Now Barr & Stroud put miniaturised thermal imaging within your grasp.

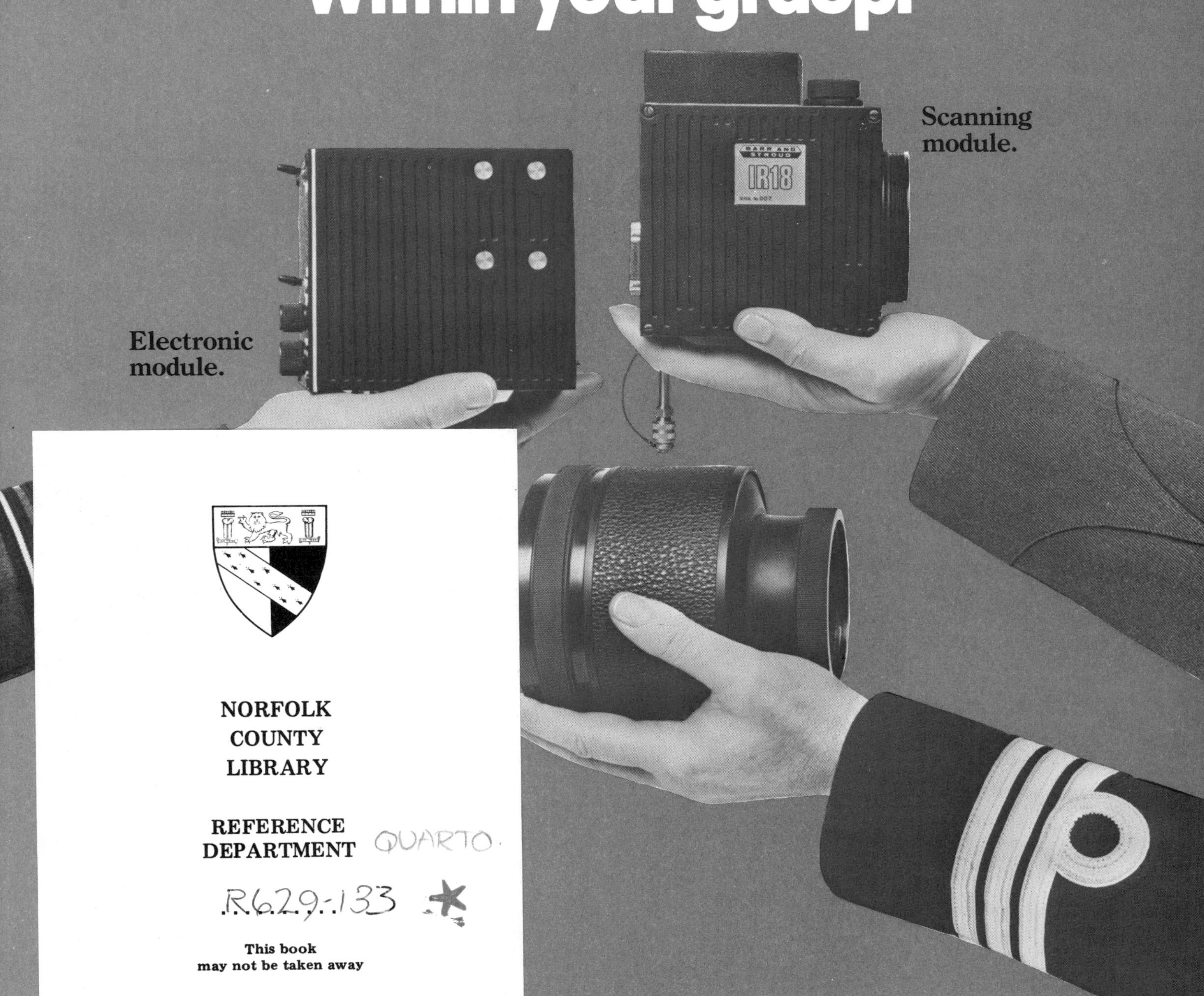

IR18 thermal imager–a breakthrough in infra-red technology.

Barr & Stroud give you the tactical advantages of thermal imaging with a compact, miniaturised scanner, no more than the size of your hand, that cuts size and weight to a minimum without sacrificing performance.

A significant breakthrough in infra-red technology, the IR18 measures only 130 x 220 x 400mm overall and weighs less than 10kg.

The result of Barr & Stroud's fifteen years research and development experience in this field, the IR18 is the first wholly passive, high performance, thermal imaging scanner designed on a modular basis and providing a standard TV picture.

An outstandingly robust and reliable system for armoured fighting vehicles, surface ships, helicopters, fixed wing aircraft and submarines. And just one aspect of our systems and equipment capability.

Whatever your defence requirements, Barr & Stroud have the scientific skills and experience, and the precision mechanical engineering expertise to help improve your watchfulness.

Barr & Stroud

Enquiries to
Barr & Stroud Limited, Melrose House, 4-6 Savile Row, London W1X 1AF
Registered Office & Works
Caxton Street, Anniesland, Glasgow, G13 1HZ
A member of the Pilkington Group

JANE'S
ALL THE WORLD'S AIRCRAFT
1979-80

A300
A310

GE Power. Because we're ready with a full spectrum of engines for the 80's.

Today, General Electric is providing the advanced, and proven, high bypass turbofan engine technology needed for tomorrow. In a broad range of power classes. For small executive aircraft, the CF34. For medium-size commercial transports, the CFM56 (through CFM International) and CF6-32. And for larger jets, the big CF6 family, including the powerful CF6-80 for the new family of commercial transports for the 80's. Across the board, GE is delivering new highs in dependability, new lows in maintenance costs and fuel consumption. When you're ready to fly into the future, take along General Electric's proven experience.

We're ready.

GENERAL ELECTRIC

Alphabetical list of advertisers

Classified list of advertisers

AC Motors
Aviaexport
Garrett Corporation
Lucas Aerospace

Accelerometers
Aeritalia
Aviaexport

Accessories
Aviaexport
Garrett Corporation

Accumulators—Cadmium Nickel
Aviaexport
SAFT

Actuators—Electric
Aviaexport
Garrett Corporation
Lucas Aerospace
Meteor

Aerials—Aircraft
Aeritalia
Dornier
Siai Marchetti
SNECMA

Aero-Auxiliary Equipment
Garrett Corporation
Lucas Aerospace
Messerschmitt-Bölkow-Blohm
Siai Marchetti

Aero-Engine Test Plant
Avco Lycoming
John Curran
FIAT
Siai Marchetti
SNECMA

Aero-Engines
Avco Lycoming
Aviaexport
FIAT
Garrett Corporation
Meteor
MTU
Omnipol
Rinaldo Piaggio
SNECMA
Turbo-Union

Aeronautical Engineers and Consultants
Aviaexport
Boeing Commercial Airplane Co
Lucas Aerospace
Siai Marchetti

Aerosystems
Boeing Commercial Airplane Co
Lucas Aerospace
Meteor

Agricultural Aircraft Spray and Dust Systems and Components
Aviaexport
Dornier
Pilatus
Siai Marchetti

Air Compressors
CIT Alcatel
Garrett Corporation

Air Compressors (Cabin) + (Engine Starting)
Garrett Corporation

Air Compressors for Engine Starting
Lucas Aerospace
Meteor

Air-Conditioning Equipment
Aviaexport
Bestobell
Garrett Corporation
Lucas Aerospace
ML Aviation

Air-Conditioning Systems
Aviaexport
Garrett Corporation

Air Control Equipment for Cabins
Aviaexport
Bestobell
Garrett Corporation
Lucas Aerospace

Air Cycle Refrigeration Packages
Aviaexport
Garrett Corporation

Air Data Computer Systems
Aviaexport
Garrett Corporation
Meteor
Selenia

Air Data Computer—Test Set
AAI Corporation

Air Traffic Control Equipment
Aeritalia
Italtel
Selenia

Airborne Surveillance Drone Systems—Recoverable—Unmanned
Canadair

Aircraft—Agricultural (Dusters & Sprayers)
Aviaexport
Dornier
Pilatus
Siai Marchetti

Aircraft—Ambulance
Aviaexport
British Aerospace Aircraft Group
Dornier
Fokker VFW
Israel Aircraft Industries
Pilatus
Rinaldo Piaggio
Siai Marchetti

Aircraft—Commercial
Aeritalia
Aérospatiale
Boeing Commercial Airplane Co
British Aerospace Aircraft Group
Dornier
Fokker VFW
Israel Aircraft Industries
Messerschmitt-Bölkow-Blohm
Rinaldo Piaggio
Saab-Scania
Siai Marchetti

Aircraft—Executive
Aeronautica Macchi
Aérospatiale
Aviaexport
Boeing Commercial Airplane Co
British Aerospace Aircraft Group
Canadair
Dornier
Fokker VFW
Garrett Corporation
Israel Aircraft Industries
Messerschmitt-Bölkow-Blohm
Rinaldo Piaggio

Aircraft—Military
Aeritalia
Aeronautica Macchi
Aérospatiale
Boeing Commercial Airplane Co
British Aerospace Aircraft Group
Dornier
Fokker VFW
GIAT
Messerschmitt-Bölkow-Blohm
Panavia
Rinaldo Piaggio
Saab-Scania
Siai Marchetti

Aircraft—Naval
Aeritalia
Boeing Commercial Airplane Co
British Aerospace Aircraft Group
Rinaldo Piaggio

Aircraft—Private
Aeronautica Macchi
British Aerospace Aircraft Group
Canadair
Dornier
Messerschmitt-Bölkow-Blohm
Omnipol
Rinaldo Piaggio
Siai Marchetti

Aircraft—Radio Controlled
Flight Refuelling
Meteor

Aircraft—Supersonic
Aeritalia
Aérospatiale
British Aerospace Aircraft Group
Panavia
Saab-Scania

Aircraft—Training
Aeritalia
Aeronautica Macchi
Boeing Commercial Airplane Co
British Aerospace Aircraft Group
Dornier
Fokker VFW
Messerschmitt-Bölkow-Blohm
Meteor
Omnipol
Pilatus
Rinaldo Piaggio
Saab-Scania
Siai Marchetti

Aircraft—Transport
Aeritalia
Boeing Commercial Airplane Co
Dornier
Fokker VFW
Israel Aircraft Industries
Messerschmitt-Bölkow-Blohm

Aircraft V/STOL
Aviaexport
Boeing Commercial Airplane Co
British Aerospace Aircraft Group
Dornier
Fokker VFW
Messerschmitt-Bölkow-Blohm
Omnipol
Pilatus
Siai Marchetti

Aircraft Arresting Gear
SNECMA

Aircraft Canopies
Aeritalia
Aeronautica Macchi
Goodyear Tyre & Rubber Co

Aircraft Development
Aeritalia
Boeing Commercial Airplane Co
Messerschmitt-Bölkow-Blohm
Meteor
Rinaldo Piaggio

Aircraft Escape Systems
Garrett Corporation

Aircraft Field Operations & Support
Boeing Commercial Airplane Co

Aircraft Floats
Dornier
Garrett Corporation
Meteor

Aircraft Freight Handling Equipment
Aviaexport
Boyd Airport Equipment
Dornier
Fokker VFW
Messerschmitt-Bölkow-Blohm

Aircraft Integrated Data Systems
Eltro
Garrett Corporation
Meteor

Aircraft Mechanical Handlers
Aviaexport
Dornier
ML Aviation

Aircraft Modifications
Boeing Commercial Airplane Co
Messerschmitt-Bölkow-Blohm

Aircraft Product Support
Messerschmitt-Bölkow-Blohm

Aircraft Propellers
Aviaexport
Snia Viscosa

Aircraft Propeller Governors
Rinaldo Piaggio
Woodward Governor

Aircraft Wire & Cable
Standard Wire & Cable

Airfield Lighting
Aviaexport
Omnipol

Airline Technical Assistance
Boeing Commercial Airplane Co
Messerschmitt-Bölkow-Blohm

Airport Ground Handling Equipment
Boyd Airport Equipment

Airports—Planning
Messerschmitt-Bölkow-Blohm

Airports—New Passenger Transport Systems
Messerschmitt-Bölkow-Blohm

Airport Maintenance Equipment
Aeronautica Macchi
Israel Aircraft Industries
ML Aviation
SNECMA

Airspeed Indicators
Aeritalia
Aviaexport
Dornier

Alternators
Aviaexport
Garrett Corporation
Lucas Aerospace

Altimeters Encoding
Aeritalia

Altitude Control Systems
Aviaexport
Eltro

Ammunition Boosters
Meteor
Snia Viscosa

Antennae
Messerschmitt-Bölkow-Blohm
Meteor

Anti-Skid Systems
Aviaexport
Goodyear Tyre & Rubber Co
SNECMA

Armaments for Aircraft
Contraves/Oerlikon
GIAT
Messerschmitt-Bölkow-Blohm
ML Aviation
SAMM
Snia Viscosa

Automatic Checkout Systems
AAI Corporation
Aviaexport
Lucas Aerospace
Selenia

Automatic Parachute Openers
Aviaexport
Meteor

Automatic Parachute Systems
Meteor

Automatic Pilots
Aviaexport
Meteor

Automatic Voltage and Current Regulators
Aviaexport
Lucas Aerospace

Auxiliary Power Plant
Aviaexport
Garrett Corporation
Lucas Aerospace

Bars—Stainless Steel & Heat Resisting Steel
Aviaexport

Batteries
Aviaexport
Meteor
SAFT

Batteries—Aviation
Aviaexport
SAFT

Battery Chargers
Aviaexport
Lucas Aerospace
SAFT

Battery Testing Equipment
SAFT

Belts—Safety
Aviaexport

Binoculars
Aeritalia
Barr & Stroud

Blades—Gas Turbine
Avco Lycoming
Aviaexport
FIAT
SNECMA

Bomb Carriers
ML Aviation

Bonding Jumpers Bus Bars
Electro-Sonic Components

Brake Linings
Goodyear Tyre & Rubber Co

Brakes for Aircraft
Aviaexport
Goodyear Tyre & Rubber Co
Israel Aircraft Industries
SNECMA

Cabin Cooling (Tropical Airfield Equipment)
Aviaexport
Garrett Corporation

Cabin Pressure Control System
Aviaexport
Garrett Corporation

Cabin Pressurising Test Equipment
Aviaexport
Garrett Corporation

Cables—Electric
Electro-Sonic Components
ML Aviation
Standard Wire & Cable

Cables—RF
Electro-Sonic Components
Standard Wire & Cable

Central Air Data Computers
Garrett Corporation
Meteor

JOHN CURRAN LTD
CARDIFF

Aero·engine test facilities for civil and military aviation

John Curran test and run-up facilities are designed to meet customer requirements to engine types, range of power and frequency of test. They can be designed to accept different types of engines in succession for test, or for adaptation to other types at a later date.

Instrument consoles are designed on the modular system to allow for future additions or re-arrangement.

Designers and manufacturers of complete aero·engine test facilities radar aerial mounts and turning gear specialist engineering projects

PO Box 72·Curran Road·CARDIFF·UK·CF1 1TE 'phone: 0222 20641

Coatings—Erosion Resistant
Avco Lycoming
Goodyear Tyre & Rubber Co
Israel Aircraft Industries
Lucas Aerospace

Combustion Systems (Gas Turbine)
Lucas Aerospace

Communications Control Systems
Racal Acoustics

Compasses—Aircraft
Lucas Aerospace

Components
Aviaexport
Bestobell
CIT Alcatel
Dornier
Flight Refuelling
Fokker VFW
Garrett Corporation
Israel Aircraft Industries
SAMM

Computers
Dornier
Hollandse Signaalapparaten
Selenia

Computers—Aerodynamic Analogue and Digital
Dornier
Garrett Corporation
Israel Aircraft Industries

Connectors/Connector Accessories
Aviaexport
Electro-Sonic Components
Garrett Corporation

Constant Speed Alternator Drive Units
Garrett Corporation
Lucas Aerospace

Control Equipment for Aircraft
Aviaexport
Dornier
Garrett Corporation
Lucas Aerospace
SNECMA

Controls—Cockpit
Aviaexport

Controls—Main Engine Fuel
Aviaexport
Lucas Aerospace

Convoluted Sleeves/Bellows
Bestobell

Cooling Compressors
Aviaexport
Garrett Corporation

Cooling Turbines
Garrett Corporation

Cryogenic Turbines
Garrett Corporation

Data Processing Equipment
CIT Alcatel
Dornier
Garrett Corporation
Meteor
Selenia
SNECMA

Data Processing Equipment for ATC
Dornier
Selenia

Data Transmission Equipment
Dornier
Elmer Montedel
Eltro
Selenia
SNECMA

DC Generators
Lucas Aerospace

DC Motors
Aviaexport
Garrett Corporation
Lucas Aerospace

De-Icing Equipment
Bestobell
Flight Refuelling
Garrett Corporation
Goodyear Tyre & Rubber Co
Lucas Aerospace

Direction Finding Equipment (Triangulation)
Aviaexport
Selenia

Drogue Guns
ML Aviation

Drones
Aeronautica Macchi
Canadair
Dornier
Meteor
Selenia

Ejection Seats
Aeronautica Macchi
SNECMA

Ejector Release Units
ML Aviation

Electric Auxiliaries
Aviaexport
Garrett Corporation
Lucas Aerospace

Electric Ground Cover Systems
Lucas Aerospace

Electric Tractors
ML Aviation

Electrical Equipment
Aviaexport
Garrett Corporation
Lucas Aerospace
ML Aviation

Electrical Wiring Assemblies
Aviaexport
Fokker VFW
ML Aviation
Standard Wire & Cable

Electrical Wire Cable Cord of all types
Standard Wire & Cable

Electro-Optical Systems
Barr & Stroud
Eltro
Saab-Scania
Selenia

Electronic Equipment
Aeritalia
Aviaexport
Boeing Commercial Airplane Co
CIT Alcatel
Garrett Corporation
Israel Aircraft Industries
Meteor
ML Aviation
Saab-Scania
SAMM
Selenia
SNECMA

Electronic Fuel Control Systems
Lucas Aerospace

Electronics & Guidance
Israel Aircraft Industries
Messerschmitt-Bölkow-Blohm
Selenia

Engine/Bulkhead Fireseals
Bestobell

Engine Compressor Cleaning Rigs
John Curran

Engine Handling Equipment
John Curran

Engine Parts Fabrication
Avco Lycoming
FIAT
Lucas Aerospace

Engine Research
General Electric

Engine Starting Equipment
Lucas Aerospace

Engine Testing Equipment
Avco Lycoming
Aviaexport
John Curran
Garrett Corporation

Engines—Aircraft
Avco Lycoming
Aviaexport
FIAT
Garrett Corporation
General Electric
Klöckner-Humboldt-Deutz
Motoravio Sud
MTU
Rinaldo Piaggio
SNECMA

The E-2C Hawkeye:
It grows on you.
Just ask the men who fly the Hawkeye.
Or those who benefit from its exceptional AEW capabilities.
E-2C is the catalyst for the Navy's vital war-at-sea missions: Airborne Early Warning, Intercept Control, Anti-ship Missile Defense, and Over-the-Horizon Targeting.
Its readiness record...one of the fleet's highest...means the Navy can count on the Hawkeye when it is needed.
But as good as the Hawkeye is, the best will get even better:
With a new anti-jam rotodome antenna.
A greatly expanded passive detection (ESM) system.
The jam-resistant Joint Tactical Information Distribution System (JTIDS).
And an expanded data processing capability.
E-2C Hawkeye. The best gets better... and will continue to grow for the next quarter century.
Grumman Aerospace Corporation, Bethpage, Long Island, New York 11714.
GRUMMAN
The reliable source
NG
9501
NAVY
763 NG
763

CLASSIFIED LIST OF ADVERTISERS

Engines—Auxiliary
Avco Lycoming
Aviaexport
General Electric
Klöckner-Humboldt-Deutz
Lucas Aerospace
MTU

Engines—V/STOL
Avco Lycoming
Aviaexport
Garrett Corporation
General Electric
SNECMA

Environmental Control Systems
Garrett Corporation
Lucas Aerospace
Messerschmitt-Bölkow-Blohm
Selenia

Executive Transport—Twin Fan Jet
Canadair

Experimental Assemblies
ML Aviation

Feel Simulator Controls
Garrett Corporation
Lucas Aerospace

Fibre Optics
Barr & Stroud

Film Resistent Hose
Bestobell

Filters—Air
Aviaexport

Filters—Electronic
Aviaexport
Barr & Stroud
CIT Alcatel
Racal Acoustics
Selenia

Filters—Fuel & Oil
Aviaexport
Flight Refuelling

Fire Suppression Systems
Eltro

Flexible Sleeves, Connectors
Bestobell

Flight Instrument Test Sets
Garrett Corporation
Israel Aircraft Industries
SNECMA

Flotation Gear
Garrett Corporation

Flow Gauges
Aviaexport

Forgings—Steel
SNECMA

Fuel Flow Proportioners
Flight Refuelling
Garrett Corporation
Lucas Aerospace

Fuel Pumps
Aviaexport
Garrett Corporation
Lucas Aerospace

Fuel Systems Protection
PRB

Fuel Systems & Refuelling Equipment
Aviaexport
Flight Refuelling
Israel Aircraft Industries
Lucas Aerospace

Fuel Tank Pressurisation Equipment
Flight Refuelling
Garrett Corporation
Israel Aircraft Industries

Furnishings & Aircraft Cabins
Aviaexport
Garrett Corporation
Rinaldo Piaggio

Gas Turbine Starting Systems
Klöckner-Humboldt-Deutz
Lucas Aerospace

Gas Turbines
Avco Lycoming
Aviaexport
FIAT
Garrett Corporation
General Electric
Klöckner-Humboldt-Deutz
Lucas Aerospace
MTU
Rinaldo Piaggio
SNECMA

Gas Turbines—Equipment & Accessories
Avco Lycoming
Aviaexport
Garrett Corporation
Lucas Aerospace
SNECMA

Gauges
Aviaexport

Generators
Aviaexport
Garrett Corporation
Lucas Aerospace

Ground Refuelling Equipment
Flight Refuelling
Goodyear Tyre & Rubber Co

Ground Support Equipment
Boyd Airport Equipment
Canadair

Ground Workshop & Hangar Equipment
Israel Aircraft Industries

Guidance Control Test Set
AAI Corporation

Guided Missile Ground Handling Equipment
AAI Corporation
Aeronautica Macchi
Eltro
Garrett Corporation
ML Aviation
Selenia

Guided Missiles
Aérospatiale
Dornier
Messerschmitt-Bölkow-Blohm
Saab-Scania
Selenia

Gunnery Training Apparatus
Contraves/Oerlikon
Saab-Scania

Hangar Test Stands
Boyd Airport Equipment

Heat Exchangers
Lucas Aerospace
SNECMA

Heat Transfer Systems
Garrett Corporation

Heated Windows
Barr & Stroud
Lucas Aerospace

Heated Windscreen Controllers
Lucas Aerospace

Helicopter Deck Restraint Systems
ML Aviation

Helicopter Winches
Agusta
Lucas Aerospace

Helicopter Parts & Components
Agusta
Aviaexport
Dornier
Israel Aircraft Industries
Messerschmitt-Bölkow-Blohm

Helicopter Searchlights
Garrett Corporation

Helicopter Training & Support
Agusta

Helicopters—Ambulance
Agusta

Helicopters—Commercial-Executive
Aérospatiale
Agusta
Aviaexport
Bell Helicopter
Boeing Commercial Airplane Co
Dornier
Messerschmitt-Bölkow-Blohm

Helicopters—Military-Navy
Aérospatiale
Agusta
Boeing Commercial Airplane Co
Messerschmitt-Bölkow-Blohm

High Pressure Couplings
Flight Refuelling

Hose Clips
Bestobell

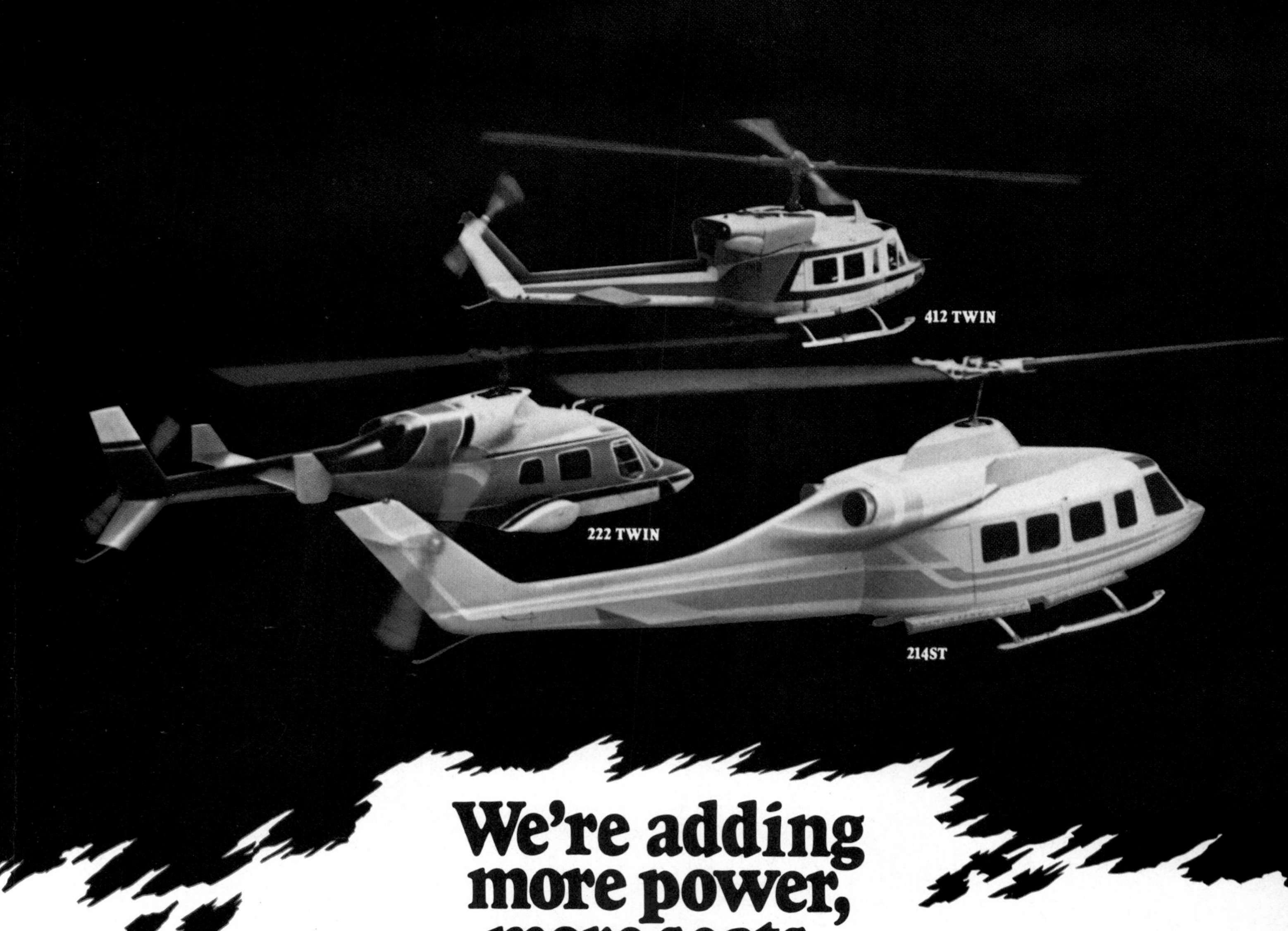
412 TWIN
222 TWIN
214ST

CLASSIFIED LIST OF ADVERTISERS

Hydraulic Equipment
Lucas Aerospace
ML Aviation
SAMM
SNECMA

Hydraulic Pressure Pumps
Lucas Aerospace
SAMM

Hydraulic Test Units—Mobile & Static
Aeronautica Macchi

Indicators—Fault Isolation
Electro-Sonic Components

Inertial Navigation Systems
Electro-Sonic Components

Inflatable Structures
Garrett Corporation

Infra-Red Linescan
Eltro

Infra-Red Materials
Barr & Stroud
Selenia

Infra-Red Systems
Barr & Stroud
Eltro
Garrett Corporation
Meteor
Selenia

Instruments—Aircraft
Aeritalia
Israel Aircraft Industries

Instruments—Electronic
Aeritalia
Israel Aircraft Industries
SNECMA

Instruments—Navigation
Aeritalia
Aérospatiale
Aviaexport

Instruments—Precision
Israel Aircraft Industries

Instruments—Test Equipment
AAI Corporation
Aeritalia
Aviaexport
John Curran
Garrett Corporation
Israel Aircraft Industries
SNECMA
Woodward Governor

Integrated Total Pneumatic Systems
Garrett Corporation
Lucas Aerospace

Intercommunication Equipment
Elmer Montedel

Jacks
Boyd Airport Equipment
Electro-Sonic Components
Lucas Aerospace
SAMM

Jet Engine Parts
Avco Lycoming
John Curran
FIAT
Garrett Corporation
Klöckner-Humboldt-Deutz
MTU
Rinaldo Piaggio
SNECMA

Jet Engine Test Plant
Avco Lycoming
John Curran
FIAT
Garrett Corporation
SNECMA

Jet Fuel Starters
Garrett Corporation
Lucas Aerospace

Jet Propulsion Engines
Avco Lycoming
FIAT
Garrett Corporation
Lucas Aerospace
SNECMA

Jet Trainer—Military
Embraer

Jointing Compound
Goodyear Tyre & Rubber Co

Lamps—Cockpit
Aviaexport
Electro-Sonic Components
Lucas Aerospace

Landing Lamps
Aviaexport
Electro-Sonic Components

Lasers
Aérospatiale
Barr & Stroud
Eltro
Garrett Corporation
Messerschmitt-Bölkow-Blohm
Selenia

Laser Rangefinder
Barr & Stroud
Eltro
Selenia

Life Saving Equipment
Garrett Corporation
Saab-Scania

Light Aircraft
Embraer

Lightweight Hose
Bestobell

Lights—Aircraft
Aviaexport

Lights—Landing
Aviaexport

Lights—Navigation
Aviaexport
Lucas Aerospace

Linear Actuators
Garrett Corporation
Lucas Aerospace

Linings—Brakes
Goodyear Tyre & Rubber Co
Lucas Aerospace

Mach Number Transducers
Garrett Corporation

Machine Tools
CIT Alcatel

Marine Engines
FIAT
Garrett Corporation

Market Intelligence Reports
DMS

Materials Technology
Aérospatiale
Boeing Commercial Airplane Co

Metal Ducting
Bestobell

Metal Duct Connectors
Bestobell

Metal Fittings
Aviaexport

Microphones
Aviaexport

Missile Optics
Barr & Stroud
Messerschmitt-Bölkow-Blohm

Missiles—Guided
Aérospatiale
Dornier
Messerschmitt-Bölkow-Blohm
Saab-Scania
Selenia

Motor Generators
Aviaexport
Garrett Corporation

Motors—Electric
Aviaexport
Garrett Corporation
Lucas Aerospace

Motors—Hydraulic
Aviaexport
CIT Alcatel
Garrett Corporation
Lucas Aerospace
SAMM

Night Vision Equipment
Barr & Stroud
Eltro
Selenia

Non-Destructive Inspect Equipment
Fokker VFW

Oil Valves
Flight Refuelling
Garrett Corporation

CLASSIFIED LIST OF ADVERTISERS

Optical Equipment
Barr & Stroud

Optical Gun Sights
Eltro
Saab-Scania
Selenia

Overhaul & Modification Kits
Dornier
Garret Corporation
Siai Marchetti

Oxygen Apparatus
Aviaexport

Oxygen Breathing Apparatus
Garrett Corporation

Parachute Flares
Bofors

Parachutes
Aviaexport
Meteor

Parachutes—Special Purpose
Aviaexport

Parts for US Built Aircraft
Garrett Corporation

Passenger Bridges (Aviobridge)
Boyd Airport Equipment
Fokker VFW

Patrol Aircraft—Maritime
Embraer

Periscopes
Barr & Stroud

Photographic Equipment
Fokker VFW

Plastic Fabrications
Aeritalia
Lucas Aerospace

Plastic Fabrications (Re-inforced with Fibreglass)
Aeritalia
Boeing Commercial Airplane Co
Fokker VFW
Israel Aircraft Industries
Lucas Aerospace
Messerschmitt-Bölkow-Blohm

Plastic Mouldings
Fokker VFW
Lucas Aerospace

Platform Trucks
Fokker VFW

Pneumatic Controls
Garrett Corporation
Lucas Aerospace

Power Control for Aircraft
Garrett Corporation
Lucas Aerospace
SAMM

Power—Solar Cell Panels & Arrays
Messerschmitt-Bölkow-Blohm

Precision Gears
FIAT

Pressure Control Equipment
Garrett Corporation

Pressure Radio Transducers
Garrett Corporation

Pressure Regulation Valves—Fluids & Gases
Flight Refuelling
Garrett Corporation
Lucas Aerospace

Pressure Switches
Lucas Aerospace
SAMM

Pressure Transducers
Garrett Corporation

Private Planes—Civil & Military
Embraer

Propeller Governors
Rinaldo Piaggio

Propeller Hubs
Meteor

Propeller Test Stands
John Curran

Propellers
Rinaldo Piaggio

Proposals for Aircraft Ground Support Operations
Boeing Commercial Airplane Co
Boyd Airport Equipment
Messerschmitt-Bölkow-Blohm
Rinaldo Piaggio
Siai Marchetti

Pumps—Agricultural Spray
Dornier

Pumps—Air Compressor
Garrett Corporation
SNECMA

Pumps—Fuel and Oil
Garrett Corporation
Israel Aircraft Industries
Lucas Aerospace
SAMM
Siai Marchetti

Pumps—Hydraulic
Garrett Corporation
Israel Aircraft Industries
Lucas Aerospace
SAMM
SNECMA

Provisioning Parts Breakdown Lists
John Curran

Radar for Navigation, Warning Interception, Fire Control & Airfield Supervision
Aviaexport
Israel Aircraft Industries
Omnipol
Selenia
SMA
SNECMA

Radar Reflectors
Fokker VFW
Selenia

Radar Test Set
AAI Corporation

Radar Turning Gears & Equipment
John Curran

Radio Equipment
Aviaexport
Elmer Montedel
Israel Aircraft Industries
Italtel
SNECMA

Radio Equipment—Ground HF & Airborne HF/VHF
Elmer Montedel
Italtel

Radio Navigation Equipment
Elmer Montedel

Rangefinders
Barr & Stroud
Eltro
Selenia

Recirculating Precision Ball-Screws
Lucas Aerospace

Refrigeration Compressors
Garrett Corporation
Lucas Aerospace

Refuelling Equipment Hose
Goodyear Tyre & Rubber Co

Repair & Maintenance of Aircraft
Aeritalia
Avco Lycoming
Boeing Commercial Airplane Co
Dornier
Fokker VFW
Garrett Corporation
Israel Aircraft Industries
Messerschmitt-Bölkow-Blohm
Meteor
Pilatus
Rinaldo Piaggio
Siai Marchetti

Repair & Overhaul of Aero-Engines
FIAT
Garrett Corporation
Rinaldo Piaggio
SNECMA

Repair of Aircraft Instruments
Aviaexport
Fokker VFW
Israel Aircraft Industries
Pilatus
Siai Marchetti

Rocket Engine Test Plant
Messerschmitt-Bölkow-Blohm
Snia Viscosa

Rocket Propulsion
Messerschmitt-Bölkow-Blohm
Snia Viscosa

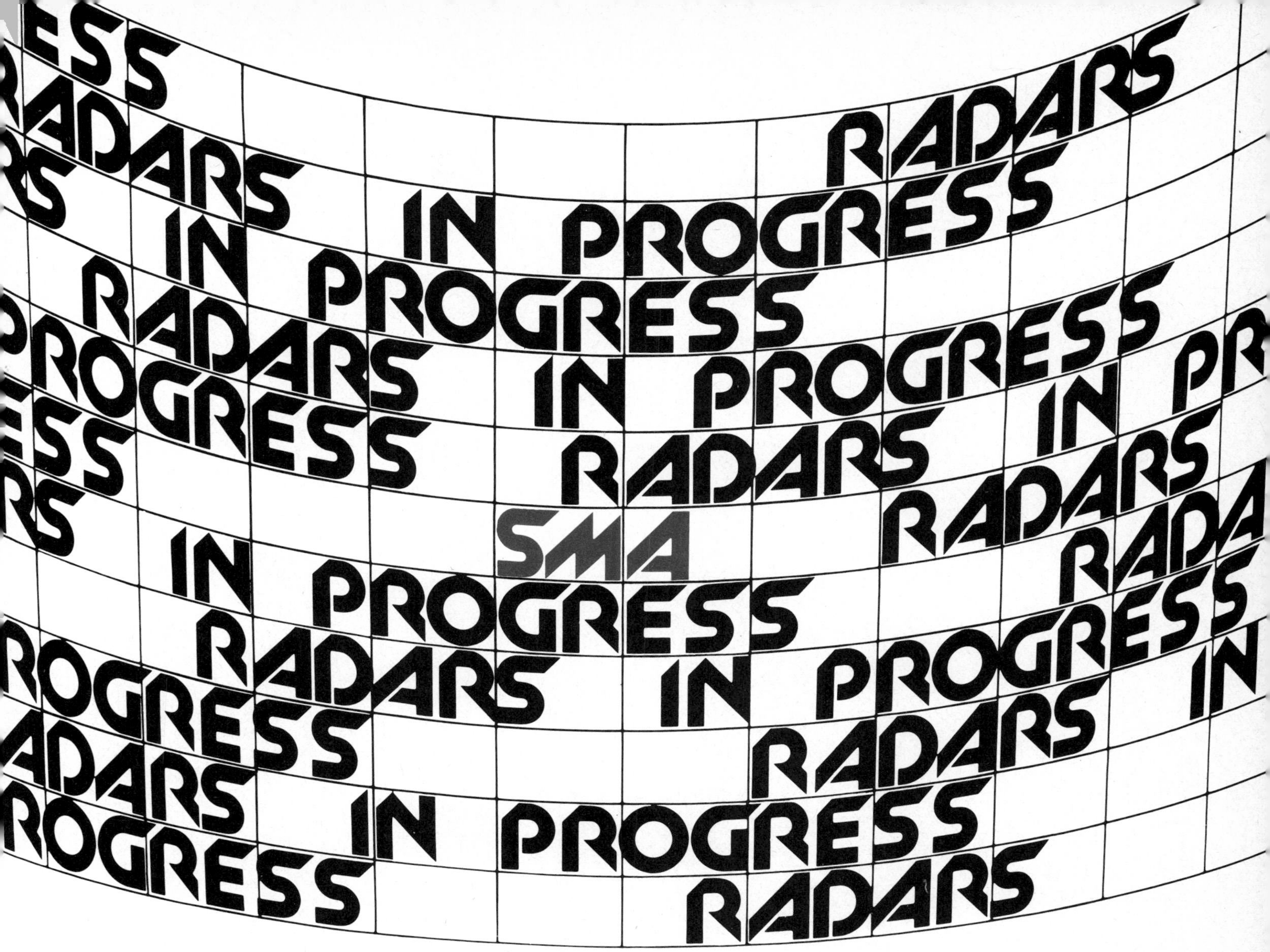

CLASSIFIED LIST OF ADVERTISERS

Rocket Sounding
Aerospatiale
Dornier
Messerschmitt-Bölkow-Blohm
Saab-Scania

Rotary Actuators
Garrett Corporation
Lucas Aerospace

RPVs
Messerschmitt-Bölkow-Blohm
Meteor

Runway Friction Measuring Equipment
ML Aviation
Saab-Scania

Seals, Gaskets
Bestobell

Seat Belts
Aviaexport

Servo Actuators
Garrett Corporation
Meteor
SAMM

Sheet Metal Work
Fokker VFW
Israel Aircraft Industries
Lucas Aerospace

Sheet Metal Working Machines
Fokker VFW

Silicone Rubber Components
Bestobell

Simulators
AAI Corporation
Dornier
Messerschmitt-Bölkow-Blohm
Selenia
Siai Marchetti

Solenoid Valves
Flight Refuelling

Space Hardware Recovery
Dornier

Space Satellites
Aeritalia
Aérospatiale
Dornier
Fokker VFW
Messerschmitt-Bölkow-Blohm
Selenia

Space Systems
Aeritalia
Aérospatiale
Boeing Commercial Airplane Co
Dornier
Fokker VFW
Messerschmitt-Bölkow-Blohm
Saab-Scania
Selenia
Snia Viscosa

Spacecraft
Aeritalia
Aérospatiale
Dornier
Messerschmitt-Bölkow-Blohm
Selenia

Spare Parts for US Built Aircraft
Goodyear Tyre & Rubber Co
Siai Marchetti

Stability Augmentation System
Aérospatiale
Dornier
Messerschmitt-Bölkow-Blohm

Stall Warning Systems
Fokker VFW

Starter Pods—Airborne
Garrett Corporation

Starting Systems—Airborne
Garrett Corporation
Lucas Aerospace

Static Inverters
Lucas Aerospace

Station Boxes
Racal Acoustics

Surveillance Systems
Canadair
Garrett Corporation
Messerschmitt-Bölkow-Blohm
Meteor

Switches
Electro-Sonic Components
Lucas Aerospace

Switches—Miniature Electrical
Electro-Sonic Components
SAMM

Switchgear
Aviaexport
Lucas Aerospace

Synthetic Rubber Mouldings—Extensions
Bestobell

Tachometers
Aviaexport

Target Release & Exchanger Mechanisms
Meteor

Target Towing Winches
Flight Refuelling
Garrett Corporation
Meteor

Technical Publications
John Curran
Dornier
Flight Refuelling
Fokker VFW
Israel Aircraft Industries
Rinaldo Piaggio
Siai Marchetti

Technical Publications—Special Studies
Dornier

Temperature Control Equipment
Garrett Corporation
Lucas Aerospace

Test Equipment
AAI Corporation
Aeronautica Macchi
Avco Lycoming
Aviaexport
John Curran
Electro-Sonic Components
Garrett Corporation
Israel Aircraft Industries
Lucas Aerospace
ML Aviation
Selenia
SNECMA

Test Equipment—Radar, Air Data Computer, Fire Control System, Avionics etc
AAI Corporation

Test Equipment—Airfield Radio
SNECMA

Test Equipment—Metal Bonding
Aviaexport
Fokker VFW
Siai Marchetti

Thermal/Acoustic Insulation
Bestobell

Thermal Imaging Systems
Barr & Stroud
Eltro

Thermo Couple Cables
Electro-Sonic Components
Israel Aircraft Industries
Standard Wire & Cable Co

Tractors—Electric
ML Aviation

Training Devices
AAI Corporation
Messerschmitt-Bölkow-Blohm

Transformer Rectifier Units
Israel Aircraft Industries
Lucas Aerospace

Tubes—Stainless Steel
Aviaexport

Turbines—Ram Air
Garrett Corporation

Turbofan Engines
Avco Lycoming
FIAT
Garrett Corporation
General Electric
MTU
SNECMA

Turnkey Airport Projects
Selenia

Tyres for Aircraft
Goodyear Tyre & Rubber Co

Undercarriage Equipment
SNECMA

Undercarriage Gear—Retractable
SNECMA

Valves
Flight Refuelling
Garrett Corporation
Israel Aircraft Industries
Lucas Aerospace
SAMM
Siai Marchetti

Valves—Control Hydraulic
Garrett Corporation
Goodyear Tyre & Rubber Co
Israel Aircraft Industries
SAMM
Siai Marchetti

Valves—Electronic
Garrett Corporation

Valves—Non-Return Fuel
Flight Refuelling
Garrett Corporation

Valves—Non-Return Hydraulic
Flight Refuelling
Garrett Corporation
SAMM

Valves—Relief Hydraulic
Garrett Corporation

Valves & Miniature Relays
Garrett Corporation

'V' Band Clamps
Bestobell

Vertical Take-off Aircraft
British Aerospace Aircraft Group
Dornier
Messerschmitt-Bölkow-Blohm

Visibility Measuring Equipment
SNECMA

Voltage & Current Regulators
Garrett Corporation
Lucas Aerospace

Water Separators
Flight Refuelling
Garrett Corporation

Wheels for Aircraft
Goodyear Tyre & Rubber Co
SNECMA

Wind Tunnel Testing Plant
Aeronautica Macchi
Boeing Commercial Airplane Co
British Aerospace Aircraft Group
John Curran
Dornier

Optimum range

Commercial transport aircraft currently in production and development by British Aerospace, either independently or in partnership with other European companies, are helping to meet worldwide requirements ranging from supersonic to subsonic travel, from feeder lines to intercontinental services, from executive transport to cargo carriage.

1. **CONCORDE** supersonic airliner†
2. **BAC ONE-ELEVEN** short/medium-range jet family
3. **HS125** executive jet family
4. **HS748** turboprop transport aircraft
5. **AIRBUS A300** and **A310** wide-body airliners*
6. **JETSTREAM** turboprop feeder-liner and VIP transport
7. **BRITISH AEROSPACE 146** wide-body fanjet feederliner

†in partnership with Aerospatiale, France. *as a full partner in Airbus Industrie

BRITISH AEROSPACE

unequalled in its range of aerospace programmes

Motoravio Sud S.p.A. originally founded in 1971 with 50% FIAT participation, became 100% FIAT during 1974, following, as regards the quality and reliability of its production, the well-known tradition of FIAT AVIAZIONE in Turin. Motoravio Sud employs about 480 people, the majority of whom are highly qualified workers.

One of the most important activities carried out by Motoravio Sud is the overhaul and repair of jet and piston engines, a field where it has acquired a remarkable experience. Because of its geographical position, highly stilled personnel and modern equipment, Motoravio Sud can be considered one of the most capable and qualified centres in the Mediterranean area.

The main aero engine programmes, to which Motoravio Sud presently participates, in both fields of manufactoring and overhaul, are shown in the picture at right.

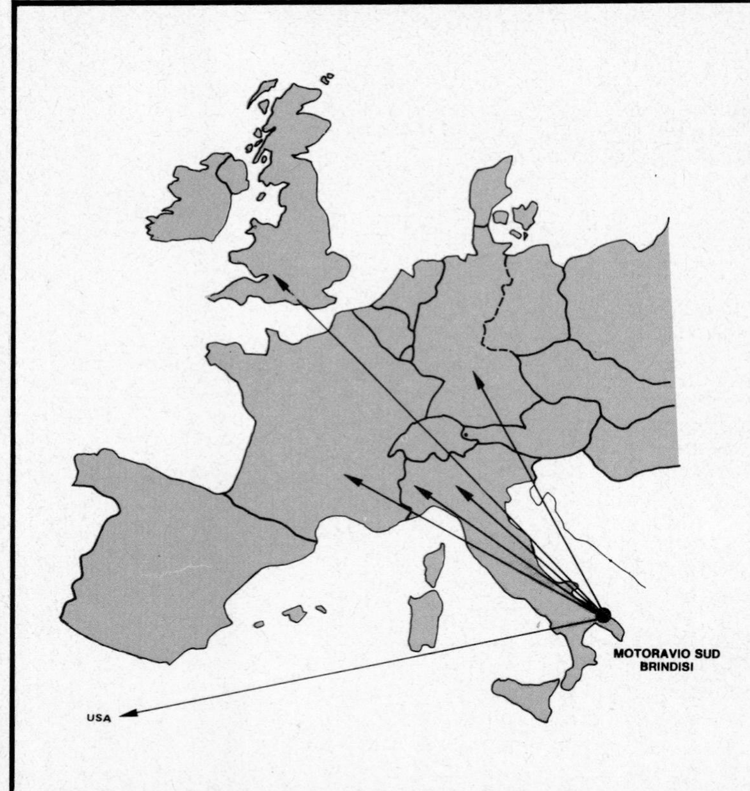

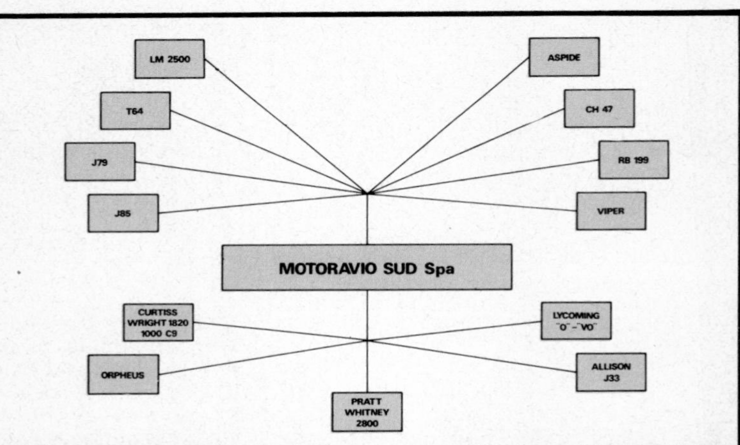

helicopters
ly,

In size, the Agusta Group is now one of world's major aerospace enterprises. It exports to 67 countries.

But size and volume is not the only story. Agusta is now also the most diversified helicopter manufacturer.

Production at Agusta this year includes twelve models, civil and military, some of Agusta original design, some under licence from Bell, Sikorsky, and Boeing-Vertol. Product support is extensive and thorough.

For anyone considering helicopter purchases, Agusta is truly an attractive source.

AGUSTA
Milan, Italy - Telex 333280

AB 212 ASW

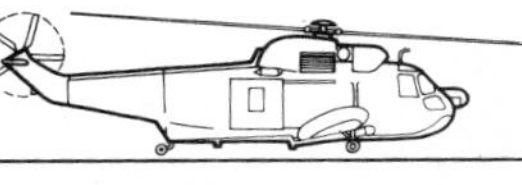

ASH-3D

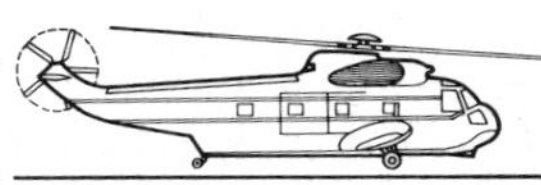

AS-61

HH-3F

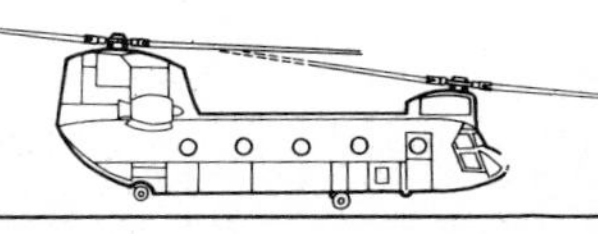

EMB-CH47C

European Leader in the avionics Market

migrator

complete COM/NAV avionics system approved in category 1

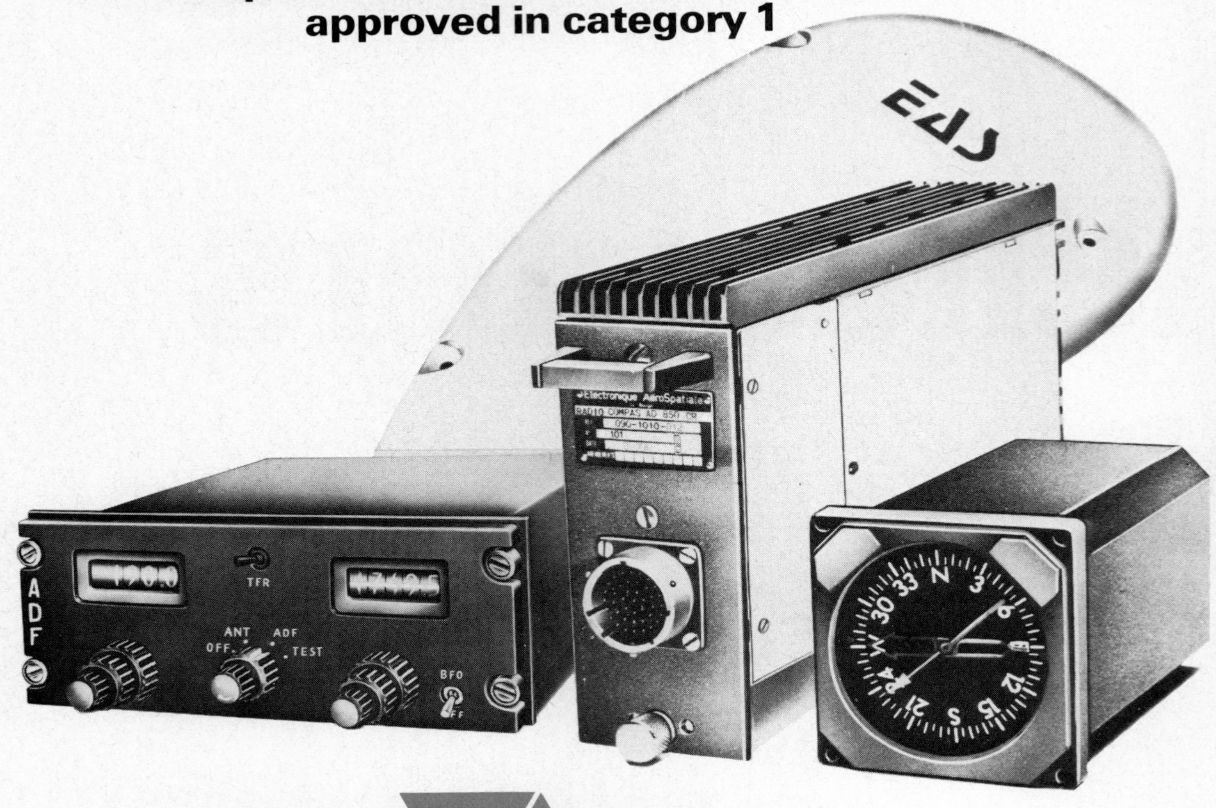

volt'air

complete line for all your requirements in`ac´generation, from light twins, to bizjets and mono/twin helicopters

EAS the french flag in avionics
Electronique Aérospatiale
B.P. 51-93350 Le Bourget-France Tél. 862.51.51-862.51.00-Télex 220809 F

Canadair is recognized around the world for excellence in aircraft design and manufacture.

In its 35 years, Canadair has produced nearly 3,900 aircraft, of which 3,000 were high-performance types and 580 were supersonic.

We have built everything from amphibians to business jets, trainers to fighters, water-bombers to four-engined transports. And many of the aircraft we built 35 years ago are still in operation.

Right now we're busy turning out our new Challenger business jet, the versatile CL-215 waterbomber and our family of surveillance drones.

Other manufacturers know Canadair's skills. We're making fuselage sections for the 747SP and major components for the P-3 and Aurora long range patrol aircraft. Soon we'll be producing aft fuselages for the Boeing 767.

We're very busy, but not too busy to discuss your needs. Call us in Montreal at (514) 744-1511.

canadair

Canadair Ltd., P.O. Box 6087, Station 'A', Montreal, Quebec, Canada H3C 3G9

ELTRO optronic know how

Helicopter in thermal image

Development · Manufacture · Maintenance

- Laser rangefinders/target illuminators/trackers
- Low-level light intensifiers-reconnaissance/aiming devices
- Optronic fire suppression systems
- Runway visual range measuring systems
- Thermal imaging systems
- Landmine detectors
- IR missile guidance

Eltro GmbH, Gesellschaft für Strahlungstechnik
Postfach 102120 · 6900 Heidelberg 1, W.-Germany

I-PIAC
P166-DL3

There is only o
can ge
tr
The new Fokker F
Great where others are too b

The new Fokker F28 gives you something no other jet can: Profitability on the short and medium haul, low to medium density routes. Where you need jet speed and comfort to meet passenger demand. Where traffic is outgrowing your turboprop capacity – but still a long way from making jets a commercially viable proposition.

With the exception of one: the new Fokker F28. Because it has been specifically designed to make a profit where other jets can't. For example, on the rapidly growing regional network of Air Anglia.

Thanks to its 80/85 passenger capacity which is just right for these routes. Generating more traffic. Offering healthy growth potential. And returning your investment with jet speed.

Thanks to its low weight which will save you money on navigation and landing fees.

e modern jet that
nerate regional
affic profitably.
28.
g.

Thanks to its fuel economy which is the best of any commercial jetliner in production.

And thanks to its fatigue-resistant airframe and low-noise Rolls-Royce RB 183 engines optimized for short cycles and long service life.

If you want to know more about the new Fokker F28 please don't hesitate to contact us at our address below.

And who knows – maybe you will be the next to order this exciting new aircraft:

The new Fokker F28.

Fokker-VFW International, Schiphol-Oost, Netherlands, Telephone: 20–5449111, Telex FINT 11526.

RAT-31S the intelligent radar

The SELENIA RAT-31S radars now being delivered to air defence forces already incorporate all those features that three-dimensional radars should have if they are to be compatible with the operational requirements of the 1980s and beyond.

RAT-31S is completely adaptive to its operational environment and incorporates such techniques as:
Phase scanning for pulse-to-pulse frequency agility over an extremely wide bandwidth.
Planar array antenna for very low sidelobe levels.
Multiple pencil beams for very high data rates giving enhanced accuracy and clutter rejection.
Monopulse for excellent height measurement accuracy compatible with pulse-to-pulse frequency agility.
Intelligent frequency selection to adapt the transmitter frequencies to the actual ECM environment.
Pulse coding for sub-clutter visibility even in pulse-to-pulse frequency agility operation.
S-band operation for compactness and easy transportation.

These and other features make of RAT-31S a very intelligent equipment which gives you more at less cost.

Designed for the 1980s - in series production to-day.

INDUSTRIE ELETTRONICHE ASSOCIATE S.p.A.
RADAR & MISSILE SYSTEMS DIVISION
Via Tiburtina Km 12.400 / 00131 ROME, ITALY
Phone: 43601 / **Telex:** 613690 SELROM I
P.O. Box: 7083, 00100 ROME, ITALY

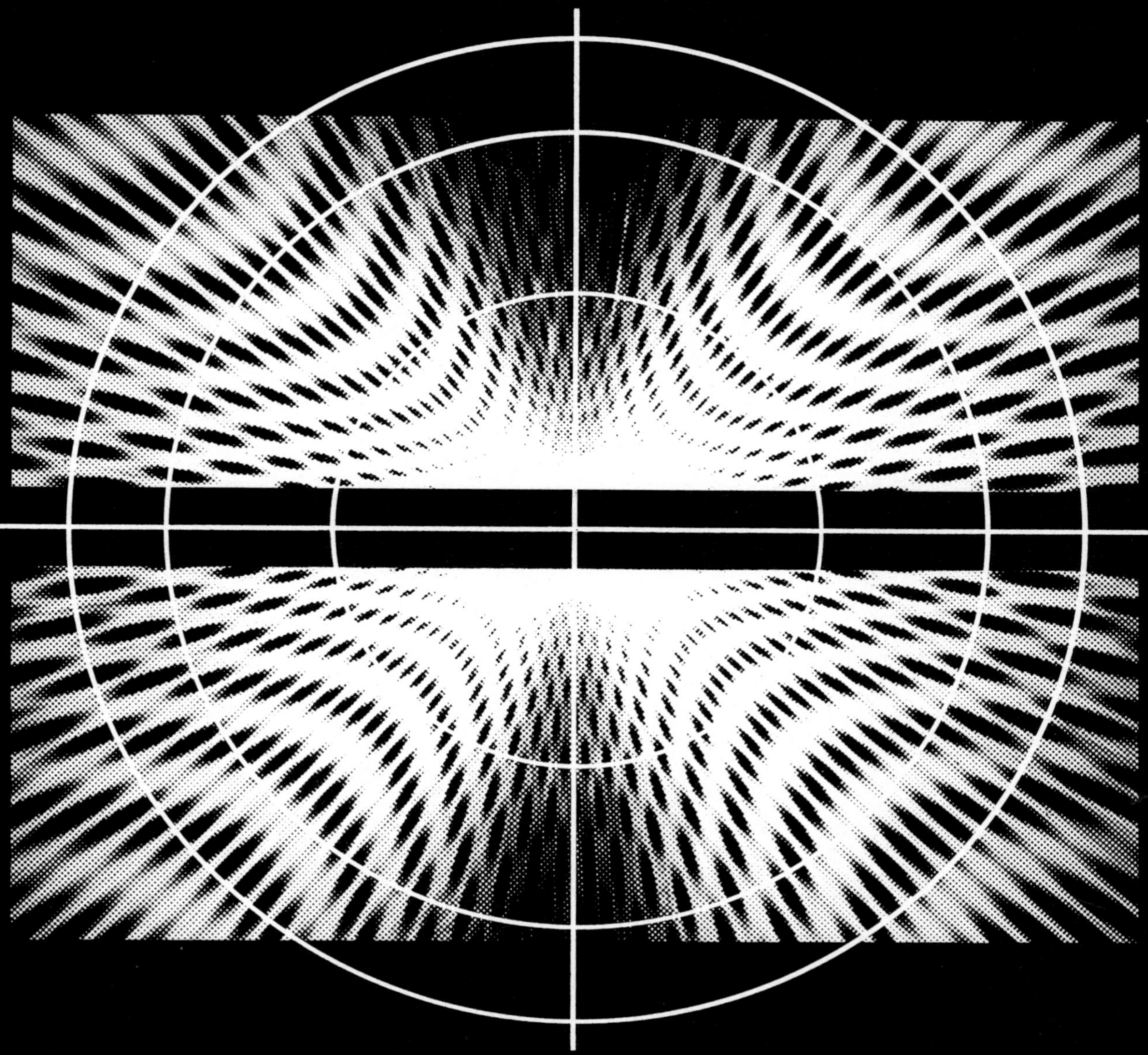

Goodyear– single source supply.

Goodyear design, manufacture, test and supply complete tyre, wheel, brake and anti-skid assemblies.

We save aircraft manufacturers costly engineering and precious flight-testing time.

And because single-source systems are simpler to maintain, the aircraft user gets speedier servicing – worldwide.

For total service, and absolute reliability, come to Goodyear.

For detailed information on all Goodyear aviation equipment – including erosion-resistant coating and jointing compounds for aviation – please contact:

Aviation Products Division,
The Goodyear Tyre and Rubber Company (G.B.) Ltd.,
Wolverhampton WV10 6DH.
Tel: Wolverhampton 22321.
Telex: 338891.

Goodyear-equipped aircraft include:- Tristar, DC-10 Series, Panavia Tornado, SN600 Corvette, Lynx, F15, DC-9 Series, Hercules C-130, Vanguard, Caravelle Series 10 and 11, Fokker Fellowship, Gulfstream 11, Herald, Jet Commander, Nord 262, Falcon 10 and 20, Boeing 707-320C, Buccaneer, Jaguar, Saab J29, J35, J37, Westland W.9.30, Westland Sea King, SA Bulldog.

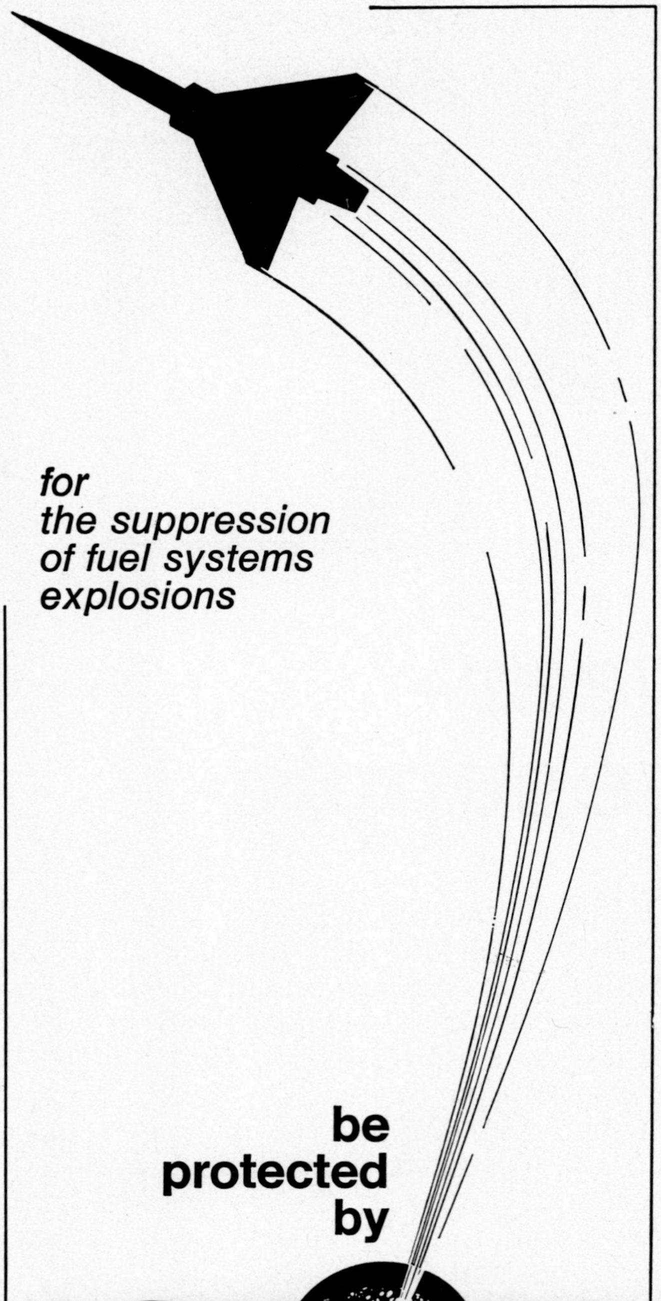

siaimarchetti
sf.260 w
....and they do this too.
sm.1019 e
SIAI
sesto calende italia tel. 0331-924421 telex 332601 SIAIAV I

JANE'S

FOR INTERNATIONAL REFERENCE

Established over three quarters of a century, **JANE'S** is a name synonymous with accuracy and authority throughout the world. Free of bias and opinion with every fact checked and re-checked, the ten **Jane's Yearbooks** are the recognised reference works on Defence, Transport, Finance and Ocean Technology.

JANE'S ALL THE WORLD'S AIRCRAFT
Edited by John W.R. Taylor
Fellow, Royal Historical Society,
Member, Royal Aeronautical Society.

JANE'S FIGHTING SHIPS
Edited by Captain J.E. Moore, Royal Navy

JANE'S WEAPON SYSTEMS
Edited by Ronald Pretty

JANE'S INFANTRY WEAPONS
Edited by Colonel John Weeks

JANE'S SURFACE SKIMMERS
Edited by Roy McLeavy

JANE'S OCEAN TECHNOLOGY
Edited by Robert L. Trillo

JANE'S FREIGHT CONTAINERS
Edited by Patrick Finlay

JANE'S WORLD RAILWAYS
Edited by Paul Goldsack

JANE'S MAJOR COMPANIES OF EUROPE
Edited by Jonathan Love

JANE'S COMBAT SUPPORT EQUIPMENT
Edited by Christopher Foss

JANE'S YEARBOOKS
Paulton House
8 Shepherdess Walk, London N1
Telephone 01-251 1666   Telex 23168   Cables MACJANES LDN

Assured through AAI's advanced state-of-the-arts test technology.

High-performance aircraft depend on sophisticated systems operating at peak efficiency for constant readiness. Air installations throughout the free world depend on AAI, a leader in test technology, for fast, accurate, and reliable testing at organizational, intermediate, and depot levels.

Our test and maintenance management expertise includes general purpose radar testers up to computerized units for special applications.

Shown here are the latest in a broad line of test systems developed and produced by AAI.

Depot and Intermediate Level ATE. Series 5565

A series of modular, ATLAS programmed ATE for support of advanced avionics systems and components. Includes microwave, analog, digital, and fully integrated test systems. Full logistics support and test programming services are provided.

Air Data Computer Test Set, AN/ASM-442

Operates on flight line or in field shop. Provides fully automatic testing of air data computers and associated indicators. Features dynamic air-speed/altitude profiles.

AAI is also a leader in simulation and training systems for aircraft:

- Electronics Warfare—SEWT, GEWTS, A-10, B-52, and EA-6B.
- Air Traffic Control—Rapcon and VFR Tower trainers.
- Flight Sub-Systems—C-141, F-106, Apollo, LEM, and spacial orientation.

General Purpose X Band Radar Test Set, AN/UPM-145

Provides complete X-Band signal generation and measurement with internal CW, Pulse, and FM modulation. Lightweight, fuly ruggedized and completely solid state. Provides direct digital readout in operating units of measurement. Independent precise control of all signal parameters.

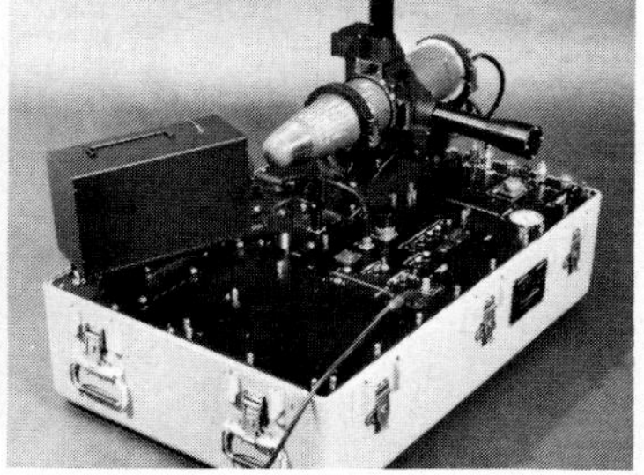

Guidance Control Test Set, TS-3621/DSQ-29 for AIM-9 Sidewinder Missile.

Features automatic testing of mission-essential guidance and control signals. Provides dynamic testing of Tracking and fin torque performance. Readiness of this microprocessor-controlled test set is assured by automatic self test.

A Subsidiary of United Industrial Corporation

P.O. Box 6767/Baltimore, Maryland USA 21204
Telephone: (301) 666-1400
TWX: 710-232-1800/Telex: 8-7849
CABLE AAICKYLV Baltimore, Md.

CORPORATION

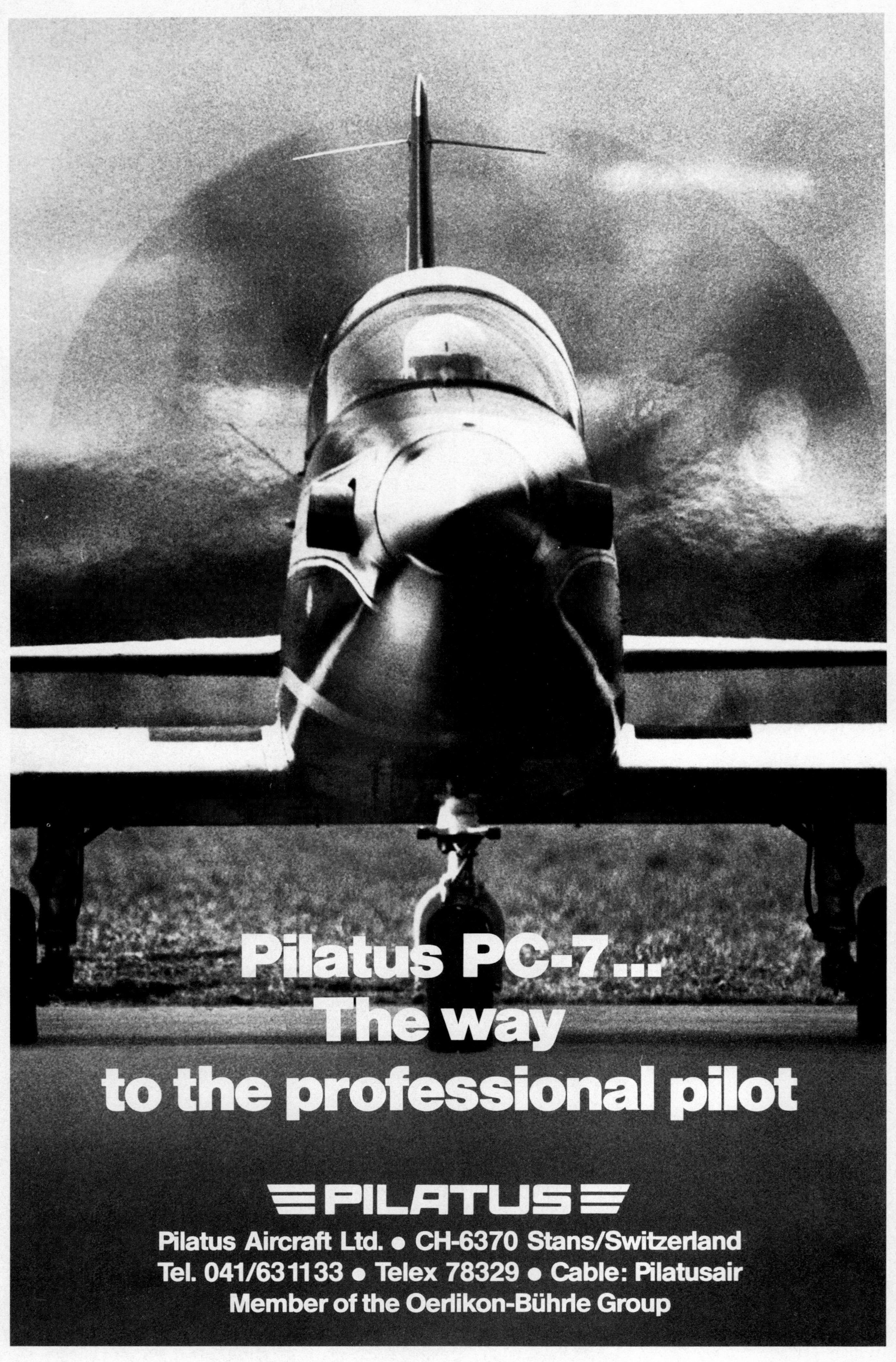
Pilatus PC-7...
The way
to the professional pilot
PILATUS
Pilatus Aircraft Ltd. • CH-6370 Stans/Switzerland
Tel. 041/631133 • Telex 78329 • Cable: Pilatusair
Member of the Oerlikon-Bührle Group

The signal-sorters

Integrating given combinations of VHF, UHF, HF, VOR, ADF and other receiver signals into a single interface obviously requires flexibility on the part of an aircraft's Communication Control System equipment.

Flexibility in CCS

And flexibility is exactly what the Racal Six-Ninety Series CCS offers.

These small, highly sophisticated units provide for the selection, control and interface of audio signals from onboard equipment and intercom.

Modular principle

Already in use in military and civil aircraft all over the world, the Series is based on a modular principle which allows equipment to be custom engineered to fit any aircraft from Piper to Jumbo.

Complete range

The station boxes shown above are just two from the complete range, which includes equipment suitable for almost any application.

For full details of the Six-Ninety Series, contact the address below.

RACAL ACOUSTICS for sound communications

Racal Acoustics Limited, Beresford Avenue, Wembley, Middlesex HA0 1RU, England.
Telephone: 01-902 8991. Telex: 926288. Telegrams & Cables: Acoustics Wembley.

THE INSIDE STORY ON THE BOEING FAMILY.

Choices. Choices. Choices. No other manufacturer in the world offers everything from 100 to 500 seats.

Five hundred miles, 1,000 miles, 3,500 miles, 6,000 miles. Boeing jetliners have the range flexibility to give airlines all sorts of opportunities to lower operating costs per seat mile.

Thin traffic. High frequency. Nonstop city pairs. High density, long-range markets. High density, short-range markets. Boeing jetliners do it all.

Single aisles. Twin aisles. Wide bodies. Six abreast. Seven abreast.

Eight abreast. Nine abreast. Ten abreast. Eleven abreast. Boeing has the options.

All-freight. Combis. Side cargo door loading. Main deck. Lower lobes. Pallets 88″ × 108″. Containers 40′ long. Virtually anything goes in Boeing jetliners.

The lineup runs like this: the intercontinental 707; 737, The Little Giant; 727, the world's most popular trijet; 747, The Queen of the Sky. And now a new generation — the 757 and 767. That's the basic family. But there are all types of choices within the product line. Gross weight. Engines. Seating. Cargo. Galley. You name it, we can do it. Or, if we haven't done it, we're probably thinking about doing it.

Everything we do has one purpose in mind — to give you the right airplane for the right market.

Our goal: to provide our customers with airplanes that perform with superior operating efficiency and have the flexibility to meet the multiple changing marketing opportunities of the '80s. And beyond.

THE BOEING FAMILY
Getting people together.

747

767

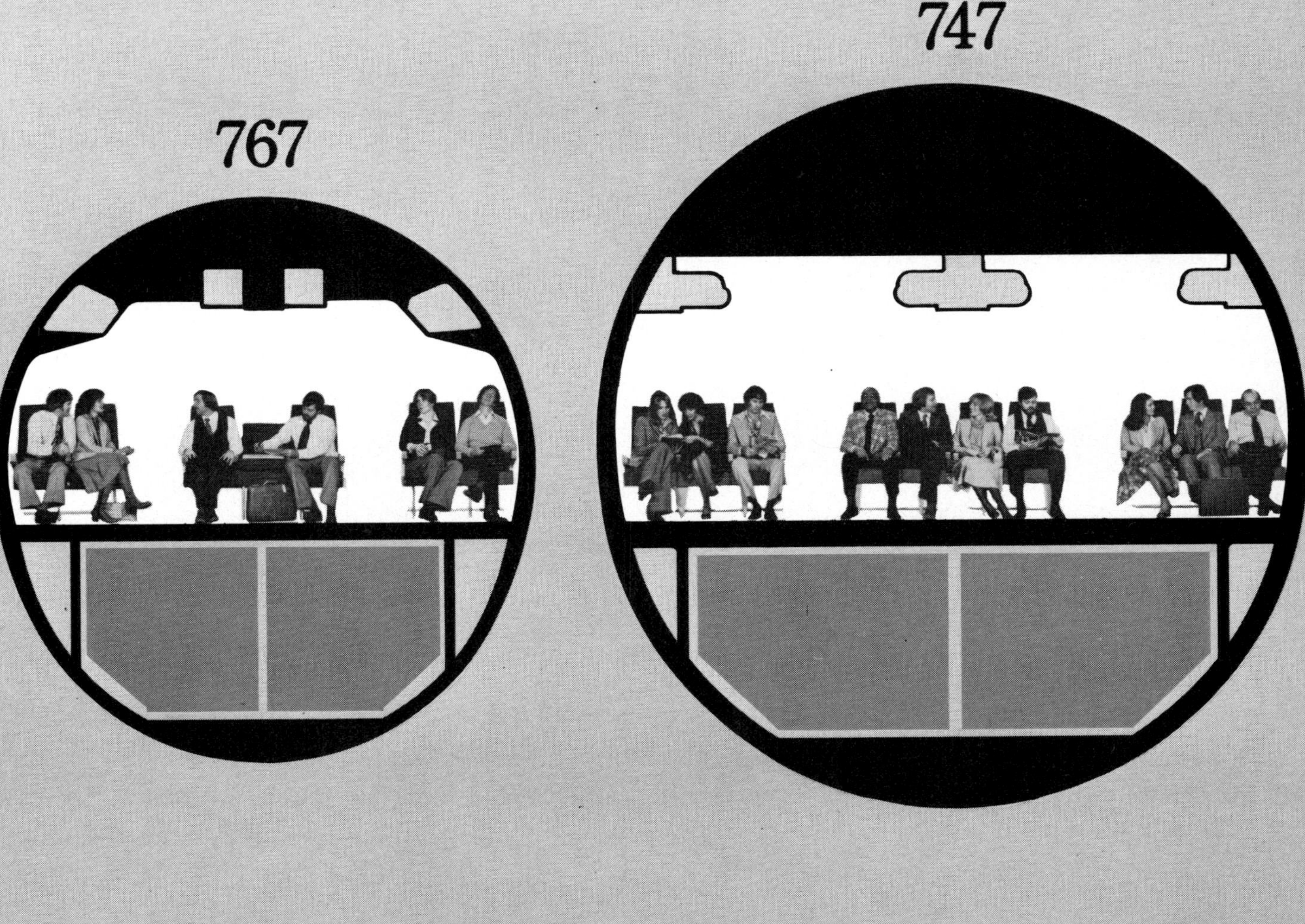

turbounion

The best form of defence is collaboration.

The Turbo-Union RB 199, powerful, compact and economical, will be familiar to you as the engine of the Tornado.

Less widely recognised, perhaps, are the advantages of its triple nationality.

Its very development was made possible only by the combined defence allocations of West Germany, the United Kingdom and Italy.

Without the pooled factory capacity and manpower skills of the three nations there would have been difficulty in meeting the initial orders for 2000.

And the amalgamation of their aero-engine know-how provided a short answer to competition.

In Rolls-Royce, MTU and Fiat Aviazione, the British, West German and Italian member companies of the Turbo-Union consortium formed in 1969, the partnership was one that had already collaborated for more than a decade.

And from the sharing of their design and engineering experience, their production resources, their management and manufacturing skills, was born the most advanced military gas turbine in the world.

All this – the RB 199 itself, the knowledge, the very partnership – is now at the service of every Allied power.

TURBO-UNION RB 199
There's really no alternative.

Turbo-Union Ltd., **Head-Office:** P. O. Box 3, Filton, Bristol BS 12 7QE, England, **Munich-Office:** Arabellastraße 4, D-8000 München 81, West Germany

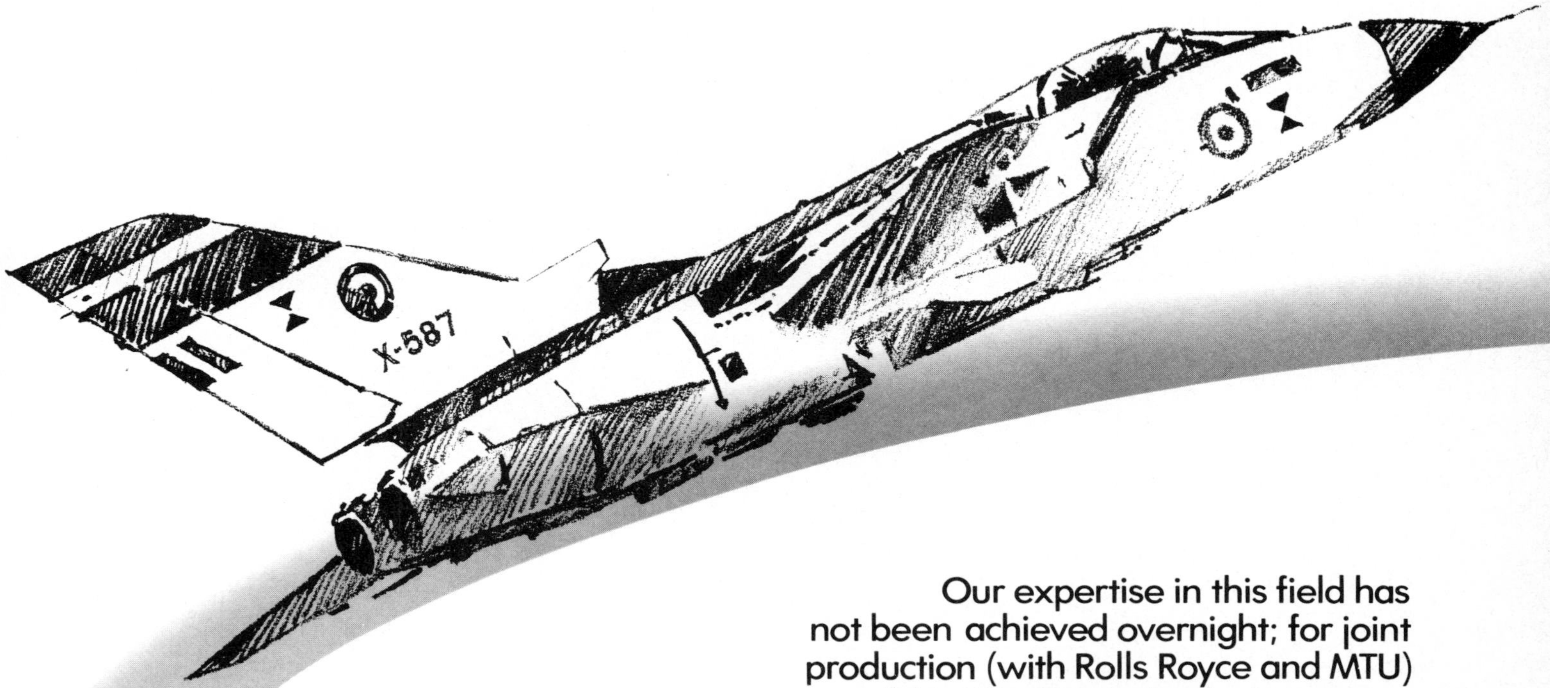

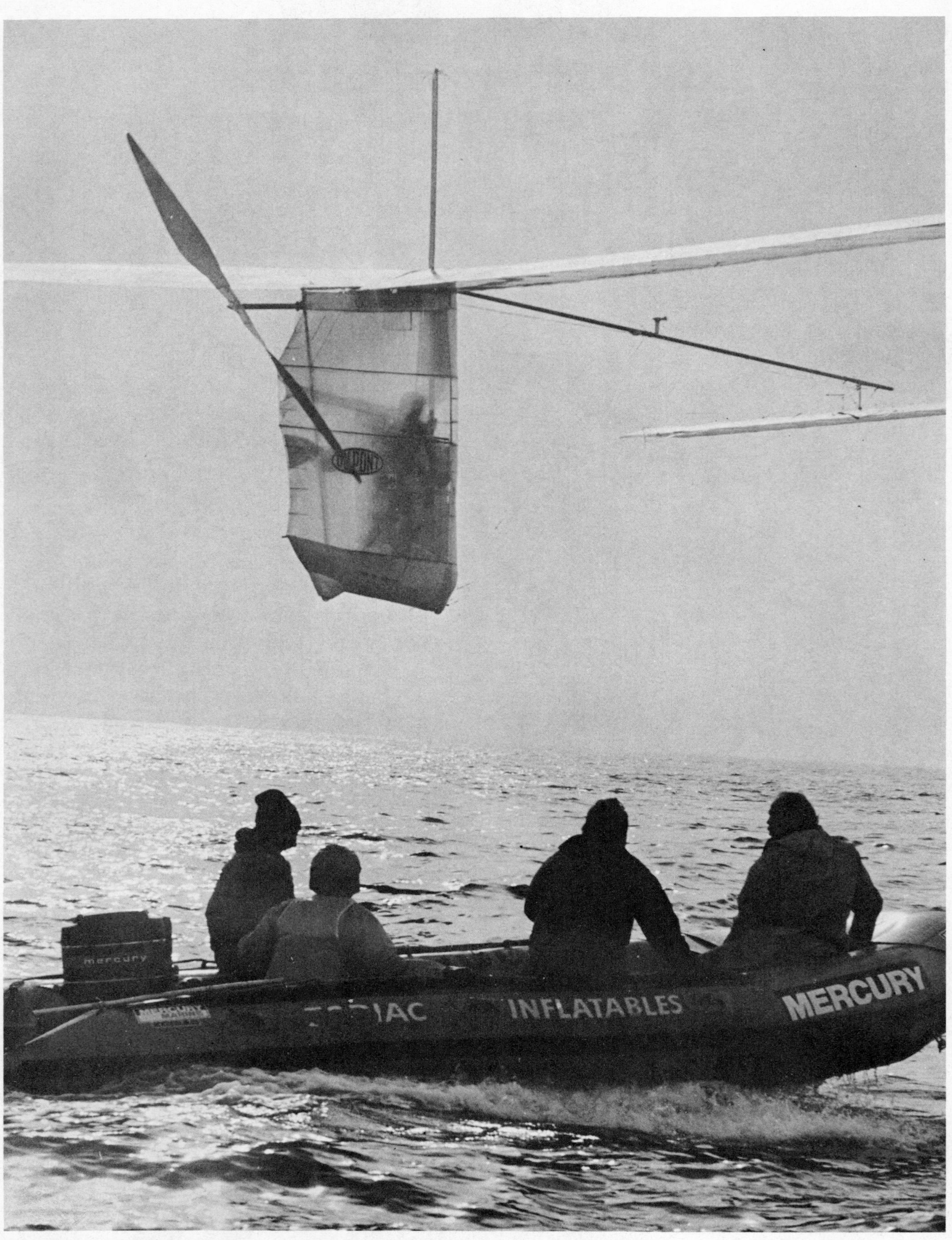

Bryan Allen, pilot and power plant, in mid-Channel with Gossamer Albatross on 12 June 1979. The historic 2 hour 40 minute crossing was completed successfully less than two years after Allen became the first person to achieve a man-powered flight around a mile-long figure-of-eight course

JANE'S ALL THE WORLD'S AIRCRAFT

FOUNDED IN 1909 BY FRED T. JANE

COMPILED AND EDITED BY
JOHN W. R. TAYLOR FRHistS, MRAeS, FSLAET
ASSISTANT EDITOR
KENNETH MUNSON, ARAeS

1979-80

ISBN 0 354 00589 8

JANE'S YEARBOOKS

LONDON

BOFORS

Turn night into day

with the SUPER LEPUS
the 7 000 000 candela aircraft parachute flare with supersonic capability.

Approved for AJ 37 Viggen, Jaguar, F-4, Harrier and many other aircraft.

AB BOFORS Ordnance Division
Box 500, S-690 20 BOFORS, Sweden
Telephone: (0)586-360 00 • Cables: Boforsco, Bofors • Telex: 73210 bofors s

CONTENTS

The Editor has been assisted in the compilation of this edition as follows:

Kenneth Munson	AIRCRAFT SECTION: ARGENTINA TO FINLAND, GREECE TO TURKEY, UNITED KINGDOM (pp 246-257); RPVs; SAILPLANES
David Mondey	AIRCRAFT SECTION: WEST GERMANY, UNITED KINGDOM (pp 223-246), UNITED STATES OF AMERICA; BALLOONS; INDEX
Bill Gunston	GLOSSARY; AERO-ENGINES
Michael Taylor	HOMEBUILTS; METRIC CONVERSIONS
Maurice Allward	SPACEFLIGHT AND RESEARCH ROCKETS
The Lord Ventry	AIRSHIPS

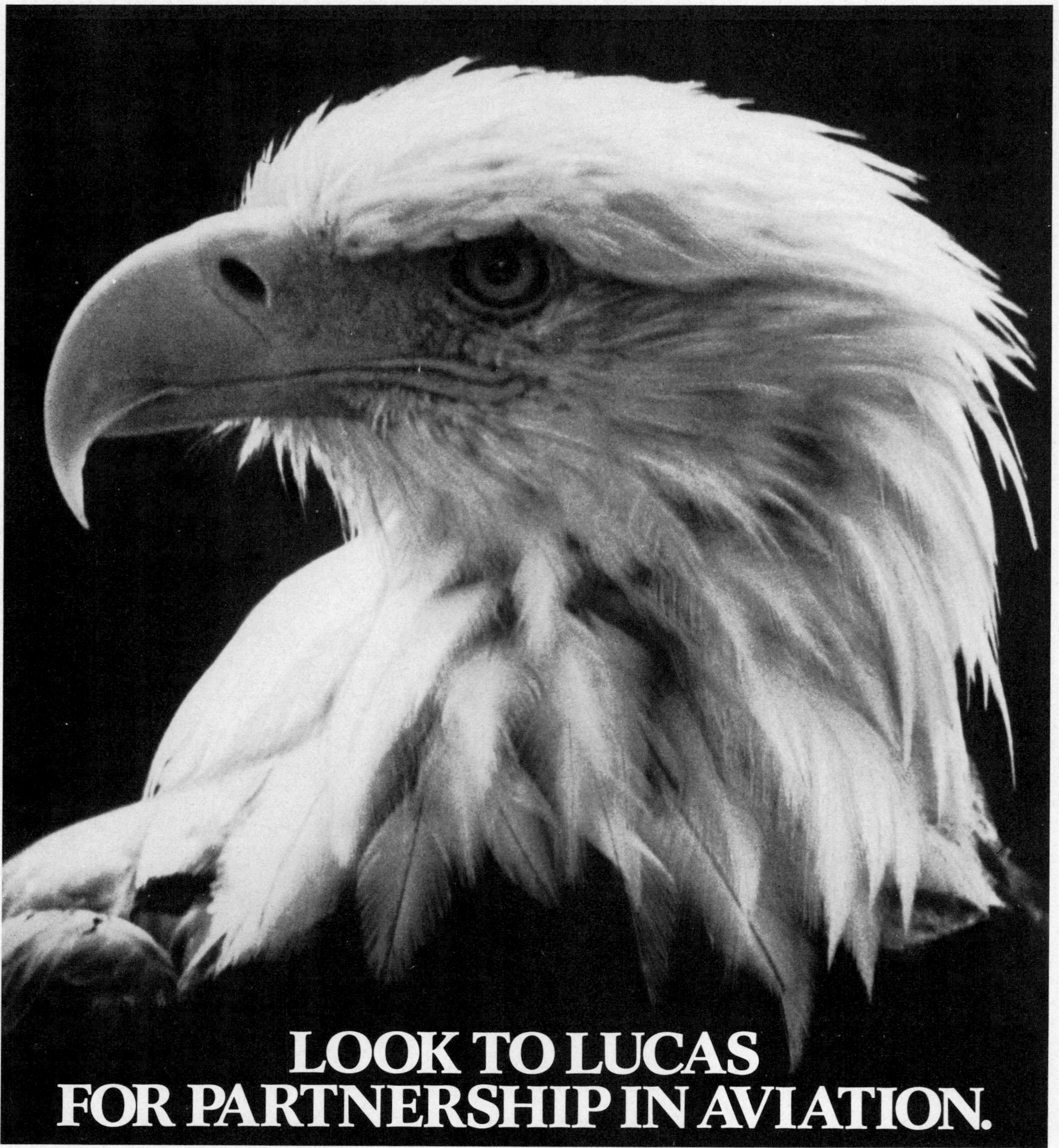
LOOK TO LUCAS
FOR PARTNERSHIP IN AVIATION.

FOREWORD

This edition marks the 70th year of publication of *Jane's All the World's Aircraft*, twenty of them under its present Editor. In an age that delights in anniversaries, it would have been appropriate to preface the contents with a catalogue of past achievements and a lighthearted survey of the current activities of the aviation industry that our book has served since 1909, the year in which Louis Blériot's flight from France to England marked the true beginning of international flying. To do so would abrogate responsibility and the trust of those who expect *Jane's* yearbooks to present their subjects in global perspective.

As we enter the decade of the 1980s, the dangers confronting our planet can be summed up in two of the sentences used by the Chairman of the US Joint Chiefs of Staff to introduce the FY 1980 *US Military Posture* statement. Noting that recent trends had "edged us another year closer to a potentially unstable and acutely dangerous imbalance in US-USSR military capability", General David C. Jones added: "I believe the days ahead may well be some of the most difficult we have ever faced".

The average citizen can be excused for finding such remarks puzzling after the USA and Soviet Union have signed two SALT (Strategic Arms Limitation Talks) agreements, aimed at restricting the numbers of long-range nuclear weapons available to both nations and ensuring a balance of power between them.

Nobody will deny that it is better to have the superpowers talking to each other rather than sitting on opposite sides of the fence snarling. But any suggestion that SALT I and II have led to meaningful force limitations, or reductions, is illusory. As a start, SALT II applies exclusively to the USA and USSR. It provides for no reduction of weapons that might annihilate the European allies of either nation in the event of major war, being concerned only with strategic arms and interpreting 'strategic' as something able to hit the USA from the Soviet Union, or vice versa. The Soviet SS-20 nuclear missiles and 'Backfire' bombers targeted against countries like Britain, West Germany, the Netherlands and Norway are not regarded as strategic in this context—a suggestion that offers little comfort to the peoples of those NATO nations.

To get an agreement on such terms may be desirable in a year preceding US Presidential elections, but some of the itemised limitations would seem laughable to the inhabitants of nations in the geographical middle were they not so ominous. America agreed, for example, that 'Backfire' need not be counted as a strategic bomber provided it was made visibly incapable of using its inherent flight refuelling capability. It now flies with the flight refuelling probe removed—no doubt safely in store at its base.

This should not imply that the Soviet Union is likely to break its word, only that SALT II does little to guarantee peace. For example, far from leading to any reduction in the US strategic attack force, the treaty provides for an *increase* in the number of operational US launch vehicles (missiles and/or manned bombers) to a total of 2,250 specified as the East/West level of balance. The Soviet Union will have to cut its own total of strategic nuclear delivery vehicles by about 250 to meet the limitation; but merely to count the launchers is no longer sufficient.

Each Soviet SS-18 ICBM is permitted to carry ten warheads, aimed to hit ten different targets (and is large enough to carry thirty!). The number of landbased MIRVed vehicles, with Multiple Independently-targetable Re-entry Vehicles of this kind, is limited by the treaty to 820 on each side. However, under the SALT agreements, the total number of Soviet nuclear warheads on ICBMs aimed at the USA and other targets has been allowed to increase from 1,050 in 1969, when the talks began, to 3,200 at the time of signing SALT II and more than 6,000 by the mid-1980s. Add to this number the Soviet submarine-launched ballistic missiles (SLBMs) and the warhead total will approach 12,000.

Soviet standards of accuracy in hitting targets is expected to match US potential by 1982. This has caused former US Secretary of State Henry Kissinger to express his belief that the Soviet Union will then be able to destroy America's landbased ICBM force with about half of the landbased MIRVed missiles that it is permitted to maintain under the SALT II treaty. Having done so, it would still have more than 300 MIRVed ICBMs, 380 MIRVed SLBMs and 500 single-warhead weapons (a total of well over 5,000 warheads) available to threaten America's civilian population and industrial potential. By contrast, Dr Kissinger believes that if SAC's entire force of Titan and Minuteman ICBMs were launched against Soviet ICBM silos, fewer than half of the Soviet missiles would be destroyed.

In each case, this assumes that the missiles under attack would be caught in their silos. More likely in this age of satellite and electronic surveillance is that the impending attack would be detected, leading to a two-way exchange of weapons. The US Congressional Office of Technology Assessment has studied the implications of such an act. According to the *Washington Post*, the study begins with the assumption that "The Soviets have dropped 4,000 megatons, and close to 100 million Americans are killed. The US counterattack on the Soviet Union has a similar devastating effect". This is no place to record the hideous scenario that follows. All the gold in Fort Knox becomes of less worth than a mug full of clean water or a sack of uncontaminated potatoes. "The president (who has survived) announces that the cease-fire is holding" . . . . but there are no victors in that kind of war.

* * * * * * *

It might be argued that these references to missile capabilities are out of place in *All the World's Aircraft*; but, once one accepts that the consequences of an ICBM exchange would be catastrophic and long-lasting as the experts predict, the piloted aeroplane reassumes its old dominant role in any defence plan.

The traditional line of thought is that fighting could begin, somewhere like the central front in Europe, as the result of deliberate aggression or over-reaction to a real or imagined provocation. America's reaction to the 'discovery' of 'Soviet combat forces' in Cuba in the Autumn of 1979—despite assurances that they had been there for 17 years, on training duties—demonstrated how sensitive the superpowers can be to such matters. It is, therefore, essential for NATO and the Warsaw Pact forces to be balanced in Europe (the main danger area) before we can hope to begin a genuine, still-balanced, scaling down of arms and create the basis for a permanent peace.

In this respect, the offer by President Brezhnev to withdraw 20,000 troops and 1,000 tanks from bases in East Germany was more realistic than half of the clauses in SALT II, and should have been welcomed.

If either side became so dominant that it could achieve a quick breakthrough on the battlefield whenever it wished, the temptation for the other to plan for the use of nuclear weapons, on a rapidly increasing scale, might be irresistible. Unfortunately, the forces on opposite sides of the border across Europe are already far from balanced. Britain's *Statement on the Defence Estimates* for 1979 includes a diagram suggesting that the Warsaw Pact countries outnumber NATO in central Europe by 2.2 to 1 in fixed-wing tactical aircraft, 2.8 to 1 in main battle tanks and 2.7 to 1 in artillery; and they are known to deploy immense numbers of anti-aircraft guns and missiles of high quality.

To superior numbers must be added the Warsaw Pact's dominance in chemical and electronic warfare, and round-the-clock competence. As long as eleven years ago, in Czechoslovakia, the Soviet forces demonstrated their ability to mount a large operation impeccably at night, after blanketing the entire border electronically to hide their approach. Despite this, too many of NATO's first-line aircraft in Europe are fair-weather types, lacking equipment or weapons for all-weather operation. By comparison, Warsaw Pact combat aircraft continue to make massive technological advances to improve their effectiveness. Pages 175-223 of this edition provide ample evidence of this, including brief references to a few of the types that will give the air forces of the eastern bloc even greater capability in the 1980s.

Of particular note is the enthusiasm and imagination with which the Soviet Union has integrated helicopters into its armed forces. Evidence suggests that nearly 6,000 Mi-8s alone have been built, mostly as military aircraft capable of carrying up to 28 troops or the heaviest firepower yet seen on any helicopter in the world. The Mi-24 is an impressive assault transport and gunship, heavily armed and armoured, with laser-guided missiles now added to its weapons. NATO has nothing comparable, and it should not be overlooked that an Mi-24 now holds the absolute speed record for helicopters, at nearly 200 knots (370 km/h; 230 mph).

The Mi-24 is best regarded as a very high-speed armoured fighting vehicle, almost an aerial tank. It has displayed its ability in action, in places like Afghanistan. Other Soviet helicopters enabled the Ethiopians and their allies to get behind Somali forces in areas of the Ogaden, complete with guns and vehicles, and so played an important part in ending that campaign. The capability of such units will be further improved, to a unique extent, when the new Mil heavy-lift helicopter known to NATO as 'Halo' enters service.

The great advantage enjoyed by the Soviet armed services is that they continue to receive the very best equipment that their industry can produce, seemingly regardless of cost. Western economy dictates a policy of cost-cutting that usually makes the best too expensive and keeps outdated equipment in service when it is long past its prime.

According to General Richard H. Ellis, Commander in Chief of SAC, the USSR now has at least three new ICBMs in production, whereas America's projected MX missile is ten years away from full deployment; and the USSR has an advanced bomber with intercontinental capabilities in production, while the US has none. Meanwhile, the 214 vintage early-model B-52s stored at Davis-Monthan AFB, some without engines, wheels and other components, are counted as nuclear delivery vehicles under SALT II. The 54 operational Titan ICBMs at the same base have developed a tendency to leak poisonous fumes from time to time.

What's new? The answer is that the DoD's FY 1980 defence budget requested a total of only 382 new combat aircraft for the USAF (60 F-15s, 175 F-16s, 144 A-10s, 3 E-3A AWACS), of which only the 63 F-15s and E-3As can be regarded as all-weather types. The US Navy requests totalled 57 combat aircraft (24 F-14s, 15 F-18s, 12 P-3Cs and 6 E-2Cs), plus 6 ECM jamming EA-6Bs, to which Congress subsequently added a few A-7Es to keep things going in Texas. Soviet fighter production alone has been maintained at the rate of more than 1,000 a year for the past six years.

The time is clearly overdue for NATO nations to make better use of their technological skills to re-equip their armed forces, rather than risk becoming the richest occupants of a future nuclear graveyard. Efforts to assure people in the UK that ground-launched cruise missiles based in East Anglia would provide an answer to the SS-20 missile are akin to equating Hitler's V-1 flying bomb with the V-2 rocket in 1944. If money can be spared for pilotless aircraft, it might be better to spend it on tens of

thousands of RPVs. These would be able to maintain permanent patrol over any potentially troublesome frontier, watching for and reporting in real time the slightest sign of abnormal activity on the other side. RPVs with different onboard equipment could be launched immediately to designate targets such as tanks or AFVs, which could be picked off by warhead-carrying RPVs at the rate of one every ten seconds per designator.

It is unlikely that they would run short of targets on the central front in Europe. America's Assault Breaker anti-armour study assumes that a primary need is "to engage the command tanks of six Soviet and Warsaw Pact armoured divisions attacking along an 18 km front—some 2,400 targets—and try to keep these from being a dominant part of the battle, at least for a couple of days and hopefully for longer than that".

Such applications for RPVs could offset some of the most worrying NATO front-line weaknesses, at a cost to which even politicians could not object. Yet this is the year in which the USAF disbanded its only RPV reconnaissance unit, despite the latter's achievements in Viet-Nam. As one highly-qualified observer commented to the Editor: "You get to be a general flying SR-71s, not RPVs".

* * * * * *

Turning now to industry, two years have elapsed since the majority of the UK's privately-owned aerospace companies were nationalised to form British Aerospace. This seemed to make little difference to its programmes and projects for a while; but by the beginning of 1979 there were signs of life. The BAe 146 transport had received a firm go-ahead, and some critics of a four-turbofan configuration for a short-haul airliner were silenced by the willingness of Avco Aerostructures of America and Saab-Scania of Sweden to put their own cash into the venture. More important still, the UK had rejoined the Airbus consortium that it should never have left, enabling BAe to contribute and benefit as a full partner in Europe's most-successful-ever commercial aircraft programme.

In the engine field, Rolls-Royce's RB.211 turbofan had proved so outstanding that Boeing had no hesitation in choosing it as the launch engine for its new 757 airliner.

With military aircraft like the Harrier, Hawk, Nimrod and Tornado, and thriving missile and space contracts to occupy its time and talents, and the unique experience of the brilliantly successful Anglo-French Concorde SST programme on which to build, one felt that Britain's industry could face the future with greater confidence than at any period for more than twenty years. The euphoria did not last. A new government, seemingly anxious to have immediate money rather than long-term prosperity, soon disturbed the calm with plans to sell back half the BAe shares to the private ownership under which the industry had declined before nationalisation. Even worse, the workforce suddenly caught the malaise that had been slowly throttling Britain's car and shipbuilding industries, by joining in strikes that reduced each 'working' week to only three days and persuaded Rolls-Royce to close completely until its employees' yearning for industrial suicide had passed.

At the time this Foreword was being written, the consequences of such action, or inaction, had still to be reckoned. With the RB.211-535 programme already eight weeks behind schedule, Eastern Air Lines is known to be studying actively the possibility of fitting General Electric CF6-32s to its Boeing 757s. Rolls's Aero-Engine Division Managing Director has told his staff that Boeing "would never let the poor performance of a supplier stand in the way of their success" and that the potential sale of RB.211s for 2,000 airliners during the 1980s is in the balance. Time is running out for evidence of shrewd leadership at the top and common-sense will to survive on the shop floor of Britain's aerospace industry. Without these once-traditional British virtues, all the skill and talent in the world are dross.

Britain is not unique in suffering from strikes, but few great nations have allowed themselves deliberately to decline, morally and industrially, at such a rate. It is utterly untypical, and one must hope for a change of attitude before it is too late, because the entire world will be poorer without Britain's once-balanced and respected example and inventive genius.

As already noted, the USA, too, has experienced years of government penny-pinching, to the detriment of its military services. Anyone who has seen the A-10 Thunderbolt II's mighty gun in action will recognise the destructive power of this 1980s Stormovik; but *all* A-10s should be to the standard of the lone two-seater prototype, to ensure their adequacy in a European environment. Equally, having evolved and tested the B-1 at great cost, there seems little sense in the proposal to produce a bargain-price penetrator by modifying this superb aircraft to "aluminium, fixed-wing, with reduced power and the bomb bays replaced by a missile launcher", as reported recently by Senator Barry Goldwater. One might as well have saved millions of pounds and francs on Concorde by making it manpowered.

The alternatives to the emasculated B-1 that were outlined by General Ellis before the Senate Armed Services Committee on SALT II, last August, were no more impressive. He said: "We fully expect the ALCM-equipped B-52G to be employed in a 'shoot and penetrate' role until 1985, at which time we recommend its transition to an all stand-off ALCM carrier. The B-52H model will be upgraded to ensure it has the ability to penetrate until the late 1980s. Then, SAC recommends that it, too, be converted to an ALCM stand-off carrier role. With the entire B-52 force in a pure ALCM role, we can delay the costly introduction of a new cruise missile carrier until the 1990s.

"Preliminary work on an advanced strategic manned penetrator for the 1990s has just started. It is now at a very low funding level, and mostly in the form of studies . . . Several agencies have looked at various alternatives to offset the serious threat in the period of uncertainty during the early 1980s. SAC believes the most promising and timely solution is the early modification of 155 FB- and F-111s into FB-111B/Cs with new engines, enlarged weapon capacity, and sharply increased range capabilities. This would provide a strategic penetrator for the entire decade of the 1980s."

* * * * * *

Whether or not such updating of an old airframe could produce a survivable penetrator for the 1980s we can only wait and see. At least it would avoid one of the major problems encountered time after time by the US Department of Defense in recent years—the danger inherent in trying to develop every part of a new weapon system concurrently. This was emphasised by Under Secretary of Defense for Research and Engineering Dr. William J. Perry. Discussing the F-16 fighter, he said it provided "an excellent example of a programme where we took a risk. We introduced high concurrency into the programme and we are paying a price for that". Stressing that the F100 engine had caused most concern, he added: "We did not know when we made the decision (to go into production) that we were about to enter a whole series of problems on the F100 engine in the F-15".

Dr. Perry reckoned that up to two years had been saved in the time needed to get the F-16 into service by using the same basic engine as that in the F-15 . . . "But if we don't get our engine problem solved and have to introduce a different engine, it will have proven a very, very poor decision."

Pratt & Whitney seems to be justifying his trust. As this edition is closing for press, the company has announced that it knows the reason for the stall stagnations that have been encountered usually when afterburning has been selected on the F-15 at high altitude and low speed, and is remedying the problem. It has already succeeded in reducing the incidence of such stalls from three or four per 1,000 engine hours to 1.38, and hopes eventually to attain a rate of 0.15 per 1,000 hours.

The US Navy has suffered similarly with its F-14A Tomcat fighters. Quoting DoD sources: "Although the F-14A has been shown to be a superb fighter aircraft, its material readiness has been inadequate. Reliability problems with the TF30 engines continue to plague the Tomcat, principally regarding compressor stalling accidents. The engine deficiencies became epidemic after 1975 . . . . approximately 33% of all F-14A losses are attributable to engine failures."

An alternative engine programme was launched, taking the core of the B-1 bomber's General Electric F101 engine as the basis for a new power plant for both the F-16 and F-14. The cost in FY 1978/80 was a relatively modest $57 million, but the eventual cost of re-engining F-14s alone was estimated at well over a billion dollars. It should not now be necessary. However, improvement programmes on eight current US engines had cost a total of $676 million by October 1979, and were expected to absorb a further $1,200 million by the mid-1980s. There is clearly a lesson here for everyone.

It explains why the US Air Force and Navy have selected four engine companies to begin studies for a new 80 kN (18,000 lb st) engine, with a thrust-to-weight ratio of 11.3:1, to power future fighters. On the basis that it usually takes 12 to 14 years and one million flying hours to mature advanced fighter engines, whereas airframes can be developed in four to six years, the new engine is required to be at the pre-production flight testing stage by 1990-91.

The kind of aircraft that it might power was displayed by Rockwell International, in the form of a full-scale mockup, at the 1979 Paris Air Show. As exciting in concept as the F-16, it was one of three competitive designs by Rockwell, Grumman and General Dynamics to meet a DARPA (Defense Advanced Research Projects Agency) specification for a Forward Swept Wing (FSW) technology demonstrator. One of the three is likely to be built for flight testing in 1982-83, and DARPA expects it to provide five major advantages compared with sweptback wings: high maximum lift at all angles of attack, because the tips remain effective as angle of attack increases; better distribution of internal volume; lower supersonic drag; improved flutter characteristics; and enhanced wing bending moment relief.

The Rockwell design is based on a 45 degree forward-swept aeroelastic wing made of composites, and a single General Electric F404 engine. Weight is calculated at only 5,900 kg (13,000 lb), complete with one M61 Vulcan gun, two air-to-air missiles and the APG-65 radar developed for the F-18. Cost is estimated at $6 million per aircraft.

* * * * * *

Study of the provisional three-view of what is claimed to represent a new Soviet combat aircraft, on page 197, suggests that the Soviet Union, too, is reverting to its familiar belief that small is beautiful in fighter design. The advances made by its design bureaus in the past decade have been impressive, particularly in the field of heavy-lift and assault helicopters. However, the US Department of Defense believes that America is still ahead in avionics, munitions and standards of pilot training. The number of hours flown annually by all but elite Soviet aircrew is said to be minimal by Western standards. Equally significant is that interceptor pilots are trained to operate under strict ground control, which limits low flying.

This last factor is becoming less significant as the Soviet air forces perfect the look-down, snap-down radar/missile techniques they have already demonstrated from MiG-23 and MiG-25 interceptors against low-flying targets. Allied to proficiency in anti-aircraft fire from the ground, on a massive scale, it may explain Foreign Minister Andrei Gromyko's much-publicised comment on US cruise missiles. When US delegates to the SALT talks expressed resentment that the USSR had insisted on restricting the range of US air-launched cruise missiles to 2,500 km, Mr. Gromyko is said to have waved his hands at the Americans and remarked: "All right; you can fly them round the world if you like".

It is tempting to regard any concession by the Soviet Union as simply a gesture by a nation so mighty that such things make no difference. Such

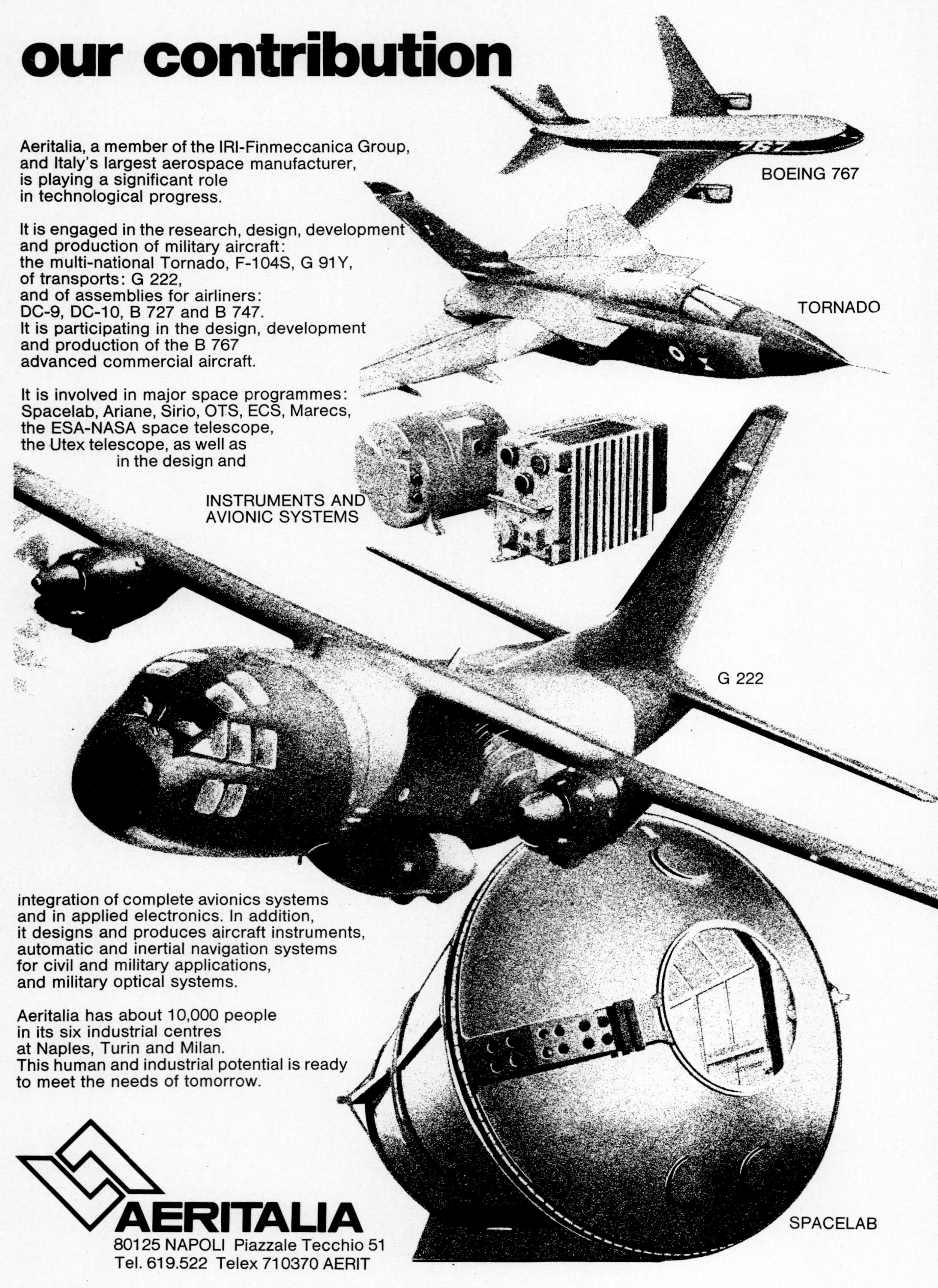
our contribution
Aeritalia, a member of the IRI-Finmeccanica Group, and Italy's largest aerospace manufacturer, is playing a significant role in technological progress.
It is engaged in the research, design, development and production of military aircraft: the multi-national Tornado, F-104S, G 91Y, of transports: G 222, and of assemblies for airliners: DC-9, DC-10, B 727 and B 747. It is participating in the design, development and production of the B 767 advanced commercial aircraft.
It is involved in major space programmes: Spacelab, Ariane, Sirio, OTS, ECS, Marecs, the ESA-NASA space telescope, the Utex telescope, as well as in the design and integration of complete avionics systems and in applied electronics. In addition, it designs and produces aircraft instruments, automatic and inertial navigation systems for civil and military applications, and military optical systems.
Aeritalia has about 10,000 people in its six industrial centres at Naples, Turin and Milan. This human and industrial potential is ready to meet the needs of tomorrow.
BOEING 767
TORNADO
INSTRUMENTS AND AVIONIC SYSTEMS
G 222
SPACELAB
AERITALIA
80125 NAPOLI Piazzale Tecchio 51
Tel. 619.522 Telex 710370 AERIT

cynicism ignores known facts. For example, the MiG-21 may not represent anything approaching current Soviet technological attainment, but it *is* the most widely-deployed combat aircraft in the world and still equips many first-line tactical squadrons of the Warsaw Pact air forces. Yet it has seldom fared well when matched against Western types. In the latest incident, six Israeli F-15s and four IAI Kfir-C2s were directed by an E-2C Hawkeye AWACS against eight Syrian MiG-21s over southern Lebanon. Six of the MiGs were shot down, five of them by the F-15s which are believed to have used Shafrir missiles in the engagement (the first ever fought by either of the US types).

Would the result have been different with Soviet pilots in the MiGs, or if they had been MiG-23s? We must pray that we never have to learn the answer.

Meanwhile, a very different aircraft provides an example of how Soviet designers triumph over temporary setbacks. Twelve months ago the Tu-144 supersonic airliner was out of service, after only six months of operation over the short Moscow-Alma Ata route. It seemed a sad end for Concorde's only rival, and a setback for all who believe that commercial flying must continue to advance in speed as well as safety and scope.

No Tu-144 appeared at the 1979 Paris Air Show; but then, on 23 June, came news that the Soviet SST had completed a proving flight over the long Moscow-Khabarovsk route for which it was originally intended. Anyone with a pocket calculator and the right kind of know-how could prove to his own satisfaction that such a nonstop journey, with a reasonable payload, was possible only for a re-engined Tu-144—a conclusion confirmed in due course by the USSR's Deputy Minister of Civil Aviation. So, at last, one can genuinely congratulate Dr. Alexei Tupolev on an achievement that even America's aerospace industry has not yet been able to match. It is only sad that none of the official information sources in Moscow has displayed the meanest subsonic speed in sending details of the Tu-144D to update *Jane's* entry on the aircraft.

* * * * * *

It is hard to believe that Concorde, having passed out of production, is making its final appearance in *Jane's* this year. The last two aircraft left the assembly lines at Toulouse and Filton without immediate operators and with no very apparent enthusiasm on anyone's part to follow up one of the major success stories in engineering history.

Yet there is hope. Seven years ago a Douglas Aircraft Company vice president, at Long Beach, remarked to the Editor that America's first SST would "look like Concorde, be made of the same materials as Concorde and fly at the same speed as Concorde, but would be twice as big so that it could operate at a healthy profit". After nearly four years of Concorde operations, his view is unlikely to have undergone any great change; so might not one still look forward to the possibility of this great US manufacturer of commercial transport aircraft getting together with Aérospatiale and BAe to build flagships for all of the world's major airlines?

With subsonic transports rolling off the line at Boeing at the rate of 28 a month, and the new 757 and 767 to ease into the programme, there is little likelihood that Douglas's northern rival would want to have a second try at supersonics for a while. Douglas itself has not had a happy year in 1979; but no manufacturer can be blamed if, as reported, customers fail to follow carefully-stated servicing procedures. It is easy to say that it should not be possible to remove engines in such a way that the operation causes serious damage. Such an interpretation of Murphy's Law would also insist that every motor car be fitted with a device that prevented its being driven into the path of a speeding juggernaut lorry on a motorway.

However great the advances made in every aspect of air safety, there will always be accidents. In the 31 days of August 1979, more than 4.6 million people travelled in the 283 DC-10s in world-wide service with 41 airlines. By then, these aircraft had carried more than 233 million passengers, in eight years. New orders placed in September brought the total to close on 400, including 53 conditional orders and options. No further comment should be needed.

* * * * * *

The degree to which Europe's aerospace industries are now working together becomes more apparent with each succeeding edition of *Jane's*. The UK continues to build HS.748s, One-Elevens, Shorts 330s and Skyvans; but the only large airliners now manufactured in Europe are the products of Airbus Industrie, drawing on the capabilities of French, West German, Dutch, Spanish and British manufacturers, with Belgium coming in on the A310. Britain, France, Sweden and Italy continue to design and build military aircraft to meet their own special needs and those of export customers; but here, too, there is growing emphasis on collaboration, evident in the programmes for the Tornado, Jaguar, Alpha Jet and new armed helicopters.

The cost of collaboration is not always as low as one might wish, which is hardly surprising when one sees Airbus wings and fuselage sections being airfreighted from Chester and Hamburg to Toulouse and counts the cost of personnel commuting from one country to another. Nevertheless, the advantages are well proved—not least that Europe would probably be out of the big transport aircraft league entirely without such a venture.

Nor should it be imagined that any of the 'big three' US manufacturers does the job on its own. This was emphasised when Boeing placed $1,000 million worth of 757 subcontracts in a single day in October 1979—covering 200 shipsets of centre fuselage wing-boxes and keel beams from Avco Aerostructures; overwing passenger cabins from Fairchild Republic; the fuselage sections immediately fore and aft of the wing from Rockwell's Tulsa Division; tailcones and tail surfaces from Vought. With other components coming from Shorts of Belfast and Hawker de Havilland of Australia, Boeing is responsible for manufacturing little but the wings and nose section. Such widespread collaboration is not unusual, as study of the entries for other US commercial aircraft, and for subcontracting companies, will reveal.

The fact is that most countries, and most manufacturers throughout the world, now depend on others to some degree. Light aircraft designed by Beech, Cessna and Piper are built under licence in Argentina, Brazil, Colombia, Poland and the UK. US combat aircraft are assembled in Belgium, Italy, Japan, South Korea, the Netherlands, Spain, Switzerland and Taiwan. Italian trainers and light attack aircraft are built in Brazil and South Africa. Spanish transport aircraft are built in Indonesia, West German helicopters in Indonesia and the Philippines . . . the list becomes endless when component manufacturers everywhere from Australia to Israel are added. Even the Soviet Union is not excluded, with Poland licensed to build the An-28 and Mi-2, and to supply major assemblies for the Il-86 airbus. No less interesting is news that McDonnell Douglas is negotiating licence manufacture of the DC-9 Super 80 in China.

Nowhere has collaboration been more freely offered than in spaceflight. Countless foreign satellites and experiments have been launched on board US and Soviet rockets through the years, and representatives of all the USSR's allies and friends are being taken into orbit, one by one, in Soyuz spacecraft. A Vostok spacecraft launched in the Cosmos series of unmanned missions in September 1979 made history by carrying thirteen US experiments with those from the Soviet Union and other countries.

Less publicised, but even more significant, is that the Soviet Union interrupted signals from three of its early warning military satellites on 1/2 September 1979, at NASA's request, to ensure that they would not interfere with transmissions from Pioneer 11 as it passed Saturn.

Such incidents reflect our industry's contribution to the concept of 'one world'. Wars will certainly become less attractive as nations realise their interdependence. There would be no 'butter mountain' for the Soviet Union to buy from a devastated Europe, and no wheat to feed its people, 25 million tons at a time, from American prairies scorched and blighted for generations by nuclear radiation. The pity is that surplus food goes at the moment mainly to those who can pay for it. With millions suffering from starvation, cargo ships and aircraft mothballed because they have nothing to do, and crews unemployed, there must be something wrong with world government.

As we have discovered increasingly in recent years, criticism of poor resources management can be applied to energy as well as food. At the first sign of petrol shortage, newspapers began to tell of shootings, stabbings and punch-ups between frustrated motorists in queues at American filling stations. At a global level, West German Chancellor Helmut Schmidt warned that wars might be precipitated by competition for oil and gas if nuclear energy was not developed quickly. It became easier to understand growing international interest in nations like Afghanistan, sitting astride routes to places where oil flows.

Such warnings are nothing new. The Foreword to the 1974-75 *Jane's* noted that: "While the increased cost of aviation fuels has created much of the present financial crisis, a greater long-term problem is depletion of the world's hydrocarbon fuel reserves. The solution may lie in the eventual use of liquid hydrogen fuel, now that manned space programmes have shown that it can be manufactured, handled and used safely in very large quantities. This is no place to examine exhaustively the ways in which liquid hydrogen might replace kerosene or gasoline in aircraft. Suffice it to say that the project design teams of some of the world's leading manufacturers have worked out the basic configurations of airliners that might run on liquid hydrogen.

"Models tested in wind tunnels by companies like McDonnell Douglas have given results suggesting that full-scale versions might be carrying passengers in everyday service by the turn of the century. One interesting conclusion is that the new fuel not only makes possible intercontinental aircraft able to carry 500 passengers at Mach 6 to Mach 9, but would be equally suitable for 1,000-seat subsonic jumbos. Furthermore, liquid hydrogen is the cleanest burning of all fuels and might offer solutions to both airport noise and inflight sonic boom problems when allied to advanced design."

We are now five years nearer the time when the tanks will run dry, with little achieved. It is, therefore, to Lockheed's credit that its engineers have come forward with a scheme that would enable the potential of liquid hydrogen fuel to be assessed realistically on a normal scheduled freight service, using aircraft that would be almost indistinguishable externally from their kerosene-fuelled counterparts.

The idea is to install in a conventional, but lengthened, TriStar two large tanks holding a total of 22,710 kg (50,070 lb) of liquid hydrogen fuel, fore and aft of the cargo hold. Such an aircraft would be capable of hauling 48,230 kg (106,330 lb) of freight for a distance of 3,500 nm (6,480 km; 4,025 miles), and the proposal is to use it on services from the USA, across the Atlantic to Western Europe and then down to the Gulf States. Lockheed believes such cargo operations could begin by 1987 if work on the project started now, and that it might not be many more years before the results were sufficiently convincing to persuade the airlines to show interest in hydrogen-powered passenger aircraft.

Feeling only slightly facetious, we can add that *Jane's*, at about the same time as that first reference to liquid hydrogen fuel, began to offer alternatives for when the hydrocarbons become scarce. A section on hang gliders appeared first in 1973-74, followed by a few pages of hot-air balloons, which found a place in *All the World's Aircraft* just 193 years after they first lifted men off the ground.

These new sections, like the 'Homebuilts', have added considerably to the interest and value of the book, for an ever-wider readership. Without a moment's hesitation, Editor and Publisher chose as the frontispiece to this year's edition a photograph of a strange aircraft that would hardly have qualified for inclusion a few years ago. Following dramatic pictures of the supersonic YF-16, B-1, Tornado and 'ski-jump' Harrier that have occupied this place of honour since the frontispiece was introduced in 1975-76, we now have the Gossamer Albatross and its pilot/engine Bryan Allen, midway over the English Channel on the first-ever manpowered crossing—an achievement that Louis Blériot would certainly have applauded.

The first two solar-powered aircraft also find a place in the book this year.

The enthusiasm shown by the makers of homebuilt and manpowered aircraft, gliders and balloons when submitting material for inclusion in *Jane's* helps to make the Editor's work a delight. The feelings of the balloonists are summed up by the correspondent at Mike Adams' Balloon Loft who wrote: "We really appreciate *Jane's* including balloons in their publications. We have received many inquiries as a result of being listed". Brian Boland, of Boland Balloons, wrote a long letter telling how his 110 lb wife, Kathy, set a series of FAI-recognised records in the world's smallest certificated experimental hot-air balloon, one of which involved being whisked to a height of 3,477 m (11,407 ft), without even the comfort and assurance provided by a basket. We men in aviation never cease to owe a great deal to our womenfolk.

* * * * * *

As always, *Jane's* owes much to many people, in literally every aircraft-manufacturing nation in the world, for without their willing and increasing help this great book would be far less comprehensive and accurate. This year's Paris Air Show— also celebrating its 70th 'birthday'—brought *Jane's* into contact with yet another of the Soviet Union's great designers, Oleg Antonov. During a long interview, he proved to be an old friend, remarking proudly that he had personal copies of *All the World's Aircraft* going back to 1922. The Show also provided an opportunity to renew links with representatives of Tehnoimportexport, who promised to end the period of unintentional non-cooperation which has made Romania the only nation not to provide update material for *Jane's* in recent years.

In this respect, readers will note a major increase in the volume of information on China's aerospace industry, which is growing rapidly in size, quality and willingness to communicate with the outside world. In particular, certain details of that nation's new large airliner correct inaccurate information that has appeared elsewhere, notably in respect of the number of engines fitted.

To all those whose contributions have made this new edition possible, the Editor offers his sincere thanks and friendship. It is not practicable to list many of them by name, but all should know how much their information, photographs, drawings and advice are valued.

In particular, the Editor records his debt to the long-serving members of his team of fellow compilers, headed by Assistant Editor Kenneth Munson and including Maurice Allward, Bill Gunston, David Mondey, Michael Taylor and the Lord Ventry. Details of their individual responsibilities are given at the top of the Contents page.

Of similar importance in creating the quality of the end product is the work of Netherwood Dalton & Co. Ltd. of Huddersfield, who can claim a longer association with *All the World's Aircraft* than anyone else, having printed every UK and US edition of the book from the start, when it was entitled *All the World's Air-Ships*. Their close collaboration with the London Office staff responsible for layout of the pages, under the experienced leadership of Christine Richards, has again ensured the compact, correctly-ordered appearance of the contents, so important in an international reference book.

After twenty years it is difficult to find anything new to say about the ever-ready assistance received from those overseas who have been loyal personal friends during a lifetime in the aviation business. So, a simple and warm "Thank you" to good friends and colleagues on the editorial staffs of *Air Force Magazine* (Washington) and *Flug Revue* (West Germany); to Delden Badcock (Australia); Pierre Sparaco (Belgium); Ronaldo S. Olive and Roberto Pereira de Andrade (Brazil); Vico Rosaspina (Italy); Eiichiro Sekigawa (Japan); Antonio Camarasa and Javier Taibo (Spain); Roland Eichenberger and Dr. Ulrich Haller (Switzerland); Norman Polmar and Tom DeFrank (USA); Wolfgang Wagner of *Deutscher Aerokurier* (West Germany); Dipl Ing Andrzej Glass and other friends of the Instytut Lotnictwa in Poland; William Green and Gordon Swanborough of *Air International* and Alan Hall of *Aviation News* (UK); and the editorial staffs at *Flight International* and *Aeroplane Monthly* (UK); *Aviation Magazine* and *Air et Cosmos* (France); *Aerophile* (USA); *FLYGvapenNYTT* (Sweden) and *de Vliegende Hollander* (the Netherlands). The high standard of the illustrations again owes much to our photographer friends Howard Levy, Gordon S. Williams, Peter M. Bowers, Jean Seele, Neil Macdougall, Austin Brown, Brian M. Service and J. M. G. Gradidge, and to Dennis Punnett and Michael Badrocke who were responsible for the new and updated three-view drawings. Established on this foundation of knowledge, experience and enthusiasm, *Jane's* at least can look forward with confidence to the challenges that will confront it in the 'eighties.

October 1979 J W R T

GLOSSARY

In response to requests from readers, the following explanations are offered of some of the more important technical terms or acronyms in the modern world of aerospace, which has become so permeated with technical shorthand that a quick-reference glossary has become essential. Comments, criticism and additions will be carefully considered for the next edition.

AAM Air-to-air missile.
AC Alternating current.
ACLS (1) Automatic carrier landing system; (2) Air cushion landing system.
ADAC Avion de Décollage et Attérrissage Court (STOL).
ADAV Avion de Décollage et Attérrissage Vertical (VTOL).
ADC (1) US Air Force Aerospace Defense Command; (2) air data computer.
ADF Automatic Direction Finding (equipment).
ADG Accessory-drive generator.
ADI Attitude/director indicator.
aeroplane (N America, airplane) Heavier-than-air aircraft with propulsion and a wing that does not rotate in order to generate lift.
AEW Airborne early warning.
AFB Air Force Base (USA).
AFCS Automatic flight control system.
afterburning Temporarily augmenting the thrust of a turbofan or turbojet by burning additional fuel in the jetpipe.
AGREE Advisory Group on Reliability in Electronic Equipment.
Ah Ampère-hours.
AHRS Attitude/heading reference system.
AIDS Airborne integrated data system.
aircraft All man-made vehicles for navigation within the atmosphere, including helicopters and balloons.
airstair Retractable stairway built into aircraft.
AM Amplitude modulation.
anhedral Downward slope of wing seen from front, from root to tip.
AP Ammonium perchlorate.
APFD Autopilot flight director.
aphelion The point in a solar (Sun-centred) orbit furthest from the Sun.
apogee The point in an Earth-centred orbit furthest from the Earth.
approach noise Measured 1 nm from downwind end of runway with aircraft passing overhead at 112·6 m (370 ft).
APU Auxiliary power unit (part of aircraft).
ARINC Aeronautical Radio Inc, company whose electronic box sizes (racking sizes) are the international standard.
ASE Automatic stabilisation equipment.
ASI Airspeed indicator.
ASIR Airspeed indicator reading.
ASM Air-to-surface missile.
aspect ratio Measure of wing (or other aerofoil) slenderness seen in plan view, usually defined as the square of the span divided by area.
ASV (1) Air-to-surface vessel; (2) Anti-surface vessel.
ASW Anti-submarine warfare.
ATC Air traffic control.
ATR Air Transport Radio, series of ARINC standard box sizes.
attack, angle of Angle at which airstream meets aerofoil (angle between mean chord and free-stream direction). Not to be confused with angle of incidence (which see).
augmented Boosted by afterburning.
autogyro Rotary-wing aircraft propelled by a propeller (or other thrusting device) and lifted by a freely running autorotating rotor.
AUW All-up weight (term meaning total weight of aircraft under defined conditions, or at specific time during flight). Not to be confused with MTOGW (which see).
avionics Aviation electronics, such as communications radio, radars, navigation systems and computers.
AWACS Airborne Warning And Control System (aircraft).

bar Non-SI unit of pressure adopted by this yearbook pending wider acceptance of Pa. 1 bar = 10^5 Pa, and ISA pressure at S/L is 1,013·2 mb, or just over 1 bar.
bare weight Undefined term meaning unequipped empty weight.
basic operating weight MTOGW minus payload (thus, including crew, fuel and oil, bar stocks, cutlery etc).
BCAR British Civil Airworthiness Requirements.
BFO Beat-frequency oscillator.
BITE Built-in test equipment.
bladder tank Fuel (or other fluid) tank of flexible material.
bleed air Hot high-pressure air extracted from gas-turbine engine compressor or combustor and taken through valves and pipes to perform useful work such as driving machinery or anti-icing by heating surfaces.
blown flap Flap across which bleed air is discharged at high (often supersonic) speed to prevent flow-breakaway.
BOW Basic operating weight.
BPR Bypass ratio.
BTU Non-SI unit of energy (British Thermal Unit) = 0·9478 J.
bus Busbar, main terminal in electrical system to which battery or generator power is supplied.
bypass ratio Airflow through fan duct (not passing through core) divided by airflow through core.

CAA Civil Aviation Administration (UK).
CAB Civil Aeronautics Board (USA).
CAB Pt 298 Sets the commercial standards for non-certificated carriers, mainly commuter airlines.
cabin altitude Height above S/L at which ambient pressure is same as inside cabin.
CAM Cockpit-angle measure (crew vision).
canards Foreplanes, fixed or controllable aerodynamic surfaces ahead of CG.
CAR Civil Airworthiness Regulations.
CAS Calibrated airspeed, unusual measure in certain supersonic aircraft equipped with ASI calibrated to allow for air compressibility according to ISA S/L.
CBR California bearing ratio, measure of ability of airfield surface (paved or not) to support aircraft.
CCV Control configured vehicle.
CEAM Centre d'Expériences Aériennes Militaires.

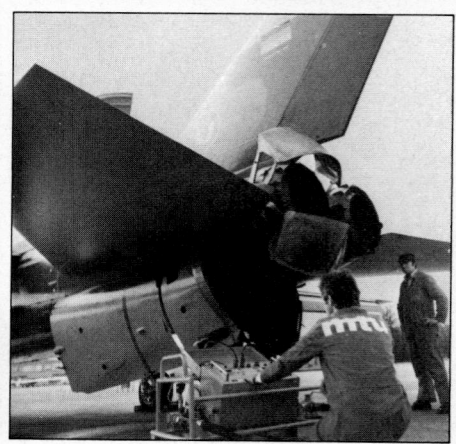

CEAT Centre d'Essais Aéronautiques de Toulouse.
CEP Circular error probability (50/50 chance of hit being inside or outside) in bombing, missile attack or gunnery.
CG Centre of gravity.
chaff Thin slivers of radar-reflective material cut to length appropriate to wavelengths of hostile radars and scattered in clouds to protect friendly aircraft.
chord Distance from leading-edge to trailing-edge measured parallel to longitudinal axis.
clean In flight configuration with landing gear, flaps, slats etc retracted.
'clean' Without any optional external stores.
composite material Made of two constituents, such as filaments or short whiskers plus adhesive.
CONUS Continental USA (ie, excluding Hawaii, etc).
core Gas generator portion of turbofan comprising compressor(s), combustion chamber and turbine(s).
CRT Cathode-ray tube.
CSAS Command and stability augmentation system (part of AFCS).
CSD Constant-speed drive (output shaft speed held steady, no matter how input may vary).

dB Decibel.
DC Direct current.
derated Engine restricted to power less than potential maximum (usually such engine is flat-rated).
design weight Different authorities have different definitions; weight chosen as typical of mission but usually much less than MTOGW.
dibber bomb Designed to cause maximum damage to concrete runways.
dihedral Upward slope of wing seen from front, from root to tip.
DINS Digital inertial navigation system.
disposable load Sum of masses that can be loaded or unloaded, including payload, crew, usable fuel etc; MTOGW minus OWE.
DME Distance-measuring equipment; gives linear distance to a beacon directly ahead.
dog-tooth A step in the leading-edge of a plane resulting from an increase in chord. (See also saw-tooth.)
Doppler Short for Doppler radar—radar using fact that received frequency is a function of relative velocity between transmitter or reflecting surface and receiver.
double-slotted flap One having an auxiliary aerofoil ahead of main surface to increase maximum lift.
dP Maximum design differential pressure between pressurised cabin and ambient (outside) atmosphere.
drone Pilotless aircraft, usually winged, following preset programme of manoeuvres.

EAA Experimental Aircraft Association (divided into local branches called Chapters).
EAS Equivalent airspeed, RAS minus correction for compressibility.
ECCM Electronic counter-countermeasures.
ECM Electronic countermeasures.
ehp Equivalent horsepower, measure of propulsive power of turboprop made up of shp plus addition due to residual thrust from jet.
ekW Equivalent kilowatts, SI measure of propulsive power of turboprop (see ehp).
elevon Wing trailing-edge control surface combining functions of aileron and elevator.
ELT Emergency locator transmitter, to help rescuers home on a disabled or crashed aircraft.
EPA Environmental Protection Agency.
EPNdB Effective perceived noise decibel, SI unit of EPNL.
EPNL Effective perceived noise level, measure of noise effect on humans which takes account of sound intensity, frequency, character and duration, and response of human ear.
EPU Emergency power unit (part of aircraft, not used for propulsion).
ERP Effective radiated power.
ESA European Space Agency.
ESM (1) Electronic surveillance (or support) measures; (2) Electronic signal monitoring.

FAA Federal Aviation Administration.
FAI Fédération Aéronautique Internationale.
fail-safe Structure or system which survives failure (in case of system, may no longer function normally).
FAR Federal Aviation Regulations.
FAR Pt 23 Defines the airworthiness of private and air-taxi aeroplanes of 5,670 kg (12,500 lb) MTOGW and below.
FAR Pt 25 Defines the airworthiness of public transport aeroplanes exceeding 5,670 kg (12,500 lb) MTOGW.
FBW Fly by wire (which see).
FDS Flight director system.
feathering Setting propeller or similar blades at pitch aligned with slipstream, to give resultant torque (not tending to turn shaft) and thus minimum drag.
FEBA Forward edge of battle area.
fence A chordwise projection on the surface of a wing, used to modify the distribution of pressure.
fenestron Helicopter tail rotor with many slender blades rotating in short duct.
ferry range Extreme safe range with zero payload.
FFAR Folding-fin (or free-flight) aircraft rocket.
FFVV Fédération Française de Vol à Voile (French gliding authority).
field length Measure of distance needed to land and/or take off; many different measures for particular purposes, each precisely defined.
flaperon Wing trailing-edge surface combining functions of flap and aileron.
flat-four Engine having four horizontally opposed cylinders; thus, flat-twin, flat-six etc.
flat-rated Propulsion engine capable of giving full thrust or power for take-off up to high airfield height and/or high ambient temperature (thus, probably derated at S/L).
FLIR Forward-looking infra-red.
fly by wire Flight control system with electrical signalling (ie, without mechanical interconnection between cockpit flying controls and control surfaces).
FM Frequency modulation.
footprint A precisely delineated boundary on the surface inside which the perceived noise of an aircraft exceeds a specified level during take-off and/or landing.
Fowler flap Moves initially aft to increase wing area and then also deflects down to increase drag.
free turbine Turbine mechanically independent of engine upstream, other than being connected by rotating bearings and the gas stream, and thus able to run at its own speed.
Frise aileron Most common manual aileron, with leading-edge that projects below wing to increase drag when aileron is raised.
FY Fiscal year (1 July to 30 June in US government affairs).

g Acceleration due to mean Earth gravity, ie of a body in free fall.
gallons Non-SI measure; I Imp gal (UK) = 4·546 litres, 1 US gal = 3·785 litres.
GCI Ground-controlled interception.
geostationary Of an Earth satellite, rotating with the Earth and thus always overhead the same point. Corresponds to altitude above Earth's surface of about 35,800 km (22,245 miles).
geostationary orbit An Earth-centred orbit at a height above the Earth's surface of about 35,800 km (22,245 miles) and lying approximately in the plane of the equator. A satellite in such an orbit travelling eastwards will hover over the same point, rotating precisely with the Earth.
geosynchronous See geostationary.
Gfk Glassfibre-reinforced plastics (German).
glide ratio Of a sailplane, distance travelled along track divided by height lost in still air.
glove In a swing-wing aeroplane with pivots well out from the centreline it is geometrically impossible to have one-piece pivoted wings because at zero sweep the inner ends would overlap; the answer is fixed inner leading portions called gloves.
GPU Ground power unit (not part of aircraft).
green aircraft Aircraft flyable but lacking furnishing and customer's choice of electronics.
gross wing area See wing area.
GRP Glassfibre-reinforced plastics.
GSE Ground-support equipment (such as special test gear, steps and servicing platforms).
GTS Gas-turbine starter (ie starter is miniature gas turbine).
gunship Helicopter designed for battlefield attack, normally with slim body carrying pilot and weapon operator only.

h Hour(s).
hardened Protected as far as possible against nuclear explosion.
hardpoint Reinforced part of aircraft to which external load can be attached, eg weapon or tank pylon.
helicopter Rotary-wing aircraft both lifted and propelled by one or more power-driven rotors turning about substantially vertical axes.
HF High frequency.
'hot and high' Adverse combination of airfield height and high ambient temperature, which lengthens required TOD.
hovering ceiling Ceiling of helicopter (corresponding to air density at which maximum rate of climb is zero), either IGE or OGE.
HP High pressure.
hp Horsepower.
HSI Horizontal situation indicator.
HUD Head-up display (bright numbers and symbols projected on pilot's windscreen and focussed on infinity so that pilot can simultaneously read display and look ahead).
HVAR High-velocity aircraft rocket.

IAS Indicated airspeed, ASIR corrected for instrument error.
IATA International Air Transport Association.
ICAO International Civil Aviation Organization.
IFF Identification friend or foe.
IFR Instrument flight rules (ie, not VFR).
IGE In ground effect: helicopter performance with theoretical flat horizontal surface just below the wheels.
ILS Instrument landing system.
IMC Instrument meteorological conditions, basically IFR.
IMK Increased manoeuvrability kit.
INAS Integrated nav/attack system.
incidence Strictly, the angle at which the wing is set in relation to the fore/aft axis. Wrongly used to mean angle of attack (which see).
inertial navigation Measuring all accelerations imparted to a vehicle and, by integrating these with respect to time, calculating speed at every instant (in all three planes) and by integrating a second time calculating total change of position in relation to starting point.
INS Inertial navigation system.
integral construction Machined from solid instead of assembled from separate parts.
integral tank Fuel or other liquid tank formed by sealing part of structure.
intercom Wired telephone system for communication within aircraft.
inverter Electric or electronic device for inverting (reversing polarity of) alternate waves in AC power to produce DC.
IP Intermediate pressure.
IR Infra-red.
IRAN Inspect and repair as necessary.
IRLS Infra-red linescan (builds TV-type picture showing cool regions as dark and hot regions as light).
ISA International Standard Atmosphere.
ISIS (1 Boeing Vertol) Integral spar inspection system; (2 Ferranti) integrated strike and interception sight.

JASDF Japan Air Self-Defence Force.
JATO Jet-assisted take-off (actually means rocket-assisted).
JCAB Japan Civil Airworthiness Board.
JDA Japan Defence Agency.
JGSDF Japan Ground Self-Defence Force.
JMSDF Japan Maritime Self-Defence Force.

Kevlar A filament-wound high-strength composite material.
kN Kilonewton (the Newton is the SI unit of force; 1 lbf = 4·448 N).
knot 1 nm per hour.
Krüger flap Hinges down and then forward from below the leading-edge.
Küchemann tip Wing tip of curving planform intended to minimise drag at high subsonic speed.
kVA Kilovolt-Ampères.
kW Kilowatt, SI measure of all forms of power (not just electrical).

LARC Low-altitude ride control.
lbf Pounds of thrust.
LBA Luftfahrtbundesamt (Federal German civil aviation authority).
LCN Load classification number, measure of 'flotation' of aircraft landing gear linking aircraft weight, weight distribution, tyre numbers, pressures and disposition.
LITVC Liquid-injection thrust vector control.
LLTV Low-light TV (thus, LLLTV, low-light-level).
Load factor (1) percentage of max payload; (2) stress limit.
LOC Localiser.
localiser Element giving steering guidance in ILS.
loiter Flight for maximum endurance, such as supersonic fighter on patrol.
longerons Principal fore-and-aft structural members (eg, in fuselage).
Loran (Long Range Navigation) Family of hyperbolic navaids based on ground radio emissions.
lox Liquid oxygen.
LP Low pressure.
LRMTS Laser ranger and marked-target seeker.

M or Mach number The ratio of the speed of a body to the speed of sound (1,116 ft; 340 m/s in air at 15°C) under the same ambient conditions.
MAC US Air Force Military Airlift Command.
MAD Magnetic anomaly detector.
Madar Maintenance analysis, detection and recording.
Madge Microwave aircraft digital guidance equipment.
marker, marker beacon Ground beacon giving position guidance in ILS.
MASTACS Manoeuvrability augmentation system for tactical air combat simulation.
MEPU Monofuel emergency power unit.
MF Medium frequency.
MLS Microwave landing system.
MLW Maximum landing weight.
MMH Monomethyl hydrazine.
MMO Maximum permitted operating Mach number.
monocoque Structure with strength in outer shell, devoid of internal bracing.
MPA Man-powered aircraft.
MRW Maximum ramp weight.

Oerlikon 8 cm Rockets

For effective engagement of point and area targets. Application in ground-to-ground or air-to-ground roles using multiple launchers or aircraft pods

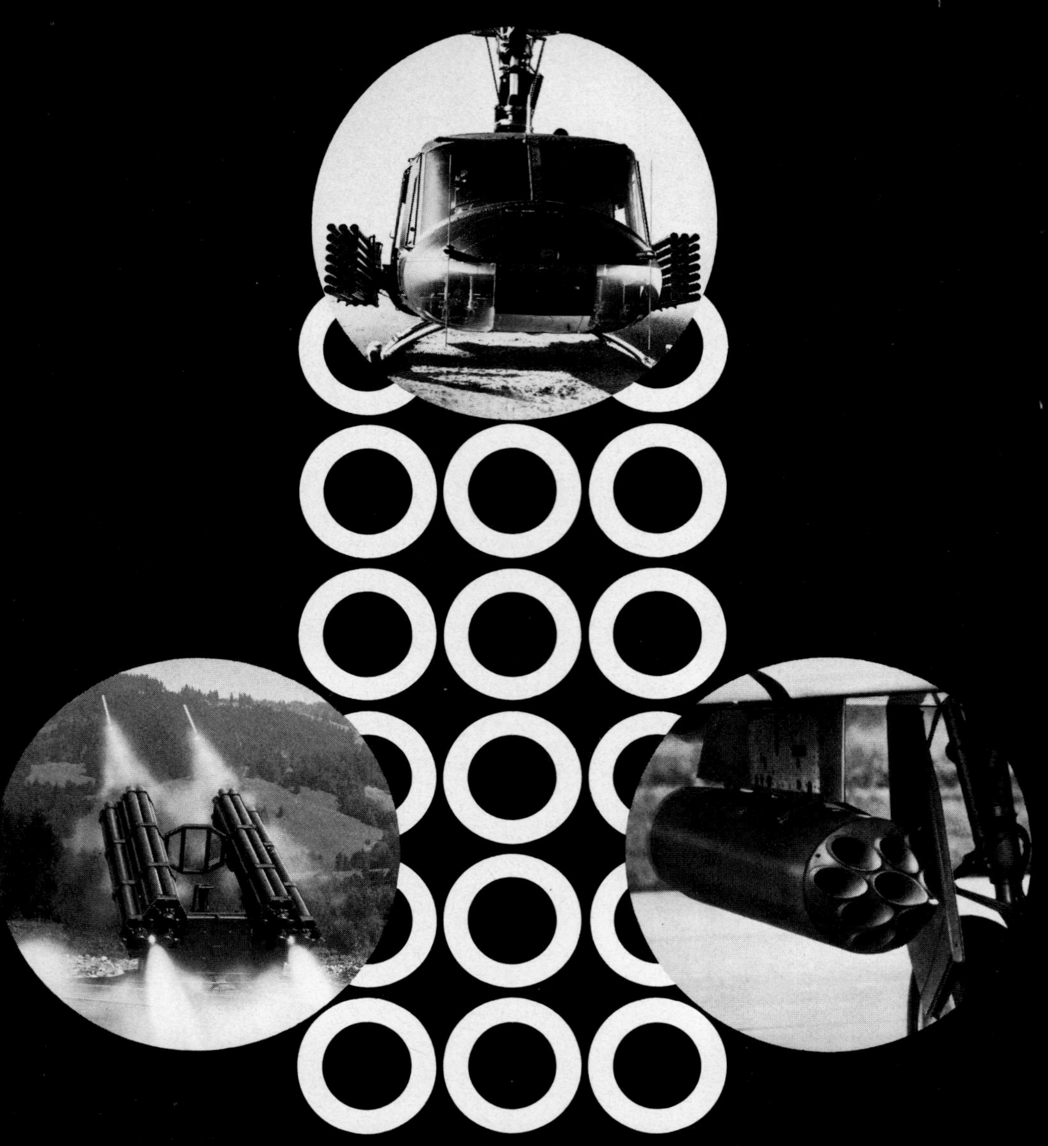

Machine Tool Works Oerlikon-Bührle Ltd., Zurich/Switzerland

30-146

MTBF Mean time between failures.
MTOGW Maximum take-off gross weight (MRW minus taxi/run-up fuel).
MZFW Maximum zero-fuel weight.

NACA US National Advisory Committee for Aeronautics (now NASA).
Nadge NATO air defence ground environment.
NASA National Aeronautics and Space Administration.
NASC US Naval Air Systems Command (also several other aerospace meanings).
NATC US Naval Air Training Command or Test Center (also several other aerospace meanings).
nm Nautical mile, 1·8532 km, 1·15152 miles.
NOAA National Oceanic and Atmospheric Administration.
NOE Nap-of-the-Earth (low flying in military aircraft, using natural cover of hills, trees, etc).
NOGS Night observation gunship.
Ns Newton-second (1 N thrust applied for 1 second).

OBS Omni-bearing selector.
OCU Operational Conversion Unit.
OGE Out of ground effect: helicopter hovering far above nearest surface.
Omega Long-range hyperbolic navaid.
OMI Omni-bearing magnetic indicator.
omni Generalised word meaning equal in all directions (as in omni-range, omni-flash beacon).
OTPI On-top position indicator (indicates overhead of submarine in ASW).
OWE Operating weight empty, MTOGW minus payload, usable fuel and oil and other consumables.

PA system Public-address.
pallet (1) for freight, rigid platform for handling by fork-lift or conveyor; (2) for missile, mounting and electronics box outside aircraft.
payload Disposable load generating revenue (passengers, cargo, mail and other paid items); in military aircraft loosely used to mean total load carried of weapons, cargo or other mission equipment.
PD radar Pulse-Doppler.
penaids Penetration aids, such as jammers, chaff or decoys to help aircraft fly safely through hostile airspace.
perigee The point in an Earth-centred orbit nearest to the Earth.
perihelion The point in a solar (Sun-centred) orbit closest to the Sun.
PFA Popular Flying Association (UK).
PHI Position and heading (or homing) indicator.
plane A lifting surface (eg, wing, tailplane).
pneumatic de-icing Covered with flexible surfaces alternately pumped up and deflated to throw off ice.
port Left side, looking forward.
power loading Aircraft weight (usually MTOGW) divided by total propulsive power or thrust at T-O.
pressure fuelling Fuelling via a leakproof connection through which fuel passes at high rate under pressure.
pressure ratio In gas-turbine engine, compressor delivery pressure divided by ambient pressure (in supersonic aircraft, divided by ram pressure downstream of inlet).
primary flight controls Those used to control trajectory of aircraft (thus, not trimmers, tabs, flaps, slats, airbrakes or lift dumpers etc).
pulse-Doppler Radar sending out pulses and measuring frequency-shift of returns from target(s).
pylon Structure linking aircraft to external load (engine nacelle, drop-tank, bomb etc). Also used in conventional sense in pylon racing.

radius In terms of performance, the distance an aircraft can fly from base and return without intermediate landing.
RAI Registro Aeronautico Italiano.
ram pressure Increased pressure in forward-facing aircraft inlet, generated by converting (relative) kinetic energy to pressure.
ramp weight Maximum weight at start of flight (MTOGW plus taxi/run-up fuel).
range Too many definitions to list, but essentially the distance an aircraft can fly (or is permitted to fly) with specified load and usually whilst making allowance for specified additional manoeuvres (diversions, stand-off, go-around etc).
RAS Rectified airspeed, IAS corrected for position error.
RATT Radio teletype.
redundant Provided with spare capacity or data channels and thus made to survive failures.
refanned Gas-turbine engine fitted with new fan of higher BPR.
rigid rotor Helicopter rotor without articulating hinges (eg, flapping hinge, drag hinge) but with pitch variation.
RLD Rijksluchtvaartdienst, Netherlands civil aviation department.
RMI Remote magnetic indicator (compass).
R/Nav Area navigation, navaid covering whole of local area instead of just crowded airways.
Rotor-kite Rotary-wing aircraft with no internal power, lifted by a freely running autorotating rotor and towed by an external vehicle.
roving Multiple strands of fibre, as in a rope (but usually not twisted).
RPV Remotely piloted vehicle (pilot in other aircraft or on ground).
RSA Réseau du Sport de l'Air.
RVR Runway visible range.

s Second(s).
SAC US Air Force Strategic Air Command.
safe-life A term denoting that a component has proved by testing that it can be expected to continue to function safely for a precisely defined period before replacement.
salmon (French saumon) Streamlined fairings, usually at wingtip of sailplane, serving same function as endplate and acting also as tip-skid.
SAR Search and rescue.
SATS (1) Small airfield for tactical support; (2) Small Arms Target System.
saw-tooth Same as dog-tooth.
second-source Production of identical item by second factory or company.
semi-active Homing on to radiation reflected from target illuminated by radar or laser energy beamed from elsewhere.
service ceiling Usually height equivalent to air density at which maximum attainable rate of climb is 100 ft/min.
servo A device which acts as a relay, usually augmenting the pilot's efforts to move a control surface or the like.
sfc Specific fuel consumption.
SGAC Secrétariat Général à l'Aviation Civile.
shaft Connection between gas turbine and compressor or other driven unit. Two-shaft engine has second shaft, rotating at different speed, surrounding the first (thus, HP surrounds inner LP or fan shaft).
Shoran Short range navigation (radio).
shp Shaft horsepower, measure of power transmitted via rotating shaft.
sideline noise EPNdB measure of aircraft landing and taking off, at point 0·25 nm (2- or 3-engined) or 0·35 nm (4-engined) from runway centreline.
SIF Selective identification facility.
signature Characteristic 'fingerprint' of all electromagnetic radiation (radar, IR etc).
single-shaft Gas-turbine in which all compressors and turbines are on common shaft rotating together.
S/L Sea level.
SLAR Side-Looking Airborne Radar.
snap-down Air-to-air interception of low-flying aircraft by AAM fired from fighter at a higher altitude.
soft target Not armoured or hardened.
specific fuel consumption Rate at which fuel is consumed divided by power or thrust developed, and thus a measure of engine efficiency. For jet engines (air-breathing, ie not rockets) unit is mg/Ns, milligrams per Newton-second; for shaft engines unit is μg/J, micrograms (millionths of a gram) per Joule (SI unit of work or energy).
specific impulse Measure of rocket engine efficiency; thrust divided by rate of fuel/oxidant consumption per second, the units for mass and force being the same so that the answer is expressed in seconds.
spool One complete axial compressor rotor; thus a two-shaft engine may have a fan plus an LP spool.
SSB Single-sideband (radio).
SSR Secondary surveillance radar.
st Static thrust.
stabiliser Fin (thus, horizontal stabiliser = tailplane).
stall strips Sharp-edged strips on wing leading-edge to induce stall at that point.
stalling speed TAS at which aircraft stalls at 1*g*, ie wing lift suddenly collapses.
standard day ISA temperature and pressure.
starboard Right side, looking forward.
static inverter Solid-state electronic inverter (ie, not rotary machine).
STOL Short take-off and landing. (Several definitions, stipulating allowable horizontal distance to clear screen height of 35 or 50 ft or various SI measures).
store Object carried as part of payload on external attachment (eg bomb, drop-tank).
substrate The underlying layer on which something (such as a solar cell or integrated circuit) is made.
supercritical wing Wing of relatively deep, flat-topped profile generating lift right across upper surface instead of concentrated close behind leading-edge.
synchronous See geostationary.
synchronous satellite Geostationary.

t Tonne, 1 Megagram, 1,000 kg.
tabbed flap Fitted with narrow-chord tab along entire trailing-edge which deflects to greater angle than main surface.
tabs Small auxiliary surfaces hinged to trailing-edge of control surfaces for purposes of trimming, reducing hinge moment (force needed to operate main surface) or in other way assisting pilot.
TAC US Air Force Tactical Air Command.
Tacan Tactical air navigation, simple military navaid using ground beacons.
taileron Left and right tailplanes used as primary control surfaces in both pitch and roll.
tailplane Main horizontal tail surface, originally fixed and carrying hinged elevator(s) but today usually a single 'slab' serving as control surface.
TANS Tactical air navigation system (Doppler-based computer, control and display unit).
TAS True airspeed, EAS corrected for density (often very large factor) appropriate to aircraft height.
TBO Time between overhauls.
TFR Terrain-following radar (for low-level attack).
T-O Take-off.
T-O noise EPNdB measure of aircraft taking off, at point directly under flight path 3·5 nm from brakes-release (regardless of altitude).
TOD Take-off distance.
TOGW Take-off gross weight (not necessarily MTOGW).
ton Imperial (long) ton = 1·016 t (Mg), US (short) ton = 0·9072 t.
track Distance between centres of contact areas of main landing wheels measured left/right across aircraft (with bogies, distance between centres of contact areas of each bogie).
transceiver Radio transmitter/receiver.
transfer orbit Orbit, or part of an orbit, linking two others at different heights around the same planetary body.
transponder Radio transmitter triggered automatically by a particular received signal.
TRU Transformer/rectifier unit.
turbofan Gas-turbine jet engine generating most thrust by a large-diameter cowled fan, with small part added by jet from core.
turbojet Simplest form of gas-turbine comprising compressor, combustion chamber, turbine and propulsive nozzle.
turboprop Gas-turbine in which as much energy as possible is taken from gas jet and used to drive reduction gearbox and propeller.
turboshaft Gas-turbine in which as much energy as possible is taken from gas jet and used to drive high-speed shaft (which in turn drives external load such as helicopter gearbox).
TVC Thrust vector control (rocket).
TWT Travelling-wave tube.
tyre sizes In simplest form, first figure is rim diameter (in or mm) and second is rim width (in or mm). In more correct three-unit form, first figure is outside diameter, second is max width and third is wheel diameter.

UHF Ultra-high frequency.
unfactored Performance level expected of average pilot, in average aircraft, without additional safety factors.
usable fuel Total mass of fuel consumable in flight, usually 95-98 per cent of system capacity.

variable-geometry Capable of grossly changing shape in flight, especially by varying sweep of wings.
VD Maximum permitted diving speed
vernier Small thruster, usually a rocket, for final precise adjustment of a vehicle's trajectory and velocity.
VFR Visual flight rules.
VHF Very high frequency.
VLF Very low frequency.
VMO Maximum permitted operating flight speed (IAS, EAS or CAS must be specified).
VNE Never-exceed speed (aerodynamic or structural limit).
VOR VHF omni-range, ground navaid usable only when flying along predetermined airways.
VTOL Vertical take-off and landing.

washout Inbuilt wing twist reducing angle of incidence towards the tip.
wheelbase Minimum distance from nosewheel or tailwheel (centre of contact area) to line joining main wheels (centres of contact areas).
wing area Total projected area of clean wing (no flaps, slats etc) including all control surfaces and area of fuselage bounded by leading- and trailing-edges projected to centreline (inapplicable to slender-delta aircraft with extremely large leading-edge sweep angle). Sometimes called gross wing area; net area excludes projected areas of fuselage, nacelles, etc.
wing loading Aircraft weight (usually MTOGW) divided by wing area.
winglet Small auxiliary aerofoil, usually sharply upturned, at tip of wing.
wire guidance Guidance of missile or RPV by signals transmitted through fine wire(s) linking it with operator.

zero-fuel weight MTOGW minus usable fuel and other consumables, in most aircraft imposing severest stress on wing.
zero/zero seat Ejection seat designed for use even at zero speed on ground.
ZFW Zero-fuel weight.

FIRST FLIGHTS

Some first flights made during the period 1 June 1978 to 1 October 1979

June 1978

4 Aero Design DG-1 (N10E), first successful flight (USA)
9 GEPAS Compact sailplane (F-CRRL) (France)
13 Dassault-Breguet Mystère-Falcon 50 (F-WFJC), third aircraft (France)
20 Dassault-Breguet/Dornier Alpha Jet 1B (AT-01), first for Belgium (International)
30 Wallerkowski Hornisse (D-EBXG) (Germany, Federal Republic)

July 1978

6 NASA/Boeing QSRA (NASA 715) (USA)
8 Mantainer MA-1 airship (VH-PSE) (Australia)
9 EAA Acro-Sport II (N9EA) (USA)
9 Thompson Metal Hurlant (USA)
19 Gulfstream American Turbo Ag-Cat D (USA)
20 Aermacchi M.B.339 (I-NEUF), first production (Italy)

August 1978

4 E-Systems E-150 mini-RPV (USA)
7 General Dynamics F-16A (78-0001), first production (USA)
9 Maule M-5-210TC Lunar Rocket (USA)
12 Pilatus PC-7 Turbo-Trainer (HB-HAO), first production (Switzerland)
13 Temple-Flügel TF-1 hang glider (Germany, Federal Republic)
14 SEPECAT Jaguar S-1, first flight with RT172-58 Adour 811 engine (International)
20 Aérospatiale Fouga 90 (F-WZJB) (France)
20 British Aerospace Sea Harrier FRS. Mk 1 (XZ450) (UK)
21 Gates Learjet 28 Longhorn, first production (USA)
24 Westland Wideye RPV (UK)
25 Canadair CL-227 RPV (Canada)
29 Mitsubishi MU-300 Diamond I (JQ8001) (Japan)

September 1978

8 Raisbeck (Rockwell) Sabreliner 60A Mark Five (N605RG), first production (USA)
11 Partenavia/Aeritalia AP.68TP (NC001) (Italy)
13 Aérospatiale AS 332 Super Puma (F-WZJA) (France)
18 Dassault Mirage 2000, second prototype (France)
26 Cox (DHC-3-T) Turbo Otter (C-FMES-X) (Canada)

October 1978

16 Lockheed L-1011-500 TriStar (N48354) (USA)
22 Neiva N622 Universal II/YT-25B (1831) (Brazil)
24 Striplin FLAC (USA)
28 Scheibe SF-H34 sailplane (D-3334) (Germany, Federal Republic)

November 1978

8 Canadair CL-600 Challenger (C-GCGR-X) (Canada)
9 McDonnell Douglas YAV-8B (158394) (USA)
15 CNPSL-PZL-Warszawa PZL-106AR Kruk (Poland)
18 McDonnell Douglas YF-18 Hornet (160775) (USA)
27 Dassault-Breguet/Dornier Alpha Jet 1B, first assembled in Belgium (International)
29 PZL-Mielec M-18 Dromader, firefighting version (Poland)

December 1978

11 General Dynamics F-16B, first European-assembled, at Gosselies, Belgium
26 Concorde 215 (F-WJAN) (International)
27 Enstrom Model 280L Hawk (N5696E) (USA)
29 Zlin 142 (Czechoslovakia)
30 General Avia F.600 Canguro (I-CANG) (Italy)

January 1979

17 CARMAM 15-38 sailplane (France)

Dassault's multi-role twin-turbofan Super Mirage 4000, first flown on 9 March 1979

February 1979

3 Aerospace Developments AD 500 airship (G-BECE) (UK)
13 Texas Helicopter Wasp II (USA)
14 Rockwell International B-1 (76-0174), fourth aircraft (USA)
19 Akaflieg München Mü 27 sailplane (Germany, Federal Republic)
26 McDonnell Douglas F-15C Eagle (78-468) (USA)
28 Aerospace Cresco (New Zealand)

March 1979

9 Dassault Super Mirage 4000 (France)
12 McDonnell Douglas YF-18A Hornet (160776), second aircraft (USA)
17 Canadair CL-600 Challenger, second aircraft (C-GCGS-X) (Canada)
22 Lockheed CP-140 Aurora (N64996) (USA)
31 Aérospatiale AS 365N Dauphin 2 (F-WZJD) (France)

April 1979

6 McDonnell Douglas YF-18A Hornet (160777), third aircraft (USA)
10 Westland WG 30 (G-BGHF) (UK)
15 Dassault Mirage 50 (France)
19 Gates Learjet 55 Longhorn (N551GL) (USA)
23 Bell XV-15, second aircraft (N703NA), first flight in helicopter mode (USA)
24 Dassault Mystère-Falcon 20FH (F-WZAH) (France)
26 Dassault Mirage 2000, third prototype (France)
28 Airbus A300B4-200 (F-WZEN), first with JT9D engines (International)

May 1979

3 General Dynamics F-16B, first assembled by Fokker, Netherlands (J-259)
4 Fairchild Republic Night/Adverse Weather A-10 (73-1664) (USA)
11 Boeing Vertol YCH-47D Chinook (USA)
14 Dornier/LCT Argus RPV (International)
24 IPE 02 sailplane (PP-ZQL) (Brazil)
30 Cessna Citation III (N650CC) (USA)

June 1979

3 PZL-Swidnik Kania/Kitty Hawk (Poland)
13 MBB/Kawasaki BK-117 (D-HBKA) (International)
13 To Solar One solar-powered sailplane (UK)
14 Dornier TNT testbed aircraft (D-IFNT) (Germany, Federal Republic)
15 Raisbeck (Rockwell) Sabreliner 80A Mark Five (USA)
22 British Aerospace HS 748 Srs 2B (G-BGJV) (UK)

July 1979

6 Delemontez-Cauchy DC-1 (France)
10 Panavia Tornado GR.Mk 1 (ZA319), first UK production (International)
14 Canadair CL-600 Challenger, third aircraft (Canada)
21 Bell Model 214ST (USA)
23 Chagnes Microstar (France)
24 Bell XV-15 (N703NA), first conversion to aeroplane mode (USA)
24 NASA/Boeing KC-135A with winglets (53129) (USA)
25 PZL 112 Mewa (SP-DKC) (Poland)
27 Panavia Tornado (43 + 01), first German production (International)
27 Pottier P.50TR Bouvreuil (HB-YBF) (France/Switzerland)
27 Rockwell/NASA/USAF HiMAT RPV, first free flight (USA)

August 1979

10 MBB/Kawasaki BK-117, first assembled in Japan (International)
20 BGA Supermunk (G-BBNA) (UK)

September 1979

26 Aérospatiale Fouga 90 (F-WZJB), re-engined with Astafan IVGs (France)
26 Westland Sea King HC.Mk 4 (ZA290) (UK)
27 Aérospatiale AS 355E Ecureuil 2/Twinstar (F-WZLA) (France)

OFFICIAL RECORDS

Corrected to September 1979

ABSOLUTE WORLD RECORDS

Seven records are classed as Absolute World Records for aeroplanes by the Fédération Aéronautique Internationale, as follows:

Distance in a straight line (USA)
Major Clyde P. Evely, USAF, in a Boeing B-52H Stratofortress, on 10-11 January 1962, from Okinawa to Madrid, Spain. 10,890·27 nm (20,168·78 km; 12,532·3 miles).

Distance in a closed circuit (USA)
Captain William M. Stevenson, USAF, in a Boeing B-52H Stratofortress, on 6-7 June 1962. Seymour Johnson AFB-Bermuda-Sondrestrom (Greenland)-Anchorage (Alaska)-March AFB-Key West-Seymour Johnson AFB. 9,851·54 nm (18,245·05 km; 11,337 miles).

Height (USSR)
Alexander Fedotov in an E-266M (MiG-25) on 31 August 1977. 37,650 m (123,523 ft).

Height in sustained horizontal flight (USA)
Captain Robert C. Helt and Major Larry A. Elliott (USAF) in a Lockheed SR-71A on 28 July 1976 at Beale AFB, California. 25,929·031 m (85,069 ft).

Height, after launch from a 'mother-plane' (USA)
Major R. White, USAF, in the North American X-15A-3 on 17 July 1962, at Edwards AFB, California. 95,935·99 m (314,750 ft).

Speed in a straight line (USA)
Captain Eldon W. Joersz and Major George T. Morgan Jr (USAF) in a Lockheed SR-71A on 28 July 1976 over a 15/25 km course at Beale AFB, California. 1,905·81 knots (3,529·56 km/h; 2,193·17 mph).

Speed in a closed circuit (USA)
Major Adolphus H. Bledsoe Jr and Major John T. Fuller (USAF) in a Lockheed SR-71A on 27 July 1976, over a 1,000 km closed circuit from Beale AFB, California. 1,818·154 knots (3,367·221 km/h; 2,092·294 mph).

Seven records are classed as Absolute World Records for manned spacecraft by the Fédération Aéronautique Internationale, as follows:

Endurance in Earth orbit (USSR)
Vladimir Kovalyonok and Alexander Ivanchenkov on board Soyuz 29/Salyut 6/Soyuz 31, from 15 June to 2 November 1978. 139 days 14 h 47 min 32 s.

Awaiting confirmation is a subsequent record of 175 days and 36 min set by Soyuz 32/Salyut 6/Soyuz 34 cosmonauts Vladimir Lyakhov and Valery Ryumin.

Altitude (USA)
F. Borman, J. A. Lovell and W. Anders in Apollo 8, on 21-27 December 1968. 203,925 nm (377,668·9 km; 234,673 miles).

Greatest mass lifted to altitude (USA)
F. Borman, J. A. Lovell and W. Anders in Apollo 8, on 21-27 December 1968. 127,980 kg (282,147 lb).

Distance in Earth orbit (USSR)
Vladimir Kovalyonok and Alexander Ivanchenkov on board Soyuz 29/Salyut 6/Soyuz 31, from 15 June to 2 November 1978. 50,184,473 nm (92,941,650 km; 57,751,263 miles).

Awaiting confirmation is the much greater distance covered by Soyuz 32/Salyut 6/Soyuz 34 cosmonauts Vladimir Lyakhov and Valery Ryumin.

Extravehicular duration (USA)
Eugene A. Cernan, from the Apollo 17 lunar module *Challenger,* on 12, 13 and 14 December 1972, during mission of 7-19 December 1972. 21 h 31 min 44 s.

Number of astronauts remaining simultaneously outside spacecraft (USSR)
A. Eliseiev and E. Khrounov, from Soyuz 4 and 5, for 37 min on 14-18 January 1969. Two astronauts.

Accumulated time in spaceflight (USSR)
Vladimir Kovalyonok, on board Soyuz 25, Soyuz 29, Salyut 6 and Soyuz 31. 141 days 15 h 31 min 32 s.

Awaiting confirmation is a subsequent record set by Soyuz 32/Salyut 6/Soyuz 34 cosmonauts Vladimir Lyakhov and Valery Ryumin.

WORLD CLASS RECORDS

Following are details of some of the more important world class records confirmed by the FAI:

CLASS C, GROUP I (Aeroplanes with piston engines)

Distance in a straight line (USA)
Cdr Thomas D. Davies, USN, and crew of three in a Lockheed P2V-1 Neptune, on 29 September-1 October 1946, from Perth, Western Australia, to Columbus, Ohio, USA. 9,763·49 nm (18,081·99 km; 11,235·6 miles).

Distance in a closed circuit (USA)
James R. Bede in the Bede BD-2, on 7-10 November 1969, between Columbus, Ohio, and Toledo, Ohio, USA. 7,797·66 nm (14,441·26 km; 8,973·38 miles).

Height (Italy)
Mario Pezzi, in a Caproni 161*bis,* on 22 October 1938. 17,083 m (56,046 ft).

Speed in a straight line (USA)
Darryl Greenamyer in a modified Grumman F8F-2 Bearcat, on 16 August 1969, over 3 km course at Edwards AFB, California. 419·249 knots (776·449 km/h; 482·463 mph).

CLASS C, GROUP II (Aeroplanes with turboprop engines)

Distance in a straight line (USA)
Lt Col E. L. Allison and crew in a Lockheed HC-130H Hercules, on 20 February 1972. 7,587·99 nm (14,052·95 km; 8,732·098 miles).

Distance in a closed circuit (USA)
Cdr Philip R. Hite and crew in a Lockheed RP-3D Orion, on 4 November 1972. 5,455·46 nm (10,103·51 km; 6,278·03 miles).

Height (USA)
Donald R. Wilson in an LTV Electrosystems L450F, on 27 March 1972, at Majors Field, Greenville, Texas. 15,549 m (51,014 ft).

Speed in a straight line (USA)
Cdr Donald H. Lilienthal and crew in a Lockheed P-3C Orion, over 15/25 km course on 27 January 1971. 435·26 knots (806·10 km/h; 500·89 mph).

Speed in a closed circuit (USSR)
Ivan Sukhomlin and crew in a Tupolev Tu-114, on 9 April 1960, carrying a 25,000 kg payload over a 5,000 km circuit. 473·66 knots (877·212 km/h; 545·07 mph).

CLASS C, GROUP III (Aeroplanes with jet engines)

Distance in a straight line, distance in a closed circuit, height, speed in straight line and speed in 1,000 km closed circuit
See Absolute World Records.

Speed over a 3 km course at restricted altitude (USA)
Darryl Greenamyer in the modified Red Baron F-104RB Starfighter, on 24 October 1977, at Mud Lake, Tonopah, Nevada. 858·77 knots (1,590·45 km/h; 988·26 mph).

Speed in a 100 km closed circuit (USSR)
Alexander Fedotov in a Mikoyan E-266 (MiG-25), on 8 April 1973. 1,406·641 knots (2,605·1 km/h; 1,618·734 mph).

Speed in a 500 km closed circuit (USSR)
M. Komarov in a Mikoyan E-266 (MiG-25), on 5 October 1967, near Moscow. 1,609·88 knots (2,981·5 km/h; 1,852·62 mph).

Speed around the World (USA)
Walter H. Mullikin and crew of four, in a Boeing 747SP of Pan American, on 1-3 May 1976, from New York City, via Delhi and Tokyo, back to New York, in 1 day 22 h 50 s. 436·95 knots (809·24 km/h; 502·84 mph).

Greatest mass lifted to a height of 2,000 m (USA)
William J. Allsopp and crew in a Boeing 747-236B with Rolls-Royce RB.211 engines, at Le Moore NAS, California, on 1 November 1976. 381,108·25 kg (840,200 lb).

CLASS C.2, ALL GROUPS (Seaplanes)

Distance in a straight line (UK)
Capt D. C. T. Bennett and First Officer I. Harvey, in the Short-Mayo Mercury, on 6-8 October 1938, from Dundee, Scotland, to the Orange River, South Africa. 5,211·66 nm (9,652 km; 5,997·5 miles).

Height (USSR)
Georgi Buryanov and crew of two in a Beriev M-10, on 9 September 1961, over the Sea of Azov. 14,962 m (49,088 ft).

Speed in a straight line (USSR)
Nikolai Andrievsky and crew of two in a Beriev M-10, on 7 August 1961, at Joukovski-Petrovskœ, over a 15/25 km course. 492·44 knots (912 km/h; 566·69 mph).

CLASS D, GROUP I (Single-seat sailplanes)

Distance in a straight line (Germany, Federal Republic)
Hans W. Grosse in a Schleicher ASW 12, on 25 April 1972. 788·77 nm (1,460·8 km; 907·70 miles).

Height (USA)
Paul F. Bickle, in a Schweizer SGS 1-23E, on 25 February 1961, at Mojave-Lancaster, California. 14,102 m (46,266 ft).

CLASS D, GROUP II (Two-seat sailplanes)

Distance in a straight line (Australia)
Ingo Renner and Hilmer Geissler in a Caproni Vizzola Calif A-21, on 27 January 1975, from Bendigo Aerodrome to Langley Station, Australia. 523·97 nm (970·4 km; 602·98 miles).

Height (USA)
L. E. Edgar and H. E. Klieforth in a Pratt-Read sailplane, on 19 March 1952, at Bishop, California. 13,489 m (44,256 ft).

CLASS E.1 (Helicopters)

Distance in a straight line (USA)
R. G. Ferry in a Hughes OH-6A, on 6-7 April 1966, 1,923·08 nm (3,561·55 km; 2,213 miles).

Height (France)
Jean Boulet in an Aérospatiale SA 315B Lama on 21 June 1972. 12,442 m (40,820 ft).

Speed in a straight line (USSR)
Gourguen Karapetyan in a Mil A-10 (Mi-24), on 21 September 1978, over a 15/25 km course near Moscow. 198·9 knots (368·4 km/h; 228·9 mph).

Speed in a 100 km closed circuit (USSR)
Boris Galitsky and crew of five in a Mil Mi-6, on 26 August 1964, near Moscow. 183·67 knots (340·15 km/h; 211·36 mph).

CLASS E.2 (Convertiplanes)

Height (USSR)
D. Efremov and crew of two, in the Kamov Ka-22 Vintokryl, on 24 November 1961 at Bykovo. 2,588 m (8,491 ft).

Speed in a straight line (USSR)
D. Efremov and crew of five, in the Kamov Ka-22 Vintokryl, on 7 October 1961, at Joukovski-Petrovskœ, over a 15/25 km course. 192·39 knots (356·3 km/h; 221·4 mph).

Speed in a 100 km closed circuit (New Zealand)
Sqd Ldr W. R. Gellatly and J. G. P. Morton, in the Fairey Rotodyne, on 5 January 1959, White Waltham-Wickham-Radley Bottom-Kintbury-White Waltham. 165·89 knots (307·22 km/h; 190·90 mph).

CLASS E.3 (Autogyros)

Height (UK)
Wing Cdr K. H. Wallis, in a Wallis WA-116/Mc, on 11 May 1968. 4,639 m (15,220 ft).

Distance in a straight line (UK)
Wing Cdr K. H. Wallis, in a Wallis WA-116/F, from Lydd Airport, Kent, to Wick, Scotland, on 28 September 1975. 472·092 nm (874·315 km; 543·274 miles).

Distance in a closed circuit (UK)
Wing Cdr K. H. Wallis, in a Wallis WA-116/F, on 13 July 1974. 361·91 nm (670·26 km; 416·48 miles).

Speed in a straight line (UK)
Wing Cdr K. H. Wallis, in a Wallis WA-116/Mc, over a 3 km course, on 12 May 1969. 96·589 knots (179 km/h; 111·225 mph).

JANE'S READERS' SERVICE

JANE'S ENCYCLOPAEDIA OF AVIATION

A major new work covering the history of flight with details of over 5,000 powered aircraft, space vehicles, gliders, airforces and airlines, containing over 60,000 words and 2,500 illustrations in colour and monochrome. For advance information and details of your local stockist please complete and return this card.

Name . . . .

Address . . . .

. . . .

Company *(if applicable)* . . . .

Occupation *(if applicable)* . . . .

JANE'S WORLD AIRCRAFT RECOGNITION HANDBOOK

The most comprehensive recognition study guide and handy reference book to be published in nearly 40 years. For information and full details of your local stockist please complete and return this card.

Name . . . .

Address . . . .

. . . .

Company *(if applicable)* . . . .

Occupation *(if applicable)* . . . .

JANE'S AEROSPACE DICTIONARY

The result of 5 years' research has produced a unique dictionary of aviation and aerospace terms which will be the essential English language reference work throughout the world. For advance information and details of your local stockist please complete and return this card.

Name . . . .

Address . . . .

. . . .

Company *(if applicable)* . . . .

Occupation *(if applicable)* . . . .

JANE'S ADVANCE INFORMATION SERVICE

To be sure of being able to obtain Jane's Yearbooks immediately on publication complete and return this card and we will automatically notify you in advance of publication dates and local stockists.

Name . . . .

Address . . . .

. . . .

Company *(if applicable)* . . . .

Occupation *(if applicable)* . . . .

Marketing Manager
Jane's Yearbooks
8 Shepherdess Walk
London N1
UK

Marketing Manager
Jane's Yearbooks
8 Shepherdess Walk
London N1
UK

Marketing Manager
Jane's Yearbooks
8 Shepherdess Walk
London N1
UK

Marketing Manager
Jane's Yearbooks
8 Shepherdess Walk
London N1
UK

AIRCRAFT

ARGENTINA

AERO BOERO
AERO BOERO SRL

HEAD OFFICE: Hipólito Irigoyen 505, 2421 Morteros, Córdoba
Telephone: Morteros 409 and 2121
DIRECTORS: Cesar E. Boero and Hector C. Boero

This company is producing and developing the Aero Boero 150 and 180 series of light aircraft, and is developing the 260 Ag agricultural aircraft.

AERO BOERO 180 RV and RVR

The original three-seat Aero Boero 180 (1972-73 *Jane's*) was followed by the Aero Boero 180 RV (standard version) and 180 RVR (glider-towing version), the first of which flew for the first time in October 1972. These current versions, to which the description applies, have extended-span all-metal wings, increased fuel capacity, a recontoured fuselage and sweptback vertical tail surfaces. A total of 45 AB 180 RV/RVRs had been built and seven more had been ordered by the Spring of 1978.

TYPE: Three-seat light aircraft.

WINGS: Strut-braced high-wing monoplane. Streamline-section V bracing strut each side. Wing section NACA 23012. Dihedral 1° 45'. Incidence 3° at root, 1° at tip. Light alloy structure, including skins. Ailerons and flaps of aluminium alloy construction.

FUSELAGE: Welded steel tube structure (SAE 4130), covered with Ceconite.

TAIL UNIT: Wire-braced welded steel tube structure, covered with Ceconite. Sweptback vertical surfaces. Ground-adjustable tab on rudder.

LANDING GEAR: Non-retractable tailwheel type, with shock-absorption by helicoidal springs inside fuselage. Main wheels carried on faired-in V struts and half-axles. Main wheels and tyres size 6·00-6, pressure 1·65 bars (24 lb/sq in). Hydraulic disc brakes on main units. Tailwheel steerable and fully castoring.

POWER PLANT: One 134 kW (180 hp) Lycoming O-360-A1A flat-four engine, driving (according to customer's choice) either a Hartzell constant-speed or McCauley 1A200 or Sensenich 76EM8 two-blade fixed-pitch propeller. Three wing fuel tanks, total capacity 201 litres (44 Imp gallons).

ACCOMMODATION: Normal accommodation for pilot and two passengers in enclosed cabin. Baggage compartment on port side, aft of cabin. Transparent roof panel in 180 RVR.

AVIONICS AND EQUIPMENT: One 40A alternator and one 12V battery. VHF radio standard. Provision for night or blind-flying instrumentation at customer's option. Towing hook in 180 RVR.

DIMENSIONS, EXTERNAL:
- Wing span: 10·72 m (35 ft 2 in)
- Wing chord (constant): 1·61 m (5 ft 3½ in)
- Wing aspect ratio: 7·05
- Length overall: 7·273 m (23 ft 10¼ in)
- Height overall: 2·10 m (6 ft 10½ in)
- Wheel track: 2·05 m (6 ft 8¾ in)
- Wheelbase: 5·10 m (16 ft 8¾ in)

AREAS:
- Wings, gross: 16·47 m² (177·3 sq ft)
- Ailerons (total): 1·84 m² (19·81 sq ft)
- Flaps (total): 1·94 m² (20·88 sq ft)
- Fin: 0·93 m² (10·01 sq ft)
- Rudder, incl tab: 0·41 m² (4·41 sq ft)
- Tailplane: 1·40 m² (15·07 sq ft)
- Elevators: 0·97 m² (10·44 sq ft)

WEIGHTS AND LOADINGS:
- Weight empty, equipped: 550 kg (1,212 lb)
- Max T-O weight: 844 kg (1,860 lb)
- Max wing loading: 52·0 kg/m² (10·7 lb/sq ft)
- Max power loading: 6·30 kg/kW (10·36 lb/hp)

PERFORMANCE (at max T-O weight, except where indicated):
- Never-exceed speed: 134 knots (249 km/h; 155 mph)
- Max level speed at S/L:
  - RV: 132 knots (245 km/h; 152 mph)
  - RVR: 122 knots (225 km/h; 140 mph)
- Max cruising speed at S/L: 114 knots (211 km/h; 131 mph)
- Stalling speed, flaps down: 41·5 knots (77 km/h; 48 mph)
- Max rate of climb at S/L: 360 m (1,180 ft)/min
- Time to 600 m (1,970 ft), 75% power, with Blanik two-seat sailplane: 3 min 10 sec
- Service ceiling: 6,700 m (22,000 ft)
- T-O run: 100 m (330 ft)
- T-O to 15 m (50 ft), two persons: 188 m (615 ft)
- Landing from 15 m (50 ft): 160 m (525 ft)
- Landing run: 60 m (195 ft)
- Range with max fuel: 636 nm (1,180 km; 733 miles)

Aero Boero 180 Ag, with ventral chemical pod and underwing spraybars

AB 180 SP biplane version of the Aero Boero 180

AERO BOERO 180 Ag

This version of the Aero Boero 180 is certificated in the Restricted category for use as an agricultural aircraft. Ten had been built and six more had been ordered by the Spring of 1978.

The description of the Aero Boero 180 RV and RVR applies also to the 180 Ag, except as follows:

WINGS: Incidence 3° 30' at root, 2° at tip.

ACCOMMODATION: Normal accommodation for pilot only in agricultural role. As AB 180 RV/RVR for non-agricultural use.

EQUIPMENT: Flush-fitting underfuselage pod containing agricultural chemical. Spraybars fitted along rear bar of V strut and horizontally below wings. Electrically-operated rotary atomisers (two each side) fitted to rear bar of V strut.

PERFORMANCE (at max T-O weight):
- Never-exceed speed: 117 knots (217 km/h; 135 mph)
- Max level speed at S/L: 109 knots (201 km/h; 125 mph)
- Max cruising speed at S/L: 100 knots (185 km/h; 115 mph)
- Econ cruising speed at S/L: 96 knots (177 km/h; 110 mph)
- Stalling speed, flaps down: 48 knots (89 km/h; 55 mph)
- Max rate of climb at S/L: 107 m (350 ft)/min
- T-O run: 213 m (700 ft)
- T-O to 15 m (50 ft): 335 m (1,100 ft)
- Landing from 15 m (50 ft): 229 m (750 ft)
- Landing run: 152 m (500 ft)
- Range with max fuel: 434 nm (804 km; 500 miles)

AERO BOERO 180 SP

By adding short-span lower wings (approx 6 m; 19 ft 8¼ in) to the basic AB 180 Ag, Aero Boero has produced this biplane version of the aircraft, with improved take-off and landing performance, wider speed range, and greater payload/range capability. Agricultural chemical tankage of approx 330 litres (72·5 Imp gallons) is provided in the lower wings, in place of the underfuselage pack of the AB 180 Ag.

PERFORMANCE:
- Max level speed: 117 knots (217 km/h; 135 mph)
- Max cruising speed: 100 knots (185 km/h; 115 mph)
- Stalling speed: 30·5 knots (56·5 km/h; 35 mph)
- Service ceiling with max payload: 3,500 m (11,480 ft)
- T-O run with max payload: 200 m (656 ft)
- T-O run without payload: 65 m (213 ft)
- Landing run without payload: 70 m (230 ft)
- Range at 75% power: 448 nm (830 km; 516 miles)
- Endurance at 75% power: 4 h 30 min

AERO BOERO 150 RV

Essentially a lower-powered version of the AB 180 RV, the Aero Boero 150 RV is certificated in the Normal category. Four had been built and five more had been ordered by the Spring of 1978.

The description of the Aero Boero 180 RV and RVR applies also to the 150 RV except as follows:

POWER PLANT: One 112 kW (150 hp) Lycoming O-320-A2B flat-four engine, driving a Sensenich 74-DM6-0-54 fixed-pitch propeller. Two wing fuel tanks, total capacity 134 litres (29·5 Imp gallons).

PERFORMANCE (at max T-O weight):
- Never-exceed speed: 132 knots (245 km/h; 152 mph)
- Max cruising speed: 114 knots (211 km/h; 131 mph)
- Stalling speed, flaps down: 42 knots (77 km/h; 48 mph)
- Max rate of climb at S/L: 270 m (885 ft)/min
- T-O run: 100 m (328 ft)
- T-O to 15 m (50 ft): 220 m (722 ft)

AERO BOERO 150 Ag

This version of the Aero Boero 150 is certificated in the Restricted category for use as an agricultural aircraft. The description of the Aero Boero 180 Ag applies also to the 150 Ag except as follows:

POWER PLANT: As Aero Boero 150 RV.

EQUIPMENT: Non-corrosive glassfibre underfuselage tank, with capacity of 270 litres (59·4 Imp gallons; 71·3 US gallons) of liquid chemical.

PERFORMANCE (at max T-O weight):
- Never-exceed speed 123 knots (228 km/h; 141 mph)
- Max level speed 119 knots (220 km/h; 137 mph)
- Econ cruising speed 82 knots (152 km/h; 94·5 mph)

Aero Boero 150 Ag agricultural aircraft (Lycoming O-320 engine)

AERO BOERO 260 Ag

Aero Boero began the design of this single-seat agricultural monoplane in mid-1971, at which time it was known as the AG.235/260. Construction of a prototype began in October 1971, and this aircraft flew for the first time on 23 December 1972. The static test programme, and flight certification, were due to be completed in April 1978.

The prototype, to which the description applies, is illustrated in an accompanying photograph. The three-view drawing shows the modifications intended for the production version, including twin landing lights in the port wing leading-edge and all-round-vision cockpit hood.

TYPE: Single-seat agricultural aircraft.

WINGS: Low-wing monoplane. Wing section NACA 23012. Dihedral 5°. Construction, including trailing-edge flaps and ailerons, is of aluminium alloy, with inverted V bracing struts on each side.

FUSELAGE: Welded SAE 4130 steel tube structure with plastics covering.

TAIL UNIT: Wire-braced welded steel tube structure with plastics covering.

LANDING GEAR: Non-retractable tailwheel type, with coil spring shock-absorbers. Hydraulic disc brakes on main wheels.

POWER PLANT: One 194 kW (260 hp) Lycoming O-540 flat-six engine, driving a McCauley P235/AFA 8456 two-blade propeller. Four wing fuel tanks, total capacity 268 litres (59 Imp gallons).

ACCOMMODATION: Pilot only, in enclosed cabin. Door on starboard side, which can be jettisoned in an emergency. Cabin heated, and ventilated by adjustable cool-air vents. Utility compartment on port side, aft of cabin.

AVIONICS AND EQUIPMENT: VHF radio standard. Non-corrosive glassfibre tank installed forward of cockpit, with capacity of 500 litres (110 Imp gallons) of liquid or 500 kg (1,102 lb) of dry chemical. Quick-dump valve, to jettison contents of tank in an emergency. Engine-driven pump.

DIMENSIONS, EXTERNAL:
- Wing span 10·90 m (35 ft 9 in)
- Wing chord (constant over most of span) 1·61 m (5 ft 3½ in)
- Wing aspect ratio 6·8
- Length overall (tail up) 7·45 m (24 ft 5¼ in)
- Height overall (tail up) 1·90 m (6 ft 2¾ in)
- Tailplane span 3·04 m (9 ft 11¾ in)
- Propeller diameter 2·13 m (7 ft 0 in)

DIMENSION, INTERNAL:
- Hopper volume 0·5 m³ (17·66 cu ft)

AREAS: As for Aero Boero 180 RV and RVR

WEIGHTS AND LOADINGS:
- Weight empty 720 kg (1,587 lb)
- Max T-O weight 1,350 kg (2,976 lb)
- Max wing loading 77·28 kg/m² (15·83 lb/sq ft)
- Max power loading 6·96 kg/kW (11·44 lb/hp)

PERFORMANCE (at max T-O weight):
- Never-exceed speed 117 knots (217 km/h; 135 mph)
- Max cruising speed at S/L 109 knots (201 km/h; 125 mph)
- Econ cruising speed 95·5 knots (177 km/h; 110 mph)
- Stalling speed, flaps down 52·5 knots (97 km/h; 60 mph)
- Max rate of climb at S/L 410 m (1,345 ft)/min
- Service ceiling 6,400 m (21,000 ft)
- T-O to 15 m (50 ft) 200 m (656 ft)
- Landing from 15 m (50 ft) 120 m (394 ft)
- Range with max fuel 593 nm (1,100 km; 683 miles)

Prototype Aero Boero 260 Ag agricultural aircraft (Lycoming O-540 engine)

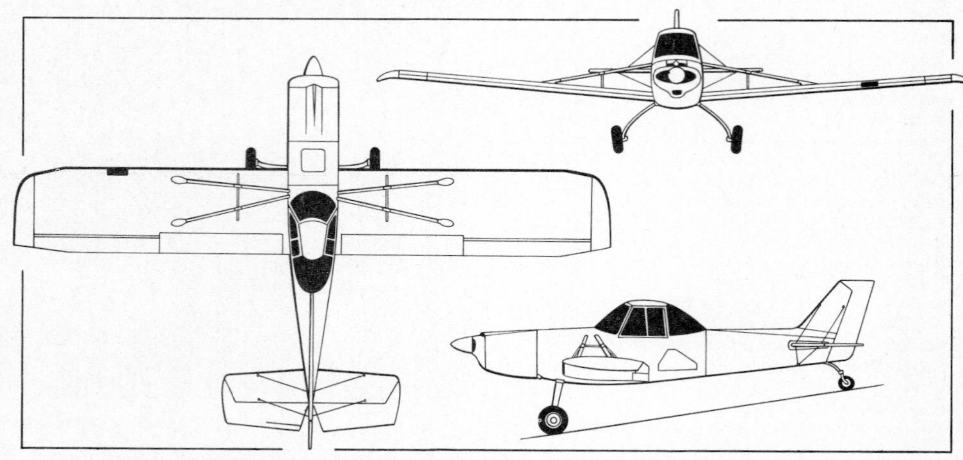

Intended production version of the Aero Boero 260 Ag *(Michael A. Badrocke)*

CHINCUL

CHINCUL S.A.C.A.I.F.I.

HEAD OFFICE: 25 de Mayo 489, 6° Piso, Buenos Aires
Telephone: 32 5671/5
Telex: 012 2706

WORKS: Calle Mendoza entre 6 y 7 (Casilla de Correo 80), San Juan

PRESIDENT: Juan José Beraza

VICE-PRESIDENT: José María Beraza

EXECUTIVE DIRECTOR: Aquiles Luis Uriarte

WORKS DIRECTOR: Héctor Carlos Delgado

CHIEF OF ENGINEERING DEPT: Fernando Leon Reisin

CHIEF OF PRODUCTION DEPT: Conrado Risso Patrón

CHIEF OF QUALITY CONTROL AND FLIGHT TEST DEPT: Roberto Lucio

This company, a wholly-owned subsidiary of La Macarena SA, Piper's Argentine distributor, concluded an agreement with Piper Aircraft Corporation in November 1971 for manufacture of a range of Piper products in Argentina. The plan called for a progression through manufacturing phases of increasing complexity, and some Chincul products (such as the Pawnee) are now more than 60% manufactured in Argentina.

Piper aircraft are built at the plant at San Juan, which has a covered area of 14,500 m² (156,075 sq ft) and a work force of 320 people; an additional facility of 2,000 m² (21,530 sq ft) is planned as a maintenance and overhaul workshop.

Prototype Chincul military trainer developed from the Piper Cherokee Arrow

Chincul's production programme includes the PA-23-250 Aztec and Turbo Aztec; the PA-25-235 Pawnee D; various Cherokees (PA-28-140, -180, -181 and -200R, and PA-32-300 and -300R); Navajos (PA-31-310 and -325 Turbo Navajo, PA-31P Pressurised Navajo and PA-31-350 Navajo Chieftain); and the PA-34-200T Seneca. The PA-36 Pawnee Brave and PA-38 Tomahawk were introduced during 1978, and the PA-31T Cheyenne in January 1979. More than 200 aircraft had been completed by January 1979, and many of these are now operating in various South American countries.

All Piper kits now being delivered to Chincul are for Phase 3 assembly, involving the assembly and riveting of wings and control surfaces, manufacture of interiors, upholstery, electrical harness, and other systems installation. Batteries, upholstery, fabrics, tyres, engine instruments, fire extinguishers and glassfibre components are of Argentine manufacture. Chincul also has an agreement with Narco Avionics under which it assembles Escort 110, Com 11, Com 120, Nav 121 and 122, ADF 31, 140 and 141, OGR 2A2-5, and Nav 11/12 sets.

The company is currently developing a fully-aerobatic two-seat military trainer based on the Piper Cherokee Arrow.

CHINCUL (PIPER) CHEROKEE ARROW TRAINER

In January 1978 Chincul was flight testing the prototype (LV-X67) of a military training aircraft which it has developed from the Piper Cherokee Arrow four-seat light aircraft. The principal modifications from the standard Arrow are a more powerful engine, a two-seat cockpit with new canopy, revised internal equipment, and provision for a built-in machine-gun and underwing weapons for armament training. Although the basic airframe of the Arrow is retained, it has been entirely restressed to permit certification in the fully-aerobatic category. Production was planned to begin in mid-1979.

TYPE: Two-seat military trainer.

WINGS, FUSELAGE, TAIL UNIT AND LANDING GEAR: Generally similar to those of Piper Arrow (see US section), but with fuselage modified in cabin area. Entire airframe restressed for aerobatic flying.

POWER PLANT: One 194 kW (260 hp) Lycoming AEIO-540 series flat-six engine, driving a two-blade propeller with spinner. Fuel tank in each wing leading-edge, combined capacity 272 litres (71·8 US gallons). Oil capacity 11·5 litres (3 US gallons).

ACCOMMODATION: Seats for instructor and pupil side by side under rearward-sliding framed canopy. Dual controls standard.

AVIONICS AND EQUIPMENT: Two VHF and one HF com; two VOR; one ILS; one DME; two ADF; audio selector panel; oxygen system.

ARMAMENT: Provision for one 7·62 mm machine-gun in lower front fuselage; underwing pylons for bombs and rockets.

DIMENSIONS, EXTERNAL:
- Wing span: 10·67 m (35 ft 0 in)
- Wing chord (constant portion inboard of ailerons): 1·60 m (5 ft 3 in)
- Wing chord at tip: 1·07 m (3 ft 6¼ in)
- Length overall: 7·25 m (23 ft 9½ in)
- Height overall: 2·23 m (7 ft 3½ in)
- Tailplane span: 3·92 m (12 ft 10½ in)
- Wheel track: 3·05 m (10 ft 0 in)
- Wheelbase: 2·40 m (7 ft 10½ in)
- Propeller diameter: 2·03 m (6 ft 8 in)

AREA:
- Wings, gross: 15·79 m² (170·0 sq ft)

WEIGHTS AND LOADINGS:
- Weight empty: 785 kg (1,730 lb)
- Max T-O weight: 1,315 kg (2,900 lb)
- Max wing loading: 83·25 kg/m² (17·06 lb/sq ft)
- Max power loading: 6·78 kg/kW (11·15 lb/hp)

PERFORMANCE (at max T-O weight):
- Max level speed: 169 knots (314 km/h; 195 mph)
- Max cruising speed (75% power): 156 knots (290 km/h; 180 mph)
- Speed for optimum climb: 87 knots (161 km/h; 100 mph)
- Stalling speed, flaps and landing gear down: 54 knots (100 km/h; 62 mph)
- Max rate of climb at S/L: 238 m (780 ft)/min
- Service ceiling: 3,962 m (13,000 ft)
- T-O run: 302 m (990 ft)
- Landing run: 227 m (744 ft)
- Range (75% power, optimum mixture, at optimum altitude): 729 nm (1,352 km; 840 miles)
- Fuel consumption (75% power): 54·5 litres (12 Imp gallons)/h

CICARÉ
CICARÉ AERONÁUTICA SC

ADDRESS: Ave Ibañez Frocham s/n, Casilla Correo 24, 7260 Saladillo, Provincia de Buenos Aires

ENQUIRIES TO: Comodoro Antonio R. Mantel, Santa Fé 1256, Buenos Aires

Telephone: Buenos Aires 41 5260

PARTNERS:
Augusto Ulderico Cicaré
Comodoro Ildefonso Domingo Durana
Comodoro Antonio Raúl Mantel

This company was formed in 1972 to develop and build small aero-engines and light helicopters. Brief details of the experimental Cicaré I and Cicaré II appeared in the 1970-71, 1973-74 and 1974-75 *Jane's*.

CICARÉ C.K.1

Design of the C.K.1, known originally as the CH-III Colibrí, began in August 1973, and prototype construction started in 1974. This work was done, under contract from the Argentine Air Force, to evolve a light helicopter suitable for training and agricultural duties.

Following considerable redesign during 1975-76, the helicopter was redesignated C.K.1 and made its first flight in September 1976. It was hoped to obtain full certification in 1978; work on a pre-series batch of five C.K.1s was then under way.

The following description applies to the prototype:

TYPE: Two/three-seat light helicopter.

ROTOR SYSTEM: Four-blade rigid main rotor and two-blade tail rotor. Blade section NACA 0015. All blades are of glassfibre construction. No rotor brake or blade folding.

ROTOR DRIVE: Ten V-belts, via a reduction gearbox, with freewheel system for autorotation. Main rotor/engine rpm ratio 1 : 6; tail rotor/engine rpm ratio 1 : 1.

FUSELAGE: Steel tube structure, with glassfibre cabin and aluminium tailboom.

LANDING GEAR: Tubular steel skid type.

POWER PLANT: One 142-149 kW (190-200 hp) 4C-27 flat-four engine. Single glassfibre fuel tank, capacity 135 litres (29·5 Imp gallons). Optional auxiliary tank, capacity 75 litres (16·5 Imp gallons).

Cicaré C.K.1 prototype two/three-seat light helicopter

ACCOMMODATION: Two or three seats side by side in enclosed cabin (instructor and pupil only in training version). Door on each side of cabin. Space for up to 45 kg (100 lb) of baggage. Cabin heated and ventilated.

AVIONICS AND EQUIPMENT: VHF radio standard. Mission equipment includes spraying or dusting gear and cargo sling.

DIMENSIONS, EXTERNAL:
- Diameter of main rotor: 7·60 m (24 ft 11¼ in)
- Main rotor blade chord: 152 mm (6 in)
- Diameter of tail rotor: 1·10 m (3 ft 7·2 in)
- Distance between rotor centres: 4·27 m (14 ft 0 in)
- Length overall: 8·53 m (28 ft 0 in)
- Height overall: 2·47 m (8 ft 1·2 in)
- Skid track: 2·01 m (6 ft 7·2 in)

AREAS:
- Main rotor disc: 43·8 m² (471·43 sq ft)
- Tail rotor disc: 0·95 m² (10·18 sq ft)

WEIGHTS AND LOADINGS:
- Weight empty, equipped: 469 kg (1,034 lb)
- Max payload: 226 kg (500 lb)
- Max T-O weight: 800 kg (1,764 lb)
- Max disc loading: 18·3 kg/m² (3·74 lb/sq ft)
- Max power loading: 5·63 kg/kW (9·28 lb/hp)

PERFORMANCE (estimated, at max T-O weight):
- Max level and cruising speed at S/L: 88 knots (163 km/h; 101 mph)
- Econ cruising speed: 65 knots (120 km/h; 74·5 mph)
- Max rate of climb at S/L: 360 m (1,180 ft)/min
- Service ceiling: 3,900 m (12,800 ft)
- Hovering ceiling out of ground effect: 1,700 m (5,575 ft)
- Range, standard fuel: 259 nm (480 km; 298 miles)

FMA (AREA DE MATERIAL CÓRDOBA)
AGRUPACIÓN AVIONES-DEPARTAMENTO INGENIERÍA, GUARNICION AÉREA CÓRDOBA

ADDRESS: Avenida Fuerza Aérea Argentina Km 5½, 5103 Córdoba

Telephone: 45011/15

Telex: 51965 AR

DIRECTOR: Brigadier Fernando Rodriguez

CHIEF ENGINEER: Enrique Alberto Corti

The original Fábrica Militar de Aviones (Military Aircraft Factory) was founded in 1927 as a central organisation for aeronautical research and production in Argentina. Its name was changed to Instituto Aerotécnico in 1943 and then to Industrias Aeronáuticas y Mecánicas del Estado (IAME) in 1952. In 1957 it became a State enterprise under the title of Dirección Nacional de Fabricaciones e Investigacióńes Aeronáuticas (DINFIA), but reverted to its original title in 1968. It is now a component of the Area de Material Córdoba division of the Argentine Air Force.

FMA comprises two large divisions. The Instituto de Investigacióńes Aeronáuticas y Espacial (IIAE) is responsible for the design, manufacture and testing of rockets, sounding equipment and other equipment. The Fábrica

IA 58A Pucará combat aircraft of the Argentinian Air Force

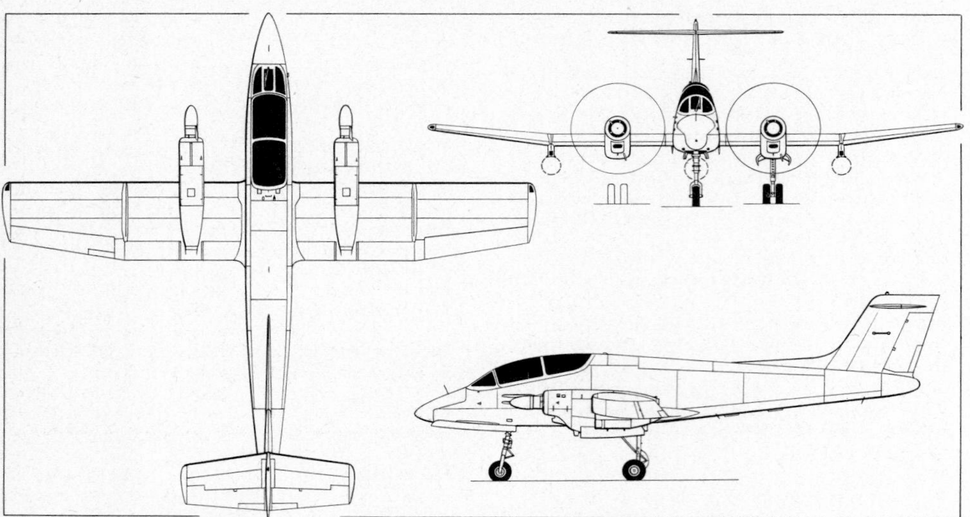

FMA IA 58A Pucará twin-turboprop counter-insurgency aircraft *(Pilot Press)*

Militar de Aviones itself controls the aircraft manufacturing facilities situated in Córdoba. The laboratories, factories and other aeronautical division buildings occupy a total covered area of 148,557 m² (1,599,059 sq ft); the Area de Material Córdoba employs 3,500 persons, of whom about 1,500 are in the FMA.

FMA's head offices are situated in Buenos Aires. It also controls the Centro de Ensayos en Vuelo (Flight Test Centre), to which all aircraft produced in Argentina are sent for certification tests.

In current production is the IA 58 Pucará, a nationally designed counter-insurgency aircraft.

The IA 62 design, referred to briefly in the 1977-78 *Jane's*, has been superseded by the IA 63, a primary and advanced jet trainer currently in the preliminary design stage.

FMA is also producing Cessna single-engined aircraft under licence, under agreements announced in October 1965 and subsequently. These aircraft are repurchased by Cessna for sale through its distributors and dealers in Latin America or sold directly by FMA to Argentinian government agencies. Forty Cessna Model 150s were ordered by the Comando de Regiones Aéreas for use as trainers by Argentinian flying clubs. The first A182J (Argentinian 182) was completed in August 1966 and delivered to its owner on 2 September 1966. A renewed and extended agreement, announced in April 1971, provided for continued production of the Cessna 182 and, in addition, for the range to be extended to include the Model 150 trainer and the AGwagon agricultural aircraft.

By the beginning of 1979, FMA had completed 146 Cessna Model A182s, 39 Model A150 trainers, 9 Model A-A150 Aerobats and 33 Model A188 AGwagons. Production continued in 1979 of the Models A182 and A188, and of the 82 kW (110 hp) Cessna Model 152.

IA 58 PUCARÁ

Design of this twin-turboprop counter-insurgency aircraft, to meet an Argentinian Air Force requirement, began in August 1966. Known originally as the Delfin (Dolphin), it was later renamed Pucará after a type of stone fortress built by the early South American Indians. An unpowered aerodynamic prototype, which first flew on 26 December 1967, was described in the 1968-69 *Jane's*. The first powered prototype, designated A-X2, flew for the first time on 20 August 1969 with 674 kW (904 ehp) AiResearch TPE 331-U-303 turboprop engines, and was described in the 1971-72 *Jane's*. It was later redesignated AX-01.

A second prototype, designated AX-02, flew for the first time on 6 September 1970, powered by 761 kW (1,022 ehp) Turboméca Astazou XVI G turboprops. This power plant was adopted as standard for the production version, for which the prototype was the similarly-powered AX-03, first flown in mid-1973; the AX-01 also was re-engined with Astazou XVI Gs.

An initial order for 30 IA 58A Pucarás, subsequently increased to 60, was placed by the Argentinian Air Force, and the first of these (A-501) flew for the first time on 8 November 1974. About 30 Pucarás had been delivered by mid-1979; these are in service with Argentinian Air Force units, including the II Escuadron de Exploracion y Ataque at Reconquista air base, with which the Pucará was deployed operationally in late 1976 against terrorist groups in north-western Argentina. The Argentinian Air Force has an eventual requirement for 100 of these aircraft, for which 211 Astazou XVI engines have already been ordered.

An **IA 58B Bravo** (Brave) version is under development. This has two 30 mm DEFA cannon, with 140 rds/gun, resulting in a slightly deeper nose section and a modified underfuselage outline aft of the wing trailing-edges. The four 7·62 mm guns are retained. Other improvements in the IA 58B, the prototype of which appeared at the Paris Air Show in June 1979, include a new avionics fit (HF, VHF/FM, DME and IFF/SSB, plus provision for the Omega navigation system and weather radar). See Addenda for photograph.

Except where indicated, the following description applies to the standard IA 58A, production of which was at the rate of approx two per month in the Summer of 1979:

Type: Twin-turboprop counter-insurgency aircraft.

Wings: Cantilever low-wing monoplane. Wing section NACA 64_2A215 at root, NACA 64_1A212 at tip. Dihedral 7° on outer panels. Incidence 2°. No sweepback. Conventional semi-monocoque fail-safe structure of duralumin. Frise-type fabric-covered duralumin ailerons, and all-dural slotted trailing-edge flaps, actuated by pushrods. No slats. Balance tab in starboard aileron, electrically-operated trim tab in port aileron. Kléber-Colombes pneumatic de-icing boots on leading-edges.

Fuselage: Conventional semi-monocoque fail-safe structure of duralumin frames and stringers.

Tail Unit: Cantilever semi-monocoque structure of duralumin. Fixed-incidence tailplane and elevators mounted near top of fin. Rudder and elevators actuated by pushrods, and each fitted with inset trim tab. Kléber-Colombes pneumatic de-icing boots on leading-edges.

Landing Gear: Retractable tricycle type. All units retract forward hydraulically, steerable nose unit into fuselage, main units into engine nacelles. Shock-absorbers of Kronprinz Ring-Feder type, designed by Vicecomodoro Ruiz. Single wheel on nose unit, twin wheels on main units, all with Dunlop tubeless Type III tyres size 7·50-10. Tyre pressures: 2·82 bars (41 lb/sq in) on main units, 2·41 bars (35 lb/sq in) on nose unit. Dunlop hydraulic disc brakes on main units. No anti-skid units.

Power Plant: Two 761 kW (1,022 ehp) Turboméca Astazou XVI G turboprop engines, each driving a Hamilton Standard 23LF/1015-0 three-blade metal propeller with spinner. Fuel in two fuselage tanks (total 800 litres; 176 Imp gallons) and one 230 litre (50·5 Imp gallon) self-sealing tank in each wing, giving overall internal capacity of 1,260 litres (277 Imp gallons). Refuelling point on top of fuselage aft of cockpit. Fuel system includes provision for up to 30 s of inverted flight. A long-range auxiliary tank, capacity 1,130 litres (248·5 Imp gallons), can be attached to the fuselage centreline pylon, and a 300 litre (66 Imp gallon) auxiliary tank on each underwing pylon. Max internal and external fuel load 2,990 litres (657·5 Imp gallons). Oil capacity 11·75 litres (2·6 Imp gallons).

Accommodation: Pilot and co-pilot in tandem on Martin-Baker Mk AP06A zero-zero ejection seats beneath transparent moulded canopy which is hinged at rear and opens upwards. Rear seat elevated 25 cm (9·8 in) above front seat. Bulletproof windscreen, with wiper. Dual controls standard.

Systems: Hydraulic system, pressure 207 bars (3,000 lb/sq in), supplied by two engine-driven pumps, actuates landing gear, flaps and wheel brakes. Wing and tail unit de-icing by engine bleed air. Electrical system includes two 28V 300A starter/generators for DC power and three 500/750VA static inverters for 115/200V AC power. One 24V 36Ah SAFT Voltabloc 4006 battery. No APU. Liquid oxygen bottle.

Avionics and Equipment: Blind-flying instrumentation standard. Electronics include Bendix DFA-73A-1 ADF, Bendix RTA-42A VHF com, Bendix RNA-2bc VHF nav, Northern N-420 HF/SSB com, amplifier and audio-selector system with AS-A-31 panel. Optional electronics include weather radar, IFF, and VHF/FM tactical communications system. Landing/taxying light in leading-edge of each underwing pylon.

Armament and Operational Equipment (IA 58A): Two 20 mm Hispano HS-2804 cannon, each with 270 rds, in underside of forward fuselage; and four 7·62 mm FN-Browning machine-guns, each with 900 rds, in sides of fuselage abreast of cockpit. Aero 7A-1 pylon on centreline beneath fuselage, capacity 1,000 kg (2,205 lb). Aero 20A-1 pylon, capacity 500 kg (1,102 lb), beneath each wing outboard of engine nacelle. Total external stores load 1,620 kg (3,571 lb), including gun and rocket pods, bombs, or auxiliary fuel tanks. Matra 83-4-3 reflector gunsight and AN/AWE-1 programmer.

Armament (IA 58B): Two 30 mm DEFA 553 cannon, with 140 rds/gun; and four 7·62 mm FN-Browning machine-guns, with 900 rds/gun. One underfuselage and two underwing hardpoints for up to twelve 125 kg bombs; one 30 mm Dassault gun pod plus four Alkan 530 rocket launchers or two drop-tanks; or six Alkan 530 launchers; or three drop-tanks.

Dimensions, external:
- Wing span: 14·50 m (47 ft 6¾ in)
- Wing chord at root: 2·24 m (7 ft 4¼ in)
- Wing chord at tip: 1·60 m (5 ft 3 in)
- Wing aspect ratio: 6·95
- Length overall: 14·25 m (46 ft 9 in)
- Length of fuselage: 13·32 m (43 ft 8½ in)
- Fuselage: Max width: 1·24 m (4 ft 0¾ in)
- Height overall: 5·36 m (17 ft 7 in)
- Tailplane span: 4·70 m (15 ft 5 in)
- Wheel track (c/l of shock-absorbers): 4·20 m (13 ft 9¼ in)
- Wheelbase: 3·48 m (11 ft 5 in)
- Propeller diameter: 2·59 m (8 ft 6 in)

Dimensions, internal:
- Cabin: Floor area: 2·90 m² (31·2 sq ft)
- Volume: 2·74 m³ (96·8 cu ft)

Areas:
- Wings, gross: 30·30 m² (326·1 sq ft)
- Ailerons (total): 3·29 m² (35·41 sq ft)
- Trailing-edge flaps (total): 3·58 m² (38·53 sq ft)
- Fin: 3·465 m² (37·30 sq ft)
- Rudder, incl tab: 1·565 m² (16·84 sq ft)
- Tailplane: 4·60 m² (49·51 sq ft)
- Elevators, incl tabs: 2·612 m² (28·11 sq ft)

Weights and Loadings (IA 58A):
- Weight empty, equipped: 4,037 kg (8,900 lb)
- Max T-O weight: 6,800 kg (14,991 lb)
- Max landing weight: 5,806 kg (12,800 lb)
- Max wing loading: 224·4 kg/m² (46 lb/sq ft)
- Max power loading: 4·46 kg/kW (7·3 lb/ehp)

Performance (IA 58A at max T-O weight except where indicated):
- Never-exceed speed: 404 knots (750 km/h; 466 mph)
- Max level speed at 3,000 m (9,845 ft): 270 knots (500 km/h; 310 mph)
- Max cruising speed at 6,000 m (19,685 ft): 259 knots (480 km/h; 298 mph)
- Econ cruising speed: 232 knots (430 km/h; 267 mph)
- Stalling speed, flaps and landing gear up: 68 knots (125 km/h; 78 mph)
- Stalling speed, flaps and landing gear down, at 4,790 kg (10,560 lb) gross weight: 77·5 knots (142·5 km/h; 89 mph)
- Max rate of climb at S/L: 1,080 m (3,543 ft)/min
- Service ceiling: 10,000 m (32,810 ft)
- Service ceiling, one engine out: 6,000 m (19,685 ft)
- T-O run: 300 m (985 ft)
- T-O to 15 m (50 ft): 705 m (2,313 ft)
- Landing from 15 m (50 ft) at 5,100 kg (11,243 lb) gross weight: 603 m (1,978 ft)
- Landing run at 5,100 kg (11,243 lb) gross weight: 200 m (656 ft)
- Range with max fuel at 5,000 m (16,400 ft): 1,641 nm (3,042 km; 1,890 miles)
- *g* limits: +6; −3

Performance (IA 58B):
- Min T-O run: 353 m (1,158 ft)
- Min landing run: 557 m (1,827 ft)
- Range on internal fuel: 728 nm (1,350 km; 838 miles)
- Endurance:
  - at 5,718 kg (12,606 lb) combat weight: 5 h 37 min
  - at 5,940 kg (13,095 lb) combat weight: 5 h 23 min

RACA
REPRESENTACIONES AERO COMERCIALES ARGENTINAS SA

Head Office: Lavalle 715, 5° Piso, 1047 Buenos Aires
Telephone: 393 7334 and 392 9488
Telex: 22844 RACA AR
Works: Aeródromo San Fernando, Provincia Buenos Aires
President: J. R. Fernández Racca

This company is the representative or dealer in Argentina for the Canadair CL-215 and CASA C-212 Aviocar aircraft, and the MBB BO 105 and Hughes helicopters. Under a licence agreement concluded in December 1972 RACA is undertaking, with Argentinian government approval (granted in mid-1973), the progressive local manufacture of a minimum of 120 Hughes Model 500 helicopters (see US section) from knock-down components. These are known locally as RACA-Hughes 500s, and are identical to the Hughes-built version described in the US section.

The programme is covering, in three phases, a period of eight years, to supply military and civil customers in Argentina and neighbouring countries. In anticipation of this programme, RACA expanded its workshop facilities at San Fernando aerodrome to a covered area of 4,600 m² (49,514 sq ft).

RRA

RONCHETTI, RAZZETTI AVIACIÓN SA

Address: Aeropuerto Internacional Rosario, Casilla Correo 7, 2132 Funes, Santa Fé Province
Telephone: Rosario 58251 or Funes 93276
President: Julio E. Razzetti
Head of Design and Development Group (RRAFAGA): Ing Norberto S. Cobelo
Head of Production: Julio Di Giuseppe

RRAFAGA J-1 MARTIN FIERRO

RRA J-1 Martin Fierro agricultural aircraft (Lycoming IO-540-K1JG engine)

The J-1 Martin Fierro is a single-seat agricultural aircraft, designed in Argentina by a team led by Ing Norberto S. Cobelo. Design began in September 1972, and construction of the first of two prototypes started three months later. This aircraft made its first flight on 18 December 1975.

Five more J-1s were under construction during 1978, including one for structural testing. Certification by the Argentinian Air Force was anticipated during that year, and plans were being made for series production.

Type: Single-seat agricultural aircraft.

Wings: Cantilever low-wing monoplane. Thickness/chord ratio 15%. Dihedral 7°. Incidence 2° at root. All-metal single box-spar structure, with detachable leading-edges. All-metal Frise-type ailerons and semi-Fowler trailing-edge flaps. No tabs.

Fuselage: Welded tube structure with detachable metal skin.

Tail Unit: Cantilever all-metal two-spar structure. Fixed-incidence tailplane. Trim tab in each elevator.

Landing Gear: Non-retractable tailwheel type, with spring steel shock-absorption. Cleveland wheels and main-wheel brakes. Goodyear tyres, size 8·50-10 (8 ply) on main units, 2·80-8 (4 ply) on tail unit.

Power Plant: One 224 kW (300 hp) Lycoming IO-540-K1JG flat-six engine, driving a Hartzell two-blade variable-pitch constant-speed propeller with spinner. Fuel in two wing-root tanks, total capacity 162 litres (35·6 Imp gallons). Refuelling point on top of each tank. Oil capacity 12 litres (2·64 Imp gallons).

Accommodation: Single seat in heated and ventilated framed cockpit. Downward-opening window/door on each side.

Systems and Equipment: 12V 60A Prestolite generator and 12V 30Ah Prestolite battery. Single hopper, forward of cockpit, of 850 litres (187 Imp gallons) capacity. Can be fitted with dusting or spraying systems, for dry or liquid chemicals.

Dimensions, external:
- Wing span 13·00 m (42 ft 7¾ in)
- Wing chord (constant) 1·60 m (5 ft 3 in)
- Wing aspect ratio 8·12
- Length overall 7·00 m (22 ft 11¾ in)
- Height overall 4·00 m (13 ft 1½ in)
- Wheelbase 2·40 m (7 ft 10½ in)
- Propeller diameter 2·13 m (7 ft 0 in)
- Propeller ground clearance 0·50 m (1 ft 7¾ in)

Areas:
- Wings, gross 20·80 m² (223·9 sq ft)
- Ailerons (total) 2·76 m² (29·71 sq ft)
- Trailing-edge flaps (total) 2·76 m² (29·71 sq ft)
- Fin 1·44 m² (15·50 sq ft)
- Rudder 0·96 m² (10·33 sq ft)
- Tailplane 2·64 m² (28·42 sq ft)
- Elevators (total, incl tabs) 1·76 m² (18·94 sq ft)

Weights and Loadings:
- Basic operating weight with spray equipment 920 kg (2,028 lb)
- Max payload 850 kg (1,874 lb)
- Max T-O and landing weight (Restricted category) 2,000 kg (4,409 lb)
- Max wing loading 96·14 kg/m² (19·69 lb/sq ft)
- Max power loading 8·93 kg/kW (14·70 lb/hp)

Performance (at max FAR Pt 23 Aerobatic T-O weight):
- Never-exceed speed 188 knots (349 km/h; 217 mph)
- Max level speed at S/L, 'clean' 130 knots (241 km/h; 150 mph)
- Econ cruising speed at S/L, 'clean' 114 knots (211 km/h; 131 mph)
- Stalling speed, flaps up 55 knots (102 km/h; 63 mph)
- Stalling speed, flaps down 43 knots (79 km/h; 49 mph)
- Max rate of climb at S/L 290 m (950 ft)/min
- Service ceiling 3,660 m (12,000 ft)
- T-O run 168 m (550 ft)
- T-O to 15 m (50 ft) 251 m (824 ft)
- Landing from 15 m (50 ft) 244 m (800 ft)
- Landing run 85 m (280 ft)
- Max range, 45 min reserves 265 nm (490 km; 305 miles)

AUSTRALIA

CAC

COMMONWEALTH AIRCRAFT CORPORATION LIMITED

Head Office and Works: 304 Lorimer Street, Port Melbourne, Victoria 3207
Telephone: 64 0771
Telex: 30721
Chairman of Directors: N. F. Stevens
Secretary: E. W. Stodden

Commonwealth Aircraft Corporation Pty Ltd was formed in 1936. On 18 August 1975 it became a public company, changing its name to Commonwealth Aircraft Corporation Limited.

In February 1971, CAC was named as the prime contractor in a programme to provide 56 Bell 206B-1 JetRanger II helicopters for the Australian Army. These were delivered between April 1973 and March 1977.

Major current programmes include repair and overhaul of RAAF Atar 9C, Avon and Viper jet engines; modification of RAAF Lockheed P-3C Orions to Australian LRMP (long-range maritime patrol) requirements; manufacture of passenger doors for the Lockheed L-1011 TriStar and escape slides for the McDonnell Douglas DC-10, and of catering equipment for Australian Airlines and Qantas. Ground support equipment is supplied through Static General Engineering Pty Ltd, a CAC subsidiary.

GAF

GOVERNMENT AIRCRAFT FACTORIES

Headquarters: Fishermen's Bend, Private Bag No. 4, Post Office, Port Melbourne, Victoria 3207
Telephone: 64 0661
Telex: AA 34397
General Manager: M. C. Morrison
Marketing Manager: E. A. Morris
Public Relations Officer: C. Collinson

The Government Aircraft Factories are units of the Defence Production facilities owned by the Australian government and operated by the Department of Productivity. They have a work force of approximately 2,500 persons. Their functions include the design, development, manufacture, assembly, maintenance and modification of aircraft, target drones and guided weapons. At Avalon airfield, subassembly of components, final assembly, modification, repair and test-flying of jet and other aircraft are undertaken.

Current activity includes development and production of the Nomad twin-turboprop STOL aircraft, the Ikara anti-submarine missile, and the Jindivik and Turana target drones.

The GAF are producing elevators for the Boeing 727 and wing flaps for the Fokker F28 Fellowship.

Twin-float version of the GAF Nomad N22B, flight-tested in the USA

GOVERNMENT AIRCRAFT FACTORIES NOMAD

The N2 prototype of the Nomad twin-turboprop light utility aircraft was flown for the first time on 23 July 1971, and received an Australian Department of Transport type certificate in August 1972. Type certificates for the N22 and N24 initial production versions, described in previous editions of *Jane's,* were issued in May 1975 and October 1977 respectively.

The N22B and N24A current versions were type certificated in August 1975 and May 1978 respectively, and in December 1978 both of these versions were awarded certification under US FAR Pt 135 Appendix A (Transport category). Type certificates have also been issued in various European, Asian, South American and Pacific countries.

Current versions are as follows:

N22B. Short-fuselage civil version, intended primarily as a STOL utility aircraft for short/medium-range transportation of up to 13 passengers and/or cargo. Also used for aerial ambulance, geophysical and geographical survey duties, particularly in areas with minimal maintenance and landing field facilities.

N22B (float and amphibious versions). Flight trials were concluded in Minneapolis, USA, in late 1978 of a Nomad equipped with twin Wipline floats. These trials showed exceptionally good surface and in-flight stability, and FAA certification was expected during 1979. An amphibious version was scheduled to fly in mid-1979.

Mission Master. Short-fuselage military version, in service in Australia, Papua New Guinea, the Philippines and Indonesia for maritime surveillance, forward area support and surveillance, and as a light military transport for personnel and equipment. Four underwing pylons, load-bearing drop doors in the cabin floor, self-sealing fuel cells, transparent flight deck roof panels, military avionics, and special equipment according to role.

N24A. Civil version with lengthened fuselage, offering seating for up to 17 passengers and a considerably improved payload capability. Design includes the insertion of a 1·14 m (3 ft 9 in) plug in the cabin, and increased forward baggage capacity. The basic aircraft includes a full commuter interior and IFR avionics.

Search Master B. Basic coastal patrol version, equipped with Bendix RDR 1400 search radar, with 46 cm (18 in) forward-looking flat-plate scanner in nose radome. In service with Indonesian Navy (12) and Papua New Guinea Defence Force.

Search Master L. More sophisticated coastal patrol version, with Litton APS-504(V)2 search radar and a 100 cm (40 in) flat-plate phased array scanner rotating 360° in undernose 'guppy' radome. Search capacity significantly increased; choice of Doppler, Omega or INS long-range navigation system also ground stabilises radar display. Both B and L versions provide a spacious cabin and excellent view for the crew, and may include optional long-range fuel tanks, floor hatch, bubble windows, underwing pylons, radar and navigation consoles. Search Master L due to enter Australian service in 1979; six ordered by Indonesian Navy.

By the middle of 1979 about 100 Nomads of all versions had been sold, customers including the Philippine Air Force (12), Indonesian Navy (18), Australian Army (11) and Aeromedical Services (8).

The following description applies generally to all versions, except where a specific model is indicated:

TYPE: Twin-turboprop STOL utility aircraft.

WINGS: Braced high-wing monoplane. Basic NACA 23018 wing section, modified to incorporate increased nose radius and camber. Dihedral 1° from roots. Incidence 2°. No sweepback. Two-spar fail-safe torsion-box structure of riveted light alloy. Full-span double-slotted trailing-edge flaps. All-metal ailerons, which droop with the flaps and transfer their motion progressively to slot-lip ailerons as the flaps extend, resulting in full-span flap. Controls actuated manually by cables and push-rods. Pneumatic de-icing of leading-edges optional. Small stub wings at cabin floor level support the main landing gear fairings from which a single strut on each side braces the main wing.

FUSELAGE: Conventional semi-monocoque riveted light alloy structure of stringers and frames.

TAIL UNIT: Cantilever all-metal structure. One-piece all-moving tailplane, with inset trim and anti-balance tab. Tailplane and rudder actuated manually by cables. Trim tab in rudder. Pneumatic de-icing of leading-edges optional. Ventral fin on floatplane version.

LANDING GEAR: Retractable tricycle type, with electrical retraction by means of single actuator in the fuselage. GAF oleo-pneumatic shock-absorbers. Single rearward-retracting steerable nosewheel, tyre size 8·00-6, pressure 3·17 bars (46 lb/sq in) on N22B, 3·03 bars (44 lb/sq in) on N24A. Twin wheels on each main unit, tyre size 8·00-6, pressure 2·34 bars (34 lb/sq in) on N22B, 2·69 bars (39 lb/sq in) on N24A. Main wheels retract forward into streamlined fairings at outer ends of stub wings. Dual hydraulically-operated single-disc brakes on main units. No anti-skid units. Provision for float gear on N22B. Amphibious gear under development.

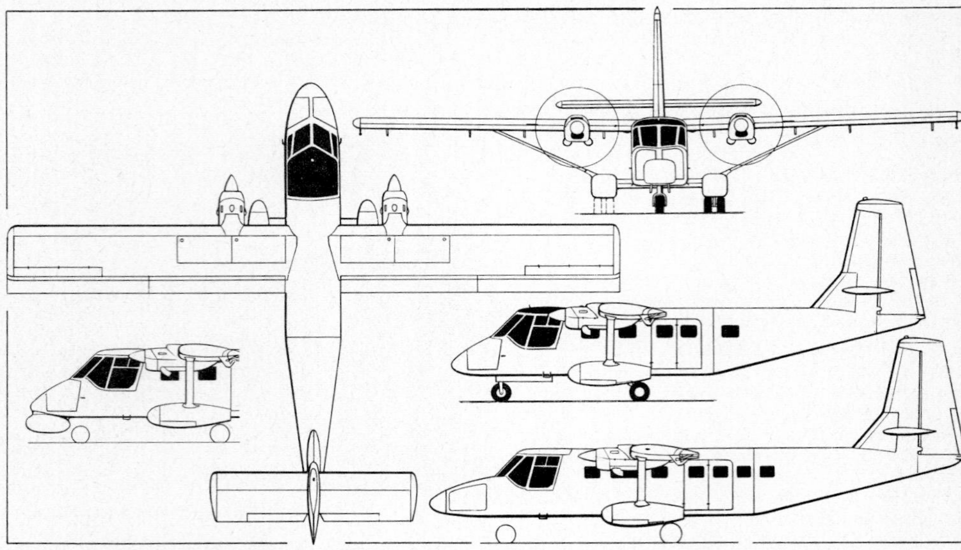

Government Aircraft Factories N22B Nomad, with additional side view (bottom) of N24A and scrap view of forward fuselage of Search Master L *(Pilot Press)*

POWER PLANT: Two 298 kW (400 shp) Allison 250-B17B turboprop engines, each driving a Hartzell three-blade constant-speed fully-feathering reversible-pitch metal propeller. Standard fuel capacity 1,018 litres (224 Imp gallons) plus 20 litres (4·4 Imp gallons) unusable in flexible bag tanks. Provision for internal auxiliary tanks for ferry purposes. An additional fuel capacity of 335 litres (73·7 Imp gallons) is provided by two optional integral tanks, one in each wingtip. Gravity refuelling via overwing point above each pair of tanks. Oil capacity 8·5 litres (1·9 Imp gallons) per engine.

ACCOMMODATION (N22B): Designed for single-pilot operation, but can accommodate crew of two on side-by-side seats. Access to flight deck by forward-opening door on each side. Main cabin has individual seats for up to 13 passengers, at 74 cm (29 in) pitch, with continuous seat tracks and readily-removable seats which allow rapid rearrangement of the cabin to suit alternative loads. Access to main cabin via double doors on port side, with single emergency exit on starboard side. Baggage compartments in nose (with door on each side) and optionally in rear of fuselage (with internal and external access). Whole interior, including flight deck, is heated and ventilated.

ACCOMMODATION (N24A): Flight deck accommodation and access as for N22B. Lengthened main cabin, with similar internal provision to N22B for up to 17 passengers, and access via double port-side doors as in N22B. Enlarged nose baggage compartment. Rear baggage compartment of same capacity as N22B. Ventilation and heating system with individual adjustable outlets.

SYSTEMS: No air-conditioning, hydraulic or pneumatic systems normally, but air-conditioning and pneumatic airframe de-icing are available optionally. Electrical system comprises a 28V 150A DC starter/generator on each engine, and a 22Ah battery with AC inverters. Other optional systems include oxygen demand system for crew and continuous-flow system for passengers; electrical de-icing for propellers, cabin floor hatch and underwing pylon racks.

AVIONICS AND EQUIPMENT: Provision is made for a wide range of nav/com equipment to meet specific customer requirements. Other optional items include full IFR instrumentation and a lightweight weather radar.

ARMAMENT AND OPERATIONAL EQUIPMENT (Mission Master/Search Master): The military variants have provision for four underwing hardpoints capable of accepting up to 227 kg (500 lb) loads, including gun and rocket pods. The nose bay can be utilised to accommodate surveillance and night vision aid equipment. Removable seat armour and self-sealing fuel tanks can be fitted for added protection. Other equipment as detailed under model listings.

DIMENSIONS, EXTERNAL:

Wing span	16·46 m (54 ft 0 in)
Wing chord (constant)	1·81 m (5 ft 11¼ in)
Wing aspect ratio	9·11
Length overall: N22B	12·56 m (41 ft 2·4 in)
N24A	14·36 m (47 ft 1¼ in)
Height overall	5·52 m (18 ft 1½ in)
Tailplane span	5·39 m (17 ft 8·4 in)
Wheel track	3·23 m (10 ft 7 in)
Wheelbase: N22B	3·65 m (11 ft 11·6 in)
N24A	4·37 m (14 ft 4 in)
Propeller diameter	2·29 m (7 ft 6 in)
Propeller ground clearance	1·22 m (4 ft 0 in)
Distance between propeller centres	4·36 m (14 ft 3·6 in)
Crew doors (each): Height	0·86 m (2 ft 10 in)
Width	0·69 m (2 ft 3 in)
Passenger double doors (port): Height	1·32 m (4 ft 4 in)
Width	1·22 m (4 ft 0 in)
Height to sill	0·89 m (2 ft 11 in)
Emergency exit (stbd): Height	0·58 m (1 ft 11 in)
Width	0·63 m (2 ft 1 in)

DIMENSIONS, INTERNAL:

Cabin, excl flight deck and rear baggage compartment:	
Length: N22B	5·18 m (17 ft 0 in)
N24A	6·27 m (20 ft 7 in)
Max width	1·30 m (4 ft 3 in)
Max height	1·58 m (5 ft 2·4 in)
Floor area: N22B	6·53 m² (70·25 sq ft)
N24A	8·08 m² (87·0 sq ft)
Volume: N22B	10·19 m³ (360·0 cu ft)
N24A	11·61 m³ (410·0 cu ft)
Baggage compartment volume (nose):	
N22B	0·76 m³ (27·0 cu ft)
N24A	1·13 m³ (40·0 cu ft)
Baggage compartment volume (optional, rear):	
N22B, N24A	0·79 m³ (28·0 cu ft)

AREAS:

Wings, gross	30·10 m² (324·0 sq ft)
Ailerons (total net)	2·55 m² (27·4 sq ft)
Trailing-edge flaps (total net)	9·81 m² (105·6 sq ft)
Fin	3·63 m² (39·1 sq ft)
Rudder, incl tab	2·89 m² (31·1 sq ft)
Tailplane, incl tabs	7·25 m² (78·0 sq ft)

WEIGHTS AND LOADINGS:

Manufacturer's basic weight empty:	
N22B	2,092 kg (4,613 lb)
N24A	2,377 kg (5,241 lb)
Typical operating weight empty:	
N22B	2,150 kg (4,741 lb)
N24A	2,377 kg (5,241 lb)
Max fuel load (usable), N22B and N24A:	
standard	803 kg (1,770 lb)
extended range	1,066 kg (2,350 lb)
Max T-O and landing weight:	
N22B	3,855 kg (8,500 lb)
N24A	4,263 kg (9,400 lb)
Max wing loading: N22B	127·9 kg/m² (26·2 lb/sq ft)
N24A	141·5 kg/m² (29·0 lb/sq ft)

N24 long-fuselage version of the GAF Nomad, seating up to 17 passengers

GAF Nomad Search Master B of the Indonesian Navy

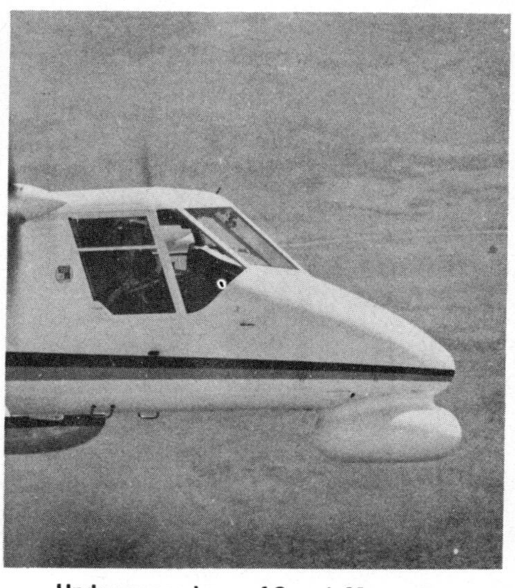

Undernose radome of Search Master L

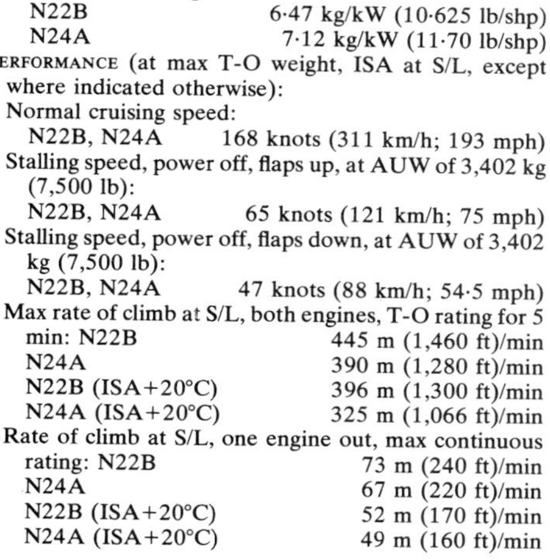

Max power loading:
- N22B 6·47 kg/kW (10·625 lb/shp)
- N24A 7·12 kg/kW (11·70 lb/shp)

Performance (at max T-O weight, ISA at S/L, except where indicated otherwise):

Normal cruising speed:
- N22B, N24A 168 knots (311 km/h; 193 mph)

Stalling speed, power off, flaps up, at AUW of 3,402 kg (7,500 lb):
- N22B, N24A 65 knots (121 km/h; 75 mph)

Stalling speed, power off, flaps down, at AUW of 3,402 kg (7,500 lb):
- N22B, N24A 47 knots (88 km/h; 54·5 mph)

Max rate of climb at S/L, both engines, T-O rating for 5 min:
- N22B 445 m (1,460 ft)/min
- N24A 390 m (1,280 ft)/min
- N22B (ISA+20°C) 396 m (1,300 ft)/min
- N24A (ISA+20°C) 325 m (1,066 ft)/min

Rate of climb at S/L, one engine out, max continuous rating:
- N22B 73 m (240 ft)/min
- N24A 67 m (220 ft)/min
- N22B (ISA+20°C) 52 m (170 ft)/min
- N24A (ISA+20°C) 49 m (160 ft)/min

Service ceiling, both engines, climbing at 30·5 m (100 ft)/min, max cruise rating:
- N22B at 3,630 kg (8,000 lb) AUW 6,400 m (21,000 ft)
- N24A at 4,082 kg (9,000 lb) AUW 6,100 m (20,000 ft)

Min ground turning radius:
- N22B, N24A 11·66 m (38 ft 3 in)

Runway LCN at max T-O weight:
- N22B 2·3
- N24A 2·5

T-O run:
- N22B (FAR 23) 223 m (730 ft)
- N24A (FAR 23) 296 m (970 ft)
- N22B (STOL) 183 m (600 ft)
- N22B (FAR 23), ISA+20°C 296 m (970 ft)
- N24A (FAR 23), ISA+20°C 366 m (1,200 ft)
- N22B (STOL), ISA+20°C 213 m (700 ft)

T-O to 15 m (50 ft):
- N22B (FAR 23) 360 m (1,180 ft)
- N24A (FAR 23) 521 m (1,710 ft)
- N22B (STOL) 320 m (1,050 ft)
- N22B (FAR 23), ISA+20°C 463 m (1,520 ft)
- N24A (FAR 23), ISA+20°C 610 m (2,000 ft)

Landing from 15 m (50 ft), AUW of 3,630 kg (8,000 lb):
- N22B (FAR 23) 338 m (1,110 ft)
- N22B (STOL) 216 m (710 ft)
- N22B (FAR 23), ISA+20°C 353 m (1,160 ft)

Landing from 15 m (50 ft), AUW of 4,082 kg (9,000 lb):
- N24A (FAR 23) 420 m (1,380 ft)
- N24A (FAR 23), ISA+20°C 439 m (1,440 ft)

Landing run, AUW of 3,630 kg (8,000 lb):
- N22B (FAR 23) 212 m (695 ft)
- N22B (STOL) 76 m (250 ft)
- N22B (FAR 23), ISA+20°C 226 m (740 ft)

Landing run, AUW of 4,082 kg (9,000 lb):
- N24A (FAR 23) 241 m (790 ft)
- N24A (FAR 23), ISA+20°C 256 m (840 ft)

Max range at 90% power, standard fuel, reserves for 45 min hold:
- N22B, N24A at S/L 580 nm (1,074 km; 668 miles)
- N22B, N24A at 3,050 m (10,000 ft) 730 nm (1,352 km; 840 miles)

HAWKER DE HAVILLAND

HAWKER DE HAVILLAND AUSTRALIA PTY LTD (Member Company of Hawker Siddeley Group)

Head Office: PO Box 30, Bankstown, NSW 2200
Telephone: 772 8111
Telex: 20719
Chairman of Directors: R. Kingsford-Smith
Managing Director: B. S. Price

Hawker de Havilland is primarily a manufacturing, maintenance and overhaul organisation, concentrating on the defence, aviation and marine fields in Australia and overseas, with centres at Bankstown, Sydney, and Guildford, Perth.

Major activities include the manufacture of components for the GAF Nomad aircraft, and sole source production of airframe and engine components for Boeing, Boeing Vertol, Lockheed, McDonnell Douglas, Pratt & Whitney, and Westland. Other aerospace products include infra-red target mini-RPVs (see RPVs and Targets section). Hawker de Havilland's main activity continues to be the provision of overhaul, modification and repair services to the Australian defence forces and a wide variety of other Australian and regional customers.

SKYCRAFT

SKYCRAFT PTY LTD

Address: 138 Bellevue Parade, Carlton, NSW 2218
Telephone: Sydney 546 2501
Director: R. G. Wheeler

SKYCRAFT SCOUT

Designed by Mr R. G. Wheeler, and first built and flown in May 1974, the Scout is described as a 'minimum aircraft' which can be quickly dismantled and carried on the roof rack of a motor car. It has been in continuous production since August 1976, when the Australian Department of Transport issued an Air Navigation Order permitting its operation subject to certain exemptions and limitations. A total of 260 had been ordered and built by early 1979.

The Scout has a wire-braced airframe of aluminium alloy tube, with Dacron-covered (single surface) wings and tail surfaces. The wings have a leading-edge spar, set at a dihedral which raises the tips 0·51 m (20 in) above the centreline, and are set at a mean incidence of 4°. There are no ailerons or wing warping. Tail surfaces are all-moving, comprising a rudder and elevators only, operated by the control column. There is no rudder bar. A non-retractable steel-leaf main landing gear is fitted, forward of the CG, below the A-frame which supports the pilot's glassfibre seat, and has size 12 in × 2·5 in wheels. A small alloy tailwheel is attached to the base of the rudder post.

The Scout is equipped with a 153 cc Aero Pixi piston engine, and a fuel tank of 2·3 litres (0·5 Imp gallon) capacity. It can also be flown power off, as a glider.

Skycraft Scout minimum aeroplane (153 cc Aero Pixi engine)

Dimensions, external:
- Wing span (nominal) 8·69 m (28 ft 6 in)
- Wing chord at root 1·75 m (5 ft 9 in)
- Wing chord at tip 0·41 m (1 ft 4 in)
- Wing aspect ratio 6·3
- Length overall 5·03 m (16 ft 6 in)
- Height overall 1·57 m (5 ft 2 in)
- Elevator span 3·00 m (9 ft 10 in)

Areas:
- Wings (total) 11·71 m² (126·0 sq ft)
- Rudder 0·77 m² (8·25 sq ft)
- Elevators (total) 1·58 m² (17·00 sq ft)

Weights and Loading:
- Weight empty, equipped 51 kg (112 lb)
- Max T-O weight 129 kg (285 lb)
- Max wing loading 10·25 kg/m² (2·1 lb/sq ft)

Performance (powered):
- Max level speed 41 knots (76 km/h; 47 mph)
- T-O and landing speed 24 knots (44·5 km/h; 28 mph)
- Stalling speed 19-21 knots (35·5-39 km/h; 22-24·5 mph)
- Rate of climb 42·5-55 m (140-180 ft)/min
- T-O run 64 m (210 ft)
- Landing run 28 m (90 ft)
- Range 24 nm (44·5 km; 28 miles)
- Endurance 40 min

Performance (unpowered):
- Best glide ratio

TRANSAVIA

TRANSAVIA CORPORATION PTY LTD

ADDRESS: 73 Station Road, Seven Hills, NSW 2147
Telephone: 624 4244
Telex: 21396
SERVICE DIVISION: Hangar 120, Bankstown Aerodrome, NSW
Telephone: 70 6968
CHAIRMAN: F. Belgiorno-Nettis, CBE
DIRECTOR: C. Salteri
GENERAL MANAGER: J. Corby

Transavia Corporation, formed in 1964, is a subsidiary of Transfield (NSW) Pty Ltd, one of Australia's largest construction companies.

TRANSAVIA PL-12 AIRTRUK

The Airtruk, designed by Mr Luigi Pellarini, was originally type-certificated on 10 February 1966, for spreading fertiliser and for seeding. Swath width is up to 32 m (35 yd) and of unusual uniformity. A liquid-spraying conversion, developed in 1968, is capable of covering a 30·2 m (33 yd) swath. This version has an engine-driven spraypump and a liquid chemical capacity of 818 litres (180 Imp gallons). The PL-12's unconventional layout keeps the tails clear of chemicals, and also permits rapid loading by a vehicle which approaches the aircraft between the tails.

The three-seat prototype Airtruk flew for the first time on 22 April 1965. Delivery of production Airtruks began in December 1966, and 100 had been built by January 1979, for customers in Australia, Europe, Asia and Africa.

Production of the PL-12 was continuing in 1979, together with that of the **PL-12-U**, a multi-purpose cargo/passenger/ambulance/aerial survey version of which a prototype flew for the first time in December 1970. Certification of this version was granted in February 1971, by which time two production aircraft had been completed, and deliveries began later in that year.

Ten Airtruks have been assembled by Flight Engineers Ltd in New Zealand (which see).

The following description applies to both the PL-12 and PL-12-U, except where a particular version is indicated:

TYPE: Single-engined agricultural (PL-12) or multi-purpose (PL-12-U) aircraft.

WINGS: Strut-braced sesquiplane. Wing section NACA 23012. Dihedral 1° 30′ on upper wings. Incidence (upper wings) 3° 30′, stub-wings 4°. Conventional all-metal structure, covered with Alclad sheet. All-metal trailing-edge flaps and ailerons, covered with ribbed Alclad sheet, and operated manually. Small stub-wings below fuselage, braced to cabin by a single strut and to upper wings by a V strut on each side.

FUSELAGE: Pod-shaped structure, of 4130 welded steel tube construction with 2024 Alclad covering and glassfibre tailcone.

TAIL UNIT: Twin units, each comprising a fin, rudder and separate T tailplane and elevator, and each carried on a cantilever tubular Alclad boom extending from the upper wings. Small bumper fairing underneath each fin. Manually-operated control surfaces. Adjustable tab in each elevator. Fixed tab on starboard rudder.

LANDING GEAR: Non-retractable tricycle type, each of the three wheels being carried on a pivoted trailing leg. Transavia patented shock-absorbers, of bonded rubber block moulded within four hinged plates forming a diamond shape, loaded at the long axis and deformed by loads to exchange long and short axes. All wheels and tyres same size, 8·00-6. Nosewheel tyre pressure 1·38 bars (20 lb/sq in); main-wheel tyre pressure 2·21 bars (32 lb/sq in). Cleveland hydraulic disc brakes with parking lock.

POWER PLANT: One 224 kW (300 hp) Rolls-Royce Continental IO-520-D flat-six engine, driving a McCauley D2A34C58/90AT-2 two-blade constant-speed metal propeller with spinner. Two upper-wing fuel tanks, total capacity 189 litres (41·5 Imp gallons). Optional long-range installation of second tank in each upper mainplane, increasing total capacity to 379 litres (83·4 Imp gallons). Refuelling point above each upper wing. Oil capacity 11·4 litres (2·5 Imp gallons).

ACCOMMODATION (PL-12): Single-seat cockpit, with door on starboard side. Two-seat cabin aft of chemical hopper/tank for carriage of ground crew, with door at rear of lower deck. Accommodation heated and ventilated.

ACCOMMODATION (PL-12-U): Single-seat cockpit as in PL-12. By removing the central hopper or tank, passenger cabin is enlarged to seat one passenger on upper deck (back to back with pilot's seat) and four more passengers on lower deck. Doors on upper deck (starboard side) and lower deck (port side). Lower-deck cabin is heated.

SYSTEM: 12V electrical system standard.

AVIONICS AND EQUIPMENT: Optional avionics for PL-12-U include VHF (available optionally for PL-12), HF, ADF, artificial horizon and directional gyro.

DIMENSIONS, EXTERNAL:
- Upper wing span: 11·98 m (39 ft 3½ in)
- Upper wing chord (constant portion): 1·76 m (5 ft 9¼ in)
- Upper wing chord at tip: 1·27 m (4 ft 2 in)
- Stub-wing span: 4·93 m (16 ft 2 in)
- Length overall: 6·35 m (20 ft 10 in)
- Length of fuselage: 4·19 m (13 ft 9 in)
- Height overall: 2·79 m (9 ft 2 in)
- Fuselage: Max width: 0·97 m (3 ft 2 in)
- Tailplane span (each): 2·13 m (7 ft 0 in)
- Distance between tailplanes: 3·48 m (11 ft 5 in)
- Wheel track: 2·44 m (8 ft 0 in)
- Wheelbase: 1·64 m (5 ft 4½ in)
- Propeller diameter: 2·23 m (7 ft 4 in)
- Min propeller ground clearance: 0·30 m (1 ft 0 in)
- Passenger door (PL-12, rear):
  - Height: 0·97 m (3 ft 2 in)
- Passenger doors (PL-12-U, stbd upper and port lower, each): Height: 0·91 m (3 ft 0 in)

DIMENSIONS, INTERNAL (PL-12):
- Rear passenger cabin: Length: 1·83 m (6 ft 0 in)
  - Max width: 0·97 m (3 ft 2 in)
  - Max height: 2·03 m (6 ft 8 in)
  - Floor area: 0·37 m² (4 sq ft)
  - Volume: Passenger cabin: 0·85 m³ (30 cu ft)
  - Chemical hopper: 1·02 m³ (36 cu ft)

DIMENSIONS, INTERNAL (PL-12-U):
- Passenger cabin: Length: 2·74 m (9 ft 0 in)
  - Max width: 0·97 m (3 ft 2 in)
  - Max height: 2·11 m (6 ft 11 in)
  - Floor area: 1·67 m² (18 sq ft)
  - Volume: 2·10 m³ (74 cu ft)

AREAS:
- Wings, gross: 23·8 m² (256 sq ft)
- Ailerons, total: 1·67 m² (18·0 sq ft)
- Trailing-edge flaps, total: 1·67 m² (18·0 sq ft)
- Fins, total: 1·30 m² (14·0 sq ft)
- Rudders, total: 0·56 m² (6·0 sq ft)
- Tailplanes, total: 2·60 m² (28·0 sq ft)
- Elevators, total, incl tabs: 1·30 m² (14·0 sq ft)

WEIGHTS AND LOADINGS:
- Weight empty: PL-12: 839 kg (1,850 lb)
  - PL-12-U: 830 kg (1,830 lb)
- Max T-O weight:
  - PL-12 (normal category): 1,723 kg (3,800 lb)
  - PL-12 (agricultural category): 1,855 kg (4,090 lb)
  - PL-12-U: 1,723 kg (3,800 lb)
- Max landing weight (both): 1,723 kg (3,800 lb)
- Max wing loading: PL-12: 79 kg/m² (16·2 lb/sq ft)
  - PL-12-U: 73 kg/m² (15·0 lb/sq ft)
- Max power loading: PL-12: 8·28 kg/kW (13·7 lb/hp)
  - PL-12-U: 7·69 kg/kW (12·7 lb/hp)

PERFORMANCE (at max T-O weight except where indicated):
- Never-exceed speed:
  - PL-12, PL-12-U: 155 knots (286 km/h; 178 mph)
- Max level speed at S/L, ISA:
  - PL-12: 103 knots (192 km/h; 119 mph)
  - PL-12-U: 112 knots (208 km/h; 129 mph)
- Max cruising speed (75% power) at S/L, ISA:
  - PL-12: 95 knots (175 km/h; 109 mph)
  - PL-12-U: 102 knots (188 km/h; 117 mph)
- Stalling speed, flaps up:
  - PL-12: 55 knots (103 km/h; 64 mph)
  - PL-12-U: 52 knots (97 km/h; 60 mph)
- Stalling speed, flaps down:
  - PL-12: 52 knots (97 km/h; 60 mph)
  - PL-12-U: 50 knots (94 km/h; 58 mph)
- Max rate of climb at S/L: PL-12: 183 m (600 ft)/min
  - PL-12-U: 244 m (800 ft)/min
- Service ceiling (both versions): 3,200 m (10,500 ft)
- *T-O run: PL-12: 334 m (1,095 ft)
  - PL-12-U: 274 m (900 ft)
- *T-O to 15 m (50 ft): PL-12: 564 m (1,850 ft)
  - PL-12-U: 457 m (1,500 ft)
- Landing run (both versions, at max landing weight): 183 m (600 ft)
- Normal range with standard fuel: 286 nm (531 km; 330 miles)
- Ferry range, standard fuel: 330 nm (611 km; 380 miles)

**DCA Australia technique*

TRANSAVIA T-300 SKYFARMER

A prototype of the Skyfarmer was flown for the first time in July 1978. This aircraft is a development of the PL-12, the significant difference being that it is powered by a 224 kW (300 hp) Lycoming IO-540-K1A5 flat-six engine, driving a 2·13 m (7 ft 0 in) diameter Hartzell HC-C3YR-1RF/F8468-2R three-blade constant-speed propeller. It also incorporates some of the improved features of the T-320.

Ten Skyfarmers had been ordered by 1 February 1979. The description of the PL-12 Airtruk applies also to the Skyfarmer, except for the power plant and the following details:

WEIGHTS AND LOADINGS:
- Weight empty: 907 kg (2,000 lb)
- Max T-O weight (agricultural category): 1,855 kg (4,090 lb)
- Max landing weight: 1,723 kg (3,800 lb)
- Max wing loading: 78·6 kg/m² (16·1 lb/sq ft)
- Max power loading: 8·28 kg/kW (13·6 lb/hp)

PERFORMANCE (at max T-O weight, ISA at S/L, except where indicated):
- Never-exceed speed: 155 knots (286 km/h; 178 mph)
- Max level speed: 111 knots (206 km/h; 128 mph)
- Max cruising speed (75% power): 106 knots (196 km/h; 122 mph)
- *Max light-weight cruising speed: 116 knots (214 km/h; 133 mph)
- Stalling speed, flaps up: 55 knots (102 km/h; 63·5 mph)
- Stalling speed, flaps down: 52 knots (96·5 km/h; 60 mph)
- *Light-weight stalling speed, flaps up, power off: 45 knots (83·5 km/h; 52 mph)
- *Light-weight stalling speed, flaps down, power off: 42 knots (78 km/h; 48·5 mph)
- Max rate of climb at S/L: 198 m (650 ft)/min
- *Max light-weight rate of climb at S/L: 538 m (1,765 ft)/min
- Service ceiling: 3,810 m (12,500 ft)
- *Light-weight service ceiling: 6,890 m (22,600 ft)
- T-O run: 275 m (902 ft)
- *Light-weight T-O run: 77 m (252 ft)
- T-O to 15 m (50 ft): 475 m (1,558 ft)
- *Light-weight landing run: 82 m (270 ft)

**Weight of empty aircraft plus pilot and 50% standard fuel*

TRANSAVIA T-320 AIRTRUK

This version of the Airtruk, certificated in January 1976, is a development of the PL-12, from which it differs principally in having a Continental Tiara 6-320-2B engine and a larger-diameter propeller; oleo-pneumatic shock-absorbers; and a 28V electrical system.

Production of the T-320 began in October 1976, and four had been built by the end of that year. A further three were assembled in New Zealand by Flight Engineers Ltd (which see) and one by Transfield (NZ) Ltd.

TYPE, WINGS, FUSELAGE AND TAIL UNIT: Similar to those of PL-12. Upper-wing fence each side of each tailboom.

LANDING GEAR: Similar to PL-12, but with oleo-pneumatic shock-absorbers and size 8·00-6 (8 ply) tyres and tubes on all units.

POWER PLANT: One 238·5 kW (320 hp) Continental Tiara 6-320-2B flat-six engine, driving (on prototype) a two-blade Hartzell HC-C2YF-1BF constant-speed propeller. Fuel and oil capacities as for PL-12.

ACCOMMODATION: As PL-12. Two-man rear cabin can carry up to 155 kg (342 lb) of equipment with seats removed.

SYSTEM: 28V electrical system and 28V battery standard.

EQUIPMENT: Standard 907 kg (2,000 lb) capacity hopper aft of cockpit, with twin nozzles for dry chemical dispersal and seeding. Optional Powermist spray system (up to 454 litres; 120 US gallons; 100 Imp gallons/min) for liquid chemical (max capacity 816 litres; 216 US gallons; 180 Imp gallons). Hopper can be filled in 15-20 s

View of Transavia T-320 Airtruk showing twin underfuselage outlets for chemical

and contents jettisoned in 3·2-4·5 s. Other optional equipment includes spray nozzles; additional wing fuel tanks; radio; cockpit heating; navigation, landing, taxi and cockpit lights; lighting system, including iodine quartz lamps, for night spraying; windscreen demister.

DIMENSIONS, EXTERNAL: As PL-12 except:
- Propeller diameter (prototype) 2·41 m (7 ft 11 in)

DIMENSION, INTERNAL:
- Hopper volume 1·02 m³ (36·0 cu ft)

AREA:
- Wings, gross 23·78 m² (256·0 sq ft)

WEIGHTS AND LOADINGS:
- Typical weight empty 816 kg (1,800 lb)
- Max T-O weight:
  - Normal category 1,723 kg (3,800 lb)
  - agricultural category 1,855 kg (4,090 lb)
- Max wing loading 79·1 kg/m² (16·2 lb/sq ft)
- Max power loading 7·66 kg/kW (12·6 lb/hp)

PERFORMANCE (A: at 1,855 kg; 4,090 lb AUW; B: at unloaded weight, S/L, ISA):
- Max level speed: A 120 knots (222 km/h; 138 mph)
  - B 125 knots (232 km/h; 144 mph)
- Cruising speed (75% power):
  - A 111 knots (206 km/h; 128 mph)
  - B 116 knots (216 km/h; 134 mph)
- Stalling speed, flaps up, power off:
  - A 50·5 knots (93·5 km/h; 58 mph)
  - B 40 knots (74 km/h; 46 mph)
- Stalling speed, flaps down, power off:
  - A 47 knots (87 km/h; 54 mph)
  - B 35 knots (64·5 km/h; 40 mph)
- Max rate of climb at S/L: A 254 m (833 ft)/min
  - B 547 m (1,795 ft)/min
- Service ceiling: A 5,260 m (17,250 ft)
  - B 6,005 m (19,700 ft)
- T-O run, grass, zero wind: A 311 m (1,020 ft)
  - B 75 m (246 ft)
- T-O to 15 m (50 ft): A 443 m (1,452 ft)
  - B 166 m (543 ft)
- Landing run, grass, zero wind: B 77 m (255 ft)
  - B at 1,723 kg (3,800 lb) AUW 169 m (555 ft)
- Swath width: liquid spray 27·5 m (90 ft)
  - dry fertiliser 29 m (96 ft)
  - insecticide dusting 30·5 m (100 ft)

VTOL
VTOL AIRCRAFT PTY LTD

ADDRESS: PO Box 5195C, Newcastle West, NSW 2302
Telephone: 43 5348
WORKS: Rutherford Aerodrome
CHAIRMAN OF DIRECTORS: Duan A. Phillips

PHILLIPS PHILLICOPTER Mk 1

Mr Phillips, assisted by Mr P. Gerakiteys, designed and built a prototype two-seat helicopter known as the Phillicopter Mk 1. Design work began in 1962, construction started in 1967, and the prototype flew for the first time in 1971.

Orders for the Phillicopter have been held in abeyance pending the completion of flight testing. In early 1979 this was continuing, and modifications to the control and rotor systems were being undertaken.

A description and illustration of the Phillicopter can be found in the 1977-78 *Jane's*.

BELGIUM

SABCA
SOCIÉTÉ ANONYME BELGE DE CONSTRUCTIONS AÉRONAUTIQUES

HEAD OFFICE: Chaussée de la Hulpe 185, B-1170 Brussels
Telephone: Brussels (02) 660 00 64
Telex: SABDG 23 244
WORKS:
Haren-Brussels, Chaussée de Haecht 1470, B-1130 Brussels
Telephone: Brussels (02) 216 80 10
Telex: SABUSH 21 237
Aéroport de Gosselies/Charleroi, B-6200 Gosselies
Telephone: Charleroi (071) 35 01 70
Telex: SABGO 51 251
CHAIRMAN: B. C. Vallières
DIRECTOR, GENERAL MANAGER: P. G. Willekens

SABCA has been since 1920 the largest aircraft manufacturer in Belgium. In addition to building aircraft and aero-engines under licence pre-war for the Belgian government and the Sabena company, it built aircraft of its own design.

Dassault-Breguet (France) and Fokker-VFW (Netherlands/Germany) have parity holdings in SABCA, through which the Belgian company now participates in various European projects.

At Haren, the company is working on components and equipment for the General Dynamics F-16; Dassault-Breguet/Dornier Alpha Jet; Dassault Mirage F1, Mirage III and Mirage 5; Fokker-VFW F27 and F28; and Aérospatiale SA 330 Puma. SABCA is also manufacturing hydraulic components and tanks for F-104G and TF-104G aircraft in European service.

At Gosselies, SABCA is assembling the Alpha Jet for the Belgian Air Force and the General Dynamics F-16 for Belgium and Denmark. The first Alpha Jet for the Belgian Air Force left the assembly line in December 1978; the first F-16 was flown on 11 December 1978 and delivered in January 1979. SABCA is also continuing to maintain and overhaul Mirage 5 and F-104G aircraft for the Belgian Air Force; is engaged in overhaul and repair of other military aeroplanes and helicopters for the Belgian and foreign armed forces; and is involved in overhaul and modification of the ground guidance systems of Nike missiles, for NATO.

First example of the General Dynamics F-16 assembled in Belgium by SABCA: a two-seat F-16B

SABCA's Electronic Division is manufacturing IFF, SATT and Doppler equipment, and a variety of aircraft electronic ground equipment. It undertakes work on electronic equipment under F-104G overhaul contracts, and is currently integrating ECM equipment in Mirage 5 aircraft. The division produces a laser tank fire control system for the Belgian, Canadian and Australian Armies and other armed forces.

SABCA is involved in space projects, including the Ariane space launcher and Spacelab. It is a member of various European industrial consortia.

In 1979 the Haren and Gosselies works occupied a total area of approx 72,000 m² (775,000 sq ft) and between them employed 1,850 people.

SONACA
SOCIÉTÉ NATIONALE DE CONSTRUCTION AÉRONAUTIQUE

HEAD OFFICE, WORKS AND AIRPORT: Route Nationale 5, B-6200 Gosselies
Telephone: Charleroi (071) 35 01 90

One of Belgium's primary aerospace manufacturers, Fairey SA (see 1977-78 *Jane's*), went into liquidation in 1977. In mid-April 1978 a new company, Sonaca, was formed at Gosselies, with an initial capital of 95 million Belgian francs, financed jointly by FN-Herstal (25 million), Sait Electronics (12·5 million), SABCA (10 million), Cartonex (2·5 million) and the Belgian government (45 million). This company occupies the 46,450 m² (499,985 sq ft) former Fairey SA works at Gosselies. It is committed only to the continuation of Fairey's military aircraft programmes, including participation in the European manufacturing programme for the General Dynamics F-16 light fighter, and employs approx 900 of the former work force of 1,600 people. The Belgian production line for the Britten-Norman Islander and Trislander has been taken over by Pilatus of Switzerland.

BRAZIL

AEROTEC
AEROTEC S/A INDUSTRIA AERONÁUTICA

HEAD OFFICE AND WORKS: Caixa Postal 286, 12200 São José dos Campos, São Paulo State
Telephone: (0123) 21 8011 and 21 8877
GENERAL AND INDUSTRIAL DIRECTOR: Eng Carlos Gonçalves
COMMERCIAL AND ADMINISTRATIVE DIRECTOR: Almir Medeiros

This company was formed in 1962. It designed and built the Uirapuru light aircraft, which, under the military designation T-23, has been ordered by the Brazilian, Bolivian and Paraguayan air forces and for civil flying clubs.

Aerotec builds wings for the EMBRAER Ipanema agricultural aircraft (which see). The company is also participating in EMBRAER's general aviation aircraft construction programme, by building fuselages for the EMB-720C Minuano, EMB-721C Sertanejo and EMB-810C Seneca II.

In 1979 Aerotec employed 110 persons and its premises occupied approx 7,000 m² (75,350 sq ft) of covered space.

AEROTEC A-122 UIRAPURU
Brazilian Air Force designation: T-23

The Uirapuru was designed as a private venture by Engs José Carlos de Souza Reis and Carlos Gonçalves. The prototype (PP-ZTF), with an 80·5 kW (108 hp) Lycoming O-235-C1 engine, flew for the first time on 2 June 1965 and was described and illustrated in the 1966-67 *Jane's*. It was followed by a second Uirapuru (PP-ZTT), with a 112 kW (150 hp) Lycoming O-320-A engine.

Two military pre-production models (0940 and 0941) were completed in early 1968, making their first flights on 23 January and 11 April respectively. These both had 150 hp engines.

In October 1967, the Brazilian Air Force placed an order for 30 **A-122A** production aircraft (Brazilian Air Force designation T-23), powered by 119 kW (160 hp) Lycoming O-320-B2B engines, increasing the total subsequently to 100, for use at the Academia da Força Aérea (Air Force Academy) in Pirassunungа, São Paulo State.

Military A-122A Uirapurus were also delivered to the air forces of Bolivia (18) and Paraguay (8).

The civil version of the Uirapuru is known as the **A-122B**. This is basically similar to the military version, except for having a cockpit canopy like that of the second prototype (see 1967-68 *Jane's*). Approx 25 have been built, including 18 delivered in 1975 to civil flying clubs supported by the Ministry of Aeronautics.

A total of 155 Uirapurus, including prototype and pre-production aircraft, had been built by early 1977, when production was suspended, but the Uirapuru remains available to order. Meanwhile, 46 Brazilian Air Force T-23s are being fitted with new engine cowlings, fuel tanks and canopies (as designed for the Uirapuru II) during IRAN work, to improve performance.

A full description of the A-122A military version can be found in the 1978-79 *Jane's*.

TYPE: Two-seat primary trainer.

POWER PLANT: One 119 kW (160 hp) Lycoming O-320-B2B flat-four engine, driving a Sensenich M-74-DM-6-060 two-blade fixed-pitch metal propeller. Variable-pitch propeller optional. Two integral fuel tanks in wing leading-edges, with total capacity of 140 litres (31 Imp gallons). Refuelling points above tanks. Optional 40 litre (8·8 Imp gallon) wingtip tanks.

ACCOMMODATION: Two fully-adjustable seats side by side under rearward-sliding transparent canopy. Two-piece windscreen. For emergency jettison, canopy separates into two pieces. Seats permit the use of either back-type or seat-type parachutes. Dual controls. Baggage compartment, capacity 30 kg (66 lb), aft of seats with access from cockpit only.

DIMENSIONS, EXTERNAL:

Wing span	8·50 m (27 ft 10¾ in)
Wing area, gross	13·50 m² (145·3 sq ft)
Wing aspect ratio	5·5
Length overall	6·60 m (21 ft 8 in)
Height overall	2·70 m (8 ft 10 in)
Wheel track	2·36 m (7 ft 9 in)
Wheelbase	1·47 m (4 ft 9¾ in)
Propeller diameter	1·87 m (6 ft 1½ in)

WEIGHTS AND LOADINGS:

Weight empty	540 kg (1,191 lb)
Max T-O weight	840 kg (1,852 lb)
Max wing loading	63·0 kg/m² (13·90 lb/sq ft)
Max power loading	7·06 kg/kW (11·41 lb/hp)

PERFORMANCE (at max T-O weight, S/L, ISA. A-122A in original form before new IRAN update):

Never-exceed speed	165 knots (307 km/h; 190 mph)
Max level speed:	
A-122A	122 knots (227 km/h; 141 mph)
A-122B	128 knots (238 km/h; 148 mph)
Max cruising speed (75% power):	
A-122A	100 knots (185 km/h; 115 mph)
A-122B	105 knots (195 km/h; 121 mph)
Econ cruising speed (65% power):	
A-122A	89 knots (164 km/h; 102 mph)
A-122B	94 knots (174 km/h; 108 mph)
Stalling speed, flaps up (both versions)	56·5 knots (104 km/h; 65 mph)
Stalling speed, flaps down (both versions)	39 knots (72 km/h; 45 mph)
Max rate of climb at S/L:	
A-122A	255 m (836 ft)/min
A-122B	273 m (895 ft)/min
Service ceiling	4,500 m (14,760 ft)
T-O run (zero wind)	200 m (656 ft)
Landing run (zero wind)	180 m (590 ft)
Max range	429 nm (800 km; 495 miles)
Endurance	4 h 30 min

Aerotec A-122B, civil version of the Uirapuru, of the Brasilia Aero Club *(Ronaldo S. Olive)*

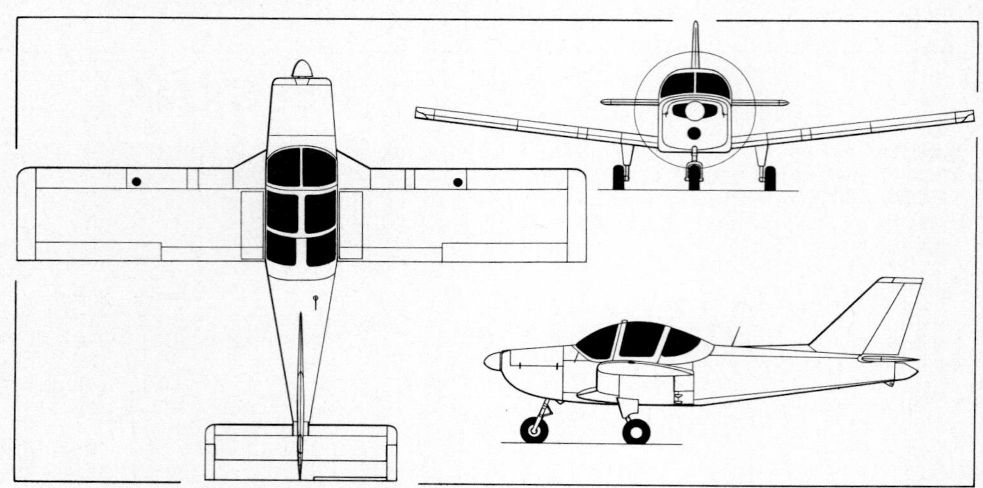

Aerotec A-132 Uirapuru II two-seat aerobatic trainer *(Pilot Press)*

AEROTEC A-132 UIRAPURU II

Aerotec began the development of a higher-powered, fully aerobatic trainer for the Brazilian Air Force, based on the A-122A but with modified wings and tail and improved cockpit layout and electronics. This has the designation A-132 Uirapuru II; it was intended to replace existing Brazilian Air Force T-23s which, after refurbishing, would be issued to civilian aero clubs.

Principal changes included a flat-sided fuselage, slightly increased wing span, enlarged vertical tail (and no underfin), and improved canopy design. Power plant was unchanged.

The A-132 programme was temporarily in abeyance in the Spring of 1979.

DIMENSIONS, EXTERNAL:

Wing span	9·00 m (29 ft 6¼ in)
Length overall	6·88 m (22 ft 6¾ in)
Height overall	2·70 m (8 ft 10 in)

WEIGHTS:

Weight empty	540 kg (1,190 lb)
Max T-O weight	840 kg (1,852 lb)

PERFORMANCE (estimated):

Max level speed at S/L	128 knots (238 km/h; 148 mph)
Max cruising speed	105 knots (195 km/h; 121 mph)
Stalling speed, flaps down	39 knots (72 km/h; 45 mph)
Max rate of climb at S/L	273 m (895 ft)/min
T-O to 15 m (50 ft)	200 m (656 ft)
Endurance	4 h 30 min

CTA
CENTRO TÉCNICO AEROESPACIAL

HEADQUARTERS: São José dos Campos, São Paulo State

The Centro Técnico Aeroespacial (Aerospace Technical Centre) is a Ministry of Aeronautics establishment for training aeronautical and aerospace personnel and for conducting aeronautical and aerospace research and development. It is composed of five institutes: the Instituto Tecnológico de Aeronáutica (ITA); the Instituto de Pesquisas e Desenvolvimento (IPD); the Instituto de Atividades Espaciais (IAE); the Instituto de Ensaios e Padrões (IEP); and the Instituto de Fomento e Coordenação Industrial (IFI).

The **ITA** is a college of engineering for aeronautical and aerospace personnel. The **IPD** conducts aeronautical research and development. The **IAE** conducts space research and development. The **IEP** is devoted to the development of aeronautical and aerospace standards in Brazil. The **IFI** is responsible for the fostering and co-ordination of the Brazilian aerospace industry. Its main activities are devoted to increasing the development rate of aeronautical and aerospace activities, by transferring the most appropriate technology to the aerospace industry and by providing incentives for the adoption of such technology by the industrial community. The IFI is also responsible for the certification of civil aircraft and approval of other aeronautical products.

EMBRAER
EMPRESA BRASILEIRA DE AERONÁUTICA SA

HEAD OFFICE AND WORKS: Av Brig Faria Lima No. 2170, Caixa Postal 343, 12200 São José dos Campos, São Paulo State

Telephone: (0123) 21 5400

Telex: (391) 1122445 EBAE BR or (391) 1125105 EBAE BR

RIO OFFICE: Aeroporto Santos Dumont, Sobreloja, Salão de Embarque No. 2, Rio de Janeiro, RJ

Telephone: (021) 222 8981

PRESIDENT: Aldo B. Franco

SUPERINTENDENT DIRECTOR: Ozires Silva

PRODUCTION DIRECTOR: Ozilio Carlos da Silva

TECHNICAL DIRECTOR: Guido Fontegalante Pessotti

FINANCIAL DIRECTOR: Alberto Franco Faria Marcondes

INDUSTRIAL RELATIONS DIRECTOR: Antonio Garcia da Silveira

COMMERCIAL DIRECTOR: Renato José da Silva

PUBLIC RELATIONS: José de Araujo Nogueira

PRESS RELATIONS: Mário Leme Galvão

EMBRAER was created on 19 August 1969, and came into operation on 2 January 1970 to promote the development of the Brazilian aircraft industry. It now has an authorised capital of Cr $2,000 million (about US $89·9 million), of which Cr $842 million (US $37·8 million) had been subscribed by 31 December 1978. The Brazilian government owns 54·42% of the voting shares, 89·22% of the subscribed capital being held by private shareholders. EMBRAER has a work force of some 4,300 persons and a factory area of 117,820 m² (1,268,200 sq ft). By the end of 1978 EMBRAER had built a total of 1,785 aircraft, of which 1,039 were Piper designs. The 1,000th aircraft, an EMB-110P Bandeirante, was delivered to Votec, a Brazilian regional airline, on 3 December 1976.

In August 1974, EMBRAER signed a comprehensive co-operative agreement with Piper Aircraft Corporation involving the assembly and eventual manufacture in Brazil of the Seneca II and Navajo Chieftain twin-engined aircraft and worldwide distribution of the products of both companies. At the beginning of 1975, this agreement was extended to include the single-engined Cherokee series. In consequence, with the co-operation of other Brazilian companies (Neiva, Aerotec, Aeromot and Motortec), EMBRAER now produces and markets these aircraft in Brazil. A similar arrangement for reciprocal marketing of each other's turboprop-engined aircraft is being discussed.

In early 1975, EMBRAER negotiated with Northrop Corporation a contract for manufacturing in Brazil components for the US company's F-5E Tiger II combat aircraft. This work was started in 1976.

EMBRAER has in current production the EMB-110 Bandeirante, the EMB-111 maritime reconnaissance version of the Bandeirante, the pressurised EMB-121 Xingu twin-turboprop transport aircraft, the EMB-326GB Xavante licence-built version of the Italian Aermacchi M.B.326GC jet trainer and ground attack aircraft, the EMB-201A Ipanema agricultural aircraft, and various EMBRAER-built versions of Piper single- and twin-engined light aircraft.

EMBRAER EMB-110 BANDEIRANTE (PIONEER)

Brazilian Air Force designations: C-95, EC-95 and R-95

The Bandeirante twin-turboprop light transport was developed to a Brazilian Ministry of Aeronautics specification calling for a general-purpose aircraft capable of carrying out missions such as transport, navigation training and aeromedical evacuation.

The first YC-95 prototype (2130) flew for the first time on 26 October 1968, followed by the second (2131) on 19 October 1969, and the basically similar third aircraft (PP-ZCN) on 26 June 1970. These prototypes, designated EMB-100, were described in the 1970-71 *Jane's*.

The first production EMB-110 Bandeirante (C-95/2133) flew for the first time on 9 August 1972, and was test-flown until December 1972 as part of the certification programme. Following the completion of testing to FAR 23, the aircraft was granted a type certificate by the Aerospace Technical Centre of the Ministry of Aeronautics, and the first three Bandeirantes were delivered to the Brazilian Air Force on 9 February 1973.

By 1 January 1979 a total of 219 Bandeirantes of various models had been sold, to some 40 operators. The 200th Bandeirante was delivered on 18 December 1978, and production was scheduled to continue during 1979-80 at a rate of five per month.

The Bandeirante is available in the following versions:

EMB-110. Basic 12-seat aircraft; 60 operated by Brazilian Air Force as **C-95.**

EMB-110A. Navaid checking and calibration version. Four operated by Brazilian Air Force as **EC-95.**

EMB-110B. Aerial photogrammetric version, with electrically-operated ventral sliding door, size 0·84 m (2 ft 9 in) × 1·86 m (6 ft 1¼ in), permitting the use of aerial cameras (Zeiss RMK A8·5/23, RMK A15/23, RMK A30/23 and Wild RC-10), a Zeiss IRU regulator, and Zeiss NT-1 navigation visors. Other equipment includes Decca 72 Doppler navigation system. Crew includes three equipment operators. Six operated by Brazilian Air Force as **R-95.** TerraFoto, a Brazilian enterprise, has an **EMB-110B1,** with quick-change aerial photogrammetric/nine-passenger executive interior. One B1 also ordered by Uruguayan Air Force, with convertible aerial photogrammetric/14-passenger feederliner interior.

EMB-110C. Standard 15-passenger commercial transport version. Entered commercial service with Transbrasil on 16 April 1973. Acquired also by Chilean Navy (three) as **EMB-110C(N)** and Uruguayan Air Force (five).

EMB-110E(J). Executive transport version with accommodation for seven passengers, four in individual seats and three on a sideways-facing sofa. Other features include a galley, wardrobe, and stereo AM/FM and tape deck.

EMB-110K1. All-cargo version, lengthened by insertion of a 0·85 m (2 ft 9½ in) plug between the flight deck and the centre-fuselage, and with upward-opening 1·80 m × 1·42 m (5 ft 10½ in × 4 ft 8 in) cargo door on port side of rear fuselage. Ventral fin. Two 559 kW (750 shp) PT6A-34 engines. Twenty ordered initially by Brazilian Air Force as **C-95A**; 20 more ordered in 1979. Described separately.

EMB-110P. Commercial third-level commuter version for 18 passengers, developed from EMB-110C. Described separately.

EMB-110P1. Quick-change version of EMB-110K1, for passenger and cargo operations. Five delivered by 1 January 1979, to operators in Gabon, Saudi Arabia and the USA; 2 more sold to operators in Australia and Finland. Described separately.

EMB-110P2. Third-level commuter transport counterpart of EMB-110K1, carrying up to 21 passengers. First flown on 3 May 1977. Total of 14 delivered by 1 January 1979; 20 sold by Spring 1979 to operators in Australia, Fiji, France, Haute Volta, Papua New Guinea and the UK. Detailed description applies to this version.

EMB-110S1. Geophysical survey version, with 559 kW (750 shp) PT6A-34 engines, increased internal fuel (1,914 litres; 421 Imp gallons), and provision for two 318 litre (70 Imp gallon) wingtip tanks. Proton magnetometer in extended tailboom, gamma ray spectrometers, Doppler navigation system and data recording system.

EMB-111. Maritime patrol version, described separately.

The following description, except where noted, applies to the standard production EMB-110P2:

Type: Twin-turboprop general-purpose transport.

Wings: Cantilever low-wing monoplane. Wing section NACA 23016 (modified) at root, NACA 23012 (modified) at tip. Sweepback 19′ 48″ at quarter-chord. Dihedral 7° at 28% chord. Incidence 3°. All-metal two-spar structure, of 2024-T3 and -T4 aluminium alloy, with detachable glassfibre wingtips. Glassfibre wing/fuselage fairing. All-metal statically-balanced ailerons and double-slotted flaps. Trim tab in port aileron. De-icing system optional.

Fuselage: All-metal semi-monocoque structure of 2024-T3 aluminium alloy. Two upward-hinged doors, one on each side of nose, provide access to avionics.

Tail Unit: Cantilever all-metal structure, with sweptback vertical surfaces. Glassfibre dorsal fin. Ventral fin (K1, P1 and P2 only). Trim tabs in rudder and port elevator. Tab in starboard elevator linked to flaps, to offset pitching moment during flap extension. De-icing system optional.

Landing Gear: Hydraulically-retractable tricycle type, with single wheel and oleo-pneumatic shock-absorber on each unit. Main-wheel tyre size 670 × 270-12 (10 ply rating), pressure 5·86-6·20 bars (85-90 lb/sq in). Steerable, forward-retracting nosewheel unit has tyre size 6·50-8, pressure 4·27-4·69 bars (62-68 lb/sq in).

Power Plant: Two 559 kW (750 shp) Pratt & Whitney Aircraft of Canada PT6A-34 turboprop engines, each driving a Hartzell HC-B3TN-3C/T10178H-8R constant-speed three-blade metal propeller with autofeathering and full reverse-pitch capability. Four integral fuel tanks in wings, with total capacity of 1,720 litres (378 Imp gallons). Oil capacity 8·7 litres (1·9 Imp gallons). Gravity refuelling point on top of each wing. Optional de-icing system for engine air inlets and propellers.

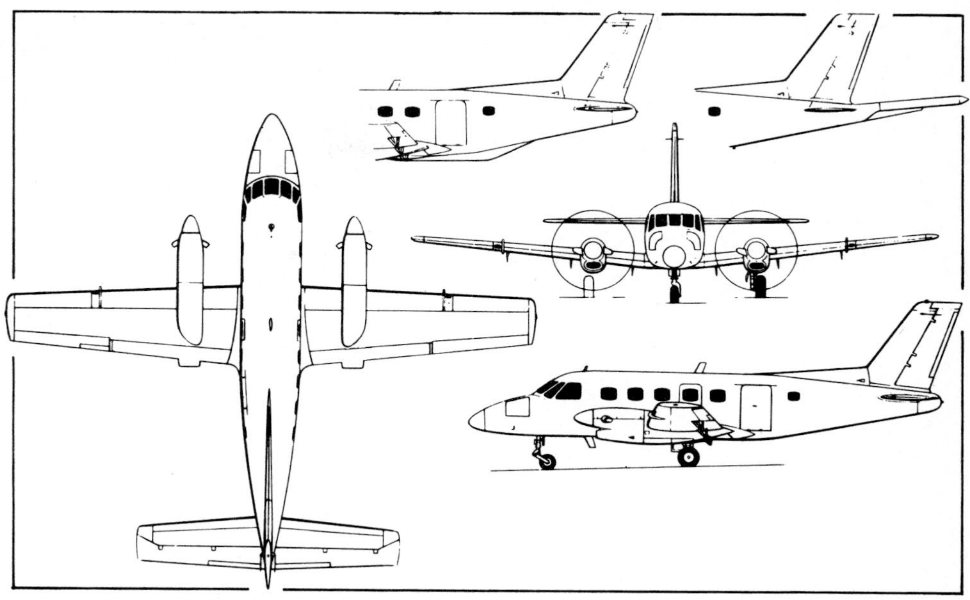

EMBRAER EMB-110P Bandeirante, with scrap views of B1 (top left) and S1 *(Pilot Press)*

Accommodation: Pilot and co-pilot side by side on flight deck. Seats for up to 21 passengers in main cabin, at 74 cm (29 in) pitch. Crew/passenger door at front and passenger/baggage door at rear, both on port side; emergency exit over wing on each side, and opposite crew/passenger door on starboard side. Crew/passenger door can also be used as emergency exit. Cabin floor stressed for uniformly distributed loads of up to 488 kg/m² (100 lb/sq ft). Baggage compartment at rear of cabin, with total capacity of 2·0 m³ (70·6 cu ft). Flush-type toilet in compartment at rear of cabin. Toilet/lavatory standard. Windscreen de-icing optional.

Systems: Air-cycle-type air-conditioning system with cooling capacity of 25,000 BTU/h and engine bleed heating. Hydraulic system, pressure 207 bars (3,000 lb/sq in), for landing gear actuation, dual independent braking systems, nosewheel steering and parking brake. Electrical system utilises two starter/generators, giving 200A continuously or 300A for one minute, and one 24V 34Ah nickel-cadmium battery with two 250VA static inverters to supply 115/26V 400Hz AC power. External power receptacle on port side of forward fuselage. Oxygen system for crew and passengers, using oxygen cylinder in rear of fuselage with capacity of 3·3 m³ (115 cu ft) at 128 bars (1,850 lb/sq in) pressure.

Avionics and Equipment: Avionics available in one of three standard packages. No. 1 package includes two Collins 618M-3 360-channel VHF transceivers, two Collins VIR-30A VOR/ILS/marker beacon receivers, two Collins DF-206 ADF receivers, and one or two Collins PN-101 gyromagnetic compass systems. No. 2 package includes one Collins 51Z-6 marker beacon receiver, two Bendix DFA-73A ADF systems, one Collins 618M-2B VHF1 system and one Whinner TC-609 VHF2 system, one Sunair ASB-100A HF system, one Collins 51R-7A/51V-5 VOR/ILS receiver, and one or two Collins PN-101 gyromagnetic compass systems. No. 3 package includes one or two King KC-55A gyromagnetic compass systems, two King KX-175BE VHF nav/com, two King KN-75 glideslope receivers, two King KR-21 marker beacon receivers, and two King KR-85 ADF receivers. Optional avionics include one Sunair ASB-100A HF/AM/SSB transceiver, one RCA AVQ-47 or Bendix RDR-1200 weather radar, Bendix M4-C or M4-D autopilot, one Collins DME-40 or two King KN-65A DME systems, one Collins TDR-90 or two King KT-76A ATC transponders, one Garrett Rescu/88L emergency locator transmitter, one Collins AVR-101 voice recorder, one Collins ALT-50 or King KRA-405 radio altimeter, entertainment radio, tape deck and PA system. Standard equipment includes engine fire detection system, propeller synchroniser, eight-day clock, annunciator panel, dual heated pitot heads, heated static port, external power socket, dual landing lights, taxi light, rotating beacons, dual map lights, instrument lighting system, soundproofing, low-profile glareshield and towbar. Optional equipment includes three-light strobe system, complete de-icing and anti-icing systems, toilet, a variety of cabinets and a range of galley equipment.

Dimensions, external:

Wing span	15·32 m (50 ft 3¼ in)
Wing chord at root	2·45 m (8 ft 0½ in)
Wing chord at tip	1·35 m (4 ft 5 in)
Wing aspect ratio	8·10
Length overall	15·10 m (49 ft 6½ in)
Length of fuselage	14·59 m (47 ft 10½ in)
Height overall	4·92 m (16 ft 1¾ in)
Fuselage: Max width	1·72 m (5 ft 7¾ in)
Tailplane span	7·54 m (24 ft 9 in)
Propeller diameter	2·36 m (7 ft 9 in)
Distance between propeller centres	4·80 m (15 ft 9 in)
Propeller ground clearance	0·276 m (10¾ in)
Wheel track	4·94 m (16 ft 2½ in)
Wheelbase	5·01 m (16 ft 5¼ in)
Passenger door (rear, port):	
Height	1·35 m (4 ft 5¼ in)
Width	0·85 m (2 ft 9½ in)
Crew/passenger door (fwd, port):	
Height	1·42 m (4 ft 8 in)
Width	0·63 m (2 ft 1 in)
Passenger emergency exits (two, each):	
Height	0·80 m (2 ft 7½ in)
Width	0·63 m (2 ft 1 in)
Crew emergency exit: Height	0·80 m (2 ft 7½ in)
Width	0·55 m (1 ft 9¾ in)

Dimensions, internal:

Cabin: Max length	9·53 m (31 ft 3¼ in)
Width	1·60 m (5 ft 3 in)
Height	1·60 m (5 ft 3 in)
Floor area	12·00 m² (129·2 sq ft)
Volume	20·4 m³ (720·4 cu ft)

R-95 (EMB-110B) photogrammetric version of the EMBRAER Bandeirante

EMB-110P2 third-level commuter transport version of the Bandeirante, seating up to 21 passengers

AREAS:
- Wings, gross 29·10 m² (313·23 sq ft)
- Ailerons (total) 2·16 m² (23·25 sq ft)
- Flaps (total) 4·90 m² (52·74 sq ft)
- Fin, excl dorsal fin 3·81 m² (41·01 sq ft)
- Dorsal fin 0·82 m² (8·83 sq ft)
- Ventral fin 0·80 m² (8·61 sq ft)
- Rudder, incl tab 1·69 m² (18·19 sq ft)
- Tailplane 5·51 m² (59·31 sq ft)
- Elevators, incl tabs 4·31 m² (46·39 sq ft)

WEIGHTS AND LOADINGS:
- Weight empty, equipped 3,516 kg (7,751 lb)
- Max payload 1,681 kg (3,706 lb)
- Max T-O weight 5,670 kg (12,500 lb)
- Max landing and max zero-fuel weight 5,450 kg (12,015 lb)
- Max wing loading 195·52 kg/m² (40·04 lb/sq ft)
- Max power loading 5·07 kg/kW (8·33 lb/shp)

PERFORMANCE (EMB-110P2 at max T-O weight, ISA, except where indicated):
- Max level speed at 2,440 m (8,000 ft) 248 knots (460 km/h; 286 mph)
- Max cruising speed at 3,050 m (10,000 ft) 225 knots (417 km/h; 259 mph)
- Econ cruising speed at 3,050 m (10,000 ft) 176 knots (326 km/h; 203 mph)
- Stalling speed at max landing weight 71 knots (132 km/h; 82 mph) CAS
- Max rate of climb at S/L 545 m (1,788 ft)/min
- Rate of climb at S/L, one engine out 136 m (446 ft)/min
- Time to 3,050 m (10,000 ft) 6 min
- Time to 4,575 m (15,000 ft) 10 min
- Service ceiling at AUW of 5,300 kg (11,684 lb) 7,350 m (24,100 ft)
- Service ceiling, one engine out, at AUW of 5,300 kg (11,684 lb) 3,780 m (12,400 ft)
- T-O run 430 m (1,410 ft)
- T-O to 15 m (50 ft) 675 m (2,215 ft)
- Landing from 15 m (50 ft) 850 m (2,790 ft)
- Landing run 565 m (1,854 ft)
- Range at 3,050 m (10,000 ft), 45 min reserves:
  - with max fuel 1,025 nm (1,900 km; 1,180 miles)
  - with 1,440 kg (3,175 lb) standard payload 268 nm (497 km; 309 miles)

EMBRAER EMB-110K1 and P1 BANDEIRANTE

Brazilian Air Force designation of EMB-110K1: C-95A

The following description applies to the K1 and P1, both of which are in current production:

WINGS: As EMB-110P2, but with optional inflatable de-icing boots on leading-edges.

FUSELAGE: As EMB-110P2, but with enlarged rear door for cargo loading.

TAIL UNIT, LANDING GEAR AND POWER PLANT: As EMB-110P2, including ventral fin.

ACCOMMODATION (EMB-110K1): Pilot and co-pilot side by side on flight deck. Crew door forward on port side; emergency exit forward of wing on starboard side. Cabin equipped for cargo only, with enlarged cargo door on port side at rear. Flush-type toilet behind co-pilot's seat.

ACCOMMODATION (EMB-110P1): As K1, but with quick-change cabin seating up to 18 persons. Overwing emergency exit on each side, making three in all.

SYSTEMS: Air-conditioning, hydraulic and electrical systems as for EMB-110P2. Oxygen system optional.

AVIONICS AND EQUIPMENT: Standard and optional avionics and equipment as for EMB-110P2.

DIMENSIONS, EXTERNAL: As EMB-110P2 plus:
- Cargo door (rear, port):
  - Height 1·42 m (4 ft 8 in)
  - Width 1·80 m (5 ft 11 in)

DIMENSIONS, INTERNAL: As EMB-110P2

AREAS: As EMB-110P2

WEIGHTS AND LOADINGS: As EMB-110P2 except:
- Max payload:
  - K1 1,804 kg (3,977 lb)
  - P1 (passenger configuration) 1,633 kg (3,600 lb)

PERFORMANCE (at max T-O weight, ISA): As EMB-110P2 except:
- Range at 3,050 m (10,000 ft), 45 min reserves:
  - K1 and P1 with max fuel 1,025 nm (1,900 km; 1,180 miles)
  - K1 with 1,750 kg (3,856 lb) standard payload 165 nm (306 km; 190 miles)
  - P1 with 1,440 kg (3,175 lb) standard payload 225 nm (417 km; 259 miles)

EMBRAER EMB-110P BANDEIRANTE

WINGS, FUSELAGE, TAIL UNIT AND LANDING GEAR: As EMB-110P2, except for shorter fuselage, fewer doors and emergency exits (see 'Accommodation' paragraph), and no ventral fin.

POWER PLANT: Two 507 kW (680 shp) Pratt & Whitney Aircraft of Canada PT6A-27 turboprop engines; otherwise as EMB-110P2.

ACCOMMODATION: Pilot and co-pilot side by side on flight deck, which is separated from main cabin by door. Cabin seats up to 18 passengers. Downward-hinged door on port side, aft of wing, with built-in airstairs. Cabin floor stressed for loads of up to 450 kg/m² (92 lb/sq ft). Emergency exit over wing on each side. Baggage compartment at rear of cabin, with total capacity of 2·0 m³ (70·6 cu ft). Toilet/lavatory standard.

SYSTEMS: As EMB-110P2.

AVIONICS AND EQUIPMENT: Standard avionics include two Collins 618M-2B 360-channel VHF transceivers, one Sunair ASB-100A HF/AM/SSB transceiver, one Collins 51R-7A VOR/ILS receiver, two Bendix DFA-73A1 ADF receivers, one Collins 51Z-6 marker beacon receiver, and one Collins 51V-5 glideslope receiver. Optional avionics include RCA AVQ-47 or Bendix RDR-1200 weather radar, Bendix M4-C or M4-D autopilot, single or dual Sperry STARS IVB or IVC flight directors, entertainment radio, tape deck, PA system, and complete de-icing and anti-icing system. Standard and optional equipment as listed for EMB-110P2.

DIMENSIONS, EXTERNAL: As EMB-110P2 except:
- Length overall 14·23 m (46 ft 8¼ in)
- Length of fuselage 13·74 m (45 ft 1 in)
- Wheelbase 4·56 m (14 ft 11½ in)
- Crew/passenger door (fwd, port) None
- Emergency exits Two only

DIMENSIONS, INTERNAL: As EMB-110P2 except:
- Cabin: Max length 8·65 m (28 ft 4½ in)
  - Floor area (incl flight deck) 10·9 m² (117·3 sq ft)
  - Volume 18·4 m³ (649·8 cu ft)

AREAS: As EMB-110P2 (except no ventral fin)

WEIGHTS AND LOADINGS:
- Weight empty, equipped 3,403 kg (7,502 lb)
- Max payload 1,645 kg (3,626 lb)
- Max T-O weight 5,600 kg (12,345 lb)
- Max landing and max zero-fuel weight 5,300 kg (11,684 lb)
- Max wing loading 193·10 kg/m² (39·55 lb/sq ft)
- Max power loading 5·52 kg/kW (9·08 lb/shp)

PERFORMANCE (at max T-O weight, ISA, except where indicated):
- Max level speed at 2,285 m (7,500 ft) 244 knots (452 km/h; 280 mph)
- Max cruising speed at 3,050 m (10,000 ft) 232 knots (430 km/h; 267 mph)
- Econ cruising speed at 3,050 m (10,000 ft) 184 knots (341 km/h; 212 mph)
- Stalling speed at max landing weight 71 knots (132 km/h; 82 mph) CAS
- Max rate of climb at S/L 442 m (1,450 ft)/min
- Rate of climb at S/L, one engine out 137 m (450 ft)/min
- Time to 3,050 m (10,000 ft) 8 min
- Time to 4,575 m (15,000 ft) 13 min
- Service ceiling at AUW of 5,300 kg (11,684 lb) 7,700 m (25,300 ft)
- Service ceiling, one engine out, at AUW of 5,300 kg (11,684 lb) 3,750 m (12,300 ft)
- T-O run 452 m (1,480 ft)
- T-O to, and landing from, 15 m (50 ft) 695 m (2,280 ft)
- Landing run 372 m (1,220 ft)
- Range at 3,050 m (10,000 ft), 45 min reserves:
  - with max fuel 1,100 nm (2,038 km; 1,266 miles)
  - with standard payload 320 nm (593 km; 368 miles)

EMBRAER EMB-111

Brazilian Air Force designation: P-95

This land-based maritime reconnaissance aircraft, based on the EMB-110 Bandeirante, was designed to meet specifications issued by the Comando Costeiro, the Brazilian Air Force's Coastal Command, which has ordered 12. The main external differences in this version are the large nose radome, housing search radar, and the addition of wingtip fuel tanks.

The first EMB-111 (2262) flew for the first time on 15

Brazilian Air Force C-95A Bandeirante (EMB-110K1), with lengthened fuselage and rear cargo door

August 1977; Brazilian Air Force aircraft, the first three of which were delivered on 11 April 1978, serve with the 1° Esquadrão of the 7° Grupo de Aviação, located at Salvador AFB, Bahia.

Six have been ordered by the Chilean Navy, and deliveries of these were expected to be completed by mid-1979. The Chilean aircraft have some mission equipment changes, including full de-icing system, and passive ECM antennae under the nose and at the tail.

TYPE: Twin-turboprop maritime reconnaissance aircraft.

WINGS: As EMB-110P2, but with reinforced leading-edges and tip-tanks.

FUSELAGE: Similar to EMB-110P2, but with large nose radome.

TAIL UNIT AND LANDING GEAR: As EMB-110P2.

POWER PLANT: Two 559 kW (750 shp) Pratt & Whitney Aircraft of Canada PT6A-34 turboprop engines, each driving a three-blade propeller with spinner. Four integral fuel tanks in wings (total capacity 1,914 litres; 421 Imp gallons), and two permanent wingtip tanks (total capacity 636 litres; 140 Imp gallons). Overall total fuel capacity 2,550 litres (561 Imp gallons), of which 2,454 litres (540 Imp gallons) are usable. Oil capacity 8·7 litres (1·9 Imp gallons).

ACCOMMODATION: Pilot and co-pilot side by side on flight deck. Main cabin accommodates search radar/radio operator, navigator and observer. Port-side door at rear, for crew and cargo, opens inwards and can be used for air-drop of paratroops and survival equipment. Galley and toilet in main cabin.

AVIONICS AND EQUIPMENT: One Collins 618T-3B HF/AM/SSB/CW transceiver, two Collins 618M-3 VHF transceivers, two Sperry C-14 gyromagnetic compasses, two Bendix DFA-74A ADF receivers, two Collins VIR-31A VOR/ILS/marker beacon receivers, one Collins AN/APX-92 IFF transponder, one Collins DF-301E VHF/DF, one Collins DME-40 DME system, one Bendix ALA-51 radio altimeter, one Litton LN-33 inertial navigation system, and one AIL AN/APS-128 (SPAR-1) search radar. Optional avionics include Bendix M4-C or M4-D autopilot, single or dual Sperry STARS IVB or IVC flight directors, entertainment radio, tape deck, PA systems and complete de-icing and anti-icing system.

ARMAMENT AND OPERATIONAL EQUIPMENT: Four underwing pylons for 127 mm air-to-surface rockets (two per pylon), or three stores pylons plus a leading-edge-mounted 50 million candlepower searchlight. For target marking, six Brazilian-built MK-6 smoke grenades are carried, as well as a Motorola SST-121 transponder. Flares of 200,000 candlepower also available for illumination of targets at night.

DIMENSIONS, EXTERNAL: As EMB-110P2 except:
- Wing span (over tip-tanks) 15·96 m (52 ft 4½ in)
- Length overall 14·83 m (48 ft 7⅞ in)
- Length of fuselage 14·34 m (47 ft 0½ in)
- Height overall 4·74 m (15 ft 6½ in)
- Propeller ground clearance 0·278 m (11 in)
- Wheelbase 4·56 m (14 ft 11½ in)

DIMENSIONS, INTERNAL:
- Cabin: Max length 8·65 m (28 ft 4½ in)
  - Width 1·60 m (5 ft 3 in)
  - Height 1·60 m (5 ft 3 in)
  - Floor area 11·60 m² (124·9 sq ft)

AREAS: As EMB-110P2

WEIGHTS AND LOADINGS:
- Weight empty, equipped 3,760 kg (8,289 lb)
- Max T-O weight 7,000 kg (15,432 lb)
- Max zero-fuel weight 5,150 kg (11,354 lb)
- Max landing weight 5,300 kg (11,684 lb)
- Max wing loading 241·38 kg/m² (49·44 lb/sq ft)
- Max power loading 6·26 kg/kW (10·29 lb/shp)

PERFORMANCE (at max T-O weight, ISA+15°C, except where indicated):
- Max cruising speed at 3,050 m (10,000 ft) 208 knots (385 km/h; 239 mph)
- Econ cruising speed at 3,050 m (10,000 ft) 190 knots (352 km/h; 218 mph)
- Stalling speed at max landing weight 71 knots (132 km/h; 82 mph) CAS
- Max rate of climb at S/L 362 m (1,190 ft)/min
- Time to 3,050 m (10,000 ft) 13 min
- Time to 4,575 m (15,000 ft) 28 min
- Service ceiling, at AUW of 5,300 kg (11,684 lb) 7,770 m (25,500 ft)
- Service ceiling, one engine out, at AUW of 5,300 kg (11,684 lb) 4,025 m (13,200 ft)
- T-O run 940 m (3,084 ft)
- T-O to 15 m (50 ft) 1,590 m (5,217 ft)
- Landing from 15 m (50 ft) 725 m (2,379 ft)
- Landing run 405 m (1,329 ft)
- Range at 3,050 m (10,000 ft), max fuel, 45 min reserves 1,590 nm (2,945 km; 1,830 miles)

EMBRAER EMB-121 XINGU

Brazilian Air Force designation: VU-9

The prototype Xingu (PP-ZXI) flew for the first time on 10 October 1976. A second airframe was completed for static and fatigue testing. First production Xingu (PP-ZCT) was flown on 20 May 1977, and Brazilian CTA certification was awarded in May 1979. Nine production Xingus had been completed by 30 March 1979, and production is scheduled to reach 28 by the end of 1980. Six VU-9s for the Grupo de Transporte Especial (the Special Transport Group) of the Brazilian Air Force at Brasilia were delivered during the first half of 1978; domestic and foreign orders totalled 16 by mid-1979.

From the 49th aircraft, production will switch to the Xingu 2, with PT6A-42 engines and an 84 cm (33 in) longer cabin. A prototype Xingu 2 is scheduled to fly in February 1980.

TYPE: Twin-turboprop general-purpose transport.

WINGS: Cantilever low-wing monoplane. Utilises same wing as EMB-110P2 (which see), but with reduced span and modified tips. Inflatable leading-edge de-icing boots optional.

FUSELAGE: All-metal semi-monocoque fail-safe structure of aluminium alloy, with circular cross-section, designed for a max operating pressure differential of 0·414 bars (6·0 lb/sq in).

TAIL UNIT: Cantilever metal T-tail, with glassfibre dorsal fin. Inflatable de-icing boots optional for fin and tailplane leading-edges. Trim and balance tabs in rudder and each elevator. Ventral fin.

LANDING GEAR: Hydraulically-retractable tricycle type, with oleo-pneumatic shock-absorber on each unit. Single main wheels, with tyres size 670 × 210-12 (10 ply rating), pressure 5·52-5·86 bars (80-85 lb/sq in). Steerable, forward-retracting twin nosewheels, with tyres size 16 × 44 (six ply rating), pressure 5·52-5·86 bars (80-85 lb/sq in).

POWER PLANT: Two 507 kW (680 shp) Pratt & Whitney Aircraft of Canada PT6A-28 turboprop engines, each driving a Hartzell HC-B3TN-3D/T10178HB-8R three-blade constant-speed metal propeller with autofeathering and full reverse-pitch capability. Four integral fuel tanks in wings, with total capacity of 1,666 litres (366 Imp gallons). Gravity refuelling point on top of each wing. Oil capacity 8·3 litres (1·8 Imp gallons).

ACCOMMODATION: Two seats side by side on flight deck. Cabin seats up to 9 passengers. Downward-hinged door on port side, aft of wing, with built-in airstairs. Cabin floor stressed for loads of up to 488 kg/m² (100 lb/sq ft). Emergency exit over wing on starboard side. Baggage compartments in nose and at rear of cabin. Toilet/lavatory standard.

AVIONICS: Standard avionics include dual RCA AVC-110A VHF transceivers, dual RCA AVN-220A VOR/ILS/marker beacon receivers, one Collins ADF-60A ADF, one VOR/ILS OBS indicator (co-pilot), dual RCA AVA-310 audio panels, one Sperry C-14

The maritime reconnaissance EMBRAER EMB-111 developed from the Bandeirante

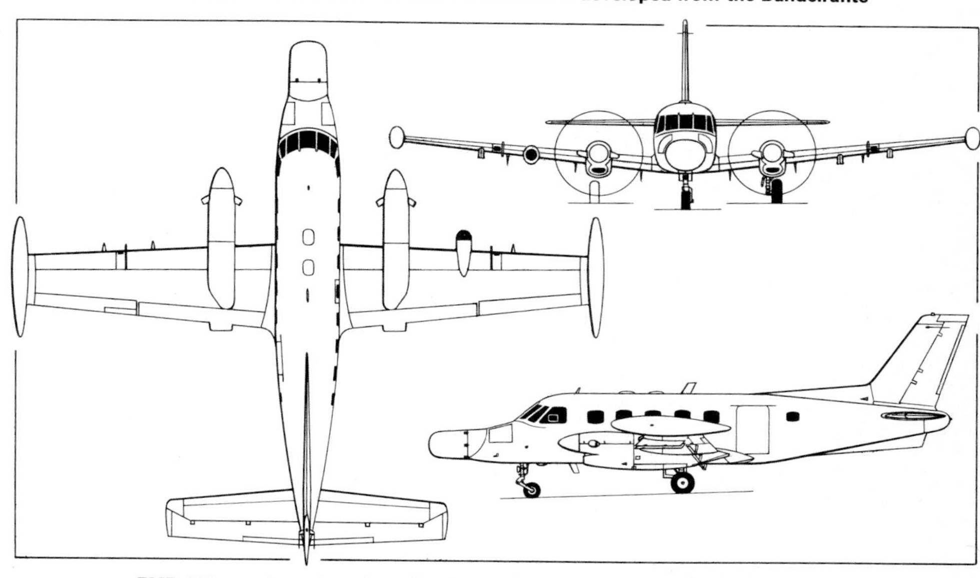
EMB-111 patrol version of the Bandeirante, developed by EMBRAER *(Pilot Press)*

First production EMBRAER EMB-121 Xingu, showing the now-standard ventral fin *(Ronaldo S. Olive)*

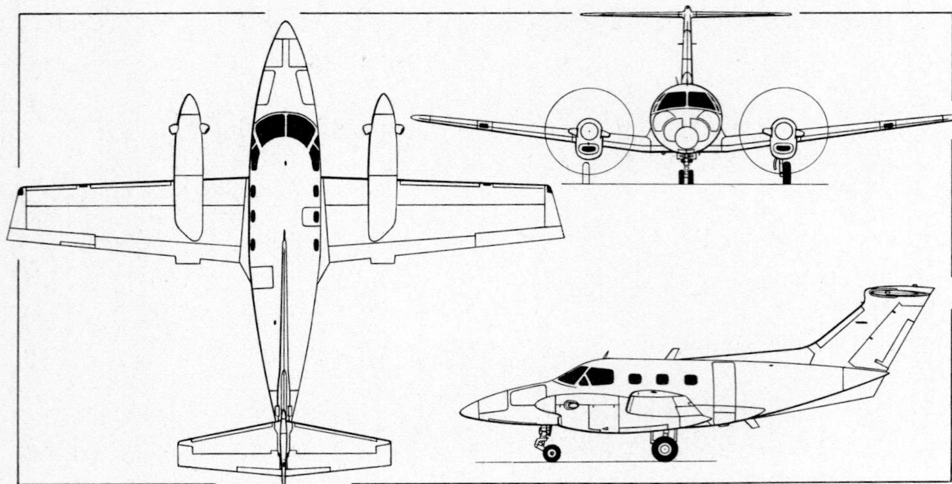

EMB-121 Xingu six/nine-passenger twin-turboprop transport *(Pilot Press)*

gyromagnetic compass with dual Sperry RD-44 course indicator (pilot), one AIM-200 DC FM directional gyro (co-pilot), one Sperry GH-14-330 gyro horizon (pilot), one AIM-500 DC FM gyro horizon (co-pilot), one Collins TDR-90 transponder with Smiths 01-200-105 encoding altimeter, one Collins DME-40 DME, dual Telex TEL-66C microphones, dual Telex A1210 pairs of earphones, dual Flite-Tronics PC-15 BC(D) static converters, and one Sunair ASB-100A HF transceiver. Optional avionics are available in three standard packages, with dual Collins DF-206 ADF, Sunair ASB-100A HF/AM/SSB, dual RCA AVA-310 and Sperry SPZ-200 autopilot common to all three. In addition, package No. 1 offers dual RCA AVC-110A VHF com, one RCA AVN-220A VHF nav and one Sperry C-14 gyromagnetic compass; package No. 2 offers dual RCA AVC-110A VHF com, dual RCA AVN-220A VHF nav, dual Sperry C-14 gyromagnetic compasses, and Garrett Rescu/88L emergency locator transmitter; package No. 3 offers dual Collins VHF-20A VHF com, dual Collins VIR-30A VHF nav, dual Sperry C-14 gyromagnetic compasses, Garrett Rescu/88L ELT, Collins ALT-50 radio altimeter, and dual Sperry STARS IVC flight directors for pilot and co-pilot. Bendix RDR-1200 or RCA Primus 40 weather radar, cabin music and PA systems are optional extras on all three packages; Collins TDR-90 transponder on packages 2 and 3; Collins DME-40 on package 3; and pilot's Sperry STARS IVB or IVC on package 2.

Equipment: Standard equipment comprises maximum permissible airspeed indicator, eight-day clock, chronometer, cabin rate of climb indicator, cabin altitude and differential pressure indicator, annunciator panel, heated stall warning system, dual heated pitot tubes and heated static ports, external power sockets, wing ice light, dual landing lights, dual taxi lights, dual strobe anti-collision lights, dual map lights, cabin dome lights, instrument lighting system, low profile glareshield, and hand-type cabin fire extinguishers. Optional equipment includes three-light strobe system, fire extinguishing system, de-icing and anti-icing system, toilet, and a range of galley equipment.

Dimensions, external:
Wing span 14·45 m (47 ft 5 in)
Wing chord at root 2·33 m (7 ft 7¾ in)
Wing chord at tip 1·49 m (4 ft 10¾ in)
Wing chord at fuselage c/l 2·47 m (8 ft 1¼ in)
Wing aspect ratio 7·18
Length overall 12·25 m (40 ft 2¼ in)
Length of fuselage 11·16 m (36 ft 7½ in)
Fuselage max width 1·86 m (6 ft 1¼ in)
Height overall 4·74 m (15 ft 6½ in)
Tailplane span 5·58 m (18 ft 3¾ in)
Wheel track 5·24 m (17 ft 2¼ in)
Wheelbase 2·88 m (9 ft 5½ in)
Propeller diameter 2·36 m (7 ft 9 in)
Distance between propeller centres 5·10 m (16 ft 8¾ in)
Passenger door (rear, port):
Height 1·31 m (4 ft 3½ in)
Width 0·63 m (2 ft 0¾ in)
Emergency exit (one overwing):
Height 0·96 m (3 ft 1¾ in)
Width 0·509 m (1 ft 8 in)

Dimensions, internal:
Pressurised cabin: Max length 5·18 m (17 ft 0 in)
Max width 1·74 m (5 ft 8½ in)
Max height 1·52 m (4 ft 11¾ in)
Baggage compartment volume:
nose 0·30 m^3 (10·6 cu ft)
rear 0·64 m^3 (22·6 cu ft)

Areas:
Wings, gross 27·50 m^2 (296·0 sq ft)
Ailerons (total) 1·84 m^2 (19·81 sq ft)
Trailing-edge flaps (total) 4·90 m^2 (52·74 sq ft)
Vertical tail surfaces (total, excl dorsal fin) 4·00 m^2 (43·06 sq ft)
Rudder, incl tab 1·30 m^2 (13·99 sq ft)
Dorsal fin 0·54 m^2 (5·81 sq ft)
Ventral fin 0·94 m^2 (10·12 sq ft)
Horizontal tail surfaces (total) 5·84 m^2 (62·86 sq ft)
Elevator, incl tabs 2·17 m^2 (23·36 sq ft)

Weights and Loadings:
Weight empty, equipped 3,500 kg (7,716 lb)
Max T-O weight 5,670 kg (12,500 lb)
Max zero-fuel weight 4,660 kg (10,273 lb)
Max landing weight 5,340 kg (11,772 lb)
Max wing loading 206·2 kg/m^2 (42·2 lb/sq ft)
Max power loading 5·59 kg/kW (9·19 lb/shp)

Performance (at max T-O weight, ISA, except where indicated):
Max cruising speed at 3,350 m (11,000 ft) 243 knots (450 km/h; 280 mph)
Econ cruising speed at 6,100 m (20,000 ft) 203 knots (376 km/h; 234 mph)
Stalling speed at max T-O weight, flaps up 96 knots (178 km/h; 111 mph)
Stalling speed at max landing weight, full flap 74 knots (137·5 km/h; 85·5 mph)
Max rate of climb at S/L 426 m (1,400 ft)/min
Service ceiling 7,925 m (26,000 ft)
Service ceiling, one engine out 3,960 m (13,000 ft)
T-O to 15 m (50 ft) 865 m (2,840 ft)
Landing from 15 m (50 ft) at max landing weight 850 m (2,790 ft)
Range with 900 kg (1,985 lb) payload at 6,100 m (20,000 ft), 45 min reserves 900 nm (1,666 km; 1,035 miles)
Range with max fuel and 610 kg (1,345 lb) payload at 6,100 m (20,000 ft), ISA, 45 min reserves 1,270 nm (2,352 km; 1,461 miles)

EMBRAER (AERMACCHI) EMB-326GB XAVANTE

Brazilian Air Force designation: AT-26

Under an agreement signed in May 1970, EMBRAER is assembling under licence the Aermacchi M.B.326GB jet trainer/ground attack aircraft for the Brazilian Air Force, by whom the type is known as the AT-26 Xavante, the name of a Brazilian Indian tribe.

The initial order called for the manufacture of 112 aircraft, at a rate of two per month; a further 40 were ordered in December 1975, three during 1976 and 20 more in 1979. The first Brazilian-assembled Xavante made its first flight on 3 September 1971, and the first two aircraft were handed over to the Brazilian Air Force a few days later. The three Xavantes ordered in 1976 were delivered to the Togolese Air Force.

By 1 January 1979 a total of 146 Xavantes had been delivered. These are in service with the Brazilian Air Force's 3° Esquadrão Misto de Reconhecimento e Ataque (3rd Mixed Reconnaissance and Attack Squadron) at Santa Cruz AFB, Rio de Janeiro; the 4° Esquadrão Misto de Reconhecimento e Ataque at Santa Maria AFB, Rio Grande do Sul State; the 4° Grupo de Aviação (4th Aviation Group) at Fortaleza, Ceará State; the CATRE (Centro de Aplicações Táticas e Recompletamento de Equipagens: Tactical and Aircrew Training Centre) at Natal, Rio Grande do Norte State; the 10° Grupo de Aviação at Cumbica AFB, São Paulo State; and other units.

A description of the standard M.B. 326GB appears in the Italian section of this edition; the version for the Brazilian Air Force is basically similar, except in the following respects:

Avionics and Equipment: Two Collins Type 618M-2B 360-channel VHF transceivers, Collins CIA-102A interphone system, Bendix DFA 73A-1 ADF, and a complete VOR/ILS system using a Collins 51RV-1 VOR/LOC/glideslope receiver, Collins 51Z-4 marker beacon receiver and AN/APX-72. Provision for IFF transponder.

Armament: Six underwing points for bombs, gun pods or other stores. Typical loads include six 250 lb bombs; two 500 lb bombs; two 500 lb bombs and two twin 7·62 mm gun pods; four 250 lb bombs and two twin 7·62 mm gun pods; two twin 7·62 mm gun pods and two underwing drop-tanks; two twin 7·62 mm gun pods and four LM-70/7 rocket pods (each with seven SBAT 70 mm folding-fin air-to-ground projectiles); two twin 7·62 mm gun pods and two LM-37/36 rocket pods (each with thirty-six SBAT 37 mm air-to-ground rockets); six LM-70/7 rocket pods; or two LM-70/19 rocket pods (each with nineteen SBAT 70 mm air-to-ground rockets); or photographic reconnaissance pods. All armament loads are designed and manufactured in Brazil.

EMBRAER EMB-312

Brazilian Air Force designation: T-27

On 6 December 1978, EMBRAER received a contract from the Departamento de Pesquisas e Desenvolvimento (Department of Research and Development) of the Brazilian Air Force to develop and construct a new basic trainer for that service. Bearing the manufacturer's designation EMB-312 and the Brazilian Air Force designation T-27, it is expected to fly for the first time in August or September 1980. The initial contract is understood to cover one flying prototype and one static test airframe; a Ministry of Aeronautics source has said that about 100 production aircraft are expected to be ordered.

Characteristics of the EMB-312 will include high manoeuvrability, short take-off and landing, the ability to operate from unprepared runways, and a high degree of stability. Designed to meet the requirements of FAR Pt 23 Appendix A, it will be built using such modern techniques as integral machining by numerical control machinery, chemical milling, and metal-to-metal bonding.

Type: Tandem two-seat basic trainer.

Wings: Cantilever low-wing monoplane. Wing section NACA 63_2A-415 at centreline, NACA 63A-212 at tip. Dihedral 5° 30′ at 30% chord. Incidence 1° 23′ at centreline. Geometric twist 2° 12′. Sweepback 0° 43′ 26″ at quarter-chord. All-metal structure, with single-slotted trailing-edge flaps and constant-chord ailerons. No tabs.

Fuselage: Conventional all-metal semi-monocoque structure.

Tail Unit: Cantilever all-metal structure, with sweptback fin and horn-balanced rudder. Non-swept horizontal surfaces, with trim tab in port elevator.

Landing Gear: Retractable tricycle type, with single wheel and oleo-pneumatic shock-absorber on each unit. Nose unit retracts rearward, main units inward into wings.

Power Plant: One 559 kW (750 shp) Pratt & Whitney Aircraft of Canada PT6A-25C turboprop engine, derated to 436 kW (585 shp) and driving a Hartzell

EMBRAER (Aermacchi) AT-26 Xavante of the Brazilian Air Force with 0·5 in gun pods *(Ronaldo S. Olive)*

three-blade constant-speed propeller. Max internal fuel capacity 727 litres (160 Imp gallons). Fuel system allows for up to 35 s of inverted flight.

ACCOMMODATION: Ejection seats for two persons in tandem under one-piece moulded canopy. Rear seat elevated. Baggage compartment in rear fuselage.

ARMAMENT: Provision for two ordnance attachment points under each wing, each stressed for a max load of 150 kg (330 lb). Typical loads, on MA-4A-22 pylons, include two MS10-21/22-10A machine-gun pods, each with 350 rds; four 25 lb MK-76 bombs; four 250 lb MK-81 general-purpose bombs; or four LM-37/7A or LM-70/7 launchers, each with seven rockets. Provision for RFR-01 fixed-reflex gunsight.

DIMENSIONS, EXTERNAL:
Wing span 11·09 m (36 ft 4½ in)
Wing chord at root 2·30 m (7 ft 6½ in)
Wing chord at tip 1·05 m (3 ft 5¼ in)
Wing mean aerodynamic chord 1·82 m (5 ft 11½ in)
Wing aspect ratio 6·44
Length overall 10·15 m (33 ft 3½ in)
Height overall 3·40 m (11 ft 1¾ in)
Fuselage: Max width 0·92 m (3 ft 0¼ in)
Tailplane span 4·30 m (14 ft 1¼ in)
Wheel track 3·66 m (12 ft 0 in)
Wheelbase 3·07 m (10 ft 0¾ in)
Propeller ground clearance (static) 0·25 m (9¾ in)

DIMENSIONS, INTERNAL:
Cockpits: Combined length 2·80 m (9 ft 2¼ in)
Max height 1·38 m (4 ft 6¼ in)
Max width 0·80 m (2 ft 7½ in)
Baggage compartment:
Floor loading 650 kg/m² (133 lb/sq ft)
Volume 0·17 m³ (6·0 cu ft)

AREAS:
Wings, gross 19·00 m² (204·5 sq ft)
Ailerons (total) 1·75 m² (18·84 sq ft)
Trailing-edge flaps (total) 2·61 m² (28·09 sq ft)

WEIGHTS AND LOADINGS:
Weight empty to be defined
Max internal fuel load 566 kg (1,247 lb)
Typical T-O weights with external load:
four MK-76 bombs 2,179 kg (4,803 lb)
four LM-37/7A rocket launchers 2,222 kg (4,898 lb)
two machine-gun pods 2,288 kg (5,044 lb)
four MK-81 bombs or four LM-70/7 rocket launchers, reduced internal fuel 2,350 kg (5,180 lb)
Max T-O and landing weight 2,350 kg (5,180 lb)
Max wing loading 124·2 kg/m² (25·4 lb/sq ft)
Max power loading 5·39 kg/kW (8·86 lb/shp)

PERFORMANCE (estimated, aircraft at max 'clean' T-O weight, ISA, except where indicated):
Never-exceed speed 324 knots (600 km/h; 373 mph)
Max level speed at 4,000 m (13,125 ft) 247 knots (457 km/h; 284 mph)
Stalling speed, flaps up 75 knots (139 km/h; 86·5 mph)
Stalling speed, flaps down 67 knots (124 km/h; 77 mph)
Max rate of climb at S/L 648 m (2,125 ft)/min
Service ceiling, AUW of 2,100 kg (4,629 lb) 9,940 m (32,600 ft)
T-O run at S/L 290 m (952 ft)
T-O to 15 m (50 ft) 510 m (1,674 ft)
Landing from 15 m (50 ft), AUW of 2,100 kg (4,629 lb) 505 m (1,657 ft)
Landing run at S/L, AUW of 2,100 kg (4,629 lb) 240 m (788 ft)
Range at long-range cruising speed at 4,570 m (15,000 ft), 30 min reserves 1,140 nm (2,112 km; 1,312 miles)
g limits (Aerobatic) +6·0/−3·0

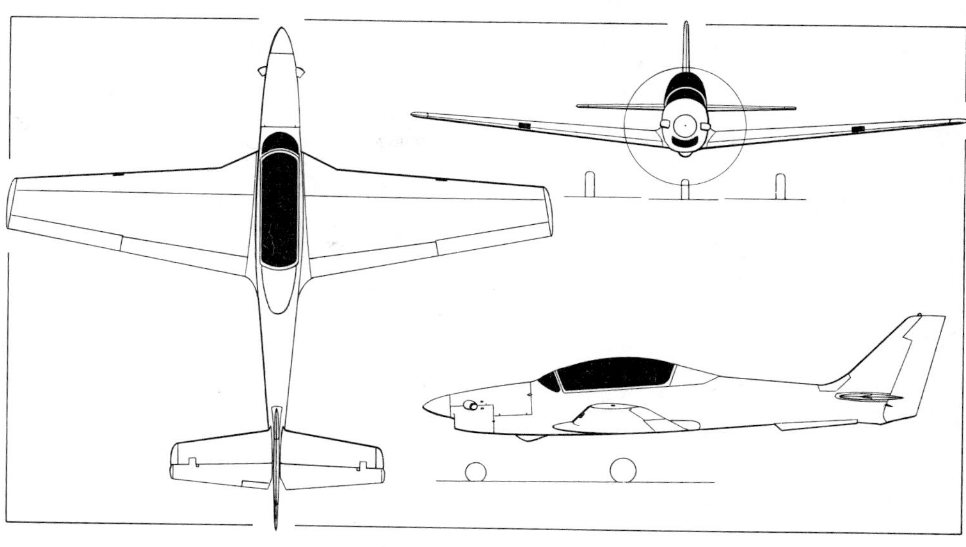
EMBRAER EMB-312 tandem two-seat trainer *(Pilot Press)*

EMBRAER EMB-201A IPANEMA

The original version of this agricultural aircraft was designed and developed to specifications laid down by the Brazilian Ministry of Agriculture. Design was started in May 1969, and the EMB-200 prototype (PP-ZIP) made its first flight on 30 July 1970. Ipanema is the name of a famous beach in Rio, and also of a farm which is the headquarters of the Agricultural Air School of the Ministry of Agriculture, where the EMB-200 was flight tested from 1970 onward. A type certificate was granted on 14 December 1971.

The following versions of the Ipanema have been produced:

EMB-200 and EMB-200A. Initial versions. Production, of 73 aircraft, completed in mid-1974. Described in 1973-74 *Jane's*.

EMB-201. Developed version, produced between mid-1974 and March 1977; total of 200 built. Described in 1976-77 *Jane's*.

EMB-201A. Current production version, first flown 10 March 1977. Incorporates several modifications requested by operators as a result of field experience, including new wing profile, wingtips and other aerodynamic improvements, improved systems, and revised cockpit layout. Detailed description applies to this version, of which 112 had been built by 1 January 1979.

EMB-201R. Glider towing version of EMB-201. Three built for Brazilian Air Force (designation **U-19**). Described and illustrated in 1977-78 *Jane's*.

EMBRAER is conducting studies for a version of the Ipanema powered by a Pratt & Whitney Aircraft of Canada PT6 turboprop engine.

The following description applies to the standard production EMB-201A:

TYPE: Single-seat agricultural aircraft.

WINGS: Cantilever low-wing monoplane. Wing section NACA 23015 (modified), with cambered leading-edges. Dihedral 7° from roots. Incidence 3°. All-metal single-spar structure of 2024 aluminium alloy with all-metal Frise-type ailerons outboard and all-metal slotted flaps on trailing-edge, and all-detachable cambered leading-edges. No tabs. Cambered wingtips standard.

FUSELAGE: Rectangular-section all-metal safe-life structure, of welded 4130 steel tube with removable skin panels of 2024 aluminium alloy. Structure is specially treated against chemical corrosion.

TAIL UNIT: Cantilever two-spar all-metal structure of 2024 aluminium alloy. Slight sweepback on fin and rudder. Fixed-incidence tailplane. Trim tab in starboard elevator.

LANDING GEAR: Non-retractable main and tail wheels, with oleo shock-absorbers on main units. Tailwheel has tapered spring shock-absorber. Main wheels and tyres size 8·50-10. Tailwheel diameter 250 mm (10 in). Tyre pressures: main, 2·07-2·41 bars (30-35 lb/sq in); tailwheel, 3·79 bars (55 lb/sq in). Hydraulic disc brakes on main wheels.

POWER PLANT: One 224 kW (300 hp) Lycoming IO-540-K1J5D flat-six engine, driving a Hartzell two-blade constant-speed metal propeller with spinner. Integral fuel tanks in each wing leading-edge, with total capacity of 292 litres (64·2 Imp gallons). Refuelling point on top of each tank. Oil capacity 12 litres (2·6 Imp gallons).

ACCOMMODATION: Single horizontally/vertically-adjustable seat in fully-enclosed cabin with bottom-hinged window/door on each side. Ventilation system in cabin. Inertial type shoulder harness standard.

SYSTEM: 28V DC electrical system supplied by a 24Ah BB639/U battery and a Bosch K.1 28V 35A alternator. Power receptacle for external battery (AN-2552-3A type) on port side of forward fuselage.

AVIONICS AND EQUIPMENT: Standard VFR electronics include 360-channel Bendix RT-241A VHF transceiver and Bendix T-12C ADF transceiver. Hopper for agricultural chemicals has capacity of 680 litres (149·5 Imp gallons) liquid or 750 kg (1,653 lb) dry. Dusting system below centre of fuselage. Spraybooms and Micronair atomisers aft of and above wing trailing-edges.

DIMENSIONS, EXTERNAL:
Wing span 11·69 m (38 ft 4¼ in)
Wing chord (constant) 1·71 m (5 ft 7½ in)
Wing aspect ratio 6·85
Length overall (tail up) 7·43 m (24 ft 4½ in)
Height overall (tail down) 2·22 m (7 ft 3½ in)
Fuselage: Max width 0·93 m (3 ft 0½ in)
Tailplane span 3·66 m (12 ft 0 in)
Wheel track 2·20 m (7 ft 2½ in)
Wheelbase 5·20 m (17 ft 7¼ in)
Propeller diameter 2·13 m (7 ft 0 in)

DIMENSIONS, INTERNAL:
Cockpit: Max length 1·20 m (3 ft 11¼ in)
Max width 0·85 m (2 ft 9½ in)
Max height 1·34 m (4 ft 4¾ in)

AREAS:
Wings, gross 19·94 m² (214·63 sq ft)
Ailerons (total) 1·60 m² (17·22 sq ft)
Trailing-edge flaps (total) 2·30 m² (24·76 sq ft)
Fin 0·58 m² (6·24 sq ft)
Rudder 0·63 m² (6·78 sq ft)
Tailplane 3·17 m² (34·12 sq ft)

WEIGHTS AND LOADINGS (N: Normal; R: Restricted category):
Max payload: N, R 750 kg (1,653 lb)
Max T-O and landing weight: N 1,550 kg (3,417 lb)
R 1,800 kg (3,968 lb)
Max wing loading: N 77·75 kg/m² (15·92 lb/sq ft)
R 90·29 kg/m² (18·49 lb/sq ft)
Max power loading: N 6·92 kg/kW (11·39 lb/hp)
R 8·03 kg/kW (13·23 lb/hp)

PERFORMANCE (at max T-O weight, 'clean' configuration, ISA):
Never-exceed speed:
N 165 knots (305 km/h; 190 mph)
R 104 knots (193 km/h; 120 mph)
Max level speed at S/L:
N 124 knots (230 km/h; 143 mph)
R 121 knots (225 km/h; 140 mph)
Max cruising speed (75% power) at 1,830 m (6,000 ft):
N 115 knots (212 km/h; 132 mph)
R 110 knots (204 km/h; 127 mph)
Stalling speed, power off (N):
flaps up 56 knots (103 km/h; 64 mph)
8° flap 54 knots (100 km/h; 62 mph)
30° flap 49·5 knots (92 km/h; 57 mph)
Stalling speed, power off (R):
flaps up 59·5 knots (109·5 km/h; 68 mph)
8° flap 57·5 knots (106·5 km/h; 66 mph)
30° flap 53 knots (98·5 km/h; 61 mph)
Max rate of climb at S/L, 8° flap:
N 283 m (930 ft)/min
R 201 m (660 ft)/min

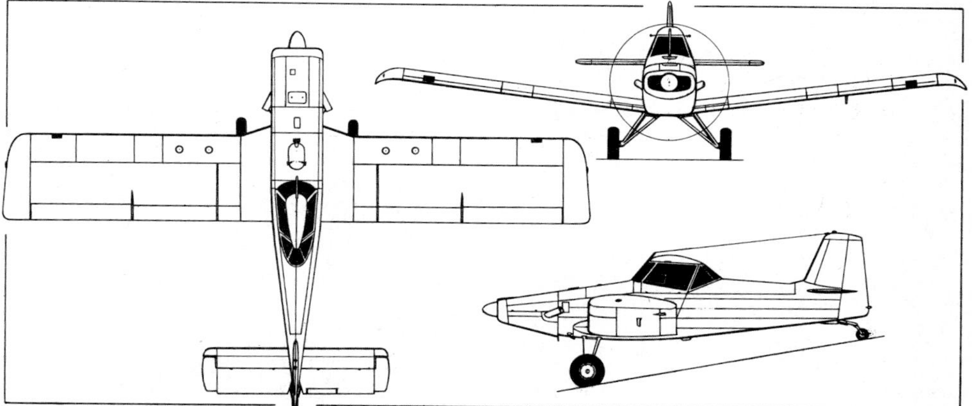
EMBRAER EMB-201A Ipanema single-seat agricultural aircraft *(Pilot Press)*

Service ceiling, 8° flap: R 3,470 m (11,385 ft)
T-O run at S/L, 8° flap, asphalt runway:
N 282 m (925 ft)
R 368 m (1,208 ft)
T-O to 15 m (50 ft), conditions as above:
N 438 m (1,437 ft)
R 707 m (2,320 ft)
Landing from 15 m (50 ft) at S/L, 30° flap, asphalt runway: N 489 m (1,605 ft)
R 507 m (1,664 ft)
Landing run, conditions as above: N 150 m (492 ft)
R 168 m (551 ft)
Range at 1,830 m (6,000 ft), no reserves:
N 506 nm (938 km; 583 miles)
R 474 nm (878 km; 545 miles)

EMB-201A Ipanema (Lycoming IO-540-K1J5D engine) in agricultural service

EMB-710C Carioca four-seat light aircraft, EMBRAER-built version of the Piper Cherokee Pathfinder

EMBRAER-PIPER LIGHT AIRCRAFT PROGRAMME

Detailed descriptions of the Piper aircraft built by EMBRAER (see introductory copy) can be found in the US section, except for the EMB-710C Carioca, which is now manufactured only in Brazil and is described separately. EMBRAER names and designations are as follows:

EMB-711C Corisco (Spark). Piper PA-28R-200 Cherokee Arrow II. Retractable landing gear. Total of 214 sold by 1 January 1979.

EMB-720C Minuano. Piper PA-32-300 Cherokee SIX, named after a wind of southern Brazil. Fixed landing gear, six seats. Total of 89 sold by 1 January 1979.

EMB-721C Sertanejo. Piper PA-32R-300 Cherokee Lance, named after a farming people of the Brazilian interior. Retractable landing gear, six seats. Total of 109 sold by 1 January 1979.

EMB-810C Seneca II. Piper PA-34-200T Seneca II. Total of 244 sold by 1 January 1979, including 10 for the Brazilian Air Force, by which they are designated **U-7**.

EMB-820C Navajo. Piper PA-31-350 Navajo Chieftain. First flight of Brazilian-built example 31 December 1975. Total of 98 sold by 1 January 1979.

EMBRAER (PIPER) EMB-710C CARIOCA

The Carioca, named after inhabitants of Rio de Janeiro, is the Brazilian licence-built version of the US Piper PA-28-235 Cherokee Pathfinder, described under the Piper heading in the 1977-78 *Jane's*. It is now manufactured only in Brazil, production by Piper having ended. A total of 195 had been sold by EMBRAER by 1 January 1979. Production scheduled to end in 1979.

TYPE: Four-seat cabin monoplane.

WINGS: Cantilever low-wing monoplane. Wing section NACA 65_2-415. Dihedral 7°. Incidence 2°. Single-spar wings, plain ailerons and slotted flaps of light alloy construction. Glassfibre wingtips. Ailerons and four-position flaps have corrugated skin. Ground-adjustable tab in port aileron.

FUSELAGE: Aluminium alloy semi-monocoque structure. Glassfibre engine cowling.

TAIL UNIT: Cantilever structure of aluminium alloy, except for glassfibre tips on fin and tailplane. Fin and rudder have corrugated metal skin. One-piece all-moving tailplane. Combined anti-servo and trim tab in rudder.

LANDING GEAR: Non-retractable tricycle type. Steerable nosewheel.

POWER PLANT: One 175 kW (235 hp) Lycoming O-540-B4B5 flat-six engine, driving a Hartzell HC-C2YK-18F constant-speed propeller with spinner. Normal fuel capacity of 189 litres (50 US gallons) is supplemented by two tanks in the wingtips, containing a total of 129 litres (34 US gallons). Total fuel capacity 318 litres (84 US gallons), of which 310 litres (82 US gallons) are usable. Oil capacity 11·5 litres (3 US gallons).

ACCOMMODATION: Four persons in enclosed, heated and ventilated cabin. Individual adjustable front seats, with dual controls; individual rear seats. Large door on starboard side. Windscreen defrosting. Baggage compartment aft of cabin, with capacity of 90 kg (200 lb). Rear seats removable to provide 1·25 m³ (44 cu ft) of cargo space.

SYSTEMS: Hydraulic system for brakes only. Electrical system includes 60A alternator and 12V battery.

AVIONICS AND EQUIPMENT: Standard avionics include King KMA-20-11 audio, King KX-175BE VHF nav/com and King KR-85 ADF. Standard equipment includes external tiedown points and wing jacking points. Optional equipment includes fire extinguisher, external power socket, alternate static source, overhead vent system, ventilation fan for air vent system, soundproofing, outside air temperature gauge, and heated pitot.

DIMENSIONS, EXTERNAL:
Wing span 9·80 m (32 ft 2 in)
Wing chord (constant) 1·60 m (5 ft 3 in)
Wing aspect ratio 6·12
Length overall 7·34 m (24 ft 1 in)
Height overall 2·70 m (8 ft 10¼ in)
Tailplane span 3·93 m (12 ft 10¾ in)
Propeller diameter 2·03 m (6 ft 8 in)
Wheel track 3·05 m (10 ft 0 in)
Wheelbase 1·98 m (6 ft 6 in)

DIMENSION, INTERNAL:
Baggage compartment volume 0·68 m³ (24·0 cu ft)

AREAS:
Wings, gross 15·79 m² (170·0 sq ft)
Ailerons (total) 0·99 m² (10·66 sq ft)
Trailing-edge flaps (total) 1·36 m² (14·64 sq ft)
Fin, excl dorsal fin 0·70 m² (7·53 sq ft)
Rudder, incl tab 0·38 m² (4·09 sq ft)
Tailplane 2·46 m² (26·48 sq ft)

WEIGHTS AND LOADINGS:
Weight empty, equipped 766 kg (1,689 lb)
Max T-O weight 1,361 kg (3,000 lb)
Max wing loading 85·9 kg/m² (17·6 lb/sq ft)
Max power loading 7·77 kg/kW (12·8 lb/hp)

PERFORMANCE (at max T-O weight, ISA, except where indicated):
Max level speed at S/L 140 knots (259 km/h; 161 mph)
Max cruising speed (75% power) at 1,830 m (6,000 ft) 133 knots (246 km/h; 153 mph)
Econ cruising speed (55% power) at 3,565 m (11,700 ft) 120 knots (222 km/h; 138 mph)
Stalling speed, flaps down 53 knots (98·5 km/h; 61 mph) IAS
Max rate of climb at S/L 244 m (800 ft)/min
Service ceiling 4,130 m (13,550 ft)
T-O run, 25° flap 259 m (850 ft)
T-O to 15 m (50 ft), 25° flap 396 m (1,300 ft)
Landing from 15 m (50 ft) 530 m (1,740 ft)
Landing run at max landing weight 317 m (1,040 ft)
Range (75% power) at 1,980 m (6,500 ft), no reserves 769 nm (1,425 km; 885 miles)
Range (55% power) at 2,745 m (9,000 ft), no reserves 867 nm (1,608 km; 999 miles)

HELIBRAS
HELICÓPTEROS DO BRASIL SA

PROVISIONAL HEAD OFFICE: CTA Hangar X-10, Caixa Postal 6031, 12200 São José dos Campos, SP
Telephone: (0123) 21 8435
WORKS: Avenida Coronel Carneiro Junior 190, Centro, Itajuba, Minas Gerais
Telephone: 55 21 230 99 20
SUPERINTENDENT DIRECTOR: Nivaldo Alves da Silva
COMMERCIAL DIRECTOR: Antonio Luiz Portugal Moura
PRODUCTION DIRECTOR: Alain Adrien Royer

Formation of this company was announced in October 1977. Owned jointly by Aérospatiale of France and the State of Minas Gerais (45% each) and Aerofoto (10%), it is embarking upon a 10-year programme involving the assembly (graduating to local manufacture) of 30 Aérospatiale SA 315B Lama and 200 AS 350B Ecureuil helicopters, at a new factory to be erected at Itajuba in Minas Gerais State. The first Lamas were due to be assembled in Brazil during the second half of 1979; the first Brazilian-produced Ecureuils will be delivered in early 1981.

NEIVA
SOCIEDADE CONSTRUTORA AERONÁUTICA NEIVA LTDA

HEAD OFFICE AND WORKS: Estrada Velha Rio-São Paulo 2176, São José dos Campos, SP, Caixa Postal 247, Código 12200
Telephone: (0123) 21 6333
Telex: 011 25951 SOAN BR
OTHER WORKS: Av Brigadeiro Faria Lima s/n, São José dos Campos, SP, Código 12200
Rua Nossa Senhora de Fátima 360, Botucatu, SP, Caixa Postal 10, Código 18600
DIRECTORS:
José Carlos de Barros Neiva (Director General)
Breno A. B. Junqueira

In early 1979 Neiva was negotiating further orders for the N621 (T-25) Universal basic trainer with potential customers in Europe, Asia, Africa and Latin America.

The company participates in EMBRAER's general aviation aircraft production programme, partially manufacturing and assembling the EMB-710C Carioca, EMB-711C Corisco and EMB-721C Sertanejo, and building components for the EMB-720C Minuano. Neiva also participates in EMBRAER's agricultural aircraft production programme, building at Botucatu the fuselage structure of the EMB-201A Ipanema.

NEIVA N621 UNIVERSAL

Brazilian Air Force designation: T-25 and T-25A

The Universal was designed by Eng Joseph Kovacs to meet a Brazilian Air Force requirement. Initial design started in January 1963, and the prototype (PP-ZTW) flew for the first time on 29 April 1966.

The first production T-25 was flown on 7 April 1971, and 132 were delivered to the Brazilian Air Force between Autumn 1971 and early 1975. Production took place at Botucatu and São José dos Campos, with wingtips, tailplanes and elevators manufactured under subcontract by Motortec in Rio de Janeiro. The Brazilian Air Force ordered eight more in 1978, and an additional order for 20 was being negotiated in early 1979. Ten T-25s were supplied to the Chilean Army; these were transferred subsequently to the Chilean Air Force.

The T-25 is in service, as an advanced trainer, with the Academia da Força Aérea (Air Force Academy) at Pirassununga, São Paulo State; and, as the T-25A, with the Brazilian Air Force's EMRAs (Reconnaissance and Attack Squadrons).

TYPE: Two/three-seat basic trainer.

WINGS: Cantilever low-wing monoplane. Wing section NACA 63_2A315 at root, NACA $63_1$212 at tip. Dihedral 6°. Incidence 2°. Single-spar structure of riveted aluminium alloy. All-metal dynamically-balanced slotted ailerons. All-metal split flaps.

FUSELAGE: Welded steel tube centre fuselage with aluminium skin panels. Semi-monocoque tailcone of riveted aluminium alloy.

TAIL UNIT: Cantilever all-metal structure, with electrically-actuated tab in port elevator.

LANDING GEAR: Retractable tricycle type. Hydraulic retraction, main units inward, nosewheel rearward. ERAM oleo shock-absorbers. Main wheels fitted with Goodyear tyres size 6·50-8 and Goodyear or OLDI disc brakes. Nosewheel steerable and fitted with Goodyear tyre size 6·00-6. Tyre pressure 2·28 bars (33 lb/sq in) on main units, 1·79 bars (26 lb/sq in) on nose unit.

POWER PLANT: One 224 kW (300 hp) Lycoming IO-540-K1D5 flat-six engine, driving a Hartzell HC-C2YK-4/C8475-A2 non-feathering two-blade constant-speed metal propeller. Six aluminium fuel tanks in wings, total capacity 332 litres (73 Imp gallons). Refuelling points above wings. Oil capacity 11·5 litres (2·5 Imp gallons).

ACCOMMODATION: Two seats side by side, with full dual controls, and optional third seat at rear. Large rearward-sliding transparent canopy. Baggage compartment aft of rear seat.

SYSTEMS: Electrically-actuated hydraulic system, pressure 103 bars (1,500 lb/sq in), for flaps and landing gear. Manual emergency pump. 28V electrical system.

AVIONICS AND EQUIPMENT: 140-channel Brazilian-made VHF radio, ADF and VOR/LOC. Complete IFR instrumentation.

ARMAMENT: Two underwing hardpoints for 7·62 mm machine-gun pods.

DIMENSIONS, EXTERNAL:
- Wing span: 11·00 m (36 ft 1 in)
- Wing chord at root: 2·00 m (6 ft 6½ in)
- Wing chord at tip: 1·08 m (3 ft 6½ in)
- Wing aspect ratio: 7·1
- Length overall: 8·60 m (28 ft 2½ in)
- Height overall: 3·00 m (9 ft 9¾ in)
- Tailplane span: 3·95 m (12 ft 11½ in)
- Wheel track: 2·65 m (8 ft 8¼ in)
- Wheelbase: 2·33 m (7 ft 7¾ in)
- Propeller diameter: 2·13 m (7 ft 0 in)
- Propeller ground clearance: 0·37 m (1 ft 2½ in)

DIMENSIONS, INTERNAL:
- Cabin: Length: 2·20 m (7 ft 2½ in)
  - Max width: 1·25 m (4 ft 1 in)
  - Max height: 1·25 m (4 ft 1 in)
  - Floor area: 3·0 m² (32 sq ft)
  - Volume: 4·00 m³ (141 cu ft)
- Baggage compartment volume: 0·35 m³ (12·5 cu ft)

AREAS:
- Wings, gross: 17·20 m² (185·14 sq ft)
- Ailerons (total): 1·47 m² (15·82 sq ft)
- Trailing-edge flaps (total): 1·34 m² (14·42 sq ft)
- Fin: 0·82 m² (8·83 sq ft)
- Rudder: 0·90 m² (9·69 sq ft)
- Tailplane: 1·72 m² (18·51 sq ft)
- Elevators, incl tab: 1·35 m² (14·53 sq ft)

WEIGHTS AND LOADINGS (A: Aerobatic; U: Utility):
- Weight empty, equipped: A, U: 1,150 kg (2,535 lb)
- Max T-O weight: A: 1,500 kg (3,306 lb)
  - U: 1,700 kg (3,747 lb)
- Max wing loading: A: 88·2 kg/m² (18·1 lb/sq ft)
  - U: 100·0 kg/m² (20·5 lb/sq ft)
- Max power loading: A: 6·70 kg/kW (11·02 lb/hp)
  - U: 7·59 kg/kW (12·49 lb/hp)

PERFORMANCE (at max T-O weight. A: Aerobatic; U: Utility):
- Never-exceed speed:
  - A, U: 269 knots (500 km/h; 310 mph)
- Max level speed at S/L:
  - A: 162 knots (300 km/h; 186 mph)
  - U: 160 knots (296 km/h; 184 mph)
- Max cruising speed (75% power) at S/L:
  - A: 153 knots (285 km/h; 177 mph)
  - U: 151 knots (280 km/h; 174 mph)
- Stalling speed, flaps up:
  - A: 63·5 knots (117 km/h; 73 mph)
  - U: 66 knots (122 km/h; 76 mph)
- Stalling speed, flaps down:
  - A: 56·5 knots (104 km/h; 65 mph)
  - U: 59·5 knots (110 km/h; 68·5 mph)
- Max rate of climb at S/L: A: 400 m (1,312 ft)/min
  - U: 320 m (1,050 ft)/min
- Service ceiling: A: 6,100 m (20,000 ft)
  - U: 5,000 m (16,400 ft)
- T-O run at S/L: A: 350 m (1,148 ft)
  - U: 455 m (1,493 ft)
- T-O to 15 m (50 ft) at S/L: A: 510 m (1,673 ft)
  - U: 650 m (2,133 ft)
- Landing from 15 m (50 ft) at S/L:
  - A: 600 m (1,970 ft)
  - U: 760 m (2,493 ft)
- Range (75% power) at 2,000 m (6,550 ft), 10% reserves: A: 539 nm (1,000 km; 621 miles)
  - U: 809 nm (1,500 km; 932 miles)

Neiva T-25 Universal two/three-seat basic training aircraft of the Brazilian Air Force

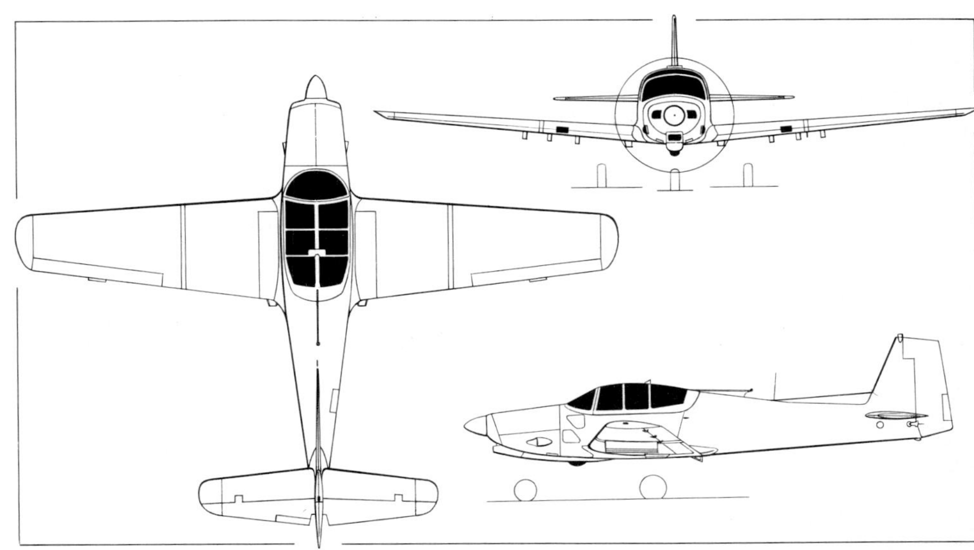

Neiva T-25B Universal II basic training aircraft under development for the Brazilian Air Force *(Pilot Press)*

YT-25B prototype of the Neiva N622 Universal II (Lycoming IO-720-D1B engine), without dorsal fin and underwing hardpoints

NEIVA N622 UNIVERSAL II

Brazilian Air Force designation: T-25B

The N622 is a more powerful version of the N621 Universal, with a 298 kW (400 hp) Lycoming IO-720-D1B flat-eight engine, driving a Hartzell HC-C3YR-4F/FC8475 three-blade constant-speed propeller, in place of the IO-540 flat-six used in the T-25. The nose is redesigned to accommodate the larger engine, increasing the aircraft's overall length to 8·78 m (28 ft 9¾ in); modifications to the vertical tail increase the aircraft's overall height to 3·40 m (11 ft 2 in). Six underwing stores attachment points are provided. Structural reinforcements permit the maximum T-O weight to be increased to 1,900 kg (4,189 lb). Provision is made for a complete avionics set, including two VHF com, and single ADF, VHF nav, marker, glideslope, transponder and audio control. Four alternative installations (Brazilian Whinner, Collins Micro-Line, Becker 2000 line and Bendix BX 2000 line) have been tested successfully. All other characteristics are very similar to those of the N621 Universal.

A YT-25B prototype of the Universal II was ordered by the Brazilian Air Force. This aircraft, converted from the second prototype N621 (serial number 1831), made its first flight on 22 October 1978.

PERFORMANCE (estimated, at AUW of 1,800 kg; 3,968 lb, 'clean'):
- Never-exceed speed: 269 knots (500 km/h; 310 mph)
- Max level speed: 173 knots (320 km/h; 199 mph)
- Cruising speed at 3,000 m (9,845 ft): 163 knots (302 km/h; 188 mph)
- Stalling speed, flaps down: 57 knots (105 km/h; 66 mph)
- Max rate of climb at S/L: 540 m (1,770 ft)/min
- Service ceiling: 5,000 m (16,400 ft)
- T-O to 15 m (50 ft): 600 m (1,970 ft)
- Landing from 15 m (50 ft): 500 m (1,640 ft)
- Range (75% power at 1,500 m; 5,000 ft, standard fuel): 277 nm (515 km; 320 miles)

RIO CLARO

AÉRO CLUBE DE RIO CLARO

ADDRESS: Rua Cinco 1152, 13500 Rio Claro (Caixa Postal 147), São Paulo State

PRESIDENT: Henrique Martins Schlittler

RIO CLARO (IPT) IPT-16 SURUBIM MODIFICADO

The original IPT-16, last described in the 1958-59 *Jane's*, was a streamlined all-wooden single-seat cabin monoplane powered by a 119 kW (160 hp) Hirth HM 506A four-cylinder inverted in-line engine and having a retractable main landing gear. It flew for the first time on 17 September 1959.

Over the next three years the Surubim (little devil) was used extensively by the IPT as a flying testbed for wooden lightplane construction. Chief test pilot during this programme was Alberto Bertelli, who later became an instructor at the Rio Claro Aero Club, and in 1962 the aircraft was donated to the club by the IPT. It continued to be used regularly until the end of 1975, when the Rio Claro club began an extensive modification programme. Details of the Surubim Modificado, as the converted aircraft is known, were given in the 1978-79 *Jane's*.

RIO CLARO IPAI-28 SUPER SURUBIM

Nearing completion in 1979, the Super Surubim is a new aircraft, design of which was started in late 1975 by Eng Sylvio de Oliveira and members of the Rio Claro Aero Club. Design parameters were calculated with the assistance of the São Carlos City Engineering School, whose current director is Eng Romeu Corsini, formerly of the IPT. Assistance was also provided by EMBRAER, including the supply of aluminium sheeting. First flight was anticipated in late 1979, with Alberto Bertelli as pilot.

TYPE: Tandem two-seat cabin monoplane; *g* limits ±8·0.

WINGS: Cantilever low-wing monoplane, with highly tapered wings. Wing section NACA 23016·7 at root, NACA 23012 at tip. Dihedral from roots. All-metal two-spar structure, with rear auxiliary spar, with skins of 2024-T3 Alclad aluminium alloy, chemically treated against corrosion. Wings built in one piece and attached to underside of fuselage by bolts. Trailing-edge split flaps between ailerons and fuselage; ailerons have 100% balancing. No tabs. 'Letterbox' fixed slots near outer leading-edges, forward of ailerons.

FUSELAGE: Conventional all-metal semi-monocoque structure of frames and longerons.

TAIL UNIT: Cantilever metal structure, of similar construction to wings. Trim tab in rudder and starboard elevator. Rudder and elevators have 100% balancing.

LANDING GEAR: Non-retractable type, with single main wheels and tailwheel. Main units have strut bracing, leg and wheel fairings, 190 mm diameter wheels from a Neiva T-25 Universal, and are fitted with Oldi brakes. Main-wheel tyre size 7·00-6, pressure 2·76 bars (40 lb/sq in). Small tailwheel, carried on leaf spring.

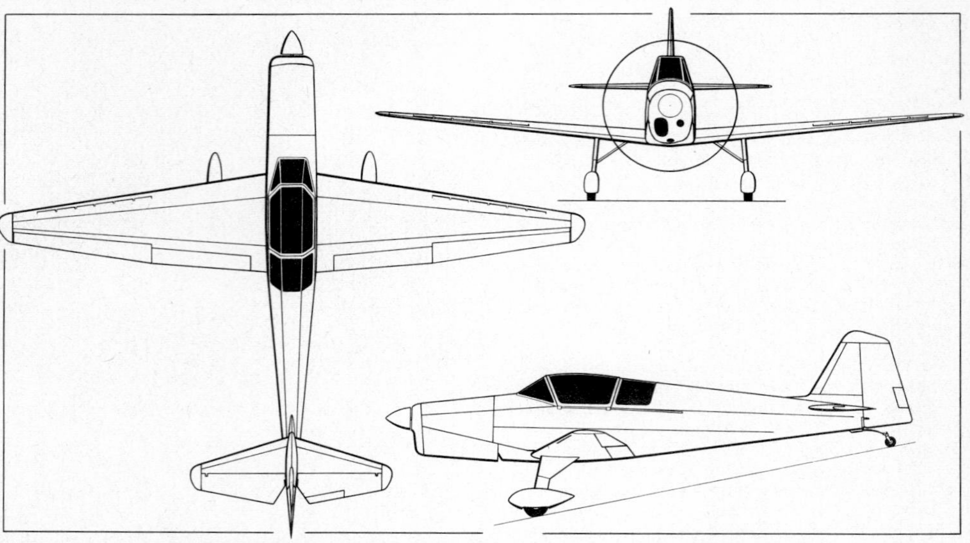

Rio Claro IPAI-28 Super Surubim tandem two-seat light aircraft *(Pilot Press)*

POWER PLANT: One 146 kW (196 hp) Ranger 6-440-C4 six-cylinder inverted in-line aircooled engine, driving a two-blade propeller with spinner. Fuel in two wing tanks, combined capacity 140 litres (30·75 Imp gallons).

ACCOMMODATION: Seats for two persons in tandem. Rearward-sliding framed canopy, jettisonable in flight.

DIMENSIONS, EXTERNAL:

Wing span	9·10 m (29 ft 10¼ in)
Wing area, gross	10·12 m² (108·9 sq ft)
Wing aspect ratio	8·18
Length overall	8·10 m (26 ft 7 in)
Height overall	2·12 m (6 ft 11½ in)
Wheel track	2·40 m (7 ft 10½ in)
Propeller diameter	2·20 m (7 ft 2½ in)

WEIGHTS AND LOADINGS:

Weight empty	650 kg (1,433 lb)
Max T-O weight	950 kg (2,094 lb)
Max wing loading	93·8 kg/m² (19·21 lb/sq ft)
Max power loading	6·5 kg/kW (10·68 lb/hp)

PERFORMANCE (estimated, at max T-O weight):

Never-exceed speed	215·5 knots (400 km/h; 248 mph)
Max level speed	146 knots (270 km/h; 168 mph)
Max cruising speed	129 knots (240 km/h; 149 mph)
Stalling speed, flaps up	59·5 knots (110 km/h; 68·5 mph)
Stalling speed, flaps down	54·5 knots (100 km/h; 62·5 mph)
Max rate of climb at S/L	320 m (1,050 ft)/min

CANADA

CANADAIR
CANADAIR LIMITED

HEAD OFFICE AND WORKS: Cartierville Airport, St Laurent, Montreal, Quebec

POSTAL ADDRESS: PO Box 6087, Station 'A', Montreal, Quebec H3C 3G9

Telephone: (514) 744 1511

Telex: 05-826747

CHAIRMAN OF THE BOARD: Léo Lavoie

PRESIDENT AND CHIEF EXECUTIVE OFFICER: Frederick R. Kearns

EXECUTIVE VICE-PRESIDENT: Harry Halton

VICE-PRESIDENTS:
- Peter J. Aird (Finance)
- Leonard B. Box (Canadair Services)
- Frank M. Francis (Development Programmes)
- James R. Humphreys (Engineering)
- Benoit I. Kérub (Public Relations)
- Conrad Kunze (Materiel)
- Jacques Ouellet (Resources)
- Jacques A. Sincennes (Technical Support)
- James B. Taylor (Marketing)
- Andreas Throner (Manufacturing)
- Harvie D. Walford (Corporate Planning)
- Robert A. Wohl (Legal and Admin)

Canadair Inc, 274 Riverside Avenue, Westport, Connecticut 06883, USA (US sales subsidiary)

Telephone: (203) 226 2581

Telex: 0096-4282

PRESIDENT: James B. Taylor

Canadair Limited, formerly the Canadian subsidiary of General Dynamics Corporation and owned since 1976 by the Canadian government, has been engaged in the development and manufacture of military and commercial aircraft since 1944. It has also been employed in the research, design, development and production of missile components, drone surveillance systems and a variety of non-aerospace products. Canadair has 232,257 m² (2·5 million sq ft) of covered floor space and a work force of nearly 5,000.

The CL-600 Challenger twin-turbofan executive transport entered production during 1978; the third series of CL-215 tanker/utility amphibians had been completed by 1979 (aircraft 51-65); production of the CL-89 and development of the CL-289 drone systems (see RPVs and Targets section) continue. Major subcontracts concern structural components for the US Navy's P-3C Orion and the CP-140 Aurora Canadian version of this aircraft (see under Lockheed in US section), various components for the McDonnell Douglas F-15, and aft fuselage sections for the Boeing 747SP and 767. Production of aircraft spares, and the modification, repair and overhaul of aircraft, are also included in the current work programme.

CANADAIR CL-600 CHALLENGER

In April 1976, Canadair acquired from the late Mr William P. Lear Sr the worldwide exclusive rights to design, manufacture, market and support the latter's LearStar 600; this concept envisaged an aircraft using an advanced-technology wing and two high bypass ratio turbofan engines. With 53 firm orders supported by deposits in hand on 29 October 1976, the programme was launched. In March 1977, major design changes were announced and the aircraft became known as the Canadair Challenger.

Construction of three Challengers began in April 1977, and the first of these (C-GCGR-X) was rolled out on 25 May 1978. First flight was made on 8 November 1978, with the initial flight of the second aircraft (C-GCGS-X) following on 17 March 1979. DoT type approval was planned for late 1979; FAA certification is expected to follow shortly thereafter.

By 5 June 1979, sales of the executive version had reached 120, including 69 to the USA, 37 to the Arab League, five in Canada, six in Europe, two in South America and one in Panama. A letter of intent had also been received from Federal Express Corporation for 25 of a stretched cargo version, design of which began in 1979 (see separate entry for Challenger E).

The following description applies to the basic passenger version:

TYPE: Twin-turbofan business, cargo and commuter transport.

WINGS: Cantilever low-wing monoplane, built in one piece. Advanced-technology wing section. Thickness/chord ratio 14% at root, 12% at leading-edge sweep break and 10% at tip. Dihedral 2° 20′. Incidence 3° at root. Sweepback at quarter-chord 25°. Two-spar structure, primarily of aluminium alloy; spars covered with skin-stringer panels to form rigid torsion box. Two-section double-slotted trailing-edge flaps. Hydraulically-powered aluminium plain ailerons and outboard roll-control spoilers. Inboard spoilers for descent control and ground lift dumping. No tabs. Thermal anti-icing of leading-edges by engine bleed air.

FUSELAGE: Aluminium alloy fail-safe semi-monocoque pressurised structure of circular cross-section, with clad frames, stringers, and chemically-milled skins.

TAIL UNIT: Cantilever multi-spar aluminium alloy T-tail, with swept vertical and horizontal surfaces. All control surfaces powered. Tailplane incidence adjusted by electric trim motor. No tabs. Tailplane leading-edges anti-iced by engine bleed air.

LANDING GEAR: Hydraulically-retractable tricycle type, with twin wheels and Dowty Rotol oleo-pneumatic shock-absorbers on each unit. Main wheels retract inward into fuselage, nose unit forward. Nose unit steerable and self-centering. Main wheels have Goodyear 26 × 6·65 tyres, pressure 11·38 bars (165 lb/sq in); nosewheels have Goodyear 18 × 4·4 tyres, pressure 8·27 bars (120 lb/sq in). Goodyear hydraulically-operated multiple-disc carbon brakes. Fully-modulated anti-skid system for main units.

POWER PLANT: Two 33·36 kN (7,500 lb st) Avco Lycoming ALF 502L turbofan engines, one pylon-mounted on each side of rear fuselage, fitted with cascade-type fan-air thrust reversers. Integral fuel tank in centre-section and two in each wing; total usable capacity 8,305 litres (1,827 Imp gallons). Oil capacity 13·6 litres (3 Imp gallons).

ACCOMMODATION: Pilot and co-pilot side by side on flight deck with dual controls. Blind-flying instrumentation standard. Typical accommodation includes three pairs of facing seats at front of cabin, with tables between; a further pair on starboard side at rear, with inward-facing three-place settee on port side. Closet (port), pull-out toilet, bar and galley (starboard) forward of cabin. Toilet and baggage area aft of cabin. Upward-opening door on port side, forward of wing. Entire accommodation heated, ventilated and air-conditioned.

SYSTEMS: Sundstrand pressurisation and AiResearch air-conditioning systems, max pressure differential 0·64 bars (9·3 lb/sq in). Three independent hydraulic systems, each of 207 bars (3,000 lb/sq in), for actuation of ailerons, spoilers, landing gear extension/retraction and main-wheel brakes. AC electrical system includes two 30kVA engine-driven generators. AiResearch gas turbine APU is standard, and will be certificated for in-flight operation. Bleed air from APU starts engines. Sundstrand bleed air anti-icing system.

AVIONICS: Radios and radar standard. Other avionics and equipment to customer's requirements.

DIMENSIONS, EXTERNAL:

Wing span	18·85 m (61 ft 10 in)
Wing chord at root	4·89 m (16 ft 0½ in)
Wing chord at tip	1·27 m (4 ft 1·9 in)
Wing aspect ratio	8·5
Length overall	20·85 m (68 ft 5 in)
Fuselage: Max diameter	2·69 m (8 ft 10 in)
Height overall	6·30 m (20 ft 8 in)
Tailplane span	6·20 m (20 ft 4 in)
Wheel track	3·18 m (10 ft 5 in)
Wheelbase	7·99 m (26 ft 2½ in)
Passenger door (port, fwd): Height	1·78 m (5 ft 10 in)
Width	0·91 m (3 ft 0 in)
Height to sill	1·61 m (5 ft 3½ in)
Baggage door (port, aft): Height	0·84 m (2 ft 9 in)
Width	0·71 m (2 ft 4 in)
Height to sill	1·61 m (5 ft 3½ in)

Second prototype of the Canadair CL-600 Challenger business transport (two Avco Lycoming ALF 502L turbofan engines)

Overwing emergency exits (two, each):
- Height 0·91 m (3 ft 0 in)
- Width 0·51 m (1 ft 8 in)

Dimensions, internal:
- Cabin: Length, incl galley, toilet and baggage area, excl flight deck 8·61 m (28 ft 3 in)
- Max width 2·49 m (8 ft 2 in)
- Max height 1·85 m (6 ft 1 in)
- Floor area, incl galley, toilet and baggage area, excl flight deck 18·81 m² (202·5 sq ft)
- Volume (freight) 26·56 m³ (938·0 cu ft)

Weights:
- Manufacturer's weight empty 7,711 kg (17,000 lb)
- Basic operating weight 9,172 kg (20,220 lb)
- Max payload 3,400 kg (7,500 lb)
- Max T-O weight 16,329 kg (36,000 lb)
- Max ramp weight 16,406 kg (36,170 lb)
- Max landing weight 14,969 kg (33,000 lb)
- Max zero-fuel weight 11,703 kg (25,800 lb)

Performance:
- See Challenger E entry

CANADAIR CL-600 CHALLENGER E

The E (for Extended) additional version of the Challenger, announced on 3 July 1979 and scheduled for delivery from 1983, has a lengthened fuselage, new power plant, increased fuel capacity and payload, and greater range. Main differences from the basic version (which see) are as follows:

Wings: Modified to include leading-edge high-lift devices and changes to trailing-edge flaps.

Fuselage: Lengthened by insertion of 1·90 m (6 ft 3 in) section forward of wings and 0·76 m (2 ft 6 in) section aft of wings.

Power Plant: Two 38·5 kN (8,650 lb st) General Electric CF34 turbofan engines. Fuel load increased from 6,763 kg (14,910 lb) to 10,251 kg (22,600 lb).

Accommodation: Room for separate cabin between main cabin and rear toilet/baggage area for, typically, two seats and inward-facing three-place settee; or private bedroom.

Dimensions:
- Length overall 23·52 m (77 ft 2 in)
- Cabin: Length, incl galley, toilet and baggage area, excl flight deck 11·28 m (37 ft 0 in)
- Floor area, as above 24·62 m² (265 sq ft)

Weights:
- Manufacturer's weight empty 8,963 kg (19,670 lb)
- Basic operating weight 11,050 kg (24,360 lb)
- Max T-O weight 21,772 kg (48,000 lb)
- Max ramp weight 21,845 kg (48,160 lb)
- Max landing weight 15,876 kg (35,000 lb)
- Max zero-fuel weight 13,041 kg (28,750 lb)

Performance (A: Challenger, B: Challenger E):
- Initial cruising altitude: A 12,500 m (41,000 ft)
  - B 11,280 m (37,000 ft)
- Time to initial cruising altitude: A 17 min
  - B 23 min
- FAR Pt 25 landing distance at max landing weight:
  - A 1,173 m (3,850 ft)
  - B 1,097 m (3,600 ft)
- FAR Pt 121 landing distance at typical landing weight:
  - A, B 1,585 m (5,200 ft)
- Balanced field length (ISA, S/L):
  - A 1,494 m (4,900 ft)
  - B 1,966 m (6,450 ft)
- Range at Mach 0·83:
  - A 3,000 nm (5,560 km; 3,455 miles)
  - B with 544 kg (1,200 lb) payload 3,850 nm (7,135 km; 4,433 miles)
- Max range, NBAA IFR reserves:
  - A with 426 kg (940 lb) payload 3,600 nm (6,671 km; 4,145 miles)
  - B with 544 kg (1,200 lb) payload at Mach 0·78 4,600 nm (8,525 km; 5,297 miles)

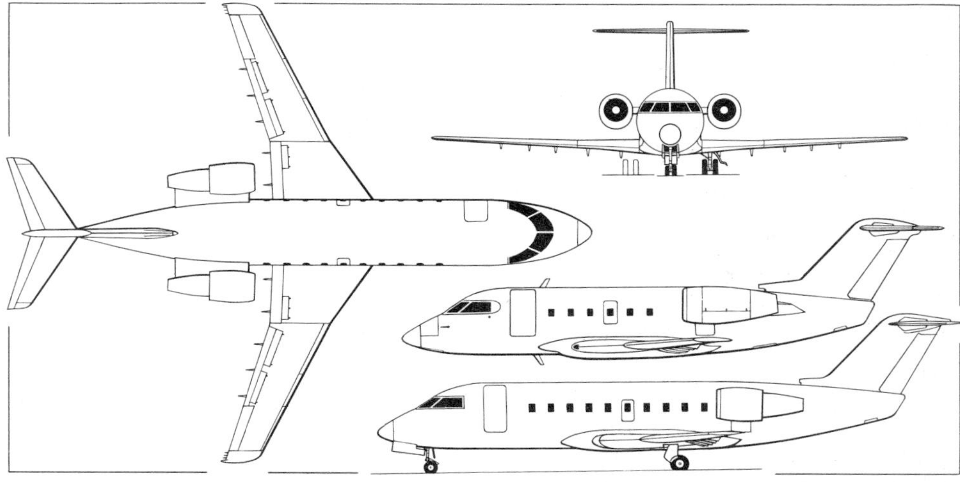

Canadair CL-600 Challenger E 'stretched' twin-turbofan executive transport, with additional side elevation (centre) of basic short-fuselage model *(Pilot Press)*

CANADAIR CL-215

The Canadair CL-215 is a twin-engined amphibian, intended primarily for firefighting but adaptable to a wide variety of other duties. It is designed for simplicity of operation and maintenance, and can operate from small airstrips, lakes, ocean bays etc.

The CL-215 made its first flight on 23 October 1967, and its first water take-off on 2 May 1968.

The Securité Civile of France has operated CL-215s since June 1969. Following an initial purchase of 10 aircraft, it took delivery of a further five. The French aircraft have seen considerable action fighting forest fires in southern France, Corsica, the Federal Republic of Germany and Italy. One French CL-215 has been fitted experimentally with a spray system to examine the feasibility of applying oil dispersants from the air.

The Province of Quebec operates 15 aircraft, mainly in a firefighting role. Several of these were converted to wide-swath liquid sprayers for a massive campaign which began in Spring 1973 to protect huge tracts of valuable timberland from budworm infestation.

The Spanish government, which has operated two aircraft since February 1971, took delivery of eight more in 1974. The later aircraft, although equipped for search and rescue, are capable of firefighting and other roles.

The Greek government took delivery of two CL-215s in 1974; three more were delivered in 1976, and a further two in 1977. The Province of Manitoba took delivery of one CL-215 in 1977, and the Royal Thai Navy has two equipped for search and rescue. In February 1979 the Venezuelan operator CVG Ferrominera Orinoco CA took delivery of two dual-purpose firefighting/passenger transport versions: these aircraft are fitted with 26 passenger seats.

Production of the third series of aircraft (Nos. 51-65) has been completed; weight and performance figures for the first and second series can be found in the 1977-78 *Jane's*.

The CL-215 offers fire protection agencies three methods of attacking fires in grass, brush or forest: (1) with pre-mixed long-term chemical retardants ground-loaded at a land base; (2) with short-term retardants mixed automatically during the water scooping operation; and (3) with plain water scooped from any 1,200 m (¾ mile) stretch of lake or ocean near the fire. It carries a maximum water or retardant load of 5,455 litres (1,200 Imp gallons). The tanks can be ground filled in 90 s or scoop filled in 16-20 s with the original scooping system, while the aircraft skims the water at about 60 knots (111 km/h; 69 mph). Pickup distance in still air, from 15 m (50 ft) above the water during landing to 15 m (50 ft) on take-off, is 1,660 m (5,450 ft) with the original installation. All new production aircraft now incorporate an improved scooping system which reduces the time to fill the tanks to 10 s and the 15 m/15 m (50 ft/50 ft) pickup distance to 1,200 m (4,000 ft).

On a number of occasions single CL-215s have made over 100 drops totalling more than 545,520 litres (120,000 Imp gallons) in one day. Full loads have been scooped from the Mediterranean in wave heights of up to 2 m (6 ft). In June 1978 a Manitoba government CL-215 made 160 drops (totalling 872,824 litres; 192,000 Imp gallons) on fires in one day. One CL-215 landed and took off safely in the open sea in conditions of high wind and swells of more than 3 m (9·8 ft).

Tests conducted at Canadair have shown that the CL-215 can be used to extinguish oil fires when loaded with a foaming material.

Type: Twin-engined multi-purpose amphibian.

Wings: Cantilever high-wing monoplane. No dihedral. All-metal one-piece fail-safe structure, with front and rear spars at 16% and 49% chord. Spars of conventional construction, with extruded caps and web stiffened by vertical members. Aluminium alloy skin, with riveted spanwise extruded stringers, is supported at 762 mm (30 in) pitch by interspar ribs. Leading-edge consists of aluminium alloy skin attached to pressed nose-ribs and spanwise stringers. Hydraulically-operated all-metal single-slotted flaps, supported by four external hinges on interspar ribs on each wing. Trim tab and geared tab in port aileron, rudder/aileron interconnect tab in starboard aileron. Detachable glassfibre wingtips.

Fuselage: All-metal single-step flying-boat hull of conventional fail-safe construction.

Tail Unit: Cantilever all-metal fail-safe structure with horizontal surfaces mounted midway up fin. Structure of aluminium alloy sheet, honeycomb panels, extrusions and fittings. Elevators and rudder fitted with dynamic balance, trim tab (port elevator only) and spring tabs and geared tabs. Provision for de-icing of leading-edges.

Landing Gear: Hydraulically-retractable tricycle type. Fully-castoring, self-centering twin-wheel nose unit retracts rearward into hull and is fully enclosed by doors. Main gear support structures retract into wells in sides of hull. A plate mounted on each main gear assembly encloses bottom of wheel well. Main-wheel tyre pressure 5·31 bars (77 lb/sq in); nosewheel tyre pressure 6·55 bars (95 lb/sq in). Hydraulic disc brakes. Non-retractable stabilising floats are each carried on a pylon cantilevered from wing box structure, with breakaway provision.

Power Plant: Two 1,566 kW (2,100 hp) Pratt & Whitney R-2800-83AM2AH, -83AM12AD or -CA3 eighteen-cylinder radial engines, each driving a Hamilton Standard Hydromatic constant-speed fully-feathering three-blade propeller, with 43E60 hub and type 6903 blades. Aircraft 31-65 have two fuel tanks, each of eight flexible cells, in wing spar box, with total usable capacity of 5,910 litres (1,300 Imp gallons). Gravity refuelling through two points above each tank. Oil in two tanks, with total capacity of 272·75 litres (60 Imp gallons), aft of engine firewalls.

Accommodation (water bomber version): Crew of two side by side on flight deck. Dual controls standard. Two 2,673 litre (588 Imp gallon) water tanks in main fuselage compartment, with retractable pickup probe in each side of hull bottom. Water-drop door in each side of hull bottom. Doors on port side of fuselage forward and aft of wings, of flush type on aircraft 31-65. Emergency exit on starboard side aft of wing trailing-edge. Emergency hatch above starboard cockpit. Mooring hatch on top of hull nose below flight deck windows.

Accommodation (utility versions): Basic aircraft is equipped with canvas folding seats for eight passengers. With the tank headers in situ, 15 passengers can be carried. Removing the tank headers provides space for a total of 19 passengers. In the search and rescue configuration the utility version has, in addition, a navigator's station on the starboard side, aft of the pilot's bulkhead; a flight engineer's station between the pilot and co-pilot; two observer's stations in the aft cabin, forward of the rear door; and provision for four seats or two banks of three stretchers each, one on the port side forward of the wheel well and one on the starboard side aft of the wheel well. Provision for up to 26 seats or nine stretchers in passenger and casualty evacuation roles respectively.

Systems: Hydraulic system, pressure 207 bars (3,000 lb/sq in), utilises two engine-driven pumps to actuate landing gear, flaps, water-drop doors and pickup probes, and wheel brakes. Electric pump in system provides power for emergency actuation of landing gear and brakes and closure of water doors. Electrical system includes two 250VA 115V 400Hz single-phase inverters, two 28V 200A DC generators, one 34Ah lead-acid battery and one aircooled petrol-engine-driven 28V 200A generator GPU. In the SAR version, two 800VA inverters are installed.

Avionics and Equipment: Standard installation includes HF, VHF and FM communications equipment, VOR/ILS, glideslope receiver, ADF, marker beacon, transponder and ELT. For the SAR version, radar, radio altimeter and DME are added to the navigation equipment; other avionics for this role include IFF/SIF, UHF intercom, and crash location communications equipment. Optional avionics include UHF, DME and radar.

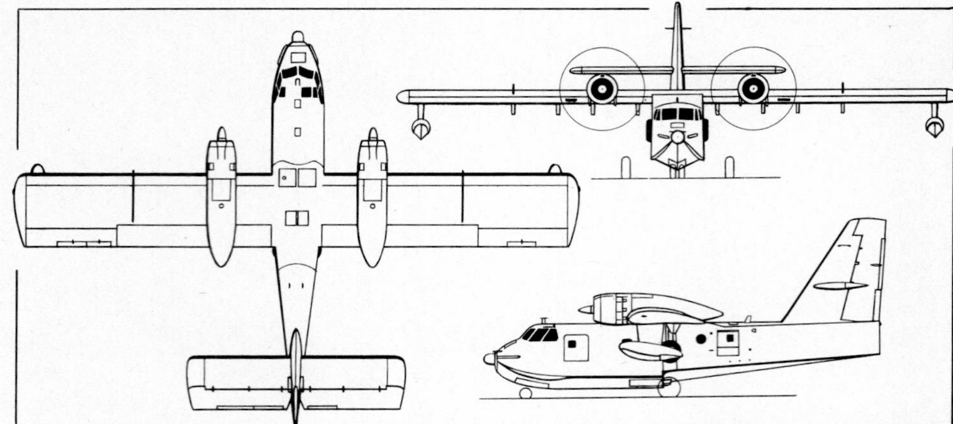

Search and rescue version of the Canadair CL-215 twin-engined amphibian, with nose radome *(Pilot Press)*

Dimensions, external:
- Wing span: 28·60 m (93 ft 10 in)
- Wing chord (constant): 3·54 m (11 ft 7½ in)
- Wing aspect ratio: 8·15
- Length overall: 19·82 m (65 ft 0½ in)
- Beam: 2·59 m (8 ft 6 in)
- Length/beam ratio: 7·5
- Height overall (on land): 8·92 m (29 ft 3 in)
- Tailplane span: 10·97 m (36 ft 0 in)
- Wheel track: 5·28 m (17 ft 4 in)
- Wheelbase: 7·23 m (23 ft 8½ in)
- Propeller diameter: 4·34 m (14 ft 3 in)
- Forward door: Height: 1·37 m (4 ft 6 in)
  - Width: 1·03 m (3 ft 4 in)
- Rear door: Height: 1·12 m (3 ft 8 in)
  - Width: 1·03 m (3 ft 4 in)
- Water-drop door: Length: 1·60 m (5 ft 3 in)
  - Width: 0·81 m (2 ft 8 in)
- Emergency exit: Height: 0·91 m (3 ft 0 in)
  - Width: 0·51 m (1 ft 8 in)

Dimensions, internal:
- Cabin, excl flight deck: Length: 9·38 m (30 ft 9½ in)
  - Max width: 2·39 m (7 ft 10 in)
  - Max height: 1·90 m (6 ft 3 in)
  - Floor area: 19·69 m² (212 sq ft)
  - Volume: 35·03 m³ (1,237 cu ft)

Areas:
- Wings, gross: 100·33 m² (1,080 sq ft)
- Ailerons (total): 8·05 m² (86·6 sq ft)
- Flaps (total): 22·39 m² (241 sq ft)
- Vertical tail surfaces (total): 17·23 m² (185·5 sq ft)
- Rudder, incl tabs: 6·02 m² (64·75 sq ft)
- Horizontal tail surfaces (total): 28·43 m² (306 sq ft)
- Elevators, incl tabs: 7·88 m² (84·8 sq ft)

Weights and Loadings (aircraft Nos. 51-65):
- Manufacturer's weight empty: 12,065 kg (26,600 lb)
- Typical operating weight empty: 12,610 kg (27,800 lb)
- Max payload: Water bomber: 5,443 kg (12,000 lb)
  - Utility version: 2,805 kg (6,185 lb)
- Max T-O weight (land): 19,731 kg (43,500 lb)
- Max T-O weight (water): 17,100 kg (37,700 lb)
- Max zero-fuel weight: 19,275 kg (42,500 lb)
- Max landing weight: on land: 15,603 kg (34,400 lb)
  - on water: 16,780 kg (37,000 lb)
- Cabin floor loading: 732 kg/m² (150 lb/sq ft)
- Max wing loading: 196·66 kg/m² (40·3 lb/sq ft)
- Max power loading: 6·23 kg/kW (10·36 lb/hp)

Performance:
- Cruising speed (max recommended power) at AUW of 18,595 kg (41,000 lb) at 3,050 m (10,000 ft): 157 knots (291 km/h; 181 mph)
- Stalling speed, 15° flap, AUW of 19,731 kg (43,500 lb): 75 knots (139 km/h; 86 mph)
- Stalling speed, 25° flap, AUW of 15,603 kg (34,400 lb), power off: 66 knots (123 km/h; 76 mph)
- Max rate of climb at S/L at AUW of 19,731 kg (43,500 lb) at max continuous power: 305 m (1,000 ft)/min
- Rate of climb at S/L, one engine out, at AUW of 17,100 kg (37,700 lb) at T-O power: 75 m (245 ft)/min
- T-O to 15 m (50 ft):
  - from land at AUW of 19,731 kg (43,500 lb): 811 m (2,660 ft)
  - from water at AUW of 17,100 kg (37,700 lb): 800 m (2,620 ft)
- Landing from 15 m (50 ft):
  - on land at AUW of 15,603 kg (34,400 lb): 732 m (2,400 ft)
  - on water at AUW of 16,780 kg (37,000 lb): 835 m (2,740 ft)
- Range with 1,587 kg (3,500 lb) payload:
  - at max cruise power: 1,000 nm (1,853 km; 1,151 miles)
  - at long-range cruise power: 1,220 nm (2,260 km; 1,405 miles)

Canadair CL-215 utility amphibian (two Pratt & Whitney R-2800 radial engines)

COX

COX AIR RESOURCES LTD

Address: Hangar No. 3, Municipal Airport, Edmonton, Alberta T5G 2Z3

President: Ray S. Cox

Chief Designer: Aimo Pitkanen

COX (DHC-3-T) TURBO OTTER

This company has produced a prototype conversion to turboprop power of the de Havilland DHC-3 Otter, substituting a Pratt & Whitney Aircraft of Canada PT6A-27 engine for the original 447 kW (600 hp) Pratt & Whitney R-1340 Wasp nine-cylinder radial piston engine. Modification began in mid-1976, and was completed in April 1978; the prototype made its first flight on 26 September 1978. Certification was to be sought under CAR Pt 3.

Approximately 270 single-engined Otters (described in detail in the 1967-68 *Jane's*) are still in operation, and Cox Air Resources estimates the potential market for this turboprop conversion at about 75 of these. Main advantages are a reduced empty weight, increased fuel and payload capability, and slight increase in performance.

Type: Single-engined STOL utility transport.

Wings, Fuselage, Tail Unit and Landing Gear: As DHC-3, except for longer nose section. Capability for interchangeable wheel/ski/float landing gear retained.

Power Plant: One 493 kW (662 shp) Pratt & Whitney Aircraft of Canada PT6A-27 turboprop engine, driving a Hartzell four-blade reversible-pitch metal propeller.

Fuel in four fuselage tanks, total capacity 991 litres (218 Imp gallons). Oil capacity 12·5 litres (2·75 Imp gallons).

Accommodation: As DHC-3.

Systems: Improved cabin heating system.

Avionics: King Silver Crown range of avionics equipment available, to customer's requirements.

Dimensions, external: As DHC-3 except:
- Length overall 13·82 m (45 ft 4 in)

Weights:
- Basic operating weight approx 1,692 kg (3,730 lb)
- Max T-O weight 3,629 kg (8,000 lb)

Performance (estimated, at max T-O weight):
- Max level and never-exceed speed 144 knots (266 km/h; 166 mph)
- Max cruising speed approx 130 knots (241 km/h; 150 mph)
- Max rate of climb at S/L 349 m (1,145 ft)/min
- Range with max fuel approx 907 nm (1,681 km; 1,045 miles)

Cox conversion of the DHC-3 Otter, with P&WC PT6A-27 turboprop engine

DE HAVILLAND CANADA

THE DE HAVILLAND AIRCRAFT OF CANADA LTD

Head Office and Works: Downsview, Ontario M3K 1Y5
Telephone: (416) 633 7310
Telex: 06-22128

Chairman: D. N. Kendall

President: John W. Sandford

Vice-Presidents:
- D. B. Annan (Senior Vice-President)
- W. J. Easdale (Personnel and Industrial Relations)
- W. T. Heaslip (Special Projects)
- R. O. Hiscocks (Engineering)
- F. A. Johnson (Customer Support)
- S. B. Kerr (Finance)
- R. G. McCall (Operations)
- J. A. Timmins (Marketing and Sales)

Chief Designer: F. H. Buller

The de Havilland Aircraft of Canada Ltd was established in early 1928 as a subsidiary of The de Havilland Aircraft Co Ltd, and became subsequently a member of the Hawker Siddeley Group. On 26 June 1974 ownership was transferred to the Canadian government, which planned to operate the company only until responsible Canadian investors were found to purchase and operate de Havilland.

Facilities in 1979 covered a total area of 113,209 m² (1,218,578 sq ft), comprising a 77,023 m² (829,070 sq ft) main plant on the southern border of Downsview airport, 30,455 m² (327,815 sq ft) of leased space on the northern boundary of the airport, and an additional 5,731 m² (61,693 sq ft) of leased storage and warehousing space. To handle the increased production rates, an expansion programme at the main plant was initiated in 1979. This will consist of a 3,326 m² (35,800 sq ft) extension for small parts manufacturing, plus a 1,951 m² (21,000 sq ft) first phase of a high-bay aircraft assembly and preparation area.

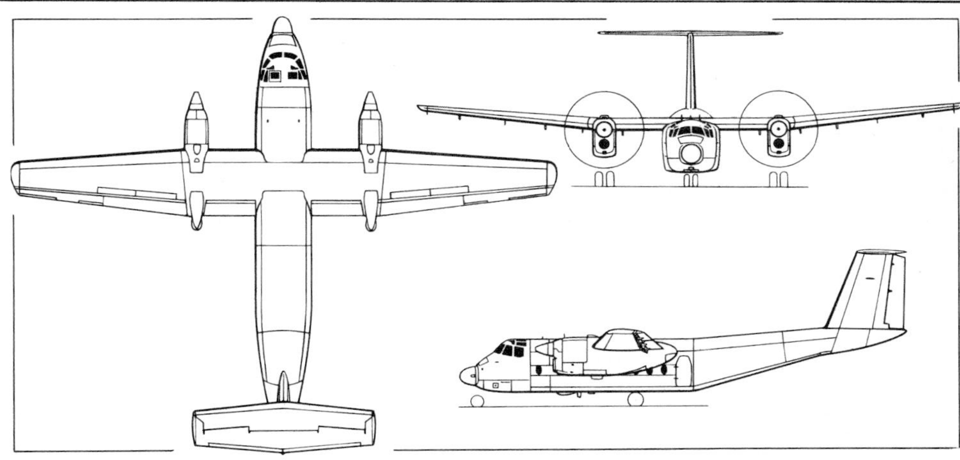

de Havilland Canada DHC-5D Buffalo twin-turboprop STOL utility transport *(Pilot Press)*

DHC-5D BUFFALO

CAF designation: CC-115
USAF designation: C-8A

The Buffalo is a developed version of the Caribou with an enlarged fuselage and two General Electric T64 turboprop engines. Development costs were shared equally by the US Army, the Canadian government and de Havilland Canada.

The first of four evaluation DHC-5s made its initial flight on 9 April 1964. Delivery of these aircraft to the US Army began in April 1965, and 15 DHC-5As were delivered to the Canadian Armed Forces in 1967-68. These aircraft, currently designated **C-8A (DHC-5)** and **CC-115 (DHC-5A)** respectively, have been described in earlier editions of *Jane's*.

Twenty-four Buffalos were delivered to the Brazilian Air Force in 1969 and 1970, and 16 to the Peruvian Air Force in 1971-72. These are designated DHC-5A/C-115, and are generally similar to the CC-115 Canadian version.

One NASA-owned C-8A was modified to evaluate the augmentor wing concept devised by de Havilland Canada and another for quiet short-haul research (QSRA) and evaluation of propulsive-lift technology. The former was described under the NASA entry in the US section of the 1978-79 *Jane's*; the latter is described under the NASA entry in this edition.

The DHC-5B and C were versions proposed in 1974 with CT64-P4C and Rolls-Royce Dart RDa.12 engines respectively.

One CC-115, modified by DHC for a joint DITC/USAF Air Cushion Landing System development programme, was described under the Bell Aerospace heading in the US section of the 1977-78 *Jane's*.

In early 1976 testing was completed of the **DHC-5D**, with a higher gross weight and improved performance. The first production DHC-5D set up, in February 1976, the following time-to-height records, which were subsequently confirmed by the FAI: 2 min 12·75 s to 3,000 m, 4 min 27·5 s to 6,000 m and 8 min 3·5 s to 9,000 m. These times qualify both in the class for turboprop-powered aircraft of unlimited weight category, and for those in the 12,000-16,000 kg weight category.

Deliveries of the DHC-5D began in early 1976 and a total of 36 had been sold by mid-1979, including aircraft for the air forces of Ecuador (two), Kenya (six), Mauritania (two), Togo (two), Zaïre (three), Zambia (seven), Oman (one), Sudan (four), Tanzania (four) and the United Arab Emirates (four). A further batch of 24 has been approved, and production was at the rate of 1½ per month in mid-1979.

A civil version of the Buffalo, known as the **Transporter**, is also available; this is described separately.

The following description applies to the military DHC-5D:

Type: Twin-turboprop STOL utility transport.

Wings: Cantilever high-wing monoplane. Wing section NACA 64_3A417·5 (mod) at root, NACA 63_2A615 (mod) at tip. Dihedral 0° inboard of nacelles, 5° outboard. Incidence 2° 30′. Sweepback at quarter-chord 1° 40′. Conventional fail-safe multi-spar structure of high-strength aluminium alloys. Full-span double-slotted aluminium alloy flaps, outboard sections functioning as ailerons. Aluminium alloy slot-lip spoilers, forward of inboard flaps, are actuated by Jarry Hydraulics unit. Spoilers coupled to manually-operated ailerons for lateral control, uncoupled for symmetrical ground operation. Electrically-actuated trim tab in starboard aileron. Geared tab in each aileron. Rudder/aileron interconnect tab on port aileron. Outer wing leading-edges fitted with electrically-controlled flush pneumatic rubber de-icing boots.

Fuselage: Fail-safe structure of high-strength aluminium alloy. Longitudinal keel members support cargo floor.

Tail Unit: Cantilever structure of high-strength aluminium alloy, with fixed-incidence T-tailplane. Elevator aerodynamically and mass balanced. Fore and trailing serially-hinged rudders are powered by tandem jacks operated by two independent hydraulic systems manufactured by Jarry Hydraulics. Trim tab in port half of elevator, spring tab in starboard half. Electrically-controlled flush pneumatic rubber de-icing boot on tailplane leading-edge.

Landing Gear: Retractable tricycle type, with twin wheels on each unit. Hydraulic retraction, nose unit aft, main units forward. Jarry Hydraulics oleo-pneumatic shock-absorbers. Goodrich main wheels and tyres, size 37 × 15-12, pressure 3·10 bars (45 lb/sq in) for STOL assault role, 4·14 bars (60 lb/sq in) as STOL transport. Goodrich nosewheels and tyres, size 8·9 × 12·5, pressure 3·17 bars (46 lb/sq in). Goodrich multi-disc anti-skid brakes.

Power Plant: Two General Electric CT64-820-4 turboprop engines, each rated at 2,336 kW (3,133 shp) and driving a Hamilton Standard 63E60-25 three-blade constant-speed reversible-pitch fully-feathering propeller with Beta control. Propellers have integral hydraulic systems and electrical de-icing of spinners, cuffs and blades. Fuel in one integral tank in each inner wing, capacity 4,841 litres (1,065 Imp gallons; 1,279 US gallons), and ten interconnected rubber bag tanks in each outer wing, capacity 3,137 litres (690 Imp gallons; 829 US gallons). Total fuel capacity 7,978 litres (1,755 Imp gallons; 2,108 US gallons). Refuelling points above wings and in side of fuselage for pressure refuelling. Total oil capacity 45·5 litres (10 Imp gallons; 12 US gallons).

Accommodation: Crew of three, comprising pilot, co-pilot and crew chief. Main cabin can accommodate roll-up troop seats or folding forward-facing seats for 41 troops or 35 paratroops, or 24 stretchers and six seats. Provision for toilet in forward part of cabin. Door on each side at rear of cabin. Loading height with rear cargo loading door up and ramp down 2·90 m (9 ft 6 in). 508 mm (20 in) grid of tiedown points, with additional tiedowns at sides of cabin.

Systems: AiResearch bleed air cabin heating and cooling system. Two independent hydraulic systems, each of 207 bars (3,000 lb/sq in), actuate landing gear, flaps, spoilers, rudders, brakes, nosewheel steering, winch and APU starting. 3·45 bar (50 lb/sq in) pneumatic system for engine starting, de-icing and environmental control. Two Lucas Aerospace engine-driven variable-frequency 3-phase 20kVA AC generators with 28V DC and 400Hz conversion subsystems. Solar T-62T-40-5 gas turbine APU in port engine nacelle provides electric (10kVA generator), hydraulic and pneumatic power for environmental control, hydraulic operation of cargo winch, electrical systems, and other utility functions.

Avionics and Equipment: Full IFR instrumentation and weather radar standard, as are 34 troop seats, cargo buffer rail, cargo winch, roller conveyors, parachute anchor cables and retrieval system, pendulum release system, Brooks and Perkins palletised loading system with integral side rail restraint, tiedown straps and chains, and crew oxygen system. Optional items include seven forward-facing troop seats, airframe de-icing, toilet, cabin oxygen system, and self-sealing fuel cells.

Dimensions, external:
- Wing span 29·26 m (96 ft 0 in)
- Wing chord at root 3·59 m (11 ft 9¼ in)
- Wing chord at tip 1·19 m (5 ft 11 in)
- Wing aspect ratio 9·75
- Length overall 24·08 m (79 ft 0 in)
- *Height overall 8·73 m (28 ft 8 in)
- Tailplane span 9·75 m (32 ft 0 in)
- Wheel track 9·29 m (30 ft 6 in)
- Wheelbase 8·48 m (27 ft 10 in)
- Propeller diameter 4·42 m (14 ft 6 in)
- Cabin doors (each side):
  - Height 1·68 m (5 ft 6 in)
  - Width 0·84 m (2 ft 9 in)
  - *Height to sill 1·17 m (3 ft 10 in)
- Emergency exits (each side, below wing leading-edge):
  - Height 1·02 m (3 ft 4 in)
  - Width 0·66 m (2 ft 2 in)
  - *Height to sill approx 1·52 m (5 ft 0 in)

de Havilland Canada DHC-5D Buffalo STOL transport aircraft (two General Electric CT64-820-4 turboprop engines)

Rear cargo loading door and ramp:
Height 6·33 m (20 ft 9 in)
Width 2·34 m (7 ft 8 in)
*Height to ramp hinge 1·17 m (3 ft 10 in)

**will vary with aircraft configuration and loading conditions*

DIMENSIONS, INTERNAL:
Cabin, excl flight deck:
Length, cargo floor 9·58 m (31 ft 5 in)
Width at floor 2·36 m (7 ft 9 in)
Max width 2·67 m (8 ft 9 in)
Max height (aft of wings) 2·08 m (6 ft 10 in)
Height forward of rear spar 1·98 m (6 ft 6 in)
Floor area 22·48 m² (242 sq ft)
Volume (rectangular) 44·74 m³ (1,580 cu ft)

AREAS:
Wings, gross 87·8 m² (945 sq ft)
Ailerons (total) 3·62 m² (39 sq ft)
Trailing-edge flaps (total, incl ailerons) 26·01 m² (280 sq ft)
Spoilers (total) 2·34 m² (25·2 sq ft)
Fin 8·55 m² (92 sq ft)
Rudder 5·57 m² (60 sq ft)
Tailplane 14·07 m² (151·5 sq ft)
Elevator, incl tabs 7·57 m² (81·5 sq ft)

WEIGHTS AND LOADINGS (A: STOL assault mission from unprepared airfield; B: STOL transport mission, firm smooth airfield surface):
Operational weight empty (incl 3 crew and 680 kg; 1,500 lb allowance for options and electronics):
A, B 11,412 kg (25,160 lb)
Max payload: A 5,370 kg (11,840 lb)
B 8,164 kg (18,000 lb)
Max normal fuel: A, B 6,212 kg (13,696 lb)
Max unit load for air drop:
A, B 2,721 kg (6,000 lb)
Manoeuvring limit load factor: A 3·0
B 2·5
Max T-O weight: A 18,597 kg (41,000 lb)
B 22,316 kg (49,200 lb)
Max landing weight: A 17,735 kg (39,100 lb)
B 21,273 kg (46,900 lb)
Max zero-fuel weight: A 16,782 kg (37,000 lb)
B 19,731 kg (43,500 lb)
Max wing loading: A 209·9 kg/m² (43·4 lb/sq ft)
B 253·9 kg/m² (52·1 lb/sq ft)
Max uniform cabin floor loading:
A, B 976 kg/m² (200 lb/sq ft)
Max power loading: A 3·98 kg/kW (6·54 lb/shp)
B 4·78 kg/kW (7·85 lb/shp)

PERFORMANCE (at max T-O weight except where indicated. A: STOL assault mission from unprepared airfield; B: STOL transport mission from firm smooth airfield surface):
Max cruising speed at 3,050 m (10,000 ft):
***A 252 knots (467 km/h; 290 mph)
*B 227 knots (420 km/h; 261 mph)
Stalling speed, 40° flap:
A at 17,690 kg (39,000 lb) AUW 67 knots (124 km/h; 77 mph)
B at 21,273 kg (46,900 lb) AUW 73 knots (135 km/h; 84 mph)
Max rate of climb at S/L, normal rated power:
A 710 m (2,330 ft)/min
B 555 m (1,820 ft)/min
Rate of climb at S/L, one engine out:
A, max power 205 m (675 ft)/min
B, military power 116 m (380 ft)/min
†Service ceiling, normal rated power:
A 9,450 m (31,000 ft)
B 8,380 m (27,500 ft)
Service ceiling, one engine out:
A, military power 5,575 m (18,300 ft)
*B, max power 3,810 m (12,500 ft)
STOL T-O run:
**A 289 m (950 ft)
B 701 m (2,300 ft)
STOL T-O to 15 m (50 ft), mid-CG:
**A 381 m (1,250 ft)
B 876 m (2,875 ft)
STOL landing from 15 m (50 ft):
**A 346 m (1,135 ft)
B 613 m (2,010 ft)
STOL landing run:
**A 168 m (550 ft)
B 259 m (850 ft)
Range at 3,050 m (10,000 ft):
A, max payload 225 nm (416 km; 259 miles)
B, max payload 600 nm (1,112 km; 691 miles)
A, B, zero payload 1,770 nm (3,280 km; 2,038 miles)

† Recommended max operating altitude of 7,620 m (25,000 ft)
** at 21,200 kg (46,737 lb) AUW*
*** with 5,443 kg (12,000 lb) payload*
****at 17,667 kg (38,950 lb) AUW*

DHC-5 BUFFALO AUGMENTOR WING JET STOL RESEARCH AIRCRAFT

In co-operation with the Canadian Department of Industry, Trade and Commerce, a NASA-owned C-8A Buffalo has been modified as a flying testbed for the 'augmentor wing' concept devised by de Havilland Canada. A full description of the modified aircraft appeared under the NASA heading in the US section of the 1978-79 edition.

Flight evaluation was resumed in June 1978, following overhaul of the Spey engines. Modifications to the jetpipe produced a significant thrust improvement, and measurements are expected to show that a noise reduction has been made. The test programme includes continued evaluation of the steep, curved descending approach, and of pilot workload using an alternate controller. Optional guidance for fuel conservation experiments is also included in the flight programme.

The 500th flight was due to be made in January 1979, at which time a total of 580 h would have been accumulated. The programme was planned to continue until the end of 1979, and to include further single-engine tests and night-flying experiments.

DHC-5 BUFFALO QUIET SHORT-HAUL RESEARCH AIRCRAFT (QSRA)

A C-8A has been acquired by NASA for evaluation of the USB (upper surface blowing) powered lift system. It has a new wing, four Lycoming YF102 turbofan engines, and a modified tail assembly furnished by NASA. The QSRA prototype was converted by Boeing Commercial Airplane Co under NASA contract. Further details can be found under the NASA heading in the US section.

DHC TRANSPORTER

Undergoing Canadian DoT type approval testing in the Spring of 1979, the Transporter civil version of the DHC-5D Buffalo will be certificated to CAR 4b and SR 442b standards for commercial operation. A demonstration aircraft (C-GTLW) was exhibited at the Paris Air Show in June 1979. Airframe, engines, propellers and APU are the same as those of the Buffalo; some systems are modified, and military installations are replaced by a civil passenger interior which can be transformed quickly for freight-carrying.

The Transporter is available with a 44-seat utility interior as standard, with seats folding into the side walls to convert for freight loading. Optional configurations include a VIP/executive version, seating up to 19 persons in two cabins; and a de luxe 'hard wall' interior with increased soundproofing and air ventilation system.

Initial certification was to be at a max T-O weight of 18,597 kg (41,000 lb), with max landing and zero-fuel weight of 18,144 kg (40,000 lb). This would permit a useful load (fuel plus payload) of 6,713 kg (14,800 lb), with which the Transporter would have an operating range of more than 600 nm (1,112 km; 691 miles). Operated to civil regulations, the Transporter would require a 1,097 m (3,600 ft) field length; but it retains the capability to operate from 457 m (1,500 ft) strips, provided a clear stopway is available at each end.

DHC-6 TWIN OTTER SERIES 300

CAF designation: CC-138
US Army designation: UV-18A
USAF designation: UV-18B

First announced in 1964, the Twin Otter is a STOL

Transporter civil passenger/cargo version of the DHC-5D Buffalo

transport powered by two Pratt & Whitney Aircraft of Canada PT6A series turboprop engines. Design began in January 1964, and construction of five aircraft began in November of the same year. The first of these (CF-DHC-X), powered by two 432 kW (579 ehp) PT6A-6 engines, flew on 20 May 1965.

The fourth and subsequent aircraft of the initial Series 100 version were fitted with PT6A-20 engines, and the first delivery of a production aircraft, to the Ontario Department of Lands and Forests, was made in July 1966, shortly after the Twin Otter received FAA Type Approval. All Series are certificated to FAR 23 Pt 135.

By 1 May 1979, a total of 670 Twin Otters had been sold in more than 75 countries, and operating hours totalled more than 5 million. The 600th DHC-6 was delivered in July 1978, and production in 1979 was increased from four to five aircraft per month.

Military operators of Twin Otters include the Argentinian Air Force (six) and Army (two); Chilean Air Force (five); Ecuadorean Air Force (three); Ethiopian Army Air Corps (three); Jamaica Defence Force (one); Royal Norwegian Air Force (four); Peruvian Air Force (twelve); the Canadian Armed Forces (eight CC-138 for SAR and utility duties); the US Army (two); and the US Air Force Academy (two).

The Twin Otter is available as a maritime surveillance aircraft. One has been modified for Greenlandair Charter for use on ice patrol/maritime surveillance duties. Changes include operation at a higher MTOGW (6,350 kg; 14,000 lb), provision of a Litton LASR-2 search radar in a chin radome, paradrop doors, four observers' stations with bubble windows, additional fuel tanks in the cabin with a max capacity of 567 kg (1,250 lb) each, a VLF navigation system, and provision for photographic equipment.

The Twin Otter is used as a photo survey aircraft in Switzerland and the Sudan. Two such aircraft were delivered to the People's Republic of China in February 1978, with another similar aircraft on order. A fourth aircraft especially modified for geophysical surveying is also on order.

Four production versions of the Twin Otter have so far been announced, of which the Series 100 (115 built), Series 200 (115 built) and Series 300S (six built) were described in the 1967-68, 1970-71 and 1976-77 *Jane's* respectively. The current production version is:

Series 300. Deliveries began in the Spring of 1969 with the 231st Twin Otter off the line. Available, with short nose, as floatplane. Ten of the 12 aircraft supplied to Peru were fitted with floats, for operation by Grupo Aéreo No. 42 of the Peruvian Air Force, based at Iquitos.

Type: Twin-turboprop STOL transport.

Wings: Strut-braced high-wing monoplane. Wing section NACA 6A series mean line; NACA 0016 (modified) thickness distribution. Dihedral 3°. No sweepback. All-metal safe-life structure, each wing being attached to the fuselage by two bolts at the front and rear spar fitting and braced by a single streamline section strut on each side. Light alloy riveted construction is used throughout except for the upper skin panels, which have spanwise corrugated stiffeners bonded to them. All-metal double-slotted full-span trailing-edge flaps. Spoilers fitted to Series 300S aircraft only. All-metal ailerons which also droop for use as flaps. Electrically-actuated tab in port aileron; geared trim tabs in both port and starboard ailerons. Optional pneumatic-boot de-icing equipment.

Fuselage: Conventional semi-monocoque safe-life structure, built in three sections. Primary structure of frames, stringers and skin of aluminium alloy. Windscreen and cabin windows of acrylic plastics. Cabin floor is of low-density aluminium-faced sandwich construction and is designed to accommodate distributed loads of up to 976 kg/m² (200 lb/sq ft).

Tail Unit: Cantilever all-metal structure of high-strength aluminium alloys. Fin and fixed-incidence tailplane are bolted to rear fuselage. Manually-operated trim tabs in rudder and elevators. A geared tab is fitted to the rudder to lighten control forces, and a tab fitted to the starboard elevator is linked to the flaps to control longitudinal trim during flap retraction and extension. Optional pneumatic-boot de-icing of tailplane leading-edge.

Landing Gear: Non-retractable tricycle type, with single wheel on each unit. Fully-steerable nosewheel. Urethane compression-block shock-absorption on main units. Oleo-pneumatic nosewheel shock-absorber. Goodyear main-wheel tyres size 11·00-12, pressure 2·62 bars (38 lb/sq in). Goodyear nosewheel tyre size 8·90-12·50, pressure 2·28 bars (33 lb/sq in). Goodrich independent, hydraulically-operated disc brakes on main wheels. Anti-skid braking system in Series 300S. Alternatively, high-flotation wheels and tyres, for operation in soft-field conditions, are available at customer's option, size 15·0-12·0 for nosewheel and main wheels. Provision for alternative wheel/ski landing gear. Twin-float gear available for short-nose Srs 300, with added wing fences and small auxiliary fins.

Power Plant: Two 486 kW (652 ehp) Pratt & Whitney Aircraft of Canada PT6A-27 turboprop engines, each driving a Hartzell HC-B3TN-3DY three-blade reversible-pitch fully-feathering metal propeller with Beta control. Two underfloor fuel tanks (eight cells), total capacity of 1,446 litres (318 Imp gallons). Refuelling point for each tank on port side of fuselage. Oil capacity 9·1 litres (2 Imp gallons) per engine. Optional electrical de-icing system for propellers and air intakes.

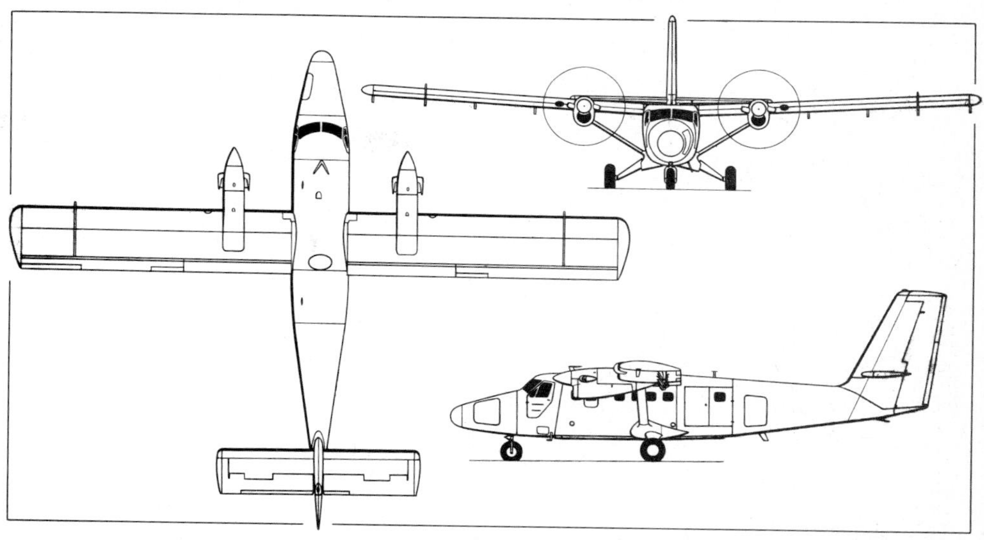

de Havilland Canada DHC-6 Twin Otter Series 300 STOL utility transport *(Pilot Press)*

Accommodation: Side-by-side seats for one or two pilots on flight deck, access to which is by a forward-opening car-type door on each side or via the passenger cabin. Dual controls standard. Windscreen demisting and defrosting standard. Cabin divided by bulkhead into main passenger or freight compartment and baggage compartment. Seats for up to 20 passengers in main cabin. Standard interior is 20-seat commuter layout, with Douglas track, carpets, double windows, individual air vents and reading lights, and airstair door. Optional layouts include 18- or 19-seat commuter versions, 13/20-passenger utility version with foldaway seats and double cargo doors with ladder, and 11-passenger layout in Series 300S. Access to cabin by door on each side of rear fuselage; airstair door on the port side. Optional double door for cargo on port side instead of airstair door. Compartments in nose and aft of main cabin, each with upward-hinged door on port side, for 136 kg (300 lb) and 227 kg (500 lb) of baggage respectively; rear baggage hold accessible from cabin in emergency. Emergency exits near front of cabin on each side. Heating of flight deck and passenger cabin by engine bleed air; ventilation via a ram-air intake on the port side of the fuselage nose. Oxygen system for crew and passengers optional. Executive, survey or ambulance interiors can be fitted at customer's option. Tiedown cargo rings are installed as standard for the freighter role.

Systems: Hydraulic system, pressure 103 bars (1,500 lb/sq in), for flaps, brakes, nosewheel steering and (where fitted) ski retraction mechanism. A hand pump in the crew compartment provides emergency pressure for standby or ground operation if the electric pump is inoperative. Accumulators smooth the system pressure pulses and provide pressure for parking and emergency braking. Optional low-pressure pneumatic system (1·24 bars; 18 lb/sq in) for operation of autopilot or wing and tail de-icing boots, if fitted. Primary electrical system is 28V DC, with one 200A starter/generator on each engine. One 40Ah 20-cell nickel-cadmium battery (optionally a 36Ah lead-acid battery) for emergency power and engine starting. Separate 3·6Ah battery supplies independent power for engine starting relays and ignition. 250VA main and standby static inverters provide 400Hz AC power for instruments and electronics. External DC receptacle aft of port side cabin door permits operation of complete system on the ground.

Avionics and Equipment: Navigation and communications equipment, including weather radar, to customer's specification. Blind-flying instrumentation standard.

Dimensions, external:

Wing span	19·81 m (65 ft 0 in)
Wing chord (constant)	1·98 m (6 ft 6 in)
Wing aspect ratio	10
Length overall: landplane	15·77 m (51 ft 9 in)
seaplane	15·09 m (49 ft 6 in)
*Height overall: landplane	5·94 m (19 ft 6 in)
seaplane	6·04 m (19 ft 10 in)
Tailplane span	6·30 m (20 ft 8 in)
Wheel track (landplane)	3·71 m (12 ft 2 in)
Wheelbase (landplane)	4·53 m (14 ft 10½ in)
Seaplane track (c/l of floats)	4·06 m (13 ft 4 in)
Propeller diameter	2·59 m (8 ft 6 in)
Passenger door (port side): Height	1·27 m (4 ft 2 in)
Width	0·76 m (2 ft 6 in)
*Height to sill	1·32 m (4 ft 4 in)
Passenger door (starboard side):	
Height	1·15 m (3 ft 9½ in)
Width	0·77 m (2 ft 6¼ in)
*Height to sill	1·32 m (4 ft 4 in)
Baggage compartment door (nose):	
Mean height	0·69 m (2 ft 3¼ in)
Width	0·76 m (2 ft 5¾ in)
*Height to sill	1·32 m (4 ft 4 in)
Baggage compartment door (port, rear):	
Max height	0·97 m (3 ft 2 in)
Width	0·65 m (2 ft 1½ in)
Cargo double door (port, rear):	
Height	1·27 m (4 ft 2 in)
Width	1·42 m (4 ft 8 in)
*Height to sill	1·32 m (4 ft 4 in)

Maritime surveillance/ice patrol version of Twin Otter Series 300, with undernose radome

*will vary with aircraft configuration and loading conditions

Dimensions, internal:

Cabin, excl flight deck, galley and baggage compartment: Length	5·64 m (18 ft 6 in)
Max width	1·61 m (5 ft 3¼ in)
Max height	1·50 m (4 ft 11 in)
Floor area	7·45 m² (80·2 sq ft)
Volume	10·87 m³ (384 cu ft)
Baggage compartment (nose): Volume	1·08 m³ (38 cu ft)
Baggage compartment (rear): Length	1·88 m (6 ft 2 in)
Volume	2·49 m³ (88 cu ft)

Areas:

Wings, gross	39·02 m² (420 sq ft)
Ailerons (total)	3·08 m² (33·2 sq ft)
Trailing-edge flaps (total)	10·42 m² (112·2 sq ft)
Fin	4·46 m² (48·0 sq ft)
Rudder, incl tabs	3·16 m² (34·0 sq ft)
Tailplane	9·29 m² (100·0 sq ft)
Elevator, incl tabs	3·25 m² (35·0 sq ft)

Weights:

Typical operating weight (20-seat commuter, incl 2 crew and 59 kg; 130 lb of electronics)	3,363 kg (7,415 lb)
Max payload for 100 nm (185 km; 115 miles)	1,941 kg (4,280 lb)
Max T-O weight	5,670 kg (12,500 lb)
Max landing weight: wheels and skis	5,579 kg (12,300 lb)
floats	5,670 kg (12,500 lb)

Performance (at max T-O weight, ISA):

Max cruising speed at 3,050 m (10,000 ft) 182 knots (338 km/h; 210 mph)

DHC-6 Twin Otter Series 300, one of two operated by the United States Air Force Academy under the designation UV-18B

Stalling speed, flaps up
74 knots (137·5 km/h; 85·5 mph) EAS
Stalling speed, flaps down
58 knots (108 km/h; 67 mph) EAS
Max rate of climb at S/L 488 m (1,600 ft)/min
Rate of climb at S/L, one engine out
104 m (340 ft)/min
Service ceiling 8,140 m (26,700 ft)
Service ceiling, one engine out 3,530 m (11,600 ft)
T-O run: STOL 213 m (700 ft)
CAR Pt 3 262 m (860 ft)
T-O to 15 m (50 ft): STOL 366 m (1,200 ft)
CAR Pt 3 457 m (1,500 ft)
Landing from 15 m (50 ft): STOL 320 m (1,050 ft)
CAR Pt 3 591 m (1,940 ft)
Landing run: STOL 157 m (515 ft)
CAR Pt 3 290 m (950 ft)
Range at long-range cruising speed with 1,134 kg (2,500 lb) payload 700 nm (1,297 km; 806 miles)
Range at long-range cruising speed with 862 kg (1,900 lb) payload and wing tanks
920 nm (1,704 km; 1,059 miles)

DHC-7 DASH 7

CAF designation: CC-132

The Dash 7 'quiet STOL' airliner project was begun by de Havilland Canada in late 1972, following a worldwide market survey of short-haul transport requirements.

Two pre-production aircraft were built, the first of these (C-GNBX-X) flying on 27 March 1975 and the second (C-GNCA-X) on 26 June 1975. A third airframe was built for structural testing and a fourth for fatigue testing. The first production Dash 7 (C-GQIW, aircraft No. 3), flew on 30 May 1977 and, together with the two pre-production aircraft, participated in the certification and flight test programme.

Certification by the Canadian Department of Transport to FAR 25 was received on 2 May 1977; STOL performance is approved under conventional FAR 25 and FAR 121 regulations. In addition, certification has been given for 7° 30′ glidescope and 10·7 m (35 ft) landing reference height adopted by the FAA for STOL aircraft.

An initial batch of 50 production Dash 7s is being built, with the production rate being increased to two per month by the end of 1979. The first to enter service was aircraft No. 4, with Rocky Mountain Airways, on 3 February 1978. By the Spring of 1978 the Dash 7 was in service in Canada (with Wardair) and Europe (Spantax). Orders and options totalled 54 by 20 August 1979; customers included Widerøe (Norway), Golden West (USA), Time Air (Canada), Canadian Armed Forces, Air Wisconsin (USA), Ransome (USA), Air Pacific (USA), Alidair (UK), Gronlandsfly (Greenland), SAHSA (Honduras), Alyemda (South Yemen), Westcoast Air Holdings (Canada), Air Oregon (USA) and Air Innsbruck (Austria).

The all-cargo version is designated **DHC-7 Series 101,** and is already in service with Wardair Canada Ltd and Emirates Air Service (Abu Dhabi). By mid-1979, further deliveries were due to have been made to Wardair, Greenlandair and the Canadian Armed Forces (two to replace CC-109 Cosmopolitan transports based in Germany).

A maritime reconnaissance variant, the **DHC-7R Ranger,** is described separately. The following description applies to the standard production DHC-7:

Type: Four-engined short/medium-range quiet STOL transport.

Wings: Cantilever high-wing monoplane, with 4° 30′ dihedral from centre-section. Wing section NACA 63A418 (modified) at root, NACA 63A415 (modified) at tip. Incidence 3° at root. Conventional all-metal two-spar bonded skin/stringer structure. Double-slotted flaps, extending over approx 80% of trailing-edge, are actuated mechanically for take-off, by irreversible screwjacks, and hydraulically for landing. Two inboard ground spoilers/lift dumpers and two outboard air spoilers in each upper surface, forward of flaps, also actuated hydraulically. Outboard sections can be operated symmetrically, or differentially in combination with the cable-operated ailerons. Trim tab in starboard aileron; servo-tab in each aileron. Pneumatic-boot de-icing of leading-edges outboard of the inner nacelles.

Fuselage: Conventional all-metal stressed-skin pressurised structure, of bonded skin/stringer construction. Basically circular cross-section, with flattened profile under floor level.

Tail Unit: Cantilever all-metal T-tail, with large dorsal fin. Fixed-incidence tailplane, and one-piece cable-operated horn-balanced elevator with trim tabs. Two-piece vertically-split rudder, actuated hydraulically. Pneumatic-boot de-icing of leading-edges of tailplane and of elevator horns.

Landing Gear: Menasco retractable tricycle type, with twin wheels on all units. Oleo-pneumatic shock-absorbers. Hydraulic retraction, main units forward into inboard engine nacelles, steerable nose unit rearward into fuselage. Main-wheel tyres size 30 × 9·00-15, pressure 7·38 bars (107 lb/sq in); nosewheel tyres size 6·50-10, pressure 5·31 bars (77 lb/sq in). Larger, low-pressure tyres optional, with pressures of 4·83 bars (70 lb/sq in) on main units, 4·76 bars (69 lb/sq in) on nose unit. Anti-skid hydraulic braking system for all units. Small retractable tailskid under rear fuselage.

Power Plant: Four 835 kW (1,120 shp) Pratt & Whitney Aircraft of Canada PT6A-50 turboprop engines, each driving a Hamilton Standard 24PF-305 constant-speed fully-feathering reversible-pitch four-blade glassfibre propeller, with Beta control, of slow-turning type (1,210 rpm) to reduce noise level. Fuel in two integral tanks in each wing, total capacity 5,602 litres (1,480 US gallons; 1,232 Imp gallons). Single pressure refuelling/defuelling point on underside of rear fuselage, aft of pressure dome. Pneumatic de-icing of engine air intakes; electrical de-icing for propellers. Oil capacity 23 litres (6 US gallons; 5 Imp gallons).

Accommodation: Flight crew of two, plus one or two cabin attendants. Seats for 50 passengers at 81 cm (32 in) pitch, in pairs on each side of centre aisle, with generous provision for underseat carry-on baggage. Outward-opening airstair door at rear on port side. Emergency exits on each side at front of cabin and on starboard side at rear. Baggage compartment in rear fuselage (capacity 998 kg; 2,200 lb), with external access on starboard side and internal access from cabin. Galley, coat rack and toilet at rear of cabin. Optional arrangements include movable bulkhead for mixed freight/passenger loads with large forward freight door on port side. Up to five standard pallets can be accommodated in an all-cargo role. Quick-change cargo handling system available optionally. Entire accommodation pressurised and air-conditioned.

Systems: Cabin pressure differential 0·294 bars (4·26 lb/sq in). Two air-cycle systems, driven by engine bleed air, for cabin air-conditioning. Two independent hydraulic systems, each of 207 bars (3,000 lb/sq in). No. 1 system actuates flaps, rudder, wing spoilers and main-wheel brakes; No. 2 system actuates landing gear, nosewheel and backup main-wheel brakes, parking brakes, nosewheel steering, rudder and outboard wing spoilers. Primary DC power provided by four Phoenix 28V 250A 7·5kW starter/generators. 115/200V three-phase AC power at 400Hz from four 10kVA Lucas brushless generators for propeller and windscreen de-icing and standby fuel pumps. Lucas static inverters supply constant-frequency 400Hz loads, including engine instrumentation and navigational systems. Nickel-cadmium batteries for engine starting. APU, for cabin air-conditioning and electrics, and engine starting, available optionally.

Avionics and Equipment: Standard avionics include crew

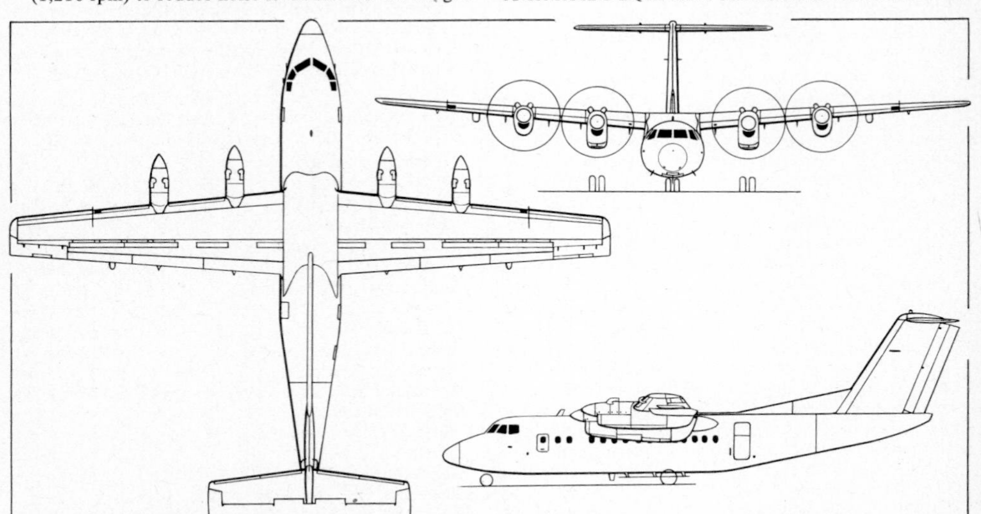

de Havilland Canada DHC-7 Dash 7 four-turboprop STOL transport *(Pilot Press)*

DHC-7 Dash 7 four-turboprop quiet STOL transport, in the insignia of Wardair Canada Ltd

interphone system; cabin PA system; flight data recorder; flight compartment voice recorder; emergency locator transmitter; two independent VHF communications systems; two independent VHF (VOR/ILS) radio navigation systems; one LF (ADF) radio navigation system; one ATC transponder; one DME; one RCA Primus 40 weather radar; one marker beacon; Sperry Flight Systems SPZ-700 autopilot/flight director system, incorporating Z-500 flight computer and ADC-200 central air data computer; Sperry STARS ADI and HSI; Sperry AA-215 radio altimeter; and two Sperry C-14 slaved gyro compasses and VG-14 vertical gyros. Provision for variety of optional avionics to customer's requirements. Standard options include Collins 618M-3 communications transceiver, Collins 51RV-4D navigation receiver, Collins 51Z-4 glideslope/marker receiver, and Collins 621A-6 transponder.

DIMENSIONS, EXTERNAL:
- Wing span 28·35 m (93 ft 0 in)
- Wing chord at root 3·81 m (12 ft 6 in)
- Wing chord at tip 1·68 m (5 ft 6 in)
- Wing mean aerodynamic chord 2·99 m (9 ft 9¾ in)
- Wing aspect ratio 10
- Length overall 24·58 m (80 ft 7·7 in)
- *Height overall 7·98 m (26 ft 2 in)
- Tailplane span 9·45 m (31 ft 0 in)
- Fuselage: Max diameter 2·79 m (9 ft 2 in)
- Wheel track 7·16 m (23 ft 6 in)
- Wheelbase 8·38 m (27 ft 6 in)
- Propeller diameter 3·43 m (11 ft 3 in)
- *Propeller ground clearance (inboard engines) 1·60 m (5 ft 3 in)
- Min propeller/fuselage clearance 0·75 m (2 ft 5·4 in)
- Passenger door (rear, port):
  - Height 1·75 m (5 ft 9 in)
  - Width 0·76 m (2 ft 6 in)
  - *Height to sill 1·09 m (3 ft 7 in)
- Emergency exit door (rear, stbd):
  - Height 1·35 m (4 ft 5 in)
  - Width 0·61 m (2 ft 0 in)
  - *Height to sill 1·09 m (3 ft 7 in)
- Emergency exit doors (fwd, each):
  - Height 0·91 m (3 ft 0 in)
  - Width 0·51 m (1 ft 8 in)
  - *Height to sill 1·55 m (5 ft 1 in)
- Baggage hold door (rear, stbd):
  - Height 1·02 m (3 ft 4 in)
  - Width 0·84 m (2 ft 9 in)
  - *Height to sill 1·47 m (4 ft 10 in)
- Cargo door (fwd, port, optional):
  - Height 1·78 m (5 ft 10 in)
  - Width 2·31 m (7 ft 7 in)
  - *Height to sill approx 1·22 m (4 ft 0 in)

**will vary with aircraft configuration and loading conditions*

DIMENSIONS, INTERNAL:
- Cabin, excl flight deck: Length 12·04 m (39 ft 6 in)
  - Max width 2·59 m (8 ft 6 in)
  - Floor width 2·13 m (7 ft 0 in)
  - Max height 1·94 m (6 ft 4½ in)
  - Height under wing 1·85 m (6 ft 1 in)
  - Volume 54·1 m³ (1,910 cu ft)
- Baggage compartment (rear fuselage):
  - Max length 2·30 m (7 ft 6½ in)
  - Volume 6·8 m³ (240 cu ft)

AREAS:
- Wings, gross 79·90 m² (860·0 sq ft)
- Ailerons (total) 2·16 m² (23·22 sq ft)
- Trailing-edge flaps (total) 27·33 m² (294·20 sq ft)
- Spoilers (total) 3·63 m² (39·04 sq ft)
- Vertical tail surfaces (total, excl dorsal fin) 15·79 m² (170·0 sq ft)
- Horizontal tail surfaces (total) 20·16 m² (217·0 sq ft)

WEIGHTS AND LOADINGS:
- Basic weight empty (standard 50-passenger layout) 12,110 kg (26,700 lb)
- Operating weight empty 12,405 kg (27,350 lb)
- Max payload (50 passengers or cargo) 5,284 kg (11,650 lb)
- Max fuel (standard tanks) 4,563 kg (10,060 lb)
- Max T-O weight 19,958 kg (44,000 lb)
- Max zero-fuel weight 17,690 kg (39,000 lb)
- Max landing weight 19,050 kg (42,000 lb)
- Max cabin floor loading 366·2 kg/m² (75 lb/sq ft)
- Max wing loading 249·8 kg/m² (51·17 lb/sq ft)
- Max power loading 5·98 kg/kW (9·82 lb/shp)

PERFORMANCE (at max T-O weight, FAR Pt 25, at S/L, ISA, except where indicated):
- Max cruising speed at 2,440 m (8,000 ft) at AUW of 18,597 kg (41,000 lb) 231 knots (428 km/h; 266 mph)
- Max cruising speed at 4,570 m (15,000 ft) at AUW of 18,597 kg (41,000 lb) 227 knots (420 km/h; 261 mph)
- En-route rate of climb, flaps and landing gear up:
  - 4 engines, max climb power 372 m (1,220 ft)/min
  - 3 engines, max continuous power 216 m (710 ft)/min
- Service ceiling at AUW of 18,597 kg (41,000 lb):
  - 4 engines, max climb power 6,980 m (22,900 ft)
  - 3 engines, max continuous power 4,510 m (14,800 ft)
- T-O field length, 25° flap 689 m (2,260 ft)
- T-O field length at 3,050 m (10,000 ft), 15° flap 1,829 m (6,000 ft)
- Landing field length at max landing weight, 45° flap 594 m (1,950 ft)
- Landing field length at 3,050 m (10,000 ft) at 18,915 kg (41,700 lb) landing weight, 45° flap 823 m (2,700 ft)
- Min ground turning radius 8·84 m (29 ft 0 in)
- Runway LCN with 32 × 11·50-15 low-pressure tyres, rigid, 30 in relative stiffness 16·2
- Range at 3,960 m (13,000 ft) with 50 passengers and baggage, at long-range cruising speed, IFR reserves 730 nm (1,352 km; 840 miles)
- Max range at 4,570 m (15,000 ft) with standard fuel and 3,040 kg (6,700 lb) payload, long-range cruising speed 1,160 nm (2,148 km; 1,335 miles)

OPERATIONAL NOISE CHARACTERISTICS (FAR Pt 36 at S/L, ISA + 10°C, confirmed):
- T-O noise level 80·5 EPNdB
- Approach noise level on 3° glideslope 91·4 EPNdB
- Sideline noise level 82·8 EPNdB

DHC-7R RANGER

First details of this maritime reconnaissance version of the Dash 7 were given on 5 September 1976, at the Farnborough International air show in the UK.

Principal differences from the standard Dash 7 airliner are increased fuel tankage, to provide approx 10-12 hour endurance at normal patrol speeds; two observers' stations in the fuselage, with bubble windows; a nose-mounted Texas Instruments search radar; and onboard avionics and equipment for a range of maritime surveillance duties including day and night photography. The Ranger can be converted easily to a standard 50-passenger transport configuration, and retains the capacity to carry up to 26 passengers without removal of the reconnaissance installation.

In addition, the advantages inherent in the basic DHC-7 design include multi-engine safety; low fuel consumption; quiet operation, with low interior vibration and noise levels; and the ability to use short, semi-prepared airstrips close to the reconnaissance area.

Development of the Ranger is continuing, and two have been ordered by the Canadian Coast Guard, for delivery in 1980. A prototype was scheduled to fly in late 1979.

TYPE: Four-turboprop maritime reconnaissance aircraft.

WINGS: As for DHC-7.

FUSELAGE: Generally as for DHC-7, except for enlarged nose radome and bubble cabin windows for observers.

TAIL UNIT AND LANDING GEAR: As for DHC-7.

POWER PLANT: Four 835 kW (1,120 shp) Pratt & Whitney Aircraft of Canada PT6A-50 turboprop engines, as in DHC-7, each driving a Hamilton Standard 24PF series constant-speed fully-feathering reversible-pitch slow-turning (1,210 rpm) propeller with four glassfibre blades. Fuel load increased from 4,626 kg (10,200 lb) in DHC-7 to 7,734 kg (17,050 lb) in DHC-7R, equivalent to increase in total tank capacity from 5,602 litres (1,232 Imp gallons; 1,480 US gallons) to 9,350 litres (2,056 Imp gallons; 2,470 US gallons).

ACCOMMODATION: Pilot and co-pilot on flight deck. Work stations in forward part of cabin for two observers (one each side), with swivelling seats and 180° bubble windows, and for navigator/tactical co-ordinator aft of starboard observer's station. Fully-equipped galley and toilet/washroom at rear of cabin. All reconnaissance installations are of modular design, permitting quick and easy removal to make entire interior available for use in transport role. Alternatives to primary reconnaissance layout include 50-passenger transport, with reconnaissance installation removed; seating for up to 26 passengers in rear of cabin without removal of reconnaissance installation at front; or mixed passenger/cargo layout with reconnaissance installation removed, freight loading door and movable cabin bulkhead added (typical load, three standard freight pallets and 18 passengers). With all of these layouts, toilet and buffet provisions at rear of cabin, and 6·8 m³ (240 cu ft) of baggage space, are standard.

SYSTEMS: Generally as described for DHC-7, including cabin pressurisation at 0·294 bars (4·26 lb/sq in); dual hydraulic systems, each of 207 bars (3,000 lb/sq in); and 115/200V AC and 28V DC electrical systems. Adequate electrical power is provided to allow mission to be completed in event of an engine shutdown.

AVIONICS: Standard avionics comprise VHF/FM

Artist's impression of the DHC-7R Ranger four-turboprop maritime patrol aircraft

(maritime), dual VHF and HF/SSB communications; Litton LTN-72 INS; Canadian Marconi CMA-734 Omega VLF navigation system; dual VHF nav with glideslope; marker beacon; DME; ATC transponder; ADF with remote magnetic indicator; radar altimeter; gyro magnetic compass system; autopilot; dual flight director system; two air data computers; flight data recorder; flight compartment voice recorder; integrated audio system; and emergency locator beacon. Optional avionics include UHF com; UHF/DF receiver; and Doppler navigation system.

OPERATIONAL EQUIPMENT: Avionics racks on port side near front of cabin, just aft of observer's station, with flare stowage and flare launcher (for night photography) to rear of these racks. Vinten reconnaissance camera mounted in fuselage. Photo annotation system records on the film the appropriate position data obtained from the aircraft's navigation system. Main camera can be supplemented by hand-held cameras at the two observers' stations. Six-man life raft at front of cabin, adjacent to starboard observer's station. Nose-mounted weather radar is optional. A range of specialised sensing equipment can be installed, to customer's requirements, for resource surveillance.

DIMENSIONS, EXTERNAL AND INTERNAL:
As for DHC-7

WEIGHTS AND LOADINGS (estimated):
Basic weight empty (standard) 12,633 kg (27,850 lb)
Operating weight empty (standard) 13,172 kg (29,040 lb)
Max payload 4,518 kg (9,960 lb)
Max fuel (standard tanks) 8,165 kg (18,000 lb)
Max T-O weight 20,865 kg (46,000 lb)
Max zero-fuel weight 17,690 kg (39,000 lb)
Max landing weight 19,050 kg (42,000 lb)
Max wing loading 255·4 kg/m² (52·3 lb/sq ft)
Max power loading 6·25 kg/kW (10·27 lb/shp)

PERFORMANCE (estimated, at max T-O weight except where indicated):
Max cruising speed at 2,440 m (8,000 ft), AUW of 19,500 kg (43,000 lb):
ISA 230 knots (426 km/h; 265 mph)
ISA +15°C 221 knots (409 km/h; 254 mph)
Rate of climb at S/L, AUW of 20,865 kg (46,000 lb), flaps up:
4 engines, max climb power:
ISA 335 m (1,100 ft)/min
ISA + 15°C 268 m (880 ft)/min
3 engines, max continuous power:
ISA 183 m (600 ft)/min
ISA + 15°C 171 m (560 ft)/min
Service ceiling (30·5 m; 100 ft/min rate of climb):
ISA 6,555 m (21,500 ft)
ISA + 15°C 5,790 m (19,000 ft)
Service ceiling, one engine out (FAR Pt 25):
ISA 4,085 m (13,400 ft)
ISA + 15°C 3,320 m (10,900 ft)
T-O to 15 m (50 ft) at S/L:
ISA 688 m (2,257 ft)
ISA + 20°C 778 m (2,554 ft)
Landing run at S/L at max landing weight:
ISA 355 m (1,164 ft)
ISA + 20°C 376 m (1,235 ft)
Typical mission profile, incl radar search at 1,525 m (5,000 ft) and 30 min inspection at 305 m (1,000 ft), at 800 nm (1,480 km; 920 miles) from base, reserves for 100 nm (185 km; 115 mile) diversion at 3,355 m (11,000 ft) and 45 min hold at 1,525 m (5,000 ft):
time on search, out and back at 3,050 m (10,000 ft) 1 h 41 min
time on search, out and back at 6,100 m (20,000 ft) 2 h 45 min
total mission time, out and back at 3,050 m (10,000 ft) 10 h 10 min
total mission time, out and back at 6,100 m (20,000 ft) 10 h 56 min
Typical patrol endurance, at long-range cruising speed at 4,570 m (15,000 ft), reserves as above:
total mission time 12 h
Range with max fuel, at long-range cruising speed at 6,100 m (20,000 ft), reserves as above:
2,480 nm (4,595 km; 2,855 miles)

DHC DASH X

Well into the project definition phase in mid-1979, the Dash X will be intermediate in size and passenger capacity between the Twin Otter and the Dash 7. At that time, general configuration was broadly similar to that of the Dash 7, but with a seating capacity of approx 32 persons and a power plant of two new fuel-efficient turboprop engines in the 1,044-1,342 kW (1,400 to 1,800 shp) class. A first flight in the early 1980s is anticipated.

HAWKER SIDDELEY

HAWKER SIDDELEY CANADA LTD (Member Company of Hawker Siddeley Group)

HEAD OFFICE: 7 King Street East, Toronto, Ontario M5C 1A3
Telephone: (416) 3622941
Telex: 06 217711
CHAIRMAN: Sir Arnold Hall, FRS
VICE-CHAIRMEN:
J. N. Paterson
F. H. Wood
PRESIDENT AND CHIEF EXECUTIVE OFFICER: E. J. White
DIRECTOR OF CORPORATE AFFAIRS: J. F. A. Painter

Known as A. V. Roe Canada Ltd until 1962, this company controls operating units and subsidiaries in Canada, the UK and the USA employing about 7,100 people.

The company's chief aviation unit is Orenda Division (see Aero-engines section).

McKINNON

McKINNON-VIKING ENTERPRISES

HEAD OFFICE AND WORKS: Hangar No. 2, Victoria International Airport (PO Box 2004), Sidney, British Columbia V8L 3S3
Telephone: (604) 656 7227
PRESIDENT, OWNER AND MANAGER: N. Christensen

McKinnon-Viking, formed in 1978, supersedes the former McKinnon Enterprises Inc, included previously in the US section. McKinnon (formerly McKinnon-Hickman Company) entered the aircraft conversion field in 1953 when it began to undertake the conversion of Grumman Widgeon twin-engined light amphibians into executive aircraft. The success of this programme led to development and manufacture of a four-engined conversion of the larger Grumman Goose amphibian, known as the McKinnon G-21 Goose, details of which can be found in the 1966-67 *Jane's.* It was superseded by the turboprop-powered G-21C and D Turbo-Goose, described in the 1976-77 *Jane's.*

Details of conversions available currently are as follows:

McKinnon G-21G Turbo-Goose, a turboprop-powered conversion of the Grumman G-21A

McKINNON G-21G TURBO-GOOSE

This version of the Turbo-Goose is an 8/12-seat conversion of the standard Grumman G-21A. Modifications to the airframe include a 0·38 m (15 in) nose extension to accommodate radar, metallising treatment of the wings and provision of a wraparound windscreen, retractable wingtip floats, rotating beacon on top of the fin, a small dorsal fin and hull vents. Optional improvements include provision of picture windows for the cabin, a centre main fuel tank of increased capacity, dual landing lights in wing leading-edges, electrically-operated retraction of landing gear and enlargement of the cabin by removing the bulkhead at station 26. McKinnon has received FAA approval for this conversion.

TYPE: Twin-turboprop light amphibian.

WINGS: Cantilever high-wing monoplane. Wing section NACA 23000. Dihedral 2° 30′. All-metal structure with metal covering. Fabric-covered metal ailerons.

FUSELAGE: All-metal semi-monocoque flying-boat hull with two steps.

TAIL UNIT: Braced all-metal structure.

LANDING GEAR: Retractable tailwheel type. All wheels retract electrically into hull, with manual extension. Bendix oleo-pneumatic shock-absorbers. Goodyear wheels and double-disc brakes. Retractable wingtip stabilising floats.

POWER PLANT: Two 507 kW (680 shp) Pratt & Whitney Aircraft of Canada PT6A-27 turboprop engines, driving Hartzell three-blade constant-speed reversible-pitch and fully-feathering propellers. Fuel tanks in wings, total capacity 2,218 litres (586 US gallons).

ACCOMMODATION: Pilot and up to 11 passengers in standard version. Bow-loading entrance and baggage space in nose. Main cabin, forward of the standard rear door, seats seven people, with four more in a cabin aft of the door. Baggage compartment, capacity 136 kg (300 lb).

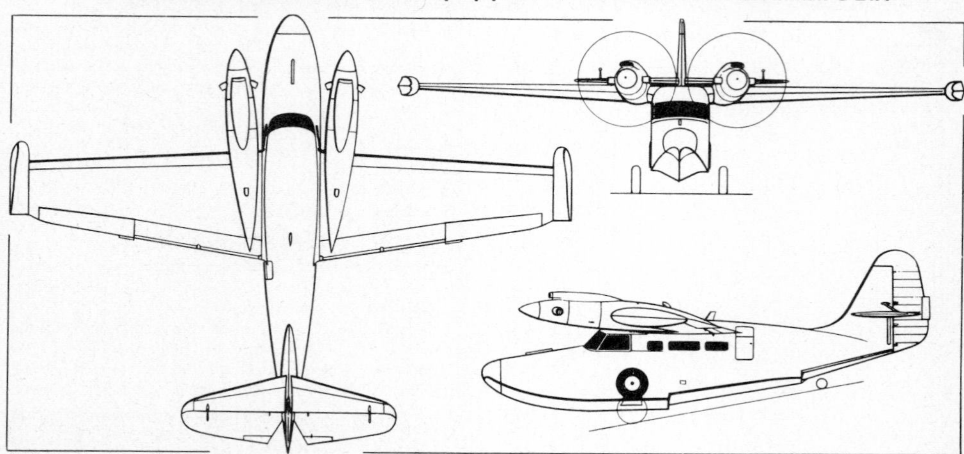

McKinnon G-21G Turbo-Goose, an 8/12-seat conversion of the Grumman G-21A *(Pilot Press)*

DIMENSIONS, EXTERNAL:
Wing span 15·49 m (50 ft 10 in)
Wing chord at root 3·05 m (10 ft 0 in)
Wing chord at tip 1·52 m (5 ft 0 in)
Wing aspect ratio 6·84
Length overall 12·07 m (39 ft 7 in)
Width of hull 1·52 m (5 ft 0 in)
Tailplane span 6·02 m (19 ft 9 in)
Wheel track 2·29 m (7 ft 6 in)
Wheelbase 5·23 m (17 ft 2 in)

AREAS:
Wings, gross 35·08 m² (377·64 sq ft)
Ailerons (total) 2·75 m² (29·64 sq ft)
Fin 1·97 m² (21·20 sq ft)
Rudder 2·49 m² (26·80 sq ft)
Tailplane 3·67 m² (39·48 sq ft)
Elevators 3·99 m² (42·92 sq ft)
Elevator tab 0·195 m² (2·10 sq ft)

WEIGHTS:
Weight empty, equipped (approx) 3,039 kg (6,700 lb)
Max T-O weight 5,670 kg (12,500 lb)

PERFORMANCE (at max T-O weight):
Max operating speed 211 knots (391 km/h; 243 mph)
Service ceiling 6,100 m (20,000 ft)
Service ceiling, one engine out 3,660 m (12,000 ft)
Range with 2,218 litres (586 US gallons) fuel 1,390 nm (2,575 km; 1,600 miles)

McKINNON TURBOPROP GOOSE CONVERSION

For owners of Goose amphibians who do not require a full conversion of their aircraft to G-21G standard, McKinnon offers a simple conversion which involves only replacement of the original R-985 piston engines with two 507 kW (680 shp) Pratt & Whitney Aircraft of Canada PT6A-27 turboprop engines driving three-blade constant-speed reversible-pitch propellers.

Any of the other modifications incorporated on the G-21G can be made during this conversion. Speed and take-off performance are comparable with those of the G-21G. Range is also comparable after fitment of the optional auxiliary tanks to provide a total fuel capacity of 2,218 litres (586 US gallons).

WEIGHTS (minimum conversion):
- Weight empty, equipped: 3,009 kg (6,635 lb)
- Max T-O weight: 5,670 kg (12,500 lb)
- Max landing weight, on land or water: 5,445 kg (12,000 lb)

McKinnon Super Widgeon with retractable wingtip floats

McKINNON SUPER WIDGEON

The Super Widgeon is an executive conversion of the Grumman Widgeon light amphibian, with the two original 149 kW (200 hp) Ranger six-cylinder in-line inverted engines replaced by two 201 kW (270 hp) Lycoming GO-480-B1D flat-six engines driving Hartzell three-blade fully-feathering propellers. Modifications to the hull and landing gear permit an increase in loaded weight. Extra tanks are provided in the outer wings to increase the fuel capacity from 408 to 582 litres (108 to 154 US gallons). Other new features include picture windows, a modern IFR instrument panel, improved soundproofing and the provision of an emergency escape hatch. Approval to install retractable floats was obtained in 1960.

The cabin is arranged to accommodate a pilot, co-pilot and three or four passengers.

Well over 70 Widgeons have been converted to Super Widgeon standard by McKinnon, and several retractable float installations have been completed.

DIMENSIONS, EXTERNAL:
- Wing span: 12·19 m (40 ft 0 in)
- Length overall: 9·47 m (31 ft 1 in)
- Height overall: 3·48 m (11 ft 5 in)

WEIGHT:
- Max T-O weight: 2,500 kg (5,500 lb)

PERFORMANCE (at max T-O weight):
- Max level speed at S/L: 165 knots (306 km/h; 190 mph)
- Cruising speed at 3,050 m (10,000 ft) (62½% power): 156 knots (290 km/h; 180 mph)
- Cruising speed at S/L (70% power): 152 knots (282 km/h; 175 mph)
- Landing speed: 54 knots (100 km/h; 62 mph)
- Max rate of climb at S/L: 534 m (1,750 ft)/min
- Service ceiling: 5,490 m (18,000 ft)
- Service ceiling, one engine out: 1,525 m (5,000 ft)
- T-O run on land: 183 m (600 ft)
- T-O from smooth water: 10 sec
- Range with max fuel, 30 min reserves: 868 nm (1,600 km; 1,000 miles)

NWI

NORTHWEST INDUSTRIES LIMITED (Subsidiary of CAE Industries Ltd)

ADDRESS: Municipal Airport, PO Box 517, Edmonton, Alberta T5J 2K5
Telephone: (403) 455 3161

NWI was awarded in 1978 a Canadian government contract valued at nearly $17 million to extend the useful service life of CF-104 ground strike support aircraft of the Canadian Armed Forces. The programme, which will extend over a three-year period and employ more than 150 of NWI's 350 personnel, will ensure the continued active role of the CF-104 in its NATO and Canadian defence assignments until replaced by the proposed NFA (New Fighter Aircraft) sought by the Canadian government.

European-based CF-104s will be airlifted from Germany to Edmonton in Lockheed L 100-30 Commercial Hercules transport aircraft of Pacific Western Airlines, operated under subcontract to NWI.

TAC

TEAL AIRCRAFT CORPORATION

HEAD OFFICE AND WORKS: Buttonville Airport, Markham, Ontario M3P 3J9
Telephone: (416) 297 3027
Telex: 06219564
PRESIDENT: R. F. English

In the Spring of 1976, Teal acquired from Schweizer Aircraft Corporation the complete production tooling and fixtures, and all rights in the **Teal** amphibian, designed by Mr David B. Thurston. Teal Aircraft Corporation is the parent company, but it produced the aircraft, in developed form as the **TSC-1A3 Marlin,** at St Augustine, Florida, until Spring 1979. Manufacture was then terminated pending further financing.

TRIDENT

TRIDENT AIRCRAFT LIMITED

ADDRESS: PO Box 2428, Sidney, British Columbia V8L 3Y4
Telephone: (604) 656 7294
PRESIDENT: D. A. Hazlewood, PEng
CHIEF ENGINEER: J. C. Galizia

TRIDENT TR-1 TRIGULL

Design of the Trigull started in Canada in 1971. The first prototype (CF-TRI-X), then powered by a 212·5 kW (285 hp) Teledyne Continental Tiara engine, flew for the first time on 5 August 1973. A second prototype made its first flight on 2 July 1976, and a third airframe was completed for static tests. Certification from the Canadian Dept of Transport and the FAA was received on 28 October and 16 December 1976 respectively. The aircraft meets the requirements of FAR Pt 23 up to amendment 13 for strength and flying qualities.

Production of the Trigull has begun, and first deliveries are scheduled for June 1980, from new facilities near Victoria, Vancouver Island. Trident is to undertake all assembly work, but may subcontract the manufacture of some components. Firm orders for 47 aircraft had been received by June 1979.

TYPE: Six-seat light amphibian.

WINGS: Cantilever high-wing monoplane. Wing section NACA 23015R-4 (modified). Dihedral 2° from roots. Incidence 2° 15′. No sweepback. Two-spar aluminium (2024-T3) stressed-skin fail-safe structure, of constant chord, with drooped leading-edges. Electrically-operated single-slotted aluminium Fowler flap and Frise-type aileron on each trailing-edge. Ground-adjustable tab on port aileron.

FUSELAGE: Flying-boat type, with single-step hull and rear boom to support tail unit. Conventional semi-monocoque structure. Cabin, above the boat hull and forward of the engine pylon, is of glassfibre/foam sandwich. Engine cowling panels and doors are of glassfibre, wingtip float bottoms and other fairings of ABS plastics.

TAIL UNIT: Cantilever type, of 2024-T3 aluminium stressed-skin construction, with single sweptback fin and rudder. Variable-incidence tailplane, actuated by screwjack, with electrical trim. Balanced elevator, with tips of ABS plastics. Trim tab on rudder.

Trident TR-1 Trigull prototype (Teledyne Continental Tiara engine)

LANDING GEAR: Fuselage hull and independently retractable wingtip floats. Manually retractable water rudder, extending from air rudder. Retractable tricycle-type gear for operation on land, with single wheel on each unit. Electrical retraction of floats, hydraulic retraction of wheeled gear. Main wheels retract outward into wings, nosewheel (which is steerable) upward to lie semi-recessed in nose to act as bumper. Oleo-pneumatic shock-absorbers. Cleveland hydraulic disc brakes and parking brake. Main wheels and tube-type tyres size 7.00-6, nosewheel tyre size 6.00-6. Tyre pressure 2·41 bars (35 lb/sq in).

POWER PLANT: One 223.5 kW (300 hp) Lycoming IO-540-M1A5D flat-six fuel-injection engine, driving a Hartzell three-blade constant-speed reversible-pitch metal pusher propeller. A 261 kW (350 hp) turbo-charged Lycoming TIO-540-J2BD engine is to be offered optionally. Fuel in single bag-type tank in lower hull, capacity 378 litres (100 US gallons). Refuelling point in hull. Oil capacity 11.4 litres (3 US gallons).

ACCOMMODATION: Seating for pilot and up to five passengers, in three pairs, in enclosed, heated, ventilated and soundproofed cabin. Access via large forward-hinged door on each side and centre-hinged bow door on starboard side. Space for 68 kg (150 lb) of baggage aft of cabin, in compartment with restraint net, tiedown points and exterior lockable door. Dual controls optional. Alternative layouts available, for use as ambulance (one stretcher and one medical attendant in addition to pilot) or freighter.

SYSTEMS: Hydraulic system for landing gear actuation; manually operated standby pump. Electrical system includes 28V 50A alternator, 24V battery, and 28V voltage regulator.

AVIONICS AND EQUIPMENT: Basic VFR and IFR instrumentation standard. Radio and other avionics to customer's specification. Standard equipment includes cabin speaker, electric clock, magnetic compass, instrument panel glareshield, sensitive altimeter, outside air temperature gauge, rate of climb indicator, audible stall warning indicator, turn co-ordinator, flap position indicator, landing gear position indicator lights and audible warning indicator, aileron and elevator control locks, instrument post lights, cabin carpeting, pilot's storm window, windscreen defroster, overhead dome light, map pockets, inertia-reel shoulder harness for crew, front and rear adjustable cabin ventilators, tiedown and docking rings, landing/strobe/navigation lights, and towbar. Optional equipment includes anchor light, cabin cargo floor, courtesy lights, ELT, engine winterisation kit, fire extinguisher, first aid kit, two floor baggage containers, passenger headrests, microphone and headset, portable oxygen system, propeller spinner, quick-drain oil valve, rear bench seat with lap belts, seaplane operating kit, and tinted windows.

DIMENSIONS, EXTERNAL:
Wing span: floats up 12·73 m (41 ft 9 in)
floats down 11·84 m (38 ft 10 in)
Wing chord, constant 1·83 m (6 ft 0 in)
Wing aspect ratio: floats up 7·11
floats down 6·55
Length overall, wheels down 8·94 m (29 ft 4 in)
Height overall 3·81 m (12 ft 6 in)
Hull: Max width 1·22 m (4 ft 0 in)
Elevator span 4·70 m (15 ft 5 in)
Wheel track 3·66 m (12 ft 0 in)
Wheelbase 3·68 m (12 ft 1 in)
Propeller diameter 2·08 m (6 ft 10 in)
Passenger doors (each): Height 1·04 m (3 ft 5 in)
Width 1·036 m (3 ft 4·8 in)
Bow door (stbd): Height 0·99 m (3 ft 3 in)
Width 0·70 m (2 ft 3·4 in)
Baggage compartment door: Height 0·39 m (1 ft 3·4 in)
Width 0·50 m (1 ft 7·7 in)

DIMENSIONS, INTERNAL:
Cabin: Max length 2·46 m (8 ft 0·8 in)
Max width 1·19 m (3 ft 11 in)
Max height 1·275 m (4 ft 2·2 in)
Volume (cargo) 3·03 m³ (107 cu ft)
Aft baggage compartment volume 0·36 m³ (12·9 cu ft)

AREAS:
Wings, gross: floats up 22·78 m² (245·2 sq ft)
floats down 21·39 m² (230·2 sq ft)
Ailerons (total) 0·89 m² (9·6 sq ft)
Trailing-edge flaps (total) 4·11 m² (44·2 sq ft)
Fin 2·91 m² (31·3 sq ft)
Rudder 0·91 m² (9·8 sq ft)
Tailplane 2·75 m² (29·6 sq ft)
Elevators (total) 2·44 m² (26·3 sq ft)

WEIGHTS AND LOADINGS:
Basic operating weight, empty 1,134 kg (2,500 lb)
Max T-O weight 1,723 kg (3,800 lb)
Max wing loading:
floats up 75·64 kg/m² (15·50 lb/sq ft)
floats down 80·57 kg/m² (16·51 lb/sq ft)
Max power loading 7·70 kg/kW (12·67 lb/hp)

PERFORMANCE (at max T-O weight):
Never-exceed speed 183 knots (339 km/h; 211 mph)
Max level speed at S/L 148 knots (274 km/h; 170 mph)
Max cruising speed (75% power) at 1,830 m (6,000 ft) 140 knots (259 km/h; 161 mph)
Cruising speed at 3,050 m (10,000 ft):
65% power 136 knots (252 km/h; 157 mph)
60% power 131 knots (243 km/h; 151 mph)
45% power 107 knots (198 km/h; 123 mph)
Stalling speed, gear or floats down, power off 50 knots (93 km/h; 58 mph) CAS
Stalling speed, gear and floats up, power off 56 knots (104 km/h; 64·5 mph) CAS
Max rate of climb at S/L 326 m (1,070 ft)/min
Max rate of climb at 3,050 m (10,000 ft) 168 m (550 ft)/min
Service ceiling 5,490 m (18,000 ft)
T-O run at S/L, ISA: from land 275 m (900 ft)
from water 408 m (1,340 ft)
T-O to 15 m (50 ft) at S/L, ISA:
from land 503 m (1,650 ft)
from water 615 m (2,015 ft)
Landing from 15 m (50 ft) at S/L, ISA:
on land 485 m (1,590 ft)
on water 415 m (1,360 ft)
Landing run at S/L, ISA: on land 265 m (870 ft)
on water 238 m (780 ft)
Range with max usable fuel and 317·5 kg (700 lb) payload, incl pilot and allowances for T-O, climb, cruise, descent and landing, plus 45 min reserves:
75% power at 1,830 m (6,000 ft) 760 nm (1,408 km; 875 miles)
65% power at 3,050 m (10,000 ft) 825 nm (1,529 km; 950 miles)
60% power at 3,050 m (10,000 ft) 868 nm (1,609 km; 1,000 miles)
45% power at 3,050 m (10,000 ft) 977 nm (1,810 km; 1,125 miles)
Range with max payload, reserves as above 109 nm (201 km; 125 miles)

ZENAIR
ZENAIR LTD

HEAD OFFICE: 236 Richmond Street, Richmond Hill, Ontario L4C 3Y8
Telephone: (416) 884 9044
WORKS: 25 King Road, Nobleton, Ontario
Telephone: (416) 859 4556
PRESIDENT AND DESIGNER: Christophe Heintz

This company was formed by M Christophe Heintz, formerly designer with Avions Pierre Robin of France, to market plans, materials, parts and complete kits of his single-seat, two-seat and three-seat Zénith light aircraft (see Homebuilt Aircraft section).

Additionally, Zenair is now building prototypes of the four-seat Zénith-CH 400, intended for eventual factory production.

HEINTZ ZÉNITH-CH 400

Design began in 1976 of a new four-seat version of the Zénith which retains the basic configuration of the earlier aircraft but in scaled-up form. Construction of three prototypes at Zenair's plant began in September 1977, and the first of these was expected to fly for the first time in late 1979. The CH 400 is scheduled to be available in 1980 as a factory-built production aircraft.

TYPE: Four-seat light aircraft.

WINGS: Cantilever low-wing monoplane. Wing section NACA 33015. Dihedral 6° 30′ on tapered outer panels. Incidence 3° 30′. Single-spar aluminium alloy structure. Frise-type ailerons and slotted flaps of aluminium alloy. No tabs.

FUSELAGE: Conventional aluminium alloy stressed-skin structure of basically rectangular section, with rounded top-decking.

TAIL UNIT: Cantilever one-piece all-moving tailplane, with automatic and controllable anti-servo trim tab, and one-piece all-moving rudder (no fin). Single-spar structures, with ribs and skins of aluminium.

LANDING GEAR: Non-retractable tricycle type, with unidirectional glassfibre spring main-gear legs. All three wheels and tyres size 6·00-6, pressure 2·21 bars (32 lb/sq in). Hydraulically-actuated disc brakes on main gear. Steerable nosewheel. Wheel fairings optional.

POWER PLANT: One 134 kW (180 hp) Lycoming O-360 flat-four engine, driving a metal fixed-pitch propeller. Fuel tanks in wings, total capacity 210 litres (46 Imp gallons). Refuelling points in top of wings. Oil capacity 9 litres (2 Imp gallons).

ACCOMMODATION: Pilot and passenger on individual front seats, with rear bench seat for two further passengers. Forward-sliding Plexiglas canopy. Baggage compartment, with two separate doors, capacity 60 kg (132 lb).

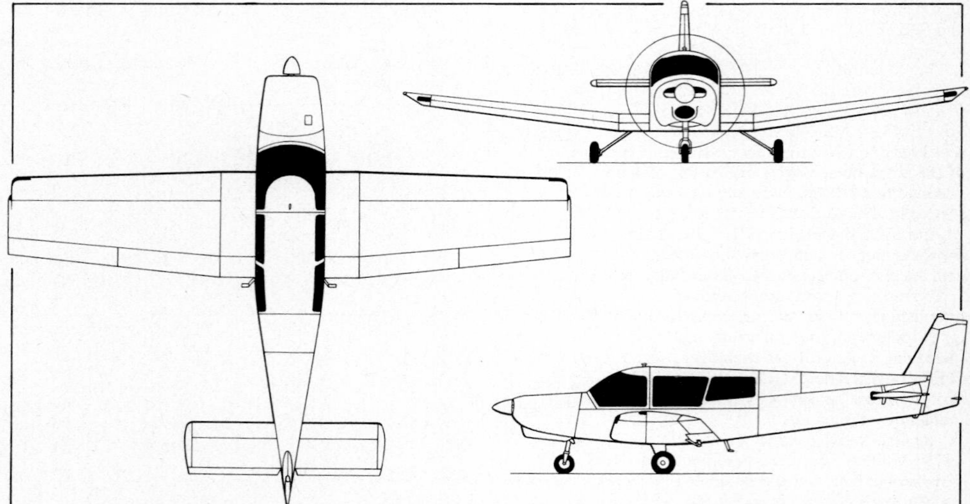

Heintz Zénith-CH 400 four-seat light aircraft (Lycoming O-360 engine) *(Michael A. Badrocke)*

SYSTEM: 12V alternator for electrical system.

AVIONICS: As required. Full IFR potential.

DIMENSIONS, EXTERNAL:
Wing span 9·20 m (30 ft 2¼ in)
Wing chord at root 1·82 m (5 ft 11¾ in)
Wing chord at tip 1·38 m (4 ft 6¼ in)
Wing aspect ratio 5·6
Length overall 7·80 m (25 ft 7 in)
Fuselage: Max width 1·12 m (3 ft 8 in)
Height overall 2·70 m (8 ft 10¼ in)
Tailplane span 3·00 m (9 ft 10 in)
Wheel track 3·00 m (9 ft 10 in)
Wheelbase 1·60 m (5 ft 3 in)
Propeller diameter 1·88 m (6 ft 2 in)
Propeller ground clearance 0·27 m (10¾ in)

AREAS:
Wings, gross 15·20 m² (163·6 sq ft)
Ailerons (total) 0·94 m² (10·12 sq ft)
Flaps (total) 1·62 m² (17·44 sq ft)
Rudder 1·15 m² (12·38 sq ft)
Tailplane (incl tabs) 2·70 m² (29·06 sq ft)

WEIGHTS AND LOADINGS:
Weight empty, equipped 650 kg (1,433 lb)
Max T-O weight 1,170 kg (2,580 lb)
Max wing loading 77 kg/m² (15·77 lb/sq ft)
Max power loading 8·73 kg/kW (14·33 lb/hp)

PERFORMANCE (estimated):
Never-exceed speed 188 knots (350 km/h; 217 mph)
Max level speed 146 knots (270 km/h; 168 mph)
Max cruising speed 135 knots (250 km/h; 155 mph)
Econ cruising speed 124 knots (230 km/h; 143 mph)
Stalling speed, flaps up 56 knots (103 km/h; 64 mph)
Stalling speed, flaps down 48·5 knots (90 km/h; 56 mph)
Max rate of climb at S/L 274 m (900 ft)/min
Service ceiling 4,875 m (16,000 ft)
T-O and landing run 244 m (800 ft)
T-O to, and landing from, 15 m (50 ft) 457 m (1,500 ft)
Range with max fuel and max payload 607 nm (1,125 km; 699 miles)
Endurance with max fuel and max payload 4 h 30 min

CHINA
(PEOPLE'S REPUBLIC)

STATE AIRCRAFT FACTORIES

WORKS: Shenyang, Liaoning Province; Sian, Shensi Province; Harbin, Heilungkiang Province; Shanghai, Chekiang Province; Peking, Hopei Province; and elsewhere

Longest-established of the Chinese national aircraft factories is the works at Shenyang, which had its origin in the Mukden plant of the Manshu Aeroplane Manufacturing Company, one of several aircraft and aero-engine manufacturing facilities established in Manchukuo (Manchuria) by the Japanese invaders in 1938. After the Communist regime became responsible for the whole of mainland China in 1949 the Manchurian factories were re-established and re-equipped with Soviet assistance. Today Shenyang (formerly Mukden), and Harbin (also known as Pinkiang) are the main centres of Chinese aircraft and aero-engine production, under the jurisdiction of the Third Ministry of Machine Building. There are design and development centres at Shenyang, Peking (now known as Beijing), Harbin and elsewhere.

In the middle and late 1950s the Shenyang factory produced in large numbers under licence several aircraft types, the first of these being the Yak-18, for which a licence agreement was signed in November 1952. In October 1954 this was followed by a licence for the Antonov An-2 biplane*, the Mil Mi-4 helicopter, and their ASh-62 and ASh-82 engines.

***CAAC airline timetables refer to the An-2 by the Chinese designation Yun-5 (Y-5), and other transports have appeared in Chinese publications with Y prefixes which have been reported in the Western press. On other occasions, the Chinese have used a prefix C when referring to the same aircraft. This is, perhaps, more logical, being consistent with use of the Westernised F, B and T for fighters, bombers and trainers respectively.**

First jet aircraft to be built in China were the single-seat MiG-15bis and two-seat MiG-15UTI, both of which have the Chinese name Sinshi-lyan Chaen-to Chi (Type 2 Fighting Aeroplane) and designation **F-2**. These were followed by the MiG-17F (Sinshi-si Chaen-to Chi: Type 4 Fighting Aeroplane, designation **F-4**) and MiG-17PF (Sinshi-wu Chaen-to Chi: Type 5 Fighting Aeroplane, designation **F-5**). The MiG fighters and their Klimov VK-1 engines were produced at Shenyang, deliveries of both the MiG-15UTI and MiG-17F beginning in late 1956; by mid-1959 these were almost totally of Chinese manufacture. A 'UTI' tandem two-seat conversion of the MiG-17F/F-4 was also produced by the Chinese: this, too, has the designation F-4, and is a standard advanced trainer type. Several hundred MiG-15s (mostly UTIs) remain in service, and over 1,000 F-4s and F-5s still equip more than 20 air regiments in air-to-air and fighter-bomber roles. A small number of F-4s also continues in service with the Aviation of the People's Navy. F-4s were exported to Albania (30), Kampuchea and North Viet-Nam. These types were followed by Chinese versions of the MiG-19 (F-6) and MiG-21 (F-7).

Aircraft built at the Sian works include the Soviet Tupolev Tu-16 bomber (Chinese designation B-6) and the Yin-an No. 1 utility aircraft. Harbin's products have included the Czechoslovak Super Aero 45 two/three-passenger twin-engined utility aircraft, the Heilungkiang No. 1 agricultural/utility aircraft resembling the Soviet Yak-12, the Soviet Ilyushin Il-28 jet bomber (Chinese B-5) and, currently, the C-11 agricultural/utility light twin. Another Yak-12 development, known as the Red Banner No. 1, was produced at Peking, together with two light piston-engined transports known as the Capital No. 1 and Peking No. 1. Most of the older types were illustrated in *Jane's* between 1959 and 1964.

The capability of China's aircraft industry has been revealed most openly by study of the F-6 single-seat day fighters supplied to Pakistan, generally similar to the Soviet MiG-19SF. An assessment of the F-6 by a western observer described the general standard of workmanship of the airframe as very good. At low altitudes this fighter was said to outmanoeuvre any type of combat aircraft in service in Asia except the F-86, and to outclimb the MiG-21 and F-104 Starfighter. The potential of the Pakistani F-6s was much enhanced by supplementing their standard cannon armament with two Sidewinder missiles.

The indications are that output of older fighters is now diminishing, with increasing emphasis being placed on the development of new aircraft making use of China's increasing technological capability. The F-6bis 'Fantan' twin-jet fighter-bomber is in production and service, and prototypes are being flown of an all-weather interceptor of indigenous design.

The Chairman of the US Joint Chiefs of Staff, in his FY 1979 Military Posture statement, reported that the Chinese Air Force of the People's Liberation Army then had an operational home defence fighter force of about 4,000 MiG-15s, -17s, -19s and -21s, and a tactical air force of more than 1,000 MiG-15s, Tupolev Tu-2s, Ilyushin Il-28s and 'Fantan-As'. The Chinese Air Force currently deploys a medium bomber force of more than 80 Tu-16s, which are nuclear-capable. About 70 MRBMs and IRBMs are also deployed in a strategic role.

SHENYANG (MIKOYAN) F-6

Chinese name: Sinshi-liyu Chaen-to Chi (Type 6 Fighting Aeroplane)

NATO reporting names: Farmer-C (MiG-19SF) and Farmer-D (MiG-19PF)

The F-6 is basically a MiG-19 fighter built under licence in China. Its original design was initiated by the Mikoyan bureau in the USSR, where the I-350 prototype flew for the first time in September 1953.

The initial production MiG-19 day fighter began to enter service with the Soviet air defence force in early 1955. Before long an all-moving tailplane replaced the former, ineffective, elevators. This new version, which also had three 30 mm guns (instead of the original armament of one 37 mm and two 23 mm cannon) and introduced an attachment under each wing for a bomb or air-to-surface rocket, was known as the MiG-19S (for Stabilisator).

With the adoption in 1957 of the Tumansky (Mikulin) R-9 axial-flow turbojet as the standard power plant, the aircraft's designation was again changed, to MiG-19SF (Forsirovanny; increased power). At the same time, another version with limited all-weather capability was put into production as the MiG-19PF (Perekhvatchik; interceptor), with a small Izumrud (Emerald) radar scanner inside its engine air intake and a ranging unit in the intake top lip. The later MiG-19PM (Modifikatsirovanny; modified) differed from the PF in having four first-generation radar-homing missiles (NATO 'Alkali') instead of guns.

In the Soviet Union the MiG-19 was phased out of production by the end of the 'fifties, but a licence agreement for its manufacture in China was signed in January 1958. Many MiG-19s had been delivered to China in knocked-down form before the deterioration of Moscow-Peking relations. The designation F-6 was given to the Chinese version of the MiG-19S fighter, which first flew in December 1961 and from mid-1962 became standard equipment in the Chinese Air Force of the People's Liberation Army.

Chinese two-seat training versions of the MiG-17F/F-4

Production of the F-6 was stepped up from about 1966, and several thousand have been built to date, including counterparts of the Soviet MiG-19PF and MiG-19SF versions. China has developed a number of variants of its own design. One of these is a tactical reconnaissance model, with a camera pack in the lower forward fuselage. The F-6 from Sinkiang air base in Fukien Province, whose pilot defected to Taiwan in July 1977, was one of the original Soviet-supplied aircraft converted to this configuration. It was equipped with a vertical/oblique camera installation in the lower forward fuselage, from which the underfuselage 30 mm cannon had been deleted. This aircraft was reported to belong to the 1st Reconnaissance Air Unit; the two wing-root cannon showed no traces of having been fired.

Another purely-Chinese development is the **TF-6**, a trainer version with a tandem two-seat cockpit installation similar to those in the UTI versions of the MiG-15 and MiG-17. The 'Fantan-A' strike fighter, derived from the F-6 and formerly referred to as the F-9, is now known to have the designation **F-6bis**; this is described separately.

Production of the F-6 series is believed to be continuing, at a rate of about 100-120 a year. Some of the limited all-weather models have a different centrebody radar housing of longer, slim-conical form.

Immediately after the Indo-Pakistan war of September 1965, China offered F-6s to Pakistan. Forty were supplied initially and the first PAF squadron was operational within a year. Subsequent deliveries brought to 150 the total of F-6s acquired by Pakistan, and by early 1978 these equipped seven PAF ground-attack squadrons. By the Spring of 1974 the Air Wing of the Tanzanian People's Defence Force had received sufficient F-6s for a single squadron; 40 have been delivered to Egypt.

In the Chinese Air Force of the PLA, the F-6 equips more than 40 air regiments, each regiment having three or four squadrons. Roles for which the aircraft are employed include air-to-air interception, battlefield interdiction, close support, counter air and tactical reconnaissance. The F-6 also serves in small numbers with the Aviation of the People's Navy.

The following description is based on known details of the basic MiG-19SF, modified where possible to apply specifically to the Chinese F-6:

TYPE: Single-seat day fighter, attack and tactical reconnaissance aircraft.

WINGS: Cantilever all-metal mid-wing monoplane. Wing section TsAGI S-12S at root, SR-7S at tip. Thickness/chord ratio (mean) 8·24%. Anhedral 4° 30'. Sweepback at quarter-chord 55°. Entire trailing-edge of each wing formed by aileron (outboard) and large Fowler-type flap, both hydraulically powered. Compressed-air emergency extension system for flaps. Trim tab in port aileron. Large full-chord boundary layer fence above each wing at mid-span to enhance aileron effectiveness.

FUSELAGE: Conventional all-metal semi-monocoque structure of circular section, with divided air intake in nose and side-by-side twin orifices at rear. Top and bottom 'pen-nib' fairings aft of nozzles. Entire rear fuselage detaches at wing trailing-edge for engine servicing. Forward-hinged door-type airbrake, operated hydraulically, on each side of fuselage aft of wing

Camera windows identify the tactical reconnaissance F-6

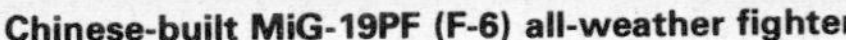

Chinese-built MiG-19PF (F-6) all-weather fighter

Note the unusual slim pointed radome fitted to the F-6 (MiG-19PF) at the rear

trailing-edge. Forward-hinged perforated door-type airbrake under centre-fuselage. Shallow ventral strake under rear fuselage. Upward-hinged pitot boom mounted on lower lip of nose intake.

Tail Unit: Conventional all-metal structure. Hydraulically-actuated one-piece horizontal surfaces, with electrical emergency actuation in the event of hydraulic failure. Anti-flutter weight projecting forward from each tailplane tip. Stick-to-tailplane gearing, via electro-mechanical linkage, reduces required stick forces during high-*g* manoeuvres. Sweepback on vertical surfaces 57° 30′. Electrically-actuated trim tab in rudder. Large dorsal fin between fin and dorsal spine enclosing actuating rods for tail control surfaces.

Landing Gear: Wide-track retractable tricycle type, with single wheel on each unit. Hydraulic actuation, nosewheel forward, main units inward into wing roots. Pneumatic emergency extension system. All units of levered-suspension type, with oleo-pneumatic shock-absorbers. Main-wheel tyres size 660 × 200 mm; max pressure 9·8 bars (142 lb/sq in). Nosewheel tyre size 500 × 180; pressure 6·9 bars (100 lb/sq in). Pneumatically-operated brakes on main wheels, with pneumatic emergency backup. Pneumatically-deployed brake parachute housed in bottom of rear fuselage above ventral strake. Small tail bumper.

Power Plant: Two Chinese-built versions of Tumansky (Mikulin bureau) R-9B turbojet, each rated at 25·5 kN (5,730 lb st) dry and 31·9 kN (7,165 lb st) with afterburning. Hydraulically-actuated nozzles. Two main fuel tanks in tandem between cockpit and engines, and two smaller tanks under forward end of engine tailpipes, total capacity 2,170 litres (477 Imp gallons). Provision for two 800 litre (176 Imp gallon) underwing drop-tanks, raising max total fuel capacity to 3,770 litres (829 Imp gallons).

Accommodation: Pilot only, on ejection seat (Martin-Baker PKD Mk 10 automatic zero-zero rocket-assisted type in Pakistani aircraft), under rearward-sliding blister canopy. In emergency canopy is jettisoned by an explosive charge at the lock, after which it is carried away by the slipstream. Fluid anti-icing system for windscreen. Cockpit pressurised, heated and air-conditioned.

Systems: Cockpit pressurised by air-conditioning system mounted in top of fuselage aft of cockpit, using compressor bleed air. Constant temperature maintained by adjustable electric thermostat. Two independent hydraulic systems. Main system, powered by pump on starboard engine, actuates landing gear retraction and extension, flaps, airbrakes and afterburner nozzle mechanism. System for tailplane and aileron boosters is powered by a pump on the port engine, and can also be supplied by the main system should the booster system fail. Electrical system powered by two DC starter/generators, supplemented by a battery, providing 27V DC, and 115V 400Hz and 36V 400Hz AC.

Avionics and Equipment: Standard avionics include VHF radio, blind-flying equipment, radio compass, radio altimeter, tail-warning system, navigation lights, taxying light on nosewheel leg and landing light in bottom of front fuselage.

Armament: Installed armament of two or three 30 mm NR-30 guns, one in each wing root and (not on MiG-19PF) one under starboard side of nose. Aircraft supplied to Pakistan have an attachment under each wing for a Sidewinder air-to-air missile, outboard of drop-tank. Alternatively, an attachment inboard of each tank for a bomb weighing up to 250 kg (or 500 lb), a rocket of up to 212 mm calibre, or a pack of eight air-to-air rockets. Optical gunsight. Gun camera in top lip of air intake of MiG-19SF; Izumrud airborne interception radar in centre of nose intake of MiG-19PF, with ranging unit in top lip of intake.

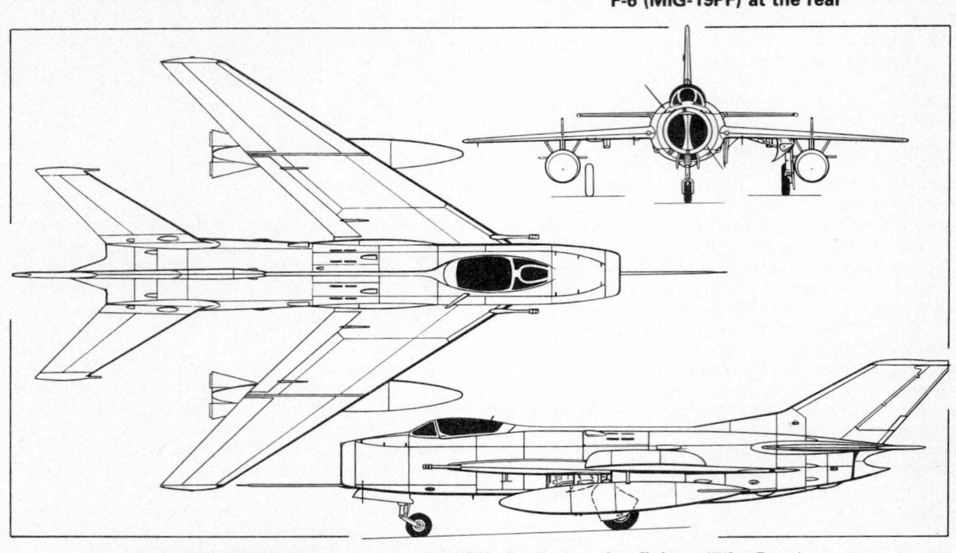

Shenyang F-6 (Chinese-built MiG-19SF) single-seat day fighter *(Pilot Press)*

Dimensions, external:

Wing span	9·00 m (29 ft 6½ in)
Wing chord, mean	3·02 m (9 ft 10¾ in)
Wing aspect ratio	3·24
Length overall (MiG-19SF):	
incl nose probe	14·90 m (48 ft 10½ in)
excl nose probe	12·60 m (41 ft 4 in)
Length of fuselage	11·82 m (38 ft 9½ in)
Height overall	4·02 m (13 ft 2¼ in)
Tailplane span	5·00 m (16 ft 4¾ in)
Wheel track	4·15 m (13 ft 7½ in)

Areas:

Wings, gross	25·00 m^2 (269 sq ft)
Airbrakes (three, total)	1·50 m^2 (16·15 sq ft)
Ventral strake	0·614 m^2 (6·61 sq ft)

Weights and Loadings:

Weight empty, nominal	5,760 kg (12,700 lb)
Normal T-O weight	7,600 kg (16,755 lb)
Max T-O weight	8,700 kg (19,180 lb)
Max wing loading	348 kg/m^2 (71·28 lb/sq ft)
Max power loading	136·4 kg/kN (1·34 lb/lb st)

Performance:

Max level speed at 10,000 m (32,800 ft)	783 knots (1,452 km/h; 902 mph)
Cruising speed	512 knots (950 km/h; 590 mph)
Stalling speed, flaps up	189 knots (350 km/h; 218 mph)
Landing speed	127 knots (235 km/h; 146 mph)
Max rate of climb at S/L	6,900 m (22,635 ft)/min
Time to service ceiling	8 min 12 s
Service ceiling	17,900 m (58,725 ft)
Absolute ceiling	19,870 m (65,190 ft)
T-O run, with afterburning	515 m (1,690 ft)
T-O run, with underwing tanks, no afterburning	900 m (2,953 ft)
T-O to 25 m (82 ft), with afterburning	1,525 m (5,000 ft)
T-O to 25 m (82 ft), with underwing tanks, no afterburning	1,880 m (6,170 ft)
Landing from 25 m (82 ft), with brake-chute	1,700 m (5,580 ft)
Landing from 25 m (82 ft), without brake-chute	1,980 m (6,495 ft)
Landing run, with brake-chute	600 m (1,970 ft)
Landing run, without brake-chute	890 m (2,920 ft)
Combat radius with external tanks	370 nm (685 km; 426 miles)
Normal range at 14,000 m (46,000 ft)	750 nm (1,390 km; 863 miles)
Max range with external tanks	1,187 nm (2,200 km; 1,366 miles)
Max endurance at 14,000 m (46,000 ft)	2 h 38 min

F-6bis

Chinese name: Sinshi-liyu-itsi Chaen-to Chi (Type 6bis Fighting Aeroplane)

NATO reporting name: Fantan-A

This twin-engined fighter-bomber, derived from the F-6/MiG-19 produced in China, was thought formerly to have the Chinese designation F-9. Its correct designation is F-6bis; photographs which became available in 1979 have enabled some earlier reports to be confirmed and some additional features of the aircraft to be observed.

The airframe is based substantially upon that of the F-6, with overall dimensions increased by about 10% to give a longer fuselage, higher aspect ratio wings and taller vertical tail surfaces. The wings retain the four external attachment points and large boundary layer fences of the F-6. The principal change of configuration occurs in the forward fuselage, which is longer than that of the F-6 and terminates in a 'solid' conical nose radome. Introduction of this radome has necessitated the provision of lateral air intakes for the twin engines, abreast of the single-seat cockpit, and the shape of these increases the area-rule 'waisting' of the central portion of the fuselage. The cockpit canopy differs from that on the F-6 in being hinged at the rear to open upwards. The centre and rear fuselage sections retain the various louvres and external airscoops of the F-6, supporting the belief that the latter's power plant of two side-by-side Chinese-built Tumansky (Mikulin bureau) R-9B turbojet engines remains basically unchanged. One report has suggested that the engines in the F-6bis are designated R-9B-811, having a rating of 25·5 kN (5,730 lb st) dry and 36·8 kN (8,267 lb st) with afterburning. The taller main fin has a smaller dorsal fin than the F-6, and the strake fairing below the tail is shorter. Horizontal tail surfaces, including anti-flutter weights at their tips, appear to be the same as those of the F-6. As on the F-6, the nosewheel retracts forward, the main units inward into the wings, and there is a brake parachute housed in the tailcone.

The F-6bis retains the two wing-mounted 30 mm cannon of the F-6, these now occupying the revised wing-root position outboard of the engine air intake trunks. The third (nose-mounted) gun carried by most versions of the F-6 appears to be omitted. Underwing weapon load is thought to be in the order of 1,000 kg (2,205 lb), typical combinations including two 500 kg or four 250 kg bombs, two 250 kg bombs and two drop-tanks, two 'Atoll' type air-to-air missiles, or four pods each with eight 57 mm air-to-surface rockets (S-5 type or similar). Drop-tanks, usually carried on the outboard pylon beneath each wing, appear to be of the same size as the 800 litre (176 Imp gallon) tanks carried in this position by the F-6. There appears to be also an internal fuselage weapons bay, capable of housing about 1,500 kg (3,300 lb) of stores, aft of the airbrake.

Details of the F-6bis avionics are necessarily speculative, but one report has suggested that the nose radar may be similar to the Soviet R2L (NATO 'Spin Scan B'); and that other equipment includes items based on, or similar to, the SRO-2 IFF (NATO 'Odd Rods'), ARK-5 radio compass, RV-UM low-altitude radio altimeter, MRP-48P marker beacon receiver, and RSIU-4 VHF com radio. Such details should, however, be regarded as highly provisional.

The majority of 'Fantan-As' are in service with tactical strike fighter squadrons of the Chinese Air Force of the People's Liberation Army, but the type is also known to serve in an air defence role with the Aviation of the People's Navy.

DIMENSIONS, EXTERNAL (estimated):
- Wing span — 10·20 m (33 ft 5 in)
- Length overall — 15·25 m (50 ft 0 in)

WEIGHTS (estimated):
- Weight empty — 6,200 kg (13,670 lb)
- Max T-O weight — 10,700 kg (23,590 lb)
- Max landing weight — 9,200 kg (20,280 lb)

PERFORMANCE (estimated):
- Max level speed at high altitude — close to Mach 2 (1,145 knots; 2,125 km/h; 1,320 mph)
- Max level speed at low altitude — Mach 1·56 (1,032 knots; 1,913 km/h; 1,188 mph)
- Service ceiling — 16,000 m (52,500 ft)
- T-O run — 620 m (2,035 ft)
- T-O to 15 m (50 ft) — 920 m (3,020 ft)
- Landing run — 900 m (2,950 ft)
- Combat radius — up to 430 nm (800 km; 500 miles)

F-6bis tactical strike fighters, in service with the Chinese Air Force

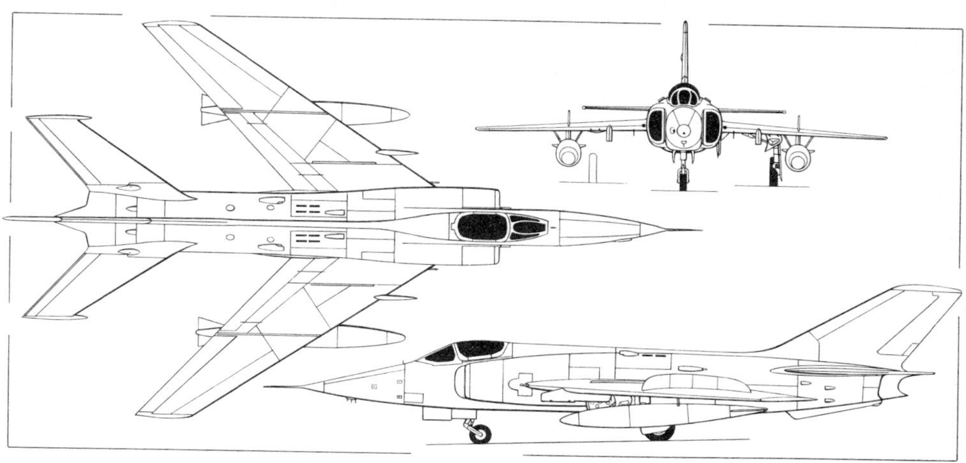
F-6bis 'Fantan-A' single-seat twin-jet combat aircraft *(Pilot Press)*

F-7 (MIKOYAN MiG-21)

Chinese name: Sinshi-tsi Chaen-to Chi (Type 7 Fighting Aeroplane)
NATO reporting name: Fishbed

Design of this Chinese copy of the Mikoyan MiG-21 fighter was based initially on that of a number of Soviet-built MiG-21Fs ('Fishbed-Cs') delivered to China prior to the political break in 1960. The difficult task of copying the airframe, R-11 afterburning turbojet and equipment was completed so quickly that the F-7 made its first flight in December 1964 and began to enter service with the Chinese Air Force of the PLA in 1965. The design was later updated by reference to Soviet-built MiG-21PFs ('Fishbed-D') when examples of the latter were staged through China en route to North Viet-Nam.

In early 1975 General George S. Brown, USAF, told the Senate Armed Services Committee that China "has produced a number of MiG-21s, but for reasons which are not yet fully clear . . .production was suspended and only a small number of PRC (People's Republic of China) produced MiG-21s are operational with the PRC Air Force. The balance of the operational MiG-21s were Soviet-provided some years ago".

Chinese production of the MiG-21 was reported to have ended in 1966 after between 60 and 80 had been completed, but may have been resumed more recently. The MiG-21/F-7 is currently believed to equip only two air regiments of the People's Liberation Army.

F-8 and F-9

These designations are now thought to apply to Chinese-designed fighters powered respectively by single and twin Tumansky R-11 turbojet engines. Neither is believed to have entered production.

F-12

Agency reports originating in Hong Kong in late 1977 referred to this new fighter, which is under development in China. It is thought possible that the F-12 may make use of technology gleaned from the Soviet MiG-23 'Flogger' variable-geometry fighter-bomber, one or more examples of which were offered to China by Egypt in 1976. Other reports of this aircraft, which should be regarded as very provisional, suggest that it is intended to have a maximum speed of up to Mach 2·4 and to be able to operate from 600 m (1,970 ft) airstrips. Gross weight is thought to be in the order of 20,000 kg (44,100 lb), the power plant probably being a pair of Rolls-Royce RB.168-25R Spey Mk 202M afterburning turbofan engines (each 54·5 kN; 12,250 lb st dry, 91·25 kN; 20,515 lb st with afterburning). First flight is not expected to take place before 1980.

Il-28U (NATO 'Mascot') tandem-cockpit training version of the Il-28 bomber

HARBIN (ILYUSHIN) B-5

Chinese name: Sinshi-wu Houng-chai Chi (Type 5 Bombing Aeroplane)
NATO reporting name: Beagle

First flown in 1948, the Il-28 three-seat tactical light bomber entered service in the Soviet Union in 1949-50. Several thousand were built subsequently in the USSR and Czechoslovakia, including variants designated Il-28R (reconnaissance-bomber), Il-28T (torpedo-carrying) and Il-28U (training). Many were exported to other Communist states, including China, where the Il-28 entered licence production at Harbin after the political break with the Soviet Union. A dual-control version is also produced in China.

According to the US FY 1979 Military Posture statement, Chinese planners "still appear to consider it an important weapon system. Four hundred Il-28s are now operational (in China); the number, if any, configured for nuclear weapons delivery is unknown".

The Il-28/B-5 is believed to equip about a dozen air regiments of the People's Liberation Army; about 100 more are in service with the Aviation of the People's Navy.

A detailed description of the Il-28 can be found in the 1963-64 *Jane's;* the following are its leading characteristics:

POWER PLANT: Two 27·07 kN (6,085 lb st) Klimov VK-1 turbojet engines. Standard internal fuel capacity 7,908 litres (1,740 Imp gallons).

ARMAMENT: Four 23 mm NR-23 cannon, two in underside of forward fuselage (each 100 rounds) and two in remotely controlled tail turret (each 225 rounds). Internal weapons bay for up to 3,000 kg (6,615 lb) of bombs or one torpedo.

DIMENSIONS, EXTERNAL:
- Wing span — 21·45 m (70 ft 4½ in)
- Wing area, gross — 60·80 m² (654·45 sq ft)
- Length of fuselage — 17·65 m (57 ft 11 in)
- Height overall — 6·20 m (20 ft 4 in)

WEIGHTS:

Weight empty	12,890 kg (28,417 lb)
Normal T-O weight	18,400 kg (40,565 lb)
Max T-O weight	23,200 kg (51,150 lb)

PERFORMANCE (at normal T-O weight except where indicated):

Max level speed:
at S/L 432 knots (800 km/h; 497 mph)
at 1,750 m (5,740 ft) 472 knots (875 km/h; 544 mph)
at 4,500 m (14,765 ft) 486 knots (900 km/h; 559 mph)
at 12,000 m (39,370 ft) 434 knots (805 km/h; 500 mph)

Max rate of climb at S/L	900 m (2,952 ft)/min
Service ceiling	12,300 m (40,350 ft)
T-O run at max T-O weight	1,620 m (5,315 ft)
Landing run at AUW of 14,850 kg (32,630 lb)	920 m (3,020 ft)

Range with max fuel:
at 18,400 kg (40,565 lb) AUW at 1,000 m (3,280 ft) 612 nm (1,135 km; 705 miles)
at 21,000 kg (46,297 lb) AUW at 10,000 m (32,800 ft) 1,176 nm (2,180 km; 1,355 miles)

SIAN (TUPOLEV) B-6

Chinese name: Sinshi-liyu Houng-chai Chi (Type 6 Bombing Aeroplane)
NATO reporting name: Badger

First steps to assemble the Tupolev Tu-16 bomber under licence in China were taken in 1958, but work was suspended in 1960 after the political break with the USSR. A production programme was reinstated some two years later, and the formidable task was undertaken of copying the design without Soviet assistance. Deliveries of the Chinese-built B-6 version did not begin until about 1968. Six of the 12 nuclear devices tested at Lop Nor up to 1971 were air-dropped from Tu-16/B-6s, but production of this aircraft has been relatively slow. By the early 1970s, about 60 had been completed.

The FY 1979 Military Posture statement by General George S. Brown, USAF, Chairman of the US Joint Chiefs of Staff, suggested that "More than 80 of these Soviet-designed bombers are now operational. Although no radical changes to the 'Badger' basic design are expected, limited production of ECM, reconnaissance or tanker variants could be initiated at any time. An air-to-surface missile carrier still remains a possibility in the future."

HARBIN (MIL) H-5

Chinese name: Sinshi-wu Chiou-sung Chi (Type 5 Vertical-flight Aeroplane)
NATO reporting name: Hound

The H-5 is the Chinese-built military version of the Mil Mi-4 general-purpose helicopter, some 300-350 of which are estimated to be in service with the Air Force of the People's Liberation Army. A further 50 or so serve with the Aviation of the People's Navy for anti-submarine and search and rescue duties.

A civil version of the Mi-4/H-5 has the Chinese name **Syuan Fen** (Whirlwind).

At least two other types of helicopter are believed to have been developed in China; one of these is an Mi-4 derivative fitted with a Pratt & Whitney Aircraft of Canada PT6T-6 Turbo Twin Pac turboshaft power plant.

SHENYANG (YAKOVLEV) BT-5

Chinese name: Sinshi-wu Kao Chi Chao Lien (Type 5 Basic Trainer)
NATO reporting name: Max

A Sino-Soviet agreement of November 1952 provided for the licence manufacture in China of the Yakovlev Yak-18 (Chinese name: Sinshi-san Tso Chi Chao Lien: Type 3 Primary Trainer) and its 119 kW (160 hp) M-11FR engine. The first example was flown in July 1954; Chinese-built engines were introduced in 1956.

The original Yak-18 was superseded by the Yak-18A, following a subsequent agreement in January 1958 for this version to be built in China, where it has the designation BT-5. Ivchenko AI-14R engines for the BT-5 were also manufactured in China as the Hou-sai-5. The BT-5 was superseded in production and service by the BT-6 (which see).

SHENYANG BT-6

Chinese name: Sinshi-liyu Kao Chi Chao Lien (Type 6 Basic Trainer)

Despite a close similarity to the Yak-18A/BT-5 (see previous entry), the BT-6 is regarded as an essentially indigenous design of the Chinese aerospace industry, and was the first such design to enter large-scale production.

Evolved to replace the BT-5 in the basic training role, the two-seat BT-6 is powered by a 213 kW (285 hp) Hou-sai-6 nine-cylinder aircooled radial engine, based on the Ivchenko AI-14RF and driving a two-blade propeller. It is reported to have been in production since 1961, with more than 2,000 delivered, including exports to North Korea, North Viet-Nam and Zambia. As shown in the accompanying illustrations, features include a tricycle landing gear and large, square-cut vertical tail surfaces.

Harbin B-5 (Il-28) bomber of the Chinese Air Force taxying out for a night exercise

WEIGHTS:

Weight empty	1,095 kg (2,415 lb)
Max fuel	110 kg (243 lb)
Max T-O weight	1,400 kg (3,088 lb)

PERFORMANCE:

Max level speed	155 knots (286 km/h; 178 mph)
Landing speed	62 knots (115 km/h; 71·5 mph)
Max rate of climb at S/L	380 m (1,248 ft)/min
Service ceiling	5,080 m (16,680 ft)
T-O run	280 m (920 ft)
Landing run	350 m (1,150 ft)
Endurance	3 h 36 min

HARBIN (ANTONOV) C-5 (Y-5)

Chinese name: Sinshi-wu Yuong-shu Chi (Type 5 Transport Aeroplane)
NATO reporting name: Colt

The Antonov An-2 general-purpose biplane was supplied to, and built under licence in, China in considerable numbers (more than 1,000). It has been used extensively in a civil capacity for agricultural and general transport work, and several hundred still serve with the Chinese Air Force.

Chinese-produced examples have included a number of variants differing from the standard Soviet- or Polish-built production models, and some of them have reportedly been fitted with turboprop power plants.

SHANGHAI C-10 (Y-10)

The first prototype jet airliner of Chinese design and manufacture was nearing completion in mid-1979. No details were then available except that it is a medium-size low-wing monoplane with three Pratt & Whitney JT3D turbofan engines and seating for about 140 passengers.

HARBIN C-11 (Y-11)

Chinese name: Sinshi-shi Yuong-shu Chi (Type 11 Transport Aeroplane)

First details of this new Chinese twin-engined utility aircraft were given on 26 August 1977, in the French/Chinese publication *Chine Nouvelle,* which stated that it had been designed and developed by the Chinese aerospace industry and was in production as a replacement for the Antonov An-2, which has the Chinese designation C-5 or Y-5. First flight is believed to have taken place in 1975, and production takes place at the Harbin Aircraft Works.

The C-11 is intended for use primarily in agricultural and forestry applications, and was described as "a new contribution towards speeding up the modernisation of agriculture" in China. In June/July 1977, it underwent operational trials for crop-dusting and spraying missions.

In overall size and general configuration the C-11 resembles the Australian GAF Nomad, in which the Chinese government reportedly expressed an interest in

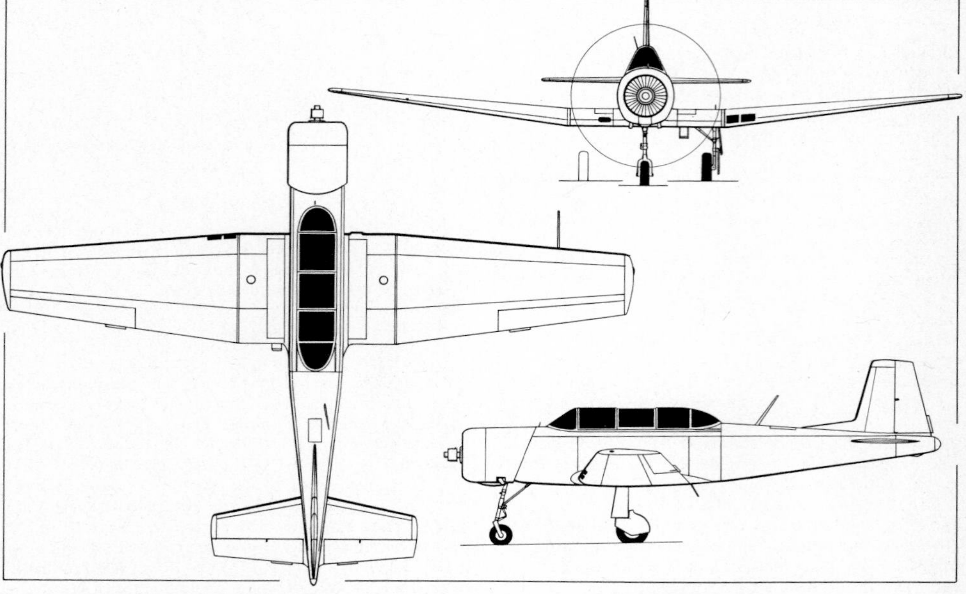

Shenyang BT-6 tandem two-seat basic training aircraft *(Pilot Press)*

Shenyang BT-6 basic trainer (Chinese-built Hou-sai-6 engine)

1976-77. Its engines are fitted with louvred intakes to control cooling, and may be related to the Soviet Vedeneev-developed Ivchenko AI-14RF.

TYPE: Twin-engined agricultural and general-purpose aircraft.

WINGS: Braced high-wing all-metal monoplane, with constant chord from root to tip. No dihedral. Drooping ailerons and two-section slotted flaps along full span of trailing-edges. Leading-edge slats from nacelle to tip of each wing, with smaller inboard flap or slat on each side between nacelle and fuselage. Small stub-wings at cabin floor level support the main landing gear units; bracing strut from each stub-wing out to approx mid-span.

FUSELAGE: Conventional semi-monocoque all-metal structure of basically rectangular cross-section, swept upward at rear.

TAIL UNIT: Cantilever non-swept metal structure, with low-set tailplane and small dorsal fin. Horn-balanced rudder and elevators. Inset tab in rudder and port elevator.

LANDING GEAR: Non-retractable tricycle type, with oleo-pneumatic shock-absorber in each unit. Twin-wheel main units, attached to underside of stub-wings. Single steerable nosewheel. Small bumper under tailcone.

POWER PLANT: Two 213 kW (285 hp) Hou-sai-6 nine-cylinder radial aircooled engines, each driving a two-blade variable-pitch propeller, underslung from wings and fitted with louvred intakes in front of cylinders to control cooling.

ACCOMMODATION: Crew of two on flight deck, with separate forward-opening door(s) for access. Dual controls. Cabin accommodates six to eight passengers or equivalent cargo. Cargo/passenger double door on port side of fuselage, in line with wing trailing-edge. Underside of rear fuselage, aft of this door, probably lets down to act as a loading ramp for bulky cargo.

AVIONICS AND EQUIPMENT: Radio; operational equipment according to mission. Agricultural version has hopper with capacity of 855 kg (1,885 lb) or 975 litres (214 Imp gallons), and six rotary atomisers for spraying.

DIMENSIONS, EXTERNAL:
Wing span 17·00 m (55 ft 9¼ in)
Wing aspect ratio 8·5
Length overall 12·017 m (39 ft 5⅛ in)
Height overall 4·64 m (15 ft 2¾ in)
Wheel track (c/l of shock-absorbers) approx 3·00 m (9 ft 10 in)
Wheelbase approx 3·70 m (12 ft 1¾ in)

DIMENSIONS, INTERNAL:
Cabin: Length 3·58 m (11 ft 9 in)
Width 1·27 m (4 ft 2 in)
Height 1·48 m (4 ft 10¼ in)

AREA:
Wings, gross 34·00 m² (365·97 sq ft)

WEIGHTS:
Weight empty 2,050 kg (4,519 lb)
Fuel load 210 kg (463 lb)
Max T-O weight 3,500 kg (7,715 lb)

PERFORMANCE:
Max level speed 119 knots (220 km/h; 137 mph)
Cruising speed, 57% power 89 knots (165 km/h; 102 mph)
Service ceiling 4,000 m (13,125 ft)
T-O and landing run 140 m (460 ft)

C-11 utility aircraft under construction at Harbin

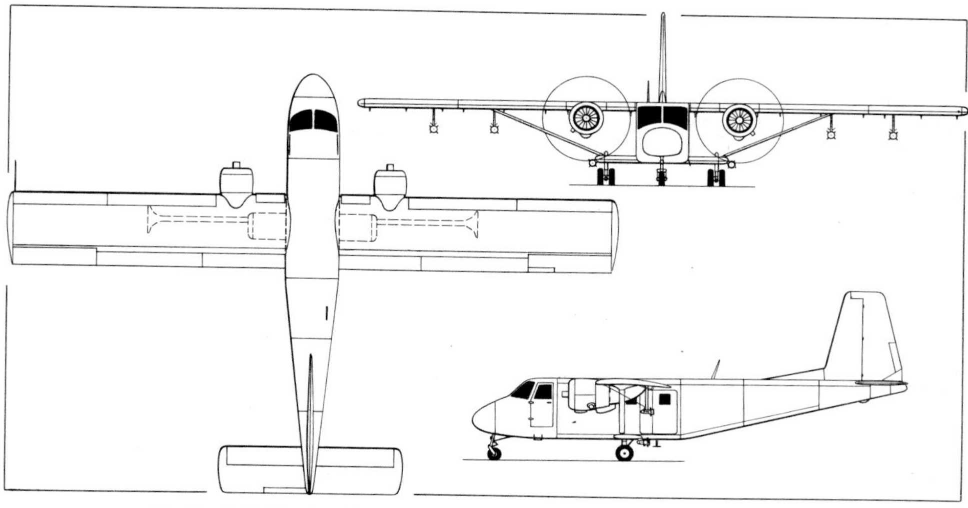

Harbin C-11 (Y-11) twin-engined agricultural and utility aircraft *(Pilot Press)*

C-11 (Y-11) twin-engined general-purpose aircraft, designed and built in China

COLOMBIA

AGRICOPTEROS

AGRICOPTEROS LTDA

ADDRESS: Apartado Aéreo 1789, Cali

PRESIDENT: Eng Maximo Tedesco

This company, which undertakes crop-spraying operations in Colombia, is assembling kits of a modified agricultural version of the Aerosport Scamp (see under USA in the Homebuilt Aircraft section).

AGRICOPTEROS (AEROSPORT) SCAMP MODEL B

Following a visit to the USA in 1976 the President of Agricopteros Ltda ordered two kits of the Aerosport Scamp homebuilt biplane, with a view to the possible adaptation of this aircraft for agricultural duties. In collaboration with Aerosport, he introduced a number of modifications into the new Scamp B version, and the first example made its initial flight on 27 May 1977.

This was the basic aircraft, in which the major changes included a slight increase in wing span, the provision of ailerons on the lower as well as the upper wings, and a different power plant. No agricultural equipment was installed at that time; this was designed subsequently by Sr Tedesco, and consists primarily of an underfuselage glassfibre chemical tank, wind-driven pressure pump, spraybars and nozzles. The entire installation weighs only 17 kg (38 lb). A T-type hydraulic valve system forces the ultra-low-volume liquid chemical into the spraybars at a pressure of 5·52 bars (80 lb/sq in), and it is discharged through the nozzles at 4·14 bars (60 lb/sq in). The tank is fitted with a quick-release trapdoor, and the entire chemical load can be jettisoned in 2 s in an emergency. If the aircraft is required for cross-country journeys, the tank can be used to carry auxiliary fuel instead of chemical.

The Scamp B is now being produced by Agricopteros by the assembly of kits supplied by Aerosport.

TYPE: Single-seat Restricted category (export) agricultural light aircraft.

WINGS: Braced biplane structure, with V-type interplane strut each side. Flying and landing wires of streamline section. Single 5 × 12·5 cm (2 × 5 in) extruded section of 6063-T3 light alloy tubing forms a pylon to support the centre-section of the upper wing. Wing section NACA 23012. Dihedral 3° on lower wings only. All-metal light alloy tubular front and main spars. Light alloy plain ailerons, with piano hinge at upper surface, on upper and lower wings. Lower ailerons actuated by slaved push/pull tube connected to upper pair. No flaps or tabs.

FUSELAGE: All-metal light alloy semi-monocoque structure.

TAIL UNIT: Braced T-tail of light alloy construction. Single bracing strut each side. Fixed-incidence tailplane. Ground-adjustable trim tab on rudder.

LANDING GEAR: Non-retractable tricycle type. Cantilever spring main-gear struts of light alloy. Wheel fairing optional for each unit.

POWER PLANT: One 74·5 kW (100 hp) Revmaster 2,100 cc modified Volkswagen engine, driving an Aerial 56-38 two-blade fixed-pitch wooden propeller. Fuel tank in fuselage nose, aft of firewall, capacity 30·5 litres (6·7 Imp gallons). Refuelling point on fuselage upper surface, forward of windscreen.

ACCOMMODATION: Single seat in open cockpit.

EQUIPMENT: Underfuselage tank for ultra-low-volume chemical or auxiliary fuel, capacity 60 litres (13·2 Imp gallons).

DIMENSIONS, EXTERNAL:
Wing span 5·94 m (19 ft 6 in)
Wing chord, constant 0·91 m (3 ft 0 in)
Wing area, gross 10·82 m² (116·5 sq ft)
Length overall 4·37 m (14 ft 4 in)
Height overall 1·73 m (5 ft 8 in)

Tailplane span 1·98 m (6 ft 6 in)
Wheel track 1·52 m (5 ft 0 in)
Wheelbase 1·22 m (4 ft 0 in)
Propeller diameter 1·42 m (4 ft 8 in)

WEIGHTS:
Weight empty 259 kg (572 lb)
Normal T-O weight 360 kg (795 lb)
Max T-O weight with chemical 428 kg (945 lb)

PERFORMANCE:
Never-exceed speed 100 knots (185 km/h; 115 mph)
Max level speed 82 knots (153 km/h; 95 mph)
Cruising speed 76 knots (140 km/h; 87 mph)
Max manoeuvring speed 72 knots (134 km/h; 83 mph)
Stalling speed 43·5 knots (81 km/h; 50 mph)
Service ceiling: tested 2,590 m (8,500 ft)
estimated 3,810 m (12,500 ft)
T-O run 122 m (400 ft)
Landing run 152 m (500 ft)
Range at cruising speed 130 nm (241 km; 150 miles)
Max range with auxiliary fuel in underfuselage tank 477 nm (885 km; 550 miles)
Max endurance with auxiliary fuel in underfuselage tank 6 h 45 min
Swath width 8·5 m (28 ft)

Agricopteros-built Aerosport Scamp B, with belly tank and spraybars

AVIONES DE COLOMBIA

AVIONES DE COLOMBIA SA

HEAD OFFICE: Calle 26 No. 4A-45 Piso 8, Bogotá
Telephone: (282) 9648, 9668 and 9728
Telex: 45 220
WORKS: Aeropuerto Guaymaral, Apartado Aéreo 6876, Bogotá
Telephone: (254) 1515 and 8831
SALES MANAGER: Rafael Urdaneta

This company, established in the 1950s and known formerly as Urdaneta y Galvez Ltda, has been a South American distributor for Cessna aircraft since 1961. In 1969 it also began assembling and partly building selected Cessna types under licence. Sixty-five aircraft were so produced in 1973, and a further 93 in 1974, some 40% of these being Cessna Model A188B AGwagons (see US section). Production in 1974 was limited to wings, tail units and seats for the Cessna range, but welding and other techniques were learnt, and the company has since become qualified to manufacture complete airframes. Facilities include 464·5 m² (5,000 sq ft) of office space in Bogotá, and 13,935 m² (150,000 sq ft) at Guaymaral, the general aviation airport for Bogotá. Service facilities include complete engine, propeller and avionics workshops. Assembly space is expected to be increased by a further 5,574 m² (60,000 sq ft) in 1980.

By 1 January 1979 the company had a work force of 338 persons, and had assembled 590 Cessna aircraft of 14 different models, as follows: 50 Model 150s, 12 Model 152s, 48 Model 172s, 17 Model 172XPs, six Model 177RGs, 70 Model 182s, 21 Model 185s, 231 Model 188s, 90 Model 206s, 25 Model 210s, five Model 310s, eight Model 337s, two Model 340s and five Model 402s. Production during 1978 averaged 10 aircraft per month; a further 114 aircraft were due for completion during 1979. About 20 per cent of total production is exported to Bolivia, Ecuador and Peru, or sold to customers in Colombia.

First prototype of the Aviones de Colombia/Cessna AgTrainer, which was due to enter production in 1979

AVIONES DE COLOMBIA/CESSNA AGTRAINER

Illustrated in an accompanying photograph, the AgTrainer is modified by Aviones de Colombia from the Cessna Model 188 AGtruck. The cabin has been widened to accommodate two persons side by side, increasing the empty weight by approx 91 kg (200 lb). Flight characteristics remain unchanged. Two prototypes have been flown (the first of them on 16 September 1976), and by 1 January 1979 these two aircraft had accumulated nearly 2,000 flying hours. The first prototype has been operated by Aeroandes, a local crop-spraying flying school.

Aviones de Colombia expected to manufacture about six production AgTrainers in 1979.

CZECHOSLOVAKIA

Central direction of the Czechoslovak aircraft industry is by a body known as the Generálni Reditelstvi Aero—Ceskoslovenské Letecke Podniky; Trust Aero—Czechoslovak Aeronautical Works, Prague-Letnany, whose General Manager is Josef Skarohlid. Principal factories concerned with aircraft manufacture are the Aero Vodochody National Corporation, Let National Corporation and Zlin Aircraft-Moravan National Corporation, whose current products appear under the appropriate headings in this section. Other Czechoslovak factories engaged in the production of aero-engines and sailplanes are listed in the relevant sections of this edition.

Sales of all aircraft products outside Czechoslovakia are handled by the Omnipol Foreign Trade Corporation, whose address is given below.

OMNIPOL

FOREIGN TRADE CORPORATION

ADDRESS: Washingtonova 11, Prague 1
Telephone: 2126
Telex: 121489, 121808 and 121077
GENERAL MANAGER: Tomás Marecek, GE
SALES MANAGER: Ing Miloslav Branný
PUBLICITY MANAGER: Jirí Matula

This concern handles the sales of products of the Czechoslovak aircraft industry outside Czechoslovakia and furnishes all information requested by customers with regard to export goods.

About 29,000 people are employed by the Czechoslovak aircraft industry.

AERO

AERO VODOCHODY NÁRODNÍ PODNIK (Aero Vodochody National Corporation)

Address: Vodochody, p. Odelená Voda, near Prague
Managing Director: Jirí Chmelícek
Vice-Directors:
Ing Josef Sedlácek (Technical)
Jan Spára (Production)
Ing Otakar Stella (Sales)
Ing Václav Klouda (Works Economy)
Chief Designer: Dipl Ing Jan Vlcek
Project Engineer, L-39: Ing Vlastimil Havelka
Chief Pilot: Vlastimil David

This factory perpetuates the name of one of the three founder companies of the Czechoslovak aircraft industry, which began activities shortly after the first World War with the manufacture of Austrian Phönix fighters. Subsequent well-known products included the A 11 military general-purpose biplane and its derivatives, and licence manufacture of the French Bloch 200 twin-engined bomber. The present works was established on 1 July 1953, since when it has seven times received the Red Banner award of the Ministry of Engineering and UVOS, as well as many other awards including those of Exemplary Exporting Corporation and the Order of Labour.

Aero's major product from 1963-74 was the L-29 Delfin jet basic and advanced trainer, of which approx 3,600 were built. A full description of this can be found in the 1974-75 edition of *Jane's*. It has now been superseded in production by the L-39, a description of which follows:

AERO L-39 ALBATROS

The L-39 basic and advanced jet trainer was developed in the Aero works at Vodochody by a team led by the chief designer, Dipl Ing Jan Vlcek. Two prototype airframes had been completed by 4 November 1968 when the 02 aircraft flew for the first time. The 01 airframe was utilised for structural testing. By the end of 1970, five flying prototypes and two for ground testing had been completed. Slightly larger and longer air intake trunks were fitted after preliminary flight tests.

A pre-production batch of 10 aircraft began to join the flight test programme in 1971, and series production started in late 1972, following official selection of the L-39 to succeed the L-29 (1974-75 *Jane's)* as the standard jet trainer of all Warsaw Pact countries except Poland. Service acceptance trials, in Czechoslovakia and the USSR, took place in 1973, and by the Spring of 1974 the L-39 had begun to enter service with the Czechoslovak Air Force.

The L-39 forms part of a comprehensive training system which includes a specially designed pilot training flight simulator (TL-39), a pilot ejection ground training simulator (NK-TL-29/39), and vehicle-mounted mobile automatic test equipment (AKZ-KL-39). The aircraft is capable of operation from unprepared runways.

By May 1977, when the L-39 made its first appearance in the west, at the Paris *Salon de l'Aéronautique et de l'Espace,* approximately 1,000 L-39s had been ordered. Of these, some 400-500 were then in service with several air forces. It is expected that the L-39 will be built in numbers comparable to those of the L-29 Delfin. Like the L-29, the Albatros is used in Czechoslovakia for all pilot training, including that of helicopter pilots.

Official Czechoslovak designations for the different L-39 versions are as follows:

L-39C (for Cvičný: training). Basic and advanced flying training version, to which the detailed description applies. In service with Czechoslovak Air Force; supplied also to air forces of Afghanistan, Bulgaria, Germany (Democratic Republic), Hungary and USSR.

L-39Z0 (Z for Zbrojní: armed). Weapon training version, with underfuselage gun (optional) and underwing weapon stations. Reinforced landing gear. Export customers include air forces of Iraq and Libya.

L-39Z. Single-seat ground attack version, with underfuselage gun and underwing weapon stations. Reinforced landing gear. Production expected to begin in second half of 1979.

The following description applies to the current production L-39C trainer version, except where indicated:

Type: Two-seat basic and advanced jet trainer (L-39C), weapons trainer (L-39Z0) and single-seat light ground attack aircraft (L-39Z).

Close-up of underfuselage gun installation on Aero L-39Z0

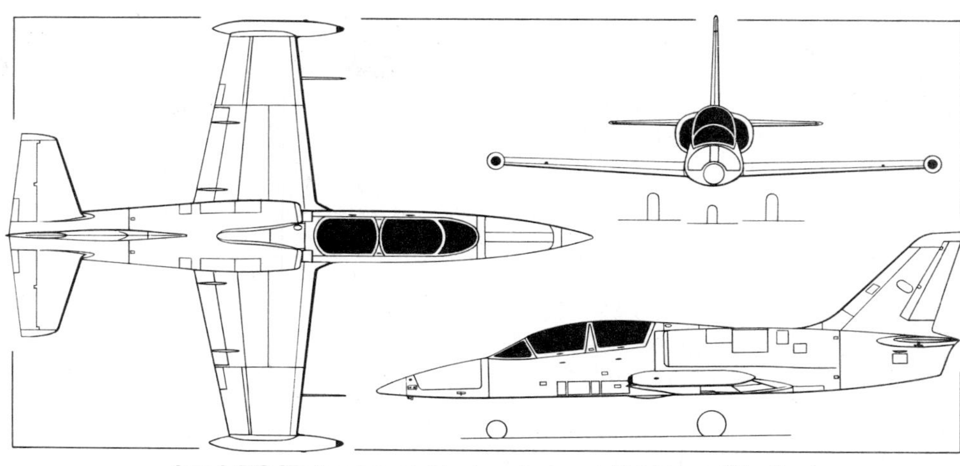

Aero L-39C Albatros two-seat basic and advanced jet trainer *(Pilot Press)*

Wings: Cantilever low-wing monoplane, with 2° 30′ dihedral from roots. Wing section NACA 64A012 mod. 5. Incidence 2°. Sweepback at quarter-chord 1° 45′. One-piece all-metal stressed-skin structure, with all-metal hydraulically-operated double-slotted trailing-edge flaps. Small fence above and below each trailing-edge between flap and aileron. Electrically-operated trim tab in each aileron. Control surfaces actuated by pushrods. Flaps deflect 25° for take-off, 44° for landing; ailerons deflect 17° up or down; airbrakes deflect 55° downward. Non-jettisonable wingtip fuel tanks, incorporating landing lights.

Fuselage: Metal semi-monocoque structure, built in two portions. Front portion consists of three sections, the first of which is a laminated glassfibre nosecone housing electrical and radio equipment and the nose landing gear. Next comes the pressurised compartment for the crew. The third section contains fuel tanks and the engine bay. The rear fuselage, carrying the tail unit, can be removed quickly to provide access for engine servicing. Two airbrakes side by side under fuselage, just forward of wing leading-edge.

Tail Unit: Conventional all-metal cantilever structure, with sweepback on vertical surfaces. Variable-incidence tailplane. Control surfaces actuated by pushrods. Electrically-operated trim tab in each elevator.

Landing Gear: Retractable tricycle type, with single wheel and oleo-pneumatic shock-absorber on each unit. Hydraulic retraction, main wheels inward into wings (with automatic braking during retraction), nosewheel forward into fuselage. Pneumatic ram-air system for emergency extension. K24 main wheels, fitted with Barum tubeless tyres size 610 × 215 mm (610 × 185 mm on early production aircraft), pressure 5·88 bars (85·34 lb/sq in). Nosewheel fitted with Barum tubeless tyre size 450 × 165 mm (430 × 150 mm on early production aircraft), pressure 3·92 bars (56·89 lb/sq in). Hydraulic disc brakes and anti-skid units on main wheels. Landing gear of L-39Z0 and L-39Z reinforced to cater for higher operating weights.

Power Plant: One 16·87 kN (3,792 lb st) Walter Titan (Motorlet-built Ivchenko AI-25-TL) turbofan engine mounted in rear fuselage, with semi-circular lateral air intake, fitted with splitter plate, on each side of fuselage above wing centre-section. L-39Z may have uprated engine of approx 18·63 kN (4,188 lb st). Fuel in five rubber bag-type main tanks aft of cockpit, with combined capacity of 1,055 litres (232 Imp gallons), and two 100 litre (22 Imp gallon) non-jettisonable wingtip tanks. Total internal fuel capacity 1,255 litres (276 Imp gallons). Provision for two 350 litre (77 Imp gallon) underwing drop-tanks, increasing total overall fuel capacity to 1,955 litres (430 Imp gallons). Space in L-39Z for additional fuselage tank in place of rear seat.

Accommodation: Crew of two in tandem, on VSI-BRI rocket-assisted ejection seats, operable at zero height and at speeds down to 81 knots (150 km/h; 94 mph), beneath individual transparent canopies which hinge sideways to starboard. Dual controls standard. L-39Z flown as single-seater, with rear seat removed.

Systems: Cabin pressurised (differential 0·27 bars; 3·92 lb/sq in) and air-conditioned. Air-conditioning system provides automatic temperature control from 10° to 28°C at ambient air temperatures from −55°C to +45°C. Two interconnected hydraulic systems, each with variable pressure pump and operating at 147 bars (2,133 lb/sq in) pressure. Main system actuates landing gear, flaps, airbrakes, ram-air turbine and wheel brakes. Emergency system incorporates three accumulators, using a 50-50 mixture of hydraulic fluid and nitrogen. Mechanical standby for actuation of landing gear, flaps and airbrakes in the event of total hydraulic failure. Pneumatic canopy seals. 27/28V DC electrical system, powered by a 9kW VG 7500JA engine-driven generator, with two 800VA static inverters (one 1000VA on early aircraft) for 115V single-phase AC power at 400Hz and one 50VA static inverter for 36V three-phase AC, also at 400Hz. If primary generator fails, a V 910 ram-air turbine is extended automatically into the airstream and generates up to 3kW of emergency power for essential services. 12V SAM 28 battery for standby power. Sapphire 5 compressed air generator and SV-35 turbine for engine starting and to power fuel flow system. Air intakes and windscreen anti-iced by engine bleed air; normally, anti-icing is sensor-activated automatically, but a manual standby system is also provided. Oxygen system for crew.

Avionics and Equipment: Standard avionics include Tesla RTL-11 air-to-ground VHF com (100-150MHz) and crew intercom, with separate intercom backup; a Soviet-built R-832 two-band VHF/UHF; RKL-41 ADF (150-1,800kHz); RV-5 radio altimeter; MRP-56P/S marker beacon receiver; and SRO-2 IFF. VOR/ILS optional. Landing light in forward end of each tip-tank.

Armament (L-39Z): Four underwing hardpoints, the inboard pair each stressed for loads of up to 500 kg (1,102 lb) and the outer pair for loads of up to 250 kg (551 lb) each; max external stores load 1,100 kg (2,425 lb). Typical underwing stores can include various combinations of bombs up to 500 kg in size; four UB-16 pods each containing sixteen S-5 57 mm air-to-surface rockets; eight 130 mm R-130 air-to-surface rockets; air-to-air missiles; gun pods; a five-camera reconnaissance pod; or (on inboard stations only) two 150 or 350 litre (33 or 77 Imp gallon) drop-tanks. Underfuselage pod, below front cockpit, housing a single 23 mm Soviet GSh-23 two-barrelled cannon; ammunition for this gun (max 150 rds) is housed in fuselage, above gun pod. Electrically-controlled ASP-3-NMU-39 gunsight and

Aero L-39Z0 weapon training version of the Albatros, with underfuselage gun pod

FKP-2-2 gun camera standard.

DIMENSIONS, EXTERNAL:
- Wing span — 9·46 m (31 ft 0½ in)
- Wing chord (mean) — 2·15 m (7 ft 0½ in)
- Wing aspect ratio (geometric) — 4·4
- Length overall — 12·32 m (40 ft 5 in)
- Height overall — 4·72 m (15 ft 5½ in)
- Tailplane span — 4·40 m (14 ft 5 in)
- Wheel track — 2·44 m (8 ft 0 in)
- Wheelbase — 4·39 m (14 ft 4¾ in)

AREAS:
- Wings, gross — 18·80 m² (202·36 sq ft)
- Ailerons (total) — 1·23 m² (13·26 sq ft)
- Trailing-edge flaps (total) — 2·68 m² (28·89 sq ft)
- Airbrakes (total) — 0·50 m² (5·38 sq ft)
- Fin — 2·77 m² (29·78 sq ft)
- Rudder — 0·71 m² (7·68 sq ft)
- Tailplane — 3·93 m² (42·30 sq ft)
- Elevators, incl tabs — 1·14 m² (12·27 sq ft)

WEIGHTS AND LOADINGS:
- Weight empty — 3,330 kg (7,341 lb)
- Fuel load:
  - fuselage tanks — 824 kg (1,816 lb)
  - wingtip tanks — 156 kg (344 lb)
  - underwing tanks (optional) — 545 kg (1,201 lb)
- Max external weapon load — 1,100 kg (2,425 lb)
- Max T-O weight:
  - 'clean', with 824 kg (1,816 lb) fuel and tip-tanks empty — 4,570 kg (10,075 lb)
  - with full internal fuel (980 kg; 2,160 lb) and four underwing rocket pods — 5,270 kg (11,618 lb)
- Max landing weight: L39C — 4,300 kg (9,480 lb)
  - L39Z — 4,600 kg (10,141 lb)
- Wing loading 'clean' — 243 kg/m² (49·77 lb/sq ft)
- Power loading 'clean' — 270·9 kg/kN (2·65 lb/lb st)

PERFORMANCE (A: at 'clean' AUW of 4,570 kg; 10,075 lb with tip-tanks empty; B: at AUW of 5,270 kg; 11,618 lb with full internal fuel and four underwing rocket pods; C: at AUW of 4,300 kg; 9,480 lb, except where indicated):
- *Max limiting Mach number (VNE) — 0·82
- Max permitted diving speed (VD) — 491 knots (910 km/h; 565 mph)
- Max level speed at S/L:
  - C — 378 knots (700 km/h; 435 mph)
- Max level speed at altitude:
  - A at 6,000 m (19,685 ft) — 421 knots (780 km/h; 485 mph)
  - B at 6,000 m (19,685 ft) — 340 knots (630 km/h; 391 mph)
  - C at 5,000 m (16,400 ft) — 405 knots (750 km/h; 466 mph)
- Cruising speed at 5,000 m (16,400 ft):
  - C — 367 knots (680 km/h; 423 mph)
- Stalling speed:
  - C, flaps up — 97 knots (180 km/h; 112 mph)
  - C, 25° flap — 90 knots (165 km/h; 103 mph)
  - C, 44° flap — 84 knots (155 km/h; 97 mph)
- Touchdown speed:
  - A at 4,300 kg (9,480 lb) AUW — 95·5 knots (177 km/h; 110 mph)
  - B at 4,600 kg (10,141 lb) AUW — 100 knots (185 km/h; 115 mph)
- Max rate of climb at S/L: A — 1,320 m (4,330 ft)/min
  - B — 960 m (3,150 ft)/min
- Optimum climbing speed:
  - C — 210 knots (390 km/h; 242 mph)
- Service ceiling: A — 11,500 m (37,730 ft)
  - B — 9,000 m (29,525 ft)
- T-O run, 25° flap, ISA:
  - at 4,300 kg (9,480 lb) AUW, concrete — 480 m (1,575 ft)
  - at 4,300 kg (9,480 lb) AUW, grass — 630 m (2,067 ft)
  - at 4,570 kg (10,075 lb) AUW — 500 m (1,640 ft)
  - at 5,270 kg (11,618 lb) AUW — 800 m (2,625 ft)
- T-O to 25 m (82 ft) from concrete:
  - at 4,300 kg (9,480 lb) AUW — 630 m (2,067 ft)
- Landing from 25 m (82 ft):
  - at 4,300 kg (9,480 lb) AUW — 1,120 m (3,675 ft)
- Landing run, 44° flap, ISA:
  - at 4,100 kg (9,039 lb) AUW — 620 m (2,034 ft)
  - at 4,300 kg (9,480 lb) AUW — 690 m (2,264 ft)
- Max range on internal fuel, 5% reserves:
  - A — 458 nm (850 km; 528 miles)
  - B — 421 nm (780 km; 485 miles)
- Max range with full internal fuel, two 350 litre drop-tanks, and no external weapons — 863 nm (1,600 km; 994 miles)
- Endurance at 5,000 m (16,400 ft), ISA:
  - with max internal fuel — 2 h 0 min
  - with max internal and external fuel — 2 h 30 min
- *g* limits:
  - at 4,200 kg (9,259 lb) AUW — +8; −4
  - at 4,400 kg (9,700 lb) AUW — +7·5; −3·75
  - at 4,600 kg (10,141 lb) AUW — +7; −3·5

**Has flown at Mach 0·85 (512 knots; 950 km/h; 590 mph) in test flights*

LET

LET NÁRODNÍ PODNIK (Let National Corporation)

ADDRESS: Uherské Hradiste-Kunovice
Telephone: Uherské Hradiste 5121
Telex: 060180 and 060181
MANAGING DIRECTOR: Ing Josef Kurz
CHIEF DESIGNER: Ing Ladislav Smrcek
CHIEF PILOT: Frantisek Srnec

The Let plant at Kunovice was established in 1950, its early activities including licence production of the Soviet Yak-11 piston-engined trainer under the Czechoslovak designation C-11. It contributed to the production of the Aero 45, was responsible for the L 200 Morava twin-engined air taxi and Z-37 Cmelák agricultural aircraft, and the L 13 Blanik sailplane; it is currently responsible for development and manufacture of the L-410 twin-turboprop light transport aircraft.

The factory also produces apparatus and equipment for radar and computer technology.

L-410UVP current production model of the Turbolet, introduced in 1979

LET L-410 TURBOLET

Design of the L-410 twin-turboprop light transport was started in 1966, by a team led by Ing Ladislav Smrcek. The first prototype (OK-YKE), powered by Pratt & Whitney Aircraft of Canada PT6A-27 turboprop engines, flew for the first time on 16 April 1969. Three additional PT6A-engined prototypes were completed subsequently; the second of these was later test-flown with Hartzell four-blade propellers in a successful attempt to reduce aircraft vibration and cabin noise levels.

The following versions of the L-410 have been announced:

L-410A. Initial passenger/cargo production version, powered by 533 kW (715 ehp) Pratt & Whitney Aircraft of Canada PT6A-27 engines. Entered service with Czechoslovak domestic operator Slov-Air in late 1971. Total of 31 built by 31 January 1979, including prototypes. Described in 1978-79 and earlier editions of *Jane's*.

L-410AF. Aerial photography/survey version, generally similar to L-410A but with larger, wider and extensively glazed nose compartment. One built, which was exported to Hungary in 1974. Other details in 1978-79 and earlier editions of *Jane's*.

L-410M. Similar to L-410A, but with Motorlet M 601 A engines and seats for up to 17 passengers. First flown 1973; first production example delivered 1976. Total of 110 built, including prototype. Superseded in 1979 by L-410UVP. Full description in 1978-79 *Jane's*; the following figures supersede those given in that edition:
- Max zero-fuel weight — 5,290 kg (11,662 lb)
- Never-exceed speed — 216 knots (400 km/h; 248 mph) EAS
- Econ cruising speed — 192 knots (355 km/h; 221 mph)
- Stalling speed, flaps up — 80 knots (148 km/h; 92 mph) EAS
- Stalling speed, flaps down — 62 knots (114 km/h; 71 mph) EAS
- Max rate of climb at S/L — 450 m (1,476 ft)/min
- Rate of climb at S/L, one engine out — 84 m (275 ft)/min
- Service ceiling — 7,770 m (25,500 ft)
- Service ceiling, one engine out — 1,700 m (5,575 ft)
- T-O run — 440 m (1,443 ft)

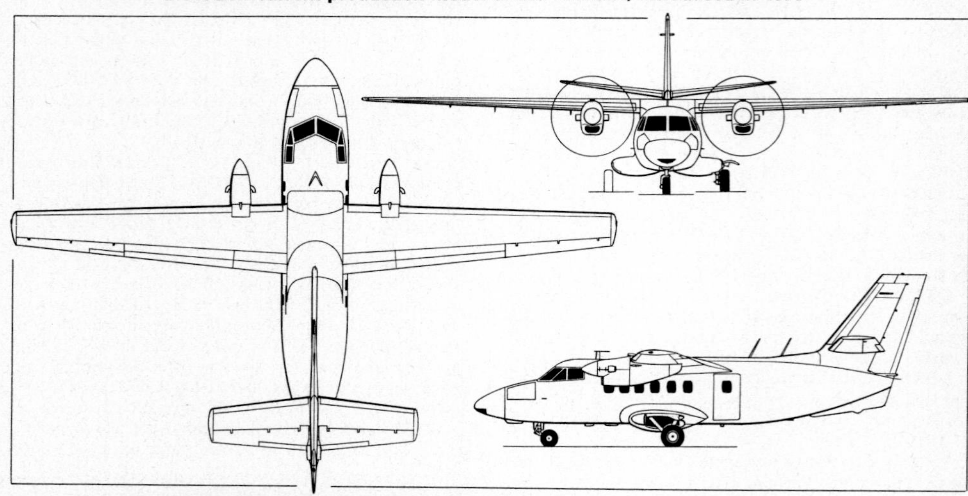
Let L-410UVP Turbolet twin-turboprop 15-passenger light transport *(Pilot Press)*

- T-O to 10 m (33 ft) — 630 m (2,067 ft)
- Landing from 15 m (50 ft) at max landing weight — 670 m (2,198 ft)
- Landing run at max landing weight — 380 m (1,247 ft)
- Range with max payload, 30 min reserves — 167 nm (310 km; 193 miles)
- Range with max fuel and 760 kg (1,675 lb) payload, 30 min reserves — 625 nm (1,160 km; 720 miles)

L-410UVP. Standard production version from beginning of 1979, prototype having first flown in 1977. Changes include increased wing span and area; lengthened fuselage; enlarged vertical tail surfaces; dihedral tailplane; improved cockpit systems and additions to standard instrumentation; introduction of spoilers, automatic pitch trim, automatic propeller feathering, and anti-skid system for main landing gear units; fabric-covered elevators and rudder; and later-model M 601 engines and V 508 propellers. Basic version is for passenger transportation, but cabin can be converted easily to all-cargo, aeromedical, parachutist or firefighting configuration; aircraft can also be equipped for aerial photography or calibration of ground navigation aids. The L-410UVP can operate from grass, sand and gravel strips as well as from paved runways, and in snow and ice conditions. It is being manufactured in large numbers, and will become standard Aeroflot equipment on Soviet internal feederline services, in company with the PZL-Mielec (Antonov) An-28. Stringent Aeroflot requirements included the ability to operate in temperatures ranging from −50°C to +45°C; systems were required to be survivable in temperatures as low as −60°C.

Production of the L-410UVP is planned to reach about 100 a year, most of them for Aeroflot.

The following description applies to the L-410UVP:

TYPE: Twin-turboprop general-purpose light transport.

WINGS: Cantilever high-wing monoplane. Wing section NACA 63A418 at root, NACA 63A412 at tip. Dihedral 1° 45′. Incidence 2° at root, −0° 30′ at tip. No sweepback at front spar. Conventional all-metal two-spar torsion-box structure, attached to fuselage by four-point mountings. Chemically machined skin with longitudinal reinforcement. Hydraulically actuated double-slotted metal flaps, with both slots variable. Spoiler forward of each flap. All-metal ailerons, forward of which are 'pop-up' pitch trim surfaces that come into operation automatically during single-engine operation and decrease the lift on the side of the running engine. Kléber-Colombes pneumatic de-icing of leading-edges.

FUSELAGE: Conventional all-metal semi-monocoque spot welded and riveted structure, built in three main portions.

TAIL UNIT: Conventional cantilever structure, of all-metal construction except for elevators and rudder, which are fabric-covered. Sweptback vertical tail surfaces, with small dorsal fin and ventral fin. One-piece tailplane, with 7° dihedral from roots, mounted part-way up fin. Balance tab in rudder and each elevator. Kléber-Colombes pneumatic de-icing of leading-edges.

LANDING GEAR: Retractable tricycle type, with single wheel on each unit. Hydraulic retraction, nosewheel forward, main wheels inward to lie flat in fairing on each side of fuselage. Technometra Radotin oleo-pneumatic shock-absorbers. Non-braking nosewheel, with servo-assisted steering, fitted with 548 × 221 mm (9·00-6) tubeless tyre, pressure 2·74 bars (39·8 lb/sq in). Main wheels fitted with 718 × 306 mm (12·50-10) tubeless tyres, pressure 3·14 bars (45·5 lb/sq in). All wheels manufactured by Moravan Otrokovice, tyres by Rudy Rijen, Gottwaldow. Moravan Otrokovice hydraulic disc brakes, parking brake and anti-skid units on main wheels. Metal ski landing gear, with plastics undersurface, optional.

POWER PLANT: Two 544 kW (730 ehp) Walter M 601 B turboprop engines, each driving an Avia V 508 B three-blade reversible-pitch fully-feathering metal propeller. De-icing for propeller blades (electrical) and lower intakes; anti-icing flaps inside each nacelle. Six (optionally eight) bag-type fuel tanks in wings, with total capacity (eight tanks) of 1,300 litres (286 Imp gallons). Four refuelling points above wings, with provision for two extra points when all eight tanks are fitted. Usable oil capacity 5·6 litres (1·25 Imp gallons) per engine.

ACCOMMODATION: Crew of one or two on flight deck. Dual controls standard. Standard accommodation in main cabin for 15 passengers, with pairs of adjustable seats on starboard side of aisle and single seats opposite, all at 76 cm (30 in) pitch. Baggage compartment (at rear, accessible from cabin), toilet and wardrobe standard in this version. Cabin heated by engine bleed air. Alternative layouts include all-cargo; ambulance, accommodating six stretchers, five sitting patients and a medical attendant; accommodation for 14 parachutists and a despatcher/instructor; firefighting configuration, carrying 12 firefighters and a pilot/observer. All-cargo version has protective floor covering, crash nets on each side of cabin, and tiedown provisions; floor is at truck-bed height. Aircraft can also be equipped for aerial photography or for calibration of ground navigation aids. Double upward-opening doors aft on port side, with stowable steps; right hand door serves as passenger entrance and exit. Both doors open for cargo loading, and can be removed for paratroop training missions. Downward-opening crew door, forward on starboard side, serves also as emergency exit.

SYSTEMS: No APU, air-conditioning or pressurisation systems. Duplicated hydraulic systems, No. 1 system actuating landing gear, flaps, spoilers, automatic pitch trim surfaces, main-wheel brakes, nosewheel steering and windscreen wipers. No. 2 system for emergency landing gear extension, flap actuation and parking brake. Electrical system includes AC power from three three-phase 36V 400Hz rotary inverters and two single-phase 115V 400Hz inverters, guaranteeing against a loss of power for essential instruments; DC power from two 5·6kW generators and two 25Ah batteries.

AVIONICS AND EQUIPMENT: Standard instrumentation provides for flight in IMC conditions, with all basic instruments duplicated and three artificial horizons. Communications include two VHF with a range of 65 nm (120 km; 75 miles) at 1,000 m (3,280 ft) altitude, and crew intercom. Standard navigation instruments include artificial horizons (three); barometric altimeters, airspeed indicators, rate of climb indicators, turn indicators, RMIs, gyro-compasses, ILS, and ARK-15M ADF with range of 97 nm (180 km; 112 miles) at 1,000 m (3,280 ft) altitude (two of each); and radio altimeter with ground proximity warning, ASI with stall warning, magnetic compass, GMK-1GE VOR, and ILS with marker beacon (one of each). Cockpit, instrument and passenger cabin lights, navigation lights, three landing lights in nose (each with two levels of light intensity), crew and cabin fire extinguishers, windscreen wipers, and alcohol spray for windscreen and wiper de-icing, are also standard.

DIMENSIONS, EXTERNAL:

Wing span	19·488 m (63 ft 11¼ in)
Wing chord at root	2·534 m (8 ft 3¾ in)
Length overall	14·467 m (47 ft 5½ in)
Height overall	5·829 m (19 ft 1½ in)
Wheel track	3·65 m (11 ft 11½ in)
Propeller diameter	2·50 m (8 ft 2½ in)
Passenger/cargo door (port, aft):	
Height	1·30 m (4 ft 3¼ in)
Width overall	1·25 m (4 ft 1¼ in)
Width (passenger door only)	0·75 m (2 ft 5½ in)
Height to sill	0·80 m (2 ft 7½ in)
Crew door/emergency exit door (stbd, fwd):	
Height	1·05 m (3 ft 5¼ in)
Width	0·66 m (2 ft 2 in)
Height to sill	0·80 m (2 ft 7½ in)

DIMENSIONS, INTERNAL:

Cabin, exl flight deck: Length	6·25 m (20 ft 6 in)
Max width	1·92 m (6 ft 3½ in)
Max height	1·658 m (5 ft 5¼ in)
Floor area	9·69 m² (104·3 sq ft)
Volume	17·86 m³ (630·7 cu ft)
Baggage compartment volume (rear)	0·77 m³ (27·2 cu ft)

WEIGHTS:

Basic weight empty	3,700 kg (8,157 lb)
Max fuel	1,000 kg (2,205 lb)
Max payload	1,310 kg (2,888 lb)
Max T-O weight	5,700 kg (12,566 lb)
Max landing weight	5,500 kg (12,125 lb)

PERFORMANCE (at max T-O weight, ISA):

Max cruising speed	197 knots (365 km/h; 227 mph)
Econ cruising speed	162 knots (300 km/h; 186 mph)
Service ceiling, one engine out	2,850 m (9,350 ft)
T-O run	400 m (1,312 ft)
Landing run	250 m (820 ft)
Max range at max cruising speed at 3,000 m (9,850 ft), 30 min reserves	561 nm (1,040 km; 646 miles)

VZLU

VYZKUMNY A ZKUSEBNÍ LETECKY USTAV (Aeronautical Research and Test Institute)

ADDRESS: Beranovych 130, Prague 9-Letnany 19905
Telephone: Prague 827041 and 826541
Telex: Prague 1493
MANAGING DIRECTOR: Ing J. Havlicek

This Institute, whose title is self-explanatory, was founded in 1922 and undertakes a range of activities corresponding broadly to those carried out by the RAE in Britain. Details of its principal facilities appeared in the 1970-71 and 1972-73 *Jane's*. It is a member of the Czechoslovak aircraft manufacturing group, under the general management of Aero (which see).

ZLIN

MORAVAN NÁRODNÍ PODNIK (Zlin Aircraft Moravan National Corporation)

ADDRESS: Otrokovice 76581
Telephone: Gottwaldov 92 2041 44
Telex: Gottwaldov 067 334
MANAGING DIRECTOR: Frantisek Klapil
VICE-DIRECTORS:
Ing Stanislav Machálka (Technical)
Jan Munclinger (Production)
Frantisek Muzny (Sales)
Ing Adolf Dolezal (Works Economy)
CHIEF DESIGNER: Ing Jirí Navrátil
CHIEF PILOT: Zdenek Polásek

The Moravan works, responsible for production of the famous range of Zlin aerobatic and light touring aircraft, was formed originally on 8 July 1935 as Zlinská Letecká Akciová Spolecnost (Zlin Aviation Joint Stock Co) in Zlin, although manufacture of Zlin aircraft was actually started two years earlier by the Masarykova Letecká Liga (Masaryk League of Aviation). The factory was renamed Moravan after the second World War. At present, in addition to production of the Zlin 42 M and Zlin 50 L, and development of the Zlin 142, Moravan is building items of aircraft equipment.

Zlin 42 M two-seat light training and touring aircraft (Avia M 137 AZ engine)

ZLIN 42 M

The prototype Zlin 42 was first flown on 17 October 1967, and in 1969 began undergoing flight trials prior to certification. Standard power plant of the initial version, which entered production in 1971 and was described in the 1973-74 *Jane's*, was the 134 kW (180 hp) M 137 A engine, with which the Z 42 conforms to FAR Pt 23 airworthiness specifications in the Aerobatic category and is suitable for service in climates with temperatures between +40° and −20°C. The principal customer for this version was the German Democratic Republic, which acquired several dozen for military liaison duties.

The following description applies to the subsequent **Zlin 42 M** production version, of which a prototype was first flown in November 1972, certification under FAR Pt 23 in the Aerobatic (+6*g* to −3·5*g*) and Normal categories being obtained in 1973. This differs from the initial version in having a constant-speed propeller and a tail fin identical to that of the Z 43 (see 1977-78 *Jane's*).

At the request of a number of operators of the initial production version, their aircraft have during overhaul been fitted retrospectively with Avia V 503 A two-blade metal propellers of the type fitted to the current production Z 42 M. The aircraft so modified are then redesignated **Zlin 42 MU**.

Production of the Zlin 42 M began in 1974, and is continuing. By early 1979, total Zlin 42 production (all versions) was in excess of 170.

TYPE: Two-seat light training and touring aircraft.

WINGS: Cantilever low-wing monoplane. Wing section NACA $63_2416{\cdot}5$. Dihedral 6° from roots. Sweep-forward 4° 20′ at quarter-chord. All-metal structure with single main spar. All-metal slotted ailerons and flaps all have same dimensions. Mass-balanced flaps and ailerons, operated mechanically by control rods. Ground-adjustable tab in each aileron.

FUSELAGE: Engine cowlings of sheet metal. Centre fuselage of welded steel tube truss construction, covered with laminated glassfibre panels. Rear fuselage is all-metal semi-monocoque structure.

TAIL UNIT: Cantilever all-metal structure. Control surfaces have partial mass and aerodynamic balance. Trim tabs on elevator and rudder. Rudder actuated by control cables, elevator by control rods.

LANDING GEAR: Non-retractable tricycle type, with nosewheel offset to port. Oleo-pneumatic nosewheel shock-absorber. Main wheels carried on flat spring steel legs. Nosewheel steering by means of rudder pedals. Single wheel on each unit. Main wheels and Barum tyres size 420 × 150, pressure 1·86 bars (27 lb/sq in); nosewheel and Barum tyre size 350 × 135, pressure 2·45 bars (35·6 lb/sq in). Hydraulic brakes on main wheels can be operated from either seat. Parking brake standard. Wheel fairings and skis optional.

POWER PLANT: One 134 kW (180 hp) Avia M 137 AZ inverted six-cylinder aircooled in-line engine, with low-pressure injection pump, driving a two-blade Avia V 503 A fully-automatic constant-speed propeller. Fuel tanks in each wing leading-edge, with total capacity of

130 litres (28·5 Imp gallons). Fuel and oil systems permit aerobatic and inverted flying. Oil capacity 12 litres (2·64 Imp gallons).

ACCOMMODATION: Individual side-by-side seats for two persons, the pilot's seat being to port. Both are adjustable for height and permit the use of back-type parachutes. Baggage space aft of seats. Cabin and windscreen heating and ventilation. Forward-opening door on each side of cabin. Dual controls standard.

SYSTEMS: Electrical system includes a 600W 27V engine-driven generator and Teledyne battery. External power source can be used for starting the engine.

AVIONICS AND EQUIPMENT: VHF radio and IFR instrumentation optional.

DIMENSIONS, EXTERNAL:
Wing span 9·11 m (29 ft 10¾ in)
Wing chord (constant) 1·42 m (4 ft 8 in)
Length overall 7·07 m (23 ft 2½ in)
Height overall 2·69 m (8 ft 10 in)
Elevator span 2·90 m (9 ft 6 in)
Wheel track 2·33 m (7 ft 7¾ in)
Wheelbase 1·66 m (5 ft 5¼ in)
Propeller diameter 2·00 m (6 ft 6¾ in)

DIMENSIONS, INTERNAL:
Cabin: Length 1·80 m (5 ft 10¾ in)
Width 1·12 m (3 ft 8 in)
Height 1·20 m (3 ft 11¼ in)
Baggage space 0·2 m³ (7·1 cu ft)

AREAS:
Wings, gross 13·15 m² (141·5 sq ft)
Ailerons (total) 1·408 m² (15·16 sq ft)
Trailing-edge flaps (total) 1·408 m² (15·16 sq ft)
Fin 0·54 m² (5·81 sq ft)
Rudder, incl tab 0·81 m² (8·72 sq ft)
Tailplane 1·23 m² (13·24 sq ft)
Elevator, incl tab 1·36 m² (14·64 sq ft)

WEIGHTS AND LOADINGS:
Basic weight, empty 645 kg (1,422 lb)
Max T-O weight: Aerobatic 920 kg (2,028 lb)
Normal 970 kg (2,138 lb)
Max wing loading: Aerobatic 70 kg/m² (14·3 lb/sq ft)
Normal 74 kg/m² (15·2 lb/sq ft)
Max power loading:
Aerobatic 6·87 kg/kW (11·27 lb/hp)
Normal 7·24 kg/kW (11·88 lb/hp)

PERFORMANCE (at max Aerobatic T-O weight):
Max level speed at S/L, ISA
122 knots (226 km/h; 140 mph)
Cruising speed at 600 m (1,975 ft), ISA
116 knots (215 km/h; 134 mph)
Stalling speed, flaps up, power off
54 knots (100 km/h; 62·5 mph) CAS
Stalling speed, flaps down, power off
49 knots (89 km/h; 56 mph) CAS
Max rate of climb at S/L 312 m (1,025 ft)/min
Service ceiling 4,250 m (13,950 ft)
T-O run 185 m (607 ft)
T-O to 15 m (50 ft) 380 m (1,245 ft)
Landing from 15 m (50 ft) 410 m (1,345 ft)
Landing run 135 m (443 ft)
Range with max standard fuel
286 nm (530 km; 329 miles)
g limits: Aerobatic +6·0; −3·5
Normal +3·8; −1·5

ZLIN 142

A prototype of the Zlin 142 was flown for the first time on 29 December 1978, and in early 1979 was undergoing certification trials. It was scheduled to be displayed at the Brno fair in September 1979, but no other details had been received at the time of closing for press.

ZLIN Z 50 L

The Z 50 L is a fully-aerobatic single-seat competition light aircraft, the design of which began in 1973. Construction of a prototype was started in 1975, and this aircraft flew for the first time on 18 July 1975. Two additional prototypes and 18 production aircraft had been completed by 1 January 1979.

Five Z 50 Ls took part in the 1976 World Aerobatic Championships at Kiev, USSR, gaining 2nd place in the team event and 3rd place in the men's individual competitions. Thirteen took part in the 1978 Championships at Hosin, Czechoslovakia, gaining 1st and 3rd places in the men's individual competitions and 1st place in the team event.

TYPE: Single-seat aerobatic aircraft.

WINGS: Cantilever low-wing monoplane. Wing section NACA 0018 at root, NACA 0012 at tip. Dihedral 1° 7′ 24″. All-metal structure, with single continuous main spar, rear auxiliary spar, and aluminium-clad duralumin skin. All-metal mass-balanced ailerons, actuated by pushrods, occupy most of each trailing-edge. Ground-adjustable tab on port outer aileron; automatic trim tab on each inboard aileron. No flaps. Provision for fitting wingtip fuel tanks for cross-country flights.

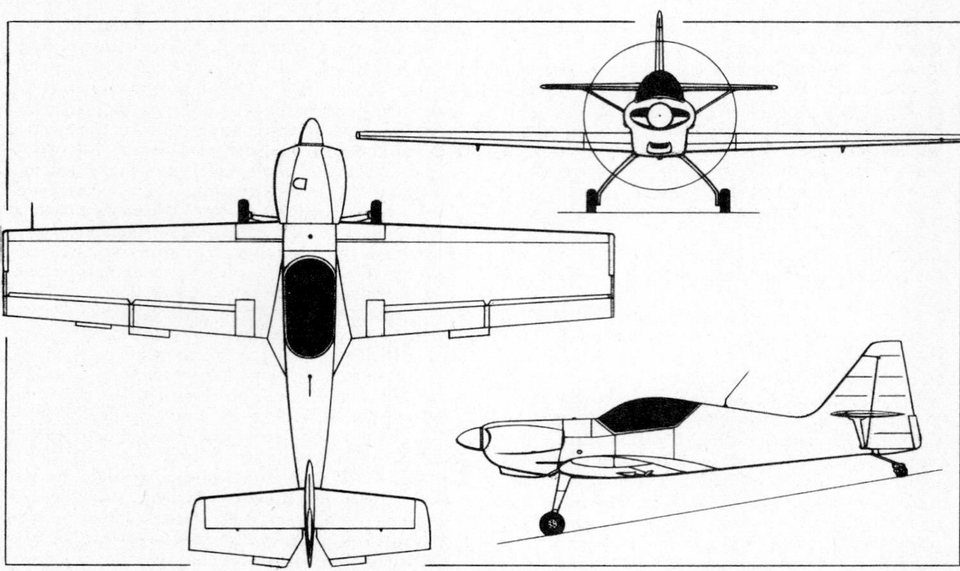

Zlin Z 50 L single-seat aerobatic aircraft *(Pilot Press)*

Zlin Z 50 L light aircraft (Lycoming AEIO-540-D4B5 engine)

FUSELAGE: All-metal semi-monocoque stressed-skin structure, with duralumin skin.

TAIL UNIT: Conventional metal structure. Braced tailplane and fin duralumin-covered, balanced elevators and rudder fabric-covered. One mechanically-adjustable tab and one automatic trim tab on elevators; automatic trim tab on rudder. Elevators actuated by pushrods, rudder by cables.

LANDING GEAR: Non-retractable tailwheel type. Main wheels carried on flat-spring titanium cantilever legs. Mechanical main-wheel brakes actuated by rudder pedals. Fully-castoring tailwheel, with flat-spring shock-absorption, has automatic locking device to maintain aircraft on a straight track during taxying, take-off and landing. Main wheels size 350 × 135 mm, pressure 2·5 bars (36 lb/sq in); tailwheel size 200 × 80 mm, pressure 1·0 bar (14·5 lb/sq in). Main-wheel fairings optional.

POWER PLANT: One 194 kW (260 hp) Lycoming AEIO-540-D4B5 flat-six engine, without reduction gear, driving a Hoffmann HO-V123K-F/200AH three-blade constant-speed variable-pitch wooden propeller with spinner. Single main fuel tank in fuselage, aft of firewall, capacity 60 litres (13·2 Imp gallons). Auxiliary 50 litre (11 Imp gallon) tank can be attached to each wingtip for cross-country flights only. Fuel and oil systems designed for full aerobatic manoeuvres, including inverted flight. Oil capacity 12 litres (2·64 Imp gallons).

ACCOMMODATION: Single seat under fully-transparent sideways-opening (to starboard) bubble canopy, which can be jettisoned in an emergency. Seat and backrest are adjustable, and permit the use of a back-type parachute. Cockpit ventilated by sliding panel in canopy.

SYSTEM: Electrical system includes an alternator as main power source and a Varley battery. External power socket in fuselage side for engine starting.

AVIONICS AND EQUIPMENT: VHF radio optional.

DIMENSIONS, EXTERNAL:
Wing span 8·58 m (28 ft 1¾ in)
Wing span over tip-tanks 9·03 m (29 ft 7½ in)
Wing chord at root 1·73 m (5 ft 8¼ in)
Wing chord at tip 1·21 m (3 ft 11¾ in)
Wing mean aerodynamic chord 1·4853 m (4 ft 10½ in)
Wing aspect ratio 5·88
Length overall (tail up) 6·62 m (21 ft 8¾ in)
Height over tail (static) 1·985 m (6 ft 6¼ in)
Elevator span 3·44 m (11 ft 3½ in)
Wheel track 1·90 m (6 ft 2¾ in)
Wheelbase 5·05 m (16 ft 7 in)
Propeller diameter 2·00 m (6 ft 6¾ in)
Propeller ground clearance (tail up)
0·31 m (1 ft 0¼ in)

AREAS:
Wings, gross 12·50 m² (134·55 sq ft)
Ailerons (total) 2·80 m² (30·14 sq ft)
Fin 0·59 m² (6·35 sq ft)
Rudder, incl tab 0·81 m² (8·72 sq ft)
Tailplane 1·66 m² (17·87 sq ft)
Elevators (total, incl tabs) 1·20 m² (12·92 sq ft)

WEIGHTS AND LOADINGS (Aerobatic category):
Weight empty, equipped 570 kg (1,256 lb)
Max T-O weight 720 kg (1,587 lb)
Max wing loading 57·6 kg/m² (11·80 lb/sq ft)
Max power loading 3·72 kg/kW (6·11 lb/hp)

PERFORMANCE (at max Aerobatic T-O weight):
Never-exceed speed
181·5 knots (337 km/h; 209 mph) CAS
Max level speed at S/L, ISA
158 knots (293 km/h; 182 mph)
Max cruising speed at 1,000 m (3,280 ft), ISA
147 knots (273 km/h; 169 mph)
Econ cruising speed at 1,000 m (3,280 ft), ISA
134 knots (248 km/h; 154 mph)
Stalling speed 53 knots (98 km/h; 61 mph) CAS
Max rate of climb at S/L 720 m (2,360 ft)/min
Service ceiling 7,000 m (2,300 ft)
T-O run 170 m (558 ft)
T-O to 15 m (50 ft) 290 m (952 ft)
Landing from 15 m (50 ft) 530 m (1,740 ft)
Landing run 250 m (820 ft)
Range with max fuel (incl wingtip tanks)
345 nm (640 km; 397 miles)
g limits: Aerobatic +9; −6

EGYPT

ABHC

ARAB BRITISH HELICOPTER CO

ADDRESS: Helwan, near Cairo

PARTICIPATING COMPANIES:

Arab Organisation for Industrialisation (AOI)
Westland Helicopters Ltd

CHAIRMAN: K. H. El Shishini, BSc (Aeronautics Engineering), MSc

VICE-CHAIRMAN: A. V. N. Reed, BSc (Tech), CEng, FRAeS, AMBIM

MANAGING DIRECTOR: B. Baxter, BEng, CEng, MIMechE, MIProdE

DEPUTY MANAGING DIRECTOR: A. Abdin, BSc, MSc

COMMERCIAL DIRECTOR: F. P. Stanton

BOARD MEMBERS:

Gen K. A. Elazayem (Egypt)
Lt Col Fadel Saeed (United Arab Emirates)
Capt Hamad Fand (Qatar)
Capt Eng M. A. R. Katouaa

The Arab Organisation for Industrialisation (AOI), funded jointly by Saudi Arabia, Qatar, the United Arab Emirates and Egypt, has embarked upon a major programme to re-establish an aircraft and aero-engine industry in Egypt, to meet the needs of the participating states.

The first step in this programme was the signing of a contract, on 27 February 1978, between the AOI and Westland Helicopters and Rolls-Royce of the UK to produce the Westland/Aérospatiale Lynx helicopter and its Gem engines in Egypt. The ABHC, and a corresponding engine company (ABEC), have been set up to manage the programme; ABHC has an initial capital of $30 million, with Westland having a 30% shareholding.

Also in the Spring of 1978, the AOI signed a similar agreement with the French government.

ABHC/WESTLAND LYNX

Under an initial £55 million contract, Westland is to supply 20 British-built Lynx helicopters to Egypt, followed by components for a further 30 which will be assembled by ABHC in manufacturing facilities to be developed adjacent to the existing Egyptian aircraft factory (formerly Factory 36) at Helwan, 29 km (18 miles) south of Cairo. Subsequently, with technical and management training assistance from Westland, Egyptian personnel will progress towards complete manufacture. Current plans are for up to 230 Lynx to be so produced, for the armed forces of Egypt, Saudi Arabia, Qatar and the United Arab Emirates; similarly, ABEC, with Rolls-Royce assistance, will produce up to 750 Gem turboshaft engines for the programme, which is expected to extend over about seven years.

FINLAND

VALMET

VALMET OY KUOREVEDEN TEHDAS

OFFICE AND WORKS: 35600 Halli

Telephone: 942 82810 Exchange

Telex: 28269 Valku SF

MANAGER: Heikki Mäntylä

PROJECT MANAGER, L-70: Pekka Kaipio

Valmet Oy Kuoreveden Tehdas (Kuorevesi Works) is affiliated to Valmet Oy, a State-owned company consisting of several metal-working factories. It continues the traditions of Ilmailuvoimien Lentokonetehdas, established in 1921, and was formerly a part of the Valmet Oy Tampere factory group, from which it was separated in 1974. It is now an independent factory directly responsible to Valmet's Head Office in Helsinki, and is currently the largest aircraft industry establishment in Finland. Since 1922, Valmet Oy Kuoreveden Tehdas and its predecessors have built 30 different types of aircraft, of which 18 have been of Finnish design. Valmet Oy was responsible for assembly of the 12 Saab 35XS Drakens ordered by Finland in 1970.

Current activities of Valmet Oy Kuoreveden Tehdas include the overhaul and repair of military and civil aircraft, piston engines and instruments. The factory has a covered area of approximately 14,000 m² (150,695 sq ft). Valmet Oy Linnavuoren Tehdas, at Siuro, is concerned primarily with the overhaul and repair of aircraft jet engines.

The Kuorevesi and Linnavuori Works are also participating in the manufacture and assembly of 46 of the 50 BAe Hawk Mk 51 jet trainers and their Adour Mk 851 jet engines, purchased by the Finnish Air Force from the UK in early 1978. Deliveries of these aircraft are to take place in 1981-85.

The latest aircraft of Finnish design to be built by Valmet is the L-70 Miltrainer piston-engined trainer. It was designed by Ilmailuteollisuuden Kehitysosasto (IKO), which was formed on 15 September 1970.

VALMET L-70 MILTRAINER

Finnish Air Force name: Vinka (Blast)

In late 1970 an aeronautical research and development group was established in Finland, its first major task being to study a Finnish Air Force requirement for a basic training aircraft to replace the Saab 91 Safir. It was decided to produce an entirely Finnish design to fulfil this need, and a development contract was placed with Valmet by the Finnish Air Force on 23 March 1973. The aircraft, which was originally designated Leko-70, an abbreviation of 'Lentokone', the Finnish word for 'aeroplane', is named Vinka by the Finnish Air Force.

The prototype made its first flight at Kuorevesi on 1 July 1975. A second prototype is being used for static and fatigue testing; a full-size cockpit mockup and components for a third aircraft have been completed.

The Finnish Air Force ordered 30 Vinkas on 28 January 1977. Deliveries of these are scheduled to take place between 1979 and January 1981. Production began on 15 January 1977.

The Miltrainer is designed for aerobatic flying as a two-seater. In civil use, in Normal or Utility category, it is capable of seating up to four persons, depending upon the amount of baggage carried.

TYPE: Two-seat training or two/four-seat touring aircraft.

WINGS: Cantilever low-wing monoplane. Wing section NACA 63_2A615 (modified). Dihedral 6° from roots. Incidence 2°. Fail-safe structure of main spar, auxiliary spar, ribs and stringers, of constant chord except for forward-swept wing-root leading-edges, and attached to fuselage by steel fittings. Riveted aluminium alloy skin. Electrically-operated slotted flaps, and mass-balanced slotted ailerons, on trailing-edges, all of aluminium alloy riveted construction. Ailerons actuated by stainless steel control cables. Flaps and ailerons have fluted skins. Adjustable geared tab in each aileron.

Valmet L-70 Miltrainer demonstrating the use of optional ski landing gear

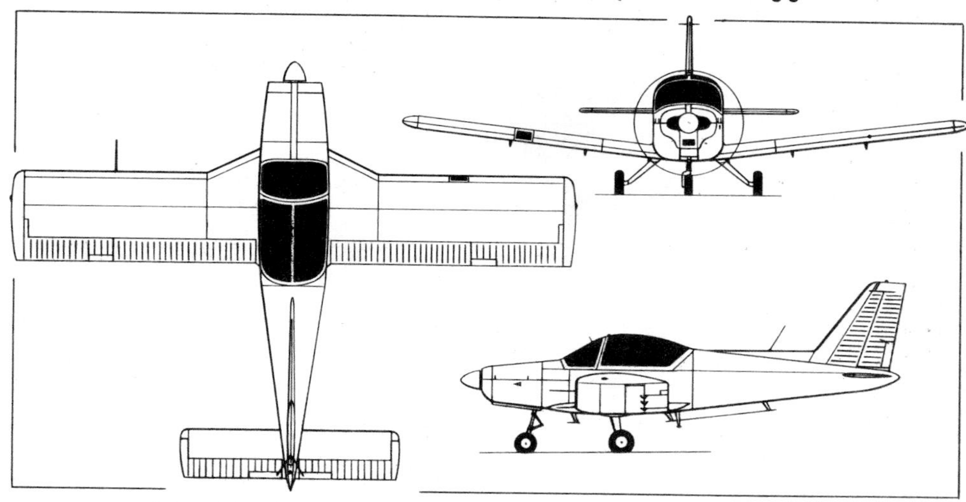
Valmet L-70 Miltrainer two/four-seat training and touring aircraft *(Pilot Press)*

FUSELAGE: Conventional aluminium alloy semi-monocoque fail-safe structure of frames and longerons, with riveted skin. Welded steel tube engine mount and wing carry-through structure; stainless steel firewall. Cockpit floor panels of bonded sandwich.

TAIL UNIT: Cantilever aluminium alloy structure, with fluted and riveted skin. Slight sweepback on vertical surfaces; shallow dorsal fin. Elevators and rudder aerodynamically and mass balanced, and actuated by stainless steel control cables. Geared trim tabs in rudder and each elevator.

LANDING GEAR: Non-retractable tricycle type. Cantilever main legs. Automotive Products oleo-pneumatic shock-absorbers on all units. Cleveland P410 main wheels, with 17·5 × 6·30-6 tyres, pressure 1·86 bars (27 lb/sq in); Goodyear 5·00-5 nosewheel, with 14·2 × 4·95-5 tyre, pressure 2·07 bars (30 lb/sq in). Cleveland 30-52K disc brakes. Provision for fitting Finncraft skis.

POWER PLANT: One 149 kW (200 hp) Lycoming AEIO-360-A1B6 flat-four engine, driving a Hartzell HC-C2YK-4F/FC 7666A-2 two-blade constant-speed propeller with spinner. Christen-801 inverted fuel and oil systems. Semi-integral bonded sandwich fuel tank in each wing root ahead of main spar; total capacity 176 litres (38·7 Imp gallons). Overwing fuelling point above each tank. Oil capacity 7·6 litres (1·7 Imp gallons).

ACCOMMODATION: Side-by-side seats for instructor and pupil in trainer version, with integral longitudinal central console which serves also to reinforce fuselage floor. Dual controls standard, but instructor's or pupil's control column can be removed if desired. Windscreen and one-piece rearward-sliding fully-transparent jettisonable canopy, with steel tube turnover frame. Canopy can be locked in partially open position if required. Provision for two more seats at rear, which can be removed to make room for additional baggage. Up to 280 kg (617 lb) of baggage or freight can be carried internally, or externally if flown as a single-seater. As ambulance, can accommodate one stretcher patient and medical attendant in addition to pilot. Cockpit heated and ventilated.

SYSTEM: 24V 70A DC electrical system, with brushless generator and 25Ah nickel-cadmium battery.

AVIONICS AND EQUIPMENT: Two VHF, one ADF, one VOR/ILS, one ATC transponder, two RMI, and one gyromagnetic compass. Blind-flying instrumentation standard. Equipment for secondary roles may include glider or target towing hook; one long-focus or four short-focus vertical cameras (provision for 35 × 40 cm; 13·8 × 15·75 in aperture, with hinged doors, in floor of rear cockpit); four underwing pylons (total capacity 300 kg; 661 lb) for external freight or supplies; and dispersal equipment for agricultural missions.

DIMENSIONS, EXTERNAL:

Wing span	9·85 m (32 ft 3¾ in)
Wing chord (constant over most of span)	1·53 m (5 ft 0¼ in)
Wing aspect ratio	6
Length overall	7·50 m (24 ft 7¼ in)

Height overall	3·31 m (10 ft 10¼ in)
Tailplane span	3·60 m (11 ft 9¾ in)
Wheel track	2·30 m (7 ft 6½ in)
Wheelbase	1·61 m (5 ft 3½ in)
Propeller diameter	1·88 m (6 ft 2 in)
Propeller ground clearance	0·25 m (9¾ in)

Areas:

Wings, gross	14·00 m² (150·70 sq ft)
Ailerons (total)	1·41 m² (15·18 sq ft)
Trailing-edge flaps (total)	1·90 m² (20·45 sq ft)
Fin	0·87 m² (9·36 sq ft)
Rudder, incl tab	0·79 m² (8·50 sq ft)
Tailplane	2·01 m² (21·64 sq ft)
Elevators, incl tabs	1·01 m² (10·87 sq ft)

Weights and Loadings:

Operating weight empty, equipped	767 kg (1,691 lb)
Max payload with full fuel	380 kg (838 lb)
Max T-O weight: Aerobatic	1,040 kg (2,293 lb)
Normal	1,250 kg (2,756 lb)
Max wing loading	89·3 kg/m² (18·3 lb/sq ft)
Max power loading	8·38 kg/kW (13·78 lb/hp)

Performance (at max Aerobatic T-O weight):

Never-exceed speed	193 knots (360 km/h; 223 mph)
Max level speed at S/L	129 knots (240 km/h; 149 mph)
Cruising speed (75% power) at 1,525 m (5,000 ft)	120 knots (222 km/h; 138 mph)
Stalling speed, flaps up, power off	53 knots (98 km/h; 61 mph)
Stalling speed, flaps down, power off	46 knots (85 km/h; 53 mph)
Max rate of climb at S/L	342 m (1,120 ft)/min
Service ceiling	5,000 m (16,400 ft)
T-O run	180 m (590 ft)
T-O to 15 m (50 ft)	260 m (855 ft)
Landing from 15 m (50 ft)	300 m (985 ft)
Landing run	150 m (490 ft)
Min ground turning radius	8·00 m (26 ft 3 in)
Range with max fuel	547 nm (1,015 km; 630 miles)
Range with max payload	464 nm (860 km; 534 miles)
g limits: Aerobatic	+6·00; −3·00
Utility	+4·40; −2·02
Normal	+3·80; −1·80

FRANCE

AÉROSPATIALE

SOCIÉTÉ NATIONALE INDUSTRIELLE AÉROSPATIALE

Head Office: 37 boulevard de Montmorency, 75781 Paris Cédex 16
Telephone: 524 43 21
Telex: AISPA X 620059 F

BOARD OF DIRECTORS

Chairman: Jacques Mitterrand

Representatives of the Shareholders:
René Ravaud, Ingénieur Général de l'Armement (President and Director General of SNECMA)
André Giraud (General Non-executive Director, Government Delegate to the Atomic Energy Commission)
Pierre Jouven (Honorary President of Péchiney Ugine Kuhlmann)
Le Crédit Lyonnais, represented by Alain Bizot (Director of Crédit Lyonnais)

Representatives of the State:
Jean-Pierre Barbery, Ingénieur Général de l'Armement (representing the Ministry of Defence)
Jacques de Larosière (Treasury Director, representing the Ministry of Economy and Finance)
Claude Abraham (Director General of Civil Aviation, representing the Secretary of State for Transport)

Representatives of the Employees:
Paul Bienfait (representing executives)
Georges Girard and Guy Carraz (representing workmen, office staff, technicians and supervisors)

GENERAL MANAGEMENT

President and Director General: Jacques Mitterrand
Director General Delegate: Roger Chevalier
Deputy General Manager, Economics and Finance: Yves Barbé
Deputy General Manager, Industrial and Technical Matters: Joseph Millara
General Secretary: Marc Robert
Director of the President's Office: Jean-Charles Poggi
Inspector General: Jean Soissons
Press and Information Adviser to the President: Jean E. Lagrange
Director of International Affairs: Michel Thomas
Director of Public Relations: Claude Loiseau
Industrial Director: Roger Berthier
Central Financial Director: Michel Euvrard
Director (Industrial Relations): André Escoulin
Director (Organisation and Training): René Dor
Director (Headquarters Establishment): Jean René Signori

AIRCRAFT DIVISION

Managing Director: André Etesse
Assistant Managing Director: René Dor
Assistant Managing Director, Programmes: Georges Roche
Military Adviser: Gen (ret) Pierre Delachenal
Technical Director: Pierre Lecomte
Commercial Director: Henri Puel
Aircraft Design Director: Gilbert Cormery
Flight Test Director: Henri Perrier
Director (Quality Assurance): André Despeyroux
Works and Facilities:
Toulouse. Director: Jean Pierson
Nantes-Bouguenais. Director: Jean-Louis Fache
Saint-Nazaire. Director: Jean Renon
Méaulte. Director: Jean-Paul Chandez

HELICOPTER DIVISION

Managing Director: François Legrand
Technical Director: Georges Petit
Director of Engineering: René Mouille
Commercial Director: Jean-Claude Rebuffel
Director (Product Support): Marc Fourcade
Flight Test Director: Jean-Marie Besse
Director (Quality Assurance): André Breton
Works and Facilities:
Marignane. Director: Fernand Carayon
La Courneuve. Director; Lucien Fournier

TACTICAL MISSILES DIVISION

Managing Director: Michel Allier
Assistant Managing Director: Philippe Girard
Director of Engineering: Jean Guillot
Works and Facilities:
Châtillon. Director: Jean-Claude Renaut
Bourges. Director: Georges Barroy

SPACE AND BALLISTIC SYSTEMS DIVISION

Managing Director: Pierre Usunier
International and Commercial Affairs (Space): Alexandre Dauguet
Assistant Managing Director—Director of Systems Subdivision: Gérard Payelle
Works and Facilities:
Aquitaine. Director: Robert Laurentjoye
Les Mureaux. Director: Séverin Golbert
Cannes. Director: Gérard Chauvallon

SUBSIDIARIES

Société Girondine d'Entretien et de Réparation de Matériel Aéronautique (SOGERMA)
Société de Construction d'Avions de Tourisme et d'Affaires (Socata)
Société d'Exploitation et de Constructions Aéronautiques (SECA)
Electronique Aérospatiale (EAS)
Société Charentaise d'Equipements Aéronautiques (SOCEA)
Aérospatiale Helicopter Corporation (USA)
European Aerospace Corporation (USA)

The Société Nationale Industrielle Aérospatiale was formed on 1 January 1970, by decision of the French government, as a result of the merger of the former Sud-Aviation, Nord-Aviation and SEREB companies. It is the biggest aerospace company in the Common Market countries on the Continent of Europe, with a registered capital of 447,400,000 francs, facilities extending over a total area of 9,790,000 m² (105,380,000 sq ft), of which 1,766,000 m² (19,009,000 sq ft) are covered, and a staff (including subsidiary companies) of 37,304 persons in mid-1979.

In the aircraft field, major products include the short/medium-range large-capacity A300/A310 European Airbus, in co-operation with Deutsche Airbus GmbH, British Aerospace, VFW-Fokker and CASA; and the Transall heavy multi-purpose transport, in co-operation with MBB and VFW-Fokker.

Aérospatiale produces a range of light piston-engined aircraft through its subsidiary, Socata (which see). It is also a major manufacturer of helicopters, guided missiles, spacecraft and research rockets.

Helicopter activities, concentrated at Marignane, involve the development and production of a wide range of turbine-powered types, described under this entry. Agreements concluded with Westland in the UK covered joint development and production of the Puma and Gazelle, and the Westland-designed Lynx, after all three types had been chosen to equip the French and British armed forces.

AÉROSPATIALE/BAe CONCORDE

Details of the Concorde programme can be found in the International section of this edition.

AÉROSPATIALE FOUGA 90

The Fouga 90 is a successor to the CM 170 Magister trainer and light tactical support aircraft, of which 929 were built between 1953 and 1969. Of these, about 650 are believed to continue in service in 16 countries, and accumulated flying time on the type totals more than three million hours.

When designing the Fouga 90, Aérospatiale retained the aerodynamics of the wing and tail unit of the Magister. The centre-fuselage has been redesigned and deepened, to accommodate pilot and instructor in the now-preferred stepped positions, to give the occupant of the rear seat an optimum forward view. More modern electronics and systems are installed; and the original Marboré turbojets are replaced by turbofans, offering much reduced specific fuel consumption and improved noise characteristics. Limiting load factors are $+7g$ and $-3g$, permitting all standard aerobatic manoeuvres. Like the Magister, the Fouga 90 is suitable for weapon training and light attack roles.

A prototype Fouga 90 flew for the first time on 20 August 1978. This is powered by Astafan IIG turbofans, as described in detail. Production aircraft will have Astafan IVGs with 22% greater thrust at high altitude, and the prototype was being re-engined with IVGs during Summer 1979.

Type: Light twin-turbofan transition trainer and tactical support aircraft.

Wings: Cantilever mid-wing monoplane. NACA 64 series wing section. Thickness/chord ratio varies from 19% at root to 12% at tip. No dihedral. Incidence 2°. Leading-edge sweepback 13°. Single-spar aluminium alloy stressed-skin structure. Servo-control ailerons. Hydraulically-operated all-metal slotted flaps. Hydraulically-actuated retractable airbrakes in upper and lower surfaces.

Fuselage: All-metal semi-monocoque structure, comprising four longerons, frames and a heavy-gauge stressed skin, without stringers.

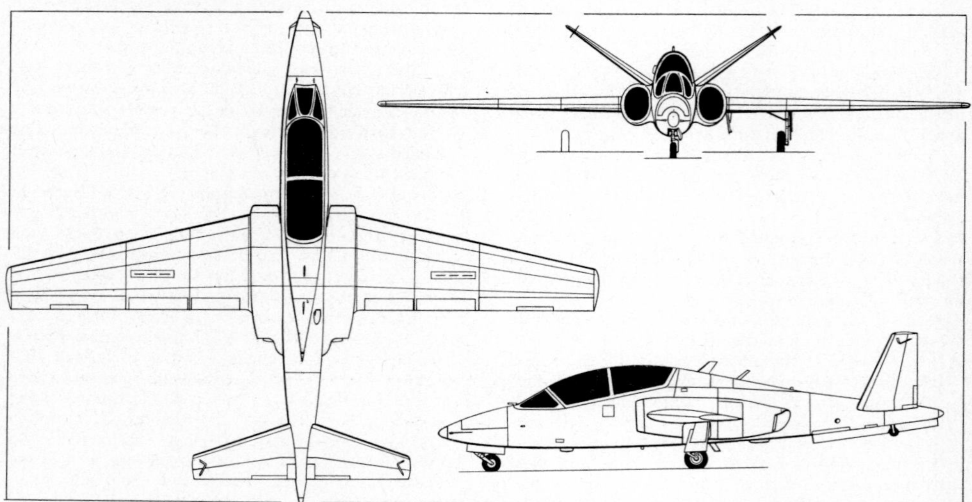

Production configuration of Aérospatiale Fouga 90, a modernised version of the CM 170 Magister basic trainer *(Pilot Press)*

TAIL UNIT: All-metal single-spar V structure, with included angle of 100°. Statically and aerodynamically balanced elevators. Long narrow-chord ventral fin, enclosing small tail bumper.

LANDING GEAR: Retractable tricycle type. Hydraulic actuation, nosewheel rearward (forward on production aircraft), main units inward into wings. Goodyear main wheels, diameter 254 mm (10 in), with hydraulic brakes. Nosewheel, diameter 102 mm (4 in), fitted with anti-shimmy device.

POWER PLANT: Prototype flew initially with two Turboméca Astafan IIG turbofan engines, each rated at 6·82 kN (1,532 lb st). Standard power plant will be two Astafan IVGs, each rated at 7·75 kN (1,740 lb st). Main fuel in two fuselage tanks, with total capacity of 720 litres (158 Imp gallons), and wing leading-edge tanks with total capacity of 500 litres (110 Imp gallons). Max total fuel capacity 1,220 litres (268 Imp gallons). Refuelling point in port side of canopy-to-fuselage fairing. Fuel system designed to permit 30 s of inverted flight. Hot-air de-icing for engine air intakes.

ACCOMMODATION: Two seats in tandem, under large individual rearward-hinged canopies on prototype. Production aircraft will have sideways-hinged one-piece canopy. Martin-Baker F10KX zero-zero ejection seats in prototype. Rear seat raised to give instructor clear view forward over head of pupil. Forward field of view 10° up and 15° down from front seat, 13° up and 5° down from rear seat. Windscreen de-iced externally by alcohol, internally by hot air.

SYSTEMS: Modernised by comparison with CM 170 Magister. Cockpits pressurised and air-conditioned. Hydraulic system includes two engine-driven pumps and a tank designed for inverted flight. System, pressure 200 bars (2,900 lb/sq in), actuates directly the airbrakes, flaps and landing gear, and through accumulators the normal and emergency braking systems. DC electrical system includes a 36Ah battery and two 6kVA starter/generators (one per engine). Main 28V bus bar can also be supplied via external power receptacle on starboard side. AC system supplied from 400Hz inverter, connected to 26V and 115V bus bars. Individual oxygen supply with regulator in each cockpit.

AVIONICS AND EQUIPMENT: Basic package includes two VHF transceivers, intercom, directional gyro, VOR/ILS/marker beacon receiver, ADF, standby compass, transponder, DME, two gyro horizons, two HSI, two RMI, two marker indicator light units, blind-flying instrumentation, two *g* meters and two clocks. Optional items include a UHF transceiver, second VOR/ILS/marker receiver, Tacan, IFF and two course indicators.

ARMAMENT (optional): Four underwing attachments for external stores; each inboard station has capacity of 250 kg (551 lb), each outboard station has capacity of 150 kg (331 lb). Weapon loads can include four 125 kg or 50 kg bombs; two 50 kg bombs and two pods each containing eighteen 68 mm rockets; or two AS.11 or AS.12 air-to-surface missiles and two 30 mm gun pods.

DIMENSIONS, EXTERNAL:

Wing span	12·04 m (39 ft 6 in)
Wing chord at root	1·98 m (6 ft 6 in)
Wing chord at tip	0·87 m (2 ft 10¼ in)
Wing aspect ratio	7·6
Length overall	10·46 m (34 ft 3¾ in)
Height overall	3·078 m (10 ft 1¼ in)
Tailplane span	4·38 m (14 ft 4½ in)
Wheel track	4·44 m (14 ft 6¾ in)
Wheelbase	4·00 m (13 ft 1½ in)

AREAS:

Wings, gross	18·38 m² (197·8 sq ft)
Ailerons (total)	1·10 m² (11·84 sq ft)
Trailing-edge flaps (total)	2·10 m² (22·60 sq ft)
Horizontal tail area (projected)	3·71 m² (39·93 sq ft)
Vertical tail area (projected)	2·60 m² (28·00 sq ft)

WEIGHTS AND LOADINGS (A, Astafan IIG; B, Astafan IVG engines):

Weight empty, equipped: A	2,600 kg (5,732 lb)
B	2,650 kg (5,840 lb)
Normal T-O weight, 'clean': A	3,500 kg (7,716 lb)
B	3,800 kg (8,380 lb)
Max T-O weight, with armament:	
A, B	4,200 kg (9,260 lb)
Normal wing loading: A	190·4 kg/m² (39·00 lb/sq ft)
B	206·7 kg/m² (42·36 lb/sq ft)
Normal power loading: A	258·9 kg/kN (2·54 lb/lb st)
B	245·2 kg/kN (2·41 lb/lb st)

PERFORMANCE (estimated, at normal T-O weight):

Never-exceed speed: A, B	Mach 0·82
Max level speed, S/L to 6,100 m (20,000 ft):	
A	345 knots (640 km/h; 398 mph)
Max level speed at 6,100 m (20,000 ft):	
B	372 knots (690 km/h; 428 mph)
Max level speed at S/L:	
B	355 knots (657 km/h; 408 mph)
Max rate of climb at S/L: A	1,158 m (3,800 ft)/min
B	1,200 m (3,935 ft)/min
Service ceiling: A	12,195 m (40,000 ft)
T-O to 10·7 m (35 ft): A	610 m (2,000 ft)
Landing from 15 m (50 ft): A	670 m (2,200 ft)
Range with max fuel:	
A	1,000 nm (1,850 km; 1,150 miles)
Endurance with max fuel, no reserves:	
A	3 h 15 min
B	3 h

Prototype of the Aérospatiale Fouga 90 tandem two-seat transition trainer

The Lockheed T-33 with modified wing section used in Aérospatiale's Pegasus programme of supercritical wing research

AÉROSPATIALE PEGASUS PROGRAMME

Aérospatiale has been engaged in supercritical wing research since 1972. Financial support by French government agencies and the Armée de l'Air made possible more extensive practical testing of supercritical aerofoils from 1975, under a programme known as Pegasus.

The basic wing section evolved by Aérospatiale was of typical supercritical form, with a thickness/chord ratio of 17%. Known as the S17a aerofoil, it was found to have shortcomings in terms of boundary layer behaviour when subjected to wind tunnel testing. However, it was realised that the Reynolds number experienced during such tests was much lower than that experienced in full-scale flight; so arrangements were made to acquire on loan a Lockheed T-33 belonging to the Armée de l'Air, for use as an aerodynamic testbed.

In May 1976, Aérospatiale began superimposing the S17a section on to the existing wing of the T-33. This was done by building up the basic form with balsa and then adding a skin of resin-coated fabric. Flight trials of the modified aircraft began on 13 April 1977, which is claimed to represent the first flight in Europe by an aircraft with a supercritical wing, and continued until 2 May 1978. They confirmed at an early stage the characteristics suggested by wind tunnel testing.

To remedy the shortcomings, Aérospatiale made minor changes to the profile on the underside of the wing, near the trailing-edge, to produce a section designated S17a1. This gave improved results in the later flight tests, proving much superior to the T-33's standard wing section at low speeds, without any decrease of the maximum Mach No. of 0·77-0·78 attainable in level flight. This research is expected to be applicable to future subsonic commercial transport programmes in which Aérospatiale participates.

AÉROSPATIALE SA 315B LAMA

Indian Army name: Cheetah

Design of the SA 315B Lama began in late 1968, initially to meet a requirement of the Indian armed forces, and a prototype was flown for the first time on 17 March 1969. French certification was granted on 30 September 1970 and FAA Type Approval on 25 February 1972.

The Lama combines features of the Alouette II and III, having the airframe (with some reinforcement) of the former and the dynamic components, including the Artouste power plant and rotor system, of the SA 316 Alouette III.

During demonstration flights in the Himalayas in 1969 a Lama, carrying a crew of two and 140 kg (308 lb) of fuel, made the highest landings and take-offs ever recorded, at a height of 7,500 m (24,600 ft).

On 21 June 1972, a Lama set a helicopter absolute height record of 12,442 m (40,820 ft). The pilot was Jean Boulet, holder of the previous record in an SE 3150 Alouette.

The production Lama is capable of transporting an external load of 1,135 kg (2,500 lb) at an altitude of more than 2,500 m (8,200 ft). In an agricultural role, it can be fitted with spraybars and an underbelly tank of 1,135 litres (300 US gallons) capacity, developed jointly by Aérospatiale Helicopter Corporation and Simplex Manufacturing Company. The tank is equipped with an electrical emergency dump system.

An alternative agricultural installation, using two side-mounted glassfibre tanks of Simplex manufacture, was shown for the first time at the 1976 US National Agriculture Aviation Association convention. Up to 1,000 kg (2,200 lb) of liquid chemicals can be carried in these tanks, which weigh 132 kg (290 lb) empty. A high-performance electric pump dispenses up to 455 litres (120 US gallons)/min at 2·10 kg/cm² (30 lb/sq in) boom pressure.

A total of 272 Lamas had been sold to 91 operators in 24 countries by 1 March 1979. In addition to manufacture by Aérospatiale, the SA 315B is produced under licence by HAL for the Indian Army under the name of Cheetah.

TYPE: Turbine-driven general-purpose helicopter.

ROTOR SYSTEM: Three-blade main and anti-torque rotors. All-metal main rotor blades, of constant chord, are on articulated hinges, with hydraulic drag-hinge dampers. Rotor brake standard.

ROTOR DRIVE: Main rotor driven through planetary gearbox, with freewheel for autorotation. Take-off drive for tail rotor at lower end of main gearbox, from where a torque shaft runs to a small gearbox which supports the tail rotor and houses the pitch-change mechanism. Cyclic and collective pitch controls are powered.

FUSELAGE: Glazed cabin has light metal frame. Centre and rear of fuselage have a triangulated steel tube framework.

LANDING GEAR: Skid type, with removable wheels for ground manoeuvring. Pneumatic floats for normal operation from water, and emergency flotation gear, inflatable in the air, are available.

POWER PLANT: One 649 kW (870 shp) Turboméca Artouste IIIB turboshaft engine, derated to 410 kW (550 shp). Fuel tank in fuselage centre-section, with capacity of 575 litres (126·5 Imp gallons), of which 573 litres (126 Imp gallons) are usable.

ACCOMMODATION: Glazed cabin seats pilot and passenger side by side in front and three passengers behind. Provision for external sling for loads of up to 1,135 kg (2,500 lb). Can be equipped for rescue (hoist capacity 160 kg; 352 lb), liaison, observation, training, agricultural, photographic and other duties. As an ambulance, can accommodate two stretchers and a medical attendant.

Aérospatiale SA 315B Lama (Turboméca Artouste IIIB turboshaft engine)

Dimensions, external:

Main rotor diameter	11·02 m (36 ft 1¾ in)
Tail rotor diameter	1·91 m (6 ft 3¼ in)
Main rotor blade chord (constant)	0·35 m (13·8 in)
Length overall, both rotors turning	12·92 m (42 ft 4¾ in)
Length of fuselage	10·26 m (33 ft 8 in)
Height overall	3·09 m (10 ft 1¾ in)
Skid track	2·38 m (7 ft 9¾ in)

Weights:

Weight empty	1,021 kg (2,251 lb)
Normal max T-O weight	1,950 kg (4,300 lb)
Max T-O weight with externally-slung cargo	2,300 kg (5,070 lb)

Performance (at AUW of 2,300 kg; 5,070 lb, with slung load):

Max cruising speed	65 knots (120 km/h; 75 mph)
Max rate of climb at S/L	234 m (768 ft)/min
Service ceiling	3,000 m (9,840 ft)
Hovering ceiling IGE	2,950 m (9,675 ft)
Hovering ceiling OGE	1,550 m (5,085 ft)

AÉROSPATIALE SA 316B ALOUETTE III

The Alouette III helicopter was evolved from the Alouette II, with larger cabin, greater power, improved equipment and higher performance. The prototype flew for the first time on 28 February 1959, and a total of 1,406 Alouette IIIs had been sold to 195 operators in 73 countries by 1 March 1979.

Those delivered up to the end of 1969 were designated **SE 3160.** The subsequent Artouste-engined **SA 316B** has strengthened main and rear rotor transmissions, higher AUW and increased payload. It flew for the first time on 27 June 1968; first deliveries were made in 1970, and this version received FAA Type Approval on 25 March 1971. The **SA 319B,** with Astazou engine, is described separately, but is included in the total sales figures above.

The sale of Alouette IIIs to India, Romania and Switzerland included a licence agreement for manufacture of the aircraft in those countries. Quantities involved were 200 in India, 130 in Romania and 60 in Switzerland.

In 1977, an SA 316B operated by Trans North Turbo Air for the Canadian Park Service evacuated a mountain climber, suffering from pulmonary edema and frostbite, from a point at the 4,235 m (13,900 ft) level on the east ridge of Mount Logan. This is thought to be the greatest height at which a hoist rescue has been effected.

Type: Turbine-driven general-purpose helicopter.

Rotor System: Three-blade main and anti-torque rotors. All-metal main rotor blades, on articulated hinges, with hydraulic drag-hinge dampers. Rotor brake standard.

Rotor Drive: Main rotor driven through planetary gearbox, with freewheel for autorotation. Take-off drive for tail rotor at lower end of main gearbox, from where a torque shaft runs to a small gearbox which supports the tail rotor and houses the pitch-change mechanism. Cyclic and collective pitch controls are powered.

Fuselage: Welded steel tube centre-section, carrying the cabin at the front and a semi-monocoque tailboom.

Tail Unit: Cantilever all-metal fixed tailplane, with twin endplate fins, mounted on tailboom.

Landing Gear: Non-retractable tricycle type, manufactured by Messier-Hispano-Bugatti. Nosewheel is fully-castoring. Provision for pontoon landing gear.

Power Plant: One 649 kW (870 shp) Turboméca Artouste IIIB turboshaft engine, derated to 425 kW (570 shp). Fuel in single tank in fuselage centre-section, with capacity of 575 litres (126·5 Imp gallons), of which 573 litres (126 Imp gallons) are usable.

Accommodation: Normal accommodation for pilot and six persons, with three seats in front and a four-person folding seat at the rear of the cabin. Two baggage holds in centre-section, on each side of the welded structure and enclosed by the centre-section fairings. Provision for carrying two stretchers athwartships at rear of cabin, and two other persons, in addition to pilot. All passenger seats removable to enable aircraft to be used for freight-carrying. Provision for external sling for loads of up to 750 kg (1,650 lb). One forward-opening door on each side, immediately in front of two rearward-sliding doors. Dual controls and cabin heating optional.

Operational Equipment (military version): In the assault role, the Alouette III can be equipped with a wide range of weapons. A 7·62 mm AA52 machine-gun (with 1,000 rds) can be mounted athwartships on a tripod behind the pilot's seat, firing to starboard, either through a small window in the sliding door or through the open doorway with the door locked open. The rear seat is removed to allow the gun mounting to be installed. In this configuration, max accommodation is for pilot, co-pilot, gunner and one passenger, although normally only the pilot and gunner would be carried. Alternatively, a 20 mm MG 151/20 cannon (with 480 rds) can be carried on an open turret-type mounting on the port side of the cabin. For this installation all seats except that of the pilot are removed, as is the port side cabin door, and the crew consists of pilot and gunner. Instead of these guns, the Alouette III can be equipped with four AS.11 or two AS.12 wire-guided missiles on external jettisonable launching rails, with an APX-Bézu 260 gyro-stabilised sight, or 68 mm rocket pods.

Dimensions, external:

Diameter of main rotor	11·02 m (36 ft 1¾ in)
Main rotor blade chord (each)	0·35 m (13·8 in)
Diameter of tail rotor	1·91 m (6 ft 3¼ in)
Length overall, rotors turning	12·84 m (42 ft 1½ in)
Length overall, blades folded	10·03 m (32 ft 10¾ in)
Width overall, blades folded	2·60 m (8 ft 6¼ in)
Height to top of rotor head	3·00 m (9 ft 10 in)
Wheel track	2·60 m (8 ft 6¼ in)

Weights:

Weight empty	1,143 kg (2,520 lb)
Max T-O weight	2,200 kg (4,850 lb)

Performance (standard version, at max T-O weight):

Max level speed at S/L	113 knots (210 km/h; 130 mph)
Max cruising speed at S/L	100 knots (185 km/h; 115 mph)
Max rate of climb at S/L	260 m (850 ft)/min
Service ceiling	3,200 m (10,500 ft)
Hovering ceiling IGE	2,880 m (9,450 ft)
Hovering ceiling OGE	1,520 m (5,000 ft)
Range with max fuel at S/L	258 nm (480 km; 298 miles)
Range at optimum altitude	290 nm (540 km; 335 miles)

AÉROSPATIALE SA 319B ALOUETTE III ASTAZOU

Indian military name: Chetak

The SA 319B Alouette III Astazou is a direct development of the SA 316B, from which it differs principally in having an Astazou XIV turboshaft engine (649 kW; 870 shp, derated to 447 kW; 600 shp) with increased thermal efficiency and a 25% reduction in fuel consumption.

A prototype SA 319 was completed in 1967. The production total is included in the figures given under the SA 316B entry.

Operational Equipment (naval version): The Alouette III can fulfil a variety of shipborne roles; features common to all naval configurations include a quick-mooring harpoon to ensure instant and automatic mooring on landing and before take-off, a nosewheel locking device, and folding main rotor blades. For detecting and destroying small surface craft such as torpedo-boats, it can be equipped with a SFENA three-axis stabilisation

Aérospatiale SA 316B Alouette III equipped with skis for operation by the French Securité Civile in mountain areas

Aérospatiale SA 321G Super Frelon of Aéronavale, equipped for development launches of Exocet anti-ship missiles

system, OMERA ORB 31 radar, APX-Bézu 260 gyro-stabilised sight and two AS.12 wire-guided missiles. For the ASW role, it can carry two Mk 44 homing torpedoes beneath the fuselage, or one torpedo and MAD (magnetic anomaly detection) gear in a streamlined container which is towed behind the helicopter on a 50 m (150 ft) cable. The aircraft can be used for air/sea rescue when the cabin floor is protected by an anti-corrosion covering to prevent sea water from reaching vital components. Rescue hoist (capacity 225 kg; 500 lb) mounted on port side of fuselage.

WEIGHTS:
- Weight empty — 1,146 kg (2,527 lb)
- Max T-O weight — 2,250 kg (4,960 lb)

PERFORMANCE (at max T-O weight):
- Max level speed at S/L — 118 knots (220 km/h;136 mph)
- Max cruising speed at S/L — 106 knots (197 km/h; 122 mph)
- Max rate of climb at S/L — 270 m (885 ft)/min
- Hovering ceiling IGE — 3,100 m (10,170 ft)
- Hovering ceiling OGE — 1,700 m (5,575 ft)
- Range with 6 passengers (80 kg; 176 lb each), T-O at S/L — 325 nm (605 km; 375 miles)

AÉROSPATIALE SA 321 SUPER FRELON

The Super Frelon is a three-engined multi-purpose helicopter derived from the smaller SA 3200 Frelon (see 1961-62 *Jane's*).

Under a technical co-operation contract, Sikorsky Aircraft, USA, provided assistance in the development of the Super Frelon, in particular with the detail specifications, design, construction and testing of the main and tail rotor systems. Under a further agreement, the main gearcase and transmission box are produced in Italy by Fiat.

The first prototype of the Super Frelon (originally designated SA 3210-01) flew on 7 December 1962, powered by three 985 kW (1,320 shp) Turmo IIIC₂ engines, and represented the troop transport version. In July 1963 this aircraft set up several international helicopter records, including a speed of 184 knots (341 km/h; 212 mph) over a 3 km course, and a speed of 189·115 knots (350·47 km/h; 217·77 mph) over a 15/25 km course.

The second prototype, flown on 28 May 1963, was representative of the naval version, with stabilising floats on the main landing gear supports. Four pre-production aircraft followed, and the French government ordered an initial production series of 17, designated SA 321G, in October 1965. By 1 March 1979, a total of 98 Super Frelons had been sold to 10 operators in 8 countries.

Passenger and utility versions of the Super Frelon are available, and the main differences between the current versions are summarised as follows:

SA 321F. Commercial airliner, designed to carry 34-37 passengers in a standard of comfort comparable to that of fixed-wing airliners, over 94 nm (175 km; 108 mile) stage lengths at a cruising speed of 124 knots (230 km/h; 143 mph), with 20 min reserve fuel. The prototype was designed in accordance with US FAR 29 regulations and flew for the first time on 7 April 1967. Type certification was granted by the SGAC on 27 June 1968 and by the FAA on 29 August 1968.

SA 321G. Anti-submarine helicopter. First version of the SA 321 to enter production. The first SA 321G flew on 30 November 1965 and deliveries began in early 1966. Twenty-four built. In service with Flottille 32F of Aéronavale, which was commissioned at Lanvéoc-Poulmic on 5 May 1970. Duties of this squadron include patrols in support of *Redoutable* class nuclear submarines entering and leaving their base on the Île Longue. The SA 321G can also be operated from the French helicopter carrier *Jeanne d'Arc*.

SA 321H. Version for air force and army service, without stabilising floats or external fairings on each side of lower fuselage. Turmo IIIE₆ engines instead of Turmo IIIC₆ in other versions. No de-icing equipment fitted.

SA 321Ja. Utility and public transport version, intended to fulfil the main roles of personnel and cargo transport. Designed to carry a maximum of 27 passengers. External loads of up to 5,000 kg (11,023 lb) can be suspended from the cargo sling and carried 27 nm (50 km; 31 miles), the aircraft returning to base without load. An internal payload of 4,000 kg (8,818 lb) can be carried over 100 nm (185 km; 115 miles) at 124 knots (230 km/h; 143 mph) with 20 min fuel reserves. The SA 321J prototype flew for the first time on 6 July 1967. A French certificate of airworthiness was granted in December 1971.

The following description applies generally to current production models of the Super Frelon, except where specific variants are indicated:

TYPE: Three-engined heavy-duty helicopter.

ROTOR SYSTEM: Six-blade main rotor and five-blade anti-torque tail rotor. Main rotor head consists basically of two six-armed star-plates carrying the drag and flapping hinges for each blade. The root of each blade carries a fitting for pitch control and each blade has an individual hydraulic damper to govern movement in the drag plane. Each main blade is 8·60 m (28 ft 2½ in) long, with constant chord and NACA 0012 section. All-metal construction, with D-section main spar forming leading-edge. Tail rotor of similar construction to main rotor, with blades 1·60 m (5 ft 3 in) long. Rearward folding of all six main rotor blades of SA 321G is accomplished automatically by hydraulic jacks, simultaneously with automatic folding of the tail rotor pylon.

ROTOR DRIVE: The driveshaft from the rear engine is geared directly to the shaft from the port forward engine. The two forward engines have a common reduction gear from which an output shaft drives the main rotor shaft through helical gearing. There are two reduction gear stages on the main rotor shaft. The tail rotor shaft is driven by gearing from the shaft linking the rear and port forward engines and incorporates two-stage reduction. The rotor can be stopped within 40 sec by a boosted disc-type rotor brake fitted to this shaft. Main rotor rpm 207 and 212. Tail rotor rpm 990.

FUSELAGE: Boat-hull fuselage of conventional metal semi-monocoque construction, with watertight compartments inside planing bottom. On the SA 321G, there is a small stabilising float attached to the rear landing gear support structure on each side. The tail section of the SA 321G folds for stowage. Small fixed stabiliser on starboard side of tail rotor pylon on all versions. The SA 321F does not have stabilising floats, but large external fairings on each side of the centre fuselage serve a similar purpose and also act as baggage containers.

LANDING GEAR: Non-retractable tricycle type, by Messier-Hispano-Bugatti. Twin wheels on each unit. Oleo-pneumatic shock-absorbers can be shortened on the SA 321G to reduce height of aircraft for stowage. Magnesium alloy wheels, all of same size. Tyre pressure 6·9 bars (100 lb/sq in). Optionally, low-pressure (3·45 bars; 50 lb/sq in) tyres may be fitted. Hydraulic disc brakes on main wheels. Nosewheel unit is steerable and self-centering.

POWER PLANT: Three 1,156 kW (1,550 shp) Turboméca Turmo IIIC₆ turboshaft engines (IIIE₆ in SA 321H); two mounted side by side forward of main rotor shaft and one aft of rotor shaft. Fuel in flexible tanks under floor of centre fuselage, with total standard capacity of 3,975 litres (874 Imp gallons) in SA 321G/H and 3,900 litres (858 Imp gallons) in SA 321Ja. Optional auxiliary fuel tankage comprises two 500 litre (110 Imp gallon) external tanks on all models, two 500 litre (110 Imp gallon) internal tanks in the SA 321G, and three 666 litre (146·5 Imp gallon) internal tanks in the SA 321H/Ja.

ACCOMMODATION (military versions): Crew of two on flight deck, with dual controls and advanced all-weather equipment. Equipment in the SA 321G, which carries a flight crew of five, includes a tactical table and a variety of devices for anti-submarine detection and attack, towing, minesweeping and other duties. This version also has provision for carrying 27 passengers. SA 321H transport accommodates 27-30 troops, 5,000 kg (11,023 lb) of internal or external cargo, or 15 stretchers and two medical attendants. Rescue hoist of 275 kg (606 lb) capacity. Main cabin is ventilated and soundproofed. Sliding door on starboard side of front fuselage. Rear loading ramp is actuated hydraulically and can be opened in flight.

ACCOMMODATION (SA 321F): Airliner seats for up to 37 passengers (34 if toilets are installed) in three-abreast rows with centre aisle. Alternative layouts for 8, 14 or 23 passengers, with toilets, or 11, 17 or 26 passengers without toilets, the remainder of the cabin space being blanked off by movable partitions and used for the carriage of freight; with these configurations, unused seats are folded against the cabin wall. All seats and interior furnishings are designed for quick removal when the helicopter is to be used for all-freight services. To cater for operations over marshland or water, the hull and lateral cargo compartments are sealed sufficiently to permit an occasional landing on water.

ACCOMMODATION (SA 321Ja): Seating for up to 27 passengers in the personnel transport role. As a cargo transport, external loads of up to 5,000 kg (11,023 lb) can be suspended from the cargo sling. Loading of internal cargo (up to 5,000 kg; 11,023 lb) is effected via the rear ramp-doors, with the assistance of a Tirefor hand winch.

OPERATIONAL EQUIPMENT: The ASW SA 321G operates normally in tactical formations of three or four aircraft, each helicopter carrying the full range of detection, tracking and attack equipment, including a self-contained navigation system associated with a Doppler radar, a 360° radar with transponder and display console, and dipping sonar. Four homing torpedoes can be carried in pairs on each side of the main cabin. Both the SA 321G and H can be fitted with an anti-surface vessel weapon system, consisting of two Exocet missiles and launch installation, associated with an OMERA-Segid Héracles ORB 31D radar for target designation.

DIMENSIONS, EXTERNAL:
- Diameter of main rotor — 18·90 m (62 ft 0 in)
- Main rotor blade chord (each) — 0·54 m (1 ft 9¼ in)
- Diameter of tail rotor — 4·00 m (13 ft 1½ in)
- Tail rotor blade chord (each) — 0·30 m (11¾ in)
- Length overall, rotors turning — 23·03 m (75 ft 6⅝ in)
- Length of fuselage, incl tail rotor — 20·08 m (65 ft 10¾ in)
- Length of fuselage — 19·40 m (63 ft 7¾ in)
- Length overall:
  - SA 321G, blades and tail folded — 17·07 m (56 ft 0 in)
- Width overall:
  - SA 321G, blades and tail folded — 5·20 m (17 ft 0¾ in)
  - SA 321F, incl baggage containers — 5·04 m (16 ft 6⅜ in)
- Width of fuselage — 2·24 m (7 ft 4¼ in)
- Height at tail rotor (normal) — 6·66 m (21 ft 10¼ in)
- Height overall:
  - SA 321G, blades and tail folded — 4·94 m (16 ft 2½ in)
- Wheel track — 4·30 m (14 ft 1 in)

Wheelbase 6·56 m (21 ft 6¼ in)
Cabin door: Height 1·55 m (5 ft 1 in)
Width 1·20 m (3 ft 11¼ in)
Rear loading ramp; Length 1·90 m (6 ft 2¾ in)
Width 1·90 m (6 ft 2¾ in)

DIMENSIONS, INTERNAL:
Cabin: Length: SA 321F 9·67 m (31 ft 9 in)
SA 321G and Ja 7·00 m (22 ft 11½ in)
Width: SA 321F 1·96 m (6 ft 5 in)
SA 321G and Ja, at floor 1·90 m (6 ft 2¾ in)
Height: SA 321F 1·80 m (5 ft 11 in)
SA 321G and Ja 1·83 m (6 ft 0 in)
Usable volume:
SA 321G and Ja 25·3 m³ (893 cu ft)

WEIGHTS:
Weight empty, standard aircraft:
SA 321G 6,863 kg (15,130 lb)
SA 321H 6,702 kg (14,775 lb)
SA 321Ja 6,868 kg (15,141 lb)
Max T-O weight 13,000 kg (28,660 lb)

PERFORMANCE (at max T-O weight):
Never-exceed speed at S/L
148 knots (275 km/h; 171 mph)
Cruising speed at S/L135 knots (250 km/h; 155 mph)
Cruising speed at S/L, one engine out
113 knots (210 km/h; 130 mph)
Max rate of climb at S/L 400 m (1,312 ft)/min
Rate of climb at S/L, one engine out
146 m (479 ft)/min
Service ceiling 3,150 m (10,325 ft)
Service ceiling, one engine out 1,200 m (3,940 ft)
Hovering ceiling IGE 2,170 m (7,120 ft)
Normal range at S/L 442 nm (820 km; 509 miles)
Normal range at S/L, one engine out
496 nm (920 km; 572 miles)
Range at S/L with 3,500 kg (7,716 lb) payload
549 nm (1,020 km; 633 miles)
Endurance in ASW role 4 h

AÉROSPATIALE SA 330 PUMA

The twin-engined SA 330 Puma was developed initially to meet a French Army requirement for a medium-sized *hélicoptère de manoeuvre,* able to operate by day or night in all weathers and all climates. In 1967, the SA 330 was selected for the RAF Tactical Transport Programme, and was included in the joint production agreement between Aérospatiale and Westland in the UK.

The first of two SA 330 prototypes flew on 15 April 1965, and the last of six pre-production models on 30 July 1968, followed in September 1968 by the first production aircraft.

Details of six early versions of the Puma can be found in the 1976-77 *Jane's.* Current production versions are as follows:

SA 330J/L. Civil (J) and military (L) versions introduced in 1976 with main rotor blades of composite materials. Increased max T-O weight.

On 25 April 1978, the SA 330J became the first helicopter outside the Soviet Union to be certificated for all-weather operations, including flight in icing conditions. Equipment for this comprises thermal de-icing of the main rotor blades; thermal anti-icing of the tail rotor blades; special lengthened air intakes to ensure normal air supply into engines regardless of ambient conditions, including protection against sand and sea spray; and installation of weather radar.

A total of 624 Pumas had been sold to 52 operators in 43 countries by 1 March 1979. Nurtanio of Indonesia is expected to begin production of Pumas in the early 1980s.

TYPE: Medium-sized transport helicopter.

ROTOR SYSTEM: Four-blade main rotor, with a fully-articulated hub and integral rotor brake. The blade cuffs, equipped with horns, are connected by link-rods to the swashplate, which is actuated by three hydraulic twin-cylinder servo-control units. Each of the moulded blades is made up of a glassfibre roving spar, a composite glass and carbon fibre fabric skin, with Moltoprene/honeycomb filler. The leading-edge is covered with a stainless steel protective section. Attachment of the blades to their sleeve by means of two pins enables them to be folded back quickly by manual methods. The five-blade tail rotor has flapping hinges only, and is located on the starboard side of the tailboom.

ROTOR DRIVE: Mechanical shaft and gear drive. Main gearbox, mounted on top of cabin behind engines, has two separate inputs from the engines and five reduction stages. The first stage drives, from each engine, an intermediate shaft directly driving the alternator and the ventilation fan, and indirectly driving the two hydraulic pumps. At the second stage the action of the two units becomes synchronised on a single main driveshaft by means of freewheeling spur gears. If one or both engines are stopped, this enables the drive gears to be rotated by the remaining turbine or the autorotating rotor, thus maintaining drive to the ancillary systems when the engines are stopped. Drive to the tail rotor is via shafting and an intermediate angle gearbox, terminating at a right-angle tail rotor gearbox. Turbine output 23,000 rpm, main rotor shaft 265 rpm. Tail rotor shaft 1,278 rpm. The hydraulically-controlled rotor brake, installed on the main gearbox, permits stopping of the rotor 15 s after engine shutdown.

Aérospatiale SA 330J Puma (two Turboméca Turmo IVC turboshaft engines)

FUSELAGE: Conventional all-metal semi-monocoque structure. Local use of titanium alloy under engine installation, which is outside the main fuselage shell. Monocoque tailboom supports the tail rotor on the starboard side and a horizontal stabiliser on the port side.

LANDING GEAR: Messier-Hispano-Bugatti semi-retractable tricycle type, with twin wheels on each unit. Main units retract upward hydraulically into fairings on sides of fuselage; self-centering nose unit retracts rearward. When landing gear is down, the nosewheel jack is extended and the main-wheel jacks are telescoped. Dual-chamber oleo-pneumatic shock-absorbers. All tyres same size (7·00-6), of Dunlop or Kléber-Colombes tubeless type, pressure 6·0 bars (85 lb/sq in) on all units. Hydraulic differential disc brakes, controlled by foot pedals. Lever-operated parking brake. Emergency pop-out flotation units can be mounted on rear landing gear fairings and forward fuselage.

POWER PLANT: Two Turboméca Turmo IVC turboshaft engines, each with max rating of 1,175 kW (1,575 shp) and fitted with intake anti-icing. Engines are mounted side by side above cabin forward of the main rotor assembly and separated by a firewall. They are coupled to the main rotor transmission box, with shaft drive to tail rotor, and form a completely independent system from the fuel tanks up to the main gearbox inputs. Fuel in four flexible tanks and one auxiliary tank beneath cargo compartment floor, with total capacity of 1,544 litres (339·5 Imp gallons). Provision for additional 1,900 litres (418 Imp gallons) in four auxiliary ferry tanks installed in cabin. External auxiliary tanks (two, each 350 litres; 77 Imp gallons capacity) are available. For long-range missions (mainly offshore) one or two special internal tanks (each 215 litres; 47·25 Imp gallons) can be fitted in the cabin. Each engine is supplied normally by a pair of interconnected primary tanks, the lower halves of which have self-sealing walls for protection against small-calibre projectiles. Refuelling point on starboard side of main cabin. Oil capacity 22 litres (4·8 Imp gallons) for engines, 25·5 litres (5·6 Imp gallons) for transmission.

ACCOMMODATION: Crew of one or two side by side on anti-crash seats on flight deck, with jump-seat for third crew member if required. Door on each side of flight deck on current versions. Internal doorway connects flight deck to cabin, with folding seat in doorway for an extra crew member or cargo supervisor. Dual controls standard. Accommodation in main cabin for 16 individually-equipped troops, six stretchers and six seated patients, or equivalent freight. The number of troops can be increased to 20 in the high-density version. Strengthened floor for cargo-carrying, with lashing points. Jettisonable sliding door on each side of main cabin; or port-side door with built-in steps and starboard-side double door in VIP or airline configurations. Removable panel on underside of fuselage, at rear of main cabin, permits longer loads to be accommodated and also serves as emergency exit on SA 330L version. Removable door with integral steps for access to baggage racks on SA 330J version. A hatch in the floor below the centreline of the main rotor is provided for carrying loads of up to 3,200 kg (7,055 lb) on an internally-mounted cargo sling. (Certification for external loads up to 3,500 kg; 7,715 lb anticipated in 1979.) A fixed or retractable rescue hoist (capacity 275 kg; 606 lb) can be mounted externally on the starboard side of the fuselage. The cabin can be equipped in 8/9/12-seat VIP, 17-seat commuter or 20-seat high-density layouts, with baggage compartment and/or toilet facilities in rear of cabin. Cabin and flight deck are heated, ventilated and soundproofed. Demisting, de-icing, washers and wipers for pilots' windscreens.

SYSTEMS: Two independent hydraulic systems, each 172 bars (2,500 lb/sq in), supplied by self-regulating pumps driven by the main gearbox. Each system supplies one set of servo unit chambers, the left-hand system supplying in addition the autopilot, landing gear, rotor brake and wheel brakes. Freewheels in main gearbox ensure that both systems remain in operation, for supplying the servo-controls, if the engines are stopped in flight. Other hydraulically-actuated systems can be operated on the ground from the main gearbox, or by external power through the ground power receptacle. There is also an independent auxiliary system, fed through a hand pump, which can be used in an emergency to lower the landing gear and pressurise the accumulator for the

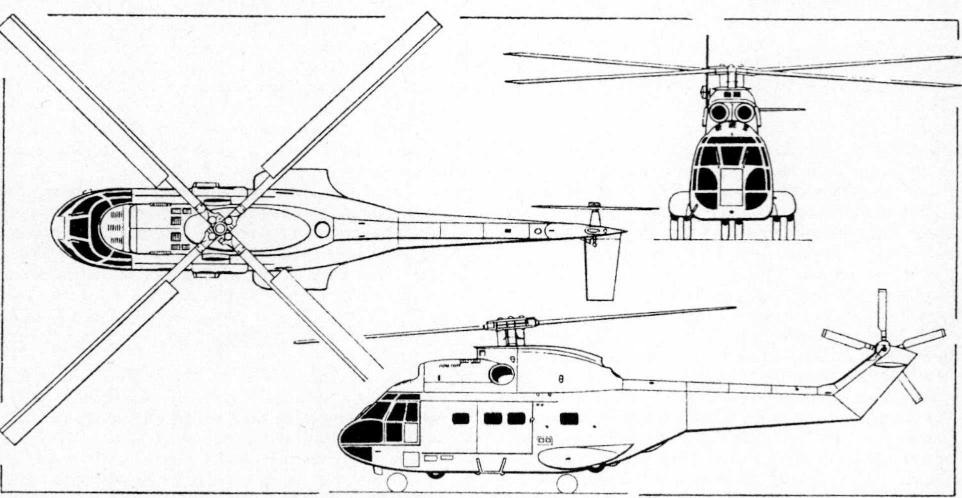

Aérospatiale SA 330 Puma transport helicopter *(Pilot Press)*

parking brake on the ground. Three-phase 200V AC electrical power supplied by two 15kVA 400Hz alternators, driven by the port side intermediate shaft from the main gearbox and available on the ground under the same conditions as the hydraulic ancillary systems. 28·5V 10kW DC power provided from the AC system by two transformer-rectifiers. Main aircraft battery used for self-starting and emergency power in flight. For the latter purpose, an emergency 400VA inverter can supply the essential navigation equipment from the battery, permitting at least 20 min continued flight in the event of a main power failure. De-icing of engines and engine air intakes by warm air bled from compressor. Anti-snow shield for Winter operations.

ELECTRONICS AND EQUIPMENT: Optional communications equipment includes VHF, UHF, tactical HF and HF/SSB radio installations and intercom system. Navigational equipment includes radio compass, radio altimeter, VLF Omega, Decca navigator and flight log, Doppler, and VOR/ILS with glidepath. Autopilot, with provision for coupling to self-contained navigation and microwave landing systems. Full IFR instrumentation available optionally. The search and rescue version has nose-mounted Bendix RDR 1400 or RCA Primus 40 or 50 search radar, Doppler, and Decca self-contained navigation system, including navigation computer, polar indicator, roller-map display, hover indicator, route mileage indicator and ground speed and drift indicator.

ARMAMENT (optional): A wide range of armament can be carried, including side-firing 20 mm cannon, axial-firing 7·62 mm machine-guns, missiles and rockets.

DIMENSIONS, EXTERNAL:

Diameter of main rotor	15·00 m (49 ft 2½ in)
Diameter of tail rotor	3·04 m (9 ft 11½ in)
Distance between rotor centres	9·20 m (30 ft 2¼ in)
Blade chord, main rotor	0·60 m (1 ft 11½ in)
Ground clearance of tail rotor	2·00 m (6 ft 6¾ in)
Length overall	18·15 m (59 ft 6½ in)
Length of fuselage	14·06 m (46 ft 1½ in)
Length, blades folded	14·80 m (48 ft 6¾ in)
Width, blades folded	3·50 m (11 ft 5¾ in)
Height overall	5·14 m (16 ft 10½ in)
Height to top of rotor hub	4·38 m (14 ft 4½ in)
Width over wheel fairings	3·00 m (9 ft 10 in)
Wheel track	2·38 m (7 ft 10¾ in)
Wheelbase	4·045 m (13 ft 3 in)
Passenger cabin doors, each:	
Height	1·35 m (4 ft 5 in)
Width	1·35 m (4 ft 5 in)
Height to sill	1·00 m (3 ft 3½ in)
Floor hatch, rear of cabin:	
Length	0·98 m (3 ft 2¾ in)
Width	0·70 m (2 ft 3½ in)

DIMENSIONS, INTERNAL:

Cabin: Length	6·05 m (19 ft 10 in)
Max width	1·80 m (5 ft 10¾ in)
Max height	1·55 m (5 ft 1 in)
Floor area	7·80 m² (84 sq ft)
Usable volume	11·40 m³ (403 cu ft)

AREAS:

Main rotor blades (each)	4·00 m² (43 sq ft)
Tail rotor blades (each)	0·28 m² (3·01 sq ft)
Main rotor disc	177·0 m² (1,905 sq ft)
Tail rotor disc	7·30 m² (78·6 sq ft)
Horizontal stabiliser	1·34 m² (14·4 sq ft)

WEIGHTS:

Weight empty, standard aircraft:	
SA 330J	3,766 kg (8,303 lb)
SA 330L	3,615 kg (7,970 lb)
Max T-O and landing weight	7,400 kg (16,315 lb)*

*Certification for T-O weight of 7,500 kg (16,535 lb), *for cargo-sling mission only*, anticipated in 1979

PERFORMANCE (SA 330J/L: A at 6,000 kg; 13,230 lb AUW, B at 7,400 kg; 16,315 lb AUW):

Never-exceed speed:	
A	158 knots (294 km/h; 182 mph)
B	142 knots (263 km/h; 163 mph)
Max cruising speed:	
A	146 knots (271 km/h; 168 mph)
B	139 knots (258 km/h; 160 mph)
Max rate of climb at S/L:	
A	552 m (1,810 ft)/min
B	366 m (1,200 ft)/min
Service ceiling (30 m; 100 ft/min rate of climb):	
A	6,000 m (19,680 ft)
B	4,800 m (15,750 ft)
Hovering ceiling IGE:	
A, ISA	4,400 m (14,435 ft)
A, ISA +20°C	3,700 m (12,135 ft)
B, ISA	2,300 m (7,545 ft)
B, ISA +20°C	1,600 m (5,250 ft)
Hovering ceiling OGE:	
A, ISA	4,250 m (13,940 ft)
A, ISA +20°C	3,600 m (11,810 ft)
B, ISA	1,700 m (5,575 ft)
B, ISA +20°C	1,050 m (3,445 ft)
Max range at normal cruising speed, no reserves:	
A	309 nm (572 km; 355 miles)
B	297 nm (550 km; 341 miles)

AÉROSPATIALE AS 332 SUPER PUMA

Design of this derivative of the SA 330 Puma was started in 1974, and the programme received a formal 'go-ahead' from the French government in June 1975. As a first stage, Aérospatiale retrofitted a Puma airframe with two Turboméca Makila turboshaft engines and an uprated transmission. This experimental helicopter, designated AS 331, flew for the first time on 5 September 1977. It was followed, on 13 September 1978, by the first flight of the prototype AS 332 Super Puma, embodying more extensive changes to provide increased payload and performance, simplified maintenance, reduced cabin noise level, reduced vulnerability to hostile fire in combat areas, and better crew survivability in a crash. Original plans to fit a 'fenestron' ducted tail rotor were dropped after evaluation of a 'fenestron' on the SA 330Z testbed (see 1976-77 *Jane's*, page 812) indicated no worthwhile performance gains.

Externally evident airframe changes compared with the SA 330 Puma include a lengthened nose; increased wheelbase and wheel track; a new landing gear with a single wheel on each of the main units, which offer an optional 'kneeling' capability to reduce overall dimensions for shipboard stowage; and an added ventral fin. The main and tail rotor blades have a new and more efficient profile.

There are two basic versions of the Super Puma:

AS 332B. Military version.

AS 332C. Civil version.

Each sub-type will be offered in standard form, accommodating up to 20 troops/17 civilian passengers, or with the cabin lengthened by 0·76 m (2 ft 6 in) to provide four more seats and two additional windows. All variants will offer all-weather flight capability, including operation in forecast icing conditions.

DGAC and FAA certification of the Super Puma is planned for late 1980, with deliveries beginning in 1981. To facilitate integration of the aircraft into existing fleets of Pumas (notably in French Army service), Aérospatiale hopes to launch a programme under which SA 330 Pumas will be retrofitted with the engines, some dynamic components and the composite-blade tail rotor of the Super Puma.

TYPE: Twin-turbine multi-role helicopter.

ROTOR SYSTEM: Four-blade main rotor, with a fully-articulated hub and integral rotor brake. Each drag hinge is fitted with an elastomeric frequency adaptor. The blade cuffs, equipped with horns, are connected by link-rods to the swashplate, which is actuated by three hydraulic twin-cylinder servo-control units. Each of the moulded blades is made up of a glassfibre roving spar and a composite glass and carbon fibre fabric skin, with Moltoprene filler. The leading-edge is covered with a titanium protective section. Attachment of the blades to their sleeve by means of two pins enables them to be folded back quickly by manual methods. The five-blade tail rotor has flapping hinges only, and is located on the starboard side of the tailboom. The rotors may be equipped with a de-icing system similar to that certificated for the Puma.

ROTOR DRIVE: Mechanical shaft and gear drive. Modular main gearbox is fitted with two torquemeters and has two separate lubrication circuits. It is mounted on top of the cabin behind the engines, has two separate inputs from the engines and five reduction stages. The first stage drives, from each engine, an intermediate shaft directly driving the alternator and indirectly driving the two hydraulic pumps, with a further shaft drive to the ventilation fan. At the second stage the action of the two units becomes synchronised on a single main driveshaft by means of freewheeling spur gears. If one or both engines are stopped, this enables the drive gears to be rotated by the remaining turbine or the autorotating rotor, thus maintaining drive to the ancillary systems when the engines are stopped. Drive to the tail rotor is via shafting and an intermediate angle gearbox, terminating at a right-angle tail rotor gearbox. Turbine output 23,840 rpm, main rotor shaft 265 rpm. Tail rotor shaft 1,278 rpm. The hydraulically-controlled rotor brake, installed on the main gearbox, permits stopping of the rotor 15 s after engine shutdown.

FUSELAGE: Conventional all-metal semi-monocoque structure, embodying anti-crash features. Local use of titanium alloy under engine installation, which is outside the main fuselage shell. Monocoque tailboom supports the tail rotor on the starboard side and a horizontal stabiliser with fixed leading-edge slat on the port side. Optional folding tailboom for aircraft that will serve on ships such as frigates.

LANDING GEAR: Retractable tricycle type, of Messier-Hispano-Bugatti high energy-absorbing design. All units retract rearward hydraulically, main wheels into fairings on sides of fuselage. Dual-chamber oleo-pneumatic shock-absorbers. Optional 'kneeling' capability for main units. Twin-wheel self-centering nose unit, tyre size 466 × 176, pressure 6.0 bars (85 lb/sq in). Single wheel on each main unit with tyre size 615 × 225-10, pressure 6.0 bars (85 lb/sq in). Hydraulic differential disc brakes, controlled by foot pedals. Lever-operated parking brake. Emergency pop-out flotation units can be mounted on main landing gear fairings and forward fuselage.

POWER PLANT: Two Turboméca Makila IA turboshaft engines, each with max rating of 1,309 kW (1,755 shp). Air intakes protected by a grille against ingestion of ice, snow and foreign objects; but multi-purpose intake is necessary for flight into sandy areas. Standard versions have five flexible fuel tanks under cabin floor, with total capacity of 1,544 litres (339·5 Imp gallons). Stretched versions have a basic fuel system of six flexible tanks with total capacity of 2,044 litres (450 Imp gallons). Provision for additional 1,900 litres (418 Imp gallons) in four auxiliary ferry tanks installed in cabin. Two external auxiliary tanks are available, with total capacity of 700 litres (154 Imp gallons). For long-range missions (mainly offshore), a special internal tank, capacity 600 litres (132 Imp gallons), and an auxiliary tank, capacity 330 litres (72·5 Imp gallons) are available; latter fits in cargo-sling well beneath cabin floor and is quickly removable to permit use of sling. Refuelling point on starboard side of cabin. Fuel system is designed to avoid fuel leakage following a crash, with flexible fuel lines and interconnections between tanks, self-sealing valves and automatic fuel pump shutdown in a crash. Options include a fuel dumping system, pressure refuelling, and crash-resistant tanks.

ACCOMMODATION: One pilot (VFR) or two pilots side by side (IFR) on flight deck, with jump-seat for third crew member or paratroop despatcher. Door on each side of flight deck and internal doorway connecting flight deck to cabin. Dual controls, co-pilot instrumentation and anti-crash flight deck floor. Standard versions accommodate in main cabin up to 20 troops in normal seating, 16 troops in anti-crash seats, six stretchers and six seated casualties/attendants, 17 civilian passengers, or eight, nine or twelve VIP passengers in special interiors with toilet and galley. Stretched versions accommodate in main cabin up to 24 troops in normal seating, 18 troops in anti-crash seats, nine stretchers and three seated casualties/attendants, 21 civilian passengers, or nine, ten or 15 VIP passengers with toilet and galley. Strengthened floor for cargo carrying, with lashing points. Jettisonable sliding door on each side of main cabin; or port side door with built-in steps and starboard-side double door in VIP or airline configura-

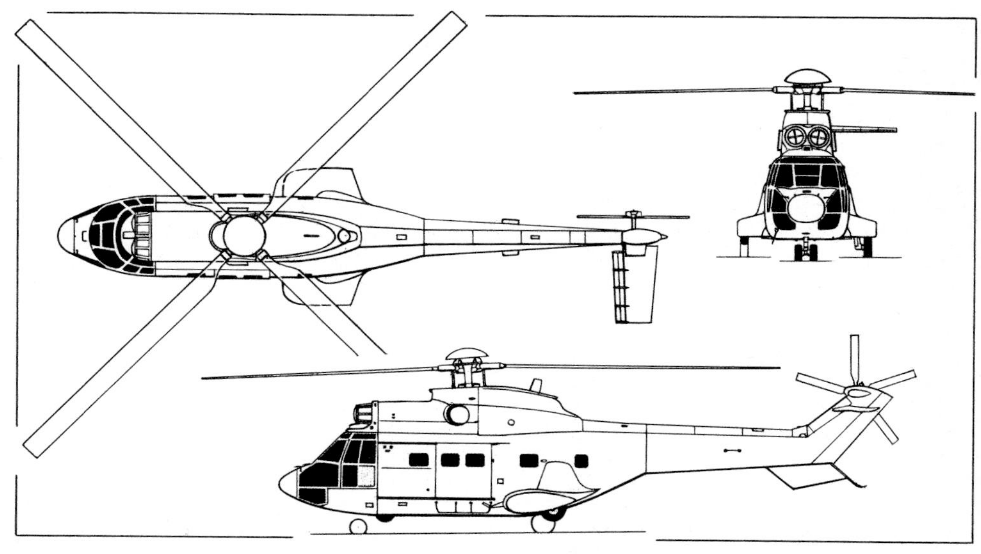

Aérospatiale AS 332 Super Puma (two Turboméca Makila turboshaft engines) *(Pilot Press)*

tions. Removable panel on underside of fuselage, at rear of main cabin, permits longer loads to be accommodated, and also serves as emergency exit. Removable door with integral steps for access to baggage racks optional. A hatch in the floor below the centreline of the main rotor is provided for carrying loads of up to 4,000 kg (8,818 lb) on an internally-mounted cargo sling. A fixed or retractable rescue hoist (capacity 275 kg; 606 lb) can be mounted externally on the starboard side of the fuselage. Cabin and flight deck are heated, ventilated and soundproofed. Demisting, de-icing, washers and wipers for pilots' windscreens.

SYSTEMS: Two independent hydraulic systems, supplied by self-regulating pumps driven by the main gearbox. Each system supplies one set of servo unit chambers, the left-hand system supplying in addition the autopilot, landing gear, rotor brake and wheel brakes. Freewheels in main gearbox ensure that both systems remain in operation, for supplying the servo-controls, if the engines are stopped in flight. Other hydraulically-actuated systems can be operated on the ground from the main gearbox (when a special disconnect system is installed to permit running of port engine with rotors stationary), or by external power through the ground power receptacle. There is also an independent auxiliary system, fed through a hand pump, which can be used in an emergency to lower the landing gear. Three-phase 200V AC electrical power supplied by two 20kVA 400Hz alternators, driven by the port side intermediate shaft from the main gearbox and available on the ground under the same conditions as the hydraulic ancillary systems. 28.5V DC power provided from the AC system by two transformer-rectifiers. Main aircraft battery used for self-starting and emergency power in flight.

AVIONICS AND EQUIPMENT: Optional communications equipment includes VHF, UHF, tactical HF and HF/SSB radio installations and intercom system. Navigational equipment includes radio compass, radio altimeter, VLF Omega, Decca navigator and flight log, Doppler, and VOR/ILS with glidepath. Autopilot, with provision for coupling to self-contained navigation and microwave landing systems. Full IFR instrumentation available optionally. The search and rescue version has nose-mounted Bendix RDR 1400 or RCA Primus 40 or 50 search radar, Doppler, and Crouzet Nadir or Decca self-contained navigation system, including navigation computer, polar indicator, roller-map display, hover indicator, route mileage indicator and ground speed and drift indicator. For naval ASW and ASV missions, aircraft can be fitted with nose-mounted OMERA type ORB 32 ASD 360° radar, linked to a tactical table.

ARMAMENT AND OPERATIONAL EQUIPMENT (optional): Typical alternatives for army/air force missions are one 20 mm gun, two 7·62 mm machine-guns, or two pods each containing twenty-two 68 mm rockets or nineteen 2·75 in rockets. Armament for naval missions includes two Exocet missiles, or two torpedoes and sonar, or MAD and sonobuoys.

DIMENSIONS, EXTERNAL:
Diameter of main rotor 15·00 m (49 ft 2½ in)
Diameter of tail rotor 3·04 m (9 ft 11½ in)
Blade chord, main rotor 0·60 m (1 ft 11½ in)
Length overall: standard 18·46 m (60 ft 6¾ in)
Length of fuselage: standard 14·76 m (48 ft 5 in)
stretched 15·52 m (50 ft 11 in)
Length, blades folded: standard 15·60 m (51 ft 2 in)
stretched 16·36 m (53 ft 8 in)
Length, blades and tail pylon folded:
standard 12·64 m (41 ft 5½ in)
stretched 13·40 m (43 ft 11½ in)
Width, blades folded 3·90 m (12 ft 9½ in)
Height overall 4·92 m (16 ft 1¾ in)
Height to top of rotor hub 4·48 m (14 ft 8½ in)
Width over wheel fairings 3·90 m (12 ft 9½ in)
Wheel track 3·00 m (9 ft 10 in)
Wheelbase 4·49 m (14 ft 8¾ in)
Passenger cabin doors, each:
Height 1·35 m (4 ft 5 in)
Width 1·35 m (4 ft 5 in)
Floor hatch, rear of cabin:
Length 0·98 m (3 ft 2¾ in)
Width 0·70 m (2 ft 3½ in)

DIMENSIONS, INTERNAL:
Cabin: Length: standard 6·05 m (19 ft 10½ in)
stretched 6·81 m (22 ft 4 in)
Max width 1·80 m (5 ft 11 in)
Max height 1·55 m (5 ft 1 in)
Floor area: standard 7·80 m² (84 sq ft)
Usable volume: standard 11·40 m³ (403 cu ft)
stretched 13·30 m³ (469·5 cu ft)

WEIGHTS:
Weight empty:
AS 332B, standard 3,850 kg (8,488 lb)
AS 332B, stretched 3,940 kg (8,686 lb)
AS 332C, standard 3,920 kg (8,642 lb)
AS 332C, stretched 4,010 kg (8,840 lb)
Max T-O weight 7,800 kg (17,196 lb)

PERFORMANCE (Basic version, at max T-O weight):
Max cruising speed at S/L
157 knots (291 km/h; 181 mph)

Aérospatiale AS 332B Super Puma twin-turbine multi-role helicopter *(J. M. G. Gradidge)*

Econ cruising speed at S/L
140 knots (260 km/h; 161 mph)
Max rate of climb at S/L 582 m (1,910 ft)/min
Service ceiling, one engine out 2,300 m (7,550 ft)
Hovering ceiling OGE: ISA 2,300 m (7,550 ft)
ISA + 20° C 1,600 m (5,250 ft)
Range at S/L, no reserves:
standard tanks 337 nm (625 km; 388 miles)
with external (2 × 350 litre) and auxiliary (330 litre) tanks 566 nm (1,050 km; 652 miles)
with external, auxiliary and cabin (600 litre) tanks
712 nm (1,320 km; 820 miles)
with external and four ferry tanks
928 nm (1,720 km; 1,068 miles)
Max endurance at S/L, no reserves:
standard tanks 3 h 20 min
with external and auxiliary tanks 5 h 35 min
with external, auxiliary and 600 litre cabin tanks
6 h 55 min

AÉROSPATIALE SA 341/342 GAZELLE

The first prototype of this five-seat lightweight helicopter (designated SA 340) made its first flight on 7 April 1967, powered by an Astazou III engine. It was followed by a second prototype on 12 April 1968 and then by four pre-production SA 341 Gazelles.

The first production SA 341 Gazelle flew for the first time on 6 August 1971, with a longer cabin than its predecessors, enlarged tail unit, additional door on the starboard side at rear (optional on production aircraft) and uprated Astazou IIIA engine.

The following versions of the Gazelle have been announced:

SA 341B. British Army version, with Astazou IIIN engine. Designated Gazelle AH. Mk 1.

SA 341C. British Navy version. Designated Gazelle HT. Mk 2.

SA 341D. Royal Air Force training version. Designated Gazelle HT. Mk 3.

SA 341E. Royal Air Force communications version. Designated Gazelle HCC. Mk 4.

SA 341F. Original French Army version, with Astazou IIIC engine; 166 procured.

SA 341G. Civil version, with Astazou IIIA engine. Certificated by SGAC on 7 June 1972 and by the FAA on 18 September 1972. In January 1975, it was announced that the SA 341G had become the first helicopter in the world authorised to be flown by a single pilot under IFR Cat I conditions. It is now certificated for IFR Cat II operation, with a ceiling of 30 m (100 ft) and 365 m (1,200 ft) forward visibility. Equipment fitted to the aircraft which qualified for this FAA certification comprised a Sperry flight director coupled to SFENA servo-dampers. A variant, known as the **Stretched Gazelle,** has the rear portion of the cabin modified to provide an additional 20 cm (8 in) of legroom for the rear-seat passengers.

SA 341H. Military export version, with Astazou IIIB engine.

SA 342J. Similar to SA 342L, for commercial operators. Higher max T-O weight. Improved 'fenestron' tail rotor. Certificated by DGAC on 27 April 1976. Deliveries began in 1977.

SA 342K. Military version, first flown on 11 May 1973 and supplied to Kuwait. 650 kW (870 shp) Astazou XIVH engine, with momentum-separation shrouds over intakes.

SA 342L. Military counterpart of SA 342J, with improved 'fenestron' tail rotor.

SA 342M. Successor to SA 341F for ALAT (French Army Light Aviation Corps). Differs from SA 342L in having an ALAT instrument panel and Astazou XIVM turboshaft with automatic start-up and high-energy ignition. Optional equipment specified by ALAT includes SFIM 85 autopilot, self-contained navigation system, exhaust deflector, and night flying equipment. Order for 160 announced in December 1978, with Hot missiles for anti-tank warfare.

Of the above, only the SA 341G and SA 342J/L/M were being marketed by Aérospatiale in the Spring of 1979.

A two-stretcher ambulance configuration has received FAA Standard Type Certification. No major modification is necessary to convert the aircraft to carry two patients longitudinally on the port side of the cabin, one above the other, leaving room for the pilot and a medical attendant in tandem on the starboard side. The dual spine board arrangement weighs 27 kg (60 lb) and stows into the baggage compartment when not in use.

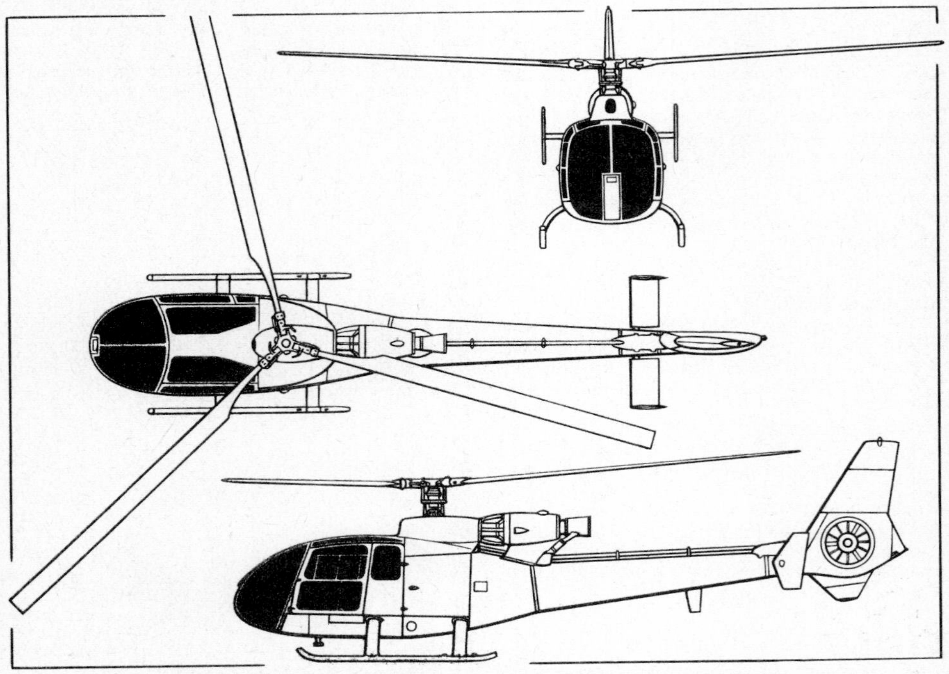

Aérospatiale SA 341 Gazelle five-seat light utility helicopter *(Pilot Press)*

Under an Anglo-French agreement signed in 1967, Gazelles are produced jointly with Westland Helicopters Ltd, and are also built under licence in Yugoslavia. A total of 820 had been sold to 130 operators in 32 countries by 1 March 1979.

Three Class E1c records were set up by the SA 341-01 at Istres on 13 and 14 May 1971. These were: 167·28 knots (310·00 km/h; 192·62 mph) in a straight line over a 3 km course; 168·36 knots (312·00 km/h; 193·87 mph) in a straight line over a 15/25 km course; and 159·72 knots (296·00 km/h; 183·93 mph) over a 100 km closed circuit.

The following details apply to all SA 341 variants:

TYPE: Five-seat light utility helicopter.

ROTOR SYSTEM: Three-blade semi-articulated main rotor and 13-blade shrouded-fan anti-torque tail rotor (known as a 'fenestron' or 'fan-in-fin'). Rotor head and rotor mast form a single unit. The main rotor blades are of NACA 0012 section, attached to NAT hub by flapping hinges. There are no drag hinges. Each blade has a single leading-edge spar of plastics material reinforced with glassfibre, a laminated glass-fabric skin and honeycomb filler. Tail rotor blades are of die-forged light alloy, with articulation for pitch change only. Main rotor blades can be folded manually for stowage. Rotor brake standard.

ROTOR DRIVE: Main reduction gearbox forward of engine, which is mounted above the rear part of the cabin. Intermediate gearbox beneath engine, rear gearbox supporting the tail rotor. Main rotor/engine rpm ratio 378·3 : 6,179. Tail rotor/engine rpm ratio 5,774 : 6,179.

FUSELAGE: Cockpit structure is based on a welded light alloy frame which carries the windows and doors. This is mounted on a conventional semi-monocoque lower structure consisting of two longitudinal box sections connected by frames and bulkheads. Central section, which encloses the baggage hold and fuel tank and supports the main reduction gearbox, is constructed of light alloy honeycomb sandwich panels. Rear section, which supports the engine and tailboom, is of similar construction. Honeycomb sandwich panels are also used for the cabin floors and transmission platform. Tailboom is of conventional sheet metal construction, as are the horizontal tail surfaces and the tail fin.

TAIL UNIT: Small horizontal stabiliser on tailboom, ahead of tail rotor fin.

LANDING GEAR: Steel tube skid type. Wheel can be fitted at rear of each skid for ground handling. Provision for alternative float or ski landing gear.

POWER PLANT (SA 341): One Turboméca Astazou IIIA turboshaft, installed above fuselage aft of cabin and delivering 440 kW (590 shp) for take-off (max continuous rating also 440 kW; 590 shp). Main fuel tank in fuselage, usable capacity 445 litres (98 Imp gallons). Provision for 90 litre (19·8 Imp gallon) auxiliary tank beneath baggage compartment and/or 200 litre (44 Imp gallon) ferry tank inside rear cabin. Total possible usable fuel capacity 735 litres (161 Imp gallons). Refuelling point on starboard side of cabin. Oil capacity 13 litres (2·8 Imp gallons) for engine, 3·5 litres (0·77 Imp gallons) for gearbox.

ACCOMMODATION: Crew of one or two on side-by-side seats in front of cabin, with bench seat to the rear for a further three persons. The bench seat can be folded into floor wells to leave a completely flat cargo floor. Access to baggage compartment via rear cabin bulkhead, or via optional door on starboard side. Cargo tie-down points in cabin floor. Forward-opening car-type door on each side of cabin, immediately behind which are rearward-opening auxiliary cargo loading doors. Baggage compartment at rear of cabin. Ventilation standard. Dual controls optional.

SYSTEMS: Hydraulic system, pressure 40 bars (570 lb/sq in), serves three pitch change jacks for main rotor head and one for tail rotor. 28V DC electrical system supplied by 4kW engine-driven generator and 40Ah battery. Optional 26V AC system, supplied by 0·5kVA alternator at 115/200V 400Hz.

ELECTRONICS AND EQUIPMENT: Optional communications equipment includes UHF, VHF, HF, intercom systems and homing aids. Optional navigation equipment includes radio compass, radio altimeter and VOR. Blind-flying instrumentation standard on SA 341B and F, optional on other versions. A variety of operational equipment can be fitted, according to role, including a 700 kg (1,540 lb) cargo sling, 135 kg (300 lb) rescue hoist, one or two stretchers (internally), or photographic and survey equipment.

ARMAMENT: Military loads can include two pods of Matra or Brandt 2·75 in or 68 mm rockets, four AS.11 or two AS.12 wire-guided missiles with APX-Bézu 334 gyro-stabilised sight, four or six Hot wire-guided missiles with APX 397 gyro-stabilised sight, two forward-firing 7·62 mm machine-guns, reconnaissance flares or smoke markers.

DIMENSIONS, EXTERNAL:

Diameter of main rotor	10·50 m (34 ft 5½ in)
Diameter of tail rotor	0·695 m (2 ft 3⅜ in)
Distance between rotor centres	5·85 m (19 ft 2¼ in)
Main rotor blade chord (constant)	0·30 m (11·8 in)
Length overall	11·97 m (39 ft 3 5/16 in)
Length of fuselage	9·53 m (31 ft 3 3/16 in)
Width, rotors folded	2·015 m (6 ft 7 5/16 in)
Height to top of rotor hub	2·72 m (8 ft 11⅛ in)
Height overall	3·15 m (10 ft 2⅝ in)
Skid track	2·015 m (6 ft 7 5/16 in)
Main cabin doors, each:	
Height	1·05 m (3 ft 4 9/16 in)
Width	1·00 m (3 ft 3¼ in)
Height to sill	0·63 m (2 ft 0¾ in)
Auxiliary cabin doors, each:	
Height	1·05 m (3 ft 4 9/16 in)
Width	0·48 m (1 ft 6¾ in)
Height to sill	0·63 m (2 ft 0¾ in)

DIMENSIONS, INTERNAL:

Cabin: Length	2·20 m (7 ft 2 9/16 in)
Max width	1·32 m (4 ft 4 in)
Max height	1·21 m (3 ft 11⅝ in)
Floor area	1·50 m^2 (16·1 sq ft)
Volume	1·80 m^3 (63·7 cu ft)
Baggage hold volume	0·45 m^3 (15·9 cu ft)

AREAS:

Main rotor blades, each	1·57 m^2 (16·9 sq ft)
Tail rotor blades, each	0·007 m^2 (0·075 sq ft)
Main rotor disc	86·5 m^2 (931 sq ft)
Tail rotor disc	0·37 m^2 (3·98 sq ft)
Fin	0·45 m^2 (4·84 sq ft)
Tailplane	1·80 m^2 (19·4 sq ft)

WEIGHTS AND LOADING:

Weight empty:	
341G	917 kg (2,022 lb)
341H	908 kg (2,002 lb)
342	955 kg (2,105 lb)
Max T-O and landing weight:	
341G/H	1,800 kg (3,970 lb)
342J	1,900 kg (4,190 lb)
Max disc loading:	
341G/H	19·5 kg/m^2 (4 lb/sq ft)

PERFORMANCE (at max T-O weight):

Never-exceed speed at S/L:	
SA 341, 342	167 knots (310 km/h; 193 mph)
Max cruising speed at S/L:	
SA 341, 342	142 knots (264 km/h; 164 mph)
Econ cruising speed at S/L:	
SA 341	126 knots (233 km/h; 144 mph)
SA 342	128 knots (238 km/h; 148 mph)
Max rate of climb at S/L:	
SA 341	540 m (1,770 ft)/min
SA 342	612 m (2,010 ft)/min
Service ceiling:	
SA 341	5,000 m (16,400 ft)
SA 342	4,300 m (14,100 ft)
Hovering ceiling IGE:	
SA 341	2,850 m (9,350 ft)
SA 342	3,650 m (11,970 ft)
Hovering ceiling OGE:	
SA 341	2,000 m (6,560 ft)
SA 342	2,875 m (9,430 ft)
Range at S/L with max fuel:	
SA 341	361 nm (670 km; 416 miles)
Range with max fuel, econ cruising speed, no reserves:	
SA 342	407 nm (755 km; 469 miles)
Range with pilot and 500 kg (1,102 lb) payload:	
SA 341	193·5 nm (360 km; 223 miles)

Aérospatiale SA 342L Gazelle, armed with six Hot missile launchers

AÉROSPATIALE AS 350 ECUREUIL/ASTAR

Intended as a successor to the Alouette, the AS 350 Ecureuil (Squirrel) was designed with an emphasis on low operating and maintenance costs, and low noise and vibration levels. It embodies Aérospatiale's Starflex type of main rotor hub, made of glassfibre, with elastomeric spherical stops and oleo-elastic frequency matchers.

The decision to build prototypes of the Ecureuil was taken in April 1973. The first of these (F-WVKH) flew on 27 June 1974, powered by an Avco Lycoming LTS 101 turboshaft engine. It was followed on 14 February 1975 by a second prototype (F-WVKI) with a Turboméca Arriel turboshaft.

The Lycoming-powered version is marketed only in North America, as the **Astar,** and the Arriel-powered **AS 350B Ecureuil** throughout the rest of the world. French certification of the AS 350B was obtained on 27 October 1977 and deliveries began in March 1978. FAA certification of the original **AS 350C** Astar was obtained on 21 December 1977 and the first production delivery was made in April 1978. The AS 350C was superseded in 1978 by the **AS 350D** with a more powerful version of the Lycoming engine. By 1 March 1979 a total of 362 Ecureuils and Astars had been sold to 149 operators in 16 countries. Production is intended to build up to 7 Ecureuils and 16 Astars per month by February 1980.

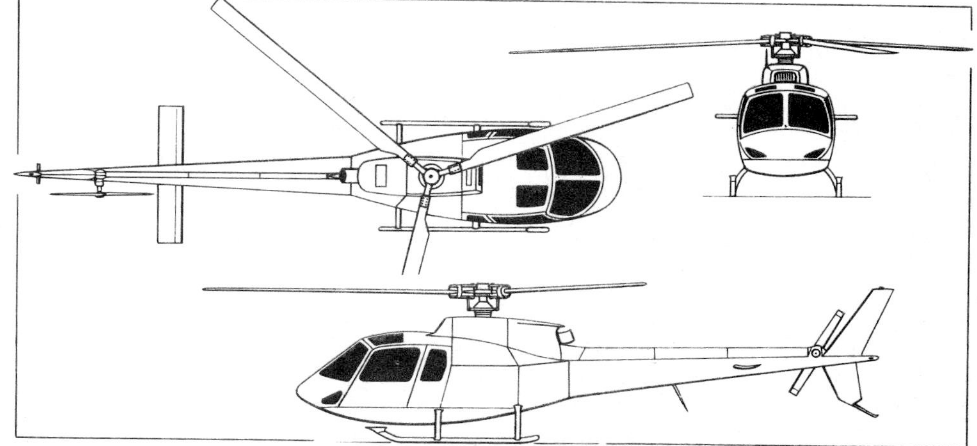

Aérospatiale AS 350 Ecureuil six-seat light helicopter *(Pilot Press)*

Aérospatiale AS 350D Astar (Avco Lycoming LTS 101-600A.2 turboshaft engine)

TYPE: Six-seat light general-purpose helicopter.

ROTOR SYSTEM: Three-blade main rotor, with Starflex glassfibre hub in which the three conventional hinges for each blade are replaced by a single ball-joint of rubber/steel sandwich construction, requiring no maintenance. Glassfibre blades, with stainless steel leading-edge sheath, produced by an entirely mechanised process. Symmetrical blade section. Two-blade tail rotor; each blade comprises a sheet metal skin around a glassfibre spar, the flexibility of which obviates the need for hinges.

ROTOR DRIVE: Simplified transmission, with single epicyclic main gear train. By comparison with Alouette II, number of gear wheels is reduced from 22 to 9 and number of bearings from 23 to 9. Tail rotor drive-shaft coupling on engine.

FUSELAGE: Basic structure of light alloy pressings, with skin mainly of thermoformed plastics, including baggage compartment doors.

TAIL UNIT: Horizontal stabiliser, of inverted aerofoil section, mid-mounted on tailboom. Sweptback fin, in two sections above and below tailboom.

LANDING GEAR: Steel tube skid type. Emergency flotation gear optional.

POWER PLANT: One 478 kW (641 shp) Turboméca Arriel (AS 350B) or 459 kW (616 shp) Avco Lycoming LTS 101-600A.2 (AS 350D) turboshaft engine, mounted above fuselage to rear of cabin. Plastics fuel tanks with total capacity of 530 litres (116·5 Imp gallons).

ACCOMMODATION: Two individual bucket seats at front of cabin and two two-place bench seats are standard. In the alternative layout the two benches are replaced by three armchair seats. Large forward-hinged door on each side. Optional sliding door at rear of cabin on port side. Baggage compartment aft of cabin, with full-width upward-hinged door on starboard side. Top of baggage compartment reinforced to provide platform on each side for inspecting and servicing rotor head.

SYSTEMS: Hydraulic system includes four single-body servo units, operating at 40 bars (570 lb/sq in) pressure, and accumulators to protect against a hydraulic power supply failure. Electrical system includes a 4·5kW engine-driven starter/generator, a 16Ah 24V nickel-cadmium battery and a ground power receptacle connected to the bus bar which distributes power to the electrical equipment. Cabin air-conditioning system optional.

AVIONICS AND EQUIPMENT: Optional com/nav radio equipment includes VHF/AM, ICS, VOR/LOC/glide-slope, marker beacon indicator, radio compass, HF/SSB, transponder and DME. IFR instrumentation optional. Available equipment includes a 750 kg (1,650 lb) cargo sling, a 900 kg (1,984 lb) sling associated with a max T-O weight of 2,100 kg (4,630 lb), and a 135 kg (297 lb) electrical hoist.

DIMENSIONS, EXTERNAL:

Diameter of main rotor	10·69 m (35 ft 0¾ in)
Diameter of tail rotor	1·86 m (6 ft 1¼ in)
Length overall	13·00 m (42 ft 8 in)
Length of fuselage	10·91 m (35 ft 9½ in)
Width of fuselage	1·80 m (5 ft 10¾ in)
Height overall	3·08 m (10 ft 1¼ in)
Skid track	2·10 m (6 ft 10¾ in)
Cabin doors (standard, each):	
Height	1·15 m (3 ft 9¼ in)
Width	1·10 m (3 ft 7¼ in)

DIMENSIONS, INTERNAL:

Cabin: Length	2·42 m (7 ft 11¼ in)
Width at rear	1·65 m (5 ft 5 in)
Height	1·35 m (4 ft 5 in)
Baggage compartment volume	1·00 m³ (35·31 cu ft)

WEIGHTS:

Weight empty: AS 350B	1,045 kg (2,304 lb)
AS 350D	1,070 kg (2,359 lb)
Max T-O weight: normal	1,950 kg (4,300 lb)
with max slung load	2,100 kg (4,630 lb)

PERFORMANCE (at T-O weight of 1,950 kg; 4,300 lb):

Never-exceed speed below 500 m (1,640 ft):	
Both versions	147 knots (272 km/h; 169 mph)
Max cruising speed:	
AS 350B	125 knots (232 km/h; 144 mph)
AS 350D	124 knots (230 km/h; 143 mph)
Max rate of climb at S/L:	
Both versions	492 m (1,615 ft)/min
Service ceiling:	
AS 350B	4,875 m (16,000 ft)
AS 350D	4,575 m (15,000 ft)
Hovering ceiling IGE:	
AS 350B	3,000 m (9,840 ft)
AS 350D	2,500 m (8,200 ft)
Hovering ceiling OGE:	
AS 350B	2,250 m (7,380 ft)
AS 350D	1,800 m (5,900 ft)
Range with max fuel at S/L, no reserves:	
AS 350B	383 nm (710 km; 441 miles)
AS 350D	410 nm (760 km; 472 miles)

AÉROSPATIALE AS 355E ECUREUIL 2/TWINSTAR

The AS 355E represents a twin-engined addition to the AS 350 Ecureuil/Astar family. Many components, such as the rotor blades, main rotor mast and head, tail rotor hub, servo units, cabin and landing gear, are identical to those of the AS 350. Major changes appear in the power plant, transmission, fuel system and fuselage structure.

Design work on the AS 355E had been completed by the end of 1978. First flight of the prototype was scheduled for September 1979, with DGAC certification for VFR operation expected by October 1980. This helicopter is intended primarily for the civil market, in particular for use by companies working in the oil industry. By 1 March 1979, sales totalled 135, to 35 operators in five countries. The version for the North American market will be known as the **Twinstar**; aircraft marketed elsewhere will be named **Ecureuil 2**.

TYPE: Twin-turbine light general-purpose helicopter.

ROTOR SYSTEM: As for AS 350.

ROTOR DRIVE: Single main gearbox, made up of three modules (epicyclic reduction gearbox, bevel gearbox and oil pump), receives power from the engines via a coupling shaft carrying two free-wheel units and power take-offs for the accessories and tail rotor.

FUSELAGE: Light alloy cabin and centre-fuselage structure, with deep-drawn sheet-metal forms of simple geometric design. Tapered tailboom of light alloy sheet wrapped and riveted around deep-drawn sheet metal cylindrical frames.

LANDING GEAR: Steel tube skid type.

POWER PLANT: Two Allison 250-C20F turboshaft engines, each rated at 317 kW (425 shp) for take-off. Two fuel tanks, with total capacity of 730 litres (160·5 Imp gallons), in body structure.

ACCOMMODATION: As for AS 350.

SYSTEMS, AVIONICS AND EQUIPMENT: As for AS 350.

DIMENSIONS, EXTERNAL AND INTERNAL: As for AS 350.

WEIGHTS:

Weight empty	1,230 kg (2,712 lb)
Max T-O weight	2,100 kg (4,630 lb)

PERFORMANCE (estimated, at max T-O weight):

Never-exceed speed (structural limitation)	147 knots (272 km/h; 169 mph)
Max level speed at S/L	129 knots (240 km/h; 149 mph)
Econ cruising speed	119 knots (220 km/h; 136 mph)
Max rate of climb at S/L	516 m (1,690 ft)/min
Service ceiling	4,000 m (13,125 ft)
Hovering ceiling IGE	2,200 m (7,215 ft)
Hovering ceiling OGE	1,500 m (4,920 ft)
Range with max fuel at S/L, no reserves	432 nm (800 km; 497 miles)

AÉROSPATIALE SA 360C DAUPHIN

The SA 360 Dauphin was developed, with the twin-engined SA 365 variant (described separately), as a replacement for the Alouette III. The first of two SA 360 prototypes (F-WSQL) flew for the first time on 2 June 1972, powered by a 730 kW (980 shp) Turboméca Astazou XVI turboshaft engine. After 180 flights, it was re-engined with an Astazou XVIIIA turboshaft and modified in certain respects, including the addition of small weights to the rotor blades, to eliminate ground resonance and reduce vibration to an unprecedented level, even at high speed. The aircraft flew for the first time in its modified form on 4 May 1973, having been joined by the second prototype (F-WSQX) on 29 January 1973.

DGAC certification of the basic SA 360C was awarded on 18 December 1975, followed by FAA certification on 31 March 1976. By 1 March 1979, Aérospatiale had received orders for a total of 74 SA 360C and SA 365 helicopters, from 30 operators in 15 countries, including the USA.

Three helicopter speed records in Class E1d (1,750 to 3,000 kg weight) were set up at Istres by the first prototype of the SA 360 on 15, 16 and 17 May 1973, piloted by Roland Coffignot. Carrying a payload equivalent to eight persons and fuel for one hour's flying, the SA 360 achieved, successively, 161·4 knots (299 km/h; 185·8 mph) over a 100 km closed circuit; 168·4 knots (312 km/h; 193·9 mph) over a 3 km course; and 163·5 knots (303 km/h; 188·3 mph) over a 15 km course.

TYPE: Turbine-powered general-purpose helicopter.

ROTOR SYSTEM: Four-blade semi-articulated main rotor and 13-blade shrouded-fan anti-torque tail rotor (known as a 'fenestron' or 'fan-in-fin'). Main rotor blades are of symmetrical NACA 0012 section, with a theoretical twist of 8° and constant chord, and are attached to the NAT hub via flapping hinges. There are no drag hinges. Each blade has a single leading-edge spar of polyester plastics, extending back to about 30% chord at top and bottom. The outer skin is of glassfibre, with an inner skin of carbon fibre, and the entire blade is filled with Nomex honeycomb. The leading-edge is formed by a layer of Vulkollan plastics with an outer protective shield of thin-gauge stainless steel. Tail rotor blades are of die-forged light alloy, with articulation for pitch change only. Main rotor blades can be folded manually for stowage. Rotor brake and main rotor blade de-icing optional.

ROTOR DRIVE: Main reduction gearbox forward of engine, which is mounted above the fuselage to the rear of the cabin. Output shaft enters main transmission box above the driveshaft to the tail rotor. Self-lubricating bearings. Main rotor rpm: 348 normal; 393 in autorotation. Tail rotor rpm: 4,700.

FUSELAGE: Conventional all-metal assembly of cabin and semi-monocoque tailboom. Cabin built on a strong box

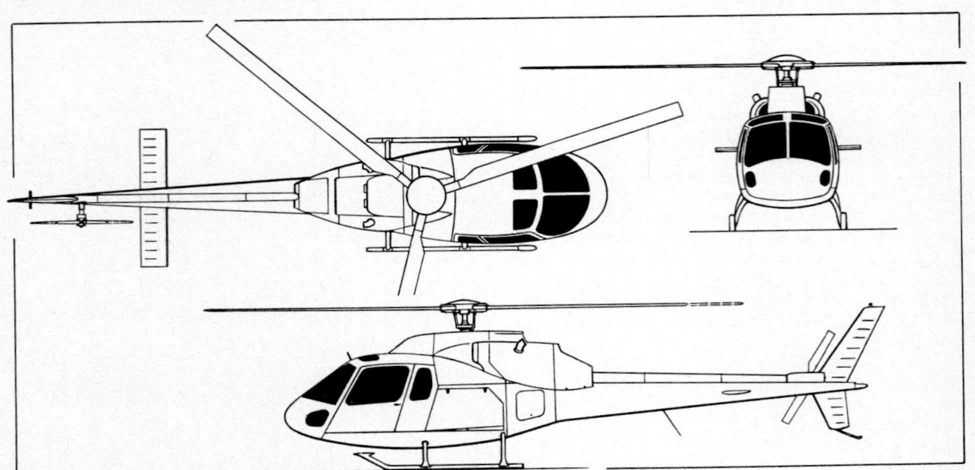

Twin-engined Aérospatiale AS 355E Ecureuil 2/Twinstar *(Pilot Press)*

structure embodying two transverse frames and the cabin floor.

Tail Unit: Horizontal stabiliser mid-set on tailboom, forward of shrouded tail rotor, with endplate fins. Tailboom terminates in large fin of unsymmetrical section, housing the tail rotor. The section of this fin is such that in cruising flight it counters the torque of the main rotor; the tail rotor is thus required to provide only yaw control, with minimal variation of pitch, requiring only small power intake.

Landing Gear: Steel tube skid type, or Eram non-retractable tailwheel-type landing gear, with single wheel on each unit. Main legs of wheel gear embody hydraulic shock-absorbers. Tailwheel carried on anti-shimmy leg which can be locked manually in central position. Dunlop main-wheel tyres size 355 × 150-4, pressure 5 bars (73 lb/sq in). Dunlop tailwheel tyre size 260 × 80-4, pressure 5 bars (73 lb/sq in). Disc brakes on main wheels. Wheel fairings standard. Provision for emergency flotation gear, and skis.

Power Plant: One Turboméca Astazou XVIIIA turboshaft engine, delivering 783 kW (1,050 shp) for take-off. Four Kléber-Colombes bag-type fuel tanks under cabin floor, total normal capacity 640 litres (141 Imp gallons) and for one ferry tank of 475 litres (104 Imp gallons) capacity on the cabin floor and one auxiliary tank of 215 litres (47 Imp gallons) capacity at the back of the cabin.

Accommodation: Standard ten-seat version has seats for pilot (to starboard) and co-pilot or passenger in front, and two rows of four seats to the rear. Interior of the cabin is clear except for a vertical duct, housing the flying control rods, positioned centrally aft of the centre row of seats. Two large forward-hinged doors on each side. Optional rearward-sliding doors. Compartment for hand baggage or coats aft of rear row of seats. Separate main baggage compartment aft of cabin, with door on starboard side. Alternative 14-seat layout has an extra row of four seats attached to the cabin rear wall, and no space for hand baggage or coats. Ambulance version carries four stretcher patients, a medical attendant and two crew. Mixed-traffic version carries six persons at front of cabin, with 2·50 m^3 (88·3 cu ft) of cargo space to the rear. The floor in this area will support a loading of 610 kg/m^2 (125 lb/sq ft). Executive versions are available with VIP interiors for four or six passengers. Cabin is heated and ventilated.

Systems: Two sets of three single-body servo controls mounted in series on the flight control channel, each supplied by an independent hydraulic system: one main set at the main rotor head, one auxiliary set capable of integrating an autopilot, and one tail rotor servo unit. Electrical system includes a 4·5kW engine-driven starter/generator, an 0·5kVA 115/200V 400Hz generator, a 23Ah nickel-cadmium battery and a ground power receptacle.

Avionics and Equipment: Optional equipment includes IFR instrumentation, an autopilot, 1,300 kg (2,865 lb) capacity cargo sling, 272 kg (600 lb) capacity rescue hoist, air-conditioning system, VHF/AM, ICS, VOR/LOC/glideslope, marker beacon indicator, HF/SSB, transponder and DME.

Dimensions, external:
Diameter of main rotor 11·50 m (37 ft 8¾ in)
Main rotor blade chord (constant) 0·35 m (1 ft 1¾ in)
Diameter of tail rotor 0·90 m (2 ft 11 7/16 in)
Length overall 13·20 m (43 ft 3½ in)
Length of fuselage 10·98 m (36 ft 0 in)
Height overall 3·50 m (11 ft 6 in)
Stabiliser span 3·15 m (10 ft 4 in)
Wheel track 1·95 m (6 ft 4¾ in)
Wheelbase 7·23 m (23 ft 8¾ in)
Cabin doors (fwd, each):
Height 1·16 m (3 ft 9½ in)
Width 1·14 m (3 ft 9 in)
Cabin doors (aft, each):
Height 1·16 m (3 ft 9½ in)
Width 0·87 m (2 ft 10¼ in)
Freight compartment door:
Height 0·56 m (1 ft 10 in)
Width 0·75 m (2 ft 5½ in)

Dimensions, internal:
Cabin: Usable length 2·30 m (7 ft 6½ in)
Height at front 1·40 m (4 ft 7 in)
Height at rear 1·06 m (3 ft 5¾ in)
Width at front 1·92 m (6 ft 3½ in)
Width at rear 1·60 m (5 ft 3 in)
Floor area 4·20 m^2 (45·20 sq ft)
Volume 5·0 m^3 (176 cu ft)
Baggage compartment volume 1·00 m^3 (35·31 cu ft)

Weights:
Basic operating weight 1,580 kg (3,483 lb)
Max payload:
internal 1,420 kg (3,130 lb)
slung 1,300 kg (2,865 lb)
Max T-O weight 3,000 kg (6,613 lb)

Performance (at AUW of 2,600 kg; 5,732 lb):
Never-exceed speed at S/L 170 knots (315 km/h; 196 mph)
Cruising speed at S/L 148 knots (275 km/h; 171 mph)

Aérospatiale SA 360C Dauphin ten-seat general-purpose helicopter, with skid landing gear

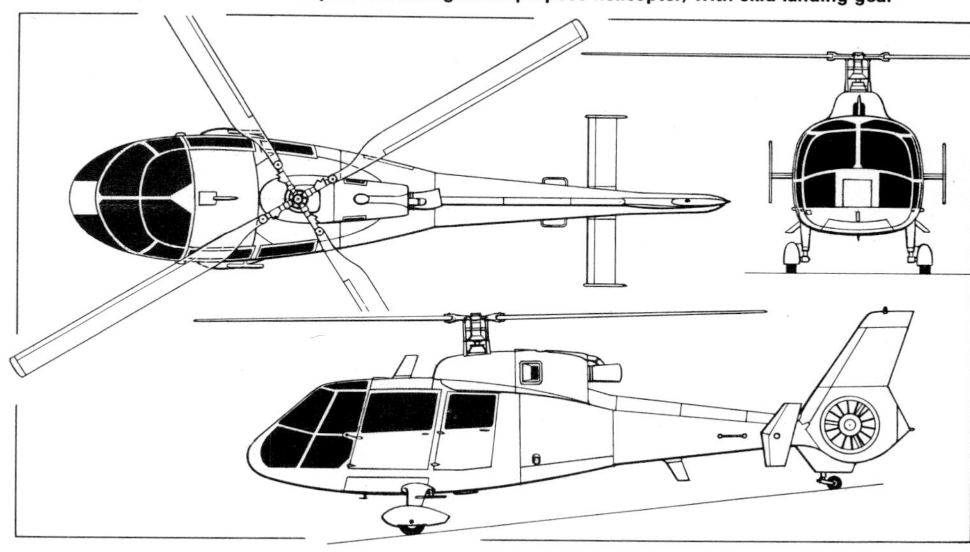

Aérospatiale SA 360C Dauphin (Turboméca Astazou XVIIIA turboshaft engine) with wheel-type landing gear *(Pilot Press)*

Max rate of climb at S/L 540 m (1,770 ft)/min
Hovering ceiling IGE 3,850 m (12,630 ft)
Range at S/L with max fuel 367 nm (680 km; 423 miles)
Endurance at S/L 4 h

AÉROSPATIALE SA 361H/HCL DAUPHIN

Although similar to the SA 360C in most respects, this military version of the Dauphin has a 1,043 kW (1,400 shp) Turboméca Astazou XXB turboshaft engine and Starflex rotor head, as described under the entry for the AS 350 Ecureuil. An SA 360 was flight tested with an Astazou XX engine as a first stage in the SA 361H/HCL development programme.

Mission capabilities of this version include anti-tank operations, armed with two four-round packs of Hot missiles; area neutralisation, with 20 mm cannon, two 19-round or 22-round packs of rockets, or two pods each containing two 7·62 mm machine-guns; and transport of 8-10 assault troops.

First firing trials with Hot missiles were completed successfully on a range at Bourges on 25 May 1978. At the Paris Air Show, in June 1979, an SA 361H/HCL* was demonstrated with eight Hot missile launchers and a nose-mounted FLIR (forward looking infra-red) system, developed by SFIM/TRT and claimed to provide night-time (starry night) anti-tank capability.

**HCL=Hélicoptère Combat Léger (Light Combat Helicopter)*

Dimensions:
As for SA 365 Dauphin 2

Weights:
Basic operating weight 1,620 kg (3,572 lb)
Max T-O weight 3,400 kg (7,495 lb)

Performance (estimated, at AUW of 3,300 kg; 7,275 lb):
Never-exceed speed at S/L 170 knots (315 km/h; 196 mph)
Cruising speed at S/L 148 knots (275 km/h; 171 mph)
Vertical rate of climb at S/L 750 m (2,460 ft)/min

Aérospatiale SA 361H/HCL Dauphin fitted with Hot missile launch packs and nose-mounted FLIR

Service ceiling	6,000 m (19,680 ft)
Hovering ceiling IGE	3,000 m (9,840 ft)
Hovering ceiling OGE	2,250 m (7,380 ft)
Range at S/L with max fuel, no reserves	302 nm (560 km; 348 miles)

AÉROSPATIALE SA 365C DAUPHIN 2

Announced in early 1973, the SA 365C is a twin-engined version of the SA 360, powered by Turboméca Arriel turboshaft engines. The prototype (F-WVKE) flew for the first time on 24 January 1975. DGAC certification for VFR flight was received in July 1978, and for IFR flight in December 1978. FAA and CAA certification was achieved by the Autumn of the same year and delivery of production SA 365Cs began in December 1978, initially to Offshore Helicopters Inc of the USA. A total of 20 had been delivered by 12 April 1979.

The SA 365C is designed for single-pilot IFR flight. It differs from the SA 360C in the following details:

ROTOR SYSTEM: Main rotor blades are attached to Starflex glassfibre hub, as described under entry for AS 350 Ecureuil.

ROTOR DRIVE: The installation of free-turbine engines has eliminated the need for a clutch in the output drive from each engine into the main gearbox.

FUSELAGE: The profile of the firewall between the two turboshaft engines is extended rearward in the form of a curved fairing which blends into the dorsal spine fairing over the tail rotor driveshaft.

TAIL UNIT: Horizontal stabiliser has inverted-camber aerofoil section, and the fixed vertical tail fins are offset to produce a lateral component which enhances the anti-torque function of the unsymmetrical surfaces. These features increase the efficiency of the 'fenestron' tail rotor, notably during hover.

POWER PLANT: Two Turboméca Arriel free-turbine turboshaft engines, each rated at 486 kW (651 shp), mounted side by side above the fuselage, aft of the main rotor driveshaft. Four separate bag-type fuel tanks, filling full width of fuselage under cabin floor. Two refuelling points aft of rear cabin door on port side.

DIMENSIONS, EXTERNAL:

Diameter of main rotor	11·68 m (38 ft 4 in)
Length overall	13·29 m (43 ft 7¼ in)

WEIGHTS:

Weight empty	1,850 kg (4,078 lb)
Max T-O weight	3,400 kg (7,495 lb)

PERFORMANCE (at AUW of 3,000 kg; 6,613 lb):

Never-exceed speed	170 knots (315 km/h; 196 mph)
Cruising speed	137 knots (255 km/h; 158 mph)
Max rate of climb at S/L	750 m (2,460 ft)/min
Service ceiling (60 m; 200 ft/min climb)	6,000 m (19,680 ft)
Hovering ceiling IGE	3,350 m (10,990 ft)
Hovering ceiling OGE	2,600 m (8,530 ft)
Max range at econ cruising speed, no reserves	251 nm (465 km; 289 miles)

OPERATING LIMITS:

Max pressure altitude	4,570 m (15,000 ft)
Max temperature	+50°C
Min temperature	−40°C

AÉROSPATIALE AS 365N DAUPHIN 2

This version of the Dauphin 2 was first stated to be under development in mid-1977, but few details were released until June 1979, when the prototype (F-WZJD) was exhibited at the Paris Air Show. First flown on 31 March 1979, it introduced more refined external lines, a fully-retractable landing gear, uprated engines and a considerably increased range, making this version particularly suitable for offshore commercial and naval applications.

It is hoped to obtain civil certification for VFR operation by October 1980, and for IFR operation by the end of the same year. Deliveries of the AS 365N would then start in early 1981. The AS 366G, with different power plant, is described separately.

TYPE: Twin-turbine military and commercial general-purpose helicopter.

ROTOR SYSTEM: Four-blade main rotor, with blades of glassfibre and carbon fibre, attached to Starflex glassfibre rotor head with quick-disconnect pins. Blades fold for stowage and a rotor brake is standard. Thirteen-blade 'fenestron' type of metal ducted-fan anti-torque tail rotor.

FUSELAGE: Conventional light alloy semi-monocoque structure.

TAIL UNIT: Horizontal stabiliser mid-set on tailboom, forward of 'fenestron', with endplate fins of different form to those on SA 365C.

LANDING GEAR: Retractable tricycle type, with twin-wheel self-centering nose unit and single wheel on each rearward-retracting main unit. Oleo-pneumatic shock-absorbers. Tyre pressure 7 bars (101 lb/sq in) for main wheels, 4 bars (58 lb/sq in) for nosewheels. Disc brakes.

POWER PLANT: Two Turboméca Arriel IC free-turbine turboshaft engines, each rated at 546 kW (735 shp). Five fuel tanks divided in two groups under cabin floor, with total capacity of 1,100 litres (242 Imp gallons). Refuelling point on port side. Oil capacity 8·5 litres (1·85 Imp gallons).

Aérospatiale SA 365C Dauphin 2 with twin Turboméca Arriel turboshaft engines

ACCOMMODATION: Standard accommodation for one pilot and nine passengers in VFR configuration. Crew of two for IFR operation. High-density seating for one pilot and 13 passengers. VIP configurations for four to six persons in addition to pilot. Three forward-opening doors on each side. Freight hold aft of cabin rear bulkhead. Cabin heated and ventilated; optional air-conditioning.

SYSTEMS: SEMCA air-conditioning system optional. Duplicated hydraulic system. Electrical system includes two 4·5kW starter/generators, one 23Ah 24V battery and two 250VA 115V 400Hz inverters. Provision for de-icing system.

AVIONICS AND EQUIPMENT: Optional avionics include VHF and HF com/nav, VOR, ILS, ADF, transponder, DME, radar and self-contained nav system. Optional equipment includes a 1,500 kg (3,300 lb) capacity cargo sling, and 275 kg (605 lb) capacity hoist with 80 m (260 ft) cable length.

ARMAMENT AND OPERATIONAL EQUIPMENT: Provision for complete ASW and ASV weapon system, including omnidirectional radar with target designation capability.

DIMENSIONS, EXTERNAL:

Diameter of main rotor	11·68 m (38 ft 4 in)
Diameter of tail rotor	0·90 m (2 ft 11⁷⁄₁₆ in)
Blade chord, main rotor	0·385 m (1 ft 3¼ in)
Length overall	13·29 m (43 ft 7¼ in)

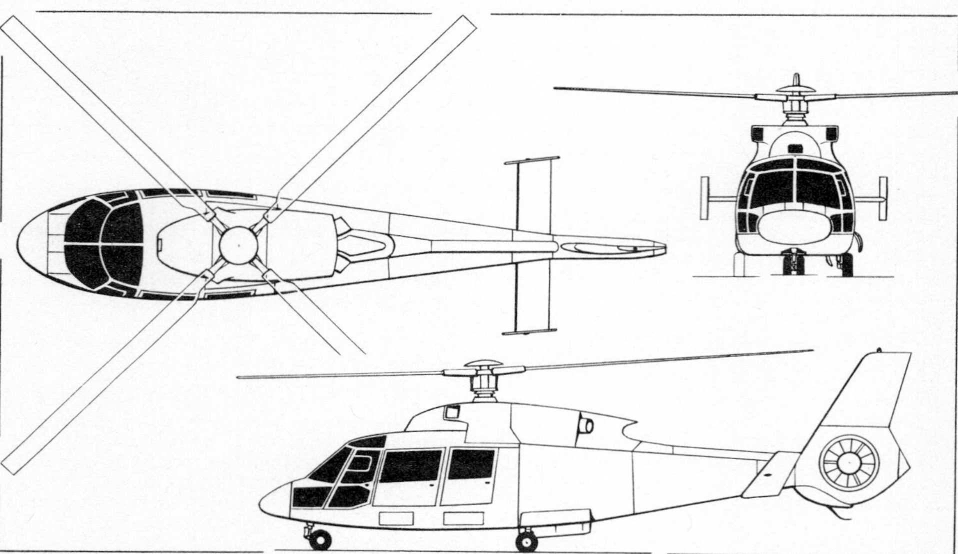

Aérospatiale AS 365N Dauphin 2 (two Turboméca Arriel IC turboshaft engines *(Pilot Press)*

Prototype of Aérospatiale AS 365N Dauphin 2 twin-turbine helicopter

Length overall, rotor blades folded
11·40 m (37 ft 4¾ in)
Width, rotor blades folded 3·21 m (10 ft 6½ in)
Height to top of rotor hub 3·30 m (10 ft 10 in)
Height overall 3·81 m (12 ft 6 in)
Wheel track 2·03 m (6 ft 8 in)
Wheelbase 3·61 m (11 ft 10¼ in)
Main cabin door (fwd, each side):
Height 1·16 m (3 ft 9½ in)
Width 1·14 m (3 ft 9 in)
Main cabin door (rear, each side):
Height 1·16 m (3 ft 9½ in)
Width 0·87 m (2 ft 10¼ in)
Baggage compartment door (stbd):
Height 0·51 m (1 ft 8 in)
Width 0·73 m (2 ft 4¾ in)
DIMENSIONS, INTERNAL:
Cabin: Length 2·30 m (7 ft 6½ in)
Max width 1·92 m (6 ft 3½ in)
Max height 1·40 m (4 ft 7 in)
Floor area 4·20 m² (45·20 sq ft)
Volume 5·00 m³ (176 cu ft)
Baggage compartment volume 2·20 m³ (77·7 cu ft)
WEIGHTS:
Weight empty, standard aircraft 1,888 kg (4,163 lb)
Max T-O weight 3,600 kg (7,936 lb)
PERFORMANCE (estimated, at max T-O weight):
Never-exceed speed at S/L
170 knots (315 km/h; 196 mph)
Max cruising speed at S/L
149 knots (277 km/h; 172 mph)
Econ cruising speed at S/L
135 knots (250 km/h; 155 mph)
Max rate of climb at S/L 630 m (2,065 ft)/min
Service ceiling (60 m; 200 ft/min climb)
5,000 m (16,400 ft)
Service ceiling, one engine out 1,750 m (5,740 ft)
Hovering ceiling IGE 2,050 m (6,725 ft)
Hovering ceiling OGE 1,250 m (4,100 ft)
Range with max fuel 470 nm (870 km; 540 miles)

AÉROSPATIALE AS 366G DAUPHIN 2

At the 1979 Paris Air Show, Aérospatiale announced that it had won with this aircraft the competition for a helicopter to perform SRR (Short Range Recovery) duties with the US Coast Guard. The initial contract is for 90 AS 366Gs, basically similar to the AS 365N but with engines and equipment of US manufacture accounting for about 60% of the total cost of each aircraft.

The AS 366G will be powered by two Avco Lycoming LTS 101-750 turboshafts; Rockwell Collins is prime contractor for the advanced communications, navigation and all-weather search equipment. Flight testing is expected to begin in August 1980, to permit civil certification in October 1981 and deliveries to the Coast Guard between the early months of 1982 and 1986.

C.A.A.R.P. — *See 'Mudry'*

DASSAULT-BREGUET
AVIONS MARCEL DASSAULT/BREGUET AVIATION

HEAD OFFICE: 27 rue du Professeur Victor Pauchet, 92420 Vaucresson
POSTAL ADDRESS: BP 32, 92420 Vaucresson
Telephone: 970 38 50 and 970 75 21
Telex: 60755 Brevau
PRESS INFORMATION OFFICE: 46 avenue Kléber, 75116 Paris
Telephone: 727 61 19
WORKS: 92210-Saint-Cloud, 77000-Melun-Villaroche, 95100-Argenteuil, 92100-Boulogne/Seine, 78140-Vélizy-Villacoublay, 33610-Martignas, 33700-Bordeaux-Mérignac, 33400-Talence, 33630-Cazaux, 31770-Toulouse-Colomiers, 64600-Biarritz-Anglet, 64200-Biarritz-Parme, 13800-Istres, 74370-Argonay, 59113-Lille-Seclin, 86000-Poitiers
FOUNDER: Marcel Dassault
PRESIDENT AND CHIEF EXECUTIVE: B. C. Vallières
GENERAL MANAGER, INTERNATIONAL AFFAIRS: H. de l'Estoile
DEPUTY GENERAL MANAGER: X. D'Iribarne
DEPUTY GENERAL MANAGER: J. Estebe
SECRETARY GENERAL: C. Edelstenne
GENERAL TECHNICAL MANAGER: J. Cabrière
TECHNICAL ADVISER: H. Deplante
EXPORT TECHNICAL MANAGER: Y. Thiriet
MILITARY AIRCRAFT SALES MANAGER: F. Serralta
MILITARY AIRCRAFT SALES MANAGER: P. E. Jaillard
CIVIL AIRCRAFT MANAGER: B. Latreille
PRODUCTION MANAGER: J. C. Veber
FLIGHT TEST MANAGER: J. F. Cazaubiel
PRESS INFORMATION MANAGER: A. Segura

Avions Marcel Dassault/Breguet Aviation resulted from the merger on 14 December 1971 of the Avions Marcel Dassault and Breguet Aviation companies. On 1 January 1979, it announced that, in accordance with an option taken in 1976, it had transferred 21% of its stock to the French government.

Dassault-Breguet is engaged in the development and production of military and civil aircraft, guided missiles and servo control equipment. In addition to the aircraft described in this entry, the company's principal current products include the Jaguar tactical support aircraft and advanced trainer (under Anglo-French collaborative programme; see SEPECAT in the International section) and the Alpha Jet basic and advanced training and strike aircraft (under Franco-German programme).

Under development are the Mirage 2000 and Super Mirage 4000 multi-role combat aircraft; and a new-generation version of the Atlantic maritime patrol aircraft for operational service from the mid-1980s.

Series production of Avions Marcel Dassault/Breguet Aviation aircraft is undertaken under a widespread subcontracting programme, with final assembly and flight testing being handled by the company. Its 15 separate works and facilities covered 620,800 m² (6,682,300 sq ft), with a total of 15,560 employees, including 3,000 engineers, in mid-1979.

Avions Marcel Dassault/Breguet Aviation has established close links with the industries of other countries. The original Atlantic programme associated manufacturers in Belgium, France, Germany, Italy and the Netherlands under the overall responsibility of their respective governments. In the same way the British and French governments are associated in the SEPECAT concern, formed to control the Dassault-Breguet/BAe Jaguar programme; and the German and French governments are associated in the Dassault-Breguet/Dornier Alpha Jet programme.

Purchase of Mirage fighters by Belgium and Spain led to Belgian and Spanish participation in Mirage III/5 and Mirage F1 production.

Dassault Mirage III-EBR fighter-bomber/intruder of the Brazilian Air Force

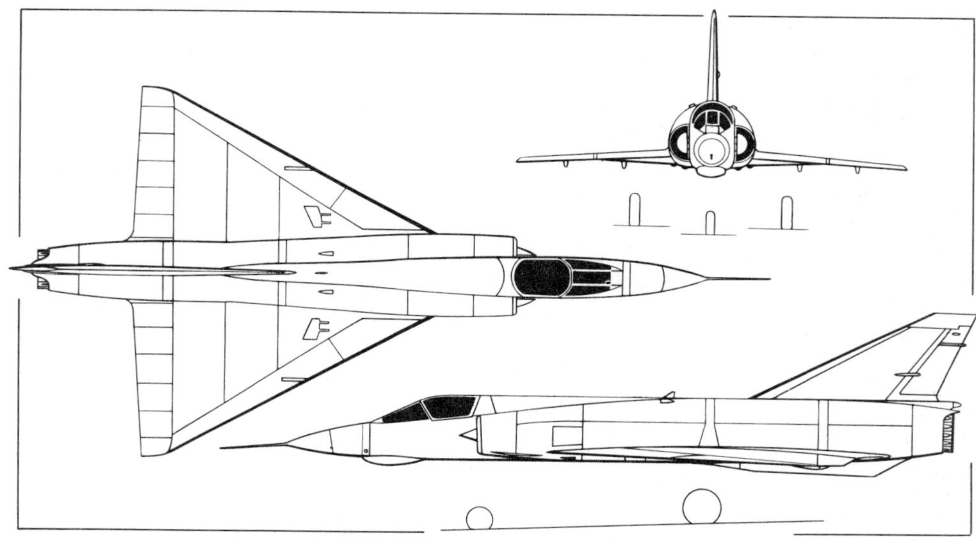

Dassault Mirage III-E single-seat combat aircraft in French Air Force configuration *(Pilot Press)*

Production by Dassault-Breguet in 1978 totalled 150 military and civil aircraft.

DASSAULT MIRAGE III

The Mirage III was designed initially as a Mach 2 high-altitude all-weather interceptor, capable of performing ground support missions and requiring only small airstrips. Developed versions include a two-seat trainer, long-range fighter-bomber and reconnaissance aircraft, and a total of more than 1,370 Mirage III/5/50s of all types had been ordered by 31 January 1979, including licence production abroad.

The experimental prototype flew for the first time on 17 November 1956, powered by a SNECMA Atar 101G turbojet with afterburner (44·1 kN; 9,900 lb st). Versions currently available include the following:

Mirage III-D. Two-seat version, built initially in Australia for the RAAF. Similar, French-built models ordered by 12 countries, including six more for Australia. Tandem seating under one-piece canopy; radar deleted, but fitted with radio beacon equipment. Intended primarily as a trainer, but suitable for strike sorties, carrying air-to-surface armament. Total of 180 Mirage III-B/III-D/5 two-seaters sold to 20 countries.

Mirage III-D2Z. For South Africa. Generally similar to III-D but with SNECMA Atar 9K-50 turbojet. Delivered 1974-75.

Mirage III-E. Long-range fighter-bomber/intruder version, of which 523 have been built for 13 air forces. First of three prototypes flew on 5 April 1961, and the first delivery of a production III-E was made in January 1964.

Mirage III-R. Reconnaissance version of III-E. Set of five OMERA type 31 cameras, in place of radar in nose, can be focused in four different arrangements for very low altitude, medium altitude, high altitude and night reconnaissance missions. Self-contained navigation system. Provision for air-to-surface armament. Two prototypes, of which the first flew in November 1961. Total of 153 production models ordered, including Mirage 5-Rs, for eight air forces.

Mirage III-R2Z. For South Africa. Generally similar to III-R but with SNECMA Atar 9K-50 turbojet. Delivered 1974-75.

Mirage III-RD. Similar to III-R but with improved Doppler navigation system in fairing under front fuselage, gyro gunsight and automatic cameras. Provision for carrying SAT Cyclope infra-red tracking equipment in ventral fairing, and two 1,700 litre (374 Imp gallon) underwing auxiliary fuel tanks. Twenty built for French Air Force.

The following description refers to the Mirage III-E, but is generally applicable to all versions:

TYPE: Single-seat fighter-bomber/intruder aircraft.

WINGS: Cantilever low-wing monoplane of delta planform, with conical camber. Thickness/chord ratio 4·5% to 3·5%. Anhedral 1°. No incidence. Sweepback on leading-edge 60° 34′. All-metal torsion-box structure with stressed skin of machined panels with integral stiffeners. Elevons are hydraulically powered by Dassault twin-cylinder actuators with artificial feel. Airbrakes, comprising small panels hinged to upper and lower wing surfaces, near leading-edge.

FUSELAGE: All-metal structure, 'waisted' in accordance with the area rule.

TAIL UNIT: Cantilever fin and hydraulically-actuated powered rudder only. Dassault twin-cylinder actuators with artificial feel.

LANDING GEAR: Retractable tricycle type, with single wheel on each unit. Hydraulic retraction, nosewheel rearward, main units inward. Messier-Hispano-Bugatti shock-absorbers and disc brakes. Main-wheel tyre pressure 5·9-9·8 bars (85·5-142 lb/sq in). Braking parachute.

POWER PLANT: One SNECMA Atar 9C turbojet engine (60·8 kN; 13,670 lb st with afterburning), fitted with an overspeed system which is engaged automatically from Mach 1·4 and permits a thrust increase of approx 8 per cent in the high supersonic speed range. Optional and jettisonable SEPR 844 single-chamber rocket motor (14·7 kN; 3,300 lb st) or interchangeable fuel tank. Movable half-cone centrebody in each air intake. Total internal fuel capacity 3,330 litres (733 Imp gallons) when rocket motor is not fitted. Provision for this to be augmented by two 625, 1,100, 1,300 or 1,700 litre (137, 242, 285 or 374 Imp gallon) underwing drop-tanks; 500 litre (110 Imp gallon) non-jettisonable supersonic tanks; JL-100 jettisonable tanks each housing both 280 litres (61 Imp gallons) fuel and air-to-surface rockets; Bidon Cyclope jettisonable tanks each housing 1,100 litres (242 Imp gallons) fuel and electronic equipment; or Bidon Homing jettisonable tanks housing 850 litres (187 Imp gallons) fuel and electronic equipment.

ACCOMMODATION: Single seat under rearward-hinged canopy. Hispano-built Martin-Baker Type RM.4 zero-altitude ejection seat.

SYSTEMS: Two separate air-conditioning systems for cockpit and avionics. Two independent hydraulic systems, pressure 207 bars (3,000 lb/sq in), for flying controls, landing gear and brakes. Power for DC electrical system from 24V 40Ah batteries and a 26·5V 9kW generator. AC electrical system power provided by one 200V 400Hz transformer and one 200V 400Hz 9kVA alternator.

AVIONICS AND EQUIPMENT: Duplicated UHF, Tacan, Doppler, CSF Cyrano II fire-control radar in nose, navigation computer, bombing computer, automatic gunsight.

The Mirage III-E has a normal magnetic detector mounted in the fin, and a central gyro and other avionics to provide accurate and stabilised heading information. The pilot's equipment determines at any instant the geographical co-ordinates of the aircraft and compares them with the co-ordinates of the target, the differences between the two being presented to the pilot as a 'course to steer' and 'distance to run'. Associated with this facility is a rotative magazine in the cockpit in which it is possible to insert up to twelve plastics punch-cards. Each card represents the co-ordinates of a geographical position. Therefore it is possible before take-off at point A to select point B on the rotating magazine. During take-off, ie after reaching 150 knots (278 km/h; 173 mph), the computer will switch on and the heading and distance to point B will be presented to the pilot. When overhead point B (assuming a pure navigational sortie) he can either select point A or the next turning point, or if required this sequence can continue until a maximum of twelve pre-set turning points have been used. Another facility available in the computer is known as the 'additional base'. Assuming that between points A and B the pilot receives instructions by radio to go to point C (and that there is no punch-card in the magazine for point C) the pilot can, by means of setting knobs, wind on the bearing and distance of point C from point B; then, when he selects the switch 'additional base', the heading to steer and distance to run to point C will be indicated.

Marconi Doppler equipment provides the ground speed and drift information for the above, while Tacan is presented as a 'bearing and distance' on the navigation indicator located on the starboard side of the instrument panel.

The Cyrano II installation in the aircraft's nose provides orthodox air-to-air interception radar, and has the additional mode available of control from the ground. In the latter case the pilot simply obeys his gunsight instructions, and radio silence is maintained. Cyrano II also functions in an air-to-ground role for high-level navigation, presenting a radar picture of the ground; for low-level navigation, presenting the obstacles above a preselected altitude; for blind descent, presenting obstacles that intercept the descent path; for anti-collision, presenting the obstacles that can be avoided by applying a 0·1g pull-up; and for distance measuring, by presenting in the sight the oblique aircraft-to-ground distance.

Allied to the Cyrano II installation is the CSF 97 sighting system, of illuminated points, dots, bars and figures, giving air-to-air facility for cannon and missiles, air-to-ground facility for dive-bombing or LABS, and navigation facility for horizon and heading.

ARMAMENT: Ground attack armament consists normally of two 30 mm DEFA cannon in fuselage, each with 125 rounds of ammunition, and two 1,000 lb bombs, or an AS.30 air-to-surface missile under the fuselage and 1,000 lb bombs under the wings. Alternative underwing stores include JL-100 pods, each with 18 rockets, and jettisonable underwing fuel tanks. For interception duties, one Matra R.530 air-to-air missile can be carried under fuselage, with optional guns and two Sidewinder missiles.

Dassault Mirage III-RD reconnaissance aircraft of the French Air Force

DIMENSIONS, EXTERNAL:
- Wing span: 8·22 m (26 ft 11½ in)
- Wing aspect ratio: 1·94
- Length overall: III-E: 15·03 m (49 ft 3½ in)
- III-R: 15·50 m (50 ft 10¼ in)
- Height overall: 4·50 m (14 ft 9 in)
- Wheel track: 3·15 m (10 ft 4 in)
- Wheelbase: III-E: 4·87 m (15 ft 11¾ in)

AREAS:
- Wings, gross: 34·85 m² (375 sq ft)
- Vertical tail surfaces (total): 4·5 m² (48·4 sq ft)

WEIGHTS AND LOADING:
- Weight empty: III-E: 7,050 kg (15,540 lb)
- III-R: 6,600 kg (14,550 lb)
- T-O weight 'clean': III-E: 9,600 kg (21,165 lb)
- Max T-O weight: III-E, R: 13,700 kg (30,200 lb)
- Max wing loading: III-E, R: 393·1 kg/m² (80·53 lb/sq ft)

PERFORMANCE (Mirage III-E, in 'clean' condition with guns installed, except where indicated):
- Max level speed at 12,000 m (39,375 ft): Mach 2·2 (1,268 knots; 2,350 km/h; 1,460 mph)
- Max level speed at S/L: 750 knots (1,390 km/h; 863 mph)
- Cruising speed at 11,000 m (36,000 ft): Mach 0·9
- Approach speed: 183 knots (340 km/h; 211 mph)
- Landing speed: 157 knots (290 km/h; 180 mph)
- Time to 11,000 m (36,000 ft), Mach 0·9: 3 min
- Time to 15,000 m (49,200 ft), Mach 1·8: 6 min 50 s
- Service ceiling at Mach 1·8: 17,000 m (55,775 ft)
- Ceiling, using rocket motor: 23,000 m (75,450 ft)
- T-O run, according to mission (up to max T-O weight): 700-1,600 m (2,295-5,250 ft)
- Landing run, using brake parachute: 700 m (2,295 ft)
- Combat radius, ground attack: 647 nm (1,200 km; 745 miles)

DASSAULT MIRAGE 5

The Mirage 5 is a ground attack aircraft using the same airframe and engine as the Mirage III-E. The basic VFR version has simplified avionics, 500 litres (110 Imp gallons) greater fuel capacity than III-E and considerably extended stores carrying capability. It combines the full Mach 2+ capability of the Mirage III, and its ability to operate from semi-prepared airfields, with simpler maintenance. In ground attack configuration, up to 4,000 kg (8,820 lb) of weapons and 1,000 litres (220 Imp gallons) of fuel can be carried externally on seven wing and fuselage attachment points. The Mirage 5 can also be flown as an interceptor, with two Sidewinder air-to-air missiles and 4,700 litres (1,034 Imp gallons) of external fuel. At customer's option, any degree of IFR/all-weather operation can be provided for, with reduced fuel or weapons load. The Mirage 5 was flown for the first time on 19 May 1967.

Up to 31 January 1979, a total of 480 Mirage 5s had been ordered for eleven air forces, including Mirage 5-R reconnaissance variants and two-seat Mirage 5-Ds. A full list of versions was published in the 1976-77 *Jane's*.

The structural description of the Mirage III-E is generally applicable to the Mirage 5, with the following exceptions:

ARMAMENT: Seven attachment points for external loads, with multiple launchers permitting a max load of more than 4 tons. Ground attack armament consists normally of two 30 mm DEFA cannon in fuselage, each with 125 rounds of ammunition, and two 1,000 lb bombs or an AS.30 air-to-surface missile under the fuselage and 1,000 lb bombs under the wings. Alternative underwing

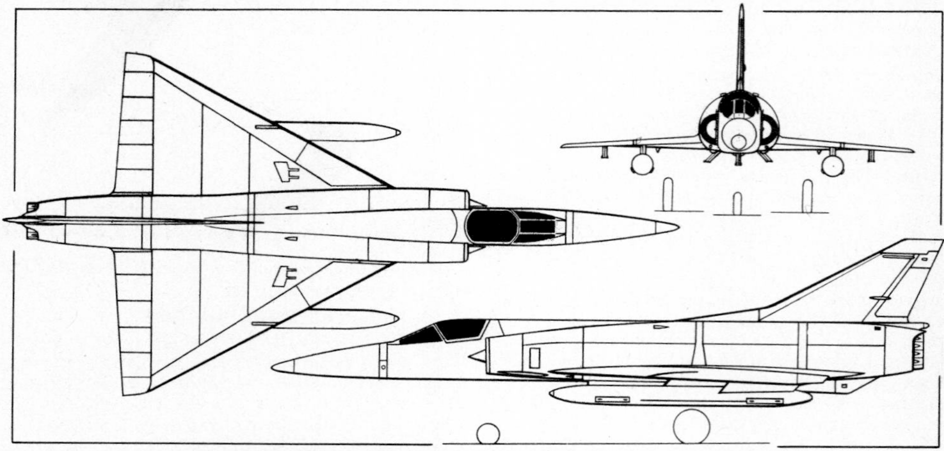

Dassault Mirage 5 single-seat ground attack aircraft *(Pilot Press)*

Dassault Mirage 5-DM two-seat trainer/combat aircraft supplied to Zaire

stores include tank/bomb carriers, each with 500 litres (110 Imp gallons) of fuel and four 500 lb or two 1,000 lb bombs, and JL-100 pods, each with eighteen 68 mm rockets and 250 litres (55 Imp gallons) of fuel. For interception duties, two Sidewinder missiles can be carried under the wings.

EQUIPMENT: Can have Aïda II radar rangefinder in nose.

DIMENSIONS, EXTERNAL:
As III-E, except:
Length overall 15·55 m (51 ft 0¼ in)

WEIGHTS AND LOADING:
As III-E, except:
Weight empty 6,600 kg (14,550 lb)

PERFORMANCE (in 'clean' condition, with guns installed, except where indicated):
As III-E, plus:
Combat radius with 907 kg (2,000 lb) bomb load:
hi-lo-hi 700 nm (1,300 km; 808 miles)
lo-lo-lo 350 nm (650 km; 404 miles)
Ferry range with three external tanks 2,158 nm (4,000 km; 2,485 miles)

DASSAULT MIRAGE 50

First displayed in representative form at the 1975 Paris Air Show, the Mirage 50 retains the basic airframe of the Mirage III/5 series, but is powered by the higher-rated SNECMA Atar 9K-50 turbojet, as fitted in the Mirage F1-Cs of the French Air Force and Mirage III-R2Zs of the South African Air Force. This gives 70·6 kN (15,873 lb st) with afterburning, representing a 16% thrust increase compared with standard Mirage III/5s.

The prototype Mirage 50 flew for the first time on 15 April 1979. First customer is the Sudanese Air Force, which is reported to have ordered 24. Chile has ordered 16.

The Mirage 50 is a multi-mission fighter, suitable for air superiority duties with guns and dogfight missiles, air patrol and supersonic interception, and ground attack combined with self-defence capability. It can carry the full range of operational stores, armament and equipment developed for the Mirage III/5 series, plus Agave or Cyrano IV multi-function radar, an inertial or Doppler nav/attack system, and head-up display. It is available in reconnaissance configuration. A two-seat training version is also projected. Improvements compared with other delta-wing Mirages include better take-off performance, higher rate of climb, faster acceleration and better manoeuvrability. Maximum internal fuel capacity is 3,475 litres (764 Imp gallons). Underwing and underfuselage tanks can increase total capacity to 4,700 litres (1,034 Imp gallons).

DIMENSIONS, EXTERNAL:
Wing span 8·22 m (27 ft 0 in)
Length overall 15·56 m (51 ft 0½ in)
Height overall 4·50 m (14 ft 9 in)

AREA:
Wings, gross 35·00 m² (376·7 sq ft)

WEIGHTS:
Weight empty, equipped 7,150 kg (15,765 lb)
T-O weight, 'clean' 9,900 kg (21,825 lb)
Max T-O weight 13,700 kg (30,200 lb)

PERFORMANCE:
Max level speed at altitude Mach 2·2 (750 knots; 1,390 km/h; 863 mph IAS)
Max rate of climb at S/L 11,100 m (36,400 ft)/min
Service ceiling at Mach 2 18,000 m (59,055 ft)
Combat radius at low altitude with two 400 kg bombs 372 nm (690 km; 428 miles)

DASSAULT MIRAGE F1

Details of the early history of the Mirage F1 can be found in the 1977-78 *Jane's*. The prototype flew for the first time on 23 December 1966 and was followed by three pre-series aircraft.

The primary role of the Mirage F1 is that of all-weather interception at any altitude, and the **F1-C** production version, to which the detailed description applies, utilises weapon systems similar to those of the Mirage III-E. It is equally suitable for attack missions, carrying a variety of external loads beneath the wings and fuselage. A ground attack version designated **F1-A** is also in production, with much of the more costly avionic equipment deleted and the space so vacated occupied by an additional fuel tank. Further versions include the **F1-B** two-seat trainer, the first of which made its first flight on 26 May 1976; the **F1-E**, similar to the F1-C but with more comprehensive nav/attack system; and the **F1-R** reconnaissance variant.

By January 1979, a total of 554 Mirage F1s had been ordered, comprising 231 for the French Air Force and 323 for service with the air forces of Ecuador, Greece (F1-C), Iraq, Kuwait (F1-C and B), Libya (F1-A, B and E), Morocco (F1-C), South Africa (F1-A and C) and Spain (F1-B and C). The first production F1 flew on 15 February 1973 and was delivered officially to the French Air Force on 14 March 1973. The first unit to receive the F1 was the 30e Escadre at Reims, which became operational in early 1974. It was followed by the 5e Escadre at Orange and the 12e Escadre at Cambrai. Each Escadre comprised two interceptor squadrons in early 1979, but creation of a third squadron at Cambrai was then being considered.

An order for 36 Mirage F1s for the Royal Jordanian Air Force was reported in the Summer of 1979.

Dassault Mirage 50 fighter (SNECMA Atar 9K-50 turbojet engine)

In February 1979, it was announced that the French Air Force had decided to purchase about 30 F1-Rs, to replace Mirage III-R/RD aircraft equipping two squadrons of the 33e Escadre de Reconnaissance, at Strasbourg. These aircraft will carry an OMERA 40 panoramic camera and an OMERA 35 camera internally, together with an infra-red sensor and an OMERA 360 sight recorder. Further electro-magnetic or optical sensors will be carried in an underbelly pod. Other new equipment will include an inertial platform and EMD navigation radar. The first F1-R squadron is expected to become operational in 1983.

By the beginning of 1979 a total of 280 Mirage F1s had been completed, with production continuing at the rate of five per month.

The Mirage F1 is produced by Dassault-Breguet in co-operation with the Belgian companies SABCA, in which Dassault-Breguet has a parity interest, and Sonaca, which is building rear fuselage sections for all Mirage F1s ordered. Dassault-Breguet also has a technical and industrial co-operation agreement with the Armaments Development and Production Corporation of South Africa Ltd, whereby the latter company has rights to build the Mirage F1 under licence.

The following description applies to the F1-C production version for the French Air Force:

TYPE: Single-seat multi-mission fighter and attack aircraft.

WINGS: Cantilever shoulder-wing monoplane. Anhedral from roots. Sweepback 47° 30′ on leading-edges, with extended chord on approximately the outer two-thirds of each wing. All-metal two-spar torsion-box structure, making extensive use of mechanically or chemically milled components. Trailing-edge control surfaces of honeycomb sandwich construction. Entire leading-edge can be drooped hydraulically (manually for T-O and landing, automatic in combat). Two differentially-operating double-slotted flaps and one aileron on each trailing-edge, actuated hydraulically by servo controls. Ailerons are compensated by trim devices incorporated in linkage. Two spoilers on each wing, ahead of flaps.

FUSELAGE: Conventional all-metal semi-monocoque structure. Primary frames are milled mechanically, secondary frames and fuel tank panels chemically. Electrical spot-welding for secondary stringers and sealed panels, remainder titanium flush-riveted or bolted and sealed. Titanium alloy also used for landing gear trunnions, engine firewall and certain other major structures. High-tensile steel wing attachment points. Nosecone over radar, and antennae fairings on fin, are of plastics. Large hydraulically-actuated door-type airbrake in forward underside of each intake trunk.

TAIL UNIT: Cantilever all-metal two-spar structure, with sweepback on all surfaces. All-moving tailplane mid-set on fuselage, and actuated hydraulically by electrical or manual control. Tailplane trailing-edge panels are of honeycomb sandwich construction. Auxiliary fin beneath each side of rear fuselage.

LANDING GEAR: Retractable tricycle type, by Messier-Hispano. Hydraulic retraction, nose unit rearward, main units upward into rear of intake trunk fairings. Twin wheels on each unit. Nose unit steerable and self-centering. Oleo-pneumatic shock-absorbers. Main-wheel tyre pressure 9-11 bars (130-160 lb/sq in), permitting operation from semi-prepared airfields. Messier-Hispano brakes and anti-skid units. Brake parachute in bullet fairing at base of rudder.

POWER PLANT: One SNECMA Atar 9K-50 turbojet engine, rated at 70·6 kN (15,873 lb st) with afterburning. Movable semi-conical centrebody in each intake. Fuel in integral tanks in wings and fuselage, on each side of intake trunks, able to be pressure-refuelled completely in about 6 min. Provision for three jettisonable auxiliary fuel tanks (each 1,200 litres; 264 Imp gallons) to be carried under fuselage and on inboard wing pylons.

ACCOMMODATION: Single SEMMB (Martin-Baker Mk 4) ejection seat for pilot, under rearward-hinged canopy. Cockpit is air-conditioned, and is heated by warm air bled from engine which also heats the radar compartment and certain equipment compartments. Intertechnique liquid oxygen system for pilot.

SYSTEMS: Two independent hydraulic systems, for landing

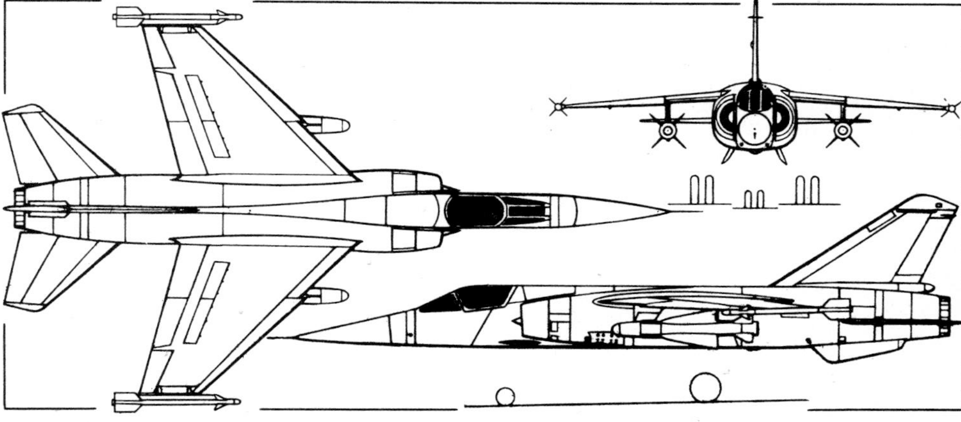

Dassault Mirage F1 single-seat multi-mission fighter and attack aircraft *(Pilot Press)*

Dassault Mirage F1 in advanced ground attack configuration

gear retraction, flaps and flying controls, supplied by pumps similar to those fitted in Mirage III. Electrical system includes two Auxilec 15kVA variable-speed alternators, either of which can supply all functional and operational requirements. Emergency and standby power provided by SAFT Voltabloc 40Ah nickel-cadmium battery and EMD static converter. DC power provided by transformer-rectifiers operating in conjunction with battery. Liquid oxygen system standard.

AVIONICS AND EQUIPMENT: Thomson-CSF Cyrano IV fire-control radar in nose. This permits all-sector interception at any altitude and incorporates a system to eliminate 'fixed' echoes when following low-flying aircraft. Two UHF transceivers (one UHF/VHF), Socrat 6200 VOR/ILS with Socrat 5600 marker, LMT Tacan, LMT NR-AI-4-A IFF, remote-setting interception system, three-axis generator, central air data computer, Bézu Sphere with ILS indicator, Crouzet Type 63 navigation indicator and SFENA 505 autopilot. CSF head-up display, with magnifying lens, provides all necessary data for flying and fire control. Equipment for attack role can include Doppler radar and bombing computer, navigation computer, position indicator, laser rangefinder and terrain-avoidance radar.

ARMAMENT AND OPERATIONAL EQUIPMENT: Standard fixed armament of two 30 mm DEFA 553 cannon, with 125 rds/gun, mounted in lower front fuselage. Two Alkan universal stores attachment pylons under each wing and one under centre fuselage, plus provision for carrying one air-to-air missile at each wingtip. Max external combat load 4,000 kg (8,820 lb). Externally-mounted weapons for interception role include Matra R.530 or Super 530 radar homing or infra-red homing air-to-air missiles on underfuselage and inboard wing pylons, and/or a Sidewinder or Matra 550 Magic infra-red homing air-to-air missile at each wingtip station. For ground attack duties, typical loads may include one AS.37 Martel anti-radar missile or AS.30 air-to-surface missile, eight 450 kg bombs, four launchers each containing 18 air-to-ground rockets, or six 600 litre (132 Imp gallon) napalm tanks. Other possible external loads include three 1,200 litre (264 Imp gallon) auxiliary fuel tanks, or two photoflash containers and a reconnaissance pod incorporating an SAT Cyclope infra-red system and EMI side-looking radar.

DIMENSIONS, EXTERNAL:
- Wing span: 8·40 m (27 ft 6¾ in)
- Length overall: 15·00 m (49 ft 2½ in)
- Height overall: 4·50 m (14 ft 9 in)
- Wheel track: 2·50 m (8 ft 2½ in)
- Wheelbase: 5·00 m (16 ft 4¾ in)

AREA:
- Wings, gross: 25·00 m² (269·1 sq ft)

WEIGHTS AND LOADING:
- Weight empty: 7,400 kg (16,314 lb)
- T-O weight, 'clean': 10,900 kg (24,030 lb)
- Max T-O weight: 15,200 kg (33,510 lb)
- Max wing loading: 608 kg/m² (124·5 lb/sq ft)

PERFORMANCE:
- Max level speed (high altitude): Mach 2·2
- Max level speed (low altitude): Mach 1·2
- Approach speed: 141 knots (260 km/h; 162 mph)
- Landing speed: 124 knots (230 km/h; 143 mph)
- Max rate of climb at S/L (with afterburning): 12,780 m (41,930 ft)/min
- Max rate of climb at high altitude (with afterburning): 14,580 m (47,835 ft)/min
- Service ceiling: 20,000 m (65,600 ft)
- Stabilised supersonic ceiling: 18,500 m (60,700 ft)
- T-O run (AUW of 11,500 kg; 25,355 lb): 450 m (1,475 ft)
- T-O run (typical interception mission): 640 m (2,100 ft)
- Landing run (AUW of 8,500 kg; 18,740 lb): 500 m (1,640 ft)
- Landing run (typical interception mission): 610 m (2,000 ft)
- Endurance: 3 h 45 min

DASSAULT MIRAGE 2000

Following cancellation of the ACF (Avion de Combat Futur) programme, described briefly in the 1975-76 *Jane's*, the Mirage 2000 was selected on 18 December 1975 as the primary combat aircraft of the French Air Force from the mid-eighties. Under French government contract, it is being developed initially as an interceptor and air superiority fighter, powered by a single SNECMA M53 turbofan engine. Dassault claims that its performance will be markedly superior to that of any current combat aircraft in these categories, and that the Mirage 2000 will be equally suitable for reconnaissance, close support, and low-altitude attack missions in areas to the rear of a battlefield.

Reversion to a Mirage III/5 type of delta-wing design, without horizontal tail surfaces, caused some surprise after Dassault's choice of a tailed sweptwing configuration for the later Mirage F1 and ACF. It resulted from considerable study of the requirements of a smaller and less ambitious aircraft than the ACF. Research left no doubt that a delta wing embodying the latest aerodynamic concepts offers an excellent compromise between structural simplicity, light weight, high speed characteristics and the demands of rapid acceleration, high rate of climb and manoeuvrability for an aeroplane of relatively modest size and installed power. In particular, a delta layout offers low drag over a wide range of angles of attack in flight, while providing the largest practicable wing area, with attendant benefits in terms of tight turning capability and high service ceiling.

Former shortcomings, such as higher landing speed than a comparable sweptwing type, are overcome by the addition of automatic leading-edge flaps which, used in conjunction with the elevons, constitute a variable-camber wing. At the same time, the adoption of fly-by-wire control for the wing surfaces and rudder, with artificial stability ensured by a central computer, permits acceptance of a far-aft centre of gravity. This makes possible a much reduced landing speed for the Mirage 2000, and improves its manoeuvrability in combat.

Having tested successfully a carbon-fibre rudder on a Mirage III, and boron horizontal tail surfaces on a Mirage F1 throughout the flight regime to Mach 2·2, Dassault decided to utilise both materials in the Mirage 2000, achieving weight saving of 15-20 per cent in the components so constructed.

Wing area of the Mirage 2000 is some 15 per cent greater than that of the Mirage III/5, enabling it to carry more internal fuel. The combined effect of all the technological advances was summarised by Général Maurice Saint-Cricq, Chief of Staff of the French Air Force, in the Spring of 1977. He said that the Mirage 2000 is intended to fly at Mach 2·2 at a height of 18,000 m (59,000 ft); to offer low-speed characteristics at least as good as those of the Mirage F1; a rate of climb twice that of the Mirage III, enabling it to attack a Mach 3 aircraft penetrating at high altitude approximately five minutes from brake release; and a 30 per cent better range than that of the Mirage III, after take-off from a 1,200 m (3,940 ft) strip, enabling it to maintain coverage of a combat area for three times as long.

Five prototypes are being built, of which four are funded by the French Air Force and one by the manufacturers. The first of these made its first flight, at Istres, on 10 March 1978, only 27 months after programme launch in December 1975. The second flew on 18 September 1978 and the third on 26 April 1979. The third prototype is the first to be fitted with the complete weapons system, including radar. No. 04 prototype and a two-seat trainer version are scheduled to fly at the beginning of 1980 and in the middle of the same year respectively. The first series production Mirage 2000 is expected to follow in the second half of 1982. The manufacturers' prototype will be used to develop equipment and other changes proposed for future variants and for export models of the Mirage 2000. Further airframes have been built for static and fatigue testing.

Initial production contracts, in 1979-82, are expected to finance 127 single-seat and two-seat Mirage 2000s in 'air defence' configuration, with an eventual requirement for 200 aircraft in this role; but only four were ordered in the 1979 budget. Dassault believes that a further 200 Mirage 2000s will be required for reconnaissance and strike duties. A single basic type would then make up a high proportion of the French Air Force's planned first-line strength of 450 combat aircraft by the second half of the 'eighties.

The following description applies to the initial single-seat air defence version of the Mirage 2000:

TYPE: Single-seat interceptor and air superiority fighter.

Dassault Mirage F1-B two-seat combat trainer

Dassault Mirage F1-C of the French Air Force, carrying two Matra 550 Magic air-to-air missiles on wingtip launchers and an underbelly R.530 missile

First prototype Dassault Mirage 2000, armed with two Matra 550 Magic and two Super 530 missiles. Also to be seen in this view are its newly-modified engine air intakes and fairings between the wing trailing-edge and fuselage

WINGS: Cantilever multi-spar low-wing monoplane of delta planform, with cambered profile. Leading-edge sweepback 58°. Large-radius root fairings. Full-span automatic leading-edge flaps operate in conjunction with two-section elevons which form entire trailing-edge of each wing, to provide variable camber in combat and during landing approach. Leading-edge flaps are retracted during all phases of acceleration and low-altitude cruise, to reduce drag. Fly-by-wire control system for elevons and flaps, with surfaces actuated by hydraulic servo-units. No tabs. Retractable airbrakes above and below each wing.

FUSELAGE: Conventional all-metal semi-monocoque structure, 'waisted' in accordance with area rule. Small fixed strake, with marked dihedral, near leading-edge of each air intake trunk.

TAIL UNIT: Cantilever fin and inset rudder only; latter actuated by fly-by-wire control system via hydraulic servo-units. Much of fin skin and all rudder skin of boron/epoxy/carbon composites. Sweepback on fin leading-edge 45°. No tab.

LANDING GEAR: Retractable tricycle type by Messier-Hispano-Bugatti, with twin nosewheels, and single wheel on each main unit. Hydraulic retraction, nosewheels rearward, main units inward. Oleo-pneumatic shock-absorbers. Electro-hydraulic nosewheel steering, through 45° to each side. Manual disconnect permits nosewheel unit to castor through 360° for ground towing. Light alloy wheels and tubeless tyres, size 360 × 135-6 on nosewheels, 750 × 230-15 on main wheels. Messier-Hispano-Bugatti hydraulically-actuated graphite composite disc brakes on main wheels, with anti-skid units. Runway arrester gear standard. Brake-chute in canister above jet nozzle.

POWER PLANT: One SNECMA M53-2 turbofan engine, rated at 83·4 kN (18,740 lb st) with afterburning, in each prototype; M53-5, rated at 88·3 kN (19,840 lb st) with afterburning, specified for production aircraft. Movable half-cone centrebody in each air intake. Internal fuel capacity 3,800 litres (835 Imp gallons). Provision for a jettisonable fuel tank of up to 1,700 litres (374 Imp gallons) capacity under each wing. Flight refuelling probe forward of cockpit on starboard side.

ACCOMMODATION: Pilot only, under transparent canopy, in air-conditioned and pressurised cockpit.

SYSTEMS: Two independent hydraulic systems, pressure 280 bars (4,000 lb/sq in), to actuate flying control servo-units, landing gear and brakes. Electrical system includes two Auxilec 20110 aircooled 20kVA 400Hz constant-frequency alternators, two Bronzavia DC transformers, a SAFT 40Ah battery and ATEI static inverter.

AVIONICS AND EQUIPMENT: Pulse Doppler radar, developed and produced by Thomson-CSF in collaboration with Electronique Marcel Dassault, with operating range of 54 nm (100 km; 62 miles), capability of detecting targets at all altitudes, and good ECCM characteristics (interchangeable with conventional Thomson-CSF Cyrano 500 radar). SAGEM-Kearfott Uliss 52 inertial platform. EMD central digital computer. Thomson-CSF VE-130 head-up and VMC-180 head-down displays. SFENA 605 autopilot. Thomson-CSF ECM, including passive radar warning, LMT Deltac Tacan and IFF, Socrat VOR/ILS/marker beacon receiver, TRT radio-altimeter and UHF and V/UHF com.

ARMAMENT: Two 30 mm DEFA cannon. Nine attachments for external stores, five under fuselage and two under each wing. Typical interception weapons comprise two Matra Super 530 missiles (inboard) and two Matra 550 Magic missiles (outboard) under wings. (Projected strike version would carry up to 5,000 kg; 11,025 lb of external stores, including nuclear weapons.)

DIMENSIONS, EXTERNAL (estimated):

Wing span	9·00 m (29 ft 6 in)
Length overall	15·33 m (50 ft 3½ in)
Wheel track	3·40 m (11 ft 1¾ in)
Wheelbase	5·00 m (16 ft 4¾ in)

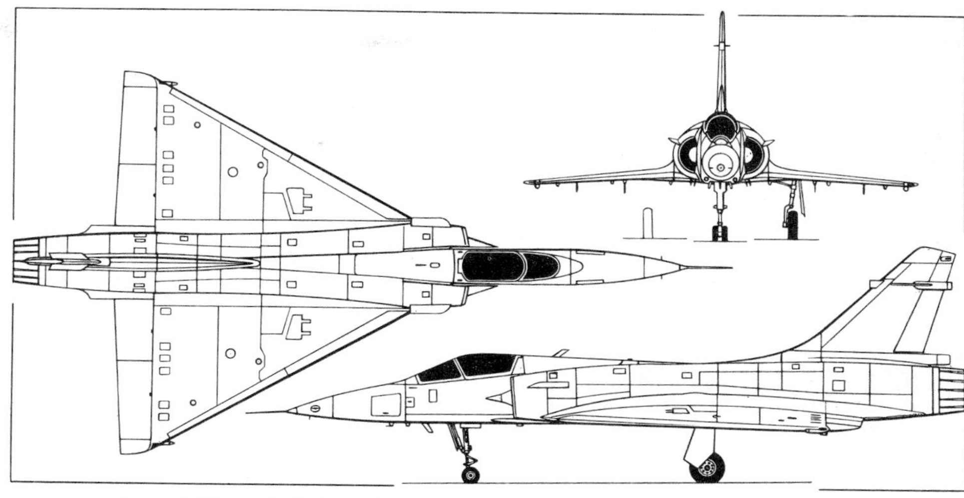

Dassault Mirage 2000 (one SNECMA M53 afterburning turbofan engine) *(Pilot Press)*

WEIGHT (estimated):

T-O weight, combat mission	9,000 kg (19,840 lb)

PERFORMANCE (estimated):

Max level speed	over Mach 2·3
Max continuous speed	Mach 2·2
Approach speed	150 knots (278 km/h; 173 mph)
Rate of climb at S/L	15,000 m (49,200 ft)/min
Time to 15,250 m (50,000 ft) and Mach 2	less than 4 min
Service ceiling	20,000 m (65,600 ft)
Range with external tanks	over 810 nm (1,500 km; 932 miles)

DASSAULT SUPER MIRAGE 4000

When the French Air Force abandoned development of the ACF (Avion de Combat Futur) programme, in favour of the single-engined Mirage 2000, M Marcel Dassault announced, in December 1975, that Dassault-Breguet would develop at the French industry's own expense a twin-turbofan scale-up of the Mirage 2000, intended primarily for interception and low-altitude penetration attacks on targets a considerable distance from its base. Potential export customers were assured that the new aircraft would offer overall performance superior to that of any aircraft in its class known to be in production or under development.

A mockup of the new type, now designated Super Mirage 4000 (originally Super Mirage Delta), was unveiled in December 1977. The prototype achieved a speed of Mach 1·2 during its first flight on 9 March 1979, Mach 1·6 on its second flight three days later, and Mach 2·2 during its sixth flight on 11 April, when an initial spin analysis was also made and it was flown at angles of attack up to 25°.

Its general configuration is shown in the accompanying illustrations. Dimensions, weights, performance, and details of armament are generally classified; but installation of two engines of the type fitted in the single-engined Mirage 2000 will give the Super Mirage 4000 a power:weight ratio well above 1:1 in an interceptor role. It was said to have taken off at a loaded weight of about 20,000 kg (44,000 lb) for early flight tests.

The Super Mirage 4000 has computer-derived aerodynamics, with a rearward CG made possible by a fly-by-wire active control system. Other features include foreplanes, a blister-type cockpit canopy giving a 360° field of view, a very large nose radome, and extensive use of boron and carbon fibre composites for structures such as the fin, rudder, elevons, fuselage access panels and foreplanes.

The following details should be regarded as provisional:

TYPE: Single-seat multi-role combat aircraft (two-seat version under study).

Dassault Super Mirage 4000 multi-role combat aircraft *(Pilot Press)*

This photograph shows clearly the difference in size between the Mirage 2000 (left) and the Super Mirage 4000

WINGS: Cantilever mid-wing monoplane of delta planform, with computer-derived aerodynamics. Large-radius root fairings. Two-section elevons form entire trailing-edge of each wing. Full-span automatic leading-edge flaps provide variable camber in combat. Fly-by-wire active control system for elevons and flaps. No tabs.

FUSELAGE: Conventional semi-monocoque structure, 'waisted' in accordance with area rule. Door-type airbrake in each intake trunk above wing-root leading-edge.

TAIL UNIT AND FOREPLANES: Cantilever fin and inset rudder; latter actuated by fly-by-wire control system. Fin is made of carbon composite and contains fuel tankage. No tab. Variable-incidence swept canard foreplane near lip of each engine air intake duct.

LANDING GEAR: Retractable tricycle type, of Messier-Hispano-Bugatti design, with twin nosewheels and single wheel on each main unit. Hydraulic retraction, nosewheels forward, main units inward. Oleo-pneumatic shock-absorbers. Electro-hydraulic nosewheel steering. Aluminium alloy main wheels, with tubeless tyres and steel disc brakes on prototype; graphite composite brakes planned on production aircraft.

POWER PLANT: Two SNECMA M53-2 turbofan engines side-by-side in rear fuselage of prototype, each rated at 83·4 kN (18,740 lb st) with afterburning. Production Super Mirage 4000 is intended to have uprated M53-2s, each giving 95 kN (21,350 lb st) with afterburning. Movable half-cone centrebody in each air intake. Provision for a large jettisonable fuel tank under each wing and under fuselage. Fuel tankage in fin helps to give total capacity about three times that of the Mirage 2000.

ACCOMMODATION: Pilot only, on Martin-Baker Mk10 zero-zero ejection seat, under sideways-opening (to starboard) transparent canopy; 360° field of view.

SYSTEMS: Messier-Hispano-Bugatti hydraulic system, pressure 280 bars (4,000 lb/sq in), powered by four advanced pumps and using lightweight titanium pipelines. Two Auxilec electrical generators. Turboméca Palouste gas turbine APU, in compartment aft of pilot's seat, for engine starting.

AVIONICS AND EQUIPMENT: Provision for a radar of 90 cm (35·4 in) diameter in nose, to provide search range of up to 65-70 nm (120-130 km; 75-80 miles). Digital autopilot, multi-mode displays, SAGEM inertial navigation system, Crouzet Type 80 air data computer, Thomson-CSF VE.120 head-up display and digital automated weapon delivery system.

ARMAMENT: Provision for two 30 mm DEFA guns in bottom of air intake trunks and a rail under each outer wing for a Matra 550 Magic air-to-air missile, plus a wide range of air-to-air and air-to-surface weapons. Total of eleven hardpoints for external stores.

DIMENSIONS, EXTERNAL:

Wing span	12·00 m (39 ft 4½ in)
Length overall	18·70 m (61 ft 4¼ in)
Wheel track	4·36 m (14 ft 3½ in)
Wheelbase	6·90 m (22 ft 7½ in)

AREA:

Wings, gross	73·00 m² (786 sq ft)

DASSAULT SUPER ETENDARD

Dassault is producing for the French Navy an updated version of its Etendard IV-M carrier-based fighter which has served with the Navy's operational squadrons since 1962, and was last described in the 1965-66 *Jane's*. The airframe and equipment of the new version, known as the Super Etendard, were expected to be 90% common with those of the Etendard IV-M, except for the nav/attack system. In fact, the installation of a more powerful turbojet engine and equipment of enhanced capability, together with the adoption of improved aerodynamic features and modern manufacturing techniques, has made the Super Etendard 90% new.

The Super Etendard is a transonic single-seat strike fighter, for low and medium altitude operations from ships in the class of the French Navy's *Clémenceau* and *Foch*. Its equipment includes a highly sophisticated and accurate nav/attack integrated avionics system. Inherent long range is increased by flight refuelling capability, and it is able to operate as a tanker for other aircraft.

The Atar 8K-50 turbojet engine is a non-afterburning version of the Atar 9K-50 used in the Mirage F1 multi-mission fighter and attack aircraft. It has a lower specific fuel consumption than the Atar 8 fitted in the Etendard IV-M. The thrust increase of about 10%, combined with a new wing leading-edge and redesigned flaps, allows a significant increase in gross weight for catapulting and, hence, permits increased fuel load and armament.

Two prototypes were produced by conversion of standard IV-M airframes. The first of these flew for the first time on 28 October 1974, and had logged a total of 620 flying hours in 520 flights by November 1977. Its programme included engine development, followed in 1978 by tests of the Super Etendard's external load-carrying capability and firing trials of the Exocet AM39 air-to-surface anti-shipping missile.

The second prototype, which flew for the first time on 25 March 1975, had logged 420 hours in 390 flights by November 1977, including tests of the Super Etendard's navigation system and bombing capabilities. Its subsequent tasks included shipboard operation under open-sea conditions in waters other than the Mediterranean, where all early trials took place.

It was intended originally to build 100 production aircraft, but the number has been reduced to 71 in order to conform with budget limitations. The first aircraft came off the production line in November 1977 and flew on 24 November. Deliveries began on 28 June 1978, when the third production aircraft was accepted officially by the French Navy, and Dassault had delivered nine Super Etendards by the beginning of 1979, with production continuing at the rate of two and a half aircraft per month. The first twelve replaced Etendard IV-Ms in service with Flottille 11F, based at Landivisiau. In 1979, the F-8E(FN) Crusaders of Flottille 14F were to be replaced at the same base, followed by deliveries to Flottille 17F, currently flying Etendard IV-Ms from Hyères.

TYPE: Single-seat transonic carrier-based strike fighter.

WINGS: Cantilever mid-wing monoplane. Thickness/chord ratio varies from 6% at root to 5% at tip. Anhedral 1°. Sweepback at quarter-chord 45°. All-metal two-spar torsion-box structure; stressed skin of machined panels with integral stiffeners. Tips fold upward for carrier stowage. Inset ailerons, hydraulically-powered by Dassault irreversible dual circuits with artificial feel. Spoiler on top surface of each wing, ahead of special double-slotted flap with second slot in form of an integral 'gutter'. Flap travel increased by comparison with Etendard IV-M. Hydraulically-powered drooping leading-edges, with extended chord on outer panels.

FUSELAGE: All-metal semi-monocoque structure, 'waisted' in accordance with area rule. Perforated airbrake under each side of centre-fuselage.

TAIL UNIT: Cantilever all-metal structure, with tailplane mid-set on fin. All surfaces swept. All-moving tailplane (with electrically-powered pitch trim) and rudder are powered in same way as ailerons.

LANDING GEAR: Retractable tricycle type, with single wheel on each unit, manufactured by Messier-Hispano-Bugatti. Nosewheel retracts rearward, main units inward into wings and fuselage. Messier-Hispano-Bugatti oleo-pneumatic shock-absorbers and disc brakes. Main-wheel tyres size 30 × 7·7-16; nosewheel tyre size 490 × 155-9. Brake-chute in fairing at junction of fin and tailplane trailing-edges.

POWER PLANT: One SNECMA Atar 8K-50 non-afterburning turbojet, rated at 49 kN (11,025 lb st). Fuel in integral tanks in wings and rubber tanks in fuselage, with total capacity of 3,200 litres (704 Imp gallons; 845 US gallons). Provision for an external tank of 1,100 litres (242 Imp gallons; 290 US gallons) under each wing, and a 600 litre (132 Imp gallon; 158 US gallon) centreline tank or flight refuelling 'buddy' pack under the fuselage. Retractable flight refuelling probe in front of windscreen.

ACCOMMODATION: Pilot only, on Hispano-built Martin-Baker SEMMB CM4 A lightweight ejection seat in pressurised and air-conditioned cockpit. Extensively armoured.

SYSTEMS: Duplicated hydraulic circuits for flying controls, landing gear, brakes and airbrakes, and wing leading-edge droop.

AVIONICS AND EQUIPMENT: SAGEM ETNA inertial navigation and attack system; Thomson-CSF/EMD Agave lightweight search/track/designation/telemetry/navigation radar; Thomson-CSF VE.120 head-up display; Crouzet Type 97 navigation display, armament control panel and selector box, and Type 66 air data computer; TRT radio altimeter; SFIM three-axis attitude indicator; LMT micro-Tacan and IFF, and SOCRAT VOR.

ARMAMENT: Two DEFA 30 mm guns, each with 125 rds, in bottom of engine air intake trunks. Underfuselage attachments for two 250 kg bombs. Four underwing attachments for 400 kg bombs, Magic air-to-air missiles or rocket pods. Optionally, one Exocet AM39 air-to-surface missile under starboard wing, and one external fuel tank under port wing.

DIMENSIONS, EXTERNAL:

Wing span	9·60 m (31 ft 6 in)
Width, wings folded	7·80 m (25 ft 7 in)
Wing aspect ratio	3·23
Length overall	14·31 m (46 ft 11½ in)
Height overall	3·86 m (12 ft 8 in)
Wheel track	3·50 m (11 ft 6 in)
Wheelbase	4·80 m (15 ft 9 in)

AREA:

Wings, gross	28·4 m² (305·7 sq ft)

WEIGHTS:

Weight empty	6,450 kg (14,220 lb)
Max fuel, incl two 1,100 litre underwing tanks	4,800 kg (10,580 lb)
Max weapon load, internal fuel only	2,100 kg (4,630 lb)
Max T-O weight	12,000 kg (26,455 lb)

PERFORMANCE:

Max level speed at height	approx Mach 1
Max level speed at low altitude	650 knots (1,204 km/h; 748 mph)

Approach speed for shipboard landing at AUW of 7,800 kg (17,200 lb) 122 knots (226 km/h; 140 mph)

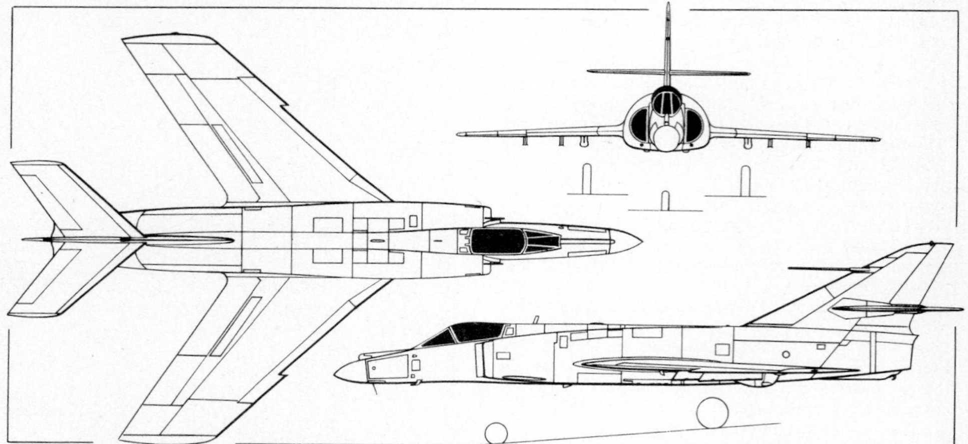

Dassault Super Etendard naval fighter (SNECMA Atar 8K-50 turbojet engine) *(Pilot Press)*

Dassault Super Etendard carrier-based fighter on the catapult of the *Foch*

Service ceiling 13,700 m (45,000 ft)
Radius of action, hi-lo-hi, with AM39 missile
390 nm (720 km; 450 miles)

DASSAULT-BREGUET/DORNIER ALPHA JET

Details of the Alpha Jet programme can be found in the International section of this edition.

DASSAULT-BREGUET/BAe JAGUAR

Details of the Jaguar programme can be found under 'SEPECAT' in the International section of this edition.

DASSAULT-BREGUET ATLANTIC ANG

The Atlantic ANG (Atlantic Nouvelle Génération) is a twin-turboprop maritime patrol aircraft derived directly from the earlier Atlantic that was produced in 1964-74 for operation by the armed services of France (40, of which 3 were sold subsequently to Pakistan), Germany (20, including 5 special-purpose ECM aircraft), Italy (18) and the Netherlands (9). Design definition of the new version was initiated by a French government instruction to proceed in July 1977, with the aim of providing a replacement for the first generation Atlantic and the Neptune during the period from 1985 to 1990. This led to launch of the development phase of the ANG programme in October 1978. Initial requirement is for 42 aircraft for the French Navy.

Two prototypes are being produced by modification of first generation Atlantic airframes. Work started in January 1979, and the prototypes are scheduled to fly in their new form in mid-1981 and at the beginning of 1982 respectively. Series production is expected to begin in 1981, to permit delivery of the first production Atlantic ANG in early 1985. The work is likely to be shared by the same European SECBAT (Société d'Etudes et de Construction du Breguet Atlantic) consortium that was responsible for the earlier programme, with possible modification of the work-split to reflect varying national interests in the ANG aircraft. The Tyne engines will be produced by SNECMA of France, Rolls-Royce of the UK, FN of Belgium and MAN of Germany; and propellers by Ratier of France and British Aerospace.

Structural changes by comparison with the first generation Atlantic will include use of a refined bonding technique, improved anti-corrosion protection, better sealing between skin panels, and design improvements offering longer fatigue life and more economical maintenance. These are intended to ensure increased serviceability, with 75% of squadron aircraft permanently available for operations; readiness to take off within 20 minutes of an order to go; and an aircraft life of more than 20 years, or at least 12,000 flying hours.

The basic mission performance requirements envisaged for the ANG are quite similar to those of the Atlantic now in service: a high cruising speed to the operational area, quick descent from cruising altitude to patrol height, lengthy patrol endurance at low altitude, and a high degree of manoeuvrability at sea level. It will be able to carry a wide variety of weapons and equipment for finding and attacking both submarines and surface targets in all weathers. Like the original Atlantic, the ANG will be able to perform minelaying, logistic support, and passenger and freight transport missions. It could be adapted for advanced AEW and flight refuelling duties, and is suitable for civilian tasks such as air/sea rescue and patrol of offshore fishing and oil interests.

Type: Twin-turboprop maritime patrol aircraft.

Wings: Cantilever mid-wing monoplane, with streamlined avionics pods on tips. Wing section NACA 64 series. Dihedral 6° on outer panels only. Incidence 3°. Tapered planform, with 9° sweepback on leading-edge. All-metal three-spar fail-safe structure, with bonded light alloy honeycomb skin panels on torsion box and on main landing gear doors. Two conventional all-metal ailerons on each wing, actuated by SAMM twin-cylinder jacks. All-metal slotted flaps, with bonded light alloy honeycomb filling, in three segments on each wing, over 75% of span. Three hinged spoilers on upper surface of each outer wing, forward of flaps. Metal airbrake above and below each wing. No trim tabs. Air Equipement/Kléber-Colombes pneumatic de-icing system on leading-edges.

Fuselage: All-metal 'double-bubble' fail-safe structure, with bonded honeycomb sandwich skin on pressurised central section of upper lobe, weapons bay doors and nosewheel door.

Tail Unit: Cantilever all-metal structure, with bonded honeycomb sandwich skin panels on torsion boxes. Fixed-incidence tailplane, with dihedral. Control surfaces operated through SAMM twin-cylinder jacks. No trim tabs. Air Equipement/Kléber-Colombes pneumatic de-icing system on leading-edges.

Landing Gear: Retractable tricycle type, supplied by Messier-Hispano-Bugatti, with twin wheels on each unit. Hydraulic retraction, nosewheels rearward, main units forward into engine nacelles. Kléber-Colombes or Dunlop tyres; size 39 × 13-20 on main wheels, pressure 12 bars (170 lb/sq in), 26 × 8-13 on nosewheels, pressure 6·5 bars (94 lb/sq in). New Messier-Hispano-Bugatti disc brakes with higher braking energy, and Modistop anti-skid units.

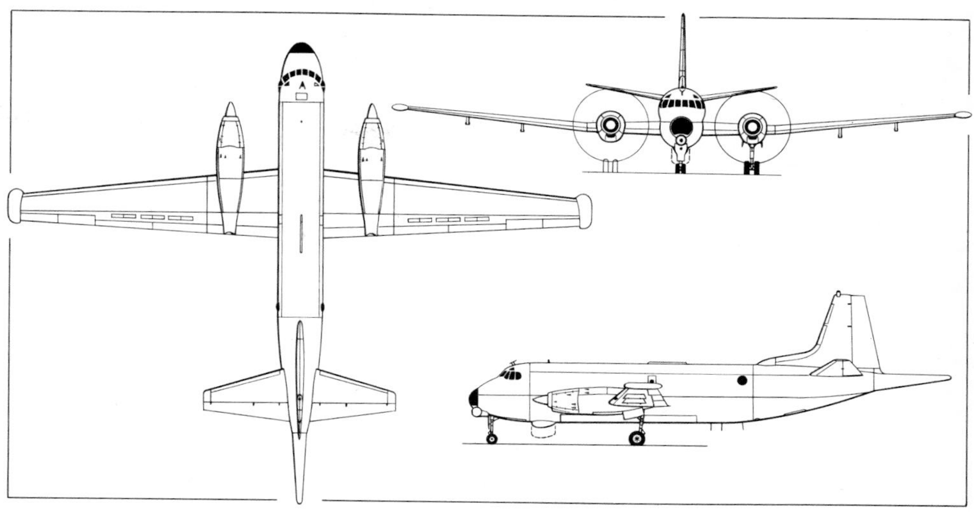

Dassault-Breguet Atlantic ANG Twin-turboprop maritime patrol aircraft *(Pilot Press)*

Power Plant: Two 4,638 kW (6,220 ehp) Rolls-Royce Tyne RTy.20 Mk 21 turboprop engines, each driving a four-blade Ratier/British Aerospace constant-speed propeller type PD 249/476/3. Six pressure-refuelled integral fuel tanks in wings, with total capacity of 23,000 litres (5,059 Imp gallons). Provision for auxiliary tankage in weapons bay, capacity 4,600 litres (1,012 Imp gallons). Updated gauging system. Oil capacity 100 litres (22 Imp gallons).

Accommodation: Normal flight crew of 12, comprising observer in nose; pilot, co-pilot and flight engineer on flight deck; a radio-navigator, ESM-ECM-MAD operator, radar-IFF operator, tactical coordinator and two acoustic sensor operators at stations on the starboard side of the tactical compartment; and two observers in beam positions at the rear. Provision for carrying relief crew, or 12 other personnel. Rest compartment, with eight seats, in centre-fuselage, forward of crew room with tables and seats, galley, toilet and wardrobe. Primary access via extending airstair door in bottom of rear fuselage. Emergency exits above and below flight deck and on each side of fuselage, above wing trailing-edge.

Systems: Air-conditioning system by ABG/Semca, supplied by two compressors driven by gearboxes. Heat exchangers and bootstrap system for cabin temperature control. Duplicated hydraulic system, to operate flying controls, landing gear, flaps, weapons bay doors and retractable radome. Three basic electrical systems: variable-frequency three-phase 115/208V AC system, with two 60/80kVA generators and modernised control and protection equipment; fixed-frequency three-phase 115/208V 400Hz AC system, with four 15kVA Auxivar generators, two on each engine; 28V DC system, with four 6kW transformer-rectifiers supplied from the variable-frequency AC system, and one 40Ah battery. One 60kVA emergency AC generator, driven at constant speed by APU. Individual oxygen bottles for emergency use. Electrical anti-icing for engine air intake lips, propeller blades and spinners. Garrett-AiResearch gas turbine APU for engine starting, emergency electrical supply, and air-conditioning on ground.

Armament and Operational Equipment: Main weapons bay in unpressurised lower fuselage can accommodate all NATO standard bombs, depth charges, eight homing torpedoes or two air-to-surface missiles (typical load comprises three torpedoes and one AM.39 Exocet missile). Four underwing attachments for stores, including rockets, missiles or containers. Up to 78 sonobuoys in compartment aft of weapons bay, where whole of upper and lower fuselage provides storage for sonobuoys and marker flares. Forward-looking infra-red sensor under nose. Thomson-CSF Iguane retractable radar immediately forward of weapons bay, with LMT IFF interrogator and SECRE decoder. Cameras in port side of nose and in bottom of rear fuselage. Crouzet-manufactured MAD in tail sting. Thomson-CSF Arar 13 radar detector for ESM. Other equipment includes HF com, Tacan and DME by LMT, VHF/AM com by Socrat, TRT radio-altimeter, Collins MF and V/UHF radio-compass, dual SAGEM Uliss 53 inertial navigation systems, Crouzet geographical display and air data computer. UHF and VHF/FM suppliers not yet designated. Thomson-CSF Sadang system for processing active and passive acoustic detection data.

Dimensions, external:
Wing span, incl wingtip pods 37·36 m (122 ft 6¾ in)
Wing aspect ratio 10·94
Length overall 31·75 m (104 ft 2 in)
Height overall 11·34 m (37 ft 2½ in)
Fuselage: Max depth 4·00 m (13 ft 1½ in)
Tailplane span 12·31 m (40 ft 4½ in)
Wheel track 9·00 m (29 ft 6¼ in)
Wheelbase 9·45 m (31 ft 0 in)
Propeller diameter 4·88 m (16 ft 0 in)
Distance between propeller centres
9·00 m (29 ft 6¼ in)
Main weapons bay:
Length 9·00 m (29 ft 6¼ in)
Width 2·10 m (6 ft 10¾ in)

Dimensions, internal:
Cabin, incl rest compartment, galley, toilet, aft observers' stations:
Length 18·50 m (60 ft 8½ in)
Max width 3·60 m (11 ft 9½ in)
Max height 2·00 m (6 ft 6¾ in)
Floor area 155 m² (1,668 sq ft)
Volume 92 m³ (3,250 cu ft)

Areas:
Wings, gross 120·34 m² (1,295·3 sq ft)
Ailerons (total) 5·26 m² (56·62 sq ft)
Flaps (total) 26·80 m² (288·48 sq ft)
Spoilers (total) 1·66 m² (17·87 sq ft)
Vertical tail surfaces (total) 16·64 m² (179·11 sq ft)
Rudder 5·96 m² (64·15 sq ft)
Horizontal tail surfaces (total) 33·00 m² (355·21 sq ft)
Elevators 8·30 m² (89·34 sq ft)

Weights and Loadings:
Weight empty, equipped, standard mission
25,000 kg (55,115 lb)
Military load: ASW mission 2,200 kg (4,850 lb)
ASV mission 3,000 kg (6,610 lb)
Max fuel 18,500 kg (40,785 lb)
Mission T-O weight: ASW 43,900 kg (96,780 lb)
ASV 45,400 kg (100,090 lb)
Max overload T-O weight 46,200 kg (101, 850 lb)
Max zero-fuel weight 29,000 kg (63,935 lb)
Normal design landing weight 36,000 kg (79,365 lb)
Max landing weight, emergency
46,000 kg (101,400 lb)
Max wing loading 385 kg/m² (78·96 lb/sq ft)
Max power loading 5·07 kg/kW (8·34 lb/ehp)

Performance (estimated, at T-O weight of 45,000 kg; 99,200 lb, except where indicated):
Never-exceed speed Mach 0·7
Max level speed at optimum height
355 knots (657 km/h; 408 mph)
Max level speed at S/L 320 knots (592 km/h; 368 mph)
Max cruising speed at 7,600 m (25,000 ft)
300 knots (555 km/h; 345 mph)
Normal patrol speed, S/L to 1,525 m (5,000 ft)
180 knots (333 km/h; 207 mph)
Stalling speed, flaps down 90 knots (167 km/h; 104 mph)
Max rate of climb at S/L, AUW of 30,000 kg (66,140 lb)
884 m (2,900 ft)/min
Max rate of climb at S/L, AUW of 40,000 kg (88,185 lb)
610 m (2,000 ft)/min
Rate of climb at S/L, one engine out, AUW of 30,000 kg (66,140 lb) 365 m (1,200 ft)/min
Rate of climb at S/L, one engine out, AUW of 40,000 kg (88,185 lb) 213 m (700 ft)/min
Service ceiling 9,100 m (30,000 ft)
Runway LCN at max T-O weight 60
T-O to 10·5 m (35 ft) 1,620 m (5,315 ft)
T-O to 10·5 m (35 ft), one engine out 2,240 m (7,350 ft)
Landing from 15 m (50 ft) 1,500 m (4,922 ft)
170-knot turning radius at AUW of 40,000 kg (88,185 lb) at:
30° bank 1,500 m (4,925 ft)
45° bank 600 m (1,970 ft)
60° bank 500 m (1,640 ft)
Ferry range with max fuel
4,400 nm (8,150 km; 5,065 miles)
Typical endurance at low altitude:
600 nm (1,110 km; 690 miles) from base 8 h
1,000 nm (1,850 km; 1,150 miles) from base 5 h
Max endurance 18 h

DASSAULT MYSTÈRE-FALCON 20 SERIES F

Details of the early history of this twin-turbofan light transport can be found in the 1977-78 *Jane's*.

Dassault builds the wings and Aérospatiale the fuselages and tail units of production aircraft, which are marketed in the USA under the name Falcon and elsewhere as Mystère 20s. The first production aircraft flew on 1 January 1965, and by mid-February 1979 sales of Mystère-Falcon 20s had reached 446, of which 157 were for customers in the areas marketed by Dassault. Of these, 393 had been delivered, including 242 to the Business Jets Division of Pan American and its successor, Falcon Jet Corporation, formed jointly by Dassault-Breguet and Pan American in 1973. Production is continuing at the rate of two aircraft per month.

Basic current production version is the **Mystère-Falcon 20 Series F,** which introduced high-lift devices to improve T-O and landing performance, more powerful engines than earlier Falcons and increased wing fuel tank capacity. The prototype was displayed at the Paris Air Show in June 1969 and deliveries began in July 1970. During 1970 the Series F became the first aircraft to receive type approval under FAA FAR Pt 36 anti-noise regulations. This approval was subsequently extended to other versions.

The **Mystère-Falcon 20 Series G** and **Series H** are described separately.

All versions of the Mystère-Falcon 20 can be modified as follows for specific duties:

Calibration: Two aircraft ordered by the SGAC and one by the Spanish government are used for the calibration of radio navigation aids. The equipment includes a removable console, thus retaining the full passenger-carrying capability of the aircraft.

Airline crew training: Since 20 September 1966, several Mystère-Falcon 20s have been used by Air France to train pilots for their jet airliners, with up to five aircraft being used simultaneously. Japan Air Lines also bought three of this version.

Cross-country: Similar to basic aircraft, but with low-pressure tyres for soft-field operation at the same take-off and landing weights. Described in 1968-69 *Jane's*.

Quick-change and cargo: A quick-change kit, consisting of an assembly of nets and supports, keeps the centre aisle free and allows direct access to nine freight compartments. Total usable volume of these compartments is 6·65 m³ (235 cu ft), and transformation from executive configuration to cargo configuration, or vice versa, takes less than one hour. A cargo version of the Falcon is also available and is described separately. For both versions an increase of the maximum zero-fuel weight from 8,900 kg (19,600 lb) to 9,980 kg (22,000 lb) allows an increased payload of up to 3,000 kg (6,615 lb).

Aerial photography: The French Institut Géographique National has a Mystère-Falcon 20 fitted with two cameras (Zeiss RMK 610 mm focal length, and Wild RC8, RC9 or RC10) and an intervalometer. This enables the aircraft to be used for high-altitude photography and photogrammetry duties.

Systems trainer: Two aircraft fitted with Mirage III-E combat radar and navigation systems are in service with the French Air Force for training its Mirage pilots. This version, known as the **Falcon ST,** has been sold also to the Libyan Republic.

Camera-equipped Mystère-Falcon 20 of the French Institut Géographique National

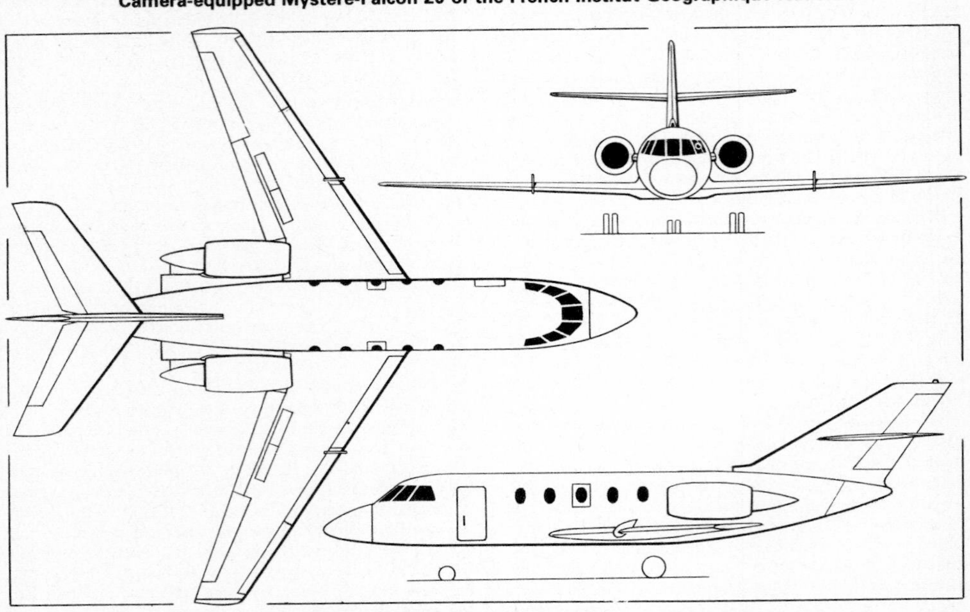
Dassault Mystère-Falcon 20 Series H *(Pilot Press)*

TYPE: Twin-turbofan executive transport.

WINGS: Cantilever low-wing monoplane. Thickness/chord ratio varies from 10·5 to 8%. Dihedral 2°. Incidence 1° 30'. Sweepback at quarter-chord 30°. All-metal (copper-bearing alloys) fail-safe torsion-box structure with machined stressed skin. Ailerons are each operated by Dassault twin-body actuators, from dual hydraulic systems, and have artificial feel. Non-slotted slats inboard of fence, and slotted slats outboard, on each wing. Hydraulically-actuated airbrakes forward of the hydraulically-actuated two-section single-slotted flaps. Leading-edges anti-iced by engine bleed air.

FUSELAGE: All-metal semi-monocoque structure of circular cross-section, built on fail-safe principles.

TAIL UNIT: Cantilever all-metal structure, with electrically-controlled variable-incidence tailplane mounted halfway up fin. Elevators and rudder each actuated by twin hydraulic servos. No trim tabs.

LANDING GEAR: Retractable tricycle type, by Messier-Hispano, with twin wheels on all three units. Hydraulic retraction, main units inward, nosewheels forward. Oleo-pneumatic shock-absorbers. Goodyear disc brakes and anti-skid units. Normal tyre pressure 9·15 bars (133 lb/sq in) on all units. Low-pressure gear (4·5 bars; 65 lb/sq in) available optionally. Steerable and self-centering nosewheels. Braking parachute standard.

POWER PLANT: Two General Electric CF700-2D-2 turbofan engines (each 20 kN; 4,500 lb st) mounted in pods on each side of rear fuselage. Fuel in two integral tanks in wings and two auxiliary tanks aft of rear pressure bulkhead in fuselage, with total capacity of 5,200 litres (1,144 Imp gallons; 1,374 US gallons). Separate fuel system for each engine, with provision for cross-feeding. Single-point pressure refuelling. Emergency refuelling by gravity.

ACCOMMODATION: Crew of two on flight deck, with full dual controls and airline-type instrumentation. Normal seating for eight or ten passengers in individual reclining chairs, with tables between forward pairs of seats and a central 'trench' aisle, or 12-14 passengers at reduced pitch without tables. Toilet at rear. Baggage space and wardrobe on starboard side, immediately aft of flight deck opposite door, and at rear of cabin. Buffet with ice-box, food and liquid storage at front of cabin on port side. Downward-opening door has built-in steps.

SYSTEMS: Duplicated air-conditioning and pressurisation system, supplied with air bled from both engines. Pressure differential 0·57 bars (8·3 lb/sq in). Two independent hydraulic systems, pressure 207 bars (3,000 lb/sq in), with twin engine-driven pumps and emergency electric pump, actuate primary flying controls, flaps, landing gear, wheel brakes, airbrakes and nosewheel steering. 28V DC electrical system with a 9kW 28V DC starter/generator on each engine, one 1500VA and two 750VA 400Hz 118/208V inverters and two 40Ah batteries. Automatic emergency oxygen system. 9kW Microturbo Saphir II APU optional.

AVIONICS AND EQUIPMENT: Standard equipment includes duplicated VHF and VOR/glideslope, single ADF and DME, marker beacon receiver, ATC transponder, cockpit audio and duplicated blind-flying instrumentation. Optional equipment includes integrated flight instrument system, weather radar, HF communications radio, autopilot, second ADF and DME, and cabin address system.

DIMENSIONS, EXTERNAL:
- Wing span: 16·30 m (53 ft 6 in)
- Wing chord (mean): 2·85 m (9 ft 4 in)
- Wing aspect ratio: 6·4
- Length overall: 17·15 m (56 ft 3 in)
- Length of fuselage: 15·55 m (51 ft 0 in)
- Height overall: 5·32 m (17 ft 5 in)
- Tailplane span: 6·74 m (22 ft 1 in)
- Wheel track: 3·69 m (12 ft 1¼ in)
- Wheelbase: 5·74 m (18 ft 10 in)
- Passenger door: Height: 1·52 m (5 ft 0 in)
  - Width: 0·80 m (2 ft 7½ in)
  - Height to sill: 1·09 m (3 ft 7 in)
- Emergency exits (each side, over wing):
  - Height: 0·66 m (2 ft 2 in)
  - Width: 0·48 m (1 ft 7 in)

DIMENSIONS, INTERNAL:
- Cabin, incl fwd baggage space and rear toilet:
  - Length: 7·08 m (23 ft 2¾ in)
  - Max width: 1·87 m (6 ft 1¾ in)
  - Max height: 1·73 m (5 ft 8 in)
  - Volume: 20·0 m³ (700 cu ft)
- Baggage compartment (fwd): 0·70 m³ (24·7 cu ft)
- Baggage compartment (aft): 0·37 m³ (13·1 cu ft)

AREAS:
- Wings, gross: 41·00 m² (440 sq ft)
- Horizontal tail surfaces (total): 11·30 m² (121·6 sq ft)
- Vertical tail surfaces (total): 7·60 m² (81·8 sq ft)

WEIGHTS:
- Weight empty, equipped: 7,530 kg (16,600 lb)
- Max payload: 1,180 kg (2,600 lb)
- Max T-O and ramp weight: 13,000 kg (28,660 lb)
- Max zero-fuel weight: 8,900 kg (19,600 lb)
- Typical landing weight: 8,930 kg (19,685 lb)

PERFORMANCE:
- Never-exceed speed at S/L: 350 knots (650 km/h; 404 mph) IAS
- Never-exceed speed at 7,000 m (23,000 ft): 390 knots (725 km/h; 450 mph) IAS
- Max cruising speed at 7,620 m (25,000 ft) at AUW of 9,071 kg (20,000 lb): 465 knots (862 km/h; 536 mph)
- Econ cruising speed at 12,200 m (40,000 ft): 405 knots (750 km/h; 466 mph)
- Stalling speed: 82 knots (152 km/h; 95 mph)
- Absolute ceiling: 12,800 m (42,000 ft)
- Service ceiling, one engine out, at AUW of 8,500 kg (18,700 lb): 7,480 m (24,500 ft)

T-O to 10·7 m (35 ft) at AUW of 12,580 kg (27,735 lb) (full tanks, 8 passengers and baggage) 915 m (3,000 ft)
FAR 25 balanced T-O field length, AUW as above 1,450 m (4,750 ft)
FAR 121 landing field length at AUW of 8,550 kg (18,870 lb) (8 passengers, 45 min reserves) 985 m (3,230 ft)
Landing from 15 m (50 ft) 590 m (1,930 ft)
Range with max fuel and 725 kg (1,600 lb) payload at econ cruising speed, with reserves for 45 min cruise 1,808 nm (3,350 km; 2,080 miles)

DASSAULT MYSTÈRE-FALCON 20 SERIES G and GUARDIAN

US Coast Guard designation: HU-25A

When Dassault-Breguet released preliminary details of the Garrett-engined version of its Mystère-Falcon 20 twin-turbofan business jet in the late Spring of 1976, it stated that the new power plant, complete with nacelles and thrust reversers, would be offered initially as a retrofit for existing aircraft, with full production of the new model, designated Mystère-Falcon 20G, scheduled for a later date.

A further statement, in the Autumn of 1976, announced that a tender by Falcon Jet Corporation, distributor and support centre for Falcons in the USA, had proved the lowest bid to meet a US Coast Guard requirement for a medium-range surveillance aircraft known by the project designation HX-XX. This was confirmed on 5 January 1977, when William T. Coleman Jr, then US Secretary of Transportation, authorised the Coast Guard to award a contract for 41 aircraft to Falcon Jet Corporation.

A prototype (F-WATF) flew for the first time on 28 November 1977, and was the 362nd Mystère-Falcon 20 to be completed. Production aircraft are expected to have 44% French content and 56% US content.

The 41 Falcon 20Gs ordered by the US Coast Guard, as **HU-25 As**, are to be delivered at the rate of one a month, from Summer 1980. In choosing the type to meet its HX-XX requirement, the Coast Guard had expressed a preference for a turbofan-powered aircraft, with a minimum cabin/cockpit volume of 17 m³ (600 cu ft), able to perform the full range of MRS (medium-range surveillance) missions. These were listed as search and rescue (28·5% of total flight hours), marine environmental protection (30·3%), enforcement of laws and treaties (18·9%), marine science activities (10·6%), logistics support (5·4%), engineering support (3·8%), domestic ice-breaking (1·7%) and short-range aids to navigation (0·8%).

The basic airframe of the HU-25A, and the similar **Falcon Guardian** for other customers such as the French Navy (five ordered 1979 to replace P-2H Neptunes for oversea surveillance) and the Japanese Maritime Safety Agency, is little changed from that of the Mystère-Falcon 20F. The most significant new features are as follows:

AIRFRAME: Fuselage is modified to embody a drop hatch, and one search window on each side. Four hardpoints under fuselage: two for 500 kg (1,100 lb) loads, two for 200 kg (440 lb) loads. Four underwing hardpoints: two for 660 kg (1,455 lb) loads, two for 230 kg (507 lb) loads.

POWER PLANT: Two Garrett-AiResearch ATF 3-6-2C turbofan engines (each 24·65 kN; 5,538 lb st), meeting current and proposed FAR Pt 36 noise standards. Entire engine open to borescope inspection. Fuel tankage, total capacity 5,770 litres (1,269 Imp gallons; 1,524 US gallons), divided into two identical halves, one for each engine with cross-feed capability. Wing feeder tanks pressurised with bleed air, so that fuel will continue to flow to engines with all pumps turned off. Provision for auxiliary fuel tank in rear of cabin. Single-point refuelling in about nine minutes. Fuel heaters and bacterial protection standard.

ACCOMMODATION: Normal crew of five to seven. Typical complement will comprise two pilots, one surveillance system operator (SSO) at a console on the starboard side at the rear of the cabin, two search crew members at side windows. A three-seat sofa is provided for passengers, on the port side. A drop-hatch for stores, with floor-mounted roller conveyor, is located towards the front of the cabin. Galley and retractable toilet on port side. Provision for carrying four stretchers.

SYSTEMS: Pressurisation and air-conditioning by engine bleed air; max pressure differential 0.585 bars (8·5 lb/sq in). Two independent hydraulic systems, with twin engine-driven pumps; electric standby pump to power primary flight control system in emergency. All primary flight controls utilise dual hydraulic actuators, artificial feel, electric trim and manual backup. Each half of the dual actuator is fed by one of the hydraulic systems; failure of either system will not affect handling, as each actuator has sufficient power for full control deflection. DC electrical system, with two 9kW engine-driven starter/generators, two nickel-cadmium batteries and two 1,000VA static inverters. Ground power receptacle. One 20kVA alternator driven by hydraulic motor, plus one 4kVA alternator driven by APU. Wings and nacelles anti-iced by engine bleed air, permitting flight under maximum icing conditions with one engine out.

Dassault Mystère-Falcon Guardian, prototype for the US Coast Guard's HU-25A

AVIONICS: Basic avionics package includes dual HF, VHF-AM, IFF, single VHF-FM and UHF. Nav equipment includes inertial sensor system, Omega, dual VOR/ILS/MB, DME, ADF, radio altimeters, area navigation system and single Tacan. Sensors include maritime search and weather radar and optional SLAR, infra-red and ultra-violet scanners, FLIR, aerial reconnaissance camera and steerable TV camera with laser illumination invisible to human eyes.

DIMENSIONS, EXTERNAL:
- Wing span 16·30 m (53 ft 6 in)
- Wing aspect ratio 7·02
- Length overall 17·15 m (56 ft 3 in)
- Height overall 5·32 m (17 ft 5 in)
- Tailplane span 6·74 m (22 ft 1 in)

AREA:
- Wings, gross 41·80 m² (450 sq ft)

WEIGHTS:
- Weight empty 8,620 kg (19,000 lb)
- Operating weight empty, with 5 crew and complete electronics package 9,475 kg (20,890 lb)
- Max fuel 4,636 kg (10,220 lb)
- Max zero-fuel weight 10,215 kg (22,520 lb)
- Max T-O weight 14,515 kg (32,000 lb)
- Max landing weight 12,510 kg (27,580 lb)

PERFORMANCE (at max T-O weight, except where indicated):
- Max cruising speed at 12,200 m (40,000 ft) Mach 0·8 (461 knots; 855 km/h; 531 mph)
- Econ cruising speed at 12,500 m (41,000 ft) Mach 0·72
- Min manoeuvring speed at low altitude 150 knots (278 km/h; 173 mph)
- Initial cruising height 12,500 m (41,000 ft)
- T-O run 1,235 m (4,050 ft)
- FAR 25 landing run at typical landing weight 625 m (2,050 ft)
- Range with 5 crew, reserves of 5% total fuel plus 30 min at S/L 2,250 nm (4,170 km; 2,590 miles)

DASSAULT MYSTÈRE-FALCON 20 SERIES H

This new version of the Mystère-Falcon 20 was announced at the 1979 Paris Air Show. It retains almost unchanged the airframe, varied configurations and operational flexibility of the Mystère-Falcon 20 Series F, but is powered by two Garrett turbofans of the type used in the Series G/HU-25A Guardian and is fitted with the new rear fuselage structural fuel tank developed for the Mystère-Falcon 50. This combination of engines with improved sfc and increased fuel capacity enables the Series H to offer a 42% longer range than the Series F with eight passengers and 45 min fuel reserves, without any sacrifice of cabin volume.

To hasten development, Dassault flew for the first time on 24 April 1979 an aircraft known as the **Mystère-Falcon 20FH** (F-WZAH), embodying the new fuselage fuel tank and associated system changes, but retaining the General Electric CF700 engines of the Series F. The same aircraft was expected to be re-engined with Garrett turbofans and to resume flying as a fully-representative Series H prototype before the end of 1979, and type certification of the new model is scheduled for the second half of 1980.

The description of the Mystère-Falcon 20F applies also to the Series H, except as follows:

POWER PLANT: Two Garrett-AiResearch ATF 3-6-2C turbofan engines (each 24·65 kN; 5,538 lb st). Fuel in two integral tanks in wings and large integral tank in rear fuselage, with total capacity of 6,100 litres (1,342 Imp gallons; 1,611 US gallons).

WEIGHTS:
- Weight empty 8,070 kg (17,790 lb)
- Max fuel 4,900 kg (10,800 lb)
- Payload with max fuel 910 kg (2,006 lb)
- T-O weight with 2 crew, 8 passengers and max fuel 13,150 kg (28,990 lb)
- Max T-O weight 14,060 kg (31,000 lb)
- Max zero-fuel weight 10,000 kg (22,050 lb)

PERFORMANCE (estimated):
- Max cruising speed at 10,050 m (33,000 ft) Mach 0·80 (470 knots; 870 km/h; 540 mph)
- Balanced T-O field length with 8 passengers and max fuel 1,520 m (5,000 ft)
- Landing field length with 8 passengers and reserves 1,000 m (3,280 ft)
- Range with 8 passengers, 45 min reserves 2,520 nm (4,670 km; 2,900 miles)

DASSAULT FALCON CARGO JET

Under contract from Pan American Business Jets, Little Rock Airmotive converted a Falcon 20 into a specialised cargo aircraft. Known as the Falcon Cargo Jet, the prototype flew for the first time on 28 March 1972. By the Summer of the same year, an operator named Federal Express Corporation, of Little Rock, had three similar aircraft in service and expanded its fleet subsequently to a total of 32 Falcon D Cargo Jets.

The cargo conversion can be applied to any Mystère-Falcon 20 and is offered on the current Series F aircraft.

Basic feature of the conversion is replacement of the standard cabin door by a hydraulically-actuated cargo door 1·88 m wide by 1·44 m high (6 ft 2 in × 4 ft 9 in), forward of the wing on the port side. This door opens upward, with its sill at cabin floor level. The flooring itself is new and offers a completely flat area 7·01 m long by 1·62 m wide (23 ft × 5 ft 4 in). Made of aluminium honeycomb, it can sustain loadings of up to 488 kg/m² (100 lb/sq ft) and affords a vast number of alternative tie-down points for retainer nets and pallets. Floor-mounted rollers are optional.

The Falcon Cargo Jet's Category II solid-state avionics standard includes dual com/nav, dual flight directors, autopilot and weather radar. Specifically, in the case of the Federal Express fleet, the fit comprises RCA com/nav with DME, dual Collins FD-108 flight directors, RCA AVQ-21 radar, Collins AP-105 autopilot, Teledyne angle-of-attack system, Collins ADF and RCA transponder. Also installed on these aircraft is a Fairchild integral electronic weight and balance system, which indicates as a cockpit readout whether or not cargo weight and distribution are within the legal limits. Standard safety provisions include a quick-release cargo restraint system able to withstand 9*g*.

Dimensions, weights and performance are largely unchanged by this conversion scheme. Nominal empty weight is 6,963 kg (15,350 lb) and max zero-fuel weight is increased to 9,980 kg (22,000 lb). Range varies from 1,215 nm (2,250 km; 1,400 miles) with max payload to 1,736 nm (3,215 km; 2,000 miles) with max fuel and a 2,040 kg (4,500 lb) payload. Usable cabin volume is 14·15 m³ (500 cu ft).

DASSAULT MYSTÈRE-FALCON 10

The Mystère-Falcon 10 is basically a scaled-down version of the Mystère-Falcon 20, with similar wing high-lift devices to those of the Mystère-Falcon 20F and powered by two small turbofans in the 14·6 kN (3,300 lb st) class. It is designed to fail-safe principles and to comply with US FAR 25 transport category requirements.

A prototype (F-WFAL), with General Electric CJ610 turbojets, made its first flight on 1 December 1970. Flight testing was resumed on 7 May 1971 following modifications to the angles of wing incidence and dihedral and an increase in wing sweepback. The modified aircraft set a 1,000 km closed-circuit speed record of 502·05 knots (930·4 km/h; 578·13 mph) in FAI Class C1f on 1 June 1971.

A second prototype (F-WTAL), with Garrett-AiResearch TFE 731-2 engines, flew for the first time on 15 October 1971, followed by a third aircraft on 14 October 1972, with similar engines. This third Mystère-Falcon 10 set a 2,000 km closed-circuit speed record of 494·83 knots (917·02 km/h; 569·809 mph) in Class C1f on 29 May 1973.

The first production Mystère-Falcon 10 with TFE 731-2 engines flew on 30 April 1973. French certification was granted on 11 September 1973, followed by FAA certification nine days later, allowing deliveries of production aircraft to begin on 1 November. A total of 142 had been delivered by July 1979, at which time 179 Mystère-Falcon 10s had been ordered. They include three **Mystère-Falcon 10MER** aircraft for the French Navy, which uses them as intruders for interception training of Super Etendard pilots, as conventional instrument and night flying trainers, for calibration of shipboard radars and for medical evacuation, as well as for communications duties. The Navy has an option on two more.

At the beginning of 1979, rate of production at the Istres assembly plant was two per month. Fuselages are provided by the Potez works at Aire-sur-Adour, which assembles components built by SOGERMA, SOCEA and Socata. Wings come from CASA of Spain; tail units and nose assemblies from IAM of Italy; and many other components such as tail fins, doors and emergency exits from Latécoère's Toulouse works.

Like the Mystère-Falcon 20, the Mystère-Falcon 10 can be equipped for liaison, executive transport, navigation/attack system training, aerial photography, radio navigation aid calibration and ambulance duties.

TYPE: Twin-turbofan executive transport.

WINGS: Cantilever low-wing monoplane with increased sweepback on inboard leading-edges. All-metal torsion-box structure, with leading-edge slats and double-slotted trailing-edge flaps and plain ailerons. Two-section spoilers above each wing, forward of flaps.

FUSELAGE: All-metal semi-monocoque structure, designed to fail-safe principles.

TAIL UNIT: Cantilever all-metal structure, similar to that of Falcon 20.

LANDING GEAR: Retractable tricycle type, manufactured by Messier-Hispano-Bugatti, with twin wheels on main gear, single wheel on nose gear. Hydraulic retraction, main units inward, nosewheel forward. Oleo-pneumatic shock-absorbers. Low-pressure tyres for soft-field operation.

POWER PLANT: Two Garrett-AiResearch TFE 731-2 turbofan engines (each 14·4 kN; 3,230 lb st), mounted in pod on each side of rear fuselage. Fuel in two integral tanks in wings and two feeder tanks aft of rear bulkhead, with total capacity of 3,340 litres (735 Imp gallons; 882 US gallons). Separate fuel system for each engine, with provision for cross-feeding. Pressure refuelling system.

ACCOMMODATION: Crew of two on flight deck, with dual controls and airline-type instrumentation. Provision for third crew member on a jump-seat. Normal seating for four passengers (two individual seats and a three-seat sofa) or for seven passengers, with two individual seats added. Each pair of single seats is separated by a table. Coat compartment on starboard side, immediately aft of flight deck opposite door; rear baggage compartment behind sofa. Galley on left of entrance. Optional front toilet compartment. Downward-opening door with built-in steps.

SYSTEMS: Duplicated air-conditioning and pressurisation systems supplied with air bled from both engines. Pressure differential 0·61 bars (8·8 lb/sq in). Two independent hydraulic systems, each of 207 bars (3,000 lb/sq in) pressure and with twin engine-driven pumps and emergency electric pump, to actuate primary flight controls, flaps, landing gear, wheel brakes, airbrakes, yaw damper and nosewheel steering. 28V DC electrical system with a 9kW DC starter/generator on each engine, three 750VA 400Hz 115V inverters and two 23Ah batteries. Automatic emergency oxygen system.

AVIONICS AND EQUIPMENT: Standard equipment includes duplicated VHF and VOR/glideslope, single ADF, marker beacon receiver, ATC transponder, autopilot, intercom system and duplicated blind-flying instrumentation. Optional equipment includes duplicated DME and flight director, second ADF, weather radar and radio altimeter.

DIMENSIONS, EXTERNAL:

Wing span	13·08 m (42 ft 11 in)
Wing chord (mean)	2·046 m (6 ft 8½ in)
Wing aspect ratio	7·1
Length overall	13·85 m (45 ft 5 in)
Length of fuselage	12·47 m (40 ft 11 in)
Height overall	4·61 m (15 ft 1½ in)
Tailplane span	5·82 m (19 ft 1 in)
Wheel track	2·86 m (9 ft 5 in)
Wheelbase	5·38 m (17 ft 8 in)
Passenger door:	
Height	1·47 m (4 ft 10 in)
Width	0·80 m (2 ft 7 in)
Height to sill	0·884 m (2 ft 10¾ in)
Emergency exit (stbd side, over wing):	
Height	0·914 m (3 ft 0 in)
Width	0·508 m (1 ft 8 in)

DIMENSIONS, INTERNAL:

Cabin, excl flight deck:	
Length	5·00 m (16 ft 5 in)
Max width	1·46 m (4 ft 9 in)
Max height	1·50 m (4 ft 11 in)
Volume	7·50 m³ (264·6 cu ft)
Baggage compartment volume:	
front (wardrobe)	0·35 m³ (12·35 cu ft)
rear	0·70 m³ (24·7 cu ft)

AREAS:

Wings, gross	24·1 m² (259 sq ft)
Horizontal tail surfaces (total)	6·75 m² (72·65 sq ft)
Vertical tail surfaces (total)	4·54 m² (48·87 sq ft)

WEIGHTS:

Weight empty, equipped	4,880 kg (10,760 lb)
Max payload	1,060 kg (2,337 lb)
Max T-O weight	8,500 kg (18,740 lb)
Max zero-fuel weight	6,120 kg (13,500 lb)
Max landing weight	8,000 kg (17,640 lb)

PERFORMANCE:

Never-exceed speed at S/L	350 knots (648 km/h; 402 mph)
Max operating Mach number	0·87
Max cruising speed	494 knots (915 km/h; 568 mph)
FAR 25 balanced T-O field length with four passengers and fuel for a 1,000 nm (1,850 km; 1,150 mile) stage, 45 min reserves	930 m (3,050 ft)
FAR 25 balanced T-O field length, with four passengers and max fuel	1,250 m (4,100 ft)
FAR 25 landing run, with four passengers and 45 min reserves	630 m (2,070 ft)
Range with four passengers and 45 min reserves	1,918 nm (3,555 km; 2,209 miles)

Dassault Mystère-Falcon 10MER radar training aircraft of the French Navy

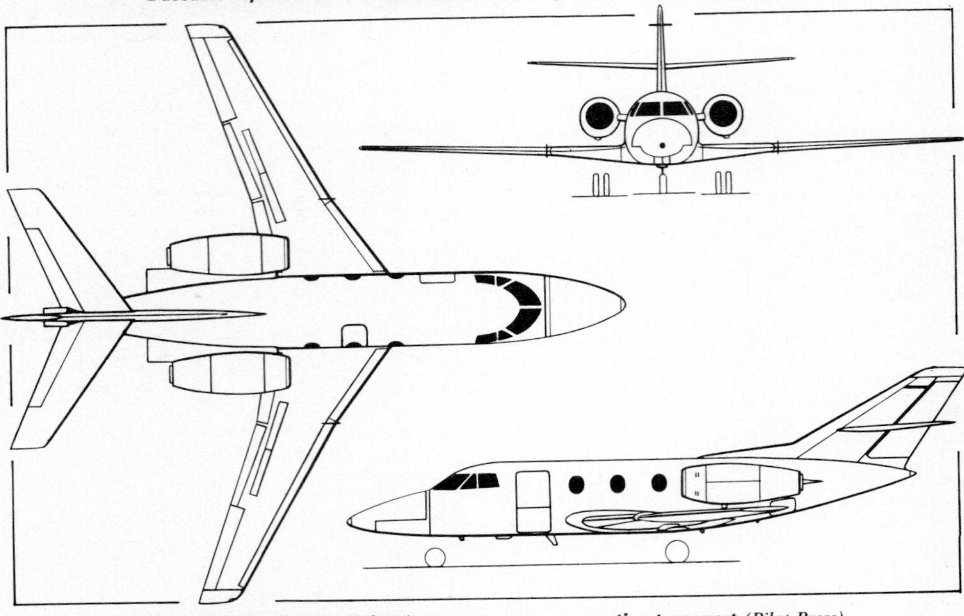

Dassault Mystère-Falcon 10 four/seven-passenger executive transport *(Pilot Press)*

DASSAULT-BREGUET MYSTÈRE-FALCON 50

The Mystère-Falcon 50 is a three-turbofan executive transport derived from the Mystère-Falcon 20, with standard accommodation for eight passengers and a crew of two. It has an entirely new wing of supercritical section, adapted to flight at high Mach numbers and embodying efficient high-lift devices, and complies with FAR Pt 36 noise requirements.

The original prototype (F-WAMD) flew for the first time on 7 November 1976, followed by a second prototype (F-WINR) on 16 February 1978 and the third (and sole pre-production) aircraft on 13 June 1978. DGAC certification was received on 27 February 1979, followed by FAA type approval on 8 March. Falcon 50 No. 4, flown on 2 March 1979, was the first built on Dassault-Breguet's Mérignac assembly line and became Falcon Jet's US demonstrator. Orders totalled 100 by mid-February 1979, and deliveries were scheduled to begin in July 1979, when Falcon 50 No. 3 was to be handed over to a customer who had owned a Falcon 20 for 12 years. In the early Autumn, the fifth aircraft was scheduled to be delivered to GLAM (Groupe de Liaisons Aériennes Militaires) for priority use by the President of the Republic. Production will build up to three per month by early 1980.

Fuselages for the Mystère-Falcon 50 are produced at Aérospatiale's Saint-Nazaire works, wings at the Col-

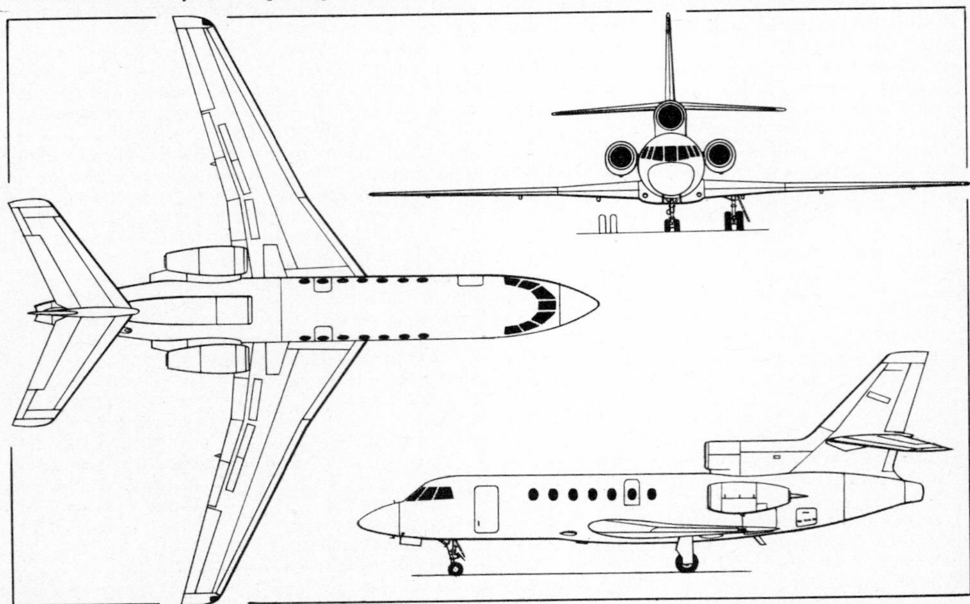

Dassault-Breguet Mystère-Falcon 50 extended-range three-turbofan executive transport *(Pilot Press)*

Dassault Mystère-Falcon 50 No. 3, which set a speed record in its class, between Chicago and Paris, on 24 September 1978

omiers plant of Dassault-Breguet, tail units by Aérospatiale at Méaulte, and cowlings by Hurel-Dubois at Vélizy-Villacoublay.

TYPE: Three-turbofan executive transport.

WINGS: Cantilever low-wing monoplane, with compound leading-edge sweepback and supercritical section. Each wing is attached to the central box structure by multiple bolts and forms an integral fuel tank. Full-span leading-edge slats, of which the outboard sections are slotted. Double-slotted trailing-edge flaps and ailerons. Three-section two-position airbrakes on top surface of each wing.

FUSELAGE: All-metal semi-monocoque structure of circular cross-section, with aft baggage compartment included in pressure-cell.

TAIL UNIT: Cantilever all-metal structure, with horizontal surfaces mounted partway up fin. Tailplane incidence adjustable by screwjack, driven by two electric motors controlled by 'normal' and 'emergency' controls located respectively on the control wheels and pedestal.

LANDING GEAR: Retractable tricycle type by Messier-Hispano-Bugatti, with twin wheels on each unit. Hydraulic retraction, main units inward, nosewheels forward. Four-disc brakes designed for 400 landings with normal-energy braking.

POWER PLANT: Three Garrett-AiResearch TFE 731-3 turbofan engines, each rated at 16·5 kN (3,700 lb st) for take-off. Two engines pod-mounted on sides of rear fuselage, the third attached by two top mounts. Thrust reverser on centre engine. Fuel in wing and fuselage tanks, with total capacity of 5,829 litres (1,540 US gallons). Single-point pressure fuelling.

ACCOMMODATION: Crew of two side-by-side on flight deck, with full dual controls and airline-type instrumentation. Normal accommodation for eight passengers in individual reclining seats, with first two rows facing each other and separated by stowable tables. Lavatory with water supply and flushing toilet at rear. Wardrobe and galley in forward part of cabin. Downward-opening airstair door. Optional layout provides a five-passenger lounge at the rear and a forward lavatory.

SYSTEMS: Air-conditioning system utilises bleed air from all three engines. Max pressure differential 0·61 bars (8·8 lb/sq in). Pressurisation maintains a max cabin altitude of 2,440 m (8,000 ft) to a flight altitude of 13,700 m (45,000 ft). Two independent hydraulic systems, pressure 207 bars (3,000 lb/sq in), with three engine-driven pumps and one emergency electric pump, actuate primary flying controls, flaps, slats, landing gear, wheel brakes, airbrakes and nosewheel steering. 28V DC electrical system, with a 9kW 28V DC starter/generator on each engine and two 23Ah batteries. Automatic emergency oxygen system. Optional 9kW Garrett-AiResearch APU.

AVIONICS: Standard items include Omega, inertial navigation system, duplicated VHF and VIR, ADF, DME, ATC and HF, radio altimeter and weather radar. Basic aircraft includes Collins AP-580 autopilot and two FCS-80 flight directors.

DIMENSIONS, EXTERNAL:

Wing span	18·86 m (61 ft 10½ in)
Wing chord (mean)	2·84 m (9 ft 3¾ in)
Wing aspect ratio	7·6
Length overall	18·30 m (60 ft 0½ in)
Length of fuselage	17·66 m (57 ft 11 in)
Height overall	6·90 m (22 ft 7½ in)
Tailplane span	7·74 m (25 ft 4¾ in)
Wheel track	3·98 m (13 ft 0¾ in)
Wheelbase	7·24 m (23 ft 9 in)
Passenger door: Height	1·52 m (4 ft 11¾ in)
Width	0·80 m (2 ft 7½ in)
Height to sill	1·30 m (4 ft 3¼ in)
Emergency exits (each side, over wing):	
Height	0·92 m (3 ft 0¼ in)
Width	0·51 m (1 ft 8 in)

DIMENSIONS, INTERNAL:

Cabin, incl forward baggage space and rear toilet:	
Length	7·14 m (23 ft 5 in)
Max width	1·86 m (6 ft 1¼ in)
Max height	1·79 m (5 ft 10½ in)
Volume	18·3 m³ (646·2 cu ft)
Baggage compartment (aft)	2·55 m³ (90 cu ft)

AREAS:

Wings, gross	46·83 m² (504·1 sq ft)
Horizontal tail surfaces (total)	13·35 m² (143·7 sq ft)
Vertical tail surfaces (total)	9·82 m² (105·7 sq ft)

WEIGHTS:

Weight empty, equipped	9,000 kg (19,840 lb)
Max payload	972 kg (2,140 lb)
Max T-O and ramp weight	17,000 kg (37,478 lb)
Max zero-fuel weight	10,250 kg (22,600 lb)
Max landing weight	15,810 kg (34,855 lb)

PERFORMANCE:

Max operating Mach No. — Mach 0·85

Max operating speed at S/L — 350 knots (648 km/h; 402 mph)IAS

Max operating speed at 7,225 m (23,700 ft) — 370 knots (685 km/h; 425 mph)IAS

Max cruising speed — Mach 0·82 or 470 knots (870 km/h; 540 mph)TAS

Service ceiling — 13,800 m (45,300 ft)

FAR 25 balanced field length with 8 passengers and fuel for 3,400 nm (6,295 km; 3,910 miles) — 1,490 m (4,900 ft)

FAR 121 landing distance with 8 passengers and FAR 121 reserves — 1,050 m (3,450 ft)

Range at Mach 0·75 with 8 passengers and FAR 121 reserves — 3,510 nm (6,500 km; 4,038 miles)

FOURNIER

FOURNIER AVIATION

OFFICE AND WORKS: Aérodrome d'Athée-Nitray, 37270 Montlouis

Telephone: (47) 50 68 30

Telex: 696 254

MANAGING DIRECTOR: René Caillet

Fournier Aviation was formed in 1978, bringing together the assets and activities of the former Avions Fournier SA and the Fournier Design Office, in close collaboration with M René Fournier. It is continuing to manufacture the RF-6B two-seat light aircraft, of which details follow.

Fournier Aviation has also developed the RF-9 motor-glider (see Sailplanes section).

FOURNIER RF-6B

The prototype of this two-seat aerobatic aircraft, designed by M René Fournier, flew for the first time on 12 March 1974; certification was obtained in April 1975.

Production of five pre-series RF-6Bs began during the first half of 1975, and the first of these (F-BVKS) flew for the first time on 4 March 1976. It has a longer nose than the prototype and a more powerful engine. By June 1979, a total of 45 RF-6Bs had been produced.

Intended primarily for use as an aerobatic or training aircraft, the RF-6B is stressed to +6*g* and −3*g*.

Fournier RF-6B (Rolls-Royce Continental O-200-A engine) *(R. Kunert)*

TYPE: Two-seat aerobatic, training and sporting aircraft.

WINGS: Cantilever low-wing monoplane. Wing section NACA 23015 at root, NACA 23013 at tip. Dihedral 3° 30′. Incidence 3°. All-wood single-spar structure with plywood and Dacron covering. Frise-type ailerons of wooden construction, Dacron covered. Plain trailing-edge flaps of wooden construction with Dacron covering.

FUSELAGE: All-wood oval structure, plywood covered.

TAIL UNIT: Cantilever structure of wood with Dacron

covering. Fixed-incidence tailplane. Trim tab in port elevator.

LANDING GEAR: Non-retractable tricycle type. Oleo-pneumatic shock-absorber in each unit. Steerable nosewheel. Main-wheel tyres size 380 × 150. Nose-wheel tyre size 300 × 100. Hydraulic disc brakes.

POWER PLANT: One 74·5 kW (100 hp) Rolls-Royce Continental O-200-A flat-four engine, driving a Hoffmann two-blade wooden fixed-pitch propeller with spinner. Fuselage fuel tank, immediately aft of firewall, capacity 80 litres (17·6 Imp gallons). Refuelling point on fuselage upper surface, forward of windscreen. Oil capacity 4 litres (0·88 Imp gallons).

ACCOMMODATION: Two seats side by side under transparent canopy, which swings upward and aft for access to cockpit. Dual controls standard. Cockpit heated and ventilated. Baggage space aft of seats.

SYSTEMS: Hydraulic system for brakes only. Electrical power supplied by 12V 40A engine-driven alternator and 12V battery.

AVIONICS AND EQUIPMENT: Nav and com radios optional. Blind-flying instrumentation optional.

DIMENSIONS, EXTERNAL:

Wing span	10·50 m (34 ft 5½ in)
Wing chord at root	1·53 m (5 ft 0¼ in)
Wing chord at tip	0·83 m (2 ft 8¾ in)
Wing aspect ratio	8·5
Length overall	7·00 m (22 ft 11¾ in)
Height overall	2·52 m (8 ft 3 in)
Tailplane span	3·40 m (11 ft 1¾ in)
Propeller diameter	1·75 m (5 ft 9 in)
Propeller ground clearance	0·28 m (11 in)

AREAS:

Wings, gross	13·00 m² (139·9 sq ft)
Ailerons (total)	1·07 m² (11·52 sq ft)
Trailing-edge flaps (total)	1·52 m² (16·36 sq ft)
Rudder	0·74 m² (7·97 sq ft)
Tailplane	1·65 m² (17·76 sq ft)
Elevators (incl tab)	1·00 m² (10·76 sq ft)

WEIGHTS AND LOADINGS:

Weight empty	500 kg (1,102 lb)
Max T-O weight: Aerobatic	720 kg (1,587 lb)
Utility	750 kg (1,653 lb)
Max wing loading	57·7 kg/m² (11·8 lb/sq ft)
Max power loading	10·07 kg/kW (16·53 lb/hp)

PERFORMANCE (at max T-O weight):

Never-exceed speed	162 knots (300 km/h; 186 mph)
Max level speed at S/L	108 knots (200 km/h; 124 mph)
Max cruising speed at S/L	97 knots (180 km/h; 112 mph)
Stalling speed	46 knots (85 km/h; 53 mph)
Min sinking speed, engine off	2·0 m (6·6 ft)/sec
Max rate of climb at S/L	210 m (690 ft)/min
Service ceiling	4,000 m (13,125 ft)
T-O to 15 m (50 ft)	290 m (950 ft)
Landing from 15 m (50 ft)	250 m (820 ft)
Landing run, no braking	200 m (655 ft)
Range with max fuel	350 nm (650 km; 404 miles)

HELICOP-JET

ADDRESS: Héliport de Paris, 4 avenue de la Porte de Sèvres, 75015 Paris

Telephone: 554 69 13

PROPRIETOR: Charles Déchaux

HELICOP-JET

A full-scale mockup of this 'cold-jet' tip-driven light helicopter was first exhibited at the Paris Air Show in June 1969. Construction of a pre-production prototype was started by Établissements Charles Déchaux in 1970, and this aircraft made its first flight in December 1976 at Issy-les-Moulineaux. It logged about 60 flying hours, powered by a 186 kW (250 hp) Turboméca Palouste air generator, with which it could lift only the pilot. Helicop-Jet plans to fit a more powerful engine in the production version, to which the detailed description applies.

The definitive prototype, with an Astazou engine, was displayed at the Paris Air Show in June 1979, and is shown in the accompanying illustration. It was expected to fly in October 1979.

TYPE: Four/five-seat tip-driven light helicopter.

ROTOR SYSTEM: One four-blade main rotor; no anti-torque rotor. Blade section NACA 23018. Constant-chord blades, each built around a hollow extruded spar and attached to the hub via a laminated torsion strap of high-strength steel. Trailing-edge of each blade consists of a light alloy sheet box structure, bonded over ribs carried by a light spar. The laminated blade attachment straps permit pitch change and flapping without need for the usual blade bearings and stops. Compressed air from engine passes through a large-diameter non-rotating steel rotor mast, via a spherical bearing to the hollow spar of each blade and thence to the blade-tip nozzle. Rotor speed 320-350 rpm.

FUSELAGE: Extensively glazed light alloy cabin made up basically of two roof sections of the Panhard B-24 motor car (lower one inverted), of which M Déchaux has bought the tooling. Twin tailbooms of elliptical section.

TAIL UNIT: Variable-incidence horizontal surface between tailbooms, which end in integral endplate fins. Central stainless steel rudder, working in jet efflux, for use particularly during hovering and low-speed flight.

LANDING GEAR: Tubular skid type, with attachments for two small ground-handling wheels. Floats optional.

POWER PLANT: One 373 kW (500 hp) Turboméca Astazou II turbo-generator, supplying compressed air for the tip-drive nozzles at a flow rate of 2·15 kg (4·75 lb)/sec and pressure ratio of 3·5:1. Residual jet thrust 20-40 kg (44-88 lb). One or two streamlined external fuel tanks, each with capacity of 100 kg (220 lb), attached to legs of landing gear.

Prototype Helicop-Jet tip-driven light helicopter *(Brian M. Service)*

ACCOMMODATION: Seats for four persons in side-by-side pairs, with provision for a fifth. Fully-transparent forward-hinged door on each side of cabin. Tinted glass optional.

EQUIPMENT: Optional equipment includes radio, intercom, night-flying equipment, baggage compartment, winch, rescue and medical equipment and stretcher.

DIMENSIONS, EXTERNAL:

Diameter of rotor	9·40 m (30 ft 10 in)
Rotor blade chord (constant)	0·23 m (9 in)
Length of fuselage	3·10 m (10 ft 2 in)
Width of fuselage	1·40 m (4 ft 7 in)
Height overall	2·64 m (8 ft 8 in)
Skid track	2·00 m (6 ft 6¾ in)

AREA:

Rotor disc	69·4 m² (747 sq ft)

WEIGHTS AND LOADING:

Weight empty	450 kg (992 lb)
Max T-O weight	1,060 kg (2,336 lb)
Max disc loading	15·3 kg/m² (3·13 lb/sq ft)

PERFORMANCE (estimated):

Max cruising speed	108 knots (200 km/h; 124 mph)
Normal cruising speed	97 knots (180 km/h; 112 mph)
Range with four persons	243 nm (450 km; 280 miles)
Range with two persons and auxiliary fuel	378-432 nm (700-800 km; 435-497 miles)

ISSOIRE
SOCIÉTÉ ISSOIRE-AVIATION

HEAD OFFICE AND WORKS: Aérodrome d'Issoire-le-Broc, BP No. 7, 63501 Issoire Cédex

Telephone: (73) 89 01 54

Telex: Issavia 990.185F

PRESIDENT AND DIRECTOR GENERAL: X. Laguette

Issoire-Aviation, formed on 1 February 1978, took over the premises at Issoire Aerodrome that had belonged to the former Wassmer company (see 1977-78 *Jane's*), following the liquidation of Wassmer on 16 September 1977. It also acquired the industrial assets of Wassmer, and thus assumed responsibility for the continued airworthiness of aircraft of Wassmer design.

Activities of Issoire-Aviation are intended to be devoted 50% to subcontract work for major French aerospace manufacturers such as Dassault, Matra and Aérospatiale, and 50% to general aviation programmes. Initially, work in the latter category includes the mainte-

Issoire IA 80 Piranha (Rolls-Royce Continental O-200-A engine) *(Flight International)*

nance and repair of aircraft, and the production of Siren E 75 and D 77 sailplanes (see Sailplanes section) and IA 80 Piranha light aircraft, developed originally by Wassmer as the WA 80.

At the beginning of April 1979, Issoire-Aviation occupied 4,000 m² (43,050 sq ft) of covered workshop area and 180 m² (1,935 sq ft) of offices at Issoire-le-Broc, and had 40 employees. Production of the E 75 sailplane had begun, with the aim of increasing output to one E 75, two D 77s and one Piranha per month.

ISSOIRE IA 80 PIRANHA

Developed by the former Wassmer company, as the WA 80 Piranha, this two-seat trainer has a fuselage generally similar to that of the four-seat Wassmer WA 51 Pacific (see 1977-78 *Jane's*) and is therefore unusually roomy.

First flown in November 1975, the Piranha is certificated in the Utility category, and spinning is permitted. When production figures were last made available, in January 1977, orders for 20 had been received and 10 had been built. In addition to the standard version, as described and illustrated, a prototype has been flight tested with a 97 kW (130 hp) engine, and a glider/banner-towing version is under consideration.

TYPE: Two-seat light training and general purpose aircraft.

WINGS: Cantilever low-wing monoplane. Wing section NACA 63418. Dihedral 6° 40′ from roots. All-plastics (polyester resin) structure produced by vacuum-forming process to give a very precise smooth surface. Sweptforward wing-root leading-edges, embodying stall strips. No sweep on outer wings at quarter-chord. Slightly-inset ailerons, with foam rubber gap seals, are operated through control rods. Manually-operated four-position flaps.

FUSELAGE: All-plastics (polyester resin) structure. Main shell and integral fin moulded in two halves. Frames and stringers also of plastics.

TAIL UNIT: Conventional cantilever configuration, with sweptback vertical surfaces and small dorsal fin. Elevators operated through control rods, rudder by cables. All-plastics (polyester resin) construction. Controllable trim tab on port elevator.

LANDING GEAR: Non-retractable tricycle type. Main wheels mounted inside each end of a one-piece laminated polyester resin spring. Nosewheel carried on steerable oleo-pneumatic leg. Disc brakes on main wheels. Small tail bumper.

POWER PLANT: One 74·5 kW (100 hp) Rolls-Royce Continental O-200-A flat-four engine, driving a two-blade fixed-pitch EVRA wooden propeller. Fuel tank in fuselage, aft of cockpit, capacity 90 litres (19·75 Imp gallons).

ACCOMMODATION: Two seats side by side, with stick-type dual controls standard. Adjustable seats. Gull-wing door on each side, port one jettisonable. Baggage compartment aft of seats, over fuel tank.

DIMENSIONS, EXTERNAL:
- Wing span: 9·40 m (30 ft 10 in)
- Wing aspect ratio: 7·1
- Length overall: 7·50 m (4 ft 7¼ in)
- Height overall: 2·10 m (6 ft 10¾ in)
- Wheel track: 2·10 m (6 ft 10¾ in)

DIMENSIONS, INTERNAL:
- Cabin: Length: 2·40 m (7 ft 10½ in)
- Max height: 1·18 m (3 ft 10½ in)
- Baggage space: 1·2 m³ (42·3 cu ft)

AREA:
- Wings, gross: 12·40 m² (133·5 sq ft)

WEIGHTS AND LOADINGS:
- Weight empty: 500 kg (1,102 lb)
- Max T-O weight: 800 kg (1,763 lb)
- Max wing loading: 64·51 kg/m² (13·2 lb/sq ft)
- Max power loading: 10·74 kg/kW (17·63 lb/hp)

PERFORMANCE (at max T-O weight):
- Never-exceed speed: 163 knots (302 km/h; 187 mph)
- Max speed at S/L: 129 knots (240 km/h; 149 mph)
- Max cruising speed at S/L: 102 knots (190 km/h; 118 mph)
- Stalling speed, flaps up: 51·5 knots (95 km/h; 59 mph)
- Stalling speed, flaps down: 43·5 knots (80 km/h; 50 mph)
- Rate of climb at S/L: 210 m (690 ft)/min
- Service ceiling: 4,000 m (13,125 ft)
- T-O run: 200 m (655 ft)
- T-O to 15 m (50 ft): 300 m (985 ft)
- Landing from 15 m (50 ft): 300 m (985 ft)
- Landing run: 150 m (495 ft)
- Range with max fuel (75% power): 378 nm (700 km; 435 miles)
- *g* limits: +4·4, −2·2

MICROTURBO
MICROTURBO SA

HEAD OFFICE: Chemin du Pont de Rupé, 31019 Toulouse Cédex
Telephone: (61) 70 07 77
Telex: 531442
DIRECTORATE: See Engines section

MICROTURBO MICROJET 200

Best known as a manufacturer of small gas turbines, Microturbo SA exhibited at the 1979 Paris Air Show a full-size mockup of an aircraft known as the Microjet 200, of which a prototype was scheduled to fly before the end of the year. Aim of the programme is to offer economies in military pilot training by use of very small high-performance jet aircraft with comparatively low initial and operating costs.

The Microjet 200 is an all-metal two-seater, of simple configuration, powered by two Microturbo TRS 18 turbojets, each rated at 0·98 kN (220·5 lb st). Mounted in the rear fuselage, the engines are supplied with air via NACA type flush inlets, on each side of the fuselage aft of the cockpit, and exhaust through lateral jetpipes forward of, and below, the V-tail (included angle 110°). The unswept wings have a relatively high thickness/chord ratio and are fitted with slotted flaps. The tricycle landing gear is retractable.

Pupil and instructor are seated side by side under the one-piece canopy, with the seats slightly staggered to minimise cockpit width. Each has a miniature control stick, mounted on a side console.

Mockup of Microturbo Microjet 200 two-seat lightweight training aircraft *(Brian M. Service)*

DIMENSIONS, EXTERNAL:
- Wing span: 7·20 m (23 ft 7½ in)
- Length overall: 6·00 m (19 ft 8¼ in)
- Height overall: 1·90 m (6 ft 2¾ in)

AREA:
- Wings, gross: 6·12 m² (65·9 sq ft)

WEIGHTS:
- Max fuel: 296 kg (652 lb)
- Max T-O weight (Utility): 870 kg (1,918 lb)

PERFORMANCE (estimated):
- Max level speed: 248 knots (460 km/h; 286 mph)
- Rate of climb at S/L at max T-O weight: 660 m (2,165 ft)/min
- T-O to 15 m (50 m) at max T-O weight: 680 m (2,230 ft)
- Service ceiling: above 9,145 m (30,000 ft)
- Range with max fuel at 8,225 m (27,000 ft), 30 min reserves: 540 nm (1,000 km; 620 miles)
- Endurance for aerobatics at 3,050 m (10,000 ft) with 156 kg (344 lb) of fuel: 40 min

MOTO-DELTA
JEAN MARC GEISER

95 boulevard Saint-Michel, 75005 Paris
Telephone: 326 50 99

MOTO-DELTA G11

The Moto-Delta G11, as the accompanying photograph shows, is a simple ultra-light powered flex-wing aircraft. It has been produced as a low-cost, economical to run, easy to fly aircraft and is road-transportable on top of a family car.

The fuselage, landing gear legs and main beam of the wing are built entirely of laminated glassfibre, with some Klégécel and polyurethane foam plastics. The tail unit consists of a fin and rudder only. A 13·5 kW (18 hp) flat-twin two-stroke engine is mounted behind the pilot's seat and drives a pusher propeller.

The first prototype flew originally as the G10 with a completely open pilot's seat, as illustrated in the 1976-77 *Jane's*. The current G11 version, displayed at the 1977 Paris Air Show, has a streamlined cockpit fairing of glassfibre, with a windscreen to protect the pilot.

The delta-shaped flex-wing is made of Dacron, mounted on a tubular duralumin frame. An overhead control arm regulates the movement of the wing. Pedals actuate the rudder and nosewheel steering.

The Moto-Delta G11 was expected to enter production before the end of 1979.

DIMENSIONS, EXTERNAL:
- Wing span: 8·00 m (26 ft 3 in)
- Wing area, gross: 14·00 m² (151 sq ft)
- Length overall: 5·00 m (16 ft 4¾ in)

WEIGHTS:
- Weight empty: 52 kg (115 lb)
- Max T-O weight: 140 kg (308 lb)

PERFORMANCE:
- Max level speed: 49 knots (90 km/h; 56 mph)
- Max cruising speed: 38 knots (70 km/h; 43·5 mph)
- Stalling speed: 16 knots (30 km/h; 19 mph)
- Max rate of climb at S/L: 90 m (295 ft)/min
- T-O run: 25 m (82 ft)
- Landing run: 15 m (49 ft)
- Endurance with max fuel: 1 h 30 min

MOTO-DELTA G20

This two-seat version of the Moto-Delta was under development in mid-1979. No details are yet available.

Geiser Moto-Delta G11 powered flex-wing-type aircraft

MUDRY
AVIONS MUDRY et CIE

ADDRESS: Aérodrome de Bernay, BP 47, 27300 Bernay
Telephone: (16-32) 43 07 93
DIRECTOR: Auguste Mudry

M Auguste Mudry established this company in the works of the former Société Aéronautique Normande at Bernay, and operated it in parallel with his other aircraft manufacturing company, C.A.A.R.P. of Beynes (see 1977-78 *Jane's*). All activities of C.A.A.R.P. were subsequently combined with those of Avions A. Mudry, at Bernay, where the CAP 10 B and CAP 20 L aerobatic light aircraft continued in production in 1979.

With a total of 49 employees, Mudry delivered in 1977 ten CAP 20L and four CAP 10 aircraft. It is developing a new single-seat light aircraft designated CAP 21.

MUDRY CAP 10 B

Developed from the Piel Emeraude two-seat light aircraft (see Homebuilts section), via the prototype C.P. 100 aerobatic version built by C.A.A.R.P., the CAP 10 is intended for use as a training, touring or aerobatic aeroplane. The prototype was flown for the first time in August 1968, and certification of the CAP 10 was granted on 4 September 1970. Construction is to French AIR 2052 (CAR 3) Category A standards for aerobatic flying, with load factors of +6*g* and −4·5*g*.

A total of 90 CAP 10s had been built by 1 May 1979, including 30 for the French Air Force. Some are in service with the Equipe de Voltige Aérienne (EVA) at Salon-de-Provence, and others with the basic flying training school at Clermont-Ferrand-Aulnat. Fourteen more of the current CAP 10 B version were ordered for the French Air Force in 1979; six were ordered simultaneously for the French Navy.

TYPE: Two-seat aerobatic light aircraft.

WINGS: Cantilever low-wing monoplane. Wing section NACA 23012. Dihedral 5° from roots. Incidence 0°. No sweepback. All-spruce single-spar torsion-box structure, with trellis ribs, rear auxiliary spar and okoumé plywood covering. Inner section of each wing is rectangular in plan, outer section semi-elliptical. Wooden trailing-edge plain flaps and slotted ailerons.

FUSELAGE: Conventional spruce girder structure, built in two halves and joined by three main frames. Of basically rectangular section with rounded top-decking. Polyester fabric covering. Forward section also has an inner plywood skin for added strength. Engine cowling panels of non-inflammable laminated plastics.

TAIL UNIT: Conventional cantilever structure. All-wood single-spar fin, integral with fuselage, and tailplane. All surfaces plywood-covered except rudder, which is covered with both plywood and polyester fabric. Tailplane incidence adjustable on ground. Trim tab in each elevator. Automatic rudder trim.

LANDING GEAR: Non-retractable tailwheel type. Main-wheel legs of light alloy, with ERAM type 9 270 C oleo-pneumatic shock-absorbers. Single wheel on each main unit, tyre size 380 × 150. Solid tailwheel tyre, size 6 × 200. Tailwheel is steerable by rudder linkage but can be disengaged for ground manoeuvring. Hydraulically-actuated main-wheel disc brakes (controllable from port seat) and parking brake. Streamline fairings on main wheels and legs.

POWER PLANT: One 134 kW (180 hp) Lycoming IO-360-B2F flat-four engine, driving a Hoffmann two-blade fixed-pitch wooden propeller. Standard fuel tank aft of engine fireproof bulkhead, capacity 72 litres (16 Imp gallons). Optional auxiliary tank, capacity 75 litres (16·5 Imp gallons), beneath baggage compartment. Fuel and oil systems modified to permit periods of inverted flying.

ACCOMMODATION: Side-by-side adjustable seats for two persons, with provision for back parachutes, under rearward-sliding and jettisonable moulded transparent canopy. Special aerobatic shoulder harness standard. Space for 20 kg (44 lb) of baggage aft of seats in training and touring models.

SYSTEMS: Electrical system includes Delco-Rémy 40A engine-driven alternator and SAFT 12V DC nickel-cadmium battery.

AVIONICS AND EQUIPMENT: CSF 262 12-channel VHF radio and *g* meter fitted. Optional equipment includes starboard brake pedals; Narco, Jolliet or Badin VHF; Narco VOR; radio compass; IFR instrumentation; navigation and landing lights; and heated pitot.

DIMENSIONS, EXTERNAL:
- Wing span — 8·06 m (26 ft 5¼ in)
- Wing aspect ratio — 5·96
- Length overall — 7·16 m (23 ft 6 in)
- Height overall — 2·55 m (8 ft 4½ in)
- Tailplane span — 2·90 m (9 ft 6 in)
- Wheel track — 2·06 m (6 ft 9 in)

DIMENSION, INTERNAL:
- Cabin: Max width — 1·054 m (3 ft 5½ in)

AREAS:
- Wings, gross — 10·85 m² (116·79 sq ft)
- Ailerons (total) — 0·79 m² (8·50 sq ft)
- Vertical tail surfaces (total) — 1·32 m² (14·25 sq ft)
- Horizontal tail surfaces (total) — 1·86 m² (20·0 sq ft)

WEIGHTS (A: Aerobatic, U: Utility):
- Weight empty, equipped:
  - A, U — 540 kg (1,190 lb)
- Fuel load:
  - A — 54 kg (119 lb)
  - U — 108 kg (238 lb)
- Max T-O weight:
  - A — 760 kg (1,675 lb)
  - U — 830 kg (1,829 lb)

PERFORMANCE (at max T-O weight):
- Never-exceed speed — 183 knots (340 km/h; 211 mph)
- Max level speed at S/L — 146 knots (270 km/h; 168 mph)
- Max cruising speed (75% power) — 135 knots (250 km/h; 155 mph)
- Stalling speed, flaps up — 52 knots (95 km/h; 59·5 mph)
- Stalling speed, flaps down — 44 knots (80 km/h; 50 mph)
- Max rate of climb at S/L — over 360 m (1,180 ft)/min
- Service ceiling — 5,000 m (16,400 ft)
- Range with max fuel — 647 nm (1,200 km; 745 miles)

CAP 10 B two-seat aerobatic light aircraft (Lycoming IO-360-B2F engine) *(J. M. G. Gradidge)*

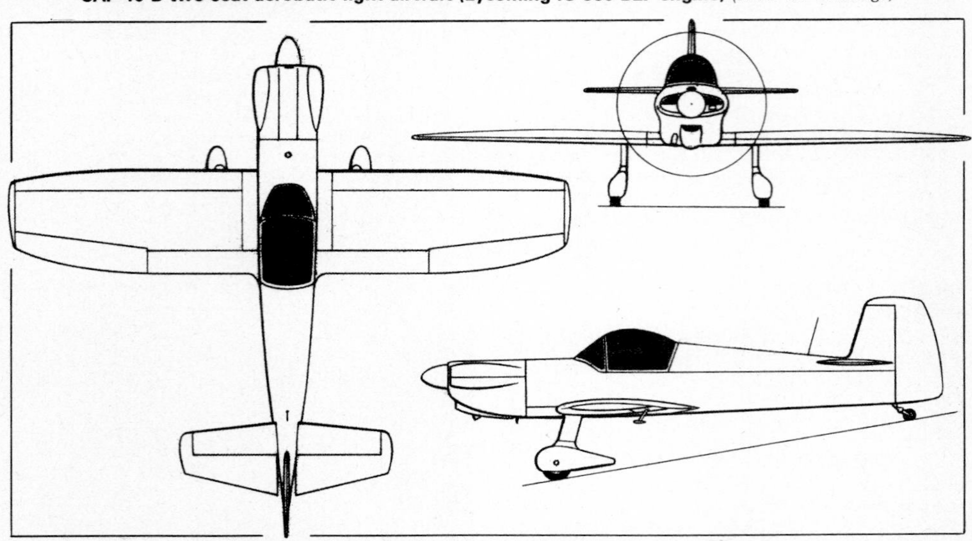

Mudry CAP 20LS-200 single-seat aerobatic aircraft *(Pilot Press)*

Prototype CAP 20L-180 (Lycoming AEIO-360 engine)

MUDRY CAP 20L

First flown on 15 January 1976, the CAP 20L ('léger') is a lightweight development of the earlier CAP 20. It is intended as both a comparatively inexpensive high-performance type for private individuals to fly in competitive aerobatics, and as an aircraft superior to any previous version of the CAP 20 for the Armée de l'Air and for international competition against the best aerobatic types of foreign design.

The prototype (F-WVKY) flew as a **CAP 20L-180**, with 134 kW (180 hp) Lycoming AEIO-360 engine. Standard production model is the **CAP 20LS-200**, with 149 kW (200 hp) Lycoming engine and constant-speed propeller, the first example of which flew for the first time on 6 November 1976.

An initial series of 25 CAP 20LS-200s is under construction, of which ten had been delivered by the beginning of 1979. The 100th aircraft of the CAP 10/20 series, delivered on 4 March 1978, was a CAP 20LS-200. The following data apply to this version:

TYPE: Single-seat aerobatic light aircraft.

WINGS: Cantilever low-wing monoplane. All-wood single-spar wings, similar in construction to those of CAP 10 but with only ailerons on trailing-edge.

FUSELAGE: Conventional all-wood structure, of basically triangular section with rounded top-decking. Wooden covering, except for laminated plastics engine cowling.

TAIL UNIT: Cantilever all-wood structure. Trim tab in rudder and each elevator.

LANDING GEAR: Non-retractable tailwheel type. Oleo-pneumatic shock-absorbers. Streamline fairings on main wheels and legs. Disc brakes.

POWER PLANT: One 149 kW (200 hp) Lycoming AIO-360-B1B flat-four engine, driving a Hartzell two-blade constant-speed metal propeller. Fuel tank aft of cockpit, capacity 80 litres (17·5 Imp gallons), with system modified to permit periods of inverted flight.

ACCOMMODATION: Single seat under transparent moulded canopy which opens sideways to starboard and is jettisonable. Special aerobatic shoulder harness.

DIMENSIONS, EXTERNAL:
- Wing span — 7·57 m (24 ft 10 in)
- Length overall — 6·46 m (21 ft 2½ in)
- Height overall — 1·52 m (5 ft 0 in)

AREA:
- Wings, gross — 10·47 m² (112·7 sq ft)

WEIGHTS:
- Weight empty — 500 kg (1,102 lb)
- Max T-O weight (Aerobatic) — 650 kg (1,433 lb)

PERFORMANCE:
- Max cruising speed (75% power) — 162 knots (300 km/h; 186 mph)
- Stalling speed — 46 knots (85 km/h; 53 mph)
- Max rate of climb at S/L — 840 m (2,755 ft)/min
- Endurance with max fuel — 2 h
- *g* limits — +8, −6

MUDRY CAP 21

The prototype of this new single-seat aerobatic competition aircraft was displayed at the 1979 Paris Air Show. It had not flown at that time, and is scheduled for certification in 1980.

The CAP 21 retains the fuselage and 149 kW (200 hp) Lycoming AIO-360-B1B engine of the CAP 20LS-200, but has an entirely new wing of V16 F section, with a different planform and built by a new production method. This wing is expected to improve the rate of roll by comparison with the CAP 20L, and facilitate the execution of snap manoeuvres.

DIMENSIONS, EXTERNAL:

Wing span	7·57 m (24 ft 10 in)
Length overall	6·46 m (21 ft 2½ in)
Height overall	1·52 m (5 ft 0 in)

WEIGHTS:

Weight empty	480 kg (1,059 lb)
Max T-O weight	630 kg (1,389 lb)

PERFORMANCE:

Max cruising speed	172 knots (320 km/h; 199 mph)
Endurance with max fuel	2 h

REIMS AVIATION

REIMS AVIATION SA

OFFICE AND WORKS: Reims-Prunay Airport, BP 2745, 51062 Reims Cédex
Telephone: (26) 06 96 55
Telex: REMAVIA 830754
PARIS OFFICE: 18 quai Alphonse le Gallo, 92100 Boulogne-Billancourt
Telephone: 604 81 36
CHAIRMAN: Pierre Clostermann
CHIEF OPERATING OFFICER AND PRODUCTION MANAGER: Jean Pichon
FINANCIAL DIRECTOR: Jean Luc Varga
ADMINISTRATIVE DIRECTOR: Armand Blang
PUBLIC RELATIONS: Frédéric Amanou
CHIEF PILOT: Franck Bardou

Under an agreement signed on 16 February 1960, the Cessna Aircraft Company of Wichita, Kansas, USA, acquired a 49% holding in this company, which was then known as Société Nouvelle des Avions Max Holste.

Reims Aviation has the right to manufacture under licence Cessna designs for sale in Europe, Africa and Asia. By 1 January 1979 it had assembled a total of 1,557 Cessna F 150 and F 152, and 351 FRA 150 and FA 152 two-seat aircraft; 1,779 F 172 and 635 FR 172, 138 F 182 and 24 FR 182 RG four-seat aircraft; and 168 F 337, FT 337P, and STOL FTB 337 six-seat aircraft. Nearly 87% of all products are exported. A total of 411 aircraft were delivered in the 1978 calendar year.

Reims Aviation is a subcontractor to Dassault-Breguet in the Mystère-Falcon 10, 20 and 50, Mirage F1 and Super Étendard programmes. It had 492 employees on 1 January 1979. Its offices and factory at Reims-Prunay Airport have an area of 23,000 m² (260,500 sq ft).

REIMS/CESSNA F 152 and FA 152 AÉROBAT

Standard and aerobatic versions of the Cessna 152 assembled under licence by Reims Aviation are designated F 152 and FA 152 Aérobat respectively. The first FA 152 was flown on 25 April 1977, followed four days later by the first F 152. Production was at the rate of 155 F 152s and 10 FA 152s a year in early 1979.

Details of the current Cessna 152 series can be found in the US section.

REIMS/CESSNA F 172 SKYHAWK/100 and FR 172K HAWK XP

Cessna Skyhawk and Skyhawk II aircraft assembled under licence by Reims Aviation are designated **F 172 Skyhawk/100** and **Skyhawk/100 II** respectively.

Until 1971, Reims Aviation retained a 145 hp Rolls-Royce Continental engine in the F 172, of which the first example was flown on 4 January 1963, with 805 delivered by the end of 1971. The current F 172 has a 119 kW (160 hp) Lycoming O-320-H2AD. Production in early 1979 was at the rate of 160 aircraft per year.

In early 1967 Reims Aviation flew the prototype of a more powerful version of the F 172, which it named the Reims Rocket. Details of this aircraft, which the company produced exclusively for worldwide sale, can be found in the 1976-77 *Jane's*. Production ended after 590 Rockets had been completed, and Reims Aviation is now manufacturing instead (and again exclusively) a variant of the Skyhawk known as the **FR 172K Hawk XP**. The prototype flew for the first time on 21 September 1976, and current rate of production is 25 per year.

The Hawk XP has a 145·5 kW (195 hp) Continental IO-360-K flat-six engine, driving a McCauley constant-speed propeller. Wing fuel tank capacity is increased to 197 litres (43·3 Imp gallons), of which 186 litres (41 Imp gallons) are usable. There is also a version with a 64 litre (14·1 Imp gallon) auxiliary fuselage tank, increasing total capacity to 261 litres (57·4 Imp gallons), of which 238 litres (52·3 Imp gallons) are usable.

Three models are available, as follows:

Hawk XP. Basic model, with heavy-duty windscreen and door windows, pre-select flap control, rudder trim control, vernier mixture control and manifold pressure gauge as standard.

Hawk XP II. As XP, but with rate of climb indicator, gyros and vacuum system, outside air temperature gauge, heated pitot, 300 Series nav/com, full-flow oil filter, map and instrument light, sun visors, adjustable pilot's seat, corrosion proofing, dual landing lights, omni-flash beacon, wheel fairings and towbar as added factory-installed items.

Hawk XP II with Nav/Pac. Full IFR package as standard, including 300 Series nav/com with 720 com and 200 nav channels, remote VOR/LOC indicator and 300 Series digital ADF with BFO.

DIMENSIONS, EXTERNAL:

Wing span	10·92 m (35 ft 10 in)
Length overall	8·28 m (27 ft 2 in)
Height overall	2·68 m (8 ft 9½ in)
Tailplane span	3·45 m (11 ft 4 in)
Wheel track	2·53 m (8 ft 3½ in)
Propeller diameter	1·93 m (6 ft 4 in)

AREA:

Wings, gross	16·16 m² (174 sq ft)

WEIGHTS AND LOADINGS:

Weight empty: XP	690 kg (1,521 lb)
XP II	725 kg (1,598 lb)
Baggage	91 kg (200 lb)
Max T-O weight	1,157 kg (2,550 lb)
Max wing loading	71·6 kg/m² (14·7 lb/sq ft)
Max power loading	7·95 kg/kW (13·1 lb/hp)

PERFORMANCE (at max T-O weight):

Max level speed at S/L — 133 knots (246 km/h; 153 mph)
Max cruising speed (80% power) at 1,830 m (6,000 ft) — 130 knots (241 km/h; 150 mph)
Stalling speed, power off, flaps up — 53 knots (98 km/h; 61 mph) CAS
Stalling speed, power off, flaps down — 46 knots (85 km/h; 53 mph) CAS

Max rate of climb at S/L	265 m (870 ft)/min
Service ceiling	5,180 m (17,000 ft)
T-O run	244 m (800 ft)
T-O to 15 m (50 ft)	415 m (1,360 ft)
Landing from 15 m (50 ft)	387 m (1,270 ft)
Landing run	189 m (620 ft)

Range with standard fuel, with allowances for starting, taxying, T-O, climb and 45 min reserve at 45% power:
80% power at 1,830 m (6,000 ft) — 480 nm (889 km; 552 miles)
econ cruise at 3,050 m (10,000 ft) — 575 nm (1,065 km; 661 miles)

Range with auxiliary fuel, allowances as above:
80% power at 1,830 m (6,000 ft) — 675 nm (1,250 km; 776 miles)
econ cruise at 3,050 m (10,000 ft) — 815 nm (1,509 km; 937 miles)

Reims/Cessna FA 152 Aérobat

Reims/Cessna FR 172K Hawk XP II (Continental IO-360-K engine)

REIMS/CESSNA F 182 and FR 182 RG

The first Reims-assembled **F 182** flew for the first time on 2 June 1975. Production was at the rate of 35 aircraft per year in early 1979.

First example of the retractable-gear version of this type was flown on 9 December 1977, as the **FR 182 RG**. Reims began deliveries in 1978.

Full descriptions of the similar Skylane and Skylane RG can be found under the Cessna entry in the US section.

REIMS/CESSNA F 337 and FT 337P PRESSURISED SKYMASTER

Production of the Reims-assembled F 337 and FT 337P has ended.

REIMS AVIATION FTB 337

In 1969 Reims Aviation began the assembly under licence of the Cessna 337 Super Skymaster six-seat twin-engined light aircraft. Primary structures were supplied by Cessna, and engines by Rolls-Royce; smaller components and equipment were French-built.

Assembly of the standard F 337 and pressurised FT 337P versions has ended, but Reims Aviation continues to produce the FTB 337, which it developed in 1974 at the request of various government agencies.

The airframe of this five/six-seat push-and-pull light twin is basically similar to that of the F 337, but embodies STOL (ADAC) modifications, comprising high-lift trailing-edge flaps, and is fitted with two 168 kW (225 hp) Rolls-Royce Continental TSIO-360-D turbocharged engines. The FTB 337 is not pressurised but can be equipped for maritime or overland patrol duties, sea or land rescue, or other specialised tasks by day and night, with four underwing pylons for containers of food and medicine, dinghies and locator beacons, radar, or equipment to detect illegal oil jettison and slicks at sea, or forest fires, including a SAT Super Cyclope infra-red sensor. The rear of the cabin can be cleared to carry cargo or two

Reims/Cessna FR 182 RG (Lycoming O-540-J3C5D engine)

stretchers. The aircraft can also be equipped for navigation and IFR training.

An FTB 337 was specially equipped with underwing containers and a belly pack and searchlight for anti-pollution operations over the English Channel in 1977.

By 1 January 1979 Reims Aviation had delivered 61 FTB 337s, and expected to build two or three more during 1979.

DIMENSIONS, EXTERNAL:
As Cessna Model 337, except:
Wing span 12·10 m (39 ft 8½ in)
Height overall 2·84 m (9 ft 4 in)

AREA:
Wings, gross 18·81 m² (202·5 sq ft)

WEIGHTS AND LOADING:
Weight empty 1,454 kg (3,206 lb)
Max T-O weight 2,100 kg (4,630 lb)
Max wing loading 113 kg/m² (23·2 lb/sq ft)

PERFORMANCE (at max T-O weight):
Max level speed at S/L 205 knots (380 km/h; 236 mph)
Cruising speed (75% power):
at 3,000 m (10,000 ft) 186 knots (344 km/h; 214 mph)
at 6,000 m (20,000 ft) 200 knots (370 km/h; 230 mph)
Stalling speed, power reduced, wheels and flaps up 67 knots (124 km/h; 77 mph)
Max rate of climb at S/L 375 m (1,230 ft)/min
Rate of climb at S/L, one engine out 100 m (328 ft)/min
Rate of climb at 3,000 m (10,000 ft) 346 m (1,135 ft)/min
Service ceiling 7,300 m (23,950 ft)
Service ceiling, one engine out 6,000 m (20,000 ft)
STOL T-O to 15 m (50 ft) 245 m (804 ft)
STOL landing from 15 m (50 ft) 260 m (853 ft)
Max range, no reserves:
75% power at 6,000 m (20,000 ft) 955 nm (1,770 km; 1,100 miles)
econ power at 3,000 m (10,000 ft) 1,085 nm (2,012 km; 1,250 miles)
econ power at 6,000 m (20,000 ft) 1,150 nm (2,132 km; 1,325 miles)
Max endurance at 120 knots (222 km/h; 138 mph), no reserves approx 5 h

Reims Aviation FTB 337 G, equipped with remote sensing systems in underbelly pack, including Super Cyclope infra-red sensor and Hasselblad electric cameras

ROBIN

AVIONS PIERRE ROBIN

HEAD OFFICE AND WORKS: BP 87, 21121 Fontaine-les-Dijon Cédex
Telex: 350818 Robin
COMMERCIAL MANAGEMENT:
Robin SA
BP 87, 21121 Fontaine-les-Dijon Cédex
Telephone: (80) 31 61 01
PRESIDENT DIRECTOR GENERAL, AVIONS PIERRE ROBIN: Pierre Robin
PRESIDENT DIRECTOR GENERAL, ROBIN SA: Thérèse Robin
SALES SUPERVISOR: Jacques Bernardin
PRODUCTION DIRECTOR: Philippe Estassy
TECHNICAL DIRECTOR: Michel Brandt

This company was formed in October 1957 as Centre Est Aéronautique to design, manufacture and sell touring aircraft. In 1969 the name of the company was changed to Avions Pierre Robin. Marketing and after-sales service of its products are the responsibility of Robin SA.

Since 1973, Avions Pierre Robin has manufactured the DR 400 series of wooden light aircraft, all of which represent highly-refined developments of the company's earlier Jodel designs and were first flown in prototype form in 1972. They are described in detail, together with the company's current range of all-metal light aircraft, some with retractable landing gear.

A total of 122 aircraft were sold in 1978; target for 1979 was 150 aircraft.

The company's works currently cover an area of about 11,000 m² (118,400 sq ft) and it employs 160 people.

ROBIN DR 400/100 2+2

Design of the 400 series, and construction of the first example of each type, began towards the end of 1971. Features common to all six designs include a transparent canopy which slides forward to give access to all seats, and lowered walls on each side of the cabin, by comparison with the earlier 300 series, to provide easier access and improved field of view.

Lowest-powered of the series, the DR 400/100 2+2 flew for the first time on 24 November 1972 and received DGAC certification on 19 December 1972.

TYPE: Two/four-seat light aircraft.

WINGS: Cantilever low-wing monoplane. Wing section NACA 23013·5 (modified). Centre-section has constant chord and no dihedral; outer wings have a dihedral of 14°. All-wood one-piece structure, with single box-spar. Leading-edge plywood-covered; polyester-fibre covering overall. Wooden ailerons, covered with polyester-fibre. Aluminium alloy flaps. Ailerons and flaps interchangeable port and starboard. Manually-operated airbrake under spar outboard of landing gear on each side. Picketing ring under each wingtip.

FUSELAGE: Wooden semi-monocoque structure of basic rectangular section, plywood-covered.

TAIL UNIT: Cantilever all-wood structure, covered with polyester-fibre. Sweptback fin and rudder. All-moving one-piece horizontal surface, with tab.

LANDING GEAR: Non-retractable tricycle type, with oleo-pneumatic shock-absorbers and Manu hydraulically-actuated drum brakes. All three wheels and tyres are size 380 × 150, pressure 1·57 bars (22·8 lb/sq in) on nose unit, 1·77 bars (25·6 lb/sq in) on main units. Nose-wheel steerable via rudder bar. Fairings over all three legs and wheels. Tailskid with damper. Parking brake.

POWER PLANT: One 74·5 kW (100 hp) Lycoming O-235-H2C flat-four engine, driving a McCauley 1A-BCM-7056 two-blade fixed-pitch metal propeller. Fuel tank in fuselage, capacity 110 litres (24 Imp gallons).

ACCOMMODATION: Basic accommodation for two persons side by side, on adjustable seats, in enclosed cabin, with access via forward-sliding jettisonable transparent canopy. Optional bench seat to rear for one or two persons. Max payload 154 kg (340 lb) total on front seats, 111 kg (244 lb) total on rear seat. Dual controls standard. Cabin heated and ventilated. Baggage compartment with internal access.

SYSTEMS AND EQUIPMENT: Standard equipment includes a 12V 50A alternator, 12V 32Ah battery, push-button starter, audible stall warning, and windscreen de-icing. Radio, blind-flying equipment, and navigation, landing and anti-collision lights to customer's requirements.

DIMENSIONS, EXTERNAL:
Wing span 8·72 m (28 ft 7¼ in)
Wing chord, centre-section (constant) 1·71 m (5 ft 7½ in)
Wing chord at tip 0·90 m (3 ft 0 in)
Wing aspect ratio 5·6
Length overall 6·96 m (22 ft 10 in)
Height overall 2·23 m (7 ft 3¾ in)
Tailplane span 3·20 m (10 ft 6 in)
Wheel track 2·60 m (8 ft 6¼ in)
Wheelbase 5·20 m (17 ft 0¾ in)
Propeller diameter 1·78 m (5 ft 10 in)

DIMENSIONS, INTERNAL:
Cabin: Length 1·62 m (5 ft 3¾ in)
Max width 1·10 m (3 ft 7¼ in)
Max height 1·23 m (4 ft 0½ in)
Baggage space, volume 0·39 m³ (13·75 cu ft)

AREAS:
Wings, gross 13·60 m² (146·39 sq ft)
Ailerons, total 1·15 m² (12·38 sq ft)
Flaps, total 0·70 m² (7·53 sq ft)
Fin 0·61 m² (6·57 sq ft)
Rudder 0·63 m² (6·78 sq ft)
Horizontal tail surfaces, total 2·88 m² (31·00 sq ft)

WEIGHTS AND LOADINGS:
Weight empty, equipped 520 kg (1,146 lb)
Max T-O and landing weight 865 kg (1,907 lb)
Max wing loading 63·6 kg/m² (13·03 lb/sq ft)
Max power loading 11·61 kg/kW (19·07 lb/hp)

PERFORMANCE (at max T-O weight):
Never-exceed speed 166 knots (308 km/h; 191 mph)
Max level speed at S/L 117 knots (216 km/h; 134 mph)
Max cruising speed (75% power) at 2,440 m (8,000 ft) 114 knots (211 km/h; 131 mph)
Econ cruising speed (55% power) 96 knots (178 km/h; 111 mph)
Stalling speed, flaps down 44·5 knots (81 km/h; 51 mph)
Stalling speed, flaps up 53·5 knots (99 km/h; 61·5 mph)
Max rate of climb at S/L 198 m (650 ft)/min
Service ceiling 3,800 m (12,460 ft)
T-O run 240 m (732 ft)
T-O to 15 m (50 ft) 510 m (1,675 ft)
Landing from 15 m (50 ft) 450 m (1,477 ft)
Landing run 180 m (590 ft)
Range with max fuel at max cruising speed, no reserves 555 nm (1,030 km; 640 miles)

ROBIN DR 400/120 PETIT PRINCE

The prototype of this DR 400 series Petit Prince flew for the first time on 15 May 1972 and received DGAC certification on the 10th of that month, followed by CAA certification in December 1972. Since 1975, the original 125 hp DR 400/125 has been superseded by the 118 hp DR 400/120, to which the following details apply:

TYPE: Three/four-seat light training and touring aircraft.

WINGS, FUSELAGE, TAIL UNIT AND LANDING GEAR: As for DR 400/100 2+2.

POWER PLANT: One 88 kW (118 hp) Lycoming O-235-L2A flat-four engine, driving a McCauley two-blade fixed-pitch metal propeller, or Hoffmann two-blade fixed-pitch wooden propeller. Fuel tank in fuselage, capacity 110 litres (24 Imp gallons); optional 50 litre (11 Imp gallon) auxiliary tank. Oil capacity 5·7 litres (1·25 Imp gallons).

ACCOMMODATION: Seats for three or four persons, in pairs, up to a max weight of 154 kg (340 lb) on front pair and 136 kg (300 lb), including baggage, at rear. Otherwise as for DR 400/100 2+2.

SYSTEMS AND EQUIPMENT: As for DR 400/100 2+2.

DIMENSIONS, EXTERNAL, INTERNAL, AND WING AREA: As DR 400/100 2+2

WEIGHTS AND LOADINGS:
Weight empty, equipped 530 kg (1,169 lb)
Max T-O and landing weight 900 kg (1,984 lb)
Max wing loading 66·2 kg/m² (13·56 lb/sq ft)
Max power loading 10·23 kg/kW (16·8 lb/hp)

PERFORMANCE (at max T-O weight):
Never-exceed speed 166 knots (308 km/h; 191 mph)
Max level speed at S/L 123 knots (228 km/h; 141 mph)
Max cruising speed at 2,440 m (8,000 ft) 118 knots (220 km/h; 136 mph)
Econ cruising speed at 3,650 m (12,000 ft) 110 knots (205 km/h; 127 mph)
Stalling speed, flaps down 45 knots (83 km/h; 52 mph)
Stalling speed, flaps up 51 knots (94 km/h; 58·5 mph)
Max rate of climb at S/L 190 m (623 ft)/min
Service ceiling 3,500 m (11,500 ft)
T-O run 360 m (1,180 ft)
T-O to 15 m (50 ft) 640 m (2,100 ft)
Range with max fuel at max cruising speed, no reserves 491 nm (910 km; 565 miles)

ROBIN DR 400/140B MAJOR

Robin was developing an improved version of this aircraft in early 1979, in the expectation of achieving higher performance and reduced specific fuel consumption. Principal changes involve use of a propeller with reduced pitch; a max fuel capacity of 190 litres (41·8 Imp gallons) to make possible a range of 742 nm (1,375 km; 854 miles) at 128 knots (238 km/h; 148 mph) at 70% power; a new instrument panel layout; addition of an external door to the baggage space; and an improved interior layout. Orders for twelve of the improved models had been received by Spring 1979, and deliveries were expected to begin in July 1979.

The following details apply to the earlier version in production at the beginning of 1979:

Type: Four-seat light monoplane.

Wings, Fuselage, Tail Unit, Landing Gear: As for DR 400/100 2+2.

Power Plant: One 119 kW (160 hp) Lycoming O-320-D flat-four engine, driving a Sensenich two-blade metal fixed-pitch propeller. Otherwise as for DR 400/120.

Accommodation: Seating for four persons, on two side-by-side adjustable front seats (max load 154 kg; 340 lb total) and rear bench seat (max load 154 kg; 340 lb total). Forward-sliding transparent canopy gives access to all seats. Up to 62 kg (137 lb) of baggage can be stowed aft of rear seats when four occupants are carried.

Systems and Equipment: As for DR 400/100 2+2.

Dimensions, external:
- As for DR 400/100 2+2, except:
- Propeller diameter 1·83 m (6 ft 0 in)

Dimensions, internal: As for DR 400/100 2+2

Areas: As for DR 400/100 2+2

Weights and Loadings:
- Weight empty, equipped 560 kg (1,235 lb)
- Max T-O and landing weight 1,000 kg (2,205 lb)
- Max wing loading 73·5 kg/m² (15·05 lb/sq ft)
- Max power loading 8·40 kg/kW (13·78 lb/hp)

Performance (at max T-O weight):
- Never-exceed speed 166 knots (308 km/h; 191 mph)
- Max level speed at S/L (60% power) 141 knots (262 km/h; 163 mph)
- Max cruising speed (60% power) at 2,440 m (8,000 ft) 125 knots (232 km/h; 144 mph)
- Econ cruising speed at 3,650 m (12,000 ft) 125 knots (232 km/h; 144 mph)
- Stalling speed, flaps down 47 knots (87 km/h; 54 mph)
- Stalling speed, flaps up 48 knots (89 km/h; 55·5 mph)
- Max rate of climb at S/L 240 m (785 ft)/min
- Service ceiling 4,560 m (14,950 ft)
- T-O run 200 m (655 ft)
- T-O to 15 m (50 ft) 500 m (1,640 ft)
- Landing from 15 m (50 ft) 490 m (1,608 ft)
- Landing run 220 m (722 ft)
- Range with max fuel at max cruising speed, no reserves 491 nm (910 km; 565 miles)

ROBIN DR 400/160 CHEVALIER

The first DR 400/160 flew on 29 June 1972. It was awarded DGAC certification on 6 September 1972, and CAA certification in December of the same year.

Type: Four-seat light aircraft.

Wings, Fuselage, Tail Unit, Landing Gear: Generally as for DR 400/100 2+2, but with external baggage door aft of cabin, in top of fuselage on port side.

Power Plant: One 119 kW (160 hp) Lycoming O-320-D flat-four engine, driving a Sensenich two-blade metal fixed-pitch propeller. Fuel tank in fuselage, capacity 110 litres (24 Imp gallons), and two tanks in wing-root leading-edges, giving total capacity of 190 litres (41·75 Imp gallons). Provision for auxiliary tank, raising total capacity to 240 litres (52·75 Imp gallons). Oil capacity 7·55 litres (1·66 Imp gallons).

Accommodation, Systems and Equipment: As for DR 400/140B, except baggage capacity 40 kg (88 lb).

Dimensions and Areas:
- As for DR 400/140B, except:
- Baggage door: Height 0·47 m (1 ft 6½ in)
- Width 0·55 m (1 ft 9½ in)
- Wing area 14·20 m² (152·8 sq ft)

Weights and Loadings:
- Weight empty, equipped 565 kg (1,245 lb)
- Max T-O and landing weight 1,050 kg (2,315 lb)
- Max wing loading 74·2 kg/m² (15·20 lb/sq ft)
- Max power loading 8·82 kg/kW (14·47 lb/hp)

Performance (at max T-O weight):
- Never-exceed speed 166 knots (308 km/h; 191 mph)
- Max level speed at S/L 143 knots (266 km/h; 165 mph)
- Max cruising speed (75% power) at 2,440 m (8,000 ft) 137 knots (255 km/h; 158 mph)

Robin DR 400/140B Major (Lycoming O-320-D engine) *(R. Kunert)*

- Econ cruising speed (60% power) at 3,650 m (12,000 ft) 127 knots (236 km/h; 146 mph)
- Stalling speed, flaps down 50 knots (93 km/h; 58 mph)
- Stalling speed, flaps up 56 knots (103 km/h; 64 mph)
- Max rate of climb at S/L 228 m (748 ft)/min
- Service ceiling 4,430 m (14,525 ft)
- T-O run 310 m (1,017 ft)
- T-O to 15 m (50 ft) 620 m (2,034 ft)
- Landing from 15 m (50 ft) 545 m (1,788 ft)
- Landing run 250 m (820 ft)
- Range with max fuel at econ cruising speed, no reserves 863 nm (1,600 km; 994 miles)

ROBIN MAJOR 80

Announced at the 1979 Paris Air Show, the Major 80 is an improved version of the DR 400/160, with a propeller of finer pitch and a new instrument panel based on experience with the Aiglon.

ROBIN DR 400/180 RÉGENT

First flown on 27 March 1972, this most powerful, four/five-seat member of the wooden DR 400 series received DGAC certification on 10 May 1972, and CAA certification in December 1972.

The DR 400/180 is generally similar to the DR 400/160 Chevalier, except in the following details:

Power Plant: One 134 kW (180 hp) Lycoming O-360-A flat-four engine. Propeller and fuel tankage as for DR 400/160.

Accommodation, Systems and Equipment: Basically as for DR 400/160, but optional seating for three persons on rear bench seat. Baggage capacity 55 kg (121 lb).

Dimensions and Areas:
- As for DR 400/160, except:
- Propeller diameter 1·93 m (6 ft 4 in)

Weights and Loadings:
- Weight empty, equipped 600 kg (1,322 lb)
- Max T-O and landing weight 1,100 kg (2,425 lb)
- Max wing loading 77·7 kg/m² (15·91 lb/sq ft)
- Max power loading 8·21 kg/kW (13·47 lb/hp)

Performance (at max T-O weight):
- Never-exceed speed 166 knots (308 km/h; 191 mph)
- Max level speed at S/L 150 knots (278 km/h; 173 mph)
- Max cruising speed (75% power) at 2,440 m (8,000 ft) 144 knots (267 km/h; 166 mph)
- Econ cruising speed (60% power) at 3,650 m (12,000 ft) 134 knots (249 km/h; 155 mph)
- Stalling speed, flaps down 51·5 knots (95 km/h;59 mph)
- Stalling speed, flaps up 56·5 knots (105 km/h; 65 mph)
- Max rate of climb at S/L 252 m (825 ft)/min
- Service ceiling 4,720 m (15,475 ft)
- T-O run 315 m (1,035 ft)
- T-O to 15 m (50 ft) 610 m (2,000 ft)

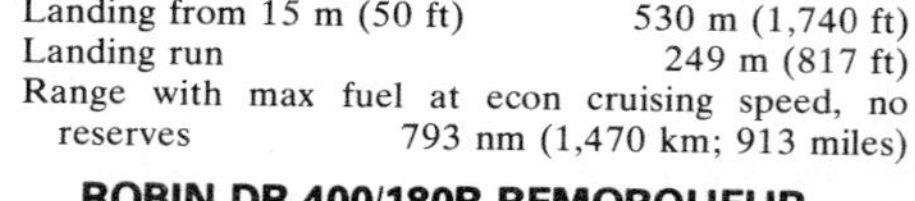

- Landing from 15 m (50 ft) 530 m (1,740 ft)
- Landing run 249 m (817 ft)
- Range with max fuel at econ cruising speed, no reserves 793 nm (1,470 km; 913 miles)

ROBIN DR 400/180R REMORQUEUR

The DR 400/180R is a member of the DR 400 range designed for use as a glider-towing aircraft, although it can also be flown as a normal four-seat tourer. The prototype first flew on 6 November 1972 and received DGAC certification on the 28th of that month. Details are generally the same as for the DR 400/180 Régent, except for the following items:

Fuselage: No external baggage door.

Power Plant: One 134 kW (180 hp) Lycoming O-360-A flat-four engine, driving (for glider-towing) a Sensenich 76 EM 8S5 058 two-blade propeller. For touring operation a Sensenich 76 EM 8S5 064 propeller of the same diameter is fitted. Fuel capacity as for DR 400/100 2+2.

Dimensions and Areas:
- As for DR 400/140B

Weights and Loadings:
- Weight empty, equipped 560 kg (1,234 lb)
- Max T-O and landing weight 1,000 kg (2,205 lb)
- Max wing loading 73·5 kg/m² (15·05 lb/sq ft)
- Max power loading 7·46 kg/kW (12·25 lb/hp)

Performance (glider tug, at max T-O weight):
- Never-exceed speed 166 knots (308 km/h; 191 mph)
- Max level speed at S/L (70% power) 124 knots (230 km/h; 143 mph)
- Max cruising speed at 2,440 m (8,000 ft) 124 knots (230 km/h; 143 mph)
- Econ cruising speed (56% power) at 3,650 m (12,000 ft) 122 knots (226 km/h; 140 mph)
- Stalling speed, flaps down 47 knots (87 km/h; 54 mph)
- Stalling speed, flaps up 53·5 knots (99 km/h; 61·5 mph)
- Max rate of climb at S/L towing Bijave sailplane 210 m (690 ft)/min
- Service ceiling 6,000 m (19,675 ft)
- T-O run 205 m (673 ft)
- T-O to 15 m (50 ft) 400 m (1,313 ft)
- Landing from 15 m (50 ft) 470 m (1,542 ft)
- Landing run 220 m (722 ft)
- Range at econ cruising speed, max fuel, no reserves 444 nm (825 km; 512 miles)

ROBIN HR 100/250TR PRESIDENT

The prototype of this model (F-WVKA) was produced by converting the 'one-off' HR 100/235TR, by installation of a Lycoming IO-540-C4B5 fuel-injection engine, driving a Hartzell constant-speed propeller.

Production began in the second half of 1975, with initial deliveries to the Centre d'Essais en Vol for training duties. About 18 were delivered to the CEV in 1976-78.

Type: Four/five-seat all-metal light aircraft.

Wings: Cantilever low-wing monoplane. Wing section NACA 64A515 (modified). Dihedral 6° 18′ from roots. Incidence 4° 41′. No sweepback. Aluminium alloy single-spar structure of constant chord. All-metal Frise-type ailerons and electrically-actuated NACA slotted flaps. No tabs.

Fuselage: Aluminium alloy semi-monocoque structure in cabin section. Rear fuselage top-decking and engine cowling are of non-stressed polyester.

Tail Unit: Cantilever structure, similar to wings in construction. Sweptback vertical surfaces. One-piece all-moving horizontal surfaces, with automatic anti-tab inboard on each trailing-edge. Trim tab in rudder.

Landing Gear: Retractable tricycle type, with single wheel on each unit. Electro-hydraulic retraction. Nosewheel protrudes slightly when retracted, to reduce damage in a wheels-up landing. Oleo-pneumatic shock-absorbers. Main-wheel tyres size 420 × 150 or 6·50-3, pressure 2·17 bars (31·5 lb/sq in). Nosewheel tyre size 330 × 130 or 5·00-5. Hydraulic disc brakes. Parking brake. Tailskid with damper.

Robin DR 400/180 Régent (Lycoming O-360-A engine)

Power Plant: One 186 kW (250 hp) Lycoming IO-540-C4B5 flat-six engine, driving a Hartzell two-blade constant-speed metal propeller. Four fuel tanks in wings, with total capacity of 440 litres (97 Imp gallons).
Accommodation: Two persons side by side in individual front bucket seats, with dual controls. Rear bench seat for two or three passengers. Access via forward-sliding jettisonable canopy. Baggage space aft of rear seats, accessible internally or by upward-opening external door on port side.
System: Electrical system includes 12V 60A alternator and 12V 45Ah battery.
Avionics and Equipment: Standard equipment includes push-button starter, audible stall warning indicator, windscreen de-icing and towbar. Optional equipment includes VHF radio, VOR, navigation and landing lights, rotating anti-collision beacon, and full IFR equipment, including autopilot.

Dimensions, external:

Wing span	9·08 m (29 ft 9½ in)
Wing chord (constant)	1·675 m (5 ft 6 in)
Wing aspect ratio	5·36
Length overall	7·59 m (24 ft 10¾ in)
Height overall	2·71 m (8 ft 10¾ in)
Tailplane span	3·20 m (10 ft 10 in)
Wheel track	3·225 m (10 ft 7 in)
Wheelbase	2·16 m (7 ft 1 in)
Propeller diameter	2·03 m (6 ft 8 in)

Dimensions, internal:

Cabin: Length	2·80 m (9 ft 2 in)
Max width	1·115 m (3 ft 8 in)
Max height	1·20 m (3 ft 11¼ in)

Areas:

Wings, gross	15·2 m² (163·6 sq ft)
Ailerons, total	1·02 m² (10·98 sq ft)
Trailing-edge flaps, total	1·55 m² (16·68 sq ft)
Fin	1·015 m² (10·93 sq ft)
Rudder	0·67 m² (7·21 sq ft)
Tailplane, incl tabs	2·76 m² (29·71 sq ft)

Weight:

Max T-O weight	1,400 kg (3,086 lb)

Performance (at max T-O weight):

Max level speed at S/L	170 knots (315 km/h; 196 mph)
Max cruising speed at 2,135 m (7,000 ft)	160 knots (297 km/h; 185 mph)
Cruising speed (65% power) at 3,050 m (10,000 ft)	154 knots (285 km/h; 177 mph)
Stalling speed, wheels and flaps up	72 knots (132·5 km/h; 82·5 mph) IAS
Stalling speed, wheels down, 30° flap	62 knots (114 km/h; 71 mph) IAS
Max rate of climb at S/L	324 m (1,065 ft)/min

ROBIN HR 100/4+2

Following Teledyne Continental's decision to end production of its Tiara engines, the Tiara-powered HR 100/4+2 has been dropped from Robin's production programme.

ROBIN R 1180 AIGLON

The R 1180 Aiglon is an all-metal four-seat light aircraft of conventional low-wing monoplane layout. It has non-retractable landing gear, and is powered by a 134 kW (180 hp) Lycoming O-360-A3AD engine which drives a two-blade Sensenich fixed-pitch propeller. Wing section is NACA 23015. Fuel capacity is 242 litres (53 Imp gallons). The prototype (F-WVKH) flew for the first time in late 1976; the first production Aiglon (F-GBAM), with a larger, tinted canopy and other changes, received DGAC certification on 19 September 1978. Orders had been received from customers in four countries by that time.

Dimensions, external:

Wing span	9·08 m (29 ft 9½ in)
Wing aspect ratio	5·46
Length overall	7·26 m (23 ft 9¾ in)
Height overall	2·38 m (7 ft 9¾ in)
Propeller diameter	1·93 m (6 ft 4 in)

Dimensions, internal:

Cabin: Length	2·00 m (6 ft 6¾ in)
Width	1·12 m (3 ft 8 in)
Height	1·22 m (4 ft 0 in)

Area:

Wings, gross	15·1 m² (162·5 sq ft)

Weights:

Weight empty	650 kg (1,433 lb)
Max T-O weight	1,150 kg (2,535 lb)

Performance (at max T-O weight):

Max level speed at S/L	135 knots (251 km/h; 156 mph)
Max cruising speed (75% power) at height	132 knots (245 km/h; 152 mph)
Cruising speed (65% power) at height	127 knots (235 km/h; 146 mph)
Stalling speed, flaps up	58 knots (107 km/h; 66·5 mph)
Stalling speed, flaps down	50 knots (92 km/h; 57 mph)
Max rate of climb at S/L	258 m (846 ft)/min
Service ceiling	5,030 m (16,500 ft)
T-O to 15 m (50 ft)	970 m (3,185 ft)
Landing from 15 m (50 ft)	460 m (1,510 ft)
Range with max fuel at 65% power, with reserves	876 nm (1,624 km; 1,009 miles)

Robin HR 100/250TR President four/five-seat light aircraft (Lycoming IO-540-C4B5 engine)

Robin R 1180 Aiglon four-seat light aircraft (Lycoming O-360 engine)

ROBIN R 2000 SERIES

First of a new generation of light aircraft designated R for Robin, the R 2160 prototype (F-WZAC) flew for the first time in September 1976 and was announced officially in the following month. Further variants of the R 2000 series have since been evolved, differing from the prototype as follows:

R 2100A. Two-seat aerobatic light aircraft, with an 80·5 kW (108 hp) Lycoming O-235-H engine, driving a McCauley fixed-pitch propeller.

R 2112. Generally similar to R 2100A, but with an 82 kW (110 hp) Lycoming engine. Second example built was demonstrated at the 1979 Paris Air Show.

R 2160 Acrobin. Generally similar to R 2100, but with a 119 kW (160 hp) Lycoming O-320-D engine. Prototype of the R 2000 series flew originally in this form. Seventeen ordered by the Service de la Formation Aéronautique in Spring 1978.

R 2160A Rafale. Differs from R 2160 in having a 119 kW (160 hp) Lycoming AEIO-320 engine. All other construction, weight and performance data unchanged.

The R 2000 series were derived from the Robin HR 200, which they superseded, and embody many components of that aircraft, including the basic fuselage and tail fin. The wing is completely new, of increased chord and different section; the rudder is larger and there is a long, shallow ventral fin to improve spinning characteristics. All R 2000 variants are being certificated in the Aerobatic Category, and are being fully tested for spin recovery, including inverted spin.

The following details refer specifically to the R 2160 Acrobin, but are generally applicable to all variants:
Type: Two-seat aerobatic light aircraft.
Wings: Cantilever low-wing monoplane. Wing section NACA 23015. Dihedral 6° 20′ from roots. Incidence 3°. No sweep. Conventional single-spar aluminium alloy structure. Entire trailing-edge of each wing comprises an inboard slotted flap and a fully balanced slotted aileron, both of aluminium alloy construction.
Fuselage: Conventional aluminium alloy semi-monocoque structure.
Tail Unit: Cantilever structure of aluminium alloy construction. All-moving single-spar horizontal surfaces, with anti-tab on trailing-edge each side. Rudder is horn-balanced, with no tab.

Robin R 2112, latest addition to the R 2000 series *(J. M. G. Gradidge)*

Robin R 2160 Acrobin two-seat aerobatic aircraft (Lycoming O-320-D engine) *(J. M. G. Gradidge)*

Landing Gear: Non-retractable tricycle type, with oleo-pneumatic shock-absorbers. All three tyres size 380 × 150. Cleveland disc brakes on main wheels. Three wheel and leg fairings standard.

Power Plant: One 119 kW (160 hp) Lycoming O-320-D flat-four engine, driving a Sensenich two-blade fixed-pitch propeller. Fuel tank in fuselage, capacity 120 litres (26·5 Imp gallons). Refuelling point at side of fuselage.

Accommodation: Two seats side by side under large transparent canopy, the front half of which slides forward for access. Seats are adjustable.

System: 12V electrical system.

Avionics and Equipment: Blind-flying instruments, radio, VOR, ADF and ILS available to customer's requirements.

Dimensions, external:

Wing span	8·33 m (27 ft 4 in)
Wing chord (constant)	1·554 m (5 ft 1¼ in)
Wing aspect ratio	5·34
Length overall	7·10 m (23 ft 3½ in)
Height overall	2·135 m (7 ft 0 in)
Tailplane span	3·04 m (9 ft 11¾ in)
Wheel track	2·91 m (9 ft 6½ in)
Wheelbase	1·434 m (4 ft 8½ in)
Propeller diameter	1·88 m (6 ft 2 in)

Dimension, internal:

Cabin: Width	1·06 m (3 ft 5¾ in)

Area:

Wings, gross	13·00 m² (140 sq ft)

Weights:

Weight empty: R 2100A	530 kg (1,169 lb)
R 2160	550 kg (1,213 lb)
Max T-O weight: R 2100A	775 kg (1,708 lb)
R 2160	800 kg (1,764 lb)

Performance (at max T-O weight):

Never-exceed speed:	
all versions	180 knots (333 km/h; 207 mph)
Max level speed at S/L:	
R 2100A	112 knots (208 km/h; 129 mph)
R 2160	138 knots (257 km/h; 160 mph)
Max cruising speed (75% power) at 2,285 m (7,500 ft):	
R 2100A	101 knots (187 km/h; 116 mph)
R 2160	130 knots (242 km/h; 150 mph)
Cruising speed (65% power) at 3,350 m (11,000 ft):	
R 2100A	94 knots (175 km/h; 108 mph)
R 2160	126 knots (234 km/h; 145 mph)
Stalling speed, flaps down:	
R 2100A	46 knots (85 km/h; 53 mph)
R 2160	47 knots (87 km/h; 54 mph)
Stalling speed, flaps up:	
R 2160	52 knots (96 km/h; 60 mph)
Max rate of climb at S/L:	
R 2100A	192 m (630 ft)/min
R 2160	312 m (1,025 ft)/min
Service ceiling:	
R 2100A	3,500 m (11,500 ft)
R 2160	4,575 m (15,000 ft)
Range with max fuel at 65% power:	
R 2100A	530 nm (980 km; 608 miles)
R 2160	430 nm (796 km; 495 miles)

Robin R 2160 side-by-side two-seat training aircraft *(Pilot Press)*

SOCATA

SOCIÉTÉ DE CONSTRUCTION D'AVIONS DE TOURISME ET D'AFFAIRES (Subsidiary of AÉROSPATIALE)

Head Office, Works and After-Sales Service: Aéroport de Tarbes-Ossun-Lourdes, BP 38, 65001 Tarbes Cédex
Telephone: (62) 93 97 30
Telex: SOCATA 520828

Sales: 37 boulevard de Montmorency, 75781 Paris Cédex 16
Telephone: 524 43 21
Telex: 620059 AIRSPA
Aéroport de Toussus-le-Noble, BP No. 2, 78530 Buc
Telephone: 956 21 00
Telex: 600 836 SOCAERO

President and Director General: Pierre Gautier

This company was formed in 1966, as a subsidiary of Aérospatiale (then Sud-Aviation), to be responsible for producing all of the group's piston-engined light aircraft.

Socata also produces components for the A300 Airbus, Mystère-Falcon 10 and 20 business aircraft, and Puma, Alouette, Dauphin and Ecureuil helicopters. It is responsible for overhaul and repair of MS 760 Paris light jet aircraft.

Socata's works cover an area of 47,672 m² (513,135 sq ft), and employed a total of 860 people in January 1979.

Aircraft of the basic Rallye series are similar externally. This light Rallye airframe is used for the Galopin, Garnement and Galérien. The more powerful variants have a heavy airframe

SOCATA RALLYE SERIES

The Rallye had its origin in a competition organised by the SFATAT in 1958 and was developed originally by the old-established Morane-Saulnier company. The prototype (67 kW; 90 hp MS 880A) Rallye-Club flew on 10 June 1959, and the initial production versions were the MS 880B Rallye-Club and the MS 885 Super Rallye. FAA certification was obtained on 21 November 1961.

The 3,000th Rallye built in France was delivered to the Aéro-Club Renault on 26 May 1977. Versions of the Rallye are also built under licence in Poland, by the PZL-Warszawa organisation (which see).

When Socata launched its 1979 production programme, on 17 May, the seven aircraft constituting the current Rallye series were given names, instead of the former designations, as follows:

Galopin (formerly Rallye 110 ST). This version may be operated either as a two-seater cleared for spinning or as a three/four-seater with spins prohibited. It has an 82 kW (110 hp) Lycoming O-235-L2A engine, driving a two-blade McCauley fixed-pitch propeller.

Garnement (formerly Rallye 160 ST). Similar to Galopin, but with 115 kW (155 hp) Lycoming O-320-D2A engine. Developed as a high-performance aircraft for flying clubs and for use in countries where high temperatures or high altitude might impose limitations on lower-powered aircraft.

Galérien (formerly Rallye 180 T). Specialised glider and banner towing version, developed to meet German noise regulations. Powered by 134 kW (180 hp) Lycoming O-360-A3A engine, driving a two-blade fixed-pitch propeller. Certificated in September 1977.

Gaillard (formerly Rallye 180 GT). Four-seat version with 134 kW (180 hp) Lycoming O-360-A3A engine, driving a fixed-pitch or constant-speed propeller, strengthened structure to permit increased AUW, larger rudder and ailerons, fillets of increased size between wing trailing-edges and fuselage, longer nosewheel leg to give increased propeller clearance, enlarged dorsal fin, modified cockpit canopy and a baggage compartment. Streamlined wheel fairings optional. Prototype flew for first time on 7 December 1964. French certification received on 27 April 1965; FAA type approval on 23 June 1971. Total of 742 built by 1 January 1979; 100 ordered by the SFACT for duty as glider tugs at French gliding centres. A variant with a TV camera pod mounted under the starboard wing was demonstrated in 1978. Known as ATAL, this equipment allows the aircraft to be used for aerial surveillance of highway traffic, transmitting images to ground stations over a radius of about 27 nm (50 km; 31 miles). The camera is steerable by the pilot, who also sees the images on a cockpit monitor.

Gabier (formerly Rallye 235 GT). High-performance version, with 175 kW (235 hp) Lycoming O-540-B4B5 engine, driving a Hartzell HC-C2YK-1/8468-6 two-blade constant-speed metal propeller, and with accommodation for four persons. Construction of prototype began in January 1975. First flight was made on 1 April 1975. Total of 103 built by 1 January 1979. A variant (formerly Rallye 235 A) is available with dual control columns instead of control wheels. Another variant (formerly Rallye 235 C) has a tailwheel type landing gear instead of the standard tricycle type.

Gaucho (formerly Rallye 235 CA). Agricultural version of Gabier with tailwheel landing gear. Described separately.

Guerrier (formerly Rallye 235 G). Military version. Described separately.

The Garnement and Gaillard are authorised for use as ambulance aircraft carrying a pilot, one stretcher patient and medical attendant. They can also be used for glider towing, and some 400 Rallyes are employed in this role, incuding more than 250 in France. Agricultural spraygear can be fitted and tests have been conducted with various models on ski landing gear.

The following details apply to all French-built versions listed:

Type: Two/four-seat light monoplane.

Wings: Cantilever low-wing monoplane. Wing section NACA 63A416 (modified). Dihedral 7°. Incidence 4°. All-metal single-spar structure. Wide-chord slotted ailerons. Full-span automatic slats. Long-span slotted flaps. Ailerons and flaps have corrugated metal skin. Ground-adjustable aileron tabs. No anti-icing equipment.

Fuselage: All-metal semi-monocoque structure.

Tail Unit: Cantilever all-metal structure with corrugated skin on the mass-balanced control surfaces. Fixed-incidence tailplane. One automatic tab and one controllable tab on elevator. One controllable tab on rudder.

Landing Gear: Non-retractable tricycle type on all but Gaucho and non-standard Gabier. Oleo-pneumatic shock-absorbers. Castoring nosewheel. Standard Gabier has Cleveland main wheels with tyres size 6·00-6, pressure 1·8 bars (26·1 lb/sq in); nosewheel tyre size 5·00-4, pressure 1·4 bars (20·3 lb/sq in). Cleveland hydraulic disc brakes. Provision for fitting skis or floats.

Power Plant: One flat-four or flat-six engine (details under entries for individual models), driving a two-blade fixed-pitch or constant-speed metal propeller. Fuel in two metal tanks in wings, with total capacity of 105 litres (23 Imp gallons) in Galopin, 184 litres (40·5 Imp gallons) in Garnement and Galérien, 235 litres (52 Imp gallons) in Gaillard, and 282 litres (62 Imp gallons) in Gabier. Refuelling points above wings. Oil capacity 6 litres (1·3 Imp gallons) in Galopin, 8 litres (1·75 Imp gallons) in Garnement, Galérien and Gaillard, 12 litres (2·6 Imp gallons) in Gabier.

ACCOMMODATION: Two seats side by side at front, and rear bench seat for one/two persons in Galopin, under large rearward-sliding canopy. Other versions are full four-seaters. Dual control columns on Galopin, Garnement, Galérien, Gaucho, Guerrier and both non-standard variants of Gabier. Dual control wheels on Gaillard and standard Gabier. Individual adjustable front seats and baggage space aft of rear seats (accessible internally) on the Gaillard, Gabier and Guerrier. Heating and ventilation standard.

SYSTEMS: Electrical system includes 12V 18A battery and 12V 40A alternator in Galopin; 12V 32A battery and 12V 40A alternator in Garnement, Galérien and Gaillard; 12V 32A battery and 12V 55A alternator in Gabier.

AVIONICS AND EQUIPMENT: The instrument panel is fitted with an anti-glare visor, and is designed to take full radio-navigation equipment to customer's requirements.

DIMENSIONS, EXTERNAL (A, Galopin; B, Garnement; C, Galérien; D, Gaillard; E, Gabier):

Wing span	9·74 m (31 ft 11 in)
Wing chord (constant)	1·30 m (4 ft 3 in)
Wing aspect ratio	7·57
Length overall:	
A, B, C, D	7·24 m (23 ft 9 in)
E	7·25 m (23 ft 9½ in)
Height overall	2·80 m (9 ft 2¼ in)
Tailplane span	3·67 m (12 ft 0½ in)
Wheel track	2·01 m (6 ft 6½ in)
Wheelbase	1·71 m (5 ft 7¼ in)

DIMENSIONS, INTERNAL:

Cabin: Length: A, B, C	1·80 m (5 ft 11 in)
D, E	2·25 m (7 ft 4 in)
Width	1·13 m (3 ft 8½ in)

AREAS:

Wings, gross	12·28 m² (132 sq ft)
Ailerons (total)	1·56 m² (16·79 sq ft)
Trailing-edge flaps (total)	2·40 m² (25·83 sq ft)
Vertical tail surfaces (total)	1·74 m² (18·73 sq ft)
Horizontal tail surfaces (total)	3·48 m² (37·50 sq ft)

WEIGHTS AND LOADINGS:

Weight empty: A	520 kg (1,145 lb)
B	540 kg (1,191 lb)
C	545 kg (1,200 lb)
D	570 kg (1,257 lb)
E	694 kg (1,530 lb)
Max T-O and landing weight: A	770 kg (1,697 lb)
B	870 kg (1,918 lb)
C	950 kg (2,094 lb)
D	1,050 kg (2,315 lb)
Max T-O weight: E	1,200 kg (2,645 lb)
Max landing weight: E	1,140 kg (2,513 lb)
Max wing loading: E	95 kg/m² (19·45 lb/sq ft)
Max power loading: E	6·69 kg/kW (10·98 lb/hp)

PERFORMANCE (at max T-O weight):

Max level speed at S/L:	
A	110 knots (204 km/h; 126 mph)
B	119 knots (220 km/h; 137 mph)
C	122 knots (226 km/h; 140 mph)
D	130 knots (240 km/h; 150 mph)
E	148 knots (275 km/h; 171 mph)
Max cruising speed (75% power):	
A	104 knots (192 km/h; 119 mph)
B	115 knots (213 km/h; 132 mph)
C	113 knots (209 km/h; 130 mph)
D	122 knots (226 km/h; 140 mph)
E	132 knots (245 km/h; 152 mph)
Econ cruising speed (65% power):	
A	95 knots (176 km/h; 109 mph)
B	109 knots (202 km/h; 125 mph)
C	111 knots (205 km/h; 127 mph)
D	115 knots (213 km/h; 132 mph)
E	125 knots (231 km/h; 144 mph)
Stalling speed, flaps down:	
A	41 knots (75 km/h; 47 mph)
B	45 knots (83 km/h; 52 mph)
C	46 knots (85 km/h; 53 mph)
D	50 knots (92 km/h; 57·5 mph)
E	54 knots (100 km/h; 62 mph)
Max rate of climb at S/L:	
A	192 m (630 ft)/min
B	246 m (805 ft)/min
C	265 m (870 ft)/min
D	231 m (760 ft)/min
E	300 m (984 ft)/min
Service ceiling:	
A	3,200 m (10,500 ft)
B	3,950 m (12,950 ft)
C	4,500 m (14,750 ft)
D	3,600 m (11,800 ft)
E	4,500 m (14,760 ft)
T-O run:	
A, B	214 m (700 ft)
C	240 m (790 ft)
D	250 m (820 ft)
E	360 m (1,180 ft)
T-O to 15 m (50 ft):	
A	418 m (1,370 ft)
B	365 m (1,200 ft)
C	408 m (1,340 ft)
D	445 m (1,460 ft)
E	500 m (1,640 ft)
Landing from 15 m (50 ft):	
A	268 m (880 ft)
B	335 m (1,100 ft)
C	342 m (1,120 ft)
D	360 m (1,180 ft)
E	397 m (1,300 ft)
Landing run:	
A	113 m (370 ft)
B	170 m (560 ft)
C	146 m (480 ft)
D	150 m (490 ft)
E	165 m (540 ft)
Range with max fuel (allowances for T-O, climb and descent, 45 min reserves):	
A	400 nm (740 km; 460 miles)
B	520 nm (963 km; 598 miles)
C	460 nm (852 km; 529 miles)
D	600 nm (1,110 km; 690 miles)
E	590 nm (1,090 km; 679 miles)

SOCATA RALLYE GUERRIER

This military aircraft (known originally as the Rallye 235 G) is generally similar to the high-performance Gabier four-seat light aircraft, with a 175 kW (235 hp) Lycoming O-540-B4B5 engine, but has four Alkan 663 underwing stores pylons which enable it to be used for a variety of armed and support missions. The pylons are attached under each wing between ribs 8 and 9, and ribs 15 and 16, and are connected to a weapon selection box installed centrally on the radio panel in the cockpit.

Stores that can be carried on these pylons include Matra F2 rocket launchers, each containing six 68 mm rockets; Type AA 52 pods, each containing two 7·62 mm machine-guns with 500 rds/gun, and large enough to retain all spent cartridge cases and links after firing; 50 kg operational or practice bombs; rescue packs for airdropping over water, desert, jungle or polar regions; flares for use during operational or rescue missions by night; a surveillance pack containing a TV camera and transmitter to send images to a ground station. The camera is fitted with a zoom lens, and can scan to 45° on each side of the aircraft, with a vertical scan of 110°. The pilot has a control box (normal and zoom), and a monitor on which to check precisely the images the camera is viewing. All underwing loads can be jettisoned in an emergency.

The cockpit of the Guerrier contains two side-by-side seats, with dual controls, enabling the aircraft to be used for both basic and operational training, as well as combat missions. A rear bench seat can be installed to permit the carriage of two passengers and a quantity of baggage or freight. Structure of the aircraft is basically unchanged, except for some reinforcement, notably to the wings in the vicinity of the weapon pylons.

PERFORMANCE:

Range/endurance:

Armed reconnaissance with 2 gun pods at 70% power, 30 min fuel reserves	5 h or 556 nm (1,030 km; 640 miles)
Armed reconnaissance with 4 rocket launchers at 70% power, 30 min fuel reserves	2 h 40 min or 286 nm (530 km; 329 miles)
Ground support with 2 gun pods at 75% power at 915 m (3,000 ft), 30 min fuel reserves, 10 min over target	243 nm (450 km; 280 miles)
Ground support with 4 rocket launchers at 75% power at 915 m (3,000 ft), 30 min fuel reserves, 10 min over target	130 nm (240 km; 149 miles)
Ground support with 2 rocket launchers and 2 gun pods at 75% power at 915 m (3,000 ft), 15 min fuel reserves, 10 min over target	43 nm (80 km; 50 miles)
Unarmed reconnaissance with TV pod at 70% power, 30 min fuel reserves	545 nm (1,010 km; 627 miles)

SOCATA RALLYE GAUCHO

The high-lift and safety characteristics inherent in the basic Rallye series well suit it for agricultural operations. It has been possible to purchase standard models adapted for spraying/dusting for some years. The Gaucho represents a more specialised development, with a tailwheel-type landing gear instead of the normal tricycle type; a faired-in rear cabin to house a 580 litre (127·5 Imp gallon) chemical tank; reinforced structure, with anti-corrosive treatment on metal surfaces; and a propeller specially designed for heavy duty at low speeds. The airframe is based on that of the Gabier, and a generally similar 175 kW (235 hp) Lycoming O-540-B2B5 engine is fitted.

The cockpit is equipped normally with a single seat, on the port side, with entrance via an upward-opening canopy/door hinged on the centreline. The forward portion of the chemical tank projects into the starboard side of the cockpit, alongside the pilot. If desired, it can be removed, and replaced by a cover plate and second seat. The aircraft can then be used as a dual-control agricultural pilot trainer, with tank capacity reduced to 500 litres (110 Imp gallons).

Between the seasons for agricultural flying, the Gaucho's cockpit canopy, cabin fairing, chemical tank, spraybars and other specialised equipment can be removed and replaced by conventional Gabier seats and sliding canopy, converting the aircraft into a four-seat touring aircraft or light freighter.

A variety of dispersal equipment is available for the Gaucho, including four Micronair units, two above each wing trailing-edge; a Sorensen underfuselage pump with a capacity of 2 to 40 litres/hectare (1 to 22 Imp gallons/acre) and spraybars with 24 or 32 nozzles; or a Transland spreader for solids. Steel wire-cutters are fitted on the front of each main landing gear leg and on the windscreen

Socata Guerrier in ground support configuration, with two F2 rocket packs and two gun pods on underwing attachments

This view of the Socata Gaucho shows the wing spraybars

centreline, with a steel cable from the latter to the tip of the fin.

The Gaucho was certificated in May 1978.

DIMENSIONS:

As for Gabier, except:

Length overall	7·26 m (23 ft 10 in)
Height overall	2·31 m (7 ft 7 in)

WEIGHTS:

Weight empty	694 kg (1,530 lb)
Max chemical payload	425 kg (935 lb)
Max T-O weight	1,350 kg (2,980 lb)

PERFORMANCE (at max T-O weight):

Max cruising speed at S/L	119 knots (220 km/h; 137 mph)
Econ cruising speed (65% power)	115 knots (213 km/h; 132 mph)
Stalling speed, flaps down	54 knots (100 km/h; 62 mph)
Spraying speed	70 knots (130 km/h; 80 mph)
Max rate of climb at S/L	300 m (984 ft)/min
T-O run	365 m (1,200 ft)
T-O to 15 m (50 ft)	495 m (1,620 ft)
Landing from 15 m (50 ft)	435 m (1,430 ft)
Landing run	315 m (1,030 ft)
Range, with allowances for T-O, climb and descent, 45 min reserves	485 nm (900 km; 558 miles)

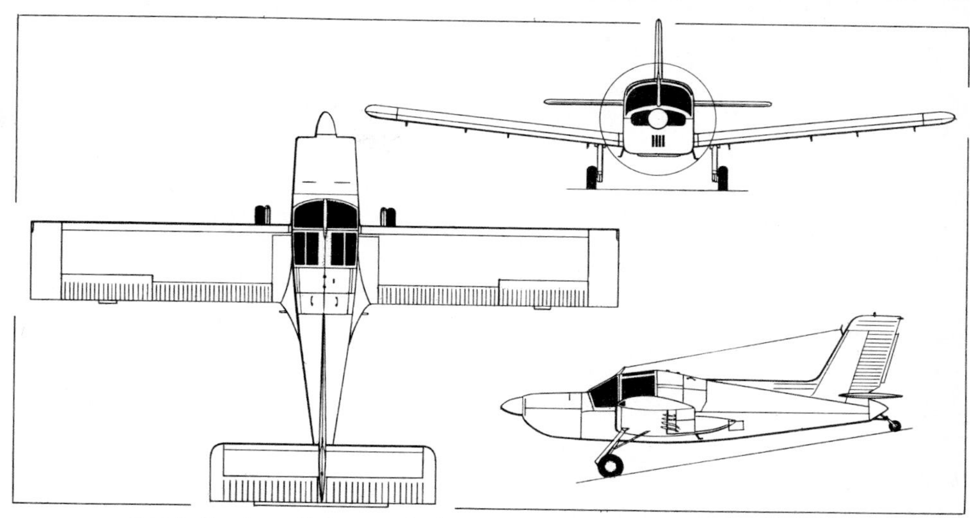

Socata Gaucho, with hopper aft of cabin and tailwheel landing gear *(Pilot Press)*

SOCATA RALLYE TAMPICO AND TOBAGO

The prototype for this new series of all-metal light aircraft was the original TB 10 (F-WZJP), of which design was initiated by Socata's Research and Development Department in February 1975, under the direction of Philippe Stuckelberger. Construction of the prototype began in February 1976, and it made a 25 min first flight at Tarbes on 23 February 1977, powered by a 119 kW (160 hp) Lycoming O-320-D2A engine. It was lost during the final phases of spin testing at the CEV on 15 December 1977.

The second prototype of the TB 10 was fitted with a 134 kW (180 hp) Lycoming engine. A further airframe underwent static tests at the CEA, Toulouse.

Following certification of the TB 10 by the DGAC, on 26 April 1979, two production versions were added to Socata's 1979 product range, as follows:

TB 9 Tampico. Four-seater, with 119 kW (160 hp) Lycoming O-320-D2A engine, fixed-pitch propeller, and fuel capacity of 155 litres (34 Imp gallons); awaiting certification in mid-1979.

TB 10 Tobago. Four/five-seater, with 134 kW (180 hp) engine.

Further versions, with more powerful engines, are planned. Installation of a retractable landing gear on later models is under consideration.

Manufacture of these aircraft is simplified by comparison with the Rallye, by the elimination of certain features such as wing leading-edge slats. The following description applies to the initial production Tobago:

TYPE: Four/five-seat all-metal light aircraft.

WINGS: Cantilever low-wing monoplane. Wing section RA 163 CW3. Thickness/chord ratio 16%. Dihedral 4° 30′ from roots. No incidence at root. No sweep. Conventional light alloy single-spar structure of constant chord. Balanced ailerons and electrically-actuated slotted flaps, of laminated plastics. No tabs.

FUSELAGE: Conventional light alloy semi-monocoque structure.

TAIL UNIT: Cantilever all-metal type, with sweptback vertical surfaces and constant-chord all-moving horizontal surfaces mounted at extreme tail, aft of rudder. Ground-adjustable tab at top of rudder. Anti-tab in horizontal surfaces.

LANDING GEAR: Non-retractable tricycle type, with steerable nosewheel. Oleo-pneumatic shock-absorbers. Wheel fairings on all three units. Disc brakes. Parking brake.

POWER PLANT: One 134 kW (180 hp) Lycoming O-360-A1AD flat-four engine, driving a Hartzell two-blade constant-speed propeller with spinner. Two fuel tanks, with total capacity of 208 litres (45·75 Imp gallons). Oil capacity 7·5 litres (1·6 Imp gallons).

ACCOMMODATION: Four/five seats in enclosed cabin. Sharply-inclined low-drag windscreen. Access via upward-hinged window/doors. Baggage compartment aft of cabin, with external door on port side. Cabin carpeted, soundproofed, heated and ventilated. Windscreen defrosting standard.

SYSTEMS: Electrical system includes 12V 60A alternator and 12V 32A battery, landing and navigation lights, four individual cabin lights and instrument panel lighting. Hydraulic system for wheel brakes only.

AVIONICS AND EQUIPMENT: Avionics to customer's specification. Standard equipment includes seat belts for all seats, armrests, glove box, map pockets, antiglare visors, stall warning indicator, tiedown fittings and towbar.

DIMENSIONS, EXTERNAL (Tampico and Tobago):

Wing span	9·76 m (32 ft 0¼ in)
Wing chord (constant)	1·22 m (4 ft 0 in)
Wing aspect ratio	8
Length overall	7·64 m (25 ft 0¾ in)
Height overall	3·20 m (10 ft 6 in)
Tailplane span	3·20 m (10 ft 6 in)
Wheelbase	1·95 m (6 ft 5 in)
Propeller diameter	1·88 m (6 ft 2 in)
Propeller ground clearance	0·10 m (4 in)
Cabin doors (each):	
Width	0·89 m (2 ft 11 in)
Height	0·76 m (2 ft 6 in)
Baggage door:	
Width	0·63 m (2 ft 1 in)
Height	0·43 m (1 ft 5 in)

DIMENSIONS, INTERNAL (Tampico and Tobago):

Cabin: Length, firewall to rear bulkhead	2·54 m (8 ft 4 in)
Length, panel to rear bulkhead	2·00 m (6 ft 6¾ in)
Max width, at rear seats	1·27 m (4 ft 2 in)
Max width, at front seats	1·15 m (3 ft 9¼ in)
Max height, floor to roof	1·12 m (3 ft 8 in)

AREAS:

Wings, gross	11·9 m² (128·1 sq ft)
Ailerons (total)	0·91 m² (9·80 sq ft)
Trailing-edge flaps (total)	3·72 m² (40·04 sq ft)
Horizontal tail surfaces (total)	2·56 m² (27·56 sq ft)

WEIGHTS (A, Tampico; B, Tobago):

Weight empty: A	650 kg (1,433 lb)
B	670 kg (1,477 lb)
Max T-O weight: A	1,060 kg (2,340 lb)
B	1,150 kg (2,530 lb)

PERFORMANCE (at max T-O weight):

Max level speed: A	125 knots (231 km/h; 144 mph)
B	133 knots (246 km/h; 153 mph)
Max cruising speed (75% power):	
A	121 knots (224 km/h; 139 mph)
B	127 knots (235 km/h; 146 mph)
Econ cruising speed (65% power):	
A	115 knots (213 km/h; 132 mph)
B	119 knots (220 km/h; 137 mph)
Stalling speed, flaps up:	
A	59 knots (110 km/h; 68 mph)
B	60 knots (111 km/h; 69 mph)
Stalling speed, flaps down:	
A	50 knots (92 km/h; 57·5 mph)
B	52 knots (97 km/h; 60 mph)
Max rate of climb at S/L:	
A	214 m (700 ft)/min
B	240 m (790 ft)/min
Service ceiling: A	4,270 m (14,000 ft)
B	3,960 m (13,000 ft)
T-O run: A	380 m (1,250 ft)
B	360 m (1,180 ft)
T-O to 15 m (50 ft): A	570 m (1,870 ft)
B	540 m (1,770 ft)
Landing from 15 m (50 ft): A	380 m (1,250 ft)
B	420 m (1,380 ft)

Socata Tobago four/five-seat light aircraft (Lycoming O-360-A1AD engine)

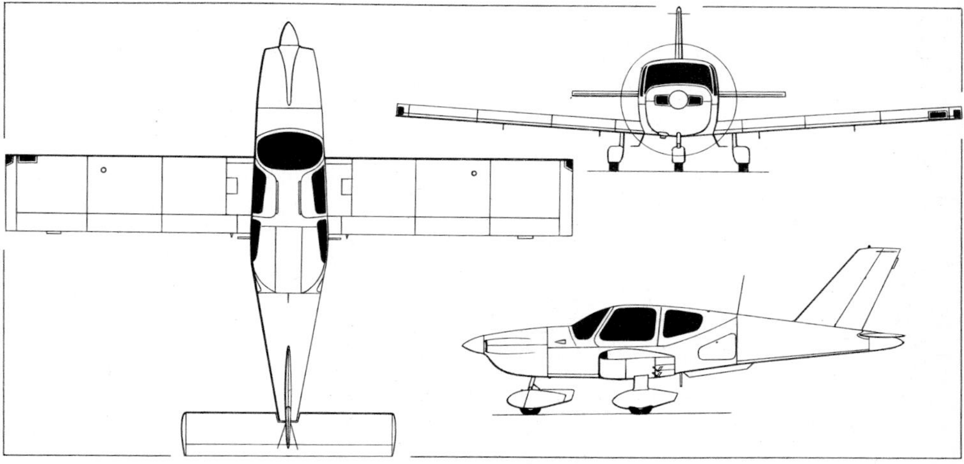

Socata Tobago four/five-seat all-metal light aircraft *(Pilot Press)*

Landing run: A	183 m (600 ft)
B	190 m (620 ft)

Range with max fuel, allowances for T-O, climb and descent, 45 min reserves:

A	460 nm (852 km; 529 miles)
B	580 nm (1,074 km; 667 miles)

AÉROSPATIALE TB 30 EPSILON

At the Farnborough Air Show, in September 1978, Aérospatiale released first details of this tandem two-seat primary trainer, which it had proposed to meet the French Air Force's 'Epsilon' requirement for a propeller-driven aircraft for use in the first stages of a more cost-effective future training sequence. In June 1979, at the Paris Air Show, the company was able to announce receipt of an order from the Air Force for two prototypes, which will adopt the name Epsilon. The first of these was expected to fly before the end of 1979. A static test airframe is also being built.

The Epsilon programme was conceived to reduce costs by curtailment of the formerly-adopted all-through jet sequence. It is claimed that the relatively high performance of the TB 30, and the fact that its cockpit layout resembles closely that of contemporary combat aircraft, will permit more satisfactory grading of pupil pilots after an initial few hours of flying, and again after completion of the basic training curriculum, covering aerobatics, blind and night flying, close formation flying, combat manoeuvres and VFR/IFR navigation, prior to advanced training for combat or transport flying.

Initial development of the TB 30 was undertaken by Aérospatiale's Aircraft Division, but design and manufacture have been entrusted to Socata at Tarbes. If the aircraft is adopted by the French Air Force, an initial order for 50 is anticipated.

TYPE: Two-seat military primary flying trainer.

WINGS: Cantilever low-wing monoplane. Wing section RA 1643 at root, RA 1243 at tip. Thickness/chord ratio 16% at root, 12% at tip. Dihedral 5°. Incidence 2°. All-metal light alloy structure, with single main spar and rear auxiliary spar, built in two panels attached directly to sides of fuselage. Press-formed ribs and heavy-gauge skin without stringers. Electrically-actuated light alloy single-slotted flaps. Light alloy mass-balanced ailerons, with controllable trim tab in one aileron.

FUSELAGE: Light alloy semi-monocoque structure of four longerons, frames and heavy-gauge skin, without stringers.

TAIL UNIT: Cantilever single-spar light alloy structure. Fixed-incidence tailplane. Balanced single-spar elevators and rudder, with controllable trim tabs.

LANDING GEAR: Hydraulically-retractable tricycle type, with single wheel on each unit. Inward-retracting main units and rearward-retracting nosewheel. Independent hydraulic single-disc brake on each main wheel.

POWER PLANT: One 224 kW (300 hp) Lycoming AEIO-540-L1A5D flat-six engine, modified for inverted flight and driving a Hoffmann HO-V123K-F/200 AH three-blade constant-speed wooden propeller, with spinner. Fuel in two wing leading-edge tanks, with total capacity of 200 litres (44 Imp gallons). Refuelling points on wing upper surface.

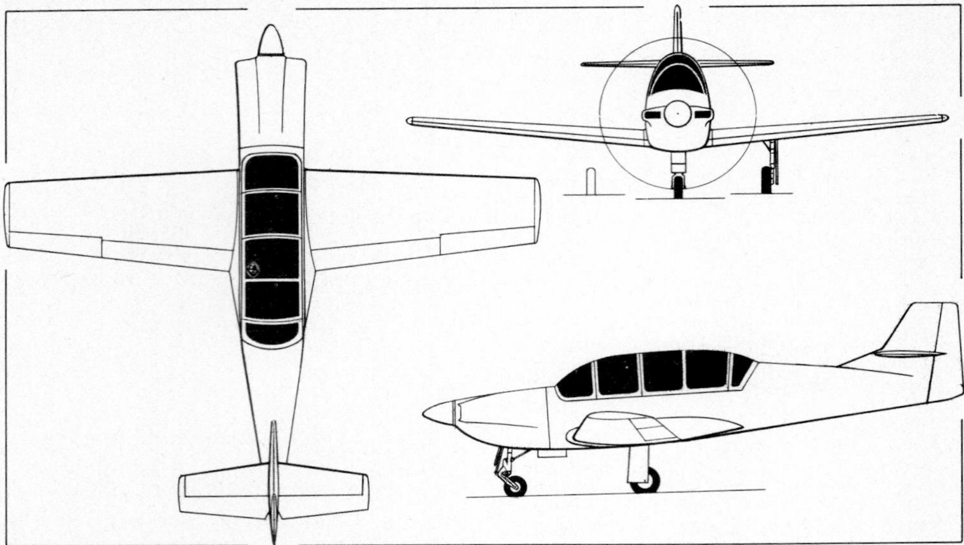

Aérospatiale TB 30 Epsilon tandem two-seat military primary trainer *(Pilot Press)*

ACCOMMODATION: Two seats in tandem, with rear seat slightly raised. Seats are electrically adjustable, up and down, and rudder pedals are mechanically adjustable fore and aft. Rearward-sliding two-section Plexiglas canopy, with emergency ejection system. Baggage compartment aft of cabin.

SYSTEMS: Hydraulic system for actuating landing gear and brakes. 28V electrical system includes engine-driven alternator, battery for engine starting and emergency use, and external power receptacle on port side of fuselage aft of wing. Cabin heated and ventilated. Windscreen demister.

AVIONICS AND EQUIPMENT: Radio com and blind-flying instrumentation standard.

DIMENSIONS, EXTERNAL:

Wing span	7·40 m (24 ft 3¼ in)
Wing chord at root	1·46 m (4 ft 9½ in)
Wing chord at tip	0·92 m (3 ft 0¼ in)
Wing aspect ratio	6
Length overall	7·40 m (24 ft 3¼ in)
Height overall	2·50 m (8 ft 2½ in)
Tailplane span	2·57 m (8 ft 5¼ in)
Wheel track	2·30 m (7 ft 6½ in)
Wheelbase	1·80 m (5 ft 10¾ in)
Propeller diameter	2·00 m (6 ft 6¾ in)
Propeller ground clearance	0·25 m (10 in)

AREAS:

Wings, gross	9·00 m² (96·88 sq ft)
Fin	1·40 m² (15·07 sq ft)
Tailplane	1·65 m² (17·76 sq ft)

WEIGHTS AND LOADINGS:

Weight empty, equipped	826 kg (1,821 lb)
T-O and landing weight (aerobatic)	1,150 kg (2,535 lb)
Max T-O and landing weight	1,175 kg (2,590 lb)
Max wing loading (aerobatic)	128 kg/m² (26·17 lb/sq ft)
Max power loading (aerobatic)	5·13 kg/kW (8·45 lb/hp)

PERFORMANCE (estimated, at max aerobatic T-O weight):

Never-exceed speed	281 knots (522 km/h; 324 mph)
Max level speed at S/L	198 knots (368 km/h; 228 mph)
Max cruising speed (75% power) at 1,830 m (6,000 ft)	184 knots (342 km/h; 212 mph)
Stalling speed, flaps down, power off	61 knots (113 km/h; 70 mph)
Max rate of climb at S/L	575 m (1,900 ft)/min
Time to 1,525 m (5,000 ft)	3 min
Service ceiling	6,900 m (22,600 ft)
T-O run	293 m (960 ft)
T-O to 50 ft (15 m)	465 m (1,525 ft)
Landing from 50 ft (15 m)	575 m (1,890 ft)
Landing run	250 m (820 ft)
Endurance	3 h
g limits	+7; −3·5

GERMANY
(FEDERAL REPUBLIC)

AIRCONCEPT
AIRCONCEPT FLUGZEUG UND GERÄTEBAU GmbH und Co KG

ADDRESS: Krichelstrasse 18, 4050 Mönchengladbach 1
Telephone: 02161 22037

The 1977-78 *Jane's* contained an illustrated entry on an ultra-lightweight single-seat sporting aircraft known as the VoWi 10, designed and built by Ing Helmut Wilden. This aircraft (D-EGWI) consisted basically of a wire-braced all-moving wing and V tail unit, linked by a light alloy tube 'backbone', and with an exposed seat for the pilot carried on a tubular structure beneath the wing. It flew for the first time on 16 April 1975, powered by two 6 kW (8 hp) Stihl-Baumsägen single-cylinder two-stroke aircooled engines.

Subsequently, the VoWi 10 was almost completely redesigned to make it suitable for series production, and the Airconcept company was formed to manufacture and market the aircraft in its developed form.

Following the death of Helmut Wilden, on 19 November 1978, no further news has been received from the company. It is believed, however, that plans are being made to continue production of this ultra-lightweight aircraft.

AIRCONCEPT VoWi 10

In its production form, the VoWi 10 is a two-seater with a fixed strut-braced wing and conventional flat-four engine. The prototype (D-ENWS) made its first flight at Mönchengladbach in the Spring of 1978, by which time manufacture of the first 15 production aircraft had started. It was then planned to build up delivery rate from two to five aircraft per month by the end of the year, and to increase to 10 a month during 1979. Orders for between 40 and 50 aircraft had been received by May 1978.

Airconcept VoWi 10 two-seat ultralight aircraft (Limbach SL 1700 AE engine) *(Brian M. Service)*

TYPE: Ultra-lightweight two-seat sporting and utility aircraft.

WINGS: Braced high-wing monoplane. Single bracing strut each side, supplemented by wire bracing to front of cabin. Gö 535 (modified) wing section. Constant chord. Dihedral from roots. No sweep. Gfk sandwich construction, without ailerons. Lateral control by cable-operated spoilers mounted at 50% chord. No flaps. Wings can be folded back alongside fuselage for storage and transport.

FUSELAGE: Basic structure of aluminium tubing; sheet aluminium cabin fairing and floor, and triangular stabilising surface between rear of cabin and 'backbone'.

TAIL UNIT: Braced V-tail, comprising twin fins and horn-balanced rudders of Gfk sandwich with aluminium tube leading-edges. Tail surfaces can be folded upward for storage and transport.

LANDING GEAR: Non-retractable tricycle type, with single wheel on each unit. Cantilever main legs of Gfk. Castoring nosewheel. Shoe brakes on main wheels.

POWER PLANT: One 44·5 kW (60 hp) Limbach SL 1700 AE flat-four engine, mounted on end of fuselage 'backbone', forward of cabin, and driving a two-blade fixed-pitch propeller, with spinner. Fuel capacity 26 litres (5·7 Imp gallons).

ACCOMMODATION: Two seats side by side in open-sided cabin. Controls accessible from either seat.

DIMENSIONS, EXTERNAL:

Wing span	11·0 m (36 ft 1 in)
Wing chord (constant)	1·34 m (4 ft 4¾ in)
Length overall	5·89 m (19 ft 4 in)

Height overall 2·22 m (7 ft 3½ in)
AREA:
Wings, gross 13·0 m² (139·9 sq ft)
WEIGHTS AND LOADINGS:
Weight empty 270 kg (595 lb)
Max T-O weight 430 kg (948 lb)
Max wing loading 33·1 kg/m² (6·78 lb/sq ft)
Max power loading 9·66 kg/kW (15·8 lb/hp)
PERFORMANCE (estimated):
Max level speed, with pilot only 86 knots (160 km/h; 99 mph)
Cruising speed 59-62 knots (110-115 km/h; 68·5-71·5 mph)
Stalling speed 28 knots (51 km/h; 32 mph)
Max rate of climb at S/L:
with pilot only 210 m (689 ft)/min
two persons 150 m (492 ft)/min
T-O run 60 m (197 ft)
T-O to 15 m (50 ft) 130 m (427 ft)
Landing from 15 m (50 ft) 120 m (394 ft)
Max endurance, 15 min reserves 2 h

DEUTSCHE AIRBUS
DEUTSCHE AIRBUS GmbH

ADDRESS: 8000 München 81, Arabellastrasse 30, Postfach 810260
Telephone: (089) 92 63 1
Telex: 5215149

CHAIRMAN OF THE SUPERVISORY BOARD: Dr Franz-Josef Strauss
MANAGEMENT:
Dipl Kfm Rolf Siebert
Dipl-Ing Klaus Hamann
PUBLIC RELATIONS: Jochen H. Eichen

This company is the German partner in the consortium formed for development and production of the European high-capacity A300 and A310 transport aircraft described under the Airbus heading in the International section.

DORNIER
DORNIER GmbH

HEAD OFFICE: Postfach 1420, 7990 Friedrichshafen/Bodensee
Telephone: Immenstaad (07545) 81+
Telex: 0734372
WORKS:
Research and Development: 7759 Immenstaad/Bodensee (near Friedrichshafen)
Production: Postfach 2160, Trimburgstrasse, 8000 München 66
AIRFIELD AND FLIGHT TEST CENTRE: 8031 Oberpfaffenhofen, near München
BONN OFFICE: Allianzplatz, 5300 Bonn
BOARD OF DIRECTORS:
Dipl-Ing Claudius Dornier Jr (Chairman)
Dipl-Ing Heinz Boldt
Dipl-Ing Dr Bernhard Schmidt
Dipl-Ing Dr jur Karl-Wilhelm Schäfer
Rainer Hainich
PUBLIC RELATIONS: Gerhard Patt

Dornier GmbH, formerly Dornier-Metallbauten, was formed in 1922 by the late Professor Claude Dornier as the successor to the 'Do' division of the former Zeppelin Werke, Lindau, GmbH. It has been operated in the form of a Gesellschaft mit beschränkter Haftung since 22 December 1972.

Member companies, in addition to Dornier GmbH, include Dornier-Reparaturwerft GmbH, at Oberpfaffenhofen (aircraft servicing and maintenance), Dornier System GmbH of Friedrichshafen (spaceflight, new technologies, electronics, management consultancy and contract research) and Lindauer Dornier GmbH of Lindau, which produces machinery for the textile industry and for the manufacture of plastics foils.

The Do 28 D Skyservant twin-engined STOL transport and utility aircraft continues in production, and is now available also in turboprop form as the Turbo-Skyservant. Dornier expects to supplement these types with a larger twin-turboprop transport designated LTA (Light Transport Aircraft), embodying advanced technology features such as a supercritical wing. As a first stage, it is flight testing a generally similar wing on a modified Skyservant testbed.

Another projected application of Dornier's new wing technology is on the amphibian flying-boat that the company has been studying for some years to meet expressed requirements for a modern search and rescue amphibian. Consideration was being given in Summer 1979 to the possibility of testing the wing on an existing Do 24 seagoing flying-boat.

Dornier is also active in development of various types of RPVs and tethered rotor platforms (see RPVs and Targets section).

The company continues in partnership with the Dassault-Breguet group in France to develop and produce the Alpha Jet training/light attack aircraft, described in the International section. Under German government contract, it will design and test a supercritical wing on one of the Alpha Jet prototypes. It is also involved in licence production of components for the McDonnell Douglas Phantom fighter; and is collaborating with Pilatus of Switzerland (which see) in marketing the latter company's Turbo-Trainer, and with Gulfstream American Corporation in marketing the Ag-Cat in Europe, Africa and parts of the Middle East. In another important programme, Dornier is responsible for integrating the operational avionics in the 18 Boeing E-3A Sentry AWACS aircraft being acquired by NATO for use in Europe.

DORNIER Do 28 D-2 SKYSERVANT

Despite its designation, the Skyservant inherited only the basic configuration of the earlier Do 28. The prototype (D-INTL) first flew on 23 February 1966. Type approval for the basic Do 28 D was granted on 24 February 1967, and for the developed Do 28 D-1 on 6 November 1967. FAA certification of the Do 28 D-1 was granted on 19 April 1968. Military type approval of the Do 28 D-1 was granted in January 1970, and of the Do 28 D-2 in late 1971, in accordance with MIL-specification standards. Initial deliveries of the Skyservant were made in the Summer of 1967; by mid-1979 sales totalled 260 aircraft, to more than 25 countries. Of these, 245 had been delivered by June 1979, including 101 Do 28 D-2s to the Federal German Luftwaffe for general duties and 20 to the Navy Air Arm for support duties. Others are in service with the air forces of Cameroun, Ethiopia, Israel, Nigeria, Somalia, Thailand, Turkey and Zambia. Production of a further batch of 20 aircraft was then under way.

Dornier Do 28 D-2 Skyservant equipped with auxiliary fuel tanks on wing pylons

On 15 March 1972 M. F. Tuytjens set six international records in a Do 28 D-1 Skyservant in Class C1e for piston-engined business aircraft in the 3,000-6,000 kg weight category. Those still standing in mid-1979 included an altitude of 8,624 m (28,294 ft) with a 1,000 kg payload; a record payload of 1,000 kg (2,205 lb) carried to a height of 2,000 m (6,562 ft); and time-to-height records of 6 min 6 s to 3,000 m (9,843 ft), 12 min 2 s to 6,000 m (19,685 ft), and 44 min 4 s to 9,000 m (29,528 ft).

The following details apply to the Do 28 D-2, which introduced a number of aerodynamic and detail refinements, including a 192 kg (423 lb) increase in AUW and more extensive standard equipment:

TYPE: Twin-engined STOL transport and utility aircraft.

WINGS: Cantilever high-wing monoplane. Wing section NACA 23018 (modified), with nose slot in the outer half of each wing. Dihedral 1° 30′. Incidence 4°. All-metal box-spar structure. Double-slotted ailerons and flaps have metal structure, partly Eonnex-covered. Balance tabs on ailerons. Pneumatic de-icing optional.

FUSELAGE: Conventional all-metal stressed-skin structure.

TAIL UNIT: Cantilever all-metal structure, with rudder and horizontal surfaces partly Eonnex-covered: All-moving horizontal surface, with combined anti-balance and trim tab. Trim tab in rudder. Pneumatic de-icing optional.

LANDING GEAR: Non-retractable tailwheel type. Dornier oleo-pneumatic shock-absorbers on main units, glassfibre sprung tailwheel unit. Main-wheel tyres size 8·50-10, pressure 3·38 bars (49 lb/sq in). Twin-contact tailwheel tyre size 5·50-4, pressure 2·76 bars (40 lb/sq in). Double-disc hydraulic brakes. Fairings on main legs and wheels standard.

POWER PLANT: Two 283 kW (380 hp) Lycoming IGSO-540-A1E flat-six engines, mounted on stub-wings and each driving a Hartzell Type HC-B3W30-2B/W10151 B-8R three-blade constant-speed and fully-feathering propeller. Fuel tanks in engine nacelles, with total usable capacity of 893 litres (196·5 Imp gallons). Refuelling points above nacelles. Provision for two underwing auxiliary fuel tanks with combined capacity of 474 litres (104 Imp gallons). Total capacity of separate oil tanks, 33 litres (7·25 Imp gallons).

ACCOMMODATION: Pilot and either co-pilot or passenger side by side on flight deck. Dual controls standard. Main cabin fitted with up to 12 seats, with aisle, or 13 inward-facing folding seats, or five stretchers and five folding seats, all layouts including toilet and/or baggage compartment and/or darkroom for aerial survey missions aft of cabin. Alternatively, cabin can be stripped for cargo-carrying. Door on each side of flight deck. Emergency exit on starboard side of cabin. Combined two-section passenger and freight door on port side of cabin, at rear.

AVIONICS AND EQUIPMENT: Standard equipment includes dual controls, dual brake system, directional slaved gyro, cabin heating, 100A alternators and provisions for de-icing system and IFR com/nav antennae installation; other avionics to customer's specifications.

DIMENSIONS, EXTERNAL:
Wing span 15·55 m (51 ft 0¼ in)
Wing chord (constant) 1·90 m (6 ft 2¾ in)
Wing aspect ratio 8·3

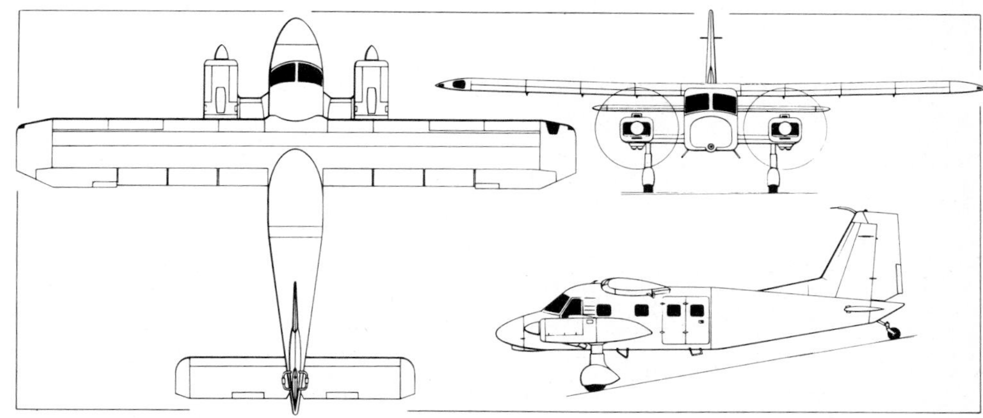
Dornier Do 28 D-2 Skyservant STOL utility transport aircraft *(Pilot Press)*

Length overall 11·41 m (37 ft 5¼ in)
Height overall 3·90 m (12 ft 9½ in)
Tailplane span 6·61 m (21 ft 8¼ in)
Wheel track 3·52 m (11 ft 6 in)
Wheelbase 8·63 m (28 ft 3¾ in)
Propeller diameter 2·36 m (7 ft 9 in)
Passenger door (port, rear):
Height 1·34 m (4 ft 4¾ in)
Width 0·65 m (2 ft 1½ in)
Height to sill 0·60 m (1 ft 11½ in)
Freight door (port, rear):
Height 1·34 m (4 ft 4¾ in)
Width 1·28 m (4 ft 2½ in)

Dimensions, internal:
Cabin, excl flight deck and rear baggage compartment:
Max length 3·97 m (13 ft 0½ in)
Max width 1·37 m (4 ft 6 in)
Max height 1·52 m (4 ft 11⅞ in)
Floor area 5·30 m² (57·05 sq ft)
Volume 8·10 m³ (286 cu ft)

Areas:
Wings, gross 29·00 m² (312·2 sq ft)
Ailerons (total) 2·64 m² (28·4 sq ft)
Trailing-edge flaps (total) 4·80 m² (51·6 sq ft)
Fin, incl dorsal fin 3·65 m² (39·3 sq ft)
Rudder, incl tab 1·40 m² (15·1 sq ft)
Tailplane, incl tab 7·65 m² (82·3 sq ft)

Weights and Loadings:
Weight empty, standard 2,328 kg (5,132 lb)
Max T-O weight 3,842 kg (8,470 lb)
Max T-O weight with optional external fuel tanks 4,015 kg (8,852 lb)
Max ramp weight 3,862 kg (8,514 lb)
Max landing weight 3,650 kg (8,050 lb)
Max wing loading 132 kg/m² (27·1 lb/sq ft)
Max power loading 6·79 kg/kW (11·14 lb/hp)

Performance (at max T-O weight):
Max level speed at 3,050 m (10,000 ft) 175 knots (325 km/h; 202 mph)
Max cruising speed at 3,050 m (10,000 ft) 165 knots (306 km/h; 190 mph)
Max cruising speed at S/L 147 knots (273 km/h; 170 mph)
Econ cruising speed, 50% power at 3,050 m (10,000 ft) 130 knots (241 km/h; 150 mph)
Stalling speed, power off, flaps down 56·5 knots (104 km/h; 65 mph)
Min control speed, power on, flaps down 35 knots (65 km/h; 40 mph)
Max rate of climb at S/L 354 m (1,160 ft)/min
Rate of climb at S/L, one engine out 55 m (180 ft)/min
Service ceiling 7,680 m (25,200 ft)
Service ceiling, one engine out 2,805 m (9,200 ft)
T-O run 280 m (920 ft)
T-O to 15 m (50 ft) 415 m (1,360 ft)
Landing from 15 m (50 ft) 390 m (1,280 ft)
Landing run 201 m (660 ft)
Range with max payload 566 nm (1,050 km; 652 miles)

DORNIER Do 28 D-6 TURBO-SKYSERVANT

Dornier flew for the first time on 9 April 1978 the Do 28 D-5X prototype of a turboprop-powered version of the Skyservant (D-IBUF). In this prototype the piston engines of the Do 28 D-2 were replaced by two 447 kW (600 shp) Avco Lycoming LTP 101-600-1A turboprop engines, derated to 298 kW (400 shp) and each driving a three-blade constant-speed metal propeller. These engines are available optionally on the production Do 28 D-6 Turbo-Skyservant, but 298 kW (400 shp) Pratt & Whitney Aircraft of Canada PT6A-110 free-turbine turboprops are standard. In other respects the airframe is generally similar to that of the Do 28 D-2 Skyservant, except that reinforced landing gear allows a higher maximum landing weight.

Delivery of the Turbo-Skyservant to operators is scheduled to begin in early 1981.

Weights and Loadings (PT6A-110 engines):
Weight empty 2,153 kg (4,747 lb)
Max payload 1,340 kg (2,954 lb)
Max T-O weight 4,300 kg (9,480 lb)
Max landing weight 4,100 kg (9,039 lb)
Max wing loading 148 kg/m² (30·4 lb/sq ft)
Max power loading 7·21 kg/kW (11·85 lb/shp)

Performance (at max T-O weight except where indicated; PT6A-110 engines):
Max cruising speed at 3,050 m (10,000 ft) 183 knots (339 km/h; 211 mph)
Cruising speed, 75% power at 3,050 m (10,000 ft) 165 knots (305 km/h; 190 mph)
Cruising speed, max range power at 3,050 m (10,000 ft) 140 knots (259 km/h; 161 mph)
Cruising speed, 50% power at 3,050 m (10,000 ft) 138 knots (256 km/h; 159 mph)
Max rate of climb at 1,525 m (5,000 ft) 389 m (1,275 ft)/min
Rate of climb at 1,525 m (5,000 ft), one engine out 44 m (145 ft)/min
Service ceiling at AUW of 3,800 kg (8,377 lb) 8,740 m (28,675 ft)
Service ceiling, one engine out at AUW of 3,800 kg (8,377 lb) 4,250 m (13,945 ft)
Range with max fuel and 656 kg (1,446 lb) payload at 3,050 m (10,000 ft), no reserves:
at 75% power 861 nm (1,595 km; 991 miles)
at max range power 899 nm (1,665 km; 1,035 miles)
Range with max payload at 3,050 m (10,000 ft), no reserves:
at 75% power 286 nm (530 km; 329 miles)
at max range power 297 nm (550 km; 342 miles)

DORNIER NEW TECHNOLOGY WING (TNT) TESTBED AIRCRAFT

The advanced technology wing (*Tragflügel Neuer Technologie:* TNT) has been developed by Dornier with support from the Federal Ministry of Research and Technology. The first phase of the TNT programme, including design, aerodynamic and structural studies, began in mid-1975 and was completed at the end of 1976. Phase II covered engineering, construction of the wing, and its installation on the testbed aircraft, a Do 28 D-2 Skyservant. This was modified by extending the centre-fuselage 1·36 m (4 ft 5½ in) and installing a longer nose; fitting standard Alpha Jet landing gear in a non-retractable form; and fitting two Garrett-AiResearch TPE 331-5-252D turboprop engines, one on each wing. The first flight of this research aircraft (D-IFNT) was made on 14 June 1979, beginning a full year of testing under Phase III of the programme.

The description of the Do 28 D-2 applies also to the TNT testbed aircraft, except as follows:

Wings: Cantilever high-wing monoplane. Special Dornier wing section. Thickness/chord ratio reduces from 16% over the full centre-section to 13% at the tip. Dihedral 0° on centre-section; 4° on outer panels. Incidence at root 2° 12′. Twist on outer panels −3°. Composite structure, with spars, panels and ribs of torsion box integrally milled from light alloy; leading-edge boxes of conventional sheet metal construction; trailing-edge boxes and sharply-swept wingtips of glassfibre sandwich. Electrically-operated single-slotted Fowler type trailing-edge flaps. Ailerons, which can be drooped up to 10°, have Flettner tabs to offload control forces, and trim tabs.

Fuselage and Tail Unit: Generally similar to Do 28 D-2, but fuselage extended in length.

Landing Gear: Non-retractable tricycle type, consisting of standard production Alpha Jet landing gear units.

Power Plant: Two 533 kW (715 shp) Garrett-AiResearch TPE 331-5-252D turboprop engines, each driving a Hartzell type HC-B4TN-SCL/L 1028+4 four-blade constant-speed metal propeller. Integral fuel tanks in wing centre-section, outside fuselage area, with combined capacity of 2,000 kg (4,409 lb).

Systems: Generally as for Do 28 D-2, but the electrical system has been modified to meet the requirements of the turboprop engines and their new location.

Avionics: Have been selected to satisfy the test assignment and meet IFR requirements.

Dimensions, external:
Wing span 16·97 m (55 ft 8 in)
Wing chord (mean aerodynamic) 2·04 m (6 ft 8¼ in)
Wing aspect ratio 9
Length overall (excl nose probe) 13·30 m (43 ft 7½ in)
Height overall 4·70 m (15 ft 5 in)
Wheel track 3·02 m (9 ft 10¾ in)
Wheelbase 4·19 m (13 ft 9 in)
Propeller diameter 2·73 m (8 ft 11½ in)

Area:
Wings, gross 32·00 m² (344·5 sq ft)

Weights and Loadings:
Weight empty 3,010 kg (6,636 lb)
Max T-O weight 4,500 kg (9,921 lb)
Max wing loading 140·6 kg/m² (28·80 lb/sq ft)
Max power loading 4·22 kg/kW (6·94 lb/shp)

Performance (estimated, at max T-O weight except where indicated):
Never-exceed speed 231 knots (428 km/h; 266 mph)
Cruising speed 185 knots (342 km/h; 213 mph)
Max rate of climb at S/L, AUW of 4,000 kg (8,818 lb) 942 m (3,091 ft)/min
Rate of climb, one engine out, conditions as above 348 m (1,142 ft)/min
T-O to 15 m (50 ft) at AUW of 4,000 kg (8,818 lb) 250 m (820 ft)

DORNIER LTA

Advanced technology features of the LTA (Light Transport Aircraft) include a high-efficiency wing of special Dornier section, which is being flight tested initially on the Dornier TNT testbed aircraft (described separately); extensive use of lightweight composite materials in the airframe; optional pressurisation; and application of OLGA gust absorption techniques developed jointly by Dornier and the DFVLR under the ZKP research programme.

Two versions of the LTA are proposed:

Basic LTA. With accommodation for a crew of two and 19 passengers, with toilet and wardrobe, in a non-pressurised fuselage.

Commuter LTA. With accommodation for a crew of two or three and 24 passengers, without toilet and ward-

Dornier Do 28 D-5X Turbo-Skyservant prototype (two Avco Lycoming LTP 101-600-1A turboprop engines)

Dornier TNT research aircraft to evaluate the company's new technology wing

robe. Seven pairs of seats on starboard side of cabin, row of four seats at rear of cabin, and six single seats on port side, with an aisle 0·45 m (1 ft 5¾ in) wide. Pressurised fuselage optional.

In mid-1979, Dornier was discussing with Hindustan Aeronautics (HAL) of India the possibility of undertaking a joint programme to develop and produce the LTA.

TYPE: Twin-turboprop light transport.

WINGS: Cantilever high-wing monoplane. Dornier Do A-5 supercritical wing section. Dihedral outboard of engines. Wing leading-edge and raked wingtips of glassfibre/Kevlar composites. Fowler-type slotted trailing-edge flaps and ailerons of carbon fibre composites. Ailerons can be drooped symmetrically to augment trailing-edge flaps, and are operated differentially to serve as conventional ailerons. Remainder of wing of light alloy construction.

FUSELAGE; Semi-monocoque light alloy structure of circular cross-section. Nose, tailcone and main landing gear housings have glassfibre/Kevlar composite skins.

TAIL UNIT: Cantilever T-tail of basic light alloy construction, with sweptback vertical surfaces. Fin and tailplane leading-edges of glassfibre/Kevlar composite construction; elevators and rudder of carbon fibre composites.

LANDING GEAR: Retractable tricycle type, with single wheel on each unit. Main units retract forward and inward into fairings built on to the lower fuselage. Nosewheel retracts forward.

POWER PLANT: Two Garrett-AiResearch TPE 331-5 or -8 (541 kW; 725 shp) or TPE 331-10 (652 kW; 875 shp) turboprop engines, each driving a Hartzell four-blade constant-speed reversible-pitch metal propeller. Alternative engines include the Avco Lycoming LTP 101-700A2 (548 kW; 735 shp) and Pratt & Whitney Aircraft of Canada PT6A-34 (567 kW; 760 shp).

ACCOMMODATION: Crew of two or three, and 19-24 passengers, as described under model listings. Seat pitch 76 cm (30 in). Door on port side, at forward end of cabin. Baggage space aft of cabin rear bulkhead, with external access door on port side. Baggage space in nose. Provision for toilet and wardrobe in 19-seat version.

SYSTEM: Pressurisation optional in Commuter version.

DIMENSIONS, EXTERNAL:

Wing span	17·81 m (58 ft 5¼ in)
Wing aspect ratio	9·32
Length overall	16·60 m (54 ft 5½ in)
Height overall	5·55 m (18 ft 2½ in)

DIMENSIONS, INTERNAL:

Cabin:	
Length	6·63 m (21 ft 9 in)
Max width	2·31 m (7 ft 7 in)
Max height	1·80 m (5 ft 10¾ in)
Floor area	11·9 m² (128 sq ft)
Volume	23·6 m³ (833 cu ft)

AREA:

Wings, gross	33·93 m² (365·2 sq ft)

WEIGHTS AND LOADINGS (estimated. A: Basic LTA; B: Commuter LTA):

Manufacturer's weight, empty:	
A, B	3,544 kg (7,813 lb)
Max fuel:	
A	2,000 kg (4,410 lb)
Max T-O weight (unpressurised):	
A	6,500 kg (14,330 lb)
B	6,850 kg (15,102 lb)
Max wing loading:	
A	191·6 kg/m² (39·24 lb/sq ft)
B	201·9 kg/m² (41·35 lb/sq ft)

Do 28 D-2 Skyservant testbed for the wing of the Dornier LTA transport aircraft *(Pilot Press)*

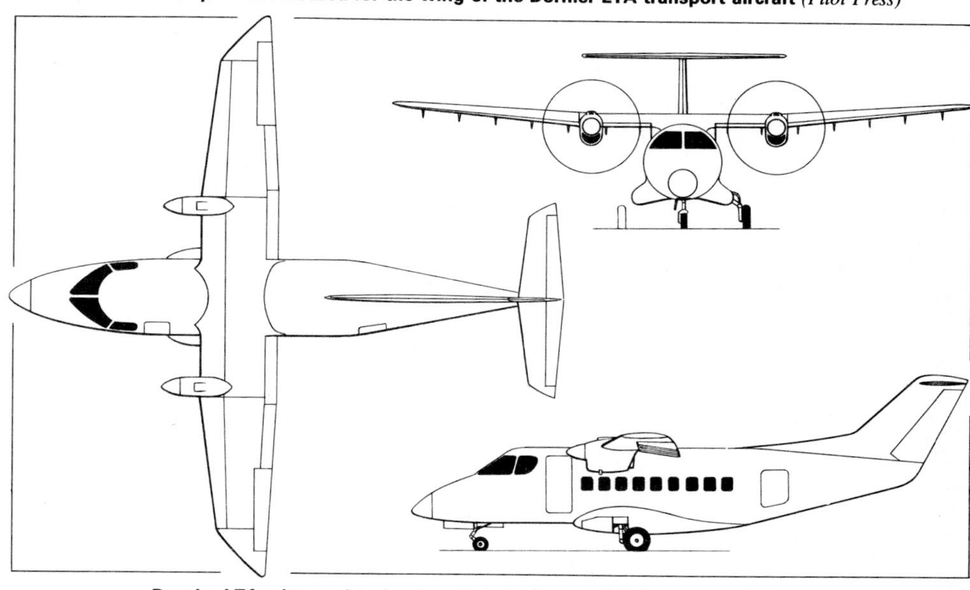

Dornier LTA advanced technology twin-turboprop light transport *(Pilot Press)*

PERFORMANCE (estimated, with TPE 331-8 engines):

Max level speed:	
A, B	241-243 knots (445-450 km/h; 277-280 mph)
Max cruising speed (80% power) at 3,000 m (9,850 ft):	
A, B	216-221 knots (400-410 km/h; 249-255 mph)
Time to 3,050 m (10,000 ft)	from 5·7 to 7·14 min
Service ceiling	8,000-10,000 m (26,250-32,810 ft)
Service ceiling, one engine out	2,500-5,000 m (8,200-16,400 ft)
T-O run at 6,000 kg (13,227 lb) AUW	675 m (2,215 ft)
T-O run at 7,500 kg (16,535 lb) AUW	950 m (3,117 ft)
Range with max fuel:	
A, with 15 passengers	810 nm (1,500 km; 930 miles)
B, with 20 passengers	430 nm (800 km; 495 miles)
B, with 24 passengers	251 nm (400 km; 250 miles)

EQUATOR
EQUATOR AIRCRAFT GESELLSCHAFT FÜR FLUGZEUGBAU mbH ULM

HEAD OFFICE: Benzstrasse 15, D-7904 Erbach
Telephone: (073) 04 6116 and 05 6116
PRESIDENT: Günther Pöschel

Günther Pöschel, President of Pöschel Aircraft GmbH, designed and built the prototype of a five/six-seat light STOL aircraft, designated P-300 Equator. Powered by a 216 kW (290 hp) Lycoming IO-540 flat-six engine, this flew for the first time on 8 November 1970, and was last described in the 1972-73 *Jane's*.

At that time it was intended to produce a turboprop-powered amphibious version of the same basic design, under the designation P-400 Equator Turbo-Stol-Amphibian, but lack of capital halted development of this aircraft. A fresh start was made when Herr Pöschel formed Equator Aircraft to resume development of the turboprop-powered version as the P-400 Turbo-Equator.

A full description and illustration of the Turbo-Equator can be found in the 1977-78 *Jane's*. Following an incident during the eighth flight in the Autumn of 1977, the configuration has undergone a major change. The definitive aircraft is now reported to be mid-wing, with a reciprocating engine mounted on a pylon above the fuselage in the P-300 version, and a turboprop in the P-400 version. The fuselage and wings of the prototype airframe were being built by the Glasflügel and Glaser-Dirks sailplane companies respectively in mid-1979, with the first flight scheduled to take place before the end of that year.

GYROFLUG
GYROFLUG INGENIEURSGESELLSCHAFT mbH

ADDRESS: Freihofstrasse 37, 7000 Stuttgart 40
Telephone: (07 11) 80 12 02

MANAGEMENT:
Dipl-Ing Wolfgang Schiller
Jörg Elzenbeck

Gyroflug was formed in July 1978 to manufacture and market, as a ready-to-fly production aircraft, a developed version of the two-seat VariEze lightweight sporting aircraft designed by Burt Rutan for amateur construction (see Rutan entry in US Homebuilt section). The company's executives had earlier built and flown, in April 1977, the first VariEze completed in Europe (D-EEEZ).

Gyroflug's development of the VariEze is known as the Speed-Canard. It is hoped to begin delivery of production aircraft in late 1980.

GYROFLUG SPEED-CANARD

As well as being slightly larger overall than the Rutan VariEze, on which it is based, the Speed-Canard differs in a number of important details. Its 18° swept wing retains the NASA winglets that have proved so successful on the original design, but utilises a new aerofoil designed by Prof Eppler which is claimed to reduce drag by 30%. Instead of retaining the glassfibre/foam core structure of the VariEze, which is well suited to amateur construction, the Speed-Canard is made of glassfibre and carbon fibre reinforced plastics laid up in female moulds, giving a lighter structure optimised for series production. The forward fuselage embodies a flush canopy similar to that of the latest sailplanes, with the rear seat raised to ensure a good field of view for both occupants.

A more powerful engine is standard, in the form of an 86 kW (115 hp) Lycoming O-235 flat-four engine, driving a Hoffmann HO-V72G/17OU-10 two-blade constant-speed pusher propeller with spinner. Gyroflug is studying the possibility of fitting two Klöckner-Humboldt-Deutz KHD 117 lightweight turbojets in a later version of the Speed-Canard, giving an estimated max level speed of 237 knots (440 km/h; 273 mph).

Construction of the moulds in which to build components of the piston-engined prototype was begun in early 1979. They were complete by the time of the Paris Air

Show, and the first flight of the Speed-Canard was scheduled for Autumn 1979.

Dimensions, external:

Wing span	7·00 m (22 ft 11½ in)
Foreplane span	3·61 m (11 ft 10⅛ in)
Foreplane chord (constant)	0·34 m (1 ft 1⅜ in)
Length overall	5·32 m (17 ft 5½ in)
Length of fuselage	4·32 m (14 ft 2 in)
Max width of fuselage	0·74 m (2 ft 5 in)
Height to top of fuselage	1·66 m (5 ft 5½ in)

Areas:

Wings, gross	5·30 m² (57·05 sq ft)
Foreplane, gross	1·22 m² (13·13 sq ft)

Weights and Loadings (estimated):

Weight empty	280 kg (617 lb)
Max fuel	130 kg (287 lb)
Max T-O weight	600 kg (1,323 lb)
Max wing loading	92·02 kg/m² (18·85 lb/sq ft)
Max power loading	6·98 kg/kW (11·5 lb/hp)

Performance (estimated, at max T-O weight):

Never-exceed speed	215 knots (400 km/h; 248 mph)
Max cruising speed, 75% power	191 knots (354 km/h; 220 mph)
Econ cruising speed, 45% power	146 knots (270 km/h; 168 mph)
Stalling speed	51 knots (94 km/h; 58·5 mph)
Max rate of climb at S/L	480 m (1,575 ft)/min
T-O run	300 m (984 ft)
Max range	1,349 nm (2,500 km; 1,553 miles)

MBB
MESSERSCHMITT-BÖLKOW-BLOHM GmbH

Head Office: Ottobrunn bei München, 8000 München 80, Postfach 80 11 09

Telephone: (089) 6000-1

Telex: 5287-0 mbbd

Works:

Augsburg, Donauwörth, Hamburg-Finkenwerder, Laupheim, Manching, Munich, Nabern/Teck, Ottobrunn, Schrobenhausen and Stade

President and General Manager: Prof Dipl-Ing Gero Madelung

Executive Vice-President and Deputy General Manager: Sepp Hort

Executive Vice-Presidents:

Dr Johannes Broschwitz
Fritz Killguss
Peter C. Küchler
Ernst-Georg Pantel

Vice-Presidents, Division Managing Directors:

Ernst-Georg Pantel (Commercial Aircraft Division)
Günther Kuhlo (Dynamics Division)
Johannes Schubert (Space Division)
Kurt Pfleiderer (Helicopter and Transport Systems Division)
Gunter Horstkotte (Ottobrunn Operations Division)

Chairman of the Supervisory Board: Max Streibl

Public Relations: Eduard Roth

In May 1969 the former Messerschmitt-Bölkow GmbH and Hamburger Flugzeugbau GmbH (see 1968-69 *Jane's)* merged to form a new group known as Messerschmitt-Bölkow-Blohm GmbH. Shareholders in this company include the city of Hamburg, which has a 20·25% interest, the estate of the late Prof Dr-Ing h.c. Willy Messerschmitt (11·05%), Dr-Ing h.c. Ludwig Bölkow (4·14%), the Blohm family (0·75%), The Boeing Company (0·99%), the Bavarian State (7·8%), the Bavarian Reconstruction Finance Institute (20·78%) and Fides GmbH (33·78%). MBB is the largest aerospace company in Germany, and is affiliated with a number of national and international corporations.

Development work on the Panavia Tornado multi-role combat aircraft, as Germany's prime contractor, is the company's main military aircraft activity. MBB has a 42·5% shareholding in Panavia Aircraft GmbH (which see), together with BAe (42·5%) and Aeritalia (15%). It is supplying PAH-1 anti-tank helicopters to the German Army, and is working with Aérospatiale of France on the second-generation PAH-2 (see International section). MBB is participating in the resumed production of the Transall C-160 military transport aircraft. Its Manching facilities are responsible for overhaul of F-104G Starfighter and F-4 Phantom aircraft flown by the German armed services.

The main civil aircraft programme involves work on the Airbus A300 and A310 for Airbus Industrie (which see). The company is also making major assemblies for the Fokker F28 Fellowship. MBB's BO 105 was the first twin-turbine lightweight utility helicopter to enter series production, and it is now working in partnership with Kawasaki Heavy Industries of Japan on a new helicopter known as the BK 117 (see International section).

MBB is also involved extensively in missile development and production, and is a prime contractor or system leader in a number of European space programmes. Details of these activities can be found in the appropriate sections of this edition.

In 1978 the company was engaged in detail study of a new generation of attack aircraft for the Luftwaffe, and was also devoting much of its market research/design effort towards new-generation European airliners.

Since 1966, MBB has been developing a new type of conventional weapon system, designated **MW-1,** which will be carried by the Tornado and can equip other types such as the F-4F Phantom. It consists of a dispenser carried under the aircraft's belly, from which a large number of small munitions can be ejected pyrotechnically. For use against tanks, the munitions may be shaped-charge bombs which detonate on impact or mines that are set off when the tanks run over them. They can be of types designed to destroy airfield runways, splinter mines with fuses triggered by aircraft movements, or a type designed to destroy aircraft inside shelters.

Top: MW-1 weapon system under an F-4F Phantom II. Above: Static firing tests of an MW-1 pack

MBB BO 105

Design of this light utility helicopter was started in July 1962 and construction of prototypes began in 1964, under Federal German government contract. The first BO 105 prototype was fitted with an existing conventional rotor and two Allison 250-C18 turboshaft engines; subsequent aircraft have had a rotor system based on a rigid titanium hub, with feathering hinges only, and hingeless flexible glassfibre blades. From the Spring of 1970 'droop-snoot' rotor blades of MBB design have been standard.

Details of subsequent prototypes, early production helicopters and special variants can be found in previous editions of *Jane's.* Current models are as follows:

BO 105 CB. Standard production version since 1975, with two Allison 250-C20B engines, operable in air temperatures ranging from −45° to +54°C, and strengthened rotor gearing. LBA certification received in November 1976.

BO 105 CBS. Version with increased seating or cargo capacity in a 0·25 m (9·8 in) longer fuselage. Available in five-seat executive or six-seat high-density configurations. Similar to the version marketed as the Executaire by Boeing Vertol of the USA (which see). Identified by small additional window aft of door on each side.

BO 105 D. Variant as supplied to the UK, with modified equipment. The BO 105 D has been approved since 1973 by the CAA for commercial single-pilot IFR operation, even in controlled airways.

BO 105 L. Variant due for certification by end of 1979, with deliveries to begin in early 1980. See Addenda.

BO 105 M (VBH). Liaison and light observation helicopter for the German Army, with uprated engines and transmission. Production of 227 examples approved by the Federal government, to permit replacement of current Alouette IIs to begin in September 1979.

BO 105 P (PAH-1). Anti-tank version, with outriggers able to carry six Euromissile Hot missiles, and with a stabilised sight above the co-pilot's position. Three prototypes have been built, and the Federal government has given approval for the procurement of 212 examples for the German Army, with initial deliveries scheduled for September 1979. Uprated engines and transmission, Singer AN/ASN-128 Doppler navigation system. Flight testing was scheduled for completion in early 1979.

In the Philippines and Indonesia, NAM and Nurtanio respectively (which see) are participating in licence assembly programmes.

The description which follows applies to the BO 105 CB production version:

Type: Five-seat light helicopter.

Rotor System: Four-blade main rotor, comprising rigid titanium hub and GRP blades, with titanium anti-erosion strip forming leading-edge of each blade. MBB-designed 'droop-snoot' blades of NACA 23012 asymmetrical section, having a specially-designed trailing-edge giving improved control in pitching moment. Flexible tension/torsion blade retention, to take up centrifugal forces. Roller bearings for pitch change. Main rotor blade folding optional. Two-blade semi-rigid tail rotor; blades of GRP, with titanium anti-erosion strip on leading-edge. Main rotor rpm 424. Tail rotor rpm 2,220.

Rotor Drive: Main transmission utilises two bevel gear input stages with freewheeling clutches and a spur collector gear stage. Planetary reduction gear; three auxiliary drives for accessories. Main transmission rated for twin-engine input of 257 kW (345 shp) per engine, or a single engine input of 283 kW (380 shp). Tail rotor

One of 20 MBB BO 105 C rescue helicopters serving under the Federal German government's 'Katastrophenschutz' scheme to provide speedy assistance after major disasters

gearbox on fin. Main rotor/engine rpm ratio 1 : 14·2. Tail rotor/engine rpm ratio 1 : 2·7.

FUSELAGE: Conventional light alloy semi-monocoque structure of pod and boom type. Glassfibre-reinforced cowling over power plant. Titanium sheet engine deck.

TAIL UNIT: Horizontal stabiliser of conventional light alloy construction with small endplate fins.

LANDING GEAR: Skid type, with cross tubes designed for energy absorption by plastic deformation in the event of a heavy landing. Inflatable emergency floats can be attached to skids.

POWER PLANT: Two 313 kW (420 shp) Allison 250-C20B turboshaft engines, each with a max continuous rating of 298 kW (400 shp). Bladder-type fuel tanks under cabin floor, capacity 580 litres (127·5 Imp gallons), of which 570 litres (125·3 Imp gallons) are usable. Fuelling point on port side of cabin. Provision for fitting auxiliary tanks in freight compartment. Oil capacity: engine 9 litres (1·98 Imp gallons), gearbox 7 kg (15·4 lb).

ACCOMMODATION: Pilot and co-pilot or passenger on individual front seats, with safety belts. Optional dual controls. Bench seat at rear for three persons, removable for cargo and stretcher carrying. Entire rear fuselage aft of seats and under power plant available as freight and baggage space, with access through two clamshell doors at rear. Two standard stretchers can be accommodated in ambulance role. One forward-opening hinged and jettisonable door and one sliding door on each side of cabin. Heating system optional.

SYSTEMS: Tandem fully-redundant hydraulic system for powered main rotor controls. Electrical system powered by two 150A 28V DC starter/generators and a 24V 22Ah nickel-cadmium battery; external power socket.

AVIONICS AND EQUIPMENT: Standard equipment includes tiedown rings in cargo compartment, cabin and cargo compartment dome lights, position lights and collision warning lights. A wide range of optional avionics and equipment is available, including search radar, Doppler navigation, emergency flotation gear, auxiliary fuel tanks, cargo hook, two-man rescue winch, windscreen wiper, engine fire extinguishing system, snow skids, searchlight, landing lights and stability augmentation system. A completely equipped ambulance version is available.

ARMAMENT (Military versions): Provision for a variety of alternative military loads, including six Hot anti-tank missiles and associated stabilised sight.

DIMENSIONS, EXTERNAL:

Diameter of main rotor	9·84 m (32 ft 3·4 in)
Diameter of tail rotor	1·90 m (6 ft 2¾ in)
Main rotor blade chord	0·27 m (10·63 in)
Tail rotor blade chord	0·18 m (7·09 in)
Distance between rotor centres	5·95 m (19 ft 6¼ in)
Length, incl main and tail rotors	11·86 m (38 ft 11 in)
Length, excl main rotor	8·56 m (28 ft 1 in)
Height to top of main rotor head	3·00 m (9 ft 10 in)
Width over skids, unladen	2·53 m (8 ft 3½ in)
Width over skids, laden	2·58 m (8 ft 5½ in)
Rear loading doors:	
Height	0·64 m (2 ft 1 in)
Width	1·40 m (4 ft 7 in)

DIMENSIONS, INTERNAL:

Cabin, incl cargo compartment:	
Length	4·30 m (14 ft 1 in)
Max width	1·40 m (4 ft 7 in)
Max height	1·25 m (4 ft 1 in)
Volume	4·80 m³ (169 cu ft)
Cargo compartment: Length	1·85 m (6 ft 0¾ in)
Max width	1·20 m (3 ft 11¼ in)
Max height	0·57 m (1 ft 10½ in)
Floor area	2·20 m² (23·7 sq ft)
Volume	1·50 m³ (53 cu ft)

WEIGHTS AND LOADINGS:

Weight empty, basic	1,189 kg (2,622 lb)
Weight empty, operating	1,279 kg (2,820 lb)
Standard fuel	460 kg (1,014 lb)
Fuel, incl auxiliary tanks	780 kg (1,720 lb)
Max T-O weight	2,300 kg (5,070 lb)
Normal disc loading	26·5 kg/m² (5·43 lb/sq ft)
Max disc loading	30·5 kg/m² (6·25 lb/sq ft)

PERFORMANCE (at normal T-O weight):

Never-exceed speed at S/L	145 knots (270 km/h; 167 mph)
Max cruising speed at S/L	132 knots (245 km/h; 152 mph)
Normal cruising speed	125 knots (232 km/h; 144 mph)
Max rate of climb at S/L	540 m (1,773 ft)/min
Vertical rate of climb at S/L	258 m (847 ft)/min
Max operating height	5,180 m (17,000 ft)
Single-engine service ceiling	1,280 m (4,200 ft)
Hovering ceiling IGE	2,900 m (9,514 ft)
Hovering ceiling OGE	1,980 m (6,500 ft)
Range with standard fuel and max payload, no reserves:	
at S/L	310 nm (575 km; 357 miles)
at 1,525 m (5,000 ft)	355 nm (656 km; 408 miles)
Ferry range with auxiliary tanks, no reserves:	
at S/L	540 nm (1,000 km; 621 miles)
at 1,525 m (5,000 ft)	600 nm (1,112 km; 691 miles)

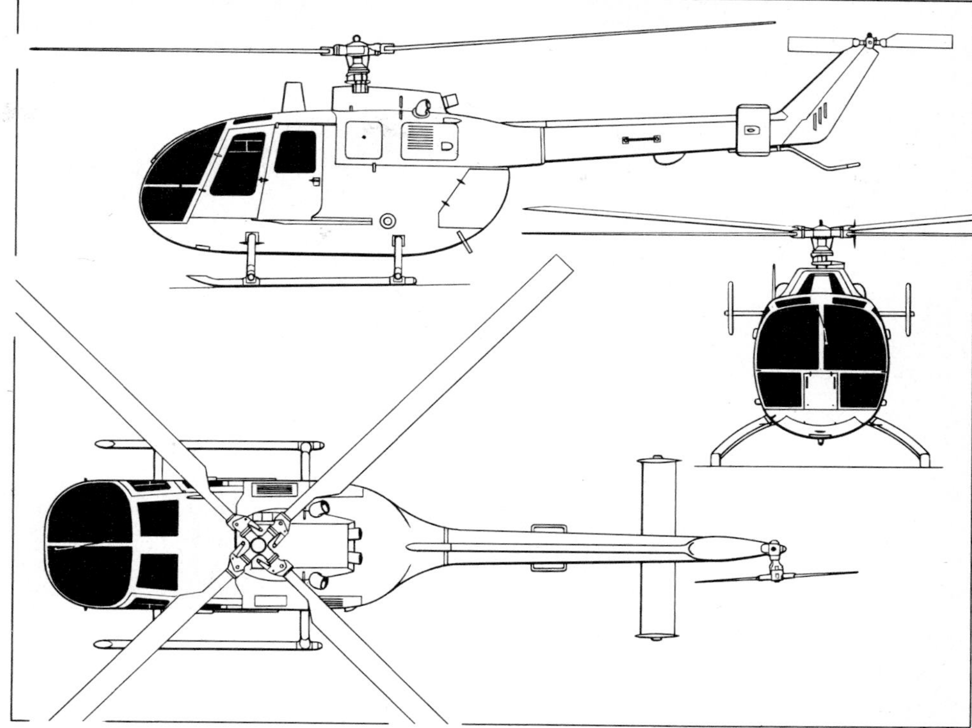

BO 105 CB five-seat light helicopter (two Allison 250-C20B turboshaft engines) *(Pilot Press)*

MBB BO 105 P (PAH-1) fitted with six Hot anti-tank missiles and SFIM stabilised target acquisition and tracking sight *(Brian M. Service)*

MBB/AÉROSPATIALE PAH-2

Details of this second-generation anti-tank helicopter can be found in the International section.

MBB/KAWASAKI BK 117

Following signature of an agreement on 25 February 1977, MBB is developing in conjunction with Kawasaki of Japan an 8/10-seat multi-purpose helicopter known as the BK 117. A description of this aircraft can be found in the International section.

MYLIUS
LEICHTFLUGZEUGE-ENTWICKLUNGEN DIPL ING HERMANN MYLIUS

ADDRESS: Kuckucksweg 6, 8011 Brunnthal

In addition to heading the light aircraft technical development activities of MBB, Dipl Ing Hermann Mylius develops and builds sporting aircraft privately.

MYLIUS MY 102 TORNADO, MY 103 MISTRAL and MY 104 PASSAT

In July 1971, Dipl Ing Mylius began privately the development of a single-seat version of the MHK 101, intended for competitive aerobatics. Construction of a prototype (D-EMYS) was started in December 1971, and this flew for the first time on 7 July 1973. Known as the MY 102 Tornado, it has achieved considerable success in competition.

Development of the MY 102 is continuing and a second prototype, embodying a number of modifications, was scheduled to fly in 1979. Two larger versions are also being developed, to provide a family of three basically similar aircraft:

MY 102 Tornado. Basic single-seat model.

MY 103 Mistral. Generally similar to Tornado, but with accommodation for pilot and one passenger. Three examples were under construction in 1978.

MY 104 Passat. Four-seat version of the MY 102, expected to fly in the Spring of 1980.

The following description applies in particular to the MY 102, but specification details of the MY 103 and MY 104 are given also:

TYPE: Single-seat sporting and aerobatic aircraft.

WINGS: Cantilever low-wing monoplane. Wing section NACA 64218 at root, NACA 64212 at tip. Dihedral 2° 30′. Incidence 2°. Sweepback 1° 24′ at quarter-chord. Single-spar all-metal structure with glassfibre wingtips. All-metal differentially-operated ailerons. Electrically-operated all-metal plain trailing-edge flaps. By removing three bolts on each side, the wings can be folded back alongside the fuselage to facilitate stowage in a confined space or to permit the aircraft to be towed on ordinary roads behind a car. Control lines to flaps and ailerons disconnect and reconnect automatically during folding and unfolding.

FUSELAGE: Conventional semi-monocoque structure of light alloy, except for glassfibre engine cowlings.

TAIL UNIT: Single all-metal fin and rudder, with sweepback on fin leading-edge and dorsal fairing from base of fin to rear of cockpit canopy. All-moving metal tailplane, with glassfibre tips, mid-mounted on extreme rear of fuselage, with cable-controlled full-span anti-servo tab.

LANDING GEAR: Tricycle type, with fixed or optionally rearward-retracting nosewheel and non-retractable main wheels. Nosewheel is steerable by means of the rudder pedals, the controls being disconnected automatically during retraction, which is accomplished electrically. Nosewheel can be locked in the down position during flight, if required. Main-gear legs are cantilever steel struts, inclined outward at 45° from fuselage main bulkhead. Cleveland wheels size 5·00-5; Continental tyres size 5·00-5 on nosewheel and 5·50-5 on main wheels. Streamlined fairings on main wheels. Cleveland hydraulically-actuated brakes. Small skid under rear fuselage, which can be fitted with an adapter for transport by road.

POWER PLANT: One 168 kW (225 hp) modified Lycoming AIO-360-B1B flat-four engine, driving a Hoffmann three-blade constant-speed metal propeller with spinner. Fuel in two tanks in wings, each with capacity of 73·4 litres (19·4 US gallons). Total fuel capacity 146·8 litres (38·8 US gallons). Refuelling point in upper surface of each wing.

ACCOMMODATION: Pilot only, beneath rearward-sliding tinted canopy.

SYSTEMS: DC electrical system for flaps, nose gear actuation and engine starting, provided by 40A engine-driven alternator and 12V 33Ah battery. Hydraulic system for brakes only.

AVIONICS: Becker AR400 radio.

DIMENSIONS, EXTERNAL (A: MY 102; B: MY 103; C: MY 104):
Wing span: A — 7·89 m (25 ft 10⅝ in)
B — 8·40 m (27 ft 6¾ in)
C — 10·46 m (34 ft 3¾ in)
Wing aspect ratio: A — 6·6
B — 6·85
C — 8
Length overall: A, B — 6·40 m (21 ft 0 in)
C — 7·60 m (24 ft 11¼ in)
Height overall: A, B — 2·31 m (7 ft 7 in)
C — 2·38 m (7 ft 9¾ in)

AREAS:
Wings, gross: A — 9·40 m^2 (101·18 sq ft)
B — 10·30 m^2 (110·87 sq ft)
C — 13·50 m^2 (145·32 sq ft)

WEIGHTS AND LOADINGS (B and C estimated):
Weight empty: A — 530 kg (1,168 lb)
B — 554 kg (1,221 lb)
C — 680 kg (1,499 lb)
Max T-O weight (Normal category):
A — 820 kg (1,808 lb)
B — 920 kg (2,028 lb)
C — 1,258 kg (2,773 lb)
Max T-O weight (Aerobatic):
A — 650 kg (1,433 lb)
B — 780 kg (1,720 lb)
Max wing loading (Normal category):
A — 87·23 kg/m^2 (17·87 lb/sq ft)
B — 89·32 kg/m^2 (18·29 lb/sq ft)
C — 93·19 kg/m^2 (19·08 lb/sq ft)
Max wing loading (Aerobatic):
A — 69·15 kg/m^2 (14·16 lb/sq ft)
B — 75·73 kg/m^2 (15·51 lb/sq ft)
Max power loading: A — 4·88 kg/kW (8·04 lb/hp)
B — 5·48 kg/kW (9·01 lb/hp)
C — 7·49 kg/kW (12·32 lb/hp)

PERFORMANCE (at max Normal T-O weight, B and C estimated):
Never-exceed speed:
A, B, C — 216 knots (400 km/h; 249 mph)
Max level speed at S/L:
A — 173 knots (320 km/h; 199 mph)
B — 167 knots (310 km/h; 193 mph)
C — 162 knots (300 km/h; 186 mph)
Cruising speed: A — 159 knots (295 km/h; 183 mph)
B — 154 knots (285 km/h; 177 mph)
C — 148 knots (275 km/h; 171 mph)
Landing speed: A — 48·5 knots (90 km/h; 56 mph)
B, C — 55 knots (102 km/h; 63 mph)
Max rate of climb at S/L: A — 750 m (2,460 ft)/min
B — 600 m (1,970 ft)/min
Service ceiling: A — 7,500 m (24,610 ft)
B — 7,000 m (22,970 ft)
C — 5,000 m (16,400 ft)
Range with max fuel, 15 min reserves:
A — 485 nm (900 km; 559 miles)
B — 647 nm (1,200 km; 745 miles)
C — 782 nm (1,450 km; 900 miles)
Endurance, at 65% power: A — 3 h 30 min
B — 4 h 18 min
C — 5 h 30 min
g limits: A — ±9
B — ±7·5
C — ±4·7

Vibration testing a Hoffmann three-blade constant-speed propeller on the MY 102 Tornado prototype

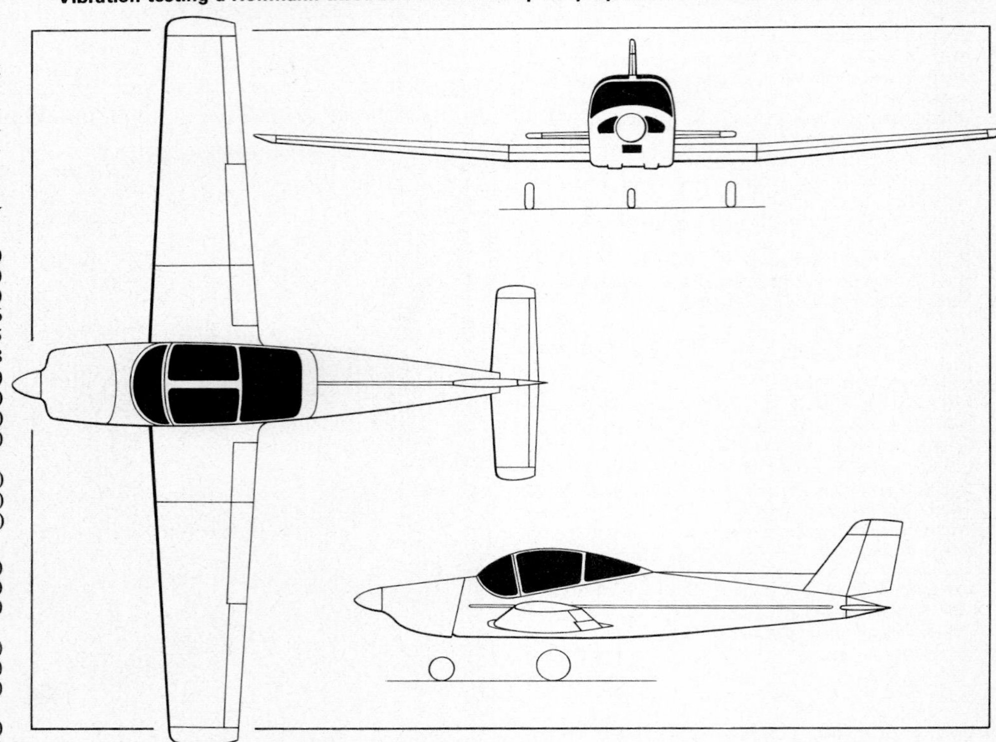

MY 104 Passat four-seat development of the MY 102 *(Michael A. Badrocke)*

RFB

RHEIN-FLUGZEUGBAU GmbH (Subsidiary of VFW-Fokker GmbH)

HEAD OFFICE AND MAIN WORKS: D-4050 Mönchengladbach 1, Flugplatz, Postfach 408
Telephone: (0 21 61) 662031
Telex: 08/52506

OTHER WORKS: D-5050 Porz-Wahn, Flughafen Köln-Bonn, Halle 6; and D-2401 Lübeck-Blankensee, Flugplatz

EXECUTIVE DIRECTORS:
Dipl-Volkswirt Wolfgang Kutscher
Dipl-Ing Alfred Schneider

This company, founded in 1956, has since 1976 held 100% of the stock of Sportavia-Pützer (which see).

RFB is engaged in the development and manufacture of airframe structural components, with particular reference to wings and fuselages made entirely of glassfibre-reinforced resins. Current programmes include series and individual production of aircraft components and assemblies made of light alloy, steel and glassfibre-reinforced resin, for aircraft in quantity production by other German companies, as well as spare parts and ground equipment.

Under contract to the German government, RFB is servicing military aircraft, and is providing target-towing flights and other services with special aircraft. It operates a factory-certificated service centre for all types of Piper aircraft and for the Mitsubishi MU-2 utility transport aircraft. General servicing of other types of all-metal aircraft is undertaken.

In the aircraft propulsion field, RFB has been engaged for some years in the development of specialised applications for ducted propellers, leading to the Fantrainer military multi-purpose training aircraft.

RFB FANTRAINER 400

This tandem two-seat training aircraft was first projected in 1970, at which time a model was exhibited at the Hanover Air Show. It utilises a ducted fan propulsion system which, in the original concept, comprised a Dowty variable-pitch fan, integral with the rear fuselage and driven by a 224 kW (300 hp) Wankel four-disc rotary engine.

In March 1975 it was announced that the Federal German Defence Ministry had awarded RFB a contract to develop and build two Fantrainer prototypes, for evaluation as potential replacements for the Piaggio P.149D primary trainers now used by the Luftwaffe. They were designed to conform to US FAR 23 specifications in the Aerobatic and Utility categories, and it is suggested that pupils might be able to make direct transition from the Fantrainer to the Alpha Jet.

The first prototype, designated **AWI-2**, flew for the first time on 27 October 1977, powered by two 112 kW (150 hp) Wankel engines driving a variable-pitch fan through a reduction gearbox, with airbrakes in the fan shroud. The **ATI-2** second prototype flew for the first time on 31 May 1978 and has one Allison 250-C20B turboshaft engine.

In 1978, the first prototype was brought up to proposed production configuration for the Luftwaffe, as the **Fantrainer 400**, with Allison 250-C20B turboshaft engine.

An uprated version, with 448 kW (600 shp) Allison 250 or Avco Lycoming LTS 101 turboshaft, has been offered to the USAF as a T-37 replacement.

The description which follows applies to the Fantrainer 400:

Type: Two-seat basic and IFR training aircraft. *g* limits +6/−3.

Wings: Cantilever mid-wing monoplane. Wing section Eppler 502. Thickness/chord ratio 15·7%. Dihedral 2° 30′. No incidence. Sweepforward 6° at quarter-chord. Constructed mainly of glassfibre and plastics tube sandwich. Frise-type ailerons and electrically-actuated Fowler-type trailing-edge flaps. No tabs.

Fuselage: The load-carrying fail-safe structure of the forward and centre-fuselage is of light alloy, with non-load-bearing glassfibre skin, sections of which are removable for servicing purposes. Cruciform metal rear fuselage is connected to the centre-fuselage at three points. The integral fan duct is free of structural loads. Large airbrake on each side of fan duct, operation of which causes no lift or stability changes.

Tail Unit: All-metal T-tail of light alloy, with conventional rudder and elevator. Servo tab in trailing-edge of each elevator. Trim tab in rudder.

Landing Gear: Retractable tricycle type, with single wheel on each unit. Electro-hydraulic actuation, with manual emergency extension. All units retract into fuselage, nosewheel forward, main units inward and upward into wing roots. Leaf-spring legs, of glassfibre-reinforced plastics. Cleveland main wheels size 15 × 6·00-6, tyre pressure 4·7 bars (68 lb/sq in). Goodyear nosewheel size 5·00-5, tyre pressure 3·45 bars (50 lb/sq in). Cleveland wheel brakes.

Power Plant: One 313 kW (420 shp) Allison 250-C20B turboshaft engine, driving a Dowty Rotol seven-blade constant-speed ducted fan. Four integral fuel tanks in wings, with combined capacity of 310 litres (68 Imp gallons). Refuelling points at wingtips. Oil capacity 16 litres (3·5 Imp gallons). Engine air intakes in wing leading-edges.

Accommodation: Two seats in tandem cockpit, meeting US MIL specifications in terms of dimensions and layout. Seats and rudder pedals adjustable. Provision for seat and back parachutes. Fighter-type side consoles. Canopy over each seat hinges sideways independently. Accommodation heated and ventilated.

Systems: Electrical system includes a starter/generator and battery. Electro-hydraulic system for operation of landing gear and airbrakes.

Dimensions, external:
- Wing span: 9·60 m (31 ft 6 in)
- Wing chord at root: 1·89 m (6 ft 2½ in)
- Wing chord at tip: 1·02 m (3 ft 4 in)
- Wing aspect ratio: 6·6
- Length overall, incl nose probe: 8·95 m (29 ft 4¼ in)
- Height overall: 2·90 m (9 ft 6 in)
- Tailplane span: 3·29 m (10 ft 9½ in)
- Wheel track: 1·94 m (6 ft 4¼ in)
- Wheelbase: 3·80 m (12 ft 5½ in)
- Fan diameter: 1·20 m (3 ft 11¼ in)

Areas:
- Wings, gross: 13·9 m² (149·6 sq ft)
- Ailerons (total): 1·19 m² (12·81 sq ft)
- Trailing-edge flaps (total): 1·40 m² (15·07 sq ft)
- Rudder, incl tab: 2·20 m² (23·68 sq ft)
- Tailplane: 2·90 m² (31·22 sq ft)
- Elevators, incl tab: 0·77 m² (8·29 sq ft)

Weights and Loadings (A: Aerobatic; B: Utility category):
- Weight empty, equipped: 925 kg (2,040 lb)
- Max T-O weight:
  - A: 1,350 kg (2,976 lb)
  - B: 1,580 kg (3,483 lb)
- Max wing loading:
  - A: 97 kg/m² (19·9 lb/sq ft)
  - B: 114 kg/m² (23·3 lb/sq ft)
- Max power loading:
  - A: 4·3 kg/kW (7·09 lb/shp)
  - B: 5·05 kg/kW (8·29 lb/shp)

Performance (at AUW of 1,580 kg; 3,483 lb):
- Max level speed at S/L: 195 knots (362 km/h; 225 mph)
- Max cruising speed at 3,000 m (9,840 ft): 178 knots (330 km/h; 205 mph)
- Max rate of climb at S/L: 610 m (2,000 ft)/min
- Service ceiling: 6,100 m (20,000 ft)
- T-O run: 230 m (755 ft)
- Landing run: 190 m (625 ft)
- Range at 30% power, 30 min reserves:
  - at 185 knots (343 km/h; 213 mph) at 760 m (2,500 ft): 400 nm (740 km; 460 miles)
  - at 158 knots (293 km/h; 182 mph) at 1,525 m (5,000 ft): 496 nm (920 km; 571 miles)
  - at 161 knots (298 km/h; 185 mph) at 3,800 m (12,500 ft): 651 nm (1,207 km; 750 miles)
- Max range at 915 m (3,000 ft), no reserves: 702 nm (1,300 km; 807 miles)

The ATI-2 second prototype of the Fantrainer, with Allison 250-C20B turboshaft engine

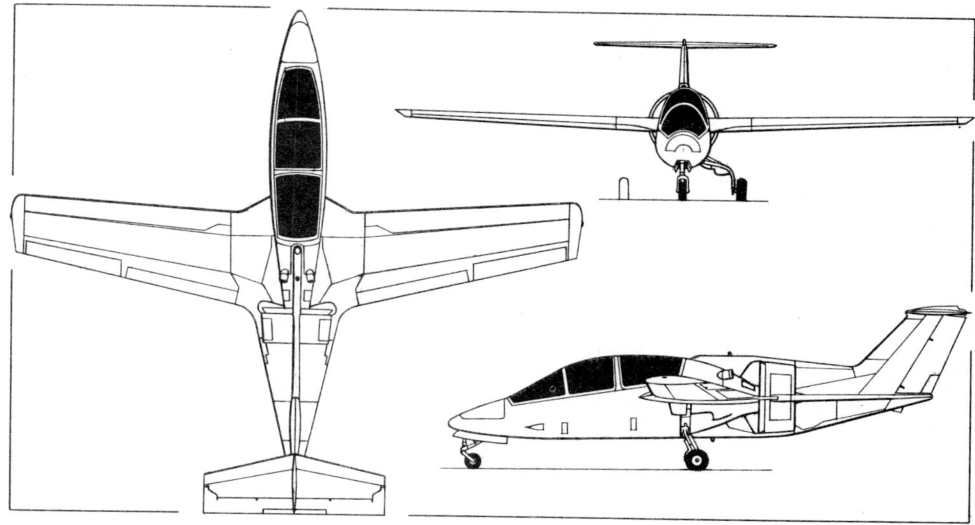

RFB Fantrainer 400 two-seat basic and IFR training aircraft *(Pilot Press)*

SPORTAVIA

SPORTAVIA-PÜTZER GmbH u Co KG

Head Office and Works: D-5377 Dahlem-Schmidtheim, Flugplatz Dahlemer Binz

Telephone: (02447) 277/8

Telex: 08 33 602

Sales Manager: Alfons Pützer

This company was formed in 1966 by Comte Antoine d'Assche, director of the French company Alpavia SA, and Herr Alfons Pützer, originally to take over from Alpavia manufacture of the Avion-Planeur series of light aircraft designed by M René Fournier.

In 1969, RFB (which see), a subsidiary of VFW-Fokker GmbH, acquired a 50% holding in Sportavia: the remaining shares were acquired in January 1977, from which date Sportavia became wholly owned by RFB.

In current production is a four-seat lightweight sporting aircraft known as the RS 180 Sportsman.

Sportavia was also responsible for developing the P.68 Observer variant of the Partenavia P.68B Victor twin-engined light aircraft (see Italian section).

SPORTAVIA RS 180 SPORTSMAN

M René Fournier began design of the Sportsman in December 1970. Construction of the first of two prototypes started fourteen months later, and this aircraft made its first flight on 1 March 1973, powered by a 93 kW (125 hp) Lycoming O-235-F2A engine.

Sportavia RS 180 Sportsman four-seat light aircraft (Lycoming O-360-A3A engine)

The second prototype, a completely new four-seat design developed by Sportavia, had the designation RF6C, and this flew for the first time on 28 April 1976. It differed from the first prototype in having a more powerful engine, increased cabin volume, and a GRP outer skin.

The RF6C entered production in late 1976. The change of designation to RS 180 took effect in early 1978, simultaneously with raising of the tailplane from its original position at the top of the fuselage.

Type: Four-seat lightweight sporting aircraft.

Wings: Cantilever low-wing monoplane. Wing section NACA 63-218 at root, NACA 63-215 at tip. Dihedral 5° from roots. Incidence 0°. One-piece single spar of laminated beech, birch plywood and pine ribs, mahogany plywood covering (upper surfaces only), and GRP outer skin. All-metal split flap on each trailing-edge, with electrical actuation. Fabric-covered wooden Frise-type ailerons, actuated by pushrods. No tabs. Turned-down wingtips.

FUSELAGE: Conventional wooden structure of frames and longerons, with mahogany plywood covering and GRP outer skin.

TAIL UNIT: Cantilever wooden structure, with GRP-covered fixed surfaces and fabric-covered control surfaces. Fixed-incidence tailplane mounted part-way up fin. Rudder and elevators actuated by pushrods. Flettner tab in port elevator.

LANDING GEAR: Non-retractable tricycle type. Main units have hydraulic shock-absorption. Steerable nosewheel, with oleo-pneumatic shock-absorber. Single wheel on each unit. Hydraulic disc brakes. Streamline fairings over all three wheels.

POWER PLANT: One 134 kW (180 hp) Lycoming O-360-A3A flat-four engine, driving a Hoffmann two-blade wooden fixed-pitch propeller for glider towing, or two-blade metal propeller for towing, in each case with spinner. Fuel tank in each wing, combined capacity 210 litres (46·2 Imp gallons), of which 206 litres (45·3 Imp gallons) are usable. Overwing refuelling point above each tank. Oil capacity 6·5 litres (1·5 Imp gallons).

ACCOMMODATION: Four seats in side-by-side pairs under rearward-sliding Perspex 'bubble' canopy. 'Solid' canopy roof is standard on production aircraft. Dual controls. Cabin heated and ventilated.

SYSTEMS: Hydraulic system for brakes. Electrical power provided by 12V 60A engine-driven generator.

AVIONICS AND EQUIPMENT: Radio, radio navigation equipment and full blind-flying instrumentation to customer's requirements.

DIMENSIONS, EXTERNAL:

Wing span	10·50 m (34 ft 5½ in)
Wing aspect ratio	7·6
Wing taper ratio	0·65
Length overall	7·15 m (23 ft 5½ in)
Height overall	2·55 m (8 ft 4⅜ in)
Propeller diameter	1·80 m (5 ft 10¾ in)

AREA:

Wings, gross	14·50 m² (156·08 sq ft)

WEIGHTS AND LOADINGS:

Weight empty	640 kg (1,411 lb)
Max T-O weight	1,100 kg (2,425 lb)
Max wing loading	75·86 kg/m² (15·54 lb/sq ft)
Max power loading	8·19 kg/kW (13·47 lb/hp)

PERFORMANCE (at max T-O weight):

Never-exceed speed	172 knots (320 km/h; 198 mph)
Cruising speed, 75% power at 2,590 m (8,500 ft):	
wood propeller	122 knots (225 km/h; 140 mph)
metal propeller	132 knots (245 km/h; 152 mph)
Stalling speed, flaps up	59 knots (110 km/h; 68·5 mph)
Stalling speed, flaps down	49 knots (90 km/h; 56 mph)
Max rate of climb at S/L	324 m (1,063 ft)/min
Service ceiling	5,400 m (17,725 ft)
T-O run	181 m (594 ft)
T-O to 15 m (50 ft)	450 m (1,476 ft)
Range with max fuel, no reserves	750 nm (1,390 km; 864 miles)

VFW-FOKKER

VEREINIGTE FLUGTECHNISCHE WERKE-FOKKER GmbH (Subsidiary of ZENTRALGESELLSCHAFT VFW-FOKKER mbH)

HEAD OFFICE: Hünefeldstrasse 1-5, 2800 Bremen 1 (Postfach 1206)

Telephone: (0421) 538-1

Telex: 245 821

WORKS: Bremen, Einswarden, Hoykenkamp, Lemwerder, Speyer and Varel

DIRECTORS:

Dipl Ing Johann Schäffler (Chairman)

Dipl Volkswirt August Ackermann (Finance)

Dipl Ing Hans E. W. Hoffmann (Research and Development)

Bernd Kosegarten (Marketing and Personnel)

PUBLIC RELATIONS MANAGER: Joseph Grendel

The Vereinigte Flugtechnische Werke GmbH (VFW) was formed at the end of 1963 by a merger of the two Bremen-based aircraft companies of Focke-Wulf GmbH and 'Weser' Flugzeugbau GmbH. They were joined in 1964 by Ernst Heinkel Flugzeugbau GmbH. Details of the history and products of these former companies can be found in earlier editions of *Jane's*.

In 1968-69, VFW acquired 65% of the shares of RFB (Rhein-Flugzeugbau GmbH, which see) but has since become 100% shareholder and has also a 50% holding in Henschel Flugzeugwerke AG of Kassel.

With effect from 1 January 1970, VFW became an equal partner with Fokker of the Netherlands in a company known as Zentralgesellschaft VFW-Fokker mbH, with headquarters in Düsseldorf. The two partners continued to operate independently, as subsidiaries of Zentralgesellschaft VFW-Fokker. The name of the VFW company was changed to VFW-Fokker GmbH as a consequence of the amalgamation.

VFW is a partner in the Fokker F28 and Transall C-160 transport programmes, and is collaborating also in development and production of the Panavia Tornado multi-role combat aircraft, General Dynamics F-16 fighter and Airbus A300/A310.

Other work includes the overhaul and repair of Transall C-160, JetStar, CH-53G and Sea King aircraft, together with modification work on the F-104G.

Through its wholly-owned subsidiary, ERNO Raumfahrttechnik GmbH, VFW-Fokker is participating in the Spacelab programme as prime contractor.

GREECE

HAI

HELLENIC AEROSPACE INDUSTRY LTD

ADDRESS: Athens Tower, 2-4 Mesogion Street, Athens 610

Telephone: 779 9678

Telex: 21-9528 HAI GR

GENERAL MANAGER: H. E. Mack

MARKETING DIRECTOR: R. P. Stone

Steps to establish a national 'aerospace support facility' in Greece were first taken by the Greek government in late 1971. A bill approving the establishment of such a facility was passed, by the government then in power, in the Summer of 1975; and on 26 November 1975 contracts worth $120 million were signed in Athens between the Greek government and the four US companies which were to design, build and operate the facility: Lockheed Corporation, the Austin Company of New York, Westinghouse Electric Corporation and General Electric.

Lockheed Aircraft International has overall responsibility for managing the centre, and for all airframe work; management, and selective technical/training personnel, were supplied initially by Lockheed Aircraft Service Co. Austin is architect and directs the construction contractors for the plant. Lockheed is responsible for the workshops, Westinghouse for overhaul and repair of electronics, and General Electric for aero-engine overhaul and maintenance.

The new facility, known as Hellenic Aerospace Industry (HAI), is being built on a 185 hectare (457 acre) site adjacent to the present Hellenic Air Force base at Tanagra, about 60 km (37 miles) north of Athens. It was officially dedicated by the Greek Prime Minister, Mr Karamanlis, on 4 February 1977, and the first building went into operation on 15 May 1978. Hangars, workshops and offices will occupy some 83,613 m² (900,000 sq ft). The facility was scheduled for completion in September 1979, but the first two Hellenic Air Force aircraft (F-4 Phantoms) were accepted for maintenance and overhaul in January 1979, and 55 aircraft were scheduled to arrive before the end of that year. HAI will provide depot level maintenance for the Hellenic Air Force, maintenance and manufacturing for airlines, and will eventually employ about 3,000 people.

INDIA

HAL

HINDUSTAN AERONAUTICS LIMITED

ADDRESS: Indian Express Building, Vidhana Veedhi, PO Box 5150, Bangalore 560 001

Telephone: 76901 (8 lines)

Telex: 845-266 HAL IN

CHAIRMAN: Air Marshal S. J. Dastur (Retd)

DIRECTORS:

A. Chandmal

P. D. Chopra (Managing Director, Bangalore Complex)

Air Marshal L. S. Grewal

L. K. Joshi

B. K. Kapur (Managing Director, Accessories Complex)

S. C. Keshu (Managing Director, MiG Complex)

Dr D. N. Prasad

Raj Mahindra (Managing Director, Design and Development)

Dr R. Ramanna

Dr S. R. Valluri

S. Vasudevan

GENERAL MANAGERS:

Bangalore Complex:

S. K. Ohri (Aircraft Division)

K. K. Kirtikar (Engine Division)

Gp Capt Willie Raj (Overhaul Division)

N. Nagaraja Rao (Foundry and Forge Division)

K. N. R. Swamy (Helicopter Division)

MiG Complex:

Harsimran Singh (Nasik Division)

G. Narasimhan (Koraput Division)

Accessories Complex:

Gp Capt R. S. Sivaswamy (Retd) (Hyderabad Division)

H. K. Singh (Lucknow Division)

Kanpur Division:

B. S. Balooja (OFFG)

Hindustan Aeronautics Limited (HAL) was formed on 1 October 1964, amalgamating the former Hindustan Aircraft Ltd (formed 1940) and Aeronautics India Ltd (formed 1963), and has 10 Divisions, five at Bangalore and one each at Nasik, Koraput, Hyderabad, Kanpur and Lucknow, with a total work force of about 40,000 people. The company, whose principal customer is the Indian Air Force, is currently manufacturing and overhauling many types of aircraft, helicopters, and their related aero-engines, avionics, instruments and accessories. It is also manufacturing components for satellites on behalf of the Indian Space Research Organisation (ISRO).

The Bangalore Complex is engaged in the manufacture of military aircraft and aero-engines, both under licence and of indigenous design. This Complex has a large organisation undertaking repair and overhaul of airframes, engines, and allied instruments and accessories. It has also a self-contained foundry and forge.

Kanpur Division has been engaged mainly in the manufacture of different versions of the British Aerospace HS 748 under licence. It is responsible for series production of the Basant agricultural aircraft, designed at the Bangalore design bureau.

Nasik, Koraput and Hyderabad Divisions are manufacturing the airframe, engine and avionics respectively of the Soviet MiG-21 fighter with the collaboration of the USSR.

Lucknow Division, formed in late 1969, is producing aircraft accessories under licence from various manufacturers in the UK, France and the USSR, including wheels and brakes, ejection seats, instruments, fuel accessories, air-conditioning and pressurisation systems. The Division has successfully developed a number of electrical and hydraulic accessories which have entered production. It is planned to begin manufacturing gyros for use in airborne systems.

In addition to its manufacturing programmes, HAL is pursuing design and development activities relating to aircraft, helicopters, avionics and accessories. The design bureau at Bangalore is engaged in the design and development of the HPT-32 piston-engined basic trainer, an armed version of the HJT-16 Kiran, and a trainer version of the Ajeet. In mid-1979, HAL and Dornier of Germany were discussing the possibility of a joint programme to develop and produce the Dornier LTA twin-turboprop light transport. The helicopter design department at Bangalore is designing an Advanced Light Helicopter (ALH) with the assistance of Aérospatiale of France. The avionics design department at Hyderabad is pursuing the design and development of airborne electronic equipment, and the design department at Lucknow is developing aircraft instruments and accessories.

BANGALORE COMPLEX

ADDRESS: Bangalore Complex 560 017 (Karnataka State)
Telephone: 53201 and 50773

The Bangalore Complex of HAL consists essentially of the former Hindustan Aircraft Limited, the activities of which, since its formation in 1940, were described in previous editions of *Jane's*. The Complex is subdivided into an Aircraft Division, Helicopter Division, Engine Division, Overhaul Division, and Foundry and Forge Division.

Bangalore Complex is engaged in producing aircraft designed and developed by the HAL design bureau, and also in manufacturing various aircraft and aero-engines under licence. The Engine Division's activities are described in the appropriate section of this edition.

Licence production of Aérospatiale SA 315B Lama and SA 316B Alouette III helicopters, undertaken initially by the Aircraft Division, is undertaken by the Helicopter Division, officially inaugurated on 19 July 1974.

The Overhaul Division of Bangalore Complex repairs and overhauls HAL HF-24 and HT-2 and Hawker Siddeley (de Havilland) Dove/Devon aircraft, DHC-4 Caribou, Fairchild C-119 Packet transports and English Electric Canberra bombers, and various piston engines. Jet engines are overhauled at the Engine Division. The branch factory at Barrackpore near Calcutta continues to concentrate on repair and overhaul of DC-3s of the Indian Air Force and non-scheduled operators.

HAL HF-24 MARUT (WIND SPIRIT)

Development of the HF-24 Marut single-seat ground attack fighter was started by HAL in 1956. The first prototype HF-24 Mk I, powered by two Bristol Orpheus 703 turbojet engines, flew for the first time on 17 June 1961. The first series production Marut flew on 15 November 1967, and the first of two prototype tandem two-seat Mk IT training versions on 30 April 1970.

Production of the Mk I (129 built) and Mk IT (18 built) ended in 1977. A full description and illustrations of these aircraft can be found in the 1977-78 *Jane's*.

Plans are in hand to develop the Mk I into a tactical air support aircraft, by fitting a new power plant and systems.

HAL HJT-16 Mk I KIRAN (RAY OF LIGHT)

In December 1959, the government of India approved the design and development by HAL of a side-by-side two-seat jet basic trainer designated HJT-16 Mk I, powered by a Rolls-Royce Viper 11 turbojet.

Detailed design work on the HJT-16 Mk I began in April 1961 under the leadership of Dr V. M. Ghatage. The first prototype flew for the first time on 4 September 1964. It was followed by a second aircraft in August 1965.

A total of 24 pre-production HJT-16 Mk Is were delivered to the Indian Air Force, the initial delivery (of six aircraft) being made in March 1968. The HJT-16 Mk I is now in series production. By 1 January 1979 a total of 144 had been produced, to meet the requirements of both the Indian Air Force and Indian Navy. Total IAF/IN requirement is for 190 aircraft.

The Kiran is suitable for use in armament training or light attack roles, and the 119th and subsequent Kirans, designated **Mk IA**, are fitted with a hardpoint beneath each wing capable of carrying weapons or a drop-tank. In addition, HAL is developing a Mk II version of the Kiran for these roles, and this is described separately.

HAL HJT-16 Mk IA Kiran two-seat jet basic trainer

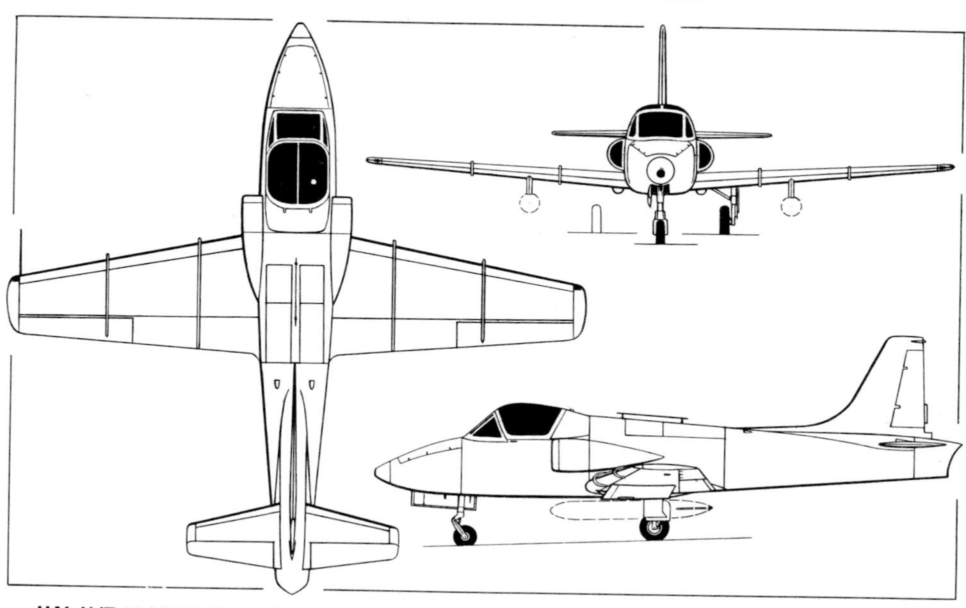

HAL HJT-16 Mk IA Kiran side-by-side two-seat jet basic trainer and light attack aircraft *(Pilot Press)*

TYPE: Two-seat jet basic trainer.

WINGS: Cantilever low-wing monoplane. Wing section NACA 23015 at root, NACA 23012 at tip. Dihedral 4° from roots. Incidence 0° 30′ at root. Conventional all-metal three-spar structure. Frise-type differential ailerons. Hydraulically-actuated trailing-edge split flaps. Two full-chord boundary layer fences on upper surface of each wing.

FUSELAGE: All-metal semi-monocoque structure of light alloy. Hydraulically-actuated door-type airbrake under centre of fuselage.

TAIL UNIT: Cantilever all-metal structure. Electrically-operated variable-incidence tailplane. Ground-adjustable tab on rudder.

LANDING GEAR: Retractable tricycle type, of HAL manufacture. Hydraulic actuation. Main units retract inward into fuselage; self-centering twin-contact non-steerable nosewheel retracts forward. Oleo-pneumatic shock-absorbers. Main-wheel tyres size 19 × 6·25-9, pressure 6·21 bars (90 lb/sq in). Nosewheel tyre size 15·4 × 4-6, pressure 4·83 bars (70 lb/sq in). Hydraulic brakes, without cooling.

POWER PLANT: One 11·12 kN (2,500 lb st) Rolls-Royce Viper 11 turbojet engine. Internal fuel in main saddle tanks in fuselage (two 209 litre; 46 Imp gallon), wing centre-section collector tank (282 litres; 62 Imp gallons) and outboard wing tanks (two 218 litre; 48 Imp gallon), giving total capacity of 1,137 litres (250 Imp gallons). Provision for two underwing tanks with total capacity of 454 litres (100 Imp gallons). System permits 30 s of inverted flight.

ACCOMMODATION: Crew of two side by side in air-conditioned and pressurised cockpit, on Martin-Baker Mk H4 HA zero-altitude fully-automatic ejection seats. Clamshell-type canopy. Dual controls and duplicated blind-flying instruments.

SYSTEMS: Air-conditioning system has max pressure differential of 0·12 bars (1·75 lb/sq in). Dowty hydraulic system for landing gear, flaps and airbrake, pressure 207 bars (3,000 lb/sq in). Accumulator for manual emergency system. Electrical system is of 28V DC single-wire earth return type, with two 24V 25Ah batteries. Normalair pressure-demand oxygen system.

AVIONICS AND EQUIPMENT: STR 9X/M 10-channel VHF transceiver, AX-3 single-channel VHF standby set and Marconi Avionics DFA-73 ADF manufactured by BEL-India. Landing light in nose.

ARMAMENT: Hardpoint beneath each wing of 119th and subsequent aircraft, each capable of carrying a 500 lb bomb, an HAL pod containing two 7·62 mm FN machine-guns, a pod containing seven 68 mm SNEB rockets, or a 227 litre (50 Imp gallon) drop-tank.

DIMENSIONS, EXTERNAL:

Wing span	10·70 m (35 ft 1¼ in)
Wing chord at root	2·35 m (7 ft 8½ in)
Wing chord at tip	1·02 m (3 ft 4 in)
Wing aspect ratio	6
Length overall	10·60 m (34 ft 9 in)
Height overall	3·635 m (11 ft 11 in)
Tailplane span	3·90 m (12 ft 9½ in)
Wheel track	2·42 m (7 ft 11 in)
Wheelbase	3·50 m (11 ft 6 in)

AREAS:

Wings, gross	19·00 m² (204·5 sq ft)
Ailerons (total)	1·55 m² (16·68 sq ft)
Flaps (total)	2·34 m² (25·19 sq ft)
Vertical tail surfaces (total)	2·10 m² (22·60 sq ft)
Rudder, incl tab	0·714 m² (7·69 sq ft)
Horizontal tail surfaces (total)	3·72 m² (40·04 sq ft)
Elevators	1·14 m² (12·27 sq ft)

WEIGHTS AND LOADINGS:

Weight empty	2,560 kg (5,644 lb)
Normal T-O weight	3,600 kg (7,936 lb)
Max T-O weight (with two 50 Imp gallon drop-tanks)	4,100 kg (9,039 lb)
Max wing loading	190 kg/m² (38·9 lb/sq ft)
Thrust/weight ratio	0·315

PERFORMANCE (at normal T-O weight):

Max level speed at S/L	375 knots (695 km/h; 432 mph)
Max level speed at 9,150 m (30,000 ft)	371 knots (688 km/h; 427 mph)
Max cruising speed	175 knots (324 km/h; 201 mph)
Stalling speed, flaps and landing gear up	81 knots (151 km/h; 94 mph)
Stalling speed, flaps and landing gear down	71 knots (132 km/h; 82 mph)
Ceiling	9,150 m (30,000 ft)
Time to 9,150 m (30,000 ft)	20 min
Min ground turning radius	5·50 m (18 ft 0½ in)
T-O run	442 m (1,450 ft)
Endurance on internal fuel at 230 knots (426 km/h; 265 mph) at 9,150 m (30,000 ft)	1 h 45 min

HAL KIRAN Mk II

This version of the Kiran, suitable for armament training or counter-insurgency duties, is being developed by the HAL design bureau at Bangalore. Principal differences include improved weapon-carrying capability, a more powerful engine, updated avionics and an improved hydraulic system. The engine is a derated version of the Orpheus 701 turbojet, rated at 15·1 kN (3,400 lb st), which gives the Kiran Mk II improved maximum speed, climb and manoeuvrability. The range, with two underwing drop-tanks fitted as standard, remains the same as for the Mk I. A prototype was flown for the first time on 30 July 1976; this is being followed by a second prototype.

ARMAMENT: Two 7·62 mm machine-guns in nose, with 250 rds/gun. Two Ferranti F 195R ISIS gunsights, with common control unit. Two hardpoints beneath each wing, the inboard ones each capable of carrying a 227 litre (50 Imp gallon) drop-tank, a 500 lb high-explosive bomb, a Type 122·1 68 mm rocket pod or a 25 lb practice bomb carrier. Each outboard pylon is capable of carrying a similar weapon load or drop-tank.

HAL AJEET (INVINCIBLE)

The Hawker Siddeley Gnat light fighter and fighter-bomber was built under licence by HAL between 1962 and 1974, as described in the 1974-75 and 1975-76 editions of *Jane's*.

The design bureau completed in 1974 the design of a Mk II version of the Gnat known as the Ajeet, with improved performance characteristics and equipment, including improved communications and navigation systems; more reliable longitudinal control; and increased combat capability. The last-named characteristic is achieved by a redesigned fuel system, dispensing with the underwing drop-tanks in favour of integral wing tanks, so permitting additional underwing armament to be carried.

The last two Gnat Mk I aircraft were converted as prototypes for the Ajeet; the first of these was flown on 5 March 1975, and the second on 5 November 1975.

First flight of a production Ajeet was made on 30 September 1976. By mid-January 1979 a total of 23 Ajeets had been completed, of approximately 80 then on order.

Type: Single-seat lightweight interceptor and ground attack aircraft.

Wings: Cantilever shoulder-wing monoplane. Sweptback wings, of RAE 102 section. Thickness/chord ratio 8%. Anhedral 5°. Sweepback 40° at quarter-chord. One-piece wing of two-spar thick-skin light alloy construction, fitting into recess in top of fuselage and secured by bolts at four points. Inboard ailerons, powered by hydraulic actuators, droop 22° to serve as flaps when the landing gear is lowered.

Fuselage: Light alloy semi-monocoque structure of pressed frames and extruded stringers.

Tail Unit: Cantilever all-metal structure. Three-spar sweptback fin, integral with fuselage. One-piece three-spar variable-incidence tailplane, operated hydraulically by modified Hobson PFC 1003 actuator. Rear portions of tailplane can be unlocked to perform as elevators; or locked to provide the functions of an all-moving tailplane. Ground-adjustable tab on rudder.

Landing Gear: Retractable tricycle type, all units retracting rearward hydraulically into fuselage. Dowty Rotol oleo-pneumatic shock-absorber struts. Wheel well fairings attached to individual landing gear units serve as airbrakes when landing gear is partly lowered, the relative movements of the airbrakes being so adjusted that no change of trim occurs at any speed. Dunlop mainwheel tyres size 20 × 5·25, pressure 9·3 bars (135 lb/sq in); twin nosewheel tyres, size 17 × 3·25, pressure 5·65 bars (82 lb/sq in). Hydraulically operated brakes and Maxaret anti-skid units on main wheels. Braking parachute in fairing at base of fin.

Power Plant: One Rolls-Royce Orpheus 701-01 non-afterburning turbojet engine, rated at 20 kN (4,500 lb st). Compressed-air starting. Air intakes in sides of fuselage. Seven crashproof flexible tanks and two metal tanks in fuselage, and two 250 litre (55 Imp gallon) integral wing tanks. Total internal fuel capacity 1,350 litres (297 Imp gallons). Fuel supplied to engine by electrically-driven booster pump in one of the tanks. Provision for two 150 litre (33 Imp gallon) underwing drop-tanks.

Accommodation: Pilot only, on Martin-Baker GF-4 zero-height/90 knot (167 km/h; 104 mph) lightweight ejection seat. Pressurised, heated and air-conditioned cockpit, with jettisonable canopy which is hinged at rear and opens upward.

Systems: Normalair air-conditioning and pressurisation system, max differential of 0·24 bars (3·5 lb/sq in) at 12,800 m (42,000 ft). Oxygen system with demand-type regulator. Dowty hydraulic system of 207 bars (3,000 lb/sq in), with Abex pump, for aileron, landing gear, main-wheel brake and tailplane actuation. 28V DC electrical system, with 3·5kW Rotax generator and two 12V 25Ah Varley batteries. Oxygen system for pilot.

Avionics and Equipment: Bendix TA/RA-22 VHF transceiver (initially; V/UHF later) and BEL AX-3 standby VHF set; Bendix DFA-73 ADF; IFF Mk 10 (BAT) transponder.

Armament: Two 30 mm Aden Mk 4 cannon in air intake fairings, one on each side of fuselage, with 90 rds/gun. Ferranti F 195R/3 ISIS weapons sight. Vinten G90 gun camera. Four underwing hardpoints able to carry two 500 lb bombs (inner pylons), four Arrow Type 122 pods each containing eighteen 68 mm rockets, or two 150 litre (33 Imp gallon) drop-tanks (outer pylons).

Dimensions, external:

Wing span	6·73 m (22 ft 1 in)
Wing chord at c/l	2·58 m (8 ft 5·6 in)
Wing chord at tip	1·17 m (3 ft 10 in)
Wing area, gross	14·65 m² (157·7 sq ft)
Wing aspect ratio	3·575
Length overall	9·04 m (29 ft 8 in)
Height overall	2·46 m (8 ft 1 in)
Tailplane span	2·84 m (9 ft 4 in)
Wheel track	1·55 m (5 ft 1 in)
Wheelbase	2·36 m (7 ft 9 in)

Weights and Loadings:

Basic weight empty	2,307 kg (5,086 lb)
T-O weight 'clean'	3,539 kg (7,803 lb)
Max T-O weight	4,170 kg (9,195 lb)
Normal landing weight	2,767 kg (6,100 lb)
Max wing loading	284·6 kg/m² (58·3 lb/sq ft)

Prototype of the HAL Kiran Mk II armament training and counter-insurgency aircraft

Prototype of the Ajeet lightweight combat aircraft, developed by HAL from the Hawker Siddeley Gnat

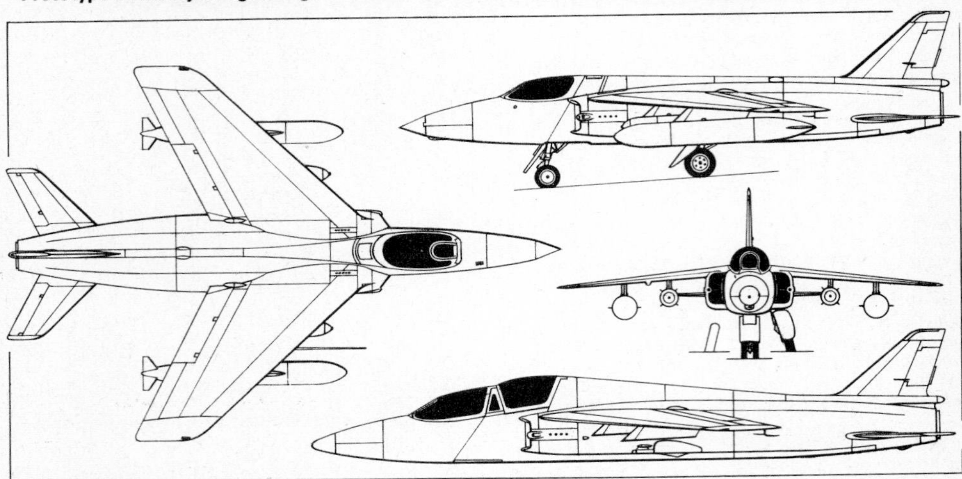
HAL Ajeet lightweight interceptor/ground attack aircraft, with additional side view (bottom) of trainer version *(Pilot Press)*

Performance (in configurations indicated; A: ISA; B: ISA + 15°C; C: ISA + 30°C):

Max Mach No. at 12,000 m (39,375 ft) at 'clean' T-O weight: A 0·96
B 0·953
C 0·948

Max level speed at S/L at 'clean' T-O weight:
A 595 knots (1,102 km/h; 685 mph)
B 612 knots (1,134 km/h; 705 mph)
C 622 knots (1,152 km/h; 716 mph)

Time to 12,000 m (39,375 ft) from brakes off, at 'clean' T-O weight: A 6 min 2 s
B 7 min 43 s
C 9 min 33 s

Service ceiling: A, B, C 13,720 m (45,000 ft)

Turning performance at 450 knots (834 km/h; 518 mph) IAS at S/L: A 5·30g
B 5·28g
C 5·00g

T-O run at S/L, zero wind, at T-O weight of 4,136 kg (9,118 lb) with two Arrow rocket pods and two 33 Imp gallon drop-tanks: A 1,034 m (3,390 ft)
B 1,180 m (3,870 ft)
C 1,376 m (4,515 ft)

Landing run 'clean' at S/L, zero wind, at normal landing weight, no brake 'chute: A 951 m (3,120 ft)
B 997 m (3,270 ft)
C 1,047 m (3,435 ft)

Landing run 'clean' at S/L, zero wind, at normal landing weight, with brake 'chute: A 658 m (2,160 ft)
B 695 m (2,280 ft)
C 725 m (2,379 ft)

Combat radius (A, B and C), low level ground attack mission:
with two 500 lb bombs on inboard stations 110 nm (204 km; 127 miles)
with two Arrow rocket pods inboard and two 33 Imp gallon drop-tanks outboard 140 nm (259 km; 161 miles)
with four Arrow rocket pods 104 nm (193 km; 120 miles)

HAL AJEET TRAINER

This tandem two-seat trainer version of the Ajeet, which retains the four underwing hardpoints and full combat capability of the single-seater, is evolved in a similar manner to that in which the T.Mk 1 trainer was evolved from the original Gnat fighter. To accommodate the second cockpit, two of the fuselage fuel tanks are deleted, although this can be offset by deleting the Aden cannon to make room for an additional 273 litres (60 Imp gallons) of fuel internally; in this event, provision is made for carrying a 7·62 mm gun pod on each of the inboard wing pylons. Sections 0·70 m (2 ft 3½ in) long are inserted in the fuselage fore and aft of the wings, increasing the overall length of the Ajeet Trainer to 10·44 m (34 ft 3 in).

The Ajeet Trainer is powered by a single Orpheus 701 turbojet engine, and retains the main hydraulic system and powered flying controls of the single-seater. Normal and emergency operation of the landing gear is also similar, but with duplicated controls and a mechanical override facility in the rear cockpit. All instruments, including those for blind flying, are duplicated in the rear cockpit, which will be illuminated, air-conditioned and pressurised similarly to the front cockpit. A gunsight is fitted in the front cockpit only. Both occupants are provided with Martin-Baker GF-4 ejection seats. Avionics and equipment include a multi-channel VHF transceiver (to be replaced eventually by a V/UHF set), ADF and IFF Mk 10.

A prototype is under construction, and is expected to undergo evaluation in 1980-81.

HAL HPT-32

Currently under development for the Indian Air Force, the HPT-32 is a fully-aerobatic piston-engined basic trainer, with side-by-side seats for instructor and pupil and a third seat at the rear. A four-seat version is under consideration for the liaison role. The trainer can be used for a wide range of ab initio training, including instrument, navigation, night flying and formation flying; for armed patrol; for observation, liaison or sport flying; or for weapon training, light strike duties, supply dropping, search and rescue, reconnaissance, or glider or target towing. The airframe, which is of all-metal construction, is designed to FAR 23, and is expected to have a fatigue life of 6,500 h.

The first prototype (X2157) made its first flight on 6 January 1977; a second was under construction in 1979.

TYPE: Two/three-seat basic trainer or four-seat liaison aircraft.

WINGS: Cantilever low-wing monoplane of all-metal construction. Dihedral 5° from roots. Incidence 2° 30′ at root. Ground-adjustable tab on each aileron.

FUSELAGE: All-metal semi-monocoque structure.

TAIL UNIT: Cantilever all-metal structure, with sweptback vertical surfaces. One-piece elevator. Trim tabs in rudder and port half of elevator.

LANDING GEAR: Non-retractable tricycle type on prototype and ab initio version. Main wheels size 6·00-6·5, nosewheel 5·00-5. Dunlop tyres on all wheels, pressure 2·41-2·76 bars (35-40 lb/sq in) on main units, 3·10 bars (45 lb/sq in) on nose unit..

POWER PLANT: Prototype powered by 194 kW (260 hp) Lycoming AEIO-540-D4B5 flat-six engine, driving a Hartzell two-blade constant-speed metal propeller with spinner. Two integral wing fuel tanks, with total capacity of 227 litres (50 Imp gallons); provision for 136·5 litre (30 Imp gallon) tank in place of rear seat. For production aircraft, an indigenous engine of similar power is under development.

ACCOMMODATION: Side-by-side seats for two persons in front, with provision for one or two seats plus baggage space at rear, under rearward-sliding jettisonable framed canopy. Front two seats adjustable in height by 127 mm (5 in); rear seat(s) not adjustable. Full dual controls, and adjustable rudder pedals, for instructor and pupil.

ARMAMENT AND EQUIPMENT: Four underwing attachments for armament or other stores, up to a total of 255 kg (562 lb). VHF radio.

DIMENSIONS, EXTERNAL:

Wing span	9·50 m (31 ft 2 in)
Wing chord at root	2·24 m (7 ft 4¼ in)
Wing chord at tip	0·92 m (3 ft 0¼ in)
Wing aspect ratio	6·013
Length overall	7·715 m (25 ft 3¾ in)
Height overall	3·27 m (10 ft 8¾ in)
Wheel track	3·45 m (11 ft 4 in)
Wheelbase	2·10 m (6 ft 10¾ in)
Propeller diameter	2·032 m (6 ft 8 in)
Propeller ground clearance (static)	0·241 m (9½ in)

AREAS:

Wings, gross	15·01 m² (161·6 sq ft)
Ailerons (total)	1·04 m² (11·19 sq ft)
Trailing-edge flaps (total)	1·83 m² (19·70 sq ft)
Fin	2·316 m² (24·93 sq ft)
Rudder, incl tab	1·078 m² (11·60 sq ft)
Tailplane	3·02 m² (32·50 sq ft)
Elevator, incl tab	1·35 m² (14·53 sq ft)

WEIGHTS AND LOADINGS:

Weight empty	926 kg (2,041 lb)
Normal T-O weight	1,250 kg (2,756 lb)
Max T-O weight	1,375 kg (3,031 lb)
Max wing loading	91·6 kg/m² (18·76 lb/sq ft)
Max power loading	7·09 kg/kW (11·66 lb/hp)

PERFORMANCE (at Normal T-O weight, ISA):

Max level speed at S/L	117 knots (217 km/h; 135 mph)
Stalling speed, flaps up	59 knots (110 km/h; 68 mph)
Stalling speed, flaps down	55 knots (102 km/h; 63 mph)
Max rate of climb at S/L	335 m (1,100 ft)/min
Service ceiling	4,750 m (15,580 ft)
T-O run	205 m (673 ft)
Range at 1,525 m (5,000 ft) with 50 Imp gallons fuel	378 nm (700 km; 435 miles)
Endurance at 1,525 m (5,000 ft) with 50 Imp gallons fuel	4 h 0 min
g limits	+6·0; −3·0

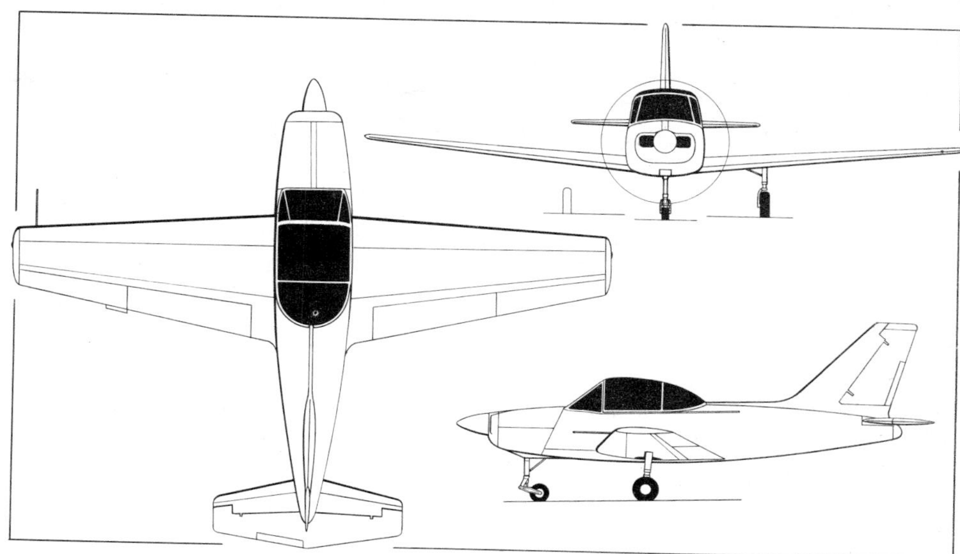

HAL HPT-32 two/three-seat basic trainer, as projected with retractable landing gear *(Pilot Press)*

First prototype HAL HPT-32 two/three-seat basic training aircraft

HAL Cheetah, Indian-assembled version of the Aérospatiale SA 315B Lama helicopter

HAL-assembled Aérospatiale Alouette III helicopter in Indian military insignia

HAL (AÉROSPATIALE) SA 315B LAMA

Indian name: Cheetah

The Bangalore Complex's Helicopter Division is building the French Aérospatiale SA 315B Lama five-seat general-purpose helicopter (which see) under licence in India, where it is known as the Cheetah.

Initial production was from French-built components. The first Indian-assembled Cheetah was test-flown on 6 October 1972, and a total of 59 had been delivered by 1 January 1979. Production of aircraft manufactured from raw materials began in 1976-77.

An agricultural version of the Cheetah is under development. Preliminary spraying trials have been conducted, and further modifications are in progress.

HAL (AÉROSPATIALE) SA 316B ALOUETTE III

Indian name: Chetak

The Bangalore Complex's Helicopter Division is building the French Aérospatiale SA 316B Alouette III under a licence granted in June 1962. The first Indian-assembled Alouette III was flown for the first time on 11 June 1965.

By 1 January 1979 a total of 216 Alouette IIIs had been manufactured by HAL. A few Alouette IIIs were presented to the Royal Nepal Army in 1974. HAL also supplies Indian-built components for French-built Alouette IIIs.

An armed version, known as the Chetak, is being developed by HAL, carrying four air-to-surface missiles on laterally-mounted booms. Target identification and fire control is via a monocular periscopic sight on the cabin roof. Successful firing trials have been carried out.

HAL LIGHT HELICOPTER

The Design Bureau of HAL has under development a single-engined high-performance light helicopter. Two versions are being developed: a standard version for Indian Air Force/Army use, and a variant for the Indian Navy. The former will have a capability for combat missions, communications duties, armed reconnaissance and surveillance, casualty evacuation, crew rescue, external cargo carrying and training. The naval version will be able to perform anti-submarine search and strike, air to surface vessel search and strike, search and rescue, reconnaissance, casualty evacuation, and vertical replenishment duties at sea.

The configuration described in the 1977-78 *Jane's* has been superseded; the ALH is now expected to be a twin-engined design with different landing gear from that originally specified.

KANPUR DIVISION

ADDRESS: Chakeri, Kanpur
Telephone: HAL PABX 62471-4
Telex: HAL KP 243

When the decision was taken to build the Hawker Siddeley (now British Aerospace) 748 twin-turboprop transport in India, as a replacement for the Dakotas of the Indian Air Force, four hangars at Kanpur were taken over, on 23 January 1960, as the IAF Aircraft Manufacturing Depot. The Depot was incorporated in Aeronautics (India) Ltd in June 1964 and subsequently became the Kanpur Division of Hindustan Aeronautics Ltd.

HAL HS 748

The first Indian-built 748 flew on 1 November 1961, followed by the second one on 13 March 1963. The first four Indian 748s were Srs 1 aircraft, utilising components imported from the UK.

The first Indian-built Srs 2 flew for the first time on 28 January 1964, and 14 were delivered to Indian Airlines in 1967-70. Since then a further three have been delivered to Indian Airlines; three more are being modified for a photographic survey role; and four others are being delivered to the Indian Directorate General of Civil Aviation (for a calibration role) and the National Remote Sensing Agency.

HAL has also produced the aircraft in several versions for the Indian Air Force. These include 10 VIP executive transports, 10 as navigation trainers and 18 as trainers for pilots of multi-engined aircraft.

A prototype HS 748(M) military freighter, developed by Kanpur Division, flew for the first time on 16 February 1972 and successfully completed flight trials with the Indian Air Force. An order for 10 more HS 748s was announced in June 1975. These aircraft are built to the military freighter standard; this order was expected to be completed in 1979. A further 10 HS 748(M)s were ordered in 1978, extending production until 1983.

HAL HA-31 Mk II BASANT (SPRING)

HAL HA-31 Mk II Basant (Lycoming IO-720-C1B engine) *(Pilot Press)*

HAL HA-31 Mk II Basant single-seat agricultural and utility aircraft

Design of this agricultural aircraft began at the Bangalore design bureau in mid-1968. The prototype, designated HA-31 Mk I, was powered by a 186 kW (250 hp) Rolls-Royce Continental engine, and was described in the 1971-72 *Jane's*. The aircraft was subsequently completely redesigned as the HA-31 Mk II, with a 298 kW (400 hp) engine, and a prototype of this version flew for the first time on 30 March 1972. A second, pre-production prototype flew in September 1972, and certification was obtained in March 1974. A pre-production batch of 20 Basants was built by the design bureau, and the first eight of these were handed over to the Indian Ministry of Food and Agriculture on 21 June 1974. Responsibility for series manufacture of the Basant was then assigned to the Kanpur Division, which is to build 100. A total of 36 had been built by 1 January 1979.

The Basant is intended primarily for aerial application of pesticides and fertilisers. It can also be used for aerial survey, fire/patrol duties and cloud seeding.

TYPE: Single-seat agricultural and utility aircraft.

WINGS: Strut-braced low-wing monoplane. Constant-chord wings, of USA 35B section with rounded tips. Thickness/chord ratio 11·6%. Dihedral 5° from roots. No incidence or sweepback. Spars (two) and ribs of light alloy, with fabric covering. Fowler-type trailing-edge flaps and Frise-type ailerons, of similar construction to wings and operated manually. Tab in port aileron. Single inverted-Vee bracing strut and cross-strut on each side, attached to fuselage forward of cockpit.

FUSELAGE: Conventional structure, of welded chrome-molybdenum steel tube with fabric covering in most areas. Structure forward of cockpit designed to absorb impact in the event of a crash. Cockpit structure, seat and attachment, seat belt and shoulder harness all designed to withstand 40*g* loads in the event of a crash.

TAIL UNIT: Conventional alloy structure, with fixed-incidence metal-skinned tailplane. One-piece elevator, with central trim tab. Fabric-covered fin and rudder. Fixed tab in rudder.

LANDING GEAR: Non-retractable tailwheel type, with HAL oleo-pneumatic shock-absorbers on all units. Size 24·7 × 7·5-10 tyres on main wheels, 11·28 × 4-3·5 on tailwheel. Tyre pressure 2·41 bars (35 lb/sq in) on main units, 2·76 bars (40 lb/sq in) on tail unit. Dunlop hydraulic disc brakes on main units.

POWER PLANT: One 298 kW (400 hp) Lycoming IO-720-C1B flat-eight engine, driving a Hartzell three-blade constant-speed metal propeller. Two inboard fuel tanks (each 91 litres; 20 Imp gallons) and two outboard tanks (each 63·5 litres; 14 Imp gallons) in each wing, and 9 litre (2 Imp gallon) collector tank. Total fuel capacity 318 litres (70 Imp gallons). Refuelling point on each tank. Oil capacity (nominal) 19·3 litres (4·25 Imp gallons).

ACCOMMODATION: Single seat in fully-enclosed cockpit. Forward-hinged door on starboard side; emergency door on port side. Cockpit heated and ventilated.

SYSTEMS: Hydraulic motor for crop spraying. Electrical power, from 24V 50A alternator and 24V 25Ah battery, for engine starting, instruments, VHF radio etc.

AVIONICS AND EQUIPMENT: VHF radio optional. Glassfibre hopper, installed between engine firewall and front wall of cockpit enclosure, has 0·93 m^3 (33 cu ft) capacity and can carry up to 605 kg (1,333 lb) of pesticide for Normal category operation and up to 907 kg (2,000 lb) in Restricted category.

DIMENSIONS, EXTERNAL:
- Wing span: 12·00 m (39 ft 4½ in)
- Wing chord (constant): 2·00 m (6 ft 6½ in)
- Wing aspect ratio: 6·17
- Length overall: 9·00 m (29 ft 6¼ in)
- Height overall: 2·55 m (8 ft 4½ in)
- Tailplane span: 3·86 m (12 ft 8 in)
- Wheel track: 2·70 m (8 ft 10¼ in)
- Wheelbase: 6·00 m (19 ft 8¼ in)
- Propeller diameter: 2·13 m (7 ft 0 in)
- Propeller ground clearance: 0·25 m (10 in)

AREAS:
- Wings, gross: 23·34 m^2 (251·23 sq ft)
- Ailerons (total): 2·14 m^2 (23·03 sq ft)
- Trailing-edge flaps (total): 2·618 m^2 (28·18 sq ft)
- Fin: 1·06 m^2 (11·41 sq ft)
- Rudder, incl tab: 0·86 m^2 (9·26 sq ft)
- Tailplane: 2·44 m^2 (26·26 sq ft)
- Elevator, incl tab: 1·80 m^2 (19·37 sq ft)

WEIGHTS AND LOADINGS:
- Weight empty: 1,200 kg (2,645 lb)
- Basic operating weight: 1,954 kg (4,300 lb)
- Max T-O weight: 2,270 kg (5,000 lb)
- Max wing loading: 97·25 kg/m^2 (19·92 lb/sq ft)
- Max power loading: 7·62 kg/kW (12·6 lb/hp)

PERFORMANCE (at basic operating weight):
- Never-exceed speed: 164 knots (305 km/h; 189 mph)
- Max level speed at S/L: 121 knots (225 km/h; 140 mph)
- Max cruising speed at 2,625 m (8,000 ft): 100 knots (185 km/h; 115 mph)
- Econ cruising speed: 87 knots (161 km/h; 100 mph)
- Stalling speed, flaps up: 52 knots (96 km/h; 60 mph)
- Stalling speed, flaps down: 49 knots (91 km/h; 57 mph)
- Max rate of climb at S/L: 228 m (750 ft)/min
- Service ceiling: 3,800 m (12,500 ft)
- Min ground turning radius: 7·00 m (22 ft 11 in)
- T-O run: 214 m (700 ft)
- T-O to 15 m (50 ft): 365 m (1,200 ft)
- Landing from 15 m (50 ft): 305 m (1,000 ft)
- Landing run: 183 m (600 ft)
- Range with max fuel, no payload: 348 nm (645 km; 400 miles)
- Endurance with max payload, 30 min reserves: 1 h

MiG COMPLEX

The MiG Complex was originally formed with the Nasik, Koraput and Hyderabad Divisions of HAL, which, under an agreement concluded in 1962, built respectively the airframes, power plants and avionics equipment of MiG-21 fighters under licence from the USSR.

As a result of the reorganisation of HAL, the Hyderabad Division, with Lucknow Division, now constitutes the Accessories Complex.

HAL (MIKOYAN) MiG-21

Indian Air Force designations: Type 66-400, 66-600, 74, 76, 77 and 96

Several versions of the MiG-21 (NATO reporting name 'Fishbed') have been supplied to or manufactured in India, including the MiG-21F (IAF designation Type 74) and MiG-21PF (Type 76) of which details can be found in the 1976-77 *Jane's;* and the MiG-21FL (Type 77) and MiG-21U (Types 66-400 and 66-600), as described in the 1977-78 *Jane's*. Other versions include:

MiG-21M. Current production version with R-11F2S-300 engine. First aircraft handed over to IAF on 14 February 1973. IAF designation **Type 96**. Fifty Soviet-built MiG-21PFMAs, to supplement Indian production, placed in service with Nos. 7 and 108 Squadrons. No. 26 Squadron is among those reportedly equipped with MiG-21M.

MiG-21MF ('Fishbed-J'). Improved production version, having more powerful Tumansky R-13-300 turbojet engine and increased fuel.

MiG-21 bis ('Fishbed-N'). Deliveries of this version, initially for service with No. 21 Squadron of IAF, reported in 1977.

A full description of the MiG-21 appears in the USSR section of this edition.

HAL-built MiG-21FL single-seat combat aircraft in Indian Air Force insignia

INDONESIA

LAPAN

LEMBAGA PENERBANGAN DAN ANTARIKSA NASIONAL (National Aeronautics and Space Institute)

HEADQUARTERS: Jalan Pemuda Persil No. 1, PO Box 3048, Djakarta Timur
Telephone: (021) 465125, 482808 and 482653
Telex: 45675 LAPAN IA
CHAIRMAN: Air Vice-Marshal Dr Sunaryo
VICE-CHAIRMAN: Prof Wiranto Arismunandar

Pusat Teknologi Dirgantara (Aerospace Technology Center)
Rumpin Airfield, Bogor, West Java
HEAD OF AEROSPACE TECHNOLOGY CENTER: Dr Haryono Djojodihardjo
MANAGER, AEROSPACE TECHNOLOGY DEVELOPMENT: Ir Jaidun Kromodihardjo

Established in 1963 under the original chairmanship of Air Vice-Marshal J. Salatun, LAPAN had 525 personnel at the beginning of 1979, accommodated within four centres: the Aerospace Technology Center at Rumpin Airfield, near Bogor; the Aerospace Study Center and the Space Applications Center, both at Jakarta; and the Atmospheric and Space Research Center at Bandung. In FY 1977 it began construction of a prototype of the XT-400 eight-seat transport aircraft, and also built and test-flew a mini-RPV, the XTG-01.

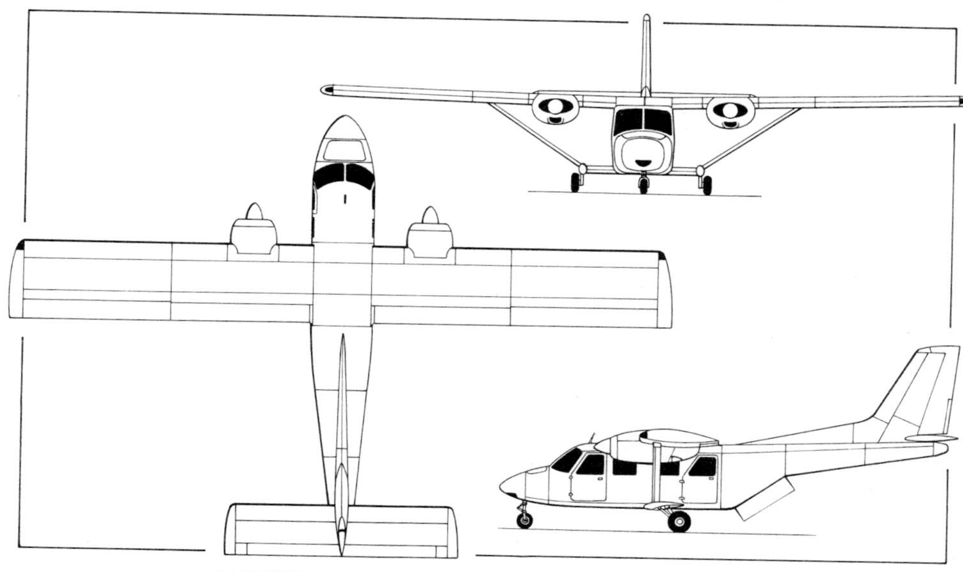

LAPAN XT-400 eight-seat STOL utility transport *(Pilot Press)*

LAPAN XT-400

In the same class as the Britten-Norman Islander, the XT-400 differs from that aircraft by having an upswept rear fuselage with clamshell rear-loading doors. Designed by a team under the leadership of Dipl-Ing Suharto, it is of all-metal construction, and is the first Indonesian aircraft of indigenous design able to accommodate more than three people. The initial version, of which the prototype is due to fly in 1980, will carry one pilot and up to seven passengers; a future version is planned, with seats for 11 passengers. Design is to FAR Pts 23 and 25 (Utility category), and the XT-400 will have STOL capability, including the ability to operate from grass or semi-prepared runways. Applications include those of passenger and cargo transport, aerial survey (equipped with photographic or geographical survey equipment), and ambulance.

The following description applies to the first prototype:

TYPE: Twin-engined light STOL transport.

WINGS: All-metal high-wing monoplane, with single streamline-section bracing strut each side which is attached to a stub-wing at fuselage floor level. Wing section NACA 2415. Dihedral 2°. Inboard half of each semi-span carries a slotted trailing-edge flap (25% of overall chord); aileron on outboard half of each semi-span. No tabs.

FUSELAGE: Conventional all-metal semi-monocoque structure, with riveted skin. Basically rectangular cross-section in main cabin area. Upswept at rear, to facilitate cargo loading.

TAIL UNIT: Cantilever all-metal structure, with slightly-swept vertical surfaces and long dorsal fin extending almost to wing trailing-edge. One-piece fixed-incidence tailplane aft of fin, with wide-span elevator. Trim tab in rudder.

LANDING GEAR: Non-retractable tricycle type, with single wheel and oleo-pneumatic shock-absorber on each unit. Main units attached to tips of stub-wings. Steerable nosewheel. Main-wheel tyres size 7·50-10, pressure 2·55 bars (37 lb/sq in); nosewheel tyre size 6·00-6, pressure 1·65 bars (24 lb/sq in).

POWER PLANT: Two 186·5 kW (250 hp) Lycoming IO-540-C flat-six engines, each driving a Hartzell constant-speed propeller with spinner. Total fuel capacity 494 litres (130·5 US gallons). Oil capacity 11·4 litres (3 US gallons).

ACCOMMODATION: Passenger version accommodates up to eight persons, including pilot, on four pairs of seats. Pilot's seat adjustable fore and aft. Aeromedical version can accommodate two stretchers and attendants. Two forward-opening car-type doors on port side of main cabin, and one on starboard side. Baggage compartment at rear of cabin, accessible via downward-opening clamshell doors in underside of upswept rear fuselage. These doors also facilitate rear loading and unloading of freight or stretchers in cargo and ambulance versions.

SYSTEMS: Internal/external lighting and other electrical services powered by 24V generator and voltage regulator.

AVIONICS AND EQUIPMENT: Optional items include blind-flying instrumentation.

DIMENSIONS, EXTERNAL:
- Wing span: 14·59 m (47 ft 10½ in)
- Wing chord, constant: 1·80 m (5 ft 10¾ in)
- Wing area, gross: 25·36 m² (273·0 sq ft)
- Wing aspect ratio: 7·8
- Length overall: 10·20 m (33 ft 5½ in)
- Height overall: 4·30 m (14 ft 1¼ in)
- Tailplane span: 5·20 m (17 ft 0¾ in)
- Wheel track: 2·84 m (9 ft 4 in)
- Wheelbase: 3·62 m (11 ft 10½ in)
- Propeller diameter: 2·03 m (6 ft 8 in)

DIMENSIONS, INTERNAL:
- Cabin: Length: 3·75 m (12 ft 3½ in)
  - Width: 1·08 m (3 ft 6½ in)
  - Height: 1·23 m (4 ft 0½ in)
  - Floor area: 3·90 m² (41·98 sq ft)
  - Volume: 4·25 m³ (150·1 cu ft)

WEIGHTS AND LOADINGS:
- Weight empty, with basic equipment: 1,422 kg (3,136 lb)
- Max payload (8 persons plus baggage): 762 kg (1,680 lb)
- Max T-O weight: 2,540 kg (5,600 lb)
- Max wing loading: 100 kg/m² (20·5 lb/sq ft)
- Max power loading: 6·8 kg/kW (11·2 lb/hp)

PERFORMANCE (estimated):
- Max level speed: 148 knots (273 km/h; 170 mph)
- Max cruising speed (75% power): 139 knots (257 km/h; 160 mph)
- Econ cruising speed (60% power): 126 knots (233 km/h; 145 mph)
- Stalling speed: 58 knots (106 km/h; 66 mph)
- Max rate of climb at S/L: 274 m (900 ft)/min
- Service ceiling: 4,665 m (15,300 ft)
- T-O to 15 m (50 ft): 300 m (980 ft)
- Landing from 15 m (50 ft): 380 m (1,250 ft)
- Range with max fuel: 521 nm (965 km; 600 miles)
- Range with max payload: 260 nm (483 km; 300 miles)
- *g* limits: +3·6; −1·5

P T NURTANIO

P T INDUSTRI PESAWAT TERBANG NURTANIO (Nurtanio Aircraft Industries Ltd)

ADDRESS: Lanuma Husein Sastranegara (Husein Sastranegara Air Force Base), Jln Pajajaran 154, Bandung
Telephone: Bandung 56191 and 56662
Telex: 28295 nur bd
PRESIDENT DIRECTOR: Prof Dr-Ing B. J. Habibie
SECRETARY TO PRESIDENT DIRECTOR: Tatang Endan

DIRECTORS:
- Untung Suwignjo (General Affairs)
- Ir Yuwono, VI (Production)
- Ir Harsono Pusponegoro (Technology)

MANAGERS:
- Ir Yuwono, VI (General Workshop Division)
- Ir Harsono Pusponegoro (Fixed Wing Division)
- Ir Ramelan (Rotary Wing Division)
- Ir Paramayuda (Aircraft Services Division)

ASST FOR COMMERCIAL AFFAIRS: Ir Subagyo
ASST FOR FINANCE: Dr Bambang Ekoyono
GENERAL INSPECTOR: Dr S. Parlin Napitupulu
CHIEF OF PUBLIC RELATIONS: Suripto Sugondo

This company was officially inaugurated in August 1976 when, as a result of a government order dated 5 April 1976, the former Lipnur (Lembaga Industri Penerbangan Nurtanio: see 1977-78 *Jane's*) combined its aircraft industry activities with those of the Pertamina oil company. It is

Nurtanio-built CASA C-212 Aviocar commercial transport, fitted with rain-making equipment, for the Thailand Department of Agriculture

named in honour of the late Air Marshal Nurtanio Pringgoadisuryo, who was largely responsible for establishing an aircraft industry in Indonesia.

In addition to the programmes listed, P. T. Nurtanio has rights to manufacture the Aérospatiale SA 330 Puma in Indonesia, and plans to begin production of this helicopter in the early 1980s.

Nurtanio is also developing a 40-seat transport aircraft of its own design.

NURTANIO (CASA) C-212 AVIOCAR

The C-212 Aviocar twin-turboprop transport aircraft has been manufactured in Indonesia since the first half of 1976, under licence from CASA of Spain (which see); 25 had been completed by mid-1979.

By the beginning of 1979 more than 12 Aviocars were in operation throughout Indonesia with Pelita Air Service, Merpati Nusantara Airlines, Bouraq Indonesia Airlines and the Indonesian Air Force. Two Aviocars equipped for rain-making have been exported to Thailand.

The Indonesian Air Force has ordered one complete squadron of Aviocars.

NURTANIO (MBB) BO 105

The BO 105 helicopter has been manufactured in Indonesia since May 1976, under licence from MBB of Germany (which see).

By the beginning of 1979 a total of 25 BO 105s had been delivered for operation with the Indonesian Army and Navy and Pelita Air Service.

The Indonesian Air Force has ordered one complete squadron of BO 105s.

Nurtanio (MBB) BO 105 multi-purpose helicopter

INTERNATIONAL PROGRAMMES

AIRBUS
AIRBUS INDUSTRIE

HEAD OFFICE: Avenue Lucien Servanty, BP No. 33, 31700 Blagnac, France
Telephone: (61) 71 11 11
Telex: AI TO A 53526 F
PARIS OFFICE: 12bis avenue Bosquet, 75007 Paris, France
Telephone: 551 40 95

AIRFRAME PRIME CONTRACTORS:
Aérospatiale, 37 boulevard de Montmorency, 75781 Paris Cédex 16, France
Deutsche Airbus GmbH, 8000 München 81, Arabellastrasse 30, Postfach 810260, Federal Republic of Germany
British Aerospace Aircraft Group, Richmond Road, Kingston upon Thames, Surrey KT2 5QS, England

CHAIRMAN OF SUPERVISORY BOARD: Dr Franz-Josef Strauss
PRESIDENT AND CHIEF EXECUTIVE: Bernard Lathière
EXECUTIVE VICE-PRESIDENT AND GENERAL MANAGER: Roger Béteille
SENIOR VICE-PRESIDENTS:
J. Roeder (Technical)
G. Warde (Commercial)
F. Kracht (Production)
G. Ville (Finance and Administration)
B. Ziegler (Flight and Support)
PROGRAMME MANAGERS:
R. Chanut (A300)
J. Plénier (A310)

Airbus Industrie was set up in December 1970 as a 'Groupement d'Intérêt Economique' to manage the development, manufacture, marketing and support of a twin-engined large-capacity short/medium-range transport aircraft known as the A300. This management now extends to the developed version known as the A310. Airbus Industrie has design leadership and is responsible for the A300/310 activities of the partner companies. These are Aérospatiale of France, which has a 37·9% interest in the programme, Deutsche Airbus (MBB and VFW-Fokker) of Germany (37·9%), British Aerospace (20%), and CASA of Spain (4·2%). Fokker-VFW (Netherlands) is an associate in the A300 and A310 programmes; Belairbus (Belgium) is an associate in the programme for the A310.

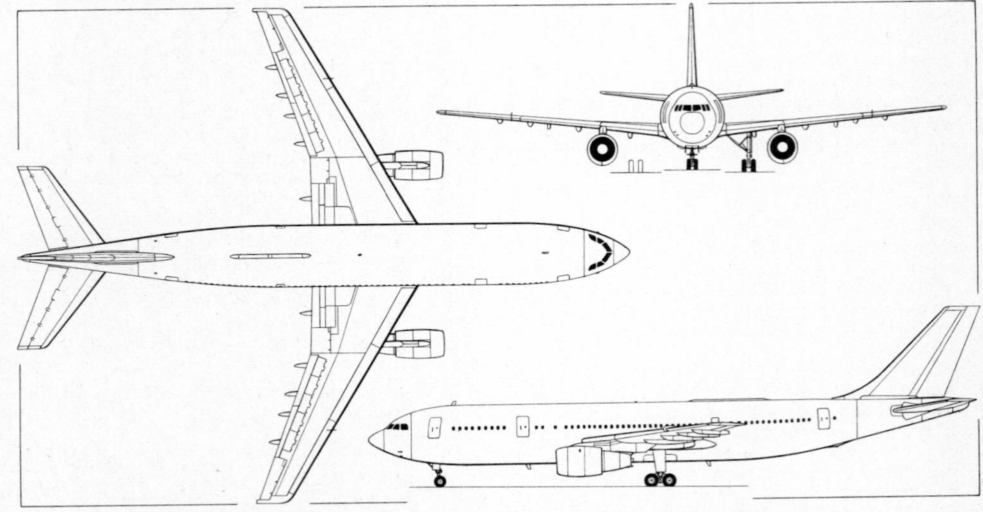

Airbus A300B4 wide-bodied short/medium-range transport (CF6 engines) *(Pilot Press)*

AIRBUS A300

The Airbus A300 is a wide-bodied aircraft with underwing pods for two turbofan engines. The early history of the project has appeared in previous editions of *Jane's*.

Construction of the first A300, a B1, began in September 1969. This aircraft (F-WUAB, later F-OCAZ) made its first flight on 28 October 1972, and was followed by the second B1 (F-WUAC) on 5 February 1973. The B1 was described in detail in the 1971-72 *Jane's*. Initial certification covered automatic approach and landing in

Category 2 weather conditions. Certification for Category 3A automatic approach and landing was granted on 30 September 1974.

The A300 is currently being offered with two General Electric CF6-50C, C1 or C2 turbofans, or two Pratt & Whitney JT9D-59As. All CF6-50 engines are now available with a weight and fuel saving 'short' nozzle. The first A300 with JT9D engines, a B4 for SAS, made its first flight on 28 April 1979. The CF6-50L2 of 240 kN (54,000 lb st), the JT9D-59B of 242·5 kN (54,500 lb st) and the Rolls-Royce RB.211-524 of up to 236 kW (53,000 lb st), are also available as customer options.

The following versions are currently available:

A300B2-100 (formerly A300B2). Initial production version. Third and fourth aircraft are to this configuration, flying for the first time on 28 June and 20 November 1973 respectively. Aircraft No. 4 subsequently delivered to Air Inter on 22 January 1977 as F-BUAE. Type certificated by DGAC and LBA on 15 March 1974; entered service, with Air France, between Paris and London on 30 May 1974. Designated **B2-101** with CF6-50C engines.

A300B2-200 (formerly A300B2K). Basically as B2-100 series, but fitted with wing-root leading-edge Krueger flaps developed originally for A300B4. With same wheels and brakes also as B4, is suitable for operation from 'hot and high' airports. First aircraft of this type, No. 32 (ZS-SDA), first flew on 30 July 1976. First delivery, of ZS-SDB to South African Airways, made on 23 November 1976. Designation 'dash' numbers, according to power plant, are **B2-201** (CF6-50C), **B2-202** (CF6-50C1) and **B2-220** (JT9D-59A).

A300B2-300. Basically as B2-200, but increased zero-fuel and landing weights for increased payload and multi-stop flexibility. Available from Autumn 1979.

A300B4-100 (formerly A300B4 Stage I and Stage II). Basic longer-range version. Developed from original A300B2, with same external dimensions and volumetric payload capacity, but with increased design weights and fuel capacity, and Krueger flaps at wing-root leading-edges to improve T-O performance. Aircraft No. 9 (F-WLGA) was the first built to this configuration, and first flew on 26 December 1974. French and German certification granted on 26 March 1975, and FAA Type Approval on 30 June 1976. First delivery, of D-AMAX to Germanair, made in May 1975; this aircraft entered service on 1 June 1975. Designation 'dash' numbers, according to power plant, are **B4-101** (CF6-50C), **B4-102** (CF6-50C1), **B4-103** (CF6-50C2) and **B4-120** (JT9D-59A).

A300B4-200 (formerly A300B4 Stage III). Announced on 19 January 1978, concurrently with order for three by Air France. Compared with -100 series, has reinforced wings and fuselage, strengthened landing gear, and size 49 × 17-20 main-wheel tyres. This allows certification at higher T-O weight, enabling full payload of passengers and cargo to be carried on stages of up to 1,954 nm (3,621 km; 2,250 miles) with standard airline reserves. Optional additional fuel tank available with this version: installed in rear cargo hold in place of two LD3 containers, it extends the range with full complement of passengers to 3,100 nm (5,740 km; 3,565 miles). Designation 'dash' numbers, according to power plant, are **B4-201** (CF6-50C), **B4-202** (CF6-50C1), **B4-203** (CF6-50C2), **B4-220** (JT9D-59A), and **B4-221** (JT9D-59B).

A300C4 Freighter conversion of B4; described separately.

A310. Developed version, with shorter fuselage and redesigned wings; described separately.

In addition, future developments are under study, including a 320/330-passenger 'stretched' version and a very-long-range 200-seater with a shortened fuselage, bigger wings and four engines. However, Airbus Industrie has stated that it will not launch any new models without a firm launching commitment.

By 10 August 1979, orders and options totalling 252 A300s (including C4s) had been received, as follows:

	Orders	*Options*
Air Afrique (B4-200)	1	—
Air France (B2/B4-100/200)	23	12
Air Inter (France) (B2-100)	7	—
Alitalia (B4-200)	8	3
Cruzeiro do Sul (Brazil) (B4-200)	3	1
Eastern Air Lines (USA) (B4-100)	23	9
Egyptair (B4-200)	3	4
Garuda (Indonesia) (B4-200)	6	6
Germanair (B4-100)	4	—
Hapag Lloyd (Germany) (B4-100/C4-200)	2	—
Iberia (B4-100)	4	4
Indian Airlines (B2-100)	8	3
Iran Air (B2-200)	6	3
Korean Air Lines (B4-100)	8	—
*Laker Airways (UK) (B4-200)	10	—
Lufthansa (Germany) (B2/B4-100)	11	—
Malaysian Airline System (B4-200)	3	1
Olympic Airways (Greece) (B4-100)	5	5
Pakistan International (B4-200)	4	6
Philippine Air Lines (B4-100)	2	2
SAS (Scandinavia) (B2-300)	4	8
Singapore Airlines (B4-200)	6	6
South African Airways (B2/B4-200)	5	1
Thai International (B4-100)	10	4
Toa Domestic Airlines (Japan) (B2-200)	6	—
Trans European Airways (Belgium) (B1)	2	—
Undisclosed	1	−1

*option for last four to be A310s

A total of 69 A300s (27 B2s and 42 B4s) had been delivered by 10 August 1979.

Aérospatiale is responsible for manufacturing the entire nose section (including the flight deck), lower centre fuselage and engine pylons, and for final assembly. Deutsche Airbus is responsible for manufacturing the forward fuselage, between the flight deck and wing box, the upper centre fuselage, the rear fuselage and the vertical tail surfaces. British Aerospace has design responsibility for the wings (for which it received the Queen's Award for Technological Achievement in 1976), builds the wing fixed structures, and is working in collaboration with Fokker-VFW, which is building the wing moving surfaces. CASA manufactures the horizontal tail surfaces, fuselage main doors and landing gear doors. Final assembly and painting in customers' colour scheme is carried out at Toulouse. Aircraft are then flown to Hamburg for installation of interior furnishings and equipment before returning to Toulouse for final customer acceptance. General Electric engines are assembled under licence by SNECMA; some components are also licence-built by SNECMA (France) and MTU (Germany). The whole power plant assembly is virtually identical to that of the McDonnell Douglas DC-10-30, and nacelles are supplied by McDonnell Douglas. Nacelles for Pratt & Whitney engines are manufactured by Rohr (Germany) and are interchangeable with those of JT9D-59-powered DC-10-40 aircraft and JT9D-70-powered Boeing 747s.

TYPE: Large-capacity wide-bodied short/medium-range transport.

WINGS: Cantilever mid-wing monoplane. Thickness/chord ratio 10·5%. Sweepback 28° at quarter-chord. Primary two-spar box-type structure, integral with fuselage and incorporating fail-safe principles, built of high-strength aluminium alloy. Third spar across inboard sections. Machined skin with open-sectioned stringers. Each wing has three-section leading-edge slats (no slat cutout over the engine pylon), and three Fowler-type double-slotted flaps on trailing-edge; a Krueger flap on the leading-edge wing root (B2-200/B4); an all-speed aileron between inboard flap and outer pair; and a low-speed aileron outboard of the outer pair of flaps. Lift dump facility by combination of three spoilers (outboard) and two airbrakes (inboard) on each wing, forward of outer pair of flaps, plus two additional airbrakes forward of inboard flap. The flaps extend over 84% of each half-span, and increase the wing chord by 25% when fully extended. The datum of the all-speed aileron is deflected downward by up to 10° with flap operation to maintain trailing-edge continuity with deflected flaps. Drive mechanisms for flaps and slats are similar to one another, each powered by twin motors driving ball screwjacks on each surface with built-in protection against asymmetric operation. Two slat positions for take-off and landing. Pre-selection of the airbrake/lift dump lever allows automatic extension of the lift dumpers on touchdown. All flight controls are powered by triplex hydraulic servo-jacks, with no manual reversion. Anti-icing of wing leading-edges, outboard of engine pods, is by hot air bled from engines.

FUSELAGE: Conventional semi-monocoque structure of circular cross-section, with frames and open Z-section stringers. Built mainly of high-strength aluminium alloy, with steel or titanium for some major components. Skin panels integrally machined in areas of high stress. Honeycomb panels or restricted glassfibre laminates for secondary structures.

TAIL UNIT: Cantilever all-metal structure, with sweepback on all surfaces. Variable-incidence tailplane and separately-controlled elevators. Tailplane powered by two motors driving a fail-safe ball screwjack. No anti-icing of leading-edges.

LANDING GEAR: Hydraulically-retractable tricycle type, of Messier-Hispano design, with Messier-Hispano shock-absorbers and wheels. Twin-wheel nose unit

B4-220 version of the twin-turbofan Airbus Industrie A300, first to be powered by JT9D engines

The first Airbus Industrie A300B4-200 wide-bodied transport aircraft, delivered to Air France in April 1979

retracts forward, main units inward into fuselage. Free-fall extension. Each four-wheel main unit comprises two tandem-mounted bogies, interchangeable left with right, with tyres size 46 × 16·20, pressure 11·6 bars (168 lb/sq in) on B2, 13·3 bars (193 lb/sq in) on B4-100 series. Tyre size 49 × 17-20, pressure 12·41 bars (180 lb/sq in), on B4-200 series. Nosewheel tyres size 40 × 14-16, pressure 7·93 bars (115 lb/sq in) on B2, 9·52 bars (138 lb/sq in) on B4. Steering angles 65°/95°. SNECMA (Hispano) hydraulic disc brakes on all main wheels. Duplex anti-skid units fitted, with a third standby hydraulic supply for wheel brakes.

Power Plant: Underwing location of the power plant enables the A300 to use any advanced technology turbofan engine in the 222·5 kN (50,000 lb thrust) class. It is currently being offered with the following engines: Two 227 kN (51,000 lb st) General Electric CF6-50C turbofans (B2-101/201 and B4-101/201);
Two 233·5 kN (52,500 lb st) General Electric CF6-50C1 (B2-202, B4-102/202) or C2 (B4-103/203); or Two 236 kN (53,000 lb st) Pratt & Whitney JT9D-59A (B2-220 and B4-120/220) or -59B (B4-221).
These engines are installed in pods interchangeable with those of the McDonnell Douglas DC-10 Series 30 and 40. For other engines available, see introductory copy.
Fuel in two integral tanks in each wing, with total usable capacity of 43,000 litres (9,460 Imp gallons) in B2. Fifth integral tank in wing centre-section of B4, increasing total usable capacity to 59,700 litres (13,133 Imp gallons). For B4-200 series, an optional self-contained fuselage fuel tank is available, capacity 6,000 litres (1,320 Imp gallons). This unit fits into the rear cargo hold, where it takes the place of two standard LD3 containers. Two standard refuelling points beneath each wing, outboard of engine pylons.

Accommodation (B2 and B4): Crew of three on flight deck, plus two observer's seats. Seating for between 220 and 320 passengers in main cabin in six, seven, eight or nine-abreast layout with 79/86 cm (31/34 in) seat pitch. Typical economy class layout has 269 seats, eight abreast with two aisles, at 86 cm (34 in) seat pitch. This layout includes one galley and one toilet forward, with provision for a second one, and one more galley and four toilets aft. Up to 336 passengers can be carried at 76 cm (30 in) seat pitch in single-class high-density layout. Closed hatracks on each side, forming baggage lockers (max individual capacity 0·062 m^3; 2·19 cu ft). Provision for central double-sided rack. Two outward parallel-opening plug-type passenger doors ahead of wing leading-edge on each side, and one on each side at rear. Underfloor baggage/cargo holds fore and aft of wings, with doors on starboard side. The forward hold will accommodate four 2·24 × 3·18 × 1·63 m (88 × 125 × 64 in) pallets or twelve LD3 or IATA A1 containers; the rear hold will accommodate eight LD3 containers each of 4·25 m^3 (150 cu ft) capacity. Additional bulk loading of freight provided for in an extreme rear compartment with usable volume of 16·0 m^3 (565 cu ft). The latter compartment can be used for the transport of livestock. Entire accommodation is pressurised, including freight, baggage and avionics compartments.

Systems: Air for air-conditioning system can be provided from engines, the APU or a high pressure ground source. Supply is controlled by separate and parallel bootstrap-type units, each of which includes a flow limiting unit, cooler unit, water separator and temperature control unit. In addition, air from each engine passes through a pressure control pre-cooler unit. Distribution in flight deck and three cabin areas, with independent regulation. Two independent automatic systems, with manual override, control the cabin altitude, its rate of change and the differential pressure. Cabin pressure differential for normal operations is 0·57 bars (8·25 lb/sq in). Hydraulic system comprises three fully-independent circuits, operating simultaneously. Fluid used is a fire-resistant phosphate-ester type, working at a pressure of 207 bars (3,000 lb/sq in). The three circuits provide triplex power for primary flying controls; if any circuit fails, full control of the aircraft is retained without any necessity for action by the crew. All three circuits supply the all-speed and low-speed ailerons, rudder and elevator; 'blue' circuit additionally supplies tail trim, spoilers, slats and rudder variable-gear unit; 'green' circuit additionally supplies airbrakes, spoilers, slats, elevator artificial feel units, flaps, steering, wheel brakes and normal landing gear requirements; 'yellow' circuit additionally supplies tail trim, airbrakes, lift dumpers, rudder variable-gear unit, elevator artificial feel unit, flaps, wheel brakes and steering. Each circuit normally powered by engine-driven self-regulating pumps, one on each engine for the green circuit and one each for the blue and yellow circuits. Dowty Rotol ram-air turbine-driven pump provides standby hydraulic power should both engines become inoperative. Main electrical power is supplied by two Westinghouse three-phase constant-frequency AC generators mounted on the engines. A third identical generator, driven by the APU, can supply power both in flight, to replace a failed engine-driven generator, and on the ground. Supply frequency is 400Hz and voltage is 115/200V. Any one generator can supply sufficient power to operate all equipment and systems necessary for take-off and landing. A conventional generator CSD system is installed, the two units being mounted on opposite sides of the engine gearbox with the CSD driving an aircooled generator at a constant 8,000 rpm. Each generator is rated at 90kVA, with overload ratings of 135kVA for 5 minutes and 180kVA for 5 seconds. The APU generator is driven at constant speed through a gearbox. Three unregulated transformer-rectifier units (TRUs) supply 28V DC power. Three 24V 25Ah nickel-cadmium batteries are used for APU starting and fuel control, engine starter control, standby lights and, by selection, emergency busbar. This busbar and a 115V 400Hz static inverter provide standby power in flight if normal power is unavailable. This system is separated completely from the main system. Hot air protection for engine intakes and slat sections on the wings outboard of the engine. Garrett-AiResearch TSCP 700-5 or GTCP 331 APU in tailcone, exhausting upward. The installation incorporates APU noise attenuation. Fire protection system is self-contained, and firewall panels protect main structure from an APU fire. The APU can be operated on the ground, in flight up to 10,675 m (35,000 ft), and in icing conditions. Relights are possible up to 7,620 m (25,000 ft). Aircraft is completely independent of ground power sources, since all major services can be operated by the APU.

Avionics and Equipment: Standard communications avionics include two VHF sets and one Selcal system, plus interphone and passenger address systems. An accident recorder and voice recorder are also installed. Standard navigation avionics include two VOR, two ILS, two radio altimeters, one marker beacon, two ADF, two DME, two ATC transponders and a weather radar. Most other avionics available to customer's requirements, only those related to the blind landing system (ILS and radio altimeter) being selected and supplied by the manufacturer. Additional optional avionics include one or two HF sets, third VHF, second marker beacon, second radar, navigation computer and pictorial display. Both the pilot and co-pilot have an integrated instrument system combining heading and attitude (three SAGEM MGC 10/ARINC 569 are standard in B2, but they can be replaced by MGC 30/ARINC 571 Mk 1 inertial sensors, which are modular with the MGC 10); SFENA autopilot/flight director system; and radio information. The SFENA/Smiths/Bodenseewerk automatic flight control system includes a comprehensive range of en-route facilities such as VOR coupling, heading select, height acquire, turbulence, rate of descent (if required) and control wheel steering, in addition to the normal height, speed, pitch-and-roll attitude and heading locks. An optional speed reference system with built-in windshear protection is available. Dual automatic landing system provides coupled approach and automatic landing facilities suitable for Category 3A operation. The system is designed to allow future extension to Category 3B automatic landing capability. An automatic braking system is available.

Dimensions, external (B2, B4):
Wing span 44·84 m (147 ft 1 in)
Wing aspect ratio 7·73
Length overall 53·62 m (175 ft 11 in)
Length of fuselage 52·03 m (170 ft 8½ in)
Fuselage max diameter 5·64 m (18 ft 6 in)
Height overall 16·53 m (54 ft 2¾ in)
Tailplane span 16·94 m (55 ft 7 in)
Wheel track 9·60 m (31 ft 6 in)
Wheelbase (c/l of shock-absorbers) 18·60 m (61 ft 0 in)
Passengers doors (each):
Height 1·93 m (6 ft 4 in)
Width 1·07 m (3 ft 6 in)
Height to sill:
fwd 4·60 m (15 ft 1 in)
centre 4·80 m (15 ft 9 in)
rear 5·50 m (18 ft 0½ in)
Emergency exits (each):
Height 1·60 m (5 ft 3 in)
Width 0·61 m (2 ft 0 in)
Height to sill 4·87 m (15 ft 10 in)
Underfloor cargo door (fwd):
Height 1·71 m (5 ft 7½ in)
Width 2·44 m (8 ft 0 in)
Height to sill 2·56 m (8 ft 4¾ in)
Underfloor cargo door (rear):
Height 1·71 m (5 ft 7½ in)
Width 1·81 m (5 ft 11¼ in)
Height to sill 2·96 m (9 ft 8½ in)
Underfloor cargo door (extreme rear):
Height 0·95 m (3 ft 1 in)
Width 0·95 m (3 ft 1 in)
Height to sill 3·30 m (10 ft 10 in)

Dimensions, internal (B2, B4):
Cabin, excl flight deck:
Length 39·15 m (128 ft 6 in)
Max width 5·35 m (17 ft 7 in)
Max height 2·54 m (8 ft 4 in)
Underfloor cargo hold:
Length:
fwd 10·60 m (34 ft 9¼ in)
rear 6·89 m (22 ft 7¼ in)
extreme rear 3·10 m (10 ft 2 in)
Max height 1·76 m (5 ft 9 in)
Max width 4·20 m (13 ft 9¼ in)
Underfloor cargo hold volume:
fwd 75·1 m^3 (2,652 cu ft)
rear 46·8 m^3 (1,652 cu ft)
extreme rear 16·0 m^3 (565 cu ft)
Max total volume for bulk loading 140·0 m^3 (4,944 cu ft)

Areas (B2, B4):
Wings, gross 260·0 m^2 (2,798·6 sq ft)
Vertical tail surfaces (total) 45·2 m^2 (486·5 sq ft)
Horizontal tail surfaces (total) 69·5 m^2 (748·1 sq ft)

Weights and Loadings:
Manufacturer's weight empty:
B2-100/120 77,062 kg (169,892 lb)
B2-200/220 77,427 kg (170,697 lb)
B4-100/120 79,070 kg (174,319 lb)
B4-200/220 79,833 kg (176,000 lb)
Typical operating weight empty:
B2-100/120, B2-200 85,910 kg (189,400 lb)
B2-220 87,500 kg (192,905 lb)
B4-100 (basic) 88,100 kg (194,227 lb)
B4-120 (basic) 89,300 kg (196,873 lb)
B4-200 (optional) 88,500 kg (195,109 lb)
B4-220 (optional) 89,700 kg (197,755 lb)
Max payload (structural):
B2-100/120 34,590 kg (76,258 lb)
B2-200 34,600 kg (76,280 lb)
B2-220 33,000 kg (72,752 lb)
B4-100 (basic) 35,900 kg (79,146 lb)
B4-120 (basic) 34,700 kg (76,500 lb)
B4-200 (optional) 35,200 kg (77,602 lb)
B4-220 (optional) 34,300 kg (75,618 lb)
Max usable fuel:
B2-200/220 (basic) 34,000 kg (74,957 lb)
B4-100/120 (basic) 47,500 kg (104,720 lb)
Max T-O weight:
B2-100 137,000 kg (302,030 lb)
or 142,000 kg (313,055 lb)
B2-200 142,000 kg (313,055 lb)
B4-100 150,000 kg (330,690 lb)
or 153,000 kg (337,305 lb)
or 157,000 kg (347,230 lb)
B4-200 165,000 kg (363,760 lb)
Max ramp weight:
B2-200 142,900 kg (315,040 lb)
B4-200 165,900 kg (365,745 lb)
Max landing weight:
B2-100 127,500-134,000 kg (281,090-295,420 lb)
B2-200 130,000-134,000 kg (286,600-295,420 lb)
B4-100 133,000-136,000 kg (293,215-299,825 lb)
B4-200 134,000 kg (295,420 lb)
Max zero-fuel weight:
B2-100 116,500-124,000 kg (256,835-273,375 lb)
B2-200 120,500 kg (265,655 lb)
or 124,000 kg (273,375 lb)
B4-100 122,000-126,000 kg (268,960-277,780 lb)
B4-200 124,000 kg (273,375 lb)
Max wing loading:
B2-200 546 kg/m^2 (111·8 lb/sq ft)
B4-100 606 kg/m^2 (124·1 lb/sq ft)
B4-200 635 kg/m^2 (130·0 lb/sq ft)
Max power loading:
B2-201 (CF6-50C) 312·8 kg/kN (3·07 lb/lb st)
B2-220 (JT9D-59A) 300·8 kg/kN (2·95 lb/lb st)
B4-101 (CF6-50C) 346·9 kg/kN (3·40 lb/lb st)
B4-102 (CF6-50C1) 337·3 kg/kN (3·31 lb/lb st)
B4-103 (CF6-50C2) 337·3 kg/kN (3·31 lb/lb st)
B4-203 (CF6-50C2) 353·3 kg/kN (3·46 lb/lb st)
B4-220 (JT9D-59A) 349·6 kg/kN (3·43 lb/lb st)
B4-221 (JT9D-59B) 340·2 kg/kN (3·34 lb/lb st)

Performance (at max T-O weight except where indicated):
Max operating speed (Mmo/Vmo):
B2
Mach 0·86 (345 knots; 639 km/h; 397 mph) CAS
B4
Mach 0·82 (345 knots; 639 km/h; 397 mph) CAS
Max cruising speed at 7,620 m (25,000 ft):
B2, B4 492 knots (911 km/h; 567 mph)
Typical high-speed cruise at 9,145 m (30,000 ft):
B2, B4 495 knots (917 km/h; 570 mph)
Typical long-range cruising speed at 9,450 m (31,000 ft): B2, B4 457 knots (847 km/h; 526 mph)
Approach speed at typical weight:
B2 131 knots (243 km/h; 151 mph) CAS
B4 128 knots (237 km/h; 147 mph) CAS
Max operating altitude: B2 10,675 m (35,000 ft)
Min ground turning radius (wingtips) 33·51 m (109 ft 11¼ in)

Runway LCN at max T-O weight:
- 0·76 m (30 in) radius of rigidity:
  - B2 63
  - B4-100/120 72
  - B4-200/220 74
- 1·02 m (40 in) radius of rigidity:
  - B2 74
  - B4-100/120 85
  - B4-200/220 88

T-O field length (S/L, ISA + 15°C):
- B2 1,951 m (6,400 ft)
- B4-100/120 2,750 m (9,020 ft)
- B4-200/220 3,000 m (9,845 ft)

Landing field length at typical weight:
- B2 1,630 m (5,350 ft)
- B4-100/120 1,660 m (5,445 ft)

Range with 269 passengers and baggage:
- B2-200/220 1,800 nm (3,334 km; 2,074 miles)
- B4-100/120 2,600 nm (4,818 km; 2,994 miles)
- B4-200/220 2,750 nm (5,095 km; 3,165 miles)

Range with max fuel:
- B2-200/220 2,300 nm (4,261 km; 2,648 miles)
- B4-100/120 3,200 nm (5,930 km; 3,685 miles)
- B4-200/220 3,200 nm (5,930 km; 3,685 miles)

Operational Noise Characteristics (FAR Pt 36):
- T-O noise level:
  - B2 90 EPNdB
  - B4-100/120 92 EPNdB
  - B4-200/220 94 EPNdB
- Approach noise level:
  - B2, B4 101 EPNdB
- Sideline noise level:
  - B2, B4 95 EPNdB

AIRBUS A300C4

Announced in late 1976, the A300C4 is a convertible freighter version of the A300B4; it, too, is available with the same range of power plant options. Main differences from the B4 are a large upper-deck cargo door, a reinforced cabin floor, a smoke detection system in the main cabin, and an interior trim adaptable to the freighter role. The upper-deck cargo door is on the opposite side to that of the underfloor holds, enabling loading or unloading to be carried out simultaneously at all positions.

In the freight mode the loading system is fitted to the existing seat rails, and permits the carriage of up to thirteen 2·24 × 3·17 m (88 × 125 in) pallets, twelve 2·44 × 3·17 m (96 × 125 in) pallets, or eight of the former plus five of the latter, in basic configurations. Total upper-deck volume thus varies between 173 m³ (6,100 cu ft) and 179 m³ (6,315 cu ft). A 9*g* barrier net is installed in the front of the cabin. Total cargo-carrying capability of the A300C4 is approx 41,000 kg (90,390 lb). Modification kits covering the forward fuselage section, in which the upper-deck cargo door is installed, are being built in Bremen by VFW-Fokker.

For customers requiring it, the A300C4 has the capability for conversion to passenger or mixed passenger/cargo configuration. Typical options include accommodation (in mainly eight-abreast seating) for up to 281 passengers on the upper deck; or 145 passengers (seven/eight-abreast) plus six 88 × 125 in pallets; or 75 passengers plus nine 88 × 125 in pallets; or fourteen 88 × 125 in or 96 × 125 in pallets; or twenty 86 × 125 in pallets.

The first A300C4, for Hapag Lloyd of Germany, made its initial flight in mid-1979; after fitting of the upper-deck cargo door, it was due to be delivered in January 1980.

Airbus Industrie has also defined an **A300F4** freighter version. This is similar to the C4, but with all passenger provisions removed completely and the cabin windows replaced by metal blanking plates.

The description of the A300B4 applies generally also to the convertible C4, except as outlined above and detailed below:

Dimensions, external: As A300B4, plus:
- Upper-deck cargo door (fwd, port):
  - Height (projected) 2·59 m (8 ft 6 in)
  - Width 3·58 m (11 ft 9 in)

Dimensions, internal: As A300B4, except:
- Cabin upper deck usable for cargo:
  - Length 31·78 m (104 ft 3 in)
  - Min height 2·16 m (7 ft 1 in)
  - Max height 2·44 m (8 ft 0 in)
  - Volume 173–179 m³ (6,100–6,315 cu ft)
- Max total volume for bulk loading (upper and lower decks) 286 m³ (10,087 cu ft)

Weights:
- Manufacturer's weight empty (basic):
  - passenger mode 81,000 kg (178,575 lb)
  - freight mode 81,900 kg (180,560 lb)
  - pure freighter 78,300 kg (172,620 lb)
- Manufacturer's weight empty (optional):
  - passenger mode 81,300 kg (179,235 lb)
  - freight mode 82,200 kg (181,220 lb)
  - pure freighter 78,600 kg (173,285 lb)
- Operating weight empty (basic):
  - *passenger mode 89,000 kg (196,210 lb)
  - freight mode 82,900 kg (182,765 lb)
  - pure freighter 79,000 kg (174,165 lb)
- Operating weight empty (optional):
  - *passenger mode 89,200 kg (196,650 lb)
  - freight mode 83,200 kg (183,425 lb)
  - pure freighter 79,400 kg (175,045 lb)
- Max payload (structural) (basic):
  - passenger mode 35,000 kg (77,160 lb)
  - freight mode 41,100 kg (90,610 lb)
  - pure freighter 45,000 kg (99,210 lb)
- Max payload (structural) (optional):
  - passenger mode 36,800 kg (81,130 lb)
  - freight mode 42,800 kg (94,360 lb)
  - pure freighter 46,600 kg (102,735 lb)
- Max T-O weight:
  - basic 157,500 kg (347,230 lb)
  - optional 165,000 kg (363,765 lb)
- Max landing weight:
  - basic 134,000 kg (295,420 lb)
  - optional 136,000 kg (299,830 lb)
- Max zero-fuel weight:
  - basic 124,000 kg (273,375 lb)
  - optional 126,000 kg (277,780 lb)

**incl weight of underfloor cargo hold containers and pallets*

Performance (estimated):
- Range with max (structural) payload, allowances for ground manoeuvring, 30 min hold at 460 m (1,500 ft), no diversion:
  - basic 2,100 nm (3,890 km; 1,825 miles)
  - optional 2,500 nm (4,635 km; 2,170 miles)
- Range with max fuel, no payload, allowances as above:
  - passenger mode 3,900 nm (7,230 km; 3,390 miles)
  - freight mode 4,100 nm (7,600 km; 3,560 miles)
  - pure freighter 4,200 nm (7,785 km; 3,650 miles)

AIRBUS A310

Known originally as the A300B10, the A310 is a short-fuselage development of the A300, and was launched in July 1978. Compared with the A300, the cabin is shorter by 11 frames and the overall fuselage by 13 frames. The cabin thus normally seats from 210–234 passengers, although the aircraft will be certificated to carry up to 255 persons. The A310 retains the same fuselage cross-section as the A300, thus being able to carry standard LD3 containers two abreast, and/or standard pallets installed crosswise. Capacity is 14 (optionally 15) standard LD3s, or three pallets and six (optionally seven) containers.

The A310 also has new, advanced-technology wings, of reduced span and area, designed by the British Aerospace Aircraft Group; a new and smaller tailplane; new 'multi-role' pylons able to support all types of engine offered; and landing gear modified to cater for these changes in size and weight.

Like the A300, the A310 can be powered by General Electric, Pratt & Whitney or Rolls-Royce turbofan engines. The customers so far identified (up to mid-1979) have selected for their aircraft the 213·5 kN (48,000 lb st) General Electric CF6-80A (Lufthansa and KLM); or the 208·6 kN (46,900 lb st) Pratt & Whitney JT9D-7R4C (Swissair); and the aircraft is to be certificated initially with these two types of engine. Studies to power the A310 with the 222·4 kN (50,000 lb st) Rolls-Royce RB.211-524B4 are under way.

At present, the A310 is offered in one basic version, the **A310-200**, for short/medium-haul operations, including transcontinental routes. However, it is to be certificated and offered at different weight options, to match different airline needs, and further developments will offer increases in payload/range capability.

First flight of the A310 is scheduled for early 1982, and entry into service for early 1983.

The following versions have been announced:

A310-100. Basic designation of short-range version. Model designations, according to power plant, include **A310-101** (CF6-45B2A), **A310-102** (CF6-80A), **A310-120** (JT9D-7R4) and **A310-140** (RB.211-524B4). None ordered by September 1979.

A310-200. Basic designation of medium-range version. Model designations, according to power plant, include **A310-201** (CF6-45B2A), **A310-202** (CF6-80A), **A310-220** (JT9D-7R4) and **A310-240** (RB.211-524B4).

A310C-200. Convertible version.

A310F-200. Freighter version.

By 10 August 1979, orders and options totalling 107 A310-200s had been received, as follows:

	Orders	*Options*
Air Afrique	2	—
Air France	5	10
KLM (Netherlands)	10	10
Lufthansa (Germany)	25	25
Swissair	10	10

Type: Large-capacity wide-bodied short/medium-range transport.

Wings: Cantilever mid-wing monoplane. Thickness/chord ratio 15·2% at root, 11·8% at 'break' in trailing-edge, and 10·8% at tip. Sweepback 28° at quarter-chord. Three-section leading-edge slats on each wing over almost full span, with no cutout over engine pylon. Two Fowler-type double-slotted flaps on each trailing-edge,

Airbus A300B4 for Hapag Lloyd of Germany, being converted in 1979 as the first A300C4 freighter

Model of the Airbus A310 developed version of the A300

with all-speed aileron between. Three roll spoilers/lift dumpers (outboard) and two airbrakes/lift dumpers (inboard) forward of each outer flap. Two further airbrakes/lift dumpers forward of each inboard flap. Construction generally similar to that of A300.

FUSELAGE: Generally similar to A300, except for reduced length (see introductory copy), resulting in deletion of two passenger doors.

TAIL UNIT: Vertical surfaces as for A300; horizontal surfaces similar to A300, but with slightly reduced dimensions.

LANDING GEAR: Generally similar to that of A300, but modified to cater for new dimensions and weights.

POWER PLANT: Currently ordered or available with the following turbofan engines:
Two 206·8 kN (46,500 lb st) General Electric CF6-45B2A (A310-101/201);
Two 213·5 kN (48,000 lb st) General Electric CF6-80A (A310-102/202);
Two 208·6 kN (46,900 lb st) Pratt & Whitney JT9D-7R4C (A310-120/220); or
Two 222·4 kN (50,000 lb st) Rolls-Royce RB.211-524B4 (A310-140/240).

ACCOMMODATION: Crew accommodation as for A300. Standard cabin arranged for 195-255 seats in eight-abreast layout; nine-abreast seating available for high-density configurations. Overhead baggage stowage as for A300, rising to average of 0·07 m³ (2·33 cu ft) per passenger with optional central stowage in 212-seat layout. Four passenger doors only, one forward and one aft on each side. Type I emergency exit over wing on each side. Underfloor baggage/cargo holds fore and aft of wings, each with door on starboard side. Forward hold will accommodate eight LD3 containers or three 2·24 × 3·17 m (88 × 125 in) standard pallets; its door is sized for the latter, but a wider door is optional, enabling 2·44 × 3·17 m (96 × 125 in) pallets to be loaded. Rear hold will accommodate six LD3 containers. Additional compartment aft of rear hold for bulk loading.

AVIONICS AND EQUIPMENT: Digital AFCS (automatic flight control system) standard, with computer-based flight control, thrust control and stability augmentation, confers capability for Category 2 landings; full provision to upgrade to Category 3 by adding second flight control computer and fail-operational capability. Basic flight management system is digital, with area navigation computer, electronic HSI and ADI, CRT displays and basic AIDS (airborne integrated data system); developed AIDS, with engine monitoring computer and digital data recorder, under evaluation. Head-up displays optional.

DIMENSIONS, EXTERNAL:

Wing span	43·90 m (144 ft 0¼ in)
Wing aspect ratio	8·8
Length overall	47·21 m (154 ft 10¾ in)
Length of fuselage	46·70 m (153 ft 2½ in)
Fuselage: Max diameter	5·64 m (18 ft 6 in)
Height overall	15·81 m (51 ft 10½ in)
Tailplane span	16·26 m (53 ft 4¼ in)
Wheel track	9·60 m (31 ft 6 in)
Wheelbase (c/l of shock-absorbers)	15·22 m (49 ft 11¼ in)

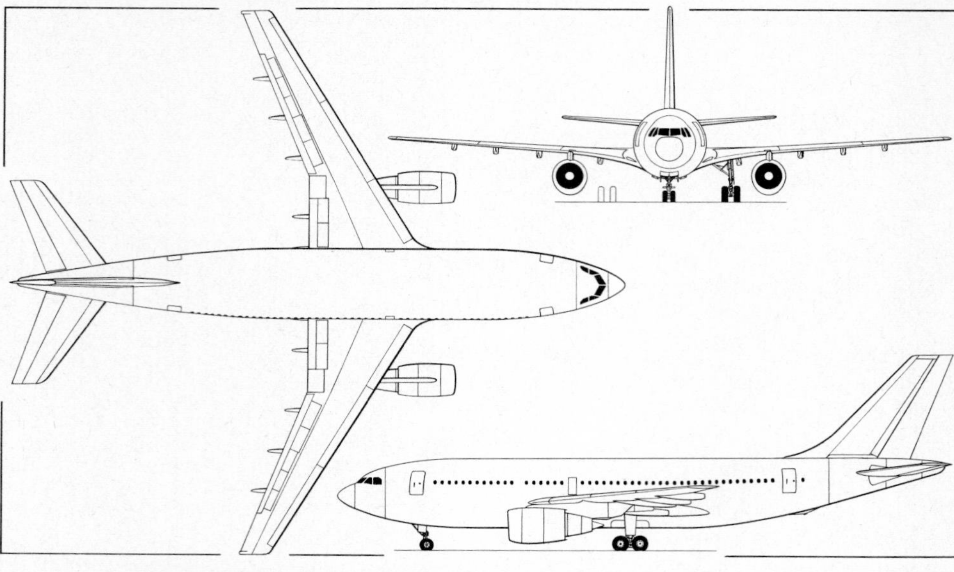

Airbus A310 short-fuselage short/medium-range transport aircraft *(Pilot Press)*

Passenger doors (four, each):	
Height	1·93 m (6 ft 4 in)
Width	1·07 m (3 ft 6 in)
Height to sill: fwd	4·32 m (14 ft 2 in)
rear	4·74 m (15 ft 6½ in)
Emergency exits (two, each):	
Height	1·40 m (4 ft 7 in)
Width	0·67 m (2 ft 2½ in)
Underfloor cargo door (fwd):	
Height	1·71 m (5 ft 7½ in)
Width	2·44 m (8 ft 0 in)
Height to sill	2·56 m (8 ft 4¾ in)
Underfloor cargo door (rear):	
Height	1·85 m (6 ft 0¾ in)
Width	1·85 m (6 ft 0¾ in)
Height to sill	2·63 m (8 ft 7½ in)

DIMENSIONS, INTERNAL:

Cabin: Max width	5·35 m (17 ft 7 in)
Max height	2·54 m (8 ft 4 in)
Underfloor cargo holds (fwd and rear):	
Max height	1·75 m (5 ft 9 in)
Max width	4·20 m (13 ft 9¼ in)
Underfloor cargo hold volume:	
fwd	50·3 m³ (1,776 cu ft)
rear	34·5 m³ (1,218 cu ft)
extreme rear	17·3 m³ (611 cu ft)
total containerised volume	62·6 m³ (2,211 cu ft)

AREAS:

Wings, gross	219·9 m² (2,367·0 sq ft)
Vertical tail surfaces (total)	45·2 m² (486·5 sq ft)
Horizontal tail surfaces (total)	64·0 m² (688·9 sq ft)

WEIGHTS:

Typical operating weight empty:	
101	75,389 kg (166,204 lb)
201	76,469 kg (168,585 lb)
202	76,100 kg (167,772 lb)
220	76,200 kg (167,992 lb)
Max payload: 202	32,400 kg (71,430 lb)
220	32,300 kg (71,209 lb)
Max usable fuel: 101	28,200 kg (62,170 lb)
202, 220	43,000 kg (94,798 lb)
Max T-O weight: 101	121,000 kg (266,760 lb)
201, 202, 220	132,000 kg (291,010 lb)
Max landing weight: 101	116,000 kg (255,735 lb)
201, 202, 220	118,500 kg (261,250 lb)
Max zero-fuel weight: 101	106,000 kg (233,690 lb)
201, 202, 220	108,500 kg (239,200 lb)

PERFORMANCE (estimated, with 234 passengers except where indicated):

Max operating speed: all versions	Mach 0·84 (360 knots; 667 km/h; 414 mph)
Approach speed at max landing weight:	
101	131 knots (243 km/h; 151 mph) CAS
201	133 knots (246 km/h; 153 mph) CAS
T-O field length at max T-O weight (S/L, ISA):	
101	1,555 m (5,100 ft)
201	1,980 m (6,500 ft)
Range, with allowances for ground manoeuvring, 250 nm (463 km; 288 mile) diversion, 30 min hold:	
101	1,830 nm (3,390 km; 2,110 miles)
201	2,710 nm (5,020 km; 3,120 miles)
202, 220	3,200 nm (5,930 km; 3,685 miles)
Range with max payload, allowances as above:	
202, 220	1,500 nm (2,780 km; 1,730 miles)
Range with max fuel, allowances as above:	
202, 220	3,750 nm (6,950 km; 4,320 miles)

OPERATIONAL NOISE CHARACTERISTICS (FAR Pt 36):

Take-off, sideline and approach noise levels:	
all versions	less than 90 EPNdB

ALPHA JET

AIRFRAME PRIME CONTRACTORS:

Avions Marcel Dassault/Breguet Aviation, 27 rue du Professeur Pauchet, BP 32, 92420 Vaucresson, France
Telephone: 970 75 21
Telex: 0734372

Dornier GmbH, Postfach 1420, 7990 Friedrichshafen, Federal Republic of Germany
Telephone: (07545) 82307
Telex: 0734372

On 22 July 1969 the French and German governments announced a joint requirement for a new subsonic basic and advanced training aircraft to enter service with the French and German armed forces in the 1970s. Each government had a potential requirement for about 200 such aircraft to replace Magister, Lockheed T-33A and Mystère IV-A trainers in service.

On 24 July 1970, it was announced that the Alpha Jet design had been selected for development to meet the requirement. The aircraft has been developed also for close air support and battlefield reconnaissance duties, following a change in Luftwaffe requirements.

First Alpha Jet E for the French Air Force, with underfuselage gun pod and underwing weapons and drop-tanks

DASSAULT-BREGUET/DORNIER ALPHA JET

Dassault-Breguet of France and Dornier of Germany are jointly producing the Alpha Jet, with Dassault-Breguet as main contractor and Dornier as industrial collaborator, the total work load being shared primarily between the two groups.

On 15 February 1971 the project definition phase of the Alpha Jet was completed, and design work for the development phase started in the Autumn of 1971. This received joint Franco-German government approval in late 1972; approval to proceed with the production phase was announced on 26 March 1975.

Four prototypes were built, the first and third assembled in France and the second and fourth in Germany, plus two airframes for static and fatigue testing. Structural testing was completed on 18 January 1977.

Flight testing was carried out predominantly in France, by both French and German pilots, each prototype having made its first few test flights in the country where it was assembled. The 01 made its first flight, at Istres, on 26 October 1973; all four had flown by the end of 1974. Details of the prototypes can be found in the 1978-79 and earlier editions of *Jane's*. By the beginning of 1979 the Alpha Jet had accumulated about 3,000 flying hours.

The French and Federal German governments have agreed to procure 400 Alpha Jets, 200 each for the Armée de l'Air and the Luftwaffe, and by the Spring of 1979 firm initial contracts had been placed for 239 of these (89 **Alpha Jet E** trainers for France and 150 close-support **Alpha Jet As** for Germany). In addition, Belgium has ordered 33 of the E version, which it designates **Alpha Jet 1B**. The Togolese Air Force has ordered five, and the air forces of the Ivory Coast 12, Morocco 24 and Nigeria 12.

Dassault-Breguet and Dornier have teamed with Lockheed-California to enter the Alpha Jet in the US Navy's VTX advanced trainer competition; if selected, it will be built under licence in the USA by Lockheed. The Alpha Jet may also be concerned in the manufacturing agreement signed in the Spring of 1978 between the French government and the Arab Organisation for Industrialisation.

The first production Alpha Jet, the E1 for the French Air Force, made its first flight at Istres on 4 November 1977. This is being used to replace the 04 prototype, for service testing by the CEV at Istres and the CEAM at Mont-de-Marsan. Deliveries to the Armée de l'Air started in the Summer of 1978, beginning with the E2 aircraft, and went first to the 314e Groupement École at Tours. This unit will receive 65 Alpha Jet Es in 1979-81, to replace Lockheed T-33As at present in service. Fourteen Alpha Jet Es had been delivered by May 1979. During 1979-80 nine Alpha Jet Es will be delivered to the French national aerobatic team, the Patrouille de France, followed by 14 to the Centre d'Entraînement au Vol Sans Visibilité in 1981, and 30 in 1982 to the 8e Escadre de Transformation at Cazaux to replace Mystère IV-As in the weapons training role.

The first Alpha Jet 1B for Belgium (AT-01, the fifth production aircraft) first flew on 20 June 1978, and was delivered to the Belgian Air Force during the following month. Eight had been delivered by May 1979. Like the French aircraft, the Belgian Alpha Jets are being used primarily for advanced flying and weapons training, for which they replace the Potez/Aérospatiale Magister.

The second production Alpha Jet to fly, on 12 April 1978, was the A1 first close support model for Germany. Deliveries of the Alpha Jet A to the Luftwaffe are scheduled to take place in 1979-82, equipping three Jagdbombergeschwader (fighter-bomber groups) at Fürstenfeldbruch, Husum and Oldenburg and replacing the Fiat G91R in the close support and reconnaissance role. Nine Alpha Jet As had been delivered by May 1979, and deliveries were scheduled to increase to six per month by October of that year.

All production Alpha Jets have identical structure, power plant, landing gear and standard equipment; there are assembly lines in France, Germany and Belgium. The outer wings, tail unit, rear fuselage, landing gear doors and cold-flow exhaust are manufactured in Germany; the forward and centre fuselage (with integrated wing centre-section) are manufactured in France. Fuselage nosecones and wing flaps are manufactured in Belgium by SABCA, which is building 32 of the 33 ordered by that country, for completion between November 1978 and April 1980. Final assembly of the trainer version takes place in France, and of the close support version in Germany. The power plant prime contractors are Turboméca and SNECMA in France, and MTU and KHD in Germany; and, for the landing gear, Messier-Hispano in France and Liebherr Aero Technik in Germany. A total of 113 Alpha Jets were due for completion by the end of 1979, by which time output should have risen to a rate of 13 per month.

TYPE: Tandem two-seat basic, low-altitude and advanced jet trainer and close support and battlefield reconnaissance aircraft.

WINGS: Cantilever shoulder-wing monoplane, with 6° anhedral from roots. Thickness/chord ratio 10·2% at root, 8·6% at tip. Sweepback 28° at quarter-chord. All-metal numerically- or chemically-milled structure, consisting of two main wing panels bolted to a centre frame. Extended chord on outer wings. Hydraulically actuated Fowler-type slotted flaps on each trailing-edge. Ailerons actuated by double-body irreversible hydraulic servo, with trimmable artificial feel system.

FUSELAGE: All-metal semi-monocoque structure, numerically or chemically milled, of basically oval cross-section. Built in three sections: nose (including cockpit), centre-section (including engine air intake trunks and main landing gear housings) and rear (including engine mounts and tail assembly). Narrow strake on each side of nose of Alpha Jet E and 1B. Pointed nose, with pitot probe, on close support version. Electrically controlled, hydraulically actuated airbrake on each side of rear upper fuselage, of carbon-fibre-reinforced epoxy resin.

TAIL UNIT: Cantilever type, of similar construction to wings, with 45° sweepback on fin leading-edge and 30° on tailplane leading-edge. Dorsal spine fairing between cockpit and fin. All-flying tailplane, with trimmable and IAS-controlled artificial feel system. Glassfibre fin tip and tailplane tips. Double-body irreversible hydraulic servo-actuated rudder, with trimmable artificial feel system. Yaw damper on close support version.

LANDING GEAR: Forward-retracting tricycle type, of Messier-Hispano/Liebherr design. All units retract hydraulically, main units into underside of engine air intake trunks. Single wheel and low-pressure tyre (approx 4 bars; 58 lb/sq in at normal T-O weight) on each unit. Tyre sizes 615 × 255-10 on main units, 380 × 150-4 on nose unit. Steel disc brakes and anti-skid units on main gear. Emergency braking system. Hydraulic nosewheel steering and arrester hook on close support version. Nosewheel offset to starboard to permit ground firing from gun pod.

POWER PLANT: Two SNECMA/Turboméca Larzac 04-C5 turbofan engines, each rated at 13·24 kN (2,976 lb st) for production aircraft, mounted on sides of fuselage. Splitter plate in front of each intake. Fuel in two integral tanks in outer wings, one in centre-section and three fuselage tanks. Internal fuel capacity 1,900 litres (418 Imp gallons). Provision for 310 litre (68·2 Imp gallon) capacity drop-tank on each outer wing pylon. Pressure refuelling standard for all tanks, including drop-tanks. Gravity system for fuselage tanks and drop-tanks. Pressure refuelling point near starboard engine air intake. Fuel system incorporates provision for short periods of inverted flying.

First of 33 production Alpha Jet 1B two-seat advanced trainers for the Belgian Air Force

ACCOMMODATION: Two persons in tandem, in pressurised cockpit under individual upward-opening canopies. Dual controls standard. Rear seat (for instructor in trainer versions) is elevated. French trainer versions fitted with Martin-Baker Mk 4 ejection seats, operable (including ejection through canopy) at zero height and speeds down to 90 knots (167 km/h; 104 mph). Aircraft for Germany fitted with licence-built (by RFB) Stencel S-III-S3AJ zero-zero ejection seats; Martin-Baker Mk 10 zero-zero seats in aircraft for Belgium. Baggage compartment in tailcone, with access door on starboard side.

SYSTEMS: Cockpit air-conditioning and demisting system. Cabin pressure differential 0·30 bars (4·3 lb/sq in). Two independent and redundant hydraulic systems, each 207 bars (3,000 lb/sq in), with engine-driven pumps (emergency electric pump on one circuit), for actuating control surfaces, landing gear, brakes, flaps, airbrakes, and (when fitted) nosewheel steering. Pneumatic system, for cockpit pressurisation and air-conditioning, occupants' pressure suits and fuel tank pressurisation, is supplied by compressed air from engines. Main electrical power supplied by two 28V 9kW starter/generators, one on each engine. Circuit includes a 36Ah nickel-cadmium battery for self-starting and two static inverters for supplying 115V AC current at 400Hz to auxiliary systems. External ground DC power receptacle in port engine air intake trunk. Hydraulic and electrical systems can be sustained by either engine in the event of the other engine becoming inoperative. Liquid-film anti-icing system; de-icing by electrical heater mats. Oxygen mask for each occupant, supplied by liquid oxygen converter of 10 litres (2·2 Imp gallons) capacity. Emergency gaseous oxygen bottle for each occupant.

AVIONICS AND EQUIPMENT: Large avionics bay in rear fuselage, containing most of the radio and navigation equipment. Standard avionics include VHF and UHF transceivers, IFF/SIF, VOR/ILS/marker, Tacan, gyro platform and intercom. Twin landing lights on nosewheel leg; taxying light in each wing leading-edge. Close support version has Kaiser/VDO KM 808 head-up display, radar altimeter, Lear Siegler LSI 6000 E attitude and heading reference system, and Litef LDN Doppler navigation system with LR-1416 navigation computer, ABE control unit and Teledyne Ryan speed sensor, and Elettronica (Italy) ECM.

ARMAMENT AND OPERATIONAL EQUIPMENT: For armament training and light close support missions, the Alpha Jet can be equipped with an underfuselage detachable pod containing a 30 mm DEFA or 27 mm Mauser cannon with 150 rds, or the same pod with a 12·7 or 7·62 mm machine-gun and up to 250 rds. Provision also for two hardpoints under each wing, with non-jettisonable adaptor pylons, the inner ones each stressed for loads of up to 665 kg (1,466 lb) and the outer ones for up to 335 kg (738 lb). On these can be carried, within the load capacity for each station, F2, M155 or F1 launchers for six, eighteen or thirty-six 68 mm rockets respectively; HE or retarded bombs of 50, 125, 250 or 400 kg; 625 lb cluster dispensers; 690 or 825 lb special-purpose tanks; combined external multistore adaptor (CEM-1) for six to eighteen rockets and four practice bombs, or one 500 lb bomb, or six penetration bombs, or grenades or other stores; practice launchers for bombs or rockets; Dassault-Breguet CC-420 30 mm gun pods; or two 310 litre (68·2 Imp gallon) drop-tanks (outer pylons only). Provision also for carrying air-to-air or air-to-surface missiles such as Magic or Maverick, target demonstration devices or reconnaissance pod. Total payload for all five stations is at present 2,250 kg (4,960 lb). Fire control system for air-to-air or air-to-ground firing, dive bombing and low-level bombing. Firing by trainee pilot (in front seat) is governed by a safety interlock system controlled by the instructor, which energises the forward station trigger circuit and illuminates a fire clearance indicator in the trainee's cockpit. Thomson-CSF/Bodenseewerk Type 902 reflector sight in French version; Kaiser/VDO KM 808 sight, head-up display and gun camera in German version.

DIMENSIONS, EXTERNAL:
- Wing span: 9·11 m (29 ft 10¾ in)
- Wing aspect ratio: 4·8
- Length overall:
  - trainer: 12·29 m (40 ft 3¾ in)
  - close support version incl probe: 13·23 m (43 ft 5 in)
- Height overall (at normal T-O weight): 4·19 m (13 ft 9 in)
- Tailplane span: 4·33 m (14 ft 2½ in)
- Wheel track: 2·71 m (8 ft 10¾ in)
- Wheelbase: 4·72 m (15 ft 5¾ in)

AREAS:
- Wings, gross: 17·50 m² (188·4 sq ft)
- Ailerons (total): 1·04 m² (11·19 sq ft)
- Trailing-edge flaps (total): 2·86 m² (30·78 sq ft)
- Airbrakes (total): 0·74 m² (7·97 sq ft)
- Fin: 2·97 m² (31·97 sq ft)
- Rudder: 0·62 m² (6·67 sq ft)
- Horizontal tail surfaces (total): 3·94 m² (42·41 sq ft)

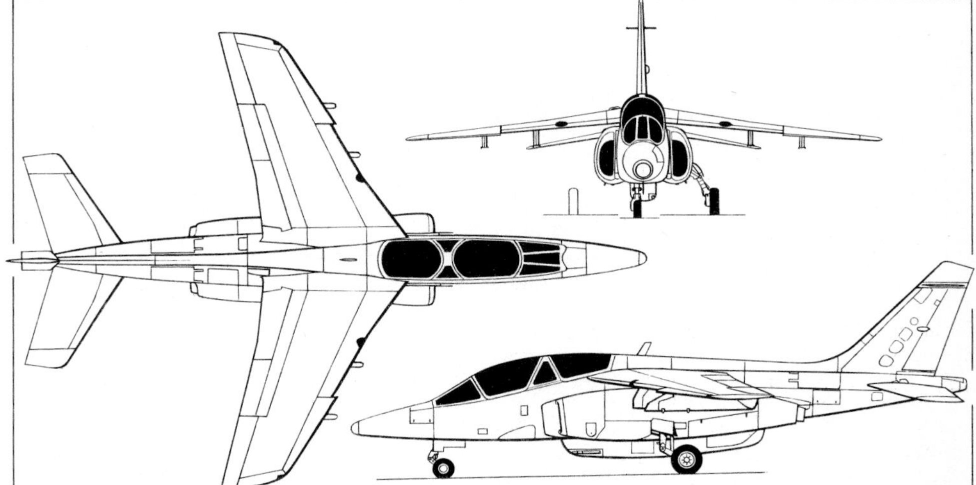

Alpha Jet E basic and advanced trainer *(Pilot Press)*

WEIGHTS:
Weight empty, equipped:
trainer 3,345 kg (7,374 lb)
close support version 3,500 kg (7,716 lb)
Max fuel load:
internal 1,415 kg (3,120 lb)
external 500 kg (1,102 lb)
Max external load 2,250 kg (4,960 lb)
Normal T-O weight:
trainer, 'clean' 5,000 kg (11,023 lb)
Max T-O weight:
with external stores 7,500 kg (16,535 lb)
Max landing weight 5,300 kg (11,684 lb)

PERFORMANCE (at normal 'clean' T-O weight, except where indicated):
Max level speed at 10,000 m (32,800 ft) Mach 0·85
Max level speed at S/L 540 knots (1,000 km/h; 622 mph)
Max speed for flap and landing gear extension 175 knots (323 km/h; 201 mph)
Approach speed 110 knots (204 km/h; 127 mph)
Stalling speed, flaps and landing gear up 116 knots (216 km/h; 134 mph)
Stalling speed, flaps and landing gear down 90 knots (167 km/h; 104 mph)
Landing speed at normal landing weight less than 92 knots (170 km/h; 106 mph)
Max rate of climb at S/L 3,420 m (11,220 ft)/min
Rate of climb at S/L, one engine out, at 4,782 kg (10,542 lb) AUW, in landing configuration 330 m (1,085 ft)/min
Time to 9,145 m (30,000 ft) less than 7 min
Service ceiling 14,020 m (46,000 ft)
T-O run 490 m (1,610 ft)
Landing run 610 m (2,000 ft)
Low altitude radius of action (trainer):
'clean', max internal fuel 232 nm (430 km; 267 miles)
with external tanks 297 nm (550 km; 342 miles)
High altitude radius of action (trainer), reserves of 15% internal fuel:
'clean', max internal fuel 593 nm (1,100 km; 683 miles)
with external tanks 739 nm (1,370 km; 851 miles)
Lo-lo-lo mission radius (close support version), incl 5 min combat at max continuous thrust:
with belly gun pod and underwing weapons 189 nm (350 km; 217·5 miles)
with belly gun pod, underwing weapons and external tanks 280 nm (520 km; 323 miles)
Hi-lo-hi mission radius (close support version), incl 5 min combat at max continuous thrust, reserves for two GCA landings:
with belly gun pod and underwing weapons 280 nm (520 km; 323 miles)
with belly gun pod, underwing weapons and external tanks 490 nm (910 km; 565 miles)
Ferry range (internal fuel and two 310 litre external tanks) 1,450 nm (2,687 km; 1,670 miles)
Endurance (internal fuel only):
low altitude more than 2 h 30 min
high altitude more than 3 h 30 min
g limits (ultimate) +12; −6·4

CONCORDE

CONCORDE SUPERSONIC TRANSPORT

AIRFRAME PRIME CONTRACTORS:

British Aerospace Aircraft Group, Richmond Road, Kingston upon Thames, Surrey KT2 5QS, England
Telephone: 01-546 7741

Aérospatiale, 37 boulevard de Montmorency, 75781 Paris Cédex 16, France
Telephone: 524 43 21

POWER PLANT PRIME CONTRACTORS:

Rolls-Royce Ltd, PO Box 3, Filton, Bristol, England
Telephone: 0272 693871

Société Nationale d'Étude et de Construction de Moteurs d'Aviation, 2 boulevard Victor, 75724 Paris Cédex 15, France
Telephone: 554 92 00

CONCORDE

Anglo-French negotiations concerning the development of a supersonic transport aircraft culminated on 29 November 1962 in the signing of two agreements, one between the French and British governments, the other between the manufacturers to whom the project was entrusted. The agreements provided for the manufacture of two Concorde prototypes, followed by two pre-production aircraft and two airframes for static and fatigue testing. The static test programme was completed in September 1973, and this airframe was tested to destruction in June 1974. Fatigue testing was programmed to continue until two aircraft 'lives' (about 48,000 flights) had been attained.

The planned flight test programme, involving the two prototype, two pre-production and first four production Concordes, achieved its target of 5,335 hr flying at the time when the full passenger-carrying certificate of airworthiness was granted by the SGAC and CAA in late 1975.

By the beginning of 1979 a total of 19 Concordes had flown, including 15 production models. In development and test flying with the manufacturers 2,930 flights had then been made, of which 1,800 involved flight at supersonic speeds. A total of 6,560 hours block time had been amassed, including 2,450 hours supersonic. In addition, up to the Summer of 1979, airline service had involved 7,600 flights amounting to 26,000 flying hours and 360,000 passengers carried. The published schedule for December 1978 amounted to 1,030 commercial hours per month for Air France and British Airways. Both airlines have approval to operate Concorde in Category 3 weather conditions.

When sonic boom considerations preclude use of the normal climb technique, sufficient power is available to increase the transonic acceleration height to over 12,200 m (40,000 ft). Normally, however, the aircraft accelerates and climbs from 200 knots (370 km/h; 230 mph) CAS at S/L to 400 knots (740 km/h; 460 mph) CAS at 1,500 m (5,000 ft), then climbs at a constant CAS of 400 knots to 9,800 m (32,150 ft) where its speed is Mach 1·06, climbs and accelerates to Mach 1·8 (530 knots; 980 km/h; 610 mph CAS) at 13,800 m (45,300 ft) and continues climbing at this CAS until the cruise Mach number is reached, finally climbing to cruising height at cruising Mach number.

Airframe development and production of the Concorde were undertaken jointly by Aérospatiale and BAe, with two final assembly lines, at Toulouse and Filton respectively. There was no duplication of main production jigs.

Aérospatiale was responsible for development and production of the rear cabin section, wings and wing control surfaces, hydraulic systems, flying controls, navigation systems, radio and air-conditioning system. The automatic flight control system was designed by Marconi in the UK and SFENA in France, under contract to Aérospatiale. BAe was responsible for the three forward sections of the fuselage, the rear fuselage and vertical tail surfaces, the engine nacelles and ducting, the electrical system, sound and thermal insulation, oxygen system, fuel system, engine installation, and fire warning and extinguishing systems.

The two prototype and two pre-production Concordes have been fully described in previous editions of *Jane's.* The first two production aircraft were flown on 6 December 1973 at Toulouse (F-WTSB) and 13 February 1974 at Filton (G-BBDG), each attaining a speed of approx 868 knots (1,610 km/h; 1,000 mph) on its first flight. Third and fourth production aircraft (F-WTSC, now F-BTSC, and G-BOAC) flew for the first time at Toulouse and Filton on 31 January and 27 February 1975 respectively. Special category certificates of airworthiness were granted in May and June 1975 by the SGAC and CAA, anticipating the full airworthiness certificates which were granted on 13 October and 5 December 1975. The fifth and sixth production aircraft (F-BVFA and G-BOAA) made their first flights on 25 October and 5 November 1975 respectively, and the next four production aircraft were delivered to Air France and British Airways (two each) in 1976. Nos. 11 and 12 (F-BVFD and G-BOAE) first flew on 10 February and 17 March 1977, followed by No. 14 on 21 April 1978, No. 13 on 26 June 1978, and No. 15 on 26 December 1978.

British Airways ordered five production Concordes, and Air France four, all of which have been delivered. Air France started a daily service to New York on 22 November 1977 and British Airways on 12 February 1978. Air France continues to operate a daily service, while British Airways has increased services to New York to 12 a week. Air France extended its Paris-Washington service to Mexico City twice a week from 20 September 1978. A joint operation between British Airways and Singapore Airlines opened a supersonic service from Bahrain to Singapore on 9 December 1977; a thrice-weekly service was suspended in early 1978, but Malaysian airspace was then cleared to Concorde for a six-month trial period, and Singapore services were reopened on 24 January 1979.

Preliminary purchasing agreements were signed by Iran Air for two Concordes (with an option on a third) and by CAAC of China for three.

On 10 February 1977, Braniff Airways of the USA announced the signing of interchange agreements with British Airways and Air France. Under the terms of these agreements Braniff was to operate Concorde arrivals and departures six days a week between Dallas/Fort Worth and Washington Dulles. This service was inaugurated on 12 January 1979, three days after the issue of Concorde's FAA Type Certificate.

In 1977-78, BAe flight-tested modifications to the wing and tail control surfaces designed to reduce drag and fuel consumption. These modifications, which consist of an approx 0·61 m (2 ft) increase in fin chord and an approx 0·05 m (2 in) increase in the chord of the elevons and rudder may, it is estimated, reduce fuel consumption by approx 680 kg (1,500 lb) on a flight of 3,500 nm (6,485 km; 4,030 miles). In 1978 also, BAe was flight-testing a new, thinner air intake lip. This modification reduces fuel consumption by approx 1,360 kg (3,000 lb) on a supersonic flight of 3,500 nm (6,485 km; 4,030 miles).

The following description applies to the production Concorde:

TYPE: Four-jet supersonic transport.

WINGS: Cantilever low wing of ogival delta planform. Thickness/chord ratio 3% at root, 2·15% from nacelle outboard. Slight anhedral. Continuous camber. Multi-spar torsion-box structure, manufactured mainly from RR.58 (AU2GN) aluminium alloy. Integrally-machined components used for highly loaded members and skin panels. In centre wing, spars are continuous across fuselage, the spars and associated frames being built as single assemblies extending between the engine nacelles. Forward wing sections built as separate components attached to each side of fuselage, spar loads being transferred to cross-members in lower part of main fuselage frames. Three elevons on trailing-edge of each wing, of aluminium alloy honeycomb construction. Each elevon is independently operated by a tandem jack, each half supplied from an independent hydraulic source and controlled by a separate electrical system. Dowty Boulton Paul power control units. Hydraulic artificial feel units protect the aircraft against excessive aerodynamic loads induced by pilot through over-control. Autostabilisation is provided. Autopilot control is by signals fed into normal control circuit. No high-lift devices. Leading-edges ahead of air intakes are de-iced electrically.

FUSELAGE: Mainly-conventional pressurised aluminium alloy semi-monocoque structure of constant cross-

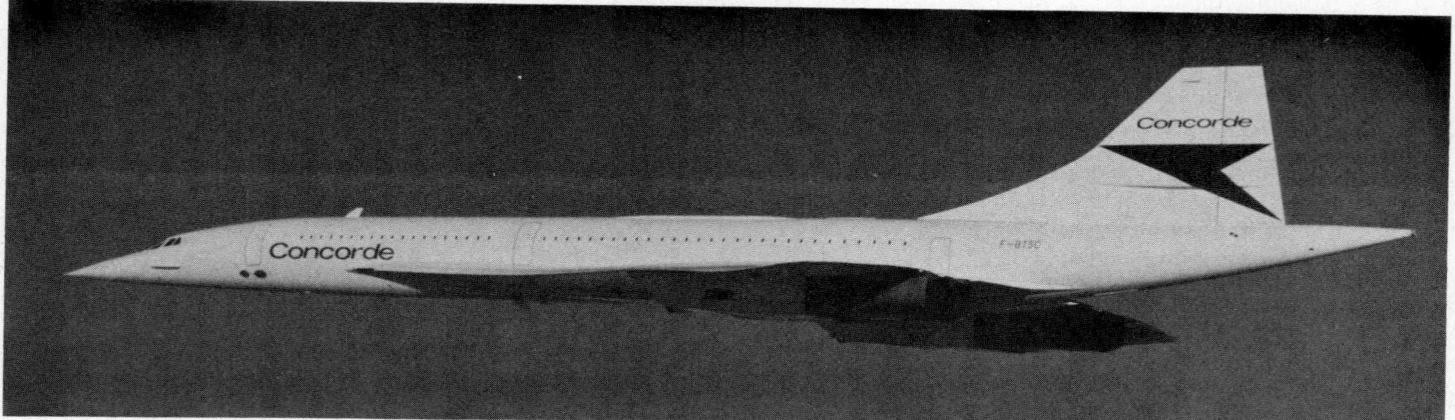

Third production Concorde, painted for its role in the film *Airport '79*

section, with unpressurised nose and tail cones. Hoop frames at approx 0·55 m (21·5 in) pitch support integrally-machined panels having closely-pitched longitudinal stringers. Window surrounds in passenger cabin formed of integral skin-stringer panels machined from aluminium alloy planks. Nose is drooped hydraulically to improve forward view during take-off, initial climb, approach and landing. Retractable visor is raised hydraulically to fair in windscreen in cruising flight.

Tail Unit: Vertical fin and rudder only. Fin is multi-spar torsion box of similar construction to wings. Two-section aluminium rudder controlled in same way as elevons. No de-icing system.

Landing Gear: Hydraulically-retractable tricycle type. Messier-Hispano nose and main units, with Kléber wheels and tyres. Twin-wheel steerable nose unit retracts forward. Four-wheel bogie main units retract inward. Oleo-pneumatic shock-absorbers. Main wheels and tyres size 47 × 15·75-22, pressure 12·9 bars (187 lb/sq in). Nosewheels and tyres size 31 × 10·75-14, pressure 12 bars (174 lb/sq in). Dunlop carbon disc brakes. SNECMA (Hispano) SPAD anti-skid units. Retractable tail bumper.

Engine Nacelles: Each consists of hydraulically-controlled variable-area (by ramp) air intake, engine bay and nozzle support structure. Intakes are of RR.58 or AU2GN aluminium alloy with steel leading-edges. The engine bay has an Inconel centre wall with aluminium alloy forward doors and titanium rear doors. The nozzle bay, aft of the rear spar, is of welded Stresskin sandwich panels and heat-resistant nickel alloys. Reverser buckets, which are also used as a secondary nozzle, are actuated by ball-screw jacks driven by compressed air through flexible shafts. Leading-edges of intakes, rear ramp sections and intake auxiliary door are electrically de-iced. Engine nose bullet and inlet guide vanes are de-iced by hot engine bleed air.

Power Plant: Four Rolls-Royce/SNECMA Olympus 593 Mk 610 turbojet engines, each rated at 169·3 kN (38,050 lb st) with 17% afterburning, and Type 28 thrust reversers. Fuel system is used also as heat sink and to maintain aircraft trim. All tanks are of integral construction and are in two groups, with total usable capacity of 119,786 litres (26,350 Imp gallons). Main group comprises five tanks in each wing and four tanks in fuselage and maintains CG automatically in cruising flight. Trim tank group (three tanks) comprises two tanks at the front and a tank of 13,150 litres (2,892 Imp gallons) capacity in fuselage beneath tail fin. This group maintains correct relationship between CG and aerodynamic centre of pressure by transferring fuel rearward during acceleration and forward during return to subsonic flight. Four pressure refuelling points in bottom fairing, two forward of each main landing gear unit. Oil capacity 22·75 litres (5 Imp gallons) per engine.

Accommodation: Pilot and co-pilot side by side on flight deck, with third crew member behind on starboard side. Provision for supernumerary seat behind pilot. Wide variety of four-abreast seating layouts to suit individual requirements of airlines. With all normal toilet and galley service facilities, up to 128 economy class passengers can be carried with 86 cm (34 in) seat pitch. A version with 144 passenger seats at 81 cm (32 in) pitch is available. Toilets at front and centre of cabin. Baggage space under forward cabin and aft of cabin. Passenger doors forward of cabin and amidships on port side, with service doors opposite. Baggage door aft of cabin on starboard side. Emergency exits in rear half of cabin on each side. Two galley areas.

Systems: BAe (Hawker Siddeley Dynamics) air-conditioning system, comprising four independent subsystems, with Hamilton Standard heat exchangers. Pressure differential 0·74 bars (10·7 lb/sq in). In each subsystem the air passes through a primary ram-air heat exchanger to an air cycle cold-air unit, and then through secondary air/air and air/fuel heat exchangers. The air is then mixed with hot air and fed to cabins, flight deck, baggage holds, landing gear, equipment and radar bays. Hydraulic services utilise two primary systems and one standby, pressure 276 bars (4,000 lb/sq in), each actuated by two engine-driven pumps. Temperature of

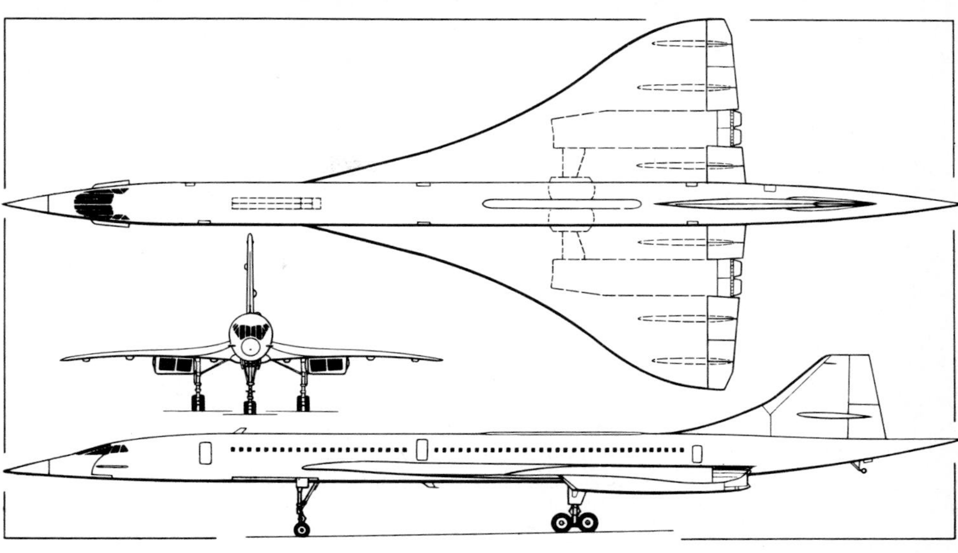

Aérospatiale/BAe Concorde supersonic transport *(Pilot Press)*

the Oronite M.2V fluid is limited by heat exchangers. Main systems actuate flying control surfaces, artificial feel units, landing gear, wheel brakes, nosewheel steering, windscreen visor, nosecone droop, engine intake ramps and fuel pumps in rear transfer tank. Electrical system powered by four 60kVA engine-driven constant-speed brushless alternators giving 200/115V AC at 400Hz. Four 150A transformer-rectifiers and two 25Ah batteries provide 28V DC supply.

Avionics: SFENA/Marconi Avionics automatic flight control system (AFCS). Litton LTN-72 primary navigation system comprises three identical inertial platforms, each coupled to a digital computer to form three self-contained units, two VOR/ILS systems, one ADF (Marconi Avionics AD-380 in British Airways aircraft), two DME systems, one marker, two RCA AVQ-X weather radars and two TRT AHV-5 radio altimeters. Plessey flight data recording system in British Airways aircraft. Provision for supplementary system including a long-distance radio fixing system of the Loran C type. Optional equipment includes a second ADF. Basic communications equipment consists of two VHF and two HF transceivers, one Selcal decoder and two ATC transponders (Cossor SSR 2700 in British Airways aircraft). Nose radome by Reinforced Microwave Plastics. Provision for a third VHF transceiver and data link equipment.

Dimensions, external:
- Wing span — 25·56 m (83 ft 10 in)
- Wing aerodynamic reference chord at root — 27·66 m (90 ft 9 in)
- Wing aspect ratio — 1·7
- Length overall — 62·10 m (203 ft 9 in)
- Height overall — 11·40 m (37 ft 5 in)
- Fin aerodynamic reference chord at base — 10·59 m (34 ft 9 in)
- Wheel track — 7·72 m (25 ft 4 in)
- Wheelbase — 18·19 m (59 ft 8¼ in)
- Passenger doors (each):
  - Height — 1·67 m (5 ft 5¾ in)
  - Width — 0·76 m (2 ft 6 in)
  - Height to sill: fwd — 4·88 m (16 ft 0 in)
  - amidships — 4·74 m (15 ft 7 in)
- Service doors (each):
  - Height — 1·22 m (4 ft 0 in)
  - Width — 0·61 m (2 ft 0 in)
  - Height to sill: fwd — 4·88 m (16 ft 0 in)
  - amidships — 4·75 m (15 ft 7 in)
- Baggage hold door (underfloor):
  - Length — 0·99 m (3 ft 3 in)
  - Width — 0·84 m (2 ft 9·2 in)
  - Height to sill — 3·54 m (11 ft 7 in)
- Baggage hold door (rear, stbd):
  - Height — 1·52 m (5 ft 0 in)
  - Width — 0·76 m (2 ft 6 in)
  - Height to sill — 4·04 m (13 ft 3 in)

Dimensions, internal:
- Cabin:
  - Length, flight deck door to rear pressure bulkhead, incl galley and toilets — 39·32 m (129 ft 0 in)
  - Width — 2·63 m (8 ft 7½ in)
  - Height — 1·96 m (6 ft 5 in)
  - Volume — 238·5 m³ (8,440 cu ft)
- Baggage/freight compartments:
  - underfloor — 6·43 m³ (227 cu ft)
  - rear fuselage (total) — 13·31 m³ (470 cu ft)

Areas:
- Wings, gross — 358·25 m² (3,856 sq ft)
- Elevons (total) — 32·00 m² (344·44 sq ft)
- Fin (excl dorsal fin) — 33·91 m² (365 sq ft)
- Rudder — 10·40 m² (112 sq ft)

Weights and Loadings:
- Operating weight empty — 78,700 kg (173,500 lb)
- Typical payload — 11,340 kg (25,000 lb)
- Max payload — 12,700 kg (28,000 lb)
- Max T-O weight — 185,065 kg (408,000 lb)
- Max zero-fuel weight — 92,080 kg (203,000 lb)
- Max landing weight — 111,130 kg (245,000 lb)
- Max wing loading — approx 488 kg/m² (100 lb/sq ft)
- Max power loading — approx 268 kg/kN (2·5 lb/lb st)

Performance (calculated, at max T-O weight):
- Max cruising speed at 15,635 m (51,300 ft)
  - Mach 2·04 or 530 knots CAS, whichever is the lesser, equivalent to TAS of 1,176 knots (2,179 km/h; 1,354 mph)
- T-O speed — 214 knots (397 km/h; 246 mph)
- Landing speed — 162 knots (300 km/h; 187 mph)
- Rate of climb at S/L — 1,525 m (5,000 ft)/min
- Service ceiling — approx 18,290 m (60,000 ft)
- Min ground turning radius — 21·7 m (71 ft 0 in)
- Runway LCN at max T-O weight — 90
- T-O to 10·7 m (35 ft) — 3,410 m (11,200 ft)
- Landing from 10·7 m (35 ft) — 2,220 m (7,300 ft)
- Range with max fuel, FAR reserves and 8,845 kg (19,500 lb) payload — 3,550 nm (6,580 km; 4,090 miles)
- Range with max payload, FAR reserves:
  - at Mach 0·95 at 9,100 m (30,000 ft) — 2,760 nm (5,110 km; 3,180 miles)
  - at Mach 2·02 cruise/climb — 3,360 nm (6,230 km; 3,870 miles)

Operational Noise Characteristics (FAR Pt 36):
- T-O noise level — 119·5 EPNdB
- *Approach noise level — 116·7 EPNdB
- Sideline noise level — 112·2 EPNdB

Under stabilised standard procedure. Air France and British Airways currently use a decelerated approach procedure which reduces approach noise level by approx 7 EPNdB

JET
JOINT EUROPEAN TRANSPORT

In March 1978 Aérospatiale, BAe, MBB and VFW-Fokker signed a memorandum of understanding covering the development, production and sale of a series of future short/medium-range civil transport aircraft. Initially, the memorandum established agreement on relationships between, and responsibilities of, the partner companies on joint programmes, including current versions of the Airbus A300 and its A310 derivative (which see), together with a new short/medium-haul aircraft known as JET (Joint European Transport).

MBB/AÉROSPATIALE

Participating Companies:

Messerschmitt-Bölkow-Blohm GmbH, Ottobrunn bei München, 8 München 80, Postfach 801220, Federal Republic of Germany
Telephone: (089) 60001

Aérospatiale, 37 boulevard de Montmorency, 75781 Paris Cédex 16, France
Telephone: 524 43 21

MBB PAH-2/AÉROSPATIALE HAC

MBB and Aérospatiale have been designated by their respective governments to design, develop and produce an anti-tank helicopter that will meet the requirements of the French and German armies for service in the second half of the 1980s. This programme is known in Germany as the PAH-2 (Panzerabwehr Hubschrauber 2) and in France as the HAC (Helicoptère Anti-Char). The programme was still in the project definition phase in the Spring of 1979, although selection of a design for further development was expected in the late Summer of that year. MBB has leadership of the programme.

MBB/KAWASAKI

AIRFRAME PRIME CONTRACTORS:

Messerschmitt-Bölkow-Blohm GmbH, Ottobrunn bei München, 8 München 80, Postfach 801220, Federal Republic of Germany
Telephone: (089) 60001

Kawasaki Heavy Industries Ltd, World Trade Center Building, 4-1 Hamamatsu-cho 2-chome, Minato-ku, Tokyo, Japan
Telephone: Tokyo (03) 435-2971

MBB/KAWASAKI BK 117

Following nearly two years of negotiations, an agreement was signed on 25 February 1977 between MBB and Kawasaki to develop jointly an 8/10-seat multi-purpose helicopter known as the BK 117. This superseded two earlier, separate projects known as the MBB BO 107 and the Kawasaki KH-7.

Development costs of the BK 117 programme are being shared equally between the two companies, with support from their governments. MBB is responsible for the main and tail rotor systems, tailboom, elevator, hydraulic system, power-amplified controls, and systems integration; Kawasaki is responsible for the fuselage, skid landing gear, transmission system and smaller items of equipment. There will be two production centres, at Munich and Gifu. First flight was made, by the second prototype (D-HBKA), in Germany on 13 June 1979. Four prototypes are being built: one each for airframe tests and FAR ground testing, plus a flying prototype in each country. A total of 48 had been sold by June 1979; deliveries are due to begin in late 1981.

The BK 117's four-blade rigid main rotor is essentially a scaled-up version of that fitted to the BO 105, from which aircraft the hydraulic system also is adapted. Kawasaki is utilising the basic transmission evolved for its earlier KH-7 design. The aircraft has a two-blade tail rotor mounted on the central fin, forward of which is a tailplane carrying twin endplate fins.

Both military and civil applications are foreseen, and the BK 117 will have many accessories interchangeable with those of the BO 105.

TYPE: Multi-purpose 8/10-seat helicopter.

POWER PLANT: Two Avco Lycoming LTS 101-650B-1 turboshaft engines, with ratings of 447 kW (600 shp) each for T-O and 410 kW (550 shp) max continuous. Standard fuel capacity 603 litres (132·5 Imp gallons). Capacity with auxiliary tanks 1,003 litres (220 Imp gallons).

ACCOMMODATION: Pilot and up to five (executive version), seven (standard or offshore IFR-equipped versions) or nine passengers (high density version). Jettisonable door on each side of flight deck. Rearward-sliding door on each side of cabin; fold-down steps on port side.

DIMENSIONS, EXTERNAL:

Diameter of main rotor	11·00 m (36 ft 1 in)
Diameter of tail rotor	1·90 m (6 ft 2¾ in)
Length overall, main and tail rotors turning	13·00 m (42 ft 8 in)
Length of fuselage	9·88 m (32 ft 5 in)
Fuselage: Max width	1·60 m (5 ft 3 in)
Max width, rotor folded (span over endplate fins)	2·57 m (8 ft 5¼ in)
Height overall, main and tail rotors turning	3·84 m (12 ft 7¼ in)
Height to top of main fin	3·30 m (10 ft 11 in)
Skid track	2·50 m (8 ft 2½ in)

First flight of the MBB/Kawasaki BK 117 on 13 June 1979

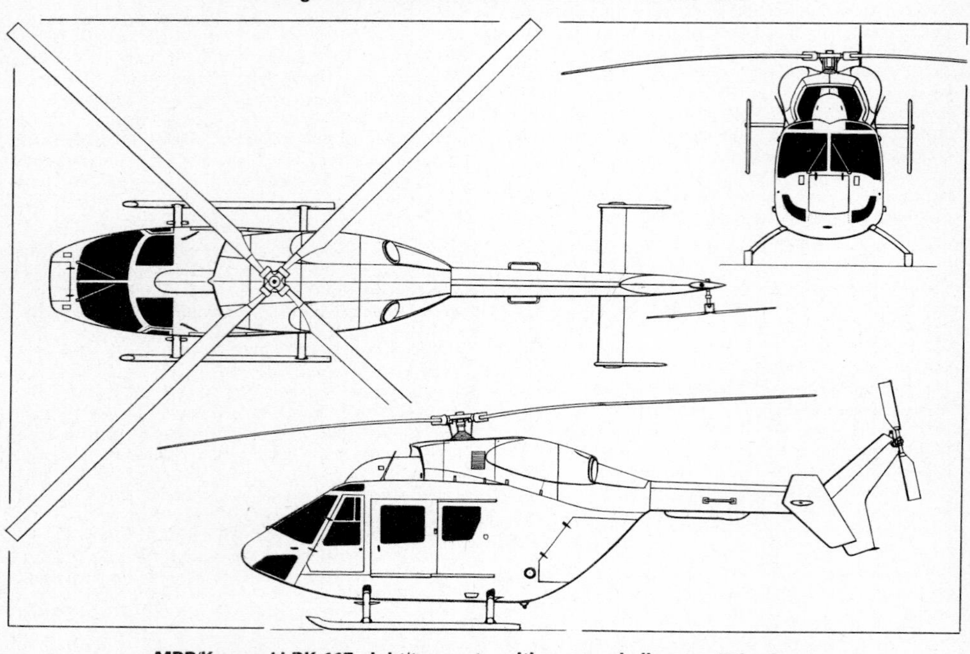

MBB/Kawasaki BK 117 eight/ten-seat multi-purpose helicopter *(Pilot Press)*

DIMENSIONS, INTERNAL:

Volume:	
passenger compartment	3·22 m³ (113·71 cu ft)
cargo compartment	1·34 m³ (47·32 cu ft)

WEIGHTS:

Weight empty, equipped	1,520 kg (3,351 lb)
Fuel (standard)	480 kg (1,058 lb)
Max T-O weight	2,800 kg (6,173 lb)

PERFORMANCE (estimated, at max T-O weight):

Max cruising speed at S/L, ISA	142 knots (264 km/h; 164 mph)
Max rate of climb at S/L	600 m (1,968 ft)/min
Max operating altitude	5,180 m (17,000 ft)
Hovering ceiling IGE	4,100 m (13,450 ft)
Hovering ceiling OGE	3,150 m (10,335 ft)
Range at S/L with max payload and standard fuel, no reserves	294 nm (545 km; 338 miles)
Endurance, conditions as above	3 h 0 min

PANAVIA

PANAVIA AIRCRAFT GmbH

HEAD OFFICE: 8 München 86, Postfach 860629, Arabellastrasse 16, Federal Republic of Germany
Telephone: (089) 92171
Telex: 05 29 825

DIRECTORS:
Prof Dipl-Ing G. Madelung (Chairman)
H. R. Baxendale
Dott R. Bonifacio (Deputy Chairman)
F. Forster-Steinberg
O. Friedrich
A. H. C. Greenwood
Dott C. Innocenti
Dott R. Mautino
Sir Frederick Page (Deputy Chairman)
H. Plückthun
Dott G. Sarzotti
I. R. Yates

MANAGING DIRECTOR: Dr C. P. Fichtmüller
DEPUTY MANAGING DIRECTOR: Dr I. A. M. Hall
FUNCTIONAL DIRECTORS:
J. L. Dell (Flight Operations)
V. von Tein (Systems Engineering, Munich)
Dr I. A. M. Hall (Programme Management)
B. O. Heath (Systems Engineering, Warton)
H. J. Klapperich (Finance and Contracts)
Prof Dr-Ing R. Riccius (Marketing)
R. Sanitz (Product Support)
Dott R. Sassi (Production)
J. A. Thornber (Procurement)

PUBLICITY MANAGER: F. Oelwein

Panavia Aircraft GmbH is a European industrial company formed on 26 March 1969 to design, develop and produce a multi-role combat aircraft (MRCA) for service from the late 1970s with the air forces of the United Kingdom, the Federal Republic of Germany and Italy, and the German Navy. This programme is one of the largest European industrial programmes ever undertaken. The three component companies of Panavia are British Aerospace (42·5% participation), MBB (42·5%) and Aeritalia (15%).

The German, British and Italian governments have set up a joint organisation known as NAMMO (NATO MRCA Management and production Organisation). This has its executive agency NAMMA (NATO MRCA Management Agency) in the same building as Panavia, in Munich.

The project was the subject of a feasibility study, which ended on 1 May 1969, when the project definition phase began. This completed the detailed design work and costing. In mid-1970 the governments announced the satisfactory outcome of the definition phase and the beginning of the development phase. A further tri-national governmental review, concluded in March 1973, preceded the production investment phase.

In March 1976 the UK government announced that full development of the air defence variant (ADV) of the aircraft had been authorised, and in this month also the name Tornado was adopted officially.

On 29 July 1976 the three governments signed a Memorandum of Understanding for the production of 809 Tornadoes (805 new, and four of the pre-production aircraft), enabling the three partner countries to embark upon the production programme.

PANAVIA TORNADO

RAF designation (IDS version): Tornado GR. Mk 1

The Tornado is a twin-engined two-seat supersonic aircraft capable of fulfilling the agreed operational requirements of its three sponsoring countries. The use of a variable-geometry wing gives it the necessary flexibility to achieve this.

The aircraft is intended to fulfil six major requirements, some of which are shared by more than one of the partners. These are:
(a) Close air support/battlefield interdiction
(b) Interdiction/counter air strike
(c) Air superiority
(d) Interception/air defence
(e) Naval strike
(f) Reconnaissance

The 809 aircraft to be produced for the participating nations will comprise 671 operational aircraft plus 138 dual-control trainers with full operational capability.

The Royal Air Force is to have 385 Tornadoes, of which 220 will be of the interdictor/strike version and 165 of the

First production Panavia Tornado GR.Mk 1 interdictor/strike aircraft

air defence version. These are due to become operational with Strike Command in 1982 and will, in the first instance, replace the Vulcans and Buccaneers of Nos. 9, 12, 15, 16, 35, 44, 50, 101 and 617 Squadrons in the overland strike and reconnaissance roles. Later, the air defence version will succeed the Phantom; and finally the Tornado will replace the Buccaneer for maritime strike tasks. Some two-thirds of the RAF's front-line aircraft will eventually be Tornadoes.

The Luftwaffe is to receive 212 Tornadoes, to replace the Lockheed F-104G in the battlefield interdiction, counter air and close air support roles. Four wings (Jabos 31, 32, 33 and 34) and one training squadron are to be equipped, starting in 1979. The 112 for MFG1 and 2 of the German Navy will be equipped for strike missions against sea and coastal targets, and for reconnaissance.

The Italian Air Force will use 54 of its 100 Tornadoes to replace F-104G and G91R aircraft of the 20°, 102°, 154° and 186° Gruppi in the air superiority, ground attack and reconnaissance roles. Of the remainder, 34 will be kept in reserve and 12 will be equipped as dual-control trainers.

Structural design of the Tornado was completed in August 1972. Nine flying prototypes have been built—four in the UK, three in Germany and two in Italy. Static tests with airframe No. 10 began at Warton in the Spring of 1974.

The 01 first prototype (D-9591), assembled by MBB, made its first flight at Manching, Germany, on 14 August 1974. The 08 (XX950) flew in the UK on 15 July 1976 (the 470th Tornado flight), and the 09 (X-587) in Italy on 5 February 1977. Details of all nine prototypes can be found in the 1978-79 and earlier editions.

Of the six pre-series Tornadoes which followed, all had flown by 1979: No. 11 in Germany on 5 February 1977, No. 12 (XZ630) in the UK on 14 March 1977, No. 13 in Germany on 10 January 1978, No. 14 in Italy on 8 January 1979, No. 15 in the UK on 24 November 1978, and No. 16 in Germany on 26 March 1979. No. 14 is fitted with production-standard wings; No. 15 with production-standard rear fuselage, tailerons, fin and actuators; and No. 16 with production-standard forward fuselage.

By June 1979, prototype and pre-series Tornadoes had accumulated a total of 2,750 hours' flying in more than 2,200 flights. During test flights the Tornado has been flown at indicated airspeeds of up to 800 knots (1,480 km/h; 920 mph) at comparatively low levels.

Tornado No. 11, the third (and first German) dual-control aircraft, has RB.199-34R-03 engines (each approx 37·8 kN; 8,500 lb st dry and 66·7 kN; 15,000 lb st with afterburning) and production-standard fin fillet and 'full-length' rudder; No. 12 also has -03 engines; and the similarly-powered No. 13 introduced a kinked leading-edge to the tailplane. The first production-standard -04 engines were fitted to the No. 1 prototype in March 1978.

With the major part (90%) of the flight envelope already cleared, delivery to service test centres began with No. 12 to the Aeroplane and Armament Experimental Establishment at Boscombe Down on 3 February 1978, followed by No. 11 to the Official Test Centre at Manching, Germany, and No. 14 to Pratica di Mare, Italy.

Three production contracts have so far been placed for the Tornado. The first, for 40 aircraft, will provide 20 Tornado GR. Mk 1 interdictor/strike versions for the RAF; three F. Mk 2 prototypes for the RAF (see separate description); and 17 Tornadoes for the Federal German Luftwaffe and Marineflieger. The second contract, for 110 Tornadoes, will provide 55 aircraft for the RAF, 40 for Germany, and 15 for the Aeronautica Militare Italiana. The third contract, signed on 6 June 1979, was for 164 aircraft (68 each for the UK and Germany and 28 for Italy), bringing the total then on firm order to 314. The first production batch is under way: the first example to be completed was BT 001 (British Trainer 001), which was rolled out at Warton on 5 June and made its initial flight on 10 July 1979. The first production German Tornado (GT 001) was rolled out at Manching on 6 June and flew for the first time on 27 July 1979. It is planned to reach a peak output of nine Tornadoes per month by 1982-83.

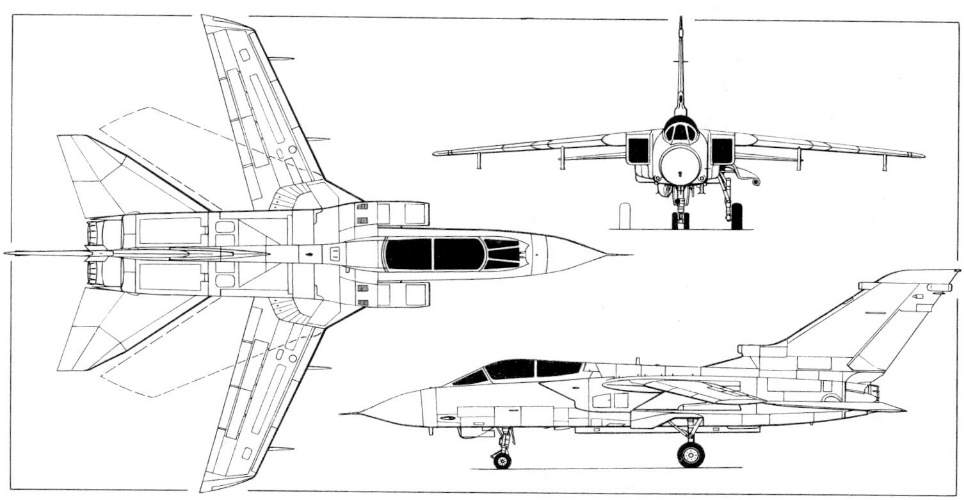

Panavia Tornado multi-role combat aircraft *(Pilot Press)*

A Tri-national Tornado Training Establishment (TTTE) has been set up at RAF Cottesmore. Anglo-German weapons training will be performed from RAF Honington. Initial production aircraft have RB.199-34R-04 Mk 101 engines, which are expected to deliver approx 40·0 kN (9,000 lb st) dry and 71·2 kN (16,000 lb st) with afterburning.

Nominal max weapons load of the IDS (interdictor/strike) Tornado is 8,165 kg (18,000 lb) on three twin hardpoints in tandem under the fuselage, two inboard points in tandem underwing, and two single outboard points underwing. A new missile designated P3T, a turbojet-powered active-radar sea-skimming development of the BAe/Matra Martel, is to be developed for the RAF's GR. Mk 1, which is also expected to have the capability to carry Pave Spike pods for laser weapons guidance. Primary armament of the German Navy Tornadoes will be four MBB Kormoran anti-shipping missiles. Italy's Tornadoes are expected to be equipped with the Selenia Aspide 1A air-to-air missile.

In partnership with Grumman Aerospace Corporation, Panavia in 1979 submitted the Tornado to the USAF as a candidate in the latter's ETF (Enhanced Tactical Fighter) programme.

The following details apply to the basic IDS (interdictor/strike) version:

Type: Twin-engined multi-purpose military aircraft.

Wings: Cantilever shoulder-wing monoplane. All-metal wings, of variable geometry, having a sweep of 25° in the fully forward position and 68° when fully swept. Wing carry-through box is of electron-beam-welded titanium alloy; majority of remaining wing structure is of aluminium alloy, with integrally stiffened skin. There is a Krueger flap on the leading-edge of each wing glove box. The wings each pivot hydraulically, on Teflon-plated bearings, from a point in the centre-section just outboard of the fuselage. The root of the outer wing mates with the pivot pin through attachment members made of titanium alloy and fixed to the upper and lower light alloy panels of the outer wing box, and a so-called 'round rib', also of titanium alloy, transmitting the normal aerodynamic force. Sweep actuators are of the ballscrew type, with hydraulic motor drive. In the event of wing sweep failure, the aircraft can land safely with the wings fully swept. High-lift devices on the outer wings include full-span leading-edge slats (three sections on each side), full-span double-slotted fixed-vane trailing-edge flaps (four sections each side), and spoilers (two on upper surface on each side). Spoilers give augmented roll control at unswept and intermediate wing positions at low speed, and also act as lift dumpers after touchdown. All flying control surfaces actuated by electrically-controlled tandem hydraulic jacks. No ailerons. Entire outer wings, including control surfaces, are Italian-built, Aeritalia having prime responsibility for final assembly and production, assisted by Aermacchi, Aeronavali Venezia, Piaggio, Saca and SIAI-Marchetti as subcontractors. Microtecnica (Italy) is prime subcontractor for the wing sweep system.

Fuselage: Conventional all-metal semi-monocoque structure, mainly of aluminium alloy, built in three main sections. MBB in Germany is prime contractor (with participation by VFW-Fokker for the prototype and pre-production aircraft) for the centre fuselage section, including the engine air intake trunks and wing centre-section box and pivot mechanism. This task includes responsibility for the surface interface between the movable wing and the fixed portion, to ensure both a smooth and slender external contour and proper sealing against aerodynamic pressure over a range of wing sweep positions. The present design uses fibre-reinforced plastics in these areas, and an elastic seal between the outer wings and the fuselage sides. Responsibility for the front fuselage, including both cockpits, and for the rear fuselage, including the engine installation, is undertaken by BAe (Warton). Radar-transparent nose-cone by AEG-Telefunken, assisted by Aeritalia and BAe, hinges sideways to starboard. Door-type airbrake on each side at top of rear fuselage.

Tail Unit: Cantilever all-metal structure, consisting of single sweptback two-spar fin and rudder, and low-set all-moving horizontal surfaces ('tailerons') which operate together for pitch control and differentially for roll control, assisted by use of the wing spoilers when the wings are not fully swept. Rudder and tailerons actuated by electrically-controlled tandem hydraulic jacks. Passive ECM antenna fairing near top of fin. Ram-air intake for heat exchanger at base of fin. Entire tail unit is the responsibility of BAe.

Landing Gear: Hydraulically-retractable tricycle type, with forward-retracting twin-wheel steerable nose unit. Single-wheel main units retract forward and upward into centre section of fuselage. Development and manufacture of the complete landing gear and associated hydraulics is headed by Dowty Rotol (UK). Dunlop aluminium alloy wheels, brakes and low-pressure tyres (to permit operation from soft, semi-prepared surfaces) and Goodyear anti-skid units. Main-wheel tyres size 30 × 11·50-14·5, Type VIII (20 ply); nosewheel tyres size 18 × 5·5, Type VIII (12 ply). Runway arrester hook beneath rear of fuselage.

Power Plant: Two Turbo-Union RB.199-34R-04 turbofan engines in production aircraft, each rated at approx 40·0 kN (9,000 lb st) dry and 71·2 kN (16,000 lb st) with afterburning, fitted with bucket-type thrust reversers and installed in rear fuselage with downward-opening doors for servicing and engine change. Four large 'blow-out' doors in top of each trunk, above the double-wedge variable-ramp intake. Dowty Boulton Paul air intake ramp actuators and afterburner control system. All integral fuel in multi-cell Uniroyal self-sealing integral fuselage tanks and/or wing box tanks, all fitted with press-in fuel sampling and water drain plugs, and all refuelled from a single-point NATO connector. Detachable and retractable in-flight refuelling probe can be mounted on starboard side of fuselage, adjacent to cockpit. System also designed to accept a buddy-to-buddy refuelling pack. Provision for drop-tanks of various sizes up to 1,500 litres (330 Imp gallons) to be carried beneath outer wings. Dowty Fuel Systems/Lucas/Microtecnica afterburning fuel control system. AEG-Telefunken intake de-icing system.

ACCOMMODATION: Crew of two on tandem Martin-Baker Mk 10A zero-zero ejection seats under Kopperschmidt/AIT one-piece canopy, which is hinged at rear and opens upward. Flat centre windscreen panel and curved side panels, built by Lucas Aerospace, incorporate Sierracote electrically-conductive heating film for de-icing and internal demisting. Seats provide safe escape at zero altitude and at speeds from zero up to 630 knots (1,166 km/h; 725 mph) IAS.

SYSTEMS: Nordmicro/BAe/Microtecnica air intake control system, and Dowty Boulton Paul/Liebherr Aerotechnik engine intake ramp control actuators. Two separate independent hydraulic systems, one driven by each engine, provide fully duplicated power for wing sweep, flaps, slats, spoilers, airbrakes, landing gear, tailerons and rudder. Main system includes Vickers pump, Dowty accumulators and Teves power pack. Fairey Hydraulics system for actuation of spoilers, rudder and taileron control. Provision for reversion to single-engine drive of both systems, via a mechanical cross-connection between the two engine auxiliary gearboxes, in the event of a single engine failure. In the event of a double engine flameout, an emergency pump in No. 1 system has sufficient duration for re-entry into the engine cold relight boundary. Flying control circuits are protected from loss of fluid due to leaks in other circuits by isolating valves which shut off the utility circuits if the reservoir contents drop below a predetermined safety limit level. Duplicated AC and DC electrical power is provided by two alternators, each driven by its respective engine auxiliary gearbox, to two separate main AC busbars and one essential AC busbar, and through two fan-cooled transformer-rectifier units (TRUs) to two main DC busbars. Lucas/Siemens 40/60kVA 200V 400Hz three-phase constant-frequency AC generating system. Either generator can cope with the full demand of the electrical systems in the event of a single generator failure. If both TRUs fail, an on-board Varta battery supplies the essential DC busbar. In the event of a total loss of power the battery also drives an electro-hydraulic pump which provides power for the primary flying controls. Under normal conditions the battery drives the KHD/Microtecnica/Lucas T312 APU for engine starting, but a DC ground supply is provided to assist starting if required. Plessey emergency power unit (EPU) and power systems controller. Normalair-Garrett precooler and cold-air unit, Marston Excelsior intercooler and Teddington temperature control system. Normalair-Garrett/Draegerwerk/OMI demand-type oxygen system, using a lox converter. KHD accessory drive gearboxes and Rotax/Lucas/Siemens integrated drive generator. Marconi flow-metering system. Eichweber fuel gauging system and Flight Refuelling flexible couplings. Graviner fire detection and extinguishing systems. Rotax contactors. Smiths engine speed and temperature indicators.

AVIONICS AND EQUIPMENT: Communications equipment includes Plessey PTR 1721 (UK and Italy) or Rohde und Schwarz (Germany) UHF/VHF transceiver; AEG-Telefunken UHF/DF (UK and Germany only); Chelton UHF homer aerial; SIT/Siemens emergency UHF with Rohde und Schwarz switch; BAe HF/SSB aerial tuning unit; Rohde und Schwarz (UK and Germany) or Montedel (Italy) HF/SSB radio; Ultra communications control system; Marconi Avionics central suppression unit; Epsylon voice recorder; and Chelton communications and landing system aerials.

Primary self-contained nav/attack system includes Texas Instruments multi-mode forward-looking radar (Marconi Avionics multi-mode airborne interception radar for RAF air defence variant); Ferranti FIN 1010 three-axis digital inertial navigation system (DINS) and combined radar display; Decca Type 72 Doppler radar system; Microtecnica air data computer; Litef Spirit 3 16-bit central digital computer; Aeritalia radio/radar altimeter; Smiths/Teldix/OMI electronic head-up display with Davall camera; Ferranti nose-mounted laser ranger and marked target receiver; Marconi Avionics TV tabular display produced in partnership with AEG and Selenia; Astronautics (USA) bearing distance heading indicator and contour map display. Defensive equipment includes Siemens (Germany) or Cossor SSR-3100 (UK) IFF transponder; Elettronica warning radar; and MSDS/Plessey/Decca passive ECM system.

Flight control system includes a Marconi Avionics/Bodenseewerk triplex command stability augmentation system (CSAS), incorporating fly-by-wire and autostabilisation; Marconi Avionics/Aeritalia autopilot and flight director (APFD), using two self-monitoring digital computers; Marconi Avionics triplex transducer unit (TTU), with analogue computing and sensor channels; Marconi Avionics terrain-following E-scope (TFE), produced in partnership with Selenia; Fairey/Marconi Avionics quadruplex electro-hydraulic actuator; and Microtecnica air data set. The APFD provides pre-selected attitude, heading or barometric height hold, heading and track acquisition, and Mach number or airspeed hold with autothrottle. Flight director operates in parallel with, and can be used as backup for, the autopilot. Automatic approach, terrain-following and radio height-holding modes are also available. Other instrumentation includes Smiths horizontal situation indicator, vertical speed indicator and standby altimeter; AEG-Telefunken ADF; Lital standby attitude and heading reference system; SEL (with Setac) or (in UK aircraft) Marconi Avionics AD2770 (without Setac) Tacan; Cossor CILS 75 ILS; Bodenseewerk attitude direction indicator; Marconi Avionics central suppression unit (CSU); and Dornier System flight data recorder.

Overall responsibility for the avionics rests with Panavia, with EASAMS (UK) as the avionics prime contractor, and ESG (Germany) and SIA (Italy) as subcontractors. The avionics systems, while standardised as far as possible, retain the flexibility necessary to perform the various roles required. They provide accurate low- and high-level navigation; precision visual attack on ground targets in blind and poor weather conditions; air-to-ground and air-to-air attack with a wide variety of weapons; manually controlled and automatic attack; and comprehensive onboard check-out and mission data recording; with minimisation of ground support facilities at bases and the front line.

ARMAMENT: Fixed armament comprises two 27 mm IWKA-Mauser cannon, one in each side of the lower forward fuselage. Other armament varies according to version, with emphasis on the ability to carry a wide range of advanced non-nuclear weapons on three underfuselage attachments and up to four swivelling hardpoints beneath the outer wings. A Marconi Avionics/Selenia stores management system is fitted, and Sandall Mace 355 and 762 mm (14 and 30 in) ejector release units are standard. Initial weapon systems evaluation will include trials in the fourth prototype of a modified Raytheon Sparrow missile, fitted with a British warhead and fuse. The battlefield interdiction version will be capable of dropping defensive 'streuwaffen' (scatter weapons) such as the MBB MW1 munitions dispenser, and of carrying weapons to suit 'hard' or 'soft' targets. The naval and interdictor strike versions will have provision for carrying additional, externally-mounted fuel tanks. The air superiority version will be able to carry a wide range of guided and semi-active homing air-to-air weapons. Among the weapons already specified for, or suitable for carriage by, the Tornado are the Sidewinder, Sky Flash, Sparrow and Aspide 1A air-to-air missiles; AS.30, Martel, P3T and Kormoran air-to-surface missiles; napalm; BL-755 600 lb cluster bombs; MK 83 or other 1,000 lb bombs; 'smart' or retarded bombs; Lepus flare bombs; active or passive ECM pods.

DIMENSIONS, EXTERNAL:
Wing span:
fully spread 13·90 m (45 ft 7¼ in)
fully swept 8·60 m (28 ft 2½ in)
Length overall 16·70 m (54 ft 9½ in)
Height overall 5·70 m (18 ft 8½ in)
Tailplane span 6·80 m (22 ft 3½ in)
Wheel track 3·10 m (10 ft 2 in)
Wheelbase 6·20 m (20 ft 4 in)

WEIGHTS (prototype/pre-series aircraft up to mid-1979, with development engines):
Weight empty, equipped 9,980-10,430 kg (22,000-23,000 lb)
Max weapon load carried 7,257 kg (16,000 lb)
Max T-O weight:
'clean', full internal fuel 20,411 kg (45,000 lb)
with external stores 26,490 kg (58,400 lb)

PERFORMANCE: (prototype/pre-series aircraft up to early 1979, with development engines):
Max level speed at altitude, 'clean' above Mach 2·0 (1,146 knots; 2,124 km/h; 1,320 mph)
Max level speed with external stores Mach 0·92 (600 knots; 1,112 km/h; 691 mph)
Max level speed at low altitude above 800 knots (1,480 km/h; 920 mph) IAS
Landing speed approx 115 knots (213 km/h; 132 mph)
Time to 9,145 m (30,000 ft) from brakes off less than 2 min
T-O and landing run approx 366 m (1,200 ft)
Max normal acceleration 7·5*g*
Max 360° rapid-roll clearance with full lateral control 4·0*g*
Radius of action with heavy weapons load, hi-lo-lo-hi 750 nm (1,390 km; 863 miles)
Ferry range approx 2,100 nm (3,890 km; 2,420 miles)
g limit +7·5

PANAVIA TORNADO ADV

RAF designation: Tornado F. Mk 2

Full-scale development of the Tornado ADV (air defence variant) was authorised by the British government on 4 March 1976. This version is being developed specifically for the RAF, which will include 165 of this long-range interceptor model, designated F. Mk 2, in its total procurement of 385 Tornadoes, to re-equip two Lightning squadrons and seven squadrons of Phantoms. Most of these 165 aircraft will be based in the United Kingdom.

Although possessing some 80% commonality with the interdictor/strike version, the Tornado F. Mk 2 will differ in several important respects, and the initial contract for 40 Tornadoes includes provision for three prototypes of this version. The first of these (ZA254), built at Warton, was rolled out on 9 August and was expected to fly in late 1979; the second and third prototypes are due to fly in 1980.

The F. Mk 2 is intended to fulfil an RAF requirement for a high-speed bomber destroyer, able to cover a wide UK defence region extending from the Atlantic approaches to the Baltic and from Iceland to the English Channel, and possessing good climb and acceleration. Its armament consists of a single 27 mm built-in IWKA-Mauser cannon in the starboard side of the lower forward fuselage, four British Aerospace (Dynamics Group) Sky Flash medium-range air-to-air missiles semi-recessed under the centre-fuselage, and two NWC AIM-9L Sidewinder short-range infra-red air-to-air missiles on the inboard outer-wing stations.

These weapons will be operated in conjunction with a new, all-British track-while-scan pulse-Doppler airborne interception radar named Foxhunter, designed and developed by Marconi Avionics, with Ferranti as subcontractor for the transmitter and aerial scanning mechanism. Foxhunter will enable the Tornado F. Mk 2 to detect targets more than 100 nm (185 km; 115 miles) away, and to track several targets simultaneously; the Sky Flash missiles will be able to engage targets at high altitude or at levels below 75 m (250 ft), in the face of heavy ECM, and at stand-off ranges of more than 22 nm (40 km; 25 miles). The first phase of Sky Flash air trials had been completed by early 1978. The Tornado F. Mk 2 carries a two-man crew, the rear (navigator's) cockpit being equipped with a Ferranti FH 31A AC-driven 3 in horizon gyro which, in

First prototype of the Tornado F. Mk 2 air defence variant for the RAF, rolled out in August 1979

addition to providing an attitude display for the navigator, feeds pitch and roll signals to other avionics systems in the aircraft in certain modes. A pilot's head-up display, ESM (electronic surveillance measures) and ECCM are also standard, as are an extremely advanced modular radar homing and warning receiver being developed by Marconi Space and Defence Systems, and a low light level TV visual augmentation system developed by Marconi Avionics. Other avionics include an IFF interrogator and an ECM-resistant data link system.

Two main airframe modifications apply to this version, of which the principal one is a 1·36 m (4 ft 5½ in) increase in fuselage length, created by the longer nose radome and the need for a small 'stretch' aft of the cockpit to allow the four Sky Flash missiles to be carried in two tandem pairs. This extension provides additional space for avionics and for an extra 909 litres (200 Imp gallons) of internal fuel. A fully-retractable flight refuelling probe is mounted in the nose, and drop-tanks can be carried on the inner underwing stations. The fixed inboard portions of the wings are extended forward at the leading-edges, to give additional chord. Power plant of production aircraft is to be an uprated version of the present standard -04 engine.

DIMENSIONS, EXTERNAL: As for IDS version, except:
Length overall 18·06 m (59 ft 3 in)

PERFORMANCE (estimated):
Normal touchdown speed
115 knots (213 km/h; 132 mph)
T-O run with normal weapon and fuel load
approx 762 m (2,500 ft)
Landing run, with thrust reversal 366 m (1,200 ft)

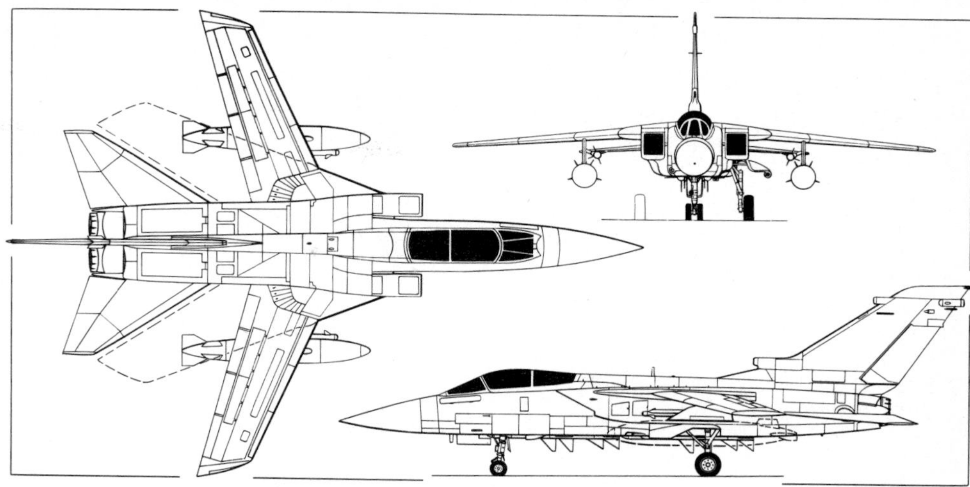
Panavia Tornado F.Mk 2, armed with Sky Flash and Sidewinder missiles *(Pilot Press)*

Radius of action (combat air patrol), loiter for more than 2 h, with sufficient fuel for interception including 10 min combat
300-400 nm (555-742 km; 345-461 miles)

SEPECAT
SOCIÉTÉ EUROPÉENNE DE PRODUCTION DE L'AVION E.C.A.T.

AIRFRAME COMPANIES:

British Aerospace Aircraft Group, Richmond Road, Kingston upon Thames, Surrey KT2 5QS, England
Telephone: 01 546 7741

Avions Marcel Dassault/Breguet Aviation, BP 32, 92420 Vaucresson, France
Telephone: 970 38 50

DIRECTORS:
P. E. Jaillard (alternate Chairman)
H. R. Baxendale (alternate Chairman)
Sir Frederick Page
J. Bonnet
C. Edelstenne
M. Berjon
T. O. Williams
I. R. Yates

PUBLIC RELATIONS:
G. B. Hill (BAe)
C. P. Raffin (Dassault-Breguet)

This Anglo-French company was formed in May 1966 by Breguet Aviation and British Aircraft Corporation, to design and produce the Jaguar supersonic strike fighter/trainer. The Jaguar project was initiated by the Defence Ministries of Britain and France on 17 May 1965. The governments of the two countries appointed an official Jaguar Management Committee to look after their interests. SEPECAT is the complementary industrial organisation.

RAF Jaguar GR.Mk 1s from (front to rear) Nos. 2 (AC), 14, 17, 20 and 31 Squadrons, based in Germany

SEPECAT JAGUAR

The Jaguar, which was evolved from the Breguet Br121 project, was designed by Breguet and BAe to meet a common requirement of the French and British air forces laid down in early 1965. This requirement called for a dual-role aircraft, to be used as an advanced and operational trainer and a tactical support aircraft of light weight and high performance, to enter French service in 1972 and with the RAF in 1973. The Jaguar M French naval version (1972-73 *Jane's*) was abandoned in 1973.

The following versions of the Jaguar have been built:

Jaguar A. French single-seat tactical support version. Prototypes (A-03 and A-04) first flown on 23 March and 27 May 1969. Total of 160 ordered.

By 1 March 1979 a total of 117 Jaguar As had been delivered. The first operational Armée de l'Air Jaguar unit (Esc. 1/7 'Provence') was formed at St Dizier in eastern France on 19 June 1973. The French Air Force has seven Jaguar A squadrons: three each with the 7th and 11th Escadres at St Dizier and Toul-Rosières, and one with the 3rd Escadre at Nancy. Two squadrons of the 92nd Escadre are forming. In December 1977 and May 1978, Jaguars of the Armée de l'Air were the first of their type to enter combat, when they were used to attack guerrilla forces in Mauritania. A Martin Marietta/Thomson-CSF target TV acquisition and laser designation pod, named ATLIS, is under development for French Jaguars.

Jaguar B (RAF designation: Jaguar T.Mk 2). British two-seat operational training version. Prototype B-08 (XW566) first flown on 30 August 1971. Total of 37 built. First T.Mk 2 delivered to RAF was XX137.

Jaguar E. French two-seat advanced training version. Prototypes (E-01 and E-02) first flown on 8 September 1968 and 11 February 1969. Total of 40 built. First production Jaguar, designated E-1, flew for the first time on 2 November 1971, and deliveries to the CEAM at Air Base 118, Mont de Marsan, began in May 1972. The first unit to equip with this version was Esc. 1/7 at St Dizier.

Jaguar S (RAF designation: Jaguar GR. Mk 1). British single-seat tactical support version, basically similar to A but with an advanced inertial navigation and weapon-aiming system (NAVWASS) controlled by a digital computer. Prototypes S-06 (XW560) and S-07 (XW563) first flown on 12 October 1969 and 12 June 1970. Total of 165 built. The first production GR. Mk 1 (XX108) flew on 11 October 1972, and this version now equips eight RAF front-line squadrons: Nos. 2 (AC), 14, 17, 20 and 31 with the Second Allied Tactical Air Force in Germany and Nos. 6, 41 and 54 at Coltishall in the UK. Nos. 2 (AC) and 41 Squadrons are reconnaissance units. Starting in 1978, RAF Jaguars are being refitted with uprated Adour engines, designated Mk 104 and equivalent to the Mk 804 which powers the Jaguar International (see following paragraph).

Jaguar International. Export version, first flown (G27-266) on 19 August 1976. Differs little from the original single-seat Jaguar S except in having more powerful Adour turbofan engines (initially the RT. 172-26 Adour Mk 804, rated at 23·40 kN; 5,260 lb st dry and 38·25 kN; 8,600 lb st with afterburning). Test flying of these engines, in a converted Jaguar S in 1975, confirmed an improved combat performance with substantially enhanced manoeuvrability and acceleration in the low-level speed range. The next standard of engine, the RT.172-58, is under development, and uprating to this standard will be possible during overhaul of the 172-26 engines. The -58 engine increases the thrust still further to +15% on take-off, and +40% under combat conditions, compared with the original Adour Mk 102. Dry thrust is also significantly improved. Flight trials with the -58 began on 14 August 1978, and in the following month the aircraft was demonstrated at the Farnborough Air Show, the demonstration including take-offs and landings on grass strips.

Other customer options include overwing pylons compatible with Magic or similar dogfight missiles; a multi-purpose radar such as the Thomson-CSF Agave, with which flight trials were completed in March 1977; anti-shipping weapons such as Harpoon, Exocet and Kormoran; and night sensors such as low light level TV. Initial orders placed by the Sultan of Oman's Air Force (12) and Ecuadorean Air Force (12). Deliveries to Ecuador were made in January-October 1977, and to Oman between March 1977 and the Spring of 1978. SOAF aircraft are fitted with a Marconi Avionics 920ATC NAVWASS computer and provision for carrying Matra R.550 Magic air-to-air missiles on overwing pylons.

An ITP (Intention to Proceed), signed on 30 October 1978 between BAe and the Indian government, was ratified in early 1979. Under this agreement, which involves 40 Jaguar Internationals, an initial quantity is purchased outright; later, others will be assembled in India from British-built components, leading eventually to full manufacture under licence by Hindustan Aeronautics Ltd, Bangalore. About three-quarters of the total will be assembled and/or built by HAL, and the contract will ensure continuation of Jaguar production into the 1980s. The first two Jaguars for India were handed over on 19 July 1979.

The Jaguar International is also being offered in a maritime strike version, similarly powered by Adour 'Dash 26' (current standard) or 'Dash 58' (optional) turbofan engines. Main differences from the standard Jaguar International are the fitting of a Thomson-CSF Agave multi-purpose nose radar, and ability to carry up to four anti-shipping missiles such as Harpoon, Exocet or Kormoran on the underwing and underfuselage hardpoints. The capacity to carry Magic air-to-air missiles on the overwing pylons is retained.

Under the terms of the production agreement signed by the British and French Defence Ministries on 9 January 1968, 202 Jaguars were built for the Royal Air Force and 200 are being built for the French air force. The first

Jaguar International in typical low-level strike configuration, carrying four 1,000 lb bombs, two underwing drop-tanks and two overwing Magic air-to-air missiles

formal production contract, placed in the Autumn of 1969, covered 50 Jaguars for France; the second was for 30 for the RAF. Subsequent contracts had brought total Anglo-French orders to 402 by early 1976. Of these, 370 had been delivered by July 1979.

Dassault-Breguet factories at Toulouse and Biarritz are responsible for the front and centre fuselage. BAe has responsibility for the rear fuselage, air intakes, wings and tail unit. There are final assembly lines for complete aircraft in both Britain and France.

The Jaguar is fully power-controlled in all three axes and is automatically stabilised as a weapons platform by gyros which sense disturbances and feed appropriate correcting data through a computer to the power control assemblies, in addition to the human pilot manoeuvre demands. The power controls are all of duplex tandem arrangement, with both mechanical and electrical servo-valves of the established Fairey platen design. Air-to-air combat capability can be enhanced by the inclusion of roll/yaw dampers, to increase lateral stability, and by increasing the slat and flap angles.

Training versions are able to operate from conventional runways only 2,000 m (6,560 ft) long, with full provision for safety in the event of an engine failure at the critical point of take-off.

The following description applies to the standard versions of the Jaguar produced for the UK and France:

Type: Single-seat tactical support aircraft (Jaguar A, S and International) and two-seat operational or advanced trainer (Jaguar B and E).

Wings: Cantilever shoulder-wing monoplane. Anhedral 3°. Sweepback 40° at quarter-chord. All-metal two-spar torsion-box structure, the skin of which is machined from solid aluminium alloy, with integral stiffeners. Entire wing unit is British-built. Main portion built as single unit, with three-point attachment to each side of fuselage. Outer panels fitted with slat which also gives effect of extended-chord leading-edge. No conventional ailerons. Lateral control by two-section spoilers, forward of outer flap on each wing, in association (at low speeds) with differential tailplane. Hydraulically-operated (by screwjack) full-span double-slotted trailing-edge flaps. Fairey Hydraulics powered flying controls. Leading-edge slats can be used in combat.

Fuselage: All-metal structure, mainly aluminium, built in three main units and making use of sandwich panels and, around the cockpit(s), honeycomb panels. Local use of titanium alloy in engine bay area. The forward and centre fuselage, up to and including the main undercarriage bays, and including cockpit(s), main systems installations, forward fuel tanks and landing gear, are of French construction. The air intakes, and entire fuselage aft of the main-wheel bays, including engine installation, rear fuel tanks and complete tail assembly, are British-built. Two door-type airbrakes under rear fuselage, immediately aft of each main-wheel well. Structure and systems, aft of cockpit(s), are identical for single-seat and two-seat versions.

Tail Unit: Cantilever all-metal two-spar structure, covered with aluminium alloy sandwich panels. Rudder and outer panels and trailing-edge of tailplane have honeycomb core. Sweepback at quarter-chord 40° on horizontal, 43° on vertical surfaces. All-moving slab-type tailplane, with 10° of anhedral, the two halves of which can operate differentially to supplement the spoilers. No separate elevators. Fairey Hydraulics powered flying controls. Ventral fins beneath the rear fuselage. Entire tail unit is British-built.

Landing Gear: Messier-Hispano retractable tricycle type, all units having Dunlop wheels and low-pressure tyres for rough-field operation. Hydraulic retraction, with oleo-pneumatic shock-absorbers. Forward-retracting main units each have twin wheels, tyre size 615 × 225-10, tyre pressure 5·8 bars (84 lb/sq in). Wheels pivot during retraction to stow horizontally in bottom of fuselage. Single rearward-retracting nose-wheel, with tyre size 550 × 250-6 and pressure of 3·9 bars (57 lb/sq in). Twin landing lights in nosewheel door. Dunlop hydraulic brakes. Anti-skid units and arrester hook standard. Irvin brake parachute of 5·5 m (18 ft 0½ in) diameter housed in fuselage tailcone.

Power Plant: Two Rolls-Royce Turboméca Adour Mk 102 turbofan engines initially (each rated at 22·75 kN; 5,115 lb st dry and 32·5 kN; 7,305 lb st with afterburning). RAF and International Jaguars: now Adour Mks 104 and 804 respectively, rated at 23·40 kN (5,260 lb st) dry and 38·25 kN (8,600 lb st) with afterburning. Lateral-type fixed-geometry air intake on each side of fuselage aft of cockpit. Fuel in six tanks, one in each wing and four in fuselage. Total internal fuel capacity 4,200 litres (924 Imp gallons). Armour protection is provided for critical fuel system components. In the basic tactical sortie the loss of fuel from one tank at the halfway point would not prevent the aircraft from regaining its base. Provision for carrying three auxiliary drop-tanks, each of 1,200 litres (264 Imp gallons) capacity, on fuselage and inboard wing pylons. Jaguar A and S equipped for in-flight refuelling, with a retractable probe forward of the cockpit on the starboard side.

Accommodation (Jaguar B and E): Crew of two in tandem on Martin-Baker Mk 9 zero-zero ejection seats (Jaguar B) or Mk 4 seats (Jaguar E) giving zero-altitude ejection at speeds down to 90 knots (167 km/h; 104 mph). Individual rearward-hinged canopies. Rear seat is 38 cm (15 in) higher than front seat. Windscreen bulletproof against 7·5 mm rifle fire.

Accommodation (Jaguar A and S): Enclosed cockpit for pilot, with rearward-hinged canopy and Martin-Baker Mk 9 (Jaguar S) or Mk 4 (Jaguar A) ejection seat as in two-seaters. Bulletproof windscreen, as in two-seat versions.

Systems: Air-conditioning and pressurisation systems maintain automatically, throughout the flight envelope, comfortable operating conditions for the crew, and also control the temperature in certain equipment bays. Two independent hydraulic systems, powered by two Vickers engine-driven pumps. Hydraulic pressure 207 bars (3,000 lb/sq in). First system (port engine) supplies one channel of each actuator for the flying controls, the hydraulic motors which actuate the flaps and slats, the landing gear retraction and extension system, the brakes and anti-skid units. The second system supplies the other half of each flying control actuator, two further hydraulic motors actuating the slats and flaps, the air-brake and landing gear emergency extension jacks, nosewheel steering system and the wheel brakes. In addition to the duplicated hydraulic power systems, there is an emergency hydraulic power transfer unit. Electrical power provided by two 15kVA AC generators, either of which can sustain functional and operational equipment without load-shedding. DC power provided by two 4kW transformer-rectifiers. Emergency power for essential instruments provided by 15Ah battery and static inverter. De-icing, rain clearance and demisting standard. Liquid oxygen system installed, which also pressurises the pilot's anti-*g* suit.

Avionics and Operational Equipment (French versions): Avionics in Jaguar E include VHF/UHF radio, VOR/ILS and IFF; Tacan with Crouzet Type 90 navigation indicator; SFIM 153-6 twin-gyro inertial platform with two SFIM 810 all-attitude roll and pitch spherical indicators; SFIM 511 directional compass; Jaeger ELDIA air data system with Jaeger altitude indicator; CSF RL 50Pj incidence probe with angle of attack indicator; CSF 121 fire control sighting unit with weapon selector and adaptor for sighting head camera. Except for the use of a SFIM 250-1 twin-gyro platform, and the addition of a vector adder to the navigation indicator, this equipment is repeated in the Jaguar A, which has in addition a panoramic camera, Dassault-built Decca RDN 72 Doppler radar, Crouzet Type 90 navigation computer with target selector, CFTH passive radar warning (ECM) detector, CSF 31 weapon aiming computer, a Dassault fire control computer for Martel anti-radar missiles and a CSF laser rangefinder. Provision for the addition to these basic installations of such other items as terrain-following radar or sighting equipment for low light level targets.

Avionics and Operational Equipment (British versions): Basic avionics of both the Jaguar B and S are similar. They include a Smiths-built Honeywell radio altimeter, slip indicator, E2B standby compass and autostabilising system, Plessey PTR 377 VHF/UHF radio and Marconi Avionics HF radio; Cossor CILS 75 ILS (being extended in 1979 to full VOR/ILS capability); IFF; Tacan; Marconi Avionics digital/inertial navigation and weapon aiming subsystem (NAVWASS) with MCS 920M digital computer, E3R three-gyro inertial platform, inertial velocity sensor, navigation control unit and projected-map display; Marconi Avionics air data computer; Smiths electronic head-up display; Smiths FS6 horizontal situation indicator; Sperry C2J gyro amplifier master unit, compass controller and magnetic detector; Plessey weapon control system. Jaguar S fitted with Ferranti laser rangefinder and Type 106 marked target seeker in modified nose. Ferranti FIN 1064 digital inertial navigation and weapon aiming equipment selected to replace major elements of NAVWASS equipment in RAF Jaguars.

Armament (Jaguar A and S): Two 30 mm cannon (DEFA 553 in Jaguar A, Aden in Jaguar S) in lower fuselage aft of cockpit. One stores attachment point on fuselage centreline and two under each wing. Centreline and inboard wing points can each carry up to 1,000 kg (2,000 lb) of weapons, and the outboard underwing points up to 500 kg (1,000 lb) each. Maximum external stores load 4,535 kg (10,000 lb). Jaguar As in service can carry the AN 52 tactical nuclear weapon. Typical alternative loads include one Martel AS.37 anti-radar missile and two 1,200 litre (264 Imp gallon) drop-tanks; eight 1,000 lb bombs; various combinations of free-fall and retarded bombs, BL755 or Beluga cluster bombs, Magic missiles and air-to-surface rockets, including the 68 mm SNEB rocket; a reconnaissance-camera pack; or two drop-tanks. The BAe-designed flush-fitting reconnaissance pod for RAF Jaguars, carried on the fuselage centreline, has optical cameras for horizon-to-horizon coverage and BAe Dynamics (HS) 401 infra-red linescan (IRLS) for additional daylight, poor weather and night capability. Cameras are installed in two rotatable drums within the pod, the forward drum (for low/medium altitude missions) containing two Vinten F95 Mk 10 and one F95 Mk 7 oblique cameras. The rear drum can carry alternative modules: two F95 Mk 10 cameras for low-level sorties, or a single F126 for

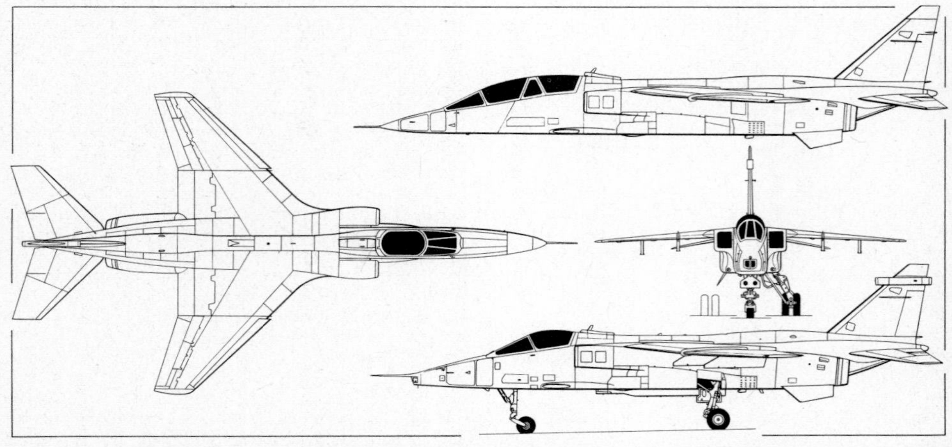

SEPECAT Jaguar S single-seat strike aircraft, with additional side view (top) of Jaguar B two-seat operational training version *(Pilot Press)*

medium altitude reconnaissance. The IRLS package is installed in the rear end of the pod, adjacent to a data conversion unit linked to the onboard NAVWASS digital computer.

ARMAMENT (Jaguar B and E): Two 30 mm DEFA 553 cannon in Jaguar E; Jaguar B has single 30 mm Aden cannon on port side. The two-seat versions have similar weapons capability to the tactical models, and can be employed for operational missions as required.

DIMENSIONS, EXTERNAL:

Wing span	8·69 m (28 ft 6 in)
Wing chord at root	3·58 m (11 ft 9 in)
Wing chord at tip	1·13 m (3 ft 8½ in)
Wing aspect ratio	3·12
Length overall, incl probe:	
A and S	16·83 m (55 ft 2½ in)
B and E	17·53 m (57 ft 6¼ in)
Length overall, excl probe:	
A and S	15·52 m (50 ft 11 in)
B and E	16·42 m (53 ft 10½ in)
Height overall	4·89 m (16 ft 0½ in)
Tailplane span	4·53 m (14 ft 10¼ in)
Wheel track	2·40 m (7 ft 10½ in)
Wheelbase	5·69 m (18 ft 8 in)

AREAS:

Wings, gross	24·00 m² (258·33 sq ft)
Leading-edge slats (total)	1·05 m² (11·30 sq ft)
Trailing-edge flaps (total)	4·12 m² (44·35 sq ft)
Spoilers (total)	0·90 m² (9·67 sq ft)
Vertical tail surfaces (total)	3·90 m² (42·00 sq ft)
Horizontal tail surfaces (total)	7·80 m² (83·96 sq ft)

WEIGHTS AND LOADINGS:

Weight empty	7,000 kg (15,432 lb)
Normal T-O weight	11,000 kg (24,000 lb)
Max T-O weight	15,500 kg (34,000 lb)
Max wing loading	604 kg/m² (126·3 lb/sq ft)
Max power loading	238·5 kg/kN (2·33 lb/lb st)

PERFORMANCE (initial production aircraft):

Max level speed at S/L
Mach 1·1 (729 knots; 1,350 km/h; 840 mph)

Max level speed at 11,000 m (36,000 ft)
Mach 1·5 (860 knots; 1,593 km/h; 990 mph)

Landing speed 115 knots (213 km/h; 132 mph)

T-O run with typical tactical load 580 m (1,900 ft)

T-O to 15 m (50 ft) with typical tactical load
940 m (3,085 ft)

Landing from 15 m (50 ft) with typical tactical load
860 m (2,825 ft)

Landing run with typical tactical load
470 m (1,545 ft)

Typical attack radius, internal fuel only:

hi-lo-hi	440 nm (815 km; 507 miles)
lo-lo-lo	310 nm (575 km; 357 miles)

Typical attack radius with external fuel:

hi-lo-hi	710 nm (1,315 km; 818 miles)
lo-lo-lo	450 nm (835 km; 518 miles)

Ferry range with external fuel
2,270 nm (4,210 km; 2,614 miles)

g limits +8·6; +12 (ultimate)

SEPECAT JAGUAR DEVELOPMENT

In addition to earlier developments listed in the previous entry, BAe is considering other means of developing the power plant and airframe for possible future versions.

The Adour engine is capable of considerable further growth, the greatest potential being represented currently by the 'Dash 63', which has 38 per cent more T-O thrust with afterburning than the Mk 102, and 65 per cent more in the combat regime. Various Adour models, with dash numbers between 58 and 63, are being studied.

BAe is also studying designs for a new wing which could either be fitted to a new aircraft with the minimum of design change, or be retrofitted to existing Jaguars.

Development contracts have already been placed for an advanced fly-by-wire installation, and for a carbon-fibre wing, for the Jaguar. The Marconi Avionics/Dowty quadruplex FBW flight control system, which has all-electric signalling and no manual backup, is being installed by BAe in an RAF Jaguar GR.Mk 1, and is due to be test-flown in 1980. BAe is also studying a version of the Jaguar with a new, larger wing with inboard extensions of the leading-edges.

SOKO/CIAR

PARTICIPANTS:

SOKO, Mostar, Yugoslavia

Centrala Industriala Aeronautica Romana, Bucharest, Romania

SOKO/CIAR ORAO (EAGLE)/IAR-93

This twin-jet ground attack fighter is under development to meet a joint requirement of the air forces of Romania and Yugoslavia. In the latter country it is known as the Orao (Eagle); its Romanian designation is IAR-93. The aircraft was known originally as the 'Jurom' (from *Ju*goslavia-*Rom*ania).

The Orao/IAR-93 was designed jointly by Yugoslav and Romanian engineers, working at the Vazduhoplovno Tehnicki Institut in Zarkovo, near Belgrade, where wind tunnel testing of the design was carried out. Manufacture of prototypes is believed to have begun simultaneously in the two countries, and the first of these, bearing serial number 25001, is thought to have flown for the first time in August 1974. On 15 April 1975 it was demonstrated publicly during the Victory Day parade at Batajnica military airfield near Belgrade. Two further prototypes have reportedly been built, followed by nine pre-production aircraft. The second prototype (25002), shown in an accompanying photograph, is a tandem two-seater; the third may have been a ground test aircraft.

More than 33 factories in Yugoslavia are involved in the Orao manufacturing programme, led by SOKO, which has prime responsibility for final assembly and flight testing.

It is anticipated that 200 or more of these aircraft may be built eventually for the two air forces, including a proportion of two-seat operational trainers. The initial production batch is reported to be nearly 40, including two-seaters.

The following description is based upon study of available photographs, and the specification data upon reports appearing in the Yugoslav and international press:

TYPE: Single-seat close support aircraft and interceptor.

WINGS: Cantilever shoulder-wing monoplane, of low aspect ratio. Anhedral approx 4° from roots. Sweepback approx 43° on leading-edges. Leading-edge slats. Two small boundary layer fences on each wing. Wide-chord Fowler-type trailing-edge flaps. Ground-adjustable tab on each aileron; trim tab in port aileron. Ailerons controlled by Dowty powered servo-actuators with autostabiliser input.

FUSELAGE: All-metal semi-monocoque structure. Door-type perforated airbrake under each side of lower front fuselage, forward of main-wheel bays. 'Pen-nib' fairing above exhaust nozzles. Space provision in nose for ranging radar.

TAIL UNIT: Cantilever metal structure, with sweepback on all surfaces. Low-set all-moving tailplane, with tip-mounted anti-flutter weights which project forward of leading-edges. Small dorsal fin. Trim tab in rudder. Tailplane and rudder controlled by Dowty powered servo-actuators with autostabiliser input. Auxiliary ventral fin on each side beneath rear fuselage.

LANDING GEAR: Messier-Hispano retractable tricycle type, built by Prva Petoljetka, with single-wheel steerable nose unit and twin-wheel main units. All units have oleo-pneumatic shock-absorbers. Hydraulic actuation, all units retracting forward into fuselage. Braking parachute in bullet fairing at base of rudder.

POWER PLANT: Two 17·8 kN (4,000 lb st) Rolls-Royce Viper Mk 632-41 non-afterburning turbojet engines in prototypes, mounted side by side in fuselage, with lateral air intakes and twin exhaust nozzles. Internal fuel capacity approx 3,070 litres (675 Imp gallons). Production aircraft may be fitted with Rolls-Royce-developed afterburners, increasing power of each engine to approx 26·5 kN (5,950 lb st).

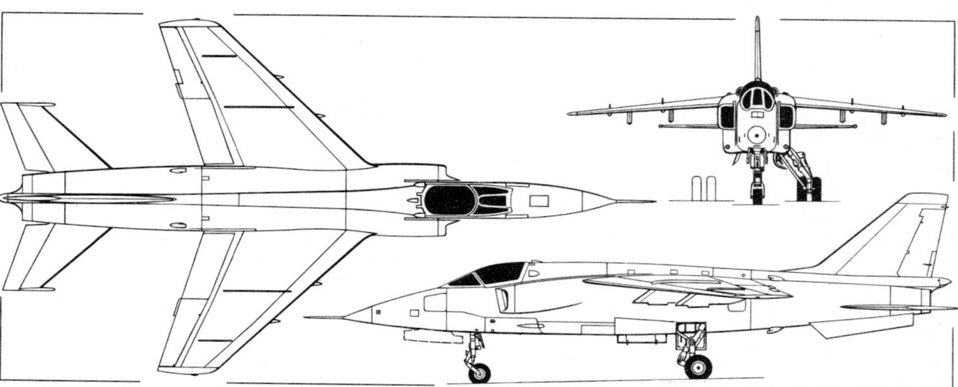
Orao/IAR-93 single-seat tactical fighter, developed jointly by Romania and Yugoslavia *(Pilot Press)*

Prototype of the Orao/IAR-93 single-seat tactical fighter (two Rolls-Royce Viper turbojet engines)

Two-seat version of the Orao/IAR-93 (foreground) with single-seater

ACCOMMODATION: Pilot only, on ejection seat beneath rear-hinged, upward-opening canopy; or crew of two in tandem under elongated canopy in operational training version.

SYSTEMS AND EQUIPMENT: Graviner Firewire and BCF fire detection and extinguishing systems. Landing lights under nose, forward of nosewheel bay, and on nose-wheel leg. Ram-air scoop aft of cockpit on each side; additional airscoops on top of fuselage, aft of canopy and at front of dorsal fin, and below rear fuselage.

ARMAMENT: Two 30 mm cannon in lower front fuselage, aft of nosewheel bay; one underfuselage and four underwing stations for external stores. Max external load approx 2,000 kg (4,410 lb) on prototypes, approx 3,000 kg (6,615 lb) on production version.

DIMENSIONS, EXTERNAL (estimated):

Wing span	7·56 m (24 ft 9¾ in)
Wing area, gross	18·00 m² (193·75 sq ft)
Wing aspect ratio	3·2
Length overall:	
incl probe	12·90 m (42 ft 4 in)
excl probe	12·45 m (40 ft 10¼ in)
Height overall	3·78 m (12 ft 4¾ in)
Wheel track (c/l of shock-struts)	2·00 m (6 ft 6¾ in)
Wheelbase	4·90 m (16 ft 1 in)

WEIGHTS AND LOADINGS (estimated; A: prototypes, B: production version):
- Weight empty, equipped: A — 4,300 kg (9,480 lb)
  - B — 4,700 kg (10,360 lb)
- Internal fuel load — approx 2,500 kg (5,510 lb)
- T-O weight 'clean': A — 7,000 kg (15,430 lb)
  - B — 7,300 kg (16,095 lb)
- Max T-O weight with external stores:
  - A — 9,000 kg (9,840 lb)
  - B — 10,300 kg (22,700 lb)
- Wing loading:
  - A at T-O weight 'clean' 388·8 kg/m² (79·6 lb/sq ft)
  - A at max T-O weight 500·0 kg/m² (102·4 lb/sq ft)
  - B at T-O weight 'clean' 405·5 kg/m² (83·0 lb/sq ft)
  - B at max T-O weight 572·2 kg/m² (117·2 lb/sq ft)
- Power loading:
  - A at T-O weight 'clean' 196·6 kg/kN (1·93 lb/lb st)
  - A at max T-O weight 252·8 kg/kN (2·48 lb/lb st)
  - B at T-O weight 'clean' 137·7 kg/kN (1·35 lb/lb st)
  - B at max T-O weight 194·3 kg/kN (1·91 lb/lb st)

PERFORMANCE (estimated; A: prototypes, without afterburning; B: production version with afterburning):
- Max level speed at low level:
  - A Mach 0·92 (609 knots; 1,128 km/h; 701 mph)
  - B Mach 1·0 (662 knots; 1,226 km/h; 762 mph)
- Max level speed at high altitude:
  - A Mach 0·95 (544 knots; 1,009 km/h; 627 mph)
  - B Mach 1·65 (946 knots; 1,752 km/h; 1,089 mph)
- Landing speed:
  - A, B 121 knots (225 km/h; 140 mph)
- Max rate of climb at S/L:
  - A 5,400 m (17,715 ft)/min
  - B 12,000 m (39,370 ft)/min
- Time to 11,000 m (36,000 ft): A 5 min 0 s
  - B 1 min 36 s
- Service ceiling: A 14,000 m (45,925 ft)
  - B 16,000 m (52,500 ft)
- T-O run:
  - A at 8,500 kg (18,740 lb) AUW 925 m (3,035 ft)
  - B at max T-O weight 1,000 m (3,280 ft)
- Landing run:
  - A at 8,500 kg (18,740 lb) AUW 1,000 m (3,280 ft)
  - B at max T-O weight 1,000 m (3,280 ft)
- Combat radius with 2,000 kg (4,410 lb) external stores:
  - A, lo-lo-lo 108 nm (200 km; 124 miles)
  - B, lo-lo-lo 175 nm (325 km; 202 miles)
  - A, hi-lo-hi 216 nm (400 km; 248 miles)
  - B, hi-lo-hi 350 nm (650 km; 404 miles)
- *g* limits: A +6·8
  - B +7·5

TRANSALL

ARBEITSGEMEINSCHAFT TRANSALL

AIRFRAME COMPANIES:

Aérospatiale, 37 boulevard de Montmorency, 75781 Paris Cédex 16, France
Telephone: 524 43 21
Telex: 620059 F

MBB, PO Box 950109, 2103 Hamburg 95, Federal Republic of Germany
Telephone: (040) 747 5164
Telex: 217684

VFW-Fokker, Hünefeldstrasse 1-5, 28 Bremen 1, Federal Republic of Germany
Telephone: (0421) 5381
Telex: 245821b

The Transall (Transporter Allianz) group was formed in January 1959 by Messerschmitt-Bölkow-Blohm, Aérospatiale and VFW-Fokker, to undertake joint development and production of the C-160 twin-turboprop military transport for the French and German air forces. Others were built for the air forces of South Africa and Turkey. Production ended in 1972, but was reinstated in 1977 to meet an additional French order and requests from other countries.

TRANSALL C-160

The Transall C-160 was developed to meet the specific requirements of the Federal German and French governments for a military transport aircraft capable of carrying troops, casualties, freight, supplies and vehicles, and of operating from semi-prepared surfaces.

Initial production, of the C-160 D (90), C-160 F (60), C-160 T (20) and C-160 Z (9), was shared between the three participating companies and ended in 1972, as described in earlier editions of *Jane's*.

An industrial agreement was signed on 29 October 1976, sharing the work on future production between Aérospatiale (50%) and the two German companies (50%), with a single final assembly line at Toulouse. Aérospatiale would build the wings and undertake final assembly; VFW-Fokker the central fuselage and tail unit; and MBB the cockpit and rear fuselage. The engines, as before, would be manufactured jointly by Rolls-Royce, SNECMA, MTU and FN.

In July 1977 the French government gave its approval to the launching of a new production series, primarily to satisfy a requirement of the French Air Force for 25-30 additional aircraft. The main improvements in this new batch are updated electronics equipment, increased max T-O weight, and extended range resulting from a reinforced wing with an optional additional fuel tank in the centre-section. New-series production began on 1 October 1977.

The following details refer to the new French Air Force/export C-160:

TYPE: Twin-engined turboprop transport.

WINGS: Cantilever high-wing monoplane. Dihedral on outer wings 3° 26′. All-metal two-spar structure designed on fail-safe principles. Wing in three sections, comprising a centre-section, which carries the engines, and two outer panels. All-metal ailerons and hydraulically-operated double-slotted flaps. Hydraulically-operated airbrakes (inboard, above and below wings) and spoilers (outboard) forward of flaps on each wing. Electrical de-icing of leading-edges.

FUSELAGE: Aluminium alloy (2024-T3) semi-monocoque structure of circular basic section, flattened at the bottom, and designed on fail-safe principles. Underside of upswept rear fuselage lowers to form loading ramp for vehicles.

TAIL UNIT: Cantilever aluminium alloy (2024-T3) structure.

LANDING GEAR: Retractable tricycle type of Messier design. Hydraulic retraction and hydraulic/pneumatic shock-absorption. Each main unit comprises two pairs of wheels in tandem and is mounted inside a fairing on the side of the fuselage. Wheels can be raised to lower the fuselage for loading. Steerable twin-wheel nose unit. Main-wheel tyres size 15·00 × 16; nosewheel tyres size 12·5 × 16. Tyre pressure 3·79 bars (55 lb/sq in) on main units, 3·14 bars (45·5 lb/sq in) on nose unit. Messier brakes.

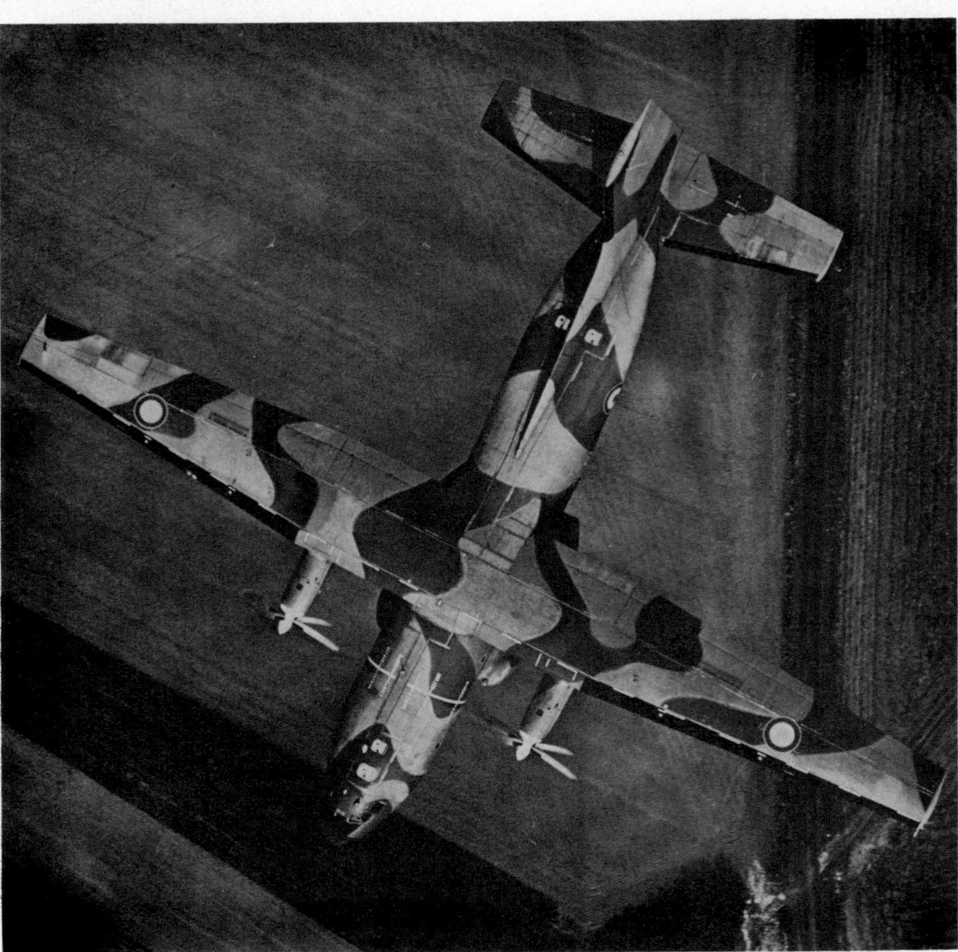

One of the original-production Transall C-160 Fs in service with the French Air Force

POWER PLANT: Two 4,549 kW (6,100 ehp) Rolls-Royce Tyne RTy.20 Mk 22 turboprop engines, each driving a Ratier Forest-built BAe Type 4/8000/6 four-blade constant-speed fully-feathering reversible-pitch propeller. Single-point pressure refuelling; gravity refuelling available optionally. Fuel in four integral wing tanks with total capacity of 19,050 litres (4,190 Imp gallons). Additional wing centre-section tank optional, capacity 9,000 litres (1,980 Imp gallons). Provision for in-flight refuelling. Water-methanol usable capacity 318·5 litres (70 Imp gallons). Oil capacity (total) 68·4 litres (15 Imp gallons).

ACCOMMODATION: Pressurised accommodation for crew of three, comprising pilot, co-pilot, and flight engineer. Typical payloads include 93 troops or 61-88 fully-equipped paratroops; 62 stretchers and four attendants; armoured vehicles, tanks and tractors not exceeding 17,000 kg (37,478 lb) total weight. Flight deck and cargo compartment air-conditioned and pressurised in flight and on the ground. Power-assisted controls. Paratroop door on each side immediately aft of the landing gear fairings; hydraulically-operated rear loading ramp. The floor and all doors are at truckbed height. The floor is provided with lashing points of 5,000 kg (11,023 lb) capacity, arranged in a 51 cm (20 in) grid, and 12,000 kg (26,455 lb) capacity on the sidewalls, and is stressed to carry large military vehicles. Loads which cannot be driven in can be taken on board rapidly by an automatic translation and stowing system. Individual loads of up to 8,000 kg (17,637 lb) can be air-dropped, including drops at low altitude (3-9 m; 10-30 ft) or during touch-and-go.

SYSTEMS: Normalair pressurisation and air-conditioning system, differential 0·302-0·322 bars (4·38-4·67 lb/sq in). Two separate primary hydraulic systems, pressure 175 bars (2,500 lb/sq in), for flying controls, loading ramp, landing gear, wheel brakes, flaps, spoilers, airbrakes, nosewheel steering and other auxiliaries. Two more systems, pressure 175 bars (2,538 lb/sq in), for emergency and ground services, as well as a hand-pump driven emergency system. AC electrical system includes two 60kVA 380-580Hz generators, one 60kVA 400Hz generator and two 9kVA 400Hz generators. 28V DC system and 40Ah batteries. AiResearch GTCP-85-160A APU in forward part of port main undercarriage fairing.

AVIONICS AND EQUIPMENT: Socrat TRAP-138 VHF; TRT TRAP-139 UHF; LMT 3527C or Collins 628T-1 HF; TEAM AS-1227B PA system; TEAM TF-AP 14 intercom; EAS RNA-720 VOR/ILS; Collins NRAN-19 or DF 206 ADF; LMT DM-820 or Collins 860E-5 (without Micro-Tacan) DME; LMT-3560 or Collins 621A-6A ATC transponder; Omera ORB-37 weather radar; TRT AHV-6 radio altimeter; EAS RM-671 or Collins 51Z-4 marker beacon; Jaeger 60571 or Jaeger 64111 encoding altimeter; SFIM-51 autopilot; and Crouzet Nadir Doppler radar. Export version available with LMT Micro-Tacan; Collins DF-301E UHF/DF (with UHF com system); Sercel Crouzet type Equinox Omega; and TRT APS-500 GPWS.

DIMENSIONS, EXTERNAL:
- Wing span — 40·00 m (131 ft 3 in)
- Wing chord at root — 4·84 m (15 ft 10½ in)
- Wing chord at tip — 2·428 m (7 ft 11½ in)
- Wing chord (mean) — 4·176 m (13 ft 8½ in)
- Wing aspect ratio — 10
- Length overall — 32·40 m (106 ft 3½ in)
- Height overall — 11·65 m (38 ft 2¾ in)

Tailplane span	14·50 m (47 ft 7 in)
Wheel track	5·10 m (16 ft 9 in)
Wheelbase	10·48 m (34 ft 4½ in)
Propeller diameter	5·486 m (18 ft 0 in)
Propeller ground clearance	1·30 m (4 ft 3¼ in)
Distance between propeller centres	10·90 m (35 ft 9¼ in)
Crew door (fwd, port):	
Height	1·22 m (4 ft 0 in)
Width	0·62 m (2 ft 0½ in)
Paratroop door (each side):	
Height	1·90 m (6 ft 2½ in)
Width	0·90 m (3 ft 0 in)
Rear loading ramp:	
Length	3·70 m (12 ft 1½ in)
Width	3·15 m (10 ft 3½ in)
Emergency exits:	
Main hold, fwd, stbd side (one):	
Height	0·88 m (2 ft 10½ in)
Width	0·54 m (1 ft 9¼ in)
Flight deck roof (one); roof of main hold, fwd (one); and two in roof of main hold at rear (one each side of dorsal fin):	
Height	0·54 m (1 ft 9¼ in)
Width	0·64 m (2 ft 1¼ in)

DIMENSIONS, INTERNAL:

Cabin, excl flight deck and ramp:	
Length	13·51 m (44 ft 4 in)
Max width	3·15 m (10 ft 3½ in)
Max height	2·98 m (9 ft 8½ in)
Floor area	42·6 m² (458·5 sq ft)
Volume	115·0 m³ (4,061 cu ft)
Cabin, incl ramp:	
Length	17·21 m (56 ft 6 in)
Floor area	54·25 m² (584 sq ft)
Volume	140·0 m³ (4,944 cu ft)

AREAS:

Wings, gross	160·00 m² (1,722 sq ft)
Ailerons (total)	6·88 m² (74·06 sq ft)
Trailing-edge flaps (total, extended)	34·54 m² (371·8 sq ft)
Spoilers (total)	0·80 m² (8·61 sq ft)
Fin:	
excl dorsal fin	29·50 m² (317·5 sq ft)
incl dorsal fin	36·00 m² (387·5 sq ft)
Rudder	10·20 m² (109·8 sq ft)
Tailplane	43·80 m² (471·5 sq ft)
Elevators	10·30 m² (110·9 sq ft)

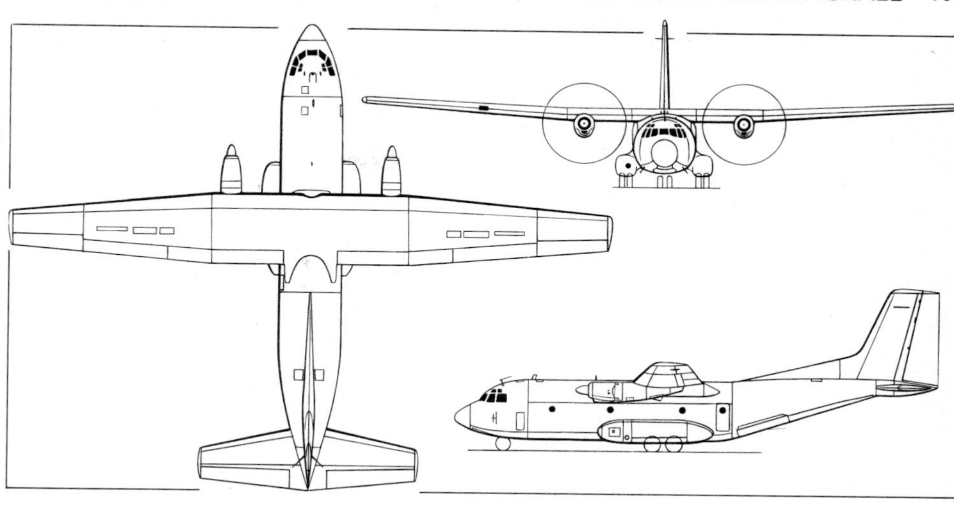

Transall C-160 twin-turboprop general-purpose transport aircraft *(Pilot Press)*

WEIGHTS AND LOADINGS:

Weight empty, equipped	27,782 kg (61,250 lb)
Min operating weight empty	28,000 kg (61,729 lb)
Typical operating weight empty	29,000 kg (63,934 lb)
Max payload	17,000 kg (37,478 lb)
Max T-O weight	51,000 kg (112,435 lb)
Max zero-fuel weight	45,000 kg (99,208 lb)
Max landing weight	47,000 kg (103,617 lb)
Max wing loading	319 kg/m² (65·34 lb/sq ft)
Max power loading	5·61 kg/kW (9·22 lb/ehp)

PERFORMANCE (at max T-O weight except where indicated, ISA):

Never-exceed speed:	
at 4,575-9,145 m; (15,000-30,000 ft)	Mach 0·64
below 4,575 m (15,000 ft)	320 knots (593 km/h; 368 mph)
Max level speed at 4,875 m (16,000 ft)	277 knots (513 km/h; 319 mph)
Stalling speed, flaps down	95 knots (177 km/h; 110 mph)
Max rate of climb at S/L	396 m (1,300 ft)/min
Rate of climb at S/L, one engine out	91 m (300 ft)/min
Service ceiling at 45,000 kg (99,208 lb) AUW	8,535 m (28,000 ft)
Service ceiling, one engine out at 45,000 kg (99,208 lb) AUW	3,050 m (10,000 ft)
T-O run, 20° flap	730 m (2,395 ft)
T-O to 15 m (50 ft), 20° flap	990 m (3,248 ft)
Landing from 15 m (50 ft), 40° flap, at max landing weight without propeller reversal	869 m (2,850 ft)
Landing run, normal	550 m (1,800 ft)
Min ground turning radius	28·60 m (93 ft 10 in)
Range, with 5% initial fuel and allowance for 30 min hold at S/L, OWE of 29,000 kg (63,934 lb):	
with 8,000 kg (17,640 lb) payload	2,750 nm (5,095 km; 3,166 miles)
with 16,000 kg (35,275 lb) payload	1,000 nm (1,852 km; 1,151 miles)
Max ferry range with centre-section wing tank	4,780 nm (8,858 km; 5,504 miles)

ZENTRALGESELLSCHAFT VFW-FOKKER mbH

ADDRESS: Gartenstrasse 15, 4000 Düsseldorf, Federal Republic of Germany
Telephone: Düsseldorf 49731
Telex: 85 84 344 ZGVF-D
BOARD OF MANAGEMENT:
Frans Swarttouw (Deputy Chairman)
Dipl Ing Johann Schäffler (Deputy Chairman)
Alan R. Buley
Friedrich-Wilhelm Freese
Hulbertus Johannes Grobben
DIRECTORS, VFW-FOKKER GmbH:
See Aircraft section (Germany)
DIRECTORS, FOKKER-VFW BV, AMSTERDAM:
See Aircraft section (Netherlands)
DIRECTORS, ERNO RAUMFAHRTTECHNIK GMBH, BREMEN:
See Spaceflight section (Germany)
DIRECTOR, AVIO-DIEPEN BV, AMSTERDAM: D. G. de Rooij

In May 1969, NVKNV Fokker, Amsterdam, and Vereinigte Flugtechnische Werke GmbH, Bremen, combined their activities on a parity basis. The effective operating date of the association was made retrospective to 1 January 1969. To accomplish the merger, a new central company named Zentralgesellschaft VFW-Fokker mbH was created, with headquarters in Düsseldorf.

Shareholders of the Zentralgesellschaft are the holding companies NVKNV Fokker, Amsterdam, and VFW-Verwaltungsgesellschaft mbH, Bremen. The Zentralgesellschaft operates through Fokker-VFW BV, Amsterdam, and VFW-Fokker mbH, Bremen, described fully in the Netherlands and German sections respectively. All marketing and product support of civil aircraft of VFW and Fokker design are undertaken by a separate company, Fokker-VFW International BV, with offices at Schiphol-Oost, Netherlands (PO Box 7600).

Companies also operating directly under Zentralgesellschaft VFW-Fokker mbH are ERNO Raumfahrttechnik GmbH, Bremen, the space division; Rhein-Flugzeugbau GmbH, Mönchengladbach (which see), for light aircraft; and Avio-Diepen BV, Amsterdam, a trading company.

The entire organisation employs about 17,000 people in 15 factories.

The company has, together with Dassault-Breguet of France, a parity interest in the Belgian company SABCA (which see), with factories at Haren and Gosselies.

IRAN

IHI
IRANIAN HELICOPTER INDUSTRY

ADDRESS: 107 Sepahbod Zahedi Avenue, Teheran
Telephone: 825041-6
Telex: 213884
MANAGING DIRECTOR: Brig Gen H. Soroudi

As a major step in a national industrialisation programme the government of Iran in 1975 selected Bell Helicopter Textron as its partner in establishing a modern aircraft industry in that country. Construction of a helicopter factory and training school was started at Isfahan by JHP, a joint US/Iranian construction partnership; the first buildings were scheduled for completion in 1979.

First products of the new Iranian industry were to have been the Bell Model 214A and Bell/IHI Model 214ST helicopters. However, the joint agreement between Bell Helicopter Textron and the government of Iran was terminated in December 1978. No information has been received from IHI concerning activities in Iran. However, development of the Model 214ST is being continued by Bell, and the description of this aircraft can now be found under that company's entry in the US section.

ISRAEL

IAI
ISRAEL AIRCRAFT INDUSTRIES LTD

HEAD OFFICE AND WORKS: Ben Gurion International Airport, Lydda (Lod)
Telephone: 03 973111
Telex: Isravia 31114
PRESIDENT: G. Gidor
EXECUTIVE VICE-PRESIDENT: A. Ostrinski
VICE-PRESIDENTS:
M. Keret (Aircraft and Airborne Systems Marketing)
N. Rosen (Naval Systems and Missiles Marketing)
A. Bar-Nir (General Manager, Bedek Aviation Division)
M. Blumkin (General Manager, Engineering Division)
A. Ezroni (General Manager, Manufacturing Division)
Y. Giladi (General Manager, Combined Technologies Division)
M. Na'aman (General Manager, Electronics Division)
M. Dvir (Research and Development)
D. Mozes (Finance)
Mrs. H. Ron (General Counsel)
Y. Zinger (Comptroller)
COMMERCIAL DIRECTOR, ARAVA: H. Pearlman
COMMERCIAL DIRECTOR, WESTWIND: S. Samach

This company was established in 1953 as Bedek Aircraft Company. The change of name, to Israel Aircraft Industries, was made on 1 April 1967.

IAI employs more than 22,000 people in all its facilities, which occupy a total covered floor area of 300,000 m² (3,229,170 sq ft). It is licensed by, among others, the Israel Civil Aviation Administration, US Federal Aviation Administration, British Civil Aviation Authority and the Israeli Air Force as an approved repair station and maintenance organisation.

Israel Aircraft Industries Ltd is composed of several divisions, plants and subsidiary companies. These underwent a major reorganisation in the latter part of 1977, and are now disposed in five divisions, as follows:

Bedek Aviation, now incorporating Turbochrome, is

an internationally approved multi-faceted single-site civil and military aircraft service centre. Present programmes include the turnaround inspection, overhaul, repair, retrofitting, outfitting and testing of 30 types of aircraft, including the Boeing 707/720 and McDonnell Douglas DC-8; 28 types of engine, including the 244·7 kN (55,000 lb st) Pratt & Whitney JT9D; and 6,000 types of components, accessories and systems. Offshore workload includes the supply of total technical support to several international operators. The division holds warranty and/or approved service centre approvals from many of the world's leading component manufacturers. Bedek has refurbished and resold numerous Boeing 707/720s, often after conversion from passenger to cargo configuration. The procedure for the structural modification was developed jointly by Boeing and Bedek Aviation.

Bedek Aviation has a total floor area of some 74,322 m² (800,000 sq ft) and in 1978 employed a staff of about 3,500.

The **Manufacturing Division** produces the Kfir fighter, the IAI-designed Arava STOL transport, and the turbofan-powered 1124 Westwind business aircraft. In addition, it is engaged in the manufacture of a vast variety of spares and assemblies for aircraft and jet engines, to meet Israeli Air Force requirements. As a subcontractor to many US and European aircraft manufacturers, the Division produces major aircraft structures, flight control surfaces, cargo loading systems and spares. It had a work force of about 5,500 in 1978.

The **Engineering Division** is responsible for engineering research, design, development and testing of aerospace systems. It provides engineering support in system analysis, aerodynamics, materials and processing, landing and control systems, and in structural, flight and environmental testing. The Division performed modification and production support for the manufacture of the Magister jet trainer for the IAF; and major structural conversions of the Boeing Model 377, for military applications such as swing-tail freighter and hose-refuelling tanker. The Division designed and developed the Arava STOL transport aircraft and developed both the 1123 and 1124 Westwind.

In 1978 the Engineering Division, which then employed about 1,500 people, was engaged in a variety of future programmes which included the development of a supercritical wing for the 1124 Westwind and a fly-by-wire system for flight testing in the Kfir; research into materials, structures and electronic countermeasures; and design studies for a utility helicopter. If it materialises, such a helicopter is likely to be powered by one or two Turboméca engines, to have a rigid rotor, and to have a max T-O weight in the region of 4,535 kg (10,000 lb). Also in the preliminary study stages is a new single-seat strike fighter known as the Arieh (Lion), intended to replace eventually the Israeli Air Force's A-4 Skyhawks and F-4 Phantoms.

The **Electronics Division** incorporates the company's former electronics subsidiary, Elta, the MBT Weapon Systems subsidiary, Tamam Precision Instruments, and MLM Systems Engineering and Integration. It specialises in the design, development and production of sophisticated electronic equipment such as airborne, ground and shipborne communications and radars, transceivers and navigational aids, general communications equipment, automatic test systems, and such electronic medical devices as cardiac resuscitation instruments. MBT participated in the development of the Gabriel shipborne surface-to-surface missile system, among others, as well as of an Electronic Warning Fence and an Audible Bomb Release Altimeter. Tamam manufactures and assembles high-precision electromechanical components and servo-systems for such mechanisms as aerosystems, torque motors and gyroscopes.

The SHL (Servo-Hydraulics Lod), PML, Ramta, MATA Helicopters and Golan Industries subsidiaries now make up the **Combined Technologies Division**. This designs, develops and manufactures hydraulic and fuel system components, hydraulic flight control servo-systems, landing gears and brake systems; produces air-actuated chucks, miniature gears, clutches and brakes; is a custom-moulder of reinforced plastics, producing parts for aircraft, cabs and trucks, concrete casting moulds and sheet products; manufactures ground support equipment, stainless steel tanks, the Dabur patrol boat and the RBY armoured vehicle; manufactures high precision metal products for the aircraft and military industries; and produces electronic assemblies and subassemblies for aircraft.

IAI-modified Dassault Super Mystère B-2, with Pratt & Whitney J52 engine and lengthened rear fuselage

IAI (DASSAULT) SUPER MYSTÈRE B-2

It was reported in mid-1977 that IAI had begun delivery to the air force of Honduras of 12 refurbished Dassault Super Mystère B-2 jet fighters formerly operated by the Israeli Air Force.

These aircraft differ considerably from the original Dassault-built aircraft, having been refitted in the early 1970s with a non-afterburning Pratt & Whitney J52-P-8A turbojet of 41·4 kN (9,300 lb st) in place of the original French Atar 101G which was rated at 44 kN (9,920 lb st) with afterburning. This modification results in a longer rear fuselage than that of the standard Super Mystère. Considerable modifications have also been made to airframe components, avionics and other systems, and the variety and weight of external stores have also been increased. The modified Super Mystère first appeared publicly in May 1973, and is said to have operated successfully in the subsequent conflict in October of that year.

IAI KFIR (LION CUB)

Following manufacture of the Nesher fighter (see 1977-78 *Jane's*), powered by an Atar turbojet, IAI developed a more extensively modified and further improved version of the same airframe, powered by a General Electric J79 afterburning turbojet engine. One of these engines was installed in a much-modified Israeli Air Force Mirage III-B, with which it was first test-flown in September 1971, and production of the J79-engined Mirage began in 1972. A prototype of the Kfir was flown in 1973, before the outbreak of the October 'Yom Kippur' war, and details of this further-modified version were made public officially for the first time on 14 May 1975, when two of the new aircraft were displayed at Ben Gurion Airport.

The Kfir utilises a basic airframe similar to that of the Dassault Mirage 5, the main changes being a shorter but larger-diameter rear fuselage, to accommodate the J79 engine; an enlarged and flattened undersurface to the forward portion of the fuselage; introduction of four small fuselage airscoops, plus a larger dorsal airscoop in place of the triangular dorsal fin, to provide cooling air for the afterburner; and a strengthened landing gear, with longer-stroke oleos. Several internal changes have also been made, including a redesigned cockpit layout, addition of a considerable amount of Israeli-built avionics equipment, and increased internal fuel tankage compared

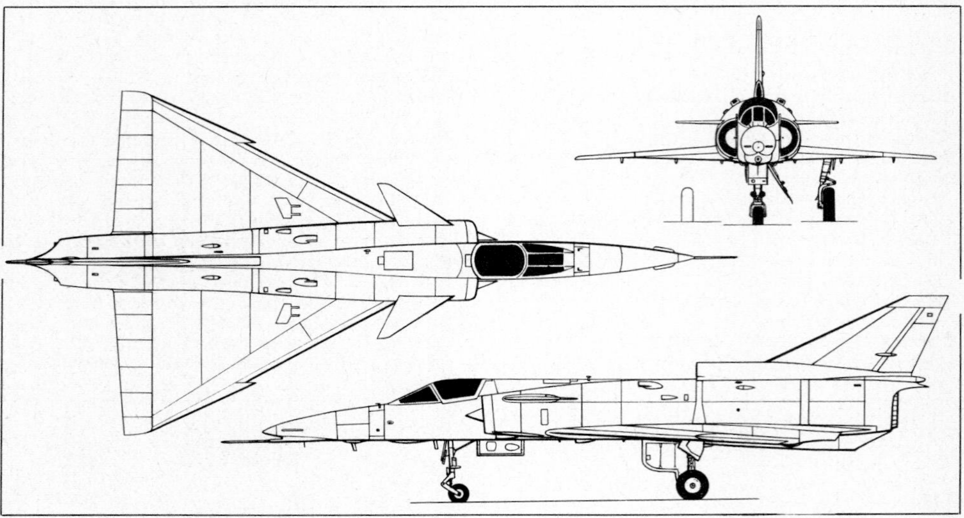

IAI Kfir-C2 (General Electric J79-J1E afterburning turbojet engine) *(Pilot Press)*

IAI Kfir-C2 single-seat interceptor, long range patrol fighter and ground attack aircraft *(Israeli Defence Force)*

with the Mirage 5. Intended for both air defence and ground attack roles, the Kfir retains the standard Mirage fixed armament of two 30 mm DEFA cannon, and can carry a variety of external weapons including the Rafael Shafrir 2 air-to-air and Luz-1 air-to-surface missiles. It has demonstrated stall-free gun firing throughout the flight envelope. Two squadrons of the Israeli Air Force were equipped with this initial Kfir-C1 version.

On 20 July 1976, at the Israeli Air Force base at Hatzerim, in the Negev, the first public demonstration took place of a modified version known as the **Kfir-C2**, which by that time was already in Israeli Air Force service, having entered production in 1974. The Kfir-C2 has a number of changes from the original C1, the most significant of which are the addition of non-retractable, sweptback canard surfaces just aft of the engine air intakes; a small strake on each side of the extreme nose; and an extended wing leading-edge, created by increasing the chord on approximately the outer 40% of each half-span.

These changes, which add some 85 kg (187 lb) to the structural weight, recall the retractable 'moustaches' fitted by Dassault to the experimental Milan version of the Mirage and described in earlier editions of *Jane's*. The canard surfaces of the Kfir-C2, however, are much larger in area than those of the Milan, and by virtue of their different location they eliminate two of the principal criticisms made of the Milan installation: impairment of the pilot's view forward and downward, and the creation of adverse wake effects in the engine air intakes. The Kfir-C2 installation is more analogous with that of the Saab 37 Viggen, though the canard surfaces are smaller. They can also be detached for missions not requiring high manoeuvrability.

The Kfir-C2 is the principal production version, both for the Israeli Air Force and for export. The modifications, which are reportedly being retrofitted to existing Kfirs, were designed to improve the aircraft's dogfighting manoeuvrability at the lower end of the speed range and to enhance take-off and landing performance. It is claimed that, in particular, they give a better sustained turning performance, with improved lateral, longitudinal and directional control; contribute to a very low gust response at all operational altitudes, especially at very low level; offer improved handling qualities at all angles of attack, high *g* loadings, and low speeds; reduce take-off and landing distances, and landing speeds; and permit a more stable (and, if required, a steeper) approach, with a flatter angle of approach and touchdown. Later versions of the C2 have Elta EL/M-2001B nose radar in an extended nose, increasing the overall length by 0·80 m (2 ft 7½ in).

A two-seat trainer version of the Kfir-C2 was reported to be under development in mid-1978, with the first flight scheduled for 1979. Overall dimensions, power plant and performance were expected to be similar to those of the single-seat version.

Approximately 150 Kfirs and Kfir-C2s were believed to have been built by the Spring of 1979, with production continuing at an approximate rate of two to three C2s per month. Twenty-four C2s were ordered in late 1976 by the Ecuadorean Air Force, but this order was later vetoed by the US government. A similar order from Taiwan, for 50 Kfir-C2s for the Chinese Nationalist Air Force, was granted US approval in July 1978.

Type: Single-seat interceptor, long range patrol fighter and ground attack aircraft.

Wings: Cantilever low-wing monoplane of delta planform, with conical camber. Thickness/chord ratio 4·5% to 3·5%. Anhedral 1°. Incidence 1°. Sweepback on leading-edges 60° 34′. All-metal torsion-box structure, with stressed skin of machined panels with integral stiffeners. Two-section elevons on each trailing-edge, with smaller elevator/trim flap inboard of inner elevon. Elevons powered by hydraulic jacks; trim flaps are servo-assisted. Small, hinged plate-type airbrake above and below each wing, near leading-edge. Kfir-C2 has additional modifications which include extended chord on outer leading-edges, and detachable sweptback canard surfaces above and forward of wings, near top lip of each engine air intake. Small leading-edge fence on some aircraft, at approx one-third span.

Fuselage: All-metal semi-monocoque structure, 'waisted' in accordance with area rule. Cross-section of forward fuselage has a wider and flatter undersurface than that of Mirage 5. Nosecone built of locally-developed composite materials, with (on Kfir-C2) a small horizontal strake or 'body fence' on each side near the tip. UHF antenna under front of fuselage, forward of nosewheel door. Enlarged-diameter rear fuselage, compared with Mirage 5, with approx 0·61 m (2 ft) shorter tailpipe. Ventral fairing under rear fuselage.

Tail Unit: Cantilever all-metal fin; rudder powered by hydraulic jack, with servo-assisted trim. UHF antenna in tip of fin. Triangular-section dorsal airscoop forward of fin, to provide cold air for afterburner cooling. No horizontal tail surfaces.

Landing Gear: Retractable tricycle type, with single SHL wheel on each unit. Electrically operated hydraulic actuation, nose unit retracting rearward, main units inward into fuselage. Longer-stroke oleos than on Mirage 5, and all units strengthened to permit higher operating weights. Low-pressure tubeless tyres on all units. Main-gear leg fairings shorter than on Mirage; inner portion of each main-leg door is integral with fuselage-mounted wheel door. Steerable nosewheel, with anti-shimmy damper. Oleo-pneumatic shock-absorbers, SHL hydraulic disc brakes and anti-skid units. Braking parachute in bullet fairing below rudder.

Power Plant: One General Electric J79-J1E turbojet engine (modified GE-17), with variable-area nozzle, rated at 52·8 kN (11,870 lb st) dry and 79·62 kN (17,900 lb st) with afterburning. Air intakes enlarged, compared with Mirage 5, to allow for higher mass flow. Adjustable half-cone centrebody in each air intake. Internal fuel in five fuselage and four integral wing tanks. Total internal capacity is probably in the order of 4,000 litres (880 Imp gallons), perhaps slightly more. There is a refuelling point on top of the fuselage, above the forward upper tank. In addition, there are wet-points for the carriage of one or two drop-tanks beneath each wing, and one under the fuselage; these tanks may be of 500, 600, 1,300 or 1,700 litres (110, 132, 286 or 374 Imp gallons) capacity. External capability should be comparable to that of the Mirage 5, which can carry up to 4,700 litres (1,034 Imp gallons) of auxiliary fuel in external drop-tanks, or 1,000 litres (220 Imp gallons) in combination with 4,000 kg (8,820 lb) of ordnance.

Accommodation: Pilot only, on Martin-Baker JM.6 zero-zero ejection seat, under rearward-hinged upward-opening canopy. Revised cockpit layout compared with Mirage 5. Cockpit pressurised, heated and air-conditioned. A two-seat version is under development, with first flight anticipated in 1979.

Systems: Two separate environmental control systems (ECS), one (using engine bleed air) for cockpit heating, pressurisation and air-conditioning, and one for avionics compartments. Two independent hydraulic systems, probably of 207 bars (3,000 lb/sq in) pressure. No. 1 system actuates flying control surfaces and landing gear; No. 2 actuates flying controls, airbrakes, landing gear, wheel brakes and utilities. Fully redundant primary AC electrical system, with two 9kVA (115/200V 400Hz) alternators, each driven by a 9kW generator and CSD (constant-speed drive) unit, and Oram static inverters connected for split-bus non-synchronised operation. DC system includes two Elta 125VA (200V 400Hz) transformer-rectifiers and a Tadiran or Oram 28V 40Ah nickel-cadmium battery. External AC and DC power receptacles. Oxygen system for pilot.

Avionics and Equipment: MBT twin-computer flight control system (ASW-41 control augmentation and ASW-42 stability augmentation systems), with Elta integrated memory unit (IMU), Tamam two-axis gyro and standby compass, autopilot, MBT radar altimeter, angle of attack transmitter and indicator, and accelerometer indicator. Elbit S-8600 multi-mode navigation (Singer-Kearfott licence) and Rafael Mahat weapon delivery system, Tamam central air data computer, Tacan, Elta EL/M-2001B or EL/M-2021 X-band air-to-air and air-to-surface pulse-Doppler target acquisition and tracking radar, IFF/SIF and fire control, Israel Electro-optics head-up display and automatic gunsight. Duplicated Tadiran UHF radio. Twin landing lights on nosewheel leg; anti-collision light in fin leading-edge.

Armament: Fixed armament of one IAI-built 30 mm DEFA 552 cannon in underside of each engine air intake (125 rds/gun on Mirage 5). Seven hardpoints (three under fuselage and two under each wing) for external stores. For interception duties, one Rafael Shafrir 2 infra-red homing air-to-air missile can be carried under each outer wing. Ground attack version can carry two 1,000 lb bombs, four 500 lb bombs, or a Rafael Luz-1 or similar air-to-surface missile under the fuselage, and two 1,000 lb or six 500 lb bombs (conventional or 'concrete dibber' type) under the wings. Alternative external stores may include IMI rocket pods; napalm; Shrike, Maverick or Hobos air-to-surface missiles; ECM pods; or drop-tanks.

Dimensions, external:
- Wing span: 8·22 m (26 ft 11½ in)
- Wing aspect ratio: 1·94
- Foreplane span (estimated): 3·90 m (12 ft 9½ in)
- Length overall: approx 16·35 m (53 ft 7¾ in)
- Height overall: 4·25 m (13 ft 11¼ in)
- Wheel track: 3·15 m (10 ft 4 in)
- Wheelbase: 4·87 m (15 ft 11¾ in)

Weights:
- Weight empty (interceptor, estimated):
  - Kfir: 7,200 kg (15,873 lb)
  - Kfir-C2: 7,285 kg (16,060 lb)
- Typical combat weight (interceptor), 50% internal fuel and two Shafrir missiles:
  - Kfir: 9,305 kg (20,514 lb)
  - Kfir-C2: 9,390 kg (20,701 lb)
- Max combat T-O weight (all versions): 14,600 kg (32,188 lb)

Performance (estimated):
- Max level speed above 11,000 m (36,100 ft):
  - Kfir: over Mach 2·2 (1,260 knots; 2,335 km/h; 1,450 mph)
  - Kfir-C2: over Mach 2·3 (1,317 knots; 2,440 km/h; 1,516 mph)
- Max rate of climb at S/L: 14,000 m (45,950 ft)/min
- Time to 11,000 m (36,100 ft): 1 min 45 s
- Stabilised ceiling (combat configuration): above 15,240 m (50,000 ft)
- T-O run at 11,000 kg (24,250 lb) AUW (Kfir): 700 m (2,300 ft)
- Landing run at 9,000 kg (19,840 lb) AUW (Kfir): 450 m (1,475 ft)
- Combat radius:
  - interceptor, two 600 litre drop-tanks: 200-288 nm (370-535 km; 230-332 miles)
  - ground attack, lo-lo-lo 351 nm (650 km; 404 miles)
  - ground attack, hi-lo-hi 700 nm (1,300 km; 807 miles)

IAI 101, 102 and 201 ARAVA

The Arava was designed to fulfil the need for a light transport with STOL performance and rough-field landing capabilities. Design work started in 1966, and construction of a prototype began towards the end of the same year. This airframe was used for structural testing; it was followed by a flying prototype (4X-IAI), which made its first flight on 27 November 1969. A second Arava (4X-IAA) began flight trials on 8 May 1971.

The following versions have been announced:

IAI 101. Civil transport version, certificated by FAA in April 1972.

IAI 102. Civil transport version, based on original IAI 101, certificated by Israel Civil Aviation Administration in April 1976. This version can accommodate 20 passengers in airline-standard four-abreast configuration, with toilet. It is available also in a VIP configuration for up to 12 passengers, as an all-cargo transport, as a medical clinic for flying doctor services, and in versions for mapping, mining research, rainmaking and bridge construction, as flying laboratories for agriculture and health ministries, and for supplying oil prospecting units.

IAI 201. Military transport version, based upon the original IAI 101. A prototype (4X-IAB) began its flight tests on 7 March 1972, and this version is now in production. The standard equipment available for the IAI 201 enables a wide variety of missions to be undertaken, and in 1977 IAI announced a version suitable for maritime surveillance duties, fitted with either an AD-9 modification to extend the range and detection capability of the standard search/weather radar, or a more advanced detection system.

IAI 202. Modified version, flight tested between mid-1976 and Spring 1977. The prototype (4X-IAO) had then flown some 75 hours and had demonstrated a 20% reduction in induced drag for only a very small trim drag penalty. It differs from the other Arava versions principally in being longer, and in having a fully 'wet' wing, containing approx 726 kg (1,600 lb) more fuel, fitted with endplate surfaces ('winglets') of NASA (Whitcomb) profile at the

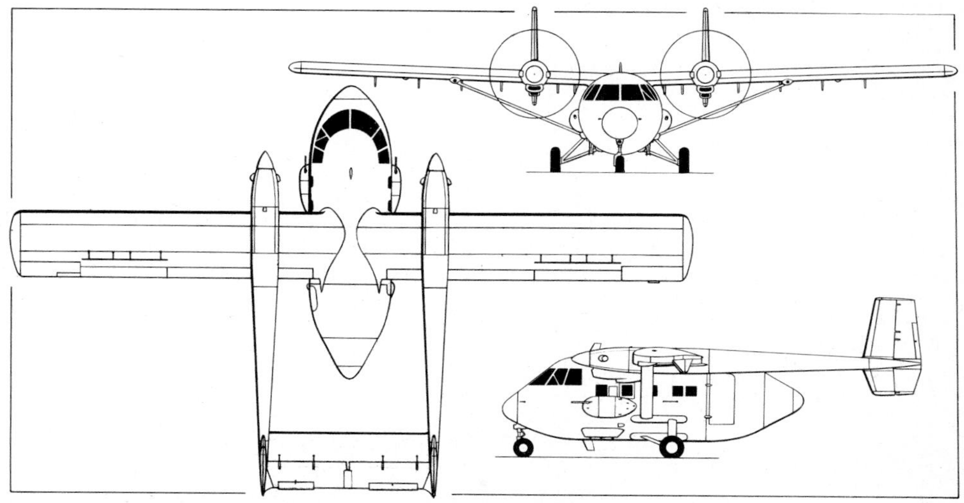

IAI 201 Arava twin-turboprop STOL light military transport *(Pilot Press)*

IAI 201 Arava twin-turboprop military transport for the Salvadorean Air Force

wingtips, and a boundary layer fence just inboard of each tip. Other features include 559 kW (750 shp) Pratt & Whitney Aircraft of Canada PT6A-36 turboprop engines, and a single-point pressure refuelling system. Performance has proved to be generally equal to that of the standard Arava, but at a max T-O weight nearly 907 kg (2,000 lb) heavier, and certification at a max T-O weight of approx 7,643 kg (16,850 lb) is anticipated. The winglet modification (but not the increased fuel capacity) is available as a retrofit modification of existing Aravas.

Prior to the October 1973 war 15 military Aravas had been ordered, 14 of them for export. During that conflict three Aravas were lease-operated by the Israeli Air Force.

Sales of the Arava had reached more than 80 by the beginning of 1979, of which more than 60 had been delivered. Customers include the Israeli Air Force (14), Bolivian Air Force (6), Ecuadorean Army (6) and Navy (3), Guatemalan Air Force (10), Honduran Air Force (3), Mexican Air Force (more than 10), Nicaraguan Air Force (2) and Salvadorean Air Force (5). Six civil Arava 102s have been sold to customers in Argentina. Production of the Arava continued during 1978 at the rate of two to three per month.

The following description applies to the IAI 201, except where indicated otherwise:

TYPE: Twin-turboprop STOL light military transport.

WINGS: Braced high-wing monoplane, with single streamline-section strut each side. Wing section NACA 63(215)A 417. Dihedral 1° 30′. Incidence 0° 27′. No sweepback. Light alloy two-spar torsion-box structure. Frise-type light alloy ailerons. Electrically-operated double-slotted light alloy flaps. Scoop-type light alloy spoilers, for lateral control, above wing at 71% chord. Electrically-actuated trim tab in port aileron.

FUSELAGE: Conventional semi-monocoque light alloy structure of stringers, frames and single-skin panels.

TAIL UNIT: Cantilever light alloy structure, with twin fins and rudders, carried on twin booms extending rearward from engine nacelles. Fixed-incidence tailplane. Geared tab and electrically-actuated trim tab in elevator and geared trim tab in each rudder. Tailbooms are built by IAI Combined Technologies Division.

LANDING GEAR: Non-retractable tricycle type, of Servo-Hydraulics Ltd manufacture, with single main wheels and steerable nosewheel. Main wheels carried on twin struts, incorporating oleo-pneumatic shock-absorbers. Main wheels size 11·00-12, tyre pressure 3·31 bars (48 lb/sq in); nosewheel size 9·00-6, tyre pressure 2·90 bars (42 lb/sq in). Disc brakes on main units. Float landing gear reportedly under development.

POWER PLANT: Two 559 kW (750 shp) Pratt & Whitney Aircraft of Canada PT6A-34 turboprop engines (PT6A-36 in IAI 202), each driving a Hartzell HC-B3TN three-blade hydraulically-actuated fully-feathering reversible-pitch metal propeller. Electrical de-icing of propellers optional. Two integral fuel tanks in each wing, with total usable capacity (except IAI 202) of 1,663 litres (366 Imp gallons). Four overwing refuelling points. Optional pressure refuelling point (standard on IAI 202) in fuselage/strut fairing. Two cabin-mounted tanks, each of 1,022 litres (225 Imp gallons), are available optionally for self-ferry flights.

ACCOMMODATION: Crew of one or two on flight deck, with door on starboard side. Main cabin of IAI 101 has folding inward-facing metal-framed fabric seats along each side, and can accommodate 20 civilian passengers. IAI 201 has similar seating for 24 fully-equipped troops or 17 paratroops and a dispatcher. IAI 102 has airline-type seating for up to 20 passengers, plus toilet. Outward-opening door at rear of cabin, opposite which, at floor level, is an emergency exit door/cargo door on the starboard side. Rear doors are built by IAI Combined Technologies Division. Aft section of fuselage is hinged to swing sideways through more than 90° to provide unrestricted access to main cabin. Alternative interior configurations available for ambulance role (12 stretchers and two sitting patients or medical attendants); as all-freight transport carrying (typically) a Jeep-mounted recoil-less rifle and its four-man crew; or as a maritime patrol aircraft fitted with search radar and other special equipment.

SYSTEMS: Hydraulic system (pressure 172 bars; 2,500 lb/sq in) for brakes and nosewheel steering only. Electrical system includes two 28V 170A DC engine-driven starter/generators, a 28V 40Ah nickel-cadmium battery, and two 250VA 115/26V 400Hz static inverters.

AVIONICS AND EQUIPMENT: Blind-flying instrumentation standard. Optional avionics include VHF, VOR/ILS, ADF, marker beacon and PA system.

ARMAMENT: Optional 0·50 in Browning machine-gun pack on each side of fuselage, above a pylon for a pod containing six 82 mm rockets. Provision for aft-firing machine-gun. Librascope gunsight.

DIMENSIONS, EXTERNAL (IAI 201):
Wing span 20·96 m (68 ft 9 in)
Wing chord (constant) 2·09 m (6 ft 10½ in)
Wing aspect ratio 10
Length overall 13·03 m (42 ft 9 in)
Length of fuselage pod 9·33 m (30 ft 7 in)
Diameter of fuselage 2·50 m (8 ft 2 in)
Height overall 5·21 m (17 ft 1 in)
Tailplane span (c/l of tailbooms) 5·21 m (17 ft 1 in)
Wheel track 4·01 m (13 ft 2 in)
Wheelbase 4·62 m (15 ft 2 in)
Propeller diameter 2·59 m (8 ft 6 in)
Propeller ground clearance 1·75 m (5 ft 9 in)
Crew door (fwd, stbd): Height 0·93 m (3 ft 0½ in)
Width 0·48 m (1 ft 7 in)
Passenger door (rear, port):
Height 1·57 m (5 ft 2 in)
Width 0·62 m (2 ft 0½ in)
Cargo drop door (rear, port):
Height 1·75 m (5 ft 9 in)
Width 2·33 m (7 ft 8 in)
Emergency/baggage door (rear, stbd):
Height 1·12 m (3 ft 8 in)
Width 0·61 m (2 ft 0 in)
Emergency window exits (each):
Height 0·66 m (2 ft 2 in)
Width 0·48 m (1 ft 7 in)

DIMENSIONS, INTERNAL:
Cabin, excl flight deck and hinged tailcone:
Length 3·87 m (12 ft 8 in)
Max width 2·33 m (7 ft 8 in)
Max height 1·75 m (5 ft 9 in)
Floor area 7·16 m² (77 sq ft)
Volume 12·7 m³ (449·2 cu ft)
Baggage compartment volume 2·60 m³ (91·8 cu ft)
Cargo door volume 3·20 m³ (113 cu ft)

AREAS (IAI 201):
Wings, gross 43·68 m² (470·2 sq ft)
Ailerons (total) 1·75 m² (18·84 sq ft)
Trailing-edge flaps (total) 8·80 m² (94·72 sq ft)
Spoilers (total) 0·85 m² (9·2 sq ft)
Fins (total) 4·86 m² (52·31 sq ft)
Rudders (total incl tabs) 3·44 m² (37·03 sq ft)
Tailplane 9·36 m² (100·75 sq ft)
Elevator, incl tabs 2·79 m² (30·03 sq ft)

WEIGHTS AND LOADINGS (IAI 201):
Basic operating weight 3,999 kg (8,816 lb)
Max payload 2,351 kg (5,184 lb)
Max T-O and landing weight 6,803 kg (15,000 lb)
Max zero-fuel weight 6,350 kg (14,000 lb)
Max wing loading 153·5 kg/m² (31·44 lb/sq ft)
Max power loading 6·08 kg/kW (10·00 lb/shp)

PERFORMANCE (IAI 201, at max T-O weight):
Never-exceed speed 215 knots (397 km/h; 247 mph)
Max level speed at 3,050 m (10,000 ft) 176 knots (326 km/h; 203 mph)
Max cruising speed at 3,050 m (10,000 ft) 172 knots (319 km/h; 198 mph)
Econ cruising speed at 3,050 m (10,000 ft) 168 knots (311 km/h; 193 mph)
Stalling speed, 0° flap 75 knots (140 km/h; 87 mph)
Stalling speed, 54° flap 62 knots (115 km/h; 71·5 mph)
Max rate of climb at S/L 393 m (1,290 ft)/min
Rate of climb at S/L, one engine out 55 m (180 ft)/min
Service ceiling 7,620 m (25,000 ft)
Service ceiling, one engine out 2,375 m (7,800 ft)
STOL T-O run 293 m (960 ft)
STOL T-O to 15 m (50 ft) 463 m (1,520 ft)
STOL landing from 15 m (50 ft) 469 m (1,540 ft)
STOL landing run 250 m (820 ft)
Range with max payload, 45 min reserves 151 nm (280 km; 174 miles)
Range with max fuel, 45 min reserves 705 nm (1,306 km; 812 miles)

PERFORMANCE (IAI 202, at max T-O weight):
Range with max payload of 2,449 kg (5,400 lb) 430 nm (797 km; 495 miles)
Range with payload of 1,587 kg (3,500 lb) 900 nm (1,668 km; 1,036 miles)
Max endurance 9 h

IAI 1124/WESTWIND I

Israeli Navy designation: 1124 Sea Scan

The IAI 1124 longer-range version of the Westwind was certificated by the FAA in the Spring of 1976. Two 1123 Westwinds (see 1976-77 *Jane's*) had been modified as flight test aircraft and the first of these made its first flight on 21 July 1975.A total of 74 had been sold by the end of 1978; at that time the production rate had been increased to three to four per month to cater for the increased demand for 1979-80 deliveries.

Aircraft from c/n 240 onwards are designated **Westwind I.** Major changes from the original 1124 are a 317 kg (700 lb) increase in fuel load, installed in a removable tank in one of the two baggage compartments; and an increase of approx 5% in cabin useful volume by relocation of some avionics and by lowering the floor in the toilet/lavatory compartment. Environmental and fuel systems have been improved, and standard avionics include an RCA Primus 400 colour radar.

Development of an advanced new version, for certification and delivery in 1982-83, was announced in mid-1979. Basic design parameters include intercontinental range, long-range cruising speed of about Mach 0·8, and economical operation.

The following maritime reconnaissance version has been announced:

1124 Sea Scan. The first operational Sea Scan was delivered in the last quarter of 1978. Several versions are available, equipped for specific operational requirements. Sea Scan is provided with external stores pylons, bubble windows, Litton APS-504(V)2 360° search radar, VLF/Omega navigation, complete VHF/UHF communications system, operators' consoles to individual customer's requirements, lavatory and refreshment centre. Additional sensor equipment for multi-mission capability can readily be accommodated, including IFF, MAD and low light level TV. Search range is 1,311 nm (2,428 km;

IAI 1124 Westwind I (two Garrett-AiResearch TFE 731-3-1G turbofan engines)

1,508 miles) at a height of 915 m (3,000 ft), covering an area of 268,056 km² (103,496 sq miles) along a 58 nm (108 km; 67 mile) search band. High-altitude search range and endurance are 2,430 nm (4,500 km; 2,795 miles) and more than 8 h respectively. Speed range is 140-440 knots (259-816 km/h; 161-507 mph).

The description which follows applies to the standard civil Westwind I in current production:

Type: Twin-turbofan business transport.

Wings: Cantilever mid-wing monoplane. Wing section NACA 64A212. Dihedral 2°. Incidence 1° at root, −1° at tip. Sweepback 4° 37′ at quarter-chord. All-metal flush-riveted two-spar fail-safe structure. Manually-operated all-metal ailerons. Electrically-operated all-metal double-slotted trailing-edge Fowler-type flaps and drooped and cambered leading-edges. Electrically-operated trim tab in port aileron. Hydraulically-actuated speed brake and two lift dumpers above each wing, forward of flap. All skins chemically milled and fully sealed. All primary control surfaces, including tabs, are fully mass-balanced. Pneumatic anti-icing boots standard.

Fuselage: All-metal semi-monocoque flush-riveted structure with pressurised fail-safe cabin and baggage compartment. Built in two main sections and joined at aft pressure bulkhead. Forward section, except for nosecone, is fully pressurised.

Tail Unit: Cantilever all-metal structure, with 28° sweep-back at quarter-chord. Variable-incidence tailplane, actuated electrically. Manually-operated statically-balanced elevators and rudder. Trim tab in rudder. Pneumatic anti-icing boots standard.

Landing Gear: Hydraulically-retractable tricycle type, main wheels retracting outward into wings, twin nose-wheels rearward. Oleo-pneumatic shock-absorbers. Single wheels on main units, pressure 10·69 bars (155 lb/sq in). Nose unit steerable and self-centering. Nose-wheel tyre pressure 3·45 bars (50 lb/sq in). Multiple-disc brakes, with fully-modulated anti-skid system having automatic computer/sensor to prevent wheel lock and maintain brake effectiveness. Parking brake fitted.

Power Plant: Two 16·46 kN (3,700 lb st) Garrett-AiResearch TFE 731-3-1G turbofan engines, with Grumman thrust reversers, mounted in pod on each side of rear fuselage. 85% of wing area forms an integral fuel tank, and additional fuel is carried separately in wingtip tanks and rear fuselage tanks. Total usable capacity 4,920 litres (1,082 Imp gallons), including wingtip tanks. Increased weight option permits additional 317 kg (700 lb) of fuel to be carried in a removable tank in one of the two baggage compartments. Single-point pressure refuelling.

Accommodation: Standard seating for two pilots and up to 10 passengers in pressurised cabin. Interior layout to customer's requirements, with galley and toilet standard. Two separate heated compartments for up to 476 kg (1,050 lb) of baggage. Passenger door at front on port side; emergency exit on each side, forward of wing. Entire accommodation heated, ventilated and air-conditioned.

Systems: Primary hydraulic system, pressure 138 bars (2,000 lb/sq in), operates through two engine-driven pumps to actuate landing gear, wheel brakes, nosewheel steering, speed brakes and lift dumpers. Electrically-operated emergency system, pressure 69 bars (1,000 lb/sq in), for brakes only. DC electrical system with two 350A 28V engine-driven starter/generators and two 37Ah long-life nickel-cadmium batteries. One main bus for each generator, connected to the central battery bus. A 400Hz 115V AC system is installed, and is powered by two solid-state static inverters, each of 1,000VA capacity, with power fed from the main DC buses. Each inverter is independently capable of supplying the entire AC load if required. Pneumatic system for anti-icing of wing and tail leading-edges only. Warm air bled from engines to prevent icing of air intakes. Windscreen is heated electrically. Garrett-AiResearch cabin environmental control system. Cabin pressure differential 0·61 bars (8·8 lb/sq in).

Avionics and Equipment: Full dual IFR instrumentation standard. Radio and other avionics include Collins NCS-31A R/Nav and control system (Global Navigation NS-500A VLF on Sea Scan), RCA Primus 40 weather radar, Collins FD-109Z flight director and AP-105 autopilot. Canadian Marconi CMA-734 Omega navigation system approved for use in US and North Atlantic airspace.

IAI 1124 Sea Scan maritime reconnaissance version of the Westwind *(Brian M. Service)*

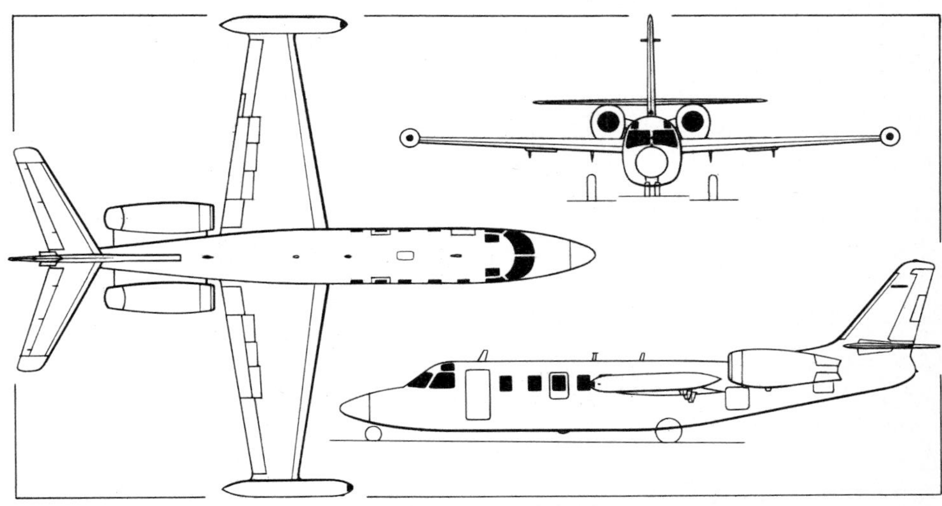

IAI 1124 Westwind twin-turbofan light executive transport *(Pilot Press)*

Dimensions, external:
- Wing span: 13·65 m (44 ft 9½ in)
- Wing chord at root: 3·20 m (10 ft 6 in)
- Wing chord at tip: 1·07 m (3 ft 6 in)
- Wing aspect ratio: 6·51
- Length overall: 15·93 m (52 ft 3 in)
- Fuselage: Max width: 1·57 m (5 ft 2 in)
  - Max depth: 1·83 m (6 ft 0 in)
- Height overall: 4·81 m (15 ft 9½ in)
- Tailplane span: 6·40 m (21 ft 0 in)
- Wheel track: 3·35 m (11 ft 0 in)
- Passenger door: Height: 1·37 m (4 ft 6 in)
  - Width: 0·61 m (2 ft 0 in)
  - Height to sill: 0·51 m (1 ft 8 in)

Dimensions, internal:
- Cabin, excl flight deck: Length: 4·72 m (15 ft 6 in)
  - Max width: 1·45 m (4 ft 9 in)
  - Max height: 1·50 m (4 ft 11 in)
  - Volume: 9·83 m³ (347 cu ft)
- Baggage compartments (3), total volume: 1·78 m³ (63 cu ft)

Areas:
- Wings, gross: 28·64 m² (308·26 sq ft)
- Ailerons (total): 1·43 m² (15·39 sq ft)
- Trailing-edge flaps (total): 3·86 m² (41·58 sq ft)
- Fin: 4·51 m² (48·60 sq ft)
- Rudder, incl tab: 0·99 m² (10·6i sq ft)
- Tailplane: 4·87 m² (52·42 sq ft)
- Elevators: 1·64 m² (17·66 sq ft)

Weights and Loadings:
- Weight empty, equipped: 5,578 kg (12,300 lb)
- Typical basic operating weight (incl two pilots and service load): 5,760 kg (12,700 lb)
- Max payload: 1,496 kg (3,300 lb) *or* 1,542 kg (3,400 lb)
- Max T-O weight: 10,364 kg (22,850 lb) *or* 10,659 kg (23,500 lb)
- Max ramp weight: 10,432 kg (23,000 lb) *or* 10,727 kg (23,650 lb)
- Max landing weight: 8,618 kg (19,000 lb)
- Max zero-fuel weight: 7,257 kg (16,000 lb) *or* 7,484 kg (16,500 lb)
- Max cabin floor loading: 976 kg/m² (200 lb/sq ft)
- Max wing loading: 361·9 kg/m² (74·13 lb/sq ft) *or* 372·2 kg/m² (76·23 lb/sq ft)
- Max power loading: 314 kg/kN (3·09 lb/lb st) *or* 324 kg/kN (3·18 lb/lb st)

Performance (at max T-O weight of 10,364 kg; 22,850 lb, except where stated):
- Max level speed, S/L to 5,900 m (19,400 ft): 471 knots (872 km/h; 542 mph)
- Max operating speed, S/L to 5,900 m (19,400 ft): 360 knots (666 km/h; 414 mph) IAS
- Max operating Mach No. from 5,900 m (19,400 ft) to 13,725 m (45,000 ft): Mach 0·765
- Econ cruising speed at 12,500 m (41,000 ft): 400 knots (741 km/h; 460 mph)
- Stalling speed, flaps and landing gear down, at max landing weight: 99 knots (183 km/h; 114 mph) CAS
- Max rate of climb at S/L: 1,524 m (5,000 ft)/min
- Max operating height: 13,725 m (45,000 ft)
- FAA T-O balanced field length: 1,495 m (4,900 ft)
- T-O balanced field length at 8,165 kg (18,000 lb) AUW: 945 m (3,100 ft)
- Landing distance from 15 m (50 ft) at max landing weight, with thrust reversal: 625 m (2,050 ft)
- Landing distance from 15 m (50 ft) at 6,350 kg (14,000 lb) AUW, with thrust reversal: 518 m (1,700 ft)
- Range with 7 passengers and baggage, IFR reserves: more than 2,150 nm (3,983 km; 2,475 miles)
- Max range with 2 passengers and baggage, 45 min reserves: more than 2,600 nm (4,815 km; 2,993 miles)
- Range with long-range fuel tank, 5 passengers and baggage, IFR reserves, at T-O weight of 10,659 kg; 23,500 lb: 2,400 nm (4,446 km; 2,763 miles)
- Range with long-range fuel tank, 2 passengers and baggage, 45 min reserves, at T-O weight of 10,659 kg; 23,500 lb: 2,900 nm (5,373 km; 3,339 miles)

Operational Noise Characteristics (FAR 36 at max T-O weight):
- T-O noise level: 84·2 EPNdB
- Approach noise level: 93·0 EPNdB
- Sideline noise level: 88·4 EPNdB

ITALY

AERITALIA

AERITALIA—SOCIETÀ AEROSPAZIALE ITALIANA p.a.

Head Office: Piazzale Vincenzo Tecchio 51 (Casella Postale 3065), 80125 Naples

Telephone: (081) 619522, 619721, 619845, 619149, 619703

Telex: N. 710370 (AERIT)

Office of the Chairman, and Branch Office (Commercial): Via Panama 52, 00198 Rome

Telephone: (06) 841441

Telex: N. 611395 (AERIT)

Honorary President: Ambassador Egidio Ortona

President and Managing Director: Ing Renato Bonifacio

Vice-President: Ing Luigi D'Agostini

General Manager: Ing Fausto Cereti

Deputy General Managers:
- Dott Franco Capanna
- Dott Michele Crosio
- Ing Mario Orlando
- Ing Giovanni Sarzotti

Board of Directors:
- Ing Fausto Cereti

Ing Giulio Ciampolini
Ing Corrado Innocenti
Ing Francesco La Via
Dott Maurizio Maspes
Dott Giorgio Massone
Dott Franco Palma
Ing Amilcare Porro
Ing Beppe Sacchi
Ing Franco Schepis

EXECUTIVE DIRECTORS:
Ing Stefano Abbà (Diversified Activities Group)
Ing Roberto Mannu (Commercial)
Dott Massimo Rizzo (General Secretary and External Relations)

PUBLIC RELATIONS AND PRESS DIRECTOR: Cesare Falessi

Aeritalia is a joint stock company which was formed on 12 November 1969 by an equal shareholding of Fiat and IRI-Finmeccanica, to combine Fiat's aerospace activities (except those which concerned aero-engines) with those of Aerfer and Salmoiraghi of the Finmeccanica group. The company became fully operational under the new title on 1 January 1972. On 28 September 1976 IRI-Finmeccanica purchased the Aeritalia stock owned by Fiat, thus acquiring complete control of the company's stock capital. Aeritalia had a total work force, in 1978, of approx 10,000.

Aeritalia's organisation is based upon a centralised general management and three operational groups: Combat Aircraft Group, Transport Aircraft Group, and the Diversified Activities Group. The production centres are located in Turin (Corso Marche, Caselle Nord and Caselle Sud), Milan (Nerviano) and Naples (Pomigliano d'Arco and Capodichino).

On 2 June 1978, Aeritalia and Aeronautica Macchi (which see) announced their intention to develop jointly new aircraft to meet the future needs of domestic and foreign markets. In August 1978 Aeritalia and Boeing of the USA signed a formal agreement under which Aeritalia is responsible for designing and manufacturing about 15% of the Boeing 767 transport aircraft, including wing control surfaces, trailing-edge flaps, leading-edge slats, wingtips, elevator, rudder and radome.

COMBAT AIRCRAFT GROUP

HEADQUARTERS AND TURIN WORKS: Corso Marche 41, 10146 Turin
Telephone: (011) 33321
Telex: N. 221076 (AERITOR)
CASELLE WORKS: Turin Airport CP, 10100 Turin
Telephone: (011) 991362
Telex: 210086

The Turin area factories are engaged in the manufacture, assembly and flight testing of the F-104S combat aircraft; in the design and construction of structural components for the Panavia Tornado (see International section); and repair, overhaul and maintenance of test equipment. Other activities include the repair, overhaul and maintenance of F-104G, F-104S and TF-104G aircraft.

TRANSPORT AIRCRAFT GROUP

HEADQUARTERS AND NAPLES AREA WORKS: 80038 Pomigliano d'Arco, Naples
Telephone: (081) 8841544
Telex: N. 710082 and 710522 (AERITPOM)
CAPODICHINO WORKS: Via del Riposo alla Doganella, Aeroporto di Capodichino, 80144 Naples
Telephone: (081) 444166
Telex: N. 710356

Aeritalia's principal activities in the Naples area comprise construction of the complete series of fuselage structural panels for the McDonnell Douglas DC-9, and fuselage upper panels and the vertical tail surfaces for the DC-10 commercial airliner; construction of engine support pylons for the Boeing 747; and manufacture, assembly and flight testing of the Aeritalia G222. Other activities include the repair, overhaul and modification of aircraft of various nations, including Italy and the United States, and the repair and maintenance of Breguet 1150 Atlantic, and G91R, G91T and G91Y aircraft.

DIVERSIFIED ACTIVITIES GROUP

HEADQUARTERS AND CASELLE WORKS: CAP 10072 Caselle-Turin
Telephone: (011) 991362
Telex: N. 210411 and 210095
AVIONICS SECTOR (CASELLE WORKS):

Since its creation within the Fiat Aircraft Division, the activities of this Sector have been extended to include research and experimentation with equipment installed in new prototypes, and the series production of electronic equipment and systems, both of original design and under licence. The Sector has also taken an important part in Italian and ESRO/NASA international space programmes. Avionics include complex electronics systems and specific equipment for aerospace applications. Design work includes both aerospace systems and new systems for other civil purposes. Activities include the manufacture, repair and overhaul of sophisticated electronics and space equipment, for both aircraft and space components of Aeritalia's own production and for the international market.

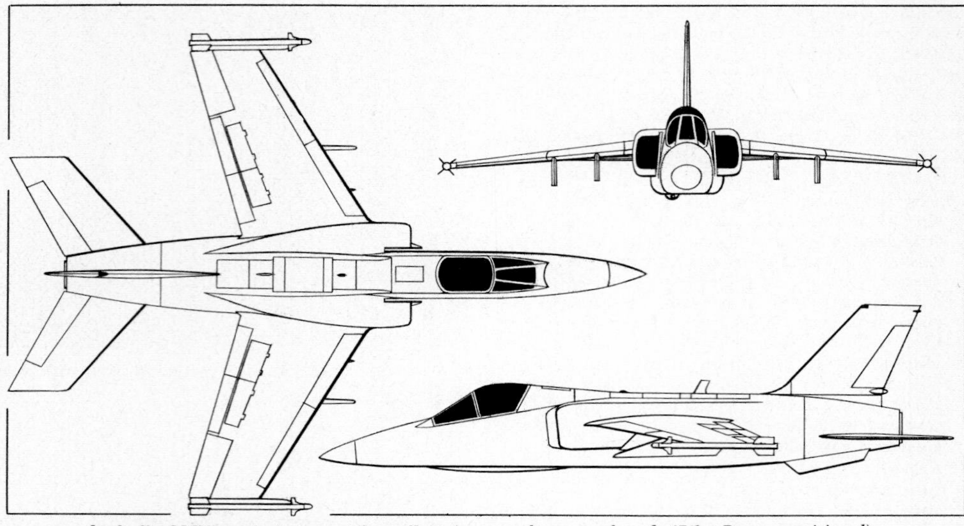

Aeritalia AMX tactical support/interdictor/reconnaissance aircraft *(Pilot Press, provisional)*

INSTRUMENTATION SECTOR:
NERVIANO WORKS: Viale Europa, 20014 Nerviano, Milan
Telephone: (0331) 587330
Telex: 330675

The Nerviano works manufactures a wide range of avionics equipment and instrumentation, including systems and instruments for aeronautical, missile and space applications.

SPACE SECTOR:
See Spaceflight section.

AERITALIA AMX

This subsonic single-seat and single-engined combat aircraft is under development to meet the requirements of the Italian Air Force. Aermacchi is an associate contractor in the programme.

In the Italian Air Force the AMX is intended to take over duties performed currently by four types of aircraft: the G91, which will be phased out of its close air support role by 1985/86; the G91Y interdictor, also due for phase-out by 1985/86; and the F-104G and F-104S versions of the Starfighter, scheduled for replacement in the strike role by 1986/87 and 1990 respectively.

The close air support and interdiction tasks could be undertaken fully by the AMX; counter-air duties would be shared with the longer-range Tornado. A total of 187 aircraft is needed to meet these re-equipment plans, with deliveries beginning ideally in 1986, to ensure initial operational capability by the Spring of 1987.

Work on the AMX project was started by Aeritalia in 1977. By early 1979 the definition phase, due to last for 18 months, had been initiated under Italian Air Force contract. Major programme milestones include a first flight scheduled to take place in late 1982. Six prototypes are expected to be built.

Basic design features include a max take-off weight of some 12,000 kg (26,455 lb), very good field performance, good gust response and high manoeuvrability rather than extreme subsonic speeds at low level. This implies use of advanced high-lift devices of a purely aerodynamic type, with valuable crossfeed from Aeritalia's current Tornado work, but not a 'swing-wing'.

Primary roles of the AMX were laid down as close interdiction over a combat radius of 180 nm (333 km; 205 miles), anti-ship operations, reconnaissance and close air support. Secondary roles are foreseen as counter-air missions, notably against enemy forward airfields, and air defence against low-level intruders. Emphasis is being placed on the ability to carry a wide variety of external weapons, on four underwing pylons, and flexibility in the avionics package; a typical combat load would comprise 1,360 kg (3,000 lb) of external ordnance, two wingtip-mounted infra-red air-to-air missiles for self-defence, one internally-mounted 20 mm rotary-barrel gun, and internal ECM equipment. The possibility of developing an advanced training version as a G91T replacement is being borne in mind.

In October 1978 the Italian Air Force officially selected as the AMX power plant a non-afterburning version of the Rolls-Royce Spey Mk 807 turbofan engine, currently rated at approx 49·1 kN (11,030 lb st). This engine is now undergoing detail definition for completion by the end of 1981.

AERITALIA G222

The G222 was originally conceived in four separate configurations, three of which were halted at the research project stage. Two prototypes were built of the military transport version, originally designated G222 TCM; the first of these (MM582) flew for the first time on 18 July 1970 and the second (MM583) on 22 July 1971. The first prototype was handed over to the Italian Air Force on 21 December 1971 for operational evaluation. One airframe was completed for static and fatigue testing.

The Italian Air Force has ordered 44 production G222s, the first of which flew on 23 December 1975. Deliveries began in late 1976, and approx 18 had been delivered by the beginning of 1979. These are in service with the 46th Brigade at Pisa, and are operated in the primary roles of troop, paratroop or cargo transport, or for aeromedical duties. The G222 can operate from semi-prepared airstrips and in all weathers.

The Argentinian Army has three G222s, and in February 1976 the Dubai government ordered one G222 (delivered in November 1976), with an option for a second.

Several major Italian airframe companies are sharing in the construction programme, including Aermacchi (outer wings); Piaggio (wing centre-section); SIAI-Marchetti (tail unit); CIRSEA (landing gear); and IAM (miscellaneous airframe components). Fuselages are built by Aeritalia's Transport Aircraft Group, in the Pomigliano d'Arco Works near Naples; final assembly, originally undertaken at Turin, was transferred to Capodichino Airport, Naples, in 1977. The first G222 produced entirely in the Naples area flew on 1 December 1977.

Design of the G222 makes it suitable for adaptation to such other roles as maritime patrol and anti-submarine warfare, and for such civil applications as firefighting, crop-spraying, aerial photogrammetry, and radio calibration. Firefighting tests with the second prototype (I-MAXB), designated **G222 SAMA** (Sistema Aeronautico Modulare Antincendio) and equipped with a dispersal system designed by Food Machinery Corporation, were completed successfully in 1976. Electronic warfare, navaid calibration and maritime surveillance versions are described separately.

To meet a reported order for 20 aircraft for the Libyan Air Force, Aeritalia is developing the **G222L** with Rolls-Royce Tyne RTy.20 turboprop engines. This version will have an operating weight empty of 18,000 kg (39,683 lb), normal max payload of 7,000 kg (15,432 lb), and max T-O weight of 28,000 kg (61,730 lb).

A projected new variant of the GE-powered aircraft is the **G222-28** with the T64-P4D engines uprated to 3,057 kW (4,100 shp), an additional 1,200 kg (2,645 lb) of centre-section fuel, accommodation for 53 troops or 42 parachute troops, and max T-O weight of 28,000 kg (61,730 lb).

The following description applies to the standard G222 military transport version currently in production, except where indicated:

TYPE: Twin-turboprop general-purpose transport aircraft.

WINGS: Cantilever high-wing monoplane, with thickness/chord ratio of 15%. Dihedral 2° 30′ on outer panels. Aluminium alloy three-spar fail-safe box structure, built in three portions. One-piece constant-chord centre-section fits into recess in top of fuselage and is secured by bolts at six main points. Outer panels tapered on leading- and trailing-edges. Upper-surface skins are of 7075-T6 alloy, lower-surface skins of 2024-T3 alloy. All control surfaces have bonded metal skins with metal honeycomb core. Double-slotted flaps extend over 60% of trailing-edge. Two-section spoilers ahead of each outboard flap segment, used also as lift dumpers on landing. Spoilers and flaps fully powered by tandem hydraulic actuators. Manually-operated ailerons, each with inset servo tab. Pneumatically-inflated de-icing boots on leading-edges, using engine bleed air.

FUSELAGE: Pressurised fail-safe structure of aluminium alloy stressed-skin construction and circular cross-section. Easily removable stiffened floor panels.

TAIL UNIT: Cantilever safe-life structure of aluminium alloy, with sweptback three-spar fin and non-swept two-spar variable-incidence tailplane. Pneumatically-inflated de-icing boots on fin and tailplane leading-edges, using engine bleed air. Rudder and elevators of metal honeycomb construction. Two tabs in each elevator; no rudder tabs. Rudder fully powered by tandem hydraulic actuators; elevators operated manually.

Landing Gear: Hydraulically-retractable tricycle type, suitable for use from prepared runways or grass fields. Messier-Hispano design, built under licence by CIRSEA (Nardi-Magnaghi). Steerable twin-wheel nose unit retracts forward. Main units, each consisting of two single wheels in tandem, retract into fairings on sides of fuselage. Oleo-pneumatic shock-absorbers. Gear can be lowered by gravity in emergency, the nose unit being aided by aerodynamic action and the main units by the shock-absorbers, which remain compressed in the retracted position. Oleo pressure in shock-absorbers is adjustable to permit variation in height and attitude of the cabin floor from the ground. Low-pressure tubeless tyres on all units, size 37·91 × 12·35 in (Type III) on main wheels, 27·56 × 10·51 in (Type III) on nosewheels. Tyre pressures 4·41 bars (64 lb/sq in) on main units, 3·92 bars (56·88 lb/sq in) on nose unit. Hydraulic multi-disc brakes. No anti-skid units.

Power Plant: Two 2,535 kW (3,400 shp) Fiat-built General Electric T64-GE-P4D turboprop engines, each driving a Hamilton Standard 63E60 three-blade variable-pitch propeller with spinner. Provision in fuselage for eight Aerojet General JATO rockets with total additional thrust of 35·3 kN (7,937 lb), for T-O with extra-heavy loads. Fuel in integral tanks: two in the outer wings, combined capacity 6,800 litres (1,495 Imp gallons), and two centre-section tanks, combined capacity 5,200 litres (1,143 Imp gallons), with cross-feed provision to either engine. Total overall fuel capacity 12,000 litres (2,638 Imp gallons). Single pressure refuelling point on starboard side of fuselage. Overwing gravity refuelling point above each tank. Electrical de-icing of spinners and propeller leading-edges. Engine intakes anti-iced by electrical/hot air system.

Accommodation: Normal crew of three (two pilots and radio operator/flight engineer) on flight deck. Provision for fourth crew member or jumpmaster when required. Standard troop transport version has 32 foldaway sidewall seats and 12 stowable seats for 44 fully-equipped troops, and carries also two 20-man life rafts stowed in the wing/fuselage fairing and a single 9-man life raft in the cargo compartment. Paratroop transport version can carry up to 32 fully-equipped paratroops, and is fitted with the 32 sidewall seats and life rafts as in the troop transport version, plus door jump platforms and static lines. Cargo transport version can accept standard pallets of up to 2·24 m (7 ft 4 in) wide, and can carry up to 9,000 kg (19,841 lb) of freight. Provision is made for 135 cargo tiedown points and a 1,500 kg (3,306 lb) capacity cargo hoist. Typical Italian military equipment loads can include two CL-52 light trucks; one CL-52 with a 105 mm L4 howitzer or one-ton trailer; Fiat AR-59 Campagnola reconnaissance vehicle with 106 mm recoilless gun or 250 kg (550 lb) trailer; or five standard A-22 freight containers. In the aeromedical role the G222 can accommodate 36 stretchers, two sitting patients and four medical attendants. A second toilet can be installed, and provision can be made to increase the water supply and to install supplementary electrical points and hooks for medical treatment bottles. In this version, the cabin oxygen system is available to all stretcher positions. Crew access door is forward of cabin on port side. Passenger doors, at front and rear of main cabin on starboard side and at rear on port side, can be used also as emergency exits. Two emergency hatches in cabin roof, forward and aft of wing carry-through structure. Hydraulically operated rear loading ramp and upward-opening door in underside of upswept rear fuselage, which can be opened in flight for air-drop operations. In cargo version, five loads of up to 1,000 kg (2,205 lb) each can be air-dropped from rear opening, or a single load of up to 5,000 kg (11,023 lb). Paratroop jumps can be made either from this opening or from the rear side doors. Windscreens and quarter-light panels are de-iced and demisted electrically. Wipers and screen wash for both windscreens. Entire accommodation pressurised and air-conditioned.

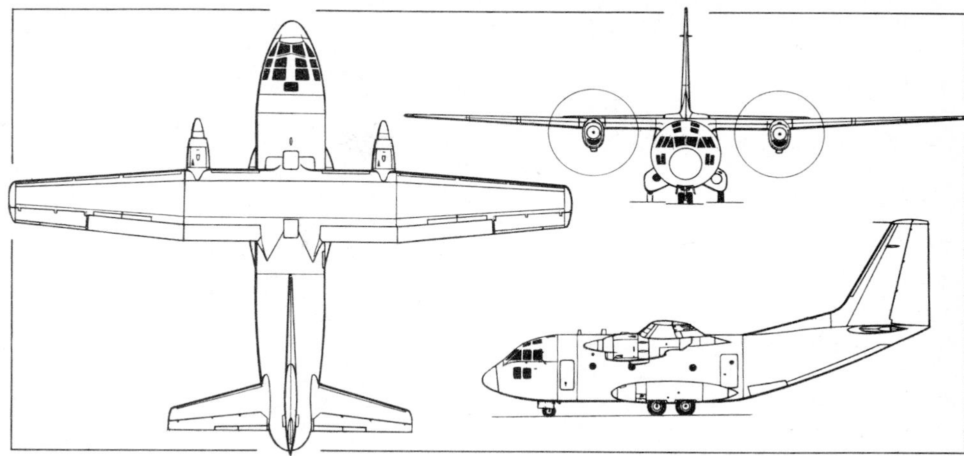

Aeritalia G222 twin-turboprop general-purpose military transport aircraft *(Pilot Press)*

Systems: Pressurisation system maintains a cabin differential of 0·41 bars (5·97 lb/sq in), giving a 1,200 m (3,940 ft) environment at altitudes up to 6,000 m (19,685 ft). Air-conditioning system uses engine bleed air during flight; on ground, it is fed by compressor bleed air from APU to provide cabin heating to a minimum of 18°C. Two independent hydraulic systems, each of 207 bars (3,000 lb/sq in) pressure. No. 1 system actuates flaps, spoilers, rudder and wheel brakes; No. 2 system actuates flaps, spoilers, rudder, wheel brakes, nosewheel steering, landing gear extension and retraction, rear ramp/door and windscreen wipers. Auxiliary hydraulic system, fed by APU-powered pump, can take over from No. 2 system in flight, if both main systems fail, to operate essential services. In addition, a standby hand pump is provided for emergency use to lower the landing gear and, on the ground, to operate the ramp/door and parking brakes. Three 45kVA alternators, one driven by each engine through constant-speed drive units and one by the APU, provide 115/200V three-phase AC electrical power at 400Hz. 28V DC power is supplied from the main AC buses via two transformer-rectifiers, with 24V 34Ah nickel-cadmium battery and static inverter for standby and emergency power. External AC power socket. Garrett-AiResearch 113·3 kW (152 hp) APU, installed in starboard main landing gear fairing, provides power for engine starting, hydraulic pump and alternator actuation, air-conditioning on ground, and all hydraulic and electrical systems necessary for loading and unloading on ground. Liquid oxygen system for crew and passengers (with cabin wall outlets); this system can be replaced by a gaseous oxygen system if required. Emergency oxygen system available for all occupants in the event of a pressurisation failure.

Avionics and Equipment: Standard communications equipment includes 3,500-channel UHF/AM, 1,630-channel emergency VHF/AM, 930-channel VHF/AM, VHF/FM, 28,000-channel HF/SSB/CW, crew intercom and PA system. Navigation equipment includes Omega dead-reckoning system, with projected-map display, Doppler radar, two-axis gyro platform, PHI and TAS computer; and an integrated ground-based system incorporating Collins autopilot, flight director, two compasses, two vertical gyros, two VOR, marker beacon, two ILS, ADF, two Tacan, and horizontal situation indicator. Other avionics include Meteo weather radar, with secondary terrain-mapping mode; radar altimeter; and IFF/ATC transponder including altitude reporting. Provision for head-up display. Landing light on nosewheel leg.

Equipment (G222 SAMA): Modular palletised firefighting pack can be installed in under two hours without any modification to the basic transport aircraft. The module consists of a 6,300 litre (1,385 Imp gallon) tank and four pressurised air containers to activate the pneumatic actuators and discharge the retardant/fertiliser through two nozzles. Length of area covered averages 300 m (985 ft).

Dimensions, external:	
Wing span	28·70 m (94 ft 2 in)
Wing chord at root	3·40 m (11 ft 1¾ in)
Wing chord at tip	1·685 m (5 ft 6¼ in)
Wing aspect ratio	9·15
Length overall	22·70 m (74 ft 5½ in)
Height overall	9·80 m (32 ft 1¾ in)
Fuselage: Max diameter	3·55 m (11 ft 7¾ in)
Tailplane span	12·40 m (40 ft 8¼ in)
Wheel track	3·668 m (12 ft 0½ in)
Wheelbase (to c/l of main units)	6·23 m (20 ft 5¼ in)
Propeller diameter	4·42 m (14 ft 6 in)
Distance between propeller centres	9·50 m (31 ft 2 in)
Rear-loading ramp/door:	
Width	2·45 m (8 ft 0½ in)
Height	2·25 m (7 ft 4½ in)
Dimensions, internal:	
Main cabin:	
Length	8·58 m (28 ft 1¾ in)
Width	2·45 m (8 ft 0½ in)
Height	2·25 m (7 ft 4½ in)
Volume	74·0 m³ (2,613 cu ft)
Areas:	
Wings, gross	82·00 m² (882·6 sq ft)
Ailerons (total)	3·65 m² (39·29 sq ft)
Trailing-edge flaps (total)	18·40 m² (198·06 sq ft)
Spoilers (total)	1·65 m² (17·76 sq ft)
Fin (incl dorsal fin)	12·19 m² (131·21 sq ft)
Rudder	7·02 m² (75·56 sq ft)
Tailplane	19·09 m² (205·48 sq ft)
Elevators (total)	4·61 m² (49·62 sq ft)
Weights and Loadings (standard transport):	
Weight empty	14,590 kg (32,165 lb)
Weight empty, equipped	15,400 kg (33,950 lb)
Operating weight empty	15,600 kg (34,392 lb)
Max payload	9,000 kg (19,841 lb)
Normal T-O weight	24,500 kg (54,013 lb)
Max T-O and landing weight	26,500 kg (58,422 lb)
Max zero-fuel weight	24,400 kg (53,792 lb)

Aeritalia G222 twin-turboprop military transport aircraft in the insignia of the Italian Air Force

Max cargo floor loading 750 kg/m² (155 lb/sq ft)
Max wing loading 323 kg/m² (66·2 lb/sq ft)
Max power loading 5·23 kg/kW (8·6 lb/shp)

WEIGHTS (G222 SAMA):
Operating weight empty 15,700 kg (34,614 lb)
SAMA equipment module 2,200 kg (4,850 lb)
Retardant 6,800 kg (14,990 lb)
Fuel 1,800 kg (3,968 lb)
Max T-O weight 26,500 kg (58,422 lb)

PERFORMANCE (standard G222 transport, at max T-O weight except where indicated):
Max level speed at 4,575 m (15,000 ft) 291 knots (540 km/h; 336 mph)
Econ cruising speed at 6,000 m (19,685 ft) 237 knots (439 km/h; 273 mph)
Air-drop speed (paratroops or cargo) 110-140 knots (204-259 km/h; 127-161 mph) IAS
Stalling speed, flaps and landing gear down 84 knots (155 km/h; 96·5 mph)
Time to 4,500 m (14,750 ft) 8 min 35 s
Max rate of climb at S/L 520 m (1,705 ft)/min
Rate of climb at S/L, one engine out 125 m (410 ft)/min
Service ceiling 7,620 m (25,000 ft)
Service ceiling, one engine out 5,000 m (16,400 ft)
T-O run 662 m (2,172 ft)
T-O to 15 m (50 ft) 1,000 m (3,280 ft)
Landing from 15 m (50 ft) 775 m (2,543 ft)
Landing run at max landing weight 545 m (1,788 ft)
Accelerate/stop distance 1,200 m (3,937 ft)
Min ground turning radius 20·80 m (68 ft 3 in)
Range with max payload, optimum cruising speed at 6,000 m (19,685 ft) 378 nm (700 km; 435 miles)
Range with 44 troops 1,198 nm (2,220 km; 1,380 miles)
Range with 36 stretchers and 4 medical attendants 1,349 nm (2,500 km; 1,553 miles)
Ferry range with max fuel 2,670 nm (4,950 km; 3,075 miles)
g limit +2·5

PERFORMANCE (G222L, estimated, at max T-O weight):
Range in still air, ISA, 10% reserves:
with max cargo 716 nm (1,326 km; 824 miles)
with 53 troops 922 nm (1,707 km; 1,061 miles)

PERFORMANCE (G222 SAMA at max T-O weight): As standard transport except:
Max cruising speed 250 knots (463 km/h; 287 mph)
Drop speed (T-O configuration) 120 knots (222 km/h; 138 mph)
Optimum height above ground during drop 50-100 m (165-330 ft)
Range with max retardant load 172 nm (320 km: 200 miles)

AERITALIA G222 (ELECTRONIC WARFARE, NAVAID CALIBRATION AND MARITIME SURVEILLANCE VERSIONS)

Aeritalia is developing an electronic warfare version of the G222 and a flight inspection (radio/radar calibration) version, and has proposed a maritime patrol, search and rescue version. Dimensions, weights and performance of all three are similar to those of the standard troop transport.

Carrying a pilot, co-pilot and up to 10 systems operators, the electronic warfare version has a modified cabin fitted with racks and consoles for detection, signal processing and data recording equipment, and an electrical system providing up to 40kW of power for its operation. Externally, it is distinguishable by a small 'thimble' radome beneath the nose and a larger 'doughnut' radome on top of the tail-fin. A prototype, designated **G222VS,** was flown for the first time on 9 March 1978.

The flight inspection version is externally similar to the standard troop transport. Known as the **G222RM,** it is equipped for flights below 3,050 m (10,000 ft) to calibrate airport flight paths and radio assistance, enabling it to check VOR, ILS, DME, Tacan, PAR, NDB, marker beacon receivers, and air traffic control systems, in addition to VHF and UHF radio transmissions. Onboard equipment includes separate receivers and displays, a central computer to collect inertial navigation data (updated continually by DME), and data on the state of the radio aid(s) being calibrated. Only one equipment operator is necessary, in addition to the two-man flight crew, and ample space remains in the rear of the hold to carry a Jeep-type vehicle for ground-based operations. This version has an optional secondary capability to perform survey missions, at altitudes between 6,100 and 7,620 m (20,000 and 25,000 ft), for multiple control of flight path assistance, using SAFI screened flight path equipment.

AERITALIA (LOCKHEED) F-104S

The first of two Lockheed-built F-104S prototypes flew during December 1966. Aeritalia is building 205 under licence for the Italian Air Force, the first of which was flown on 30 December 1968. Deliveries began in the Spring of 1969, and the 200th F-104S was flown in May 1976. These aircraft are in service with the 4°, 5°, 6°, 9°, 36°, 51° and 53° Wings of the Italian Air Force. Forty were delivered to the Turkish Air Force between December 1974 and mid-1976. Production for the Italian Air Force was continuing in early 1979.

Prototype of the Aeritalia G222VS electronic warfare aircraft

A programme to modernise the R21G radar system of the F-104S was announced in the Spring of 1974. The improved R21G/H installation, built under licence by CGE-Fiar in Italy, incorporates a moving-target indication and tracking capability based upon a Rockwell Missile Systems Division moving-target detection processor. CGE-Fiar has itself developed an improved antenna and a number of ECCM (electronic counter-countermeasures).

Details of Lockheed production of earlier models of the F-104 Starfighter can be found in the 1972-73 and earlier editions of *Jane's*. The following description applies to the Aeritalia-built F-104S:

TYPE: Single-seat multi-purpose combat aircraft.

WINGS: Cantilever mid-wing monoplane. Bi-convex supersonic wing section with a thickness/chord ratio of 3·36%. Anhedral 10°. No incidence. Sweepback 18° 6′ at quarter-chord. All-metal structure with two main spars and top and bottom one-piece skin panels. Each half-wing is a separate structure cantilevered from five forged frames in fuselage. Full-span electrically-actuated drooping leading-edge. Entire trailing-edge hinged, with inboard sections serving as landing flaps and outboard sections as ailerons. Ailerons are of aluminium, each powered by a servo control system which is irreversible and hydraulically powered, and each actuated by ten small hydraulic cylinders. Trim control is applied to position the aileron relative to the servo control position. An electric actuator positions the aileron trim. Flaps are of aluminium, actuated electrically. Above each flap is the air delivery tube of a boundary layer control system, which ejects air bled from the engine compressor over the entire flap span when the flaps are lowered to the landing position.

FUSELAGE: All-metal monocoque structure. Hydraulically-operated aluminium airbrake on each side of rear fuselage.

TAIL UNIT: T-type cantilever unit with 'all-flying' one-piece horizontal tail surface hinged at mid-chord point at top of the vertical fin and powered by a hydraulic servo. Tailplane has similar profile to wing and is all-metal. Rudder is fully powered by a hydraulic servo. Trim control is applied to position the tailplane relative to the servo control position, by means of an electric actuator. Rudder trim is operated by an electric actuator located in the fin. The rudder itself is trimmed in the same way as the tailplane. Narrow-chord ventral fin on centreline and two smaller lateral fins under fuselage to improve stability.

LANDING GEAR: Retractable tricycle type with Dowty patent liquid-spring shock-absorbers on main units, oleo-pneumatic shock-absorbers on nose unit. Hydraulic actuation. Main wheels raised in and forward. Steerable nosewheel retracts forward into fuselage. Main-wheel legs are hinged on oblique axes so that the wheels lie flush within the fuselage when retracted. Main wheels size 26 × 8·0, with Goodrich tyres size 26 × 8·0 type VIII (18-ply rating), pressure 11·93 bars (173 lb/sq in). Nosewheel tyre size 18 × 5·5 type VII (14-ply rating). Bendix hydraulic disc brakes with Goodyear anti-skid units. Arrester hook under rear of fuselage. Braking parachute in rear fuselage.

POWER PLANT: One General Electric J79-GE-19 turbojet engine, rated at 52·8 kN (11,870 lb st) dry and 79·62 kN (17,900 lb st) with afterburning. Electrical de-icing elements fitted to air intakes. Most of the aircraft's hydraulic equipment mounted inside large engine bay door under fuselage to facilitate servicing. Internal fuel in five bag-type fuselage tanks with total standard capacity of 3,392 litres (896 US gallons). Provision for external fuel in two 740 litre (195 US gallon) pylon tanks and two 645 litre (170 US gallon) wingtip tanks. Pressure refuelling of all internal and external tanks through single point on upper port fuselage just forward of air intake duct. Gravity fuelling point for internal tanks aft of pressure refuelling point, with individual gravity fuelling of external tanks. In-flight refuelling can be provided through Lockheed-designed probe-drogue system. Probe, mounted below port sill of cockpit, is removable but when installed is non-retractable. Oil capacity 15 litres (4 US gallons).

ACCOMMODATION: Pressurised and air-conditioned cockpit well forward of wings. Canopy hinged to starboard for access. Martin-Baker IQ-7A zero-zero ejection seat.

SYSTEMS: Air-conditioning package by AiResearch, using engine bleed air. Pressure differential 0·34 bars (5 lb/sq in). Two completely separate hydraulic systems, using engine-driven pumps operating at 207 bars (3,000 lb/sq in). No. 1 system operates one side of tailplane, rudder and ailerons, also the automatic pitch control actuator and autopilot actuators. No. 2 system operates other half of tailplane, rudder and ailerons, also the landing gear, wheel brakes, airbrakes, nosewheel steering and constant-frequency electrical generator. Emergency ram-air turbine supplies emergency hydraulic pump and 4·5kVA 115/200V electric generator. Electrical system supplied by two engine-driven 20kVA 115/200V variable-frequency (320-520Hz) generators. Constant-speed hydraulic motor drives 2·5kVA 115/200V generator to supply fixed-frequency AC. 28V DC power supplied by two nickel-cadmium batteries and a 120A transformer-rectifier.

AVIONICS AND EQUIPMENT: Integrated avionics system in which various communications and navigation components may be installed as a series of interconnecting but

Aeritalia-built Lockheed F-104S combat aircraft in the insignia of the Italian Air Force

self-sustaining units which may be varied to provide for different specific missions. Equipment includes autopilot with 'stick steering', which includes modes for pre-selecting and holding altitude, speed, heading and constant rate of turn; multi-purpose R21G/H radar for air-to-air interception, ground and contour mapping, and terrain avoidance modes of operation; fixed-reticle gunsight; bombing computer; air data computer; dead reckoning navigation device; Tacan radio air navigation system; provision for data link-time division set and AN/ARC-552 UHF radio; Litton LN-3-2A lightweight fully-automatic inertial navigation system; Sperry C-2G compass system; AN/APN-198 radar altimeter; AIC-18 intercom; and AN/APX-46 IFF/SIF. Provision for fitting a camera pod under the fuselage for reconnaissance duties.

ARMAMENT: Nine external attachment points, at wingtips, under wings and under fuselage, for bombs, rocket pods, auxiliary fuel tanks and air-to-air missiles. Normal primary armament consists of two Raytheon AIM-7 Sparrow air-to-air missiles under wings and/or two Sidewinders under fuselage and either a Sidewinder or 645 litre (170 US gallon) fuel tank on each wingtip. Alternatively, an M-61 20 mm multi-barrel rotary cannon can be fitted in the port underside of the fuselage instead of the AIM-7 missile control package. Max external weapon load 3,402 kg (7,500 lb).

DIMENSIONS, EXTERNAL:
- Wing span without tip-tanks 6·68 m (21 ft 11 in)
- Wing chord (mean) 2·91 m (9 ft 6·6 in)
- Wing aspect ratio 2·45
- Length overall 16·69 m (54 ft 9 in)
- Length of fuselage 15·62 m (51 ft 3 in)
- Height overall 4·11 m (13 ft 6 in)
- Tailplane span 3·63 m (11 ft 11 in)
- Wheel track 2·74 m (9 ft 0 in)
- Wheelbase 4·59 m (15 ft 0½ in)

AREAS:
- Wings, gross 18·22 m² (196·1 sq ft)
- Ailerons (total) 0·85 m² (9·2 sq ft)
- Trailing-edge flaps (total) 2·11 m² (22·7 sq ft)
- Leading-edge flaps (total) 1·51 m² (16·2 sq ft)
- Airbrakes (total) 0·77 m² (8·25 sq ft)
- Fin 3·50 m² (37·7 sq ft)
- Ventral fin (centreline) 0·47 m² (5·1 sq ft)
- Rear fuselage strakes (total) 0·71 m² (7·6 sq ft)
- Rudder, incl tab 0·51 m² (5·5 sq ft)
- Tailplane 4·48 m² (48·2 sq ft)

WEIGHTS AND LOADING:
- Weight empty 6,760 kg (14,900 lb)
- Max internal fuel load 2,641 kg (5,824 lb)
- Max internal and external fuel load 5,153 kg (11,362 lb)
- T-O weight ('clean') 9,840 kg (21,690 lb)
- Max T-O weight 14,060 kg (31,000 lb)
- Max zero-fuel weight ('clean') 6,806 kg (15,006 lb)
- Max zero-fuel weight (fighter-bomber) 7,148 kg (15,760 lb)
- Max wing loading 772 kg/m² (158 lb/sq ft)
- Max power loading, with afterburning 176·6 kg/kN (1·73 lb/lb st)

PERFORMANCE (at 9,840 kg; 21,690 lb AUW except where indicated):
- Never-exceed speed Mach 2·2
- Max level speed at 11,000 m (36,000 ft) Mach 2·2 (1,259 knots; 2,330 km/h; 1,450 mph)
- Max level speed at S/L Mach 1·2 (790 knots; 1,464 km/h; 910 mph)
- Max cruising speed at 11,000 m (36,000 ft) 530 knots (981 km/h; 610 mph)
- Econ cruising speed Mach 0·85
- T-O speed at S/L, interceptor with two AIM-7 missiles 189 knots (350 km/h; 217 mph)
- Typical landing speed at S/L 159 knots (295 km/h; 183 mph)
- Max rate of climb at S/L 16,765 m (55,000 ft)/min
- Service ceiling 17,680 m (58,000 ft)
- Zoom altitude more than 27,400 m (90,000 ft)
- Time to accelerate from Mach 0·92 to Mach 2·0 2 min
- Time to climb to 10,670 m (35,000 ft) 1 min 20 s
- Time to climb to 17,070 m (56,000 ft) 2 min 40 s
- T-O run at S/L, interceptor with two AIM-7 missiles 823 m (2,700 ft)
- Typical landing run at S/L 762 m (2,500 ft)
- Radius with max fuel 673 nm (1,247 km; 775 miles)
- Ferry range (excl flight refuelling) 1,576 nm (2,920 km; 1,815 miles)

AERMACCHI
AERONAUTICA MACCHI SpA

HEAD OFFICE: Corso Vittorio Emanuele 15, 20122 Milan
OFFICES AND WORKS: Via Silvestro Sanvito 80, Casella Postale 246, 21100 Varese
Telephone: (0332) 283100
Telex: 38070 Aviomacc
PRESIDENT: Dott Ing Paolo Foresio
VICE-PRESIDENT AND MANAGING DIRECTOR: Gen Ing Mario Matacotta
VICE-PRESIDENT AND GENERAL MANAGER: Dott Fabrizio Foresio
GENERAL MANAGER: Dott Ing Ermanno Bazzocchi
TECHNICAL DIRECTOR: Dott Ing Alberto Notari
SALES MANAGER: Dott Ing Gianni Cattaneo
PRESS AND PUBLIC RELATIONS: Andrea Artoni

The Macchi company was founded in 1912 in Varese and its first aeroplane was built in 1913. In addition to its former factory area of 36,900 m² (397,200 sq ft), a new plant has been built at Venegono airfield, with a covered area of about 20,000 m² (215,280 sq ft).

Lockheed Aircraft International acquired a substantial minority interest in Aermacchi in December 1959, and Aermacchi subsequently built the Lockheed 60 light utility transport as the Aermacchi-Lockheed AL.60 (see 1972-73 *Jane's*). In association with Aeritalia, Aermacchi also built the AM.3C military AOP and liaison monoplane.

In current production are various single- and two-seat versions of Aermacchi's own design, the M.B. 326. The M.B. 339 two-seat trainer is in series production for the Italian Air Force.

On 2 June 1978, Aermacchi and Aeritalia (which see) announced their intention to develop jointly new aircraft to meet the future needs of domestic and foreign markets.

AERMACCHI M.B. 326

The first prototype of the original Aermacchi M.B. 326 jet trainer flew for the first time on 10 December 1957, powered by a Rolls-Royce Viper 8 turbojet engine. The more powerful Viper 11 engine powers six production versions of the aircraft built for the air forces of Italy (M.B. 326 and 326E), Tunisia (M.B. 326B), Ghana (M.B. 326F), Australia (M.B. 326H) and South Africa (M.B. 326M), and one version built for Alitalia (M.B. 326D).

The initial South African Air Force version, built by Atlas (which see), was the Impala Mk 1; an improved version, the Impala Mk 2, is currently in production.

Other versions with more powerful Viper engines, armament changes and other modifications are as follows:

M.B. 326E. Two-seat advanced trainer and weapons trainer: 12 built (including six conversions) for the Italian Air Force's Scuola di Volo Basico Iniziale at Lecce. Viper 11 engine (11·12 kN; 2,500 lb st), plus strengthened wings and six underwing hardpoints of the M.B. 326GB. New avionics and equipment include UHF radio, miniaturised Tacan, gyroscopic weapons sight and gun camera. Further details in 1978-79 *Jane's*.

M.B. 326GB. Two-seat dual-control advanced training and attack version, with airframe modifications and Viper 20 Mk 540 engine. M.B. 326G prototype flew for first time in Spring 1967; similar M.B. 326GB is production version. Customers include Argentinian Navy (8), air forces of Zaïre (17) and Zambia (20). In addition, 167 similar **M.B.326GCs** are being assembled in Brazil under licence by EMBRAER (which see) for the Brazilian Air Force, as the **AT-26 Xavante**, and for the air force of Togo (three). Currently in production only in Brazil.

Aermacchi M.B. 326KT single-seat training and attack aircraft built for Tunisia

M.B. 326K. Single-seat operational trainer and light ground attack version. Retains most of structure and systems of M.B. 326GB, but has more powerful Viper 632 engine, no second cockpit, additional fuselage fuel tanks, increased weapon-carrying capacity. Prototype with Viper 540 engine first flown 22 August 1970; second prototype, with Viper 632, first flew 1971. Delivered to Dubai Defence Force (nine), Ghana Air Force (six), South African Air Force (four reported), Tunisian Air Force (eight) and Zaïre Air Force (eight). In South Africa, Atlas Impala Mk 2 (which see) is a Viper 540 powered version based on the M.B. 326K.

M.B. 326L. Two-seat advanced trainer, combining airframe of single-seat M.B. 326K with standard two-seat dual control cockpit installation. One delivered to Dubai and four to Tunisian Air Force.

A full description of these later models of the M.B. 326 can be found in the 1978-79 *Jane's*. The principal characteristics are as follows:

TYPE: Two-seat basic and advanced trainer (GB, GC and L) or single-seat operational trainer (K); all versions have light ground attack capability.

POWER PLANT (GB): One Rolls-Royce Viper 20 Mk 540 turbojet engine, rated at 15·17 kN (3,410 lb st). Fuel in flexible rubber main tank in fuselage, capacity 782 litres (172 Imp gallons), and two 305 litre (67 Imp gallon) non-jettisonable wingtip tanks. Total standard fuel capacity 1,392 litres (306 Imp gallons). Provision for two 332 litre (73 Imp gallon) jettisonable underwing tanks, to give total capacity of 2,056 litres (452 Imp gallons). Single-point pressure refuelling receptacle under fuselage. Fuel dump valves permit quick emptying of tip-tanks.

POWER PLANT (K and L): One Rolls-Royce Viper Mk 632-43 turbojet engine, rated at 18·79 kN (4,000 lb st). M.B. 326L fuel capacity same as for GB. Fuel in M.B. 326K contained in three rubber fuselage tanks and two permanent wingtip tanks, total usable capacity 1,660 litres (366 Imp gallons). Provision to install self-sealing fuselage tanks and reticulated foam anti-explosive

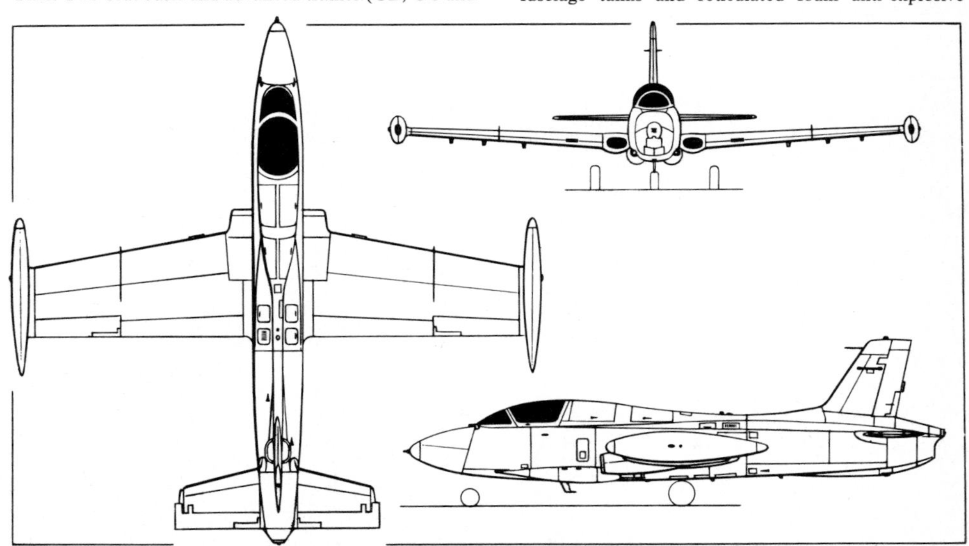

Aermacchi M.B. 326K single-seat training and light ground attack aircraft *(Pilot Press)*

filling in all tanks, including those at wingtips. Two underwing stations equipped normally to carry jettisonable auxiliary tanks of up to 340 litres (75 Imp gallons) each. Single-point pressure refuelling receptacle and auxiliary gravity refuelling points.

ACCOMMODATION (GB and L): Crew of two in tandem under a one-piece moulded Perspex canopy which hinges sideways to starboard. Pressurised cockpit, differential 0·21 bars (3·0 lb/sq in) in GB, 0·24 bars (3·5 lb/sq in) in L. Dual controls and instruments. Blind-flying screens for pupil. Martin-Baker Mk 04A lightweight ejection seats in GB; Mk 06A zero-zero seats in L.

ACCOMMODATION (K): Pilot only, on Martin-Baker Mk 6 zero-zero rocket ejection seat in pressurised and air-conditioned cockpit (differential 0·24 bars; 3·5 lb/sq in). Separately-controlled canopy jettison system provided, but seat is fitted with breakers to permit ejection through canopy in extreme emergency. Canopy hinges sideways to starboard. Provision for armour protection for pilot and other vital areas.

ARMAMENT (GB and L): Provision for up to 1,814 kg (4,000 lb) of armament on six underwing attachments. Typical weapon loads include following alternatives: two LAU-3/A packs each containing nineteen 2·75 in FFAR rockets and two packs each containing eight Hispano-Suiza SURA 80 mm rockets; two 12·7 mm gun pods and four packs each containing six SURA 80 mm rockets; one 7·62 mm Minigun, one 12·7 mm gun pod, two Matra 122 rocket packs and two packs each containing six SURA 80 mm rockets; two 500 lb bombs and eight 5 in HVAR rockets; two AS.12 missiles; one 12·7 mm gun pod, one reconnaissance pack containing four Vinten cameras and two 272 kg (600 lb) drop-tanks, or two Matra SA-10 packs each containing a 30 mm Aden gun and 150 rounds. SFOM type 83 fixed gunsight or Ferranti LFS 5/102A gyro-sight. Gun camera in nose.

ARMAMENT (K): Standard fixed armament of two 30 mm DEFA electrically-operated cannon in lower front fuselage, with 125 rds/gun. Six underwing pylons, the inboard four stressed to carry up to 454 kg (1,000 lb) each and the outboard pair up to 340 kg (750 lb) each. Max external military load (with reduced fuel) is 1,814 kg (4,000 lb). Each pylon fitted with standard NATO 355 mm (14 in) MA-4A stores rack. Typical loads may include two 750 lb and four 500 lb bombs, four napalm containers, two AS.11 or AS.12 air-to-surface missiles, two machine-gun pods, two Matra 550 air-to-air missiles, six SUU-11A/A 7·62 mm Minigun pods, and various Matra or other launchers for 37 mm, 68 mm, 100 mm, 2·75 in or 5 in rockets. A four-camera tactical reconnaissance pod can be carried on the port inner pylon without affecting the weapon capability of the other five stations.

DIMENSIONS, EXTERNAL:
- Wing span over tip-tanks:
  - GB — 10·854 m (35 ft 7¼ in)
  - K — 10·850 m (35 ft 7 in)
- Wing area, gross — 19·30 m² (207·7 sq ft)
- Wing aspect ratio — 6·08
- Length overall — 10·673 m (35 ft 0¼ in)
- Height overall — 3·72 m (12 ft 2 in)
- Wheel track — 2·485 m (8 ft 2 in)
- Wheelbase — 4·157 m (13 ft 7½ in)

WEIGHTS AND LOADINGS (M.B. 326GB. A: Trainer; B: Attack):
- Basic operating weight, excl crew:
  - A — 2,685 kg (5,920 lb)
  - *B — 2,558 kg (5,640 lb)
- Max zero-fuel weight:
  - A — 2,849 kg (6,280 lb)
  - *B — 2,640 kg (5,820 lb)
- Max T-O weight (full internal fuel, wingtip and underwing tanks):
  - A — 4,577 kg (10,090 lb)
  - B, no armament — 4,447 kg (9,805 lb)
  - B, with 769 kg (1,695 lb) armament — 5,216 kg (11,500 lb)
- Max T-O weight (max armament):
  - *B, with fuel in fuselage tank only and 1,962 kg (4,325 lb) armament — 5,216 kg (11,500 lb)
- Max wing loading — 269·5 kg/m² (55·2 lb/sq ft)
- Max power loading — 343·8 kg/kN (3·37 lb/lb st)

* *Without tip-tanks and aft ejection seat*

WEIGHTS AND LOADINGS (M.B. 326K):
- Weight empty, equipped — 3,123 kg (6,885 lb)
- T-O weight ('clean') — 4,645 kg (10,240 lb)
- Typical operational T-O weights:
  - patrol and visual reconnaissance — 5,048 kg (11,130 lb)
  - photographic reconnaissance — 5,111 kg (11,270 lb)
- Max T-O weight — 5,897 kg (13,000 lb)
- Max landing weight — 5,443 kg (12,000 lb)
- Normal design landing weight — 4,535 kg (10,000 lb)
- Max wing loading — 305 kg/m² (62·4 lb/sq ft)
- Max power loading — 313·8 kg/kN (3·25 lb/lb st)

WEIGHTS AND LOADINGS (M.B. 326L):
See 1978-79 *Jane's*

PERFORMANCE (M.B. 326GB. A: Trainer at typical weight of 3,937 kg (8,680 lb), representing max T-O weight without underwing tanks; B: Attack version at combat weight of 4,763 kg (10,500 lb); C: Attack version at max T-O weight):
- Never-exceed speed:
  - A Mach 0·82 (469 knots; 871 km/h; 541 mph EAS)
  - B Mach 0·75 (419 knots; 778 km/h; 483 mph EAS)
- Max level speed:
  - A — 468 knots (867 km/h; 539 mph)
- Max cruising speed:
  - A — 430 knots (797 km/h; 495 mph)
- Max rate of climb at S/L:
  - A — 1,844 m (6,050 ft)/min
  - B — 1,082 m (3,550 ft)/min
  - C — 945 m (3,100 ft)/min
- Time to 3,050 m (10,000 ft): B — 3 min 10 s
  - C — 4 min 0 s
- Time to 6,100 m (20,000 ft): A — 4 min 10 s
  - B — 8 min 0 s
  - C — 9 min 20 s
- Time to 9,150 m (30,000 ft): A — 7 min 40 s
  - B — 15 min 0 s
  - C — 18 min 40 s
- Time to 12,200 m (40,000 ft): A — 13 min 5 s
- Service ceiling: A — 14,325 m (47,000 ft)
  - B — 11,900 m (39,000 ft)
- T-O run, ISA: A — 412 m (1,350 ft)
  - B — 640 m (2,100 ft)
  - C — 845 m (2,770 ft)
- T-O to 15 m (50 ft), ISA: A — 555 m (1,820 ft)
  - B — 866 m (2,840 ft)
  - C — 1,140 m (3,740 ft)
- Landing from 15 m (50 ft), ISA:
  - A at landing weight of 3,175 kg (7,000 lb) — 631 m (2,070 ft)
  - B at landing weight of 4,195 kg (9,250 lb) — 802 m (2,630 ft)
- Range (A, with 113 litres; 25 Imp gallons reserve):
  - fuselage and tip-tanks — 998 nm (1,850 km; 1,150 miles)
  - fuselage, tip and underwing tanks — 1,320 nm (2,445 km; 1,520 miles)
- Combat radius (C):
  - max fuel, 769 kg (1,695 lb) armament, 90 kg (200 lb) fuel reserve, out at 6,100 m (20,000 ft), return at 7,620 m (25,000 ft) — 350 nm (648 km; 403 miles)
  - fuselage tank only, 1,814 kg (4,000 lb) armament, 90 kg (200 lb) fuel reserve, cruise at 3,050 m (10,000 ft), five minutes over target — 69 nm (130 km; 80 miles)
  - max fuel, 771 kg (1,700 lb) armament, 90 kg (200 lb) fuel reserve, cruise at 3,050 m (10,000 ft), 1 h 50 min patrol at 150 m (500 ft) over target — 49·5 nm (92 km; 57 miles)

PERFORMANCE (M.B. 326K. A: aircraft 'clean', at AUW of 4,390 kg; 9,680 lb; B: armed aircraft at 5,443 kg; 12,000 lb AUW):
- Max design limit speed at S/L — 500 knots (927 km/h; 576 mph) EAS
- Max limiting Mach number — 0·82
- Max level speed at 1,525 m (5,000 ft):
  - A — 480 knots (890 km/h; 553 mph)
- Max level speed at 9,150 m (30,000 ft):
  - B — 370 knots (686 km/h; 426 mph)
- Stalling speed, flaps up:
  - A — 102 knots (190 km/h; 118 mph) CAS
  - B — 113 knots (211 km/h; 131 mph) CAS
- Stalling speed, flaps down:
  - A — 91 knots (169 km/h; 105 mph) CAS
  - B — 102 knots (190 km/h; 118 mph) CAS
- Max rate of climb at S/L:
  - A — 1,980 m (6,500 ft)/min
  - B — 1,143 m (3,750 ft)/min
- Time to 10,670 m (35,000 ft):
  - A — 9 min 30 s
  - B — 23 min 0 s
- Runway LCN at max T-O weight — 5
- T-O run, ISA:
  - A — 411 m (1,350 ft)
  - B — 670 m (2,200 ft)
- T-O run, ISA + 20°C:
  - A — 518 m (1,700 ft)
  - B — 815 m (2,675 ft)
- T-O to 15 m (50 ft), ISA:
  - A — 572 m (1,875 ft)
  - B — 914 m (3,000 ft)
- T-O to 15 m (50 ft), ISA + 20°C:
  - A — 709 m (2,325 ft)
  - B — 1,158 m (3,800 ft)
- Typical combat radius:
  - B (internal fuel and 1,280 kg; 2,822 lb external weapons), lo-lo-lo — 145 nm (268 km; 167 miles)
  - B (reduced fuel and 1,814 kg; 4,000 lb external weapons), lo-lo-lo — 70 nm (130 km; 81 miles)
  - visual reconnaissance with two external fuel tanks — 400 nm (740 km; 460 miles)
  - photo reconnaissance with two auxiliary tanks and camera pod, hi-lo-hi — 560 nm (1,036 km; 644 miles)
- Max ferry range (two underwing tanks) — more than 1,149 nm (2,130 km; 1,323 miles)
- *g* limits — +7·33; −3·5

PERFORMANCE (M.B. 326L):
See 1978-79 *Jane's*

AERMACCHI M.B. 339A

The M.B. 339 tandem two-seat trainer/ground attack aircraft is based essentially upon the airframe and Viper 632 power plant of the M.B. 326K (which see), but has a reshaped forward fuselage, an improved two-seat cockpit, uprated avionics and equipment, and other detail changes.

The first of two M.B. 339X flying prototypes (I-NOVE) was flown for the first time on 12 August 1976. The second aircraft (I-NINE), which made its first flight on 20 May 1977, was built to pre-production standard; the third airframe was used for static and fatigue testing. They are being followed by 100 production M.B.339As for the Italian Air Force, of which the first 15 were ordered in FY 1978 and the next 40 in FY 1979; the final 45 are to be ordered in FY 1980. The first production aircraft (I-NEUF) flew for the first time on 20 July 1978, and deliveries to the Italian Air Force began in Summer 1979.

TYPE: Two-seat basic and advanced trainer and ground attack aircraft.

AIRFRAME: Structural design criteria based on MIL-A-008860A; 8*g* limit load factor in 'clean' configuration. Cockpit designed for 40,000 pressurisation cycles. Service life requirement 10,000 flying hours and 20,000 landings in the training role. Entire structure specially treated to prevent corrosion.

WINGS: Cantilever low/mid-wing monoplane. Wing section NACA 64A-114 (mod) at c/l, NACA 64A-212 (mod) at tip. Leading-edge swept back 11° 18′. Sweepback at quarter-chord 8° 29′. All-metal stressed-skin structure, with single main spar and auxiliary rear spar, built in two portions and bolted to fuselage. Skin stiffened by spanwise stringers, closely spaced ribs and false ribs. Wingtip tanks permanently attached. Single fence on each wing at approx two-thirds span. Servo-powered ailerons embody 'Irving'-type aerodynamic balance provisions, and are statically balanced along their entire span. Electrically-actuated balance tabs facilitate reversion to manual operation in the event of servo failure. Hydraulically-actuated single-slotted flaps, operated by push/pull rods.

FUSELAGE: All-metal semi-monocoque structure, built in two main portions: forward (nose to engine mounting bulkhead) and rear (engine bulkhead to tailcone). Forward portion built of C-section frames, four C-section spars, longitudinal L-section stringers, and skin panels. Rear section fabricated entirely from aluminium alloy except for firewall and most of tailcone, which are of stainless steel; four-bolt attachment to forward fuselage to facilitate access to engine. Hydraulically actuated,

First production Aermacchi M.B. 339A for the Italian Air Force (Rolls-Royce Viper Mk 632-43 turbojet engine)

electrically controlled airbrake under centre of fuselage, just forward of CG.

TAIL UNIT: Cantilever all-metal structure, of similar construction to wings. Slightly sweptback vertical surfaces. Rudder and elevators are statically balanced, each having an electrically-actuated balance and trim tab. Two auxiliary fins under rear fuselage.

LANDING GEAR: Hydraulically-retractable tricycle type, with oleo-pneumatic shock-absorbers; suitable for operation from semi-prepared runways. Nosewheel retracts forward, main units outward into wings. Steerable nosewheel, fitted with shimmy damper. Low-pressure main-wheel tubeless tyres size 545 × 175-10 (12 ply rating); nosewheel tubeless tyre size 380 × 150-4 (6 ply rating). Emergency extension system. Hydraulic disc brakes with anti-skid system.

POWER PLANT: One Rolls-Royce Viper Mk 632-43 turbojet engine, rated at 17·8 kN (4,000 lb st). Engines built in Italy under Rolls-Royce/Fiat licence; final assembly by Piaggio. Fuel in two-cell rubber fuselage tank, capacity 781 litres (172 Imp gallons), and two integral wingtip tanks, combined capacity 632 litres (139 Imp gallons). Total internal capacity 1,413 litres (311 Imp gallons) usable. Single-point pressure refuelling receptacle in port side of fuselage, below wing trailing-edge. Gravity refuelling points on top of fuselage and each tip-tank. Provision for two drop-tanks, each of 325 litres (71·5 Imp gallons) capacity, on centre underwing stations. Anti-icing system for engine air intakes optional.

ACCOMMODATION: Crew of two in tandem, on Martin-Baker Mk IT-10F zero-zero ejection seats in pressurised cockpit. Rear seat elevated 32·5 cm (12¾ in). Rearview mirror for each occupant. Two-piece moulded transparent jettisonable canopy, opening sideways to starboard.

SYSTEMS: Hydraulic system, pressure 176 bars (2,600 lb/sq in), for actuation of flaps, aileron servos, airbrake, landing gear, wheel brakes and nosewheel steering. Backup system for wheel brakes and emergency extension of landing gear. Main electrical DC power from one 28V 9kW engine-driven starter/generator and one 28V 6kW secondary generator. Two 24V 22Ah nickel-cadmium batteries for engine starting. Fixed-frequency 115/26V AC power from two 600VA single-phase static inverters. External power receptacle. Cockpit pressurised (differential 0·24 bars; 3·5 lb/sq in); bootstrap-type air-conditioning system, which also provides air for windscreen and canopy demisting. Low-pressure demand-type oxygen system, operating at 27·6 bars (400 lb/sq in).

AVIONICS AND EQUIPMENT: Typical avionics installation includes Elmer/Magnavox AN/ARC-150(V) UHF or Elmer/Magnavox SRT-194B VHF primary com transceiver; Collins 618M-3A VHF/AM or equivalent ARINC 566A, or Collins AN/ARC-186(V) VHF/AM & FM secondary com transceiver; Collins IA-210 interphone; Collins AN/ARN-118(V)1 Tacan or Collins 860E-5 DME nav system; Fiar/Bendix AN/APX-100(V) IFF; Collins 51RV-4D VOR/ILS, including localiser and glideslope receivers; Collins MKI-3 marker beacon; Collins ADF-60A ADF; or (M.B.339A) Marconi Avionics AD-620C computerised area and dead reckoning navigation system. Standard instrumentation includes ARU-2B/A attitude director indicator, AQU-6/A HSI, Aeritalia-Sperry AS-339 attitude and heading reference system, AG-5 standby attitude indicator, and flight director system. Retractable landing light beneath port wing; taxying light on nosewheel leg.

ARMAMENT AND OPERATIONAL EQUIPMENT: Up to 1,815 kg (4,000 lb) of external stores can be carried on six underwing hardpoints, the inner four of which are stressed for loads of up to 454 kg (1,000 lb) each and the outer two for up to 340 kg (750 lb) each. Provisions are made, on the two inner stations, for the installation of two Macchi gun pods, each containing either a 30 mm DEFA cannon with 120 rds, or a 12·7 mm AN/M-3 machine-gun with 350 rds. Other typical loads include two Matra 550 or AIM-9 Sidewinder air-to-air missiles; four 1,000 lb or six 750 lb bombs; six SUU-11A/A 7·62 mm Minigun pods with 1,500 rds/pod; six Matra 155 launchers, each for eighteen 68 mm rockets; six Matra F-2 practice launchers, each for six 68 mm rockets; six LAU-68/A or LAU-32G launchers, each for seven 2·75 in rockets; six Aerea AL-25-50 or AL-18-50 launchers, each with twenty-five or eighteen 50 mm rockets respectively; six Aerea AL-12-80, each with twelve 81 mm rockets; four LAU-10A launchers, each with four 5 in Zuni rockets; six Aerea BRD 1395 bomb/rocket dispensers; six Aermacchi 11B29-003 bomb/flare dispensers; or two 325 litre (71·5 Imp gallon) drop-tanks; or a photographic pod with four 70 mm Vinten cameras. Provision for Aeritalia 8.105.924 fixed reflector sight, Saab RGS 2 gunsight or Thomson-CSF RD 21 self-contained gyroscopic sight; a gunsight can also be installed in rear cockpit, to enable instructor to evaluate manoeuvres performed by student pilot. All gunsights can be equipped with fully automatic Teledyne TSC 116-2 gun camera. Head-up display system under study. Provision for towing type A-6B (1·83 × 9·14 m; 6 × 30 ft) aerial banner target; tow attachment point on inner surface of ventral airbrake.

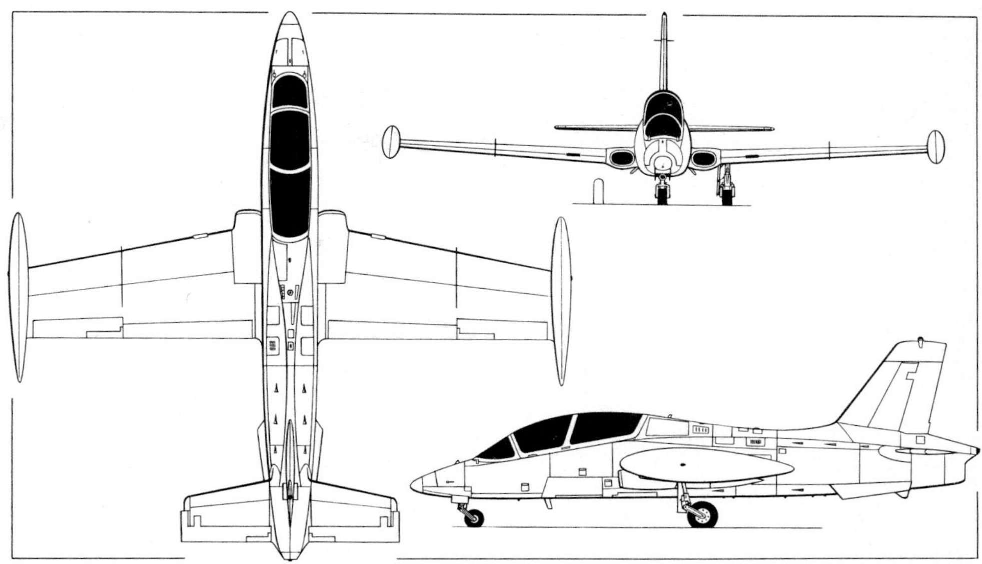

Aermacchi M.B. 339A two-seat jet trainer and light attack aircraft *(Pilot Press)*

DIMENSIONS, EXTERNAL:

Wing span over tip-tanks	10·858 m (35 ft 7½ in)
Wing aspect ratio	5·26
Length overall	10·972 m (36 ft 0 in)
Height overall	3·600 m (11 ft 9¾ in)
Tailplane span	4·164 m (13 ft 8 in)
Wheel track	2·483 m (8 ft 1¾ in)
Wheelbase	4·369 m (14 ft 4 in)

AREAS:

Wings, gross	19·30 m² (207·74 sq ft)
Ailerons (total)	1·328 m² (14·29 sq ft)
Trailing-edge flaps (total)	2·552 m² (27·47 sq ft)
Airbrake	0·520 m² (5·60 sq ft)
Fin	2·370 m² (25·51 sq ft)
Rudder, incl tab	0·610 m² (6·57 sq ft)
Tailplane	3·380 m² (36·38 sq ft)
Elevators (total, incl tabs)	0·979 m² (10·54 sq ft)

WEIGHTS:

Weight empty	3,075 kg (6,780 lb)
Weight empty, equipped	3,125 kg (6,889 lb)
Fuel load (internal, usable)	1,100 kg (2,425 lb)
T-O weight, 'clean'	4,400 kg (9,700 lb)
Max T-O weight, with external stores	5,897 kg (13,000 lb)
Landing weight with 10% fuel reserves	3,425 kg (7,550 lb)

PERFORMANCE (at 'clean' T-O weight, ISA, except where stated):

EAS limit/Mach limit
Mach 0·82 (500 knots; 926 km/h; 575 mph)

Max level speed at S/L
485 knots (898 km/h; 558 mph)

Max level speed at 9,150 m (30,000 ft)
Mach 0·77 (441 knots; 817 km/h; 508 mph)

Max speed for landing gear extension
170 knots (315 km/h; 195 mph) IAS

Approach speed over 15 m (50 ft) obstacle
98 knots (182 km/h; 113 mph) IAS

Landing speed 89 knots (165 km/h; 102·5 mph) IAS

Stalling speed 80 knots (148·5 km/h; 92·5 mph)

Max rate of climb at S/L 2,010 m (6,595 ft)/min

Time to 9,150 m (30,000 ft) 7 min 6 s

Service ceiling (30·5 m; 100 ft/min rate of climb)
14,630 m (48,000 ft)

Min ground turning radius 8·45 m (27 ft 8¾ in)

T-O run at S/L:
- 'clean' T-O weight 465 m (1,525 ft)
- max T-O weight 915 m (3,000 ft)

T-O to, and landing from, 15 m (50 ft)
700 m (2,296 ft)

Landing run at S/L:
- 'clean' landing weight 415 m (1,362 ft)
- ground attack mission landing weight of 3,630 kg (8,000 lb) 427 m (1,400 ft)

Max range (internal fuel), 10% reserves
950 nm (1,760 km; 1,093 miles)

Max endurance at 9,150 m (30,000 ft) (internal fuel), 10% reserves 2 h 50 min

Max ferry range with two underwing drop-tanks, 10% reserves 1,140 nm (2,110 km; 1,310 miles)

Max endurance at 7,620 m (25,000 ft) with two underwing drop-tanks, 10% reserves 3 h 45 min

g limits:
- 'clean' T-O weight +8·0; −4·0
- max T-O weight +5·5; −2·0

WEIGHTS (armed configuration):

Typical T-O weights with crew of one and armament indicated:

- A: two Macchi 30 mm gun pods 4,822 kg (10,630 lb)
- B: two Macchi 30 mm gun pods and two drop-tanks 5,475 kg (12,070 lb)
- C: two Macchi 30 mm gun pods and four Mk 82 bombs 5,881 kg (12,965 lb)
- D: four Mk 82 bombs and two drop-tanks 5,897 kg (13,000 lb)
- E: six Mk 82 bombs 5,897 kg (13,000 lb)
- F: two Macchi 30 mm gun pods, two LR-25-0 rocket launchers and two drop-tanks 5,808 kg (12,805 lb)
- G: four LR-25-0 launchers and two drop-tanks 5,642 kg (12,440 lb)
- H: six LR-25-0 launchers 5,323 kg (11,735 lb)

PERFORMANCE (armed configuration, at T-O weights given above):

Dash speed at S/L:

A	440 knots (815 km/h; 507 mph)
B	400 knots (741 km/h; 461 mph)
C, D	390 knots (723 km/h; 449 mph)
E	395 knots (732 km/h; 455 mph)
F, G, H	365 knots (676 km/h; 420 mph)

Radius of action, hi-lo-hi (no run-in or run-out):

A	223 nm (413 km; 257 miles)
B	323 nm (598 km; 372 miles)
C	176 nm (326 km; 203 miles)
D	320 nm (593 km; 368 miles)
E	212 nm (393 km; 244 miles)
F	275 nm (510 km; 317 miles)
G	305 nm (565 km; 351 miles)
H	165 nm (306 km; 190 miles)

Radius of action, lo-lo-lo (no run-in or run-out):

A	150 nm (278 km; 173 miles)
B	205 nm (380 km; 236 miles)
C	135 nm (250 km; 155 miles)
D	200 nm (371 km; 230 miles)
E	146 nm (271 km; 168 miles)
F	190 nm (352 km; 219 miles)
G	193 nm (358 km; 222 miles)
H	123 nm (228 km; 142 miles)

Radius of action, hi-lo-hi (30 nm; 56 km; 34·5 mile run-in and run-out):

A	150 nm (278 km; 173 miles)
B	260 nm (482 km; 299 miles)
C	122 nm (226 km; 140 miles)
D	240 nm (445 km; 276 miles)
E	138 nm (256 km; 159 miles)
F	218 nm (404 km; 251 miles)
G	230 nm (426 km; 265 miles)
H	112 nm (208 km; 129 miles)

Radius of action, lo-lo-lo (30 nm; 56 km; 34·5 mile run-in and run-out):

A	130 nm (241 km; 150 miles)
B	188 nm (348 km; 216 miles)
C	120 nm (222 km; 138 miles)
D	180 nm (334 km; 207 miles)
E	124 nm (230 km; 143 miles)
F	172 nm (319 km; 198 miles)
G	173 nm (321 km; 199 miles)
H	103 nm (191 km; 119 miles)

AGUSTA
THE AGUSTA GROUP

HEAD OFFICES:
Viale del Ghisallo 20, 20151 Milan
Telephone: (0332) 30706
Telex: 333280
Via Abruzzi 11, 00187 Rome
Telephone: (06) 4756551
Telex: 614398
GROUP MANAGEMENT:
Cav del Lavoro Conte Corrado Agusta (Joint President)
Dott Ing P. Fascione (Joint President)
Dott Ing G. Brazzelli (General Manager)

In 1977, four major Italian aerospace companies were combined under a single management structure. They are Costruzioni Aeronautiche Giovanni Agusta; SIAI-Marchetti SpA (which see); Elicotteri Meridionali SpA (see EM entry in this section); and Industria Aeronautica Meridionale. Together, they form the Agusta Group.

COSTRUZIONI AERONAUTICHE GIOVANNI AGUSTA SpA

HEAD OFFICE AND WORKS: Casella Postale 480, 21017 Cascina Costa, Gallarate
Telephone: (0331) 220478
Telex: 332569
CHAIRMAN AND PRESIDENT: Conte Corrado Agusta
DEPUTY CHAIRMAN: E. Marelli
CHIEF EXECUTIVE OFFICER: P. Fascione
GENERAL MANAGER: A. Antichi
TECHNICAL DIRECTOR: L. Passini

This company was established in 1907 by Giovanni Agusta and built many experimental and production aircraft before the second World War.

In 1952 Agusta acquired a licence to manufacture the Bell Model 47 helicopter and the first Agusta-built Model 47G made its maiden flight on 22 May 1954.

Agusta is producing under licence in Italy the Bell Models 205, 206 and 212. It is also collaborating with Bell Helicopter Textron (see US section) in developing the Model 412 version of the Bell 212, fitted with a new four-blade rotor system.

Under licence from Sikorsky, production of SH-3D helicopters began in 1967, and production of the HH-3F (S-61R) started in 1974. Agusta is also engaged, together with Meridionali, SIAI-Marchetti and other Italian companies, in production under licence of the Boeing Vertol CH-47C Chinook helicopter (see EM entry). It will collaborate with Westland Helicopters of the UK in developing the WG 34 Sea King replacement (see under Westland in UK section).

Details are given hereafter, following the descriptions of the A 109A and A 129 helicopters designed by Agusta.

AGUSTA A 109A

The Agusta A 109A is a high-speed, high-performance twin-engined helicopter. The basic version accommodates a pilot and seven passengers, and has a large baggage compartment in the rear of the fuselage. Alternatively, the A 109A can be adapted for freight-carrying, as an ambulance, or for search and rescue. Military and naval versions are described separately.

The first of three A 109 flying prototypes (NC7101) flew for the first time on 4 August 1971. RAI and FAA certification, including single-pilot IFR operation, was announced on 1 June 1975; delivery of production aircraft, designated A 109A, started in early 1976.

Agusta has successfully carried out trials of a four-unit flotation gear for the A 109A, manufactured by Garrett Air Cruisers of New Jersey. An 11-seat version, designated A-119, is under consideration.

The following description applies to the standard A 109A, production of which was at the rate of eight per month in 1978.

TYPE: Twin-engined general-purpose helicopter.

ROTOR SYSTEM AND DRIVE: Fully-articulated four-blade single main rotor and two-blade semi-rigid delta-hinged tail rotor. Main transmission assembly is housed in fairing above the passenger cabin, driving the main rotor through a coupling gearbox and main reduction gearbox, and the tail rotor through a 90° gearbox. Main rotor blades can be folded back for stowage. Main rotor/engine rpm ratio 1 : 15·62. Tail rotor/engine rpm ratio 1 : 2·88. Rotor brake optional.

FUSELAGE AND TAIL UNIT: Pod and boom type, of aluminium alloy construction, built in four main sections: nose, cockpit, passenger cabin and tailboom. Sweptback vertical fins (above and below fuselage), and non-swept elevators, mounted on rear of tailboom. Tail rotor on port side.

LANDING GEAR: Retractable tricycle type, with single main wheels and self-centering steerable nosewheel. Hydraulic retraction, nosewheel forward, main wheels upward into fuselage. Hydraulic emergency retraction. Brakes on main wheels, locking mechanism on nosewheel. All tyres are of tubeless type, size 360 × 135-6, pressure 5·9 bars (85 lb/sq in). Emergency flotation gear optional.

POWER PLANT: Two Allison 250-C20B turboshaft engines (each 313 kW; 420 shp for T-O, 287 kW; 385 shp max continuous power, 276 kW; 370 shp max cruise power, derated to 258 kW; 346 shp for twin-engine operation), mounted side by side in upper rear fuselage and separated from passenger cabin and from each other by firewalls. Fuel tank in lower rear fuselage, usable capacity 550 litres (121 Imp gallons). Oil capacity 7·7 litres (1·7 Imp gallons) for each engine and 9·5 litres (2·1 Imp gallons) for transmission.

ACCOMMODATION: Crew of one or two on flight deck, which has a door on each side. Dual controls. Main cabin seats up to six passengers, in two rows of three at 81 cm (32 in) pitch, with large space at rear for baggage. A seventh passenger can be carried in lieu of second crew member. Door to passenger cabin on each side. First row of seats removable to permit use as freight transport. Ambulance version can accommodate two stretchers, one above the other, and two medical attendants, in addition to the pilot. An external freight load of 907 kg (2,000 lb) can be transported on a centre-of-gravity hook. A side-mounted hoist and sliding doors can be installed for rescue missions.

Agusta A 109A general-purpose helicopter (two Allison 250-C20B turboshaft engines)

SYSTEMS: Utility hydraulic system, with emergency accumulators, for landing gear operation, wheel and rotor braking and nosewheel locking. Two separate hydraulic systems provide for dual flight servo-controls. 28V DC electrical system, using two 150A starter/generators, and one 24V 13Ah battery. 115V 400Hz AC power from two 250VA static inverters.

AVIONICS AND EQUIPMENT: Additional instrumentation for IFR operations and equipment to customer's requirements, including provision for VHF/FM, UHF/AM, VOR (with Area Navigation if required), ILS, DME, ADF, automatic stabilisation equipment.

DIMENSIONS, EXTERNAL:	
Diameter of main rotor	11·00 m (36 ft 1 in)
Diameter of tail rotor	2·03 m (6 ft 8 in)
Length overall, rotors turning	13·03 m (42 ft 9 in)
Length of fuselage	10·73 m (35 ft 2½ in)
Height overall	3·32 m (10 ft 10¾ in)
Elevator span	2·88 m (9 ft 5½ in)
Wheel track	2·45 m (8 ft 0½ in)
Wheelbase	3·535 m (11 ft 7¼ in)
Passenger doors (each): Height	1·06 m (3 ft 5¾ in)
Width	1·15 m (3 ft 9¼ in)
Height to sill	0·65 m (2 ft 1½ in)
DIMENSIONS, INTERNAL:	
Cabin, excl flight deck: Length	1·62 m (5 ft 3¾ in)
Width	1·42 m (4 ft 8 in)
Height	1·29 m (4 ft 2¾ in)
Volume	2·82 m^3 (100 cu ft)
Baggage compartment volume	0·52 m^3 (18·4 cu ft)
AREAS:	
Main rotor blades (each)	1·84 m^2 (19·8 sq ft)
Tail rotor blades (each)	0·203 m^2 (2·185 sq ft)
Main rotor disc	95·00 m^2 (1,022·6 sq ft)
Tail rotor disc	3·23 m^2 (34·75 sq ft)
WEIGHTS AND LOADINGS:	
Weight empty	1,415 kg (3,120 lb)
Max T-O weight	2,600 kg (5,730 lb)
Max disc loading	27·4 kg/m^2 (5·60 lb/sq ft)
Max power loading	4·15 kg/kW (6·82 lb/shp)

PERFORMANCE (at AUW of 2,450 kg; 5,400 lb. A: ISA, B: ISA + 20°C):

Never-exceed speed	168 knots (311 km/h; 193 mph)
Max cruising speed at max continuous power: A	144 knots (266 km/h; 165 mph)
Optimum cruising speed at S/L: A	125 knots (231 km/h; 143 mph)
Max rate of climb at S/L: A	493 m (1,620 ft)/min
Rate of climb at S/L, one engine out: A	103 m (340 ft)/min
Max operating height	4,572 m (15,000 ft)
Service ceiling: A	4,968 m (16,300 ft)
Service ceiling, one engine out: A	1,370 m (4,500 ft)
Hovering ceiling IGE: A	3,050 m (10,000 ft)
B	2,133 m (7,000 ft)
Hovering ceiling OGE: A	2,042 m (6,700 ft)
B	1,219 m (4,000 ft)
Max range at S/L: A	305 nm (565 km; 351 miles)
Max endurance at S/L: A	3 h 30 min

AGUSTA A 109 MILITARY VERSION

Five military A 109s have been ordered by the Italian Army for evaluation, and delivery of these began in early 1977. Three of these aircraft are each equipped to carry four TOW air-to-surface missiles, the other two being equipped for transport and liaison duties. General configuration, structure and power plant are similar to those of the A 109A (which see). Changes in the military version include dual controls and instrumentation; rotor brake; tail rotor control magnetic brake; sliding doors; environmental control system; emergency flotation gear; non-retractable landing gear; armoured seats; crashworthy fuel tanks; heavy-duty battery; particle separator; external cargo hook; multi-purpose universal supports for

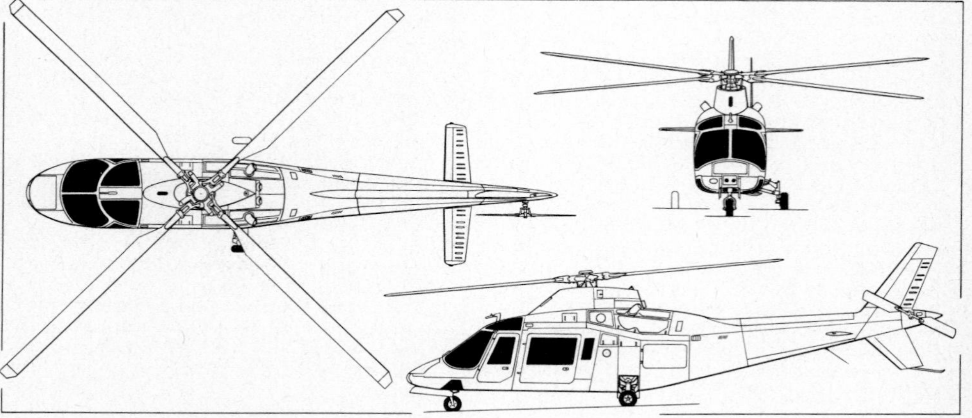

Agusta A 109A twin-engined general-purpose helicopter *(Pilot Press)*

external loads; rescue hoist; high-load cargo floor; and infra-red suppression system.

The military A 109 has also been ordered by the Argentinian Army and other foreign operators.

ACCOMMODATION: Standard seating for a pilot and seven troops. Ambulance version can accommodate two stretcher patients and two medical attendants.

ARMAMENT: Basically two 7·62 mm flexibly-mounted machine-guns, with stabilised sight system, and two XM-157 rocket launchers, each with seven 2·75 in rockets. Alternative weapons include Hot or TOW missiles; an electrically-operated 7·62 mm Minigun on flexible mounting, with 1,000 rounds; a fully-automatic MG3 7·62 mm machine-gun with 5,000 rounds; an XM-159C launcher for nineteen 2·75 in rockets, Agusta launcher for seven 81 mm rockets, or 200A-1 launcher for nineteen 2·75 in rockets.

AGUSTA A 109 NAVAL VERSION

A naval version of the A 109A is in an advanced stage of development for several navies. The main missions to be carried out by the A 109 in the naval configuration are: anti-surface-vessel, anti-submarine, electronic warfare, armed patrol (stand-off missile guidance, TG-2), coastguard patrol, SAR, aerial ambulance and utility.

The naval A 109, maintaining the general configuration, structure, power plant, reliability and performance of the A 109A, has been specially designed for shipboard compatibility. Besides the weapon systems appropriate to specific missions, the helicopter is equipped with four-axis ASE, radar altimeter, internal auxiliary fuel tanks, rotor brake, dual controls and instrumentation, particle separator, heavy duty battery, non-retractable landing gear, rescue hoist, universal supports for external loads, search radar, emergency flotation gear, anchorage points for deck lashings, and an automatic navigation system.

ACCOMMODATION: Standard seating for a crew of three or four. Ambulance version accommodates two stretchers and two medical attendants.

SYSTEMS: Standard duplicated hydraulic systems for flight controls, as in A 109A, and for automatic stabilisation equipment. Third, self-contained system for MAD and other utilities. Electrical system capacity increased to cater for higher power demand.

AVIONICS AND EQUIPMENT: Complete instrumentation for day and night sea operation in all weathers. Equipment common to all roles includes navigation, cabin and cockpit lights, two fixed landing lights, two anti-collision beacons, first aid kits, and hand-type fire extinguisher for cabin. Optional equipment common to all roles includes a four-axis cross-country autopilot system, UHF/VHF transceiver with homing, AG 03 crew intercom, VOR/ILS, DME, LF/ADF, radar altimeter, tactical air navigation system with Doppler radar, dual controls, and emergency flotation gear.

ARMAMENT AND OPERATIONAL EQUIPMENT: For the ASW role specialised equipment includes two homing torpedoes and six marine markers. Detection of the submarine can be carried out either by the parent ship (in which case the A 109 is acting as a weapon carrier system) or by the helicopter's onboard retractable classification and localisation equipment (MAD). For the ASV role the naval A 109 carries a high-performance long-range search radar with high discrimination in rough sea conditions. The surface attack is performed with AS.12 or AM-10 air-to-surface wire-guided missiles. For the TG-2 mission, the helicopter is equipped with a special guidance system to control and guide a ship-launched Otomat missile. Provisions are also incorporated for the installation of the most advanced ESM systems. A special ECM version of the naval A 109 has been studied by Agusta, and the equipment that can be installed in the helicopter includes a radar warning display, direction finder equipment, an interferometer, an electromagnetic emission analyser, and jamming equipment. For armed patrol, the naval A 109 is equipped with a search radar and armament to customer's requirements. The coastguard patrol configuration includes a search radar, a low light level TV camera and a special installation for external high efficiency loudspeakers. For the search and rescue role, the naval A 109 is fitted with a 150 kg (330 lb) capacity electrically operated hoist, emergency flotation gear and search radar. The naval A 109 can be equipped for several other duties including firefighting and crash rescue, reconnaissance, military command post, and liaison.

AGUSTA A 129-19 MANGUSTA (MONGOOSE)

This light anti-tank helicopter is now in the detail design stage for the Italian Army. First flight is expected in 1981.

A narrow fuselage, 0·95 m (37·5 in) wide, accommodates the pilot's and co-pilot/gunner's seats in tandem, with the pilot to the rear. Each crew position is fitted with flying controls, instruments and an armoured seat. Two stub wings are standard, each with two external stores stations.

POWER PLANT: Two Avco Lycoming LTS101-850 turboshaft engines, each rated at 596 kW (800 shp) for T-O and derated to 391 kW (525 shp) for normal operations. In the event of failure of one engine, the remaining

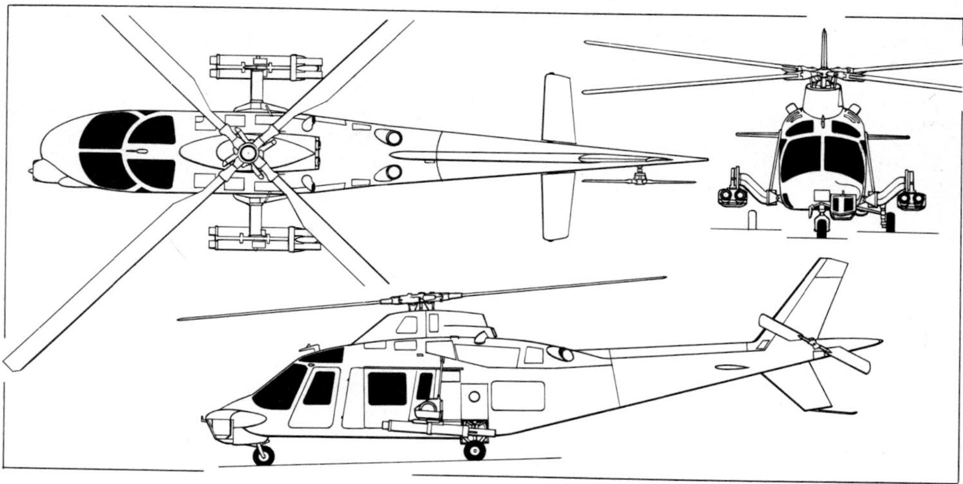

Agusta A 109 anti-tank version armed with TOW missiles *(Pilot Press)*

Military Agusta A 109 fitted with four TOW missile launchers and a nose-mounted stabilised sight

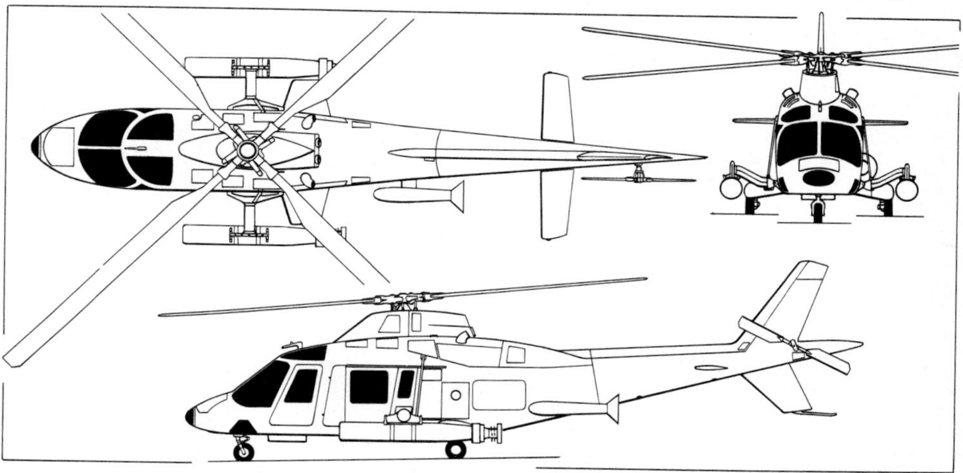

Agusta A 109 naval version, with homing torpedoes and towed MAD *(Pilot Press)*

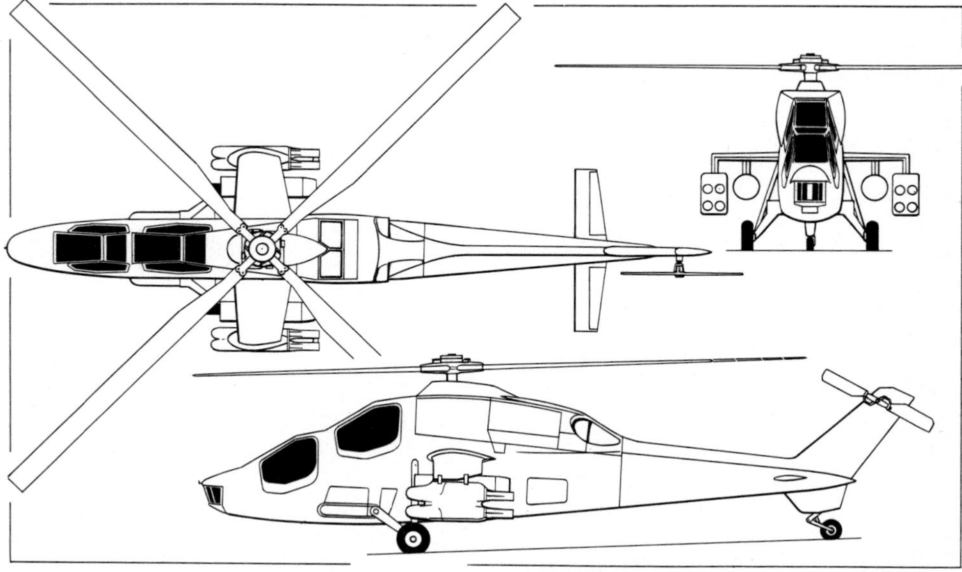

Agusta A 129-19 Mangusta twin-turboshaft anti-tank helicopter *(Pilot Press)*

engine can be operated at 484·5 kW (650 shp) to provide adequate single-engine performance.

ARMAMENT: Eight Hot or TOW anti-tank missiles; air-to-surface rockets; 7·62 mm Minitat machine-gun system. Inner stores stations can each carry 270 kg (595 lb) loads; outer stations can each carry 200 kg (441 lb).

DIMENSIONS, EXTERNAL:
- Diameter of main rotor: 11·90 m (39 ft 0½ in)
- Diameter of tail rotor: 2·00 m (6 ft 6¾ in)
- Wing span: 3·10 m (10 ft 2 in)
- Length overall, tail rotor turning: 12·50 m (41 ft 0 in)
- Fuselage max width: 0·95 m (3 ft 1½ in)
- Height over tail fin, tail rotor horizontal: 2·65 m (8 ft 8¼ in)
- Height to top of rotor hub: 3·20 m (10 ft 6 in)
- Tailplane span: 3·00 m (9 ft 10 in)
- Wheel track: 2·00 m (6 ft 6¾ in)
- Wheelbase: 7·14 m (23 ft 5 in)

WEIGHTS:
- Weight empty, equipped: 2,257 kg (4,976 lb)
- Fuel load (max internal): 650 kg (1,433 lb)
- Mission T-O weight: 3,350 kg (7,385 lb)
- Max T-O weight: 3,500 kg (7,716 lb)

PERFORMANCE (estimated: A at mission T-O weight, B at max T-O weight):
- Max permissible diving speed, with 28 rockets:
  - A: 168 knots (311 km/h; 193 mph)
  - B: 165 knots (305 km/h; 190 mph)
- Max level speed at 1,000 m (3,280 ft), ISA + 2°C:
  - A, 'clean': 175 knots (325 km/h; 202 mph)
  - B, 'clean': 172 knots (318 km/h; 198 mph)
  - A with 8 TOW: 154 knots (285 km/h; 177 mph)
  - B with 8 TOW: 151 knots (280 km/h; 174 mph)
- Max rate of climb at S/L: A: 600 m (1,970 ft)/min
  - B: 528 m (1,732 ft)/min
- Max rate of climb at S/L, one engine out:
  - A: 120 m (394 ft)/min
  - B: 90 m (295 ft)/min
- Hovering ceiling IGE, ISA + 20°C:
  - A: 3,400 m (11,155 ft)
  - B: 2,500 m (8,200 ft)
- Hovering ceiling OGE, ISA + 20°C:
  - A: 2,600 m (8,530 ft)
  - B: 2,000 m (6,560 ft)
- Endurance (anti-tank mission):
  - A, B: 2 h 30 min, plus 20 min reserves
- Max endurance at 70 knots (130 km/h; 81 mph):
  - A, B: 3 h 0 min, plus 20 min reserves
- Max self-ferry range at 135 knots (249 km/h; 155 mph):
  - A, B (internal fuel): 340 nm (629 km; 391 miles)
  - A, B (internal plus 400 kg; 882 lb external fuel): 600 nm (1,112 km; 691 miles)

AGUSTA-BELL 205

The Agusta-Bell Model 205 is a multi-purpose utility helicopter, corresponding to the UH-1D/UH-1H versions adopted by the US armed forces and described in the US section. The cabin will accommodate a pilot and 13 or 14 passengers, and there is a 0·8 m³ (28·25 cu ft) baggage compartment in the tailboom. The AB 205 is fitted with IFR and night flying instruments, and for normal operation only one pilot is needed. Power plant is a 1,044 kW (1,400 shp) Lycoming T53-L-13B turboshaft engine, derated to 932 kW (1,250 shp) for take-off.

The AB 205 is in service with the Italian armed forces and has been ordered by many other countries.

Production was at the rate of 12 aircraft per month in 1978.

DIMENSIONS, EXTERNAL: As Bell Model 205 except:
- Main rotor diameter: 14·72 m (48 ft 3½ in)
- Width overall: 2·76 m (9 ft 0½ in)
- Height overall: 4·48 m (14 ft 8 in)

WEIGHTS: As Bell Model 205 except:
- Weight empty (standard): 2,177 kg (4,800 lb)
- Normal T-O weight: 3,860 kg (8,500 lb)

PERFORMANCE (at Normal T-O weight):
- Max level speed at S/L: 120 knots (222 km/h; 138 mph)
- Cruising speed: 115 knots (212 km/h; 132 mph)
- Max rate of climb at S/L: 548 m (1,800 ft)/min
- Hovering ceiling IGE: 5,180 m (17,000 ft)
- Hovering ceiling OGE: 3,350 m (11,000 ft)
- Max range, standard tanks, no reserves: 312 nm (580 km; 360 miles)
- Max endurance, standard tanks, no reserves: 3 h 48 min

AGUSTA-BELL 206B JETRANGER III

The Agusta-Bell 206 JetRanger has been manufactured under licence from Bell since the end of 1967; deliveries began in 1972 of the Agusta-Bell 206B JetRanger II, and of the current production version, the JetRanger III, at the end of 1978. Powered by a 313 kW (420 shp) Allison 250-C20B turboshaft engine, the JetRanger III incorporates many improvements derived from the production of, and operating experience with, many thousands of earlier commercial and military JetRangers. A description of the JetRanger III appears under the Bell Helicopter Textron entry in the US section.

AGUSTA-BELL 206L-1 LONGRANGER II

This aircraft is a seven-seat single-engined light helicopter, derived from the AB 206B and powered by a 373 kW (500 shp) Allison 250-C28B turboshaft engine, as described under the Bell Helicopter Textron entry in the US section.

AGUSTA-BELL 212

The Agusta-Bell 212 is a twin-engined utility transport helicopter particularly suited to military or civilian passenger transport duties. Its general configuration is similar to that of the Bell Model 212 Twin Two-Twelve, described in the US section.

Latest customers for the AB 212 include the Austrian Army, which ordered 24 to replace its AB 204s that entered service in 1957. They will be used for transport, rescue and casualty evacuation duties, some carrying armament.

The extensively-modified AB 212ASW naval version produced by Agusta is described separately.

DIMENSIONS, EXTERNAL:
- Diameter of main rotor: 14·63 m (48 ft 0 in)
- Diameter of tail rotor: 2·59 m (8 ft 6 in)
- Length overall, rotors turning: 17·40 m (57 ft 1 in)
- Fuselage length: 14·02 m (46 ft 0 in)
- Height to top of cabin roof: 2·34 m (7 ft 8 in)
- Height overall, tail rotor turning: 4·40 m (14 ft 5 in)
- Elevator span: 2·84 m (9 ft 4 in)
- Width over skids: 2·64 m (8 ft 8 in)

WEIGHTS: As Bell Model 212 except:
- Weight empty (standard): 2,630 kg (5,800 lb)

PERFORMANCE (at AUW of 4,536 kg; 10,000 lb, ISA):
- Cruising speed at S/L: 110 knots (204 km/h; 127 mph)
- Max rate of climb at S/L: 567 m (1,860 ft)/min
- Service ceiling: 5,180 m (17,000 ft)
- Hovering ceiling IGE: 3,960 m (13,000 ft)
- Hovering ceiling OGE: 3,050 m (10,000 ft)
- Max range at 1,525 m (5,000 ft) with standard fuel, no reserves:
  - on two engines: 267 nm (494 km; 307 miles)
  - on one engine: 318 nm (589 km; 366 miles)

AGUSTA-BELL 212ASW

The AB 212ASW is an extensively modified version of the AB 212, intended primarily for anti-submarine search and attack missions, and for attacks on surface vessels, but suitable also for search and rescue and utility roles. It benefits from considerable naval operational experience gained with the single-engined AB 204AS, and because of its similarity in size to the 204AS can operate from the same small ship decks.

The AB 212ASW is produced at a rate of approximately four to five per month and is being delivered to meet orders from several navies.

Apart from some local strengthening and the provision of deck-mooring equipment, the airframe structure remains essentially similar to that of the commercial Model 212 and military UH-1N, described under the Bell Helicopter Textron entry in the US section. Main differences from the Agusta-Bell 212 are as follows:

TYPE: Twin-engined anti-submarine and anti-surface-vessel helicopter.

POWER PLANT: One Pratt & Whitney Aircraft of Canada PT6T-6 Turbo Twin Pac, rated at 1,398 kW (1,875 shp). Protection against salt water corrosion. Provision for one internal or two external auxiliary fuel tanks.

ACCOMMODATION: Normal crew of three or four. Volume of cabin is 6·1 m³ (215 cu ft), with floor area of 5·0 m² (54 sq ft). With sonar installed, volume is reduced to 5·1 m³ (180 cu ft). Naval 212 can accommodate two pilots and seven passengers; or two pilots, four stretcher patients and attendant. Single sliding door, with jettisonable emergency exit panel, on each side.

SYSTEMS: Standard duplicated hydraulic systems for flight controls, as in AB 212. The hydraulic system operates the automatic flight control system. Self-contained hydraulic system for operation of sonar, rescue hoist and other utilities. Electrical system capacity increased to cater for higher power demand (28V DC, and three-phase 200/115V or single-phase 26V AC at 400Hz); the two standard generators are integrated with a 20kVA alternator.

AVIONICS AND EQUIPMENT: Complete instrumentation for day and night sea operation in all weathers. Avionics installed are AN/ARC-159 UHF transceiver, Collins SSB/DSB 718 U-5 HF transceiver, and Agusta AG-03-M intercom, for communications; Marconi Avionics AD 370B ADF, Hoffman AN/ARN-91 Tacan and Collins AN/ARA-50 homing UHF, for navigation assistance; Aeritalia (Honeywell) AN/APN-171 radar altimeter, Canadian Marconi AN/APN-208(V)2 Doppler radar, Canadian Marconi CMA-708B/ASW navigation computer, and automatic flight control system with General Electric SR-3 gyro platform, Agusta ASE-531A automatic stabilisation equipment and Agusta AATH-547A automatic approach to hover, for automatic navigation; Siemens AN/APX-77 IFF/SIF transponder; SMA/APS series search radar and Motorola SST-119X radar transponder; and Bendix AN/AQS-13B sonar for ASW search.

ARMAMENT AND OPERATIONAL EQUIPMENT: Weapons may consist of two homing torpedoes, depth charges or two

Agusta-Bell 206L-1 LongRanger II seven-seat light helicopter

Agusta-Bell 212ASW anti-submarine and anti-surface-vessel helicopter

Agusta-Sikorsky SH-3D ASW/ASV helicopter, armed with homing torpedoes and air-to-surface missiles

air-to-surface missiles. Rescue hoist, capacity 270 kg (600 lb), standard. Provisions for auxiliary installations such as a 2,270 kg (5,000 lb) capacity cargo sling, inflatable emergency pontoons, internal and external auxiliary fuel tanks, according to mission.

ASW MISSION: The basic sensor system employed for the ASW search and attack mission is a low-frequency variable-depth sonar, with a max operating depth of 137 m (450 ft). The automatic navigation system permits the positioning of the helicopter over any desired 'dip' point of a complex search pattern. The position of the helicopter, computed by the automatic navigation system, is integrated with sonar target information in the radar tactical display where both the surface and the underwater tactical situations can be continuously monitored. Additional navigation and tactical information is provided by accurate UHF direction-finding equipment, from an A/A mode-capable Tacan and from a radar transponder. The automatic flight control system (AFCS) integrates the basic automatic stabilisation equipment with signal output from the radar altimeter, the Doppler radar, sonar cable angle signals and outputs from the dry cable transducer. The effectiveness of this system results in hands-off flight from cruise condition to sonar hover in all weathers and under rough sea conditions. A specially designed cockpit display shows the pilots all flight parameters for each phase of the ASW operation. The attack mission is carried out with two homing torpedoes, or with depth charges.

ASV MISSION: For this mission the AB 212ASW carries a high-performance long-range search radar, with a very efficient scanner design and installation possessing high discrimination in rough sea conditions. Provisions have also been made to permit incorporation of future radar system developments. The automatic navigation systems and the search radar are integrated to permit a continuously updated picture of the tactical situation. Provisions are also incorporated for the installation of the most advanced ECM systems. The surface attack is performed with air-to-surface wire-guided missiles. In operation, the co-pilot aims and 'flies' the missiles to the target through an XM-58 gyro-stabilised sight system.

STAND-OFF MISSILE GUIDANCE MISSION: In this mission the AB 212ASW, with special equipment, can provide mid-course passive guidance for the ship-launched Otomat 2 surface-to-surface missile. Equipment includes an SMA/APS series search radar and a TG-2 real-time target data transmission system for guidance of the missile.

DIMENSIONS, EXTERNAL: As AB 212, except:
- Max width:
  - with torpedoes 3·95 m (12 ft 11½ in)
  - with missiles 4·17 m (13 ft 8¼ in)

WEIGHTS (A: ASW mission with Mk 46 torpedoes; B: ASV mission with AS.12 missiles; C: search and rescue mission; all at S/L, ISA):
- Weight empty, equipped:
  - A, B, C 3,420 kg (7,540 lb)
- Crew of three: A, B, C 240 kg (529 lb)
- Mission equipment:
  - A (two Mk 46 torpedoes) 490 kg (1,080 lb)
  - B (AS.12 installation and XM-58 sight) 180 kg (396 lb)
  - C (rescue hoist) 40 kg (89 lb)
- Full fuel (normal tanks) 1,021 kg (2,250 lb)
- Auxiliary external tanks 32 kg (70 lb)
- Auxiliary fuel 356 kg (785 lb)
- Mission T-O weight: A 5,070 kg (11,176 lb)
  - B 4,973 kg (10,961 lb)
  - C 4,937 kg (10,883 lb)

PERFORMANCE (at max T-O weight, except where indicated, ISA):
- Never-exceed speed 130 knots (240 km/h; 150 mph)
- Max level speed at S/L 106 knots (196 km/h; 122 mph)
- Max cruising speed with armament 100 knots (185 km/h; 115 mph)
- Max rate of climb at S/L: A 396 m (1,300 ft)/min
- Rate of climb at S/L, one engine out:
  - A 61 m (200 ft)/min
- Hovering ceiling IGE: A 3,200 m (10,500 ft)
- Hovering ceiling OGE:
  - A at AUW of 4,763 kg (10,500 lb) 396 m (1,300 ft)
- Search endurance (A) with 50% at 90 knots (167 km/h; 103·5 mph) cruise and 50% hovering out of ground effect, 10% reserve fuel 3 h 12 min
- Search range (B) with 10% reserve fuel 332 nm (615 km; 382 miles)
- Endurance (B), no reserves 4 h 7 min
- Endurance (C) at 90 knots (167 km/h; 103·5 mph) search speed 5 h 4 min
- Max range with auxiliary tanks, 100 knots (185 km/h; 115 mph) cruise at S/L, 15% reserves 360 nm (667 km; 414 miles)
- Max endurance with auxiliary tanks, no reserves 5 h 0 min

AGUSTA-SIKORSKY SH-3D

During 1967, Agusta began the construction under licence of Sikorsky SH-3D anti-submarine helicopters for the Italian Navy. Deliveries began in 1969. Additional orders have since been placed, both for the Italian armed forces and for other navies, in various configurations including ASW, VIP transport and rescue. The VIP transport version is designated **SH-3D/TS** (Trasporto Speciale), and serves with the 31° Stormo of the Italian Air Force.

Apart from some local strengthening and an improved horizontal tail surface, the Agusta-built airframe remains essentially similar to that of the SH-3D described under the Sikorsky heading in the US section of this edition. The Agusta SH-3D is capable of operation in the roles of anti-submarine search, classification and strike; anti-surface-vessel (ASV); anti-surface-missile defence (ASMD); electronic warfare (EW); tactical troop lift; search and rescue (SAR); vertical replenishment; and casualty evacuation.

POWER PLANT: Two 1,118 kW (1,500 shp) General Electric T58-GE-100 turboshaft engines, mounted side by side above the cabin. An optional anti-ice/sand shield can be provided. Fuel in underfloor bag tanks with a total capacity of 3,180 litres (840 US gallons). Internal auxiliary fuel tank may be fitted for long-range ferry purposes. Pressure and gravity refuelling points.

ACCOMMODATION: Crew of four in ASW role; accommodation for up to 31 paratroops in troop lift role, 15 stretchers and a medical attendant in casualty evacuation configuration, and up to 25 survivors in SAR role.

SYSTEMS: Three main hydraulic systems. Primary and auxiliary systems operate main rotor control. Utility system for landing gear, winches and blade folding, pressure 207 bars (3,000 lb/sq in). Electrical system includes two 20kVA 200V three-phase 400Hz engine-driven generators, a 26V single-phase AC supply fed from the aircraft's 22Ah nickel-cadmium battery through an inverter, and DC power provided as a secondary system from two 200A transformer-rectifier units.

OPERATIONAL EQUIPMENT (ASW/ASV role): As equipped for this role the Agusta SH-3D is a fully integrated all-weather weapon system, capable of operating independently of surface vessels, and has the following equipment and weapons to achieve this task: low-frequency 360° depth sonar; Doppler radar and ASW automatic navigation system; SMA/APS series radar with one or two transceivers, with ventral radome for 360° coverage; radio altimeter; AFCS; marine markers and smoke floats; four homing torpedoes or four depth charges. The AFCS provides three-axis stabilisation in pilot-controlled manoeuvres, attitude hold, heading hold and height hold in cruising flight; controlled transition manoeuvres to and from hover; automatic height control and plan position control in the hover; and trim facility. According to the threat, the Agusta SH-3D can be equipped with medium-range (four AS.12 air-to-surface wire-guided) missiles or long-range (two Sea Killer Mk 2 or Exocet AM-39/Harpoon type) missiles. The Sistel Sea Killer Mk 2 is an all-weather day and night anti-ship missile with a range of 13·5 nm (25 km; 15·5 miles); guidance: sea skimming in elevation, radar in azimuth. The SMA/APS series radar has been specially designed to operate in a dense electronic emission environment and has a special interface to draw out target data to feed the computer for the long-range missiles. Provisions are also incorporated for the installation of the most advanced EW systems.

OPERATIONAL EQUIPMENT (Search and rescue and transport roles): The Agusta SH-3D has a variable-speed hydraulic rescue hoist of 272 kg (600 lb) capacity mounted above the starboard side cargo door. With search radar fitted, a total of 25 survivors and medical staff can be seated. In the casualty evacuation role, 15 stretchers and medical attendant can be accommodated. In the troop transport role the Agusta SH-3D can accommodate 31 troops and carry this load over a range of 314 nm (582 km; 362 miles). As a cargo transport the aircraft has an internal capacity of 2,720 kg (6,000 lb) or a max external load capacity of 3,630 kg (8,000 lb) when a low-response sling is fitted.

PERFORMANCE (at max T-O weight of 9,525 kg; 21,000 lb):
- Never-exceed speed 144 knots (267 km/h; 165 mph)
- Max rate of climb at S/L 670 m (2,200 ft)/min
- Service ceiling 3,720 m (12,200 ft)
- Hovering ceiling IGE 2,500 m (8,200 ft)
- Hovering ceiling OGE 1,130 m (3,700 ft)
- Range with max standard fuel 680 nm (1,260 km; 783 miles)

AGUSTA-SIKORSKY S-61A-4

The AS S-61A-4 is a derivative of the AS SH-3D, and is suitable for a wide range of duties including troop and cargo transport, medical evacuation, and search and rescue. Power plant comprises two 1,118·5 kW (1,500 shp) General Electric T58-GE-100 turboshaft engines. Accommodation is provided for a crew of three and up to 31 fully-equipped troops or 15 stretcher patients. Three have been built for the Italian Air Force.

AGUSTA-SIKORSKY HH-3F (S-61R)

In 1974 Agusta began production of this multi-purpose rescue helicopter. Twenty are being built initially, 12 for SAR duties with the Italian Air Force and others for foreign operators. Deliveries started in 1976; production in 1978 was at the rate of one per month.

Details of the HH-3F can be found under the Sikorsky heading in the US section of this edition.

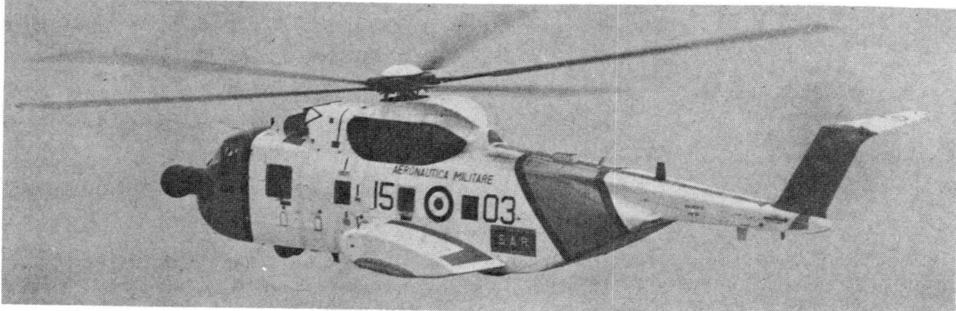

Agusta-Sikorsky HH-3F (S-61R) rescue helicopter of the Italian Air Force

BREDANARDI
BREDANARDI COSTRUZIONI AERONAUTICHE SpA

Head Office and Works: Casella Postale 108, 63039 San Benedetto del Tronto, Ascoli Piceno
Telephone: (0735) 67246/7/8/9
Telex: 560165
International Marketing Office: Via XXIV Maggio 46, 00187 Rome
Telephone: 679 68 34 and 679 73 60
Telex: 614111 BRENAR I
President: Ing Riccardo Baldini
Managing Director: Dott Elto Nardi
Director, International Marketing: Nathaniel R. Hoskot

The Nardi association with aerospace began in 1933 with the establishment of Nardi Costruzioni Aeronautiche SpA, in Milan, by the four Nardi brothers. In 1969 the Nardi brothers acquired a long-term exclusive licence from Hughes Helicopters (USA) to manufacture and market the Model 300 (269) and Model 500 (369) series of helicopters. In 1971 this licence was transferred to BredaNardi, a partnership of Nardi and EFIM, a state-owned financial organisation.

Production of the three-seat piston-engined NH-300C and the five/seven-seat turbine-powered NH-500D is undertaken at the company's 20,000 m² (215,280 sq ft) facility located at Ascoli Piceno, on Italy's Adriatic coast. The major product is the NH-500 M-D equipped with the TOW missile system. Details of these helicopters can be found under the Hughes heading in the US section of this edition.

In addition to helicopter manufacture, the Nardi brothers produce aircraft wheels, brakes (Bendix licence), retractable landing gear, hydraulic and electrical aircraft controls, fuel pumps, armament installations and aircraft accessories generally. Among these are landing gear and other accessories for F-104G and F-104S Starfighters, and the nosewheel unit and arrester hook for the Panavia Tornado.

CAPRONI VIZZOLA
CAPRONI VIZZOLA COSTRUZIONI AERONAUTICHE SpA

Head Office: Via Durini 24, 20122 Milan
Telephone: (02) 700826 and 781975

CAPRONI VIZZOLA C22J

The C22J is a two-seat lightweight training aircraft, developed by Caproni Vizzola as a private venture. Its configuration bears a close resemblance to that of the company's A-21J Calif jet-powered sailplane (which see); construction is largely of metal, with the forward fuselage skin, some fairings and other unstressed areas of glassfibre.

Intended primarily for student pilot screening, basic and proficiency training, the C22J is also suitable for ECM evaluation, ground and air navaid calibration, ecological survey and high-speed liaison. It can be converted easily for photographic survey duties, or for use as an RPV.

A prototype was nearing completion in June 1979; first flight was scheduled to take place before the end of 1979.

Type: Two-seat basic training aircraft.

Wings: Cantilever shoulder-wing monoplane. Constant-chord wings, of Wortmann FX-67K-170 section. Single-spar structure, with aluminium alloy skin. Electrically-actuated trailing-edge flaps can be set in any position throughout their full range of movement. Flaps operate in conjunction with airbrakes/spoilers, of which there is one in the upper surface of each wing, forward of the flap. Airbrakes are opened manually, but move with the flaps to provide balanced control. Aerodynamically balanced ailerons operate differentially and can be drooped to provide additional flap area. All movable surfaces are of extruded aluminium alloy, and are operated by push/pull rods. No tabs.

Fuselage: Tadpole-shaped structure, designed as a laminar lifting body. Primary load-bearing structure is of light alloy, forward portion having a moulded glassfibre skin. NACA-type flush engine air inlet in top of fuselage, aft of cockpits. Tailboom is of light alloy, with undersurface skin of glassfibre.

Tail Unit: Cantilever T tail, tailplane being of all-metal stressed-skin construction. Full-span balanced elevator is a chemically milled extrusion, and is fitted with electrically actuated spring trim. All-metal two-spar stressed-skin fin, bolted to tailboom. All control surfaces operated by push/pull rods. No tabs. Rudder pedals adjustable in flight.

Landing Gear: Retractable tricycle type, actuated electrically with manual backup. Cantilever spring steel main legs. Independent hydraulic brakes on main wheels. Steerable nosewheel, linked to rudder pedals. Safety lock for up and down positions. Electrical warning system.

Power Plant: Two KHD T 317 turbojet engines, each rated at 1·08 kN (242·5 lb st), mounted side by side in fuselage aft of cockpits. Production version may be fitted with Microturbo TRS 18 turbojets. Integral fuel tank in each wing, combined capacity 250 litres (55 Imp gallons). Fuel system incorporates fuselage collector tank which permits up to 30 s of inverted flight. Provision for two underwing auxiliary fuel tanks, each of 112 litres (24·5 Imp gallons) capacity.

Accommodation: Seats for two persons side by side under jettisonable canopy which is hinged at rear and opens upward. Seats are semi-supine. Dual flying controls. Single instrument panel and centre console, eliminating need for dual instruments and avionics. Rearview mirror for each occupant.

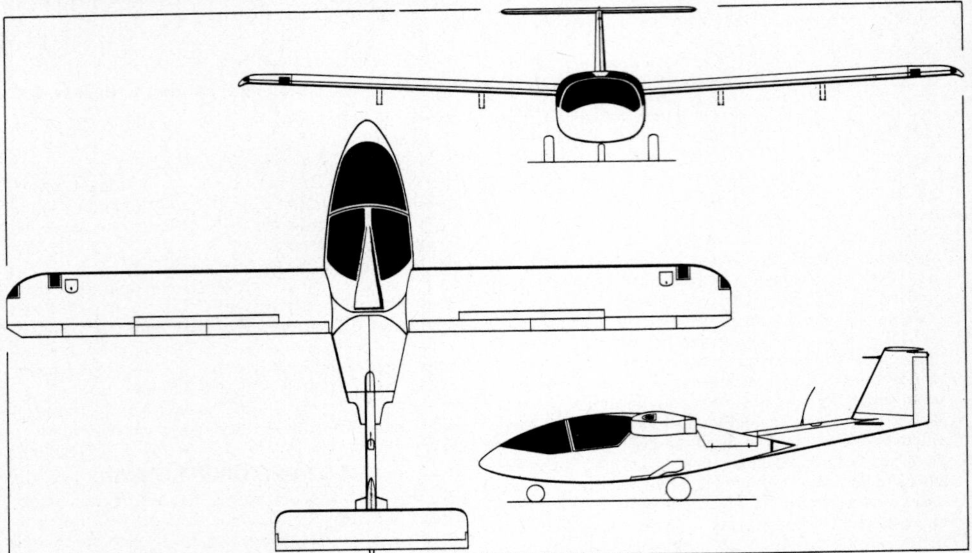

Caproni Vizzola C22J two-seat basic training aircraft *(Pilot Press)*

Systems: Hydraulic system for main-wheel brakes only. No pneumatic system. Electrical system is 28V DC, incorporating a starter/generator and a 24V 18Ah lead-acid battery. Cockpit ventilation and defrosting by heat exchangers on jetpipes. Demand-type low-pressure oxygen system for each occupant.

Avionics and Equipment: Avionics bay in top of fuselage, aft of cockpits. Navigation, landing and anti-collision lights standard.

Armament: Provision for two or four standard NATO underwing pylons, for a wide range of stores (max external load 200 kg; 440 lb) for gunnery/weapon training, photographic reconnaissance and target-towing missions. Typical loads include one auxiliary fuel tank and one three-camera pod; two auxiliary fuel tanks; two 7·62 mm gun pods and 500 rds of ammunition; two Simpres AL-18-50 pods with eighteen 2 in rockets; four SAMP EU70 50 kg general-purpose bombs; four Mk 70 11 kg or M38-A2 50 kg practice bombs; or two Dornier DATS 1 50 kg towed targets.

Dimensions, external:
- Wing span: 10·00 m (32 ft 9¾ in)
- Wing area, gross: 8·75 m² (94·18 sq ft)
- Wing aspect ratio: 11·42
- Length overall: 6·188 m (20 ft 3½ in)
- Height overall: 1·88 m (6 ft 2 in)

Weights and Loadings:
- Weight empty: 510 kg (1,124 lb)
- Max T-O weight: 'clean': 900 kg (1,984 lb)
  - with external stores: 1,100 kg (2,425 lb)
- Max wing loading: 'clean': 102·8 kg/m² (21·06 lb/sq ft)
  - with external stores: 125·7 kg/m² (25·76 lb/sq ft)

Performance (estimated, at max 'clean' T-O weight):
- Max permissible diving speed: 377 knots (700 km/h; 435 mph) EAS
- Max level speed at 2,500 m (8,200 ft): 286 knots (530 km/h; 329 mph)
- Max cruising speed:
  - at S/L: 251 knots (465 km/h; 289 mph)
  - at 5,000 m (16,400 ft): 254 knots (470 km/h; 292 mph)
- Max design manoeuvring speed: 218 knots (405 km/h; 252 mph) EAS
- Max design speed with airbrakes fully deployed: 178 knots (330 km/h; 205 mph) EAS
- Econ cruising speed at 3,000 m (9,845 ft): 162 knots (300 km/h; 186 mph)
- Max landing gear extension speed: 108 knots (200 km/h; 124 mph) EAS
- Design stalling speed, flaps down, power off: 65 knots (120 km/h; 75 mph) EAS
- Max rate of climb: at S/L: 552 m (1,810 ft)/min
  - at 3,000 m (9,845 ft): 384 m (1,260 ft)/min
  - at 6,000 m (19,685 ft): 216 m (708 ft)/min
- Time to climb to 5,000 m (16,400 ft): 12 min
- Service ceiling: 9,000 m (29,525 ft)
- T-O run at S/L, ISA, zero wind: 350 m (1,150 ft)
- T-O to 15 m (50 ft), conditions as above: 550 m (1,805 ft)
- T-O to 15 m (50 ft) at 1,500 m (4,920 ft), ISA, zero wind: 800 m (2,625 ft)
- Max range on internal fuel, 10% reserves: 572 nm (1,060 km; 658 miles)
- Max endurance: 3 h 18 min
- *g* limits: +7·0; −3·5

EM
ELICOTTERI MERIDIONALI SpA

Works: Via Giovanni Agusta 1, Frosinone
Telephone: (0775) 82801
Telex: Elmef 611377 and Emf 614171
Chairman and President: Conte Corrado Agusta
President, Chief Executive Officer: P. Fascione
General Manager: Piero Tana

This company was formed with assistance from Agusta (which see) and began to operate in October 1967. Initially, its activities consisted of overhauling helicopters of the Italian armed forces and other organisations, and the manufacture of helicopter components and sub-assemblies. In 1968 Meridionali acquired rights to the co-production, marketing and servicing of the Boeing Vertol CH-47C Chinook transport helicopter for customers in Italy, Austria, Switzerland and the Middle East. Italian production of the CH-47C airframe is undertaken

Italian-built Boeing Vertol CH-47C helicopter in the insignia of Italian Army Aviation

by SIAI-Marchetti, another member of the Agusta group.

Meridionali, whose works occupy a total area of more than 300,000 m² (3,229,170 sq ft), participates in the manufacturing programmes for the Agusta A 109A, Agusta-Bell 205, 206B and 212, and Agusta-Sikorsky SH-3D helicopters (see under Agusta in this section). Meridionali is also distributor in Italy for the Allison 250 series of turboshaft engines, and has complete facilities for overhaul, repair and field assistance.

EM (BOEING VERTOL) CH-47C

Italian manufacture of the CH-47C began in the Spring of 1970 initially to meet orders for the Imperial Iranian Army and Air Force. Production has since continued for other military customers, including Libya and Morocco, and was at the rate of one per month in 1978-79.

GENERAL AVIA
GENERAL AVIA COSTRUZIONI AERONAUTICHE Srl

ADDRESS: Via Trieste 24, 20096 Pioltello, Milan
Telephone: 9046774
TECHNICAL DIRECTOR: Dott Ing Stelio Frati
SECRETARY-TREASURER: Lamberto Frati
PRODUCTION: Enrico Fanoli
PUBLIC RELATIONS: Carla Bielli

Dott Ing Stelio Frati is well known for the many successful light aircraft which, as a freelance designer, he has evolved since 1950. These have been built in prototype and production series by several Italian manufacturers, and have included the Procaer F15 Picchio and the F.250, now manufactured by SIAI-Marchetti as the SF.260.

General Avia was established by Dott Ing Frati in early 1970, primarily to develop prototypes of his own design for production by other companies. These have included the F15F, a derivative of the Procaer F15E Picchio which is to be placed in production by Procaer; and the F.20 Pegaso, originally intended for production by Italair (see 1975-76 *Jane's*) but now being manufactured by General Avia under an agreement with Italair.

Currently, General Avia is also developing the larger F.600 Canguro transport aircraft.

GENERAL AVIA F.20 PEGASO

Design of the F.20 Pegaso six-seat light business twin was started in January 1970. Two prototypes were built by General Avia, these making their first flights on 21 October 1971 and 11 August 1972, as described in previous editions of *Jane's*. Following type certification by the RAI (19 November 1974) and FAA (14 May 1975), the Pegaso was to have been placed in production by Italair. However, under a recent agreement with Italair, the production version is now to be manufactured by General Avia, the first series-built example being due for completion in July 1979 and the second in September/October 1979.

The production version introduces a number of improvements compared with the prototypes. These include better cabin heating and soundproofing, and the use of three-blade propellers to improve certain aspects of performance.

The Pegaso is also available in a four-seat military version, the F.20 **Condor**, suitable for weapon training, long-range maritime surveillance, and search and rescue. This has lower-powered engines and can be fitted with three stores pylons under each wing, the centre one on each side being capable of carrying a 250 litre (55 Imp gallon) auxiliary fuel tank.

The following description applies to the civil Pegaso, except where indicated:

TYPE: Twin-engined six-seat light executive transport aircraft.

WINGS: Cantilever low-wing monoplane. Wing section NACA 65_2-415. Dihedral 5° from roots. Incidence 1° 45′. All-metal single-spar structure in light alloy, with flush-riveted stressed skin. Differentially-operated all-metal ailerons and electrically actuated double-slotted metal trailing-edge flaps. No tabs. Anti-icing optional.

FUSELAGE: All-metal semi-monocoque structure, with flush-riveted aluminium alloy skin.

TAIL UNIT: Cantilever all-metal structure with flush-riveted skin. Fixed-incidence tailplane. Trim tabs in rudder and each elevator. Anti-icing optional.

LANDING GEAR: Retractable tricycle type, with single wheel on each unit. Nosewheel steerable 18° to left and right. Electrical actuation, with manual backup. Oleo-pneumatic shock-absorbers. Main wheels and tyres size 7·00-6, pressure 3·24 bars (47 lb/sq in); nosewheel and tyre size 6·00-6, pressure 1·86 bars (27 lb/sq in). Cleveland brakes.

POWER PLANT: Two 223·5 kW (300 hp) (212·4 kW; 285 hp in Condor) Continental IO-520-K flat-six engines, each driving a Hartzell PHC-C3YF-2UF three-blade constant-speed fully-feathering propeller. Fuel in two wing tanks, each of 124 litres (27·25 Imp gallons), and two wingtip tanks each of 126 litres (27·7 Imp gallons) capacity. Total capacity 500 litres (110 Imp gallons). Provision in Condor for further 500 litres to be carried in two underwing auxiliary tanks. Oil capacity 22·8 litres (5 Imp gallons). Electrical propeller de-icing available optionally.

ACCOMMODATION: Normal seating, in fully enclosed cabin, for six persons (four in Condor), including pilot. Space for up to 104 kg (230 lb) of baggage in four compartments in forward and rear fuselage and each engine nacelle. Access to cabin via large door on each side. Cabin heated, ventilated and soundproofed, with glass-wool insulation.

AVIONICS AND EQUIPMENT: IFR instrumentation and dual controls standard; other installations to customer's requirements.

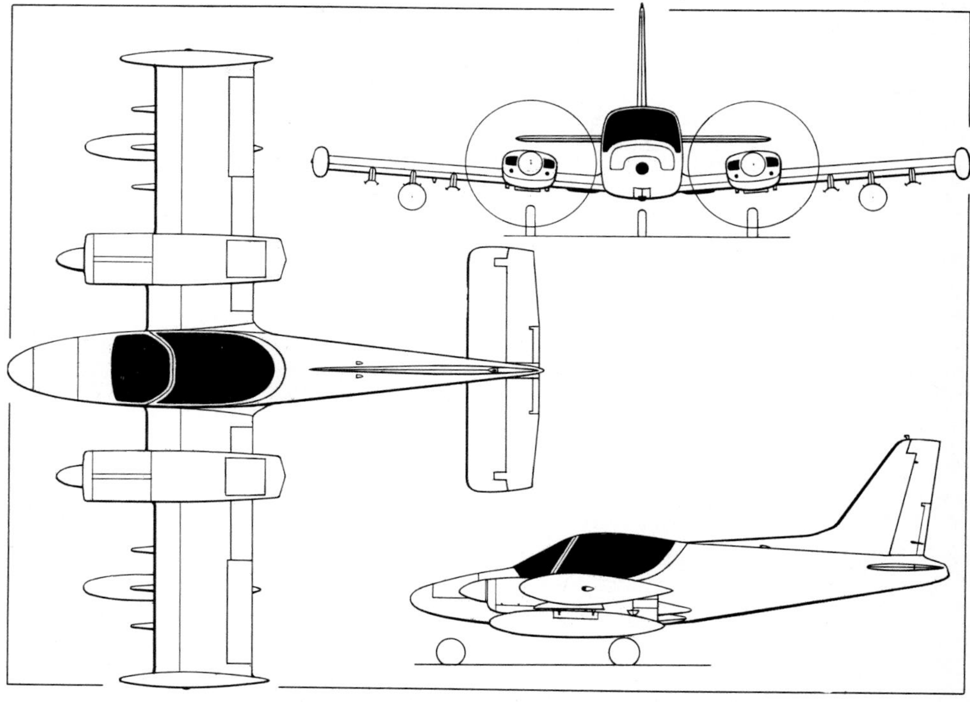

Condor four-seat military version of the General Avia F.20 Pegaso *(Pilot Press)*

DIMENSIONS, EXTERNAL:
- Wing span over tip-tanks: 10·34 m (33 ft 11 in)
- Wing chord at root: 1·65 m (5 ft 5 in)
- Wing chord at tip: 1·50 m (4 ft 11 in)
- Wing aspect ratio: 6·67
- Length overall: 8·22 m (26 ft 11½ in)
- Height overall: 3·50 m (11 ft 5¾ in)
- Tailplane span: 4·10 m (13 ft 5½ in)
- Wheel track: 3·50 m (11 ft 5¾ in)
- Wheelbase: 2·40 m (7 ft 10½ in)
- Propeller diameter: 1·98 m (6 ft 6 in)
- Min propeller ground clearance: 0·20 m (8 in)
- Distance between propeller centres: 3·42 m (11 ft 2½ in)

DIMENSIONS, INTERNAL:
- Cabin: Max length: 3·66 m (12 ft 0 in)
  - Max width: 1·17 m (3 ft 10 in)
  - Max height: 1·13 m (3 ft 8½ in)
- Baggage compartments (four):
  - Total volume: 0·70 m³ (25 cu ft)

AREAS:
- Wings, gross: 16·02 m² (172·4 sq ft)
- Ailerons (total): 1·42 m² (15·28 sq ft)
- Trailing-edge flaps (total): 1·59 m² (17·13 sq ft)
- Fin: 1·24 m² (13·35 sq ft)
- Rudder, incl tab: 0·79 m² (8·50 sq ft)
- Tailplane: 2·46 m² ((26·48 sq ft)
- Elevators, incl tabs: 1·95 m² (20·99 sq ft)

WEIGHTS AND LOADINGS (A: Pegaso; B: Condor without underwing tanks; C: Condor with underwing tanks):
- Weight empty, equipped: A 1,510 kg (3,330 lb); B 1,500 kg (3,307 lb); C 1,600 kg (3,527 lb)
- Max payload: A 514 kg (1,134 lb)
- Max T-O and landing weight: A 2,250 kg (4,960 lb); B 2,200 kg (4,850 lb); C 2,500 kg (5,511 lb)
- Max wing loading: A 145·0 kg/m² (29·7 lb/sq ft); B 137·3 kg/m² (28·12 lb/sq ft); C 156·0 kg/m² (31·95 lb/sq ft)
- Max power loading: A 5·30 kg/kW (8·71 lb/hp); B 5·18 kg/kW (8·51 lb/hp); C 5·89 kg/kW (9·66 lb/hp)

PERFORMANCE (at max T-O weight except where indicated):
- Never-exceed speed (A, B, C): 232 knots (431 km/h; 267 mph)
- Max level speed at S/L: A 216 knots (400 km/h; 249 mph); B 208 knots (385 km/h; 239 mph); C 188 knots (350 km/h; 217 mph)
- Max cruising speed (75% power) at 2,440 m (8,000 ft): A 203 knots (377 km/h; 234 mph); B 194 knots (360 km/h; 224 mph); C 178 knots (330 km/h; 205 mph)
- Econ cruising speed (60% power) at 3,660 m (12,000 ft): A, B 183 knots (340 km/h; 211 mph); C 167 knots (310 km/h; 193 mph)
- Stalling speed, flaps down: A 66 knots (121 km/h; 76 mph); B at 2,000 kg (4,409 lb) AUW 62 knots (115 km/h; 71·5 mph); C at 2,000 kg (4,409 lb) AUW 68 knots (125 km/h; 78 mph)
- Max rate of climb at S/L: A 550 m (1,805 ft)/min; B 600 m (1,970 ft)/min; C 480 m (1,575 ft)/min
- Rate of climb at S/L, one engine out: A 120 m (394 ft)/min
- Service ceiling: A 6,250 m (20,500 ft); B 6,000 m (19,685 ft); C 5,000 m (16,400 ft)
- Service ceiling, one engine out: A 2,290 m (7,515 ft); B 1,900 m (6,235 ft); C 1,500 m (4,920 ft)
- T-O run: A 230 m (755 ft); B 220 m (722 ft); C 300 m (984 ft)
- T-O to 15 m (50 ft): A 320 m (1,050 ft)
- Landing run from 15 m (50 ft): A 380 m (1,250 ft)
- Landing run: A, B 260 m (853 ft); C 300 m (984 ft)
- Range:
  - A with max fuel 955 nm (1,770 km; 1,100 miles)
  - A with max payload 547 nm (1,013 km; 630 miles)
  - B at 75% power 809 nm (1,500 km; 932 miles)
  - B at 60% power 917 nm (1,700 km; 1,056 miles)
  - C at 75% power 1,511 nm (2,800 km; 1,740 miles)
  - C at 60% power 1,618 nm (3,000 km; 1,864 miles)
- Max endurance: B 5 h; C 10 h

GENERAL AVIA F.600 CANGURO (KANGAROO)

A prototype of the F.600 Canguro (I-CANG) made its first flight on 30 December 1978. It had accumulated about 40 hours' flying by late May 1979, and RAI certification was expected shortly. Production is expected to be undertaken by SIAI-Marchetti.

TYPE: Twin-engined freight, ambulance and general utility transport.

WINGS: Cantilever high-wing monoplane. Wing section GAW-1, with 17% thickness/chord ratio. Dihedral 2°. Incidence (constant) 1° 30′. All-metal riveted structure in light alloy, with stressed skin. Centre-section has main spar and two auxiliary spars; outboard of engines, wings have two spars. All-metal ailerons and electrically-operated double-slotted flaps.

FUSELAGE: All-metal semi-monocoque structure, with stressed skin.

Tail Unit: Cantilever all-metal stressed-skin structure. Trim tabs in rudder and each elevator. Small dorsal and ventral fins.

Landing Gear: Non-retractable tricycle type, with oleo-pneumatic shock-absorption. Twin-wheel main units; single steerable nose unit. Wheel and tyre sizes 7·00-6 (main), 6·00-6 (nose). Tyre pressure (all units) 2·48 bars (36 lb/sq in).

Power Plant: Two 261 kW (350 hp) Lycoming TIO-540-J flat-six engines, each driving a Hartzell fully-feathering constant-speed propeller. Alternatively, may be powered by two 298 kW (400 shp) Allison 250-B17 turboprop engines. Fuel in four wing tanks, total capacity 900 litres (198 Imp gallons). Oil capacity 11·4 litres (2·5 Imp gallons).

Accommodation: Pilot and co-pilot or passenger on flight deck. Cabin accommodates up to 9 passengers or paratroops, or four stretcher patients and two medical attendants, or 907 kg (2,000 lb) of freight. Forward door on each side for crew and passengers; third, wider door at rear on starboard side for freight loading.

Dimensions, external:
Wing span 14·50 m (47 ft 7 in)
Wing chord (constant) 1·60 m (5 ft 3 in)
Wing aspect ratio 9·1
Length overall 12·15 m (39 ft 10½ in)
Height overall 4·60 m (15 ft 1 in)
Tailplane span 5·06 m (16 ft 7¼ in)
Wheel track 2·40 m (7 ft 10½ in)
Wheelbase 4·88 m (16 ft 0 in)
Propeller diameter 2·03 m (6 ft 8 in)
Crew/passenger doors (fwd, each):
Height 1·14 m (3 ft 9 in)
Width 0·86 m (2 ft 10 in)
Height to sill 0·90 m (2 ft 11½ in)
Cargo door (stbd, rear):
Height 1·13 m (3 ft 8½ in)
Width 1·49 m (4 ft 10¾ in)
Height to sill 0·90 m (2 ft 11½ in)

Dimensions, internal:
Cabin, excl flight deck:
Length 5·05 m (16 ft 6¾ in)
Width 1·23 m (4 ft 0½ in)
Height 1·27 m (4 ft 2 in)
Floor area 5·57 m² (60 sq ft)
Volume 7·08 m³ (250 cu ft)

Areas:
Wings, gross 23·10 m² (248·65 sq ft)
Ailerons (total) 1·28 m² (13·78 sq ft)
Trailing-edge flaps (total) 2·32 m² (24·97 sq ft)
Fin 1·46 m² (15·72 sq ft)
Rudder, incl tab 0·90 m² (9·69 sq ft)
Tailplane 3·06 m² (32·94 sq ft)
Elevators (total, incl tabs) 2·50 m² (26·91 sq ft)

Weights (A: TIO-540 engines; B: Allison 250 engines):
Weight empty, equipped, cargo version:
A 1,950 kg (4,299 lb)
B 1,760 kg (3,880 lb)

Prototype of the General Avia F.600 Canguro during its first flight

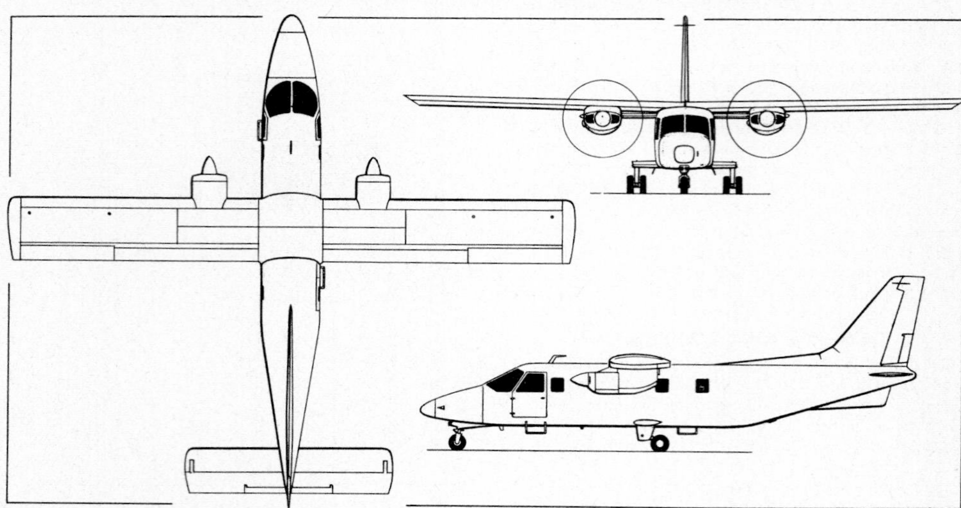

General Avia F.600 Canguro (two Lycoming TIO-540-J engines) *(Pilot Press)*

Max payload: A, B 1,050 kg (2,315 lb)
Max T-O weight: A 3,100 kg (6,834 lb)
B 3,200 kg (7,054 lb)

Performance (estimated, at max T-O weight A: TIO-540 engines; B: Allison 250 engines):
Max level speed at 4,570 m (15,000 ft):
A 183 knots (340 km/h; 211 mph)
B 194 knots (360 km/h; 224 mph)
Cruising speed at 3,660 m (12,000 ft):
A (60% power) 146 knots (270 km/h; 168 mph)
B (75% power) 167 knots (310 km/h; 193 mph)
Stalling speed, flaps down:
A 59·5 knots (110 km/h; 68·5 mph)
B 62·5 knots (116 km/h; 72 mph)
Max rate of climb at S/L: A 402 m (1,319 ft)/min
B 408 m (1,338 ft)/min
Rate of climb at S/L, one engine out:
A 84 m (276 ft)/min
B 108 m (354 ft)/min
Service ceiling: A 7,100 m (23,300 ft)
B 7,300 m (23,950 ft)
Range with max fuel (cargo version), IFR reserves:
A, 400 kg (882 lb) payload
1,025 nm (1,900 km; 1,180 miles)
B, 600 kg (1,323 lb) payload
917 nm (1,700 km; 1,056 miles)

PARTENAVIA
PARTENAVIA COSTRUZIONI AERONAUTICHE SpA

Head Office and Works: Via Cava, CP 2179, 80026 Casoria (Naples)
Telephone: (081) 7596311 (PBX)
Telex: 73199 Partenav
President: Prof Ing Luigi Pascale
Directors:
Dott G. Bulgari
Dott G. Fiore
Dott D. Marchiorello
Ing G. Regazzoni
Production Director: Ing Nino Pascale
International Marketing: Ian A. Forbes

This company was founded in 1957 by Prof Ing Luigi Pascale and his brother, Ing Nino Pascale, and has since built a series of light aircraft designed by Prof Ing Pascale.

On 1 March 1974 the company moved from its small factory at Arzano, near Naples, to a 12,000 m² (129,165 sq ft) facility on Capodichino Airport, Naples, where it is now concentrating on production and development of the P.68B Victor twin-engined seven-seat light aircraft and its derivatives, and on the P.66C Charlie.

PARTENAVIA P.66C-160 CHARLIE

This two/four-seat basic training aircraft is an improved version of the P.64B/P.66B Oscar series (see 1975-76 *Jane's*), and is certificated in the FAR Pt 23 Utility category, with clearance for all positive-*g* aerobatic manoeuvres and six-turn spins. The prototype P.66C, with a 112 kW (150 hp) Lycoming O-360-A1A engine, flew in early January 1976, and was certificated in Spring 1976.

The P.66C has been chosen by the Aero Club d'Italia as the standard basic trainer for aero clubs throughout Italy, and an order for 70 P.66C Charlies has been placed, with an option to increase this order to 250. Deliveries began at the end of 1977, and had totalled 57 by June 1979; a further 15 were due to be delivered by the end of that year.

Partenavia P.66C Charlie two/four-seat basic training aircraft

Type: Two/four-seat light monoplane.

Wings: Braced high-wing monoplane with single streamline-section bracing strut each side. Wing section NACA 63 series. Thickness/chord ratio 15%. Dihedral 1° 30′. Incidence at root 1° 40′. No sweepback. Stressed-skin single-spar torsion-box structure of aluminium alloy, with one-piece glassfibre-reinforced plastics moulded leading-edges. Ailerons and electrically-operated slotted trailing-edge flaps of similar construction to wings.

Fuselage: Forward portion, to rear of cabin, has a welded steel tube basic structure to which are attached light alloy skin panels. Rear fuselage is of conventional light alloy stressed-skin construction.

Tail Unit: Cantilever stressed-skin metal structure with sweptback vertical surfaces. All-moving tailplane in two symmetrical halves joined by steel cross-tube. Anti-balance tab in trailing-edge of tailplane, over 80% of span.

Landing Gear: Non-retractable tricycle type, with steerable nosewheel. Cantilever spring steel main legs. Oleo nosewheel shock-absorber. Cleveland main wheels type 40-28, with Pirelli tyres size 6·00-6. Goodyear nosewheel tyre size 5·00-5. Cleveland type 30-18 hydraulic disc brakes.

Power Plant: One 119 kW (160 hp) Lycoming O-320-H2AD flat-four engine, driving a Hoffmann HO 23-183.150 two-blade fixed-pitch propeller. Two integral fuel tanks in wing roots, total usable capacity 130 litres (28·5 Imp gallons). Refuelling points above wings. Oil capacity 7·5 litres (1·66 Imp gallons).

Accommodation: Enclosed cabin seating two or four persons in pairs; front seats are of the adjustable sliding type. Three forward-hinged doors: one by each front seat and on starboard side at rear. Baggage space aft of rear seats, with separate door on starboard side. Dual controls, heating, ventilation and soundproofing standard.

AVIONICS AND EQUIPMENT: Optional items include full IFR instrumentation, Grimes rotating beacon, VHF radio, VOR and ADF.

DIMENSIONS, EXTERNAL:

Wing span	9·986 m (32 ft 9¼ in)
Wing chord (constant)	1·36 m (4 ft 5½ in)
Wing aspect ratio	7·45
Length overall	7·24 m (23 ft 9 in)
Height overall	2·77 m (9 ft 1 in)
Tailplane span	3·10 m (10 ft 2 in)
Wheel track	2·10 m (6 ft 10½ in)
Wheelbase	1·63 m (5 ft 4¼ in)
Propeller diameter	1·88 m (6 ft 2 in)

DIMENSIONS, INTERNAL:

Cabin: Max width	1·06 m (3 ft 5¾ in)
Max height	1·20 m (3 ft 11¼ in)

AREAS:

Wings, gross	13·40 m² (144·2 sq ft)
Ailerons (total)	1·29 m² (13·88 sq ft)
Trailing-edge flaps (total)	1·71 m² (18·40 sq ft)
Fin	0·73 m² (7·86 sq ft)
Rudder	0·45 m² (4·84 sq ft)
Tailplane, incl tab	2·17 m² (23·36 sq ft)

WEIGHTS AND LOADINGS:

Weight empty	600 kg (1,322 lb)
Max T-O and landing weight	990 kg (2,183 lb)
Max wing loading	73·88 kg/m² (15·13 lb/sq ft)
Max power loading	8·30 kg/kW (13·63 lb/hp)

PERFORMANCE (at max T-O weight, ISA):

Max level speed at S/L	130 knots (241 km/h; 150 mph)
Max cruising speed (75% power) at 1,980 m (6,500 ft)	118 knots (218 km/h; 135 mph)
Econ cruising speed (65% power) at 2,745 m (9,000 ft)	111 knots (206 km/h; 128 mph)
Stalling speed at S/L: flaps up	53 knots (98·5 km/h; 61·5 mph)
flaps down (T-O)	50 knots (93 km/h; 58 mph)
flaps down (landing)	44 knots (82 km/h; 51 mph)
Max rate of climb at S/L	289 m (950 ft)/min
Service ceiling	4,570 m (15,000 ft)
T-O run at S/L	245 m (805 ft)
T-O to 15 m (50 ft) at S/L	420 m (1,378 ft)
Landing from 15 m (50 ft) at S/L	350 m (1,148 ft)
Landing run at S/L	150 m (492 ft)
Range at 1,980 m (6,500 ft), 75% power, with reserves	370 nm (685 km; 426 miles)
Range at 2,745 m (9,000 ft), 65% power, with reserves	422 nm (782 km; 486 miles)
Endurance at 1,980 m (6,500 ft), 75% power, with reserves	3 h 8 min
Endurance at 2,745 m (9,000 ft), 65% power, with reserves	3 h 48 min

PARTENAVIA P.68B VICTOR

Developed from the P.68, which was designed by Prof Ing Luigi Pascale in 1968 and described in the 1975-76 *Jane's*, the P.68B Victor twin-engined light transport has been in production in Partenavia's factory at Naples Airport since the Spring of 1974.

By mid-1979, approx 190 aircraft had been delivered, more than 100 of them for export to operators in Australia, Austria, Belgium, the République Populaire du Congo, Denmark, England, Finland, France, Germany, Israel, Kenya, the Middle East, Morocco, the Netherlands, Niugini, Norway, South Africa, Sweden, Switzerland, Tanzania, the USA and Venezuela. By the beginning of 1979 the whole of that year's production had been allocated, and outstanding orders extended into the first half of 1980.

TYPE: Six/seven-seat light transport and trainer.

WINGS: Cantilever high-wing monoplane. Wing section NACA 63_3-515. Dihedral 1°. Incidence 1° 30′. No sweepback. Stressed-skin single-spar torsion-box structure, of aluminium alloy except for area forward of main spar (30% of total area) which is of GRP. All-metal ailerons and electrically-operated single-slotted trailing-edge flaps. Hoerner wingtips. Trim tab on port aileron.

FUSELAGE: Conventional all-metal semi-monocoque structure of frames and longerons, with four main longerons and stressed-skin covering. Fuselage/wing intersection mainly of GRP.

TAIL UNIT: Cantilever stressed-skin metal structure. All-moving tailplane, in two symmetrical halves joined by steel cross-tube and of constant chord except for increase at leading-edge roots. Balance tab in tailplane trailing-edge, over 80% of span. Sweptback fin and rudder, with small dorsal fin. Trim tab in rudder.

LANDING GEAR: Non-retractable tricycle type, with steerable nosewheel. Cantilever spring steel main legs. Oleo-pneumatic shock-absorber on nosewheel. Cleveland main wheels, type 40-96, with Pirelli tyres size 6·00-6. Goodyear nose-wheel tyre, size 5·00-5. Cleveland type 30-61 hydraulic disc brakes. Streamlined wheel fairings optional.

POWER PLANT: Two 149 kW (200 hp) Lycoming IO-360-A1B6 flat-four engines, each driving a Hartzell HC-C2YK-2C/C-7666A-4 two-blade variable-pitch constant-speed fully-feathering propeller. Integral fuel tank in each outer wing, total capacity 410 litres (90 Imp

Partenavia P.68B Victor six/seven-seat light aircraft in the insignia of a United States customer

gallons). Two optional long-range tanks, each of 40 litres (8·8 Imp gallons) capacity. Refuelling point above each wing. Oil capacity 15 litres (3·3 Imp gallons).

ACCOMMODATION: Seating for seven persons in cabin, including pilot, in two rows of two seats and a rear bench seat for three persons. A 'club' seating arrangement is available optionally, having the two middle seats facing rearward with a folding table between them and the bench seat. Front seats are of the adjustable sliding type. Access to all seats via large car-type door on port side of cabin. Access to baggage compartment via separate large door on starboard side. Two stretchers can be carried when all passenger seats are removed. Dual controls, cabin heating, ventilation and soundproofing standard.

SYSTEMS AND AVIONICS: Electrical power supplied by two 24V 50A alternators. Bendix FCS 810 autopilot system and Goodrich pneumatic de-icing system optional. Optional avionics include full IFR instrumentation, two 360-channel VHF transceivers, two navigation receivers, VOR/ILS, marker beacon, ADF and DME.

DIMENSIONS, EXTERNAL:

Wing span	12·00 m (39 ft 4½ in)
Wing chord (constant)	1·55 m (5 ft 1 in)
Wing aspect ratio	7·74
Length overall	9·35 m (30 ft 8 in)
Height overall	3·40 m (11 ft 1¾ in)
Tailplane span	3·90 m (12 ft 9½ in)
Wheel track	2·40 m (7 ft 10½ in)
Wheelbase	3·50 m (11 ft 5¾ in)
Propeller diameter	1·88 m (6 ft 2 in)
Baggage door, stbd: Height	0·80 m (2 ft 7½ in)
Width	0·80 m (2 ft 7½ in)

DIMENSIONS, INTERNAL:

Cabin: Length	4·00 m (13 ft 1½ in)
Max width	1·16 m (3 ft 9½ in)
Max height	1·21 m (3 ft 11½ in)
Baggage space	0·57 m³ (20 cu ft)

AREAS:

Wings, gross	18·60 m² (200 sq ft)
Ailerons (total)	1·79 m² (19·27 sq ft)
Trailing-edge flaps (total)	2·37 m² (25·51 sq ft)
Fin	1·59 m² (17·11 sq ft)
Rudder, incl tab	0·44 m² (4·74 sq ft)
Tailplane, incl tab	4·41 m² (47·47 sq ft)

WEIGHTS AND LOADINGS:

Weight empty	1,260 kg (2,778 lb)
Max T-O weight	1,960 kg (4,321 lb)
Max landing weight	1,860 kg (4,100 lb)
Max wing loading	105 kg/m² (21·6 lb/sq ft)
Max power loading	6·58 kg/kW (10·80 lb/hp)

PERFORMANCE (at max T-O weight):

Max level speed at S/L	174 knots (322 km/h; 200 mph)
Max cruising speed (75% power) at 2,285 m (7,500 ft)	165 knots (306 km/h; 190 mph)
Cruising speed (65% power) at 3,350 m (11,000 ft)	160 knots (296 km/h; 184 mph)
Cruising speed (55% power) at 3,660 m (12,000 ft)	152 knots (282 km/h; 175 mph)
Stalling speed, flaps up	65 knots (120 km/h; 75 mph)
Stalling speed, flaps down	56 knots (104 km/h; 64·5 mph)
Max rate of climb at S/L	457 m (1,500 ft)/min
Rate of climb at S/L, one engine out	98 m (320 ft)/min
Service ceiling	6,100 m (20,000 ft)
Service ceiling, one engine out	2,135 m (7,000 ft)
T-O run	228 m (750 ft)
T-O to 15 m (50 ft)	344 m (1,130 ft)
Landing from 15 m (50 ft)	427 m (1,400 ft)
Landing run	210 m (690 ft)
Optimum cruising range, no reserves: 75% power	830 nm (1,538 km; 955 miles)
65% power	894 nm (1,656 km; 1,029 miles)
55% power	965 nm (1,788 km; 1,111 miles)

PARTENAVIA P.68R

The P.68R retractable landing gear version of the P.68B, described in the 1978-79 *Jane's*, flew for the first time in December 1976, and certification flight trials were completed during the Spring of 1977.

There are no immediate plans for the production of this model.

PARTENAVIA P.68RTC

This variant of the P.68B has the retractable landing gear of the P.68R and is fitted with two 156·5 kW (210 hp) Lycoming TIO-360 turbocharged engines.

PERFORMANCE (estimated):

Max level speed at S/L	218 knots (404 km/h; 251 mph)
Cruising speed (75% power) at 6,100 m (20,000 ft)	204 knots (378 km/h; 235 mph)
Cruising speed (65% power) at 5,490 m (18,000 ft)	190 knots (352 km/h; 219 mph)
Stalling speed, flaps up	66 knots (122 km/h; 76 mph)
Stalling speed, flaps down	58 knots (108 km/h; 67 mph)
Max rate of climb at S/L	449 m (1,472 ft)/min
Max rate of climb at S/L, one engine out	106 m (348 ft)/min
Service ceiling	9,450 m (31,000 ft)
Service ceiling, one engine out	4,570 m (15,000 ft)

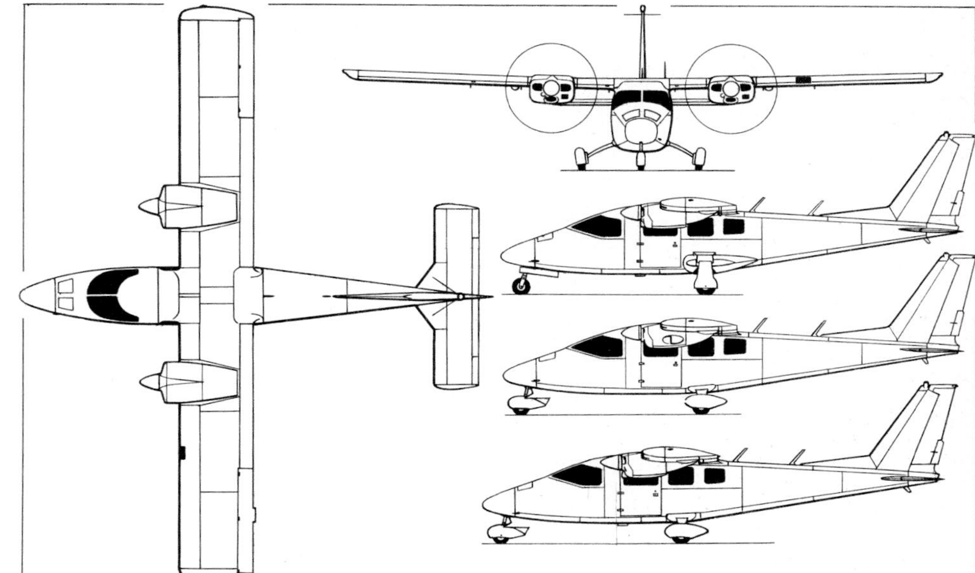

Partenavia P.68C Victor, with additional side views of P.68C-R (top) and P.68C-TC (centre) *(Pilot Press)*

T-O run 260 m (853 ft)
T-O to 15 m (50 ft) 455 m (1,491 ft)
Landing from 15 m (50 ft) 417 m (1,369 ft)
Landing run 262 m (861 ft)

PARTENAVIA P.68C

This six/seven-seat twin-engined aircraft is an improved version of the P.68B. Principal differences are a lengthened nose, for easier installation of weather radar; oleo-type nosewheel strut; single integral fuel tank (capacity 568 litres; 125 Imp gallons) in each wing; annunciator panel warning light system; individual reading lights; improved soundproofing; internally-opening baggage door, providing an additional emergency exit; modified rear bench seat back, for easier access to baggage compartment from inside cabin; and landing gear speed fairings. Power plant and dimensions are the same as for the P.68B.

WEIGHTS:
Weight empty 1,269 kg (2,797 lb)
Max T-O weight 1,990 kg (4,387 lb)
Max landing weight 1,890 kg (4,166 lb)

PERFORMANCE (estimated):
Max level speed at S/L 174 knots (322 km/h; 200 mph)
Max cruising speed at 2,290 m (7,500 ft) 166 knots (307 km/h; 191 mph)
Stalling speed, flaps up 66 knots (122 km/h; 76 mph)
Stalling speed, flaps down 60 knots (111 km/h; 69 mph)
Max rate of climb at S/L 488 m (1,600 ft)/min
Rate of climb at S/L, one engine out 85·5 m (280 ft)/min
Service ceiling 6,100 m (20,000 ft)
Service ceiling, one engine out 2,135 m (7,000 ft)
Range with max fuel (65% power) at 3,355 m (11,000 ft) 1,100 nm (2,037 km; 1,266 miles)

PARTENAVIA P.68C-R

The P.68C-R is a retractable landing gear version of the P.86C described in the preceding entry.

PARTENAVIA P.68C-TC

This variant of the P.68C is fitted with two Lycoming TIO-360-C1A6D turbocharged engines, each rated at 156·5 kW (210 hp).

WEIGHTS:
Weight empty 1,320 kg (2,910 lb)
Max T-O weight 1,990 kg (4,387 lb)
Max landing weight 1,890 kg (4,166 lb)

PERFORMANCE (estimated):
Max level speed at 4,875 m (16,000 ft) 200 knots (370 km/h; 230 mph)
Max cruising speed (75% power) at 3,660 m (12,000 ft) 180 knots (333 km/h; 207 mph)
Stalling speed, flaps up 66 knots (122 km/h; 76 mph)
Stalling speed, flaps down 60 knots (111 km/h; 69 mph)
Max rate of climb at S/L 518 m (1,700 ft)/min
Max rate of climb at S/L, one engine out 91·5 m (300 ft)/min
Service ceiling 8,230 m (27,000 ft)
Service ceiling, one engine out 4,420 m (14,500 ft)
Range with max fuel (65% power) at 6,400 m (21,000 ft) 1,100 nm (2,037 km; 1,266 miles)

PARTENAVIA P.68 FLOATPLANE/AMPHIBIAN

A P.68B modified for the installation of both amphibious and non-amphibious floats has been flown on an experimental basis with glassfibre floats manufactured by SEFA of Cannes, France.

Further development of a floatplane version of the P.68B was expected to take place in the USA. The estimated performance of a floatplane version of the P.68B is as follows:

PERFORMANCE (estimated):
Max level speed at S/L 148 knots (274 km/h; 170 mph)
Cruising speed (75% power) at 1,675 m (5,500 ft) 140 knots (259 km/h; 161 mph)
Cruising speed (65% power) at 2,745 m (9,000 ft) 136 knots (253 km/h; 157 mph)
Max rate of climb at S/L 335 m (1,100 ft)/min
Service ceiling 4,875 m (16,000 ft)
Service ceiling, one engine out 762 m (2,500 ft)
T-O run 335 m (1,100 ft)

PARTENAVIA P.68 OBSERVER

In collaboration with Sportavia-Pützer, Partenavia's West German distributor, a version of the P.68 known as the Observer has been developed, with a forward and downward view for the crew equal to that of a helicopter.

The new Plexiglas nose, cockpit and associated structure were designed by Sportavia-Pützer; the prototype (D-GERD) was constructed at that company's Dahlemer-Binz factory, and first flew on 20 February 1976. Dimensions, weights and performance are essentially as given for the P.68B Victor; the electrical system utilises 70A alternators.

With its good low-speed handling characteristics, the Observer is considered to be capable of performing many roles allocated normally to helicopters. It is intended particularly for patrol and observation operations. The prototype was evaluated in mid-1978 by the Rhineland-Palatinate police department with considerable success, and several orders for this version have been received from German and other police departments.

Prototype Partenavia P.68 Observer, modified from a standard P.68B by Sportavia-Pützer in Germany

PARTENAVIA/AERITALIA AP.68TP

This turbine-engined version of the P.68R, known originally as the P.68 Turbo, is being developed in association with Aeritalia. The installation of two Allison 250-B17B turboprop engines, each flat rated at 246 kW (330 shp), offers an improved power/weight ratio which is claimed to give the AP.68TP the lowest operating costs of any aircraft in its class. Multi-role versatility includes the ability to carry a wide variety of external stores on four underwing and two fuselage-side hardpoints, to cover a broad spectrum of possible missions. These include air taxi, liaison, executive or cargo transport, training, ground support, or (possibly with a 'goldfish bowl' nose similar to that of the P.68 Observer) for reconnaissance, coastal patrol and aerial survey.

The prototype AP.68TP (NC 6001; I-PAIT) flew for the first time on 11 September 1978, at Naples, piloted by Comm Lionello Bellio, an Aeritalia test pilot. The following description applies to this aircraft. Certification of the AP.68TP is expected by May 1980, and deliveries are scheduled to begin in late 1980 or early 1981. Production may be undertaken by a consortium.

WINGS, FUSELAGE AND TAIL UNIT: As P.68B, except for local strengthening in vicinity of wing and fuselage hardpoints, and lengthening of fuselage by 0·195 m (7·7 in) forward of wings.

LANDING GEAR: Retractable tricycle type, with single wheel on each unit. Electro-hydraulic actuation, nosewheel retracting forward, main units inward into fairings on fuselage sides.

POWER PLANT: Two Allison 250-B17B turboprop engines, each flat rated at 246 kW (330 shp) for T-O and max continuous operation, with a max cruise rating at 3,050 m (10,000 ft) of 232 kW (311 shp), and each driving a Hartzell HC-B3TF-7A/T101-73B-11R three-blade fully-feathering reversible-pitch propeller. Fuel in two main and two auxiliary tanks in wings, total capacity 660 litres (145 Imp gallons).

ACCOMMODATION: Seating for seven persons in cabin, including pilot, in two rows of two individual seats and a rear bench seat for three persons. Access to all seats via large car-type door on port side of cabin. Access to baggage compartment via separate large door on starboard side. Dual controls, cabin heating, ventilation and soundproofing standard.

SYSTEMS: Primary electrical power from two 150A 28V DC starter/generators. Nickel-cadmium battery for engine starting. Inverter for 28V DC/115V AC power in event of loss of primary source. Pneumatic anti-icing system for wing and tail leading-edges; electrical anti-icing of propeller blades; engine intakes anti-iced by hot air bled from engine compressor. Oxygen system optional.

AVIONICS: To customer's requirements. Typical installations may include dual VHF/AM com, HF, dual NAV/ILS, ADF, DME, ATC transponder, marker beacon, Omega navigation system, weather radar, autopilot, audio control and gyro compass in civil version; or VHF/FM com and homing, UHF, Tacan and IFF/ATC in military version.

ARMAMENT AND OPERATIONAL EQUIPMENT (military version): Hardpoint for a 113·5 kg (250 lb) store on each side of lower forward fuselage; four underwing hardpoints, each of 182 kg (400 lb) capacity, with standard NATO MA-4A racks. Typical loads may include four SUU-11B/A 7·62 mm Minigun pods, four LAU-32B/A rocket launchers (each containing seven rockets), four 400 lb bombs, flare dispensers, air-to-surface missiles, supply containers, or auxiliary fuel tanks.

DIMENSIONS, EXTERNAL:
Wing span 12·00 m (39 ft 4½ in)
Wing chord, constant 1·55 m (5 ft 1 in)
Wing area, gross 18·60 m² (200·2 sq ft)

Partenavia/Aeritalia AP.68TP seven-seat twin-turboprop civil version of the P.68B

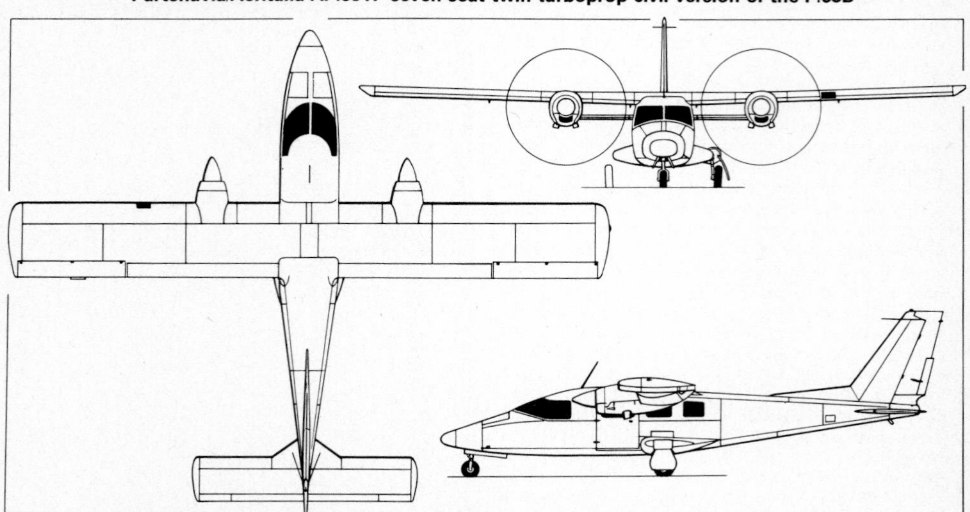
Partenavia/Aeritalia AP.68TP (two Allison 250-B17B turboprop engines) *(Pilot Press)*

Wing aspect ratio 7·55
Length overall 9·844 m (32 ft 3½ in)
Height overall 3·48 m (11 ft 5 in)
Wheel track 2·115 m (6 ft 11¼ in)
Wheelbase 3·613 m (11 ft 10¼ in)
Propeller diameter 2·13 m (7 ft 0 in)

WEIGHTS (civil version):
Weight empty 1,350 kg (2,976 lb)
Operating weight empty (one pilot and 27 kg; 60 lb of avionics and optional equipment) 1,476 kg (3,254 lb)
Max T-O and landing weight 2,400 kg (5,291 lb)
Max zero-fuel weight 2,000 kg (4,409 lb)

PERFORMANCE (at max T-O weight, ISA):
Max cruising speed at 3,050 m (10,000 ft) 220 knots (407 km/h; 253 mph)
Econ cruising speed at 3,050 m (10,000 ft) 176 knots (326 km/h; 203 mph)
Stalling speed, flaps and landing gear up 71 knots (132 km/h; 82 mph) CAS
Stalling speed, flaps and landing gear down 65 knots (121 km/h; 75 mph) CAS
Max rate of climb at S/L 762 m (2,500 ft)/min
Rate of climb at S/L, one engine out 290 m (950 ft)/min
Service ceiling 7,620 m (25,000 ft)
Service ceiling, one engine out 5,500 m (18,050 ft)
T-O to 15 m (50 ft) 396 m (1,300 ft)
Landing from 15 m (50 ft) 448 m (1,470 ft)
Range at max cruising speed with 544 kg (1,200 lb) payload 410 nm (760 km; 472 miles)
Range at econ cruising speed with 884·5 kg (1,950 lb) payload 615 nm (1,139 km; 708 miles)

PARTENAVIA P.78

Up to mid-1979, the P.78 specification had not been finalised. All known details were given in the 1978-79 *Jane's*.

PIAGGIO

INDUSTRIE AERONAUTICHE E MECCANICHE RINALDO PIAGGIO SpA

HEAD OFFICE: Viale Brigata Bisagno 14, Casella Postale 1396, 16129 Genoa
Telephone: 540 521
Telex: 270695 AERPIA I
BRANCH OFFICE: Via A. Gramsci 34, Rome
WORKS: Genoa-Sestri P. (Aircraft Division); Finale Ligure (Aero-Engine Division)
CHAIRMAN AND MANAGING DIRECTOR: Dott Rinaldo Piaggio
VICE-PRESIDENT AND CHIEF EXECUTIVE OFFICER: Dott Lucio Lotti
DIRECTOR GENERAL: Ing Umberto Barnato
DIRECTOR OF INTERNATIONAL PROGRAMMES: Ing B. Mori
TECHNICAL CONSULTANT: Ing Giovanni P. Casiraghi
TECHNICAL DIRECTOR: Ing Alessandro Mazzoni
MARKETING DIRECTOR: Commander G. B. Pizzinato

The original Piaggio company began the construction of aeroplanes in its Genoa-Sestri plant in 1916, and later in the Finale Ligure works. The present company was formed on 29 February 1964, and has since operated as an independent concern. It employs about 1,300 people and has a total covered works area (Genoa-Sestri and Finale-Ligure) of approx 100,000 m² (1,076,390 sq ft). In addition to building aircraft of its own design, Piaggio is producing components for the Aeritalia G222 and Panavia Tornado military aircraft.

The company is organised into two production Divisions: the activities of the Aero-Engine Division are described in the appropriate section of this edition.

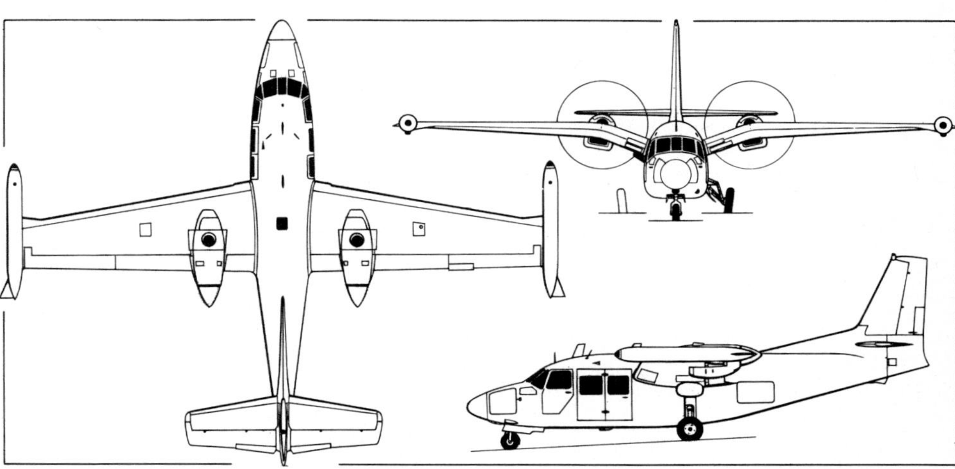

P.166-DL3 version of the Piaggio P.166, with two Avco Lycoming LTP 101 turboprop engines *(Pilot Press)*

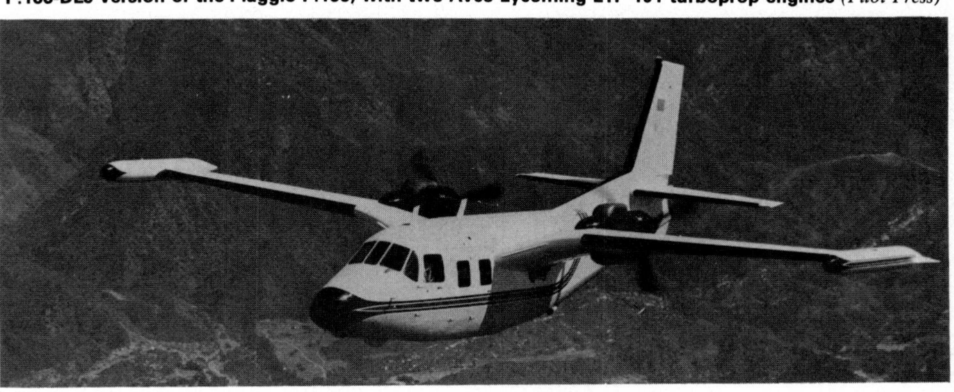

R. Piaggio P.166-DL3 twin-turboprop light transport

R. PIAGGIO P.166-DL3

The P.166 has been produced in several basic versions, of which the original P.166 production version (32 built) was described in the 1963-64 *Jane's*; the military P.166M (51 built), the P.166B Portofino (5 built) and P.166C (2 built) in the 1971-72 *Jane's*; the P.166S search and surveillance version (20 built) in the 1974-75 *Jane's*; and the P.166-DL2 (4 built) in the 1978-79 *Jane's*.

The current version is:

P.166-DL3. Turboprop-powered version, first flown on 3 July 1976. FAA and RAI certification obtained in 1978. Ten production aircraft being built.

TYPE: Twin-turboprop light transport.

WINGS: Shoulder gull-wing cantilever monoplane. NACA 230 wing section. Dihedral 21° 30′ on inner portion, 2° 8′ on outer wings. Incidence 2° 43′. Aluminium alloy flush-riveted structure. All-metal slotted ailerons, with geared and trim tab in starboard aileron. All-metal slotted flaps. Rubber-boot leading-edge de-icing optional.

FUSELAGE: Aluminium alloy flush-riveted semi-monocoque structure.

TAIL UNIT: Cantilever aluminium alloy flush-riveted structure. Geared and trim tabs in elevators; trim tab in rudder.

LANDING GEAR: Retractable tricycle type. Magnaghi oleo-pneumatic shock-absorbers. Hydraulic retraction. Nosewheel retracts rearward, main units outward. Goodyear main wheels with size 25·65 × 8·70-10 tyres, pressure 3·59 bars (52 lb/sq in). Goodyear nosewheel with size 17·5 × 6·30-6 tyre, pressure 2·90 bars (42 lb/sq in). Goodyear or Magnaghi hydraulic brakes.

POWER PLANT: Two Avco Lycoming LTP 101-600 turboprop engines, each developing 438 kW (587 shp) at take-off, and each driving a Hartzell HC-B3TN-3/T10282-95 three-blade feathering constant-speed pusher propeller. Fuel in two internal tanks in outer wings (each 212 litres; 46·6 Imp gallons), and two external wingtip tanks (each 323 litres; 71 Imp gallons). Two optional underwing tanks (each 284 litres; 62·5 Imp gallons). Total fuel capacity, normal and optional tanks, 1,638 litres (360·2 Imp gallons).

ACCOMMODATION: Standard seating for pilot and five passengers in individual seats, with toilet and bar at rear. Alternative layouts include an eight-seat executive version, with two facing rows of three seats in cabin; high-density 10-seat version with three individual seats on each side of central aisle in cabin, and curved rear twin seats in place of toilet and bar; cargo version with stripped cabin; ambulance and air survey versions. Main door in centre of cabin on port side. Separate door to flight deck on each side. Emergency exit forward of wing on starboard side. Outside door to baggage compartment aft of cabin on port side. Dual controls standard.

SYSTEMS: Hydraulic system, pressure 127 bars (1,840 lb/sq in), operates landing gear, flaps and brakes. 28V engine-driven DC generator for electrical system.

AVIONICS AND EQUIPMENT: Optional avionics include VHF radio, VOR, ADF, marker beacon receiver, glideslope receiver and Sperry SPL 45 or Collins AP 106 autopilot and horizon gyro unit.

DIMENSIONS, EXTERNAL:
Wing span: without tip-tanks 13·51 m (44 ft 4 in)
with tip-tanks 14·69 m (48 ft 2½ in)
Wing chord at root 2·40 m (7 ft 10½ in)
Wing chord at tip 1·15 m (3 ft 9¼ in)
Wing aspect ratio 7·3
Length overall 11·90 m (39 ft 3 in)
Height overall 5·00 m (16 ft 5 in)
Tailplane span 5·10 m (16 ft 9 in)
Wheel track 2·66 m (8 ft 9 in)
Wheelbase 4·71 m (15 ft 5½ in)
Cabin door: Height 1·38 m (4 ft 6 in)
Width 1·28 m (4 ft 2 in)

DIMENSIONS, INTERNAL:
Cabin: Length 3·55 m (11 ft 8 in)
Max width 1·57 m (5 ft 2 in)
Max height 1·76 m (5 ft 9 in)
Floor area 5·14 m² (55·3 sq ft)
Volume 6·63 m³ (234·1 cu ft)
Baggage compartment (front) 0·77 m³ (27·2 cu ft)
Baggage compartment (rear) 1·80 m³ (63·6 cu ft)

AREAS:
Wings, gross 26·56 m² (285·9 sq ft)
Ailerons (total) 1·95 m² (21·00 sq ft)
Trailing-edge flaps (total) 2·38 m² (25·60 sq ft)
Fin 1·62 m² (17·44 sq ft)
Rudder, incl tab 1·23 m² (13·24 sq ft)
Tailplane 3·50 m² (37·67 sq ft)
Elevators, incl tabs 1·29 m² (13·88 sq ft)

WEIGHTS AND LOADINGS:
Basic weight empty 2,126 kg (4,688 lb)
Max payload 1,306 kg (2,680 lb)
Max T-O weight 4,300 kg (9,480 lb)
Max zero-fuel weight 3,800 kg (8,377 lb)
Max landing weight 3,800 kg (8,377 lb)
Max wing loading 162 kg/m² (33·2 lb/sq ft)
Max power loading 4·91 kg/kW (8·07 lb/shp)

PERFORMANCE (at AUW of 3,855 kg; 8,500 lb except where indicated):
Max level speed at 3,050 m (10,000 ft) 225 knots (417 km/h; 259 mph)
Max cruising speed at 3,050 m (10,000 ft) 218 knots (404 km/h; 250 mph)
Econ cruising speed at 3,050 m (10,000 ft) 162 knots (300 km/h; 186 mph)
Stalling speed, flaps and wheels down, at max landing weight 63 knots (117 km/h; 72 mph)
Max rate of climb at S/L 549 m (1,800 ft)/min
Rate of climb, one engine out 198 m (650 ft)/min
Service ceiling 7,465 m (24,500 ft)
Service ceiling, one engine out 4,267 m (14,000 ft)
T-O run 274 m (900 ft)
T-O to 15 m (50 ft) 500 m (1,640 ft)
Landing from 15 m (50 ft), at AUW of 3,400 kg (7,500 lb) and using reverse thrust 300 m (984 ft)
Range with normal fuel tanks, 30 min reserves 930 nm (1,723 km; 1,070 miles)
Range with normal and optional tanks, 30 min reserves 1,450 nm (2,687 km; 1,667 miles)
Range with max payload, 30 min reserves 400 nm (741 km; 460 miles)

PROCAER

PROGETTI COSTRUZIONI AERONAUTICHE SpA

ADDRESS: Via Gramsci 2, 20091 Bresso (Milan)
Telephone: 6105742
PRESIDENT: Dott Ing Rico Neeff

Production by this company in recent years has concentrated on various versions of the F15 four-seat light aircraft. The latest of these are the all-metal F15E Picchio, and a developed version initiated by General Avia (which see) and known as the F15F. Both are part of a licence package being offered by Procaer.

The production programmes for both aircraft had been delayed in early 1979, when licensing negotiations were pending.

PROCAER F15E PICCHIO

The F15E prototype (I-PROM) flew for the first time on 21 December 1968. The aircraft has been certificated by both the RAI and FAA, in November 1970 and July 1971 respectively. A second prototype, embodying modifications, was flight tested in 1976 and was the subject of a tender to the Aero Club d'Italia. The first production F15E (I-PROD) was certificated on 19 November 1977.

The following description applies to the first prototype:

TYPE: Four-seat light aircraft.

WINGS: Cantilever low-wing monoplane. NACA 64-215/64-210 wing sections. Dihedral 6° from roots. Incidence 4°. One-piece metal structure with single main spar, rear spar carrying aileron and flap hinges, and short front spar to carry landing gear loads. All-metal Frise ailerons and electrically actuated Fowler flaps.

FUSELAGE: All-metal semi-monocoque structure.

TAIL UNIT: Cantilever all-metal structure. Trim tab on rudder and in starboard elevator.

LANDING GEAR: Retractable tricycle type. Electrical or mechanical actuation. Oleo-pneumatic shock-absorbers. Inward-retracting main wheels, size 6·00-6. Steerable, rearward-retracting nosewheel, size 5·00-5. Hydraulic disc brakes.

POWER PLANT: One 224 kW (300 hp) Continental IO-520-F flat-six engine, driving a Hartzell HC-C2YF-1B/8475-6 two-blade constant-speed metal propeller. Fuel in two wing tanks and two wingtip tanks, total capacity 318 litres (70 Imp gallons). Oil capacity 11·5 litres (2·5 Imp gallons).

ACCOMMODATION: Four persons in pairs in enclosed cabin. Forward-opening door on each side. Space for 45 kg (100 lb) of baggage behind rear bench seat. Dual controls. Cabin soundproofed, heated and ventilated.

SYSTEMS AND EQUIPMENT: Two 12V 35Ah batteries, connected in series, provide power for landing gear and flap actuation. 600W engine-driven generator. Blind-flying instruments and radio optional.

DIMENSIONS, EXTERNAL:

Wing span over tip-tanks	9·90 m (32 ft 5¾ in)
Wing chord at root	1·72 m (5 ft 8 in)
Wing chord at tip	0·85 m (2 ft 9 in)
Wing aspect ratio	7·37
Length overall	7·50 m (24 ft 7¼ in)
Height overall	2·80 m (9 ft 2½ in)
Tailplane span	3·55 m (11 ft 8 in)
Wheel track	2·78 m (9 ft 1¼ in)
Wheelbase	1·73 m (5 ft 8½ in)
Propeller diameter	1·98 m (6 ft 6 in)

DIMENSIONS, INTERNAL:

Cabin: Length	2·75 m (9 ft 0 in)
Max width	1·20 m (3 ft 11¼ in)
Max height	1·35 m (4 ft 5¼ in)

AREAS:

Wings, gross	13·30 m² (143·2 sq ft)
Ailerons (total)	1·19 m² (12·81 sq ft)
Trailing-edge flaps (total)	1·72 m² (18·50 sq ft)
Fin	0·88 m² (9·50 sq ft)
Rudder, incl tab	0·49 m² (5·27 sq ft)
Tailplane	1·67 m² (17·97 sq ft)
Elevators, incl tab	1·27 m² (13·67 sq ft)

First production example of the Procaer F15E Picchio four-seat light aircraft

Prototype of the F15F, with modified canopy, lower-powered engine and no tip-tanks

WEIGHTS AND LOADINGS:

Weight empty	842 kg (1,856 lb)
Weight empty, equipped	861 kg (1,900 lb)
Max T-O weight: Normal	1,360 kg (3,000 lb)
Utility	1,225 kg (2,700 lb)
Max wing loading:	
Normal	101·8 kg/m² (20·85 lb/sq ft)
Utility	92·0 kg/m² (18·85 lb/sq ft)
Max power loading:	
Normal	6·42 kg/kW (10·55 lb/hp)
Utility	5·75 kg/kW (9·45 lb/hp)

PERFORMANCE (N: at max Normal T-O weight; U: at max Utility T-O weight):

Never-exceed speed:	
N	191 knots (354 km/h; 220 mph)
U	200 knots (370 km/h; 230 mph)
Max level speed:	
N	173 knots (320 km/h; 199 mph)
U	174 knots (322 km/h; 200 mph)
Max cruising speed:	
N, U	165 knots (306 km/h; 190 mph)
Econ cruising speed:	
N, U	144 knots (267 km/h; 166 mph)
Stalling speed, flaps and landing gear up:	
N	68 knots (127 km/h; 78·5 mph)
U	63 knots (118 km/h; 73 mph)
Stalling speed, flaps and landing gear down:	
N	60 knots (111 km/h; 69 mph)
U	56 knots (103 km/h; 64 mph)
Service ceiling: N, U	5,300 m (17,390 ft)
T-O run: N, U	360 m (1,181 ft)
T-O to 15 m (50 ft): N, U	560 m (1,837 ft)
Landing from 15 m (50 ft): N, U	625 m (2,050 ft)
Landing run: N, U	375 m (1,230 ft)
Max range (N, U), no reserves:	
at max cruising speed	647 nm (1,200 km; 746 miles)
at econ cruising speed	863 nm (1,600 km; 994 miles)
Max endurance (N, U):	
at max cruising speed	5 h 0 min
at econ cruising speed	6 h 0 min

PROCAER/GENERAL AVIA F15F

The F15F is a derivative of the F15E Picchio, designed by Dott Ing Frati of General Avia. The prototype (I-PROL), completed by General Avia, made its first flight on 20 October 1977. Certification was expected in 1978; manufacture of a pre-production series was to be undertaken by Procaer.

Principal differences from the F15E are as follows:

TAIL UNIT: Modified dorsal fin.

POWER PLANT: One 149 kW (200 hp) Lycoming IO-360-A1B1 flat-four engine, driving a two-blade constant-speed metal propeller. Wingtip fuel tanks deleted.

ACCOMMODATION: Four seats, in two pairs, as in F15E; but fully-transparent moulded canopy instead of enclosed cabin.

DIMENSIONS, EXTERNAL:

Length overall	7·75 m (25 ft 5¼ in)

WEIGHTS AND LOADINGS:

Weight empty	765 kg (1,686 lb)
Max T-O weight (Utility)	1,225 kg (2,700 lb)
Max wing loading	92·0 kg/m² (18·85 lb/sq ft)
Max power loading	8·22 kg/kW (13·45 lb/hp)

PERFORMANCE (at max T-O weight):

Max level speed	164 knots (305 km/h; 189 mph)
Cruising speed	151 knots (280 km/h; 174 mph)
Stalling speed	55·5 knots (102 km/h; 63·5 mph)
Max rate of climb at S/L	270 m (885 ft)/min
Service ceiling	5,200 m (17,050 ft)

SIAI-MARCHETTI
SIAI-MARCHETTI SOCIETA PER AZIONI

MANAGEMENT: Via Indipendenza 2, 21018 Sesto Calende (Varese)
Telephone: (0331) 924421
Telex: 39601 Siaiavio

AERODROME AND MAIN WORKS: Vergiate (Varese)

OTHER WORKS: Sesto Calende (Varese), Malpensa and Borgomanero

ROME OFFICE: Via Barberini 36, 00187 Rome
Telephone: (06) 482811

PRESIDENT: Dott Ermenegildo Marelli

MANAGING DIRECTOR: Dott Ing Giovanni Angiola

Founded in 1915, the SIAI-Marchetti company was known originally as Savoia-Marchetti. It has produced a wide range of military and civil landplanes and flying-boats, but is now increasingly involved in helicopter manufacture, in association with Agusta and Elicotteri Meridionali. Its current products include civil and military light aircraft of its own design or development, and co-production with Agusta (which see) of Boeing Vertol CH-47C (see EM entry in this section), Bell 212, and Sikorsky SH-3D and HH-3F helicopters.

SIAI-Marchetti is engaged in the overhaul and repair of various types of large aircraft (notably the C-130 Hercules) serving with the Italian Air Force. It also participates in national or multi-national programmes for the Aeritalia G222, Aeritalia (Lockheed) F-104S and Panavia Tornado.

The company's works at Vergiate, Sesto Calende, Malpensa and Borgomanero total 1,345,000 m² (14,477,450 sq ft) in area, of which 116,000 m² (1,248,600 sq ft) are covered, and employ more than 2,500 people.

SIAI-MARCHETTI SF.260 (MILITARY VERSIONS)

The prototype for the SF.260 series, known as the F.250, was designed by Dott Ing Stelio Frati and built by Aviamilano. Flown for the first time on 15 July 1964, it was powered by a 186·5 kW (250 hp) Lycoming engine and was certificated for aerobatic flying. A description appeared in the 1965-66 *Jane's*.

The version developed initially, for civil production, was manufactured, at first under licence from Aviamilano, by SIAI-Marchetti, and is designated SF.260. It received FAA type approval on 1 April 1966. Subsequently SIAI-Marchetti became the official holder of the type certificate and of all manufacturing rights in the SF.260; it has continued to develop the civil version, described separately, and has also evolved three basic versions for military use. The three military models are as follows:

SF.260M. Two/three-seat military trainer, developed from the initial civil SF.260A and flown for the first time on 10 October 1970. Introduced a number of important structural and aerodynamic improvements, many of which were subsequently applied to the later civil versions. Meets the necessary requirements for basic flying training; instrument flying; aerobatics, including deliberate spinning and recovery; night flying; navigation flying; and formation flying.

Production to date of SF.260Ms has included orders from the Italian Air Force (25 SF.260AMI), Belgian Air Force (36 SF.260M), Bolivian Air Force (6), Burmese Air Force (10 SF.260MB), Ecuadorean Air Force (12 SF.260ME), Libyan Arab Air Force (200 SF.260ML), Moroccan Air Force (2 SF.260MM), Philippine Air Force (32 SF.260MP), Singapore Air Defence Command (16 SF.260MS), Royal Thai Air Force (12 SF.260MT), Tunisian Air Force (6), Zaïre Air Force (23 SF.260MC) and Zambian Air Force (8 SF.260MZ). Singapore ordered six more in 1979. About half of the Libyan order may be built under licence in that country, for resale to other Arab countries.

SF.260W Warrior. Trainer/tactical support version of SF.260M, first flown (I-SJAV) in May 1972. Two or four underwing pylons, for up to 300 kg (661 lb) of external stores, and cockpit stores selection panel. Able to undertake a wide variety of roles, including low-level strike; forward air control; forward air support; armed reconnaissance; and liaison. Also meets same requirements as SF.260M for use as a trainer.

Customers to date include the Dubai Police Air Wing (1

SF.260WD), Irish Air Corps (10 SF.260WE, of which the first four were handed over on 4 March 1977), Philippine Air Force (16 SF.260WP), Tunisian Air Force (12 SF.260WT), Union of Burma Air Force (nine) and Comore Islands (8 SF.260WC).

SF.260SW Sea Warrior. Version of SF.260W for surveillance, search and rescue, and supply missions. Retains the underwing pylons of the W, and is equipped also with specially designed enlarged tip-tanks containing a lightweight radar system (port) and photographic reconnaissance system (starboard). Operational flight testing of the SF.260SW has been completed. No orders had been announced up to mid-1979.

By mid-1979 more than 600 civil and military SF.260s of all models had been completed, of which most were for export. Total sales were then in excess of 700.

The following description applies primarily to the SF.260M, but is generally applicable to other military SF.260 models unless otherwise stated:

TYPE: Two/three-seat fully-aerobatic military light aircraft.

WINGS: Cantilever low-wing monoplane. Wing section NACA 64_1-212 (modified) at root, NACA 64_1-210 (modified) at tip. Dihedral 6° 20′ from roots. Incidence 2° 45′ at root, 0° at tip. No sweepback. Increased leading-edge radius compared with SF.260A, with lower datum line to improve stall characteristics. All-metal light alloy safe-life structure, with single main spar and auxiliary rear spar, built in two portions bolted together at centreline and attached to fuselage by six bolts. Press-formed ribs, with dimpled stiffening holes. Skin, which is butt-joined and flush-riveted, stiffened by stringers between main and rear spars. Differentially-operating Frise-type light alloy mass-balanced ailerons, and electrically-actuated light alloy single-slotted flaps. Flaps operated by torque tube and mechanical linkage, ailerons by pushrods and cables. Servo tab in each aileron.

FUSELAGE: Semi-monocoque safe-life structure of frames, stringers and flush-riveted skin, exclusively of light alloy except for welded steel tube engine mounting, glassfibre front panel of engine cowling, stainless steel firewall and detachable glassfibre tailcone.

TAIL UNIT: Cantilever light alloy safe-life structure, with sweptback vertical surfaces, fixed-incidence tailplane and one-piece elevator. Two-spar fin and one-piece tailplane, bolted to fuselage; single-spar elevator, statically and aerodynamically balanced, and balanced rudder. Military models have reinforced tail unit/fuselage joints compared with SF.260C. Rudder and elevator operated by cables. Controllable trim tab in starboard half of elevator; ground-adjustable tab on rudder.

LANDING GEAR: Electrically-retractable tricycle type, with manual emergency actuation. Inward-retracting main gear, of trailing-arm type, and rearward-retracting nose unit, each embodying Magnaghi oleo-pneumatic shock-absorber (type 2/22028 on main units). Each welded steel tube main leg is hinged to the main and rear spars. Nose unit is of leg-and-fork type, with co-axial shock-absorber and torque strut. Cleveland P/N 3080A main wheels, with size 6·00-6 tube and tyre (6-ply rating), pressure 2·45 bars (35·5 lb/sq in). Cleveland P/N 40-77A nosewheel, with size 5·00-5 tube and tyre (6-ply rating), pressure 1·96 bars (28·4 lb/sq in). Cleveland P/N 3000-500 independent hydraulic single-disc brake and parking brake on each main wheel. Nosewheel steering (20° to left or right) is operated directly by the rudder pedals, to which it is linked by pushrods. Up-lock secures main gear in retracted position during flight; anti-retraction system prevents main gear from retracting whenever strut is compressed by weight of aircraft. Compared with SF.260C, the military models have a reinforced nosewheel drag brace attachment and landing gear retraction supports; increased use of light alloy forgings, instead of welded steel, in certain landing gear components; and an improved retraction locking mechanism. On all models, the mooring point beneath the rear fuselage acts as a tail bumper.

POWER PLANT: One 194 kW (260 hp) Lycoming O-540-E4A5 flat-six engine, driving a Hartzell HC-C2YK-1BF/8477-8R two-blade constant-speed metal propeller with spinner. Fuel in two light alloy tanks in wings, capacity of each 49·5 litres (10·9 Imp gallons); and two permanent wingtip tanks, capacity of each 72 litres (15·85 Imp gallons). Total internal fuel capacity 243 litres (53·5 Imp gallons), of which 235 litres (51·7 Imp gallons) are usable. Individual refuelling point on top of each tank. In addition, SF.260W and SW may be fitted with two 83 litre (18·25 Imp gallon) auxiliary tanks on underwing pylons. Oil capacity (all models) 11·4 litres (2·5 Imp gallons).

ACCOMMODATION (SF.260M; W and SW similar): Side-by-side front seats (for instructor and pupil in SF.260M), with third seat centrally at rear. Front seats are individually adjustable fore and aft, and have forward-folding backs and provision for back-type parachute packs. Dual controls standard. All three seats equipped with lap belts and shoulder harnesses. Baggage compartment aft of rear seat. One-piece fully-transparent rearward-sliding Plexiglas canopy, upper portion of which is tinted. Emergency canopy release handle for each front seat occupant. Steel tube windscreen frame for protection in the event of an overturn. Cabin carpeted, air-conditioned, heated and ventilated; walls thermally insulated and soundproofed by a glassfibre lining. Slots at base of windscreen admit air for windscreen defrosting.

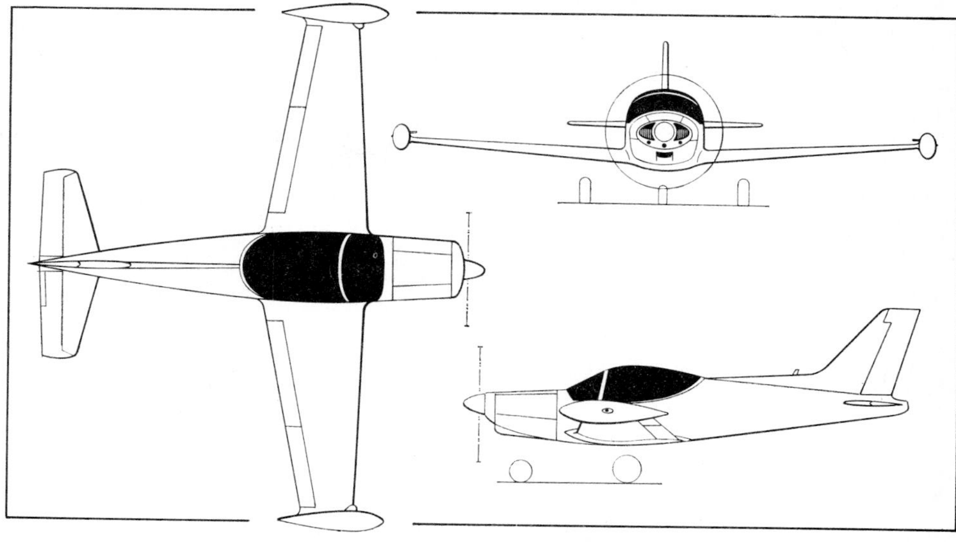

SIAI-Marchetti SF.260M military trainer (Lycoming O-540-E4A5 engine) *(Roy J. Grainge)*

SYSTEMS (SF.260M; other models generally similar): Hydraulic equipment for main-wheel brakes only. No pneumatic system. 24V DC electrical system of single-conductor negative earth type, including 70A Prestolite engine-mounted alternator/rectifier and 24V 24Ah Varley battery, for engine starting, flap and landing gear actuation, fuel booster pumps, electronics and lighting. Sealed battery compartment in rear of fuselage on port side. Connection of an external power source automatically disconnects the battery. Heating system for carburettor air intake. Emergency electrical system for extending landing gear if normal electrical actuation fails; provision for mechanical extension in the event of total electrical failure. Cabin heating, and windscreen de-icing and demisting, by heat exchanger using engine exhaust air. Additional manually controlled warm-air outlets for general cabin heating. Oxygen system optional.

AVIONICS AND EQUIPMENT (SF.260M; W and SW generally similar): Basic instrumentation and military equipment to customer's requirements. Blind-flying instrumentation and communications equipment optional: typical selection includes dual Collins 20B VHF com; Collins VIR-31A VHF nav; Collins ADF-60A ADF; Collins TDR-90 ATC transponder; Collins PN-101 compass; ID-90-000 RMI; and Gemelli AG04-1 intercom. Landing light in nose, below spinner. Instrument panel can be slid rearward to provide access to rear of instruments. Compared with SF.260C, SF.260M has various improvements to flight controls, engine controls (duplicated propeller and throttle controls), electrical system, radio and other installations.

ARMAMENT (SF.260W): Two or four underwing hardpoints, able to carry external stores on NATO standard pylons up to a maximum of 300 kg (661 lb) when flown as a single-seater. Typical alternative loads can include one or two SIAI gun pods, each with one 7·62 mm FN machine-gun and 500 rds; two Matra MAC AAF1 7·62 mm gun pods; two Simpres AL-8-70 launchers each with eight 2·75 in FFAR rockets; two LAU-32 launchers each with seven 2·75 in FFAR rockets; two Simpres AL-18-50 launchers each with eighteen 2 in SNIA ARF/8M2 rockets; two Matra F2 launchers each with six 68 mm SNEB 253 rockets; two Matra 181 launchers each with eighteen 37 mm rockets; two SAMP EU 32 125 kg general purpose bombs or EU 13 120 kg fragmentation bombs; two SAMP EU 70 50 kg general purpose bombs; Mk 76 11 kg practice bombs; two Alkan 500B cartridge throwers for Lacroix 74 mm explosive cartridges, F 725 flares, or F 130 smoke cartridges; one Alkan 500B cartridge thrower and one photo-reconnaissance pod with two 70 mm automatic cameras; or two 83 litre (18·25 Imp gallon) auxiliary fuel tanks.

OPERATIONAL EQUIPMENT (SF.260SW): Retains the underwing pylons and gunsight of the SF.260W, but is equipped also with crew survival kit and specially designed enlarged tip-tanks incorporating a lightweight radar and a photographic reconnaissance system. Bendix RDR-1400 digital radar and transmitter-receiver in forward portion of port tip-tank for search, ground mapping, beacon identification and weather avoidance. Radar control and display units are mounted at co-pilot's station, but a radar reconnaissance can be flown without a separate radar operator. Forward-looking obliquely-mounted 70 mm camera in front portion of starboard tip-tank. Rear portion of each tip-tank contains same amount of fuel (72 litres; 15·85 Imp gallons) as the smaller tip-tanks of the SF.260W. The SW can also be used for search and rescue or air supply delivery with various underwing survival kits (land or sea type) and emergency packs. Survival kit, in droppable underwing containers, is parachute-stabilised and includes 10-place (or Matra Samar 8-place) life raft, tents, rations, signals, or other equipment, depending upon prevailing climatic conditions.

DIMENSIONS, EXTERNAL:

Wing span over tip-tanks:	
M, W	8·35 m (27 ft 4¾ in)
SW	8·70 m (28 ft 6½ in)
Wing chord at root	1·60 m (5 ft 3 in)
Wing mean aerodynamic chord	1·325 m (4 ft 4¼ in)
Wing chord at tip	0·784 m (2 ft 6⅞ in)
Wing aspect ratio (excl tip-tanks)	6·33
Wing taper ratio	2·24
Length overall	7·10 m (23 ft 3½ in)
Fuselage: Max width	1·10 m (3 ft 7¼ in)
Max depth	1·042 m (3 ft 5 in)
Height overall	2·41 m (7 ft 11 in)
Elevator span	3·01 m (9 ft 10½ in)
Wheel track	2·274 m (7 ft 5½ in)
Wheelbase	1·66 m (5 ft 5¼ in)
Propeller diameter	1·93 m (6 ft 4 in)
Propeller ground clearance	0·32 m (1 ft 0½ in)

DIMENSIONS, INTERNAL:

Cabin: Length	1·66 m (5 ft 5¼ in)
Max width	1·00 m (3 ft 3¼ in)
Height (seat cushion to canopy)	0·92 m (3 ft 0¼ in)

SIAI-Marchetti SF.260W light strike aircraft of the Irish Air Corps, with two underwing 7·62 mm gun pods

Volume 1·50 m³ (53 cu ft)
Baggage compartment volume 0·18 m³ (6·36 cu ft)

AREAS:
Wings, gross 10·10 m² (108·70 sq ft)
Ailerons (total, incl tabs) 0·762 m² (8·20 sq ft)
Trailing-edge flaps (total) 1·18 m² (12·70 sq ft)
Fin 0·76 m² (8·18 sq ft)
Dorsal fin 0·16 m² (1·72 sq ft)
Rudder, incl tab 0·60 m² (6·46 sq ft)
Tailplane 1·46 m² (15·70 sq ft)
Elevator, incl tab 0·96 m² (10·30 sq ft)

WEIGHTS AND LOADINGS:
Manufacturer's basic weight empty:
W 770 kg (1,697 lb)
SW 775 kg (1,708 lb)
Weight empty, equipped: M 799 kg (1,761 lb)
W 814 kg (1,794 lb)
SW 857 kg (1,889 lb)
Fuel:
in-wing and wingtip tanks (all versions) 169 kg (372·5 lb)
underwing tanks (W and SW only) 114 kg (251·5 lb)
Typical mission weights:
M, trainer ('clean') 1,140 kg (2,513 lb)
W, two 47 kg (103·5 lb) machine-gun pods and full internal fuel 1,163 kg (2,564 lb)
W, one Alkan 500B cartridge thrower, one two-camera reconnaissance pod and full internal fuel 1,182 kg (2,605 lb)
W, trainer with 94 kg (207 lb) external stores 1,249 kg (2,753 lb)
W, self-ferry with two 83 litre (18·25 Imp gallon) underwing tanks 1,285 kg (2,833 lb)
W, two 125 kg bombs and 150 kg (331 lb) internal fuel 1,300 kg (2,866 lb)
W, two AL-8-70 rocket launchers and 160 kg (353 lb) internal fuel 1,300 kg (2,866 lb)
SW, reconnaissance patrol 1,246 kg (2,747 lb)
SW, search and rescue with two 90 kg (198·5 lb) survival kits, 60 kg (132 lb) of external weapons, and full internal fuel 1,264 kg (2,786 lb)
SW, armed patrol 1,300 kg (2,866 lb)
SW, surveillance with two 90 kg (198·5 lb) survival kits, two 47 kg (103·5 lb) gun pods, and full internal fuel 1,300 kg (2,866 lb)
Max T-O weight:
M, Aerobatic 1,100 kg (2,425 lb)
M, Utility 1,200 kg (2,645 lb)
W, SW, max permitted 1,300 kg (2,866 lb)
Max wing loading: M 119 kg/m² (24·4 lb/sq ft)
W, SW 129 kg/m² (26·4 lb/sq ft)
Max power loading:
M 6·19 kg/kW (10·17 lb/hp)
W, SW 6·70 kg/kW (11·01 lb/hp)

PERFORMANCE (M at AUW of 1,200 kg; 2,645 lb, W and SW at 1,300 kg; 2,866 lb, unless stated otherwise):
Never-exceed speed:
M 235 knots (436 km/h; 271 mph)
Max level speed at S/L:
M 183 knots (340 km/h; 211 mph)
W 170 knots (315 km/h; 196 mph)
SW 164 knots (304 km/h; 189 mph)
Max cruising speed (75% power) at 1,500 m (4,925 ft):
M 174 knots (322 km/h; 200 mph)
W 155 knots (287 km/h; 178 mph)
SW 148 knots (275 km/h; 171 mph)
Stalling speed, flaps and landing gear up:
M 74 knots (137 km/h; 85·5 mph)
W, SW 88 knots (163 km/h; 101·5 mph)
Stalling speed, flaps and landing gear down:
M 64 knots (118 km/h; 73·5 mph)
W, SW 75 knots (139 km/h; 86·5 mph)
Max rate of climb at S/L: M 475 m (1,558 ft)/min
W 335 m (1,099 ft)/min
SW 270 m (885 ft)/min
Time to 1,500 m (4,925 ft): M 4 min 0 s
W 6 min 20 s
SW 7 min 30 s
Time to 2,300 m (7,550 ft): M 6 min 50 s
W 10 min 20 s
SW 14 min 45 s
Time to 3,000 m (9,850 ft): M 10 min 0 s
W 18 min 40 s
Service ceiling: M 4,665 m (15,300 ft)
T-O run at S/L: M 384 m (1,260 ft)
T-O to 15 m (50 ft) at S/L: M 606 m (1,988 ft)
W, SW 825 m (2,707 ft)
Landing from 15 m (50 ft) at S/L:
M 539 m (1,768 ft)
W, SW 645 m (2,116 ft)
Landing run at S/L: M 345 m (1,132 ft)
Operational radius:
W, 6 h 25 min single-seat armed patrol mission at 1,163 kg (2,564 lb) AUW, incl 5 h 35 min over operating area, 20 kg (44 lb) fuel reserves 50 nm (92 km; 57 miles)
W, 3 h 38 min single-seat strike mission, incl two 5 min loiters over separate en-route target areas, 20 kg (44 lb) fuel reserves 250 nm (463 km; 287 miles)

SIAI-Marchetti SF.260C three-seat light aircraft, in the insignia of a Belgian customer

W, 4 h 54 min single-seat strike mission, incl 5 min over target area, 20 kg (44 lb) fuel reserves 300 nm (556 km; 345 miles)
W, 4 h 30 min single-seat photo-reconnaissance mission at 1,182 kg (2,605 lb) AUW, incl three 1 h loiters over separate en-route operating areas, 20 kg (44 lb) fuel reserves 150 nm (278 km; 172 miles)
W, 6 h 3 min two-seat self-ferry mission with two 83 litre (18·25 Imp gallon) underwing tanks, at 1,285 kg (2,833 lb) AUW, 30 kg (66 lb) fuel reserves 926 nm (1,716 km; 1,066 miles)
SW, 5 h 17 min two-seat surveillance mission, incl 3 h 40 min over operating area at 105 knots (195 km/h; 121 mph), 20 kg (44 lb) fuel reserves 100 nm (185 km; 115 miles)
SW, 5 h 13 min two-seat surveillance mission, incl 2 h 0 min over operating area at 105 knots (195 km/h; 121 mph), 20 kg (44 lb) fuel reserves 200 nm (370 km; 230 miles)
SW, 5 h 27 min two-seat SAR mission at 1,264 kg (2,786 lb) AUW, incl 2 h 15 min over operating area, 5 kg (11 lb) fuel reserves 200 nm (370 km; 230 miles)
Range with max fuel:
M (two-seat) 890 nm (1,650 km; 1,025 miles)
g limits (M):
at max Aerobatic T-O weight +6·0; —3·0
at max Utility T-O weight without external load +4·4; —2·2

SIAI-MARCHETTI SF.260C (CIVIL VERSION)

As indicated in the preceding entry, the SF.260 was developed from the F.250 prototype originally as a civil aircraft.

Aircraft from the **SF.260A** first series, marketed in the USA under the name **Waco Meteor,** still hold two FAI Class C1b speed records set in 1969. The first of these is for a speed of 174 knots (322·52 km/h; 200·4 mph) over a 1,000 km closed circuit near Santa Monica, California, on 25 March 1969. The second, set up on 29 March 1969 near Los Angeles, is for a speed of 199·4 knots (369·43 km/h; 229·6 mph) over a 100 km closed circuit.

The second civil series **(SF.260B)**, certificated by the FAA on 10 June 1974, incorporated many of the structural and aerodynamic improvements introduced by the SF.260M. Customers included Air France, Royal Air Maroc and Sabena, which ordered the SF.260 for airline crew training.

Approx 30-40 civil SF.260s, including SF.260As and SF.260Bs, had been built by the Spring of 1978.

The current civil version, certificated by the RAI and FAA on 23 October and 30 December 1976 respectively, is designated **SF.260C**. The following description applies to this version:

TYPE: Three-seat fully-aerobatic light aircraft.

WINGS: As SF.260M/W/SW except dihedral 5°.

FUSELAGE: As SF.260M/W/SW.

TAIL UNIT: As SF.260M/W/SW, but without extra reinforcement.

LANDING GEAR: See description for SF.260M/W/SW.

POWER PLANT: As for SF.260M/W/SW, but driving a Hartzell HC-C2YK-1BF/8477-8R or HC-C2YK-4F/FC-8477-8R two-blade constant-speed metal propeller with spinner. Fuel capacity 49·5 litres (10·9 Imp gallons) in each wing tank and 72 litres (15·8 Imp gallons) in each wingtip tank; total internal capacity 243 litres (53·4 Imp gallons). Oil capacity as for military versions.

ACCOMMODATION: Three seats in enclosed cockpit, two side by side in front, one at rear. Two children with a combined weight not exceeding 113 kg (250 lb) may occupy rear seat. One-piece fully-transparent rearward-sliding Plexiglas canopy, with rubber-cord canopy release. Baggage compartment, capacity 40 kg (88 lb), aft of rear seat. Cabin heated, ventilated and soundproofed with glassfibre.

SYSTEMS, AVIONICS AND EQUIPMENT: Generally similar to SF.260M.

DIMENSIONS, EXTERNAL: As SF.260M/W

DIMENSIONS, INTERNAL: As SF.260M/W/SW

AREAS: As SF.260M/W/SW

WEIGHTS AND LOADINGS:
Weight empty, equipped 755 kg (1,664 lb)
Max T-O weight: Aerobatic 1,000 kg (2,205 lb)
Utility 1,102 kg (2,430 lb)
Max wing loading 109 kg/m² (22·4 lb/sq ft)
Max power loading 5·68 kg/kW (9·33 lb/hp)

PERFORMANCE (at max Utility T-O weight):
Max level speed at S/L 187 knots (347 km/h; 215 mph)
Max cruising speed (75% power) at 3,050 m (10,000 ft) 178 knots (330 km/h; 205 mph)
Stalling speed, flaps and landing gear down 60 knots (111 km/h; 70 mph)
Max rate of climb at S/L 546 m (1,791 ft)/min
Service ceiling 5,790 m (19,000 ft)
T-O run at S/L on concrete 250 m (820 ft)
T-O run at S/L on grass 290 m (952 ft)
T-O to 15 m (50 ft) at S/L 472 m (1,550 ft)
Landing from 15 m (50 ft) at S/L 490 m (1,608 ft)
Landing run at S/L 345 m (1,132 ft)
Range with max fuel (two persons) 1,106 nm (2,050 km; 1,274 miles)
g limits: Aerobatic +6·0; −3·0
Utility +4·4; −2·2

SIAI-MARCHETTI S.205/20R and S.208A

Full details can be found in the 1972-73 *Jane's* of the S.205 light aircraft, and in the 1974-75 and 1976-77 editions of the S.208 series.

SIAI-Marchetti has offered, since early 1977, further-improved versions of these aircraft, which have the same basic airframe. Improvements applicable to both types include a new cockpit and cabin layout, with better cabin soundproofing; modified flaps and landing gear; and new heating and ventilation system.

SIAI-Marchetti demonstrator for the S.205/20R and S.208A four/five-seat light aircraft

Differences between the current versions are as follows:

S.205/20R. Four-seater, with 149 kW (200 hp) Lycoming IO-360 engine. Selected as second-level trainer by Italian Aero Club, to which deliveries (of an order for 140 designated **S.205AC**) began in 1977.

S.208A. Five-seater with 194 kW (260 hp) Lycoming O-540 engine. Also available in cargo, ambulance or agricultural versions.

Power Plant (S.205/20R): One 149 kW (200 hp) Lycoming IO-360-A1B6D flat-four engine, driving a Hartzell HC-C2YK-1BF/F7666A-2 two-blade constant-speed propeller with spinner. Fuel in two wing tanks, total capacity 210 litres (46·2 Imp gallons).

Power Plant (S.208A): One 194 kW (260 hp) Lycoming O-540-E4A5 flat-six engine, driving a Hartzell HC-C2YK two-blade constant-speed propeller. Fuel in two wing tanks, total capacity 215 litres (47·3 Imp gallons), and two wingtip tanks, total capacity 115 litres (25·3 Imp gallons). Overall total fuel capacity 330 litres (72·6 Imp gallons).

Accommodation: Seats for four persons in S.205/20R (five in S.208A), in fully-enclosed cabin. Baggage space aft of rear seats. Forward-opening car-type door on each side of cabin. Additional small window at rear of cabin on each side in S.208A.

Dimensions, external:
- Wing span (S.205/20R) 10·86 m (35 ft 7½ in)
- Wing span over tip-tanks (S.208A) 11·24 m (36 ft 10½ in)
- Wing area, gross (both) 16·09 m² (173·2 sq ft)
- Length overall: S.205/20R 8·00 m (26 ft 3 in)
  - S.208A 8·10 m (26 ft 7 in)
- Height overall (both) 2·89 m (9 ft 5¾ in)

Dimensions, internal (both):
- Cabin: Max length 2·80 m (9 ft 2¼ in)
  - Max width 1·14 m (3 ft 9 in)
  - Max height 1·32 m (4 ft 4 in)
  - Volume 3·00 m³ (106 cu ft)

Weights and Loadings:
- Weight empty, equipped:
  - S.205/20R 761 kg (1,677 lb)
  - S.208A 835 kg (1,841 lb)
- Max T-O weight: S.205/20R 1,300 kg (2,866 lb)
  - S.208A 1,505 kg (3,318 lb)
- Max wing loading:
  - S.205/20R 80·8 kg/m² (16·55 lb/sq ft)
  - S.208A 87·0 kg/m² (17·82 lb/sq ft)
- Max power loading:
  - S.205/20R 8·72 kg/kW (14·3 lb/hp)
  - S.208A 7·76 kg/kW (12·7 lb/hp)

Performance (at max T-O weight):
- Max level speed at S/L:
  - S.205/20R 119 knots (221 km/h; 137 mph)
  - S.208A 173 knots (320 km/h; 199 mph)
- Max cruising speed:
  - S.205/20R 107 knots (199 km/h; 124 mph)
  - S.208A 162 knots (300 km/h; 186 mph)
- Stalling speed, flaps down:
  - S.205/20R 41·5 knots (76 km/h; 47·5 mph)
  - S.208A 50 knots (92 km/h; 57·5 mph)
- Max rate of climb at S/L:
  - S.205/20R 252 m (826 ft)/min
  - S.208A 300 m (984 ft)/min
- Service ceiling: S.205/20R 4,750 m (15,575 ft)
  - S.208A 5,400 m (17,725 ft)
- T-O run: S.205/20R 260 m (853 ft)
  - S.208A 302 m (991 ft)
- Landing run: S.205/20R 300 m (984 ft)
  - S.208A 171 m (561 ft)
- Max range:
  - S.205/20R 679 nm (1,258 km; 782 miles)
  - S.208A 971 nm (1,800 km; 1,118 miles)

SIAI-MARCHETTI SM.1019E

The SM.1019 light STOL aircraft is suitable for observation, light ground attack or utility duties. Its design was started in January 1969, and construction of a prototype began two months later. This aircraft (I-STOL) flew for the first time on 24 May 1969, with an Allison 250-B15C engine, and was granted Normal and Utility category certification by the RAI on 25 October 1969.

A second prototype (I-SJAR), which flew for the first time on 18 February 1971, was designated SM.1019A. It had an improved fuel system, two doors and two instrument panels, and received RAI civil certification in the Normal and Utility categories.

Production began in 1974 of an initial series of 80 SM.1019EIs for the Aviazione Leggera dell'Esercito (ALE, or Italian Army Light Aviation), and all of these had been delivered by the Summer of 1978.

Type: Two-seat STOL light aircraft.

Wings: High-wing monoplane, braced by single strut on each side. Wing section NACA 2412. Dihedral 2° 8'. Incidence 1° 30'. Washout 3°. Conventional all-metal structure, with detachable tapered outer panels. Metal Frise-type ailerons and electrically-actuated trailing-edge slotted flaps. Trim tab in starboard aileron. Tiedown point at each wingtip.

Fuselage: Conventional all-metal stressed-skin structure.

Tail Unit: Conventional cantilever all-metal structure, with horizontal surfaces mounted on top of fuselage. Dorsal fin. Fixed-incidence tailplane. Elevators and rudder horn-balanced. Manually-operated mechanically-actuated trim tab in starboard elevator; servo tab in port elevator. Ground-adjustable trim tab on rudder.

SIAI-Marchetti SM.1019E demonstration aircraft with an AS.12 air-to-surface missile beneath each wing

Landing Gear: Non-retractable tailwheel type, with cantilever leaf-type spring steel main-wheel legs. Goodyear 511960 main wheels, with low-pressure tyres, size 7·00-6, pressure 2·07 bars (30 lb/sq in); Scott 3200A tailwheel, with size 8-3·00 tyre, pressure 2·41 bars (35 lb/sq in). Goodyear independent hydraulic single-disc brakes on main wheels, controllable from either seat. Parking brake. Combined wheel/ski gear, with hydraulic retraction and extension of skis, is optional.

Power Plant: One 298 kW (400 shp) Allison 250-B17 turboprop engine, driving a Hartzell HC-B3TF-7/T10173-11R three-blade constant-speed reversible-pitch metal propeller. Fuel in two tanks in each wing, each of 80 litres (17·5 Imp gallons; 21 US gallons) capacity; total capacity 320 litres (70 Imp gallons; 84 US gallons). Refuelling point for each tank on top of wings. Provision for auxiliary underwing tanks. Oil capacity 8 litres (1·75 Imp gallons; 2·1 US gallons).

Accommodation: Pilot and co-pilot or observer/systems operator seated in tandem in fully-enclosed and extensively-glazed cabin. Two forward-hinged doors on starboard side. Cabin heated, by engine bleed air, and ventilated. Dual controls standard.

Systems: 28V DC electrical power provided by 30V 150A Lear Siegler P/N230320020 engine-driven starter/generator and 24V 25Ah nickel-cadmium battery. External ground power receptacle. Windscreen defrosting and engine compressor inlet heating standard. Oxygen system optional.

Avionics and Equipment: Choice of VHF/UHF/HF communication systems. VLF/Omega navigation. ADF; IFF; high-performance intercom and compass system. Provision for specialised avionics (VHF/FM, radar warning, Tacan and microwave landing system) to customer's requirements. Twin taxying and landing lights in port outer wing leading-edge. Anti-collision light on top of rudder.

Armament and Operational Equipment (SM.1019EI): Two hardpoints beneath each wing for 2·75 in rocket launchers, gun pods, missiles, bombs, auxiliary fuel tanks or a reconnaissance pod. Electronic, photographic and navigation equipment for use as day or night reconnaissance aircraft.

Dimensions, external:
- Wing span 10·972 m (36 ft 0 in)
- Wing chord at root 1·63 m (5 ft 4¼ in)
- Wing chord at tip 1·09 m (3 ft 7 in)
- Wing aspect ratio 7·44
- Length overall (tail up) 8·52 m (27 ft 11½ in)
- Height overall (tail down) 2·86 m (9 ft 4½ in)
- Tailplane span 3·42 m (11 ft 2¾ in)
- Wheel track 2·29 m (7 ft 6¼ in)
- Wheelbase 6·23 m (20 ft 5¼ in)
- Propeller diameter 2·29 m (7 ft 6 in)
- Propeller ground clearance 0·23 m (9 in)
- Cabin doors, each: Height 1·06 m (3 ft 5¾ in)
  - Width 0·60 m (1 ft 11½ in)
- Baggage door: Height 0·47 m (1 ft 6½ in)
  - Width 0·53 m (1 ft 9 in)
  - Height to sill 0·62 m (2 ft 0¼ in)

Dimensions, internal:
- Cabin: Max length 2·00 m (6 ft 6¾ in)
  - Max width 0·63 m (2 ft 0¾ in)
  - Max height 1·25 m (4 ft 1¼ in)
  - Volume 1·10 m³ (38·8 cu ft)
- Baggage compartment volume 0·1 m³ (3·5 cu ft)

Areas:
- Wings, gross 16·16 m² (173·95 sq ft)
- Ailerons (total) 1·70 m² (18·30 sq ft)
- Trailing-edge flaps (total) 1·96 m² (21·10 sq ft)
- Fin 0·957 m² (10·30 sq ft)
- Rudder 1·295 m² (13·94 sq ft)
- Tailplane 1·896 m² (20·41 sq ft)
- Elevators (total) 1·584 m² (17·05 sq ft)

Weights and Loadings (without external stores):
- Weight empty, equipped 690 kg (1,521 lb)
- Basic weight empty 730 kg (1,609 lb)
- T-O weight:
  - SM.1019A (Utility category), SM.1019EI (training) 1,300 kg (2,866 lb)
- Max T-O weight:
  - SM.1019A (Normal category), SM.1019EI (helicopter escort, reconnaissance) 1,450 kg (3,196 lb)
- Wing loading at 1,300 kg (2,866 lb) AUW 80·4 kg/m² (16·5 lb/sq ft)
- Max wing loading 89·7 kg/m² (18·4 lb/sq ft)
- Power loading at 1,300 kg (2,866 lb) AUW 4·36 kg/kW (7·2 lb/shp)
- Max power loading 4·87 kg/kW (8·0 lb/shp)

Performance (A: Utility, AUW of 1,300 kg; 2,866 lb. B: helicopter escort, AUW of 1,450 kg; 3,196 lb. C: reconnaissance, AUW of 1,450 kg; 3,196 lb, except where indicated):
- Never-exceed speed 169 knots (313 km/h; 194 mph)
- Max cruising speed at S/L:
  - A 160 knots (296 km/h; 184 mph)
  - B, C 152 knots (281 km/h; 175 mph)
- Max cruising speed at 2,500 m (8,200 ft):
  - A 162 knots (300 km/h; 186 mph)
  - B, C 154 knots (285 km/h; 177 mph)
- Cruising speed (75% power) at 2,500 m (8,200 ft):
  - A 152 knots (281 km/h; 175 mph)
  - B, C 145 knots (268 km/h; 167 mph)
- Stalling speed, flaps up, with fuel injection:
  - A 53 knots (98 km/h; 61 mph)
  - B, C 58 knots (107 km/h; 66·5 mph)
- Stalling speed, flaps down, with fuel injection:
  - A 38 knots (70 km/h; 43·5 mph)
  - B, C 46 knots (85 km/h; 53 mph)
- Max rate of climb at S/L: A 551 m (1,810 ft)/min
  - B, C 499 m (1,640 ft)/min
- Operational ceiling: A, B, C 7,620 m (25,000 ft)
- T-O run at S/L: A 112 m (368 ft)
  - B, C 218 m (716 ft)
- T-O to 15 m (50 ft) at S/L: A 220 m (722 ft)
  - B, C 361 m (1,185 ft)
- Landing from 15 m (50 ft) at S/L:
  - A 220 m (722 ft)
  - B, C 281 m (922 ft)
- Landing run at S/L: A 91·5 m (300 ft)
  - B, C 135 m (443 ft)
- Typical operational radius:
  - B, with two rocket launchers, at AUW of 1,400 kg (3,086 lb) 60 nm (111 km; 69 miles)
- Max range at S/L: A 499 nm (925 km; 575 miles)
  - B 421 nm (780 km; 485 miles)
  - C 610 nm (1,130 km; 702 miles)
- Max range at 3,000 m (9,845 ft):
  - A 588 nm (1,090 km; 677 miles)
  - B 505 nm (935 km; 581 miles)
  - C 723 nm (1,340 km; 832 miles)
- Max range with two external tanks, AUW of 1,400 kg (3,086 lb): C, at 610 m (2,000 ft) 623 nm (1,154 km; 717 miles)
  - C, at 2,745 m (9,000 ft) 730 nm (1,352 km; 840 miles)
- Max endurance at S/L: A 5 h 45 min
  - B 5 h 0 min
  - C 7 h 20 min
- Max endurance at 3,000 m (9,845 ft): A 6 h 40 min
  - B 6 h 5 min
  - C, with auxiliary fuel tanks 8 h 45 min

SIAI-MARCHETTI S.211

Intended as a lightweight, low-cost basic trainer and light attack aircraft, the S.211 was first revealed in the form of a model at the Paris Air Show in May/June 1977. It is of tandem two-seat configuration, and is powered by a non-afterburning turbofan engine.

A mockup of the S.211 was exhibited at the Paris Air Show in June 1979. First flight is expected to take place in mid-1981.

TYPE: Turbofan-engined basic trainer and light attack aircraft.

WINGS: Cantilever shoulder-wing monoplane, with supercritical section evolved by computer with the assistance of the US universities of New York and Kansas. Thickness/chord ratio 15% at root, 13% at tip. Incidence 2° 13′ at root, −1° 17′ at tip. Anhedral 2° from roots. Sweepback 15° 30′ at quarter-chord. Two-spar metal torsion box structure, forming integral fuel tank; attached to fuselage by four bolts. Upper and lower skins each formed by two one-piece panels joined along centreline and to the spars. Ailerons and large-area Fowler-type flaps on trailing-edges. Trim tab in each aileron.

FUSELAGE: Conventional metal semi-monocoque structure. Hydraulically actuated airbrake under centre-fuselage. Equipment bay in nose.

TAIL UNIT: Cantilever metal structure. Sweptback fin and rudder, tapered leading-edge on tailplane. No tabs.

LANDING GEAR: Hydraulically-retractable tricycle type. All units retract forward into fuselage (main units into undersides of engine air intake trunks). Main wheels size 6·50-8; nosewheel size 5·00-5. Designed for sink rate of 4 m (13 ft)/s. Provision for emergency free-fall extension.

POWER PLANT: One 9·8 kN (2,200 lb st) Pratt & Whitney Aircraft of Canada JT15D-1 non-afterburning turbofan engine mounted in rear of fuselage; lateral intake each side of fuselage. Fuel in 600 litre (132 Imp gallon) integral wing tank and 150 litre (33 Imp gallon) fuselage main tank; total usable capacity 750 litres (165 Imp gallons). Single-point gravity refuelling. Provision for two 350 litre (77 Imp gallon) drop-tanks on inboard underwing stores points. Oil capacity 10 kg (22 lb).

ACCOMMODATION: Seats for two persons in tandem in pressurised and air-conditioned cockpit under one-piece canopy opening sideways to starboard: pupil in front, instructor on rear seat elevated 28 cm (11 in). Martin-Baker Mk 8 or Mk10 ejection seats for both occupants, capable of operation at all altitudes and at speeds between 60-400 knots (111-741 km/h; 69-461 mph), including ejection through canopy.

SYSTEMS: Environmental control system for cockpit pressurisation and air-conditioning, using engine bleed air. Max pressure differential 0·27 bars (4·0 lb/sq in). Hydraulic system, pressure 103·5 bars (1,500 lb/sq in), for landing gear and airbrake actuation. Primary electrical system is 28V DC, using an engine-driven starter/generator; nickel-cadmium battery; two static inverters supply AC power for instruments and avionics. Demand-type main oxygen system, sufficient to supply both occupants for 4 hours, plus emergency oxygen supply.

AVIONICS AND EQUIPMENT: To customer's requirements. Communications system normally comprises dual U/VHF, and HF/SSB, all with dual control. Choice of ADF, Tacan or VOR/ILS nav. Provision for IFF, flight director, radio altimeter, Doppler radar, nose-mounted attack radar, head-up display, radar warning system and ECM.

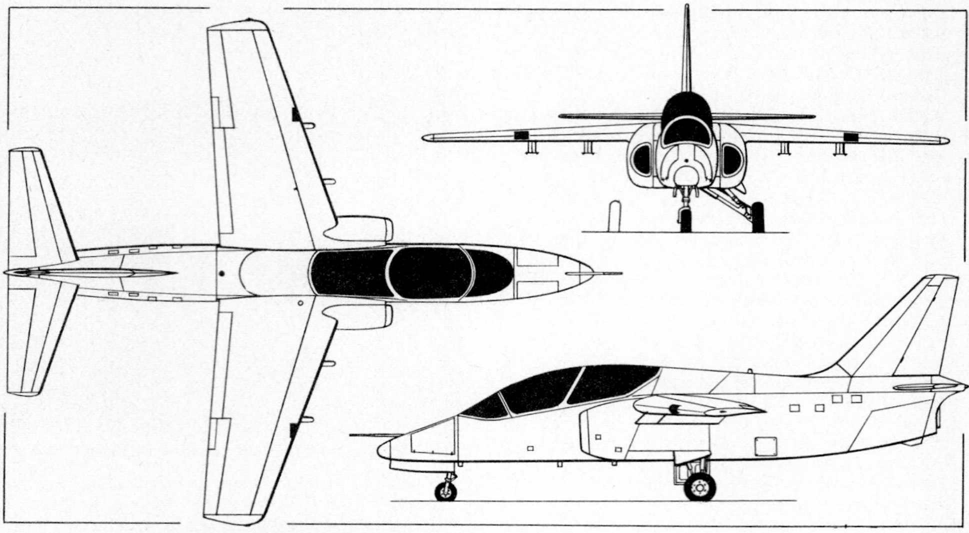

SIAI-Marchetti S.211 basic trainer and light attack aircraft *(Pilot Press)*

ARMAMENT: Four underwing hardpoints, stressed for loads of up to 300 kg (660 lb) inboard, 150 kg (330 lb) outboard; max external load 600 kg (1,320 lb). Typical loads can include four SUU-11B 7·62 mm Minigun pods, four 12·7 mm gun pods, or (inboard only) two 20 mm gun pods; four AL-18-50 (18 × 50 mm), Matra F2 (6 × 68 mm), LAU-32 (7 × 2·75 in), or AL-6-80 (6 × 81 mm) rocket launchers, or (inboard only) two Matra 155 (18 × 68 mm) or SNORA RWK-020 (12 × 81 mm) launchers; two Sidewinder or Magic air-to-air, or two Maverick air-to-surface, missiles on the inboard points; four bombs or practice bombs of up to 150 kg size, or (inboard only) two bombs or napalm containers of up to 300 kg; four 74 mm cartridge throwers; or (inboard only) two photo-reconnaissance pods each with four cameras and infra-red linescan; or two 350 litre (77 Imp gallon) auxiliary fuel tanks.

DIMENSIONS, EXTERNAL:
- Wing span — 8·00 m (26 ft 3 in)
- Wing chord at root — 2·151 m (7 ft 0¾ in)
- Wing chord at tip — 1·00 m (3 ft 3¼ in)
- Wing chord (mean aerodynamic) — 1·646 m (5 ft 4¾ in)
- Wing aspect ratio — 5·08
- Length overall — 9·28 m (30 ft 5½ in)
- Height overall — 3·73 m (12 ft 2¾ in)
- Tailplane span — 3·96 m (13 ft 0 in)
- Wheel track — 2·29 m (7 ft 6 in)
- Wheelbase — 4·02 m (13 ft 2¼ in)

AREAS:
- Wings, gross — 12·60 m² (135·63 sq ft)
- Airbrake — 0·42 m² (4·52 sq ft)
- Vertical tail surfaces (total) — 1·936 m² (20·84 sq ft)
- Horizontal tail surfaces (total) — 3·378 m² (36·36 sq ft)

WEIGHTS:
- Weight empty, equipped — 1,420 kg (3,130 lb)
- Max T-O weight: trainer, 'clean' — 2,200 kg (4,850 lb)
- armed version — 2,800 kg (6,173 lb)

PERFORMANCE (estimated, at 2,200 kg; 4,850 lb AUW):
- Never-exceed speed — Mach 0·80 (400 knots; 741 km/h; 461 mph EAS)
- Max level speed at 7,620 m (25,000 ft) — 360 knots (667 km/h; 414 mph)
- Max cruising speed at 7,620 m (25,000 ft) — 345 knots (639 km/h; 397 mph)
- Stalling speed, flaps down — 68 knots (125 km/h; 78 mph)
- Max rate of climb at S/L — 1,188 m (3,900 ft)/min
- Service ceiling — 12,200 m (40,000 ft)
- T-O and landing run — approx 305 m (1,000 ft)
- T-O to 15 m (50 ft) — 440 m (1,445 ft)
- Landing from 15 m (50 ft) — 536 m (1,760 ft)
- Min air turning radius at S/L — less than 305 m (1,000 ft)
- Range at 9,145 m (30,000 ft) with max fuel, 30 min reserves — 1,080 nm (2,000 km; 1,245 miles)
- Endurance, 30 min reserves — 4 h 15 min
- Sustained *g* limit at 4,575 m (15,000 ft) — 2·55
- Design *g* limits — +6; −3

SILVERCRAFT
SILVERCRAFT SpA

HEAD OFFICE AND WORKS: Strada del Sempione 114, Casella Postale 37, 21018 Sesto Calende (Varese)

Silvercraft was established in early 1962 to develop a light multi-purpose helicopter, which flew for the first time in October 1963. This was subsequently developed into the Silvercraft SH-4, last described in the 1976-77 *Jane's*.

The later SH-200 two-seat light helicopter flew for the first time on 12 April 1977; it was described in the 1978-79 edition.

Silvercraft has now ceased its aviation activities.

SSVV
SEZIONE SPERIMENTALE VOLO A VELA

ADDRESS: Viale delle Rimembranze 22, 20068 Linate Paese (Peschiera Borromeo)

Telephone: 50 61 990

MANAGING DIRECTOR: Felice Gonalba

SSVV STINSON L-5 235 HP

During 1942-45, well over 3,000 L-5 Sentinel liaison aircraft were built in the USA by the Stinson Division of Consolidated Vultee Aircraft Corporation. Twenty years later, there were 81 L-5s registered in Europe, of which 75 were in Italy, and the L-5 is still used extensively in that country in the role of glider tug. In the early 1970s, SSVV was asked by the Aero Club Valle d'Aosta to produce a modified version of the Sentinel suitable for use at its airfield (which is situated in the Alps some 500 m; 1,640 ft above sea level) and capable of towing a 1,000 kg (2,205 lb) sailplane to an altitude of 1,000 m (3,280 ft).

The first 'Super Stinson' conversion was flown in the Spring of 1972, and trials with Blanik and suitably ballasted Calif A-21 sailplanes demonstrated a performance well in excess of that requested. This included the ability to climb at a rate of more than 120 m (394 ft)/min with a 1,000 kg glider in tow, compared with the 60 m (197 ft)/min required by US regulation AC 43.13—2 CHG 5—Chapter 8, Section 1.

This reduction in aero-tow time, and corresponding reduction in fuel consumption (notwithstanding the higher-powered engine), led to requests by several other Italian gliding clubs for similar conversions, and by October 1977 a total of 10 such conversions had been flown. No more recent news has been received, but SSVV then expected that, owing to the difficulty of obtaining spares for the L-5's original Lycoming O-435 engine, most of the remaining airworthy L-5s in Italy would eventually be converted to the new standard.

SSVV 235 hp conversion of the Stinson L-5 Sentinel, for glider towing

The basic modification involved in the Stinson L-5 235 hp conversion is replacement of the original 138 kW (185 hp) Lycoming O-435 engine with a 175 kW (235 hp) Lycoming O-540-B1A5 flat-six engine, driving a fixed-pitch propeller. The engine is supported on a new dynafocal mounting, and is enclosed by a new, fire-resistant glassfibre cowling fitted with a large controllable cooling gill. The fuel, lubrication and electrical systems have been completely reworked, the fuel system to allow for uninterrupted flow in extreme attitudes, since the original gravity-feed system is no longer adequate at the steeper climbing angles of which the new version is capable.

TYPE: Two-seat glider towing and touring aircraft.

WINGS: High-wing braced monoplane. NACA 4412 wing section. Incidence 2°. Structure consists of spruce spars and ribs, steel tube compression struts and internal wire bracing, with fabric covering. Leading-edge slots. Ailerons and slotted flaps on trailing-edges. V-type steel tube bracing strut on each side.

FUSELAGE: Welded steel tube structure with fabric covering.

TAIL UNIT: Cantilever unit. Framework of steel tube and wood, with fabric covering. Fin built integrally with fuselage. Fixed-incidence tailplane. Horn-balanced control surfaces, with trim tab in port elevator.

LANDING GEAR: Non-retractable cantilever type, with long-stroke oleo spring shock-absorbers on main units. Hydraulically operated main-wheel brakes. Castoring tailwheel, with leaf spring shock-absorber and self-centering damper.

POWER PLANT: One 175 kW (235 hp) Lycoming O-540-B1A5 flat-six engine, driving a Hoffmann two-blade fixed-pitch wooden propeller. (Use of a constant-speed propeller under study in late 1977, to improve cross-country and ferry performance.) Spinner optional. Fuel tank in each wing root.

ACCOMMODATION: Enclosed cabin seating two persons in tandem, with dual controls. Entire roof of cabin glazed. Two doors on starboard side. External rearview mirror.

EQUIPMENT: SSVV aero-tow hook in tailcone, stressed for max load of 2,000 kg (4,409 lb).

DIMENSIONS, EXTERNAL:
- Wing span: 10·36 m (34 ft 0 in)
- Length: with spinner: 7·49 m (24 ft 7 in)
  - without spinner: 7·21 m (23 ft 7¾ in)
- Height overall: 2·16 m (7 ft 1 in)
- Propeller diameter: 2·20 m (7 ft 2½ in)

AREA:
- Wings, gross: 14·40 m² (155·0 sq ft)

WEIGHTS:
- Weight empty: 714 kg (1,574 lb)
- Fuel: 100 kg (220 lb)
- Max T-O weight: 1,021 kg (2,250 lb)

PERFORMANCE (at max T-O weight):
- Max level speed at S/L: 113 knots (209 km/h; 130 mph)
- Max rate of climb at S/L: 510 m (1,673 ft)/min
- Rate of climb at 1,000 m (3,280 ft) with 520 kg (1,146 lb) glider: 204 m (669 ft)/min

JAPAN

CTDC

ZAIDAN HOJIN MINKAN YUSOOKI KAIHATSU KYOKAI (Civil Transport Development Corporation)

HEAD OFFICE: Toranomon Daiichi Building, No. 2-3, 1-chome, Toranomon, Minato-ku, Tokyo 105
Telephone: Tokyo (03) 503 3211
Telex: 2222863 NAMC J

DIRECTORS:
Kiyoshi Yotsumoto (Chairman)
Reizo Wakasugi (Senior Managing Director)
Kyoku Hirano (Managing Director)

GENERAL MANAGER, GENERAL AFFAIRS DEPT: Masanori Yamaguchi

CTDC was established on 1 April 1973 to manage, on behalf of the Japanese government and aerospace industry, the YX civil transport aircraft programme.

Chairman of the board of directors is the current president of Kawasaki Heavy Industries Ltd; other board members include the chairman of Shin Meiwa; the presidents of Fuji, Mitsubishi, Nippi, Ishikawajima-Harima, All Nippon Airways, Japan Air Lines and Toa Domestic Airlines; and the managing directors of Fuji, Kawasaki and Mitsubishi.

YX PROGRAMME

With substantial support from the Japanese government, the Japanese aerospace industry is to develop a civil transport aircraft in collaboration with Boeing and Aeritalia.

In 1978 the Boeing 767 was chosen as the subject of this programme, and a contract between the three organisations, signed on 23 September that year, provides for Boeing and Aeritalia to assume responsibility for 68% and 15% of the programme respectively. The Japanese share of 17% will be divided between Fuji (wing/fuselage fairings), Kawasaki (front and centre fuselage sections, and wing ribs), Mitsubishi (rear fuselage sections) and other Japanese companies. The contract covers the first 500 Model 767s; the Japanese government will provide the finance for 75% of its country's share of the programme.

FUJI

FUJI HEAVY INDUSTRIES LTD (Fuji Jukogyo Kabushiki Kaisha)

HEAD OFFICE: Subaru Building, 7-2, 1-chome, Nishi-shinjuku, Shinjuku-ku, Tokyo
Telephone: Tokyo (03) 347 2505
Telex: 0-232-2268

AIRCRAFT FACTORY (UTSUNOMIYA MANUFACTURING DIVISION): Utsunomiya City, Tochigi Prefecture
Telephone: Utsunomiya (0286) 58 1111

CHAIRMAN OF THE BOARD: Eiichi Ohara
PRESIDENT: Sadamichi Sasaki
SENIOR EXECUTIVE VICE-PRESIDENT: Nobuhiro Sakata

EXECUTIVE MANAGING DIRECTORS:
Sukemitsu Irie
Shoji Nagashima

MANAGING DIRECTORS:
Iwao Shibuya
Kiyoyuki Kawabata
Yoshishige Suzuki
Hiroshi Yamamoto
Kiyoshi Ogawa

GENERAL MANAGER OF AIRCRAFT DIVISION: Atsushi Kasai
MANAGER OF AIRCRAFT SALES DEPARTMENT: Kenshi Miura
SUPERINTENDENT OF UTSUNOMIYA AIRCRAFT FACTORY: Takehiko Ihoji

Fuji Heavy Industries Ltd was established on 15 July 1953. It is a successor to the Nakajima Aircraft Company, which was established in 1914 and built 29,925 aircraft up to the end of the second World War.

The present Utsunomiya Manufacturing Division (Aircraft and Rolling Stock Factories) occupies a site of 512,070 m² (5,511,870 sq ft) including a floor area of 161,532 m² (1,738,710 sq ft) and in 1979 employed 3,315 people.

Under licence from Cessna, Fuji produced 22 L-19E Bird Dog observation aircraft for the Japan Ground Self-Defence Force. Under licence from Beech, it built also the Beechcraft Mentor, and several modified versions of the Mentor designated LM-1 Nikko, LM-2, KM and KM-2. Five additional KM-2s were ordered for the JMSDF in FY 1979; earlier details can be found in previous editions of *Jane's*. The modified KM-2B, combining features of the KM-2 and the Beechcraft T-34A, has been ordered by the JASDF as the T-3 primary trainer.

Fuji is also producing the Bell Model 204/205 series of helicopters. The first 204B covered by the agreement arrived in Japan in kit form in May 1962 for assembly.

Fuji will manufacture wing assemblies for the Lockheed P-3C Orion maritime patrol aircraft being built under licence in Japan for the Maritime Self-Defence Force.

First aircraft designed entirely by Fuji was the T-1 intermediate two-seat jet trainer (1967-68 *Jane's*). It was followed by a four-seat light aeroplane known as the FA-200 Aero Subaru.

Fuji built the VTOL testbed designed by the National Aerospace Laboratory (1972-73 *Jane's*), and since 1972 has continued the study of VTOL research aircraft under contract to NAL.

The twin-engined six/eight-seat Models 700 and 710 are being produced jointly with Rockwell International.

Fuji is currently studying a proposal to meet the JASDF's MT-X requirement for a new jet trainer, acquisition of which is expected to form a part of the 6th defence buildup programme (1982-87). Its FT-20 design would be powered by two 15·6 kN (3,500 lb st) IHI F3 turbofan engines.

Fuji FA-200-180 Aero Subaru four-seat light aircraft (Lycoming IO-360-B1B engine)

FUJI FA-200 AERO SUBARU

Fuji began detail design of this light aircraft in 1964 and the prototype flew for the first time on 12 August 1965. Subsequently, refinements were made to the aircraft, and it went into production as the FA-200-160 and FA-200-180. One example was also produced of the FA-203S STOL version, and this was described in the 1970-71 *Jane's*.

Current versions are designated as follows:

FA-200-160. Basic four-seat light aircraft, with 119 kW (160 hp) Lycoming engine. Received Japan Civil Aviation Bureau Normal category type certificate as a four-seater on 1 March 1966, Utility category certification as a three-seater on 6 July 1966 and Aerobatic category certification as a two-seater on 29 July 1967. FAA Type Approval in all three categories followed on 26 September 1967.

FA-200-180. Developed version with 134 kW (180 hp) Lycoming engine. Certification by JCAB in Normal (four-seat), Utility (four-seat) and Aerobatic (two-seat) categories was received on 28 February 1968, and FAA Type Approval in all three categories on 25 April 1968.

FA-200-180AO. Version with 134 kW (180 hp) Lycoming engine and fixed-pitch propeller. Certificated by JCAB in Normal (four-seat), Utility (four-seat) and Aerobatic (two-seat) categories on 27 September 1973; and by FAA in all three categories on 1 February 1974.

Production of the FA-200 began in March 1968, and 293 had been completed by 1 February 1979, of which more than 170 were for export.

The following description applies generally to all three current versions, except where a specific version is indicated. 'Subaru' is the Japanese name for the Pleiades group of six stars in the constellation of Taurus, and was chosen to represent the six companies which merged to form Fuji Heavy Industries Ltd.

TYPE: Four-seat light monoplane.

WINGS: Cantilever low-wing monoplane. Dihedral 7°. Incidence 2° 30′. All-metal structure, with single extruded main spar at 42% chord. All-metal riveted Frise-type ailerons and single-slotted flaps. Trim tab on each aileron.

FUSELAGE: All-metal semi-monocoque structure of frames and stringers.

TAIL UNIT: Cantilever all-metal structure, with swept vertical surfaces. One-piece tailplane. Trim tab on port elevator. Manually-adjustable tab on rudder.

LANDING GEAR: Non-retractable tricycle type. Oleo-pneumatic shock-absorbers on all units. Nosewheel steerable. Tube-type 4-ply tyres size 6·00-6 on main wheels, 5·00-5 on nosewheel. Hydraulic disc brakes. Parking brake. Streamlined wheel fairings optional.

POWER PLANT: One 119 kW (160 hp) Lycoming O-320-D2A (134 kW; 180 hp Lycoming IO-360-B1B in FA-200-180 and 134 kW; 180 hp Lycoming O-360-A5AD in FA-200-180AO) flat-four engine, driving a McCauley 1C 160/FGM 7656 two-blade fixed-pitch metal propeller in FA-200-160 (McCauley B2D34C53/74E-0 two-blade constant-speed metal propeller in FA-200-180, and McCauley 1A 170/EFA 7658 two-blade fixed-pitch metal propeller in FA-200-180AO). Fuel in two integral tanks in inner wings with total capacity of 204·5 litres (45 Imp gallons). Overwing refuelling point for each tank. Oil capacity 7 litres (1·5 Imp gallons).

ACCOMMODATION: Four seats in pairs in enclosed cabin. Individual adjustable front seats, with dual controls. Optional shoulder harness on each of the four seats. Large rearward-sliding canopy, which can be opened in flight. Two tinted roof windows optional. Cabin heating and ventilation, and windscreen defrosting, standard. Baggage compartment in rear of fuselage, capacity 80 kg (176 lb). Baggage shelf aft of rear seats, capacity 20 kg (44 lb).

AVIONICS AND EQUIPMENT: Standard electrical equipment includes 12V 50/60A alternator and 12V 38Ah battery. Optional extras include HF and VHF radio, full blind-flying instrumentation, VOR, ADF, ILS, ATC transponder, landing and navigation lights, cabin lights, instrument lights and anti-collision light.

DIMENSIONS, EXTERNAL:
Wing span 9·42 m (30 ft 11 in)
Wing chord (constant) 1·525 m (5 ft 0 in)
Wing aspect ratio 6·34
Length overall 8·17 m (26 ft 9½ in)
Height overall 2·59 m (8 ft 6 in)
Tailplane span 3·47 m (11 ft 4½in)
Wheel track 2·63 m (8 ft 7½ in)
Wheelbase 1·75 m (5 ft 8¾ in)
Propeller diameter: 160, 180AO 1·93 m (6 ft 4 in)
180 1·88 m (6 ft 2 in)

DIMENSIONS, INTERNAL:
Cabin: Length 1·74 m (5 ft 8½ in)
Width 1·03 m (3 ft 4½ in)

AREAS:
Wings, gross 14·0 m^2 (150·7 sq ft)
Ailerons (total) 1·13 m^2 (12·11 sq ft)
Flaps (total) 1·87 m^2 (20·13 sq ft)
Fin 1·50 m^2 (16·11 sq ft)
Rudder, incl tab 0·89 m^2 (9·58 sq ft)
Tailplane 3·32 m^2 (35·74 sq ft)
Elevators, incl tab 1·43 m^2 (15·4 sq ft)

WEIGHTS AND LOADINGS (N: Normal; U: Utility; A: Aerobatic category):
Weight empty: 160 620 kg (1,366 lb)
180 650 kg (1,433 lb)
180AO 640 kg (1,411 lb)
Max T-O weight: N (160) 1,060 kg (2,335 lb)
N (180) 1,150 kg (2,535 lb)
N (180AO) 1,140 kg (2,513 lb)
U (160) 970 kg (2,138 lb)
U (180/180AO) 1,100 kg (2,425 lb)
A (160) 880 kg (1,940 lb)
A (180/180AO) 940 kg (2,072 lb)
Max wing loading: N (160) 75·7 kg/m^2 (15·5 lb/sq ft)
N (180) 82·1 kg/m^2 (16·8 lb/sq ft)
Max power loading: N (160) 8·91 kg/kW (14·59 lb/hp)
N (180) 8·58 kg/kW (14·08 lb/hp)

PERFORMANCE (N: Normal category; A: Aerobatic category, at max T-O weight):
Max level speed at S/L:
N (160) 120 knots (222 km/h; 138 mph)
N (180) 126 knots (233 km/h; 145 mph)
N (180AO) 123 knots (229 km/h; 142 mph)
A (160) 122 knots (225 km/h; 140 mph)
A (180) 128 knots (237 km/h; 147 mph)
A (180AO) 126 knots (233 km/h; 145 mph)
Max cruising speed (75% power):
N (160) at 1,525 m (5,000 ft)
106 knots (196 km/h; 122 mph)
N (180) at 1,525 m (5,000 ft)
110 knots (204 km/h; 127 mph)
N (180AO) at 1,525 m (5,000 ft)
112 knots (208 km/h; 129 mph)
A (160) at 2,290 m (7,500 ft)
114 knots (211 km/h; 131 mph)
A (180 and 180AO) at 2,290 m (7,500 ft)
119 knots (220 km/h; 137 mph)
Econ cruising speed (55% power):
N (160) at 1,525 m (5,000 ft)
89 knots (164 km/h; 102 mph)
N (180) at 1,525 m (5,000 ft)
90 knots (167 km/h; 104 mph)
N (180AO) at 1,525 m (5,000 ft)
92 knots (171 km/h; 106 mph)
A (160) at 2,290 m (7,500 ft)
96 knots (177 km/h; 110 mph)
A (180) at 2,290 m (7,500 ft)
100 knots (185 km/h; 115 mph)
A (180AO) at 2,290 m (7,500 ft)
102 knots (190 km/h; 118 mph)
Stalling speed, flaps down:
N (160) 49 knots (90 km/h; 56 mph)
N (180) 53 knots (97 km/h; 60 mph)
N (180AO) 52 knots (95 km/h; 59 mph)
A (160) 45·5 knots (84 km/h; 52·5 mph)
A (180 and 180AO) 47 knots (87 km/h; 54 mph)
Max rate of climb at S/L: N (160) 207 m (680 ft)/min
N (180) 232 m (760 ft)/min
N (180AO) 204 m (670 ft)/min
A (160) 302 m (991 ft)/min
A (180) 344 m (1,129 ft)/min
A (180AO) 311 m (1,020 ft)/min
Service ceiling: N (160 and 180AO) 3,480 m (11,400 ft)
N (180) 4,175 m (13,700 ft)
A (160) 4,725 m (15,500 ft)
A (180) 5,790 m (19,000 ft)
A (180AO) 5,640 m (18,500 ft)
T-O run: A (160) 160 m (525 ft)
A (180 and 180AO) 190 m (623 ft)
T-O to 15 m (50 ft): N (160) 465 m (1,530 ft)
N (180 and 180AO) 500 m (1,640 ft)
A (160) 310 m (1,020 ft)
A (180 and 180AO) 305 m (1,000 ft)
Landing from 15 m (50 ft): N (160) 340 m (1,115 ft)
N (180 and 180AO) 350 m (1,150 ft)
A (160) 315 m (1,033 ft)
A (180 and 180AO) 325 m (1,066 ft)
Landing run: A (160) 115 m (377 ft)
A (180 and 180AO) 125 m (410 ft)

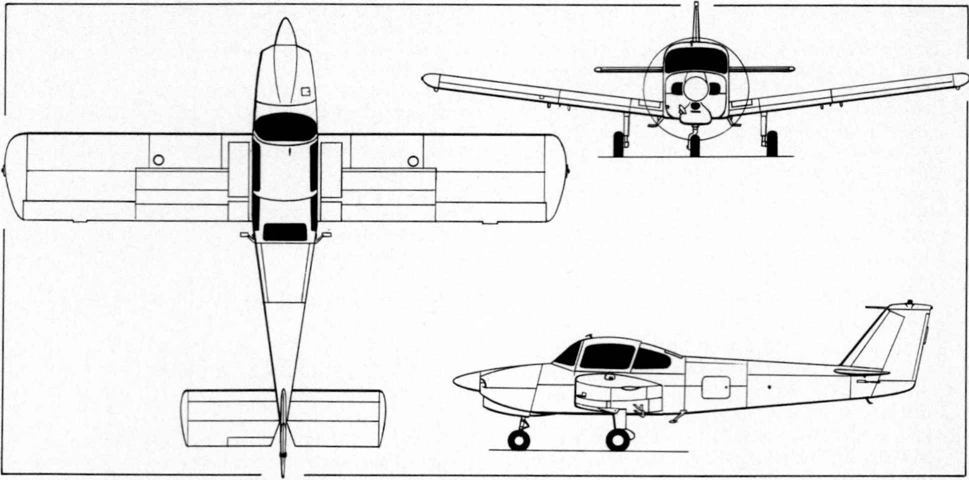

Fuji FA-200-180AO four-seat light aircraft *(Pilot Press)*

Range with max fuel (55% power at 2,290 m; 7,500 ft, no reserves):
N (160) 655 nm (1,215 km; 755 miles)
N (180) 725 nm (1,343 km; 835 miles)
N (180AO) 675 nm (1,252 km; 778 miles)
A (160) 816 nm (1,512 km; 940 miles)
A (180) 755 nm (1,400 km; 870 miles)
A (180AO) 748 nm (1,387 km; 862 miles)

FUJI/ROCKWELL COMMANDER FA-300/MODEL 700

Design and development of the FA-300/Model 700 twin-engined six/eight-seat pressurised light aircraft began in Japan in the latter half of 1971. It is currently proceeding as a collaborative venture between Fuji and Rockwell International, and is described under the latter company's heading in the US section.

For type certification trials, two prototypes were flown in Japan and three in the USA. Certification by the JCAB and FAA was granted on 16 May and 30 September 1977 respectively. External noise level satisfies the 80 dB (A) 1980 requirements of FAR Pt 36.

Airframe assemblies are manufactured in Japan; assembly is completed by the use of US-manufactured avionics, power plant, wheels, tyres and brakes.

FUJI/ROCKWELL COMMANDER FA-300/MODEL 710

This more powerful version of the FA-300 family (335 kW; 450 hp engines) is being developed jointly by Fuji and Rockwell International (which see). The first flight was made on 22 December 1976. Two prototypes were flown in Japan and two are for FAA certification in the USA. After about 580 h of flight testing by the two prototypes in Japan, JCAB certification was awarded in the early Spring of 1979. Like the Model 700, the 710 also satisfies the 1980 requirements of FAR Pt 36.

In mid-1979, one Japanese prototype was being flight-tested with NASA wingtip 'winglets'.

FUJI KM-2B

JASDF designation: T-3

The KM-2B is a modification of the original KM-2 development of the Beechcraft T-34A Mentor, described in the 1969-70 *Jane's*, combining the airframe and power plant of the KM-2 with the two-seat cockpit installation of the T-34A. The first KM-2B (JA3725) was flown for the first time on 26 September 1974, and received JCAB category A certification on 28 November 1974.

In 1975 the JASDF announced that it had selected the KM-2B to replace the T-34A in the primary trainer role. Purchase of 54 is planned as T-3s, of which 44 had been ordered by the Spring of 1979. The first of six pre-production T-3s made its first flight on 17 January 1978. The first production aircraft was completed on 7 March 1978, and was delivered to the JASDF later that month.

A version of the KM-2B for liaison and short-range rescue duties is under consideration.

The following description applies to the T-3:

TYPE: Two-seat primary trainer.

WINGS: Cantilever low-wing monoplane. Wing section NACA 23016·5 at root, NACA 23012 at tip. Dihedral 6° from roots. Incidence 4° at root. 3° geometric twist. No sweep at quarter-chord. All-metal tapered two-spar structure with stressed skin. Aluminium alloy single-slotted flaps and plain ailerons. Servo tab in each aileron; port tab controllable for trim.

FUSELAGE: Conventional all-metal semi-monocoque structure.

TAIL UNIT: Cantilever all-metal structure. Fixed-incidence tailplane, with elevators. Controllable tab in each elevator; anti-servo tab in rudder.

LANDING GEAR: Electrically retractable tricycle type, with single wheel and oleo-pneumatic shock-absorber on each unit. Nosewheel retracts rearward, main wheels inward into wings. Goodyear wheels and Type III tyres on all units: size 6·50-8 (6 ply), pressure 2·34 bars (34 lb/sq in) on main units; size 5·00-5 (4 ply), pressure 2·76 bars (40 lb/sq in) on nose unit. Goodyear automatically adjustable single-disc brakes on main units.

POWER PLANT: One 254 kW (340 hp) Lycoming IGSO-480-A1F6 flat-six engine, driving a Hartzell HC-A3V20-1F/V9333N-3 three-blade constant-speed propeller with spinner. One metal and one bladder-type fuel tank in each wing, total capacity 265 litres (70 US gallons; 58·3 Imp gallons). Refuelling points on top of wings. Oil capacity 11·35 litres (3 US gallons; 2·5 Imp gallons).

ACCOMMODATION: Crew of two in tandem, on adjustable seats in heated and ventilated cabin. Dual controls standard. Framed canopy, with rearward-sliding section over each seat. Space for 13·6 kg (30 lb) of baggage aft of rear seat.

SYSTEMS AND AVIONICS: Blind-flying instrumentation standard. Electrical system includes 28V 100A DC generator and two 160VA static inverters. Standard avionics include ICS, VHF, Tacan, and ATC transponder with Mode C.

DIMENSIONS, EXTERNAL:
Wing span 10·004 m (32 ft 10 in)
Wing chord at root 2·13 m (7 ft 0 in)

Fuji T-3 (KM-2B) two-seat primary trainer of the JASDF (Lycoming IGSO-480-A1F6 engine)

Wing chord at tip 1·07 m (3 ft 6 in)
Wing aspect ratio 6·1
Length overall 8·036 m (26 ft 4¼ in)
Height overall 3·023 m (9 ft 11 in)
Tailplane span 3·712 m (12 ft 2¼ in)
Wheel track 2·924 m (9 ft 7 in)
Wheelbase 2·266 m (7 ft 5¼ in)
Propeller diameter 2·286 m (7 ft 6 in)
Propeller ground clearance 0·25 m (9¾ in)

DIMENSIONS, INTERNAL:
Cabin: Max width approx 0·90 m (2 ft 11½ in)
Max height approx 1·30 m (4 ft 3¼ in)

AREAS:
Wings, gross 16·50 m² (177·6 sq ft)
Ailerons (total) 1·07 m² (11·52 sq ft)
Trailing-edge flaps (total) 1·98 m² (21·31 sq ft)
Fin 0·97 m² (10·44 sq ft)
Rudder, incl tab 0·61 m² (6·57 sq ft)
Tailplane 3·46 m² (37·24 sq ft)
Elevators, incl tab 1·39 m² (14·96 sq ft)

WEIGHTS AND LOADINGS:
Weight empty 1,136 kg (2,504 lb)
Normal operational T-O weight 1,510 kg (3,329 lb)
Max T-O weight 1,542 kg (3,400 lb)
Max wing loading 93·5 kg/m² (19·15 lb/sq ft)
Max power loading 6·07 kg/kW (10·00 lb/hp)

PERFORMANCE (at normal operational T-O weight):
Never-exceed speed 223 knots (413 km/h; 257 mph) EAS
Max level speed at 4,875 m (16,000 ft) 203 knots (377 km/h; 234 mph)
Max cruising speed at 2,440 m (8,000 ft) 177 knots (328 km/h; 204 mph)
Econ cruising speed at 2,440 m (8,000 ft) 137 knots (254 km/h; 158 mph)
Stalling speed, flaps up 66 knots (123 km/h; 76 mph)
Stalling speed, flaps down 54 knots (100 km/h; 62 mph)
Max rate of climb at S/L 463 m (1,520 ft)/min
Service ceiling 8,170 m (26,800 ft)
T-O run 265 m (870 ft)
T-O to 15 m (50 ft) 503 m (1,650 ft)
Landing from 15 m (50 ft) 436 m (1,430 ft)
Landing run 238 m (780 ft)
Range with max fuel 520 nm (965 km; 600 miles)

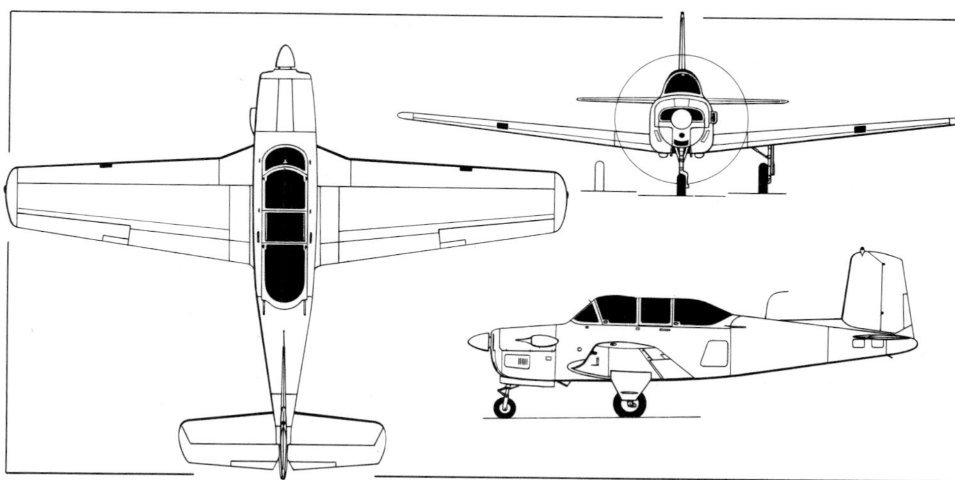

Fuji T-3 two-seat primary trainer, developed from the KM-2 and Beechcraft T-34A *(Pilot Press)*

Fuji-Bell UH-1H medium helicopter of the JGSDF (Lycoming T53-K-13B turboshaft engine)

FUJI-BELL 204B/204B-2 and 205A-1/UH-1H

Fuji is manufacturing Bell Model 204B and UH-1H helicopters under sub-licence from Mitsui and Co Ltd, Bell's Japanese licensee. By March 1979 a total of 47 Fuji-Bell 204B/204B-2s had been produced for civilian operators.

Following the delivery of 90 UH-1Bs (military version of the 204B) to the Japan Ground Self-Defence Force by early 1973, Fuji production continued with the UH-1H version, of which the first example flew for the first time on 17 July 1973; 59 had been ordered by March 1979.

The Fuji-Bell 204B is identical with that built by Bell Helicopter Textron (1971-72 *Jane's*). It is powered by an 820 kW (1,100 shp) Kawasaki-built Lycoming T53-K-11A turboshaft engine. The Fuji-Bell UH-1H has the same airframe and dynamic components as the Bell-built UH-1H, but has a tractor-type tail rotor and is powered by a 1,044 kW (1,400 shp) Kawasaki-built Lycoming T53-K-13B turboshaft engine.

In October 1973 Fuji developed a higher-powered version of the 204B. Powered by a 1,044 kW (1,400 shp) Lycoming T53-K-13B turboshaft engine, it has the same basic airframe and dynamic components as the 204B, but has a tractor-type tail rotor. The first example of this version, which is designated **204B-2**, was delivered to the Asahi Helicopter Co in early 1974.

The following details apply to the standard Fuji-Bell 204B/204B-2/UH-1H:

DIMENSIONS, EXTERNAL:
Diameter of main rotor 16·63 m (48 ft 0 in)
Diameter of tail rotor 2·59 m (8 ft 6 in)
Length overall, tail rotor turning:
204B/B-2 13·61 m (44 ft 7¾ in)
UH-1H 13·67 m (44 ft 10 in)
Length of fuselage: 204B/B-2 12·31 m (40 ft 4¾ in)
UH-1H 12·37 m (40 ft 7 in)
Height overall, tail rotor turning 4·42 m (14 ft 6 in)
Height to top of rotor hub:
204B/B-2 3·77 m (12 ft 4½ in)
UH-1H 3·98 m (13 ft 0¾ in)
Max width over landing skids:
204B/B-2 2·64 m (8 ft 8 in)
UH-1H 2·60 m (8 ft 6½ in)
Tailplane span 2·84 m (9 ft 4 in)

WEIGHTS AND LOADINGS:
Weight empty: 204B/B-2 2,177 kg (4,800 lb)
UH-1H 2,390 kg (5,270 lb)
Max T-O weight:
204B/B-2, internal load 3,855 kg (8,500 lb)
204B/B-2, external load 4,309 kg (9,500 lb)
UH-1H 4,309 kg (9,500 lb)
Max disc loading 25·6 kg/m² (5·25 lb/sq ft)
Max power loading:
204B 5·25 kg/kW (8·64 lb/shp)
204B-2, UH-1H 4·13 kg/kW (6·78 lb/shp)

PERFORMANCE (at max T-O weight):
Max level and cruising speed 110 knots (204 km/h; 127 mph)
Max rate of climb at S/L:
204B 463 m (1,520 ft)/min
204B-2 588 m (1,930 ft)/min
UH-1H 488 m (1,600 ft)/min
Service ceiling: 204B 4,480 m (14,700 ft)
204B-2 5,790 m (19,000 ft)
UH-1H 3,840 m (12,600 ft)
Hovering ceiling IGE: 204B 2,985 m (9,800 ft)
204B-2 4,635 m (15,200 ft)
UH-1H 4,145 m (13,600 ft)
Hovering ceiling OGE: 204B 1,310 m (4,300 ft)
204B-2 3,200 m (10,500 ft)
UH-1H 335 m (1,100 ft)
Range at S/L: 204B 206 nm (381 km; 237 miles)
204B-2 207 nm (383 km; 238 miles)
UH-1H 252 nm (467 km; 290 miles)

KAWASAKI
KAWASAKI JUKOGYO KABUSHIKI KAISHA (Kawasaki Heavy Industries Ltd)

HEAD OFFICE: 2-16-1 Nakamachi-Dori, Ikuta-ku, Kobe
TOKYO AND AIRCRAFT GROUP OFFICE: World Trade Center Building, 4-1, Hamamatsu-cho 2-chome, Minato-ku, Tokyo
Telephone: Tokyo (03) 435 2971
Telex: J22672 and J26888
CHAIRMAN: Kiyoshi Yotsumoto
PRESIDENT: Zenji Umeda
EXECUTIVE VICE-PRESIDENTS:
Tsuneo Ando
Toraichi Imai
WORKS: Gifu
GENERAL MANAGER, AIRCRAFT GROUP: Teruaki Yamada
ASST GENERAL MANAGER, AIRCRAFT GROUP, AND GENERAL MANAGER, AIRCRAFT SALES DIVISION: Noriyasu Muroi

With effect from 1 April 1969, Kawasaki Aircraft Co Ltd was amalgamated with the Kawasaki Dockyard Co Ltd and the Kawasaki Rolling Stock Mfg Co Ltd, to form Kawasaki Heavy Industries Ltd. The Aircraft Division of the former Kawasaki Aircraft Co Ltd, which employs some 3,200 people, continues its activities as the Aircraft Group of this company. Kawasaki has a 36·8% holding in Nippi (which see).

In addition to extensive overhaul work, Kawasaki has built many US aircraft under licence since 1953, including 48 Lockheed P2V-7 (P-2H) Neptune anti-submarine aircraft and 239 Bell Model 47 helicopters, plus another 211 Model KH-4 helicopters developed from the Bell 47 by its own design staff. From the Neptune it developed the P-2J anti-submarine aircraft, of which it delivered 82. Production of this aircraft has now ended.

Design studies are being undertaken for a new intermediate jet trainer, provisionally designated KA-840, to succeed the Lockheed T-33A, of which the company built 210 under licence during 1956-59. The KA-840 is also intended as a possible replacement for the Fuji T-1.

Kawasaki is to be a prime contractor for licence production of the Lockheed P-3C /Update II Orion, 45 of which are to be purchased by the JMSDF during the next 11 years. The first eight of these were ordered in the FY 1978 budget. The company is also a subcontractor for certain components of the McDonnell Douglas F-15 Eagles being licence-built in Japan by Mitsubishi (which see).

Kawasaki is also developing, jointly with MBB of Germany, the BK-117 twin-engined multi-purpose helicopter described in the International section.

Kawasaki has exclusive rights to manufacture and sell the twin-engined Boeing Vertol 107 Model II helicopter and its own KV-107/IIA development of it. The Hughes Model 369 (500D and 500M) light observation helicopter is also being assembled by Kawasaki under a licence agreement concluded in October 1967. By 31 March 1979 a total of 121 KV-107 helicopters had been delivered to customers in Japan and other countries including Saudi Arabia, Sweden, Thailand and the USA; and a total of 179 Hughes 500s to government and commercial operators in Japan.

Kawasaki is prime contractor for the JASDF's C-1 transport; and builds main wing and tail assemblies under subcontract for Japanese-built (see Mitsubishi entry) F-4EJ Phantom II fighters for the JASDF. Cargo and passenger doors for the Lockheed L-1011 TriStar jet transport are manufactured at the Gifu works, and Kawasaki has a Boeing contract to manufacture outboard trailing-edge flaps for the Boeing 747SP transport aircraft.

In February 1977 Kawasaki was awarded a JDA contract to produce an experimental variable-stability aircraft (VSA) by converting a P2V-7 of the JMSDF. This aircraft has a large panel above and below each wing, a fly-by-wire control system, direct-lift-control flaps, and a miniature computer.

Kawasaki is engaged in missile development and production; its aero-engine activities are described in the appropriate section of this edition.

Kawasaki P-2J patrol aircraft of the Japan Maritime Self-Defence Force (two T64 turboprop engines and two J3-IHI-7D auxiliary turbojets)

KAWASAKI P-2J

JMSDF designations: P-2J and UP-2J

The P-2J was developed by Kawasaki, originally under the designation GK-210, to meet a JMSDF requirement for a new anti-submarine aircraft to replace its P2V-7 Neptunes in service during the 1970s. Design, based very closely upon that of the P2V-7 (P-2H), began in October 1961. Work on the conversion of a standard P2V-7 as the P-2J prototype began in June 1965, and this aircraft flew for the first time on 21 July 1966.

The first production P-2J was flown on 8 August 1969, and was delivered to the JMSDF on 7 October. A further 81 P-2Js were built, and the last of these was delivered during March 1979. The FY 1978 budget included funds for the conversion of one P-2J to **UP-2J** configuration for the target-towing role. Three further similar conversions are planned.

A full description of the P-2J can be found in the 1978-79 *Jane's*.

TYPE: Four-engined anti-submarine and maritime patrol aircraft.

POWER PLANT: Two 2,282 kW (3,060 ehp) Japanese-built General Electric T64-IHI-10E turboprop engines, with water methanol injection, mounted on wing centre-section and each driving a Sumitomo Precision 63E60-19 three-blade variable-pitch metal propeller. Outboard of these, on underwing pylons, are two pod-mounted Ishikawajima-Harima J3-IHI-7D turbojets, each rated at 15·2 kN (3,417 lb st). Fuel in inboard and outboard wing tanks with total capacity of 11,433 litres (2,515 Imp gallons; 3,020 US gallons), plus 1,514 litres (333 Imp gallons; 400 US gallons) in port wingtip tank. For ferry purposes a 2,650 litre (583 Imp gallon; 700 US gallon) auxiliary tank can be installed in the weapons bay. Oil capacity 23·5 litres (5·2 Imp gallons; 6·2 US gallons) for each turboprop and 11 litres (2·4 Imp gallons; 2·9 US gallons) for each turbojet engine.

ACCOMMODATION: Crew of 12, including two pilots on flight deck, seven men in tactical compartment in forward fuselage and three aft of centre-section wing box beam. Aft of the tactical compartment, in centre fuselage, are an ordnance room, galley and toilet. Crew escape hatches in flight deck, tactical and ordnance compartments. All accommodation heated, ventilated and air-conditioned.

DIMENSIONS, EXTERNAL:

Wing span	29·78 m (97 ft 8½ in)
Wing span over tip-tanks	30·87 m (101 ft 3½ in)
Wing area, gross	92·9 m² (1,000 sq ft)
Wing aspect ratio	10
Length overall	29·23 m (95 ft 10¾ in)
Height overall	8·93 m (29 ft 3½ in)
Tailplane span	10·36 m (34 ft 0 in)
Wheel track (c/l of shock-absorbers)	7·62 m (25 ft 0 in)
Wheelbase	8·84 m (29 ft 0 in)
Propeller diameter	4·43 m (14 ft 6¼ in)

DIMENSIONS, INTERNAL (tactical compartment):

Cabin: Length	5·49 m (18 ft 0 in)
Max width	2·03 m (6 ft 8 in)
Max height (at c/l)	1·55 m (5 ft 1 in)
Floor area	11·15 m² (120 sq ft)
Volume	14·16 m³ (500 cu ft)

WEIGHTS AND LOADINGS:

Weight empty	19,277 kg (42,500 lb)
Max T-O weight	34,019 kg (75,000 lb)
Max zero-fuel weight	23,087 kg (50,900 lb)
Max landing weight	28,122 kg (62,000 lb)
Max wing loading	366·2 kg/m² (75·00 lb/sq ft)
Max power loading	8·00 kg/kW (13·16 lb/ehp)

PERFORMANCE (at max T-O weight):

Never-exceed speed	350 knots (649 km/h; 403 mph)
Max cruising speed	217 knots (402 km/h; 250 mph)
Econ cruising speed at 3,050 m (10,000 ft)	200 knots (370 km/h; 230 mph)
Stalling speed, flaps down	90 knots (166 km/h; 103 mph)
Max rate of climb at S/L	550 m (1,800 ft)/min
Service ceiling	9,150 m (30,000 ft)
T-O to 15 m (50 ft)	1,100 m (3,600 ft)
Landing from 15 m (50 ft)	880 m (2,880 ft)
Range with max fuel	2,400 nm (4,450 km; 2,765 miles)

KAWASAKI P2V-7 (P-2H) VSA VARIABLE STABILITY AIRCRAFT

Under a $3 million contract awarded in February 1977 by the Technical Research and Development Institute of the Japan Defence Agency, Kawasaki modified the 39th production P2V-7 (P-2H) Neptune ASW aircraft to experimental configuration as a Variable Stability Aircraft (VSA).

The aircraft, which has the company project designation KA-353, made its first flight at Gifu on 23 December 1977, and was handed over to the 51st Air Squadron of the JMSDF for evaluation in 1978. After two years of experimental flying, it will become a training aircraft for JMSDF test pilots, and will be used, among other things, to develop STOL approaches, with the aid of ventral airbrakes, at glideslope angles of up to 6°-7°.

Seven major modifications have been made to the basic P2V-7 aircraft:

1. Installation of a fly-by-wire control system, with mechanical backup.

2. Installation, with flight control computer monitoring, of variable stability system to measure (a) variable control feelings such as hysteresis, breakout forces etc; and (b) variable aircraft response, both lateral and longitudinal.

3. Removal of outboard trailing-edge flaps and replacement with direct lift control (DLC) flaps of 4·27 m (14 ft 0 in) span, with 20° upward and 40° downward travel. Vortex generators added forward of DLC flaps.

4. Addition of aerofoil-section, all-moving side force surface (SFS), extending above and below each wing, outboard of jet engine pod, with 30° travel to left or right. Each SFS is 4·40 m (14 ft 5¼ in) high.

5. Attachment of perforated airbrake to inside of each weapons bay door.

6. Removal of all ASW equipment, including APS-20 radome, though retaining MAD tailcone.

7. Installation of flight instrumentation and recorders, including angle of attack/sideslip sensors above nose. Addition of two control operators' consoles in tactical compartment of fuselage.

AREAS:

DLC flaps (two, each)	3·92 m² (42·19 sq ft)
SFS sections (on each wing)	5·50 m² (59·20 sq ft)
Airbrakes (two, each)	1·40 m² (15·07 sq ft)

WEIGHT:

Max T-O weight	12,245 kg (26,995 lb)

KAWASAKI C-1

The C-1 is a medium-sized troop and freight transport designed to meet the JASDF's requirement for a replacement for its former fleet of Curtiss C-46s. Preliminary design was started by NAMC in 1966, and in 1968 a prototype development contract was awarded. Following the completion of a full-size mockup in March 1968, construction by NAMC began in the following Autumn of two XC-1 flying prototypes and one airframe for static tests. The first flying prototype, assembled at Kawasaki's Gifu factory, made its first flight on 12 November 1970, followed by the second on 16 January 1971. These were handed over to the JDA on 24 February and 20 March 1971 respectively. Further development and evaluation tests by the JDA were completed in March 1973.

Two pre-production aircraft had been delivered by the end of February 1974. Airframe fatigue testing by the JDA was completed in November 1974.

Eleven production C-1s were ordered in FY 1972, of which the first was delivered in December 1974; all 11 had been delivered by the end of March 1976. An additional 13 C-1s were ordered during FY 1975; these had all been delivered by the end of February 1978, including two long-range aircraft with an additional 4,732 litre (1,250 US gallon) wing centre-section fuel tank. Two more long-range C-1s were ordered during FY 1977, and one in FY 1979; further production is anticipated. All C-1s are to be camouflaged by 1981.

Future derivatives of the C-1 under study in 1979 included an electronic warfare version, a minelaying version, a tanker version, a weather reconnaissance version, and an improved tactical transport version with an extended fuselage.

The National Aerospace Laboratory (see NAL entry) is building an experimental STOL aircraft utilising the airframe of a C-1. The prototype C-1 is also to serve until

Kawasaki P2V-7 (P-2H) Variable Stability Aircraft, with side force panels above and below each wing, fly-by-wire control system, and other modifications *(K. Hinata)*

Kawasaki C-1 medium-range military transport aircraft of the JASDF in new camouflage finish *(K. Hinata)*

1981 as a flying testbed for engines under development, for targets, and for other purposes.

Prime contractor in the C-1 programme is Kawasaki, which builds the front fuselage and wing centre-section and undertakes final assembly and flight testing. Major subcontractors are Fuji (outer wing panels); Mitsubishi (centre and aft fuselage sections and tail surfaces); Nihon Hikoki (Nippi) (flaps, slats, spoilers, ailerons, engine pylons and pods); and Shin Meiwa (cargo loading equipment).

TYPE: Twin-turbofan medium-range transport.

WINGS: Cantilever high-wing monoplane. Wings have 20° sweepback at quarter-chord, with slightly increased leading-edge sweep inboard of the engine pylons. Thickness/chord ratio 12% at root, 11% at tip. Anhedral 5° 30′ from centre-section. Conventional two-spar fail-safe structure of aluminium alloy, including control surfaces. Two quadruple-slotted flaps on each trailing-edge. Forward of these, on each wing, are three flight spoilers and a ground spoiler. Drooping leading-edge slats, in four sections, on each wing. Manually-operated aileron outboard of each outer flap. Trim tab in port aileron. Thermal anti-icing of leading-edges, using engine bleed air.

FUSELAGE: Conventional semi-monocoque fail-safe structure of aluminium alloy, with a circular cross-section.

TAIL UNIT: Aluminium alloy cantilever T-tail, with sweepback on all surfaces (30° at fin quarter-chord, 25° at tailplane quarter-chord). Tailplane has 5° anhedral. Variable-incidence tailplane, with elevators. Balance tab in each elevator and anti-balance tab in rudder. Elevators and rudder are each operated by two independent hydraulic actuator systems; the elevators can be operated manually in an emergency. Thermal de-icing of tailplane, using electric heater mat.

LANDING GEAR: Hydraulically-retractable tricycle type, of Sumitomo design. Each main unit has two pairs of wheels in tandem, retracting forward into fairings built on to the sides of the fuselage. Forward-retracting nose unit has twin wheels. Main-wheel tyres size 35 × 10·7-16, nosewheel tyres size 28 × 9-12; tyre pressure (all units) 6·21 bars (90 lb/sq in). Oleo shock-absorbers. Kayaba wheels with Dunlop tyres, which on main units have pressure of 5·17 bars (75 lb/sq in). Kayaba hydraulic brakes (two-rotor on first 10 production aircraft, three-rotor from 11th aircraft onward); Sumisei anti-skid units.

POWER PLANT: Two 64·5 kN (14,500 lb st) Mitsubishi (Pratt & Whitney) JT8D-M-9 turbofan engines, installed in pylon-mounted underwing pods and fitted with thrust reversers. Four integral wing fuel tanks with total capacity of 15,200 litres (3,344 Imp gallons). Single pressure refuelling point for all tanks, plus overwing gravity refuelling point for each tank.

ACCOMMODATION: Crew of five, comprising pilot, co-pilot, navigator, flight engineer and load supervisor. Escape hatch in flight deck roof on starboard side. Flight deck and main cabin pressurised and air-conditioned. Standard complements are as follows: troops (max) 60, paratroops (max) 45, stretchers 36 plus attendants. As a cargo carrier, loads can include a 2½ ton truck, a 105 mm howitzer, two ¾ ton trucks or three jeeps. Up to three preloaded freight pallets, 2·24 m (7 ft 4 in) wide and 2·74 m (9 ft 0 in) long, can be carried. Floor is stressed for loads of up to 7 kg/cm^2 (100 lb/sq in). Access to flight deck via downward-opening door, with built-in stairs, on port side of forward fuselage. Paratroop door on each side of fuselage, aft of wing trailing-edge. For air-dropping, the rear-loading ramp/door can be opened in flight to the full cabin cross-section.

SYSTEMS: Pressurisation and air-conditioning systems utilise engine bleed air. APU in front section of starboard landing gear fairing supplies electrical power on ground and in the air, and bleed air on ground. Three independent hydraulic systems, each 207 bars (3,000 lb/sq in). No. 1 system actuates flight controls; No. 2 actuates flight controls, high-lift devices, landing gear, nosewheel steering and brakes; No. 3 system is used for cargo door operation, and provides emergency backup for brakes and high-lift devices. Electrical power supplied by three 40kVA AC generators, two engine-driven and aircooled, and one driven by the APU. 28V DC power is obtained from AC source through a transformer-rectifier. One 24V 30Ah nickel-cadmium battery for emergency DC power.

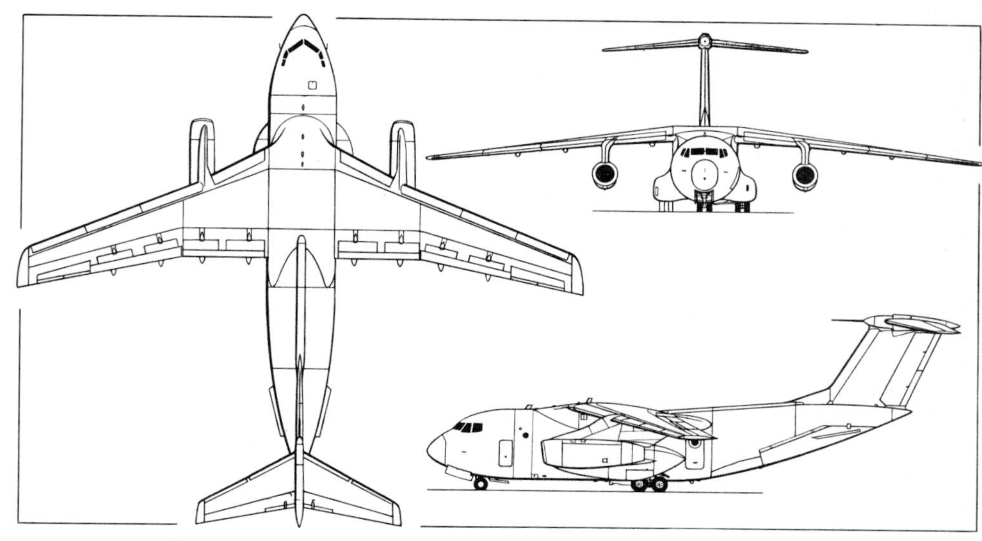

Kawasaki C-1 twin-turbofan medium-range military transport *(Pilot Press)*

AVIONICS AND EQUIPMENT: Standard avionics include autopilot, Doppler radar, radio altimeter, HF, VHF and UHF radio, ADF, UHF/DF, marker beacon, VOR/ILS, Tacan, SIF, dual compass system and flight director system. Optional avionics include Loran and weather radar.

DIMENSIONS, EXTERNAL:

Wing span	30·60 m (100 ft 4¾ in)
Wing chord at root	6·30 m (20 ft 8 in)
Wing chord at tip	2·00 m (6 ft 6¾ in)
Wing aspect ratio	7·8
Length overall	29·00 m (95 ft 1¾ in)
Length of fuselage	26·50 m (86 ft 11¼ in)
Height overall	9·99 m (32 ft 9¼ in)
Tailplane span	11·30 m (37 ft 1 in)
Wheel track	4·40 m (14 ft 5¼ in)
Wheelbase	9·33 m (30 ft 7¼ in)
Rear-loading ramp/door:	
Length	2·67 m (8 ft 9¼ in)
Width	2·70 m (8 ft 10¼ in)
Height to sill	1·25 m (4 ft 1¼ in)

DIMENSIONS, INTERNAL:

Cabin: Max length	10·80 m (35 ft 5¼ in)
Max width	3·60 m (11 ft 9¾ in)
Max height	2·55 m (8 ft 4½ in)
Floor area	28·6 m^2 (308 sq ft)
Volume (excl ramp area)	73·8 m^3 (2,606 cu ft)

AREAS:

Wings, gross	120·5 m^2 (1,297 sq ft)
Ailerons (total)	3·4 m^2 (36·6 sq ft)
Trailing-edge flaps (total)	22·9 m^2 (246·5 sq ft)
Spoilers (total)	8·9 m^2 (95·8 sq ft)
Fin	15·8 m^2 (170·1 sq ft)
Rudder, incl tabs	6·4 m^2 (68·9 sq ft)
Tailplane	18·3 m^2 (197·0 sq ft)
Elevators, incl tabs	6·5 m^2 (70·0 sq ft)

WEIGHTS AND LOADINGS:

Weight empty	23,320 kg (51,410 lb)
Weight empty, equipped	24,300 kg (53,572 lb)
Normal payload	7,900 kg (17,416 lb)
Max payload	11,900 kg (26,235 lb)
Normal T-O weight	38,700 kg (85,320 lb)
Max T-O weight	45,000 kg (99,210 lb)
Max wing loading	373·4 kg/m^2 (76·48 lb/sq ft)
Max power loading	350 kg/kN (3·42 lb/lb st)

PERFORMANCE (at normal T-O weight except where indicated):

Max level speed at 7,620 m (25,000 ft) at 35,450 kg (78,150 lb) AUW 435 knots (806 km/h; 501 mph)

Econ cruising speed at 10,670 m (35,000 ft) at 35,450 kg (78,150 lb) AUW 354 knots (657 km/h; 408 mph)

Max rate of climb at S/L	1,065 m (3,500 ft)/min
Service ceiling	11,580 m (38,000 ft)
Service ceiling, one engine out	5,485 m (18,000 ft)
T-O run	640 m (2,100 ft)
T-O to 15 m (50 ft)	910 m (3,000 ft)

Landing from 15 m (50 ft) at 36,860 kg (81,260 lb) weight 823 m (2,700 ft)

Landing run at 36,860 kg (81,260 lb) weight 455 m (1,500 ft)

Range with max fuel and 2,200 kg (4,850 lb) payload 1,810 nm (3,353 km; 2,084 miles)

Range with 7,900 kg (17,416 lb) payload 700 nm (1,300 km; 807 miles)

KAWASAKI KA-840

Under the company designation KA-840, Kawasaki is developing an intermediate jet trainer to meet a JASDF requirement for a replacement for its Lockheed T-33As and Fuji T-1s. The KA-840 has a tandem two-seat cockpit arrangement, and will be powered by two approx 15·7 kN (3,530 lb st) F-3 turbofan engines, the production version of the XF-3 currently under development by the Technical

Research and Development Institute of the Japan Defence Agency. It will have an additional capability for light attack, carrying underwing 250 kg bombs.

The KA-840 is one of two designs being submitted for JASDF consideration, the other being a Fuji project known as the FT-20. The JASDF is expected to select one of these for development by mid-1981, with a prototype first flight scheduled for FY 1985.

The following details are provisional:

SPECIFICATION:

Wing area, gross	21·6 m² (232·5 sq ft)
Max T-O weight	approx 7,500 kg (16,535 lb)
Max cruising speed	Mach 0·75 (495 knots; 917 km/h; 570 mph at S/L)
Max range with 454 litre (120 US gallon; 100 Imp gallon) external tanks	900 nm (1,670 km; 1,035 miles)

KAWASAKI (BOEING VERTOL) KV-107/II and KV-107/IIA

Swedish Navy designation: HKP 4C

Kawasaki has exclusive rights to manufacture and sell the Boeing Vertol 107 Model II helicopter. The first KV-107 to be produced by Kawasaki under this licence agreement flew for the first time in May 1962.

In 1965, Kawasaki obtained world-wide sales rights in the KV-107 from The Boeing Company's Vertol Division. In November 1965, it was awarded a type certificate for the KV-107 by the FAA.

An improved model, the **KV-107/IIA**, is available in any of the KV-107/II forms, powered by two 1,044 kW (1,400 shp) General Electric CT58-140-1 or Ishikawajima-Harima CT58-IHI-140-1 turboshaft engines (max continuous rating 932 kW; 1,250 shp), which give improved performance during VTOL and in 'hot and high' conditions. Fuel capacity 1,324 litres; 350 US gallons (standard), 3,785 litres; 1,000 US gallons (max). A prototype (JA9509) was converted from a standard KV-107/II-2 and first flown on 3 April 1968. Type approval granted by JCAB on 26 September 1968 and by FAA on 15 January 1969.

The following versions of the KV-107/II and IIA have been announced:

KV-107/II-1. Basic utility helicopter. None yet built.

KV-107/II-2. Basic airline helicopter. Eleven built. Some now operated by Columbia Helicopters Inc of USA (five) and Air Lift Inc of Japan (two). Prototype (JA9509) upgraded as IIA-2 prototype, currently used as a company test aircraft.

KV-107/II-3. Mine countermeasures (MCM) helicopter for JMSDF with extended-range fuel tanks, towing hook and cargo sling. Nine ordered, all of which had been delivered by February 1975, including seven of the **KV-107/IIA-3** version with uprated power. All of these are fitted with minesweeping and retrieval equipment and serve with the 111th Air Wing of the JMSDF.

KV-107/II-4. Tactical cargo/troop transport for JGSDF, with foldable seats for 26 troops or 15 casualty litters. Strengthened floor for carrying heavy vehicles. Orders for 59 placed, of which 57 had been delivered by March 1979, including one equipped as a VIP transport for Cabinet use. The latest 16 aircraft are of the **KV-107/IIA-4** version with uprated power, and five of them are fitted with extended-range fuel tanks.

KV-107/II-5. Long-range search and rescue helicopter for JASDF. Orders for 30 placed, of which 27 had been delivered by early 1979, including eight uprated **KV-107/IIA-5s**. Extended-range fuel tank each side of fuselage, making total capacity 3,785 litres (1,000 US gallons). Extensive nav/com equipment, four searchlights, domed observation window and rescue hoist. The last aircraft is equipped with a Kawasaki/Boeing automatic flight control system, enabling it to cruise at preselected altitude and speed, descend at a programmed rate and distance, and come to hover at a preselected altitude. Also provided are automatic climb-out to the cruise mode; standard distance approach; a turns coupler to a preselected heading; altitude sensing, with dual radar altimeters, for added safety in IFR operations; and a vernier flight control to permit critical positioning during rescue hoist operations. Eight aircraft supplied to Swedish Navy in 1972-74 have Kawasaki-built airframes and rotor assemblies but were fitted in Sweden with Rolls-Royce Gnome H.1200 turboshaft engines and a Decca navigation system. Details of other equipment fitted to Swedish aircraft as listed in 1977-78 *Jane's*.

KV-107/II-6. De luxe transport version. None yet built.

KV-107/II-7. De luxe VIP transport with 6-11 seats. One built: currently owned by Columbia Helicopters Inc of USA.

KV-107/IIA-17. Long-range passenger and cargo transport version for Tokyo Metropolitan Police Department; one delivered in February 1973. Cabin divided into two compartments: front section with 12 passenger seats, rear section capable of accommodating 2,268 kg (5,000 lb) of cargo, six stretcher patients or 12 passengers.

KV-107/IIA-SM-1. Firefighting version for Saudi Arabian government. Four ordered, all of which had been delivered by early 1979. All can be fitted with specially designed equipment for various forms of firefighting (foam agent, chemical powder, water, and co-ordinated firefighting). Additional order for two anticipated.

Kawasaki KV-107/IIA-SM-1 firefighting helicopter for the Saudi Arabian government, with firefighting boom

KV-107/IIA-SM-2. Rescue and aeromedical version for Saudi Arabian government, with external rescue hoist, medical equipment, stretcher kit and other rescue gear; 303 litre (80 US gallon) additional fuel tank can be mounted on each side of fuselage. Two ordered, both of which had been delivered by November 1978; additional order for one anticipated. For self-ferry flights. both SM-1 and SM-2 can be fitted with internally-mounted 1,893 litre (500 US gallon) auxiliary fuel tank.

The description which follows applies to the commercial KV-107/II-2, except where shown:

TYPE: Twin-engined transport helicopter.

ROTOR SYSTEM: Two three-blade rotors in tandem, rotating in opposite directions. Each blade is made up of a steel D spar to which is bonded a trailing-edge box constructed of aluminium ribs and glassfibre or aluminium skin.

ROTOR DRIVE: Power is transmitted from each engine through individually-overrunning clutches into the aft transmission, which combines the engine outputs, thereby providing a single power output to the interconnecting shaft which enables both rotors to be driven by either engine.

FUSELAGE: Basically square-section semi-monocoque structure built primarily of high-strength bare and Alclad aluminium alloy. Transverse bulkheads and built-up frames support transmission, power plant and landing gear. Loading ramp forms undersurface of upswept rear fuselage on utility and military models. Baggage container replaces ramp on airliner version. Fuselage is sealed to permit operation from water.

LANDING GEAR: Non-retractable tricycle type, with twin wheels on all three units. Oleo-pneumatic shock-absorbers. Tubeless tyres, size 18 × 5·5, pressure 10·34 bars (150 lb/sq in), on all wheels. Disc brakes. Wheel/ski gear optional.

POWER PLANT (KV-107/II): Two 932 kW (1,250 shp) General Electric CT58-110-1 or Ishikawajima-Harima CT58-IHI-110-1 turboshaft engines, mounted side by side at base of rear rotor pylon. Alternatively, two Rolls-Royce Gnome H.1200 turboshafts (in HKP 4C). Fuel tanks in sponsons, capacity 1,324 litres (350 US gallons). KV-107/IIA has more powerful CT58 engines and provision for increased fuel capacity (see introductory copy).

ACCOMMODATION: Standard accommodation for two pilots, stewardess and 25 passengers in airliner version. Seats in eight rows, in pairs on port side and single seats on starboard side (two pairs at rear of cabin) with central aisle. Airliner fitted with parcel rack and a roll-out baggage container, with capacity of approximately 680 kg (1,500 lb), located in underside of rear fuselage. Ramp of utility model is power-operated on the ground or in flight and can be removed or left open to permit carriage of extra-long cargo.

AVIONICS AND EQUIPMENT: Standard avionics include stability augmentation system (SAS) and automatic speed trim system (AST). Optional avionics include automatic stabilisation equipment (ASE); automatic flight control system (AFCS); Doppler radar; radio altimeter; HF, VHF and UHF radio; ADF; VOR/ILS; Tacan; compass system and attitude director indicator system; and intercom system.

DIMENSIONS, EXTERNAL:	
Rotor diameter (each)	15·24 m (50 ft 0 in)
Length overall, blades turning	25·40 m (83 ft 4 in)
Length of fuselage	13·59 m (44 ft 7 in)
Height to top of rear rotor hub	5·09 m (16 ft 8½ in)
Wheel track	3·92 m (12 ft 10½ in)
Wheelbase	7·57 m (24 ft 10 in)
Passenger door (fwd):	
Height	1·60 m (5 ft 3 in)
Width	0·91 m (3 ft 0 in)
DIMENSIONS, INTERNAL:	
Cabin, excl flight deck:	
Length	7·37 m (24 ft 2 in)
Normal width	1·83 m (6 ft 0 in)
Max height	1·83 m (6 ft 0 in)
Floor area	13·47 m² (145 sq ft)
Volume (usable)	24·5 m³ (865 cu ft)
AREAS:	
Rotor blades (each)	3·48 m² (37·50 sq ft)
Rotor discs (total)	364·6 m² (3,925 sq ft)
WEIGHTS AND LOADINGS:	
Weight empty, equipped:	
II-2	4,868 kg (10,732 lb)
IIA-1	4,589 kg (10,118 lb)
IIA-2	5,250 kg (11,576 lb)
Max T-O and landing weight	8,618 kg (19,000 lb)
	or 9,706 kg (21,400 lb)

Kawasaki KV-107/IIA-5 rescue helicopter of the JASDF, with rescue hoist, searchlights and AFCS

Max disc loading 23·6 kg/m² (4·84 lb/sq ft)
Max power loading 4·62 kg/kW (7·6 lb/shp)

PERFORMANCE (A: KV-107/II-2 at 8,618 kg; 19,000 lb AUW. B: KV-107/IIA at same AUW):

Never-exceed speed:
A, B 146 knots (270 km/h; 168 mph)
Max speed at S/L, normal rated power:
A 136 knots (253 km/h; 157 mph)
B 137 knots (254 km/h; 158 mph)
Cruising speed at 1,525 m (5,000 ft):
A, B 130 knots (241 km/h; 150 mph)
Max rate of climb at S/L:
A, normal rated power 463 m (1,520 ft)/min
B 625 m (2,050 ft)/min
Max vertical rate of climb at S/L:
B 381 m (1,250 ft)/min
Service ceiling:
A, normal rated power 4,570 m (15,000 ft)
B 5,180 m (17,000 ft)
Service ceiling, one engine out:
A, military power, yaw, 248 rpm 107 m (350 ft)
B 1,740 m (5,700 ft)
Hovering ceiling IGE:
A 2,895 m (9,500 ft)
B 3,565 m (11,700 ft)
Hovering ceiling OGE:
A 1,890 m (6,200 ft)
B 2,680 m (8,800 ft)
Min landing area (A, B):
Length 38 m (126 ft)
Width 23 m (75 ft)
T-O to 15 m (50 ft):
B 131 m (430 ft)
Landing from 15 m (50 ft), one engine out:
B 84 m (275 ft)
Range:
A with 3,000 kg (6,600 lb) payload, 10% reserves 94 nm (175 km; 109 miles)
B with standard fuel 192 nm (357 km; 222 miles)
B with max fuel 592 nm (1,097 km; 682 miles)

KAWASAKI (HUGHES) 369/MODEL 500 and 500C

JGSDF and JMSDF designation: OH-6J

A total of 131 Model 369HM helicopters, manufactured by Kawasaki under licence from Hughes Helicopters, had been delivered to the JGSDF (127), JMSDF (3) and a civil operator (1) by the end of 1978; Japanese production of this model has now ceased.

Manufacture continues of the Model 369HS, of which 47 had been delivered to civil operators by the beginning of 1979, including 16 Model 500Cs. Power plants are built in Japan by Mitsubishi.

DIMENSIONS AND AREAS: As for Hughes OH-6A/500/500C (see US section)

WEIGHTS AND LOADING: As for OH-6A/500/500C except:
Weight empty:
OH-6J, 500 537 kg (1,185 lb)
500C 545 kg (1,203 lb)

PERFORMANCE (at max T-O weight, ISA): As for OH-6A/500/500C except:
Max level and never-exceed speed 130 knots (241 km/h; 150 mph)
Range with max fuel:
OH-6J, 500 307 nm (568 km; 353 miles)
500C 301 nm (557 km; 346 miles)
Max endurance:
OH-6J, 500 3 h 36 min
500C 3 h 24 min

Kawasaki (Hughes) Model 369HS fitted with Kawasaki 'super-swath' agricultural spreader system

KAWASAKI (HUGHES) 369D/MODEL 500D

JGSDF designation: OH-6D

The first Model 369D (500D) built by Kawasaki under licence from Hughes Helicopters was flown for the first time on 2 December 1977; JCAB Normal category certification was awarded on 20 April 1978. Four or more Model 369Ds were due to have been delivered to civil operators by mid-1979.

MITSUBISHI

MITSUBISHI JUKOGYO KABUSHIKI KAISHA (Mitsubishi Heavy Industries Ltd)

HEAD OFFICE: 5-1, Marunouchi 2-chome, Chiyoda-ku, Tokyo 100
Telephone: Tokyo (03) 212 3111
Telex: J22381 and J22443
NAGOYA AIRCRAFT WORKS: 10, Oye-cho, Minato-ku, Nagoya 455
CHAIRMAN OF BOARD OF DIRECTORS: Gakuji Moriya
PRESIDENT: Masao Kanamori
EXECUTIVE VICE-PRESIDENTS:
Okichi Saito
Makoto Nakano
Kaname Taniguchi
Soichiro Suenaga
Masao Suzuki
MANAGING DIRECTOR AND GENERAL MANAGER OF AIRCRAFT AND SPECIAL VEHICLE HEADQUARTERS: Teruo Tojo
DIRECTOR AND DEPUTY GENERAL MANAGER OF AIRCRAFT AND SPECIAL VEHICLE HEADQUARTERS: Kenji Ikeda
ASST GENERAL MANAGER OF AIRCRAFT AND SPECIAL VEHICLE HEADQUARTERS: Yoshiaki Kato
GENERAL MANAGER, AIRCRAFT AND SPECIAL VEHICLE ADMINISTRATION DEPARTMENT: Hiroshi Hamada
GENERAL MANAGER, AIRCRAFT DEPARTMENT: Hideaki Ito
GENERAL MANAGER, AIRCRAFT EQUIPMENT DEPARTMENT: Seiichi Tsukada
GENERAL MANAGER, SPACE SYSTEM DEPARTMENT: Masahiko Hamada
DIRECTOR AND GENERAL MANAGER, SPECIAL VEHICLE DEPARTMENT: Takashi Tamaki
MANAGER OF MU-2 ADMINISTRATION SECTION: Yukiya Naramoto
GENERAL MANAGER, NAGOYA AIRCRAFT WORKS: Yoshio Sasaki

Mitsubishi began the production of aircraft in the present Oye plant of its Nagoya Engineering Works in 1921, and manufactured a total of 18,000 aircraft of approximately 100 different types during the 24 years prior to the end of the second World War in 1945. The company was also one of the leading aero-engine manufacturers in Japan, and produced a total of 52,000 engines in the 1,000-2,500 hp range. The conclusion of the Peace Treaty in 1952 enabled the aircraft industry in Japan to recommence, and in December of that year the company constructed its present Komaki South plant. This factory, together with Mitsubishi's Oye, Daiko and Komaki North plants, was later separated from the original Nagoya Engineering Works and consolidated as Nagoya Aircraft Works, with a combined floor area of 247,500 m² (2,750,000 sq ft).

Mitsubishi-built F-4EJ Phantom II fighters of the Japan Air Self-Defence Force

Contracts to overhaul F-86 Sabre fighters led, in June 1955, to the selection of Mitsubishi as the company to manufacture 300 F-86F fighters for the Japan Air Self-Defence Force under a licence agreement with North American Aviation Inc. It subsequently produced a total of 230 Lockheed F-104J and F-104DJ Starfighters, in co-operation with Kawasaki.

In co-operation with Kawasaki as subcontractor, Mitsubishi is the JDA's prime contractor in producing F-4EJ Phantom tactical fighters for the JASDF, under licence from McDonnell Douglas Corporation. The first two F-4EJs, built by McDonnell Douglas, were delivered and ferried to Japan in July 1971. The next eight were assembled from knock-down subassemblies, the first of these making its first flight on 12 May 1972. The remaining 130, of which the first was delivered to the JASDF in September 1974, are being built entirely in Japan. The first JASDF unit to equip with the F-4EJ was the 301st Squadron at Hyakuri, which was formed in August 1972, and a total of 118 F-4EJs had been delivered to the JASDF by 1 March 1979. The remaining F-4EJ units are the 302nd Squadron at Chitose, the 303rd at Komatsu, the 304th at Tsuiki and the 305th at Hyakuri. Fourteen US-built RF-4EJs were delivered by mid-1975, and these are in service with the 501st Squadron.

Mitsubishi is also designated as prime contractor for 100 McDonnell Douglas F-15 Eagles to be ordered for the JASDF, of which funds for the first 23 were approved in the FY 1978 budget. The first eight Eagles (including six two-seat F-15DJs), will be imported US-built aircraft; the next eight will be assembled in Japan from knock-down assemblies, and the remainder entirely Japanese-built.

Mitsubishi's overhaul work on Sikorsky S-55 helicopters, started in 1954, led to licence manufacture of 44 helicopters of this type; 20 S-58/HSS-1s and 25 S-62As were subsequently assembled, mainly for Japanese customers, as detailed in previous editions of *Jane's*.

Today, Mitsubishi holds licence agreements to manufacture the Sikorsky S-61A, S-61A-1, S-61B (HSS-2) and S-61B-1 (HSS-2A) helicopters. By 31 March 1979, Mitsubishi had delivered three S-61As and one S-61A-1 (for the JMSDF, for use in support of the Japanese Antarctic Expedition) and had delivered two S-61A-1s (of four ordered) to the JMSDF for rescue duties. It had also delivered 83 of an order for 99 S-61Bs (HSS-2s) and S-61B-1s (HSS-2As) to the JMSDF for anti-submarine duties. From 1979, two S-61A-1s for rescue duties, and 16 S-61B-1s for anti-submarine duties with the JMSDF, are expected to be produced.

Mitsubishi is producing a twin-turboprop utility transport designated MU-2; is prime contractor for the T-2 supersonic trainer and F-1 close-support combat aircraft for the JASDF, with Fuji, Nippi and Shin Meiwa as principal subcontractors; and is a subcontractor in the production programme for the Kawasaki C-1 (which see).

Current activities at the Daiko plant include various aero-engine activities; these are described in the appropriate section of this edition.

MITSUBISHI MU-2

The MU-2 is a twin-turboprop STOL utility transport, the basic design of which was begun in 1960. Prototype construction began in 1962 and the first aircraft was flown on 14 September 1963. By March 1979, total orders for the MU-2 (all versions) had reached 570, including 524 for export and 46 for Japanese customers. Fifteen versions have been announced, of which the MU-2A (3 built), MU-2B (34 built), MU-2C (4 built), MU-2D (18 built), MU-2E (16 built), MU-2F (95 built), MU-2G (46 built), MU-2J (108 built), MU-2K (83 built), MU-2L (36 built), MU-2M (27 built), MU-2N (36 built) and MU-2P (31 built) have been described in the 1965-66 and subsequent editions of *Jane's*. The two current versions are:

Marquise. Basically similar to MU-2N (1978-79 *Jane's*), but with AiResearch TPE 331-10-501M turboprop engines, four-blade propellers and increased fuel capacity. Manufacturer's designation MU-2B-60. First flown 13 September 1977. Certificated 2 March 1978. Seven built by early 1979.

Solitaire. Basically similar to MU-2P (1978-79 *Jane's*), but with AiResearch TPE 331-10-501M turboprop engines, rated in this installation at 495·5 kW (665 shp) each. Propeller and fuel capacity details as for Marquise. Manufacturer's designation MU-2B-40. First flown 28 October 1977. Certificated 2 March 1978. Three built by early 1979.

A subsidiary company, Mitsubishi Aircraft International Inc, in San Angelo, Texas, was established on 1 October 1967 for final assembly in the USA of semi-finished MU-2s shipped from Japan and for marketing of the aircraft in the western hemisphere.

Type: Twin-turboprop utility transport.

Wings: Cantilever high-wing monoplane. Wing section NACA 64A415 at root, NACA 63A212 (modified) at tip. No dihedral. Incidence 2°. Washout 3°. Sweepback 0° 21′ at quarter-chord. One-piece two-spar all-metal structure with chemically milled skins of 2024 and 7075 aluminium alloy. Spoilers for lateral control, between rear spar and flaps. Electrically-actuated full-span double-slotted Fowler-type flaps of aluminium alloy and plastics construction. Outboard flap section each side incorporates trim aileron. All primary controls manually-operated. Pneumatic de-icing rubber boots.

Fuselage: Circular-section aluminium alloy semi-monocoque structure.

Tail Unit: Cantilever structure of aluminium alloy, except for top of fin, which is of reinforced plastics. Small auxiliary fin beneath each side of rear fuselage on Marquise. Trim tab in rudder and each elevator. Pneumatic de-icing rubber boots.

Landing Gear (Marquise): Retractable tricycle type, with single wheel on each main unit and twin-wheel steerable nose unit. All wheels retract electrically, nosewheel forward, main wheels upward into fairings on fuselage sides. Manual backup system provided. Oleo-pneumatic shock-absorbers. Main-wheel tyres Type III, size 8·50-10 (10-ply). Nosewheel tyres Type III, size 5·00-5 (6-ply). Tyre pressure 2·76-4·34 bars (40-63 lb/sq in) on main units, 3·79 bars (55 lb/sq in) on nose unit. Goodrich double-disc hydraulic brakes. No anti-skid units or brake cooling.

Landing Gear (Solitaire): Retractable tricycle type, with single wheel on each main unit and twin-wheel steerable nose unit. All wheels retract rearward electrically. Manual backup system provided. Oleo-pneumatic shock-absorbers. Main-wheel tyres Type III 8·50-10 (10-ply). Nosewheel tyres Type III 5·00-5 (6-ply). Main-wheel tyre pressure 2·76-4·34 bars (40-63 lb/sq in), nosewheel tyre pressure 3·79 bars (55 lb/sq in). Goodrich double-disc hydraulic brakes. No anti-skid units or brake cooling.

Power Plant (Marquise): Two Garrett-AiResearch TPE 331-10-501M turboprop engines, each rated at 533 kW (715 shp) and driving a Hartzell HC-B4TN-5DL/LT10282B-5·3R four-blade fully-feathering constant-speed reversible-pitch propeller. Fuel in five integral wing tanks, total usable capacity 844 litres (223 US gallons; 185·7 Imp gallons) and two fixed wingtip tanks with total usable capacity of 682 litres (180 US gallons; 150 Imp gallons). Max total usable fuel capacity of 1,526 litres (403 US gallons; 335·7 Imp gallons). Oil capacity 11·8 litres (3·1 US gallons; 2·6 Imp gallons).

Power Plant (Solitaire): Two Garrett-AiResearch TPE 331-10-501M turboprop engines, each rated at 495·5 kW (665 shp). Propeller, fuel and oil details as for Marquise.

Accommodation (Marquise): Seats for pilot and co-pilot or passenger on flight deck. Seating in pressurised main cabin for seven to nine persons. Separate compartment at rear of cabin provides coat locker, toilet and baggage compartment. Door at rear of cabin on port side with built-in steps. Emergency exit door under wing on starboard side.

Accommodation (Solitaire): Seats for pilot and co-pilot or passenger on flight deck. Standard seating for six or seven passengers in pressurised main cabin. Pressurised baggage compartment over main-wheel bays, capacity 100 kg (220 lb). Baggage compartments aft of main-wheel bays, capacity 70 kg (154 lb); port compartment of Solitaire pressurised, others non-pressurised. Space for coats and small baggage at rear of cabin. Door under wing on port side. Emergency exit door opposite main door.

Mitsubishi Solitaire twin-turboprop transport aircraft

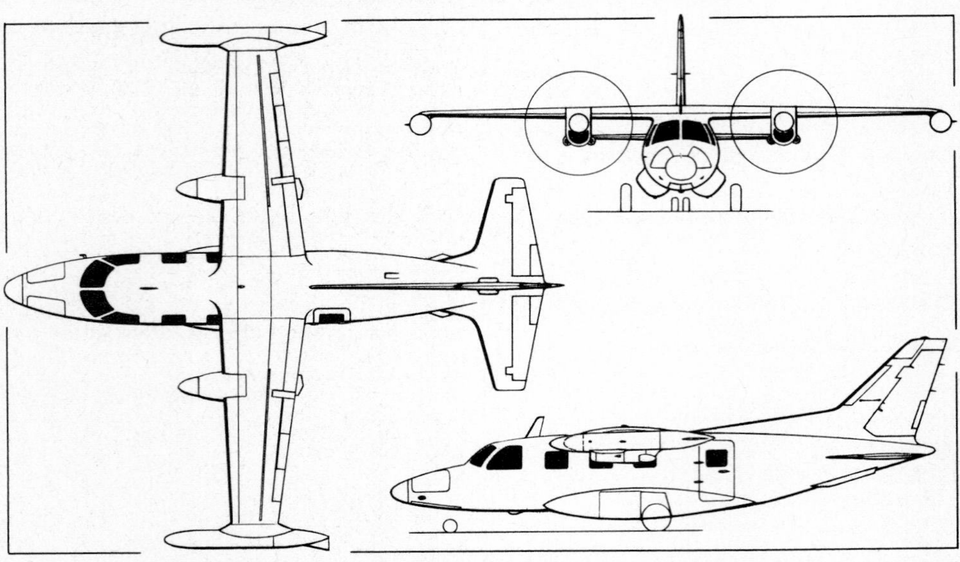

Mitsubishi Marquise twin-turboprop utility transport *(Pilot Press)*

Systems: AirResearch pressurisation and Hamilton Standard air-conditioning systems, using engine bleed air. Differential 0·41 bars (6·0 lb/sq in). Hydraulic braking system. 28V DC primary electrical system, supplemented by 115V AC system (two static inverters) for instruments and avionics. DC power supplied by two 30V 200A starter/generators and two 24V 40Ah nickel-cadmium batteries. Scott automatic flow pressure-type oxygen system, with outlet for each seat. Rubber-boot pneumatic de-icing of wing and tail leading-edges; hot-air anti-icing of engine air intakes; heated windscreens; electrically heated propellers and oil cooler inlets.

Avionics and Equipment: Blind-flying instrumentation standard. Radio and radar to customers' requirements. Standard avionics include VOR/LOC, glideslope, ADF and marker beacon receivers; ATC transponder; DME; VHF or other communications systems; Sperry SPZ-500 integrated autopilot/flight director system; VG-14A vertical gyro; dual C-14 compass systems; and weather radar.

Dimensions, external:

Wing span over tip-tanks	11·94 m (39 ft 2 in)
Wing chord (mean)	1·54 m (5 ft 1 in)
Wing aspect ratio	7·71
Length overall: Marquise	12·02 m (39 ft 5 in)
Solitaire	10·13 m (33 ft 3 in)
Length of fuselage: Marquise	11·84 m (38 ft 10 in)
Solitaire	9·98 m (32 ft 9 in)
Fuselage: Max diameter	1·65 m (5 ft 5 in)
Height overall: Marquise	4·17 m (13 ft 8 in)
Solitaire	3·94 m (12 ft 11 in)
Tailplane span	4·80 m (15 ft 9 in)
Wheel track: Marquise	2·40 m (7 ft 11 in)
Solitaire	2·36 m (7 ft 9 in)
Wheelbase: Marquise	4·40 m (14 ft 5 in)
Solitaire	4·52 m (14 ft 10 in)
Propeller diameter	2·48 m (8 ft 2 in)
Distance between propeller centres	4·50 m (14 ft 9 in)
Propeller ground clearance:	
Marquise	0·66 m (2 ft 2 in)
Solitaire	0·53 m (1 ft 9 in)
Cabin door: Height	1·17 m (3 ft 10 in)
Width	0·74 m (2 ft 5 in)
Height to sill: Marquise	0·38 m (1 ft 3 in)
Solitaire	0·51 m (1 ft 8 in)
Emergency exit door: Height	0·71 m (2 ft 4 in)
Width	0·69 m (2 ft 3 in)

Dimensions, internal:

Cabin, incl flight deck and baggage compartment:	
Length: Marquise	6·76 m (22 ft 2 in)
Solitaire	4·88 m (16 ft 0 in)
Max width	1·47 m (4 ft 10 in)
Max height	1·30 m (4 ft 3 in)
Volume: Marquise (usable)	9·83 m³ (347 cu ft)
Solitaire (total)	6·94 m³ (245 cu ft)
Baggage volume (total):	
Marquise	1·95 m³ (69·0 cu ft)
Solitaire	1·22 m³ (43·0 cu ft)

Areas (all versions):

Wings, gross	16·55 m² (178 sq ft)
Flaps (total)	3·90 m² (42·00 sq ft)
Spoilers (total)	0·54 m² (5·82 sq ft)
Fin: Marquise	2·85 m² (30·70 sq ft)
Solitaire	2·77 m² (29·80 sq ft)
Rudder, incl tab	1·17 m² (12·60 sq ft)
Tailplane	4·01 m² (43·30 sq ft)
Elevators, incl tabs	1·40 m² (15·00 sq ft)

Weights and Loadings:

Weight empty, equipped:	
Marquise	3,470 kg (7,650 lb)
Solitaire	3,180 kg (7,010 lb)
Max payload: Marquise	1,043 kg (2,300 lb)
Solitaire	1,220 kg (2,690 lb)
Max ramp weight: Marquise	5,270 kg (11,625 lb)
Solitaire	4,770 kg (10,520 lb)
Max T-O weight: Marquise	5,250 kg (11,575 lb)
Solitaire	4,750 kg (10,470 lb)
Max landing weight: Marquise	5,000 kg (11,025 lb)
Solitaire	4,515 kg (9,955 lb)
Max zero-fuel weight: Marquise	4,513 kg (9,950 lb)
Solitaire	4,400 kg (9,700 lb)
Max wing loading: Marquise	317·4 kg/m² (65·0 lb/sq ft)
Solitaire	287·9 kg/m² (59·0 lb/sq ft)
Max power loading: Marquise	5·30 kg/kW (8·70 lb/shp)
Solitaire	4·79 kg/kW (7·87 lb/shp)

PERFORMANCE (at max T-O weight, except where indicated):
Max operating speed (both, all weights)
Mach 0·57 (250 knots; 463 km/h; 288 mph) CAS
Max cruising speed:
Marquise at 4,880 m (16,000 ft)
308 knots (571 km/h; 355 mph)
Solitaire at 6,100 m (20,000 ft)
321 knots (595 km/h; 370 mph)
Econ cruising speed at 6,100 m (20,000 ft):
Marquise 295 knots (547 km/h; 340 mph)
Solitaire 313 knots (579 km/h; 360 mph)
Stalling speed, power off, flaps up:
Marquise, AUW of 4,626 kg (10,200 lb)
100 knots (185 km/h; 115 mph)
Solitaire, AUW of 4,173 kg (9,200 lb)
97 knots (180 km/h; 112 mph)
Stalling speed, power off, flaps down:
Marquise, AUW of 4,626 kg (10,200 lb)
76 knots (141 km/h; 87·5 mph)
Solitaire, AUW of 4,173 kg (9,200 lb)
73 knots (135 km/h; 84 mph)
Max rate of climb at S/L:
Marquise 670 m (2,200 ft)/min
Solitaire 716 m (2,350 ft)/min
Rate of climb at S/L, one engine out:
Marquise 125 m (410 ft)/min
Solitaire 145 m (475 ft)/min
Service ceiling: Marquise 8,960 m (29,400 ft)
Solitaire 10,210 m (33,500 ft)
Service ceiling, one engine out:
Marquise 4,510 m (14,800 ft)
Solitaire 5,150 m (16,900 ft)
Min ground turning radius:
Marquise (port) 32·61 m (107 ft 0 in)
Marquise (stbd) 35·81 m (117 ft 6 in)
Solitaire (port) 31·39 m (103 ft 0 in)
Solitaire (stbd) 35·61 m (116 ft 10 in)
T-O run: Marquise 556 m (1,825 ft)
Solitaire 472 m (1,550 ft)
T-O to 15 m (50 ft): Marquise 660 m (2,170 ft)
Solitaire 550 m (1,800 ft)
Landing from 15 m (50 ft):
Marquise 671 m (2,200 ft)
Solitaire 594 m (1,950 ft)
Landing run at max landing weight:
Marquise 402 m (1,320 ft)
Solitaire 357 m (1,170 ft)
Range with max fuel at 9,450 m (31,000 ft), 45 min reserves:
Marquise 1,395 nm (2,584 km; 1,606 miles)
Solitaire 1,600 nm (2,964 km; 1,842 miles)

MITSUBISHI MU-300 DIAMOND I

Mitsubishi has completed two prototypes (JQ8001 and 8002) of the MU-300 twin-turbofan business aircraft, powered by 11·1 kN (2,500 lb st) Pratt & Whitney Aircraft of Canada JT15D-4 engines. First flight was made on 29 August 1978, and by mid-April 1979 the two prototypes had between them accumulated a total of 317 h of flying. In July 1979 they were to be transferred to the USA for FAA certification; JCAB certification was to be sought later.

The principal design objectives of the MU-300 are speed, low noise level, cabin comfort, fuel economy, reliability and maintainability.

DIMENSIONS, EXTERNAL:
Wing span 13·24 m (43 ft 5¼ in)
Length overall 14·74 m (48 ft 4¼ in)
Height overall 4·29 m (14 ft 0¾ in)
Tailplane span 4·98 m (16 ft 4 in)

DIMENSIONS, INTERNAL:
Cabin: Max length, incl flight deck
6·38 m (20 ft 11 in)
Length, excl flight deck 4·77 m (15 ft 7¾ in)
Max width 1·50 m (4 ft 11 in)
Max height 1·47 m (4 ft 10 in)
Volume, incl flight deck 11·30 m³ (400 cu ft)
Volume, excl flight deck 8·64 m³ (305 cu ft)

WEIGHTS:
Weight empty, equipped 3,651 kg (8,049 lb)
Max fuel 1,964 kg (4,330 lb)
Max T-O weight 6,300 kg (13,890 lb)
Max ramp weight 6,368 kg (14,040 lb)
Max landing weight 6,000 kg (13,225 lb)

PERFORMANCE (estimated):
Max operating Mach No. 0·78
Max cruising speed 431 knots (800 km/h; 497 mph)
Landing speed 100 knots (185 km/h; 115 mph)
Stalling speed 77 knots (142 km/h; 88·5 mph)
Operating altitude 12,500 m (41,000 ft)
Max range, 45 min reserves
1,565 nm (2,900 km; 1,802 miles)

MITSUBISHI T-2

The T-2, the first supersonic aircraft developed by the Japanese aircraft industry, is a twin-engined two-seat jet trainer designed to meet the requirements of the JASDF.

Mitsubishi was selected as prime contractor for the development programme in September 1967. Preliminary and detailed design, under the leadership of Dr Kenji Ikeda, were followed by the completion of a full-size mockup and a development contract for prototype construction. The first XT-2 prototype (19-5101) flew for the first time on 20 July 1971, and flew supersonically for the first time in level flight (Mach 1·03) during its 30th flight, on 19 November 1971. The first flight of the second prototype (29-5102) followed on 2 December 1971. These two aircraft were delivered to the JASDF in December 1971 and March 1972 respectively for further flight testing. A static test airframe was delivered in March 1971. Two additional development aircraft made their first flights on 28 April and 20 July 1972; the flight test programme was completed in March 1974. A fatigue test airframe was delivered in January 1975.

Production orders have been placed for 73 T-2s (31 **T-2** advanced trainers, 40 **T-2A** combat trainers, and two as prototypes for the F-1 close-support fighter version, described separately). Fifty-two of the T-2/2As had been delivered by March 1979, to the 4th Air Wing at Matsushima. The current schedule calls for the 21 remaining T-2/2As to be delivered by March 1982. Aircraft Nos. 5, 8-24 and 47-56 are unarmed; Nos. 25-46 and 57-66 are fitted with a 20 mm Vulcan multi-barrel cannon, for armament training. The T-2/2As are assigned to the 21st and 22nd Squadrons of the JASDF.

Mitsubishi, as prime contractor, is responsible for fuselage construction, final assembly and flight testing of production aircraft. Major programme subcontractors are Fuji (wings and tail unit), Nippi (pylons and launchers) and Shin Meiwa (drop-tanks).

Under contract to the Technical Research and Development Institute, Mitsubishi is to convert one T-2A as a CCV (control configured vehicle). Initially, this is to fly in 1981 with canard foreplanes and a fly-by-wire control system; later, it will be fitted with a completely new wing, and will flight test such other features as a head-up display, high-*g* ejection seat, manoeuvring flaps, electronic engine controls, and composite-structure components.

TYPE: Two-seat supersonic jet trainer.

WINGS: Cantilever all-metal shoulder-wing monoplane. Wing section NACA 65 series (modified). Thickness/chord ratio 4·66%. Anhedral 9° from roots. Sweepback on leading-edges 68° at root, 42° 29′ inboard of outer extended-chord panels and 36° on outer panels; basic sweepback at quarter-chord 35° 47′. Multi-spar torsion box machined from tapered thick panels and constructed mainly of 7075 and 7079 aluminium alloy. Electrically-actuated aluminium honeycomb leading-edge flaps, the outer portions of which have extended chord. Electrically-actuated all-metal single-slotted flaps, with aluminium honeycomb trailing-edges over 70% of each half-span. No conventional ailerons. Lateral control by hydraulically-actuated all-metal two-section slotted spoilers ahead of flaps.

FUSELAGE: Conventional all-metal semi-monocoque structure, mainly of 7075 and 7079 aluminium alloy. Approx 10% of structure, by weight, is of titanium, mostly around engine bays. Two hydraulically-actuated door-type airbrakes under rear fuselage, aft of main-wheel bays.

TAIL UNIT: Cantilever all-metal structure. One-piece hydraulically-actuated all-moving swept tailplane, with 15° anhedral. Inner leading-edges of titanium; outer

Second prototype of the Mitsubishi MU-300 Diamond I twin-turbofan business aircraft

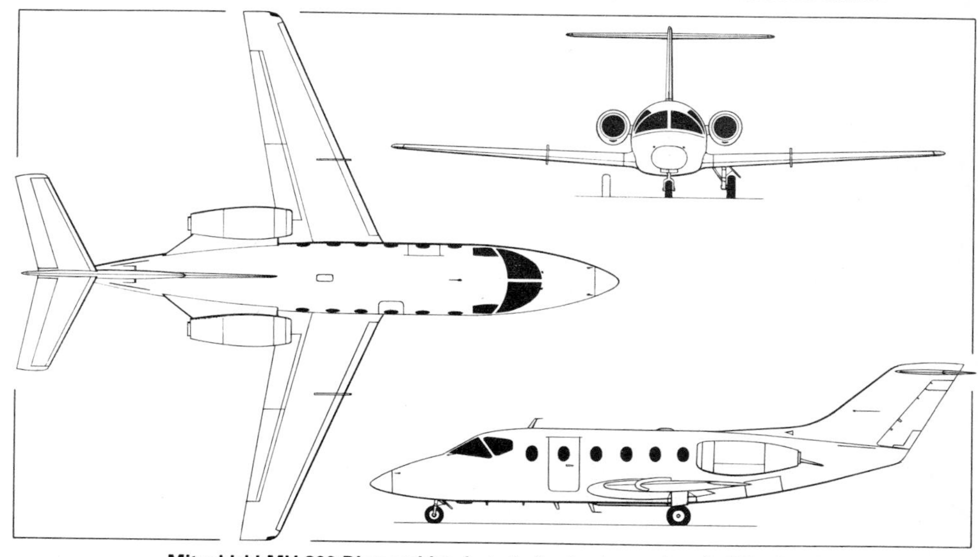
Mitsubishi MU-300 Diamond I twin-turbofan business aircraft *(Pilot Press)*

Mitsubishi T-2 twin-turbofan supersonic jet trainer for the JASDF

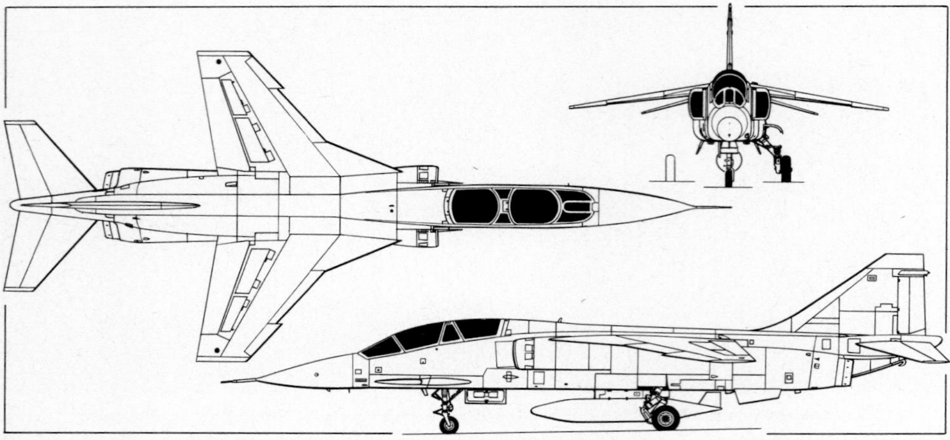

Mitsubishi T-2 tandem two-seat supersonic jet trainer *(Pilot Press)*

leading-edges of aluminium. Trailing-edges of aluminium honeycomb construction. Small ventral fin under each side of fuselage at rear. Hydraulically-actuated rudder.

LANDING GEAR: Hydraulically-retractable tricycle type, with pneumatic backup for emergency extension. Main units retract forward into fuselage, nose unit rearward. Single wheel on each unit. Nosewheel steerable through 72°. Oleo-pneumatic shock-absorbers. Hydraulic brakes and Hydro-Aire anti-skid units. Runway arrester hook beneath rear fuselage. Brake parachute in tailcone.

POWER PLANT: Two Rolls-Royce Turboméca Adour turbofan engines, each rated at 22·75 kN (5,115 lb st) dry and 32·5 kN (7,305 lb st) with afterburning, mounted side by side in centre of fuselage. (Engines licence-built by Ishikawajima-Harima, under designation TF40-IHI-801A.) Fixed-geometry air intake, with auxiliary 'blow-in' intake doors, on each side of fuselage aft of rear cockpit. Fuel in seven fuselage tanks with total capacity of 3,823 litres (841 Imp gallons; 1,010 US gallons). Pressure refuelling point in starboard side of fuselage, forward of main-wheel bay. Provision for carrying up to three 833 litre (183 Imp gallon; 220 US gallon) drop-tanks under wings and fuselage.

ACCOMMODATION: Crew of two in tandem on Daiseru-built Weber ES-7J zero-zero ejection seats in pressurised and air-conditioned cockpits, separated by windscreen. Rear seat elevated 0·28 m (11 in) above front seat. Individual manually-operated rearward-hinged jettisonable canopies. Liquid oxygen equipment.

SYSTEMS: Cockpit air-conditioning system. Two independent hydraulic systems, each 207 bars (3,000 lb/sq in), for flight controls, landing gear and utilities. Pneumatic bottle for landing gear emergency extension. Primary electrical power from two 12/15kVA AC generators.

AVIONICS AND EQUIPMENT: Mitsubishi Electric J/ARC-51 UHF. Nippon Electric J/ARN-53 Tacan and Toyo Communication J/APX-101 SIF/IFF. Mitsubishi Electric search and ranging radar in nose, with Mitsubishi Electric (Thomson-CSF) J/AWG-11 head-up display in cockpit. Lear 5010BL attitude and heading reference system.

ARMAMENT (combat trainer version): One Vulcan JM-61A-1 multi-barrel 20 mm cannon in lower fuselage, aft of cockpit on port side. Attachment point on underfuselage centreline and two under each wing for drop-tanks or other stores. Wingtip attachments for air-to-air missiles.

DIMENSIONS, EXTERNAL:

Wing span	7·88 m (25 ft 10¼ in)
Wing chord at root	4·172 m (13 ft 8¼ in)
Wing chord at tip	1·133 m (3 ft 8½ in)
Wing aspect ratio	3
Wing taper ratio	3·7
Length overall, incl probe	17·84 m (58 ft 6¼ in)
Length of fuselage	17·31 m (56 ft 9½ in)
Height overall	4·38 m (14 ft 4¼ in)
Wheel track	2·82 m (9 ft 3 in)
Wheelbase	5·72 m (18 ft 9 in)

AREAS:

Wings, gross	21·18 m^2 (228·0 sq ft)
Airbrakes (total)	0·952 m^2 (10·25 sq ft)
Vertical tail surfaces (total, excl ventral fins)	5·00 m^2 (53·82 sq ft)
Horizontal tail surfaces (total)	6·70 m^2 (72·12 sq ft)

WEIGHTS:

Operational weight empty	6,302 kg (13,893 lb)
Max T-O weight, 'clean'	9,805 kg (21,616 lb)

PERFORMANCE (at max 'clean' T-O weight except where indicated):

Max level speed at 11,000 m (36,000 ft)	Mach 1·6
Max rate of climb at S/L	10,670 m (35,000 ft)/min
Service ceiling	15,240 m (50,000 ft)
Required field length	1,525 m (5,000 ft)
Max ferry range with external tanks	1,400 nm (2,593 km; 1,610 miles)

MITSUBISHI F-1

Following the JASDF's decision to develop a single-seat close air support fighter from the T-2 supersonic trainer, design began in 1972. During the development period the fighter was provisionally designated FS-T2-Kai, as described in previous editions of *Jane's*.

The second and third production T-2 trainers (59-5106 and 59-5107) were converted as prototypes, in which form they made their first flights on 7 and 3 June 1975 respectively. These aircraft retained the rear cockpit and canopy of the T-2, but this area was occupied by the fire control system and test equipment instead of a second occupant. Externally, they differed from the T-2 by the presence of a tubular fairing at the top of the fin, housing a passive warning radar antenna.

These prototypes were delivered to the ASDF Air Proving Wing at Gifu in July and August 1975, and after a year of flight test and evaluation the aircraft was type approved in November 1976 and officially designated F-1.

Production orders had been placed by July 1978 for a total of 59 F-1s, of an anticipated total order for about 70. The first production F-1 (70-8201) made its first flight on 16 June 1977, and was delivered to the JASDF on 26 September 1977. Twenty-six F-1s had been delivered, to the 3rd Squadron of the 3rd Air Wing at Misawa, by March 1979.

TYPE: Single-seat close-support fighter.

AIRFRAME, POWER PLANT AND SYSTEMS: Generally similar to T-2, but with the rear cockpit area modified as electronics compartment for bombing computer, inertial navigation system and radar warning system. Up to three 821 litre (180 Imp gallon; 217 US gallon) auxiliary fuel tanks can be carried beneath the wings and fuselage.

ACCOMMODATION: Generally similar to T-2, but without rear seat and with 'solid' fairing in place of second canopy.

AVIONICS AND EQUIPMENT: Dual UHF; Tacan; IFF/SIF; Mitsubishi Electric nose-mounted air-to-air and air-to-ground radar, with Mitsubishi Electric (Thomson-CSF) J/AWG-12 head-up display; Ferranti 6TNJ-F inertial navigation system; radio altimeter; air data computer; Mitsubishi Electric fire control system and bombing computer; strike camera system; radar homing and warning system; attitude and heading reference system.

ARMAMENT: Single JM-61 multi-barrel 20 mm cannon. One underfuselage and four underwing hardpoints, as in T-2, with detachable multiple ejector racks. Bombs of 250, 500 or 750 lb can be carried on all five external stations, up to a maximum weight of 2,721 kg (twelve 500 lb bombs). The four underwing stations can each be used for rocket pods such as the JLAU-3A (with nineteen 70 mm), RL-7 (seven 70 mm) and RL-4 (four 125 mm). Primary weapon will be the Mitsubishi ASM-1 air-to-surface missile now under development; two of these can be carried on underwing stations. For air-to-air combat the F-1 can carry up to four AIM-9 Sidewinder missiles, one at each wingtip and one on each of the outboard underwing hardpoints. For long-range missions, the F-1 can carry up to three auxiliary fuel tanks (see 'Power Plant' paragraph).

DIMENSIONS AND AREAS:

As for T-2

WEIGHTS:

Operational weight empty	6,358 kg (14,017 lb)
Max T-O weight	13,674 kg (30,146 lb)

PERFORMANCE (at max 'clean' T-O weight except where indicated):

Generally similar to T-2 'clean', except for:

Time to 11,000 m (36,000 ft)	2 min
T-O run	1,280 m (4,200 ft)
Combat radius with four Sidewinders, internal fuel only, incl reserves	150 nm (278 km; 173 miles)
Combat radius (lo-lo-lo-hi) with eight 500 lb bombs and external tanks	190 nm (351 km; 218 miles)
Combat radius (hi-lo-hi) with two ASM-1s and one 821 litre drop-tank, incl reserves	300 nm (556 km; 346 miles)

First production Mitsubishi F-1 single-seat close-support fighter for the JASDF

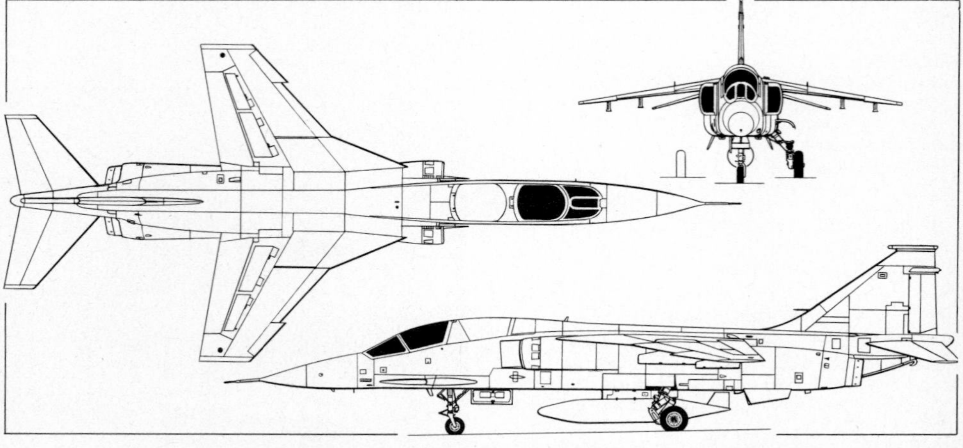

Mitsubishi F-1 (two Rolls-Royce Turboméca Adour turbofan engines) *(Pilot Press)*

NAL

NATIONAL AEROSPACE LABORATORY

ADDRESS: 1880 Jindaiji-machi, Chofu City, Tokyo
Telephone: Musashino (0422) 47 5911
DIRECTOR-GENERAL: Dr Toshio Kawasaki
DEPUTY DIRECTOR-GENERAL: Dr Shun Takeda
DIRECTOR OF V/STOL AIRCRAFT RESEARCH GROUP: Dr Norio Inumaru

The National Aerospace Laboratory (NAL) is a government establishment responsible for research and development in the field of aeronautical and space sciences. Since 1962 it has extended its activity in the field of V/STOL techniques.

NAL QSTOL RESEARCH AIRCRAFT

The NAL was allotted Y3,136 million in the FY 1979 budget for continuation of an eight-year programme to develop a large experimental Quiet STOL transport aircraft. This will be based upon the airframe of the Kawasaki C-1 tactical transport (which see), with the following modifications: replacement of the two Pratt & Whitney JT8D engines by four MITI/NAL FJR-710-600S high bypass ratio turbofan engines, installed above and far ahead of the wing leading-edges in nacelles with upper surface blowing, as on the Boeing YC-14; replacement of the existing manually-operated ailerons by larger-area 'flaperons'; fitting of a larger rudder, of the double-hinged type, and an increased-span tailplane; structural strengthening of the fuselage and landing gear; and installation of a stability augmentation system, a variable stability system and hydraulically operated control systems.

The basic and detailed design work is expected to take four years; aircraft modification began in 1979; first flight is due in 1983. Total cost of the development programme is estimated at Y17,000 million, including flight testing. Data obtained from this programme will, it is hoped, enable NAL to develop, in co-operation with the Japanese aerospace industry, a commercial STOL transport aircraft able to operate from 900 m (2,955 ft) runways with 150 passengers, and to cruise at around Mach 0·7. Tentative plans call for development of this to begin in mid-1980 and to be completed in 1990.

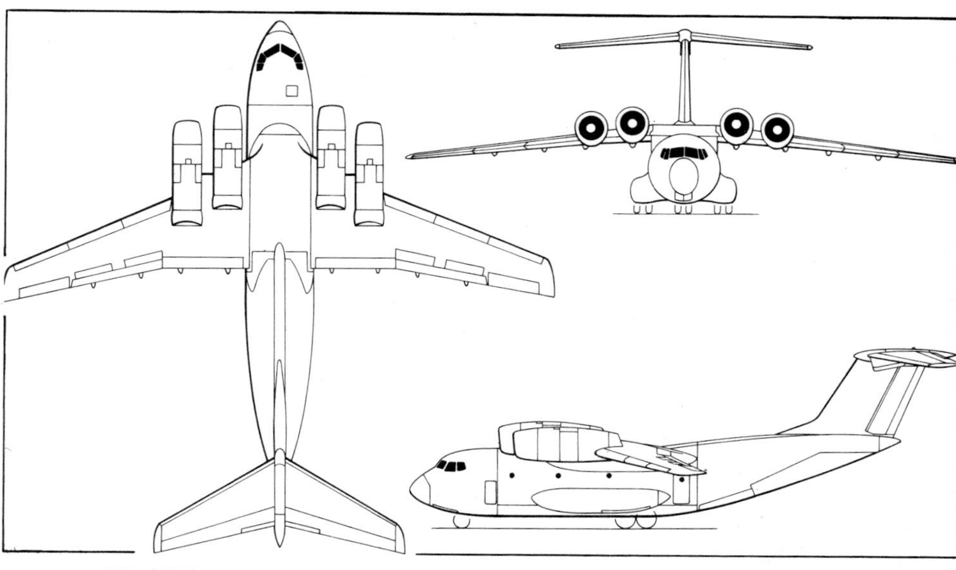

NAL QSTOL research aircraft, based on a Kawasaki C-1 airframe *(Michael A. Badrocke)*

DIMENSIONS, EXTERNAL:
- Wing span: 30·60 m (100 ft 4¾ in)
- Length overall: 30·30 m (99 ft 5 in)
- Height overall: 9·99 m (32 ft 9¼ in)
- Wheel track: 4·40 m (14 ft 5¼ in)
- Wheelbase: 9·33 m (30 ft 7¼ in)

WEIGHTS (estimated):
- Weight empty: 28,038 kg (61,813 lb)
- Max T-O weight: 38,700 kg (85,320 lb)

PERFORMANCE (estimated):
- Cruising speed: Mach 0·7
- Landing speed: 71·5 knots (133 km/h; 82·5 mph)
- T-O run: 396 m (1,300 ft)
- Max range: 1,450 nm (2,687 km; 1,670 miles)

NAMC

NIHON KOKUKI SEIZO KABUSHIKI KAISHA (Nihon Aeroplane Manufacturing Co Ltd)

HEAD OFFICE: Toranomon Daiichi Building, No. 2-3, 1-chome, Toranomon, Minato-Ku, Tokyo 105
Telephone: Tokyo (03) 503 3211
Telex: 222 2863 (NAMC J)
PRESIDENT: Kaichiro Abiru

As detailed in previous editions of *Jane's,* NAMC was responsible for the development and production of the YS-11 twin-turboprop transport aircraft, and also built the two XC-1 prototypes of the Kawasaki C-1 military transport for the JASDF (which see). It continues to be responsible for YS-11 after-sales support.

Full descriptions of the various versions of the YS-11 can be found in the 1967-68 and subsequent editions of *Jane's.*

NIPPI

NIHON HIKOKI KABUSHIKI KAISHA (Japan Aircraft Manufacturing Co Ltd)

HEAD OFFICE AND SUGITA WORKS: No. 3175 Showa-machi, Kanazawa-ku, Yokohama 236
Telephone: Yokohama (045) 771 1251
Telex: (3822) 267
OTHER WORKS: Atsugi
PRESIDENT: Masao Nagahisa
PUBLIC RELATIONS MANAGER: Taketoshi Kitamura

Nippi's Sugita plant, to which the head office was transferred in early 1971, has a floor area of 49,939 m² (537,538 sq ft) and employs 896 persons. The Atsugi plant, which employs 709 persons, has a floor area of 35,918 m² (386,618 sq ft). Kawasaki has a 36·8% holding in Nippi.

The Atsugi plant is engaged chiefly in the overhaul, repair and maintenance of various types of aircraft and helicopters, including those of the Japan Defence Agency and Maritime Safety Agency, and carrier-based aircraft of the US Navy. The Sugita plant manufactures inter-spar ribs for the Boeing 767; components and assemblies for the Kawasaki C-1, Mitsubishi T-2, F-4EJ, F-15 (pylons and launchers) and MU-2, and Shin Meiwa PS-1; airframe and dynamic components for the Kawasaki KV-107; dynamic components for the Fuji-Bell UH-1 and Kawasaki-Hughes OH-6J; engine nacelles for Japanese licence-built examples of the Lockheed P-3C; body structures for Japanese satellites; and tail units for Japanese-built rocket vehicles.

The Nippi Pilatus B4 Standard Class sailplane and Nippi NP-100A Albatross motor glider are described in the Sailplanes section.

SHIN MEIWA

SHIN MEIWA INDUSTRY Co Ltd

TOKYO OFFICE: c/o Shin Ohtemachi Building, 5th Floor, 2-1, 2-chome, Ohtemachi, Chiyoda-ku, Tokyo 100
Telephone: Tokyo (03) 279 3531
Telex: 222 2431 SMICAIR TOK
HEAD OFFICE: 1-5-25, Kosone-Cho, Nishinomiya-Shi, Hyogo-Ken
Telephone: Nishinomiya (0798) 47 0331
Telex: 5644493
WORKS (AIRCRAFT DIVISION): Konan and Itami
PRESIDENT: Yoshio Yagi
EXECUTIVE MANAGING DIRECTOR: Itaru Morita
MANAGING DIRECTOR AND GENERAL MANAGER, AIRCRAFT DIVISION: Hajime Kawanishi
ASSISTANT GENERAL MANAGER: Susumu Ishimoto (Director)
SENIOR TECHNICAL CONSULTANT: Dr Shizuo Kikuhara
TECHNICAL CONSULTANT: Dr Koichi Tokuda
SALES MANAGER AND PUBLIC RELATIONS (Tokyo Office): Shigemi Matsui

The former Kawanishi Aircraft Company became Shin Meiwa in 1949 and established itself as a major overhaul centre for Japanese and US military and commercial aircraft.

Shin Meiwa's principal current activities concern the series production of the PS-1 medium-range STOL flying-boat for the JMSDF, an amphibious search and rescue version, the US-1, and overhaul work on flying-boats and amphibians.

Shin Meiwa is engaged in the manufacture of components for other aircraft, including underwing drop-tanks for the Mitsubishi T-2 supersonic jet trainer and Japanese-built examples of the McDonnell Douglas F-15 Eagle jet fighter; the cargo loading system for the Kawasaki C-1 transport aircraft; and nose and tail components for Japanese licence-built examples of the Lockheed P-3C. Shin Meiwa will also take part in co-production of the Boeing 767 (see CTDC entry in this section).

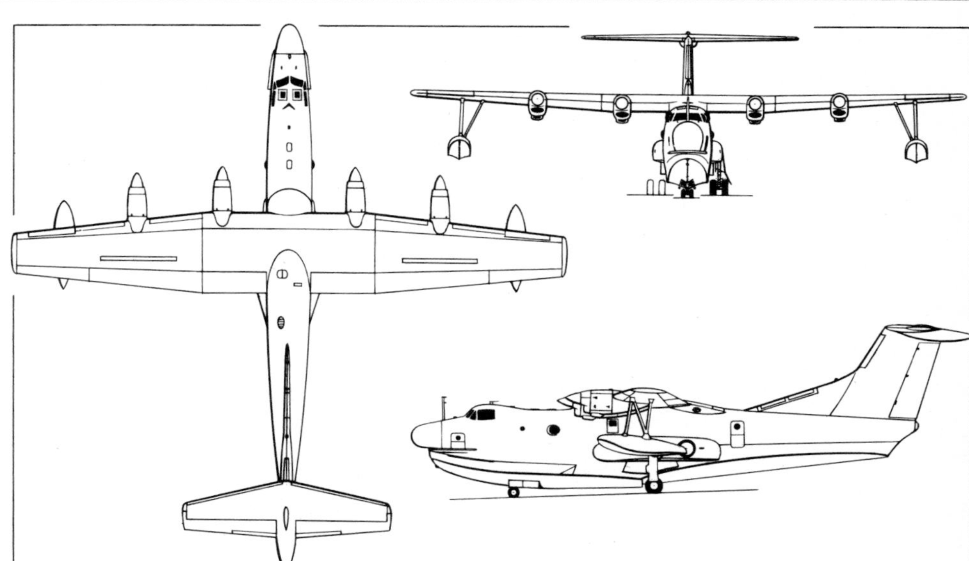

Shin Meiwa US-1 search and rescue amphibian, developed from the PS-1 *(Pilot Press)*

SHIN MEIWA SS-2 and SS-2A

JMSDF designations: PS-1 and US-1

Shin Meiwa was awarded a contract in January 1966 to develop a new anti-submarine flying-boat for the Japan Maritime Self-Defence Force. Company designation for the basic flying-boat is **SS-2**; in ASW configuration this has the JMSDF designation **PS-1**. When adapted for amphibious operation the basic aircraft has the company designation **SS-2A**. The search and rescue version of this amphibian has the JMSDF designation **US-1**.

The first PS-1 prototype (5801) flew for the first time on 5 October 1967, and the second on 14 June 1968. These aircraft were delivered to the 51st Flight Test Squadron of the JMSDF at Iwakuni. JDA type approval was granted in Autumn 1970.

In addition to the two prototypes, Shin Meiwa had by March 1979 delivered 22 production PS-1s. These are in service with the 31st Air Group of the JMSDF for ASW duties, most of them with No. 31 Squadron at Iwakuni. One more PS-1 has been ordered.

Design of the US-1 began in June 1970; the first example (9071) made its first flight, following a waterborne take-off, on 16 October 1974, and its first flight from a land base on 3 December 1974. The first US-1 was delivered on 5 March 1975, the second in July 1975 and the third in early February 1976. These amphibians are at present in service, for search and rescue duties, with No. 71 SAR Squadron of the JMSDF, also based at Iwakuni. The fourth will be delivered in March 1980; three more had been funded by early 1979.

In co-operation with the JMSDF and the National Fire Agency, Shin Meiwa converted the PS-1 first prototype into a water bombing testbed. The results of tests using tanks of 8·1 tons total capacity were analysed in 1978, and Shin Meiwa plans to achieve eventually a 14 ton water load capacity. The testbed aircraft can, in 3·6 h, deliver a maximum of 185 tonnes (182·1 tons) of water, picked up at 38 nm (70 km; 43·5 miles) from base, to a site 5·4 nm (10 km; 6 miles) away. The proposed production version, with increased capacity, could deliver 315 tonnes (310 tons) to a site the same distance from its base before needing to refuel. Simulated operational tests were to be carried out by the National Fire Agency in 1979

To make possible very low landing and take-off speeds, the PS-1 and US-1 have both a boundary layer control system and extensive flaps for propeller slipstream deflection. Control and stability in low-speed flight are enhanced by 'blowing' the rudder, flaps and elevators, and by use of an automatic flight control system.

The PS-1 is designed to dip its large sonar deep into the sea during repeated landings and take-offs, and can land on very rough water, in winds of up to 25 knots (47 km/h; 29 mph). Take-offs and landings have been made successfully in seas with wave heights of up to 3·0 m (10 ft). To resist salt-water corrosion, much of the structure is of 2024C-T3, 2024-T62, 7075-T73 and similar alloys, coated with a watertight polyurethane compound developed by Shin Meiwa.

The following description applies to both the PS-1 and US-1, except where a specific version is indicated:

TYPE: Four-turboprop STOL anti-submarine flying-boat (PS-1) or air/sea rescue amphibian (US-1).

WINGS: Cantilever high-wing monoplane. Conventional all-metal two-spar structure with rectangular centre-section and tapered outer panels. High-lift devices include outboard leading-edge slats extending over nearly 17% of the span and large outer and inner blown trailing-edge flaps extending 60° and 80° respectively. Two spoilers in front of outer flap on each wing. Powered ailerons. Leading-edge de-icing boots.

FUSELAGE: All-metal semi-monocoque hull, with high length/beam ratio. V-shaped single-step planing bottom, with curved spray suppression strakes along sides of nose and spray suppressor slots in fuselage undersides aft of inboard propeller line. Double-deck interior.

TAIL UNIT: Cantilever all-metal T-tail. Large dorsal fin. Tailplane has slats and de-icing boots on leading-edge. Blown rudder and elevators. Tab in each elevator.

ALIGHTING AND BEACHING GEAR (PS-1): Hull; and fixed stabilising floats near wingtips. Retractable tricycle-type beaching gear installed, with aft-retracting single-wheel main gear unit on each side of hull and forward-retracting twin steerable nosewheels, making aircraft independent of ground beaching aids.

LANDING GEAR (US-1): Hull, as PS-1, plus hydraulically-retractable Sumitomo tricycle landing gear with twin wheels on all units. Steerable nose unit. Oleo-pneumatic shock-absorbers. Main units, which retract rearward into fairings on hull sides, have size 40 × 14-22 (Type VII) tyres, pressure 7·79 bars (113 lb/sq in). Nosewheel tyres size 25 × 6·75-18 (Type VII), pressure 20·69 bars (300 lb/sq in). Three-rotor hydraulic disc brakes. No anti-skid units.

POWER PLANT: Four 2,282 kW (3,060 ehp) Ishikawajima-built General Electric T64-IHI-10 turboprop engines, each driving a Sumitomo-built Hamilton Standard 63E60-19 three-blade constant-speed reversible-pitch propeller. Additionally, one 1,044 kW (1,400 ehp) Ishikawajima-built General Electric T58-IHI-10 gas turbine (932 kW; 1,250 shp T58-IHI-10-M1 in US-1) is housed in the upper centre portion of the fuselage to provide power for boundary layer control system on rudder, flaps and elevators. Fuel in two bladder-type rear-fuselage tanks and five wing tanks, with total usable capacity of 19,500 litres (4,290 Imp gallons) in PS-1. US-1 fuel is in wing tanks (10,851 litres; 2,387 Imp gallons) and fuselage tanks (11,649 litres; 2,563 Imp gallons); total capacity 22,500 litres (4,950 Imp gallons). Pressure refuelling point on port side, near bow hatch. Oil capacity 152 litres (33·4 Imp gallons). The PS-1 and US-1 can both be refuelled on open sea, either from a surface vessel or from another PS-1 fitted with detachable at-sea refuelling equipment.

ACCOMMODATION (PS-1): Two pilots and flight engineer on flight deck, which has wide-view bulged windows at sides. Aft of this on the upper deck is a tactical compartment, housing two sonar operators, a navigator, MAD operator, radar operator, radio operator and a tactical co-ordinator. Electronic, magnetic and sonic equipment is installed on starboard side, with crew's rest area and bunks on port side. Aft of tactical compartment is the weapons compartment. On the lower deck, from nose to rear, are the avionics compartment, oxygen-bottle bay, main gear bay and two fuel tanks. Door on port side of rear fuselage.

ACCOMMODATION (US-1): Search and rescue version has accommodation for crew of nine and 20 seated survivors or 12 stretchers, one auxiliary seat and two observers' seats. Sliding rescue door on port side of fuselage, aft of wing. Transport version can seat up to 69 passengers in mainly four-abreast seating with centre aisle; rear portion of cabin convertible to cargo compartment.

SYSTEMS: Cabin air-conditioning system. Two independent hydraulic systems, each 207 bars (3,000 lb/sq in). No. 1 system actuates ailerons, outboard flaps, spoilers, elevators, rudder and control surface 'feel'; No. 2 system actuates ailerons, inboard and outboard flaps, wing leading-edge slats, elevators, rudder, landing gear extension/retraction and lock/unlock, nosewheel steering, main-wheel brakes and windscreen wipers. Emergency system, also of 207 bars (3,000 lb/sq in), driven by 24V DC motor, for actuation of inboard flaps, landing gear extension/retraction and lock/unlock, and main-wheel brakes. Air/sea rescue version has oxygen system for all crew and stretcher stations. AiResearch GTCP85-131J APU provides power for starting main engines and shaft power for 40kVA emergency AC generator. BLC system includes a C-2 compressor, driven by T58-IHI-10 gas turbine, which delivers compressed air at 14 kg (30·9 lb)/s and pressure of 1·86 bars (27 lb/sq in) for ducting to inner and outer flaps, rudder and elevators. Electrical system includes 115/200V three-phase 400Hz constant-frequency AC and three transformer-rectifiers to provide 28V DC. Two 40kVA AC generators, driven by Nos. 2 and 3 main engines. Emergency 40kVA AC generator driven by APU. 24V emergency DC power from two 34Ah nickel-cadmium batteries. Anti-icing, air-conditioning, fire detection and extinguishing systems standard on US-1.

AVIONICS AND EQUIPMENT (PS-1): AN/ARA-50 UHF direction finder, AN/ARN-52 Tacan, HRN-4 Loran, HPN-101B wave height meter, AN/APN-153 Doppler radar, AN/AYK-2 navigation computer, A/A24G-9 TAS transmitter, AN/APS-80 search radar, HGC-102 teletypewriter, AN/APA-125A indicator group, HRN-101 ADF, N-PT-3 dead reckoning plotting board, AN/APX-68 SIF, N-OA-35/HSA tactical plotting group, HLR-1 countermeasure device, AN/ARR-52A sonobuoy receiver, AN/ASQ-10A magnetic anomaly detector, N-MX-143/HSQ error voltage monitor, HQS-101B dipping sonar, AN/ASA-20B recorder group, AN/AQA-5 sonobuoy recorder, AN/AQA-1 sonobuoy indicator group, N-R-86/HRA OTPI (on top position indicator), AN/ASA-16 integrated display system, AN/ASA-50 computer group, HQH-101 sonobuoy data recorder, HSA-1 SDDS, RRC-15 emergency transmitter, HSA-2 automatic magnetic compensator device, N-CU-58/HRC antenna coupler, N-ID-66/HRN BDHI, N-RO-14B BT recorder, HIC-3 interphone and HRC-7 HF.

Shin Meiwa PS-1 first prototype, converted as a water bomber testbed

AVIONICS AND EQUIPMENT (US-1): HIC-3 interphone, HRC-107 HF, N-CU-58/HRC antenna coupler, HGC-102 teletypewriter, HRC-106 radio, HRC-110 radio, HRN-101 ADF, AN/ARA-50 UHF/DF, HRN-105 Tacan, HRN-104 Loran, HRN-3 marker beacon receiver, AN/APN-171 (N2) radar altimeter, HPN-101B wave height meter, AN/APN-153 Doppler radar, AN/AYK-2 navigation computer, A/A24G-9 TAS transmitter, N-PT-3 dead reckoning plotting board, N-OA-35/HSA tactical plotter group, AN/APS-80N search radar, AN/APA-125N indicator group, AN/APX-68N IFF transponder, RRC-15 emergency transmitter and N-ID-66/HRN BDHI.

ARMAMENT AND OPERATIONAL EQUIPMENT (PS-1): Weapons bay on upper deck, aft of tactical compartment, in which are stored AQA-3 Jezebel passive long-range acoustic search equipment with 20 sonobuoys and their launchers, Julie active acoustic echo ranging with 12 explosive charges, four 330 lb anti-submarine bombs, and smoke bombs. External armament includes underwing pod between each pair of engine nacelles, each containing two homing torpedoes, and a launcher beneath each wingtip for three 5 in air-to-surface rockets. Searchlight below starboard outer wing.

Shin Meiwa US-1 air/sea rescue amphibian (four Ishikawajima/General Electric T64-IHI-10 turboprop engines)

OPERATIONAL EQUIPMENT (US-1): Marker launcher, 10 marine markers, 6 green markers, 2 droppable message cylinders, 10 float lights, pyrotechnic pistol, parachute flares, 2 flare storage boxes, binoculars, 2 rescue equipment kits, 2 droppable life-raft containers, rescue equipment launcher, lifeline pistol, lifeline, 3 lifebuoys, loudspeaker, hoist unit, rescue platform, lifeboat with outboard motor, camera, and 12 stretchers. Stretchers can be replaced by troop seats.

OPERATIONAL EQUIPMENT (water bomber): Water is picked up by two retractable ventral scoops just aft of the hull step and collected in a 'midships tank with a capacity of more than 8,100 litres (1,782 Imp gallons; 2,140 US gallons)—a water weight of more than 8,083 kg (17,820 lb). An injection system mounted on the water tank enables this to be mixed with a retardant compound which is carried in a separate container to the rear of the water tank. Dispersal is via two water dump doors in the underside of the hull, just forward of the step.

DIMENSIONS, EXTERNAL:
- Wing span: 33·15 m (108 ft 9 in)
- Wing chord at root: 5·00 m (16 ft 4¾ in)
- Wing chord at tip: 2·39 m (7 ft 10 in)
- Wing aspect ratio: 8
- Length overall: 33·46 m (109 ft 9¼ in)
- Height overall:
  - PS-1 (on beaching gear): 9·82 m (32 ft 2¾ in)
  - US-1: 9·82 m (32 ft 2¾ in)
- Tailplane span: 12·36 m (40 ft 8½ in)
- Wheel track: PS-1: 3·10 m (10 ft 2 in)
  - US-1: 3·56 m (11 ft 8¼ in)
- Wheelbase: PS-1: 8·20 m (26 ft 10¾ in)
  - US-1: 8·33 m (27 ft 4 in)
- Propeller diameter: 4·42 m (14 ft 6 in)
- Rescue hatch, US-1 (port side, rear fuselage):
  - Height: 1·50 m (4 ft 11 in)
  - Width: 1·60 m (5 ft 3 in)

AREAS:
- Wings, gross: 135·8 m² (1,462 sq ft)
- Ailerons (total): 6·40 m² (68·9 sq ft)
- Inner flaps (total): 9·40 m² (101·18 sq ft)
- Outer flaps (total): 14·20 m² (152·85 sq ft)
- Leading-edge slats (total): 6·01 m² (64·7 sq ft)
- Spoilers (total): 2·10 m² (22·60 sq ft)
- Fin: 17·56 m² (189 sq ft)
- Dorsal fin: 6·32 m² (68·03 sq ft)
- Rudder: 7·01 m² (75·5 sq ft)
- Tailplane: 23·05 m² (248 sq ft)
- Elevators, incl tab: 8·78 m² (94·5 sq ft)

WEIGHTS AND LOADINGS (PS-1):
- Weight empty: 26,300 kg (58,000 lb)
- Normal T-O weight: 36,000 kg (79,365 lb)
- Max T-O weight: 43,000 kg (94,800 lb)
- Max wing loading: 316·6 kg/m² (64·84 lb/sq ft)
- Max power loading: 4·71 kg/kW (7·74 lb/ehp)

WEIGHTS (PS-1 water bomber testbed):
- Weight empty: 25,200 kg (55,555 lb)
- Water payload: 8,100 kg (17,857 lb)
- Max T-O and landing weight: 43,000 kg (94,800 lb)

WEIGHTS AND LOADINGS (US-1, search and rescue):
- Manufacturer's weight empty: 23,300 kg (51,367 lb)
- Weight empty, equipped: 25,500 kg (56,218 lb)
- Usable fuel: JP-4: 17,518 kg (38,620 lb)
  - JP-5: 18,397 kg (40,560 lb)
- Max oversea operating weight: 36,000 kg (79,365 lb)
- Max T-O weight from water: 43,000 kg (94,800 lb)
- Max T-O weight on land: 45,000 kg (99,200 lb)
- Max wing loading: 331·4 kg/m² (67·9 lb/sq ft)
- Max power loading: 4·93 kg/kW (8·11 lb/ehp)

PERFORMANCE (PS-1 at normal T-O weight):
- Max level speed at 1,525 m (5,000 ft): 295 knots (547 km/h; 340 mph)
- Cruising speed at 1,525 m (5,000 ft):
  - 4 engines: 230 knots (426 km/h; 265 mph)
  - 2 engines: 170 knots (315 km/h; 196 mph)
- Approach speed: 47 knots (87 km/h; 54 mph)
- Touchdown speed: 41 knots (76 km/h; 47 mph)
- Stalling speed: 40 knots (75 km/h; 46 mph)
- Max rate of climb at S/L: 690 m (2,264 ft)/min
- Service ceiling: 9,000 m (29,500 ft)
- Time to 3,050 m (10,000 ft): 5 min
- T-O run: 250 m (820 ft)
- Landing run: 180 m (590 ft)
- Min ground turning radius: 25·00 m (82 ft 0 in)
- Normal range: 1,169 nm (2,168 km; 1,347 miles)
- Max ferry range: 2,560 nm (4,744 km; 2,948 miles)
- Endurance: 15 h

PERFORMANCE (PS-1 water bomber testbed, estimated):
- Max level speed: 265 knots (491 km/h; 305 mph)

PERFORMANCE (US-1, search and rescue, at max T-O weight on land, except where indicated):
- Max level speed: 260 knots (481 km/h; 299 mph)
- Max level speed at 3,050 m (10,000 ft), AUW of 36,000 kg (79,365 lb): 268 knots (496 km/h; 308 mph)
- Cruising speed at 3,050 m (10,000 ft): 230 knots (426 km/h; 265 mph)
- Max rate of climb at S/L, at max land T-O weight: 460 m (1,510 ft)/min
- Max rate of climb at S/L, AUW of 36,000 kg (79,365 lb): 725 m (2,380 ft)/min
- Service ceiling at max land T-O weight: 6,520 m (21,400 ft)
- Service ceiling, AUW of 36,000 kg (79,365 lb): 8,230 m (27,000 ft)
- T-O to 15 m (50 ft) from land, 30° flap, BLC on: 620 m (2,035 ft)
- T-O to 15 m (50 ft) from water, AUW of 43,000 kg (94,800 lb), 40° flap, BLC on: 600 m (1,970 ft)
- Landing from 15 m (50 ft) on land, AUW of 36,000 kg (79,365 lb), 50° flap, BLC on, with reverse pitch: 810 m (2,655 ft)
- Landing from 15 m (50 ft) on water, AUW of 43,000 kg (94,800 lb), 60° flap, BLC on: 290 m (950 ft)
- Min ground turning radius:
  - self-powered: 21·20 m (69 ft 6¾ in)
  - towed: 18·80 m (61 ft 8¼ in)
- Runway LCN requirement at AUW of 43,000 kg (94,800 lb): 42
- Radius of search operation at AUW of 45,000 kg (99,200 lb), incl 2·3 h search: 900 nm (1,665 km; 1,035 miles)
- Max range at 230 knots (426 km/h; 265 mph) at 3,050 m (10,000 ft): 2,270 nm (4,207 km; 2,614 miles)

SHOWA

SHOWA HIKOKI KOGYO KABUSHIKI KAISHA (Showa Aircraft Industry Co Ltd)

HEAD OFFICE AND SALES OFFICE: Mitsui Building, No. 3, 3-chome, Nihonbashi-Muromachi, Chuo-ku, Tokyo
Telephone: Tokyo (03) 270 1451 and 279 1451
WORKS: No. 600 Tanaka-machi, Akishima-shi, Tokyo
NARITA SERVICE CENTRE: 20 Araizumi, Naritasi, Chiba
PRESIDENT: Teiji Asano

Showa was the first Japanese aircraft manufacturing company to resume post-war operations when it undertook the overhaul and repair of USAF aircraft.

The company's present activities comprise mainly the manufacture of wingtip floats, tail fin, partition and other doors, torpedo pods and hatches for the Shin Meiwa PS-1 flying-boat; and the supply of aluminium and non-metal honeycomb and honeycomb sandwich panels for aircraft floors and airframe construction. Showa also manufactures a variety of airborne equipment.

KOREA
(REPUBLIC)

KAL

KOREAN AIR LINES

ADDRESS: KAL Building, CPO Box 864, Seoul
Telephone: 771 66 and 771 67
Telex: KALHO K27526
PRESIDENT: C. H. Cho
SENIOR VICE-PRESIDENT, SPECIAL PROJECT DEVELOPMENT: W. B. Lee

Following delivery by Hughes Helicopters of the USA of 34 Model 500M-D Defender light helicopters to the Republic of Korea Air Force (of which four had been delivered by the end of 1976), Korean Air Lines had by early 1979 begun to manufacture about 12 Hughes Model 500D commercial helicopters, for sale to customers in Korea during the first half of that year.

A description of the Model 500D can be found under the Hughes entry in the US section of this edition.

KAL-built example of the Hughes Model 500D light helicopter

LIBYA

It was reported in 1978 that a new aircraft factory was under construction in Libya, approx 216 nm (400 km; 248 miles) from Tripoli, with assistance from SIAI-Marchetti of Italy. Main purpose of the new factory was the licence assembly of more than 100 **SIAI-Marchetti SF.260s**, of an overall total of 240 ordered by Libya for its own and other Arab air forces. Libyan production was expected to begin in 1980.

MEXICO

AAMSA

AERONAUTICA AGRICOLA MEXICANA SA

(Subsidiary of Industrias Unidas SA)

ADDRESS: 171 Oriente No. 398, Colonia Aragon, Apartado 14783, Mexico 14, DF
Telephone: (905) 517 5280
ADMINISTRATIVE DIRECTOR: Luis Diez de Bonilla

As the result of an agreement between Rockwell International Corporation of the USA (which see) and Industrias Unidas SA of Mexico, this company was formed in 1971 to take over from the former's Commercial Products Group the manufacture of Aero Commander Quail Commander and Sparrow Commander agricultural aircraft.

Aeronautica Agricola Mexicana SA purchased the type design, tooling and all production materials for the Sparrow and Quail Commander agricultural aircraft, in order to build them at a new manufacturing complex in Pasteje,

Mexico. Up to the end of 1975, only a dozen of these aircraft had been completed in Mexico, and the Sparrow programme was terminated. The Quail Commander, now known as the AAMSA Quail A-9B, supersedes an earlier version designated A-9 with a 175 kW (235 hp) Lycoming O-540-B2B5 engine and lower operating weights.

AAMSA QUAIL A-9B

The Quail A-9B agricultural aircraft has a 795 litre (210 US gallon) hopper and low operating cost. The entire primary structure is coated with Copon, an epoxy resin catalyst paint resistant to all known agricultural chemicals.

Component sets of the Quail A-9B are sent by AAMSA to its subsidiary, Aircraft Parts and Development Corporation of Laredo, Texas, which holds the FAA type certificate and is responsible for marketing the aircraft. A total of 43 AAMSA-built Quails had been completed by 1 January 1978. An output of 50 during 1978 was planned, all against firm orders.

Type: Single-seat agricultural monoplane.

Wings: Braced low-wing monoplane. Modified Clark Y wing section. Dihedral 5° 8′. Incidence 0° 20′. Composite structure with spruce spars, metal-covered leading-edge and Eonnex fabric covering on remainder of wing. Multiple steel tube overwing bracing struts on each side. Hoerner wingtips. Fabric-covered wooden ailerons. Flaps and drooping ailerons.

Fuselage: Steel tube structure with Eonnex fabric covering. Removable side panels.

Tail Unit: Wire-braced steel tube structure with Eonnex fabric covering. Trim tab in starboard elevator.

Landing Gear: Non-retractable tailwheel type. CallAir spring shock-absorbers. Cleveland main wheels, with Goodyear tyres, size 8·50-6 (6-ply). Scott 203 mm (8 in) steerable tailwheel. Cleveland toe-actuated brakes. Parking brake. Wire-cutters on main legs.

Power Plant: One 224 kW (300 hp) Lycoming IO-540-K1A5 flat-six engine, driving a McCauley Type 1A200-DFA9050 two-blade fixed-pitch metal propeller. Two-position adjustable-pitch McCauley Type 2D34CT-84HF two-blade metal propeller optional. Fuel tank in each wing, combined capacity 151 litres (40 US gallons). Oil capacity 11 litres (3 US gallons).

Accommodation: Single seat in enclosed cockpit aft of hopper. Side doors. Steel tube overturn structure. Cabin heater standard.

Systems: Electrical system includes 12V 50A starter/generator and 30Ah battery.

Avionics and Equipment: Radio and other avionics to customer's requirements. Standard equipment includes 0·64 m³ (22·5 cu ft) glassfibre/polyester hopper, capacity 643 litres (170 US gallons) of liquid or 545 kg (1,200 lb) of dry chemical; wing tiedown rings; landing gear and windscreen wire-cutters; canopy-to-fin deflector cable; and electrically-operated auxiliary fuel pumps. Optional equipment includes Transland Boommaster or Micronair spray system, Transland Swathmaster dry spreader system, lights for night flying, 0·17 m³ (6·0 cu ft) hopper extension increasing capacity to 795 litres (210 US gallons) or 725 kg (1,600 lb), invert emulsion spray system or low volume spray system, bottom-loading equipment, rotating beacon, and 30 × 13-6 main wheels.

Dimensions, external:
Wing span 10·59 m (34 ft 9 in)
Wing chord, constant 1·59 m (5 ft 2¾ in)
Length overall (tail up) 7·32 m (24 ft 0 in)
Height overall 2·34 m (7 ft 8 in)
Tailplane span 3·20 m (10 ft 6 in)
Wheel track 2·08 m (6 ft 10 in)
Wheelbase 5·21 m (17 ft 1 in)
Propeller diameter: standard 2·29 m (7 ft 6 in)
optional 2·13 m (7 ft 0 in)

Areas:
Wings, gross 16·90 m² (182 sq ft)
Ailerons (total) 1·99 m² (21·4 sq ft)
Fin 0·80 m² (8·6 sq ft)
Rudder 0·84 m² (9·0 sq ft)
Tailplane 1·47 m² (15·8 sq ft)
Elevators (total) 1·30 m² (14·0 sq ft)

Weights and Loadings:
Weight empty 817 kg (1,800 lb)
Max payload 725 kg (1,600 lb)
Max T-O weight 1,725 kg (3,800 lb)
Max wing loading 102 kg/m² (20·88 lb/sq ft)
Max power loading 7·70 kg/kW (12·67 lb/hp)

Performance (at max T-O weight, except where indicated):
Max level speed at S/L 104 knots (193 km/h; 120 mph)
Max cruising speed (75% power) at 1,360 kg (3,000 lb) AUW 100 knots (185 km/h; 115 mph)
Normal operating speed 78-87 knots (145-161 km/h; 90-100 mph)
Stalling speed 52 knots (97 km/h; 60 mph)
Stalling speed as usually landed 35 knots (65 km/h; 40 mph)
Max rate of climb at S/L 259 m (850 ft)/min
Service ceiling 4,875 m (16,000 ft)
T-O run 328 m (1,000 ft)
Landing run at normal landing weight 136 m (447 ft)
Range at 50% power 260 nm (483 km; 300 miles)

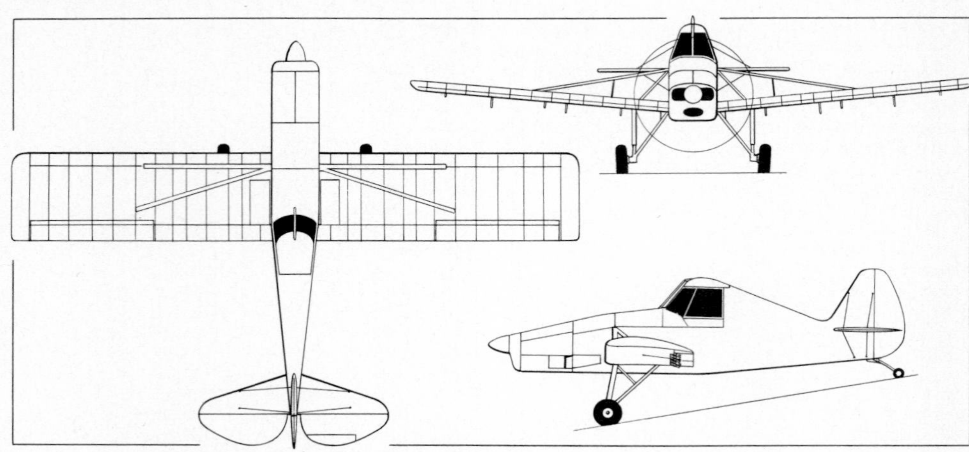

AAMSA Quail A-9B (Lycoming IO-540-K1A5 engine) *(Pilot Press)*

AAMSA Quail A-9B single-seat agricultural monoplane, in spraying configuration

ANAHUAC

FABRICA DE AVIONES ANAHUAC SA

Address: Calzada Adolfo López Mateos 478, Aeropuerto Internacional, Mexico 9, DF

Telephone: 558 27 57

President, Founder and General Administrator: Dr Alejandro Elizondo

Chief Executives:
Ing Arno Gjumlich (Designer and Chief Engineer)
Capt Marcial Sanchez (Chief Production and Flight Test Pilot)
Capt Hector Mariscal (Sales Manager)
Luis Ortega (International Public Relations Manager)

This company was formed to initiate in Mexico the development of aircraft suited to the particular needs of agricultural aviation in that country, taking its name from the former Aztec valley where Mexico City is now situated. Anahuac's first product is a single-seat agricultural aircraft known as the Tauro.

Anahuac Tauro 350 (Jacobs R-755-SM turbocharged engine)

ANAHUAC TAURO 350 (BULL)

Design of the Tauro was begun in January 1967, and the prototype first flew on 3 December 1968.

The first production Tauro was flown on 5 June 1970, following the award on 8 August 1969 of the Mexican DGAC's approved type certificate No. 1. By the end of 1971 Anahuac had built seven production aircraft, each powered by a 224 kW (300 hp) Jacobs R-755-A2M1 radial piston engine and designated **Tauro 300**; for a description and illustration of this version see the 1974-75 *Jane's*.

During 1972 and part of 1973, studies were made for an improved version, incorporating a number of improvements suggested as a result of early operational use of the Tauro 300. The result is the Tauro 350, to which the following description applies; this is in production, and three had been delivered by early 1978. A further six were scheduled for completion by the Spring of 1978.

Type: Single-seat agricultural aircraft.

Wings: Strut-braced low-wing monoplane. Wing section US 35B. Thickness/chord ratio approx 10%. Dihedral 5° from roots. Incidence 2°. No sweepback. Braced by inverted V-strut above each wing. All-metal (aluminium) spars and ribs, covered with Grade AA cotton fabric. Ailerons, of similar construction, actuated mechanically by push/pull rods. No flaps or tabs.

Fuselage: Basic structure of 4130 steel tube, covered with removable aluminium side panels. Impact-absorbing structure forward of cockpit.

Tail Unit: Single, slightly-sweptback fin and balanced rudder, and non-swept fixed-incidence tailplane and balanced elevators, of 4130 steel tube with fabric covering. Trim tab in port elevator. Horizontal surfaces wire-braced above and below.

Landing Gear: Non-retractable tailwheel type, with spring shock-absorbers on main units, leaf spring on tail unit. Main units have Cleveland 6·00-6 wheels with Goodyear 8·50-6 tyres, pressure 2·07 bars (30 lb/sq in). Cleveland plate-type brakes.

POWER PLANT: One 261 kW (350 hp) Jacobs R-755-SM turbocharged seven-cylinder radial aircooled engine, driving a Sensenich 5404/MA 96K two-blade ground-adjustable (or, optionally, constant-speed) propeller. Aluminium fuel tank in each wing root, total capacity 140 litres (31 Imp gallons; 37 US gallons). Refuelling point above tank in each wing. Provision for optional auxiliary tank in fuselage. Oil capacity 20 litres (4·4 Imp gallons; 5·3 US gallons).

ACCOMMODATION: Single adjustable seat in fully-enclosed cockpit, with downward-hinged window/door on each side. Cabin ventilated.

SYSTEMS: Electrical system includes 12V 35Ah Rebat R-35 battery for engine starting.

AVIONICS AND EQUIPMENT: King VHF radio optional. No blind-flying instrumentation. Hopper in fuselage, forward of cockpit at CG, capacity 870 litres (191 Imp gallons; 230 US gallons) of liquid or 800 kg (1,764 lb) of dry chemical. Transland dispersal equipment.

DIMENSIONS, EXTERNAL:

Wing span	11·44 m (37 ft 6½ in)
Wing chord (constant)	1·77 m (5 ft 9¾ in)
Wing aspect ratio	6·4
Length overall	8·21 m (26 ft 11¼ in)
Height overall	2·34 m (7 ft 8 in)
Tailplane span	3·50 m (11 ft 5¾ in)
Wheel track	2·50 m (8 ft 2½ in)
Propeller diameter	2·44 m (8 ft 0 in)
Propeller ground clearance (in flying attitude)	0·30 m (1 ft 0 in)

DIMENSIONS, INTERNAL:

Cabin: Max length	1·12 m (3 ft 8 in)
Max width	0·86 m (2 ft 10 in)
Max height	1·295 m (4 ft 3 in)
Floor area	0·93 m² (10·0 sq ft)

AREAS:

Wings, gross	20·24 m² (217·89 sq ft)
Ailerons (total)	1·67 m² (18·00 sq ft)
Fin	1·02 m² (11·00 sq ft)
Rudder	1·30 m² (14·00 sq ft)
Tailplane	1·49 m² (16·00 sq ft)
Elevators, incl tab	1·39 m² (15·00 sq ft)

WEIGHTS AND LOADINGS:

Weight empty	958 kg (2,112 lb)
Max T-O and landing weight	2,064 kg (4,552 lb)
Max wing loading	101·98 kg/m² (20·89 lb/sq ft)
Max power loading	7·91 kg/kW (13·00 lb/hp)

PERFORMANCE (at max T-O weight):

Never-exceed speed	121 knots (225 km/h; 140 mph)
Max level speed at S/L	104 knots (193 km/h; 120 mph)
Max cruising speed at S/L	78 knots (145 km/h; 90 mph)
Econ cruising speed at 1,525 m (5,000 ft)	74 knots (137 km/h; 85 mph)
Stalling speed	36·5 knots (68 km/h; 42 mph)
Max rate of climb at S/L	259 m (850 ft)/min
Service ceiling	5,790 m (19,000 ft)
T-O run	275 m (900 ft)
T-O to, and landing from, 15 m (50 ft)	350 m (1,150 ft)
Landing run	250 m (820 ft)
Range with max fuel	202 nm (375 km; 233 miles)

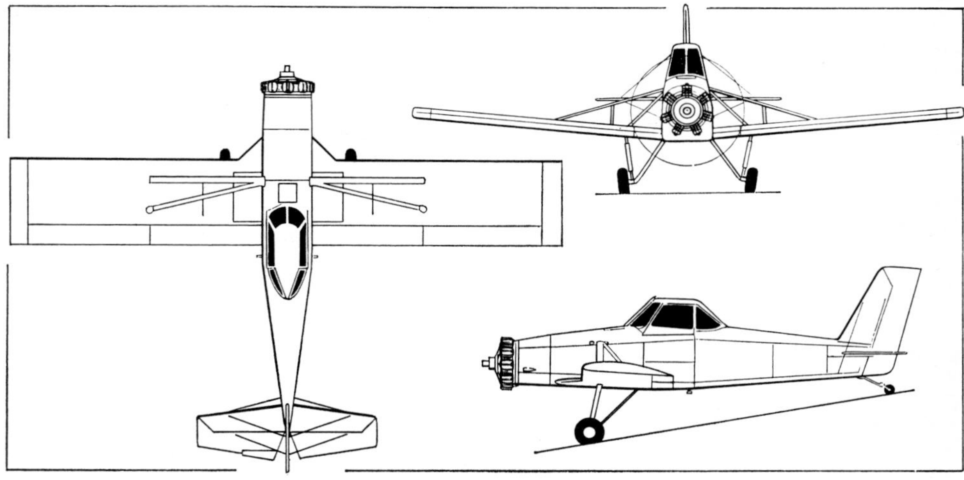

Anahuac Tauro 300 and 350 agricultural aircraft *(Pilot Press)*

NETHERLANDS

FOKKER-VFW

FOKKER-VFW BV (Subsidiary of Zentralgesellschaft VFW-Fokker mbH)

HEAD OFFICE AND MAIN FACTORY: PO Box 7600, 1117 ZJ Schiphol-Oost (Amsterdam Airport)
Telephone: Amsterdam (020) 5449111
Telex: 12227 SIFO NL

OTHER FACTORIES AND COMPANIES:
Fokker-VFW BV, Drechtsteden Division, with plants at Papendrecht, Dordrecht and Hoogeveen
Fokker-VFW BV, Avio-Fokker Division, with Ypenburg Works at Ypenburg Air Base, near the Hague; and Woensdrecht Works at Woensdrecht Air Base, near Bergen op Zoom
Trading Company Avio-Diepen BV

SUPERVISORY BOARD:
H. Buiter
Prof Dr W. H. J. Reynaerts

BOARD OF MANAGEMENT:
F. Swarttouw (Chairman)
H. J. Grobben (Vice-Chairman)
J. Donders (Personnel and Social Affairs)
D. Krook (Marketing)
J. Cornelis (Development)
A. van Wijlen (Production)

MANAGER, PUBLIC RELATIONS: Nol van Fenema

Fokker-VFW BV, Netherlands Aircraft Factories, is the Dutch manufacturing company of the Zentralgesellschaft VFW-Fokker mbH (see International section), which was formed when the 50-year-old Royal Netherlands Aircraft Factories Fokker and Vereinigte Flugtechnische Werke GmbH of Germany joined forces on a parity basis in 1969. Marketing and product support of civil airliners produced by the two companies is undertaken by a separate company, Fokker-VFW International BV, whose offices are at PO Box 7600, Schiphol-Oost, Netherlands.

Fokker-VFW BV forms the entire aircraft industry in the Netherlands, with six plants, in which about 7,100 people are employed. Earlier collaborative ventures, other than those with VFW, included participation in the manufacturing programmes for the Gloster Meteor, Hawker Hunter and Lockheed F-104G, with final assembly lines at Schiphol; and for the Breguet Atlantic and Canadair (Northrop) CF-5/NF-5. Fokker-VFW has an important share in the European manufacturing programme for the General Dynamics F-16 fighter, being responsible for centre-fuselages and wing moving surfaces for 617 aircraft (for the Dutch final assembly line for 174 F-16s for the Netherlands and Norway; and the remainder for General Dynamics, for aircraft to be delivered to the USAF). Delivery to the RNethAF of F-16s assembled by Fokker-VFW began in June 1979, following the first flight at Schiphol by a Dutch-assembled F-16 (J-259) on 3 May 1979.

Some 4,250 people are employed at the Schiphol-Oost works, which accommodates the company headquarters and administration together with the main F27 and F28 assembly lines and test flying facilities. Production is continuing of the F27 and F28, each in various versions, and wing moving surfaces are being produced for the Airbus A300. Also at Schiphol are the design offices, research department, numerically-controlled milling department, metal bonding department, electronics division, space division and scientific and administrative computer facilities.

The Drechtsteden plant, formed by the integrated production facilities at Dordrecht, Papendrecht and Hoogeveen, employs some 1,450 people. Most of these are engaged on detail production and component assembly for the General Dynamics F-16, Fokker F27 and F28 and Airbus A300; other work includes the manufacture of antennae and other specialised products. Several types of Aviobridge airport passenger gangways are also manufactured at Papendrecht.

Avio-Fokker is a Division of Fokker-VFW, employing some 1,380 people, and comprises the former Avio-Diepen plant at Ypenburg Air Base near the Hague and the former Aviolanda plant at Woensdrecht Air Base. At both facilities the installation of F-16 centre-fuselages, and maintenance, overhaul, repair and modification work on a wide variety of military and civil aircraft, are carried out. Production of outer wings and struts for the Shorts 330 has been undertaken at Woensdrecht since 1975.

Reinforced plastics components for the Friendship, Fellowship, Airbus A300 and Shorts 330, and radomes and fairings for the Westland Lynx helicopter, are manufactured at Ypenburg.

At Woensdrecht the ELMO division produces electrical and electronic systems and wire harnesses.

Hoogeveen Division, a facility of the Drechtsteden plant, is engaged in the manufacture of parts for the aerospace industry, radar and telecommunications and other industries. Quantity production of LD3 freight containers is also undertaken in this factory.

First General Dynamics F-16, a two-seat F-16B, to be assembled by Fokker-VFW

FOKKER F27 FRIENDSHIP

The first of two F27 prototypes made its first flight on 24 November 1955, and was designed to accommodate 28 passengers in a 22·3 m (73 ft) long fuselage. The second, which flew on 29 January 1957, was representative of Series 100 production aircraft, with Dart 511 engines and 32 seats in a 23·1 m (76 ft) fuselage. Two further airframes were built for static and fatigue testing.

The F27 has been in series production for many years, both by Fokker and, for a period, by Fairchild Industries in the United States. Deliveries by Fokker began in November 1958. US production of the F-27 and FH-227 totalled 205; details have appeared in previous editions of *Jane's*. Fokker-VFW has recently introduced a modernised flight deck and new-style cabin interior.

Outer wings for the F27 are manufactured in Belgium by SABCA; mid- and aft fuselage sections in France by Dassault-Breguet; dorsal fins, flaps and ailerons in Germany by VFW-Fokker.

The following F27 orders by airlines, air forces and government agencies had been announced by 9 July 1979:

Mk 100 (1967-68 *Jane's;* 83 built, incl 2 corporate; orders listed in 1971-72 *Jane's)*

Mk 200 (115 built, incl 1 corporate; orders listed in 1973-74 *Jane's)*

Mk 300 (1967-68 *Jane's;* 13 built; orders listed in 1971-72 *Jane's)*

Mk 400/600 (197 sold, incl 9 corporate); orders as listed in 1974-75 and 1977-78 *Jane's,* plus:

Air Ivoire (Mk 600)	2
Air Niger (Mk 600)	1
Air Tanzania (Mk 600)	1
Burma Airways (Mk 600)	1
GATL (Mk 400)	1

Libyan Arab Airlines (Mk 600)	2
Senegal government	6
Swift Aire Lines (USA) (Mk 600)	3

Mk 500 (70 sold, incl 4 corporate); orders listed in 1974-75 and 1977-78 *Jane's*, plus:

Air New Zealand	2
KLM (NLM CityHopper)	3

Mk 700 (1 sold to Icelandair; see 1977-78 *Jane's*)

By 9 July 1979, total sales by Fokker-VFW (including one more to the Argentinian government, six to the Bolivian government and 7 to undisclosed customers), had reached 491, bringing overall Dutch/US sales to 696. This total includes sales of the F27 Maritime, described separately.

Fokker is standardising currently on the Mks 200, 400M, 500 and 600, but any of the following versions of the F27 are available to order:

F27 Mk 200. Basic airliner or executive model with Dart RDa.7 Mk 536-7R turboprops. First flight 20 September 1959.

F27 Mk 400 Combiplane. Available on request only. Details in 1978-79 *Jane's*.

F27 Mk 400M. Military version, with accommodation for 46 parachute troops, 6,025 kg (13,283 lb) of freight or 24 stretchers and 9 attendants. Large cargo door and enlarged parachuting door on each side. First flight 24 April 1965. Four Imperial Iranian Air Force Mk 400Ms were modified by Fokker in 1977 for target towing duties.

F27 Mk 400M cartographic version. Aerial survey version with two super-wide-angle cameras, remotely controlled from central navigation station, and navigation sight. Inertial navigation system, with digital readout at navigation station and recorded on each picture. Photography through optical glass window panes. Electrically-operated window doors. First flight 24 August 1973.

F27 Mk 500. Similar to F27 Mk 200, but with lengthened fuselage and large cargo door. The 15 aircraft for the French Ministère des Postes et Télécommunications (Air France) have special large doors on both sides. First flight 15 November 1967.

F27 Mk 500M. Available on request only. Details in 1978-79 *Jane's*.

F27 Mk 600. Similar to Mk 200, but with a large cargo door. Does not have the reinforced and watertight flooring of the Combiplane. Can be fitted with quick-change interior, featuring roller tracks and palletised seats and/or cargo pallets. First flight 28 November 1968.

Any of the above models can be fitted, at customer's option, with a Dowty Rotol very-rough-field landing gear having two-stage oleos with a 100 mm (4 in) increase in stroke, giving increased overall height and propeller ground clearance. Rough-field gear versions are currently in operation with Air Tanzania, Aramco, Burma Airways and Somali Airlines.

Type: Twin-turboprop medium-range airliner.

Wings: Cantilever high-wing monoplane. Wing section NACA 64-421 at root, 64-415 at tip. Dihedral 2° 30′. Incidence 3° 30′. All-metal riveted and metal-bonded two-spar stressed-skin structure, consisting of centre-section and two detachable outer sections. Detachable honeycomb-core sandwich leading-edges with rubber-boot de-icers. GRP trailing-edges. Mechanically-operated single-slotted flaps, divided by engine nacelles. Electrically-operated trim tab in each aileron.

Fuselage: All-metal stressed-skin structure, built to fail-safe principles, with cylindrical portions metal bonded and conical parts riveted. Fuselage is pressurised between rear bulkhead of nosewheel compartment and circular pressure bulkhead aft of the baggage compartment. Length of pressurised section 16·16 m (53 ft 0 in), except for Mk 500 in which the pressurised section is 17·66 m (57 ft 11 in) long. The slightly flattened fuselage bottom is reinforced by underfloor members.

Tail Unit: Cantilever all-metal stressed-skin structure. Fin and tailplane, as well as leading-edges of surfaces, are detachable. Trim tab in each elevator. Pneumatic-boot anti-icing.

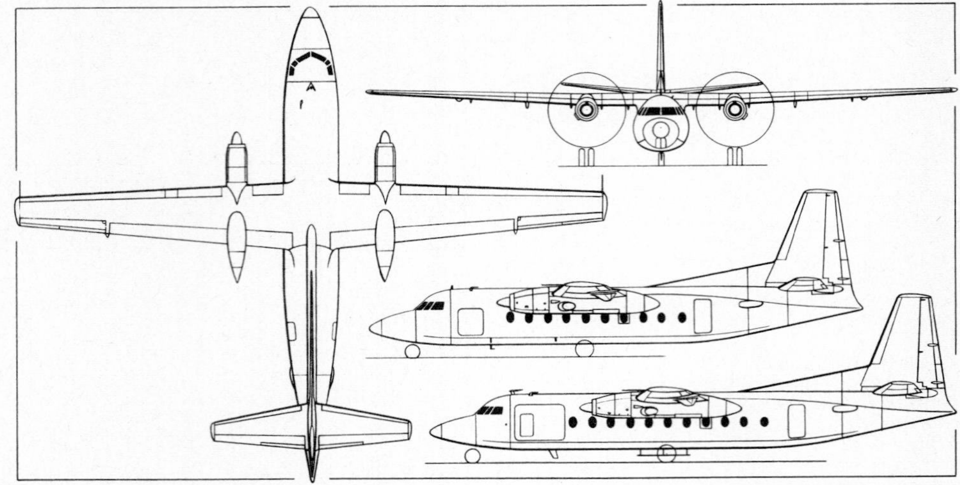

Fokker F27 Friendship Mk 200, with additional side view (bottom) of Friendship Mk 500 *(Pilot Press)*

Landing Gear: Retractable tricycle type. Pneumatic retraction. Dowty oleo-pneumatic shock-absorbers. Twin-wheel main units retract backward into engine nacelles. Single-wheel steerable nose unit retracts forward into non-pressurised nosecone. Main-wheel tyre pressure 5·62 bars (81·5 lb/sq in), nosewheel tyre pressure 3·87 bars (56 lb/sq in). Pneumatic brakes on main wheels, with Dunlop Maxaret automatic anti-skid system. Provision on all currently-available models for Dowty Rotol very-rough-field landing gear in which, at 19,730 kg (43,500 lb) AUW, the total stroke in the main gear is lengthened from 305 mm (12 in) to 406 mm (16 in), increasing the aircraft's static height and propeller ground clearance by 76 mm (3 in). Low-pressure main-wheel tyres are fitted, pressure 4·2 bars (61 lb/sq in) below 18,143 kg (40,000 lb) AUW and 4·57 bars (66 lb/sq in) at higher operating weights. Nose unit is of levered-suspension type, with tyre pressure of 3·87 bars (56 lb/sq in).

Power Plant (all current versions): Two Rolls-Royce Dart Mk 536-7R (RDa.7 rating) turboprop engines, each developing 1,596 kW (2,140 shp) plus 2·34 kN (525 lb st) for take-off. Four-blade Dowty Rotol constant-speed propellers. Integral fuel tanks in outer wings, capacity 5,136 litres (1,130 Imp gallons). Optionally, wing bag tanks for an additional 2,289 litres (503·5 Imp gallons) may be fitted. Overwing fuelling, but pressure refuelling optional. Provision for carrying two 950 litre (209 Imp gallon) external fuel tanks under wings. Methyl-bromide fire-extinguishing system with flame detectors.

Accommodation (Mks 200 and 600): Flight compartment seats two pilots side by side, with folding seat for third crew member if required. Main cabin has standard four-abreast seating for 44 passengers at 78/84 cm (31/33 in) pitch; alternative arrangements allow this number to be increased to 48 in Mk 200. Passenger door at rear of cabin, on port side, with toilet opposite. Standard cargo door at front of Mk 200 on port side; large cargo door in same position on Mk 600, with sill at truck-bed level. Cargo holds forward and aft of main cabin, size dependent on interior arrangement.

Accommodation (executive and VIP versions): Can be furnished to customer's specification, but a basic layout is available. In this, the cabin is divided into three sections: a conference room with six seats, a rest room with settee and divan, and a lounge with four seats. Toilet, galley, wardrobe, baggage space and seat for attendant in forward fuselage. Second toilet and baggage space at rear.

Accommodation (Mk 400M): Folding canvas seats, with safety harnesses, along cabin sides for up to 46 paratroops. Toilet and provision for medical supply box or pantry unit at rear. Ambulance version can accommodate 24 USAF-type stretchers, in eight tiers of three, with seats at front and rear for up to nine medical attendants or sitting casualties. All-cargo version fitted with skid strips, tiedown fittings, protection plates and hinged hatracks. Dispatch door on each side of fuselage at rear for dropping supplies and personnel.

Accommodation (Mk 500): Main cabin has standard seating for 52 passengers four abreast at 89·5 cm (35·25 in) seat pitch; alternative layouts enable up to 60 passengers to be carried at 72 cm (28·5 in) pitch.

Systems: Pressurisation and air-conditioning system utilises two Rootes-type engine-driven blowers. Choke heating and air-to-air heat exchanger; optional boot-strap cooling system. Pressure differential 0·29 bars (4·16 lb/sq in) in Mks 500 and 600; 0·38 bars (5·5 lb/sq in) in Mk 200. No hydraulic system. Pneumatic system, pressure 235 bars (3,400 lb/sq in), for landing gear retraction, nosewheel steering and brakes. Emergency pneumatic circuits for landing gear extension and brakes. Primary 28V electrical system supplied by two 375A 28V DC engine-driven generators. Secondary system supplied via two 115V 400Hz AC constant-frequency inverters. Variable-frequency AC power supply, from 120/208V 15kVA engine-driven alternators, for anti-icing and heating. Two 24V 40Ah nickel-cadmium batteries. 1·12 m³ (39·4 cu ft) oxygen system for pilots.

Avionics and Equipment: VHF and HF transceivers, VHF navigation system (including glideslope), ADF, ILS, marker beacon, dual gyrosyn compass system, intercom system, weather radar and autopilot.

Dimensions, external:

Wing span	29·00 m (95 ft 2 in)
Wing chord at root	3·45 m (11 ft 4 in)
Wing chord at tip	1·40 m (4 ft 7 in)
Wing aspect ratio	12
Length overall: except Mk 500	23·56 m (77 ft 3½ in)
Mk 500	25·06 m (82 ft 2½ in)

Fokker F27 Mk 600 version of the Friendship in the insignia of Air Niger

Fuselage: Max width 2·70 m (8 ft 10¼ in)
Max height 2·79 m (9 ft 1¾ in)
Height overall, standard landing gear:
except Mk 500 8·50 m (27 ft 11 in)
Mk 500 8·71 m (28 ft 7¼ in)
Height overall, rough-field landing gear:
except Mk 500 8·59 m (28 ft 2 in)
Tailplane span 9·75 m (32 ft 0 in)
Wheel track (c/l shock-absorbers) 7·20 m (23 ft 7½ in)
Wheelbase: except Mk 500 8·74 m (28 ft 8 in)
Mk 500 9·74 m (31 ft 11¼ in)
Propeller diameter 3·50 m (11 ft 6 in)
Propeller ground clearance:
standard landing gear:
except Mk 500 0·94 m (3 ft 1 in)
Mk 500 0·99 m (3 ft 3 in)
rough-field landing gear:
except Mk 500 1·02 m (3 ft 4¼ in)
Passenger door (aft, port):
Height 1·65 m (5 ft 5 in)
Width 0·74 m (2 ft 5 in)
Height to sill: except Mk 500 1·22 m (4 ft 0 in)
Mk 500 1·39 m (4 ft 6¾ in)
Service/emergency door (aft, stbd):
Height 1·12 m (3 ft 8 in)
Width 0·74 m (2 ft 5 in)
Height to sill 0·99 m (3 ft 3 in)
Standard cargo door (Mk 200 only):
Height 1·19 m (3 ft 11 in)
Width 1·04 m (3 ft 5 in)
Height to sill 0·99 m (3 ft 3 in)
Large cargo door (Mks 500 and 600):
Height 1·78 m (5 ft 10 in)
Width 2·32 m (7 ft 7½ in)
Height to sill: except Mk 500 0·99 m (3 ft 3 in)
Mk 500 1·03 m (3 ft 4½ in)
Dispatch doors (Mk 400M only, aft, port and stbd, each): Height 1·65 m (5 ft 5 in)
Width 1·19 m (3 ft 11 in)
Height to sill 1·22 m (4 ft 0 in)

DIMENSIONS, INTERNAL:
Cabin, excl flight deck:
Length: except Mk 500 14·46 m (47 ft 5 in)
Mk 500 15·96 m (52 ft 4 in)
Max width 2·55 m (8 ft 4½ in)
Max height 2·02 m (6 ft 7½ in)
Floor area (excl toilet):
except Mk 500 26·0 m² (280 sq ft)
Mk 500 30·2 m² (325 sq ft)
Volume (excl toilet):
except Mk 500 56·0 m³ (1,978 cu ft)
Mk 500 65·5 m³ (2,313 cu ft)
Freight hold (fwd), max: Mk 200 4·78 m³ (169 cu ft)
Mks 500, 600 5·58 m³ (197 cu ft)
Freight hold (aft), max:
all versions 2·83 m³ (100 cu ft)

AREAS:
Wings, gross 70·00 m² (753·5 sq ft)
Ailerons (total) 3·51 m² (37·80 sq ft)
Trailing-edge flaps (total) 12·72 m² (136·90 sq ft)
Vertical tail surfaces (total) 14·20 m² (153 sq ft)
Horizontal tail surfaces (total) 16·00 m² (172 sq ft)

WEIGHTS AND LOADINGS:
Manufacturer's weight, empty:
Mk 200, 44 seats 10,177 kg (22,436 lb)
Mk 400M 10,596 kg (23,360 lb)
Mk 500, 52-56 seats 10,695 kg (23,578 lb)
Mk 600, 44 seats 10,336 kg (22,786 lb)
Operating weight empty:
Mk 200, 44 seats 11,164 kg (24,612 lb)
Mk 400M, all-cargo 10,862 kg (23,947 lb)
Mk 400M, medical evacuation 11,286 kg (24,880 lb)
Mk 400M, paratrooper 11,039 kg (24,336 lb)
Mk 500, 56 seats 11,950 kg (26,345 lb)
Mk 600, 44 seats 11,314 kg (24,943 lb)
Max payload (weight limited):
Mk 200, 44 seats 5,846 kg (12,888 lb)
Mk 400M, all-cargo 6,148 kg (13,553 lb)
Mk 400M, medical evacuation 5,721 kg (12,612 lb)
Mk 400M, paratrooper 5,971 kg (13,164 lb)
Mk 500, 56 seats 5,967 kg (13,155 lb)
Mk 600, 44 seats 5,696 kg (12,557 lb)
Fuel load: standard 4,062 kg (8,955 lb)
with optional wing bag tanks (Mk 500) 5,885 kg (12,975 lb)
with optional wing bag tanks (Mk 600) 5,870 kg (12,941 lb)
Max T-O weight: all versions 20,410 kg (45,000 lb)
Max landing weight:
Mks 200, 400M and 600 18,600 kg (41,000 lb)
Mk 500 19,731 kg (43,500 lb)
Max zero-fuel weight:
Mks 200, 400M and 600 17,010 kg (37,500 lb)
Mk 500 17,900 kg (39,500 lb)
Max wing loading:
all versions 291·5 kg/m² (59·7 lb/sq ft)
Max power loading:
all versions 6·39 kg/kW (10·5 lb/shp)

PERFORMANCE (at weights indicated):
Normal cruising speed at 6,100 m (20,000 ft) and AUW of 17,237 kg (38,000 lb):
all versions 259 knots (480 km/h; 298 mph)
Rate of climb at S/L, AUW of 18,143 kg (40,000 lb):
all civil versions 451 m (1,480 ft)/min
military versions 494 m (1,620 ft)/min
Service ceiling at AUW of 17,237 kg (38,000 lb):
all civil versions 8,990 m (29,500 ft)
military versions 9,145 m (30,000 ft)
Service ceiling, one engine out, at AUW of 17,237 kg (38,000 lb):
all civil versions 3,565 m (11,700 ft)
military versions 4,055 m (13,300 ft)
Runway LCN at max T-O weight, hard runway, standard landing gear 16
Required T-O field length (ICAO-PAMC) at AUW of 18,143 kg (40,000 lb), all civil versions:
S/L, ISA 988 m (3,240 ft)
S/L, ISA +15°C 1,088 m (3,570 ft)
914 m (3,000 ft), ISA 1,210 m (3,970 ft)
Required T-O field length (military) at AUW of 18,143 kg (40,000 lb), military versions:
S/L, ISA 704 m (2,310 ft)
S/L, ISA +15°C 765 m (2,510 ft)
914 m (3,000 ft), ISA 838 m (2,750 ft)
Required landing field length (ICAO-PAMC) at AUW of 16,329 kg (36,000 lb), all civil versions:
S/L 1,003 m (3,290 ft)
1,525 m (5,000 ft) 1,076 m (3,530 ft)
Required landing field length (military) at AUW of 17,010 kg (37,500 lb), military versions:
S/L 579 m (1,900 ft)
914 m (3,000 ft) 622 m (2,040 ft)
Range (ISA, zero wind conditions) with FAR 121.645 reserves for alternate, 30 min hold at 3,050 m (10,000 ft) and 10% flight fuel:
Mks 200 and 600, 44 passengers 1,020 nm (1,926 km; 1,197 miles)
Mk 500, 52 passengers 935 nm (1,741 km; 1,082 miles)
Military transport range (ISA, zero wind conditions) at max T-O weight, reserves for 30 min hold at S/L and 5% initial fuel:
Mk 400M, all-cargo, max standard fuel 1,195 nm (2,213 km; 1,375 miles)
Mk 400M, all-cargo, max possible fuel 2,370 nm (4,389 km; 2,727 miles)
Military combat radius, conditions as above:
Mk 400M, all-cargo, max standard fuel 625 nm (1,158 km; 719 miles)
Mk 400M, all-cargo, max possible fuel 1,230 nm (2,278 km; 1,416 miles)
Max endurance at 6,100 m (20,000 ft):
Mk 400M, max standard fuel 7 h 25 min
Mk 400M, max possible fuel 12 h 47 min

OPERATIONAL NOISE CHARACTERISTICS (FAR Pt 36):
T-O noise level 90·6 EPNdB
Approach noise level (Mk 500) 98·9 EPNdB
Approach noise level (Mk 600) 100·3 EPNdB
Sideline noise level 92·2 EPNdB

FOKKER F27 MARITIME

The F27 Maritime is a medium-range maritime patrol version of the Friendship, designed to meet the requirements of various coastal agencies throughout the world which require a cost-effective surveillance aircraft for coastal patrol, fishery protection, search and rescue, and similar offshore duties. The basic design was defined in July 1975, and shortly afterwards Fokker-VFW began converting an ex-airline F27 to serve as a prototype/demonstration aircraft (PH-FCX). This prototype made its first flight in February 1976. Two Mk 400 F27 Maritimes have been delivered to the Peruvian government, and three Mk 200 Maritimes (for search and rescue duties) were delivered to the Spanish government during the first six months of 1979.

The duties of the F27 Maritime include patrol of fishery areas and coastal shipping lanes, surveillance of offshore oil industry operations, search and rescue, environmental control and similar duties. It is operated by a crew of up to six persons, and the standard fuel capacity of 9,326 litres (2,051 Imp gallons; 2,463 US gallons) in centre-wing bag tanks and wing pylon tanks gives the aircraft an endurance of 10-12 h, or a range of up to 2,700 nm (5,000 km; 3,107 miles), depending on the mission to be flown.

TYPE: Twin-turboprop maritime patrol aircraft.

WINGS, FUSELAGE AND TAIL UNIT: As described for F27, except that airframe is heavily treated with anti-corrosive measures; in tail unit, only the port elevator has a trim tab; and 'teardrop' windows are fitted to flight deck.

LANDING GEAR: As described for F27, but with tyre pressures of 5·52 bars (80 lb/sq in) on main units and 3·80 bars (55 lb/sq in) on nose unit. With long-stroke main gear fitted, pressure in the low-pressure main-wheel tyres is 4·50 bars (65 lb/sq in), and in tyre on the levered-suspension nose unit is 3·80 bars (55 lb/sq in).

POWER PLANT: Two Rolls-Royce Dart Mk 536-7R (RDa.7 rating) turboprop engines, each developing 1,730 kW (2,320 shp) for T-O. Four-blade Dowty Rotol propellers. Integral fuel tanks in outer wings, total capacity 5,140 litres (1,130 Imp gallons; 1,357 US gallons). Overwing (gravity) and pressure refuelling. Additional centre-wing tank of 2,310 litres (508 Imp gallons; 610 US gallons) capacity, and two 938 litre (206·5 Imp gallon; 248 US gallon) tanks on underwing pylons, giving overall total fuel capacity of 9,326 litres (2,051 Imp gallons; 2,463 US gallons). Methyl bromide fire extinguishing system, with flame detectors. Water-methanol tank in each engine nacelle, combined capacity 303 litres (67 Imp gallons; 80 US gallons).

ACCOMMODATION: Flight compartment seats two pilots side by side, with folding seat for third crew member if required. Main cabin fitted out as tactical compartment (for a minimum of two operators), containing advanced avionics, galley, toilet and crew rest area. Bubble windows for observers are provided aft in main cabin. Rear cabin door is openable in flight. Standard cargo door at front on port side, with sill at truckbed height. Cargo holds forward and aft of main cabin.

SYSTEMS: Generally as described for F27, except that bootstrap cooling system is standard; cabin pressure differential is 0·38 bars (5·5 lb/sq in); secondary electrical system has a third 115V 400Hz AC constant-frequency inverter; and oxygen system includes individual supply for each tactical crew member.

AVIONICS AND EQUIPMENT: Com/nav equipment comprises Collins 618T-3 HF transceiver, two Collins 618M-3 VHF transceivers, Collins AN/ARC-159 UHF transceiver, interphone, Litton LTN-72 inertial navigation system, IDC air data computer, dual Sperry C-9 gyro compasses, Collins DF-206 radio compass, Collins 51Z-4 marker beacon receiver, Honeywell AN/APN-198 radar altimeter, Collins DF-301E VHF/UHF direction finder, two Collins 51RV-4 VOR/ILS receivers, two Collins HSIs, Smiths SEP-2E/M autopilot, Collins 621A-6A ATC transponder. Operational equipment includes Litton AN/APS-504(V)-2 search radar, with 360° coverage, mounted in ventral radome.

DIMENSIONS: As for F27 Mks 200/400/600, except:
Height overall 8·70 m (28 ft 6½ in)
Cabin volume (excl flight deck) 60·5 m³ (2,136 cu ft)

WEIGHTS AND LOADINGS:
Weight empty 12,212 kg (26,923 lb)
Normal max T-O weight 20,410 kg (45,000 lb)
Operational necessity weight 21,320 kg (47,500 lb)
Max landing weight 18,600 kg (41,000 lb)
Max zero-fuel weight 17,900 kg (39,500 lb)
Max wing loading 291·5 kg/m² (59·7 lb/sq ft)
Max power loading 6·39 kg/kW (10·5 lb/shp)

Fokker F27 Maritime coastal patrol aircraft, built for the Spanish government

PERFORMANCE (at normal max T-O weight except where indicated):
Never-exceed speed, AUW of 17,237 kg (38,000 lb), S/L to 6,100 m (20,000 ft)
259 knots (480 km/h; 298 mph) CAS
Normal cruising speed at 6,100 m (20,000 ft), AUW of 17,237 kg (38,000 lb)
250 knots (463 km/h; 287 mph)
Normal operating speed at 6,100 m (20,000 ft), AUW of 17,237 kg (38,000 lb)
227 knots (420 km/h; 261 mph) CAS
Patrol speed at 457 m (1,500 ft)
150-180 knots (277-333 km/h; 172-207 mph)
Stalling speed, flaps up
96 knots (178 km/h; 111 mph) CAS
Max rate of climb at S/L, ISA, AUW of 18,143 kg (40,000 lb) 442 m (1,450 ft)/min
Service ceiling 8,990 m (29,500 ft)
Service ceiling, one engine out 3,565 m (11,700 ft)
Runway LCN (42% tyre deflection) at 15,875 kg (35,000 lb) AUW:
rigid pavement, L = 76·2 cm (30 in) 10·4
flexible pavement, h = 25·4 cm (10 in) 11·4
flexible pavement, h = 12·7 cm (5 in) 9·0
Runway LCN (42% tyre deflection) at 20,410 kg (45,000 lb) AUW:
rigid pavement, L = 76·2 cm (30 in) 16·0
flexible pavement, h = 25·4 cm (10 in) 14·8
flexible pavement, h = 12·7 cm (5 in) 12·0
Runway CBR, unpaved soil, h = 25·4 cm (10 in), 3,000 passes:
AUW of 15,875 kg (35,000 lb) 6·2%
AUW of 20,410 kg (45,000 lb) 7·8%
T-O run at S/L:
ISA 975 m (3,200 ft)
ISA + 20°C 1,080 m (3,545 ft)
Landing distance (unfactored, ISA at S/L):
AUW of 19,731 kg (43,500 lb) 610 m (2,000 ft)
AUW of 13,607 kg (30,000 lb) 530 m (1,740 ft)
Transport range at 6,100 m (20,000 ft) with 4,536 kg (10,000 lb) payload, 30 min loiter and 5% reserves
1,000 nm (1,850 km; 1,150 miles)

FOKKER F28 FELLOWSHIP

The F28 Fellowship twin-turbofan short/medium-haul transport was developed in collaboration with other European aircraft manufacturers and with equal financial support from the Netherlands Aircraft Development Board and through a loan guaranteed by the Dutch government.

Production is undertaken by Fokker-VFW in association with MBB and VFW-Fokker in Germany and Short Bros in the UK. Fokker-VFW is responsible for the front fuselage, to a point just aft of the flight deck, the centre fuselage and wing-root fairings. MBB builds the fuselage from the wing trailing-edge to the rear pressure bulkhead, and the engine nacelles and support stubs. VFW-Fokker is responsible for the rear fuselage and tail unit, and for the cylindrical fuselage section between the wing leading-edge and flight deck. Shorts are responsible for wings (including the slatted wings for the Mk 6000), and other components, including main-wheel and nosewheel doors.

First flight of the first prototype F28 (PH-JHG) was made on 9 May 1967, and the second prototype, PH-WEV, flew on 3 August 1967. The third F28 (PH-MOL) flew for the first time on 20 October 1967 and was brought up to production standard in the early Summer of 1968.

The Dutch RLD granted a C of A to the F28 on 24 February 1969, and the first delivery (of the fourth aircraft, to LTU) was made on the same day. The aircraft received FAA type approval on 24 March 1969, German certification on 30 March 1969 and British CAA type approval in June 1979. RLD certification for operation from unpaved runways was granted in mid-1972. The Mk 1000 was granted FAA-approved noise certification on 31 December 1971. The 100th Fellowship, a Mk 1000 for the Peruvian Air Force, was delivered on 30 March 1976.

A total of 146 Fellowships had been ordered by 5 September 1979, as follows:

Mk 1000/1000C (97 ordered, incl 7 Mk 1000C; orders listed in 1975-76 *Jane's,* plus 5 Mk 1000 for Garuda)
Mk 2000 (10 ordered; orders listed in 1975-76 *Jane's*)
Mk 3000

Argentina	3
Cimber Air	2
Garuda Indonesian Airways	7
Ghanaian government	1
Royal Swazi National Airways	1
Tanzanian government	1

Mk 4000

Air Anglia	2
Burma Airways	1
GATL/Air Ivoire	3
KLM-NLM	4
Linjeflyg (Sweden)	10 (plus 5 on option)
Nigeria Airways	2
Pelita Air Service	2

Seven versions have been announced, of which production of the Mks 1000 and 2000 (1976-77 *Jane's*) ended in 1976 in favour of the Mks 3000, 4000 and 6000. The Mk 5000, referred to in the 1975-76 *Jane's,* can be produced to special order.

Current versions are as follows:

Mk 3000. Similar to Mk 4000, but with short fuselage seating up to 65 passengers. Available also in 15-passenger VIP or executive layout, with range of up to 2,200 nm (4,074 km; 2,533 miles). Two of those ordered by Garuda have the optional large cargo door.

Mk 4000. High-density long-fuselage version, first flown on 20 October 1976, to seat up to 85 passengers at 74 cm (29 in) pitch. Airframe basically as Mk 6000, except for omission of leading-edge slats. Uprated Spey Mk 555-15H power plant. Two additional overwing emergency exits (making a total of four).

An extensive demonstration tour was flown in early 1978 by an improved Mk 4000 with uprated Mk 555-15 Spey engines, higher design weights, to enable more fuel to be carried, a strengthened wing of increased span, an engine noise reduction kit, new-look cabin decor and improved flight deck layout.

Mk 6000. Long-fuselage version, similar to Mk 2000 except for slatted wings and improved Spey engines. Prototype, modified from F28 first prototype (previously used for Mk 2000 certification flying) and fitted with modified wings from the second prototype, made its first flight on 27 September 1973. Dutch certification granted on 30 October 1975. Normal max seating capacity 79 passengers, but up to 85 can be carried with reduced fuel load. Two built by 1 January 1979.

Mk 6600. 'Stretched' version of Mk 6000, offered to Japan in 1978 primarily to meet a requirement of Japanese domestic airlines for a YS-11 replacement. Fuselage lengthened by 2·21 m (7 ft 3 in), increasing max passenger seating capacity to 100; Mk 555-15K Spey engines, with automatic power reserve; improved airfield and operating performance.

Super F28. Long-term developed version, with more efficient wing. Described separately.

The following details apply generally to all current production versions, except where a specific model is indicated:

TYPE: Twin-turbofan short/medium-range airliner.

WINGS: Cantilever low/mid-wing monoplane. Wing section NACA 0000-X 40Y series with camber varying along span. Thickness/chord ratio up to 14% on inner panels, 10% at tip. Dihedral 2° 30'. Sweepback at quarter-chord 16°. Single-cell two-spar light alloy torsion-box structure, comprising centre-section, integral with fuselage, and two outer panels. Fail-safe construction. Lower skin made of three planks. Taper-rolled top skin. Forged ribs in centre-section, built-up ribs in outer panels. Double-skin leading-edge with ducts for hot-air de-icing. Irreversible hydraulically-operated ailerons. Emergency manual operation of ailerons, through tabs. Hydraulically-operated Fowler double-slotted flaps over 70% of each half-span with electrical emergency extension. Five-section hydraulically-operated lift dumpers in front of flaps on each wing. Trim tab in each aileron. Wings of Mk 6000 have full-span hydraulically-operated leading-edge slats.

FUSELAGE: Circular-section semi-monocoque light alloy fail-safe structure, made up of skin panels with Redux-bonded Z-stringers. Bonded doubler plates at door and window cutouts. Quickly-detachable sandwich (metal/end-grain balsa) floor panels. Hydraulically-operated petal airbrakes form aft end of fuselage.

TAIL UNIT: Cantilever light alloy structure, with hydraulically-actuated variable-incidence T tailplane. Electrical emergency actuation of tailplane. Hydraulically-boosted elevators. Hydraulically-operated rudder with duplicated actuators and emergency manual operation. Honeycomb sandwich skin panels used extensively, in conjunction with multiple spars. Double-skin leading-edges for hot-air de-icing.

LANDING GEAR: Retractable tricycle type of Dowty Rotol manufacture, with twin wheels on each unit. Hydraulic retraction, nosewheels forward, main units inward into fuselage. Oleo-pneumatic shock-absorbers. Goodyear wheels, tyres and electronically-controlled braking system. Steerable nosewheel. Main-wheel tyres size 39 × 13, 16-ply rating, pressure 7·59 bars (110 lb/sq in) on Mks 3000, 4000 and 6000. Nosewheel tyres size 24·5 × 8·5, 10-ply rating, pressure 5·3 bars (77 lb/sq in) on Mk 6000. Low-pressure tyres optional on all units (main-wheel tyre pressure 5·34 bars; 77·5 lb/sq in on Mks 3000, 4000 and 6000).

POWER PLANT (Mks 3000/4000/6000): Two Rolls-Royce RB.183-2 Spey Mk 555-15H turbofan engines with blade-cooling (each 44 kN; 9,900 lb st, flat rated to 29·7°C), mounted in pod on each side of rear fuselage and fitted with acoustic liners and exhaust silencers. No water injection or thrust reversers. Thermal anti-icing for air intakes. Integral fuel tank in each outer wing panel with total usable capacity of 9,740 litres (2,143 Imp gallons) in Mks 3000/4000; 9,682 litres (2,130 Imp gallons) in Mk 6000. Optional seven bladder-type tank units in wing centre-section with total usable capacity of 3,300 litres (726 Imp gallons). Single refuelling point under starboard wing, near root.

ACCOMMODATION: Crew of two side by side on flight deck, with jump-seat for third crew member. Electrically-heated windscreen. Pantry/baggage space immediately aft of flight deck on starboard side, followed by entrance lobby with hydraulically-operated airstair door on port side, service and emergency door on starboard side, and seat for cabin attendant. Additional emergency door on each side of main cabin, over wing (two each side on Mk 4000). Main cabin layout of Mk 3000 can be varied to accommodate 55, 60 or 65 passengers five abreast at 94, 81/84 or 79 cm (37, 32/33 or 31 in) seat pitch respectively. In Mk 6000, layout can accommodate up to 79 passengers at 79 cm (31 in) seat pitch, and in Mks 4000/6000 up to 85 passengers at 74 cm (29 in) pitch. Aft of cabin are a wardrobe (port), baggage compartment (port) and toilet compartment (starboard). Underfloor cargo compartments fore and aft of wing, with single door on starboard side of forward hold, with one door on rear hold of each version.

Fokker F28 Fellowship Mk 4000 short/medium-range transport, in the insignia of Air Anglia

SYSTEMS: AiResearch air-conditioning system, using engine bleed air. Max pressure differential 0·51 bars (7·45 lb/sq in). Two independent hydraulic systems, pressure 207 bars (3,000 lb/sq in). Primary system for flight controls, landing gear, nosewheel steering and brakes; secondary system for duplication of certain essential flight controls. Flying control hydraulic components supplied by Jarry Hydraulics. All-AC electrical system utilises two 20kVA Westinghouse engine-driven generators to supply three-phase constant-frequency 115/200V 400Hz power. One 20Ah battery for starting APU and for emergency power. AiResearch GTCP 36-4A APU, mounted aft of rear pressure bulkhead, for engine starting, ground air-conditioning and ground electrical power, and to drive a third AC generator for standby use on essential services in flight.

AVIONICS AND EQUIPMENT: Standard avionics include VHF transceivers, VHF navigation system (with glideslope), DME, marker beacon, weather radar, ADF, ATC transponder, dual compass system, interphone and public address systems, Smiths SEP6 autopilot, Collins FD 108 flight director, flight guidance caution system, flight data recorder and voice recorder. Thermal bleed air system for wing leading-edges (slats on Mks 5000/6000), tailplane leading-edge and engine air intakes. Stick pusher system on Mk 6000. Optional equipment to customer's requirements, including equipment for operation in Cat. 2 weather minima.

DIMENSIONS, EXTERNAL (3000/4000/6000):
- Wing span: 25·07 m (82 ft 3 in)
- Wing chord at root: 4·80 m (15 ft 9 in)
- Length overall: 3000: 27·40 m (89 ft 10¾ in)
  - 4000, 6000: 29·61 m (97 ft 1¾ in)
- Length of fuselage: 3000: 24·55 m (80 ft 6½ in)
  - 4000, 6000: 26·76 m (87 ft 9½ in)
- Fuselage: Max width: 3·30 m (10 ft 10 in)
- Height overall: 8·47 m (27 ft 9½ in)
- Tailplane span: 8·64 m (28 ft 4¼ in)
- Wheel track (c/l of shock-absorbers): 5·04 m (16 ft 6½ in)
- Wheelbase: 3000: 8·90 m (29 ft 2½ in)
  - 4000, 6000: 10·35 m (33 ft 11½ in)
- Passenger door (fwd, port):
  - Height: 1·93 m (6 ft 4 in)
  - Width: 0·86 m (2 ft 10 in)
- Service/emergency door (fwd, stbd):
  - Height: 1·27 m (4 ft 2 in)
  - Width: 0·61 m (2 ft 0 in)
- Emergency exits (centre, each):
  - Height: 0·91 m (3 ft 0 in)
  - Width: 0·51 m (1 ft 8 in)
- Freight hold doors (each):
  - Height (fwd, each): 0·90 m (2 ft 11½ in)
  - Height (aft): 0·80 m (2 ft 7½ in)
  - Width (fwd, each): 0·95 m (3 ft 1½ in)
  - Width (aft): 0·89 m (2 ft 11 in)
  - Height to sill (fwd, each): 1·47 m (4 ft 10 in)
  - Height to sill (aft): 1·59 m (5 ft 2½ in)
- Baggage door (rear, port, optional):
  - Height: 0·60 m (1 ft 11½ in)
  - Width: 0·51 m (1 ft 8 in)
- Cargo door (fwd, port, optional):
  - Height: 1·87 m (6 ft 1¾ in)
  - Width: 2·49 m (8 ft 2 in)
  - Height to sill: 2·24 m (7 ft 4¼ in)

DIMENSIONS, INTERNAL (3000/4000/6000):
- Cabin, excl flight deck:
  - Length: 3000: 13·10 m (43 ft 0 in)
    - 4000, 6000: 15·31 m (50 ft 3 in)
  - Max length of seating area:
    - 3000: 10·74 m (35 ft 2¾ in)
    - 4000, 6000: 12·95 m (42 ft 6¾ in)
  - Max width: 3·10 m (10 ft 2 in)
  - Max height: 2·02 m (6 ft 7¼ in)
  - Floor area: 3000: 38·4 m² (413·3 sq ft)
    - 4000, 6000: 44·8 m² (482·2 sq ft)
  - Volume: 3000: 71·5 m³ (2,525 cu ft)
    - 4000, 6000: 83·0 m³ (2,931 cu ft)
- Freight hold (underfloor, fwd):
  - 3000: 6·90 m³ (245 cu ft)
  - 4000, 6000: 8·70 m³ (308 cu ft)
- Freight hold (underfloor, rear):
  - 3000: 3·80 m³ (135 cu ft)
  - 4000, 6000: 4·80 m³ (160 cu ft)
- Baggage hold (aft of cabin), max:
  - all versions: 2·30 m³ (81·22 cu ft)

AREAS (3000/4000/6000):
- Wings, gross: 79·00 m² (850 sq ft)
- Ailerons (total): 2·67 m² (28·74 sq ft)
- Trailing-edge flaps (total): 14·00 m² (150·7 sq ft)
- Fuselage airbrakes (total): 3·62 m² (38·97 sq ft)
- Fin (incl dorsal fin): 12·30 m² (132·4 sq ft)
- Rudder: 2·30 m² (24·6 sq ft)
- Tailplane: 19·50 m² (209·9 sq ft
- Elevators (total): 3·84 m² (41·33 sq ft)

WEIGHTS AND LOADINGS (3000/4000/6000):
- Manufacturer's weight empty:
  - 6000, 79 seats: 15,638 kg (34,477 lb)
- Operating weight empty:
  - 3000, 65 seats: 16,620 kg (36,642 lb)
  - 4000, 85 seats: 17,359 kg (38,269 lb)
  - 6000, 85 seats: 17,919 kg (39,504 lb)
- Max weight-limited payload:
  - 3000: 8,985 kg (19,810 lb)
  - 4000: 8,963 kg (19,760 lb)
  - 6000: 9,555 kg (21,065 lb)
- Fuel load:
  - standard (3000, 4000): 7,703 kg (16,982 lb)
  - standard (6000): 7,658 kg (16,882 lb)
  - with optional centre-section tanks (3000, 4000): 10,313 kg (22,736 lb)
  - with optional centre-section tanks (6000): 10,268 kg (22,637 lb)
- Max T-O weight:
  - 3000, 4000: 33,110 kg (73,000 lb)
  - 6000 (85 passengers, extended range): 33,110 kg (73,000 lb)
- Max zero-fuel weight:
  - 3000: 25,400 kg (56,000 lb)
  - 4000: 28,118 kg (62,000 lb)
  - 6000: 27,215 kg (60,000 lb)
- Max landing weight:
  - 3000: 29,030 kg (64,000 lb)
  - *4000, 6000: 30,160 kg (66,500 lb)
- Max wing loading:
  - 3000, 4000: 407 kg/m² (83·4 lb/sq ft)
  - 6000, 79 passengers (normal range): 406 kg/m² (83·3 lb/sq ft)
  - 6000, 79 passengers (extended range): 419 kg/m² (85·8 lb/sq ft)
- Max cabin floor loading:
  - all passenger versions: 366 kg/m² (75 lb/sq ft)
- Max power loading:
  - 3000, 4000: 367·5 kg/kN (3·6 lb/lb st)
  - 6000, 79 passengers (normal range): 366·4 kg/kN (3·6 lb/lb st)
  - 6000, 79 passengers (extended range): 378 kg/kN (3·7 lb/lb st)

* *in process of certification 1979*

PERFORMANCE (Mks 3000, 4000 and 6000 at AUW of 29,000 kg; 63,934 lb, ISA, except where indicated):
- Never-exceed speed: Mach 0·83 (390 knots; 723 km/h; 449 mph) EAS
- Max permissible operating speed: Mach 0·75 (330 knots; 611 km/h; 380 mph) EAS
- Max cruising speed at 7,000 m (23,000 ft): 455 knots (843 km/h; 523 mph)
- Econ cruising speed at 9,150 m (30,000 ft): 366 knots (678 km/h; 421 mph)
- Threshold speed at max landing weight:
  - 6000: 110 knots (204 km/h; 127 mph) EAS
- Max cruising altitude: 10,675 m (35,000 ft)
- Min ground turning radius:
  - 3000: 9·60 m (31 ft 6 in)
  - 4000, 6000: 10·90 m (35 ft 9 in)
- Runway LCN at max T-O weight (hard runway):
  - standard tyres:
    - 3000: 32
    - 4000: 31
    - 6000: 33
  - low-pressure tyres:
    - 3000, 4000: 25
    - 6000: 27
- Runway LCN at max T-O weight (flexible runway):
  - standard tyres:
    - 3000, 4000: 25
    - 6000: 26
  - low-pressure tyres:
    - 3000, 4000: 20
    - 6000: 21
- FAR T-O field length at max T-O weight (3000, 4000):
  - S/L: 1,590 m (5,217 ft)
  - S/L, ISA + 10°C: 1,635 m (5,364 ft)
  - S/L, ISA + 15°C: 1,710 m (5,610 ft)
  - 610 m (2,000 ft): 1,710 m (5,610 ft)
  - 915 m (3,000 ft): 1,940 m (6,365 ft)
- FAR T-O field length at max T-O weight (6000):
  - S/L: 1,335 m (4,380 ft)
  - S/L, ISA + 10°C: 1,375 m (4,510 ft)
  - S/L, ISA + 15°C: 1,515 m (4,970 ft)
  - 610 m (2,000 ft): 1,480 m (4,855 ft)
  - 915 m (3,000 ft): 1,680 m (5,510 ft)
- FAR landing field length at max landing weight (3000, 4000):
  - S/L: 965 m (3,166 ft)
  - 1,525 m (5,000 ft): 1,090 m (3,576 ft)
- FAR landing field length at max landing weight (6000):
  - S/L: 915 m (3,000 ft)
  - 1,525 m (5,000 ft): 1,030 m (3,379 ft)
- Range, high-speed schedule, FAR 121.645 reserves:
  - *3000, 65 passengers: 975 nm (1,805 km; 1,122 miles)
  - 4000, 85 passengers and 6000, 79 passengers: 900 nm (1,667 km; 1,036 miles)
- Range, long-range schedule, FAR 121.645 reserves:
  - *3000, 65 passengers: 1,400 nm (2,593 km; 1,611 miles)

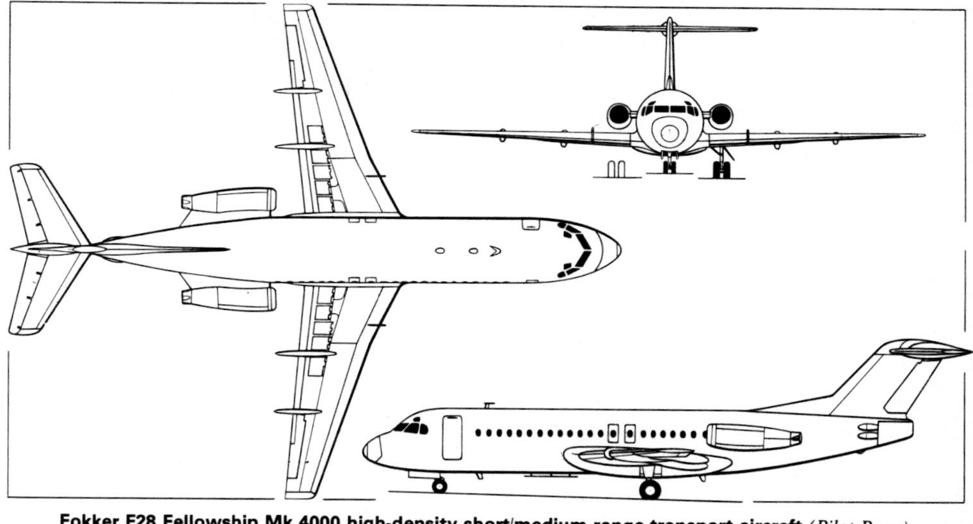
Fokker F28 Fellowship Mk 4000 high-density short/medium-range transport aircraft *(Pilot Press)*

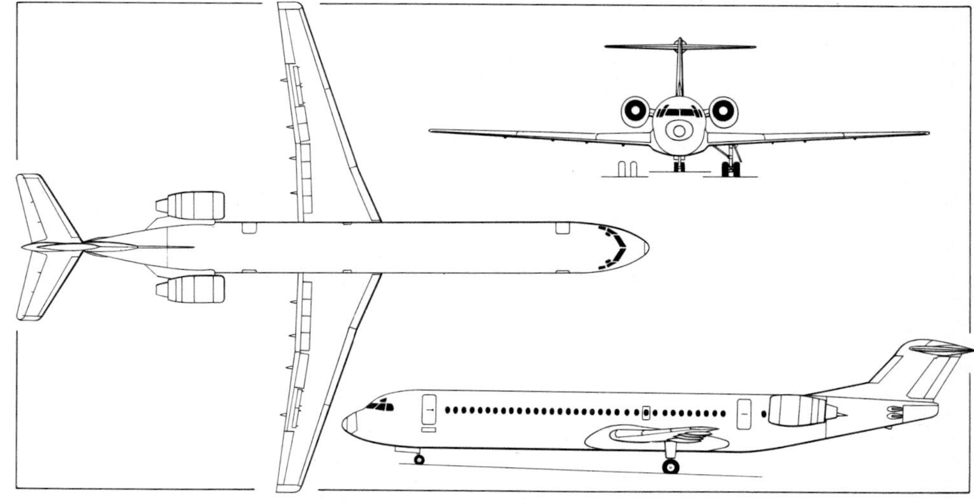
Fokker Super F28 twin-turbofan 115/130-seat airliner *(Pilot Press)*

4000, 85 passengers
1,000 nm (1,852 km; 1,151 miles)
6000, 79 passengers
1,030 nm (1,908 km; 1,185 miles)
Range (6000) at 33,110 kg (73,000 lb) max T-O weight, FAR 121.645 reserves (centre wing tanks included):
85 passengers, high-speed configuration
840 nm (1,556 km; 967 miles)
85 passengers, long-range configuration
920 nm (1,704 km; 1,059 miles)
75 passengers, high-speed configuration
1,010 nm (1,871 km; 1,163 miles)
75 passengers, long-range configuration
1,120 nm (2,076 km; 1,290 miles)
**With wing centre-section tanks*

Operational Noise Characteristics (FAR Pt 36):

T-O noise level:	
3000, 4000 (both estimated)	91·5 EPNdB
6000	92·7 EPNdB
Approach noise level:	
3000, 4000 (both estimated)	98 EPNdB
6000	96·6 EPNdB
Sideline noise level:	
3000, 4000 (both estimated)	97·5 EPNdB
6000	98·6 EPNdB

FOKKER SUPER F28

As a further development of the F28 Fellowship, Fokker-VFW is studying a project for a Super F28, fitted with a new wing of increased span and more efficient section, and having a further-lengthened fuselage. Design highlights also include high bypass ratio turbofan engines of some 71·2 kN (16,000 lb st); standard seating for 115 passengers at 86 cm (34 in) pitch, with a maximum of 130 seats at 76 cm (30 in) pitch; generous cargo volume; rear-fuselage airbrake; and basic two-man flight crew. The Super F28 will have better direct operating costs, lower noise levels, improved fuel economy, and will be able to operate from the same runways as the current F28 models.

The following description applies to the Super F28 as envisaged in early 1979:

Power Plant: Two rear-mounted high bypass ratio turbofan engines. One candidate is the Rolls-Royce RB.432-03; Fokker is also considering the CFM International CFM56-DR-18, and it is probable that either type of engine may be available at customer's choice. Thrust reversal will be available optionally.

Dimensions, external:

Wing span	31·20 m (102 ft 4½ in)
Wing sweepback	16°
Wing area, gross	97·34 m² (1,048 sq ft)
Wing aspect ratio	10
Length overall	39·35 m (129 ft 1¼ in)
Length of fuselage	36·89 m (121 ft 0½ in)
Height overall	9·14 m (29 ft 11¾ in)
Fuselage: Max width	3·30 m (10 ft 10 in)
Max depth	3·71 m (12 ft 2 in)
Wheel track	6·35 m (20 ft 10 in)
Wheelbase	15·63 m (51 ft 3½ in)

Dimensions, internal:

Cabin, excl flight deck:	
Length	25·08 m (82 ft 3½ in)
Max width	3·06 m (10 ft 0½ in)
Max height	2·01 m (6 ft 7 in)
Underfloor freight holds: front	19·13 m³ (675 cu ft)
rear	14·14 m³ (500 cu ft)

Weights:

Typical operating weight empty	27,480 kg (60,583 lb)
Max payload	13,900 kg (30,645 lb)
Fuel load	15,110 kg (33,310 lb)
Max T-O weight	48,680 kg (107,320 lb)
Max landing weight	46,250 kg (101,960 lb)
Max zero-fuel weight	41,380 kg (91,225 lb)

Performance (estimated):
Max designed operating speed
Mach 0·77 (330 knots; 611 km/h; 380 mph EAS)
Typical cruising speed
450 knots (833 km/h; 518 mph) TAS
Range with standard 115-passenger payload
up to 1,500 nm (2,775 km; 1,725 miles)

NEW ZEALAND

AEROSPACE
NEW ZEALAND AEROSPACE INDUSTRIES LIMITED

Head Office and Works: Hamilton Airport, R.D.2, Hamilton
Telephone: Hamilton 436 144 and 436 069
Telex: NZASIL 21242
General Manager: G. H. Willetts
Assistant General Manager: P. W. Goldsbro'
Chief Designer: P. W. C. Monk
Marketing Manager: H. J. I. Baxter
Engineering Manager: L. C. Burrows
Company Secretary: J. D. Linch

Aero Engine Services Ltd and Air Parts (NZ) Ltd (see 1972-73 *Jane's*) amalgamated on 1 April 1973 to form New Zealand Aerospace Industries Ltd. This company has a share capital of $NZ 1·6 million, half of which is held by Air New Zealand (representing government support), one-third by New Zealand's largest agricultural operator, and the remainder by shareholders of the two constituent companies.

The company now produces the Fletcher FU-24 piston-engined series of agricultural aircraft, and the turboprop-powered Cresco agricultural aircraft, in a 5,574 m² (60,000 sq ft) main facility located at Hamilton Airport.

Aerospace Fletcher FU-24-954, fitted with an Easton hopper box under the fuselage

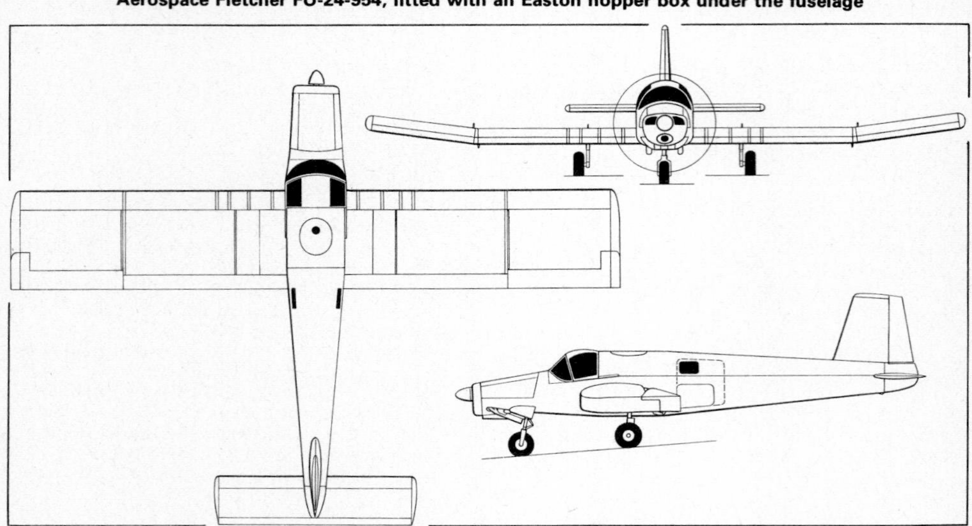
Aerospace Fletcher FU-24-954 with standard port-side door and (dotted line) optional large rear door *(Pilot Press)*

AEROSPACE FLETCHER FU-24-954

The FU-24 was developed by the Sargent-Fletcher Company of El Monte, California, initially for agricultural top-dressing work in New Zealand. The prototype flew in July 1954, followed by the first production aircraft five months later. Type certification was granted on 22 July 1955. All manufacturing and sales rights for the FU-24 were acquired by Air Parts (NZ) Ltd in 1964, and production was undertaken subsequently in that company's factory at Hamilton Airport, New Zealand.

The initial production series of 100 was delivered to New Zealand operators for top-dressing work. By June 1978, a total of 264 completed Fletcher aircraft had been produced, including 54 for export to Australia, Bangladesh, Iraq, Pakistan, Thailand, Uruguay and the United States. Up to early 1979 all foreign deliveries had been effected by solo delivery flights, but export was then due to begin of PKD and CKD (parts knock-down and component knock-down) aircraft to Frontier Aerospace Ltd, a subsidiary in Long Beach, California, USA.

The current model is the FU-24-954, to which the following description applies:

Type: Agricultural and general-purpose aircraft.

Wings: Cantilever low-wing monoplane. NACA 4415 wing section. Dihedral (outer wings) 8°. Incidence 2°. All-metal two-spar structure. All-metal plain-hinged ailerons. All-metal single-slotted flaps.

Fuselage: All-metal semi-monocoque structure. Cockpit area stressed for 25*g* impact.

Tail Unit: Cantilever all-metal structure. All-movable horizontal tail with anti-servo tab.

Landing Gear: Non-retractable tricycle type, with steerable nosewheel. Fletcher air-oil shock-absorber struts. Cleveland wheels and hydraulic disc brakes on main units. Goodyear tyres, size 8·50-6 (6-ply), pressure range 0·76-2·07 bars (11-30 lb/sq in).

Power Plant: One 298 kW (400 hp) Lycoming IO-720-A1A or A1B flat-eight engine, driving a Hartzell HC-C3YR-1R/847SR three-blade constant-speed variable-pitch metal propeller with spinner. Fuel tanks in wing leading-edges; total usable capacity 254 litres (67 US gallons), normal, 481 litres (127 US gallons) with optional long-range tanks.

Accommodation (Agricultural models): Enclosed cockpit for pilot and one passenger on side-by-side seats under rearward-sliding canopy. Cockpit reinforced for overturn/crash protection. Optional features include large cargo door on port side, additional cargo floor area, small rear door, and dual controls.

Accommodation (Utility models): Enclosed cabin for pilot and up to seven passengers or equivalent freight. Dual controls optional. Rearward-sliding hood over front two seats. Large passenger/cargo door on port side.

Agricultural Equipment: Glassfibre hopper aft of cockpit, capacity 1,045 litres (230 Imp gallons; 276 US gallons) of liquid, 1,066 kg (2,350 lb) of dry chemicals. Hopper outlets for spreading of solids (fertiliser, dry ice, poison bait, etc). Transland Swathmaster for top-dressing, seeding and high-volume spraying. Transland Boommaster for liquid spraying with booms, nozzles, fan-driven pump, etc, for low- and high-volume spraying. Micronair spraying equipment with electrically- or fan-driven pump, varied control systems, side-loading valve for liquids, and special adaptor plate for interchangeability of equipment.

Optional Equipment (all models): Full blind-flying instrumentation with ADF, VHF, VOR and DME. Full dual controls; dual main wheels and brakes, wheel and leg fairings; long-range fuel tanks; cabin heating and air-conditioning systems; metric instrumentation.

Dimensions, external:

Wing span	12·81 m (42 ft 0 in)
Wing chord (constant)	2·13 m (7 ft 0 in)
Wing aspect ratio	6
Length overall	9·70 m (31 ft 10 in)
Height to top of fin	2·84 m (9 ft 4 in)
Tailplane span	4·22 m (13 ft 10 in)
Wheel track	3·71 m (12 ft 2 in)
Wheelbase	2·28 m (7 ft 6 in)
Propeller diameter	2·18 m (7 ft 2 in)
Propeller ground clearance	0·33 m (12·8 in)

Passenger/cargo door (port, rear):
Height 0·97 m (3 ft 2 in)
Width 0·94 m (3 ft 1 in)
Optional small cargo door (rear):
Height 0·44 m (1 ft 5½ in)
Width 0·76 m (2 ft 6 in)

DIMENSIONS, INTERNAL:
Cabin: Length 3·18 m (10 ft 5 in)
Max width 1·22 m (4 ft 0 in)
Max height 1·27 m (4 ft 2 in)
Floor area 3·87 m² (41·7 sq ft)
Hopper volume 1·05 m³ (37 cu ft)

AREAS:
Wings, gross 27·31 m² (294 sq ft)
Ailerons (total) 1·82 m² (19·6 sq ft)
Trailing-edge flaps (total) 3·16 m² (34·0 sq ft)
Fin 1·26 m² (13·6 sq ft)
Rudder 0·64 m² (6·9 sq ft)
Tailplane 4·00 m² (43·1 sq ft)
Tailplane tab 0·45 m² (4·9 sq ft)

WEIGHTS AND LOADINGS:
Weight empty, equipped 1,188 kg (2,620 lb)
Max payload (agricultural) 1,052 kg (2,320 lb)
Normal max T-O weight 2,204 kg (4,860 lb)
Max agricultural T-O weight 2,463 kg (5,430 lb)
Cabin floor loading 1,885 kg/m² (386 lb/sq ft)
Normal wing loading 80·6 kg/m² (16·5 lb/sq ft)
Normal power loading 7·40 kg/kW (12·15 lb/hp)

PERFORMANCE (at Normal max T-O weight):
Never-exceed speed 143 knots (265 km/h; 165 mph)
Max level speed at S/L
126 knots (233 km/h; 145 mph)
Max cruising speed (75% power)
113 knots (209 km/h; 130 mph)
Operating speed for spraying (75% power)
90-115 knots (167-212 km/h; 104-132 mph)
Stalling speed:
flaps up 55 knots (102 km/h; 63·5 mph)
flaps down 49 knots (91 km/h; 57 mph)
Max rate of climb at S/L 280 m (920 ft)/min
Service ceiling 4,875 m (16,000 ft)
T-O run 244 m (800 ft)
T-O to 15 m (50 ft) 372 m (1,220 ft)
Landing from 15 m (50 ft) 390 m (1,280 ft)
Landing run 207 m (680 ft)
Swath width (agricultural models):
oily 23 m (75 ft)
aqueous 21·3-24·4 m (70-80 ft)
dust 7·6-15·2 m (25-50 ft)
Range with max normal fuel, 45 min reserves
383 nm (709 km; 441 miles)

AEROSPACE CRESCO

This latest development in the FU-24 series first flew on 28 February 1979. Powered by an Avco Lycoming LTP 101 turboprop engine, it has many components interchangeable with the standard FU-24-954. Use of the LTP 101, together with some structural refinement, permits a reduction in empty weight and a substantial increase in agricultural max T-O weight.

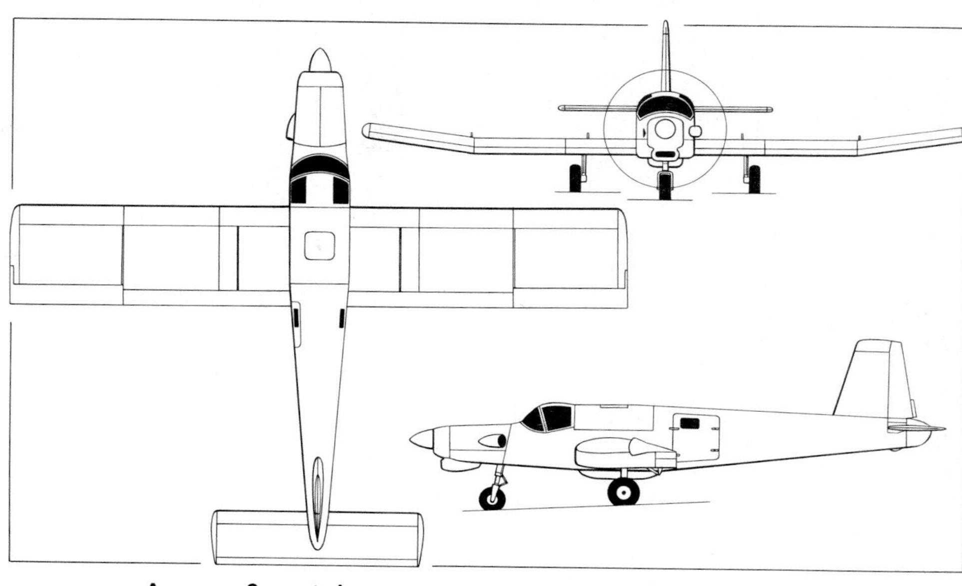

Aerospace Cresco turboprop-powered development of the FU-24 *(Pilot Press)*

The Cresco differs from the FU-24-954 in the following respects:

POWER PLANT: One 447 kW (600 shp) Avco Lycoming LTP 101 turboprop engine, driving a Hartzell HC-B3TN-3D/T1D282H three-blade propeller with spinner. Fuel load 113·4 kg (250 lb) for one hour's agricultural operation, 430 kg (948 lb) maximum.

AGRICULTURAL EQUIPMENT: Hopper capacity increased to 1,893 litres (416·4 Imp gallons; 500 US gallons).

DIMENSIONS, EXTERNAL:
Length overall 11·07 m (36 ft 4 in)
Tailplane span 4·27 m (14 ft 0 in)
Wheel track 3·76 m (12 ft 4 in)
Wheelbase 2·59 m (8 ft 6 in)
Propeller diameter 2·59 m (8 ft 6 in)

DIMENSION, INTERNAL:
Hopper volume 1·80 m³ (63·5 cu ft)

AREAS:
Ailerons (total) 2·00 m² (21·50 sq ft)
Trailing-edge flaps (total) 3·14 m² (33·80 sq ft)
Tailplane 4·69 m² (50·50 sq ft)

WEIGHTS (estimated):
Basic weight empty 1,133 kg (2,498 lb)
Payload with max fuel 1,531 kg (3,375 lb)
Max payload 1,860 kg (4,100 lb)
Normal category T-O weight 2,925 kg (6,450 lb)
Agricultural T-O weight with 1 hour's fuel
3,175 kg (7,000 lb)

PERFORMANCE (estimated, at Normal category T-O weight except where indicated, ISA at S/L):
Max level speed 141 knots (261 km/h; 162 mph)
Cruising speed (75% power)
122 knots (226 km/h; 140 mph)
Stalling speed, flaps down
52·5 knots (96·5 km/h; 60 mph)
Stalling speed, flaps down, at typical landing weight
36 knots (66 km/h; 41 mph)
Max rate of climb 265 m (870 ft)/min
T-O to 15 m (50 ft), optimum flap
451 m (1,480 ft)
Landing from 15 m (50 ft) 427 m (1,400 ft)
Landing from 15 m (50 ft) with propeller thrust reversal 335 m (1,100 ft)
Max range at 75% power
373 nm (692 km; 430 miles)
Max endurance at 75% power 3 h 53 min

FLIGHT ENGINEERS

FLIGHT ENGINEERS LTD

ADDRESS: PO Box 177, Papakura, Auckland
Telephone: Papakura 89 384
WORKS: Ardmore Aerodrome, Ardmore, Auckland
MANAGING DIRECTOR: J. T. Barr

As indicated in earlier editions of *Jane's,* Flight Engineers Ltd undertakes licence assembly or conversion in New Zealand of the Transavia PL-12 Airtruk, described in the Australian section. Limited production, which began in the early 1970s, was halted in 1975 due to unfavourable economic conditions.

No new Airtruks were built in New Zealand in 1977-78, but four standard O-520-engined examples were converted to T-320 Tiara-engined models by Flight Engineers Ltd and Transfield (NZ) Ltd before closure of the Tiara production line. Investigation was being undertaken in 1979 into the possibility of using Stage II and Geschwender Aeromotive engines in New Zealand-built Airtruks.

PAKISTAN

According to the French magazine *Air et Cosmos*, a new aircraft overhaul and maintenance facility was inaugurated in the Summer of 1978 at Kamra, about 65 km (40 miles) from Rawalpindi. The factory, intended as the nucleus of a Pakistani aircraft manufacturing industry, will overhaul Shenyang F-6 (MiG-19) and Dassault Mirage aircraft of the Pakistan Air Force, and will also, it is reported, undertake production of the **Mushaak**, a training aircraft said to be of Swedish origin — presumably the Saab Supporter, a number of which have already been supplied to Pakistan by Sweden.

PHILIPPINES

PADC

PHILIPPINE AEROSPACE DEVELOPMENT CORPORATION

ADDRESS: PADC Building, Domestic Terminal Avenue, Pasay, Metro Manila
Telephone: 839081 to 839088
Telex: 63883 PADC PN and 2114 AER PH
PRESIDENT: Roberto H. Lim
EXECUTIVE VICE-PRESIDENT: Elias G. Lavadia
TREASURER: Ruben C. Ruiz
CONTROLLER: Eloisa Valerio
DIRECTOR, MANAGEMENT SERVICES: Leandro R. Isberto
BOARD OF DIRECTORS:
Alfredo L. Juinio
Juan Ponce Enrile
Vicente Paterno
Geronimo Velasco
Panfilo Domingo
Roberto H. Lim
Placido Mapa Jr
Roman Cruz Jr

SUBSIDIARIES:
National Aero Manufacturing Corporation (NAM) (aircraft manufacture and assembly)
Philippine Aero Transport Inc (PATI) (air cargo operations)
Philippine Helicopter Services Inc (PHSI) (maintenance and overhaul of BO 105 helicopters)
Phillippine Resource Helicopters Inc (PRHI) (helicopter support and services for oil drilling operations)

PADC is a government corporation established in 1973 by President Ferdinand E. Marcos to promote the development of an aerospace industry in the Philippines.

NAM

NATIONAL AERO MANUFACTURING CORPORATION (A subsidiary of Philippine Aerospace Development Corporation)

ADDRESS: PO Box 2023, Makati Commercial Centre; or Manila International Airport, Pasay City
WORKS: PADC Hangar No. 3, MIA Road, Pasay City; PADC Hangar No. 4, Sangley Point, Cavite City
PRESIDENT: Pedro Q. Molina
VICE-PRESIDENT AND GENERAL MANAGER: Romulo H. Monasterio

PADC (MBB) BO 105

In 1974, PADC began an assembly and manufacturing programme for the BO 105C helicopter, under a licence agreement with MBB of Germany. By the end of 1978 a total of 37 had been assembled from knocked-down kits.

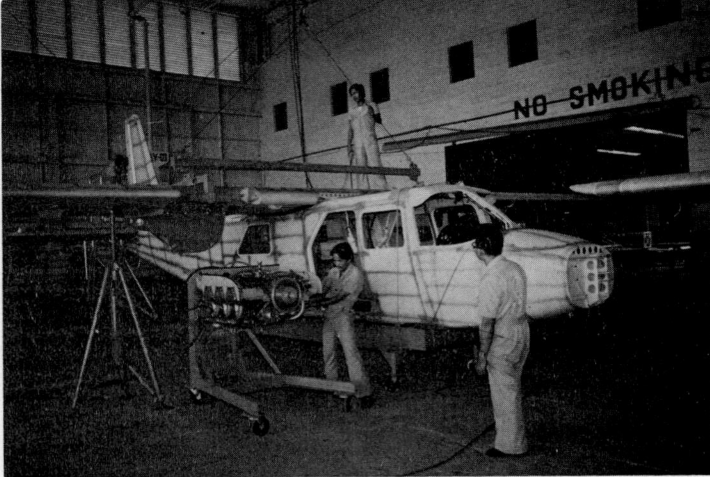

NAM assembly lines for the MBB BO 105 helicopter (left) and Pilatus Britten-Norman Islander (right)

One more remained to be assembled by NAM to complete the original programme.

In mid-1979, MBB was negotiating a new programme for six additional helicopters for export, and another six for PADC's own marketing needs.

NAM assembles/fabricates 45 per cent of the necessary components, importing the rest and exporting some components to MBB, including cargo and battery doors, oil drip pans, main relay boxes, overhead panels, nose doors, tailbooms, windscreen wipers and duct halves.

PADC (PILATUS BRITTEN-NORMAN) ISLANDER

Under an agreement made in 1974 between PADC and Britten-Norman (Bembridge) Ltd, six Islanders were delivered to PADC from the UK during the first phase. The second phase involved completion of 14 unpainted aircraft, delivered to PADC without cabin trim, furnishings and avionics. These were completed in 1975.

In 1976 NAM completed the third phase, assembling 35 Islanders from completely knocked-down Britten-Norman kits. This phase included local manufacture by NAM of ailerons, flaps, elevators, tailplanes, vertical fins, rudders, left centre boxes, fuselages and GRP parts.

The fourth phase, involving the assembly of 60 aircraft (of which 25 were to have been repurchased by Britten-Norman), was suspended when Pilatus of Switzerland acquired Britten-Norman in 1978. In 1979, PADC and Pilatus were discussing the possibility of a larger-scale Islander manufacturing and assembly programme by NAM.

A programme to equip the Islander with floats is temporarily suspended, pending funding. One float-equipped Islander has been tested successfully.

PADC/NSDB FIXED-WING AIRCRAFT PROTOTYPE

This prototype development project is a joint venture between PADC and the Philippine government's National Science Development Board (NSDB); the Metals Industry Research and Development Center (MIRDC) is co-operating in the programme.

The aircraft is an all-metal, externally-braced high-wing monoplane, accommodating four persons including the pilot. It is intended to carry passengers or cargo, and will be easily convertible into an agricultural crop dusting or seeding aircraft, with the necessary manoeuvrability to carry out such operations over small field areas.

Phase 1 of the programme, which began in October 1975, covered the preliminary design and engineering studies necessary to ensure smooth development; phase 2, which began in January 1976, concerns the detail design, construction and flight testing of a prototype.

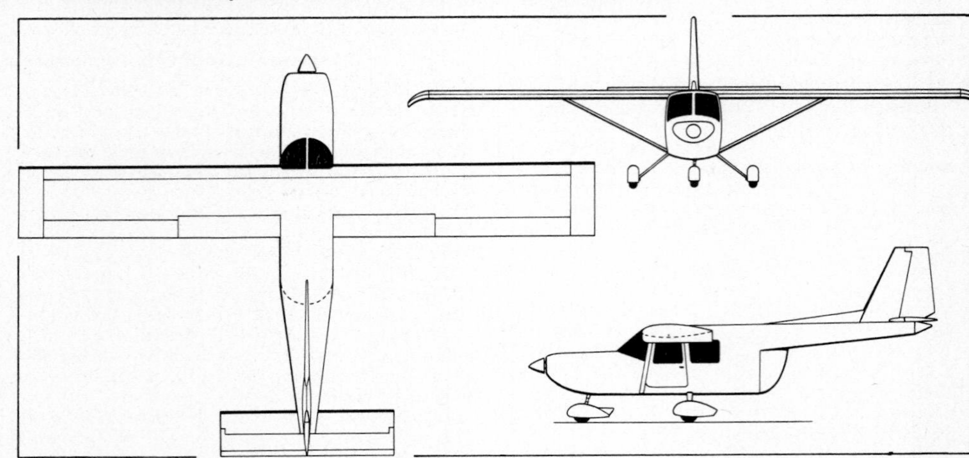

General arrangement of the PADC/NSDB prototype four-seat utility aircraft *(Michael A. Badrocke)*

TYPE: Four-seat light utility and agricultural aircraft.

WINGS: High-wing monoplane, braced by a single strut on each side. Wing section NACA 2415 (constant). No anhedral, dihedral or sweepback. Incidence 2°. Trailing-edge flaps and ailerons over virtually entire span. Turned-down wingtips.

FUSELAGE: All-metal pod and boom type.

TAIL UNIT: Cantilever all-metal structure, with slight sweepback on vertical surfaces. Shallow dorsal fin. Balanced rudder and balanced one-piece elevator.

LANDING GEAR: Non-retractable tricycle type. All three wheels same size. Streamline wheel fairing on each unit.

POWER PLANT: One 224 kW (300 hp) Lycoming IO-540-K1B5 flat-six engine, driving a Hartzell constant-speed variable-pitch propeller with spinner. Fuel tank in each wing, combined capacity 189 litres (50 US gallons; 41·5 Imp gallons). Overwing refuelling point above each tank. Oil capacity 11·4 litres (3 US gallons; 2·5 Imp gallons).

ACCOMMODATION: Pilot and up to three passengers, in pairs, in fully-enclosed cabin. Forward-opening car-type door on each side, each with pull-in window for emergency exit. Freight/baggage space aft of rear pair of seats, access to which is via clamshell rear-loading doors. Cabin ventilated.

DIMENSIONS, EXTERNAL:
- Wing span — 11·66 m (38 ft 3 in)
- Wing chord (constant) — 1·52 m (5 ft 0 in)
- Wing aspect ratio — 7·65
- Length overall — 8·43 m (27 ft 8 in)
- Height overall — 3·55 m (11 ft 7¾ in)
- Tailplane span — 3·48 m (11 ft 5 in)
- Wheel track — 2·40 m (7 ft 10½ in)
- Wheelbase — 2·20 m (7 ft 2½ in)
- Propeller diameter — 1·95 m (6 ft 4¾ in)
- Propeller ground clearance — 0·25 m (10 in)

DIMENSIONS, INTERNAL:
- Cabin: Length — 2·95 m (9 ft 8 in)
  - Max width — 1·04 m (3 ft 5 in)
  - Max height — 1·22 m (4 ft 0 in)
  - Floor area — 3·07 m² (33·0 sq ft)
  - Volume — 3·82 m³ (135·0 cu ft)
- Baggage compartment volume — 0·85 m³ (30·0 cu ft)
- Freight compartment volume — 1·69 m³ (59·6 cu ft)

AREAS:
- Wings, gross — 17·77 m² (191·3 sq ft)
- Ailerons (total) — 2·14 m² (23·0 sq ft)
- Trailing-edge flaps (total) — 1·95 m² (21·0 sq ft)
- Fin — 1·67 m² (18·0 sq ft)
- Rudder — 0·84 m² (9·0 sq ft)
- Tailplane — 3·34 m² (36·0 sq ft)
- Elevator — 1·51 m² (16·2 sq ft)

WEIGHTS AND LOADINGS (estimated):
- Weight empty — 992 kg (2,188 lb)
- Max T-O weight — 1,496 kg (3,300 lb)
- Max wing loading — 84·2 kg/m² (17·25 lb/sq ft)
- Max power loading — 3·72 kg/kW (11·0 lb/hp)

PERFORMANCE (estimated, at max T-O weight):
- Max level speed at S/L — 168·5 knots (312 km/h; 194 mph)
- Max cruising speed at S/L — 154·5 knots (286 km/h; 178 mph)
- Stalling speed, flaps up — 55·5 knots (103 km/h; 64 mph)
- Stalling speed, flaps down — 46·5 knots (86 km/h; 53·5 mph)
- Max rate of climb at S/L — 372 m (1,220 ft)/min
- Service ceiling — 5,300 m (17,400 ft)
- T-O run — 204 m (669 ft)
- T-O to 15 m (50 ft) — 436 m (1,430 ft)
- Landing from 15 m (50 ft) — 568 m (1,865 ft)
- Landing run — 305 m (1,000 ft)
- Max range — 424 nm (785 km; 488 miles)

PAF
PHILIPPINE AIR FORCE

ADDRESS: Headquarters PAF, Nichols Air Base, Pasay City

PAF XT-001

First news of this three-seat primary trainer prototype appeared in the late Summer of 1975. Built by the Self-Reliance Development Wing of the Philippine Air Force, reportedly using locally designed and manufactured jigs and fixtures, it bears a close and obvious resemblance (apart from the modified wingtips and cockpit) to the SIAI-Marchetti SF.260MP two/three-seat trainer, of which 32 were purchased by the PAF. It is thought likely that the prototype is, in fact, a converted SF.260MP; all known details, and a photograph of this aircraft, can be found in the 1978-79 *Jane's*.

PAF (AJI) T-610 CALI (SUPER PINTO)

The Self-Reliance Development Wing of the PAF has acquired from American Jet Industries the prototype of the latter company's tandem two-seat COIN version of the Temco TT-1 Pinto, together with the works drawings and the rights to the design and production of this aircraft.

The Super Pinto, last described in the 1972-73 edition of *Jane's*, is a light strike version of the TT-1 trainer, powered by a 12·7 kN (2,850 lb st) General Electric CJ610-4 turbojet engine (in place of the original Turboméca Marboré) and equipped with six underwing hardpoints for external stores.

Up to the Autumn of 1978 no production had been undertaken of the Super Pinto, which has the Philippine name Cali. The following brief details apply to the AJI-built prototype:

TYPE: Tandem two-seat jet trainer and light close support aircraft.

POWER PLANT: One 12·7 kN (2,850 lb st) General Electric CJ610-4 turbojet engine, with air intakes in wing roots. Fuel in four tanks in wings, total capacity 783·5 litres (207 US gallons; 172 Imp gallons). Provision for two 208 litre (55 US gallon; 46 Imp gallon) wingtip tanks and two 454 litre (120 US gallon; 100 Imp gallon) underwing drop-tanks.

ACCOMMODATION: Crew of two in tandem under upward-opening canopy.

DIMENSIONS, EXTERNAL:

Wing span (without tip-tanks)	9·14 m (30 ft 0 in)
Wing area, gross	13·93 m² (150 sq ft)
Length overall, incl probe	9·58 m (31 ft 5 in)
Height overall	3·48 m (11 ft 5 in)
Wheel track	4·04 m (13 ft 3 in)
Wheelbase	4·10 m (13 ft 5¼ in)

WEIGHTS AND LOADINGS (without tip-tanks):

Weight empty	1,466 kg (3,233 lb)
Max T-O weight	2,268 kg (5,001 lb)
Max wing loading	162·8 kg/m² (33·34 lb/sq ft)
Max power loading	178·6 kg/kN (1·75 lb/lb st)

PAF Cali (AJI T-610 Super Pinto) in Philippine Air Force insignia

PERFORMANCE (at max T-O weight except where indicated):

Max level speed	450 knots (834 km/h; 518 mph)
Max limiting Mach No.	Mach 0·76
Max rate of climb at S/L at AUW of 2,086 kg (4,600 lb)	2,743 m (9,000 ft)/min
Absolute ceiling	14,630 m (48,000 ft)
T-O to 15 m (50 ft)	183 m (600 ft)

PATS/NSDB

PHILIPPINE AIR TRANSPORT & TRAINING SERVICES INC (PATS School of Aeronautics)/ NATIONAL SCIENCE DEVELOPMENT BOARD

PRESIDENT: Ambrosio R. Valdez Sr

As a joint venture, the PATS School of Aeronautics and the National Science Development Board have undertaken two fairly simple aeronautical projects designed to utilise local raw materials. These are the Project 7307En light aircraft and the XG-001 two-seat sailplane.

PATS/NSDB RESEARCH PROJECTS

In a research programme, PATS and the NSDB conducted a project (No. 7307En) entitled 'Research on local fabric, local woods and local aluminium for aircraft use'. Tests were carried out, and the results of evaluation were utilised in the construction of the **PATS Bamboo Aircraft**, which logged more than 26 h of extensive testing. A proposal to continue with this project was awaiting approval in mid-1979.

In a related programme (No. 7714En, entitled 'Research on the utilisation of alcohol and/or alcohol/gasoline as fuel for light aircraft'), research was continuing in 1979. Extensive ground and flight testing with three engines had been conducted, and the encouraging test data were being evaluated. Service trials with a number of aircraft were anticipated within the following year.

POLAND

PZL

POLSKIE ZAKLADY LOTNICZE, ZJEDNOCZENIE PRZEMYSLU LOTNICZEGO I SILNIKOWEGO PZL (Polish Aviation Works, Aircraft and Engine Industry Union)

HEAD OFFICE: ul. Miodowa 5, 00251 Warsaw
Telephone: Warsaw 279985
Telex: 814281
GENERAL MANAGER: Ing Krzysztof Kuczynski
VICE-DIRECTOR: Ing Kazimierz Brejnak (Technical)

The Polish aircraft industry is under the central direction of the Zjednoczenie Przemyslu Lotniczego i Silnikowego PZL (Aircraft and Engine Industry Union).

The original PZL works was established in 1928. The principal factories concerned with aircraft manufacture today are the CNPSL-PZL Warszawa, WSK-PZL Mielec and WSK-PZL Swidnik. Between them, these three factories have manufactured some 13,000 aircraft and 4,500 helicopters since the end of the second World War. Other Polish factories, engaged in the production of sailplanes and aero-engines, are listed in the relevant sections of this edition. Altogether, 96,000 people are employed in the PZL aircraft industry.

The Polish aircraft industry manufactures several aircraft of Polish design, including the PZL-104 Wilga, PZL-106 Kruk, PZL M-15, and PZL M-18 Dromader. It builds under Soviet licence the Antonov An-2 biplane and Mil Mi-2 helicopter, and components for the Ilyushin Il-86 airbus. In 1979 it was due to begin production of the Antonov An-28, as well as licence manufacture of the French Socata Rallye (as the PZL-110 Koliber) and the US Piper Seneca II (as the PZL M-20 Mewa).

The export sales of all Polish aviation products are handled by Pezetel Foreign Trade Enterprise, whose address is given below:

Pezetel Foreign Trade Enterprise of Aviation Industry

ADDRESS: PO Box 371, 00950 Warsaw
Telephone: Warsaw 28071
Telex: 813430
GENERAL MANAGER: Jerzy Krazlewicz, MSc
MANAGER OF AVIATION DEPARTMENT: Stanislaw Ferenstein
MANAGER OF PUBLICITY DEPARTMENT: Ing Janusz Matuszewski

IL

INSTYTUT LOTNICTWA (Aeronautical Institute)

ADDRESS: Al. Krakowska 110/114, 02-256 Warsaw-Okecie
Telephone: Warsaw 460993
Telex: 813537
MANAGING DIRECTOR: Ing Zbigniew Pawlak
DEPUTY DIRECTOR: Dipl Ing Jerzy Grzegorzewski
SCIENTIFIC DIRECTOR: Dr Czeslaw Skoczylas
CHIEF OF TECHNICAL INFORMATION DIVISION: Dipl Ing Andrzej Glass

The Instytut Lotnictwa was founded in 1926. It belongs to the PZL Polish Aviation Works group, under the general management of the PZL Aircraft and Engine Industry Union. The IL is responsible for the control of all research and development work in the Polish aircraft industry. It conducts scientific research, including the investigation of problems associated with low-speed and high-speed aerodynamics, static and fatigue tests, development and testing of aero-engines, flight instruments and other equipment, flight tests, and materials technology. It is also responsible for the construction of experimental aircraft and aero-engines.

CNPSL-PZL WARSZAWA

CENTRUM NAUKOWO-PRODUKCYJNE SAMOLOTOW LEKKICH PZL WARSZAWA (Light Aircraft Science and Production Centre, PZL Warsaw)

HEAD OFFICE AND WORKS: 02-256 Warsaw-Okecie, Al. Krakowska 110/114
Telephone: Warsaw 461173 and 460031
MANAGERS:
Jozef Lipinski, Eng MSc (General Manager)
Jerzy Milczarek, Eng (Technical)
Zbigniew Pesko, MSc (Sales)
PUBLIC RELATIONS: Jerzy Pasterski, Eng MSc

The Okecie factory is responsible for light aircraft development and production, and for the design and manufacture of associated agricultural equipment for its own aircraft and for those built at other factories in the Aircraft and Engine Industry Union. Formerly known as WSK-PZL-Okecie, it adopted its present title on 1 July 1976.

PZL-104 WILGA 35 (THRUSH)

The PZL-104 Wilga is a light general-purpose aircraft intended for a wide variety of general aviation and flying club duties. The original prototype (SP-PAZ), known as the Wilga 1, with a 180 hp WN-6B engine, flew for the first time on 24 April 1962. This aircraft, and the Wilga 2, C and 3 prototypes, 3A and 3S production versions and other early models, were described in the 1968-69 *Jane's*.

In 1967 the basic design was further modified, with

PZL-104 Wilga 35A four-seat utility aircraft, in Swiss markings

improved cabin comfort, redesigned landing gear and glassfibre tailwheel leg. This version is known as the Wilga 35 (first flight 28 July 1967) when fitted with a 194 kW (260 hp) AI-14R engine, and as the Wilga 32 (first flown 12 September 1967) with a 171·5 kW (230 hp) Continental O-470-K, -L or -R engine and shorter landing gear. Both the Wilga 32 (see 1974-75 *Jane's*) and Wilga 35 received a Polish type certificate on 31 March 1969, having entered production in 1968. A modified version of the Wilga 32 was produced in Indonesia as the Lipnur Gelatik 32 (see 1975-76 *Jane's*). Details of the Wilga 40 and 43 experimental versions were given in the 1972-73 *Jane's*.

The Wilga 35 continues in production, current models being the **Wilga 35A** (Aeroclub), **35P** (Passenger/liaison), **35R** (agricultural version, described separately) and **35S** (ambulance). Examples of the Wilga 35A have been sold to customers in Austria, Bulgaria, Czechoslovakia, Egypt, Germany (Democratic Republic), Germany (Federal Republic), Hungary, Romania, Spain, Switzerland, the UK, the USA, the USSR and Venezuela.

By early 1979 more than 460 Wilgas, of all versions, had been built in Poland. Deliveries during 1978 included 36 to the USSR, 15 to East Germany, 12 to Romania and one to Hungary.

The following description applies to the current Wilga 35A:

TYPE: Single-engined general-purpose monoplane.

WINGS: Cantilever high-wing monoplane. Wing section NACA 2415. Dihedral 1°. All-metal single-spar structure, with leading-edge torsion box and beaded metal skin. Each wing attached to fuselage by three bolts, two at spar and one at forward fitting. All-metal aerodynamically and mass-balanced slotted ailerons, with beaded metal skin. Ailerons can be drooped to supplement flaps during landing. Manually-operated all-metal slotted flaps with beaded metal skin. Fixed metal slat on the leading-edge along the full span of the wing and over the fuselage. Tab on starboard aileron.

FUSELAGE: All-metal semi-monocoque structure in two portions, riveted together. Forward section incorporates main wing spar carry-through structure. Rear section is in the form of a tailcone. Beaded metal skin. Floor in cabin is of sandwich construction, with a paper core, covered with foam rubber.

TAIL UNIT: Braced all-metal structure, with sweptback vertical surfaces. Stressed-skin single-spar tailplane attached to fuselage by a single centre fitting and supported by a single aluminium alloy strut on each side. Stressed-skin two-spar fin structure of semi-monocoque construction. Rudder and one-piece elevator are aerodynamically horn-balanced and mass-balanced, with counterweights in the form of metal slats attached to the front section of the elevator. Controllable trim tab at centre of elevator trailing-edge.

LANDING GEAR: Non-retractable tailwheel type. Semi-cantilever legs, of rocker type, have PZL oleo-pneumatic shock-absorbers. Stomil tubeless low-pressure tyres size 500 × 200 mm on main wheels. Hydraulic brakes. Steerable tailwheel, size 255 × 110 mm, carried on rocker frame with oleo-pneumatic damper. Retractable metal ski landing gear optional.

POWER PLANT: One 194 kW (260 hp) Ivchenko AI-14RA nine-cylinder supercharged radial aircooled engine, driving a US-122000 two-blade constant-speed wooden propeller. Two removable fuel tanks in each wing, with total capacity of 195 litres (43 Imp gallons). Refuelling point on each side of fuselage, at junction with wing. Oil capacity 16 litres (3·5 Imp gallons). It is intended to power this version with an AI-14RC engine having electrical starting. Power plant can be fitted optionally with a silencer which reduces engine noise level to 67 dB (A).

ACCOMMODATION: Passenger version accommodates four persons in pairs, with adjustable front seats. Baggage compartment aft of seats. Upward-opening door on each side of cabin, jettisonable in emergency. In the parachute training version the starboard door is removed and replaced by a tubular upright with a horizontal strap, and the starboard front seat is rearward-facing. Backrests of the rear seats are removable, and jumps are facilitated by a step on the starboard side and by a parachute hitch. A controllable towing hook can be attached to the tail landing gear permitting the Wilga, in this role, to tow a single glider of up to 650 kg (1,433 lb) weight or two or three gliders with a total combined weight of 1,125 kg (2,480 lb).

SYSTEMS: Hydraulic system pressure 39 bars (570 lb/sq in). Engine starting is effected pneumatically by a built-in system of 7 litres (427 cu in) capacity with a pressure of 49 bars (710 lb/sq in); electrical system powered by GSK-1500 DC generator and 24V 10Ah battery.

AVIONICS AND EQUIPMENT: Standard equipment includes blind-flying instrumentation. Optional avionics include RS-6102, R-860 II, R860 IIM, King KY-195 or Bendix radio; and ARL-1601, ARK-9, King KR-85 or Bendix AV-200 ADF.

DIMENSIONS, EXTERNAL:
Wing span 11·12 m (36 ft 5¾ in)
Wing chord (constant) 1·40 m (4 ft 7¼ in)
Wing aspect ratio 7·95
Length overall 8·10 m (26 ft 6¾ in)

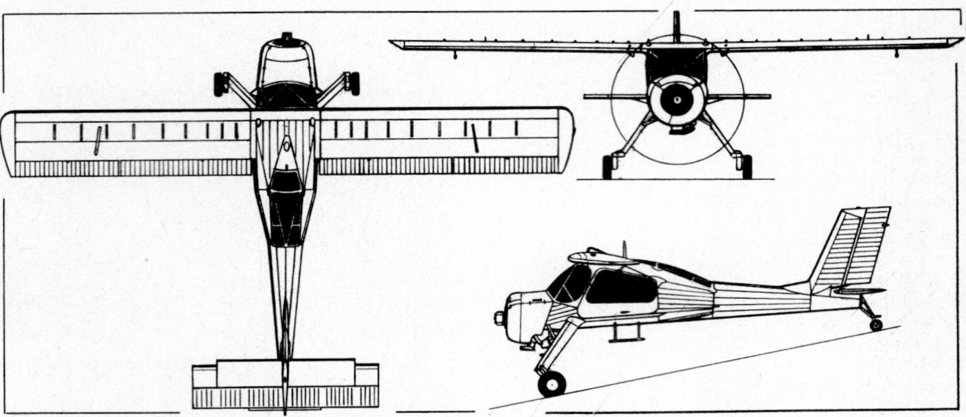

PZL-104 Wilga 35A general-purpose monoplane *(Pilot Press)*

Height overall 2·94 m (9 ft 7¾ in)
Tailplane span 3·70 m (12 ft 1¾ in)
Wheel track 2·85 m (9 ft 4¼ in)
Wheelbase 6·70 m (21 ft 11¾ in)
Propeller diameter 2·65 m (8 ft 8 in)
Passenger doors (each): Height 1·00 m (3 ft 3¼ in)
Width 1·50 m (4 ft 11 in)

DIMENSIONS, INTERNAL:
Cabin: Length 2·20 m (7 ft 2½ in)
Max width 1·20 m (3 ft 10 in)
Max height 1·50 m (4 ft 11 in)
Floor area 2·20 m² (23·8 sq ft)
Volume 2·40 m³ (85 cu ft)
Baggage compartment 0·50 m³ (17·5 cu ft)

AREAS:
Wings, gross 15·50 m² (166·8 sq ft)
Ailerons (total) 1·57 m² (16·90 sq ft)
Trailing-edge flaps (total) 1·97 m² (21·20 sq ft)
Fin 0·97 m² (10·44 sq ft)
Rudder 0·92 m² (9·90 sq ft)
Tailplane 3·16 m² (34·01 sq ft)
Elevator, incl tab 1·92 m² (20·67 sq ft)

WEIGHTS AND LOADINGS:
Weight empty, equipped 850 kg (1,874 lb)
Max T-O and landing weight 1,300 kg (2,866 lb)
Max wing loading 83·9 kg/m² (17·18 lb/sq ft)
Max power loading 6·70 kg/kW (11·02 lb/hp)

PERFORMANCE (at 1,230 kg; 2,711 lb AUW):
Never-exceed speed 150 knots (279 km/h; 173 mph)
Max level speed 108 knots (201 km/h; 125 mph)
Max cruising speed 104 knots (193 km/h; 120 mph)
Econ cruising speed 69·5 knots (128 km/h; 80 mph)
Stalling speed, power on 37 knots (68 km/h; 42·5 mph)
Max rate of climb at S/L 378 m (1,240 ft)/min
Service ceiling 4,580 m (15,025 ft)
T-O run 80 m (260 ft)
T-O to 15 m (50 ft) 186 m (610 ft)
Landing from 15 m (50 ft) 230 m (755 ft)
Landing run 95 m (310 ft)
Range with max fuel, 30 min reserves 366 nm (680 km; 422 miles)

PERFORMANCE AS GLIDER TUG:
Rate of climb at S/L: with 1 glider 234 m (770 ft)/min
with 2 gliders 204 m (670 ft)/min
with 3 gliders 132 m (435 ft)/min
Service ceiling: with 1 glider 4,000 m (13,125 ft)
with 2 gliders 3,900 m (12,800 ft)
with 3 gliders 2,500 m (8,200 ft)
Time to reach service ceiling:
with 1 glider 37 min 12 s
with 2 gliders 43 min 12 s
with 3 gliders 36 min 36 s
Range:
with 1 glider 344 nm (637 km; 395 miles)
with 2 gliders 272 nm (504 km; 313 miles)
with 3 gliders 227 nm (420 km; 260 miles)

PZL-104 WILGA 35R (AGRICULTURAL VERSION)

First flown on 13 February 1978, this agricultural version of the Wilga 35 takes advantage of the STOL capabilities of this aeroplane, its steep angles of climb and descent, and its ability to make tight turns, particularly over small fields where approach is a problem.

The agricultural equipment can be installed with any type of landing gear except floats, and is made entirely of materials resistant to chemical corrosion. Maximum chemical load, in addition to fuel for 1 hour's flying, is 270 kg (595 lb), and the limited carrying capacity qualifies the aircraft for ultra-low-volume spraying missions. With dual controls, this version can be used to give practical training to future agricultural pilots under genuine field conditions.

AGRICULTURAL EQUIPMENT: Laminated hopper for chemicals, attached beneath fuselage between main landing gear units; centrifugal pump, attached to port landing gear leg and driven by a six-blade fan; control valves; filter; spraybooms, supported well beneath wings on V-struts and fitted with four Micronair atomisers or 40 pressurised spray outlets; fluid pressure gauges; Micronair flow meter. Pump brake actuated pneumatically; cut-off and release valves, and jettison system, operated manually.

PZL-106A KRUK (RAVEN)

In the early 1960s the WSK-Okecie design team began project studies for an agricultural aircraft to replace the PZL-101 Gawron (Rook), of which WSK-Okecie manufactured more than 330 in the period 1958-73. The initial design, known as the PZL-101M Kruk (Raven), was an extensively redesigned development of the Gawron, with a 194 kW (260 hp) Ivchenko AI-14R radial engine. Progressive refinement led to the current PZL-106A Kruk, with a more powerful engine and the braced low-wing monoplane configuration that is more customary for agricultural aircraft.

The PZL-106 was designed in early 1972 by a team led by Andrzej Frydrychewicz. The first prototype (SP-PAS) flew for the first time on 17 April 1973, powered by a 298 kW (400 hp) Lycoming IO-720 engine. It was followed by a second Lycoming-engined prototype (SP-PBG) and four prototypes fitted with the 447 kW (600 hp) PZL-3S radial engine intended for PZL-106A production aircraft.

To meet the requirements of potential customers, the PZL-106A has a greater chemical load, in a larger hopper. Manufacture of some 600 aircraft for the member coun-

Agricultural version of the Wilga 35, with underfuselage hopper and spraybooms

PZL-106A Kruk, tropical version

PZL-106A Kruk agricultural aircraft in East German markings; note new-style engine cowling

tries of the CMEA (Council for Mutual Economic Aid) is anticipated.

Production of the PZL-106A began in 1976; the first export delivery, to Hungary, was made in 1977, and a total of 58 had been built by the Autumn of 1978, of which 10 were delivered to the German Democratic Republic, two to Hungary and two to Czechoslovakia. East Germany has ordered 19 more for 1979 delivery and 10 have been ordered by Iraq. A tropical version of the standard PZL-106A, with uncowled engine, is available.

Two aircraft have been equipped, for evaluation and certification, with a two-seat cockpit, dual controls, and a 400 litre (88 Imp gallon) hopper; this modification is available on any production PZL-106A. Warsaw-Okecie is also evaluating a version known as the **PZL-106AR**, first flown on 15 November 1978: this is powered by a geared PZL-3SR engine (gear ratio 0·7), driving a 3·10 m (10 ft 2 in) diameter PZL-US133000 propeller.

TYPE: Single-engined agricultural aircraft.

WINGS: Braced low-wing monoplane with upward-cambered tips. Clark Y wing section throughout span, except at tips. Thickness/chord ratio 11·7%. Dihedral 4° from roots. Incidence 6° 6′. Sweepback 4° at quarter-chord. All-metal two-spar structure, of constant chord throughout most of span. Metal and synthetic fabric covering. Full-span six-section fixed leading-edge slats. Fabric-covered duralumin slotted ailerons, each with ground-adjustable tab. No flaps. Streamline-section V bracing struts, with jury struts.

FUSELAGE: Welded steel tube structure, covered with light alloy and GRP. Steel tube structure can be pressure-tested for crack detection.

TAIL UNIT: Conventional duralumin structure, with single bracing strut each side. Fixed surfaces metal-covered; rudder and mass-balanced elevators synthetic fabric-covered. Trim tab in port elevator, balance tab in starboard elevator; ground-adjustable tab on rudder.

LANDING GEAR: Non-retractable tailwheel type, with CNPSL-PZL Warszawa wheel and oleo-pneumatic shock-absorber on each unit. Main wheels, with Stomil-Poznan low-pressure tyres (size 800 mm × 260 mm), each carried on side V and half-axle. Main-wheel tyre pressure 2·0 bars (29 lb/sq in). Pneumatically-operated CNPSL-PZL Warszawa oleo-pneumatic disc brakes on main wheels. Steerable tailwheel, with Stomil-Poznan tubeless tyre size 355 mm × 135 mm, pressure 2·5 bars (36·25 lb/sq in).

POWER PLANT: One 447 kW (600 hp) PZL-3S seven-cylinder radial aircooled engine, driving a PZL US-132000/A four-blade constant-speed metal propeller. Fuel in two wing tanks, total capacity 310 litres (68 Imp gallons). Gravity refuelling point on each wing; pressure refuelling point on starboard side of fuselage. Oil capacity 54 litres (11·9 Imp gallons) max, 7 litres (1·54 Imp gallons) min. Air filter fitted.

ACCOMMODATION: Pilot in enclosed, ventilated and air-conditioned cockpit. Second (mechanic's) rearward-facing seat to rear. Combined window/door on each side of cabin with emergency opening on port side. Underfloor baggage compartment, with external access, can be used to transport agricultural equipment. Cockpit fan and heater available optionally. Cockpit area strengthened to resist 40*g* impact.

SYSTEMS: Pneumatic system, rated at 50 bars (725 lb/sq in), for brakes and agricultural equipment. Electrical power, from 27·5V DC alternator and batteries, for engine starting, pneumatic system control, aircraft lights, instruments and pressure refuelling.

EQUIPMENT: VHF transceiver. Easily removable non-corrosive (glassfibre-reinforced plastics) hopper/tank, forward of cockpit, can carry 1,000 kg (2,205 lb) of dry or liquid chemical, and has a maximum capacity of 1,400 litres (308 Imp gallons). The hopper has a quick-dump system that can release 1,000 kg of chemical in less than 5 s. A pneumatically operated intake for the loading of dry chemicals is optional. Distribution system for liquid chemical is powered by a fan-driven centrifugal pump. A precise and reliable dispersal system, with positive on/off action for dry chemicals, gives effective swath widths of 10-35 m (33-115 ft).

DIMENSIONS, EXTERNAL:
Wing span	14·80 m (48 ft 6½ in)
Wing chord (constant)	1·90 m (6 ft 2¾ in)
Wing aspect ratio	7·8
Length overall	9·10 m (29 ft 10¼ in)
Height overall	3·32 m (10 ft 10¾ in)
Tailplane span	5·77 m (18 ft 11¼ in)
Wheel track	3·10 m (10 ft 2¼ in)
Wheelbase	7·41 m (24 ft 3¾ in)
Propeller diameter	2·62 m (8 ft 7 in)
Propeller ground clearance (tail up)	0·28 m (11 in)
Crew doors (each): Height	0·91 m (2 ft 11¾ in)
Width	1·06 m (3 ft 5¾ in)
Baggage door: Height	0·70 m (2 ft 3½ in)
Width	0·60 m (1 ft 11¾ in)

DIMENSIONS, INTERNAL:
Cabin: Length	1·37 m (4 ft 6 in)
Max width	1·25 m (4 ft 1¼ in)
Max height	1·30 m (4 ft 3¼ in)
Floor area	1·12 m² (12·05 sq ft)
Baggage compartment: Length	1·40 m (4 ft 7 in)
Width	1·00 m (3 ft 3¼ in)
Depth	0·60 m (1 ft 11¾ in)

AREAS:
Wings, gross	28·40 m² (305·7 sq ft)
Ailerons (total)	2·46 m² (26·50 sq ft)
Fin	1·26 m² (13·56 sq ft)
Rudder, incl tab	1·62 m² (17·44 sq ft)
Tailplane	3·34 m² (35·95 sq ft)
Elevators, incl tab	4·22 m² (45·42 sq ft)

WEIGHTS AND LOADINGS:
Weight empty, equipped	1,575 kg (3,472 lb)
Max chemical payload	1,000 kg (2,205 lb)
Normal T-O weight	2,800 kg (6,173 lb)
Max T-O and landing weight	3,000 kg (6,614 lb)
*Max ramp weight	3,000 kg (6,614 lb)
Max wing loading	105·6 kg/m² (21·63 lb/sq ft)
Max power loading	6·7 kg/kW (11·02 lb/hp)

* *Aircraft stressed for 3,000 kg (6,614 lb) T-O weight in Normal Category, BCAR Section K*

PERFORMANCE (at Normal T-O weight):
Never-exceed speed	140 knots (260 km/h; 161 mph)
Max level speed at S/L	114 knots (211 km/h; 131 mph)

Prototype two-seat PZL-106A Kruk agricultural aircraft, with cockpit for instructor in place of hopper

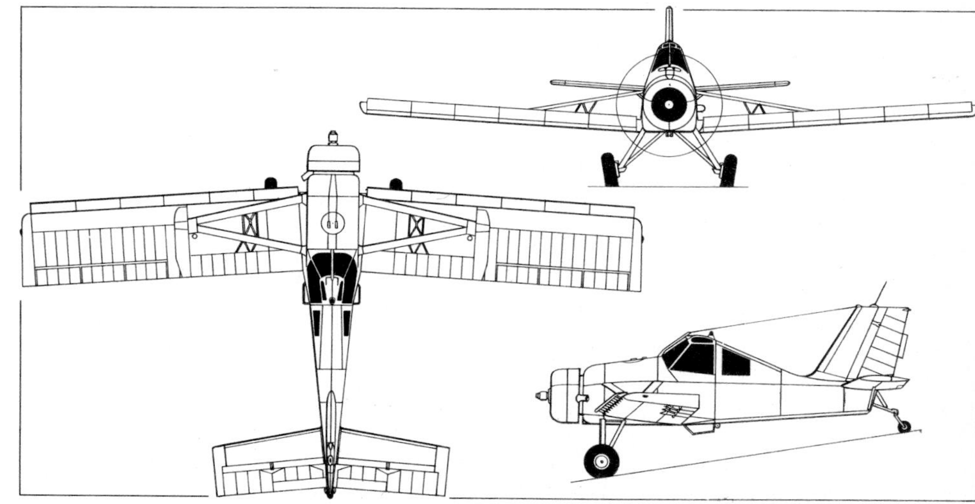

PZL-106A production version of the Kruk (PZL-3S engine) *(Pilot Press)*

Max cruising speed at S/L 97 knots (180 km/h; 112 mph)
Operating speed with 1,000 kg (2,205 lb) of chemical 65-86·5 knots (120-160 km/h; 74·5-99·5 mph)
Stalling speed at S/L 50 knots (92 km/h; 57·5 mph)
Max rate of climb at S/L with 1,000 kg (2,205 lb) of chemical 240 m (787 ft)/min
*T-O run 220 m (722 ft)
*T-O to 15 m (50 ft) 480 m (1,575 ft)
*Landing from 15 m (50 ft) 410 m (1,345 ft)
*Landing run 210 m (689 ft)
Min ground turning radius 10·00 m (32 ft 10 in)
Range with max fuel 215 nm (400 km; 248 miles)
* *with agricultural equipment*

PZL-110 KOLIBER (HUMMING-BIRD)

Under this designation, CNPSL-PZL Warszawa is producing under licence the lowest-powered version of the French Socata Rallye two/four-seat light aircraft, modified to receive a 93 kW (125 hp) PZL-Franklin engine. The first PZL-110 made its initial flight on 18 April 1978.

A description of the standard Rallye can be found under the Socata heading in the French section. The PZL-110 version differs in the following details:

Power Plant: One 93 kW (125 hp) PZL-built Franklin 4A-235-B3 flat-four engine, driving a US 135000 two-blade fixed-pitch propeller. Aluminium alloy fuel tank in each wing, combined capacity 105 litres (23 Imp gallons). Refuelling points above wings. Oil capacity 6·2 litres (1·4 Imp gallons).

Systems and Equipment: 12V electrical system, with alternator and 18Ah battery. VHF transceiver optional. Optional equipment includes ADF, and electrically powered gyro attitude indicator, turn and slip indicator and direction indicator.

PZL-110 Koliber, Polish-built version of the Socata Rallye

Dimensions, external: As Rallye 100 ST except:
Length overall 7·20 m (23 ft 7½ in)
Propeller diameter 1·82 m (5 ft 11¾ in)

Areas: As Rallye 100 ST except:
Wings, gross 12·76 m² (137·3 sq ft)

Weights and Loading:
Weight empty, equipped 530 kg (1,169 lb)
Max T-O and landing weight (Normal category) 850 kg (1,874 lb)
Max T-O weight (Utility category) 770 kg (1,700 lb)
Max wing loading 66·6 kg/m² (13·65 lb/sq ft)

Performance (at max Normal T-O weight except where indicated):
Never-exceed speed 145 knots (270 km/h; 167 mph)
Max level speed at S/L 105 knots (195 km/h; 121 mph)
Max cruising speed at S/L 92 knots (170 km/h; 106 mph)
Stalling speed, flaps up 48 knots (89 km/h; 55·5 mph)
Stalling speed, flaps down 41·5 knots (76 km/h; 47·5 mph)
Max rate of climb at S/L at AUW of 830 kg (1,830 lb) 171 m (560 ft)/min
Service ceiling 3,500 m (11,480 ft)
T-O run 140 m (459 ft)
Range with max fuel 345 nm (640 km; 397 miles)

WSK-PZL MIELEC

WYTWORNIA SPRZETU KOMUNIKACYJNEGO-PZL MIELEC (Transport Equipment Manufacturing Centre, Mielec)

Head Office and Works: ul. Ludowego Wojska Polskiego 3, 39-301 Mielec
Telephone: Mielec 70
Telex: 83293
General Manager: Dipl Ing Tadeusz Ryczaj

Largest and best-equipped aircraft factory in Poland, the WSK at Mielec has approx 278,700 m² (3 million sq ft) of floor area and a work force of some 18,000 people. It was engaged mainly in licence production of MiG single-seat jet fighters for several years. These aircraft carry the Polish designation of LiM, meaning Licence MiG, and included the LiM-1 (MiG-15), SBLiM-1 (MiG-15 UTI), LiM-2 (MiG-15 bis) and LiM-5 (MiG-17). Polish-developed versions of the LiM-5 were designated LiM-5M and LiM-6 bis. Licence production of MiG fighters ceased in Poland in about 1959.

Following a reduction in orders for combat aircraft in 1955, Mielec began production in 1956 of 240 TS-8 Bies basic trainers, described in the 1962-63 *Jane's*. Four years later, the Soviet-designed An-2 general utility biplane went into production at Mielec. In parallel production with the An-2 at the present time is the TS-11 Iskra jet trainer and light attack aircraft. In 1977 Mielec began to manufacture components, including fins, tailplanes, engine pylons, and wing slats and flaps, for the Ilyushin Il-86 Soviet wide-bodied transport, and in 1978 it was announced that Mielec would assume responsibility for series production of the Soviet Antonov An-28 twin-turboprop light general-purpose aircraft. Mielec exported its 8,500th aircraft in January 1979.

There is a design office at the factory for development of original aircraft. Its most recent designs are the M-15 agricultural aircraft, M-17 light aircraft, and M-18 Dromader agricultural aircraft, of which the M-15 and M-18 are now in production.

PZL MIELEC (ANTONOV) An-2

NATO reporting name: Colt

The prototype of the An-2, designed to a specification of the Ministry of Agriculture and Forestry of the USSR, made its first flight on 31 August 1947. It was powered by a 567 kW (760 hp) ASh-21 engine and was known as the SKh-1 (Selskokhozyaistvennyi-1: agricultural-economic-1). This designation was dropped subsequently and in 1948 the design went into production in the USSR as the An-2, with a 746 kW (1,000 hp) ASh-62 engine.

By 1960, more than 5,000 An-2s had been built in the Soviet Union for service with the Soviet armed forces, Aeroflot and other civilian organisations and the various Soviet-built versions have been fully described in previous editions of *Jane's*. Many were exported, to all of the Socialist States, and to Greece, Afghanistan, Mali, Nepal, India and Cuba, and licence rights were granted to China, where the first locally-produced An-2 was completed in December 1957.

Since 1960, apart from a small Soviet-built quantity of a developed version known as the An-2M (see 1971-72 *Jane's*), the continued production of the An-2 has been the responsibility of the PZL factory at Mielec, the original licence arrangement providing for two basic versions: the An-2T transport and An-2R agricultural version. The first 10 Polish-built An-2s were completed in 1960 (first example flown on 23 October 1960), and Mielec has since built considerable numbers of this aircraft for domestic use and for export to the USSR, Bulgaria, Czechoslovakia, Egypt, France, the German Democratic Republic, Hungary, North Korea, Mongolia, the Netherlands, Romania, Sudan, Tunisia and Yugoslavia. The 5,000th Polish-built An-2 was delivered, to the USSR, on 3 February 1973. Since beginning An-2 production, Mielec has made numerous improvements to the airframe of the An-2R, resulting in an increase in TBO from 900 hr in 1961 to 1,500 hr in 1970 and 2,000 hr in 1973.

PZL Mielec (Antonov) An-2 operated by the Instytut Lotnictwa, with ski landing gear

By the beginning of 1979 about 8,200 An-2s (all versions) had been built at Mielec, including 3,800 of the An-2R agricultural version. More than 90 per cent of these were for export, including about 7,500 to the USSR. Production was continuing in 1979, at a rate of approx 250 a year.

The Polish-built versions have different designations from those built in the USSR. These are as follows:

An-2P. Passenger version, with seating for 12 adult passengers and two children. Compared with Soviet-built An-2P (see 1971-72 *Jane's*) has improvements in passenger cabin layout and comfort, better soundproofing, a new propeller and spinner, and weight-saving instrumentation and equipment. Entered production in 1968.

An-2PK. Five-seat executive version, having two seats on starboard side and three on port side, with foldaway table between pairs of seats on each side.

An-2P-Photo. Photogrammetry version.

An-2PR. Television relay version.

An-2R. Agricultural version, with 1,350 kg (2,976 lb) capacity glassfibre-reinforced epoxy-resin hopper or tank for dry or liquid chemicals. Similar to Soviet-built An-2S. Agricultural equipment being modernised.

An-2S. Ambulance version, equipped to carry six stretcher patients and their medical attendants.

An-2T. Basic general-purpose version, with accommodation for 12 passengers and baggage or 1,500 kg (3,306 lb) of cargo.

An-2TD. Paratroop transport and training version with six tip-up seats along each side of cabin. Granted French type certificate No. IM-55 (for import licence) in 1972.

An-2TP. Cargo/passenger version, similar to AN-2TD with six tip-up seats along each side of cabin.

An-2M. Twin-float version of An-2T, similar to Soviet-built An-2V. Built in small numbers only.

An-2 Geofiz. Geophysical survey version, developed for the State Prospecting Company in Warsaw.

The following details apply to the PZL Mielec An-2P:

Type: Single-engined general-purpose biplane.

Wings: Unequal-span single-bay biplane. Wing section RPS 14% (constant). Dihedral, both wings, approx 2° 48′. All-metal two-spar structure, fabric-covered aft of front spar. I-type interplane struts. Differential ailerons and full-span automatic leading-edge slots on upper wings, slotted trailing-edge flaps on both upper and lower wings. Flaps operated electrically, ailerons mechanically by cables and push/pull rods. Electrically-operated trim tab in port aileron.

Fuselage: All-metal stressed-skin semi-monocoque

structure of circular section forward of cabin, rectangular in the cabin section and oval in the tail section.

Tail Unit: Braced metal structure. Fin integral with rear fuselage. Fabric-covered tailplane. Elevators and rudder operated mechanically by cables and push/pull rods. Electrically-operated trim tab in rudder and port elevator.

Landing Gear: Non-retractable split-axle type, with long-stroke oleo shock-absorbers. Main-wheel tyres size 800 × 260 mm, pressure 2·25 bars (32·7 lb/sq in). Pneumatic shoe brakes on main units. Fully-castoring and self-centering tailwheel with electro-pneumatic lock. For rough-field operation the oleo-pneumatic shock-absorbers can be charged from a compressed air cylinder installed in the rear fuselage. Interchangeable ski landing gear available optionally.

Power Plant: One 746 kW (1,000 hp) Shvetsov ASz-62IR nine-cylinder radial aircooled engine, driving an AW-2 four-blade variable-pitch metal propeller. Six fuel tanks in upper wings, with total capacity of 1,200 litres (264 Imp gallons). Oil capacity 120 litres (26·4 Imp gallons).

Accommodation: Crew of two on flight deck, with access via passenger cabin. Standard accommodation for 12 passengers, in four rows of three with centre aisle. Two foldable seats for children in aisle between first and second rows, and infant's cradle at front of cabin on starboard side. Toilet at rear of cabin on starboard side. Overhead racks for up to 160 kg (352 lb) of baggage, with space for coats and additional 40 kg (88 lb) of baggage between rear pair of seats and toilet. Emergency exit on starboard side at rear. Walls of cabin are lined with glass-wool mats and inner facing of plywood to reduce internal noise level. Cabin floor is carpeted. Cabin heating and starboard windscreen de-icing by engine bleed air; port and centre windscreens are electrically de-iced. Cabin ventilation by ram-air intakes on underside of top wings. Air-conditioning system in An-2R.

Systems: Compressed air cylinder, of 8 litres (490 cu in) capacity, for pneumatic charging of shock-absorbers and operation of tailwheel lock at 49 bars (711 lb/sq in) pressure and operation of main-wheel brakes at 9·80 bars (142 lb/sq in). Contents of cylinder are maintained by AK-50 M engine-driven compressor, with AD-50 automatic relief device to prevent overpressure. DC electrical system is supplied with basic 27V power (and 36V or 115V where required) by an engine-driven generator and a storage battery. CO_2 fire extinguishing system with automatic fire detector.

Avionics and Equipment: Dual controls and blind-flying instrumentation standard. R-842 short wave and R-860 ultra short wave lightweight radio transceivers, RW-UM radio altimeter, ARK-9 radio compass, MRP-56P marker, GIK-1 gyro compass, GPK-48 gyroscopic direction indicator and SPU-7 intercom.

Dimensions, external:

Wing span: upper	18·18 m (59 ft 8½ in)
lower	14·24 m (46 ft 8½ in)
Wing chord (constant): upper	2·40 m (7 ft 10½ in)
lower	2·00 m (6 ft 6¾ in)
Wing aspect ratio: upper	7·57
lower	7·12
Wing gap	2·17 m (7 ft 1½ in)
Length overall: tail up	12·74 m (41 ft 9½ in)
tail down	12·40 m (40 ft 8¼ in)
Height overall: tail up	6·10 m (20 ft 0 in)
tail down	4·00 m (13 ft 1½ in)
Tailplane span	7·20 m (23 ft 7½ in)
Wheel track	3·45 m (11 ft 3¾ in)
Wheelbase	3·36 m (11 ft 0¼ in)
Propeller diameter	3·60 m (11 ft 9¾ in)
Propeller ground clearance	0·70 m (2 ft 3½ in)
Emergency exit (stbd, rear):	
Height	0·65 m (2 ft 1½ in)
Width	0·51 m (1 ft 8 in)

Areas:

Wings, gross: upper	43·6 m² (469 sq ft)
lower	28·0 m² (301 sq ft)
Ailerons (total)	5·90 m² (63·5 sq ft)
Trailing-edge flaps (total)	9·60 m² (103 sq ft)
Fin	5·85 m² (62·97 sq ft)
Rudder, incl tab	2·65 m² (28·52 sq ft)
Tailplane	12·28 m² (132·18 sq ft)
Elevators (total, incl tab)	4·72 m² (50·81 sq ft)

Weights and Loadings:

Weight empty	3,450 kg (7,605 lb)
Max T-O weight	5,500 kg (12,125 lb)
Max landing weight	5,250 kg (11,574 lb)
Max wing loading	76·82 kg/m² (15·7 lb/sq ft)
Max power loading	7·38 kg/kW (12·13 lb/hp)

Performance (at AUW of 5,250 kg; 11,574 lb):

Max level speed at 1,750 m (5,740 ft)	139 knots (258 km/h; 160 mph)
Econ cruising speed	100 knots (185 km/h; 115 mph)
Min flying speed	49 knots (90 km/h; 56 mph)
T-O speed	43 knots (80 km/h; 50 mph)
Landing speed	46 knots (85 km/h; 53 mph)
Max rate of climb at S/L	210 m (689 ft)/min
Service ceiling	4,400 m (14,425 ft)
Time to 4,400 m (14,425 ft)	30 min
T-O run: hard runway	150 m (492 ft)
grass	170 m (558 ft)
T-O to 10·7 m (35 ft): hard runway	300 m (984 ft)
grass	320 m (1,050 ft)
Landing run: hard runway	170 m (558 ft)
grass	185 m (607 ft)
Range at 1,000 m (3,280 ft) with 500 kg (1,102 lb) payload	485 nm (900 km; 560 miles)

Antonov An-28 light general-purpose transport (Glushenkov TVD-10B turboprop engines) *(Tass)*

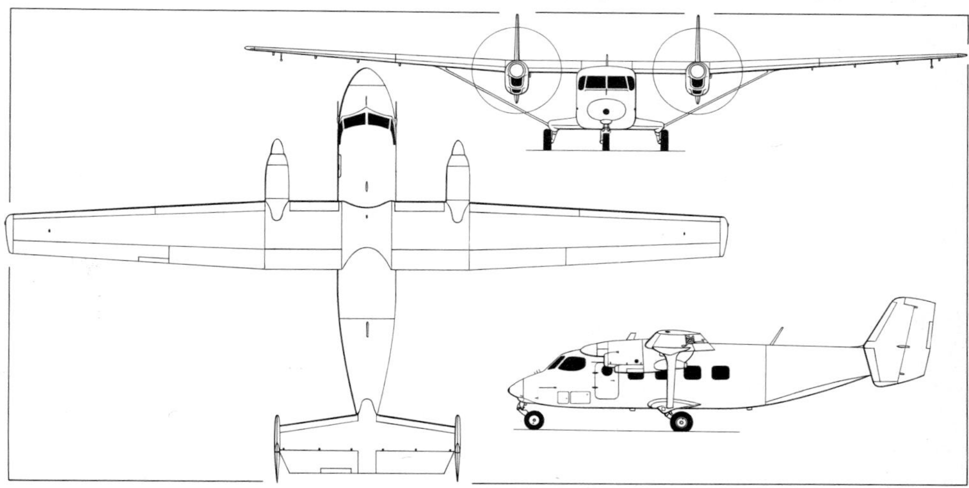

Antonov An-28 light transport, of which production is to be undertaken in Poland by WSK-PZL Mielec *(Pilot Press)*

PZL MIELEC (ANTONOV) An-28

NATO reporting name: Cash

Oleg Antonov first referred to planned production of an enlarged turboprop version of the piston-engined An-14 light general-purpose aircraft in the early 1960s, but until the Spring of 1972 there was no proof that such an aircraft had been built. Photographs of the prototype (CCCP-1968) were then published in the Polish press. It had flown for the first time in the USSR in September 1969, powered by two 604 kW (810 shp) Isotov TVD-850 turboprop engines, and was described in this form in the Soviet section of the 1974-75 and previous editions of *Jane's*.

Initially, the new aircraft was designated An-14M. Its official flight testing was completed in 1972, and during 1973 it was allocated the production designation An-28. The first pre-production An-28 (CCCP-19723) retained the original TVD-850 engines, but flight trials suggested that field performance and climb, in particular, could be improved by fitting more powerful engines. Thus, in April 1975, the same development aircraft (re-registered CCCP-19753) flew for the first time with 716 kW (960 shp) Glushenkov TVD-10 turboprop engines, which were specified also for production An-28s. It won a subsequent competitive evaluation against the Be-30, in which the emphasis was placed by the evaluators on concept rather than detail design.

Following Polish-Soviet talks in February 1978, it was announced that series production of the An-28 was to be entrusted to PZL Mielec. Mr Antonov stated at the Paris Air Show in June 1979 that the aircraft was at the final stages of testing for certification prior to production, which is expected to begin in 1980-81. The second pre-production aircraft (originally CCCP-19754, now CCCP-48105) was displayed at the Show. A total of 1,700 development flights had been completed by that time, including tests with ski landing gear.

In general configuration the An-28 differs from the piston-engined An-14 mainly in having a much-enlarged fuselage to carry up to 20 passengers or equivalent alternative payloads. The original An-14M had a retractable landing gear, with small fairings on the sides of the fuselage into which the main units retracted. Subsequently it was decided that retraction was unnecessary for flights over short distances at low speeds, and the pre-production An-28s have fixed gear. The shape of the vertical tail surfaces was also changed as a result of early flight testing.

The Antonov design bureau evolved the An-28 for service on Aeroflot's shortest routes, particularly those operated by An-2 biplanes into places which are relatively inaccessible to other types of fixed-wing aircraft. The turboprop engines make possible full-payload operation under high-temperature conditions and in mountainous regions; and the An-28 is described as being suitable for carrying passengers, cargo and mail, for scientific expeditions, geological surveying, forest fire patrol, firefighting, air ambulance or rescue operations, and parachute training. In agricultural form it can carry an 800 kg (1,764 lb) chemical payload for dusting and spraying operations.

Mr Antonov has stated that Aeroflot pilots will begin their flying careers on the An-28, which will not stall, even with the control column held in the extreme rearward position, because of the action of its automatic slots. If an engine fails, the upper-surface spoiler forward of the aileron on the opposite wing is opened automatically; as a result, the wing bearing the 'dead' engine drops only 12° in 5 s instead of the 30° that it would drop through loss of lift without the action of the Antonov-patented spoiler. The fixed tailplane slot, also patented, improves handling during a high angle of attack climb-out. Under icing conditions, if the normal anti-icing system fails, ice collects on the slat rather than the tailplane, to retain controllability.

Type: Twin-turboprop light general-purpose aircraft.

Wings: Braced high-wing monoplane, with single streamline-section bracing strut each side. Conventional two-spar structure. Automatic leading-edge slots. Entire trailing-edges hinged, the single-slotted ailerons being designed to droop with the large flaps. No tabs. Spoiler forward of each aileron. Short stub-wing extends from each side of the lower fuselage, carrying the main landing gear units, and providing lower attachments for the wing bracing struts. Anti-icing of wing leading-edges by engine bleed air.

Fuselage: Conventional all-metal semi-monocoque structure, longer, wider and deeper than that of the piston-engined An-14. Underside of rear fuselage upswept and made up of clamshell doors.

Tail Unit: Cantilever all-metal structure. Twin fins and rudders mounted vertically on a tailplane that lacks the dihedral of that on the An-14. Fixed leading-edge slat under full span of tailplane leading-edge. Anti-icing of leading-edges by engine bleed air. Twin tabs in each rudder.

Landing Gear: Non-retractable tricycle type, with single wheel on each unit. Wide-tread balloon tyres, size 720 × 320, pressure 3·5 bars (51 lb/sq in), on main units.

Steerable and self-centering nosewheel, with size 595 × 185 tyre. Brakes on main wheels. Provision for skis or floats.

POWER PLANT: Two 715 kW (960 shp) flat-rated Glushenkov TVD-10B turboprop engines (Polish designation PZL-10), each driving an AW-24AN three-blade variable-pitch metal propeller. Two 310 litre (68 Imp gallon) centre-wing and two 670 litre (147 Imp gallon) outer-wing integral fuel tanks; total fuel capacity 1,960 litres (430 Imp gallons). Oil capacity 30 litres (6·5 Imp gallons) per engine. Electrical anti-icing of propellers and engine air intakes.

ACCOMMODATION: Crew of one or two on flight deck, which has bulged side windows. Crew door forward of cabin on port side. Cabin of passenger version contains 15 seats in five rows at 72 cm (28 in) pitch, or up to 20 seats in high-density configuration, with double units on starboard side of aisle. Seats fold back against walls when aircraft is operated as a freighter or in mixed passenger/cargo role. Provision for baggage and toilet compartments and wardrobe space. Electrically-actuated ramp-door under upswept rear fuselage can slide forward under cabin to facilitate direct loading from trucks on to cabin floor. Overhead winch on rails, capacity 250 kg (550 lb), for handling cargo. Emergency exit at rear on starboard side. Six/seven-passenger executive version has four folding tables, which can be joined together in pairs to give working tops measuring 160 × 55 cm (63 × 21·5 in). Ambulance version accommodates six stretchers, five seated patients, a medical attendant and medical equipment. Can also be equipped to carry six parachutists and a dispatcher.

AVIONICS AND EQUIPMENT: Flight and navigation equipment includes R-80W UHF, Karat short-wave, RSB-5 medium-wave, Landysz-5 and R-851 radios; Wint-2 navigation computer; DISS Maszt-FK and ARK-U2 'special installations'; ADF; emergency locator transmitter; DWS-8 airspeed indicator; AR-C7 turn indicator; MS-61 drift recorder; three-axis autopilot; and dual AK-59P astrocompasses. Landing light in nose. Current level of equipment is intended to permit operation in ICAO Category II conditions, with extension later to Category III.

DIMENSIONS, EXTERNAL:

Wing span	22·06 m (72 ft 4½ in)
Wing chord at root	2·20 m (7 ft 2½ in)
Wing area, gross	40·28 m² (433·5 sq ft)
Wing aspect ratio	12
Length overall	12·98 m (42 ft 7 in)
Height overall	4·60 m (15 ft 1 in)
Tailplane span	5·20 m (17 ft 0¾ in)
Wheel track	3·41 m (11 ft 2 ¼ in)
Wheelbase	4·35 m (14 ft 3¼ in)
Propeller diameter	2·80 m (9 ft 2¼ in)

DIMENSIONS, INTERNAL:

Cabin, excl flight deck: Length	5·26 m (17 ft 3 in)
Max width	1·66 m (5 ft 5 in)
Max height	1·70 m (5 ft 7 in)
Floor area	8·73 m² (93·97 sq ft)
Volume	14·84 m³ (524 cu ft)

WEIGHTS AND LOADINGS:

Weight empty (approx)	3,500 kg (7,716 lb)
Normal payload	1,550 kg (3,415 lb)
Max payload	1,700 kg (3,750 lb)
Normal T-O weight	5,800 kg (12,785 lb)
Max T-O weight	6,100 kg (13,450 lb)
Max wing loading	151·4 kg/m² (31·03 lb/sq ft)
Max power loading	4·22 kg/kW (6·93 lb/shp)

PERFORMANCE (A: at normal T-O weight; B: at max T-O weight):

Max cruising speed:	
A, B	188 knots (350 km/h; 217 mph)
Econ cruising speed:	
A, B	162 knots (300 km/h; 186 mph)
Stalling speed, flaps up:	
A	70 knots (130 km/h; 81 mph)
B	73 knots (135 km/h; 84 mph)
Stalling speed, flaps down:	
A	65 knots (120 km/h; 75 mph)
B	67·5 knots (125 km/h; 78 mph)
Max rate of climb at S/L: A	750 m (2,460 ft)/min
B	708 m (2,320 ft)/min
Rate of climb at S/L, one engine out:	
A	192 m (630 ft)/min
B	174 m (570 ft)/min
T-O run: A	180 m (590 ft)
B	210 m (690 ft)
T-O to 15 m (50 ft): A	330 m (1,085 ft)
B	360 m (1,180 ft)
Landing from 15 m (50 ft): A	287 m (942 ft)
B	305 m (1,000 ft)
Landing run: A	150 m (492 ft)
B	170 m (558 ft)
Range at econ cruising speed at 3,000 m (9,850 ft), 30 min reserves:	
A, 15 passengers	356 nm (660 km; 410 miles)
A, 18 passengers	202 nm (375 km; 233 miles)
B, 18 passengers	372 nm (690 km; 428 miles)
B, 20 passengers	275 nm (510 km; 317 miles)
A, max fuel	702 nm (1,300 km; 807 miles)
B, max fuel	696 nm (1,290 km; 801 miles)

Single-seat Iskra-Bis C reconnaissance version of the PZL Mielec TS-11

Standard two-seat Iskra-Bis D trainer

PZL MIELEC TS-11 ISKRA (SPARK)

Designed in 1957 under the supervision of Docent Ing T. Soltyk, the TS-11 Iskra two-seat jet trainer was produced as a replacement for the piston-engined TS-8 Bies. Four prototypes were built during 1958-59, the first of these being used for static testing. First flight, on 5 February 1960, was made by the second aircraft, followed later in the same year by the third and fourth prototypes. Type approval was received in mid-1961, and quantity production began at Mielec in 1963. The formal handing over of the first Iskra to the Polish Air Force took place in March 1963, and the aircraft entered service in 1964. Iskras of the Polish Air Force logged a total of 100,000 flying hours by 1978. Another 30,000 flying hours had been accumulated in India.

Early production aircraft were powered by a 7·66 kN (1,720 lb st) HO-10 Polish-designed axial flow turbojet engine. In April 1964, flight testing began using the intended power plant, the more powerful SO-1; from the latter half of the 1960s, production Iskras were powered either by the SO-1 or by the modified but similarly rated SO-3.

About 500 Iskras had been built by mid-1979, in the following versions:

Iskra-Bis A. Basic two-seat version, for primary and advanced training. Two underwing hardpoints for external weapons.

Iskra-Bis B. Two-seat primary and advanced trainer, with four underwing attachments for missiles or other weapons. Prototype designated Iskra 100. In production.

Iskra-Bis C. Single-seat reconnaissance version. Prototype, designated Iskra 200, first flew in June 1972. Increased fuel capacity for greater range; camera pod on starboard side of nose.

Iskra-Bis D. Similar to Bis B, but able to carry a wider selection of external weapons. Prototype also designated Iskra 200. Export version supplied to Indian Air Force (50) in 1976. In production.

Iskra-Bis DF. Single-seat combat and reconnaissance trainer, with increased armament capability of Bis D, plus provision for three cameras in pod on starboard side of nose. In production.

The following description applies to the current production Iskra-Bis B, D and DF, except where indicated:

TYPE: Fully aerobatic two-seat jet primary and advanced trainer (A, B and D) and single-seat reconnaissance aircraft (C and DF).

WINGS: Cantilever mid-wing monoplane. Wing section NACA 64209 at root, NACA 64009 at tip. Sweepback at quarter-chord 7°. Marked dihedral. All-metal torsion box structure with two steel main spars and duralumin stressed skin. Hydraulically servo-assisted, aerodynamically-balanced ailerons. Hydraulically-actuated two-section double-slotted flaps and airbrakes (max deflection 87°). One boundary layer fence on each wing. Anti-flutter weight fairing projecting from each wing near tip.

FUSELAGE: All-metal semi-monocoque structure of pod and boom type.

TAIL UNIT: Cantilever all-metal structure. Two-spar fin, integral with fuselage. Variable-incidence two-spar tailplane, actuated electrically. Mass- and aerodynamically-balanced elevators and rudder. Anti-flutter weight fairing projecting from each half of tailplane at tip. Ground-adjustable tab on rudder; fixed balance tab in port elevator.

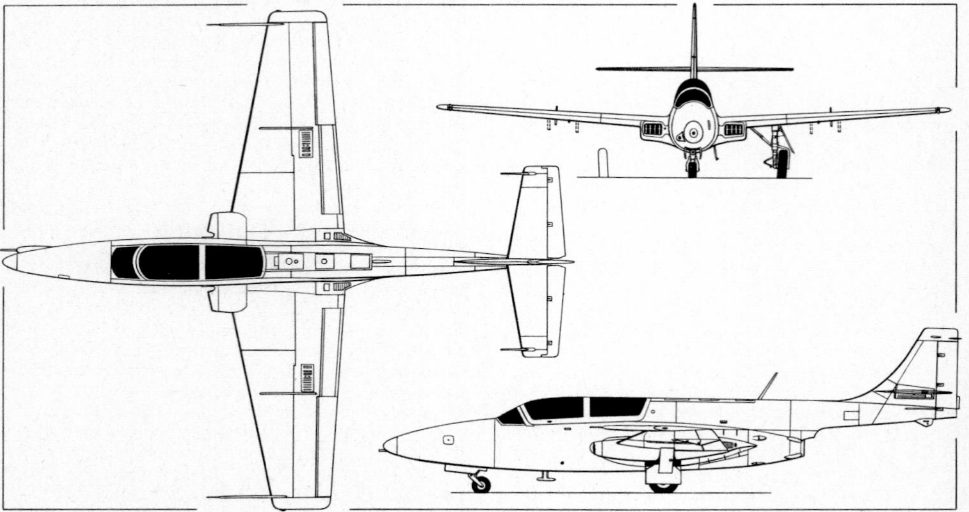

PZL Mielec Iskra-Bis D two-seat trainer, with four underwing pylons *(Pilot Press)*

LANDING GEAR: Retractable tricycle type with single wheel on each unit. Nosewheel retracts forward, main wheels inward into wing-root air intake trunks. Hydraulic actuation, with pneumatic emergency extension. Main wheels size 600 × 180, tyre pressure 5·38 bars (78 lb/sq in). Nosewheel size 400 × 150, tyre pressure 3·45 bars (50 lb/sq in). Oleo-pneumatic shock-absorbers. Disc brakes on main wheels. Castoring and self-centering nosewheel, with shimmy damper.

POWER PLANT: One SO-3 turbojet, rated at 9·81 kN (2,205 lb st), mounted in fuselage aft of cockpit section, with nozzle under tailboom. Fuel in two 315 litre (69 Imp gallon) integral wing tanks, one rubber 500 litre (110 Imp gallon) fuselage main tank (700 litre; 154 Imp gallon in single-seaters) and one rubber 70 litre (15·5 Imp gallon) fuselage collector tank. Total fuel capacity 1,200 litres (263·5 Imp gallons) in two-seaters, 1,400 litres (308 Imp gallons) in single-seaters. Fuel system permits up to 40 s of inverted flight.

ACCOMMODATION: Crew of one, or two in tandem, on lightweight ejection seat(s), under a one-piece hydraulically-actuated rearward-hinged upward-opening jettisonable canopy. Cockpit pressurised and air-conditioned. Rear seat of trainers slightly raised.

SYSTEMS: Hydraulic system, pressure 138 bars (2,000 lb/sq in), for actuation of ailerons, flaps, airbrakes, landing gear, canopy, and main-wheel brakes. Pneumatic system, pressure 118 bars (1,710 lb/sq in), for cockpit pressurisation, anti-icing and gun charging. Emergency pneumatic system for landing gear extension, flaps and emergency braking. Electrical power provided by 28·5V AW-30 generator and 24V 28Ah battery, for engine starting, instruments, lights and armament control system; 115V converter for AC power. Air-conditioning, oxygen, ethyl alcohol anti-icing and CO_2 fire extinguishing systems standard.

AVIONICS AND EQUIPMENT: Trainers have complete dual controls and instrumentation, including blind-flying panels. Standard avionics also include R-800, R-802G or R-802W VHF com; ARK-9 radio compass; RW-UM radio altimeter; MRP-56P marker beacon receiver; SPU-2P crew intercom in two-seaters; and IFF.

ARMAMENT: Forward-firing 23 mm cannon in nose on starboard side, with S-13 gun camera. Two or four attachments for a variety of underwing stores, including bombs of up to 100 kg (220 lb), eight-barrel rocket pods and 7·62 mm gun pods.

DIMENSIONS, EXTERNAL:
Wing span — 10·06 m (33 ft 0 in)
Wing chord at root — 2·254 m (7 ft 4¾ in)
Wing chord at tip — 1·162 m (3 ft 9¾ in)
Wing aspect ratio — 5·71
Length overall — 11·15 m (36 ft 7 in)
Height overall — 3·50 m (11 ft 5½ in)
Tailplane span — 3·84 m (12 ft 7¼ in)
Wheel track — 3·47 m (11 ft 4½ in)
Wheelbase — 3·44 m (11 ft 3½ in)

AREAS:
Wings, gross — 17·50 m² (188·37 sq ft)
Ailerons (total) — 1·48 m² (15·93 sq ft)
Trailing-edge flaps (total) — 1·74 m² (18·73 sq ft)
Fin — 1·55 m² (16·68 sq ft)
Rudder (incl tab) — 0·70 m² (7·53 sq ft)
Tailplane — 2·38 m² (25·62 sq ft)
Elevators (incl tab) — 1·16 m² (12·48 sq ft)

WEIGHTS AND LOADINGS:
Weight empty (trainer versions):
B — 2,494 kg (5,498 lb)
D/DF — 2,560 kg (5,644 lb)
Normal T-O weight with 570 litres (125·5 Imp gallons) internal fuel: B — 3,184 kg (7,019 lb)
D/DF — 3,243 kg (7,150 lb)
Normal T-O weight with 1,200 litres (263·5 Imp gallons) internal fuel: B — 3,704 kg (8,166 lb)
D/DF — 3,734 kg (8,232 lb)
T-O weight (reconnaissance version):
DF — 3,787 kg (8,349 lb)
Max T-O weight with full external armament:
B — 3,810 kg (8,400 lb)
D/DF — 3,840 kg (8,465 lb)
Max wing loading:
D/DF — 219 kg/m² (44·85 lb/sq ft)
Max power loading:
D/DF — 387·4 kg/kN (3·8 lb/lb st)

PERFORMANCE (at normal T-O weight with full internal fuel, except where indicated):
Never-exceed speed — Mach 0·8 (404 knots; 750 km/h; 466 mph)
Max level speed at 5,000 m (16,400 ft):
B, D/DF — 388 knots (720 km/h; 447 mph)
Normal cruising speed:
B, D/DF — 324 knots (600 km/h; 373 mph)
Unstick speed:
B, D/DF — 102 knots (190 km/h; 118 mph)
Landing speed:
B, D/DF — 92 knots (170 km/h; 106 mph)
Stalling speed, power off, flaps down:
B, D/DF — 81 knots (150 km/h; 93·5 mph)
Max rate of climb at S/L:
B, D/DF — 840 m (2,755 ft)/min
Time to 6,000 m (19,685 ft): B, D/DF — 9 min 36 s
Time to 7,000 m (22,975 ft): B, D/DF — 13 min 36 s
Service ceiling: B — 11,140 m (36,550 ft)
D/DF — 11,000 m (36,000 ft)
T-O run: B — 725 m (2,380 ft)
D/DF — 750 m (2,460 ft)
T-O to 15 m (50 ft), flaps down:
B — 1,100 m (3,609 ft)
D/DF — 1,190 m (3,904 ft)
Landing from 15 m (50 ft), flaps down:
B — 1,000 m (3,280 ft)
D/DF — 1,110 m (3,642 ft)
Landing run: B — 660 m (2,165 ft)
D/DF — 700 m (2,300 ft)
Range at 7,000 m (22,975 ft):
B with 570 litres fuel 235 nm (435 km; 270 miles)
D/DF with 570 litres fuel 243 nm (450 km; 280 miles)
B with 1,200 litres fuel 626 nm (1,160 km; 720 miles)
g limits (ultimate): B, D/DF — +8·0; −4·0

PZL MIELEC M-15 BELPHEGOR

As recorded in earlier editions of *Jane's*, the Polish and Soviet governments discussed in 1971 the development of a new, large agricultural aircraft known as the M-15, together with associated agricultural and ground support equipment. The Soviet government indicated a requirement for about 3,000 such aircraft, and on 2 December 1971 signed an agreement with the Polish government for large-scale production of the M-15.

Initial design of the M-15 was undertaken by a design bureau at Mielec under Soviet chief consulting engineer R. A. Ismailov and Polish designer K. Gocyla, and staffed by Polish and Soviet specialists. The agricultural equipment for the aircraft was developed jointly by the Instytut Lotnictwa at Warsaw (which see) and the Soviet Research Institute of Special and Utility Aviation at Krasnodar.

A prototype, designated LLP-M15, was flown on 30 May 1973; the first fully-representative M-15 prototype made its first flight on 9 January 1974. On 2 April 1975 five pre-series M-15s were sent to the USSR for evaluation; Soviet acceptance tests were completed successfully in 1976 and were followed by the award of a provisional Soviet GosAvia certificate of airworthiness. About 100 M-15s had been built by mid-1977, and by 1 January 1979 about 50 had been supplied to the Soviet Union for operating trials at Voronezh, Pyatigorsk, Poltava and Maykop, and over cottonfields in central Asia.

Firefighting and cargo-carrying versions are expected to be developed.

The following description refers to the agricultural production version:

TYPE: Three-seat agricultural aircraft.

WINGS: Biplane wings, of mainly metal construction and unequal span, built chiefly of aluminium and steel alloys and glassfibre laminates. The upper wing has a constant-chord centre-section and tapered outer panels; dihedral at tips is increased on current aircraft. The centre-section is faired to the top of the engine pod. The shorter-span lower wings, which house the agricultural dispersal pipes, are of generally similar planform and are joined to the fuselage nacelle at floor level. The entire trailing-edge of the upper wing is hinged, and is made up of hydraulically-operated double-slotted flaps and single-slotted ailerons. There are automatically-operated slats on the leading-edge. In line with each tailboom, and occupying the full depth of the gap between the upper and lower wings, is a narrow streamlined hopper for agricultural chemical, and there is a single outward-sloping bracing strut outboard of each hopper fairing. Trim tab in port aileron.

FUSELAGE: Central semi-monocoque nacelle, of narrow rectangular section, built of same materials as wings.

TAIL UNIT: Cantilever metal/glassfibre structure, consisting of twin sweptback endplate fins and rudders, bridged by a high-mounted tailplane and full-span elevators, supported on two slender tailbooms located at approx one-quarter span on the upper wing.

LANDING GEAR: Non-retractable tricycle type, with single wheel on each unit. Main wheels and tyres size 720 × 320, tyre pressure 2·5-3·0 bars (36-43 lb/sq in); nosewheel and tyre size 700 × 250, tyre pressure 2·0-2·5 bars (29-36 lb/sq in). Nosewheel steerable hydraulically, 50° to left or right. Brakes on main wheels.

POWER PLANT: One 14·7 kN (3,306 lb st) Ivchenko AI-25 turbofan engine, mounted in a pod on top of the fuselage. Eight fuel tanks in upper wing, total capacity 1,460 litres (321 Imp gallons).

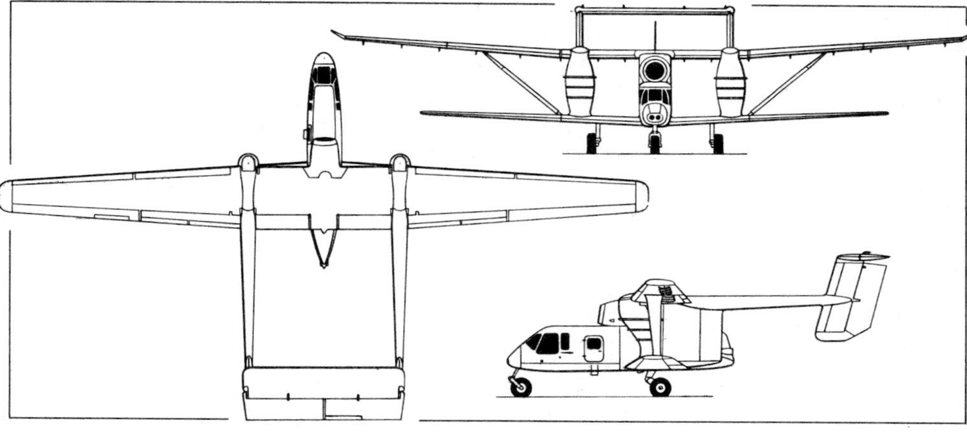

PZL Mielec M-15 turbofan-engined agricultural aircraft *(Pilot Press)*

PZL Mielec M-15 agricultural biplane (Ivchenko AI-25 turbofan engine)

New version of PZL Mielec M-15 (CCCP-15127) with lengthened nose and twin undernose strakes

ACCOMMODATION: Seat for pilot in fully-enclosed cockpit in extreme nose of fuselage. Two seats in cabin, to rear of pilot's compartment, for carrying ground staff during ferry flights. Cockpit air-conditioning by engine compressor bleed air.

AVIONICS AND EQUIPMENT: Full flight and navigation instrumentation, including stall-warning indicator. VFR radio/navigation equipment optional. The two between-wings hoppers have a combined capacity for 2,900 litres (638 Imp gallons) of liquid or 2,200 kg (4,850 lb) of dry (powdered or granulated) chemical. Ivchenko AI-9 APU, normally removed from aircraft during agricultural operations, provides power for engine starting, ground refuelling and filling of hoppers with liquid chemical. Twin landing lights in nose.

DIMENSIONS, EXTERNAL:
Wing span: upper 22·33 m (73 ft 3 in)
lower 16·428 m (53 ft 10¾ in)
Wing mean aerodynamic chord (upper) 1·84 m (6 ft 0½ in)
Length overall 13·135 m (43 ft 1 in)
Height overall 5·339 m (17 ft 6¼ in)
Height of fuselage above ground 1·008 m (3 ft 3½ in)
Wheel track 4·319 m (14 ft 2 in)
Wheelbase 4·879 m (16 ft 0 in)
Distance between c/l of hoppers 5·20 m (17 ft 0¾ in)

AREAS:
Wings (total) 67·50 m² (726·6 sq ft)
Ailerons (total) 9·03 m² (97·20 sq ft)
Trailing-edge flaps (total) 4·99 m² (53·71 sq ft)
Fins (total) 5·53 m² (59·52 sq ft)
Rudders (total) 4·00 m² (43·06 sq ft)
Tailplane 5·92 m² (63·72 sq ft)
Elevators (total) 4·08 m² (43·92 sq ft)

WEIGHTS AND LOADINGS:
Weight empty: dusting 3,230 kg (7,120 lb)
spraying 3,270 kg (7,210 lb)
with atomisers 3,275 kg (7,220 lb)
Max T-O weight 5,750 kg (12,675 lb)
Max landing weight 4,000 kg (8,815 lb)
Max wing loading 85·19 kg/m² (17·44 lb/sq ft)
Max power loading 391·19 kg/kN (3·83 lb/lb st)

PERFORMANCE (at max T-O weight):
Max cruising speed 108 knots (200 km/h; 124 mph)
Normal operating speed 86-95 knots (160-175 km/h; 99-109 mph)
Stalling speed, flaps up 60·5 knots (112 km/h; 70 mph)
Stalling speed, flaps down 48 knots (89 km/h; 55·5 mph)
Max rate of climb at S/L 300 m (985 ft)/min
T-O run: on grass 330 m (1,083 ft)
on concrete 260 m (853 ft)
Landing run: on grass 190 m (624 ft)
on concrete 200 m (656 ft)
Max range at 3,000 m (9,850 ft) 216 nm (400 km; 248 miles)
Swath width: dusting 65 m (213 ft)
spraying 40 m (131 ft)
with atomisers 70 m (230 ft)
Application rate:
dusting 10-50 kg (22-110 lb)/s
spraying 0-25 litres (0-5·5 Imp gallons)/s
with atomisers 0·2-6·5 litres (0·05-1·4 Imp gallons)/s

PZL MIELEC M-17

Development of the M-17 twin-boom two/three-seat light aircraft has been halted. A full description and illustration appeared in the 1978-79 *Jane's*.

PZL MIELEC M-18 DROMADER (DROMEDARY)

Although superficially similar to the CNPSL-PZL Warszawa PZL-106A Kruk, the M-18 Dromader is an entirely different and much larger agricultural aircraft. Designed to meet the requirements of FAR Pt 23, it was developed with the co-operation of Rockwell International of the USA and utilises the outer wing panels and other components of the Thrush Commander S-2R. Particular attention was paid in the design to pilot safety, and all parts of the structure exposed to contact with chemicals are treated with polyurethane or epoxy enamels, or manufactured from stainless steel.

The M-18 was first flown on 27 August 1976, and one of the three prototypes made the aircraft's public debut at the Paris Air Show in May/June 1977. The prototypes were followed by 10 pre-series aircraft, of which two were used for static and fatigue testing. Five of the remainder were employed for operating trials, two of them spraying and dusting cotton in Egypt during the Summer of 1978, prior to the award of a Polish type certificate on 27 September 1978. Other pre-series aircraft were exhibited and demonstrated in 1978 in Hungary, Iraq, Italy, the USA and Yugoslavia. A total of 60 was scheduled to be built by the end of 1979, including 40 for export.

A firefighting version of the Dromader was flown for the first time on 29 November 1978.

The following description refers to the standard agricultural version:

TYPE: Single-seat agricultural aircraft; *g* limits +3·4/−1·4 (FAR 23); +2·8 (CAM 8).

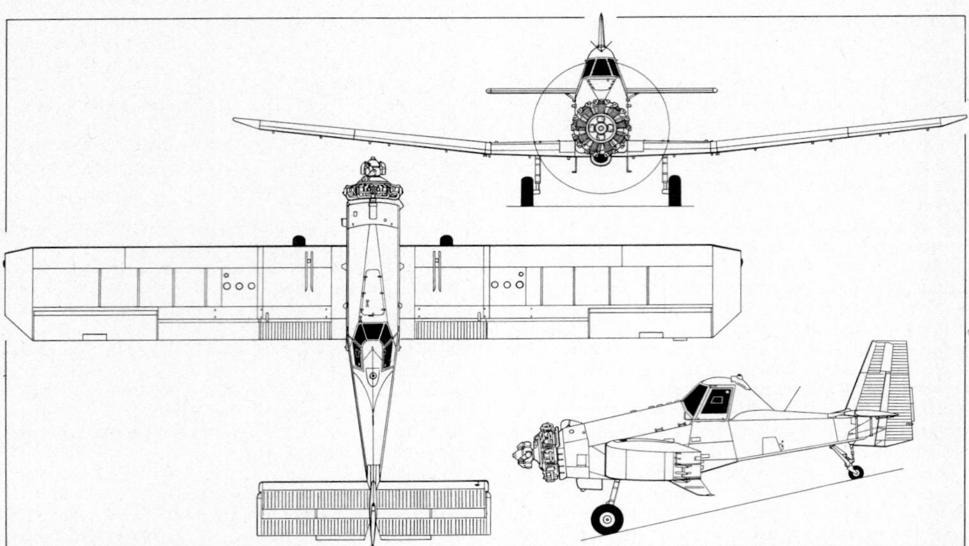

Three-view drawing *(Pilot Press)* **and photograph of the PZL Mielec M-18 Dromader agricultural aircraft**

WINGS: Cantilever all-metal low-wing monoplane, of constant chord, with 1° 15′ dihedral on centre-section and 6° on outer panels. Wing sections NACA 4416 at root, NACA 4412 at tip. Incidence 3°. Steel-capped wing spar. All-metal two-section trailing-edge flaps, actuated hydraulically. All-metal slotted ailerons, mass and aerodynamically balanced, actuated by pushrods. Electrically-actuated trim tab in starboard aileron; Flettner tab in port aileron; ground-adjustable tab on starboard aileron.

FUSELAGE: All-metal structure. Main frame, of helium-arc welded 4130N chrome-molybdenum steel tube, oiled internally against corrosion. Duralumin side panels, detachable for airframe inspection and cleaning.

TAIL UNIT: All-metal structure, with braced tailplane. Aerodynamically balanced rudder and elevators. Trim tab on each elevator, actuated by pushrods; electrically-actuated trim tab on rudder.

LANDING GEAR: Non-retractable tailwheel type. Main units have tyres size 800 × 260 mm, pressure 3·0 bars (43 lb/sq in), and are fitted with hydraulic disc brakes, parking brake and wire cutters. Fully-castoring tailwheel, lockable for take-off and landing, with size 360 × 150 mm tyre, pressure 3·43 bars (49·75 lb/sq in).

POWER PLANT: One 746 kW (1,000 hp) PZL Kalisz ASz-62IR nine-cylinder supercharged radial aircooled engine, driving a PZL Warszawa AW-2-30 four-blade constant-speed aluminium propeller. Fuel tank in each outer wing panel, combined usable capacity 400 litres (88 Imp gallons; 105·7 US gallons). Gravity-feed header tank in fuselage.

ACCOMMODATION: Single adjustable seat in fully enclosed, sealed and ventilated cockpit which is stressed to withstand 40*g* impact. Adjustable shoulder-type safety harness. Adjustable rudder pedals. Baggage compartment aft of seat. Quick-opening door on each side.

SYSTEMS: Hydraulic system, pressure 98-137 bars (1,421-1,987 lb/sq in), for flap actuation, disc brakes and dispersal system. Electrical system powered by 28·5V 100A generator, with 24V 25Ah nickel-cadmium battery and overvoltage protection relay.

AVIONICS AND EQUIPMENT: King KX-170B communications transceiver and KI-201C navigation receiver. Navigation lights, cockpit light, instrument panel lights, night working lights, taxying light, and two rotating beacons. Built-in jacking and tiedown points in wings and aft fuselage; towing lugs on main landing gear. Cockpit fire extinguisher and first aid kit.

AGRICULTURAL EQUIPMENT: Glassfibre epoxy hopper, with stainless steel tube bracing, forward of cockpit; capacity 2,500 litres (550 Imp gallons; 660 US gallons) of liquid or 1,500 kg (3,306 lb) of dry chemical. Deflector cable from cabin roof to fin. Transland gatebox, control valve and strainer, Root pump, and 48/96-nozzle spraybooms for spraying; Transland gatebox, control valve and high output spreader for dusting with dry chemical; or eight AV 3000 atomisers for fine spraying. Aircraft can also be fitted with Rockwell International water bombing installation for fire suppression.

DIMENSIONS, EXTERNAL:
Wing span 17·70 m (58 ft 0¾ in)
Wing chord (constant) 2·286 m (7 ft 6 in)
Wing aspect ratio 7·83
Length overall 9·48 m (31 ft 1¼ in)
Height overall 3·10 m (10 ft 2 in)
Tailplane span 5·60 m (18 ft 4½ in)
Wheel track 3·48 m (11 ft 5 in)
Propeller diameter 3·30 m (10 ft 10 in)
Propeller ground clearance (tail up) 0·23 m (9 in)

AREAS:
Wings, gross 40·00 m² (430·56 sq ft)
Ailerons and flaps (total) 9·53 m² (102·6 sq ft)
Vertical tail surfaces (total) 3·55 m² (38·2 sq ft)
Horizontal tail surfaces (total) 7·49 m² (80·6 sq ft)

WEIGHTS AND LOADINGS:
Weight empty 2,560 kg (5,644 lb)
Payload: FAR 23 1,500 kg (3,306 lb)
CAM 8 2,600 kg (5,732 lb)
Max T-O weight: FAR 23 4,200 kg (9,259 lb)
CAM 8 5,300 kg (11,684 lb)
Max landing weight 3,200 kg (7,055 lb)
Max wing loading (FAR 23) 105·0 kg/m² (21·51 lb/sq ft)
Max power loading (FAR 23) 5·63 kg/kW (9·26 lb/hp)

PERFORMANCE (at 4,200 kg; 9,259 lb max T-O weight, ISA. A: without agricultural equipment; B: with spreader equipment):
Never-exceed speed: A 151 knots (280 km/h; 174 mph)
Max level speed: A 138 knots (256 km/h; 159 mph)
B 128 knots (237 km/h; 147 mph)
Cruising speed: A 110 knots (205 km/h; 127 mph)
B 102 knots (190 km/h; 118 mph)
Operating speed:
B 92-110 knots (170-185 km/h; 106-115 mph)
Stalling speed, power off, flaps up:
A, B 69 knots (127 km/h; 79 mph)
Stalling speed, power off, flaps down:
A, B 63 knots (116 km/h; 72 mph)
Max rate of climb at S/L: A 414 m (1,358 ft)/min
B 348 m (1,141 ft)/min
Service ceiling: A 7,000 m (22,975 ft)
T-O run: A 190 m (625 ft)
B 220 m (722 ft)
Landing run: A, B 250 m (820 ft)
Max range, no reserves:
A 280 nm (520 km; 323 miles)

PZL MIELEC M-20 MEWA (GULL)

It was announced in early 1977 that Pezetel had signed an agreement with Piper Aircraft Corporation of the USA whereby the Polish aircraft industry will assemble, manufacture and distribute in Eastern Europe the Piper Seneca II twin-engined business aircraft.

This work, which will be undertaken by PZL Mielec, will begin with the assembly of imported kits, and will progress eventually to full licence manufacture. The aircraft (production of 400 or more has been authorised by the US government) will be powered by 164 kW (220 hp) PZL-Franklin 6A-350C-1L/R engines, and will be known as the M-20 Mewa. The first Polish prototype was awaiting completion in early 1979.

Piper-built Seneca II, which PZL Mielec is to produce as the M-20 Mewa

WSK-PZL SWIDNIK

WYTWORNIA SPRZETU KOMUNIKACYJNEGO Im. ZYGMUNTA PULAWSKIEGO-PZL SWIDNIK (Zygmunt Pulawski Transport Equipment Manufacturing Centre, Swidnik)

Head Office and Works: 21-045 Swidnik k/Lublina
Telephone: Lublin 12061 and 12071
Telex: 0642301a
General Manager: Dipl Ing Jan Czogala

The factory at Swidnik was built in 1951-52 and was engaged initially in manufacturing components for the LiM-1 (MiG-15) jet fighter.

In 1955, when the manufacture of combat aircraft was drastically reduced in Poland, the WSK at Swidnik began licence production of the Soviet-designed Mi-1 helicopter, some 1,700 of which were built under the designation SM-1. A small design office was formed subsequently at the factory to work on variants and developments of the basic SM-1 design and on original projects.

In September 1957, the Swidnik works was named after the famous pre-war PZL designer Zygmunt Pulawski, and currently employs about 10,000 people. Production is concentrated now on various versions of the Soviet-designed Mil Mi-2 turbine-powered helicopter.

Contrary to the report in the 1978-79 *Jane's*, Spitfire Helicopters of the USA has only limited rights to market the Mi-2 in that country; the name Taurus 2 does not have PZL Swidnik approval.

PZL SWIDNIK (MIL) Mi-2

NATO reporting name: Hoplite

The Mil Mi-2, announced in the Autumn of 1961, was designed in the USSR by the Mikhail L. Mil bureau. It retains the basic configuration of the earlier Mi-1 helicopter, but instead of a single piston engine has two Isotov turboshaft engines mounted side by side above the cabin.

Development of the Mi-2 prototype continued in the USSR until the helicopter had completed its initial State trials programme of flying. Then, in accordance with an agreement signed in January 1964, further development, production and marketing of the Mi-2 were assigned exclusively to the Polish aircraft industry, which flew its own first example of the Mi-2 on 4 November 1965.

Production at Swidnik began in 1965, and this factory has since built more than 2,800 in 24 different civil and military versions; the majority of these have been exported, including more than 2,000 to the USSR. Among the operators of the Mi-2 are the air forces of Czechoslovakia, Poland, Romania and the USSR, and civil operators in European and various developing countries. Production was continuing in 1978-79 at a rate of approx 300 a year.

In recent years Swidnik has undertaken a development programme to improve and modernise the original design. The first new version has uprated engines of 335 kW (450 shp) each and is essentially similar to the basic Mi-2. It flew for the first time in 1974. On another version, the metal stabiliser, tail rotor blades and main rotor blades were replaced with similar components made of plastics, intended to simplify production and improve performance. The new rotor blades were designed, manufactured and tested at the Swidnik transport equipment plant.

There are several versions of the basic Mi-2, as follows:

(a) Convertible passenger/cargo transport;
(b) Passengers-only version, for six or eight passengers;
(c) Ambulance version (Mi-2R);
(d) Agricultural version, known in Poland as the **Bazant** (Pheasant). In service in Bulgaria, Czechoslovakia, Denmark, Egypt, Finland, Iran, Iraq, Libya, Poland, Sudan, Sweden and USSR;
(e) Search and rescue version, with electrically-operated external hoist;
(f) Freighter version, with external cargo sling;
(g) Pilot training version, designed by WSK-Swidnik;
(h) Photogrammetric version;
(i) Television version (for transmission from the air);
(j) Version with 260 kg (573 lb) capacity hoist;

The following details apply specifically to the basic Mi-2, except where indicated:

Type: Twin-turbine general-purpose light helicopter.

Rotor System: Three-blade main rotor fitted with hydraulic blade vibration dampers. All-metal blades of NACA 230-13M section. Flapping, drag and pitch hinges on each blade. Main rotor blades and those of two-blade tail rotor each consist of an extruded duralumin spar with bonded honeycomb trailing-edge pockets. Anti-flutter weights on leading-edges, balancing plates on trailing-edges. Hydraulic boosters for longitudinal, lateral and collective pitch controls. Coil spring counterbalance mechanism in main and tail rotor systems. Pitch-change centrifugal loads on tail rotor carried by ribbon-type steel torsion elements. Rotors do not fold. Electrical blade de-icing system for main and tail rotors. Rotor brake fitted.

Rotor Drive: Main rotor shaft driven via gearbox on each engine; three-stage WR-2 main gearbox, intermediate gearbox and tail rotor gearbox. Main rotor/engine rpm ratio 1 : 24·6; tail rotor/engine rpm ratio 1 : 4·16. Main gearbox provides drive for auxiliary systems and take-off for rotor brake. Freewheel units permit disengagement of a failed engine and also autorotation.

Fuselage: Conventional semi-monocoque structure of pod and boom type, made up of three main assemblies: the nose (including cockpit), central section and tailboom. Construction is of sheet duralumin, bonded and spot-welded or riveted to longerons and frames. Main load-bearing joints are of steel alloy.

Tail Unit: Variable-incidence horizontal stabiliser controlled by collective-pitch lever.

Landing Gear: Non-retractable tricycle type, plus tailskid. Twin-wheel nose unit. Single wheel on each main unit. Oleo-pneumatic shock-absorbers on all units, including tailskid. Main shock-absorbers designed to cope with both normal operating loads and possible ground resonance. Main-wheel tyres size 600 × 180, pressure 4·41 bars (64 lb/sq in). Nosewheel tyres size 300 × 125, pressure 3·45 bars (50 lb/sq in). Pneumatic brakes on main wheels. Metal ski landing gear optional.

Power Plant: Two 298 or 335 kW (400 or 450 shp) Polish-built Isotov GTD-350P turboshaft engines, mounted side by side above cabin. Fuel in single rubber tank, capacity 600 litres (131 Imp gallons), under cabin floor. Provision for carrying a 238 litre (52·4 Imp gallon) external tank on each side of cabin. Refuelling point in starboard side of fuselage. Oil capacity 25 litres (5·4 Imp gallons). Engine air intake de-icing by engine bleed air.

Accommodation: Normal accommodation for one pilot on flight deck (port side). Seats for up to eight passengers in air-conditioned cabin, there being back-to-back bench seats for three persons each, with two optional extra starboard side seats at the rear, one behind the other. All seats are removable for carrying up to 700 kg (1,543 lb) of internal freight. Access to cabin via forward-hinged doors on each side at front of cabin and aft on port side. Pilot's sliding window jettisonable in emergency. Ambulance version has accommodation for four stretchers and a medical attendant or for two stretchers and two sitting casualties. Side-by-side seats and dual controls in pilot training version. Cabin heating, ventilation and air-conditioning standard. Electrical de-icing of windscreen.

Operational Equipment: Bazant agricultural version carries a hopper on each side of the fuselage (total capacity 1,000 litres; 220 Imp gallons of liquid or 750 kg; 1,650 lb of dry chemical) and either a spraybar to the rear of the cabin on each side or a distributor for dry chemicals under each hopper. Swath width covered by the spraying version is 40-45 m (130-150 ft). As a search and rescue aircraft, an electric hoist, capacity 120 kg (264 lb), is fitted. In the freight role an underfuselage hook can be fitted for suspended loads of up to 800 kg (1,763 lb).

Systems: Cabin heating, by engine bleed air, and ventilation; heat exchangers warm atmospheric air for ventila-

Armed version of the PZL Swidnik Mi-2, with four pylon-mounted air-to-surface missiles

PZL Swidnik (Mil) Mi-2 twin-turbine helicopter used by the Instytut Lotnictwa

tion system during cold weather. Hydraulic system, pressure 59-78·6 bars (855-1,140 lb/sq in), for cyclic and collective pitch control boosters. Pneumatic system, pressure 49 bars (710 lb/sq in), for main-wheel brakes. AC electrical system, with two STG-3 3kW engine-driven starter/generators and 208V 16kVA three-phase alternator. 24V DC system, with two 28Ah lead-acid batteries.

AVIONICS AND EQUIPMENT: Standard equipment includes two transceivers (medium and short wave), gyro compass, radio compass, radio altimeter, intercom system and blind-flying panel. Electrically-operated wiper for pilot's windscreen. Fire extinguishing system, for engine bays and main gearbox compartment, is generally similar to, but simpler than, the Freon system fitted to the Soviet Mil Mi-8, and can be actuated automatically or manually.

ARMAMENT: Some Mi-2s of the Polish Air Force are equipped with rocket pods or air-to-surface missiles mounted on pylons on each side of the cabin.

DIMENSIONS, EXTERNAL:
- Diameter of main rotor 14·50 m (47 ft 6¾ in)
- Main rotor blade chord (constant, each) 0·40 m (1 ft 3¾ in)
- Diameter of tail rotor 2·70 m (8 ft 10¼ in)
- Length overall, rotors turning 17·42 m (57 ft 2 in)
- Length of fuselage 11·94 m (39 ft 2 in)
- Height to top of rotor hub 3·75 m (12 ft 3½ in)
- Stabiliser span 1·85 m (6 ft 0¾ in)
- Wheel track 3·05 m (10 ft 0 in)
- Wheelbase 2·71 m (8 ft 10¾ in)
- Tail rotor ground clearance 1·59 m (5 ft 2¾ in)
- Cabin door (port, rear):
  - Height 1·065 m (3 ft 5¾ in)
  - Width 1·115 m (3 ft 8 in)
- Cabin door (stbd, front):
  - Height 1·11 m (3 ft 7¾ in)
  - Width 0·75 m (2 ft 5½ in)
- Cabin door (port, front):
  - Height approx 1·40 m (4 ft 7 in)
  - Width approx 1·20 m (3 ft 11¼ in)

DIMENSIONS, INTERNAL:
- Cabin:
  - Length, incl flight deck 4·07 m (13 ft 4¼ in)
  - Length, excl flight deck 2·27 m (7 ft 5½ in)
  - Mean width 1·20 m (3 ft 11¼ in)
  - Mean height 1·40 m (4 ft 7 in)

AREAS:
- Main rotor blades (each) 2·40 m² (25·83 sq ft)
- Tail rotor blades (each) 0·22 m² (2·37 sq ft)
- Main rotor disc 166·4 m² (1,791·11 sq ft)
- Tail rotor disc 5·73 m² (61·68 sq ft)
- Horizontal stabiliser 0·70 m² (7·53 sq ft)

WEIGHTS AND LOADING:
- Weight empty, equipped:
  - passenger version 2,402 kg (5,295 lb)
  - cargo version 2,372 kg (5,229 lb)
  - ambulance version 2,372 kg (5,229 lb)
  - Bazant 2,372 kg (5,229 lb)
- Basic operating weight, empty:
  - single-pilot versions 2,365 kg (5,213 lb)
  - dual-control version 2,424 kg (5,344 lb)
- Max payload, excl pilot, oil and fuel 800 kg (1,763 lb)
- Normal T-O weight (and max T-O weight of Bazant) 3,550 kg (7,826 lb)
- Max T-O weight 3,700 kg (8,157 lb)
- Max disc loading 22·4 kg/m² (4·6 lb/sq ft)

PERFORMANCE (at 3,550 kg; 7,826 lb T-O weight):
- Max level speed at 500 m (1,640 ft) 113 knots (210 km/h; 130 mph)
- Max cruising speed at 500 m (1,640 ft):
  - Bazant (without agricultural equipment) 102 knots (190 km/h; 118 mph)
  - other versions 108 knots (200 km/h; 124 mph)
- Max level speed with agricultural equipment (Bazant) 84 knots (155 km/h; 96 mph)
- Econ cruising speed for max range at 500 m (1,640 ft) 102 knots (190 km/h; 118 mph)
- Econ cruising speed for max endurance at 500 m (1,640 ft) 54 knots (100 km/h; 62 mph)
- Max rate of climb at S/L 270 m (885 ft)/min
- Service ceiling 4,000 m (13,125 ft)
- Hovering ceiling IGE approx 2,000 m (6,560 ft)
- Hovering ceiling OGE approx 1,000 m (3,280 ft)
- Time to 1,000 m (3,280 ft) 5 min 30 s
- Time to 4,000 m (13,125 ft) 26 min 0 s
- Min landing area 30 × 30 m (100 × 100 ft)
- Range at 500 m (1,640 ft) with max internal and auxiliary fuel, 30 min reserves 313 nm (580 km; 360 miles)
- Range at 500 m (1,640 ft) with max payload, 5% fuel reserves 91 nm (170 km; 105 miles)
- Endurance (Bazant), 5% reserves:
  - spraying 40 min
  - dusting 50 min

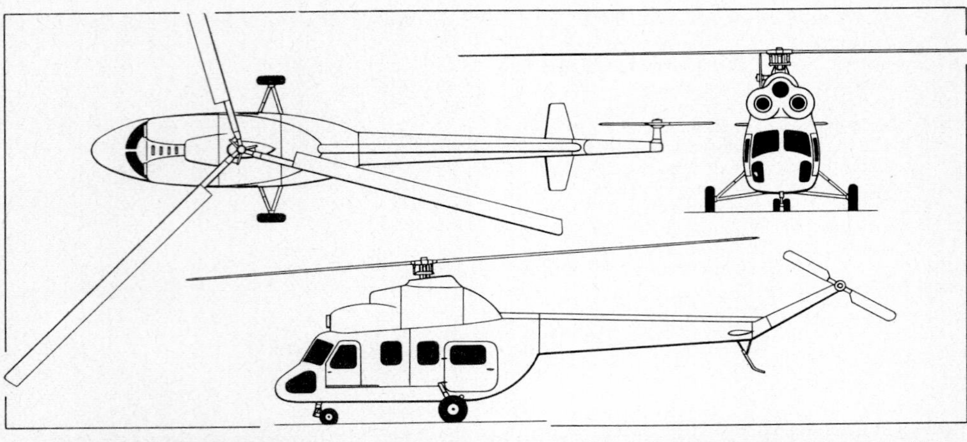

PZL Swidnik Kania/Kitty Hawk twin-turbine general-purpose light helicopter developed from the Mi-2 *(Pilot Press)*

PZL SWIDNIK KANIA/KITTY HAWK

In collaboration with the Detroit Diesel Allison Division of General Motors Corporation in the USA, PZL Swidnik is developing a modified version of the Mi-2 light helicopter, known as the Kania or Kitty Hawk, powered by two Allison 250-C20B turboshaft engines. In addition to a standard passenger version, the Kania is intended for cargo, agricultural, ambulance and other roles, similar to those performed by the Mi-2.

TYPE: Twin-turboshaft general-purpose light helicopter.

ROTOR SYSTEM: Three-blade fully articulated main rotor and two-blade seesaw tail rotor. Three hydraulic boosters for longitudinal, lateral and collective pitch control of main rotor. Rotor brake fitted. Electrical anti-icing of rotor blades optional.

ROTOR DRIVE: Transmission driven via main rotor, intermediate and tail rotor gearboxes, each with oil sight gauge and magnetic plug. Oil temperature gauge, oil cooling system, pressure indicator and tachometer for main gearbox. Anti-friction bearings on tail rotor shaft.

FUSELAGE AND TAIL UNIT: Conventional semi-monocoque fuselage, with circular-section monocoque tailboom. Horizontal stabiliser at end of tailboom. Hoist and cargo sling attachment points standard.

LANDING GEAR: Non-retractable tricycle type, plus tail-skid. Twin-wheel castoring nose unit, single wheel on each main unit. Pneumatic brakes on main wheels.

POWER PLANT: Two Allison 250-C20B turboshaft engines, mounted side by side above cabin; each rated at 313 kW (420 shp) for T-O and 30 min power, 298 kW (400 shp) max continuous, and 276 kW (370 shp) for max cruise. Standard usable fuel capacity of 600 litres (131 Imp gallons), with provision for additional 480 litres usable (105·5 Imp gallons) in optional auxiliary tanks.

ACCOMMODATION: Pilot (port side), and co-pilot or passenger, on adjustable and removable front seats, each fitted with safety belt. Dual controls optional. Accommodation for up to eight more persons, on two three-person bench seats and a single or double seat at rear of cabin, all with safety belts. Seats removable for carriage of cargo, stretchers, agricultural or other equipment. Access to cabin via jettisonable door on each side at front (port door of sliding type) and larger passenger/cargo door at rear on port side. Pilot's windscreen wiper standard. Cabin heating or air-conditioning, and electrical anti-icing of pilot's windscreen, optional.

SYSTEMS: Electrical system includes two 28V 150A DC starter/generators, two 115V 250A 400Hz static inverters, two 26V/115V 55VA 400Hz transformers, and a 25Ah nickel-cadmium battery. 16kVA AC generator for anti-icing system optional. External power receptacle. Dual fire detection and extinguishing systems for engines, single systems for transmission.

AVIONICS AND EQUIPMENT: King KX-175BE com/nav, KR-85 digital ADF, KT-76 transponder, and VFR instrumentation, all standard. Optional avionics include King KWX-50 digital weather radar, KRA-10 radar altimeter and KN-65A-03 DME. Dual instrument lighting systems, pilot's cabin extension light, cabin dome light, three hold dome lights, three position lights, adjustable landing light, and anti-collision light, are all standard, as are cargo and stretcher tiedown rings. Optional equipment includes dual controls, co-pilot's windscreen wiper, and auxiliary fuel tanks. Cabin carpet, standard or executive passenger seats, heating and air-conditioning systems, and sand filters, are also optional.

OPERATIONAL EQUIPMENT: According to mission, the Kania can be equipped with a 1,000 kg (2,205 lb) capacity stabilised cargo sling; 120 kg (265 lb) capacity hoist; stretchers and casualty care equipment; agricultural spraying or dusting gear.

DIMENSIONS, EXTERNAL:
- Diameter of main rotor 14·56 m (47 ft 9¼ in)
- Diameter of tail rotor 2·70 m (8 ft 10¼ in)
- Length overall, rotors turning 17·41 m (57 ft 1½ in)
- Length of fuselage 11·95 m (39 ft 2½ in)
- Fuselage: Max width 1·60 m (5 ft 3 in)
- Height to top of rotor hub 3·75 m (12 ft 3½ in)
- Stabiliser span 1·84 m (6 ft 0½ in)
- Wheel track 3·25 m (10 ft 8 in)
- Wheelbase 2·71 m (8 ft 10¾ in)
- Tail rotor ground clearance 1·80 m (5 ft 10¾ in)

DIMENSIONS, INTERNAL:
- Cabin: Length, incl flight deck 4·07 m (13 ft 4¼ in)
  - Max width 1·50 m (4 ft 11 in)
  - Height at front 1·30 m (4 ft 3¼ in)
  - Mean height at rear 1·51 m (4 ft 11½ in)
  - Max height at rear 1·62 m (5 ft 3¾ in)
  - Floor area 5·68 m² (61·1 sq ft)
  - Volume 7·766 m³ (274·25 cu ft)

AREAS:
- Main rotor disc 166·50 m² (1,792·2 sq ft)
- Tail rotor disc 5·725 m² (61·6 sq ft)

WEIGHTS:
- Weight empty, standard 2,140 kg (4,717 lb)
- Normal T-O weight 3,350 kg (7,385 lb)
- Max T-O weight 3,550 kg (7,826 lb)

PERFORMANCE (estimated, for 'clean' aircraft at S/L, ISA, zero wind. A: at 3,150 kg; 6,944 lb gross weight; B: at normal T-O weight; C: at max T-O weight):
- Max cruising speed:
  - A, B, C 113 knots (210 km/h; 130 mph)
- Econ cruising speed:
  - A, B 105 knots (195 km/h; 121 mph)
  - C 104·5 knots (194 km/h; 120·5 mph)
- Rate of climb: A 504 m (1,653 ft)/min
  - B 450 m (1,476 ft)/min
  - C 402 m (1,319 ft)/min
- Rate of climb, one engine out:
  - A 96 m (315 ft)/min
  - B 66 m (216 ft)/min
  - C 42 m (138 ft)/min
- Service ceiling (30·5 m; 100 ft/min climb rate):
  - A, B above 4,000 m (13,125 ft)
  - C 4,000 m (13,125 ft)
- Hovering ceiling IGE at T-O power:
  - A 2,560 m (8,400 ft)
  - B 1,940 m (6,365 ft)
  - C 1,320 m (4,330 ft)
- Hovering ceiling OGE at T-O power:
  - A 1,860 m (6,100 ft)
  - B 1,240 m (4,070 ft)
  - C 480 m (1,575 ft)
- Max range at econ cruising speed, standard fuel, no reserves: A 282 nm (522 km; 324 miles)
  - B 275 nm (510 km; 317 miles)
  - C 268 nm (497 km; 309 miles)
- Max endurance, conditions as above:
  - A 3 h 41 min
  - B 3 h 27 min
  - C 3 h 15 min

PZL SWIDNIK W-3

This all-new Polish helicopter was under development in 1978 and was expected to make its first flight in 1979. Larger than the Mi-2/Kania, it is expected to seat up to 12 persons and have a max T-O weight approaching 6,000 kg (13,225 lb). Power plant is a pair of 715 kW (960 shp) PZL-10 (Polish-built Glushenkov TVD-10) turboshaft engines.

PORTUGAL

OGMA

OFICINAS GERAIS DE MATERIAL AERONÁUTICO (GENERAL AERONAUTICAL MATERIAL WORKSHOPS)

WORKS: 2615-Alverca
Telephone: 2580 786; 2581 803, 882, 923 and 979
Telex: 14479 OGMA P
DIRECTOR: Brig Gen Eng Rui do Carmo da Conceição Espadinha
ASST DIRECTOR: Col Eng António Pedro da Silva Gonçalves

OGMA was founded in 1918 and has been in continuous operation since then. It is the Air Force department responsible for maintenance and repair, at depot level, of all aircraft, avionics, engines, structures, ground communications and radar equipment of the Portuguese Air Force.

OGMA has a total covered area of 110,000 m² (1,184,030 sq ft), and a work force of approx 3,000 people.

OGMA performs major overhaul and IRAN work on aircraft, aero-engines and components for the Portuguese Air Force. Under a contract signed in 1959, it also undertakes IRAN, refurbishing and rehabilitation, periodic inspection and emergency maintenance and crash repair of USAF and US Navy aircraft.

Under an important contract with Aérospatiale of France, OGMA is manufacturing tail structures for the SA 315B Lama and SA 318 Alouette II helicopters, and small structural components for the SA 330 Puma. Other component manufacture is undertaken for Socata, SIAI-Marchetti, OMERA and Turboméca.

ROMANIA

CIAR

CENTRALA INDUSTRIALA AERONAUTICA ROMANA (Industrial Centre for Romanian Aviation)

HEADQUARTERS: 133 Calea Victoriei, Sector 1, Bucharest

Romania has had a tradition of aviation since the earliest days of flying, dating from the first monoplane built in France in early 1906 by the Romanian engineer Traian Vuia, the original monoplane of Aurel Vlaicu which, on 17 June 1910, became the first nationally-designed aeroplane to be flown in Romania, and the aeroplanes designed and built in France and Britain by Henri Coanda in 1910-14.

Since that time the Romanian aircraft industry (IAR) has produced some 80 different types of landplane (of which 70 were Romanian-designed) and three types of seaplane (two being of Romanian design), and about 40 different types of sailplane. Many other achievements in the fields of theoretical and experimental aerodynamics have been made by teams of Romanian engineers led by Prof Elie Carafoli, Prof Ion Stroiescu, Prof Ion Grosu, Ing Radu Manicatide, Ing Iosif Silimon and others.

Before the second World War the Romanian aircraft industry employed more than 20,000 people, the most important centre being the IAR (Industria Aeronautica Romana) at Brasov, with 8,000 employees. The IAR factory, destroyed by bombing in 1944, was rebuilt after the war for the manufacture of tractors, and resumed its aeronautical activities with the IAR-811 training aircraft designed by Dipl Ing Radu Manicatide and flown for the first time in March 1949. Known until 1959 as URMV-3 (aircraft component repair factory 3), the Brasov factory during that period produced more than 200 aircraft of different types and more than 20 types of sailplane. At the same time a number of sailplanes were produced at the Combinatul de Lemn (wood factory) at Reghin by Vladimir Novitzchi; and two repair factories, subordinate to the Ministry of Military Forces, were set up at Medias (ARMV-1) and Bucharest (ARMV-2).

The IAR-93/Orao single-seat fighter, built in partnership by Romania and Yugoslavia and described in the International section *(Front Magazine)*

In 1959 the URMV-3 was dissolved and its staff divided into two teams. One was placed under the leadership of Dipl Ing Manicatide at ARMV-2, and renamed IRMA (Intreprinderea de Reparat Material Aeronautic). The other, led by Dipl Ing Silimon, was set up at Ghimbav as a division of IIL-Brasov, to concentrate on sailplane design. Up to 1968 IRMA, which was then responsible to the Ministry of Transport, had built more than 140 aircraft for ambulance, training, agricultural and other duties.

The Romanian aeronautical industry was again reorganised in 1968, and its activities are now undertaken, within the Ministry of Machine Building Industry, by the CIAR. The major activities of CIAR are carried out in two factories: Intreprinderea de Reparat Material Aeronautic (IRMA-Bucuresti) and Intreprinderea de Constructii Aeronautice (ICA-Brasov). These two factories have a combined work force of about 5,000 persons. Aeronautical research and development are undertaken by the Institute of Fluid Mechanics and Aerospace Construction (IMFCA-Bucuresti).

The Romanian industry has an agreement with British Aerospace covering manufacture of BAe One-Eleven transport aircraft under licence in Romania, by the Grupul Aeronautic Bucuresti (GAB).

The Engineering Faculty for Aerospace Construction at the Polytechnic Institute of Bucharest, which is charged with the selection and training of specialist workers, has sections devoted to aircraft, propulsion systems and avionics.

The Romanian aircraft industry is collaborating with that of Yugoslavia in the development of the Orao/IAR-93 twin-jet fighter and ground attack aircraft to meet a requirement of the air forces of the two countries. All known details of this aircraft can be found in the International section.

GAB

GRUPUL AERONAUTIC BUCURESTI (Bucharest Aircraft Group)

ADDRESS: Bucharest

GAB is the Romanian contractor for the manufacture in Bucharest of BAe One-Eleven Series 475 and 500 twin-turbofan transports under a licensing agreement signed initially in the UK on 15 June 1978 and confirmed by a series of contracts concluded in June 1979. British programme contractor is the Weybridge-Bristol Division of British Aerospace. A corresponding programme provides for Romanian manufacture of the Rolls-Royce Spey engines.

Initially, three complete aircraft will be delivered from British Aerospace's Hurn (Bournemouth) factory. The transfer of industrial technology will take place in seven stages, permitting manufacture of the first 22 aircraft by 1985, after which production of complete aircraft will continue both to cover domestic requirements and for export.

IRMA-BUCURESTI

INTREPRINDEREA DE REPARAT MATERIAL AERONAUTIC (Aircraft Component Repair Factory)

ADDRESS: Baneasa Airport, Bucharest

IRMA was formed in 1959 from part of the former URMV-3 at Brasov, having also an aircraft design and production centre under the leadership of Dipl Ing Radu Manicatide. It specialises in the repair and overhaul of various large and small aircraft and aero-engines on behalf of various airlines, including Tarom, the Romanian state airline. It is also the agent and repair centre for Lycoming engines. IRMA was responsible for series production of the IAR-818 ambulance and agricultural aircraft (1965-66 *Jane's*) and the IAR-821 and 821B (1973-74 *Jane's*); and for building the IAR-822 and 822B prototypes listed under the ICA-Brasov heading. Currently, IRMA-Bucuresti is manufacturing under licence the Pilatus Britten-Norman Islander.

Pilatus Britten-Norman BN-2A-27 Islander built in Romania by IRMA *(S. R. P. Thomson)*

IRMA (PILATUS BRITTEN-NORMAN) ISLANDER

In 1968 it was announced that the Pilatus Britten-Norman Islander (see UK section) was to be manufactured under licence in Romania, and the aircraft has since been in production by IRMA. The first Romanian-built example flew for the first time at Baneasa Airport, Bucharest, on 4 August 1969. A total of 312 had been completed by June 1979, and production is continuing.

ICA-BRASOV

INTREPRINDEREA DE CONSTRUCTII AERONAUTICE (Aircraft Construction Factory)

ADDRESS: Brasov

ICA-Brasov, created in 1968, continues the work that was begun in 1926 by IAR-Brasov and was then undertaken in 1950-59 as URMV-3 Brasov. Today, it manufactures aircraft and sailplanes of its own design.

In addition, ICA-Brasov undertakes the repair and overhaul of light aircraft; participates in the manufacturing programme for the Pilatus Britten-Norman Islander; and manufactures the Aérospatiale SA 316B Alouette III helicopter under licence in Romania. It was responsible for building prototypes of the IAR-823, IAR-826 and IAR-827 aircraft.

IAR-822 and IAR-826

Design of the **IAR-822** utility/agricultural aircraft was initiated at IMFCA in October 1968; the prototype, built by IRMA, flew for the first time in March 1970. Certification of the standard version was granted in October 1971, and of the agricultural version in January 1972.

In 1971 series manufacture began at ICA-Brasov, and the first production IAR-822 was flown for the first time in August 1971. The first 20 aircraft were of mixed construction; from 1973, the aircraft became available also in all-metal form as the **IAR-826.** Neither type is now in production: descriptions and illustrations can be found in the 1978-79 *Jane's*. The developed **IAR-827** is described separately.

IAR-822B

Production of this tandem two-seat version of the IAR-822 has ended. A description and illustration can be found in the 1978-79 *Jane's*.

IAR-823

Design of the IAR-823 two/five-seat training and touring light aircraft was started at IMFCA in May 1970, by a team led by Dipl Ing Radu Manicatide. Construction of a prototype began at ICA-Brasov in the Autumn of 1971, and this aircraft made its first flight in July 1973. The first production aircraft flew in 1974, and by mid-1979 about 50 had been delivered to the Romanian Air Force and Romanian flying clubs.

As a two-seater, the IAR-823 is fully aerobatic and is intended for training duties. With a rear bench seat for up to three more persons it is suitable as an executive, taxi or touring aircraft. Provision is made for two underwing pylons for the carriage of drop-tanks or practice weapons.

TYPE: Two/five-seat cabin monoplane.

WINGS: Cantilever low-wing monoplane. Wing section NACA 23012 (modified). Dihedral 7° from roots. Incidence 3° at root, 1° at tip. Conventional all-metal structure, with single main spar and rear auxiliary spar; three-point attachment to fuselage. Riveted spars, ribs and skin of corrosion-proof aluminium alloy. Leading-edges riveted, and sealed to ribs and main spar to form main torsion box and integral fuel tanks. Electrically-actuated fabric-covered metal single-slotted flaps and fabric-covered Frise-type slotted metal ailerons. Ground-adjustable tab.

FUSELAGE: All-metal semi-monocoque structure. Glassfibre engine cowling.

TAIL UNIT: Cantilever metal structure. Two-spar duralumin-covered fin and tailplane; fabric-covered duralumin horn-balanced rudder and elevators. Electrically-actuated automatic trim tabs in elevators; controllable tab in rudder.

LANDING GEAR: Retractable tricycle type, with steerable nosewheel. Electrical retraction, main units inward, nose unit rearward. Emergency manual actuation. Oleo-pneumatic shock-absorbers. Main-wheel tyres size 6·00-6, pressure 2·93 bars (42·5 lb/sq in). Nosewheel tyre size 355 × 150 mm. Independent hydraulic main-wheel brakes, pedal-controlled from left front seat. Shimmy damper on nose unit. No wheel doors.

POWER PLANT: One 216 kW (290 hp) Lycoming IO-540-G1D5 flat-six engine, driving a Hartzell two-blade variable-pitch constant-speed metal propeller. Fuel in four integral wing tanks, total capacity 360 litres (79 Imp gallons). Provision for two 70 litre (15·4 Imp gallon) drop-tanks on underwing pylons.

ACCOMMODATION: Fully-enclosed cabin, seating two persons side by side on individual adjustable front seats, with removable bench seat at rear for up to three more people. Dual controls standard in training version, optional in other versions. Upward-hinged door (optionally jettisonable) on each side of cabin, which is soundproofed, heated and ventilated. Compartment at rear of cabin for up to 40 kg (88 lb) of baggage. Equipment and layout can be varied for use as air taxi, executive or freight transport, ambulance, liaison or photographic aircraft.

SYSTEMS AND AVIONICS: Electrical system, including 50A alternator and 24V 30Ah battery, for engine starting, elevator tab and landing gear actuation, radio communications, landing and navigation lights and cabin and instrument lighting. Standard avionics include VFR instrumentation and Bendix RT 221-AE transceiver. Optional equipment, according to mission, includes blind-flying instrumentation and, in civil transport version, marker beacon, nav/com radio, VOR/ILS, ADF and autopilot.

DIMENSIONS, EXTERNAL:

Wing span	10·00 m (32 ft 9¾ in)
Wing chord at c/l	2·00 m (6 ft 6¾ in)
Wing chord at tip	1·00 m (3 ft 3¼ in)
Wing aspect ratio	6·66
Length overall	8·24 m (27 ft 0¼ in)
Height overall	2·52 m (8 ft 3¼ in)
Wheel track	2·48 m (8 ft 1¾ in)
Wheelbase	1·86 m (6 ft 1¼ in)
Propeller diameter	2·23 m (7 ft 4 in)

AREAS:

Wings, gross	15·00 m² (161·5 sq ft)
Ailerons (total)	1·20 m² (12·92 sq ft)
Trailing-edge flaps (total)	1·78 m² (19·16 sq ft)
Horizontal tail surfaces (total)	3·30 m² (35·52 sq ft)
Vertical tail surfaces (total)	1·50 m² (16·15 sq ft)

IAR-823 two/five-seat light aircraft (Lycoming IO-540 engine) *(Peter R. March)*

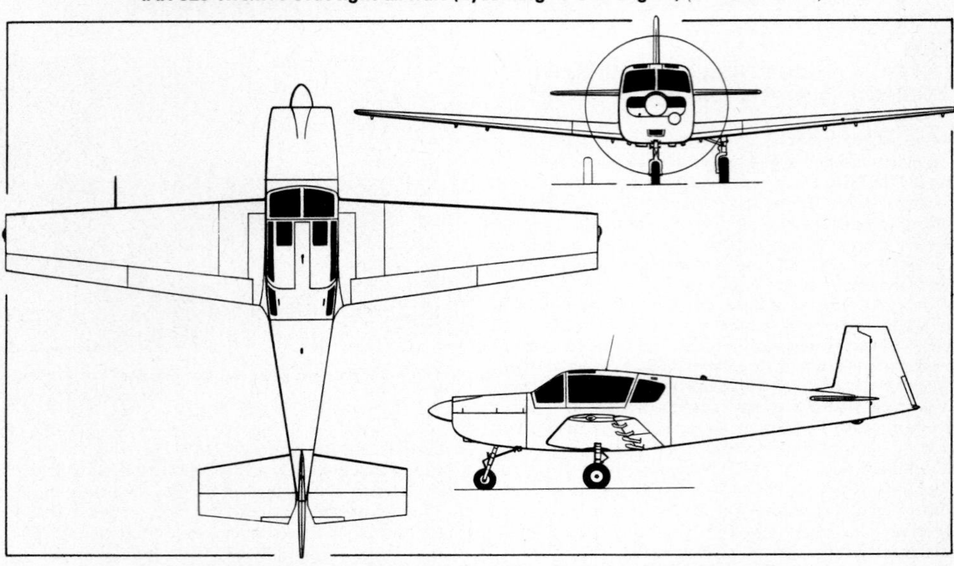

ICA-Brasov IAR-823 light touring and training aircraft *(Pilot Press)*

WEIGHTS AND LOADINGS (A: Aerobatic; U: Utility category):

Weight empty: A	900 kg (1,984 lb)
U	910 kg (2,006 lb)
Max T-O weight: A	1,190 kg (2,623 lb)
U	1,380 kg (3,042 lb)
Max permissible weight for special missions	1,500 kg (3,307 lb)
Max normal wing loading: A	79·0 kg/m² (16·2 lb/sq ft)
U	92·0 kg/m² (18·8 lb/sq ft)
Max normal power loading: A	5·51 kg/kW (9·15 lb/hp)

PERFORMANCE (at 1,400 kg; 3,086 lb AUW except where indicated):

Never-exceed speed	215 knots (400 km/h; 248 mph)
Max level speed at S/L	167 knots (310 km/h; 192·5 mph)
Max cruising speed (75% power) at 1,750 m (5,750 ft)	162 knots (300 km/h; 186 mph)
Econ cruising speed (60% power) at 3,050 m (10,000 ft)	156 knots (290 km/h; 180 mph)
Landing speed	56·5 knots (105 km/h; 65 mph)
Stalling speed, flaps up	62·5 knots (115 km/h; 71·5 mph)
Stalling speed, flaps down, power off	53 knots (98 km/h; 61 mph)
Max rate of climb at S/L	450 m (1,475 ft)/min
Time to 1,000 m (3,280 ft)	2 min 20 s
Service ceiling	5,600 m (18,375 ft)
T-O run	160 m (525 ft)
T-O to 15 m (50 ft)	310 m (1,017 ft)
Landing run	200 m (656 ft)
Range, according to mission and payload, 1 h reserves	431-970 nm (800-1,800 km; 497-1,118 miles)
Endurance, according to mission and payload	3-6 h
g limits (at 1,190 kg; 2,623 lb AUW)	+6; −3

IAR-824

Design of the IAR-824, under the leadership of Dipl Ing Iosif Silimon, began at ICA-Brasov in the Winter of 1969 and is based largely upon that of the IS-23A (see 1973-74 *Jane's*). The IS-24 prototype (YR-ISB) flew for the first time on 24 May 1971, and certification was granted on 13 May 1972. Its production status is uncertain.

TYPE: Six-seat light multi-purpose aircraft.

WINGS: Cantilever high-wing monoplane. Wing section NACA 64_2-413·5 (constant). No dihedral or sweepback. Two-spar constant-chord all-metal structure of ribs and stringers, with light alloy skin. Automatic leading-edge slats over almost full span. Electrically-operated trailing-edge flaps. Rod- and cable-actuated ailerons, which can be operated differentially or in conjunction with flaps. No tabs.

FUSELAGE: Corrosion-protected aluminium alloy semi-monocoque structure. Engine cowling of metal and glassfibre.

TAIL UNIT: Cantilever metal structure, with variable-incidence tailplane, one-piece elevator and sweptback fin and rudder. Balanced elevator and rudder, with fluted skins. Elevator controlled by rods, tailplane and rudder by cables. Trim tab in rudder.

LANDING GEAR: Non-retractable tricycle type, with hydraulic telescopic shock-absorber on each main unit. Nosewheel steerable by rudder pedals. Main-wheel

IS-24 prototype of the ICA-Brasov IAR-824 general-purpose monoplane (Lycoming IO-540 engine)

tyres size 600 × 180; nosewheel tyre size 440 × 130. Hydraulic main-wheel brakes.

POWER PLANT: One 216 kW (290 hp) Lycoming IO-540-C1D5 flat-six engine, driving a Hartzell HC.92.WK.1D-W9350-4·6 two-blade constant-speed metal propeller. Integral fuel tank in wing spar box, capacity 325 litres (71·5 Imp gallons). Reserves in wing-tip tanks.

ACCOMMODATION: Enclosed, heated, ventilated and soundproofed cabin, accommodating in standard passenger version up to six persons. Passenger seats may be removed for cargo carrying.

DIMENSIONS, EXTERNAL:

Wing span	12·40 m (40 ft 8¼ in)
Wing chord (constant)	1·90 m (6 ft 4 in)
Wing aspect ratio	6·6
Length overall	9·10 m (29 ft 10½ in)
Height overall	3·44 m (11 ft 3½ in)
Wheel track	3·30 m (10 ft 10 in)
Wheelbase	2·30 m (7 ft 6½ in)

AREAS:

Wings, gross	23·60 m² (254 sq ft)
Ailerons (total)	2·40 m² (25·83 sq ft)
Trailing-edge flaps (total)	2·56 m² (27·56 sq ft)
Horizontal tail surfaces (total)	4·00 m² (43·06 sq ft)
Vertical tail surfaces (total)	1·56 m² (16·79 sq ft)

WEIGHTS AND LOADING:

Weight empty	1,240 kg (2,733 lb)
Payload	500 kg (1,102 lb)
Max T-O weight	1,900 kg (4,188 lb)
Max wing loading	81·5 kg/m² (16·7 lb/sq ft)

PERFORMANCE (at max T-O weight):

Max level speed at S/L	110 knots (205 km/h; 127 mph)
Max cruising speed at S/L	97 knots (180 km/h; 112 mph)
Stalling speed	40·5 knots (75 km/h; 47 mph)
Max rate of climb at S/L	180 m (591 ft)/min
Service ceiling	3,000 m (9,850 ft)
T-O run	190 m (623 ft)
Landing run	110 m (361 ft)
Max range	485 nm (900 km; 559 miles)

IAR-827

The IAR-827 is a developed version of the all-metal IAR-826 (see 1978-79 *Jane's*), with increased payload, more powerful engine and improved flying and operating characteristics.

Design, by Ing Manicatide at IMFCA with the assistance of a design team from IRMA, began in the early part of 1973. The objective was to evolve an agricultural aircraft with an airframe life of 4,000 hours (equivalent to 22,000 flights) and able to carry a useful load equivalent to 2 kg (4·4 lb) for every horsepower. Particular attention was paid to the minimising of corrosion problems.

Static testing was completed before the first flight, which is believed to have taken place on or about 22 July 1976. Fatigue testing was to be carried out with the second aircraft. Initially, certification was anticipated by March 1977, and five pre-series aircraft were due to have been delivered by the end of 1977; but early flight testing revealed the need for a more powerful engine, and the original 298 kW (400 hp) Lycoming was to be replaced by a 447 kW (600 hp) PZL-3S radial engine. Certification of the intended production version, presumably with this engine, was nearing completion in mid-1979.

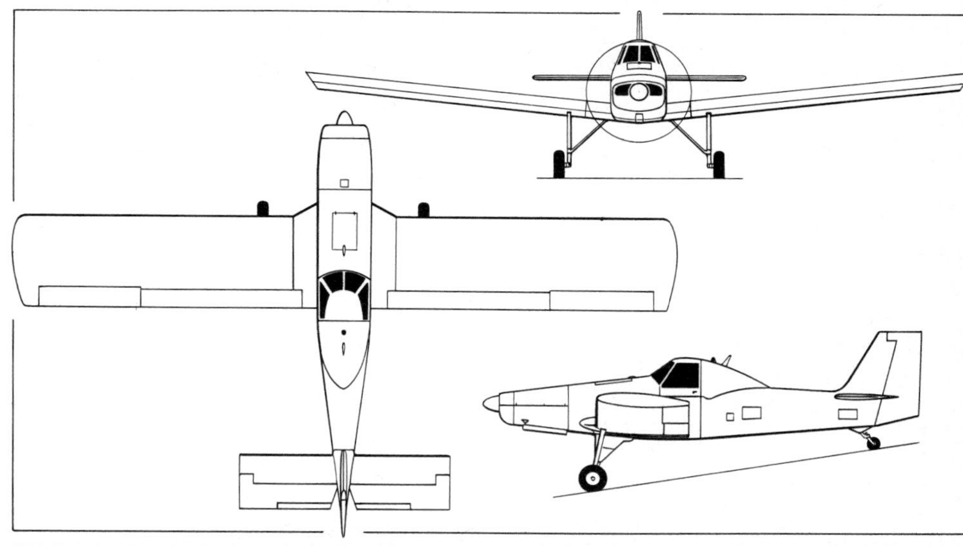

ICA-Brasov IAR-827 single/two-seat agricultural aircraft, in original form with Lycoming engine *(Pilot Press)*

The following description applies to the prototype in its Lycoming-engined form:

TYPE: Single/two-seat agricultural aircraft.

WINGS: Cantilever low-wing monoplane. Wing section NACA 23014. Constant-chord safe-life structure, with dihedral from roots. Welded chrome-molybdenum steel tube centre-section with duralumin skin. All-metal single-spar outer panels. Plain ailerons. Electrically-operated single-slotted Fowler-type flaps.

FUSELAGE: Forward structure of welded steel tube, with glassfibre skin panels attached by quick-release fastenings. Rear fuselage is an all-metal semi-monocoque.

TAIL UNIT: Cantilever all-metal structure, with slightly-sweptback fin and rudder. Balanced elevators, each with inset tab.

LANDING GEAR: Non-retractable tailwheel type. Main units comprise 140 mm stroke hydraulic shock-struts and side Vs, and are fitted with Dunlop wheels (tyre size 620 × 225) and brakes. Gear is of Romanian design and is designed to withstand a vertical velocity of 6 m (19·5 ft)/s or a free drop of 1·2 m (3 ft 11¼ in).

POWER PLANT: One 298 kW (400 hp) Lycoming IO-720-DA1B flat-eight engine, driving a Hartzell two-blade constant-speed metal propeller with spinner. Fuel tank in each wing leading-edge, each of 100 litres (22 Imp gallons) capacity.

ACCOMMODATION: Side-by-side seats for pilot and mechanic in fully-enclosed cockpit, with window/door on each side. Provision for dual controls and (on production aircraft) emergency door jettison. Seat height and rudder pedals adjustable. Crash pylon in fairing aft of seats. Cockpit is heated and ventilated and, on production aircraft, will be sealed and slightly pressurised to exclude dust.

AVIONICS: Prototype has Bendix 720-channel VHF radio and a US artificial horizon; most other instrumentation is of Soviet origin.

EQUIPMENT: All-glassfibre hopper in forward fuselage, with a volume of 1·23 m³ (43·44 cu ft). Hopper stressed for loads of up to 1,000 kg (2,205 lb), but normal max load will be 800 kg (1,763 lb) of dry or 1,200 litres (264 Imp gallons) of liquid chemical.

DIMENSIONS, EXTERNAL:

Wing span	14·00 m (45 ft 11¼ in)
Length overall	9·60 m (31 ft 6 in)
Height overall	2·60 m (8 ft 6½ in)
Tailplane span	approx 4·50 m (14 ft 9 in)
Wheel track	3·42 m (11 ft 2¾ in)
Wheelbase	6·20 m (20 ft 4 in)
Propeller diameter	2·16 m (7 ft 1 in)

AREA:

Wings, gross	29·00 m² (312·15 sq ft)

WEIGHTS:

Weight empty, with agricultural equipment	1,280 kg (2,822 lb)
Max T-O weight	2,350 kg (5,180 lb)

PERFORMANCE (estimated, with agricultural equipment, at max T-O weight):

Max level speed	113 knots (210 km/h; 130 mph)
Cruising speed	94 knots (175 km/h; 109 mph)
Operating speed range	75·5-92 knots (140-170 km/h; 87-106 mph)
Stalling speed, flaps up, power off	59·5 knots (110 km/h; 68·5 mph)
Max rate of climb at S/L	210 m (690 ft)/min
Service ceiling	3,500 m (11,475 ft)
T-O to 15 m (50 ft)	440 m (1,445 ft)
Max endurance	2 h 30 min

ICA (AÉROSPATIALE) IAR-316 ALOUETTE III

ICA-Brasov and Aérospatiale concluded an agreement in 1971 for an initial quantity of 50 SA 316B Alouette III helicopters (current total 130) to be built in Romania. Production of these continues. Romanian-built components were also supplied for incorporation in French-built Alouette IIIs.

SOUTH AFRICA

AERONICS
AERONICS (PTY) LTD

ADDRESS: PO Box 391090, Bramley 2018
Telephone: (011) 786 9600
DIRECTOR: J. M. Cohoe

Aeronics (Pty) Ltd has production rights to produce exclusively in South Africa the Sequoia Models 300 and 301 light aircraft, following an agreement signed in November 1978 with Sequoia Aircraft Corporation of Richmond, Virginia, USA.

AERONICS (SEQUOIA) MODELS 300 and 301

Design of the Sequoia light aircraft, which began in 1975, was undertaken for Sequoia Aircraft Corporation by Mr David Thurston, a consultant whose other designs include the Teal and Marlin amphibians. In addition to planned availability for construction by homebuilders, it is now to be a factory-produced aircraft, manufactured in South Africa by Aeronics (Pty) Ltd.

The Sequoia is configured basically as a two-seater in two forms, the Model 300 with side-by-side seating and the Model 301 with tandem seats; in addition, the Model 300 can be made available in a '2 + 2' layout.

A detailed description of the Sequoia 300/301 can be found in the Homebuilts section.

ATLAS
ATLAS AIRCRAFT CORPORATION OF SOUTH AFRICA (PTY) LIMITED

HEAD OFFICE AND WORKS: PO Box 11, Atlas Road, Kempton Park 1620, Transvaal
Telephone: 973 0111
Telex: 87965
GENERAL MANAGER: G. W. Ward
COMMERCIAL MANAGER (ACTING): A. J. Bester

Atlas built the Impala Mk 1 (M.B. 326M) jet trainer under licence from Aermacchi. Its present programmes include production of a developed Mk 2 version of the Impala and of the Atlas C4M, a STOL light transport aircraft developed in South Africa.

Additionally, Atlas is manufacturing under licence components for the Dassault Mirage F1-CZ and -AZ multi-purpose combat aircraft currently in service with No. 3 Squadron of the South African Air Force. Atlas also undertakes maintenance and overhaul of SAAF aircraft.

Atlas Impala Mk 2 single-seat light strike aircraft, based on the Aermacchi M.B. 326K

ATLAS IMPALA Mk 2

Manufacture by Atlas of the two-seat Aermacchi M.B. 326M for the South African Air Force (SAAF designation Impala Mk 1) was described in previous editions of *Jane's*. About 150 are reported to have been built.

The Impala Mk 2 is an improved version, based on the single-seat M.B. 326K. It was developed by Atlas as an advanced trainer for the SAAF and is now in production. Four M.B. 326Ks are reported to have been delivered initially by Aermacchi. No details of the Impala Mk 2 have yet been released officially, except that it has a Rolls-Royce Viper Mk 540 turbojet engine; a description of the Aermacchi M.B. 326 series can be found in the Italian section of this edition.

ATLAS C4M

South African Air Force name: Kudu

The C4M is a six/eight-seat light transport aircraft, developed by Atlas, which can be converted rapidly from the passenger to the freight role, and vice versa, and can operate from unprepared surfaces. The prototype (ZS-IZF) flew for the first time on 16 February 1974, and certification to FAR Pt 23 was granted on 16 June 1975. The third C4M (ZS-IZG) flew shortly afterwards.

A military prototype flew for the first time on 18 June 1975, and was later handed over to the South African Air Force (SAAF serial number 961) for evaluation. A military C4M bearing the SAAF serial number 978, and belonging to No. 41 Squadron, was displayed at the Air Africa air show in 1977, indicating that the C4M is in production. No confirmation of its status has been given by Atlas.

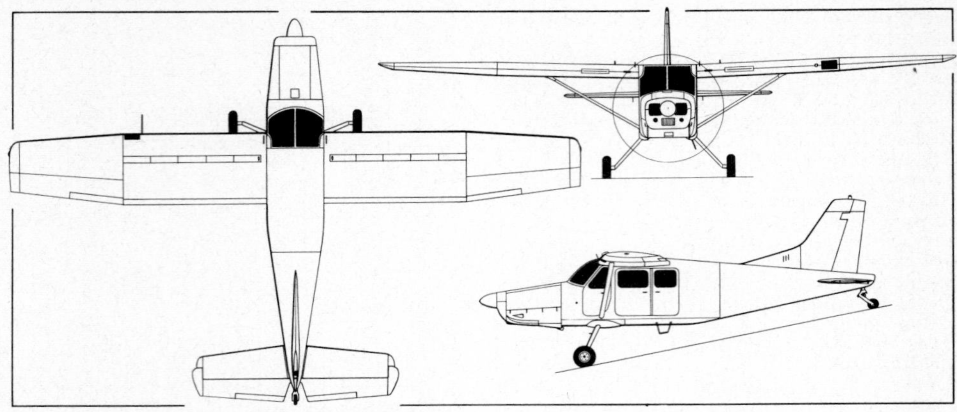

Atlas C4M six/eight-seat STOL utility light transport *(Pilot Press)*

Atlas C4M Kudu light transport (Lycoming GSO-480-B1B3 engine) of No. 41 Squadron, SAAF *(Philip J. Birtles)*

TYPE: Single-engined cabin monoplane.

WINGS: High-wing monoplane, with single elliptical-section bracing strut each side. Wing section NACA 23016 at root, NACA 4412 (modified) at tip. Dihedral 3°. Incidence 4° at root, 0° 27′ at tip. All-metal D-spar torsion-box structure, bolted to fuselage. Electrically-operated Fowler flaps, of all-metal two-spar construction, interchangeable right with left. All-metal piano-hinged ailerons, with inset electrically-operated trim tab (port) and balance tab (starboard). Vortex generators forward of ailerons. Glassfibre wingtips.

FUSELAGE: All-metal stressed-skin structure, comprising a sturdy floor, bulkheads and stringers, of basically rectangular section. No longerons. Titanium alloy firewall. Glassfibre tailcone.

TAIL UNIT: Cantilever all-metal structure. Electrically-operated variable-incidence tailplane, with manual standby. Aerodynamically and mass balanced elevators and rudder. Balance tab in port elevator. Servo tab in each elevator. Vortex generators forward of elevators.

LANDING GEAR: Non-retractable tailwheel type. Main units each have an independent cantilever leg, and are connected to oleo-pneumatic shock-absorbers mounted below cabin floor level in small underfuselage blister fairings. Main-wheel tube-type tyres size 7·00-8, 6-ply rating, pressure 2·55 bars (37 lb/sq in). Single-disc hydraulic brakes. Steerable tailwheel, mounted on oleo-pneumatic levered-suspension strut, has a size 5·00-4 6-ply tube-type tyre, pressure 2·45 bars (35·5 lb/sq in).

POWER PLANT: One 254 kW (340 hp) Piaggio-built Lycoming GSO-480-B1B3 flat-six engine, driving a Hartzell HC-B3R20-4/R10160-1 three-blade constant-speed variable-pitch metal propeller with spinner. Three removable and partially self-sealing bag-type fuel tanks in each wing, total capacity 432 litres (95 Imp gallons). Overwing refuelling points. Oil capacity 11·3 litres (2·5 Imp gallons).

ACCOMMODATION: Pilot and co-pilot side by side at front, with four individual seats in pairs at rear, or two bench seats each for three persons. Baggage compartment aft of seats. Passenger seats can be removed to provide space for up to 560 kg (1,235 lb) of cargo. Heating, ventilation and windscreen demisting standard. Forward-hinged door on each side for pilot and co-pilot. Main cabin door is on port side, and is in two sections: forward-opening front section for passengers, rearward-opening rear section for loading cargo. A sliding door at the rear of the cabin on the starboard side may be opened in flight for parachuting and is available for emergency exit. A trap-door is provided in the cabin floor for aerial survey or supply dropping purposes.

SYSTEMS: Hydraulic system for main-wheel brakes only. 28V DC electrical system supplied by an engine-driven generator and a 24V 15Ah battery. Static inverter provides 115/26V AC power for instruments and radio.

AVIONICS AND EQUIPMENT: To customer's specification, but probably including two VHF transceivers, intercom, HF radio and ADF. Blind-flying instrumentation standard.

DIMENSIONS, EXTERNAL:

Wing span	13·075 m (42 ft 10¾ in)
Wing chord at root	1·727 m (5 ft 8 in)
Wing chord at tip	1·168 m (3 ft 10 in)
Wing aspect ratio	8·07
Length overall (tail down)	9·31 m (30 ft 6½ in)
Height overall (tail down)	3·66 m (12 ft 0 in)
Elevator span	4·79 m (15 ft 8½ in)
Wheel track (full fuel, no load)	2·935 m (9 ft 7½ in)
Wheelbase	6·625 m (21 ft 9 in)
Propeller diameter	2·54 m (8 ft 4 in)
Propeller ground clearance	0·233 m (9¼ in)
Crew doors (each): Height	1·16 m (3 ft 9¾ in)
Mean width	0·53 m (1 ft 9 in)
Double doors (port): Height	1·05 m (3 ft 5¼ in)
Width	1·42 m (4 ft 8 in)
Sliding door (stbd): Height	1·04 m (3 ft 5 in)
Width	0·74 m (2 ft 5 in)
Trap-door (floor): Length	0·70 m (2 ft 3½ in)
Width	0·50 m (1 ft 7¾ in)

DIMENSIONS, INTERNAL:

Cabin: Length, incl flight deck	3·20 m (10 ft 6 in)
Max width	1·14 m (3 ft 9 in)
Height at front	1·31 m (4 ft 3½ in)
Height at rear	1·14 m (3 ft 9 in)

AREAS:

Wings, gross	20·971 m² (225·7 sq ft)
Ailerons (total)	2·620 m² (28·19 sq ft)
Trailing-edge flaps (total)	3·774 m² (40·62 sq ft)
Fin	1·625 m² (17·49 sq ft)
Rudder	0·945 m² (10·17 sq ft)
Tailplane	3·430 m² (36·92 sq ft)
Elevators, incl tabs	2·063 m² (22·21 sq ft)

WEIGHTS AND LOADINGS:

Weight empty	1,230 kg (2,711 lb)
Max payload	560 kg (1,235 lb)
Max T-O and landing weight	2,040 kg (4,497 lb)
Max wing loading	97·3 kg/m² (19·93 lb/sq ft)
Max power loading	8·03 kg/kW (13·23 lb/hp)

PERFORMANCE (at max T-O weight):

Never-exceed speed	165 knots (305 km/h; 190 mph) IAS
Max level speed at 2,440 m (8,000 ft)	140 knots (259 km/h; 161 mph) TAS
Max cruising speed at 3,050 m (10,000 ft)	126 knots (233 km/h; 145 mph) TAS
Econ cruising speed at 3,050 m (10,000 ft)	108 knots (200 km/h; 124 mph) TAS
Stalling speed, flaps up, power on	65 knots (121 km/h; 75 mph) IAS
Stalling speed, flaps down, power on	48 knots (89 km/h; 55·5 mph) IAS
Max rate of climb at S/L	244 m (800 ft)/min
Service ceiling	4,270 m (14,000 ft)
T-O run	215 m (705 ft)
T-O to 15 m (50 ft)	370 m (1,214 ft)
Landing from 15 m (50 ft)	260 m (853 ft)
Landing run	140 m (460 ft)
Range with max fuel, 45 min reserves	700 nm (1,297 km; 806 miles)
Range with 400 kg (882 lb) payload, 45 min reserves	400 nm (740 km; 460 miles)
Endurance with max fuel, no reserves	8 h

CSIR

COUNCIL FOR SCIENTIFIC AND INDUSTRIAL RESEARCH (National Institute for Aeronautics and Systems Technology)

ADDRESS: PO Box 395, Pretoria 0001

Telephone: (012) 74 9111

Telex: 3-633 SA

HEAD OF AERONAUTICS DEPARTMENT: Dr C. G. van Niekerk, FRAeS

Initially, the CSIR concentrated on the spin-off from aeronautical research. This work led to the establishment in 1952 of a small aerodynamics division which grew into the Aeronautics Research Unit, established in 1968. In 1978 this Unit joined another CSIR group to form the National Institute for Aeronautics and Systems Technology.

Current activities include research into lifting rotors, airframe fatigue, synthetic materials, separation of underwing stores, aircraft and missile stability, flutter, atmospheric turbulence, and aircraft noise problems.

The prototype CSIR (ARU) SARA II (South African Research Autogyro) made its first free flight in Pretoria during November 1972; a description of this can be found in the 1975-76 *Jane's*.

CSIR SARA 3

A new, modified SARA 3 (ZS-UIT) was designed and constructed during 1976-77, and techniques were developed for the design and manufacture of GRP rotor blades. This aircraft made its first flight on 1 August 1977, and its first public appearance three months later, at the Air Africa International display.

The rotor head of SARA 3 is of novel design (patented) which makes possible remarkably short take-off runs. The design incorporates a simple but fully-automatic variable-geometry head which allows high-speed rotor spin-up on the ground at zero-lift blade pitch angle, but changes the angle to 4°, as required for flight, when the rotor disc is tilted backward during the take-off run. The change of angle is brought about by the blades coning upward along an oblique hinge line, against stops.

TYPE: Two-seat experimental autogyro.

ROTOR SYSTEM: Single two-blade teetering rotor with fully-automatic variable-geometry head. Blades, which are of constant chord and NACA 23015 section, are constructed of GRP. No rotor brake.

ROTOR DRIVE: For rotor spin-up only, the aircraft has a belt/clutch power take-off connected to a dog clutch on the rotor by steel tube shafting via a two-stage 90° gearbox.

FUSELAGE: Space-frame of light alloy, with GRP fairings.

Tail Unit: Twin fins and rudders, bridged by a fixed-incidence tailplane and supported on twin strut-braced tailbooms. All tail surfaces of light alloy stressed-skin construction. Half-span trim tabs on tailplane.

Landing Gear: Non-retractable tricycle type. Steerable nosewheel. Oleo-pneumatic shock-absorber and single wheel on each unit.

Power Plant: One 134 kW (180 hp) Lycoming O-360-A flat-four engine, driving a Hartzell two-blade pusher propeller. Power take-off for rotor spin-up. Spherical glassfibre-reinforced fuel tanks in fuselage, total capacity 80 litres (17·6 Imp gallons). Oil capacity 9 litres (2 Imp gallons).

Accommodation: Crew of two, with dual controls, on side-by-side seats. Access by means of forward-opening 'bubble' canopy.

Avionics: 12V battery and radio.

Dimensions, external:

Rotor diameter	10·50 m (34 ft 5½ in)
Rotor blade chord	0·322 m (1 ft 0¾ in)
Length of fuselage	3·78 m (12 ft 4¾ in)
Width of fuselage	1·35 m (4 ft 5¼ in)
Height to top of rotor hub	2·69 m (8 ft 10 in)
Wheel track	2·15 m (7 ft 0¾ in)
Wheelbase	1·95 m (6 ft 4¾ in)
Propeller diameter	1·83 m (6 ft 0 in)

Dimensions, internal:

Cabin: Max width	1·20 m (3 ft 11¼ in)
Max height	1·00 m (3 ft 3¼ in)

Areas:

Rotor disc	86·59 m² (932·05 sq ft)
Rotor blades (each)	1·51 m² (16·25 sq ft)
Fins (total)	1·40 m² (15·07 sq ft)
Rudders (total)	0·49 m² (5·27 sq ft)
Tailplane	1·24 m² (13·35 sq ft)

Weights:

Weight empty	480 kg (1,058 lb)
Max T-O weight	735 kg (1,620 lb)

CSIR SARA 3 two-seat experimental autogyro (Lycoming O-360-A engine)

Performance (at max T-O weight):

Max level speed at S/L	81 knots (150 km/h; 93 mph)
Normal cruising speed at S/L	59 knots (110 km/h; 68 mph)
Min speed in level flight	26 knots (48 km/h; 30 mph)
Max rate of climb at S/L	300 m (984 ft)/min
T-O run, still air	20 m (66 ft)
T-O to 15 m (50 ft), still air	85 m (279 ft)
Landing from 15 m (50 ft), still air	75 m (246 ft)
Landing run, still air	10 m (33 ft)
Max range, no reserves	108 nm (200 km; 124 miles)
Max endurance, no reserves	1 h 50 min

NATIONAL DYNAMICS

NATIONAL DYNAMICS (PTY) LTD

Address: PO Box 20163, Virginia Airport, Durban North 4016

Telephone: Durban 845350

Directors:

S. J. Reed (Managing)

S. Reed (Marketing)

This company was formed in 1975 following the acquisition in May of that year by Dr Maitland Reed of the prototype and all rights to the (formerly Patchen) Explorer/Observer four-seat cabin monoplane. It was later decided to suspend series production testing of this aircraft.

National Dynamics took over from Air Nova (see 1975-76 *Jane's*) the Falcon aerobatic biplane. In addition, it is engaged in aviation systems manufacture, and is developing the Observer mini-RPV (see RPVs & Targets section).

NATIONAL DYNAMICS (REED) FALCON

As described in the 1975-76 *Jane's*, the Falcon is a redesign of the modified Rooivalk prototype ZS-UDU (1972-73 *Jane's*), designed by Dr Maitland Reed and the late Capt J. H. Rautenbach. It is basically a single-seat aircraft, designed for unlimited aerobatics, but is to be made available also as a two-seater. It was hoped to begin production flight testing in the Autumn of 1978.

The following description applies to the single-seat prototype Falcon, which was acquired from the University of Natal in April 1974:

Type: Single-seat aerobatic biplane.

Wings: Strut-braced biplane. Wing section NACA 0012. No anhedral or dihedral. Incidence 0°. Sweepback 10° at quarter-chord. Sitka spruce main spars and ribs, covered with Dacron. Single I bracing strut each side, faired to upper and lower wings; centre-section of upper wing supported by a pair of inverted V struts forward of cockpit. Internally-balanced ailerons, of spruce and ply, on both upper and lower wings. No tabs.

Fuselage: Welded chrome-molybdenum steel tube (4130) structure, Dacron-covered.

Tail Unit: Single fin and rudder, with wire-braced tailplane. Welded steel tube structure, Dacron-covered. Trim tab in each elevator. No rudder tab.

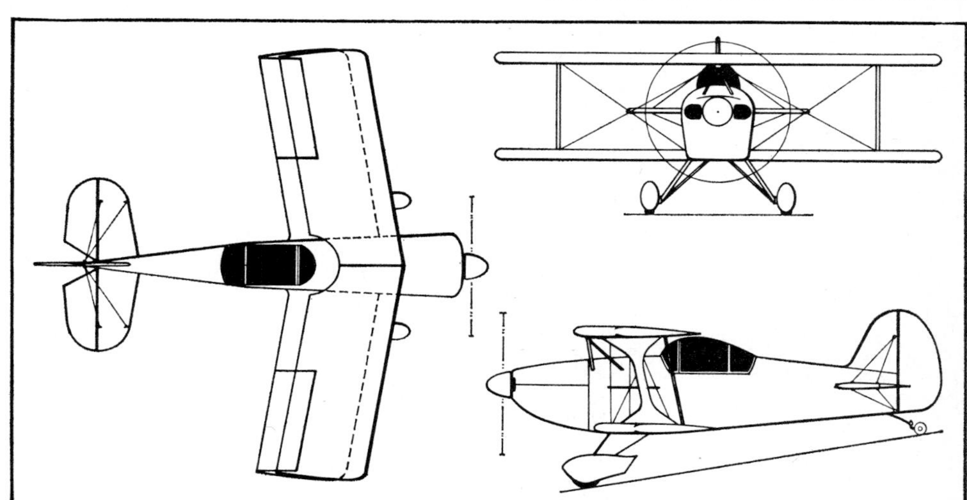

National Dynamics (Reed) Falcon single-seat aerobatic biplane *(Roy J. Grainge)*

Landing Gear: Non-retractable tailwheel type. V-type independently-sprung main legs, with rubber-cord shock-absorption. Cleveland main wheels and tyres, size 5·00-5, pressure 2·07 bars (30 lb/sq in). Cleveland hydraulic brakes on main units. Streamline fairings over main wheels.

Power Plant: One 156·5 kW (210 hp) Continental IO-360-C flat-six engine, driving a two-blade constant-speed propeller with spinner. Three fuel tanks in fuselage, total capacity 127 litres (28 Imp gallons), including one 63·6 litre (14 Imp gallon) tank for ferry purposes. Oil capacity 9 litres (2 Imp gallons).

Accommodation: Single cockpit, with fully-transparent rearward-sliding canopy. Design can be adapted to two-seat configuration.

Dimensions, external:

Wing span (upper and lower)	5·87 m (19 ft 3 in)
Wing chord (constant, each)	1·17 m (3 ft 10 in)
Length overall	5·87 m (19 ft 3 in)
Height overall	2·13 m (7 ft 0 in)

Area:

Wings (total)	12·45 m² (134·0 sq ft)

Weights:

Weight empty	408 kg (900 lb)
Max T-O weight	657 kg (1,450 lb)

Performance (estimated, 156·5 kW; 210 hp engine):

Never-exceed speed	195 knots (362 km/h; 225 mph)
Max level speed	148 knots (274 km/h; 170 mph)
Stalling speed	51·5 knots (95 km/h; 59 mph)
Max rate of climb at S/L	732 m (2,400 ft)/min
Range with max fuel	450 nm (830 km; 515 miles)

VLIÔM

VLIÔM DEVELOPMENT CO (PTY) LTD

Address: PO Box 50548, 2125 Randburg, Transvaal

Telephone: 706 3197

Directors: Dr I. E. Bock and Mrs J. N. Bock

VLIÔM

The Vliôm, designed by Dr I. E. Bock, is being developed as a novel form of VTOL vehicle with potential civil applications as a personal aircraft, sports vehicle or commuter transport. The name Vliôm is derived from the Afrikaans *Vlieg Hom* (Fly it).

The airframe consists basically of a shrouded-propeller lift/propulsion system, comprising a vertically-mounted engine and a propeller turning in the horizontal plane, the propeller and craft tilting slightly during forward movement, like a helicopter. The flat shroud-ring around the propeller gives a 60% augmentation in the thrust of the propeller, making possible the use of a small-diameter high-speed propeller. The propeller is fixed-pitch and non-articulated. A description of its method of operation can be found in the 1978-79 *Jane's*.

Design began in 1967, and powered model tests started in 1971. The present concept evolved from the results of these tests, and from the fundamental functional needs of a commuter air vehicle, designed to meet very high

The 1/10th scale model of the Vliôm photographed from the starboard side

demands of safety, simplicity of control, and economy. Tests conducted with a 1/10th scale model concentrated upon the fundamental aerodynamics and the inherent stability and simplicity of control of the craft. The main work is now concerned primarily with safety during the phase immediately after take-off, before it achieves forward speed.

Design studies give the following parameters for a four-seat commuter version, powered by an 89·5 kW (120 hp) lightweight piston engine driving a two-blade fixed-pitch propeller:

DIMENSIONS, EXTERNAL:
- Diameter of shroud-ring: 4·27 m (14 ft 0 in)
- Diameter of propeller: 2·44 m (8 ft 0 in)
- Height overall: 2·44 m (8 ft 0 in)
- Height of propeller above ground: 2·13 m (7 ft 0 in)
- Wheel track: 2·44 m (8 ft 0 in)

WEIGHTS (approx):
- Weight empty: 363 kg (800 lb)
- Max T-O weight: 726 kg (1,600 lb)

PERFORMANCE (estimated):
- Max level speed: 104 knots (193 km/h; 120 mph)
- Max cruising speed (suburban use): 61 knots (112 km/h; 70 mph)

SPAIN

AISA
AERONAUTICA INDUSTRIAL SA

HEAD OFFICE, WORKS AND AIRFIELD: Cuatro Vientos (Carabanchel Alto), Apartado 984, Madrid 25
Telephone: 208 52 40 and 208 96 40
Telex: 23593 E Madrid
PRESIDENT: Juan B. Fábregas
VICE-PRESIDENT: Gonzalo Suárez
MANAGING DIRECTOR: José A. Delgado
AIRCRAFT DESIGN MANAGER: Juan del Campo
PLANT MANAGER: Angel Romero

This company has been engaged since 1923 in the manufacture, repair and maintenance of fixed-wing aircraft and helicopters.

During recent years, the AISA design office has been responsible for several liaison, training and sporting aircraft, including the I-11, I-11B, AVD-12 and I-115.

AISA is also engaged in IRAN repair and maintenance and general overhaul of several types of US aircraft, in particular the North American T-6, Beechcraft B55, C90 and F33 Bonanza, and Piper PA-23 aircraft operated by the Spanish Air Force and the National School of Aeronautics.

In recent years, AISA has been awarded several US government contracts for IRAN repair work on Sikorsky S-55 and S-58 helicopters. It is also engaged in the repair and overhaul of Bell 47, 204, 205 and 206, and Boeing Vertol CH-47 helicopters, and their dynamic components, for the Spanish Army, Spanish Air Force and civilian operators.

The Cuatro Vientos factory has a covered area of 8,000 m² (86,110 sq ft) and employs some 140 persons.

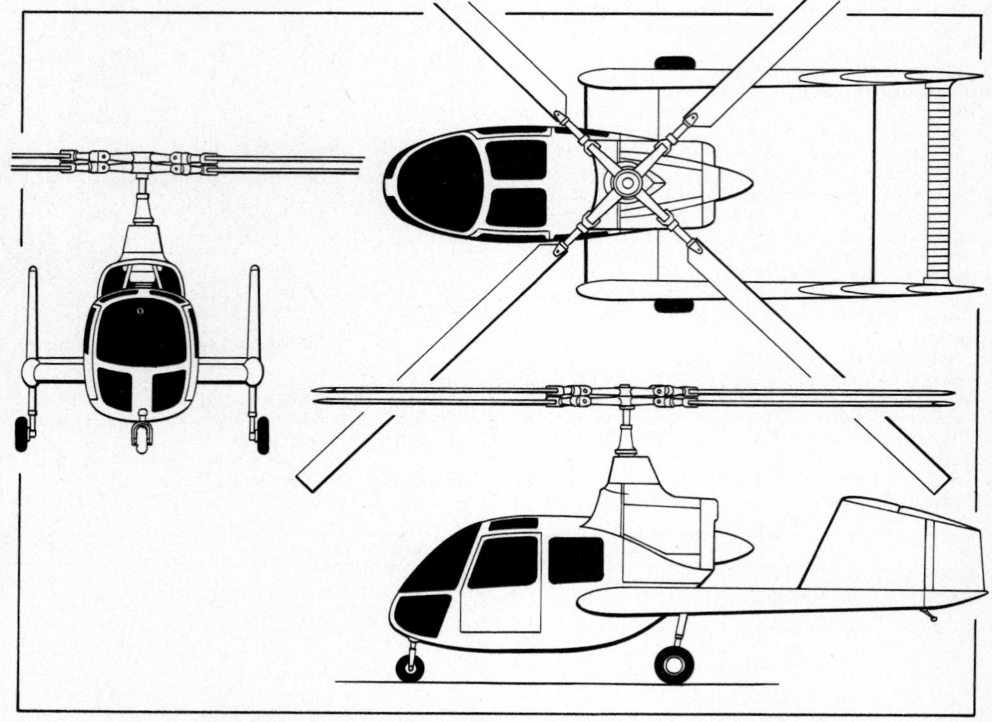

AISA autogyro GN (Lycoming IO-540-K1A5 engine) *(Roy J. Grainge)*

AISA AUTOGYRO GN

AISA, which in 1927 built some of the earliest Cierva Autogiros, is currently developing this four-seat autogyro. Construction of two prototypes (one for ground testing) began in 1978, and first flight is planned for early 1980.

The GN, which will have a jump take-off capability, is powered by a 224 kW (300 hp) Lycoming IO-540-K1A5 flat-six engine, driving a two-blade constant-speed Hartzell pusher propeller. It has accommodation for a pilot and three passengers, with a single door on each side of the cabin. A four-blade articulated rotor, with rotor brake, is fitted, and the aircraft has short-span wings of NACA 0024 section. The pod-shaped fuselage is an aluminium alloy semi-monocoque structure, with moulded Plexiglas transparencies; the twin tailbooms, tailplane, elevator and twin fins and rudders are also of all-metal construction. A non-retractable tricycle landing gear is fitted, with single wheel on each unit.

DIMENSIONS, EXTERNAL:
- Rotor diameter: 11·76 m (38 ft 7 in)
- Rotor blade chord (each): 0·28 m (11 in)
- Wing span (incl tailbooms): 2·60 m (8 ft 6¼ in)
- Wing chord (constant): 0·85 m (2 ft 9½ in)
- Length of fuselage: 6·50 m (21 ft 4 in)
- Height overall: 3·20 m (10 ft 6 in)
- Propeller diameter: 2·14 m (7 ft 0 in)
- Doors (each): Height: 1·085 m (3 ft 6¾ in)
  - Width: 0·93 m (3 ft 0½ in)

AREA:
- Rotor disc: 108·62 m² (1,169·2 sq ft)

WEIGHTS:
- Weight empty: 948 kg (2,090 lb)
- Max payload: 308 kg (679 lb)
- Max T-O weight: 1,400 kg (3,086 lb)

PERFORMANCE (estimated, at max T-O weight):
- Max level speed at S/L: 129 knots (240 km/h; 149 mph)
- Max cruising speed at S/L: 114 knots (212 km/h; 132 mph)
- Min speed, power on: 29 knots (54 km/h; 33·5 mph)
- Max rate of climb at S/L: 360 m (1,180 ft)/min
- Landing run (zero wind): 0-5 m (0-16·5 ft)
- Range with max fuel: 431 nm (800 km; 497 miles)

CASA
CONSTRUCCIONES AERONAUTICAS SA

HEAD OFFICE: Rey Francisco 4, Apartado 193, Madrid 8
Telephone: 247 25 00
Telex: 27418
WORKS: Getafe, Seville, San Pablo, Cádiz, Madrid and Ajalvir
HONORARY PRESIDENT: José Ortiz Echagüe
CHAIRMAN AND PRESIDENT: Dr Carlos Marin Ridruejo
VICE-CHAIRMAN OF THE BOARD: Dr Eugenio Aguirre Castillo
GENERAL DIRECTOR: Dr Restituto Estirado
EXECUTIVE DIRECTOR, SALES/MARKETING: Pablo de Bergia Gonzalez
DIRECTOR OF SALES: Juan Alonso Castro

This company was formed in March 1923 for the primary purpose of producing metal aircraft for the Spanish Air Force. It began by building under licence the Breguet XIX and has since manufactured many other aircraft of foreign design, the most recent being the Northrop F-5 fighter. It is assembling the 60 MBB BO 105 helicopters ordered for

CASA C-212 Series 200 Aviocar twin-turboprop transport aircraft (Garrett-AiResearch TPE 331-10-501C engines)

the Spanish Army in July 1979.

CASA's own Project Office has designed several aircraft under contract to the Spanish Air Ministry, including the C-212 Aviocar transport and the C-101 Aviojet jet trainer, both of which are currently in production. It also undertakes design and development work for foreign companies and, for example, collaborated in the design of the MBB HFB 320 Hansa executive transport; MBB in turn co-operated in the design of the Aviocar.

Under contract to Dassault-Breguet (which see), CASA is responsible for manufacturing outer wings for the Falcon 10 light business aircraft. It is a full member (4·2%) of Airbus Industrie (see International section), and manufactures the horizontal tail surfaces, landing gear doors and forward passenger doors for the Airbus A300 wide-bodied transport aircraft. It also manufactures glassfibre honeycomb components, including underwing fillets for McDonnell Douglas DC-10 and upper-rudder segments of Boeing jet transports, and wing units for the Otomat air-launched missile.

CASA undertakes maintenance and modernisation work for the Spanish Air Force and for the US Air Force in Europe. Its principal current activities of this kind concern overhaul and maintenance of McDonnell Douglas F-4 combat aircraft and Bell 47G, 204 and 205 and Sikorsky H-19 helicopters.

In 1972 the former Hispano Aviación SA (see 1972-73 *Jane's*) was merged with CASA, the latter company taking over all of Hispano's offices and other facilities, aircraft production programmes and personnel. In June 1973 ENMASA (Empresa Nacional de Motores de Aviación) was merged into CASA, and now constitutes the CASA División de Motores (see Aero-Engines section). CASA has six factories, employing about 7,900 people in early 1978. Including Hispano production, the company had by early 1979 manufactured more than 3,500 aircraft and overhauled approx 6,250. CASA has a total covered area in the region of 200,000 m² (2,152,780 sq ft); majority shareholder in the company is the INI (Instituto Nacional de Industria).

CASA C-212 AVIOCAR

Spanish Air Force designations: TR.12A and T.12B

The C-212 Aviocar twin-turboprop light utility STOL transport was evolved by CASA to fulfil a variety of military or civil roles, but primarily to replace the mixed fleet of Junkers Ju 52/3m (T.2), Douglas DC-3 (T.3) and CASA-207 Azor (T.7) transport aircraft formerly in service with the Spanish Air Force. The first prototype flew for the first time on 26 March 1971, the second on 23 October 1971.

The C-212 is able to fill six main roles—as a 16-seat paratroop transport, military freighter, ambulance, photographic aircraft, crew trainer or 19-seat passenger transport—and has been certificated to joint military and civil standards by the Instituto Nacional de Técnica Aeroespacial (INTA), which was also responsible for the flight test programme. It has a STOL capability that enables it to use unprepared landing strips about 400 m (1,310 ft) in length, and has been optimised for operation in remote areas with a poor infrastructure.

Eight pre-production Aviocars were ordered initially by the Spanish Air Ministry; the first of these made its first flight on 17 November 1972, and all had flown by February 1974.

By mid-1979 a total of 172 Aviocars had been sold, and production was then at the rate of 35 aircraft per year.

The following versions are in service:

C-212A (Spanish Air Force designation T.12B). Military utility transport, ordered by the air forces of Indonesia (45), Jordan (3), Portugal (20) and Spain (55), and for civil internal use by the government of Nicaragua (5) and two customers in South America (10). First C-212A delivered on 20 May 1974. First Spanish Air Force squadron is No. 461, based at Gando in the Canary Islands.

C-212AV. VIP transport operated by the air forces of Jordan (1) and Spain (5). First example delivered 13 May 1976.

C-212B (Spanish Air Force designation TR.12A). Photographic survey version. Six of the eight pre-production Aviocars were completed to this configuration for the Spanish Air Force, and are each equipped with two Wild RC-10 aerial survey cameras. Four others have been delivered to the Portuguese Air Force.

C-212C. Commercial transport. Three ordered by the Indonesian company Pertamina, for operation by Pelita Air Service. First example (PK-PCK) delivered on 16 July 1975. Also operated by Merpati Nusantara Air Lines, Bouraq Air Lines (three) and Companie PT Deraya (three) of Indonesia, Bursa Hava Yollari of Turkey (two) and Air Logistic Co of Alaska (one). Two sold to Royal Thailand Rain Industry can be converted quickly from rainmaking configuration, by removal of chemical containers through ventral door, for personnel and/or cargo transportation. Certificated by the FAA to FAR Pt 25 requirements at an AUW of 5,670 kg (12,500 lb) as the C-212CA, and at an AUW of 6,500 kg (14,330 lb) as the C-212CB.

C-212E. Navigation trainer. Two of the eight pre-production Aviocars were completed to this configuration for the Spanish Air Force, which later increased its order to five of this version. First example delivered 15 December 1976.

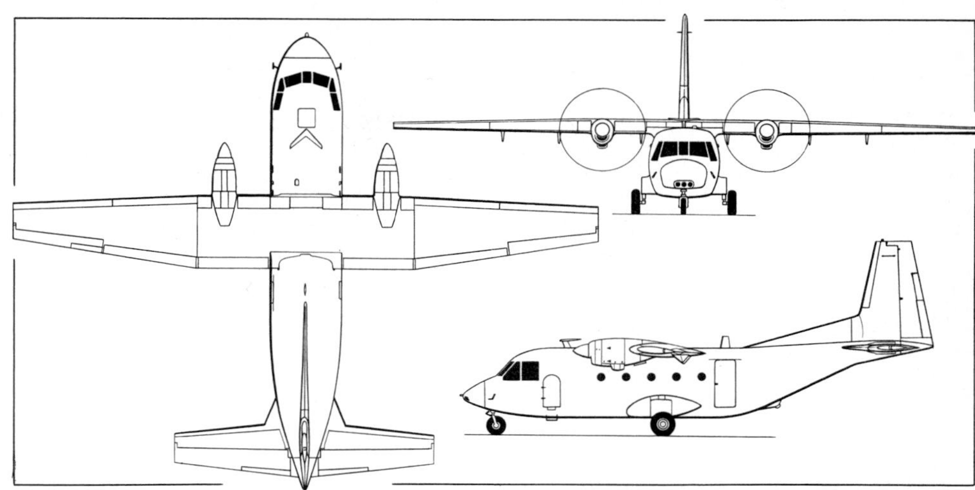

CASA C-212 Series 200 Aviocar twin-turboprop light transport aircraft *(Pilot Press)*

The aforementioned versions have the collective designation C-212-5, and are no longer in production. The current production model, from 1979, is:

C-212 Series 200. Improved version, with more powerful TPE 331-10 engines and increased max T-O weight. Aircraft Nos. 138 and 139 served as prototypes for this version, making their first flights on 30 April and 20 June 1978 respectively.

In order to promote sales in the Far East, CASA has established a C-212 assembly line in Indonesia, as well as full after-sales support in that area (see Nurtanio entry in Indonesian section). Aircraft sold and assembled by Nurtanio are included in the totals listed under individual versions of the Aviocar.

The following description applies to both the C-212-5 and the Series 200, except where a specific model is indicated:

TYPE: Twin-turboprop STOL utility transport.

WINGS: Cantilever high-wing monoplane. Wing section NACA 65_3-218. Incidence 2° 30′. No dihedral or sweepback. All-metal light alloy fail-safe structure. All-metal ailerons and double-slotted trailing-edge flaps. Trim tab in port aileron. Rubber-boot de-icing of leading-edges.

FUSELAGE: Semi-monocoque fail-safe structure of light alloy construction.

TAIL UNIT: Cantilever two-spar all-metal structure, with dorsal fairing forward of fin. Tailplane mid-mounted on rear of fuselage. Trim tab in rudder and each elevator. Rubber-boot de-icing of leading-edges. Wider-span horizontal surfaces on Series 200.

LANDING GEAR (C-212-5): Non-retractable tricycle type, with single main wheels and single steerable nosewheel. CASA oleo-pneumatic shock-absorbers. Dunlop wheels and tyres, main units size 11·00-12 (8-ply) Type III, nose unit size 8·00-7 Type III. Tyre pressure (all units) 3·10 bars (45 lb/sq in). Dunlop hydraulic disc brakes on main wheels.

LANDING GEAR (C-212 Srs 200): As C-212-5, but Goodyear wheels and tyres: main units size 11·00-12 Type III (10-ply rating), pressure 3·72 bars (54 lb/sq in); nose unit size 24-7·7 Type VII (8-ply rating), pressure 3·52 bars (51 lb/sq in). Goodyear hydraulic disc brakes on main wheels.

POWER PLANT (C-212-5): Two 559 kW (750 shp) Garrett-AiResearch TPE 331-5-251C turboprop engines, each driving a Hartzell HC-B4TN-5CL/LT10282HB+4 four-blade constant-speed (Beta mode on ground) metal propeller (three-blade HC-B3TN-5E in prototype and early pre-series aircraft). Fuel in four outer-wing tanks, with total capacity of 2,100 litres (462 Imp gallons). Oil capacity 6 litres (1·32 Imp gallons) per engine.

POWER PLANT (C-212 Srs 200): Two Garrett-AiResearch TPE 331-10-501C turboprop engines, each flat-rated at 634 kW (850 shp) and driving a Hartzell HC-B4MV-5AL four-blade constant-speed propeller (Beta mode on ground). Fuel and oil capacities as for C-212-5.

ACCOMMODATION (C-212-5): Crew of two on flight deck. For the troop transport role, the main cabin can be fitted with 16 inward-facing seats along the cabin walls, to accommodate 15 paratroops and an instructor/jumpmaster; or seats for 18 fully-equipped troops. As an ambulance, the cabin would normally be equipped to carry 12 stretcher patients and two medical attendants. As a freighter, the Aviocar can carry up to 2,100 kg (4,630 lb) of cargo in the main cabin, including light vehicles. Photographic version is equipped with two Wild RC-10 vertical cameras and a darkroom. Navigation training version accommodation consists of individual desks for an instructor and five pupils, in two rows, fitted with appropriate instrument installations. The civil passenger transport version has standard seating for 19 persons in five rows of three (one to port and two to starboard of centre aisle) at 79 cm (31 in) pitch, plus two rows of two seats. VIP transport version can be furnished to customer's requirements: those of the Spanish and Royal Jordanian Air Forces have seats for 12 passengers (four forward and eight aft, with cabin divider), with two foldaway tables in forward section and toilet forward and baggage compartment aft of main passenger areas. Access to main cabin is via two doors on the port side, one aft of (and providing access to) the flight deck and one aft of the wing trailing-edge. In addition, there is a two-section underfuselage loading ramp/door aft of the main cabin; this door is openable in flight for the discharge of paratroops or cargo, and is fitted with external wheels, to allow the door to remain open during ground manoeuvring. There is an emergency exit door aft of the wing trailing-edge on the starboard side. All versions have a toilet at the forward end of the main cabin on the starboard side, with a baggage compartment opposite on the port side. In the civil transport version, the interior of the rear-loading door can be used for additional baggage stowage.

ACCOMMODATION (C-212 Srs 200): Troop transport has 20 inward-facing seats plus three forward-facing seats, for 23 paratroops and instructor/jumpmaster; or seats for 24 fully-equipped troops. Cargo payload is 2,250 kg (4,960 lb). Civil transport version seats up to 25 passengers, with provision for quick change to all-cargo or mixed passenger/cargo interior. Toilet and baggage compartment are not standard.

SYSTEMS: Unpressurised cabin. Hydraulic system, pressure 138 bars (2,000 lb/sq in), operates main-wheel brakes, flaps, nosewheel steering and ventral cargo door. Electrical system is supplied by two 9kW starter/generators.

AVIONICS AND EQUIPMENT: Radio and radar equipment includes VHF, UHF, VOR/ILS and one ADF. Blind-flying instrumentation standard. Optional avionics include Tacan, SIF/IFF, and a second ADF.

DIMENSIONS, EXTERNAL:

Wing span	19·00 m (62 ft 4 in)
Wing chord at root	2·50 m (8 ft 2½ in)
Wing chord at tip	1·50 m (4 ft 11 in)
Wing aspect ratio	9
Length overall	15·16 m (44 ft 9 in)
Height overall	6·68 m (21 ft 11 in)
Tailplane span: C-212-5	7·40 m (24 ft 3¼ in)
C-212 Srs 200	8·40 m (27 ft 6¾ in)
Wheel track	3·10 m (10 ft 2 in)
Wheelbase	5·55 m (18 ft 2½ in)
Propeller diameter	2·69 m (8 ft 10 in)
Distance between propeller centres	5·30 m (17 ft 4¾ in)
Passenger door (port, aft):	
Max height	1·58 m (5 ft 2¼ in)
Max width	0·70 m (2 ft 3½ in)
Crew and servicing door (port, fwd):	
Max height	1·10 m (3 ft 7¼ in)
Max width	0·60 m (1 ft 11⅝ in)
Rear-loading door: Max length	3·66 m (12 ft 0 in)
Max width	1·70 m (5 ft 7 in)
Max height	1·80 m (5 ft 11 in)

DIMENSIONS, INTERNAL:

Cabin (between flight deck and rear-loading door):	
Length	6·50 m (21 ft 4 in)
Max width	2·10 m (6 ft 10¾ in)
Max height	1·80 m (5 ft 11 in)
Floor area	10·50 m² (113·0 sq ft)
Volume	22·00 m³ (776·9 cu ft)

AREAS:

Wings, gross	40·0 m² (430·56 sq ft)
Ailerons (total)	2·45 m² (26·37 sq ft)
Trailing-edge flaps (total)	7·38 m² (79·44 sq ft)
Fin	4·25 m² (45·75 sq ft)
Rudder, incl tab	2·02 m² (31·74 sq ft)
Tailplane: C-212-5	7·36 m² (79·22 sq ft)
C-212 Srs 200	12·57 m² (135·30 sq ft)
Elevators, incl tabs	4·36 m² (46·93 sq ft)

WEIGHTS AND LOADINGS (C-212-5):
Manufacturer's weight empty 3,700 kg (8,157 lb)
Weight empty, equipped 3,905 kg (8,609 lb)
Max payload 2,100 kg (4,630 lb)
Fuel load 1,600 kg (3,527 lb)
Max T-O weight 6,500 kg (14,330 lb)
Max zero-fuel weight 6,000 kg (13,227 lb)
Max landing weight 6,250 kg (13,780 lb)
Max wing loading 162·5 kg/m^2 (33·3 lb/sq ft)
Max power loading 5·81 kg/kW (9·55 lb/shp)
WEIGHTS (C-212 Srs 200):
Manufacturer's weight empty 3,915 kg (8,631 lb)
Weight empty, equipped 4,115 kg (9,072 lb)
Max payload 2,250 kg (4,960 lb)
Fuel load 1,600 kg (3,527 lb)
Max T-O weight 7,300 kg (16,093 lb)
Max landing weight 7,000 kg (15,432 lb)
PERFORMANCE (C-212-5, at max T-O weight except where indicated):
Never-exceed speed
253 knots (471 km/h; 292 mph) EAS
Max level speed at 3,660 m (12,000 ft)
194 knots (359 km/h; 223 mph)
Econ cruising speed at 3,660 m (12,000 ft)
148 knots (275 km/h; 171 mph)
Stalling speed, flaps up 74 knots (137 km/h; 85·5 mph)
Stalling speed, flaps down
61·5 knots (113 km/h; 70·5 mph)
Max rate of climb at S/L 518 m (1,700 ft)/min
Max rate of climb at S/L, one engine out
93 m (305 ft)/min
Service ceiling 8,140 m (26,700 ft)
Service ceiling, one engine out 4,115 m (13,500 ft)
T-O run 350 m (1,148 ft)
T-O to 15 m (50 ft) 484 m (1,588 ft)
Landing from 15 m (50 ft) 518 m (1,700 ft)
Landing run 331 m (1,085 ft)
Range at 3,050 m (10,000 ft):
with max fuel and 1,045 kg (2,303 lb) payload
949 nm (1,760 km; 1,093 miles)
with max payload 258 nm (480 km; 298 miles)
PERFORMANCE (C-212 Srs 200, at max T-O weight, ISA):
Max cruising speed at 3,050 m (10,000 ft)
210 knots (389 km/h; 242 mph)
Max rate of climb at S/L 527 m (1,730 ft)/min
Service ceiling 8,535 m (28,000 ft)
T-O run 370 m (1,215 ft)
T-O to 15 m (50 ft) 565 m (1,855 ft)
Landing from 15 m (50 ft) 430 m (1,410 ft)
Landing run 280 m (920 ft)
Range at max cruising speed, no reserves:
with max payload 410 nm (760 km; 472 miles)
with max fuel 928 nm (1,720 km; 1,070 miles)

CASA C-101 AVIOJET

On 16 September 1975, CASA and the Spanish Ministerio del Aire signed a development contract for a new basic and advanced military jet trainer aircraft. This has the manufacturer's designation C-101. The contract covered design, development, and the construction of six prototype aircraft: four for flight test and two for static and fatigue testing. First flights of the four flying prototypes were made on 27 June and 30 September 1977, and 26 January and 17 April 1978. All four were handed over to the Spanish Air Force, for service trials, in 1978.

To minimise cost and maintenance, the C-101 is built on modular lines, with ample space within the airframe for equipment for any training mission likely to be required in the 1980s. The C-101 is fully aerobatic, and will be able to carry out such additional duties as ground attack, reconnaissance, escort, weapons training, electronic countermeasures (ECM), and photographic missions.

The C-101 was designed by CASA with the co-operation of MBB (Germany) and Northrop (USA), the latter company providing assistance with the inlet design and that of the 'Norcasa' wing section. Manufacture of production aircraft is carried out entirely by CASA except for the nosewheel unit, which is produced in the UK by Dowty Rotol. Wings and main landing gear units are built at Getafe and fuselages at Seville.

Production of the first 10 aircraft started at the beginning of 1978, and the first of these was scheduled for completion in August 1979. A total of 60 has been ordered by the Spanish Air Force, which has an overall requirement for about 120. Deliveries were expected to begin in October 1979, with entry into service following in 1980 to replace HA 200/220 Saetas.

TYPE: Tandem two-seat basic and advanced trainer and light tactical aircraft.

WINGS: Cantilever low-wing monoplane. Wing section Norcasa 15, thickness/chord ratio 15%. Dihedral 5°. Incidence 1°. Sweepback at quarter-chord 1° 53′. All-metal (aluminium alloy) three-spar fail-safe stressed-skin structure. Plain ailerons and slotted trailing-edge flaps, of glassfibre/honeycomb sandwich construction. Ailerons actuated hydraulically, with manual backup. Ground-adjustable tab on port aileron.

FUSELAGE: All-metal semi-monocoque fail-safe structure. Hydraulically-operated aluminium honeycomb airbrake under centre of fuselage.

TAIL UNIT: Cantilever all-metal structure, with variable-incidence tailplane. Aluminium honeycomb rudder and elevators. Optional electrically-actuated trim tab in rudder.

Fourth prototype CASA C-101 Aviojet trainer/close support aircraft

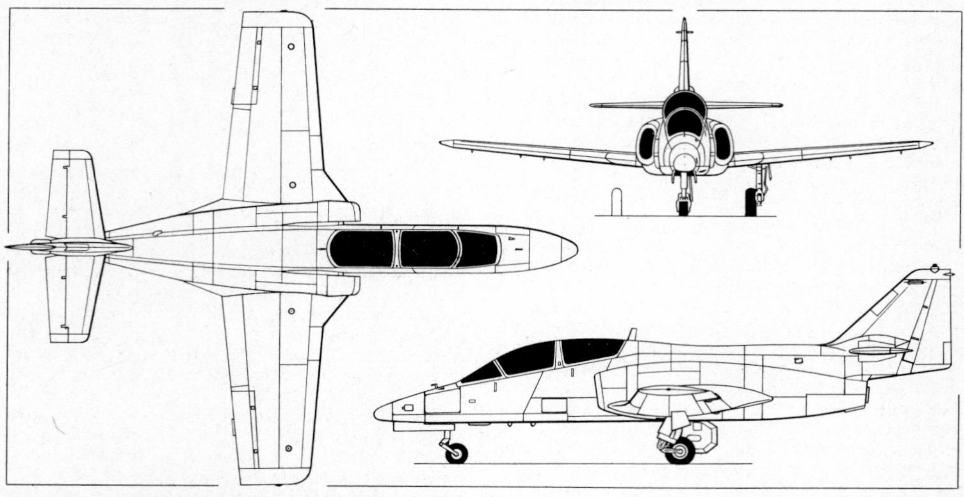

CASA C-101 Aviojet basic/advanced training and light strike aircraft *(Pilot Press)*

LANDING GEAR: Hydraulically-retractable tricycle type, with single wheel and oleo-pneumatic shock-absorber on each unit. Forward-retracting Dowty Rotol nose unit, with steerable nosewheel size 450 × 140-8. Inward-retracting main units, wheel size 615 × 225-10, with disc brakes.

POWER PLANT: One Garrett-AiResearch TFE 731-2-2J non-afterburning turbofan engine (15·57 kN; 3,500 lb st) installed in rear fuselage. Lateral intake on each side of fuselage, abreast of second cockpit. Fuel in one 1,125 litre (247 Imp gallon) fuselage bag tank, one 575 litre (126 Imp gallon) integral tank in wing centre-section, and two outer-wing integral tanks each of 335 litres (74 Imp gallons). Total internal fuel capacity 2,370 litres (521 Imp gallons). Refuelling point in port air intake. Oil capacity 8·5 litres (1·8 Imp gallons).

ACCOMMODATION: Crew of two in tandem, on Martin-Baker Mk E 10 zero-zero ejection seats, under individual canopies which open sideways to starboard and separated by internal windscreen. Rear seat elevated 0·325 m (1 ft 0¾ in). Cockpit pressurised and air-conditioned. Dual controls standard.

SYSTEMS: Hamilton Standard three-wheel bootstrap-type air-conditioning and pressurisation system, differential 0·28 bars (4·1 lb/sq in). Single hydraulic system, pressure 207 bars (3,000 lb/sq in), for landing gear, ailerons, airbrake and parking brake. Pneumatic system for air-conditioning, pressurisation and canopy seal. 9kW electrical system. High-pressure oxygen system.

AVIONICS AND EQUIPMENT: Magnavox RT-1168/ARC-164 UHF; Wilcox AN/ARC-134 VHF; Bendix AN/ARN-127 VOR/ILS/marker; Collins AN/ARN-118 Tacan; Teledyne Electronic RT-1063B/APX-101 IFF/SIF; Sperry SPI-402 flight director system, including Tarsyn vertical and directional gyro package, dual HZ-444 attitude director indicators, RD-500A horizontal situation indicators with remote course selection, RH-405 radio magnetic indicators and 807A com transceivers.

ARMAMENT AND OPERATIONAL EQUIPMENT: Large bay below rear cockpit suitable for quick-change packages, including 30 mm DEFA cannon pod, a twin 12·7 mm gun pod, reconnaissance camera, ECM package or laser designator. Six underwing hardpoints, capacities 500 kg (1,102 lb) inboard, 375 kg (827 lb) centre and 250 kg (551 lb) outboard. Typical armament may include one 30 mm cannon or two 12·7 mm guns in the fuselage; and six LAU-10 pods of 5 in rockets, six LAU-68 pods of 2·75 in rockets, six BR-250 250 kg bombs, four BR-375 375 kg bombs, two BR-500 500 kg bombs, four BLU-27 napalm canisters or six SUU-25 flare pods under the wings.

DIMENSIONS, EXTERNAL:
Wing span 10·60 m (34 ft 9⅜ in)
Wing chord at c/l 2·36 m (7 ft 9 in)
Wing chord at tip 1·41 m (4 ft 7½ in)
Wing aspect ratio 5·6
Length overall 12·25 m (40 ft 2¼ in)
Height overall 4·25 m (13 ft 11¼ in)
Tailplane span 4·32 m (14 ft 2 in)
Wheel track 2·97 m (9 ft 9 in)
Wheelbase 4·87 m (15 ft 11¾ in)
AREAS:
Wings, gross 20·00 m^2 (215·3 sq ft)
Ailerons (total) 1·60 m^2 (17·22 sq ft)
Trailing-edge flaps (total) 2·50 m^2 (26·91 sq ft)
Fin 1·90 m^2 (20·45 sq ft)
Rudder 1·30 m^2 (13·99 sq ft)
Tailplane 3·44 m^2 (37·03 sq ft)
Elevators 1·00 m^2 (10·76 sq ft)
WEIGHTS AND LOADINGS:
Basic operating weight 3,300 kg (7,275 lb)
Max internal fuel weight 1,860 kg (4,100 lb)
T-O weight: trainer, 'clean' 4,700 kg (10,361 lb)
ground attack 5,600 kg (12,345 lb)
Wing loading: trainer 235·0 kg/m^2 (48·13 lb/sq ft)
ground attack 280·0 kg/m^2 (57·35 lb/sq ft)
Power loading: trainer 302 kg/kN (2·96 lb/lb st)
ground attack 359 kg/kN (3·53 lb/lb st)
PERFORMANCE (at 4,400 kg; 9,700 lb AUW):
Max limiting Mach No. Mach 0·80
Max level speed at S/L 370 knots (685 km/h; 426 mph)
Max level speed at 8,230 m (27,000 ft)
Mach 0·69 (416 knots; 771 km/h; 479 mph)
Econ cruising speed at 9,145 m (30,000 ft)
Mach 0·56 (396 knots; 734 km/h; 456 mph)
Stalling speed, flaps up
99 knots (183 km/h; 114 mph)
Stalling speed, flaps down
88 knots (164 km/h; 102 mph)
Max rate of climb at S/L 1,097 m (3,600 ft)/min
Time to 7,620 m (25,000 ft) 10 min
Service ceiling 12,500 m (41,000 ft)
T-O and landing run 580 m (1,903 ft)
T-O to 15 m (50 ft) 890 m (2,920 ft)
Landing from 15 m (50 ft) 910 m (2,985 ft)
Typical combat radius:
interdiction (lo-lo-lo) with four 500 lb bombs, two 19 × 2·75 in rocket launchers and 30 mm gun, 5 min over target, 15 min reserves
100 nm (185 km; 115 miles)
close air support with four 19 × 2·75 in rocket launchers and 30 mm gun, 1 h loiter over battle area, 15 min reserves 150 nm (278 km; 173 miles)
armed patrol with 30 mm or two 12·7 mm guns, no underwing stores, 3 h at 200 knots (370 km/h; 230 mph) at S/L, 20 min reserves
160 nm (296 km; 184 miles)
ECM, 3 h 15 min loiter over target, 20 min reserves
330 nm (611 km; 380 miles)
interdiction (hi-lo-hi) with two 500 lb bombs and 30 mm gun, 5 min over target, 15 min reserves
450 nm (833 km; 518 miles)
photo-reconnaissance (hi-lo-hi), 20 min reserves
520 nm (964 km; 599 miles)
Ferry range, 30 min reserves
2,055 nm (3,807 km; 2,366 miles)

Typical endurance, training missions:
General handling, incl 10 min aerobatics 1 h 15 min
High-level navigation 2 h 0 min
Low-level navigation 1 h 30 min
Weapons training, incl 1 h over firing range 1 h 35 min

CASA C-102

Under this designation CASA is developing, with assistance from AISA, a side-by-side two-seat primary training aircraft with a tricycle landing gear and a 74·5-112 kW (100-150 hp) engine.

SWEDEN

SAAB-SCANIA

SAAB-SCANIA AKTIEBOLAG

Head Office: S-581 88 Linköping
Telephone: Int. +46 13 11 54 00
Telex: 50040 SAABLGS
President: Sten Gustafsson

Aerospace Division

Telephone: Int. +46 13 12 90 20
Head of Division: T. Gullstrand
Head of Missile and Electronics Sector: I. K. Olsson
Information: Hans G. Andersson

The original Svenska Aeroplan AB was founded at Trollhättan in 1937 for the production of military aircraft. In 1939 this company was amalgamated with the Aircraft Division (ASJA) of the Svenska Järnvägsverkstäderna rolling stock factory in Linköping. Following this merger, Saab moved its head office and engineering departments to Linköping, which is now the main aerospace factory.

In 1950, Saab acquired a factory at Jönköping for development and manufacture of airborne equipment. Other post-war expansions include a bombproof underground factory in Linköping, as well as important new production and engineering facilities in Linköping, Jönköping, Trollhättan and Gothenburg. The company's name was changed to Saab Aktiebolag in May 1965.

During 1968 Saab merged with another large Swedish automotive concern, Scania-Vabis, to strengthen the two companies' position in automotive product development, production and export. Malmö Flygindustri (MFI) was acquired in the same year.

Saab-Scania has nearly 40,000 employees, organised in four operating divisions. Of these, about 6,000 are employed by the Aerospace Division, including 4,400 at Linköping, 500 at Jonköping, 50 at Malmö, 35 at Norrköping and 25 at Gothenburg.

Saab-Scania's current and recent aerospace products include the Saab 37 Viggen supersonic multi-purpose STOL combat aircraft, the Saab 35 Draken single-seat all-weather fighter-bomber, the Saab 105 multi-purpose military aircraft and the Safari/Supporter series of piston-engined trainer and army co-operation aircraft. Since 1949 Saab-Scania has delivered more than 2,000 military jet aircraft to the air forces of four nations. It has also delivered more than 1,500 piston-engined aircraft to military and civil customers around the world. Since 1962, Saab-Scania has also had a dealership for Hughes helicopters in Scandinavia and Finland. In 1978 it received a contract to manufacture the inboard wing flaps and vanes for the McDonnell Douglas DC-9 Super 80 twin-turbofan transport aircraft; the first set of flaps was delivered in January 1979. In December 1978 Saab-Scania signed an agreement to participate in the production of the BAe 146 four-turbofan feederliner. For this aircraft, it is manufacturing tailplanes, elevators, rudders, ailerons and spoilers.

Saab-Scania has greatly expanded its activities in the electronics field. Current production items include computer systems, autopilots, fire control and bombing systems for piloted aircraft, and electronics for guided missiles. A major production programme is the airborne computer for the Saab 37. The Saab RGS2 lead-computing optical sighting system has been selected for the Royal Netherlands Air Force Northrop NF-5A, the Italian Air Force Aermacchi M.B.339A, and the British Aerospace Hawks for the Finnish Air Force. Space-borne computers, optronic fire control systems and field artillery computer systems are also under development and in production.

Saab-Scania manufactured the Saab 05A air-to-surface missile for the Swedish Air Force and a modernised Saab 04E version of the Air Force RB04 homing anti-shipping missile carried by the AJ 37 Viggen. Its guided missile activities are now conducted by Saab-Bofors Missile Corporation, formed jointly with AB Bofors. Initial task of this company is to develop a new anti-ship weapon, the RBS 15.

In addition, Saab-Scania is a member of the MESH space technology consortium which delivered the TD-1A solar research satellite to ESRO. In 1973 ESRO/ESA ordered from MESH the OTS satellite, and subsequently the MAROTS maritime communications satellite.

SAAB 37 VIGGEN (THUNDERBOLT)

Swedish Air Force designations: AJ 37, JA 37, SF 37, SH 37 and SK 37

The Saab 37 Viggen multi-mission combat aircraft is the major component in the System 37 manned weapon system for the Swedish Air Force. System 37 comprises the Saab 37 and its power plant, airborne equipment, armament, ammunition and photographic equipment; ground servicing equipment, including test equipment; and training equipment, including simulators. Particular attention is paid to the optimum adaptation of System 37 to the SwAF base organisation and air defence control system (STRIL 60).

Saab JA 37 interceptor version of the Viggen, in the markings of F13 Wing of the Swedish Air Force

The Saab 37 is designed as a basic platform which can be readily adapted to fulfil the four primary roles of attack, interception, reconnaissance and training. The aircraft has an advanced aerodynamic configuration, using a foreplane, fitted with flaps, in combination with a main delta wing to confer STOL characteristics. Its Swedish development of the American Pratt & Whitney JT8D turbofan engine, with a very powerful Swedish-designed afterburner, enables the Viggen to cruise economically and to have the acceleration and climb performance required for interception duties; the combination of advanced aerodynamic features with this engine, thrust reverser, automatic speed control during landing, and head-up display, enables it to operate from narrow runways of about 500 m (1,640 ft) length.

The first of seven prototypes flew for the first time on 8 February 1967, and by April 1969 all six single-seat prototypes were flying. The seventh Viggen was the prototype for the two-seat SK 37 operational trainer. A number of airframe parts were also completed for static testing.

The following versions have been announced:

AJ 37. Single-seat all-weather attack version, with secondary interceptor capability. Initial production version, which began to replace the A 32A Lansen from mid-1971. First production AJ 37 flew on 23 February 1971 and deliveries began on 21 June 1971. First AJ 37 unit was F7 Wing at Såtenäs. The AJ 37 equips two squadrons of F6 Wing at Karlsborg, two squadrons of F7, and one squadron of F15 at Söderhamn.

JA 37. Single-seat interceptor, with Volvo Flygmotor RM8B engine, of improved performance and with secondary capability for attack missions. Preliminary design work began in 1968. Flight testing of selected systems, including the radar, was initiated in early 1973 in a modified Saab 32 Lansen development aircraft. Four modified AJ 37s were used in the JA 37 development programme, as detailed in the 1976-77 *Jane's*. The JA 37 has four elevon hydraulic actuators under each wing, instead of three as on other versions, and a modified, taller tail-fin similar to that of the SK 37.

A British Aerospace contract with FMV (Forsvarets Material Verk) provided for technical assistance to Saab-Scania and L. M. Ericsson in integrating the Sky Flash air-to-air missile with the Viggen airframe and radar for trials carried out in 1977-78.

An initial batch of 30 JA 37s was ordered in September 1974, out of a planned total procurement of 149 to re-equip eight Draken fighter squadrons of the Swedish Air Force in 1979-85. Two further batches, of 60 and 59, were ordered in May 1978. First flight by a production JA 37 (serial No. 301) was made on 4 November 1977. Deliveries, to F13 at Norrköping, began in 1979.

SF 37. Single-seat all-weather armed photographic reconnaissance version to replace the S 35E Draken. A production contract was awarded in early 1973. Intended normally for overland reconnaissance, the SF 37 has a modified nose containing cameras and other equipment, permitting reconnaissance at any hour of the day or night, at high or low altitudes and at long distances from its base. First flown on 21 May 1973. Deliveries, to F13 at Norrköping, began in April 1977.

SH 37. Single-seat all-weather maritime reconnaissance version, to replace the S 32C version of the Lansen. Production ordered at same time as the SF 37. Primarily intended to survey, register, and report activities in the neighbourhood of Swedish territory. Can also be used for attack missions. Prototype first flown on 10 December 1973. First production SH 37 delivered on 19 June 1975. In service with F13 at Norrköping (one squadron); deliveries to F17 at Kallinge and F21 at Luleå began in 1978.

SK 37. Tandem two-seat dual-control training version, in which the rear cockpit takes the place of some electronics and the forward fuselage fuel tank, and is fitted with bulged hood and twin periscopes. Modified, taller tail-fin of increased area. Capable of secondary attack role, with full range of attack armament as in AJ 37. Prototype first flown on 2 July 1970. First production SK 37 delivered in June 1972. In service with conversion unit of F15 at Söderhamn.

Saab 37X. Proposed export version, essentially similar to JA 37.

A 20. Proposed future attack version. Described separately.

Initially, 175 aircraft of the AJ 37, SF/SH 37 and SK 37 versions were ordered for the Swedish Air Force; in December 1973 it was announced that five more aircraft (AJ 37s) were to be built within the same overall budget cost. More than 200 of the 329 Viggens ordered by mid-1979 had been delivered by that time.

The following details refer generally to all versions of the Viggen, except where specific versions are indicated:

Type: Single-seat all-weather multi-purpose combat aircraft and (SK 37) two-seat operational trainer.

Wings: Tandem arrangement of canard foreplane, with trailing-edge flaps, and a rear-mounted delta main wing with two-section hydraulically-actuated powered elevons on each trailing-edge, which can be operated differentially or in unison. Main wing has compound sweep on leading-edge. Outer sections have extended leading-edge. Extensive use of metal-bonded honeycomb panels for wing control surfaces, foreplane flaps and main landing gear doors.

Fuselage: Conventional all-metal semi-monocoque structure, using light metal forgings and heat-resistant plastics bonding. Local use of titanium for engine firewall and other selected areas. Four plate-type airbrakes, one on each side and two below fuselage. Metal-bonded honeycomb construction is used to a large extent. Quick-release handle permits nosecone to be pulled forward on tracks to give access to radar compartment.

Tail Unit: Vertical surfaces only, comprising main fin and powered rudder, supplemented by a small ventral fin.

Saab SF 37 all-weather photographic reconnaissance version of the Viggen

Rudder of metal-bonded honeycomb construction. The main fin can be folded downward to port.

LANDING GEAR: Retractable tricycle type of Saab origin, built by Motala Verkstad and designed for a max rate of sink of 300 m (985 ft)/min. Power-steerable twin-wheel nose unit retracts forward. Each main unit has two main wheels in tandem and retracts inward into main wing and fuselage. Main oleos shorten during retraction. Nosewheel tyres size 18 × 5·5, pressure 10·7 bars (155 lb/sq in). Main-wheel tyres size 26 × 6·6, pressure 14·8 bars (215 lb/sq in). Goodyear wheels and brakes. Dunlop anti-skid system.

POWER PLANT (AJ 37, SF/SH 37, SK 37): One Volvo Flygmotor RM8A (supersonic development of the Pratt & Whitney JT8D-22) turbofan engine, fitted with a Swedish-developed afterburner and thrust reverser. This engine is rated at 65·7 kN (14,770 lb st) dry and 115·7 kN (26,015 lb st) with afterburning. Thrust reverser doors are actuated automatically by the compression of the oleo as the nose gear strikes the runway, the thrust being deflected forward via three annular slots in the ejector wall. The ejector is normally kept open at subsonic speeds to reduce fuselage base drag; at supersonic speeds, with the intake closed, the ejector serves as a supersonic nozzle. Fuel is contained in one tank in each wing, a saddle tank over the engine, one tank in each side of the fuselage, and one aft of the cockpit. Electrically-powered pumps deliver fuel to the engine from the central fuselage tank, which is kept filled continuously from the peripheral tanks. Pressure refuelling point beneath starboard wing. Provision for jettisonable external auxiliary tank (normally permanent on SK 37) on underfuselage centreline pylon.

POWER PLANT (JA 37, Saab 37X): One Volvo Flygmotor RM8B turbofan engine, rated at 72·1 kN (16,203 lb st) dry and 125 kN (28,108 lb st) with afterburning. Thrust reverser and fuel system similar to other versions.

ACCOMMODATION: Pilot only, on Saab-Scania fully-adjustable rocket-assisted ejection seat beneath rearward-hinged clamshell canopy. Cockpit pressurisation, heating and air-conditioning by engine bleed air, via Delaney Gallay heat exchangers, cooling turbines and water separator. Birdproof windscreen. JA 37 cockpit redesigned and optimised for interceptor mission. SK 37 has twin periscopes, and tandem ejection seats under individual canopies.

SYSTEMS: Two independent hydraulic systems, each of 207 bars (3,000 lb/sq in) pressure, each with engine-driven pump; auxiliary electrically-operated standby pump for emergency use. Three-phase AC electrical system supplies 210/115V 400Hz power via a General Electric 60kVA liquid-cooled brushless generator (Westinghouse 75kVA in JA 37), which also provides 28V DC power via 24V nickel-cadmium batteries and rectifier. Emergency standby power from 6kVA turbogenerator, which is extended automatically into the airstream in the event of a power failure. External power receptacle on port side of fuselage. Graviner fire detection system.

AVIONICS AND FLIGHT EQUIPMENT: Altogether, about 50 avionics units, with a total weight of approx 600 kg (1,323 lb), are installed in the Saab 37. Flight equipment includes an automatic speed control system, a Marconi Avionics (in AJ 37) or Smiths (JA 37) electronic head-up display, AGA aircraft attitude instruments and radio, Phillips (AJ 37) or Garrett-AiResearch (JA 37) air data computer and instruments, L.M. Ericsson radar, Honeywell radar altimeter, Decca Doppler Type 72 navigation equipment, SATT radar warning system, Svenska Radio radar display system and electronic countermeasures, and AIL Tactical Instrument Landing System (TILS), a microwave scanning beam landing guidance system. Most of the avionics equipment in the Viggen is connected to the central digital computer, which is programmed to check out and monitor these systems both on the ground and during flight. The JA 37 has a ram-air intake on the underfuselage centreline, for cooling the avionics compartment.

ARMAMENT AND OPERATIONAL EQUIPMENT (AJ 37): All armament is carried externally on seven permanent attachment points, three under the fuselage and two under each wing, with standard 750 mm (29·5 in) store ejection racks. Each wing can be fitted with an additional hardpoint if required. Primary armament is the Swedish RB04E air-to-surface homing missile for use against naval targets; the Saab RB05A air-to-surface missile for use against ground, naval and certain airborne targets; or the TV-guided Hughes Maverick (RB 75). To these can be added pods of Bofors 135 mm air-to-surface rockets, up to 16 bombs, or 30 mm Aden gun pods. The AJ 37 version can be adapted to perform interception missions armed with RB24 (Sidewinder) or RB28 (Falcon) air-to-air missiles. Computations in connection with various phases of an attack, including navigation, target approach and fire control calculations, are handled by a Saab-Scania CK-37 miniaturised digital computer. This computer, which performs 48 specific tasks within the aircraft and is capable of 200,000 calculations per second, also provides data to the head-up display in the cockpit, thus freeing the pilot for concentration on other aspects of a flight. Continuous monitoring of the flight paths and fuel situation is provided throughout the mission; the computer can also, when required, release the weapons automatically.

ARMAMENT AND OPERATIONAL EQUIPMENT (JA 37): Permanent underbelly pack, offset to port side of centreline, containing one 30 mm Oerlikon KCA long-range cannon with a muzzle velocity of 1,050 m (3,445 ft)/s, a rate of fire of 1,350 rds/min, and a projectile weight of 0·36 kg (0·79 lb). Improved fire control equipment. This gun installation permits retention of the three underfuselage stores attachment points, as in the AJ 37, in addition to the four underwing hardpoints. Advanced target search and acquisition system, based on a high-performance long-range L.M. Ericsson UAP-1023 X-band pulse-Doppler radar which is unaffected by variations of weather and altitude. This radar is not disturbed by ground clutter, and is highly resistant to ECM. Singer-Kearfott SKC-2037 central digital computer and Garrett-AiResearch LD-5 digital air data computer. Singer-Kearfott KT-70L inertial measuring equipment. Honeywell/Saab-Scania SA07 digital automatic flight control system. Weapon system includes provision for medium- and short-range homing air-to-air missiles.

ARMAMENT AND OPERATIONAL EQUIPMENT (SF 37 and SH 37): Both reconnaissance versions can carry two air-to-air missiles, on the outboard wing stations, for self-defence. Equipment in the SF 37 includes a special optical sight, data camera, tape recorder and other registration equipment. The data camera collects and stores on its film co-ordination figures, aircraft position, course, altitude, target location and other data. Four vertical or oblique low-level cameras and two long-range vertical high-altitude cameras and a VKA 702 infra-red camera are installed in the nose, together with the camera sight, an infra-red sensor, and ECM registration equipment. Systems configuration also makes possible the detection of camouflaged targets and horizon-to-horizon (180°) photo coverage. Typical external mission equipment, in addition to air-to-air missiles, includes drop-tanks on the underfuselage stations, and an active or passive ECM pod on each of the inboard underwing pylons.

Internal equipment of the SH 37 includes a nose-mounted surveillance radar similar to that of the AJ 37, a camera for photographing the radar display, ECM registration equipment, and various other registration systems including a data camera and a tape recorder. The inboard and outboard wing pylons can be occupied, respectively, by active or passive ECM pods and air-to-air missiles, as on the SF 37. The underfuselage attachments can carry a drop-tank on the centreline station, a night reconnaissance pod on the port station and a long-range camera pod or a Red Baron night reconnaissance pod on the starboard station.

DIMENSIONS, EXTERNAL:
- Main wing span — 10·60 m (34 ft 9¼ in)
- Main wing aspect ratio — 2·45
- Foreplane span — 5·45 m (17 ft 10½ in)
- Length overall (incl probe):
  - except JA 37, Saab 37X — 16·30 m (53 ft 5¾ in)
  - JA 37, Saab 37X — 16·40 m (53 ft 9¾ in)
- Length of fuselage:
  - except JA 37, Saab 37X — 15·45 m (50 ft 8¼ in)
  - JA 37, Saab 37X — 15·58 m (51 ft 1½ in)
- Height overall: AJ 37 — 5·80 m (19 ft 0¼ in)
  - JA 37 — 5·90 m (19 ft 4¼ in)
- Height overall, main fin folded — 4·00 m (13 ft 1½ in)
- Wheel track — 4·76 m (15 ft 7½ in)
- Wheelbase (c/l of shock-absorbers):
  - except JA 37, Saab 37X — 5·60 m (18 ft 4½ in)
  - JA 37, Saab 37X — 5·69 m (18 ft 8 in)

AREAS:
- Main wings, gross — 46·00 m² (495·1 sq ft)
- Foreplanes, outside fuselage — 6·20 m² (66·74 sq ft)

WEIGHTS (approx):
- T-O weight:
  - AJ 37 — 15,000-20,500 kg (33,070-45,195 lb)
  - JA 37 'clean' — 15,000 kg (33,070 lb)
  - JA 37 (normal armament) — 17,000 kg (37,478 lb)

PERFORMANCE (JA 37):
- Max level speed: at high altitude — above Mach 2
  - at 100 m (300 ft) — above Mach 1·1
- Approach speed: approx 119 knots (220 km/h; 137 mph)
- Time to 10,000 m (32,800 ft) from brakes off, with afterburning — less than 1 min 40 s
- T-O run — approx 400 m (1,310 ft)
- Landing run — approx 500 m (1,640 ft)
- Required landing field length:
  - conventional landing — 1,000 m (3,280 ft)
  - no-flare landing — 500 m (1,640 ft)

Saab SH 37 Viggen sea surveillance and attack aircraft

Saab JA 37 Viggen firing a BAe Sky Flash air-to-air missile

Tactical radius with external armament:

hi-lo-hi	over 540 nm (1,000 km; 620 miles)
lo-lo-lo	over 270 nm (500 km; 310 miles)

SAAB A 20

As part of a future defence study known as Attack Aircraft System 85, the Swedish Air Force proposed the re-equipment of its medium attack units in the mid-1980s with two new aircraft types. One of these, provisionally designated A 20, would be a modified development of the JA 37 version of the Viggen. The other, of which development was cancelled for budgetary reasons, was the Saab B3LA (see 1978-79 *Jane's*).

SAAB SAFARI/SUPPORTER

The original Safari and Supporter were described and illustrated in the 1978-79 *Jane's*. Production ended in August 1978, at which time 250 had been built.

These models were then superseded by the Safari TS with turbocharged engine.

SAAB SAFARI TS

The prototype Safari (formerly Saab-MFI 15) flew for the first time on 11 July 1969 with a 119 kW (160 hp) engine. After being re-engined with a 149 kW (200 hp) Lycoming IO-360-A1B6, it resumed flying on 26 February 1971. The initial production version with this engine was described and illustrated in the 1978-79 *Jane's*.

From August 1978 it was superseded in production by the Safari TS version with a turbocharged engine; the description which follows applies to this model, which is intended initially as a military trainer.

The Safari TS conforms to FAR Pt 23 in the Normal, Utility and Aerobatic categories, and can be adapted to carry up to 300 kg (660 lb) of external stores. Other typical missions include reconnaissance; liaison; rescue operations; ambulance role (with internally-stowed stretcher); coastal, forest fire or border patrol; road traffic control; and a wide range of basic flying training roles.

A tricycle landing gear is standard, but a tailwheel gear is available optionally, and conversion from one to the other can be accomplished quickly.

TYPE: Two/three-seat light aircraft.

WINGS: Braced shoulder-wing monoplane, with single bracing strut each side. Thickness/chord ratio 10%. Dihedral 1° 30′. All-metal structure, swept forward 5° from roots. Mass-balanced all-metal ailerons. Electrically-operated all-metal plain sealed flaps. Servo tab in starboard aileron.

FUSELAGE: Metal box structure. Glassfibre tailcone, engine cowling panels and wing strut/landing gear attachment fairings.

TAIL UNIT: Cantilever metal structure comprising swept fin and rudder and one-piece mass-balanced horizontal 'stabilator' with large anti-servo and trimming tab. Glassfibre fin tip. Trim tab in rudder.

LANDING GEAR: Non-retractable tricycle (standard) or tailwheel type. Cantilever composite spring main legs. Goodyear 6·00-6 main wheels and either a 5·00-5 steerable nosewheel or a tailwheel. Cleveland disc brakes on main units. Landes or Finncraft skis, or Edo floats, optional.

POWER PLANT: One 157 kW (210 hp) Continental turbocharged flat-six engine, driving a two-blade constant-speed metal propeller with spinner. Two integral wing fuel tanks, total capacity 190 litres (41·8 Imp gallons). Oil capacity 7·5 litres (1·6 Imp gallons). From 10-20 s inverted flight (limited by oil system) permitted.

ACCOMMODATION: Side-by-side adjustable seats, with provision for back-type or seat-type parachutes, for two persons beneath fully-transparent upward-hinged canopy. Dual controls standard. Space aft of seats for 100 kg (220 lb) of baggage (with external access on port side) or, optionally, a rearward-facing third seat. Upward-hinged door, with window, beneath wing on port side. Cabin heated and ventilated.

SYSTEM: 28V 50A DC electrical system.

AVIONICS AND EQUIPMENT: Provision for full blind-flying instrumentation and radio. Six underwing attachments for up to 300 kg (660 lb) of external stores. Landing light in nose.

ARMAMENT: Six underwing hardpoints, the inner two stressed to carry up to 150 kg (330 lb) each and the outer four up to 100 kg (220 lb) each. Typical loads may include two 7·62 mm machine-gun pods, two Abel pods each with seven 75 mm air-to-surface rockets, four Abel pods each with seven 68 mm rockets, eighteen 75 mm Bofors rockets, or six Bofors Bantam wire-guided anti-tank missiles.

DIMENSIONS, EXTERNAL:

Wing span	8·85 m (29 ft 0½ in)
Wing chord (outer panels, constant)	1·36 m (4 ft 5½ in)
Length overall: nosewheel	7·10 m (23 ft 3½ in)
tailwheel	6·85 m (22 ft 5¾ in)
Height overall: nosewheel	2·60 m (8 ft 6½ in)
tailwheel (tail down)	1·90 m (6 ft 2¾ in)
Tailplane span	2·80 m (9 ft 2¼ in)
Wheel track: nosewheel	2·30 m (7 ft 6½ in)
tailwheel	2·025 m (6 ft 7¾ in)
Wheelbase: nosewheel	1·59 m (5 ft 2¾ in)
tailwheel	4·75 m (15 ft 7 in)
Propeller diameter	1·88 m (6 ft 2 in)
Cabin door (port): Height	0·78 m (2 ft 6¾ in)
Width	0·52 m (1 ft 8½ in)

DIMENSIONS, INTERNAL:

Cabin: Max width	1·10 m (3 ft 7¼ in)
Max height (from seat cushion)	1·00 m (3 ft 3¼ in)

AREAS:

Wings, gross	11·90 m² (128·1 sq ft)
Ailerons (total)	0·98 m² (10·55 sq ft)
Flaps (total)	1·55 m² (16·68 sq ft)
Fin	0·77 m² (8·29 sq ft)
Rudder, incl tab	0·73 m² (7·86 sq ft)
Horizontal tail surfaces (total)	2·10 m² (22·6 sq ft)

WEIGHTS AND LOADINGS:

Weight empty, equipped	680 kg (1,499 lb)
Max T-O weight: Normal	1,200 kg (2,645 lb)
Utility	1,125 kg (2,480 lb)
Aerobatic	900 kg (1,984 lb)
Max wing loading: Normal	101 kg/m² (20·7 lb/sq ft)
Utility	95 kg/m² (19·5 lb/sq ft)
Aerobatic	76 kg/m² (15·6 lb/sq ft)
Max power loading: Normal	7·64 kg/kW (12·6 lb/hp)
Utility	7·17 kg/kW (11·8 lb/hp)
Aerobatic	5·73 kg/kW (9·5 lb/hp)

PERFORMANCE (at max T-O weight, ISA; N: Normal category; U: Utility category; A: Aerobatic category):

Max level speed at S/L:	
N	137 knots (254 km/h; 158 mph)
U	138 knots (256 km/h; 159 mph)
A	142 knots (263 km/h; 163 mph)
Cruising speed (75% power) at 3,660 m (12,000 ft):	
N	131 knots (243 km/h; 151 mph)
U	133 knots (246 km/h; 153 mph)
A	138·5 knots (257 km/h; 160 mph)
Cruising speed (75% power) at S/L:	
N	120 knots (222 km/h; 138 mph)
U	121 knots (224 km/h; 139 mph)
A	125 knots (232 km/h; 144 mph)
Stalling speed, flaps up, power off:	
N	60 knots (111 km/h; 70 mph) IAS
U	58 knots (107 km/h; 67 mph) IAS
A	55·5 knots (102 km/h; 63·5 mph) IAS
Stalling speed, flaps down, power off:	
N	56·5 knots (104 km/h; 65 mph) IAS
U	54 knots (100 km/h; 62·5 mph) IAS
A	50·5 knots (93 km/h; 58 mph) IAS
Max rate of climb at S/L: N	288 m (945 ft)/min
U	324 m (1,063 ft)/min
A	462 m (1,516 ft)/min
Rate of climb at 3,660 m (12,000 ft):	
N	246 m (807 ft)/min
U	282 m (925 ft)/min
A	420 m (1,378 ft)/min
Time to 1,525 m (5,000 ft): N	5 min 30 s
U	5 min 0 s
A	3 min 30 s
Time to 3,660 m (12,000 ft): N	13 min 30 s
U	12 min 0 s
A	8 min 0 s
Service ceiling:	
N, U, A	above 6,100 m (20,000 ft)
T-O run at S/L: N	200 m (656 ft)
U	185 m (607 ft)
A	100 m (328 ft)
T-O to 15 m (50 ft) at S/L: N	375 m (1,230 ft)
U	345 m (1,132 ft)
A	210 m (689 ft)
Landing from 15 m (50 ft) at S/L:	
N	400 m (1,312 ft)
U	390 m (1,280 ft)
A	315 m (1,034 ft)
Landing run at S/L: N	160 m (525 ft)
U	155 m (509 ft)
A	125 m (410 ft)
g limits: A	+6·0; −3·0

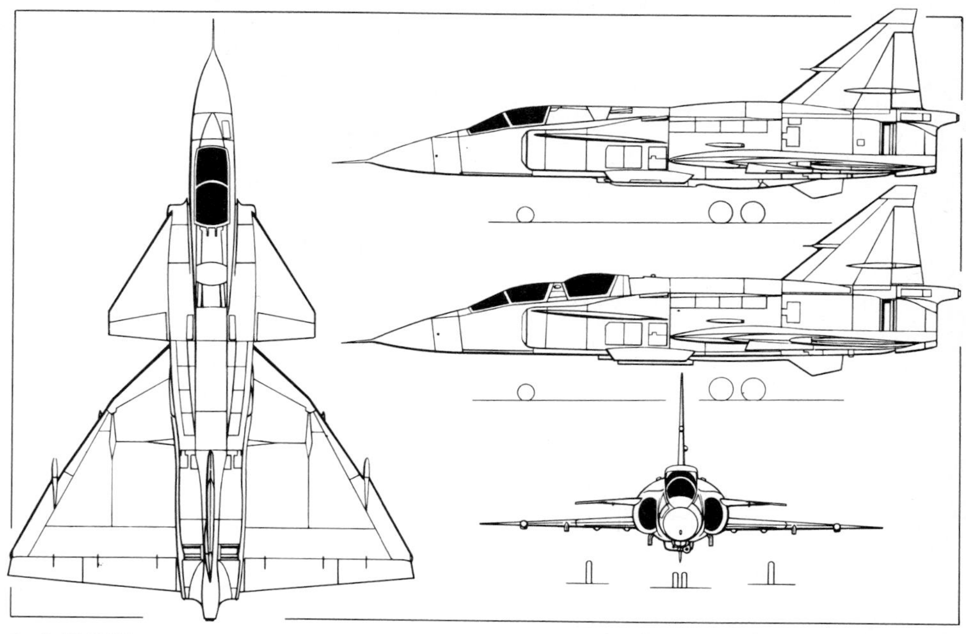

Saab JA 37 Viggen single-seat interceptor, with additional side view (centre) of two-seat SK 37 *(Pilot Press)*

Saab Safari TS two/three-seat light aircraft (Continental turbocharged engine)

SWITZERLAND

FFA
FLUG- UND FAHRZEUGWERKE AG ALTENRHEIN

HEAD OFFICE AND WORKS: CH-9423 Altenrhein
Telephone: (071) 43 01 01
Telex: 77 230 ffa ch
PRESIDENT, BOARD OF MANAGEMENT: Dr C. Caroni
DIRECTOR: Dipl Ing H. Eisenring
CHIEF ENGINEER: Dipl Ing P. Spalinger

This company, known formerly as AG für Dornier Flugzeuge, was originally the Swiss branch of the German Dornier company. It is now an entirely Swiss company.

FFA's current activities include production of the AS.202 Bravo light aircraft, and the overhaul, modification and servicing of military and civil aircraft. Marketing of the Bravo is undertaken by Repair AG, an FFA subsidiary.

The company has about 800 employees, approximately one-quarter of whom are engaged in its aviation activities.

FFA AS.202 BRAVO

Following an agreement concluded with SIAI-Marchetti of Italy, FFA is engaged in production and development of the AS.202 Bravo light trainer and sporting aircraft.

The first Bravo to fly was a Swiss-assembled AS.202/15 prototype (HB-HEA), which flew for the first time on 7 March 1969. The Italian-built second prototype flew on 7 May 1969. The third aircraft (HB-HEC) made its first flight on 16 June 1969, and the first production aircraft on 22 December 1971.

Three versions are available, as follows:

AS.202/15. Two/three-seat initial production version, with 112 kW (150 hp) Lycoming O-320-E2A engine. Optional third seat. Swiss certification granted on 15 August 1972; FAA certification awarded on 16 November 1973. In production: 32 ordered by February 1978, of which 28 had been delivered.

AS.202/18A. Two/three-seat aerobatic version with a 134 kW (180 hp) Lycoming engine, Hartzell constant-speed propeller and inverted oil system. First example (HB-HEY) flew for the first time on 22 August 1974. Swiss certification granted on 12 December 1975; FAA certification awarded on 17 December 1976. In production: 72 ordered by Summer 1978, including 48 AS.202/18A-1s for the Iraqi Air Force.

Aircraft currently in production incorporate a number of modifications, including riveted wing skins, rubber fuel tanks, and a glassfibre engine cowling. More than 115 Bravos had been sold by mid-1979, in Switzerland and to foreign customers including Royal Air Maroc, the Royal Flight of Oman, the Uganda Central Flying School, and the air forces of Iraq (48) and Morocco (14).

AS.202/26A. First flown in 1978. Two/three-seat training and aerobatic version with a 194 kW (260 hp) Lycoming engine and systems for unlimited inverted flying.

The following description applies to all versions of the Bravo, except where a specific model is indicated:

TYPE: Two/three-seat light aircraft.

WINGS: Cantilever low-wing monoplane. Wing section NACA 63_2618 (modified) at centreline, 63_2415 at tip. Thickness/chord ratio 17·63% at root, 15% at tip. Dihedral 5° 43′ from roots. Incidence 3°. Sweepback at quarter-chord 0° 40′. Conventional aluminium single-spar fail-safe structure, with honeycomb laminate skin. Aluminium single-slotted flaps and single-slotted ailerons. Ground-adjustable tab on each aileron.

FUSELAGE: Conventional aluminium semi-monocoque fail-safe structure, with several glassfibre fairings.

TAIL UNIT: Cantilever aluminium single-spar structure with sweptback vertical surfaces. Rudder mass-balanced, with provision for anti-collision beacon. Fixed-incidence tailplane. Two-piece elevator with full-span trim tab on starboard half. Ground-adjustable tab on rudder.

LANDING GEAR: Non-retractable tricycle type, with steerable nosewheel. Rubber-cushioned shock-absorber struts of SIAI-Marchetti design. Main-wheel tyres size 6·00-6; nosewheel tyre size 5·00-5. Tyre pressure (all units) 2·41 bars (35 lb/sq in). Independent hydraulically-operated disc brake on each main wheel.

POWER PLANT (AS.202/15): One 112 kW (150 hp) Lycoming O-320-E2A flat-four engine, driving a McCauley 1C172 MGM two-blade fixed-pitch metal propeller with spinner. Two wing leading-edge fuel tanks with total capacity of 170 litres (37·4 Imp gallons). Refuelling point above each wing. Oil capacity 7·6 litres (1·6 Imp gallons). Additional exhaust muffler available optionally.

POWER PLANT (AS.202/18A): One 134 kW (180 hp) Lycoming AEIO-360-B1F flat-four engine, driving a Hartzell HC-C2YK-1BF/F7666A-2 two-blade constant-speed propeller with spinner. Hoffmann three-blade propeller optional. Fuel capacity as for AS.202/15; starboard tank has additional flexible fuel intake for aerobatics. Christen 801 fully-aerobatic oil system, capacity 7·6 litres (1·6 Imp gallons).

POWER PLANT (AS.202/26A): One 194 kW (260 hp) Lycoming fuel-injection engine, driving a Hartzell constant-speed propeller. Fuel capacity 174 litres (38·3 Imp gallons). Fuel and oil systems permit unrestricted inverted flight.

AS.202/18A version of the FFA Bravo (Lycoming AEIO-360 engine)

ACCOMMODATION: Seats for two persons side by side, in Aerobatic versions, under rearward-sliding jettisonable transparent canopy. Space at rear in Utility versions for a third seat or 100 kg (220 lb) of baggage. Dual controls, cabin ventilation and heating standard.

SYSTEMS: Hydraulic system for brake actuation. One 12V 60A engine-driven alternator and one 25Ah battery provide electrical power for engine starting, lighting, instruments, communications and navigation installations. 28V electrical system optional.

AVIONICS AND EQUIPMENT: Provision for VHF radio, VOR, ADF, Nav-O-Matic 200A autopilot, blind-flying instrumentation or other special equipment at customer's option. Clutch-and-release mechanism for glider towing optional.

DIMENSIONS, EXTERNAL:	
Wing span	9·75 m (31 ft 11¾ in)
Wing chord at root	1·88 m (6 ft 2 in)
Wing chord at tip	1·16 m (3 ft 9½ in)
Wing aspect ratio	6·51
Length overall	7·50 m (24 ft 7¼ in)
Length of fuselage	7·15 m (23 ft 5½ in)
Height overall	2·81 m (9 ft 2¾ in)
Tailplane span	3·67 m (12 ft 0½ in)
Wheel track	2·25 m (7 ft 4½ in)
Wheelbase	1·78 m (5 ft 10 in)
Propeller diameter	1·88 m (6 ft 2 in)
Propeller ground clearance	0·31 m (1 ft 0¼ in)
DIMENSIONS, INTERNAL:	
Cabin: Max length	2·15 m (7 ft 0½ in)
Max width	1·02 m (3 ft 4¼ in)
Max height	1·10 m (3 ft 7¼ in)
Floor area	2·15 m² (23·14 sq ft)
AREAS:	
Wings, gross	13·86 m² (149·2 sq ft)
Ailerons (total)	1·09 m² (11·7 sq ft)
Trailing-edge flaps (total)	1·49 m² (16·04 sq ft)
Fin	0·45 m² (4·84 sq ft)
Rudder, incl tab	0·94 m² (10·12 sq ft)
Tailplane	1·88 m² (20·24 sq ft)
Elevators, incl tab	0·76 m² (8·18 sq ft)
WEIGHTS AND LOADINGS:	
Weight empty, equipped: 15	630 kg (1,388 lb)
18A	700 kg (1,543 lb)
26A	793 kg (1,748 lb)
Max payload: 15, Aerobatic	175 kg (386 lb)
15, Utility	270 kg (595 lb)
18A, Aerobatic	172 kg (379 lb)
18A, Utility	258 kg (568 lb)
26A, Aerobatic	188 kg (414 lb)
26A, Utility	292 kg (643 lb)
Max T-O and landing weight:	
15, Aerobatic	885 kg (1,951 lb)
15, Utility	999 kg (2,202 lb)
18A, Aerobatic	950 kg (2,094 lb)
18A, Utility	1,050 kg (2,315 lb)
26A, Aerobatic	1,075 kg (2,370 lb)
26A, Utility	1,200 kg (2,645 lb)
Max wing loading: 15	72·2 kg/m² (14·8 lb/sq ft)
18A	75·8 kg/m² (15·52 lb/sq ft)
26A	86·6 kg/m² (17·75 lb/sq ft)
Max power loading:	
15, Utility	8·92 kg/kW (14·68 lb/hp)
18A, Utility	7·84 kg/kW (12·86 lb/hp)
26A, Utility	6·18 kg/kW (10·17 lb/hp)

PERFORMANCE (Utility versions, at max T-O weight):	
Never-exceed speed:	
15, 18A	173·5 knots (322 km/h; 200 mph)
26A	208 knots (386 km/h; 240 mph)
Max level speed at S/L:	
15	114 knots (211 km/h; 131 mph)
18A	130 knots (241 km/h; 150 mph)
Max cruising speed (75% power) at 2,440 m (8,000 ft):	
15	114 knots (211 km/h; 131 mph)
18A	122·5 knots (227 km/h; 141 mph)
26A	138 knots (256 km/h; 159 mph)
Econ cruising speed at 3,050 m (10,000 ft):	
15 (66% power)	109·5 knots (203 km/h; 126 mph)
18A (55% power)	109·5 knots (203 km/h; 126 mph)
Stalling speed, flaps up, power off:	
15	59·5 knots (110 km/h; 68·5 mph)
18A	60·5 knots (112 km/h; 70 mph)
26A	63 knots (116 km/h; 72 mph)
Stalling speed, flaps down, power off:	
15	48·5 knots (89 km/h; 55·5 mph)
18A	47 knots (87 km/h; 54 mph)
26A	53 knots (98 km/h; 61 mph)
Max rate of climb at S/L:	
15	193 m (633 ft)/min
18A	274 m (900 ft)/min
26A	358 m (1,175 ft)/min
Service ceiling: 15	4,265 m (14,000 ft)
18A	5,490 m (18,000 ft)
26A	5,670 m (18,600 ft)
T-O run at S/L: 15	235 m (771 ft)
18A	210 m (689 ft)
26A	184 m (605 ft)
T-O to 15 m (50 ft) at S/L: 15	475 m (1,558 ft)
18A	400 m (1,312 ft)
26A	340 m (1,115 ft)
Landing from 15 m (50 ft): 15	415 m (1,362 ft)
18A	466 m (1,527 ft)
26A	465 m (1,525 ft)
Landing run: 15	130 m (427 ft)
18A, 26A	210 m (690 ft)
Range with max fuel, no reserves:	
15	480 nm (890 km; 553 miles)
18A	521 nm (965 km; 600 miles)
26A	460 nm (853 km; 530 miles)
Max endurance: 18A	5 h 30 min
26A	4 h 54 min

FFA AS 32T TURBO TRAINER

FFA's subsidiary Repair AG released preliminary details of the proposed AS 32T during the Paris Air Show in June 1979. The accompanying photograph illustrates the general configuration of the design, which features an electrically-retractable tricycle landing gear. The wing and tailplane are almost identical with those of the AS.202 Bravo, which Repair AG distributes for FFA.

TYPE: Tandem two-seat basic and advanced trainer.

POWER PLANT: One 313 kW (420 shp) Allison 250-B17 turboprop engine, flat rated to 239 kW (320 shp) and driving a Hartzell HC-B3TF-2 three-blade constant-speed propeller. Fuel capacity 300 litres (66 Imp gallons).

DIMENSIONS, EXTERNAL:	
Wing span	9·75 m (31 ft 11¾ in)
Wing area, gross	13·86 m² (149·2 sq ft)
Length overall	8·85 m (29 ft 0½ in)
Height overall	3·04 m (9 ft 11¾ in)
Wheel track	2·60 m (8 ft 6½ in)
Propeller diameter	2·18 m (7 ft 2 in)
WEIGHTS:	
Weight empty, equipped	800 kg (1,764 lb)
Max T-O weight	1,300 kg (2,866 lb)
Max landing weight	1,200 kg (2,645 lb)

PERFORMANCE (estimated, at AUW of 1,200 kg; 2,645 lb, ISA, zero wind):
Never-exceed speed
243 knots (450 km/h; 280 mph) EAS

Cruising speed at 3,000 m (9,845 ft):
- 80% power: 185 knots (343 km/h; 213 mph)
- 55% power: 165 knots (306 km/h; 190 mph)

Rate of climb at 500 m (1,640 ft) 534 m (1,752 ft)/min
Service ceiling 9,450 m (31,000 ft)
T-O run at 500 m (1,640 ft) 165 m (540 ft)
T-O to 15 m (50 ft) 330 m (1,080 ft)
Landing from 15 m (50 ft) 460 m (1,510 ft)
Landing run 210 m (690 ft)
Range with max fuel, 55% power, no reserves 651 nm (1,207 km; 750 miles)
Max endurance at 915 m (3,000 ft), 55% power, no reserves 4 h

Model of FFA's proposed AS 32T Turbo Trainer

PILATUS

PILATUS FLUGZEUGWERKE AG

HEAD OFFICE AND WORKS: CH-6370, Stans, near Lucerne
Telephone: (041) 63 11 33
Telex: 78 329
GENERAL MANAGER: H. Uehlinger
MANAGERS:
Aerospace Division:
D. C. Klöckner
Dr A. Canal (Marketing and PR)
W. Damerum (Sales)
W. Volkart (Product Support)
K. G. Trautmann (Projects)
O. Masefield (Engineering)
Production: W. Gubler
Administration: P. Ebner

Pilatus Flugzeugwerke AG was formed in December 1939; details of its early history can be found in previous editions of *Jane's*. It is part of the Oerlikon-Bührle Group.

Current Pilatus products are the Turbo-Porter single-engined utility transport and the PC-7 Turbo-Trainer.

On 25 July 1978 it was announced that Pilatus was to purchase the assets of Britten-Norman (Bembridge) Ltd of the UK, thus acquiring exclusive production and marketing rights to all Britten-Norman products. Part and licence production of the Islander is planned to continue in the Philippines, Romania and, eventually, other countries under new agreements. The final takeover took place on 21 September 1979, and Britten-Norman is operated under the name Pilatus Britten-Norman Ltd (which see) as a subsidiary of Pilatus Aircraft Ltd.

PILATUS PC-6 TURBO-PORTER

US Army designation: UV-20 Chiricahua

The Pilatus PC-6 is a single-engined multi-purpose utility aircraft, with STOL characteristics permitting operation from unprepared strips under harsh environmental and terrain conditions. The aircraft can be converted rapidly from a pure freighter to a passenger transport, and can be adapted for a great number of different missions, including supply dropping, ambulance, aerial survey and photography, parachuting, crop spraying, water bombing and target towing as well as operation from soft ground, snow, glacier or water, and long-range operations.

Design work began in 1957, and the first of five PC-6 piston-engined prototypes made its first flight on 4 May 1959. Twenty pre-series PC-6s, with 253·5 kW (340 hp) Lycoming engines, had been delivered by the Summer of 1961.

Subsequent versions have included the piston-engined PC-6 and PC-6/350 Porters; the PC-6/A, A1, A2, B and C2-H2 Turbo-Porters, with various turboprop power plants. Descriptions of all these can be found in the 1974-75 and earlier editions of *Jane's*.

Swiss-built piston-engined variants have the name Porter, and turboprop-powered variants are known as Turbo-Porters. In the USA, where the PC-6 was manufactured by Fairchild, it is known simply as the Porter, irrespective of the type of power plant fitted.

The current production version is the **PC-6/B2-H2 Turbo-Porter,** certificated on 30 June 1970 and powered by a 410 kW (550 shp) PT6A-27 turboprop engine. Other versions can be made available on request.

By 1 April 1979, more than 440 PC-6 aircraft, of all models, had been built (including US licence manufacture), and were operating in more than 50 countries. Military operators include the air forces of Angola, Argentina, Australia, Austria, Bolivia, Burma, Chad, Ecuador, Oman, Peru, Sudan, Switzerland, Thailand and the US Army. Production by Pilatus was continuing at a rate of approx two to three per month.

Pilatus PC-6 Turbo-Porter (Pratt & Whitney Aircraft of Canada PT6A-27 turboprop engine)

Pilatus markets a Q-STOL (Quiet STOL) conversion kit for the B1 and B2 Turbo-Porters fitted with PT6A-20 or -27 turbine engines. This includes a system whereby propeller speed can be altered independently of the engine power setting, and is claimed to reduce the noise level by more than 10 dB for T-O and 20 dB for landing.

The structural description which follows is applicable to the current B2-H2 version. Details of the agricultural Turbo-Porter are given separately.

TYPE: Single-engined STOL utility transport.

WINGS: Braced high-wing monoplane, with single streamline-section bracing strut each side. Wing section NACA 64-514 (constant). Dihedral 1°. Incidence 2°. Single-spar all-metal structure. Entire trailing-edge hinged, inner sections consisting of electrically-operated all-metal double-slotted flaps and outer sections of all-metal single-slotted ailerons. No airbrakes or de-icing equipment. Trim tabs and/or Flettner tabs on ailerons optional; ground-adjustable tabs are mandatory if these are not fitted.

FUSELAGE: All-metal semi-monocoque structure.

TAIL UNIT: Cantilever all-metal structure. Variable-incidence tailplane. Flettner tabs on elevator.

LANDING GEAR: Non-retractable tailwheel type. Oleo shock-absorbers of Pilatus design on all units. Steerable/lockable tailwheel. Goodyear Type II main wheels and GA 284 tyres size 24 × 7 or 7·50 × 10 (pressure 2·21 bars; 32 lb/sq in); oversize Goodyear Type III wheels and tyres optional, size 11·0 × 12, pressure 0·88 bars (12·8 lb/sq in). Goodyear tailwheel with size 5·00-4 tyre. Goodyear disc brakes. Pilatus wheel/ski gear or Edo 58-4580 or 679-4930 floats optional.

POWER PLANT (PC-6/B2-H2): One 410 kW (550 shp) Pratt & Whitney Aircraft of Canada PT6A-27 turboprop engine, driving a Hartzell HC-B3TN-3D/T-10178 propeller. Standard fuel in integral wing tanks, capacity 480 litres (127 US gallons; 105·5 Imp gallons) normal, 644 litres (170 US gallons; 142 Imp gallons) maximum. Two underwing auxiliary tanks, each of 190 litres (50 US gallons; 42 Imp gallons), available optionally.

ACCOMMODATION: Cabin has pilot's seat forward on port side, with one passenger seat alongside, and is normally fitted with six quickly-removable seats, in pairs, to the rear of these for additional passengers. Up to 10 persons can be carried in high-density layout. Floor is level, flush with door sill, and is provided with seat rails. Forward-opening door beside each front seat. Large rearward-sliding door on starboard side of main cabin. Double doors, without central pillar, on port side. Hatch in floor 0·58 × 0·90 m (1 ft 10¾ in × 2 ft 11½ in), openable from inside cabin, for aerial camera or for supply dropping. Hatch in cabin rear wall 0·50 × 0·80 m (1 ft 7 in × 2 ft 7 in) permits stowage of six passenger seats or accommodation of freight items up to 5·0 m (16 ft 5 in) in length. Walls lined with lightweight soundproofing and heat-insulation material. Adjustable heating and ventilation systems provided. Dual controls optional.

SYSTEMS: Cabin heated by engine bleed air. Scott 8500 oxygen system optional. 200A 30V starter/generator and 24V 34Ah nickel-cadmium battery.

EQUIPMENT: Generally to customer's requirements, but can include agricultural equipment (see separate description) or a 1,300 litre (286 Imp gallon) water tank in cabin, with quick-release system, for firefighting role.

DIMENSIONS, EXTERNAL:

Wing span	15·13 m (49 ft 8 in)
Wing span over navigation lights	15·20 m (49 ft 10½ in)
Wing chord (constant)	1·90 m (6 ft 3 in)
Wing aspect ratio	7·96
Length overall	10·90 m (35 ft 9 in)
Height overall (tail down)	3·20 m (10 ft 6 in)
Elevator span	5·12 m (16 ft 9½ in)
Wheel track	3·00 m (9 ft 10 in)
Wheelbase	7·87 m (25 ft 10 in)
Propeller diameter	2·56 m (8 ft 5 in)
Cabin double door (port) and sliding door (starboard):	
Height	1·04 m (3 ft 5 in)
Width	1·58 m (5 ft 2¼ in)

DIMENSIONS, INTERNAL:

Cabin, from back of pilot's seat to rear wall:	
Length	2·30 m (7 ft 6½ in)
Max width	1·16 m (3 ft 9½ in)
Max height (at front)	1·28 m (4 ft 2½ in)
Height at rear wall	1·18 m (3 ft 10½ in)
Floor area	2·67 m² (28·6 sq ft)
Volume	3·28 m³ (107 cu ft)

AREAS:

Wings, gross	28·80 m² (310 sq ft)
Ailerons (total)	3·83 m² (41·2 sq ft)
Flaps (total)	3·76 m² (40·5 sq ft)
Fin	1·70 m² (18·3 sq ft)

Rudder, incl tab 0·96 m² (10·3 sq ft)
Tailplane 4·03 m² (43·4 sq ft)
Elevator, incl tab 4·22 m² (45·4 sq ft)

WEIGHTS AND LOADINGS:
Weight empty, equipped 1,215 kg (2,678 lb)
Max T-O and landing weight:
Normal (CAR 3) 2,200 kg (4,850 lb)
Restricted (CAR 8) 2,770 kg (6,100 lb)
Max cabin floor loading 488 kg/m² (100 lb/sq ft)
Max wing loading (Normal) 76·4 kg/m² (15·65 lb/sq ft)
Max power loading (Normal) 5·37 kg/kW (8·82 lb/shp)

PERFORMANCE (at max T-O weight, Normal category):
Never-exceed speed 151 knots (280 km/h; 174 mph) IAS
Max cruising speed at 3,050 m (10,000 ft) 140 knots (259 km/h; 161 mph)
Econ cruising speed at 3,050 m (10,000 ft) 129 knots (240 km/h; 150 mph)
Stalling speed, power off, flaps up 50 knots (93·5 km/h; 58 mph)
Stalling speed, power off, flaps down 44 knots (82 km/h; 51 mph)
Max rate of climb at S/L 482 m (1,580 ft)/min
Service ceiling 9,150 m (30,025 ft)
T-O run 110 m (360 ft)
T-O to 15 m (50 ft) 235 m (771 ft)
Landing from 15 m (50 ft) 220 m (722 ft)
Landing run 73 m (240 ft)
Max range, no reserves:
internal fuel only 560 nm (1,036 km; 644 miles)
with external fuel 875 nm (1,620 km; 1,007 miles)
Endurance: internal fuel only 4 h 20 min
with external fuel 6 h 45 min
g limits +3·72; −1·50

PILATUS PC-6 TURBO-PORTER (AGRICULTURAL VERSIONS)

The Turbo-Porter can, if required, be equipped for agricultural duties, the necessary equipment being easily removable when not required, to permit the use of the aircraft for other work.

For liquid spraying, a stainless steel tank (capacity 1,330 litres; 292·5 Imp gallons; 351·4 US gallons) is installed behind the two front seats, and 46- or 62-nozzle spraybooms are fitted beneath the wings. In this configuration the aircraft can cover a swath width of 45 m (148 ft). An ultra-low-volume system, using four to six atomisers or two to four Micronairs, is also available, permitting increase in swath width up to 400 m (1,310 ft).

For dusting with granulated materials, the lower part of the standard tank can be replaced by a discharge and dispersal door permitting coverage of a swath width of up to 20 m (66 ft). A Transland spreader can be fitted for dust application (swath up to 30 m; 100 ft). Effective swath width of these versions is 13-40 m (43-131 ft), the optimum being approx 20 m (66 ft).

Both versions are fitted with small doors in the fuselage sides, giving access to the tank/hopper for servicing, removal or replenishment, and two single seats or a bench seat for three persons can be installed aft of the tank. Optional items include an engine air intake screen and a loading door for chemical in the top of the fuselage.

AVIONICS AND EQUIPMENT: Optional avionics include Decca Mk 8A navigator, Decca Hi-Fix radio, Decca Doppler 72 radar, gyrosyn CL-11 compass and SR 54A radio altimeter.

WEIGHTS (L: liquid spray system; D: dry chemicals system):
Weight empty: L, D 1,215 kg (2,678 lb)
Agricultural installation: L 133 kg (293 lb)
D 105 kg (231 lb)
Chemical: L 1,132 kg (2,497 lb)
D 1,160 kg (2,559 lb)
Fuel, oil and pilot: L, D 286 kg (630 lb)
Max T-O and landing weight:
L, D 2,770 kg (6,100 lb)

PERFORMANCE (liquid spray version, PT6A-27 engine, at max T-O weight):
Operating speed approx 90 knots (167 km/h; 104 mph)
Operating height 6-8 m (20-26 ft)
Spraying duration with full spray tank 6 min

PC-6/B1 Turbo-Porter agricultural aircraft fitted with 46-nozzle sprayboom

PILATUS PC-7 TURBO-TRAINER

Pilatus announced in the Spring of 1975 details of the PC-7 Turbo-Trainer fully aerobatic two-seat training aircraft, fitted with a 410 kW (550 shp) Pratt & Whitney Aircraft of Canada PT6A-25A turboprop engine.

The PC-7 can be used for basic, transition and aerobatic training, and, with suitable equipment installed, for IFR and tactical training. It meets the requirements of FAR 23 (Aerobatic and Utility categories) and is also designed to comply with a selected group of US Air Force military specifications (Trainer category). As a single-seater, it is flown from the front seat. The tactical trainer version has six underwing hard points, the inner pair stressed for 250 kg (551 lb) loads, the centre pair for 160 kg (353 lb) each and the outer pair for 110 kg (242·5 lb) each. Max external load comprises 1,040 kg (2,293 lb) of underwing stores.

Certification under FAR Pt 23 was awarded on 5 December 1978, following the first flight by a production PC-7 on 12 August that year. Deliveries to customers began immediately after certification, and had reached about 30 by the Summer of 1979. Several contracts and follow-on orders have been signed with international customers (including 8 for Bolivia, 34 for Burma, 12 for Guatemala and 12 for Mexico), and the backlog of orders will absorb the production capacity until 1981. The Swiss Air Force has integrated two leased PC-7s into its regular training course, for a final operational evaluation with a view to possible procurement in the early 1980s.

Production in 1979 was at the rate of four to five a month, with the capability to increase to six per month, depending upon market requirements. Dornier GmbH is collaborating with Pilatus in marketing the PC-7 in Germany.

TYPE: Single-engined single/two-seat training aircraft.

WINGS: Cantilever low-wing monoplane. Wing section NACA 64_2A series at root, NACA 64_1A series at tip. Thickness/chord ratio 15% at root, 12% at tip. Dihedral 7° on outer panels. Sweepback 1° at quarter-chord. One-piece all-metal single-spar structure, with auxiliary spars and ribs. Constant-chord centre-section and tapered outer panels. Aluminium alloy (2022 or 2024) skin, reinforced by stringers. Some fairings of glassfibre-reinforced plastics. Plain mass-balanced ailerons; split trailing-edge flaps, extending under fuselage. Trim tab in port aileron.

FUSELAGE: All-metal semi-monocoque structure, with aluminium alloy skin. Some fairings of glassfibre-reinforced plastics.

TAIL UNIT: Cantilever all-metal structure, of similar construction to wings. Trim tabs in rudder and starboard elevator. All control surfaces mass-balanced.

LANDING GEAR: Retractable tricycle type. Electrical actuation, with emergency manual extension. Main wheels retract inward, nosewheel rearward. Oleo-pneumatic shock-absorbers on all units. Castoring nosewheel, with shimmy dampers. Goodrich main wheels and tyres, size 6·50-8, pressure 4·83 bars (70 lb/sq in). Goodrich hydraulic disc brakes on main wheels. Parking brake.

POWER PLANT: One Pratt & Whitney Aircraft of Canada PT6A-25A turboprop engine, flat rated at 410 kW (550 shp), driving a Hartzell HC-B3TN-2 three-blade constant-speed fully-feathering propeller with spinner. Fuel in integral tanks in wings, total usable capacity 476 litres (105 Imp gallons). Fuel system permits up to 30 s of inverted flight. Provision for underwing drop-tanks.

ACCOMMODATION: Adjustable seats for two persons in tandem, beneath rearward-sliding jettisonable Plexiglas canopy. Cockpits ventilated and heated by engine bleed air, which can also be used for windscreen de-icing. Space for 25 kg (55 lb) of baggage aft of seats, with external access.

SYSTEMS: Hydraulic system for main-wheel brakes only. No pneumatic system. 28V DC operational (24V nominal) electrical system, incorporating 30V 200A Lear Siegler starter/generator and 24V 34Ah or 40Ah nickel-cadmium battery. Ground power receptacle fitted.

AVIONICS AND EQUIPMENT: Dual controls standard.

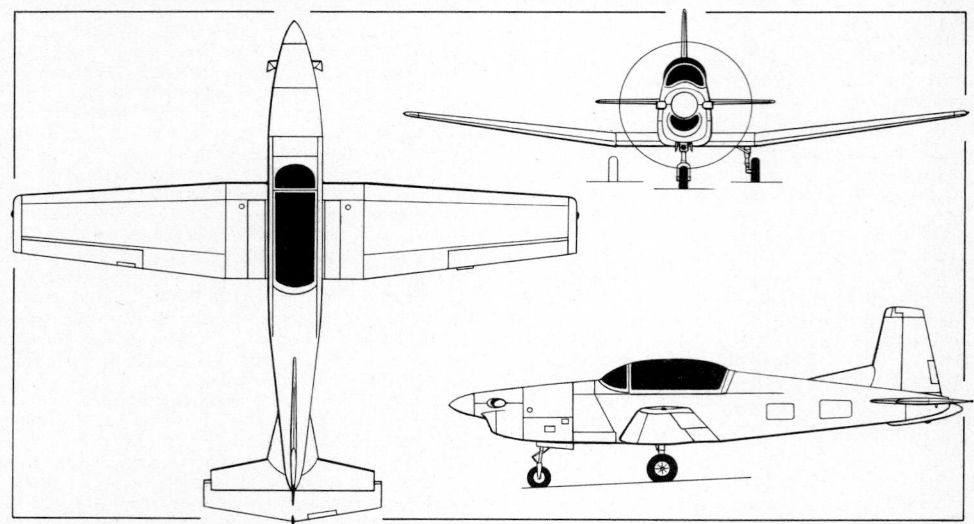

Pilatus PC-7 Turbo-Trainer, the subject of a joint programme with Dornier of Germany *(Pilot Press)*

Production line-up of the Pilatus PC-7 Turbo-Trainer (Pratt & Whitney Aircraft of Canada PT6A-25A turboprop engine)

Optional equipment includes IFR training shield, to screen rear cockpit; Rosemount Srs 92 angle of attack equipment; radio, oxygen and air-conditioning.

DIMENSIONS, EXTERNAL:

Wing span	10·40 m (34 ft 1½ in)
Wing mean aerodynamic chord	1·64 m (5 ft 4½ in)
Wing mean geometric chord	1·59 m (5 ft 2·6 in)
Wing aspect ratio	6·52
Length overall	9·75 m (32 ft 0 in)
Height overall	3·21 m (10 ft 6½ in)
Propeller diameter	2·36 m (7 ft 9 in)

AREA:

Wings, gross	16·60 m² (178·7 sq ft)

WEIGHTS AND LOADINGS:

Weight empty, equipped	1,270 kg (2,800 lb)
Normal T-O weight, 'clean'	1,900 kg (4,188 lb)
Max T-O weight, with external stores	2,700 kg (5,952 lb)
Max landing weight	2,565 kg (5,655 lb)
Normal wing loading, 'clean'	114·5 kg/m² (23·44 lb/sq ft)
Max wing loading	162·7 kg/m² (33·31 lb/sq ft)
Normal power loading, 'clean'	4·63 kg/kW (7·61 lb/shp)
Max power loading	6·59 kg/kW (10·82 lb/shp)

PERFORMANCE (A: at 1,900 kg; 4,188 lb AUW. B: at 2,700 kg; 5,952 lb AUW):

Never-exceed speed:	
A, B	270 knots (500 km/h; 310 mph) EAS
Max structural cruising speed:	
A, B	270 knots (500 km/h; 310 mph) EAS
Max cruising speed at 5,000 m (16,400 ft):	
A, 100% power	235 knots (435 km/h; 271 mph)
A, 75% power	175 knots (325 km/h; 202 mph)
Max cruising speed at S/L:	
A, 100% power	207 knots (385 km/h; 239 mph)
Manoeuvring speed:	
A	174 knots (322 km/h; 200 mph) EAS
B	185 knots (342 km/h; 212 mph) EAS
Max speed with flaps and landing gear down:	
A, B	135 knots (250 km/h; 155 mph) EAS
Stalling speed, flaps up, power off:	
A	71 knots (131 km/h; 81·5 mph) EAS
B	85 knots (158 km/h; 98 mph) EAS
Stalling speed, flaps down, power off:	
A	61 knots (113 km/h; 70·5 mph) EAS
B	72 knots (133 km/h; 83 mph) EAS
Normal rate of climb:	
A at S/L	630 m (2,065 ft)/min
B at S/L	330 m (1,080 ft)/min
A at 3,050 m (10,000 ft)	588 m (1,930 ft)/min
B at 3,050 m (10,000 ft)	280 m (918 ft)/min
A at 6,100 m (20,000 ft)	336 m (1,105 ft)/min
B at 6,100 m (20,000 ft)	120 m (393 ft)/min
Time to 5,000 m (16,400 ft): A	10 min
B	27 min
Service ceiling: A	10,000 m (32,800 ft)
B	6,500 m (21,325 ft)
T-O run at S/L, zero wind: A	230 m (755 ft)
B	540 m (1,772 ft)
T-O to 15 m (50 ft) at S/L, zero wind:	
A	360 m (1,182 ft)
B	990 m (3,250 ft)
Landing from 15 m (50 ft) at S/L, zero wind:	
A	390 m (1,280 ft)
B	540 m (1,772 ft)
Landing run at S/L, zero wind:	
A	230 m (755 ft)
B	345 m (1,132 ft)
Max range at cruise power at 5,000 m (16,400 ft), 5% plus 20 min reserves:	
A, B	810 nm (1,500 km; 932 miles)
Max endurance: A, B	4 h 30 min
g limits (ultimate): A	+6·0; −3·0
B	+4·5; −2·25

SWISS FEDERAL AIRCRAFT FACTORY

EIDGENÖSSISCHES FLUGZEUGWERK—FABRIQUE FÉDÉRALE D'AVIONS—FABBRICA FEDERALE D'AEROPLANI

HEAD OFFICE AND WORKS: CH-6032 Emmen
Telephone: (041) 59 41 11
Telex: 7 84 80 fwead ch
DIRECTOR: Lucien Othenin-Girard
DEPUTY DIRECTOR: Dr Peter Burkhardt
CHIEF DESIGNERS:
Hansjoerg Kobelt (Electronics)
Heinz Rhomberg (Structures)
HEAD OF RESEARCH DEPARTMENT: Heini Kamber
HEAD OF PRODUCTION: Hanspeter Arnold

The F+W is the Swiss government's official aircraft establishment for research, development, production, maintenance and modification of military aircraft. It employs about 600 people in a works located at Emmen, near Lucerne, covering 35,300 m² (380,000 sq ft). Included are four wind tunnels for speeds of up to Mach 4·5, test cells for piston and turbojet engines with or without afterburners, and a modern data acquisition and processing system.

The F+W is made up of six technical departments. Research Department operates the wind tunnel facilities and performs scientific research and development in the fields of aerodynamics, thermodynamics, systems analysis and flight mechanics. Engineering Department is responsible for the design and development of aircraft, aircraft subsystems and components, and the development of space hardware. Electronics Department undertakes maintenance and modification of the avionics of the Swiss Air Force's aircraft, and provides support for flight evaluations. Quality Assurance Department assures maintenance of high quality and adherence to standards in the production and maintenance of the aircraft and space hardware. The M & P Department maintains up-to-date awareness of new materials and processes, and develops its own process techniques to meet particular requirements. Thus, for example, fabrication of titanium parts and Inconel pressure vessels is undertaken at the F+W. Production Department is competent to undertake the fabrication of aircraft subassemblies and components, as well as final assembly and checkout of complete aircraft.

The Factory is taking part in the assembly programme of Northrop F-5E/F Tiger IIs for the Swiss Air Force, which began in 1976 and involves an initial total of 72 aircraft (see 1978-79 *Jane's*). More than 12 of these had been completed by February 1979, at which time the Swiss Defence Minister announced that Switzerland would probably require an additional 40-50 of these aircraft after delivery of the current series.

The F+W conducts wind tunnel programmes for foreign aircraft manufacturers, ground transportation developers and users, and for the building industry. It also offers proprietary products to potential customers, including an electronic audio warntone generator, water separators for aircraft conditioning systems, strain-gauge force measuring scales, and the POHWARO hot water rockets. Details of these rockets can be found in the 1977-78 *Jane's*.

TAIWAN

AIDC/CAF

AERO INDUSTRY DEVELOPMENT CENTER—CHINESE AIR FORCE

ADDRESS: PO Box 8676-1, Taichung, Taiwan 400
Telephone: Taichung (042) 223051 and 223052
Telex: 51140
OTHER WORKS: Kang Shan
DIRECTOR: Lieutenant General Y. C. Lee
DEPUTY DIRECTORS:
Dr Hsichun M. Hua (Engineering and Research)
Major General E. Y. Chu (Manufacturing)

The Aero Industry Development Center was established on 1 March 1969 as a successor to the Bureau of Aircraft Industry (BAI), which was established in 1946 in Nanking and moved to Taiwan in 1948. It now employs approx 2,000 people.

In October 1968 the Aeronautical Research Laboratory, then a branch of BAI, constructed the first Chinese-built PL-1A (see 1970-71 *Jane's*), a slightly modified version of the US Pazmany PL-1 which flew for the first time on 26 October 1968. After further modifications, 35 PL-1B Chienshou production models were built by AIDC in 1970, and two further batches of 10 in 1972 and 1974. These aircraft have been used extensively as primary trainers for CAF air cadets. A full description and illustration of the PL-1B appeared in the 1975-76 *Jane's*.

Between 1969 and 1976, the AIDC produced in Taiwan 118 examples of the Bell UH-1H (Bell Model 205) helicopter under licence for the Chinese Nationalist Army.

The AIDC is currently engaged in licence building 187 Northrop F-5E Tiger II tactical fighter aircraft (see US section) and 21 two-seat F-5Fs for the Chinese Nationalist Air Force. The first Chinese-built F-5E (CAF name **Chung Cheng**) was rolled out on 30 October 1974, and more than 130 had been delivered by the beginning of 1979.

The AIDC designed and developed the T-CH-1 tandem two-seat turboprop trainer, and this is now in production for the Chinese Air Force. The Lycoming T53 engines for the T-CH-1 are licence-built at Kang Shan. Under development are two other indigenous designs, the XC-2 twin-turboprop transport and a tandem two-seat twin-engined military trainer designated XAT-3.

AIDC/CAF-built Chung Cheng (Northrop F-5E Tiger II) for the Chinese Nationalist Air Force

AIDC T-CH-1

This aircraft is a tandem two-seat trainer, the design of which was started by AIDC in November 1970. Two prototypes were ordered, designated XT-CH-1A and XT-CH-1B; construction began in January 1972.

The first aircraft was completed in September 1973 and was flown for the first time on 23 November 1973; it was described and illustrated in the 1974-75 *Jane's*.

The second prototype (63-3002), designated XT-CH-1B, was a modified version able to perform weapon delivery training and counter-insurgency missions. It flew for the first time on 27 November 1974.

The following description applies to the T-CH-1, of which production began in May 1976. Fifty have been ordered for the Chinese Air Force, of which more than 30 had been delivered by early 1979.

TYPE: Turboprop-powered trainer and light ground attack aircraft.

WINGS: Cantilever low-wing monoplane. Wing section NACA 64-2A215 (constant). Dihedral 8° from roots. Incidence 2°. No sweepback. Conventional aluminium alloy stressed-skin structure, with aluminium alloy ailerons and slotted trailing-edge flaps. Link-balance type trim tab in each aileron.

FUSELAGE: Conventional semi-monocoque structure of aluminium alloy.

TAIL UNIT: Cantilever aluminium alloy structure, with fixed-incidence tailplane. Dorsal fin. Link-balance type trim tabs in rudder and each elevator.

LANDING GEAR: Retractable tricycle type. Hydraulic retraction, main wheels inward into wings, nosewheel rearward. Telescopic shock-absorbers. Goodyear brakes. Small tail bumper under rear fuselage.

POWER PLANT: One 1,082 kW (1,451 ehp) Taiwan-built Lycoming T53-L-701 turboprop engine, driving a Hamilton Standard 53C51-27 three-blade metal propeller with spinner. Fuel in two tanks in each wing and one in fuselage, with total capacity of 963 litres (212 Imp gallons). Oil capacity 30 litres (6·6 Imp gallons).

ACCOMMODATION: Crew of two in tandem. Rearward-sliding fully-transparent canopy over each cockpit. Cockpits heated and ventilated.

SYSTEMS: Midland-Ross Corporation heating and ventilating system. 115V 300A system provides AC electrical power at 250VA 400Hz. 28V DC system includes 24V 34Ah battery. Oxygen bottle with volume of 3·5 litres (2,100 cu in).

AVIONICS AND EQUIPMENT: Collins AN/ARC-51BX UHF radio and Collins AN/ARN-83 ADF.

DIMENSIONS, EXTERNAL:

Wing span	12·19 m (40 ft 0 in)
Wing chord at root	2·44 m (8 ft 0 in)
Wing chord at tip	1·52 m (5 ft 0 in)
Wing aspect ratio	6

Production line-up of AIDC/CAF T-CH-1 basic trainers for the Chinese Air Force

Length overall 10·26 m (33 ft 8 in)
Height overall 3·66 m (12 ft 0 in)
Tailplane span 5·56 m (18 ft 3 in)
Wheel track 3·86 m (12 ft 8 in)
Wheelbase 2·39 m (7 ft 10 in)
Propeller diameter 3·05 m (10 ft 0 in)
Propeller ground clearance 0·74 m (2 ft 5 in)

AREAS:
Wings, gross 25·18 m² (271·0 sq ft)
Ailerons (total) 2·42 m² (26·0 sq ft)
Flaps (total) 5·02 m² (54·0 sq ft)
Fin 1·67 m² (18·0 sq ft)
Rudder, incl tab 1·11 m² (12·0 sq ft)
Elevators, incl tabs 1·81 m² (19·5 sq ft)

WEIGHTS AND LOADINGS:
Weight empty 2,608 kg (5,750 lb)
T-O weight: 'clean' 3,402 kg (7,500 lb)
max 5,057 kg (11,150 lb)
Max wing loading 200·9 kg/m² (41·14 lb/sq ft)
Max power loading 4·68 kg/kW (7·68 lb/ehp)

PERFORMANCE (at AUW of 3,447 kg; 7,600 lb):
Never-exceed speed 370 knots (685 km/h; 426 mph)
Max level speed at 4,570 m (15,000 ft) 320 knots (592 km/h; 368 mph)
Max cruising speed at 4,570 m (15,000 ft) 220 knots (407 km/h; 253 mph)
Econ cruising speed at 4,570 m (15,000 ft) 170 knots (315 km/h; 196 mph)
Stalling speed 50 knots (93 km/h; 58 mph)
Max rate of climb at S/L 1,036 m (3,400 ft)/min
Service ceiling 9,755 m (32,000 ft)
T-O run 146 m (480 ft)
T-O to 15 m (50 ft) 244 m (800 ft)
Landing from 15 m (50 ft) 381 m (1,250 ft)
Landing run 183 m (600 ft)
Range with max fuel 1.085 nm (2,010 km; 1,250 miles)

AIDC XC-2

The basic design of the XC-2 twin-turboprop transport, which was started in January 1973, incorporates features of common interest to military and civil operators, including quick-change capability and the ability to operate from short fields and unprepared surfaces. The XC-2 can carry up to 38 passengers or 3,855 kg (8,500 lb) of cargo.

The first prototype (serial number 68-5001) was rolled out on 31 October 1978, and was due to make its first flight in early 1979.

TYPE: Twin-turboprop transport aircraft.

WINGS: Cantilever high-wing monoplane. Wing section NACA 65_3-218. Incidence 4°. No dihedral or sweepback at quarter-chord. Light alloy three-spar fail-safe structure, in three sections: constant-chord centre-section and tapered outer panels. All-metal manually-operated ailerons and hydraulically-actuated Fowler-type trailing-edge flaps. Servo tab in each aileron.

FUSELAGE: Conventional all-metal semi-monocoque fail-safe structure, of basically rectangular section, upswept at rear to provide clearance for rear loading. Cabin pressurisation optional.

TAIL UNIT: Cantilever aluminium alloy three-spar structure, with sweptback fin and rudder and non-swept horizontal surfaces. Dorsal fin. Horizontal surfaces mounted halfway up fin. Trim and balance tab in rudder and each elevator.

LANDING GEAR: Retractable tricycle type, with hydraulically-steerable twin-wheel nose unit. Single-wheel main units retract into fairings on sides of fuselage.

POWER PLANT: Two 1,082 kW (1,451 ehp) Lycoming T53-L-701A turboprop engines, each driving a Hamilton Standard 53C51-27 three-blade variable-pitch metal propeller with spinner. Fuel in rubber tanks in wings, with combined standard capacity of 3,028 litres (666 Imp gallons).

ACCOMMODATION: Crew of three (pilot, co-pilot and flight engineer) on flight deck. Standard seating in main cabin for 38 passengers, four abreast at 79 cm (31 in) pitch. Interior layout has quick-change capability to passenger/cargo or all-cargo configuration. Access to main cabin via forward and rear doors on port side; single door on starboard side; and a two-section loading ramp/door in underside of rear fuselage, aft of main cabin, which is openable in flight for airdrop operations. Provision for toilet, galley and baggage compartment in passenger version.

SYSTEMS: Anti-icing and cabin heating systems standard. Hydraulic system, pressure 207 bars (3,000 lb/sq in), for flaps, landing gear and nosewheel steering. 28V DC primary electrical system, with 300A starter/generator on each engine. Two nickel-cadmium batteries for engine starting and emergency power.

AVIONICS AND EQUIPMENT: Standard avionics include UHF and VHF com; and ADF, Tacan and transponder navigation equipment. Optional avionics include VOR/ILS and HF.

DIMENSIONS, EXTERNAL:
Wing span 24·90 m (81 ft 8·4 in)
Wing chord (centre-section, constant) 3·05 m (10 ft 0 in)
Wing aspect ratio 9·5
Length overall 20·10 m (65 ft 11·3 in)
Height overall 7·72 m (25 ft 3·8 in)
Tailplane span 9·12 m (29 ft 10·9 in)
Wheel track 3·86 m (12 ft 7·8 in)
Wheelbase 7·10 m (23 ft 3·5 in)
Propeller diameter 3·05 m (10 ft 0 in)
Propeller ground clearance 0·90 m (2 ft 11·5 in)

DIMENSIONS, INTERNAL:
Cabin, excl flight deck:
Length 8·095 m (26 ft 6·7 in)
Width 2·57 m (8 ft 5 in)
Height 2·23 m (7 ft 3·7 in)
Floor area 20·85 m² (224·4 sq ft)
Volume 45·45 m³ (1,605·0 cu ft)

AREAS:
Wings, gross 65·40 m² (704·00 sq ft)
Ailerons (total) 4·24 m² (45·63 sq ft)
Trailing-edge flaps (total) 11·69 m² (125·80 sq ft)
Fin (incl dorsal fin) 9·35 m² (100·64 sq ft)
Rudder (incl tabs) 4·75 m² (51·12 sq ft)
Tailplane 10·41 m² (112·05 sq ft)
Elevators (incl tabs) 8·97 m² (96·55 sq ft)

WEIGHTS AND LOADINGS:
Weight empty 7,031 kg (15,500 lb)
Max payload 3,855 kg (8,500 lb)

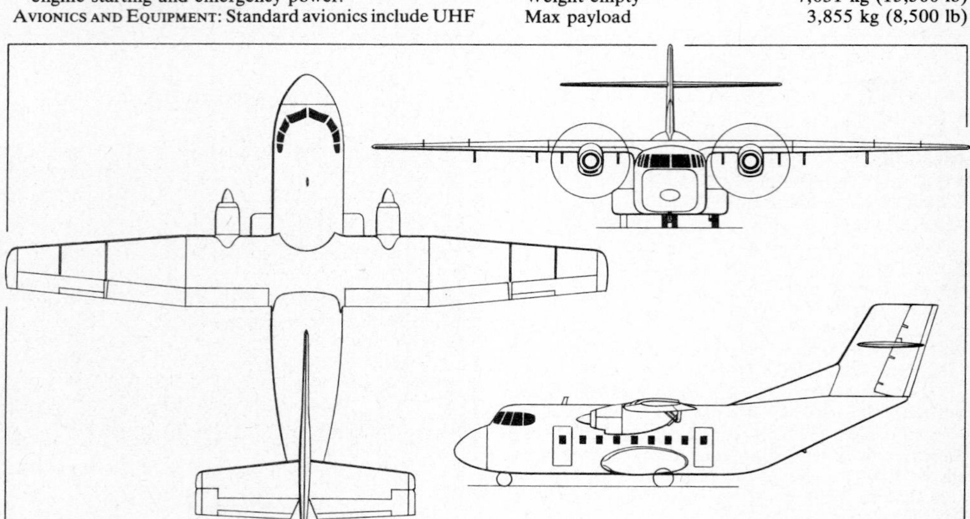

AIDC XC-2 twin-turboprop utility transport aircraft *(Pilot Press)*

First prototype of the AIDC/CAF XC-2 twin-turboprop transport aircraft

Max T-O weight 12,474 kg (27,500 lb)
Max landing weight 12,247 kg (27,000 lb)
Max zero-fuel weight 11,254 kg (24,810 lb)
Max wing loading 190·7 kg/m² (39·06 lb/sq ft)
Max power loading 5·77 kg/kW (9·48 lb/ehp)
PERFORMANCE (estimated, at max T-O weight):
Never-exceed speed 250 knots (463 km/h; 287 mph)
Max level speed at S/L 212 knots (392 km/h; 244 mph)
Max cruising speed at 3,050 m (10,000 ft) 200 knots (370 km/h; 230 mph)
Econ cruising speed at 3,050 m (10,000 ft) 180 knots (333 km/h; 207 mph)
Stalling speed, flaps down 78 knots (145 km/h; 90 mph)
Max rate of climb at S/L 457 m (1,500 ft)/min
Service ceiling 8,015 m (26,300 ft)
Service ceiling, one engine out 2,740 m (9,000 ft)
T-O run 625 m (2,050 ft)
T-O to 15 m (50 ft) 778 m (2,550 ft)
Landing from 15 m (50 ft) 826 m (2,710 ft)
Landing run 582 m (1,910 ft)
Range with max payload, reserves for 87 nm (161 km; 100 mile) alternate and 45 min hold 259 nm (480 km; 298 miles)
Range with max fuel, 45 min reserves 897 nm (1,661 km; 1,032 miles)

TURKEY

TURKISH AIR FORCE

ADDRESS: Air Reinforcement Centre, Kayseri

MAV ISIK 78-XA

This designation has been given to an agricultural aircraft which was undergoing flight test in the Summer of 1979 at the Turkish Air Force's Air Reinforcement Centre at Kayseri. Said to be of 85% Turkish design, the Mav Isik 78-XA apparently resembles current Cessna low-wing agricultural aircraft, except for a high-mounted two-seat cockpit, and is thought to be powered by a Continental flat-six engine. It is planned to produce the aircraft at an initial rate of 20 per year.

TUSAS
TURK UCAK SANAYII ANONIM SIRKETI

DIRECTOR: Prof Mehmet Akyurt

Preliminary steps have been taken by the Turkish government to establish the headquarters at Kayseri of an aircraft manufacturing facility, to be known as TUSAS, financed jointly by the Turkish government (55%) and the Turkish Armed Forces Foundation (45%).

TUSAS was officially established with effect from 11 July 1973 with an initial capital of 300 million Turkish lire; this figure has since been increased to more than 1,000 million lire.

Plans envisage an initial programme for the manufacture in Turkey of selected aircraft for the Turkish Air Force. The first type is intended to be a jet trainer/light attack aircraft, and it was announced on 25 October 1977 that the Aermacchi M.B.339 had been selected to fill this requirement. Plans were for TUSAS to assemble 60 of these aircraft over a 64-month period, initially from Italian-built components but progressing eventually to 90% manufacture of the airframe in Turkey. Electronics and Rolls-Royce Viper 632 engines would be imported.

However, a meeting called in Turkey on 26 October 1977 to sign a firm contract for this programme was postponed until further notice, and no further progress had been reported before this page closed for press.

UNION OF SOVIET SOCIALIST REPUBLICS

ANTONOV

GENERAL DESIGNER IN CHARGE OF BUREAU: Oleg Konstantinovich Antonov

After establishing his reputation with a series of successful glider and sailplane designs, Oleg K. Antonov became one of Russia's leading designers of transport aircraft, particularly those types intended for short-field operation.

In addition to the current products described in this section, his design bureau is studying the requirements of a large transport to replace the An-22.

ANTONOV An-2

NATO reporting name: Colt

Following manufacture of the An-2M specialised agricultural version of this large single-engined biplane, in the mid-sixties, production of the An-2 came to an end in the Soviet Union. Details of the various versions that were built can be found in the 1971-72 *Jane's*.

Several versions of the An-2 continue in production under licence in Poland (see WSK-PZL Mielec entry).

ANTONOV An-3

It was reported in the Spring of 1972 that the Antonov design bureau was engaged on design studies for a turboprop development of the An-2 biplane (see WSK-PZL-Mielec in Polish section). Further details were given by Mr Oleg Antonov during the 1975 Paris Air Show.

Designated An-3, the aircraft was intended specifically for agricultural duties and was then expected to compete with the Polish turbofan-engined WSK-Mielec M-15 as the next-generation agricultural aircraft for use throughout the countries of eastern Europe and the Soviet Union.

At the 1979 Paris Air Show, Mr Antonov emphasised his continued interest in agricultural aircraft, and confirmed that a prototype had been produced by converting an An-2 to have a 716 kW (960 shp) Glushenkov TVD-10B turboprop engine, driving a slow-turning large-diameter propeller optimised for an aircraft operating speed of 75-97 knots (140-180 km/h; 87-112 mph). He added that an important feature was the ability of the turboprop to ensure adequate cockpit air-conditioning during operation in ambient temperatures of 40-45°C.

ANTONOV An-12

NATO reporting name: Cub

The basic An-12 is a military and civil freight-carrying version of the now-retired An-10 passenger transport, with redesigned rear fuselage and tail unit. A loading ramp for freight and vehicles, in the underside of the upswept rear fuselage, can be lowered in flight for air-drop operations. The built-in freight-handling gantry has a capacity of 2,300 kg (5,070 lb). The cargo floor is designed for loadings of up to 1,500 kg/m² (307 lb/sq ft).

About 850 An-12s are reported to have been built for military and civil use before production ended in 1973. Versions in service with the Soviet air forces, and identified by unclassified NATO reporting names, are as follows:

Cub-A. Standard Soviet military paratroop and freight transport for many years. At peak strength, 'Cub-As' could carry two full army divisions, totalling 14,000 men and their equipment, over a radius of 651 nm (1,207 km; 750 miles). In 1979, about 85% of the 700 aircraft equipping the VTA (Military Transport Aviation) comprised 'Cub-As', designated **An-12BP** in the USSR, although replacement with Ilyushin Il-76s had started in 1974. Sixteen An-12s were supplied to the Indian Air Force. Others are operated by the air forces of Algeria, Bangladesh, Egypt, Indonesia, Iraq, Poland, Sudan, Syria and Yugoslavia. Civil An-12s serve with Aeroflot, Polish Airlines (LOT), Bulair and Cubana.

Cub-B. Conversion of 'Cub-A' for electronic intelligence (elint) duties. Example photographed off Sweden had four additional blister fairings under forward and centre fuselage, plus other antennae.

Cub-C. Used by Soviet Air Force and Navy for ECM duties. Ogival 'solid' fuselage tailcone, housing electronic equipment, instead of gun position. Additional electronic pods faired into forward fuselage and ventral surfaces. Glazed nose and undernose radar of other versions retained. Has operated in Egyptian insignia.

'Cub-A' has a tail gunner's position. In the converted military An-12 which Ghana Airways operated for a time, this was fitted out as a toilet. In the refined commercial version, first demonstrated at the 1965 Paris Air Show, the turret is removed and replaced by a streamlined fairing.

Equipment for all-weather operation is standard on all versions. Current Soviet Air Force An-12s have a larger undernose radome than that originally fitted.

The following details apply to the standard military An-12BP transport. Additional information on the late commercial model can be found in the 1977-78 *Jane's*.

TYPE: Four-engined cargo transport.

WINGS: Cantilever high-wing monoplane. All-metal two-spar structure in five panels, comprising centre-section, intermediate wings and tip sections. TsAGI wing sections: S-5-18 at centreline, S-3-16 at intermediate station, S-3-14 at tip. Anhedral 4° on tip sections. Sweepback 6° 30′ at quarter-chord. Manually-operated aerodynamically-balanced ailerons. Double-slotted Fowler flaps in two portions each side, hydraulically-actuated. Electro-thermal de-icing.

FUSELAGE: Stressed-skin semi-monocoque structure of circular section.

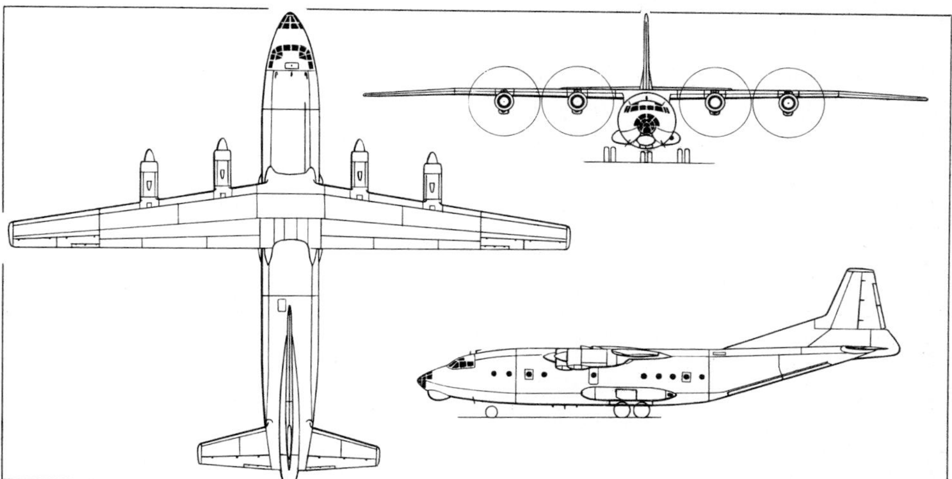

Antonov An-12 ('Cub-A') four-turboprop general-purpose commercial transport aircraft *(Pilot Press)*

Electronic intelligence version of the Antonov An-12 known to NATO as 'Cub-B' *(Swedish Air Force)*

TAIL UNIT: Cantilever all-metal structure. Electrically-operated trim tabs. All controls are manually operated and aerodynamically balanced. Electro-thermal de-icing of fin and tailplane.

LANDING GEAR: Retractable tricycle type. Hydraulic actuation. Shock-absorbers use nitrogen instead of air and have stroke of 340 mm (13·4 in). Four-wheel bogie on each side retracts into blister on side of fuselage. Hydraulically-steerable dual nosewheels. Main-wheel tyres size 1,050 × 300 mm; pressure 5·52-6·55 bars (80-95 lb/sq in). Hydraulic disc brakes. Optional skis for operation on snow.

POWER PLANT: Four 2,983 kW (4,000 ehp) Ivchenko AI-20K turboprops, driving AV-68 four-blade reversible-pitch propellers. All fuel in 22 bag-type tanks in wings, total normal capacity 13,900 litres (3,058 Imp gallons). Max capacity 18,100 litres (3,981 Imp gallons).

ACCOMMODATION: Pilot and co-pilot side by side on flight deck. Engineer's station on starboard side, behind co-pilot. Radio operator in well behind pilot, facing outward. Navigator in glazed nose compartment. Rear gunner in tail turret. Crew door on port side forward of wing. Access to freight hold via ramp-door at rear, under upswept rear fuselage. Ramp-door is divided into two longitudinal halves, which can be hinged upward inside cabin to provide access for direct loading of freight from trucks. Undersurface of fuselage aft of ramp is formed by door which hinges upward into fuselage to facilitate loading and unloading. Equipped to carry 100 paratroops, all of whom can be despatched in under one minute, with ramp-doors folded upward.

SYSTEMS: Entire accommodation air-conditioned and pressurised to differential of 0·49 bars (7·1 lb/sq in). Hydraulic system operates landing gear retraction, nosewheel steering, flaps, brakes and rear loading ramp and door.

ARMAMENT: Two 23 mm NR-23 guns in tail turret.

DIMENSIONS, EXTERNAL:

Wing span	38·00 m (124 ft 8 in)
Wing chord (mean)	3·452 m (11 ft 4 in)
Wing aspect ratio	11·85
Length overall	33·10 m (108 ft 7¼ in)
Height overall	10·53 m (34 ft 6½ in)
Tailplane span	12·20 m (40 ft 0¼ in)
Wheel track	5·42 m (17 ft 9½ in)
Wheelbase	10·82 m (35 ft 6 in)
Propeller diameter	4·50 m (14 ft 9 in)
Rear loading hatch:	
Length	7·70 m (25 ft 3 in)
Width	2·95 m (9 ft 8 in)

DIMENSIONS, INTERNAL:

Cargo hold:	
Length	13·50 m (44 ft 3½ in)
Max width	3·50 m (11 ft 5¾ in)
Max height	2·60 m (8 ft 6¼ in)
Volume	97·2 m³ (3,432·6 cu ft)

AREAS:

Wings, gross	121·70 m² (1,310 sq ft)
Ailerons (total)	7·84 m² (84·39 sq ft)
Trailing-edge flaps (total)	27·00 m² (290·63 sq ft)
Vertical tail surfaces	21·53 m² (231·75 sq ft)
Rudder	6·53 m² (70·29 sq ft)
Horizontal tail surfaces	26·95 m² (290·09 sq ft)
Elevators	7·11 m² (76·53 sq ft)
Elevator trim tabs (total)	0·78 m² (8·40 sq ft)

WEIGHTS AND LOADINGS:

Weight empty	28,000 kg (61,730 lb)
Max payload	20,000 kg (44,090 lb)
Normal T-O weight	55,100 kg (121,475 lb)
Max T-O weight	61,000 kg (134,480 lb)
Normal wing loading	461 kg/m² (94·4 lb/sq ft)
Normal power loading	4·62 kg/kW (7·5 lb/ehp)

PERFORMANCE:

Max level speed	419 knots (777 km/h; 482 mph)
Max cruising speed	361 knots (670 km/h; 416 mph)
Min flying speed	88 knots (163 km/h; 101 mph)
Landing speed	108 knots (200 km/h; 124 mph)
Max rate of climb at S/L	600 m (1,970 ft)/min
Service ceiling	10,200 m (33,500 ft)
T-O run	700 m (2,300 ft)
Landing run	500 m (1,640 ft)
Range with max payload	1,942 nm (3,600 km; 2,236 miles)
Range with max fuel	3,075 nm (5,700 km; 3,540 miles)

ANTONOV An-14 PCHELKA (LITTLE BEE)

NATO reporting name: Clod

The An-14 Pchelka is a twin-engined light general-purpose aircraft, the first prototype of which made its first flight on 15 March 1958. Production began in 1965 at the Progress Plant at Arsenyev in the far east of the Soviet Union, for both Aeroflot and the Soviet armed forces. Several hundred were built; none had been involved in a fatal accident up to mid-1979.

The military An-14 was first seen at the Domodedovo air display in July 1967 and does not appear to differ externally from the civilian passenger version. It serves also with the air forces of Bulgaria, the German Democratic Republic and Guinea.

ECM version of the Antonov An-12 ('Cub-C') in Egyptian Air Force insignia

TYPE: Twin-engined light general-purpose aircraft.

WINGS: Braced high-wing monoplane with single streamline-section bracing strut each side. Dihedral 2°. Conventional all-metal two-spar structure. Full-span leading-edge slats, in three sections on each wing. Section between fuselage and engine nacelle on each wing is extended pneumatically when the flaps are lowered 35-40°. The remaining four sections are actuated automatically by the airflow over the wing. Entire trailing-edges hinged, each comprising a double-slotted flap, with the slat of the flap extending to the wingtip and built into the single-slotted aileron as a leading-edge structure. Flaps operated pneumatically. Trim tab in port aileron. Small stub-wing carries each main landing gear unit and provides lower attachment for bracing strut.

FUSELAGE: Conventional all-metal semi-monocoque pod and boom structure.

TAIL UNIT: Cantilever all-metal structure, with 9° dihedral on tailplane. Twin fins and rudders, mounted at right-angles to the tips of the tailplane, so that they toe inwards at the top. Trim tab in port rudder and in each elevator. Leading-edges of fins and tailplane embody both warm air and electrical anti-icing systems.

LANDING GEAR: Non-retractable tricycle type, with single wheel on each unit. Main units carried on short stub-wings. Wide-tread tyres, size 700 × 250, on all three units. Tyre pressure: main units 3·45 bars (50 lb/sq in); nosewheel 2·93 bars (42·5 lb/sq in). Nosewheel is fully-castoring and steerable to 70° each way, and is self-centering for take-off. Pneumatic brakes on main wheels. Skis can be fitted for operation from snow, or floats for operation from water.

POWER PLANT: Two 224 kW (300 hp) Ivchenko AI-14RF nine-cylinder radial aircooled engines, each driving a V-530 two-blade or three-blade variable-pitch propeller. Each engine draws its fuel normally from an inboard metal tank and outer flexible tank in the wing on which it is mounted, with a cross-feed to enable either engine to be supplied from both tank groups in the event of an engine failure. Total fuel capacity 383 litres (84 Imp gallons).

ACCOMMODATION: Pilot and one passenger side by side on flight deck. Main cabin normally seats six persons in pairs in individual forward-facing armchair seats, each by a large window and with central aisle. Provision for seven seats in main cabin in high-density version. Cabin soundproofed and provided with heating and ventilation systems. Door from cabin to flight deck. Passengers enter cabin through clamshell rear doors which form underside of upswept rear fuselage. Executive version offers de luxe accommodation for five passengers and their baggage, with tables between facing seats. All seats quickly removable to provide an unobstructed cabin for cargo carrying. Ambulance version can accommodate six stretchers, in tiers of three on each side of cabin, with an attendant. Dual controls available for pilot training, and a variety of equipment can be fitted for geological survey, aerial photography and agricultural duties. Chemical tank capacity of agricultural version is 1,000 litres (220 Imp gallons).

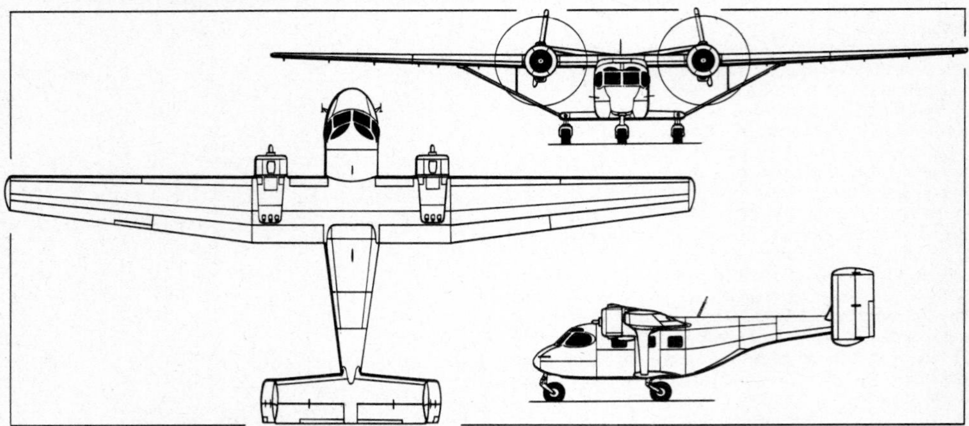

Antonov An-14 Pchelka twin-engined light general-purpose aircraft *(Pilot Press)*

Antonov An-14 Pchelka (two Ivchenko AI-14RF engines) of the Bulgarian Air Force

Antonov An-22 Antheus long-range heavy transport aircraft (four Kuznetsov NK-12MA turboprop engines) *(Tass)*

SYSTEMS: Pneumatic system, pressure 49 bars (710 lb/sq in), for wheel brakes, flap and slat actuation, engine starting, cabin heating and anti-icing. Main 27V DC electrical system supplied by two 3kW engine-driven generators. Two converters to supply 115V 400Hz AC power.

AVIONICS AND EQUIPMENT: Standard equipment includes an artificial horizon, gyro-compass, magnetic compass, altimeter, airspeed indicator, clock, rate-of-climb indicator, turn indicator, outside air temperature gauge and ice-warning device. Com/nav equipment can include duplicated transceivers, ADF, VOR, marker beacon and radio altimeter.

DIMENSIONS, EXTERNAL:
- Wing span: 21·99 m (72 ft 2 in)
- Wing chord, mean: 1·89 m (6 ft 2½ in)
- Wing aspect ratio: 12·15
- Length overall: 11·44 m (37 ft 6½ in)
- Height overall: 4·63 m (15 ft 2½ in)
- Tailplane span: 5·00 m (16 ft 4¾ in)
- Wheel track: 3·60 m (11 ft 9¾ in)
- Wheelbase: 3·71 m (12 ft 2 in)
- Propeller diameter: 2·90 m (9 ft 6 in)
- Cabin door:
  - Length: 1·90 m (6 ft 3 in)
  - Width: 0·85 m (2 ft 9½ in)

DIMENSIONS, INTERNAL:
- Cabin, excl flight deck:
  - Length: 3·10 m (10 ft 2 in)
  - Width: 1·53 m (5 ft 0 in)
  - Height: 1·60 m (5 ft 3 in)

AREA:
- Wings, gross: 39·72 m² (427·5 sq ft)

WEIGHTS AND LOADINGS:
- Weight empty: 2,000 kg (4,409 lb)
- Max payload (normal): 720 kg (1,590 lb)
- Max T-O weight: 3,600 kg (7,935 lb)
- Max wing loading: 90·8 kg/m² (18·6 lb/sq ft)
- Max power loading: 8·04 kg/kW (13·2 lb/hp)

PERFORMANCE (at max T-O weight):
- Max level speed at 1,000 m (3,280 ft): 120 knots (222 km/h; 138 mph)
- Normal cruising speed at 2,000 m (6,560 ft): 97 knots (180 km/h; 112 mph)
- Operating speed, agricultural duties: 76 knots (140 km/h; 87 mph)
- Landing speed: 46 knots (85 km/h; 53 mph)
- Max rate of climb at S/L: 306 m (1,000 ft)/min
- Service ceiling: 5,200 m (17,060 ft)
- T-O run, on concrete: 100 m (328 ft)
- T-O to 15 m (50 ft): 200 m (656 ft)
- Landing from 15 m (50 ft): 300 m (985 ft)
- Landing run: 70 m (230 ft)
- Range:
  - with max payload: 350 nm (650 km; 404 miles)
  - with 550 kg (1,212 lb) payload: 385 nm (715 km; 444 miles)
  - with max fuel: 431 nm (800 km; 497 miles)

ANTONOV An-22 ANTHEUS

NATO reporting name: Cock

The prototype of this very large transport aircraft flew for the first time on 27 February 1965. Production aircraft were delivered to both the Soviet Air Force and Aeroflot, which uses the An-22 mainly in underdeveloped areas of the northern USSR, Siberia and the Far East. Deliveries were completed during 1974, after 30 to 50 aircraft had been delivered to the military air transport force (VTA). In 1978 they remained the only Soviet transports capable of airlifting the T-62 tank.

On 26 October 1967, an An-22 set up fourteen payload-to-height records, piloted by I. Davydov and with a crew of seven. It reached a height of 7,848 m (25,748 ft) with a payload of 100,000 kg of metal blocks, qualifying also for records with 35,000, 40,000, 45,000, 50,000, 55,000, 60,000, 65,000, 70,000, 75,000, 85,000, 90,000 and 95,000 kg. Max payload lifted to a height of 2,000 m was 100,444·6 kg (221,443 lb). Take-off run with this load was stated to be just over one kilometre. The flight lasted 78 minutes.

A further series of ten records, for speed with payload, was set up in February 1972 by an An-22 captained by Marina Popovich, wife of the Soviet cosmonaut Pavel Popovich. The aircraft averaged 320·161 knots (593·318 km/h; 368·671 mph) around a 2,000 km closed circuit with a 50,000 kg payload, qualifying also for records with 30,000, 35,000, 40,000 and 45,000 kg, on 19 February. Two days later, it averaged 328·326 knots (608·449 km/h; 378·073 mph) around 1,000 km with the same payload.

The An-22 also holds three records for speed with payload over a 5,000 km closed circuit. On 21 October 1974, piloted by S. Dedoukh, a payload of 30,000 kg was carried at a speed of 322·300 knots (597·283 km/h; 371·134 mph). On 24 October 1974, piloted by Y. Romanov, a payload of 35,000 kg was carried at a speed of 317·636 knots (588·639 km/h; 365·763 mph). On 17 April 1975, piloted by G. Pakilev, a payload of 40,000 kg was carried at a speed of 315·156 knots (584·042 km/h; 362·907 mph).

The following details refer to the production version as illustrated:

TYPE: Long-range heavy turboprop transport.

WINGS: Cantilever high-wing monoplane. Marked anhedral on outer panels. All-metal structure, appearing to have three main spars which attach to three strong fuselage ring-frames. Double-slotted trailing-edge flaps. Tab in each aileron.

FUSELAGE: All-metal semi-monocoque structure, with upswept rear fuselage containing loading-ramp/door for direct loading. Retractable jacks support rear fuselage at point where rear loading ramp is hinged.

TAIL UNIT: Cantilever all-metal structure. Twin fins and rudders (each in two sections, above and below tailplane) mounted outboard of mid-span. Bullet fairing forward of each fin tip. Tabs in each elevator and in each of the four rudder sections.

LANDING GEAR: Retractable tricycle type, designed to permit off-runway operation. Steerable twin-wheel nose unit. Each main gear consists of three twin-wheel levered-suspension units in tandem, each unit mounted at the bottom of one of the fuselage ring frames that also picks up a wing spar. Main units retract upward into fairings built on to sides of fuselage. Tyre pressure adjustable in flight or on ground to suit airfield surface.

POWER PLANT: Four 11,186 kW (15,000 shp) Kuznetsov NK-12MA turboprop engines, each driving a pair of four-blade contra-rotating propellers.

ACCOMMODATION: Crew of five or six. Navigator's station in nose. Cabin for 28-29 passengers aft of flight deck, separated from main cabin by bulkhead containing two doors. Uninterrupted main cabin, with reinforced titanium floor, tiedown fittings and rear loading ramp. When ramp lowers, a large door which forms the underside of the rear fuselage retracts upward inside fuselage to permit easy loading of tall vehicles. Rails in roof of cabin for four travelling gantries continue rearward on underside of this door. Two winches, used in conjunction with the gantries, each have a capacity of 2,500 kg (5,500 lb). Door in each landing gear fairing, forward of wheels, for crew and passengers.

AVIONICS AND EQUIPMENT: Pressurisation equipment and APU in forward part of starboard landing gear fairing. Two radars, in nose 'thimble' and undernose fairings.

DIMENSIONS, EXTERNAL:
- Wing span: 64·40 m (211 ft 4 in)
- Length overall (prototype): 57·80 m (189 ft 7 in)
- Height overall: 12·53 m (41 ft 1½ in)
- Propeller diameter: 6·20 m (20 ft 4 in)

DIMENSIONS, INTERNAL:
- Main cabin: Length: 33·0 m (108 ft 3 in)
  - Max width: 4·4 m (14 ft 5 in)
  - Max height: 4·4 m (14 ft 5 in)

AREA:
- Wings, gross: 345 m² (3,713 sq ft)

WEIGHTS:
- Weight empty, equipped: 114,000 kg (251,325 lb)
- Max payload: 80,000 kg (176,350 lb)
- Max fuel: 43,000 kg (94,800 lb)
- Max T-O weight: 250,000 kg (551,160 lb)

PERFORMANCE:
- Max level speed: 399 knots (740 km/h; 460 mph)
- T-O run: 1,300 m (4,260 ft)
- Landing run: 800 m (2,620 ft)
- Range with max fuel and 45,000 kg (99,200 lb) payload: 5,905 nm (10,950 km; 6,800 miles)
- Range with max payload: 2,692 nm (5,000 km; 3,100 miles)

ANTONOV An-24

NATO reporting name: Coke

Development of this twin-turboprop transport was started in 1958, to replace piston-engined types on Aeroflot's internal feederline routes. The first prototype flew in April 1960 and the An-24 entered service on Aeroflot's routes from Moscow to Voronezh and Saratov in September 1963. By 1976, a total of about 1,100 An-24s had been produced, several hundred of them for

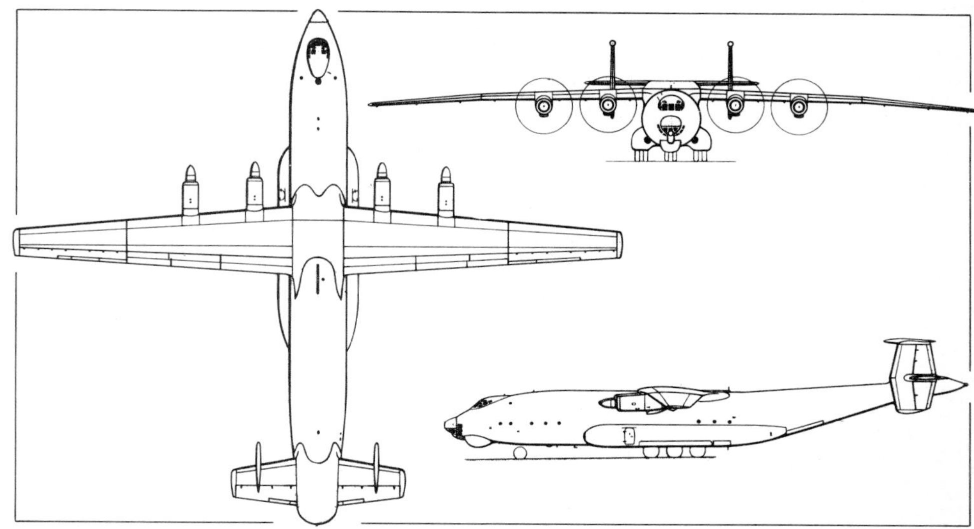

Antonov An-22 Antheus long-range heavy transport aircraft *(Pilot Press)*

Antonov An-24RV twin-turboprop transport fitted with new eight-blade propellers that are claimed to offer considerably reduced noise characteristics *(Tass)*

Aeroflot. A list of 14 other airlines known to have operated a total of 74 An-24s can be found in the 1976-77 *Jane's*. The An-24 was also supplied for military service, usually in small numbers, with the air forces of the USSR, Bangladesh, the Republic of Congo (Brazzaville), Czechoslovakia, Egypt, East Germany, Hungary, Iraq, North Korea, Mongolia, Poland, Romania, the Somali Republic, North Viet-Nam and South Yemen. Six were acquired by the Laotian government, for unspecified duties, in 1977. Production ended in 1978, when the last aircraft off the assembly line was delivered to the Romanian airline Tarom. It was stated to be the 750th aircraft of the An-24/26 series exported by that time.

The An-24 was built in a variety of forms, as follows:

An-24V Srs II. Standard version. Superseded Srs I (with 2,550 ehp AI-24 engines) in 1968. Powered by two Ivchenko AI-24A turboprop engines, with water injection. Mixed passenger/freight, convertible cargo/passenger, all-freight and executive versions were available.

An-24P. Firefighting *(Pozharny)* version, which underwent evaluation in the USSR in 1971. Special provisions for enabling firefighters to be parachuted from a height of 800-1,200 m (2,625-3,940 ft) to deal with forest fires.

An-24RV. Generally similar to Srs II version of An-24V, but with Type RU 19-300 auxiliary turbojet engine in starboard nacelle instead of starter/generator. This turbojet is used for engine starting, to improve take-off performance and to improve performance in the air. It permits take-off with a full payload from airfields up to 3,000 m (9,840 ft) above S/L and at temperatures up to ISA + 30°C. It also ensures considerably improved stability and handling characteristics after a failure of one of the turboprop engines in flight. Max T-O weight is increased by 800 kg (1,760 lb) at S/L ISA and by 2,000 kg (4,410 lb) at S/L ISA + 30°C by use of the auxiliary turbojet.

An accompanying photograph, issued in March 1979, shows an An-24RV fitted experimentally with eight-blade propellers which were stated to offer considerably reduced noise characteristics. The aircraft was photographed at Sheremetyevo Airport, Moscow.

An-24T. Generally similar to An-24V Srs II but equipped as specialised freighter. Normal passenger door at rear of cabin is deleted and replaced by a belly freight door at the rear of the cabin. This hinges upward and to the rear, providing a hatchway for cargo loading. An electrically-powered winch, capacity 1,500 kg (3,300 lb), is used to hoist crates through the hatch and runs on a rail in the cabin ceiling to position the payload inside the cabin. Electrically or manually powered conveyor, capacity 4,500 kg (9,920 lb), flush with cabin floor. Fewer windows. Folding seats along walls of cabin. Emergency exit hatches in side and in floor at front of cabin. Rear cargo door permits air-dropping of payload or parachutists. Provision for stretcher-carrying in air ambulance role. Single ventral fin replaced by twin ventral fins, forming V, aft of cargo door.

An-24RT. Generally similar to An-24T but with Type RU auxiliary turbojet in starboard nacelle, as on An-24RV.

The following description is generally applicable to all versions:

Type: Twin-turboprop short-range transport.

Wings: Cantilever high-wing monoplane, with 2° anhedral on outer panels. Incidence 3°. Sweepback at quarter-chord on outer panels 6° 50′. All-metal two-spar structure, built in five sections: centre-section, two inner wings and two outer wings. Wing skin is attached by electrical spot-welding. Mass-balanced servo-compensated ailerons, with large trim tabs of glassfibre construction. Hydraulically-operated Fowler flaps along entire wing trailing-edges inboard of unpowered ailerons; single-slotted flaps on centre-section, double-slotted outboard of nacelles. Servo and trim tabs in each aileron. Thermal de-icing system.

Fuselage: All-metal semi-monocoque structure in front, centre and rear portions, of bonded/welded construction.

Tail Unit: Cantilever all-metal structure, with ventral fin (two ventral fins on An-24T/RT versions). 9° dihedral on tailplane. All controls manually operated. Balance tabs in elevators. Trim tab and spring tab in rudder. All leading-edges incorporate thermal de icing system.

Landing Gear: Retractable tricycle type with twin wheels on all units. Hydraulic retraction. Emergency extension by gravity. All units retract forward. Main wheels size 900 × 300-370, tyre pressure 3·45-4·90 bars (50-71 lb/sq in). Nosewheels size 700 × 250, tyre pressure 2·45-3·45 bars (35·5-50 lb/sq in). Tyre pressures variable to cater for different types of runway. Disc brakes on main wheels. Steerable and castoring nosewheel unit.

Power Plant (all versions): Two 1,902 kW (2,550 ehp) Ivchenko AI-24A turboprop engines (with provision for water injection; weight of water 68 kg; 150 lb), each driving an AV-72 four-blade constant-speed fully-feathering propeller. Electrical de-icing system for propeller blades and hubs; hot air system for engine air intakes. Fuel in integral tanks immediately outboard of nacelles, and four bag-type tanks in centre-section, total capacity 5,550 litres (1,220 Imp gallons). Provision for four additional tanks in centre-section. Pressure refuelling socket in starboard engine nacelle. Gravity fuelling point above each tank. Carbon dioxide inert gas system to create fireproof condition inside fuel tanks. Oil capacity 53 litres (11·5 Imp gallons). TG-16 self-contained starter/generator in rear of starboard engine nacelle of An-24V and An-24T; this is replaced by one 8·83 kN (1,985 lb st) Type RU 19-300 auxiliary turbojet in starboard nacelle of An-24RV and An-24RT. Provision for fitting rocket-assisted take-off units on cargo versions.

Accommodation (An-24V/RV): Crew of three (pilot, co-pilot/radio operator/navigator and one stewardess). Provision for carrying navigator, radio operator and engineer. Normal accommodation for 44-52 passengers in air-conditioned and pressurised cabin. Standard layout has baggage and freight compartments on each side aft of flight deck; then the main cabin with 52 forward-facing reclining seats, in pairs at a pitch of 72 cm (28·3 in), on each side of centre aisle (optionally two small sofas for babies at rear, instead of two of the seats); buffet and stewardess's seat, and toilet, opposite door to rear of cabin; and wardrobes at rear. Passenger door on port side, aft of cabin, is of airstair type. Door on starboard side for freight hold (front). All doors open inward. The 46-seat version has a removable partition aft of the fifth row of seats, instead of one row of seats. The mixed passenger/cargo version is laid out normally for 36 passengers, with 14 m³ (495 cu ft) forward hold for baggage, freight and mail, and rear wardrobe and baggage hold (2·8 m³; 99 cu ft). A typical de luxe or executive layout retains the forward and aft baggage and freight holds of the airliner version but has the main cabin divided into three compartments. The forward compartment contains four pairs of seats, in aft-facing and forward-facing pairs with tables between, and a buffet. Next comes a similar cabin without the buffet, followed by a sleeping compartment, with a sofa, two seats and table. At the rear is the standard toilet compartment opposite the airstair door, and a large wardrobe space.

Accommodation (An-24T/RT): Provision for crew of up to five, with optional cargo handler. Door at front of cabin on starboard side. Upward-opening cargo door in belly at rear of cabin. Max overall dimensions of cargo packages that can be handled are 1·1 × 1·5 × 2·6 m (43·3 × 59 × 102 in) or 1·3 × 1·5 × 2·1 m (51·2 × 59 × 82·7 in). Toilet (port side) and emergency exit door in belly, immediately aft of flight deck. Folding seats, in two-, three- and four-place units, for 30 paratroops or 38 equipped soldiers along walls of main cabin. Ambulance configuration is equipped to carry 24 stretcher cases and one medical attendant. Cargo loading system includes rails in floor, electric winch, overhead gantry, tiedown fittings, nets and harness. Electrical de-icing system for windscreens.

Systems: Air-conditioning system uses hot air tapped from the 10th compressor stage of each engine, with a heat exchanger and turbocooler in each nacelle. Cabin pressure differential 0·29 bars (4·27 lb/sq in). Main and emergency hydraulic systems, pressure 151·7 bars (2,200 lb/sq in), for landing gear retraction, nosewheel

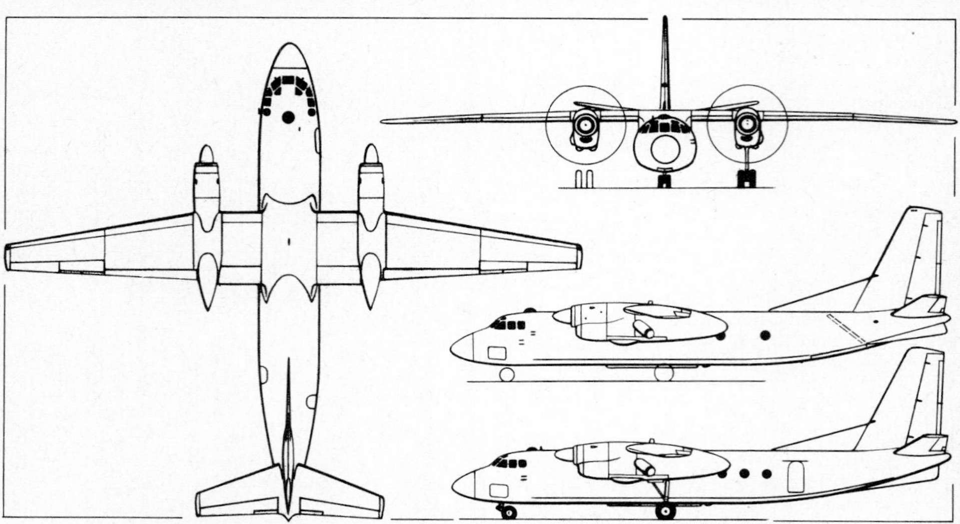

Antonov An-24V transport, with additional side view of the An-24T (centre) *(Pilot Press)*

steering, flaps, brakes, windscreen wipers, propeller feathering and, on An-24T, operation of cargo and emergency escape doors. Hand-pump to operate doors only and build up pressure in main system. Electrical system includes two 27V DC starter/generators, two alternators to provide 115V 400Hz AC supply and two inverters for 36V 400Hz three-phase AC supply. An-24T has permanent oxygen system for pilot, installed equipment for other crew members and three portable bottles for personnel in cargo hold.

AVIONICS AND EQUIPMENT (An-24T/RT): Standard radio equipment includes two R-802V VHF transceivers, R-836 HF transmitter and US-8 receiver, SPU-7 intercom, two ARK-11 ADF, RV-2 radio altimeter, SP-50 ILS with KRP-F glidepath receiver, GRP-2 glideslope receiver and MRP-56 marker receiver, and RPSN-2AN weather, obstruction and navigation radar. Flight and navigational equipment includes an AP-28L1 autopilot, TsGV-4 master vertical gyro, GPK-52AP directional gyro, GIK-1 gyro compass, two ZK-2 course setting devices, two AGD-1 artificial horizons, AK-59P astro-compass, NI-50BM-K ground position indicator and other standard blind-flying instruments, plus three clocks. Optional OPB-1R sight for pinpoint dropping of cargo and determination of navigational data.

DIMENSIONS, EXTERNAL:
Wing span 29·20 m (95 ft 9½ in)
Wing aspect ratio 11·7
Length overall 23·53 m (77 ft 2½ in)
Height overall 8·32 m (27 ft 3½ in)
Width of fuselage 2·90 m (9 ft 6 in)
Depth of fuselage 2·50 m (8 ft 2½ in)
Tailplane span 9·08 m (29 ft 9½ in)
Wheel track (c/l shock-struts) 7·90 m (25 ft 11 in)
Wheelbase 7·89 m (25 ft 10½ in)
Propeller diameter 3·90 m (12 ft 9½ in)
Propeller ground clearance 1·145 m (3 ft 9 in)
Passenger door (port, aft, except on An-24T):
Height 1·40 m (4 ft 7 in)
Width 0·75 m (2 ft 5½ in)
Height to sill 1·40 m (4 ft 7 in)
Freight compartment door (stbd, fwd):
Height 1·10 m (3 ft 7¼ in)
Width 1·20 m (3 ft 11¼ in)
Height to sill 1·30 m (4 ft 3 in)
Baggage compartment door (stbd, aft, except on An-24T):
Height 1·41 m (4 ft 7½ in)
Width 0·75 m (2 ft 5½ in)
Cargo door (belly, rear, An-24T only):
Length 2·85 m (9 ft 4 in)
Width:
max 1·40 m (4 ft 7 in)
min 1·10 m (3 ft 7¼ in)
Height above ground 1·25-1·62 m (4 ft 1 in to 5 ft 4 in)
Emergency exit (An-24T, side):
Height 0·60 m (1 ft 11½ in)
Width 0·50 m (1 ft 7½ in)
Emergency exit (An-24T, underfuselage):
Length 1·155 m (3 ft 9½ in)
Width 0·70 m (2 ft 3½ in)

DIMENSIONS, INTERNAL:
Main passenger cabin (52-seater):
Length 9·69 m (31 ft 9½ in)
Max width 2·76 m (9 ft 1 in)
Max height 1·91 m (6 ft 3 in)
Floor area 39·95 m² (430 sq ft)
Cargo hold (An-24T):
Length 15·68 m (51 ft 5½ in)
Width 2·17 m (7 ft 1½ in)
Height 1·765 m (5 ft 9½ in)
Volume 50 m³ (1,765 cu ft)

AREAS:
Wings, gross 74·98 m² (807·1 sq ft)
Horizontal tail surfaces (total) 17·23 m² (185·5 sq ft)
Vertical tail surfaces (total, excl dorsal fin) 13·38 m² (144·0 sq ft)

WEIGHTS AND LOADINGS:
Weight empty:
An-24V 13,300 kg (29,320 lb)
An-24T 14,060 kg (30,997 lb)
Basic operating weight:
An-24T 14,698 kg (32,404 lb)
Fuel weight:
An-24T with max payload 1,800 kg (3,968 lb)
An-24T for max range 4,760 kg (10,494 lb)
Max payload (ISA, S/L):
An-24V, An-24RV 5,500 kg (12,125 lb)
An-24T 4,612 kg (10,168 lb)
An-24RT 5,700 kg (12,566 lb)
Max ramp weight:
An-24T 21,110 kg (46,540 lb)
Max T-O and landing weight:
An-24V, An-24T, S/L,ISA 21,000 kg (46,300 lb)
An-24V, An-24T, S/L, ISA + 30°C 19,800 kg (43,650 lb)
An-24RV, An-24RT, S/L, ISA or ISA + 30°C 21,800 kg (48,060 lb)
Max wing loading:
An-24V 276 kg/m² (56·53 lb/sq ft)

PERFORMANCE (at max T-O weight):
Normal cruising speed at 6,000 m (19,700 ft) 243 knots (450 km/h; 280 mph)
Max range cruising speed at 7,000 m (23,000 ft) 243 knots (450 km/h; 280 mph)
T-O speed:
An-24T 97-100 knots (180-185 km/h; 112-115 mph)
Landing speed:
An-24V 89 knots (165 km/h; 103 mph) CAS
An-24T 87-95 knots (160-175 km/h; 100-109 mph)
Max rate of climb at S/L:
An-24V 114 m (375 ft)/min
An-24RV 204 m (670 ft)/min
Rate of climb at S/L, one engine out:
An-24V, ISA 84 m (275 ft)/min
An-24V, ISA + 30°C, with water injection 84 m (275 ft)/min
An-24RV, ISA 174 m (570 ft)/min
An-24RV, ISA + 30° 90 m (295 ft)/min
Service ceiling:
An-24V, An-24T 8,400 m (27,560 ft)
An-24RV, An-24RT 9,000 m (29,525 ft)
Service ceiling, one engine out:
An-24T 2,750 m (9,020 ft)
T-O run:
An-24V 600 m (1,970 ft)
An-24T 640 m (2,100 ft)
Balanced T-O runway:
An-24T, ISA 1,720 m (5,645 ft)
An-24T, ISA + 15°C 1,750 m (5,745 ft)
Landing run at AUW of 20,000 kg (44,100 lb):
An-24T 880 m (1,903 ft)
Landing from 15 m (50 ft) at AUW of 20,000 kg (44,100 lb):
An-24T 1,590 m (5,217 ft)
Range with max payload, with reserves:
An-24V, An-24RV 296 nm (550 km; 341 miles)
An-24T, An-24RT 344 nm (640 km; 397 miles)
Range with max fuel:
An-24V, 45 min fuel reserves 1,293 nm (2,400 km; 1,490 miles)
An-24T, with 1,612 kg (3,554 lb) payload, no reserves 1,618 nm (3,000 km; 1,864 miles)

ANTONOV An-26

NATO reporting name: Curl

First displayed in public at the 1969 Paris Air Show, the An-26 was known initially as the 'An-24T with an enlarged freight door'. It is, in fact, generally similar to the An-24RT, but has more powerful AI-24T turboprop engines and a completely redesigned rear fuselage of the 'beaver-tail' type. Although intended primarily for cargo-carrying, with airdrop capability, the An-26 can be adapted easily for passenger-carrying, ambulance or paratroop transport duties. Production was continuing in 1979.

The Air Wing of the Bangladesh Defence Force has a small number of An-26s, as well as one An-24. Other An-26s serve with the Cuban, Hungarian, Peruvian, Polish and Romanian Air Forces. The Soviet Air Force has a total of about 200 An-24s and An-26s.

The basic structural description of the An-24 applies also to the An-26, except for the following details:

TYPE: Twin-turboprop short-haul transport.

WINGS: Made in three sections: centre-section and two outer panels which contain integral fuel tanks.

FUSELAGE: Skin on lower portion of fuselage is made of 'bimetal' (duralumin-titanium) sheet for protection during operations from unpaved airfields.

LANDING GEAR: Shock-absorbers are of oleo-nitrogen type. Main wheels are fitted with hydraulic disc brakes and anti-skid units. Nosewheels can be steered hydraulically through 45° each side while taxying and are controllable through ±10° during take-off and landing. Main-wheel tyres size 1,050 × 400, pressure 3·93 bars (57 lb/sq in). Nosewheel tyres size 700 × 250, pressure 4·41 bars (64 lb/sq in).

POWER PLANT: Two 2,103 kW (2,820 ehp) Ivchenko AI-24T turboprop engines, each driving a four-blade constant-speed fully-feathering propeller. One 8·83 kN (1,985 lb st) RU 19-300 auxiliary turbojet in starboard nacelle for use, as required, at take-off, during climb and in level flight, and for self-contained starting of main engines. Fuel load 5,500 kg (12,125 lb).

ACCOMMODATION: Basic crew of five (pilot, co-pilot, radio operator, flight engineer and navigator), with station at rear of cabin on starboard side for loading supervisor or load despatcher. Toilet on port side aft of flight deck; small galley and oxygen bottle stowage on starboard side. Emergency escape hatch in floor immediately aft of flight deck. Large downward-hinged rear ramp-door, which can also slide forward under fuselage for direct loading on to cabin floor or for air-dropping of freight. Electrically-powered mobile winch, capacity 1,500 kg (3,300 lb), hoists crates through rear entrance and runs on a rail in the cabin ceiling to position payload in cabin. Electrically- or manually-operated conveyor, capacity 4,500 kg (9,920 lb), built-in flush with cabin floor, facilitates loading and air-dropping of freight. Can accommodate a variety of motor vehicles, including GAZ-69 and UAZ-469 military vehicles, or cargo items up to 1·50 m (59 in) high by 2·10 m (82·6 in) wide. Height of rear edge of cargo door surround above the cabin floor is 1·50 m (4 ft 11 in). Cabin is pressurised and air-conditioned, and is fitted with a row of tip-up seats along each wall to accommodate up to 40 paratroops. Conversion to troop transport role, or to an ambulance for 24 stretcher patients and a medical attendant, takes 20 to 30 minutes in the field.

SYSTEMS: Basically as for An-24. Electrical system includes two 27V DC starter/generators on engines, a standby generator on the auxiliary turbojet, and three storage batteries for emergency use. Two engine-driven alternators provide 115V 400Hz single-phase AC supply, with standby inverter. Basic source of 36V 400Hz three-phase AC supply is two inverters, with standby transformer.

AVIONICS AND EQUIPMENT: Standard com/nav avionics comprise two VHF transceivers, HF, intercom, two ADF, radio altimeter, glidepath receiver, glideslope receiver, marker receiver, weather/navigation radar, directional gyro and flight recorder. Optional equipment includes a flight director system, astro-compass and autopilot. Standard operational equipment includes parachute static line attachments and retraction devices, tiedowns, jack to support ramp sill, flight deck curtains, sun visors and windscreen wipers. Optional items include a navigator's observation blister on port side of flight deck, OPB-1R sight for pinpoint dropping of freight, medical equipment and liquid heating system.

DIMENSIONS, EXTERNAL:
As for An-24, except:
Length overall 23·80 m (78 ft 1 in)
Height overall 8·575 m (28 ft 1½ in)
Tailplane span 9·973 m (32 ft 8¾ in)
Wheelbase 7·651 m (25 ft 1¼ in)
Propeller ground clearance 1·227 m (4 ft 0¼ in)
Crew door (stbd, front):
Height 1·40 m (4 ft 7 in)
Width 0·60 m (1 ft 11¾ in)
Height to sill 1·47 m (4 ft 9¾ in)
Loading hatch (rear):
Length 3·40 m (11 ft 1¾ in)
Width at front 2·40 m (7 ft 10½ in)
Width at rear 2·00 m (6 ft 6¾ in)
Height to sill 1·47 m (4 ft 9¾ in)
Height to top edge of hatchway 3·014 m (9 ft 10¾ in)

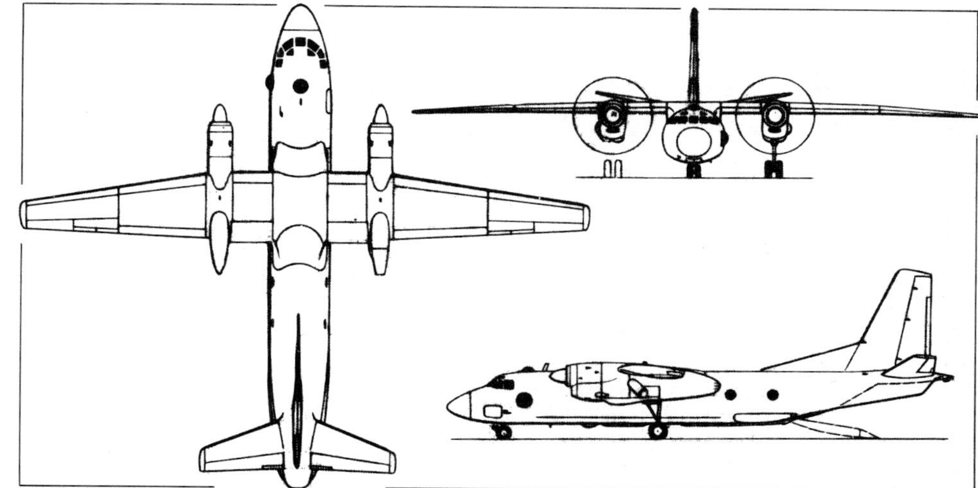

Antonov An-26 twin-turboprop short-haul transport *(Pilot Press)*

Five Antonov An-26 transports which passed through Gatwick Airport, en route to Cuba, in December 1978 *(British Airports Authority, Gatwick)*

Emergency exit (floor at front):
- Length: 1·02 m (3 ft 4¼ in)
- Width: 0·70 m (2 ft 3½ in)

Emergency exit (top):
- Diameter: 0·65 m (2 ft 1½ in)

Emergency exits (each side of hold, two):
- Height: 0·60 m (1 ft 11¾ in)
- Width: 0·50 m (1 ft 7½ in)

DIMENSIONS, INTERNAL:

Cargo hold:
- Length of floor: 11·50 m (37 ft 8¾ in)
- Width of floor: 2·40 m (7 ft 10½ in)
- Max height: 1·91 m (6 ft 3 in)

AREAS:
- Wings, gross: 74·98 m² (807·1 sq ft)
- Horizontal tail surfaces (total): 19·83 m² (213·45 sq ft)
- Vertical tail surfaces (total, incl dorsal fin): 15·85 m² (170·61 sq ft)

WEIGHTS:
- Weight empty: 15,020 kg (33,113 lb)
- Normal payload: 4,500 kg (9,920 lb)
- Max payload: 5,500 kg (12,125 lb)
- Normal T-O and landing weight: 23,000 kg (50,706 lb)
- Max T-O and landing weight: 24,000 kg (52,911 lb)

PERFORMANCE (at normal T-O weight):
- Cruising speed at 6,000 m (19,675 ft): 229-234 knots (425-435 km/h; 264-270 mph)
- T-O speed: 108 knots (200 km/h; 124 mph) CAS
- Landing speed: 102 knots (190 km/h; 118 mph) CAS
- Max rate of climb at S/L: 480 m (1,575 ft)/min
- Service ceiling: 8,100 m (26,575 ft)
- T-O run, on concrete: 780 m (2,559 ft)
- T-O to 15 m (50 ft): 1,240 m (4,068 ft)
- Landing from 15 m (50 ft): 1,740 m (5,709 ft)
- Landing run, on concrete: 730 m (2,395 ft)
- Min ground turning radius: 22·3 m (73 ft 2 in)
- Range, with allowance for taxying and 580 kg (1,278 lb) reserve fuel:
  - with 4,500 kg (9,920 lb) payload: 485 nm (900 km; 559 miles)
  - with 2,126 kg (4,687 lb) payload: 1,214 nm (2,250 km; 1,398 miles)

ANTONOV An-28

NATO reporting name: Cash

Responsibility for An-28 production has been allocated to the WSK-PZL Mielec works in Poland (see Polish section).

ANTONOV An-30

NATO reporting name: Clank

Described as the first specialised aerial survey aeroplane produced in the Soviet Union, the An-30 is evolved from the An-24RT and An-26 twin-turboprop transports, to which it is generally similar. The major modifications are made to the nose, which is extensively glazed to give the navigator a wide field of view, and to the flight deck, which is raised to improve the pilots' view and increase the size of the navigator's compartment. There are fewer windows in the main cabin, which contains a darkroom and film storage cupboard, as well as survey cameras and a control desk. Other amenities include a toilet, buffet and crew rest area with armchairs and couches.

Photography can be automatic or semi-automatic if required, but two photographer/surveyors are normally carried, in addition to a flight crew of five (pilot, co-pilot, flight engineer, radio operator and navigator).

For the primary task of air photography for map-making, the An-30 is equipped with large survey cameras. These are mounted in the cabin above apertures, of which there are four, each covered by a door. A crew photographer uncovers the apertures, as required, by remote control from his desk in the aircraft.

Standard equipment includes radio topographic distance measuring equipment and a radio altimeter, with recording units. The pre-programmed flight path of the aircraft over the area to be photographed is fed into an onboard computer, controlled from the navigator's station, which maintains the correct speed, altitude and direction of flight throughout the mission. The cartographic An-30 has an AFA-41/7·5 wide-angle camera, in a TAU-M gyro-stabilised mounting, over No. 1 aperture; and an AFA-54/50 long focal-length camera over No. 3 aperture, each mounted vertically. Two further AFA-54/50 cameras take oblique photographs at 28° to the vertical, port and starboard, through Nos. 4 and 5 apertures. One photogrammetric version has two vertically mounted AFA-41/7·5 cameras, one in a TAU-M mount. Another has the same installation without the gyroscopic mounting. An OPB-1R viewfinder and automatic exposure meter is mounted above aperture No. 2 in all versions.

If required, the cameras can be replaced by other kinds of survey equipment, such as those used for mineral prospecting or for microwave radiometer survey, which measures the heat emission of land and ocean to obtain data on ocean surface characteristics, sea and lake ice, snow cover, flooding, seasonal vegetation changes, and soil types.

The power plant comprises two 2,103 kW (2,820 ehp) Ivchenko AI-24VT turboprop engines, with water injection, each driving an AV-72T four-blade constant-speed fully-feathering and reversible-pitch propeller. Main engines are supplemented by an 8·83 kN (1,985 lb st) RU 19A-300 auxiliary turbojet in the rear of the starboard engine nacelle. The latter is used for engine starting, and for take-off, climb and cruise power in the event of failure of the primary power plant. Engine TBO was 4,000 h in 1977. Max fuel capacity is 6,200 litres (1,364 Imp gallons).

Conversion into a transport aircraft is provided for, with cover plates to place over the camera apertures. The standard An-24 cabin door, on the port side of the fuselage at the rear, is retained, together with the standard forward freight compartment door on the starboard side.

The prototype An-30 flew for the first time in 1974. Operators include the Romanian Air Force, which has at least three.

Antonov An-30 (two AI-24VT turboprops and RU 19A-300 auxiliary turbojet) *(Pilot Press)*

Antonov An-30 aerial survey development of the An-24 twin-turboprop transport aircraft, with glazed nose and other modifications *(M. D. West)*

Antonov An-32, a version of the An-26 transport with a major increase in engine power for take-off from 'hot and high' airfields

DIMENSIONS, EXTERNAL:

Wing span	29·20 m (95 ft 9½ in)
Wing aspect ratio	11·4
Length overall	24·26 m (79 ft 7 in)
Height overall	8·31 m (27 ft 3¼ in)
Tailplane span	9·973 m (32 ft 8¾ in)
Fuselage, nominal diameter	2·90 m (9 ft 6¼ in)
Wheel track (c/l of oleos)	7·90 m (25 ft 11 in)
Propeller diameter	3·90 m (12 ft 9½ in)
Propeller ground clearance	1·20 m (3 ft 11¼ in)

WEIGHTS:

Basic operating weight	15,590 kg (34,370 lb)
Max T-O weight	23,000 kg (50,705 lb)

PERFORMANCE:

Max level speed	291 knots (540 km/h; 335 mph)
Cruising speed	232-256 knots (430-475 km/h; 267-295 mph)
Landing speed	95 knots (175 km/h; 109 mph)
Service ceiling	8,300 m (27,230 ft)
Range at 237 knots (440 km/h; 273 mph) at 6,000 m (19,700 ft)	1,274 nm (2,360 km; 1,466 miles)

ANTONOV An-32

NATO reporting name: Cline

This short/medium-range transport, of which first details were released in May 1977, is a developed version of the An-26, intended for operation in high-temperature or high-altitude environments. Except for having much enlarged ventral fins and a full-span slotted tailplane, the airframe appears to be generally similar to that of the An-26.

The An-32 is powered by two 3,862 kW (5,180 ehp) Ivchenko AI-20M turboprop engines, each driving a four-blade propeller. The large increase in power is intended specifically to improve take-off performance, service ceiling and payload. Thus, the An-32 is able to operate from airfields 4,000-4,500 m (13,125-14,750 ft) above sea level in an ambient temperature of 25°C, and can transport 3 tonnes of freight over a 594 nm (1,100 km; 683 mile) stage length, with fuel reserves. The overwing location of the engines requires nacelles of considerable depth, as the main landing gear units continue to retract into the underwing portions.

A rear loading hatch and forward-sliding ramp/door, similar to those of the An-26, are retained; but hoist capacity is increased to 2,000 kg (4,409 lb) to facilitate handling of the maximum payload of 6 tonnes of freight. Alternative payloads include 39 passengers or 30 parachutists on a row of tip-up seats along each cabin wall, or 24 stretcher patients and a medical attendant; the normal crew of five comprises pilot, co-pilot, navigator, radio operator and flight engineer.

Low-pressure tyres (of the same sizes as those on the An-26) permit operation from unpaved strips; and the high position of the engines reduces the possibility of stone or debris ingestion. A TG-16M APU, housed in the rear of the starboard landing gear fairing, helps to make the An-32 independent of ground servicing equipment by providing on-board engine starting capability at airfields up to 4,500 m (14,750 ft) above sea level.

Only a single prototype of the An-32 had been built by mid-1979. It was exhibited at the 1977 Paris Air Show; at the 1979 Show, Mr Antonov commented that production would be undertaken only if sufficient orders were received in advance to justify such a move.

DIMENSIONS, EXTERNAL AND INTERNAL:

As for An-26, except:

Propeller diameter	4·70 m (15 ft 5 in)

WEIGHT:

Max T-O weight	26,000 kg (57,320 lb)

PERFORMANCE:

Normal cruising speed	275 knots (510 km/h; 317 mph)
Max cruising height	8,000 m (26,250 ft)
Service ceiling	9,500 m (31,150 ft)
Service ceiling, one engine out	5,000 m (16,400 ft)
T-O run	500 m (1,640 ft)
Range with max payload, 45 min reserves	432 nm (800 km; 497 miles)
Range with max fuel, 45 min reserves	1,188 nm (2,200 km; 1,367 miles)

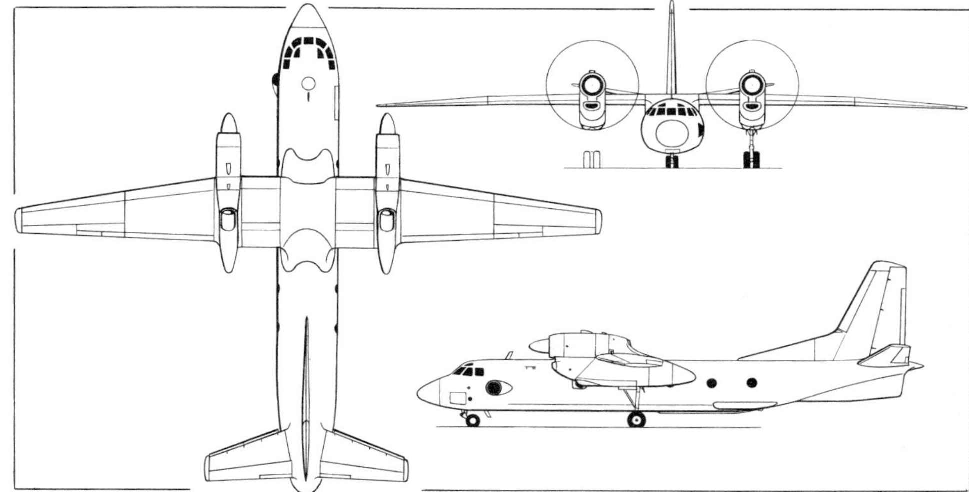

Antonov An-32 short/medium-range transport (two Ivchenko AI-20M turboprop engines) *(Pilot Press)*

ANTONOV An-40

At the 1979 Paris Air Show, Mr Antonov stated that the designation An-40 was given to an intended replacement for the An-12 which was subsequently abandoned.

ANTONOV An-72

NATO reporting name: Coaler

Two prototypes of this experimental twin-turbofan STOL transport had been built by mid-1979, with a third airframe nearing completion for static testing. First photographs of one of these aircraft (CCCP-19774) were released by the Soviet Tass news agency shortly after its reported first flight on 22 December 1977. By the time of the 1979 Paris Air Show the two An-72s had logged a total of just over 1,000 hours in about 300 flights, and were described by Mr Antonov as "progressing faster than the An-28", which is itself entering production at Mielec in Poland.

The An-72 is being evaluated as a STOL replacement for the An-26 twin-turboprop transports flown by Aeroflot and other airlines, and is able to operate from unprepared airfields or from surfaces covered with ice or snow. The military potential of a transport able to utilise natural landing areas in undeveloped countries, or even small fields in Europe, is obvious. In particular, the An-72 might be an ideal aircraft with which to support operations by the new generation of V/STOL combat aircraft that will follow the Yak-36. Its low-pressure tyres and bogie landing gear are well suited to such tasks, and the high-set engines avoid problems caused by foreign object ingestion.

As on the Boeing YC-14, which has a similar engine arrangement, the efflux is ejected over the upper surface of the wing and down over the very large multi-slotted flaps. By taking advantage of the so-called 'Coanda effect', which causes the airflow to 'attach to' the extended flaps, a considerable increase in lift can be achieved.

Mr Antonov anticipates few changes to the design if a

First prototype of the Antonov An-72 twin-turbofan STOL transport, with ventral fins *(Tass)*

Second prototype of the An-72 with modified rear fuselage and other changes, as shown at 1979 Paris Air Show *(Tass)*

decision is taken to put the An-72 into series production. However, he is not convinced that so small a transport has much to gain from complications such as the deflector doors at the rear of the engine nacelles which 'spread' the exhaust flow for optimum effectiveness during take-off and landing.

Particular care has been taken to ensure easy handling of the An-72 in the air, and the designer commented that the aircraft had proved outstanding in this respect. Its Doppler-based automatic navigation system, linked to an onboard computer, is preprogrammed before take-off on a push-button panel to the right of the large cockpit map display. Failure warning panels above the windscreen display red lights for critical failures, yellow lights for non-critical failures, to minimise the time that needs to be spent on monitoring instruments and equipment.

Type: Twin-turbofan light STOL transport.

Wings: Cantilever high-wing monoplane, with approx 25° sweepback on leading-edges and straight trailing-edges. Short constant-chord centre-section, without dihedral or anhedral. Approx 10° anhedral on outer panels. Wing upper-surface blowing requires engines to be mounted above and forward of wings, to exhaust over upper surface. Hydraulically-actuated full-span leading-edge flaps outboard of nacelles. Wide-span trailing-edge flaps, double-slotted inboard in exhaust efflux, triple-slotted on outer panels. Normal T-O flap setting 25-30°; max deflection 60°. Five-section spoilers forward of flaps on each side; some sections opened automatically on touchdown by sensors actuated by weight on main landing gear. Conventional ailerons outboard of flaps, with tab in port aileron.

Fuselage: Conventional all-metal semi-monocoque structure of circular cross-section. Underside of upswept rear fuselage made up of two outward-hinged clamshell doors and downward-opening ramp-door.

Tail Unit: Cantilever all-metal T tail, with wide-chord sweptback vertical surfaces. Double-hinged rudder, with tab in lower portion of two-section aft panel. Tailplane leading-edge sweep slightly greater than that of wings, with straight trailing-edge on horn-balanced elevators. Two tabs in each elevator. Tapered fairing forward of fin/tailplane junction. Two large outward-canted ventral fins, probably associated with airdrop testing from open ramp, on CCCP-19774; not fitted on CCCP-83966 when shown in Paris, June 1979.

Landing Gear: Retractable tricycle type. Twin wheels on rearward-retracting steerable nose unit. Each main unit comprises two trailing-arm legs in tandem, retracting inward through 90° so that wheels lie horizontally in bottom of large fairings, outside fuselage pressure cell. Low-pressure tyres, size 720 × 310 on nosewheels, 1050 × 400 on main wheels.

Power Plant: Two Lotarev D-36 high bypass ratio turbofan engines, each rated at 63·74 kN (14,330 lb st).

Accommodation: Pilot and copilot/navigator side by side on very roomy flight deck. Optional flight engineer's seat, at rear on starboard side, slides forward on tracks to position between and slightly aft of pilots, to give access to controls on central console. Main cabin designed primarily for freight, but with folding seats for 32 passengers along side walls and provision for carrying 24 casualties and attendant in ambulance configuration. Large downward-hinged rear ramp-door for loading trucks and tracked vehicles. As on An-26, ramp-door can be arranged to slide forward under fuselage to facilitate direct loading from a truck on to cabin floor, or for airdropping of freight. Winch, capacity 2,500 kg (5,510 lb), assists loading of containers up to 1·90 × 2·44 × 1·46 m (6 ft 3 in × 8 ft × 4 ft 9½ in) in size, pallets 1·90 × 2·42 × 1·46 m (6 ft 3 in × 7 ft 11 in × 4 ft 9½ in) in size, and other bulky items. Provision for building roller conveyors into floor. Main crew and passenger door at front of cabin on port side. Small emergency exit and servicing door at rear of cabin on starboard side.

System: Air-conditioning system provides comfortable environment to altitude of 10,000 m (32,800 ft), and can also be used to refrigerate main cabin when perishable goods are carried.

Avionics and Equipment: Large radome over navigation/weather radar in nose. Doppler-based automatic navigation system, with map display on flight deck.

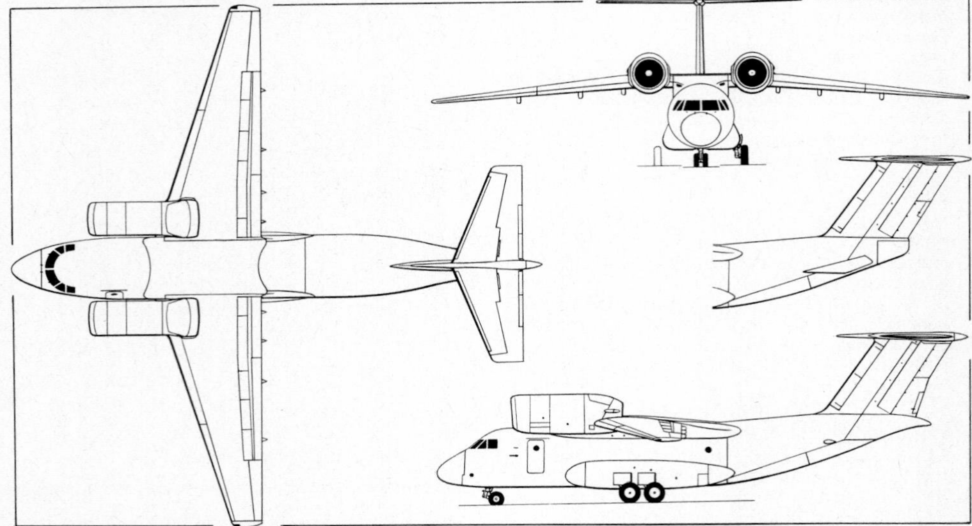

Antonov An-72 (two Lotarev D-36 turbofan engines), with scrap view of rear fuselage of first prototype *(Pilot Press)*

Dimensions, external:
- Wing span: 25·83 m (84 ft 9 in)
- Length overall: 26·576 m (87 ft 2¼ in)
- Height overall: 8·235 m (27 ft 0¼ in)

Dimensions, internal:
- Main cabin: Length: 9·00 m (29 ft 6¼ in)
  - Width at floor level: 2·10 m (6 ft 10¾ in)
  - Height: 2·20 m (7 ft 2½ in)

Weights:
- Max payload: 7,500 kg (16,535 lb)
- Max T-O weight:
  - from 1,000 m (3,280 ft) runway: 26,500 kg (58,420 lb)
  - from 1,200 m (3,935 ft) runway: 30,500 kg (67,240 lb)

Performance:
- Max cruising speed: 388 knots (720 km/h; 447 mph)
- T-O speed with light load: 81 knots (150 km/h; 94 mph)
- T-O speed with heavier load: 92 knots (170 km/h; 106 mph)
- Max operating height: 11,000 m (36,100 ft)
- Normal operating height: 8,000-10,000 m (26,250-32,800 ft)
- Range with max fuel, 30 min reserves: 1,725 nm (3,200 km; 1,985 miles)
- Range with max payload, 30 min reserves: 540 nm (1,000 km; 620 miles)

BERIEV

Georgi Mikhailovich Beriev, whose death was reported in July 1979, was a graduate of the Leningrad Polytechnic Institute. He took up seaplane design in 1928 and became subsequently the best-known Soviet designer of water-based aircraft. He was appointed chief designer of the seaplane group at the TsKB (Central Design Bureau of Aviatrust) in 1930, and his first complete design, the twin-engined MBR-2 flying-boat, was flown for the first time two years later, entering production in 1934. Other pre-war designs included the KOR-1 twin-float shipboard reconnaissance seaplane and the KOR-2 flying-boat, later redesignated Be-2 and Be-4 respectively.

In 1945 the Beriev bureau at Taganrog became the centre for all Soviet seaplane development, and the piston-engined Be-6 (first flown in 1947) was a standard military flying-boat during the 1950s. It was described in the 1959-60 *Jane's*. Only limited production was undertaken of the Be-8, also flown in 1947; and Beriev's next major flying-boat was the sweptwing twin-jet Be-10, based on the Be-R-1 prototype of 1949. This entered service in about 1960, and was described in the 1966-67 *Jane's*.

A more recent maritime aircraft of Beriev design is the M-12 (Be-12) twin-turboprop amphibian, which is in standard service with Soviet Naval Air Force units as a successor to the Be-6. The Be-30 twin-turboprop light transport (see 1972-73 *Jane's*) did not enter series production. A developed version, the Be-32, set up two time-to-height records, as noted briefly in the 1977-78 *Jane's*.

BERIEV M-12 (Be-12) TCHAIKA (SEAGULL)

NATO reporting name: Mail

This twin-turboprop medium-range maritime reconnaissance amphibian was displayed for the first time in the 1961 Aviation Day flypast at Tushino Airport, Moscow. Subsequently, during the period 23-27 October 1964, it established six officially-recognised international height records in Class C3 Group II. Data submitted in respect of these records revealed that the designation of the aircraft was M-12 and the power plant two 4,000 shp Ivchenko AI-20D turboprop engines. The aircraft was also, clearly, able to lift a payload of around 10 tons under record conditions.

The records set by the M-12 in 1964 were altitude of

12,185 m (39,977 ft) without payload, altitude of 11,366 m (37,290 ft) with payloads of 1,000 kg and 2,000 kg, altitude of 10,685 m (35,055 ft) with 5,000 kg payload, altitude of 9,352 m (30,682 ft) with 10,000 kg payload, and maximum payload of 10,100 kg (22,266 lb) lifted to a height of 2,000 m (6,560 ft). In each case, the crew consisted of M. Mikhailov, I. Kouprianov and L. Kuznetsov.

These 1964 records have never been bettered. Subsequent record attempts, often improving successfully on earlier performances by the M-12, have ensured that this aircraft retains all 21 FAI records listed in Class C3 Group II, as follows:

On 24 April 1968, A. Souchko set a speed record of 298·013 knots (552·279 km/h; 343·169 mph) over a 500 km closed circuit. On 9 October 1968, the same pilot set a speed record of 293·919 knots (544·693 km/h; 338·456 mph) over a 1,000 km circuit. On 25 October 1973, Vladimir Svyatochnuk and crew covered a closed-circuit distance of 1,382·968 nm (2,562·897 km; 1,592·510 miles).

Three speed-with-payload records over a 1,000 km closed circuit were set in 1970. A. Suchov attained 283·841 knots (526·011 km/h; 326·848 mph) with 1,000 kg on 21 April; A. Smirnov averaged 286·267 knots (530·504 km/h; 329·640 mph) with 2,000 kg on 8 July; and A. Zakharov averaged 284·163 knots (526·606 km/h; 327·218 mph) with 5,000 kg on 9 July.

On 31 October 1972, P. Yakouchine and crew of three achieved 300·450 knots (556·789 km/h; 345·973 mph) over a 2,000 km closed circuit, raising the record for no payload and 1,000 kg payload, and setting a new record with 2,000 kg. The current record of 263·720 knots (488·722 km/h; 303·678 mph) with a 5,000 kg payload was set by A. Souchko and crew on 30 October 1975. On 5 November 1974, V. Averchine set a time to height record to 6,000 m in 12 min 24·6 s; on 14 November 1974. A. Zakharov climbed to 3,000 m in 5 min 6·2 s. On 29 April 1975, V. Efimov climbed to 9,000 m in 27 min 3·4 s. V. Svyatochnuk and crew of three achieved a speed of 322·092 knots (596·514 km/h; 370·656 mph) over a 100 km closed circuit on 19 April 1976; and a record of 9,368 m (30,735 ft) for altitude maintained in horizontal flight on 3 May 1976.

The M-12 also holds all 17 current records in Class C2 Group II, for turboprop flying-boats. On 25 April 1968, E. Nikitine set a 500 km closed-circuit speed record of 305·064 knots (565·347 km/h; 351·290 mph), followed on 12 October 1968 by a speed record of 297·793 knots (551·871 km/h; 342·916 mph) over a 1,000 km closed circuit. On 21 April 1970, A. Zakharov set a speed record of 289·272 knots (536·074 km/h; 333·101 mph) over a 1,000 km closed circuit with a 1,000 kg payload. P. Yakushin averaged 288·848 knots (535·288 km/h; 332·613 mph) over the same distance with 2,000 kg on 8 July 1970; and on the following day E. Nikitine averaged 285·454 knots (528·998 km/h; 328·704 mph) over 1,000 km with a 5,000 kg payload.

On 30 October 1972, A. Zakharov and crew of three averaged 300·015 knots (555·983 km/h; 345·472 mph) over a 2,000 km circuit, claiming also the speed record over this distance with a 1,000 kg payload. Over this same distance, V. Averchine and crew averaged 295·999 knots (548·542 km/h; 340·848 mph) with a 2,000 kg payload on 28 October 1973, followed by E. Nikitine and crew who averaged 258·727 knots (479·470 km/h; 297·929 mph) with 5,000 kg on the next day. The closed-circuit distance record was raised to 1,393·071 nm (2,581·62 km; 1,604·144 miles) on 20 November 1973, by G. Efimov and crew.

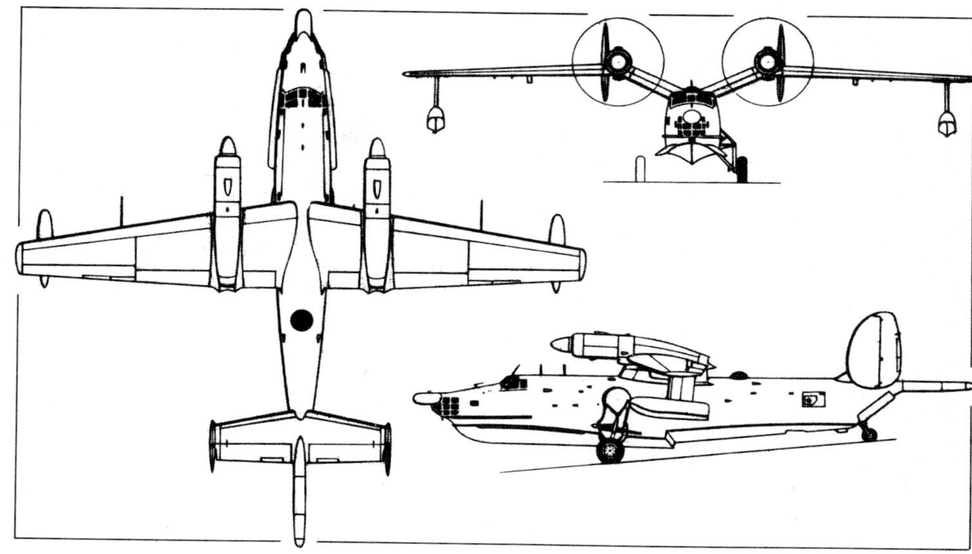

Beriev M-12 (Be-12) Tchaika twin-turboprop maritime reconnaissance amphibian *(Pilot Press)*

On 5 November 1974, V. Belov set a time to height record to 3,000 m in 5 min 9·8 s; on 14 November 1974, E. Nikitine climbed to 6,000 m in 11 min 57·4 s. The current record of 8,223 m (26,975 ft) for sustained altitude in horizontal flight was set by V. Averchine on 28 April 1975. The same pilot set a time-to-height record next day, climbing to 9,000 m in 22 min 9·8 s. G. Efimov and crew achieved a speed of 322·538 knots (597·340 km/h; 371·170 mph) over a 100 km closed circuit on 19 April 1976. Finally, on 2 November 1977, Eduard Kolkov and crew set an altitude record of 9,159 m (30,049 ft), and Nikolai Chkourko and crew climbed to 9,043 m (29,668 ft) with a 1,000 kg payload.

Layout and construction of the M-12 are conventional. The single-step hull has a high length-to-beam ratio and is fitted with two long strakes, one above the other, on each side of the nose to prevent spray from enveloping the propellers at take-off. There is a glazed observation and navigation station in the nose, with a long radar 'thimble' built into it, and an astrodome type of observation position above the rear fuselage. The nose radome on current aircraft is wider and somewhat flatter in section than that on early M-12s. A long MAD (magnetic anomaly detection) 'sting' extends from the tail, and there appears to be an APU exhaust on the port side of the rear fuselage.

The sharply-cranked high-set wing, with non-retractable wingtip floats, is reminiscent of that of the Be-6, and is intended to raise the AI-20 turboprop engines well clear of the water. The cowlings of the turboprops open downward in two halves, so that they may be used as servicing platforms. The tail unit, with twin fins and rudders at the tips of a 'dihedral' tailplane, is also similar to that of the Be-6.

The tailwheel landing gear consists of single-wheel main units, which retract upward through 180° to lie flush within the sides of the hull, and a rearward-retracting tailwheel.

In addition to an internal bomb bay aft of the step, there is provision for one large and one small external stores pylon under each outer wing panel.

When three M-12s took part in the 1967 air display at Domodedovo, the commentator said that the unit to which they belonged was "one of those serving where the country's military air force began", implying that the aircraft were then in operational service. M-12s have since been identified in standard service at Soviet Northern and Black Sea Fleet air bases and were reported to be operational for a period from bases in Egypt. About 100 are believed to have been built, of which about 90 remain in service.

DIMENSIONS, EXTERNAL (approx):

Wing span	29·70 m (97 ft 6 in)
Length overall	32·90 m (107 ft 11¼ in)
Height overall	7·00 m (22 ft 11½ in)
Propeller diameter	4·85 m (16 ft 0 in)
AREA:	
Wings, gross	95·69 m² (1,030 sq ft)
WEIGHT (estimated):	
Max T-O weight	29,500 kg (65,035 lb)
PERFORMANCE (estimated):	
Max level speed	329 knots (610 km/h; 379 mph)
Normal operating speed	172 knots (320 km/h; 199 mph)
Rate of climb at S/L	912 m (2,990 ft)/min
Service ceiling	11,280 m (37,000 ft)
Max range	2,158 nm (4,000 km; 2,485 miles)

Beriev M-12 (Be-12) Tchaika maritime patrol amphibian flying-boat of the Soviet Naval Air Force *(Swedish Air Force)*

ILYUSHIN

DESIGN BUREAU HEADQUARTERS: Moscow Central Airport, Khodinka, Moscow

GENERAL DESIGNER: G. Novozhilov

Sergei Vladimirovich Ilyushin, who died on 9 February 1977, at the age of 83, began his aviation career as a member of the ground staff at an airport. One of the aircraft he designed in the 'thirties made a record flight from Moscow to North America, but he is best remembered for his Il-2 and Il-10 Shturmovik close support aircraft of the Second World War. He was awarded the Order of Lenin and a third Hammer and Sickle gold medal on 29 March 1974, in recognition of his service in the development of aviation technology and the Soviet aircraft industry.

Aircraft designed by Ilyushin and currently in service include the veteran Il-28 twin-jet bomber and Il-14 piston-engined light transport, of which details have been given in earlier editions of *Jane's*, and the four-turboprop Il-18 transport which has been in scheduled service with Aeroflot and other airlines and air forces for many years. More recent types from the Ilyushin bureau include an anti-submarine variant of the Il-18, designated Il-38; a four-turbofan rear-engined airliner known as the Il-62; the Il-76 turbofan-engined heavy freighter; and a large wide-bodied transport designated Il-86.

ILYUSHIN Il-18

NATO reporting name: Coot

The Il-18 prototype, named Moskva (Moscow), flew for the first time on 4 July 1957 and production models entered service with Aeroflot in 1959. In 20 years they have logged 12 million flying hours with Aeroflot, carrying 235 million passengers on 5·5 million flights. Production is believed to have exceeded 700 aircraft, of which more than 100 were exported for use by commercial airlines. Known civilian operators were listed in the 1975-76 *Jane's*. Military operators of Il-18s include the air forces of Afghanistan, Algeria, Bulgaria, China, Czechoslovakia, Poland, the Soviet Union, Syria and Yugoslavia, mostly in comparatively small numbers.

An anti-submarine derivative, the Il-38 (NATO reporting name 'May'), is in service and is described separately. Another military variant of the Il-18, seen for the first time in 1978, is the ECM or elint aircraft known to NATO as **Coot-A** and shown in accompanying illustrations. In this case, the airframe appears to be basically unchanged by comparison with the transport. It carries under its fuselage a container about 10·25 m long and 1·15 m deep (33 ft 7½ in × 3 ft 9 in), which is assumed to house side-looking radar. There is a further container, about 4·4 m long and 0·88 m deep (14 ft 5 in × 2 ft 10½ in) on each side of the forward fuselage, containing a door over a camera or other sensor. Numerous other antennae and blisters can be seen, about eight of them on the undersurface of the centre and rear fuselage, with two large plates projecting above the forward fuselage. Further variants of the Il-18, adapted for military support tasks, will probably appear as the airliners are replaced by jets.

Versions of the Il-18 commercial transport are as follows:

Il-18V. Standard version for Aeroflot, with four 2,983 kW (4,000 ehp) AI-20K turboprops and fuel capacity of 23,700 litres (5,213 Imp gallons). Accommodation for 110 mixed tourist/economy class passengers, or 90 in all-tourist configuration.

Il-18E. Developed version with 3,169 kW (4,250 ehp) AI-20M engines. Same fuel capacity as Il-18V. Accommodation can be increased to 122 mixed class or 110 tourist class in Summer, by deleting coat storage space essential in Winter time.

Il-18D. Generally similar to Il-18E, but with additional centre-section fuel tankage, increasing total capacity to 30,000 litres (6,600 Imp gallons). Increased all-up weight.

TYPE: Four-engined passenger transport.

WINGS: Cantilever low-wing monoplane. Mean thickness/chord ratio 14%. All-metal structure. Three spars in centre-section, two in outer wings. All-metal ailerons are mass-balanced and aerodynamically-compensated, and fitted with spring tabs. Manually-operated flying controls. Electrically-actuated double-slotted flaps. Electro-thermal de-icing.

FUSELAGE: Circular-section all-metal monocoque structure. The structure is of the fail-safe type, and appears to employ rip stop doublers around window cutouts, door frames and the more-heavily loaded skin panels.

TAIL UNIT: Cantilever all-metal structure. Trim tabs in rudder and elevators. Additional spring tab in rudder. Manually-operated flying controls. Electro-thermal de-icing.

LANDING GEAR: Retractable tricycle type. Hydraulic actuation. Four-wheel bogie main units, with 930 mm × 305 mm tyres and hydraulic brakes. Steerable (45° each way) twin nosewheel unit, with 700 mm × 250 mm tyres. Tyre pressures: main 7·86 bars (114 lb/sq in), nose 5·86 bars (85 lb/sq in). Hydraulic brakes and nosewheel steering. Pneumatic emergency braking.

POWER PLANT: Four Ivchenko AI-20 turboprops (details under model listings), driving AV-68I four-blade reversible-pitch propellers. Ten flexible bag-type fuel tanks in inboard panel of each wing and integral tank in outboard panel, with a total capacity of 23,700 litres (5,213 Imp gallons). The Il-18D has additional bag tanks in centre-section, giving a total capacity of 30,000 litres (6,600 Imp gallons). Pressure fuelling through four international standard connections in inner nacelles. Provision for overwing fuelling. Oil capacity 58·5 litres (12·85 Imp gallons) per engine.

ACCOMMODATION: Crew of five, comprising two pilots, navigator, wireless operator and flight engineer. Flight deck is separated from remainder of fuselage by a pressure bulkhead to reduce the hazards following a sudden decompression of either. Standard 110-seat high-density version has a forward cabin containing 24 seats six-abreast; then, successively, an entrance lobby with two toilets on the starboard side, two large wardrobes in line with the propellers, the main cabin containing 71 seats in six-abreast rows, a galley/pantry opposite the rear door, a rear cabin containing 15 seats five-abreast, and a rear toilet compartment. Deletion of the wardrobes enables two more rows of seats to be installed in the main cabin in Summer, increasing max capacity to 122 seats. In 90-seat configuration, all seating is five-abreast, with 20 passengers in the front cabin, 55 in centre cabin and 15 in rear cabin. Again, two more rows of seats can replace the wardrobes in Summer, increasing the capacity to 100 seats. The 65-seat layout of the Il-18D has 14 seats (5-5-4) in front cabin, 43 seats (4-5-5-5-5-5-5-5-4) in centre cabin and 8 seats (4-4) in rear cabin. Pressurised cargo holds under floor forward and aft of the wing, and a further,unpressurised, hold aft of the rear pressure bulkhead.

SYSTEMS: Cabin pressurised to max differential of 0·49 bars (7·1 lb/sq in). Electrical system includes eight 12kW DC generators and 28·5V single-phase AC inverters. Hydraulic system, pressure 207 bars (3,000 lb/sq in), for landing gear retraction, nosewheel steering, brakes and flaps.

AVIONICS AND EQUIPMENT: Equipment includes dual controls and blind-flying panels, weather radar and ILS indicators, automatic navigation equipment, two automatic radio compasses, radio altimeter.

DIMENSIONS, EXTERNAL:	
Wing span	37·4 m (122 ft 8½ in)
Wing chord at root	5·61 m (18 ft 5 in)
Wing chord at tip	1·87 m (6 ft 2 in)
Wing aspect ratio	10
Length overall	35·9 m (117 ft 9 in)
Height overall	10·17 m (33 ft 4 in)
Tailplane span	11·8 m (38 ft 8½ in)
Wheel track	9·0 m (29 ft 6 in)
Wheelbase	12·78 m (41 ft 10 in)
Propeller diameter	4·50 m (14 ft 9 in)
Passenger doors (each):	
Height	1·40 m (4 ft 7 in)
Width	0·76 m (2 ft 6 in)
Height to sill	2·90 m (9 ft 6 in)
Freight hold doors (underfloor, each):	
Height	0·90 m (2 ft 11 in)
Width	1·20 m (3 ft 11 in)
DIMENSIONS, INTERNAL:	
Flight deck:	
Volume	9·36 m^3 (330 cu ft)
Cabin, excl flight deck:	
Length	approx 24·0 m (79 ft 0 in)
Max width	3·23 m (10 ft 7 in)
Max height	2·00 m (6 ft 6 in)
Volume	238 m^3 (8,405 cu ft)
Baggage and freight holds (underfloor and aft of cabin: total)	29·3 m^3 (1,035 cu ft)
AREAS:	
Wings, gross	140 m^2 (1,507 sq ft)
Ailerons (total)	9·11 m^2 (98·05 sq ft)

Ilyushin Il-18 medium-range transport in service with Polish Airlines (LOT)

Close-up of the forward fuselage of 'Coot-A' *(Royal Air Force)*

ECM or electronic intelligence (elint) version of the Ilyushin Il-18 (NATO 'Coot-A'), photographed in early 1978 *(Royal Air Force)*

Ilyushin Il-38 anti-submarine/maritime patrol aircraft (four Ivchenko AI-20 turboprop engines), photographed from a Nimrod of No. 120 Squadron, RAF Kinloss

Trailing-edge flaps (total)	27·15 m² (292·2 sq ft)
Vertical tail surfaces (total)	17·93 m² (193·0 sq ft)
Rudder	6·83 m² (73·52 sq ft)
Horizontal tail surfaces (total)	27·79 m² (299·13 sq ft)
Elevators (total)	11·80 m² (127·0 sq ft)

WEIGHTS AND LOADINGS:

Weight empty, equipped (90-seater):	
Il-18E	34,630 kg (76,350 lb)
Il-18D	35,000 kg (77,160 lb)
Max payload	13,500 kg (29,750 lb)
Max T-O weight:	
Il-18V, E	61,200 kg (134,925 lb)
Il-18D	64,000 kg (141,100 lb)
Max wing loading (Il-18D)	457 kg/m² (93·6 lb/sq ft)
Max power loading (Il-18D)	5·05 kg/kW (8·30 lb/ehp)

PERFORMANCE (at max T-O weight):

Max cruising speed:	
Il-18V	351 knots (650 km/h; 404 mph)
Il-18E, D	364 knots (675 km/h; 419 mph)
Econ cruising speed:	
Il-18V	324 knots (600 km/h; 373 mph)
Il-18E, D	337 knots (625 km/h; 388 mph)
Operating height:	
Il-18D	8,000-10,000 m (26,250-32,800 ft)
T-O run:	
Il-18E	1,100 m (3,610 ft)
Il-18D	1,300 m (4,265 ft)
Landing run:	
Il-18E, D	850 m (2,790 ft)
Range with max fuel, 1-hour reserves:	
Il-18E	2,805 nm (5,200 km; 3,230 miles)
Il-18D	3,508 nm (6,500 km; 4,040 miles)
Range with max payload, 1-hour reserves:	
Il-18E	1,728 nm (3,200 km; 1,990 miles)
Il-18D	1,997 nm (3,700 km; 2,300 miles)

ILYUSHIN Il-38

NATO reporting name: May

This anti-submarine/maritime patrol development of the Il-18 airliner represents a conversion similar to that by which the US Navy's P-3 Orion was evolved from the Lockheed Electra transport. It has a lengthened fuselage fitted with an undernose radome similar in shape to that of the Ka-25 ASW helicopter but housing a different radar, an MAD tail 'sting', other specialised electronic equipment and a weapon-carrying capability.

The main cabin of the Il-38 has few windows. The complete wing assembly is much further forward than on the Il-18, to cater for the effect on the CG position of internal equipment and stores. A crew of twelve is reported to be carried.

The Il-38 is a standard shore-based maritime patrol aircraft of the Soviet Naval Air Force, operating widely over the Atlantic and Mediterranean. In the latter area, some aircraft carried Egyptian Air Force insignia for a period, but are believed to have been manned by Soviet aircrew, operating from North African bases such as Matru, near Cairo. More recently, Il-38s of the Soviet Navy have operated over the Indian Ocean from an airfield in the People's Democratic Republic of Yemen.

In 1975, the Indian Navy ordered an initial batch of four Il-38s, of which delivery began in 1977, to equip INAS 315 at Dabolim, Goa. About 60 are believed to be operational with Soviet naval units.

DIMENSIONS, EXTERNAL:

Wing span	37·4 m (122 ft 8½ in)
Length overall	39·6 m (129 ft 10 in)
Height overall	10·17 m (33 ft 4 in)

PERFORMANCE (estimated):

Max cruising speed at 8,230 m (27,000 ft)	347 knots (645 km/h; 400 mph)
Max range	3,910 nm (7,240 km; 4,500 miles)

ILYUSHIN Il-62

NATO reporting name: Classic

Announced on 24 September 1962, when the first prototype (CCCP-06156) was inspected by the late Premier Krushchev, the standard Il-62 is a long-range airliner, with four Kuznetsov turbofan engines mounted in horizontal pairs on each side of the rear fuselage. It accommodates up to 186 passengers and was designed to fly on ranges equivalent to Moscow-New York (about 4,155 nm; 7,700 km; 4,800 miles) with more than 150 passengers and reserve fuel.

The Kuznetsov engines were not ready in time for the first flight of the first prototype, which took place in January 1963, with four 73·55 kN (16,535 lb st) Lyulka AL-7 engines installed. This aircraft was followed by a second prototype and three pre-production aircraft. Series production then started at Kazan, and Aeroflot introduced the Il-62 on to its Moscow-Montreal service on 15 September 1967, as a replacement for the Tu-114.

The Il-62 inaugurated Aeroflot's Moscow-New York service in July 1968, and has been used subsequently on many other routes, including Moscow-Paris and Moscow-Tokyo. Production is reported to have totalled 125 by December 1976, including export sales to CSA Czechoslovakian Airlines (7), Interflug of East Germany (6), Polish Airlines LOT (5), CAAC of China (5), Tarom of Romania (3), Cubana (1) and the Czechoslovakian government for VIP operation (1).

The Il-62's automatic flight control system is capable of taking over from a height of 200 m (650 ft) after take-off to a similar height during the landing approach. It can maintain a predetermined speed during climb and descent, and a selected cruising height, and can follow automatically a programmed track under command of the navigation computer.

The Il-62 is designed for an airframe service life of 25,000-30,000 flying hours, including 7,000-8,000 take-offs and landings.

A re-engined version, designated Il-62M, was flown for the first time in 1971. Details of this aircraft, and the further developed Il-62MK, are given separately, after the following description of the standard Il-62:

TYPE: Four-turbofan long-range airliner.

WINGS: Cantilever low-wing monoplane. Sweepback 35° at quarter-chord. Extended-chord leading-edge on outer two-thirds of each wing. All-metal three-spar structure. Each wing fitted with three-section manually-operated ailerons, electrically-actuated double-slotted flaps and two hydraulically-operated spoiler sections forward of flaps. Trim tab and spring-loaded servo tab in each centre aileron, spring-loaded

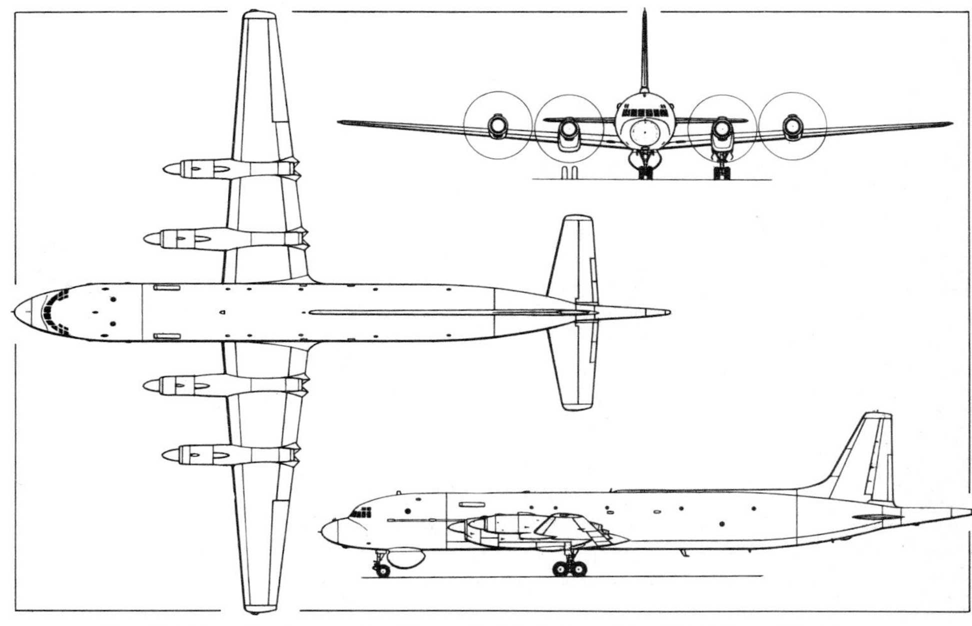

Ilyushin Il-38 anti-submarine/maritime patrol derivative of the Il-18 airliner *(Pilot Press)*

servo tab in each inner aileron. Hot-air anti-icing of leading-edges.

FUSELAGE: Conventional all-metal semi-monocoque structure. Frames are duralumin stampings and pressings. Integrally pressed skin panels at highly-stressed areas. Floors are sandwich panels with foam plastics filler. Nosecone hinges upward for access to radar.

TAIL UNIT: Cantilever all-metal structure, with electrically-actuated variable-incidence tailplane mounted at tip of fin. All surfaces sweptback. Manually-operated rudder, fitted with yaw damper, trim tab and spring servo tab. Manually-operated elevators have two automatic trim tabs and two manual trim tabs. Hot-air leading-edge anti-icing system.

LANDING GEAR: Hydraulically-retractable tricycle type. Forward-retracting twin-wheel steerable nose unit. Emergency extension by gravity. Oleo-nitrogen shock-absorber on each unit. Each main unit carries a four-wheel bogie and retracts inward into wing-roots. Main-wheel tyres size 1450 × 450, pressure 9·31 bars (135 lb/sq in). Nosewheel tyres size 930 × 305, pressure 7·86 bars (114 lb/sq in). Hydraulic disc brake and inertia-type electric anti-skid unit on each main wheel, supplemented by large tail parachute. Parking brakes. Hydraulic twin-wheel strut is extended downward to support rear fuselage during loading and unloading.

POWER PLANT: Four Kuznetsov NK-8-4 turbofan engines, each rated at 103 kN (23,150 lb st), mounted in horizontal pairs on each side of rear fuselage. Thrust reverser on each outboard engine. Hot-air anti-icing system for engine intakes. Automatically-controlled fuel system, with seven integral tanks extending through entire wing from tip to tip. Each engine has its own independent fuel system, with cross-feed. Total fuel capacity 100,000 litres (21,998 Imp gallons). Four standard international underwing pressure refuelling sockets. Eight gravity refuelling sockets. Total oil capacity 204 litres (45 Imp gallons).

ACCOMMODATION: Crew of five (two pilots, navigator, radio operator and flight engineer) on flight deck. Provision for two supernumerary pilot/navigators. Basic two-cabin layout, and galley, toilet and wardrobe facilities, are unchanged in the three main versions, only the width and pitch of the seats being varied. In the 186-passenger version, there are 72 seats in the forward cabin and 114 in the rear cabin, all six-abreast and all at a seat pitch of 86 cm (34 in). In the 168-seat configuration, increased pitch reduces capacity to 66 in the forward cabin and 102 in the rear cabin. The 114-passenger version has 45 seats in the forward cabin and 69 in the rear cabin, all five-abreast, except for four-abreast rear row by door. A first class/de luxe version for 85 passengers is available, with 45 seats in forward cabin and 40 four-abreast sleeperette chairs with footrests in rear cabin. Passenger doors forward of front cabin and between cabins on port side. Total of five toilets, opposite forward door, between cabins (starboard) and aft of rear cabin (both sides). Electrically-powered galley/pantry amidships and wardrobes in each version. Two pressurised baggage and freight compartments under cabin floor, forward and aft of wing. Unpressurised baggage/cargo compartment at extreme rear of fuselage. All compartments have tiedown fittings and rails in floor, and removable nets to restrain cargo.

SYSTEMS: Air-conditioning and pressurisation system maintains sea level conditions up to 7,000 m (23,000 ft) and gives equivalent of 2,100 m (6,900 ft) at 13,000 m (42,600 ft). Pressure differential 0·62 bars (9·0 lb/sq in). Hydraulic system, pressure 207 bars (3,000 lb/sq in), for landing gear retraction, nosewheel steering, brakes, spoilers and windscreen wipers. Emergency hydraulic system, powered by electric motor, for nosewheel steering, main-wheel extension and spoiler control. Three-phase 200/115V AC electrical supply from four 40kVA engine-driven generators (optional 27V DC system with eight 18kW engine-driven generators). Four transformer-rectifiers and four batteries for DC supply. Electrical windscreen de-icing. Type TA-6 APU in tail-cone.

AVIONICS: Standard avionics include two-channel autopilot, navigation computer, air data system, HF and UHF radio, VOR/ILS, RMI, Doppler, radio altimeter and weather radar. Polyot automatic flight control system optional.

DIMENSIONS, EXTERNAL:
- Wing span: 43·20 m (141 ft 9 in)
- Length overall: 53·12 m (174 ft 3½ in)
- Length of fuselage: 49·00 m (160 ft 9 in)
- Height overall: 12·35 m (40 ft 6¼ in)
- Tailplane span: 12·23 m (40 ft 1½ in)
- Fuselage width: 4·10 m (13 ft 5½ in)
- Fuselage height: 3·75 m (12 ft 3½ in)
- Wheel track: 6·80 m (22 ft 3½ in)
- Wheelbase: 24·49 m (80 ft 4½ in)
- Passenger doors (each):
  - Height: 1·83 m (6 ft 0 in)
  - Width: 0·86 m (2 ft 9¾ in)
  - Height to sill: 3·55 m (11 ft 8 in)
- Emergency exit (galley service) door:
  - Height: 1·37 m (4 ft 6 in)
  - Width: 0·61 m (2 ft 0 in)
- Front cargo hold door:
  - Height: 1·31 m (4 ft 3½ in)
  - Width: 1·26 m (4 ft 1½ in)
  - Height to sill: 1·92 m (6 ft 3½ in)
- Second cargo hold door:
  - Height: 1·00 m (3 ft 3½ in)
  - Width: 1·26 m (4 ft 1½ in)
  - Height to sill: 1·92 m (6 ft 3½ in)
- Third cargo hold door:
  - Height: 0·70 m (2 ft 3½ in)
  - Width: 0·70 m (2 ft 3½ in)
  - Height to sill: 2·32 m (7 ft 7¼ in)
- Rear cargo hold door:
  - Height: 1·15 m (3 ft 9 in)
  - Width: 1·07 m (3 ft 6 in)
  - Height to sill: 3·62 m (11 ft 10½ in)

DIMENSIONS, INTERNAL:
- Cabin:
  - Max height: 2·12 m (6 ft 11½ in)
  - Max width: 3·49 m (11 ft 5¼ in)
  - Volume: 163 m^3 (5,756 cu ft)
- Total volume of pressure cell: 396 m^3 (13,985 cu ft)
- Cargo hold volume:
  - Underfloor (two, total): 39·1 m^3 (1,380 cu ft)
  - Rear fuselage: 5·8 m^3 (205 cu ft)

AREAS:
- Wings, gross: 279·6 m^2 (3,010 sq ft)
- Ailerons (total): 16·25 m^2 (174·9 sq ft)
- Spoilers (total): 9·54 m^2 (102·7 sq ft)
- Flaps (total): 43·48 m^2 (468·0 sq ft)
- Horizontal tail surfaces (total): 40·00 m^2 (430·5 sq ft)
- Vertical tail surfaces (total): 35·60 m^2 (383·2 sq ft)

WEIGHTS AND LOADING:
- Weight empty: 66,400 kg (146,390 lb)
- Operating weight, empty: 69,400 kg (153,000 lb)
- Max payload: 23,000 kg (50,700 lb)
- Max fuel: 83,325 kg (183,700 lb)
- Max ramp weight: 167,000 kg (368,000 lb)
- Max T-O weight: 162,000 kg (357,150 lb)
- Max landing weight: 105,000 kg (231,500 lb)
- Max zero-fuel weight: 93,500 kg (206,130 lb)
- Max wing loading: 572 kg/m^2 (117·2 lb/sq ft)

PERFORMANCE (at max T-O weight):
- Normal cruising speed: 442-486 knots (820-900 km/h; 510-560 mph)
- Normal cruising height: 10,000-12,000 m (33,000-39,400 ft)
- Landing speed: 119-129 knots (220-240 km/h; 137-149 mph)
- Max rate of climb at S/L: 1,080 m (3,540 ft)/min
- FAR T-O field length:
  - ISA at S/L: 3,250 m (10,660 ft)
  - ISA+20°C at S/L: 3,915 m (12,840 ft)
- FAR landing field length:
  - ISA at S/L: 2,800 m (9,185 ft)
  - ISA+20°C at S/L: 2,950 m (9,680 ft)
- Range with max payload, 66,700 kg (147,050 lb) fuel, 1 hour fuel reserves: 3,612 nm (6,700 km; 4,160 miles)
- Range with 80,000 kg (176,370 lb) fuel and 10,000 kg (22,045 lb) payload, 1 hour fuel reserves: 4,963 nm (9,200 km; 5,715 miles)

ILYUSHIN Il-62M / MK

First displayed publicly at the 1971 Paris Air Show, the **Il-62M** is a developed version of the Il-62, with no dimensional changes to the airframe. It is fitted with more powerful turbofans, of a different type, with clamshell thrust reversers on the outboard engine of each pair, offering a lower approach speed and improved airflow over the rear of the nacelles. An additional fuel tank is installed in the tail-fin, contributing (with the improved specific fuel consumption of the engines) to the longer range of this version.

Revised layout of the flight deck equipment, and new navigation and radio communications equipment, are features of the Il-62M. Control wheels of new design allow the pilots a better field of view, and the aircraft's automatic flight control system permits automatic landings in ICAO Category II conditions, with extension to Category III conditions envisaged later. The wing spoilers of this version can be utilised differentially to enhance roll control.

Additional emergency and rescue equipment is installed on the Il-62M. Unlike the Il-62, it has a containerised baggage and freight system, with mechanised loading and unloading.

The Il-62M exhibited in Paris in 1971 and 1973 was the prototype (CCCP-86673). Production models entered service on Aeroflot's Moscow-Havana route in 1974 and have taken over progressively all of the airline's very-long-distance services. Four have been acquired by Cubana de Aviacion.

A variant announced in 1978 is the **Il-62MK,** still dimensionally unchanged and with the same power plant as the Il-62M, but with a strengthened wing for longer airframe life. Although the output of each engine is derated to 107·9 kN (24,250 lb st), max T-O weight is increased to 167,000 kg (368,170 lb) and max landing weight to 110,000 kg (242,500 lb), permitting the carriage of up to 195 passengers. To ensure adequate cabin service with so many passengers, the interior has been redesigned to permit the more efficient use of service trolleys. Range with max fuel and 10,000 kg (22,045 lb) payload is 5,180 nm (9,600 km; 5,965 miles). Max payload is 25,000 kg (55,115 lb).

The basic structural description of the Il-62 applies also to the Il-62M. The main innovations are as follows:

POWER PLANT: Four Soloviev D-30KU turbofan engines, each rated at 112·8 kN (25,350 lb st), mounted in horizontal pairs on each side of rear fuselage. Clamshell-type thrust reverser on each outboard engine. Remainder of power plant installation basically as for Il-62, but additional fuel tank in tail-fin with capacity of 5,000 litres (1,100 Imp gallons).

ACCOMMODATION: Alternative configurations for up to 186 economy class, 168 tourist class or 140 mixed class passengers. In the economy class version there are two toilets opposite the forward door, on the starboard side, aft of the flight deck. The forward cabin contains 66 seats, all six-abreast in threes with centre aisle. Galley/pantry and toilet amidships. Rear cabin contains 106 seats, six-abreast in threes with centre aisle. Two toilets and wardrobe to rear of this cabin. Doors as on Il-62. Forward underfloor baggage and freight hold accommodates nine containers, each weighing approximately 45 kg (100 lb) empty and with a capacity of 600 kg (1,322 lb) and 1·6 m^3 (56·5 cu ft). Rear hold accommodates five similar containers. Two compartments for non-containerised cargo. Total baggage and freight capacity 48 m^3 (1,695 cu ft)

SYSTEMS AND EQUIPMENT: See introductory notes.

AVIONICS: Duplicated SAU-1T automatic flight control system provides for automatic control from a height of 200 m (660 ft) after take-off to a height of 30 m (100 ft) on the approach to land. DISS-013 Doppler indicator and NV-PB-1 navigation computer. TKS-P course sensing system. TsGV-10P vertical master gyros. SVS-PN-15 air data system. Kurs-MP-2 radio navigation system, utilising VOR, ILS or SP-50 beacons. GROZA radar.

Ilyushin Il-62M long-range airliner (four Soloviev D-30KU turbofan engines) of Cubana, photographed at San Juan, Puerto Rico *(Austin J. Brown)*

SD-67 DME. ARK-15 ADF. RV-5 radio altimeter. SO-70 IFF transponder. MIKRON 2-24MHz HF radio. LANDASH 118-135MHz VHF radio. VESHANIE public address and in-flight entertainment system.

DIMENSIONS AND AREAS:

Same as for Il-62

WEIGHTS (Il-62M):

Max payload	23,000 kg (50,700 lb)
Max T-O weight	165,000 kg (363,760 lb)
Max landing weight	105,000 kg (231,500 lb)
Max zero-fuel weight	94,600 kg (208,550 lb)

PERFORMANCE (Il-62M, at max T-O weight):

Normal cruising speed
458-486 knots (850-900 km/h; 528-560 mph)

Normal cruising height
10,000-12,000 m (33,000-39,400 ft)

Balanced T-O distance (ISA, S/L) 3,000 m (9,845 ft)

Landing run (ISA, S/L) 2,800 m (9,185 ft)

Range with max payload, with reserves
4,315 nm (8,000 km; 4,970 miles)

Range with 10,000 kg (22,045 lb) payload, with reserves 5,400 nm (10,000 km; 6,215 miles)

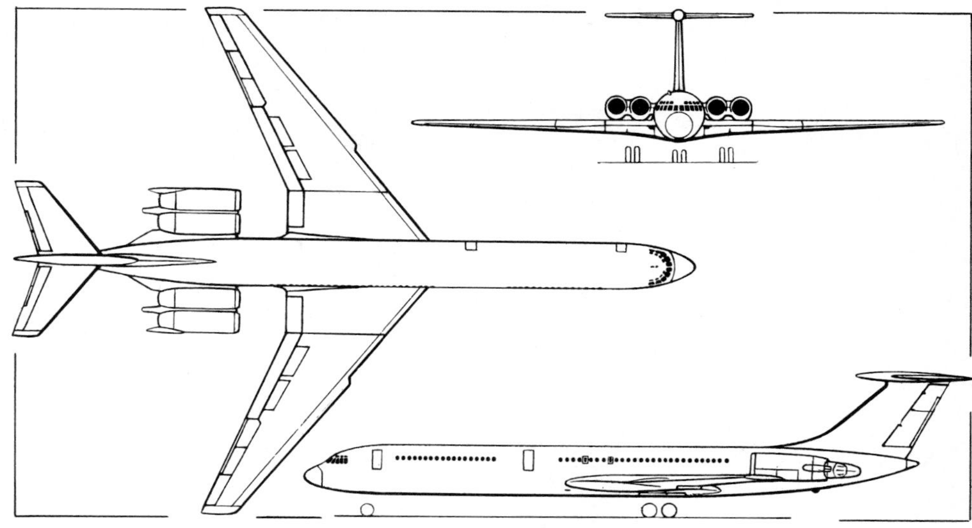

Ilyushin Il-62M long-range four-turbofan transport *(Pilot Press)*

ILYUSHIN Il-76T

NATO reporting name: Candid

Flown for the first time on 25 March 1971, the Il-76T prototype (CCCP-86712) made its public debut at the 29th Salon de l'Aéronautique et de l'Espace in Paris in May 1971.

It is a high-performance pressurised heavy transport of conventional layout, powered by four turbofan engines of similar basic type to those installed in the Il-62M. The clamshell thrust reversers, fitted to all four engines, are of different configuration, stowing above and below the nozzle when not in use, instead of to each side.

Nominal task of the Il-76T is to transport 40 tonnes of freight for a distance of 2,700 nm (5,000 km; 3,100 miles) in less than six hours, as a replacement for the turboprop An-12. It can take off from short unprepared airstrips and an official statement in 1971 said that it would be used first during the period of the then-current five-year plan (1971-75) in Siberia, the north of the Soviet Union and the Far East, where operation of other types of transport is difficult. It was announced in 1978 that, following extensive testing in Siberia, the Il-76T was to enter service on the Moscow-Japan route of Aeroflot.

It was clear from the start that the Il-76 had considerable potential as a military transport. It has been in service with the Soviet Air Force since 1974, and is superseding the An-12 as the standard equipment of Transport Aviation units, with about 100 currently in first-line squadrons. The military Il-76 has a turret mounting two guns at the tail.

A version of the Il-76 was evaluated as a flight refuelling tanker for the 'Backfire' supersonic strategic bombers of the Soviet Air Force and Naval Air Fleet, as a successor to modified M-4 ('Bison') aircraft, and is expected to enter service in this role at an early date. First export deliveries of the military Il-76 were to be made to Iraq in 1978. Other customers are reported to include Czechoslovakia and Poland.

Aircraft seen and photographed since 1973 embody a number of modifications compared with the prototype. Most important is that the hinge-line of each rear clamshell door is higher on the fuselage of at least one aircraft, giving a larger door and permitting taller and wider loads to pass between the doors when they are open. Other new features include a modified rear fin fillet and strengthening of the upper fuselage.

In July 1975, the Il-76 set a total of 24 officially recognised records for speed and altitude with payload. Piloted by Yakov I. Vernikov, on 4 July, it raised to 70,121 kg (154,590 lb) the record for greatest payload carried to a height of 2,000 m. The same flight recorded an altitude of 11,875 m (38,960 ft) with payloads of 60,000 kg, 65,000 kg and 70,000 kg. Also on 4 July, Alexander Turumine averaged 462·283 knots (856·697 km/h; 532·327 mph) around a 2,000 km circuit in an Il-76 carrying a payload of 55,000 kg, qualifying for additional records with 35,000 kg, 40,000 kg, 45,000 kg and 50,000 kg. On 7 July, Turumine averaged 462·801 knots (857·657 km/h; 532·923 mph) around 1,000 km, claiming nine records for payloads from 30,000 kg to 70,000 kg. The same pilot averaged 440·305 knots (815·968 km/h; 507·019 mph) around a 5,000 km circuit on 10 July, claiming records with 15,000 kg, 20,000 kg, 25,000 kg, 30,000 kg, 35,000 kg and 40,000 kg payloads.

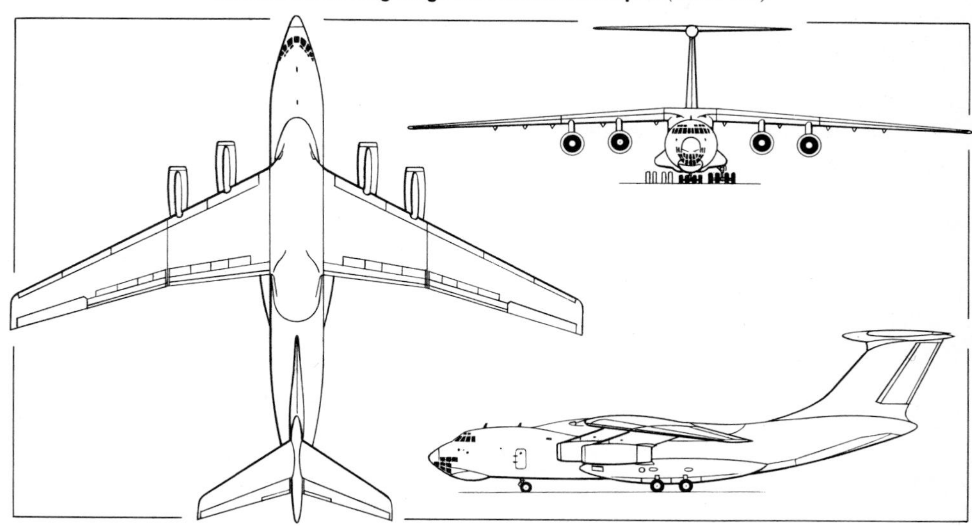

Ilyushin Il-76T four-turbofan heavy freight-carrying transport *(Pilot Press)*

TYPE: Four-turbofan medium/long-range freight transport.

WINGS: Cantilever monoplane, mounted above fuselage to leave interior unobstructed, and with marked anhedral from roots. Sweepback 25° at quarter-chord. All-metal structure. Two-section double-slotted flaps over full span from wing root to inboard edge of aileron each side. Spoilers forward of flaps. Leading-edge slats over almost entire span. Tabs in each aileron.

FUSELAGE: All-metal semi-monocoque structure of basically circular section. Underside of upswept rear fuselage made up of two outward-hinged clamshell doors, upward-hinged panel between these doors, and downward-hinged loading ramp.

TAIL UNIT: Cantilever all-metal structure, with tailplane mounted at tip of fin. All surfaces sweptback. Tabs in rudder and each elevator.

LANDING GEAR: Retractable tricycle type, designed for operation from prepared and unprepared runways. Nose unit made up of two pairs of wheels, side by side, with central oleo. Each main-wheel bogie made up of four pairs of wheels in two rows. Low-pressure tyres size 1,300 × 480 on main wheels, 1,100 × 330 on nosewheels. Nosewheels retract forward. Main units retract inward into two large ventral fairings under fuselage, with an additional large fairing on each side of lower fuselage over actuating gear. During retraction main-wheel axles rotate around leg, so that wheels stow with axles parallel to fuselage axis (ie: wheels remain vertical but at 90° to direction of flight). Tyre pressure can be varied in flight from 2·5 to 5 bars (36-73 lb/sq in) to suit different landing strip conditions.

POWER PLANT: Four Soloviev D-30KP turbofan engines, each rated at 117·7 kN (26,455 lb st), in individual underwing pods. Each pod is carried on a large forwardly-inclined pylon and is fitted with a clamshell

Ilyushin Il-76T freight transport (four Soloviev D-30KP turbofan engines) *(Tass)*

Parachute troops preparing to embark on a Soviet military Il-76. Note the rear gun turret

thrust reverser. Total fuel capacity reported to be 81,830 litres (18,000 Imp gallons). No fuel is carried in the wings.

ACCOMMODATION: Conventional side-by-side seating for pilot and co-pilot on spacious flight deck. Station for navigator below flight deck in glazed nose. Forward-hinged door on each side of fuselage forward of wing. Cabin loaded via rear ramp. Entire accommodation is pressurised, and advanced mechanical handling systems are provided for containerised and other freight. Quick configuration changes are made by the use of modules, each able to accommodate 30 passengers in four-abreast seating, litter patients and medical attendants, or cargo. Three such modules can be carried, each approx 6·10 m (20 ft) long, 2·4 m (8 ft) wide and 2·4 m (8 ft) high. They are loaded through the rear doors by means of two overhead travelling cranes, and are secured to the cabin floor with cargo restraints.

AVIONICS AND EQUIPMENT: Full equipment for all-weather operation by day and night, including a computer for automatic flight control and automatic landing approach. Large ground-mapping radar in undernose radome. APU in port side landing gear fairing.

DIMENSIONS, EXTERNAL:

Wing span	50·50 m (165 ft 8 in)
Length overall	46·59 m (152 ft 10½ in)
Height overall	14·76 m (48 ft 5 in)

DIMENSIONS, INTERNAL:

Cabin:	
Length, excl ramp	20·00 m (65 ft 7½ in)
Length, incl ramp	24·50 m (80 ft 4½ in)
Width	3·46 m (11 ft 4¼ in)
Height	3·40 m (11 ft 1¾ in)

AREA:

Wings, gross	300·0 m² (3,229·2 sq ft)

WEIGHTS:

Max payload	40,000 kg (88,185 lb)
Max T-O weight	170,000 kg (374,785 lb)

PERFORMANCE:

Cruising speed
405-432 knots (750-800 km/h; 466-497 mph)

T-O speed 114 knots (210 km/h; 131 mph)

Approach and landing speed
119-130 knots (220-240 km/h; 137-149 mph)

Normal cruising height
9,000-12,000 m (29,500-39,350 ft)

T-O run 850 m (2,790 ft)

Landing run 450 m (1,475 ft)

Nominal range with max payload
2,700 nm (5,000 km; 3,100 miles)

Max range, with reserves
3,617 nm (6,700 km; 4,163 miles)

ILYUSHIN Il-86

NATO reporting name: Camber

First indication that this aircraft was under development was given at the 1971 Paris Air Show. Mr Genrikh Novozhilov, successor to the late Sergei Ilyushin as chief of the Ilyushin design bureau, told visitors that a new wide-bodied transport known as the Il-86 was then in the early project design stage.

No final decision on the configuration, or number of engines, had been taken at that time; but in the Spring of 1972 a model of one projected configuration was displayed publicly in Moscow. This design was similar in layout to the Il-62, with four rear-mounted turbofan engines and a T-tail, but was intended to be much larger, with a two-deck fuselage. It was described and illustrated in the 1972-73 *Jane's*.

Simultaneously with the display of this original model, it became known that the Il-86 had been chosen for development, after a competition in which it was matched against proposals from the Antonov and Tupolev design teams.

By the end of 1972, it was evident that the design of the Il-86 had evolved along different lines to those suggested by the model displayed six months earlier. In particular the engines had been repositioned into four underwing pods, permitting the tailplane to be lowered on to the rear fuselage. The first of two prototypes (CCCP-86000), in this form, made a first flight of about 40 min after taking off in 1,700 m (5,575 ft) from an 1,820 m (5,970 ft) runway at the old Moscow Central Airport of Khodinka, where the Ilyushin Bureau has its headquarters, to the official flight test centre on 22 December 1976, piloted by Hero of the Soviet Union A. Kuznetsov.

The Novosti official press agency announced in September 1977 that more than 100 test flights had been made and that basic testing was expected to be completed by 7 November 1977, the 60th anniversary of the October Revolution. The Soviet Civil Air Minister, Mr Boris Bugayev, has said that the Il-86 will enter service with Aeroflot in time to carry visitors from Prague, Sofia and Berlin to the 1980 Olympic Games in Moscow; the first flight over an Aeroflot route, from Moscow to Mineralnye Vody, was made in September 1978, three months ahead of schedule. US reports suggest that the aim was to complete 1,200 hours of flight testing before deliveries began in late 1979. Aircraft CCCP-86002, which flew for the first time at Voronezh on 24 October 1977, was described as the first production Il-86.

The Il-86 is likely to be used also by the Soviet Air Force, and the evolution of an AWACS version has been suggested as a possibility by Western sources. The airframe is believed to be designed for 40,000 flying hours or 20,000 landings.

For production aircraft, wings, including flaps and slats, pylons to carry the engine pods, and vertical and horizontal tail surfaces are being manufactured in Poland. Final assembly is centred at Voronezh.

The following details should be regarded as provisional:

TYPE: Four-turbofan wide-bodied passenger transport.

WINGS: Cantilever low-wing monoplane of all-metal construction, made at Voronezh. Dihedral from roots. Sweepback 35° at quarter-chord. Large double-slotted trailing-edge flaps, in two sections along entire span of each wing inboard of aileron. Multi-section spoilers in top surface, forward of all four flap sections. Full-span leading-edge slats, with small cutaway to clear each inboard engine pylon. Shallow fence on top surface in line with each pylon.

FUSELAGE: Conventional semi-monocoque light alloy structure of circular cross-section.

TAIL UNIT: Conventional sweptback cantilever structure, with tailplane dihedral. Each control surface in two sections. Tail unit made at Kiev.

LANDING GEAR: Retractable four-unit type. Forward-retracting steerable twin-wheel nose unit, and three four-wheel bogie main units. Two of the latter retract inward into the wing-root fairings; the third unit is mounted centrally under the fuselage, slightly forward of the others, and retracts forward. Main landing gear made at Kuibyshev. Main-wheel tyres size 1300 × 480; nosewheel tyres size 1120 × 450.

POWER PLANT: Four Kuznetsov NK-86 turbofan engines, each rated at 127·5 kN (28,660 lb st), mounted on pylons forward of wing leading-edges. Engines fitted with combined thrust reversers/noise attenuators. Fuel capacity 70,000-80,000 litres (15,400-17,600 Imp gallons). Provision for APU in tailcone (space occupied by three-stage parachute for stall tests in prototype).

ACCOMMODATION: Standard flight crew comprises two pilots and a flight engineer, with provision for a navigator if required. Upper deck, on which all seats are located, is divided into three separate cabins by wardrobes, serving areas connected by elevators to lower-deck galleys, and cabin staff accommodation, with a total of eight toilets at front and rear of the aircraft. Cabins feature unusually large windows, indirect lighting in walls and in ceiling panels, and enclosed baggage lockers at top of side walls. Preponderance of metal and natural fibre materials rather than plastics throughout cabins to enhance safety in an emergency. Up to 350 passengers in basic nine-abreast seating throughout, with two aisles. Suggested mixed-class alternative layout provides for 28 passengers six-abreast in the front cabin, and 206 passengers eight-abreast in the other two cabins. Passengers are intended to enter via three airstair-type doors, made in Kharkov, which hinge down from the port side of the lower deck. One of these doors is forward of the wing; the others are aft of the wing. Four further doors at upper-deck level on each side, for emergency use and for use at airports where the utilisation of high-level boarding steps or bridges is preferred. Coats and hand baggage are intended to be stowed on the lower deck before passengers climb one of three fixed staircases to the main deck. Cargo holds are designed to accommodate heavy or registered baggage and freight in 16 standard LD3 containers. Access is via upward-hinged doors forward of the starboard wing-root leading-edge and at the side of the rear hold. Containers can be loaded and unloaded by means of a self-propelled truck with built-in roller conveyor. Films will be shown in flight, and there will be a choice of 12 tape-recorded programmes to listen to.

DIMENSIONS, EXTERNAL:

Wing span	48·06 m (157 ft 8¼ in)
Length overall	59·54 m (195 ft 4 in)
Diameter of fuselage	6·08 m (19 ft 11½ in)
Height overall	15·81 m (51 ft 10½ in)
Tailplane span	20·57 m (67 ft 6 in)
Wheel track (c/l of outer shock-struts)	11·15 m (36 ft 7 in)

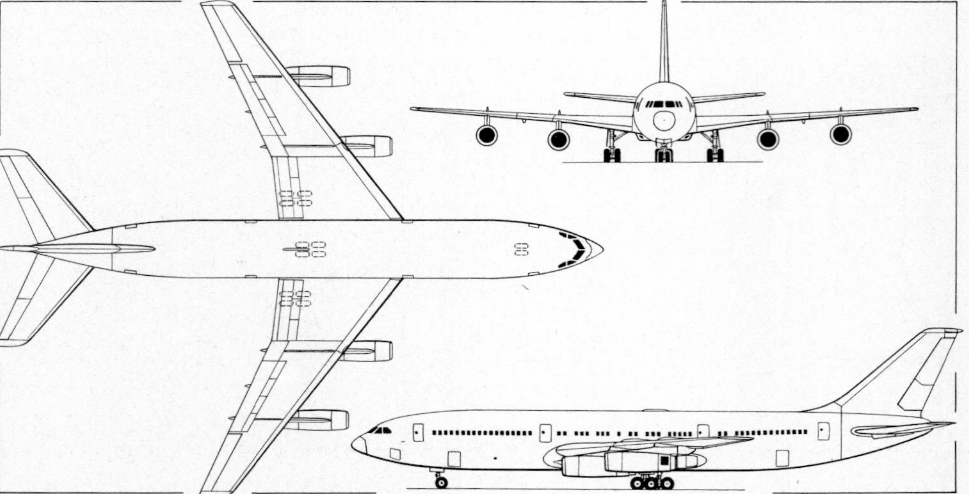

Ilyushin Il-86 four-turbofan wide-bodied passenger transport *(Pilot Press)*

Ilyushin Il-86 wide-bodied transport at 1979 Paris Air Show *(Brian M. Service)*

Wheelbase 21·34 m (70 ft 0 in)
DIMENSIONS, INTERNAL:
Main cabins: Height 2·61 m (8 ft 7 in)
Max width approx 5·70 m (18 ft 8½ in)
AREA:
Wings, gross 320 m² (3,444 sq ft)
WEIGHTS:
Max payload 42,000 kg (92,600 lb)
Max fuel 86,000 kg (189,600 lb)
Max T-O weight (dependent on size and type of runway) 190,000-206,000 kg (418,875-454,150 lb)
Max landing weight 175,000 kg (385,800 lb)
PERFORMANCE (estimated):
Normal cruising speed at 9,000-11,000 m (30,000-36,000 ft)
485-512 knots (900-950 km/h; 560-590 mph)
Approach speed
130-141 knots (240-260 km/h; 149-162 mph)
Field length for take-off and landing
2,300-2,600 m (7,550-8,530 ft)
Range with max payload
1,944 nm (3,600 km; 2,235 miles)
Range with max fuel
2,480 nm (4,600 km; 2,858 miles)

KAMOV

CHIEF OF DESIGN BUREAU: S. Mikhéev

Nikolai I. Kamov, who died on 24 November 1973, aged 71, had been a leading designer of rotating-wing aircraft since the late 1920s and, with N. K. Skrzhinskii, was responsible for the first successful Soviet rotorcraft, the KaSkr-I, in 1929. He became well known internationally when he designed a series of one-man lightweight helicopters of the 'flying motorcycle' type in the late 1940s.

The Ka-15 and Ka-18 helicopters, developed by Kamov and his design team, under chief engineer Vladimir Barshevskii, were both put into large-scale production and service. Details of them can be found in the 1962-63 and 1963-64 editions of *Jane's* respectively.

Later Kamov types are the Ka-25 turbine-powered anti-submarine helicopter; a flying-crane version of the same design, designated Ka-25K; and a twin-engined general-purpose helicopter designated Ka-26. All available details of these types follow:

KAMOV Ka-25

NATO reporting name: Hormone

The prototype of this military helicopter was first shown in public in the Soviet Aviation Day flypast over Tushino Airport, Moscow, in July 1961. It was allocated the NATO code name 'Harp', but this was changed to 'Hormone' for the production versions, of which about 460 were built in 1966-75. Together with the newer Mil helicopters known to NATO as 'Haze-A', these have largely replaced piston-engined Mi-4s in the Soviet Navy's ship and shore based force of around 250 helicopters. Nine are operated on coastal anti-submarine duties by the Syrian Air Force and others by India and Yugoslavia.

Basically, the Ka-25 follows the formula established by earlier Kamov designs such as the Ka-15 and Ka-18, with two three-blade co-axial contra-rotating rotors, a pod-and-boom fuselage, multi-fin tail unit, and four-wheel landing gear. It is powered by two small turboshaft engines mounted side by side above the cabin, and this has left the cabin space clear for personnel, operational equipment, fuel and payload.

In its ship-based anti-submarine version, the Ka-25 operates from cruisers of the 'Kresta' and 'Kara' classes, the new carrier/cruiser *Kiev,* and the helicopter carrier/cruisers *Moskva* and *Leningrad,* each of which accommodates about 18 aircraft. It has a search radar installation in an undernose radome with a diameter of 1·25 m (4 ft 1 in). Other equipment includes a towed magnetic anomaly detector, dipping sonar housed in a compartment at the rear of the cabin, and an electro-optical sensor. A major shortcoming is said to be lack of night and all-weather sonar-dipping capability.

Each landing wheel can be surrounded by an inflatable pontoon surmounted by inflation bottles to provide flotation in the event of an emergency alighting on the water. The rear legs are pivoted to retract upward about their wishbone supports, so that the wheels can be moved to a position where they offer least interference to signals from the nose radar.

The two so-called 'air-to-surface missiles' carried on outriggers on each side of the cabin of the prototype during its Tushino appearance were dummies, but there is reason to believe that Ka-25s are being armed with newly-developed 'fire-and-forget' air-to-surface guided missiles. Many, but not all, have an internal weapons bay for stores, including ASW torpedoes and nuclear depth charges.

Kamov Ka-25 ('Hormone-A') anti-submarine helicopter (two Glushenkov turboshaft engines) *(US Navy)*

'Hormone-B' target acquisition variant of ship-based Ka-25, with enlarged undernose radome and cylindrical radome under rear of cabin, but without belly weapon-bay doors *(US Navy)*

As well as serving as an anti-submarine and missile guidance aircraft, the Ka-25 fulfils a variety of other military roles. Only two versions may be identified at present by NATO reporting names:

Hormone-A. Basic anti-submarine version, as described above and below.

Hormone-B. Special electronics variant, able to acquire targets for ship-launched missiles. Larger undernose radome with more spherical undersurface. Cylindrical radome under rear of cabin. Data link equipment.

The Ka-25K, described separately, is a commercial counterpart of the Ka-25. It can be assumed that the two types are similar in details such as basic structure, overall dimensions, power plant, weights and performance, except that the military version is a little shorter, with an estimated fuselage length of 9·75 m (32 ft 0 in).

TYPE: Twin-turbine anti-submarine and general-purpose helicopter.

AIRFRAME AND POWER PLANT: Basically as for Ka-25K, except for pivoted main landing gear. Provision for carrying an external fuel tank on each side of main cabin.
ACCOMMODATION: Pilot and co-pilot side by side on flight deck, with rearward-sliding door on each side. Entry to main cabin is via a rearward-sliding door to rear of main landing gear on port side. Cabin is large enough to contain 12 folding seats for passengers.
AVIONICS AND EQUIPMENT: Equipment available for all versions includes autopilot, navigational system, radio compass, radio communications installations, and lighting system for all-weather operation by day or night. Dipping sonar housed in compartment at rear of main cabin, immediately forward of tailboom, and search radar under nose of anti-submarine version, which carries also a towed magnetic anomaly detector. Some aircraft have a blister fairing over equipment mounted at the base of the centre tail-fin; others have a cylindrical housing, with a transparent top, above the central point of the tailboom (see illustration), with a shallow blister fairing to the rear of this. Doors under the fuselage of some aircraft enclose a weapons bay for ASW torpedoes, nuclear depth charges and other stores.

Kamov Ka-25K flying-crane helicopter (two Glushenkov GTD-3 turboshaft engines) *(S. P. Peltz)*

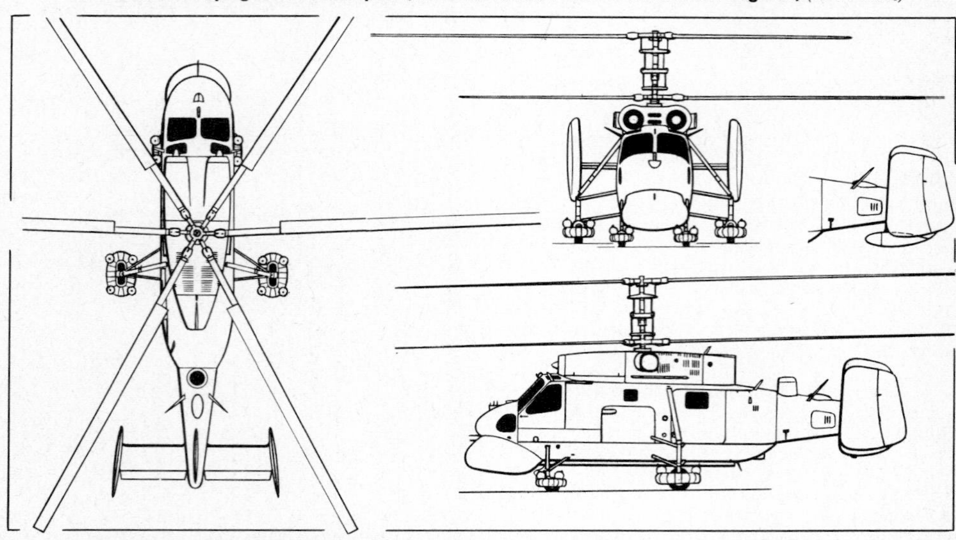
'Hormone-A' anti-submarine version of the Kamov Ka-25 helicopter. Scrap view shows optional blister fairing at base of central tail-fin *(Pilot Press)*

KAMOV Ka-25K

NATO reporting name: Hormone

This flying-crane helicopter was shown publicly for the first time at the 1967 Paris Air Show. Instead of the undernose radome of the anti-submarine version of the Ka-25, it has a removable gondola giving an exceptional field of view for the occupant.

One of the pilots occupies this gondola during loading, unloading and positioning of externally-slung cargoes, while the helicopter is hovering. His seat faces rearward, giving him an unobstructed view of the operation, and he is able to control the aircraft by means of a set of dual flying controls fitted in the gondola. This distribution of duty, with one pilot controlling the aircraft during loading and unloading operations and the other pilot controlling it in cruising flight, is claimed to increase the precision and safety of payload handling and to offer a reduction in the overall time required to do a particular job.

The Ka-25K is claimed to combine high payload-to-AUW ratio with good manoeuvrability and minimum dimensions. The rotors, transmission and engines, with their auxiliaries, form a single self-contained assembly, which can be removed in one hour.

TYPE: Twin-turbine flying-crane helicopter.
ROTOR SYSTEM: Two three-blade co-axial contra-rotating rotors. Automatic blade-folding.
FUSELAGE: Conventional all-metal semi-monocoque structure of pod and boom type. Detachable gondola under nose.
TAIL UNIT: Cantilever all-metal structure, with central fin, ventral fin and twin endplate fins and rudders which are toed inward.
LANDING GEAR: Non-retractable four-wheel type. Oleo-pneumatic shock-absorbers. Nosewheels are smaller than main wheels and are of castoring type. Each wheel can be enclosed in an inflatable pontoon surmounted by inflation bottles.
POWER PLANT: Two 671 kW (900 shp) Glushenkov GTD-3 turboshaft engines, mounted side by side above cabin, forward of rotor driveshaft.
ACCOMMODATION: Crew of two side by side on flight deck. Rearward-facing pilot's seat with dual flying controls in undernose gondola for use during loading and unloading. Main cabin, normally used for freight carrying, contains 12 folding seats for passengers. Rearward-sliding door on each side of flight deck. Large rearward-sliding door at rear of main cabin on port side. Hatchway in cabin floor, with two downward-opening doors, through which sling cable passes from winch on CG.
AVIONICS AND EQUIPMENT: Optional equipment includes autopilot, navigational system, radio compass, radio communications installation, and lighting system for all-weather operation by day or night.

DIMENSIONS, EXTERNAL:

Diameter of rotors (each)	15·74 m (51 ft 8 in)
Length of fuselage	9·83 m (32 ft 3 in)
Height to top of rotor head	5·37 m (17 ft 7½ in)
Width over tail-fins	3·76 m (12 ft 4 in)
Wheel track: front	1·41 m (4 ft 7½ in)
rear	3·52 m (11 ft 6½ in)
Cabin door: Height	1·10 m (3 ft 7¼ in)
Width	1·20 m (3 ft 11¼ in)

WEIGHTS:

Weight empty	4,400 kg (9,700 lb)
Max payload	2,000 kg (4,400 lb)
Max T-O weight	7,300 kg (16,100 lb)

PERFORMANCE:

Max level speed	119 knots (220 km/h; 137 mph)
Normal cruising speed	104 knots (193 km/h; 120 mph)
Service ceiling	3,500 m (11,500 ft)
Range with standard fuel, with reserves	217 nm (400 km; 250 miles)
Range with max fuel, with reserves	351 nm (650 km; 405 miles)

KAMOV Ka-26

NATO reporting name: Hoodlum

First details of this twin-engined light helicopter were announced in January 1964, and the prototype flew for the first time in the following year. Kamov described it as an ideal helicopter for agriculture, possessing all the virtues of the Ka-15 (which was used in about a dozen countries) but able to lift three times as much chemical payload, and the Ka-26 entered large-scale service as an agricultural aircraft in the Soviet Union in 1970, being used primarily over orchards and vineyards. It is also used widely on Aeroflot's air ambulance services and is suitable for many other applications, including cargo and passenger transport, forest firefighting, mineral prospecting, pipeline construction and laying transmission lines.

The usual Kamov contra-rotating co-axial three-blade rotor system is retained, with hydraulic dampers fitted to each rotor head and the rotor shafts inclined forward at 6° to the vertical. The blades, made of glass-textolyte (plastics) materials, weigh only 25 kg (55 lb) each and are completely interchangeable. They, and the cabin windscreen, are equipped with an anti-icing system, activated automatically by a radioisotope ice warning device and utilising an alcohol glycerine mixture.

A powered control system is standard. The jacks are actuated by a single hydraulic system, with manual override in case of system failure.

The fully-enclosed cabin, with a door on each side, is fitted out normally for operation by a single pilot, but a second seat and dual controls are optional. The cabin is warmed and demisted by air from a combustion heater, which also heats the passenger compartment when fitted.

The tailplane, with twin fins and rudders toed inward at 15°, is carried on two plastics tailbooms. Short high-mounted stub-wings carry the two podded 242·5 kW (325 hp) M-14V-26 aircooled radial piston engines, designed by I. M. Vedeneev, and the main units of the non-retractable four-wheel landing gear. Each engine is cooled by a fan in the front of its nacelle, which absorbs about 18·6 kW (25 hp) from the engine output. Dust filters are fitted in the air delivery ducts, to protect the engines, each of which is connected to the rotor transmission by a shaft and two flexible couplings. Both rotors can be driven by either engine if the other fails; disengagement of the failed engine is automatic, and an autorotative landing can be made if both engines fail.

All four landing gear units embody oleo-pneumatic shock-absorbers. The forward wheels are of the castoring type and are not fitted with brakes. The rear wheels are fitted with pneumatically-operated brakes. Tyre size is 595 × 185 on the main wheels, 300 × 125 on the forward wheels.

The space aft of the cabin, between the main landing gear units and under the rotor transmission, is able to accommodate a variety of interchangeable payloads. For agricultural work the chemical hopper (capacity 900 kg; 1,985 lb) and dust-spreader or spraybars are fitted in this position, on the aircraft's centre of gravity. This equipment is quickly removable and can be replaced by a cargo/passenger pod accommodating six persons, with provision for a seventh passenger beside the pilot. Alternatively, the Ka-26 can be operated with either an open platform for hauling freight or a hook for slinging bulky loads at the end of a cable or in a cargo net.

A version for geophysical survey has an electromagnetic pulse generator in the cabin and is encircled by a huge 'hoop' antenna. It carries on the port side of the fuselage a mounting for the receiver 'bird' which is towed at the end of a cable, beneath the helicopter, when in use. The receiver is lowered by an electric winch and the cable is cut by automatic shears if its traction should exceed the authorised limit.

An aerial survey model is available with an AFA-31-MA camera mounted in the cabin. This aircraft can photograph 5 km² (2 sq miles) per hour at a scale of 1 : 10,000.

As an air ambulance, the Ka-26 can carry two stretcher patients, two seated casualties and a medical attendant. A winch, with a capacity of up to 150 kg (330 lb), enables it to be used for rescue duties.

When operating as an agricultural sprayer, the Ka-26 discharges its chemical payload at 1·5-12 litres/s (0·33-2·65 Imp gallons/s). The rate of discharge in a dusting role is 1·5-12 kg/s (3·3-26·5 lb/s). Up to 120 hectares (296 acres) can be sprayed during each flying hour at the rate of 50 kg/ha (44·5 lb/acre). As a duster, 140 ha (346 acres) can be treated at the same discharge rate. 50 ha (123 acres) can be topdressed with chemical fertilisers each flying hour, at a rate of 100 kg/ha (89 lb/acre).

To protect the pilot against toxic chemicals in the agricultural role, the cabin is lightly pressurised by a blower and air filter system which ensures that the cabin air is always clean. The flying and navigation equipment are adequate for all-weather operation, by day and night. VHF and HF radio are fitted, together with a radio compass and radio altimeter.

Because of its small size and manoeuvrability, the Ka-26 can be operated from platforms on small ships such as whalers and icebreakers, and a Soviet fishing boat operating in the North Atlantic in early 1970 carried a Ka-26 for fish-spotting duties. This aircraft was equipped with inflated pontoons to permit alighting on the water.

In mid-1969, a Ka-26 was tested in Siberia and the north-west USSR in a forest protection version able to deliver six firemen and their equipment speedily to the site of a forest fire. In the Spring of 1972, Ka-26s joined Mi-1, Mi-2 and Mi-4 helicopters in operations to clear ice from Soviet rivers, by landing demolition teams on thick ice-floes and destroying thinner ice-fields from the air.

More than 600 Ka-26s had been produced by 1977. They are in civilian service in Bulgaria, East Germany, West Germany, Hungary, Japan, Romania and Sweden, as well as in the USSR. Military operators include the air forces of Hungary and Sri Lanka.

Mr S. Mikhéev, chief of the Kamov design bureau, stated that a new version of the Ka-26 was under development in 1979.

Dimensions, external:
- Diameter of rotors (each) 13·00 m (42 ft 8 in)
- Vertical separation between rotors 1·17 m (3 ft 10 in)
- Length of fuselage 7·75 m (25 ft 5 in)
- Height overall 4·05 m (13 ft 3½ in)
- Width over engine pods 3·64 m (11 ft 11½ in)
- Width over agricultural spraybars 11·20 m (36 ft 9 in)
- Tailplane span 4·60 m (15 ft 1 in)
- Wheel track:
  - Main wheels 2·42 m (7 ft 11½ in)
  - Nosewheels 0·90 m (2 ft 11½ in)
- Wheelbase 3·48 m (11 ft 5 in)
- Passenger pod door:
  - Height 1·40 m (4 ft 7 in)
  - Width 1·25 m (4 ft 1¼ in)

Dimensions, internal:
- Passenger pod:
  - Length, floor level 1·83 m (6 ft 0 in)
  - Width, floor level 1·25 m (4 ft 1¼ in)
  - Headroom 1·40 m (4 ft 7 in)

Weights:
- Operating weight, empty:
  - Stripped 1,950 kg (4,300 lb)
  - Cargo/platform 2,085 kg (4,597 lb)
  - Cargo/hook 2,050 kg (4,519 lb)
  - Passenger 2,100 kg (4,630 lb)
  - Agricultural 2,216 kg (4,885 lb)
- Fuel weight:
  - Transport 360 kg (794 lb)
  - Other versions 100 kg (220 lb)
- Payload:
  - Transport 900 kg (1,985 lb)
  - Agricultural duster 1,065 kg (2,348 lb)
  - Agricultural sprayer 900 kg (1,985 lb)
  - With cargo platform 1,065 kg (2,348 lb)
  - Flying crane 1,100 kg (2,425 lb)
- Normal T-O weight:
  - Transport 3,076 kg (6,780 lb)
  - Agricultural 2,980 kg (6,570 lb)
- Max T-O weight:
  - all versions 3,250 kg (7,165 lb)

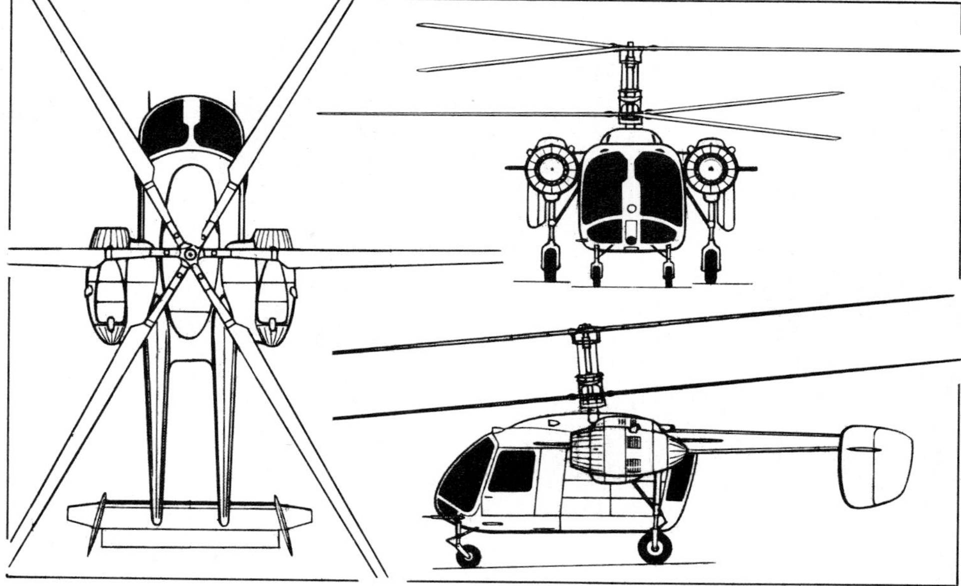

Kamov Ka-26 twin-engined light general-purpose helicopter in passenger-carrying form *(Pilot Press)*

Kamov Ka-26 used by Asahi Helicopter Co of Japan, mainly for crop-spraying in rice fields

Performance (at max T-O weight):
- Max level speed 91 knots (170 km/h; 105 mph)
- Max cruising speed 81 knots (150 km/h; 93 mph)
- Econ cruising speed 49-59 knots (90-110 km/h; 56-68 mph)
- Agricultural operating speed range 16-62 knots (30-115 km/h; 19-71 mph)
- Service ceiling 3,000 m (9,840 ft)
- Service ceiling, one engine out 500 m (1,640 ft)
- Hovering ceiling IGE at AUW of 3,000 kg (6,615 lb) 1,300 m (4,265 ft)
- Hovering ceiling OGE at AUW of 3,000 kg (6,615 lb) 800 m (2,625 ft)
- Range with 7 passengers, 30 min fuel reserves 215 nm (400 km; 248 miles)
- Max range with auxiliary tanks 647 nm (1,200 km; 745 miles)
- Endurance at econ cruising speed 3 h 42 min

MiG

Colonel-General Artem I. Mikoyan, who died on 9 December 1970 at the age of 65, was head of the design bureau responsible for the MiG series of fighter aircraft. With Mikhail I. Gurevich, a mathematician, he collaborated in the design of the first of the really-modern Soviet jet-fighters, the MiG-15, which began to appear in squadron service in numbers in 1949.

The MiG-17, a progressive development of the MiG-15, appeared in Soviet squadrons in 1953 or 1954, and was followed into service by the supersonic MiG-19, which appeared in 1955 and has been manufactured also in large numbers in China (which see).

All available details of aircraft designed by the Mikoyan bureau which are currently in production or under development follow:

MIKOYAN MiG-21

NATO reporting names: Fishbed and Mongol

The Soviet design bureau that was led by the late Colonel-General Artem I. Mikoyan developed the MiG-21 air superiority fighter on the basis of experience of jet-to-jet combat between MiG-15s and US aircraft during the war in Korea. The emphasis was placed on good transonic and supersonic handling, high rate of climb, small size and light weight, using a turbojet engine of medium power, in contrast with the heavier and much more powerful Sukhoi Su-7 and Su-9 fighters that were developed simultaneously. The first versions of the MiG-21 were, therefore, day fighters of limited range, with comparatively light armament and limited avionics. Subsequent development of the type has been aimed primarily at improvements in range, weapons and all-weather capability, and the MiG-21 is the most widely-used fighter in the world, as well as forming for many years the backbone of Soviet tactical air power.

'Fishbed-H' reconnaissance version of MiG-21, with underbelly sensor pack, underwing fuel tanks and wingtip ECM *(Flug Revue)*

The E-5 prototype of the MiG-21 flew for the first time in 1955, and made its public debut during the flypast in the Soviet Aviation Day display at Tushino Airport, Moscow, on 24 June 1956. The initial production version (NATO 'Fishbed-A') was built in only limited numbers, with a Tumansky R-11 turbojet engine rated at 38·25 kN (8,600 lb st) dry and 50 kN (11,240 lb st) with afterburning, and with an armament of two 30 mm NR-30 cannon. Meanwhile, the Soviet Union had been developing a small infra-red homing air-to-air missile, designated K-13 (NATO 'Atoll') and generally similar to the US AIM-9B Sidewinder 1A. Underwing pylons for two K-13s were fitted on the MiG-21F, the suffix 'F' standing for *Forsirovanny* (boosted) and indicating that this model also

MiG-21PFMA (NATO 'Fishbed-J') with four 'Atoll' missiles under its wings

Mikoyan MiG-21bis multi-role fighters, known to NATO as 'Fishbed-N'

had a slightly more powerful turbojet. To save weight and provide room for avionics associated with the missiles, the port NR-30 cannon was removed and its blast-tube fairing on the lower fuselage was blanked off. Further details of this and subsequent versions of the MiG-21 are as follows:

MiG-21F (Fishbed-C). First major production version, built also in Czechoslovakia. Short-range clear-weather fighter, with radar ranging equipment and a Tumansky R-11 turbojet rated at 42·25 kN (9,500 lb st) dry and 56·4 kN (12,676 lb st) with afterburning (designation of engine given in Soviet press statements as TDR Mk R37F). Two underwing pylons for UV-16-57 pods, each containing sixteen 57 mm rockets, or K-13 air-to-air missiles, and one NR-30 cannon in starboard side of fuselage (one each side on early aircraft and on the ten supplied to India). Internal fuel capacity of 2,340 litres (515 Imp gallons), plus under-fuselage pylon for external fuel tank of 490 litres (108 Imp gallons) capacity. Small nose air intake of approximately 69 cm (27 in) diameter, with small movable three-shock centrebody housing the radar ranging equipment. Under-nose pitot boom, which folds upward on the ground to reduce risk of ground personnel walking into it. Transparent blister cockpit canopy which hinges upward about base of integral flat bulletproof windscreen. Transparent rear-view panel (not on aircraft built in Czechoslovakia) aft of canopy at front of shallow dorsal spine fairing. Large blade antenna at rear of this panel, with small secondary antenna midway along spine. Fowler-type flap between fuselage and aileron on each trailing-edge, with fairing plate under wing at outer extremity. Small forward-hinged airbrake under fuselage, forward of ventral fin; two further forward-hinged airbrakes, on each side of underfuselage in line with wing-root leading-edges, integral with part of cannon fairings. Brake-parachute housed inside small door on port underside of rear fuselage, with cable attachment under rear part of ventral fin. Semi-encapsulated escape system, in which canopy is ejected with seat, forming shield to protect pilot from slipstream, until the seat has been slowed by its drogue chute. Leading-edge of fin extended forward on all but early aircraft, to increase chord.

MiG-21PF (Fishbed-D). Basic model of second series of operational versions with forward fuselage of less-tapered form. Intake enlarged to diameter of approximately 91 cm (36 in) and housing larger centrebody for R1L search/track radar (NATO 'Spin Scan A') to enhance all-weather capability (designation suffix letter 'P', standing for *Perekhvatchik,* is applied to aircraft adapted for all-weather interception from an earlier designed role). Remainder of airframe generally similar to that of MiG-21F, but pitot boom repositioned above air intake; cannon armament and fairings deleted, permitting simplified design for forward airbrakes; larger main wheels and tyres, requiring enlarged blister fairing on each side of fuselage, over wing, to accommodate wheel in retracted position; dorsal spine fairing widened and deepened aft of canopy, to reduce drag and house additional fuel tankage, and rear-view panel deleted; primary blade antenna repositioned to mid-spine and secondary antenna deleted. Uprated R-11 turbojet, giving 58·4 kN (13,120 lb st) with afterburning. Internal fuel capacity increased to 2,850 litres (627 Imp gallons) in seven fuselage tanks. Late production aircraft have attachments for a rocket-assisted take-off unit (RATOG) aft of each main landing gear bay, and provision for a flap-blowing system known as *Sduva Pogranichnovo Sloya* (SPS), which reduces the normal landing speed by some 22 knots (40 km/h; 25 mph). Flaps are larger than original Fowler type, do not move aft, and lack outboard fairing plates. Prototype shown at Tushino in 1961 had dummy metal centrebody. Production aircraft in service with many air forces.

Fishbed-E. Basically similar to 'Fishbed-C' with broad-chord vertical tail surfaces. Parachute-brake repositioned into acorn fairing, made up of clamshell doors, at base of rudder, above jet nozzle. Provision for GP-9 underbelly pack, housing GSh-23 twin-barrel 23 mm gun, in place of centreline pylon, with associated predictor sight and electrical ranging system. Identified in 1964.

MiG-21FL. Export version of late-model MiG-21PF series, with broad-chord vertical tail surfaces and parachute-brake housing at base of rudder but no provision for SPS or RATOG. About 200 were initially assembled and later built under licence in India by Hindustan Aeronautics Ltd (which see), with the IAF designation Type 77. R-11-300 turbojet rated at 38·25 kN (8,598 lb st) dry and 60·8 kN (13,668 lb) with afterburning. Suffix letter 'L' *(Lokator)* indicates the installation of Type R2L ('Spin Scan B') search/track radar. Can be fitted with GP-9 underbelly gun pack. Identified in 1966.

MiG-21PFS or MiG-21PF(SPS). Similar to 'Fishbed-D', but with SPS as standard production installation.

MiG-21PFM (Fishbed-F). Successor to interim MiG-21PFS, embodying all the improvements introduced progressively on the PF and PFS, the suffix letter 'M' indicating an exportable version of an existing design. Leading-edge of fin extended forward a further 45 cm (18 in). Small dorsal fin fillet eliminated. Additional refinements, including sideways-hinged (to starboard) canopy and conventional windscreen quarter-lights; simple ejection seat instead of semi-encapsulated type; and large dielectric portion at tip of tail-fin. R2L radar reported to have lock-on range of under 7 nm (13 km; 8 miles) and to be ineffective at heights below about 915 m (3,000 ft) because of ground 'clutter'. Max permissible speed at low altitude is reported to be 593 knots (1,100 km/h; 683 mph). Built also in Czechoslovakia.

Analogue. Based on a standard MiG-21PF airframe, this aircraft was fitted with a scaled-down replica of the original 'ogee' delta wing of the Tu-144 supersonic transport, for aerodynamic flight testing and development before the Tu-144 prototype was completed. It had no horizontal tail surfaces. Following its several dozen research flights, modifications were made to the full-size wing. One only.

Fishbed-G. Experimental STOL version of MiG-21PFM, with a pair of vertically-mounted lift-jet engines in lengthened centre-fuselage. Demonstrated in the air display at Domodedovo in July 1967, and described and illustrated in the 1970-71 *Jane's.* Prototype only.

MiG-21PFMA (Fishbed-J). Multi-role version. Basically similar to MiG-21PFM but with deeper dorsal fairing containing fuel tankage above fuselage, giving straight line from top of canopy to fin. Pitot tube remains above air intake but is offset to starboard. Provision for GP-9 underbelly gun pack as alternative to centreline fuel tank. Four underwing pylons, instead of former two, for a variety of ground attack weapons and stores, as alternative or supplementary to two or four air-to-air missiles. Latter can include radar-homing 'Advanced Atoll' as well as infra-red K-13A 'Atoll'. Able to carry two underwing tanks in addition to standard underbelly tank, offsetting reduced internal fuel capacity of 2,600 litres (572 Imp gallons). Zero-speed zero-altitude ejection seat. Small boat-shape fairing with angle-of-attack indicator on port side of nose. Later production aircraft can have the GSh-23 gun installed inside the fuselage, with a shallow underbelly fairing for the twin barrels and splayed cartridge-ejection chutes to clear each side of centreline store.

MiG-21M. Generally similar to MiG-21PFMA with internal GSh-23 gun pack. R-11F2S-300 engine. Has superseded MiG-21FL on Hindustan Aeronautics production line in India, with IAF designation Type 88. First Indian-built MiG-21M was handed over officially to IAF on 14 February 1973.

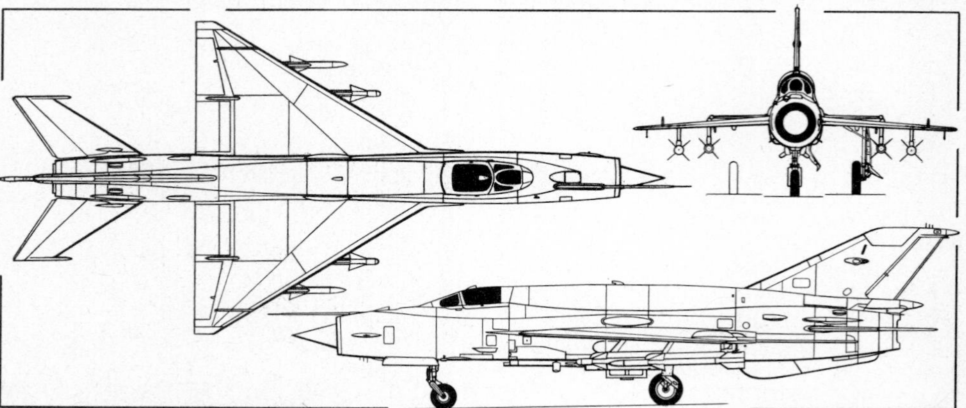

Mikoyan MiG-21SMT 'Fishbed-K' single-seat multi-role fighter *(Pilot Press)*

Two-seat training version of the MiG-21, known as 'Mongol-B', in Soviet Air Force service *(Flug Revue)*

MiG-21R (Fishbed-H). Tactical reconnaissance version, basically similar to MiG-21PFMA. Equipment includes an external pod for forward-facing or oblique cameras, infra-red sensors or ECM devices, and fuel, on fuselage centreline pylon. Suppressed antenna at mid-fuselage and optional ECM equipment in wingtip fairings.

MiG-21MF (Fishbed-J). Generally similar to MiG-21PFMA but re-engined with a Tumansky R-13-300 turbojet, lighter in weight and with higher performance ratings. Small rearview mirror above cockpit canopy. Debris deflector beneath each suction relief door forward of wing root. Entered service with Soviet Air Force in 1970.

MiG-21RF (Fishbed-H). Tactical reconnaissance version of MiG-21MF. Equipment as for MiG-21R.

MiG-21SMT (Fishbed-K). Similar to MiG-21MF, except for having deep dorsal spine extended rearward as far as parachute-brake housing, to provide maximum possible fuel tankage and optimum aerodynamic form. Able to carry ECM equipment in small removable wingtip pods. Deliveries to Warsaw Pact air forces reported to have begun in 1971. Like the MiG-21PFMA and MiG-21MF, this version can carry K-13A 'Atoll' infra-red missiles and/or radar-homing 'Advanced Atolls'.

MiG-21bis (Fishbed-L). Third-generation multi-role air combat/ground attack version, with updated avionics and generally improved construction standards. Wider and deeper dorsal fairing.

Note: The reporting name 'Fishbed-M' has been omitted by NATO, to avoid confusion with 'MiG-21M'.

MiG-21bis (Fishbed-N). Advanced version of 'Fishbed-L' with Tumansky R-25 turbojet engine, rated at 73·6 kN (16,535 lb st) with afterburning. Further improvement of avionics indicated by 'bow and arrow' antenna under nose. Radar detection range believed to be 16 nm (30 km; 18·5 miles). Standard equipment in Soviet Air Force for several years. Empty weight reported to be 5,200 kg (11,465 lb), normal T-O weight 7,960 kg (17,550 lb).

MiG-21U (Mongol). Two-seat training versions. Initial version, 'Mongol-A', is generally similar to the MiG-21F but has two cockpits in tandem with sideways-hinged (to starboard) double canopy, larger main wheels and tyres of MiG-21PF, one-piece forward airbrake, and pitot boom repositioned above intake. Cannon armament is deleted. Later models, 'Mongol-B', have the broader-chord vertical tail surfaces and under-rudder brake-parachute housing of the later operational variants, with a deeper dorsal spine and no dorsal fin fillet.

MiG-21US (Mongol-B). Similar to later MiG-21U but with provision for SPS flap-blowing, and retractable periscope for instructor in rear seat.

MiG-21UM (Mongol-B). Two-seat trainer counterpart of MiG-21MF with R-13 turbojet and four underwing stores pylons.

Alternative designations, allocated by the Soviet authorities to MiG-21s used to set up FAI-recognised international records, are as follows:

E-33. This designation has been applied to MiG-21U 'Mongol' trainers used to establish women's records. Those confirmed by the FAI include an altitude of 24,336 m (79,842 ft) set up by Natalya Prokhanova on 22 May 1965, and a sustained altitude of 19,020 m (62,402 ft) in horizontal flight established by Lydia Zaitseva on 23 June 1965.

E-66. Aircraft of basic MiG-21F series, used by Col Georgi Mossolov to set up a world absolute speed record (since beaten) of 1,288·6 knots (2,388 km/h; 1,484 mph) over a 15/25 km course on 31 October 1959. Engine described as a 58·35 kN (13,120 lb st) Type TDR Mk R37F.

E-66A. Variant of E-66 used by Mossolov to raise the world height record to 34,714 m (113,892 ft) on 28 April 1961, from an aerodrome near Moscow. Powered additionally by a 29·4 kN (6,615 lb st) GRD Mk U2 rocket engine in underbelly pack, exhausting between twin ventral fins. Other changes compared with then-standard operational model included a widened dorsal spine and repositioned blade antenna, as standardised for the MiG-21PF, and a blister fairing above the nose.

E-66B. Used by Svetlana Savitskaya to set four women's time-to-height records on 15 November 1974, from an aerodrome near Moscow. Described as having one 68·7 kN (15,432 lb st) PDM engine (presumably afterburning turbojet) and two 22·6 kN (5,070 lb st) TTPDs (possibly assisted take-off rockets). Times recorded were 41·2 s to 3,000 m, 1 min 0·1 s to 6,000 m, 1 min 21 s to 9,000 m, and 1 min 59·3 s to 12,000 m.

E-76. Designation allocated to apparently-standard MiG-21PFs used by Soviet women pilots to establish international records. Those confirmed by the FAI are for a speed of 1,112·7 knots (2,062 km/h; 1,281·27 mph) over a 500 km closed circuit by Marina Solovyova on 16 September 1966; a speed of 485·78 knots (900·267 km/h; 559·40 mph) over a 2,000 km closed circuit by Yevgenia Martova on 11 October 1966; a speed of 1,148·7 knots (2,128·7 km/h; 1,322·7 mph) over a 100 km closed circuit by Miss Martova on 18 February 1967; and a speed of 700·5 knots (1,298·16 km/h; 806·64 mph) over a 1,000 km closed circuit by Lydia Zaitseva on 28 March 1967.

There is reason to believe that the similar designations E-74, E-77 and E-88 apply to versions of the export MiG-21F, MiG-21FL and MiG-21M respectively.

About 1,750 of the 4,600 aircraft estimated to equip Soviet tactical air forces are MiG-21s, including 300 of the reconnaissance versions ('Fishbed-H'). In addition, MiG-21s have been supplied to the Afghan, Algerian, Bangladesh, Bulgarian, Chinese, Cuban, Czech, Egyptian, Ethiopian, Finnish, East German, Hungarian, Indian, Indonesian, Iraqi, North Korean, Laotian, Malagasy, Polish, Romanian, South Yemeni, Sudanese, Syrian, Tanzanian, North Vietnamese, Yemen Arab Republic and Yugoslav air forces.

A version of the MiG-21 has been built in China under the designation F-7.

The Chinese industry is assisting with spares and overhaul services for the MiG-21s, MiG-17s and MiG-19s operated by Egypt. Ferranti and Smiths Industries of the UK are collaborating in a scheme to provide the Egyptian MiG-21s with a digital inertial navigation, weapon aiming and head-up display system (Hudwac).

The following details refer to the MiG-21MF ('Fishbed-J'):

Type: Single-seat multi-role fighter.

Wings: Cantilever mid-wing monoplane of clipped-delta planform, with slight anhedral from roots. No leading-edge camber. Sweepback approximately 57°. Small pointed fairing on each side of fuselage forward of wing-root leading-edge. Small boundary-layer fence above each wing near tip. All-metal construction. Inset ailerons, actuated hydraulically. Large 'blown' plain trailing-edge flaps, actuated hydraulically.

Fuselage: Circular-section all-metal semi-monocoque structure. Ram-air intake in nose, with three-position movable centrebody. Large dorsal spine fairing along top of fuselage from canopy to fin. Forward-hinged door-type airbrake on each side of underfuselage below wing leading-edge. A further forward-hinged airbrake under fuselage forward of ventral fin. All airbrakes actuated hydraulically. Blister fairings above and below wing on each side to accommodate main wheels when retracted.

Tail Unit: Cantilever all-metal structure, with all surfaces sharply swept. Conventional fin and hydraulically-powered rudder. Hydraulically-actuated one-piece all-moving horizontal surface, with two gearing ratios for use at varying combinations of altitude and airspeed. Tailplane trim switch on control column. No trim tabs. Single large ventral fin.

Landing Gear: Hydraulically-retractable tricycle type, with single wheel on each unit; all units housed in fuselage when retracted. Forward-retracting non-steerable nosewheel unit; inward-retracting main wheels which turn to stow vertically inside fuselage. Tyres on main wheels inflated to approximately 7·93 bars (115 lb/sq in), ruling out normal operation from grass runways. Pneumatic braking on all three wheels, supplied from compressed-air bottles. Steering by differential main-wheel braking. Wheel doors remain open when legs are extended. Brake parachute housed inside acorn fairing at base of rudder.

Power Plant: One Tumansky R-13-300 turbojet engine, rated at 50 kN (11,240 lb st) dry and 64·73 kN (14,550 lb st) with afterburning. Fuel tanks in fuselage, with total capacity of 2,600 litres (572 Imp gallons), of which approx 1,800 litres (396 Imp gallons) are usable within CG limits at low speed. Provision for carrying one finned external fuel tank, capacity 490 litres (108 Imp gallons), on underfuselage pylon and two similar drop-tanks on outboard underwing pylons. Two jettisonable solid-propellant JATO rockets can be fitted under rear fuselage, aft of wheel doors.

Accommodation: Pilot only, on ejection seat with spring-loaded arm at top which ensures that seat cannot be operated unless hood is closed. Canopy is sideways-hinged, to starboard, and is surmounted by a small rearview mirror. Flat bullet-proof windscreen. Cabin air-conditioned. Armour plating forward and aft of cockpit.

Systems: Duplicated hydraulic system, supplied by engine-driven pump, with backup by battery-powered electric pump, and emergency electric tailplane trim and manual operation of flying controls. Autostabilisation in pitch and roll only.

Avionics and Equipment: Search and track radar in intake centrebody, with search range of approx 10·4 nm (19·3 km; 12 miles). Other standard avionics include VOR/ADF and warning radar with an indicator marked in 45° sectors in front of and behind the aircraft. Gyro gunsight is reported to topple at 2·75*g*. Automatic rang-

Two views of the MiG-23S 'Flogger-B' single-seat variable-geometry air combat fighter of the Soviet Air Force. Note the large splitter plates forward of variable-geometry intakes on this version, on the two-seat MiG-23U and on all export models of this family of fighters. Stripes on the stores under the wings of the aircraft in the lower picture imply that they are missile simulators

ing can be fed into gunsight. Full blind-flying instrumentation, with attitude and heading indicators driven by remote central gyro platform.

ARMAMENT: One twin-barrel 23 mm GSh-23 gun, with 200 rounds, in belly pack. Four underwing pylons for weapons or drop-tanks. Typical loads for interceptor role include two K-13A 'Atoll' air-to-air missiles on inner pylons and two radar-homing 'Advanced Atolls' or two UV-16-57 rocket packs (each sixteen 57 mm rockets) on outer pylons; four K-13As/'Advanced Atolls'; or two drop-tanks and two K-13As or 'Advanced Atolls'. Typical loads for ground attack role are four UV-16-57 rocket packs; two 500 kg and two 250 kg bombs; or four S-24 240 mm air-to-surface missiles.

DIMENSIONS, EXTERNAL:
- Wing span: 7·15 m (23 ft 5½ in)
- Length, incl pitot boom: 15·76 m (51 ft 8½ in)
- Length, excl pitot boom and intake centrebody: 13·46 m (44 ft 2 in)
- Height overall: 4·10 m (13 ft 5½ in)
- Wheel track: 2·69 m (8 ft 10 in)

AREA:
- Wings, gross: 23 m² (247 sq ft)

WEIGHTS:
- T-O weight:
  - with four K-13A missiles: 8,200 kg (18,078 lb)
  - with two K-13A missiles and two 108 Imp gallon drop-tanks: 8,950 kg (19,730 lb)
  - with two K-13As and three drop-tanks: 9,400 kg (20,725 lb)

PERFORMANCE:
- Max level speed above 11,000 m (36,000 ft): Mach 2·1 (1,203 knots; 2,230 km/h; 1,385 mph)
- Max level speed at low altitude: Mach 1·06 (701 knots; 1,300 km/h; 807 mph)
- Landing speed: 146 knots (270 km/h; 168 mph)
- Service ceiling: 18,000 m (59,050 ft)
- T-O run at normal AUW: 800 m (2,625 ft)
- Landing run: 550 m (1,805 ft)
- Range, internal fuel only: 593 nm (1,100 km; 683 miles)
- Ferry range, with three external tanks: 971 nm (1,800 km; 1,118 miles)

MIKOYAN MiG-23

NATO reporting names: Flogger-A, B, C, E, F and G

The prototype of this variable-geometry air combat fighter was first displayed in public during the 1967 Aviation Day flypast at Domodedovo Airport, Moscow. Initial deliveries of pre-series aircraft to the Soviet Air Force were made in 1970, but deployment of the MiG-23 in large numbers did not begin until 1973. Two Soviet fighter regiments, with a total of about 75 aircraft, were based in East Germany in 1973/74, and deliveries to the Soviet Air Force of all versions of the MiG-23 and the related MiG-27 were estimated to total over 1,500 aircraft by the Spring of 1979. Others had been supplied to the Bulgarian and Czechoslovak Air Forces. Export versions, with a lower equipment standard, are operated by the Algerian, Cuban, Egyptian, Ethiopian, Iraqi, Libyan and Syrian Air Forces.

US press reports suggest that two former Egyptian-operated MiG-23s are being flown by the USAF in the USA; at least one other is believed to have been presented to China.

There appear to be at least six versions of the MiG-23 of which details can be published:

MiG-23 (Flogger-A). Prototype shown at Domodedovo on 9 July 1967. Illustrated in 1973-74 and preceding editions of *Jane's*. It is now known that one or two development squadrons of 'Flogger-As' entered service with the Soviet Air Force. Experience with these dictated almost total redesign of the major production versions which followed.

MiG-23S (Flogger-B). Single-seat air combat fighter which is rapidly displacing the MiG-21 as the primary air-to-air tactical aircraft of the Soviet Air Forces, deployed in both forward areas and the interior of the USSR. Design changes compared with prototype include movement further rearward of all tail surfaces except ventral fin, giving much increased gap between wing and tailplane; a much larger dorsal fin; and the introduction of fixed inboard wing leading-edges. The US *Military Posture* statement for FY 1979 described 'Flogger-B' as "the first Soviet aircraft with a demonstrated ability to track and engage targets flying below its own altitude".

MiG-23U (Flogger-C). Tandem two-seat version suitable for both operational training and combat use. Individual canopy over each seat. Rear seat slightly higher than forward seat, with retractable periscopic sight for occupant. Dorsal fairing of increased depth aft of rear canopy. Otherwise identical to early MiG-23S (with R-27 engine). In service with Soviet Air Force and air forces of other countries, including Cuba, Czechoslovakia and Egypt.

MiG-23S (Flogger-E). Export version of 'Flogger-B'. Generally similar to Soviet Air Force version, but equipped to a lower standard. Smaller radar (NATO 'Jay Bird': search range 15 nm; 29 km; 18 miles, tracking range 10 nm; 19 km; 12 miles) in shorter nose radome. No under-nose laser rangefinder or Doppler navigation equipment. Armed with 'Atoll' missiles and GSh-23 gun.

MiG-23– (Flogger-F). Export counterpart of Soviet Air Force's MiG-27 ('Flogger-D') ground attack/interdictor version. Has the nose shape, cockpit external armour plate and larger, low-pressure tyres of MiG-27, but retains the power plant, variable-geometry intakes and GSh-23 twin-barrel gun of the MiG-23 interceptor. Operated by Czechoslovak, Cuban, Egyptian, Ethiopian, Iraqi, Libyan and Syrian Air Forces.

MiG-23S (Flogger-G). First identified when six aircraft from the air base of Kubinka made goodwill visits to Finland and France in the Summer of 1978. Although basically similar to 'Flogger-B', these aircraft had a much smaller dorsal fin. Absence of operational equipment, such as underwing pylons and laser rangefinder, may suggest that only a few aircraft have been modified to this standard for improved aerobatic capability as a display team.

Early production aircraft were powered by a Tumansky R-27 turbofan engine, rated at 68·65 kN (15,430 lb st) dry and 100·0 kN (22,485 lb st) with afterburning. This power plant continues in use in the two-seat MiG-23U, but the current MiG-23S and MiG-27 have a Tumansky R-29B turbojet.

'Flogger-E', the export version of 'Flogger-B', with smaller radome and other changes

The two-seat MiG-23U, identical to the MiG-23S except for second cockpit *(Flug Revue)*

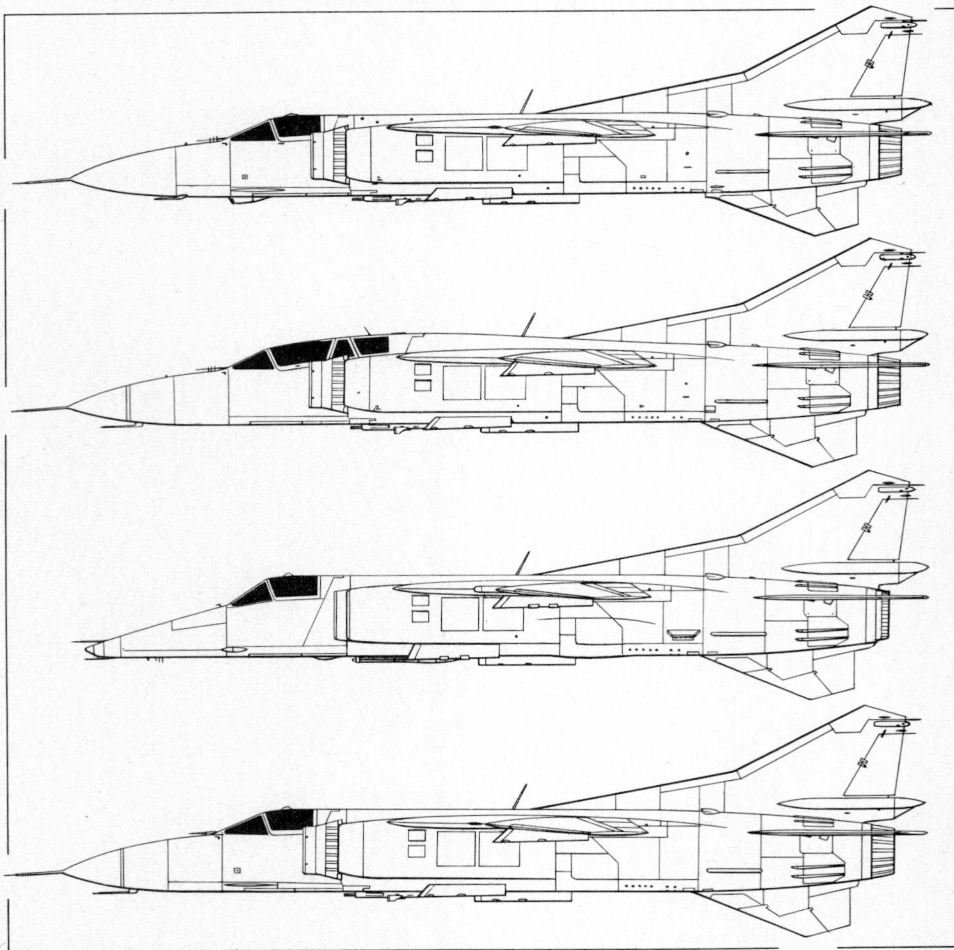

Top to bottom: Side views of the 'Flogger-B', 'Flogger-C', 'Flogger-D' and 'Flogger-E' variants of the MiG-23/27 series *(Pilot Press)*

The following description refers specifically to the current single-seat MiG-23S as supplied to the Soviet Air Force:

TYPE: Single-seat variable-geometry air combat fighter.

WINGS: Cantilever shoulder wing. Sweepback of main panels variable in flight or on the ground by manual control, reportedly at 16°, 45° or 72°. Fixed triangular inboard panels, with leading-edges swept at approximately 72°. Full-span trailing-edge single-slotted flaps, each in three sections, permitting independent actuation of outboard sections when wings are fully swept. Top-surface spoilers/lift dumpers forward of flaps, for differential operation in conjunction with horizontal tail surfaces, and for collective operation for improved runway adherence and braking after touchdown. Leading-edge flap on outboard two-thirds of each main (variable-geometry) panel.

FUSELAGE: Conventional semi-monocoque structure of basic circular section; flattened on each side of cockpit, forward of lateral air intake trunks which blend into circular shape of rear fuselage. Large flat boundary layer splitter plate forms inboard face of each intake. Two small rectangular 'blow-in' air intakes in each trunk, under inboard wing leading-edge. Perforations under rear fuselage, aft of main-wheel bays, are pressure-relief vents. Four door-type airbrakes, mounted two on each side of rear fuselage.

TAIL UNIT: All-moving horizontal surfaces, swept back at approximately 57° on leading-edge, operate both differentially and symmetrically to provide aileron and elevator function respectively. Conventional fin, swept back at approximately 65° on leading-edge, with inset rudder. Large dorsal fin. No tabs. Large ventral fin in two portions. Lower portion is hinged to fold to starboard when landing gear is extended, to increase ground clearance.

LANDING GEAR: Retractable tricycle type, with single wheel on each main unit and steerable twin-wheel nose unit. Main units retract inward into rear of air intake trunks. Main fairings to enclose these units are attached to legs. Small inboard fairing for each wheel bay hinged to fuselage belly. Nose unit, fitted with small mudguard, retracts rearward. Brake parachute housed in cylindrical fairing at base of rudder.

POWER PLANT: One Tumansky R-29B turbojet engine, rated at 78·45 kN (17,635 lb st) dry and 112·8 kN (25,350 lb st) with max afterburning. Max internal fuel capacity 5,750 litres (1,265 Imp gallons). Variable-geometry air intakes and variable nozzle. Provision for carrying external fuel tank, capacity 800 litres (176 Imp gallons), on underfuselage centreline pylon.

ACCOMMODATION: Single seat in air-conditioned cockpit, under small rearward-hinged canopy.

AVIONICS AND EQUIPMENT: Radar dish (NATO 'High Lark': search range 46 nm; 85 km; 53 miles, tracking range 29 nm; 54 km; 34 miles) behind dielectric nosecone. ILS antenna (NATO 'Swift Rod') under radome; yaw sensor above fuselage forward of windscreen; angle of attack sensor on port side. Small cylindrical fairings forward of starboard underwing pylon and above rudder are believed to contain ECM equipment. Undernose laser rangefinder, Sirena 3 radar warning system, and Doppler equipment standard on Soviet Air Force version. Dr Robert C. Seamans, then US Secretary of the Air Force, stated his belief in early 1973 that the contemporary radar and missile systems were comparable with those of the USAF's F-4 Phantom II. Retractable landing light under nose, aft of radome.

ARMAMENT: One 23 mm GSh-23 twin-barrel gun in fuselage belly pack, with large flash eliminator around muzzles. One pylon under centre-fuselage, one under each engine air intake duct, and one under each fixed inboard wing panel, for rocket packs, air-to-air missiles (NATO 'Apex' and 'Aphid') or other external stores.

DIMENSIONS, EXTERNAL (estimated):

Wing span:

fully spread	14·25 m (46 ft 9 in)
fully swept	8·17 m (26 ft 9½ in)
Length overall	16·80 m (55 ft 1½ in)

WEIGHT (estimated):

T-O weight 12,700-15,000 kg (28,000-33,050 lb)

PERFORMANCE (estimated):

Max level speed at height with external stores	Mach 2·3
Max level speed at S/L	Mach 1·1
Service ceiling	18,600 m (61,000 ft)
T-O and landing run	900 m (2,950 ft)
Combat radius	520 nm (960 km; 600 miles)

MIKOYAN MiG-27

NATO reporting name: Flogger-D

Although the single-seat ground attack aircraft known to NATO as 'Flogger-D' has many airframe features in common with the MiG-23, it differs in important respects and is designated MiG-27. Use of fixed air intakes and a fixed nozzle is consistent with the primary requirement of high subsonic speed at low altitude.

The forward portion of the fuselage is completely redesigned by comparison with the MiG-23. Instead of an ogival radome, 'Flogger-D' has a nose that is sharply-tapered in side elevation, with a small sloping window covering a laser rangefinder and marked target seeker, and additional armour on the flat sides of the cockpit. A six-barrel 23 mm Gatling-type underbelly gun replaces the GSh-23 of the interceptor, and there are five pylons for external stores, including tactical nuclear weapons and, probably, the air-to-surface missile known to NATO as 'Kerry'. There is provision for carrying an external fuel

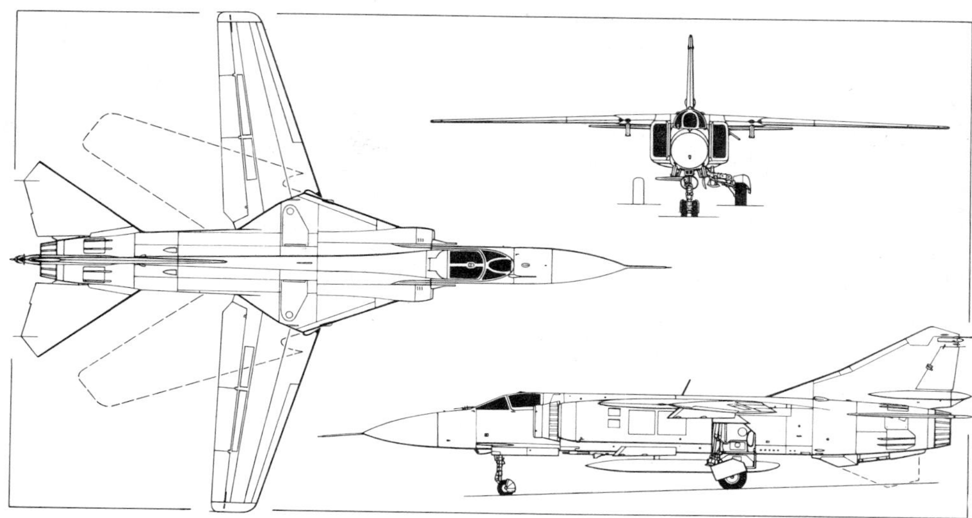

A shorter dorsal fin identifies the 'Flogger-G' version of the MiG-23S *(Pilot Press)*

MiG-27 ('Flogger-D') landing, with wings extended and ventral fin folded *(Flug Revue)*

MiG-27 variable-geometry interdictor ('Flogger-D') of the Soviet Air Force. Note the fixed-geometry intakes, laser rangefinder in nose, and dielectric panels *(Tass)*

MiG-23S with modified tail ('Fishbed-G') photographed during a goodwill visit to France in 1978 *(Colair)*

tank for ferry flights under each outer wing, which must be kept in a fully-forward position when the tank is in place. Equipment includes an ECM antenna above the port glove pylon.

The somewhat similar aircraft known to NATO as 'Flogger-F' is a member of the MiG-23 series, with variable-geometry intakes and a GSh-23 twin-barrel gun, although having the nose-shape and larger, low-pressure tyres of 'Flogger-D'. It represents the export counterpart of 'Flogger-D', with lower standards of equipment and performance, and is described under the MiG-23 entry.

The following data are estimated for the MiG-27 operated by the Soviet Air Force:

POWER PLANT: Generally similar to MiG-23S. Provision for three external tanks, each of 800 litres (176 Imp gallons) capacity, under fuselage and each outer wing.

DIMENSIONS, EXTERNAL: As MiG-23, plus:
- Wing aspect ratio (spread) 7·45
- Tailplane span 5·75 m (18 ft 10¼ in)

AREAS:
- Wings, gross (spread) 27·26 m² (293·4 sq ft)
- Horizontal tail surfaces 6·88 m² (74·06 sq ft)

WEIGHTS:
- Max weapon load 3,000 kg (6,610 lb)
- Max T-O weight, 'clean' 15,500 kg (34,170 lb)
- Max T-O weight 20,100 kg (44,310 lb)

PERFORMANCE (estimated):
- Max level speed at height Mach 1·75
- Max level speed at S/L Mach 0·95
- T-O to 15 m (50 ft) at AUW of 15,700 kg (34,600 lb) 800 m (2,625 ft)
- Max ferry range with three external tanks 1,350 nm (2,500 km; 1,550 miles)

MIKOYAN MiG-25 (E-266)

NATO reporting name: Foxbat

Development of the MiG-25 was initiated as a high-priority programme to counter the threat of the USAF's Mach 3 B-70 strategic bomber, for which North American Aviation Inc was chosen as prime contractor in December 1957. When the B-70 was cut back to a research project by President Kennedy, in March 1961, work on the MiG-25 continued, with increasing emphasis on the reconnaissance potential of the design.

First indication that the prototype had flown came with a Soviet claim, in April 1965, that a twin-engined aircraft designated E-266 had set a 1,000 km closed-circuit speed record of 1,251·9 knots (2,320 km/h; 1,441·5 mph), carrying a 2,000 kg payload. The attempt was made at a height of 21,000-22,000 m (69,000-72,200 ft) by Alexander Fedotov, who had earlier set a 100 km record in the Mikoyan E-166 research aircraft.

The same pilot set a payload-to-height record of 29,977 m (98,349 ft) with a 2,000 kg payload in the E-266 on 5 October 1967, after a rocket-assisted take-off. This qualified also for the record with a 1,000 kg payload. Photographs of the E-266 issued subsequently in the Soviet Union identified it as the twin-finned single-seat fighter of which four examples had taken part in the Domodedovo display in July 1967, and the designation MiG-25 was confirmed later. NATO had, meanwhile, allocated the reporting name 'Foxbat' to the type.

The aircraft's performance in level flight was demonstrated further on 5 October 1967, when M. Komarov set a speed record of 1,608·83 knots (2,981·5 km/h; 1,852·61 mph) over a 500 km closed circuit. On 27 October, P. Ostapenko raised the 1,000 km closed-circuit record to 1,576·00 knots (2,920·67 km/h; 1,814·81 mph) in an E-266, carrying a 2,000 kg payload and qualifying also for records with 1,000 kg payload and no payload. On 8 April 1973, Fedotov achieved a speed of 1,405·741 knots (2,605·1 km/h; 1,618·734 mph) over a 100 km closed circuit. Next, on 25 July 1973, he set an absolute height record by climbing to 36,240 m (118,898 ft) in an E-266.

Three time-to-height records were established by the E-266 on 4 June 1973, when Boris Orlov climbed to 20,000 m in 2 min 49·8 s, and P. Ostapenko climbed to 25,000 m in 3 min 12·6 s and 30,000 m in 4 min 3·86 s. All three records were beaten by the McDonnell Douglas F-15 *Streak Eagle* in January-February 1975; but two of them were recaptured by an E-266M (with uprated power plant) on 17 May 1975. Fedotov climbed to 25,000 m in 2 min 34·2 s and Ostapenko reached 30,000 m in 3 min 9·7 s. Fedotov also set a new record by climbing to 35,000 m in 4 min 11·3 s.

The current absolute height record was set by Fedotov on 31 August 1977, when he climbed to 37,650 m (123,524 ft) in an E-266M. He had, on 22 July, climbed to 37,080 m (121,654 ft) carrying a 2,000 kg payload, qualifying also for the record with 1,000 kg.

Four MiG-25 reconnaissance aircraft were deployed with Soviet Air Force units in Egypt in the Spring of 1971, having been airlifted to that country in An-22 transports. Between the Autumn of 1971 and the Spring of 1972, these aircraft were despatched in pairs from Cairo West airfield on at least four occasions to carry out high-speed reconnaissance missions off the Israeli coastline or down the full length of the Israeli-occupied Sinai Peninsula. Phantom interceptors sent up by the Israeli defence forces failed to make contact with the MiGs, which remained in Egypt until September 1975. In 1977, MiG-25 reconnaissance aircraft were based in the Soviet Union, at Brieg in Silesia, and in Syria. Operators in 1979 were reported to include the Algerian and Libyan Air Forces.

In early 1973 Dr Robert C. Seamans, then US Secretary of the Air Force, described the MiG-25 as "probably the best interceptor in production in the world today", and added "This Mach 3 aircraft performs both interceptor and reconnaissance missions, can operate at 24,400 m (80,000 ft), and has a highly capable avionics and missile system". In his FY 1975 US Defense Department Report, then-Secretary Schlesinger commented: "Should the Soviet Union develop and deploy an AWACS/'Foxbat' 'look-down, shoot-down' air defence system, we would have to counter it with new penetration devices and techniques such as the cruise missile, bomber defence missiles and improved ECM".

A first opportunity to study the MiG-25 interceptor outside the Soviet Union came when Lt Viktor Belenko defected in one from the Soviet air base of Sikharovka, 200 km (120 miles) from Vladivostok, to Hakodate airport, Japan, on 6 September 1976. Statements attributed to this pilot suggest that more than 400 MiG-25s had been built by that time, and that his particular aircraft left the production line less than three years earlier. Japanese and US military technicians who examined the aircraft reported that the airframe is constructed mainly of steel, with titanium only in places subjected to extreme heating such as the wing leading-edges. The inevitable weight penalty restricts the amount of equipment that can be carried. Belenko said that the aircraft took a considerable time to accelerate to high speeds, which were then difficult to maintain.

Examination of the aircraft is said to have shown that the fuselage weighs about 13,600 kg (30,000 lb) with the wings, tail surfaces and afterburners removed; the fire control system is bulky and lacking in advanced technology, with its very high power (600 kW) devoted to anti-jamming capability rather than range, and with vacuum tubes rather than solid-state circuitry throughout the avionics; ECM standards are high; the number of cockpit instruments was described as 50% of those in F-4EJ Phantoms of the JASDF, with a smaller and less versatile weapon sight; and the Machmeter has a 'red-line' limit at

MiG-25 'Foxbat-A' interceptor, armed with four air-to-air missiles (NATO 'Acrid')

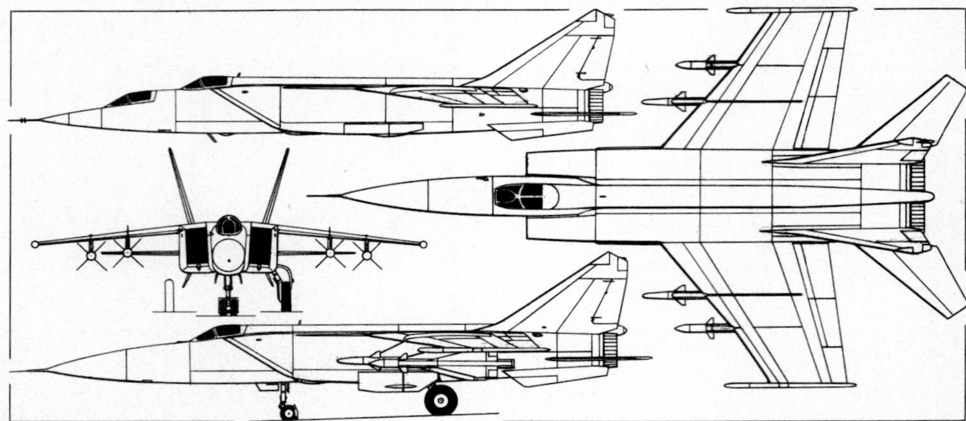

Mikoyan MiG-25 single-seat fighter (NATO 'Foxbat-A'), with additional side view (top) of two-seat MiG-25U *(Pilot Press)*

The reconnaissance version of the MiG-25 known to NATO as 'Foxbat-B'. Note the camera-carrying nose and dielectric panels *(Flug Revue)*

Mach 2·8, which almost certainly represents a never-exceed speed when carrying missiles and pylons rather than the maximum speed of which the 'clean' aircraft is capable. Of particular interest is the aircraft's high-quality airborne computer which, in conjunction with a ground-based flight control system, enables the interceptor to be vectored automatically on to its target over long ranges.

There are now five variants of the MiG-25, as follows:

MiG-25 (Foxbat-A). Basic interceptor, with large radar (NATO 'Fox Fire') in nose and armed with four air-to-air missiles on underwing attachments. Slightly reduced wing leading-edge sweep towards tips. CW target illuminating radar in nose of wingtip anti-flutter bodies.

MiG-25R (Foxbat-B). Basic reconnaissance version, with five camera windows and various flush dielectric panels aft of very small dielectric nosecap for radar. Equipment believed to include Doppler navigation system and side-looking airborne radar (SLAR). No armament. Slightly reduced span. Wing leading-edge sweep constant from root to tip.

MiG-25U (Foxbat-C). Trainer, of which first photographs were published towards the end of 1975. Generally similar to operational versions, but with new nose, containing separate cockpit with individual canopy, forward of standard cockpit and at a lower level. No search radar or reconnaissance sensors in nose. The aircraft designated **E-133** in which Svetlana Savitskaya set a women's world speed record of 1,448·942 knots (2,683·44 km/h; 1,667·412 mph) on 2 June 1975 is believed to have been a MiG-25U. She has since set a women's sustained height record of 21,209·9 m (69,586 ft) in an E-133 on 31 August 1977, and a women's speed record of 1,331·70 knots (2,466·31 km/h; 1,532·49 mph) around a 500 km closed circuit on 21 October 1977.

MiG-25R (Foxbat-D). Generally similar to 'Foxbat-B', but with larger SLAR (side-looking airborne radar) dielectric panel, further aft on starboard side of nose, and no cameras.

E-266M. Designation of experimental aircraft which set three time-to-height records in 1975 and now holds also the absolute height record. Lt Belenko has referred to a developed interceptor in which the airframe has been strengthened to permit supersonic flight near the ground; the engines have been uprated to give 137·3 kN (30,865 lb st) with afterburning; the avionics have been improved; and two fuselage attachments have been added to make possible the carriage of a total of six air-to-air missiles. Installation of a gun is also likely.

In tests against simulated cruise missiles, a MiG-25 flying at 6,000 m (19,685 ft) has detected a target flying below 60 m (200 ft) at a range of 11 nm (20 km; 12·5 miles), fired an unarmed missile against it and achieved a theoretical 'kill'.

The following description of the MiG-25 ('Foxbat-A') interceptor should be regarded as provisional:

Type: Single-seat interceptor.

Wings: Cantilever high-wing monoplane. Anhedral 4° from roots. Sweepback on leading-edge approx 42° inboard, 40° outboard of each outer missile attachment. Wing structure basically of steel, with titanium leading-edge. Upper surface fence in line with each inboard weapon attachment; shorter shallow fence in line with each outer attachment. Long anti-flutter body at each wingtip. Light alloy aileron at centre of each semi-span, with simple light alloy flap on inboard 37% of trailing-edge. No other movable wing surfaces.

Fuselage: Basic fuselage is quite slim, but is blended into the rectangular air intake trunks, which have wedge inlets. Inner walls of intakes are curved at top and do not run parallel with outer walls; a hinged panel forms the lower lip of each intake, enabling intake area to be varied electronically. Structure mainly of steel.

Tail Unit: Cantilever structure comprising twin outward-canted fins with inset rudders, and all-moving horizontal surfaces. All surfaces sweptback, without tabs. Main structures of steel, with titanium leading-edges and light alloy rear sections. Two outward-canted ventral fins. Large areas of each main and ventral fin form flush antennae.

Landing Gear: Retractable tricycle type. Single wheel, with high-pressure tyre of 1·20 m (47·25 in) diameter, on each forward-retracting main unit. Wheel stows vertically between air intake duct and outer skin of each trunk. Twin-wheel nose unit. Twin brake-chutes in fairing above and between jet nozzles.

Power Plant: Two Tumansky R-31 (R-266) single-shaft turbojet engines, each rated at 107·9 kN (24,250 lb st) with afterburning. Water-methanol injection standard. Fuel in two structural tanks in fuselage, between cockpit and engine bay, in saddle tanks around intake ducts, and in integral tank in each wing, filling almost the entire volume inboard of outer fence. Total fuel capacity approx 14,000 kg (30,865 lb).

Close-up of tandem cockpits in nose of MiG-25U 'Foxbat-C' *(Flug Revue)*

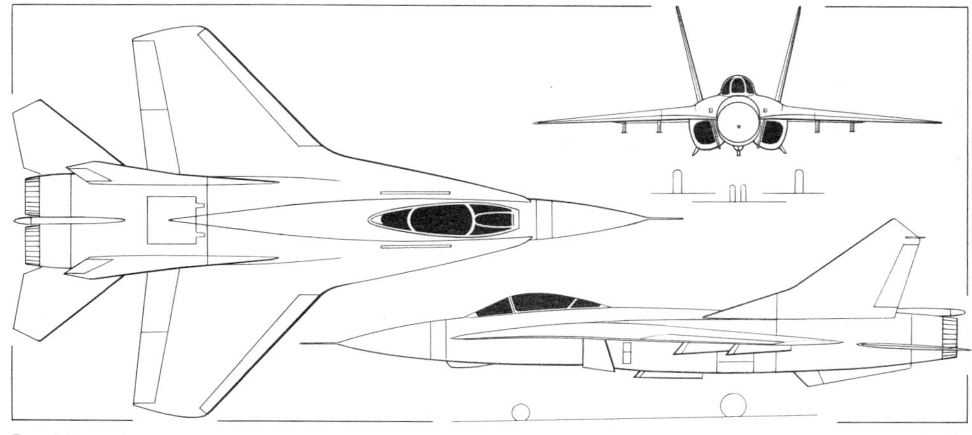

Provisional drawing of the single-seat twin-jet fighter said to have been identified by reconnaissance satellite and to be known in Washington as Ram L *(Pilot Press)*

Accommodation: Pilot only, on zero-height, 80 knot (150 km/h; 93 mph) ejection seat similar to that fitted to some versions of MiG-21. Canopy hinged to open sideways, to starboard.

Avionics and Equipment: Main fire-control radar (NATO 'Fox Fire': range believed to be 54 nm; 100 km; 62 miles) in nose, forward of electronics compartment housing navigation radar. SRZO-2 IFF and SOD-57M ATC/SIF, with antennae in starboard fin tip. Sirena 3 360° radar warning system with receivers in centre of each wingtip anti-flutter body and starboard fin tip. Unidentified ECCM, decoys and jammers. RSB-70/RPS HF, RSIU-5 VHF, R-831 UHF communications equipment, SP-50 ILS, and MRP-56P beacon receiver. Retractable landing light under front of each intake trunk.

Armament: Four air-to-air missiles on underwing attachments. These may comprise one infra-red and one radar homing example of the missile known to NATO as 'Acrid' under each wing. More usually, it is believed that one 'Apex' and one 'Aphid' are carried under each wing. Backup optical weapon sight.

Dimensions, external (estimated):
- Wing span:
  - 'Foxbat-A' — 13·95 m (45 ft 9 in)
  - 'Foxbat-B' — 13·40 m (44 ft 0 in)
- Wing aspect ratio — 3·3
- Length overall — 22·30 m (73 ft 2 in)
- Height overall — 5·60 m (18 ft 4¼ in)

Area:
- Wings, gross:
  - 'Foxbat-A' — 56 m² (603 sq ft)

Weights (estimated):
- Basic operating weight:
  - 'Foxbat-A' — at least 20,000 kg (44,100 lb)
  - 'Foxbat-B' — 19,600 kg (43,200 lb)
- Max T-O weight:
  - 'Foxbat-A' — 36,200 kg (79,800 lb)
  - 'Foxbat-B' — 33,400 kg (73,635 lb)

Performance (estimated):
- Max level speed at height:
  - 'Foxbat-B', 'clean' — Mach 3·2
- Never-exceed combat speed:
  - 'Foxbat-A', with missiles — Mach 2·8
- Max level speed at low altitude:
  - 'Foxbat-A' — Mach 0·85
- Max rate of climb at S/L:
  - 'Foxbat-A' — 12,480 m (40,950 ft)/min
- Time to 11,000 m (36,000 ft) with afterburning:
  - 'Foxbat-A' — 2 min 30 s
- Service ceiling:
  - 'Foxbat-A' — 24,400 m (80,000 ft)
- T-O run:
  - 'Foxbat-A' — 1,380 m (4,525 ft)
- Landing run:
  - 'Foxbat-A' — 2,180 m (7,150 ft)
- Normal combat radius:
  - 'Foxbat-A' — 610 nm (1,130 km; 700 miles)
- Max combat radius, econ power:
  - 'Foxbat-A' — 700 nm (1,300 km; 805 miles)

NEW MIKOYAN FIGHTER

Inevitably, there have been persistent reports in recent years concerning new fighter designs emanating from the Mikoyan bureau. The accompanying three-view drawing depicts an air superiority fighter in the class of the projected Northrop F-18L which is said to have been at the advanced flight testing stage in Spring 1979. US reports suggest that it is known in Washington as Ram L, having been identified initially on a photograph taken by reconnaissance satellite over Ramenskoye flight test centre in the USSR.

The drawing of this single-seat twin-jet fighter should be regarded as highly provisional. The aircraft's T-O weight is said to be in the 11,340 kg (25,000 lb) class.

MIL

General Designer in Charge of Bureau: Marat N. Tishchenko

M. L. Mil was connected with Soviet gyroplane and helicopter development from at least 1930. His achievements were recognised by the award of the Order of Lenin on his 60th birthday in November 1969. He died on 31 January 1970.

His original Mi-l, which was designed in 1949, first flown in 1950 and introduced into squadron service in 1951, was the first helicopter to enter series production in the Soviet Union and was also produced in Poland. It was followed by the larger Mi-4 in a number of variants, and these types are still in service, in civil and military forms.

Subsequent products of the bureau that was headed by Mikhail Mil include the Mi-6, a very large passenger and freight helicopter, the Mi-10 (V-10) and Mi-10K crane versions of the Mi-6, the smaller turbine-powered Mi-2 (V-2) and Mi-8 (V-8) passenger helicopters, the Mi-12 (V-12), which is the largest helicopter yet flown anywhere in the world, the Mi-14 coastal patrol development of the Mi-8, and the Mi-24 military assault helicopter. Avia-export has sold helicopters of Mil design in 38 countries.

MIL Mi-2 (V-2)

Built exclusively in Poland and described under Polish aircraft industry entry for WSK-PZL Swidnik.

Mil Mi-4 helicopter ('Hound-C') fitted with communications jamming equipment

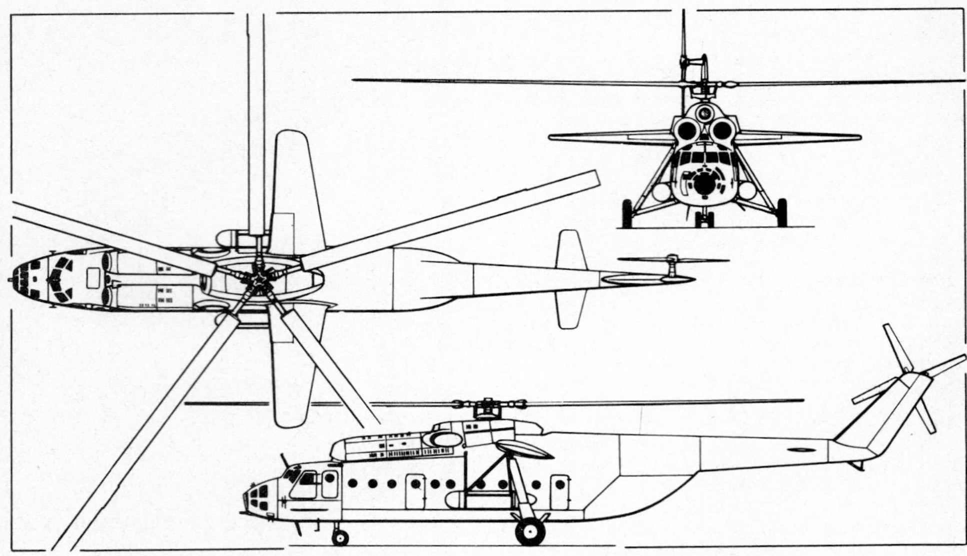

Military version of Mil Mi-6 heavy general-purpose helicopter *(Pilot Press)*

Mil Mi-6 heavy general-purpose helicopter (two Soloviev D-25V turboshaft engines) *(Martin Fricke)*

MIL Mi-4

NATO reporting name: Hound

Although Mi-4s have been largely replaced by turbine-powered helicopters in their original transport and anti-submarine roles, they continue in service with support units. A version first identified in 1977 is shown in an accompanying illustration. The multiple antennae projecting from the front and rear of the cabin, on each side, are communications jammers.

The designations given by NATO to military variants of the Mi-4 may now be listed, as follows:

Hound-A. Basic transport helicopter.

Hound-B. ASW version, with undernose radar, etc.

Hound-C. ECM version, shown in an accompanying illustration.

The Mil Mi-4 was last described in the 1971-72 *Jane's.* About 3,500 were built in 1952-69.

MIL Mi-6

NATO reporting name: Hook

First announced in the Autumn of 1957, the Mi-6 was then the largest helicopter flying anywhere in the world. From it were evolved the Mi-10 and Mi-10K flying crane helicopters, and its dynamic components were used in duplicated form on the V-12 (Mi-12).

Layout of the Mi-6 is conventional. Clamshell rear loading doors and folding ramps facilitate the loading of bulky freight and vehicles. Freight can also be carried externally, suspended from a hook on the CG. When the aircraft is operated in this flying crane role, the small wings which normally offload the rotor in flight can be removed, permitting an increase in payload.

The stub-wings are deleted also from the firefighting version. First demonstrated at the 1967 Paris Air Show, this carries several tons of water in tanks inside its cabin and can either spray this slowly from nozzles or dump it through the hoist cutout in its belly.

In setting up 14 FAI-recognised records in Class E1, the Mi-6 has lifted payloads of up to 20,117 kg (44,350 lb). Records still standing in mid-1979 included a 100 km closed-circuit speed record of 183·54 knots (340·15 km/h; 211·36 mph), set up by Boris Galitsky on 26 August 1964. On 15 September 1962 the same pilot, and crew, in an Mi-6 had flown at 162·08 knots (300·377 km/h; 186·64 mph) over a 1,000 km circuit, setting the current records for speed with payload of 1,000 kg and payload of 2,000 kg. On 11 September 1962 Vasily Kolochenko and crew of four averaged 153·44 knots (284·354 km/h; 176·69 mph) over a 1,000 km closed circuit, with a payload of 5,000 kg.

Five Mi-6s are reported to have been built for development testing, followed by an initial pre-series of 30 and subsequent manufacture of some 800 for military and civil use. Rate of production was reported to be eight per month in 1970. Six were supplied to the Indonesian Air Force; many others have been delivered to the Bulgarian, Egyptian, Iraqi, Syrian and North Vietnamese air forces and to the government of Peru.

Type: Heavy transport helicopter.

Rotor System: Five-blade main rotor and four-blade tail rotor. Main rotor blades each have a tapered steel tube spar, to which are bonded built-up metal aerofoil sections. Blades have coincident flapping and drag hinges and fixed tabs. Main rotor shaft inclined forward at 5° to vertical. Control via large welded swashplate. Hydraulically-actuated powered controls. All rotor blades incorporate electro-thermal de-icing system.

Fuselage: Conventional all-metal riveted semi-monocoque structure of pod and boom type.

Wings: Two small cantilever shoulder wings, mounted above main landing gear struts, offload rotor by providing some 20% of total lift in cruising flight. Removed when aircraft is operated as flying crane.

Tail Unit: Tail rotor support acts as vertical stabiliser. Variable-incidence horizontal stabiliser, near end of tailboom, for trim purposes.

Landing Gear: Non-retractable tricycle type, with steerable twin-wheel nose unit and single wheel on each main unit. Twin-chamber oleo-pneumatic (high-presssure and low-pressure) main landing gear shock-struts. High-pressure chambers interconnected through overflow system incorporating spring damper, to damp out oscillations at full landing gear loading and so eliminate ground resonance. Main wheels size 1,325 × 480 mm. Nosewheels size 720-310. Brakes on main wheels. Small tail-bumper under end of tailboom.

Power Plant: Two 4,101 kW (5,500 shp) Soloviev D-25V (TV-2BM) turboshaft engines, mounted side by side above cabin, forward of main rotor shaft. Eleven internal fuel tanks, with total capacity of 6,315 kg (13,922 lb), and two external tanks, on each side of cabin, with total capacity of 3,490 kg (7,695 lb). Provision for two additional ferry tanks inside cabin, with total capacity of 3,490 kg (7,695 lb). Automatic fuel-flow control system with manual override. Side panels of engine cowlings are opened and closed hydraulically and are used as platforms for inspection and maintenance of engines and rotor head.

Accommodation: Crew of five, consisting of two pilots, navigator, flight engineer and radio operator. Four jettisonable doors on flight deck. Equipped normally for cargo operation, with tip-up seats along side walls. When these seats are supplemented by additional seats installed in centre of cabin, 65 passengers can be carried, with cargo or baggage in the aisles. As an air ambulance, 41 stretcher cases and two medical attendants on tip-up seats can be carried. One of attendant's stations is provided with intercom to flight deck, and provision is made for portable oxygen installations for the patients. Cabin floor is stressed for loadings of 2,000 kg/m² (410 lb/sq ft), with provision for cargo tiedown rings. Rear clamshell doors and ramps are operated hydraulically. Standard equipment includes an electric winch of 800 kg (1,765 lb) capacity and pulley block system. External cargo sling system for bulky loads. Central hatch in cargo floor. Two passengers doors, fore and aft of main landing gear on port side.

Avionics and Equipment: Standard equipment includes VHF and HF communications radio, intercom, radio altimeter, radio compass, autopilot, marker beacon, directional gyro and full all-weather instrumentation.

Systems: Main, standby and auxiliary hydraulic systems, each with separate pump mounted on main gearbox. Operating pressure 118-152 bars (1,705-2,205 lb)sq in). Main 27V DC electrical system, supplied by two 12kW starter/generators, with batteries for 30 min emergency supply. De-icing system and some radio equipment supplied by three-phase 360V 400Hz AC system, utilising two 90kVA generators. Trolley-mounted APU, consisting of 74·5 kW (100 hp) AI-8 gas turbine and 24kW generator, carried on board.

Armament: A few Mi-6s are fitted with a gun of unknown calibre in the fuselage nose.

Dimensions, external:

Diameter of main rotor	35·00 m (114 ft 10 in)
Diameter of tail rotor	6·30 m (20 ft 8 in)
Distance between rotor centres	21·09 m (69 ft 2½ in)
Length overall, rotors turning	41·74 m (136 ft 11½ in)
Length of fuselage	33·18 m (108 ft 10½ in)
Height overall	9·86 m (32 ft 4 in)
Wing span	15·30 m (50 ft 2½ in)
Span of horizontal stabiliser	5·04 m (16 ft 6½ in)
Wheel track	7·50 m (24 ft 7¼ in)
Wheelbase	9·10 m (29 ft 10½ in)
Rear loading doors:	
Height	2·70 m (8 ft 10¼ in)
Width	2·65 m (8 ft 8¼ in)

Mil Mi-8 ('Hip-E') military helicopter. This differs from the commercial version in having circular cabin windows, a nose gun and weapon-carriers on outriggers *(see Addenda)*

Passenger doors:
  Height: front 1·71 m (5 ft 7¼ in)
    rear 1·62 m (5 ft 3¾ in)
  Width 0·81 m (2 ft 7¾ in)
  Sill height: front 1·40 m (4 ft 7¼ in)
    rear 1·30 m (4 ft 3¼ in)
Central hatch in floor
  1·44 m (4 ft 9 in) × 1·93 m (6 ft 4 in)

DIMENSIONS, INTERNAL:
Cabin:
  Length 12·00 m (39 ft 4½ in)
  Max width 2·65 m (8 ft 8¼ in)
  Max height:
    at front 2·01 m (6 ft 7 in)
    at rear 2·50 m (8 ft 2½ in)
  Cabin volume 80 m³ (2,825 cu ft)

WEIGHTS:
Weight empty 27,240 kg (60,055 lb)
Max internal payload 12,000 kg (26,450 lb)
Max slung cargo 9,000 kg (19,840 lb)
Max T-O weight with slung cargo at altitudes under 1,000 m (3,280 ft) 37,500 kg (82,675 lb)
Normal T-O weight 40,500 kg (89,285 lb)
Max T-O weight for VTO 42,500 kg (93,700 lb)

PERFORMANCE (at max T-O weight):
Max level speed 162 knots (300 km/h; 186 mph)
Max cruising speed 135 knots (250 km/h; 155 mph)
Service ceiling 4,500 m (14,750 ft)
Range with 6,000 kg (13,228 lb) payload
  350 nm (650 km; 404 miles)
Range with external tanks and 4,300 kg (9,480 lb) payload 566 nm (1,050 km; 652 miles)
Max ferry range (tanks in cabin)
  781 nm (1,450 km; 900 miles)

MIL Mi-8 (V-8)

NATO reporting name: Hip

This turbine-powered helicopter was shown in public for the first time during the 1961 Soviet Aviation Day display. Since then, nearly 6,000 Mi-8s have been delivered for military and civil use. With Mi-24s, they form the standard equipment of Soviet tactical helicopter regiments, in a variety of forms, some carrying extremely heavy weapon loads. Military Mi-8s have also been supplied to the Afghan, Algerian, Anguilla, Bangladesh, Bulgarian, Czechoslovak, Egyptian, Ethiopian, Finnish, East German, Hungarian, Indian, Iraqi, North Korean, Laotian, Libyan, Malagasy, Pakistani, Peruvian, Polish, Romanian, Sudanese, Syrian, North Vietnamese, North Yemen, South Yemen and Yugoslav armed forces.

The commercial Mi-8, with larger, square windows in place of the circular cabin windows of the military version, is in service with Aeroflot for transport and air ambulance duties, and is operated by this airline in support of Soviet activities in the Antarctic. Standard Mi-8s are used there for ice patrol and reconnaissance, for rescue operations, and for carrying supplies and equipment to Vostok Station, near the South Pole.

Three international women's helicopter records for distance and speed in a 2,000 km closed circuit were credited to the Mi-8 in mid-1979.

The original prototype (NATO **'Hip-A'**) had a single 2,013 kW (2,700 shp) Soloviev turboshaft engine and four-blade main rotor. When fitted with the five-blade rotor that became standard on subsequent aircraft, it was redesignated **'Hip-B'**. The second prototype, which flew for the first time on 17 September 1962, introduced the now-standard Isotov twin-turbine power plant and became **'Hip-C'** to NATO in both civil and military forms. Later versions include the **'Hip-E'**, described in US Congress as the world's most heavily armed helicopter.

In an emergency, the rotor blades of the Mi-8 and intermediate and tail gearboxes are interchangeable with those of the piston-engined Mi-4, although this prevents use of the de-icing system.

There are three civil versions, as follows:

Mi-8. Passenger version, with standard seating for 28 persons in main cabin.

Mi-8T. General utility version, equipped normally to carry internal or external freight, but able to accommodate 24 passenger seats.

Mi-8 Salon. De luxe version. Main cabin is furnished for eleven passengers, with an eight-place couch facing inward on the port side, and two chairs and a swivelling seat on the starboard side. There is a table on each side. An air-to-ground radio telephone and removable ventilation fans are standard equipment. Forward of the main cabin is a compartment for a hostess, with buffet and crew wardrobe. Aft of the main cabin are a toilet (port) and passenger wardrobe (starboard), to each side of the entrance. The Mi-8 Salon has a max T-O weight of 10,400 kg (22,928 lb) and range of 205 nm (380 km; 236 miles) with 30 min fuel reserve. In other respects it is similar to the standard Mi-8.

TYPE: Twin-engined transport helicopter.

ROTOR SYSTEM: Five-blade main rotor and three-blade tail rotor. Transmission comprises a type VR-8 main gearbox giving main rotor shaft/engine rpm ratio of 0·016 : 1, intermediate and tail gearboxes, main rotor brake and drives off the main gearbox for the tail rotor, fan, AC generator, hydraulic pumps and tachometer generators. Main rotor shaft inclined forward at 4° 30′ to vertical. All-metal main rotor blades of basic NACA 230 section; solidity 0·0777. Each main blade is made up of an extruded light alloy spar carrying the blade root fitting, 21 trailing-edge pockets and the blade tip. Pockets are honeycomb-filled. Main rotor blades are fitted with balance tabs, and are interchangeable. Their drag and flapping hinges are a few inches apart, and they are carried on a machined spider. Controls hydraulically-powered. All-metal tail rotor blades, each made up of a spar and honeycomb-filled trailing-edge. Automatically-controlled electro-thermal de-icing system on all blades.

FUSELAGE: Conventional all-metal semi-monocoque structure of pod and boom type.

TAIL UNIT: Tail rotor support acts as small vertical

Mil Mi-8 (V-8) passenger helicopter (two Isotov TV2-117A turboshaft engines) *(Brian M. Service)*

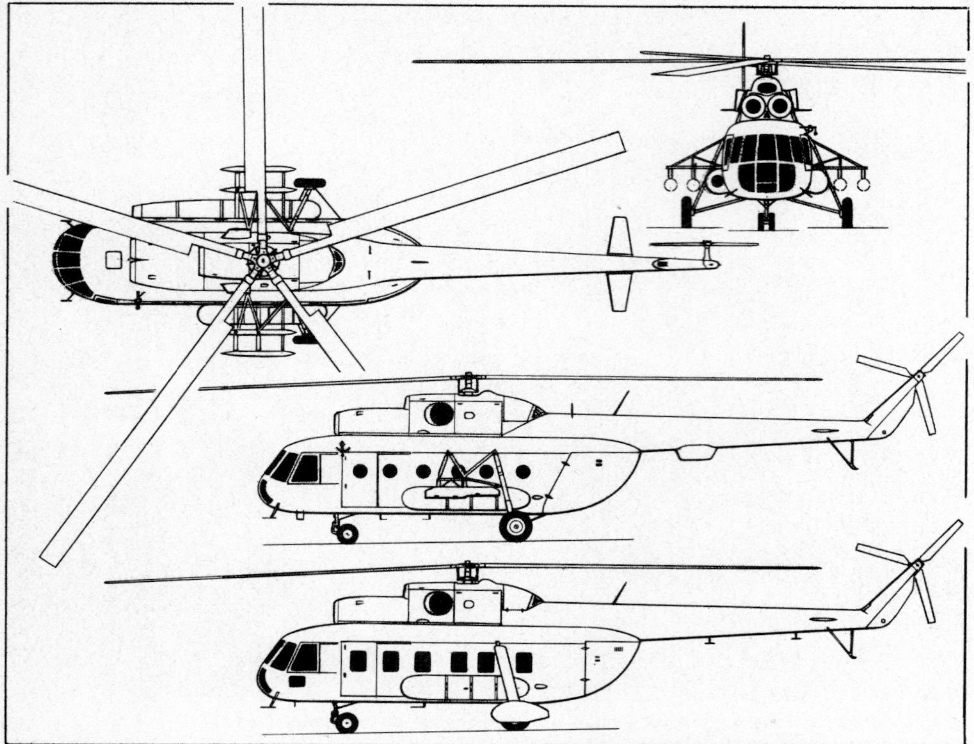

'Hip-C' military version of Mil Mi-8 twin-turbine helicopter, with additional side view (bottom) of commercial version *(Pilot Press)*

stabiliser. Horizontal stabiliser near end of tailboom.

LANDING GEAR: Non-retractable tricycle type, with steerable twin-wheel nose unit and single wheel on each main unit. All units embody oleo-pneumatic (gas) shock-absorbers. Main-wheel tyres size 865 × 280; nosewheel tyres size 595 × 185. Pneumatic brakes on main wheels. Pneumatic system can also recharge tyres in the field, using air stored in main landing gear struts. Optional main-wheel fairings.

POWER PLANT: Two 1,118·5 kW (1,500 shp) Isotov TV2-117A turboshaft engines. Main rotor speed governed automatically, with manual override. Single flexible internal fuel tank, capacity 445 litres (98 Imp gallons), and two external tanks, on each side of cabin, with capacity of 745 litres (164 Imp gallons) in the port tank and 680 litres (149·5 Imp gallons) in the starboard tank. Total standard fuel capacity 1,870 litres (411·5 Imp gallons). Provision for carrying one or two additional ferry tanks in cabin, raising max total capacity to 3,700 litres (814 Imp gallons). Fairing over starboard external tank houses optional cabin air-conditioning equipment at front. Engine cowling side panels form maintenance platforms when open, with access via hatch on flight deck. Engine air intake de-icing standard. Total oil capacity 60 kg (132 lb).

ACCOMMODATION: Two pilots side by side on flight deck, with provision for a flight engineer's station. Windscreen de-icing standard. Basic passenger version is furnished with 28 four-abreast track-mounted tip-up seats at a pitch of 72-75 cm (28·3-29·5 in), with a centre aisle 32 cm (12·6 in) wide, a wardrobe and baggage compartment; or 32 seats without wardrobe. Seats and bulkheads of basic version are quickly removable for cargo-carrying. Mi-8T has cargo tiedown rings in floor, a winch of 200 kg (440 lb) capacity and pulley block system to facilitate the loading of heavy freight, an external cargo sling system, and 24 tip-up seats along the side walls of the cabin. All versions can be converted for air ambulance duties, with accommodation for 12 stretchers and a tip-up seat for a medical attendant. The large windows on each side of the flight deck slide rearward. The sliding, jettisonable main passenger door is at the front of the cabin on the port side. An electrically-operated rescue hoist can be installed at this doorway. The rear of the cabin is made up of large clamshell freight-loading doors, with a downward-hinged passenger airstair door inset centrally at the rear. Hook-on ramps are used for vehicle loading.

SYSTEMS: Standard heating system can be replaced by full air-conditioning system. Two independent hydraulic systems, each with own pump; operating pressure 44-64 bars (640-925 lb/sq in). DC electrical supply from two 27V 18kW starter/generators and six 28Ah storage batteries. AC supply for de-icing system and some radio equipment supplied by 208/115/36/7·5V 400Hz generator, with 36V three-phase standby system. Provision for oxygen system for crew and, in ambulance version, for patients. Freon fire-extinguishing system in power plant bays and service fuel tank compartments, actuated automatically or manually. Two portable fire extinguishers for use in cabin.

AVIONICS AND EQUIPMENT: Standard equipment includes a type R-842 HF transceiver with frequency range of 2 to 8 MHz and range of up to 540 nm (1,000 km; 620 miles), type R-860 VHF transceiver operating on 118 to 135·9 MHz over ranges of up to 54 nm (100 km; 62 miles), intercom, radio telephone, type ARK-9 automatic radio compass, type RV-3 radio altimeter with 'dangerous height' warning, and four-axis autopilot to give yaw, roll and pitch stabilisation under any flight conditions, stabilisation of altitude in level flight or hover, and stabilisation of pre-set flying speed, navigation equipment and instrumentation for all-weather flying by day and night, including two gyro horizons, two airspeed indicators, two main rotor speed indicators, turn indicator, two altimeters, two rate of climb indicators, magnetic compass, radio altimeter, radio compass and astro-compass for Polar flying.

ARMAMENT: Military versions can be equipped with a great variety of weapons. 'Hip E' has a flexibly-mounted 12·7 mm machine-gun in the nose, and a triple rack for external stores, including anti-tank missiles, bombs and pods each containing sixteen or thirty-two 57 mm rockets, on an outrigger structure on each side of the main cabin.

DIMENSIONS, EXTERNAL:
- Diameter of main rotor: 21·29 m (69 ft 10¼ in)
- Diameter of tail rotor: 3·90 m (12 ft 9½ in)
- Distance between rotor centres: 12·65 m (41 ft 6 in)
- Length overall, rotors turning: 25·24 m (82 ft 9¾ in)
- Length of fuselage: 18·31 m (60 ft 0¾ in)
- Height overall: 5·65 m (18 ft 6½ in)
- Wheel track: 4·50 m (14 ft 9 in)
- Wheelbase: 4·26 m (13 ft 11¾ in)
- Fwd passenger door: Height: 1·41 m (4 ft 7¼ in)
  - Width: 0·82 m (2 ft 8¼ in)
- Rear passenger door: Height: 1·70 m (5 ft 7 in)
  - Width: 0·84 m (2 ft 9 in)
- Rear cargo door: Height: 1·82 m (5 ft 11½ in)
  - Width: 2·34 m (7 ft 8¼ in)

DIMENSIONS, INTERNAL:
- Passenger cabin: Length: 6·30 m (20 ft 7¾ in)
  - Width: 2·34 m (7 ft 8¼ in)
  - Height: 1·82 m (5 ft 11¾ in)
- Cargo hold (freighter):
  - Length at floor: 5·34 m (17 ft 6¼ in)
  - Width: 2·34 m (7 ft 8¼ in)
  - Height: 1·82 m (5 ft 11¾ in)
  - Volume: approx 23 m³ (812 cu ft)

AREA:
- Main rotor disc: 355 m² (3,828 sq ft)

WEIGHTS:
- Weight empty:
  - Passenger version: 7,261 kg (16,007 lb)
  - Cargo version: 6,816 kg (15,026 lb)
- Max payload: internal: 4,000 kg (8,820 lb)
  - external: 3,000 kg (6,614 lb)
- Normal T-O weight: 11,100 kg (24,470 lb)
- T-O weight with 28 passengers, each with 15 kg (33 lb) of baggage: 11,570 kg (25,508 lb)
- T-O weight with 2,500 kg (5,510 lb) of slung cargo: 11,428 kg (25,195 lb)
- Max T-O weight for VTO: 12,000 kg (26,455 lb)

PERFORMANCE:
- Max level speed at 1,000 m (3,280 ft):
  - Normal AUW: 140 knots (260 km/h; 161 mph)
- Max level speed at S/L:
  - Normal AUW: 135 knots (250 km/h; 155 mph)
  - Max AUW: 119 knots (220 km/h; 137 mph)
  - With 2,500 kg (5,510 lb) of slung cargo: 97 knots (180 km/h; 112 mph)
- Max cruising speed:
  - Normal AUW: 122 knots (225 km/h; 140 mph)
  - Max AUW: 97 knots (180 km/h; 112 mph)
- Service ceiling: 4,500 m (14,760 ft)
- Hovering ceiling IGE at normal AUW: 1,900 m (6,233 ft)
- Hovering ceiling OGE at normal AUW: 800 m (2,625 ft)
- Ranges:
  - Cargo version at 1,000 m (3,280 ft), with standard fuel, 5% reserves:
    - Normal AUW: 259 nm (480 km; 298 miles)
    - Max AUW: 248 nm (460 km; 285 miles)
  - Passenger version at 1,000 m (3,280 ft), with 20 min fuel reserves: 229 nm (425 km; 264 miles)
  - Ferry range of cargo version, with auxiliary fuel, 5% reserves: 647 nm (1,200 km; 745 miles)

MIL Mi-10 (V-10)

NATO reporting name: Harke

This flying crane development of the Mi-6 was demonstrated at the 1961 Soviet Aviation Day display at Tushino, having flown for the first time in the previous year. Above the line of the cabin windows the two helicopters are almost identical, but the depth of the fuselage is reduced considerably on the Mi-10, and the tailboom is deepened so that the flattened undersurface runs unbroken to the tail. The Mi-10 also lacks the fixed wings of the Mi-6.

Items which are interchangeable between the Mi-6 and Mi-10 include the power plant, transmission system and reduction gearboxes, swashplate assembly, main and tail rotors, control system and most items of equipment. The power of the Soloviev turboshaft engines remains constant up to 3,000 m (9,850 ft) and to an ambient air temperature of 40°C at sea level. The aircraft will maintain level flight on one engine. Full navigation equipment and an autopilot permit all-weather operation, by day and night.

The tall long-stroke quadricycle landing gear, with wheel track exceeding 6·0 m (19 ft 8 in) and clearance under the fuselage of 3·75 m (12 ft 3½ in) with the aircraft fully loaded, enables the Mi-10 to taxi over a load it is to carry and to accommodate loads as bulky as a prefabricated building.

Use can be made of interchangeable wheeled cargo platforms which are held in place by hydraulic grips controllable from either the cockpit or a remote panel. Using these grips without a platform, cargos up to 20 m (65 ft 7 in) long, 10 m (32 ft 9½ in) wide and 3·1 m (10 ft 2 in) high can be lifted and secured in 1½ to 2 minutes. The cabin can accommodate additional freight or passengers.

A closed-circuit TV system, with cameras scanning forward from under the rear fuselage and downward through the sling hatch, is used to observe the payload and main landing gear, touchdown being by this reference. The TV system replaces the retractable undernose 'dustbin' fitted originally.

The following details refer to the standard Mi-10, which has been operated by both Aeroflot and the Soviet armed forces and is available for export. About 55 are believed to have been delivered by 1977, with production resuming at a modest rate after a six-year break. Some have been exported to Iraq.

TYPE: Heavy flying-crane helicopter.

ROTOR SYSTEM: Same as for Mi-6, except that main rotor shaft is inclined forward at an angle of only 45′.

FUSELAGE: Conventional all-metal riveted semi-monocoque structure.

TAIL UNIT: Same as for Mi-6.

LANDING GEAR: Non-retractable quadricycle type, with twin wheels on each unit. All units fitted with oleo-pneumatic shock-absorbers. Telescopic main legs. Main wheels size 1,230 × 260 mm, each with brake. Levered-suspension castoring nose units. Nosewheels size 950 × 250. All landing gear struts are faired. The port nose gear fairing incorporates steps to the crew door. Despite the height of the gear, the Mi-10 can make stable landing and take-off runs at speeds up to 54 knots (100 km/h; 62 mph).

POWER PLANT: Two 4,101 kW (5,500 shp) Soloviev D-25V turboshaft engines, mounted side by side above cabin, forward of main rotor drive-shaft. Single fuel tank in fuselage and two external tanks, on sides of cabin, with total capacity of 6,340 kg (13,975 lb). Provision for carrying two auxiliary tanks in cabin, to give total fuel capacity of 8,260 kg (18,210 lb). Engine cowling side panels (opened and closed hydraulically) can be used as maintenance platforms when open.

ACCOMMODATION: Two pilots and flight engineer accommodated on flight deck, which has bulged side windows to provide an improved downward view. Flight deck is heated and ventilated and has provision for oxygen equipment. Crew door is immediately aft of flight deck on port side. Main cabin can be used for freight and/or passengers, 28 tip-up seats being installed along the side walls. Freight is loaded into this cabin through a door on the starboard side, aft of the rear landing gear struts, with the aid of a boom and 200 kg (440 lb) capacity electric winch. In addition to the cargo platform described earlier, the Mi-10 has external sling gear as standard equipment. This can be used in conjunction with a winch controlled from a portable control panel inside the cabin. The winch can be also be used to raise loads of up to 500 kg (1,100 lb) while the aircraft is hovering on rescue and other duties, via a hatch in the cabin floor.

Avionics, Equipment and Systems: Generally as for Mi-6, including APU.

Dimensions, external:
- Diameter of main rotor 35·00 m (114 ft 10 in)
- Diameter of tail rotor 6·30 m (20 ft 8 in)
- Distance between rotor centres 21·24 m (69 ft 8 in)
- Length overall, rotors turning 41·89 m (137 ft 5½ in)
- Length of fuselage 32·86 m (107 ft 9¾ in)
- Ground clearance under fuselage 3·75 m (12 ft 3½ in)
- Height overall 9·80 m (32 ft 2 in)
- Wheel track (c/l shock-struts):
  - nosewheels 6·01 m (19 ft 8¾ in)
  - main wheels 6·92 m (22 ft 8½ in)
- Wheelbase 8·29 m (27 ft 2½ in)
- Cargo platform: Length 8·53 m (28 ft 0 in)
  - Width 3·54 m (11 ft 7¼ in)
- Crew door: Height 1·35 m (4 ft 5¼ in)
  - Width 0·78 m (2 ft 6¾ in)
  - Height to sill 3·91 m (12 ft 10¼ in)
- Freight loading door: Height 1·56 m (5 ft 1½ in)
  - Width 1·26 m (4 ft 1½ in)
  - Height to sill 3·92 m (12 ft 10½ in)
- Cabin floor hatch:
  - Diameter 1·00 m (3 ft 3½ in)

Dimensions, internal:
- Cabin: Length 14·04 m (46 ft 0¾ in)
  - Width 2·50 m (8 ft 2½ in)
  - Height 1·68 m (5 ft 6 in)
  - Volume approx 60 m³ (2,120 cu ft)

Weights:
- Weight empty 27,300 kg (60,185 lb)
- Max payload on platform, incl platform 15,000 kg (33,070 lb)
- Max slung payload 8,000 kg (17,635 lb)
- T-O weight with slung cargo 38,000 kg (83,775 lb)
- Max T-O weight 43,700 kg (96,340 lb)

Performance:
- Max level speed at max T-O weight 108 knots (200 km/h; 124 mph)
- Cruising speed at max T-O weight 97 knots (180 km/h; 112 mph)
- Service ceiling (limited) 3,000 m (9,850 ft)
- Range with platform payload of 12,000 kg (26,455 lb) 135 nm (250 km; 155 miles)

MIL Mi-10K

First displayed publicly in Moscow on 26 March 1966, the Mi-10K is a development of the Mi-10 with a number of important design changes, most apparent of which are a reduction in the height of the landing gear and a more slender tail rotor support structure.

It can be operated by a crew of only two pilots. This is made possible by the provision of an additional cockpit gondola under the front fuselage, with full flying controls and a rearward-facing seat. By occupying this seat, one of the pilots can control the aircraft in hovering flight and, at the same time, have an unrestricted view of cargo loading, unloading and hoisting, which are also under his control.

In the Mi-10K, the maximum slung payload is 11,000 kg (24,250 lb) and is expected to be increased further to 14,000 kg (30,865 lb) by using Soloviev D-25VF turboshaft engines, uprated to 6,500 shp each, in due course. Fuel capacity of the Mi-10K, in standard internal and external tanks, is 9,000 litres (1,980 Imp gallons). The rotor turns at 120 rpm.

Dimensions, external:
- Generally as for Mi-10, except:
- Height overall 7·80 m (25 ft 7 in)
- Wheel track 5·00 m (16 ft 4¾ in)
- Wheelbase 8·74 m (28 ft 8 in)
- Door sill heights:
  - Crew door 1·81 m (5 ft 11 in)
  - Freight door 1·82 m (5 ft 11½ in)

Weights:
- Weight empty 24,680 kg (54,410 lb)
- Max payload, slung cargo 11,000 kg (24,250 lb)
- Max fuel load with ferry tanks in cabin 8,670 kg (19,114 lb)
- Max T-O weight with slung cargo 38,000 kg (83,776 lb)

Performance:
- Cruising speed, empty 135 knots (250 km/h; 155 mph)
- Max cruising speed with slung load 109 knots (202 km/h; 125 mph)
- Service ceiling 3,000 m (9,850 ft)
- Ferry range with auxiliary fuel 428 nm (795 km; 494 miles)

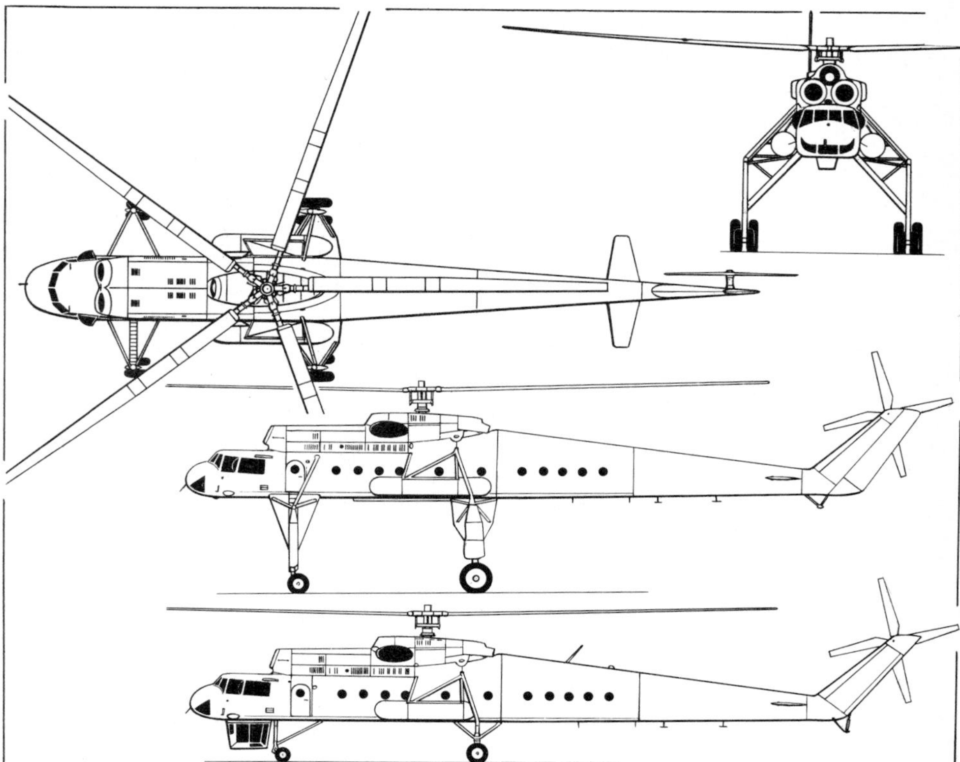

Mil Mi-10 flying crane derivative of the Mi-6, with additional side view (bottom) of Mi-10K *(Pilot Press)*

MIL Mi-14 (V-14)

NATO reporting name: Haze

An accompanying photograph shows a shore-based anti-submarine helicopter which is in standard service with the Soviet Navy as a replacement for the Mi-4. Clearly derived from the Mi-8, it is known to NATO as 'Haze'.

No details are available officially. Features evident in the photograph include a boat-hull planing bottom on the fuselage, and a sponson on each side at the rear, to provide a degree of amphibious capability; a large undernose radome; and a towed magnetic anomaly detection (MAD) bird stowed against the rear of the fuselage pod. The landing gear of 'Haze' is fully retractable.

Dimensions, power plant and dynamic components must be generally similar to those of the Mi-8.

It is generally assumed that 'Haze' is the 'float-equipped version of the Mi-8' which was reported to be under test in the Soviet Union in early 1974, with the designation V-14. About 50 are believed to have been delivered by 1977, with production continuing at a rate of 25 per year.

MIL Mi-24

NATO reporting name: Hind

This assault helicopter was known to exist for some two years before photographs became available to the technical press in early 1974. The two versions shown in those first photographs were each capable of carrying a squad of eight combat-equipped troops, and had attachments under their auxiliary wings for a variety of ordnance, to keep down the heads of enemy troops in the drop zone and to attack ground targets, including tanks. At least two units of approximate squadron strength were based in eastern Europe by the Spring of 1974. Since that time the Mi-24 has developed in two complementary forms, one configured for optimum efficiency as an assault transport, while retaining heavy armament; the other as an advanced gunship with secondary transport capability. Deliveries of all models are believed to exceed 1,000, with production continuing at a rate of 30 a month. Full regiments of Mi-24s are based at Parchim and Stendal, northwest and west of Berlin, near the border with West Germany. About 30 are reported to have been supplied to Afghanistan and others to Libya and East Germany.

The basic airframe, power plant and transmission system appear to be common to all versions of the Mi-24, with differences in armament, operational equipment and tail rotor location. In addition, the gunship has completely new crew accommodation forward of the engine inlets and above the fuselage floor. Five major variants of which

Mil Mi-10K preparing to lift a 10-tonne sheet steel drum to the top of a tower at the Sinarski pipe works in Kamenski Uralski *(Tass)*

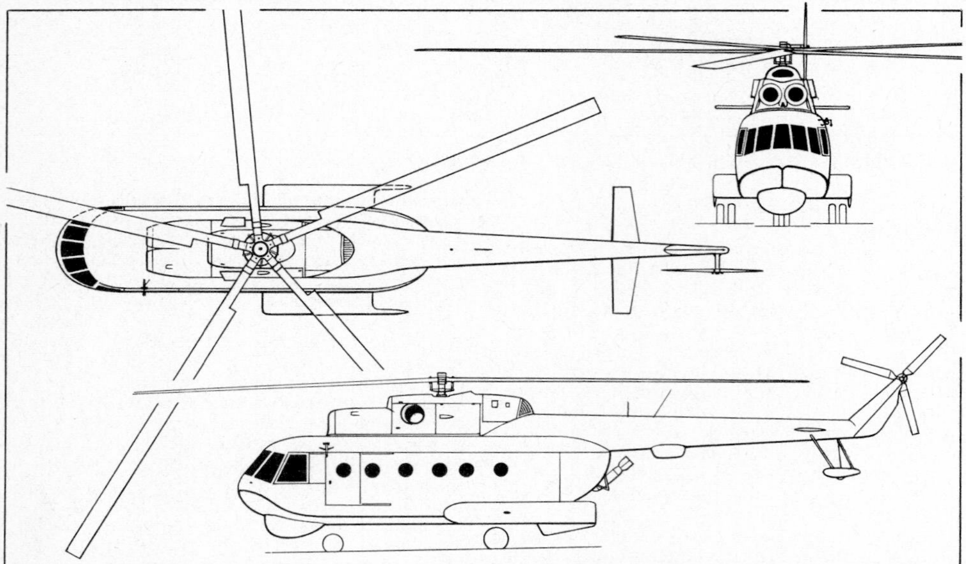

Photograph and three-view drawing *(Pilot Press)* **of the Mil Mi-14 (V-14) ASW helicopter (NATO 'Haze')**

details may be published are known by the following NATO reporting names:

Hind-A. Armed assault helicopter, with large enclosed flight deck for crew of four, comprising pilot, co-pilot, gunner-navigator and forward observer. Auxiliary wings, with considerable anhedral, each carry three weapon stations for heavy armament, supplemented by large-calibre machine-gun in nose. Anti-torque rotor, originally on starboard side of offset tail pylon, repositioned to port side on later and converted aircraft. Initial production Mi-24s were of this version.

Hind-B. Similar to 'Hind-A' except that auxiliary wings have neither anhedral nor dihedral, and carry only the two inboard weapon stations on each side. This version is believed to have preceded 'Hind-A' and was not built in large numbers.

Hind-C. Generally similar to late-model 'Hind-A' but without nose gun and undernose blister fairing, and no missile rails at wingtips.

Hind-D. Basically similar to late-model 'Hind-A', with tail rotor on port side, but with front fuselage completely redesigned for primary gunship role. Tandem stations for weapon operator (in nose) and pilot have individual canopies. Front canopy hinged to open sideways, to starboard; footstep under starboard side of fuselage for access to pilot's rearward-hinged door. Rear seat raised to give pilot an unobstructed forward view. Probe fitted forward of top starboard corner of bulletproof windscreen at extreme nose may be similar to US low-airspeed sensing equipment, to indicate optimum conditions for minimum dispersion of 57 mm rockets. Under nose is a four-barrel Gatling-type large-calibre machine-gun in a turret with a wide range of movement in azimuth and elevation, providing air-to-air as well as air-to-surface capability. Undernose pack for sensors, possibly including radar and low-light-level TV. (Reports that forward-looking infra-red might be fitted were premature, as such equipment is not expected to be ready for service in the Soviet Union for several years.) Wing armament of 'Hind-A' retained, but forward-looking (electro-optical?) sensor transferred from top of port inner pylon to wingtip. Many small antennae and blisters. Extended nosewheel leg to increase ground clearance of sensor pack; nosewheels semi-exposed when retracted.

Hind-F. Variant reported to be based in East Germany in 1979, with armament of six anti-tank guided missiles.

Other developments reported in 1979 were the introduction on some 'Hinds' of a 30 mm Gatling-type nose gun and a laser seeker.

Except where indicated, the following details apply to all current versions:

Rotor System: Five-blade main rotor and three-blade tail rotor; latter now on port side of offset tail fin. Main rotor blades believed to be of glassfibre, on cast titanium head. Balance tab and electrical leading-edge de-icing on each blade.

Fuselage: Conventional all-metal semi-monocoque structure of pod and boom type. Forward portion, above shallow floor structure, differs with role.

Auxiliary Wings: Cantilever shoulder wings of tapered planform, with marked anhedral and incidence. No movable surfaces.

Tail Unit: Swept fin, offset a few degrees, serves also as tail rotor pylon. Variable-incidence horizontal stabiliser at base of fin.

Landing Gear: Tricycle type, with rearward-retracting twin-wheel nose unit, and single-wheel main units with oleo-pneumatic shock-absorbers and low-pressure tyres. Main units retract rearward and inward into the aft end of the fuselage pod, turning through 90° to stow almost vertically, discwise to the longitudinal axis of the fuselage, under prominent blister fairings. Tubular tripod skid assembly protects tail rotor in a tail-down take-off or landing.

Power Plant: Two 1,118·5 kW (1,500 shp) Isotov turboshaft engines, related to the TV2-117A engines of the Mi-8 but shorter, mounted side by side above the cabin, with their output shafts driving rearward to the main rotor shaft through a combining gearbox. (These may have been superseded by 1,640 kW; 2,200 shp TV3-117s in later aircraft; see entry on Mil A-10.)

Accommodation ('Hind-A'): Crew of four; eight fully-equipped troops in main cabin. Access to flight deck via large rearward-sliding blistered transparent panel which forms the aft flight deck window on the port side, and a large upward-hinged window forward of this. At front of passenger cabin on each side is a large door, divided horizontally into two sections which are hinged to open upward and downward respectively. Optically

'Hind-A', first major production version of the Mil Mi-24 assault helicopter, with original starboard-side tail rotor

flat bulletproof glass window in nose, with wiper, for gunner. Armour protection for crew and some vital components.

SYSTEMS: Dual electrical system, with three generators. Stability augmentation system. Electro-thermal de-icing system for main and tail rotor blades.

AVIONICS: Include ADF navigation system with map display.

ARMAMENT ('Hind-A'): One 12·7 mm machine-gun in nose, probably slaved to undernose sighting system. Rails for four 'Swatter' anti-tank missiles under end-plate pylons at wingtips. Four underwing pylons for rocket pods (each thirty-two 57 mm rockets), special bombs, or other stores. Entering service on the Mi-24 is a tube-launched 'fire-and-forget' anti-tank guided missile (NATO 'Spiral'), which is reported to have a range of 3·75-5·3 nm (7-10 km; 4·3-6·2 miles) and to home on targets illuminated by a laser designator.

DIMENSIONS, EXTERNAL (estimated):

Diameter of main rotor	17·00 m (55 ft 9 in)
Diameter of tail rotor	3·90 m (12 ft 9½ in)
Length overall	17·00 m (55 ft 9 in)
Height overall	4·25 m (14 ft 0 in)

WEIGHTS (estimated):

Max external weapons	1,275 kg (2,800 lb)
Normal T-O weight	10,000 kg (22,000 lb)

MIL A-10

In the Summer of 1975, a total of seven helicopter records in class E1 were set by a Soviet women's crew in a helicopter designated A-10. All that was then known about the A-10 was that it had been designed by the Mil bureau and was powered at that time by two 1,118·5 kW (1,500 shp) Isotov TV2-117A turboshaft engines, as fitted to the Mi-8. The performance capability represented by the records suggested that the A-10 might be related to the Mi-24, and east European press reports confirmed this in 1979. The front fuselage is of 'Hind-C' configuration.

Pilot on all 1975 record flights was Galina Rastorgoueva, a test pilot and engineer. She was accompanied by Ludmila Polyanskaya, who is employed as navigator on Il-18 airliners of Aeroflot. On 18 July 1975, they averaged 180·480 knots (334·464 km/h; 207·826 mph) around a 100 km circuit, setting a new women's speed record. On 1 August, a speed of 178·624 knots (331·023 km/h; 205·688 mph) around 500 km set both general and women's records, as did an average speed of 179·500 knots (332·646 km/h; 206·697 mph) over 1,000 km on 13 August. Two women's time-to-height helicopter records followed, with a time of 2 min 33·5 s to 3,000 m on 8 August, and 7 min 43 s to 6,000 m on 26 August.

Latest A-10 record confirmed by the FAI is a speed of 198·9 knots (368·4 km/h; 228·9 mph) set by Gourguen Karapetyan over a 15/25 km course near Moscow on 21 September 1978. Of interest is that this A-10 had two TV3-117 turboshaft engines, each rated at 1,640 kW (2,200 shp).

MIL HEAVY-LIFT HELICOPTER

NATO reporting name: Halo

A statement to Congress on the US Army's FY 1980 budget appropriations contained a comment that the Russians "may be on the verge of developing an operational heavy-lift helicopter—a system we do not possess. They have been flying prototypes of a helicopter called 'Homer' for several years (see 1977-78 *Jane's*). This is capable of carrying company-size units and is the same size as a Boeing 727. They have never deployed this system for reasons known only to themselves (probably technical). They now, however, have developed prototypes of a new heavy-lift helicopter called 'Halo'."

No details of 'Halo' have been released officially, but it is reported to have a single main rotor/tail rotor configuration, with clamshell rear loading doors. Representatives of the Mil bureau have discussed their current involvement in heavy-lift helicopters with a total installed power of around 18,650 kW (25,000 shp).

MIL NAVAL HELICOPTER

The US *Military Posture* statement for FY 1979 contained the remark: "Another new (Soviet) naval helicopter is projected in the mid-1980s for ASW and reconnaissance roles". No details were given.

The completely redesigned nose of the Mi-24 ('Hind-D') gunship is shown clearly in this close-up

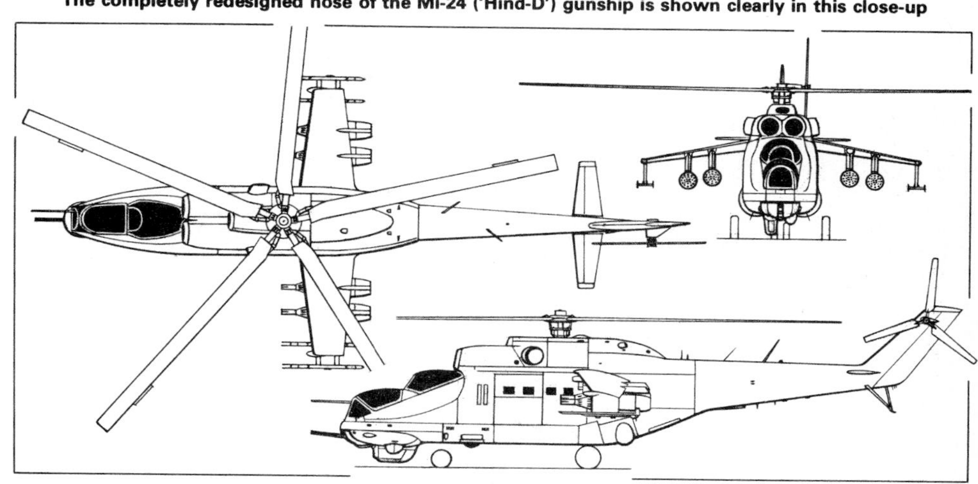

The gunship version of the Mil Mi-24 known to NATO as 'Hind-D' *(Pilot Press)*

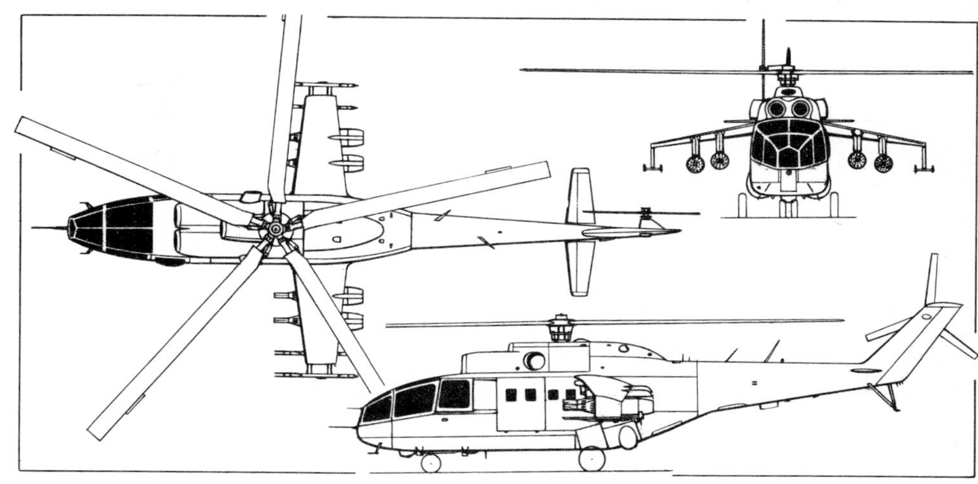

Mil Mi-24 assault helicopter, in the form known to NATO as 'Hind-A', with original tail rotor *(Pilot Press)*

MYASISHCHEV

Professor Vladimir Mikhailovich Myasishchev died on 14 October 1978, at the age of 76. Although his work was little publicised, he was responsible for the development of several important types. They included the four-jet M-4 bomber (known in the West by the reporting name of 'Bison') which remains in service for maritime reconnaissance and as a flight refuelling tanker.

Myasishchev later designed a long-range four-jet heavy bomber to replace the M-4. This was allocated the NATO code name of 'Bounder' and was described in the 1964-65 *Jane's*. Changing requirements limited 'Bounder' to a research role.

MYASISHCHEV M-4

NATO reporting name: Bison

Three major production versions of this four-jet aircraft have been identified by NATO code names, as follows:

Bison-A. The Soviet Union's first operational four-jet strategic bomber, displayed initially over Moscow in May 1954. Comparable with early versions of Boeing B-52 Stratofortress. Powered by four 85·3 kN (19,180 lb st) Mikulin AM-3D turbojets, buried in wing-roots. Range reported to be 6,075 nm (11,250 km; 7,000 miles) at 450 knots (835 km/h; 520 mph) with 4,500 kg (10,000 lb) of nuclear or conventional free-fall bombs. Defensive armament of ten 23 mm cannon in twin-gun turrets in tail, above fuselage fore and aft of wing and under fuselage fore and aft of bomb bays, believed necessary because of aircraft's operational ceiling of only 13,700 m (45,000 ft). In early 1975, the Chairman of the US Joint Chiefs of Staff commented that all 85 M-4s then serving in the Soviet bomber force were available for conversion into flight refuelling tankers for the 'Backfire' supersonic bomber force, but that a tanker version of the Il-76 transport would probably be preferred. About 45 'Bison-As' are, in fact, serving as tankers for other M-4s and Tu-95 'Bears' of the Soviet strategic bomber force, carrying a hose-reel unit in the bomb bay.

Bison-B. Maritime reconnaissance version identified in service in 1964. 'Solid' nose radome in place of hemispherical glazed nose of 'Bison-A,' with large superimposed flight refuelling probe. Numerous underfuselage blister fairings for specialised avionic equipment. Forward portion of centre bomb bay doors bulged. Aft gun turrets above and below fuselage deleted, reducing armament to six 23 mm cannon.

Bison-C. Generally similar configuration to 'Bison-B' but with large search radar faired neatly into new and longer nose, aft of centrally-mounted flight refuelling probe. Prone bombing/observation station, with optically-flat glass panels, below and to rear of radar; further small windows and a domed observation (and probably gunnery aiming) window on each side; underfuselage blister fairings, bulged bomb bay and armament; all as 'Bison-B'. An example of this version with the experimental aircraft designation 201-M was used to set up a number of official records in 1959 and was exhibited statically in the Soviet Aviation Day display at Domodedovo Airport, Moscow, in 1967. Powered by four 127·5 kN (28,660 lb st) Soloviev D-15 turbojet engines, this testbed aircraft established seven payload-to-height records, including a weight of 55,220 kg (121,480 lb) lifted to 2,000 m (6,560 ft) and height of 15,317 m (50,253 ft) with a 10,000 kg payload.

DIMENSIONS, EXTERNAL (A, 'Bison-A'; C, 'Bison-C'):

Wing span: A	50·48 m (165 ft 7½ in)
C	51·82 m (170 ft 0 in)
Length overall: A	47·20 m (154 ft 10 in)
C	49·38 m (162 ft 0 in)
Tailplane span	15·00 m (49 ft 2½ in)

WEIGHTS (A, 'Bison-A'; C, 'Bison-C'):

Max T-O weight: A	158,750 kg (350,000 lb)
C	165,000 kg (363,760 lb)

PERFORMANCE (A, 'Bison-A'; C, 'Bison C', estimated):

Max level speed at 3,000 m (9,850 ft):	
C	572 knots (1,060 km/h; 658 mph)
Max level speed at 11,000 m (36,000 ft):	
A	485 knots (900 km/h; 560 mph)
Max level speed at 12,000 m (39,370 ft):	
C	515 knots (955 km/h; 593 mph)
Cruising speed at 12,000 m (39,370 ft):	
C	450 knots (835 km/h; 519 mph)
Service ceiling:	
C	15,600 m (51,180 ft)

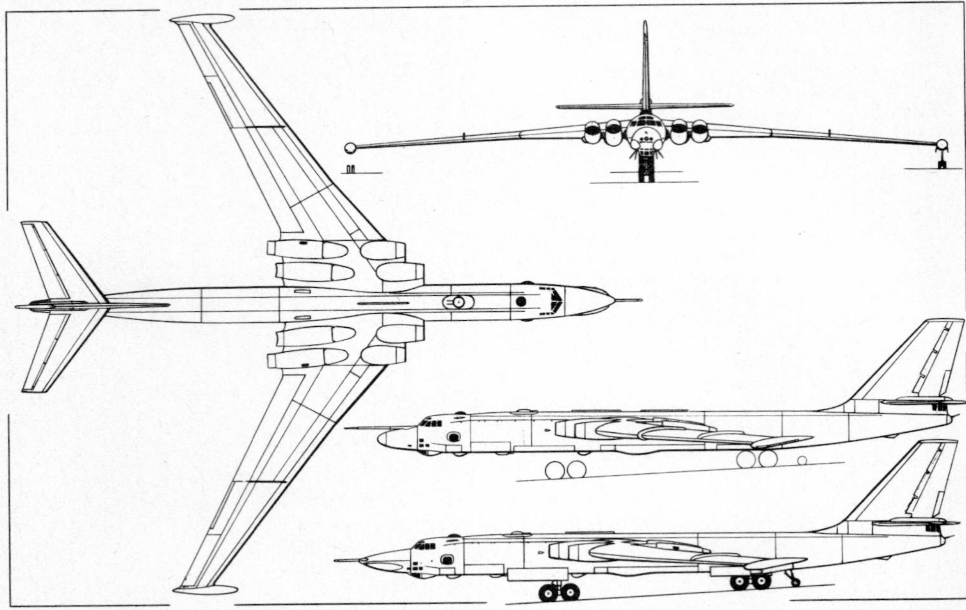

Myasishchev M-4, in the form known to NATO as 'Bison-C', with additional side view (centre) of 'Bison-B' *(Pilot Press)*

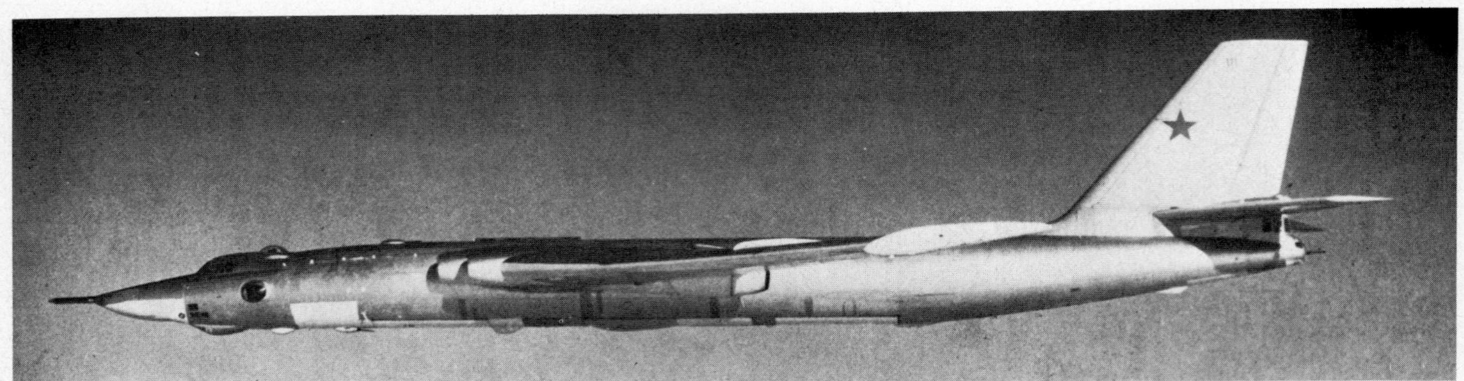

This photograph of the 'Bison-C' version of the M-4 shows clearly its modified nose *(Royal Air Force)*

SUKHOI

Pavel Osipovich Sukhoi, who headed this design bureau until his death in September 1975, helped to design the ANT-25 and had a share in the construction of the 'Rodina' before the second World War; his Su-2 attack aeroplane was used in the war. He was also responsible for one of the jet aircraft in the 1947 Soviet Aviation Day display.

Nearly a decade later, on 24 June 1956, there appeared over Tushino new sweptwing and delta-wing fighters from Sukhoi's design team. Both aircraft subsequently entered squadron service with the Soviet Air Force, as the Su-7 and Su-9, and have been followed by other Sukhoi designs.

SUKHOI Su-7B

NATO reporting names: Fitter-A and Moujik

The **Su-7B** single-seat ground attack fighter (NATO reporting name **Fitter-A**) was first seen in prototype form during the 1956 Soviet Aviation Day Display and appeared in formations of up to 21 aircraft at the 1961 Tushino display. It subsequently became the standard tactical fighter-bomber of the Soviet Air Force, with which about 400 continue in service. Others have been supplied to Afghanistan, Algeria, Cuba, Czechoslovakia, Egypt, Hungary, India, Iraq, North Korea, Peru, Poland, Romania, Syria and North Viet-Nam.

The fuselage and tail unit of the Su-7B are almost identical with those of the delta-wing Su-11. Early production models had the pitot boom mounted centrally above the air intake, but it is offset to starboard on current versions. Another change was made in the brake-chute installation. Early aircraft had a single ribbon-type parachute, attached under the rear fuselage; later Su-7Bs have twin brake-chutes, in a housing at the base of the rudder. The size of the blast panels on the sides of the front fuselage by the wing-root guns was also increased, implying that the cannon now fitted have a higher muzzle velocity or rate of fire.

Among further changes that led to use of the revised designation **Su-7BM** (for *Modifikatsirovanny:* modified) was the introduction of a low-pressure nosewheel tyre, requiring blistered doors to enclose it when retracted.

A variant of the Su-7 seen first at Domodedovo in 1967 is the two-seat **Su-7U**, with the second cockpit in tandem, aft of the standard cockpit and with a slightly raised canopy. A prominent dorsal 'spine' extends from the rear of the aft canopy to the base of the tail fin. The two-seater is a standard operational trainer and has the NATO reporting name **Moujik**.

The following description applies to the standard Su-7BM:

TYPE: Single-seat ground attack fighter.

WINGS: Cantilever mid-wing monoplane. No dihedral or anhedral. Sweepback approx 60° on leading-edges. Conventional all-metal construction. Wing-root chord is extended, giving a straight trailing-edge on inboard section of each wing. Very large area-increasing flaps over entire trailing-edge from root to inboard end of aileron on each wing. No slats or tabs. Two boundary-layer fences on each wing, at approx mid-span and immediately inboard of tip.

FUSELAGE: Conventional all-metal semi-monocoque structure of circular section. Two slim duct fairings along top of centre-fuselage. Two door-type airbrakes, at top and bottom, on each side of rear fuselage.

TAIL UNIT: Cantilever all-metal structure, with sweepback on all surfaces. All-moving horizontal surfaces, with anti-flutter bodies projecting forward from tips. Conventional rudder. No tabs.

LANDING GEAR: Retractable tricycle type, with single wheel on each unit. Nosewheel retracts forward, main units inward into wings. Twin brake-chutes in large fairing at base of rudder.

POWER PLANT: One Lyulka AL-7F-1 turbojet engine, rated at 68·65 kN (15,432 lb st) dry or 98·1 kN (22,046 lb st) with afterburning. Total internal fuel capacity 3,175 kg (7,000 lb). Provision for two external tanks, side-by-side under fuselage, with total capacity of 952 kg (2,100 lb). Two JATO solid-propellant rocket units can be attached under rear fuselage to shorten T-O run.

ACCOMMODATION: Pilot only, on rocket-powered ejection seat, under rearward-sliding blister canopy.

ARMAMENT: Two 30 mm NR-30 guns, each with 70 rounds, in wing-root leading-edges. Four underwing attachments for rocket pods or bombs (usually two 750 kg and two 500 kg). When underbelly fuel tanks are fitted, max external weapon load is 1,000 kg (2,200 lb).

DIMENSIONS, EXTERNAL:

Wing span	8·93 m (29 ft 3½ in)
Length overall, incl probe	17·37 m (57 ft 0 in)
Height overall	4·57 m (15 ft 0 in)

WEIGHTS:

Weight empty	8,620 kg (19,000 lb)
Normal T-O weight	12,000 kg (26,450 lb)
Max T-O weight	13,500 kg (29,750 lb)

Sukhoi Su-7B close support fighter of the Soviet Air Force with underfuselage rocket pods *(Flug Revue)*

PERFORMANCE:
Max level speed at 11,000 m (36,000 ft):
'clean'
Mach 1·6 (917 knots; 1,700 km/h; 1,055 mph)
with external stores
Mach 1·2 (685 knots; 1,270 km/h; 788 mph)
Max level speed at S/L without afterburning
approx 460 knots (850 km/h; 530 mph)
Max rate of climb at S/L
approx 9,120 m (29,900 ft)/min
Service ceiling 15,150 m (49,700 ft)
Combat radius
172-260 nm (320-480 km; 200-300 miles)
Max range 780 nm (1,450 km; 900 miles)

Su-7U (NATO 'Moujik'), in service with the Soviet Air Force

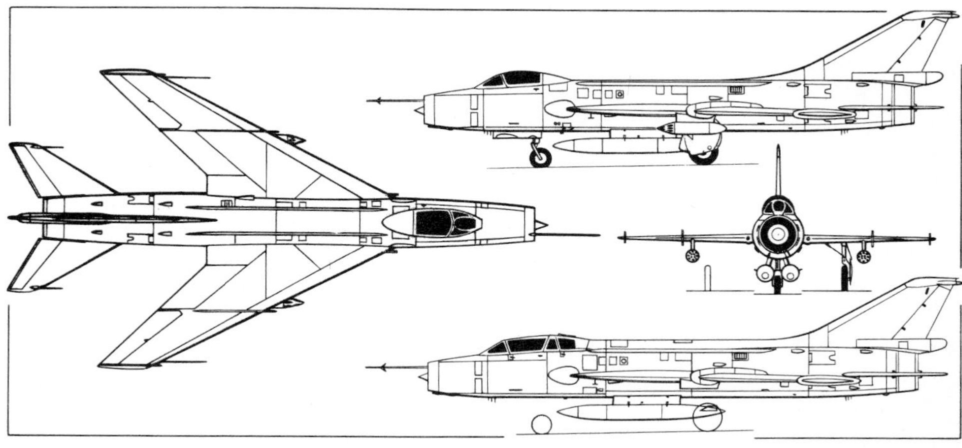

Sukhoi Su-7BM single-seat close support fighter, with additional side view (bottom) of two-seat Su-7U *(Pilot Press)*

SUKHOI Su-9 and Su-11

NATO reporting names: Fishpot and Maiden

First seen at Tushino during the 1956 Aviation Day Display, the prototype of these single-seat all-weather fighters (allocated the NATO reporting name 'Fishpot-A') had a small conical radome above its engine air intake. This was replaced by a centrebody air intake on the production version, which entered standard service in the Soviet Air Force in two forms as follows:

Su-9 (Fishpot-B). Initial version, operational since 1959 and still in service. Powered by 88·25 kN (19,840 lb st) Lyulka AL-7F afterburning turbojet. Small-diameter air intake and centrebody housing R1L (NATO 'Spin Scan') S-band radar. Examples included in the Tushino display of 1961 carried four of the Soviet Air Force's then-standard radar-homing air-to-air missiles (NATO reporting name 'Alkali') on underwing attachments, plus two underfuselage fuel tanks side by side. No fixed armament.

Su-11 (Fishpot-C). First seen publicly at the Domodedovo Aviation Day display in 1967, the Su-11 is a much-improved development of the Su-9, with a Lyulka AL-7F-1 turbojet (98·1 kN; 22,046 lb st with afterburning) and a standard armament of two underwing missiles (NATO 'Anab'), one with radar homing head and one with infra-red homing head. It also has a lengthened nose of less-tapered form than that of the Su-9, with an enlarged centrebody for the Uragan 5B (NATO 'Skip Spin') X-band radar, and two slim duct fairings along the top of the centre-fuselage, as on the Su-7B. The fuselage and tail unit of the two types are, in fact, almost identical.

There is also a tandem two-seat training version (NATO reporting name **Maiden**), with a cockpit layout similar to that of the two-seat Su-7 ('Moujik').

Although the Su-9 and Su-11 are generally similar in layout to their Mikoyan contemporary, the MiG-21, they are larger and heavier aircraft, with a much more powerful afterburning turbojet. They are less limited in all-weather capability than early versions of the MiG-21. The Sukhoi and Mikoyan 'tailed deltas' were, therefore, regarded as complementary rather than competitive when ordered into production in the late 'fifties. In 1977, the Su-9 and Su-11 continued to form 25 per cent of the Soviet home defence interceptor force.

The Su-9 and Su-11 can be distinguished from the MiG-21 by their cleaner airframe, and the absence of both a ventral stabilising fin and fairings on the fuselage forward of the wing-root leading-edges. The cockpit canopy of the single-seat versions is rearward-sliding, whereas that of the MiG-21 is hinged to open either forward about the base of the windscreen or sideways.

The tricycle landing gear of the Su-9 and Su-11 has a wide track, with a single wheel on each unit. The main units retract inward into the wings, the nosewheel forward. Control surfaces appear to be conventional, with a one-piece all-moving tailplane, carrying the anti-flutter body projection at each tip that is found on many Soviet combat aircraft. There are four petal-type airbrakes, in pairs on each side of the rear fuselage.

Sukhoi Su-9 all-weather fighter, with four underwing mountings for 'Alkali' missiles *(Tass)*

Sukhoi Su-11 single-seat fighter, armed with two of the missiles known to NATO as 'Anab' *(Novosti)*

DIMENSIONS, EXTERNAL (Su-11, estimated):
Wing span 8·43 m (27 ft 8 in)
Length overall, incl probe 17·0 m (56 ft 0 in)
WEIGHT (Su-11, estimated):
Max T-O weight 13,600 kg (30,000 lb)
PERFORMANCE (Su-11, estimated):
Max level speed at 11,000 m (36,000 ft)
Mach 1·8 (1,033 knots; 1,915 km/h; 1,190 mph)
Service ceiling 17,000 m (55,700 ft)

SUKHOI Su-15

NATO reporting name: Flagon

Ten examples of this single-seat twin-jet delta-wing fighter participated in the flying display at Domodedovo in July 1967. First to appear was a single black-painted machine, piloted by Vladimir Ilyushin, son of the famous designer and known to be a test pilot for Sukhoi. When a formation of nine similar aircraft appeared later, the identity of the design bureau responsible for them was confirmed by the obvious 'family likeness' to the Su-9 and Su-11 in the shape of the wings and tail unit.

It is now clear that this aircraft was developed to meet a Soviet Air Force requirement for a Mach 2·5 interceptor to replace the Su-11. It is in service with the Soviet Air Force in several forms:

Flagon-A. Has simple delta wings (estimated span 9·15 m; 30 ft), identical in form to those of the Su-11. Conical nose radome. Turbojets reported to be Tumansky R-11F2-300s, as used in MiG-21 series, each rated at 60·8 kN (13,668 lb st) with afterburning. Probably restricted to small initial quantity.

Flagon-B. This STOL version appeared at Domodedovo in 1967, with three lift-jet engines mounted vertically in the centre-fuselage and wings of compound sweep similar to, but different in detail from, those of the 'Flagon D/F' combat aircraft. Tested only as an R and D prototype, it was described briefly in the 1970-71 *Jane's*.

Flagon-C. Two-seat training version of 'Flagon-D', with probable combat capability. Individual rearward hinged canopy over each seat. Periscope fitted above rear canopy for forward view.

Flagon-D. Generally similar to 'Flagon-A', but with longer-span wings of compound sweep, produced by reducing the sweepback at the tips via a very narrow unswept section. Conical radome. First major production version.

Flagon-E. Wings similar to those of 'Flagon-D'. New and more powerful propulsion system, increasing speed and range. Turbojets reported to be Tumansky R-13F-300s, as used in second-generation MiG-21MF, each rated at 64·73 kN (14,550 lb st). Uprated avionics. Major production version; operational since second half of 1973.

Flagon-F. Latest version in service. Can be identified by ogival nose radome. Generally similar to 'Flagon-E'.

About 1,000 Su-15s were believed to form the back-

Sukhoi Su-11 single-seat all-weather interceptor *(Pilot Press)*

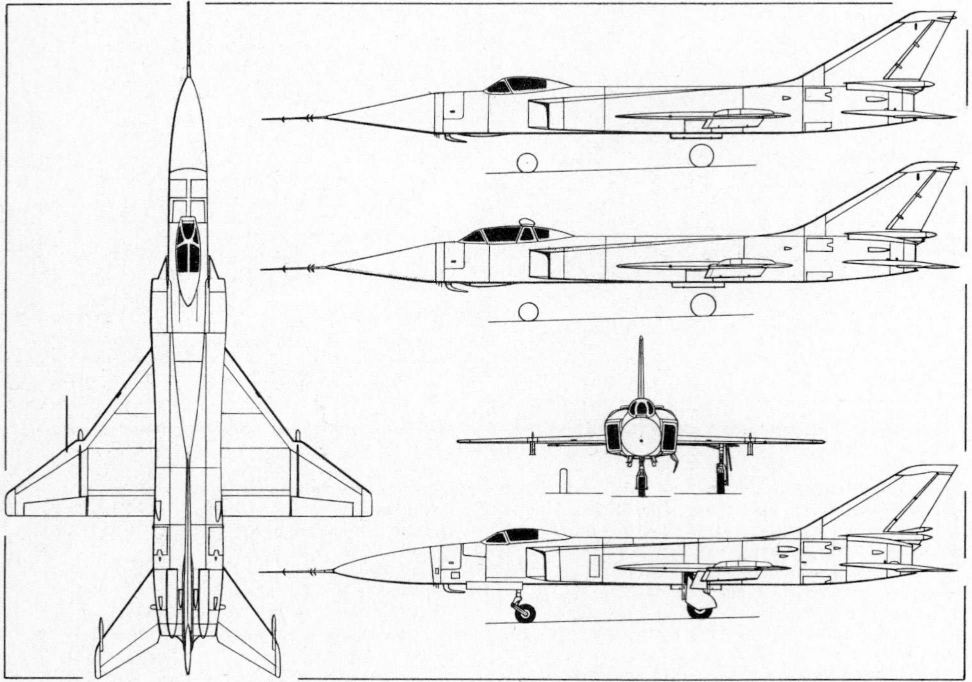

Sukhoi Su-15, 'Flagon-F', with additional side views of two-seat 'Flagon-C' (centre) and 'Flagon-D' (top) *(Pilot Press)*

bone of the PVO-Strany's force of 2,600 interceptors in 1979, all based in the Soviet Union.

The following details apply to 'Flagon-F':

TYPE: Single-seat twin-jet all-weather interceptor.

WINGS: Cantilever mid-wing monoplane, basically similar to those of Su-11, but with new and extended tips. Sweepback approx 53° on inner wings, 37° on tips. No dihedral or anhedral. All-metal structure. Single boundary-layer fence above each wing at approx 70% span. Large area-increasing flap extends from inboard end of aileron to fuselage on each side.

FUSELAGE: Cockpit section is basically circular with large ogival dielectric nosecone. Centre fuselage is faired into rectangular-section air intake ducts. Two door-type airbrakes at top and bottom on each side of rear fuselage, forward of tailplane.

TAIL UNIT: Cantilever all-metal structure, with sweepback on all surfaces. All-moving tailplane, with anhedral, mounted slightly below mid position and fitted with anti-flutter bodies near tips. Conventional rudder. No trim tabs.

LANDING GEAR: Tricycle type, with single wheel on each unit. Main wheels retract inward into wings and intake ducts; nosewheel retracts forward.

POWER PLANT: Two turbojets, with variable-area nozzles, mounted side by side in rear fuselage. These are reported to be Tumansky R-13F2-300s, each rated at 70·6 kN (15,875 lb st) with afterburning. Ram air intakes, with variable ramps on splitter plates, embodying vertical slots for boundary layer control. Blow-in auxiliary inlets midway between main intake and wing leading-edge in each duct.

ACCOMMODATION: Single seat in enclosed cockpit, with rearward-sliding blister canopy. Rear-view mirror above canopy of some aircraft.

ARMAMENT: Single pylon for external store under each wing, in line with boundary-layer fence. Normal armament comprises one radar homing and one infra-red homing air-to-air missile (NATO 'Anab'). Side-by-side pylons under centre-fuselage for further weapons or external fuel tanks.

AVIONICS AND EQUIPMENT: Large X-band radar (NATO 'Skip Spin') in nose, SOD-57M ATC/SIF nav system, SRO-2 (NATO 'Odd Rods') IFF, Sirena 3 radar warning system.

DIMENSIONS, EXTERNAL (estimated):

Wing span	10·53 m (34 ft 6 in)
Length overall	20·5 m (68 ft 0 in)

WEIGHT (estimated):

Max T-O weight	16,000 kg (35,275 lb)

PERFORMANCE (estimated):

Max level speed above 11,000 m (36,000 ft):	
with external stores	Mach 2·3
'clean'	Mach 2·5
Time to 11,000 m (36,000 ft)	2 min 30 s
Service ceiling	20,000 m (65,600 ft)
Combat radius	390 nm (725 km; 450 miles)

SUKHOI Su-17

NATO reporting names: Fitter-C and D

First of two variable-geometry fighter aircraft demonstrated at Domodedovo in July 1967 was an adaptation of the Su-7, which was allocated the NATO reporting name 'Fitter-B'. It was externally identical with the standard operational Su-7 except for the movable outer wing panels and associated fences, outboard of the main landing gear.

This variable-geometry Su-7 was thought at first to be no more than an economically-produced aerodynamic testbed aircraft, built to gain experience with the technique. However, this simple adaptation of a standard fighter offers much improved take-off and landing performance, and the ability to disperse squadrons to emergency wartime airfields. It was announced in the USA in 1972 that at least one or two squadrons of 'improved Fitter-Bs' had been identified as operational with the Soviet Air Force. They were allocated the NATO reporting name **Fitter-C**, and several hundred aircraft of this type are now deployed, under the Soviet designation Su-17. Units completely equipped with Su-17s included the Soviet ground attack regiment based at Finsterwalde in East Germany by the Spring of 1977. The FY 1979 US *Military Posture* statement says of the type: "'Fitter-C' with its more powerful engine and improved avionics, is in a completely different class from the earlier A and B variants".

Wing sweep is varied manually. The movable part of each wing is about 4·0 m (13 ft) long and is fitted with a full-span leading-edge slat. Its entire trailing-edge is also hinged, forming slotted ailerons and flaps. The large main fence on each side is square-cut at the front and incorporates attachments for external stores. There are two shorter and shallower fences inboard of the main fence on each side, on the sweptback portion of the centre-section trailing-edge which aligns with the trailing-edge of the outer panel when it is fully swept. The standard flap is retained on the inner portion of the centre-section on each side.

The Su-17 has an uprated Lyulka AL-21F-3 turbojet engine (80·1 kN; 18,000 lb st dry; 109 kN; 24,500 lb st with afterburning), with a better sfc than the Su-7's AL-7F-1. Variations in rear fuselage contours suggest that the Su-20 and Su-22 'export' versions (which see) may retain the AL-7F-1.

At the nose there is a pitot tube on the port side and a transducer to provide data for the fire control computer on the starboard side. Between the intake and two auxiliary inlets on the port side is an angle of attack sensor.

Including the wing fence stores attachments, eight weapon pylons can be fitted under the wings and fuselage, for up to 5,000 kg (11,023 lb) of bombs, rocket pods and guided missiles such as the air-to-surface AS-7 (NATO 'Kerry'); the 30 mm NR-30 wing-root guns of the Su-7 are retained. There is a prominent dorsal spine fairing on the fuselage, in place of the Su-7's twin ducts. This, presumably, houses the control runs, some avionics and fuel. Equipment is thought to include SRD-5M (NATO 'High Fix') centrebody radar, ASP-5ND fire control system, Sirena 3 360° radar homing and warning system, SRO-2M

Two views of the tandem two-seat combat trainer version of the Sukhoi Su-15, known to NATO as 'Flagon-C'

IFF, SOD-57M ATC/SIF, RSIU-5/R-831 VHF/UHF and R5B-70 HF.

There is a container for twin brake-chutes between the base of the rudder and the tailpipe. Immediately above this is a slimmer cylindrical housing for the ATC/SIF and rear Sirena 3 antennae. The two forward Sirena 3 antennae are in the leading-edges of the fixed wing panels, between the two fences on each side.

A variant of which the accompanying photograph became available in mid-1977 is **Fitter-D**. This has a small undernose radome and a laser marked target seeker in its centrebody.

Both 'Fitter-C' and 'Fitter-D' have also been assigned to Soviet Naval Aviation units in the Baltic Sea area, where they could be employed in limited anti-shipping strike roles or to support amphibious operations.

DIMENSIONS, EXTERNAL (estimated):
- Wing span:
  - spread (28° sweep): 14·00 m (45 ft 11¼ in)
  - swept (62° sweep): 10·60 m (34 ft 9½ in)
- Wing aspect ratio: spread: 4·9
  - swept: 3·0
- Length overall, incl probe: 18·75 m (61 ft 6¼ in)
- Fuselage length: 15·40 m (50 ft 6¼ in)
- Height overall: 4·75 m (15 ft 7 in)

AREAS (estimated):
- Wings, gross: spread: 40·1 m² (431·6 sq ft)
  - swept: 37·2 m² (400·4 sq ft)

WEIGHTS (estimated):
- Weight empty: 10,000 kg (22,046 lb)
- Max internal fuel: 3,700 kg (8,157 lb)
- T-O weight, 'clean': 14,000 kg (30,865 lb)
- Max T-O weight: 17,700 kg (39,020 lb)

PERFORMANCE (estimated for 'clean' aircraft, 60% internal fuel, except where indicated):
- Max level speed at height: Mach 2·17
- Max level speed at S/L: Mach 1·05
- Touchdown speed: 143 knots (265 km/h; 165 mph)
- Max rate of climb at S/L: 13,800 m (45,275 ft)/min
- Service ceiling: 18,000 m (59,050 ft)
- T-O run at AUW of 17,000 kg (37,478 lb): 620 m (2,035 ft)
- T-O to 15 m (50 ft) at AUW of 17,000 kg (37,478 lb): 835 m (2,740 ft)
- Landing run: 600 m (1,970 ft)
- Combat radius with 2,000 kg (4,409 lb) external stores:
  - hi-lo-hi: 340 nm (630 km; 391 miles)
  - lo-lo-lo: 195 nm (360 km; 224 miles)

SUKHOI Su-19

NATO reporting name: Fencer

This variable-geometry attack aircraft was identified as a major new operational type by Admiral Thomas H. Moorer, Chairman of the US Joint Chiefs of Staff, in early 1974, when he described it as "the first modern Soviet fighter to be developed specifically as a fighter-bomber for the ground attack mission". Designated Su-19 in the Soviet Union, it is in the same class as the USAF's F-111.

No clear photographs or officially-released details of the Su-19 had been made available by mid-1979. However, it is believed that the accompanying drawing reflects the aircraft's major characteristics.

Seating for the crew of two (pilot and weapon systems officer) is shown to be side by side in a slim and clean fuselage typical of Sukhoi designs. The wings are pivoted much further inboard than on the Su-17/20 or Tupolev 'Backfire'. Each is shown with flying control surfaces and high-lift devices similar in principle to those of the F-111, comprising full-span leading-edge and trailing-edge flaps, with airbrake/lift dumpers forward of the latter operating also as spoilers for lateral control at low speeds. This implies that the all-moving horizontal tail surfaces operate both differentially and symmetrically to provide aileron and elevator functions.

Wing leading-edge sweep appears to be approximately 23° in the fully-spread position, and 70° fully swept. The wings are shown without dihedral or anhedral.

Except for the two-seat cockpit, the overall lines of the fuselage, air intake trunks and vertical tail surfaces have much in common with those of the Su-15. It is further suggested that the Su-19 may be powered by two Lyulka AL-21F turbojets of the kind fitted to the single-engined Su-17. Armament includes more than 4,535 kg (10,000 lb) of guided and unguided air-to-surface weapons on six pylons under the fuselage, wing-root gloves and outer wings, in addition to a GSh-23 twin-barrel 23 mm gun. The pivoting pylons under the outer wings are the first observed on a Soviet aircraft.

The Su-19 entered squadron service in December 1974. In the Spring of 1979 at least 250 were serving with first-line squadrons in the European theatre, including units in Lusatia and a regiment at Chernyakhovsk, near Kaliningrad on the Soviet Baltic coast. None has been seen outside the Soviet Union or its home waters.

DIMENSIONS, EXTERNAL (estimated):
- Wing span: spread: 17·15 m (56 ft 3 in)
  - swept: 9·53 m (31 ft 3 in)
- Length overall: 21·29 m (69 ft 10 in)

WEIGHT (estimated):
- Max T-O weight: 30,850 kg (68,000 lb)

'Flagon-F' version of the Su-15, armed with 'Anab' missiles *(Swedish Air Force)*

Two views of Sukhoi Su-17 single-seat variable-geometry fighter with wings extended *(Flug Revue)*

Sukhoi Su-17 ('Fitter-D') with undernose radar

Sukhoi Su-20 variable-geometry ground attack fighter in service with the Polish Air Force

Artist's impression of Sukhoi Su-19 variable-geometry attack aircraft *(Michael A. Badrocke)*

Only photograph yet released of the Sukhoi Su-19

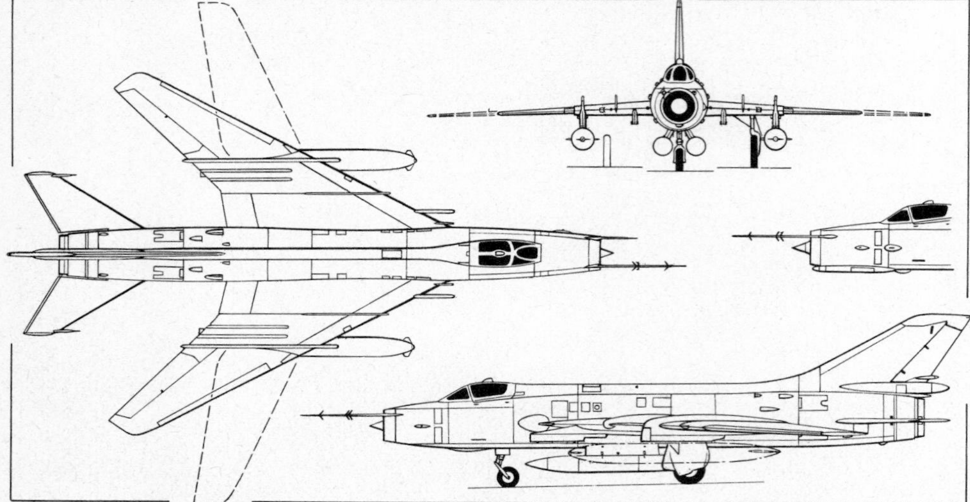

PERFORMANCE (estimated):
Max speed at height — above Mach 2
Combat radius, lo-lo-lo — over 174 nm (322 km; 200 miles)

SUKHOI Su-20 and Su-22

NATO reporting name: Fitter-C

The operational **Su-20** is an 'export' version of the Su-17, to which it is generally similar except, perhaps, for having a lower-rated engine and different equipment. Operators include the Algerian, Czechoslovak, Egyptian, Iraqi, Libyan and Syrian Air Forces and about ten squadrons of the Polish Air Force, whose aircraft fly normally with two very large jettisonable fuel tanks on the wing fence attachments, instead of the twin centreline tanks usually carried by the Su-7 and Su-9/11.

The **Su-22** is a variant of the Su-20, with further-reduced equipment standards. It is reported to have a Sirena 2 limited-coverage radar warning receiver and virtually no navigation aids. Weapons include 'Atoll' air-to-air missiles. Delivery of 36 to Peru began in 1977.

Sukhoi Su-20 variable-geometry tactical combat aircraft ('Fitter-C'), with scrap view of 'Fitter-D' nose *(Pilot Press)*

TUPOLEV

CHIEF DESIGNER (Tu-144): Dr Alexei A. Tupolev
CHIEF DESIGNER (Tu-154): Dmitry Markov
DEPUTY CHIEF OF BUREAU: Andrei Kandolov

Andrei Tupolev, born in 1888, was a leading figure in the Central Aero-Hydrodynamic Institute (TsAGI) in Moscow from the time when it was founded, in 1929, until his death on 23 December 1972. He was for long the Soviet Union's outstanding designer, and the recent products of his design team range from turbofan civil transports to the first Soviet supersonic bomber to enter service and the first supersonic transport aircraft. Also in production in the Soviet Union are small amphibious aerosleighs of Tupolev design, powered by aircraft piston engines and capable of travelling over both water and snow. Current chief designers of the Tupolev bureau include Andrei Tupolev's son, Dr Alexei A. Tupolev.

TUPOLEV Tu-16

NATO reporting name: Badger

This Tupolev bomber made its first major public appearance in 1954; yet nearly half of the 2,000 that were built remain operational. About 300 are deployed with medium-range units of the Soviet strategic nuclear force, supported by a few Tu-16 in-flight refuelling tankers, using a unique wingtip-to-wingtip transfer technique, and more than 100 of various reconnaissance and ECM variants. Naval units have about 275 Tu-16s carrying air-to-surface missiles, 90 tankers and 70 reconnaissance and ECM models.

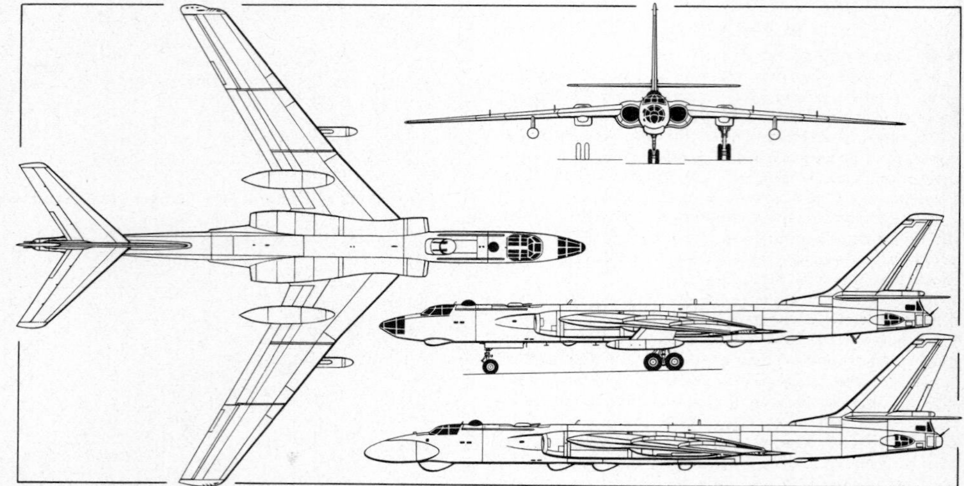

Tupolev Tu-16, in the form known to NATO as 'Badger-F', with additional side view (bottom) of 'Badger-D' *(Pilot Press)*

Ten versions of the Tu-16 have been identified by unclassified NATO reporting names. All except 'Badger-B' (see 1975-76 *Jane's*) remain in first-line service, as follows:

Badger-A. First Soviet long-range strategic jet bomber. Still operational with Dalnaya Aviatsiya, including tankers for wingtip-to-wingtip flight refuelling. Crew of seven. Glazed nose, with small undernose radome. Defensive

'Badger-H' version of the Tupolev Tu-16 twin-jet bomber, for stand-off or escort ECM duties

armament of seven 23 mm cannon. Nine supplied to Iraq. More than 80 operational with Chinese air force, mostly built in China.

Badger-C. Anti-shipping version, first seen at 1961 Soviet Aviation Day display. Large air-to-surface winged missile (NATO reporting name 'Kipper') carried under fuselage. Wide nose radome, in place of glazing and nose gun of 'Badger-A'.

Badger-D. Maritime/electronic reconnaissance version. Nose similar to that of 'Badger-C'. Enlarged undernose radome; three blister fairings in tandem under centre-fuselage.

Badger-E. Similar to 'Badger-A' but with cameras in bomb bay.

Badger-F. Basically similar to 'Badger-E' but with electronic intelligence pod on a pylon under each wing.

Badger-G. Similar to 'Badger-A' but with underwing pylons for two rocket-powered air-to-surface missiles (NATO reporting name 'Kelt'). One photographed by pilot of Japanese F-86F in December 1977 carried a new missile (NATO 'Kingfish') on port underwing pylon. Some Gs were included in the 25 Tu-16s supplied to Egypt as replacements for aircraft lost in the October 1973 war with Israel.

Badger-H. Stand-off or escort ECM aircraft, with primary function of chaff dispensing. The chaff dispensers are probably located in the bomb bay area. Hatch aft of bomb bay. Two teardrop radomes, fore and aft of bomb bay. Two blade antennae aft of bomb bay.

Badger-J. Specialised ECM jamming aircraft, with at least some of the equipment located in a canoe-shape radome inside the bomb bay.

Badger-K. Electronic reconnaissance variant. Two teardrop radomes, inside and forward of bomb bay.

Maritime reconnaissance versions of 'Badger' make regular flights over units of the US Navy and other NATO naval forces at sea in the Atlantic, Pacific and elsewhere, and have been photographed while doing so. The aircraft often operate in pairs, with one 'Badger-F' accompanied by a different version. They also make electronic intelligence (elint) sorties around the coastlines of NATO and other non-Communist countries.

TYPE: Twin-jet medium bomber and maritime reconnaissance/attack aircraft.

WINGS: Cantilever high mid-wing monoplane with slight anhedral and with 35° of leading-edge sweep on outer panels; increased sweep on inboard panels. Thickness/chord ratio 12½%.

FUSELAGE: All-metal semi-monocoque structure of circular cross-section.

TAIL UNIT: Cantilever all-metal structure, with sweepback on all surfaces. Trim tabs in rudder and each elevator.

LANDING GEAR: Retractable tricycle type. Twin-wheel nose unit retracts rearward. Main four-wheel bogies retract into housings projecting beyond the wing trailing-edge.

POWER PLANT: Two Mikulin AM-3M turbojet engines, each rated at about 93·2 kN (20,950 lb st) at sea level. Fuel in wing and fuselage tanks, with total capacity of approx 45,450 litres (10,000 Imp gallons). Provision for underwing auxiliary fuel tanks and for flight refuelling. Tu-16 tankers trail hose from starboard wingtip; receiving equipment is in port wingtip extension.

ACCOMMODATION: Normal crew of seven, with two pilots side by side on flight deck. Navigator in glazed nose of 'Badger-A, E and F'. Manned tail position plus lateral observation blisters in rear fuselage under tailplane.

ARMAMENT: Forward dorsal and rear ventral barbettes each containing two 23 mm cannon. Two further cannon in tail position controlled by an automatic gun-ranging radar set. Seventh, fixed, cannon on starboard side of nose of versions without nose radome. Bomb load of up to 9,000 kg (19,800 lb) delivered from weapons bay about 6·5 m (21 ft) long in standard bomber. Naval versions can carry air-to-surface winged stand-off missiles.

AVIONICS AND EQUIPMENT: Radio and radar aids probably include HF and VHF R/T equipment, as well as IFF and a radio compass and radio altimeter. Other equipment differs according to role.

DIMENSIONS, EXTERNAL:

Wing span	32·93 m (108 ft 0½ in)
Length overall	34·80 m (114 ft 2 in)
Height overall	10·80 m (35 ft 6 in)

AREA:

Wings, gross	164·65 m² (1,772·3 sq ft)

WEIGHT:

Normal T-O weight	approx 68,000 kg (150,000 lb)

PERFORMANCE (estimated, at max T-O weight):

Max level speed at 10,700 m (35,000 ft)
510 knots (945 km/h; 587 mph)

Service ceiling 13,000 m (42,650 ft)

Range with max bomb load
2,605 nm (4,800 km; 3,000 miles)

Range at 417 knots (770 km/h; 480 mph) with 3,000 kg (6,600 lb) of bombs
3,450 nm (6,400 km; 3,975 miles)

TUPOLEV Tu-95

NATO reporting name: Bear

This huge Tupolev bomber flew for the first time in the late Summer of 1954, was first seen at Tushino in July 1955, and subsequently became standard equipment in the Soviet Air Force. It is often referred to as the Tu-20, but its correct Soviet designation is Tu-95.

As well as maintaining its important strategic attack role, as the Soviet counterpart of the USAF's B-52 Stratofortress, the Tu-95 is in major service with the Soviet Naval Air Force for maritime reconnaissance and to provide targeting data to the launch control and guidance stations responsible for both air-to-surface and surface-to-surface anti-shipping missiles.

Six versions have been identified by NATO reporting names, and all remain operational:

Bear-A. Basic strategic bomber, with chin radar, and defensive armament comprising three pairs of 23 mm cannon in remotely-controlled dorsal and ventral barbettes and manned tail gun turret. Two glazed blisters on rear fuselage, under tailplane, are used for sighting by the gunner controlling all these weapons. The dorsal and ventral barbettes can also be controlled from a station aft of the flight deck. Internal stowage for two nuclear or a variety of conventional free-fall weapons. A braking parachute may be used to reduce landing run. Total of about 100 'Bear-As' and 'Bear-Bs' remain operational with the Soviet bomber force.

Bear-B. First seen in 1961 Aviation Day flypast, with additional radar equipment in wide undernose radome, replacing the original glazing, and carrying a large air-to-surface missile (NATO reporting name 'Kangaroo') with estimated range of 350 nm (650 km; 400 miles). Some 'Bears' of Dalnaya Aviatsiya now carry 'Kitchen' air-to-

Tupolev Tu-16 specialised ECM jamming aircraft ('Badger-J')

The latest electronic reconnaissance variant of the Tupolev Tu-16 ('Badger-K')

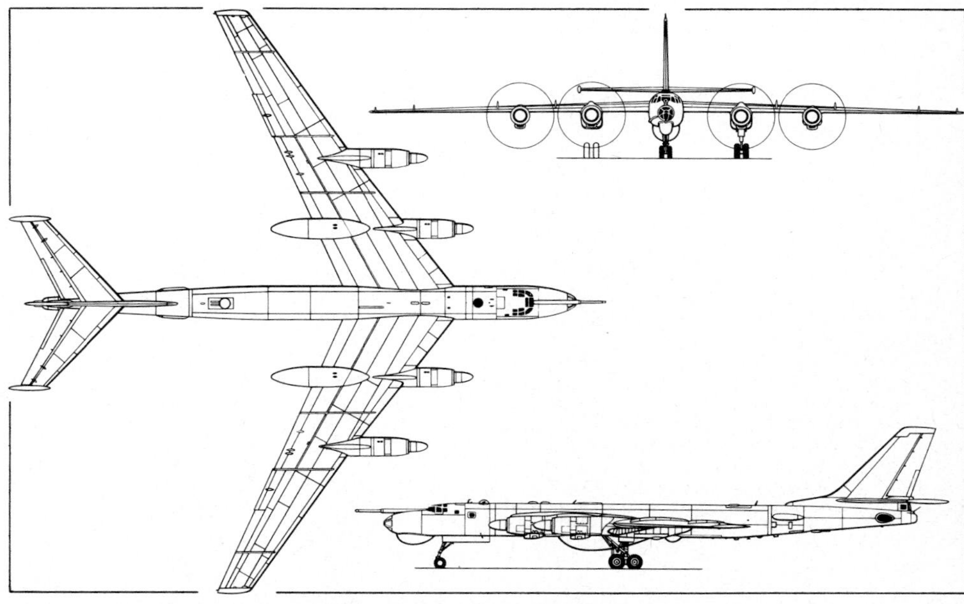

The version of the Tupolev Tu-95 known to NATO as 'Bear-D' *(Pilot Press)*

Camera ports under the bomb bay are a recognition feature of the 'Bear-E' version of the Tu-95 *(Royal Air Force)*

The faired tail, housing special equipment, on a 'Bear-D' photographed in 1978

The version of 'Bear-F' with an undernose radome

surface missiles. 'Bear-B' is used also for maritime patrol, with flight refuelling nose-probe and, sometimes, a streamlined blister fairing on the starboard side of the rear fuselage. Defensive armament retained. One aircraft observed recently with a pointed canister under each wing, presumably for air sampling.

Bear-C. Maritime patrol version, first identified when it appeared in vicinity of NATO naval forces during Exercise Teamwork in September 1964. Generally similar to 'Bear-B' but with streamlined blister fairing on *both* sides of rear fuselage. Refuelling probe standard.

Bear-D. This version was first photographed extensively when several examples (together with Tu-16s) made low passes over the US Coast Guard icebreakers *Edisto* and *Eastwind* off Severnaya Zemlya, in the Soviet Arctic, in August 1967. These aircraft differed in detail, but each had a glazed nose, an undernose radar scanner, a large underbelly radome for X-band radar, a blister fairing on each side of the rear fuselage like 'Bear-C', a nose refuelling probe, and a variety of other blisters and antennae, including a streamlined fairing on each tailplane tip. The rearward-facing radar above the tail turret is much larger than on previous versions of the Tu-95. It is now known that 'Bear-D' has an extremely important function in support of operations involving surface-to-surface and air-to-surface missiles. It provides data on the location and nature of potential targets to missile launch crews on board ships and aircraft which are themselves too distant from the target to ensure precise missile aiming and guidance. About 45 serve with Soviet Naval air fleet.

A 'Bear-D' photographed in the second half of 1978, after interception by US Navy F-4s, had in place of the normal tail turret and associated radome a faired tail housing special equipment (see accompanying illustration).

Bear-E. Maritime reconnaissance version basically similar in configuration to 'Bear-A' but with a refuelling probe above its glazed nose and the rear fuselage blister fairings of 'Bear-C'. Six bomb bay windows, in pairs in line with the wing flaps, indicate the presence of reconnaissance cameras, sometimes with a seventh window to the rear on the starboard side.

Bear-F. First identified in 1973, this much-refined anti-submarine version has enlarged and lengthened fairings aft of its inboard engine nacelles, for purely aerodynamic reasons. The undernose radar of 'Bear-D' is missing on some aircraft; others have a radome in this position, but of considerably modified form. On both models the main underfuselage X-band radar housing is considerably further forward than on 'Bear-D' and smaller in size; the forward portion of the fuselage is longer; there are no large blister fairings under and on the sides of the rear fuselage; and the nosewheel doors are bulged prominently, suggesting the use of larger or low-pressure tyres. 'Bear-F' has two stores bays in its rear fuselage, one of them replacing the usual rear ventral gun turret and leaving the tail turret as the sole defensive gun position. About 15 of this version were operational in early 1979.

Examples of all versions of the Tu-95 have made reconnaissance flights over units of the US Fleet at sea and have been photographed by US naval fighters whilst doing so. They are also encountered frequently over the North Sea by the RAF and Royal Navy, and off the US east coast during transits between Murmansk and Cuba, and elint missions from Cuba.

Type: Four-turboprop long-range bomber and maritime reconnaissance aircraft.

Wings: Cantilever mid-wing monoplane. Sweepback 37° at quarter-chord on inner panels, 35° at quarter-chord on outer panels. All-metal three-spar structure. All-metal hydraulically-powered ailerons and Fowler flaps. Trim tabs in ailerons. Spoilers in top surface of wing forward of inboard end of ailerons. Three boundary layer fences on top surface of each wing. Thermal anti-icing system in leading-edges.

Fuselage: All-metal semi-monocoque structure of circular section, containing three pressurised compartments. Those forward and aft of the weapons bay are linked by a crawlway tunnel. The tail gunner's compartment is not accessible from the other compartments.

Tail Unit: Cantilever all-metal structure, with sweepback on all surfaces. Adjustable tailplane incidence. Hydraulically-powered rudder and elevators. Trim tabs in rudder and each elevator.

Landing Gear: Retractable tricycle type. Main units consist of four-wheel bogies, with tyres approx 1·50 m (5 ft) diameter and hydraulic internal expanding brakes. Twin wheels on nose unit. All units retract rearward, main units into nacelles built on to wing trailing-edge. Retractable tail bumper consisting of two small wheels.

Power Plant: Four Kuznetsov NK-12MV turboprop engines, each originally with max rating of approx 8,948 kW (12,000 ehp) but now uprated to 11,033 kW (14,795 ehp) and driving eight-blade contra-rotating reversible-pitch Type AV-60N propellers. Fuel in wing tanks, with normal capacity of 72,980 litres (16,540 Imp gallons).

Accommodation and Armament: See notes applicable to individual versions and under 'Fuselage'.

Operational Equipment ('Bear-D'): Large X-band radar in blister fairing under centre fuselage, for reconnaissance and to provide data on potential targets for anti-shipping aircraft or surface vessels. In latter mode, PPI presentation is data-linked to missile launch station. Four-PRF range J-band circular and sector scan bombing and navigation radar (NATO 'Short Horn'). I-band tail warning radar (NATO 'Bee Hind') in housing at base of rudder.

Dimensions, external ('Bear-F', approx):
- Wing span: 51·10 m (167 ft 8 in)
- Length overall: 49·50 m (162 ft 5 in)
- Height overall: 12·12 m (39 ft 9 in)

Weight (estimated):
- Max T-O weight: 188,000 kg (414,470 lb)

Performance ('Bear-A'):
- Over-target speed at 12,500 m (41,000 ft): 435 knots (805 km/h; 500 mph)
- Max range with 11,340 kg (25,000 lb) bomb load: 6,775 nm (12,550 km; 7,800 miles)

TUPOLEV Tu-126

NATO reporting name: Moss

An officially-released Soviet documentary film, shown in the West in 1968, included sequences depicting a military version of the Tu-114 four-turboprop transport (see 1972-73 *Jane's*), carrying above its fuselage a rotating 'saucer' type early warning radar with a diameter of about 11 m (36 ft). This was a logical development, as the Tu-114 had a fuselage of larger diameter than the military Tu-95, and could accommodate more easily the extensive avionic equipment and large crew required by a long-endurance early-warning and fighter control aircraft. The new aircraft, designated Tu-126 in the Soviet Union, also has wings similar to those of the Tu-114, with extended-chord trailing-edge flaps, rather than the 'straight' trailing-edge of the Tu-95. Its power plant comprises four 11,033 kW (14,795 ehp) Kuznetsov NK-12MV turboprop engines.

The general appearance of the Tu-126, which has the NATO reporting name 'Moss', is shown in the accompanying illustrations. It can be seen to have a flight refuelling nose-probe, ventral tail-fin and numerous additional antennae and blisters for electronic equipment.

In the AWACS (airborne warning and control system) role, the Tu-126 is intended to work in conjunction with advanced interceptors. After locating incoming low-level strike aircraft, the Tu-126 would ideally direct towards them fighters armed with 'snap-down' air-to-air missiles able to be fired from a cruising height of 6,100 m (20,000 ft) or higher. It has a further, obvious application in assisting strike aircraft to elude enemy interceptors picked up by its radar.

At least ten or twelve Tu-126s are operational with the Soviet air defence forces. They are said, by US defence experts, to have worked in overwater exercises but to be ineffective over land at the present stage of development.

The Tu-126 airborne warning and control system (AWACS) aircraft, known to NATO as 'Moss'

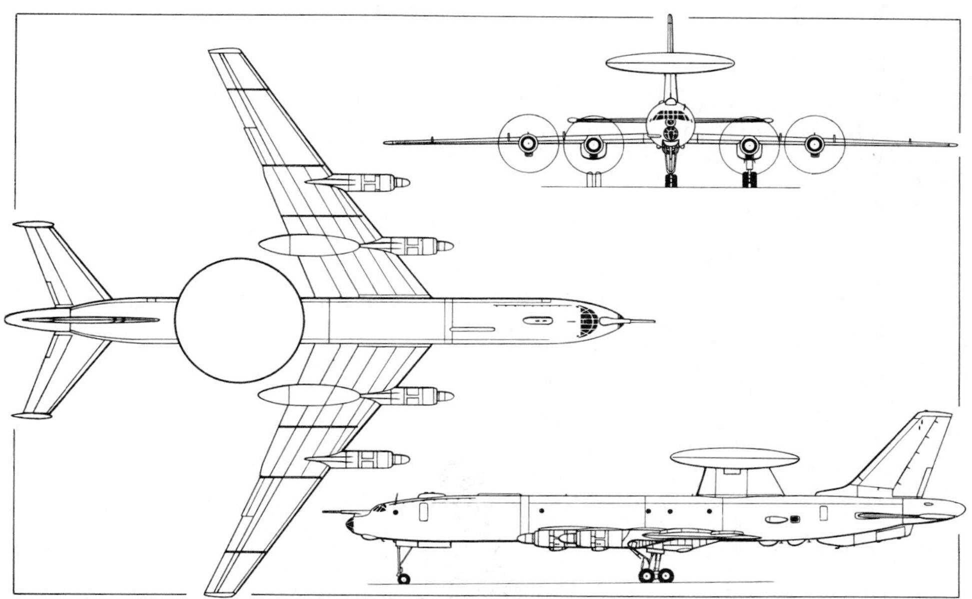

Tupolev Tu-126 (four Kuznetsov NK-12MV turboprops) *(Pilot Press)*

DIMENSIONS, EXTERNAL:

Wing span	51·20 m (168 ft 0 in)
Wing aspect ratio	10·4
Length overall	55·20 m (181 ft 1 in)
Height overall	16·05 m (52 ft 8 in)
Wheel track	13·70 m (44 ft 11½ in)
Propeller diameter	5·60 m (18 ft 4½ in)

AREA:

Wings, gross	311·1 m² (3,349 sq ft)

WEIGHT (estimated):

Max T-O weight	170,000 kg (374,785 lb)

TUPOLEV Tu-22

NATO reporting name: Blinder

First shown publicly in the 1961 Aviation Day flypast over Moscow, the Tu-22 was the first operational Soviet supersonic bomber. Of the ten examples which took part in that display, only one carried visible weapons, in the form of an air-to-surface missile (NATO reporting name 'Kitchen'), some 11 m (36 ft) long, semi-submerged in the underside of its fuselage. This aircraft had also a wider nose radome.

A total of 22 Tu-22s took part in the 1967 display at Domodedovo. One was escorted by six MiG-21PFs, permitting a more accurate calculation of its overall dimensions than had previously been possible. Most carried 'Kitchen' missiles; all had a partially-retractable nose refuelling probe and the wide radome seen on the single missile-armed aircraft in 1961.

About 250 Tu-22s were built, in four versions, as follows:

Blinder-A. Basic reconnaissance bomber, with fuselage weapon bay for free-fall bombs. 'Blinder-A' entered only limited service, its max range of 1,215 nm (2,250 km; 1,400 miles) being inadequate for the originally intended strategic role.

Blinder-B. Generally similar to 'Blinder-A' but equipped to carry air-to-surface nuclear missile (NATO reporting name 'Kitchen') recessed in weapon bay. Larger radar in nose. Partially-retractable flight refuelling probe on nose. About 125 'Blinder-As' and 'Blinder-Bs' are believed to remain operational with the Soviet bomber force, plus about 24 serving with the Libyan Air Force.

Blinder-C. Maritime reconnaissance version, with battery of six cameras in weapon bay and camera windows in weapon bay doors. Modifications to nosecone, dielectric panels, etc, suggest possible electronic intelligence role or equipment for electronic countermeasures (ECM) duties. About 60 delivered, for operation primarily over sea approaches to the Soviet Union, from bases in the Southern Ukraine and Estonia.

Blinder-D. Training version. Cockpit for instructor in raised position aft of standard flight deck, with stepped-up canopy.

A missile-armed long-range interceptor version of 'Blinder' has been reported in service, as a possible replacement for the Tu-28P.

The following details apply to 'Blinder-A and B' but are generally applicable to all versions except as noted under model descriptions:

TYPE: Twin-jet supersonic bomber and maritime patrol aircraft.

WINGS: Cantilever mid-wing monoplane. Constant small anhedral from roots. Sweepback approx 45° on leading-edge outboard of fence and 50° inboard of fence, increasing to acute sweep at roots. Conventional all-metal structure. Fully-powered two-section ailerons, with tab on each inboard section. Fowler flaps inboard and outboard of wheel pod on each wing trailing-edge.

FUSELAGE: All-metal semi-monocoque structure of circular section, with area-rule 'waisting' at wing-roots.

TAIL UNIT: Cantilever all-metal structure, with sweepback on all surfaces. Fully-powered slab-type horizontal surfaces at bottom of fuselage. Aerodynamically balanced rudder, with inset tab.

LANDING GEAR: Retractable tricycle type. Wide-track four-wheel bogie main units retract rearward into pods built on to wing trailing-edges. Oleo-pneumatic shock-absorbers. Main legs also designed to swing rearward for additional cushioning during taxying and landing on rough runways. Twin-wheel nose unit retracts rearward. Small retractable skid to protect rear fuselage in tail-down landing or take-off.

POWER PLANT: Two turbojet engines, each reportedly rated at 120·1 kN (27,000 lb st) with afterburning, mounted in pods above rear fuselage, on each side of tail fin. Lip of each intake is in the form of a ring which can be translated forward by jacks for take-off. Air entering ram intake is then supplemented by air injected through annular slot between ring and main body of pod. Original nozzles had short fluted final section aft of short fixed section, with annular space between this and outer fairing. Current nozzles have longer-chord convergent-divergent nozzle inside the outer fairing, believed to have resulted in increased thrust and range. Semi-

Tupolev Tu-22 photographed from an investigating interceptor of the Swedish Air Force

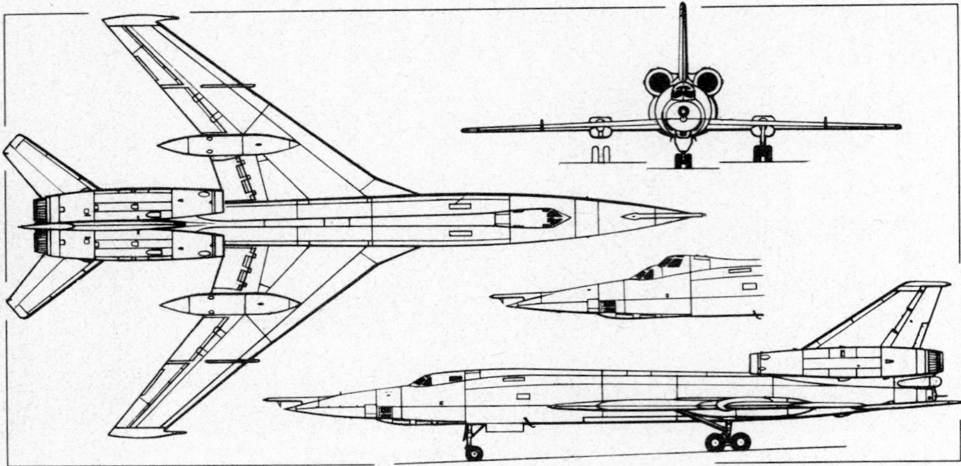

Tupolev Tu-22 twin-jet supersonic bomber ('Blinder-A') with additional view of nose of 'Blinder-D' training version *(Pilot Press)*

The tandem-cockpit training version of the Tu-22, known to NATO as 'Blinder-D'

retractable flight refuelling probe on nose, with triangular guard underneath to prevent drogue damaging fuselage nosecone.

Accommodation: Crew of three in tandem. Row of windows in bottom of fuselage, aft of nose radome, at navigator/systems operator's station. Pilot has upward-ejection seat; other crew members have downward-ejection seats.

Armament and Operational Equipment: Weapons bay in centre-fuselage, with double-fold doors. Special doors with panels shaped to accommodate recessed 'Kitchen' missile on 'Blinder-B' version. Single 23 mm NS-23 gun in radar-directed tail turret, beneath 'Bee Hind' tail-warning radar antenna. Radar in nose (larger type in 'Blinder-B'). Chaff/flare countermeasures dispensers and bombing assessment cameras carried in rear of wheel pods of some aircraft.

Dimensions, external (estimated):

Wing span	27·70 m (90 ft 10½ in)
Length overall	40·53 m (132 ft 11½ in)
Height overall	10·67 m (35 ft 0 in)

Weight (estimated):

Max T-O weight	83,900 kg (185,000 lb)

Performance (estimated):

Max level speed at 12,200 m (40,000 ft)	Mach 1·4 (800 knots; 1,480 km/h; 920 mph)
Service ceiling	18,300 m (60,000 ft)
Max range	1,215 nm (2,250 km; 1,400 miles)

TUPOLEV Tu-26 (Tu-22M)

NATO reporting name: Backfire

Official NATO sources first acknowledged the existence of a Soviet variable-geometry ('swing-wing') medium bomber in the Autumn of 1969. Such an aircraft was not unexpected, as the Tu-22 (NATO 'Blinder') was clearly incapable of fulfilling the long-range strategic bombing role for which it had been intended.

A prototype of the new bomber is said to have been observed in July 1970, on the ground near the Tupolev works at Kazan in Central Asia. Subsequent official statements confirmed the aircraft as a twin-engined design by the Tupolev bureau. At least two prototypes were built; up to twelve pre-production models followed, for development testing, weapons trials and evaluation, by the beginning of 1973. Their official designation was said to be Tu-26, but the Soviet Union referred to them as **Tu-22Ms** in the SALT 2 treaty talks. This seems illogical if 'Blinder' is the Tu-22, as the suffix 'M' normally signifies a modification of an existing type, and is clearly inapplicable in the case of these very different aircraft. The NATO reporting name allocated to the aircraft is 'Backfire'.

When drawing up the basic parameters for the bomber, the Tupolev bureau is believed to have aimed at a maximum unrefuelled range of 4,775-5,200 nm (8,850-9,650 km; 5,500-6,000 miles) at high altitude. Unwillingness to depart from the Tupolev practice of retracting the main landing gear bogies into fairings on the wing trailing-edges limited the variable geometry to the outer wings, as on the Sukhoi Su-17 and Su-20. There is evidence to believe that the large size of these fairings, with the wheels stowed beneath the wing, caused excessive drag, so that 'Backfire's' range fell short of what had been planned. Redesign almost eliminated the fairings from later aircraft, after the main landing gear had been revised to retract inward into the fuselage. This accounts for the two versions of the Tu-26/Tu-22M currently identified by NATO reporting names:

Backfire-A. Initial version, with large landing gear fairing pods on the wing trailing-edges. Believed to equip only one squadron.

Backfire-B. Developed version, with landing gear fairing pods eliminated except for shallow underwing fairings, no longer protruding beyond the trailing-edge. Increased wing span.

The photograph of a 'Backfire-B' which illustrates this entry was taken from a Saab Draken interceptor of the Swedish Air Force, over international waters, during a Soviet combined-services exercise in the Baltic in June 1978. Points to note include the removal of the flight refuelling probe (although the housing remains), and the external stores racks under the air intake trunks, which must impose speed limitations and may be fitted only for exercises or for short-range ground support missions.

Performance data given at the end of this entry conform with the latest estimates published openly by the Swedish Air Force and by other agencies. Some expert opinion continues to credit the 'Backfire' with a maximum speed in the Mach 2·25/2·5 bracket and a range adequate to cover virtually all of the continental USA with the aid of Arctic staging and flight refuelling, from bases in the USSR.

More than 125 'Backfire-Bs' are in service, with production continuing at the rate of about 30 aircraft per year. Many of them have been allocated to medium-range bomber squadrons of the Soviet Strategic Nuclear Forces; but at least 50 are deployed in a maritime role by Soviet Naval Aviation, and a former RAF Chief of Air Staff, Sir Andrew Humphrey, said in December 1975: "Russian fast, wide-ranging, and high-performance aircraft like 'Backfire', armed with stand-off missiles, may soon become an even greater danger to allied shipping than the relatively slow-moving Russian submarines". It is expected that the 'Backfire' strategic/maritime force will be built up gradually to a total of 250-400 aircraft. One unit was reported to be based at Komsomol'sk, about 430 nm (800 km; 500 miles) north of Vladivostok, in the Far East of the USSR, in Spring 1979.

Type: Twin-engined medium bomber and maritime reconnaissance/attack aircraft.

Wings: Cantilever mid-wing monoplane, made up of a large-span fixed centre-section and two variable-geometry outer panels. No anhedral or dihedral, but wing section is so thin that considerable flexing of the outer panels takes place in flight. Leading-edge fence towards tip of centre-section on each side. Each outer wing panel is believed to be fitted with a full-span leading-edge slat, aileron, and slotted trailing-edge flaps

'Backfire-B' version of the Tupolev Tu-26/Tu-22M photographed from a Draken interceptor of the Swedish Air Force

aft of spoilers/lift dumpers. Wing sweep is believed to be variable from fully spread (20°) to fully swept (55°), rather than limited to one intermediate position as on the MiG-23.

FUSELAGE: Forward of wings, fuselage is basically circular with large ogival dielectric nosecone. Centre-fuselage is faired into rectangular-section air intake trunks, each fitted with a large splitter plate and assumed to embody complex variable-geometry ramps. There is no evidence to suggest external area-rule 'waisting' of these trunks.

TAIL UNIT: Cantilever structure, with sweepback on all surfaces. All-moving horizontal surfaces; conventional inset rudder.

LANDING GEAR: Retractable tricycle type, of which details remain largely speculative. Each main unit is assumed to carry a multi-wheel bogie, which pivots inward from the vestigial fairing under the centre-section into the bottom of the adjacent intake trunk.

POWER PLANT: Two turbofan engines with afterburners, mounted side by side in the rear fuselage. It is not yet possible to identify positively the type of engine fitted, but US sources have suggested the use of Kuznetsov turbofans similar to those installed in Tupolev's Tu-144 supersonic transport. This would be logical, as each engine is rated at 196·1 kN (44,090 lb st) with afterburning in the Tu-144. Uprated for military use, such engines would give an increase of at least 70% over the installed power in the Tu-22. A less-likely alternative is the turbofan evolved by the Kolesov bureau as a backup for the Tu-144, and which is said to be capable of supporting supersonic cruise without use of reheat. Fuel tankage is believed to include integral tanks in the entire fixed portion of the wings and much of the centre-fuselage above the weapon bay. A flight refuelling nose-probe can be fitted; after one observed refuelling, a 'Backfire' prototype is said to have remained airborne for a further 10 h.

ACCOMMODATION: Pilot and co-pilot side by side on flight deck. Other crew members further aft, as indicated by position of windows between flight deck and air intakes.

ARMAMENT: Aircraft observed to date have usually carried a primary armament of one of several different versions of 'Kitchen' air-to-surface missile semi-submerged in the underside of the centre-fuselage. Aircraft shown in accompanying photograph has multiple racks for stores under the air intake trunks. US reports have suggested that the Soviet Union is developing decoy missiles to assist penetration of advanced defence systems, in addition to very advanced ECM and ECCM. Twin 23 mm guns in radar-directed tail mounting.

AVIONICS AND EQUIPMENT: Large bombing and navigation radar (NATO 'Down Beat') inside dielectric nosecone. Radar (NATO 'Fan Tail') for tail turret, above guns.

DIMENSIONS, EXTERNAL:

Wing span: fully spread	34·45 m (113 ft)
fully swept	26·21 m (86 ft)
Length overall	40·23 m (132 ft)
Height overall	10·06 m (33 ft)

WEIGHTS:

Nominal weapon load	9,435 kg (20,800 lb)
Max T-O weight	122,500 kg (270,000 lb)

PERFORMANCE (estimated):

Max speed at high altitude*	Mach 2·0
Max speed at low altitude	Mach 0·9
Max unrefuelled combat range*	4,350 nm (8,050 km; 5,000 miles)

**See introductory copy.*

TUPOLEV Tu-28P/Tu-128

NATO reporting name: Fiddler

Largest fighter ever put into squadron service, this supersonic twin-jet interceptor was seen for the first time at Tushino in July 1961, with a large delta-wing air-to-air missile (NATO 'Ash') mounted under each wing. It is thought to have the service designation Tu-28P (US Department of Defense has used Tu-128); its NATO reporting name is 'Fiddler'.

The Tu-28P has a large ogival nose radome and carries a crew of two in tandem. The shoulder intakes for its two afterburning turbojet engines have half-cone shock-bodies, and the jet-pipes are side by side in the bulged tail. Each engine is estimated to have a max rating of about 120·1 kN (27,000 lb st).

The sharply-swept wings are mid-set, with slight anhedral, and have considerably increased chord on the inboard panels, which have both increased sweep and a straight trailing-edge. The wide-track main landing gear units, comprising four-wheel bogies, retract into large fairings built on to the wing trailing-edges.

The tail unit is also sharply swept, and the two aircraft seen in 1961 were each fitted with two ventral fins. These were missing on the three Tu-28Ps which flew past at Domodedovo in July 1967, as was the large bulged fairing fitted under the fuselage in 1961.

The current armament is double that seen in 1961, each aircraft being equipped to carry two 'Ash' missiles under each wing, one usually of the radar homing type and the other of the infra-red homing type. This was confirmed as the standard armament of first-line service aircraft in a film released in 1969, showing units of the Soviet armed forces taking part in defence exercises.

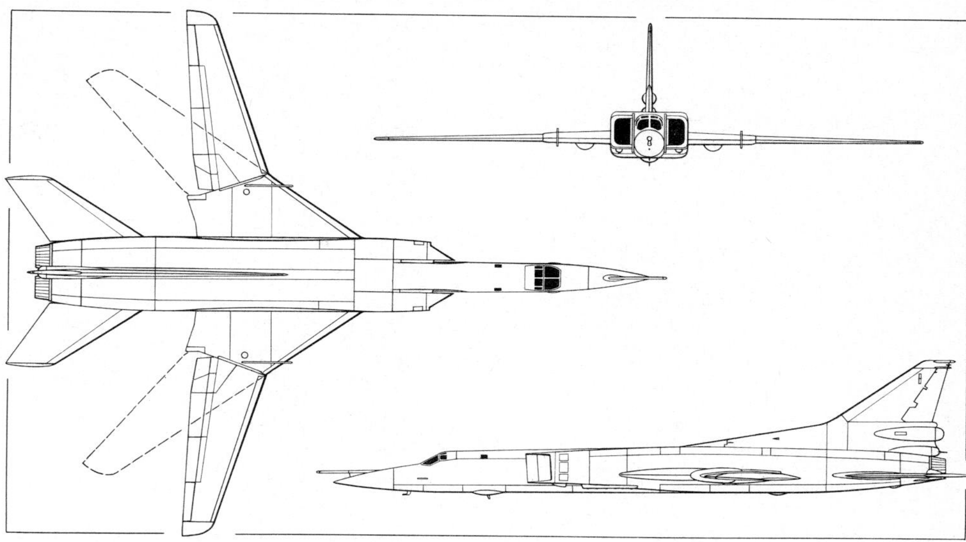

Tupolev Tu-26/Tu-22M (NATO 'Backfire-B') bomber and maritime reconnaissance/attack aircraft *(Pilot Press)*

It has been suggested that the Tu-28P is being replaced in service by an interceptor version of the Tu-22.

DIMENSIONS, EXTERNAL (estimated):

Wing span	20·00 m (65 ft 0 in)
Length overall	26·00 m (85 ft 0 in)

WEIGHT (estimated):

Max T-O weight	45,000 kg (100,000 lb)

PERFORMANCE (estimated):

Max speed at 11,000 m (36,000 ft)	Mach 1·75 (1,000 knots; 1,850 km/h; 1,150 mph)
Service ceiling	20,000 m (65,620 ft)
Range with max fuel	2,692 nm (4,989 km; 3,100 miles)

NEW TUPOLEV HEAVY BOMBER

In the Department of Defense Annual Report for Fiscal Year 1979, Secretary Harold Brown stated: "The Soviet heavy bomber capability continues to rest principally in the small and aging 'Bison-Bear' force consisting of 100 turboprop 'Bears' and 40 'Bisons'. However, we now expect to see the first prototype of a new modern heavy bomber in the near future. If deployed, this aircraft would presumably replace the 'Bisons' and 'Bears' as the backbone of the Soviet intercontinental bomber force." The new bomber has variable-geometry (swing) wings and was expected to fly during 1979.

Tu-28P all-weather interceptor with 'Ash' infra-red missiles on inboard underwing pylons and 'Ash' radar homing missiles on outboard pylons

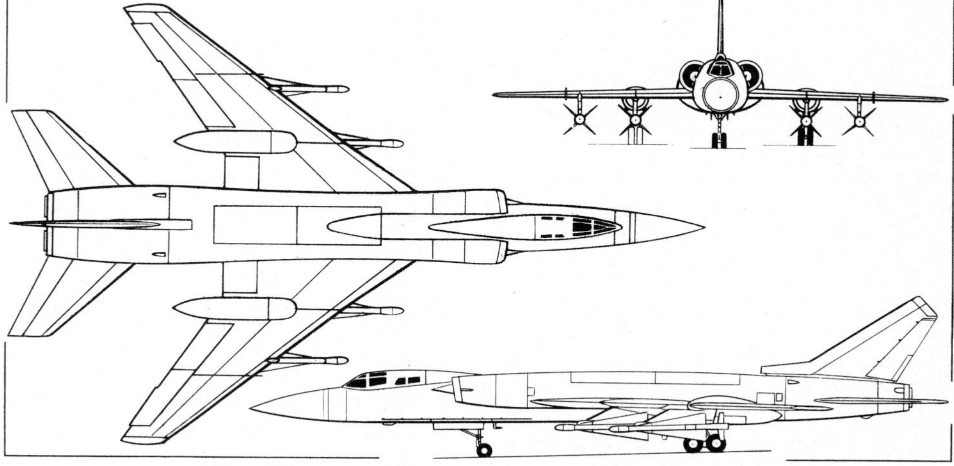

Tupolev Tu-28P supersonic twin-jet all-weather interceptor *(Pilot Press)*

Tupolev Tu-134A medium-range transport (two Soloviev D-30 turbofan engines) of Aeroflot with glazed nose and undernose radar

TUPOLEV Tu-134

NATO reporting name: Crusty

Known originally as the Tu-124A, this aircraft is a rear-engined twin-turbofan development of the Tu-124 (described in earlier editions of *Jane's*). It had completed more than 100 test flights when first details and photographs were released in mid-September 1964. The prototype was followed by five pre-production aircraft and the Tu-134 then went into series production at Kharkov. It entered international service on Aeroflot's Moscow-Stockholm route in September 1967, after a period on internal services, and was joined by the 'stretched' Tu-134A in the Autumn of 1970. The two versions differ as follows:

Tu-134. Initial version, with Soloviev D-30 turbofans, accommodating 64-72 passengers. Export orders included eleven for Interflug (East Germany), six for Balkan Bulgarian Airlines, five for LOT (Poland), six for Malev (Hungary) and three for Aviogenex (Yugoslavia). Described in detail in 1978-79 *Jane's*.

Tu-134A. Fuselage lengthened by 2·10 m (6 ft 10½ in) to accommodate 76-80 passengers and increase baggage space by 2·0 m³ (71 cu ft). Wider seats. Wings strengthened locally. Main landing gear units strengthened and fitted with Il-18 wheels and brakes. Thrust reversers on Soloviev D-30-II engines. New radio and navigation equipment to international standards. APU for self-contained engine starting, electrical power supply and air-conditioning on the ground. More than 200 Tu-134s and Tu-134As are believed to be in service with Aeroflot. Export orders for the Tu-134A have included eleven for CSA (Czechoslovakia), three for Malev, seven for Balkan Bulgarian Airlines, five for LOT, and six for Aviogenex. In some cases these replaced Tu-134s operated earlier.

The third aircraft delivered to Aviogenex differed from all Tu-134s seen previously in having the original glazed nose and undernose radome replaced by a more conventional conical nose radome. Subsequently this became optional on both the Tu-134 and the Tu-134A.

The following details apply to the Tu-134A:

Type: Twin-turbofan short/medium-range transport aircraft.

Wings: Cantilever low-wing monoplane. Sweepback at quarter-chord 35°. Anhedral 1° 30′. Conventional all-metal two-spar structure. Two-section aileron on each wing, operated manually through geared tabs, and fitted also with trim tabs. Electro-mechanically-actuated all-metal double-slotted flaps. Hydraulically-actuated spoilers. Hot-air de-icing system.

Fuselage: Conventional all-metal semi-monocoque structure of circular section. Electro-mechanically-actuated airbrake under fuselage, to steepen angle of approach.

Tail Unit: Cantilever all-metal structure, with variable-incidence tailplane mounted at top of fin. Elevators operated manually through geared tabs. Rudder control is hydraulically powered, with yaw damper. Trim tabs in elevators. Fin leading-edge de-iced by hot air; tailplane leading-edge de-iced electrically.

Landing Gear: Retractable tricycle type. All units retract rearward. Main units consist of four-wheel bogies retracting into fairings built on to wing trailing-edge. Oleo-pneumatic shock-absorbers, supplemented by ability of legs to swing rearward to cushion taxying and landing on rough runways. Main wheels size 930 × 305, tyre pressure 5·86 bars (85 lb/sq in). Steerable twin nosewheels size 660 × 200, tyre pressure 6·38-6·90 bars (92·5-100 lb/sq in). Disc brakes and anti-skid units standard.

Power Plant: Two Soloviev D-30 Srs II turbofan engines, each rated at 66·7 kN (14,990 lb st), in pod on each side of rear fuselage, available with thrust reversers, constant-speed drives and AC generators. Standard capacity of Tu-134A wing fuel tanks is 16,600 litres (3,650 Imp gallons), with optional increase to 18,000 litres (3,960 Imp gallons). Single-point refuelling socket in starboard wing-root leading-edge, Gravity fuelling point above each tank. Hot-air de-icing system for nacelle intakes. Fire-warning and freon extinguishing system.

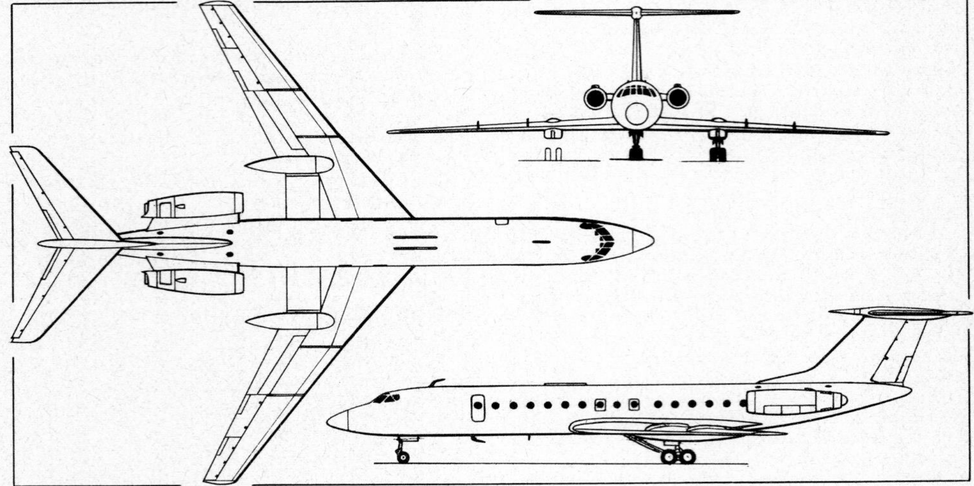

Tupolev Tu-134A twin-turbofan short/medium-range transport with conical nose radome *(Pilot Press)*

Accommodation: Flight crew of three, consisting of two pilots and a navigator, plus two stewardesses. All configurations have 28 seats in four-abreast rows in rear cabin. Front cabin seats 44, 48 or 52 passengers, four-abreast, with tables between front two rows. Seat pitch 75 cm (29·5 in). In each version there is a galley on the starboard side and baggage compartment and galley on the port side immediately aft of the flight deck, two toilets at the rear and a large baggage and freight compartment aft, in line with the engines. Three wardrobes forward of main cabin on 72-seat version, one on other versions. Reduced forward baggage space on 80-seater. Max loading on floor of freight compartment 400 kg/m² (82 lb/sq ft). The passenger door is on the port side, forward of the front cabin. There are two cargo doors, on the starboard side by the baggage compartments, and an emergency exit on each side over the wing. Crew cabin and canopy observation panel de-iced by electric heater and hot air.

Systems: Air-conditioning system, pressure differential 0·56 bars (8·10 lb/sq in), fed with bleed air from engine compressors. Hydraulic system operating pressure 207 bars (3,000 lb/sq in). Electrical system includes 27V DC supply from four 12kW starter/generators and two batteries, single-phase 115V 400Hz AC supply from two inverters and three-phase 36V 400Hz AC supply. APU available. Oxygen available continuously for pilot, from 92 litre bottle, with 1 h supply for other crew members and portable supply for emergency use by passengers.

Avionics and Equipment: Typical installation includes two ARK-15 radio compasses, Mikron HF communications radio, two UHF transceivers, RV-5 radio altimeter, two 'Course MP-2' VOR/ILS, two SO-70 transponders, ROZ-1 weather radar and DISS-013 Doppler.

Dimensions, external:

Wing span	29·01 m (95 ft 2 in)
Wing chord at root	8·66 m (28 ft 5 in)
Wing chord at tip	1·92 m (6 ft 3½ in)
Wing aspect ratio	7·3
Length overall	37·05 m (121 ft 6½ in)
Length of fuselage	33·17 m (108 ft 10 in)
Fuselage max diameter	2·90 m (9 ft 6 in)
Height overall	9·14 m (30 ft 0 in)
Tailplane span	11·80 m (38 ft 8½ in)
Wheel track	9·45 m (31 ft 0 in)
Wheelbase	16·04 m (52 ft 7½ in)
Passenger door: Height	1·30 m (4 ft 3 in)
Width	0·70 m (2 ft 3½ in)
Height to sill	2·60 m (8 ft 6½ in)
Baggage compartment doors:	
Height	0·90 m (2 ft 11½ in)
Width: fwd	1·10 m (3 ft 7¼ in)
aft	1·20 m (3 ft 11¼ in)
Height to sill	2·40 m (7 ft 10½ in)

Dimensions, internal:

Cabin (portion containing seats only):	
Width	2·71 m (8 ft 10½ in)
Height	1·96 m (6 ft 5 in)
Volume	68·0 m³ (2,400 cu ft)
Baggage compartment (fwd):	
Volume	4·0-6·0 m³ (141-212 cu ft)
Baggage compartment (aft):	
Height (mean)	1·75 m (5 ft 9 in)
Length (mean)	2·80 m (9 ft 2 in)
Width (mean)	1·75 m (5 ft 9 in)
Floor area	4·5 m² (48·4 sq ft)
Volume	8·50 m³ (300 cu ft)

Areas:

Wings, gross	127·3 m² (1,370·3 sq ft)
Ailerons (total)	9·68 m² (104·2 sq ft)
Trailing-edge flaps (total)	22·50 m² (242·2 sq ft)
Spoilers (total)	4·48 m² (48·2 sq ft)
Vertical tail surfaces (total)	20·03 m² (215·6 sq ft)
Rudder	5·76 m² (62·0 sq ft)
Horizontal tail surfaces (total)	30·68 m² (330·2 sq ft)
Elevators	6·42 m² (69·1 sq ft)

Weights (Tu-134A):

Operating weight empty	29,000 kg (63,950 lb)
Max fuel	14,400 kg (31,800 lb)
Max payload	8,200 kg (18,075 lb)
Max ramp weight	47,200 kg (104,000 lb)
Max T-O weight	47,000 kg (103,600 lb)
Max landing weight	43,000 kg (94,800 lb)

Performance (Tu-134A):

Max cruising speed at AUW of 42,000 kg (92,600 lb) at 10,000 m (32,800 ft)
477 knots (885 km/h; 550 mph)

Normal cruising speed
405-458 knots (750-850 km/h; 466-528 mph)

Service ceiling at max T-O weight
11,900 m (39,000 ft)
Landing run at standard landing weight
780 m (2,560 ft)
Range at max AUW, cruising at 405 knots (750 km/h; 466 mph) at 10,000 m (32,800 ft), with 1 hour fuel reserve:
with max payload
1,020 nm (1,890 km; 1,174 miles)
with payload of 5,000 kg (11,025 lb)
1,630 nm (3,020 km; 1,876 miles)

TUPOLEV Tu-144

NATO reporting name: Charger

A detailed history of the development of this supersonic transport aircraft can be found in the 1977-78 *Jane's*.

The first of the two prototypes of the Tu-144 (CCCP-68001) flew for the first time on 31 December 1968, this being the first flight by a supersonic airliner anywhere in the world. On 5 June 1969 the Tu-144 exceeded Mach 1 for the first time, at a height of 11,000 m (36,000 ft), half-an-hour after take-off. On 26 May 1970 it became the first commercial transport to exceed Mach 2, by flying at 1,160 knots (2,150 km/h; 1,335 mph) at a height of 16,300 m (53,475 ft) for several minutes. Highest speed reported subsequently was Mach 2·4, probably with the aircraft in its almost totally redesigned production form.

Regular supersonic flights by Aeroflot began on 26 December 1975, between Moscow's Domodedovo Airport and Alma-Ata, capital of Kazakhstan. Carrying a payload of freight and mail, Tu-144 No. CCCP-77106 took 1 h 59 min for the journey of about 1,760 nm (3,260 km; 2,025 miles), flying for most of the time at 1,187 knots (2,200 km/h; 1,367 mph) at a height of 16,000-18,000 m (52,500-59,000 ft).

Scheduled passenger flights began on 1 November 1977, when aircraft CCCP-77109 flew from Moscow to Alma-Ata in just under two hours, with 80 of its 140 seats occupied. A public holiday and bad weather led to cancellation or postponement of five of the next six services; but reliability improved from 20 December and a total of 102 flights was made by 1 June 1978. However, the service was then terminated, following an accident to one of the Tu-144s on a non-commercial flight. There was no further news of route flying by the aircraft until the Tu-144D, with new engines, made a proving flight from Moscow to Khabarovsk in June 1979 (see separate entry on Tu-144D).

Thirteen Tu-144s were built, including prototypes.

Construction of the Tu-144 is mainly of VAD-23 light alloy, with extensive use of integrally-stiffened panels, produced by both chemical milling and machining from solid metal. Stainless steel and titanium are used for the leading-edges, elevons, rudder and undersurface of the rear fuselage, and the aircraft is stated to embody 10,000 parts made of plastics.

The wings have a double-delta planform, with a sweepback in the order of 76° on the inboard portions and 57° on the main panels. They are cambered over the full area, with a downward-curving trailing-edge like that of the Concorde. The structure is multi-spar, with large honeycomb panels. The powered control surfaces consist of four separate elevons on each wing and a two-section rudder, each operated by two separate actuators.

The fuselage blends with the low-set wings, giving a flat undersurface which contributes to fuselage lift and directional stability. There are doors forward of the passenger cabins and in the centre on the port side, and six emergency exits.

The 'moustache' foreplanes are pivoted from points near the top of the fuselage, immediately aft of the flight deck. Each is fitted with a double-slotted trailing-edge flap and a fixed leading-edge double-slat. The foreplanes retract rearward, protruding only a little externally but restricting to a narrow passage the space between flight deck and cabin. When extended, during take-off and landing only, they have anhedral but no sweep.

The twin-wheel steerable nose unit of the landing gear retracts forward into the fuselage. Each main eight-wheel bogie (two rows of four) retracts forward and up into one of the engine ducts, between the divided air-intake trunks. This requires the bogie first to pivot sideways through 90° about the base of the leg, before retraction. Nosewheel tyres are size 950 × 300. The main wheels are fitted with size 950 × 400 tyres and quadruple steel disc brakes. All wheel-bays are thermally insulated, and the nosewheel tyres are blown with cooling air after retraction, throughout cruising flight.

The first flight of the Tu-144 prototype was also the first time that the Kuznetsov NK-144 turbofan engine, selected for the original version of the aircraft, had been tested in the air. At that time the engine max ratings were 127·5 kN (28,660 lb st) without afterburning and 171·6 kN (38,580 lb) with full afterburning. On production aircraft the rating with full afterburning was raised to 196·1 kN (44,090 lb st). The engines were paired in two separate ducts; each intake trunk contained a central vertical wall, giving an individual flow of air to each engine. The intakes had fully-automatic movable ramps, with manual reversion, and with airflow dump doors midway from the inlet to the engines. Afterburning was normally maintained at 30% to 40% of its maximum additional thrust throughout cruising flight. No thrust reversers were installed, but a twin brake-parachute was fitted solely for use on short runways.

Total fuel capacity was about 95,000 kg (209,440 lb), with a transfer tank in the fuselage tailcone to counterbalance CG movement in flight.

A flight crew of three is normally carried by both versions of the aircraft, consisting of two pilots and a flight engineer. The pilots have fully-adjustable armchair seats. During cruising flight, their windscreen is faired in by a retractable visor which has birdproof side windows and a 'solid' top. The entire nose can be drooped for improved view during take-off and landing.

The basic interior layout is for a total of 140 passengers in three cabins. The front cabin contains 11 seats for first class passengers, basically three-abreast, with tables between the front two rows. It is divided by a movable partition from the forward tourist class cabin, which contains six rows of five-abreast seats, with the three-seat units on the port side of the centre aisle. The rear tourist class cabin contains 15 rows of five-abreast seating at the front and six rows of four-abreast seating at the rear. Seat pitch is normally 102 cm (40 in) for first class and 87 cm (34·25 in) for tourist class; but alternative layouts are available.

Forward of the passenger accommodation there are toilet (starboard) and cloakroom compartments (port), with a bench seat for two cabin staff by the forward door. A second cloakroom, toilet and buffet kitchen are located between the two tourist class cabins, with two further toilets at the rear. Aft of these, in line with the engines, is a large compartment for containerised baggage and freight, which are loaded and unloaded semi-automatically through a large door on the starboard side of the hold, at the rear. There are no underfloor holds.

Little information is yet available on aircraft systems. The prototype had three independent hydraulic systems and two separate systems for pressurisation and air-conditioning. Preparation for flight, ground air-conditioning and engine starting can be performed independently of airport services. Advanced automatic flight control and navigation systems are standard, with the intention of progressing eventually to full automatic landing under all weather conditions. Six landing and taxi lights are mounted on the nosewheel leg.

DIMENSIONS, EXTERNAL:
Wing span 28·80 m (94 ft 6 in)

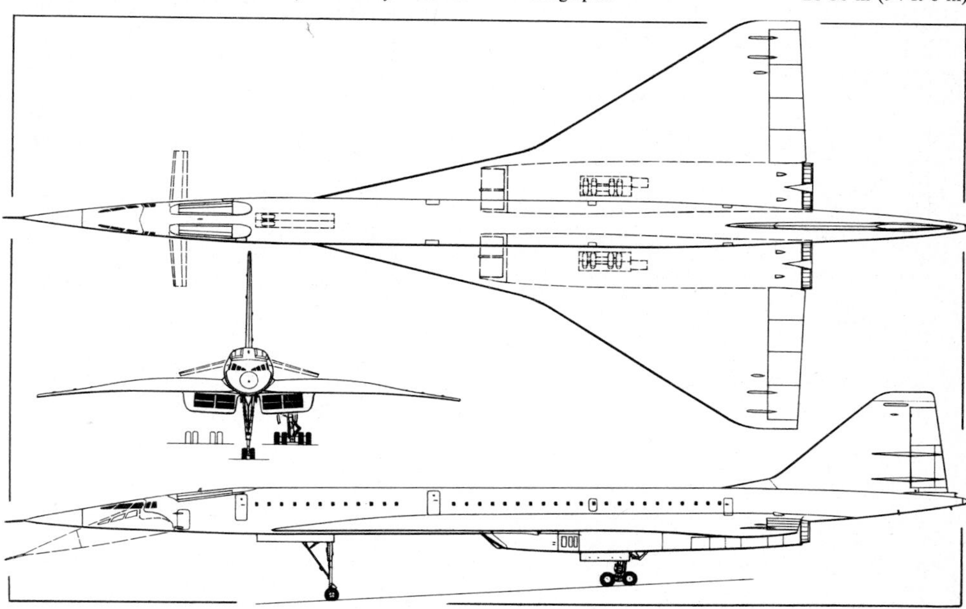

Tupolev Tu-144 supersonic transport in its first production form *(Pilot Press)*

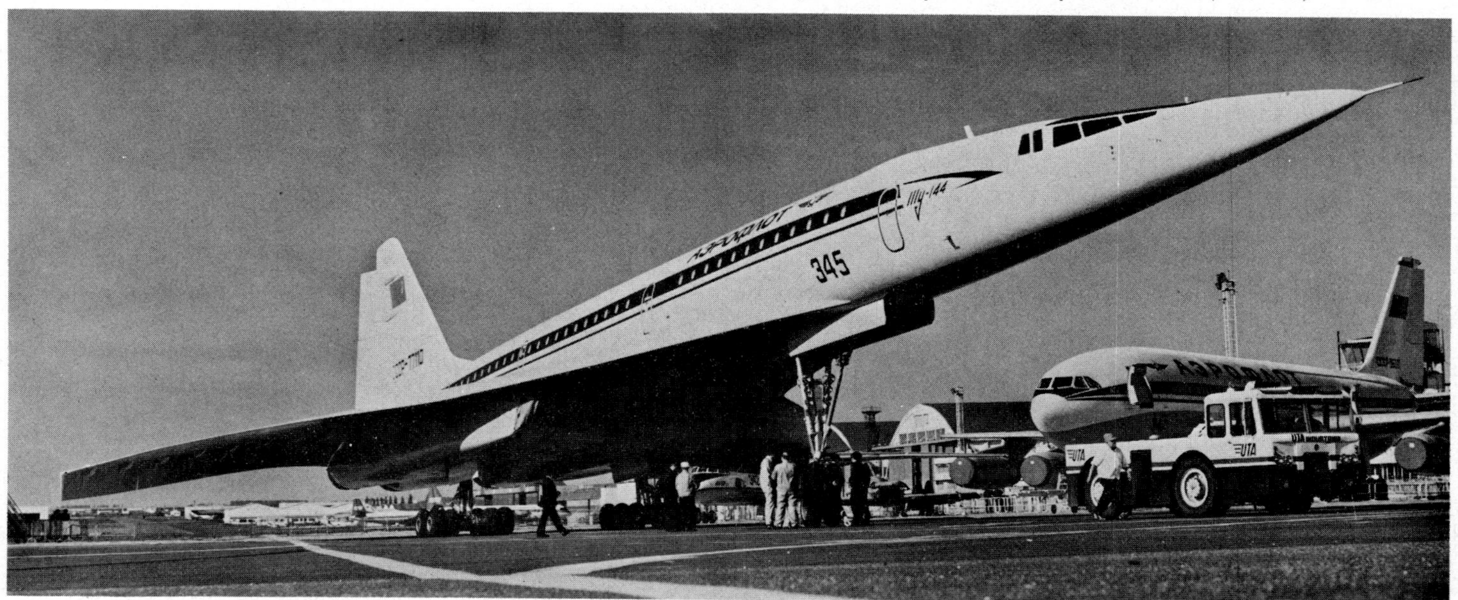

Tupolev Tu-144 supersonic transport, in initial production form. This aircraft was displayed at the 1977 Paris Air Show *(Brian M. Service)*

Length overall 65·70 m (215 ft 6½ in)
Height, wheels up 12·85 m (42 ft 2 in)
Wheel track 6·05 m (19 ft 10¼ in)
Wheelbase 19·60 m (64 ft 3½ in)

DIMENSIONS, INTERNAL:
Cabin: Headroom 1·93 m (6 ft 4 in)
Baggage/cargo hold capacity 20 m³ (706 cu ft)

AREA:
Wings, gross 438 m² (4,714·5 sq ft)

WEIGHTS:
Operating weight empty 85,000 kg (187,400 lb)
Max fuel 95,000 kg (209,440 lb)
Max payload (space limited) 14,000 kg (30,865 lb)
Max payload (structure limited) 15,000 kg (33,070 lb)
Max ramp weight 185,000 kg (407,850 lb)
Max T-O weight 180,000 kg (396,830 lb)
Max zero-fuel weight 100,000 kg (220,460 lb)
Max landing weight 110,000-120,000 kg (242,500-264,550 lb)

PERFORMANCE (nominal):
Max cruising speed Mach 2·35 (1,350 knots; 2,500 km/h; 1,550 mph)
Normal cruising speed Mach 2·2 (1,240 knots; 2,300 km/h; 1,430 mph)
Landing speed 151 knots (280 km/h; 174 mph)
Cruising height 16,000-18,000 m (52,500-59,000 ft)
Balanced field length at max T-O weight (approx):
ISA, S/L 3,000 m (9,845 ft)
ISA+15°C, S/L 3,200 m (10,500 ft)
Landing run 2,600 m (8,530 ft)
Max range with 140 passengers, at an average speed of Mach 1·9 (1,080 knots; 2,000 km/h; 1,243 mph) 3,500 nm (6,500 km; 4,030 miles)

TUPOLEV Tu-144D

Nato reporting name: Charger

First news of the development of this improved version of the Tu-144 was given after it had completed its first route proving flight from Moscow to Khabarovsk, in the Soviet Far East, on 23 June 1979. Time taken for the 3,340 nm (6,185 km; 3,840 mile) flight was 3 h 21 min. Passengers included the aircraft's designer, Dr Alexei A. Tupolev.

After this proving operation, Mr Ivan Razumovsky, Soviet Deputy Minister for Civil Aviation, said that the Tu-144D has new engines by comparison with the original Tu-144. Reported to be the Koliesov variable bypass engines first mentioned briefly in *Jane's* in 1973-74, these were said by the Minister to be 50% more economical in operation, making possible a max range of 3,780 nm (7,000 km; 4,350 miles), and to meet international requirements in terms of noise emission.

No other details of the Tu-144D had become available by mid-September 1979. It was not in regular service at that time, but was stated to be ready for series production.

TUPOLEV Tu-154

NATO reporting name: Careless

The three-engined Tu-154, announced in the Spring of 1966, was intended to replace the Tu-104, Il-18 and An-10 on medium/long stage lengths of up to 3,240 nm (6,000 km; 3,725 miles). It is able to operate from airfields with a class B surface, including packed earth and gravel. Normal flight can be maintained after shutdown of any one engine. Single-engine flight is possible at a lower altitude.

The first of six prototype and pre-production models flew for the first time on 4 October 1968. The seventh Tu-154 was delivered to Aeroflot for initial route proving and crew training in early 1971. Mail and cargo flights began in May. Initial passenger-carrying services were flown for a few days in the early Summer of 1971 between Moscow and Tbilisi. Regular services began on 9 February 1972, over the 700 nm (1,300 km; 800 mile) route between Moscow and Mineralnye Vody, in the North Caucasus. International services began with a proving flight between Moscow and Prague on 1 August 1972.

The following details apply to the basic Tu-154. This version was superseded in production successively by the Tu-154A and Tu-154B, which are described separately.

TYPE: Three-engined medium/long-range transport aircraft.

WINGS: Cantilever low-wing monoplane. Sweepback 35° at quarter-chord. Conventional all-metal three-spar fail-safe structure; centre spar extending to just outboard of inner edge of aileron on each wing. Five-section slat on outer 80% of each wing leading-edge. Triple-slotted flaps. Four-section spoilers on each wing. Outboard sections supplement ailerons for roll control. Section inboard of landing gear housing serves as airbrake and lift-dumper; two middle sections can be used as airbrakes in flight. All control surfaces hydraulically actuated and of honeycomb construction. Hot-air de-icing of wing leading-edge. Slats are electrically heated.

FUSELAGE: Conventional all-metal semi-monocoque fail-safe structure of circular section.

TAIL UNIT: Cantilever all-metal structure, with variable-incidence T tailplane. Rudder and elevator of honeycomb construction. Sweepback of 40° at quarter-chord on horizontal surfaces, 45° on leading-edge of vertical surfaces. Control surfaces hydraulically actuated by irreversible servo-controls. Leading-edges of fin and tailplane and engine air intake de-iced by hot air.

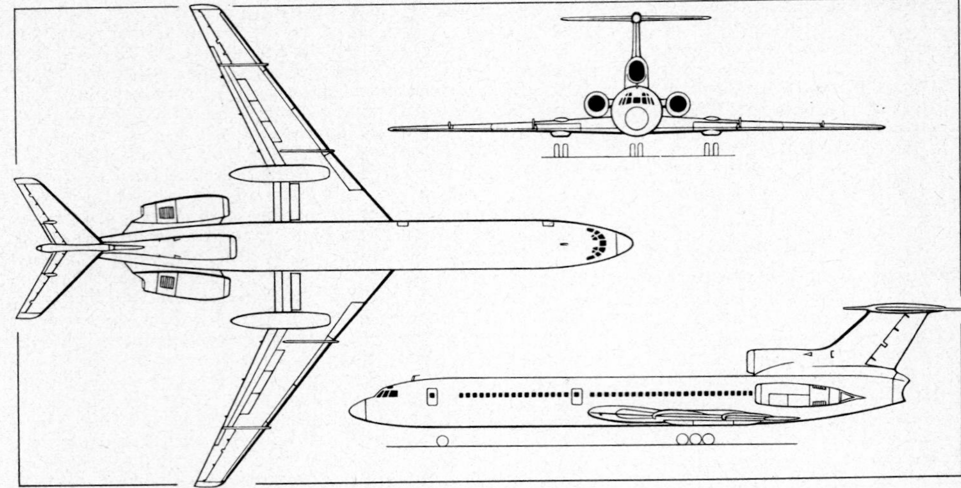

Tupolev Tu-154 medium/long-range three-turbofan transport aircraft *(Pilot Press)*

LANDING GEAR: Retractable tricycle type. Hydraulic actuation. Main units retract rearward into fairings on wing trailing-edge. Each consists of a bogie made up of three pairs of wheels, size 930 × 305, in tandem; tyre pressure 7·86 bars (114 lb/sq in). Steerable anti-shimmy twin-wheel nose unit has wheels size 800 × 225 and retracts forward. Disc brakes and anti-skid units on main wheels.

POWER PLANT: Three Kuznetsov NK-8-2 turbofan engines, each rated at 93·2 kN (20,950 lb st), one on each side of rear fuselage and one inside extreme rear of fuselage. Two lateral engines fitted with upper and lower thrust-reversal grilles. Integral fuel tanks in wings; standard capacity 41,140 litres (9,050 Imp gallons). Max fuel capacity 46,825 litres (10,300 Imp gallons). Single-point refuelling standard.

ACCOMMODATION: Flight crew of two pilots and flight engineer; provision for navigator aft of pilot and folding seats for additional pilots or instructors. There are basic passenger versions for a total of 167, 158, 152, 146 and 128 passengers. Each has a toilet at the front (starboard), removable galley amidships and three toilets aft. Coat storage, folding seat and inflatable evacuation chute in each entrance lobby. Standard economy class version has 54 seats in six-abreast rows, with two tables between front rows, in forward cabin; and 104 seats in six-abreast rows (rear two rows four-abreast) in rear cabin at seat pitch of 75 cm (29·5 in). The 167-seat high-density version differs in having one further row of six seats in the forward cabin and reduced galley facilities. The tourist class versions carry 146 passengers at a seat pitch of 81 cm (31·9 in) or 152 at a pitch of 87 cm (34·25 in) with reduced galley facilities. The 128-seat version has only 24 first class seats, four-abreast at a pitch of 102 cm (40 in), in the forward cabin. There is also an all-cargo version. Passenger doors are forward of front cabin and between cabins on the port side, with emergency and service doors opposite. All four doors open outwards. Four emergency exits, two over wing on each side. Two pressurised baggage holds under main cabin floor, with two inward-opening doors. Normal provision for mechanised loading and unloading of baggage and freight in containers. Smaller unpressurised hold under rear cabin for carrying spare parts or special cargo such as radioactive isotopes.

AVIONICS AND EQUIPMENT: Automatic flight control system standard, including automatic navigation on pre-programmed route under control of navigational computer with en-route checks by ground radio beacons (including VOR, VOR/DME) or radar, and automatic approach by ILS to ICAO Category II standards (development to Category III standard in hand). Moving-map ground position indicator, HF and VHF radio, and radar standard. Safety equipment includes four inflatable life-rafts, each for 26 persons.

SYSTEMS: Air-conditioning system pressure differential 0·62 bars (9·0 lb/sq in). Three independent hydraulic systems; working pressure 207 bars (3,000 lb/sq in). No. 1 system, powered by two pumps driven by centre engine and port engine, operates landing gear, brakes and all control surfaces. No. 2 system, powered by a pump driven by centre engine, actuates nosewheel steering, the second flying controls circuit and landing gear emergency extension. No. 3 system, powered by pump on starboard engine, actuates the third flying controls circuit and second landing gear emergency extension circuit. Three-phase 200/115V AC electrical system, supplied by three 40kVA alternators. 28V DC system. APU standard, driving 40kVA alternator and 12kW starter/generator.

DIMENSIONS, EXTERNAL:
Wing span 37·55 m (123 ft 2½ in)
Length overall 47·90 m (157 ft 1¾ in)
Height overall 11·40 m (37 ft 4¾ in)
Diameter of fuselage 3·80 m (12 ft 5½ in)
Tailplane span 13·40 m (43 ft 11½ in)
Wheel track 11·50 m (37 ft 9 in)
Wheelbase 18·92 m (62 ft 1 in)
Passenger doors (each): Height 1·73 m (5 ft 7 in)
Width 0·80 m (2 ft 7½ in)
Height to sill 3·10 m (10 ft 2 in)
Servicing door: Height 1·28 m (4 ft 2½ in)
Width 0·61 m (2 ft 0 in)
Emergency door: Height 1·28 m (4 ft 2½ in)
Width 0·64 m (2 ft 1¼ in)
Emergency exits (each): Height 0·90 m (2 ft 11½ in)
Width 0·48 m (1 ft 7 in)
Main baggage hold doors (each):
Height 1·20 m (3 ft 11¼ in)
Width 1·35 m (4 ft 5 in)
Height to sill 1·80 m (5 ft 11 in)
Rear (unpressurised) hold:
Height 0·90 m (2 ft 11½ in)
Width 1·10 m (3 ft 7¼ in)
Height to sill 2·20 m (7 ft 2½ in)

DIMENSIONS, INTERNAL:
Cabin: Width 3·58 m (11 ft 9 in)
Height 2·02 m (6 ft 7½ in)
Volume 163·2 m³ (5,763 cu ft)
Main baggage holds: Front 21·5 m³ (759 cu ft)
Rear 16·5 m³ (582 cu ft)
Rear underfloor hold 5·0 m³ (176 cu ft)

AREAS:
Wings, gross 201·45 m² (2,169 sq ft)
Horizontal tail surfaces 40·55 m² (436·48 sq ft)
Vertical tail surfaces 31·72 m² (341·43 sq ft)

WEIGHTS:
Operating weight empty 43,500 kg (95,900 lb)
Normal payload 16,000 kg (35,275 lb)
Max payload 20,000 kg (44,090 lb)
Max fuel 33,150 kg (73,085 lb)
Max ramp weight 90,300 kg (199,077 lb)
Normal T-O weight 84,000 kg (185,188 lb)
Max T-O weight 90,000 kg (198,416 lb)
Normal landing weight 68,000 kg (149,915 lb)
Max landing weight 80,000 kg (176,370 lb)
Max zero-fuel weight 63,500 kg (139,994 lb)

PERFORMANCE (at max T-O weight, except where indicated):
Max level speed:
above 11,000 m (36,000 ft) Mach 0·90
at low altitudes 283 knots (525 km/h; 326 mph) IAS
Max cruising speed at 9,500 m (31,150 ft) 526 knots (975 km/h; 605 mph)
Best-cost cruising speed at 11,000-12,000 m (36,000-39,350 ft) Mach 0·85 (486 knots; 900 km/h; 560 mph)
Long-range cruising speed at 11,000-12,000 m (36,000-39,350 ft) Mach 0·80 (459 knots; 850 km/h; 528 mph)
Approach speed 127 knots (235 km/h; 146 mph)
Min ground turning radius 24·60 m (80 ft 8½ in)
T-O run at normal T-O weight, ISA 1,140 m (3,740 ft)
Balanced runway length at max T-O weight, FAR standard:
ISA, S/L 2,100 m (6,890 ft)
ISA+20°C, S/L 2,420 m (7,940 ft)
Landing field length, at max landing weight, FAR standard:
ISA, S/L 2,060 m (6,758 ft)
ISA+20°C, S/L 2,217 m (7,273 ft)
Range at 11,000 m (36,000 ft) with standard fuel, reserves for 1 hour and 6% of total fuel:
at 486 knots (900 km/h; 560 mph), with T-O weight of 84,000 kg and max payload (158 passengers, baggage and 5 tonnes of cargo and mail) 1,360 nm (2,520 km; 1,565 miles)

Tupolev Tu-154B-2 medium/long-range transport aircraft (three Kuznetsov NK-8-2U turbofan engines) in service with Malev *(Antonio Camarasa)*

as above, T-O weight of 90,000 kg
1,867 nm (3,460 km; 2,150 miles)
at 459 knots (850 km/h; 528 mph), with T-O weight of 84,000 kg and max payload as above
1,510 nm (2,800 km; 1,740 miles)
as above, T-O weight of 90,000 kg
2,050 nm (3,800 km; 2,360 miles)
max range with 13,650 kg (30,100 lb) payload
2,850 nm (5,280 km; 3,280 miles)
Range at 11,000 m (36,000 ft) with optional centre-wing tanks, reserves as above:
with 9,000 kg (19,840 lb) payload (95 passengers)
3,453 nm (6,400 km; 3,977 miles)
with 6,700 kg (14,770 lb) payload (70 passengers)
3,723 nm (6,900 km; 4,287 miles)

TUPOLEV Tu-154A and Tu-154B

NATO reporting name: Careless

A developed version of the Tu-154, with the designation **Tu-154A,** was reported in early 1973, with the first flight scheduled for later that year. An article in the April 1975 issue of the Soviet magazine *Grazhdanskaya Aviatsiya* recorded that this aircraft had entered service with Aeroflot in April 1974 and that production Tu-154As were to be put into scheduled operation during 1975.

The Tu-154A is dimensionally unchanged by comparison with the original model, and is able to carry a normal payload of 152 passengers in Summer and 144 in Winter. Alternative configurations provide seats for 168 passengers on high-density routes, or 12 first class and 128 tourist class. Changes have centred mainly on the power plant, equipment and systems, to permit an increased gross weight, improve performance and reliability, and reduce servicing requirements.

The power plant consists of three Kuznetsov NK-8-2U turbofan engines, each uprated to 103 kN (23,150 lb st). Increased max take-off and landing weights allow extra fuel to be carried, raising the maximum capacity to 39,750 kg (87,630 lb). An additional tank, capacity 6,600 kg (14,550 lb), is mounted between the front and centre spars in the centre-section. It is intended primarily as a ballast tank for ferrying, and the fuel it contains can be pumped into the main system only on the ground. When the aircraft carries less than a full payload, this tank can be filled and its contents can be transferred to the main tanks at a destination airport, so reducing purchases of fuel outside the operator's home country. Other fuel system improvements have been made to the anti-icing fluid additive system; the centre-section tanks can be purged with CO_2 in the event of a forced landing with the wheels retracted.

The controls for the flaps, leading-edge slats and tailplane are interconnected, so that when the flaps are operated the tailplane is trimmed 3° down. An override switch caters for CG conditions which require a movement of more than 3°.

Additional emergency exits in the rear fuselage meet international requirements. The floor of the baggage holds has been strengthened to prevent damage by sharp-edged packages and baggage; and a smoke warning system has been introduced in the holds.

The electrical system has been modified by comparison with the Tu-154 and employs three alternators, on separate supply circuits, to provide 200/115V AC power. Two circuits supply all electrical services; the third supplies the electrical anti-icing system for the leading-edge slats. If one alternator fails, the remaining primary alternator can provide for all essential services, supplemented by the alternator on the APU. The duplicated DC electrical system embodies three rectifiers, of which one is for emergency use in the event of a failure of either of the others.

An ABSU automatic approach and landing system is fitted. This met ICAO Category I requirements initially, but was to be uprated to Category II later. Other equipment changes include the provision of duplicated radio compass, radio altimeter and DME; and the introduction of two-speed windscreen wipers and a system to indicate angle-of-bank limitations. An MSRP-64 flight recorder covers some 80 parameters, and a Mars-B voice recorder with open microphone is standard.

Servicing requirements and costs were reduced considerably on the Tu-154A, for which the servicing cycle is 300/900/1,800 hours.

In 1977, production was switched to a further-improved version, designated **Tu-154B**, since refined as the **Tu-154B-2**. This retains the NK-8-2U turbofans of the Tu-154A, but is fitted with Thomson-CSF/SFIM automatic flight control and navigation equipment approved for Category II automatic landings. Max take-off and zero-fuel weights have been increased; and rearward extension of the usable cabin space enables up to 180 passengers to be carried despite the introduction of two more emergency exits, immediately forward of the engine nacelle on each side. A typical seating arrangement, employed by Malev, has 8 first class passengers at the front, 36 economy class in the forward cabin and 98 in the rear. Improvements have been made to the electronics, notably to simplify take-off and landing procedures. A different radar is fitted, and the fuel tank used as ballast on the Tu-154A can be used normally, as part of the standard fuel system of the Tu-154B/B-2.

Production of all versions of the Tu-154 exceeded 250 by mid-1979. More than 200 were operated by Aeroflot, others by Balkan Bulgarian Airlines (12), Malev (7) and Tarom (5).

Weights (A, Tu-154A; B, Tu-154B):
Basic operating weight: B 50,775 kg (111,940 lb)
Normal payload: A 16,000 kg (35,275 lb)
Max payload: A, B 18,000 kg (39,680 lb)
Max T-O weight: A 94,000 kg (207,235 lb)
B 96,000 kg (211,650 lb)
Max zero-fuel weight: B 71,000 kg (156,525 lb)
Max landing weight (normal):
A 78,000 kg (171,960 lb)
Max landing weight (emergency):
A 92,000-94,000 kg (202,825-207,235 lb)

Performance (A, Tu-154A; B, Tu-154B, at max T-O weight, except where indicated):
Max level speed:
A 310 knots (575 km/h; 357 mph) IAS, except with less than 7,150 kg (15,763 lb) fuel at heights above 7,000 m (23,000 ft)
Normal cruising speed:
A Mach 0·85 (486 knots; 900 km/h; 560 mph)
Range with payload of 16,000 kg (35,275 lb):
A 1,725-1,780 nm (3,200-3,300 km; 1,985-2,050 miles)
Range with 120 passengers and baggage:
B 2,160 nm (4,000 km; 2,485 miles)
Range with max payload:
B 1,485 nm (2,750 km; 1,708 miles)

YAKOVLEV

General Designer in Charge of Bureau:
Alexander Sergeivich Yakovlev

Yakovlev is one of the most versatile Russian designers and products of his design bureau have ranged from transonic long-range fighters to the Yak-24 tandem-rotor helicopter, an operational VTOL carrier-based fighter and a variety of training and light general-purpose aircraft. Types in current production and service, or under development, are described hereafter.

YAKOVLEV Yak-18T

Details of this extensively-redesigned cabin version of the Yak-18 were given for the first time at the 1967 Paris Air Show, where an unregistered example was displayed statically. The first prototype flew for the first time in the Summer of that year, powered, like the Yak-18A and 18PM, with a 224 kW (300 hp) Ivchenko AI-14RF nine-cylinder radial engine, driving a two-blade variable-pitch propeller.

An initial evaluation programme of 450 test flights was completed by two prototypes during 1968-69. Together with experience gained during several months of operation at the Sasov flying school, this suggested that a number of improvements would be worthwhile. Most important of these was the installation of a more powerful M-14P radial engine of the type evolved by Vedeneev from the AI-14 and chosen also for the Kamov Ka-26 helicopter. In addition, improvements were made to the cabin layout and ventilation, and elevator effectiveness was reduced.

An aircraft embodying the modifications was approved by the Research Institute of the Soviet Ministry of Civil Aviation. Four others logged 605 flying hours, including 1,591 take-offs and landings, over a five-month period of testing on every kind of airfield, under a wide variety of weather conditions. The Yak-18T was pronounced superior to earlier versions of the Yak-18 for basic training, and far more economical to operate than the An-2, which was also widely used.

Full production was ordered at Smolensk, and by 1974 it was possible to train the complete intake of 100 pupil pilots at Sasov on the new aircraft. Seventeen were then available for use at the school, of which two were being flown at double the normal rate of utilisation under a Research Institute programme.

As the standard basic trainer at Aeroflot flying schools, the Yak-18T is used for circuits, instrument training and navigation training, and as a flying classroom for an instructor and three pupils. Only one pupil accompanies the instructor on aerobatic flights.

Next to enter service, as a successor to the Yak-12, will be the ambulance version, with light communications and forest fire patrol versions under consideration. A floatplane version is under development and the Yak-18T will also operate eventually on skis.

Designer responsible for this variant of the Yak-18 was Mr Y. Yankievich.

Type: Four-seat multi-purpose light aircraft.

Wings: Cantilever low-wing monoplane, in three sections: a constant-chord centre-section, integral with the fuselage, and two tapered outer panels. Wing section Clark YH, with thickness/chord ratio of 14·5% at root and 9·3% at tip. Dihedral on outer panels only. Two-spar light alloy construction. Light alloy covering on centre-section and on leading-edges of outer panels; inboard 25% of outer panels covered with light alloy, remainder with fabric. Slotted ailerons of light alloy construction, each hinged at three points and partly fabric-covered. Light alloy split flap across entire span of centre-section, actuated by two pneumatic servo-motors. Fixed step at port wing-root trailing-edge, with corrugated upper surface walkway to door on each side. Ailerons operated by pushrods. Ground-adjustable tab on each aileron.

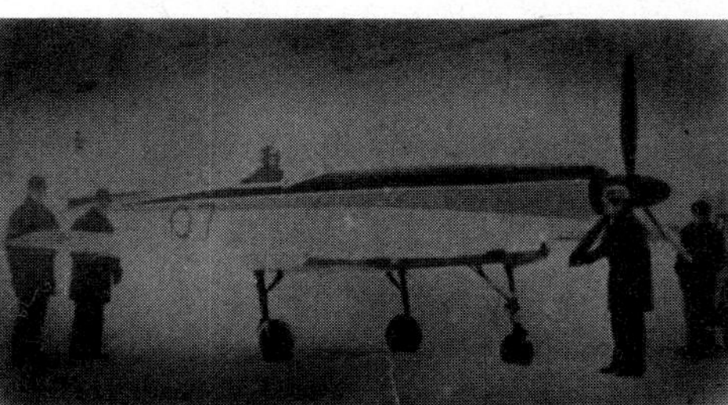

During 1979 this photograph was received, showing a Yak-18 fitted experimentally with a Glushenkov TVD-10 turboprop engine. No details have been made available

Yakovlev Yak-18T basic trainer (Vedeneev M-14P engine)

FUSELAGE: Conventional light alloy semi-monocoque structure, of basically square section. Skin on rear fuselage spot welded to frames and stringers.

TAIL UNIT: Braced light alloy structure, with wire bracing above tailplane and strut bracing below. All surfaces fabric-covered. Control surfaces operated by both pushrods and cables. Controllable trim tab in each elevator.

LANDING GEAR: Fully-retractable tricycle type, with single wheel on each unit. Pneumatic retraction, nosewheel rearward, main units inward into centre-section. No main-wheel doors. Oleo-nitrogen shock-absorbers. Castoring but non-steerable self-centering nosewheel with shimmy damper. All three tyres size 500-150. Differential pneumatic brakes on main wheels, with override button on instructor's control wheel.

POWER PLANT: One 269 kW (360 hp) Vedeneev M-14P nine-cylinder aircooled radial engine, driving a two-blade variable-pitch metal propeller, without spinner. Louvres in front of cowling to regulate cooling. Two-part cowling, split on horizontal centreline. Fuel tanks in wing roots.

ACCOMMODATION: Car-type cabin, seating four persons in pairs. Large forward-hinged door on each side, jettisonable in emergency. Provision for upholstered or parachute-type front seats. Bench-type rear seat removable for freight carrying. Ambulance configuration available, for pilot, stretcher patient and medical attendant. Large baggage compartment aft of rear seat, with external access on port side. Stretcher of ambulance version is loaded through this large baggage door. Cabin furnishings of non-inflammable synthetic materials. Dual control wheels. Glareshield above panel. Heating and ventilation standard.

SYSTEMS: Pneumatic system for actuating landing gear and flaps. Electrical system includes instrument panel red lighting, navigation and landing lights, and anti-collision beacon at top of fin.

AVIONICS AND EQUIPMENT: Standard equipment includes UHF radio, intercom, radio compass, radio altimeter and flight recorder.

DIMENSIONS, EXTERNAL:

Wing span	11·16 m (36 ft 7¼ in)
Length overall	8·35 m (27 ft 4¾ in)

AREA:

Wings, gross	18·75 m² (201·8 sq ft)

WEIGHTS AND LOADINGS (A, with instructor and one pupil; B, with instructor and three pupils):

Max payload: A	306 kg (675 lb)
B	436 kg (960 lb)
Max T-O weight: A	1,500 kg (3,307 lb)
B	1,650 kg (3,637 lb)
Max wing loading: A	80 kg/m² (16·4 lb/sq ft)
B	88 kg/m² (18·0 lb/sq ft)
Max power loading: A	5·59 kg/kW (11·0 lb/hp)
B	6·15 kg/kW (12·1 lb/hp)

PERFORMANCE (at max T-O weight: A, with instructor and one pupil; B, with instructor and three pupils):

Max level speed:	
A, B	159 knots (295 km/h; 183 mph)
Max cruising speed:	
B	135 knots (250 km/h; 155 mph)
Max rate of climb at S/L: B	300 m (985 ft)/min
Service ceiling: A, B	5,500 m (18,000 ft)
T-O run: A	330 m (1,085 ft)
B	400 m (1,315 ft)
Landing run: A	400 m (1,315 ft)
B	500 m (1,640 ft)
Range with max fuel, with reserves:	
A	350 nm (650 km; 403 miles)
B	485 nm (900 km; 560 miles)

YAKOVLEV Yak-28

NATO reporting names: Brewer, Firebar and Maestro

First seen in considerable numbers in the 1961 Soviet Aviation Day flypast were three successors to the Yak-25/27 series (see 1971-72 *Jane's*), described by the commentator as supersonic multi-purpose aircraft and identified subsequently by the designation Yak-28. These aircraft are shoulder-wing monoplanes, whereas all versions of the Yak-25, 26 and 27 were mid-wing. The Yak-28 series were, in fact, produced as entirely new designs, following only the general configuration of the earlier types.

The landing gear comprises two twin-wheel units in tandem, with the forward unit under the pilot's cockpit and the rear unit moved further aft than on the Yak-25/27, to a point immediately in front of the ventral fin. Wingtip balancer wheels are retained. The entire wing-root leading-edge has been extended forward and the height of the fin and rudder increased. Tailplane sweep is also increased.

Several versions of the basic design have been reported, with the following NATO reporting names:

Brewer-A to C (Yak-28). Two-seat tactical attack versions. Single cockpit for pilot, with blister canopy, and glazed nose for navigator/bomb aimer. Corresponding to Yak-26 ('Mangrove') and produced to replace the Il-28 in the Soviet Air Force. Most examples have blister radome under fuselage just forward of wings. On some aircraft, long engine nacelles extend forward as far as the front of this radome. Others have shorter nacelles. Guns semi-submerged in each side of the fuselage on some aircraft; on starboard side only on others. Internal bomb bay between the underfuselage radome and the rear main landing gear unit. Now used only in places of secondary importance.

Brewer-D. Reconnaissance version, with cameras in bomb bay.

Brewer-E. First Soviet operational ECM escort aircraft, deployed in 1970. Underfuselage radome deleted. Active ECM pack built into bomb bay, from which it projects in form of a semi-cylindrical pack. Attachment under each outer wing, outboard of external fuel tank, for a rocket pod.

Firebar. Tandem two-seat all-weather fighter derivative of Yak-28, corresponding to Yak-27. Nose radome. Internal weapons bay deleted. 'Anab' air-to-air missile under each wing instead of guns. Identified as **Yak-28P** (Perekhvatchik; interceptor) at 1967 Domodedovo dis-

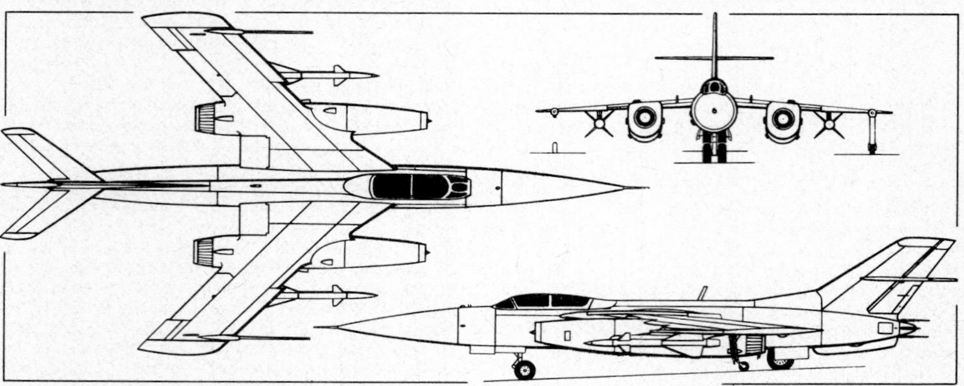

The long-nose version of the Yakovlev Yak-28P two-seat all-weather fighter ('Firebar') *(Pilot Press)*

Yak-28P ('Firebar') fitted with original short radome and carrying two 'Anab' missiles *(Flug Revue)*

Version of the Yak-28 known to NATO as 'Brewer-C' *(Flug Revue)*

play, the suffix 'P' indicating that the design had been *adapted* for the fighter role. Example shown in static park had a much longer dielectric nosecone than the standard operational 'Firebars' in the flying display and had two missile pylons under each wing, one for an 'Atoll' and one for an 'Anab'. This suggested that it was a weapons development aircraft. However, the lengthened nosecone has since been fitted retrospectively on many Yak-28Ps in squadron service. This does not indicate any increase in radar capability or aircraft performance.

Maestro (Yak-28U). Trainer version of 'Firebar'. Normal cockpit layout replaced by two individual single-seat cockpits in tandem, each with its own canopy. Front canopy sideways-hinged to starboard; rear canopy rearward-sliding.

More than 300 Yak-28P 'Firebars' continue to form a significant component of the Soviet home defence interceptor force. The Yak-28 'Brewer' series is changing gradually from first-line attack to support roles, with the emphasis on ECM, reconnaissance and operational training.

The following details refer specifically to the Yak-28P, but are generally applicable to the other versions of the Yak-28:

TYPE: Two-seat transonic all-weather interceptor.

WINGS: Cantilever shoulder-wing monoplane of basically constant chord. Extended leading-edge on outer wings and also between fuselage and each engine nacelle. Outer extensions are drooped. Slotted flap, with unswept trailing-edge, between fuselage and each engine nacelle. Basic wing sweepback 45°. Anhedral from root. Single fence on upper surface of each wing, between fuselage and engine nacelle. Large trailing-edge flap and short aileron, with tab, outboard of nacelle on each wing. Balancer-wheel fairings, inset from wing-tips, are extended forward as lead-filled wing balance weights.

FUSELAGE: All-metal semi-monocoque structure of basically circular section. Finely-tapered dielectric nosecone over radar scanner.

TAIL UNIT: Cantilever all-metal structure. Variable-incidence tailplane mounted midway up fin. All surfaces sweptback. Trim tab in rudder. Dorsal fin fairs into spine along top of fuselage. Shallow ventral stabilising fin.

LANDING GEAR: Two twin-wheel main units in tandem, retracting into fuselage. Front unit retracts forward, rear unit rearward. Small balancer wheel near each wingtip, retracting rearward under wing; fairing integral with leg.

POWER PLANT: Two afterburning turbojet engines, believed to be of same basic type as Tumansky R-11 fitted to MiG-21, with rating of 58·35 kN (13,120 lb st). Each fitted with centrebody shock-cone. A pointed slipper-type external fuel tank can be carried under the leading-edge of each wing, outboard of the engine nacelle.

ACCOMMODATION: Crew of two in tandem on ejection seats in pressurised cabin under long transparent blister canopy.

ARMAMENT: Pylon under each outer wing for 'Anab' air-to-air missile, with alternative infra-red or semi-active radar homing heads.

OPERATIONAL EQUIPMENT: Reported to include tail warning radar.

DIMENSIONS, EXTERNAL (estimated):
- Wing span: 12·95 m (42 ft 6 in)
- Length overall:
  - Yak-28: 21·65 m (71 ft 0½ in)
- Height overall: 3·95 m (12 ft 11½ in)

WEIGHT (estimated):
- Max T-O weight:
  - Yak-28P: 15,875 kg (35,000 lb)

PERFORMANCE (Yak-28P, estimated):
- Max level speed at 10,670 m (35,000 ft): Mach 1·1 (636 knots; 1,180 km/h; 733 mph)
- Cruising speed: 496 knots (920 km/h; 571 mph)
- Service ceiling: 16,750 m (55,000 ft)
- Max combat radius: 500 nm (925 km; 575 miles)
- Max range: 1,040-1,390 nm (1,930-2,575 km; 1,200-1,600 miles)

YAKOVLEV Yak-36

NATO reporting name: Forger

This is the VTOL combat aircraft deployed by the Soviet Navy on the *Kiev* and *Minsk*, the first two of its 40,000 ton carrier/cruisers to put to sea. Two versions have been observed on the ships, as follows:

Forger-A. Basic single-seat combat aircraft. At least nine appear to be operational on each ship, in addition to about 15 Kamov Ka-25 anti-submarine and missile targeting helicopters. Primary operational roles are assumed to be reconnaissance, strikes against small ships, and fleet defence against shadowing, unarmed maritime reconnaissance aircraft.

Forger-B. Two-seat training version, of which one example was seen on the *Kiev* and another on the *Minsk*. A second cockpit is located forward of the normal cockpit, with the ejector seat at a lower level, under a continuous transparent canopy. To compensate for the longer nose, a 'plug' is inserted in the fuselage aft of the wing, lengthening the constant-section portion without requiring modification of the tapering rear fuselage assembly. In other respects this version appears to be identical to 'Forger-A', but has no ranging radar or weapon pylons.

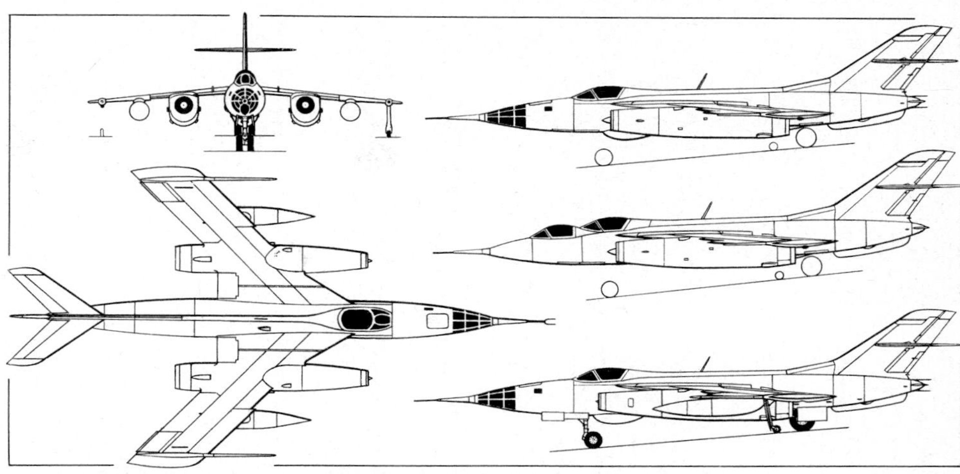

The version of the Yak-28 two-seat tactical attack aircraft known to NATO as 'Brewer-C', with additional side views of 'Brewer-B' (top) and the Yak-28U ('Maestro') tandem-cockpit trainer (centre) *(Pilot Press)*

The likelihood that an aircraft of this type was under development in the Soviet Union was first confirmed in 1974 by Admiral Thomas H. Moorer, then Chairman of the US Joint Chiefs of Staff. In his annual report, he said of the *Kiev:* "This ship is over 900 ft in length and should displace 30-40,000 tons. The deck configuration and the lack of catapults or arresting gear indicate that this ship apparently is designed to operate V/STOL aircraft and helicopters. It should be capable of carrying 25 V/STOL aircraft or 36 helicopters. It is believed, however, that a mixture of new V/STOL tactical aircraft and 'Hormone' (Ka-25) helicopters is the most likely complement".

The 1975-76 *Jane's* contained the remark that a strike/reconnaissance V/STOL aircraft was thought to have been evolved from the experimental VTOL aircraft known as 'Freehand' by the Yakovlev bureau, utilising a mixture of vectored thrust and direct jet-lift. This belief was confirmed when the *Kiev* entered the Mediterranean in July 1976 and subsequently operated its complement of 'Forgers' extensively during passage through that sea and the Atlantic en route to Murmansk. These aircraft, and those seen subsequently on the sister-ship *Minsk,* are assumed to be operated by a development squadron.

The general appearance of the single-seat 'Forger-A' is shown in the accompanying illustrations. Its basic configuration is conventional, except that VTOL capability has permitted the mid-set wings to be made relatively small in area. They fold upward at approximately mid-span, for stowage on board ship. No leading-edge devices are fitted, but the entire trailing-edge of each wing is made up of an aileron on the outboard (folding) panel and a large Fowler-type flap on the inboard panel. Sweepback is approximately 45° on the leading-edge, and there is considerable anhedral from the wing roots.

All tail surfaces are swept, with conventional rudder and elevators. 'Puffer-jet' stability control orifices are apparent above and below the tailcone and at each wingtip.

Each leg of the trailing-link tricycle landing gear carries a single wheel. The nose gear retracts rearward, the main units forward into the fuselage. A small bumper is fitted under the upward-curving rear fuselage.

Primary propulsion is by a single large turbojet, exhausting through a single pair of vectoring side-nozzles aft of the wing. No afterburner is fitted. The large lateral air intake ducts do not appear to embody splitter plates.

Two lift-jets are installed in tandem in the fuselage immediately aft of the cockpit, under a rearward-hinged louvred door of the kind fitted to the Mikoyan and Sukhoi STOL prototypes demonstrated in 1967. The position of the corresponding underfuselage doors implies that the lift-jets are mounted at an angle, in such a way that their thrust is exerted both upward and slightly forward. As the main vectored-thrust nozzles also turn up to 10° forward of vertical during take-off and landing, the total of four

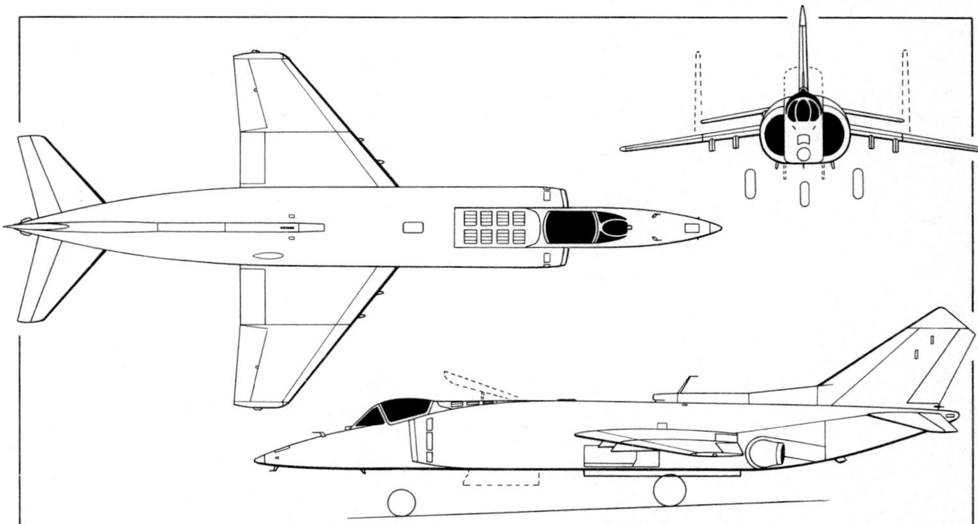

Yakovlev single-seat VTOL carrier-based combat aircraft (NATO 'Forger-A') *(Michael A. Badrocke)*

Yak-36 ('Forger-A') without auxiliary intake doors, approaching the carrier/cruiser *Kiev (US Navy)*

'Forger-A' single-seat version of the Yak-36 taking off. This aircraft, with painted flag further aft, has a row of small auxiliary intake doors aft of each intake *(Royal Navy)*

The two-seat training version of the Yak-36 ('Forger-B')

exhaust effluxes can be envisaged as forming a V under the fuselage. There appears to be a small intake for cooling air at the front of the dorsal fin fairing.

Observers of deck flying by 'Forger-As' report that the aircraft appear to be extremely stable during take-off and landing. Take-offs are made vertically, with a smooth conversion about 5 to 6 m (15-20 ft) above the deck, initiated by lowering the aircraft's nose about 5° below the horizon and maintaining this attitude until the aircraft has accelerated to 30-40 knots (55-75 km/h; 35-46 mph). At this speed, a 5° nose-up attitude is assumed, and the accelerating transition is continued by vectoring aft the nozzles of the propulsion engine.

Landing procedure begins with a gradual descent from far astern, with the last 400 m (1,300 ft) flown essentially level, about 30 m (100 ft) above the water. The aircraft crosses the ship's stern with about a 5 knot (10 km/h; 6 mph) closure rate, 10-14 m (35-45 ft) above the flight deck, then flares gently to a hover and descends vertically. Landings are so precise that some form of control from the ship during take-off and approach has been suggested, perhaps in association with laser devices lining each side of the rear deck.

At no time was a STOL take-off observed, as practised by the Harrier/AV-8A combat aircraft of the Royal Air Force and US Marine Corps to increase their load-carrying capability. It is suggested that anything but direct vertical take-off might be difficult for the pilot of 'Forger-A', as take-off with forward speed over the deck would impose formidable stability and safety problems. The Soviet aircraft must also lack the Harrier's ability to increase its combat manoeuvrability by the use of thrust vectoring in forward flight (VIFF).

Estimates put the thrust of 'Forger-A's' primary power plant (based possibly on the Lyulka AL-21) at around 78 kN (17,500 lb), and the thrust of each Koliesov lift-jet at 25 kN (5,600 lb). This would appear adequate to permit a considerable weight of fuel and weapons to be carried. Gun pods and rocket packs have been photographed on four pylons under the aircraft's inner wing panels. Operational equipment includes radar ranging and an infra-red sensor.

DIMENSIONS, EXTERNAL (estimated):
- Wing span: 7·00 m (23 ft 0 in)
- Length overall:
  - 'Forger-A': 15·00 m (49 ft 3 in)
  - 'Forger-B': 17·66 m (58 ft 0 in)

WEIGHT (estimated):
- Max T-O weight:
  - 'Forger-A': 10,000 kg (22,050 lb)

PERFORMANCE (estimated):
- Max level speed at height: Mach 1·3
- Max rate of climb at S/L: 4,500 m (14,750 ft)/min
- Service ceiling: 12,000 m (39,375 ft)

YAKOVLEV Yak-40

NATO reporting name: Codling

This three-turbofan short-haul jet transport was designed to replace the Li-2 (Soviet-built DC-3) and to operate from Class 5 (grass) airfields. The prototype flew for the first time on 21 October 1966 and the Yak-40 made its first passenger flight in Aeroflot service on 30 September 1968.

By the Summer of 1976, more than 800 Yak-40s had been built. Most are in service with Aeroflot, some as air ambulances carrying patients to medical centres and to Black Sea convalescent centres. Others have been sold in Afghanistan, Bulgaria, Czechoslovakia, France, West Germany, Italy, Poland and Yugoslavia. Military operators include the Soviet, Bangladesh, Polish, Syrian and Yugoslav air forces. Production in the Soviet Union has ended, but a company named ICX Aviation Inc (which see) has announced plans to manufacture a re-engined version in the USA, as the X-Avia.

All Soviet production Yak-40s are structurally similar, with AI-25 engines, and differ only in their standard of accommodation, usually for 27 or 32 airline passengers in a single class, 16 or 20 passengers in two-class layouts, or up to 11 passengers in an executive layout. All have clamshell thrust reversers aft of the centre engine.

A freighter version is in service, with a cargo door, size approximately 1·50 m × 1·60 m (5 ft × 5 ft 2½ in), in the port side of the fuselage.

A full description of the Yak-40 can be found in the 1978-79 *Jane's*.

POWER PLANT: Three Ivchenko AI-25 turbofan engines, each rated at 14·7 kN (3,300 lb st). Fin and boundary layer splitter beneath and forward of intake for centre engine. Clamshell thrust reverser fitted to airframe aft of this engine. Hot-air anti-icing system for all three engine air intakes. Fire warning and extinguishing systems standard. Fuel in integral tanks between front auxiliary spar and main spar in each wing, from outboard of the fuselage to the inner end of the aileron, total capacity 3,910 litres (860 Imp gallons). Type AI-9 turbine APU mounted in rear of top engine intake fairing for engine starting. Provision for starting from ground compressed air supply.

ACCOMMODATION: Two pilots side by side on flight deck, on adjustable seats, with dual controls. Central jump seat at rear for third person. Automatically-actuated electrical windscreen de-icing system. Main cabin normally laid out for 27 passengers in three-abreast rows, with two-chair units on starboard side of aisle. Seat pitch 755 mm (29·7 in). Individual ventilator by each seat. Rack for hand baggage on starboard side of cabin ceiling. Cloakroom (port), buffet, baggage compartment and toilet (starboard) aft of main cabin. Seat for stewardess against rear face of partition separating cabin from rear compartments, on port side. Normal access via hydraulically-actuated ventral airstair door at rear. Service door on port side of cabin, at front. For high-density services, twin-seat units can be installed on each side of aisle, giving a total of 32 seats in only eight rows. Seat pitch is unchanged, enabling the rear cabin partition to be moved forward and so giving a larger baggage compartment. The 16-seat mixed class version has two passenger cabins, separated by a partition. The forward cabin has two swivelling chairs, on each side of a table, on the port side; and an inward-facing four-place settee on the starboard side, with small cupboards fore and aft. Alternatively, two more swivelling seats and a table can replace the settee. The rear cabin contains 12 seats in standard three-abreast rows. A lobby between the flight deck and forward cabin provides access for the crew without passing through the main cabins, and contains a cloakroom (starboard) and seat for the stewardess. Compartments aft of the rear cabin are as in the standard 27-seat version. The 20-seat version differs from the 16-seater in having 16 seats four-abreast in the rear cabin. The executive version has a toilet and other facilities in a large compartment aft of the flight deck; a centre lounge furnished with a four-place settee, three armchairs, a writing desk and a sideboard; and rear cabin containing six seats, three-abreast. There is a further toilet aft, and the galley is equipped to special standards. A bar with two adjustable tables is built into the wall between the flight deck and lounge, on the port side. A freight-carrying version is in service.

AVIONICS AND EQUIPMENT: Standard equipment includes full blind-flying instrumentation, two Landysh-5 VHF

Yakovlev Yak-40 short-range transport (three Ivchenko AI-25 turbofan engines) in Aeroflot markings

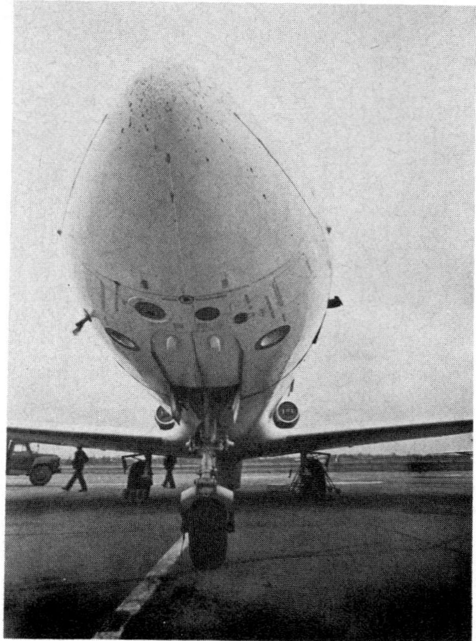

Yak-40 equipped with special TV to register contact with the environment of charged particles injected from a spacecraft *(Tass)*

radio communications installations, an ARK-10 automatic radio compass, KURS-MP-2 VOR/ILS system, RV-5 radio altimeter, Type SO 70 transponder, Grosa-40 weather radar, PRIVOD-ANE-1 flight director system, Kremenj 40E autopilot, AGD 1 artificial horizon and GMK-1GE gyro-compass, permitting automatic approach to ICAO Category II standards.

DIMENSIONS, EXTERNAL:
- Wing span: 25·0 m (82 ft 0¼ in)
- Wing aspect ratio: 9
- Length overall: 20·36 m (66 ft 9½ in)
- Length of fuselage: 17·00 m (55 ft 9 in)
- Diameter of fuselage: 2·40 m (7 ft 10½ in)
- Height overall: 6·50 m (21 ft 4 in)
- Tailplane span: 7·50 m (24 ft 7¼ in)
- Wheel track: 4·52 m (14 ft 10 in)
- Wheelbase: 7·47 m (24 ft 6 in)
- Rear cabin door:
  - Height: 1·74 m (5 ft 8½ in)
  - Width: 0·94 m (3 ft 1 in)
- Service door:
  - Height: 1·20 m (3 ft 11¼ in)
  - Width: 0·55 m (1 ft 9½ in)

DIMENSIONS, INTERNAL:
- Cabin: Length: 7·07 m (23 ft 2½ in)
  - Max width: 2·15 m (7 ft 0¾ in)
  - Max height: 1·85 m (6 ft 0¾ in)

AREA:
- Wings, gross: 70·00 m² (753·5 sq ft)

WEIGHTS AND LOADINGS (A: 27 seats, B: 32 seats, C: 16 seats, D: executive version):
- Weight empty:
  - A: 9,010-9,400 kg (19,865-20,725 lb)
  - B: 9,400 kg (20,725 lb)
  - D: 9,560-9,850 kg (21,075-21,715 lb)
- Max payload:
  - A: 2,300 kg (5,070 lb)
  - B: 2,720 kg (6,000 lb)
  - C: 1,360 kg (3,000 lb)
  - D: 990 kg (2,180 lb)
- Max fuel weight:
  - A: 2,125-4,000 kg (4,685-8,820 lb)
  - B: 4,000 kg (8,820 lb)
  - D: 3,000-4,000 kg (6,615-8,820 lb)
- Normal T-O weight:
  - A: 12,360-15,500 kg (27,250-34,170 lb)
  - B: 15,500 kg (34,170 lb)
  - D: 12,360-15,000 kg (27,250-33,070 lb)
- Max T-O weight:
  - A, B: 16,000 kg (35,275 lb)
  - C: 15,310 kg (33,750 lb)
  - D: 15,400 kg (33,950 lb)
- Max wing loading:
  - A, B: 230 kg/m² (47·1 lb/sq ft)

PERFORMANCE (corresponding to weights given above):
- Max level speed at S/L: Mach 0·7 (324 knots; 600 km/h; 373 mph) IAS
- Max cruising speed at 7,000 m (23,000 ft): 297 knots (550 km/h; 342 mph)
- T-O speed:
  - A, B: 86 knots (160 km/h; 100 mph)
  - D: 81-84 knots (150-156 km/h; 93-97 mph)
- Max rate of climb at S/L: 480 m (1,575 ft)/min
- Normal T-O run:
  - A, B: 700 m (2,297 ft)
  - C: 650 m (2,133 ft)
  - D: 660 m (2,165 ft)
- Normal landing run:
  - A, C, D: 320 m (1,050 ft)
  - B: 360 m (1,182 ft)
- Range with max payload at 254 knots (470 km/h; 292 mph) at 8,000 m (31,500 ft), with reserves:
  - A, C, D: 971 nm (1,800 km; 1,118 miles)
  - B: 782 nm (1,450 km; 900 miles)
- Range with max fuel at 254 knots (470 km/h; 292 mph) at 8,000 m (26,250 ft), with reserves:
  - All versions: 971 nm (1,800 km; 1,118 miles)
- Max range at 254 knots (470 km/h; 292 mph) at 8,000 m (26,250 ft), no reserves:
  - All versions: 1,080 nm (2,000 km; 1,240 miles)

YAKOVLEV Yak-42

NATO reporting name: Clobber

On the basis of experience with the Yak-40, the Yakovlev design bureau is developing for Aeroflot this larger civil airliner with a similar three-engined layout. According to Alexander Yakovlev, the basic design objectives were simple construction, reliability in operation, economy and the ability to operate in remote areas with widely differing climatic conditions. Up to 2,000 aircraft in this category are needed, for use particularly on feederline services extending north and south from the main east-west trans-Siberian trunk routes.

Three prototypes of the Yak-42 were ordered initially. The first of these (CCCP-1974) flew for the first time on 7 March 1975, with a wing sweepback of 11°, and was furnished as a 100-passenger local-service version with carry-on baggage and coat stowage fore and aft of the cabin. The second prototype (CCCP-1975) had 23° of wing sweep, and cabin windows which extended further forward and rearward on each side, indicating that it was representative of the 120-seat version with three more rows of seats and no carry-on baggage areas. The third prototype (CCCP-1976; re-registered subsequently as CCCP-42303) differed from the second only in detail, having hot-air de-icing on the tail surfaces as well as the wings; fairing discs over the main wheels and longer leg fairings to improve airflow over the doorless main landing gear when retracted; and movement further forward of the overwing emergency exits.

It was made known that a decision on the degree of wing sweep to be standardised for production aircraft would be taken after simultaneous evaluation of the prototypes, in terms of high-speed cruise, economy and low-speed handling characteristics. The 23° wing showed itself superior, and aircraft No. CCCP-42303, exhibited at the 1977 Paris Salon, was typical of the first series of 200 production Yak-42s, which will replace Tu-134s currently in Aeroflot service.

Each aircraft is furnished throughout with six-abreast seats at a pitch of 80 cm (31·5 in). Access to the cabin is by airstair doors under the rear fuselage and at the front of the cabin on the port side, making the aircraft independent of airport ground equipment. There is a fifth emergency exit door, on the starboard side, opposite the forward airstair.

Two holds are provided for cargo-carrying, with a chain-drive handling system built into the aircraft's floor. The forward hold can accommodate six containers, each with a capacity of 2·2 m³ (77·7 cu ft); the rear hold takes three similar containers.

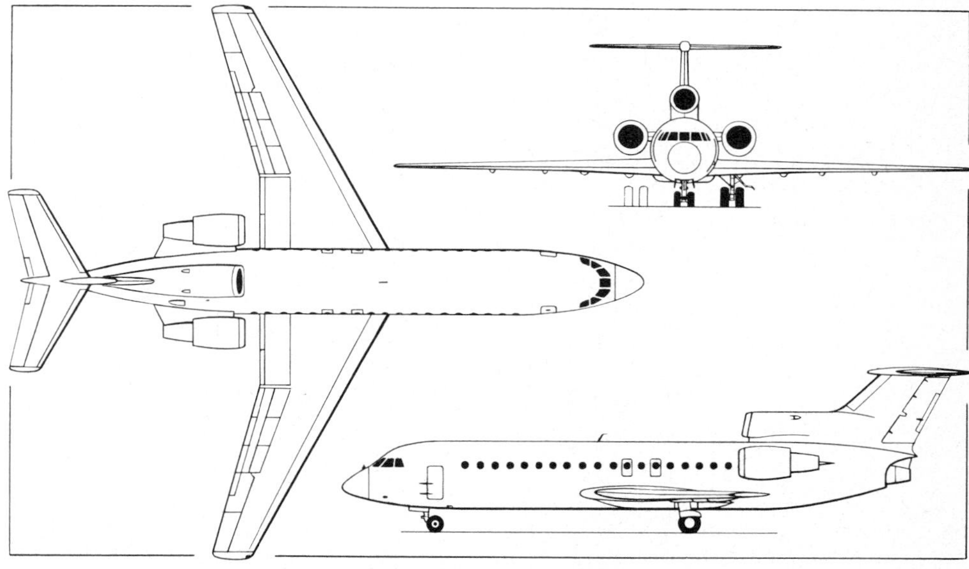

Yakovlev Yak-42 three-turbofan short-range passenger transport *(Pilot Press)*

Yakovlev Yak-42 short-range transport (three Lotarev D-36 turbofan engines) *(Brian M. Service)*

A flight crew of two is normal, with provision for a high degree of automation, including an area navigation system. Control surfaces are actuated hydraulically. To cater for rough-field operations, a heavy-duty tricycle landing gear is fitted, with twin wheels on each unit and low-pressure tyres, size 1300 × 480 on main wheels, 930 × 305 on nosewheels.

The Yak-42 is powered by three D-36 high bypass ratio (5·34 : 1) turbofan engines, designed under the leadership of Vladimir Lotarev at the Zaporozhye engine works. Take-off rating of each engine is 63·2 kN (14,200 lb st), and the Yak-42 is intended to use all three engines at cruise power during flight. Special care has been taken during design to ensure that the D-36 will conform with national and international limits on smoke and noise; and the Yak-42 is intended to operate in temperatures ranging from −50°C to +50°C. Thrust reversers will be fitted to the two outer engines of production aircraft. An APU will also be standard, for engine starting and ground services.

DIMENSIONS, EXTERNAL:
- Wing span: 34·20 m (112 ft 2½ in)
- Wing sweepback: 23°
- Length overall: 36·38 m (119 ft 4¼ in)
- Height overall: 9·80 m (32 ft 1¾ in)
- Tailplane span: 10·80 m (35 ft 5 in)
- Wheel track: 5·63 m (18 ft 5¾ in)
- Wheelbase: 14·78 m (48 ft 6 in)

DIMENSION, INTERNAL:
- Cabin: Max width: 3·80 m (12 ft 6 in)

AREA:
- Wings, gross: 150 m² (1,615 sq ft)

WEIGHTS:
- Weight empty: 28,960 kg (63,845 lb)
- Max payload: 14,500 kg (32,000 lb)
- Max T-O weight: 52,000 kg (114,640 lb)

PERFORMANCE (estimated):
- Normal cruising speed at 7,600 m (25,000 ft): 442 knots (820 km/h; 510 mph)
- Approach speed: 114-119 knots (210-220 km/h; 131-137 mph)
- T-O field length: 1,800 m (5,900 ft)
- Landing from 15 m (50 ft): 1,100 m (3,610 ft)
- Range with max fuel 1,620 nm (3,000 km; 1,860 miles)
- Range with normal 10,500 kg (23,150 lb) payload, with reserves: 1,000 nm (1,850 km; 1,150 miles)
- Range with max payload, with reserves: 540 nm (1,000 km; 620 miles)

YAKOVLEV Yak-50

A Novosti Press Agency bulletin, dated 30 June 1975, stated that tests of a new Yakovlev sporting aircraft, designated Yak-50, had been carried out near Arsenyev in the Soviet far east. Mr Nikolai Sazykin, director of the Progress Engineering Works in which all Yakovlev sporting aircraft are assembled, was quoted as saying that the Yak-50 was intended to participate in the 1976 world aerobatic championships.

No descriptive details, specification or illustrations of the new aircraft were released. Test pilot Anatoly Sergeyev stated only that it was more advanced than the familiar Yak-18 training and aerobatic monoplane, with a more powerful engine, better manoeuvrability, a speed of over 215 knots (400 km/h; 248 mph) in a dive, and the ability to perform all aerobatics with its landing gear retracted or extended.

When six Yak-50s participated in the 1976 world aerobatic championships at Kiev, their evolution from the Yak-18 was apparent, but with significant changes. Basic configuration is little different from that of the single-seat Yak-18PS, with tailwheel-type landing gear. This was deliberate, to keep the handling characteristics of the two types as similar as possible. However, overall dimensions are reduced; control surface hinge-lines have been moved to keep control forces light; and overall structural strength has been increased by switching entirely to metal covering. In particular, the fuselage is now semi-monocoque instead of steel tube with fabric covering to the rear of the cockpit. Designers responsible for these and other changes were Sergei Yakovlev (son of Alexander Yakovlev) and Yuri Yankievich.

The wings dispense with the Yak-18's centre-section and have 2° dihedral and 2° incidence, and retain an asymmetric section. To ensure a high power/weight ratio in such a large aircraft, the power plant is a 268 kW (360 hp) Vedeneev (Ivchenko) M-14P aircooled radial piston engine, driving a V-530TA-D35 two-blade variable-pitch propeller, instead of the 224 kW (300 hp) Ivchenko AI-14RF of the Yak-18PS. Main-wheel tyre size is 500 × 150, nosewheel tyre size 200 × 80. The main fuel tank, capacity 55 litres (12 Imp gallons), is aft of the engine firewall, the electrical system battery behind the pilot's seat. A Zyablik radio transceiver is standard.

Observers at the world championships at Kiev reported that the Yak-50s performed the all-important Aresti manoeuvres with smooth precision, their primary shortcoming being excessive directional stability. Yak-50s flown by V. Letsko and I. Egorov finished first and second in the men's competition. Others came fifth, seventh and ninth, to win the team prize. First five places in the women's championship were taken by Yak-50s.

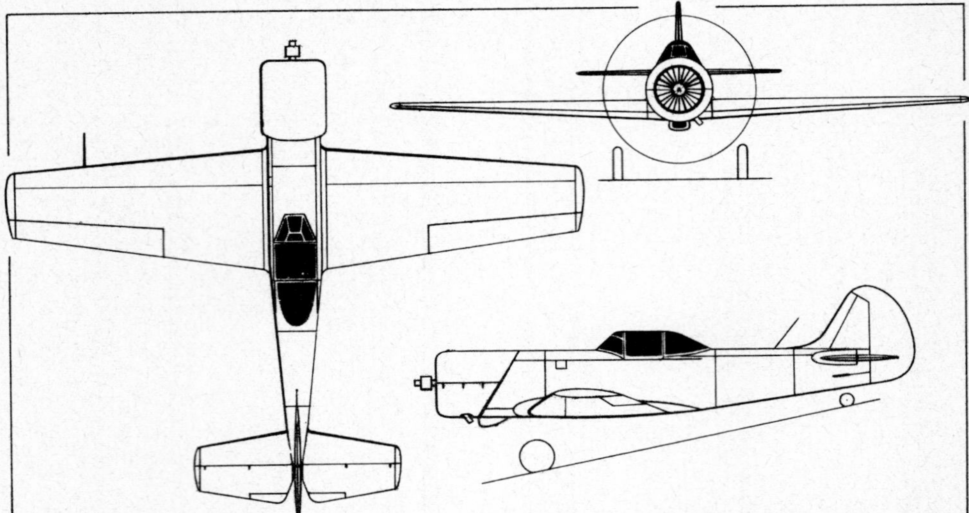

Photograph and three-view drawing *(Pilot Press)* **of the Yakovlev Yak-50, winner of the 1976 world aerobatic championships**

DIMENSIONS, EXTERNAL:
- Wing span: 9·50 m (31 ft 2 in)
- Length overall: 7·676 m (25 ft 2¼ in)
- Tailplane span: 3·16 m (10 ft 4½ in)
- Wheel track: 2·00 m (6 ft 6¾ in)
- Wheelbase: 5·10 m (16 ft 8¾ in)
- Propeller diameter: 2·00 m (6 ft 6¾ in)

AREAS:
- Wings, gross: 15·00 m² (161·5 sq ft)
- Ailerons (total): 1·95 m² (21·00 sq ft)
- Vertical tail surfaces (total): 1·48 m² (15·93 sq ft)
- Horizontal tail surfaces (total): 2·86 m² (30·78 sq ft)

WEIGHTS AND LOADINGS:
- Weight empty, equipped: 765 kg (1,686 lb)
- Max T-O weight: 900 kg (1,984 lb)
- Max wing loading: 60 kg/m² (12·29 lb/sq ft)
- Max power loading: 3·36 kg/kW (5·51 lb/hp)

PERFORMANCE:
- Never-exceed speed: 226 knots (420 km/h; 261 mph)
- Max level speed: 173 knots (320 km/h; 199 mph)
- T-O speed: 65 knots (120 km/h; 75 mph)
- Rate of climb at S/L: 960 m (3,150 ft)/min
- Service ceiling: 5,500 m (18,045 ft)
- T-O run: 200 m (657 ft)
- Landing run: 250 m (820 ft)
- Max range at 1,000 m (3,280 ft), with 120 litres (26·4 Imp gallons) auxiliary fuel, reserve of 10 litres (2·2 Imp gallons): 267 nm (495 km; 307 miles)
- Endurance at 500 m (1,640 ft) with 52 litres (11·4 Imp gallons) auxiliary fuel, reserve of 10 litres (2·2 Imp gallons): 48 min
- *g* limits: +9; −6

YAKLOVLEV YAK-52

Announced in late 1978, the Yak-52 is a tandem-cockpit variant of the Yak-50, with unchanged span and length, but with a semi-retractable tricycle landing gear. Although aesthetically unattractive, this last feature is intended to reduce damage in a wheels-up landing.

The Yak-52 is expected to replace the Yak-18, which has been the standard *ab initio* trainer for Soviet pilots since the mid-1940s. Alexander Yakovlev has believed for many years that aeroplanes to be flown by young people should be designed by members of the Komsomol youth brigades and light aircraft enthusiasts, under experienced leadership. The enthusiasm engendered by this policy led to first flight of the prototype Yak-52 less than a year after its design was started. Flight testing was then undertaken by pilots qualified as Soviet Masters of Sport, as well as professional test pilots. Production may be entrusted to the Romanian aircraft industry, under the COMECON

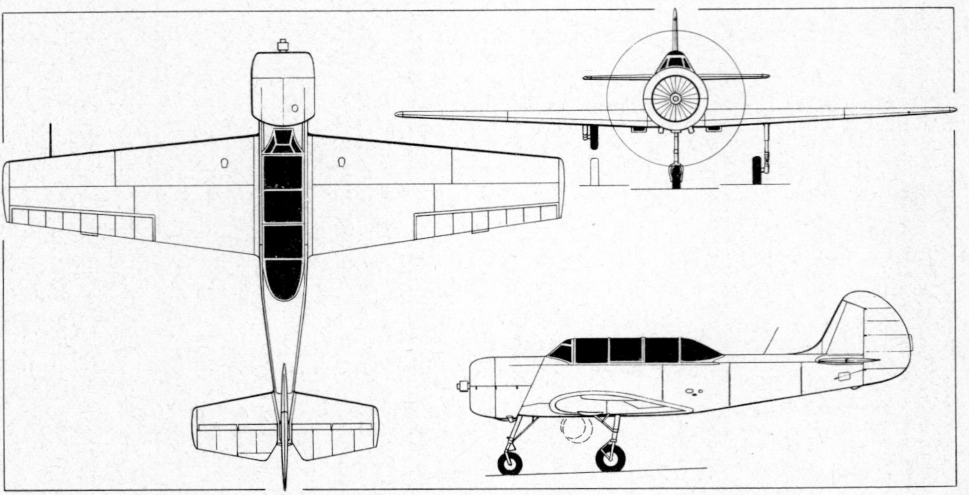

Yakovlev Yak-52 tandem two-seat primary trainer *(Pilot Press)*

The semi-retractable landing gear of the Yak-52 can be seen clearly in this photograph

(Council for Mutual Economic Assistance) programme.

TYPE: Tandem two-seat piston-engined primary trainer.

WINGS: Cantilever low-wing monoplane of single-spar stressed-skin all-metal construction. Each wing comprises a single straight-tapered panel, attached directly to the side of the fuselage. Fabric-covered slotted ailerons. Light alloy split trailing-edge flaps. Ground-adjustable tab on each aileron.

FUSELAGE: Conventional light alloy semi-monocoque structure.

TAIL UNIT: Cantilever light alloy structure. Fixed surfaces metal covered; control surfaces fabric covered. Horn-balanced rudder, with ground-adjustable tab. Mass-balanced elevators. Controllable tab in port elevator.

LANDING GEAR: Semi-retractable tricycle type, with single wheel on each unit. Pneumatic retraction, nosewheel rearward, main units forward. All three wheels remain fully exposed to airflow, against the undersurface of the fuselage and wings respectively, to offer greater safety in the event of a wheels-up emergency landing. Oleo-pneumatic shock-absorbers. Main-wheel tyre size 500 × 150; nosewheel tyre size 400 × 150. Pneumatic brakes. Skis can be fitted in place of wheels for Winter operations, permissible at temperatures down to −42°C.

POWER PLANT: One 269 kW (360 hp) Vedeneev M-14P nine-cylinder aircooled radial engine, driving a two-blade variable-pitch propeller type V-530TA-D35, without spinner. Louvres in front of cowling to regulate cooling. Two-part cowling, split on horizontal centreline. Two fuel tanks, in wing roots forward of spar, each with capacity of 65 litres (14·25 Imp gallons). Additional tank of 5·5 litres (1·25 Imp gallons) capacity supplies engine during inverted flight. Oil capacity 20 litres (4·5 Imp gallons).

ACCOMMODATION: Tandem seats for pupil and instructor (at rear) under long 'glasshouse' canopy, with separate rearward-sliding hood over each seat. Seats and dual flying controls are adjustable. Sides of cockpit have a soft synthetic lining. Heating and ventilation standard.

SYSTEMS: No hydraulic system. Independent main and emergency pneumatic systems, for flap actuation, landing gear retraction, engine starting, and wheel brake control. Pneumatic systems supplied by two compressed air bottles, mounted behind rear seat and recharged in flight by an AK-50T compressor. GSR-3000M engine-driven generator supplies 27V electrical system. Battery in port wing.

AVIONICS AND EQUIPMENT: Dual engine and flying instruments. Equipment includes GMK-1A gyro-compass, ARK-15M automatic radio compass, Landysh-5 VHF com and SPU-9 intercom.

DIMENSIONS, EXTERNAL:

Wing span	9·50 m (31 ft 2 in)
Length overall	7·676 m (25 ft 2¼ in)
Height overall	2·95 m (9 ft 8¼ in)
Propeller diameter	2·40 m (7 ft 10½ in)

AREA:

Wings, gross	15·00 m² (161·5 sq ft)

WEIGHTS AND LOADINGS:

Basic operating weight	1,000 kg (2,205 lb)
Max T-O weight	1,290 kg (2,844 lb)
Max wing loading	86·0 kg/m² (17·61 lb/sq ft)
Max power loading	4·80 kg/kW (7·90 lb/hp)

PERFORMANCE:

Never-exceed speed	194 knots (360 km/h; 223 mph)
Max level speed	154 knots (285 km/h; 177 mph)
Landing speed	60 knots (110 km/h; 69 mph)
Max rate of climb at S/L	600 m (1,970 ft)/min
Service ceiling	6,000 m (19,700 ft)
T-O run	170 m (558 ft)
Landing run	200 m (656 ft)
Range with max fuel	297 nm (550 km; 341 miles)
Endurance with max fuel	2 h 50 min
g limits	+7; −5

UNITED KINGDOM

AIRCRAFT DESIGNS

AIRCRAFT DESIGNS (BEMBRIDGE) LTD

ADDRESS: Bembridge Fort, Sandown, Isle of Wight
Telephone: Brading (098372) 461
Telex: 86448 Micair G

CHAIRMAN: R. C. Britten

DIRECTORS:
J. M. McMahon
N. J. R. James, MA (Cantab)
F. H. Mann

TECHNICAL DIRECTOR AND CHIEF EXECUTIVE:
D. A. Berryman, CEng, FRAeS

In 1976 the late John Britten resigned from the board of The Fairey Company, which had acquired Britten-Norman in 1972, in order to concentrate on aircraft design. Following his death in mid-1977 the Sheriff project (see Addenda to the 1977-78 *Jane's*) was resumed under the Chairmanship of Mr Robin Britten, who invited Mr Denis Berryman, CEng, FRAeS, to take up the post of Technical Director of Aircraft Designs (Bembridge), a company owned jointly by Air Bembridge and Crop Culture (Aerial) Ltd.

The initial Sheriff project, for an economical twin-engined trainer, has now developed into a lower/middle range four-seat touring or air taxi aircraft, while still retaining the originally conceived option of a lower-powered twin-engined trainer, particularly suitable for low-cost military training.

Construction of a prototype began in March 1979, at which time it was anticipated that a first flight would be made in the early months of 1980. Certification is scheduled for early 1981.

BRITTEN SHERIFF

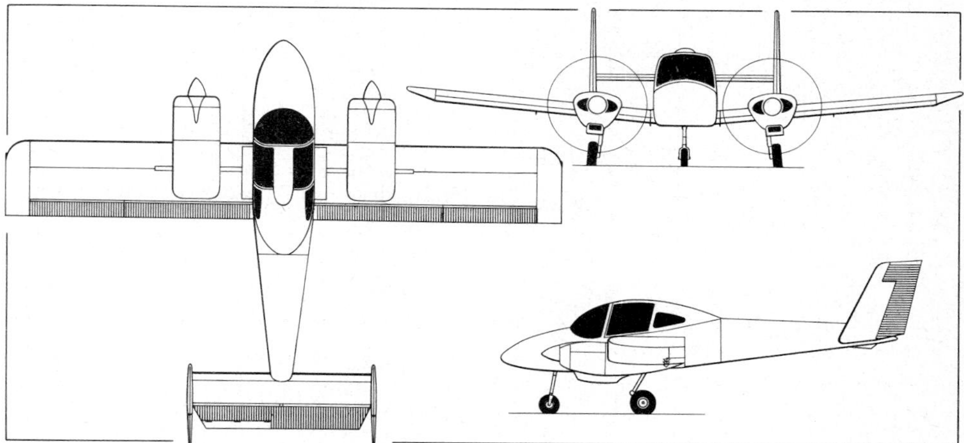

Aircraft Designs (Britten) Sheriff two/four-seat training and utility aircraft *(Pilot Press)*

TYPE: Two/four-seat lightweight training and utility aircraft.

WINGS: Cantilever low-wing monoplane. Wing section NACA 23015. Conventional single-spar structure of 2024 light alloy. The main spar is a built-up I-section, and the basic structure includes light alloy ribs and a stressed leading-edge skin, part of which forms an integral fuel tank in each wing. Frise-type light alloy ailerons with corrugated skins. Plain light alloy trailing-edge flaps with corrugated skins. No tabs.

FUSELAGE: Simple single-curvature rectangular box structure of 2024 light alloy. Four longerons and light alloy formers. Nosecone and fairings of glassfibre. Electronics/equipment bay in nose.

TAIL UNIT: Cantilever structure of 2024 light alloy, with twin endplate fins and rudders. Elevator and rudders have corrugated skins. Trim tab in port half of elevator.

LANDING GEAR: Non-retractable (optionally retractable) tricycle type with single wheel on each unit. Trailing-link main legs, with shock-absorption by air/oil struts. Nosewheel has oleo-pneumatic shock-strut and is fully castoring. Main wheels and tyres size 6·00-6. Nosewheel and tyre size 5·00-5.

POWER PLANT: Tourer has two 119 kW (160 hp) Lycoming O-320-H flat-four engines, each driving a two-blade constant-speed fully-feathering metal propeller with spinner. Club trainer has two 85·7 kW (115 hp) Lycoming O-235-L2C flat-fours, each driving a two-blade fixed-pitch metal propeller. Integral wing fuel tanks with total capacity of 277 litres (61 Imp gallons). Refuelling point in leading-edge of each wing.

ACCOMMODATION: Tourer has four forward-facing seats. Trainer has two side-by-side seats, with dual controls as standard. Two 'gull-wing' doors provide access.

DIMENSIONS, EXTERNAL:

Wing span	10·06 m (33 ft 0 in)
Wing chord (constant)	1·40 m (4 ft 7 in)
Wing aspect ratio	7·26
Length overall	6·98 m (22 ft 11 in)
Propeller diameter	1·83 m (6 ft 0 in)

AREAS:

Wings, gross	13·94 m² (150·0 sq ft)
Vertical tail surfaces (total)	2·60 m² (28·0 sq ft)
Horizontal tail surfaces (total)	3·25 m² (35·0 sq ft)

WEIGHTS AND LOADINGS (estimated. A: four-seat tourer/air taxi with fixed landing gear; B: four-seat tourer/air taxi with retractable landing gear; C: two-seat club trainer):

Weight empty: A	810 kg (1,785 lb)
B	855 kg (1,885 lb)
C	716 kg (1,579 lb)
Max T-O weight: A	1,270 kg (2,800 lb)
B	1,338 kg (2,950 lb)
C	975 kg (2,150 lb)
Max wing loading: A	91·3 kg/m² (18·7 lb/sq ft)
B	96·0 kg/m² (19·7 lb/sq ft)
C	69·8 kg/m² (14·3 lb/sq ft)
Max power loading: A	5·34 kg/kW (8·75 lb/hp)
B	6·08 kg/kW (9·95 lb/hp)
C	5·69 kg/kW (9·35 lb/hp)

PERFORMANCE (estimated, A: engines 110 kW; 148 hp at 2,500 rpm at 1,270 kg; 2,800 lb T-O weight; B: engines 110 kW; 148 hp at 2,500 rpm at 1,338 kg; 2,950 lb T-O weight; C: engines 85·7 kW; 115 hp at 975 kg; 2,150 lb T-O weight):

Max level speed:	
A	139 knots (257 km/h; 160 mph)
B	150 knots (278 km/h; 173 mph)
C	127 knots (235 km/h; 146 mph)
Cruising speed at 75% power:	
A	127 knots (235 km/h; 146 mph)
B	137 knots (254 km/h; 158 mph)
C	122 knots (225 km/h; 140 mph)
Cruising speed at 60% power:	
A	115 knots (212 km/h; 132 mph)
B	123 knots (229 km/h; 142 mph)
Max rate of climb at S/L: A	405 m (1,330 ft)/min
B	396 m (1,300 ft)/min
C	350 m (1,150 ft)/min
Rate of climb at S/L, one engine out:	
A	91 m (300 ft)/min

B 94 m (310 ft)/min
C 49 m (160 ft)/min
T-O to 15 m (50 ft): A 367 m (1,205 ft)
B 421 m (1,380 ft)
C 381 m (1,250 ft)
Landing from 15 m (50 ft): A 480 m (1,575 ft)
B 501 m (1,645 ft)
C 369 m (1,210 ft)
Range with max fuel, no reserves:
A 540 nm (1,000 km; 621 miles)
B 580 nm (1,075 km; 668 miles)
C (132 litres; 29 Imp gallons)
310 nm (575 km; 357 miles)

BAe
BRITISH AEROSPACE

HEADQUARTERS: Brooklands Road, Weybridge, Surrey KT13 0SJ
Telephone: Weybridge (0932) 45522
Telex: 27111
LONDON OFFICE: 100 Pall Mall, London SW1Y 5HR
Telephone: 01 930 1020
Telex: 24353
CORPORATION BOARD:
The Rt Hon The Lord Beswick, PC (Chairman)
A. H. C. Greenwood, CBE, JP, CEng, FRAeS (Deputy Chairman)
L. W. Buck (Industrial Relations)
Air Chief Marshal Sir Peter Fletcher, KCB, OBE, DFC, AFC, RAF(Retd) (Corporate Strategy and Planning)
B. E. Friend, FCA (Financial Director)
D. O. Gladwin, CBE, JP (part-time member)
G. R. Jefferson, CBE, BSc (Eng), CEng, MIMechE, FRAeS, FRSA (Chairman and Chief Executive, Dynamics Group)
Sir Frederick Page, KB, CBE, FRS, MA, CEng, FRAeS (Chairman and Chief Executive, Aircraft Group)
Dr A. W. Pearce, CBE, PhD (part-time member)
E. G. Rubython, CBE (Deputy Chief Executive, Aircraft Group)
J. T. Stamper, MA, CEng, FRAeS (Technical Director)
SECRETARY/LEGAL ADVISER: B. Cookson, LLB
TREASURER: J. D. Hanson, LLB, FCA
PUBLIC RELATIONS CONSULTANT: W. Simpson
PUBLIC RELATIONS OFFICER (HQ): D. A. Dorman

British Aerospace was established by the Aircraft and Shipbuilding Industries Act 1977, as a result of which, on 29 April 1977, the ownership of British Aircraft Corporation (Holdings) Ltd, Hawker Siddeley Aviation Ltd, Hawker Siddeley Dynamics Ltd and Scottish Aviation Ltd was vested in the Corporation. Initially, these four companies continued to trade under their existing names. With effect from 1 January 1978, a new structure for British Aerospace was implemented, whereby the Corporation functions through two operating groups, an Aircraft Group and a Dynamics Group (see Air-launched Missiles section).

British Aerospace has the following overseas subsidiaries: British Scandinavian Aviation AB, British Aerospace Australia Ltd, British Aerospace Inc; and the following UK subsidiaries: British Aerospace (Insurance Brokers) Ltd, British Aerospace (Insurance) Ltd, British Aircraft Corporation (Pension Fund Trustees) Ltd and HSA/HSD (Pension Fund Trustees) Ltd.

Its associated companies are SEPECAT (formed in May 1966 by BAC and Breguet Aviation to control the development and production of the Jaguar tactical strike fighter and trainer), Panavia Aircraft GmbH (formed in March 1969 by BAC, MBB and Aeritalia to manage the development and production of the Tornado multi-role combat aircraft), Dulles International Aeroservices Inc (formed in 1976 by BAC (USA) Inc and Rolls-Royce Aero Engines of the USA to build and operate a new facility at Washington's Dulles International Airport to supply customers in North America with spares and engineering support), Arab-British Dynamics Ltd (inaugurated in 1977 by BAC Guided Weapons Division and the Arab Organisation for Industrialisation to manufacture the Swingfire missile in Egypt), Frames Travel (Fylde) Ltd and Remploy Services Ltd.

BRITISH AEROSPACE AIRCRAFT GROUP

HEADQUARTERS: Richmond Road, Kingston upon Thames, Surrey KT2 5QS
Telephone: 01 546 7741
Telex: 23726
GROUP BOARD:
Sir Frederick Page, KB, CBE, FRS, MA, CEng, FRAeS, FBIM (Chairman & Chief Executive)
E. G. Rubython, CBE (Deputy Chief Executive)
A. F. Atkin, CBE, BSc (Hons), DipAe (Hull), CEng, FIMechE, FRAeS (Managing Director, Military)
J. L. Thorne (Managing Director, Civil)
G. W. Carr, FCIS, MRAeS (Administration Director)
J. L. Glasscock, BA, FCIS, JP (Commercial Director)
P. Jefferson, CEng, MRAeS, MIMechE (Production Director)
F. E. Roe, DIC, BSc, CEng, ACGI, FRAeS (Resources Director)
R. H. Sawyer, FCA, FCMA, JDip, MA (Financial Director)
J. T. Stamper, MA, CEng, FRAeS (Technical Director)
A. S. Watson (Marketing Director, Military)
N. V. Barber, BA, MSc (Divisional Managing Director, Manchester Division)
C. M. Chandler, ACWA (Divisional Managing Director, Kingston-Brough Division)
M. J. Goldsmith, DIC, CEng, FRAeS (Divisional Managing Director, Hatfield-Chester Division)
L. Phillimore, BSc, CEng, FRAeS (Divisional Managing Director, Scottish Division)
J. Ferguson Smith, FCA (Deputy Managing Director, Civil; Divisional Chairman, Weybridge-Bristol Division; and Marketing Director, Civil)
M. G. Wilde, OBE, BSc, DipAe, CEng, FRAeS (Divisional Managing Director, Weybridge-Bristol Division)
I. R. Yates, BEng, CEng, FRAeS, FIMechE (Divisional Managing Director, Warton Division)
GROUP SECRETARY: V. H. Lidstone
MILITARY ADVISER: Air Chief Marshal Sir Denis Smallwood, GBE, KCB, DSO, DFC
PUBLIC RELATIONS MANAGER: R. A. C. Gardner

British Aerospace Aircraft Group was formed officially on 1 January 1978 by the reorganisation of the airframe interests of British Aircraft Corporation, Hawker Siddeley Aviation and Scottish Aviation. The Group is organised into six Divisions: Kingston-Brough; Manchester; Warton; Hatfield-Chester; Weybridge-Bristol; and Scottish.

Civil aircraft programmes include development and production of the British Aerospace 146 four-turbofan feederliner, the twin-turbofan HS 125 business aircraft and BAC One-Eleven transport, and the twin-turboprop HS 748 and Jetstream transports. Military aircraft programmes include manufacture of the Harrier and Sea Harrier V/STOL combat aircraft, Hawk ground attack/trainer and Bulldog basic and aerobatic trainer. Development of the Nimrod for anti-submarine warfare and airborne early warning duties continues. BAe also offers HS 748 variants for military transport and maritime patrol missions.

Major international collaborative programmes include the AV-8B development of the Harrier with McDonnell Douglas in the USA, the Tornado multi-role combat aircraft with MBB of Germany and Aeritalia of Italy, the Jaguar with Dassault-Breguet of France, the One-Eleven with Romania, and the Concorde supersonic transport with Aérospatiale of France. In 1978, British Aerospace became a full 20% risk-sharing partner in the Airbus Industrie A300 wide-body airliner programme.

In defence support, British Aerospace holds large contracts in the Middle East, notably in Saudi Arabia where a continuing programme of training and maintenance for the Royal Saudi Air Force involves more than 2,000 expatriate employees.

BRITISH AEROSPACE AIRCRAFT GROUP, HATFIELD/CHESTER DIVISION

ADDRESS: Hatfield, Hertfordshire AL10 9TL
Telephone: Hatfield (07072) 62345
Telex: 22411
OTHER WORKS: Broughton, near Chester, Clwyd
DIVISIONAL BOARD:
J. L. Thorne (Chairman)
M. J. Goldsmith, DIC, CEng, FRAeS, (Managing Director)
J. P. Smith, CBE, CEng, FRAeS (Deputy Managing Director)
C. F. Bethwaite (Project Director, BAe 146)
B. J. Champion, CA(SA) (Resources Director; and Finance Director, Chester)
P. Edwards (Director; and General Manager, Chester)
J. Humphreys, ACCA (Financial Director)
J. A. Johnstone, OBE, CEng, FRAeS, AMSLAET (Marketing Director)
R. C. Meakins, MBIM (Administration Director; and Commercial Director, Chester)
P. R. Owen, CEng, FRAeS (Technical Director)
J. S. Paterson, CA (Commercial Director)
G. R. Wilkinson (Production Director)
SECRETARY: R. F. Kirkby
PUBLIC RELATIONS MANAGER: J. E. Scott

Main activities of this Division include development of the HS 125 and variants; design, development and production of A300 and A310 wings for Airbus Industrie; development and production of the British Aerospace 146, work on which is also taking place at other Group factories; responsibility for Trident aircraft in service.

BRITISH AEROSPACE AIRCRAFT GROUP, KINGSTON/BROUGH DIVISION

ADDRESS: Richmond Road, Kingston upon Thames, Surrey KT2 5QS
Telephone: 01 546 7741
Telex: 23726
OTHER WORKS: Dunsfold Aerodrome, Godalming, Surrey; Hamble, Hants; Brough, North Humberside; Holme-on-Spalding Moor Aerodrome, Yorks; Bitteswell Aerodrome, Lutterworth, Leicestershire
DIVISIONAL BOARD:
A. F. Atkin, CBE, BSc, DipAe, CEng, FIMechE, FRAeS (Chairman)
C. M. Chandler, ACWA (Managing Director)
R. G. Adolphus, BSc, CEng, FRAeS (Production Director)
K. Essex-Crosby, DipAe, CEng, FRAeS (Director)
J. W. Fozard, DCAe, BSc, CEng, FRAeS, FIMechE (Marketing Director)
R. H. Hill, CEng, MRAeS (Director)
R. S. Hooper, DCAe, DAe, CEng, MIMechE, FRAeS (Technical Director)
A. E. Lane (Resources Director; and General Manager, Hamble)
L. W. Milsom (Director; and General Manager, Brough)
A. C. Spencer (Director)
J. F. White, FCA, MBIM, MRAeS (Financial Director)
A. H. Whitehouse, TEng, MRAeS (Administration Director; and General Manager, Bitteswell)
SECRETARY: T. A. Fletcher
PUBLIC RELATIONS MANAGER: A. D. F. Lewis

Main activities of this Division include design, development and production of the Harrier, Sea Harrier and Hawk; production of components for the A300 Airbus; product support of the Buccaneer and Phantom; Phantom wing modifications; overhaul and conversion of Hunter, Shackleton, Vulcan, Gnat and Buccaneer aircraft.

BRITISH AEROSPACE AIRCRAFT GROUP, MANCHESTER DIVISION

ADDRESS: Greengate, Middleton, Manchester M24 1SA
Telephone: 061 681 2020
Telex: 667015
OTHER WORKS: Woodford Aerodrome, Woodford, Cheshire
DIVISIONAL BOARD:
A. F. Atkin, CBE, BSc, DipAe, CEng, FIMechE, FRAeS (Chairman)
N. V. Barber, BA, MSc (Managing Director)
H. T. Healy, ACMA (Financial Director)
J. E. Perry, BSc, MSc, CEng, MIMechE, MIProdE (Production Director)
J. B. Scott-Wilson, MA, FRAeS (Director)
B. F. W. Tull, CBE (Marketing Director)
S. C. Ward, BSc (Commercial Director)
G. A. Whitehead, CBE, CEng, FIMechE, FRAeS, AMCT (Technical Director)
SECRETARY: S. C. Ward, BSc
PUBLIC RELATIONS OFFICER: J. R. Gray

Main activities of this Division include design, development and production of the HS 748 and Nimrod; development of the AEW Nimrod; production of A300 Airbus components.

BRITISH AEROSPACE AIRCRAFT GROUP, SCOTTISH DIVISION

ADDRESS: Prestwick International Airport, Ayrshire KA9 2RW
Telephone: Prestwick (0292) 79888
Telex: 77432

DIVISIONAL BOARD:
J. L. Thorne (Chairman)
L. Phillimore, BSc, CEng, FRAeS (Managing Director)
W. Agnew (Production Director)
D. McConnell (Commercial Director)
J. R. Woods (Administration Director)

SECRETARY: J. W. Connell
SALES ADMINISTRATOR/PUBLICITY: R. Watt

Main activities of this Division include Bulldog and Jetstream production; production of fuselages for Lockheed C-130 Hercules and components for Lockheed TriStars; engine production and overhaul.

BRITISH AEROSPACE AIRCRAFT GROUP, WARTON DIVISION

ADDRESS: Warton Aerodrome, Preston, Lancashire PR4 1AX
Telephone: Preston (0772) 633333
Telex: 67627

OTHER WORKS: Preston, Lancashire; Samlesbury Aerodrome, Blackburn, Lancashire

DIVISIONAL BOARD:
A. F. Atkin, CBE, BSc, DipAe, CEng, FIMechE, FRAeS (Chairman)
I. R. Yates, BEng, CEng, FRAeS, FIMechE (Managing Director)
F. E. Roe, DIC, BSc, CEng, ACGI, FRAeS (Deputy Managing Director)
R. Dickson, MA (Cantab), CEng, FRAeS (Research Director)
R. H. Evans (Commercial Director and Director-in-charge, India)
S. Gillibrand, MSc, CEng, FRAeS (Production Director)
J. Glover, FCMA (Financial Director)
B. O. Heath, BSc, DIC, CEng, MRAeS, Hon MIED (Technical Director and Panavia Director of Systems Engineering; Warton)
Air Chief Marshal Sir Frederick Rosier, GCB, CBE, DSO (Director, Saudi Arabia)
T. O. Williams, MA, CEng, FIMechE, MIEE (Administration Director)

SECRETARY: L. F. Trueman, FCCA
PUBLICITY MANAGER: A. F. Johnston

Main activities of this Division include design, development and production with MBB and Aeritalia of the Panavia Tornado; joint development and production with Dassault-Breguet of the SEPECAT Jaguar; product support of the Jet Provost, Lightning and Strikemaster; conversion programmes for the Canberra; provision of advanced defence support programmes.

BRITISH AEROSPACE AIRCRAFT GROUP, WEYBRIDGE/BRISTOL DIVISION

ADDRESS: Brooklands Road, Weybridge, Surrey KT13 0SF
Telephone: Weybridge (0932) 45522
Telex: 27111

OTHER WORKS: Filton House, Filton, Bristol; Bournemouth (Hurn) Airport, Christchurch, Dorset

DIVISIONAL BOARD:
J. Ferguson Smith, FCA, FRAeS (Chairman)
M. G. Wilde, OBE, BSc, DipAe, CEng, FRAeS (Managing Director)
K. Bentley, MA, CEng, MRAeS (Technical Director)
W. R. Coomber, CEng, FRAeS (Resources Director; and Chief Executive, Weybridge)
G. Hanby, FCA, FCWA (Commercial Director)
J. T. Jefferies, CEng, FIProdE (Administration Director; and Chief Executive, Filton)
L. J. Rogers, OBE, MA (Marketing Director)
A. E. Rowland (Production Director)
B. G. Thomas (Project Director, One-Eleven and Romania)
J. L. Thorne (Director)
E. B. Trubshaw, CBE, MVO, FRAeS (Director of Flight Test and Concorde)
D. Wynne, FCWA (Financial Director)

SECRETARY: H. T. Fream
DIVISIONAL PUBLIC RELATIONS MANAGER: N. A. Barfield
PUBLIC RELATIONS MANAGER, FILTON: H. Berry

Main activities of this Division include development and production of the One-Eleven; support for the One-Eleven, Concorde, VC10, Vanguard, Viscount, Britannia and Bristol Freighter; major subcontract work; major component manufacture for the BAe 146.

Two contracts, announced on 23 May 1978, involve Filton in replacing the windscreens of 45 General Dynamics F-111 aircraft from the USAF base at Lakenheath, Suffolk, and replacing the pyrotechnic ejection systems and other maintenance tasks on a further 19 aircraft. Another major contract is for the conversion of five VC10 and four Super VC10 commercial transports to tanker configuration for the Royal Air Force.

Artist's impression of one of the VC10 flight refuelling tankers to be produced at Weybridge/Bristol Division by conversion of ex-airline transports

BAe JETSTREAM SERIES 200

RAF designation: Jetstream T. Mk 1
Royal Navy designation: Jetstream T. Mk 2

The original H.P. 137 Jetstream was designed and developed between 1966 and 1970 by Handley Page Ltd, and was described in *Jane's* at that time. A number of Handley Page-built Jetstream Mk 1s are in service; others have been converted to Series 200 standard. This model originated with Handley Page and was developed subsequently by Jetstream Aircraft Ltd (see 1972-73 *Jane's*). A total of 32 civil Jetstreams were in service in the UK and the USA in mid-1979. A full UK type certificate in the transport category (passenger), for operations in performance group C, was awarded on 22 November 1972.

Twenty-six military Series 200s (Model 201) were built for the Royal Air Force, under the designation Jetstream T.Mk 1. One was written off; the remainder were put temporarily in store at St Athan, pending a decision on future requirements. It was announced in October 1976 that eight would be used by the RAF in the multi-engine pilot training role; 16 were to be converted to T. Mk 2s, with MEL E 190 airborne weather and terrain-mapping radar in a 'thimble' radome in the nose, for observer training with the Royal Navy; one was to be retained as a spare.

The first of the stored RAF Jetstreams were redelivered in November/December 1976, to No. 2 FTS at Leeming, Yorkshire, and the Central Flying School. Jetstream XX488, the aerodynamic prototype for the T.Mk 2 version, made its first flight on 7 April 1977. On 26 October 1978, the first T.Mk 2 was delivered to the Royal Navy, and the Jetstream began to replace Hunting Sea Princes then in service with No. 750 Squadron at Culdrose, Cornwall.

After assessing the marketing prospects for an improved version of the basic aircraft, Scottish Division of BAe was authorised to initiate production of the new Jetstream 31 in December 1978. This is described separately. Details of the Jetstream Series 200 can be found in the 1978-79 *Jane's*.

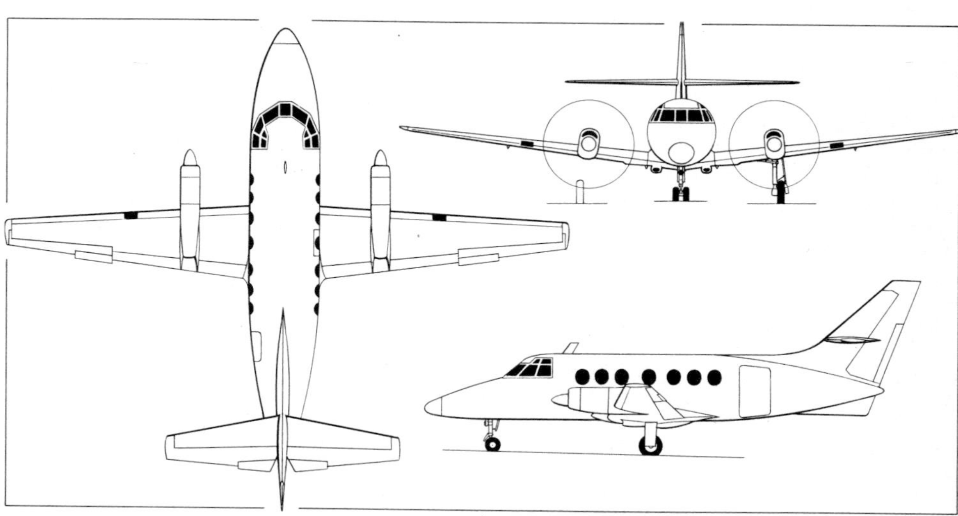

BAe Jetstream 31 twin-turboprop light commuter/executive transport *(Pilot Press)*

BAe JETSTREAM 31

The decision to proceed with development and production of this new version of the Jetstream was announced by British Aerospace on 5 December 1978. It will be available in three versions, as follows:

Commuter. Basic version, designed to carry 18/19 passengers and baggage, and able to operate three 87 nm (160 km; 100 mile) stage lengths without refuelling.

Corporate. Executive version, designed for eight to ten passengers, and able to carry eight passengers for 870 nm (1,610 km; 1,000 miles). Cabin design for North American market undertaken by Dave Ellies Industrial Design Inc, for fitting out at completion centres in the USA.

Special. Intended for military operation, and specialist roles such as airfield calibration, resources survey and protection.

It is intended to obtain FAA certification to FAR Pt 25; the Jetstream 31 will qualify for the currently proposed amendment to FAR Pt 23, and also the longer-term proposal for FAR Pt 24 which applies to commuter airlines. The first prototype was scheduled to fly in late 1979, and initial production deliveries will be made in 1981.

TYPE: Light commuter/executive transport.

WINGS: Cantilever low-wing monoplane. Wing section NACA 63A418 at root, NACA 63A412 at tip. Dihedral 7° from roots. Incidence 2° at root, 0° at tip. Sweepback 0° 34′ at quarter-chord. Aluminium alloy fail-safe structure. Aluminium alloy manually-operated

BAe Jetstream T.Mk 2 for observer training with the Royal Navy

Frise-type ailerons. Hydraulically-operated aluminium alloy double-slotted flaps. No slats or leading-edge flaps. Trim tab in each aileron. Goodrich pneumatic rubber-boot de-icing system for leading-edges.

Fuselage: Conventional aluminium alloy semi-monocoque fail-safe structure, with chemically-milled skin panels. Fully pressurised.

Tail Unit: Cantilever two-spar aluminium alloy structure. Fixed-incidence tailplane. Manually-operated control surfaces. Trim tabs in rudder and each elevator. Goodrich pneumatic rubber-boot de-icing system for leading-edges.

Landing Gear: Retractable tricycle type, with nosewheel steering. Hydraulic retraction, main wheels inward into wings, twin nosewheels forward. British Aerospace oleo-pneumatic shock-absorbers on all units. Dunlop wheels and tyres: main-wheel tyres size 28 × 9·00-12, pressure 3·93 bars (57 lb/sq in); nosewheel tyres size 6·00-6, pressure 2·34 bars (34 lb/sq in). No brake cooling. Anti-skid units.

Power Plant: Two 671 kW (900 shp) Garrett-AiResearch TPE 331-10 turboprop engines, each driving a Dowty Rotol four-blade variable- and reversible-pitch fully-feathering metal propeller. Fuel in integral tank in each wing, total capacity 1,745 litres (384 Imp gallons; 461 US gallons). Refuelling point on top of each outer wing.

Accommodation: Two seats side by side on flight deck, with provision for dual controls, though aircraft can be approved (subject to local regulations) for single-pilot operation. Main cabin can be furnished in commuter layout for up to 18 passengers, or with executive interior for 8/10 passengers, but optional layouts are available. Downward-opening passenger door, with integral airstairs, at rear of cabin on port side. Emergency exit over wing on starboard side. Baggage compartment in rear of cabin, aft of main door. Entire accommodation pressurised, heated, ventilated and air-conditioned. Toilet, galley and bar optional.

Systems: Air-conditioning system with cabin pressurisation at max differential of 0·38 bars (5·5 lb/sq in), providing a 2,440 m (8,000 ft) cabin altitude at 7,620 m (25,000 ft). Single hydraulic system with dual engine-driven pumps, for actuation of flaps, landing gear, brakes and nosewheel steering. Details of electrical and oxygen systems not finalised by Spring 1979. APU optional.

Avionics and Equipment: Not defined by Spring 1979.

Dimensions, external:

Wing span	15·85 m (52 ft 0 in)
Wing chord at root	2·19 m (7 ft 2½ in)
Wing chord at tip	0·80 m (2 ft 7¼ in)
Wing aspect ratio	10
Length overall	14·37 m (47 ft 1½ in)
Length of fuselage	13·40 m (43 ft 11½ in)
Height overall	5·32 m (17 ft 5½ in)
Fuselage: Max diameter	1·98 m (6 ft 6 in)
Tailplane span	6·60 m (21 ft 8 in)
Wheel track	5·94 m (19 ft 6 in)
Wheelbase	4·60 m (15 ft 1 in)
Propeller diameter	2·69 m (8 ft 10 in)
Passenger door: Height	1·42 m (4 ft 8 in)
Width	0·86 m (2 ft 10 in)
Emergency exit: Height	0·91 m (3 ft 0 in)
Width	0·56 m (1 ft 10 in)

Dimensions, internal:

Cabin, excl flight deck: Length	7·32 m (24 ft 0 in)
Max width	1·83 m (6 ft 0 in)
Max height	1·80 m (5 ft 11 in)
Floor area	8·35 m² (90 sq ft)
Volume	16·92 m³ (598 cu ft)
Baggage compartment volume (according to layout)	1·94-2·53 m³ (68·5-89·5 cu ft)

Areas:

Wings, gross	25·08 m² (270 sq ft)
Ailerons, aft of hinge line (total)	1·52 m² (16·4 sq ft)
Trailing-edge flaps (total)	3·25 m² (35·0 sq ft)
Vertical tail surfaces (total)	7·72 m² (83·1 sq ft)
Horizontal tail surfaces (total)	7·80 m² (84·0 sq ft)

Weights and Loadings (estimated):

Manufacturer's weight empty	3,450 kg (7,606 lb)
Max T-O and landing weight	6,350 kg (14,000 lb)
Max ramp weight	6,400 kg (14,110 lb)
Max zero-fuel weight	6,100 kg (13,448 lb)
Max wing loading	253·19 kg/m² (51·85 lb/sq ft)
Max power loading	4·73 kg/kW (7·78 lb/shp)

Performance (estimated, at max T-O weight):

Max level speed	263 knots (488 km/h; 303 mph)
Max cruising speed	253 knots (469 km/h; 291 mph)
Stalling speed, flaps down	96 knots (179 km/h; 111 mph)
Max rate of climb at S/L	680 m (2,230 ft)/min
Rate of climb at S/L, one engine out	163 m (535 ft)/min
Service ceiling	9,630 m (31,600 ft)
Service ceiling, one engine out	4,665 m (15,300 ft)
T-O to 15 m (50 ft)	858 m (2,815 ft)
Landing from 15 m (50 ft)	818 m (2,684 ft)
Range with max fuel, six passengers, 30 min reserves at cruising power at optimum altitude, plus 5%	1,108 nm (2,053 km; 1,275 miles)
Range with max payload, reserves as above	420 nm (778 km; 484 miles)

BAe HS 125 SERIES 700

The BAe HS (formerly de Havilland) 125 Srs 700 is a twin-turbofan business aircraft which is also suitable for use by armed forces in the communications role, as a troop carrier, as an ambulance aircraft, for airways inspection, and as an economical trainer for pilots, navigators and specialised radio and radar operators. All Series of HS 125s can operate from unpaved runways without modification.

The HS 125 was developed as a private venture, and the first of two prototypes flew for the first time on 13 August 1962. Deliveries to customers began in September 1964. By 12 September 1979 a total of 459 HS 125s had been sold, more than 80 per cent of them for export.

Production of the Hawker Siddeley 125 Series 1 (8 built), 1A (64 built), 1B (13 built), 2 (RAF Dominie T. Mk 1, 20 built), 3 (2 built), 3A (12 built), 3B (15 built), 3A-R and 3A-RA (20 built), 3B-RA (16 built), 400A (69 built), 400B (47 built), 600A (33 built) and 600B (39 built) has ended, and these versions have been described in previous editions of *Jane's*. The current versions are:

HS 125 Srs 700A and 700B. Introduced in 1976. Use of Garrett-AiResearch TFE 731-3-1H turbofan engines gives an improved specific fuel consumption by comparison with that of the turbojets in earlier versions of the HS 125. The Series 700 also meets all existing and proposed international noise regulations. The prototype (G-BFAN) was produced by conversion of a Series 600 airframe and flew for the first time on 28 June 1976. Similar conversions of existing turbojet-powered HS 125s are offered; but new-production Series 700 aircraft embody many refinements in addition to the change of power plant. As in the case of earlier versions, the intended market is indicated by a suffix letter: the **Series 700A** is for the North American market, **Series 700B** for the rest of the world.

Improvements to the airframe, to reduce drag and enhance its appearance, include redesign of the wing keel skid, use of countersunk rivets instead of mushroom-head types in the flap bottom skin, replacement of the lower airbrake leading-edge castellations by internal castellations, replacement of the mushroom-head bolts and rivets in the inner tank doors and aileron trailing-edges by countersunk types, redesign of the ventral fin and adjacent fairings in glassfibre and enlargement of the area of the ventral fin to improve directional stability, deletion of the NACA cooling air intake introduced in the nose of the Series 600, addition of fairings over the windscreen wiper blades and two ADF loop aerials, and use of Harper radius countersunk rivets instead of mushroom-head rivets in the fuselage and tail unit.

New interior equipment and furnishings include the use of figured walnut veneer on cabin tables and toilet consoles, leather trim, provision of a Blaupunkt Bamberg combined radio/cassette stereo player and recorder, a luxury toilet compartment, digital cabin clock, slide-out portable bar box, full harness on sideways-facing seats, improved life-jacket stowage under seats, improved plug-in meal tray for divan occupants, and a new range of interior colour schemes.

The first flight of a production HS 125 Series 700 was made on 8 November 1976. UK certification was received on 7 April 1977. The first sale had been made before completion of the prototype, and by 12 September 1979 the sale of 101 Series 700s had been announced, including about 60 for customers in North America. Military operators include the Irish Air Corps.

The following description applies specifically to the Series 700:

Type: Twin-turbofan business transport aircraft.

Wings: Cantilever low-wing monoplane. Thickness/chord ratio 14% at root, 11% at tip. Dihedral 2°. Incidence 2° 6′ at root, −0° 24′ at tip. Sweepback 20° at quarter-chord. Wings built in one piece and dished to pass under fuselage, to which they are attached by four vertical links, a side link and a drag spigot. All-metal two-spar fail-safe structure, with partial centre spar of approx two-thirds span, sealed to form integral fuel tankage which is divided into two compartments by centreline rib. Skins are single-piece units on each of the upper and lower semi-spans. Detachable leading-edges. Fence on each upper surface at approx two-thirds span. Mass-balanced ailerons, operated manually by cable linkage. Trim tab and geared tab in port aileron, two geared tabs in starboard aileron. Aileron fences to improve lateral stability. Large, four-position double-slotted flaps, actuated hydraulically via a screwjack on each flap. Mechanically-operated hydraulic cutout prevents asymmetric operation of the flaps. Airbrakes above and below each wing, forming part of flap shrouds, provide lift-dumping facility during landing, and have intercon-

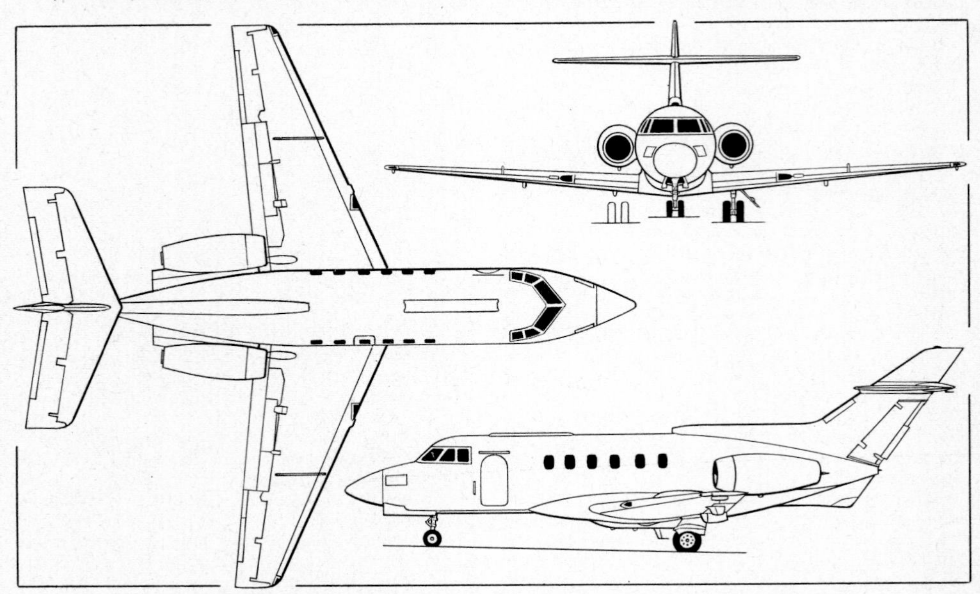

BAe HS 125 Srs 700 light twin-turbofan business transport *(Pilot Press)*

BAe HS 125 Series 700 light twin-turbofan business transport (two Garrett-AiResearch TFE 731 engines)

nected controls to prevent asymmetric operation. TKS liquid system, using porous stainless steel leading-edge panels, for de-icing or anti-icing.

Fuselage: All-metal semi-monocoque fail-safe structure, making extensive use of Redux bonding. Constant circular cross-section over much of its length.

Tail Unit: Cantilever all-metal structure, with fixed-incidence tailplane mounted on fin. Small fairings on tailplane undersurface to eliminate turbulence around elevator hinge cutouts. Triangular ventral fin, and extended dorsal fin. Control surfaces operated manually via cable linkage. Tabs in rudder and each elevator. TKS liquid de-icing or anti-icing of fin and tailplane leading-edges.

Landing Gear: Retractable tricycle type, with twin wheels on each unit. Hydraulic retraction of all units; nosewheels forward, main wheels inward, into wings. Oleo-pneumatic shock-absorbers. Fully-castoring nose unit, steerable 45° to left or right. Dunlop main wheels and 10-ply tyres, size 23 × 7-12, pressure 8·75 bars (127 lb/sq in). Dunlop nosewheels and 6-ply tyres, size 18 × 4·25-10, pressure 5·51 bars (80 lb/sq in). Dunlop double-disc hydraulic brakes with Maxaret anti-skid units on all main wheels.

Power Plant: Two 16·46 kN (3,700 lb st) Garrett-AiResearch TFE 731-3-1H turbofan engines, mounted in rear fuselage pods designed and manufactured by Grumman Aerospace. Engine intake anti-icing by engine bleed air. Integral fuel tanks in wings, with total capacity of 4,628 litres (1,018 Imp gallons). Single pressure refuelling point in lower starboard side of rear fuselage. Overwing refuelling point near each wingtip. Rear underfuselage tank of 509 litres (112 Imp gallons) capacity, with refuelling point on starboard side, and 232 litre (51 Imp gallon) dorsal fin tank, raising overall total capacity to 5,369 litres (1,181 Imp gallons; 1,418 US gallons) of which 5,323 litres (1,171 Imp gallons; 1,406 US gallons) are usable.

Accommodation: Crew of two on flight deck, which is fully soundproofed, insulated and air-conditioned. Dual controls standard. Seat provided for third crew member. Standard executive layout has seating for eight passengers, with forward baggage compartment, refreshment bar and coat compartment (forward) and toilet (aft). There are individual recessed lights and air louvres. Cabin styling offers the operator a choice of interchangeable furnishing units to suit individual requirements. The wide seats, which on the Srs 700A swivel through 180°, are adjustable fore and aft and sideways, have adjustable lumbar support, and can be reclined hydraulically up to 40°. Typical executive furnishing includes a couch for three persons, five individual seats, and individual foldaway wall tables. Alternative high-density layout is available, seating up to 14 passengers. Outward-opening door at front on port side, with integral airstairs. Emergency exit over wing on starboard side. Edge-heating for the windscreen is introduced on the Series 700. Electrical windscreen anti-icing, with methanol spray backup.

Systems: AiResearch air-conditioning and pressurisation system. Max cabin differential 0·58 bars (8·35 lb/sq in), maintaining S/L cabin pressure up to 6,550 m (21,500 ft). Oxygen system standard, with dropout masks for passengers. Hydraulic system, pressure 186-207 bars (2,700-3,000 lb/sq in), for operation of landing gear, main-wheel doors, flaps, spoilers, nosewheel steering, main-wheel brakes and anti-skid units. Two accumulators provide emergency hydraulic power for wheel brakes in case of a main system failure. Independent auxiliary system for lowering landing gear and flaps in the event of a main system failure. DC electrical system utilises two 12kW engine-driven starter/generators and two 24V 25Ah nickel-cadmium batteries. A 24V 3·5Ah battery provides separate power for igniter and starter control circuits. AC electrical system includes two 115V 2·5kVA 400Hz three-phase static inverters and one 250VA solid-state standby inverter for electronics, and one engine-driven 120V 4·4kVA frequency-wild alternator for windscreen anti-icing. Ground power receptacle on starboard side at rear of fuselage for 28V external DC supply. AiResearch GTCP-30-92 auxiliary power unit is standard on Srs 700B. Engine ice protection system supplied by engine bleed air. Graviner triple FD Firewire fire warning system and two BCF engine fire extinguishers.

Avionics and Equipment: Standard avionics include dual Collins VHF-20A com transceivers, Collins VIR-30A VHF nav receivers with dual marker indicators, dual Collins DF-206 ADF, dual Collins MC-103 compasses, Collins DME-40 DME, Marconi AD1540 audio control and passenger address system, RCA Primus 400 weather radar, Collins TDR-90 ATC transponder and Blaupunkt Bamberg stereo tape and AM/FM radio. Provisions for Collins 718U-5 HF com transceiver and second transponder and DME. Collins APS-80 autopilot and FDS-80 flight director system standard, to provide altitude hold, altitude pre-select, airspeed hold, Mach number hold, vertical speed hold, aircraft heading, VOR/LOC, ILS approach and pitch with electric trim.

Dimensions, external:

Wing span	14·33 m (47 ft 0 in)
Wing chord (mean)	2·29 m (7 ft 6¼ in)
Wing aspect ratio	6·25
Length overall	15·46 m (50 ft 8½ in)
Height overall	5·36 m (17 ft 7 in)
Fuselage: Max diameter	1·93 m (6 ft 4 in)
Tailplane span	6·10 m (20 ft 0 in)
Wheel track (c/l of shock-absorbers)	2·79 m (9 ft 2 in)
Wheelbase	6·34 m (20 ft 9½ in)
Passenger door (fwd, port):	
Height	1·30 m (4 ft 3 in)
Width	0·69 m (2 ft 3 in)
Height to sill	1·07 m (3 ft 6 in)
Emergency exit (overwing, stbd):	
Height	0·91 m (3 ft 0 in)
Width	0·51 m (1 ft 8 in)

Dimensions, internal:

Cabin (excl flight deck): Length	6·50 m (21 ft 4 in)
Max width	1·80 m (5 ft 11 in)
Max height	1·75 m (5 ft 9 in)
Floor area	5·11 m² (55·0 sq ft)
Volume	17·10 m³ (604·0 cu ft)
Baggage compartment	0·84 m³ (29·6 cu ft)

Areas:

Wings, gross	32·8 m² (353·0 sq ft)
Ailerons (total)	2·76 m² (29·76 sq ft)
Trailing-edge flaps (total)	5·21 m² (56·06 sq ft)
Fin, incl dorsal fin	5·31 m² (57·15 sq ft)
Ventral fin	0·61 m² (6·61 sq ft)
Horizontal tail surfaces (total)	9·29 m² (100 sq ft)

Weights and Loadings:

Weight empty	5,826 kg (12,845 lb)
Typical operating weight empty	6,270 kg (13,822 lb)
Max payload	1,010 kg (2,228 lb)
Max T-O weight	11,249 kg (24,800 lb)
Max ramp weight	11,340 kg (25,000 lb)
Max zero-fuel weight	7,280 kg (16,050 lb)
Max landing weight	9,979 kg (22,000 lb)
Max wing loading	343 kg/m² (70·3 lb/sq ft)
Max power loading	341 kg/kN (3·35 lb/lb st)

Performance (at max T-O weight except where indicated):

Never-exceed speed: Mach 0·85

Max level speed at S/L: 320 knots (592 km/h; 368 mph) IAS

Max cruising speed at 8,380 m (27,500 ft): 436 knots (808 km/h; 502 mph) TAS

Econ cruising speed at 11,275-12,500 m (37,000-41,000 ft): 390 knots (723 km/h; 449 mph) TAS

Stalling speed, flaps down: 83 knots (155 km/h; 96 mph) EAS

Service ceiling: 12,500 m (41,000 ft)

T-O run: 1,204 m (3,950 ft)

T-O to 10·7 m (35 ft), unfactored: 1,346 m (4,415 ft)

T-O balanced field length: 1,798 m (5,900 ft)

Landing from 15 m (50 ft) at landing weight of 7,167 kg (15,800 lb), unfactored: 619 m (2,030 ft)

Landing run at landing weight of 6,804 kg (15,000 lb): 1,231 m (4,040 ft)

Range with max fuel, allowances for T-O, approach, landing, taxying and 45 min reserves: 2,330 nm (4,318 km; 2,683 miles)

Range with max payload, allowances as above, and 45 min reserves: 2,120 nm (3,930 km; 2,442 miles)

Operational Noise Characteristics (FAR Pt 36):

T-O noise level	87·6 EPNdB
Approach noise level	96·3 EPNdB
Sideline noise level	88·9 EPNdB

BAe HS 748 SERIES 2B

Design of the HS 748 short/medium-range turboprop airliner started in January 1959. The first prototype flew on 24 June 1960, followed by a second on 10 April 1961. UK production of the Series 1 (18 built) and Series 2 (including two Andover CC.Mk 2s for The Queen's Flight and four for Air Support Command), described in previous editions of *Jane's*, has been completed. These models were followed by the Series 2A (see 1977-78 *Jane's*), which continues to be available to order.

In early 1979 the BAe HS 748 Series 2A was replaced as the standard version by a new **Series 2B** basic model, with improved 'hot and high' Dart 536-2 engines, a 1·22 m (4 ft) greater span wing with reduced drag, modified tail surfaces, and other refinements. Prototype for this version was G-BCDZ, flown earlier as the demonstration model of the Coastguarder. The Srs 2B is available in the same civil, military and Coastguarder configurations as the Srs 2A (see following paragraphs), and modification kits are available to existing Srs 2A operators. First production Srs 2B (G-BGJV) made its initial flight on 22 June 1979.

HS 748 Civil Transport. In addition to the basic transport configuration, the Series 2B is available optionally with a large rear freight door which has an opening of 2·67 m by 1·72 m (8 ft 9 in × 5 ft 7¾ in), together with a strengthened cabin floor capable of supporting an overall floor loading of 976 kg/m² (200 lb/sq ft).

HS 748 Military Transport. The military transport version has the large rear freight door and strengthened floor that are available for the civil transport and has, in addition, fixed fittings to undertake a wide range of military roles. Optional military overload take-off and landing weights give improved payload/range capabilities. A total of 52 military HS 748 Srs 2As had been exported by the Summer of 1979, of which 28 were fitted with the rear freight door and strengthened floor. These were for the air forces of Belgium (3), Brazil (12), Ecuador (5), three undisclosed air forces (6), the Royal Brunei Army (1), and the Nepal Royal Flight (1).

HS 748 Coastguarder. Variant for search and rescue and maritime surveillance roles. Described separately.

Sales of all Series (including 31 Andover C.Mk 1s for the RAF: see 1968-69 *Jane's*) totalled 343 by mid-June 1979, including 289 for export. Of these, 328 had been delivered. Nine aircraft were sold with Dart RDa.8 engines, seven being supplied to Bundesanstalt für Flugsicherung (Germany) with calibration equipment for radio navigational aids and two to the Royal Australian Navy with navigational and electronic training equipment. Six Andover C.Mk 1s have been modified for flight checking and calibration duties, and redelivered to the RAF since 1977 to replace Argosy E.Mk 1 aircraft in this role. The modified Andovers are designated **E.Mk 3**.

The HS 748 is the subject of a manufacturing agreement with the Indian government, and 89 aircraft (included in above overall totals) are being assembled from British-built components by Hindustan Aeronautics Ltd. Of these, 17 are for Indian Airlines and 72 for the Indian Air Force.

BAe HS 748 Series 2B, photographed during its first flight on 22 June 1979

The following description applies to the 1979 production HS 748 Series 2B, except where indicated:

TYPE: Twin-engined passenger or freight transport.

WINGS: Cantilever low-wing monoplane. Wing section NACA 23018 at root, NACA 4412 at tip. Dihedral 7°. Incidence 3°. Sweepback 2° 54′ at quarter-chord. All-metal two-spar fail-safe structure. No cutouts in spars for engines or landing gear. All-metal set-back hinge, shielded horn-balance, manually-operated ailerons and electrically-actuated Fowler flaps. Geared tab in each aileron. Trim tab in starboard aileron. Pneumatic leading-edge de-icing boots.

FUSELAGE: All-metal semi-monocoque riveted fail-safe structure, of circular section.

TAIL UNIT: Cantilever all-metal structure. Fixed-incidence tailplane. Manually-operated controls. Trim tabs in elevators and rudder. Spring tab in rudder.

LANDING GEAR: Retractable tricycle type, with hydraulically-steerable nose unit. All wheels retract forward hydraulically. Main wheels retract into bottom of engine nacelles forward of front wing spar. Dowty Rotol shock-absorbers. Twin wheels, with Dunlop tyres, on all units. Main wheels size 32 × 10·75-14. Nosewheels size 25·65 × 8·5-10. Standard tyre pressures: main wheels 5·03 bars (73 lb/sq in); nosewheels 3·79 bars (55 lb/sq in). Minimum tyre pressures: main wheels 4·48 bars (65 lb/sq in); nosewheels 3·45 bars (50 lb/sq in). Dunlop disc brakes with Maxaret anti-skid units. No brake cooling.

POWER PLANT (Srs 2B): Two 1,700 kW (2,280 ehp) Rolls-Royce Dart RDa.7 Mk 536-2 turboprop engines, each driving a Dowty Rotol four-blade constant-speed fully-feathering propeller. Provision for automatic injection of water methanol into live engine in the event of an engine failure on take-off. Fuel in two integral wing tanks, with total capacity of 6,550 litres (1,440 Imp gallons). Tanks modified to provide increased wing bending relief. Underwing pressure refuelling and overwing gravity refuelling. Oil capacity 14·2 litres (25 Imp pints) per engine.

ACCOMMODATION: Crew of two on flight deck, and cabin attendant. Normal accommodation for 40-58 passengers in paired seats on each side of central gangway. Baggage compartment forward of cabin, with provision for steward's seat. Galley, toilet and baggage compartment aft of cabin. Forward baggage compartment and steward's seat can be replaced by freight hold with moving partition between hold and passenger cabin. Main passenger door, on port side at rear, with smaller door on starboard side to serve as baggage door and emergency exit. Crew and freight door on port side at front. Hydraulically-operated stairs.

ACCOMMODATION (military transport): Up to 60 troops in airline type seats. Provision for forward and aft baggage compartments and hydraulically-operated airstairs. In paratroop role up to 48 paratroops and despatchers can be accommodated on sidewall folding seats with safety harness. Dropping by static line or free fall. For casualty evacuation up to 24 stretchers and nine nursing staff can be carried, with provision for medical supplies and equipment. For supply dropping a guided roller conveyor system allows twelve 340 kg (750 lb) or six 680 kg (1,500 lb) loads to be dropped within six seconds. Capacity for 5,886 kg (12,976 lb) freight. Large cargo door will accept items up to 1·42 m × 1·42 m × 3·66 m (4 ft 8 in × 4 ft 8 in × 12 ft) or small diameter pipes over 12 m (39 ft 4 in) in length. On-board freight hoist and palletised freight system available. Quickly-removable VIP cabin available, and a variety of VIP layouts, with separate toilet, telephone and wide range of options.

SYSTEMS: Normalair automatic pressurisation and air-conditioning system, giving equivalent altitude of 2,440 m (8,000 ft) at 7,620 m (25,000 ft). Pressure differential 0·38 bars (5·5 lb/sq in). Hydraulic system, pressure 172 bars (2,500 lb/sq in), for landing gear retraction, nose-wheel steering, brakes and propeller brakes. No pneumatic system. One 9kW 28V DC generator and one 22kVA alternator on each engine. Two 1,800VA static inverters.

AVIONICS AND EQUIPMENT: Collins or Bendix solid-state radio and radar. Blind-flying instrumentation and Bendix RDR colour weather radar. Sperry SPZ-500 multi-mode autopilot/flight director system. Provision for flight data recorder. Marconi ARC 340 communications and homing system in Royal Brunei Army aircraft.

DIMENSIONS, EXTERNAL:

Wing span: Srs 2A	30·02 m (98 ft 6 in)
Srs 2B	31·23 m (102 ft 5½ in)
Wing chord at root	3·49 m (11 ft 5¼ in)
Wing chord at tip: Srs 2A	1·34 m (4 ft 5 in)
Wing aspect ratio: Srs 2A	11·967
Srs 2B	12·668
Length overall	20·42 m (67 ft 0 in)
Fuselage: Max diameter	2·67 m (8 ft 9 in)
Height overall	7·57 m (24 ft 10 in)
Tailplane span	10·97 m (36 ft 0 in)
Wheel track	7·54 m (24 ft 9 in)
Wheelbase	6·30 m (20 ft 8 in)
Propeller diameter	3·66 m (12 ft 0 in)
Propeller ground clearance	0·61 m (2 ft 0 in)
Passenger door (port, rear):	
Height	1·57 m (5 ft 2 in)
Width	0·76 m (2 ft 6 in)

BAe HS 748 Series 2A military transport aircraft with large rear freight door, in Belgian Air Force insignia

Height to sill 1·84 m (6 ft 0½ in)
Freight and baggage door (fwd):
Height 1·37 m (4 ft 6 in)
Width 1·22 m (4 ft 0 in)
Height to sill 1·84 m (6 ft 0½ in)
Baggage door (rear, stbd):
Height 1·24 m (4 ft 1 in)
Width 0·64 m (2 ft 1 in)
Height to sill 1·84 m (6 ft 0½ in)
Optional freight door (rear, port):
Height 1·72 m (5 ft 7¾ in)
Width 2·67 m (8 ft 9 in)

Dimensions, internal:
Cabin, excl flight deck: Length 14·17 m (46 ft 6 in)
Max width 2·46 m (8 ft 1 in)
Max height 1·92 m (6 ft 3½ in)
Floor area 27·5 m² (296 sq ft)
Volume 56·35 m³ (1,990 cu ft)
Max total freight holds 9·54 m³ (337 cu ft)

Areas:
Wings, gross: Srs 2A 75·35 m² (810·75 sq ft)
Srs 2B 77·00 m² (828·87 sq ft)
Ailerons (total) 3·98 m² (42·90 sq ft)
Trailing-edge flaps (total) 14·83 m² (159·80 sq ft)
Fin 9·81 m² (105·64 sq ft)
Rudder, incl tabs 3·66 m² (39·36 sq ft)
Tailplane 17·55 m² (188·9 sq ft)
Elevators, incl tabs 5·03 m² (54·10 sq ft)

Weights and Loadings (A: standard Srs 2A; B: Srs 2A military transport; C: standard Srs 2B; D: Srs 2B military transport):
Basic operating weight, incl crew:
A 12,159 kg (26,806 lb)
B 11,577 kg (25,524 lb)
C 12,226 kg (26,953 lb)
D 11,644 kg (25,671 lb)
Max payload: A 5,304 kg (11,694 lb)
B 5,886 kg (12,976 lb)
B, optional overload 7,927 kg (17,476 lb)
C 5,238 kg (11,547 lb)
D 5,819 kg (12,829 lb)
D, optional overload 7,860 kg (17,329 lb)
Max T-O weight: A, B, C, D 21,092 kg (46,500 lb)
B, D, optional overload 23,133 kg (51,000 lb)
Max zero-fuel weight:
A, B, C, D 17,463 kg (38,500 lb)
B, D, optional overload 19,504 kg (43,000 lb)
Max landing weight: A, B, C, D 19,504 kg (43,000 lb)
B, D, optional overload 21,546 kg (47,500 lb)
Max wing loading: A 279·8 kg/m² (57·3 lb/sq ft)
C 273·9 kg/m² (56·1 lb/sq ft)
Max power loading: A, C 6·20 kg/kW (10·2 lb/ehp)

Performance (A: standard Srs 2A at max T-O weight unless otherwise indicated; B: military Srs 2A at normal max T-O weight with 20% fuel reserves; C: military Srs 2A at optional overload T-O weight with 20% fuel reserves; D: provisional figures for standard Srs 2B at max T-O weight unless otherwise indicated):
Cruising speed:
A, D at 17,236 kg (38,000 lb) 244 knots (452 km/h; 281 mph)
Max rate of climb at S/L:
A, D at 17,236 kg (38,000 lb) 433 m (1,420 ft)/min
Service ceiling: A, D 7,620 m (25,000 ft)
Min ground turning radius:
A, B, C, D 11·82 m (39 ft)
Runway LCN: A, D 9 to 18
T-O run: A (BCAR) 1,225 m (4,020 ft)
B 756 m (2,480 ft)
C 945 m (3,100 ft)
D (BCAR) 1,134 m (3,720 ft)
Balanced field length:
A (BCAR) 1,640 m (5,380 ft)
A (BCAR, 650 nm; 1,203 km; 748 mile sector, 40 passengers and reserves for 200 nm; 370 km; 230 miles plus 45 min hold) 892 m (2,925 ft)
D (BCAR) 1,393 m (4,570 ft)
D (BCAR, 840 nm; 1,557 km; 967 mile sector, 44 passengers and reserves for 200 nm; 370 km; 230 miles plus 45 min hold) 963 m (3,160 ft)
T-O to 15 m (50 ft): B 927 m (3,040 ft)
C 1,158 m (3,800 ft)
Landing field length:
A, D (BCAR) 1,036 m (3,400 ft)
Landing from 15 m (50 ft): B 567 m (1,860 ft)
C 625 m (2,050 ft)
Landing run: B 347 m (1,140 ft)
C 387 m (1,270 ft)
Radius of action:
B, supply drop mission with 12 × 340 kg (750 lb) containers 625 nm (1,158 km; 720 miles)
Range with max payload:
A, with reserves for 200 nm (370 km; 230 miles) plus 45 min hold 735 nm (1,361 km; 846 miles)
B 925 nm (1,714 km; 1,066 miles)
C 840 nm (1,556 km; 967 miles)
D, with reserves for 200 nm (370 km; 230 miles) plus 45 min hold 705 nm (1,306 km; 812 miles)
Range with max fuel:
A, with 3,662 kg (8,074 lb) payload, reserves for 200 nm (370 km; 230 miles) plus 45 min hold 1,340 nm (2,483 km; 1,543 miles)

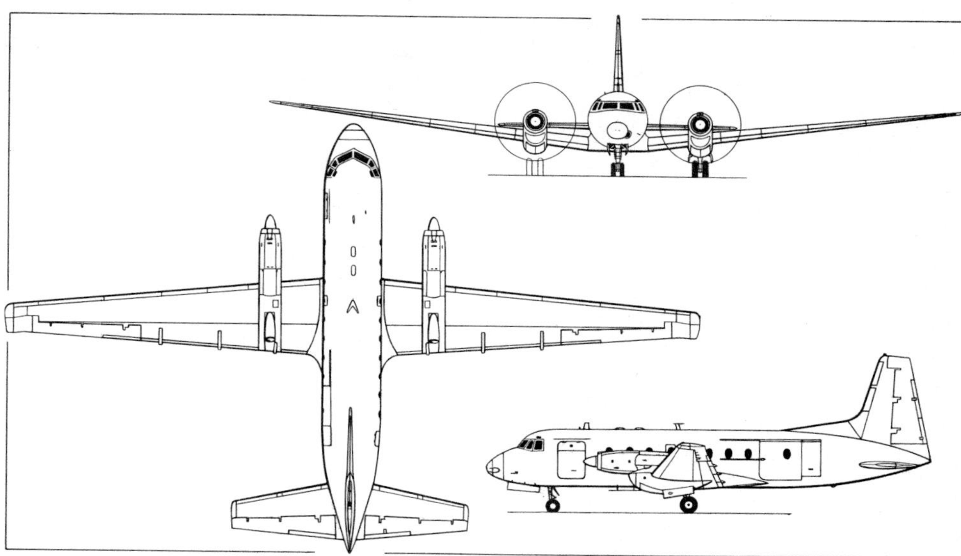
BAe HS 748 Srs 2B twin-turboprop transport aircraft *(Pilot Press)*

B, with 4,321 kg (9,527 lb) payload 1,410 nm (2,613 km; 1,624 miles)
C, with 6,363 kg (14,027 lb) payload 1,280 nm (2,372 km; 1,474 miles)
D, with 3,532 kg (7,787 lb) payload, reserves for 200 nm (370 km; 230 miles) plus 45 min hold 1,345 nm (2,492 km; 1,549 miles)

Operational Noise Characteristics (FAR Pt 36):
T-O noise level 92·5 EPNdB
Approach noise level 103·8 EPNdB
Sideline noise level 96·3 EPNdB

BAe HS 748 COASTGUARDER

The Coastguarder is a medium-range maritime patrol aircraft, based on the HS 748. Its development was initiated to meet the need for an aircraft in this category suitable for surface surveillance, fishery protection, pollution/contraband control, search and rescue, tactical surveillance and offshore oilfield patrol. A prototype/demonstration aircraft (G-BCDZ), constructed from an ex-airline HS 748 Series 2A, flew for the first time on 18 February 1977. Demonstration activity with this aircraft was intense during 1977-78, with visits to Europe, Scandinavia, South and Central America, and the Far East. It has since been modified as the prototype of the new HS 748 Series 2B.

The airframe of the Coastguarder is generally similar to that of the standard HS 748 civil and military transport; but there is crew accommodation for two pilots, two beam observers and a tactical navigator, to enable the Coastguarder to fulfil its primary roles. A 0·30 m (1 ft 0 in) diameter chute is mounted in the aft fuselage for the air launch of five-man rescue dinghies, and smoke or flame floats. Two optically flat, inward opening windows in the forward fuselage allow high definition photographs to be taken, with optional data annotation. The standard radio, radar and navigation equipment has been expanded to cover the normal naval radio frequencies, and to provide adequate navigation aids for long overwater flights.

The tactical navigator's station is situated midway down the cabin, on the starboard side, and is equipped with an MEL MAREC radar display and plotting board, Decca 72 Doppler, and a Decca 9447 TANS computer/display. The MAREC radar was chosen as standard on the basis of experience gained in previous ASV, ASW and SAR applications. It has an underfuselage antenna, a 0·43 m (1 ft 5 in) diameter main display and plotting board, with a 0·13 m (5 in) repeat display for the pilot. Used in conjunction with the Doppler, TANS computer and Marconi Omega VLF navigation system, the resulting tactical navigation system can, in addition to satisfying all normal search and navigation requirements, provide effective tactical plotting to control an exercise involving a group of friendly vessels and other radar targets, including aircraft. MAREC provides up to 210 nm (389 km; 242 miles) display range in all directions for the tactical navigator and up to 250 nm (460 km; 285 miles) for the pilot's repeater display. A choice of presentation scale between 1 and 30 nm (1·9-55·6 km; 1·2-34·5 miles) per inch allows enlargement of any selected part of the display.

To provide the additional range required for a maritime reconnaissance role, the fuel tankage has been increased to 10,047 litres (2,210 Imp gallons). The standard Coastguarder may be used for a number of maritime and other roles without any change to the basic configuration. Additional passengers can be accommodated by fitting seats to the standard rails which run the full length of the cabin. The optional rear freight door provides an air-dropping capability, allowing the despatch of large dinghies or supplies in an air/sea rescue role. As many as twelve 30-man dinghies can be transported and dropped for the rescue of a large number of aircraft/ship survivors. The Coastguarder can also be converted easily for cargo carrying, by removal of the tactical navigator's station and other equipment.

The description of the standard HS 748 Series 2B applies also to the Coastguarder, except as follows:

Type: Twin-turboprop maritime patrol aircraft.

Power Plant: Two 1,700 kW (2,280 ehp) Rolls-Royce Dart RDa.7 Mk 535-2 turboprop engines, each driving a Dowty Rotol four-blade metal constant-speed fully-feathering propeller. Fuel in integral wing tanks with a max combined capacity of 10,047 litres (2,210 Imp gallons). Underwing pressure refuelling and overwing gravity refuelling. Oil capacity 14·2 litres (25 Imp pints) per engine.

Accommodation: Standard Coastguarder layout has two pilots on flight deck; two beam observers seated at aft end of cabin, one each side, with domed windows; and tactical navigator approximately midway down cabin at tactical station on starboard side. Toilet on starboard side at aft end of cabin, with galley opposite. Main door on port side at rear of cabin; smaller door for emergency exit on starboard side. Crew door on port side at front of cabin. Large rear freight door optional. Four airline-type seats, forward of tactical navigator's station, on starboard side, serve as crew rest area.

BAe HS 748 Coastguarder twin-turboprop maritime patrol aircraft

AVIONICS AND EQUIPMENT: Avionics include Sylvania VHF/FM com transceiver, dual Collins 618M-3 VHF com transceivers, dual Collins 51RV-4B VHF nav receivers, Collins AN/ARC-159 UHF com transceiver, Collins 51Z-4 marker beacon receiver, dual Collins DF 206 ADF, Collins DF 301E UHF D/F, Collins 618T-3 HF transceiver, Collins 346D-1 address system, Ultra UA 60 interphone, Sperry RN 200 radio navigation display, Honeywell AN/APN-171 radio altimeter, MEL MAREC radar with 0·43 m (1 ft 5 in) main display and 0·13 m (5 in) pilot's repeat display, Marconi CMA 771 Omega VLF nav system, Decca 72 Doppler, and Decca 9447 TANS computer/display. Attitude stabilised antenna, size 0·91 m × 0·53 m (3 ft 0 in × 1 ft 9 in), in underfuselage radome provides 360° azimuth viewing, plus selected sector scan facilities. Provisions for optional ATC transponder, DME, and height encoding altimeter. Standard equipment includes a 0·30 m (1 ft 0 in) launch chute for five-man rescue dinghies and smoke or flame floats. Optional equipment includes large rear freight door, additional passenger seats, large dinghies, and other rescue equipment.

WEIGHTS AND LOADINGS:

*Typical operating weight empty	12,722 kg (28,048 lb)
Max T-O weight	21,092 kg (46,500 lb)
Max zero-fuel weight	17,463 kg (38,500 lb)
Max landing weight	19,504 kg (43,000 lb)
Max wing loading	279·8 kg/m² (57·3 lb/sq ft)
Max power loading	6·20 kg/kW (10·2 lb/ehp)

depending upon customer requirements

PERFORMANCE (at max T-O weight, unless stated otherwise):

Cruising speed at 4,570 m (15,000 ft) at AUW of 18,144 kg (40,000 lb) 233 knots (431 km/h; 268 mph)

Typical search speed at 610 m (2,000 ft) 140 knots (259 km/h; 161 mph)

Service ceiling 7,620 m (25,000 ft)

T-O to 15 m (50 ft), unfactored:

S/L, ISA 951 m (3,120 ft)

S/L, ISA +20° C 1,045 m (3,430 ft)

Landing from 15 m (50 ft) at max landing weight, unfactored:

S/L, ISA 570 m (1,870 ft)

S/L, ISA +20° C 608 m (1,995 ft)

Range with 4,536 kg (10,000 lb) payload, 20% fuel reserves, ISA 960 nm (1,779 km; 1,105 miles)

Range with max fuel, 20% reserves, ISA 2,300 nm (4,262 km; 2,648 miles)

Time on station at 200 nm (370 km; 230 miles) radius of action, at 3,050 m (10,000 ft), 20% fuel reserves, ISA 9 h 24 min

BAe 146

In August 1973, Hawker Siddeley announced that it was to produce with government support a four-turbofan quiet-operating transport aircraft known as the HS (now BAe) 146. Within a few months economic problems in the UK halted this programme, but research and design continued on a limited basis. With the absorption of Hawker Siddeley into British Aerospace in April 1977, BAe continued to provide limited funding to allow the manufacture of assembly jigs, systems test rigs, and continuing design and wind tunnel testing. On 10 July 1978, the British Aerospace Board's decision to give the 146 programme a full go-ahead was approved by the government, and production is to be undertaken in several BAe factories, including Brough, Filton, Manchester and Prestwick. Following the production decision, risk-sharing agreements were signed with Avco Aerostructures (USA) for the manufacture of 20 sets of wing boxes; and with Saab-Scania (Sweden) for 20 sets of tailplanes and control surfaces. Under an initial contract, Short Brothers (UK) are to manufacture 100 pods for the Avco Lycoming ALF 502 engines which will power the 146. Final assembly will take place at BAe's Hatfield plant.

The basic aims of the BAe 146 are to provide a passenger seating standard comparable with present wide-bodied transports, combined with competitive operating costs, good airfield performance and low operating noise levels.

Two series will be available:

Series 100. Designed to operate from short semi-prepared airstrips with minimal ground facilities, with a normal seating capacity of 71-88. A mixed passenger/freight version is planned.

Series 200. For operation from paved runways only, with seating capacity of 82-109 and greater range. Fuselage lengthened by four frame pitches (2·21 m; 7 ft 3 in). Increased maximum T-O weight and zero-fuel weight. Underfloor cargo volume increased by 35%. Reduced max operating speed.

The first flight of the Series 100 prototype is scheduled to be made in November 1980. Full transport category CAA certification of the Series 100 is expected to be obtained by February 1982, with initial deliveries of production aircraft simultaneously. The eighth aircraft will be the first Series 200, with first flight scheduled for February 1982 and certification by August 1982.

Freight-carrying and military versions are planned; the latter is described separately.

The following description applies to the BAe 146 Series 100, except where indicated:

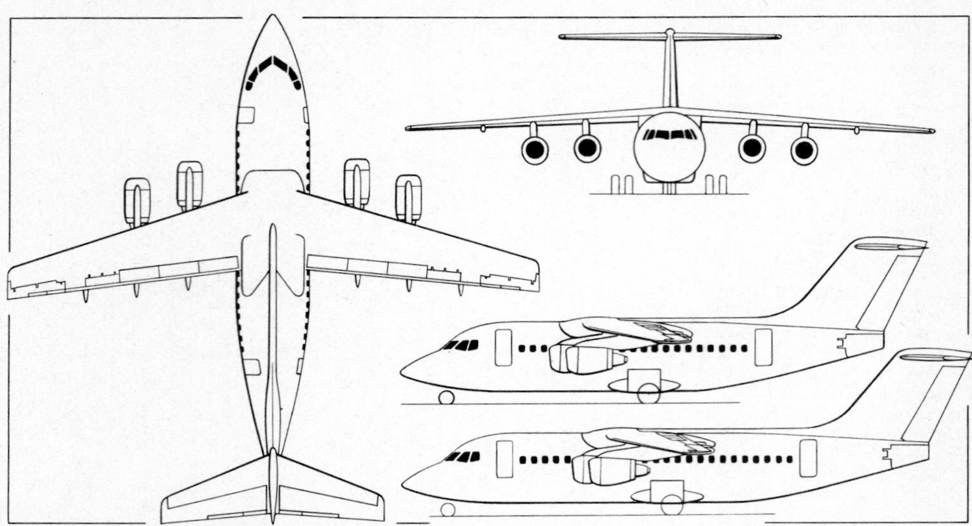

BAe 146 Series 100, with additional side view (bottom) of Series 200 *(Pilot Press)*

TYPE: Four-turbofan short-range transport aircraft.

WINGS: Cantilever high-wing monoplane. British Aerospace high-lift aerofoil section. Thickness/chord ratio 15·3% adjacent to fuselage, 12·2% at tip. Anhedral 3° at trailing edge. Incidence 3° 6′ at fuselage side, 0° at tip. Sweepback 15° at quarter-chord. All-metal fail-safe structure of light alloy with machined skins, integrally machined spars and ribs. Single-section hydraulically-actuated tabbed Fowler flaps of light alloy spanning 66% of each wing trailing-edge. Mechanically-actuated balanced ailerons, with hydraulically-operated power boost spoilers on upper surfaces. Trim and spring tab in each aileron. No leading-edge lift devices. Hot-air anti-icing of leading-edges.

FUSELAGE: All-metal fail-safe pressurised semi-monocoque structure. Flight deck and tailcone areas free of stringers. Remainder of structure has 'top hat' stringers bonded to skins above keel area. 'Z' section stringers 'wet' assembled with bonding agent and riveted to skin in keel area. Chemically-etched skins of light alloy. Petal-type airbrakes form tailcone when closed.

TAIL UNIT: Cantilever sweptback T-tail, of all-metal construction. Chemically-etched light alloy skins bonded to 'top-hat' section stringers. Fixed-incidence tailplane. Manually-operated balanced elevators, each with trim and spring tab. Powered rudder. Hot-air anti-icing of tailplane leading-edges.

LANDING GEAR: Hydraulically-retractable tricycle type, of Dowty Rotol design, with twin wheels on each unit. Main units retract inward into fairings on fuselage sides; steerable nose unit retracts forward. Oleo-pneumatic shock-absorbers with wheels mounted on trailing axle. Simple telescopic nosewheel strut. Main-wheel tyres size 13·00-16 Type III, pressure (Series 100) 7·52 bars (109 lb/sq in). Nosewheel tyres size 7·50-10 Type III, pressure (Series 100) 6·14 bars (89 lb/sq in). Low-pressure tyres optional. Multi-disc carbon brakes operated by duplicated hydraulic systems. Brake cooling and rudder pedal steering optional. Anti-skid units in both primary and secondary brake systems.

POWER PLANT: Four Avco Lycoming ALF 502R-3 turbofan engines, each rated at 29·8 kN (6,700 lb st), installed in pylon-mounted underwing pods. Fuel in two integral wing tanks and integral centre-section tank (the latter with a vented and drained sealing diaphragm above passenger cabin), having a combined capacity of 11,547 litres (2,540 Imp gallons). Optional auxiliary tanks in wing-root fairings, with combined capacity of 1,363 litres (300 Imp gallons), giving total optional capacity of 12,910 litres (2,840 Imp gallons). Single-point pressure refuelling, with coupling situated in starboard wing outboard of outer engine.

ACCOMMODATION: Crew of two pilots on flight deck, and two or three cabin staff. Optional observer's seat. Series 100 has accommodation in main cabin for 71 passengers with five-abreast seating at 84 cm (33 in) pitch, and a maximum of 88 seats six-abreast at 79 cm (31 in) pitch. Series 200 will have maximum capacity for 109 passengers with six-abreast seating at 79 cm (31 in) pitch. Various alternative layouts for mixed passenger/freight configurations. All seating layouts have two toilets, one forward and one aft, and a forward galley as standard. One outward-opening passenger door forward and one aft on port side of cabin. Built-in airstairs optional. Servicing doors, one forward and one aft, on starboard side of cabin. Freight and baggage holds under cabin floor. All accommodation air-conditioned. Windscreen electrical anti-icing and demisting standard. Rain repellent system optional.

SYSTEMS: Cabin air-conditioning and pressurisation from engine bleed air. Electro-pneumatic pressurisation control with discharge valves at fore and aft of cabin. Max differential 0·45 bars (6·5 lb/sq in). Hydraulic system, duplicated for essential services, for landing gear, flaps, rudder, roll and lift spoilers, airbrakes, nosewheel steering, brakes and auxiliary fuel pumps; pressure 207 bars (3,000 lb/sq in). Electrical power supplied by two 40 kVA integrated-drive alternators to feed 115/200V 3-phase 400Hz primary systems. 28V DC power supplied by transformer-rectifier in each channel. Hydraulically-powered emergency electrical power unit. AiResearch GTCP 36-100 APU for ground air-conditioning and electrical power generation optional. High-pressure gaseous oxygen system, pressure 124 bars (1,800 lb/sq in).

AVIONICS: Automatic flight control system incorporates a simplex Cat 1 autopilot with a flight director display and separate attitude reference for each pilot. Addition of extra equipment and wiring permits coupled approaches to Cat 2 minima. Standard ARINC interface with radio nav system allows choice of radio equipment. Basic avionics include dual VHF com, audio system, passenger address system, cockpit voice recorder, dual compass systems, dual ADIs with separate attitude reference driven by single computer, marker, weather radar, radio altimeter, ground proximity warning system, DME, ATC transponder, dual VHF nav and an ADF. Optional avionics include third VHF com, area navigation system, Selcal, tape reproducer, single or dual HF com, and second ADF, DME, transponder, weather radar display and radio altimeter.

DIMENSIONS, EXTERNAL:

Wing span	26·34 m (86 ft 5 in)
Wing aspect ratio	8·98
Length overall:	
Series 100	26·16 m (85 ft 10 in)
Series 200	28·37 m (93 ft 1 in)
Height overall	8·61 m (28 ft 3 in)
Fuselage diameter	3·56 m (11 ft 8 in)
Tailplane span	11·07 m (36 ft 4 in)
Wheel track	4·72 m (15 ft 6 in)
Wheelbase: Series 100	10·10 m (33 ft 1½ in)
Series 200	11·20 m (36 ft 9 in)
Passenger doors (port, fwd and rear):	
Height	1·83 m (6 ft 0 in)
Width	0·85 m (2 ft 9½ in)
Height to sill	1·93 m (6 ft 4 in)
Servicing doors (stbd, fwd and rear):	
Height	1·47 m (4 ft 10 in)
Width	0·85 m (2 ft 9½ in)
Height to sill	1·93 m (6 ft 4 in)
Underfloor freight hold door (stbd, fwd):	
Height	1·07 m (3 ft 6 in)
Width	1·22 m (4 ft 0 in)
Height to sill	0·86 m (2 ft 10 in)
Underfloor freight hold door (stbd, aft):	
Height	1·07 m (3 ft 6 in)
Width	0·91 m (3 ft 0 in)
Height to sill	1·07 m (3 ft 6 in)

DIMENSIONS, INTERNAL:

Cabin (excl flight deck, incl galley and toilets): Length:	
Series 100	15·42 m (50 ft 7 in)
Series 200	17·63 m (57 ft 10 in)
Max width	3·38 m (11 ft 1 in)
Max height	2·04 m (6 ft 8½ in)
Floor area: Series 100	49·24 m² (530 sq ft)
Series 200	56·39 m² (607 sq ft)
Baggage/freight holds, underfloor:	
Series 100	14·16 m³ (500 cu ft)
Series 200	19·09 m³ (674 cu ft)

AREAS:

Wings, gross	77·30 m² (832 sq ft)
Ailerons (total)	3·53 m² (38 sq ft)
Trailing-edge flaps (total)	19·32 m² (208 sq ft)
Spoilers (total)	9·66 m² (104 sq ft)
Fin	11·61 m² (125 sq ft)
Rudder	9·20 m² (99 sq ft)
Tailplane	15·61 m² (168 sq ft)
Elevators, incl tab	10·03 m² (108 sq ft)

WEIGHTS AND LOADINGS (estimated):

Typical operating weight empty:	
Series 100	19,958 kg (44,000 lb)
Series 200	21,092 kg (46,500 lb)
Max payload: Series 100	7,824 kg (17,250 lb)
Series 200	9,979 kg (22,000 lb)
Max T-O weight:	
Series 100, standard	33,497 kg (73,850 lb)
Series 100, optional	35,835 kg (79,000 lb)
Series 200	39,690 kg (87,500 lb)
Max ramp weight: Series 100	33,724 kg (74,350 lb)
Series 200	39,916 kg (88,000 lb)
Max zero-fuel weight:	
Series 100	27,782 kg (61,250 lb)
Series 200	31,070 kg (68,500 lb)
Max landing weight:	
Series 100	32,590 kg (71,850 lb)
Series 200	34,926 kg (77,000 lb)
Max wing loading:	
Series 100, standard	433·6 kg/m² (88·8 lb/sq ft)
Series 200	513·6 kg/m² (105·2 lb/sq ft)
Max power loading:	
Series 100, standard	281 kg/kN (2·76 lb/lb st)
Series 200	333 kg/kN (3·26 lb/lb st)

PERFORMANCE (estimated, at max standard T-O weight, except where indicated):

Max operating speed:
- Series 100: Mach 0·70 (315 knots; 584 km/h; 363 mph CAS)
- Series 200: Mach 0·70 (300 knots; 555 km/h; 345 mph CAS)

Max cruising speed:
- Series 100 at 6,705 m (22,000 ft): 427 knots (791 km/h; 492 mph)
- Series 200 at 7,315 m (24,000 ft): 422 knots (782 km/h; 486 mph)

Econ cruising speed, Series 100 and 200 at 9,145 m (30,000 ft): 364 knots (674 km/h; 419 mph)

Stalling speed, 40° flap:
- Series 100: 91 knots (169 km/h; 105 mph) EAS
- Series 200: 99 knots (183 km/h; 114 mph) EAS

Stalling speed, 45° flap, at max landing weight:
- Series 100: 87 knots (161 km/h; 100 mph) EAS
- Series 200: 90 knots (168 km/h; 104 mph) EAS

T-O to 10·7 m (35 ft), S/L, ISA:
- Series 100: 1,091 m (3,580 ft)
- Series 200: 1,509 m (4,950 ft)

FAR landing distance from 15 m (50 ft), S/L, ISA, at max landing weight:
- Series 100: 1,009 m (3,310 ft)
- Series 200: 1,067 m (3,500 ft)

Range with max fuel, incl 293 kg (645 lb) fuel for ground and airborne manoeuvres, plus fuel for 150 nm (278 km; 173 mile) diversion and 45 min hold at 1,525 m (5,000 ft):
- Series 100: 1,480 nm (2,743 km; 1,704 miles)
- Series 200: 1,465 nm (2,715 km; 1,687 miles)

Range with max payload, allowances as above:
- Series 100: 565 nm (1,048 km; 651 miles)
- Series 200: 1,040 nm (1,928 km; 1,198 miles)

OPERATIONAL NOISE CHARACTERISTICS (FAR Pt 36-9, estimated):

T-O noise level:
- Series 100: 83 EPNdB
- Series 200: 88 EPNdB

Approach noise level:
- Series 100 and 200: 95 EPNdB

Sideline noise level:
- Series 100 and 200: 89 EPNdB

BAe 146M

British Aerospace has proposed the development of a military version of the BAe 146 short-range transport. Utilising the same power plant as the civil transport, it is envisaged as a medium-lift aircraft suitable for a variety of missions, including the airlift of vehicles and palletised cargo; the delivery of heavy vehicles to forward airstrips, and casevac mission on the return flight; airdrop of paratroops and supplies, the latter by free-fall or parachute extraction technique; and troop or VIP transport, with mixed passenger/freight layouts optional.

Generally similar to the civil BAe 146, the proposed military version differs primarily in having a changed landing gear to simplify operation from unprepared surfaces at forward landing strips, and in redesign of the aft fuselage to provide rear ramp loading. All available details follow:

TYPE: Short-range multi-role military transport.

WINGS: As for BAe 146.

FUSELAGE: All-metal fail-safe pressurised semi-monocoque structure, with a new aft fuselage which has a hydraulically-operated ramp, and doors which open outward and upwards, to permit straight-in loading of military vehicles and other cargo.

TAIL UNIT: As for BAe 146.

LANDING GEAR: Hydraulically-retractable tricycle type, specially designed for operation from unprepared surfaces. Nose unit, with twin wheels, retracts forward. Main landing gear has two large-diameter wheels with low-pressure tyres mounted in tandem on each side. Wheels are independently mounted on trailing arms which operate a dual-piston shock-absorber. Main units retract into a long fairing on each side of the lower fuselage. Anti-skid brake units standard.

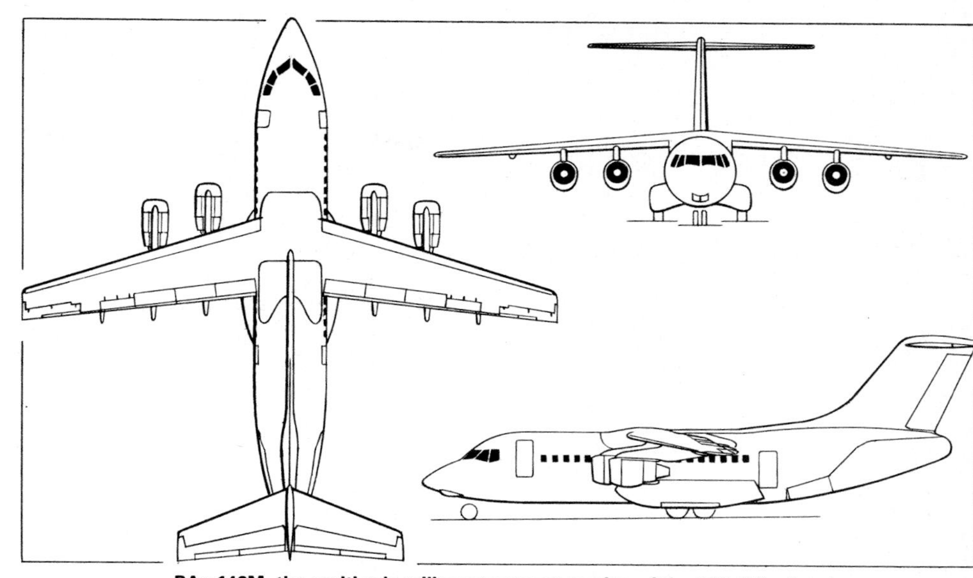

BAe 146M, the multi-role military transport version of the 146 *(Pilot Press)*

POWER PLANT: As for BAe 146, except standard fuel capacity 12,910 litres (2,840 Imp gallons), contained in integral wing tanks and wing root fillet tanks. Provision for 5,455 litres (1,200 Imp gallons) of optional fuel.

ACCOMMODATION: Crew of two on flight deck, with seat for supernumerary crew member and provision for optional navigator's station. Constant-section cargo hold/cabin can accommodate a typical military load comprising a 105 mm light gun, a one ton truck and a half ton truck, plus their operating personnel. A Scorpion tank and its crew can be carried. A total of five 2·74 × 2·24 m (108 × 88 in) pallets can be loaded, using a side guidance system and rollers. A winch to simplify loading is available optionally. Accommodation is provided for up to 60 paratroops and two dispatchers, and two sticks of 30 men can be dispatched simultaneously through two rear paratroop exits. For supply drops the 146M can carry items ranging from two medium-stressed platforms, to 18 'one ton' type containers. As a troop transport, up to 70 seats can be provided in a five-abreast layout, which includes also two toilets and 9·49 m³ (335 cu ft) of baggage space. A maximum of 84 passengers, seated six-abreast, can be accommodated in an all-passenger configuration, with two toilets and 9·63 m³ (340 cu ft) of baggage space.

SYSTEMS: Generally as for BAe 146. Optional APU in nose of starboard main landing gear fairing.

AVIONICS: Basic installation would include passenger address and audio systems, flight deck voice recorder, dual ADI, marker beacon receiver, weather radar, radio altimeter, DME, ADF, dual VHF nav, flight data recorder, dual VHF/UHF com, dual compass systems, Doppler, IFF with civil mode, TANS, and HF com. Options could add a second ADF, DME, IFF, radio altimeter and HF, Selcal, Tacan, Omega, DF/homer and an inertial navigation system.

DIMENSIONS, EXTERNAL:

Wing span	26·34 m (86 ft 5 in)
Length overall	27·38 m (89 ft 10 in)
Height overall	8·94 m (29 ft 4 in)
Wheel track	4·19 m (13 ft 9 in)
Wheelbase	10·95 m (35 ft 11 in)

DIMENSIONS, INTERNAL:

Cabin/hold:	
Length (excl ramp)	12·50 m (41 ft 0 in)
Floor width	2·73 m (8 ft 11½ in)
Max width of doorway	2·82 m (9 ft 3 in)
Floor area (excl ramp)	34·19 m² (368 sq ft)
Volume	91·32 m³ (3,225 cu ft)

AREA:

Wings, gross	77·30 m² (832 sq ft)

WEIGHTS AND LOADINGS (estimated):

Max T-O weight	39,916 kg (88,000 lb)
Max landing weight	38,555 kg (85,000 lb)
Max zero-fuel weight	31,071 kg (68,500 lb)
Max wing loading	516·4 kg/m² (105·8 lb/sq ft)
Max power loading	335 kg/kN (3·28 lb/lb st)

PERFORMANCE (estimated, at max T-O weight except where indicated):

Max level speed above 6,100 m (20,000 ft): more than 400 knots (742 km/h; 461 mph)

Max rate of climb at S/L at AUW of 36,287 kg (80,000 lb): 780 m (2,560 ft)/min

Max operating altitude: 9,145 m (30,000 ft)

Service ceiling, one engine out, at AUW of 36,287 kg (80,000 lb): 6,920 m (22,700 ft)

T-O run, ISA + 20°C at S/L: 1,317 m (4,320 ft)

T-O to 15 m (50 ft), ISA + 20°C at S/L: 1,625 m (5,330 ft)

Landing from 15 m (50 ft) at max landing weight, ISA + 20°C at S/L: 617 m (2,025 ft)

Landing run at max landing weight, ISA + 20°C at S/L: 378 m (1,240 ft)

Range with max payload, standard fuel, 10% reserves: 1,260 nm (2,335 km; 1,451 miles)

BAe (BAC) ONE-ELEVEN

Details of the One-Eleven were announced on 9 May 1961, simultaneously with the news that British United Airways had ordered ten. Design and manufacture are shared between three Weybridge/Bristol Division factories, at Weybridge, Filton and Hurn.

Five commercial versions have been produced, and details of the Series 200 (56 built), 300 (nine built) and 400 (69 built) can be found in the 1974-75 *Jane's*. Two versions are currently in production, as follows:

Series 475. Combines standard fuselage and accommodation of Series 400 with wings and power plant of Series 500 and a modified landing gear system, using low-pressure tyres, to permit operation from secondary low-strength runways with poorer-grade surfaces. The Srs 400/500 development aircraft (G-ASYD) was converted

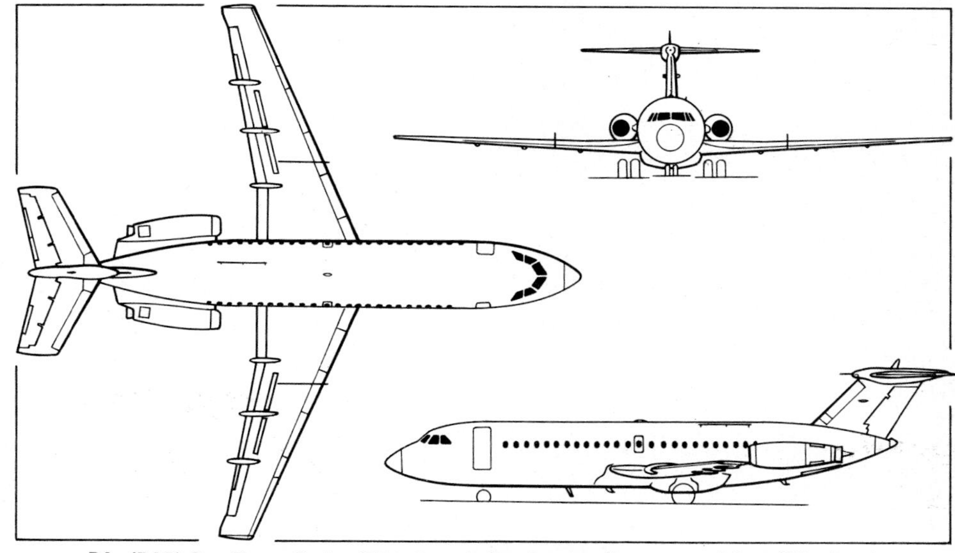

BAe (BAC) One-Eleven Series 475 twin-turbofan short/medium-range airliner *(Pilot Press)*

BAe (BAC) One-Eleven Series 475 with forward upward-opening freight door, for service with the Air Force of the Sultanate of Oman

to serve as prototype and flew for the first time on 27 August 1970. First production Series 475 (G-AYUW) flew for the first time on 5 April 1971. Certification and first production delivery (to Faucett of Peru) in July 1971. The three Srs 475s supplied to the Sultan of Oman's Air Force have a quick-change passenger/cargo interior layout and a 3·05 × 1·85 m (10 ft 0 in × 6 ft 1 in) forward freight door. The first executive Series 475, for a Saudi Arabian customer, was delivered in May 1978. Nine had been sold by 1 June 1979.

Series 500. Derived from Series 300/400, this version incorporates a lengthened fuselage (2·54 m; 100 in fwd of wing, 1·57 m; 62 in aft) which accommodates 97-119 passengers, with a flight crew of two. Wingtip extensions increase span by 1·52 m (5 ft). Take-off performance improved by increased wing area and by installation of two Rolls-Royce Spey Mk 512 DW turbofans, each rated at 55·8 kN (12,550 lb st). Main landing gear strengthened and heavier wing planks used to cater for increased AUW. Prototype, converted from Srs 400 development aircraft (G-ASYD), flew for the first time on 30 June 1967. First Srs 500 production aircraft (G-AVMH) flew on 7 February 1968. ARB certification 15 August 1968. Deliveries to BEA (now British Airways) began on 29 August 1968, and regular services on 17 November 1968. Total of 84 sold by 1 June 1979.

In addition, executive and freighter versions of the One-Eleven are available. More than 40 examples of the former are now in service, notably in the USA and with the Australian government, with interior and long-range tank conversions being made either by BAe or by specialist contractors. The One-Eleven freighter incorporates a 3·05 m by 1·85 m (10 ft 0 in by 6 ft 1 in) upward-opening hydraulically-powered loading door in the forward fuselage, together with a quickly-removable freight floor overlay and cargo handling system. First to be delivered, in November 1975, was one of three Series 475 freighters operated by the Sultan of Oman's Air Force.

In May 1977, BAe concluded an agreement with CIAR of Romania for the Series 475 and Series 500 to be built under licence in Romania by GAB (which see). Orders for 227 One-Elevens (not including those to be built in Romania) had been received by 1 June 1979.

A One-Eleven 'hush kit', comprising an intake duct lining, a by-pass duct lining, an acoustically-lined jetpipe, and a six-chute exhaust silencer, was flown for the first time, on the Srs 475 development aircraft G-ASYD, on 14 June 1974. It is designed to reduce the area within the 90 EPNdB noise contour by approximately 50 per cent, giving a noise footprint equivalent to that of a twin-turboprop aircraft. The first production aircraft to be fitted with 'hush kits' were five One-Eleven 500s for Tarom, the Romanian state airline, which were delivered between March and August 1977. In May 1979 Monarch Airlines in the UK became the first operator to order 'hush kits' for retrospective fitting to its fleet of One-Eleven Srs 500s.

The following description applies to the Series 475 and 500:

Type: Twin-turbofan short/medium-range transport.

Wings: Cantilever low-wing monoplane. Modified NACA cambered wing section. Thickness/chord ratio 12½% at root, 11% at tip. Dihedral 2°. Incidence 2° 30′. Sweepback 20° at quarter-chord. All-metal structure of copper-based aluminium alloy, built on fail-safe principles. Three-shear-web torsion box with integrally-machined skin/stringer panels. Ailerons of Redux-bonded light alloy honeycomb, manually operated through servo tabs. Port servo tab used for trimming. Light alloy Fowler flaps hydraulically operated through Hobson actuators. Light alloy spoiler/airbrakes on upper surface of wing, operated hydraulically through Dowty Boulton Paul actuators. Hydraulically-actuated lift dumpers, inboard of spoilers, are standard. Flaps on Series 475 have a glassfibre coating. Thermal de-icing of wing leading-edges with engine bleed air.

Fuselage: Conventional circular-section all-metal fail-safe structure with continuous frames and stringers. Skin made from copper-based aluminium alloy.

Tail Unit: Cantilever all-metal fail-safe structure, with variable-incidence T tailplane, controlled through duplicated Hobson hydraulic units. Fin integral with rear fuselage. Elevators and rudder actuated hydraulically through Dowty Boulton Paul tandem jacks. Leading-edges of fin and tailplane de-iced by engine bleed air.

Landing Gear: Retractable tricycle type, with twin wheels on each unit. Hydraulic retraction, nose unit forward, main units inward. Oleo-pneumatic shock-absorbers manufactured by BAC. Hydraulic nosewheel steering. Dunlop wheels, tubeless tyres and 5-plate heavy-duty hydraulic disc brakes. Hytrol Mk III anti-skid units. Main-wheel tyres size 40 × 12 on Srs 500, pressure 11·03 bars (160 lb/sq in). Dunlop 44 × 16 tyres on Srs 475, pressure 5·72 bars (83 lb/sq in). Nosewheel tyres size 24 × 7·25 on Srs 500, pressure 7·58 bars (110 lb/sq in). Dunlop 24 × 7·7 tyres on Srs 475, pressure 7·24 bars (105 lb/sq in). All tyre pressures are given for aircraft at mid-CG position and max taxi weight.

Power Plant: Two Rolls-Royce Spey Mk 512 DW turbofan engines, each rated at 55·8 kN (12,550 lb st), mounted in pod on each side of rear fuselage. Fuel in integral wing tanks of 10,160 litres (2,235 Imp gallons) and centre-section tank of 3,864 litres (850 Imp gallons) capacity; total fuel capacity 14,024 litres (3,085 Imp gallons). Optional 1,591 litre (350 Imp gallon) and 3,182 litre (700 Imp gallon) fuel tanks are available to increase total fuel capacity. Pressure refuelling point in fuselage forward of wing on starboard side. Provision for gravity refuelling. Oil capacity (total engine oil) 13·66 litres (3 Imp gallons) per engine.

Accommodation (Srs 475): Crew of two on flight deck and up to 89 passengers in main cabin. Single class or mixed class layout, with movable divider bulkhead to permit any first/tourist ratio. Typical mixed class layout has 16 first class (four abreast) and 49 tourist (five abreast) seats. Galley units normally at front on starboard side. Coat space available on port side aft of flight deck. Ventral entrance with hydraulically-operated airstair. Forward passenger door on port side incorporates optional power-operated airstair. Galley service door forward on starboard side. Two baggage and freight holds under floor, fore and aft of wings, with doors on starboard side. Forward freight door on Srs 475s for Sultan of Oman's Air Force. Entire accommodation air-conditioned.

Accommodation (Srs 500): Crew of two on flight deck and up to 119 passengers in main cabin. Two additional overwing emergency exits, making two on each side. One toilet on each side of cabin at rear. Otherwise generally similar to Srs 475.

Systems: Fully-duplicated air-conditioning and pressurisation systems with main components by Normalair-Garrett. Air bled from engine compressors through heat exchangers. Max pressure differential 0·52 bars (7·5 lb/sq in). Hydraulic system, pressure 207 bars (3,000 lb/sq in), operates flaps, spoilers, rudder, elevators, tailplane, landing gear, brakes, nosewheel steering, ventral and forward airstairs and windscreen wipers. No pneumatic system. Electrical system utilises two 30kVA Plessey/Westinghouse AC generators, driven by Plessey constant-speed drive and starter units, plus a similar generator mounted on the APU and shaft-driven. AiResearch gas-turbine APU in tailcone to provide ground electrical power, air-conditioning and engine starting, also some system checkout capability. APU is run during take-off to eliminate performance penalty of bleeding engine air for cabin air-conditioning.

Avionics and Equipment: Communications and navigation avionics generally to customers' requirements. Typical installation includes dual VHF com to ARINC 546, dual VHF nav to ARINC 547A, including glideslope receivers, marker receiver, flight/service interphone system, Marconi AD 370, Bendix DFA 73 or Collins DF 203 ADF, ATC transponder to ARINC 532D, Collins 860 E2 DME, Ekco E 190 or Bendix RDR 1E weather radar. Sperry C9 or CL11 compass systems and Collins FD 108 flight director system (dual) are also installed. Elliott 2000 Series autopilot system. Provision on the Srs 500 for additional equipment, including automatic

BAe (BAC) One-Eleven Series 500 of Tarom photographed over the south coast of England

throttle control, for low weather minima operation.

DIMENSIONS, EXTERNAL:
Wing span 28·50 m (93 ft 6 in)
Wing chord at root 5·12 m (16 ft 9⅝ in)
Wing chord at tip 1·65 m (5 ft 5 in)
Wing aspect ratio 8·5
Length overall: Srs 475 28·50 m (93 ft 6 in)
Srs 500 32·61 m (107 ft 0 in)
Length of fuselage: Srs 475 25·55 m (83 ft 10 in)
Srs 500 29·67 m (97 ft 4 in)
Height overall 7·47 m (24 ft 6 in)
Tailplane span 8·99 m (29 ft 6 in)
Wheel track 4·34 m (14 ft 3 in)
Wheelbase: Srs 475 10·06 m (33 ft 0 in)
Srs 500 12·60 m (41 ft 4 in)
Passenger door (fwd, port):
Height 1·73 m (5 ft 8 in)
Width 0·82 m (2 ft 8 in)
Height to sill 2·13 m (7 ft 0 in)
Ventral entrance: Height 1·83 m (6 ft 0 in)
Width 0·66 m (2 ft 2 in)
Height to sill 2·13 m (7 ft 0 in)
Freight door (fwd, starboard):
Height (projected) 0·79 m (2 ft 7 in)
Width 0·91 m (3 ft 0 in)
Height to sill 1·09 m (3 ft 7 in)
Freight door (rear, starboard):
Height (projected) 0·66 m (2 ft 2 in)
Width 0·91 m (3 ft 0 in)
Height to sill 1·30 m (4 ft 3 in)
Freight door (fwd, Srs 475 SOAF):
Height 1·85 m (6 ft 1 in)
Width 3·05 m (10 ft 0 in)
Galley service door (fwd, starboard):
Height (projected) 1·22 m (4 ft 0 in)
Width 0·69 m (2 ft 3 in)
Height to sill 2·13 m (7 ft 0 in)

DIMENSIONS, INTERNAL (Srs 475):
Cabin, excl flight deck:
Length 17·31 m (56 ft 10 in)
Max width 3·16 m (10 ft 4 in)
Max height 1·98 m (6 ft 6 in)
Floor area approx 47·0 m^2 (506 sq ft)
Freight hold, fwd 10·02 m^3 (354 cu ft)
Freight hold, rear 4·42 m^3 (156 cu ft)

DIMENSIONS, INTERNAL (Srs 500):
Cabin, excl flight deck:
Length 21·44 m (70 ft 4 in)
Total floor area approx 61·78 m^2 (665 sq ft)
Freight holds (total volume) 19·45 m^3 (687 cu ft)

AREAS (Srs 475, 500):
Wings, gross 95·78 m^2 (1,031 sq ft)
Ailerons (total) 2·86 m^2 (30·8 sq ft)
Flaps (total) 15·89 m^2 (171 sq ft)
Spoilers (total) 2·30 m^2 (24·8 sq ft)
Vertical tail surfaces (total) 10·90 m^2 (117·4 sq ft)
Rudder, incl tab 3·05 m^2 (32·8 sq ft)
Horizontal tail surfaces (total) 23·90 m^2 (257·0 sq ft)
Elevators, incl tab 6·55 m^2 (70·4 sq ft)

WEIGHTS AND LOADINGS:
Operating weight empty:
Srs 475 23,348 kg (51,473 lb)
Srs 500 24,454 kg (53,911 lb)
Max payload: Srs 475 9,764 kg (21,527 lb)
Srs 500 12,286 kg (27,089 lb)
Max T-O weight:
Srs 475 41,730-44,678 kg (92,000-98,500 lb)
Srs 500 45,200-47,400 kg (99,650-104,500 lb)
Max ramp weight: Srs 475 44,905 kg (99,000 lb)
Srs 500 47,625 kg (105,000 lb)
Max landing weight:
Srs 475 38,100-39,462 kg (84,000-87,000 lb)
Srs 500 39,462 kg (87,000 lb)
Max zero-fuel weight: Srs 475 33,112 kg (73,000 lb)
Srs 500 36,741 kg (81,000 lb)
Max wing loading:
Srs 475 435·5 kg/m^2 (89·2 lb/sq ft)
Srs 500 472 kg/m^2 (96·7 lb/sq ft)
Max power loading:
Srs 475 400·3 kg/kN (3·92 lb/lb st)
Srs 500 424·7 kg/kN (4·16 lb/lb st)

PERFORMANCE (at max T-O weight):
Never-exceed speed (structural)
410 knots (760 km/h; 472 mph) EAS
Max level and cruising speed at 6,400 m (21,000 ft)
470 knots (871 km/h; 541 mph)
Fuel econ cruising speed at 7,620 m (25,000 ft)
400 knots (742 km/h; 461 mph)
Stalling speed (T-O flap setting):
Srs 475 99 knots (184 km/h; 114 mph) EAS
Srs 500 105 knots (195 km/h; 121 mph)
Rate of climb at S/L at 300 knots (555 km/h; 345 mph)
EAS: Srs 475 756 m (2,480 ft)/min
Srs 500 695 m (2,280 ft)/min
Max cruising height 10,670 m (35,000 ft)
Min ground turning radius:
Srs 475 17·07 m (56 ft 0 in)
Srs 500 17·98 m (59 ft 0 in)
Runway LCN at max weight, rigid pavement (1: 40):
Srs 475 32
Srs 500 53
T-O run at S/L, ISA: Srs 475 1,676 m (5,500 ft)
Srs 500 1,981 m (6,500 ft)
Balanced T-O to 10·7 m (35 ft) at S/L, ISA:
Srs 475 1,798 m (5,900 ft)
Srs 500 2,225 m (7,300 ft)
Landing distance (BCAR) at S/L, ISA, at max landing weight: Srs 475, Srs 500 1,463 m (4,800 ft)
Still-air range with max fuel, ISA, with reserves for 200 nm (370 km; 230 mile) diversion and 45 min hold:
Srs 475 1,997 nm (3,700 km; 2,300 miles)
Srs 500 1,880 nm (3,484 km; 2,165 miles)
Still-air range with typical capacity payload, ISA, reserves as above:
Srs 475 at 44,678 kg (98,500 lb)
1,619 nm (3,000 km; 1,865 miles)
Srs 500 at 47,400 kg (104,500 lb)
1,480 nm (2,744 km; 1,705 miles)
Srs 475 executive aircraft with additional 3,182 litres (700 Imp gallons) fuel has equivalent range of
2,549 nm (4,725 km; 2,936 miles)

BAe (HS) TRIDENT

The BAe (HS) (originally de Havilland D.H.121) Trident was ordered into production initially to meet BEA's requirements for a short-haul 520 knot (965 km/h; 600 mph) airliner for service from 1963-64 onwards. Design was started in 1957 and the first Trident (G-ARPA), a production aircraft for BEA, flew for the first time on 9 January 1962.

Five versions were produced: the Trident 1 (24 built), 1E (15 built), 2E (50 built), 3B (26 built) and Super 3B (2 built). Production of the Trident has ended, and all versions have been described fully in previous editions of *Jane's*. Of the 33 Trident 2Es supplied to China, 15 are operated (plus two Super 3Bs) by CAAC, the state airline. The remaining 18, plus four others acquired from Pakistan International Airlines, were allocated to the Air Force of the People's Liberation Army.

BAe SA-3-120 BULLDOG SERIES 120

The Bulldog originated in 1968 as a military trainer version of the Beagle Pup, from which it differs substantially in having a fully-transparent canopy, increased wing span, and strengthened construction to allow full aerobatic operation.

First flight of the Beagle-built prototype (G-AXEH) was made on 19 May 1969. A second prototype (G-AXIG), completed by Scottish Aviation, was flown on 14 February 1971, and a third airframe was completed for static and fatigue tests.

All versions ordered so far are basically similar, except for the equipment fitted. The first production Bulldog, completed by Scottish Aviation, flew for the first time on 22 June 1971 and received full ARB certification on 30 June 1971. The first 98 production Bulldogs were of the Series 100 version, described in the 1972-73 *Jane's*. The second prototype was refurbished, issued with a Normal category C of A, and delivered to a private owner under the designation Model 104.

Production continued with the Series 120, which was awarded full CAA certification on 12 February 1973.

By January 1979 orders for the Bulldog Series 120 were as follows:

Model 121. For Royal Air Force, by whom it is designated **T. Mk 1.** Total of 130 ordered, of which the first (XX513) flew for the first time on 30 January 1973 and was delivered to the A & AEE at Boscombe Down on 20 February 1973. By February 1976, all had been delivered, and were in service with No. 2 FTS at Leeming, the CFS at Leeming, and University Air Squadrons.

Model 122. For Ghana Air Force. Six ordered initially, delivery of which was completed in September 1973. Further seven ordered in December 1974 **(Mk 122A)**, delivery of which was completed by February 1976.

Model 123. For Nigerian Air Force. Twenty ordered initially. Delivery of these completed December 1974. Further 12 delivered in 1978.

Model 124. One aircraft (G-ASAL) used as company demonstration aircraft.

Model 125. Built for Jordanian Royal Academy of Aeronautics. Total of 13 delivered, in three batches, between 1974 and 1976. All transferred to Royal Jordanian Air Force in 1978.

Model 126. For Lebanese Air Force. Six ordered. Delivery completed in October 1975.

Model 127. For undisclosed customer (reportedly Kenya). Nine ordered. Delivery completed December 1976.

Model 128. For Royal Hong Kong Auxiliary Air Force. Two ordered. Delivered in 1977.

The following description applies to the Bulldog Series 120:

TYPE: Two/three-seat primary trainer.

WINGS: Cantilever low-wing monoplane. Wing section NACA 63_2615. Dihedral 6° 30′. Incidence 1° 9′ at root. Conventional single-spar riveted stressed-skin structure of light alloy. Electrically-operated slotted trailing-edge flaps and slotted ailerons of similar construction. Ground-adjustable tab on starboard aileron.

FUSELAGE: Conventional light alloy stressed-skin semi-monocoque structure.

TAIL UNIT: Cantilever two-spar light alloy stressed-skin structure. Fixed-incidence tailplane. Full-span trim tab in starboard elevator. Manually-operated trim tab in rudder. Ventral fin.

LANDING GEAR: Non-retractable tricycle type, with single wheel on each unit. Steerable nosewheel with Automotive Products oleo-pneumatic shock-absorber and Goodyear wheel and tyre, size 5·00-5, pressure 2·76 bars (40 lb/sq in). Main units have Automotive Products oleo-pneumatic shock-absorbers and Goodyear wheels and tyres, size 6·00-6, pressure 2·07 bars (30 lb/sq in). Goodyear hydraulic disc brakes on main wheels. Optional ski landing gear.

POWER PLANT: One 149 kW (200 hp) Lycoming IO-360-A1B6 flat-four engine, driving a Hartzell HC-C2YK-4F/FC7666A-2 two-blade constant-speed metal propeller with spinner. Lycoming AEIO-360-A1B6 engine available optionally, permitting up to 20 sec of inverted flight. Four removable metal fuel tanks, two in each wing, with total usable capacity of 145·5 litres (32 Imp gallons). Refuelling point on top of each wing. Oil capacity 7·6 litres (1·67 Imp gallons).

ACCOMMODATION: Enclosed cabin seating pilot and co-pilot or trainee side by side with dual controls, with space at rear for observer's seat or up to 100 kg (220 lb) of baggage. Rearward-sliding jettisonable transparent canopy. Cabin heated and ventilated.

SYSTEMS: Heat exchanger for cabin heating. Hydraulic system, pressure 40 bars (580 lb/sq in), for main-wheel brakes only. Vacuum-type pneumatic system available optionally. 24V DC power from engine-driven alternator and 24V 25Ah storage battery. No oxygen or de-icing systems.

AVIONICS AND EQUIPMENT: VHF, UHF or HF com radio to individual customer's requirements; panel can accommodate dual VHF nav, DME, ATC transponder, ADF and other navaids. Blind-flying instrumentation standard. Glider towing attachment optional.

ARMAMENT AND OPERATIONAL EQUIPMENT: Standard aircraft is unarmed, but has provision for installation of four underwing hardpoints to which can be attached various loads including unguided or wire-guided air-to-surface projectiles; 7·62 mm machine-gun pods; grenade launchers; practice or active bombs of up to 50 kg; markers; supply containers; leaflet dispensers; and rescue and survival equipment. Maximum underwing load 290 kg (640 lb).

DIMENSIONS, EXTERNAL:
Wing span 10·06 m (33 ft 0 in)
Wing chord at root 1·51 m (4 ft 11¼ in)
Wing chord at tip 0·86 m (2 ft 9¾ in)
Wing aspect ratio 8·4
Length overall 7·09 m (23 ft 3 in)
Height overall 2·28 m (7 ft 5¾ in)
Tailplane span 3·35 m (11 ft 0 in)
Wheel track 2·03 m (6 ft 8 in)
Wheelbase 1·40 m (4 ft 7 in)
Propeller diameter 1·88 m (6 ft 2 in)
Propeller ground clearance 0·26 m (10¼ in)

BAe Scottish Division Bulldog Model 121 trainer in service with the RAF

DIMENSIONS, INTERNAL:
Cabin: Length 2·11 m (6 ft 11 in)
Max width 1·14 m (3 ft 9 in)
Max height 1·02 m (3 ft 4 in)

AREAS:
Wings, gross 12·02 m² (129·4 sq ft)
Ailerons (total) 0·87 m² (9·4 sq ft)
Trailing-edge flaps (total) 1·30 m² (13·95 sq ft)
Vertical tail surfaces (total) 2·11 m² (22·72 sq ft)
Horizontal tail surfaces (total) 2·55 m² (27·50 sq ft)

WEIGHTS AND LOADINGS:
Weight empty, equipped 649 kg (1,430 lb)
Basic operating weight empty 669 kg (1,475 lb)
Max T-O weight:
normal and semi-aerobatic 1,066 kg (2,350 lb)
fully aerobatic 1,015 kg (2,238 lb)
Max wing loading 88·6 kg/m² (18·15 lb/sq ft)
Max power loading 7·15 kg/kW (11·75 lb/hp)

PERFORMANCE (at max T-O weight):
Never-exceed speed (structural) 210 knots (389 km/h; 241 mph)
Max level speed at S/L 130 knots (241 km/h; 150 mph)
Max cruising speed at 1,220 m (4,000 ft) 120 knots (222 km/h; 138 mph)
Econ cruising speed at 1,220 m (4,000 ft) 105 knots (194 km/h; 121 mph)
Stalling speed, flaps down, power off 53 knots (98 km/h; 61 mph) EAS
Max rate of climb at S/L 315 m (1,034 ft)/min
Service ceiling 4,875 m (16,000 ft)
Min ground turning radius 9·75 m (32 ft 0 in)
T-O run 274 m (900 ft)
T-O to 15 m (50 ft) 427 m (1,400 ft)
Landing from 15 m (50 ft) 363 m (1,190 ft)
Landing run 153 m (500 ft)
Range with max fuel, 55% power, no reserves 540 nm (1,000 km; 621 miles)
Endurance with max fuel, conditions as above 5 h 0 min
g limits: semi-aerobatic +4·4; −1·8
fully aerobatic +6; −3

BAe (BAC 167) STRIKEMASTER

The BAe Strikemaster was developed from the BAC 145 series (see 1972-73 *Jane's*). It has the same airframe, but is powered by a Rolls-Royce Viper Mk 535 turbojet engine (15·2 kN; 3,410 lb st) and has four underwing hardpoints, enabling it to carry up to 1,360 kg (3,000 lb) of stores.

The first Strikemaster flew for the first time on 26 October 1967, and a total of 146 (including five BAC 145s) were ordered. By the end of 1978 deliveries had been completed, including a further batch of 12 Mk 80As ordered by Saudi Arabia in 1977 (not 10, as reported in 1978-79 *Jane's*); but 10 aircraft were built for stock in anticipation of further orders.

Details of the Strikemaster can be found in the 1978-79 *Jane's*.

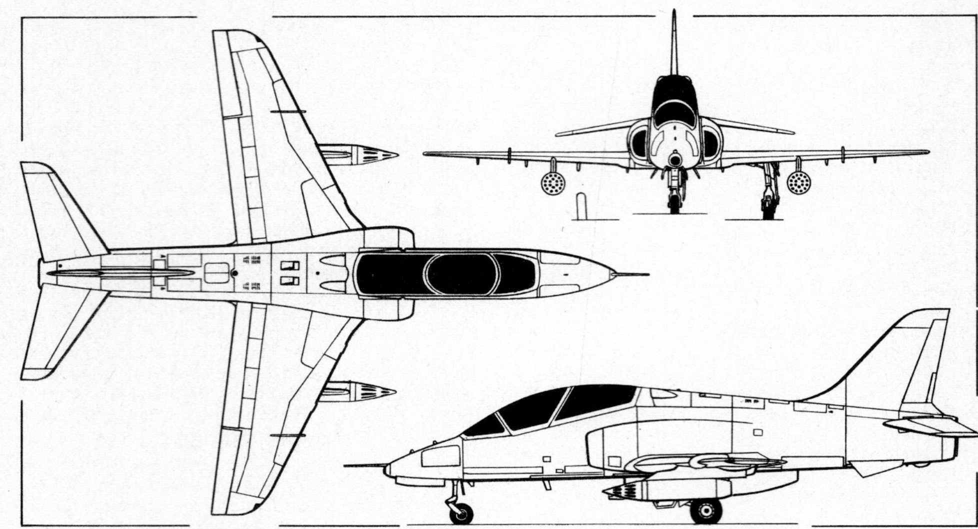
British Aerospace Hawk two-seat jet trainer/close support aircraft *(Pilot Press)*

BAe HAWK

RAF designation: Hawk T. Mk 1

After examining designs submitted by BAC and Hawker Siddeley to meet an RAF requirement for a basic and advanced jet trainer, the Ministry of Defence announced in October 1971 that the Hawker Siddeley 1182 had been selected to meet this requirement. Selection of a non-afterburning version of the Rolls-Royce Turboméca Adour to power the aircraft was announced on 2 March 1972, and later in the same month the Ministry of Defence confirmed an initial order for 176 HS 1182s, which were given the RAF name of Hawk. These were to consist of one pre-production aircraft (XX154), which first flew on 21 August 1974, and 175 production Hawks. There were no separate prototypes; instead, the first five production aircraft were allocated to the development programme. The first two production Hawks (XX162 and 163) were delivered to the Advanced Flying Training School at RAF Valley on 4 November 1976, and 100 had been delivered by 27 March 1979. The possibility of a follow-on order from the RAF was mentioned at that time.

The Hawk is designed to be fully aerobatic (it is stressed to +8 and −4*g*) and to have a fatigue life of 6,000 hours. It is replacing the Jet Provost, Gnat Trainer and Hunter in RAF service for advanced flying training, and for radio, navigation and weapons training. The basic design is capable of development for other operational roles, and studies of a number of variants have been made. One outcome of this is that a substantial number of RAF Hawks will be modified to carry two AIM-9L Sidewinder air-to-air missiles (see accompanying illustration) to supplement home defence fighter squadrons in an emergency. The RAF's premier aerobatic team, the Red Arrows, was re-equipping with the Hawk in late 1979.

The Finnish government has ordered 50 Hawk **Mk 51** trainers to replace its Fouga Magisters, with initial deliveries scheduled for early 1980. Components for 46 of these, and final assembly, will be undertaken in Finland by Valmet (which see). British Aerospace announced on 5 April 1978 the receipt of a contract for the supply of eight Hawk ground attack/trainer aircraft for the Indonesian Air Force. An African country (reportedly Kenya) has ordered 12.

In January 1979, it was announced that the US Naval Air Development Center had awarded BAe Aircraft Group a contract to study modification of the Hawk to meet the Navy's VTX-TS requirement for a replacement for the T-2C Buckeye and TA-4J Skyhawk. The modification would make the Hawk capable of operation from aircraft carriers.

TYPE: Two-seat basic and advanced jet trainer, with capability for close support role.

WINGS: Cantilever low-wing monoplane. Thickness/chord ratio 10·9% at root, 9% at tip. Dihedral 2°. Sweepback 26° on leading-edge, 21° 30′ at quarter-chord. One-piece wing, with six-bolt attachment to fuselage, employing a machined spars-and-skin torsion box, the greater part of which forms an integral fuel tank. Hydraulically-operated double-slotted flaps and ailerons, the latter operated by Automotive Products tandem actuators.

FUSELAGE: Conventional all-metal structure of frames and stringers, cut out to accept the one-piece wing. Large airbrake under rear of fuselage, aft of wing.

TAIL UNIT: Cantilever all-metal structure, with sweepback on all surfaces. One-piece all-moving power-operated anhedral tailplane, with Automotive Products tandem hydraulic actuators. Manually-operated rudder, with electrically-actuated trim tab.

LANDING GEAR: Wide-track retractable tricycle type, with single wheel on each unit. Hydraulic actuation, using Automotive Products jacks. Main units retract inward into wing, ahead of front spar; nosewheel retracts forward. Main wheels and tyres size 6·50-10, pressure 9·86 bars (143 lb/sq in). Nosewheel and tyre size 4·4-16, pressure 8·27 bars (120 lb/sq in). Tail bumper fairing under rear fuselage. Anti-skid wheel brakes. Tail braking parachute.

POWER PLANT: One Rolls-Royce Turboméca RT.172-06-11 Adour Mk 151 non-afterburning turbofan engine, with average rating of 23·75 kN (5,340 lb st). Air intake on each side of fuselage, forward of wing leading-edge. Engine starting by integral gas turbine starter. Fuel in one fuselage bag tank (841 litres; 185 Imp gallons) and integral wing tank (864 litres; 190 Imp gallons); total fuel capacity 1,705 litres (375 Imp gallons). Pressure refuelling point near front of port engine air intake trunk. Provision for carrying one 455 litre (100 Imp gallon) drop-tank on each inboard underwing pylon.

ACCOMMODATION: Crew of two in tandem under one-piece fully-transparent sideways-opening canopy. Fixed front windscreen and separate internal windscreen in front of rear cockpit. Rear seat elevated. Martin-Baker Mk 10B zero-zero rocket-assisted ejection seats, with MDC (miniature detonation cord) system to break canopy before seats eject. The MDC can also be operated from outside the cockpit in case of a ground emergency. Dual controls standard. Entire accommodation pressurised, heated and air-conditioned.

SYSTEMS: BAe Dynamics cockpit air-conditioning and pressurisation systems, using engine bleed air. Duplicated hydraulic systems, each 207 bars (3,000 lb/sq in),

BAe Hawk T.Mk 1 two-seat basic and advanced jet trainer

BAe Hawk, camouflaged and carrying a full load of underwing stores

for actuation of control jacks, flaps, airbrake, landing gear and anti-skid wheel brakes. Compressed nitrogen accumulators provide emergency power for flaps and landing gear. Hydraulic accumulator for emergency operation of wheel brakes. No pneumatic system. DC electrical power from single brushless generator, with two static inverters to provide AC power and two batteries for standby power. Gaseous oxygen system for crew. Pop-up Dowty Rotol ram-air turbine in upper rear fuselage provides emergency power for flying controls in the event of an engine or No. 2 pump failure.

Avionics and Equipment: The RAF standard of flight instrumentation includes Ferranti gyros and inverter, two Sperry Gyroscope RAI-4 4 in remote attitude indicators and a magnetic detector unit, and Louis Newmark compass system. Radio and navigation equipment includes Sylvania UHF and VHF, Cossor CAT.7000 Tacan, Cossor ILS with CILS.75/76 localiser/glideslope receiver and marker receiver, and IFF/SSR (Cossor 2720 Mk 10A IFF in aircraft for Finland).

Armament and Operational Equipment: Ferranti F.195 weapon sight and camera recorder in each cockpit. (Saab RGS2 sighting system in aircraft for Finland.) Trainer version has underfuselage centreline-mounted 30 mm Aden gun and ammunition pack, and two inboard underwing points each capable of carrying a nominal 454 kg (1,000 lb) stores load. Typical underwing armament training loads include two Matra 155 launchers, each with eighteen 2·75 in air-to-surface rockets, or two clusters of four practice bombs. Provision for two outboard underwing pylons, and a pylon in place of the ventral gun pack, also each capable of a 1,000 lb load (2,567 kg; 5,660 lb total external stores load), for close support role. The Hawk has demonstrated its ability to carry a total external load of 3,084 kg (6,800 lb). In RAF training roles the normal max external load is reported to be about 680 kg (1,500 lb). AIM-9L Sidewinder air-to-air missiles will be carried by RAF Hawks modified for operational use in an emergency.

Dimensions, external:

Wing span	9·39 m (30 ft 9¾ in)
Wing chord at root	2·65 m (8 ft 8¼ in)
Wing chord at tip	0·90 m (2 ft 11½ in)
Wing aspect ratio	5·284
Length overall, excl probe	11·17 m (36 ft 7¾ in)
Height overall	3·99 m (13 ft 1¼ in)
Tailplane span	4·39 m (14 ft 4¾ in)
Wheel track	3·34 m (10 ft 11½ in)

Areas:

Wings, gross	16·69 m² (179·6 sq ft)
Ailerons (total)	1·05 m² (11·30 sq ft)
Trailing-edge flaps (total)	2·50 m² (26·91 sq ft)
Airbrake	0·53 m² (5·70 sq ft)
Fin	2·51 m² (27·02 sq ft)
Rudder, incl tab	0·58 m² (6·24 sq ft)
Tailplane	4·33 m² (46·61 sq ft)

Weights:

Weight empty	3,647 kg (8,040 lb)
T-O weight:	
trainer, 'clean'	5,035 kg (11,100 lb)
trainer, armed	5,572 kg (12,284 lb)
Max T-O weight	7,755 kg (17,097 lb)
Max landing weight	4,649 kg (10,250 lb)

Performance:

Max level speed
540 knots (1,000 km/h; 621 mph) IAS

Max Mach number	1·17
Time to 9,145 m (30,000 ft)	6 min 6 s
Service ceiling	15,240 m (50,000 ft)
T-O run	550 m (1,800 ft)
Landing run	488 m (1,600 ft)

Combat radius:
with 2,540 kg (5,600 lb) weapon load
300 nm (556 km; 345 miles)
with 1,360 kg (3,000 lb) weapon load
560 nm (1,038 km; 645 miles)
Ferry range 'clean' 1,313 nm (2,433 km; 1,510 miles)
Ferry range with two 455 litre (100 Imp gallon) drop-tanks 1,669 nm (3,093 km; 1,922 miles)
Endurance approx 4 h 0 min

BAe HARRIER

RAF designations: Harrier GR.Mk 3 and T.Mk 2A and 4

USMC designations: AV-8A (Mk 50) and TAV-8A (Mk 54)

Spanish Navy designation: Matador (AV-8S and TAV-8S)

The Harrier was the world's first operational fixed-wing V/STOL strike fighter. Developed from six years of operating experience with the P.1127/Kestrel series of aircraft (see 1968-69 *Jane's*), it is an integrated V/STOL weapon system, incorporating a Ferranti FE 541 inertial navigation and attack system and Smiths head-up display. The first of six single-seat prototypes (XV276) flew for the first time on 31 August 1966; the following versions have since been built:

Harrier GR. Mk 1, 1A and 3. Single-seat close-support and tactical reconnaissance versions for the Royal Air Force. First of initial series of 78 production aircraft (XV738) flew on 28 December 1967. Entered service with the Harrier OCU, No. 233 Squadron, at RAF Wittering, on 1 April 1969. Delivered to No. 1 Squadron at Wittering and Nos. 3, 4 and 20 in Germany.

A Harrier GR. Mk 1A, piloted by Sqn Ldr T. L. Lecky-Thompson, set up two international time-to-height records after VTO, in Class H for jet-lift aircraft, on 5 January 1971. The aircraft, after a vertical take-off, reached 9,000 m (29,528 ft) in 1 min 44·7 s and 12,000 m (39,370 ft) in 2 min 22·7 s. The same RAF pilot also set up a Class H altitude record of 14,040 m (46,063 ft) in a Harrier GR. Mk 1A on 2 January 1971.

Harrier GR. Mk 1 aircraft were fitted initially with 84·5 kN (19,000 lb st) Pegasus 101 engines. When retrofitted subsequently with the 89·0 kN (20,000 lb st) Pegasus 102 engine they were redesignated GR.Mk 1A. Aircraft now in service have Pegasus 103 engine and are designated GR. Mk 3. A further 12 single-seat Harrier GR. Mk 3s, ordered for the RAF in March 1976, have been delivered; an additional batch of 24 GR. Mk 3s was ordered in 1977.

In early 1978 flight testing began of a Harrier GR. Mk 3 fitted with cushion augmentation devices (CADS) and wing leading-edge root extensions (LERX), both intended to improve lift capability. The CADS system consists of ventral strakes fitted to the underfuselage gun pods which, like the lift improvement devices (LIDS) employed on the McDonnell Douglas AV-8B Advanced Harrier, trap the exhaust air from the engine as it rebounds from the ground; the air is prevented from re-entering the intakes by a laterally-positioned surface fixed across the front of the two pods.

Harrier T. Mk 2, 2A and 4. Two-seat versions, retaining the full combat capability of the single-seater in terms of equipment fit and weapon carriage. There is a large degree of commonality in structure and system components, ground support equipment and flight and ground crew training. Differences include a new, longer nose section forward of the wing leading-edge, with two cockpits in tandem; a tailcone approx 1·83 m (6 ft) longer than that of the single-seat model; and enlarged fin surfaces. The two-seat Harrier may be used operationally with the rear seat and compensating tail ballast removed, thus minimising the weight penalty over its single-seat counterpart. First development aircraft (XW174) flew on 24 April 1969, and the first of 21 production aircraft (XW264) on 3 October 1969. The two-seater entered RAF service in July 1970.

The Harrier T. Mk 2, like the GR. Mk 1, was powered originally by the Pegasus 101 engine. The designations T. Mk 2A and T. Mk 4 apply to aircraft retrofitted with, respectively, the Pegasus 102 and 103.

Harrier Mk 50 (USMC designation AV-8A). Single-seat close-support and tactical reconnaissance version for the US Marine Corps. Dimensionally the same as GR. Mk 3, but with modifications to customer's specification, including provision for the carriage of Sidewinder missiles. Initial quantity of 12 ordered in 1969. Subsequent orders brought this total to 102. The last order for the USMC included eight Harrier **Mk 54s** with Pegasus 103 engines (a two-seat version designated **TAV-8A**) for operational training; the last of these was delivered in 1977.

The first AV-8A was delivered to the USA on 26 January 1971. The first 10 AV-8As had Pegasus 102 engines; the next 92 aircraft are powered by Pegasus 103s, which have also been fitted retrospectively to the earlier aircraft. McDonnell Douglas acquired licence rights to manufacture 'any significant numbers' ordered if the US government decided to build in the USA.

The AV-8As equip three USMC combat squadrons: VMA 513, VMA 542 and VMA 231 at Cherry Point, North Carolina. A training squadron, VMA(T) 203, is also based at Cherry Point. Six **Mk 55** AV-8As and two TAV-8As were ordered, through the USA, for the Spanish Navy, by whom they are known as **Matadors** and designated **T/AV-8S**. These were handed over in November 1976, and equip the 8a Escuadrilla of the Spanish Navy at Rota, Cadiz. A further five AV-8Ss were ordered later.

Harrier Mk 52. One aircraft built as a demonstrator using HSA and equipment suppliers' private funding. It is similar to the Harrier T. Mk 4, and is fitted with a Pegasus 103 engine; in recognition of its status as the first civil-registered jet V/STOL aircraft in the UK, it was granted the civil registration G-VTOL. First flight was made on 16 September 1971, with a Pegasus 102 fitted initially.

An Advanced Harrier study was completed in December 1973 by Hawker Siddeley, Rolls-Royce, McDonnell Douglas and Pratt & Whitney. This was funded jointly by the UK and US governments on behalf of the RAF, RN, USMC and USN, but in March 1975 the UK Secretary of State for Defence, Mr Roy Mason, stated that "there is not enough common ground on the Advanced Harrier for us to join in the programme with the US". The US **AV-8B** advanced version of the Harrier is, therefore, described under the McDonnell Douglas heading in this edition.

Following proposals by Lt Cdr D. R. Taylor, RN, tests were carried out successfully in 1977 with a 'ski-jump' launching ramp designed to boost the short take-off performance of vectored-thrust aircraft. This technique makes possible substantial benefits in Harrier operation both at sea and ashore. A ski-jump with a 20° angle enables the Harrier to take off at a 30 knot (55·5 km/h; 34·5 mph) lower speed than from a flat deck and at 60 knots (111 km/h; 69 mph) less than from a runway, so conserving fuel for the flight itself. It also permits more than 907 kg (2,000 lb) of extra fuel or weapons to be carried than would be possible in the same distance with a flat-deck take-off.

The following details apply generally to the Harrier GR. Mk 3 and T. Mk 4, except where a specific version is indicated:

Type: V/STOL close support and reconnaissance aircraft.

Wings: Cantilever shoulder-wing monoplane. Wing section of BAe (HS) design. Thickness/chord ratio 10% at root, 5% at tip. Anhedral 12°. Incidence 1° 45′. Sweepback at quarter-chord 34°. One-piece aluminium alloy three-spar safe-life structure with integrally-machined skins, manufactured by Brough factory of BAe, with

BAe Harrier GR. Mk 3 of No. 1 Squadron, RAF, with special camouflage for Exercise Cold Winter, held in Norway in 1979 *(Rolls-Royce)*

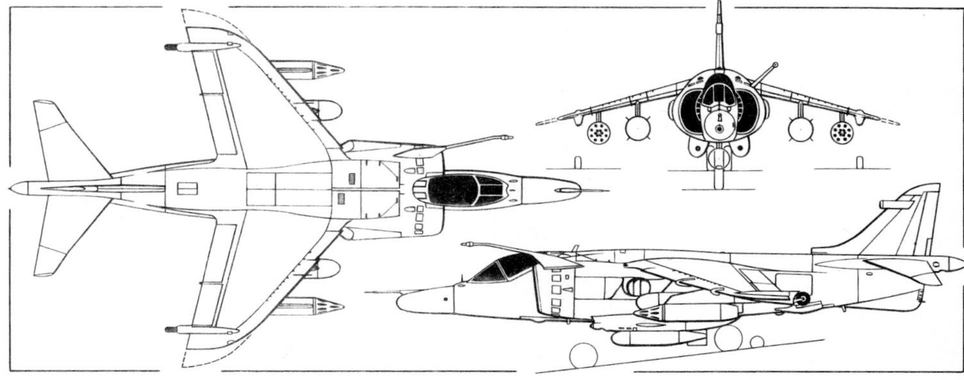

BAe Harrier GR. Mk 3 single-seat V/STOL close support and reconnaissance aircraft *(Pilot Press)*

BAe AV-8S Harrier of the Spanish Navy, by which it is known as the Matador

BAe Harrier two-seat combat trainer of the RAF's No. 4 Squadron, based at Gutersloh in Germany

six-point attachment to fuselage. Plain ailerons and flaps, of bonded aluminium alloy honeycomb construction. Ailerons irreversibly operated by Fairey tandem hydraulic jacks. Jet reaction control valve built into front of each outrigger wheel fairing. Entire wing unit removable to provide access to engine. For ferry missions, the normal 'combat' wingtips can be replaced by bolt-on extended tips to increase ferry range.

FUSELAGE: Conventional semi-monocoque safe-life structure of frames and stringers, mainly of aluminium alloy, but with titanium skins at rear and some titanium adjacent to engine and in other special areas. Access to power plant through top of fuselage, ahead of wing. Jet reaction control valves in nose and in extended tailcone. Large forward-hinged airbrake under fuselage, aft of main-wheel well.

TAIL UNIT: One-piece variable-incidence tailplane, with 15° of anhedral, irreversibly operated by Fairey tandem hydraulic jack. Rudder and trailing-edge of tailplane are of bonded aluminium honeycomb construction. Rudder is operated manually. Trim tab in rudder. Ventral fin under rear fuselage. Fin tip carries suppressed VHF aerial.

LANDING GEAR: Retractable bicycle type of Dowty Rotol manufacture, permitting operation from rough unprepared surfaces of CBR as low as 3% to 5%. Hydraulic actuation, with nitrogen bottle for emergency extension of landing gear. Single steerable nosewheel retracts forward, twin coupled mainwheels rearward, into fuselage. Small outrigger units retract rearward into fairings slightly inboard of wingtips. Nosewheel leg is of levered-suspension Liquid Spring type. Dowty Rotol telescopic oleo-pneumatic main and outrigger gear. Dunlop wheels and tyres, size 26·00 × 8·75-11 (nose unit), 27·00 × 7·74-13 (main units) and 13·50 × 6·4 (outriggers). GR. Mk 3 tyre pressures 6·21 bars (90 lb/sq in) on nose and main units, 6·55 bars (95 lb/sq in) on outriggers. T. Mk 4 tyre pressures 6·90 bars (100 lb/sq in) on nose unit, 6·55 bars (95 lb/sq in) on main and outrigger units. Dunlop multi-disc brakes and Dunlop-Hytrol adaptive anti-skid system.

POWER PLANT: One Rolls-Royce Pegasus Mk 103 vectored-thrust turbofan engine (95·6 kN; 21,500 lb st), with four exhaust nozzles of the two-vane cascade type, rotatable through 98° from fully-aft position. Engine bleed air from HP compressor used for jet reaction control system and to power duplicated air motor for nozzle actuation. The low-drag intake cowls, with outward-cambered lips, each have 8 automatic suction relief doors aft of the leading-edge to improve intake efficiency by providing extra air for the engine at low forward or zero speeds. Fuel in five integral tanks in fuselage and two in wings, with total capacity of approx 2,865 litres (630 Imp gallons). This can be supplemented by two 455 litre (100 Imp gallon) jettisonable combat tanks or two 1,500 litre (330 Imp gallon) ferry tanks on the inboard wing pylons. Ground refuelling point in port rear nozzle fairing. Provision for in-flight refuelling probe above the port intake cowl.

ACCOMMODATION: Crew of one (Mk 3) or two (Mk 4) on Martin-Baker Type 9A Mk 2 zero-zero rocket ejection seats which operate through the miniature detonating cord equipped canopy of the pressurised, heated and air-conditioned cockpit. AV-8A Harriers of the USMC retrofitted with Stencel SIIIS-3 ejection seats. Manually-operated canopy, rearward-sliding on single-seat, sideways-opening (to starboard) on two-seat versions. Birdproof windscreen, with hydraulically-actuated wiper. Windscreen de-icing.

SYSTEMS: Three-axis limited-authority autostabiliser for V/STOL flight. Pressurisation system of BAe design, with Normalair-Garrett and Marston major components; max pressure differential 0·24 bars (3·5 lb/sq in). Duplicated hydraulic systems, each of 207 bars (3,000 lb/sq in), actuate Fairey flying control and general services and include a retractable ram-air turbine inside top of rear fuselage, driving a small hydraulic pump for emergency power. AC electrical system with transformer-rectifiers to provide required DC supply. One 12kVA Lucas alternator. Two 28V 25Ah batteries, one of which energises a 24V motor to start Lucas gas-turbine starter/APU. This unit drives a 6kVA auxiliary alternator for ground readiness servicing and standby. Normalair-Garrett liquid oxygen system of 5 litres (1 Imp gallon) capacity. Bootstrap-type cooling unit for equipment bay, with intake at base of dorsal fin.

AVIONICS AND EQUIPMENT: Plessey U/VHF, Ultra standby UHF, Hoffman Tacan and Cossor IFF, Ferranti FE 541 inertial navigation and attack system (INAS), with Sperry C2G compass, Smiths electronic head-up display of flight information and Smiths air data computer. INAS can be aligned equally well at sea or on land. The weapon aiming computer provides a general solution for manual or automatic release of free-fall and retarded bombs, and for the aiming of rockets and guns, in dive and straight-pass attacks over a wide range of flight conditions and very considerable freedom of manoeuvre in elevation. Communication equipment ranges through VHF in the 100-156MHz band to UHF in the 220-400MHz band. Ferranti Type 106 Laser Ranger and Marked Target Seeker (LRMTS) retrofitted to all RAF Harriers.

ARMAMENT AND OPERATIONAL EQUIPMENT: Optically-flat panel in nose, on port side, for F.95 oblique camera, which is carried as standard. A cockpit voice recorder with in-flight playback facility supplements the reconnaissance cameras, and facilitates rapid debriefing and mission evaluation. No built-in armament. Combat load is carried on four underwing and one underfuselage pylons, all with ML ejector release units. The inboard wing points and the fuselage point are stressed for loads of up to 910 kg (2,000 lb) each, and the outboard underwing pair for loads of up to 295 kg (650 lb) each; the two strake fairings under the fuselage can each be replaced by a 30 mm Aden gun pod and ammunition. At present, the Harrier is cleared for operations with a maximum external load exceeding 2,270 kg (5,000 lb), but has flown with a weapon load of 3,630 kg (8,000 lb). The Harrier is able to carry 30 mm guns, bombs, rockets and flares of UK and US designs, and in addition to its fixed reconnaissance camera can also carry a five-camera reconnaissance pod on the underfuselage pylon. A typical combat load comprises a pair of 30 mm Aden gun pods, a 1,000 lb bomb on the underfuselage pylon, a 1,000 lb bomb on each of the inboard underwing pylons, and a Matra 155 launcher with 19 × 68 mm SNEB rockets on each outboard underwing pylon. A Sidewinder installation is provided in the AV-8A version, to give the aircraft an effective air-to-air capability in conjunction with the two 30 mm Aden guns.

DIMENSIONS, EXTERNAL:

Wing span: combat — 7·70 m (25 ft 3 in)
  ferry — 9·04 m (29 ft 8 in)
Wing chord at root — 3·56 m (11 ft 8 in)
Wing chord at tip — 1·26 m (4 ft 1½ in)
Wing aspect ratio: combat — 3·175
  ferry — 4·08
Length overall: single-seat — 13·87 m (45 ft 6 in)
  single-seat (laser nose) — 13·91 m (45 ft 7·8 in)
  two-seat — 17·00 m (55 ft 9½ in)
Height overall:
  single-seat — 3·45 m (11 ft 4 in)
  two-seat — 4·17 m (13 ft 8 in)
Tailplane span — 4·24 m (13 ft 11 in)
Outrigger wheel track — 6·76 m (22 ft 2 in)
Wheelbase, nosewheel to main wheels — approx 3·45 m (11 ft 4 in)

AREAS:

Wings, gross: combat — 18·68 m² (201·1 sq ft)
  ferry — 20·1 m² (216 sq ft)
Ailerons (total) — 0·98 m² (10·5 sq ft)
Trailing-edge flaps (total) — 1·29 m² (13·9 sq ft)
Fin (excl ventral fin):
  single-seat — 2·40 m² (25·8 sq ft)
  two-seat — 3·57 m² (38·4 sq ft)
Rudder, incl tab — 0·49 m² (5·3 sq ft)
Tailplane — 4·41 m² (47·5 sq ft)

WEIGHTS AND LOADING:

Basic operating weight, empty, with crew:
  GR.Mk 3 and Mk 50 — 5,580 kg (12,300 lb)
  T.Mk 4 (solo for combat) — 5,896 kg (13,000 lb)
  T.Mk 4 (dual) — 6,237 kg (13,750 lb)
Internal fuel — 2,295 kg (5,060 lb)
Max T-O weight (single-seat) — over 11,340 kg (25,000 lb)
Max wing loading (single-seat) — 610 kg/m² (125 lb/sq ft)

PERFORMANCE:

Max speed at low altitude — over 640 knots (1,186 km/h; 737 mph) EAS
Max Mach number (in a dive) — 1·3
Time to 12,200 m (40,000 ft) from vertical T-O — 2 min 22·7 s
Ceiling — more than 15,240 m (50,000 ft)
Endurance with one in-flight refuelling — more than 7 h
Range with one in-flight refuelling — more than 3,000 nm (5,560 km; 3,455 miles)

BAe BIG WING HARRIER

British Aerospace Kingston-Brough Division has a research contract to design an advanced wing for the Harrier V/STOL combat aircraft, which will provide high subsonic performance, good manoeuvring capability and increased internal fuel capacity. Known simply as the Big Wing, the new structure embodies the latest UK supercritical technology and has a much greater thickness/chord ratio than the wing of the current operational versions of the Harrier. This reduces the structural weight penalty of the increased-area wing (approx 23·2 m²; 250 sq ft) and accommodates a further 1,114 litres (245 Imp gallons) of fuel.

The Big Wing is designed to fit on to the existing Harrier GR. Mk 3 or T.Mk 4 fuselage with a minimum of modification. Changes are limited mainly to the addition of wiring and controls for the outboard stores pylons, and

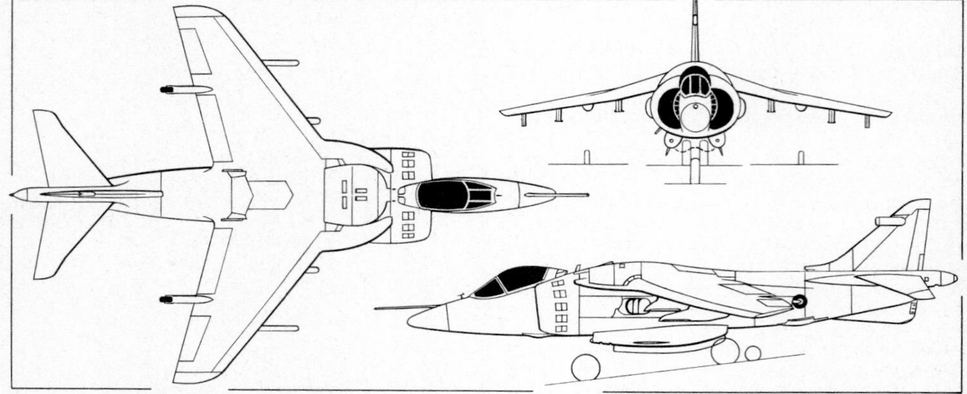

British Aerospace's Big Wing as it would appear on a new-production Harrier with Pegasus 11-35 engine
(Pilot Press)

the provision of new wing fairings, engine access doors and hardpoints to locate the forward ends of the leading-edge root extensions (LERX). Addition of cushion augmentation devices (CADS), to improve VTOL performance and handling, also necessitates some modification of the underfuselage.

If the Big Wing is adopted to enhance the capability of RAF Harriers, it is likely that retrofits to existing squadron aircraft will be followed by new production of aircraft fitted with both the Big Wing and the uprated Rolls-Royce Pegasus 11-35 turbofan, which develops about 102 kN (23,000 lb st) and would require slightly larger air intakes.

BAe SEA HARRIER

RN designation: FRS. Mk 1

On 15 May 1975, the British government announced its decision to proceed with full development of a maritime version of the Harrier, subsequently designated Sea Harrier FRS. Mk 1. The initial orders are for 34 aircraft, to equip the Royal Navy's new 'Invincible' class of anti-submarine cruisers and the anti-submarine carrier *Hermes*. The Naval Intensive Flying Trials Unit for the Sea Harrier (No. 700A Squadron) was scheduled to form at RNAS Yeovilton in the latter half of 1979. It will eventually become the shore-based HQ squadron, with eight aircraft. Front-line units, each with five aircraft, will be Nos. 800, 801 and 802 Squadrons, forming in late 1979, early 1980 and early 1981 respectively. In addition, one standard, non-navalised T.Mk 4 two-seater is to be procured by the Royal Navy for land-based training.

A 7° 'ski-jump' T-O ramp is fitted to HMS *Invincible*. Ramps on HMS *Hermes* and later ships of the 'Invincible' class may be more steeply angled.

The first Sea Harrier to fly (XZ450), made its first flight on 20 August 1978, and the first for the Royal Navy (XZ451) was handed over on 18 June 1979. Major changes compared with the Harriers in service with the Royal Air Force, Spanish Navy and US Marine Corps comprise the elimination of magnesium components, introduction of a raised cockpit, revised operational avionics, and installation of multi-mode Ferranti radar in a redesigned nose that folds to port for carrier stowage. Known by the name Blue Fox, this radar has been under development since March 1973, when the Electronic Systems Department of Ferranti was awarded a study and preliminary development contract. It is a derivative of the frequency-agile Sea Spray radar fitted in the Lynx helicopter, but embodies changes to suit its different role, with air-to-air intercept and air-to-surface modes of operation. Two specially modified Hawker Hunter T. Mk 8s, redesignated T.Mk 8M, have been fitted with nose-mounted Blue Fox radars. Intended to speed the development of this radar and a new nav/attack system, they will be used subsequently for radar training. Equipment of the Sea Harrier includes ECM in a container near the tip of the tail-fin and underwing attachments for air-to-air missiles of the Sidewinder type.

The Royal Navy's Sea Harrier FRS. Mk 1 has a Rolls-Royce Pegasus 104 vectored-thrust turbofan engine, with the same rating as the Pegasus 103 fitted to current RAF Harriers. The two variants differ little in design, except that the Pegasus 104 incorporates additional anti-corrosion features and has the capability to generate more electrical power.

Harriers have already accumulated thousands of take-offs and landings at sea, from a total of 30 different ships of nine naval services, in a wide range of weather, sea and climatic conditions. These operations have proved that no changes are needed to the aircraft's V/STOL design features to permit routine deployment at sea.

Estimated weights, loadings and detailed performance figures are not yet available for the Sea Harrier. It is expected that the Navy's FRS.Mk 1 will operate at approximately the same weights as the GR.Mk 3, and will be capable of lifting a full military payload with a 152 m (500 ft) flat deck run into an overdeck wind of 30 knots (55·5 km/h; 34·5 mph).

The description of the GR.Mk 3 applies also to the FRS.Mk 1, except as follows:

TYPE: V/STOL fighter, reconnaissance and strike aircraft.

POWER PLANT: As GR.Mk 3, except one Rolls-Royce Pegasus Mk 104 vectored-thrust turbofan engine of 95·6 kN (21,500 lb st). Internal fuel capacity 2,277 kg (5,060 lb). External combat fuel capacity 730 kg (1,600 lb).

ACCOMMODATION: As GR.Mk 3, but with pilot raised 28 cm (11 in), on Martin-Baker Type 10 rocket ejection seat.

SYSTEMS: As GR.Mk 3, except autopilot function on Fairey Hydraulics, giving throughput to aileron and tailplane power controls as well as to three-axis auto-stabs. Pressurisation system of BAe design with major components from Normalair-Garrett and Delaney Gallay. British Oxygen liquid oxygen system of 5 litres (1 Imp gallon) capacity. Lucas Mk 2 GTS/APU.

AVIONICS AND EQUIPMENT: Ferranti multi-mode Blue Fox nose-mounted radar, with TV-raster daylight-viewing tube which conveys flight information, as well as radar data, to pilot. New and larger Smiths electronic head-up display and digital weapon aiming computer. Decca Doppler 72. Ferranti self-aligning attitude reference platform and digital navigation computer. Radio nav aids include UHF homing, Tacan with offset facility and I-band transponder. Radio com by multi-channel Plessey PTR 377 U/VHF, with VHF standby via D 403M transceiver. Passive electronic surveillance and warning of external radar illumination by receiver with forward and rear hemisphere antennae in fin and tailcone respectively.

ARMAMENT AND OPERATIONAL EQUIPMENT: As GR.Mk 3, except for addition of Sidewinder installation similar to that of AV-8A, and provision for two air-to-surface missiles of Martel or Harpoon type.

DIMENSIONS, EXTERNAL: As GR.Mk 3 except:
- Wing span 7·70 m (25 ft 3¼ in)
- Length overall 14·50 m (47 ft 7 in)
- Length overall, nose folded 12·88 m (42 ft 3 in)
- Height overall 3·71 m (12 ft 2 in)

PERFORMANCE:
- Typical cruising speed:
  - High altitude, for well over 1 h on internal fuel above Mach 0·8
  - Low altitude 350-450 knots (650-833 km/h; 404-518 mph), with rapid acceleration to 600 knots (1,110 km/h; 690 mph)
- Time from alarm to 30 nm (55 km; 35 miles) combat area under 6 min
- High altitude intercept radius, with 3 min combat and reserves for VL 400 nm (750 km; 460 miles)

First of the BAe Sea Harrier FRS Mk 1 combat aircraft for the Royal Navy, on board HMS *Hermes (Rolls-Royce)*

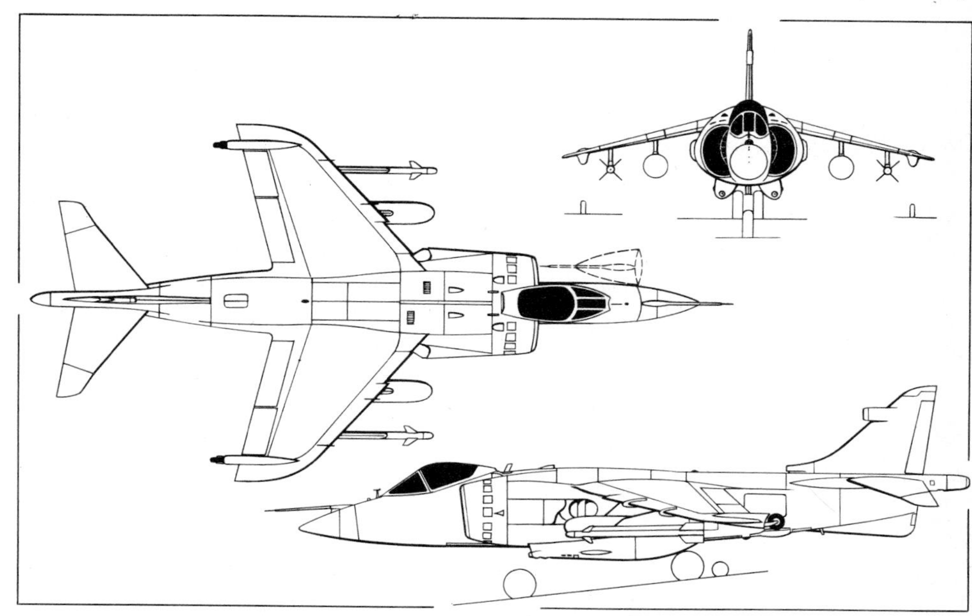

BAe Sea Harrier FRS. Mk 1 for the Royal Navy *(Pilot Press)*

HAWKER HUNTER T.Mk 8M

As part of the Sea Harrier development programme, two Hunter T.Mk 8 two-seat trainers of the Royal Navy were converted by British Aerospace at Brough to carry the complete suite of operational equipment selected for the Sea Harrier, including the Ferranti Blue Fox radar. The first of these aircraft, which have the designation **T.Mk 8M**, flew for the first time on 9 January 1978. They are being used for nav/attack system development trials, one by BAe at Dunsfold and the other by the RSRE at RAE Bedford. After completion of these trials, in 1981, the converted Hunters will be returned to the Royal Navy for service as Sea Harrier airborne weapons system trainers.

BAe HS BUCCANEER

The BAe (HS; originally Blackburn) Buccaneer strike aircraft flew for the first time on 30 April 1958, and was produced initially for the Royal Navy (20 development aircraft, 40 S.Mk 1 and 84 S.Mk 2) and the South African Air Force (16 S.Mk 50). Descriptions of these versions were given in the 1970-71 *Jane's*.

Most Royal Navy S.Mk 2s were later transferred to the RAF, the first four being delivered to No. 12 Squadron at RAF Honington on 1 October 1969. Those operated by the RAF are designated **S.Mk 2A** (without Martel capability) and **S.Mk 2B** (with Martels). Other airframe and equipment differences exist between these models, but the

Hawker Hunter T.Mk 8M, converted to speed development of the Sea Harrier's Ferranti Blue Fox radar

capability to carry Martel air-to-ground missiles is the fundamental definition of aircraft standard. The RAF, in addition to the ex-RN aircraft, ordered 43 new-production S.Mk 2Bs, the first of which flew on 8 January 1970. Production deliveries were completed in 1977, but the jigs have remained available to cope with repairs and modifications.

Buccaneers which were in Royal Navy service had the designations **S.Mk 2C** without, and **S.Mk 2D** with, Martel capability; all existing aircraft have been transferred to the RAF.

A description of the S.Mk 2A/2B Buccaneer can be found in the 1977-78 *Jane's*.

BAe HS NIMROD

The Nimrod was evolved to replace the Shackleton maritime reconnaissance aircraft of RAF Strike Command, with which it is scheduled to serve until well into the 1990s. Design of the Nimrod, as the Hawker Siddeley 801, began in June 1964, and government authority to proceed was announced in June 1965.

Based substantially upon the airframe of the Hawker Siddeley (de Havilland) Comet 4C, the Nimrod is a new-production aircraft with a 1·98 m (6 ft 6 in) shorter, modified pressurised fuselage; an unpressurised, underslung pannier for operational equipment and weapons; and Rolls-Royce Spey turbofan engines (instead of the Avon turbojets of the Comet), with wider air intakes to allow for the greater mass flow. Other external changes include enlarged flight deck main windows and 'eyebrow' windows; ESM and MAD equipment, in glassfibre fairings on top of the fin and in the tailboom respectively; and a searchlight in the starboard wing external fuel tank. The search radar is housed in a streamlined glassfibre fairing which forms the nose section of the unpressurised lower fuselage.

The Nimrod was designed to combine the advantages of high-altitude, fast transit speed with low wing loading and good low-speed manoeuvring capabilities when operating in its primary roles of anti-submarine warfare, surveillance and anti-shipping strike. When required, two of the four Spey engines can be shut down to extend endurance, and the aircraft can cruise and climb on only one engine. A wide range of weapons can be carried in the 14·78 m (48 ft 6 in) long bomb bay, and large numbers of sonobuoys and markers can be carried and released from the pressurised rear fuselage area.

In addition to its surveillance and ASW roles, the Nimrod can be used for day and night photography. As supplied originally to the RAF, these aircraft had a stand-off surface missile capability. This has since been deleted but could be reactivated if required. The Nimrod MR. Mk 1 can carry 16 additional personnel in the self-support role; the MR. Mk 2 can also carry support personnel, but only 10 without the removal of equipment.

Two prototypes were built, both utilising existing Comet 4C airframes. The first of these (XV148), fitted with Spey engines, flew for the first time on 23 May 1967 and was used for aerodynamic testing. The second (XV147) retained its original Avon engines, was first flown on 31 July 1967, and was used for development of the nav/tac system and special maritime equipment.

The following versions have been produced:

Nimrod MR. Mk 1. Initial production version, to which the detailed description applies. Thirty-eight ordered initially (XV226-263), the first of which was flown on 28 June 1968. Deliveries began on 2 October 1969 and were completed in August 1972. The MR. Mk 1 was delivered initially to No. 236 OCU, RAF Strike Command, at St Mawgan, Cornwall, and is in service with No. 42 Squadron, also at St Mawgan; and Nos. 120, 201 and 206 Squadrons at Kinloss, Scotland. An order for eight additional Nimrods was announced in January 1972 and delivery of these began in 1975. Only the first five were to be delivered to Mk 1 standard; three others will be used as development aircraft, one for the MR. Mk 2, and two for the Nimrod AEW. Mk 3.

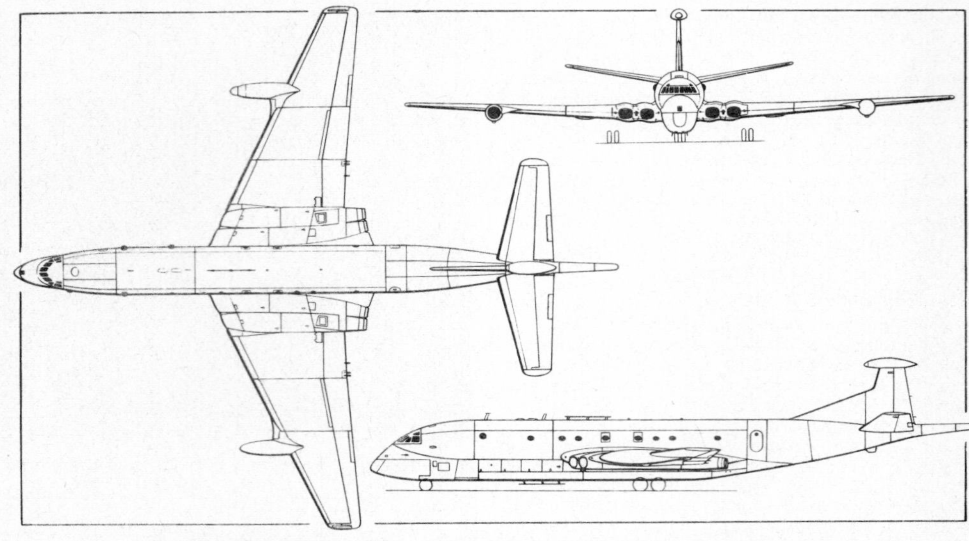

BAe HS Nimrod MR. Mk 1 four-turbofan maritime patrol aircraft *(Pilot Press)*

BAe HS Nimrod R.Mk 1 of No. 51 Squadron, RAF. Note the modified tailcone in place of the MAD boom and the revised contours of the port wing leading-edge pod *(Swedish Air Force)*

Nimrod R. Mk 1. Designation of three aircraft (additional to the 46 MR. Mk 1s ordered for RAF Strike Command) delivered in 1971 to No. 51 Squadron at Wyton, Huntingdonshire. These aircraft (XW664-666), which replaced Comet 2s, are said to be employed for electronic reconnaissance and to monitor hostile radio and radar transmissions, although official statements have referred only to radio/radar calibration duties connected with RAF equipment. They can be identified by the absence of an MAD tailboom.

Nimrod MR. Mk 2. Thirty-two aircraft of the RAF's Nimrod MR. Mk 1 fleet are being refitted with new communications equipment, and advanced tactical sensor, ESM and navigation systems, under a programme which was started in 1975. Re-delivery began on 23 August 1979 with XV236, the first completely refitted aircraft. After refit these aircraft are redesignated MR. Mk 2, and are being repainted in a new NATO-approved camouflage colour scheme. Equipment in this version includes an advanced search radar, offering greater range and sensitivity coupled with a higher data processing rate; and a new acoustic processing system, developed by Marconi Avionics Systems, which is compatible with a wide range of existing and projected sonobuoys. Armament includes Stingray homing torpedoes.

Nimrod AEW. Mk 3. Airborne early warning version; described separately.

Ample space and power is available in the basic Nimrod design to accept additional or alternative sensors such as sideways-looking radar, forward-looking infra-red, infra-red linescan, low light level TV, digital processing of intercepted ESM signals and other new developments.

TYPE: Four-turbofan maritime patrol aircraft.

WINGS: Cantilever low/mid-wing monoplane, of metal construction. Sweepback 20° at quarter-chord. All-metal two-spar structure, comprising a centre-section, two stub-wings and two outer panels. Extensive use of Redux metal-to-metal bonding. All-metal ailerons, operated through duplicated hydraulic and mechanical units. Trim tab in each aileron. Plain flaps outboard of engines, operated hydraulically. Hot-air anti-icing system.

FUSELAGE: All-metal semi-monocoque structure. The circular-section cabin space is fully pressurised. Below this is an unpressurised pannier housing the bomb bay, radome and additional space for operational equipment. Segments of this pannier are free to move relative to each other, so that structural loads in the weapons bay are not transmitted to the pressure-cell. A glassfibre nose radome and tailboom are provided.

TAIL UNIT: Cantilever all-metal structure. Rudder and elevators operated through duplicated hydraulic and mechanical units. A glassfibre pod on top of the fin houses ESM equipment. Trim tab in each elevator. Hot-air anti-icing system.

BAe HS Nimrod MR. Mk 1 four-turbofan maritime patrol aircraft of RAF Strike Command

LANDING GEAR: Retractable tricycle type. Four-wheel tandem-bogie main units, with size 36 × 10-18 Dunlop tyres, pressure 12·76 bars (185 lb/sq in). Twin-wheel nose unit, with size 30 × 9-15 Dunlop tyres, pressure 6·21 bars (90 lb/sq in).

POWER PLANT: Four Rolls-Royce RB. 168-20 Spey Mk 250 turbofan engines, each rated at 54 kN (12,140 lb st). Reverse thrust fitted on two outer engines. Fuel in fuselage keel tanks, integral wing tanks, and permanent external tank on each wing leading-edge, with total capacity of 48,780 litres (10,730 Imp gallons), equivalent to a fuel weight of 38,940 kg (85,840 lb). Provision for up to six removable tanks to be carried in the weapons bay, increasing max fuel weight to 45,785 kg (100,940 lb) and max overload T-O weight of aircraft to 87,090 kg (192,000 lb).

ACCOMMODATION: Normal crew of 12, comprising pilot, co-pilot, and flight engineer on flight deck; routine navigator, tactical navigator, radio operator, radar operator, two sonics systems operators, ESM/MAD operator, and two observers/stores loaders in main (pressurised) cabin, which is fitted out as a tactical compartment. In this compartment, from front to rear, are a toilet on the port side; stations for the two navigators (stbd), radio and radar operators (port), and sonics systems operators (stbd) in the forward section; ESM/MAD operator's station, galley, four-seat dining area, rest quarters and sonobuoy stowage in the middle section; and buoy and marker launch area in the rear section. Three hemispherical observation windows forward of wings (one port, two stbd), giving 180° field of view. Two normal doors, emergency door, and four overwing emergency exits. Weapons bay can be utilised for additional fuel tanks (see under 'Power Plant') or for the carriage of freight. Provision is made for a trooping role, in which configuration 45 passengers can be accommodated if some rear-fuselage equipment is removed.

SYSTEMS: Air-conditioning by engine bleed air; Smith-Kollsman pressurisation system, with additional Normalair-Garrett conditioning pack on Mk 2 aircraft, max differential 0·603 bars (8·75 lb/sq in). Anti-icing and bomb-bay heating by engine bleed air. Lockheed hydraulic system, pressure 172 bars (2,500 lb/sq in), for duplicated flying control power units, landing gear shock-absorbers, steering and door jacks, weapons bay door jacks, camera aperture door jacks, and self-sealing couplings for water charging, ground test, engine bay and ancillary services. Lucas APU provides high-pressure air for engine starting. Electrical system utilises four 60kVA engine-driven alternators, with English Electric constant-speed drives, to provide 200V 400Hz three-phase AC supply. Secondary AC comes from two 115V three-phase static transformers, with duplicate 115/26V two-phase static transformers which also feed a 1kVA frequency changer providing a 115V 1,600Hz single-phase supply for radar equipment. Emergency supplies for flight instruments are provided by a 115V single-phase static inverter. DC supply is by four 28V transformer-rectifier units backed up by two nickel-cadmium batteries.

AVIONICS AND EQUIPMENT (MR. Mk 1): Routine navigation by Decca Doppler Type 67M/Marconi E3 heading reference system, with reversionary heading from a Sperry GM7 duplicated gyro compass system, operating in conjunction with a Ferranti routine dynamic display. Tactical navigation, and stores selection and release, by Marconi nav/attack system utilising an 8K Marconi 920B digital computer. Tactical display station provides continually-updated information about aircraft position, with present and past track, sonobuoy positions, range circles from sonobuoys, ESM bearings, MAD marks, radar contacts and visual bearings. Course information can be displayed automatically to the pilots on the flight director system; alternatively, the computer can be coupled to the autopilot to allow the tactical navigator to direct the aircraft to a predicted target interception, weapon release point, or any other point on the tactical display. ASW equipment includes Sonics 1C sonar and a new long-range sonar system; EMI ASV-21D air-to-surface-vessel detection radar in nose; Thomson-CSF ESM (electronic support measures) equipment in pod on top of fin; and Emerson Electronics ASQ-10A MAD (magnetic anomaly detector) in extended tailboom. Strong Electric 70 million candle-power searchlight at front of starboard external wing fuel tank. Aeronautical and General Instruments F.126 and F.135 cameras for day and night photography respectively, the latter having Chicago Aero Industries electronic flash equipment. Smiths SFS.6 automatic flight control system, embodying SEP.6 three-axis autopilot, integrated with the navigation and tactical system. Twin Plessey PTR 175 UHF/VHF, and Marconi AD 470 HF, communications transceivers; twin Marconi AD 260 VOR/ILS; Hoffman ARN 72 Tacan; Decca Loran C/A; Marconi AD 360 ADF; Honeywell AN/APN-171(V) radar altimeter. Yaw damper and Mach trim standard.

AVIONICS AND EQUIPMENT (MR. Mk 2): New and more flexible operational system, using three separate processors for tactical navigation, radar and acoustics. Marconi central tactical system, based on a 920 ATC computer with a greater storage capacity than that of MR. Mk 1, to provide improved computing and display facilities and, in conjunction with a Ferranti inertial navigation system, improved navigation capabilities. EMI Searchwater long-range air-to-surface-vessel radar, with its own data processing subsystem incorporating a Ferranti FM 1600D digital computer. This system presents a clutter-free picture, can detect and classify surface vessels, submarine snorts and periscopes at extreme ranges, can track several targets simultaneously, and is designed to operate in spite of countermeasures. AQS 901 acoustics processing and display system, based on twin Marconi 920 ATC computers, is compatible with a wide range of passive and active sonobuoys, either in existence or under development, including the Australian BARRA passive directional sonobuoy, the Canadian TANDEM, the US SSQ-41 and SSQ-53, and the new Ultra A-size X17255 Command Active Multi-Beam Sonobuoys (CAMBS), with a performance similar to that of helicopter-mounted dipping sonars. Communications are being improved by the installation of twin Marconi AD 470 HF transceivers (instead of the original single AD 470), and a radio teletype and encryption system.

ARMAMENT (MR. Mk 1): 14·78 m (48 ft 6 in) long weapons bay, with two pairs of doors, in unpressurised lower fuselage pannier, able to carry up to six lateral rows of ASW weapons, including up to nine torpedoes as well as bombs. (Capability of carrying depth charges and mines is not used by RAF.) Alternatively, to give greater range and endurance, up to six auxiliary fuel tanks can be fitted in the weapons bay, or a combination of fuel tanks and weapons can be carried. To ensure weapon serviceability, the weapons bay is heated when the ambient temperature falls below +5°C. Bay approx 9·14 m (30 ft) long in rear pressurised part of fuselage for storing and launching of active and passive sonobuoys and marine markers. Two rotary launchers, each capable of holding six size A sonobuoys, are used when the cabin is unpressurised; two single-barrel launchers are used when the aircraft is pressurised. A hardpoint is provided beneath each wing, just outboard of the main-wheel doors, on which can be carried air-to-surface missiles, rocket or cannon pods, or mines, according to mission requirements. The missile capability has been deleted from RAF Nimrods, but could be reactivated if required.

DIMENSIONS, EXTERNAL:
Wing span 35·00 m (114 ft 10 in)
Wing chord at root 9·00 m (29 ft 6 in)
Wing chord at tip 2·06 m (6 ft 9 in)
Wing aspect ratio 6·2
Length overall 38·63 m (126 ft 9 in)
Height overall 9·08 m (29 ft 8½ in)
Tailplane span 14·51 m (47 ft 7¼ in)
Wheel track 8·60 m (28 ft 2½ in)
Wheelbase 14·24 m (46 ft 8½ in)

DIMENSIONS, INTERNAL:
Cabin (incl flight deck, navigation and ordnance areas, galley and toilet): Length 26·82 m (88 ft 0 in)
Max width 2·95 m (9 ft 8 in)
Max height 2·08 m (6 ft 10 in)
Volume 124·14 m³ (4,384 cu ft)

AREAS:
Wings, gross 197·0 m² (2,121 sq ft)
Ailerons (total) 5·63 m² (60·6 sq ft)
Trailing-edge flaps (total) 23·37 m² (251·6 sq ft)
Fin and rudder (above tailplane centreline) 10·96 m² (118 sq ft)
Dorsal fin 5·67 m² (61 sq ft)
Tailplane 40·41 m² (435 sq ft)
Elevators (incl tabs) 12·57 m² (135·3 sq ft)

WEIGHTS (MR. Mk 1):
Typical weight empty 39,000 kg (86,000 lb)
Max disposable payload 6,120 kg (13,500 lb)
Normal max T-O weight 80,510 kg (177,500 lb)
Max overload T-O weight 87,090 kg (192,000 lb)
Typical landing weight 54,430 kg (120,000 lb)

PERFORMANCE (MR. Mk 1):
Max operational necessity speed, ISA + 20°C 500 knots (926 km/h; 575 mph)
Max transit speed, ISA + 20°C 475 knots (880 km/h; 547 mph)
Econ transit speed, ISA + 20°C 425 knots (787 km/h; 490 mph)
Typical low-level patrol speed (two engines) 200 knots (370 km/h; 230 mph)
Operating height range S/L to 12,800 m (42,000 ft)
Min ground turning radius 27·1 m (89 ft 0 in)
Runway LCN at T-O weight of 82,550 kg (182,000 lb) 50
T-O run at 80,510 kg (177,500 lb) AUW, ISA at S/L 1,463 m (4,800 ft)
Unfactored landing distance at 54,430 kg (120,000 lb) landing weight, ISA at S/L 1,615 m (5,300 ft)
Typical ferry range 4,500-5,000 nm (8,340-9,265 km; 5,180-5,755 miles)
Typical endurance 12 h

BAe HS NIMROD AEW. Mk 3

Hawker Siddeley Aviation designed an airborne early warning (AEW) version of the Nimrod which is intended specifically for European defence. On 31 March 1977 the British Defence Secretary announced the government's intention to proceed with the procurement of eleven of these aircraft for the RAF. The AEW Nimrod has been made possible by the development by Marconi Avionics of a new radar system which, in addition to an essential maritime capability, satisfies also the air defence requirements of central Europe. The aircraft could provide, at long range and at low or high altitude, detection, tracking and classification of aircraft, missiles and ships; interceptor control; direction of strike aircraft; air defence; air traffic control; and search and rescue facilities.

Designed specifically for installation in this modified version of the maritime reconnaissance Nimrod, the radar requires modification to the nose and tail to permit installation of the newly developed and identically-shaped scanners in fore and aft positions. The aircraft's performance is likely to be affected only marginally by the structural changes and a reduction in directional stability is compensated by a 0·91 m (3 ft 0 in) increase in fin height.

Mounting the scanners at the extremities of the airframe ensures good all-round coverage, and they do not suffer from airframe obscuration effects. Designed for very low sidelobe level, they are synchronised and each sweeps through 180° in azimuth, the Cossor Jubilee Guardsman IFF interrogator using the same scanners to aid correlation of IFF and radar returns. With automatic roll- and pitch-stabilisation by ,dual INS, which compensates for structural flexing, these scanners are able to overcome the cyclic error which is present in other systems.

The associated radar is a pulsed Doppler system that, in addition to the detection of aircraft, has a ship surveillance capability. The rate at which pulses are transmitted can be varied to provide maximum detection in differing terrain conditions or sea states. The system has also highly sophisticated anti-jamming features to cope with the growing efficiency of electronic countermeasures.

The radar passes target plots in terms of range, azimuth, radial velocity and altitude to the advanced digital data handling system; this is based on an airborne computer that controls the flow of data from the scanners and correlates track information between the AEW aircraft and a surface control station. A total of six operator consoles is

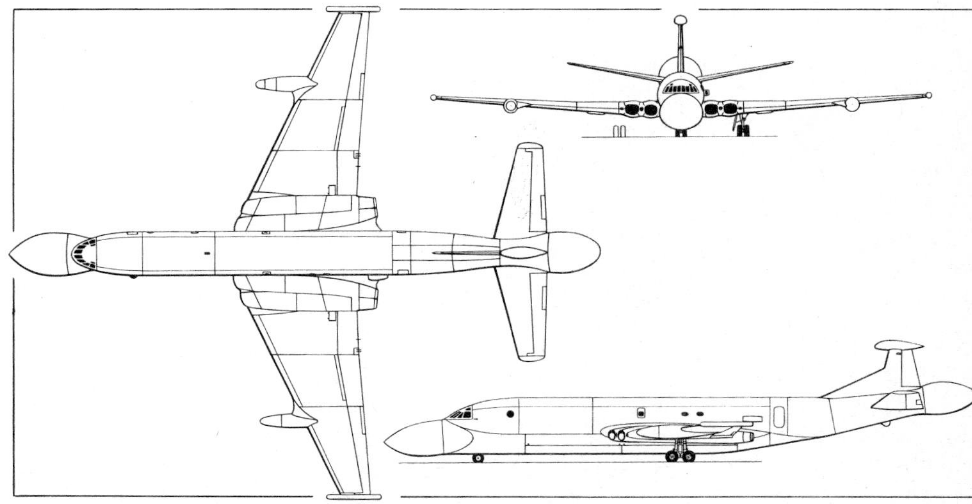

The AEW.Mk 3 version of the BAe HS Nimrod *(Pilot Press)*

planned. Each has a tactical situation display, showing the tracks selected by the operator, and a tabular display for the selective presentation of detailed track and control information. Much of the data control is fully automatic; thus, association of radar, IFF and ESM, track initiation, tracking and data storage requires no action from the operator. Control of the data handling system is achieved by rolling ball and functionally arranged keyboards, the operator interfacing with the system to carry out system control, track classification, fighter control and data link management.

High standards of communications and navigation are essential to complement the advanced radar and data handling system. For communications the AEW Nimrod will carry tactical UHF transceivers, SIMOP HF transceivers, pilot's U/VHF, RATT, secure voice com, LF receiver and data links. Primary navigation electronics will consist of dual inertial navigation systems (INS). The secondary navigation system will include a gyro magnetic compass, air data computer, twin VOR/ILS, ADF, Tacan, autopilot and a flight director. ESM (electronic support measures) equipment is housed in the two pods at the wingtips. Other features of special significance for this role are the spacious cabin for electronics and crew, high transit speed and sound low-speed characteristics.

The first of five development aircraft, a converted Comet 4C (XW626), was rolled out at Woodford on 1 March 1977 and made its first flight on 28 June 1977. This aircraft carries nose-mounted radar only. Two of the development aircraft will be from the batch of eight extra Nimrod MR. Mk 1s ordered in 1972, but will be completed instead as AEW. Mk 3s. The first of these (XZ286), scheduled to fly in 1979, will be the first aerodynamically representative AEW. Mk 3 airframe. The Nimrod AEW.Mk 3 is expected to enter RAF service in 1981/82.

Dimensions, external:
- Wing span: 35·08 m (115 ft 1 in)
- Length overall: 41·76 m (137 ft 5½ in)
- Height overall: 10·06 m (33 ft 0 in)

Performance:
- Endurance: in excess of 10 h

BRITTEN-NORMAN: *See 'Pilatus Britten-Norman'*

CRANFIELD
CRANFIELD INSTITUTE OF TECHNOLOGY

Address: College of Aeronautics, Cranfield Institute of Technology, Cranfield, Bedford MK43 0AL
Telephone: Bedford (0234) 750111
Telex: 825072
Chief Designer: Prof D. Howe

CRANFIELD A1 Mk 2

The A1 (G-BCIT) is an aerobatic aircraft produced to the requirements of the late Neil Williams, for use by the British aerobatic team. Design began in 1968 and construction of the prototype was initiated in 1971. Lack of finance stopped any major work until 1975, when the project was assisted by Mr Alan Curtis.

The A1 was flown for the first time on 23 August 1976, and by mid-1977 had made some 60 flights totalling 40 hours. The results were sufficiently encouraging to justify the replacement of the original Rolls-Royce Continental IO-360-D engine of the aircraft in its Mk 1 form (see 1977-78 *Jane's*) by one of greater power, and a Lycoming IO-540-D engine was installed. The aircraft first flew with this new power plant at the end of August 1977, and all aspects of performance and handling were considerably improved.

Subsequently, the aircraft was fitted with modified ailerons and a rudder with increased height and horn balance, and in this form is known as the Mk 2. The intended *g* limits of the aircraft are +12 and −8 (ultimate). In the original configuration the flight envelope had been explored to 230 knots (426 km/h; 265 mph) and at stresses of +7*g* and −5*g*. Weight and performance figures which follow are for the prototype in its Mk 2 configuration.

A Certificate of Airworthiness was granted in August 1978, permitting unlimited aerobatics within +7/−5*g* at an AUW of 876 kg (1,931 lb).

Although the A1 is intended specifically for competition aerobatics, it is envisaged that alternative versions of the aircraft could be used for crop-spraying and military applications.

Cranfield A1 Mk 2 (Lycoming IO-540-D engine) in its latest, modified, form

Type: Single-seat aerobatic aircraft; two seats for training and ferrying.

Wings: Cantilever low-wing monoplane. NACA 23 series wing section. Thickness/chord ratio 15% at root, 12% at tip. 2° washout at tips. Dihedral 3°. Incidence ground-adjustable. Sweepback at quarter-chord 9° 36'. One-piece wing of light alloy skin-stringer construction, with machined extrusions for centre of front spar. Some fail-safe features. Light alloy mass-balanced Frise-type ailerons, fabric-covered aft of spar; ground-adjustable tab on port aileron. No flaps or spoilers.

Fuselage: Welded T45 steel tube structure, with light alloy floor and wooden formers, fabric-covered except for plywood top-decking.

Tail Unit: Light alloy construction, similar to wings, except for rudder which is fabric-covered. Rudder and elevators horn-balanced. Dorsal fin. Trim tab in starboard elevator. Ground-adjustable tailplane incidence.

Landing Gear: Non-retractable tailwheel type from Chipmunk. Main-wheel tyres of 0·36 m (14 in) diameter, pressure 1·72 bars (25 lb/sq in). Castoring tailwheel, with tyre of 0·127 m (5 in) diameter, pressure 2·76 bars (40 lb/sq in). Hydraulic disc brakes.

Power Plant: One 208·7 kW (280 hp) Lycoming IO-540-D (Special), with a Christen wet sump inverted oil system, driving a Hoffmann three-blade variable-pitch metal propeller with spinner. Main fuel tank in fuselage; two auxiliary tanks in wing leading-edges.

Accommodation: Single seat under sideways-opening (to port) jettisonable bubble canopy in aerobatic configuration. Two seats for training and ferrying.

Systems: Electrical system, supplied by 28V DC engine-driven alternator and optional lead-acid batteries.

Dimensions, external:
- Wing span: 10·00 m (32 ft 10 in)
- Wing chord at root: 2·08 m (6 ft 10 in)
- Wing chord at tip: 0·91 m (3 ft 0 in)
- Wing area: 15 m² (161·5 sq ft)
- Wing aspect ratio: 6·7
- Length overall: 8·05 m (26 ft 5 in)
- Height overall: 2·70 m (8 ft 10¼ in)
- Tailplane span: 3·11 m (10 ft 2½ in)
- Wheel track: 2·96 m (9 ft 8½ in)
- Wheelbase: 4·74 m (15 ft 6½ in)
- Propeller diameter: 2·00 m (6 ft 6¾ in)

Weights and Loadings:
- Aerobatic T-O weight, single-seat: 850 kg (1,874 lb)
- Max T-O weight, two seats: 1,000 kg (2,205 lb)
- Max wing loading:
  - single-seat: 58 kg/m² (11·82 lb/sq ft)
  - two-seat: 67 kg/m² (13·65 lb/sq ft)
- Max power loading: 4·17 kg/kW (7·88 lb/hp)

Performance (at Aerobatic T-O weight):
- Never-exceed speed: 207 knots (384 km/h; 239 mph)
- Max level speed at S/L: 148 knots (274 km/h; 170 mph)
- Stalling speed: 49 knots (90 km/h; 56 mph)
- Max rate of climb at S/L: 688 m (2,255 ft)/min
- Service ceiling: approx 5,000 m (16,400 ft)
- T-O run: 170 m (558 ft)
- Landing run: 200 m (660 ft)
- Range with max fuel: approx 108 nm (200 km; 124 miles)
- Max endurance: approx 1 h 30 min

EDGLEY
EDGLEY AIRCRAFT LTD

Address: 31 Smith Street, Elsworth, Cambridgeshire
Telephone: Elsworth (09547) 402
Directors:
J. K. Edgley, BSc, DIC, AMRAeS
F. M. Edgley
E. J. R. F. Hood
Consultant: D. Kent

Edgley Aircraft Ltd was formed in 1974 to design, build and market an unorthodox observation aircraft, the EA7 Optica. Its designer, Mr John Edgley, was a director of Scenic Flying Ltd, which in 1972 projected and subsequently patented a slow-flying touring aircraft in which the pilot sat behind the two passengers. In 1974 Mr Edgley began the final aerodynamic design of what eventually became the Optica, and this underwent wind tunnel testing at the Imperial College, London, where Mr Edgley was then a post-graduate student, in the Summer of 1975. The Optica's three-abreast seating configuration was introduced in 1977, and since Scenic Flying did not wish to be concerned directly in its production Edgley Aircraft Ltd was formed to continue its development. Mr David Kent, who was connected with the Tawney Owl light aircraft last described in the 1961-62 *Jane's*, joined Edgley Aircraft in 1976, assisting Mr Edgley in the final stages of design, stress analysis and construction of the Optica prototype, which began in August of that year in a London workshop. In mid-1978, with most of the airframe complete, the project was moved to the College of Aeronautics at Cranfield for final assembly; this was completed in the Summer of 1979.

EDGLEY EA7 OPTICA

Due to make its first flight in the Autumn of 1979, the EA7 Optica is a most unusual design for a three-seat observation aircraft, particularly in the fields of pipeline and powerline inspection; forestry and coastal patrol; police and frontier patrol; film, TV and press reporting; and touring. The cabin configuration, as can be seen in the accompanying illustration, is based upon that of an insect's eye, to give the best possible all-round view from a fixed-wing aircraft. Power plant is a ducted propulsor unit, utilising a Lycoming O-320 flat-four engine and offering excellent quietness, both within the cabin and from the ground. The Optica is designed for low-speed flying, one feature being the inboard pair of wing flaps which are set at an angle of 10° for en-route cruising. A low wing loading, and low stalling speed, facilitate continuous flight at low speeds, and the generous flap area confers short take-off and landing capability from both hard and soft strips.

The Optica is intended for low volume production (up to 100 a year), using a minimum of sophisticated tooling. Methods of achieving this under consideration in mid-1979 included extending the present company into a full production company; having a specific number of Opticas built initially by another company under subcontract or licence; and setting up a direct link with an existing manufacturing organisation.

TYPE: Three-seat observation aircraft.

WINGS: Cantilever mid-wing monoplane. Wing section NASA GA(W)-1, thickness/chord ratio 17%. Dihedral 3° on outer panels. Incidence 0°. Constant-chord single-spar non-swept wings of aluminium alloy stressed-skin construction. Wingtips (also fin/tailplane fillets, nosewheel mudguard and some power plant fairings) of glassfibre. Electrically actuated Fowler trailing-edge flaps inboard and outboard of tailbooms; outboard flaps adjustable from 0-10° for en-route flight and from 10-40° for landing; inboard flaps set permanently at 10°. Top-hinged, mass balanced plain ailerons outboard of outer flaps. No spoilers, airbrakes or tabs.

CABIN: 'Insect eye' shaped structure, built of aluminium alloy with Suntex vacuum formed acrylic windows. Cabin attached to fan shroud and rest of airframe by six stators of steel tube and aluminium alloy shear web construction. Steel tube and aluminium alloy nose beam supporting cabin floor. Horizontal window frame member, just above floor level, designed to act in combination with forward-running nosewheel box to act as skid in case of nosewheel failure. Entire cabin structure designed to withstand 9g impact. Depending upon number of occupants, a 12 kg (26·5 lb) balance weight can be installed in either the cabin or the port fin, to adjust the CG position.

TAIL UNIT: Twin-tailboom configuration, of aluminium alloy stressed-skin tubular construction. Tailboom pick-up points at extremities of wing centre-section. Angular, inward-canted fins and balanced rudders. Fixed-incidence tailplane, with elevator, bridging space between tops of fins. Inset trim tab occupies port half of elevator trailing-edge; no rudder tabs.

LANDING GEAR: Non-retractable tricycle type, with steerable nosewheel offset to port. Modified Piper main-wheel legs, with rubber-in-compression shock-absorption. Nosewheel shock-absorption by bungee rubber in tension. Single wheel on each unit, tyre sizes 6·00-6 (main) and 5·00-5 (nose). Disc brakes on main wheels. Retractable parking strut, operated from cabin, extends below fan shroud to keep aircraft level when empty on the ground.

POWER PLANT: Ducted propulsor unit, with engine and fan forming a power pod separate from the main shroud. Pod is attached by four stators of steel channel and aluminium alloy shear web construction, with steel tube engine bearers. Five-blade fixed-pitch birch fan, driven by a single 119 kW (160 hp) Lycoming O-320-B2B flat-four engine mounted in a duct downstream of the fan. Fuel tank of 91 litres (20 Imp gallons) in each wing leading-edge, immediately outboard of tailbooms and forward of wing spar. Tanks are of full wing section, but are designed not to be stressed by wing bending and torsion. Total fuel capacity 182 litres (40 Imp gallons). Refuelling point in upper surface of each wing. Oil capacity approx 9 litres (2 Imp gallons).

Edgley EA7 Optica three-seat observation aircraft in almost completed form *(Flight International)*

ACCOMMODATION: Cabin designed to seat up to three persons side by side, with either single- or two-pilot operation (left hand and centre seats). Dual controls optional. Fixed seats in prototype; adjustable seats optional. Baggage space aft of seats. Alternative accommodation for two stretchers, or one stretcher and one medical attendant, in addition to pilot. Single elliptical door on each side, hinged at front and opening forward. Cabin heated, by hot air from engine, and ventilated.

SYSTEMS: Hydraulics for main-wheel brakes only. Prototype has 12V electrical system (battery and alternator) for engine starting, flap actuation and under-shroud strut; it has no lights. 24V system under consideration for production version.

DIMENSIONS, EXTERNAL:

Wing span	12·00 m (39 ft 4½ in)
Wing chord (basic, constant)	1·32 m (4 ft 4 in)
Wing chord (over 10° fixed flaps)	1·52 m (5 ft 0 in)
Wing aspect ratio	9·1
Length overall	8·10 m (26 ft 7 in)
Height over fan shroud	1·95 m (6 ft 4¾ in)
Diameter of fan shroud	1·68 m (5 ft 6¼ in)
Diameter of fan	1·20 m (3 ft 11¼ in)
Shroud ground clearance	0·27 m (10¾ in)
Height over tailplane	2·50 m (8 ft 2½ in)
Tailplane span (c/l of tailbooms)	3·40 m (11 ft 1¾ in)
Wheel track	3·40 m (11 ft 1¾ in)
Wheelbase	2·78 m (9 ft 1½ in)
Doors (each): Long axis	1·34 m (4 ft 4¾ in)
Short axis	0·96 m (3 ft 1¾ in)
Height to sill	0·45 m (1 ft 5¾ in)

DIMENSIONS, INTERNAL:

Cabin: Length	2·45 m (8 ft 0½ in)
Max width	1·76 m (5 ft 9¼ in)
Max height	1.35 m (4 ft 5¼ in)
Floor area	approx 0·72 m² (7·53 sq ft)

AREAS:

Wings, gross	15·84 m² (170·5 sq ft)
Ailerons (total)	1·55 m² (16·68 sq ft)
Trailing-edge flaps: inboard (total)	0·61 m² (6·57 sq ft)
outboard (total)	1·49 m² (16·04 sq ft)
Fins (total)	2·74 m² (29·49 sq ft)
Rudders (total)	1·26 m² (13·56 sq ft)
Tailplane	1·70 m² (18·30 sq ft)
Elevator, incl tab	1·22 m² (13·13 sq ft)

*WEIGHT:

Max T-O weight (provisional) 1,134 kg (2,500 lb)

*PERFORMANCE (estimated):

Design never-exceed speed 155 knots (288 km/h; 178 mph)

Max cruising speed above 100 knots (185 km/h; 115 mph)

Stalling speed below 50 knots (93 km/h; 57 mph)

**More exact figures to be released after first flight*

LOCKSPEISER

LOCKSPEISER AIRCRAFT LTD

REGISTERED OFFICE: Royal Chambers, High Street, Weston-super-Mare, Avon BS23

Telephone: Weston-super-Mare (0934) 29467

MANAGING DIRECTOR: David Lockspeiser, MRAeS, CEng

COMPANY SECRETARY: Christopher E. Bean, FCA

LOCKSPEISER LDA-01

Mr David Lockspeiser designed a utility aeroplane known as the LDA, or Land Development Aircraft, the production version of which is intended for operation as a passenger, freight or vehicle transport, as an agricultural, ambulance, survey or firefighting aircraft, or for other duties. In a military version, for use as a light troop transport or battlefield support aircraft, the initials stand for Light Defence Aircraft.

The basic concept of the LDA is that of an 'aerial Land-Rover', offering a wide variety of applications, low initial cost and economy of operation, and capable of being easily assembled, inspected and repaired. Many of the major components are interchangeable, and the aircraft can carry a complete set of its own spares, including wings. A primary design consideration was ease of construction for licensed manufacture and assembly. A flush-fitting removable ventral container serves as an interchangeable 'mission pack' and facilitates the quick conversion of the aircraft from one role to another.

A 70% scale prototype, registered G-AVOR and known as the LDA-01, was flown for the first time by Mr Lockspeiser on 24 August 1971. Powered at that time by a 63 kW (85 hp) Continental engine, it took off in less than 91 m (300 ft). A description of it with this engine appeared in the 1972-73 *Jane's*.

Development flying with the LDA-01 has defined the proposed full-size LDA-1 as a 12·04 m (39 ft 6 in) span aircraft, with 7·08 m³ (250 cu ft) of usable cargo space, a disposable load of 907 kg (2,000 lb) and a max T-O weight of 1,814 kg (4,000 lb). As an alternative to the removable mission pack the LDA-01, to which the following description applies, has been flown with a side-loading double door on the port side.

TYPE: Single-engined general utility aeroplane.

WINGS: Strut-braced main wings at rear and cantilever foreplane at front. Main wings and foreplane are of constant NACA 23012 section and constant chord. Dihedral 3° on main wings; 0° on foreplane. Main wing incidence 0°, foreplane 3° (adjustable on ground). Conventional all-metal alloy construction, with parallel main and rear spars and pop-riveted stressed-skin covering. Built in three basically identical and interchangeable units, two forming the main wings and the third being used as the foreplane. Each panel has four strongpoints at the centre. These serve as attachment points to the fuselage when the panel is positioned as a foreplane; when it is positioned as a port or starboard mainplane they serve as fin-post attachments or as lift-strut and picketing points. They can also be located on a 'luggage rack' under the fuselage when a panel is carried as a spare by an aircraft of the same type. Main wings have trailing-edge flaps inboard and ailerons outboard; in addition to their normal function these are operated in unison to perform the function of an elevator. The foreplane is fitted with a screwjack-operated flap which also doubles as a pitch trimmer. This system of control gives greater safety at the stall, the foreplane being designed to stall before the main wings. Main wings fitted with fences to contain vortex disturbance from the foreplane tips.

Lockspeiser LDA-01 prototype Land Development or Light Defence Aircraft *(Anthony Young)*

FUSELAGE: Conventional box-shaped structure, consisting of space frame of 19 mm (¾ in) square 22 gauge T.35 steel, welded on a flat jig and covered with light alloy skin. Two outward-opening freight doors on port side.

TAIL UNIT: Twin wire-braced fins and twin rudders, above and below main wings, of welded steel tube construction with fabric covering.

LANDING GEAR: Non-retractable tricycle type, with cantilever spring steel main-gear legs at rear. Goodyear single or twin nosewheel(s) and tyre(s), size 5·00-5·5, pressure 1·035 bars (15 lb/sq in), steerable from rudder bar. Ackerman steering of nose leg(s). Goodyear 6·00-6 main wheels and tyres, pressure 2·07 bars (30 lb/sq in). Goodyear hydraulic brakes on main wheels.

POWER PLANT: One 119 kW (160 hp) Lycoming O-320-D1A flat-four engine, at rear of fuselage, driving a Hoffmann HO-V-72 two-blade constant-speed metal pusher propeller with spinner. Two fuel tanks in fuselage, one forward and one aft of cargo bay, each of 69 litres (15·2 Imp gallons) capacity. Refuelling points on starboard side.

ACCOMMODATION: Pilot in enclosed cabin. Sideways-opening canopy, hinged on port side. Side-opening doors in fuselage for passengers or freight. Floor is fitted with lashing points, and has apertures for vertical photography. Production LDA-1 will have either the optional side-loading double doors, 1·98 m (6 ft 6 in) wide and 1·22 m (4 ft 0 in) in height, or the removable container, and will also have access via the roof so that conventional loaders can be used when the aircraft is employed in an agricultural role. Proposed Light Defence Aircraft military version capable of carrying six soldiers and their equipment, or of being fitted with anti-tank missiles or machine-gun pods.

SYSTEMS AND AVIONICS: 12V electrical system. Rabat Type 35 battery. Bendix VHF and VOR nav/com system.

DIMENSIONS, EXTERNAL:

Main wing span	9·27 m (30 ft 5 in)
Foreplane span	4·39 m (14 ft 5 in)
Main wing chord, constant	1·14 m (3 ft 9 in)
Foreplane chord, constant	1·14 m (3 ft 9 in)
Main wing aspect ratio	8·2
Foreplane aspect ratio	5·2
Length overall	7·14 m (23 ft 5¼ in)
Fuselage: Max width	0·91 m (3 ft 0 in)
Max depth	1·07 m (3 ft 6 in)
Height overall	2·77 m (9 ft 1 in)
Wheel track	2·08 m (6 ft 10 in)
Wheelbase	3·91 m (12 ft 10 in)
Propeller diameter	1·80 m (5 ft 11 in)
Fuselage floor/ground clearance	0·57 m (1 ft 10½ in)
Removable payload container:	
Length	1·98 m (6 ft 6 in)
Width	0·91 m (3 ft 0 in)
Depth	0·38 m (1 ft 3 in)

DIMENSION, INTERNAL:

Centre fuselage: total internal volume 1·7 m³ (60 cu ft)

AREAS:

Main wings, gross	10·46 m² (112·55 sq ft)
Foreplane, gross	3·74 m² (40·25 sq ft)
Mainplane flaps (total)	0·93 m² (10·0 sq ft)
Ailerons (total)	1·49 m² (16·0 sq ft)
Foreplane flaps (total)	0·93 m² (10·0 sq ft)
Fins (total)	1·58 m² (17·0 sq ft)
Rudders (total)	1·07 m² (11·5 sq ft)

WEIGHTS AND LOADINGS:

Basic weight empty	561 kg (1,236 lb)
Operating weight empty	635 kg (1,401 lb)
Normal T-O weight	733 kg (1,617 lb)
Normal operating weight	771 kg (1,700 lb)
Design max T-O weight	1,043 kg (2,300 lb)
Max wing loading	99·7 kg/m² (20·43 lb/sq ft)
Normal max power loading at 771 kg (1,700 lb) AUW	6·48 kg/kW (10·6 lb/hp)
Max power loading at design max T-O weight	8·76 kg/kW (14·3 lb/hp)

PERFORMANCE:

Cruising speed	92 knots (170 km/h; 106 mph)
Optimum climbing speed	68 knots (126 km/h; 78 mph)
Stalling speed	42 knots (78 km/h; 49 mph)
T-O run, flaps up	183 m (600 ft)
Landing run, flaps up	116 m (380 ft)
Range	260 nm (481 km; 299 miles)

MARSHALL

MARSHALL OF CAMBRIDGE (ENGINEERING) LTD (Aircraft Division)

HEAD OFFICE AND WORKS: Airport Works, Cambridge CB5 8RX

Telephone: Cambridge (0223) 61133

Telex: 81208

MANAGING DIRECTOR: Sir Arthur Marshall, OBE

COMMERCIAL DIRECTOR: R. D. Horsbrough

CHIEF ENGINEER: R. O. Gates

SALES MANAGER: Norman Sellars

The Aircraft Division of this company (known as Marshalls Flying School Ltd until 1962) has specialised for many years in the modification, overhaul and repair of military and commercial aircraft, including the design and installation of interior furnishing for executive transports and of avionics fits up to and including the complete outfitting of various aircraft for calibration and electronic countermeasures roles.

The company's design department is both CAA and MoD(PE) approved. As an approved service and repair centre for the Lockheed Hercules, Gulfstream American and Cessna Citation aircraft, Marshall of Cambridge also has FAA approval covering most types of American aircraft. The company's conversion, modification and overhaul facilities, which include some of the largest heated hangars in England, with workshop support to full aircraft factory standard, have enabled it to undertake numerous major programmes of work on Viscounts, Britannias, Comets, VC10s, Canberras and a vast number of other civil and military aircraft. It has a separate hangar for specialised painting of the largest aircraft, and a sculpture milling shop for manufacture of major aircraft components.

In 1966, Marshall of Cambridge was appointed the designated centre for the Royal Air Force Hercules C. Mk 1 transport aircraft, and in 1973 the company completed the conversion of an RAF Hercules C. Mk 1 to W. Mk 2 configuration.

Marshall of Cambridge designed and manufactured the variable-geometry nose and visor for the pre-production Concorde aircraft, and the flight deck, associated electrics and ground equipment.

It converted two Hawker Siddeley Buccaneer Mk 2s as trials aircraft in the Panavia Tornado development programme, as described in the 1977-78 *Jane's*.

MARSHALL (LOCKHEED) HERCULES CONVERSIONS

The **Hercules W. Mk 2** long-range meteorological aircraft was adapted by Marshall from a Hercules C. Mk 1 (XV208), for the RAF's Meteorological Research Flight. It flew for the first time on 21 March 1973, and participated in the multi-national Project GATE in 1974.

Full details of the equipment and other changes made in the W. Mk 2 were given in the 1974-75 *Jane's*.

The dimensions, weights and performance of the Hercules C. Mk 1 (Lockheed C-130K), as given in the US section of this edition, apply generally also to the W. Mk 2, except in the following respects:

DIMENSIONS, EXTERNAL:

Length overall, incl boom	36·58 m (120 ft 0 in)
Height overall	11·71 m (38 ft 5 in)

WEIGHTS:

Weight empty	32,059 kg (70,678 lb)
Weight empty, equipped	37,149 kg (81,900 lb)
Max normal T-O weight	70,310 kg (155,000 lb)
Max zero-fuel weight	58,422 kg (128,800 lb)
Max landing weight	58,970 kg (130,000 lb)

It was announced in 1978 by the Ministry of Defence that a contract had been signed with Lockheed Corporation to modify 30 Hercules C. Mk 1s (C-130Ks) of the Royal Air Force to **Hercules C. Mk 3** configuration. The modification involves 'stretching' the fuselage by the insertion of a 2·54 m (8 ft 4 in) plug forward of the wings and a 2·03 m (6 ft 8 in) plug aft of the wings, thus producing the same fuselage dimensions and capacity as those of the L 100-30 Commercial Hercules (see US section). The first aircraft was being modified by Lockheed in Marietta, Georgia, during the last quarter of 1979; the remaining 29 are to be modified by Marshall of Cambridge in 1980-83.

Examples of volumetric and load differences include:

Cabin volume, incl ramp:	
C. Mk 1	127·4 m³ (4,500 cu ft)
C. Mk 3	171·5 m³ (6,057 cu ft)
Palletised loads:	
C. Mk 1	5
C. Mk 3	7
Land-Rovers plus trailers:	
C. Mk 1	3 + 2
C. Mk 3	4 + 3

NDN

NDN AIRCRAFT LTD

ADDRESS: Goodwood Aerodrome, nr Chichester, Sussex

Telephone: 0243 784337/8

Telex: 21120 Ref 1531

DIRECTORS:

N. D. Norman, CBE, MRAeS (Managing Director)
K. A. F. Burke, ACA
A. J. Coombe, BSc (Technical)
B. E. Norman

Mr N. D. Norman founded NDN Aircraft Ltd in the early months of 1977 to develop and subsequently produce or arrange licence production of a new two-seat basic military trainer known as the NDN 1 Firecracker.

NDN 1 FIRECRACKER

The first prototype Firecracker (G-NDNI) made its initial flight on 26 May 1977, and a British C of A in the Aerobatic category was issued by the CAA on 24 May 1979. The aircraft's design meets the requirements of FAR Pt 23-14.

The following description applies to the first prototype; a second Firecracker, powered by a turboprop engine, was under construction in mid-1979.

TYPE: Two-seat training aircraft.

WINGS: Cantilever low-wing monoplane. Wing section NACA 23012 (modified). Dihedral 5° on outer wing panels only. Incidence 3°. Leading-edge of inner wing panels swept back approximately 20°. Light alloy structure, including aerodynamically and mass balanced ailerons and hydraulically-operated single-slotted trailing-edge flaps. Trim tab in starboard aileron; geared tab in each aileron. All controls manually operated.

FUSELAGE: Semi-monocoque stressed-skin structure of light alloy. Hydraulically-operated light alloy door-type airbrake in fuselage undersurface, at wing trailing-edge.

TAIL UNIT: Cantilever stressed-skin structure of light alloy. Fixed-incidence tailplane. Trim tab in starboard half of elevator and in rudder.

LANDING GEAR: Hydraulically retractable tricycle type, steerable nosewheel retracting aft, main units inward. Oleo-pneumatic shock-absorber and single wheel on each unit. Cleveland type 551-751 main wheels, with size 6·00-6 Goodyear tyres. Cleveland type 551-753 nosewheel, with size 5·00-5 Goodyear tyre. Cleveland type 551-705 hydraulically-operated disc brakes.

Prototype of the NDN 1 Firecracker two-seat military training aircraft

POWER PLANT: One 194 kW (260 hp) Lycoming AEIO-540-B4D5 flat-six engine, driving a Hoffmann HO-V123K/200AH5 three-blade constant-speed propeller. Four integral wing fuel tanks with a combined capacity of 427 litres (94 Imp gallons). Refuelling points on wing upper surface. Fuel and Christen oil systems permit inverted flight.

ACCOMMODATION: Two seats in tandem beneath sideways-opening (to starboard) transparent canopy. Canopy can be jettisoned in emergency. Rear seat is raised 10 cm (4 in) above level of forward seat for improved view. Baggage space (0·25 m³; 9 cu ft) aft of rear seat. Accommodation heated and ventilated.

SYSTEMS: Hydraulic system, pressure 103·5 bars (1,500 lb/sq in), supplied by electro-hydraulic pump with hand-operated emergency pump. Gas bottle for emergency nosewheel extension. Electrical system powered by a Prestolite engine-driven 24V 70A alternator. 12V 35Ah battery for aerobatics. Air-conditioning and oxygen systems optional.

AVIONICS AND EQUIPMENT: Typical avionics will include dual VHF com/nav, plus ILS, DME, ADF, transponder and marker beacon receiver. Blind-flying instrumentation is standard. Optional equipment includes target towing facilities, underwing weapon pylons, gunsight, survey camera and autopilot.

DIMENSIONS, EXTERNAL:

Wing span	7·92 m (26 ft 0 in)
Wing chord at root	1·83 m (6 ft 0 in)
Wing chord at tip	1·45 m (4 ft 9 in)
Wing aspect ratio	5·36
Length overall	7·70 m (25 ft 3 in)
Height overall	3·00 m (9 ft 10 in)
Tailplane span	2·90 m (9 ft 6 in)
Wheel track	3·05 m (10 ft 0 in)
Wheelbase	2·08 m (6 ft 10 in)
Propeller diameter	1·93 m (6 ft 4 in)

AREAS:

Wings, gross	11·71 m² (126 sq ft)
Ailerons (total)	1·23 m² (13·2 sq ft)

Trailing-edge flaps (total) 1·23 m² (13·2 sq ft)
Fin 0·60 m² (6·5 sq ft)
Rudder, incl tab 0·65 m² (7·0 sq ft)
Tailplane 1·28 m² (13·8 sq ft)
Elevator, incl tab 1·11 m² (12·0 sq ft)

WEIGHTS AND LOADINGS (estimated):
Weight empty, equipped 875 kg (1,930 lb)
Max T-O weight, fully aerobatic 1,288 kg (2,840 lb)
Max landing weight 1,225 kg (2,700 lb)
Max wing loading 109·9 kg/m² (22·5 lb/sq ft)
Max power loading 6·64 kg/kW (10·9 lb/hp)

PERFORMANCE (at max landing weight, ISA at S/L, zero wind, unless otherwise stated):
Never-exceed speed 238 knots (441 km/h; 274 mph) EAS
Max level speed at S/L 176 knots (326 km/h; 203 mph)
Max cruising speed, 75% power at 2,286 m (7,500 ft) 167 knots (309 km/h; 192 mph)
Stalling speed, flaps down 56·5 knots (105 km/h; 65 mph) EAS
Max rate of climb at S/L 442 m (1,450 ft)/min
Service ceiling 5,485 m (18,000 ft)
Absolute ceiling 6,100 m (20,000 ft)
T-O run 271 m (890 ft)
T-O to 15 m (50 ft) 360 m (1,180 ft)
Landing from 15 m (50 ft) 396 m (1,300 ft)
Landing run 259 m (850 ft)
Range with max fuel, no reserves 1,220 nm (2,260 km; 1,405 miles)

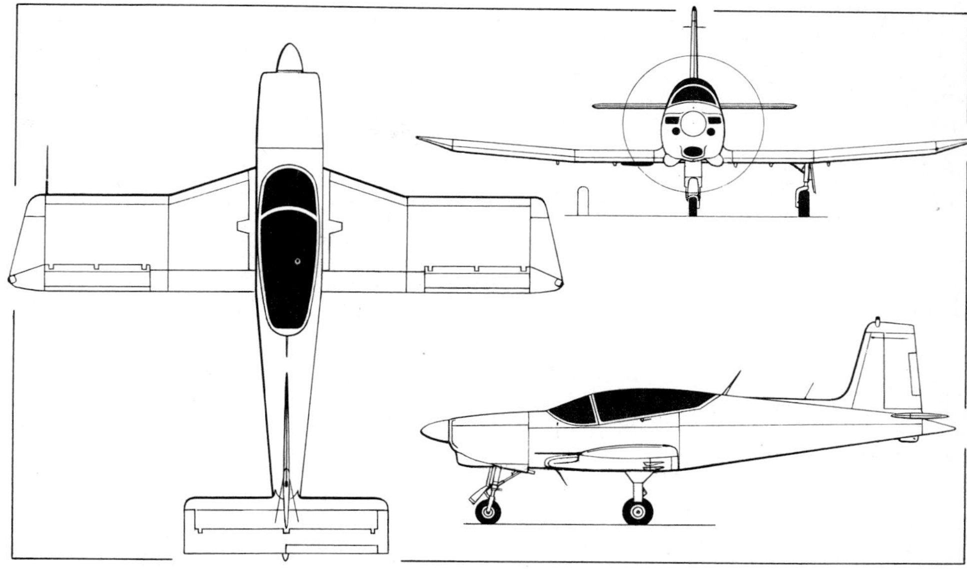

NDN 1 Firecracker (Lycoming AEIO-540-B4D5 engine) *(Pilot Press)*

PILATUS BRITTEN-NORMAN

PILATUS BRITTEN-NORMAN LTD (a subsidiary of Pilatus Aircraft Ltd)

HEAD OFFICE: Bembridge Airport, Bembridge, Isle of Wight PO35 5PR
Telephone: 098387 2511/5
Telex: 86277

DIRECTORS:
D. C. Kloeckner (Managing)
P. Desai (Marketing)
J. Keller (Production)
D. A. Berryman (Technical)

The previous history of this company can be found in the 1978-79 and earlier editions of *Jane's*. It produces the Islander and Trislander transport aircraft; the Islander is manufactured also in Romania by IRMA (which see). In addition to the Bembridge and Romanian production lines, Philippine Aerospace Development Corporation has an Islander production line in Manila, for the production of 115 aircraft under licence in four phases during the period 1975-1980. This programme is described under the NAM entry in the Philippines section.

By mid-1978, Britten-Norman had begun production of the latest series of the Islander, the BN-2B. Development of the Turbo Islander, Defender, Trislander and other versions of this widely used family of aircraft is continuing at Bembridge.

On 25 July 1978 it was announced that Pilatus Aircraft Ltd of Switzerland was to acquire all assets of Britten-Norman (Bembridge) Ltd, including the facilities on the Isle of Wight and the former Fairey SA Islander/Trislander production hardware at Gosselies in Belgium. Final takeover took place in September 1979. Part and licence production of Islanders in the Philippines and Romania, and eventually in other countries, is to continue under the new agreements.

PILATUS BRITTEN-NORMAN BN-2B ISLANDER II

The Islander is a modern replacement for aircraft in the class of the de Havilland Dragon Rapide, Detail design work began in April 1964 and construction of the prototype (G-ATCT) was started in September of the same year. It flew for the first time on 13 June 1965, powered by two 157 kW (210 hp) Rolls-Royce Continental IO-360-B engines and with wings of 13·72 m (45 ft) span. Subsequently, the prototype was re-engined with more powerful Lycoming O-540 engines, with which it flew for the first time on 17 December 1965. The wing span was also increased by 1·22 m (4 ft) to bring the prototype to production standard.

The production prototype BN-2 Islander (G-ATWU) flew for the first time on 20 August 1966. The Islander received its domestic C of A on 10 August 1967 and an FAA Type Certificate on 19 December 1967.

Deliveries of Islanders began in August 1967, and by June 1979 more than 900 aircraft of the various models had been delivered to operators in approx 120 countries.

Large-scale production in the Philippines began in 1974 with the delivery of the first of six 224 kW (300 hp) Islanders. Phase two involved 14 unpainted aircraft without cabin trim, furnishing and electronics, which were finished by NAM. Phase three called for the assembly by NAM of 35 aircraft supplied in knockdown kit form. The final phase covers 60 aircraft for which subassemblies and certain components are manufactured in Manila, using jigs and detailed parts supplied from the UK. Of these 60 aircraft, about 25 will be repurchased by Pilatus Britten-Norman for sale throughout the world.

Pilatus Britten-Norman BN-2A Islander for the Desert Locust Control Organisation *(S. R. P. Thomson)*

Initial production aircraft were designated **BN-2**. Those built from 1 June 1969 until 1978 had the designation **BN-2A**, as described in the 1977-78 *Jane's*. The current standard model is the **BN-2B Islander II**, which has a higher max landing weight and improved interior design. Features include a new range of passenger seats and covers, more robust door locks, improved door seals, improved stainless steel sills, redesigned fresh air system to improve ventilation in hot and humid climates, smaller diameter propellers to decrease cabin noise, and redesigned flight deck and instrument panel.

Military versions known as the **Defender** and **Maritime Defender** and the three-engined civil **Trislander** are described separately.

The basic Islander II is available with a choice of two alternative power plants and either standard 14·94 m (49 ft 0 in) span wings or wingtip extensions having raked tips and containing auxiliary fuel tanks. A series of modification kits is available as standard or as an option for new production aircraft, and can also be supplied to operators in the field for retrospective fitting to existing aircraft. The version with 224 kW (300 hp) fuel-injection engines was first introduced in 1970, deliveries beginning in November of that year. An extended nose, incorporating 0·62 m³ (22 cu ft) of additional baggage space, was introduced as an optional feature in 1972.

A Rajay turbocharging installation was developed in the United States by Jonas Aircraft, the New York based distributors for Britten-Norman aircraft. The Rajay installation is a bolt-on unit, for manual operation, which can be fitted on to standard 194 kW (260 hp) engines. The superchargers have the effect of increasing the single-engined ceiling to 3,810 m (12,500 ft) and twin-engined ceiling to 7,925 m (26,000 ft). Cruising speed is also increased, from 139 knots (257 km/h; 160 mph) at 2,135 m (7,000 ft) to 146 knots (270 km/h; 168 mph) at 3,050 m (10,000 ft).

The following description applies to the standard landplane BN-2B, unless otherwise stated:

TYPE: Twin-engined feederline transport.

WINGS: Cantilever high-wing monoplane. NACA 23012 constant wing section. No dihedral. Incidence 2°. No sweepback. Conventional riveted two-spar torsion-box structure in one piece, using L72 aluminium-clad aluminium alloys. Flared-up wingtips of Britten-Norman design. Raked-back extended wingtips optional. Slotted ailerons and single-slotted flaps of metal construction. Flaps operated electrically, ailerons by pushrods and cables. Ground-adjustable tab on starboard aileron. BTR-Goodrich pneumatic de-icing boots optional.

FUSELAGE: Conventional riveted four-longeron semi-monocoque structure of pressed frames and stringers and metal skin, using L72 aluminium-clad aluminium alloys. Optional 1·15 m (3 ft 9¼ in) nose extension for baggage stowage.

TAIL UNIT: Cantilever two-spar structure, with pressed ribs and metal skin, using L72 aluminium-clad aluminium alloys. Fixed-incidence tailplane and mass-balanced elevator. Rudder and elevator are actuated by pushrods and cables. Trim tabs in rudder and elevator. Pneumatic de-icing of tailplane and fin optional.

LANDING GEAR: Non-retractable tricycle type, with twin wheels on each main unit and single steerable nose-wheel. Cantilever main legs mounted aft of rear spar. All three legs fitted with Lockheed oleo-pneumatic shock-absorbers. All five wheels and tyres size 16 × 7-7, supplied by Goodyear. Tyre pressure: main 2·41 bars (35 lb/sq in); nose 2·00 bars (29 lb/sq in). Foot-operated aircooled Cleveland hydraulic brakes on main units. Parking brake. Wheel/ski gear available optionally.

POWER PLANT: Two Lycoming flat-six engines, each driving a Hartzell HC-C2YK-2B or -2C two-blade metal constant-speed feathering propeller. Propeller synchronisers optional. Standard power plant is the 194 kW (260 hp) O-540-E4C5, but the 224 kW (300 hp) IO-540-K1B5 can be fitted at customer's option. Optional Rajay turbocharging installation on 194 kW (260 hp) engines, to improve high-altitude performance. Integral fuel tank between spars in each wing, outboard of engine. Total fuel capacity (standard) 518 litres (114 Imp gallons; 137 US gallons). With auxiliary tanks in wingtip extensions, total capacity is increased to 741 litres (163 Imp gallons; 196 US gallons). Additional pylon-mounted underwing auxiliary tanks, each of 227 litres (50 Imp gallons; 60 US gallons) capacity, available optionally. Refuelling point in upper surface of wing above each internal tank. Total oil capacity 22·75 litres (5 Imp gallons).

ACCOMMODATION: Up to 10 persons, including pilot, on side-by-side front seats and four bench seats. No aisle. Seat backs fold forward. Access to all seats via three forward-opening doors, forward of wing and at rear of cabin on port side and forward of wing on starboard side. Baggage compartment at rear of cabin, with port-side loading door in standard versions. Exit in emergency by removing door windows. Special execu-

Prototype of the Pilatus Britten-Norman BN-2B Islander II *(S. R. P. Thomson)*

tive layouts available. Can be operated as freighter, carrying more than a ton of cargo; in this configuration the passenger seats can be stored in the rear baggage bay. In ambulance role, up to three stretchers and two attendants can be accommodated. Other layouts possible, including photographic and geophysical survey, parachutist transport or trainer (with accommodation for up to eight parachutists and a dispatcher), firefighting, public health spraying and crop spraying.

SYSTEMS: Southwind cabin heater standard. 45,000 BTU Stewart Warner combustion unit, with circulating fan, provides hot air for distribution at floor-level outlets and at windscreen demisting slots. Fresh air, boosted by propeller slipstream, is ducted to each seating position for on-ground ventilation. Electrical DC power, for instruments, lighting and radio, from one or two engine-driven 24V 50A self-rectifying alternators and a controller to main busbar and circuit-breaker assembly in nose bay. Emergency busbar with automatic changeover provides a secondary route for essential services. Two 24V 17Ah heavy-duty lead-acid batteries for independent operation. Ground power receptacle provided. Optional electrical de-icing of propellers and windscreen, and pneumatic de-icing of wing and tail unit leading-edges. Intercom system, including second headset, and passenger address system are standard. Oxygen system available optionally for all versions.

AVIONICS AND EQUIPMENT: Standard items include blind-flying instrumentation, autopilot, dual flying controls and brake system, and a wide range of VHF or HF communications and navigation equipment.

DIMENSIONS, EXTERNAL:
- Wing span: standard — 14·94 m (49 ft 0 in)
  - with extended tips — 16·15 m (53 ft 0 in)
- Wing chord (constant) — 2·03 m (6 ft 8 in)
- Wing aspect ratio: standard — 7·4
  - with extended tips — 7·95
- Length overall: standard — 10·86 m (35 ft 7¾ in)
  - optional nose extension — 12·02 m (39 ft 5¼ in)
- Fuselage: Max width — 1·21 m (3 ft 11½ in)
  - Max depth — 1·46 m (4 ft 9¾ in)
- Height overall — 4·18 m (13 ft 8¾ in)
- Tailplane span — 4·67 m (15 ft 4 in)
- Wheel track (c/l of shock-absorbers) — 3·61 m (11 ft 10 in)
- Wheelbase: standard — 3·99 m (13 ft 1¼ in)
  - optional nose extension — 4·90 m (16 ft 0¾ in)
- Propeller diameter — 1·98 m (6 ft 6 in)
- Cabin door (front, port):
  - Height — 1·10 m (3 ft 7½ in)
  - Width: top — 0·64 m (2 ft 1¼ in)
  - Height to sill — 0·59 m (1 ft 11¼ in)
- Cabin door (front, starboard):
  - Height — 1·10 m (3 ft 7½ in)
  - Max width — 0·86 m (2 ft 10 in)
  - Height to sill — 0·57 m (1 ft 10½ in)
- Cabin door (rear, port):
  - Height — 1·09 m (3 ft 7 in)
  - Width: top — 0·635 m (2 ft 1 in)
  - bottom — 1·19 m (3 ft 11 in)
  - Height to sill — 0·52 m (1 ft 8½ in)
- Baggage door (rear, port):
  - Height — 0·69 m (2 ft 3 in)

DIMENSIONS, INTERNAL:
- Passenger cabin, aft of pilot's seat:
  - Length — 3·05 m (10 ft 0 in)
  - Max width — 1·09 m (3 ft 7 in)
  - Max height — 1·27 m (4 ft 2 in)
  - Floor area — 2·97 m² (32 sq ft)
  - Volume — 3·68 m³ (130 cu ft)
- Baggage space aft of passenger cabin:
  - standard — 0·85 m³ (30 cu ft)
  - maximum — 1·39 m³ (49 cu ft)
- Nose baggage compartment (optional) — 0·62 m³ (22 cu ft)
- Freight capacity:
  - aft of pilot's seat, incl rear cabin baggage space — 4·70 m³ (166 cu ft)
  - with four bench seats folded into rear cabin baggage space — 3·68 m³ (130 cu ft)

AREAS:
- Wings, gross: standard — 30·19 m² (325·0 sq ft)
  - with extended tips — 31·31 m² (337·0 sq ft)
- Ailerons (total) — 2·38 m² (25·6 sq ft)
- Flaps (total) — 3·62 m² (39·0 sq ft)
- Fin — 3·41 m² (36·64 sq ft)
- Rudder, incl tab — 1·60 m² (17·2 sq ft)
- Tailplane — 6·78 m² (73·0 sq ft)
- Elevator, incl tabs — 3·08 m² (33·16 sq ft)

WEIGHTS AND LOADINGS (A: standard wings, B: extended wings, C: 194 kW; 260 hp and D: 224 kW; 300 hp engines):
- Weight empty, equipped (without avionics):
  - C — 1,638 kg (3,612 lb)
  - D — 1,695 kg (3,738 lb)
- Max T-O and landing weight (A, B) — 2,993 kg (6,600 lb)
- Max zero-fuel weight (BCAR):
  - A, C, D — 2,855 kg (6,300 lb)
  - B, C, D — 2,810 kg (6,200 lb)
- Max wing loading: A — 99·1 kg/m² (20·3 lb/sq ft)
  - B — 95·7 kg/m² (19·6 lb/sq ft)
- Max floor loading, without cargo panels — 586 kg/m² (120 lb/sq ft)
- Max power loading: C — 7·71 kg/kW (12·7 lb/hp)
  - D — 6·68 kg/kW (11·0 lb/hp)

PERFORMANCE (C: at 2,855 kg; 6,300 lb AUW, ISA, 194 kW; 260 hp engines. D: at max T-O weight, ISA, 224 kW; 300 hp engines):
- Never-exceed speed:
  - C, D (standard wings) — 177 knots (327 km/h; 203 mph) IAS
  - C, D (extended wings) — 184 knots (340 km/h; 211 mph) IAS
- Max level speed at S/L:
  - C — 148 knots (274 km/h; 170 mph)
  - D — 151 knots (280 km/h; 173 mph)
- Max cruising speed (75% power) at 2,135 m (7,000 ft):
  - C — 139 knots (257 km/h; 160 mph)
  - D — 142 knots (264 km/h; 164 mph)
- Cruising speed (67% power) at 2,750 m (9,000 ft):
  - C — 134 knots (248 km/h; 154 mph)
  - D — 137 knots (254 km/h; 158 mph)
- Cruising speed (59% power) at 3,660 m (12,000 ft):
  - C — 130 knots (241 km/h; 150 mph)
  - D — 132 knots (245 km/h; 152 mph)
- Stalling speed, flaps up:
  - C — 50 knots (92 km/h; 57 mph) IAS
- Stalling speed, flaps down:
  - C, D — 43 knots (79 km/h; 49 mph) IAS
- Max rate of climb at S/L: C — 290 m (950 ft)/min
  - D — 344 m (1,130 ft)/min
- Rate of climb at S/L, one engine out:
  - C — 58·5 m (192 ft)/min
  - D — 61 m (200 ft)/min
- Absolute ceiling: C — 4,938 m (16,200 ft)
  - D — 5,974 m (19,600 ft)
- Service ceiling: C — 4,450 m (14,600 ft)
  - D — 5,485 m (18,000 ft)
- Service ceiling, one engine out:
  - C, standard wings — 1,737 m (5,700 ft)
  - C, extended wings — 1,981 m (6,500 ft)
  - D, standard wings — 1,890 m (6,200 ft)
  - D, extended wings — 2,133 m (7,000 ft)
- Min ground turning radius — 9·45 m (31 ft 0 in)
- T-O run at S/L, zero wind, hard runway:
  - C — 169 m (555 ft)
  - D — 203 m (665 ft)
- T-O run at 1,525 m (5,000 ft):
  - D — 296 m (970 ft)
- T-O to 15 m (50 ft) at S/L, zero wind, hard runway:
  - C — 332 m (1,090 ft)
  - D — 335 m (1,100 ft)
- T-O to 15 m (50 ft) at 1,525 m (5,000 ft):
  - D — 475 m (1,560 ft)
- Landing from 15 m (50 ft) at S/L, zero wind, hard runway:
  - C — 292 m (960 ft)
  - D — 299 m (980 ft)
- Landing from 15 m (50 ft) at 1,525 m (5,000 ft):
  - D — 357 m (1,170 ft)
- Landing run at 1,525 m (5,000 ft):
  - D — 168 m (550 ft)
- Landing run at S/L, zero wind, hard runway:
  - C — 137 m (450 ft)
  - D — 140 m (460 ft)
- Range at 75% power at 2,135 m (7,000 ft):
  - C, standard wings — 622 nm (1,153 km; 717 miles)
  - C, extended wings — 903 nm (1,673 km; 1,040 miles)
  - D, standard wings — 555 nm (1,028 km; 639 miles)
  - D, extended wings — 816 nm (1,513 km; 940 miles)
- Range at 67% power at 2,750 m (9,000 ft):
  - C, standard wings — 713 nm (1,322 km; 822 miles)
  - C, extended wings — 1,036 nm (1,920 km: 1,193 miles)
  - D, standard wings — 577 nm (1,070 km; 665 miles)
  - D, extended wings — 847 nm (1,569 km; 975 miles)
- Range at 59% power at 3,660 m (12,000 ft):
  - C, standard wings — 755 nm (1,400 km; 870 miles)
  - C, extended wings — 1,096 nm (2,032 km; 1,263 miles)
  - D, standard wings — 613 nm (1,136 km; 706 miles)
  - D, extended wings — 905 nm (1,677 km; 1,042 miles)

PILATUS BRITTEN-NORMAN DEFENDER

The Defender is a variant of the civil Islander which can be adapted for a wide variety of government and military roles such as search and rescue, internal security, long-range patrol, forward air control, troop transport, logistic support and casualty evacuation.

The Defender is available with the same choices of power plant and wing configuration as the current civil versions and can be equipped with a wide range of highly sophisticated electronics, including nose-mounted weather radar, providing the aircraft with a marine search capability. Optional equipment includes four NATO standard underwing pylons for a variety of external stores, the inboard pair each carrying up to 317·5 kg (700 lb) and the outboard pair up to 204 kg (450 lb).

Typical underwing loads include twin 7·62 mm machine-guns in pod packs, 250 lb or 500 lb GP bombs, Matra rocket packs, SURA rocket clusters, wire-guided missiles, 5 in reconnaissance flares, anti-personnel grenades, smoke bombs, marker bombs and 227 litre (60 US gallon) drop-tanks.

Internal capacity for passengers, stretcher cases or cargo is the same as that of the civil Islander. Static and air-to-

Pilatus Britten-Norman Defender of the Botswana Defence Force, with underwing stores *(S. R. P. Thomson)*

ground firing trials were successfully completed in 1971. The Defender is cleared for forward and beam firing of two pairs of 7·62 mm machine-guns, and the forward firing of SURA and 68 mm SNEB rockets.

Britten-Norman Defenders/Islanders are in service with the Abu Dhabi Defence Force, Belgian Army, Botswana Defence Force, British Army Parachute Association, Ghana Air Force, Guyana Defence Force, Indian Navy, Jamaica Defence Force, Malagasy Air Force, Philippine Navy, Presidential Flight of the Mexican Air Force, Royal Hong Kong Auxiliary Air Force, Panamanian Air Force, Sultan of Oman's Air Force, Mauritania Islamic Defence Force, and in Malawi and Rwanda. Those operated by the air forces of Iraq, Israel and Qatar are military Islanders, and are not equipped to carry offensive weapons. Those supplied to the Indian Navy are Maritime Defenders.

The description given for the BN-2B Islander applies also to the Defender, except as follows:

Power Plant: Two 224 kW (300 hp) Lycoming IO-540-K1B5 flat-six engines standard.

Avionics: Typical installation comprises King 360-channel VHF nav/com transceivers with VOR/LOC and VOR/ILS, ADF, marker beacon, KT76 transponder, Sunair ASB 100A HF transceiver, RCA or Bendix radar and Brittain B5 three-axis autopilot.

Weights and Loadings:

Weight empty, equipped (excl avionics) 1,824 kg (4,020 lb)
Max T-O weight 2,993 kg (6,600 lb)
Max landing weight 2,855 kg (6,300 lb)
Max wing loading 95·7 kg/m² (19·6 lb/sq ft)
Max power loading 6·68 kg/kW (11·0 lb/hp)

Performance (at max T-O weight, ISA. A: no stores on pylons; B: pylons loaded):

Max level speed:
A 151 knots (280 km/h; 174 mph)
B 144 knots (266 km/h; 166 mph)
Cruising speed, 67% power at 3,050 m (10,000 ft):
A 138 knots (255 km/h; 159 mph)
B 131 knots (242 km/h; 150 mph)
Cruising speed, 59% power at 610 m (2,000 ft):
A 123 knots (227 km/h; 141 mph)
B 116 knots (215 km/h; 133 mph)
Stalling speed, flaps down:
A, B 39 knots (73 km/h; 45 mph)
Max rate of climb at S/L: A 396 m (1,300 ft)/min
B 357 m (1,170 ft)/min
Service ceiling: A, B 5,180 m (17,000 ft)
Absolute ceiling: A, B 6,100 m (20,000 ft)
T-O to 15 m (50 ft): A, B 320 m (1,050 ft)
Landing from 15 m (50 ft): A, B 303 m (995 ft)
Range with max payload:
A 363 nm (672 km; 418 miles)
B 326 nm (603 km; 375 miles)
Range with standard fuel:
A 1,096 nm (2,027 km; 1,260 miles)
B 1,000 nm (1,850 km; 1,150 miles)
Max range with auxiliary fuel, no reserves, at full mission weight with max endurance power setting 1,497 nm (2,772 km; 1,723 miles)

PILATUS BRITTEN-NORMAN MARITIME DEFENDER

Generally similar to the Defender, the Maritime Defender differs by having a modified nose with a larger search radar, capable of detecting a 100 m² (1,076 sq ft) target in sea state 4-5 at a range of 36 nm (67 km; 41·5 miles). Scanning 60° on each side of the flight path, the radar provides a search width of 60 nm (111 km; 69 miles) at optimum altitude. The interior layout provides for pilot and co-pilot, a radar operator at a mid-cabin position on the starboard side, and two observers in the rear of the cabin, one aft of the radar operator, and one adjacent to a window on the port side.

Intended for coastal patrol, fishery and oil rig protection duties, as well as search and rescue support, the Maritime Defender is suitable for all-weather operation, by day or night, and carries the equipment necessary to fulfil such roles. This can include Collins PN 101 compass/HSI, horizon gyro (radar stabilisation), autopilot, Bendix RDR 1300 radar, Marconi CMA 734 Omega, Plessey PVI 712 radio altimeter, dual Collins VHF 20 com, dual Collins VIR 30M VHF nav/ILS, VHF marine band com, Collins ADF 60, Collins TDR 90 transponder, Collins DME 40, encoding altimeter, and Sunair ASB 100A SSB HF com. Specialised equipment includes a searchlight installation and hand-held camera; the four underwing pylons can be used to carry a loudspeaker pod, flares, parachute dinghy packs and a variety of weapons.

The description of the Defender applies also to the Maritime Defender, except that overall length is increased to 11·07 m (36 ft 3¾ in).

PILATUS BRITTEN-NORMAN BN-2A Mk III TRISLANDER

In the Autumn of 1970 Britten-Norman introduced an enlarged development of the twin-engined Islander, having a third engine mounted at the rear and a lengthened fuselage seating up to 17 passengers.

The prototype Trislander was produced by converting the second prototype of the twin-engined Islander (G-ATWU), adding a 2·29 m (7 ft 6 in) length of parallel-section fuselage forward of the wing, reinforcing the rear fuselage and fitting a new main landing gear with larger wheels and tyres. The tail unit was modified to act as a mount for the third engine. This aircraft made its first flight on 11 September 1970, appearing at the SBAC Display at Farnborough later the same day. Production aircraft have additional fin area above the rear engine.

Pilatus Britten-Norman Maritime Defender, with enlarged nose radome *(S. R. P. Thomson)*

The prototype was later dismantled and its fuselage used for structural testing. By the end of 1970 construction had begun of three production aircraft by converting standard Islander airframes from the current production line, and this system has been adopted for all production aircraft, thus maintaining maximum flexibility on what is now a completely integrated Islander/Trislander assembly line. The first production Trislander (G-AYTU) was flown on 6 March 1971, and the first delivery (to Aurigny Air Services in the Channel Islands) was made on 29 June 1971.

ARB certification of the Trislander, granted on 14 May 1971, approved the aircraft for both VFR and IFR operation and for full public transport with one pilot and up to 17 passengers. FAA certification followed on 4 August 1971, to FAR Pt 23 and to the latest air taxi requirements of SFAR Pt 23 and Appendix A of FAR Pt 135. The Appendix A standard is higher than that met by most other commuter aircraft currently offered on world markets, and is achieved primarily because of continued take-off capability and fatigue-free structure.

By mid-1979 orders had been received for more than 80 Trislanders. Of these more than 60 had been delivered, to customers in the UK, Africa, Australasia, USA, Canada, Indonesia and South America.

The following versions of the Trislander are currently in production:

BN-2A Mk III-2. Standard version with extended nose containing baggage compartment.

BN-2A Mk III-3. As Mk III-2, with an autofeather system which feathers the propeller automatically should an engine fail on take-off.

BN-2A Mk III-4. As Mk III-3, plus a standby rocket engine to provide additional thrust should an engine fail on take-off.

Type: Three-engined feederline transport.

Wings: Cantilever high-wing monoplane. NACA 23012 constant wing section. No dihedral. Incidence 2°. No sweepback. Conventional riveted two-spar torsion-box structure in one piece, using aluminium-clad aluminium alloys. Increases in skin gauges and spar laminates compared with twin-engined versions. Structure is strictly 'safe-life', but exhibits several fail-safe features and principles. Flared-up wingtips of Britten-Norman design, with raked tips. Slotted ailerons and electrically-operated single-slotted permanently-drooped flaps of metal construction. Ground-adjustable tab in starboard aileron. BTR-Goodrich pneumatic de-icing boots optional.

Fuselage: Conventional riveted four-longeron semi-monocoque structure of pressed frames and stringers and metal skin, using L72 aluminium-clad aluminium alloys. Some reinforcement of fuselage aft of wing to support weight of rear engine. Structure is strictly 'safe-life', but has several fail-safe features and principles.

Tail Unit: Cantilever structure, using L72 aluminium-clad aluminium alloys, with low aspect ratio main fin which also acts as mount for the third engine. Fixed-incidence tailplane (with raked tips) and elevators are similar in construction to those of Islander. Trim tab in rudder. BTR-Goodrich pneumatic de-icing boots for tailplane optional.

Landing Gear: Non-retractable tricycle type, with twin-wheel main units and single steerable nosewheel. Cantilever main legs mounted aft of rear spar. All five wheels and tyres are Cleveland size 7·00-6. Tyre pressure 3·10 bars (45 lb/sq in) on main units, 2·00 bars (29 lb/sq in) on nose unit. Cleveland foot-operated air-cooled hydraulic disc brakes on main units. Parking brake. No anti-skid units. Fairings fitted to main gear extension tubes below the engine nacelle and above the shock-absorber attachment bolts.

Power Plant: Three 194 kW (260 hp) Lycoming O-540-E4C5 flat-six engines (two mounted on wings and one on vertical tail), each driving a Hartzell HC-C2YK-2G/C8477-4 two-blade constant-speed fully-feathering metal propeller. Automatic feathering device available as an option. Standby rocket engine, mounted just below rear of tail-engine nacelle, is available as an option; weighing 21 kg (46·2 lb), this provides 1·56 kN (350 lb st) for 12 seconds. Fuel in two integral tanks between front and rear wing spars, outboard of the engine nacelles, and two tanks in wingtips. Total fuel capacity 746 litres (164 Imp gallons; 197 US gallons). Overwing refuelling point above each tank. Oil capacity 34 litres (7·5 Imp gallons; 9 US gallons).

Accommodation: Up to 18 persons, including pilot, in pairs on bench seats at approx 79 cm (31 in) pitch. Access to all seats provided by five broad-hinged rearward-opening car-type doors, two on port side and three on starboard side. Baggage compartment at rear of cabin, with external baggage door on port side. Exit in emergency by removing window panels in front four passenger doors. Heating, ventilation and sound insulation standard. Ambulance or VIP interior layouts at customer's option. Dual controls optional.

Systems: One Southwind cabin heater fitted as standard. DC electrical system includes two 24V 50A self-rectifying alternators, supplying the instruments, lighting and radio, and a 24V 17Ah battery. No hydraulic or pneumatic systems, except for self-contained hydraulic brakes.

Avionics and Equipment: Optional avionics include Bendix M4C or Mitchell Century III autopilot, a wide range of Bendix, King or Narco VHF or HF nav/com equipment, including ADF and DME. Optional equipment includes windscreen de-icing, second cabin heater, cargo tiedowns, anti-collision strobe beacons, emergency exit beta lights, electric propeller de-icing and pneumatic airframe de-icing systems.

Dimensions, external:

Wing span 16·15 m (53 ft 0 in)
Wing chord (constant) 2·03 m (6 ft 8 in)
Wing aspect ratio 7·95
Length overall 15·01 m (49 ft 3 in)
Fuselage: Max width 1·21 m (3 ft 11½ in)
Max depth 1·46 m (4 ft 9¾ in)

Pilatus Britten-Norman BN-2A Mk III-2 Trislander three-engined feederline transport *(S. R. P. Thomson)*

Height overall 4·32 m (14 ft 2 in)
Tailplane span 6·48 m (21 ft 3 in)
Wheel track (c/l of shock-absorbers) 3·35 m (11 ft 0 in)
Wheelbase 7·12 m (23 ft 4¼ in)
Propeller diameter 2·03 m (6 ft 8 in)
Propeller ground clearance 0·69 m (2 ft 3 in)
Distance between propeller centres (wing engines) 3·61 m (11 ft 10 in)
Passenger doors (stbd, fwd and centre):
Height 1·10 m (3 ft 7½ in)
Max width 0·89 m (2 ft 10·9 in)
Height to sill 0·57 m (1 ft 10½ in)
Passenger doors (port, fwd and rear):
Height 1·09 m (3 ft 7 in)
Max width 1·21 m (3 ft 11·9 in)
Height to sill 0·57 m (1 ft 10½ in)
Passenger door (stbd, rear):
Height 1·09 m (3 ft 7 in)
Width 0·75 m (2 ft 5½ in)
Baggage compartment door (rear, port):
Height 0·66 m (2 ft 1·95 in)
Width 0·44 m (1 ft 5·2 in)
Nose baggage compartment door (port, optional):
Width 0·79 m (2 ft 7 in)

DIMENSIONS, INTERNAL:
Cabin: Length, excl flight deck but incl rear baggage compartment 8·24 m (27 ft 0½ in)
Max width 1·09 m (3 ft 7 in)
Max height 1·27 m (4 ft 2 in)
Floor area 7·85 m² (84·45 sq ft)
Volume 9·54 m³ (337 cu ft)
Rear baggage compartment volume 0·71 m³ (25·0 cu ft)
Nose baggage compartment volume (optional) 0·62 m³ (22·0 cu ft)

AREAS:
Wings, gross 31·31 m² (337·0 sq ft)
Ailerons (total) 2·38 m² (25·6 sq ft)
Trailing-edge flaps (total) 3·62 m² (39·0 sq ft)
Fin 5·83 m² (62·7 sq ft)
Rudder, incl tab 1·13 m² (12·2 sq ft)
Tailplane 8·36 m² (90·0 sq ft)
Elevators 2·42 m² (26·0 sq ft)

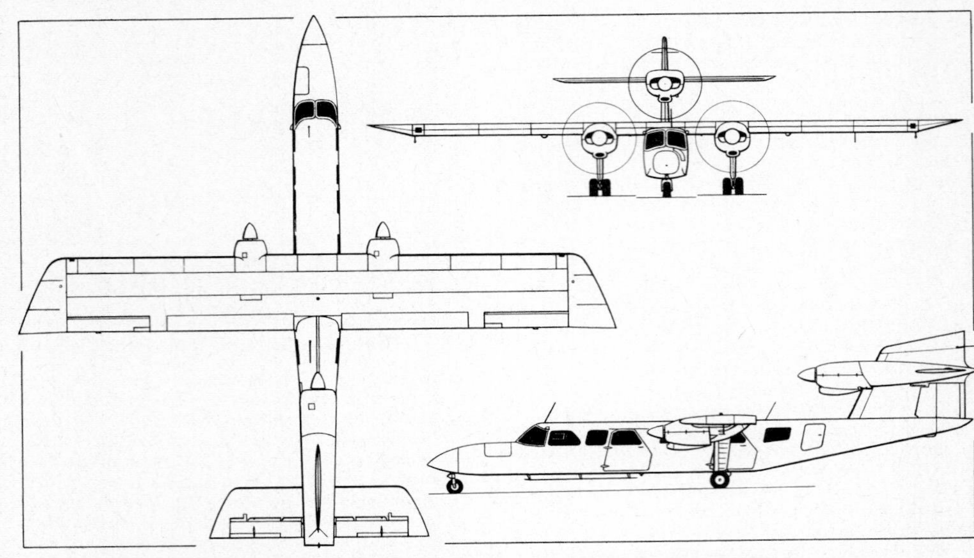

Pilatus Britten-Norman BN-2A Mk III-2 Trislander feederline transport *(Pilot Press)*

WEIGHTS AND LOADINGS:
Weight empty, equipped (without electronics) 2,650 kg (5,843 lb)
Max T-O and landing weight 4,536 kg (10,000 lb)
Max wing loading 144·8 kg/m² (29·67 lb/sq ft)
Max power loading 7·79 kg/kW (12·8 lb/hp)

PERFORMANCE (at max T-O weight, ISA):
Max level speed at S/L 156 knots (290 km/h; 180 mph)
Cruising speed (75% power) at 1,980 m (6,500 ft) 144 knots (267 km/h; 166 mph)
Cruising speed (67% power) at 2,470 m (9,000 ft) 138 knots (256 km/h; 159 mph)
Cruising speed (59% power) at 3,960 m (13,000 ft) 130 knots (241 km/h; 150 mph)
Max rate of climb at S/L 298 m (980 ft)/min
Rate of climb at S/L, one engine out 86 m (283 ft)/min
Absolute ceiling 4,450 m (14,600 ft)
Service ceiling 4,010 m (13,150 ft)
Service ceiling, one engine out 2,105 m (6,900 ft)
T-O run at S/L, zero wind, hard runway 393 m (1,290 ft)
T-O to 15 m (50 ft) at S/L, zero wind, hard runway 594 m (1,950 ft)
Landing from 15 m (50 ft) at S/L, zero wind, hard runway 440 m (1,445 ft)
Landing run at S/L, zero wind, hard runway 259 m (850 ft)
Max still-air range at 59% cruising power 868 nm (1,610 km; 1,000 miles)

SHORTS

SHORT BROTHERS LIMITED

HEAD OFFICE, WORKS AND AERODROME: PO Box 241, Airport Road, Belfast BT3 9DZ, Northern Ireland
Telephone: 0232 58444
Telex: 74688
OTHER FACTORIES: Newtownards, Castlereagh, Belfast (3)
LONDON OFFICE: Berkeley Square House, Berkeley Square, London W1X 5LB
CHAIRMAN: Sir George Leitch, KCB
MANAGING DIRECTOR: P. F. Foreman, CBE
DIRECTORS:
F. F. H. Charlton
D. W. G. L. Haviland, CB
James Sim
Dr Llewellyn Smith, CBE
H. E. Trevan-Hawke
SECRETARY: Gordon Bruce
EXECUTIVE DIRECTORS:
B. Carlin (Manufacturing)
B. P. Laight, OBE (Engineering)
A. R. Manvell (Missiles)
R. McNulty (Finance and Administration)
A. F. C. Roberts, OBE (Aircraft)
K. W. Tyson (Commercial)
CONTROLLER OF PERSONNEL SERVICES: R. M. Armour, OBE
CHIEF TEST PILOT: L. L. Cumming
PUBLICITY MANAGER: G. H. Edgar
MANAGER, PUBLIC RELATIONS SERVICES: Derek S. Jones

Short Brothers were first established, as aeronauts, in 1898, and in 1901 they began the manufacture of balloons at Hove, Sussex. Works were later established in London, first at premises off the Tottenham Court Road and, in 1906, at Battersea. In March 1909 Shorts opened the United Kingdom's first purpose-built aircraft factory at Shellbeach, Isle of Sheppey. (The Short No. 1 had been ordered by F. T. McClean in January 1909.) The contract placed with Shorts by the Wright brothers in March 1909, for six Flyers, was the first aircraft production contract to be placed in the UK. The main aircraft works moved to Eastchurch in 1909-10, and to Rochester in 1913-14.

In June 1936 Short Brothers, in collaboration with Harland & Wolff Ltd, formed a new company known as Short & Harland Ltd to build aircraft in Belfast, and in 1947 activities were concentrated in Belfast under the name Short Bros & Harland Ltd. The name Short Brothers Ltd was re-adopted on 1 June 1977.

The British government now owns, directly or indirectly, 98 per cent of the issued shareholding. In 1976 the company received the Queen's Award to Industry for the ninth time. It had 6,400 employees in 1978.

The company's current products include the Shorts 330, a 30-seat commuter airliner, and the Skyvan turboprop STOL light transport, in use throughout the world for passenger, freight, survey, military and miscellaneous operations.

In April 1979 an agreement with Piper Aircraft Corporation of the USA was announced, under which Shorts are to produce the Piper Tomahawk light aircraft at a rate of 10 per month. Deliveries were scheduled to begin in the late Summer of 1979. To handle Tomahawk production, Shorts have formed Shorlac (Shorts Light Aircraft Company Ltd), a wholly-owned subsidiary with 4,645 m² (50,000 sq ft) premises on the perimeter of Belfast Harbour Airport.

Internationally, Shorts is collaborating as risk-sharing partner with Fokker-VFW, MBB and VFW-Fokker in production of the F28 Fellowship transport, with responsibility for the wings; and holds contracts to produce ailerons, spoilers, wingtips, landing gear doors, galley doors, environmental control system doors and tail unit rib assemblies for the Lockheed L-1011 TriStar, and landing gear doors for the Boeing 747. During 1967, Shorts began the design and manufacture of pods for Rolls-Royce jet engines, and is responsible for podding Rolls-Royce RB.211 turbofan engines for the TriStar. Deliveries of these direct to Lockheed at Palmdale began in the early Summer of 1970. The company is also podding RB.211 engines for the Boeing 747s of British Airways, and has produced pods for more than 500 RB.211s. A contract to produce pods for the Avco Lycoming ALF 502 turbofans of the British Aerospace 146 was announced in January 1979.

To cope with its involvement in the TriStar programme, Shorts installed some of Europe's most advanced facilities for the hot-forming of titanium and the manipulation of high-temperature creep-resistant alloys. It is conducting advanced research into jet-engine noise reduction and metal bonding. Shorts is also quality-approved subcontractor to many major US and UK aerospace companies. Conversely, production of the wings for the Shorts 330 is undertaken jointly by British Aerospace and Fokker-VFW, and production of the 330 landing gear by Menasco in Canada.

In addition to its activities in the field of piloted aircraft, Shorts is engaged in missile development and production, production of supersonic target drones, including production to MoD contract of the MATS-B target drone.

The company's Flying Services Division operates maintenance units and airfields for various civil and military organisations, and flies and maintains aircraft and target drones for the Ministry of Defence. This includes operation of the Llanbedr target aircraft base, and the target service, supply and recovery flight at the Woomera range in Australia.

SHORTS 330

The Shorts 330 (originally SD3-30) is a 30-passenger twin-turboprop transport aircraft designed primarily for commuter and regional air service operators whose current 18/20-seat aircraft require replacement by larger aircraft.

Design of the 330 is derived from that of the Skyvan STOL utility transport, and it retains many of the latter type's well-proven characteristics, including the large cabin cross-section. The same fail-safe concept and design philosophy is employed in the structural components. The cabin, including the toilet and galley compartments, is 3·78 m (12 ft 5 in) longer than that of the Skyvan Srs 3.

Two prototypes and the first production aircraft were used for the development programme. The first prototype (G-BSBH) flew for the first time on 22 August 1974. Eight days earlier, the first order for the 330 was placed by Command Airways of Poughkeepsie, New York, for three aircraft. CAA certification to full Transport Category requirements was granted on 18 February 1976; this was followed on 18 June 1976 by US FAR Pt 25 and Pt 36 approval, and subsequently by approvals from the Canadian Dept of Transport and the West German LBA. The 330 conforms with CAB Pt 298 (US) and meets the noise requirements of FAR Pt 36 by a substantial margin. Initial deliveries began in June 1976; first to enter service, on 24 August 1976, was a Time Air 330.

Firm orders for 43 Shorts 330s had been placed by 1 June 1979, as follows:

Operator	Number
Air North (Vermont)	2
ALM Antillean Airlines (Curaçao)	2
Chautauqua Airlines (New York)	2
Command Airways (New York)	3
DLT (Germany)	7
Golden West Airlines (California)	4
Hawaiian Air	3
Henson Aviation (Maryland)	3
Loganair (Scotland)	2
Metro Airlines (Texas)	5
Mississippi Valley Airlines (Wisconsin)	3
Suburban Airlines (Pennsylvania)	4
Time Air (Canada)	3

Of these, 27 had been delivered. They had carried one million passengers by 9 March 1979.

A military version, the **SD3-M**, has also been proposed. This would be capable of a variety of roles, including the tactical transportation of troops, cargo and vehicles, paratrooping, supply dropping, casualty evacuation and search and rescue, and would be able to carry up to 32 troops or 3,630 kg (8,000 lb) of cargo.

The following description applies to both the 330 and the SD3-M:

Shorts 330 wide-bodied commuter airliner in the insignia of Hawaiian Air Lines

Type: Twin-turboprop transport aircraft.

Wings: Braced high-wing monoplane, of all-metal fail-safe construction, built in three sections. Wing sections NACA 63A series (modified). Thickness/chord ratio 18% at root, 14% on outer panels. Dihedral 3° on outer panels. Centre-section, integral with top of centre-fuselage, has taper on leading- and trailing-edges, and is a two-spar single-cell box structure of light alloy with conventional skin and stringers. The strut-braced outer panels, which are pin-jointed to the centre-section, are reinforced Skyvan constant-chord units, built of light alloy, and each consists of a two-cell box having wing skins made up of a smooth outer skin bonded to a corrugated inner skin. All-metal single-slotted ailerons. Geared trim tabs in ailerons. All-metal single-slotted flaps, each in three sections. Primary control surfaces are rod-actuated.

Fuselage: Light alloy structure, built in two main portions: nose (including flight deck, nosewheel bay and forward baggage compartment); and the centre (including main wing spar attachment frames and lower transverse beams which carry the main landing gear and associated fairings) and rear portion (including aft baggage compartment and tail unit attachment frames). The nose and rear underfuselage are of conventional skin/stringer design. The remainder is composed of a smooth outer skin bonded to a corrugated inner skin and stabilised by frames.

Tail Unit: Cantilever all-metal two-spar structure with twin fins and rudders, basically similar to that of the Skyvan. Fixed-incidence tailplane, with reinforced leading-edge. Full-span elevator, aerodynamically balanced by set-back hinges. Rudders each have an unshielded horn aerodynamic balance. Primary control surfaces are rod-actuated. Geared trim tabs in elevator and starboard rudder (port rudder, trim only).

Landing Gear: Menasco retractable tricycle type, with single wheel on each unit. Main units carried on short sponsons, into which the wheels retract hydraulically. Oleo-pneumatic shock-absorbers. Nosewheel is steerable. Normal tyre pressures: main units 5·38 bars (78 lb/sq in), nose unit 3·79 bars (55 lb/sq in). Special requirements for rough-field operation have been catered for in the design.

Power Plant: Two 862 kW (1,156 shp) (max continuous rating 761 kW; 1,020 shp) Pratt & Whitney Aircraft of Canada PT6A-45A turboprop engines, each driving a Hartzell five-blade low-speed propeller. Fuel in main tanks in wing centre-section/fuselage fairing, total capacity 2,182 litres (480 Imp gallons). Normal cross-feed provisions to allow for pump failure. Provision to increase total fuel capacity for special requirements.

Accommodation (330): Crew of two on flight deck, plus cabin attendant. Dual controls standard. Standard seating for 30 passengers, in ten rows of three at 76 cm (30 in) pitch, with wide aisle. Seat rails fitted to facilitate changes in configuration. Galley, toilet and cabin attendant's seat at rear. Large overhead baggage lockers. Entire accommodation soundproofed and air-conditioned. Baggage compartments in nose (1·27 m³; 45 cu ft) and to rear of cabin (2·83 m³; 100 cu ft), each with external access and capable of holding a combined total of 454 kg (1,000 lb) of baggage. Passenger door is at rear of cabin on port side. Passenger version has two emergency exits on the starboard side, two on the port side (including passenger door) and one in the flight deck roof. Mixed-traffic version has full access to these emergency exits. For mixed passenger/freight operation a partition divides the cabin into a rear passenger area (typically for 18 persons) and a forward cargo compartment, the latter being loaded through a large port-side door, capable of admitting ATA 'D' type containers. In all-cargo configuration the cabin can accommodate up to seven 'D' type containers, with ample space around them for additional freight. Cabin floor is flat throughout its length, and is designed to support loadings of 181 kg (400 lb) per foot run at 610·3 kg/m² (125 lb/sq ft). Locally-reinforced areas of higher strength are also provided. Seat rails can be used as cargo lashing points. Freight loading is facilitated by the low-level cabin floor.

Systems: Hydraulic system of 207 bars (3,000 lb/sq in), supplied by engine-driven pumps, operates landing gear, nosewheel steering, flaps and brakes (at lower pressure) and includes emergency accumulators. Main electrical system, for general services, is 28V DC and is of the split busbar type with cross-coupling for essential services. Lucas 28V 250A DC starter/generator for engine starting and aircraft services, with separate 1·5kW 200V AC output for windscreen anti-icing and demisting. Special AC sources of 115V and 26V available at 400Hz for certain instruments. De-icing/anti-icing system for wing and tail leading-edges; optional inertial anti-icing system for engine intake ducts; electric mat de-icing for inlet lips and propellers. Full air-conditioning system.

Avionics and Equipment: Passenger safety equipment standard. Wide range of radio and navigation equipment available to customer's requirements. Typical standard avionics comprise duplicated VHF communications and navigation systems, two glideslope/markers, two ILS repeaters, two radio magnetic indicators, one ADF, one transponder, one DME, PA system, flight data recorder, voice recorder and weather radar.

Dimensions, external:

Wing span	22·76 m (74 ft 8 in)
Wing chord (standard mean)	1·85 m (6 ft 0·7 in)
Length overall	17·69 m (58 ft 0½ in)
Height overall	4·95 m (16 ft 3 in)
Tailplane span	5·68 m (18 ft 7¾ in)
Wheel track	4·24 m (13 ft 11 in)
Wheelbase	6·15 m (20 ft 2 in)
Propeller diameter	2·82 m (9 ft 3 in)
Propeller ground clearance	1·83 m (6 ft 0 in)
Cabin floor: height above ground	0·94 m (3 ft 1 in)
Passenger door (port, rear):	
Height	1·57 m (5 ft 2 in)
Width	0·71 m (2 ft 4 in)
Forward cargo door (port):	
Height	1·68 m (5 ft 6 in)
Width	1·42 m (4 ft 8 in)

Dimensions, internal:

Cabin: Max length, incl toilet	9·47 m (31 ft 1 in)
Max width	1·98 m (6 ft 6 in)
Max height	1·98 m (6 ft 6 in)
Floor area	18·77 m² (202 sq ft)
Volume (all-cargo)	34·83 m³ (1,230 cu ft)
Baggage compartments volume (total usable)	4·11 m³ (145 cu ft)
Cabin overhead lockers (total)	1·13 m³ (40 cu ft)

Areas:

Wings, gross	42·1 m² (453·0 sq ft)
Ailerons (total, aft of hinges)	2·55 m² (27·5 sq ft)
Trailing-edge flaps (total)	7·74 m² (83·3 sq ft)
Fins (total)	8·65 m² (93·1 sq ft)
Rudders (total, aft of hinges)	2·24 m² (24·1 sq ft)
Tailplane	7·77 m² (83·6 sq ft)
Elevator (total, aft of hinges)	2·54 m² (27·3 sq ft)

Weights and Loadings:

Weight empty, equipped (incl crew of three):	
330 for 30 passengers	6,652 kg (14,665 lb)
Fuel: standard tanks	1,741 kg (3,840 lb)
Max payload for normal max T-O weight:	
30 passengers and baggage	2,653 kg (5,850 lb)
cargo	3,400 kg (7,500 lb)
Max T-O weight	10,160 kg (22,400 lb)
Max landing weight	10,024 kg (22,100 lb)
Max wing loading	241·4 kg/m² (49·45 lb/sq ft)
Max power loading	5·89 kg/kW (9·7 lb/shp)

Performance (at max T-O weight, ISA at S/L, except where indicated):

Max cruising speed at 3,050 m (10,000 ft), AUW of 9,525 kg (21,000 lb)	190 knots (352 km/h; 218 mph)
Econ cruising speed at 3,050 m (10,000 ft), AUW of 9,525 kg (21,000 lb)	160 knots (296 km/h; 184 mph)
Stalling speed, flaps and landing gear up	92 knots (171 km/h; 106 mph)
Stalling speed at max landing weight, flaps and landing gear down	74 knots (137 km/h; 85 mph)
Max rate of climb at S/L	335 m (1,100 ft)/min
Service ceiling, one engine out, AUW of 8,618 kg (19,000 lb)	4,265 m (14,000 ft)
T-O distance (FAR Pt 25 and BCAR Gp A):	
ISA	1,128 m (3,700 ft)
ISA + 15°C	1,310 m (4,300 ft)
Landing distance, AUW of 8,618 kg (19,000 lb):	
BCAR	1,100 m (3,610 ft)
FAR	993 m (3,260 ft)

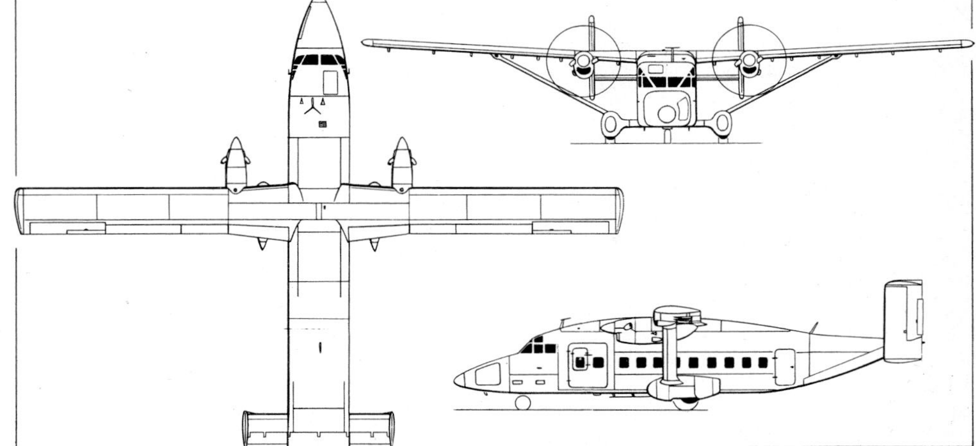

Shorts 330 twin-turboprop commuter and utility transport *(Pilot Press)*

Runway LCN at max T-O weight 10·4
Range with max passenger payload, cruising at 3,050 m (10,000 ft), no reserves:
415 nm (768 km; 477 miles)
Range with max fuel, cruising at 3,050 m (10,000 ft), no reserves:
passenger version, 1,778 kg (3,920 lb) payload
758 nm (1,403 km; 872 miles)
cargo version, 2,118 kg (4,670 lb) payload
758 nm (1,403 km; 872 miles)

Operational Noise Characteristics (FAR Pt 36):

Take-off	88·5 EPNdB
Sideline	83·9 EPNdB
Approach	92·8 EPNdB

SHORTS SD3-MR SEEKER

Shorts have proposed a version of the 330, known as the SD3-MR Seeker, for fishery protection, search and rescue, and various other maritime operations. Performance figures would be basically as for the 330/SD3-M but with greatly enhanced range/endurance capabilities afforded by an internal fuel tank which would virtually double the existing capacity.

Other changes from the standard specification would include blister windows at the forward cabin stations, observers' seats, long-range VLF/Omega navigation, search/weather radar, installation of a data-recording oblique camera, and a crew rest area. Full 360° scan radar, navigator and radar operator stations, flare launch tube and survival equipment stowage and deployment facilities, could readily be installed. The existing 330 galley/toilet and interior soundproofing and trim would be retained to ensure low crew fatigue on long sorties.

Allowing reserves for a 50 nm (92·5 km; 57·5 mile) diversion and 45 min holding, a typical on-station endurance would be 8·5 h at 610 m (2,000 ft) at 200 nm (370 km; 230 miles) from base. This represents a total endurance capability of over 12 h.

SHORTS SC.7 SKYVAN

Design of the SC.7 Skyvan was started as a private venture in 1959, and construction of the first prototype began in 1960. This aircraft (G-ASCN) flew for the first time on 17 January 1963, with two 290 kW (390 hp) Continental GTSIO-520 piston engines, and completed its flight trials by mid-1963. It was then re-engined with 388 kW (520 shp) Astazou II turboprops and first flew in its new form on 2 October 1963.

The following versions of the Skyvan have been built:

Skyvan Srs 1 and Srs 1A. Designation of first prototype, with Continental engines (Srs 1) and later with Astazou IIs (Srs 1A).

Skyvan Srs 2. Three development and 16 initial production aircraft, with Astazou XII turboprop engines. Several subsequently re-engined to Srs 3 standard. Descriptions in 1968-69 and 1970-71 *Jane's*.

Skyvan Srs 3. Current civil version, which superseded Srs 2 in 1968. First Srs 3 to fly was the second development aircraft, G-ASZI, which had been equipped originally with Astazous. The first flight with AiResearch engines was made on 15 December 1967, and a second aircraft (G-ASZJ) re-engined with TPE 331s flew on 20 January 1968. Total of 61 ordered by June 1979, recent customers including Gulf Air and the government of Saudi Arabia.

Skyvan Srs 3A. Introduced in September 1970. Complies with BCAR Passenger Transport Category, in Performance Group A: max T-O weight 6,215 kg (13,700 lb), max landing weight 6,075 kg (13,400 lb). One ordered.

Skyvan Srs 3M. Military version of Srs 3, modified internally to accept optional equipment for typical military missions. Prototype (G-AXPT) flew for the first time in early 1970. Suitable for paratrooping and supply dropping, assault landing, troop transport, casualty evacuation, staff transport, and vehicle or ordnance transport.

A total of 56 had been ordered by March 1979, for armed services including the Argentinian Naval Prefectura (5), Austrian Air Force (2), Botswana Defence Force (2), Ecuador Army Air Force (1), Ghana Air Force (6), Indonesian Air Force (3), Lesotho Police (2), Mauritanian Air Force (2), Royal Nepalese Army (2), No. 2 Squadron of the Sultan of Oman's Air Force (16), Panama National Guard (1), Singapore Air Force (6), Royal Thai Police (3), Yemen Arab Republic Air Force (2), and undisclosed customers (4). Three of the Singapore aircraft are equipped for search and rescue duties. Those of the Indonesian Air Force are equipped to civil standard and operate social services on behalf of the Ministry of the Interior.

Skyliner. Limited-production de luxe all-passenger version of Series 3/3A. Total of nine sold (orders listed in 1976-77 *Jane's*).

Total orders for Series 3/3A/3M Skyvans and Skyliners had reached 127 by June 1979. In February 1970 the Skyvan became the first aircraft to be certificated under the British Air Registration Board's new Civil Airworthiness Requirements for STOL operations.

The following description applies to the standard current civil Srs 3 and military Srs 3M:

Type: Light civil or military STOL utility transport.

Wings: Braced high-wing monoplane. Wing section NACA 63A series (modified). Thickness/chord ratio 14%. Dihedral 2° 2′. Incidence 2° 30′. Light alloy structure consisting of a two-cell box with wing skins made up of a uniform outer sheet bonded to a corrugated inner sheet. All-metal single-slotted ailerons. Geared tabs on port and starboard ailerons, with manual trim on starboard aileron. All-metal single-slotted flaps. Provision for sintered leading-edge de-icing system.

Fuselage: Light alloy structure. Nose and crew cabin section is of conventional skin/stringer design. Elsewhere, the fuselage structure consists of double-skin panels (flat outer sheets bonded to inner corrugated sheets), stabilised by frames.

Tail Unit: Cantilever all-metal two-spar structure, with twin fins and rudders. Fixed-incidence tailplane. Geared trim tabs in outer elevators and rudders. Provision for sintered leading-edge de-icing system.

Landing Gear: Non-retractable tricycle type. Single wheel on each unit. Steerable nosewheel. Main units carried on short sponsons. Electro-Hydraulics oleo-pneumatic shock-absorbers. Main-wheel tyres size 11·00-12, nosewheel tyre size 7·50-10. Tyre pressure (all units) 2·76 bars (40 lb/sq in). Hydraulically-operated disc brakes, with differential braking for steering. Low-pressure tyres available optionally.

Power Plant: Two 533 kW (715 shp) Garrett-AiResearch TPE 331-201 turboprop engines, each driving a Hartzell HC-B3TN-5/T10282H three-blade (optionally four-blade) variable-pitch propeller. Fuel in four tanks in pairs on top of fuselage between wing roots, each pair consisting of one tank of 182 litres (40 Imp gallons) capacity and one of 484 litres (106·5 Imp gallons) capacity. Total fuel capacity of 1,332 litres (293 Imp gallons). Provision for increase in total fuel capacity to 1,773 litres (390 Imp gallons) by installing four specially-designed tanks in spaces between fuselage frames on each side, beneath main fuel tank. Oil capacity 7·73 litres (1·7 Imp gallons).

Accommodation: Crew of one, with provision for two. Accommodation (Srs 3) for up to 19 passengers, or 12 stretcher patients and attendants, or 2,085 kg (4,600 lb) of freight, vehicles or agricultural equipment. Srs 3M can accommodate 22 equipped troops; 16 paratroops and a dispatcher; 12 stretcher cases and two medical attendants, or 2,358 kg (5,200 lb) of freight. It carries its own lightweight vehicle loading ramps and has a one-piece door which leaves the fuselage threshold entirely clear of appendages. Executive version provides luxury accommodation and equipment for nine passengers. Full-width rear loading door, and forward door on each side of crew compartment. Rear door can be opened in flight to permit the parachuting of loads up to 1·37 m (4 ft 6 in) in height. Cockpit and cabin heated by engine bleed air mixed with fresh air from intake in nose. Cabin unpressurised. Some aircraft fitted with Rolamat cargo loading equipment.

Systems: Hydraulic system, pressure 172 bars (2,500 lb/sq in), operates flaps, wheel brakes and nosewheel steering. No pneumatic system. Electrical system utilises two busbars, operating independently, each connected to a 28V 125A DC starter/generator, a battery and a 115V 400Hz static inverter. General services are 28V DC; some radio and instruments 115V AC.

Avionics and Equipment: Radio optional. Typical installation for operations in Europe and USA consists of duplicated VHF, duplicated VOR/ILS, marker beacon and ADF. Provision for HF, DME, transponder, Bendix M4D autopilot and weather radar. Blind-flying instrumentation standard.

Equipment (Srs 3M): Port-side blister window for an air dispatcher; two anchor cables for parachute static lines; a guard rail beneath the tail to prevent control surface fouling by the static lines; inward-facing paratroop seats with safety nets; parachute signal light; mounts for NATO-type stretchers; and roller conveyors for easy loading and paradropping of pallet-mounted supplies.

Dimensions, external:

Wing span	19·79 m (64 ft 11 in)
Wing chord (constant)	1·78 m (5 ft 10 in)
Wing aspect ratio	11
Length overall: without radome	12·21 m (40 ft 1 in)
with radome	12·60 m (41 ft 4 in)
Height overall	4·60 m (15 ft 1 in)
Tailplane span	5·28 m (17 ft 4 in)
Wheel track	4·21 m (13 ft 10 in)
Wheelbase	4·52 m (14 ft 10 in)
*Propeller diameter	2·59 m (8 ft 6 in)
Propeller ground clearance	1·52 m (5 ft 0 in)
Crew and passenger doors (fwd, port and stbd):	
Height	1·52 m (5 ft 0 in)
Width	0·51 m (1 ft 8 in)
Height to sill	1·14 m (3 ft 9 in)
Rear loading door: Height	1·98 m (6 ft 6 in)
Width	1·96 m (6 ft 5 in)
Height to sill	0·74 m (2 ft 5 in)

**Optional four-blade propellers of 2·51 m (8 ft 3 in) diameter*

Dimensions, internal:

Cabin, excl flight deck: Length	5·67 m (18 ft 7 in)
Max width	1·98 m (6 ft 6 in)
Max height	1·98 m (6 ft 6 in)
Floor area	11·15 m² (120 sq ft)
Volume	22·09 m³ (780 cu ft)

Areas:

Wings, gross	34·65 m² (373 sq ft)
Ailerons (total)	3·00 m² (32·3 sq ft)
Trailing-edge flaps (total)	5·86 m² (63·1 sq ft)
Fins	7·62 m² (82·0 sq ft)
Rudders, incl tabs	2·41 m² (25·9 sq ft)
Tailplane	7·53 m² (81·0 sq ft)
Elevators, incl tabs	3·62 m² (39·0 sq ft)

Shorts Skyvan Srs 3 twin-turboprop transport aircraft in the insignia of Gulf Air

WEIGHTS AND LOADINGS (with 1,332 litres; 293 Imp gallons of fuel):
Basic operating weight: 3 — 3,331 kg (7,344 lb)
3M — 3,356 kg (7,400 lb)
Typical operating weight as freighter:
3 — 3,447 kg (7,600 lb)
3M — 3,456 kg (7,620 lb)
Typical operating weight with passengers or troops:
3 — 3,674 kg (8,100 lb)
3M — 3,778 kg (8,330 lb)
Max payload for normal T-O weight:
3 — 2,086 kg (4,600 lb)
3M — 2,358 kg (5,200 lb)
Max payload for overload T-O weight:
3M — 2,721 kg (6,000 lb)
Max T-O weight: 3, normal — 5,670 kg (12,500 lb)
3M, normal — 6,214 kg (13,700 lb)
3M, overload — 6,577 kg (14,500 lb)
Max landing weight: 3 — 5,670 kg (12,500 lb)
3M — 6,123 kg (13,500 lb)
Max wing loading: 3 — 163·6 kg/m² (33·5 lb/sq ft)
3M — 179·1 kg/m² (36·7 lb/sq ft)
Max power loading: 3 — 5·32 kg/kW (8·74 lb/shp)
3M — 6·17 kg/kW (9·58 lb/shp)

PERFORMANCE (at max T-O weight, with 1,332 litres; 293 Imp gallons of fuel):
Never-exceed speed — 217 knots (402 km/h; 250 mph) EAS
Max cruising speed at 3,050 m (10,000 ft):
max continuous power — 176 knots (327 km/h; 203 mph)
cruise power — 169 knots (314 km/h; 195 mph)
Econ cruising speed at 3,050 m (10,000 ft) — 150 knots (278 km/h; 173 mph)
Stalling speed, flaps down:
3 — 60 knots (111 km/h; 69 mph) EAS
3M — 62 knots (115 km/h; 71 mph) EAS
Max rate of climb at S/L: 3 — 500 m (1,640 ft)/min
3M — 466 m (1,530 ft)/min
Service ceiling (30 m; 100 ft/min climb):
3 — 6,858 m (22,500 ft)
3M — 6,705 m (22,000 ft)
Service ceiling, one engine out (15 m; 50 ft/min climb):
3 — 3,810 m (12,500 ft)
3M — 2,895 m (9,500 ft)
Min ground turning radius — 3·76 m (12 ft 4 in)
Runway LCN at AUW of 5,670 kg (12,500 lb):
standard tyres — 3·5
low-pressure tyres — 3·0
T-O run, STOL, unfactored: 3 — 213 m (700 ft)
3M — 238 m (780 ft)
T-O run (normal): 3 (BCAR) — 512 m (1,680 ft)
T-O to 10·7 m (35 ft), Transport Group A, ISA at S/L — 1,020 m (3,350 ft)
T-O to 15 m (50 ft), STOL, unfactored:
3 — 320 m (1,050 ft)
3M — 384 m (1,260 ft)
T-O to 15 m (50 ft):
3 (BCAR, normal) — 610 m (2,000 ft)
3 (BCAR, STOL) — 482 m (1,580 ft)
3 (FAR Pt 23) — 488 m (1,600 ft)
Landing from 15 m (50 ft):
3 (BCAR, normal) — 622 m (2,040 ft)
3 (BCAR, STOL) — 567 m (1,860 ft)
3 (FAR Pt 23) — 451 m (1,480 ft)
3M (STOL, unfactored) — 425 m (1,395 ft)
Landing from 15 m (50 ft), Transport Group A, ISA at S/L — 1,010 m (3,320 ft)
Landing from 9 m (30 ft):
3 (STOL, unfactored) — 351 m (1,150 ft)
3 (BCAR, STOL) — 500 m (1,640 ft)
Landing run: 3M (STOL, unfactored) 212 m (695 ft)
Range at long-range cruising speed, 45 min reserves:
3 — 600 nm (1,115 km; 694 miles)
3M — 580 nm (1,075 km; 670 miles)
Range (typical freighter) at long-range cruising speed, 45 min reserves:
3 with 1,814 kg (4,000 lb) payload — 162 nm (300 km; 187 miles)
3M with 2,268 kg (5,000 lb) payload — 208 nm (386 km; 240 miles)

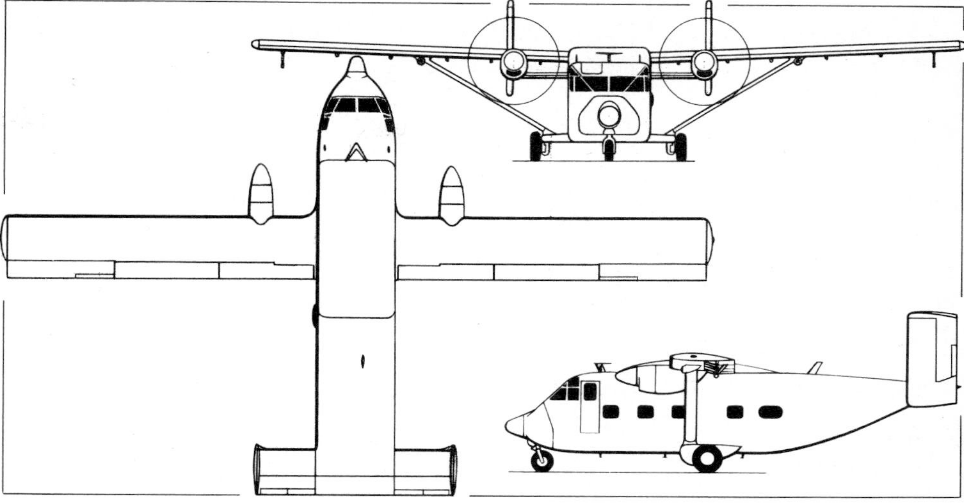

Shorts Skyvan transport aircraft with nose radome *(Pilot Press)*

WALLIS

WALLIS AUTOGYROS LTD

HEAD OFFICE: Reymerston Hall, Norfolk NR9 4QY
Telephone: 036 285 418
DIRECTORS:
Wg Cdr K. H. Wallis, CEng, FRAeS, FRSA, RAF (Retd)
P. M. Wallis

The Wallis prototype single-seat ultralight autogyro (G-ARRT, flown for the first time in August 1961) introduced many patented features, including a rotor head with offset gimbal system to provide hands and feet off stability and to eliminate pitch-up and 'tuck-under' hazards; a high-speed flexible rotor spin-up shaft with positive disengagement during flight; an automatic system of controlling rotor drive on take-off which allows power to be applied until the last moment; centrifugal stops to control rotor blade teetering; and a novel safe starting arrangement.

All Wallis autogyros are built for special purposes, and are not on public sale. Suffixes indicate the type of engine fitted.

WALLIS WA-116 and WA-116-T

The WA-116 represents the original Wallis design, of which the prototype (G-ARRT) flew for the first time on 2 August 1961, powered by a 54 kW (72 hp) modified McCulloch 4318 piston engine. Four more WA-116s were built by Beagle and five by Wg Cdr Wallis, as described in the 1973-74 *Jane's*. The last of these was later dismantled for construction of G-AXAS, a tandem two-seat version (WA-116-T) flown for the first time on 3 April 1969.

The WA-116 currently holds the height record for autogyros in Classes E3 and E3a, at 4,639 m (15,220 ft), set on 11 May 1968 by the prototype with its original 54 kW (72 hp) McCulloch engine; and the Class E3 and E3a records for speed in a straight line (96·589 knots; 179·000 km/h; 111·225 mph), set on 12 May 1969 by the same aircraft re-engined with a 67 kW (90 hp) McCulloch.

The WA-116 has remained potentially one of the most promising of the Wallis autogyro designs, particularly following the refitting of G-ASDY in 1971 with a 44 kW (60 hp) Franklin 2A-120-A engine. It is currently fitted with a Franklin 2A-120-B engine, and has been brought up to 'working WA-116/F' standard.

The WA-116/F has undergone progressive refinements which included, on the latest Franklin conversions, experiments with two different four-blade propellers. These propellers have since been replaced by specially-designed two-blade types.

A particularly successful conversion to WA-116/F was that of the WA-116/Mc G-ATHM. This underwent more extensive conversion than its predecessors, mainly to increase fuel capacity and pilot comfort to fit it for special long-range flights. It has a 50 litre (11 Imp gallon) internal fuel tank, and began test flying, for range, in April 1974. Fitted also with a 36 litre (8 Imp gallon) jettisonable long-range ventral tank, it set up on 13 July 1974 new Class E3 and E3a world records, for nonstop distance in a closed circuit, of 361·91 nm (670·26 km; 416·48 miles). Additionally, this flight set new 100 km (Class E3a only) and 500 km (Class E3 and E3a) closed-circuit speed records of 70·51 knots (130·67 km/h; 81·19 mph) and 68·07 knots (126·14 km/h; 78·38 mph) respectively. A 91 litre (20 Imp gallon) ventral tank was next fitted, and on 28 September 1975, with this tank containing some 70 litres (15·5 Imp gallons), Wg Cdr Wallis made a nonstop flight from Lydd, Kent, to Wick, Caithness. This flight set Class E3 and E3a records for nonstop distance in a straight line of 472·092 nm (874·315 km; 543·274 miles). In fact, the actual distance flown, to avoid airfield zones and other hazardous areas, was in the order of 521 nm (966 km; 600 miles), flown in 6 h 25 min at an average speed of approx 81 knots (150 km/h; 93 mph). The ventral tank was not jettisoned after being emptied, and the WA-116/F landed with sufficient fuel remaining for a further 65 nm (121 km; 75 miles). Its time of 6 h 25 min was later confirmed by the FAI as a record for duration in both Class E3 and Class E3a. Thus, WA-116s now hold all the major autogyro world records for speed, height, range and endurance.

Wg Cdr Wallis reports that G-ATHM could now improve very substantially on its 1974 performance. Recent minor modifications include duplicated mechanical main fuel pumps, in addition to the long-range tank fuel pumping system. The aircraft has been adapted to carry ciné cameras, and has been operated on air-to-ground filming for television.

The McCulloch-engined WA-116-T/Mc, G-AXAS, remains the lightest two-seater in the Wallis range. As a result, it is expected to improve even further upon the 3·14 : 1 ratio of all-up weight to empty weight, established at RAE Bedford in 1971. It has made more than 130 flights in a programme of multi-spectral experiments by Plessey Radar on behalf of the Home Office. The programme, intended to evaluate this method of detecting illicit graves (eg of murder victims) from the air, entails taking detailed photographs from about 30 m (100 ft) directly above the suspected sites. Most WA-116s have been converted to accept the Plessey Radar multi-band remote sensing equipment, to provide flexibility in operations for the police, water resources survey and other agencies. The WA-116-T/Mc has undergone minor refinement of the control system and the rotor spin-up drive system.

DIMENSIONS (WA-116/F):
Rotor diameter — 6·20 m (20 ft 4 in)
Length of fuselage — 3·38 m (11 ft 1 in)
Height to top of rotor head — 1·85 m (6 ft 1 in)
Wheel track — 1·63 m (5 ft 4 in)
Wheelbase — 1·07 m (3 ft 6 in)

Wg Cdr Wallis demonstrating the 'hands and feet off' stability of the WA-116-T/Mc at a pre-selected and trimmed airspeed

Left: Wg Cdr Wallis in the WA-116/F, holder of seven world speed and distance records for autogyros, set in 1974-75; right, the WA-117/R-R with Rolls-Royce Continental engine and Type 751 Vinten panoramic camera installation

WEIGHTS (WA-116/F):
Weight empty 143 kg (316 lb)
Max T-O weight 317·5 kg (700 lb)
PERFORMANCE (WA-116/F):
Max level speed not fully explored
Cruising speed without long-range tank 87 knots (161 km/h; 100 mph)
Max rate of climb at S/L 305 m (1,000 ft)/min
Max range with long-range tank (estimated) 651 nm (1,207 km; 750 miles)

WALLIS WA-117/R-R

Started in 1964, the WA-117 was intended to combine proven features of the WA-116 airframe with a fully-certificated engine, the 74 kW (100 hp) Rolls-Royce Continental O-200-B. An experimental test vehicle (G-ATCV) flew for the first time on 24 March 1965; this was later dismantled for the construction of a true WA-117 prototype (G-AVJV), which made its first flight on 28 May 1967. This aircraft took part in the Loch Ness investigations in 1970, and was evaluated as a carrying vehicle for HSD Linescan 212 infra-red sensor equipment. More recently, fitted with an HSD Type 213 Linescan and a photographic pack containing an electric-drive 70 mm wide-angle camera, it has been operating in experimental detection of leaks in main water pipelines buried 2·45 m (8 ft) underground. It has also been fitted with a Vinten Type 751 panoramic camera, with which excellent results have been obtained. With its special silencers and special four-blade 'quiet' propeller, G-AVJV is one of the quietest powered aircraft of any kind yet built. A third WA-117 (G-AXAR) was lost in 1970.

WEIGHT:
Max T-O weight approx 317·5 kg (700 lb)
PERFORMANCE:
Max level speed 104 knots (193 km/h; 120 mph)
Cruising speed 78 knots (145 km/h; 90 mph)
Max rate of climb approx 305 m (1,000 ft)/min

WALLIS WA-118/M METEORITE

Design of the WA-118 Meteorite (G-ATPW) was started in April 1965 and it flew for the first time on 6 May 1966. The 89 kW (120 hp) supercharged Italian Meteor Alfa 1 engine was brought up to then-current standards during 1969-70.

The aircraft, intended for speeds of up to 174 knots (322 km/h; 200 mph), was also fitted with a bubble canopy, reclining cockpit and other modifications and was rebuilt as G-AVJW, making its first flight in this form on 9 August 1969. Intended for a long-term test programme, it has been completely redesigned and rebuilt to bring it into line with the latest features of the Wallis range. The eventual objective of this programme is to achieve altitudes in excess of 9,145 m (30,000 ft). The aircraft is being fitted with a partially stress-bearing cockpit nacelle of glassfibre-reinforced plastics. Capable of being used as an open cockpit or, in inclement weather, of accepting an optional hardtop (not yet tested), this nacelle is being used as a prototype for a planned Franklin-powered autogyro of even better performance than the WA-116/F G-ATHM. The objective is to provide more space and comfort for the pilot, without sacrificing performance, and the cockpit will permit the internal stowage of oxygen equipment and an approved recording barograph.

WALLIS WA-120/R-R

Construction of the WA-120 began in early 1970, under the original designation WA-117-S. It subsequently developed into more than a re-engined version of the WA-117, so justifying the use of a new designation.

The WA-120 (G-AYVO) is powered by a 97 kW (130 hp) Rolls-Royce Continental O-240-A flat-four engine and cruises at a fuel consumption of 15·9 litres (3·5 Imp gallons)/h. It flew for the first time on 13 June 1971; the original horizontal tail surface was removed after tests in varying climatic conditions.

The WA-120 has a forward-sliding transparent cockpit canopy, and can be flown at speeds of up to 60 knots (111 km/h; 69 mph) with this canopy partly open.

During 1977 the WA-120/R-R was loaned to the Science Museum in London, where for approx three years it is forming part of an exhibition on the theme of 'Exploration', fitted with four Vinten 70 mm reconnaissance cameras in a multi-band pack.

WALLIS WA-121

The WA-121, currently in the flight development stage, is the smallest and lightest Wallis autogyro to date. At present, three versions are envisaged: a high-speed version **(WA-121/Mc)** with a Wallis-McCulloch engine of about 74 kW (100 hp); a cross-country version **(WA-121/F)** with a 44·5 kW (60 hp) Franklin 2A-120-B engine; and a high-altitude version **(WA-121/M Meteorite 2)** with a supercharged 89 kW (120 hp) Meteor Alfa 1 radial two-stroke engine and transistorised ignition.

The prototype (G-BAHH) has a high-mounted tailplane and an open cockpit, and made its first flight on 28 December 1972. With the McCulloch engine, it has already exceeded unofficially the speed and altitude records set up by the WA-116 prototype G-ARRT. It employs a number of improvements in control system design, resulting in greater stability at speed, better head resistance and greater pilot comfort. Special features in the rotor head suspension, originally incorporated in the WA-117 prototype G-AVJV, are incorporated also in the WA-120 and WA-121. Now fitted with a wider-track main landing gear, to standardise it with other autogyros in the Wallis range, the WA-121 was to have been used for high-speed experimental flying in 1978.

Wallis WA-120/R-R, on display at the Science Museum, London *(Science Museum)*

The next version to be built will probably be the WA-121/F, but this is currently awaiting the completion of other projects and the evaluation of further experience to be gained with the WA-116/F.

The McCulloch-engined WA-121 high-speed autogyro

WESTLAND

WESTLAND AIRCRAFT LTD

HEAD OFFICE, WORKS AND AIRFIELD: Yeovil, Somerset BA20 2YB
LONDON OFFICE: 8 The Sanctuary, Westminster, London SW1P 3JU
CHAIRMAN: The Rt Hon Lord Aldington, PC, KCMG, CBE, DSO
VICE-CHAIRMAN AND CHIEF EXECUTIVE: B. D. Blackwell, MA, BSc(Eng), FEng, FIMechE, FRAeS, FBIM
VICE-CHAIRMAN: Walter Oppenheimer, FCA
DIRECTORS:
The Rt Hon Lord Aberconway
Sir David Collins, CBE, DSc, FEng
Sir Christopher Hartley, KCB, CBE, DFC, AFC, BA
Sir Ronald Melville, KCB
Sir Eric Mensforth, CBE, DSc, FEng
W. T. C. Miller, OBE, MA, CEng, MIMechE, MInstM
J. Speechley, OBE, MSc, FEng, FRAeS
Sir John Treacher, KCB, FRAeS
S. W. Wiltshire
SECRETARY: J. R. Bayley, LLB
PUBLIC RELATIONS EXECUTIVE: John Teague, CEng, MRAeS, MIM

Westland Aircraft Ltd was formed in July 1935, to take over the aircraft branch of Petters Ltd, previously known as the Westland Aircraft Works, which had been engaged in aircraft design and construction since 1915.

Westland entered the helicopter industry in 1947 by acquiring the licence to build the Sikorsky S-51, of which it produced 133 under the name Westland Dragonfly. This technical association with Sikorsky has continued, and it was decided subsequently to concentrate on the design, development and construction of helicopters.

In 1959, Westland acquired Saunders-Roe Ltd. In 1960 it acquired the Helicopter Division of Bristol Aircraft Ltd and Fairey Aviation Ltd, and is now the only major helicopter design and manufacturing organisation in the United Kingdom.

Since 1 October 1966, the company's helicopter business has been conducted through a wholly-owned company named Westland Helicopters Ltd.

Through the British Hovercraft Corporation Ltd, Westland is continuing development of the Hovercraft type of vehicle pioneered by Saunders-Roe.

One of Westland's subsidiary companies, Normalair-Garrett Ltd, specialises in the design, development and production of aircraft pressure control, air-conditioning, oxygen breathing and hydraulic systems. Most British pressurised aircraft, civil and military, use Normalair-Garrett equipment, as do the Panavia Tornado and many aircraft of foreign design. In addition, this company produces data loggers, trace readers and hydraulic equipment for aircraft flying controls.

WESTLAND HELICOPTERS LTD

HEAD OFFICE, WORKS AND AIRFIELD: Yeovil, Somerset BA20 2YB

Telephone: Yeovil (0935) 5222

Telex: 46277

CHAIRMAN: B. D. Blackwell, MA, BSc(Eng), FEng, FIMechE, FRAeS, FBIM

MANAGING DIRECTOR: J. Speechley, OBE, MSc, FEng, FRAeS

ACCOUNTING DIRECTOR AND SECRETARY: A. R. B. Hobbs, FCCA

FINANCE DIRECTOR: Malcolm Jones, BSc(Econ), FCMA, MBIM

DIRECTOR OF ADVANCED ENGINEERING: J. P. Jones, PhD, BSc(Eng), CEng, FRAeS

COMMERCIAL DIRECTOR: A. V. N. Reed, BSc(Tech), CEng, FRAeS, AMBIM

SALES AND PRODUCT SUPPORT DIRECTOR: A. M. Cundick, BSc(Eng), CEng, FRAeS, MBIM

WORKS DIRECTOR: J. W. Bower, CEng, MIMechE, MBIM

TECHNICAL DIRECTOR: V. A. B. Rogers, MSc, CEng, FRAeS, FIMechE

Helicopters in current production at the Yeovil headquarters of Westland Helicopters are the Sea King, Commando, Gazelle and Lynx. The Gazelle and Lynx, together with the Puma, form part of the Anglo-French helicopter co-operation programme.

Gazelles are in production for the British and French armed forces. Production of the Lynx began in 1975, and Westland is actively involved with production of component sets for Pumas built by Aérospatiale.

WESTLAND WG 34

This new large helicopter is being developed under Ministry of Defence (Navy) contract, initially as a replacement for the Royal Navy's Sea King HAS. Mk 2 shipboard anti-submarine helicopters.

In the Spring of 1977 the MoD(N) completed a series of feasibility studies to examine how an SKR (Sea King Replacement) would operate, and what sensors and performance standards it would require. These studies demonstrated:

(a) the need for the aircraft to operate at long ranges from its base, and independently of other units;

(b) that this autonomy of operation would best be served by the use of sonobuoys instead of the traditional active dipping sonar;

(c) the need for an automated data handling system to exploit the capability of the acoustic sensors, and to control the variety of supporting sensors required (radar, radar intercept equipment, and magnetic anomaly detector);

(d) that a payload capability greater than that of the present Sea King was needed to carry the required weight of sensors, avionics, weapons, and the fuel load necessary to achieve a useful endurance; and

(e) that a rotating-wing aircraft of similar dimensions to the Sea King would best meet these requirements while remaining compatible with the size of ships which would carry the new aircraft.

The WG 34, which is marginally smaller than the Sea King but has substantially more payload capability, was selected for development in the late Summer of 1978, and precise airframe, systems, and avionics specifications are currently being defined. It is intended that the WG 34 will be developed and built by Westland in collaboration with Aérospatiale (France) and Agusta (Italy). The Italian Navy has a requirement broadly similar to that of the Royal Navy, and a number of European armies are seeking a troop transport of similar size and weight to the WG 34. Negotiations towards a collaborative solution were in progress in early 1979; civil applications are also foreseen.

The following provisional description of the SKR version of the WG 34 is based on details released up to mid-1979:

TYPE: Three/four-seat anti-submarine helicopter.

AIRFRAME: For general appearance, see accompanying illustration. Landing gear is fully retractable, main units retracting into fairings on fuselage sides.

POWER PLANT: Probably three (or two) turboshaft engines of an existing type. Engine intakes face sideways, to assist anti-icing.

ACCOMMODATION: Crew of three normally (pilot, observer, and acoustics systems operator); provision for co-pilot if required.

SYSTEMS AND OPERATIONAL EQUIPMENT: Marconi Avionics acoustics processing and display systems, developed from the AQS-901 system now being fitted to the BAe Nimrod MR. Mk 2. Ferranti search radar, developed from the Sea Spray currently fitted in the Royal Navy's Lynx HAS. Mk 2. Decca ESM (electronic support measures) equipment, also developed from that in the Lynx HAS. Mk 2. Decca Doppler or Omega navigation system. ECM-resistant Joint Tactical Information Distribution System (JTIDS) data link equipment. Magnetic anomaly detector (MAD) of the towed 'bird' type, probably the US ASQ-81, stowed internally in rear fuselage when not in use. Secure voice communications. Ferranti automated tactical data handling system for effective management of sensors. Airframe anti-icing system.

Artist's impression of Westland WG 34 Sea King replacement

ARMAMENT: Fully enclosed weapons bay, capable of accommodating a homing torpedo or other weapons, in forward portion of each fuselage main landing gear fairing. No details of individual weapons yet available.

DIMENSIONS:

Diameter of main rotor	16·92 m (55 ft 6 in)
Length overall, rotors turning	20·57 m (67 ft 6 in)
Length of fuselage	17·30 m (56 ft 9 in)
Height overall, rotors turning	5·44 m (17 ft 10 in)
Height to top of main rotor head	4·11 m (13 ft 6 in)
Tailplane span	5·03 m (16 ft 6 in)
Wheel track (c/l of main units)	3·05 m (10 ft 0 in)

WEIGHT:

Max T-O weight	approx 10,886 kg (24,000 lb)

WESTLAND SEA KING

The Sea King was developed originally by Westland to meet the Royal Navy's requirement for an advanced anti-submarine helicopter with prolonged endurance. It can also undertake secondary roles, such as search and rescue, tactical troop transport, casualty evacuation, cargo carrying and long-range self-ferry. A land-based general-purpose version, the Commando, is described separately.

The Sea King development programme stemmed from a licence agreement for the S-61 helicopter concluded originally with Sikorsky in 1959. This permitted Westland to utilise the basic airframe and rotor system of the Sikorsky SH-3D, of which a description can be found in the US section. Considerable changes were made in the power plant and in specialised equipment, to meet British requirements.

The fuselage is essentially similar to that of the basic Sikorsky aircraft, with a watertight hull which allows water landing in an emergency. The retractable main landing gear is housed in sponsons braced to the fuselage by fixed struts. To improve the lateral stability and flotation capability of the helicopter with the rotor stopped, inflatable buoyancy bags are fitted to the outside of each sponson.

The following versions of the Sea King had been announced up to mid-1979:

Sea King HAS. Mk 1. ASW version for Royal Navy, ordered in 1967. First production HAS. Mk 1 (XV642) flown for the first time on 7 May 1969. Total of 56 built, delivery of which was completed in May 1972. In service with Nos. 814, 819, 820, 824 and 826 Squadrons. Described in previous editions of *Jane's*. Currently being uprated by Royal Navy to Mk 2 standard.

Sea King HAS. Mk 2. Uprated version for ASW and SAR duties with the Royal Navy. Twenty-one ordered; first flown (XZ570) on 18 June 1976. Equipment includes Marconi Avionics LAPADS (Lightweight Acoustic Processing And Display System) passive sonobuoy processor to improve detection capability. To be upgraded to Mk 5 standard with MEL improved radar and other modifications.

Sea King HAR. Mk 3. Uprated version for SAR duties with the Royal Air Force. Sixteen ordered, to equip No. 202 Squadron at Lossiemouth, Scotland. First HAR. Mk 3 flew on 6 September 1977, and deliveries began in August 1978. Fifteen delivered by early 1979.

Sea King HC. Mk 4. Utility version of Commando Mk 2 (which see) for Royal Navy.

Sea King Mk 41. Search and rescue version for Federal German Navy. First example (89 + 50) flown for the first

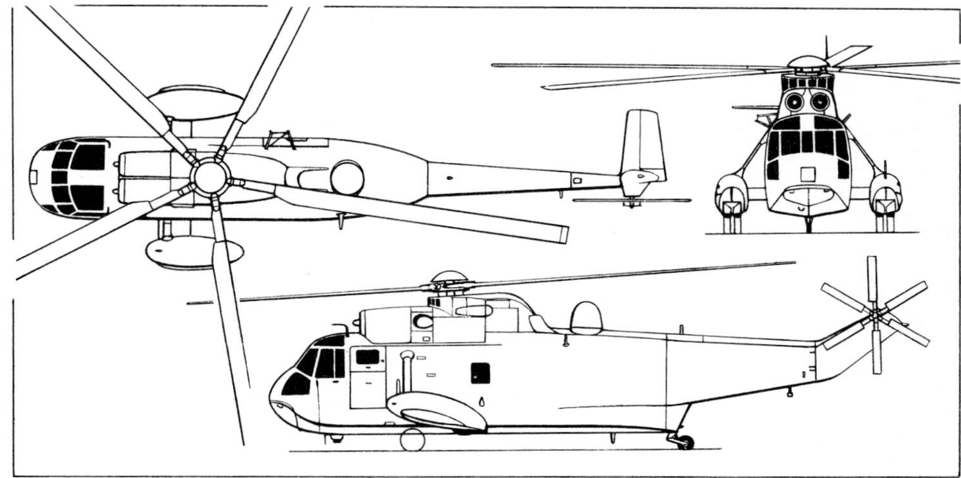
Westland Sea King HAS.Mk 2 anti-submarine helicopter *(Pilot Press)*

Westland Sea King HAR. Mk 3 search and rescue helicopter of the Royal Air Force

time on 6 March 1972. Twenty-two ordered, of which production and delivery were completed in 1974. First unit to equip with these aircraft was MFG.5, based at Kiel-Holtenau.

Sea King Mk 42. ASW version for Indian Navy. Original order for six, which are in service with No. 330 Squadron. Delivery of a further six was completed in 1974, and these are in service with Nos. 330 and 336 Squadrons. Follow-on order announced in June 1977 for three uprated aircraft, designated **Mk 42A**, with hauldown capability for small-ship operation.

Sea King Mk 43. SAR version for Norwegian Air Force. Ten ordered initially, all of which were delivered in 1972. In service with No. 330 Squadron at Bodo. Follow-on order in June 1977 for additional aircraft to uprated standard.

Sea King Mk 45. ASW version for Pakistan Navy. Six ordered, delivery of which was completed during 1975.

Sea King Mk 47. ASW version. Six ordered by Saudi Arabia on behalf of Egyptian Navy.

Sea King Mk 48. SAR version for Belgian Air Force. Five ordered, including one aircraft with VIP interior capability. Delivery completed in November 1976. In service with No. 40 Squadron at Coxyde.

Sea King Mk 50. Version, developed from Mk 1, for No. 817 Squadron of the Royal Australian Navy, which ordered 10. First flight 30 June 1974. Production included offset manufacture in Australia to 30% of the contract value. Deliveries began in the Autumn of 1974. The Mk 50 was the first fully-uprated version of the Sea King to fly. It is capable of operation in the roles of anti-submarine search and strike, vertical replenishment, tactical troop lift, search and rescue, casualty evacuation, and self-ferry.

A total of 233 Sea King and Commando aircraft had been ordered by mid-1979.

A description of the Sea King Mk 1, which is applicable also to most export versions except the Mks 47, 48 and 50, has appeared in previous editions of *Jane's*. Current production Sea Kings (Mk 2/3 standard) have uprated Gnome engines and transmission, a six-blade tail rotor, increased max T-O weight and other detail improvements; the following description applies to the current version. Most of the improvements are incorporated also in the Mk 50s built for Australia, and in certain other export versions.

Power Plant (all current versions): Two 1,238 kW (1,660 shp) (max contingency rating) Rolls-Royce Gnome H.1400-1 turboshaft engines, mounted side by side above cabin. Transmission rating 2,012 kW (2,700 shp). Fuel in underfloor bag tanks, total capacity (SAR versions) 3,636 litres (800 Imp gallons). Internal auxiliary tank may be fitted for long-range ferry purposes. Pressure refuelling point on starboard side, two gravity points on port side.

Accommodation: Crew of four in ASW role; accommodation for up to 22 survivors in SAR role. Two-section airstair door at front on port side, cargo door at rear on starboard side. Entire accommodation heated and ventilated. Cockpit doors and windows, and two windows each side of cabin, can be jettisoned in an emergency.

Systems: Three main hydraulic systems. Primary and auxiliary systems operate main rotor control. Utility system (207 bars; 3,000 lb/sq in) for main landing gear, sonar and rescue winches and blade folding. Pressure for windscreen wipers 86 bars (1,250 lb/sq in). Electrical system includes two 20kVA 200V three-phase 400Hz engine-driven generators, a 26V single-phase AC supply fed from the aircraft's 22Ah nickel-cadmium battery through an inverter, and DC power provided as a secondary system from two 200A transformer-rectifier units.

Operational Equipment (ASW models): As equipped for this role, the Sea King is a fully-integrated all-weather hunter-killer weapon system, capable of operating independently of surface vessels, and has the following equipment and weapons to achieve this task: Plessey Type 195 dipping sonar, Bendix AN/AQS-13B dipping sonar (Mk 50), Marconi AD 580 Doppler navigation system, AW 391 search radar in dorsal radome, transponder beneath rear fuselage, Honeywell AN/APN-171 radio altimeter, Sperry GM7B Gyrosyn compass system, Louis Newmark Mk 31 automatic flight control system, two No. 4 marine markers, four No. 2 Mk 2 smoke floats, Ultra Electronics mini-sonobuoys, up to four Mk 46 homing torpedoes, or four Mk 11 depth charges or one Clevite simulator. Observer/navigator has tactical display on which sonar contacts are integrated with search radar and navigational information. Radio equipment comprises Plessey PTR 377 UHF/VHF and homer, Ultra D 403M standby UHF, Collins 618-T3 HF radio, Ultra UA 60M intercom, Telebrief system and IFF provisions. For secondary role a mounting is provided on the aft frame of the starboard door for a general-purpose machine-gun. The Mk 31 AFCS provides radio altitude displays for both pilots; artificial horizon displays; three-axis stabilisation in pilot-controlled manoeuvres; attitude hold, heading hold and height hold in cruising flight; controlled transition manoeuvres to and from the hover; automatic height control and plan position control in the hover; and an auxiliary trim facility.

Operational Equipment (non-ASW models): A wide range of radio and navigation equipment may be installed, including VHF/UHF communications, VHF/UHF homing, radio compass, Doppler navigation system, radio altimeter, VOR/ILS, radar and transponder, of Collins, Plessey, Honeywell and Marconi manufacture. A Sperry compass system and a Louis Newmark automatic flight control system are also installed. Sea Kings equipped for search and rescue have in addition a Breeze BL 10300 variable-speed hydraulic rescue hoist of 272 kg (600 lb) capacity mounted above the starboard-side cargo door. Automatic main rotor blade folding and spreading is standard with this version, and for shipboard operation the tail pylon can also be folded. With search radar fitted, a total of 18 survivors and medical staff can be carried; this total can be increased to 22 if the search radar is omitted . In the casualty evacuation role, the Sea King can accommodate up to 9 stretchers and two medical attendants, or intermediate combinations of seats and stretchers; a typical layout might provide for 14 seats and two stretchers. In the troop transport role, the Sea King can accommodate 22 troops, with the majority of seats at 42 cm (16·5 in) pitch, and can carry this load over a range of 300 nm (555 km; 345 miles) under ISA sea level conditions. As a cargo transport, the aircraft has an internal capacity of 2,720 kg (6,000 lb) or a max external load capacity of 2,948 kg (6,500 lb) when a low-response sling is fitted.

Dimensions, external:
- Diameter of main rotor — 18·90 m (62 ft 0 in)
- Diameter of tail rotor — 3·16 m (10 ft 4 in)
- Length overall (rotors turning) — 22·15 m (72 ft 8 in)
- Length of fuselage — 17·01 m (55 ft 9¾ in)
- Length overall (main rotor folded) — 17·42 m (57 ft 2 in)
- Length overall (rotors and tail folded) — 14·40 m (47 ft 3 in)
- Height overall (rotors turning) — 5·13 m (16 ft 10 in)
- Height overall (rotors spread and stationary) — 4·85 m (15 ft 11 in)
- Height to top of rotor hub — 4·72 m (15 ft 6 in)
- Width overall (rotors folded):
  - with flotation bags — 4·98 m (16 ft 4 in)
  - without flotation bags — 4·77 m (15 ft 8 in)
- Wheel track (c/l of shock-absorbers) — 3·96 m (13 ft 0 in)
- Cabin door (port): Height — 1·68 m (5 ft 6 in)
  - Width — 0·91 m (3 ft 0 in)
- Cargo door (stbd): Height — 1·52 m (5 ft 0 in)
  - Width — 1·73 m (5 ft 8 in)
  - Height to sill — 1·14 m (3 ft 9 in)

Dimensions, internal:
- Cabin: Length:
  - ASW — 5·87 m (19 ft 3 in)
  - SAR — 7·59 m (24 ft 11 in)
  - Max width — 1·98 m (6 ft 6 in)
  - Max height — 1·92 m (6 ft 3½ in)
  - Floor area (incl area occupied by radar, sonar etc):
    - ASW — 12·08 m^2 (130 sq ft)
    - SAR — 13·94 m^2 (150 sq ft)

Weights and Loadings (A: anti-submarine, B: SAR, C: troop transport, D: casualty evacuation, E: internal cargo):
- Basic weight (depending on version) — approx 5,896 kg (13,000 lb)
- Weight, equipped: A — 6,201 kg (13,672 lb)
  - B, C — 5,613 kg (12,376 lb)
  - D — 5,797 kg (12,781 lb)
  - E — 5,558 kg (12,253 lb)
- Max T-O weight:
  - all current versions — 9,525 kg (21,000 lb)
- Max disc loading — 34·62 kg/m^2 (7·09 lb/sq ft)
- Max power loading — 4·73 kg/kW (7·77 lb/shp)

Performance (at max T-O weight, all current versions):
- Cruising speed at S/L — 112 knots (208 km/h; 129 mph)
- Max rate of climb at S/L — 616 m (2,020 ft)/min
- Max vertical rate of climb at S/L — 119 m (390 ft)/min
- Service ceiling, one engine out — 1,220 m (4,000 ft)
- Hovering ceiling IGE — 1,525 m (5,000 ft)
- Hovering ceiling OGE — 975 m (3,200 ft)
- Range with max standard fuel — 664 nm (1,230 km; 764 miles)
- Ferry range with max standard and auxiliary fuel — 814 nm (1,507 km; 937 miles)

WESTLAND COMMANDO

First flown on 12 September 1973, the Commando is a tactical helicopter based on the Sea King.

The payload/range performance and endurance capabilities of the Sea King have been optimised in the design of the Commando, which is intended to operate

Westland Commando Mk 2 tactical military helicopter, in the insignia of the Qatar Emiri Air Force

with maximum efficiency in the primary roles of tactical troop transport, logistic support and cargo transport, and casualty evacuation. In addition, the Commando can operate effectively in the secondary roles of air-to-surface strike and search and rescue.

The following versions have been announced:

Commando Mk 1. Designation of first five Commandos, part of a larger order placed on behalf of the Egyptian Air Force by the Saudi Arabian government. Minimally-modified version able to transport up to 21 troops. First two delivered to Egypt in January/February 1974. All five now delivered.

Commando Mk 2. Major production version, to which the following description applies. Flew for first time (G-17-12) on 16 January 1975. The Saudi Arabian order for Sea King/Commando helicopters includes 17 Mk 2s and two VIP Mk 2Bs for the Egyptian Air Force. In addition, four Mk 2s (three Mk 2As and one VIP Mk 2C) were ordered by the Qatar Emiri Air Force.

Sea King HC. Mk 4. Utility version of Commando Mk 2 for Royal Navy. Incorporates folding main rotor blades of Sea King, but retains non-retractable wheeled landing gear of Commando. Designed to carry up to 28 troops in cabin or 3,400 kg (7,500 lb) slung load. Equipped for parachuting and abseiling. Revised avionics, including Decca TANS with chart display and Decca 71 Doppler navigation system. For service with Nos. 845 and 846 (Naval Air Commando) Squadrons. Fifteen ordered, of which first four were due to be delivered by Winter 1979/80, remainder during 1980-81.

TYPE: Twin-turboshaft tactical military helicopter.

ROTOR SYSTEM: Five-blade single main rotor and six-blade tail rotor. Main rotor blades, of NACA 0012 section, attached to hub by multiple bolted joint. Blade construction consists of a light alloy extruded spar, with light alloy trailing-edge pockets. Tail rotor blades are of similar construction. Rotor brake fitted. Tail section folds for stowage; main rotor blades do not.

ROTOR DRIVE: Twin input four-stage reduction main gearbox, with single bevel intermediate and tail gearboxes. Main rotor/engine rpm ratio 93·43; tail rotor/engine rpm ratio: 15·26.

FUSELAGE: Light alloy stressed-skin structure, unpressurised. Sea King sponsons replaced by stub-wings.

TAIL UNIT: Similar to Sea King, with starboard-side half-tailplane at top of tail rotor pylon.

LANDING GEAR: Non-retractable tailwheel type, with twin-wheel main units. Oleo-pneumatic shock-absorbers. Main-wheel tyres size 6·50-10, tailwheel tyre size 6·00-6.

POWER PLANT: As for current versions of Sea King (which see).

ACCOMMODATION: Crew of two on flight deck. Seats along cabin sides, and single jump seat, for up to 28 troops. Two-piece airstair door at front on port side, cargo door at rear on starboard side. Entire accommodation heated and ventilated. Cockpit doors and windows, and two windows each side of main cabin, are jettisonable in an emergency.

SYSTEMS: Primary and secondary hydraulic systems for flight controls. No pneumatic system. Electrical system includes two 20kVA alternators.

AVIONICS AND EQUIPMENT: Blind-flying instrumentation standard. Wide range of radio, radar and navigation equipment available to customer's requirements. Cargo sling and rescue hoist optional.

ARMAMENT: Wide range of guns, missiles, etc may be carried, according to customer's requirements.

DIMENSIONS, EXTERNAL:

Diameter of main rotor	18·90 m (62 ft 0 in)
Diameter of tail rotor	3·16 m (10 ft 4 in)
Distance between rotor centres	11·10 m (36 ft 5 in)
Main rotor blade chord	0·46 m (1 ft 6¼ in)
Length overall (rotors turning)	22·15 m (72 ft 8 in)
Length of fuselage	17·02 m (55 ft 10 in)
Height overall (rotors turning)	5·13 m (16 ft 10 in)
Height to top of rotor hub	4·72 m (15 ft 6 in)
Wheel track (c/l of shock-absorbers)	3·96 m (13 ft 0 in)
Wheelbase	7·21 m (23 ft 8 in)
Passenger door (fwd, port): Height	1·68 m (5 ft 6 in)
Width	0·91 m (3 ft 0 in)
Cargo door (aft, stbd): Height	1·52 m (5 ft 0 in)
Width	1·73 m (5 ft 8 in)

DIMENSIONS, INTERNAL: As Sea King (SAR version)

AREAS:

Main rotor disc	280·5 m² (3,019 sq ft)
Tail rotor disc	7·79 m² (83·86 sq ft)
Main rotor blades (each)	4·14 m² (44·54 sq ft)
Tail rotor blades (each)	0·23 m² (2·46 sq ft)
Tailplane	1·80 m² (19·40 sq ft)

WEIGHTS:

Operating weight empty (troop transport, 2 crew)	5,700 kg (12,566 lb)
Max T-O weight	9,525 kg (21,000 lb)

PERFORMANCE (at max T-O weight): As given for Sea King, plus:

Range with max payload (28 troops), reserves for 30 min stand-off and T-O — 240 nm (445 km; 276 miles)

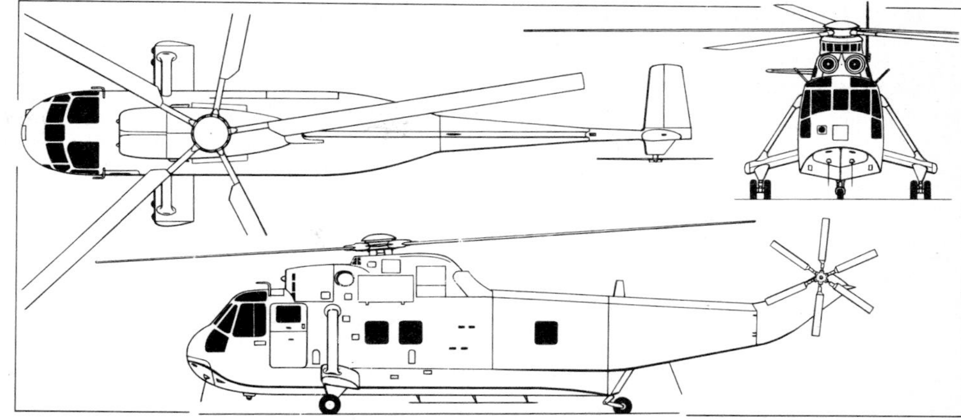

Westland Commando Mk 2 twin-turboshaft tactical military helicopter *(Pilot Press)*

WESTLAND LYNX

The Lynx is one of three types of aircraft (Puma, Gazelle and Lynx) covered by the Anglo-French helicopter agreement first proposed in February 1967 and confirmed on 2 April 1968. Westland has design leadership in the Lynx, which is a medium-sized helicopter intended to fulfil general-purpose, naval and civil transport roles. It is the first British aircraft to be designed entirely on a metric basis.

The first of 13 Lynx prototypes (XW835) flew for the first time on 21 March 1971 and was followed by XW837, the third prototype (second Lynx to fly), on 28 September 1971.

Details of the subsequent development aircraft can be found in the 1975-76 *Jane's*. One example of the Army version and two of the naval version began final type testing and certification trials at the A & AEE, Boscombe Down, in mid-1975.

A Lynx Intensive Flying Trials Unit, No. 700L Naval Air Squadron, was formed in September 1976 at RNAS Yeovilton, Somerset, as a joint Royal Navy/Royal Netherlands Navy operational evaluation unit. Deck handling tests, on board HMS *Birmingham* off Portland, were completed in February 1977.

The following versions of the Lynx have been announced:

Lynx AH. Mk 1. General-purpose and utility version for the British Army. Capable of operation on tactical troop transport, logistic support, armed escort of troop-carrying helicopters, anti-tank strike, search and rescue, casualty evacuation, reconnaissance and command post duties. Total of 100 ordered by early 1978. First production aircraft (XZ170) flown on 11 February 1977; 25 delivered by early 1979. Operational flight formed on completion of Army intensive flight trials in December 1977.

A Westland-owned aircraft (G-LYNX, first flown in May 1979), has demonstrated the helicopter's multi-role capability with a wide range of weapons which have included Hughes TOW and Euromissile Hot anti-tank guided missiles; SURA 80 mm, SNEB 68 mm and ZN 2·75 in rockets; twin 7·62 mm machine-gun pods and 20 mm automatic cannon; Matra Magic 550 air-to-air missiles; an AN/ALE-39 countermeasures dispenser with ECM chaff; and ECM warning equipment. It can also carry mine dispensers, or anti-tank teams armed with Milan missiles.

Lynx HAS. Mk 2. Version for Royal Navy, for advanced shipborne anti-submarine and other duties. Ferranti Sea Spray search and tracking radar in modified nose. Capable of operation on anti-submarine classification and strike, air to surface vessel search and strike, search and rescue, reconnaissance, troop transport, fire support, communication and fleet liaison, and vertical replenishment duties. Total of 60 ordered by mid-1978. First production aircraft (XZ229) flown on 10 February 1976; 24 delivered by early 1979. First operational RN unit is No. 702 Squadron, formed on completion of Navy intensive flight trials in December 1977. Serving in 1979 with nine Ships' Flights (five in Type 21 frigates, two in 'Leander' class frigates, and two in Type 42 destroyers). May be fitted with additional submarine detection gear, possibly of the dipping sonar type.

Lynx (French Navy). Navy version, generally similar to British HAS. Mk 2 but with Alcatel dunking sonar, French radar and radio, and AS.12 wire-guided missiles. Total of 26 ordered by early 1978; 19 delivered by early 1979 (the first on 28 September 1978).

In addition to orders from the British and French armed forces, 24 naval Lynx were ordered by the Royal Netherlands Navy, of which 18 are at the increased AUW of 4,763 kg (10,500 lb). The first batch of six (Dutch naval designation **UH-14A**) have been delivered, and are being used for search and rescue (with No. 7 Squadron), communications and training duties. The other 18 are for use in the ASW role: 10 (designation **SH-14B**) will be equipped with Alcatel dunking sonar and eight (designation **SH-14C**) with MAD. The first SH-14B was handed over on 3 September 1979.

Nine naval Lynx have been delivered to the Brazilian Navy, two to the Argentinian Navy, and three to Qatar. The Royal Danish Navy and Royal Norwegian Air Force have ordered seven and six respectively, and the Federal German Navy 12. An initial order for 50 Lynx has also been placed, following the signing of an agreement by Westland and the Arab Organisation for Industrialisation (AOI), to build Lynx helicopters in Egypt (which see). The total number of Lynx on order by June 1979 was 299.

Lynx production is shared in the ratio of 70% by Westland to 30% by Aérospatiale, and was at an approximate rate of four per month in early 1979.

The following description applies to both the military general-purpose and naval versions with the standard Gem power plant, except where otherwise indicated:

TYPE: Twin-engined multi-purpose helicopter.

ROTOR SYSTEM: Single four-blade semi-rigid main rotor and four-blade tail rotor. The main rotor blades, which are interchangeable, are of cambered aerofoil section and embody mass taper. Each blade consists of a two-piece, two-channel stainless steel D-shaped box-spar, to which is bonded a glassfibre-reinforced plastics rear skin stabilised by a Nomex plastics honeycomb core. Blade tips are of moulded glassfibre-reinforced plastics, with a stainless steel anti-erosion sheath forward of the 50% chord line. Each blade is attached to the main rotor hub by titanium root attachment plates and a flexible arm; the inboard portion of each arm accommodates most of the flapping movement of each blade, while the outer portion provides freedom in the lag plane. The rotor hub and inboard portions of the flexible arms are built as a complete unit, in the form of a titanium monobloc forging. A feathering hinge, comprising double needle bearings, is incorporated between the inboard and outboard flexible arms. The feathering hinge bearings are relieved of centrifugal loading by a flexible torsion bar

British Army Westland Lynx during firing trials with Hot anti-tank missiles

Westland Lynx AH.Mk 1 helicopter, with additional side view (top) of Lynx HAS. Mk 2 *(Pilot Press)*

which joints the inboard and outboard section of each arm. A two-pin jaw for blade attachment and manual blade folding is provided. Each of the tail rotor blades has a light alloy spar, machined integrally with the root attachment, which forms the nose portion of the aerofoil section and has a flush-fitting stainless steel sheath on the leading-edge. The rear section of each blade is of similar construction to that of the main rotor blades. The tail rotor hub has conventional flapping and feathering hinges, and incorporates torsionally flexible tiebars which carry the centrifugal loads inboard to the flapping hinges. Tail rotor blades are replaceable in opposing pairs, and each blade is attached to the hub by the outboard tiebar pin and a six-bolt root-end flanged joint. Main rotor blades of both versions can be folded, and tail rotor pylon of naval version can be folded and spread manually, to reduce overall length for stowage.

Rotor Drive: Transmission consists of three interconnected gearboxes, transmitting power to the main and tail rotors. The engines are mounted from extensions of the gearbox casing through gimbal and flexible couplings which permit a degree of angular misalignment. The drives are taken from the front of the engines into the main gearbox, which is mounted above the cabin forward of the engines. This gearbox interconnects the two engines, with the speed reduction being carried out in two stages. The first stage uses an involute-form spiral bevel pinion and gear. The second stage comprises a conformal pinion meshing with a gear fixed directly to the main rotor drive-shaft. In flight, the accessory gears, which are all at the front of the main gearbox, are driven by one of the two through shafts from the first-stage reduction gears. For system checking on the ground without the rotor turning, the accessories can be driven by the port engine via a through shaft, a lockout freewheel unit being selected manually to isolate the main rotor transmission from the port engine input drive. Freewheel units are mounted in each engine gearbox shaft, and also within the accessory drive chain of gears. Rotor head controls are actuated by three identical tandem servojacks, trunnion-mounted from the main rotor gearbox and powered by two independent hydraulic systems. The collective jack is mounted centrally on the forward end of the main gearbox, with the cyclic jacks positioned at 45° on each side. Duplex autostabiliser actuators are integral with each jack. Cyclic and collective inputs from the three control jacks are translated to the lower bearing housing of a four-arm spider which is located within, and rotates with, the main rotor shaft. The spider is mounted universally within a splined section of the main shaft, above its bearing housing, and is linked to the blade pitch-change levers by four adjustable-length track rods. Rod and lever control runs are employed on both the cyclic and collective systems, and are carried within protective ducts below the cockpit floor, up to cabin roof level on both sides of the aircraft, and finally to the rotor head. Yaw control runs are initially by rod and lever, and then to cables which transmit pedal movements along the tailboom to the tail rotor control jacks, which in turn effect blade pitch changes. Spring feel units and electric trim motors for the cyclic control channels are installed below the cockpit floor. Yaw control pedals are adjustable separately over a wide range. Control system incorporates a simple stability augmentation system, which acts in a single channel to provide improved stability in pitch. Provision is made for in-flight blade tracking. Each engine embodies an independent control system which provides full-authority rotor speed governing, pilot control being limited to selection of the desired rotor speed range. In the event of an engine failure, this system will restore power up to single-engine maximum contingency rating to maintain the power turbine/rotor governed speed within the prescribed limits. A single, centrally-mounted rotor speed select lever, with a limited authority, sets the datum of the power turbine/rotor speed governing system. This system meters fuel to maintain the selected speed throughout the flight condition range. A fine-adjustment trimming control is provided to facilitate accurate matching of each engine. On the naval versions, the main rotor can provide negative thrust to increase stability on deck after touchdown. Tail rotor drive is taken from the main ring gear. A hydraulically-operated rotor brake is mounted on the main gearbox at the tail rotor drive-shaft coupling, the shaft continuing aft to the single-stage, bevel reduction type intermediate and tail rotor gearboxes. Pitch variation of the tail rotor blades is controlled by a spider, actuated by hydraulic jack via a pushrod which extends through the centre of the tail rotor gearbox.

Fuselage and Tail Unit: Conventional semi-monocoque pod and boom structure, mainly of light alloy, including a cantilever floor structure with unobstructed surface. Glassfibre components used for access panels, doors and fairings. The forward fuselage is free from bulkheads, giving an unrestricted field of view. Single large window in each of the main cabin sliding doors. Provision for internally-mounted defensive armament, and for universal flange mountings on each side of the exterior to carry weapons or other stores. Tailboom is a light alloy monocoque structure bearing the sweptback vertical fin/tail rotor pylon, which has a half-tailplane near the tip on the starboard side. Tailplane leading- and trailing-edges, and bullet fairing over tail rotor gearbox, are of glassfibre.

Landing Gear (general-purpose version): Non-retractable tubular skid type. Provision for a pair of adjustable ground handling wheels on rear of each skid. Flotation gear optional.

Landing Gear (naval versions): Non-retractable oleo-pneumatic tricycle type. Single-wheel main units, mounted on sponsons near rear of main fuselage, are fixed at 27° toe-out for deck landing, and can be manually turned into line and locked fore and aft for movement of aircraft into and out of ship's hangar. Twin-wheel nose unit can be castored hydraulically through 90° by the pilot. Designed for high shock-absorption to facilitate take-off from, and landing on, small decks under severe sea and weather conditions. Sprag brakes (wheel locks) fitted to each wheel prevent rotation on landing or inadvertent deck roll. These locks are disengaged hydraulically and will automatically re-engage in the event of hydraulic failure. Friction brakes may be fitted for shore use. Flotation gear, and hydraulically-actuated harpoon deck-lock securing system, optional.

Power Plant: Two Rolls-Royce BS.360-07-26 Gem turboshaft engines. Each has a max continuous rating of 559 kW (750 shp), a take-off and inter-contingency rating of 619 kW (830 shp), and a max contingency rating (2½ min) of 671 kW (900 shp). Engines mounted side by side on top of the fuselage upper decking, aft of the main rotor shaft and gearbox, and separated from fuselage, transmission area and each other by firewalls. Engine air intakes de-iced electrically. Fuel in five crashproof bag-type tanks, all within the fuselage structure, comprising two main tanks each of 204 kg (450 lb) capacity, two side-by-side collector tanks each of 93 kg (204·5 lb) capacity, and a 148 kg (326 lb) capacity underfloor tank at the forward end of the cabin. Total fuel capacity 733 kg (1,616 lb). Cross-feed system allows fuel to be supplied from both collector tanks to one engine or from one tank to both engines. If required, ferry range can be increased by installing in rear of cabin two metal auxiliary tanks with a combined capacity of 654 kg (1,442 lb). Single-point pressure refuelling (3·79 bars; 55 lb/sq in max) and defuelling; two points for gravity refuelling. A removable 114 litres (25 Imp gallons)/min pressure refuelling/defuelling pack can be fitted in the cabin which, with port engine running, can be used to refuel aircraft from dump stocks on ground or containers suspended from hoist. It is also possible to raise fuel about 5 m (15 ft) while the aircraft is hovering. Fuel jettison capability for main and forward tanks. Provision for self-sealing of both collector tanks (except in Royal Navy version) to provide protection against small-arms fire. Engine oil tank capacity 6·8 litres (1·5 Imp gallons). Main rotor gearbox oil capacity 18 litres (4 Imp gallons). Engine access doors manufactured in Australia by Hawker Pacific.

Accommodation: Pilot and co-pilot or observer on side-by-side seats which can accommodate back-type dinghies and are adjustable fore and aft and for height. Inertia-reel shoulder harness for pilot and co-pilot. Dual controls optional. Additional crew members (eg, gunner, hoist operator) according to role. Individual forward-hinged cockpit door and large rearward-sliding cabin door on each side; all four doors jettisonable. Main cabin doors manufactured by Hawker Pacific in Australia. Cockpit accessible from cabin area. Maximum high-density layout (general-purpose version) for one pilot and 10 armed troops or paratroops, on lightweight bench seats in soundproof cabin. Alternative VIP layouts for four to seven passengers, with additional cabin soundproofing. Seats can be removed quickly to permit the carriage of up to 907 kg (2,000 lb) of freight internally. Tiedown rings are provided at approx 51 cm (20 in) intervals on main cabin floor, which is stressed for loads of up to 976 kg/m² (200 lb/sq ft). Alternatively, loads of up to 1,360 kg (3,000 lb) can be carried externally on freight hook mounted below the cabin floor and fitted, in naval version, with electrically-operated emergency release system. In the casualty evacuation role, with a crew of two, the Lynx can accommodate three standard stretchers and a medical attendant; electrically-heated casualty bags can be provided. Both versions have secondary capability for search and rescue (up to nine survivors) and other roles (see introductory copy and 'Equipment' paragraphs).

Systems: Two independent hydraulic systems in all versions, pressure 141 bars (2,050 lb/sq in). Pumps powered by accessory drive from main rotor gearbox, enabling full power to be drawn from both main systems in event of engine failure. If either No. 1 or No. 2 main system fails, the other maintains adequate flying control. No. 1 system, additionally, actuates tail rotor yaw control and rotor brake. Tail rotor operation reverts to mechanical control if No. 1 system fails. A third hydraulic system, at the same pressure, is provided in the naval version when sonar equipment, MAD or a hyd-

Westland naval Lynx, one of two for the Argentinian Navy

raulic winch system are installed. When this third hydraulic system is installed, the deck-lock harpoon is also operated by this system. No pneumatic system. 28V DC electrical power supplied by two 6kW engine-driven starter/generators and an alternator. Engines can also be started from external 28V DC power source. 24V 23Ah (optionally 40Ah) nickel-cadmium battery fitted for essential services and emergency engine starting. 200V three-phase AC power available at 400Hz from two 15kVA transmission-driven alternators. AC and DC external ground power sockets on starboard side of fuselage. Graviner Triple FD engine fire detection system; two separate fire suppression systems fitted, but interconnected to permit contents of both bottles to be directed to one engine if necessary. All versions fitted with centralised standard warning system which provides visual and audio warnings of major emergencies, visual warnings for secondary failure, and visual indications of an advisory nature. Optional cabin heating and ventilation system, using mixing unit combining engine bleed air with outside air. Optional supplementary cockpit heating system. Electrical anti-icing and demisting of windscreen, and electrically-operated windscreen wipers, standard; windscreen washing system optional.

Avionics and Flight Equipment: Main equipment bays are in nose (under upward-hinged door) and at rear of cabin. All versions equipped as standard with navigation, cabin and cockpit lights; adjustable landing light under nose; anti-collision beacon; first aid kit(s); and hand-type fire extinguishers for cabin. Optional avionics common to all roles (general-purpose and RN versions) include simplex two-axis cross-country autopilot system; Plessey PTR 377 UHF/VHF transceiver with homing; Ultra D 403M standby UHF; S.G. Brown three-position crew intercom. Optional role equipment or installations for both versions include Marconi automatic flight control system (AFCS); ARC-340 VHF/FM; Collins 718 U-5 HF; VOR/ILS; DME; AN/ARN-118 Tacan (general-purpose version only); I-band transponder (naval version only); Sperry GM9 Gyrosyn compass system; E2C standby compass; Sperry RL8E heading indicator (Royal Naval version); Louis Newmark 8462/05 vertical gyro; Plessey PTR 446 IFF transponder; AD 3703 and 3805 radio compass (general-purpose version only); Marconi AD-380 ADF (Royal Danish Navy version); Honeywell AN/APN-198 radar altimeter; Decca Tactical Air Navigation System (TANS) with Decca Type 71 Doppler radar; Decca Mk 19 flight log; and vortex-type sand filter for engine air intakes. Additional units are fitted in naval version, when sonar is fitted, to provide automatic transition to the hover and automatic Doppler hold in the hover. Other optional equipment (both versions) includes signal pistol and cartridges, Aldis lamp and stowage.

Armament and Operational Equipment: For armed escort, anti-tank or air-to-surface strike missions, general-purpose version can be equipped with one 20 mm AME 621 or similar cannon, with 1,500 rds, or a pintle-mounted 7·62 mm GEC Minigun inside cabin; or a Minigun beneath cabin, in Emerson Minitat installation, with 3,000 rds. External pylon can be fitted on each side of cabin for a variety of stores, including two Minigun or other self-contained gun pods; two pods of eighteen or two of seven 68 mm or 2·75 in rockets; or up to six Aérospatiale AS.11, or eight Aérospatiale/MBB Hot or Hughes TOW, or similar air-to-surface missiles. An additional six or eight missiles can be carried in cabin, for rearming in forward areas, and Avimo-Ferranti 530 lightweight stabilised sight (or other sight applicable to weapon system) is fitted for target detection and missile direction. British Army Lynx aircraft equipped with TOW missiles have roof-mounted Hughes sight manufactured under licence by Dynamics Group of British Aerospace. The Lynx can also transport mobile anti-tank teams of three gunners with missiles and launchers. For search and rescue role, with a crew of three, both versions can be fitted with a waterproof floor, eight 4 in flares in utility version (or six 4·5 in flares in naval version), and a 272 kg (600 lb) capacity electrically-operated 'clip-on' hoist in starboard side of cabin. Alternative option of hydraulically-operated hoist in naval version when third hydraulic system is installed. Hoist, which can lift a load through 76 m (250 ft) at 30·5 m (100 ft)/min, can be swung back into cabin when not in use, permitting sliding door to be closed. General-purpose version can also be equipped for several other duties, including firefighting and crash rescue, reconnaissance, military command post, liaison, customs and border control, and pilot and operational training. Optional equipment, according to role, can include lightweight sighting system with alternative target magnification, vertical and/or oblique cameras, up to six 4·5 in flares for night operation, low light level TV, infra-red linescan, searchlight, and specialised communications equipment. Naval version can carry out a number of these roles, but has specialised equipment for its primary duties. For ASW role, this includes two Mk 44 or Mk 46 homing torpedoes, one each on an external pylon on each side of fuselage, and six marine markers; or two Mk 11 depth charges. Detection of submarine can either be carried out by parent ship (in which case the Lynx carries retractable classification and localisation equipment), or the Lynx can itself be equipped for this function, with Alcatel D.U.A.V.4 lightweight dunking sonar, and hydraulically-powered winch and cable hover mode facilities within the AFCS. Ferranti Sea Spray lightweight search and tracking radar, for detecting small surface targets in low visibility/high sea conditions. Armament includes BAe CL834 Sea Skua semi-active homing missiles for attacking light surface craft; alternatively, four AS.12 or similar wire-guided missiles can be employed in conjunction with AF 530 or APX-334 lightweight stabilised optical sighting system.

Dimensions, external (A: general-purpose version; N: naval version):
Diameter of main rotor (A, N) 12·802 m (42 ft 0 in)
Diameter of tail rotor (A, N) 2·21 m (7 ft 3 in)
Main rotor blade chord (A, N, constant, each) 0·359 m (1 ft 3½ in)
Tail rotor blade chord (A, N, constant, each) 180 mm (7·1 in)
Length overall, both rotors turning (A, N) 15·163 m (49 ft 9 in)
Length overall:
A, main rotor blades folded 13·165 m (43 ft 2·3 in)
N, main rotor blades and tail folded 10·618 m (34 ft 10 in)
Length of fuselage, nose to tail rotor centre:
A 12·06 m (39 ft 6·8 in)
N 11·92 m (39 ft 1·3 in)
Width overall, main rotor blades folded:
A, N 2·94 m (9 ft 7·75 in)
Height overall, both rotors turning:
A 3·66 m (12 ft 0 in)
N 3·60 m (11 ft 9¾ in)
Height overall, both rotors stopped:
A 3·504 m (11 ft 6 in)
N 3·365 m (11 ft 0·5 in)
Height to top of rotor hub: A 2·964 m (9 ft 8·7 in)
Height overall, main rotor blades and tail folded:
N 3·20 m (10 ft 6 in)
Tail rotor ground clearance: A 1·41 m (4 ft 7·5 in)
N 1·38 m (4 ft 6·3 in)
Tailplane half-span (from fuselage c/l):
A, N 1·776 m (5 ft 9·9 in)
Skid track: A 2·032 m (6 ft 8 in)
Wheel track: N 2·778 m (9 ft 1·4 in)
Wheelbase: N 3·014 m (9 ft 10·7 in)
Cabin door openings (A, N, each):
Mean width 1·372 m (4 ft 6 in)
Height 1·194 m (3 ft 11 in)

Dimensions, internal:
Cabin, from back of pilots' seats:
Min length 2·057 m (6 ft 9 in)
Max width 1·778 m (5 ft 10 in)
Width at rear 1·409 m (4 ft 7·5 in)
Max internal floor width 1·715 m (5 ft 7·5 in)
Max height 1·422 m (4 ft 8 in)
Floor area 3·72 m² (40·04 sq ft)
Volume 5·21 m³ (184 cu ft)

Weights (A: general-purpose version, N: naval version):
Manufacturer's bare weight: A 2,578 kg (5,683 lb)
N 2,679 kg (5,906 lb)
Manufacturer's basic weight: A 2,658 kg (5,860 lb)
N 2,780 kg (6,129 lb)
Operating weight empty, equipped:
A, troop transport (pilot and 10 troops) 2,787 kg (6,144 lb)
A, anti-tank strike (incl weapon pylons, firing equipment and sight) 3,072 kg (6,772 lb)
A, search and rescue (crew of three) 2,963 kg (6,532 lb)
N, anti-submarine strike 3,101 kg (6,836 lb)
N, reconnaissance (crew of two) 3,082 kg (6,794 lb)
N, anti-submarine classification and strike 3,192 kg (7,037 lb)
N, air to surface vessel search and strike (crew of two and two Sea Skuas) 3,162 kg (6,971 lb)
N, search and rescue (crew of three) 3,210 kg (7,076 lb)
N, dunking sonar search and strike 3,409 kg (7,515 lb)
Normal max T-O weight: A, N 4,309 kg (9,500 lb)
Max T-O weight: A, N 4,763 kg (10,500 lb)

Performance (at normal max T-O weight at S/L, ISA, except where indicated. A: general-purpose version; N: naval version):
Max continuous cruising speed:
A 152 knots (282 km/h; 175 mph)
N 145 knots (269 km/h; 167 mph)
A, N (ISA + 20°C) 141 knots (261 km/h; 162 mph)
Max continuous cruising speed (1 h), one engine out:
A 122 knots (225 km/h; 140 mph)
N 113 knots (209 km/h; 130 mph)
A (ISA + 20°C) 103 knots (192 km/h; 119 mph)
N (ISA + 20°C) 94 knots (174 km/h; 108 mph)
Speed for max endurance:
A, N (ISA and ISA + 20°C) 70 knots (130 km/h; 81 mph)
Min flying speed (max contingency rating, one engine out): A, N 25 knots (46·5 km/h; 29 mph)
A, N (ISA + 20°C) 36 knots (67 km/h; 41·5 mph)
Max forward rate of climb: A 664 m (2,180 ft)/min
N 616 m (2,020 ft)/min
A (ISA + 20°C) 495 m (1,625 ft)/min
N (ISA + 20°C) 485 m (1,590 ft)/min
Max forward rate of climb (1 h power), one engine out:
A 174 m (570 ft)/min
N 162 m (530 ft)/min
A (ISA + 20°C) 73 m (240 ft)/min
N (ISA + 20°C) 61 m (200 ft)/min
Max vertical rate of climb:
A, N 376 m (1,235 ft)/min
A, N (ISA + 20°C) 346 m (1,135 ft)/min
Hovering ceiling OGE: A, N 2,920 m (9,580 ft)
Typical range, with reserves:
A, troop transport 292 nm (540 km; 336 miles)
Radius of action, out and back at max sustained speed, max hover weight 4,309 kg (9,500 lb), allowances for T-O and landing, 15 min loiter in search area, 2 min hover for each survivor, and reserves for 20 min loiter at end of mission:
A, search and rescue (crew of 3 and 8 survivors) 134 nm (248 km; 154 miles)
N, search and rescue (crew of 3 and 2 survivors) 136 nm (253 km; 157 miles)
N, search and rescue (crew of 3 and 8 survivors) 120 nm (222 km; 138 miles)
Time on station at 50 nm (93 km; 58 miles) radius, out and back at max sustained speed, with 2 torpedoes and 6 marine markers, allowances for T-O and landing and reserves for 20 min loiter at end of mission:
N, anti-submarine classification and strike, loiter speed on station 1 h 55 min
N, anti-submarine strike, loiter on station 2 h 24 min
N, dunking sonar search and strike, 50% loiter speed and 50% hover on station 39 min
Time on station at 50 nm (93 km; 58 miles) radius, out and back at max sustained speed, with crew of 2 and 2 Sea Skuas, allowances and reserves as above:
N, air to surface vessel strike, en-route radar search and loiter speed on station 2 h 5 min
Max range: A 356 nm (660 km; 410 miles)
N 339 nm (628 km; 390 miles)
A (ISA + 20°C) 356 nm (660 km; 410 miles)
N (ISA + 20°C) 338 nm (626 km; 389 miles)
Max endurance: A, N (ISA + 20°C) 3 h 26 min
Max ferry range with auxiliary cabin tanks:
A 724 nm (1,342 km; 834 miles)
N 565 nm (1,046 km; 650 miles)

WESTLAND WG 30

Westland Helicopters first undertook studies leading to this enlarged, twin-engined development of the Lynx helicopter as a private venture in early 1976. Detail design of the bigger fuselage began about a year later, and the construction of two prototypes was authorised in January 1978. The first of these, registered G-BGHF, was rolled out on 23 March 1979 and made its first flight on 10 April 1979, two weeks ahead of schedule. By the end of May it had accumulated 30 h of flying in 30 flights. The second prototype made its first public debut at the Paris Air Show in June 1979.

Main differences from the Lynx are the completely new and more spacious fuselage; retractable landing gear; increased-diameter main and (on the production version) tail rotor; a noise and vibration reducing 'raft' mounting for the twin engines and main rotor head; a dynamic system developed from that of the Lynx and retaining more than 85% of the proven system in that aircraft; increased fuel capacity; new automatic flight control system; and simplified electrical system. Payload/range capability is increased, and the manoeuvrability of the Lynx is retained.

Initially, the WG 30 is planned to meet military needs for a tactical transport, battlefield support and aeromedical helicopter. The basic aircraft is, however, also suitable for the civil market, for such roles as passenger and/or cargo transport, executive and VIP use, offshore rig support, and Arctic operation. Military approvals and full Category A civil certification are expected to be obtained during 1980, and deliveries to begin towards the end of 1981.

Type: Twin-turboshaft general-purpose military and civil helicopter.

Rotor System: Four-blade semi-rigid main rotor and four-blade tail rotor. Main rotor blades, which can be folded for stowage, are of constant-chord and cambered section; each has a stainless steel spar and a bonded GRP skin. Forged titanium hingeless main rotor head. Main rotor system, engines and main rotor gearbox are mounted on a structural 'raft' which reduces rotor-induced vibration, so improving passenger comfort, and also improves structural and systems reliability. This raft comprises two fore-and-aft steel beams and three cross-beams, the latter (from front to rear) being of

Westland WG 30 twin-turboshaft general-purpose helicopter, first flown on 10 April 1979

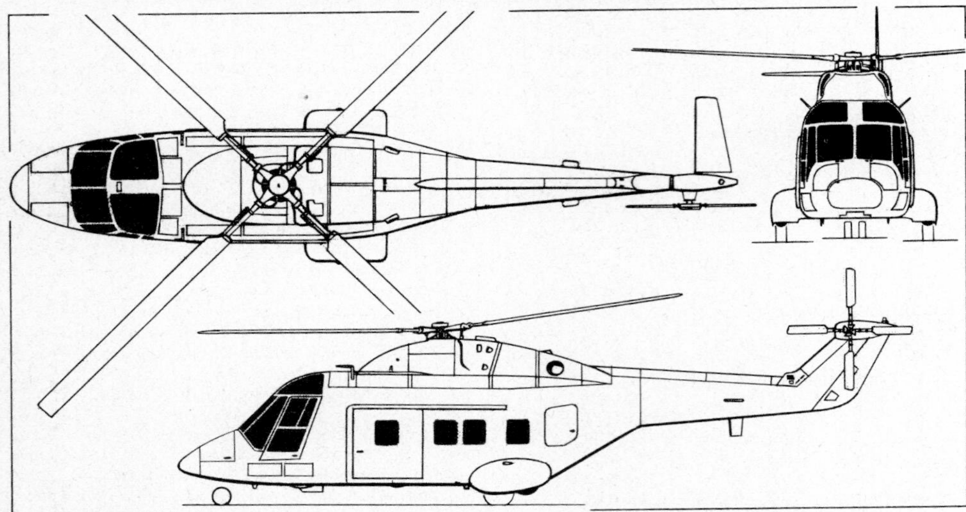

Westland WG 30 (two Rolls-Royce Gem 41-1 turboshaft engines) *(Pilot Press)*

machined light alloy, fabricated light alloy and steel. The raft 'floats' on four Lord elastomeric suspension blocks which, in turn, are mounted on two pairs of fore-and-aft beams bridging the main lift frames. First prototype has a standard Lynx tail rotor; later aircraft will have a rotor of slightly larger diameter, with composite blades, which will rotate in the opposite direction and will be quieter.

Rotor Drive: Engines drive directly into standard Lynx conformal main gearbox, thence by driveshafts to intermediate and tail rotor gearboxes.

Fuselage: Main cabin, which is of basically rectangular cross-section, is a conventional semi-monocoque structure of light alloy frames and stringers, with stringer spacing constant throughout the airframe. Roof panels, fuel tank surrounds and bulkheads are of aluminium honeycomb, floor panels of Ciba-Geigy Fibrelam GRP.

Landing Gear: Hydraulically retractable tricycle type, with oleo-pneumatic shock-absorber on each unit. Fairey Hydraulics main units each have a single Goodyear wheel and tyre of the size fitted to the Westland Sea King; they retract into fairings on the fuselage sides at the rear of the cabin, the wheels remaining partly exposed when retracted. Fairey nose unit, which is castoring, is fully retractable rearwards, and is fitted with twin Goodyear wheels and tyres.

Power Plant: Two Rolls-Royce Gem 41-1 turboshaft engines mounted side by side above cabin, each rated at 835 kW (1,120 shp) max contingency, 790 kW (1,060 shp) intermediate contingency, 746 kW (1,000 shp) for T-O, and 671 kW (900 shp) max continuous. Engine intakes as for Lynx. Fuel in two FPT tanks, each of 499 kg (1,100 lb) capacity, one under front seats and one under rear seats in cabin. Intertechnique booster pumps, with provision for crossfeed to either engine.

Accommodation: Crew of two on flight deck, with provision for one-pilot operation. Large flight deck windows provide excellent field of view for crew. Windscreen washers and wipers on both front transparencies. Main cabin can accommodate, in military version, 14 troops each weighing 127 kg (280 lb) including full equipment; 17 troops with less equipment; or a maximum of 22 troops in high-density configuration; or, in cargo configuration, ammunition, anti-tank missile launch teams, fuel, and supplies for battlefield support. Aeromedical version can accommodate six stretchers plus 8/10 sitting casualties/medical attendants. Civil passenger version can provide three/four-abreast seating for up to 17 persons in airline standards of comfort. This version, too, has a high-density layout, in which up to 22 passengers can be accommodated in two forward-facing rows of five and two inward-facing rows of six. Various other civil layouts include executive/VIP transport (six/eight seats, toilet and galley unit), offshore oil support, all-cargo, and mixed passenger/cargo. Large rearward-sliding door on each side of cabin. Four large square cabin windows each side, including one in each door. Step each side to facilitate access to flight deck. Baggage compartment in port side of rear fuselage, aft of cabin, with external access door. Stowages for safety equipment, liferafts, lifejackets and aircraft flotation gear for overwater operation.

Systems: Two independent hydraulic systems (each 141 bars; 2,050 lb/sq in), as in Lynx; No. 1 system actuates landing gear. Electrical compartment in starboard side of rear fuselage, aft of cabin. DC system as in Lynx (28V from two 6kW engine-driven starter/generators, alternator and battery); AC power provided by two 500V static inverters, but alternators are available at customer's option. Air-conditioning system optional.

Avionics and Equipment: Nose compartment for avionics and radio. Standard aircraft is VFR equipped, but IFR package (to include VOR/ILS, DME and ADF) is under development. Louis Newmark duplex automatic flight control system for all three axes, with computer-based control and duplex heading hold. SFENA spring feel units (one each for pitch and roll). Other flying controls essentially similar to Lynx; rods connecting hand and foot controls to operating jacks are of the type fitted to Wessex and Sea King. Duplicated three-axis automatic stabilisation equipment. Communications and security systems to customer's requirements.

Dimensions, external:
Diameter of main rotor 13·31 m (43 ft 8 in)
Diameter of tail rotor:
first prototype 2·21 m (7 ft 3 in)
production 2·44 m (8 ft 0 in)
Length overall, rotors turning 15·90 m (52 ft 2 in)
Length overall, main rotor blades folded 14·33 m (47 ft 0 in)
Width overall, main rotor blades folded 3·30 m (10 ft 10 in)
Height overall, rotors turning 4·39 m (14 ft 5 in)
Height overall (minimum) 4·04 m (13 ft 3 in)
Cabin doors (each): Height 1·37 m (4 ft 6 in)
Width 1·22 m (4 ft 0 in)
Height to sill 0·58 m (1 ft 10¾ in)

Dimensions, internal:
Cabin, excl flight deck: Length 4·42 m (14 ft 6 in)
Width 1·98 m (6 ft 6 in)
Height 1·68 m (5 ft 6 in)
Volume 13·03 m^3 (460 cu ft)
Baggage compartment volume (rear) 1·05 m^3 (37 cu ft)

Areas:
Main rotor disc 139·14 m^2 (1,497·7 sq ft)
Tail rotor disc: first prototype 3·80 m^2 (40·9 sq ft)
production 4·68 m^2 (50·4 sq ft)

Weights and Loading:
Manufacturer's bare weight, with basic minimum equipment 2,914 kg (6,424 lb)
Max fuel load 998 kg (2,200 lb)
Typical operating weights (tactical troop transport):
1 crew, VFR equipped 3,120 kg (6,878 lb)
2 crew, IFR equipped 3,311 kg (7,300 lb)
Max weight for hovering OGE, ISA 5,035 kg (11,100 lb)
Max T-O weight 5,330 kg (11,750 lb)
Max cabin floor loading 976 kg/m^2 (200 lb/sq ft)

Performance (estimated, at max T-O weight except where indicated):
Max level and cruising speed at S/L:
ISA 135 knots (250 km/h; 155 mph)
ISA + 20°C 125 knots (232 km/h; 144 mph)
Max level speed at S/L, one engine out 110 knots (204 km/h; 126 mph)
Min level speed at S/L, one engine out 30 knots (56 km/h; 35 mph)
Hovering ceiling IGE 2,135 m (7,000 ft)
Hovering ceiling OGE 1,525 m (5,000 ft)
Radius of action (offshore oil support, IFR), 45 min hold, 227 kg (500 lb) fuel reserves 135 nm (250 km; 155 miles)
Range with 1,815 kg (4,000 lb) payload:
carried internally 75 nm (140 km; 85 miles)
carried externally 45 nm (85 km; 50 miles)
Max ferry range (S/L, ISA), with reserves nearly 400 nm (740 km; 460 miles)

WESTLAND/AÉROSPATIALE SA 330 PUMA

Following the completion of 40 Puma HC.Mk 1s for the RAF in 1972 (7 more ordered in 1979), Westland is building Puma component sets for the French production line.

The Puma is described fully under the Aérospatiale heading in the French section.

WESTLAND/AÉROSPATIALE SA 341 GAZELLE

The Gazelle, described fully under the Aérospatiale heading in the French section, is in joint production in Britain and France under the same Anglo-French agreement as the Puma. The Gazelle has been ordered by the British Army (158 **AH. Mk 1** initially; increased in 1978), Royal Navy (30 **HT. Mk 2**) and Royal Air Force (14 **HT. Mk 3**).

The first Gazelle HT. Mk 2 (XW845) was flown on 6 July 1972. The first HT. Mk 3 was delivered to the RAF Central Flying School on 16 July 1973. The AH. Mk 1 entered service on 6 July 1974, with No. 660 Squadron of the Army Air Corps at Soest, Germany; and the HT. Mk 2 with No. 705 Squadron at RNAS Culdrose on 10 December 1974.

British Army Gazelles began to be equipped in 1977 with Decca Doppler 80 radar and automatic chart display.

WHE

W. H. EKIN (ENGINEERING) CO LTD

Address: 158 King's Gate, Aberdeen AB2 6BR, Scotland

Telephone: Aberdeen (0224) 33463

Registered Office: c/o 4 Malone Hill Park, Belfast BT9 6RL, Northern Ireland

Directors:
Dr William H. Ekin, PhD, BSc(Hons), CEng, MIMechE, DMS
Mrs M. J. H. Ekin

This company was formed in March 1969 to undertake the production of six McCandless Mk IV Gyroplanes (see 1972-73 *Jane's*), and the first of these made its first flight in February 1972. An extensive redesign was embarked upon by WHE in Autumn 1971 and a new prototype (G-AXXN) flew for the first time on 1 February 1973. The modified aircraft is known as the WHE Airbuggy.

WHE AIRBUGGY

The first production Airbuggy (G-AXYX) was delivered to an English customer in October 1975, and the second in July 1976. A third, ordered in August 1978, was due for delivery in Spring 1979, and a fourth was due to begin flight testing in the same year.

Type: Single-seat light autogyro.

Rotor System and Drive: Two-blade semi-rigid teetering rotor with an offset gimbal head, through the centre of which runs the rotor spin-up drive. Blades are secured to hub by bolts, and are of Rotordyne bonded metal construction. Rotor spin-up effected via V-belt drive to 9·667 : 1 worm reduction gearbox and universal and sliding joints. No rotor brake or blade folding.

Fuselage: Space-frame of T35 and T45 steel tube, assembled by sifbronze welding.

Tail Unit: Fin, rudder and tailplane formed from plywood sandwich. Ground-adjustable trim tab on rud-

First production example of the WHE Airbuggy single-seat autogyro

der. Endplate auxiliary fins on tailplane of prototype.

LANDING GEAR: Non-retractable tricycle type. All three wheels have rubber bungee for shock-absorption. Nosewheel steerable. Main wheels with tyres sized from 12 × 2·5 to 13·5 × 5 and nosewheel from 12 × 2·5 to 12 × 3·8 according to surface from which aircraft operates. Internal expanding drum brake on nosewheel only.

POWER PLANT: One 56 kW (75 hp) 1,600-1,800 cc modified Volkswagen engine, driving a Hoffmann two-blade pusher propeller via a 1·5 : 1 reduction drive. Drive transmitted by 10 V belts. Fuel capacity 29·5 litres (6·5 Imp gallons), in gravity tank mounted above engine, with refuelling point on top of tank. Oil capacity 2·5 litres (4·5 Imp pints).

ACCOMMODATION: Single seat in open cockpit behind large windscreen. Door on starboard side.

SYSTEM: A 12V 25Ah ground rechargeable battery is installed to power an electric engine starter motor and to supply instruments and radio. The starters have been removed from the first two aircraft, as the engines have been found to start satisfactorily without them, using only the hand lever.

AVIONICS: Prototype has Parkair Nipper 24-channel com transceiver.

DIMENSIONS, EXTERNAL:

Diameter of rotor	6·63 m (21 ft 9 in)
Rotor blade chord	0·188 m (7·4 in)
Propeller diameter	1·45 m (4 ft 9 in)
Length overall	3·51 m (11 ft 6 in)
Height overall	2·21 m (7 ft 3 in)
Wheel track	1·63 m-1·68 m (5 ft 4 in-5 ft 6 in)
Wheelbase	1·32 m (4 ft 4 in)

AREAS:

Rotor blades (each)	0·52 m² (5·6 sq ft)
Rotor disc	37·63 m² (405 sq ft)
Fin	0·31 m² (3·3 sq ft)
Rudder	0·49 m² (5·3 sq ft)

WEIGHTS AND LOADINGS:

Weight empty	161 kg (355 lb)
Max T-O and landing weight	295 kg (650 lb)
Max disc loading	8·5 kg/m² (1·75 lb/sq ft)
Max power loading	5·27 kg/kW (8·7 lb/hp)

PERFORMANCE (at max T-O weight):

Never-exceed speed	69 knots (128 km/h; 80 mph)
Max level speed at S/L	69 knots (128 km/h; 80 mph)
Max cruising speed	61 knots (113 km/h; 70 mph)
Econ cruising speed	52 knots (97 km/h; 60 mph)
Max rate of climb at S/L	305 m (1,000 ft)/min
T-O run	46-92 m (150-300 ft)
Landing run, still air	9 m (30 ft)
Landing run in 13 knot (24 km/h; 15 mph) wind	Nil
Range with max fuel, no allowances	121 nm (225 km; 140 miles)
Range with max payload, no allowances	86 nm (161 km; 100 miles)

UNITED STATES OF AMERICA

AERONCA

AERONCA INC

HEAD OFFICE: 1712 Germantown Road, Middletown, Ohio 45042

Telephone: (513) 422 2751

PRESIDENT AND CHIEF EXECUTIVE OFFICER: Donald A. Bordlemay

SENIOR VICE-PRESIDENT: George P. Irwin

Aeronca Inc, founded in 1928, and responsible for construction of the Champion series of two-seat lightplanes during the mid/late 1940s, came to an agreement with Foxjet International to build the Foxjet twin-turbofan light transport. This arrangement has now been terminated, and details of the Foxjet can be found under the Foxjet International entry in this edition of *Jane's*.

AEROSPACE GENERAL

AEROSPACE GENERAL COMPANY

ADDRESS: Route 1, Box 208, Odessa, Texas 79763

Telephone: (915) 332 8233

PRESIDENT: Gilbert Magill

This company was formed by Mr Gilbert Magill who, as former President of Rotor-Craft Corporation, was responsible for the RH-1 Pinwheel ultra-light one-man helicopter described and illustrated in the 1960-61 *Jane's*. The same basic concept, including the use of rotor-tip rockets for propulsion, was embodied later in a powered pilot rescue vehicle known as the Mini-Copter. Three prototypes were ordered by the US Navy for evaluation and development, but the programme was terminated in 1977, when the prototypes were transferred to the US Army. In early 1979 four aircraft of this type were acquired by the Army for test and evaluation in an Individual Tactical Air Vehicle (ITAV) role. Details of this helicopter, and of a generally similar civil MC-8 Mini-Copter, can be found in the 1978-79 *Jane's*.

AHRENS

AHRENS AIRCRAFT CORPORATION

HEAD OFFICE: 2800 Teal Club Road, Oxnard, California 93030

Telephone: (805) 985 2000

Telex: 659 240 Ahrens Air ONX

AHRENS AIRCRAFT INC

WORKS: Hangar 403 (PO Box 432), Ramey Station, Aguadilla, Puerto Rico 00604

Telephone: (809) 891 2033

Telex: 3859451

PRESIDENT: Peter W. Ahrens

VICE-PRESIDENTS:
Kim K. Ahrens (Engineering)
Edd H. Ahrens (Production)

The parent Ahrens Aircraft Corporation provides subassembly and shipping services for the main production and assembly plant of Ahrens Aircraft Inc, located at the

Ahrens AR 404 passenger/cargo transport prototype, with production-type retractable main landing gear

former Ramey AFB, Puerto Rico.

AHRENS AR 404

Ahrens Aircraft Corporation initiated the design of the AR 404 in January 1975; the aim was to evolve a simple and robust multi-purpose transport aircraft that would be easy to operate and maintain. A constant-section square fuselage was adopted to provide maximum volume and simplify the loading of containers; the wing was mounted on the fuselage upper surface, eliminating the need for any wing carry-through structure within the fuselage. A modular concept was chosen for all systems to simplify maintenance, and it is claimed that an engine can be removed for replacement within 20 minutes.

Construction of a prototype began in August 1975, and this aircraft (N404AR) made its first flight on 1 December 1976. The first flight of a production aircraft was scheduled to be made in June 1979, and FAA certification under FAR Pt 25 is anticipated during the first quarter of 1980. The company expected to build four production aircraft during 1979, increasing delivery rate to one per month in 1980. The current labour force in the Puerto Rico works is approximately 100, but this is expected to almost double during 1980.

The details which follow apply to the production version of the AR 404, which will have a longer cabin than the prototype:

Type: Passenger/cargo transport.

Wings: Cantilever high-wing monoplane. Wing section NACA 64_3-618. Dihedral 0°. Incidence 0°. Three-spar fail-safe light alloy structure, with light alloy skins. Electrically-operated two-section single-slotted trailing-edge flaps of light alloy construction on each wing. Manually-actuated plain ailerons of light alloy construction, with electrically-operated trim tab in each. Modified Hoerner-type wingtips.

Fuselage: Semi-monocoque square constant-section fail-safe structure of light alloy.

Tail Unit: Cantilever structure of light alloy. Manually-actuated control surfaces. Trim tabs in elevator and rudder.

Landing Gear: Prototype made first six flights with retractable nosewheel and fixed main units. It was then converted to production configuration, with hydraulically-retractable tricycle gear, all units retracting forward to simplify free-fall extension in emergency. Main units retract into sponson on each side of fuselage. Oleo-pneumatic shock-absorber and twin wheels on each unit. Hydraulically-steerable nose unit has wheels and tyres size 6·00-6. Main wheels and tyres size 7·00-8. Hydraulically-operated disc brakes.

Power Plant: Four 314 kW (420 shp) Allison 250-B17B turboprop engines, each driving a Hartzell three-blade constant-speed and fully-reversible metal propeller. Four wing fuel tanks, capacity 1,892 litres (500 US gallons). Two optional leading-edge auxiliary tanks, capacity 946 litres (250 US gallons). Propeller blades de-iced electrically.

Accommodation: Crew of two side by side on flight deck, with dual controls. Up to 30 passengers can be accommodated in commuter version, with a 'two and one' seating arrangement having an aisle width of 0·38 m (1 ft 3 in). Five-track seat/cargo restraint system in cabin floor may be used for seat attachment, direct cargo tiedown, or for the fitting of rollers to facilitate the handling of palletised cargo. Four standard D-3 containers can be accommodated. Twelve cabin windows on each side. Passenger door aft of wing on each side. Crew door on port side; communicating door between flight deck and cabin. Split cargo door forms undersurface of aft fuselage, lower half serving also as a loading ramp, which can be left open to permit the carriage of outsize cargo or to allow the air-dropping of paratroops and supplies. Accommodation air-conditioned and heated.

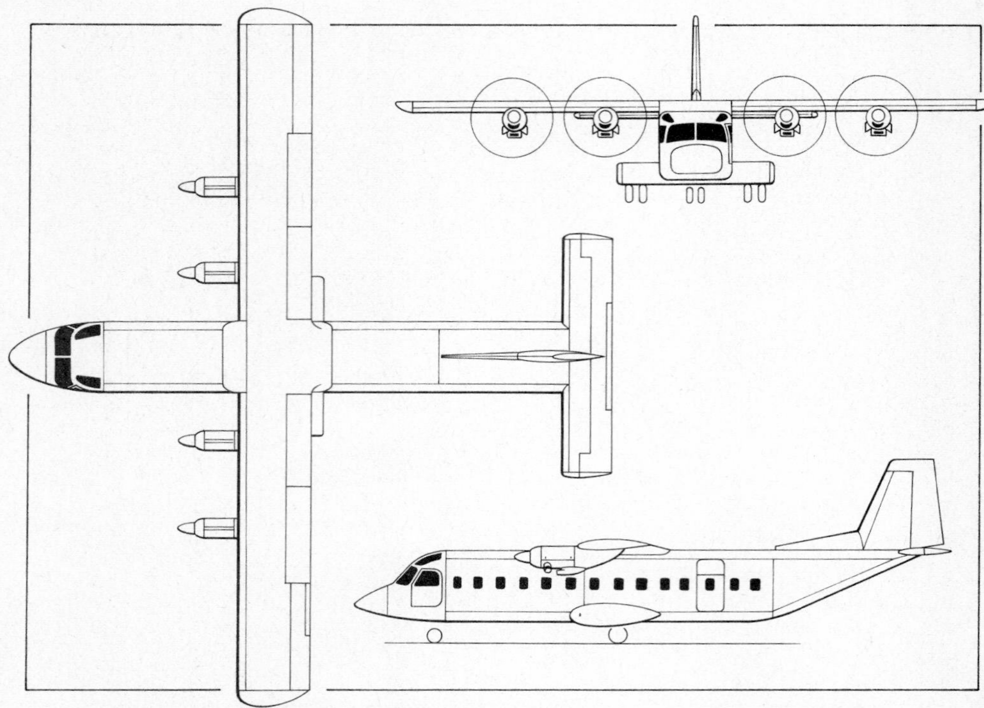

Production version of the Ahrens AR 404 utility transport aircraft *(Michael A. Badrocke)*

Systems: Hydraulic system for landing gear retraction, brakes and nosewheel steering. Electrical system powered by four Lear Siegler engine-driven generators, each developing 28V 150A DC. Dual storage batteries and external power sockets. A small APU driving a 28V 150A generator is housed in one sponson and is intended for emergency electricity supply and for battery charging.

Avionics and Equipment: Collins AP 106 autopilot, blind-flying instrumentation, navigation and communications transceivers and transponder are standard. Weather radar and other avionics optional.

Dimensions, external:

Wing span	20·12 m (66 ft 0 in)
Wing chord, constant	1·98 m (6 ft 6 in)
Wing aspect ratio	10·1
Length overall	16·08 m (52 ft 9 in)
Height overall	5·33 m (17 ft 6 in)
Tailplane span	7·32 m (24 ft 0 in)
Wheel track	4·27 m (14 ft 0 in)
Propeller diameter	2·29 m (7 ft 6 in)
Propeller ground clearance	1·45 m (4 ft 9 in)
Cabin doors (each): Height	1·52 m (5 ft 0 in)
Width	0·76 m (2 ft 6 in)
Rear cargo doors (upper and lower): Width	1·63 m (5 ft 4 in)

Dimensions, internal:

Cabin: Length	8·53 m (28 ft 0 in)
Max width	1·85 m (6 ft 1 in)
Max height	1·83 m (6 ft 0 in)
Floor area	15·8 m² (170 sq ft)
Volume	28·55 m³ (1,008 cu ft)

Areas:

Wings, gross	39·20 m² (422 sq ft)
Ailerons (total, incl tabs)	3·99 m² (43 sq ft)
Trailing-edge flaps (total)	5·95 m² (64 sq ft)
Vertical tail surfaces (incl tab)	4·83 m² (52 sq ft)
Horizontal tail surfaces (incl tab)	11·15 m² (120 sq ft)

Weights and Loadings (estimated):

Weight empty, equipped	3,719 kg (8,200 lb)
Max T-O weight	7,711 kg (17,000 lb)
Max wing loading	196·7 kg/m² (40·3 lb/sq ft)
Max power loading	6·16 kg/kW (10·1 lb/shp)

Performance (estimated, at max T-O weight):

Max level speed at 1,525 m (5,000 ft)	190 knots (352 km/h; 219 mph)
Max cruising speed at 1,525 m (5,000 ft)	170 knots (315 km/h; 195 mph)
Stalling speed, flaps down	75 knots (139 km/h; 86·5 mph)
Max rate of climb at S/L	366 m (1,200 ft)/min
Service ceiling	5,500 m (18,000 ft)
T-O run	488 m (1,600 ft)
Landing run	396 m (1,300 ft)
Range with standard fuel, no reserves	850 nm (1,574 km; 978 miles)
Range with auxiliary fuel, no reserves	1,280 nm (2,370 km; 1,473 miles)

AIR TRACTOR

AIR TRACTOR INC

Address: PO Box 485, Municipal Airport, Olney, Texas 76374

Telephone: (817) 564 5641

President: Leland Snow

The Air Tractor series of agricultural aircraft are new designs embodying more than 20 years' experience by their designer, Mr Leland Snow, who designed, developed, certificated and put into production the earlier Snow S-2 series of agricultural aircraft. The latter, which later became the Rockwell S-2R Thrush, have been described in previous editions of *Jane's*.

Three versions of the Air Tractor series were available in 1979: the Model AT-301 with Pratt & Whitney radial engine, and the Models AT-302 and AT-302A, each with an Avco Lycoming turboprop engine.

Air Tractor Model AT-301 Air Tractor single-seat agricultural aircraft

AIR TRACTOR MODEL AT-301 AIR TRACTOR

Design of the Model AT-301 Air Tractor was initiated in January 1971, and construction of the first prototype/pre-production aircraft started in August 1972. This aircraft flew for the first time in September 1973, and received FAA certification under FAR Pt 23 in November of that year. At that time the aircraft was also flight tested to meet FAR Pt 8 requirements. By 1 January 1979, a total of 244 AT-301s had been ordered, of which 176 had been completed, and production was continuing at a rate of six aircraft per month.

Type: Single-seat agricultural aircraft.

Wings: Cantilever low-wing monoplane. Wing section NACA 4415. Dihedral 3° 30′. Incidence 2°. No sweepback. Conventional two-spar structure of 2024-T3 light alloy. Ailerons of light alloy construction, interconnected with trailing-edge flaps to droop 10° at maximum flap deflection of 30°. Electrically-operated Fowler-type trailing-edge flaps of light alloy construction. No trim tabs. Wing ribs and skins zinc chromated before assembly. Wing roots and skin overlaps sealed against chemical entry.

Fuselage: Welded structure of 4130N steel tube, oven stress relieved and oiled internally. Quickly detachable skins of 2024-T3 light alloy.

Tail Unit: Light alloy structure, with cantilever fin and strut-braced tailplane. Fabric-covered rudder and elevators. Trim tab in each elevator.

Landing Gear: Non-retractable tailwheel type. Cantilever spring steel main gear; flat spring suspension for castoring and lockable tailwheel. Cleveland main wheels with tyres 26·0 × 10, pressure 2·83 bars (41 lb/sq in). Tailwheel tyre size 12·50 × 4, pressure 2·42 bars (35 lb/sq in). Cleveland type 30-89 hydraulic disc brakes.

POWER PLANT: One 447·4 kW (600 hp) Pratt & Whitney R-1340 aircooled radial engine, driving a Hamilton Standard two-blade metal constant-speed propeller type 12D40. Fuel contained in two integral wing tanks with combined capacity of 288 litres (76 US gallons). Refuelling points on upper surface of wings at root. Oil capacity 30·3 litres (8 US gallons).

ACCOMMODATION: Single seat in enclosed cabin which is sealed to prevent chemical ingress. Cabin ventilation by 0·08 m (3 in) diameter airscoop.

SYSTEMS: Agricultural dispersal system comprises a 1,211 litre (320 US gallon) glassfibre hopper, mounted in the forward fuselage; Transland gatebox, Agrinautics valve and strainer, 0·05 m (2 in) Root pump, 0·05 m (2 in) stainless steel plumbing, and up to 68 nozzles in spraybars mounted below and just aft of wing trailing-edges. Electrical system 24V, supplied by 30A engine-driven alternator.

DIMENSIONS, EXTERNAL:
- Wing span — 13·72 m (45 ft 0 in)
- Wing chord, constant — 1·83 m (6 ft 0 in)
- Wing aspect ratio — 7·5
- Length overall — 8·23 m (27 ft 0 in)
- Height overall — 2·59 m (8 ft 6 in)
- Propeller diameter — 2·77 m (9 ft 1 in)

AREAS:
- Wings, gross — 25·08 m² (270 sq ft)
- Ailerons (total) — 3·55 m² (38·2 sq ft)
- Trailing-edge flaps (total) — 3·34 m² (36·0 sq ft)
- Fin — 0·82 m² (8·8 sq ft)
- Rudder — 1·12 m² (12·1 sq ft)
- Tailplane — 2·42 m² (26·0 sq ft)
- Elevators (incl tabs) — 2·36 m² (25·4 sq ft)

WEIGHTS AND LOADINGS:
- Weight empty, equipped — 1,656 kg (3,650 lb)
- Max T-O weight (CAM 8) — 3,130 kg (6,900 lb)
- Max wing loading — 124·8 kg/m² (25·6 lb/sq ft)
- Max power loading — 7·0 kg/kW (11·5 lb/hp)

PERFORMANCE (at max T-O weight, unless stated otherwise):
- Never-exceed speed — 155 knots (286 km/h; 178 mph)
- Max level speed at S/L — 143 knots (266 km/h; 165 mph)
- Max cruising speed at 1,830 m (6,000 ft) — 130 knots (241 km/h; 150 mph)
- Econ cruising speed at 2,440 m (8,000 ft) — 122 knots (225 km/h; 140 mph)
- Stalling speed, flaps down, at normal landing weight — 46 knots (85·5 km/h; 53 mph)
- Max rate of climb at S/L — 488 m (1,600 ft)/min
- T-O run — 259 m (850 ft)
- Landing run at normal landing weight — 91 m (300 ft)
- Range with max fuel, no allowances — 304 nm (563 km; 350 miles)

Air Tractor's turboprop-powered Model AT-302 Air Tractor

AIR TRACTOR MODEL AT-302/302A AIR TRACTOR

Design of the basic **AT-302** turboprop-powered version of the Air Tractor was initiated in September 1976, and construction of the prototype started two months later. It flew for the first time in June 1977. The first flight of a production aircraft was made in November 1977, and certification under FAR Pt 23 was awarded during the following month. Apart from installation of the Avco Lycoming turboprop engine, and the structural modifications necessary to accept this power plant, the Model AT-302 is basically similar to the piston-engined AT-301. A total of 30 had been ordered by 1 January 1979, of which nine had been delivered.

The Model **AT-302A**, introduced for 1979, is identical to the AT-302 except for the installation of a 1,457 litre (385 US gallon) hopper, with a 0·97 m (3 ft 2 in) wide gatebox for high application rates of dry chemicals.

WINGS, FUSELAGE, TAIL UNIT, LANDING GEAR: As for Model AT-301.

POWER PLANT: One 447·5 kW (600 shp) Avco Lycoming LTP 101-600A turboprop engine, driving a Hartzell three-blade metal constant-speed propeller. Fuel system as for AT-301. Oil capacity 7·5 litres (2 US gallons). Air intake has two large dry paper type automobile air filters to avoid ingestion of chemicals.

ACCOMMODATION, SYSTEMS: As for Model AT-301, except electrical system supplied by 24V 150A engine-driven generator.

DIMENSIONS, EXTERNAL: As for Model AT-301, except:
- Length overall — 8·99 m (29 ft 6 in)
- Propeller diameter — 2·74 m (9 ft 0 in)

DIMENSIONS, INTERNAL, AND AREAS: As for Model AT-301

WEIGHTS AND LOADINGS (A: AT-302; B: AT-302A):
- Weight empty:
  - A, spray equipped — 1,474 kg (3,250 lb)
  - B, duster equipped — 1,520 kg (3,350 lb)
- Max T-O weight: A — 2,994 kg (6,600 lb)
  - B — 3,266 kg (7,200 lb)
- Max wing loading: A — 119·4 kg/m² (24·44 lb/sq ft)
  - B — 130·2 kg/m² (26·67 lb/sq ft)
- Max power loading: A — 6·7 kg/kW (11·0 lb/shp)
  - B — 7·3 kg/kW (12·0 lb/shp)

PERFORMANCE (AT-302, at max T-O weight unless stated otherwise):
- Never-exceed speed — 155 knots (286 km/h; 178 mph)
- Max level speed at S/L — 148 knots (274 km/h; 170 mph)
- Max cruising speed at 2,440 m (8,000 ft) — 143 knots (266 km/h; 165 mph)
- Econ cruising speed at 2,440 m (8,000 ft) — 130 knots (241 km/h; 150 mph)
- Stalling speed, flaps down, at normal landing weight — 44·3 knots (82 km/h; 51 mph)
- Max rate of climb at S/L (hopper empty) — 610 m (2,000 ft)/min
- Rate of climb at S/L (hopper full) — 366 m (1,200 ft)/min
- T-O run — 238 m (780 ft)
- Landing run at normal landing weight — 91 m (300 ft)
- Range with max fuel, no allowances — 347 nm (644 km; 400 miles)

AJI
AMERICAN JET INDUSTRIES INC

This company name has ceased to exist, following the acquisition of Grumman American Corporation by AJI. Grumman American is known now as Gulfstream American Corporation, under which heading details of the AJI Hustler and Peregrine can be found.

AJI itself is now known as Gulfstream American Corporation of California (which see). Details of AJI's earlier activities can be found in the 1978-79 and earlier editions of *Jane's*.

AMES
AMES INDUSTRIAL CORPORATION

ADDRESS: 55 Orville Drive, Bohemia, NY 11716
Telephone: (516) 567 3780

PRESIDENT: M. Berlon
VICE-PRESIDENT AND GENERAL MANAGER: H. A. Iversen

This company was awarded a NASA contract to develop and build a small manned aircraft, embodying the pivoting-wing concept and designated **AD-1**. Details can be found under the NASA entry in this section.

ARCTIC
ARCTIC AIRCRAFT COMPANY

ADDRESS: PO Box 6-141, Anchorage, Alaska 99502
Telephone: (907) 243 1580
SECRETARY: C. J. Diehl

Arctic Aircraft is constructing and marketing, as the S1B2 Arctic Tern, an updated and improved version of the Interstate S1A, first flown more than 30 years ago.

ARCTIC AIRCRAFT INTERSTATE S1B2 ARCTIC TERN

TYPE: Two-seat sporting and general utility aircraft.

WINGS: High-wing monoplane, with V bracing struts each side and auxiliary struts. Wing section NACA 23012. Composite structure with Sitka spruce spars, light alloy ribs and Dacron covering. Hoerner-type wingtips of glassfibre. Fowler-type single-slotted trailing-edge flaps. Plain inset ailerons.

FUSELAGE: Welded structure of 4130 chrome-molybdenum steel tube, Dacron covered. Two-piece engine cowling of glassfibre.

TAIL UNIT: Wire-braced structure of welded 4130 steel tube with Dacron covering. Trim tab in elevator.

LANDING GEAR: Non-retractable tailwheel type. Main wheels carried in two side Vs and half-axles hinged to fuselage. Shock-absorption by hydraulic/coil spring oleo unit. Cleveland main wheels with US Uniroyal tyres size 8·50-6. Maule tailwheel, diameter 203 mm (8 in). Scott toe-operated brakes. Parking brake optional. Peekay 1800 or Edo 2000 floats or 2500 skis optional.

POWER PLANT: One 112 kW (150 hp) Lycoming O-320 flat-four engine, driving a McCauley two-blade fixed-pitch metal propeller. One fuel tank in each wing, total capacity 151 litres (40 US gallons). Belly-mounted auxiliary fuel tank optional.

ACCOMMODATION: Two seats in tandem; rear seat removable to provide additional space for cargo. Cabin door on starboard side, beneath wing. Cabin step. Baggage space in rear fuselage, with external door on starboard side. Tinted windows and cabin skylight optional. Safety belts and fittings standard. Dual controls standard. Cabin soundproofed, heated and ventilated. Windscreen de-icing by hot air. Cabin floor carpeted.

SYSTEM: Electrical system includes 55A engine-driven alternator, 12V DC storage battery, engine starter and navigation lights.

AVIONICS AND EQUIPMENT: A range of radios is available. Standard features include epoxy priming, three-colour paint scheme, ground manoeuvring handles and engine quick oil drain. Optional items include instrument lights, Alcor exhaust gas analyser, folding front seat, shoulder harness, cabin dome lights, landing lights, belly-mounted cargo pack, lumber rack and salt water corrosion proofing.

DIMENSIONS, EXTERNAL:
- Wing span — 10·97 m (36 ft 0 in)
- Length overall — 7·32 m (24 ft 0 in)
- Height overall — 2·13 m (7 ft 0 in)

DIMENSIONS, INTERNAL:
- Cabin volume — 1·38 m³ (48·7 cu ft)
- Baggage volume — 0·84 m³ (29·63 cu ft)

Arctic Aircraft Interstate S1B2 Arctic Tern two-seat general utility aircraft

AREA:
Wings, gross 17·28 m² (186·0 sq ft)
WEIGHTS AND LOADINGS:
Weight empty 487 kg (1,073 lb)
Max T-O weight 862 kg (1,900 lb)
Max wing loading 49·9 kg/m² (10·2 lb/sq ft)
Max power loading 7·7 kg/kW (12·67 lb/hp)
PERFORMANCE:
Never exceed speed 152 knots (282 km/h; 175·5 mph)
Max cruising speed at S/L, 75% power 102 knots (188 km/h; 117 mph)
Cruising speed, 65% power at optimum altitude 96 knots (178 km/h; 111 mph)
Stalling speed, flaps down 28 knots (51·5 km/h; 32 mph)
Max rate of climb at S/L, at max T-O weight 389 m (1,275 ft)/min
Service ceiling 5,790 m (19,000 ft)
Absolute ceiling 6,400 m (21,000 ft)
T-O run at max T-O weight 99 m (325 ft)
T-O to 15 m (50 ft) at max T-O weight 152 m (500 ft)
Landing from 15 m (50 ft) 137 m (450 ft)
Range with max fuel, 45 min reserves:
75% power 479 nm (888 km; 552 miles)
65% power 566 nm (1,049 km; 652 miles)

ASTEC

ADVANCED SYSTEMS TECHNOLOGY INC

HEAD OFFICE AND WORKS: Snohomish County Airport, Everett, Washington 98204
Telephone: (206) 355 8700
Telex: Astec Evt 15 2954

ASTEC/CESSNA EAGLE

Advanced Systems Technology (ASTEC) was founded in 1971 to provide consulting services in aerodynamics and aircraft structural design, and continued this work until, in 1976, the company initiated studies for a major aircraft modification. The Cessna Citation 500 was chosen, with the initial object of increasing cruising speed; but a market survey showed the major requirement to be extended range. Using computerised design and analysis techniques, ASTEC developed a wing modification to reduce drag and increase fuel capacity. To test the flight characteristics of this wing, a Citation 500 was flown with the new wing contours fabricated by the addition of polyurethane foam and glassfibre. A metal production prototype wing was then constructed and flight tested. FAA approval and issue of an STC for modification of Cessna Citation 500 and Citation I aircraft to the same standard was awarded on 4 August 1978.

Changes to the basic Citation 500 wing include use of an advanced technology aerofoil section of increased thickness and length over the inboard portion of the wing; wingtip extensions of 0·51 m (1 ft 8 in), and the addition of cove seals to the trailing-edge flaps. The thickened wing and the wingtip extensions contain an additional 490 kg (1,080 lb) of fuel, accounting for some 77% of the approximate 650 nm (1,205 km; 748 mile) increase in range over the basic Citation 500. The remainder of the increase is due to improved aerodynamic efficiency of the ASTEC wing.

An STC was received in May 1979 for similar modification of the Cessna Citation 501, this being known as the ASTEC/Cessna **Eagle SP** after conversion. It is certificated under FAR Pt 23 and approved for single-pilot operation.

Production conversions were being carried out at a rate of 2½ per month in early 1979, but it was planned to increase this to 4½ per month towards the end of the year. The description of the Citation I under Cessna's entry in this edition applies also to the Eagle, except as detailed below:

WINGS: Thickness/chord ratio of inboard portions increased from 14% to 19%, and supercritical technology incorporated to improve wing/fuselage airflow. Span increased, by comparison with Citation 500, by addition of wingtip extensions.

POWER PLANT: As for Citation 500, except increased fuel capacity provided in the thicker wing centre-section and wingtip extensions.

DIMENSIONS, EXTERNAL:
Wing span 14·35 m (47 ft 0½ in)
Wing chord at root 2·95 m (9 ft 8⅛ in)
Wing chord at tip 0·93 m (3 ft 0½ in)
Wing aspect ratio 7·92
Length overall 13·26 m (43 ft 6 in)
Height overall 4·36 m (14 ft 3¾ in)
Wheel track 3·84 m (12 ft 7⅛ in)
Wheelbase 4·78 m (15 ft 8¼ in)
WEIGHTS:
Weight empty 2,971 kg (6,550 lb)
Max fuel 2,064 kg (4,550 lb)
Max T-O weight 5,670 kg (12,500 lb)

First production example of the ASTEC/Cessna Eagle, a conversion of the Citation 500

Max zero-fuel weight 4,309 kg (9,500 lb)
Max landing weight 5,148 kg (11,350 lb)
PERFORMANCE (at max T-O weight except where indicated):
Max cruising speed, average cruise weight, at 10,670 m (35,000 ft) 344 knots (637 km/h; 396 mph)
Cruising speed, average cruise weight, at 12,500 m (41,000 ft) 320 knots (592 km/h; 368 mph)
Stalling speed 78 knots (145 km/h; 90 mph)
Max certificated altitude 12,500 m (41,000 ft)
Balanced field length 907 m (2,975 ft)
Landing field length 602 m (1,974 ft)
Range, VFR, with 454 kg (1,000 lb) payload 1,900 nm (3,521 km; 2,188 miles)
Range, IFR, with 454 kg (1,000 lb) payload 1,400 nm (2,594 km; 1,612 miles)

ASTEC/GRUMMAN EAGLE II

ASTEC is developing an all-new wing for the Gulfstream II aircraft. Employing advanced technology aerodynamic concepts, it will be offered as a retrofit package for existing Gulfstream II aircraft, to provide greater range through increased fuel volume, and improved take-off, climb and landing performance as a result of aerodynamic advances. A prototype wing, with new contours formed from polyurethane foam and glassfibre, was due to be flight tested in late 1979.

The new wing will have an increase in area of 16·5% by comparison with the original, and will also be thicker. Thickness/chord ratio near the wing root will be approximately 14%, tapering to 10·5% at the tip. New trailing-edge flaps, ailerons, spoilers and landing gear supports will be included, but changes to the hydraulic and electrical systems of the Gulfstream II will be limited to changed runs and lengths of hydraulic lines and electrical wires in the wing. In addition to the provision of greater fuel capacity, modified venting and pressure fuelling schemes will be incorporated. A new wing/body fairing will be provided, but no other modifications will be made to the fuselage, tail unit, landing gear or engines.

Modified aircraft will be renamed Eagle II.

DIMENSIONS, EXTERNAL:
Wing span 24·38 m (80 ft 0 in)
Wing chord at aircraft c/l 5·51 m (18 ft 1 in)
Wing chord at tip (theoretical) 1·52 m (5 ft 0 in)
Wing chord, mean aerodynamic 3·89 m (12 ft 9¼ in)
Wing aspect ratio 6·93
Length overall 24·36 m (79 ft 11 in)
Height overall 7·47 m (24 ft 6 in)
AREAS:
Wings, gross 85·84 m² (924 sq ft)
Ailerons (total) 2·79 m² (30 sq ft)
Trailing-edge flaps (total) 14·31 m² (154 sq ft)
Spoilers (ground) 1·86 m² (20 sq ft)
Spoilers (flight) 2·88 m² (31 sq ft)
WEIGHTS (estimated):
Operating weight empty 16,284 kg (35,900 lb)
Max T-O weight 31,071 kg (68,500 lb)
Max ramp weight 31,525 kg (69,500 lb)
Max zero-fuel weight 19,051 kg (42,000 lb)
Max landing weight 26,535 kg (58,500 lb)
PERFORMANCE (estimated, at max T-O weight except where indicated):
Max operating speed below 7,345 m (24,100 ft) 367 knots (681 km/h; 423 mph) CAS
Max operating Mach No. above 7,345 m (24,100 ft) Mach 0·85
Long-range cruising speed at 13,105 m (43,000 ft) Mach 0·75
Certificated altitude 13,105 m (43,000 ft)
FAA T-O field length 1,737 m (5,700 ft)
FAA landing field length 792 m (2,600 ft)
Range with 14,061 kg (31,000 lb) fuel, long-range cruising power, and NBAA IFR reserves 4,000 nm (7,413 km; 4,606 miles)

AYRES

AYRES CORPORATION

ADDRESS: PO Box 3090, Albany, Georgia 31706
Telephone: (912) 883 1440
Telex: 547629

AYRES THRUSH

Ayres Corporation acquired the manufacturing and world marketing rights of the Rockwell Thrush Commander-600 and -800 from Rockwell International's General Aviation Division in late November 1977, and is now offering the following versions of this large agricultural aircraft:

Thrush-600. Basic version with Pratt & Whitney R-1340 Wasp aircooled radial engine.

Turbo-Thrush S-2R. As Thrush-600, but with a Pratt & Whitney Aircraft of Canada PT6A-34 or -15 turboprop engine. Described separately.

Details of two-seat versions developed in 1979 can be found in the Addenda.

Ayres took over the leased facility in Albany covering 23,226 m² (250,000 sq ft) at which Rockwell formerly built the Thrush, and retained the supervisory management and production personnel, amounting to 150 persons, who worked previously for Rockwell's General Aviation Division. In early 1979 production was continuing at a rate of 10 aircraft per month.

The Thrush-600 has a 1·50 m³ (53 cu ft) hopper able to contain up to 1,514 litres (400 US gallons) of liquid or 1,487 kg (3,280 lb) of dry chemicals. Corrosion-proofing is of activated Copon, and it is certificated to both CAR 3 Normal category and CAM 8 Restricted category requirements.

The following details refer to the basic single-seat Thrush-600:

TYPE: Single-seat agricultural aircraft.

WINGS: Cantilever low-wing monoplane. Dihedral 3° 30′. Two-spar structure of light alloy throughout, except for main spar caps of heat-treated SAE 4000 Series steel. Leading-edge formed by heavy main spar and the nose-skin. Light alloy plain ailerons. Electrically-operated flaps. Wing roots sealed against chemical entry.

FUSELAGE: Welded chrome-molybdenum steel tube structure covered with quickly-removable light alloy panels. Underfuselage skin of stainless steel.

TAIL UNIT: Wire-braced welded chrome-molybdenum steel tube structure, fabric-covered. Streamline-section heavy-duty stainless steel wire bracing and heavy-duty stainless steel attachment fittings. Light alloy controllable trim tab in each elevator. Deflector cable from cockpit to fin-tip.

LANDING GEAR: Non-retractable tailwheel type. Main units have rubber-in-compression shock-absorption and 29 × 11·00-10 wheels with 10-ply tyres. Hydraulically-operated disc brakes. Parking brakes. Wire cutters on main gear. Steerable, locking tailwheel, size 12·5 × 4·5 in.

POWER PLANT: One 448 kW (600 hp) Pratt & Whitney R-1340 Wasp nine-cylinder aircooled radial engine, driving a Hamilton Standard type 12D40/EAC AG-100-2 two-blade constant-speed metal propeller. One 200·5 litre (53 US gallon) integral tank in each wing, giving total fuel capacity of 401 litres (106 US gallons), of which 378·5 litres (100 US gallons) are usable.

ACCOMMODATION: Single adjustable seat in 'safety pod' sealed cockpit enclosure, with steel tube overturn structure. Two overhead windows for improved view in turns. Downward-hinged door on each side. Tempered safety-glass windscreen. Dual inertia-reel safety harness standard. Baggage compartment. Windscreen wiper and washer.

SYSTEM: Electrical system powered by a 24V 50A engine-driven alternator; 70A alternator optional. Lightweight 24V 35Ah battery.

AVIONICS AND EQUIPMENT: Hopper forward of cockpit with capacity of 1·50 m³ (53 cu ft) or 1,514 litres (400 US gallons). Hopper has a 0·33 m² (3·56 sq ft) lid, openable by two handles. Standard equipment includes Universal spray system with external 50 mm (2 in) stainless steel plumbing, 50 mm Root Model 67 pump with wooden fan, Transland gate, 50 mm valve, quick-disconnect pump mount and strainer. Streamlined spraybooms with outlets for 68 nozzles, 36 nozzles installed. Micro-adjust valve control (spray) and calibrator (dry). A 63 mm (2·5 in) side-loading system is installed on the port side. Navigation lights, instrument lights and two rotating beacons. Optional equipment includes Transland high-volume spreader with micro-adjust calibrator, agitator installation, extra-high-density spray configuration with 70 nozzles installed; Agrinautics electrically-operated three-way valve, emergency shut-off valve, pump in lieu of Root pump and strainer in lieu of Transland strainer; Agevenco 6520 pump in lieu of Root pump. Six- or eight-unit AU3000 Micronair installation in lieu of standard booms and nozzles. Transland S-2 Boommaster with Q-D flange in lieu of standard gate and Root pump, and S-2R Boommaster replacement units; night working lights including wingtip turn lights, cockpit fire extinguisher, and water bomber configuration. Optional avionics include basic installation kit, Bendix T-12C ADF or T-12D digital ADF; King KX170B, KX170BE, KX175B or KX175BE nav/com; KI201C converter indicator; Narco Com-11A or Com-11B com transceiver; and Nav-11 nav receiver.

DIMENSIONS, EXTERNAL:
- Wing span: 13·51 m (44 ft 4 in)
- Length overall (tail up): 8·95 m (29 ft 4½ in)
- Height overall: 2·79 m (9 ft 2 in)
- Tailplane span: 4·86 m (15 ft 11½ in)
- Wheel track: 2·72 m (8 ft 11 in)
- Propeller diameter: 2·74 m (9 ft 0 in)

AREA:
- Wings, gross: 30·34 m² (326·6 sq ft)

WEIGHTS AND LOADINGS:
- Weight empty, equipped: 1,678 kg (3,700 lb)
- Max T-O weight (CAR 3): 2,721 kg (6,000 lb)
- Max T-O weight (CAM 8): 3,130 kg (6,900 lb)
- Max wing loading: 103·0 kg/m² (21·1 lb/sq ft)
- Max power loading: 6·99 kg/kW (11·5 lb/hp)

PERFORMANCE (with spray equipment installed and at CAR 3 max T-O weight, unless indicated otherwise):
- Max level speed: 122 knots (225 km/h; 140 mph)
- Max cruising speed, 70% power: 108 knots (200 km/h; 124 mph)
- Working speed, 70% power: 91-100 knots (169-185 km/h; 105-115 mph)
- Stalling speed, flaps up: 61 knots (113 km/h; 70 mph)
- Stalling speed, flaps down: 57·5 knots (107 km/h; 66 mph)
- Stalling speed at normal landing weight, flaps up: 50 knots (92 km/h; 57 mph)
- Stalling speed at normal landing weight, flaps down: 48 knots (89 km/h; 55 mph)
- Max rate of climb at S/L: 274 m (900 ft)/min
- Service ceiling: 4,575 m (15,000 ft)
- T-O run: 236 m (775 ft)
- Landing run: 152 m (500 ft)
- Ferry range with max fuel at 70% power: 350 nm (648 km; 403 miles)

Ayres Thrush-600 agricultural aircraft (Pratt & Whitney R-1340 engine)

AYRES TURBO-THRUSH S-2R

This turbine-engined version of the Thrush has as standard a 559 kW (750 shp) Pratt & Whitney Aircraft of Canada PT6A-34 turboprop, driving a three-blade constant-speed and reversible-pitch metal propeller. The lower-powered (507 kW; 680 shp) PT6A-15 engine is available optionally. To compensate for the small size and light weight of the turboprop, it is mounted well forward of the firewall, in a slender cowling. Current installations have cowlings which comprise individual panels to improve access. Innovations include an oil cooler with an airscoop on top of the cowling, new exhaust outlets for the PT6A, and a special air induction system utilising large perforated aluminium panels at the aft end of the cowling side panels. Air entering via these panels is ducted to large centrifugal air filters, able to remove 98 per cent of all foreign matter in the airflow before it enters the engine. Another important modification involves resiting of the cabin air inlet, which is now high on the side of the canopy to ensure that the cabin is not contaminated by fumes from the turbine engine.

A 1,514 litre (400 US gallon) hopper is standard for the Turbo-Thrush, but a 1,893 litre (500 US gallon) hopper is available optionally, and is suitable for installation with either the standard or optional power plant.

Advantages claimed for this conversion include greatly improved take-off and climb performance; improved short landing capability; a 454 kg (1,000 lb) increase in payload due to reduced power plant weight; ability to operate on aviation turbine fuel, avgas or diesel fuel; a TBO of more than 3,000 hours; quieter operation; and the ability to stop the propeller without shutting down the engine, because of the free-turbine configuration.

First flight of the prototype was made on 9 September 1975. More than 60 Turbo-Thrushes were in operation in January 1979, at which time production was at a rate of four turbine-powered aircraft per month.

DIMENSIONS, EXTERNAL:
- Wing span: 13·54 m (44 ft 5 in)
- Length overall: 10·06 m (33 ft 0 in)
- Height overall: 2·79 m (9 ft 2 in)
- Tailplane span: 4·86 m (15 ft 11½ in)
- Wheel track: 2·74 m (9 ft 0 in)

AREA:
- Wings, gross: 30·34 m² (326·6 sq ft)

WEIGHTS AND LOADINGS (A: standard hopper; B: optional 1,893 litre: 500 US gallon hopper):
- Weight empty: A: 1,633 kg (3,600 lb)
  - B: 1,769 kg (3,900 lb)
- Max T-O weight (CAR 3):
  - A, B: 2,722 kg (6,000 lb)
- Typical operating weight (CAM 8):
  - A: 3,719 kg (8,200 lb)
  - B: 3,856 kg (8,500 lb)
- Max wing loading: 127·1 kg/m² (26·0 lb/sq ft)
- Max power loading: 7·6 kg/kW (14·17 lb/shp)

PERFORMANCE (A and B, at max T-O weight unless specified otherwise):
- Max level speed, with spray equipment: 138 knots (256 km/h; 159 mph)
- Cruising speed, 50% power: 130 knots (241 km/h; 150 mph)
- Working speed, 30-50% power: 82·5-130 knots (153-241 km/h; 95-150 mph)
- Stalling speed, flaps up: 61 knots (113 km/h; 70 mph)
- Stalling speed, flaps down: 57 knots (106 km/h; 66 mph)
- Stalling speed at normal landing weight, flaps up: 51 knots (95 km/h; 59 mph)
- Stalling speed at normal landing weight, flaps down: 49·5 knots (92 km/h; 57 mph)
- Max rate of climb at S/L: 533 m (1,750 ft)/min
- Service ceiling: 7,620 m (25,000 ft)
- T-O run: 183 m (600 ft)
- Landing run: 152 m (500 ft)
- Landing run with propeller reversal: 91 m (300 ft)
- Ferry range at 40% power: 391 nm (724 km; 450 miles)

Ayres Turbo-Thrush S-2R (Pratt & Whitney Aircraft of Canada PT6A-34 turboprop engine)

BALL-BARTOE

BALL-BARTOE AIRCRAFT CORPORATION (a subsidiary of Ball Corporation)

HEAD OFFICE: PO Box 1857, Boulder, Colorado 80306
Telephone: (303) 441 4100
Telex: 45-605
PRESIDENT: O. E. Bartoe Jr

This company designed and built the prototype of a single-seat research aircraft designated JW-1 Jetwing. It is powered by a 9·79 kN (2,200 lb st) turbofan engine, the jet efflux from which is ducted so that the entire flow from the engine blows the upper surface of the wing, over 70% of the span. Design originated in March 1973, and construction of the prototype began six months later. In December 1976 the aircraft was subjected to full-scale wind tunnel testing, and the first flight was made on 11 July 1977. By 1 January 1978 a total of 65 flights had been recorded, and the company stated that preliminary performance figures were very close to the estimates given.

Further flight testing of the JW-1 was to be carried out during 1979 at the University of Tennessee Space Institute. Details and illustrations can be found in the 1978/79 *Jane's*.

BEECHCRAFT
BEECH AIRCRAFT CORPORATION

HEAD OFFICE AND MAIN WORKS: Wichita, Kansas 67201
Telephone: (316) 681 7111
BRANCH DIVISIONS: Liberal, Kansas; Salina, Kansas; and Boulder, Colorado

CHAIRMAN OF THE BOARD: Mrs O. A. (Walter H.) Beech
PRESIDENT: Frank E. Hedrick
EXECUTIVE VICE-PRESIDENT: Edward C. Burns
SENIOR VICE-PRESIDENTS:
Seymour Colman (Administration)
Michael G. Neuburger (International Division)
VICE-PRESIDENTS:
Stewart M. Ayton
Harold W. Deets (Materiel)
Max P. Eaton (Production)
Glenn Ehling (Manufacturing)
Gary M. Hanssen (Industrial Relations)
E. C. Nikkel (Aerospace Programmes)
John A. Pike (Research and Development)
C. A. Rembleske (Engineering)
Austin Rising
William G. Robinson (Corporate Communications)
George D. Rodgers (Domestic Commercial Marketing)
William G. Rutherford (Government Relations)
William D. Wise (Advanced Technology)
SECRETARY-TREASURER: C. W. Dieker
ASSISTANT SECRETARY: I. Alumbaugh
ASSISTANT SECRETARY AND CONTROLLER: L. R. Damon
ASSISTANT TREASURER AND CHIEF ACCOUNTANT:
D. C. Cullinane
ASSISTANT TREASURER: Wey D. Kenny
DIRECTOR, ADVERTISING AND SALES PROMOTION:
R. James Yarnell
DIRECTOR, PUBLIC RELATIONS: Stephen M. Caine

Founded jointly in 1932 by Mrs Olive Ann Beech and the late Walter H. Beech, pioneer designer and builder of light aeroplanes in the United States, the Beech Aircraft Corporation is currently engaged in the production of civil and military aircraft, missile targets, aircraft and missile components and cryogenic equipment for spacecraft.

Deliveries by Beech in 1978 were made up of 300 King Airs, 34 Dukes, 300 Barons, 434 Bonanzas, 120 Duchesses, 31 Sierras, 115 Sundowners and 79 Sports. By 1 January 1979 Beech had delivered 2,897 pressurised aircraft since introducing the King Air 90 in 1964, a record exceeding that of any other general aviation manufacturer. Total production of Beechcraft aeroplanes exceeded 42,000 by the beginning of 1979.

A milestone attained in 1978 was delivery of the 2,000th King Air in September. This total comprised 457 Super King Airs, 284 King Air 100s and 1,259 King Air 90s.

Deliveries of the Beechcraft C-12 twin-turboprop transport to the US Army continued throughout 1978. Contracts totalling $57 million awarded in late 1977 and 1978 will extend deliveries of C-12Cs for the US Army until November 1979, and UC-12Bs for the US Navy until April 1981.

During 1978 Beech continued deliveries of the US Navy T-34C turboprop trainer for student primary training at NAS Milton, Florida. Beech has received contracts totalling $72 million for 184 T-34Cs and provision of engineering services. Production of an international version, designated T-34C-1, continued in 1978, and deliveries to the Argentinian Navy, Ecuadorean Air Force, Indonesian Air Force, Royal Moroccan Air Force and Peruvian Navy have been completed.

Production of the Beechcraft T-44A twin-turboprop advanced trainer for the US Navy continued, with the first delivery in April 1977, for advanced pilot training at NAS Corpus Christi, Texas. With receipt of an $11·8 million Navy award in December 1977, contracts to Beech for 61 T-44As, testing and contract logistics support, totalled $46 million. Production was scheduled to continue until October 1979.

Production deliveries of the Beechcraft Duchess 76 began in May 1978. FAA certification of the Model 77 Skipper trainer was awarded in March 1979, and initial deliveries of production aircraft were scheduled for later in the year.

During 1978 more powerful versions of the Baron 58P and 58TC were introduced, and in Spring 1979 deliveries began of the Bonanza A36TC, the company's first turbocharged single-engined aircraft.

Production of airframes for the Bell Helicopter Textron JetRanger, continuous at Beech since 1967, was extended until December 1979 by receipt of a $3·7 million contract in August 1978. Commercial JetRanger helicopter contracts with Beech exceed $75 million, the company building the complete airframe, including fuselage, cowling, tailboom and skid landing gear, at Wichita and the Salina, Kansas, division.

In early 1977 Beech established a wholly-owned subsidiary, Beech Aerospace Services Inc (BASI), to expand worldwide support of Beechcraft aerospace products. Beech Aircraft has contracts for total logistics support from the US Army, Navy and Air Force, which includes responsibility for furnishing technicians, spares, and ground support equipment. BASI activities cover the Army and Air Force C-12A, USN T-34C and T-44A, as well as subsonic and supersonic missile targets for the Army. By the beginning of 1979, BASI had trained 388 service technicians, stationed them at 31 bases in 24 countries, and established supply routes to each base. BASI headquarters for administration, spare parts, publications central supply and training is based at Wichita.

Beech production of subassemblies for the McDonnell Douglas F-4 Phantom II fighter has entered its seventeenth consecutive year.

Beech Aircraft occupies 283,717 m² (3,054,000 sq ft) of plant area at its four major facilities in Wichita, Liberal and Salina, Kansas, and Boulder, Colorado, and at its centres in Selma, Alabama, and Newton, Kansas.

The Salina division supplies all wings used in Wichita production and is responsible for manufacture and final assembly of the six-seat Beechcraft Duke and the pressurised Beechcraft Baron 58P.

All assembly, flight testing and delivery of the Beechcraft Duchess 76, Sierra, Sundowner and Skipper are carried out at the Liberal Division, which also manufactures control surfaces for all Beech aircraft.

Work at Boulder involves space vehicle or missile applications, and included design, development, final assembly and testing of the cryogenic gas storage system for NASA's Apollo and Skylab spacecraft. This same system was utilised in the US-USSR Apollo-Soyuz Test Programme carried out in July 1975. Boulder engineers have developed for NASA cryogenic tanks with the capacity of supporting space missions of as long as six months. These tanks can store 50 times as much oxygen and 120 times as much hydrogen as those used in the Apollo programme.

In January 1974 Beech was awarded a subcontract to produce the power reactant storage assembly for NASA's Space Shuttle Orbiter. The assembly includes two liquid oxygen and two liquid hydrogen tanks to supply the Orbiter's fuel cells and environmental control/life support system. Design, development, test and production are being carried out at the Boulder division. The first delivery of oxygen and hydrogen cryogenic tanks for the power reactant storage assembly was completed in November 1978. During 1975-76 Beech received three additional contracts to develop Space Shuttle ground support equipment systems, which will be used at both the Kennedy Space Center and Vandenberg AFB launch sites. Beech contracts on the Space Shuttle programme total $22·9 million.

Boulder also produces aircraft assemblies for other Beech divisions and AQM-37A and MQM-107 (VSTT) missile target systems for the US Army and Navy (see RPVs and Targets section).

In late 1978, Beech announced the lease of a 5,388 m² (58,000 sq ft) facility at Craig Field, Selma, Alabama, for aircraft modification. Beech will continue to manufacture basic aircraft at its Wichita facility, and fly them to its Selma Modification Center for specialised work. First aircraft scheduled for modification at Selma were special maritime versions of the Super King Air for Japan's Maritime Safety Agency.

In June 1978, Beech anounced the introduction of an innovative charter service through the Beechcraft Aviation Centers. Known as the Beechcraft Executive Flight plan, it makes available to businessmen on a guaranteed annual charter basis such aircraft as the Baron 58P and 58TC, and the single-engined Bonanza series. The company believes that this will make a new sector of the business community aware of the economic advantages of private air transport.

Wholly-owned subsidiaries of the parent company include Beech Acceptance Corporation Inc, which is engaged in business aircraft retail finance and leasing; Beechcraft AG, which has its headquarters in Zurich, Switzerland, and supports in Europe the sales, liaison and other activities of the parent company; Travel Air Insurance Company Ltd, a Bermuda-based company organised during 1972 to provide aircraft liability insurance; Beech Holdings Inc, which provides marketing support to the parent company; Beech International Sales Corporation, Wichita, through which all Beech export sales are made; Beech Aerospace Services Inc, which provides worldwide support of Beechcraft military aircraft, missile targets and related products; Fuel and Line Service Inc, Wichita; and the following product sales outlets: Hedrick Beechcraft, Colorado Springs, Colorado; Houston-Beechcraft Inc, Houston, Texas; Denver-Beechcraft Inc, Denver, Colorado and Aircraftco Division, Broomfield, Colorado; United Beechcraft Inc, Wichita, Kansas; Beechcraft West Hayward, Van Nuys, Bakersfield and Fresno, California; Mission Beechcraft, Santa Ana, California; Indiana Beechcraft Inc, Indianapolis, Indiana; Beechcraft East Inc, Farmingdale, New York; and Baton Rouge Aircraft, Baton Rouge, Louisiana.

BEECHCRAFT MODEL T-34C

US Navy designation: T-34C

In March 1953 the USAF selected the Beechcraft Model 45 as its new primary trainer and, under the designation T-34A Mentor, a total of 450 were eventually acquired. Power plant consisted of a 168 kW (225 hp) Continental O-470-13 flat-six engine. Just over a year later the US Navy reached a similar decision, and a total of 423 T-34B Mentors were built for that service.

In 1973 Beech received a USN R & D contract to modify two T-34Bs to see whether the type could be upgraded for a continuing training role. This involved the installation of a turboprop engine and the latest avionics equipment, the primary object being to let student pilots have experience of operating turbine-powered aircraft from the beginning of their flight training. The power plant selected was the PT6A-25, which has a torque limiter in this application to restrict engine output to 298 kW (400 shp), ensure long engine life, and provide constant performance over a wide range of temperature and altitude.

Design of the modifications to update the aircraft began in March 1973, and conversion of two T-34Bs (140784 and 140861) started in May 1973. Designated YT-34C, the first of these aircraft (described in previous editions of *Jane's*) flew for the first time on 21 September 1973.

Beech has received USN contracts totalling approx $72 million for 184 new-production T-34Cs. The first of these were delivered to the Naval Air Training Command at Whiting Field, Milton, Florida, in November 1977. Student training in the T-34C began in January 1978, and 163 had been delivered by 1 March 1979. An export civil version, known as the **Turbine Mentor 34C**, is in service at the Algerian National Pilot Training School, which received six in 1979.

Production T-34Cs incorporate improvements developed during the flight test programme; structural strength was increased to permit high limit speeds and a fatigue life of 16,000 hours in a primary flight training role.

A **T-34C-1** armament systems trainer version is also available and, in addition to its basic role, is capable of carrying out forward air control (FAC) and tactical strike missions. Contracts were received for the supply of 12 T-34C-1s to the Air Force of Morocco, 20 for the Air Force of Ecuador, 16 for the Air Force of Indonesia, 6 for the Peruvian Navy, and 15 for the Navy of Argentina. Delivery of all of these has been completed.

TYPE: Two-seat turbine-powered primary training aircraft.

Beechcraft Turbine Mentor 34C trainers for the national pilot training school of Algeria

WINGS: Cantilever low-wing monoplane. Wing section NACA 23016·5 (modified) at root, NACA 23012 at tip. Dihedral 7°. Incidence 4° at root, 1° at tip. No sweepback. Conventional box beam structure of light alloy. Ailerons of light alloy construction. Single-slotted trailing-edge flaps of light alloy. Manually operated trim tab in port aileron. Servo tabs in both ailerons.

FUSELAGE: Semi-monocoque light alloy structure.

TAIL UNIT: Cantilever structure of light alloy. Fixed-incidence tailplane. Manually-operated trim tabs in elevators and rudder. Twin ventral fins under rear fuselage.

LANDING GEAR: Electrically-retractable tricycle type. Main units retract inward, nosewheel aft. Beech oleo-pneumatic shock-absorbers. Single wheel on each unit. Main wheels size 7·00-8. Nosewheel and tyre size 5·00-5. Goodyear multiple-disc hydraulic brakes.

POWER PLANT: One 533 kW (715 shp) Pratt & Whitney Aircraft of Canada PT6A-25 turboprop engine, torque limited to 298 kW (400 shp), driving a Hartzell three-blade metal constant-speed fully-feathering propeller. Version of same engine derated to 410 kW (550 shp) is available optionally. Two bladder-type fuel cells in each wing, with a total usable capacity of 492 litres (130 US gallons). Oil capacity 15·1 litres (4 US gallons).

ACCOMMODATION: Instructor and pupil in tandem beneath rearward-sliding cockpit canopy. Cockpit ventilated, heated by engine bleed air and air-conditioned. Dual controls standard. All armament controls in forward cockpit of T-34C-1.

SYSTEMS: Hydraulic system for brakes only. Pneumatic system for emergency opening of cockpit canopy. Diluter demand gaseous oxygen system, pressure 103·5 bars (1,500 lb/sq in). Electrical power supplied by 200A starter/generator. Freon-type air-conditioner for cockpit cooling.

AVIONICS AND EQUIPMENT: Standard avionics can include UHF or VHF com, VOR or Tacan nav, DME, transponder, angle of attack indicator, ADF, marker beacon, compass and intercom system. Area-NAV, Loran, HF and specialised tactical systems available to customer's requirements. Blind-flying instrumentation standard. Electrically-heated pitot.

ARMAMENT (T-34C-1): CA-513 fixed-reticle reflector gunsight. Four underwing hardpoints are provided for the carriage of stores. The inboard stations are rated at 272 kg (600 lb) each, the outboard stations at 136 kg (300 lb) each, with a maximum load of 272 kg (600 lb) each side and 544 kg (1,200 lb) total. Weapons which can be carried on MA-4 racks include AF/B37K-1 bomb containers with practice bombs or flares, LAU-32 or LAU-59 rocket pods, MK 81 bombs, SUU-11 Minigun pods, BLU-10/B incendiary bombs, AGM-22A wire-guided anti-tank missiles and TA8X towed target equipment.

DIMENSIONS, EXTERNAL:
- Wing span: 10·16 m (33 ft 3⅞ in)
- Wing chord at root: 2·55 m (8 ft 4½ in)
- Wing chord at tip: 1·05 m (3 ft 5¼ in)
- Wing aspect ratio: 6·22
- Length overall: 8·75 m (28 ft 8½ in)
- Height overall: 3·02 m (9 ft 10⅞ in)
- Tailplane span: 3·71 m (12 ft 2⅛ in)
- Wheel track: 2·91 m (9 ft 6½ in)
- Wheelbase: 2·41 m (7 ft 11 in)
- Propeller diameter: 2·29 m (7 ft 6 in)
- Propeller ground clearance: 0·45 m (1 ft 5¾ in)

DIMENSIONS, INTERNAL:
- Cabin: Length: 2·74 m (9 ft 0 in)
  - Max width: 0·86 m (2 ft 10 in)
  - Max height: 1·22 m (4 ft 0 in)

AREAS:
- Wings, gross: 16·71 m² (179·9 sq ft)
- Ailerons (total): 1·06 m² (11·4 sq ft)
- Trailing-edge flaps (total): 1·98 m² (21·3 sq ft)
- Fin: 1·31 m² (14·1 sq ft)

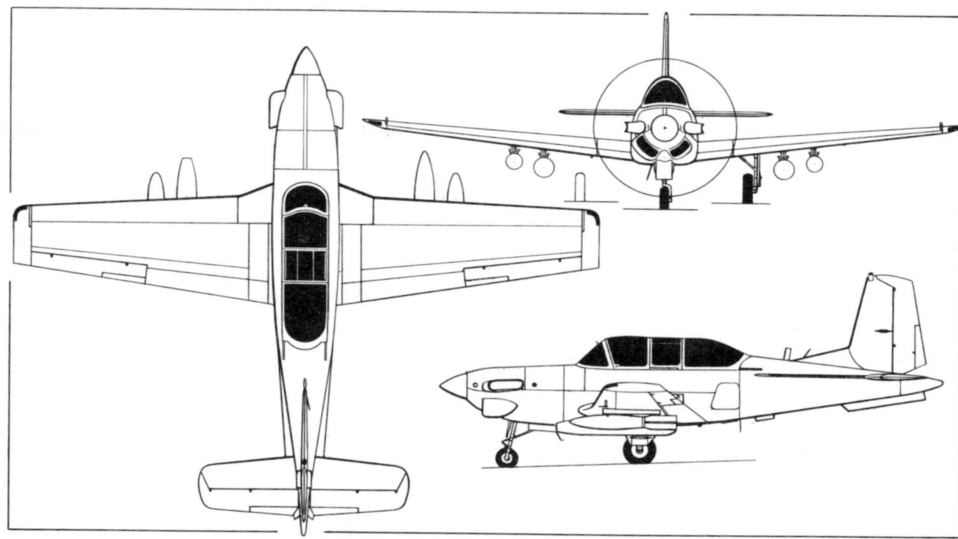

Beechcraft Model T-34C-1 turboprop-powered training/attack aircraft *(Pilot Press)*

- Rudder, incl tab: 0·76 m² (8·16 sq ft)
- Tailplane: 2·95 m² (31·8 sq ft)
- Elevators, incl tabs: 1·50 m² (16·2 sq ft)

WEIGHTS AND LOADING:
- Weight empty: T-34C: 1,334 kg (2,940 lb)
  - T-34C-1: 1,356 kg (2,990 lb)
- Max T-O and landing weight:
  - T-34C: 1,950 kg (4,300 lb)
  - T-34C-1, strike role: 2,495 kg (5,500 lb)
- Max wing loading: T-34C 108·3 kg/m² (22·2 lb/sq ft)

PERFORMANCE (T-34C, preliminary results at max T-O weight):
- Never-exceed speed 280 knots (518 km/h; 322 mph)
- Max cruising speed at 5,335 m (17,500 ft) 214 knots (397 km/h; 247 mph)
- Stalling speed, flaps up 55 knots (102 km/h; 63·3 mph) CAS
- Max rate of climb at 3,050 m (10,000 ft) 388 m (1,275 ft)/min
- Service ceiling over 9,145 m (30,000 ft)
- Range at 6,100 m (20,000 ft) 650 nm (1,205 km; 749 miles)

PERFORMANCE (T-34C-1 with 298 kW; 400 shp engine, estimated. A with two stores at AUW of 2,222 kg; 4,900 lb. B with four stores at AUW of 2,495 kg; 5,500 lb):
- Max level speed at 5,500 m (18,000 ft):
  - A: 192 knots (355 km/h; 221 mph)
  - B: 172 knots (318 km/h; 198 mph)
- Stalling speed, flaps down, idle power:
  - A: 65 knots (120 km/h; 75 mph) CAS
  - B: 69 knots (128 km/h; 80 mph) CAS
- Max rate of climb at S/L: A: 268 m (880 ft)/min
  - B: 170 m (560 ft)/min
- Typical combat radius:
  - FAC mission at AUW of 2,429 kg (5,355 lb), with four stores and optional max fuel, incl 2·6 h loiter over target and 20 min +5% reserves 100 nm (185 km; 115 miles)
  - Strike mission at AUW of 2,473 kg (5,452 lb), with four stores and optional max fuel, incl 20 min +5% reserves 300 nm (555 km; 345 miles)

BEECHCRAFT MODEL 77 SKIPPER

Beech announced on 17 April 1979 that the Model 77 Skipper, mentioned briefly in the 1978-79 *Jane's*, had received FAA certification in the Utility category, and that deliveries of production aircraft would begin later that month. The first aircraft were allocated to Beech Aero Centers for flying training duties.

Beechcraft Model 77 Skipper lightweight training aircraft (Lycoming O-235 engine)

Following design definition, which began in late 1973, a five-year development programme had been undertaken to evolve an efficient and economical two-seat general aviation trainer. The prototype, designated PD 285, flew for the first time on 6 February 1975, and was described briefly in the 1975-76 *Jane's*. It was fitted after a time with a T-tail, which offered aerodynamic improvements. Inherent design features included a wing of NASA-developed GAW-1 section, which resulted from NASA/Beech research into supercritical aerofoils with high-lift characteristics; extensive use of bonded metal construction; a one-piece bonded door on each side of the cabin; and all-round tinted cabin windows.

TYPE: Two-seat training aircraft, approved for six-turn spins.

WINGS: Cantilever low-wing monoplane, of NASA GAW-1 section. Dihedral 6° from roots. Tubular spar formed of wrapped light alloy sheet and glassfibre adhesive to ensure required bonding stiffness at all wing stations; auxiliary rear spar, light alloy ribs and bonded light alloy skins. Plain ailerons with corrugated skins. Ground-adjustable trim tab on each aileron. Plain trailing-edge flaps with corrugated skins. Flaps and ailerons actuated via torque tubes.

FUSELAGE: Semi-monocoque structure of light alloy. Lower cabin section is of bonded construction.

TAIL UNIT: Cantilever T-tail of light alloy. Fixed-incidence tailplane, leading-edge of fin, large portion of tailplane, elevator trim tabs and rudder are of bonded construction. Trim tab in each elevator; rudder trim standard.

LANDING GEAR: Non-retractable tricycle type with single wheel on each unit. Cantilever main legs. Steerable nosewheel.

POWER PLANT: One 85·5 kW (115 hp) Lycoming O-235-L2C flat-four engine, driving a Sensenich fixed-pitch two-blade metal propeller with spinner. Fuel in integral wing tanks with combined usable capacity of 110 litres (29 US gallons). Refuelling point on upper surface of each wing.

ACCOMMODATION: Two seats side by side in enclosed cabin. Door on each side. Tinted cabin windows. Carpeted floor. Dual controls standard.

DIMENSIONS, EXTERNAL:
- Wing span: 9·14 m (30 ft 0 in)
- Length overall: 7·29 m (23 ft 11 in)
- Height overall: 2·30 m (7 ft 6½ in)
- Tailplane span: 3·00 m (9 ft 10 in)
- Wheel track: 2·54 m (8 ft 4 in)
- Wheelbase: 1·50 m (4 ft 11 in)
- Propeller diameter: 1·83 m (6 ft 0 in)

WEIGHTS:
- Weight empty: 499 kg (1,100 lb)
- Max T-O and landing weight: 760 kg (1,675 lb)
- Max ramp weight: 762 kg (1,680 lb)

PERFORMANCE (at max T-O weight):
- Max cruising speed, 80% power at 1,370 m (4,500 ft) 105 knots (195 km/h; 121 mph)
- Econ cruising speed, 53% power at 1,370 m (4,500 ft) 88 knots (163 km/h; 101 mph)
- Cruising speed, 61% power at 2,590 m (8,500 ft) 96 knots (177 km/h; 110 mph)
- Econ cruising speed, 51% power at 2,590 m (8,500 ft) 85 knots (137 km/h; 99 mph)
- Stalling speed, flaps up 49 knots (91 km/h; 56·5 mph) CAS
- Stalling speed, flaps down 47 knots (87 km/h; 54 mph) CAS
- Max rate of climb at S/L: 219 m (720 ft)/min
- Service ceiling: 3,930 m (12,900 ft)
- Absolute ceiling: 4,570 m (15,000 ft)
- T-O run: 238 m (780 ft)
- T-O to 15 m (50 ft): 390 m (1,280 ft)
- Landing from 15 m (50 ft): 400 m (1,313 ft)

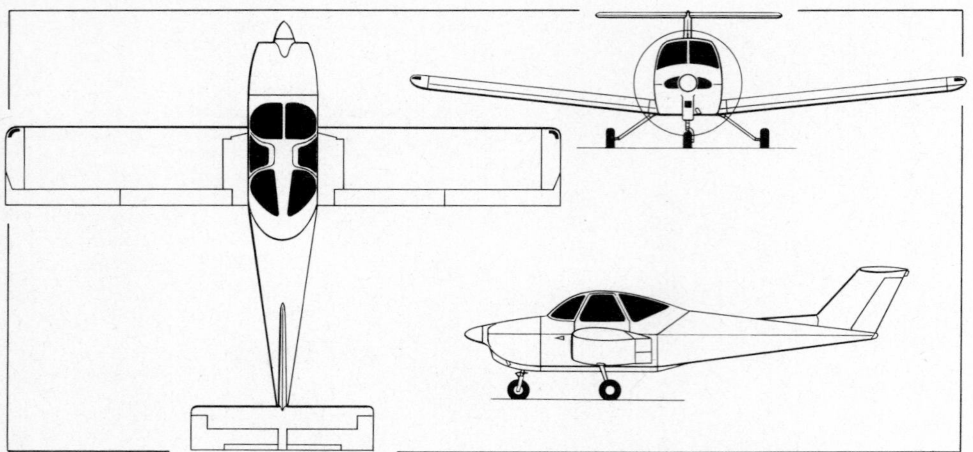
Beechcraft Model 77 Skipper two-seat training aircraft *(Pilot Press)*

Landing run 204 m (670 ft)
Range, max cruising speed at 1,370 m (4,500 ft), with reserves 327 nm (607 km; 377 miles)
Range, econ cruising speed at 1,370 m (4,500 ft), with reserves 410 nm (760 km; 472 miles)
Range, cruising speed (61% power) at 2,590 m (8,500 ft), with reserves 388 nm (719 km; 447 miles)
Range, econ cruising speed at 2,590 m (8,500 ft), with reserves 413 nm (766 km; 476 miles)

BEECHCRAFT SIERRA 200 and SUNDOWNER 180

In December 1971, Beech introduced a new light aircraft marketing programme centred around three models, which were given individual exterior paint schemes and renamed from their previous Musketeer designations (see 1971-72 *Jane's*).

In 1974 these designations were changed again to indicate the engine horsepower rating, so becoming Beechcraft Sierra 200 (formerly Model A24R Musketeer Super R), Sundowner 180 (Model C23, formerly Musketeer Custom), and Sport 150 (Model B19, formerly Musketeer Sport). The fourth aircraft in the former Musketeer line, the Super, was discontinued at the end of 1971 after a total of 368 had been built; and production of the Sport 150 (Model B19) ended in September 1978 after 903 had been built. Details of the Sport 150 can be found in the 1978-79 *Jane's*.

The Sierra 200 was recertificated in 1974 and redesignated Model B24R, due to the installation of a new engine, improved cowling and redesign of control features. Designated Model C24R in 1977, improvements included a propeller of increased diameter to enhance performance, and wheel well fairings to reduce drag when the wheels are retracted.

Details of the two current models are as follows:

Sundowner 180. Basic four-seat version with 134 kW (180 hp) Lycoming O-360-A4K engine, driving a Sensenich Type 76EM8S5-0-60 two-blade fixed-pitch metal propeller, and non-retractable landing gear. Aerobatic version is approved for rolls, Immelmann turns, loops, spins, chandelles and other manoeuvres, carrying two persons. Three windows standard on each side of cabin.

Sierra 200. Generally similar to the Sundowner but with accommodation for four to six persons, a 149 kW (200 hp) Lycoming IO-360-A1B6 engine, driving a Hartzell Type HC-M2YR-1BF/F7666A two-blade metal constant-speed propeller, and retractable tricycle landing gear. Electrically-actuated hydraulic system based on a self-contained unit in the rear fuselage, comprising electrically-driven hydraulic pump, fluid reservoir and valves. An emergency valve, sited adjacent to the pilot's feet, allows selection of the landing gear to free-fall within three seconds. Main wheels retract outward into wings; nosewheel turns through 90° as it retracts rearwards. Four windows standard on each side of cabin.

Factory-installed optional equipment packages are as follows:

Weekender. Includes sun visors; lighting group comprising rotating beacon, navigation, cabin dome, overhead instrument and map lights; cabin boarding steps; dual controls and pedal-operated brakes for co-pilot; tinted windscreen and windows; and acrylic enamel paint; adding 7·3 kg (16 lb) to basic empty weight.

Holiday. As above, plus wing-mounted landing light; 35Ah battery; instrument group comprising 3 in horizon and directional gyros with vacuum system, turn co-ordinator, rate-of-climb indicator, coat hook and garment hanger in baggage compartment, electric clock, and outside air temperature gauge; adding 15·9 kg (35 lb) to basic empty weight.

Professional. As above, plus wing-mounted taxi light; heated pitot tube; electrically-operated tailplane trim and control wheel switch; true airspeed indicator; two headrests and instrument post lights; adding 18·1 kg (40 lb) to basic empty weight.

Ten factory-installed avionics packages are available optionally, and include com transceiver, nav receiver-converter, ADF, transponder and audio panel from Collins, King, Edo-Aire Mitchell or Narco, plus cabin speaker, microphone with jack and related antennae. An extensive selection of additional avionics is also available optionally.

Production is centred in Beech's Liberal, Kansas, plant. A total of 4,798 Musketeers, Sundowners, Sports and Sierras had been delivered by 1 February 1979. They included 20 aircraft supplied to the Mexican government for military training, 25 for the Canadian Armed Forces, 21 for the Indonesian Department of Transportation, Communication and Tourism for its primary training programme, and 19 for the University of Illinois Institute of Aviation. Three Sierra 200s were delivered in 1979 to the national pilot training school of Algeria.

The following details apply to both current models:

Type: Four- or four/six-seat cabin monoplane.

Wings: Cantilever low-wing monoplane. Wing section NACA 63_2A415. Dihedral 6° 30′. Incidence 3° at root, 1° at tip. Single extruded main spar at 50% chord. Aluminium skin and stringers are bonded to honeycomb Trussgrid ribs on forward 50% of wing; rear 50% of wing is riveted. Slotted all-metal riveted ailerons and mechanically-controlled (optionally electrically-actuated) flaps have corrugated skin. No trim tabs. Plastics wingtips.

Fuselage: Cabin section has basic keel formed by floor and lower skin, with rolled skin side panels, stringers, a minimum number of bulkheads and structural top. Conventional semi-monocoque rear fuselage.

Tail Unit: Cantilever all-metal structure, with swept vertical surfaces. One-piece all-moving horizontal surface with full-span anti-servo tab. Optional electric tailplane trim. Rudder and aileron controls interconnected for easy cross-country flying.

Landing Gear (Sundowner): Non-retractable tricycle type. Beech rubber-disc shock-absorbers. Nosewheel with tube-type tyre size 15 × 6·00-6, pressure 2·76 bars (40 lb/sq in). Main wheels have tube-type tyres size 17·5 × 6·00-6, pressure 1·52 bars (22 lb/sq in). Cleveland disc-type hydraulic brakes with toe-operated control. Steerable nosewheel. Parking brake.

Landing Gear (Sierra): Tricycle type, with electrically-actuated hydraulic retraction. Main units retract outwards and upwards into wing wells; steerable nosewheel unit turns through 90° and retracts rearward to fold flat into a fairing behind the nosewheel. Beech rubber-disc shock-absorbers. Main wheels fitted with tube-type tyres size 17·5 × 6·00-6, pressure 2·21 bars (32 lb/sq in). Nosewheel tyre size 14·2 × 5·00-5, pressure 2·41 bars (35 lb/sq in). Cleveland hydraulic disc brakes with toe-operated control. Parking brake.

Power Plant: One flat-four engine (details given under model listings). Two fuel tanks in inboard wing leading-edges, with usable capacity of 216 litres (57 US gallons). Refuelling points above tanks. Oil capacity 7·5 litres (2 US gallons).

Accommodation: Pilot and three or five passengers (Sierra); pilot and three passengers (Sundowner); in pairs, in enclosed cabin with door on each side. Compartment for 122 kg (270 lb) baggage, with external door on port side. In-flight adjustable seats, pilot's storm window, windscreen defroster, instrument panel glareshield, air vents, map stowage, wall-to-wall carpeting. Optional aerobatic kit for Sundowner includes *g* meter and quick-release door.

Systems: Electrical system supplied by 60A alternator, 12V 25Ah battery. 35Ah battery optional. Hydraulic system for brakes only, except on Sierra which has electro-hydraulic actuation system for landing gear. Vacuum system for instruments optional.

Avionics and Equipment: Optional avionics as listed earlier. Standard equipment includes sensitive altimeter, fore and aft adjustable front seats with reclining backs, shoulder harness and lap belts, pilot's storm window, map stowage, emergency locator transmitter, stall warning device, control locks and towbar. Optional equipment includes headrests, Hobbs hour meter, exhaust gas temperature and outside air temperature gauges, true airspeed indicator, instrument post lights, rear cabin 'family' seat, tinted windscreen and windows, electrically operated trailing-edge flaps, vacuum system, two-light strobe system, wing-mounted taxi light, external power socket, heated pitot, electric tailplane trim, alternate static source, internal corrosion proofing and acrylic enamel exterior finish. An aerobatic kit is available for the Sundowner, and a 'Magic Hand' landing gear safety system for the Sierra.

Dimensions, external:

Wing span	9·98 m (32 ft 9 in)
Wing chord, constant	1·34 m (4 ft 4¾ in)
Wing aspect ratio	7·5
Length overall	7·85 m (25 ft 9 in)
Height overall: Sundowner	2·51 m (8 ft 3 in)
Sierra	2·46 m (8 ft 1 in)
Tailplane span	3·30 m (10 ft 10 in)
Wheel track: Sundowner	3·61 m (11 ft 10 in)
Sierra	3·86 m (12 ft 8 in)
Wheelbase: Sundowner	1·93 m (6 ft 4 in)
Sierra	1·83 m (6 ft 0¼ in)
Propeller diameter	1·93 m (6 ft 4 in)
Propeller ground clearance	0·36 m (1 ft 2 in)
Cabin doors: Height	0·97 m (3 ft 2 in)
Width	1·03 m (3 ft 4 in)
Baggage compartment door:	
Sundowner: Height	0·47 m (1 ft 6½ in)
Width	0·60 m (1 ft 11¾ in)
Sierra: Height	0·91 m (3 ft 0 in)
Width	0·61 m (2 ft 0 in)

Dimensions, internal:

Cabin, aft of instrument panel:	
Length	2·41 m (7 ft 11 in)
Max width	1·18 m (3 ft 8 in)
Max height	1·22 m (4 ft 0½ in)
Floor area	2·4 m² (25·84 sq ft)
Volume	2·92 m³ (103·2 cu ft)
Baggage compartment	0·55 m³ (19·5 cu ft)

Areas:

Wings, gross	13·57 m² (146 sq ft)
Ailerons (total)	0·92 m² (9·9 sq ft)

Beechcraft Sundowner 180 four-seat light aircraft

Beechcraft Sierra 200 four/six-seat light aircraft

Flaps (total) 1·74 m² (18·7 sq ft)
Fin 0·99 m² (10·61 sq ft)
Rudder 0·43 m² (4·62 sq ft)
Tailplane, incl anti-servo tab 2·51 m² (27·0 sq ft)

WEIGHTS AND LOADINGS:
Weight empty (incl oil and unusable fuel):
Sundowner 670 kg (1,477 lb)
Sierra 768 kg (1,693 lb)
T-O weight, Utility category:
Sundowner 920 kg (2,030 lb)
Max T-O weight: Sundowner 1,111 kg (2,450 lb)
Sierra 1,247 kg (2,750 lb)
Max wing loading:
Sundowner 81·9 kg/m² (16·78 lb/sq ft)
Sierra 91·9 kg/m² (18·84 lb/sq ft)
Max power loading:
Sundowner 8·29 kg/kW (13·61 lb/hp)
Sierra 8·37 kg/kW (13·75 lb/hp)

PERFORMANCE (at max T-O weight):
Max level speed at S/L:
Sundowner 123 knots (228 km/h; 141 mph)
Sierra 142 knots (262 km/h; 163 mph)
Cruising speed:
Sundowner, 84% power 123 knots (228 km/h; 141 mph)
Sundowner, 59% power 98 knots (182 km/h; 113 mph)
Sierra, 75% power 137 knots (254 km/h; 158 mph)
Sierra, 55% power 115 knots (213 km/h; 132 mph)
Stalling speed, flaps down, power off:
Sundowner 51 knots (94·5 km/h; 59 mph) IAS
Sierra 60 knots (111 km/h; 69 mph) IAS
Max rate of climb at S/L:
Sundowner 241 m (792 ft)/min
Sierra 283 m (927 ft)/min
Service ceiling: Sundowner 3,840 m (12,600 ft)
Sierra 4,690 m (15,385 ft)
Absolute ceiling: Sundowner 4,390 m (14,400 ft)
Sierra 5,315 m (17,430 ft)
Min ground turning radius 7·29 m (23 ft 11 in)
T-O run: Sundowner 344 m (1,130 ft)
Sierra 361 m (1,185 ft)
T-O to 15 m (50 ft): Sundowner 596 m (1,955 ft)
Sierra 506 m (1,660 ft)
Landing from 15 m (50 ft):
Sundowner 452 m (1,484 ft)
Sierra 446 m (1,462 ft)
Landing run: Sundowner 214 m (703 ft)
Sierra 249 m (816 ft)
Range with max fuel, allowances for warm-up, T-O, climb and 45 min reserves:
Sundowner, 2,300 rpm at 1,370 m (4,500 ft) 597 nm (1,106 km; 687 miles)
Sierra, 2,400 rpm at 3,050 m (10,000 ft) 686 nm (1,271 km; 790 miles)

BEECHCRAFT BONANZA MODEL V35B

The prototype Bonanza flew for the first time on 22 December 1945 and the type went into production in 1947. In February 1977 the 10,000th V-tail Bonanza Model 35 was completed, and this aircraft entered its 33rd year of production in 1979. The current version is designated Model V35B.

The Bonanza Model A36 and A36TC utility aircraft, and Model F33 series with conventional tail unit, are described separately.

The Bonanzas for 1979 are equipped with a dual-duct fresh air system to increase cabin airflow. Safety features include single diagonal strap shoulder harness with inertia reel for all occupants as standard equipment. Five optional factory-installed IFR avionics packages include dual communication, navigation, marker beacon, glideslope, DME, and transponder. Four packages meet FAA Technical Standard Order (TSO). Beech was in 1972 the first general aviation manufacturer to acquire IFR approval for factory installation of area navigation equipment on production aircraft with this equipment.

In 1979 Beech was offering five 'Super Utility' packages of optional equipment, which includes a large cargo door on the Models V35B and F33A and club seating arrangement on the Models A36 and A36TC, 280 litre (74 US gallon) extended-range fuel tanks, gyro horizon and directional gyro with pressure system, heated pitot, alternate static source, super soundproofing and a choice of Edo-Aire Mitchell Century I, III or IV, Bendix FCS-810 or King KFC 200 autopilot.

Other optional extras available on the Bonanza include the Beech-designed 'Magic Hand' landing gear safety system. Designed to eliminate the possibility of wheels-up landing or inadvertent retraction of the landing gear on the ground, it lowers the gear automatically on approach when the engine manifold pressure falls below approximately 508 mm (20 in) and airspeed has been reduced to 104 knots (193 km/h; 120 mph). On take-off, it keeps the gear down until the aircraft is airborne and has accelerated to 78 knots (145 km/h; 90 mph) IAS. The system can be switched off by the pilot at will.

An optional 12,000 BTU refrigeration-type air-conditioning system was introduced during 1975, comprising an evaporator located beneath the pilot's seat, condenser mounted on the lower fuselage and an engine-mounted compressor. Air outlets are located on the centre console, and a two-speed blower is provided for air distribution (except on A36TC).

Beechcraft's V-tail V35B Bonanza four/five-seat light aircraft

TYPE: Four/five-seat light cabin monoplane.

WINGS: Cantilever low-wing monoplane. Wing section Beech modified NACA 23016·5 at root, modified NACA 23012 at tip. Dihedral 6°. Incidence 4° at root, 1° at tip. Sweepback 0° at quarter-chord. Each wing is a two-spar semi-monocoque box-beam of conventional aluminium alloy construction. Symmetrical-section ailerons and single-slotted flaps of aluminium alloy construction. Ground-adjustable trim tab in each aileron.

FUSELAGE: Conventional aluminium alloy semi-monocoque structure. Hat-section longerons and channel-type keels extend forward from cabin section, making the support structure for the engine and nosewheel an integral part of the fuselage.

TAIL UNIT: Cantilever V tail, with tailplane and elevators set at 33° dihedral angle. Semi-monocoque construction. Fixed surfaces have aluminium alloy structure and skin. Control surfaces, aft of the light alloy spar, are primarily of magnesium alloy, with large controllable trim tab in each. Tail surfaces are interchangeable port and starboard, except for tabs and actuator horns. Electrically-operated elevator trimming optional.

LANDING GEAR: Electrically-retractable tricycle type, with steerable nosewheel. Main wheels retract inward into wings, nosewheel aft. Beech oleo-pneumatic shock-absorbers on all units. Cleveland main wheels, size 6·00-6, and tyres, size 7·00-6, pressure 2·28-2·76 bars (33-40 lb/sq in). Cleveland nosewheel and tyre, size 5·00-5, pressure 2·76 bars (40 lb/sq in). Cleveland ring-disc hydraulic brakes. Parking brake.

POWER PLANT: One 212·5 kW (285 hp) Continental IO-520-BB flat-six engine, driving a McCauley two-blade metal constant-speed propeller. Three-blade McCauley propeller optional. Manually-adjustable engine cowl flaps. Two standard fuel tanks in wing leading-edges, with total usable capacity of 166·5 litres (44 US gallons). Optionally, these can be replaced by tanks with total usable capacity of 280 litres (74 US gallons). Refuelling points above tanks. Oil capacity 11·5 litres (3 US gallons).

ACCOMMODATION: Enclosed cabin seating four or five persons on individual seats. Centre windows open for ventilation on ground and have release pins to permit their use as emergency exits. Pilot's storm window, port side. Cabin structure reinforced for protection in turnover. Space for up to 122·5 kg (270 lb) of baggage aft of seats. Passenger door and baggage access door both on starboard side. Cabin heated and ventilated.

SYSTEMS: Electrical system supplied by 28V 50A alternator, 24V 15Ah battery; a 100A alternator is available as an option. Hydraulic system for brakes only. Pneumatic system for instrument gyros and refrigeration-type air-conditioning system optional.

AVIONICS AND EQUIPMENT: Standard avionics comprise King KX 170B 720-channel com transceiver, 200-channel nav receiver with KC 208 VOR/LOC converter-indicator, microphone, headset, cabin speaker, and Beechcraft B11-1 nav/com/GS antenna. A wide range of optional avionics is available, by Bendix, Collins, Edo-Aire, King and Narco. Standard equipment includes sensitive altimeter, rate of climb indicator, electric turn co-ordinator, outside air temperature gauge, electric clock, instrument panel floodlights, electroluminescent sub-panel lighting, glove compartment, sun visors, pilot's storm window, ultraviolet-proof windscreen and windows, wall-to-wall carpeting, in-flight storage pockets, coat hooks, cabin dome light, reading lights, four fore and aft adjustable and reclining seats, armrests, headrests for all seats, shoulder harness and lap belt for all seats, rear cabin utility shelf, landing light, taxi light, full-flow oil filter, ventilation system, stall warning device, emergency locator transmitter, exterior urethane paint finish, three-position flap system, and towbar. Optional equipment includes co-pilot's brakes, control wheel clock, dual control wheels, 3 in gyro horizon and directional gyro with pressure system, exhaust gas temperature gauge, instrument post lights, internally-lighted instruments, control wheel map lights, large cargo door, entrance door courtesy light, fifth seat, super soundproofing, rotating beacons, three-light strobe system, air-conditioner or oxygen system, standby generator system, 'Magic Hand' landing gear system, heated pitot, external power socket, 100A alternator, three-blade propeller, alternate static source, and static wicks.

DIMENSIONS, EXTERNAL:
Wing span 10·21 m (33 ft 6 in)
Wing chord at root 2·13 m (7 ft 0 in)
Wing chord at tip 1·07 m (3 ft 6 in)
Wing aspect ratio 6·2
Length overall 8·05 m (26 ft 5 in)
Height overall 2·31 m (7 ft 7 in)
Tailplane span 3·10 m (10 ft 2 in)
Wheel track 2·92 m (9 ft 7 in)
Wheelbase 2·13 m (7 ft 0 in)
Propeller diameter: two-blade 2·13 m (7 ft 0 in)
three-blade 2·03 m (6 ft 8 in)
Passenger door: Height 0·91 m (3 ft 0 in)
Width 0·94 m (3 ft 1 in)
Baggage compartment door:
Height 0·47 m (1 ft 6½ in)
Width 0·57 m (1 ft 10½ in)

DIMENSIONS, INTERNAL:
Cabin, aft of firewall: Length 3·07 m (10 ft 1 in)
Max width 1·07 m (3 ft 6 in)
Max height 1·27 m (4 ft 2 in)
Volume 3·31 m³ (117 cu ft)
Baggage space 0·99 m³ (35 cu ft)

AREAS:
Wings, gross 16·80 m² (181 sq ft)
Ailerons (total) 1·06 m² (11·4 sq ft)
Trailing-edge flaps (total) 1·98 m² (21·3 sq ft)
Fixed tail surfaces 2·20 m² (23·8 sq ft)
Movable tail surfaces, incl tabs 1·34 m² (14·4 sq ft)

WEIGHTS AND LOADINGS:
Weight empty, equipped 949 kg (2,093 lb)
Max T-O and landing weight 1,542 kg (3,400 lb)
Max wing loading 91·8 kg/m² (18·80 lb/sq ft)
Max power loading 7·26 kg/kW (11·93 lb/hp)

PERFORMANCE (at max T-O weight, except cruising speeds at mid-cruise weight):
Max level speed at S/L 182 knots (338 km/h; 209 mph)
Cruising speed:
75% power at 1,830 m (6,000 ft) 172 knots (319 km/h; 198 mph)
66% power at 3,050 m (10,000 ft) 168 knots (311 km/h; 193 mph)
55% power at 3,660 m (12,000 ft) 157 knots (291 km/h; 181 mph)
45% power at 2,440 m (8,000 ft) 136 knots (253 km/h; 157 mph)
Stalling speed, power off, flaps up 64 knots (118 km/h; 74 mph) IAS
Stalling speed, power off, 30° flap 51 knots (94 km/h; 59 mph) IAS
Max rate of climb at S/L 356 m (1,167 ft)/min
Service ceiling 5,445 m (17,860 ft)
T-O run 305 m (1,002 ft)
T-O to 15 m (50 ft) 539 m (1,769 ft)
Landing from 15 m (50 ft) 404 m (1,324 ft)
Landing run 233 m (763 ft)
Range with 280 litres (74 US gallons) usable fuel, allowances for engine start, taxi, T-O, climb and 45 min reserves at 45% power:
75% power at 1,830 m (6,000 ft) 716 nm (1,326 km; 824 miles)
66% power at 3,050 m (10,000 ft) 777 nm (1,440 km; 894 miles)
55% power at 3,660 m (12,000 ft) 838 nm (1,553 km; 964 miles)
45% power at 2,440 m (8,000 ft) 889 nm (1,648 km; 1,023 miles)

Beechcraft Model F33A Bonanza (foreground) and A36 six-seat Bonanza

BEECHCRAFT BONANZA MODEL F33A/C

The **F33A** version of the Bonanza is a four/five-seat single-engined executive aircraft, similar in general configuration to the Bonanza Model V35B, but distinguished by a conventional tail unit with sweptback vertical surfaces. The prototype flew for the first time on 14 September 1959, and the production models were known as Debonairs until 1967.

The **F33C** is generally similar to the A, but approved for both aerobatic and utility operation.

The Model G33 was discontinued in early 1973 after 49 had been produced.

A total of 2,189 Model 33s had been built by 6 April 1978. Twenty-one were bought for pilot training by Lufthansa in Germany; Pacific Southwest Airlines acquired ten G33s for airline crew training; and the Netherlands Government Flying School has ordered 16 F33Cs. Deliveries of F33As and aerobatic F33Cs to foreign air forces were as follows: Imperial Air Force of Iran, 16 F33Cs; Mexican Navy, 5 F33Cs; Spanish Air Ministry and Air Force, 74 F33s in service in 1977.

Optional extras include the 'Magic Hand' automatic landing gear control system, air-conditioning system and other items described under the Model V35B Bonanza entry, except that the large cargo door, air-conditioning and fifth seat are not available for the Bonanza F33C.

TYPE: Four/five-seat cabin monoplane.

WINGS: As for V35B Bonanza.

FUSELAGE: As for Bonanza V35B series.

TAIL UNIT: Conventional cantilever all-metal stressed-skin structure, primarily of aluminium alloy but with corrugated magnesium skin on elevators. Large trim tab in each elevator. Fixed tab in rudder.

LANDING GEAR: As for Bonanza V35B series. Main wheels size 6·00-6, with tyres size 7·00-6, pressure 2·28-2·76 bars (33-40 lb/sq in); nosewheel size 5·00-5, tyre pressure 2·76 bars (40 lb/sq in).

POWER PLANT: As for Bonanza V35B.

ACCOMMODATION: Enclosed cabin with four individual seats in pairs as standard, plus optional forward-facing fifth seat (F33A only). Baggage compartment and hat shelf aft of seats. Passenger door and baggage compartment door on starboard side. Heater standard. Large cargo door, on starboard side of fuselage, optional on F33A.

SYSTEMS: As for V35B.

AVIONICS AND EQUIPMENT: As for V35B.

DIMENSIONS, EXTERNAL: As for V35B except:

Length overall	8·13 m (26 ft 8 in)
Height overall	2·51 m (8 ft 3 in)
Tailplane span	3·71 m (12 ft 2 in)
Propeller diameter	2·13 m (7 ft 0 in)

DIMENSIONS, INTERNAL: As for V35B.

AREAS: As for V35B except:

Fin	0·85 m² (9·1 sq ft)
Rudder, incl tab	0·43 m² (4·6 sq ft)
Tailplane	1·75 m² (18·82 sq ft)
Elevators, incl tabs	1·24 m² (13·36 sq ft)

WEIGHTS AND LOADINGS:

Weight empty	958 kg (2,113 lb)
Max T-O and landing weight	1,542 kg (3,400 lb)
Max wing loading	91·8 kg/m² (18·8 lb/sq ft)
Max power loading	7·26 kg/kW (11·93 lb/hp)

PERFORMANCE: As for V35B

BEECHCRAFT BONANZA MODEL A36

This version of the Bonanza, introduced in mid-1968, is a full six-seat utility aircraft developed from the Bonanza Model V35B. It is generally similar to the V35B, but has a conventional tail unit with sweptback vertical surfaces, similar to that of the F33 series of Bonanzas. In addition, the A36 has large double doors on the starboard side of the fuselage aft of the wing root, to facilitate loading and unloading of bulky cargo when used in a utility role. The cabin volume is increased by 0·54 m³ (18·9 cu ft) compared with the V35B, due to a fuselage extension of 0·25 m (10 in), and an increase of 0·28 m³ (10 cu ft) in the baggage compartment volume.

Like all Bonanzas, the Model A36 is licensed in the FAA Utility category at full gross weight, with no limitation of performance. A total of 1,266 civil versions of the Model 36/A36 had been built by 6 April 1978.

The current version of the Bonanza Model A36 introduced the improvements noted for the Bonanza V35B as well as options which include a club-seating interior layout with rear-facing third and fourth seats, executive writing desk, reading lights and fresh air outlets for fifth and sixth seats. Optional extras include the 'Magic Hand' automatic landing gear control system, refrigeration-type air-conditioning system and all other items mentioned under the Model V35B Bonanza entry, except for the large cargo door.

TYPE: Four/six-seat utility light cabin monoplane.

WINGS: As for Model V35B.

FUSELAGE: As for Model V35B but lengthened by 0·25 m (10 in).

TAIL UNIT: Conventional cantilever all-metal stressed-skin structure, primarily of aluminium alloy but with corrugated magnesium skin on elevators. Large trim tab in each elevator. Fixed tab in rudder.

LANDING GEAR: Electrically-retractable tricycle type, similar to that of Baron. Main units retract inward into wings, nosewheel rearward. Beech oleo-pneumatic shock-absorbers. Steerable nosewheel. Cleveland main wheels, size 6·00-6, with tyres size 7·00-6, pressure 2·28-2·76 bars (33-40 lb/sq in). Cleveland nosewheel and tyre size 5·00-5, pressure 2·76 bars (40 lb/sq in). Cleveland ring-disc hydraulic brakes. Parking brake.

POWER PLANT: As for Model V35B.

ACCOMMODATION: Enclosed cabin seating four to six persons on individual seats. Two rear removable seats and two folding seats permit rapid conversion to utility configuration. Optional club-seating layout with rear-facing third and fourth seats, executive writing desk, headrests for third and fourth seats, reading lights and fresh air outlets for fifth and sixth seats. Double doors of bonded aluminium honeycomb construction on starboard side facilitate loading of cargo. As an air ambulance, one stretcher can be accommodated with ample room for a medical attendant and/or other passengers. Extra windows provide improved view for passengers. Stowage for 181 kg (400 lb) of baggage.

SYSTEMS: Electrical system supplied by 28V 50A alternator, 24V 15Ah battery; a 100A alternator is available as an option. Hydraulic system for brakes only. Pneumatic system for instrument gyros and refrigeration-type air-conditioning system optional.

AVIONICS AND EQUIPMENT: Standard avionics include King KX 170B 720-channel nav/com, with KI 208 VOR/LOC Omni converter/indicator and Beechcraft antenna, but a wide range of optional electronics equipment is available. Optional items of equipment are as detailed for the V35B Bonanza, except as noted.

DIMENSIONS, EXTERNAL: As for V35B except:

Length overall	8·38 m (27 ft 6 in)
Height overall	2·57 m (8 ft 5 in)
Wheelbase	2·39 m (7 ft 10¼ in)
Rear passenger/cargo door:	
Height	1·02 m (3 ft 4 in)
Width	1·14 m (3 ft 9 in)

DIMENSIONS, INTERNAL:

Cabin, aft of firewall: Length, incl extended baggage compartment	3·84 m (12 ft 7 in)
Max width	1·07 m (3 ft 6 in)
Max height	1·27 m (4 ft 2 in)
Volume	3·85 m³ (135·9 cu ft)

AREA:

Wings, gross	16·8 m² (181 sq ft)

WEIGHTS AND LOADINGS:

Weight empty, equipped	980 kg (2,161 lb)
Max T-O weight	1,633 kg (3,600 lb)
Max wing loading	97·2 kg/m² (19·9 lb/sq ft)
Max power loading	7·68 kg/kW (12·6 lb/hp)

PERFORMANCE (at max T-O weight, except cruising speeds at mid-cruise weight):

Max level speed	179 knots (332 km/h; 206 mph)
Cruising speed:	
75% power at 1,830 m (6,000 ft)	168 knots (311 km/h; 193 mph)
66% power at 3,050 m (10,000 ft)	163 knots (303 km/h; 188 mph)
55% power at 3,660 m (12,000 ft)	150 knots (278 km/h; 173 mph)
45% power at 2,440 m (8,000 ft)	127 knots (235 km/h; 146 mph)
Stalling speed, flaps up, power off	62 knots (115 km/h; 71 mph) IAS
Stalling speed, 30° flap, power off	52 knots (96·5 km/h; 60 mph) IAS
Max rate of climb at S/L	314 m (1,030 ft)/min
Service ceiling	5,060 m (16,600 ft)
T-O run	347 m (1,140 ft)
T-O to 15 m (50 ft)	622 m (2,040 ft)
Landing from 15 m (50 ft)	442 m (1,450 ft)
Landing run	256 m (840 ft)
Range with 280 litres (74 US gallons) usable fuel, allowances for engine start, taxi, T-O, climb and 45 min reserves at 45% power:	
75% power at 1,830 m (6,000 ft)	697 nm (1,292 km; 802 miles)
66% power at 3,050 m (10,000 ft)	748 nm (1,386 km; 861 miles)
55% power at 3,660 m (12,000 ft)	790 nm (1,464 km; 909 miles)
45% power at 2,440 m (8,000 ft)	824 nm (1,527 km; 948 miles)

BEECHCRAFT TURBO BONANZA MODEL A36TC

Beech introduced for 1979 a turbocharged version of the A36 Bonanza, following FAA certification on 7 December 1978. This addition to the Beechcraft range is generally similar to the A36, except as detailed:

WINGS, FUSELAGE, TAIL UNIT AND LANDING GEAR: As for Model A36.

POWER PLANT: One 223·7 kW (300 hp) Continental TSIO-520-UB turbocharged flat-six engine, driving a McCauley three-blade constant-speed metal propeller. Two fuel tanks in wing leading-edges, with total usable capacity of 166·5 litres (44 US gallons). Optionally, these can be replaced by tanks with total usable capacity of 280 litres (74 US gallons). Refuelling points above tanks. Oil capacity 11·5 litres (3 US gallons).

ACCOMMODATION AND SYSTEMS: As for Model A36, except that air-conditioning is not available as an option.

AVIONICS AND EQUIPMENT: As detailed for Model V35B, except that rear cabin utility shelf, exhaust gas temperature gauge, three-blade propeller, standby generator and air-conditioning are not available. A turbine inlet temperature gauge is standard.

DIMENSIONS, EXTERNAL: As for Model A36, except:

Propeller diameter	2·03 m (6 ft 8 in)
Propeller ground clearance	0·24 m (9½ in)

DIMENSIONS, INTERNAL, AND AREAS: As for Model A36

WEIGHTS AND LOADINGS:

Max T-O and landing weight	1,655 kg (3,650 lb)
Max ramp weight	1,663 kg (3,666 lb)
Max wing loading	98·6 kg/m² (20·17 lb/sq ft)
Max power loading	7·40 kg/kW (12·17 lb/hp)

PERFORMANCE (at max T-O weight):

Never-exceed speed	203 knots (377 km/h; 234 mph) IAS
Max operating altitude	7,620 m (25,000 ft)

BEECHCRAFT DUCHESS 76

The Duchess 76, a four-seat twin-engined light aircraft, flew for the first time on 24 May 1977, and received FAA certification on 24 January 1978. A testbed version of this aircraft, designated PD 289, had been undergoing a comprehensive flight test programme since September 1974. Following certification in the Normal category for day and night VFR and IFR, the first production deliveries were made in May 1978, at which time more than 350 had been ordered. A total of 120 Duchesses had been delivered by 1 January 1979.

The Duchess 76 is planned for use by Beech Aero Centers, and is designed for the personal light twin, light charter and multi-engine flight trainer markets. Emphasis has, therefore, been placed on good low speed flight and single-engine handling characteristics, and opposite-rotating propellers are fitted.

Factory-installed optional equipment packages are available as follows:

Weekender. Comprising sun visors; acrylic enamel paint; tinted windscreen and windows; landing, navigation, strobe, cabin dome, map, overhead instrument and instrument post lights; cabin boarding steps; and propeller unfeathering accumulators; adding 12·2 kg (27 lb) to basic empty weight.

Holiday. As above, plus coat hook and garment hanger in baggage compartment; instrument group comprising 3 in gyro horizon, 3 in directional gyro, pressure system, turn co-ordinator, rate of climb indicator, electric clock, exhaust temperature gauge, and external air temperature gauge; and wing-mounted landing light; adding 22·2 kg (49 lb) to basic empty weight.

Professional. As above, plus electric elevator trim with control wheel switch; two seat headrests; heated pitot tube; wing-mounted taxi lights; and true airspeed indicator; adding 26·3 kg (58 lb) to basic empty weight.

Ten factory-installed avionics packages are also available optionally, and include com transceiver; nav receiver-converter, with VOR/LOC indicator: ADF; transponder; and audio panel; from Collins, Edo-Aire Mitchell, King and Narco. An extensive selection of additional avionics, including autopilot, DME, glideslope receiver and marker beacon systems, are available optionally from these manufacturers and also from Bendix.

TYPE: Four-seat cabin monoplane.

WINGS: Cantilever low-wing monoplane. Wing section NACA 63_2A415 with modified root section. Dihedral 6°30′. Incidence 3° at root, 0°45′ at tip. Wings and modified Frise-type ailerons of light alloy bonded honeycomb construction. Electrically-operated single-slotted trailing-edge flaps of light alloy. No tabs.

FUSELAGE: Semi-monocoque structure of light alloy.

TAIL UNIT: Conventional cantilever T-tail structure of light alloy with swept vertical surfaces. Fixed-incidence tailplane. Trim tab in rudder and each elevator.

LANDING GEAR: Hydraulically-retractable tricycle type, with single wheel on each unit. Self-centering steerable nosewheel retracts forward, main units inward. Oleo-pneumatic shock-absorbers. Main wheels with tube type tyres size 17·5 × 6·00-6. Nosewheel with tube type tyre size 5·00-5. Hydraulic brakes. Parking brake.

POWER PLANT: Two 134·2 kW (180 hp) Lycoming O-360-A1G6D counter-rotating flat-four engines, each driving a Hartzell two-blade metal constant-speed fully-feathering propeller type HC-M2YR-2C(L)EUF/F(J)C 7666A. One fuel tank in each wing, with a combined usable capacity of 378·5 litres (100 US gallons). Refuelling point on upper surface of each wing. Oil capacity 15 litres (4 US gallons).

ACCOMMODATION: Two individual front seats, adjustable fore and aft, with reclining seatbacks. Rear bench seat for two passengers. Shoulder harness and lap belt for all seats. Door on each side of cabin. Baggage compartment (capacity 90 kg; 200 lb) with external access door on port side. Pilot's storm window. Accommodation heated and ventilated. Windscreen defroster.

SYSTEMS: Electrical system supplied by two 12V 60A engine-driven alternators, 12V 35Ah battery. Electrically-driven hydraulic pump for landing gear retraction. Separate hydraulic system for brakes. 45,000 BTU heater.

AVIONICS AND EQUIPMENT: Optional avionics as listed earlier. Standard equipment includes sensitive altimeter, stall warning device, super soundproofing, carpeted floor, armrests, instrument panel glareshield, map stowage, storage pockets, rear accessory storage shelf, towbar, tiedown rings, control lock, and emergency locator transmitter. Optional equipment includes ventilation blower, Hobbs hour meter, internal corrosion proofing, external power socket and third and fourth split seat in lieu of standard bench seat.

DIMENSIONS, EXTERNAL:

Wing span	11·58 m (38 ft 0 in)
Wing chord at root	1·71 m (5 ft 7½ in)
Wing chord at tip	1·36 m (4 ft 5¾ in)
Wing aspect ratio	7·973
Length overall	8·86 m (29 ft 0½ in)
Height overall	2·90 m (9 ft 6 in)
Tailplane span	3·81 m (12 ft 6 in)
Wheel track	3·20 m (10 ft 6 in)
Wheelbase	2·13 m (7 ft 0 in)
Propeller diameter	1·93 m (6 ft 4 in)
Propeller ground clearance	0·25 m (10 in)
Cabin doors (port, stbd): Height	0·97 m (3 ft 2 in)
Width	0·97 m (3 ft 2 in)
Baggage door (port): Height	0·91m (3 ft 0 in)
Width	0·60 m (1 ft 11½ in)

DIMENSIONS, INTERNAL:

Cabin: Length	2·41 m (7 ft 11 in)
Max width	1·12 m (3 ft 8 in)
Max height	1·23 m (4 ft 0½ in)
Baggage compartment	0·55 m³ (19·5 cu ft)

AREAS:

Wings, gross	16·81 m² (181 sq ft)
Ailerons (total)	0·99 m² (10·7 sq ft)
Trailing-edge flaps (total)	2·29 m² (24·7 sq ft)
Fin	1·69 m² (18·23 sq ft)
Rudder (incl tab)	0·68 m² (7·3 sq ft)
Tailplane	3·66 m² (39·4 sq ft)
Elevators (incl tabs)	1·28 m² (13·77 sq ft)

Beechcraft Duchess 76 four-seat light aircraft (two Lycoming O-360-A1G6D engines)

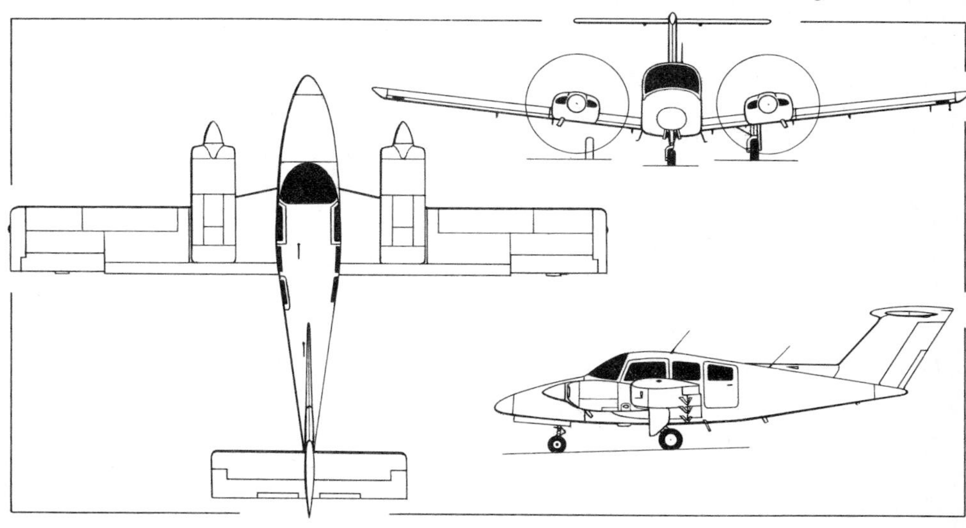

Beechcraft Duchess 76 four-seat light twin *(Pilot Press)*

WEIGHTS AND LOADINGS:

Weight empty	1,109 kg (2,446 lb)
Max T-O and landing weight	1,769 kg (3,900 lb)
Max ramp weight	1,776 kg (3,916 lb)
Max zero-fuel weight	1,587 kg (3,500 lb)
Max wing loading	105·2 kg/m² (21·5 lb/sq ft)
Max power loading	6·59 kg/kW (10·8 lb/hp)

PERFORMANCE (at max T-O weight):

Never-exceed speed 171 knots (317 km/h; 197 mph)

Max cruising speed at 1,830 m (6,000 ft) 166 knots (308 km/h; 191 mph)

Recommended cruising speed at 3,050 m (10,000 ft) 158 knots (293 km/h; 182 mph)

Econ cruising speed at 3,660 m (12,000 ft) 151 knots (280 km/h; 174 mph)

Stalling speed, power off, flaps up 70 knots (130 km/h; 81 mph) IAS

Stalling speed, power off, flaps down 60 knots (111 km/h; 69 mph) IAS

Max rate of climb at S/L 380 m (1,248 ft)/min

Rate of climb at S/L, one engine out 72 m (235 ft)/min

Service ceiling	5,990 m (19,650 ft)
Service ceiling, one engine out	1,880 m (6,170 ft)
T-O run	310 m (1,017 ft)
T-O to 15 m (50 ft)	646 m (2,119 ft)
Landing from 15 m (50 ft)	573 m (1,881 ft)
Landing run	305 m (1,000 ft)

Range with max fuel, incl allowances for start, taxi, T-O, climb, and 45 min reserves at econ cruise power:

Max cruising speed at 1,830 m (6,000 ft) 623 nm (1,155 km; 717 miles)

Recommended cruising speed at 3,050 m (10,000 ft) 711 nm (1,317 km; 818 miles)

Econ cruising speed at 3,660 m (12,000 ft) 780 nm (1,445 km; 898 miles)

BEECHCRAFT BARON MODEL 95-B55

US Army designation: T-42A Cochise

The original Baron Model 95-55 was a four/five-seat cabin monoplane developed from the earlier Travel Air but with more power, better all-weather capability and airframe refinements that included a swept tail-fin. It first flew in prototype form on 29 February 1960 and was licensed in the FAA Normal category in November 1960. The Baron Model 95-B55 was similarly licensed in September 1963.

The current Barons are optional four-, five- or six-seaters, with interior features as described for the Bonanza.

In February 1965 the US Army selected the Model 95-B55 as winner of its competition for a twin-engined fixed-wing instrument trainer. Beech identified the military trainer as the Model 95-B55B, and this received FAA Type Approval in the Normal and Utility categories in August 1964. The US Army ordered 65, which were delivered under the designation T-42A. During 1971 Beech delivered five more T-42As to the US Army, for service with the army of Turkey, under the Military Assistance Programme. Export deliveries of the standard Model 95-B55 have also been made, including 19 for the Spanish Air Ministry and six for the Civil Air Bureau of Japan. These aircraft are used as instrument trainers.

A total of 2,280 civil and military Barons of the Model 95-55 series had been delivered by 1 January 1979.

TYPE: Four/six-seat cabin monoplane.

WINGS: Cantilever low-wing monoplane. Wing section NACA 23016·5 at root, NACA 23010·5 at tip. Dihedral 6°. Incidence 4° at root, 0° at tip. No sweepback. Each wing is a two-spar semi-monocoque box beam of conventional aluminium alloy construction. Symmetrical-section ailerons of light alloy construction, with beaded skins. Electrically-operated single-slotted light alloy trailing-edge flaps, with beaded skins. Manually-operated trim tab in port aileron. Pneumatic rubber de-icing boots optional.

FUSELAGE: Semi-monocoque aluminium alloy structure. Hat-section longerons and channel-type keels extend forward from the cabin section, making the support structure for the forward nose section and nosewheel gear an integral part of the fuselage.

TAIL UNIT: Cantilever all-metal structure. Elevators have smooth magnesium alloy skins. Manually-operated trim tab in each elevator and in rudder. Pneumatic rubber de-icing boots optional.

LANDING GEAR: Electrically-retractable tricycle type. Main units retract inward into wings, nosewheel aft. Beech oleo-pneumatic shock-absorbers on all units. Steerable nosewheel with shimmy damper. Cleveland wheels, with 6·50-8 main-wheel tyres, pressure 3·45-3·72 bars (50-54 lb/sq in). Nosewheel tyre size 5·00-5, pressure 3·31-3·59 bars (48-52 lb/sq in). Cleveland ring-disc hydraulic brakes. Parking brake.

POWER PLANT: Two 194 kW (260 hp) Continental IO-470-L flat-six engines, each driving a Hartzell two-blade constant-speed fully-feathering propeller.

Beechcraft Baron Model 95-B55 four/six-seat cabin monoplane

Optional Hartzell three-blade propellers. Manually-operated cowl flaps. Standard fuel system comprises two interconnected tanks in each wing leading-edge, with total usable capacity of 378 litres (100 US gallons). Optional interconnected fuel tanks may be added in each wing to provide a total usable capacity of 515 litres (136 US gallons). Single refuelling point in each wing for the standard or optional fuel systems. Optional fuel system includes a mechanical sight gauge in each wing leading-edge to give partial fuelling information. Oil capacity 23 litres (6 US gallons). Propeller de-icing optional.

Accommodation: Standard model has four individual seats in pairs in enclosed cabin, with door on starboard side. Single diagonal strap shoulder harness with inertia reel standard on all seats. Optional wider door for cargo. Folding airline-style fifth and sixth seats optional, complete with shoulder harness and inertia reel. Baggage compartments aft of cabin and in nose, both with external doors on starboard side and with capacity of 181 kg (400 lb) and 136 kg (300 lb) respectively. An extended rear compartment providing for an additional 54 kg (120 lb) of baggage is optional. Pilot's storm window, port side. Openable windows adjacent to the third and fourth seats are used for ground ventilation and as emergency exits. Cabin heated and ventilated. Windscreen defrosting standard. Alcohol de-icing for port side of windscreen optional.

Systems: Cabin heated by Janitrol 50,000 BTU heater, which serves also for windscreen defrosting. Oxygen system of 1·41 m³ (49·8 cu ft) or 1·87 m³ (66 cu ft) capacity optional. Electrical system includes two 24V 25A generators. One 24V 17Ah battery. Two 24V 50A engine-driven alternators and/or two 12V 25Ah batteries optional. Hydraulic system for brakes only. Pneumatic pressure system for air-driven instruments, and optional wing and tail unit de-icing system.

Avionics and Equipment: Standard avionics comprise King KX 170B 720-channel com transceiver and 200-channel nav receiver with KC 208 VOR/LOC converter indicator, microphone, headset, cabin speaker and Beechcraft B6 com and B38 nav antennae. A wide range of optional avionics by Bendix, Collins, King, Edo-Aire Mitchell and Narco is available to customer's requirements. Standard equipment includes airspeed indicator, sensitive altimeter, blind-flying instrumentation, electric turn co-ordinator, outside air temperature gauge, clock, air pressure gauge, flap position indicator, adjustable and retractable starboard side rudder pedals, instrument panel floodlights, trim tab position indicator lights, map light, sun visors, pilot's storm window, cabin dome light, passenger reading lights, ultraviolet-proof windscreen and windows, soundproofing, wall-to-wall carpeting, glove compartment, in-flight storage pockets, armrests, headrests for passenger seats, hat shelf, nose baggage light, two landing lights, navigation lights, position lights, heated pitot, heated fuel vents, towbar, winterisation kit and emergency locator transmitter. Optional equipment includes control wheel clock or chronograph, dual control wheels, engine hour and flight hour recorders, instantaneous vertical speed indicator, exhaust gas temperature gauge, dual tachometer with synchroscope, instrument post lights, internally illuminated instruments, co-pilot's brake system, extended baggage compartment, cargo door, cabin fire extinguisher, entrance door courtesy light, fifth and sixth seats, rotating beacons, strobe lights, taxi light, wing ice lights, 50A alternators, two 12V 25Ah batteries, de-icing and anti-icing systems, oxygen system, external power socket, propeller synchroniser, three-blade propellers, propeller unfeathering accumulators, alternate static source, static wicks and super soundproofing.

Dimensions, external:

Wing span	11·53 m (37 ft 10 in)
Wing chord at root	2·13 m (7 ft 0 in)
Wing chord at tip	0·90 m (2 ft 11·6 in)
Wing aspect ratio	7·16
Length overall	8·53 m (28 ft 0 in)
Height overall	2·92 m (9 ft 7 in)
Tailplane span	4·19 m (13 ft 9 in)
Wheel track	2·92 m (9 ft 7 in)
Wheelbase	2·13 m (7 ft 0 in)
Propeller diameter: two-blade	1·98 m (6 ft 6 in)
three-blade	1·93 m (6 ft 4 in)
Passenger door: Height	0·91 m (3 ft 0 in)
Width	0·94 m (3 ft 1 in)
Height to step	0·41 m (1 ft 4 in)
Baggage door (fwd): Height	0·56 m (1 ft 10 in)
Width	0·64 m (2 ft 1 in)
Baggage door (rear):	
Standard: Height	0·57 m (1 ft 10½ in)
Width	0·47 m (1 ft 6½ in)
Height to sill	0·71 m (2 ft 4 in)
Optional: Height	0·57 m (1 ft 10½ in)
Width	0·97 m (3 ft 2 in)

Dimensions, internal:

Cabin: Length	3·07 m (10 ft 1 in)
Max width	1·07 m (3 ft 6 in)
Max height	1·27 m (4 ft 2 in)
Baggage compartment (fwd)	0·34 m³ (12 cu ft)
Baggage compartment (rear)	0·99 m³ (35 cu ft)

Areas:

Wings, gross	18·50 m² (199·1 sq ft)
Ailerons (total)	1·06 m² (11·40 sq ft)
Trailing-edge flaps (total)	2·39 m² (25·70 sq ft)
Fin	1·02 m² (11·00 sq ft)
Rudder, incl tab	1·08 m² (11·60 sq ft)
Tailplane	4·46 m² (48·06 sq ft)
Elevators, incl tabs	1·51 m² (16·20 sq ft)

Weights and Loadings:

Weight empty	1,463 kg (3,226 lb)
Max T-O and landing weight	2,313 kg (5,100 lb)
Max ramp weight	2,322 kg (5,121 lb)
Max wing loading	120·5 kg/m² (25·6 lb/sq ft)
Max power loading	5·96 kg/kW (9·8 lb/hp)

Performance (at max T-O weight, except cruising speeds at average cruise weight):

Max level speed at S/L	201 knots (372 km/h; 231 mph)
Max cruising speed, 77% power at 1,830 m (6,000 ft)	188 knots (348 km/h; 216 mph)
Cruising speed, 66% power at 3,050 m (10,000 ft)	184 knots (341 km/h; 212 mph)
Econ cruising speed, 56% power at 3,660 m (12,000 ft)	173 knots (320 km/h; 199 mph)
Stalling speed, flaps up, power off	79 knots (146 km/h; 91 mph) IAS
Stalling speed, flaps down, power off	73 knots (135 km/h; 84 mph) IAS
Max rate of climb at S/L	516 m (1,693 ft)/min
Rate of climb at S/L, one engine out	121 m (397 ft)/min
Service ceiling	5,880 m (19,300 ft)
Service ceiling, one engine out	1,950 m (6,400 ft)
Min ground turning radius	9·00 m (29 ft 6 in)
Runway LCN	2
T-O run	427 m (1,400 ft)
T-O to 15 m (50 ft)	657 m (2,154 ft)
Landing from 15 m (50 ft)	655 m (2,148 ft)
Landing run	447 m (1,467 ft)

Range with 515 litres (136 US gallons) usable fuel, with allowances for engine start, taxi, T-O, climb and 45 min reserves at econ cruise power:

max cruising speed at 1,830 m (6,000 ft)	798 nm (1,479 km; 918 miles)
cruising speed at 3,050 m (10,000 ft)	907 nm (1,680 km; 1,044 miles)
econ cruising speed at 3,660 m (12,000 ft)	991 nm (1,836 km; 1,141 miles)

BEECHCRAFT BARON MODEL E55

The Baron E55 had its origin in the Baron 95-B55 when the Model 95-C55 was added to the Baron series of twin-engined aircraft in August 1965. The 95-C55 had Continental IO-520-C engines, a pneumatic vacuum system for instrument gyros and the optional wing and tail unit de-icing system, two 24V 50A engine-driven alternators, increased tailplane span, swept vertical surfaces and an extended nose baggage compartment. It was followed by the D55 in October 1967, this model introducing a pneumatic pressure system in place of the pneumatic vacuum system. The subsequent Model E55, which has an improved interior and systems accessory refinements, was licensed in the FAA Normal category on 12 November 1969.

Beech had delivered a total of 1,146 of this Baron series by 1 January 1979.

Type: Four/six-seat cabin monoplane.

Wings: As for Model 95-B55.

Fuselage: As for Model 95-B55, except nose extended by 0·305 m (1 ft 0 in).

Tail Unit: As for Model 95-B55, except tailplane span increased.

Landing Gear: As for Model 95-B55, except main-wheel tyre pressure 3·59-3·86 bars (52-56 lb/sq in); nosewheel tyre pressure 3·79-4·14 bars (55-60 lb/sq in).

Power Plant: Two 212·5 kW (285 hp) Continental IO-520-C flat-six engines, each driving a Hartzell two-blade metal constant-speed and fully-feathering propeller. Hartzell three-blade propellers optional. Fuel system as for Model 95-B55, except optional total usable capacity 628 litres (166 US gallons). Oil capacity 23 litres (6 US gallons). Full-flow oil filters standard; propeller de-icing optional.

Accommodation: As for Model 95-B55, except that extended rear compartment, providing for an additional 54 kg (120 lb) of baggage, is standard.

Systems: As for Model 95-B55, except standard electrical system supplied by two 24V 50A gear-driven alternators with alternator failure lights and one 24V 17Ah battery. Two 85A alternators and two 12V 25Ah batteries optional. Cabin air-conditioning system optional.

Avionics and Equipment: Standard and optional avionics as for Model 95-B55, except that a King KR 85 ADF with KI 225 indicator is standard. Standard and optional equipment as for Model 95-B55, except cabin door courtesy light and extended rear baggage compartment standard. Electric elevator trim optional.

Dimensions, external: As for Model 95-B55, except:

Length overall	8·84 m (29 ft 0 in)
Height overall	2·79 m (9 ft 2 in)
Tailplane span	4·85 m (15 ft 11 in)
Wheelbase	2·46 m (8 ft 1 in)

Dimensions, internal: As for Model 95-B55, except:

Cabin: Length (incl extended rear baggage compartment)	3·58 m (11 ft 9 in)
Baggage compartment (fwd)	0·51 m³ (18 cu ft)
Baggage compartment (rear)	0·99 m³ (35 cu ft)
Extension to rear baggage compartment	0·28 m³ (10 cu ft)

Areas: As for Model 95-B55, except:

Tailplane	4·95 m² (53·30 sq ft)
Elevators, incl tabs	1·84 m² (19·80 sq ft)

Weights and Loadings:

Weight empty	1,470 kg (3,241 lb)
Max T-O and landing weight	2,405 kg (5,300 lb)
Max ramp weight	2,415 kg (5,324 lb)
Max wing loading	130·0 kg/m² (26·6 lb/sq ft)
Max power loading	5·66 kg/kW (9·3 lb/hp)

Performance (at max T-O weight, except cruising speeds at average cruise weight):

Max level speed at S/L	208 knots (386 km/h; 239 mph)
Max cruising speed, 77% power at 1,830 m (6,000 ft)	200 knots (370 km/h; 230 mph)
Cruising speed, 66% power at 3,050 m (10,000 ft)	195 knots (362 km/h; 224 mph)
Econ cruising speed, 56% power at 3,660 m (12,000 ft)	184 knots (341 km/h; 212 mph)
Stalling speed, flaps up, power off	83 knots (154 km/h; 96 mph) IAS
Stalling speed, flaps down, power off	73 knots (135 km/h; 84 mph) IAS
Max rate of climb at S/L	513 m (1,682 ft)/min
Rate of climb at S/L, one engine out	118 m (388 ft)/min
Service ceiling	5,820 m (19,100 ft)
Service ceiling, one engine out	2,010 m (6,600 ft)
T-O run	401 m (1,315 ft)
T-O to 15 m (50 ft)	625 m (2,050 ft)
Landing from 15 m (50 ft)	671 m (2,202 ft)
Landing run	377 m (1,237 ft)

Range with 628 litres (166 US gallons) usable fuel, with allowances for engine start, taxi, T-O, climb and 45 min reserves at econ cruise power:

max cruising speed at 1,830 m (6,000 ft)	933 nm (1,728 km; 1,074 miles)
cruising speed at 3,050 m (10,000 ft)	1,032 nm (1,912 km; 1,188 miles)
econ cruising speed at 3,660 m (12,000 ft)	1,135 nm (2,103 km; 1,306 miles)

BEECHCRAFT BARON MODEL 58

In late 1969 Beech introduced a new version of the Baron, designated Model 58. Developed from the Baron D55, it differed by having the forward cabin section extended by 0·254 m (10 in), allowing the windscreen, passenger door, instrument panel and front seats to be moved forward and so provide a more spacious cabin. This change was made without affecting the wing main spar location, but the wheelbase was extended by moving the nosewheel forward, to improve ground handling. New features included double passenger/cargo doors on the starboard side of the cabin, extended propeller hubs, redesigned engine nacelles to improve cooling, and a fourth window on each side of the cabin. The Model 58 Baron was licensed by the FAA in the Normal category on 19 November 1969.

Beech had delivered 1,258 of this Baron series (including Baron 58Ps and 58TCs) by 1 January 1979.

TYPE: Four/six-seat cabin monoplane.

WINGS: As for Model 95-B55.

FUSELAGE: As for Model E55, except forward cabin section extended by 0·254 m (10 in).

TAIL UNIT: As for Model E55.

LANDING GEAR: As for Model E55, except wheelbase extended by 0·254 m (10 in).

POWER PLANT: As for Model E55, except that the standard and optional Hartzell propellers have extended hubs, and the engine nacelles are lengthened to accommodate these. The standard fuel system has a usable capacity of 514 litres (136 US gallons), with optional usable capacity of 628 litres (166 US gallons). Optional 'wet wingtip' installation also available, increasing usable capacity to 734 litres (194 US gallons).

ACCOMMODATION: As for Model E55, except that folding fifth and sixth seats, or club seating comprising folding fifth and sixth seats and aft-facing third and fourth seats, are optional. Executive writing desk available as option with club seating. Double passenger/cargo doors on starboard side of cabin provide access to space for 181 kg (400 lb) of baggage or cargo behind the third and fourth seats.

SYSTEMS: As for Model E55.

AVIONICS AND EQUIPMENT: Standard and optional avionics as for Model E55. Equipment as for Model E55, except double passenger/cargo doors with door-ajar warning light standard. Hartzell three-blade propellers with extended hubs, and club seating arrangement, as described above, with executive writing desk, optional.

DIMENSIONS, EXTERNAL, AND AREAS:
As for Model E55, except:
Length overall 9·09 m (29 ft 10 in)
Height overall 2·90 m (9 ft 6 in)
Wheelbase 2·72 m (8 ft 11 in)
Rear passenger/cargo doors:
Max height 1·02 m (3 ft 4 in)
Width 1·14 m (3 ft 9 in)

DIMENSIONS, INTERNAL: As for Model E55, except:
Cabin, incl rear baggage area:
Length 3·84 m (12 ft 7 in)
Floor area 3·72 m² (40 sq ft)
Volume 3·85 m³ (135·9 sq ft)

WEIGHTS AND LOADINGS:
Weight empty 1,522 kg (3,356 lb)
Max T-O and landing weight 2,449 kg (5,400 lb)
Max wing loading 132·3 kg/m² (27·1 lb/sq ft)
Max power loading 5·76 kg/kW (9·5 lb/hp)

PERFORMANCE (at max T-O weight, except cruising speeds at average cruise weight):
Max level speed at S/L 208 knots (386 km/h; 239 mph)
Max cruising speed, 77% power at 1,830 m (6,000 ft) 200 knots (370 km/h; 230 mph)
Cruising speed, 66% power at 3,050 m (10,000 ft) 195 knots (362 km/h; 224 mph)
Econ cruising speed, 56% power at 3,660 m (12,000 ft) 184 knots (341 km/h; 212 mph)
Stalling speed, flaps up, power off 84 knots (156 km/h; 97 mph) IAS
Stalling speed, flaps down, power off 74 knots (137 km/h; 85 mph) IAS
Max rate of climb at S/L 506 m (1,660 ft)/min
Rate of climb at S/L, one engine out 119 m (390 ft)/min
Service ceiling 5,670 m (18,600 ft)
Service ceiling, one engine out 2,135 m (7,000 ft)
T-O run 407 m (1,336 ft)
T-O to 15 m (50 ft) 640 m (2,101 ft)
Landing from 15 m (50 ft) 761 m (2,498 ft)
Landing run 439 m (1,439 ft)
Range with 734 litres (194 US gallons) usable fuel, with allowances for engine start, taxi, T-O, climb and 45 min reserves at econ cruise power:
max cruising speed at 1,830 m (6,000 ft) 1,108 nm (2,054 km; 1,275 miles)
cruising speed at 3,050 m (10,000 ft) 1,224 nm (2,268 km; 1,409 miles)
econ cruising speed at 3,660 m (12,000 ft) 1,339 nm (2,482 km; 1,541 miles)

BEECHCRAFT BARON MODEL 58P

Design of this pressurised version of the Model 58 Baron started in June 1972; the first flight of the prototype was made in August 1973. Certification under FAR Part 23 was received in May 1974; the first production aircraft flew later the same year. Examples of the Model 58P produced prior to 1979 are powered by two 231 kW (310 hp) Continental TSIO-520-L (or -LB) engines. The production aircraft for 1979 have more powerful TSIO-520-WB engines.

Beechcraft Baron Model 58 four/six-seat cabin monoplane

Deliveries of production aircraft began in late 1975, and a total of 180 Baron 58Ps had been delivered by 1 January 1979. Four were delivered to the US Forest Service in December 1978, for use as lead aircraft in smoke-jumping operations, as well as for reconnaissance, administration and cargo missions.

TYPE: Four/six-seat cabin monoplane.

WINGS: As for Model 95-B55.

FUSELAGE: As for Model 58, except structural reinforcement to cater for pressurisation.

TAIL UNIT: As for Model 58.

LANDING GEAR: Main gear as for Duke, except mainwheel tyre pressure 5·24 to 5·66 bars (76 to 82 lb/sq in). Nosewheel unit as for Model 58. Goodrich single-disc hydraulic brakes. Parking brake.

POWER PLANT: Two 242 kW (325 hp) Continental TSIO-520-WB turbocharged flat-six engines, each driving a Hartzell three-blade metal constant-speed and fully-feathering propeller. Electrically-operated engine cowl flaps. Integral fuel tanks in wings, with standard capacity of 651 litres (172 US gallons) of which 628 litres (166 US gallons) are usable. Optional maximum capacity of 742 litres (196 US gallons) of which 719 litres (190 US gallons) are usable. Refuelling points in outboard leading-edge of wings and, for optional maximum fuel, in wingtips. Oil capacity 22·7 litres (6 US gallons). Electrical anti-icing for propellers optional.

ACCOMMODATION: Standard accommodation has four individual seats in pairs, facing forward, with shoulder harness and inertia reel. Fifth and sixth seats optional, as is club layout. Doors on starboard side, adjacent to co-pilot, and at trailing-edge of wing on port side. Baggage space in aft cabin and in fuselage nose, with door on starboard side of nose. Openable storm window for pilot on port side. Cabin heated and pressurised. Air-conditioning optional. Windscreen defrosting by hot air. Windscreen electrical or alcohol anti-icing optional.

SYSTEMS: AiResearch pressurisation with max differential of 0·26 bars (3·7 lb/sq in) in aircraft manufactured prior to 1979, providing a 3,050 m (10,000 ft) cabin environment to an altitude of 6,460 m (21,200 ft). Aircraft manufactured subsequently have AiResearch pressurisation with max differential of 0·27 bars (3·9 lb/sq in), giving a 3,050 m (10,000 ft) cabin environment to a height of 6,705 m (22,000 ft). Beechcraft 14,000 BTU air-conditioning optional. Janitrol 35,000 BTU heater. Engine-driven compressors supply air for flight instruments, pressurisation control and optional pneumatic de-icing boots. Electrical system powered by two 24V 50A alternators, with two 12V 24Ah storage batteries. Two 24V 100A alternators optional. Hydraulic system for brakes only. Oxygen system of 0·42 m³ (15 cu ft) optional.

AVIONICS AND EQUIPMENT: Standard avionics package comprises King KX 170B nav/com (720-channel com transceiver and 200-channel nav receiver) with KI 208 VOR/LOC converter-indicator, KR 85 ADF with KI 225 indicator, microphone, headset, cabin speaker and B38 nav and B6 com antennae. Optional avionics by Bendix, Collins, King, Narco, Edo-Aire Mitchell, Sperry and RCA. Standard equipment as for Model E55, plus heated stall warning vane, dual rotating beacons, step light, door-ajar warning lights, nose baggage compartment light, emergency locator transmitter and exterior acrylic enamel paint. Optional equipment includes elevator electric trim, internally illuminated instruments, engine and flight hour recorders, instrument post lights, co-pilot brakes, dual control wheels, control wheel chronometer, executive writing desk, cabin fire extinguisher, a variety of interior furnishings, strobe lights, wing ice lights, propeller synchroniser and unfeathering accumulators, and static wicks.

DIMENSIONS, EXTERNAL:
Wing span 11·53 m (37 ft 10 in)
Wing chord at root 2·13 m (7 ft 0 in)
Wing chord at tip 0·90 m (2 ft 11½ in)
Length overall 9·09 m (29 ft 10 in)
Height overall 2·79 m (9 ft 2 in)
Tailplane span 4·85 m (15 ft 11 in)
Wheel track 2·92 m (9 ft 7 in)
Wheelbase 2·72 m (8 ft 11 in)
Propeller diameter 1·98 m (6 ft 6 in)
Propeller ground clearance 0·28 m (10¾ in)
Passenger door (starboard, fwd):
Height 0·91 m (3 ft 0 in)
Width 0·94 m (3 ft 1 in)
Height to sill 0·51 m (1 ft 8 in)
Passenger door (port, aft):
Height 0·99 m (3 ft 3 in)
Width 0·56 m (1 ft 10 in)
Height to sill 0·79 m (2 ft 7 in)
Baggage door (nose, stbd):
Height 0·38 m (1 ft 3 in)
Width 0·64 m (2 ft 1 in)

DIMENSIONS, INTERNAL: As for Model 58

AREAS: As for Model 58

WEIGHTS AND LOADINGS:
Weight empty, equipped 1,814 kg (3,999 lb)
Max T-O and landing weight 2,812 kg (6,200 lb)
Max ramp weight 2,830 kg (6,240 lb)
Max zero-fuel weight 2,585 kg (5,700 lb)
Max wing loading 152·0 kg/m² (31·14 lb/sq ft)
Max power loading 5·81 kg/kW (9·54 lb/hp)

PERFORMANCE (at max T-O weight, except cruising speeds at average cruise weight):
Max level speed 261 knots (484 km/h; 301 mph)

Beechcraft Baron Model 58P, pressurised version of the Baron 58

Max cruising speed at approx 77% power:
at 3,050 m (10,000 ft) 212 knots (393 km/h; 244 mph)
at 4,570 m (15,000 ft) 222 knots (411 km/h; 256 mph)
at 6,100 m (20,000 ft) 232 knots (430 km/h; 267 mph)
at 7,620 m (25,000 ft) 241 knots (447 km/h; 277 mph)
Cruising speed at approx 71% power:
at 3,050 m (10,000 ft) 203 knots (376 km/h; 234 mph)
at 4,570 m (15,000 ft) 214 knots (396 km/h; 246 mph)
at 6,100 m (20,000 ft) 223 knots (413 km/h; 257 mph)
at 7,620 m (25,000 ft) 231 knots (428 km/h; 266 mph)
Cruising speed at approx 62% power:
at 3,050 m (10,000 ft) 190 knots (352 km/h; 219 mph)
at 4,570 m (15,000 ft) 201 knots (372 km/h; 231 mph)
at 6,100 m (20,000 ft) 210 knots (389 km/h; 242 mph)
at 7,620 m (25,000 ft) 218 knots (404 km/h; 251 mph)
Econ cruising speed at approx 53% power:
at 3,050 m (10,000 ft) 175 knots (324 km/h; 201 mph)
at 4,570 m (15,000 ft) 186 knots (344 km/h; 214 mph)
at 6,100 m (20,000 ft) 194 knots (359 km/h; 223 mph)
at 7,620 m (25,000 ft) 202 knots (375 km/h; 233 mph)
Stalling speed, flaps up, power off 83 knots (155 km/h; 96 mph)
Stalling speed, flaps down, power off 79 knots (147 km/h; 91 mph)
Max rate of climb at S/L 451 m (1,481 ft)/min
Rate of climb at S/L, one engine out 82 m (270 ft)/min
Service ceiling above 7,620 m (25,000 ft)
Service ceiling, one engine out 4,110 m (13,490 ft)
T-O run 474 m (1,555 ft)
T-O to 15 m (50 ft) 806 m (2,643 ft)
Landing from 15 m (50 ft) 761 m (2,498 ft)
Landing run 448 m (1,471 ft)
Range with 719 litres (190 US gallons) usable fuel, and allowances for engine start, taxi, T-O, climb and 45 min reserves at econ cruising speed:
at approx 77% power:
at 3,050 m (10,000 ft) 884 nm (1,638 km; 1,017 miles)
at 4,570 m (15,000 ft) 916 nm (1,697 km; 1,054 miles)
at 6,100 m (20,000 ft) 958 nm (1,775 km; 1,102 miles)
at 7,620 m (25,000 ft) 1,008 nm (1,868 km; 1,160 miles)
at approx 71% power:
at 3,050 m (10,000 ft) 956 nm (1,772 km; 1,100 miles)
at 4,570 m (15,000 ft) 983 nm (1,822 km; 1,131 miles)
at 6,100 m (20,000 ft) 1,021 nm (1,892 km; 1,175 miles)
at 7,620 m (25,000 ft) 1,071 nm (1,984 km; 1,232 miles)
at approx 62% power:
at 3,050 m (10,000 ft) 1,076 nm (1,994 km; 1,239 miles)
at 4,570 m (15,000 ft) 1,096 nm (2,031 km; 1,261 miles)
at 6,100 m (20,000 ft) 1,120 nm (2,075 km; 1,289 miles)
at 7,620 m (25,000 ft) 1,153 nm (2,136 km; 1,327 miles)
at approx 53% power:
at 3,050 m (10,000 ft) 1,179 nm (2,185 km; 1,357 miles)
at 4,570 m (15,000 ft) 1,198 nm (2,220 km; 1,379 miles)
at 6,100 m (20,000 ft) 1,217 nm (2,255 km; 1,400 miles)
at 7,620 m (25,000 ft) 1,229 nm (2,277 km; 1,414 miles)

BEECHCRAFT BARON MODEL 58TC

This turbocharged version of the Baron Model 58 is generally similar to the Model 58P, with the same power plant, but is unpressurised, with detail differences in the airframe and equipment. The design originated in July 1974, and construction of a prototype to production aircraft standard began in February 1975. The first flight of this aircraft was made on 31 October 1975 and FAA certification, in the Normal category, was granted on 23 January 1976. Deliveries began in June 1976, and a total of 86 had been delivered by 1 January 1979.

Type: Four/six-seat cabin monoplane.

Wings: Generally similar to Model 58P.

Fuselage: Generally similar to Model 58.

Tail Unit: Generally similar to Model 58.

Landing Gear: Generally similar to Model 58P.

Power Plant: As Model 58P.

Accommodation: Generally similar to that of Model 58, except windscreen electrical anti-icing optional. Baggage/cargo space aft of 3rd and 4th seats for 272 kg (600 lb). By removing these seats 408 kg (900 lb) baggage/cargo can be stowed aft of pilot and co-pilot seats with restraining net.

Systems: Generally similar to Model 58P, except Beech Freon air-conditioning system optional. 50,000 BTU heater standard. Hydraulic system for brakes and propeller unfeathering only. Electrical power from two 24V 50A alternators, with 24V 17Ah storage battery. Two 100A alternators and a 24V 25Ah storage battery optional. Oxygen system to supply crew and passengers.

Avionics and Equipment: As for Baron 58P.

Dimensions, external: As for Model 58P except:
Utility double door (starboard, aft):
Height 1·02 m (3 ft 4 in)
Width 1·14 m (3 ft 9 in)
Baggage door (nose, starboard):
Height 0·56 m (1 ft 10 in)
Width 0·64 m (2 ft 1 in)
Emergency exit window (port and stbd):
Height 0·53 m (1 ft 9 in)
Width 0·61 m (2 ft 0 in)

Dimensions, internal: As for Model 58

Areas:
Wings, gross 17·47 m² (188·1 sq ft)
Ailerons (total, incl tabs) 1·08 m² (11·58 sq ft)
Trailing-edge flaps (total) 1·98 m² (21·3 sq ft)
Fin 1·46 m² (15·67 sq ft)
Rudder, incl tab 1·08 m² (11·6 sq ft)
Tailplane 5·11 m² (55·05 sq ft)
Elevators, incl tabs 1·84 m² (19·8 sq ft)

Weights and Loadings:
Weight empty, equipped 1,715 kg (3,780 lb)
Max T-O and landing weight 2,812 kg (6,200 lb)
Max ramp weight 2,830 kg (6,240 lb)
Max zero-fuel weight 2,585 kg (5,700 lb)
Max wing loading 160·96 kg/m² (32·96 lb/sq ft)
Max power loading 5·81 kg/kW (9·54 lb/hp)

Performance (at 2,812 kg; 6,200 lb AUW, except cruising speeds at average cruise weight):
Max level speed 261 knots (484 km/h; 301 mph)
Max cruising speed at approx 77% power:
at 3,050 m (10,000 ft) 212 knots (393 km/h; 244 mph)
at 4,570 m (15,000 ft) 222 knots (411 km/h; 256 mph)
at 6,100 m (20,000 ft) 232 knots (430 km/h; 267 mph)
at 7,620 m (25,000 ft) 241 knots (447 km/h; 277 mph)
Cruising speed at approx 71% power:
at 3,050 m (10,000 ft) 203 knots (376 km/h; 234 mph)
at 4,570 m (15,000 ft) 214 knots (396 km/h; 246 mph)
at 6,100 m (20,000 ft) 223 knots (413 km/h; 257 mph)
at 7,620 m (25,000 ft) 231 knots (428 km/h; 266 mph)
Cruising speed at approx 62% power:
at 3,050 m (10,000 ft) 190 knots (352 km/h; 219 mph)
at 4,570 m (15,000 ft) 201 knots (372 km/h; 231 mph)
at 6,100 m (20,000 ft) 210 knots (389 km/h; 242 mph)
at 7,620 m (25,000 ft) 218 knots (404 km/h; 251 mph)
Econ cruising speed at approx 53% power:
at 3,050 m (10,000 ft) 175 knots (324 km/h; 201 mph)
at 4,570 m (15,000 ft) 186 knots (344 km/h; 214 mph)
at 6,100 m (20,000 ft) 194 knots (359 km/h; 223 mph)
at 7,620 m (25,000 ft) 202 knots (375 km/h; 233 mph)
Stalling speed, power off:
flaps up 84 knots (156 km/h; 97 mph)
flaps down 78 knots (145 km/h; 90 mph)
Max rate of climb:
at S/L 432 m (1,418 ft)/min
at 4,575 m (15,000 ft) 368 m (1,208 ft)/min
Rate of climb, one engine out:
at S/L 82 m (270 ft)/min
at 1,525 m (5,000 ft) 67 m (220 ft)/min
Service ceiling above 7,620 m (25,000 ft)
Service ceiling, one engine out 4,250 m (13,940 ft)
T-O run 474 m (1,555 ft)
T-O to 15 m (50 ft) 806 m (2,643 ft)
Landing from 15 m (50 ft) 740 m (2,427 ft)
Landing run 420 m (1,378 ft)
Range at average cruise weight with 719 litres (190 US gallons) usable fuel, allowances for start, taxi, T-O, climb and 45 min reserves:
at approx 77% power:
at 3,050 m (10,000 ft) 884 nm (1,638 km; 1,017 miles)
at 4,570 m (15,000 ft) 916 nm (1,697 km; 1,054 miles)
at 6,100 m (20,000 ft) 958 nm (1,775 km; 1,102 miles)
at 7,620 m (25,000 ft) 1,008 nm (1,868 km; 1,160 miles)
at approx 71% power:
at 3,050 m (10,000 ft) 956 nm (1,772 km; 1,100 miles)
at 4,570 m (15,000 ft) 983 nm (1,822 km; 1,131 miles)
at 6,100 m (20,000 ft) 1,021 nm (1,892 km; 1,175 miles)
at 7,620 m (25,000 ft) 1,071 nm (1,984 km; 1,232 miles)
at approx 62% power:
at 3,050 m (10,000 ft) 1,076 nm (1,994 km; 1,239 miles)
at 4,570 m (15,000 ft) 1,096 nm (2,031 km; 1,261 miles)
at 6,100 m (20,000 ft) 1,120 nm (2,075 km; 1,289 miles)
at 7,620 m (25,000 ft) 1,153 nm (2,136 km; 1,327 miles)
at approx 53% power:
at 3,050 m (10,000 ft) 1,179 nm (2,185 km; 1,357 miles)
at 4,570 m (15,000 ft) 1,198 nm (2,220 km; 1,379 miles)
at 6,100 m (20,000 ft) 1,217 nm (2,255 km; 1,400 miles)
at 7,620 m (25,000 ft) 1,229 nm (2,277 km; 1,414 miles)

BEECHCRAFT DUKE B60

Design work on the original version of this 4/6-seat pressurised and turbocharged light twin-engined transport started in early 1965. Construction of the prototype began in January 1966, and the first flight was made on 29 December 1966. FAA Type Approval was granted on 1 February 1968.

The current version of the B60 has an AiResearch Lexan pressurisation system, with a mini controller that allows selection of cabin altitude prior to take-off or landing. This system can also change the aircraft cabin altitude at any desired rate from 15-610 m (50-2,000 ft)/min.

A total of 484 Dukes had been produced by 1 January 1979.

Type: Four/six-seat cabin monoplane.

Wings: Cantilever low-wing monoplane. Wing section NACA 23016·5 at root, NACA 23010·5 at tip. Thickness/chord ratio 13·7% at root, 10·5% at tip. Dihedral 6°. Incidence 4° at root, 0° at tip. Each wing is a two-spar semi-monocoque box beam of conventional aluminium alloy construction. Overhang-balance ailerons constructed of aluminium alloy. Conventional hinged trim tab in port aileron. Electrically-operated single-slotted aluminium alloy flaps. Pneumatic rubber de-icing boots optional.

Fuselage: Semi-monocoque aluminium alloy structure. Heavy-gauge chemically-milled aluminium alloy skins.

Tail Unit: Cantilever all-metal structure. Aluminium spars and end ribs; magnesium alloy skins reinforced with metal bonded honeycomb stiffeners running chordwise. Dorsal fin. Swept vertical and horizontal surfaces. Tailplane dihedral 10°. Trim tabs in rudder and port elevator. Pneumatic rubber de-icing boots optional.

Landing Gear: Electrically-retractable tricycle type. Main units retract inward, nosewheel aft; all three units have fairing doors. Beechcraft oleo-pneumatic shock-absorbers. Goodrich main wheels and tyres size 19·50 × 6·75-8 10-ply rating, pressure 5·52 bars (80 lb/sq in). Goodyear steerable nosewheel with shimmy damper, tyre size 15 × 6·00-6, pressure 3·45 bars (50 lb/sq in). Goodrich single-disc hydraulic brakes. Parking brake.

Power Plant: Two 283 kW (380 hp) Lycoming TIO-541-E1C4 turbocharged flat-six engines, each driving a Hartzell three-blade metal constant-speed and fully-feathering propeller. Propeller unfeathering accumulators and electric anti-icing optional. Electrically-operated engine cowl flaps. Two interconnected fuel cells in each wing containing 269 litres (71 US gallons); total usable capacity 538 litres (142 US gallons). Optionally, four interconnected fuel cells in each wing containing 382 litres (101 US gallons); total usable capacity 764 litres (202 US gallons); or five interconnected fuel cells in each wing containing 439 litres (116 US gallons), with total usable capacity of 878 litres (232 US gallons). Refuelling points in each leading-edge, near wingtip. Oil capacity 24·5 litres (6·5 US gallons).

Accommodation: Standard model has four individual seats in pairs, each complete with headrest and inertia-reel shoulder harness, in enclosed cabin with centre aisle. Door, hinged at forward edge, on port side at rear of cabin. Baggage hold in the nose, capacity 0·91 m³ (32 cu ft), with external access door on port side of nose. Additional stowage for 0·80 m³ (28·25 cu ft) of baggage at rear of cabin. Optional extras include fifth and sixth seats, rearward-facing third and fourth seats, curtain separating passenger and pilot seating, writing desks, refreshment cabinets, toilet, windscreen electrical anti-icing and cabin fire extinguishers.

Systems: Cabin pressurisation system, differential 0·32 bars (4·6 lb/sq in), supplied by engine turbocharger bleed air, maintains cabin altitude equivalent to 3,050 m (10,000 ft) at 7,560 m (24,800 ft). Combustion heater of 45,000 BTU standard. Optional engine-driven vapour-cycle air-conditioning system of 14,000 BTU. Automatic altitude controller for cabin pressurisation system standard. Oxygen system optional, with 0·31 m³ (11 cu ft), 0·62 m³ (22 cu ft) or 1·39 m³ (49 cu ft) bottle. Hydraulic system for brakes only. Pneumatic system for pressure-operated instruments and de-icing boots only. 24V 125A generators standard; two 12V 25Ah batteries.

Avionics and Equipment: Standard avionics comprise Collins VHF-251 VHF transceiver with PWC-150 power adaptor and B3 com antenna, Collins VIR-351 Omni No. 1 receiver with IND-351 VOR/ILS indicator and B38 antenna, Collins AMR-350 audio panel, Collins marker beacon incorporated in AMR-350, with single set marker lights and B16 antenna, Collins ADF-650 ADF with IND-650 indicator and ANT-650A antenna, Collins GLS-350 glideslope receiver with A-326A antenna, Collins TDR-950 transponder with B18 antenna, Beech metal radio panel, radio accessories, static wicks, microphone key button in pilot's control wheel, white lighting, dual microphones and headsets, single cockpit speaker, and avionics master switch. Optional avionics include an extensive range of Bendix, Collins, King, Edo-Aire Mitchell, Sperry and RCA equipment. Standard equipment includes blind-flying instrumentation, electric turn co-ordinator, outside air temperature gauge, eight-day clock, map light, instrument post lights, instrument floodlights, sun visors, bad weather window for pilot, passengers' reading lights, cabin dome light, entrance light, ventilation system with provisions for air-conditioning, tinted cabin side windows, super soundproofing, wall-to-wall carpet, in-flight storage pockets, armrests, headrests, baggage straps, dual landing lights, taxi light, navigation lights, rotating beacons, nose baggage compartment light, retracting exterior step, full-flow oil filters, alternate static source, heated pitot tube, external power socket, fuel vent anti-icer, heated stall warning device, polyurethane paint, and towbar. Optional equipment includes de luxe instrument panel with duplicated blind-flying instrumentation for co-pilot, instantaneous vertical speed indicator, tachometer with synchroscope, flight and engine hour recorders, pilot's control wheel chronometer, co-pilot's control wheel map light, co-pilot's toe brakes, internally lighted instruments, propeller synchroniser, pilot's relief tube, wing ice light and strobe lights.

Dimensions, external:

Wing span	11·96 m (39 ft 3 in)
Wing chord at fuselage c/l	2·80 m (9 ft 2⅛ in)
Wing chord at tip	0·90 m (2 ft 11⅝ in)
Wing aspect ratio	7·243
Length overall	10·31 m (33 ft 10 in)
Height overall	3·76 m (12 ft 4 in)
Tailplane span	5·18 m (17 ft 0 in)
Wheel track	3·43 m (11 ft 3 in)
Wheelbase	2·81 m (9 ft 2½ in)
Propeller diameter	1·88 m (6 ft 2 in)
Passenger door: Height	1·21 m (3 ft 11½ in)
Width	0·67 m (2 ft 2½ in)
Height to sill	0·81 m (2 ft 8 in)
Baggage compartment door:	
Height	0·60 m (1 ft 11½ in)
Width	0·95 m (3 ft 1½ in)
Height to sill	0·95 m (3 ft 1½ in)

Dimensions, internal:

Cabin: Length	3·61 m (11 ft 10 in)
Max width	1·27 m (4 ft 2 in)
Max height	1·32 m (4 ft 4 in)
Floor area	3·36 m² (36·2 sq ft)
Volume	4·80 m³ (169·6 cu ft)

Areas:

Wings, gross	19·78 m² (212·9 sq ft)
Ailerons (total)	1·06 m² (11·4 sq ft)
Trailing-edge flaps (total)	2·76 m² (29·7 sq ft)
Fin	1·52 m² (16·38 sq ft)
Rudder, incl tab	1·15 m² (12·4 sq ft)
Tailplane	4·24 m² (45·6 sq ft)
Elevators, incl tab	1·52 m² (16·4 sq ft)

Weights and Loadings:

Weight empty, equipped	1,988 kg (4,383 lb)
Max T-O and landing weight	3,073 kg (6,775 lb)
Max ramp weight	3,093 kg (6,819 lb)
Max wing loading	155·3 kg/m² (31·8 lb/sq ft)
Max power loading	5·43 kg/kW (8·9 lb/hp)

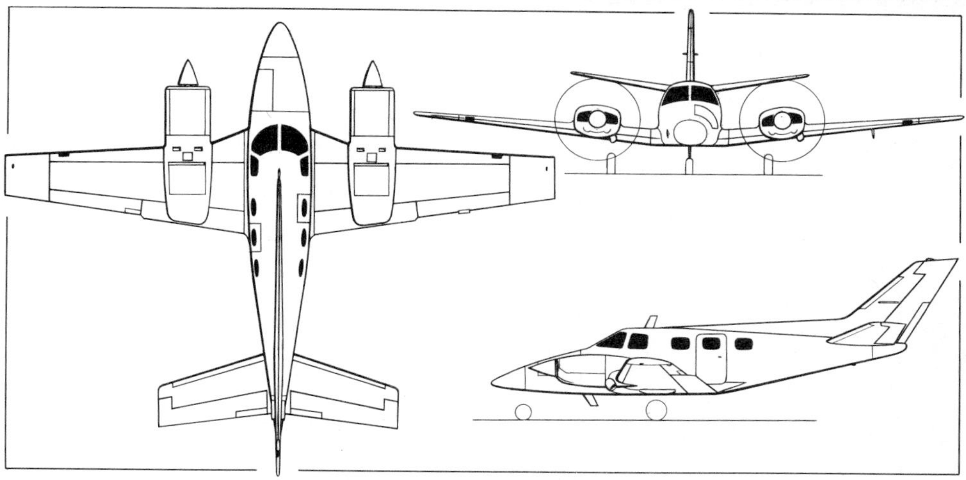

Photograph and three-view drawing *(Pilot Press)* **of the Beechcraft Duke B60 four/six-seat pressurised transport**

Performance (at max T-O weight, except cruising speeds at average cruise weight):

Max level speed at 7,010 m (23,000 ft)
246 knots (455 km/h; 283 mph)

Max cruising speed:
approx 78% power at 7,620 m (25,000 ft)
239 knots (443 km/h; 275 mph)
approx 78% power at 6,100 m (20,000 ft)
231 knots (428 km/h; 266 mph)
approx 78% power at 4,570 m (15,000 ft)
220 knots (407 km/h; 253 mph)

Cruising speed:
approx 74% power at 7,620 m (25,000 ft)
233 knots (431 km/h; 268 mph)
approx 74% power at 6,100 m (20,000 ft)
225 knots (417 km/h; 259 mph)
approx 74% power at 4,570 m (15,000 ft)
214 knots (396 km/h; 246 mph)
approx 68% power at 7,620 m (25,000 ft)
225 knots (417 km/h; 259 mph)
approx 68% power at 6,100 m (20,000 ft)
215 knots (399 km/h; 247 mph)
approx 68% power at 4,570 m (15,000 ft)
205 knots (380 km/h; 236 mph)
approx 63% power at 7,620 m (25,000 ft)
217 knots (402 km/h; 250 mph)
approx 63% power at 6,100 m (20,000 ft)
209 knots (388 km/h; 241 mph)
approx 63% power at 4,570 m (15,000 ft)
199 knots (369 km/h; 229 mph)

Stalling speed, wheels and flaps up, power off
81 knots (150·5 km/h; 93 mph)

Stalling speed, wheels and flaps down, power off
72 knots (133·5 km/h; 84 mph)

Max rate of climb at S/L	488 m (1,601 ft)/min
Rate of climb at S/L, one engine out	94 m (307 ft)/min
Service ceiling	9,145 m (30,000 ft)
Service ceiling, one engine out	4,600 m (15,100 ft)
Runway LCN	4
T-O run	632 m (2,075 ft)
T-O to 15 m (50 ft)	800 m (2,626 ft)
Landing from 15 m (50 ft)	934 m (3,065 ft)
Landing run	402 m (1,318 ft)

Range with max optional fuel and allowances for engine start, taxi, take-off, climb to altitude and 45 min fuel reserves at 45% power, ISA:
approx 78% power at 7,620 m (25,000 ft)
1,045 nm (1,936 km; 1,203 miles)
approx 78% power at 6,100 m (20,000 ft)
967 nm (1,793 km; 1,113 miles)
approx 78% power at 4,570 m (15,000 ft)
916 nm (1,698 km; 1,054 miles)
approx 74% power at 7,620 m (25,000 ft)
1,072 nm (1,986 km; 1,234 miles)
approx 74% power at 6,100 m (20,000 ft)
1,010 nm (1,872 km; 1,163 miles)
approx 74% power at 4,570 m (15,000 ft)
964 nm (1,786 km; 1,110 miles)
approx 68% power at 7,620 m (25,000 ft)
1,112 nm (2,060 km; 1,280 miles)
approx 68% power at 6,100 m (20,000 ft)
1,070 nm (1,983 km; 1,232 miles)
approx 68% power at 4,570 m (15,000 ft)
1,028 nm (1,905 km; 1,183 miles)
approx 63% power at 7,620 m (25,000 ft)
1,168 nm (2,165 km; 1,344 miles)
approx 63% power at 6,100 m (20,000 ft)
1,122 nm (2,079 km; 1,291 miles)
approx 63% power at 4,570 m (15,000 ft)
1,083 nm (2,007 km; 1,247 miles)

BEECHCRAFT QUEEN AIR B80 and QUEEN AIRLINER B80

Production of these aircraft has ended. Full details can be found in the 1978-79 *Jane's*.

BEECHCRAFT KING AIR MODEL C90

USAF designation: VC-6B

Introduced in September 1970, the King Air C90 is a pressurised 6/10-seat twin-turboprop business aircraft which superseded the original Models 90, A90 and B90 King Air. It is powered by Pratt & Whitney Aircraft of Canada PT6A-21 turboprop engines, which provide improved performance over a wide range of altitudes and temperatures. Increases in take-off and climb power offer improvements in high altitude and hot weather operation and, since these engines also run cooler, increases in useful life and lower overhaul costs result.

The C90 King Air utilises the more advanced cabin pressurisation and heating system of the King Air 100. This comprises a dual engine bleed air system for cabin pressurisation, with a max differential of 0·32 bars (4·6 lb/sq in).

The 1979 King Air C90 has as standard dual bleed air pressurisation and cabin heating, including supplementary electric heating, air-conditioning, super soundproofing, a full anti-icing system, four cabin seats in club arrangement, forward cabin partition with curtain, aft starboard cabin partition with curtain, polarised cabin windows, exterior urethane paint scheme and a comprehensive avionics package which includes dual nav/com, transpon-

1979 Beechcraft King Air C90

der, DME, ADF, marker beacon, glideslope and dual blind-flying instrumentation.

A total of 1,334 commercial and military King Air 90s had been delivered by 1 January 1979. One was provided for the USAF's 1254th Special Air Missions Squadron at Andrews AFB, Maryland, for VIP transport duties under the designation **VC-6B**. Beech has delivered 10 King Air C90s to the Spanish Air Force and Civil Aviation School for instrument training and liaison.

TYPE: Six/ten-seat twin-turboprop business aircraft.

WINGS: Cantilever low-wing monoplane. Wing section NACA 23014·1 (modified) at root, NACA 23016·22 (modified) at outer end of centre-section, NACA 23012 at tip. Dihedral 7°. Incidence 4° 48′ at root, 0° at tip. No sweepback at quarter-chord. Two-spar aluminium alloy structure. All-metal ailerons of magnesium, with adjustable trim tab on port aileron. Single-slotted aluminium alloy flaps. Automatic pneumatic de-icing boots on leading-edges standard.

FUSELAGE: Aluminium alloy semi-monocoque structure.

TAIL UNIT: Cantilever all-metal structure with sweptback vertical surfaces. Fixed-incidence tailplane, with 7° dihedral. Trim tabs in rudder and each elevator. Automatic pneumatic de-icing boots on leading-edges of fin and tailplane.

LANDING GEAR: Electrically-retractable tricycle type. Nosewheel retracts rearward, main wheels forward into engine nacelles. Main wheels protrude slightly beneath nacelles when retracted, for safety in a wheels-up emergency landing. Steerable nosewheel with shimmy damper. Beech oleo-pneumatic shock-absorbers. B.F. Goodrich main wheels with tyres size 8·50-10, pressure 3·79 bars (55 lb/sq in). B.F. Goodrich nosewheel with tyre size 6·50-10, pressure 3·59 bars (52 lb/sq in). Goodrich heat-sink and aircooled multi-disc hydraulic brakes. Parking brakes.

POWER PLANT: Two 410 kW (550 ehp) Pratt & Whitney Aircraft of Canada PT6A-21 turboprop engines, each driving a Hartzell three-blade constant-speed fully-feathering propeller. Propeller electro-thermal anti-icing, auto ignition system, environmental fuel drain collection system, and magnetic chip detector standard. Fuel in two tanks in engine nacelles, each with capacity of 231 litres (61 US gallons), and bladder type auxiliary tanks in outer wings, each with capacity of 496 litres (131 US gallons). Total fuel capacity 1,454 litres (384 US gallons). Refuelling points in top of each engine nacelle and in wing leading-edge outboard of each nacelle. Oil capacity 13·2 litres (3·5 US gallons). Engine anti-icing system standard.

ACCOMMODATION: Two seats side by side in cockpit with dual controls standard. Normally, four reclining seats are provided in the main cabin, in pairs facing each other fore and aft. Standard furnishings include cabin forward partition, with fore and aft partition curtain and coat rack, hinged nose baggage compartment door, seat belts and inertia-reel shoulder harness for all seats. Optional arrangements seat up to eight persons, some with two- or three-place couch, lateral tracking chairs, and refreshment cabinets. Baggage racks at rear of cabin on starboard side, with optional toilet on port side. Door on port side aft of wing, with built-in airstairs. Emergency exit on starboard side of cabin. Entire accommodation pressurised and air-conditioned. Electrically-heated windscreen standard.

SYSTEMS: Pressurisation by dual engine bleed air system with pressure differential of 0·32 bars (4·6 lb/sq in). Cabin heated by 45,000 BTU dual engine bleed air system and auxiliary electrical heating system. Electrical system utilises two 28V 250A starter/generators, 24V 45Ah aircooled nickel-cadmium battery with failure detector. Complete de-icing and anti-icing equipment. Oxygen system, 0·62 m^3 (22 cu ft), 1·39 m^3 (49 cu ft) or 1·81 m^3 (64 cu ft) capacity, optional. Vacuum system for flight instruments.

AVIONICS AND EQUIPMENT: Standard avionics package comprises dual Collins VHF-251 VHF transceivers with PWS-150 power adaptors and B3 antennae; dual Collins VIR-351 Omni nav receivers, one with Collins 331A-3G indicator and B17 antenna, the other with IND-351 on B17 antenna; Collins AMR-350 audio system; Collins ADF-650A ADF, with IND-650 indicator and ANT-650 antenna; Collins marker receiver integral with AMR-350, plus marker lights and B16 antenna; Collins GLS-350 glideslope receiver with B35 antenna; Collins DME-451, with IND-451 indicator, Nav1/Nav 2 switching, DME hold and B18 antenna; Collins PN-101 compass system (pilot); Standard Electric gyro horizon (pilot); CF gyro horizon and directional gyro (co-pilot); dual Flite-Tronics PC-14B 125VA inverters with failure light; avionics transient protection; dual flight instrumentation; sectional instrument panel; white lighting; radio accessories, static wicks and Beech metal radio panel; microphone key button in pilot and co-pilot control wheels; dual microphones, headsets and cockpit speakers; and avionics master switch. Optional avionics include a wide range of equipment by Bendix, Collins, King, Edo-Aire Mitchell, RCA and Sperry. Standard equipment includes dual blind-flying instrumentation with sensitive altimeters, standby magnetic compass, outside air temperature gauge, eight-day clock, vacuum gauge, de-icing pressure gauge, dual map lights, primary and secondary instrument light systems, pilot and co-pilot four-way adjustable seats with shoulder harness, map pockets, dual electrically-heated windscreens, windscreen defroster, dual storm windows, sun visors, windscreen wipers, dual cockpit speakers, control locks, cabin rate of climb indicator, cabin altitude and differential pressure indicators, indirect cabin lighting, two overhead cabin spotlights, entrance door light, adjustable reading lights, fresh air outlets, cabin windows with adjustable polarised shades, wall-to-wall carpet, 'No smoking–Fasten seat belt' sign, wing ice lights, dual landing lights, taxi light, position lights, dual rotating beacons, aft compartment lights, tail floodlight, automatic fuel heater system, heated stall warning device, dual heated pitot heads, external power socket, heated fuel vents, static wicks, emergency locator transmitter, internal corrosion proofing and external polyurethane paint. Optional equipment includes control wheel mounted chronographs, flight hour recorder, instantaneous vertical speed indicator, cockpit and cabin fire extinguishers, a range of cabin seats, cabinets, storage drawers and toilets, entrance door step lights, strobe lights, wingtip recognition lights, engine fire detection and extinguishing system, oxygen system of 0·62 m^3 (22 cu ft), 1·39 m^3 (49 cu ft), or 1·81 m^3 (64 cu ft) capacity, automatic propeller feathering, reversible-pitch propellers and propeller synchrophaser.

DIMENSIONS, EXTERNAL:

Wing span	15·32 m (50 ft 3 in)
Wing chord at root	2·15 m (7 ft 0½ in)
Wing chord at tip	1·07 m (3 ft 6 in)
Wing aspect ratio	8·57
Length overall	10·82 m (35 ft 6 in)
Height overall	4·33 m (14 ft 2½ in)
Tailplane span	5·25 m (17 ft 2½ in)
Wheel track	3·89 m (12 ft 9 in)
Wheelbase	3·75 m (12 ft 3½ in)
Propeller diameter	2·36 m (7 ft 9 in)
Passenger door: Height	1·31 m (4 ft 3¾ in)
Width	0·69 m (2 ft 3 in)
Height to sill	1·17 m (3 ft 10 in)

DIMENSIONS, INTERNAL:

Total pressurised length	5·43 m (17 ft 10 in)
Cabin: Length	3·86 m (12 ft 8 in)
Max width	1·37 m (4 ft 6 in)
Max height	1·45 m (4 ft 9 in)
Floor area	6·50 m^2 (70 sq ft)
Volume	8·89 m^3 (314 cu ft)
Baggage compartment, aft	1·51 m^3 (53·5 cu ft)

AREAS:

Wings, gross	27·31 m^2 (293·94 sq ft)
Ailerons (total)	1·29 m^2 (13·90 sq ft)
Trailing-edge flaps (total)	2·72 m^2 (29·30 sq ft)
Fin	2·20 m^2 (23·67 sq ft)
Rudder, incl tab	1·30 m^2 (14·00 sq ft)
Tailplane	4·39 m^2 (47·25 sq ft)
Elevators, incl tabs	1·66 m^2 (17·87 sq ft)

WEIGHTS AND LOADINGS:

Weight empty	2,618 kg (5,772 lb)
Max T-O weight	4,377 kg (9,650 lb)
Max ramp weight	4,402 kg (9,705 lb)
Max landing weight	4,159 kg (9,168 lb)
Max wing loading	160·1 kg/m^2 (32·8 lb/sq ft)
Max power loading	5·34 kg/kW (8·8 lb/ehp)

PERFORMANCE (at max T-O weight, except where indicated):

Max cruising speed at 3,660 m (12,000 ft)
222 knots (412 km/h; 256 mph)

Max cruising speed at 4,880 m (16,000 ft) at AUW of 3,794 kg (8,365 lb)
219 knots (406 km/h; 252 mph)

Max cruising speed at 6,400 m (21,000 ft) at AUW of 3,794 kg (8,365 lb)
216 knots (401 km/h; 249 mph)

Stalling speed, wheels and flaps up, power off
89 knots (164 km/h; 102 mph) IAS

Stalling speed, wheels and flaps down, power off
76 knots (140 km/h; 87 mph) IAS

Max rate of climb at S/L 596 m (1,955 ft)/min

Rate of climb at S/L, one engine out
164 m (539 ft)/min

Service ceiling	8,565 m (28,100 ft)
Service ceiling, one engine out	4,587 m (15,050 ft)
Min ground turning radius	11·58 m (38 ft 0 in)
Runway LCN	4
T-O to 15 m (50 ft)	689 m (2,261 ft)
Accelerate/stop distance	1,066 m (3,498 ft)

Landing from 15 m (50 ft) without propeller reversal at AUW of 4,159 kg (9,168 lb) 613 m (2,010 ft)

Landing run, without propeller reversal, at AUW of 4,159 kg (9,168 lb) 328 m (1,075 ft)

Range with max fuel at max cruising speed, incl allowance for starting, taxi, take-off, climb, descent and 45 min reserves at max range power, ISA, at:

6,400 m (21,000 ft)
1,202 nm (2,227 km; 1,384 miles)

4,875 m (16,000 ft)
1,059 nm (1,962 km; 1,219 miles)

3,660 m (12,000 ft)
957 nm (1,773 km; 1,102 miles)

Max range at econ cruising power, allowances as above, at:

6,400 m (21,000 ft)
1,281 nm (2,374 km; 1,474 miles)

4,875 m (16,000 ft)
1,159 nm (2,147 km; 1,334 miles)

3,660 m (12,000 ft)
1,068 nm (1,979 km; 1,229 miles)

BEECHCRAFT KING AIR E90

On 1 May 1972 Beech announced an addition to the King Air range of business aircraft. Designated King Air E90, this combines the airframe of the King Air C90 with the 507 kW (680 ehp) Pratt & Whitney Aircraft of Canada PT6A-28 turboprop engines that power the King Air A100, each flat rated to 410 kW (550 ehp). The US Navy ordered 15 King Air 90s in 1976 as **T-44A** advanced trainers to meet its VTAM (X) requirement, and this version is described separately.

The description of the King Air C90 in this edition applies also to the King Air E90, except as follows:

LANDING GEAR: As King Air C90, except main-wheel tyre pressure 3·93 bars (57 lb/sq in).

POWER PLANT: Two 507 kW (680 ehp) Pratt & Whitney Aircraft of Canada PT6A-28 turboprop engines, flat rated to 410 kW (550 ehp), each driving a Hartzell three-blade metal fully-feathering and reversible-pitch constant-speed propeller. Standard fuel capacity 1,794 litres (474 US gallons).

AVIONICS AND EQUIPMENT: Standard avionics include dual Collins VHF-20A VHF transceivers with Gables controls and B3 antennae; Collins VIR-30 MGM Omni No. 1 receiver, with 331A-3G indicator, Gables control and B17 antenna; Collins VIR-30M Omni No. 2 receiver with 331H-3G indicator and Gables control; Collins 356C-4 isolation amplifier and 356F-3 speaker amplifier with single set of audio switches; Collins ADF-650 ADF with IND-650 indicator, Gables control, voice range filter and ANT-650 antenna; Collins marker beacon integral with VIR-30 No. 1, with marker lights and B16 antenna; Collins glideslope receiver integral with VIR-30 No. 1, with B35 antenna; dual flight instrumentation; Collins DME-40 with 339F-12 indicator, Nav 1/Nav 2 switching, DME hold, and 237Z-1 antenna; Collins TDR-950 transponder with 237Z-1 antenna; Collins PN-101 compass system (pilot); Standard Electric gyro horizon (pilot); CF gyro horizon and directional gyro (co-pilot); dual Flite-Tronics PC-14B 125VA inverters with failure light; avionics transient protection; Beech edge-lighted radio panel, radio accessories and static wicks; white lighting; microphone key button in pilot and co-pilot control wheels; dual microphones, headsets and cockpit speakers; and avionics master switch. Optional avionics include a wide range of equipment by Bendix, Collins, King, Edo-Aire Mitchell, RCA and Sperry. Standard and optional equipment generally as listed for King Air C90.

WEIGHTS AND LOADINGS:

Weight empty	2,745 kg (6,052 lb)
Max T-O weight	4,581 kg (10,100 lb)
Max ramp weight	4,608 kg (10,160 lb)
Max landing weight	4,400 kg (9,700 lb)
Max wing loading	168·0 kg/m² (34·4 lb/sq ft)
Max power loading	5·59 kg/kW (9·18 lb/ehp)

PERFORMANCE (at max T-O weight, except where indicated):

Max cruising speed at 3,660 m (12,000 ft) 249 knots (462 km/h; 287 mph)

Cruising speed at max recommended cruise power:
- at 4,875 m (16,000 ft) 247 knots (459 km/h; 285 mph)
- at 6,400 m (21,000 ft) 245 knots (454 km/h; 282 mph)

Cruising speed for max range 197 knots (365 km/h; 227 mph)

Stalling speed, power off, wheels and flaps up 86 knots (159 km/h; 99 mph) IAS

Stalling speed, power off, wheels and flaps down 77 knots (143 km/h; 89 mph) IAS

Max rate of climb at S/L 570 m (1,870 ft)/min

Rate of climb at S/L, one engine out 143 m (470 ft)/min

Service ceiling 8,419 m (27,620 ft)

Service ceiling, at 3,629 kg (8,000 lb) AUW 9,421 m (30,910 ft)

Service ceiling, one engine out 4,386 m (14,390 ft)

Service ceiling, one engine out, at 3,629 kg (8,000 lb) AUW 6,218 m (20,400 ft)

Min ground turning radius 11·58 m (38 ft 0 in)

Runway LCN 4·5

T-O run 473 m (1,553 ft)

T-O to 15 m (50 ft) 617 m (2,024 ft)

Landing distance, 5° approach angle, full flap, at max landing weight:
- landing from 15 m (50 ft) 643 m (2,110 ft)
- landing run 314 m (1,030 ft)

Accelerate/stop distance, incl 2 s failure recognition time 1,139 m (3,736 ft)

Cruising range at max recommended cruise power:
- at 4,875 m (16,000 ft) 1,125 nm (2,084 km; 1,295 miles)
- at 6,400 m (21,000 ft) 1,309 nm (2,425 km; 1,507 miles)

Cruising range at max range power:
- at 4,875 m (16,000 ft) 1,479 nm (2,741 km; 1,703 miles)
- at 6,400 m (21,000 ft) 1,624 nm (3,009 km; 1,870 miles)

Range at max T-O weight, max recommended power at 6,400 m (21,000 ft), 45 min reserves, five occupants, 73 kg (160 lb) baggage and 1,440 kg (3,176 lb) fuel before engine start 1,309 nm (2,425 km; 1,507 miles)

BEECHCRAFT T-44A (KING AIR 90)

In 1976 Beech Aircraft won an industry-wide competition for a twin-turboprop advanced pilot training aircraft to meet the US Navy's VTAM(X) requirement. The aircraft selected was a version of the King Air 90, incorporating features of both the Model C90 and E90, with modifications to meet Navy special requirements. This aircraft has the USN designation T-44A, and by the end of 1978 Beech had received contracts to build 61 aircraft with options on 10 more; of these, 40 had then been delivered.

The first T-44A was delivered to USN Training Command at NAS Corpus Christi, Texas, on 5 April 1977, and student pilot training began in July 1977. T-44As replace TS-2As and TS-2Bs in the USN's training aircraft inventory.

The Navy's T-44As differ primarily from other King Air 90s by their power plant, consisting of two 560 kW (750 ehp) Pratt & Whitney Aircraft of Canada PT6A-34B turboprop engines, flat rated to 410 kW (550 ehp). They have also an engine compressor wash system. The fuel capacity is as for the civil King Air C90.

The avionics systems comprise a complete commercial package, plus Tacan, UHF, and UHF-DF. A 'failure mode selector box' is provided also, enabling the instructor to initiate any of 10 avionics/instrument failures on the student's instrument panel.

The description of the civil King Air C90 applies generally to the T-44A, except as described above, and it has the same maximum T-O weight.

PERFORMANCE (at max T-O weight):

Cruising speed at 4,570 m (15,000 ft) 240 knots (445 km/h; 276 mph)

Max rate of climb at S/L	597 m (1,960 ft)/min
Service ceiling	8,990 m (29,500 ft)
T-O to 15 m (50 ft)	625 m (2,050 ft)
Landing from 15 m (50 ft)	619 m (2,030 ft)

Range with max fuel at 7,620 m (25,000 ft) 1,265 nm (2,344 km; 1,456 miles)

BEECHCRAFT SUPER KING AIR F90

Details of this new, T-tailed version of the King Air are given in the Addenda.

The US Navy's T-44A version of the Beechcraft King Air

BEECHCRAFT COMMUTER C99, 1300 and 1900

Beech announced on 7 May 1979 the company's intention to re-enter the commuter airliner market. Plans include production of an updated version of the Beechcraft 99 Airliner, last described in the 1977-78 *Jane's*. Improvements will include new 559 kW (750 shp) engines instead of the 507 kW (680 shp) turboprops which powered the B99 versions when production ended. It is anticipated that production aircraft could be available for delivery during 1981, as Beechcraft Commuter C99s.

Beech is also accepting orders for two new aircraft which, subject to sufficient market interest, the company proposes to add to its commuter range. First of these is the Beechcraft Commuter 1300, a high-density pressurised model with accommodation for 13 passengers, and for which an optional cargo pod will be available. The company states that production examples of this aircraft could be available for delivery within 15 months of development being initiated.

The third aircraft in this series, the Beechcraft Commuter 1900, would be a T-tailed, 19-seat pressurised aircraft, of which the development period is estimated at 3 to 3½ years. Beech is also studying a new pressurised commuter airliner in the 35-seat category.

The Commuter 1900 would be powered by two turboprop engines of approx 746 kW (1,000 shp), would cruise at about 260 knots (483 km/h; 300 mph), have a max T-O weight of 6,915 kg (15,245 lb), and a fully-loaded cruising range of 555 nm (1,028 km; 639 miles), with IFR reserves, under ISA conditions. Fore and aft airstair doors would be standard, seats would be designed for quick removal for conversion to cargo configuration, and options would include a 1·32 × 1·32 m (52 × 52 in) cargo door. An executive transport version is also under consideration.

A letter of intent to purchase six Commuter 1900s was received from Henson Aviation in Summer 1979.

BEECHCRAFT KING AIR A100

US Army designation: U-21F

Beech Aircraft announced on 26 May 1969 the addition of a new version of the King Air to its fleet of corporate transport aircraft. Designated King Air 100, this is a pressurised transport with increased internal capacity and more powerful engines, enabling it to carry a useful load of more than two short tons. By comparison with the King Air 90 series, it has a fuselage 1·27 m (4 ft 2 in) longer, reduced wing span, larger rudder and elevator and twin-wheel main landing gear. It is available in a variety of interior configurations, seating six to eight in executive versions, or up to 13 in high-density arrangement, plus crew of two.

The King Air 100 has been approved for Category 2 landing minima by the FAA. Initial deliveries were made in August 1969, following FAA certification. A total of 296 commercial and military King Air 100s had been delivered by 1 January 1979.

First deliveries of the advanced Model A100, comprising five U-21Fs for the Department of the Army, began in October 1971. Supplied under a $2·5 million contract, they represented the first pressurised aircraft in the Army's inventory. Two A100s were supplied to the Spanish Air Force.

Two aircraft equipped with a Beech-developed UNACE package (Universal Aircraft Com/Nav Evaluation) have been delivered to Belgium and Indonesia. UNACE-configured aircraft, which provide an economical means of inspecting and calibrating aviation navigation aids, are operating also in Algeria, Canada, Malaysia, Mexico and the USA. Beech is able to modify King Airs for aerial photography, and deliveries of camera-equipped aircraft have been made to Canada, Chile, France, Jamaica, Saudi Arabia and Thailand, as well as to various US organisations.

TYPE: Twin-turboprop light passenger, freight or executive transport.

WINGS: Cantilever low-wing monoplane. Wing section NACA 23018 at root, NACA 23016·5 at centre-section joint with outer panel, NACA 23012 at tip. Dihedral 7°. Incidence 4° 48′ at root, 0° at tip. Two-spar all-metal light alloy structure. All-metal ailerons of magnesium. Trim tab in port aileron. Single-slotted light alloy trailing-edge flaps. Pneumatic de-icing boots standard.

FUSELAGE: All-metal light alloy semi-monocoque structure.

TAIL UNIT: Cantilever all-metal structure with swept vertical surfaces and a ventral stabilising fin. Trim tab in rudder. Electrically-operated adjustment of tailplane incidence. Pneumatic de-icing boots standard.

LANDING GEAR: Retractable tricycle type with single steerable nosewheel and twin wheels on each main unit. Electrical retraction, nosewheel rearward, main units forward into engine nacelles. Hydraulic retraction system optional. Beech oleo-pneumatic shock-absorbers. Goodrich main wheels and tubeless tyres size 18 × 5·5,

Artist's impression of the proposed Beechcraft Commuter 1900

pressure 7·10 bars (103 lb/sq in). Nosewheel with tubeless tyre size 6·50 × 10, pressure 3·93 bars (57 lb/sq in). B. F. Goodrich heat sink and aircooled single-disc hydraulic brakes.

POWER PLANT: Two 507 kW (680 ehp) Pratt & Whitney Aircraft of Canada PT6A-28 turboprop engines, each driving a Hartzell four-blade fully-feathering and reversible-pitch constant-speed propeller. Rubber fuel cells in wings, with total capacity of 1,779 litres (470 US gallons). Automatic fuel heating systems; inertial engine inlet de-icing system; engine inlet lips de-iced by electro-thermally heated boots; auto ignition system; environmental fuel drain collector system; magnetic chip detector. Goodrich electrical propeller anti-icing system.

ACCOMMODATION: Crew of two side by side on flight deck, with full dual controls and instruments. Easily removable partition with sliding door between flight deck and cabin. Six fully-adjustable individual cabin chairs standard, with removable headrests, with a variety of alternative layouts, for up to 13 passengers in commuter role. Seat belts and inertia-reel shoulder harness for all seats. Polarised cabin windows. Dual storm windows. Fully-carpeted floor. External access door to forward radio compartment. Aft fuselage maintenance access door. Plug-type emergency exit at forward end of cabin on starboard side. Passenger door at rear of cabin on port side, with integral airstair. Easily removable aft cabin partition with sliding doors. Lavatory installation and stowage for up to 186 kg (410 lb) baggage in aft fuselage. Other standard cabin equipment includes reading lights and fresh air outlets for all passengers, cabin coat rack and dual 'No smoking—Fasten seat belt' signs. Electro-thermally heated windscreen, hot air windscreen defroster and windscreen wipers standard. Optional equipment includes cabin fire extinguisher, additional cabin window, flush toilet and a variety of interior cabinets.

SYSTEMS: Cabin pressurisation by dual engine bleed air with a differential of 0·32 bars (4·6 lb/sq in). Cabin heated by 27,000 BTU electrical heating system. Oxygen system for flight deck and 0·62 m³ (22 cu ft) oxygen system for cabin standard. Cabin oxygen system of 1·39 m³ (49 cu ft), or 1·81 m³ (64 cu ft) optional. Dual vacuum system for instruments. Hydraulic system for brakes only. Pneumatic system for wing and tail unit de-icing only. Two 250A starter/generators. Aircooled nickel-cadmium 28V 45Ah battery with failure detector. Engine fire detection system.

AVIONICS AND EQUIPMENT: Standard avionics comprise dual King KTR 905 VHF transceivers, with Gables controls and B3 antennae; King KNR 630 Omni No. 1, with Collins 331A-3G indicator, Gables control and B17 antenna; King KNR 630 Omni No. 2, with Collins 331H-3G indicator and Gables control; dual Omni range filters; dual Collins 356F-3 audio amplifiers, each with 356C-4 isolation amplifiers and audio switches; King KDF 805 ADF less indicator, with KFS 580B control, voice range filter, and Beech flush sense antenna; King KMR 675 marker beacon receiver, with dual marker lights and B16 antenna; dual glideslope receivers integral with No. 1 and No. 2 Omni, with B35 antenna; Bendix RDR-130 weather radar, with phased array antenna and digital scope; Sperry C-14-43 compass system with servo amplifier (pilot); King KNI 581 RMI with VOR-1/ADF on single needle, VOR-2/ADF on double needle; King KXP 755 transponder, with Gables control and B18 antenna; King KDM 705A DME with KDI 571 indicator, Nav-1/Nav-2 switching, DME hold and B18 antenna; dual Flite-Tronics PC-15B 250VA inverters with failure light; avionics transient protection; sectional instrument panel; Standard Electric gyro horizon (pilot); CF gyro horizon and directional gyro (co-pilot); Beech edge-lighted radio panel, radio accessories, microphone button in pilot and co-pilot control wheels, static wicks and white lighting; dual microphones, headsets and cockpit speakers; and avionics master switch. A wide range of optional avionics equipment is available, by Bendix, Collins, King, RCA, Sperry and SunAir. Heated main landing gear brake de-icing and tail floodlight offered as optional equipment. Other standard and optional equipment generally as listed for King Air C90.

DIMENSIONS, EXTERNAL:

Wing span	13·98 m (45 ft 10½ in)
Wing chord at root	2·15 m (7 ft 0½ in)
Wing chord at tip	1·07 m (3 ft 6 in)
Wing aspect ratio	7·51
Length overall	12·18 m (39 ft 11⅜ in)
Height overall	4·68 m (15 ft 4¼ in)
Tailplane span	6·81 m (22 ft 4½ in)
Wheel track	3·96 m (13 ft 0 in)
Wheelbase	4·55 m (14 ft 11 in)
Propeller diameter	2·29 m (7 ft 6 in)
Propeller ground clearance	0·34 m (1 ft 1½ in)

DIMENSIONS, INTERNAL:

Cabin: Length (excl flight deck)	5·08 m (16 ft 8 in)
Max width	1·37 m (4 ft 6 in)
Max height	1·45 m (4 ft 9 in)
Volume, avionics compartment in nose	0·45 m³ (16 cu ft)
Volume, aft baggage compartment	1·51 m³ (53·5 cu ft)

WEIGHTS AND LOADINGS:

Weight empty	3,083 kg (6,797 lb)
Max T-O weight	5,216 kg (11,500 lb)
Max ramp weight	5,247 kg (11,568 lb)
Max zero-fuel weight	4,354 kg (9,600 lb)
Max landing weight	5,084 kg (11,210 lb)
Max wing loading	199 kg/m² (40·8 lb/sq ft)
Max power loading	5·14 kg/kW (8·46 lb/ehp)

PERFORMANCE (at max T-O weight, unless otherwise quoted):

Max cruising speed at 4,762 kg (10,500 lb) AUW:	
at 6,400 m (21,000 ft)	235 knots (436 km/h; 270 mph)
at 4,875 m (16,000 ft)	243 knots (450 km/h; 280 mph)
at 3,050 m (10,000 ft)	248 knots (459 km/h; 285 mph)
Stalling speed, power off, wheels and flaps up	89 knots (164 km/h; 102 mph)
Stalling speed, power off, wheels and flaps down	75 knots (139 km/h; 86 mph)
Max rate of climb at S/L	598 m (1,963 ft)/min
Rate of climb at S/L, one engine out	138 m (452 ft)/min
Service ceiling	7,575 m (24,850 ft)
Service ceiling, one engine out	2,835 m (9,300 ft)
Min ground turning radius	12·2 m (40 ft 0 in)
Runway LCN	4·5
T-O run: flaps up	628 m (2,060 ft)
30% flap	565 m (1,855 ft)
T-O to 15 m (50 ft): flaps up	989 m (3,245 ft)
30% flap	817 m (2,681 ft)
Landing from 15 m (50 ft) at max landing weight, without propeller reversal	897 m (2,944 ft)
Landing run at max landing weight, without propeller reversal	545 m (1,787 ft)
*Accelerate/stop distance, flaps up	1,303 m (4,275 ft)
*Accelerate/stop distance, 30% flap	1,182 m (3,877 ft)
Range at high cruise power, with 1,779 litres (470 US gallons) fuel, incl allowances for starting, taxi, take-off, climb, descent and 45 min reserves:	
at 6,400 m (21,000 ft)	1,212 nm (2,247 km; 1,395 miles)
at 4,875 m (16,000 ft)	1,064 nm (1,971 km; 1,225 miles)
at 3,050 m (10,000 ft)	900 nm (1,667 km; 1,036 miles)
Range at long range cruise power, fuel and allowances as above:	
at 6,400 m (21,000 ft)	1,340 nm (2,483 km; 1,542 miles)
at 4,875 m (16,000 ft)	1,272 nm (2,358 km; 1,464 miles)
at 3,050 m (10,000 ft)	1,152 nm (2,136 km; 1,326 miles)

**Includes allowance for failure recognition*

BEECHCRAFT KING AIR B100

On 20 March 1975 Beech recorded the first flight of a new version of the King Air. Designated King Air B100, it is generally similar to its predecessors, except for the installation of two 533 kW (715 shp) AiResearch TPE 331-6-252B turboprop engines, giving improved performance.

The description of the King Air A100 applies also to the B100, except as follows:

TYPE: Twin-turboprop light passenger, freight or executive transport.

WINGS, FUSELAGE, TAIL UNIT, LANDING GEAR: As for Model A100.

POWER PLANT: Two 533 kW (715 shp) Garrett-AiResearch TPE 331-6-252B turboprop engines, each driving a four-blade metal constant-speed and fully-feathering propeller. Fuel system and anti-icing system as for Model A100.

ACCOMMODATION, SYSTEMS, AVIONICS AND EQUIPMENT: As for Model A100, except for slight variations in ancillary equipment associated directly with the power plant.

DIMENSIONS, EXTERNAL: As for Model A100, except:

Propeller ground clearance	0·39 m (1 ft 3½ in)

DIMENSIONS, INTERNAL, AND AREAS: As for Model A100

WEIGHTS AND LOADINGS:

Weight empty, equipped	3,215 kg (7,088 lb)
Max T-O weight	5,352 kg (11,800 lb)
Max ramp weight	5,386 kg (11,875 lb)
Max zero-fuel weight	4,354 kg (9,600 lb)
Max landing weight	5,085 kg (11,210 lb)
Max wing loading	206·0 kg/m² (42·2 lb/sq ft)
Max power loading	5·02 kg/kW (8·25 lb/shp)

Beechcraft King Air B100 twin-turboprop light passenger, freight or executive transport

PERFORMANCE (at max T-O weight):
Max level speed and max cruising speed:
at 3,660 m (12,000 ft) 265 knots (491 km/h; 305 mph)
at 6,400 m (21,000 ft) 262 knots (486 km/h; 302 mph)
Stalling speed, flaps up 93 knots (172·5 km/h; 107 mph) IAS
Stalling speed, flaps down 83 knots (154·5 km/h; 96 mph) IAS
Max rate of climb at S/L 652 m (2,139 ft)/min
Rate of climb at S/L, one engine out 152 m (501 ft)/min
Service ceiling 8,870 m (29,100 ft)
Service ceiling, one engine out 3,695 m (12,120 ft)
T-O run 579 m (1,898 ft)
T-O run, 30% flap 535 m (1,755 ft)
T-O to 15 m (50 ft) 899 m (2,951 ft)
T-O to 15 m (50 ft), 30% flap 821 m (2,694 ft)
Landing from 15 m (50 ft) without propeller reversal 1,040 m (3,413 ft)
Landing from 15 m (50 ft) with propeller reversal 817 m (2,679 ft)
Landing run without propeller reversal 503 m (1,651 ft)
Landing run with propeller reversal 393 m (1,290 ft)
Range with 1,779 litres (470 US gallons) usable fuel, with allowances for start, taxi, T-O, climb, descent and 45 min reserves at max range power, ISA:
at max cruising power at:
3,660 m (12,000 ft) 1,015 nm (1,881 km; 1,168 miles)
4,875 m (16,000 ft) 1,119 nm (2,074 km; 1,288 miles)
6,400 m (21,000 ft) 1,264 nm (2,343 km; 1,455 miles)
at econ cruising power at:
3,660 m (12,000 ft) 1,108 nm (2,053 km; 1,275 miles)
4,875 m (16,000 ft) 1,205 nm (2,232 km; 1,387 miles)
6,400 m (21,000 ft) 1,325 nm (2,456 km; 1,525 miles)

BEECHCRAFT SUPER KING AIR 200

US military designations: C-12 and RU-21J

Design of the Super King Air 200 began in October 1970, construction of the first prototype and first pre-production aircraft starting simultaneously a year later. The first prototype, serial BB-1, flew for the first time on 27 October 1972, followed by the second aircraft, BB-2, on 15 December 1972. While the flight tests and testing of a static fuselage were under way, construction of the first production aircraft began in June 1973. FAA certification under FAR Part 23 was awarded on 14 December 1973, the aircraft satisfying also the icing requirements of FAR Part 25.

By comparison with the King Air 100, the Super King Air 200 has increased wing span, basically the same fuselage, a new T-tail, more powerful engines, additional fuel capacity, increased cabin pressurisation and a higher gross weight. The cargo door fitted to some military versions (see below) became available as an option on civil Super King Airs in 1979; first deliveries were for air ambulance use in Libya and commuter operations in Australia.

In August 1974, Beech received a military contract to build and support 34 modified versions of the Super King Air, designated **C-12A**. Subsequently, many more C-12s have been ordered, in four versions, as follows:

C-12A. Initial version for US Army (60) and USAF (30), with two 559 kW (750 shp) Pratt & Whitney Aircraft of Canada PT6A-38 turboprop engines, each driving a Hartzell three-blade constant-speed fully-feathering and reversible-pitch propeller. Total of 90 ordered by mid-1979.

UC-12B. US Navy version, with 634 kW (850 shp) PT6A-41 turboprop engines, cargo door and high-flotation landing gear. Total of 44 ordered by mid-1979, of planned procurement of 66 which will extend deliveries into 1981.

C-12C. As C-12A, for US Army (14), but with PT6A-41 engines.

C-12D. As C-12C, for US Army, but with cargo door. Six ordered by mid-1979.

Contract value of all 154 C-12s (80 for the Army, 30 for the Air Force, and 44 for the Navy) totals $118 million.

Worldwide deployment of the C-12s began in July 1975. They are described as 'standard off-the-shelf Super King Air types, modified slightly to meet military flight requirements and to orient the control systems for two-pilot operation which is standard military practice'. Accommodation is provided for eight passengers, plus two pilots, with easy conversion to cargo missions. The large baggage area has provisions for storing survival gear.

In addition, during 1974 the US Army added three Super King Airs to its fleet of special mission aircraft, with the designation **RU-21J.** Under an R and D contract, Beech had modified these antenna-laden aircraft for the US Army's Cefly Lancer programme. They are approved for take-off at a special AUW of 6,804 kg (15,000 lb).

In February 1977 Beech delivered to the French Institut Géographique National two specially-modified Super King Airs. These have twin Wild RC-10 Superaviogon camera installations and Doppler navigation systems, and were the first Super King Airs to be equipped with optional wingtip fuel tanks, which increase the total usable fuel capacity from 2,059 litres (544 US gallons) to 2,457 litres (649 US gallons) to provide a max endurance of 10·3 hours. Designated Beech **Model 200Ts**, they are fitted with high-flotation main landing gear, and are being operated under a special French airworthiness certificate which allows max T-O and landing weights of 6,350 kg (14,000 lb) and 6,123 kg (13,500 lb) respectively. The aircraft can be operated with or without the wingtip tanks, for high-altitude photographic and weather observation missions.

Beech Aircraft announced on 25 April 1977 the company's intention to introduce a specially-equipped maritime patrol version of the Super King Air, the **Maritime Monitor 200T**. With advanced surveillance and monitoring systems, plus the 10·3 h endurance conferred by wingtip auxiliary tanks, it is considered to be ideally suited for pollution monitoring, offshore patrol, and search and rescue missions. Airborne search radar, in an undernose radome, is capable of detecting small boats up to 43·5 nm (80·5 km; 50 miles) away and larger vessels as far as 125 nm (232 km; 144 miles) away. A VLF or inertial navigation system is available optionally. A Super King Air of this type, leased by the government of Ireland, entered service with the Irish Army Air Corps in early 1977 for coastal fishery patrol duties.

During 1978 Beech announced supply to the Egyptian government of a Super King Air which is being used to continue water, uranium and other natural resources exploration in the Sinai and Egyptian deserts which was originated by US ERTS-1 and Landsat satellites. This aircraft is equipped with remote sensing equipment, specialised avionics, and sophisticated cameras. In June 1978, the Japan Maritime Safety Agency announced selection of the Super King Air for maritime patrol in connection with Japan's 174 nm (322 km; 200 mile) fishing limit. A total of 13 aircraft are required at a cost of more than $26 million, and deliveries of the first aircraft were scheduled for mid-1979. Also in June 1978, Beech delivered to the government of Taiwan a Super King Air equipped to check ground-based navigation systems. A second special-mission aircraft was scheduled for delivery to Taiwan's Ministry of the Interior in May 1979. In late 1978 Beech won an industry-wide competition for the lease of four Super King Airs to the border patrol fleet of the US Customs Service, and these were delivered in Spring 1979.

By 1 January 1979 Beech had delivered 433 Super King Airs to commercial and private operators and 94 military C-12s to the USAF, US Navy and US Army.

TYPE: Twin-turboprop passenger or executive light transport.

WINGS: Cantilever low-wing monoplane. Wing section NACA 23018·5 (modified) at root, NACA 23011·3 at tip. Dihedral 6°. Incidence 3°48′ at root, −1° 7′ at tip. No sweepback at quarter-chord. Two-spar light alloy structure. Conventional ailerons of light alloy construction, with trim tab in port aileron. Single-slotted trailing-edge flaps of light alloy construction. Pneumatic de-icing boots standard.

FUSELAGE: Light alloy semi-monocoque structure of safe-life design.

TAIL UNIT: Conventional cantilever T-tail structure of light alloy with swept vertical and horizontal surfaces. Fixed-incidence tailplane. Trim tab in each elevator. Anti-servo tab in rudder. Pneumatic de-icing boots standard, on leading-edge of tailplane only.

LANDING GEAR: Electrically-retractable tricycle type, with twin wheels on each main unit. Single wheel on steerable nose unit, with shimmy damper. Main units retract forward, nosewheel aft. Beech oleo-pneumatic shock-absorbers. Goodrich main wheels and tyres size 18 × 5·5, pressure 7·25 bars (105 lb/sq in). Goodrich nosewheel size 6·50 × 10, with tyre size 22 × 6·75-10, pressure 3·93 bars (57 lb/sq in). Goodrich hydraulic multiple-disc brakes. Parking brake.

POWER PLANT: Two 634 kW (850 shp) Pratt & Whitney Aircraft of Canada PT6A-41 turboprop engines, each driving a three-blade metal constant-speed fully-feathering and reversible propeller; PT6A-38 engines in C-12A, as noted in introductory copy. Bladder type fuel cells in each wing, with main system capacity of 1,461 litres (386 US gallons) and auxiliary system capacity of 598 litres (158 US gallons). Total fuel capacity 2,059 litres (544 US gallons). Two refuelling points in upper surface of each wing. Oil capacity 29·5 litres (7·8 US gallons). Anti-icing of engine air intakes by hot air from engine exhaust is standard. Electro-thermal anti-icing for propellers. Wingtip tanks optional.

ACCOMMODATION: Pilot only, or crew of two side by side, on flight deck, with full dual controls and instruments as standard. Six cabin seats standard, each equipped with seat belts and inertia-reel shoulder harness; alternative layouts for a maximum of 13 passengers in cabin and 14th beside pilot. Partition with sliding door between

Beechcraft Super King Air 200 eight/fifteen-seat pressurised transport (two Pratt & Whitney Aircraft of Canada PT6A-41 turboprop engines)

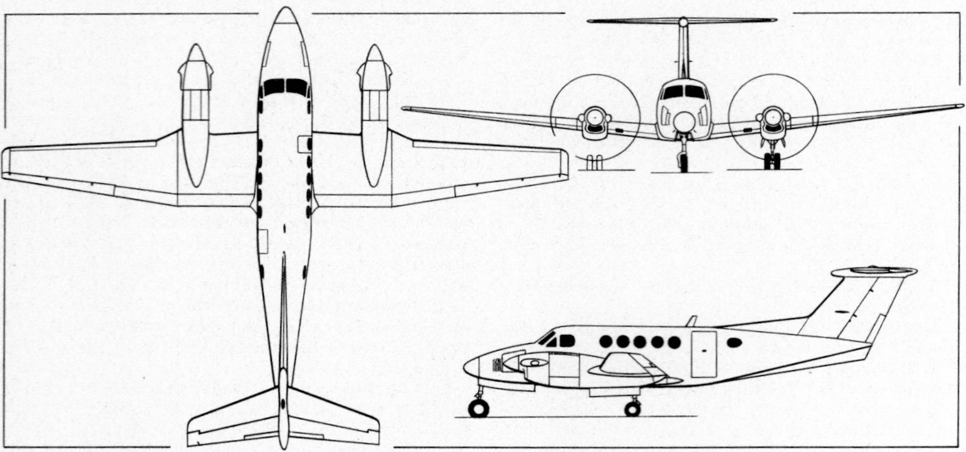

Beechcraft Super King Air 200 twin-turboprop transport *(Pilot Press)*

cabin and flight deck, and partition at rear of cabin. Door at rear of cabin on port side, with integral airstair. Large cargo door optional. Inward-opening emergency exit on starboard side over wing. Lavatory and stowage for up to 186 kg (410 lb) baggage in aft fuselage. Maintenance access door in rear fuselage; radio compartment access doors in nose. Standard equipment includes reading lights and fresh air outlets for all passengers, triple cabin windows with polarised glare control, fully-carpeted floor, 'No smoking—Fasten seat belt' sign, cabin coat rack, fluorescent cabin lighting, aisle and door courtesy lights. Electrically-heated windscreens, hot air windscreen defroster, dual storm windows, sun visors, map pockets and windscreen wipers. Cabin is air-conditioned and pressurised, and can be provided with optional radiant heat panels.

Systems: Cabin pressurisation by engine bleed air, with a maximum differential of 0·41 bars (6·0 lb/sq in). Cabin air-conditioner of 34,000 BTU capacity. Auxiliary cabin heating by radiant panels optional. Oxygen system for flight deck, and 625 litre (22 cu ft) oxygen system for cabin, with automatic drop-down face masks; standard system of 1,390 litres (49 cu ft), 1,810 litres (64 cu ft), or 2·15 m^3 (76 cu ft) optional. Dual vacuum system for instruments. Hydraulic system for brakes only. Pneumatic system for wing and tailplane de-icing. Electrical system has two 250A 28V starter/generators and 24V 45Ah aircooled nickel-cadmium battery with failure detector. AC power provided by dual 250VA inverters.

Avionics and Equipment: Standard avionics include dual Collins VHF-20A VHF transceivers, with Gables controls and B3 antennae; Collins VIR-30AGM automatic Omni No. 1, with 331A-3G indicator, Gables control and B17 antenna; Collins VIR-30AG automatic Omni No. 2, with 331H-3G indicator and Gables control; dual Omni range filters; Collins dual 356-F3 audio amplifiers, each with 356C-4 isolation amplifiers and audio switches; Collins ADF-60A ADF less indicator, with Gables control, voice range filter and ANT-60 antenna; Collins marker beacon, integral with VIR-30 No. 1, with dual marker lights and B16 antenna; dual Collins glideslopes, integral with VIR-30 No. 1 and No. 2, with B35 glideslope antenna; Bendix RDR-130 weather radar, with phased array antenna and digital scope; Sperry C-14-43 compass system, with servo amplifier (pilot); Collins 332C-10 RMI, with Nav 1/ADF on single needle, Nav 2/ADF on double needle; Collins TDR-90 transponder, with Gables control and 237Z-1 antenna; Collins DME-40 with 339F-12 indicator, Nav 1/Nav 2 switching, DME hold and 237Z-1 antenna; dual Flite-Tronics PC-15B 250VA inverters with failure light; sectional instrument panel; dual flight instrumentation; Standard Electric gyro horizon (pilot); CF gyro horizon and directional gyro (co-pilot); Beech edge-lighted radio panel, radio accessories, microphone key button in pilot's and co-pilot's control wheels, static wicks, and white lighting; dual microphones, headsets and cockpit speakers; and avionics master switch. A wide range of optional avionics by Bendix, Collins, King, RCA, Sperry and SunAir is available to customer's requirements. Standard equipment is generally as listed for King Air C90, plus dual max allowable airspeed indicators, control wheel mounted chronographs, toilet, fluorescent cabin lighting instead of indirect lighting, aisle courtesy light, transistor controlled blue/white cockpit lighting, entrance door light, engine fire detection system, rudder boost system, and yaw damper system. Optional equipment includes a flight hour recorder, instantaneous vertical speed indicator, cockpit and cabin fire extinguishers, a range of cabin chairs, cabinets and table, flushing toilet, aft cabin air-conditioning installation, radiant heating system, entrance door step lights, wingtip recognition lights, strobe lights, fin illumination lights, engine fire extinguishing system, automatic propeller feathering, propeller synchrophaser, electric pitch trim, oversize and/or 10-ply main-wheel tyres.

Dimensions, external:
Wing span 16·61 m (54 ft 6 in)
Wing chord at root 2·18 m (7 ft 1¾ in)
Wing chord at tip 0·90 m (2 ft 11⅝ in)
Wing aspect ratio 9·8
Length overall 13·34 m (43 ft 9 in)
Height overall 4·57 m (15 ft 0 in)
Tailplane span 5·61 m (18 ft 5 in)
Wheel track 5·23 m (17 ft 2 in)
Wheelbase 4·56 m (14 ft 11½ in)
Propeller diameter 2·50 m (8 ft 2½ in)
Propeller ground clearance 0·37 m (1 ft 2½ in)
Distance between propeller centres 5·23 m (17 ft 2 in)
Passenger door: Height 1·31 m (4 ft 3½ in)
Width 0·68 m (2 ft 2¾ in)
Height to sill 1·17 m (3 ft 10 in)
Cargo door (optional):
Height 1·32 m (4 ft 4 in)
Width 1·32 m (4 ft 4 in)
Nose electronics service doors (port and stbd):
Max height 0·57 m (1 ft 10½ in)
Width 0·63 m (2 ft 1 in)
Height to sill 1·37 m (4 ft 6 in)
Emergency exit door (stbd):
Height 0·66 m (2 ft 2 in)
Width 0·50 m (1 ft 7¾ in)

Dimensions, internal:
Cabin (from forward to aft pressure bulkhead):
Length 6·71 m (22 ft 0 in)
Max width 1·37 m (4 ft 6 in)
Max height 1·45 m (4 ft 9 in)
Floor area 7·80 m^2 (84 sq ft)
Volume 11·10 m^3 (392 cu ft)
Baggage hold, rear of cabin:
Volume 1·50 m^3 (53 cu ft)

Areas:
Wings, gross 28·15 m^2 (303 sq ft)
Ailerons (total) 1·67 m^2 (18·0 sq ft)
Trailing-edge flaps (total) 4·17 m^2 (44·9 sq ft)
Fin 3·46 m^2 (37·2 sq ft)
Rudder, incl tab 1·40 m^2 (15·1 sq ft)
Tailplane 4·52 m^2 (48·7 sq ft)
Elevators, incl tabs 1·79 m^2 (19·3 sq ft)

Weights and Loadings:
Weight empty 3,373 kg (7,437 lb)
Max T-O and landing weight 5,670 kg (12,500 lb)
Max ramp weight 5,710 kg (12,590 lb)
Max zero-fuel weight 4,717 kg (10,400 lb)
Max wing loading 201·6 kg/m^2 (41·3 lb/sq ft)
Max power loading 4·47 kg/kW (7·35 lb/shp)

Weights and Loadings (C-12A): As Super King Air, except:
Basic empty weight 3,538 kg (7,800 lb)
Max ramp weight 5,708 kg (12,585 lb)
Max power loading 5·07 kg/kW (8·33 lb/shp)

Performance (at max T-O weight, ISA, unless specified):
Never-exceed speed
Mach 0·52 (260 knots; 482 km/h; 299 mph) CAS
Max level speed, average cruise weight at 4,570 m (15,000 ft) 289 knots (536 km/h; 333 mph)
Max cruising speed, average cruise weight at 7,620 m (25,000 ft) 278 knots (515 km/h; 320 mph)
Econ cruising speed, average cruise weight at 7,620 m (25,000 ft) 272 knots (503 km/h; 313 mph)
Stalling speed, flaps up
99 knots (183 km/h; 114 mph) IAS
Stalling speed, flaps down
75 knots (139·5 km/h; 86·5 mph) IAS
Max rate of climb at S/L 747 m (2,450 ft)/min
Rate of climb at S/L, one engine out
226 m (740 ft)/min
Service ceiling above 9,450 m (31,000 ft)
Service ceiling, one engine out 5,835 m (19,150 ft)
T-O run 592 m (1,942 ft)
T-O run, 40% flap 566 m (1,856 ft)
T-O to 15 m (50 ft), flaps up 1,020 m (3,345 ft)
T-O to 15 m (50 ft), 40% flap 786 m (2,579 ft)
Landing from 15 m (50 ft), full flap, without propeller reversal 867 m (2,845 ft)
Landing from 15 m (50 ft) with propeller reversal
632 m (2,074 ft)
Landing run, full flap, without propeller reversal
536 m (1,760 ft)
Landing run with propeller reversal 341 m (1,120 ft)
Range with 2,059 litres (544 US gallons) usable fuel, with allowances for start, taxi, climb, descent and 45 min reserves at max range power, ISA:
max cruising power at:
5,485 m (18,000 ft)
1,190 nm (2,204 km; 1,370 miles)
7,620 m (25,000 ft)
1,485 nm (2,750 km; 1,709 miles)
9,450 m (31,000 ft)
1,757 nm (3,254 km; 2,022 miles)
econ cruising power at:
5,485 m (18,000 ft)
1,487 nm (2,755 km; 1,712 miles)
7,620 m (25,000 ft)
1,737 nm (3,217 km; 1,999 miles)
9,450 m (31,000 ft)
1,887 nm (3,495 km; 2,172 miles)

Performance (C-12A at max T-O weight, except as noted otherwise):
Max level speed at 4,265 m (14,000 ft) and AUW of 4,536 kg (10,000 lb) 260 knots (482 km/h; 299 mph)
Max cruising speed at 9,145 m (30,000 ft) and AUW of 4,536 kg (10,000 lb) 236 knots (437 km/h; 272 mph)
Service ceiling 9,450 m (31,000 ft)
Service ceiling, one engine out 5,365 m (17,600 ft)
T-O to 15 m (50 ft) 860 m (2,820 ft)
Landing from 15 m (50 ft) 766 m (2,514 ft)
Range at max cruising speed
1,584 nm (2,935 km; 1,824 miles)

BEECHCRAFT MARITIME PATROL 200T

Interest in the Maritime Monitor 200T, referred to under the Super King Air heading, encouraged Beech to develop a special maritime patrol aircraft based on the Super King Air 200. The company announced on 9 April 1979 that such an aircraft, designated Maritime Patrol 200T, was undergoing a flight test programme for FAA certification prior to worldwide demonstration in the following Summer.

Equipped to carry out such missions as monitoring ex-

Beechcraft Maritime Patrol 200T with removable wingtip fuel tanks

clusive economic zones, detecting pollution, inspecting offshore installations and conducting search and rescue flights, the 200T can be equipped optionally for special missions which include aerial photography, environmental and ecological research, airways and ground-based navigation equipment checks, and air ambulance duties.

Modifications to the standard Super King Air for the Maritime Patrol 200T configuration include new outboard wing assemblies, which permit the mounting of a 200·5 litre (53 US gallon) removable fuel tank at each wingtip; strengthened landing gear to cater for higher take-off and landing weights; provision of a bubble observation window in the aft cabin for visual search and photography, and of a hatch for dropping survival equipment; and installation of a search radar with full 360° scan in a radome mounted beneath the fuselage. Advanced navigational equipment is available, especially for maritime patrol use, and standard avionics include VLF/Omega which provides ground stabilisation and is coupled with the autopilot. This permits a search pattern to be programmed before take-off or en route. Optional avionics include INS, VHF/FM com, HF and VHF com, FLIR, LLLTV, a multispectral scanner and a tactical navigation computer. Two search radar systems are available, both offering 360° scan and weather avoidance capability.

Two of 13 aircraft bought by Japan's Maritime Safety Agency were undergoing modification to Maritime Patrol 200T standard in April 1979, and the aircraft was to be demonstrated to the US Air Force and US Navy later that year.

The description of the Super King Air 200 applies also to the 200T, except as follows:

TYPE: Twin-turboprop maritime patrol or multi-mission aircraft.

WINGS: As for Super King Air 200, except for new outboard wing assemblies to permit mounting of removable wingtip tanks.

LANDING GEAR: Strengthened to cater for higher operating weights.

POWER PLANT: As for Super King Air 200, plus provision for removable wingtip tanks to increase maximum fuel capacity by 401 litres (106 US gallons), to a total of 2,460 litres (650 US gallons).

Underfuselage radome and bubble window in cabin of Maritime Patrol 200T

AVIONICS AND EQUIPMENT: Standard and optional items as detailed in introductory description.

DIMENSIONS, INTERNAL: As for Super King Air 200, except:
- Cabin: Length (excl flight deck) 5·08 m (16 ft 8 in)

WEIGHTS (A: Normal category; B: Restricted category):
- Weight empty: A, B 3,744 kg (8,255 lb)
- Max T-O weight: A 5,670 kg (12,500 lb)
- B 6,350 kg (14,000 lb)
- Max landing weight: A 5,670 kg (12,500 lb)
- B 6,123 kg (13,500 lb)

PERFORMANCE (at max T-O weight):
- Max cruising speed, AUW of 4,990 kg (11,000 lb) at 4,265 m (14,000 ft) 265 knots (491 km/h; 305 mph)
- Typical patrol speed 140 knots (259 km/h; 161 mph)
- Range with max fuel, patrolling at 227 knots (420 km/h; 261 mph) at 825 m (2,700 ft), 45 min reserves 1,790 nm (3,317 km; 2,061 miles)
- Typical endurance at 140 knots (259 km/h; 161 mph), at 610 m (2,000 ft), 45 min reserves 6 h 36 min

BELL

BELL AEROSPACE TEXTRON (Division of Textron Inc)

HEAD OFFICE AND WORKS: PO Box 1, Buffalo, New York 14240

Telephone: (716) 297 1000

PRESIDENT: William G. Gisel

EXECUTIVE VICE-PRESIDENT: Norton C. Willcox

VICE-PRESIDENTS:
- Dr Clifford F. Berninger (Research and Engineering)
- Donald F. Bonhardt (Product Assurance)
- John R. Clark Jr (Eastern Region)
- Robert W. Hussa (Manufacturing)
- John J. Kelly (New Orleans Operations)
- John W. McKinney (Finance)
- John H. Pamperin (President, Dalmo Victor Operations)
- Joseph R. Piselli (Marketing)

Bell Aerospace is active in aircraft, missile, propulsion and electronics systems development and advanced technology for aerospace and defence programmes. Its research and development programmes include air cushion vehicles, air cushion landing systems and high-energy lasers.

Production of liquid-propellant rocket engines for Lockheed's Agena satellite programme continues and is described in the Aero-Engines section.

As an outgrowth of its AN/SPN-42 Automatic Carrier Landing System (ACLS), in operation on board US Navy aircraft carriers, Bell received contracts to update land-based versions at US Naval air stations where the systems are used to train pilots and operators in the carrier-based system. Both the land- and carrier-based systems permit fully-automatic hands-off landings, and can handle up to 120 aircraft an hour.

Other electronics work is concerned with precision inertial equipment, transoceanic satellite-relay air traffic control systems, and airborne target location and fire control systems.

BELL AIR CUSHION LANDING GEAR (ACLG)

Bell Aerospace Textron initiated the ACLG by modifying a Lake LA-4 amphibian for initial testing of the concept. This led to a joint US/Canadian test programme over the period 1969 to 1977, involving a specially modified de Havilland Canada Buffalo STOL military transport. The programme was completed in 1977; details can be found in the 1977-78 and earlier editions of *Jane's*.

Further conceptual studies are continuing under the auspices of NASA.

BELL HELICOPTER TEXTRON (Division of Textron Inc)

HEAD OFFICE: PO Box 482, Fort Worth, Texas 76101

Telephone: (817) 280 2011

PRESIDENT: James F. Atkins

SENIOR VICE-PRESIDENTS:
- Hans Weichsel Jr (Product Development)
- L. M. ('Jack') Horner (Marketing & Programmes)
- Robert R. Lynn (Research & Engineering)

VICE-PRESIDENTS:
- John A. Buyers (Model 222 Programme)
- James C. Fuller (Public Relations)
- William L. Humphrey (General Manager, Amarillo Facility)
- Webb F. Joiner (Finance)
- Dwayne K. Jose (Commercial Marketing)
- Clifford J. Kalista (Marketing & Programmes, Iran)
- Gainor J. Lindsey (Administration)
- Joseph Mashman (Special Projects)
- R. K. (Dick) May (Operations)
- C. M. McKeen Jr (Procurement)
- Phil C. Norwine (Government Marketing)
- Warren T. Rockwell (Washington Operations)
- Frank M. Sylvester (International Marketing)
- Ted R. Treff (Treasurer)

Available details of the range of military and commercial helicopters in current production, or under development, by Bell Helicopter Textron are published in this entry. Some models are also built under licence by Agusta in Italy and Fuji in Japan (which see).

During 1972 Bell achieved a major breakthrough in the elimination of vibration in helicopters with what is known as the nodalisation concept, flight test data and analytical results suggesting that 70 to 90 per cent vibration isolation was practicable. This concept is based on the scientific fact that any beam subjected to vertical vibratory forces, such as those induced by a rotor, will develop flexing to produce a wave form. Points of no relative motion, called the nodal points, appear at equal distances from the centre of the induced wave form, and it is at these points that Bell suspends the helicopter fuselage. Since the nodes have no relative motion, the fuselage becomes virtually free from rotor-induced vibration. Flight tests of a Model 206 JetRanger with its fuselage suspended from a nodalised beam were so convincing that Bell decided to utilise this 'Noda-Matic' technique on new production helicopters, beginning with the Models 206L LongRanger and 214.

Approximately 9,000 people were employed by Bell in 1979. The company has produced more than 23,500 helicopters.

BELL MODEL 205

US military designations: UH-1D/H, EH-1H and HH-1H Iroquois

Canadian military designation: CH-118 Iroquois

Although basically similar to the earlier Model 204 (see 1971-72 *Jane's*), the Model 205 introduced a longer fuselage, increased cabin space to accommodate a much larger number of passengers, and other changes. Details of the full range of military variants have been recorded in previous editions of *Jane's*. The final production version is the **UH-1H**. Deliveries of this version to the US Army began in September 1967 and 1,242 had been built by 1976, including nine for the RNZAF. Production of the UH-1H continued in 1978 to satisfy export orders and a new contract for 27 for the US Army.

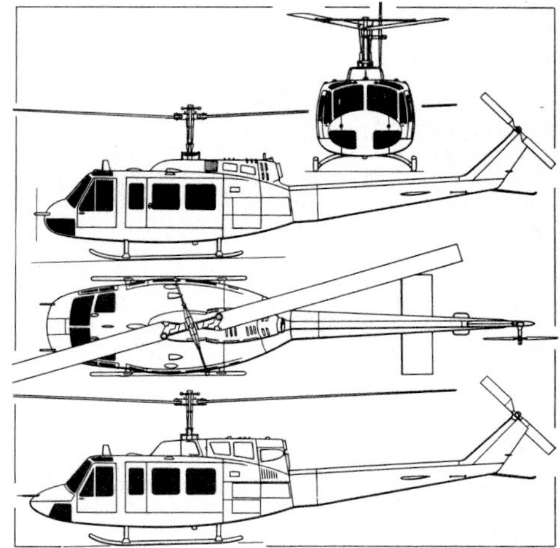

Bell UH-1H Iroquois, with additional side view (bottom) of UH-1N *(Pilot Press)*

The FY 1980 budget requests included $18·8 million to modify five UH-1Hs to **EH-1H** electronic countermeasures configuration, with the Phase II Quick Fix system, AN/APR-39V2 radar warning receiver, XM-130 chaff/flare dispenser and AN/ALQ-144 infra-red jammer. FY 1981 requests include $5·5 million to convert initial Quick Fix IA systems in the EH-1H to Phase IB configura-

Bell UH-1H Iroquois general-purpose helicopter

tion, and $3·2 million for survivability equipment to protect the aircraft against known and postulated threats, including hot metal/plume suppression.

Four aircraft have been modified for field evaluation of the US Army Standoff Target Acquisition System (SOTAS). General Dynamics Electronics Division is prime contractor for this system, which will give battlefield commanders real-time radar moving target information on the battle situation, relayed from the helicopters. Added equipment includes a large plank-like antenna under the fuselage and Sperry coupled four-axis autopilot and three-cue flight director for precise helicopter stabilisation at very low speeds.

Under a licensing agreement concluded in 1969, the Republic of China produced 118 UH-1Hs for the Nationalist Chinese Army, with much of the manufacturing and assembly carried out at Taichung, Taiwan.

The following details refer specifically to the military UH-1H. The commercial Model 205A-1 is described separately.

Type: Single-rotor general-purpose helicopter.

Rotor System: Two-blade all-metal semi-rigid main rotor with interchangeable blades, built up of extruded aluminium spars and laminates. Stabilising bar above and at right angles to main rotor blades. Underslung feathering axis hub. Two-blade all-metal tail rotor of honeycomb construction. Blades do not fold.

Rotor Drive: Shaft-drive to both main and tail rotors. Transmission rating 820 kW (1,100 shp). Main rotor rpm 294-324.

Fuselage: Conventional all-metal semi-monocoque structure.

Tail Surface: Small synchronised elevator on rear fuselage is connected to the cyclic control to increase allowable CG travel.

Landing Gear: Tubular skid type. Lock-on ground handling wheels and inflated nylon float-bags available.

Power Plant: One 1,044 kW (1,400 shp) Lycoming T53-L-13 turboshaft mounted aft of the transmission on top of the fuselage and enclosed in cowlings. Five interconnected rubber fuel cells, total capacity 799 litres (211 US gallons). Overload fuel capacity of 511 US gallons obtained by installation of kit comprising two 568 litre (150 US gallon) internal auxiliary fuel tanks interconnected with the basic fuel system.

Accommodation: Cabin space of 6·23 m^3 (220 cu ft) provides sufficient room for pilot and 11-14 troops, or six litters and a medical attendant, or 1,759 kg (3,880 lb) of freight. Crew doors open forward and are jettisonable. Two doors on each side of cargo compartment; front door is hinged to open forward and is removable, rear door slides aft. Forced air ventilation system.

Avionics and Equipment: FM, UHF, VHF radio sets, IFF transponder, Gyromatic compass system, direction finder set, VOR receiver and intercom standard. Optional nav/com systems. Standard equipment includes bleed air heater and defroster, comprehensive range of engine and flight instruments, power plant fire detection system, 30V 300A DC starter/generator, navigation, landing and anti-collision lights, controllable searchlight, hydraulically-boosted controls. Optional equipment includes external cargo hook, auxiliary fuel tanks, rescue hoist, 150,000 BTU muff heater.

Dimensions, external:
- Diameter of main rotor 14·63 m (48 ft 0 in)
- Diameter of tail rotor 2·59 m (8 ft 6 in)
- Main rotor blade chord 0·53 m (1 ft 9 in)
- Tail rotor blade chord 0·213 m (8·4 in)
- Length overall (main rotor fore and aft) 17·62 m (57 ft 9⅝ in)
- Length of fuselage 12·77 m (41 ft 10¾ in)
- Height overall 4·42 m (14 ft 6 in)

Areas:
- Main rotor disc 168·06 m^2 (1,809 sq ft)
- Tail rotor disc 5·27 m^2 (56·7 sq ft)

Weights and Loadings:
- Weight empty 2,363 kg (5,210 lb)
- Basic operating weight (troop carrier mission) 2,520 kg (5,557 lb)
- Mission weight 4,100 kg (9,039 lb)
- Max T-O and landing weight 4,309 kg (9,500 lb)
- Max zero-fuel weight 3,660 kg (8,070 lb)
- Max disc loading 25·6 kg/m^2 (5·25 lb/sq ft)
- Max power loading 4·13 kg/kW (8·63 lb/shp)

Performance (at max T-O weight):
- Never-exceed speed 110 knots (204 km/h; 127 mph)
- Max level and cruising speed 110 knots (204 km/h; 127 mph)
- Econ cruising speed at 1,735 m (5,700 ft) 110 knots (204 km/h; 127 mph)
- Max rate of climb at S/L 488 m (1,600 ft)/min
- Service ceiling 3,840 m (12,600 ft)
- Hovering ceiling IGE 4,145 m (13,600 ft)
- Hovering ceiling OGE 1,220 m (4,000 ft)
- Range with max fuel, no allowances, no reserves, at S/L 276 nm (511 km; 318 miles)

BELL MODEL 205A-1

The Model 205A-1 is a fifteen-seat commercial utility helicopter developed from the UH-1H, with 1,044 kW (1,400 shp) Lycoming T5313B turboshaft, derated to 932 kW (1,250 shp) for take-off. It is designed for rapid conversion for alternative air freight, flying crane, ambulance, rescue and executive roles. Total cargo capacity is 7·02 m^3 (248 cu ft) including baggage space in tailboom, with 2·34 m (7 ft 8 in) by 1·24 m (4 ft 1 in) door openings on each side of the cabin to facilitate loading of bulky freight. External load capacity in flying crane role is 2,268 kg (5,000 lb). The ambulance version can accommodate six litter patients and one or two medical attendants.

Normal fuel capacity is 814 litres (215 US gallons); optional capacity is 1,495 litres (395 US gallons).

The Model 205A-1 is produced under licence in Italy by Agusta (which see) as the AB 205A-1.

The description of the Bell UH-1H applies also to the Model 205A-1, except for the following details:

Type: Fifteen-seat commercial utility helicopter.

Avionics and Equipment: Standard equipment includes vertical gyro system, 5 in gyro attitude indicator, gyro compass, master caution panel, bleed air heater, force trim hydraulic boost controls, soundproof headliner, dual windscreen wipers, cabin and engine fire extinguishers, map case and retractable passenger boarding steps. Optional items include dual controls, float landing gear, rotor brake, external cargo suspension, rescue hoist, auxiliary fuel tanks, litter installations, high-output cabin heater, protective covers and customised interiors. Standard avionics comprise 360-channel VHF transceiver and intercom system. Extensive range of optional nav/com systems available.

Dimensions, external:
- Length of fuselage 12·65 m (41 ft 6 in)
- Height overall 4·39 m (14 ft 4¾ in)

Weights:
- Weight empty, equipped 2,414 kg (5,323 lb)
- Normal T-O weight 4,309 kg (9,500 lb)
- Max T-O weight, external load 4,763 kg (10,500 lb)

Performance (at normal T-O weight):
- Max level speed from S/L to 915 m (3,000 ft) 110 knots (204 km/h; 127 mph)
- Max cruising speed at S/L 110 knots (204 km/h; 127 mph)
- Max cruising speed at 2,440 m (8,000 ft) 96 knots (179 km/h; 111 mph)
- Max rate of climb at S/L 512 m (1,680 ft)/min
- Max vertical rate of climb at S/L 259 m (850 ft)/min
- Service ceiling 4,480 m (14,700 ft)
- Hovering ceiling IGE 3,170 m (10,400 ft)
- Hovering ceiling OGE 1,830 m (6,000 ft)
- Range at S/L, at max cruising speed 270 nm (500 km; 311 miles)
- Range at 2,440 m (8,000 ft) at max cruising speed, no reserves 298 nm (553 km; 344 miles)

BELL MODEL 206B JETRANGER III

In the Summer of 1977, Bell began delivery of the Model 206B JetRanger III, which subsequently replaced in production the lower-powered JetRanger II, of which 1,619 were delivered.

Power plant of the JetRanger III is the Allison 250-C20B turboshaft, which Bell was able to install with minimal modification of the original airframe to meet requests for higher performance under hot-day/high-altitude conditions. This enables Bell to offer modification kits to convert JetRanger IIs to JetRanger III standard.

The uprated power plant increases power-limited airspeeds in high altitude/temperature conditions. For example, at 3,050 m (10,000 ft) ISA, airspeed increases by 5 knots (9 km/h; 6 mph). Greater improvements are achieved at above-standard temperatures. Hovering weights are increased by up to 91 kg (200 lb) at the same altitude, and hovering ceilings by as much as 610 m (2,000 ft) at higher altitudes and temperatures.

Under a succession of major contracts, Beech Aircraft has produced airframes for all the commercial and military versions of the JetRanger, the first airframe being delivered to Bell on 1 March 1968. The work involves manufacture of the fuselage, skid gear, tailboom, spars, stabiliser and two rear fairing assemblies.

By January 1979, Bell and its licensees had manufactured well over 6,000 helicopters of the Model 206 series, more than 2,279 of them for commercial customers.

Type: Turbine-powered general-purpose light helicopter.

Rotor System: Two-blade semi-rigid see-saw type main rotor, employing pre-coning and underslinging to ensure smooth operation. Blades are of standard Bell 'droop-snoot' section. They have a D-shape aluminium spar, bonded aluminium alloy skin, honeycomb core and a trailing-edge extension. Each blade is connected to the hub by means of a grip, pitch-change bearings and a tension-torsion strap assembly. Two tail rotor blades have bonded aluminium skin but no core. Main rotor blades do not fold, but modification to permit manual folding is possible. Rotor brake available as optional kit.

Rotor Drive: Rotors driven through tubular steel alloy shafts with spliced couplings. Initial drive from engine through 90° spiral bevel gear to single-stage planetary main gearbox. Shaft to tail rotor single-stage bevel gearbox. Freewheeling unit ensures that main rotor continues to drive tail rotor when engine is disengaged. Main rotor/engine rpm ratio 1 : 15; main rotor rpm 374-394. Tail rotor/engine rpm ratio 1 : 2·3.

Fuselage: Forward cabin section is made up of two aluminium alloy beams and 25 mm (1 in) thick aluminium honeycomb sandwich. Rotor, transmission and engine are supported by upper longitudinal beams. Upper and lower structures are interconnected by three fuselage bulkheads and a centrepost to form an integrated structure. Intermediate section is of aluminium

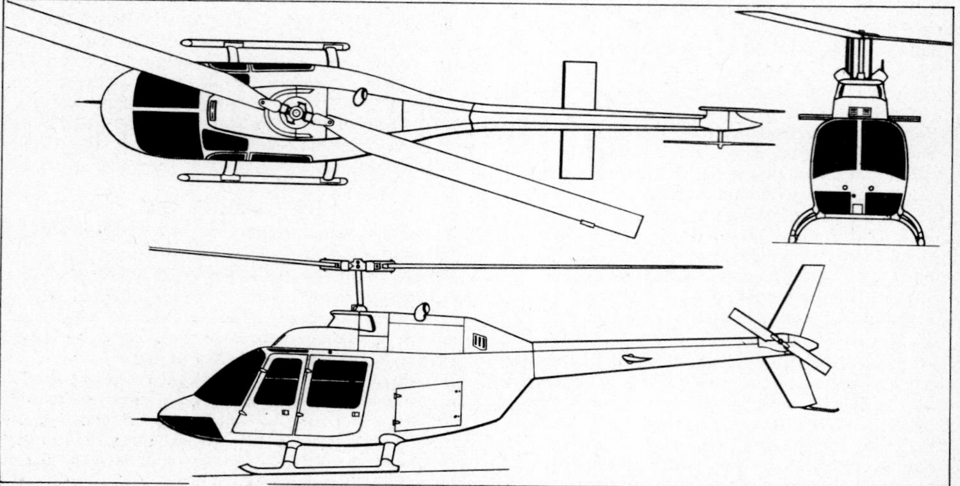

Bell 206B JetRanger III light utility helicopter *(Pilot Press)*

alloy semi-monocoque construction. Aluminium monocoque tailboom.

TAIL UNIT: Fixed stabiliser of aluminium monocoque construction, with inverted aerofoil section. Fixed vertical tail-fin in sweptback upper and ventral sections, made of aluminium honeycomb with aluminium alloy skin.

LANDING GEAR: Aluminium alloy tubular skids bolted to extruded cross-tubes. Tubular steel skid on ventral fin to protect tail rotor in tail-down landing. Special high skid gear (0·254 m; 10 in greater ground clearance) available for use in areas with high brush. Inflated bag-type pontoons or stowed floats capable of in-flight inflation available as optional kits.

POWER PLANT: One 313 kW (420 shp) Allison 250-C20B turboshaft engine. Fuel tank below and behind rear passenger seat, capacity 288 litres (76 US gallons). Refuelling point on starboard side of fuselage, aft of cabin. Oil capacity 5·2 litres (5·5 US quarts).

ACCOMMODATION: Two seats side by side in front and rear bench seat for three persons. Dual controls optional. Two forward-hinged doors on each side, made of formed aluminium alloy with transparent panels. Baggage compartment aft of rear seats, capacity 113 kg (250 lb), with external door on port side.

SYSTEMS: Hydraulic system, pressure 41·5 bars (600 lb/sq in), for cyclic, collective and directional controls. Electrical supply from 150A starter/generator. One 24V 13Ah nickel-cadmium battery.

AVIONICS AND EQUIPMENT: Full range of avionics available in form of optional kits, including VHF communications and omni navigation kit, glideslope kit, ADF, DME, marker beacon, transponder and intercom and speaker system. Standard equipment includes night lighting, dynamic flapping restraints, door locks, fire extinguishers and first aid kit. Optional items include custom seating, external cargo sling with 545 kg (1,200 lb) capacity, heater, high-intensity night lights, turn and slip indicator, clock, engine oil vent, fire detection system, engine fire extinguisher, fairing kit, camera access door, engine hour meter, internal litter kit and stability and control augmentation system.

DIMENSIONS, EXTERNAL:
- Diameter of main rotor: 10·16 m (33 ft 4 in)
- Main rotor blade chord: 0·33 m (1 ft 1 in)
- Distance between rotor centres: 5·96 m (19 ft 6½ in)
- Length overall, blades turning: 11·82 m (38 ft 9½ in)
- Length of fuselage: 9·50 m (31 ft 2 in)
- Height overall: 2·91 m (9 ft 6½ in)
- Stabiliser span: 1·96 m (6 ft 5¼ in)
- Width over skids: 1·92 m (6 ft 3½ in)

DIMENSIONS, INTERNAL:
- Cabin: Length: 2·13 m (7 ft 0 in)
  - Max width: 1·27 m (4 ft 2 in)
  - Max height: 1·28 m (4 ft 3 in)
- Baggage compartment: 0·45 m³ (16 cu ft)

AREAS:
- Main rotor blades (total): 3·35 m² (36·1 sq ft)
- Tail rotor blades (total): 0·22 m² (2·37 sq ft)
- Main rotor disc: 81·1 m² (873 sq ft)
- Tail rotor disc: 2·14 m² (23·00 sq ft)
- Stabiliser: 0·90 m² (9·65 sq ft)

WEIGHTS:
- Weight empty, equipped, incl oil and lubricants: 732 kg (1,615 lb)
- Max T-O weight: 1,451 kg (3,200 lb)

PERFORMANCE (at max T-O weight, ISA):
- Never-exceed speed at S/L: 122 knots (225 km/h; 140 mph)
- Max cruising speed at 1,525 m (5,000 ft): 116 knots (216 km/h; 134 mph)
- Max cruising speed at S/L: 115 knots (214 km/h; 133 mph)
- Max rate of climb at S/L: 384 m (1,260 ft)/min
- Vertical rate of climb at S/L: 91 m (300 ft)/min
- Service ceiling: 4,115 m (13,500 ft)
- Hovering ceiling IGE: 3,900 m (12,800 ft)
- Hovering ceiling OGE: 2,680 m (8,800 ft)
- Range with max fuel and max payload at S/L, no reserves: 296 nm (549 km; 341 miles)
- Range with max fuel and max payload at 1,525 m (5,000 ft), no reserves: 328 nm (608 km; 378 miles)

BELL KIOWA

US Army designation: OH-58
Canadian military designation: CH-136

On 8 March 1968 the US Army named Bell as winner of its reopened light observation helicopter competition, and awarded the company the first increment of a planned total order for 2,200 **OH-58A** Kiowa aircraft generally similar to the Model 206A. Major difference concerns the main rotor, that of the Kiowa having an increased diameter. There are also differences in the internal layout and avionics.

The first OH-58A was delivered to the US Army on 23 May 1969 and deployment in Viet-Nam began in the early Autumn of 1969.

Seventy-four COH-58As (from US Army production) were delivered to the Canadian Armed Forces between December 1971 and October 1972. In January 1973 the US Army ordered an additional 74 OH-58As, but these represented replacements for the COH-58As delivered to the Canadian Armed Forces and the total US Army order remained at 2,200 aircraft; the delivery of these was completed by the end of 1973. The Canadian aircraft are now designated **CH-136**.

Bell Model 206B JetRanger III light helicopter (Allison 250-C20B turboshaft engine)

Under a co-production agreement with the Australian government 56 Model 206B-1 Kiowa military light observation helicopters (similar to the OH-58A) were delivered over an eight-year period. The initial 12 206B-1s were built by Bell, and the first of these was handed over officially at Eagle Farm Airport, Brisbane, on 22 November 1971. Commonwealth Aircraft Corporation was prime Australian licensee, with responsibility for final assembly of the remainder. Only the engines and avionics were supplied from US sources. Delivery of 12 **OH-58Bs** to the Austrian Air Force was completed in 1976.

Under a US Army development qualification contract placed on 30 June 1976, Bell converted an OH-58A to an improved standard, under the designation **OH-58C**. This involved installation of a flat glass canopy to reduce glint, an uprated (313 kW; 420 shp) Allison T63-A-720 turboshaft engine, and an IR reduction package. Two additional OH-58As were modified to OH-58C configuration, for pre-production flight testing by Bell and the US Army, and production modification of 275 OH-58As to OH-58C standard began in March 1978 at Bell Helicopter, Amarillo. The final configuration includes a new instrument panel, modifications to reduce vulnerability in combat, CONUS (Continental US) navigation equipment, day optics, improved avionics and improved maintenance features. The additional power significantly improves high-altitude, hot-weather performance.

The following details apply specifically to the OH-58A:

TYPE: Turbine-powered light observation helicopter.

ROTOR SYSTEM: Two-blade semi-rigid see-saw type main rotor, employing pre-coning and underslinging to ensure smooth operation. Blades of standard Bell 'droop-snoot' section, with D-shape aluminium spar, bonded light alloy skin, honeycomb core and trailing-edge extension. Each blade is connected to the hub by means of a grip, pitch-change bearings and a tension-torsion strap assembly. The two tail rotor blades have bonded aluminium skin but no core. Main rotor blades do not fold, but modification to permit manual folding is possible. Rotor brake available as optional kit.

ROTOR DRIVE: Rotors driven through tubular steel alloy shafts with spliced couplings. Initial drive from engine through 90° spiral bevel gear to single-stage planetary main gearbox. Shaft to tail rotor single-stage bevel gearbox. Freewheeling unit ensures that main rotor continues to drive tail rotor when engine is disengaged. Main rotor/engine rpm ratio 1 : 17·44; main rotor rpm 354. Tail rotor/engine rpm ratio 1 : 2·353.

FUSELAGE: Forward cabin section is made up of two aluminium alloy beams and 25 mm (1 in) thick aluminium honeycomb sandwich. Rotor, transmission and engine are supported by upper longitudinal beams. Upper and lower structures are interconnected by three fuselage bulkheads and a centrepost to form an integrated structure. Intermediate section is a light alloy semi-monocoque. Aluminium monocoque tailboom.

TAIL UNIT: Fixed stabiliser of aluminium monocoque construction, with inverted aerofoil section. Fixed vertical fin in sweptback upper and ventral sections, constructed of aluminium honeycomb with light alloy skins.

LANDING GEAR: Light alloy tubular skids bolted to extruded cross-tubes. Tubular steel skid on ventral fin to protect tail rotor in tail-down landing. Special high skid gear available, with 0·254 m (10 in) greater ground clearance, for use in areas with high brush. Inflated bag-type pontoons, or stowed floats capable of in-flight inflation, available as optional kits.

POWER PLANT: One 236·4 kW (317 shp) Allison T63-A-700 turboshaft engine. Fuel tank below and behind aft passenger seat, total usable capacity 276 litres (73 US gallons). Refuelling point on starboard side of fuselage, aft of cabin. Oil capacity 5·6 litres (1·5 US gallons).

ACCOMMODATION: Forward crew compartment seats pilot and co-pilot/observer side by side. Entrance to this compartment is provided by single door on each side of fuselage. The cargo/passenger compartment, which has its own access doors, one on each side, provides approximately 1·13 m³ (40 cu ft) of cargo space, or provision for two passengers by installation of two seat cushions, seat belts and shoulder harnesses.

SYSTEMS: Hydraulic system, pressure 41·5 bars (600 lb/sq in) for cyclic and collective controls. Electrical supply from 150A starter/generator. One 24V 13Ah nickel-cadmium battery.

AVIONICS (OH-58A): C-6533/ARC intercommunication subsystem, AN/ARC-114 VHF-FM, AN/ARC-115 VHF-AM, AN/ARC-116 UHF-AM, AN/ARN-89 ADF, AN/ASN-43 gyro magnetic compass, AN/APX-72 transponder, TSEC/KY-28 communications security set, C-8157/ARC control indication, MT-3802/ARC mounting, TS-1843/APX transponder test set and mounting, KIT-1A/TSEC computer and mounting, and duplicate AN/ARC-114.

AVIONICS (OH-58C only): Has, in addition to the above, AN/ARN-123(V)1 CONUS nav, AN/APN-209 radar altimeter, AN/APR-39 radar warning, YG-1054 proximity warning, ID-1351 C/A HBI, ID-1347 C/ARN CDI, plus AN/APX-100 IFF transponder in lieu of AN/APX-72.

ARMAMENT: Standard equipment is the M-27 armament kit, utilising the 7·62 mm Minigun.

DIMENSIONS, EXTERNAL: As JetRanger III, except:
- Diameter of main rotor: 10·77 m (35 ft 4 in)
- Length overall, blades turning: 12·49 m (40 ft 11¾ in)
- Length of fuselage: 9·93 m (32 ft 7 in)

AREAS: As JetRanger III, except:
- Main rotor blades (total): 3·55 m² (38·26 sq ft)
- Main rotor disc: 90·93 m² (978·8 sq ft)

WEIGHTS AND LOADINGS (A: OH-58A; C: OH-58C):
- Weight empty: A: 664 kg (1,464 lb)
  - C: 719 kg (1,585 lb)
- Operating weight: A: 1,049 kg (2,313 lb)
  - C: 1,104 kg (2,434 lb)
- Max T-O and landing weight: A: 1,360 kg (3,000 lb)
  - C: 1,451 kg (3,200 lb)
- Max zero-fuel weight: A: 1,145 kg (2,525 lb)
  - C: 1,200 kg (2,646 lb)
- Max disc loading: A: 14·9 kg/m² (3·07 lb/sq ft)
  - C: 15·9 kg/m² (3·27 lb/sq ft)

PERFORMANCE (OH-58A at observation mission gross weight of 1,255 kg; 2,768 lb, ISA, except where indicated):
- Never-exceed speed at S/L: 120 knots (222 km/h; 138 mph)
- Cruising speed for max range: 102 knots (188 km/h; 117 mph)
- Loiter speed for max endurance: 49 knots (90·5 km/h; 56 mph)
- Max rate of climb at S/L: 543 m (1,780 ft)/min
- Service ceiling: 5,760 m (18,900 ft)
- Hovering ceiling IGE: 4,145 m (13,600 ft)
- Hovering ceiling OGE: 2,682 m (8,800 ft)
- Hovering ceiling OGE (armed scout mission at 1,360 kg; 3,000 lb): 1,828 m (6,000 ft)
- Max range at S/L, 10% reserves: 259 nm (481 km; 299 miles)
- Max range at S/L, armed scout mission at 1,360 kg (3,000 lb), no reserves: 264 nm (490 km; 305 miles)
- Endurance at S/L, no reserves: 3 h 30 min

BELL MODEL 206L-1 LONGRANGER II

First announced on 25 September 1973, Bell's LongRanger was intended to satisfy a requirement for a turbine-powered general-purpose light helicopter in a size and performance range between the five-seat JetRanger II and 15-seat Model 205A-1. The current LongRanger II, with more powerful engine and detail improvement, was certificated on 17 May 1978 and replaced the original model on the production line. It introduced a new version of the Allison 250 power plant, the 373 kW (500 shp) 250-C28B, which has a max continuous rating of 365 kW (489 shp), and includes in its design an integral particle separator. A new transmission is rated at 324 kW (435 shp) for take-off, its continuous rating remaining

Bell Model 206L-1 LongRanger II seven-seat general-purpose light helicopter

Bell's experimental four-blade soft-in-plane glassfibre rotor under test on the Model 206L-M LongRanger *(Howard Levy)*

unchanged at 276 kW (370 shp). Main rotor rpm is 394. Fuel capacity remains the same, at 371 litres (98 US gallons). Production rate was increased to 170 a year in 1979.

The LongRanger II incorporates Bell's Noda-Matic cabin suspension system, which gives a substantial reduction in rotor-induced vibration and results in a standard of comfort comparable with that of turboprop-powered fixed-wing aircraft.

With a cabin volume of 2·35 m^3 (83 cu ft), compared with the 1·39 m^3 (49 cu ft) of the JetRanger II, utility is enhanced by innovations that allow the maximum use of this space. For example, the port forward passenger seat has a folding back to allow loading of a container measuring 2·44 × 0·91 × 0·30 m (8 × 3 × 1 ft), making possible the carriage of such items as survey equipment, skis, and long components that cannot be accommodated in any other light helicopter. Double doors on the port side of the cabin provide an opening 1·52 m (5 ft 0 in) in width, for easy straight-in loading of litter patients or utility cargo; in an ambulance or rescue role two litter patients and two ambulatory patients/attendants may be carried. With a crew of two, the standard cabin layout accommodates five passengers in two canted aft-facing seats and three forward-facing seats. An optional executive cabin layout has four individual passenger seats.

Detail improvements introduced in the LongRanger II include a redesigned aft cabin to provide 0·05 m (2 in) more headroom for passengers in aft cabin seats; new cowlings, firewall, engine mountings, and engine deck area structure; new freewheeling unit, input shaft, forward tail rotor drive shaft, and increased diameter tail rotor; new engine oil system, oil tank, cooler, and transition duct; deletion of the water/alcohol system required formerly; and increased capacity 17Ah battery. Optional kits include emergency flotation gear, a 907 kg (2,000 lb) cargo hook, and an engine bleed air environmental control system. FAA certification was gained in December 1978 for the LongRanger II equipped with a Collins AP-107H autopilot, this providing single-pilot IFR capability.

A LongRanger designated Model 206L-M was used in 1978 as testbed for Bell's experimental four-blade soft-in-plane rotor. A production rotor of this type is fitted to the new Bell Model 412 (which see).

DIMENSIONS, EXTERNAL:
- Diameter of main rotor 11·28 m (37 ft 0 in)
- Diameter of tail rotor 1·65 m (5 ft 5 in)
- Length overall 12·46 m (40 ft 10½ in)

WEIGHTS:
- Weight empty, standard configuration 978 kg (2,156 lb)
- Max T-O weight 1,837 kg (4,050 lb)

PERFORMANCE (ISA at max T-O weight):
- Max level speed at S/L 130 knots (241 km/h; 150 mph)
- Max cruising speed at 1,525 m (5,000 ft) 116 knots (215 km/h; 134 mph)
- Max rate of climb at S/L 463 m (1,520 ft)/min
- Service ceiling at max cruise power 5,945 m (19,500 ft)
- Hovering ceiling IGE 4,025 m (13,200 ft)
- Hovering ceiling OGE 2,470 m (8,100 ft)
- Range at S/L, no reserves 297 nm (550 km; 342 miles)
- Range at 1,525 m (5,000 ft), no reserves 335 nm (621 km; 386 miles)

BELL MODEL 209 HUEYCOBRA and SEACOBRA

US Army designations: AH-1G, AH-1Q and AH-1R
US Navy/Marine Corps designations: AH-1J and AH-1T
Spanish Navy designation: Z.16

Bell Helicopter Textron initiated the Model 209 in March 1965 as a company-funded development of the UH-1B/C Iroquois intended specifically for armed helicopter missions. The original design combined the basic transmission and rotor system and (in its standard form) the power plant of the UH-1C with a new, streamlined fuselage designed for maximum speed, armament load and crew efficiency. Relatively small, its low silhouette and narrow profile make it easy to conceal with small camouflage nets or to move under cover of trees. Tandem seating provides the best possible field of view for the crew of two.

The Model 209 prototype made its first flight on 7 September 1965, and was sent to Edwards AFB in December 1965 for US Army evaluation. The Army's intention to order the aircraft was announced on 11 March 1966, the initial model being known as the AH-1G HueyCobra. Total orders to date exceed 1,800.

Versions announced so far are as follows:

AH-1G HueyCobra. Original version for US Army, powered by a single 1,044 kW (1,400 shp) Lycoming T53-L-13 turboshaft engine, derated to 820 kW (1,100 shp) for T-O and max continuous rating. Development contract for two pre-production aircraft placed on 4 April 1966, followed on 13 April by an initial order for 110 aircraft plus long-lead-time spares. Subsequent contracts raised the total US Army order to 1,078 by mid-1971. Deliveries began in June 1967, and two months later the AH-1G was deployed operationally in Viet-Nam; it played a particularly important part in the Tet offensive in 1968, and in Laos in the Spring of 1971. The US Marine Corps acquired 38 AH-1Gs during 1969, for transition training and initial deployment pending deliveries of the AH-1J; these are included in the above total. The Spanish Navy received 20, for anti-shipping strike duties, and six were supplied to Israel in 1974. A number of AH-1Gs have been converted to **TH-1G** dual-control trainers. Following the decision to equip the HueyCobra with TOW missiles, 93 AH-1Gs were converted to interim AH-1Q standard; most of these have been updated further to Mod AH-1S standard. One AH-1G was converted to **JAH-1G**, as a testbed aircraft for the Hellfire laser-guided air-launched missile.

AH-1J SeaCobra. Initial twin-turboshaft version for US Marine Corps, powered by a 1,342 kW (1,800 shp) Pratt & Whitney Aircraft of Canada T400-CP-400 coupled free-turbine turboshaft engine, a military version of the PT6T-3 Turbo Twin Pac. Engine and transmission flat rated at 820 kW (1,100 shp) continuous output, with increase to 932 kW (1,250 shp) available for T-O or 5 min emergency power. Following an initial USMC order for 49, placed in May 1968, a pre-production example was displayed to representatives of the US armed forces at Enless, Texas, on 14 October 1969. Deliveries of these 49 began in mid-1970 and were completed in 1971; a further 20, ordered in early 1973, were delivered between April 1974 and February 1975. The last two of this batch were converted later as prototypes for the AH-1T. Under a \$38.5 million contract announced on 22 December 1972, 202 TOW-capable AH-1Js were supplied to the Imperial Iranian Army Aviation from 1974, the US Army acting as purchasing agent.

AH-1Q HueyCobra. Interim anti-armour version for US Army, converted from AH-1G to fire Hughes TOW anti-tank missiles. First of eight 'pre-production' examples delivered in early 1973; first 'production' deliveries on 10 June 1975. Of 93 converted, 20 have since been further upgraded by Bell to Mod AH-1S standard. A further 62, based in Germany, are being upgraded locally to the same standard by Dornier under a May 1978 US Army contract; the first three of these were re-delivered to the US Army on 16 June 1978.

AH-1R HueyCobra. As AH-1G, but with 1,342 kW (1,800 shp) T53-L-703 turboshaft engine. No TOW missile installation.

AH-1S HueyCobra. Advanced and modernised TOW-capable version for US Army; described separately.

AH-1T Improved SeaCobra. Improved version of twin-engined AH-1J for US Marine Corps. Last two of 69 AH-1Js modified as prototypes under a US Army Aviation Systems Command contract, with uprated compo-

Bell AH-1S TOW/Cobra with flat plate canopy and missile launchers

nents for significantly increased payload and performance. Incorporates features of AH-1J airframe, but embodies dynamic system of Bell Model 214, some technology developed for Bell Model 309 Kingcobra, and upgraded power plant (1,529 kW; 2,050 shp T400-WV-402) and transmission. Lengthened fuselage. Initial contract for 10 announced in June 1975; total of 57 ordered by 1979, of which 23 are scheduled to be modified to TOW configuration. First AH-1T (USN serial number 59228) delivered to USMC on 15 October 1977.

Under US Navy contract, Hughes is adapting its Black Hole infra-red suppression system (developed for the YAH-64) for interchangeable use on the AH-1J and AH-1T.

The following description applies primarily to the AH-1G and AH-1Q, except where indicated otherwise:

TYPE: Single-engined (AH-1G/Q/R/S) and twin-engined (AH-1J/T) close support and attack helicopters.

ROTOR SYSTEM AND DRIVE (AH-1G/J/Q/R): Model 540 two-blade wide-chord 'door-hinge' main rotor, similar to that of UH-1C. Interchangeable blades, built up of extruded aluminium spars and laminates. Rotor brake fitted. Blades do not fold. Two-blade all-metal flex-beam tractor tail rotor on starboard side, of honeycomb construction; blade chord increased on AH-1J, which also has push/pull tail rotor controls. Shaft drive to both main and tail rotors. Main rotor rpm 294-324.

ROTOR SYSTEM AND DRIVE (AH-1T): Similar to that of Bell Model 214, with strengthened main rotor hub incorporating Lord Kinematics Lastoflex elastomeric and Teflon-faced bearings. Main rotor blades have increased chord, and swept tips which reduce noise and improve high-speed performance. Tail rotor also similar to that of Model 214, with increased diameter and blade chord.

WINGS: Small mid-mounted stub-wings, to carry armament and offload rotor in flight.

FUSELAGE: Conventional all-metal semi-monocoque structure, with low silhouette and narrow profile. AH-1T has forward fuselage lengthened by insertion of a 0·305 m (1 ft 0 in) plug, to accommodate tankage for additional 181·5 kg (400 lb) of fuel, and tailboom lengthened by 0·79 m (2 ft 7 in).

TAIL UNIT: Sweptback vertical fin/tail rotor pylon, strengthened on twin-engined models to cater for increased power. Elevator, of inverted aerofoil section, mid-mounted on tailboom forward of fin.

LANDING GEAR: Non-retractable tubular skid type. Ground handling wheels optional.

POWER PLANT: Single or twin turboshaft engines, as detailed under model listings. Fuel capacity (G and J) 1,014 litres (268 US gallons). (Fuel loads, where known, are given under 'Weights' heading.) Refuelling point in port side of fuselage, aft of cockpits.

ACCOMMODATION: Crew of two in tandem, with co-pilot/gunner in front seat and pilot at rear. Crew are protected by seats and side panels of Norton Co 'Noroc' armour; other panels protect vital areas of aircraft.

SYSTEMS: Hydraulic system, with Abex pumps, for flight controls and other services. Battery-powered 28V DC electrical system. Environmental control and fire detection systems.

AVIONICS: Communications equipment in AH-1G includes AN/ARC-54/131 FM radio; AN/ARC-51 and AN/ARC-134 voice com; KY-28 secure voice system.

ARMAMENT AND OPERATIONAL EQUIPMENT (AH-1G): Initial production AH-1Gs were fitted with GAU-2B/A 7·62 mm Minigun in Emerson Electric TAT-102A undernose turret (see 1978-79 *Jane's*). This was superseded by an M-28 turret, able to mount either two Miniguns (each with 4,000 rds), or two M-129 40 mm grenade launchers (each with 300 rds), or one Minigun and one M-129. The Miniguns in these turrets have two rates of fire, controlled by the gunner's trigger: 1,600 rds/min for searching or registry fire, or 4,000 rds/min for attack. The M-129 fires at a single rate of 400 rds/min. Four external stores attachments under stub-wings can accommodate seventy-six 2·75 in rockets in four M-159 launchers, 28 similar rockets in four M-157 launchers, or two M-18E1 Minigun pods. An initial batch of six AH-1Gs were delivered to the US Army in December 1969 equipped with a Bell/General Electric M-35 armament subsystem. This unit consists of an M-61 six-barrel 20 mm automatic cannon on the port inboard wing station, having a firing rate of 750 rds/min. Two ammunition boxes faired flush to the fuselage below the stub-wings each accommodate 500 rds, and total installed weight of the system is 531 kg (1,172 lb). A total of 350 M-35 kits was ordered subsequently by the US Army. All wing stores are symmetrically or totally jettisonable. In normal operation, the co-pilot/gunner controls and fires the turret armament, and the pilot (aided by an M-73 adjustable reflex rocket sight) normally fires the wing stores. The pilot can fire the turreted weapons only in the stowed (ie, dead ahead) position; the turret returns to the stowed position automatically when the gunner releases his grip on the slewing switch. The gunner also has the capability to fire the wing stores if required. Other operational equipment on the AH-1G includes an M-130 chaff dispenser.

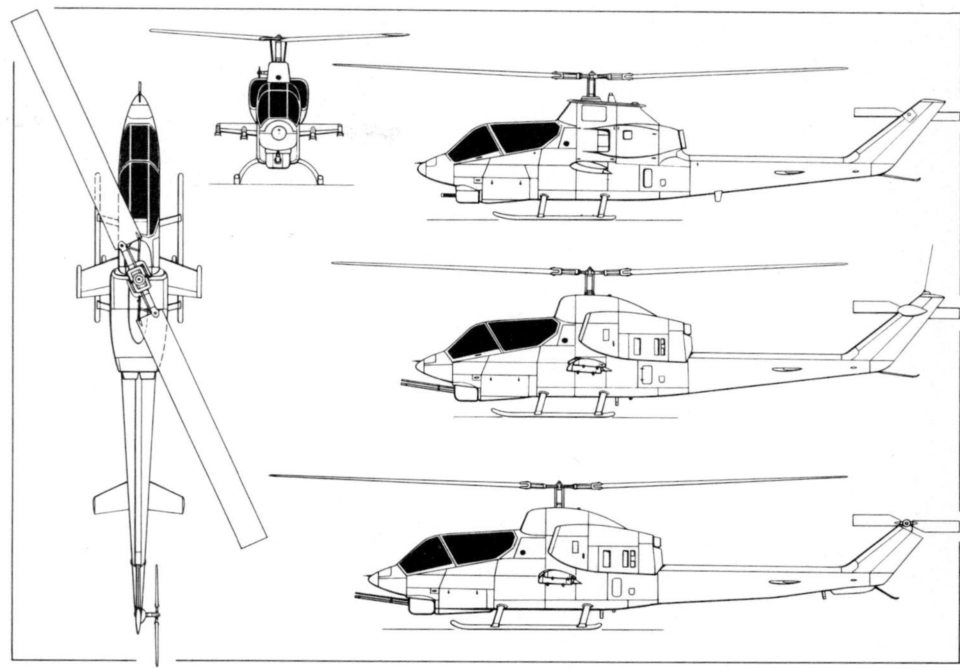

Bell AH-1T SeaCobra, with additional side views of AH-1J (centre) and AH-1G (top) *(Pilot Press)*

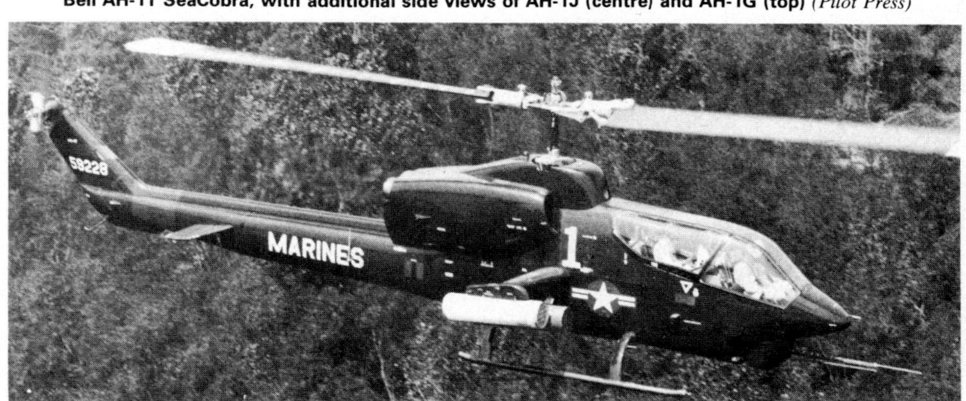

Bell AH-1T, improved version of the Model 209 SeaCobra for the US Marine Corps

ARMAMENT (AH-1J): Electrically operated General Electric undernose turret, housing an M-197 three-barrel 20 mm weapon (a lightweight version of the M-61 cannon). A 750-rd ammunition container is located in the fuselage directly aft of the turret; firing rate is 750 rds/min, but a 16-round burst limiter is incorporated in the firing switch. Barrel length of 1·52 m (5 ft) makes it imperative that the M-197 is centralised before wing stores are fired. Gun can be tracked 110° to each side, 18° upward, and 50° downward. Four attachments under stub-wings for various loads, including LAU-68A/A (seven-tube) or LAU-61A/A (19-tube) 2·75 in rocket launchers, or M-18E1 Minigun pods. Total possible armament load 245 kg (542 lb) internal, 998 kg (2,200 lb) external.

ARMAMENT (AH-1Q): M-28 turreted weapons as for AH-1G. Anti-armour configuration involves installation of eight Hughes TOW missile containers, disposed as two two-round pods on each of the outboard underwing stations. The inboard wing stations remain available for other stores, as listed for AH-1G. In the TOW configuration, a Sperry Univac helmet sight is used by both crew members to cue the turreted weapon or the TOW stabilised sight. In addition, the co-pilot/gunner may use the 2x or 13x magnification offered by the M-65 TOW system's telescopic sight unit for turret weapon engagements.

DIMENSIONS, EXTERNAL:
Diameter of main rotor: G, J, Q, R 13·41 m (44 ft 0 in)
T 14·63 m (48 ft 0 in)
Main rotor blade chord: G, J, Q, R 0·69 m (2 ft 3 in)
T 0·84 m (2 ft 9 in)
Diameter of tail rotor: G, J, Q, R 2·59 m (8 ft 6 in)
T 2·96 m (9 ft 8½ in)
Tail rotor blade chord: G, Q, R 0·21 m (8·4 in)
J 0·29 m (11½ in)
T 0·305 m (1 ft 0 in)
Wing span (all) 3·15 m (10 ft 4 in)
Length overall, main rotor fore and aft:
G, Q, R 16·14 m (52 ft 11½ in)
J 16·26 m (53 ft 4 in)
T 17·68 m (58 ft 0 in)
Length of fuselage: G, J, Q, R 13·59 m (44 ft 7 in)
T 14·68 m (48 ft 2 in)
Width of fuselage: G, Q, R 0·965 m (3 ft 2 in)
J, T 0·98 m (3 ft 2½ in)
Height overall: G, Q, R 4·12 m (13 ft 6¼ in)
J 4·15 m (13 ft 8 in)
Elevator span (all) 2·11 m (6 ft 11 in)
Width over skids (all) 2·13 m (7 ft 0 in)
Width over TOW missile pods:
G, Q 3·26 m (10 ft 8¾ in)

AREAS:
Main rotor disc: G, J, Q, R 141·26 m² (1,520·53 sq ft)
T 168·11 m² (1,809·56 sq ft)
Tail rotor disc: G, J, Q, R 5·27 m² (56·75 sq ft)
T 6·88 m² (74·03 sq ft)

WEIGHTS:
Operating weight empty, incl amounts shown for crew, fluids, avionics and armour:
G (404 kg; 891 lb) 2,754 kg (6,073 lb)
J (398 kg; 877 lb) 3,294 kg (7,261 lb)
Weight empty: T 3,635 kg (8,014 lb)
Operating weight empty: T 3,904 kg (8,608 lb)
Mission fuel load:
G (871 litres; 230 US gallons) 680 kg (1,500 lb)
J 725 kg (1,600 lb)
Max useful load (fuel and disposable ordnance):
J 1,144 kg (2,523 lb)
T 2,445 kg (5,392 lb)
Mission weight: G 4,266 kg (9,407 lb)
J 4,523 kg (9,972 lb)
Max T-O and landing weight:
G, Q, R 4,309 kg (9,500 lb)
J 4,535 kg (10,000 lb)
T 6,350 kg (14,000 lb)

PERFORMANCE (at max T-O weight, ISA):
Never-exceed speed:
G, Q, R 190 knots (352 km/h; 219 mph)
J 180 knots (333 km/h; 207 mph)
Max level speed: G, Q 149 knots (277 km/h; 172 mph)
J 180 knots (333 km/h; 207 mph)
Max crosswind speed for hovering:
J 40 knots (74 km/h; 46 mph)
Max rate of climb at S/L, normal rated power:
G, Q 375 m (1,230 ft)/min
J 332 m (1,090 ft)/min
Service ceiling, normal rated power:
G, Q 3,475 m (11,400 ft)
J 3,215 m (10,550 ft)
Hovering ceiling IGE: G, Q 3,015 m (9,900 ft)
J 3,794 m (12,450 ft)

Range with max fuel:
G, Q, both at S/L, 8% reserves
310 nm (574 km; 357 miles)
J, no reserves 311 nm (577 km; 359 miles)

BELL MODEL 209 HUEYCOBRA (MODERNISED VERSION)

US Army designation: AH-1S

The AH-1S is an advanced version of the single-engined TOW-capable HueyCobra for the US Army, with upgraded power plant, gearbox, transmission and many other improvements. Current Army planning calls for the acquisition of 690 of this model by mid-1981, and the supply of an undisclosed number to Israel has been authorised. Two are being delivered to Japan in 1979-80, and will be evaluated by the JGSDF for potential large-scale procurement.

The first of a succession of US Army contracts was placed in 1975, and 680 had been ordered by the beginning of 1979, as follows:

Mod AH-1S. This designation (the 'Mod' in this case indicating 'Modified') applies to 290 AH-1Gs already brought up to 'Production AH-1S' standard and redelivered to the US Army. These include 82 of the 93 AH-1Gs previously converted to AH-1Qs, 20 of which have since been further modified by Bell to Mod AH-1S; 62 others, remaining in Germany, are being brought up to the same standard locally by Dornier, under a US Army contract dated 2 May 1978. The first three Dornier-modified aircraft were redelivered to the US Army in Germany on 16 June 1978.

Production AH-1S. Under Step 1 of a three-step new-production programme, 100 Production AH-1S HueyCobras were built and delivered to the US Army between March 1977 and September 1978. These aircraft have a new flat-plate canopy, improved nap-of-the-earth (NOE) instrument panel layout, continental United States (CONUS) navigation equipment, radar altimeter, improved communication radios, uprated engine and transmission, push/pull anti-torque controls, and (from the 67th aircraft onwards) new Kaman-developed composite rotor blades. First unit to receive this version, in August 1977, was the 82nd Airborne Division at Fort Bragg, North Carolina.

Up-gun AH-1S. The next 98 new-production aircraft (Step 2) have all the improvements detailed for the Production AH-1S, plus a new universal 20/30 mm gun turret, an improved wing stores management system for the 2·75 in rockets, automatic compensation for off-axis gun firing, and a 10kVA alternator to provide the necessary additional electric power. Deliveries of this version began in September 1978 and were scheduled for completion in October 1979.

Modernised AH-1S. This version, not to be confused with the 'Mod AH-1S' referred to earlier, represents the fully-upgraded standard for the AH-1S, and will be reached beginning with the 199th new-production aircraft. To the improvements already mentioned for the two preceding stages will be added, as Step 3, a new fire control subsystem (comprising a laser rangefinder and tracker, ballistics computer, low-airspeed sensor, and pilot's head-up display), air data system, Doppler navigation system, IFF transponder, infra-red jammer, hot-metal and plume infra-red suppressor, closed-circuit refuelling, and new secure voice communications. Deliveries of the 99 Modernised AH-1S so far ordered are scheduled to take place between November 1979 and June 1981.

The US Army hopes eventually to bring all of its AH-1S HueyCobras up to the full Modernised AH-1S standard over a period of about five years. Current plans envisage, first, the conversion of a further 372 AH-1Gs to Modernised AH-1S in 1979-82; the 290 'Mod AH-1S' aircraft would then be upgraded to Modernised AH-1S in 1982-83; and finally, the 100 Step 1 aircraft (in 1983-84) and 98 Step 2 aircraft (in 1984) would be brought up to the full Step 3 standard.

The major differences between the AH-1S and earlier single-engined HueyCobras may be summarised as follows:

TYPE: Anti-armour attack helicopter.

ROTOR SYSTEM AND DRIVE: Upgraded gearbox and transmission, the latter rated at 962 kW (1,290 shp). From 67th new-production AH-1S onward, new main rotor blades of composite construction are fitted, developed by Kaman Aerospace Corporation and equipped with tungsten carbide bearing sleeves. The outer 15% of these blades, which are tolerant of damage by weapons of up to 23 mm calibre, is tapered in both chord and thickness.

FUSELAGE: Tailboom strengthened to increase survivability against weapons of up to 23 mm calibre. Entire airframe has an anti-infra-red paint finish.

POWER PLANT: One 1,342 kW (1,800 shp) Lycoming T53-L-703 turboshaft engine. Closed-circuit refuelling on Modernised AH-1S.

ACCOMMODATION: New flat-plate canopy has seven planes of viewing surfaces, designed to minimise glint and reduce possibility of visual detection during nap-of-the-earth (NOE) flying; it also provides increased headroom for pilot. Improved instrument layout and lighting, compatible with use of night vision goggles. Improved, independently-operating window/door ballistic jettison system to facilitate crew escape in emergency.

SYSTEMS: 10kVA AC alternator added to electrical system. Battery-driven Abex standby pump, for use in event of main hydraulic system failure, can be used for collective pitch control and for boresighting turret and TOW missile system. Improved environmental control and fire detection systems.

AVIONICS AND EQUIPMENT: Standard lightweight avionics equipment (SLAE) includes AN/ARC-114 FM, AN/ARC-164 UHF/AM voice com, and E-Systems (Memcor Division) AN/ARC-115 VHF/AM voice com (compatible with KY-58 single-channel secure voice system). Other avionics include AN/ARN-123 CONUS navigation system with VOR/ILS receivers, glideslope, marker beacon and indicator lights (Doppler navigation system in Modernised AH-1S); HSI; VSI; radar altimeter; push/pull anti-torque controls for tail rotor; co-pilot's standby magnetic compass.

ARMAMENT AND OPERATIONAL EQUIPMENT: M-65 system with eight TOW missiles on outboard underwing stations, as in AH-1Q. Beginning with the 101st new-production AH-1S (the first 'Up-gun' example), the M-28 (7·62/40 mm) turret in earlier HueyCobras is replaced by a new electrically-powered General Electric universal turret, designed to accommodate either a 20 mm or a 30 mm weapon and to improve stand-off capability. Initially, the 20 mm M-197 three-barrel Vulcan (with 750 rds) is mounted in this turret, with the 30 mm Hughes XM-230E1 single-barrel Chain Gun (with 500 rds) scheduled for installation in mid-1981. Rate of fire of both guns is 730 rds/min. Turret position is controlled by the pilot or co-pilot/gunner through helmet sights, or by the co-pilot using the M-65 TOW missile system's telescopic sight unit. Field of fire is up to 110° to each side of aircraft, 20·5° upward and 50° downward. Also from the first 'Up-gun' AH-1S, the helicopter is equipped with a new Baldwin Electronics XM-138 wing stores management subsystem, providing the means to select and fire, singly or in groups, any one of five types of external 2·75 in rocket store. These are mounted in launchers each containing from 7 to 19 tubes, and are additional to the TOW missile capability. In addition to these installations the 199th new-built AH-1S (the first to full 'Modernised' standard) introduces a fire control subsystem which includes a Kaiser head-up display for the pilot, Teledyne Systems digital fire control computer for the turreted weapon and underwing rockets, omnidirectional airspeed system to improve cannon and rocket accuracy, Hughes laser rangefinder (accurate to 10,000 m; 32,800 ft), and AN/AAS-32 airborne laser tracker. Other operational equipment includes a Marconi Avionics air data subsystem, AN/APX-100 solid-state IFF transponder, Sanders AN/ALQ-144 infra-red jammer, suppressor for infra-red signature from engine hot metal and exhaust plume, AN/APR-39 radar warning receiver, AN/ALQ-136 radar jammer (with M-130 chaff system as backup), Perkin-Elmer laser warning receiver.

DIMENSIONS, EXTERNAL: As AH-1G except:
Main rotor blade chord (from 67th new-production AH-1S) 0·76 m (2 ft 6 in)
Tail rotor blade chord 0·29 m (11½ in)

WEIGHTS:
Operating weight empty 2,939 kg (6,479 lb)
Mission weight 4,524 kg (9,975 lb)
Max T-O and landing weight 4,535 kg (10,000 lb)

PERFORMANCE (at max T-O weight, ISA):
Never-exceed speed (TOW configuration) 170 knots (315 km/h; 196 mph)
Max level speed (TOW configuration) 123 knots (227 km/h; 141 mph)
Max rate of climb at S/L, normal rated power 494 m (1,620 ft)/min
Service ceiling, normal rated power 3,720 m (12,200 ft)
Hovering ceiling IGE 3,720 m (12,200 ft)
Range at S/L with max fuel, 8% reserves 274 nm (507 km; 315 miles)

BELL MODEL 212 TWIN TWO-TWELVE

US military designation: UH-1N
Canadian military designation: CH-135

Bell announced on 1 May 1968 that the Canadian government had approved development of a twin-engined UH-1 helicopter to be powered by a Pratt & Whitney Aircraft of Canada PT6T power plant. Subsequently, the Canadian government ordered 50 of these aircraft (designated CUH-1N) for the Canadian Armed Forces, with options on 20 more. Simultaneously, orders totalling 141 aircraft for the United States services were announced, comprising 79 for the USAF, 40 for the USN and 22 for the USMC, all having the designation **UH-1N**. Subsequent orders covered the delivery of 159 more UH-1Ns to the US Navy and Marine Corps in 1973-78.

Initial deliveries for the USAF began in 1970, and the first CUH-1N for the Canadian Armed Forces was handed over officially at Uplands Airport, Ottawa, on 3 May 1971; the Canadian order was completed one year later. Deliveries to the USN and USMC began during 1971. Canadian aircraft are now designated **CH-135**. Six were delivered to the air force of Bangladesh in early 1977, and the Argentinian Air Force ordered eight in 1978.

A commercial version, known as the Twin Two-Twelve, is also in full-scale production. This received FAA type certification in October 1970, and on 30 June 1971 the Two-Twelve was granted FAA Transport Type Category A certification. The Model 212 has the capability of carrying an external load of 2,268 kg (5,000 lb), and the military UH-1N a load of 1,814 kg (4,000 lb).

Bell announced in January 1973 that two Twin Two-Twelves had been modified and flown in a programme to gain IFR certification from the UK's CAA and America's FAA. Conversion of the Model 212 from VFR to IFR configuration requires a new avionics package, new instrument panel and aircraft stabilisation controls. The Model 212 has also qualified for IFR certification by the Norwegian DCA and the Canadian DoT. In June 1977, it became the first helicopter FAA-certificated for single-pilot IFR operations with fixed floats.

An order for nine Model 212s, to support energy and natural resources development in China, was announced in February 1979. This was the first order from China received by a US helicopter manufacturer.

ROTOR SYSTEMS: Two-blade all-metal semi-rigid main rotor with interchangeable blades, built up of extruded aluminium spars and laminates. Stabilising bar above and at right angles to main rotor blades. Underslung feathering axis hub. Two-blade all-metal tail rotor. Main rotor blades do not fold. Rotor brake standard.

ROTOR DRIVE: Shaft drive to both main and tail rotors.

FUSELAGE: Conventional all-metal semi-monocoque structure.

TAIL SURFACE: Small fixed stabiliser on rear fuselage.

LANDING GEAR: Tubular skid type. Lock-on ground handling wheels, fixed floats and inflatable nylon float-bags optional.

POWER PLANT: Pratt & Whitney Aircraft of Canada PT6T-3 Turbo Twin Pac, comprising two PT6 turboshaft engines coupled to a combining gearbox with a single output shaft. Producing 1,342 kW (1,800 shp), the Twin Pac is flat rated to 962 kW (1,290 shp) for T-O and 842 kW (1,130 shp) for continuous operation. In the event of an engine failure, the remaining engine can deliver 671 kW (900 shp) for 30 minutes or 596 kW (800 shp) continuously. Five interconnected rubber fuel cells, total capacity 814 litres (215 US gallons). Auxiliary fuel tanks optional, to provide a max total capacity of 1,495 litres (395 US gallons). Single-point refuelling on starboard side of cabin.

ACCOMMODATION: Pilot and up to 14 passengers. In cargo configuration there is a total internal volume of 7·02 m^3 (248 cu ft), including baggage space in tailboom. Forward door on each side of fuselage, opening forward. Two doors on each side of cabin; forward door hinged to open forward, rear door sliding aft. Accommodation heated and ventilated. AiResearch air-cycle environmental control unit available optionally.

Bell UH-1N of Antarctic Development Squadron Six (VXE-6), US Navy

Systems: Dual hydraulic systems. 28V DC electrical system supplied by two completely independent 30V 200A starter/generators. Secondary AC power supplied by two completely independent 250VA single-phase solid-state inverters. A third inverter can acquire automatically the load of a failed inverter.

Avionics and Equipment: Optional IFR avionics include dual King KTR 900A com transceivers; dual King KNR 660A VOR/LOC/RMI receivers; King KDF 800 ADF; King KMD 700A DME; King KXP 750A transponder; King KGM 690 marker beacon/glideslope receiver; dual Sperry Tarsyn-444 three-axis gyro units; stability control augmentation system; and an automatic flight control system. Optional equipment includes a cargo sling, rescue hoist, emergency pop-out flotation gear and high skid gear.

Dimensions, external:
- Diameter of main rotor (with tracking tips) 14·69 m (48 ft 2¼ in)
- Diameter of tail rotor 2·59 m (8 ft 6 in)
- Main rotor blade chord 0·59 m (1 ft 11¼ in)
- Tail rotor blade chord 0·292 m (11½ in)
- Length overall (main rotor fore and aft) 17·46 m (57 ft 3¼ in)
- Length of fuselage 12·92 m (42 ft 4¾ in)
- Height overall 4·53 m (14 ft 10¼ in)
- Width overall (main rotor fore and aft) 2·86 m (9 ft 4½ in)

Areas:
- Main rotor disc 168·06 m² (1,809 sq ft)
- Tail rotor disc 5·27 m² (56·74 sq ft)

Weights:
- VFR empty weight plus usable oil 2,787 kg (6,143 lb)
- Max T-O weight and mission weight 5,080 kg (11,200 lb)

Performance (at max T-O weight):
- Never-exceed speed at S/L 140 knots (259 km/h; 161 mph)
- Max cruising speed at S/L 124 knots (230 km/h; 142 mph)
- Max rate of climb at S/L 402 m (1,320 ft)/min
- Service ceiling 4,330 m (14,200 ft)
- Hovering ceiling IGE 3,350 m (11,000 ft)
- Max range with standard fuel at S/L, no reserves 227 nm (420 km; 261 miles)

BELL MODEL 214B BIGLIFTER

Bell announced its intention to develop the Model 214B on 4 January 1974, claiming that it would have a lift capability better than that of any existing commercial helicopter in the medium category. FAA certification was received on 27 January 1976.

Powered by a 2,185 kW (2,930 shp) Lycoming T5508D turboshaft engine, the 214B has the same rotor drive and transmission system as the military Model 214A that was exported to Iran (see Model 214ST entry). The engine is flat rated at a maximum of 1,678 kW (2,250 shp) and the transmission is rated at 1,529 kW (2,050 shp) for take-off, with a maximum continuous power output of 1,379·5 kW (1,850 shp). The main rotor has a Wortmann blade section, swept tips, and an advanced rotor hub with elastomeric bearings on the flapping axis. The tail rotor hub requires no lubrication. Other features include an automatic flight control system, with stability augmentation and attitude retention; nodalised suspension; separate dual hydraulic systems; and a large engine deck that serves also as a maintenance platform. Differences from the military Model 214A include the addition of an engine fire extinguishing system, push-out escape windows in the cargo doors, and commercial electronics.

The standard **Model 214B** can cruise at 140 knots (259 km/h; 161 mph) with an internal load of 1,814 kg (4,000 lb). A passenger configuration provides seats for 14 persons, in addition to the crew of two. It is able to carry external loads in excess of 3,175 kg (7,000 lb) on its cargo hook, which is certificated for a maximum of 3,629 kg (8,000 lb). In an agricultural role this allows nearly four US tons of chemicals to be lifted, or 3,025 litres (800 US gallons) of water or suppressant in a firefighting role.

The **Model 214B-1** differs only in having its max T-O weight for internal load-carrying limited to 5,670 kg (12,500 lb) to meet different certification standards.

A new main rotor blade developed for the Model 214B became the first glassfibre blade of US manufacture to receive FAA certification on 24 July 1978. Assembled as a two-blade rotor for this helicopter, it has a diameter of 15.24 m (50 ft 0 in) and chord of 0·84 m (2 ft 9 in). Testing had exceeded 400 flying hours at the date of certification, and initial FAA approval is for a retirement life of 2,400 hours. Bell is confident that a retirement life of at least 10,000 hours will be achieved when in-plant and service testing have been completed.

Production glassfibre blades will be delivered initially as replacements for conventional blades in service on Model 214Bs. When full-scale manufacture is established, they will become standard on all 214Bs coming off the assembly line.

The production version of the blade has a spar consisting entirely of machine-made elements. An orbital machine winds the spar caps, which are of spanwise-orientated S_2 glass fibres that carry bending loads and centrifugal force. The fibres of these spar caps wrap around the sleeve of the attachment bolt to the hub, forming integral attachment lugs to the hub. Torsional loads in the spar are carried by layers of filament-wound crossply material located inside and outside the spanwise spar caps.

The blade skins consist of layers of non-woven crossply E-glass. A layer of woven cloth is applied to the outside of the skin to minimise foreign object damage, and the skins are supported by a Nomex non-metallic honeycomb core. The leading-edge of the blade is protected by a full-length titanium abrasion strip. The paint finish incorporates a semi-conductive graphite layer to aid the dissipation of static electricity.

Tests have shown that this method of blade construction does not dent as easily as metal. A fatigue crack usually will not grow from a small hole or puncture, and skin patches can be applied with less risk of subsequent cracking. Blades tested by the Lightning and Transient Research Institute of St Paul, Minnesota, were not damaged structurally by lightning strikes of 200,000 amperes, which is equivalent to the highest strikes recorded on aircraft. In ballistic tolerance tests, one blade virtually 'swallowed' a 23 mm high-explosive impact round rather than permitting it to exit.

Dimensions, external:
- Main rotor diameter 15·24 m (50 ft 0 in)
- Main rotor blade chord 0·84 m (2 ft 9 in)
- Tail rotor diameter 2·95 m (9 ft 8 in)
- Tail rotor blade chord 0·305 m (1 ft 0 in)

Weights:
- Max T-O weight:
  - internal loading, 214B 6,260 kg (13,800 lb)
  - internal loading, 214B-1 5,670 kg (12,500 lb)
  - external loading, 214B and 214B-1 7,257 kg (16,000 lb)

BELL MODEL 214ST

Bell Helicopters announced on 22 December 1972 the receipt of an order for 287 advanced **Model 214A** 16-seat utility helicopters, which were being acquired by Iran through the US government; an additional six examples were ordered in March 1977. The first Model 214A for Iran flew for the first time on 13 March 1974, and deliveries began on 26 April 1975. In February 1976, 39 generally similar **Model 214Cs** were ordered, with equipment for search and rescue duties.

The Model 214A, of which brief details can be found in the 1978-79 *Jane's*, was to have been the first product of the Iranian Helicopter Industry, in which the Iranian government and Bell Helicopter Textron were in partnership. As a result of changed national policy, Bell has withdrawn from this partnership, and is to continue by itself development and production of the improved **Model 214ST**, which was being developed specifically for major production and service in Iran. This aircraft was expected to serve initially as a military transport helicopter; but Bell will now develop the 214ST as a commercial transport with multi-mission capability. Originally, the suffix ST indicated Stretched Twin: Bell is retaining these initials to

Bell Model 212 twin-turbine general-purpose helicopter

Bell Model 214B BigLifter utility helicopter (Lycoming T5508D turboshaft engine) *(Phil Hanson)*

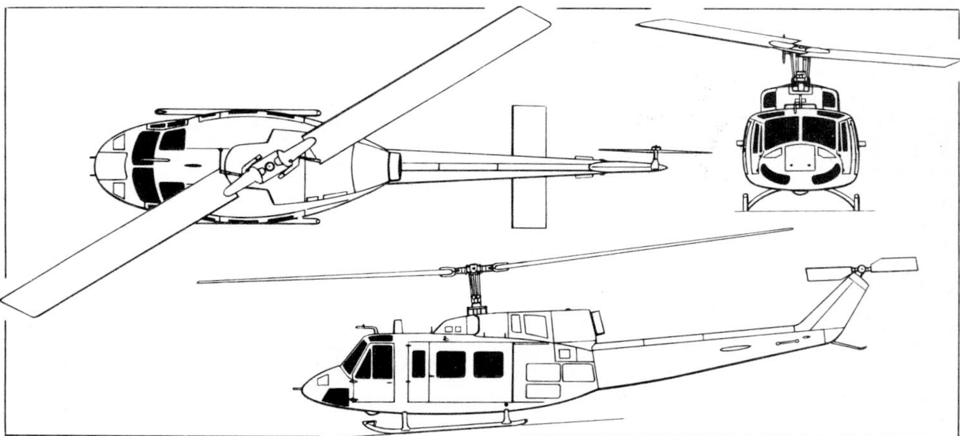

Bell Model 214B medium-size commercial heavy-lift helicopter *(Pilot Press)*

represent Super Transport.

The prototype 214ST built by Bell has been flying since February 1977, and construction of three pre-production examples began in 1978. Certification under FAR Pt 29 was scheduled for early 1980.

TYPE: Twin-turboshaft commercial transport helicopter.

ROTOR SYSTEM: Two-blade advanced technology main rotor. Each blade has a unidirectionally laid glassfibre spar, with a ±45°-wound torque casing of glassfibre cloth. The trailing-edge is also of unidirectional glassfibre, and the space between spar and trailing-edge is filled by a Nomex honeycomb core. The entire blade is then bonded together by glassfibre wrapping, with the leading-edge protected by a titanium abrasion strip and the tip by a replaceable stainless steel cap. Two-blade tail rotor; interchangeable blades, each with a stainless steel leading-edge spar and covering, aluminium honeycomb core and glassfibre trailing-edge strip. Main rotor hub incorporates elastomeric bearings. Second-generation Noda-Matic nodal suspension system. Nodal beam requires no lubrication. Main rotor brake standard.

ROTOR DRIVE: Main transmission, which has a one-hour run-dry capability, has a maximum rating of 1,678 kW (2,250 shp), maximum continuous rating of 1,380 kW (1,850 shp), and single-engine rating of 1,212 kW (1,625 shp). Combining, intermediate and tail rotor gearboxes, each with one-hour run-dry capability.

FUSELAGE: Conventional all-metal semi-monocoque structure, incorporating roll-over protection ring.

TAIL SURFACE: Electronically-controlled elevator, which minimises trim changes with alterations of power and CG, and improves longitudinal stability.

LANDING GEAR: Energy-absorbing non-retractable tubular skid type.

POWER PLANT: Two 1,212 kW (1,625 shp) General Electric CT7-2 turboshaft engines, connected to a combining gearbox. In the event of an engine failure, the remaining engine is able to provide continued flight capability. Standard fuel capacity 1,560 litres (412 US gallons), contained in seven interconnected cells, arranged to provide two independent fuel systems as required by FAR Pt 29. Single-point refuelling. Auxiliary fuel system optional, consisting of two tanks in rear of cabin.

ACCOMMODATION: Standard seating for pilot, co-pilot and 16 passengers, with alternative layout for 17 passengers. Dual controls under development. Crew seats adjustable. All seats have lap belt and shoulder harness. Jettisonable crew door each side. Large cabin door on port side for passengers or easy loading of cargo. Three emergency exits on each side. Baggage space aft of cabin, capacity 1·84 m³ (65 cu ft). Passenger seating removable to provide 8·95 m³ (316 cu ft) of cargo capacity. Cabin heated and ventilated.

SYSTEMS: Dual engine-driven hydraulic pumps for fully redundant hydraulic system. Redundant electrical system with dual engine-driven generators. Stability and control augmentation system (SCAS). Attitude/altitude retention system (AARS). Automatic elevator trim system.

AVIONICS AND EQUIPMENT: Avionics to provide full IFR capability, radar, and VLF navigation system, are under development. Equipment under development includes emergency flotation gear, external cargo suspension system, and internal rescue hoist.

DIMENSIONS, EXTERNAL:

Diameter of main rotor	15·85 m (52 ft 0 in)
Diameter of tail rotor	2·95 m (9 ft 8 in)
Main rotor blade chord	0·84 m (2 ft 9 in)
Tail rotor blade chord	0·36 m (1 ft 2 in)
Length overall, rotors turning	18·95 m (62 ft 2¼ in)
Length of fuselage	15·24 m (50 ft 0 in)
Height overall	4·84 m (15 ft 10½ in)
Skid track	2·64 m (8 ft 8 in)

DIMENSIONS, INTERNAL:

Cabin: Length, instrument panel to centre rear bulkhead	3·42 m (11 ft 2¾ in)
Length, max	4·13 m (13 ft 6¾ in)
Max width	2·41 m (7 ft 11 in)
Volume	7·73 m³ (273 cu ft)

AREAS:

Main rotor disc	197·32 m² (2,124 sq ft)
Tail rotor disc	6·82 m² (73·39 sq ft)

WEIGHTS:

Max T-O weight: internal load	7,030 kg (15,500 lb)
external load	7,484 kg (16,500 lb)

PERFORMANCE (at max T-O weight, unless detailed otherwise):

Max cruising speed at S/L	142 knots (264 km/h; 164 mph)
Max cruising speed at 1,220 m (4,000 ft)	140 knots (259 km/h; 161 mph)
Long-range average cruising speed	140 knots (259 km/h; 161 mph)
Service ceiling, one engine out	2,865 m (9,400 ft)
Hovering ceiling IGE	3,840 m (12,600 ft)
Hovering ceiling OGE	1,005 m (3,300 ft)
Range, ISA, VFR, standard fuel, no reserves	451 nm (835 km; 519 miles)
Ferry range with auxiliary fuel, pilot only, no payload, no reserves	over 600 nm (1,112 km; 691 miles)

BELL MODEL 222

In April 1974, Bell announced its intention of developing the Model 222, described as the first commercial light twin-engined helicopter to be built in the USA. Construction of the five prototypes began on 1 September 1974 and the first of these flew for the first time on 13 August 1976; FAA certification was received on 16 August 1979, and deliveries of production aircraft were planned to begin in October 1979. Orders totalled 135 in mid-January 1979.

The general appearance of the Model 222 is shown in the accompanying illustration. It was designed to meet FAR Pt 29 Transport Category requirements, and before taking a development decision Bell displayed a full-scale concept mockup, designated D306, at the annual convention of the Helicopter Association of America, in San Diego, in January 1974. The response of potential operators encouraged the development go-ahead, and customer suggestions were embodied in the definitive Model 222 design. In particular, the lower glazing of the flight deck was revised to provide increased visibility for rooftop landings, and the cabin was both lengthened and widened at the rear to give more spacious accommodation in high-density passenger-carrying configuration.

Production aircraft are offered in three configurations, as follows:

Basic 222. Standard model, as described.

222 Executive. Fully equipped for both single and dual pilot IFR flight. Sperry coupled automatic flight control system to provide stability augmentation and automatic hold for attitude, altitude, heading and airspeed, plus VOR/LOC course and glideslope hold during approach. Collins Proline avionics include dual VHF com, dual VOR nav with glideslope, ADF, marker beacon, transponder, DME and area navigation. Luxury accommodation for five or six passengers, with automatic temperature control, fluorescent and reading lights, window curtains and ceiling speakers. Optional stereo system and refreshment cabinet.

222 Offshore. Equipped for dual pilot IFR operations over water, with emergency flotation system, auxiliary fuel tanks and Collins Microline avionics.

TYPE: Twin-turbine light commercial helicopter.

ROTOR SYSTEM: Two-blade main rotor. Blade section Wortmann 090. Thickness/chord ratio 8%. Blades constructed of stainless steel and glassfibre, each attached to the hub by two chordwise bolts. Small trim tab on each blade. Completely dry main rotor hub has conical elastomerics. Two-blade tail rotor of stainless steel construction. Rotor blades do not fold. A rotor brake is standard.

ROTOR DRIVE: Rotors shaft-driven through gearbox with two spiral bevel reductions and one planetary reduction. Main rotor/engine rpm ratio 1 : 27·4; tail rotor/engine rpm ratio 1 : 5·08.

SPONSONS: Short-span cantilever sponson set low on each side of fuselage. Section NACA 0035. Dihedral 3° 12′. Incidence 5°. Sweepback at quarter-chord 3° 30′. All-metal structure of light alloy sheet and honeycomb. No movable surfaces.

FUSELAGE: Semi-monocoque structure of light alloy, with limited use of light alloy honeycomb panels. Fail-safe structure in critical areas.

TAIL UNIT: Cantilever structure of light alloy. Fixed vertical fin in sweptback upper and lower sections. Tailplane, with endplate fins, mounted midway along rear fuselage. Small skid below ventral fin for protection in tail-down landing.

LANDING GEAR: Hydraulically-retractable tricycle type, all units retracting forward. Free-fall extension in emergency. Oleo-pneumatic shock-absorbers, with scissored yoke. Self-centering nosewheel, swivelling through 360°. Single wheel and tyre on each unit. Main-wheel tyres size 6·00-6, pressure 5·18 bars (75 lb/sq in). Nosewheel tyre size 5·00-5, pressure 4·14 bars (60 lb/sq in). Hydraulic disc brakes. Water-activated emergency floats on Offshore version.

POWER PLANT: Two Avco Lycoming LTS 101-650C-2 turboshaft engines, mounted in a streamlined housing above the cabin and aft of the rotor pylon. Each engine is rated at 503·3 kW (675 shp) max for 2½ min, 469·8 kW (630 shp) for 30 min and 440 kW (590 shp) max continuous; transmission rated at 633·8 kW (850 shp) from two engines or 503·3 kW (675 shp) from one engine. Bell focused pylon with nodalisation. Fuel contained in three internal bladders, in fuselage and sponsons, with total capacity of 715 litres (189 US gallons). Single-point refuelling on starboard side of fuselage. Oil capacity 3·2 litres (6·85 US quarts) per engine.

ACCOMMODATION: Pilot and seven passengers in standard 2-3-3 layout; alternatively pilot, co-pilot and six passengers. Two additional passengers can be accommodated in a high-density 2-2-3-3 arrangement. Crew door at forward end of cabin on each side; cabin door on each side immediately forward of wing. Space for 1·05 m³ (37 cu ft) of baggage aft of cabin, with external door on starboard side. Ventilation standard; air-conditioning and heating optional.

SYSTEMS: Dual hydraulic systems, pressure 103·5 bars (1,500 lb/sq in). Electrical system supplied by dual 150A DC generators. Dual 250VA AC inverters, and 13Ah nickel-cadmium storage battery.

AVIONICS AND EQUIPMENT: VHF radio and Sperry IFR equipment standard. Other avionics, blind-flying

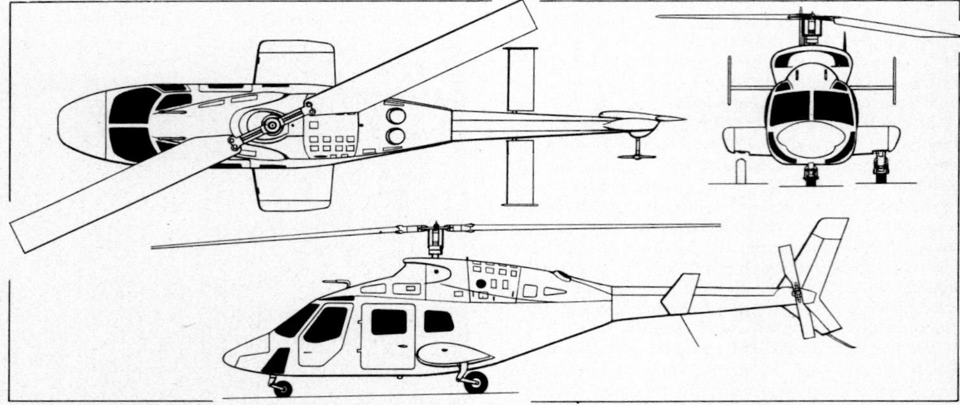

Bell Model 222 (two Avco Lycoming LTS 101 turboshaft engines) *(Pilot Press)*

Bell Model 222 eight/ten-seat twin-turbine light commercial helicopter

instrumentation and equipment, including 1,588 kg (3,500 lb) capacity cargo hook kit, to customer's requirements.

DIMENSIONS, EXTERNAL:
- Diameter of main rotor: 12·12 m (39 ft 9 in)
- Diameter of tail rotor: 1·98 m (6 ft 6 in)
- Main rotor blade chord: 0·73 m (2 ft 4·6 in)
- Tail rotor blade chord: 0·254 m (10 in)
- Sponson chord at root: 1·55 m (5 ft 1 in)
- Sponson chord at tip: 1·49 m (4 ft 10¾ in)
- Length of fuselage: 10·98 m (36 ft 0¼ in)
- Width overall: 3·18 m (10 ft 5 in)
- Height overall: 3·51 m (11 ft 6 in)
- Wheel track: 2·77 m (9 ft 1 in)
- Wheelbase: 3·70 m (12 ft 1¾ in)
- Passenger doors (each): Height: 1·30 m (4 ft 3 in)
  - Width: 0·99 m (3 ft 3 in)
  - Height to sill: 0·46 m (1 ft 6 in)
- Baggage door (stbd, aft): Height: 0·62 m (2 ft 0½ in)
  - Width: 0·89 m (2 ft 11 in)
  - Height to sill: 1·14 m (3 ft 9 in)

DIMENSIONS, INTERNAL:
- Cabin (passenger area): Length: 2·01 m (6 ft 7 in)
  - Max width: 1·41 m (4 ft 7½ in)
  - Max height: 1·30 m (4 ft 3 in)
- Volume, incl crew area: 5·52 m^3 (195 cu ft)
- Baggage hold: 1·05 m^3 (37 cu ft)
- Hat box (aft of cabin seats): 0·14 m^3 (5 cu ft)

AREAS:
- Main rotor blades (each): 4·40 m^2 (47·37 sq ft)
- Tail rotor blades (each): 0·21 m^2 (2·29 sq ft)
- Main rotor disc: 115·29 m^2 (1,241 sq ft)
- Tail rotor disc: 2·15 m^2 (23·18 sq ft)
- Vertical tail surfaces (total): 1·72 m^2 (18·53 sq ft)
- Horizontal tail surfaces (total): 1·37 m^2 (14·8 sq ft)

WEIGHTS AND LOADING:
- Weight empty, equipped: 2,064 kg (4,550 lb)
- Max T-O and landing weight: 3,470 kg (7,650 lb)
- Max disc loading: 30·1 kg/m^2 (6·16 lb/sq ft)

PERFORMANCE (at max T-O weight):
- Never-exceed speed: 160 knots (296 km/h; 184 mph)
- Max level and max cruising speed at S/L: 143 knots (265 km/h; 165 mph)
- Econ cruising speed at 2,440 m (8,000 ft): 130 knots (241 km/h; 150 mph)
- Max rate of climb at S/L: 527 m (1,730 ft)/min
- Vertical rate of climb at S/L: 262 m (860 ft)/min
- Service ceiling: 6,100 m (20,000 ft)
- Service ceiling, one engine out, ISA: 1,950 m (6,400 ft)
- Hovering ceiling IGE, ISA: 3,140 m (10,300 ft)
- Hovering ceiling OGE, ISA: 1,950 m (6,400 ft)
- Range with max fuel, 20 min reserves: 347 nm (644 km; 400 miles)

BELL MODEL 301

US Army designation: XV-15

Bell Helicopter announced in May 1973 that it had been chosen by NASA and the US Army to build and test two twin-engined tilt-rotor research aircraft. Estimated cost of the six-year programme is $45 million.

The company has been working on tilt-rotor technology since the mid-1950s, proving the concept feasible with its XV-3 prototype, described in the 1962-63 *Jane's*. Since that time development of tilt-rotor systems has progressed steadily, leading to the Model 301 which Bell proposed to meet the NASA/Army requirement. The two research aircraft, on which design work was started in July 1973, have the official designation XV-15. The fuselages and tail units were built under subcontract by Rockwell International's Tulsa Division.

The airframe structure is basically that of a conventional fixed-wing aircraft. However, the wingtip-mounted engines and rotors can be swivelled to a vertical position for VTOL operations, and are then moved forward gradually to provide transition to cruising flight at speeds in excess of 300 knots (556 km/h; 345 mph).

The XV-15 is fitted with a stability and control augmentation system to improve the handling qualities and enhance pilot efficiency. Ejection seats are installed as a safety feature during flight trials.

Future commercial and military aircraft which might be derived from the XV-15 would have a wing span of about 10·67 m (35 ft) and fuselage length of 12·50 m (41 ft). They would carry 15 troops in military service or 12 passengers as civil transports.

The programme is being funded and managed jointly by the NASA Ames Research Center and the US Army's Air Mobility Research and Development Laboratory. The two XV-15s are being used in a research programme to prove the concept, explore the limits of the operational flight envelope and assess its application to military and civil transport needs.

The first aircraft (702) made its first free hovering flight on 3 May 1977. The second aircraft (703) was transferred to Bell's Arlington, Texas, flight test facility for systems checks in late August 1977. Wind tunnel tests of the first XV-15 were carried out at NASA's Ames Research Center in June/July 1978, up to tunnel maximum speeds of 180 knots (333 km/h; 207 mph). Flight tests of the second XV-15 in helicopter mode began on 23 April 1979. The first full in-flight conversion to aeroplane mode was made by this second XV-15 (N703NA) on 24 July 1979. It achieved speeds of up to 160 knots (296 km/h; 184 mph) during the 40 min flight.

Bell XV-15 tilt-rotor research aircraft in hovering flight

TYPE: Tilt-rotor research aircraft.

ROTOR SYSTEM: Two three-blade rotors, stiff in plane and gimballed, with an elastomeric hub spring to increase control power and damping. Stainless steel blades of high-twist design, suitable for both helicopter and high-speed aircraft flight modes. Blade section is Bell-modified NACA 6-series. Blades attached to titanium hub by tension-torsion straps and roller pitch bearings.

ROTOR DRIVE: Each rotor is driven by individual engine via reduction gear, engine coupling, rotor planetary gear and shaft centrebox. Rotor/engine rpm ratio 1 : 35·11. Interconnected drive shafts and redundant tilting mechanisms permit single-engine operation and fail-operative tilt capability.

WINGS: Cantilever high-wing monoplane. Wing section Bell-modified NACA 64A223. Dihedral 2°. Incidence 3°. Forward sweep at quarter-chord 6° 30'. All-metal conventional structure, with light alloy ribs and honeycomb panels. Flap/aileron of light alloy construction on outer two-thirds of each wing trailing-edge, powered by HRT hydraulic actuators. Plain light alloy trailing-edge flap on inboard third of each wing, operated by SPECO electrical control box, with Curtiss-Wright power hinges. No tabs.

FUSELAGE: Semi-monocoque fail-safe structure of light alloy.

TAIL UNIT: Cantilever structure of light alloy, with end-plate fin and rudder mounted at each tailplane tip. Tailplane incidence ground-adjustable. Elevators and rudders powered by HRT hydraulic actuators. No tabs.

LANDING GEAR: Hydraulically-retractable tricycle type, with twin wheels on each unit. Main units retract forward, nose unit aft. Menasco oleo-pneumatic shock-absorbers. Nosewheel unit of self-centering type. Goodyear magnesium main wheels with Goodyear tyres size 6·50-8, pressure 3·8 bars (55 lb/sq in). Goodyear magnesium nosewheels with Goodyear tyres size 5·00-4, pressure 3·8 bars (55 lb/sq in). Goodyear hydraulic disc brakes.

POWER PLANT: Two 1,156 kW (1,550 shp) Avco Lycoming LTC1K-4K turboshaft engines, each with a two-minute contingency rating of 1,343 kW (1,800 shp), wingtip-mounted with tilt mechanism. Two fuel tanks in each wing, total capacity 867 litres (229 US gallons). Refuelling point on upper surface of each wing. Oil capacity 11·4 litres (3 US gallons).

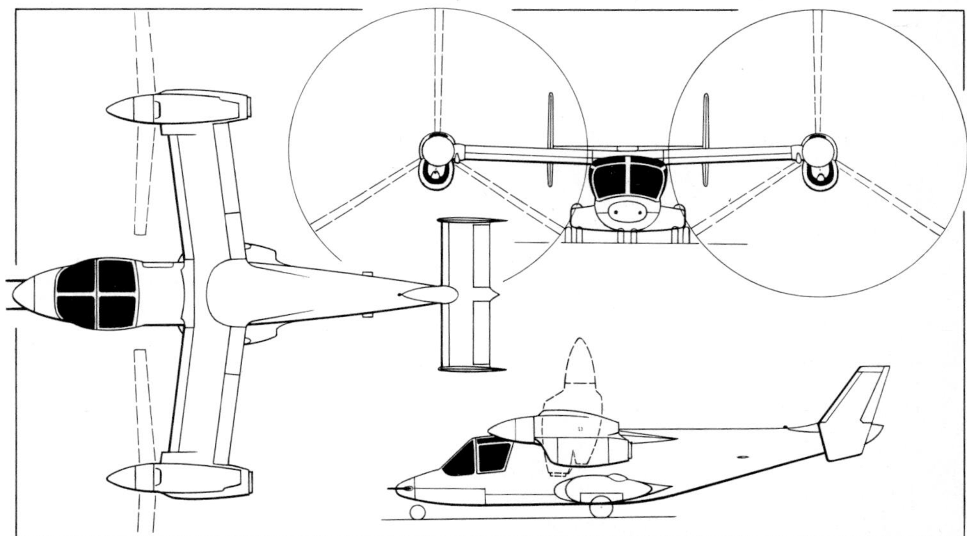

Bell XV-15 prototype tilt-rotor research aircraft *(Pilot Press)*

Bell XV-15, photographed after first in-flight conversion to aeroplane mode

Accommodation: Pilot and co-pilot side by side on flight deck, with access to cabin. Currently in austere test configuration for research equipment, cabin could accommodate nine personnel. Cabin door on starboard side. Accommodation heated, ventilated and air-conditioned. Overhead and side windows jettisonable ballistically in emergency.

Systems: AiResearch air-cycle environmental control unit. No pressurisation. Triplex hydraulic system, pressure 207 bars (3,000 lb/sq in): dual system for rotor and flight controls, with utility system as backup. Pneumatic system, pressure 207 bars (3,000 lb/sq in), for emergency actuation of landing gear. DC electrical system supplied by two 30V 300A generators. Two 28V 13Ah nickel-cadmium storage batteries. Oxygen system at pressure of 124 bars (1,800 lb/sq in). Engine inlet strut anti-icing.

Avionics and Equipment: King VHF, UHF, VOR, ILS, marker beacon indication and DME. Blind-flying instrumentation fitted.

Dimensions, external:
- Diameter of rotors (each): 7·62 m (25 ft 0 in)
- Distance between rotor centres: 9·80 m (32 ft 2 in)
- Rotor blade chord: 0·36 m (1 ft 2 in)
- Wing span: 10·72 m (35 ft 2 in)
- Wing aspect ratio: 6·7
- Wing chord, constant: 1·60 m (5 ft 3 in)
- Length overall: 12·83 m (42 ft 1 in)
- Height overall: 4·67 m (15 ft 4 in)
- Wheel track, c/l of shock-absorbers: 2·64 m (8 ft 8 in)
- Wheelbase: 4·80 m (15 ft 9 in)
- Cabin door (stbd): Height: 1·37 m (4 ft 6 in)
  - Width: 0·81 m (2 ft 8 in)
  - Height to sill: 0·56 m (1 ft 10 in)

Dimensions, internal:
- Cabin (excl flight deck):
  - Length: 4·53 m (14 ft 10½ in)
  - Max width: 1·52 m (5 ft 0 in)
  - Max height: 1·52 m (5 ft 0 in)
  - Floor area: 5·40 m² (58·1 sq ft)
  - Volume: 8·50 m³ (300 cu ft)

Areas:
- Rotor blades (each): 1·36 m² (14·6 sq ft)
- Rotor discs (each): 45·61 m² (491 sq ft)
- Wings, gross: 15·70 m² (169 sq ft)
- Flap/ailerons (total): 1·88 m² (20·2 sq ft)
- Trailing-edge flaps (total): 1·02 m² (11·0 sq ft)
- Fins (total): 3·99 m² (43·0 sq ft)
- Rudders (total): 0·70 m² (7·5 sq ft)
- Tailplane: 3·46 m² (37·25 sq ft)
- Elevators (total): 1·21 m² (13·0 sq ft)

Weights and Loading:
- Weight empty: 4,354 kg (9,600 lb)
- Design T-O weight: 5,897 kg (13,000 lb)
- Max T-O weight (STOL): 6,804 kg (15,000 lb)
- Max disc loading: 74·2 kg/m² (15·2 lb/sq ft)

Performance (estimated, at design T-O weight):
- Never-exceed speed: 364 knots (675 km/h; 419 mph)
- Max level speed at 5,180 m (17,000 ft): 332 knots (615 km/h; 382 mph)
- Max cruising speed at 4,970 m (16,300 ft): 303 knots (562 km/h; 349 mph)
- Econ cruising speed at 6,100 m (20,000 ft): 200 knots (371 km/h; 230 mph)
- Max rate of climb at S/L: 960 m (3,150 ft)/min
- Service ceiling: 8,840 m (29,000 ft)
- Service ceiling, one engine out: 4,570 m (15,000 ft)
- Hovering ceiling OGE: 2,635 m (8,650 ft)
- Range with max fuel: 445 m (825 km; 512 miles)

Prototype Bell Model 412, an improved 212 with four-blade advanced technology rotor

BELL MODEL 412

Bell announced on 8 September 1978 its intention to develop a variant of the twin-turbine Model 212 with a four-blade main rotor of advanced design. The new aircraft, designated Model 412, will be the first production helicopter with a four-blade rotor to be manufactured by Bell, although the company has flown many helicopters with multi-blade rotors for research purposes.

Two new fully-certificated Model 212s have been modified for use in the development and certification programme for the Model 412. The first of these began its flight trials in early August 1979, with FAA type approval in accordance with FAR Pt 29 expected by the end of 1980, permitting deliveries of the Model 412 to begin early the following year. CAA certification will also be obtained, and production will be undertaken simultaneously by Bell and its Italian licensee, Agusta.

Introduction of the new rotor has not only improved performance and reduced noise, but has reduced vibration significantly without requiring a costly redesign of the fuselage structure to introduce nodal suspension.

The description of the Model 212 applies also to the Model 412, except as follows:

Rotor System: Four-blade flex-beam soft-in-plane advanced technology main rotor. Blades are of similar construction to those described for the Model 214ST, but have lightning-protection mesh moulded into the structure and there are provisions for inclusion of de-icing heater elements. New-design main rotor hub of steel and light alloy construction, with elastomeric bearings and dampers. Main rotor can be folded. Rotor brake standard. Two-blade tail rotor of all-metal construction.

Rotor Drive, Fuselage, Tail Surface and Landing Gear: As for Model 212, except for shorter main rotor mast. Transmission T-O rating 975 kW (1,308 shp).

Power Plant: Pratt & Whitney Aircraft of Canada PT6T-3B Turbo Twin Pac, comprising two PT6 turboshaft engines coupled to a combining gearbox with a single output shaft. Producing 1,342 kW (1,800 shp), the Twin Pac is flat rated to 975 kW (1,308 shp) for take-off and 843 kW (1,130 shp) for continuous operation. In the event of an engine failure the remaining engine can deliver up to 764 kW (1,025 shp) for 2½ minutes, or 723 kW (970 shp) for 30 minutes. Five interconnected rupture-resistant fuel cells, with automatic shut-off valves (breakaway fittings), have a combined capacity of 814 litres (215 US gallons). Optional auxiliary fuel tanks provide a maximum total capacity of 1,495 litres (395 US gallons). Single-point refuelling on starboard side of cabin.

Accommodation and Systems: As for Model 212.

Avionics and Equipment: Optional IFR avionics include dual King KTR 900A com transceivers, dual King KNR 660A VOR/LOC/RMI receivers, King KDF 800 ADF, King KMD 700A DME, King KXP 750A transponder, King KGM 690 marker beacon/glideslope receiver, dual three-axis gyro units, stability control augmentation system, and an automatic flight control system. Optional equipment includes a cargo sling, rescue hoist, emergency pop-out flotation gear and high skid gear.

Dimensions, external:
- Diameter of main rotor: 14·02 m (46 ft 0 in)
- Diameter of tail rotor: 2·59 m (8 ft 6 in)
- Main rotor blade chord: at root: 0·40 m (1 ft 3·9 in)
  - at tip: 0·22 m (8½ in)
- Tail rotor blade chord: 0·29 m (11½ in)
- Length overall (rotors turning): 17·46 m (57 ft 3¼ in)
- Length of fuselage: 12·92 m (42 ft 4¾ in)
- Height overall: 4·32 m (14 ft 2¼ in)
- Width overall (rotor folded): 2·86 m (9 ft 4½ in)

Areas:
- Main rotor disc: 154·40 m² (1,662 sq ft)
- Tail rotor disc: 5·27 m² (56·75 sq ft)

Weights:
- Weight empty plus usable oil: 2,753 kg (6,070 lb)
- Max T-O weight: 5,216 kg (11,500 lb)

Performance (estimated, at max T-O weight):
- Never-exceed speed at S/L: 140 knots (259 km/h; 161 mph)
- Max cruising speed at S/L: 124 knots (230 km/h; 143 mph)
- Max rate of climb at S/L: 433 m (1,420 ft)/min
- Service ceiling: 4,330 m (14,200 ft)
- Hovering ceiling IGE: 3,350 m (11,000 ft)
- Max range with standard fuel at S/L, no reserves: 227 nm (420 km; 261 miles)

BELLANCA

BELLANCA AIRCRAFT CORPORATION (subsidiary of Anderson, Greenwood and Co)

Head Office and Works: PO Box 69, Municipal Airport, Alexandria, Minnesota 56308

Telephone: (612) 762 1501

President and Chief Operating Officer:
Robert E. Howard, Jr

Chairman of the Board and Chief Executive Officer:
James Elder

Vice-Presidents:
John Hall (Marketing and General Manager)
James L. Brown
Lloyd Cox (Production)

Known originally as International Aircraft Manufacturing Inc (Inter-air), Bellanca Sales Company (a subsidiary of Miller Flying Service) acquired the assets of Champion Aircraft Corporation on 30 September 1970. Following the merger, the name Bellanca Aircraft Corporation was adopted, and Bellanca now markets both its own products and those of Champion Aircraft.

The Anderson, Greenwood company of Houston, Texas, of which Bellanca Aircraft Corporation is now a wholly-owned subsidiary, obtained FAA certification on 28 July 1976 for its T-250 prototype four-seat light aircraft, now known as the Aries. Production planning for the T-250 began in November 1978, and the first production examples were scheduled for delivery in October 1979.

Bellanca is also responsible for manufacture of the Eagle agricultural biplane (see Eagle Aircraft Company entry in this section).

BELLANCA VIKING SERIES

There are three current aircraft in the Viking series, developed from the earlier Bellanca 260C and Standard Viking 300 (see 1971-72 *Jane's*), as follows:

Model 17-30A Super Viking 300A. Powered by a 224 kW (300 hp) Continental IO-520-K flat-six engine, driving a McCauley two- or three-blade metal constant-speed propeller.

Model 17-31A Super Viking 300A. This is identical to the foregoing version except for the installation of a 224 kW (300 hp) Lycoming IO-540-K1E5 engine, driving a Hartzell three-blade constant-speed propeller. Total of 823 Super Vikings (both models) delivered by 1 January 1979.

Model 17-31ATC Turbo Viking 300A. Powered by a 224 kW (300 hp) Lycoming IO-540-K1E5 engine with two Rajay turbochargers. Hartzell three-blade constant-speed propeller. Total of 150 Turbo Vikings delivered by 1 January 1979.

By 1 January 1979 a total of 1,598 Vikings of all models had been built.

Type: Four-seat light business aircraft.

Wings: Cantilever low-wing monoplane. Bellanca B wing section. Dihedral 4° 30′. Incidence 0° at root, −3° at tip. Structure consists of two laminated Sitka spruce spars, mahogany plywood and spruce ribs and mahogany plywood skin, covered with Dacron. Dacron-covered wooden ailerons and electrically-actuated flaps.

Fuselage: Welded 4130 steel tube structure, covered with Dacron. Two-piece glassfibre engine cowling, suspended from firewall.

Tail Unit: Strut-braced welded 4130 steel tube structure, covered with Dacron. Sweptback vertical surfaces. Trim tab in port elevator.

Landing Gear: Tricycle type, with Auto-Axion electro-hydraulic retraction, which lowers gear automatically during approach if pilot omits to do so, and prevents accidental retraction on ground. Manual emergency extension. Nosewheel retracts rearward, main wheels forward into underwing fairings, optionally enclosed by doors. Spring-air-oil shock-absorbers. Main-wheel tyres size 6·00-6 six-ply. Steerable nosewheel. Goodyear type 2-747 hydraulic disc brakes. Parking brakes.

Power Plant: One flat-six engine (details given under model descriptions). Six fuel tanks in wings with total usable capacity of 257 litres (68 US gallons). Optional auxiliary fuel tank in fuselage, increasing max usable capacity to 314 litres (83 US gallons). Refuelling points above each wing and on starboard side of fuselage. Oil capacity 11·5 litres (3 US gallons).

Accommodation: Four seats in pairs in enclosed cabin. Dual controls standard, with brakes on port side only. Moulded glassfibre door on starboard side of cabin. Tinted glass. Baggage space, capacity 84 kg (186 lb), aft of rear seats, with glassfibre external door and in-flight access. Provision for tube for carrying skis, max weight 9 kg (20 lb). Heating, ventilation and windscreen defrosting standard.

SYSTEMS: 12V electrical system, with Prestolite 60A alternator, solid-state regulator and 12V 33Ah battery. Hydraulic system for brakes only. Partial provisions for oxygen system.

AVIONICS AND EQUIPMENT: Standard equipment includes cylinder head temperature gauge, manifold pressure gauge, sensitive altimeter, internally-illuminated instruments with rheostat controls, stall warning system, anti-glare instrument panel cover, individually adjustable seats with shoulder harness, arm and headrests, pilot's storm window, tinted windows, map pockets, super soundproofing, dome light, map light, landing/taxi light, navigation lights, quick oil drain, tiedown rings and towbar. With factory-installed radio equipment the following additional equipment is standard: Narco omni antenna, Electro Voice microphone, power cable, Narco VP-10 broad-band transmitting antenna and microphone jacks. Mitchell Century I, II or III autopilot optional, with optional accessories which include radio tracker, radio coupler and automatic trim for Century II or III, glideslope coupler for Century III, electric trim and switch kits. Optional radio and navigation equipment includes Bendix, Collins, King and Narco VHF transceivers, transponders and marker beacon receivers; Bendix, Collins, King, Kett and Narco ADF radio receivers; King and Narco DME and Narco course line computer. Miscellaneous optional equipment includes full blind-flying instrumentation, turn co-ordinator, outside air temperature gauge, vacuum gauge, 8-day clock, exhaust gas temperature gauge, strobe lights, heated pitot, emergency locator transmitter, boom microphone and control wheel switch, co-pilot brakes, cabin fire extinguisher, golf club/ski container, reclining front seats, inertia reel shoulder harness for each seat, cabin entry step, sun visor, external power socket, electrical operation of elevator trim, stereo tape player, Whelen strobe lights, Alcor engine analyser, Avicon digital engine analyser, Astrotech elapsed digital timer, alternate static source, altitude encoder, true airspeed indicator and Hobbs flight hour meter.

DIMENSIONS, EXTERNAL:

Wing span	10·41 m (34 ft 2 in)
Length overall	8·02 m (26 ft 4 in)
Height overall	2·24 m (7 ft 4 in)
Tailplane span	3·71 m (12 ft 2 in)
Wheel track	2·74 m (9 ft 0 in)
Wheelbase	2·24 m (7 ft 4 in)
Propeller diameter	2·03 m (6 ft 8 in)
Cabin door: Height	0·95 m (3 ft 1½ in)
Max width	0·88 m (2 ft 10½ in)
Baggage compartment door: Height	0·61 m (2 ft 0 in)
Width	0·51 m (1 ft 8¼ in)

DIMENSIONS, INTERNAL:

Cabin: Length, firewall to rear wall	3·10 m (10 ft 2 in)
Max width	1·09 m (3 ft 7 in)
Max height	1·19 m (3 ft 11 in)
Baggage compartment volume	0·34 m³ (12·08 cu ft)

AREAS:

Wings, gross	15·00 m² (161·5 sq ft)
Ailerons (total)	1·09 m² (11·77 sq ft)
Trailing-edge flaps (total)	1·50 m² (16·16 sq ft)

WEIGHTS (A: IO-520, B: IO-540, C: turbocharged IO-540):

Weight empty: A	991 kg (2,185 lb)
B	1,019 kg (2,247 lb)
C	1,076 kg (2,372 lb)
Max T-O weight	1,508 kg (3,325 lb)

Bellanca Super Viking 300A four-seat light aircraft

PERFORMANCE (at max T-O weight, A: IO-520, B: IO-540, C: turbocharged IO-540):

Never-exceed speed: A, B, C	196 knots (363 km/h; 226 mph)
Max level speed at S/L: A	181 knots (335 km/h; 208 mph)
B	174 knots (322 km/h; 200 mph)
Max cruising speed (75% power): A	175 knots (325 km/h; 202 mph)
B	165 knots (306 km/h; 190 mph)
C at 7,315 m (24,000 ft)	193 knots (357 km/h; 222 mph)
Cruising speed (65% power): A	159 knots (295 km/h; 183 mph)
B	163 knots (303 km/h; 188 mph)
C at 7,315 m (24,000 ft)	175 knots (325 km/h; 202 mph)
Stalling speed, wheels and flaps down: A, B, C	61 knots (113 km/h; 70 mph) CAS
Max rate of climb at S/L: A	369 m (1,210 ft)/min
B, C	356 m (1,170 ft)/min
Service ceiling: A	6,100 m (20,000 ft)
B	5,550 m (18,200 ft)
Certificated ceiling: C	7,315 m (24,000 ft)
T-O to 15 m (50 ft): A, B, C	433 m (1,420 ft)
Landing from 15 m (50 ft): A, B, C	409 m (1,340 ft)
Max range with max optional fuel, cruise at 75% power, with allowances for start, taxi, S/L T-O, climb and descent, no reserves: A	929 nm (1,722 km; 1,070 miles)
B	821 nm (1,521 km; 945 miles)
C	802 nm (1,485 km; 923 miles)

CHAMPION (BELLANCA) CITABRIA

The Citabria ('airbatic' spelled backwards) represents Bellanca's advanced development of the Model 7 Champion airframe. There are three current versions, as follows:

Citabria Standard. Formerly Model 7ECA. Basic version, with 85·5 kW (115 hp) Lycoming O-235-K2C engine and standard wings. Design and prototype construction started on 1 January 1964. Prototype 7ECA flew for the first time on 1 May 1964 and first production model on 18 August 1964. FAA certification received 5 August 1964. During 1969 the Model 7ECA received FAA certification for operation on Edo floats.

Citabria 150. Formerly Model 7GCAA. Generally similar to above, but with 112 kW (150 hp) Lycoming O-320-A2D engine, and landing gear speed fairings, de luxe spinner and landing light as standard equipment. Design started 15 February 1965. Construction of prototype 7GCAA began on 1 May 1965, and it flew on 30 May, followed by the first production model on 20 July 1965. FAA certification received 30 July 1965.

Citabria 150S. Formerly Model 7GCBC. Generally similar to Citabria 150, with same additional equipment as standard, but with wing of increased span and trailing-edge flaps. Sale of 40 to Turkish Army, for use as primary trainers, announced in mid-1979.

By the beginning of 1979 a total of 4,976 Citabrias of all models had been built.

TYPE: Two-seat light cabin monoplane.

WINGS: Braced high-wing monoplane. NACA 4412 wing section. Dihedral 2°. Incidence 1°. Two Sitka spruce spars, aluminium ribs, Dacron covering. Steel tube V bracing struts. Single-spar Dacron-covered aluminium ailerons. No flaps. Glassfibre-reinforced polyester wingtips.

FUSELAGE: Welded chrome-molybdenum steel tube structure, covered with Dacron.

TAIL UNIT: Wire-braced welded steel tube structure, with Dacron covering. Fixed-incidence tailplane. Counter-balanced elevators. Controllable trim tab in elevator.

LANDING GEAR: Non-retractable tailwheel type. All aircraft produced since January 1968 have cantilever spring steel main gear with 6·00-6 wheels and 4-ply tyres as standard. Tyre pressure 1·65 bars (24 lb/sq in). Steerable tailwheel, with 203 mm (8 in) pneumatic tyre. Cleveland disc brakes. Parking brake. Wheel fairings optional on Standard, and included as standard on Citabria 150 and 150S. Pee Kay 1800 or Edo floats, and Federal A-200-A skis, available on Standard Citabria.

POWER PLANT: One flat-four engine, as described under individual model listings. McCauley two-blade fixed-pitch metal propeller: type 1C90ALM on 85·5 kW (115 hp) model, and type 1C172AGM on 112 kW (150 hp) models. Two aluminium fuel tanks in wings, total capacity 136 litres (36 US gallons), of which 132 litres (35 US gallons) are usable. Refuelling points above tanks. Oil capacity 5·75 litres (1·5 US gallons) on version with 85·5 kW (115 hp) engine, 7·5 litres (2 US gallons) on 112 kW (150 hp) versions.

ACCOMMODATION: Enclosed cabin seating two persons in tandem. Dual controls. Heater standard. Quick-jettison door on starboard side. Space for 45 kg (100 lb) baggage.

SYSTEMS: Hydraulic system for brakes only. Electrical system powered by 12V 60A engine-driven alternator and 12V battery.

AVIONICS AND EQUIPMENT: Wide range of King and Narco radio equipment optional, including omni, ILS and ADF. Blind-flying instrumentation optional. Standard equipment includes navigation lights, rotating beacon, sensitive altimeter, soundproofing, de luxe instrument panel with anti-glare cover, cabin step, corrosion protection, pilot's storm window, lap belts and inertia-reel shoulder harness for front seats; back seats have lap belts and harness without inertia reel. Wheel speed fairings, de luxe propeller spinner and landing light optional for Citabria Standard, but these are standard equipment for Citabria 150 and 150S. A wide range of optional equipment is available.

DIMENSIONS, EXTERNAL (A: Standard; B: 150; C: 150S):

Wing span: A, B	10·19 m (33 ft 5 in)
C	10·49 m (34 ft 5 in)

Champion Citabria two-seat aerobatic light aircraft

Wing chord (constant) 1·52 m (5 ft 0 in)
Wing aspect ratio: A, B 6·72
C 6·97
Length overall 6·92 m (22 ft 8·4 in)
Height overall 2·35 m (7 ft 8·4 in)
Wheel track 1·93 m (6 ft 4 in)
Wheelbase 4·90 m (16 ft 1 in)
Cabin door: Height 0·94 m (3 ft 1 in)
Width 0·94 m (3 ft 1 in)
Height to sill 0·44 m (1 ft 5½ in)

AREAS (A: Standard; B: 150; C: 150S):
Wings, gross: A, B 15·33 m² (165 sq ft)
C 15·79 m² (170 sq ft)
Ailerons (total) 1·53 m² (16·5 sq ft)
Fin 0·65 m² (7·02 sq ft)
Rudder 0·63 m² (6·83 sq ft)
Tailplane 1·14 m² (12·25 sq ft)
Elevators, incl tab 1·35 m² (14·58 sq ft)

WEIGHTS AND LOADINGS (A: Standard; B: 150; C: 150S):
Weight empty, equipped: A 484 kg (1,067 lb)
B 517 kg (1,140 lb)
C 522 kg (1,150 lb)
Max T-O and landing weight:
landplanes 748 kg (1,650 lb)
Max wing loading: A, B 48·8 kg/m² (10 lb/sq ft)
C 47·3 kg/m² (9·7 lb/sq ft)
Max power loading: A 8·72 kg/kW (14·35 lb/hp)
B, C 6·68 kg/kW (11·0 lb/hp)

PERFORMANCE (at max T-O weight. A: Standard; B: 150; C: 150S):
Never-exceed speed 140 knots (261 km/h; 162 mph)
Max level speed at S/L:
A 109 knots (201 km/h; 125 mph)
A seaplane 75 knots (138 km/h; 86 mph)
B 115 knots (212 km/h; 132 mph)
C 113 knots (209 km/h; 130 mph)
Max cruising speed (75% power) at optimum height:
A 107 knots (198 km/h; 123 mph)
B 112 knots (207 km/h; 129 mph)
C 111 knots (206 km/h; 128 mph)
Cruising speed (65% power):
A 102 knots (189 km/h; 117 mph)
B, C 107 knots (198 km/h; 123 mph)
Stalling speed: A, B 44·5 knots (82 km/h; 51 mph)
C 39 knots (72 km/h; 45 mph)
Max rate of climb at S/L: A 221 m (725 ft)/min
A seaplane 157 m (515 ft)/min
B 341 m (1,120 ft)/min
C 349 m (1,145 ft)/min
Service ceiling: A 3,660 m (12,000 ft)
B, C 5,180 m (17,000 ft)
T-O run: A 139 m (455 ft)
B 116 m (382 ft)
C 93 m (305 ft)
T-O to 15 m (50 ft): A 273 m (895 ft)
B 202 m (663 ft)
C 173 m (567 ft)
Landing from 15 m (50 ft): A 236 m (775 ft)
B 230 m (755 ft)
C 210 m (690 ft)
Landing run: A, B 121 m (400 ft)
C 95 m (310 ft)
Max range with max fuel, cruise at 75% power, with allowances for start, taxi, S/L T-O, climb and descent, no reserves: A 442 nm (819 km; 509 miles)
B 437 nm (810 km; 503 miles)
C 431 nm (799 km; 496 miles)
Range with max fuel, 55% power, allowances as above, no reserves: A 623 nm (1,154 km; 717 miles)
B 527 nm (977 km; 607 miles)
C 521 nm (966 km; 600 miles)
g limits +5; −2

BELLANCA MODEL 8GCBC SCOUT

This version of the Scout, with a 134 kW (180 hp) Lycoming engine, received type approval on 30 April 1974, and went into immediate production to meet large orders. By the beginning of 1979 a total of 278 8GCBC Scouts had been produced.

The description of the basic Citabria applies also to the Scout, except for the following details:

WINGS: As for Citabria, except increased wing span and provision of 27° trailing-edge flaps. Dihedral reduced to 1°. Hoerner wingtips.

FUSELAGE: Removable metal skin panels on undersurface.

TAIL UNIT: As for Citabria, but areas increased.

LANDING GEAR: Non-retractable tailwheel type. Cantilever spring steel main gear with wheels and tyres size 7·00-6. Heavy-duty Scott tailwheel. Ski installations approved are Aero Ski M2000 and M3000, Fluidyne 2000 and Airgas Landis 2000A; approved floats are Edo 2000, Pee Kay 2000 and Canadian Aircraft Products 2000A. Hydraulic disc brakes. Parking brake.

POWER PLANT: One 134 kW (180 hp) Lycoming O-360-C2E flat-four engine, driving a McCauley 1A200HFA8041 two-blade metal fixed-pitch propeller. Optional O-360-C1E engine and Hartzell HC-C2YR-1BF/F7666A-0 constant-speed propeller. Two fuel tanks in wings with a total capacity of 136 litres (36 US gallons), of which 132 litres (35 US gallons) are usable. Optional fuel system to provide max usable capacity of 265 litres (70 US gallons). Refuelling points above tanks. Oil capacity 7·5 litres (2 US gallons).

Bellanca Model 8GCBC Scout two-seat cabin monoplane (Lycoming O-360-C2E engine)

ACCOMMODATION: Enclosed cabin seating two persons in tandem. Accommodation heated and ventilated.

SYSTEMS: Electrical system powered by a 14V 60A engine-driven alternator with 12V battery in sealed and vented container. Hydraulic system for brakes only.

AVIONICS AND EQUIPMENT: An extensive range of optional avionics is available. Standard equipment includes navigation lights, wingtip strobe lights, landing lights, sensitive altimeter, soundproofing, dual controls, dual toe brakes, inertia reel harness for front seat, lap belt and shoulder strap for rear seat, alternate static source, pilot's storm window, cargo restraint system, cabin step, corrosion proofing, stall warning device, tiedown rings and quick oil drain. Optional items include a 340 litre (90 US gallon) Sorensen belly tank and underwing spraybooms, glider towing hook, and ski and float installations.

DIMENSIONS, EXTERNAL:
Wing span 11·02 m (36 ft 2 in)
Wing chord (constant) 1·52 m (5 ft 0 in)
Length overall 6·93 m (22 ft 9 in)
Height overall 2·64 m (8 ft 8 in)
Tailplane span 3·10 m (10 ft 2¼ in)
Wheel track 2·10 m (6 ft 10½ in)
Wheelbase, tail up 5·02 m (16 ft 5½ in)
Propeller diameter 2·03 m (6 ft 8 in)

AREAS:
Wings, gross 16·7 m² (180 sq ft)
Vertical tail surfaces 1·53 m² (16·5 sq ft)
Horizontal tail surfaces 2·42 m² (26 sq ft)

WEIGHTS:
Weight empty 597 kg (1,315 lb)
Normal category payload 379 kg (835 lb)
Restricted category payload 583 kg (1,285 lb)
Max T-O weight: Normal 975 kg (2,150 lb)
Restricted 1,179 kg (2,600 lb)

PERFORMANCE (A: standard fixed-pitch propeller; B: optional constant-speed propeller, at Normal category max T-O weight):
Never-exceed speed
140 knots (260 km/h; 162 mph) CAS
Max level speed at S/L
117 knots (217 km/h; 135 mph)
Cruising speed at 75% power:
A 106 knots (196 km/h; 122 mph)
B 113 knots (209 km/h; 130 mph)
Stalling speed, flaps down, power off
45 knots (84 km/h; 52 mph)
Max rate of climb at S/L: A 329 m (1,080 ft)/min
B 311 m (1,020 ft)/min
T-O run 156 m (510 ft)
Range with standard fuel at 75% power, allowances for start, taxi, T-O, climb and descent, no reserves:
A 333 nm (618 km; 384 miles)
B 343 nm (636 km; 395 miles)
Range with optional fuel at 75% power, allowances as above, no reserves:
A 680 nm (1,260 km; 783 miles)
B 700 nm (1,297 km; 806 miles)
Range with optional fuel at 55% power, allowances as above, no reserves:
A 779 nm (1,444 km; 897 miles)
B 802 nm (1,487 km; 924 miles)

CHAMPION (BELLANCA) DECATHLON

The Decathlon is an aerobatic competition aircraft designed for loads of $+6g$ and $-5g$, and has been arbitrarily cleared for two minutes of inverted flight, although the aircraft has been flown inverted in excess of four minutes without loss of oil or oil pressure. FAA certification under FAR 23, for both Normal and Aerobatic categories, was granted on 16 October 1970.

Following sale of the first hand-built production batch of 14 aircraft (first one delivered on 24 February 1971), Bellanca decided to begin full-scale production with the 15th aircraft, thus making the Decathlon the only unlimited aerobatic competition aircraft in production in the USA. By the beginning of 1979 a total of 406 Decathlons had been produced.

Three versions are available currently:

Decathlon. Formerly Model 8KCAB. Basic version with 112 kW (150 hp) Lycoming AEIO-320-E2B engine, driving a Sensenich fixed-pitch propeller.

Decathlon CS. As above, but with a 112 kW (150 hp) Lycoming AEIO-320-E1B engine, driving a Hartzell aerobatic constant-speed propeller, and with a Custom Sport package as standard, comprising wingtip strobe lights, rheostat for cabin lights, competition harness for front seat, quick oil drain, and three-colour exterior paint scheme.

Super Decathlon. As Decathlon CS, except that the 112 kW (150 hp) engine is replaced by a 134 kW (180 hp) Lycoming AEIO-360-H1A, driving a Hartzell constant-speed propeller.

TYPE: Two-seat light cabin monoplane.

Champion Super Decathlon two-seat aerobatic monoplane (Lycoming AEIO-360-H1A engine)

WINGS: Braced high-wing monoplane. Wing section NACA 1412 modified. Dihedral 1°. Incidence 1° 30′. Size of front spar substantially increased and ribs stronger and more closely-spaced by comparison with Citabria. Trusses added between front and rear spars in aileron area. Wings and ailerons Dacron covered. Glassfibre wingtips. Aluminium (front) and steel tube (rear) V bracing struts each side, of enlarged section.
FUSELAGE: Welded steel tube structure, with wood and steel formers and Dacron covering.
TAIL UNIT: Wire-braced welded steel tube structure, with Dacron covering. Fixed-incidence tailplane. Trim tab in port elevator.
LANDING GEAR: Non-retractable tailwheel type. Cantilever spring steel main legs. Main-wheel tyres size 17 × 6-6, pressure 1·66 bars (24 lb/sq in). Tailwheel tyre size 8·30 × 2·50-2·80, pressure 2·07 bars (30 lb/sq in) Cleveland disc brakes. Glassfibre wheel fairings standard.
POWER PLANT: One flat-four engine, driving a two-blade metal propeller, as detailed in the model listings. Two aluminium wing fuel tanks, with total usable capacity of 151·4 litres (40 US gallons). Oil capacity 7·5 litres (2 US gallons).
ACCOMMODATION: Enclosed cabin seating two persons in tandem. Quick-jettison door on starboard side. Space for 45 kg (100 lb) baggage. Cabin heated and ventilated.
SYSTEMS, AVIONICS AND EQUIPMENT: Generally as described for Citabria.
DIMENSIONS, EXTERNAL:
Wing span 9·75 m (32 ft 0 in)
Wing chord (constant) 1·63 m (5 ft 4 in)
Length overall 6·98 m (22 ft 10¾ in)
Height overall 2·36 m (7 ft 9 in)
Tailplane span 3·10 m (10 ft 2¼ in)
Wheel track 1·98 m (6 ft 6 in)
Wheelbase 4·93 m (16 ft 2¼ in)
Propeller diameter:
Decathlon, Super Decathlon 1·88 m (6 ft 2 in)
Decathlon CS 1·83 m (6 ft 0 in)
Door: Height 0·91 m (3 ft 0 in)
Width 0·94 m (3 ft 1 in)
DIMENSIONS, INTERNAL:
Cabin: Length 2·69 m (8 ft 10 in)
Max width 0·73 m (2 ft 5 in)
Max height 1·31 m (4 ft 3½ in)
AREAS:
Wings, gross 15·71 m² (169·1 sq ft)
Ailerons (total) 1·92 m² (20·68 sq ft)
Fin 0·65 m² (7·02 sq ft)
Rudder 0·63 m² (6·83 sq ft)
Tailplane 1·14 m² (12·25 sq ft)
Elevators, incl tab 1·35 m² (14·58 sq ft)
WEIGHTS AND LOADINGS (A: Decathlon; B: Decathlon CS; C: Super Decathlon):
Weight empty: A 572 kg (1,260 lb)
B 581 kg (1,280 lb)
C 596 kg (1,315 lb)
Max T-O weight: A, B, C 816 kg (1,800 lb)
Max wing loading: A, B, C 51·75 kg/m² (10·6 lb/sq ft)
Max power loading: A, B 7·28 kg/kW (12·0 lb/hp)
C 6·08 kg/kW (10·0 lb/hp)
PERFORMANCE (A: Decathlon; B: Decathlon CS; C: Super Decathlon, at max T-O weight):
Max level speed at 2,315 m (7,500 ft):
A, B 128 knots (237 km/h; 147 mph)
C 137 knots (254 km/h; 158 mph)
Cruising speed, 75% power, at 2,315 m (7,500 ft):
A, B 119 knots (220 km/h; 137 mph)
C 130 knots (241 km/h; 150 mph)
Stalling speed: A, B, C 47 knots (87 km/h; 54 mph)
Max rate of climb at S/L: A 305 m (1,000 ft)/min
B 268 m (880 ft)/min
C 375 m (1,230 ft)/min
Service ceiling: A, C 4,875 m (16,000 ft)
B 4,570 m (15,000 ft)
T-O run: A, B, C 192 m (630 ft)
T-O to 15 m (50 ft): A, B, C 360 m (1,180 ft)
Landing from 15 m (50 ft): A, B, C 432 m (1,416 ft)
Landing run: A, B, C 190 m (622 ft)
Range with max fuel, 75% power, with allowances for start, taxi, S/L T-O, climb and descent, no reserves:
A, B 515 nm (954 km; 593 miles)
C 510 nm (945 km; 587 miles)
Range with max fuel, 55% power, with allowances as above, no reserves:
A 587 nm (1,088 km; 676 miles)
B 582 nm (1,078 km; 670 miles)
C 543 nm (1,005 km; 625 miles)

BELLANCA ARIES T-250

Designed by Anderson, Greenwood and Company, the four-seat T-250 is the product of a research and development programme which had spanned approximately nine years by the time the aircraft received FAA certification on 28 July 1976. It first flew on 10 July 1973. Production planning was initiated in November 1978, and deliveries of the first production examples were scheduled for October 1979. Turbocharged and six-seat versions are under consideration.
TYPE: Five-seat cabin monoplane.
WINGS: Cantilever low-wing monoplane. Wing section NACA 600412 modified. Dihedral 6°. Conventional structure of light alloy. Cambered leading-edge. Plain ailerons of light alloy construction. Spring servo-tab in each aileron. Electrically-operated trailing-edge flaps of light alloy construction. Flaps can be operated manually in emergency.
FUSELAGE: Conventional light alloy structure of basic rectangular cross-section.
TAIL UNIT: Cantilever structure of light alloy, with T tailplane. All-moving horizontal surfaces, with tab.
LANDING GEAR: Electrically-retractable tricycle type. Main wheels retract inward, nosewheel aft, and all wheels are enclosed when retracted. Wheels can be raised and lowered manually in emergency. Oleo-pneumatic shock-absorbers.
POWER PLANT: One 186·4 kW (250 hp) Lycoming O-540-A4D5 flat-six engine, driving a Hartzell two-blade metal constant-speed propeller. Fuel tanks in wings, with total capacity of 288 litres (76 US gallons). Refuelling point in upper surface of each wing. Oil capacity 11·5 litres (3 US gallons).
ACCOMMODATION: Seats for pilot and up to four passengers. Dual controls standard. Door on starboard side. Space for 113 kg (250 lb) baggage at aft end of cabin when fifth seat is folded, with external access door on starboard side.
AVIONICS: Prototype has dual nav/com radio installations and a transponder.
DIMENSIONS, EXTERNAL:
Wing span 9·55 m (31 ft 4 in)
Wing chord (constant) 1·68 m (5 ft 6 in)
Length overall 7·98 m (26 ft 2 in)
Height overall 2·62 m (8 ft 7 in)
Tailplane span 3·81 m (12 ft 6 in)
Wheel track 1·68 m (5 ft 6 in)
Wheelbase 2·36 m (7 ft 9 in)
Propeller diameter 1·96 m (6 ft 5 in)
Propeller ground clearance 0·32 m (1 ft 0½ in)
DIMENSIONS, INTERNAL:
Cabin: Length 2·92 m (9 ft 7 in)
Max height 1·23 m (4 ft 0½ in)
Max width 1·14 m (3 ft 9 in)
Baggage compartment volume 0·76 m³ (27 cu ft)
AREA:
Wings, gross 15·79 m² (170 sq ft)
WEIGHTS AND LOADINGS:
Weight empty 839 kg (1,850 lb)
Max T-O weight 1,429 kg (3,150 lb)
Max wing loading 90·5 kg/m² (18·5 lb/sq ft)
Max power loading 7·67 kg/kW (12·6 lb/hp)
PERFORMANCE (at max T-O weight):
Never-exceed speed 211 knots (392 km/h; 244 mph)
Max level speed at S/L 187 knots (346 km/h; 215 mph)
Max cruising speed, 75% power
181 knots (335 km/h; 208 mph)
Cruising speed, 65% power
174 knots (322 km/h; 200 mph)
Stalling speed, wheels and flaps up
62·5 knots (116 km/h; 72 mph)
Stalling speed, wheels and flaps down
55·5 knots (103 km/h; 64 mph)
Max rate of climb at S/L 378 m (1,240 ft)/min
Service ceiling 5,515 m (18,100 ft)
Range with four occupants, max fuel, 45 min reserves at 45% power:
75% power 860 nm (1,593 km; 990 miles)
65% power 946 nm (1,754 km; 1,090 miles)
55% power 1,016 nm (1,883 km; 1,170 miles)
Range with five occupants, 189 litres (50 US gallons) fuel, reserves as above 586 nm (1,086 km; 675 miles)

The prototype Bellanca Aries T-250 five-seat light aircraft

BELLANCA
BELLANCA AIRCRAFT ENGINEERING INC

HEAD OFFICE AND WORKS: PO Box 70, Scott Depot, nr Charleston, West Virginia 25560
Telephone: (304) 755 4354
PRESIDENT: August T. Bellanca
MANAGING DIRECTOR: Henry E. Payne

The original Bellanca Aircraft Corporation of New Castle, Delaware, merged with companies not engaged in aircraft manufacture and lost its identity in 1959. The present company, formed by Mr August Bellanca and his father, the late G. M. Bellanca, bought all of the original Bellanca aircraft designs with the exception of the Model 14-19. On 1 December 1971 the company was re-organised and acquired corporate offices and production plant at Scott Depot, West Virginia.

BELLANCA MODEL 19-25 SKYROCKET II

Research and design of this aircraft were initiated in 1956 by the late G. M. Bellanca and his son, August T. Bellanca. The early decision to fabricate this aircraft from glassfibre composites resulted from much research and testing. Basically, the advantages are that smooth aerodynamic surfaces are obtained, together with high strength. The materials used in the Model 19-25 Skyrocket have a higher strength-to-weight ratio than aluminium, with better durability and fatigue resistance. Because of the extremely smooth surface finish, the Skyrocket II has a very low drag coefficient (Cdo = 0·016), and was being tested by NASA in early 1979 to evaluate application of these principles to general aviation.

Prototype of the Bellanca Model 19-25 Skyrocket II six-seat light aircraft

Since the first flight in March 1975, the Skyrocket II prototype has demonstrated its capabilities by setting record speeds of 245·80 knots (455·23 km/h; 282·86 mph) over a 100 km closed circuit, 257·64 knots (477·15 km/h; 296·49 mph) over 500 km, and 261·67 knots (484·62 km/h; 301·13 mph) over 1,000 km in the 1,000-1,750 kg weight class; and speeds of 283·72 knots (525·45 km/h; 326·50 mph) over 500 km, and 272·84 knots (505·31 km/h; 313·98 mph) over 1,000 km in the 1,750-3,000 kg class. Orders have been received for some 70 aircraft, and production plans were being formulated in 1979.
TYPE: Six-seat light cabin monoplane.
WINGS: Cantilever low-wing monoplane. NACA 63_2215

laminar-flow wing section. Dihedral 2°. Incidence 2°. Composite structure of glassfibre epoxy laminate and light alloy honeycomb sandwich, made in two half-shells, with two glassfibre/carbon spars. Plain ailerons and trailing-edge flaps of similar construction. Anti-icing of wing leading-edges by hot air.

FUSELAGE: Semi-monocoque fail-safe pressurised structure of glassfibre epoxy laminate. Airbrake in fuselage undersurface. Glassfibre stringers. Fuselage is moulded in two halves, each with an integral wing root, vertical fin half and tailplane root.

TAIL UNIT: Cantilever structure of glassfibre epoxy laminate with light alloy honeycomb sandwich. Electrically-adjustable variable-incidence tailplane. No trim tabs. Anti-icing of leading-edges by hot air.

LANDING GEAR: Hydraulically-retractable tricycle type. Nosewheel retracts aft, main units inward. Ozone oleo-pneumatic shock-absorbers with single wheel on each unit. Goodyear main wheels and tyres size 15 × 6·00-6.

POWER PLANT: One 324 kW (435 hp) Continental GTSIO-520-F flat-six engine, flat rated to an altitude of 5,790 m (19,000 ft), driving a Hartzell three-blade metal constant-speed propeller. One integral fuel tank in each wing with a combined capacity of 605·5 litres (160 US gallons), of which 568 litres (150 US gallons) are usable. Refuelling points at wingtips. Oil capacity 14·2 litres (3·75 US gallons).

ACCOMMODATION: Pilot and five passengers in enclosed cabin. Door on starboard side. Stowage for 90·7 kg (200 lb) of baggage.

DIMENSIONS, EXTERNAL:

Wing span	10·67 m (35 ft 0 in)
Wing aspect ratio	6·7
Length overall	8·81 m (28 ft 11 in)
Height overall	2·82 m (9 ft 3 in)
Propeller diameter	2·08 m (6 ft 10 in)

AREA:

Wings, gross	16·96 m² (182·6 sq ft)

WEIGHTS AND LOADINGS:

Weight empty	1,043 kg (2,300 lb)
Max T-O weight	1,860 kg (4,100 lb)
Max wing loading	109·37 kg/m² (22·4 lb/sq ft)
Max power loading	5·74 kg/kW (9·43 lb/hp)

PERFORMANCE (at max T-O weight):

Max cruising speed, 83% power at 8,840 m (29,000 ft) 287 knots (532 km/h; 331 mph)

Cruising speed, 75% power at 7,300 m (24,000 ft) 262 knots (486 km/h; 302 mph)

Cruising speed, 65% power at 4,570 m (15,000 ft) 221 knots (410 km/h; 255 mph)

Stalling speed, flaps down 56·5 knots (105 km/h; 65 mph)

Max rate of climb at S/L	579 m (1,900 ft)/min
Service ceiling	above 9,145 m (30,000 ft)
T-O run	274 m (900 ft)
T-O to 15 m (50 ft)	546 m (1,790 ft)
Landing from 15 m (50 ft)	507 m (1,665 ft)
Landing run	241 m (790 ft)

Range, 75% power, at 4,570 m (15,000 ft) more than 1,055 nm (1,955 km; 1,215 miles)

Range, 65% power, at 4,570 m (15,000 ft) more than 1,272 nm (2,357 km; 1,465 miles)

BOEING

THE BOEING COMPANY

HEAD OFFICE: PO Box 3707, Seattle, Washington 98124

ESTABLISHED: July 1916

CHAIRMAN OF THE BOARD AND CHIEF EXECUTIVE OFFICER: T. A. Wilson

PRESIDENT: Malcolm T. Stamper

SENIOR VICE-PRESIDENTS:
- H. W. Haynes (Executive Vice-President, Chief Financial Officer)
- W. M. Maulden

VICE-PRESIDENTS:
- R. R. Albrecht (Counsel and Secretary)
- R. E. Bateman (General Manager, Boeing Marine Systems)
- W. L. Hamilton (International Business)
- H. K. Hebeler (President, Boeing Engineering and Construction Division)
- V. F. Knutzen (Controller)
- R. B. Light (Manager, Washington DC Office)
- S. M. Little (Industrial and Public Relations)
- H. W. Neffner (Contract Negotiations and Pricing)
- J. E. Steiner (Corporate Product Development)
- R. W. Tharrington (President, Boeing Computer Services)
- B. M. Wheat (Senior Vice-President, Boeing Computer Services)
- Other Vice-Presidents are listed under individual company headings

TREASURER: J. B. L. Pierce

PUBLIC RELATIONS AND ADVERTISING DIRECTOR: R. P. Bush

Boeing Commercial Airplane Company:
PO Box 707, Renton, Washington 98055

PRESIDENT: E. H. Boullioun

EXECUTIVE VICE-PRESIDENT: Richard W. Welch

VICE-PRESIDENTS:
- W. W. Buckley (Operations)
- Ernest V. Fenn (General Manager, 757 Division)
- W. T. Hamilton (Research and Development)
- Kenneth F. Holtby (New Programmes)
- Donald McLaren (Finance and Contracts)
- V. C. Moe (Contracts)
- George D. Nible (Customer Services)
- Lynn M. Olason (General Manager, 747 Division)
- O. M. Roetman (International Sales)
- William L. Shineman (General Manager, Fabrication Division)
- Frank A. Shrontz (General Manager, 707/727/737 Division)
- Joseph F. Sutter (Operations and Product Development)
- John M. Swihart (Domestic and Canadian Sales)
- R. W. Taylor (Special Assistant to President)
- Dean D. Thornton (General Manager, 767 Division)
- Donald D. Whitford (Operations, 747 Division)
- C. F. Wilde (Sales and Marketing)
- H. W. Withington (Engineering)
- Brien S. Wygle (Flight Operations)

Boeing Aerospace Company:
Kent, Washington

PRESIDENT: O. C. Boileau

VICE-PRESIDENTS:
- R. L. Brock (General Manager, Army Systems)
- J. H. Goldie (Executive Vice-President, Department Management)
- D. E. Graves (Aerospace Sales)
- R. W. Hager (General Manager, Ballistic Missiles and Space)
- J. C. Maxwell (General Manager, Military Airplane Development)
- M. K. Miller (Systems Acquisition)
- B. T. Plymale (Business Development)
- Howard N. Stuverude (Programme Management)

Boeing Wichita Company:
3801 South Oliver, Wichita, Kansas 67210

PRESIDENT: L. D. Alford

VICE-PRESIDENT: A. M. S. Goo (Military Systems Development and Management)

Boeing Vertol Company:
PO Box 16858, Philadelphia, Pennsylvania 19142

PRESIDENT: O. H. Smith

VICE-PRESIDENT: C. W. Ellis (Helicopter Development and Programme Management)

In May 1961 The Boeing Airplane Company changed its proprietary name to The Boeing Company as a recognition of its diversified interests. On 19 December 1972 it was announced that three of the company's operating organisations had been designated as companies, comprising Boeing Commercial Airplane Company, Renton, Washington; Boeing Aerospace Company, Kent, Washington; and Boeing Vertol Company, Philadelphia, Pennsylvania.

The Boeing Wichita Company at Wichita, Kansas, continues modification programmes, 707, 727, 737 and 747 parts fabrication, research, programmes on military aircraft currently in use with the armed forces (B-52 and KC-135), and other support functions.

A factory with an area of 75,000 m² (807,300 sq ft) at St James-Assiniboia Airport, near Winnipeg, produces 747 components.

BOEING COMMERCIAL AIRPLANE COMPANY (BCAC)

The Boeing Commercial Airplane Company, with headquarters at the company's Renton, Washington, facility just south of Seattle, has five divisions. The 707/727/737 Division at Renton and the 747 Division at Everett continue to manufacture aircraft of those series; the 767 Division has been established to develop this new wide-body transport, which will be built at Everett; the 757 Division will handle that programme at the Renton facility; and the Fabrication Division serves the other operating groups with its massive NC machine capability. A separate Engineering Organisation, reporting to company headquarters, is responsible for such functions as technology, quality control and flight operations.

During 1978, orders for Boeing jetliners reached a record total of 490, comprising six Model 707s, 131 Model 727s, 146 Model 737s, 83 Model 747s, and 40 and 84 of the new Models 757 and 767 respectively. At the end of 1978 Boeing had delivered 3,248 turbine-powered transports of these commercial series. Production rates of airliners being manufactured in August 1979 were one 707 every two months, and twelve 727s, eight and a half 737s and seven 747s per month.

BOEING MODEL 707

US Air Force designation: VC-137

The prototype for the Boeing Model 707, designated Model 367-80, was the first jet transport designed as such to be completed and flown in the United States. It made its first flight on 15 July 1954, and a developed version was ordered in large numbers as a flight refuelling tanker/transport for the USAF under the designation KC-135. A KC-135 modernisation programme is described under the Boeing Wichita heading in this section.

On 13 July 1955 Boeing was given clearance by the USAF to build commercial developments of the prototype

Boeing Model 707-320C four-turbofan commercial transport in the insignia of Libyan Arab Airlines

concurrently with the production of KC-135s. These transport aircraft have the basic designations of Boeing 707 and 720, but were made available in many versions, of which a total of 941 had been sold and 934 delivered by 1 September 1979. These totals include five specially-equipped aircraft delivered to the USAF under the designations VC-137A (now VC-137B) and VC-137C, and 19 aircraft (9 delivered) for completion under the E-3A AWACS (Airborne Warning and Control System) programme.

The Boeing Company and CFM International SA (which see) have signed an agreement leading towards certification of a 707 powered by CFM56 turbofan engines and designated **707-700**. The aim of this development and flight test programme is to find additional military and commercial markets for the 707, and flight testing was planned to begin in November 1979. The CFM56 will be offered initially at a sea level static thrust of 97·9 kN (22,000 lb). It will provide up to 15 per cent better range, improved fuel consumption, and reduced noise levels (FAR 36 standards).

The only version of the 707 available in 1979 was as follows:

707-320C Convertible. Certificated to carry up to 219 passengers, this version can also operate mixed passenger/cargo or all-cargo services. Loading is through a 2·34 m × 3·40 m (92 in × 134 in) forward cargo door, with cargo on pallets or in containers. A Boeing-developed cargo handling system is installed on seven rows of seat tracks in the floor. Upper-deck cargo space comprises 161·21 m³ (5,693 cu ft) palletised and lower deck 48·14 m³ (1,700 cu ft) bulk. The cargo system can carry thirteen 2·24 m × 3·18 m (88 in × 125 in) or 2·24 m × 2·74 m (88 in × 108 in) 'A' type containers. There is a crew rest area aft of the flight deck. Received FAA Type Approval on 30 April 1963, and first entered service with Pan American in June 1963. Five were delivered to the Canadian Armed Forces during 1970-71 to serve as troop and staff transports and military cargo carriers. Two of these are equipped as flight refuelling tankers, utilising wingtip pods containing a hinged boom and trailing hose and drogue manufactured by Beech.

TYPE: Four-turbofan airliner.

WINGS: Cantilever low-wing monoplane. Dihedral 7°. Incidence 2°. Sweepback at quarter-chord 35°. All-metal two-spar fail-safe structure. Centre-section continuous through fuselage. Normal outboard aileron and small inboard aileron on each wing, built of aluminium honeycomb panels. Two Fowler flaps and one fillet flap of aluminium alloy on each wing. Full-span leading-edge flaps. Four hydraulically-operated aluminium alloy spoilers on each wing, forward of flaps. Primary flying controls are aerodynamically balanced and manually operated through spring tabs. Lateral control at low speeds by all four ailerons, supplemented by spoilers which are interconnected with the ailerons. Lateral control at high speeds by inboard ailerons and spoilers only. Operation of flaps adjusts linkage between inboard and outboard ailerons to permit outboard operation with extended flaps. Spoilers may also be used symmetrically as speed brakes. Thermal anti-icing of wing leading-edges.

FUSELAGE: All-metal semi-monocoque fail-safe structure with cross-section made up of two circular arcs of different radii, the larger above, faired into smooth-contoured ellipse.

TAIL UNIT: Cantilever all-metal structure. Anti-balance tab and trim tab in rudder. Trim and control tabs in each elevator. Electrically and manually operated variable-incidence tailplane. Powered rudder.

LANDING GEAR: Hydraulically-retractable tricycle type. Main units are four-wheel bogies which retract inward into underside of thickened wing-root and fuselage. Dual nosewheel unit retracts forward into fuselage. Landing gear doors close when legs fully extended. Gear can be extended in flight to give maximum rate of descent of 4,570 m/min (15,000 ft/min) when used in conjunction with spoilers. Boeing oleo-pneumatic shock-absorbers. Main wheels and tyres size 46 × 16. Nosewheels and tyres size 39 × 13. Tyre pressures: main wheels 12·41 bars (180 lb/sq in), nosewheels 7·93 bars (115 lb/sq in). Multi-disc brakes by Goodyear. Hydro-Aire flywheel detector type anti-skid units.

POWER PLANT: Four Pratt & Whitney JT3D-7 turbofan engines, each developing 84·5 kN (19,000 lb st), in pods under wings. Fuel in four main, two reserve and one centre main integral wing tanks with total capacity of 90,299 litres (23,855 US gallons). Provision for both pressure and gravity refuelling. Total oil capacity 114 litres (30 US gallons).

ACCOMMODATION: Max accommodation for up to 219 passengers. Typical arrangement has 14 first class seats, a 4-seat lounge and 133 coach class seats, with four galleys and five toilets. There are two passenger doors, forward and aft on port side. Galley servicing doors forward and aft on starboard side. Baggage compartments fore and aft of wing in lower segment of fuselage below cabin floor. Entire accommodation, including baggage compartments, air-conditioned and pressurised.

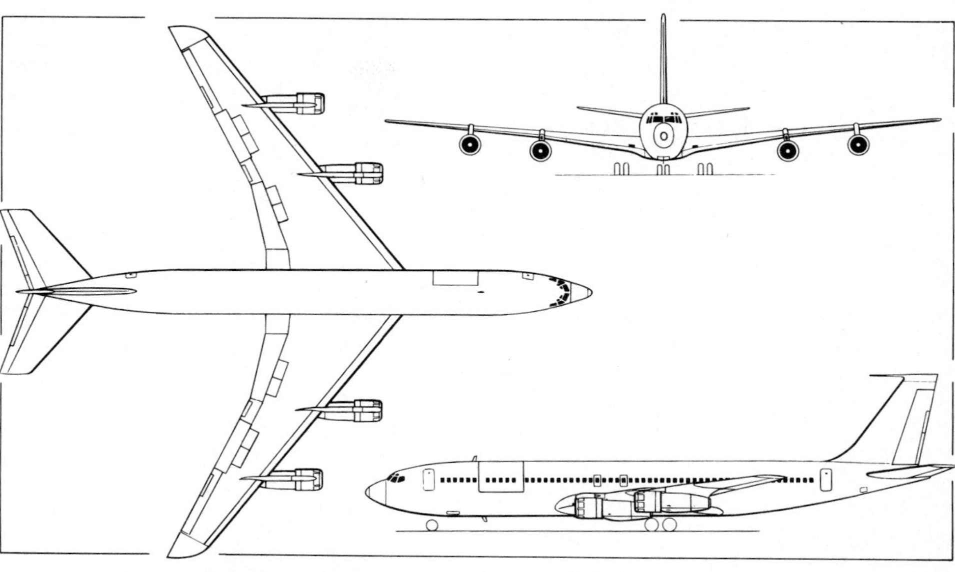

Boeing 707-320C four-turbofan passenger/cargo transport aircraft *(Pilot Press)*

SYSTEMS: Air-cycle air-conditioning and pressurisation system, using three AiResearch engine-driven turbo-compressors. Pressure differential 0·59 bars (8·6 lb/sq in). Hydraulic system, pressure 207 bars (3,000 lb/sq in), for landing gear retraction, nosewheel steering, brakes, flaps, flying controls and spoilers. Electrical system includes four 30kVA or 40kVA 115/200V 3-phase 400Hz AC alternators and four 75A transformer-rectifiers giving 28V DC. APU optional.

AVIONICS AND EQUIPMENT: To customer's specification.

DIMENSIONS, EXTERNAL:

Wing span	44·42 m (145 ft 9 in)
Wing chord at root	10·33 m (33 ft 10·7 in)
Wing chord at tip	2·84 m (9 ft 4 in)
Wing aspect ratio	7·056
Length overall	46·61 m (152 ft 11 in)
Length of fuselage	44·35 m (145 ft 6 in)
Width of fuselage	3·76 m (12 ft 4 in)
Height overall	12·93 m (42 ft 5 in)
Tailplane span	13·95 m (45 ft 9 in)
Wheel track	6·73 m (22 ft 1 in)
Wheelbase	17·98 m (59 ft 0 in)
Passenger doors (each): Height	1·83 m (6 ft 0 in)
Width	0·86 m (2 ft 10 in)
Height to sill: fwd	3·25 m (10 ft 8 in)
aft	3·20 m (10 ft 6 in)
Cargo door: Height	2·34 m (7 ft 8 in)
Width	3·40 m (11 ft 2 in)
Height to sill	3·20 m (10 ft 6 in)
Forward baggage compartment door:	
Height	1·27 m (4 ft 2 in)
Width	1·22 m (4 ft 0 in)
Height to sill	1·55 m (5 ft 1 in)
Rear baggage compartment door (fwd):	
Height	1·24 m (4 ft 1 in)
Width	1·22 m (4 ft 0 in)
Height to sill	1·47 m (4 ft 10 in)
Rear baggage compartment door (aft):	
Height	0·89 m (2 ft 11 in)
Width	0·76 m (2 ft 6 in)
Height to sill	1·93 m (6 ft 4 in)

DIMENSIONS, INTERNAL:

Cabin, excl flight deck:	
Length	33·93 m (111 ft 4 in)
Max width	3·55 m (11 ft 8 in)
Max height	2·34 m (7 ft 8 in)
Floor area	106·18 m² (1,143 sq ft)
Volume	228·6 m³ (8,074 cu ft)
Baggage compartment (fwd)	23·65 m³ (835 cu ft)
Baggage compartment (rear)	24·50 m³ (865 cu ft)

AREAS:

Wings, gross	283·4 m² (3,050 sq ft)
Ailerons (total)	11·24 m² (121 sq ft)
Trailing-edge flaps (total)	44·22 m² (476 sq ft)
Leading-edge flaps	14·31 m² (154 sq ft)
Fin	30·47 m² (328 sq ft)
Rudder, incl tabs	9·48 m² (102 sq ft)
Tailplane	58·06 m² (625 sq ft)
Elevators, incl tabs	14·03 m² (151 sq ft)

WEIGHTS AND LOADINGS:

Basic operating weight, empty:	
Passenger	66,406 kg (146,400 lb)
Cargo	64,000 kg (141,100 lb)
Max payload: Cargo	40,324 kg (88,900 lb)
Max T-O weight	151,315 kg (333,600 lb)
Max ramp weight	152,405 kg (336,000 lb)
Max zero-fuel weight	104,330 kg (230,000 lb)
Max landing weight	112,037 kg (247,000 lb)
Max wing loading	537·1 kg/m² (110·0 lb/sq ft)
Max power loading	448 kg/kN (4·39 lb/lb st)

PERFORMANCE (at average cruising weight, unless indicated otherwise):

Never-exceed speed	Mach 0·95
Max level speed	545 knots (1,010 km/h; 627 mph)
Max cruising speed at 7,620 m (25,000 ft)	525 knots (973 km/h; 605 mph)
Econ cruising speed	478 knots (886 km/h; 550 mph)
Stalling speed (flaps down, at max landing weight)	105 knots (195 km/h; 121 mph)
Max rate of climb at S/L	1,219 m (4,000 ft)/min
Service ceiling	11,885 m (39,000 ft)
CAR T-O to 10·7 m (35 ft)	3,054 m (10,020 ft)
CAR landing from 15 m (50 ft)	1,095 m (6,250 ft)
Landing run	785 m (2,575 ft)
Range with max fuel, 14 first class and 133 tourist class passengers, long-range step cruise, international reserves	5,000 nm (9,265 km; 5,755 miles)
Range with 36,287 kg (80,000 lb) cargo, long-range step cruise, international reserves	3,150 nm (5,835 km; 3,625 miles)

BOEING MODEL 727

Boeing announced its intention to supplement the four-jet 707/720 series with the three-engined short/medium-range 727 on 5 December 1960. The 727 switched to a rear-engined configuration, but has an upper fuselage section identical with that of the 707/720 and many parts and systems are interchangeable between the three types.

The 727-100, 727-100C, 727-100QC and 727-100 Business Jet versions of the Model 727 are no longer in production; details of these can be found in the 1973-74 *Jane's*. Versions which remain in production are as follows:

727-200. Lengthened version announced on 5 August 1965 with basic accommodation for 163 passengers and maximum capacity of 189 passengers. Fuselage extended by 3·05 m (10 ft) both forward and aft of main undercarriage wheel well. Structural modification corresponding to higher loads. Revised centre engine air intake. Three JT8D turbofan engines with full sound attenuation and thrust reversers are standard. Construction of the first 727-200 began in September 1966 and the first flight was made on 27 July 1967. FAA certification was awarded on 30 November 1967.

Advanced 727-200. On 12 May 1971, Boeing announced it was offering the Advanced 727-200 at 86,635 kg (191,000 lb) gross ramp weight, and initial deliveries of this version began in June 1972. Increased fuel capacity gives a range capability at least 694 nm (1,287 km; 800 miles) greater than that of the earlier 727-200. The interior features the 'Superjet-look', and a large 'Carry-all' compartment is available at no extra cost. The Advanced 727-200 is certificated for Category IIIA 15 m (50 ft) decision height, 213 m (700 ft) RVR landing. This option was first purchased by Alaska, Delta, and Western Airlines. Improved overhead duct air-conditioning is now standard. A performance data computer system has been added as standard equipment to provide onboard information for optimisation of flight profile and fuel consumption.

A version first ordered by Sterling Airways, in May 1972, has Pratt & Whitney JT8D-15 engines, ramp weight of 95,254 kg (210,000 lb) and more fuel.

A total of 1,698 Model 727s had been sold by 6 September 1979, of which 1,516 had been delivered. The 727 is the only commercial transport aircraft of which more than 1,500 have been delivered, the 1,500th example being handed over to United Air Lines on 2 July 1979. More than 1,000 of those sold are of the 727-200 series.

TYPE: Three-turbofan airliner.

Boeing Model 727-200 three-turbofan short/medium-range transport in the insignia of Alaska Airlines

WINGS: Cantilever low-wing monoplane. Special Boeing aerofoil sections. Thickness/chord ratio from 9% to 13%. Dihedral 3°. Incidence 2°. Sweepback at quarter-chord 32°. Primary structure is a two-spar aluminium alloy box with conventional ribs. Upper and lower surfaces are of riveted skin-stringer construction. There are no chordwise splices in the primary structure from the fuselage to the wingtip. Advanced 727-200s at gross weight options have modified stringers and in-spar webs, as well as upper and lower surface wing skins of increased gauge. Structure is fail-safe. Hydraulically-powered aluminium ailerons, in inboard (high speed) and outboard (low speed) units, operate in conjunction with flight spoilers. Triple-slotted trailing-edge flaps constructed primarily of aluminium and aluminium honeycomb. Four aluminium leading-edge slats on outer two-thirds of wing. Three Krueger leading-edge flaps on inboard third of wing, made from magnesium or aluminium castings. Seven spoilers on each wing, consisting of five flight spoilers outboard and two ground spoilers inboard. Spoilers function also as airbrakes. Balance tab in each outboard aileron; control tab in each inboard aileron. Controls are hydraulically-powered dual systems with automatic reversion to manual control. Actuators manufactured primarily by Weston, National Waterlift and Bertea. Thermal anti-icing of wing leading-edges by engine bleed air.

FUSELAGE: Semi-monocoque fail-safe structure, with aluminium alloy skin reinforced by circumferential frames and longitudinal stringers.

TAIL UNIT: Cantilever structure, built primarily of aluminium alloys, with tailplane mounted near tip of fin. Dual-powered variable-incidence tailplane, with direct manual reversion. Hydraulically-powered dual elevator control system with control tab manual reversion. Hydraulically-powered rudders, utilising two main systems with backup third system for lower rudder. Anti-balance tabs; rudder trim by displacing system neutral.

LANDING GEAR: Hydraulically-retractable tricycle type, with twin wheels on all three units. Nosewheels retract forward, main gear inward into fuselage. Boeing oleo-pneumatic shock-absorbers. B.F. Goodrich nose-gear wheels, tyres and brakes are standard on all models. Goodrich and Bendix are both approved suppliers of main-gear wheels, tyres and brakes for all Model 727s. Nosewheels and tyres are size 32 × 11·5 Type VIII. Main-gear wheels size 49 × 17, with tyres size 50 × 21 Type VII, are standard.

POWER PLANT: Three Pratt & Whitney JT8D-9A turbofan engines with thrust reversers and full sound attenuation, each flat rated at 64·5 kN (14,500 lb st) to 29°C, are standard. Optionally, JT8D-15s rated at 68·9 kN (15,500 lb st), JT8D-17s rated at 71·2 kN (16,000 lb st), or JT8D-17Rs with automatic performance reserve (APR) and rated at 72·9 kN (16,400 lb st) can be fitted. APR senses any significant loss in thrust by an engine during take-off and initial climb, automatically increasing thrust on the other engines to 77·4 kN (17,400 lb). This feature significantly improves performance from hot/high airports. Each engine has individual fuel system fed from integral tanks in wings, but all three tanks are interconnected. Optional fuselage fuel tanks can be installed, displacing forward and/or aft cargo compartment volume. Standard total fuel capacity 30,623 litres (8,090 US gallons). Modular design bladder cell tanks with dual fuel barrier can be installed to contain up to approximately 9,387 litres (2,480 US gallons). Single pressure fuelling point, rated at 2,271 litres (600 US gallons)/min, near wing leading-edge on underside of starboard wing at mid-span. Total usable oil capacity 45·5 litres (12 US gallons).

ACCOMMODATION: Crew of three on flight deck. Basic accommodation for 145 passengers (14 first class, 131 tourist class, 4-6 abreast). Max capacity 189 passengers. Two galleys forward and two aft. One toilet forward and two aft. Other layouts to customer's specification. A 'Superjet-look' passenger interior design is standard. The wide-body effect is achieved (without any changes in cross-section dimensions) by lighting and architectural redesign. Retrofit kits for the 'Superjet-look' are offered, as are kits for larger 'Carry-all' compartments. Entry via hydraulically-operated integral aft stairway under centre engine and door at front on port side with optional Weber Aircraft electrically-operated airstairs. Two Type III emergency exits in mid-cabin on each side and aft service door on each side. The starboard forward service door is opposite the port forward passenger door. Two heated and pressurised baggage and freight compartments under floor, forward and aft of main landing gear bay. Each compartment has one outward-opening cargo door; a second cargo door is optional for the aft compartment.

SYSTEMS: AiResearch air-conditioning and pressurisation system, using engine bleed air combined with air-cycle refrigeration. Pressure differential 0·59 bars (8·6 lb/sq in). Three independent 207 bar (3,000 lb/sq in) hydraulic systems, utilising Boeing Material Specification BMS 3-11 hydraulic fluid, provide power for flying controls, landing gear and aft airstairs. Electrical system includes three 40kVA 400Hz constant-frequency AC generators, three 50A transformer-rectifier units, one 22Ah battery. AiResearch APU provides electrical power and compressed air for engine starting and air-conditioning on ground.

AVIONICS AND EQUIPMENT: Standard avionics include dual Wulfsberg 2000 VHF com installations, Motorola NA-134D2 Selcal, flight and service attendants' interphone, passenger address system, ARINC 542 flight recorder and remote encoder, Collins 642C1 voice recorder, dual Collins 51RV-2B VHF nav systems, ARINC 570 ADF, dual King KDM 7000 DME, dual King KXP ATC, Collins 51Z-4 marker beacon, RCA Primus 90 colour weather radar, Sperry SP-150 single-channel Mod Blk V autopilot, dual yaw dampers, dual vertical gyros, dual Sperry C-9D compasses, Honeywell HG 7502 radio altimeter, instrument comparison and warning system, ARINC 545 digital air data system, variable instrument switching, dual FD-108 flight directors, and Sundstrand ground proximity warning system. Optional avionics include Collins FD-110 or Sperry Z-15 flight directors, Sperry C-11 compass system, HF com, Collins or King VHF, third VHF, Bendix weather radar, dual weather radar systems, Bendix DFA-73A-1 ADF, dual ADF, dual DME, autothrottles, speed command, dual autopilot channels, roll monitor and flare coupler, Omega and dual INS.

DIMENSIONS, EXTERNAL:

Wing span	32·92 m (108 ft 0 in)
Wing chord at root	7·70 m (25 ft 3 in)
Wing chord at tip	2·34 m (7 ft 8 in)
Wing aspect ratio	7·07
Length overall	46·69 m (153 ft 2 in)
Length of fuselage	41·51 m (136 ft 2 in)
Height overall	10·36 m (34 ft 0 in)
Tailplane span	10·90 m (35 ft 9 in)
Wheel track	5·72 m (18 ft 9 in)
Wheelbase	19·28 m (63 ft 3 in)
Passenger door (ventral): Height	1·93 m (6 ft 4 in)
Width	0·81 m (2 ft 8 in)
Passenger door (fwd): Height	1·83 m (6 ft 0 in)
Width	0·86 m (2 ft 10 in)
Height to sill	2·67 m (8 ft 9 in)
Service door (fwd): Height	1·65 m (5 ft 5 in)
Width	0·84 m (2 ft 9 in)
Service doors (aft, each): Height	1·52 m (5 ft 0 in)
Width	0·76 m (2 ft 6 in)
Baggage hold door (fwd): Height	1·07 m (3 ft 6 in)
Width	1·37 m (4 ft 6 in)
Baggage hold door (aft): Height	1·12 m (3 ft 8 in)
Width	1·37 m (4 ft 6 in)

DIMENSIONS, INTERNAL:

Cabin (aft of flight deck to rear pressure bulkhead):	
Length	28·24 m (92 ft 8 in)
Max width	3·55 m (11 ft 8 in)
Max height	2·11 m (6 ft 11 in)
Floor area	91·05 m² (980 sq ft)
Volume	188·4 m³ (6,652 cu ft)
Baggage hold (fwd)	20·1 m³ (710 cu ft)
Baggage hold (aft): standard	23·1 m³ (815 cu ft)
with optional 2nd door	21·1 m³ (745 cu ft)

AREAS:

Wings, gross	157·9 m² (1,700 sq ft)
Ailerons (total)	5·30 m² (57 sq ft)
Trailing-edge flaps, retracted (total)	26·10 m² (281 sq ft)
Trailing-edge flaps, extended (total)	36·04 m² (388 sq ft)
Flight spoilers (total)	7·41 m² (79·8 sq ft)
Fin	33·07 m² (356 sq ft)
Rudder, incl tabs	6·13 m² (66 sq ft)
Tailplane	34·93 m² (376 sq ft)
Elevators, incl tabs	8·83 m² (95 sq ft)

WEIGHTS AND LOADINGS (A: brake release weight of 83,820 kg (184,800 lb), B: brake release weight of 86,405 kg (190,500 lb), C: brake release weight of 95,027 kg (209,500 lb)):

Operating weight empty (basic specification):	
727-200 (A)	44,588 kg (98,300 lb)
727-200 (B)	45,132 kg (99,500 lb)
727-200 (C)	46,021 kg (101,460 lb)
Operating weight empty (typical airline):	
727-200 (A)	45,360 kg (100,000 lb)

Max payload (structural, based on airline operating weight empty):
727-200 (A) 18,144 kg (40,000 lb)
Max T-O weight:
727-200 (A) 83,820 kg (184,800 lb)
727-200 (B) 86,405 kg (190,500 lb)
727-200 (C) 95,027 kg (209,500 lb)
Max ramp weight:
727-200 (A) 84,275 kg (185,800 lb)
727-200 (B) 86,635 kg (191,000 lb)
727-200 (C) 95,254 kg (210,000 lb)
Max zero-fuel weight:
727-200 (A) 62,595 kg (138,000 lb)
727-200 (B) 63,500 kg (140,000 lb)
727-200 (C) 65,315 kg (144,000 lb)
Max landing weight:
727-200 (A, B) 70,080 kg (154,500 lb)
727-200 (C) 73,028 kg (161,000 lb)
Max wing loading:
727-200 (A) 530·7 kg/m² (108·7 lb/sq ft)
727-200 (B) 544·4 kg/m² (111·5 lb/sq ft)
727-200 (C) 595·7 kg/m² (122 lb/sq ft)
Max power loading:
727-200 (A) 392 kg/kN (4·2 lb/lb st)
727-200 (B) 404·5 kg/kN (4·1 lb/lb st)
727-200 (C) 445 kg/kN (4·4 lb/lb st)

PERFORMANCE (727-200 (A) at brake release weight of 83,820 kg (184,800 lb), 727-200 (B) at brake release weight of 86,405 kg (190,500 lb), and 727-200 (C) at brake release weight of 95,027 kg (209,500 lb), except where indicated):
Max operating speed Mach 0·90
Max level speed:
727-200 (A) at 6,585 m (21,600 ft) 549 knots (1,017 km/h; 632 mph)
727-200 (B, C) at 6,250 m (20,500 ft) 539 knots (999 km/h; 621 mph)
Max cruising speed:
727-200 (A) at 6,705 m (22,000 ft) 514 knots (953 km/h; 592 mph)
727-200 (B) at 7,530 m (24,700 ft) 520 knots (964 km/h; 599 mph)
Econ cruising speed at 9,145 m (30,000 ft) 495 knots (917 km/h; 570 mph)
Stalling speed at S/L, flaps down:
at 72,575 kg (160,000 lb) 106 knots (197 km/h; 122 mph)
Initial cruise altitude 10,060 m (33,000 ft)
Min ground turning radius (Advanced 727-200) 24·49 m (80 ft 4 in)
Runway LCN (Advanced 727-200) at max weight of 86,635 kg (191,000 lb), optimum tyre pressure and 0·51 m (20 in) flexible pavement:
50 × 21 tyres 70
CAR T-O distance to 10·7 m (35 ft):
727-200 (A) 2,938 m (9,640 ft)
727-200 (B) 2,591 m (8,500 ft)
727-200 (C) 3,140 m (10,300 ft)
CAR landing distance from 15 m (50 ft):
at 71,668 kg (158,000 lb) 1,430 m (4,690 ft)
Range at long-range cruising speed, with fuel load as specified and payload of 12,474 kg (27,500 lb), ATA domestic reserves:
727-200 (A) with 30,623 litres (8,090 US gallons) 2,000 nm (3,706 km; 2,303 miles)
727-200 (B) with 33,878 litres (8,950 US gallons) 2,200 nm (4,077 km; 2,533 miles)
727-200 (C) with 36,831 litres (9,730 US gallons) 2,400 nm (4,447 km; 2,763 miles)
Range with 18,144 kg (40,000 lb) payload, at long-range cruising speed, ATA domestic reserves:
727-200 (A) 1,450 nm (2,685 km; 1,670 miles)
727-200 (B) 1,605 nm (2,970 km; 1,845 miles)
727-200 (C) approx 2,140 nm (3,966 km; 2,464 miles)

OPERATIONAL NOISE CHARACTERISTICS (Advanced 727-200, with JT8D-15 engines, FAR Pt 36):
T-O noise level at brake release weight of 86,405 kg (190,500 lb) 100 EPNdB
Approach noise level at 70,080 kg (154,500 lb) landing weight and 30° flap 100·4 EPNdB
Sideline noise level 102·2 EPNdB

BOEING MODEL 737

US Air Force designation: T-43A

The decision to build this short-range transport was announced by Boeing on 19 February 1965. Simultaneously, a first order for 21 aircraft was placed by Lufthansa.

The original Model 737 was designed to utilise many components and assemblies already in production for the Boeing 727. Design began on 11 May 1964, and the first Model 737 flew on 9 April 1967. Deliveries began before the end of 1967, following FAA certification on 15 December. Sales of the 737 totalled 732 by 1 September 1979, of which 594 had been delivered. These totals include 19 Model 737-200s modified as T-43A navigation trainers for the USAF (see 1975-76 *Jane's*). A production increase to eight and a half aircraft per month was made in 1979.

Details of the early production versions of the Model 737, and of subsequent design development, can be found in the 1974-75 *Jane's*. Versions currently available are as follows:

Advanced 737-200. Current standard model, with max ramp weight of 52,605 kg (116,000 lb) and max T-O weight of 52,390 kg (115,500 lb). JT8D-9A engines (each 64·5 kN; 14,500 lb st) standard; JT8D-15 (68·9 kN; 15,500 lb st); or JT8D-17 (71·2 kN; 16,000 lb st) engines optional; basic fuel capacity of 19,532 litres (5,160 US gallons). Accommodation for 115 passengers and baggage, with 86 cm (34 in) pitch seating, or up to 130 passengers in 74 cm (29 in) pitch seating with no reduction in cabin facilities. A gross weight option with a max ramp weight of 53,295 kg (117,500 lb) and max T-O weight of 53,070 kg (117,000 lb) is available.

Advanced 737-200C/QC. Standard convertible passenger/cargo model with strengthened fuselage and floor, and a large two-position upper-deck cargo door with effective opening of 2·15 m × 3·40 m (7 ft 0½ in × 11 ft 2 in). The quick-change (QC) feature allows more rapid conversion by using palletised passenger seating and other special interior furnishings. A gross weight option with a max ramp weight of 53,295 kg (117,500 lb) and max T-O weight of 53,070 kg (117,000 lb) is available.

Advanced 737-200 Executive Jet. Same as standard Advanced 737-200, except interiors are adapted to special business and executive luxury requirements. Executive interiors can be obtained from vendors. A limited kit selection is available from Boeing. Additional fuel capacity offered by installation of fuel cells in lower cargo compartments. With max fuel this model can carry 15 passengers up to 3,000 nm (5,560 km; 3,455 miles).

Advanced 737-200 High Gross Weight Structure. Higher gross weight models of the Advanced 737-200C, for longer-range use, are available in two versions. One has a maximum taxi weight of 56,700 kg (125,000 lb) and a maximum T-O weight of 56,472 kg (124,500 lb) with JT8D-15, -17, or -17R (proposed) engines, and a fuel capacity of either 20,951 litres (5,535 US gallons) or 22,598 litres (5,970 US gallons). The additional capacity for increased range capability is provided by a 1,419 litre (375 US gallon) or a 3,066 litre (810 US gallon) fuel tank installed in the aft lower cargo compartment. The second version, with a maximum taxi weight of 58,332 kg (128,600 lb), maximum T-O weight of 58,105 kg (128,100 lb), design landing weight of 48,534 kg (107,000 lb), and maximum zero-fuel weight of 43,091 kg (95,000 lb), has approximately 650 nm (1,204 km; 748 miles) greater range capability than the standard Advanced 737-200 (130 passenger payload). Sectors of 2,300 nm (4,262 km; 2,648 miles) can be served with a 130 passenger payload and typical fuel reserves. Aircraft is identical to the current Advanced 737-200 except for the auxiliary fuel tank, new wheels, tyres and brakes, and strengthened landing gear and wing structure.

All higher gross weight versions meet FAR Pt 36 and ICAO Annex 16 in respect of noise characteristics.

An FAA-certificated kit is available which enables the Model 737 to operate from unpaved or gravel runways. The kit includes a vortex dissipator for each engine, consisting of a short hollow boom that protrudes from under each engine's forward edge. The boom is capped by a plug with downward-facing orifices. Pressurised engine bleed air forced through these orifices destroys any ground-level vortex and prevents small pieces of gravel being ingested by the engines. Other items include a gravel deflection 'ski' on the nosewheel, deflectors between the main landing gear wheels, protective shields over hydraulic tubing and speed brake cable on the main gear strut, glassfibre reinforcement of lower inboard flap surfaces, application of Teflon-base paint to fuselage and wing undersurfaces and provision of more robust DME, ATC and VHF antennae.

TYPE: Twin-turbofan short-range transport.

WINGS: Cantilever low-wing monoplane. Special Boeing wing sections. Average thickness/chord ratio 12·89%. Dihedral 6°. Incidence 1° at root. Sweepback at quarter-chord 25°. Aluminium alloy dual-path fail-safe two-spar structure. Ailerons of aluminium honeycomb construction. Boeing-developed triple-slotted trailing-edge flaps, all of aluminium with trailing-edges of aluminium honeycomb. Aluminium alloy Krueger flaps on leading-edge, inboard of nacelles. Three leading-edge slats of aluminium alloy with aluminium honeycomb trailing-edge on each wing from engine to wingtip. Two-section aluminium honeycomb flight spoilers on each outer wing serve both as airbrakes in the air and for lateral control, in association with ailerons. Two-section aluminium honeycomb ground spoilers on each wing, inboard of engine, are used only during landing. Ailerons are hydraulically powered by two hydraulic systems with manual reversion. Trailing-edge flaps are hydraulically powered, with electrical backup. Leading-edge slats and Krueger flaps are symmetrically powered by one hydraulic system normally, and by a second hydraulic system for alternate extension. Flight spoilers are symmetrically powered by the two main individual hydraulic systems. Engine bleed air for anti-icing supplied to engine nose cowls and all wing leading-edge slats.

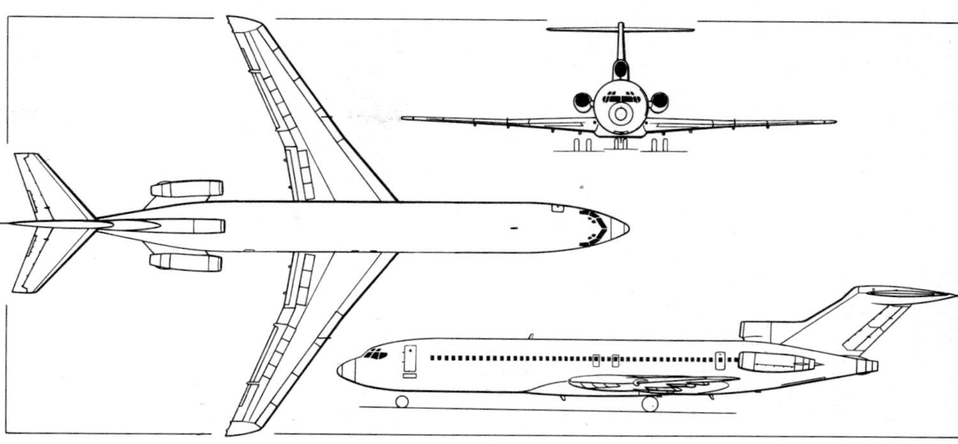

Boeing 727-200 three-turbofan short/medium-range transport *(Pilot Press)*

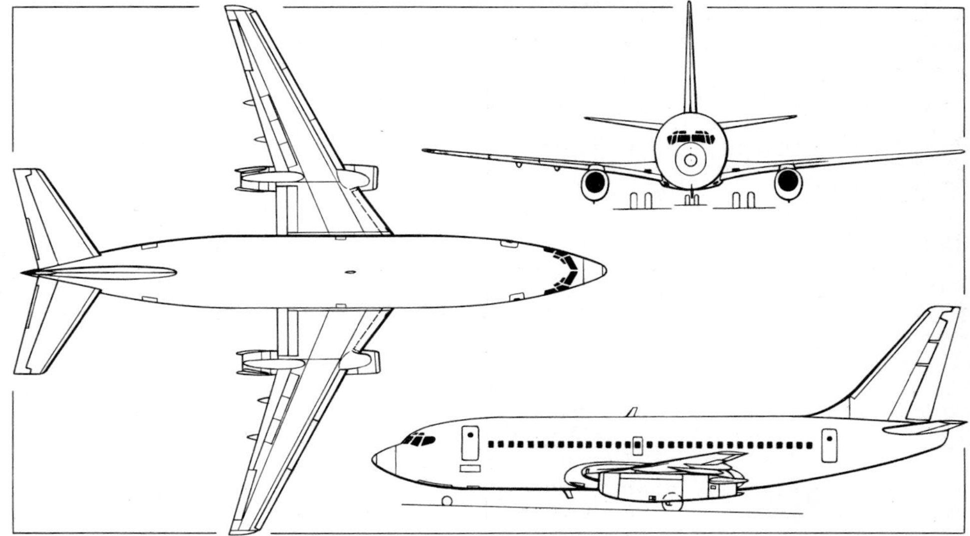

Boeing 737-200 twin-turbofan short-range transport *(Pilot Press)*

Boeing Model 737-200 twin-turbofan short-range transport in the insignia of Far Eastern Air Transport

FUSELAGE: Aluminium alloy semi-monocoque fail-safe structure.

TAIL UNIT: Cantilever aluminium alloy multi-spar structure. Variable-incidence tailplane. Elevator has dual hydraulic power, with manual reversion. Rudder is powered by a dual actuator from two main hydraulic systems, with a standby hydraulic actuator and system. Tailplane trim has dual electric drive motors, with manual backup. Elevator control tabs for manual reversion are locked out during hydraulic actuation.

LANDING GEAR: Hydraulically-retractable tricycle type, with free-fall extension. Nosewheels retract forward, main units inward. No main gear doors: wheels form wheel-well seal. Twin wheels on each main and nose unit. Boeing oleo-pneumatic shock-absorbers. Main wheels and tyres size 40 × 14-16 (low-pressure 40 × 18-17 tyres, or C40 × 14-21/H40 × 14·5-19 tyres with heavy-duty wheel brakes, are available optionally). Nosewheels and tyres size 24 × 7·7 (low-pressure 24·5 × 8·5 tyres available optionally). Bendix multi-disc brakes. Hydro-Aire Mk III anti-skid units and automatic brakes standard.

POWER PLANT: Two Pratt & Whitney JT8D turbofan engines (details under individual model listings), in underwing pods. High-performance target-type thrust reversers, with full sound attenuation quiet nacelles. Advanced models have standard fuel capacity of up to 19,532 litres (5,160 US gallons), with integral fuel cells in wing centre-section as well as two integral wing tanks. Long-range version has auxiliary fuel tank in aft lower cargo compartment, giving max fuel capacity of 22,598 litres (5,970 US gallons). Single-point pressure refuelling through leading-edge of starboard wing. Fuelling rate 1,135 litres (300 US gallons)/min. Auxiliary overwing fuelling points. Total oil capacity 41·5 litres (11 US gallons).

ACCOMMODATION: Crew of two side by side on flight deck. Details of passenger accommodation given under individual model descriptions. Passenger versions are equipped with forward airstair; an aft airstair is optional. Convertible passenger/cargo versions have the aft airstair as standard and forward airstair optional. One plug-type door at each corner of cabin, with passenger doors on port side and service doors on starboard side. Overwing escape hatches on each side. Basic passenger cabin has one lavatory and one galley at each end. Large-volume hand baggage overhead bins. Provision for a large variety of interior arrangements. Freight holds forward and aft of wing, under floor.

SYSTEMS: Air-conditioning and pressurisation system utilises engine bleed air. Max differential 0·52 bars (7·5 lb/sq in). Two independent hydraulic systems, using fire-resistant hydraulic fluid, for flying controls, flaps, slats, landing gear, nosewheel steering and brakes; pressure 207 bars (3,000 lb/sq in). No pneumatic system. Electrical supply provided by engine-driven generators. AiResearch APU for air supply and electrical power in flight and on the ground, as well as engine starting.

AVIONICS AND EQUIPMENT: Equipment to satisfy FAA Category II low weather minimum criteria is standard. Autopilot, specially designed for ILS localiser and glideslope control, with control wheel steering. Optional equipment will permit Category IIIA capability. Very Low Frequency (VLF-Omega) navigation systems are available as standard options.

DIMENSIONS, EXTERNAL:
Wing span 28·35 m (93 ft 0 in)
Wing chord at root 4·71 m (15 ft 5·6 in)
Wing chord at tip 1·60 m (5 ft 3 in)
Wing aspect ratio 8·83
Length overall 30·48 m (100 ft 0 in)
Length of fuselage 29·54 m (96 ft 11 in)
Height overall 11·28 m (37 ft 0 in)
Tailplane span 10·97 m (36 ft 0 in)
Wheel track 5·23 m (17 ft 2 in)
Wheelbase 11·38 m (37 ft 4 in)
Main passenger door (port, front):
Height 1·83 m (6 ft 0 in)
Width 0·86 m (2 ft 10 in)
Height to sill 2·62 m (8 ft 7 in)
Passenger door (port, rear):
Height 1·83 m (6 ft 0 in)
Width 0·76 m (2 ft 6 in)
Width with airstair 0·86 m (2 ft 10 in)
Height to sill 2·72 m (8 ft 11 in)
Galley service door (stbd, front):
Height 1·65 m (5 ft 5 in)
Width 0·76 m (2 ft 6 in)
Height to sill 2·62 m (8 ft 7 in)
Service door (stbd, rear):
Height 1·65 m (5 ft 5 in)
Width 0·76 m (2 ft 6 in)
Height to sill 2·72 m (8 ft 11 in)
Freight hold door (stbd, fwd):
Height 1·30 m (4 ft 3 in)
Width 1·22 m (4 ft 0 in)
Height to sill 1·30 m (4 ft 3 in)
Freight hold door (stbd, rear):
Height 1·22 m (4 ft 0 in)
Width 1·22 m (4 ft 0 in)
Height to sill 1·45 m (4 ft 9 in)

DIMENSIONS, INTERNAL:
Cabin, incl galley and toilet:
Length 20·88 m (68 ft 6 in)
Max width 3·52 m (11 ft 6½ in)
Max height 2·18 m (7 ft 2 in)
Floor area 63·8 m² (687 sq ft)
Volume 131·28 m³ (4,636 cu ft)
Freight hold (fwd) volume 10·48 m³ (370 cu ft)
Freight hold (rear) volume 14·30 m³ (505 cu ft)

AREA:
Wings, gross 91·04 m² (980 sq ft)

WEIGHTS AND LOADINGS (standard aircraft at brake release weight of 52,390 kg; 115,500 lb except where indicated):
Operating weight empty:
Adv 737-200 27,465 kg (60,550 lb)
Adv 737-200C all passenger 28,848 kg (63,600 lb)
Adv 737-200C all cargo 27,306 kg (60,200 lb)
Adv 737-200QC all passenger 30,241 kg (66,670 lb)
Adv 737-200QC all cargo 27,646 kg (60,950 lb)
Max payload:
Adv 737-200 15,626 kg (34,450 lb)
Adv 737-200C all passenger 14,243 kg (31,400 lb)
Adv 737-200C all cargo 17,599 kg (38,800 lb)
Adv 737-200QC all passenger 12,850 kg (28,330 lb)
Adv 737-200QC all cargo 17,259 kg (38,050 lb)
Adv 737-200 Executive Jet 2,268 kg (5,000 lb)
Max T-O weight:
All models, basic 52,390 kg (115,500 lb)
Optional: 53,070 kg (117,000 lb)
or 56,472 kg (124,500 lb)
or 58,105 kg (128,100 lb)
Max ramp weight:
All models, basic 52,615 kg (116,000 lb)
Optional: 53,297 kg (117,500 lb)
or 56,700 kg (125,000 lb)
or 58,332 kg (128,600 lb)
Max zero-fuel weight:
All models, basic 43,091 kg (95,000 lb)
Optional for 200C up to 44,906 kg (99,000 lb)
Max landing weight:
All models, basic 46,720 kg (103,000 lb)
Optional: 47,627 kg (105,000 lb)
or 48,534 kg (107,000 lb)
Wing loading:
All models, basic 575·5 kg/m² (117·9 lb/sq ft)
Max optional 638·2 kg/m² (130·7 lb/sq ft)
Power loading (JT8D-17):
All models, basic 368 kg/kN (3·61 lb/lb st)
Max optional 408 kg/kN (4·00 lb/lb st)

WEIGHTS AND LOADINGS (at brake release weight of 56,472 kg; 124,500 lb):
Operating weight empty 27,760 kg (61,200 lb)
Max payload 15,331 kg (33,800 lb)
Max T-O weight 56,472 kg (124,500 lb)
Max ramp weight 56,700 kg (125,000 lb)
Max zero-fuel weight 43,091 kg (95,000 lb)
Max landing weight 48,534 kg (107,000 lb)
Max wing loading 620·24 kg/m² (127·04 lb/sq ft)
Max power loading (JT8D-17) 397 kg/kN (3·9 lb/lb st)

PERFORMANCE (ISA, with JT8D-15 engines):
Max operating speed, all models Mach 0·84
Max level speed, all models, at 7,165 m (23,500 ft) 509 knots (943 km/h; 586 mph)
Max cruising speed, 737-200 at an average cruise weight of 40,823 kg (90,000 lb) at 6,890 m (22,600 ft) 500 knots (927 km/h; 576 mph)
Econ cruising speed at 9,145 m (30,000 ft) Mach 0·73
Stalling speed, flaps down, at max landing weight 99 knots (184 km/h; 114 mph)
Runway LCN (Advanced 737-200 at max taxi weight of 52,615 kg; 116,000 lb, optimum tyre pressure and 20 in flexible pavement): 40 × 14-16 tyres 51
40 × 14-21 tyres 51
40 × 18-17 tyres 36
FAR T-O distance to 10·7 m (35 ft), 737-200 at 49,435 kg (109,000 lb) AUW and 28·9°C (84°F):
JT8D-9 engines 2,073 m (6,800 ft)
JT8D-17 engines 1,615 m (5,300 ft)
FAR landing distance from 15 m (50 ft), 737-200 at max landing weight 1,341 m (4,400 ft)
Min ground turning radius 17·58 m (57 ft 8 in)
Range, cruising at 10,060 m (33,000 ft), including 3,016 kg (6,650 lb) reserve fuel, 737-200 at 52,615 kg (116,000 lb) taxi weight with 115 passengers 1,900 nm (3,521 km; 2,188 miles)
Range, all conditions as above, except 58,332 kg (128,600 lb) taxi weight 2,400 nm (4,448 km; 2,764 miles)
Range, conditions as above, 737-200 with 130 passengers 2,300 nm (4,262 km; 2,648 miles)

OPERATIONAL NOISE CHARACTERISTICS (Advanced 737-200 with JT8D-9 engines and nacelle acoustic treatment, FAR Pt 36):
T-O noise level at 52,390 kg (115,500 lb) brake release weight 95·3 EPNdB
Sideline noise level at 52,390 kg (115,500 lb) brake release weight 100·6 EPNdB
Approach noise level at 46,720 kg (103,000 lb) max landing weight 101·1 EPNdB

BOEING MODEL 747

USAF designation: E-4

First details of this wide-body commercial transport were announced on 13 April 1966, simultaneously with the news that Pan American had placed a $525 million contract for 25 Boeing 747s, including spares. Programme go-ahead date was officially 25 July 1966.

There was no prototype. The first 747 made its first flight on 9 February 1969 and FAA certification was granted on 30 December 1969. The first 747 to be delivered was received by Pan American on 12 December 1969, and this company inaugurated commercial service with the type on its New York/London route on 22 January 1970. Orders for differing versions of the 747 totalled 501 by 17 September 1979; by 31 August, 390 had been delivered. The total 747 fleet operating in Autumn 1979 carried about 3·6 million passengers each month, and had flown more than 7 million hours in revenue service.

Versions of the Boeing 747 are available as follows:

747-100B. As from September 1977, this improved version, with increased strength wing, fuselage and landing gear structure, replaced the original 747-100. Versions with max taxi weights of 323,411 kg (713,000 lb), 334,751 kg (738,000 lb), and 341,555 kg (753,000 lb) allow for the installation of a variety of optional engines in addition to the basic 208·8 kN (46,950 lb st) Pratt & Whitney JT9D-7A. These include the 216 kN (48,570 lb st) JT9D-7AW, 213·5 kN (48,000 lb st) JT9D-7F, 222·4 kN (50,000 lb st) JT9D-7FW, 222·4 kN (50,000 lb st) JT9D-7J, 233·5 kN (52,500 lb st) General Electric CF6-50E/E1/E2, 206·8 kN (46,500 lb st) CF6-45A/A2 and CF6-45B/B2, and 222·8 kN (50,100 lb st) Rolls-Royce RB.211-524B. First order, by Iran Air, was placed in 1978, with JT9D-7F engines specified.

747-100 Combi. A version of the basic 747-100, modified by the installation of a 3·05 × 3·40 m (120 × 134 in) cargo door in the port side of the fuselage, aft of the wing, to allow simultaneous carriage of passengers and up to 12 pallets/containers on the main deck. The passenger and cargo areas are separated by a removable bulkhead. The first such modification was carried out on a 747-100 of Sabena, redelivery being made in February 1974.

747SP. Lighter-weight, shorter-bodied derivative of the 747-100. Described separately.

747SR. This short-range version of the 747-100B embodies structural changes required for high take-off and landing cycles. The purchase of four 747SRs by Japan Air Lines was announced on 30 October 1972, and these aircraft have max taxi weights of 273,515 kg (603,000 lb) and 237,225 kg (523,000 lb). The first 747SR flew on 4 September 1973 and was delivered on 26 September 1973. Seven had been delivered to JAL by early 1977. The 747SR is available at max taxi weights up to 341,555 kg (753,000 lb) with the same engines as available to the 747-100B.

747-200B. Passenger version, with same accommodation as 747-100B. First flown on 11 October 1970 and certificated on 23 December 1970; deliveries began on 15 January 1971. Basic version had max T-O weight of 351,530 kg (775,000 lb) and increased fuel capacity. Available now with 216 kN (48,570 lb st) JT9D-7AW engines and max T-O weight of 356,070 kg (785,000 lb); 222·4 kN (50,000 lb st) JT9D-7FW and max T-O weight of 365,140 kg (805,000 lb); 222·4 kN (50,000 lb st) JT9D-7J engines and max T-O weight of 362,880 kg (800,000 lb); 235·7 kN (53,000 lb st) JT9D-7Q engines and max T-O weight of 371,950 kg (820,000 lb); 235·7 kN (53,000 lb st) JT9D-70A engines and max T-O weight of 371,950 kg (820,000 lb); 233·5 kN (52,500 lb st) General Electric CF6-50E/E1/E2 engines and max T-O weight of 371,950 kg (820,000 lb); and 222·8 kN (50,100 lb st) Rolls-Royce RB.211-524B2 or 229·5 kN (51,600 lb st) RB.211-524C2 engines and max T-O weight of 371,950 kg (820,000 lb).

FAA certification for the RB.211-524B engine for the 747-200B was received on 4 May 1977. On 1 November 1976, during a certification test flight, one of these aircraft took off from NAS Lemoore, California, at a gross weight of 381,108 kg (840,200 lb) and climbed to 2,000 m (6,560 ft) in 6 min 33 s, setting a new record for the maximum mass lifted to that altitude.

747-200B Combi. A version of the basic 747-200B, modified by the installation of a 3·05 × 3·40 m (120 × 134 in) cargo door in the port side of the fuselage, aft of the wing. This permits main deck layouts for all passengers or for passengers and up to 12 pallets/containers, with passenger and cargo areas separated by removable bulkhead. The first 747-200B Combi was rolled out in October 1974, and delivered to Air Canada in March 1975.

747-200C Convertible. Version of 747-200B which can be converted from all-passenger to all-cargo, or a combination of both. The first 747-200C flew on 23 March 1973, was certificated on 17 April, and was delivered to World Airways on 27 April 1973. Max T-O weight of 356,070 kg (785,000 lb) with Pratt & Whitney JT9D-7AW engines; 365,140 kg (805,000 lb) with JT9D-7FW engines; 362,880 kg (800,000 lb) with JT9D-7J engines; and 371,950 kg (820,000 lb) with JT9D-7Q, JT9D-70A, General Electric CF6-50E/E1/E2 or Rolls-Royce RB.211-524B2/C2 engines.

747-200F. Freighter version, capable of delivering 90,720 kg (200,000 lb) of palletised cargo over a range of 3,900 nm (7,227 km; 4,490 miles). Certification of the first 747-200F, which is described separately, was awarded by the FAA on 7 March 1972. T-O weights as detailed for 747-200C.

The Advanced Airborne Command Post version of the 747, developed for the USAF as the **E-4**, is described separately under the Boeing Aerospace heading.

The following details apply specifically to the basic Model 747 passenger airliner:

Type: Four-turbofan heavy commercial transport.

Wings: Cantilever low-wing monoplane. Special Boeing wing sections. Thickness/chord ratio 13·44% inboard, 7·8% at mid-span, 8% outboard. Dihedral 7°. Incidence 2°. Sweepback 37° 30′ at quarter-chord. Aluminium alloy dual-path fail-safe structure. Low-speed outboard ailerons; high-speed inboard ailerons. Triple-slotted trailing-edge flaps. Six aluminium honeycomb spoilers on each wing, comprising four flight spoilers outboard and two ground spoilers inboard. Ten variable-camber leading-edge flaps outboard and three-section Krueger flaps inboard on each wing leading-edge. All controls fully powered.

Fuselage: Conventional semi-monocoque structure, consisting of aluminium alloy skin, longitudinal stiffeners and circumferential frames. Structure is of fail-safe design, utilising riveting, bolting and structural bonding.

Tail Unit: Cantilever aluminium alloy dual-path fail-safe structure. Variable-incidence tailplane. No trim tabs. All controls fully powered.

Landing Gear: Hydraulically-retractable tricycle type. Twin-wheel nose unit retracts forward. Main gear comprises four four-wheel bogies: two, mounted side by side under fuselage at wing trailing-edge, retract forward; two mounted under wings retract inward. Cleveland Pneumatic oleo-pneumatic shock-absorbers. All 18 wheels and tubeless tyres of Model 747-100 are size 46 × 16 Type VII. Tyre pressure: main wheels 14·49 bars (210 lb/sq in), nosewheels 13·11 bars (190 lb/sq in). Main wheels and tyres size 49 × 17 on 747-200B model, pressure 14·15 bars (205 lb/sq in). The high gross weight aircraft has 49 × 19 tyres at a pressure of 13·46 bars (195 lb/sq in). Disc brakes on all main wheels, with individually-controlled anti-skid units.

Power Plant: Four Pratt & Whitney, General Electric or Rolls-Royce turbofan engines, as detailed in model listings, in pods pylon-mounted on wing leading-edges. Fuel in seven integral tanks. Capacity of centre wing tank varies according to version: 747-100: 49,966 litres (13,200 US gallons); 747-200B and 747-200F: 64,956 litres (17,160 US gallons). Remaining tanks common to all versions: two inboard main tanks, each 47,505 litres (12,550 US gallons); two outboard main tanks, each 16,977 litres (4,485 US gallons); two inboard reserve tanks, each 2,021 litres (534 US gallons). Outboard mains are reduced by 1,287 litres (340 US gallons) when CF6-50E or JT9D-70A engines are installed. 747-200B also available with two outboard reserve tanks, each 2,971 litres (785 US gallons). Total capacity, including manifolds, 747-100: 183,630 litres (48,510 US gallons); 747-200B and 747-200F: 198,390 litres (52,410 US gallons). Refuelling point on each wing between inboard and outboard engines. Total usable oil capacity 19 litres (5 US gallons).

Accommodation: Normal operating crew of three, on flight deck above level of main deck. Observer station and provision for second observer station are provided. Basic accommodation for 442 passengers, made up of 28 first class and 414 economy class, which includes a 16-passenger upper deck. Alternative layouts accommodate 447 economy class passengers in nine-abreast seating or 516 ten-abreast, with 32 passengers on upper deck. All versions have two aisles. Five passenger doors on each side, of which two forward of wing on each side are normally used. Freight holds under floor, forward and aft of wing, with doors on starboard side. One door on forward hold, two on rear hold. Aircraft is designed for fully-mechanical loading of baggage and freight. An optional side cargo door is available for passenger, convertible and freighter versions of the Model 747. Installed aft of door 4 on the port side of the fuselage, it provides a clear opening 3·40 m (11 ft 2 in) wide and 3·05 m (10 ft 0 in) in height. This door makes it possible to carry main-deck cargo on passenger versions. Addition of this door to the freighter allows loads up to 3·05 m (10 ft) in height to be accommodated aft of the flight deck, and also makes possible simultaneous nose and side cargo handling.

Systems: Air-cycle air-conditioning system. Pressure differential 0·61 bars (8·9 lb/sq in). Four independent hydraulic systems, pressure 207 bars (3,000 lb/sq in), each with one engine-driven and one pneumatically-driven pump. The latter pumps supplement or substitute for engine-driven pumps. A small AC-powered electric pump is installed to charge the brake accumulator during towing of the aircraft. Electrical supply from four aircooled 60kVA generators mounted one on each engine. Two 60kVA generators (supplemental cooling allows 90kVA each) mounted on APU for ground operation and to supply primary electrical power when engine-mounted generators are not operating. Three-phase 400Hz constant-frequency AC generators, 115/200V output. 28V DC power obtained from transformer-rectifier units. 24V 30Ah nickel-cadmium battery for selected ground functions and as in-flight backup. Gas-turbine APU for pneumatic and electrical supplies.

Avionics and Equipment: Standard avionics include two ARINC 566 VHF communications systems, two ARINC 533A HF communications systems, one ARINC 531 Selcal, three ARINC 547 VOR/ILS navigation systems, two ARINC 570 ADF, marker beacon, two ARINC 568 DME, two ARINC 572 ATC, two ARINC 552 low-range radio altimeters, two ARINC 564 weather radar units, three ARINC 561 inertial navigation systems, two heading reference systems, ARINC 412 interphone, passenger address system, passenger entertainment system, ARINC 573 flight recorder, ARINC 557 cockpit voice recorder, integrated electronic flight control system with autothrottle and rollout guidance to provide automatic stabilisation, path control and pilot assist functions for category II and III landing conditions, two ARINC 565 central air data systems, stall warning system, central instrument warning system, ground proximity warning system, attitude and navigation instrumentation, and standby attitude indication.

Boeing Model 747-200B Combi four-turbofan commercial transport in the insignia of Air Madagascar

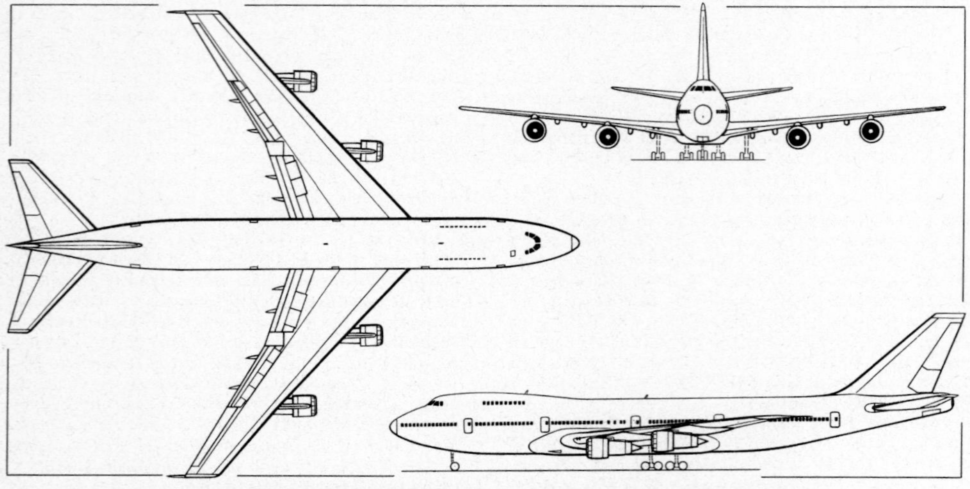

Boeing 747-200B four-turbofan heavy transport aircraft *(Pilot Press)*

DIMENSIONS, EXTERNAL:
Wing span 59·64 m (195 ft 8 in)
Wing chord at root 16·56 m (54 ft 4 in)
Wing chord at tip 4·06 m (13 ft 4 in)
Wing aspect ratio 6·96
Length overall 70·51 m (231 ft 4 in)
Length of fuselage 68·63 m (225 ft 2 in)
Height overall 19·33 m (63 ft 5 in)
Tailplane span 22·17 m (72 ft 9 in)
Wheel track 11·00 m (36 ft 1 in)
Wheelbase 25·60 m (84 ft 0 in)
Passenger doors (ten, each):
Height 1·93 m (6 ft 4 in)
Width 1·07 m (3 ft 6 in)
Height to sill approx 4·88 m (16 ft 0 in)
Baggage door (front hold):
Height 1·73 m (5 ft 8 in)
Width 2·64 m (8 ft 8 in)
Height to sill approx 2·64 m (8 ft 8 in)
Baggage door (forward door, aft hold):
Height 1·73 m (5 ft 8 in)
Width 2·64 m (8 ft 8 in)
Height to sill approx 2·69 m (8 ft 10 in)
Bulk loading door (rear door on aft hold):
Height 1·22 m (4 ft 0 in)
Width 1·12 m (3 ft 8 in)
Height to sill approx 2·90 m (9 ft 6 in)
Optional cargo door (port):
Height 3·05 m (10 ft 0 in)
Width 3·40 m (11 ft 2 in)

DIMENSIONS, INTERNAL:
Cabin, incl toilets and galleys:
Length 57·00 m (187 ft 0 in)
Max width 6·13 m (20 ft 1½ in)
Max height 2·54 m (8 ft 4 in)
Floor area, passenger deck 327·9 m² (3,529 sq ft)
Volume, passenger deck 789 m³ (27,860 cu ft)
Baggage hold (fwd, containerised) volume 78·4 m³ (2,768 cu ft)
Baggage hold (aft, containerised) volume 68·6 m³ (2,422 cu ft)
Bulk volume 28·3 m³ (1,000 cu ft)

AREAS:
Wings, reference area 511 m² (5,500 sq ft)
Ailerons (total) 20·6 m² (222 sq ft)
Trailing-edge flaps (total) 78·7 m² (847 sq ft)
Leading-edge flaps (total) 48·1 m² (518 sq ft)
Spoilers (total) 30·8 m² (331 sq ft)
Fin 77·1 m² (830 sq ft)
Rudder 22·9 m² (247 sq ft)
Tailplane 136·6 m² (1,470 sq ft)
Elevators 32·5 m² (350 sq ft)

WEIGHTS (the following suffixes are used to denote engine installations: (T) CF6-45A/A2 or -45B/B2; (U) RB.211-524B2/C2; (V) JT9D-7A/-7AW; (W) JT9D-7F/-7FW/-7J; (X) JT9D-7Q; (Y) CF6-50E/E1/E2; (Z) JT9D-70A):
Operating weight empty (approx) for max available gross weights:
747-100B (442 pass):
(T, Y) 171,000 kg (377,000 lb)
(U) 173,725 kg (383,000 lb)
(V, W) 169,190 kg (373,000 lb)
747SR (516 pass):
(T, Y) 161,030 kg (355,000 lb)
(U) 163,750 kg (361,000 lb)
(V, W) 159,210 kg (351,000 lb)
747-200B (442 pass):
(U) 175,995 kg (388,000 lb)
(V, W) 171,000 kg (377,000 lb)
(X) 172,365 kg (380,000 lb)
(Y) 173,270 kg (382,000 lb)
(Z) 175,085 kg (386,000 lb)
747-200B Combi (equipped for 232 pass and 12 pallets):
(U) 175,540 kg (387,000 lb)
(V, W) 170,550 kg (376,000 lb)
(X) 171,910 kg (379,000 lb)
(Y) 172,820 kg (381,000 lb)
(Z) 174,635 kg (385,000 lb)
747-200C (442 pass):
(U) 180,530 kg (398,000 lb)
(V, W) 175,085 kg (386,000 lb)
(X) 176,900 kg (390,000 lb)
(Y) 177,810 kg (392,000 lb)
(Z) 179,620 kg (396,000 lb)
747-200C (28 pallets):
(U) 167,830 kg (370,000 lb)
(V, W) 162,385 kg (358,000 lb)
(X) 164,200 kg (362,000 lb)
(Y) 165,110 kg (364,000 lb)
(Z) 166,920 kg (368,000 lb)
Max payload:
747-100B (442 pass):
(T, Y) 67,810 kg (149,500 lb)
(U) 65,090 kg (143,500 lb)
(V, W) 69,625 kg (153,500 lb)
747SR (516 pass):
(T, Y) 77,790 kg (171,500 lb)
(U) 75,070 kg (165,500 lb)
(V, W) 79,605 kg (175,500 lb)
747-200B (442 pass):
(U) 62,820 kg (138,500 lb)
(V, W) 67,810 kg (149,500 lb)
(X) 66,450 kg (146,500 lb)
(Y) 65,545 kg (144,500 lb)
(Z) 63,730 kg (140,500 lb)
747-200B Combi (equipped for 232 pass and 12 pallets):
(U) 71,670 kg (158,000 lb)
(V, W) 76,660 kg (169,000 lb)
(X) 75,300 kg (166,000 lb)
(Y) 74,390 kg (164,000 lb)
(Z) 72,575 kg (160,000 lb)
747-200C (442 pass):
(U) 58,290 kg (128,500 lb)
(V, W) 63,730 kg (140,500 lb)
(X) 61,915 kg (136,500 lb)
(Y) 61,010 kg (134,500 lb)
(Z) 59,190 kg (130,500 lb)
747-200C (28 pallets):
(U) 99,790 kg (220,000 lb)
(V, W) 105,230 kg (232,000 lb)
(X) 103,420 kg (228,000 lb)
(Y) 102,510 kg (226,000 lb)
(Z) 100,700 kg (222,000 lb)
Max T-O weight:
747-100B:
(T, U, V, W, Y) 322,050 kg (710,000 lb)
or 332,480 kg (733,000 lb)
or 340,190 kg (750,000 lb)
747SR:
(T, U, V, W, Y) 235,870 kg (520,000 lb)
or 258,550 kg (570,000 lb)
or 272,160 kg (600,000 lb)
or as 747-100B weights, above
747-200B, -200B Combi, -200C:
(V) 351,530 kg (775,000 lb)
or 356,070 kg (785,000 lb)
(W) 362,880 kg (800,000 lb)
or 365,140 kg (805,000 lb) wet
(U, X, Y, Z) 362,880 kg (800,000 lb)
or 371,950 kg (820,000 lb)
Max ramp weight:
747-100B, 747SR:
(T, U, V, W, Y) 341,560 kg (753,000 lb)
747-200B, -200B Combi, -200C:
(V, W) 366,500 kg (808,000 lb)
(U, X, Y, Z) 373,310 kg (823,000 lb)
Max zero-fuel weight:
747-100B:
(T, U, V, W, Y) 238,816 kg (526,500 lb)
747SR:
(T, U, V, W, Y) 219,992 kg (485,000 lb)
or 238,816 kg (526,500 lb)
747-200B:
(U, V, W, X, Y, Z) 238,816 kg (526,500 lb)
747-200B Combi:
(U, V, W, X, Y, Z) 247,208 kg (545,000 lb)
747-200C:
(U, V, W, X, Y, Z) 267,620 kg (590,000 lb)
Max landing weight:
747-100B:
(T, U, V, W, Y) 255,826 kg (564,000 lb)
or 265,352 kg (585,000 lb)
747SR:
(T, U, V, W, Y) 255,826 kg (564,000 lb)
747-200B:
(U, V, W, X, Y, Z) 255,826 kg (564,000 lb)
or 265,352 kg (585,000 lb)
or 285,763 kg (630,000 lb)
747-200B Combi:
(U, V, W, X, Y, Z) 265,352 kg (585,000 lb)
or 285,763 kg (630,000 lb)
747-200C:
(U, V, W, X, Y, Z) 285,763 kg (630,000 lb)

PERFORMANCE (at max T-O weight except where indicated):
Max level speed:
747-100, JT9D-7A engines and AUW of 272,160 kg (600,000 lb) at 9,145 m (30,000 ft)
522 knots (967 km/h; 601 mph)
747-200B, CF6-50E engines and AUW of 317,515 kg (700,000 lb) at 9,145 m (30,000 ft)
523 knots (969 km/h; 602 mph)
Cruise ceiling, all versions 13,715 m (45,000 ft)
Min ground turning radius 22·86 m (75 ft 0 in)
Runway LCN (A: 334,750 kg; 738,000 lb, B; 341,560 kg; 753,000 lb, C: 366,500 kg; 808,000 lb, D: 373,310 kg; 823,000 lb max taxi weight on h=0·51 m; 20 in flexible pavement): A 81
B 83
C 86
D 87
Runway LCN (weights as above, on l=1·02 m; 40 in rigid pavement): A 87
B 89
C 93
D 94
FAR T-O distance to 10·7 m (35 ft) at S/L, ISA:
747-100 (JT9D-7A engines at AUW of 332,480 kg (733,000 lb) 2,880 m (9,450 ft)
747-200B (JT9D-7FW engines at AUW of 365,142 kg (805,000 lb) 3,338 m (10,950 ft)
747-200B, C, F, CF6-50E engines at AUW of 371,950 kg (820,000 lb) 3,155 m (10,350 ft)
747-200B, C, JT9D-7Q/-70A engines at AUW of 371,950 kg (820,000 lb) 3,094 m (10,150 ft)
FAR landing field length, at max landing weights:
747-100, -200B at 255,826 kg (564,000 lb)
1,881 m (6,170 ft)
747-100, -200B at 265,352 kg (585,000 lb)
1,942 m (6,370 ft)
747-200B, C, F at 285,763 kg (630,000 lb)
2,109 m (6,920 ft)
Range (long-range cruise, FAR 121.645 reserves):
747-100B at T-O weight of 340,190 kg (750,000 lb), with 442 passengers and baggage
4,500 nm (8,330 km; 5,180 miles)
747-200B at T-O weight of 365,140 kg (805,000 lb), with 442 passengers and baggage
5,200 nm (9,630 km; 5,980 miles)
747-200B at T-O weight of 371,950 kg (820,000 lb), with 442 passengers and baggage
5,600 nm (10,370 km; 6,440 miles)
Ferry range (long-range cruise, FAR 121.645 reserves):
747-200B 6,700 nm (12,400 km; 7,710 miles)

OPERATIONAL NOISE CHARACTERISTICS (As per FAR Pt 36, A: JT9D-7A engines at brake release weight (BRW) of 332,480 kg; 733,000 lb and landing weight of 255,826 kg; 564,000 lb, B: JT9D-7FW at BRW of 365,140 kg; 805,000 lb and landing weight of 255,826 kg; 564,000 lb, C: CF6-50E at BRW of 371,950 kg; 820,000 lb and landing weight of 285,763 kg; 630,000 lb):
T-O noise level: A 106 EPNdB
B 109 EPNdB
C 107 EPNdB
Approach noise level: A 106 EPNdB
B 107 EPNdB
C 106 EPNdB
Sideline noise level: A 98 EPNdB
B 99 EPNdB
C 98 EPNdB

BOEING MODEL 747SP

The Boeing Company announced on 3 September 1973 that it intended to proceed 'incrementally' with development of a lower-weight longer-range version of the basic Model 747, for use on lower-density routes. A week later came the news that Pan American had placed an order for 10 747SP (Special Performance) aircraft, with an option on 15 more. Other orders have been received from Braniff

(3), China Air (2), Iran Air (4), South African Airways (6), Syrian Arab (2), Saudi Arabian (1), TWA (3) and CAAC (3).

Retaining a 90 per cent commonality of components with the standard Model 747, the major change is a reduction in overall length of 14·20 m (46 ft 7 in). Construction of the first production aircraft began in April 1974, with rollout on 19 May 1975, first flight on 4 July 1975, and FAA certification on 4 February 1976. First delivery was made on 5 March that year.

On 23-24 March 1976, taking off at a gross weight of 323,547 kg (713,300 lb) with 50 passengers, the first 747SP for South African Airways made a delivery flight from Paine Field, Washington, to Cape Town of 8,936 nm (16,560 km; 10,290 miles), a world record for nonstop distance flown by a commercial aircraft. The aircraft landed with fuel remaining for a further 2 h 27 min of flight.

A 747SP of Pan American, commanded by Capt Walter H. Mullikin, set a round-the-world speed record of 436·95 knots (809·24 km/h; 502·84 mph), by circumnavigating the globe in 1 day 22 h 50 s on 1-3 May 1976. The same pilot circumnavigated the world via the North and South Poles in a 747SP on 28-31 October 1977, covering 22,926 nm (42,459 km; 26,382·75 miles) in 54 h 7 min 12 s at an average speed of 423·49 knots (784·31 km/h; 487·35 mph). Start and finish were at San Francisco, with en route landings at London, Cape Town and Auckland, New Zealand.

The description of the basic Model 747 applies also to the 747SP, except for the following details:

Wings: As Model 747, except that trailing-edge flaps are of single-slotted variable pivot type, and wing structural materials are of reduced gauge. Large flap track fairings replaced by small link fairings. New wing/body fairings and leading-edge fillets.

Fuselage: As Model 747, except length reduced.

Tail Unit: Similar to 747, but tailplane span increased by 3·05 m (10 ft). Two-segment elevators. Height of fin increased by 1·52 m (5 ft 0 in). Double-hinged rudder.

Landing Gear: As Model 747, except structural weight reduced. Main-wheel tyres size 46 × 16, pressure 12·63 bars (183 lb/sq in). Nosewheel tyres size 49 × 17, pressure 13·8 bars (200 lb/sq in). Higher gross weight aircraft uses 747-100 wheels and brakes. Modified 747-100 steel brakes by Bendix.

Power Plant: Four Pratt & Whitney JT9D-7A turbofan engines, each 208·8 kN (46,950 lb st); or JT9D-7F of 213·5 kN (48,000 lb st); JT9D-7AW of 216 kN (48,570 lb st); JT9D-7FW of 222·4 kN (50,000 lb st); JT9D-7J of 222·4 kN (50,000 lb st); or four General Electric CF6-45A/B turbofan engines, each of 206·8 kN (46,500 lb st); or four Rolls-Royce RB.211-524B turbofan engines, each of 222·8 kN (50,100 lb st). Fuel system, fuel capacity and oil capacity as for Model 747-100B, except Model 747SP has an additional 5,943 litres (1,570 US gallons) reserve fuel.

Accommodation: Normal operating crew of three on flight deck above level of main deck. Observer station and provision for second observer station are provided. Basic accommodation for 288 passengers on main deck, with 28 first class seats in forward area and ten-abreast seating throughout the major part of the main cabin. Seating for 16/32 passengers in upper-deck first class lounge optional, giving total optional capacity of 305/321 passengers. Max high-density accommodation for 400 passengers. Four doors on each side, two forward and two aft of the wing. Crew door on starboard side giving access to upper deck. Freight holds under floor, forward and aft of wing box, each with one door on starboard side.

Systems, Avionics and Equipment: As for Model 747.

Dimensions, external: As for Model 747 except:

Length overall	56·31 m (184 ft 9 in)
Height overall	19·94 m (65 ft 5 in)
Tailplane span	25·22 m (82 ft 9 in)
Wheelbase	20·52 m (67 ft 4 in)

Dimensions, internal:

Cabin, incl toilets and galleys:

Length	42·27 m (138 ft 8 in)
Max width	6·13 m (20 ft 1½ in)
Max height	2·54 m (8 ft 4 in)
Floor area, passenger deck	253·2 m² (2,725 sq ft)
Volume, passenger deck	613·34 m³ (21,660 cu ft)
Baggage hold volume (fwd)	48·99 m³ (1,730 cu ft)
Baggage hold volume (aft, containerised)	48·99 m³ (1,730 cu ft)
Bulk compartment volume (aft)	11·33 m³ (400 cu ft)

Areas: As for Model 747 except:

Ailerons (total)	20·37 m² (219·3 sq ft)
Trailing-edge flaps (total)	78·78 m² (848 sq ft)
Fin	82·22 m² (885 sq ft)
Tailplane	142·51 m² (1,534 sq ft)

Weights: (the following suffixes are used to denote engine installations: (T) CF6-45A/A2 or -45B/B2; (U) RB.211-524B; (V) JT9D-7A/-7AW; (W) JT9D-7F -7FW/-7J):

Operating weight empty (approx, with 321 passengers):

(T)	148,330 kg (327,000 lb)
(U)	151,050 kg (333,000 lb)
(V, W)	146,060 kg (322,000 lb)

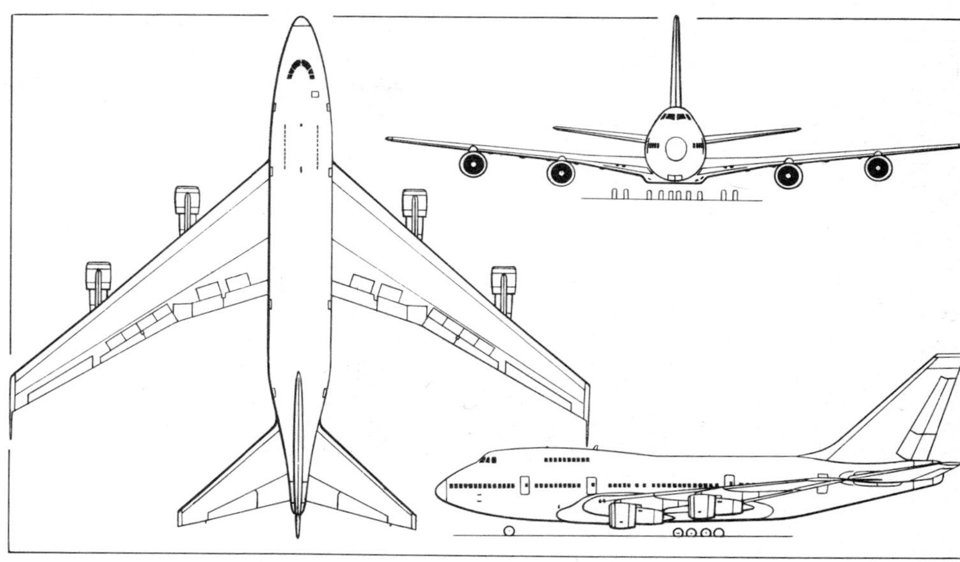

Boeing 747SP short-fuselage long-range version of the 747 *(Pilot Press)*

Max T-O weight (dry engines):

(T, U, V, W)	285,763 kg (630,000 lb)
	or 299,371 kg (660,000 lb)
	or 303,907 kg (670,000 lb)
	or 312,979 kg (690,000 lb)
	or 315,700 kg (696,000 lb)

Max ramp weight:

(T, U, V, W)	302,093 kg (666,000 lb)
	or 306,628 kg (676,000 lb)
	or 315,700 kg (696,000 lb)
	or 318,875 kg (703,000 lb)

Max zero-fuel weight:

(T, U, V, W)	185,973 kg (410,000 lb)
	or 192,777 kg (425,000 lb)

Max landing weight:

(T, U, V, W)	204,117 kg (450,000 lb)
	or 210,920 kg (465,000 lb)

Performance (at max T-O weight, except where indicated):

Never-exceed speed — Mach 0·92

Max level speed, AUW of 226,795 kg (500,000 lb) at 9,145 m (30,000 ft) — 529 knots (980 km/h; 609 mph)

Service ceiling — 13,745 m (45,100 ft)

Min ground turning radius over outer wingtip — 22·25 m (73 ft 0 in)

Runway LCN (A: 302,093 kg; 666,000 lb, B: 315,700 kg; 696,000 lb max taxi weight on h = 0·51 m; 20 in flexible pavement):

A	70
B	74

Runway LCN (weights as above, on l = 1·02 m; 40 in rigid pavement):

A	76
B	79

FAR T-O distance to 10·7 m (35 ft) at S/L, ISA (A: 299,371 kg; 660,000 lb, B: 312,979 kg; 690,000 lb max T-O weight):

(T)	A	2,362 m (7,750 ft)
	B	2,637 m (8,650 ft)
(U)	A	2,118 m (6,950 ft)
	B	2,347 m (7,700 ft)
(V)	A	2,393 m (7,850 ft)
	B	2,667 m (8,750 ft)
(W)	A	2,164 m (7,100 ft)
	B	2,377 m (7,800 ft)

FAR landing field length:

at max landing weight	1,594 m (5,230 ft)
at optional max landing weight	1,646 m (5,400 ft)

Range (long-range step cruise, FAR 121.645 reserves, with 321 passengers and baggage at A: 299,371 kg; 660,000 lb, B: 312,979 kg; 690,000 lb AUW):

A	5,350 nm (9,915 km; 6,161 miles)
B	5,850 nm (10,841 km; 6,736 miles)

Ferry range (long-range step cruise, FAR 121.645 reserves) — 7,250 nm (13,435 km; 8,348 miles)

BOEING MODEL 747-200F FREIGHTER

The Boeing Model 747-200F is a freighter version of the standard Model 747-200, capable of delivering 90,720 kg (200,000 lb) of containerised or palletised cargo over a range of 4,000 nm (7,410 km; 4,605 miles).

The first 747-200F flew for the first time on 30 November 1971. It was certificated on 7 March 1972 and delivered to Lufthansa two days later.

To ensure maximum utilisation, the 747-200F has a special loading system that enables two men to handle and stow the maximum load of up to 113,400 kg (250,000 lb) in 30 min. This system was fully described in the 1977-78 *Jane's*.

The 747-200F can carry up to 29 containers measuring 3·05 m × 2·44 m × 2·44 m (10 ft long, 8 ft high and 8 ft wide), plus 30 lower-lobe containers, each of 4·90 m³ (173

Nose-loading demonstration of a Boeing Model 747-200F freighter

Boeing Model 747SP four-turbofan special performance long-range transport in the insignia of China Airlines

cu ft) capacity, and 22·65 m³ (800 cu ft) of bulk cargo. The main deck can accommodate ANSI/ISO containers of up to 12·2 m (40 ft) in length, and many combinations of pallets and igloos. The lower hold can accommodate combinations of IATA-A1 or -A2, and ATA LD-1 or -3 half-width containers, full-width or main-deck baggage containers, and many combinations of pallets and igloos.

The nose loading door, which is hinged just below the flight deck to allow it to swing forward and upward, gives clear access to the main deck to facilitate the handling of long or large loads. A side cargo door is available as an option, allowing simultaneous nose and side loading. The side cargo door will accept palletised loads up to 3·05 m (10 ft 0 in) in height.

The description of the Model 747-200B applies also to the Model 747-200F except as follows:

Type: Four-turbofan heavy commercial freighter.

Fuselage: As for Model 747-200B, except nose cargo loading door, which is hinged at the top and opens forward and upward.

Accommodation: Normal operating crew of three on flight deck. Nose cargo loading door, hinged at top. Lower lobe cargo doors, on starboard side, one forward and one aft of wing. Bulk compartment cargo door, on starboard side, aft of lower lobe cargo door. Two doors for crew on port side of aircraft. Aircraft is designed for fully-mechanical loading of freight.

Dimensions, external: As for Model 747-200B except:
- Crew doors (two, each): Height 1·93 m (6 ft 4 in)
  - Width 1·07 m (3 ft 6 in)
  - Height to sill approx 4·88 m (16 ft 0 in)
- Nose cargo loading door: Height 2·49 m (8 ft 2 in)
  - Width at top (min) 2·64 m (8 ft 8 in)
  - Max width 3·45 m (11 ft 4 in)
  - Height to sill approx 4·90 m (16 ft 1 in)

Dimensions, internal:
- Main cargo deck: Height 2·54 m (8 ft 4 in)
  - Max width 5·92 m (19 ft 5 in)
- Lower lobe: Width at floor level 3·18 m (10 ft 5 in)
- Total cargo volume 670·83 m³ (23,690 cu ft)

Areas: As for Model 747-200B

Weights (the following suffixes are used to denote engine installations: (U) RB.211-524B; (V) JT9D-7A/-7AW; (W) JT9D-7F/-7FW/-7J; (X) JT9D-7Q; (Y) CF6-50E/E1/E2; (Z) JT9D-70A):
- Operating weight, empty (approx, with 29 pallets):
  - (U) 159,670 kg (352,000 lb)
  - (V, W) 154,220 kg (340,000 lb)
  - (X) 156,040 kg (344,000 lb)
  - (Y) 156,950 kg (346,000 lb)
  - (Z) 158,760 kg (350,000 lb)
- Max payload (29 pallets):
  - (U) 107,960 kg (238,000 lb)
  - (V, W) 113,400 kg (250,000 lb)
  - (X) 111,590 kg (246,000 lb)
  - (Y) 110,680 kg (244,000 lb)
  - (Z) 108,860 kg (240,000 lb)
- Max T-O weight: (U) 362,880 kg (880,000 lb)
  - (V) 351,530 kg (775,000 lb) or 356,070 kg (785,000 lb)
  - (W) 362,880 kg (800,000 lb) or 365,140 kg (805,000 lb) wet
  - (X, Y, Z) 362,880 kg (800,000 lb) or 371,950 kg (820,000 lb)
- Max ramp weight: (V, W) 366,500 kg (808,000 lb)
  - (U, X, Y, Z) 373,310 kg (823,000 lb)
- Max zero-fuel weight:
  - (U, V, W, X, Y, Z) 267,620 kg (590,000 lb)
- Max landing weight:
  - (U, V, W, X, Y, Z) 285,770 kg (630,000 lb)

Performance (at max T-O weight except where indicated):
- Max level speed at AUW of 272,160 kg (600,000 lb), at 9,145 m (30,000 ft) 528 knots (978 km/h; 608 mph)
- Cruise ceiling 13,715 m (45,000 ft)
- Min ground turning radius 22·86 m (75 ft 0 in)
- FAR T-O distance to 10·7 m (35 ft) at S/L, ISA:
  - JT9D-7FW engines, at AUW of 365,140 kg (805,000 lb) 3,338 m (10,950 ft)
  - CF6-50E/E1/E2 engines, at AUW of 371,950 kg (820,000 lb) 3,155 m (10,350 ft)
  - JT9D-7Q/-70A engines, at AUW of 371,950 kg (820,000 lb) 3,094 m (10,150 ft)
- FAR landing field length, at max landing weight 2,103 m (6,900 ft)
- Range, long-range step cruise, FAR 121.645 reserves, with 90,720 kg (200,000 lb) payload:
  - T-O weight of 356,070 kg (785,000 lb)
    - (V, W) 3,200 nm (5,920 km; 3,680 miles)
  - T-O weight of 371,950 kg (820,000 lb)
    - (U, Y, Z) 3,800 nm (7,030 km; 4,370 miles)
    - (X) 4,000 nm (7,400 km; 4,600 miles)
- Ferry range with max fuel, long-range cruise, FAR 121.645 reserves 7,000 nm (12,950 km; 8,050 miles)

BOEING 747-123 SPACE SHUTTLE ORBITER CARRIER (NASA 905)

Boeing modified a Model 747-123, which NASA acquired from American Airlines in August 1974, as a carrier for the Space Shuttle Orbiter. The modifications enable the 747, now registered NASA 905, to carry the Space Shuttle Orbiter aircraft 'piggy-back' fashion.

The initial taxi tests were completed by 15 February 1977, and the first flight of the NASA 905/*Enterprise* combination was made successfully from the Dryden Flight Research Center, Edwards AFB, California, on 18 February. The planned test programme was completed during 1977, as recorded in the 1978-79 *Jane's*. For further details see the NASA entry in this section.

BOEING MODEL 757

In the early months of 1978, The Boeing Company announced a proposal to develop a new family of advanced technology commercial aircraft, to which it gave the Model designations 757, 767 and 777. The short/medium-range 757 was intended to differ considerably from the other two, being based on a lengthened Boeing 727 fuselage. Improved performance would come from two new high bypass engines and an advanced technology wing, with less sweepback than that of the Model 727.

On 31 August 1978 Eastern Air Lines and British Airways announced their intention to purchase 21 and 19 Model 757s respectively, the former taking an option on an additional 24. Following the signature in early 1979 of formal contracts by both of these airlines, Boeing announced on 23 March 1979 that the company had initiated full production of the Model 757. First flight is scheduled for February 1982, with first deliveries in early 1983. Aircraft for both British Airways and Eastern Air Lines will be designated **Model 757-200** and powered by two 165·9 kN (37,300 lb st) class Rolls-Royce RB.211-535C turbofan engines. This was the first time that Boeing had launched a new airliner with a non-American engine. On a typical 400 nm (740 km; 460 mile) stage, the Model 757-200 with RB.211-535 engines is expected to use up to 37 per cent less fuel per passenger than current medium-range aircraft.

The Model 757 retains the same fuselage cross-section as the 707/727/737 family, with an overall length 5·97 m (19 ft 7 in) longer than that of the 727-200. The original design provided for a T-tail configuration, but as a result of wind tunnel testing it was decided to mount the tailplane on the fuselage.

Avionics equipment will include a Honeywell inertial reference system (IRS). In this IRS, conventional mechanical gyroscopes are replaced by laser gyroscopes, and utilisation, in both the Models 757 and 767, will represent their first commercial application. The IRS will provide position, velocity, and attitude information to flight deck displays, and for the flight management computer system (FMCS) and digital air data computer (DADC), to be supplied by Sperry Flight Systems. The FMCS will provide automatic en-route and terminal navigation capability, and will also compute and command both lateral and vertical flight profiles for optimum fuel efficiency, maximised by electronic linkage of the FMCS with automatic flight control and thrust management systems.

Landing Gear: Retractable tricycle type, with main and nose units manufactured by Menasco. Each main unit comprises a four-wheel bogie. Twin-wheel nose unit.

Power Plant: Two Rolls-Royce RB.211-535 or General Electric CF6-32 turbofan engines in the 160 kN (36,000 lb st) class, mounted in underwing pods.

Accommodation: Typical accommodation for 178 mixed class or 196 tourist class passengers, in four/six-abreast seating with central aisle. Seat pitch in the all-tourist configuration is 86 cm (34 in).

Systems and Avionics: AiResearch environmental control system; General Electric engine thrust management system; Sundstrand electrical power generating system and ram-air turbines; and AiResearch GTCP 331-200 APU. Honeywell inertial reference system (IRS); Sperry flight management computer system (FMCS) and digital air data computer (DADC); Collins digital autopilot flight director system (DAFDS), radio dis-

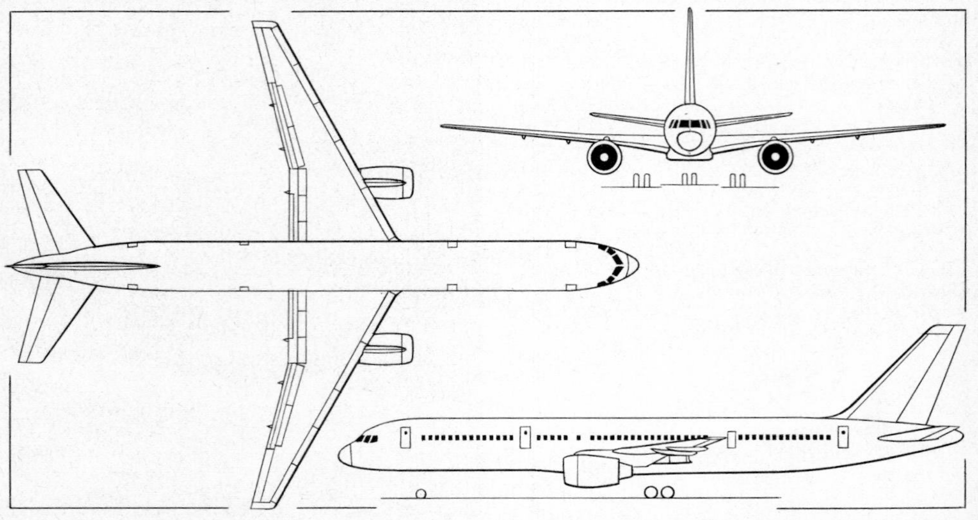

Boeing Model 757 twin-turbofan short/medium-range transport aircraft *(Pilot Press)*

tance magnetic indicator (RDMI) and optional radio magnetic indicator (RMI).

DIMENSIONS, EXTERNAL:
Wing span 37·95 m (124 ft 6 in)
Wing sweepback 25°
Wing area, gross 185·24 m^2 (1,994 sq ft)
Length overall 47·14 m (154 ft 8 in)
Length of fuselage 46·89 m (153 ft 10 in)
Height overall 13·59 m (44 ft 7 in)
Tailplane span 14·99 m (49 ft 2 in)
Wheel track 7·32 m (24 ft 0 in)
Passenger doors (two, fwd, port):
Height 1·83 m (6 ft 0 in)
Width 0·89 m (2 ft 9 in)
Service door (fwd, stbd):
Height 1·65 m (5 ft 5 in)
Width 0·76 m (2 ft 6 in)
Service door (stbd, opposite 2nd passenger door):
Height 1·65 m (5 ft 5 in)
Width 0·89 m (2 ft 9 in)
Service doors (aft, port and stbd):
Height 1·83 m (6 ft 0 in)
Width 0·76 m (2 ft 6 in)
Emergency exits (two, aft of wings):
Height 1·32 m (4 ft 4 in)
Width 0·61 m (2 ft 0 in)

DIMENSIONS, INTERNAL:
Underfloor cargo volume (bulk loading):
fwd 24·0 m^3 (847 cu ft)
aft 31·5 m^3 (1,112 cu ft)
Underfloor cargo volume (with optional containers):
fwd (8 containers) 17·7 m^3 (624 cu ft)
aft (6 containers) 13·2 m^3 (468 cu ft)
additional bulk aft 9·3 m^3 (330 cu ft)

WEIGHTS (with 178 passengers. A: 165·9 kN/37,300 lb st RB.211-535 engines; B: 161·6 kN/36,330 lb st CF6-32s):
Operating weight empty: A 58,042 kg (127,960 lb)
B 57,919 kg (127,690 lb)
Max basic T-O weight: A, B 99,790 kg (220,000 lb)
Max T-O weight (optional) 104,325 kg (230,000 lb)
Max landing weight: A, B 87,545 kg (193,000 lb)

PERFORMANCE (with 178 passengers, typical domestic operations; at max basic T-O weight and with engines as above):
Cruising speed: A, B Mach 0·80
Approach speed:
A, B 135 knots (250 km/h; 155 mph)
Initial cruising height: A 11,340 m (37,200 ft)
B 11,765 m (38,600 ft)
T-O field length (S/L, 29°C): A 1,965 m (6,450 ft)
B 2,035 m (6,670 ft)
Max range: A 2,340 nm (4,336 km; 2,695 miles)
B 2,400 nm (4,447 km; 2,763 miles)

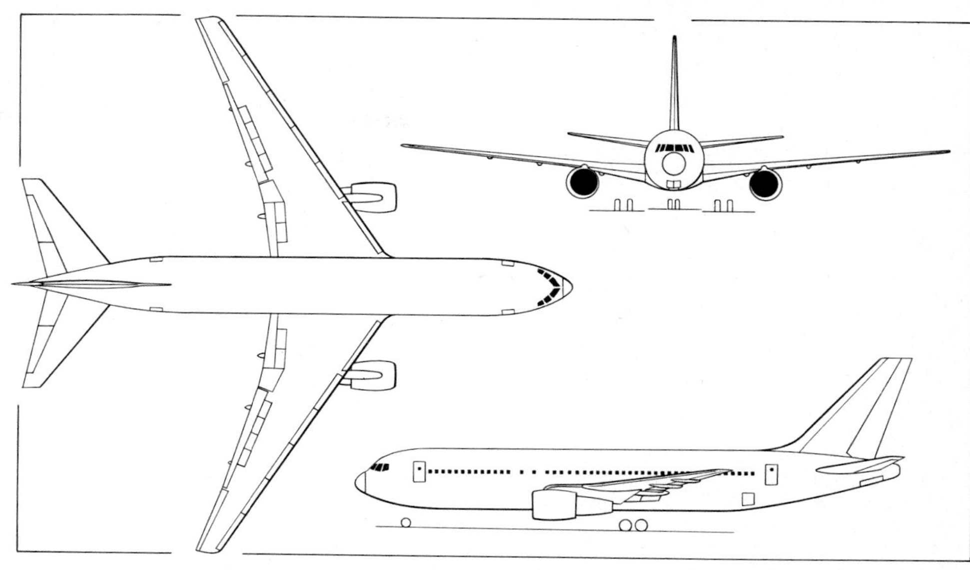

Boeing Model 767-200 wide-bodied medium-range commercial transport aircraft *(Pilot Press)*

BOEING MODEL 767

Construction of the first Model 767 began on 6 July 1979. This aircraft has a completely new airframe, with a fuselage 1·24 m (4 ft 1 in) wider than that of the Model 757, permitting a two-aisle seating layout. It was proposed initially in two forms:

767-100. Accommodation for approximately 180 passengers.

767-200MR. Increased accommodation for 208 to 255 passengers.

On 14 July 1978, Boeing announced its intention to launch full-scale development of the Model 767, following receipt of an order from United Air Lines for thirty 767-200MRs, with initial deliveries scheduled for mid-1982. This airline had participated actively in defining the design of the Model 767, as it did with the design of the Model 727 in 1959-60. It is estimated that when these aircraft enter service with United, powered by Pratt & Whitney JT9D engines, they will be 35 per cent more fuel-efficient than the aircraft they will replace, and will comply also with the stringent noise regulations which are foreseen for 1984. Pacific Western Airlines of Canada has ordered four 767-200s, with options for two more.

Following the initial order from United Air Lines, Boeing announced a version with increased gross weight, the transcontinental-range **Model 767-200TC**. Sixty-two of this version had been ordered by mid-1979, including 30 for American Airlines (with options for 20 more) and 20 for Delta Air Lines (with options for 22 more), each powered by two 213·5 kN (48,000 lb st) class General Electric CF6-80A turbofan engines. Pratt & Whitney JT9D engines are available optionally, and JT9D-7R4s of 213·5 kN (48,000 lb st) will power the aircraft ordered by Air Canada (12, with options for 18 more). Boeing is also studying the Rolls-Royce RB.211 as an alternative option. Fuel capacity of the 767-200TC is increased to 56,688 litres (15,240 US gallons), by inclusion of an auxiliary tank in the wing centre-section. The basic interior arrangements of all versions are identical.

Boeing has awarded manufacturing subcontracts to Grumman Aerospace Corporation (wing centre-section, an adjacent lower fuselage section, and fuselage bulkheads); to Vought Corporation (horizontal tail); and to Canadair Ltd (rear fuselage). In two other major work-sharing programmes announced in August and September 1978, Boeing gave details of co-production agreements whereby Aeritalia of Italy and Civil Transport Development Corporation (CTDC) of Japan will participate as follows:

Aeritalia: Wing control surfaces, flaps and leading-edge slats; wingtips; elevators; fin, rudder; and nose radome.

CTDC: Wing fairings and main landing gear doors (Fuji); centre-fuselage body panels, exit hatches and wing in-spar ribs (Kawasaki); rear-fuselage body panels, stringers, passenger and cargo doors, and dorsal fin (Mitsubishi).

The following details apply to the basic Model 767-200MR:

TYPE: Twin-turbofan medium-range commercial transport.

WINGS: Cantilever low-wing monoplane. Special Boeing wing sections. Thickness/chord ratio 15·1% at root, 10·3% at tip. Dihedral 6°. Incidence 3° 48′. Sweepback 31° 30′ at quarter-chord. Fail-safe structure of 2324 and 7150 aluminium alloy. Plain inboard and outboard ailerons of graphite hybrid composites. Single-slotted linkage-supported aluminium honeycomb trailing-edge flaps. Conventional inboard and outboard spoilers of graphite composite construction are provided for roll control, to act as airbrakes, and for lift dumping. Track-mounted leading-edge slats of light alloy construction. Roll trim through spring feel system. All control surfaces are powered hydraulically. Anti-icing of outboard wing leading-edges.

FUSELAGE: Conventional semi-monocoque structure of 2024 light alloy, consisting of skin, longitudinal stringers and circumferential frames. Structure is of fail-safe design, and is pressurised except for tailcone aft of passenger cabin, landing gear wheel wells and air cycle machine wells.

TAIL UNIT: Cantilever fail-safe structure of 2024 light alloy and aluminium honeycomb. Variable-incidence tailplane. Elevators of single-hinge type with redundant parallel actuators. No trim tabs. All controls are powered hydraulically. Yaw trim through spring feel system. No tail unit anti-icing.

LANDING GEAR: Hydraulically-retractable tricycle type. Twin-wheel nose unit retracts forward. Cleveland Pneumatic main gear, comprising two four-wheel bogies which retract inward. Oleo-pneumatic shock-absorbers. Bendix wheels and brakes. Main-wheel tyres size 43 × 15·5-20, pressure 11·73 bars (170 lb/sq in). Nosewheel tyres size 37 × 14-15, pressure 8·28 bars (120 lb/sq in). Steel disc brakes on all main wheels. Electronically-controlled anti-skid units.

POWER PLANT: Two high bypass turbofan engines in the 177·9 to 222·4 kN (40,000 to 50,000 lb st) class, in pods pylon-mounted on the wing leading-edges. Pratt & Whitney JT9D-7R and General Electric CF6-80A engines had been specified by customers up to mid-1979, and Boeing has future alternative Rolls-Royce RB.211 engines under study. Fuel in one integral tank in each wing, with total fuel capacity of 83,276 litres (22,000 US gallons). Refuelling point in port outer wing. Anti-icing of engine air inlets.

ACCOMMODATION: Normal operating crew of three on flight deck. Basic accommodation for 208 passengers, made up of 18 first class passengers forward in six-abreast seating at 96·5 cm (38 in) pitch, and 190 tourist class in mainly seven-abreast seating at 86 cm (34 in) pitch. Type A inward-opening plug doors are provided at both the front and rear of the cabin on each side of the fuselage, with a Type III emergency exit over the wing on each side. A total of five toilets is installed, two centrally in the main cabin, two aft in the main cabin, and one forward in the first class section. Galleys are situated at forward and aft ends of the cabin. Alternative layouts provide for 218 tourist passengers, seated mainly seven-abreast at 86 cm (34 in) pitch; 241 passengers seated seven-abreast at 81 cm (32 in) pitch, or 255 passengers mainly eight-abreast (two-four-two) at 81 cm (32 in) pitch. Underfloor cargo holds can accommodate, typically, up to 22 LD-67 or 11 LD-3 containers. Forward and aft cargo doors of equal size are standard, but a larger (1·75 by 3·40 m; 5 ft 9 in by 11 ft 2 in) forward cargo door is optional, to permit loading of Type 2 pallets. Overhead stowage for carry-on baggage. Cabin is air-conditioned, cargo holds heated.

SYSTEMS: Hamilton Standard dual air-cycle air-conditioning system. Pressure differential 0·59 bars (8·6 lb/sq in). Electrical supply from two engine-driven 90kVA three-phase 400Hz constant-frequency AC generators, 115/200V output. 90 kVA generator mounted on APU for ground operation or for emergency use. Three hydraulic systems at 207 bars (3,000 lb/sq in), for flight control and utility functions, supplied from Garrett bleed air powered hydraulic pump or APU. Nitrogen chlorate oxygen generators plus gaseous oxygen. Anti-icing for air data sensors and windscreen. APU to provide ground and in-flight electrical power and pressurisation.

AVIONICS AND EQUIPMENT: Standard avionics include ARINC 700 Series equipment, Collins caution annunciator, dual digital flight management systems, and triple digital flight control computers. Honeywell IRS, and Sperry Flight Systems FMCS and DADC, as described in Boeing Model 757 entry.

DIMENSIONS, EXTERNAL:
Wing span 47·24 m (155 ft 0 in)
Wing chord at root 8·57 m (28 ft 1¼ in)
Wing chord at tip 2·29 m (7 ft 6 in)
Wing aspect ratio 7·9
Length overall 48·51 m (159 ft 2 in)
Length of fuselage 47·24 m (155 ft 0 in)
Fuselage width, max 5·03 m (16 ft 6 in)
Height overall 15·85 m (52 ft 0 in)
Tailplane span 18·62 m (61 ft 1 in)
Wheel track 9·30 m (30 ft 6 in)
Wheelbase 19·69 m (64 ft 7 in)
Passenger doors (two, fwd and aft, port):
Height 1·88 m (6 ft 2 in)
Width 1·07 m (3 ft 6 in)
Galley service doors (two, stbd, each):
Height 1·83 m (6 ft 0 in)
Width 1·07 m (3 ft 6 in)
Emergency exits (two, each):
Height 0·91 m (3 ft 0 in)
Width 0·51 m (1 ft 8 in)
Cargo doors (two, fwd and aft):
Height 1·75 m (5 ft 9 in)
Width 1·78 m (5 ft 10 in)
Optional cargo door (fwd, port):
Height 1·75 m (5 ft 9 in)
Width 3·40 m (11 ft 2 in)

DIMENSIONS, INTERNAL:
Cabin, excl flight deck:
Length 33·93 m (111 ft 4 in)
Max width 4·72 m (15 ft 6 in)
Max height 2·87 m (9 ft 5 in)
Floor area 157·6 m^2 (1,696 sq ft)
Volume 435 m^3 (15,348 cu ft)
Volume, flight deck 14·1 m^3 (498 cu ft)
Baggage holds (containerised) volume 74·8 m^3 (2,640 cu ft)
Bulk cargo hold volume 13·0 m^3 (460 cu ft)

AREAS:
Wings, gross 283·3 m^2 (3,050 sq ft)

Ailerons (total)	11·6 m² (125 sq ft)
Trailing-edge flaps (total)	37·2 m² (400 sq ft)
Leading-edge flaps (total)	28·2 m² (304 sq ft)
Spoilers (total)	15·9 m² (171 sq ft)
Fin	29·5 m² (318 sq ft)
Rudder	15·0 m² (162 sq ft)
Tailplane	77·1 m² (830 sq ft)
Elevators	19·0 m² (205 sq ft)

WEIGHTS (estimated; A: 767-200MR; B: 767-200TC):

Weight empty: A	73,356 kg (161,720 lb)
B	73,981 kg (163,100 lb)
Operating weight empty: A	80,830 kg (178,200 lb)
B	81,547 kg (179,780 lb)
Max payload: A	26,762 kg (59,000 lb)
Max T-O weight: A	127,006 kg (280,000 lb)
B	136,078 kg (300,000 lb)
Max ramp weight: A	127,459 kg (281,000 lb)
Max zero-fuel weight: A	108,862 kg (240,000 lb)
B	112,491 kg (248,000 lb)
Max landing weight: A	115,666 kg (255,000 lb)
B	122,470 kg (270,000 lb)

PERFORMANCE (estimated, with JT9D-7R engines, at max T-O weight unless noted otherwise):

Max level speed at 8,840 m (29,000 ft):	
A, B	Mach 0·86
Normal cruising speed at 11,885 m (39,000 ft):	
A, B	Mach 0·80
Approach speed at max landing weight:	
A	130 knots (241 km/h; 150 mph)
B	134 knots (248 km/h; 154 mph)
Max certification altitude:	
A, B	12,800 m (42,000 ft)
Service ceiling, one engine out:	
A	4,905 m (16,100 ft)
B	5,000 m (16,400 ft)
T-O field length: A	1,966 m (6,450 ft)
B	2,042 m (6,700 ft)
Landing field length: A	1,600 m (5,250 ft)
B	1,676 m (5,500 ft)
Range with max payload:	
A	2,030 nm (3,763 km; 2,338 miles)
B	2,810 nm (5,208 km; 3,236 miles)

BOEING MODEL 777-100

Announced simultaneously with the Models 757 and 767, Boeing's Model 777-100 is proposed as a long-range derivative of the Model 767-200. It differs in having an extended fuselage, with a 3·91 m (12 ft 10 in) fuselage plug inserted forward of the wing-root leading-edge, and a 1·68 m (5 ft 6 in) fuselage section removed from aft of the wing-root trailing-edge. A third turbofan engine is installed in the aft fuselage, at the base of the fin, and a 1·52 m (5 ft 0 in) tip extension is added to each wing. Alternative power plants are available from General Electric and Pratt & Whitney.

Intended for international route operations, the 777-100 would accommodate 212 passengers in a mixed-class arrangement, or 222 passengers in an all-tourist version.

No further details were available in early 1979.

BOEING AEROSPACE COMPANY

The Boeing Aerospace Company has its headquarters at the company's space centre at Kent, Washington, some 12 miles south of Seattle. It consists of Aerospace Operations, Business Development, Electronic Support Division, Navy Systems and Advanced Project Division, Logistic Support and Services Division, Missiles and Space Division, Army Systems Division, Aircraft Armament and Information Systems Division, Automated Transportation Systems, and Military Airplane Development. Responsible for much of Boeing's military, space and diversification efforts, it has a labour force of approximately 17,000. Among its principal current activities are the AWACS and cruise missile programmes, Minuteman modernisation, advanced surface transportation programmes, military applications of commercial transports, and space projects.

BOEING E-3 SENTRY

USAF designations: EC-137D and E-3A

The E-3A Sentry AWACS (Airborne Warning And Control System) aircraft offers the potential of long-range high- or low-level surveillance of all air vehicles, manned or unmanned, in all weathers and above all kinds of terrain. Its data storage and processing capability can provide real-time assessment of enemy action, and of the status and position of friendly resources. By centralising the co-ordination of complex, diverse and simultaneous air operations in wartime, such an aircraft can command and control the total air effort: strike, air superiority, support, airlift, reconnaissance and interdiction.

In USAF service, the system has a dual use: as a command and control centre to support quick-reaction deployment and tactical operations by Tactical Air Command units; and as a survivable early-warning airborne command and control centre for identification, surveillance and tracking of airborne enemy forces, and for the command and control of NORAD (North American Air Defense) forces over the continental USA. The E-3A provides comprehensive surveillance out to a range of more than 200 nm (370 km; 230 miles) for low-flying targets, and still further for targets flying at higher altitudes.

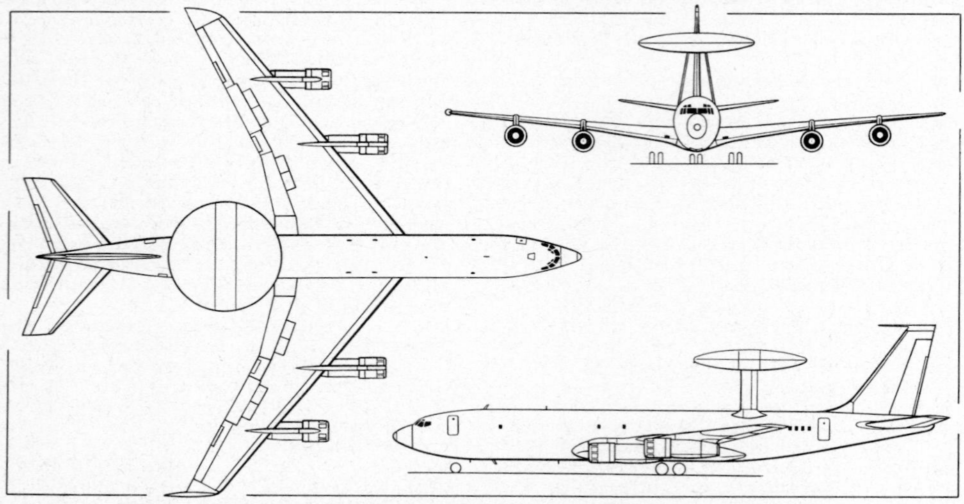
Boeing E-3A Sentry airborne warning and control system aircraft *(Pilot Press)*

Boeing E-3A Sentry airborne warning and control system (AWACS) aircraft for the USAF

Boeing's Aerospace Group was awarded an initial contract as prime contractor and systems integrator for the AWAC system on 23 July 1970. Its design submission was based on the airframe of the Model 707-320B commercial jet transport. Two of these aircraft, with the prototype designation EC-137D, were modified initially for comparative trials with prototype downward-looking radars designed by Hughes Aircraft Company and Westinghouse Electric Corporation.

After several months of airborne tests the Westinghouse radar was selected, on 5 October 1972. On 26 January 1973 the USAF announced that, following satisfactory completion of Phase 1, approval had been given for full-scale development of AWACS, and production was authorised in the Spring of 1975. The full-scale development test programme involved a fleet of three aircraft completely equipped with mission avionics, and a fourth aircraft equipped for airworthiness testing, and was completed at the end of 1976.

In December 1976 Boeing awarded Westinghouse a contract to develop a maritime surveillance capability that could be incorporated in the E-3A radar. If the USAF proceeds with development of such a capability, flight tests of the expanded radar would be followed by the retrofitting of operational E-3As.

The first production E-3A, now named Sentry, was delivered on 24 March 1977 to Tactical Air Command's 552nd Airborne Warning and Control Wing, based at Tinker AFB, Oklahoma. A total of five were delivered by the end of 1977, followed by nine more during 1978. E-3As achieved initial operational status in April 1978, and have since completed deployments to Alaska, Iceland and the Pacific. They began assuming a role in US continental air defence on 1 January 1979, when 30 NORAD personnel started to augment TAC E-3A flight crews on all operational NORAD missions from Tinker AFB. This unit was expected to be fully operational by Summer 1979.

Funding for a total of 25 E-3As had been approved by mid-1979, and three more will be requested under each Fiscal Year budget until the planned force of 34 USAF AWACS is complete. In addition, NATO has approved the acquisition of 18, under a cost-sharing agreement, to be based in the Federal Republic of Germany. For these, much of the avionics will be produced in Germany, with Dornier as systems integrator; deliveries to NATO will begin in 1982.

TYPE: Airborne early-warning and command post aircraft.

WINGS, FUSELAGE, TAIL UNIT AND LANDING GEAR: Basically as Boeing 707-320B, with strengthened fuselage structure and installation of rotodome.

POWER PLANT: Four Pratt & Whitney TF33-PW-100/100A turbofan engines, each rated at 93·4 kN (21,000 lb st), mounted in pods beneath the wings.

ACCOMMODATION: Basic operational crew of 17 includes a flight crew complement of four plus thirteen AWACS specialists, though this latter number can vary for tactical and defence missions. Aft of flight deck, from front to rear of fuselage, are communications, data processing and other equipment bays; multi-purpose consoles; communications, navigation and identification equipment; and crew rest area.

SYSTEMS: A liquid cooling system provides protection for the radar transmitter. An air-cycle pack system and a closed-loop ram-cooled environmental control system ensure a suitable environment for crew and avionics equipment. Electrical power generation has a 600kVA capability. The distribution centre for mission equipment power and remote avionics is located in the lower forward cargo compartment. The aft cargo compartment houses the radar transmitter and an APU. External sockets allow intake of power when the aircraft is on the ground. Two separate and independent hydraulic systems power flight-essential and mission-essential equipment, but either system has the capability of satisfying the requirements of both equipment groups in an emergency.

Avionics and Equipment: Prominent above the fuselage is the elliptical cross-section rotodome which is 9·14 m (30 ft) in diameter and 1·83 m (6 ft) in depth. It comprises four essential elements: a strut-mounted turntable, supporting the rotary joint assembly to which are attached sliprings for electrical and waveguide continuity between rotodome and fuselage; a structural centre section of aluminium skin and stiffener construction, which supports the AN/APY-1 surveillance radar and IFF/TADIL C antennae, radomes, auxiliary equipment for radar operation and environmental control of the rotodome interior; liquid cooling of the radar antenna; and two radomes constructed of multi-layer glassfibre sandwich material, one for the surveillance radar and one for the IFF/TADIL C array. For surveillance operations the rotodome is hydraulically driven at 6 rpm, but during non-operational flights it is rotated at only ¼ rpm, to keep the bearings lubricated. The Westinghouse radar operates in the S band; by use of pulse Doppler technology, with a high pulse repetition frequency, this radar features long range and accuracy in addition to a normal downlook capability. Its antenna, spanning about 7·32 m (24 ft), and 1·52 m (5 ft) deep, scans mechanically in azimuth, and electronically from ground level up into the stratosphere. Heart of the data processing is an IBM 4 Pi CC-1 high-speed computer, the entire group consisting of arithmetic control units, input/output units, main storage units, peripheral control units, mass memory drums, magnetic tape transports, punched tape reader, line printer, and an operator's control panel. Processing speed is in the order of 740,000 operations/sec; input/output data rate has a maximum of 710,000 words/s; main memory size is 114,688 words (expandable to 180,224), and mass memory size 802,816 words (expandable to 1,204,224). An interface adapter unit developed by Boeing is the key integrating element interconnecting functional data between AWACS avionics subsystems, data processing group, radar, communications, navigation/guidance, display, azimuth and identification. Data display and control is provided by Hazeltine Corporation multi-purpose consoles (MPC) and auxiliary display units (ADU); in present configuration each AWACS aircraft carries nine MPCs and two ADUs. Navigation/guidance relies upon three principal sources of information: two Delco AN/ASN-119 (Carousel IV) inertial platforms; a Northrop AN/ARN-120 Omega navigation set; and a Ryan AN/APN-213 Doppler velocity sensor. Communications equipment, supplied by Collins Radio, Electronic Communications Inc, E-Systems, and Hughes Aircraft, provides HF, VHF and UHF communication channels by means of which information can be transmitted or received in clear or secure mode, in voice or digital form. Identification is based on an AN/APX-103 interrogator set being developed by Cutler-Hammer's AIL Division. It is the first airborne IFF interrogator set to offer complete AIMS Mk X SIF air traffic control and Mk XII military identification friend or foe (IFF) in a single integrated system. Simultaneous Mk X and Mk XII multi-target and multi-mode operations will allow the operator to obtain instantaneously the range, azimuth and elevation, code identification and IFF status of all targets within radar range.

Dimensions, external:
- Wing span: 44·42 m (145 ft 9 in)
- Length overall: 46·61 m (152 ft 11 in)
- Height overall: 12·60 m (41 ft 4 in)

Weight:
- Max T-O weight: 147,400 kg (325,000 lb)

Performance:
- Max level speed: 460 knots (853 km/h; 530 mph)
- Service ceiling: over 8,850 m (29,000 ft)
- Endurance on station, 870 nm (1,600 km; 1,000 miles) from base: 6 h

BOEING ADVANCED AIRBORNE COMMAND POST

USAF designation: E-4

On 28 February 1973 the USAF's Electronic Systems Division announced from its headquarters at Hanscom Field, Bedford, Massachusetts, that it had awarded The Boeing Company a $59 million fixed-price contract for the supply of two Model 747Bs to be adapted as **E-4A** airborne command posts under the 481B Advanced Airborne Command Post (AABNCP) programme. A contract valued at more than $27·2 million was awarded, in July 1973, for a third aircraft; in December 1973 the fourth aircraft was contracted at $39 million.

The third and fourth aircraft differed initially from the first two in having General Electric F103-GE-100 turbofan engines, each rated at 233·5 kN (52,500 lb st), instead of the JT9Ds that were then fitted normally to aircraft of the 747 series; F103-GE-100s were fitted retrospectively to the first two aircraft during 1976. The fourth aircraft is fitted with more advanced equipment (see below) and is designated **E-4B**.

On 15 January 1976 it was stated that the total planned force was six E-4Bs, comprising the fourth aircraft, two more similar aircraft, and the three E-4As brought up to the same standard retrospectively. However, no funds have yet been approved for this continuation of the programme.

The E-4s were intended to replace EC-135 Airborne Command Posts of the National Military Command System and Strategic Air Command, which are military variants of the Model 707. E-Systems Inc of Greenville, Texas, won a contract to install interim equipment in the first three E-4As. This involved transfer and integration of equipment removed from EC-135s, providing aircraft with increased endurance and the ability to carry an expanded battle staff. The E-4A's 429·2 m² (4,620 sq ft) of floor space accommodates almost three times the payload of the EC-135. The main deck is divided into six areas: the National Command Authorities' (NCA) work area, conference room, briefing room, battle staff work area, communications control centre and rest area. The flight deck accommodates the flight crew, navigation station and flight crew rest area. Lobe areas, beneath the main deck, house a technical control facility and a limited onboard maintenance storage area.

The first E-4A flew for the first time on 13 June 1973, and was delivered to Andrews AFB, Maryland, in December 1974. The second and third, also consigned to Andrews AFB, were received in May and September 1975. In their present form, they are able to operate as National Emergency Airborne Command Posts (NEACPs), and provided operational experience that proved invaluable in finalising the design of equipment installed in the E-4B.

In early 1974, Boeing and a team comprising Computer Sciences Corporation of Falls Church, Virginia; Electro-space Systems Inc of Richardson, Texas; and E-Systems Inc, won the contract to design and install the advanced command post equipment in the first E-4B. As a first step, this was delivered to the USAF in August 1975 in testbed configuration, with flight refuelling equipment installed but without the planned command, control and communications equipment. Next stage involved installation of the 1,200kVA electrical system (two 150kVA generators on each engine) that had been designed to support the advanced electronics. Finally the operational systems were added, and the first flight of the fully equipped E-4B took place in June 1978. USAF tests of operational capability began later that year.

The E-4B, when it enters service, will have accommodation for a larger battle staff than that carried by the E-4A; an air-conditioning system of 226·5 m³ (8,000 cu ft)/min capacity to cool electronic components; nuclear thermal shielding; acoustic controls; an improved technical control facility; and new super high frequency (SHF) and Collins LF/VLF communications systems, the latter employing a trailing-wire antenna that is trailed behind the aircraft in flight.

Strategic Air Command (SAC) is now sole operational manager of the AABNCP force. Transfer of operational responsibility from Headquarters Command USAF to SAC began in October 1975 and became effective as from 1 November 1975. The main operating base for the E-4 fleet is at Offutt AFB, Nebraska.

BOEING YC-14 (AMST)

Looking ahead for potential replacements for its fleet of Lockheed C130 Hercules transport aircraft, the USAF issued requests for proposals to nine US aerospace companies in early 1972. From these proposals, those of Boeing and McDonnell Douglas were selected, and on 10 November 1972 these two companies were each awarded a contract to develop, construct and flight test two aircraft to compete in a prototype fly-off competition. Boeing's prototypes, which were allocated the USAF designation YC-14, were built under a $105·9 million contract.

A significant design feature of the YC-14 is the use of a relatively small supercritical wing, with an overwing installation of the power plant. Benefits accruing from this layout include the presentation of a low infra-red signature to ground-based detectors; an engine-free underwing surface, simplifying the carriage of external stores, including RPVs; efficient thrust reversal; and a reduced noise footprint. Significant improvement of cargo compartment loading efficiency resulted from the adoption of the wide-body fuselage concept.

The first YC-14 prototype (01873) was flown for the first time on 9 August 1976. The second prototype (01874) made its first flight on 21 October 1976, and the flight test programme was completed in August 1977, after accumulating more than 600 hours' flying. Funding for continuation of the AMST (advanced medium STOL transport) was withheld from the FY 1979 defence budget.

All available details of the Boeing YC-14 can be found in the 1978-79 *Jane's*.

Boeing E-4B advanced airborne command post operated by the USAF Strategic Air Command

BOEING WICHITA COMPANY

Boeing Wichita Company is responsible for all work on the B-52 Stratofortress bomber and KC-135 jet tanker-transport series. It manufactures parts and assemblies for the Boeing Model 707, 727, 737 and 747 series of commercial transports, and is preparing to produce the nose section of the new Model 767. It also undertakes conversion of Boeing aircraft from passenger to freight-carrying configurations, installs new interiors and embodies structural modifications.

BOEING B-52 STRATOFORTRESS

Designed originally as an intercontinental, high-altitude nuclear bomber, the B-52, which first entered US Air Force service in 1955, has undergone numerous improvement programmes over the years to ensure that its operational capabilities meet changing defence needs. The USAF expects that more than 300 B-52s will remain in its active inventory for the remainder of this century.

The early development history of the B-52 has been recorded in previous editions of *Jane's,* and a structural description can be found in the 1964-65 edition. The three versions still in squadron service (other than the B-52F, which is used for training) are the B-52D, G and H, of which a combined total of 465 was built. A total of 349 of these remain operational, serving with the 2nd, 7th, 19th, 42nd, 68th, 97th, 379th, 410th and 416th Bomb Wings of the Eighth Air Force; the 5th, 22nd, 28th, 92nd, 93rd, 96th, 319th and 320th Bomb Wings of the Fifteenth Air Force; and the 43rd Strategic Wing of the 3rd Air Division of SAC. An additional 187 B-52s are kept in inactive storage.

Several programmes involving the **B-52G** and **H** have been undertaken or are now in progress to improve the electronics, equipment and operational capability. Under a 1971 contract, 281 of these two models were modified to carry the Boeing SRAM (short range attack missile), which has completely replaced the underwing Hound Dog missiles formerly carried.

The USAF's Rivet Ace programme, initiated in 1974, is progressively updating about 270 B-52Gs and B-52Hs with what are known as 'Phase VI' ECM (electronic countermeasures). These aircraft have already an AN/ASQ-151 Electro-optical Viewing System (EVS) to improve low level penetration capability, the EVS sensors being housed in two steerable, side-by-side chin turrets. The starboard turret houses a Hughes Aircraft AAQ-6 forward-looking infra-red (FLIR) scanner, while the port turret contains a Westinghouse AVQ-22 low light level TV camera.

By 1981 the B-52G and H will be fitted with Motorola ALQ-122 SNOE (Smart Noise Operation Equipment) countermeasures, and Northrop AN/ALQ-155(V) advanced ECM; between 1978 and 1982 with an AFSATCOM kit permitting worldwide communication via satellite; and by 1984 with a Northrop ALT-28 updated transmitter and power management system, to provide automated control of radio frequency power to reduce the effectiveness of enemy radar. Other Phase VI electronics include an ALR-46 digital radar warning receiver, and two tail-mounted ITT Avionics ALQ-117 noise/deception jammers. Development and testing have been completed of an RCA ALQ-127 pulse-Doppler tail warning radar system, which will be able to detect an enemy aircraft approaching from the rear and dispense, automatically, the appropriate countermeasures. Requests for proposals were issued to AIL/Cutler-Hammer (AN/ALQ-154) and Westinghouse (AN/ALQ-153) for alternative tail warning systems, and procurement of the selected system was expected to begin by 1979.

Sedco Systems has an Air Force contract to design and develop the prototype of an electronically steerable antenna system (ESAS) for the B-52G and H, to improve their defensive electronics (jamming) capability. Boeing Wichita has a USAF contract to define and design an Offensive Avionics System (OAS) to upgrade the navigation and weapons delivery of the B-52G and H. At a significantly reduced life-cycle cost, this will be a digital (instead of analogue) based, solid-state system, and will include Tercom (terrain comparison) guidance. During 1978 and 1979, Westinghouse has been ground and flight testing an Electronic Agile Radar (EAR) as a replacement for the present B-52G/H bombing and navigation radar. A Honeywell AN/ASN-131 inertial navigation system is also to be installed in the B-52D, G and H.

In addition, whatever the result of the 1979 fly-off between Boeing's ALCM-B and the General Dynamics Tomahawk cruise missile, the B-52G will be adapted as carrier aircraft for the selected weapon, and development for this role is continuing in support of the cruise missile programme. Full-scale development of B-52 carrier aircraft equipment, as an integral part of the cruise missile programme, began in early 1978, and three B-52Gs were modified for use in the fly-off programme at Edwards AFB, California.

Boeing B-52G fitted with AN/ASQ-151 Electro-optical Viewing System and with other recent modifications

At an estimated cost, in 'then-year' dollars, of $1·4 billion, a second development phase in updating the B-52G and H is scheduled to take place between FY 1979 to 1983, with procurement of production items following in FY 1983 or 1984 and completion of equipment fits by about 1990. This phase will be devoted to a continued updating of the aircraft's electronics equipment as a cruise missile carrier, and to its penetration ability as a bomber, and will probably include such items as new forward-looking radar, automatic terrain-following guidance, and a new flight control system.

Power Plant (B-52D): Eight 44·5 kN (10,000 lb st) Pratt & Whitney J57-P-19W or -29W turbojet engines. Fuel capacity 135,140 litres (35,700 US gallons) internally, plus two 11,355 litre (3,000 US gallon) underwing drop-tanks.

Power Plant (B-52G): Engine 61·2 kN (13,750 lb st) J57-P-43WB turbojet engines. Fuel capacity 174,130 litres (46,000 US gallons) internally, plus two 2,650 litre (700 US gallon) underwing drop-tanks.

Power Plant (B-52H): Eight 75·6 kN (17,000 lb st) Pratt & Whitney TF33-P-3 turbofan engines. Fuel capacity as for B-52G.

Accommodation (B-52D/G/H): Crew of six (pilot and co-pilot, side by side on flight deck, navigator, radar navigator, ECM operator and gunner).

Armament (B-52D): Four 0·50 in machine-guns in occupied tail turret. Up to eighty-four 500 lb bombs in fuselage weapons bay, and a further twenty-four 750 lb bombs on underwing pylons: total bomb load 27,215 kg (60,000 lb).

Armament (B-52G): Four 0·50 in machine-guns in tail turret, remotely operated by AGS-15 fire control system, remote radar control, or closed circuit TV. Up to 20 Boeing AGM-69 SRAM short-range attack missiles: eight on rotary launcher in internal weapons bay, and six under each wing, plus nuclear free-fall bombs.

Armament (B-52H): As B-52G, except for single 20 mm Vulcan multi-barrel cannon in tail turret instead of four machine-guns.

Dimensions, external:
Wing span 56·39 m (185 ft 0 in)
Wing area, gross 371·6 m² (4,000 sq ft)
Length overall: G, H 49·05 m (160 ft 10·9 in)
Height overall: D 14·74 m (48 ft 4½ in)
G, H 12·40 m (40 ft 8 in)
Width of fuselage 3·00 m (9 ft 10 in)
Tailplane span: G, H 15·85 m (52 ft 0 in)
Wheel track (c/l of shock-struts) 2·51 m (8 ft 3 in)
Wheelbase 15·48 m (50 ft 3 in)

Dimension, internal:
Weapons bay volume 29·53 m³ (1,043 cu ft)

Weights:
Max T-O weight: D 204,115 kg (450,000 lb)
G, H 221,350 kg (488,000 lb)

Performance (B-52G/H):
Max level speed at high altitude
Mach 0·90 (516 knots; 957 km/h; 595 mph)
Cruising speed at high altitude
Mach 0·77 (442 knots; 819 km/h; 509 mph)
Penetration speed at low altitude
Mach 0·53 to 0·55
(352-365 knots; 652-676 km/h; 405-420 mph)
Service ceiling 16,765 m (55,000 ft)
T-O run: G 3,050 m (10,000 ft)
H 2,900 m (9,500 ft)
Range with max fuel, without in-flight refuelling:
G 6,513 nm (12,070 km; 7,500 miles)
H 8,685 nm (16,093 km; 10,000 miles)

BOEING KC-135A STRATOTANKER

The first of 732 KC-135A tanker-transports built by Boeing for the USAF flew on 31 August 1956. In early 1979, a total of 615 remained operational to support Strategic Air Command aircraft and those of other USAF commands, the US Navy and Marine Corps, and other nations.

Since 1975 Wichita has been engaged in a programme to extend the flying life of each KC-135A by 27,000 hours, by replacing the lower wing skins. This will enable the aircraft to remain fully operational well past the year 2000, and has justified a programme to retrofit modern technology engines, to improve fuel economy and reduce noise. It was hoped to select the most suitable engine and begin designing the installation in 1979.

On 10 June 1977, Boeing Wichita received a contract to design, install and flight test on a KC-135A a set of winglets that could reduce fuel consumption by an estimated 8 per cent. This would save 140 million litres (37 million US gallons) of fuel annually; the winglets are also expected to improve take-off performance, and slightly enhance fuel offload capability. Flight testing of the winglets on the KC-135A began in 1979 (see NASA entry).

BOEING VERTOL COMPANY

Boeing Vertol Company, established in 1960, has produced and delivered some 2,500 tandem-rotor helicopters to the US military services, as well as to many foreign nations. The CH-47 Chinook is the company's current production helicopter for the US Army, and is in service also with the armed forces of eight nations. Boeing Vertol markets the BO 105 C helicopter, developed and manufactured in Germany by Messerschmitt-Bölkow-Blohm GmbH (which see), in the United States, Canada and Mexico under a licence agreement.

BOEING VERTOL MODEL 107

US Navy and Marine Corps designation: CH-46/UH-46 Sea Knight

Details of the Boeing Vertol Model 107, of which production by Boeing Vertol has ended, can be found in the 1971-72 *Jane's.* A derivative, the KV-107, is being produced currently in Japan under licence by Kawasaki Heavy Industries Ltd (which see).

A total of 624 basically similar CH/UH-46 aircraft were delivered to the USMC and USN in the 1964-1971 period. With a view to modernising the Marine Corps' fleet of CH-46s, two prototypes were modified by Boeing Vertol in 1975 and have since completed flight testing. The USMC now plans to update 273 CH-46s to **CH-46E** configuration, this involving the installation of 1,394 kW (1,870 shp) General Electric T58-GE-16 turboshaft engines, each developing 33·6% more power than the 1,044 kW (1,400 shp) T58-GE-10s installed in production CH-46D/F aircraft. Other modifications include the provision of crash attenuating seats for pilot and co-pilot, a crash and combat resistant fuel system, and improved rescue system. Initial fleet modifications began during 1977, and the first CH-46E modified at the Cherry Point, NC, Naval Air Rework Facility was rolled out on 3 August 1977.

In April 1975 Boeing Vertol received a contract from Naval Air Systems Command to initiate the development of glassfibre main rotor blades for the H-46 fleet. In early 1977 glassfibre rotor blades for testing purposes were being manufactured by Boeing Vertol, and these were bench tested, whirl tested and flight tested during the remainder of the year. Due to the satisfactory progress of this programme, the USMC began in-service testing of these blades in early 1978. The first production order for these glassfibre rotor blades was issued by the US Navy in December 1977.

Boeing Vertol updated CH-46E, for the US Marine Corps, with General Electric T58-GE-16 turboshaft engines

BOEING VERTOL MODELS 114 and 414

US Army designation: CH-47 Chinook
Canadian Armed Forces designation: CH-147
Royal Air Force designation: Chinook HC. Mk 1

Development of the CH-47 Chinook series of helicopters began in 1956, and Boeing Vertol was awarded an initial contract for five YCH-47As (formerly YHC-1B) by the US Army in June 1959. The first hovering flight was made on 21 September 1961. Since then, the effectiveness of the CH-47 has been increased by successive product improvement programmes. A total of 939 Chinooks had been ordered by 1 January 1979, of which 848 had been delivered; of these, 147 orders and 92 deliveries were from licence production by the Agusta group in Italy (which see).

The CH-47 was designed to meet the US Army's requirement for an all-weather medium transport helicopter and, depending upon the series model, is capable of transporting specified payloads under severe combinations of altitude and temperature conditions. The primary mission radius criterion established by the US Army is 100 nm (185 km; 115 miles). The primary mission take-off gross weight is based on the capability of hovering out of ground effect at 1,830 m/35°C (6,000 ft/95°F). The CH-47C has demonstrated its ability to hover out of ground effect with a useful load of 11,453 kg (25,250 lb) at sea level under standard atmospheric conditions.

Three versions of the Chinook have been produced:

CH-47A. Initial production version, powered by two 1,640 kW (2,200 shp) Lycoming T55-L-5 or 1,976 kW (2,650 shp) T55-L-7 turboshaft engines. Operation of the CH-47A by the Viet-Nam Air Force (VNAF) began in 1971. Four delivered to Royal Thai Air Force. Production completed. Transmissions being uprated to CH-47C standard under 1978 Army contract.

CH-47B. Developed version with 2,125 kW (2,850 shp) T55-L-7C turboshaft engines, redesigned rotor blades with cambered leading-edge, blunted rear rotor pylon, and strakes along rear ramp and fuselage for improved flying qualities. First of two prototypes flew for the first time in early October 1966. Deliveries began on 10 May 1967. Production completed. Transmissions being uprated to CH-47C standard under 1978 Army contract.

CH-47C. The current model achieves increased performance from a combination of strengthened transmissions, two 2,796 kW (3,750 shp) T55-L-11A engines and increased integral fuel capacity. First flight of the original model CH-47C was made on 14 October 1967, and deliveries of production aircraft began in the Spring of 1968. They were first deployed in Viet-Nam in September 1968.

Deliveries of nine CH-47Cs to Canada began in September 1974. Designated **CH-147** by Canada, these aircraft have T55-L-11C engines, ISIS, CWFS, forward door rescue hoist, ferry range tank kit, up to 44 troop seats, advanced flight control system, rear ramp with water dam, 12,700 kg (28,000 lb) cargo hook, T-O weight of 22,680 kg (50,000 lb), and weight for water operations of 16,330 kg (36,000 lb) normal or 20,865 kg (46,000 lb) emergency.

Following extensive development work on a Crashworthy Fuel System (CWFS), and an Integral Spar Inspection System (ISIS), these safety features were made available during 1973. Incorporation of the CWFS on US Army CH-47Cs was accomplished by retrofit kits, deliveries of which began in March 1973. All Chinooks delivered to Australia and Canada have this system, which provides a total fuel capacity of 3,944 litres (1,042 US gallons).

Boeing Vertol is engaged in the modernisation of three Chinooks to **CH-47D** standard under a US Army R & D programme. If the development programme of these prototypes is successful, it could lead to a contract for the modernisation of 361 of the US Army's inventory of Chinook aircraft. One example of each of the CH-47A, B and C models is involved in the programme. They are being fitted with Lycoming T55-L-712 engines, uprated transmissions, a T-62T-28 APU, an advanced flight control system, and glassfibre rotor blades, testing of which began on a CH-47C testbed on 22 May 1978. The first CH-47D, converted from an A-model airframe, was rolled out on 6 March 1979, and was expected to begin its flight testing two months later.

Chinook HC.Mk 1. Version for Royal Air Force, which has ordered 33 for delivery between August 1980 and the end of 1981. Generally similar to Canadian CH-147, with Lycoming T55-L-11E turboshaft engines, but will have provision for glassfibre/carbon fibre rotor blades and three external cargo hooks (capacity 12,700 kg; 28,000 lb on centre hook, or 9,072 kg; 20,000 lb total on forward and rear hooks); accommodation for up to 44 troops or 24 standard NATO stretchers; engine and windscreen de-icing; provision for two self-ferry fuel tanks in cabin; and amphibious capability in sea states of up to 3. Intended for use on logistic support, tactical troop lift, casualty evacuation, air-mobility, and external load-carrying duties. Extensive range of British avionics and equipment, including Decca tactical navigation system; Marconi Avionics ARC340 VHF/FM com and homing system, AD120 VHF/AM com, AD380 ADF, AD2770 Tacan and AD27733 interface unit; and Lucas 40kVA generators.

CH-47 helicopters are in service in many places, including Alaska, Australia, Germany, Hawaii, Iran, Italy, Korea, Spain and Thailand as well as at numerous US National Guard and US Army installations within the continental United States. Total US Army procurement of CH-47A/B/C models had reached 721 by 1 January 1979. Of these 358 then equipped active Army units, with 94 more in Reserve/ANG service. Other customers for US-built CH-47Cs include Argentina (3, for 1979 delivery), Australia (12), Spain (10), Thailand (4), and the UK (33, for 1980-81 delivery). Customers for Agusta/EM-built CH-47Cs include the air forces of Italy (26, all delivered), Iran (95, of which 54 delivered by the end of 1978), Libya (20, of which 12 delivered) and Morocco (6, for 1978-79 delivery).

In addition, Boeing Vertol has announced a commercial version, the **Model 234LR**; this is described separately.

Details of the CH-47A and -47B can be found in the 1974-75 *Jane's*. Those which follow apply specifically to the current CH-47C:

TYPE: Twin-engined medium transport helicopter.

ROTOR SYSTEM: Two three-blade rotors, rotating in opposite directions and driven through interconnecting shafts which enable both rotors to be driven by either engine. Rotor blades, of a modified NACA 0012 section, have cambered leading-edge, a strengthened steel spar structure and honeycomb-filled trailing-edge boxes. Two blades of each rotor can be folded manually. Rotor heads are fully articulated, with pitch, flapping and drag hinges. All bearings are submerged completely in oil.

ROTOR DRIVE: Power is transmitted from each engine through individual overrunning clutches, into the combiner transmission, thereby providing a single power output to the interconnecting shafts. Rotor/engine rpm ratio 64 : 1.

FUSELAGE: Square-section all-metal semi-monocoque structure. Loading ramp forms undersurface of upswept rear fuselage. Fairing pods along bottom of each side are made of metal honeycomb sandwich and are sealed and compartmented, as is the underfloor section of the

CH-47C CHINOOK WEIGHTS AND PERFORMANCE

	Condition 1	Condition 2	Condition 3	Condition 4
Weight empty	9,736 kg (21,464 lb)	9,736 kg (21,464 lb)	9,812 kg (21,633 lb)	9,599 kg (21,162 lb)
Payload	5,284 kg (11,650 lb)	2,903 kg (6,400 lb)	9,843 kg (21,700 lb)	—
T-O weight	17,463 kg (38,500 lb)	14,968 kg (33,000 lb)	20,593 kg (45,400 lb)	20,865 kg (46,000 lb)
Max speed, S/L, ISA at normal rated power	155 knots (286 km/h; 178 mph)	164 knots (304 km/h; 189 mph)	127 knots (235 km/h; 146 mph)	—
Average cruising speed	139 knots (257 km/h; 160 mph)	137 knots (254 km/h; 158 mph)	114 knots (211 km/h; 131 mph)	133 knots (246 km/h; 153 mph)
Max rate of climb, S/L, ISA at normal rated power	649 m (2,130 ft)/min	878 m (2,880 ft)/min	421 m (1,380 ft)/min	402 m (1,320 ft)/min
Service ceiling, ISA, normal rated power	3,290 m (10,800 ft)	4,570 m (15,000 ft)	2,560 m (8,400 ft)	2,440 m (8,000 ft)
Hovering ceiling OGE, ISA, max power	2,805 m (9,200 ft)	4,145 m (13,600 ft)	Sea level	—
Mission radius	100 nm (185 km; 115 miles)	100 nm (185 km; 115 miles)	20 nm (37 km; 23 miles)	—
Ferry range	—	—	—	1,156 nm (2,142 km; 1,331 miles)

Condition 1 Criteria: Take-off gross weight equals gross weight to hover OGE at 1,830 m/35°C (6,000 ft/95°F). Radius of action 100 nm (185 km; 115 miles). Fuel reserve 10%. Payload carried internally.

Condition 2 Criteria: Take-off gross weight equals design gross weight. Radius of action 100 nm (185 km; 115 miles). Fuel reserve 10%. Payload carried internally.

Condition 3 Criteria: Take-off gross weight equals gross weight to hover OGE at S/L ISA. Radius of action 20 nm (37 km; 23 miles). Fuel reserve 10%. Payload carried externally. Except for the mission average cruising speed, all other performance is predicated on internal loading of cargo.

Condition 4 Criteria: Take-off gross weight represents alternative design gross weight. Max ferry range (integral and internal auxiliary fuel only), cruise at optimum altitude and standard temperature, no payload, 10% fuel reserves.

First Boeing Vertol CH-47D Chinook, converted from a CH-47A that completed two operational tours of duty in Viet-Nam

fuselage, for buoyancy during operation from water.

Landing Gear: Menasco non-retractable quadricycle type, with twin wheels on each forward unit and single wheels on each rear unit. Oleo-pneumatic shock-absorbers on all units. Rear units fully castoring and steerable; power steering installed on starboard rear unit. All wheels are government-furnished size 24 × 7·7-VII, with tyres size 8·50-10-III, pressure 4·62 bars (67 lb/sq in). Two single-disc hydraulic brakes. Provision for fitting detachable wheel-skis.

Power Plant: Two 2,796 kW (3,750 shp) Lycoming T55-L-11A turboshaft engines, mounted on each side of rear rotor pylon. Combined transmission rating 5,369 kW (7,200 shp); max single-engine transmission limit 3,430 kW (4,600 shp). Self-sealing fuel tanks in external pods on sides of fuselage. Total fuel capacity is 4,137 litres (1,093 US gallons), or 3,944 litres (1,042 US gallons) when equipped with Crashworthy Fuel System. Refuelling points above tanks. Total oil capacity 14 litres (3·7 US gallons).

Accommodation: Two pilots on flight deck, with dual controls. Jump seat is provided for crew chief or combat commander. Jettisonable door on each side of flight deck. Depending on seating arrangement, 33 to 44 troops can be accommodated in main cabin, or 24 litters plus two attendants, or vehicles and freight. Typical loads include a complete artillery section with crew and ammunition. All components of the Pershing missile system are transportable by Chinooks. Extruded magnesium floor designed for distributed load of 1,465 kg/m² (300 lb/sq ft) and concentrated load of 1,136 kg (2,500 lb) per wheel in tread portion. Floor contains eighty-three 2,270 kg (5,000 lb) tiedown fittings and eight 4,540 kg (10,000 lb) fittings. Rear loading ramp can be left completely or partially open, or can be removed to permit transport of extra-long cargo and in-flight parachute or free-drop delivery of cargo and equipment. Main cabin door, at front on starboard side, comprises upper hinged section which can be opened in flight and lower section with integral steps. Lower section is jettisonable. Up to 12,700 kg (28,000 lb) can be carried on external cargo hook.

Systems: Cabin heated by 200,000 BTU heater-blower. Hydraulic system provides pressures of 207 bars (3,000 lb/sq in) for flying controls, and 276 bars (4,000 lb/sq in) for engine starting. Electrical system includes two 20kVA alternators driven by transmission drive system. Solar T62 APU runs accessory gear drive, thereby operating all hydraulic and electrical systems.

Avionics and Equipment: All government furnished, including UHF communications and FM liaison sets, transponder, intercom, omni-receiver, ADF and marker beacon receiver. Blind-flying instrumentation standard. Special equipment includes dual electro-hydraulic stability augmentation system, automatic/manual speed trim system, hydraulically-powered winch for rescue and cargo handling purposes, cargo and rescue hatch in floor, integral work stands and steps for maintenance, rearview mirror, provisions for paratroops' static lines and for maintenance davits for removal of major components.

Dimensions, external:
Diameter of rotors (each) 18·29 m (60 ft 0 in)
Main rotor blade chord 0·64 m (2 ft 1¼ in)
Distance between rotor centres 11·94 m (39 ft 2 in)
Length overall, rotors turning 30·18 m (99 ft 0 in)
Length of fuselage 15·54 m (51 ft 0 in)
Width, rotors folded 3·78 m (12 ft 5 in)
Height to top of rear rotor hub 5·68 m (18 ft 7·8 in)
Wheel track (c/l of shock-absorbers) 3·20 m (10 ft 6 in)
Wheelbase 6·86 m (22 ft 6 in)
Passenger door (fwd, stbd):
Height 1·68 m (5 ft 6 in)
Width 0·91 m (3 ft 0 in)
Height to sill 1·09 m (3 ft 7 in)
Rear loading ramp entrance:
Height 1·98 m (6 ft 6 in)
Width 2·31 m (7 ft 7 in)
Height to sill 0·79 m (2 ft 7 in)

Dimensions, internal:
Cabin, excl flight deck: Length 9·20 m (30 ft 2 in)
Width (mean) 2·29 m (7 ft 6 in)
Width at floor 2·51 m (8 ft 3 in)
Height 1·98 m (6 ft 6 in)
Floor area 21·0 m² (226 sq ft)
Usable volume 41·7 m³ (1,474 cu ft)

Areas:
Rotor blades (each) 5·86 m² (63·1 sq ft)
Main rotor discs (total) 525·3 m² (5,655 sq ft)

Weights (CH-47C: see accompanying table. CH-47D as follows, A: guaranteed; B: estimated, based on whirl test results):
Internal payload over 100 nm (185 km; 115 miles) at 1,220 m (4,000 ft), hovering OGE at T-O:
A 5,896 kg (13,000 lb)
B 6,496 kg (14,322 lb)
External payload over 30 nm (55·5 km; 34·5 miles) at 1,220 m (4,000 ft), 61 m (200 ft)/min vertical climb at T-O, 35°C: A 6,803 kg (15,000 lb)
B 7,155 kg (15,775 lb)
Gross weight, hovering OGE at S/L, ISA:
A 22,680 kg (50,000 lb)
B 24,267 kg (53,500 lb)

Performance (CH-47C: see accompanying table. CH-47D: as follows):
Max level speed at S/L, ISA, at AUW of 14,968 kg (33,000 lb): A 155 knots (287 km/h; 178 mph)
B 161 knots (298 km/h; 185 mph)
OEI service ceiling at 14,968 kg (33,000 lb) AUW, ISA: A 3,050 m (10,000 ft)
B 4,270 m (14,000 ft)

BOEING VERTOL MODEL 234 COMMERCIAL CHINOOK

Announced in the late Summer of 1978, this development of the military CH-47 Chinook has been developed for use as a commercial passenger transport, as a cargo carrier, and for specialised tasks such as servicing offshore oil and natural gas rigs, remote resources exploration and extraction, logging, and construction work.

The airframe of the Model 234 is based on that of the latest military Chinook, but has many new features. These include the use of wide-chord glassfibre rotor blades, instead of the usual metal blades; redesign of the fuselage-side fairings in two different forms; a lengthened nose to accommodate the weather radar antenna; and movement further forward of the front landing gear units.

Two basic versions of the commercial Model 234 are offered:

Long-range model. Identified by continuous fuselage-side fairings, approximately twice as large as those of the military Chinook and containing large fuel tanks. Equipped to airline standards as a passenger, passenger/freight 'combi' or all-cargo transport.

Utility model. Fuselage-side fuel tanks replaced by two drum-shape internal tanks, mounted longitudinally side by side at the front of the cabin. Fuselage-side fairings removed, leaving only an individual streamlined blister around each landing gear mounting. As well as reducing weight, this enhances the helicopter's lifting capability by reducing the airframe surface area on which the rotor downwash impinges.

Conversion from one configuration of the Model 234 to another is estimated to take eight hours, and requires four persons to handle the fuel tanks of the utility model and the ramp baggage bins of the passenger-carrying helicopter. Initial cost of the glassfibre blades is significantly greater than that of metal blades, but manufacturing time is reduced by 25% and in-service maintenance costs by 71%. Mean time between blade removal is estimated at 3,200 h. The three blades of any one rotor are interchangeable, but blades cannot be interchanged from one hub to another. Current engine TBO is 1,800 h.

Initial order for the Model 234 was placed by British Airways Helicopters, which ordered three in 1978, with an option on three more, primarily for North Sea oil rig support operations. Other early customers were Columbia Helicopters and Erickson Air Crane, both based in Oregon, USA. Assembly of the first aircraft began in mid-1979. First flight is scheduled for mid-1980, with full certification in mid-1981.

Type: Twin-turbine commercial transport helicopter.

Rotor System: Two three-blade rotors in tandem, turning in opposite directions and driven through interconnecting shafts which enable both rotors to be driven by either engine. Wide-chord glassfibre blades, with VR7 section over inboard 85% of span, and VR8 section on outer 15% of span; thickness/chord ratio 12% and 8% respectively. Overall blade twist 12°. Each blade comprises a laminated glassfibre skin over a glassfibre D spar, forming the front half of the section, and with the rear half filled with Nomex honeycomb. An aluminium screen inserted in the skin provides lightning protection, discharging strikes via the titanium leading-edge. Out-

Three views on left depict the Boeing Vertol CH-47D military helicopter. Plan view at top right shows the Model 234 commercial utility model. Remaining three views depict the long-range commercial model *(Pilot Press)*

board 25% of leading-edge capped with replaceable nickel section. Blade balancing by tracking weights in tips. Two blades of each rotor can be folded manually. Hubs fully articulated, with pitch, flapping and drag hinges. All bearings submerged completely in oil. Auxiliary transmission lubrication system enables flight to be completed after total loss of oil in primary system. Blades embody electrical de-icing blankets, permitting addition of a de-icing kit if required. Rotor rpm 225.

Rotor Drive: Power is transmitted from each engine through individual overrunning clutches, into the combiner transmission, thereby providing a single power output to the interconnecting shafts.

Fuselage: All-metal semi-monocoque structure of basically square section. Loading ramp forms undersurface of upswept rear fuselage. External fuel pods of long-range model made of advanced composites, including glassfibre, graphite/epoxy and Nomex nylon honeycomb. These fairing pods provide flotation capability adequate to meet British airworthiness requirements applicable to a sea state seven (9·15 m; 30 ft waves. Wave length-to-height ratio 15) without added flotation gear.

Landing Gear: Non-retractable quadricycle type, with twin wheels on each forward unit and single wheels on each rear unit. Oleo-pneumatic shock-absorbers on all units. Rear units fully castoring and steerable. Hydraulic disc brakes.

Power Plant: Two Avco Lycoming AL 5512 turboshaft engines, pod-mounted on each side of rear rotor pylon. Each engine has max T-O rating of 3,039 kW (4,075 shp), max continuous rating of 2,205 kW (2,957 shp), and 30 min contingency rating of 3,246 kW (4,353 shp). Transmission rated at 5,592 kW (7,500 shp) at 225 rotor rpm, and 3,430 kW (4,600 shp) for single-engine operation. Long-range model has two fuel tanks, one in each fuselage-side fairing, with total capacity of 7,911 litres (2,090 US gallons). Utility model has two drum-shape internal tanks, with total capacity of 2,271 litres (600 US gallons). Single-point pressure refuelling.

Accommodation: Two pilots side by side on flight deck, with dual controls. Passenger cabin of long-range model seats up to 44 persons four-abreast, with centre aisle. Each seat has overhead bin and underseat stowage for carry-on baggage; larger items are stowed over the rear ramp in the main baggage compartment. Galley, with cabin attendant's seat, and toilet, are standard, between flight deck and cabin. Typical 'combi' configuration accommodates 18 passengers forward and 7,250 kg (16,000 lb) of freight, loaded via rear ramp. All passenger facilities can be removed for freight-only service. Passenger door at front of cabin on starboard side. Crew door on each side of flight deck. Cabin floor supported by dynamically tuned fittings to reduce vibration. Hydraulically powered cargo ramp can be stopped at any intermediate position to match the level of the loading vehicle being used. Single central cargo hook is standard on utility model for carrying external loads of up to 12,700 kg (28,000 lb). Optional dual tandem hooks for precision operations and for load stability in high-speed flight; or three tandem hooks for delivering multiple loads.

Systems: Heating and ventilation systems maintain comfortable flight deck/cabin temperature in ambient temperatures down to −32°C. Duplicated flying control, hydraulic and electrical systems. Solar T62T-2B APU, rated at 71 kW (95 shp), drives auxiliary gearbox on rear transmission to start engines and provide power for two flying control system hydraulic pumps and two alternators. All critical systems heated to inhibit ice build-up.

Avionics and Equipment: Duplicated full blind-flying instrumentation, weather radar, and dual four-axis automatic flight control system with built-in test equipment, provide all-weather capability. Optional equipment includes passenger interior furnishings for the utility model, 'combi' interior, downward-shining cargo load light, cargo winch of 5,440 kg (12,000 lb) capacity operable via floor hatch or loading ramp, rescue hoist of 272 kg (600 lb) capacity, a power-down rear loading ramp to drive the ramp below water when required, a water dam to prevent water entering the cabin when the ramp is down, glassfibre wheel-skis, an ice detector probe, and ditching equipment that includes two liferafts, each with an overload capacity of 36 persons. Standard items include integral work platforms, and a maintenance panel that allows 26 separate checks to be made from a single ground-level position.

Dimensions, external:

Rotor diameter (each)	18·29 m (60 ft 0 in)
Rotor blade chord (constant)	0·813 m (2 ft 8 in)
Length overall, rotors turning	30·18 m (99 ft 0 in)
Length of fuselage	16·08 m (52 ft 9 in)
Height overall	5·68 m (18 ft 7·8 in)
Width over fuselage-side fairings	4·78 m (15 ft 8 in)

Dimensions, internal:

Passenger cabin: Length	9·19 m (30 ft 2 in)
Max width	2·51 m (8 ft 3 in)
Max height	1·98 m (6 ft 6 in)
Baggage compartment volume	4·42 m³ (156 cu ft)
Utility model, cargo hold volume	41·03 m³ (1,449 cu ft)

Weights (estimated: L, long-range model; U, utility model):

Weight empty: L	11,090 kg (24,449 lb)
U	9,219 kg (20,323 lb)
Fuel load: L	6,361 kg (14,024 lb)
U	1,826 kg (4,026 lb)
Max payload: L	10,229 kg (22,551 lb)
U, internal	11,843 kg (26,109 lb)
U, external	12,700 kg (28,000 lb)
Max T-O weight:	
L and U, internal load	21,318 kg (47,000 lb)
U, external load	23,133 kg (51,000 lb)

Performance (estimated: L, long-range model; U, utility model):

Never-exceed speed:
L, U 165 knots (305 km/h; 190 mph)

Max cruising speed at 610 m (2,000 ft):
L, U, internal load, at 21,318 kg (47,000 lb) AUW 142 knots (263 km/h; 163 mph)

Cruising speed for optimum range, at 610 m (2,000 ft):
L, U, internal load, at 18,150 kg (40,000 lb) AUW 137 knots (253 km/h; 157 mph)
L, U, internal load, at 21,318 kg (47,000 lb) AUW 135 knots (250 km/h; 155 mph)

Max rate of climb at S/L:	
L, U, internal load	410 m (1,350 ft)/min
Service ceiling:	
L, U, internal load	4,570 m (15,000 ft)
Hovering ceiling IGE:	
L	2,790 m (9,150 ft)
U	3,155 m (10,350 ft)
Hovering ceiling OGE:	
L	1,450 m (4,750 ft)
U	2,180 m (7,150 ft)
Range with 45 min IFR reserves:	
L with 44 passengers	545 nm (1,010 km; 627 miles)
L with max fuel	740 nm (1,371 km; 852 miles)
U with max internal load	180 nm (333 km; 207 miles)
U with max external load	135 nm (250 km; 155 miles)
Max endurance:	
L	5 h 30 min
U, internal load	1 h 24 min

Boeing Vertol BO 105 Executaire, a lengthened-cabin version of the West German light helicopter

BOEING VERTOL BO 105 EXECUTAIRE

The BO 105C has been marketed in the United States, Canada and Mexico since 1972 by Boeing Vertol, under licence agreement with MBB (which see).

A number of product improvements have been made each year to increase the BO 105's operational capability, reliability and maintainability. The latest of these improvements is the installation of Allison Model 250-C20B engines and a 2F-72B transmission which provides improved twin-engine and one-engine-out performance.

On 18 March 1975, Boeing Vertol first flew a modified version known as the Executaire, of which 21 examples had been sold by 1 January 1978. The Executaire is aimed specifically at the US executive transport helicopter market. The primary modification involves lengthening the aft passenger compartment by 0·25 m (10 in), to give more legroom for passengers, as well as to provide space for improved cabin accessories and better temperature control and noise levels. The rear sliding doors are replaced by hinged doors, and an extra window is added each side, adjacent to the rear passengers' seats. In a utility interior, an additional passenger seat can be installed to accommodate six persons, including the pilot. The Executaire modification adds about 16 kg (35 lb) to the empty weight of the basic BO 105, which is described under the MBB entry in the German section.

BRANTLY-HYNES

BRANTLY-HYNES HELICOPTER INC

Head Office and Works: PO Box 1046, Frederick, Oklahoma 73542

Telephone: (405) 335 2256

President: Michael K. Hynes

This company, formed on 1 January 1975, replaced Brantly Operators Inc which acquired all rights in Brantly helicopters in late 1970. Mr M. K. Hynes acquired also ownership of the Type Certificates for the Brantly B-2, B-2A, B-2B and Model 305.

Brantly-Hynes has put the two-seat B-2B and five-seat Model 305 back into production, and planned to introduce an agricultural version of the Model 305 towards the end of 1979. Eleven B-2Bs were delivered during 1978.

BRANTLY-HYNES MODEL B-2B

Type: Two-seat light helicopter.

Rotor System: Three-blade main rotor. Articulated inboard flapping hinges offset 0·07 m (2·67 in) from hub, and coincident flap and lag hinges offset 1·31 m (4 ft 3¾ in) from hub. Symmetrical blade section with 29% thickness ratio on inboard portion; NACA 0012 section outboard of hinge. Inboard portion of each blade is rigid, built around a steel spar blade. Outboard portion is flexible, with an extruded aluminium leading-edge spar and polyurethane core; aluminium skin is bonded to core and riveted to spar. Blades are attached to hub by flapping links and do not fold. A rotor brake is standard equipment. Two-blade all-metal anti-torque tail rotor.

Rotor Drive: Through centrifugal clutch and planetary reduction gears. Bevel gear take-off from main transmission with flexible coupling to tail rotor drive-shaft. Main rotor/engine rpm ratio 1 : 6·158. Tail rotor/engine rpm ratio 1 : 1.

Fuselage: Stressed-skin all-metal structure with conical tail section. Tail rotor on swept-up boom extension.

Landing Gear: Alternative skid, wheel or float gear. Skid type has small retractable wheels for ground handling, fixed tailskid and four shock-absorbers with rubber in compression. Tyres size 10 × 3½, pressure 4·14 bars (60 lb/sq in). Alternative non-retractable tricycle landing gear has oleo-pneumatic shock-absorbers for all units, with single wheels on main units and twin nosewheels. Inflatable pontoons, which attach to standard skids, are available to permit operation from water.

Power Plant: One 134 kW (180 hp) Lycoming IVO-360-A1A flat-four engine, mounted vertically, with dual fan cooling system. Rubber bag-type fuel tank under engine, capacity 117 litres (31 US gallons). Refuelling point on port side of fuselage. Oil capacity 5·7 litres (1·5 US gallons).

Accommodation: Totally-enclosed circular-section cabin for two persons seated side by side. Forward-hinged door on each side. Dual controls, cabin heater and demisting fan standard. Compartment for 22·7 kg (50 lb) baggage in forward end of tail section.

Avionics and Equipment: Provision for all standard nav/com radios. Blind-flying instrumentation available as an option, but the Model B-2B is not certificated for instrument flight. Twin landing lights in nose.

Dimensions, external:
- Diameter of main rotor — 7·24 m (23 ft 9 in)
- Main rotor blade chord: inboard — 0·225 m (8·85 in)
- outboard — 0·203 m (8·0 in)
- Diameter of tail rotor — 1·29 m (4 ft 3 in)
- Length overall, rotor turning — 8·53 m (28 ft 0 in)
- Length of fuselage — 6·62 m (21 ft 9 in)
- Height overall — 2·06 m (6 ft 9 in)
- Skid track — 1·73 m (5 ft 8¼ in)
- Passenger doors (each): Height — 0·79 m (2 ft 7 in)
- Width — 0·86 m (2 ft 9¾ in)
- Baggage compartment door:
- Mean height — 0·25 m (9¾ in)
- Length — 0·55 m (1 ft 9¾ in)

Dimensions, internal:
- Max width of cabin — 1·27 m (4 ft 2 in)
- Baggage compartment — 0·17 m³ (6 cu ft)

Areas:
- Main rotor blades (each) — 0·69 m² (7·42 sq ft)
- Main rotor disc — 41·06 m² (442 sq ft)
- Tail rotor disc — 1·21 m² (13 sq ft)

Weights and Loadings:
- Weight empty with skids — 463 kg (1,020 lb)
- Weight empty with floats — 481 kg (1,060 lb)
- Max T-O weight — 757 kg (1,670 lb)
- Max disc loading — 18·4 kg/m² (3·77 lb/sq ft)
- Max power loading — 5·65 kg/kW (9·27 lb/hp)

Performance (at max T-O weight):
- Max level speed at S/L — 87 knots (161 km/h; 100 mph)
- Max cruising speed (75% power) — 78 knots (145 km/h; 90 mph)
- Max rate of climb at S/L — 580 m (1,900 ft)/min
- Service ceiling — 3,290 m (10,800 ft)
- Hovering ceiling IGE — 2,040 m (6,700 ft)
- Range with max fuel, with reserves — 217 nm (400 km; 250 miles)

Brantly-Hynes Model B-2B light helicopter (Lycoming IVO-360-A1A engine)

Brantly-Hynes Model 305 light helicopter carrying 181 kg (400 lb) underslung load

BRANTLY-HYNES MODEL 305

The Model 305 is a five-seat helicopter of similar configuration to the Model B-2B, but larger in every respect. The prototype of the original Model 305 flew for the first time in January 1964, and FAA Type Approval was received on 29 July 1965.

Type: Five-seat light helicopter.

Rotor System: Three-blade main rotor. Articulated inboard flapping hinges, offset 0·09 m (3·625 in) from hub, and coincident flap and lag hinges outboard. Inboard portion of each blade is rigid, built around a steel spar blade. All-metal outboard portion has a D-spar and is foam-filled. Two-blade all-metal tail rotor. Each blade has a forged aluminium leading-edge spar, ribs and riveted aluminium skin. Main rotor blades do not fold. Rotor brake is standard.

Rotor Drive: Main rotor shaft-driven through centrifugal clutch and planetary reduction gears. Bevel gear take-off from main transmission, with flexible coupling, through tail rotor drive-shaft and intermediate gearbox to tail gearbox. Main rotor/engine rpm ratio 1 : 6·666. Tail rotor/engine rpm ratio 1 : 0·998.

Fuselage: Stressed-skin all-metal structure, with conical tail section. Tail rotor carried on swept-up boom extension.

Tail Unit: Small variable-incidence horizontal stabiliser of all-metal stressed-skin construction.

Landing Gear: Alternative skid, wheel or float gear. Skid landing gear has four oleo struts, two on each side, and small retractable ground handling wheels. The wheel gear has two main wheels and twin nosewheels, all on oleo-pneumatic shock-absorbers. Goodyear main wheels and tyres size 6·00-6, pressure 2·07 bars (30 lb/sq in). Goodyear nosewheels and tyres size 5·00-5, pressure 1·93 bars (28 lb/sq in). Goodyear single-disc hydraulic brakes on main wheels.

Power Plant: One 227·5 kW (305 hp) Lycoming IVO-540-A1A flat-six engine, mounted vertically, with dual cooling fans. One rubber-cell fuel tank under engine, capacity 163 litres (43 US gallons). Refuelling point in port side of fuselage. Oil capacity 9·5 litres (2·5 US gallons).

Accommodation: Two individual seats side by side with

dual controls. Rear bench seat for three persons. Door on each side. Rear compartment for 113 kg (250 lb) of baggage, with downward-hinged door on starboard side.

AVIONICS AND EQUIPMENT: King or Narco radio, to customer's specification. Blind-flying instrumentation is available, but helicopter is not certificated for instrument flight.

DIMENSIONS, EXTERNAL:

Diameter of main rotor	8·74 m (28 ft 8 in)
Main rotor blade chord (constant)	0·254 m (10 in)
Diameter of tail rotor	1·30 m (4 ft 3 in)
Length overall, rotor turning	10·03 m (32 ft 11 in)
Length of fuselage	7·44 m (24 ft 5 in)
Height overall	2·44 m (8 ft 0⅛ in)
Wheel track	2·10 m (6 ft 10¾ in)
Wheelbase	2·15 m (7 ft 0½ in)
Passenger doors (each): Height	0·82 m (2 ft 8⅛ in)
Width	1·02 m (3 ft 3⅞ in)
Baggage compartment door: Mean height	0·30 m (1 ft 0¼ in)
Width	0·69 m (2 ft 3 in)

DIMENSIONS, INTERNAL:

Cabin: Length	2·30 m (7 ft 6½ in)
Max width	1·39 m (4 ft 6¾ in)
Max height	1·22 m (4 ft 0½ in)
Baggage compartment	0·47 m³ (16·7 cu ft)

AREAS:

Main rotor blades (each)	1·09 m² (11·79 sq ft)
Tail rotor blades (each)	0·05 m² (0·50 sq ft)
Main rotor disc	3·33 m² (35·8 sq ft)
Tail rotor disc	1·32 m² (14·18 sq ft)

WEIGHTS AND LOADINGS:

Weight empty	817 kg (1,800 lb)
Max T-O and landing weight	1,315 kg (2,900 lb)
Max zero-fuel weight	1,224 kg (2,700 lb)
Max disc loading	22·7 kg/m² (4·65 lb/sq ft)
Max power loading	5·78 kg/kW (9·84 lb/hp)

PERFORMANCE (at max T-O weight):

Max level speed at S/L	104 knots (193 km/h; 120 mph)
Max cruising speed at S/L	96 knots (177 km/h; 110 mph)
Max rate of climb at S/L	297 m (975 ft)/min
Service ceiling	3,660 m (12,000 ft)
Hovering ceiling IGE	1,245 m (4,080 ft)
Range with max fuel and max payload, with 15 min reserves	191 nm (354 km; 220 miles)

CAL POLY
CALIFORNIA POLYTECHNIC STATE UNIVERSITY

ADDRESS: San Luis Obispo, California 93407

Dr John Nicolaides, head of Cal Poly's Aeronautical Engineering Department since 1975, has been actively developing the parafoil wing for many years. Using such an aerofoil as the lifting medium, he designed a powered parafoil known as the N-Flyer in the mid-1960s. It was first evolved to meet a USAF requirement for a pilot rescue device that would allow aircrew to escape from a seriously damaged aircraft and fly out of enemy territory, but was developed to practicality too late to be used in Viet-Nam.

CAL POLY N-FLYER

Since 1975, Dr John Nicolaides and Dr Doral R. Sandlin, together with a team of students, have been testing parafoils and refining the design of the original powered parafoil designed by Dr Nicolaides. In its current form, as the N-Flyer, it consists of a lightweight, wheeled unit of tubular light alloy construction which, at its forward end, is carried on three lightweight bicycle-type wheels, the nosewheel of which is steerable, and by two small wide-tracked wheels fitted with brakes at the rear. Accommodation for the pilot is provided by a single open seat at the forward end of the unit; immediately behind him is mounted a 41 kW (55 hp) snowmobile engine driving, via belts, a two-blade wooden fixed-pitch pusher propeller. At the aft end of the unit is mounted a fin, rudder, and a small all-moving tailplane. At each side of the unit a triangular frame of light alloy tubing provides a mounting, at the apex of each triangle, for a transverse tube to which the shroud lines of the nylon fabric parafoil are attached.

As the parafoil needs to be inflated and formed to its semi-rigid aerofoil section by a stream of air passing through the tubular channels formed by the nylon fabric, a major problem was to evolve a technique that would permit a more-or-less conventional take-off. Once airborne the N-Flyer, which weighs just over 136 kg (300 lb), is reported to be easy to manoeuvre and has a max speed of approx 22 knots (40 km/h; 25 mph).

Interest in the parafoil aircraft has been shown by the US Navy and Coast Guard, and additional development work on the N-Flyer has been carried out by the Cal Poly team under contract to these services. The team has also perfected a technique for in-flight deployment of the parafoil, using a Navy RPV as the research vehicle. Two stages are involved: release of the parafoil behind the aircraft, and raising it to a flying position to serve as that craft's primary lifting surface after it has become filled with air. This latter technique appears to have applications for the recovery of cruise missiles and large RPVs.

Early model of the Nicolaides parafoil aircraft taking off

CALSPAN
CALSPAN CORPORATION

HEAD OFFICE: PO Box 400, Buffalo, New York 14225
Telephone: (716) 632 7500
Telex: 91-270

Calspan Corporation which, for a number of years, has specialised in the design and construction of variable-stability systems for research/simulation aircraft, was acquired by Arvin Industries Inc in 1978.

Since 1970, under contract to the US Naval Air Systems Command, Calspan Corporation has been operating the Bell/Navy X-22A VTOL research aircraft, last described in the 1970-71 *Jane's*. In this continuing programme, research is focused on the evaluation of desirable VTOL flying qualities, using in-flight simulation techniques. This is made possible by the installation of programmable systems for control, guidance, stability and electronic displays.

In 1977, Calspan was awarded a contract funded jointly by the US Navy and the USAF's Aeronautical Systems Division, for the conversion of a Lockheed T-33 jet trainer to serve as a variable-stability research aircraft. Under the designation NT-33A, this is being used primarily in a project known as Display Evaluation Flight Test (DEFT). This programme provides the necessary link between flight hardware and software technology, aircraft dynamics, and the pilot's information requirements. The programmable display system consists initially of a head-up display (HUD), but has growth potential to a head-down display system and energy manoeuvrability displays. DEFT flight tests, scheduled to begin in July 1979, offer a new capability to study the interaction of aircraft dynamics and display characteristics. This is of importance in developing displays for a wide range of existing and proposed aircraft.

The basic variable display system comprises the head-up display, a digital computer, mode-control panel, magnetic tape data recording system, inertial navigation system, and interface and associated equipment. General Electric Company's Aircraft Equipment Division in Utica, New York, is prime contractor for the DEFT avionics, and serves also as overall systems integrator for both hardware and software programmes.

Initial flight test objectives of the DEFT programme include in-flight checking of the variable display equipment; demonstration of the usefulness of a HUD for take-off, climb and landing; and demonstration of a take-off flight director, several landing flight directors, and a particular HUD format for landing.

Bell/US Navy X-22A VTOL research aircraft in its current form

Lockheed NT-33A DEFT research aircraft for in-flight simulation research

CAMAIR

CAMAIR AIRCRAFT CORPORATION

Head Office: PO Box 231, Remsenburg, Long Island, New York 11960

Telephone: (516) 325 0120

President: Fred Garcia Jr

CAMAIR TWIN NAVION

The Camair Twin Navion is a twin-engined version of the North American/Ryan Navion light aircraft. It embodies structural modifications to cater for the increased power and weight, together with design and aerodynamic refinements which provide improved performance, comfort and styling. Versions are as follows:

CTN-A. Prototype only. Built and flown in 1953 with two 168 kW (225 hp) Continental engines.

CTN-B. Powered by two 179 kW (240 hp) Continental O-470-B engines. First flown in early 1954. Total of 28 delivered in 1955-59.

CTN-C. First flown in 1960, with two 194 kW (260 hp) Continental IO-470-D engines. A number of Model Bs have been converted to Model C configuration.

CTN-D. The prototype of this version was powered by two 224 kW (300 hp) Continental IO-520 engines

Production of new aircraft has been suspended; but Camair is able to modify B and C models to the later model D configuration, and continues to supply spares to Twin Navion owners.

Details of the CTN-D can be found in the 1978-79 *Jane's*. The CTN-A, -B and -C versions were described in earlier editions.

CESSNA

CESSNA AIRCRAFT COMPANY

Head Office and Works: Wichita, Kansas 67201

Telephone: (316) 685 9111

President, Chairman of the Board and Chief Executive Officer:
Russell W. Meyer Jr

Senior Vice-Presidents:
R. P. Bauer (Treasurer and Controller)
William A. Boettger (Pawnee Division)
Robert D. Dickerson (Wallace Division)
Malcolm S. Harned (Technology)
Charles B. Husick (Fluid Power and Aircraft Systems Division)
R. L. Lair (Commercial Aircraft Marketing)
J. Derek Vaughan (Commercial Jet Marketing Division)
William L. Worford (Personnel and Community Relations)

Vice-Presidents:
Pierre Clostermann (President, Reims Aviation)
John W. Dussault (McCauley Accessory Division)
Richard B. Foster (Aircraft Radio and Control Division)
L. C. Gartin (Commercial Aircraft Product Support)
Homer G. Nester (Controller and Assistant Treasurer)
Thane L. Woolsey (Fluid Power Division)

Secretary: David R. Edwards

Cessna Aircraft Company was founded by the late Clyde V. Cessna, a pioneer in US aviation in 1911, and was incorporated on 7 September 1927.

By the beginning of January 1979 the company had produced a total of 151,542 aircraft. Pawnee Division delivered its 100,000th single-engined aeroplane, a Skyhawk II, on 21 July 1975.

Cessna has four plants in Wichita engaged on production of commercial and military aircraft, and The Fluid Power Division in Hutchinson, Kansas, which manufactures fluid power systems.

Subsidiary companies owned by Cessna are Aircraft Radio and Control Division at Boonton, New Jersey, the McCauley Accessories Division of Dayton, Ohio, Cessna Fluid Power Ltd of Glenrothes, Fife, Scotland, Cessna Finance Corporation and Cessna International Finance Corporation in Wichita. It has a 49% interest in Reims Aviation of France.

In early 1979 Cessna had in production 56 types of commercial aircraft; during 1978 its commercial sales totalled 9,197 aircraft, including units assembled in France by Reims Aviation (which see).

Military subcontract programmes include manufacture of assemblies, including missile ejection racks, wing tank and missile pylons, for the McDonnell Douglas F-4 Phantom II, and crew door subassemblies for Bell helicopters.

CESSNA MODEL 152

During 1977 Cessna introduced a new two-seat cabin monoplane to replace the Model 150, which had been in production for almost 20 years. Designated Model 152, it differed primarily in having a more powerful engine using low-lead 100 octane fuel, an improved 'gull wing' propeller, and power plant installation and cowling changes to reduce engine noise and vibration.

The 1979 version of the Model 152 introduced a number of improvements, including improved engine ignition, a four-cylinder priming system, a new glareshield, redesigned throttle control, new brake master cylinder, new alternator control unit, and a modified split nose-cap to improve access to the engine. New options included instrument post lights, and a new avionics control panel.

Further improvements on the 1980 model, designed mainly to facilitate cold-weather operations, include an accelerator pump which injects fuel directly into the throat of the carburettor, a slower-turning starter, dual windscreen defrosters, improved heating system for the cabin, more readable and accurate engine instruments, a manifold battery which eliminates the need for a separate battery box, and an optional economy mixture gauge.

Two versions are available for 1980:

Model 152. Standard version, as described.

Model 152/II. As Model 152, but including as standard a factory installed avionics and equipment package which includes a Cessna Series 300 nav/com, dual controls, true airspeed indicator, navigation light detectors, heated pitot, courtesy lights, omni-flash beacon, alternate static source, and emergency locator transmitter.

A total of 3,569 Model 152s had been built by 1 January 1979, including 129 F-152s built by Reims Aviation in France.

Type: Two-seat cabin monoplane.

Wings: Braced high-wing monoplane. Wing section NACA 2412 (tips symmetrical). Dihedral 1°. Incidence 1° at root, 0° at tip. All-metal structure of light alloy. Conical camber glassfibre wingtips optional. Modified Frise-type ailerons and electrically-actuated NACA single-slotted trailing-edge flaps of light alloy construction. No trim tabs.

Fuselage: Conventional semi-monocoque structure of light alloy.

Tail Unit: Cantilever structure of light alloy with swept vertical surfaces. Trim tab in starboard elevator. Ground-adjustable rudder tab.

Landing Gear: Non-retractable tricycle type. Land-O-Matic cantilever main legs, each comprising a one-piece machined conically-tapered spring steel tube. Steerable nosewheel on oleo-pneumatic shock-absorber strut. Main wheels size 6·00-6 with nylon tube-type tyres, pressure 2·07 bars (30 lb/sq in). Nosewheel size 5·00-5 with nylon tube-type tyre, pressure 2·07 bars (30 lb/sq in). Toe-operated single-disc hydraulic brakes. Rudder pedal extensions and wheel fairings optional.

Power Plant: One 82 kW (110 hp) Lycoming O-235-L2C flat-four engine, driving a McCauley two-blade metal fixed-pitch propeller with spinner. Fuel tanks in wings, with total capacity of 98 litres (26 US gallons), of which 92·75 litres (24·5 US gallons) are usable. Optional long-range tanks have a total capacity of 147·5 litres (39 US gallons), of which 142 litres (37·5 US gallons) are usable. Refuelling points on upper surface of wing. Oil capacity 5·7 litres (1·5 US gallons).

Accommodation: Enclosed cabin seating two side by side. Vertically-adjustable seats for pilot and co-pilot; inertia-reel shoulder harness and dual controls optional on standard model. Baggage compartment behind seats, backs of which hinge forward. Baggage capacity 54 kg (120 lb). Optional 'family seat' can be fitted in baggage space, for two children not exceeding 54 kg (120 lb) in combined weight. Door, with opening window, on each side. Heating and ventilation standard. Dual windscreen defrosters standard. Cabin skylight windows optional.

Systems: Hydraulic system for brakes only. Electrical system includes a 28V 60A alternator and 28V battery.

Avionics and Equipment: Optional avionics include Cessna Series 300 nav/com (standard on 152/II), Series 300 transceiver, Series 300 nav/com with remote VOR/LOC or VOR/ILS indicator, Series 300 ADF, marker beacon with three lights and aural signal, transponder with 4096 code capability, single unit avionics control panel, slimline microphone, and padded headset with attached microphone and control wheel operating button. Standard equipment includes stall warning indicator, variable intensity instrument panel red floodlights, cabin dome lights, navigation lights, map compartment, safety belts, baggage retaining net, and control locks. Optional equipment (standard on 152/II) includes dual controls, true airspeed indicator, navigation light detectors, heated pitot, courtesy lights, omni-flash beacon, alternate static source, and emergency locator transmitter. Other optional equipment includes rate of climb indicator, turn co-ordinator, sensitive altimeter, directional and horizon gyros, turn and bank indicator, flight hour recorder, economy mixture indicator gauge, outside air temperature gauge, electric clock, rearview mirror, control-wheel-mounted map light, tinted windows, cowl-mounted landing light, white strobe lights, instrument post lights, cabin fire extinguisher, winterisation kit, anti-precipitation static kit, full-flow oil filter, quick drain oil valve and external power socket.

Dimensions, external:
Wing span: standard 9·97 m (32 ft 8½ in)
with optional conical wingtips 10·11 m (33 ft 2 in)
Wing chord at root 1·63 m (5 ft 4 in)
Wing chord at tip 1·13 m (3 ft 8½ in)
Wing aspect ratio 6·7
Length overall 7·34 m (24 ft 1 in)
Height overall 2·59 m (8 ft 6 in)
Tailplane span 3·05 m (10 ft 0 in)
Wheel track 2·32 m (7 ft 7¼ in)
Wheelbase 1·47 m (4 ft 10 in)
Propeller diameter 1·75 m (5 ft 9 in)
Passenger doors (each): Width 0·86 m (2 ft 10 in)

Areas:
Wings, gross: standard 14·59 m² (157·0 sq ft)
with optional conical wingtips 14·82 m² (159·5 sq ft)

Weights and Loadings (A: standard 152; B: 152/II):
Weight empty: A 503 kg (1,109 lb)
B 518 kg (1,142 lb)
Max T-O and landing weight: A, B 757 kg (1,670 lb)
Max ramp weight: A, B 760 kg (1,675 lb)
Max wing loading 51·3 kg/m² (10·5 lb/sq ft)
Max power loading 9·24 kg/kW (15·2 lb/hp)

Performance (at max T-O weight):
*Max level speed at S/L
110 knots (204 km/h; 127 mph)
*Max cruising speed, 75% power at 2,440 m (8,000 ft)
107 knots (198 km/h; 123 mph)
Stalling speed, flaps up, power off
48 knots (89·5 km/h; 55·5 mph) CAS
Stalling speed, flaps down, power off
43 knots (80·5 km/h; 50 mph) CAS
Max rate of climb at S/L 218 m (715 ft)/min
Service ceiling 4,480 m (14,700 ft)
T-O run 221 m (725 ft)
T-O to 15 m (50 ft) 408 m (1,340 ft)
Landing from 15 m (50 ft) 366 m (1,200 ft)
Landing run 145 m (475 ft)
Range, recommended lean mixture with allowance for start, taxi, T-O, climb and 45 min reserves at 45% power:
standard fuel, 75% power at 2,440 m (8,000 ft)
320 nm (592 km; 368 miles)
max fuel, 75% power at 2,440 m (8,000 ft)
545 nm (1,009 km; 627 miles)
standard fuel, econ cruising power at 3,050 m (10,000 ft) 415 nm (769 km; 478 miles)
max fuel, econ cruising power at 3,050 m (10,000 ft)
690 nm (1,278 km; 794 miles)

**With wheel fairings which increase speeds by approximately 2 knots (3·7 km/h; 2·3 mph)*

Cessna Model 152/II for 1980, with factory installed avionics and equipment package

CESSNA MODEL 152 AEROBAT

The Model 152 Aerobat combines the economy and versatility of the standard Model 152 with aerobatic capability. Structural changes allow the Aerobat to perform 'unusual attitude' manoeuvres and it is licensed in the Aerobatic category for load factors of +6*g* and —3*g* at full gross weight, permitting the performance of barrel and aileron rolls, snap rolls, loops, Immelmann turns, Cuban eights, spins, vertical reversements, lazy eights and chandelles.

Equipment of the aircraft differs only slightly from that of the standard 152. Quick-release cabin doors, removable seat cushions and backs, quick-release lapstraps, and shoulder harnesses, are standard, as are two tinted skylights in the cabin roof which offer extra field of view. Distinct external styling provides immediate recognition of the Aerobat's role. The improvements for 1979/80 and 152/II package detailed for the Model 152 apply also to the Aerobat.

DIMENSIONS AND AREAS: As for Model 152

WEIGHTS AND LOADINGS: As for Model 152 except:
Weight empty 515 kg (1,135 lb)

PERFORMANCE (at max T-O weight): As for Model 152 except:
*Max level speed at S/L 109 knots (202 km/h; 126 mph)
*Max cruising speed, 75% power at 2,440 m (8,000 ft) 106 knots (196 km/h; 122 mph)
Range, recommended lean mixture with allowance for engine start, taxi, T-O, climb and 45 min at 45% power:
standard fuel, 75% power at 2,440 m (8,000 ft) 315 nm (583 km; 362 miles)
max fuel, 75% power at 2,440 m (8,000 ft) 540 nm (1,000 km; 621 miles)
standard fuel, econ cruising power at 3,050 m (10,000 ft) 410 nm (760 km; 472 miles)
max fuel, econ cruising power at 3,050 m (10,000 ft) 680 nm (1,260 km; 783 miles)

**With wheel speed fairings which increase speeds by approximately 2 knots (3·7 km/h; 2·3 mph)*

CESSNA SKYHAWK

Two versions of the Skyhawk are currently available:

Skyhawk. This improved version of the Skyhawk, powered by a 119 kW (160 hp) engine able to operate on 100 octane low-lead fuel, was first introduced in 1977. The 1979 model included as standard improved flap mechanism to permit higher extension speed, a new alternator control unit, new brake master cylinder, and improved throttle control. New options included an exhaust gas temperature gauge and a cabin ventilation fan. Further improvements for 1980 are designed mainly to increase comfort and visibility. They include easier access to the front seats, slimmer front door posts, dual windscreen defrosters, new engine instruments, a manifold battery which does not require a separate battery box, and new interior and exterior styling.

Skyhawk II. As Skyhawk, but including as standard a 300 Series nav/com with 360-channel com and 160-channel nav, dual controls, true airspeed indicator, navigation light detectors, heated pitot, courtesy lights, omni-flash beacon, alternate static source and emergency locator transmitter. It can be equipped optionally with a Nav Pac which adds a second nav/com, a 300 Series ADF and a transponder.

The Skyhawk is certificated for operation as a floatplane, and can be fitted with skis. A version designated F-172 is produced in France by Reims Aviation.

A total of 30,654 aircraft in the Model 172/Skyhawk series had been built by 1 January 1979, including 1,659 F-172s built in France.

TYPE: Four-seat cabin monoplane.

WINGS: Braced high-wing monoplane. NACA 2412 wing section. Dihedral 1° 44′. Incidence 1° 30′ at root, −1° 30′ at tip. All-metal structure, except for conical-camber glassfibre wingtips. Single bracing strut on each side. Modified Frise all-metal ailerons. Electrically-controlled NACA all-metal single-slotted flaps inboard of ailerons.

FUSELAGE: All-metal semi-monocoque structure.

TAIL UNIT: Cantilever all-metal structure. Sweepback on fin 35° at quarter-chord. Trim tab in starboard elevator. Ground-adjustable trim tab in rudder, in-flight adjustable trim tab optional.

LANDING GEAR: Non-retractable tricycle type. Cessna Land-O-Matic cantilever main legs, each comprising a one-piece machined conically-tapered spring steel tube. Nosewheel is carried on an oleo-pneumatic shock-strut and is steerable with rudder up to 10° and controllable up to 30° on either side. Cessna main wheels size 6·00-6 and nosewheel size 5·00-5 (optionally 6·00-6), with nylon cord tube-type tyres. Tyre pressure: main wheels 1·59 bars (23 lb/sq in), nosewheel 1·79 bars (26 lb/sq in). Hydraulic disc brakes. Optional wheel fairings. Alternative float and ski gear.

POWER PLANT: One 119 kW (160 hp) Lycoming O-320-H2AD flat-four engine, driving a two-blade fixed-pitch metal propeller. One fuel tank in each wing, total capacity 163 litres (43 US gallons). Usable fuel 151·4 litres (40 US gallons). Provision for long-range tanks, giving total capacity of 204 litres (54 US gallons), of which 189 litres (50 US gallons) are usable. Oil capacity 5·7 litres (1·5 US gallons).

ACCOMMODATION: Cabin seats four in two pairs, with optional fully-articulating front seats. Baggage space aft of rear seats, capacity 54 kg (120 lb). An optional fold-away seat can be fitted in baggage space, for one or two children not exceeding 54 kg (120 lb) total weight. Door on each side of cabin, giving access to all seats, simplifies loading if rear seats are removed and cabin used for freight. Pilot's window opens; co-pilot's opening side window and dual controls optional on Skyhawk; dual controls standard on Skyhawk II. Baggage door on port side. Combined heating and ventilation system; air-conditioning optional. Dual windscreen defrosters. Glassfibre soundproofing. Optional overhead skylights.

Cessna Skyhawk II four-seat lightplane for 1980 (Lycoming O-320-H2AD engine)

SYSTEM: Electrical system of 28V includes electric engine starter and 24V battery. Air-conditioning system of 14,000 BTU capacity optional.

AVIONICS AND EQUIPMENT: Optional avionics include Cessna Series 300 720-channel transceiver, 720-channel nav/com with remote VOR indicator, 720-channel nav/com with remote VOR/LOC indicator or VOR/ILS indicator, ADF, marker beacon with three lights and aural signal, transponder with 4096 code capability, DME, 10-channel HF transceiver, Nav-O-Matic autopilot with heading control plus VOR, Series 400 glideslope receiver, boom microphone with control-wheel switch, padded headset with boom microphone, and speaker sidetone facility. Optional equipment (standard on Skyhawk II) includes true airspeed indicator, courtesy lights, emergency locator transmitter, alternate static source, navigation light detectors, heated pitot and omni-flash beacon. Other optional equipment includes control-wheel map light, sensitive altimeter, directional gyro with movable heading index, electric clock, outside air temperature gauge, exhaust gas temperature gauge, rate of climb indicator, turn co-ordinator, map and instrument panel light, carburettor air temperature gauge, turn and bank indicator, horizon and directional gyros with vacuum system, sun visors, flight hour recorder, headrests, rearview mirror, front seats with articulating recline and vertical adjustment, inertia reel shoulder harnesses, rudder pedal extensions, overhead skylights, hinged window on starboard side, cabin fire extinguisher, child's foldaway seat, rear seats with individual reclining backs, utility shelf, safety belts for third and fourth seats, rear seat ventilation system, cabin ventilation fan, tinted windows, internal corrosion proofing, dual cowl-mounted landing lights, beacon, wingtip strobe lights, towbar, anti-precipitation static kit, portable stretcher, full-flow oil filter, engine primer system, wing-strut and fuselage steps and handles for easy refuelling, quick-drain oil valve, floatplane kit, winterisation kit, external power socket, glider tow hook, and tailplane abrasion boots.

DIMENSIONS, EXTERNAL (L: landplane; F: floatplane):
Wing span 10·92 m (35 ft 10 in)
Wing chord at root 1·63 m (5 ft 4 in)
Wing chord at tip 1·12 m (3 ft 8½ in)
Wing aspect ratio 7·52
Length overall: L 8·20 m (26 ft 11 in)
F 8·13 m (26 ft 8 in)
Height overall: L 2·68 m (8 ft 9½ in)
F 3·63 m (11 ft 11 in)
Tailplane span 3·45 m (11 ft 4 in)
Wheel track: L 2·53 m (8 ft 3½ in)
Wheelbase: L 1·63 m (5 ft 4 in)
Propeller diameter: L 1·91 m (6 ft 3 in)
F 2·03 m (6 ft 8 in)
Passenger doors (each): Height 1·01 m (3 ft 3¾ in)
Width 0·89 m (2 ft 11 in)

AREAS:
Wings, gross 16·17 m² (174 sq ft)
Ailerons (total) 1·70 m² (18·3 sq ft)
Trailing-edge flaps (total) 1·97 m² (21·20 sq ft)
Fin 1·04 m² (11·24 sq ft)
Rudder 0·69 m² (7·43 sq ft)
Tailplane 2·00 m² (21·56 sq ft)
Elevators, incl tab 1·35 m² (14·53 sq ft)

WEIGHTS AND LOADINGS (Skyhawk landplane: L; floatplane: F):
Weight empty, equipped: L 636 kg (1,403 lb)
F 718 kg (1,582 lb)
Skyhawk II 649 kg (1,430 lb)
Max T-O and landing weight: L 1,043 kg (2,300 lb)
F 1,007 kg (2,220 lb)
Skyhawk II 1,043 kg (2,300 lb)
Max ramp weight:
L, and Skyhawk II 1,046 kg (2,307 lb)
F 1,010 kg (2,227 lb)
Max wing loading: L 64·4 kg/m² (13·2 lb/sq ft)
F 62·0 kg/m² (12·7 lb/sq ft)
Skyhawk II 64·4 kg/m² (13·2 lb/sq ft)
Max power loading: L 8·74 kg/kW (14·4 lb/hp)
F 8·44 kg/kW (13·9 lb/hp)
Skyhawk II 8·74 kg/kW (14·4 lb/hp)

PERFORMANCE (L: Skyhawk and Skyhawk II landplane; F: floatplane, at max T-O weight):
Never-exceed speed:
L 151 knots (280 km/h; 174 mph)
Max level speed at S/L:
L 125 knots (232 km/h; 144 mph)
F 96 knots (178 km/h; 111 mph)
Max cruising speed (75% power):
L, at 2,440 m (8,000 ft) 122 knots (225 km/h; 140 mph)
F, at 1,220 m (4,000 ft) 95 knots (176 km/h; 109 mph)
Stalling speed, flaps up:
L 50 knots (92 km/h; 57 mph) CAS
F 48 knots (88·5 km/h; 55 mph) CAS
Stalling speed, flaps down:
L, F 44 knots (82 km/h; 51 mph) CAS
Max rate of climb at S/L: L 235 m (770 ft)/min
F 226 m (740 ft)/min
Service ceiling: L 4,330 m (14,200 ft)
F 4,570 m (15,000 ft)
T-O run: L 236 m (775 ft)
F 427 m (1,400 ft)
T-O to 15 m (50 ft): L 424 m (1,390 ft)
F 658 m (2,160 ft)
Landing from 15 m (50 ft): L 381 m (1,250 ft)
F 410 m (1,345 ft)
Landing run: L 158 m (520 ft)
F 180 m (590 ft)
Range, at recommended lean mixture, with allowances for engine start, taxi, T-O, climb and 45 min reserves at 45% power:
Max cruising speed:
L, standard fuel 455 nm (842 km; 523 miles)
F, standard fuel 360 nm (666 km; 414 miles)
L, max fuel 600 nm (1,111 km; 690 miles)
F, max fuel 475 nm (879 km; 546 miles)
Econ cruising speed at 3,050 m (10,000 ft):
L, standard fuel 575 nm (1,066 km; 662 miles)
F, standard fuel 435 nm (806 km; 501 miles)
L, max fuel 750 nm (1,390 km; 864 miles)
F, max fuel 565 nm (1,046 km; 650 miles)

CESSNA MODEL R172E

US Army designation: T-41B Mescalero
US Air Force designations: T-41C/D Mescalero

The Cessna Model R172E is a more powerful version of the original Model 172. Its design was started in late 1963, and a prototype was then built, with a 134 kW (180 hp) Continental O-360 engine. Type Approval was received in 1964, but the original power plant was replaced in the production Model R172E by a fuel-injection IO-360 engine.

In August 1966, the US Army ordered 255 aircraft of this type, under the designation **T-41B**, for training and installation support duties. Delivery of these was completed in March 1967.

In October 1967, the US Air Force ordered 45 similar aircraft, with fixed-pitch propellers, under the designation **T-41C**, for cadet flight training at the USAF Academy in Colorado. A total of 52 had been produced by 1 February 1976. Thirty **T-41Ds**, with constant-speed propellers and 28V electrical systems, were ordered initially for the Colombian Air Force, and deliveries of this version to all operators totalled 311 by 1 January 1979.

A version known as the Reims Rocket was produced by Reims Aviation in France (which see) until the end of the 1976 model year, by which time a total of 572 had been built.

The description of the Skyhawk applies also to the R172E, except for the following details:

POWER PLANT: One 156·5 kW (210 hp) Continental IO-360-D flat-six engine, driving a McCauley 2A34-C209/78CCA-2 constant-speed propeller. Two fuel tanks in wings with total capacity of 197 litres (52 US gallons), of which 174 litres (46 US gallons) are usable. Provision for long-range tanks, giving total usable capacity of 238 litres (63 US gallons). Refuelling points above wing. Oil capacity 9·5 litres (2·5 US gallons).

ACCOMMODATION: Basically as for Skyhawk. The T-41B has special crew seatbacks and shoulder harnesses, with forward-hinged door on each side of cabin by crew seats. Baggage capacity 90·5 kg (200 lb).

AVIONICS AND EQUIPMENT: The T-41B, C and D have variations in their avionics and other equipment consistent with their military roles.

DIMENSIONS, EXTERNAL:
Propeller diameter 1·93 m (6 ft 4 in)

WEIGHTS AND LOADINGS:
Weight empty, equipped 637 kg (1,405 lb)
Max T-O and landing weight 1,156 kg (2,550 lb)
Max wing loading 71·3 kg/m² (14·6 lb/sq ft)
Max power loading 7·39 kg/kW (12·1 lb/hp)

PERFORMANCE (at max T-O weight):
Never-exceed speed 158 knots (293 km/h; 182 mph)
Max level speed at S/L 133 knots (246 km/h; 153 mph)
Max cruising speed at 1,675 m (5,500 ft) 126 knots (233 km/h; 145 mph)
Econ cruising speed at 3,050 m (10,000 ft) 91 knots (169 km/h; 105 mph)
Stalling speed, flaps up 55·6 knots (103 km/h; 64 mph)
Stalling speed, flaps down 46 knots (85 km/h; 53 mph)
Max rate of climb at S/L 268 m (880 ft)/min
Service ceiling 5,180 m (17,000 ft)
T-O run 226 m (740 ft)
T-O to 15 m (50 ft) 375 m (1,230 ft)
Landing from 15 m (50 ft) 387 m (1,270 ft)
Landing run 189 m (620 ft)
Range with max fuel at econ cruising speed at 3,050 m (10,000 ft) 877 nm (1,625 km; 1,010 miles)

CESSNA MODEL R172 HAWK XP

On 23 June 1976, Cessna introduced the Model R172 Hawk XP, and a similar model is being produced by Reims Aviation in France (which see), known as the Model FR172/Reims Hawk XP. A total of 1,043 had been sold by 1 January 1979, this total including 43 Reims-built FR172s. Eighteen Hawk XPs were supplied to the Chilean Army in 1978.

Two versions are available:

Hawk XP. Standard version, powered by one 145·4 kW (195 hp) Continental IO-360-K engine. Available also as floatplane.

Hawk XP/II. Version of the above, equipped in a VFR and IFR configuration. It can be equipped optionally with Nav Pac which adds a second nav/com system and other avionics.

The 1980 versions of the Hawk XP introduce as standard the improvements detailed for the Skyhawk. TBO for the engine is increased from 1,500 to 2,000 h.

The description of the Skyhawk applies also to the Hawk XP, except as follows:

POWER PLANT: One 145·4 kW (195 hp) Continental IO-360-KB flat-six fuel-injection engine, driving a McCauley two-blade metal constant-speed propeller type ZA34C203/90DCA-14, with spinner. Two fuel tanks in wings with a combined capacity of 197 litres (52 US gallons), of which 185 litres (49 US gallons) are usable. Optional integral fuel cells provide a maximum usable capacity of 250 litres (66 US gallons).

ACCOMMODATION: As for Skyhawk, except that Hawk XP has restyled sidewalls and overhead console to improve appearance. Overhead console change provides better access to overhead floodlighting. New control yokes and addition of control for constant-speed propeller. Baggage space has capacity of 91 kg (200 lb).

DIMENSIONS, EXTERNAL (L: landplane; F: floatplane):
As for Skyhawk except:
Length overall: L 8·28 m (27 ft 2 in)
F 8·18 m (26 ft 10 in)
Height overall: F 3·78 m (12 ft 5 in)

WEIGHTS AND LOADINGS (L: Hawk XP landplane; F: floatplane):
Weight empty: L 698 kg (1,538 lb)
F 817 kg (1,800 lb)
Hawk XP II 710 kg (1,565 lb)
Max T-O and landing weight 1,157 kg (2,550 lb)
Max ramp weight: L, F 1,160 kg (2,558 lb)
Max wing loading 71·8 kg/m² (14·7 lb/sq ft)
Max power loading 7·96 kg/kW (13·08 lb/hp)

PERFORMANCE (at max T-O weight):
Max level speed at S/L:
L 133 knots (246 km/h; 153 mph)
F 118 knots (219 km/h; 136 mph)
Max cruising speed (80% power at 1,830 m; 6,000 ft):
L 130 knots (241 km/h; 150 mph)
F 116 knots (215 km/h; 134 mph)
Stalling speed, flaps up, power off:
L 53 knots (98 km/h; 61 mph) CAS
F 50 knots (93 km/h; 58 mph) CAS
Stalling speed, flaps down, power off:
L 46 knots (85 km/h; 53 mph) CAS
F 44 knots (82 km/h; 51 mph) CAS
Max rate of climb at S/L:
L, F 265 m (870 ft)/min
Service ceiling: L 5,180 m (17,000 ft)
F 4,725 m (15,500 ft)
T-O run: L 244 m (800 ft)
F 346 m (1,135 ft)
T-O to 15 m (50 ft): L 415 m (1,360 ft)
F 564 m (1,850 ft)
Landing from 15 m (50 ft): L 387 m (1,270 ft)
F 404 m (1,325 ft)
Landing run: L 189 m (620 ft)
F 201 m (660 ft)
Range (recommended lean mixture, allowances for engine start, taxi, T-O, climb, and 45 min reserves at 45% power):
80% power at 1,830 m (6,000 ft) with 185 litres (49 US gallons) usable fuel:
L 440 nm (815 km; 506 miles)
F 395 nm (731 km; 454 miles)
80% power at 1,830 m (6,000 ft) with 250 litres (66 US gallons) usable fuel:
L 635 nm (1,176 km; 730 miles)
F 570 nm (1,055 km; 656 miles)
Econ cruising power at 3,050 m (10,000 ft) with 185 litres (49 US gallons) usable fuel:
L 575 nm (1,065 km; 662 miles)
F 495 nm (916 km; 569 miles)
Econ cruising power at 3,050 m (10,000 ft) with 250 litres (66 US gallons) usable fuel:
L 815 nm (1,510 km; 938 miles)
F 705 nm (1,305 km; 811 miles)

CESSNA CUTLASS

See Addenda for details of this new development of the Skyhawk with retractable landing gear.

CESSNA CARDINAL CLASSIC

In September 1967, Cessna introduced the single-engined four-seat Model 177. Renamed subsequently as the Cardinal Classic, a total of 4,239 had been built, including Cardinal RGs, and Reims Cardinal RGs built by Reims Aviation in France (which see), before production ceased at the end of 1978. Details of these aircraft can be found in the 1978-79 and earlier editions of *Jane's*.

CESSNA CARDINAL RG and RG II

In December 1970, Cessna introduced a version of the Cardinal with retractable landing gear. Production of this model ended in late 1978; details can be found in the 1978-79 *Jane's*.

CESSNA MODEL 180 SKYWAGON

The Model 180 Skywagon has a typical Cessna braced high-wing monoplane layout, but with a tailwheel type of landing gear. Two commercial versions are available for 1979:

Model 180 Skywagon. Basic model, as described, which introduces as standard improvements for 1979 a new tailcone access panel to simplify maintenance, and new exterior styling. Wheel and brake fairings are introduced as a new option.

Model 180 Skywagon II. As Skywagon, plus factory-installed avionics package which includes Series 300 nav/com with remote VOR indicator, ADF and an emergency locator transmitter. Optional Nav Pac provides a second nav/com, with Series 400 glideslope and marker beacon. Standard equipment is as Model 180, plus long-range fuel tanks with a total usable capacity of 284 litres (75 US gallons), horizontal and directional gyros, vertical speed indicator, turn co-ordinator, heated pitot, external air temperature gauge, clock, map light, sun visor, dual controls, quick-drain oil plug, and external power socket.

A total of 6,002 Model 180s had been built by 1 January 1979.

TYPE: One/six-seat cabin monoplane.

WINGS: Generally similar in construction to those of Skyhawk. Dihedral 1° 44′.

FUSELAGE: All-metal semi-monocoque structure. Identical to fuselage of Cessna 185, except for firewall and mounting brackets for dorsal fin.

TAIL UNIT: Unswept cantilever all-metal structure with adjustable-incidence tailplane. Normally no trim tabs; manually-operated rudder trim available optionally.

LANDING GEAR: Non-retractable tailwheel type. Cessna cantilever spring steel main legs. Tailwheel has tapered tubular spring. Main wheels and nylon tube-type tyres size 6·00-6 (optionally 8·00-6). Cessna tailwheel size 8·00 × 2·80. Tyre pressure, main wheels 2·07 bars (30 lb/sq in), tailwheel 3·79-4·48 bars (55-65 lb/sq in) according to load. Hydraulic disc brakes. Parking brake. Wheel and brake fairings optional. Alternative Edo Model 628-296 floats, snow ski or amphibian gear.

POWER PLANT: One 171·5 kW (230 hp) Continental O-470-U flat-six engine, driving a McCauley 2A34C203/90DA-8 two-blade constant-speed metal propeller. Two fuel tanks in wings, with total standard capacity of 333 litres (88 US gallons), of which 318 litres (84 US gallons) are usable. Oil capacity 11·5 litres (3 US gallons).

ACCOMMODATION: Standard seating is for a pilot only, with a choice of three optional arrangements. Maximum seating is for six persons in three pairs, without baggage space. With fewer seats there is space at rear of cabin for up to 181 kg (400 lb) of baggage. Door on each side of cabin, plus optional cargo door and baggage compartment door on port side. Starboard door has quick-release hinge pins so that it can be removed when loading bulky cargo. Fifth and sixth passenger seats, attached to aft wall of cabin, can be folded when space is required for cargo. Hinged window each side. Instrument lighting controls are transistorised. Heating and ventilation standard. Fully-articulating seats for pilot and co-pilot, child's foldaway seat for the rear cabin and safety belts for rear-seat passengers are available optionally. Dual controls optional (standard on Skywagon II).

SYSTEMS: Hydraulic system for brakes only. Electrical system powered by 28V 60A alternator. 24V 33Ah battery. Oxygen system, 1·36 m³ (48 cu ft) capacity, optional.

AVIONICS AND EQUIPMENT: Optional avionics include Cessna Series 300 360-channel com transceiver, 360-channel nav/com with 160-channel nav and remote VOR indicator, 720-channel com and 200-channel nav with remote VOR/LOC indicator or VOR/ILS indicator, ADF with digital tuning, marker beacon with three lights and aural signal, transponder with 4096 code capability, DME, Nav-O-Matic single-axis autopilot with heading control and VOR intercept and track; or Series 400 720-channel com transceiver, 720-channel nav/com with remote VOR/LOC or VOR/ILS indicator, transponder with 4096 code capability, glideslope receiver and ADF with digital tuning. Standard avionics for Skywagon II include Cessna 300 Series nav/com with remote VOR indicator, ADF and an emergency locator transmitter. Standard equipment includes audible stall warning indicator, instrument panel red floodlights, control locks, windscreen defroster, cabin dome light, landing and taxi lights, and baggage restraint net. Optional equipment, standard on Skywagon II, includes blind-flying instrumentation, heated pitot tube, outside air temperature gauge, electric clock, map light, sun visor, dual controls, quick-drain oil valve, external power socket, and long-range fuel tanks. Other optional equipment includes boom microphone, control wheel with map light and microphone switch, carburettor air temperature gauge, true airspeed indicator, economy mixture indicator, turn and bank indicator, instrument panel post lights, auxiliary instrument lights, courtesy lights, co-pilot's seat installation, navigation light detectors, omni-flash beacon, alternate static source, rudder pedal extensions, flight hour recorder, pilot and co-pilot headrests, twin beverage pack, cargo tiedown fittings, tinted windows, internal corrosion proofing, photographic provisions, stretcher installation, cabin fire extinguishers, de luxe interior, inertia-reel shoulder harness, bubble windows, amphibian kit, floatplane kit, wheel and brake fairings, jack pad, strobe light, tailwheel lock, ski axles, ski provisions, emergency locator transmitter, non-congealing oil cooler, oil dilution system, engine winterisation kit, overall paint scheme, agricultural sprayer system and tailplane abrasion boots.

DIMENSIONS, EXTERNAL:
Wing span 10·92 m (35 ft 10 in)
Wing chord at root 1·63 m (5 ft 4 in)
Wing chord at tip 1·11 m (3 ft 7¾ in)

Cessna Model R172 Hawk XP/II, which has a factory-installed VFR/IFR package

Wing aspect ratio 7·52
Length overall: Landplane 7·81 m (25 ft 7½ in)
Skiplane 8·47 m (27 ft 9½ in)
Floatplane 8·23 m (27 ft 0 in)
Amphibian 8·38 m (27 ft 6 in)
Height overall:
Landplane, skiplane 2·36 m (7 ft 9 in)
Floatplane 3·71 m (12 ft 2 in)
Amphibian 3·86 m (12 ft 8 in)
Tailplane span 3·35 m (11 ft 0 in)
Wheel track, landplane 2·33 m (7 ft 8 in)
Propeller diameter:
Landplane, skiplane 2·08 m (6 ft 10 in)
Floatplane, amphibian 2·29 m (7 ft 6 in)
Passenger doors (each): Height 1·01 m (3 ft 3¾ in)
Width 0·89 m (2 ft 11 in)

AREAS:
Wings, gross 16·16 m² (174 sq ft)
Ailerons (total) 1·70 m² (18·3 sq ft)
Trailing-edge flaps (total) 1·97 m² (21·23 sq ft)
Fin 0·84 m² (9·01 sq ft)
Dorsal fin 0·19 m² (2·04 sq ft)
Rudder 0·68 m² (7·29 sq ft)
Tailplane 1·94 m² (20·94 sq ft)
Elevators 1·40 m² (15·13 sq ft)

WEIGHTS AND LOADINGS:
Weight empty, equipped:
Skywagon landplane 745 kg (1,643 lb)
Skywagon II landplane 768 kg (1,694 lb)
Floatplane 885 kg (1,950 lb)
Skiplane 810 kg (1,785 lb)
Amphibian 1,000 kg (2,205 lb)
Max T-O weight:
Landplane, skiplane 1,270 kg (2,800 lb)
Floatplane, amphibian 1,338 kg (2,950 lb)
Max ramp weight: Landplane 1,274 kg (2,810 lb)
Max wing loading:
Landplane, skiplane 78·6 kg/m² (16·1 lb/sq ft)
Floatplane, amphibian 83·0 kg/m² (17·0 lb/sq ft)
Max power loading:
Landplane, skiplane 7·41 kg/kW (12·2 lb/hp)
Floatplane, amphibian 7·80 kg/kW (12·8 lb/hp)

PERFORMANCE (at max T-O weight):
Never-exceed speed:
Landplane 167 knots (309 km/h; 192 mph)
Max level speed at S/L:
*Landplane 148 knots (274 km/h; 170 mph)
Floatplane, amphibian, skiplane
129 knots (240 km/h; 149 mph)
Max cruising speed (75% power) at 2,440 m (8,000 ft):
*Landplane 142 knots (264 km/h; 164 mph)
Floatplane, amphibian
123 knots (228 km/h; 142 mph)
Skiplane 124 knots (230 km/h; 143 mph)
Econ cruising speed at 3,050 m (10,000 ft):
Landplane 105 knots (195 km/h; 121 mph)
Floatplane, amphibian 99 knots (183 km/h; 114 mph)
Skiplane 88 knots (162 km/h; 101 mph)
Stalling speed, flaps up, power off:
All versions 53 knots (98·5 km/h; 61 mph) CAS
Stalling speed, flaps down, power off:
All versions 48 knots (88·5 km/h; 55 mph) CAS
Max rate of climb at S/L:
Landplane 335 m (1,100 ft)/min
Floatplane, amphibian 296 m (970 ft)/min
Skiplane 277 m (910 ft)/min
Service ceiling: Landplane 5,395 m (17,700 ft)
Floatplane, amphibian 4,663 m (15,300 ft)
Skiplane 4,480 m (14,700 ft)
T-O run: Landplane 190 m (625 ft)
Floatplane 354 m (1,160 ft)
Amphibian, on land 213 m (700 ft)
Amphibian, on water 354 m (1,160 ft)
T-O to 15 m (50 ft): Landplane 367 m (1,205 ft)
Floatplane 579 m (1,900 ft)
Amphibian, on land 401 m (1,315 ft)
Amphibian, on water 579 m (1,900 ft)
Landing from 15 m (50 ft):
Landplane 416 m (1,365 ft)
Floatplane 524 m (1,720 ft)
Amphibian, on land 442 m (1,450 ft)
Amphibian, on water 524 m (1,720 ft)
Landing run: Landplane 146 m (480 ft)
Floatplane 224 m (735 ft)
Amphibian, on land 226 m (740 ft)
Amphibian, on water 224 m (735 ft)
Range, at recommended lean mixture with allowances for start, taxi, T-O, climb and 45 min reserves at 45% power:
Max fuel, max cruising speed at 2,440 m (8,000 ft):
Landplane 825 nm (1,529 km; 950 miles)
Floatplane, amphibian
715 nm (1,324 km; 823 miles)
Skiplane 720 nm (1,334 km; 829 miles)
Max fuel, econ cruising speed at 3,050 m (10,000 ft):
Landplane 1,010 nm (1,872 km; 1,163 miles)
Floatplane, amphibian
825 nm (1,529 km; 950 miles)
Skiplane 820 nm (1,519 km; 944 miles)

These speeds are 1 knot (1·9 km/h; 1·2 mph) higher with optional speed fairings installed

Cessna Model 180 Skywagon one/six-seat cabin monoplane (Continental O-470-U engine)

CESSNA SKYLANE

Three variants of this aircraft were available, of which the Model 182 was the basic standard version. This was discontinued in 1976, leaving two commercial versions currently available:

Skylane. Standard version.

Skylane II. As Skylane, plus factory-installed avionics package which includes Cessna Series 300 nav/com with 720-channel com and 200-channel nav with remote VOR/LOC, ADF, transponder and 200A Nav-O-Matic autopilot with VOR/LOC track and intercept. It is available optionally with a Nav Pac, which adds a second 300 nav/com plus VOR/ILS, Series 400 glideslope receiver with VOR/ILS indicator and Series 400 marker beacon. Standard equipment includes true airspeed indicator, dual controls, navigation light detectors, external power socket, heated pitot, courtesy lights, omni-flash beacon, alternate static source, and emergency locator transmitter.

The 1979 versions of the Skylane introduce as standard improvements an increase in standard fuel capacity and reduction in the quantity of unusable fuel, a redesigned brake master cylinder, a new alternator control unit, an improved throttle control, lighter-weight main landing gear components, and new interior and exterior styling. New options include an ARC two-axis autopilot and a digital clock.

A version designated F182 Skylane is produced for the European market by Reims Aviation in France (which see).

A total of 17,847 Model 182/Skylanes had been built by 1 January 1979, including 94 F182s built by Reims Aviation.

TYPE: Four-seat cabin monoplane.

WINGS: Braced high-wing monoplane. Wing section NACA 2412, modified. Incidence at root 0° 47′, at tip −2° 50′. Dihedral 1° 44′. Wing structure similar to Skyhawk, except metal-to-metal bonded leading-edge.

FUSELAGE: All-metal semi-monocoque structure.

TAIL UNIT: Cantilever all-metal structure with swept fin and rudder. Trim tab in starboard elevator. Electrically-operated elevator trim optional.

LANDING GEAR: Non-retractable tricycle type. Land-O-Matic cantilever main legs, each comprising a one-piece machined conically-tapered spring steel tube. Steerable nosewheel with oleo-pneumatic shock-absorption. Cessna main wheels and tyres size 6·00-6, pressure 2·90 bars (42 lb/sq in). Cessna nosewheel and tyre size 5·00-5, pressure 3·38 bars (49 lb/sq in). Cessna hydraulic disc brakes. Parking brake. Optional wheel fairings.

POWER PLANT: Similar to that of Model 180, except for McCauley propeller type 2A34C203/90DCA-8. Standard fuel capacity 348 litres (92 US gallons), of which 333 litres (88 US gallons) are usable. Refuelling point on upper surface of each wing. Oil capacity 11·5 litres (3 US gallons).

ACCOMMODATION: Generally similar to Skyhawk, with standard seating for four; four seat belts and two shoulder harnesses standard. Optional child's seat. Baggage space aft of rear seats and hatshelf with total capacity of 91 kg (200 lb), with external baggage door. Cargo tiedown net standard. Front seat inertia-reel shoulder harness, rear seat shoulder harness, leather seating, air vent for rear-seat passengers, and openable starboard window optional. Dual controls optional on Skylane.

SYSTEMS: Electrical system powered by 60A 28V engine-driven alternator. 24V battery. Hydraulic system for brakes only. Vacuum system optional. Oxygen system of 1·36 m³ (48 cu ft) capacity optional.

AVIONICS AND EQUIPMENT: Standard avionics for Skylane II, optional on Skylane, include Cessna 200 Series 200A Nav-O-Matic autopilot, 300 Series 720-channel nav/com with remote VOR/LOC or VOR/ILS indicator, ADF with digital tuning, marker beacon with three lights and aural signal and transponder with 4096 code capability. Other optional avionics include DME, 10-channel HF transceiver, 300A Nav-O-Matic single-axis autopilot with heading control plus VOR intercept and track, 400 Series glideslope receiver, ADF with digital tuning and transponder with 4096 code capability. Standard equipment includes audible stall warning device, variable-intensity instrument panel red floodlights, pedestal lights, control locks, armrests, windscreen defrosters, cabin dome light, baggage restraint net, adjustable cabin ventilators, tinted windscreen and windows, landing, taxi and navigation lights and cabin steps. Optional equipment includes blind-flying instrumentation, sensitive altimeter, electric clock, outside air temperature gauge, turn co-ordinator indicator, rate of climb indicator, control wheel with map light and microphone switch, carburettor air temperature gauge, economy mixture indicator, instrument post lights, flight hour recorder, sun visors, rearview mirror, inertia reel shoulder harness for front seats, rear window curtain, cabin fire extinguisher, headrests, shoulder harness for rear seats, leather seating, child's seat, skylights, stretcher installation, utility shelf, internal corrosion proofing, omni-flash beacon, wingtip strobe lights, non-congealing oil cooler, full-flow oil filter, quick drain oil valve, engine winterisation kit, engine priming system, overall paint scheme, towbar, heated stall warning transmitter, glider tow hook, tailplane abrasion boots and tailcone lift handles. True airspeed indicator, dual controls, navigation light detectors, external power socket, heated pitot, courtesy lights and emergency locator transmitter are standard for Skylane II, optional for Skylane.

DIMENSIONS, EXTERNAL:
Wing span 10·92 m (35 ft 10 in)
Wing chord at root 1·63 m (5 ft 4 in)
Wing chord at tip 1·09 m (3 ft 7 in)
Length overall 8·53 m (28 ft 0 in)
Height overall 2·82 m (9 ft 3 in)
Tailplane span 3·55 m (11 ft 8 in)
Wheel track 2·74 m (9 ft 0 in)
Wheelbase 1·69 m (5 ft 6½ in)
Propeller diameter 2·08 m (6 ft 10 in)

Cessna Skylane four-seat cabin monoplane (Continental O-470-U engine)

Passenger doors (each): Height 1·02 m (3 ft 4¼ in)
Width 0·90 m (2 ft 11¼ in)

AREAS:
Wings, gross 16·16 m² (174 sq ft)
Ailerons (total) 1·70 m² (18·3 sq ft)
Trailing-edge flaps (total) 1·97 m² (21·20 sq ft)
Fin 1·08 m² (11·62 sq ft)
Rudder 0·65 m² (6·95 sq ft)
Tailplane 2·13 m² (22·96 sq ft)
Elevators 1·47 m² (15·85 sq ft)

WEIGHTS AND LOADINGS:
Weight empty, equipped: Skylane 771 kg (1,700 lb)
Skylane II 796 kg (1,754 lb)
Max T-O and landing weight 1,338 kg (2,950 lb)
Max ramp weight 1,342 kg (2,960 lb)
Max wing loading 82·5 kg/m² (16·9 lb/sq ft)
Max power loading 7·80 kg/kW (12·8 lb/hp)

PERFORMANCE (at max T-O weight):
Max level speed at S/L
148 knots (273 km/h; 170 mph)
Max cruising speed, 75% power at 2,440 m (8,000 ft) 144 knots (267 km/h; 166 mph)
Stalling speed, flaps up
56 knots (103 km/h; 64 mph) CAS
Stalling speed, flaps down
50 knots (92 km/h; 57 mph) CAS
Max rate of climb at S/L 308 m (1,010 ft)/min
Service ceiling 5,030 m (16,500 ft)
T-O run 215 m (705 ft)
T-O to 15 m (50 ft) 411 m (1,350 ft)
Landing from 15 m (50 ft) 411 m (1,350 ft)
Landing run 180 m (590 ft)
Range, recommended lean mixture, with allowances for start, taxi, T-O, climb and 45 min reserves at 45% power:
Max fuel, 75% power at 2,440 m (8,000 ft)
880 nm (1,630 km; 1,013 miles)
Max fuel, econ cruising speed at 3,050 m (10,000 ft)
1,095 nm (2,029 km; 1,261 miles)

CESSNA SKYLANE RG and TURBO-SKYLANE RG

Introduced in late 1977, the retractable landing gear version of the Skylane is available in four models for 1979:

Skylane RG. Standard version, powered by Lycoming O-540-J3C5D flat-six engine, derated to 175 kW (235 hp), and driving a two-blade metal constant-speed propeller with spinner.

Skylane RG II. As Skylane RG, plus additional avionics and equipment detailed for the Skylane II.

Turbo-Skylane RG. Generally similar to Skylane RG, but powered by a 175 kW (235 hp) Lycoming O-540-L3C5D flat-six engine with turbocharger, driving a two-blade metal constant-speed propeller.

Turbo-Skylane RG II. As Turbo-Skylane RG, plus additional avionics and equipment detailed for the Skylane II, except that the Series 300 transponder is replaced by the Series 400 model. Optional Nav Pac provides IFR capability with addition of a second Series 300 nav/com and indicator, and Series 400 glideslope and marker beacon.

All versions of the Skylane RG have as standard the improvements detailed for the 1979 Skylane models. By 1 January 1979 a total of 760 Skylane RGs had been built, including 18 built by Reims Aviation in France as Reims 182 Skylane RGs.

The description of the Cessna Skylane applies also to the Skylane RG and Turbo-Skylane RG, except as follows:

LANDING GEAR: Hydraulically-retractable tricycle type. Tubular spring steel main gear struts, retracting rearward into fuselage. Nosewheel, which retracts forward, is carried on a short-stroke oleo-pneumatic shock-absorber with hydraulic damper, and is steerable. Nosewheel enclosed by doors when retracted. Hydraulic brakes. Parking brake.

POWER PLANT: One Lycoming flat-six engine, as detailed in model listings. Standard fuel capacity 348 litres (92 US gallons), of which 333 litres (88 US gallons) are usable. Refuelling point on upper surface of each wing. Oil capacity 8·5 litres (2·25 US gallons).

SYSTEMS: As described for Skylane, except self-contained electro-hydraulic system for operation of landing gear and brakes.

DIMENSIONS, EXTERNAL: As for Skylane except:
Length overall 8·72 m (28 ft 7½ in)
Height overall 2·72 m (8 ft 11 in)

WEIGHTS AND LOADINGS (A: Skylane RG; B: Skylane RG II; C: Turbo-Skylane RG; D: Turbo-Skylane RG II):
Weight empty: A 786 kg (1,732 lb)
B 809 kg (1,783 lb)
C 800 kg (1,764 lb)
D 823 kg (1,815 lb)
Max T-O and landing weight:
All versions 1,406 kg (3,100 lb)
Max ramp weight:
All versions 1,412 kg (3,112 lb)
Max wing loading:
All versions 86·9 kg/m² (17·8 lb/sq ft)
Max power loading:
All versions 8·03 kg/kW (13·2 lb/hp)

PERFORMANCE (at max T-O weight):
Max level speed at S/L:
A, B 160 knots (296 km/h; 184 mph)
Max level speed at 6,100 m (20,000 ft):
C, D 187 knots (346 km/h; 215 mph)
Max cruising speed, 75% power at 2,285 m (7,500 ft):
A, B 156 knots (290 km/h; 180 mph)
Max cruising speed, 75% power at 6,100 m (20,000 ft):
C, D 173 knots (320 km/h; 199 mph)
Max cruising speed, 75% power at 3,050 m (10,000 ft):
C, D 158 knots (293 km/h; 182 mph)
Stalling speed, flaps up, power off:
All versions 54 knots (100 km/h; 62 mph)
Stalling speed, flaps down, power off:
All versions 50 knots (92·5 km/h; 57·5 mph)
Max rate of climb at S/L:
A, B 347 m (1,140 ft)/min
C, D 317 m (1,040 ft)/min
*Service ceiling: A, B 4,360 m (14,300 ft)
Max certificated operating altitude:
C, D 6,100 m (20,000 ft)
T-O run: All versions 250 m (820 ft)
T-O to 15 m (50 ft): All versions 479 m (1,570 ft)
Landing from 15 m (50 ft):
All versions 402 m (1,320 ft)
Landing run: All versions 183 m (600 ft)
Range with max fuel, recommended lean mixture, with allowances for start, taxi, T-O, climb and 45 min reserves at 45% power:
75% power at 2,285 m (7,500 ft):
A, B 890 nm (1,650 km; 1,025 miles)
75% power at 6,100 m (20,000 ft):
C, D 875 nm (1,622 km; 1,008 miles)
75% power at 3,050 m (10,000 ft):
C, D 840 nm (1,556 km; 967 miles)
econ cruising power at 3,050 m (10,000 ft):
A, B 1,135 nm (2,103 km; 1,307 miles)
econ cruising power at 6,100 m (20,000 ft):
C, D 1,015 nm (1,881 km; 1,169 miles)
econ cruising power at 3,050 m (10,000 ft):
C, D 1,035 nm (1,918 km; 1,192 miles)

* *Service ceiling is 5,485 m (18,000 ft) if optional EGT gauge is used to set best power mixture*

CESSNA MODEL 185 SKYWAGON

US military designation: U-17

The prototype of the Model 185 Skywagon flew for the first time in July 1960 and the first production model was completed in March 1961. It is generally similar to the Model 180 Skywagon, except for installation of a 224 kW (300 hp) Continental IO-520 engine.

Two versions are available for 1979:

Model 185 Skywagon. Standard version.

Model 185 Skywagon II. As Skywagon, plus factory-installed avionics package which includes Series 300 nav/com, ADF, and emergency locator transmitter. Optional Nav Pac provides a second nav/com with Series 400 glideslope and marker beacon. Standard equipment as for Model 185, plus horizontal and directional gyros, sensitive altimeter, vertical speed indicator, turn co-ordinator, heated pitot and stall warning tubes, external air temperature gauge, clock, map light, sun visor, dual controls, quick-drain oil valve, and external power socket.

The Model 185 Skywagon can be fitted with Edo 628-2960 floats, or Edo Model 597 amphibious floats, or Fli-Lite skis, and is suitable for agricultural duties, using quickly-removable Sorensen spraygear. It can carry under its fuselage a detachable glassfibre Cargo-Pack, more than 2·75 m long and 0·79 m wide (9 ft × 2 ft 7 in), with a volume of 0·61 m³ (21·5 cu ft) and capacity of 136 kg (300 lb). The Pack incorporates loading doors on the side and at the rear.

The 1979 version has the same improvements as those detailed for the Model 180 Skywagon. Wheel and brake fairings are introduced as a new option.

Cessna has received important contracts to supply U-17A/B/C Skywagons to the US Air Force for delivery to overseas countries, under the US Military Assistance Programme.

A total of 3,130 Model 185 Skywagons, including U-17A/B/Cs, had been built by 1 January 1979.

TYPE: One/six-seat cabin monoplane.

WINGS AND FUSELAGE: Similar to Model 180.

TAIL UNIT: Same as for Model 180, except for fin of increased area and manually-operated rudder trim as standard equipment.

LANDING GEAR: Similar to Model 180, except for tyre pressures: main wheels (6·00-6) 2·41 bars (35 lb/sq in), main wheels (8·00-6) 1·72 bars (25 lb/sq in), tailwheel 3·79-4·83 bars (55-70 lb/sq in) depending on load. Manual tailwheel lock standard. Wheel and brake fairings optional. Optional amphibian, float or ski gear.

POWER PLANT: One 224 kW (300 hp) Continental IO-520-D flat-six engine, driving a McCauley two-blade metal constant-speed propeller. Three-blade McCauley propeller optional. Fuel in two tanks in wings, total capacity 333 litres (88 US gallons), of which 318 litres (84 US gallons) are usable. Oil capacity 11·5 litres (3 US gallons).

ACCOMMODATION, AVIONICS AND EQUIPMENT: Generally as for Model 180, except omni-flash beacon and manual tailwheel lock standard.

DIMENSIONS: As for Model 180, except:
Propeller diameter, standard:
Landplane 2·08 m (6 ft 10 in)
Floatplane, amphibian, skiplane 2·18 m (7 ft 2 in)
Propeller diameter, optional:
Landplane 2·03 m (6 ft 8 in)

AREAS: As for Model 180, except:
Fin 1·29 m² (13·86 sq ft)

WEIGHTS AND LOADINGS:
Weight empty, equipped:
Skywagon landplane 762 kg (1,681 lb)
Floatplane 901 kg (1,986 lb)
Amphibian 1,017 kg (2,241 lb)
Skiplane 827 kg (1,823 lb)
Skywagon II landplane 785 kg (1,731 lb)
Max T-O and landing weight:
Landplane, skiplane 1,519 kg (3,350 lb)
Floatplane 1,506 kg (3,320 lb)
Amphibian, land take-off 1,481 kg (3,265 lb)
Amphibian, water take-off 1,406 kg (3,100 lb)
Max ramp weight:
Landplane 1,525 kg (3,362 lb)
Max wing loading:
Landplane, skiplane 94·2 kg/m² (19·3 lb/sq ft)
Floatplane 93·3 kg/m² (19·1 lb/sq ft)
Amphibian 91·8 kg/m² (18·8 lb/sq ft)
Max power loading:
Landplane, skiplane 6·78 kg/kW (11·2 lb/hp)
Floatplane 6·72 kg/kW (11·1 lb/hp)
Amphibian 6·61 kg/kW (10·9 lb/hp)

PERFORMANCE (at max T-O weight):
Never-exceed speed:
Landplane 182 knots (338 km/h; 210 mph)
Max level speed at S/L:
*Landplane 155 knots (286 km/h; 178 mph)
Floatplane 141 knots (261 km/h; 162 mph)
Amphibian, skiplane
136 knots (252 km/h; 157 mph)
Max cruising speed (75% power) at 2,285 m (7,500 ft):
*Landplane 145 knots (269 km/h; 167 mph)
Floatplane 134 knots (248 km/h; 154 mph)
Amphibian 129 knots (240 km/h; 149 mph)
Skiplane 132 knots (245 km/h; 152 mph)
Stalling speed, flaps up, power off:
Landplane, skiplane, floatplane
56 knots (104 km/h; 64·5 mph) CAS
Amphibian 55 knots (102 km/h; 63 mph) CAS
Stalling speed, flaps down, power off:
Landplane, skiplane
49 knots (90·5 km/h; 56 mph) CAS
Amphibian 51 knots (94 km/h; 58 mph) CAS
Floatplane 52 knots (96 km/h; 60 mph) CAS
Max rate of climb at S/L:
Landplane 308 m (1,010 ft)/min

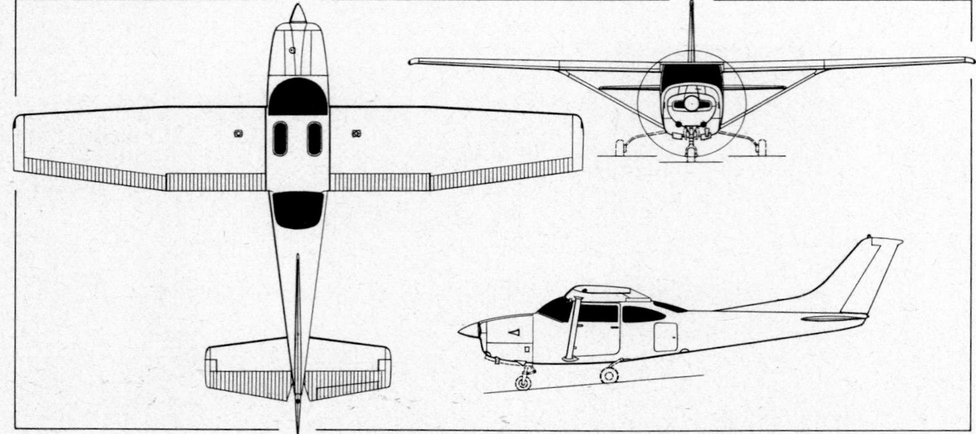

Cessna Skylane RG with retractable landing gear *(Pilot Press)*

Floatplane 293 m (960 ft)/min
Amphibian 296 m (970 ft)/min
Skiplane 247 m (810 ft)/min
Service ceiling: Landplane 5,229 m (17,150 ft)
Floatplane 5,000 m (16,400 ft)
Amphibian 4,663 m (15,300 ft)
Skiplane 4,055 m (13,300 ft)
T-O run: Landplane 235 m (770 ft)
Floatplane 337 m (1,105 ft)
Amphibian, on land 204 m (670 ft)
Amphibian, on water 270 m (885 ft)
T-O to 15 m (50 ft): Landplane 416 m (1,365 ft)
Floatplane 530 m (1,740 ft)
Amphibian, on land 389 m (1,275 ft)
Amphibian, on water 436 m (1,430 ft)
Landing from 15 m (50 ft):
Landplane 427 m (1,400 ft)
Floatplane 466 m (1,530 ft)
Amphibian, on land 378 m (1,240 ft)
Amphibian, on water 450 m (1,480 ft)
Landing run: Landplane 146 m (480 ft)
Floatplane 195 m (640 ft)
Amphibian, on land 238 m (780 ft)
Amphibian, on water 183 m (600 ft)
Range with max fuel (recommended lean mixture, with allowances for engine start, taxi, T-O, climb and 45 min reserves at 45% power):
75% power at 2,285 m (7,500 ft):
Landplane 680 nm (1,260 km; 783 miles)
Floatplane 625 nm (1,159 km; 720 miles)
Amphibian 600 nm (1,112 km; 691 miles)
Skiplane 610 nm (1,130 km; 702 miles)
econ cruising power at 3,050 m (10,000 ft):
Landplane 835 nm (1,548 km; 962 miles)
Floatplane 740 nm (1,371 km; 852 miles)
Amphibian 690 nm (1,279 km; 795 miles)
Skiplane 715 nm (1,324 km; 823 miles)

These speeds are 1 knot (1·9 km/h; 1·2 mph) higher with optional speed fairings installed.

Cessna Model 185 Skywagon one/six-seat cabin monoplane (Continental IO-520-D engine)

Cessna AGtruck agricultural aircraft (Continental IO-520-D engine)

CESSNA AGWAGON and AGTRUCK

On 8 December 1971, Cessna announced the introduction of four new agricultural aircraft, three of them based on the earlier AGwagon low-wing monoplane. Of these, the AGpickup (53 built) was discontinued in 1976.The high-wing AGcarryall is described separately.

The current AGwagon and AGtruck are of all-metal construction and have special corrosion proofing, heavy-duty spring steel Land-O-Matic landing gear and Cessna's Camber-Lift wing to provide better control during low-speed operations. Wing fences are used to smooth airflow over the wing. Special attention has been paid to safety features, and these include ensolite padding on the upper instrument panel, urethane padding on tubular structures in the cabin area and around doors, safe flush switch and control locations and quick-release door hinges. Other standard features include wide wing walks, large hopper loading doors, and fresh-air scoops that slightly pressurise the cockpit and tailcone to prevent the ingress of dust and fumes.

Optional equipment includes a special night operations package to provide brilliant illumination for night operations. This comprises a 100A 24V alternator, taxi/landing lights, instrument panel lights, overhead floodlight, two 600W retractable spray lights, lighting angle control for spray lights, wingtip turning lights, hopper quantity light and a control stick grip incorporating light switches.

Differences between the two models are as follows:

AGwagon. Basic model, powered by a 224 kW (300 hp) Continental IO-520-D flat-six engine, driving a constant-speed propeller. Standard equipment includes a 757 litre (200 US gallon) hopper, a liquid and dry material dispersal control system, cockpit canopy with all-round view, tailplane abrasion boots, oversize 8·00-8 × 22 main-wheel tyres, 10 in tailwheel tyre, wire cutters, cable deflector, tailcone lift handles, hopper side-loading system on port side, navigation lights, pilot's four-way adjustable seat, control stick lock, quick oil drain, auxiliary fuel pump, steerable tailwheel and remote fuel strainer drain control. Options include an automatic flagman and cockpit air-conditioning.

AGtruck. As AGwagon, except for 1,060 litre (280 US gallon) hopper. Additional standard equipment includes a 22-nozzle engine-driven hydraulic spray system with manually-controlled spray valve and gatebox without agitator, wing fuel tanks, extended conical-cambered wingtips, automatic inertia reel for the safety belt system, sensitive altimeter, pilot's foul weather windows, strobe lights, instrument panel lights, landing and taxi lights, three-colour exterior styling, and oversize 10 in main and tailwheel tyres. Options include air-conditioning and a six-way articulating seat.

By 1 January 1979 deliveries totalled 1,531 AGwagons and 1,691 AGtrucks.

TYPE: Single-seat agricultural monoplane.

WINGS: Braced low-wing monoplane, with single streamline-section bracing strut each side. Wing section NACA 2412, modified. Dihedral 9°. Incidence 1° 30′ at root, −1° 30′ at tip. All-metal structure with NACA all-metal single-slotted flaps inboard of Frise all-metal ailerons. Aileron leading-edge gaps sealed. Wing fences immediately outboard of bracing strut attachment points. Conical-cambered wingtips, extended on AGtruck.

FUSELAGE: Rectangular-section welded steel tube structure with removable metal skin panels forward of cabin. All-metal semi-monocoque rear fuselage.

TAIL UNIT: Cantilever all-metal structure. Fixed-incidence tailplane. Trim tab in starboard elevator.

LANDING GEAR: Non-retractable tailwheel type. Land-O-Matic cantilever main legs of heavy-duty spring steel. Tapered tubular tailwheel spring shock-absorber. Main wheels and tyres size 8·00-8 × 22 on AGwagon, with oversize 10 in main-wheel tyres on AGtruck. AGwagon has 10 in tailwheel tyre and AGtruck an oversize 10 in tailwheel tyre. Hydraulic disc brakes and parking brake. Wheel fenders optional.

POWER PLANT: One 224 kW (300 hp) Continental IO-520-D flat-six engine, driving a McCauley two-blade metal constant-speed propeller. Larger two-blade, or three-blade, propeller optional. Two fuel tanks in wings with combined capacity of 204 litres (54 US gallons), of which 197 litres (52 US gallons) are usable. Oil capacity 11·5 litres (3 US gallons).

ACCOMMODATION: Pilot only, on vertically and longitudinally adjustable seat, in enclosed cabin. Steel overturn structure. Combined window and door on each side, hinged at bottom. Heating and ventilation standard.

SYSTEM: Electrical system has a 60A 12V alternator and 12V 24Ah battery as standard. A 60A 24V or a 100A 24V alternator is available optionally.

EQUIPMENT: Standard equipment is as detailed in model listings. Optional equipment includes fan-driven or engine-driven hydraulic spray systems; 22, 44 or 64 nozzle spraybooms; two spreader systems for either medium or high-volume applications; electric spray control valve; a Cessna-designed gatebox; wing leading-edge repair kit; and a tailcone jack point.

DIMENSIONS, EXTERNAL (A: AGwagon; B: AGtruck):
Wing span: A 12·41 m (40 ft 8½ in)
B 12·70 m (41 ft 8 in)
Wing chord at root 1·63 m (5 ft 4 in)
Wing chord at tip 1·12 m (3 ft 8 in)
Length overall 7·90 m (25 ft 11 in)
Height overall 2·49 m (8 ft 2 in)
Tailplane span 3·35 m (11 ft 0 in)
Wheel track 2·16 m (7 ft 1 in)
Propeller diameter: standard 2·08 m (6 ft 10 in)
optional: 2-blade 2·18 m (7 ft 2 in)
3-blade 2·03 m (6 ft 8 in)

AREAS:
Wings, gross: A 18·77 m² (202 sq ft)
B 19·05 m² (205 sq ft)

WEIGHTS AND LOADINGS:
Weight empty, approx, with no dispersal equipment installed: A 906 kg (1,998 lb)
B 931 kg (2,052 lb)
Weight empty, with liquid dispersal system gatebox and engine-driven hydraulic pump:
A 982 kg (2,164 lb)
B 1,008 kg (2,222 lb)
T-O weight, Normal category 1,496 kg (3,300 lb)
Max T-O weight, Restricted category:
A 1,814 kg (4,000 lb)
B 1,905 kg (4,200 lb)
Max landing weight 1,496 kg (3,300 lb)
Wing loading, Normal category:
A 79·6 kg/m² (16·3 lb/sq ft)
B 78·6 kg/m² (16·1 lb/sq ft)
Max wing loading, Restricted category:
A 96·6 kg/m² (19·8 lb/sq ft)
B 100·0 kg/m² (20·5 lb/sq ft)
Power loading, Normal category:
A, B 6·68 kg/kW (11·0 lb/hp)
Max power loading, Restricted category:
A 8·10 kg/kW (13·3 lb/hp)
B 8·50 kg/kW (14·0 lb/hp)

PERFORMANCE (A: AGwagon, B: AGtruck. At max T-O weight with liquid dispersal equipment):
Max level speed at S/L:
A 105 knots (195 km/h; 121 mph)
B 104 knots (193 km/h; 120 mph)
Max cruising speed, 75% power at 1,980 m (6,500 ft):
A 97 knots (180 km/h; 112 mph)
B 96 knots (179 km/h; 111 mph)
Stalling speed, flaps up, power off:
A 58 knots (108 km/h; 67 mph) CAS
B 60 knots (111 km/h; 69 mph) CAS
Stalling speed, flaps down, power off:
A 55 knots (102 km/h; 64 mph) CAS
B 56 knots (104 km/h; 65 mph) CAS
Max rate of climb at S/L: A 168 m (550 ft)/min
B 149 m (490 ft)/min
Service ceiling: A 2,775 m (9,100 ft)
B 2,470 m (8,100 ft)
T-O run: A 367 m (1,205 ft)
B 415 m (1,360 ft)
T-O to 15 m (50 ft): A 575 m (1,885 ft)
B 652 m (2,140 ft)
Landing from 15 m (50 ft): A, B 386 m (1,265 ft)
Landing run: A, B 128 m (420 ft)
Range, recommended lean mixture, allowances for engine start, taxi, T-O, climb, and 45 min reserves at 45% power:
Max fuel, 75% power at 1,980 m (6,500 ft):
A 226 nm (418 km; 260 miles)
B 217 nm (402 km; 250 miles)

CESSNA AGHUSKY

Cessna introduced for 1979 a fourth model to its line of agricultural aircraft. Named the AGhusky, it is a turbocharged version of the AGtruck, the 231 kW (310 hp) engine providing improved performance at varying operational altitudes.

The description of the AGtruck applies also to the AGhusky, except as follows:

POWER PLANT: One 231 kW (310 hp) Continental TSIO-520-T turbocharged flat-six engine, driving a three-blade metal constant-speed propeller. Two fuel tanks in wings with combined capacity of 204 litres (54 US gallons), of which 197 litres (52 US gallons) are usable. Oil capacity 11·5 litres (3 US gallons).

EQUIPMENT: Standard equipment includes a 1,060 litre (280 US gallon) hopper, a Cessna hydraulic dispersal system with electric spray valve and 22-nozzle sprayboom, and a special lighting package.

DIMENSIONS, EXTERNAL: As for AGtruck, except:
Length overall 8·08 m (26 ft 6 in)
Propeller diameter 2·03 m (6 ft 8 in)

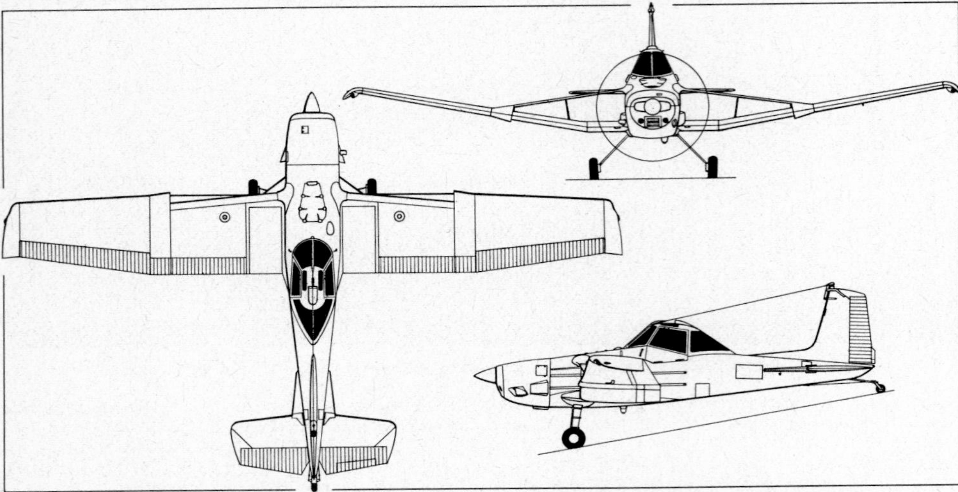

Photograph and three-view drawing *(Pilot Press)* **of the Cessna AGhusky, a turbocharged version of the extensively-built AGtruck**

Weights and Loadings:
- Weight empty, standard 1,040 kg (2,293 lb)
- Max T-O weight, Restricted category 1,996 kg (4,400 lb)
- Max landing weight 1,497 kg (3,300 lb)
- Max wing loading 104·78 kg/m² (21·5 lb/sq ft)
- Max power loading 8·64 kg/kW (14·2 lb/hp)

Performance (at max T-O weight, unless detailed otherwise):
- Max level speed at S/L 109 knots (203 km/h; 126 mph)
- Max cruising speed, 75% power at 1,980 m (6,500 ft) 102 knots (190 km/h; 118 mph)
- Stalling speed, flaps up, power off 62 knots (114 km/h; 71 mph) CAS
- Stalling speed, flaps down, power off 58 knots (108 km/h; 67 mph) CAS
- Max rate of climb at S/L 155 m (510 ft)/min
- Max certificated operating altitude 4,265 m (14,000 ft)
- T-O run 422 m (1,385 ft)
- T-O to 15 m (50 ft) 602 m (1,975 ft)
- Landing from 15 m (50 ft) 386 m (1,265 ft)
- Landing run 128 m (420 ft)
- Range with max fuel, 75% power at 1,980 m (6,500 ft), recommended lean mixture, allowances for engine start, taxi, T-O, climb, and 45 min reserves at 45% power 213 nm (394 km; 245 miles)

CESSNA AGCARRYALL

First announced by Cessna on 8 December 1971, the AGcarryall represented a new multi-purpose concept in this specialised category of aircraft. It is intended for use as a demonstrator of spraying techniques, as a runabout for moving people, equipment or cargo when operating in the field, as a backup aircraft for peak seasonal workloads, as an agricultural pilot trainer, and for use by the farmer who requires spraying capability plus transportation.

Based upon the Model 185, the AGcarryall has two seats as standard, and optional seating for four additional passengers, and is provided with removable spraybooms and a 571 litre (151 US gallon) chemical tank.

The 1979 version introduced as standard a number of improvements, including larger fuel tanks, and redesigned spray control installation, brake master cylinder, and fin cable deflector bracket.

A total of 95 AGcarryalls had been delivered by 1 January 1979.

Type: One/six-seat agricultural utility monoplane.

Wings: Generally similar to Model 185. Provision for attachment of streamline-section V struts on undersurface of each wing to support outer end of sprayboom.

Fuselage and Tail Unit: As for Model 185.

Landing Gear: Non-retractable tailwheel type. Land-O-Matic cantilever main legs of heavy-duty spring steel. Tapered tubular tailwheel spring shock-absorber. Hydraulic disc brakes. Parking brake. Wire cutters on main legs.

Power Plant: As for Model 185. Increased fuel.

Accommodation: Standard seating is for a pilot and passenger, side by side, on four-way adjustable seats. Optional seating for four additional passengers, in two pairs. Door on each side of cabin with quick-release hinges. Extended baggage floor. Cabin heated and ventilated. Wire cutters on windscreen.

System: Electrical system with 60A 28V engine-driven alternator and 24V 24Ah battery standard.

Avionics and Equipment: Series 300 nav/com standard. Standard equipment includes corrosion proofing, windscreen defrosting system, remote fuel strainer drain control, interior lights, landing and taxi lights, navigation lights, aft cabin baggage net, cable deflector, two-colour external paint scheme, and wind-driven spray system with associated 30-nozzle boom, liquid material controls, underfuselage chemical tank with capacity of 571 litres (151 US gallons), omni-flash beacon, overhead floodlight, stowable starboard rudder pedals, safety belts for pilot and co-pilot. Optional equipment includes inertia-reel shoulder harness for two front seats, ground assist handles, tailcone jack point, improved static discharge system and seating for three to six people.

Dimensions, external: As for Model 185, except:
- Height overall 2·40 m (7 ft 10½ in)
- Wheel track 2·26 m (7 ft 5 in)

Areas: As for Model 185

Weights and Loadings (with Sorensen spray system):
- Weight empty 860 kg (1,895 lb)
- Max T-O and landing weight 1,519 kg (3,350 lb)
- Max ramp weight 1,525 kg (3,362 lb)
- Max wing loading 94·2 kg/m² (19·3 lb/sq ft)
- Max power loading 6·78 kg/kW (11·2 lb/hp)

Performance (at max T-O weight, with Sorensen spray system):
- *Max level speed at S/L 129 knots (238 km/h; 148 mph)
- *Max cruising speed at 2,285 m (7,500 ft) 122 knots (225 km/h; 140 mph)
- Stalling speed, flaps up 57 knots (105 km/h; 65 mph) CAS
- Stalling speed, flaps down 49 knots (91 km/h; 56 mph) CAS
- Max rate of climb at S/L 258 m (845 ft)/min
- Service ceiling 4,085 m (13,400 ft)
- T-O run 270 m (885 ft)
- T-O to 15 m (50 ft) 442 m (1,450 ft)
- Landing from 15 m (50 ft) 427 m (1,400 ft)
- Landing run 146 m (480 ft)
- Range, recommended lean mixture, with allowances for start, taxi, T-O, climb and 45 min reserves at 45% power:
  - Max cruising speed at 2,285 m (7,500 ft) with max fuel 564 nm (1,046 km; 650 miles)

**With spraybooms removed, max level speed and cruising speed are increased by 8·7 knots (16 km/h; 10 mph)*

CESSNA STATIONAIR 6

Cessna re-named the former U206 Skywagon and TU206 Turbo-Skywagon as the Stationair and Turbo-Stationair respectively. In 1978 a name change to Stationair 6 and Turbo-Stationair 6 highlighted the six-seat capacity of these cargo/utility aircraft, and the considerable differences between them and the Model 185 Skywagon. In particular, they have swept vertical tail surfaces, a tricycle landing gear, a tailplane of greater span, wide-span flaps, and double cargo doors on the starboard side of the fuselage which permit the easy loading and unloading of a crate more than 1·22 m long, 0·91 m wide and 0·91 m deep (4 ft × 3 ft × 3 ft).

The two basic versions of the Stationair 6 are as follows:

Stationair 6. Standard cargo utility model with 224 kW (300 hp) Continental IO-520-F engine and double loading doors, as described in detail.

Turbo-Stationair 6. Similar to the Stationair 6 but with 231 kW (310 hp) Continental TSIO-520-M turbocharged engine in modified cowling and provided with a manifold pressure relief valve to prevent overboost.

A utility version of the Stationair is also available, with a single seat for the pilot as standard, vinyl floor covering, two-colour paint scheme and no wheel fairings. Up to five passenger seats can be supplied optionally.

The 1979 models of the two basic Stationair 6 versions introduced a number of improvements as standard, including increased-capacity fuel tanks, and a new cargo door latch assembly.

A total of 5,362 Model 206 Skywagons and Stationairs had been built by 1 January 1979, including 643 de luxe Super Skylanes of similar basic design.

Type: Single-engined cargo/utility aircraft.

Wings: Braced high-wing monoplane. Single streamlined-section bracing strut each side. Wing section NACA 2412, modified. Dihedral 1° 44′. Incidence 1° 30′ at root, —1° 30′ at tip. All-metal structure. Glassfibre conical camber tips. Modified Frise-type wide-chord ailerons. Electrically-operated long-span NACA single-slotted flaps. No tabs.

Fuselage: Conventional all-metal semi-monocoque structure.

Tail Unit: Cantilever all-metal structure, with sweptback vertical surfaces. Large trim tab in starboard elevator. Electrical operation of trim tab optional.

Landing Gear: Non-retractable tricycle type. Cessna Land-O-Matic cantilever spring steel main legs. Steerable nosewheel with oleo-pneumatic shock-absorbers. Cessna wheels, tubeless tyres and hydraulic disc brakes. Parking brake. Main wheels and tyres size 6·00-6, pressure 2·90 bars (42 lb/sq in). Nosewheel and tyre size

Cessna AGcarryall utility aircraft (Continental IO-520-D engine)

5·00-5, pressure 3·10 bars (45 lb/sq in). Main-wheel tyres size 8·00-6, nosewheel tyre size 6·00-6 and oversize wheel fairings optional. Floats and wheel-skis optional.

POWER PLANT: One Continental flat-six engine (details given under model listings), driving a McCauley three-blade metal constant-speed propeller type D2A32C90/82NC-2 (Stationair) or D3A-32C88/82NC-2 (Turbo-Stationair). Two fuel cells in wings, with total standard capacity of 348 litres (92 US gallons), of which 333 litres (88 US gallons) are usable. Oil capacity 11·5 litres (3 US gallons).

ACCOMMODATION: Standard seating for pilot, co-pilot and up to four passengers, front seats with inertia safety belts. Club seating arrangement optional, with centre row of seats facing aft. Utility version has only pilot's seat as standard. Pilot's door on port side. Large double cargo doors on starboard side; forward door hinged to open forward, rear door hinged to open rearward. Aircraft can be flown with cargo doors removed for photography, air dropping of supplies or parachuting. Openable starboard window optional. Fully articulating seats for pilot and co-pilot and safety harness for four rear seats optional. Cabin heated and ventilated.

SYSTEMS: Electrical system powered by an engine-driven 60A 28V alternator. 24V 33Ah battery. Hydraulic system for brakes and optional wheel-skis. Oxygen system of 2·10 m³ (74 cu ft) capacity standard on Turbo-Stationair 6; 1·36 m³ (48 cu ft) system optional for Stationair 6. Vacuum system optional.

AVIONICS AND EQUIPMENT: Optional avionics as detailed for the Skylane, plus Series 400 Nav-O-Matic two-axis autopilot with heading control, VOR intercept and track and altitude control, Series 400 nav/com, DME, RNAV, a non-slaved HSI (with autopilot installation), audio/marker beacon panel, padded headset and electro-luminescent panel lighting, plus the optional avionics detailed for the Skylane II. Standard equipment as for the Skylane, plus sensitive altimeter, electric clock, turn co-ordinator indicator, outside air temperature gauge, glareshield, overall paint scheme, and sun visors. Optional equipment, less the above items, is as detailed for the Skylane, plus ambulance kits, casket kit, photographic provisions, glider towing provisions and skydiving kit. The child's seat and skylights are not available for the Stationair 6. The Turbo-Stationair 6 has an overboost control valve, absolute pressure controller, pressurised fuel system, turbine access door, pilot's all-purpose control wheel, non-congealing oil cooler, full flow oil filter and alternate static source as standard.

DIMENSIONS, EXTERNAL (L: landplane; F: floatplane):
Wing span 10·92 m (35 ft 10 in)
Wing chord at root 1·63 m (5 ft 4 in)
Wing chord at tip 1·09 m (3 ft 7 in)
Wing aspect ratio 7·63
Length overall:
Stationair 6: L 8·61 m (28 ft 3 in)
Stationair 6: F 9·04 m (29 ft 8 in)
Turbo-Stationair 6 8·61 m (28 ft 3 in)
Height overall: L 2·83 m (9 ft 3½ in)
F 4·31 m (14 ft 1½ in)
Tailplane span 3·96 m (13 ft 0 in)
Wheel track: L 2·46 m (8 ft 1 in)
Propeller diameter: L 2·03 m (6 ft 8 in)
F 2·18 m (7 ft 2 in)
Pilot's door (port):
Height, mean 1·03 m (3 ft 4 in)
Cargo double door (stbd):
Height 0·98 m (3 ft 2½ in)
Width 1·13 m (3 ft 8½ in)
Height to sill 0·64 m (2 ft 1 in)

DIMENSIONS, INTERNAL:
Cabin: Length 3·66 m (12 ft 0 in)
Max width 1·12 m (3 ft 8 in)
Max height 1·26 m (4 ft 1½ in)
Volume available for payload 2·87 m³ (101·2 cu ft)

AREAS:
Wings, gross 16·17 m² (174·0 sq ft)
Ailerons (total) 1·60 m² (17·32 sq ft)
Trailing-edge flaps (total) 2·63 m² (28·35 sq ft)
Fin 1·08 m² (11·62 sq ft)
Rudder, incl tab 0·65 m² (6·95 sq ft)
Tailplane 2·31 m² (24·84 sq ft)
Elevators, incl tab 1·86 m² (20·08 sq ft)

WEIGHTS AND LOADINGS (L: landplane; F: floatplane):
Weight empty:
Utility Stationair 6: L 824 kg (1,817 lb)
F 988 kg (2,178 lb)
Utility Stationair 6/II: L 851 kg (1,877 lb)
F 1,015 kg (2,238 lb)
Stationair 6: L 870 kg (1,919 lb)
F 1,026 kg (2,261 lb)
Stationair 6/II: L 898 kg (1,980 lb)
F 1,053 kg (2,321 lb)
Utility Turbo-Stationair 6 853 kg (1,881 lb)
Utility Turbo-Stationair 6/II 881 kg (1,942 lb)
Turbo-Stationair 6 900 kg (1,984 lb)
Turbo-Stationair 6/II 927 kg (2,044 lb)

Cessna Stationair 6 one/six-seat cargo/utility aircraft

Max T-O and landing weight:
Stationair 6: L 1,633 kg (3,600 lb)
F 1,587 kg (3,500 lb)
Turbo-Stationair 6 1,633 kg (3,600 lb)
Max ramp weight:
Stationair 6: L 1,638 kg (3,612 lb)
Turbo-Stationair 6: L 1,640 kg (3,616 lb)
Max wing loading:
Stationair 6: L 101·1 kg/m² (20·7 lb/sq ft)
F 98·1 kg/m² (20·1 lb/sq ft)
Turbo-Stationair 6 101·1 kg/m² (20·7 lb/sq ft)
Max power loading:
Stationair 6: L 7·29 kg/kW (12·0 lb/hp)
F 7·08 kg/kW (11·7 lb/hp)
Turbo-Stationair 6 7·07 kg/kW (11·6 lb/hp)

PERFORMANCE (L: landplane; F: floatplane):
Max level speed:
Stationair 6 at S/L:
L 156 knots (290 km/h; 180 mph)
F 138 knots (256 km/h; 159 mph)
Turbo-Stationair 6 at 5,180 m (17,000 ft):
L 174 knots (322 km/h; 200 mph)
Max cruising speed (75% power):
Stationair 6 at 1,980 m (6,500 ft):
L 147 knots (272 km/h; 169 mph)
F 132 knots (245 km/h; 152 mph)
Turbo-Stationair 6, 80% power at 6,100 m (20,000 ft):
L 167 knots (309 km/h; 192 mph)
Turbo-Stationair 6, 80% power at 3,050 m (10,000 ft): L 152 knots (282 km/h; 175 mph)
Stalling speed, flaps up, power off:
Stationair 6: L 62 knots (115 km/h; 71·5 mph) CAS
F 56 knots (104 km/h; 64·5 mph) CAS
Turbo-Stationair 6:
L 62 knots (115 km/h; 71·5 mph) CAS
Stalling speed, flaps down, power off:
Stationair 6: L 54 knots (101 km/h; 62·5 mph) CAS
F 51 knots (95 km/h; 59 mph) CAS
Turbo-Stationair 6:
L 54 knots (101 km/h; 62·5 mph) CAS
Max rate of climb at S/L:
Stationair 6: L 280 m (920 ft)/min
F 282 m (925 ft)/min
Turbo-Stationair 6: L 308 m (1,010 ft)/min
Service ceiling:
Stationair 6: L 4,511 m (14,800 ft)
F 4,237 m (13,900 ft)
Turbo-Stationair 6: L 8,230 m (27,000 ft)
T-O run:
Stationair 6: L 274 m (900 ft)
F 559 m (1,835 ft)
Turbo-Stationair 6: L 255 m (835 ft)
T-O to 15 m (50 ft):
Stationair 6: L 543 m (1,780 ft)
F 860 m (2,820 ft)
Turbo-Stationair 6: L 500 m (1,640 ft)
Landing from 15 m (50 ft):
Stationair 6: L 425 m (1,395 ft)
F 511 m (1,675 ft)
Turbo-Stationair 6: L 425 m (1,395 ft)
Landing run:
Stationair 6: L 224 m (735 ft)
F 238 m (780 ft)
Turbo-Stationair 6: L 224 m (735 ft)
Range, Stationair 6, recommended lean mixture, with allowances for start, taxi, T-O, climb and 45 min reserves at 45% power:
Max cruising speed at 1,980 m (6,500 ft) with max fuel: L 725 nm (1,344 km; 835 miles)
F 650 nm (1,204 km; 748 miles)
Econ cruising speed at 3,050 m (10,000 ft) with max fuel: L 900 nm (1,667 km; 1,036 miles)
F 770 nm (1,427 km; 887 miles)
Range, Turbo-Stationair 6, recommended lean mixture, with allowances for start, taxi, T-O, climb and 45 min reserves at 45% power:
Max cruising speed at 6,100 m (20,000 ft) with max fuel: L 690 nm (1,279 km; 795 miles)
Max cruising speed at 3,050 m (10,000 ft) with max fuel: L 655 nm (1,213 km; 754 miles)
Econ cruising speed at 6,100 m (20,000 ft) with max fuel: L 785 nm (1,455 km; 904 miles)
Econ cruising speed at 3,050 m (10,000 ft) with max fuel: L 805 nm (1,492 km· 927 miles)

CESSNA STATIONAIR 7 and TURBO-STATIONAIR 7

On 19 February 1969 Cessna announced two new seven-seat versions of its Skywagon utility aircraft. Generally similar to the earlier Model 206 Super Skywagon, the Skywagon had been 'stretched' to provide improved load-carrying ability while retaining the single engine and operating economy of the Model 206.

In addition to the longer fuselage, new features included a door for the co-pilot or passenger on the starboard side at the front of the cabin, and a separate baggage compartment forward of the cabin, accessible through an external door, also on the starboard side of the fuselage.

Design of this model started in November 1967 and the prototype flew for the first time on 11 May 1968. The first production aircraft, a Model 207, was completed on 13 December 1968 and made its first flight on 3 January 1969, followed three days later by the first flight of a T207 Turbo-Skywagon. Both models received FAA certification on 31 December 1968. A total of 498 Model 207s had been delivered by 1 January 1979.

For 1978 these two models were renamed Stationair 7 and Turbo-Stationair 7 respectively. The avionics equipment detailed as standard and optional for the Stationair 6 and Turbo-Stationair 6 is available respectively for the Stationair 7 and Turbo-Stationair 7.

There are two current versions, as follows:

Stationair 7. Standard passenger/cargo utility model with 224 kW (300 hp) Continental IO-520-F engine.

Turbo-Stationair 7. Generally similar to Stationair 7, but with 231 kW (310 hp) Continental TSIO-520-M turbocharged engine, driving a McCauley three-blade metal constant-speed propeller. Absolute pressure controller, pressurised fuel system, non-congealing oil cooler, full-flow oil filter, overboost control valve, alternate static source and oxygen system standard.

The following description applies to the Stationair 7, except where stated otherwise:

TYPE: Single-engined utility aircraft.

WINGS: Braced high-wing monoplane. Single streamline-section bracing strut each side. Wing section NACA 2412 from root to just inboard of tip; wingtip is symmetrical. Dihedral 1° 44'. Incidence 1° 30' at root, —1° 30' at tip. All-metal structure. Glassfibre conical-camber tips. Modified Frise-type all-metal wide-chord ailerons. Electrically-operated long-span NACA single-slotted all-metal flaps. No trim tabs.

FUSELAGE: Conventional all-metal semi-monocoque structure.

TAIL UNIT: Cantilever all-metal structure, with sweptback vertical surfaces. Tailplane fixed with —3° incidence. Large trim tab in starboard elevator. Electrical operation of trim tab optional. Rudder trimmed by adjustment of bungee.

LANDING GEAR: Non-retractable tricycle type. Improved Cessna Land-O-Matic cantilever main legs of one-piece tapered steel tube. Steerable nosewheel with Cessna oleo-pneumatic shock-absorber and hydraulic shimmy damper. Cessna wheels, tubeless tyres and hydraulic disc brakes. Main wheels and tyres size 6·00-6, pressure 3·79 bars (55 lb/sq in). Nosewheel and tyre size 5·00-5, pressure 3·38 bars (49 lb/sq in). Optional 8·00-6 main-wheel tyres, pressure 2·41 bars (35 lb/sq in), nosewheel tyre size 6·00-6, pressure 2·00 bars (29 lb/sq in). Wheel fairings standard; oversize wheel fairings optional.

POWER PLANT: One 224 kW (300 hp) Continental IO-520-F flat-six engine, driving a McCauley three-blade metal constant-speed propeller. A bladder-type fuel tank, capacity 115·5 litres (30·5 US gallons), is located in the inboard section of each wing. Total fuel capacity 231 litres (61 US gallons), of which 204 litres (54 US

Cessna Stationair 7 one/seven-seat utility aircraft (Continental IO-520-F engine)

gallons) are usable. Optional tankage increases capacity to 151·5 litres (40 US gallons) in each wing, giving a total capacity of 303 litres (80 US gallons), of which 276 litres (73 US gallons) are usable. Refuelling points in upper surface of each wing. Oil capacity 11·4 litres (3 US gallons).

ACCOMMODATION: Pilot's seat only standard. Optional individual seats for up to seven persons, arranged in three pairs, two abreast, with a single seat at the rear of cabin. Pilot's door on port side, co-pilot's door on starboard side at front. Large double cargo doors on starboard side at rear of cabin; forward door hinged to open forward, rear door hinged to open rearward. Aircraft can be flown with cargo doors removed for photography, air dropping of supplies or parachuting; optional equipment includes a spoiler for use when the aircraft is flown in this configuration. Openable window, port side; openable window starboard side optional. Separate baggage compartment, forward of cabin, capacity 54 kg (120 lb), accessible through top-hinged door on starboard side. External glassfibre cargo pack, capacity 136 kg (300 lb), carried beneath the fuselage, is available as an optional extra.

SYSTEMS: Hydraulic system for brakes. Electrical system powered by a 28V 60A engine-driven alternator. 24V 33Ah battery. Oxygen system of 2·15 m³ (76 cu ft) capacity standard on Turbo-Stationair 7; 1·36 m³ (48 cu ft) system optional on Stationair 7.

AVIONICS AND EQUIPMENT: As described for the Model 180, but with electric clock, sensitive altimeter, outside air temperature gauge, flap position indicator, rate of climb indicator, turn co-ordinator, elevator and rudder trim controls, sun visors, electro-luminescent lights for switch and comfort control panels, instrument panel glareshield light, triple dome lights, tinted windscreen and windows, baggage tiedown rings, dual-beam landing lights, emergency locator transmitter, cabin steps and towbar standard. Additional optional items include Cessna Series 400 avionics, instrument post lights, rear-view mirror, articulating and vertically adjustable front seats, inertia-reel shoulder harness for pilot and co-pilot, openable starboard window, centre armrests, shoulder harness for five passenger seats, ambulance kit comprising stretcher, oxygen and attendant's seat, heated stall warning transmitter and pitot, anti-precipitation static kit, flush com antenna, glider tow hook and skydiving kit.

DIMENSIONS, EXTERNAL:

Wing span	10·92 m (35 ft 10 in)
Wing chord at root	1·63 m (5 ft 4 in)
Wing chord at tip	1·09 m (3 ft 7 in)
Wing aspect ratio	7·46
Length overall	9·80 m (32 ft 2 in)
Height overall	2·92 m (9 ft 7 in)
Tailplane span	3·96 m (13 ft 0 in)
Wheel track	3·09 m (10 ft 1¾ in)
Wheelbase	2·11 m (6 ft 11¼ in)
Propeller diameter	2·03 m (6 ft 8 in)
Forward cabin doors (each):	
Height	1·05 m (3 ft 5½ in)
Width	0·89 m (2 ft 11½ in)
Height to sill	0·71 m (2 ft 4 in)
Cargo double doors (stbd):	
Height	0·97 m (3 ft 2 in)
Width	1·13 m (3 ft 8½ in)
Height to sill	0·76 m (2 ft 6 in)
Baggage door (stbd): Height	0·61 m (2 ft 0 in)
Width	0·34 m (1 ft 1½ in)
Height to sill	1·02 m (3 ft 4 in)

DIMENSIONS, INTERNAL:

Cabin: Length	4·27 m (14 ft 0 in)
Max width	1·13 m (3 ft 8½ in)
Max height	1·24 m (4 ft 1 in)
Floor area	4·38 m² (47·1 sq ft)
Volume	4·40 m³ (155·5 cu ft)
Forward baggage compartment:	
Length	0·43 m (1 ft 5 in)
Max width	1·05 m (3 ft 5½ in)
Max height	0·69 m (2 ft 3 in)
Floor area	0·46 m² (4·9 sq ft)
Volume	0·27 m³ (9·5 cu ft)
Underfuselage cargo pack	0·34 m³ (12·0 cu ft)

AREAS:

Wings, gross	16·17 m² (174·0 sq ft)
Ailerons (total)	1·60 m² (17·32 sq ft)
Trailing-edge flaps (total)	2·66 m² (26·60 sq ft)
Fin	0·84 m² (9·04 sq ft)
Rudder	0·65 m² (6·95 sq ft)
Tailplane	2·31 m² (24·84 sq ft)
Elevators, incl tab	1·86 m² (20·08 sq ft)

WEIGHTS AND LOADINGS:

Weight empty: Utility Stationair 7	894 kg (1,971 lb)
Utility Stationair 7/II	925 kg (2,040 lb)
Stationair 7	942 kg (2,076 lb)
Stationair 7/II	973 kg (2,145 lb)
Utility Turbo-Stationair 7	931 kg (2,052 lb)
Utility Turbo-Stationair 7/II	962 kg (2,121 lb)
Turbo-Stationair 7	978 kg (2,157 lb)
Turbo-Stationair 7/II	1,010 kg (2,226 lb)
Max T-O and landing weight:	
Stationair 7 and Turbo-Stationair 7	1,723 kg (3,800 lb)
Max ramp weight: Stationair 7	1,729 kg (3,812 lb)
Turbo-Stationair 7	1,731 kg (3,816 lb)
Max wing loading:	
Stationair 7 and Turbo-Stationair 7	106·44 kg/m² (21·8 lb/sq ft)
Max power loading:	
Stationair 7	7·69 kg/kW (12·7 lb/hp)
Turbo-Stationair 7	7·46 kg/kW (12·3 lb/hp)

PERFORMANCE (at max T-O weight and with optional wheel fairings, which increase speed by 3-4 knots; 5·5-7·5 km/h; 3·5-4·5 mph, with corresponding difference in range. A: Stationair 7; B: Turbo-Stationair 7):

Never-exceed speed:	
A, B	182 knots (338 km/h; 210 mph)
Max level speed:	
A at S/L	150 knots (278 km/h; 173 mph)
B at 5,180 m (17,000 ft)	170 knots (315 km/h; 196 mph)
Max cruising speed:	
A, 75% power at 1,980 m (6,500 ft)	143 knots (266 km/h; 165 mph)
B, 80% power at 6,100 m (20,000 ft)	161 knots (298 km/h; 185 mph)
B, 80% power at 3,050 m (10,000 ft)	148 knots (274 km/h; 170 mph)
Stalling speed, flaps up, power off:	
A, B	65 knots (121 km/h; 75 mph) CAS
Stalling speed, flaps down, power off:	
A, B	58 knots (108 km/h; 67 mph) CAS
Max rate of climb at S/L: A	247 m (810 ft)/min
B	270 m (885 ft)/min
Service ceiling: A	4,054 m (13,300 ft)
B	7,925 m (26,000 ft)
T-O run: A	335 m (1,100 ft)
B	314 m (1,030 ft)
T-O to 15 m (50 ft): A	600 m (1,970 ft)
B	567 m (1,860 ft)
Landing from 15 m (50 ft): A, B	457 m (1,500 ft)
Landing run: A, B	233 m (765 ft)

Range, A at recommended lean mixture, with allowances for engine start, taxi, T-O, climb and 45 min reserves at 45% power:

Max cruising speed at 1,980 m (6,500 ft) with standard fuel	390 nm (723 km; 449 miles)
Max cruising speed at 1,980 m (6,500 ft) with max fuel	565 nm (1,047 km; 651 miles)
Econ cruising speed at 3,050 m (10,000 ft) with standard fuel	470 nm (871 km; 541 miles)
Econ cruising speed at 3,050 m (10,000 ft) with max fuel	690 nm (1,279 km; 795 miles)

Range, B with allowances as above:

Max cruising speed at 6,100 m (20,000 ft) with standard fuel	350 nm (648 km; 403 miles)
Max cruising speed at 3,050 m (10,000 ft) with standard fuel	345 nm (639 km; 397 miles)
Max cruising speed at 6,100 m (20,000 ft) with max fuel	525 nm (972 km; 604 miles)
Max cruising speed at 3,050 m (10,000 ft) with max fuel	510 nm (944 km; 587 miles)
Econ cruising speed at 6,100 m (20,000 ft) with standard fuel	385 nm (713 km; 443 miles)
Econ cruising speed at 3,050 m (10,000 ft) with standard fuel	415 nm (769 km; 478 miles)
Econ cruising speed at 6,100 m (20,000 ft) with max fuel	585 nm (1,083 km; 673 miles)
Econ cruising speed at 3,050 m (10,000 ft) with max fuel	610 nm (1,130 km; 702 miles)

CESSNA CENTURION and CENTURION II

The original prototype Model 210, which flew in January 1957, followed the general formula of the Cessna series of all-metal high-wing monoplanes, but was the first to have a retractable tricycle landing gear.

Later versions of the Model 210 have a fully-cantilever wing, eliminating the bracing struts used on earlier models. Their design was started on 24 October 1964 and construction of a prototype began on 29 November 1964. The first T210 with the new wing flew on 18 June 1965.

On 3 December 1970 Cessna announced the introduction of two new versions of the Model 210 to be known as Centurion II and Turbo-Centurion II. These differ from the Centurion and Turbo-Centurion by having as standard equipment a factory-installed IFR avionics package which offers a cost saving on avionics equipment, plus a gyro panel, dual controls, articulating front seats and all-purpose control wheel. A Pressurised Centurion was introduced in late 1977, and this is described separately.

Standard improvements for the 1979 versions of the Centurion include elimination of the main landing gear doors to save weight, decrease retraction time and facilitate maintenance, lighter-weight landing gear components, redesigned integral hydraulic-electric unit for landing gear retraction, and simplified removal of forward and centre seats for maintenance purposes.

The six current production versions of the Centurion are as follows:

Centurion. Standard model, with 224 kW (300 hp) Continental IO-520-L flat-six engine, driving a McCauley D3A32C88/82NC-2 three-blade metal constant-speed propeller.

Centurion II. Identical to Centurion but with a 720-channel Cessna Series 300 nav/com, ADF, transponder, all-purpose control wheel, instrument post lights, true airspeed indicator, horizon and directional gyro with vacuum system and suction gauge, economy mixture indicator, dual controls, reclining and vertically-adjustable co-pilot's seat, emergency locator transmitter, ground power socket, navigation light detectors, heating system

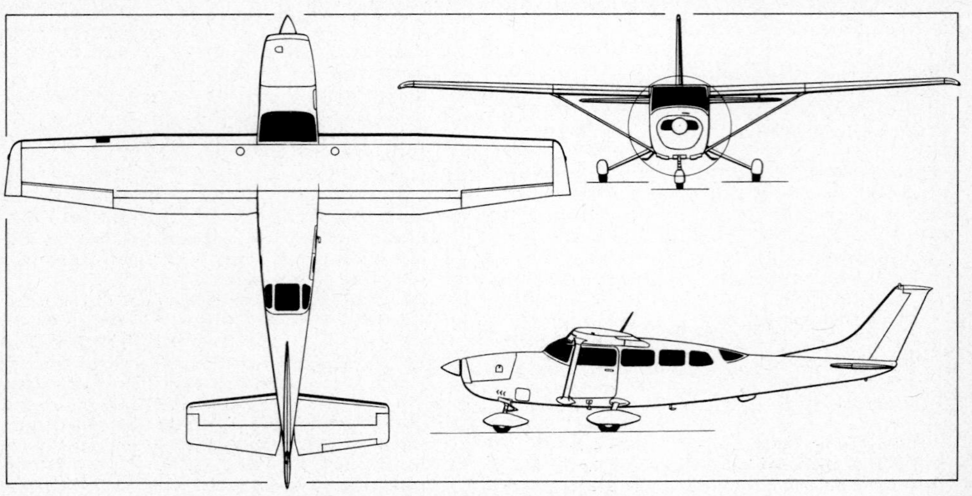

Cessna Stationair 7 utility aircraft *(Pilot Press)*

for pitot and stall warning transmitter, omni-flash beacon, two courtesy lights and alternate static source as standard. Nav-O-Matic 200A autopilot and Bendix RDR-160 weather radar optional. A Nav Pac is also optional, this including a second Series 300 nav/com, with Series 400 glideslope and marker beacon.

Turbo-Centurion. Generally similar to Centurion, but powered by a 231 kW (310 hp) Continental TSIO-520-R turbocharged engine, driving a McCauley three-blade metal constant-speed propeller. Absolute pressure controller, full-flow oil filter, pressurised fuel system, oxygen system, non-congealing oil cooler and overboost control valve standard.

The Turbo-Centurion version holds an international altitude record for aircraft of this class with a height of 12,906·5 m (42,344 ft).

Turbo-Centurion II. Identical to Turbo-Centurion but with additional standard equipment as detailed for Centurion II, except that transponder is Series 400. The same optional avionics are available also.

Pressurised Centurion/Pressurised Centurion II. Introduced in late 1977, these pressurised versions of the Centurion are described separately.

The original versions received FAA Type Approval on 23 August 1966. A total of 6,506 Model 210/Centurions, plus an additional 158 Pressurised Centurions, had been delivered by 1 January 1979.

TYPE: Six-seat cabin monoplane.

WINGS: Cantilever high-wing monoplane. Wing section NACA 64_2A215 at root, NACA 64_1A412 (A=0·5) at tip. Dihedral 1° 30′. Incidence 1° 30′ at root, −1° 30′ at tip. All-metal structure, except for glassfibre conical-camber tips. All-metal Frise-type ailerons. Electrically-actuated all-metal Fowler-type flaps. Ground-adjustable tab in each aileron. Pneumatic de-icing system optional.

FUSELAGE: All-metal semi-monocoque structure.

TAIL UNIT: Cantilever all-metal structure with 36° sweepback on fin. Fixed-incidence tailplane. Controllable trim tabs in rudder and starboard elevator. Electrical operation of elevator tab optional. Pneumatic de-icing system optional.

LANDING GEAR: Hydraulically-retractable tricycle type with single wheel on each unit. Nose unit retracts forward, main units aft and inward. Chrome vanadium tapered steel tube main legs. Steerable nosewheel with oleo-pneumatic shock-absorber. Cessna main wheels and tube-type tyres, size 6·00-6, pressure 2·90 bars (42 lb/sq in). Cessna nosewheel and tyre, size 5·00-5, pressure 3·10 bars (45 lb/sq in). Cessna hydraulic disc brakes. Parking brake.

POWER PLANT: One flat-six engine, as described under model listings. Electrical de-icing system for propeller optional. Integral fuel tanks in wings, with max total capacity of 340 litres (90 US gallons). Refuelling points above wing. Oil capacity 9·5 litres (2·5 US gallons) in Centurions, 10·5 litres (2·75 US gallons) in Turbo-Centurions.

ACCOMMODATION: Six persons in pairs in enclosed cabin. Front two seats of fully-articulating type on Centurion II and Turbo-Centurion II (pilot's seat only on other versions). Fifth and sixth seats have folding backs to accommodate articles up to 2·01 m (6 ft 7 in) long. Openable window on port side standard; optional for starboard side. Dual controls standard on Centurion II and Turbo-Centurion II (optional on other models). Forward-hinged door on each side of cabin. Baggage space aft of rear seats, capacity 109 kg (240 lb), with outside door on port side. Combined heating and ventilation system. Windscreen electrical anti-icing optional.

SYSTEMS: Integral hydraulic-electric unit for landing gear retraction. Hydraulic system for brakes. Electrical power supplied by 24V 60A engine-driven alternator. 24V battery. Oxygen system standard on Turbo-Centurion, optional for Centurion.

AVIONICS AND EQUIPMENT: Optional avionics as for Stationair, except that Series 300 or 400 integrated flight control system is available when the Series 200A, 300A, or 400 Nav-O-Matic autopilot is replaced by the Series 400A two-axis autopilot, which has automatic pitch trim and an optional ILS coupler. Automatic Radial Centering (ARC) is optional with Series 300 nav indicators. Series 400 avionics, including 400B Integrated Flight Control System, Series 800 encoding altimeter with altitude alert system, and Bendix RDR-160 weather radar, are also available as options. Standard equipment includes sensitive altimeter, rate of climb indicator, electric clock, outside air temperature gauge, audible landing gear and stall warning indicators, turn co-ordinator indicator, electroluminescent lights for switch and comfort control panels, glareshield and map lights, variable-intensity instrument panel red floodlights, sun visors, control locks, armrests, windscreen defroster, dome lights, baggage restraint net, adjustable cabin air ventilation, tinted windscreen and windows, landing lights, taxi light, navigation lights, quick fuel drains and sampler cup, overall paint scheme, cabin steps and towbar. Optional equipment includes a gyro panel, fully-articulating co-pilot seat, all-purpose control wheel, control wheel map light, boom microphone, turn and bank indicator, flight hour recorder, rearview mirror, electric elevator trim system, true airspeed indicator, economy mixture indicator, instrument post lights, emergency locator transmitter, navigation light detectors, pitot and stall warning heating system, omni-flash beacon and two courtesy lights for Centurion and Turbo-Centurion, cabin fire extinguisher, headrests, stretcher installation, internal corrosion proofing, ice detector light, engine priming system, glider tow hook, wingtip-mounted strobe lights, tailplane abrasion boots and static dischargers. Optional for the Centurion and Centurion II only are a full-flow oil filter, non-congealing oil cooler, and engine winterisation kit.

Cessna Centurion, standard version of this six-seat cabin monoplane

DIMENSIONS, EXTERNAL:
- Wing span — 11·20 m (36 ft 9 in)
- Wing chord at root — 1·68 m (5 ft 6 in)
- Wing chord at tip — 1·22 m (4 ft 0 in)
- Wing aspect ratio — 7·66
- Length overall — 8·59 m (28 ft 2 in)
- Height overall — 2·95 m (9 ft 8 in)
- Tailplane span — 3·96 m (13 ft 0 in)
- Wheel track — 2·64 m (8 ft 8 in)
- Wheelbase — 1·75 m (5 ft 9 in)
- Propeller diameter — 2·03 m (6 ft 8 in)
- Passenger doors (each):
  - Height — 1·02 m (3 ft 4¼ in)
  - Width — 0·90 m (2 ft 11¼ in)
  - Height to sill — 0·91 m (3 ft 0 in)
- Baggage compartment door:
  - Height — 0·57 m (1 ft 10½ in)
  - Width — 0·74 m (2 ft 5 in)

DIMENSIONS, INTERNAL:
- Cabin: Length — 3·50 m (11 ft 6 in)
  - Max width — 1·08 m (3 ft 6½ in)
  - Max height — 1·23 m (4 ft 0½ in)
  - Floor area — 2·69 m^2 (29·0 sq ft)
  - Volume — 3·96 m^3 (139·9 cu ft)
- Baggage space — 0·46 m^3 (16·25 cu ft)

AREAS:
- Wings, gross — 16·25 m^2 (175 sq ft)
- Ailerons (total) — 1·75 m^2 (18·86 sq ft)
- Trailing-edge flaps (total) — 2·74 m^2 (29·50 sq ft)
- Fin, incl dorsal fin — 0·95 m^2 (10·26 sq ft)
- Rudder, incl tab — 0·65 m^2 (6·95 sq ft)
- Tailplane — 1·73 m^2 (18·57 sq ft)
- Elevators, incl tab — 1·87 m^2 (20·08 sq ft)

WEIGHTS AND LOADINGS:
- Weight empty: Centurion — 966 kg (2,129 lb)
  - Centurion II — 995 kg (2,194 lb)
  - Turbo-Centurion — 1,007 kg (2,221 lb)
  - Turbo-Centurion II — 1,037 kg (2,287 lb)
- Max T-O and landing weight:
  - Centurion, Centurion II — 1,724 kg (3,800 lb)
- Max T-O weight:
  - Turbo-Centurion, Turbo-Centurion II — 1,814 kg (4,000 lb)
- Max landing weight:
  - Turbo-Centurion, Turbo-Centurion II — 1,724 kg (3,800 lb)
- Max ramp weight:
  - Centurion, Centurion II — 1,729 kg (3,812 lb)
  - Turbo-Centurion, Turbo-Centurion II — 1,822 kg (4,016 lb)
- Max wing loading:
  - Centurion, Centurion II — 106 kg/m^2 (21·7 lb/sq ft)
  - Turbo-Centurion, Turbo-Centurion II — 111·6 kg/m^2 (22·8 lb/sq ft)
- Max power loading:
  - Centurion, Centurion II — 7·69 kg/kW (12·7 lb/hp)
  - Turbo-Centurion, Turbo-Centurion II — 7·85 kg/kW (12·9 lb/hp)

PERFORMANCE (at max T-O weight):
- Max level speed:
  - Centurion, Centurion II at S/L — 175 knots (325 km/h; 202 mph)
  - Turbo-Centurion, Turbo-Centurion II at 5,180 m (17,000 ft) — 204 knots (378 km/h; 235 mph)
- Max cruising speed:
  - Centurion, Centurion II, 75% power at 1,980 m (6,500 ft) — 171 knots (317 km/h; 197 mph)
  - Turbo-Centurion, Turbo-Centurion II, 80% power:
    - at 6,100 m (20,000 ft) — 196 knots (364 km/h; 226 mph)
    - at 3,050 m (10,000 ft) — 180 knots (333 km/h; 207 mph)
- Stalling speed, flaps up, power off:
  - Centurion, Centurion II — 65 knots (121 km/h; 75 mph) CAS
  - Turbo-Centurion, Turbo-Centurion II — 67 knots (124 km/h; 77 mph) CAS
- Stalling speed, flaps down, power off:
  - Centurion, Centurion II — 56 knots (104 km/h; 64·5 mph) CAS
  - Turbo-Centurion, Turbo-Centurion II — 58 knots (108 km/h; 67 mph) CAS
- Max rate of climb at S/L:
  - Centurion, Centurion II — 290 m (950 ft)/min
  - Turbo-Centurion, Turbo-Centurion II — 283 m (930 ft)/min
- Service ceiling:
  - Centurion, Centurion II — 5,275 m (17,300 ft)
  - Turbo-Centurion, Turbo-Centurion II — 8,230 m (27,000 ft)
- T-O run:
  - Centurion, Centurion II — 381 m (1,250 ft)
  - Turbo-Centurion, Turbo-Centurion II — 396 m (1,300 ft)
- T-O to 15 m (50 ft):
  - Centurion, Centurion II — 619 m (2,030 ft)
  - Turbo-Centurion, Turbo-Centurion II — 658 m (2,160 ft)
- Landing from 15 m (50 ft):
  - All versions — 457 m (1,500 ft)
- Landing run: All versions — 233 m (765 ft)
- Range, Centurion and Centurion II with max fuel, at recommended lean mixture with allowances for engine start, taxi, T-O, climb and 45 min reserves at 45% power:
  - Max cruising speed at 1,980 m (6,500 ft) — 855 nm (1,585 km; 985 miles)
  - Econ cruising speed at 3,050 m (10,000 ft) — 1,065 nm (1,973 km; 1,226 miles)
- Range, Turbo-Centurion and Turbo-Centurion II with max fuel, allowances as above:
  - Max cruising speed at 3,050 m (10,000 ft) — 780 nm (1,445 km; 898 miles)
  - Max cruising speed at 6,100 m (20,000 ft) — 815 nm (1,506 km; 938 miles)
  - Econ cruising speed at 3,050 m (10,000 ft) — 960 nm (1,778 km; 1,105 miles)
  - Econ cruising speed at 6,100 m (20,000 ft) — 940 nm (1,741 km; 1,082 miles)

CESSNA PRESSURISED CENTURION and PRESSURISED CENTURION II

On 10 November 1977, Cessna announced the introduction of a pressurised version of the Centurion. It is available in two versions:

Pressurised Centurion. Standard model, generally similar to Centurion, except for installation of 231 kW (310 hp) Continental TSIO-520-P engine with a special high-capacity turbocharger to support the pressurisation system, and pressure cabin. Easily identified by four smaller windows on each side of cabin.

Pressurised Centurion II. Identical to Pressurised Centurion, with additional standard avionics and equipment as described for Centurion II, except that autopilot is Nav-O-Matic 300A and transponder is Series 400.

These Centurions have a cabin pressure differential of 0·23 bars (3·35 lb/sq in), providing a cabin altitude of 3,695 m (12,127 ft) at 7,010 m (23,000 ft). Cabin heat is provided by a double heat exchange system using exhaust system heat. Unlike the average combustion heating unit, this system uses no fuel and is reported to offer outstanding performance even in extremely cold temperatures. A total of 158 Pressurised Centurions had been delivered by 1 January 1979.

The description of the Centurion applies also to the Pressurised Centurion, except as follows:

FUSELAGE: Conventional semi-monocoque structure of light alloy, with fail-safe structure in the pressurised section.

POWER PLANT: One 231 kW (310 hp) Continental TSIO-520-P flat-six engine; otherwise as for Centurion. Oil capacity 10·4 litres (2·75 US gallons).

ACCOMMODATION: As for Centurion, except forward-hinged door on port side of cabin. Large emergency exit on starboard side. Baggage space aft of cabin area, capacity 91 kg (200 lb). Four windows each side of

Cessna Pressurised Centurion six-seat cabin monoplane (one Continental TSIO-520-P engine)

cabin, two overhead windows above the rear seats. Cabin pressurised, heated and ventilated.

SYSTEMS: As for Centurion, except cabin pressurisation system by engine bleed air, max differential 0·23 bars (3·35 lb/sq in). Cabin heated by double heat exchange system using exhaust system heat.

DIMENSIONS, INTERNAL: As for Centurion except:
- Baggage space — 0·52 m³ (18·3 cu ft)

WEIGHTS AND LOADINGS (A: Pressurised Centurion; B: Pressurised Centurion II):
- Weight empty: A — 1,059 kg (2,334 lb)
- B — 1,088 kg (2,399 lb)
- Max T-O weight: A, B — 1,814 kg (4,000 lb)
- Max landing weight: A, B — 1,723 kg (3,800 lb)
- Max ramp weight: A, B — 1,821 kg (4,016 lb)
- Max wing loading: A, B — 111·8 kg/m² (22·9 lb/sq ft)
- Max power loading: A, B — 7·85 kg/kW (12·9 lb/hp)

PERFORMANCE (at max T-O weight, except where indicated):
- *Max level speed at 5,180 m (17,000 ft) — 206 knots (381 km/h; 237 mph)
- *Max cruising speed, 80% power at 6,100 m (20,000 ft) — 200 knots (370 km/h; 230 mph)
- *Max cruising speed, 80% power at 3,050 m (10,000 ft) — 182 knots (338 km/h; 210 mph)
- Stalling speed, flaps up — 67 knots (124 km/h; 77·5 mph) CAS
- Stalling speed, flaps down — 58 knots (108 km/h; 67 mph) CAS
- Max rate of climb at S/L — 283 m (930 ft)/min
- Rate of climb at 3,050 m (10,000 ft) — 248 m (815 ft)/min
- Rate of climb at 6,100 m (20,000 ft) — 157 m (515 ft)/min
- Max certificated operating altitude — 7,010 m (23,000 ft)
- T-O run — 396 m (1,300 ft)
- T-O to 15 m (50 ft) — 658 m (2,160 ft)
- Landing from 15 m (50 ft) — 457 m (1,500 ft)
- Landing run — 233 m (765 ft)
- Range with max fuel, recommended lean mixture, with fuel allowance for engine start, taxi, T-O, climb and 45 min reserves at 45% power:
  - 80% power at 6,100 m (20,000 ft) — 770 nm (1,427 km; 887 miles)
  - 80% power at 3,050 m (10,000 ft) — 735 nm (1,363 km; 846 miles)
  - 70% power at 6,100 m (20,000 ft) — 845 nm (1,566 km; 973 miles)
  - 70% power at 3,050 m (10,000 ft) — 820 nm (1,519 km; 944 miles)
  - Econ cruising speed at 6,100 m (20,000 ft) — 910 nm (1,687 km; 1,048 miles)
  - Econ cruising speed at 3,050 m (10,000 ft) — 925 nm (1,714 km; 1,065 miles)

**Speeds based on estimated mid-cruise weight*

CESSNA MODEL 303

Cessna announced, on 17 February 1978, the first flight (on 14 February) of a new lightweight four-seat twin-engined aircraft, to which the company has allocated the designation Model 303.

To be certificated to the latest FAR 23 regulations, this aircraft has a NASA-developed supercritical wing, and makes extensive use of bonded structures. The spacious cabin has a passenger door with airstairs on the starboard side. Power plant consists of two 119 kW (160 hp) Lycoming flat-four engines. Intended to serve as a multi-engine trainer, or as a fast business aircraft, the Model 303 has a max T-O weight of 1,633 kg (3,600 lb), max cruising speed of 174 knots (322 km/h; 200 mph), and range of 868 nm (1,609 km; 1,000 miles). It was planned originally to begin delivery of production aircraft in late 1979, but no further information was available in the early months of 1979.

CESSNA MODEL 310 and 310 II

The Model 310 is a twin-engined five/six-seat cabin monoplane, the prototype of which flew on 3 January 1953. It went into production in 1954. The Turbo 310 was added in late 1968, and the first production model was delivered in December 1968. On 21 December 1973 Cessna announced two new versions of the Model 310, known as the 310 II and the Turbo 310 II, which have factory-installed IFR avionics plus other comfort and convenience features as standard. A total of 4,903 examples of the Model 310 had been completed by 1 January 1979.

There are four current versions of the Model 310, as follows:

310. Standard model, as described in detail, powered by two 212·5 kW (285 hp) Continental IO-520-MB flat-six engines, driving McCauley three-blade fully-feathering constant-speed metal propellers.

310 II. Identical to 310, but having as standard equipment dual 300 Series nav/com with 720-channel com, 200-channel nav, VOR/LOC and VOR/ILS indicators; 300 Series ADF with digital tuning; 400 Series glideslope receiver; marker beacon; transponder; 400B Nav-O-Matic autopilot with approach coupler; associated antennae; avionics cooling kit and panel; six individual seats; dual controls; starboard landing light; taxi light; rotating beacon; outside air temperature gauge; economy mixture indicator; auxiliary fuel system of 238·5 litres (63 US gallons); locator beacon, nosewheel fender, static dischargers; external power socket; and large baggage door.

Turbo T310. Similar to 310, but with two 212·5 kW (285 hp) Continental TSIO-520-BB turbocharged engines, with automatic propeller synchronisation, full-flow oil filters, absolute and pressure ratio controllers, overboost control valves and engine cowl flaps as standard.

Turbo T310 II. Identical to T310, but with the additional standard equipment as detailed for the 310 II.

The 1979 versions of the Model 310 introduce a number of improvements as standard, including a more corrosion-resistant exhaust system, and the provision of an FAA-approved flight manual.

TYPE: Twin-engined five- or six-seat monoplane.

WINGS: Cantilever low-wing monoplane. Wing section NACA 23018 at centreline, NACA 23009 at tip. Dihedral 5°. Incidence 2° 30′ at root, −0° 30′ at tip. All-metal structure. Electrically-operated split flaps. Trim tab in port aileron. Pneumatic de-icing system optional.

FUSELAGE: All-metal semi-monocoque structure.

TAIL UNIT: Cantilever all-metal structure, with 40° sweepback on fin at quarter-chord. Small ventral fin. Trim tabs in rudder and starboard elevator. Electrically-operated elevator trim optional. Pneumatic de-icing system optional.

LANDING GEAR: Retractable tricycle type. Electro-mechanical retraction. Cessna oleo shock-absorber struts. Nosewheel steerable to 15° and castoring from 15° to 55° each side. Main wheels size 6·50-10, tyre pressure 4·14 bars (60 lb/sq in). Nosewheel size 6·00-6, tyre pressure 2·76 bars (40 lb/sq in). Goodyear single-disc hydraulic brakes. Hydraulic parking brake.

POWER PLANT: Two flat-six engines, as described under individual model listings, driving three-blade propellers. Automatic propeller unfeathering system and propeller de-icing optional; automatic propeller synchroniser standard for T310 and T310 II, optional for 310 and 310 II. Standard fuel in two permanently attached canted wingtip tanks, each holding 193 litres (51 US gallons), of which 189 litres (50 US gallons) are usable. Cross-feed fuel system. Optional fuel in two 77·5 litre (2·5 US gallon) rubber fuel cells installed between the wing spars outboard of each engine nacelle, two 43·5 litre (11·5 US gallon) rubber fuel cells further outboard in each wing, and two 77·5 litre (20·5 US gallon) wing locker fuel tanks, providing a maximum fuel capacity of 783 litres (207 US gallons), of which 768 litres (203 US gallons) are usable. Oil capacity 24·6 litres (6·5 US gallons).

ACCOMMODATION: Cabin normally seats five, two in front and three on cross-bench behind. Four alternative seating arrangements are available, with up to six individual seats in pairs, all of which can tilt and have fore and aft adjustment, individual air vents, reading lights and magazine pockets. Dual controls optional. Inertia seat-belts for two front seats (optional for rear seats). Pilot's storm window, port side. Cabin windows are double-glazed to reduce noise level. Large door on starboard side giving access to all seats. Cargo door, 1·02 m (3 ft 4 in) wide, for loading of bulky items, standard on 310 II and T310 II, optional on 310 and T310. Baggage compartment at rear of cabin, capacity 163 kg (360 lb), with internal and external access; locker for a further 54·5 kg (120 lb) of baggage in the rear of each engine nacelle; and baggage compartment in extended nose with capacity of 158 kg (350 lb). Total baggage capacity 430 kg (950 lb). Optional cabin accessories include writing desk, window curtains, electrical adjustment of pilot and co-pilot seats, all-leather seats, oxygen system and photographic survey provisions. Windscreen defrosting standard; windscreen alcohol de-icing system optional.

SYSTEMS: Electrical system powered by two 50A 28V engine-driven alternators and 24V 25Ah battery. 100A alternators optional. Oxygen system of 2·17 m³ (76·6 cu ft) or 1·37 m³ (48·3 cu ft) capacity optional; an automatic altitude compensating regulator is standard with this installation. Janitrol 45,000 BTU thermostatically-controlled blower-type heater for cabin heating and windscreen defrosting. Cabin air-conditioning system rated at 12,000 BTU optional. Vacuum system supplied by two engine-driven pumps with adequate capacity to cater for the pneumatic de-icing boots and flight instruments. Hydraulic system for brakes only.

AVIONICS AND EQUIPMENT: Optional avionics include Series 300 nav/com transceiver with 720-channel com and 200-channel nav with remote VOR/LOC or VOR/ILS indicator, ADF with digital tuning, 10-channel HF and flight director system; Series 400 nav/com transceiver with 720-channel com and 200-channel nav with remote VOR/LOC or VOR/ILS indicator, 40-channel glideslope, ADF with digital tuning and BFO, transponder with 4096 code capability, encoding altimeter, Nav-O-Matic 400A two-axis autopilot and integrated flight control system with optional RMI or HSI; or Series 1000 com transceiver, nav receiver, ADF, and glideslope receiver, with Series 800 DME and RNAV system. Additional avionics options include PN-101 pictorial navigation system, X-band weather radar, KNC-610 area nav, AVQ-75 DME, KN-65 DME, radar altimeter, locator beacon, yaw damper, boom microphone and headset. Standard equipment includes sensitive altimeter, quartz crystal clock, blind-flying instrumentation, audible landing gear and stall warning indicators, heater overheat light, variable-intensity emergency floodlight, map light, alternator failure lights, instrument post lights, control locks, navigation light detectors, sun visors, pilot and co-pilot safety belts, hat shelf, super soundproofing, cabin radio speaker, baggage straps, adjustable cabin air ventilators, emergency exit window, aft omni-vision window, tinted dual-pane windows, armrests, reading lights, landing light, navigation lights, full-flow oil coolers, nosewheel fender, heated pitot, heated fuel vents and stall-warning transmitter, quick-drain fuel valves, overall paint scheme, retractable cabin step and towbar. Optional equipment includes digital clock, relief tube, flight hour recorder, co-pilot's blind-flying instrumentation, angle of attack indicator, true airspeed indicator, economy mixture indicator, outside air temperature

Cessna Model 310 twin-engined five/six-seat cabin monoplane

gauge, instantaneous rate of climb indicator, electroluminescent panel lighting, turn co-ordinator, synchronous tachometer, rudder pedal locks, boom microphone/headset, rearview mirror, electrically-adjustable seats and inertia-reel shoulder harness for pilot and co-pilot, all-leather seats, cabin curtain, rear window curtains, writing desk, 'total flood' cabin fire extinguisher, cabin fire extinguisher, eight-track stereo with cabin speakers, stereo headsets, nacelle and nose baggage compartment courtesy lights, courtesy light timer, internal corrosion proofing, fuselage ice protection plates, ice detection light, rotating beacon, second retractable landing light, wing walk and cabin step lights, three-light strobe system, taxi light, photographic provisions, carpet for nose baggage area, engine fire detection and extinguishing system, external power socket, emergency locator transmitter, electric windshield panel, anti-icing kit, anti-collision light, heated dual static source, static dischargers and radome nose. Additional optional items for the Model 310 and 310 II include automatic propeller synchroniser and partial oxygen system plumbing.

DIMENSIONS, EXTERNAL:

Wing span	11·25 m (36 ft 11 in)
Wing chord at root	1·71 m (5 ft 7½ in)
Wing chord at tip	1·16 m (3 ft 9½ in)
Wing aspect ratio	7·3
Length overall	9·74 m (31 ft 11½ in)
Height overall	3·25 m (10 ft 8 in)
Tailplane span	5·18 m (17 ft 0 in)
Wheel track	3·59 m (11 ft 9½ in)
Wheelbase	2·80 m (9 ft 2¼ in)
Propeller diameter: 310, 310 II	1·94 m (6 ft 4½ in)
T310, T310 II	1·98 m (6 ft 6 in)

DIMENSIONS, INTERNAL:

Baggage compartment (cabin)	1·26 m³ (44·6 cu ft)
Baggage compartments (nacelles, total)	0·52 m³ (18·5 cu ft)
Baggage compartment (nose)	0·59 m³ (21 cu ft)

AREAS:

Wings, gross	16·63 m² (179 sq ft)
Ailerons (total)	1·06 m² (11·44 sq ft)
Trailing-edge flaps (total)	2·13 m² (22·90 sq ft)
Fin	1·33 m² (14·30 sq ft)
Rudder	1·09 m² (11·76 sq ft)
Tailplane	2·99 m² (32·15 sq ft)
Elevators	2·05 m² (22·10 sq ft)

WEIGHTS AND LOADINGS:

Weight empty: 310	1,521 kg (3,353 lb)
310 II	1,634 kg (3,603 lb)
T310	1,575 kg (3,473 lb)
T310 II	1,689 kg (3,723 lb)
Max ramp weight: All versions	2,511 kg (5,535 lb)
Max T-O weight: All versions	2,495 kg (5,500 lb)
Max landing weight: All versions	2,449 kg (5,400 lb)
Max zero-fuel weight:	
310, 310 II	2,223 kg (4,900 lb)
T310, T310 II	2,275 kg (5,015 lb)
Max wing loading:	
All versions	150 kg/m² (30·73 lb/sq ft)
Max power loading:	
All versions	5·87 kg/kW (9·65 lb/hp)

PERFORMANCE (at max T-O weight, except speeds at mid-cruise weight):

Max level speed:	
310 at S/L	207 knots (383 km/h; 238 mph)
T310 at 4,875 m (16,000 ft)	237 knots (439 km/h; 273 mph)
Max cruising speed:	
310, 75% power at 2,285 m (7,500 ft)	195 knots (361 km/h; 225 mph)
T310, 73·6% power at 3,050 m (10,000 ft)	201 knots (372 km/h; 231 mph)
T310, 73·6% power at 6,100 m (20,000 ft)	223 knots (413 km/h; 257 mph)
Econ cruising speed with max fuel:	
310 at 3,050 m (10,000 ft)	144 knots (267 km/h; 166 mph)
T310 at 6,100 m (20,000 ft)	175 knots (325 km/h; 202 mph)
Min control speed (VMC):	
All versions	81 knots (150 km/h; 93 mph)
Stalling speed, flaps up, power off:	
All versions	78 knots (145 km/h; 90 mph) CAS
Stalling speed, flaps down, power off:	
All versions	70 knots (130 km/h; 81 mph) CAS
Max rate of climb at S/L:	
310	507 m (1,662 ft)/min
T310	518 m (1,700 ft)/min
Rate of climb at S/L, one engine out:	
310	113 m (370 ft)/min
T310	119 m (390 ft)/min
Service ceiling: 310	6,020 m (19,750 ft)
T310	8,350 m (27,400 ft)
Service ceiling, one engine out:	
310	2,255 m (7,400 ft)
T310	5,245 m (17,200 ft)
T-O run: 310	407 m (1,335 ft)
T310	398 m (1,306 ft)
T-O to 15 m (50 ft): 310	518 m (1,700 ft)
T310	507 m (1,662 ft)
Landing from 15 m (50 ft):	
All versions, at 2,449 kg (5,400 lb)	546 m (1,790 ft)
Landing run:	
All versions, at 2,449 kg (5,400 lb)	195 m (640 ft)

Range, recommended lean mixture, allowances for start, taxi, T-O, climb and 45 min reserves at 45% power:

310, 310 II, max cruising speed at 2,285 m (7,500 ft) with 272 kg (600 lb) usable fuel
494 nm (916 km; 569 miles)

310, 310 II, as above with 552 kg (1,218 lb) usable fuel
1,132 nm (2,097 km; 1,303 miles)

310, 310 II, econ cruising speed at 3,050 m (10,000 ft) with 272 kg (600 lb) usable fuel
616 nm (1,141 km; 709 miles)

310, 310 II, as immediately above with 552 kg (1,218 lb) usable fuel
1,511 nm (2,800 km; 1,740 miles)

T310, T310 II, max cruising speed at 6,100 m (20,000 ft) with 272 kg (600 lb) usable fuel
521 nm (966 km; 600 miles)

T310, T310 II, as immediately above with 552 kg (1,218 lb) usable fuel
1,250 nm (2,316 km; 1,439 miles)

T310, T310 II, econ cruising speed at 6,100 m (20,000 ft) with 272 kg (600 lb) usable fuel
571 nm (1,057 km; 657 miles)

T310, T310 II, as immediately above with 552 kg (1,218 lb) usable fuel
1,440 nm (2,668 km; 1,658 miles)

CESSNA MODEL 337 SKYMASTER and SKYMASTER II

USAF designation: O-2

This unorthodox all-metal 4/6-seat business aircraft resulted from several years of study by Cessna aimed at producing a twin-engined aeroplane that would be simple to fly, low in cost, safe and comfortable, while offering all the traditional advantages of two engines. Construction of a full-scale mockup was started in February 1960 and completed two months later. The prototype flew for the first time on 28 February 1961, followed by the first production model in August 1962. FAA Type Approval was received on 22 May 1962 and deliveries of the original Model 336 Skymaster, with non-retractable landing gear, began in May 1963.

A total of 195 Model 336 Skymasters had been built by January 1965. In the following month, this version was superseded by the Model 337 Skymaster, with increased wing incidence, retractable landing gear, and other changes, making it virtually a new aeroplane. A total of 1,978 Model 336/337 Skymasters had been built by 1 January 1979, plus an additional 66 Reims Skymasters by Reims Aviation in France.

In addition, 544 examples of two military versions (O-2A and O-2B) were delivered to the USAF and Imperial Iranian Air Force, as detailed in the 1977-78 and earlier editions of *Jane's*. Similar aircraft are now available from Summit Aviation (which see), by conversion of standard Skymasters.

Six commercial versions of the Model 337 Skymaster are available for 1979:

Skymaster. Basic version, powered by two 156·5 kW (210 hp) Continental IO-360-GB flat-six engines, each driving a McCauley two-blade constant-speed and fully-feathering metal propeller. Detailed description applies to this version.

Skymaster II. Generally similar to the Skymaster, but including the following equipment as standard: dual Series 300 nav/coms, Series 300 ADF, Series 400 transponder, glideslope, marker beacon, and Nav-O-Matic autopilot (400A Nav-O-Matic or Series 400 IFCS offered as alternative exchanges). Optional equipment includes directional and horizon gyros with associated vacuum system and suction gauge, true airspeed indicator, dual controls, extended-range fuel system, ground power socket, heated pitot and stall warning, emergency locator transmitter, alternate static source.

Turbo-Skymaster. Generally similar to Skymaster, but powered by two 156·5 kW (210 hp) Continental TSIO-360-H flat-six turbocharged engines, each driving a two-blade constant-speed and fully-feathering metal propeller.

Turbo-Skymaster II. Identical to Turbo-Skymaster, but with additional standard avionics and equipment as detailed for Skymaster II.

Pressurised Skymaster/Pressurised Skymaster II. Described separately.

The 1979 versions of the Skymaster/Turbo-Skymaster have a number of standard and optional detail improvements to Series 400 avionics equipment.

TYPE: Tandem-engined cabin monoplane.

WINGS: Braced high-wing monoplane, with single streamlined bracing strut each side. Wing section NACA 2412 at root, NACA 2409 at tip. Dihedral 3°. Incidence 4° 30′ at root, 2° 30′ at tip. Conventional all-metal two-spar structure. Conical-camber glassfibre wingtips. All-metal Frise ailerons. Electrically-operated all-metal single-slotted flaps. Ground-adjustable tab in port aileron. Pneumatic de-icing system optional.

FUSELAGE: Conventional all-metal semi-monocoque structure.

TAIL UNIT: Cantilever all-metal structure with twin swept-back fins and horn-balanced rudders, carried on two slim metal booms. Trim tab in starboard side of elevator, with optional electrical actuation. Optional pneumatic de-icing system.

LANDING GEAR: Hydraulically-retractable tricycle type. Cantilever spring steel main legs. Steerable nosewheel with oleo-pneumatic shock-absorber. Main wheels and tyres size 6·00-6. Nosewheel and tyre size 15 × 6·00-6. Main-wheel tyre pressure 3·80 bars (55 lb/sq in). Hydraulic disc brakes. Parking brake. Oversize wheels and heavy-duty brakes optional.

POWER PLANT: Two Continental flat-six engines, as detailed in model listings. Electrically-operated cowl flaps. Propeller de-icing optional for forward propeller. Fuel in two main tanks in each wing, with total usable capacity of 333 litres (88 US gallons); two additional tanks in wings, with total usable capacity of 227 litres (60 US gallons), provide optional long-range system. Total usable capacity with optional tanks 560 litres (148 US gallons). Refuelling points above wings. Oil capacity (Skymaster/Skymaster II) 15 litres (4 US gallons); (Turbo-Skymaster/Turbo-Skymaster II) 17 litres (4·5 US gallons).

ACCOMMODATION: Standard accommodation for pilot and co-pilot on individual seats, with individual track-mounted seats for two passengers. Dual controls optional. Alternative arrangements include individual seats for fifth and sixth passengers. Optional cabin equipment includes fully-articulating individual seats for passengers and matching headrests. Optional centre seats can be moved fore and aft to ease access to other seats. Space for 165 kg (365 lb) of baggage in four-seat version, with external loading door. Airstair door on starboard side. Cabin is heated, ventilated and soundproofed. Adjustable air vents and reading lights available to each passenger. Provision for carrying glassfibre cargo pack, with capacity of 136 kg (300 lb), under fuselage; this reduces cruising speed by only 2·6 knots (5 km/h; 3 mph).

SYSTEMS: Electrical system supplied by two 38A 28V engine-driven alternators. 24V battery. Hydraulic system for landing gear retraction and brakes.

AVIONICS AND EQUIPMENT: Optional avionics include Cessna Series 300 nav/com with 720-channel com and 200-channel nav with remote VOR/LOC or VOR/ILS indicator, ADF with digital tuning, marker beacon with three lights and aural signal, DME, 10-channel HF transceiver, and Nav-O-Matic single-axis autopilot and integrated flight control system; or Series 400 nav/com with 720-channel com and 200-channel nav with VOR/LOC or VOR/ILS indicator, 40-channel glideslope receiver, ADF with digital tuning and BFO, transponder with 4096 code capability, Nav-O-Matic 400 or 400A two-axis autopilot and integrated flight control system, non-slaved HSI, aural/visual altitude alert system with coupling to IFCS when installed, and Bendix RDR 160 weather radar. Standard equipment includes sensitive altimeter, airspeed indicator, rate of climb indicator, electric clock, outside air temperature gauge, audible stall warning device, engine synchronisation indicator, turn co-ordinator indicator, map light, sun visors, all-weather window, hinged window starboard side, navigation light detectors, elevator and aileron control locks, windscreen defroster, tinted windscreen and windows, dome light, reading lights, baggage net, omni-flash beacon, taxi light, anti-precipitation static kit, retractable tiedown rings, towbar, polyurethane external paint scheme and quick drain fuel tank valves. Optional equipment includes all-purpose control wheel with provision for map light, boom microphone switch, pitch trim switch, autopilot/electric trim disengage switch, blind-flying instrumentation, economy mixture indicator, true airspeed indicator, instrument post lights, approach plate holder, flight hour recorder, windscreen anti-icing panel, cabin fire extinguisher, baggage net, wall-mounted table, safety belts for 3rd, 4th, 5th and 6th seats, internal corrosion proofing, emergency exit window port side, portable stretcher, cargo tiedown installation, full-flow oil filters, external power socket, propeller synchrophaser, winterisation kit, alternate static source, oxygen system, ice detection system, white strobe lights, photographic provisions, static wicks, pitot heating system, flush glideslope antenna, telescoping towbar, and cargo rack.

DIMENSIONS, EXTERNAL:

Wing span	11·63 m (38 ft 2 in)
Wing chord at root	1·83 m (6 ft 0 in)
Wing chord at tip	1·22 m (4 ft 0 in)
Wing aspect ratio	7·18
Length overall: Skymaster	9·07 m (29 ft 9 in)
Turbo-Skymaster	9·09 m (29 ft 10 in)
Height overall	2·79 m (9 ft 2 in)
Tailplane span	3·06 m (10 ft 0½ in)
Wheel track	2·49 m (8 ft 2 in)
Wheelbase	2·39 m (7 ft 10 in)
Propeller diameter: Front	1·98 m (6 ft 6 in)
Rear	1·93 m (6 ft 4 in)

Passenger door: Height 1·17 m (3 ft 10 in)
Width 0·91 m (3 ft 0 in)
DIMENSIONS, INTERNAL:
Cabin: Length 3·02 m (9 ft 11 in)
Max width 1·12 m (3 ft 8¼ in)
Max height 1·30 m (4 ft 3¼ in)
Volume 3·62 m³ (128 cu ft)
Baggage space 0·50 m³ (17 cu ft)
AREAS:
Wings, gross 18·81 m² (202·5 sq ft)
Ailerons (total) 1·43 m² (15·44 sq ft)
Trailing-edge flaps (total) 3·43 m² (36·88 sq ft)
Fins (total) 2·85 m² (30·68 sq ft)
Rudders (total) 0·99 m² (10·70 sq ft)
Tailplane 3·05 m² (32·82 sq ft)
WEIGHTS AND LOADINGS (A: Skymaster; B: Skymaster II; C: Turbo-Skymaster; D: Turbo-Skymaster II):
Weight empty: A 1,270 kg (2,800 lb)
B 1,335 kg (2,943 lb)
C 1,306 kg (2,879 lb)
D 1,371 kg (3,022 lb)
Max T-O weight: All versions 2,100 kg (4,630 lb)
Max ramp weight: A, B 2,108 kg (4,648 lb)
C, D 2,110 kg (4,652 lb)
Max landing weight: All versions 1,996 kg (4,400 lb)
Max wing loading: All versions 112 kg/m² (22·9 lb/sq ft)
Max power loading: All versions 6·71 kg/kW (11·0 lb/hp)
PERFORMANCE (at max T-O weight):
Max level speed:
A, B at S/L 172 knots (319 km/h; 198 mph)
C, D at 6,100 m (20,000 ft) 207 knots (383 km/h; 238 mph)
Max cruising speed:
A, B, 75% power at 1,675 m (5,500 ft) 169 knots (314 km/h; 195 mph)
C, D, 80% power at 6,100 m (20,000 ft) 200 knots (370 km/h; 230 mph)
C, D, 80% power at 3,050 m (10,000 ft) 182 knots (338 km/h; 210 mph)
Stalling speed, flaps up, power off:
All versions 70 knots (130 km/h; 81 mph) CAS
Stalling speed, flaps down, power off:
All versions 61 knots (113 km/h; 70 mph) CAS
Max rate of climb at S/L: A, B 287 m (940 ft)/min
C, D 354 m (1,160 ft)/min
Rate of climb at S/L, front engine only:
A, B 91 m (300 ft)/min
Rate of climb at S/L, rear engine only:
A, B 98 m (320 ft)/min
Single-engine rate of climb at S/L:
C, D 102 m (335 ft)/min
Service ceiling: A, B 4,970 m (16,300 ft)
A, B, front engine only 2,105 m (6,900 ft)
A, B, rear engine only 2,165 m (7,100 ft)
C, D, single-engine 5,030 m (16,500 ft)
Max certificated operating altitude:
C, D, single- or twin-engine 6,100 m (20,000 ft)
T-O run: All versions 305 m (1,000 ft)
T-O to 15 m (50 ft): All versions 511 m (1,675 ft)
Landing from 15 m (50 ft): All versions 503 m (1,650 ft)
Landing run: All versions 213 m (700 ft)
Range, recommended lean mixture, allowances for start, taxi, T-O, climb, and 45 min reserves at 45% power: A, B:
75% power at 1,675 m (5,500 ft) with 239 kg (528 lb) usable fuel 545 nm (1,011 km; 628 miles)
75% power at 1,675 m (5,500 ft) with 403 kg (888 lb) usable fuel 990 nm (1,835 km; 1,140 miles)
Econ cruising power at 3,050 m (10,000 ft) with 239 kg (528 lb) usable fuel 670 nm (1,242 km; 772 miles)
Econ cruising power at 3,050 m (10,000 ft) with 403 kg (888 lb) usable fuel 1,235 nm (2,288 km; 1,422 miles)
C, D:
80% power at 6,100 m (20,000 ft) with 239 kg (528 lb) usable fuel 520 nm (964 km; 599 miles)
80% power at 3,050 m (10,000 ft) with 239 kg (528 lb) usable fuel 490 nm (908 km; 564 miles)
80% power at 6,100 m (20,000 ft) with 403 kg (888 lb) usable fuel 975 nm (1,807 km; 1,123 miles)
80% power at 3,050 m (10,000 ft) with 403 kg (888 lb) usable fuel 905 nm (1,677 km; 1,042 miles)
Econ cruising power at 6,100 m (20,000 ft) with 239 kg (528 lb) usable fuel 590 nm (1,093 km; 679 miles)
Econ cruising power at 3,050 m (10,000 ft) with 239 kg (528 lb) usable fuel 580 nm (1,075 km; 668 miles)
Econ cruising power at 6,100 m (20,000 ft) with 403 kg (888 lb) usable fuel 1,125 nm (2,084 km; 1,295 miles)
Econ cruising power at 3,050 m (10,000 ft) with 403 kg (888 lb) usable fuel 1,080 nm (2,002 km; 1,244 miles)

CESSNA MODEL P337 PRESSURISED SKYMASTER and PRESSURISED SKYMASTER II

On 8 December 1971 Cessna introduced a pressurised version of the Skymaster. Design and construction of the prototype began in January 1971, and the first prototype made its initial flight on 23 July 1971. Construction of pre-production and production aircraft began simultaneously in May 1971, and FAA certification was granted on 2 February 1972. Deliveries began in May 1972.

The pressurised version is distinguished easily from the standard Skymaster in having four, instead of three, windows on each side of the cabin. Pressurisation is provided from the turbocharged engines, either of which can maintain full pressurisation and air-conditioning. With a maximum differential of 0·23 bars (3·35 lb/sq in), a cabin altitude of 3,050 m (10,000 ft) can be maintained to 6,100 m (20,000 ft). Pilot setting of departure and landing field altitudes on the pressurisation controls is all that is necessary for the system to begin automatic operation.

Two versions of the Model P337 are available for 1979:

Pressurised Skymaster. Basic version, to which the detailed description applies.

Pressurised Skymaster II. Pressurised version of Skymaster II, to which it is identical except for pressurisation installation; a Series 400A Nav-O-Matic autopilot is standard, with Series 400 IFCS offered in exchange.

The 1979 versions of the P337 introduce the improvements detailed for the Model 337. A total of 290 Model P337 Skymasters had been built by 1 January 1979, plus an additional 27 Reims Pressurised Skymasters built by Reims Aviation in France.

TYPE: Tandem-engine, pressurised cabin monoplane.

WINGS: As Model 337 Skymaster.

FUSELAGE: Conventional all-metal semi-monocoque structure, with fail-safe structure in the pressurised section extending between the two engine bulkheads, but excluding aft lower area below cabin floor.

TAIL UNIT: As Model 337 Skymaster.

LANDING GEAR: Hydraulically-retractable tricycle type, main units retracting aft, nosewheel forward. Cantilever spring steel main units. Steerable nosewheel with oleo-pneumatic shock-absorber. Main-wheel tyres size 6·00-6, pressure 3·79 bars (55 lb/sq in). Nosewheel tyre size 15·00 × 6·00-6, pressure 2·90 bars (42 lb/sq in). Cleveland hydraulic disc brakes. Parking brake. Heavy-duty wheels, brakes and tyres optional.

POWER PLANT: Two 168 kW (225 hp) Continental TSIO-360-C turbocharged flat-six engines, each driving a McCauley two-blade constant-speed fully-feathering metal propeller. Propeller de-icing optional for forward propeller. Four interconnected fuel tanks in each wing with a combined usable capacity of 280 litres (74 US gallons). Total usable fuel capacity 560 litres (148 US gallons). Refuelling points in wing upper surfaces. Oil capacity 17 litres (4·5 US gallons).

ACCOMMODATION: Standard accommodation for pilot and co-pilot on individual seats, with rear bench seat for two passengers. A third passenger seat at rear of cabin is optional. Space for 165 kg (365 lb) of baggage in four-seat version. Bench seat slides fore and aft to provide easy access to baggage area. Two-section door on starboard side, lower half opening downward and incorporating airstairs. Upper half opens upward. Cabin is heated and ventilated. Double-pane windows. Individual adjustable air ventilators and reading lights for passengers. Windscreen defrosting standard. Windscreen de-icing optional.

SYSTEMS: Electrical system powered by two 28V 38A engine-driven self-rectifying alternators. 24V battery. Electrically-driven hydraulic pump for landing gear retraction. Vacuum system optional for blind-flying instrumentation. Oxygen system optional. Cabin pressurised by engine bleed air, max differential 0·23 bars (3·35 lb/sq in). Cabin heated by 25,000 BTU gasoline heater and/or hot air from the compression section of the pressurisation system.

AVIONICS AND EQUIPMENT: Optional avionics are as detailed for the Model 337 Skymaster. Standard equipment is the same as for the Skymaster, plus a manual cabin altitude control, cabin rate-of-climb, cabin differential pressure and cabin altitude gauges, propeller synchrophaser and altitude warning light. Optional equipment includes a true airspeed computer, emergency locator beacon, solid-state oxygen system, engine priming system, cargo pack, and automatic propeller unfeathering system, in addition to the options detailed for the Skymaster.

DIMENSIONS, EXTERNAL:
As for Model 337 except:
Length overall 9·09 m (29 ft 10 in)
Propeller ground clearance: Front 0·23 m (9 in)
Rear 0·51 m (1 ft 8 in)
Passenger door: Height 1·15 m (3 ft 9¼ in)
Width 0·90 m (2 ft 11¼ in)
Height to sill 0·56 m (1 ft 10 in)
DIMENSIONS, INTERNAL:
Cabin: Length 3·02 m (9 ft 11 in)
Max width 1·11 m (3 ft 7¾ in)
Max height 1·29 m (4 ft 2¾ in)
Floor area 2·10 m² (22·6 sq ft)
Volume 3·62 m³ (128 cu ft)
Baggage space 0·50 m³ (17 cu ft)
AREAS: As for Model 337
WEIGHTS AND LOADINGS:
Weight empty:
Pressurised Skymaster 1,388 kg (3,059 lb)
Pressurised Skymaster II 1,438 kg (3,171 lb)
Max T-O weight 2,131 kg (4,700 lb)
Max ramp weight 2,142 kg (4,724 lb)
Max landing weight 2,025 kg (4,465 lb)
Max wing loading 113·3 kg/m² (23·2 lb/sq ft)
Max power loading 6·34 kg/kW (10·4 lb/hp)
PERFORMANCE (at max T-O weight):
Max level speed at 6,100 m (20,000 ft) 212 knots (393 km/h; 244 mph)
Max cruising speed, 75% power at 6,100 m (20,000 ft) 205 knots (380 km/h; 236 mph)
Max cruising speed, 75% power at 3,050 m (10,000 ft) 186 knots (344 km/h; 214 mph)
Stalling speed, flaps and wheels up, power off 70 knots (130 km/h; 81 mph) CAS
Stalling speed, flaps and wheels down, power off 62 knots (115 km/h; 71 mph) CAS
Max rate of climb at S/L 357 m (1,170 ft)/min
Rate of climb at S/L, one engine out 114 m (375 ft)/min
Max certificated operating altitude 6,100 m (20,000 ft)
Service ceiling, one engine out 5,700 m (18,700 ft)
Min ground turning radius 2·54 m (8 ft 4 in)
T-O run 288 m (945 ft)
T-O to 15 m (50 ft) 457 m (1,500 ft)
Landing from 15 m (50 ft) at max landing weight 511 m (1,675 ft)
Landing run at max landing weight 242 m (795 ft)
Range, recommended lean mixture, with allowances for start, taxi, T-O, climb and 45 min reserves at 45% power:
75% power at 6,100 m (20,000 ft) with 403 kg (888 lb) usable fuel 985 nm (1,825 km; 1,134 miles)
75% power at 3,050 m (10,000 ft) with 403 kg (888 lb) usable fuel 915 nm (1,694 km; 1,053 miles)
Econ cruising power at 6,100 m (20,000 ft) with 403 kg (888 lb) usable fuel 1,155 nm (2,140 km; 1,330 miles)
Econ cruising power at 3,050 m (10,000 ft) with 403 kg (888 lb) usable fuel 1,110 nm (2,056 km; 1,278 miles)

Model P337 pressurised version of the Cessna Skymaster

CESSNA MODEL 340A, 340A II and 340A III

Cessna announced on 8 December 1971 the introduction of a pressurised twin-engined business aircraft designated Model 340. Developed from the Model 310, it had a wing and landing gear generally similar to those of the Model 414, a pressurised fuselage of fail-safe design, a tail unit similar to that of the Model 310 and 212·5 kW (285 hp) Continental TSIO-520-K engines. The Model 340 II followed, with factory-installed avionics as standard, and in 1978 a Model 340A III was introduced.

Versions of the Model 340 available in 1979 are as follows:

340A. Standard model, as described in detail.

340A II. Identical to Model 340A, but with dual Series 300 nav/coms with 720-channel com and 200-channel nav and VOR/LOC and VOR/ILS indicators, ADF, Series 400 DME, marker beacon, glideslope, transponder and 400B two-axis Nav-O-Matic autopilot, basic avionics kit, avionics cooling kit panel, and emergency locator transmitter as standard. Other standard equipment includes dual controls, a variable cabin pressure control system, external power socket, starboard landing light, taxi light, strobe lights, economy mixture indicator, outside air temperature gauge, 238·5 litre (63 US gallon) auxiliary fuel system, nosewheel fender, static dischargers, and all necessary antennae for onboard avionics.

340A III. As Model 340A, plus an avionics package comprising dual Series 400 nav/coms, one with HSI and the other with Automatic Radial Centering (ARC), Series 400 dual glideslope, RNAV, ADF, marker beacon, DME, transponder, 400B IFCS, Series 800 encoding altimeter and altitude alerter, Series 1000 RMI, Bendix RDR-160 weather radar, yaw damper, basic avionics kit, avionics cooling, audio system, all essential antennae, hand fire extinguisher, and 100A alternators added and/or substituted for the equipment installed on the 340A II. Standard equipment is as detailed for the Model 340A II.

All 1979 models have as standard improvements a more corrosion-resistant exhaust system and an FAA-approved flight manual. The optional air-conditioning system has a new lightweight motor.

A total of 826 Model 340s had been delivered by 1 January 1979.

Type: Six-seat pressurised business aircraft.

Wings: Cantilever low-wing monoplane, with 'Stabila-tip' fixed wingtip fuel tanks. Wing section NACA 23018 (modified) at aircraft centreline, NACA 23015 (modified) at centre-section/outer wing junction, NACA 23009 (modified) at tip. Dihedral 5° on outer panels. Incidence 2° 30′ at root, −0° 30′ at tip. All-metal two-spar structure. All-metal ailerons of single-spar construction; controllable trim tab in starboard aileron. Electrically-actuated all-metal split trailing-edge flaps, of single-spar construction with lower skin, comprising an inboard and outboard panel on each wing. Optional pneumatic de-icing system.

Fuselage: All-metal semi-monocoque structure. The pressurised cabin section, extending from station 100·00 aft to station 252·00, is of fail-safe construction. All openings are reinforced with doublers and frame members, and longitudinal continuity is provided by lightweight extruded T-section stringers.

Tail Unit: Cantilever all-metal structure with swept vertical surfaces. Fixed-incidence tailplane of conventional two-spar construction. Elevators of single-spar construction, with controllable trim tab in starboard elevator. Rudder, built up on a formed channel spar and transverse ribs, has a controllable trim tab. Optional pneumatic de-icing system.

Landing Gear: Retractable tricycle type, with single wheel on each unit. Electro-mechanical retraction, main units inward into wings and faired by doors when retracted, nose unit rearward into the fuselage nose and faired by two doors when retracted. Mechanically-operated emergency gear extension system. Cessna oleo-pneumatic shock-absorbers. Steerable nosewheel with shimmy damper and self-centering device. Mainwheel tyres size 6·50-10 (8-ply); nosewheel tyre size 6·00-6 (6-ply). Single-disc hydraulic brakes. Parking brake.

Power Plant: Two 231 kW (310 hp) Continental TSIO-520-NB flat-six turbocharged fuel-injection engines, each driving a McCauley three-blade metal constant-speed and fully-feathering propeller. Fuel system, max usable capacity 768 litres (203 US gallons), as described for Model 310. Manifold pressure relief valves to prevent engines from overboosting are standard equipment. Oil capacity 24·6 litres (6·5 US gallons).

Accommodation: Standard seating for pilot and co-pilot on tilting and individually adjustable seats. Individual seats for four passengers, two forward-facing on the port side, one aft-facing and one forward-facing on starboard side. Door, on port side aft of wing, is two-piece type with built-in airstairs in bottom portion. Plug-type emergency escape hatch on starboard side of cabin, over wing. Foul-weather window for pilot. Baggage accommodated in nose compartment with external access doors, capacity 159 kg (350 lb), two wing lockers, capacity 54·5 kg (120 lb) each, and in rear cabin area, capacity 154 kg (340 lb). Total baggage capacity 422 kg (930 lb). Cabin pressurised, heated and ventilated. Air-conditioning optional. Windscreen defroster standard; windscreen de-icing optional.

Systems: Electrical system powered by two 28V 50A engine-driven alternators and 24V 25Ah battery. 100A alternators optional, standard on 340A III. Vacuum system supplied by two engine-driven pumps. Hydraulic system for brakes only. Cabin pressurised by engine bleed air, max differential 0·29 bars (4·2 lb/sq in). Cabin heated by Stewart Warner 45,000 BTU gasoline heater. Lightweight air-conditioning system optional. Oxygen system, 0·31 m³ (11·0 cu ft) or 2·17 m³ (76·6 cu ft) capacity, optional.

Avionics and Equipment: Optional avionics for the Model 340A are as detailed for the Model 310. Standard equipment of Model 340A includes sensitive altimeter, rate of climb indicator, cabin altitude and differential pressure indicator, digital fuel flow gauge with computer, blind-flying instrumentation, quartz crystal clock, audible stall warning device, variable intensity floodlights and instrument post lights, aileron and elevator control lock, safety belts for pilot and co-pilot, sun visors, heater overheat indicator light, 'Not Locked' light for cabin door, courtesy lights, individual reading lights, super soundproofing, cabin radio speaker, full-flow oil filters, quick drain fuel valves and sampler cup, propeller synchroniser, navigation lights with flasher unit, heating system for fuel vents, pitot and stall warning device, retractable landing light in port wing, all-over paint scheme, two rotating beacons, and towbar. Optional items, except as detailed in model listings, include turn co-ordinator, economy mixture and instantaneous rate of climb indicators, flight hour recorder, true airspeed indicator, angle of attack indicator, electric elevator trim control, inertia-reel shoulder harness for pilot and co-pilot, boom microphone, digital clock, blind-flying instrumentation for co-pilot, windscreen alcohol de-icing system, emergency locator transmitter, rudder pedal lock, cabin writing desk, window curtains, flight deck divider curtain, refreshment centres, headrests, all-leather seats, tinted double-pane cabin windows, internal corrosion proofing, stereo system, cabin fire extinguisher, baggage courtesy lights, courtesy light timer relay, 'total flood' fire extinguisher system for cabin, ice detection lights, taxi light, white strobe lights, propeller unfeathering system, 100A alternators, engine fire detection and extinguishing system, heated dual static source, nosewheel fender, propeller de-icing system, fuselage ice impact panels, radome nose, static wicks, and dual pitot system.

Cessna Model 340A six-seat pressurised business aircraft

Dimensions, external:

Wing span	11·62 m (38 ft 1·3 in)
Wing chord at root	1·714 m (5 ft 7·4 in)
Wing chord, mean aerodynamic	1·57 m (5 ft 1·68 in)
Wing chord at tip	1·156 m (3 ft 9·6 in)
Wing aspect ratio	7·2
Length overall	10·46 m (34 ft 4 in)
Height overall	3·84 m (12 ft 7 in)
Tailplane span	5·18 m (17 ft 0 in)
Wheel track	3·93 m (12 ft 10·7 in)
Wheelbase	3·12 m (10 ft 2·7 in)
Propeller diameter	1·94 m (6 ft 4½ in)
Passenger door: Height	1·18 m (3 ft 10½ in)
Width	0·53 m (1 ft 9 in)
Emergency hatch: Height	0·48 m (1 ft 7 in)
Width	0·66 m (2 ft 2 in)

Dimensions, internal:

Cabin: Length, incl baggage compartment	3·86 m (12 ft 8 in)
Max width	1·18 m (3 ft 10½ in)
Max height	1·24 m (4 ft 1 in)
Volume (total)	4·6 m³ (162·4 cu ft)
Baggage space: Cabin	0·52 m³ (18·5 cu ft)
Nose	0·44 m³ (15·5 cu ft)
Engine nacelles (each)	0·13 m³ (4·625 cu ft)

Areas:

Wings, gross	17·09 m² (184 sq ft)
Ailerons (total)	1·06 m² (11·44 sq ft)
Trailing-edge flaps (total)	2·14 m² (23·06 sq ft)
Fin	1·51 m² (16·20 sq ft)
Rudder, incl tab	1·09 m² (11·76 sq ft)
Tailplane	2·99 m² (32·15 sq ft)
Elevators, incl tab	1·97 m² (21·25 sq ft)

Weights and Loadings:

Weight empty: 340A	1,773 kg (3,909 lb)
340A II	1,879 kg (4,143 lb)
340A III	1,921 kg (4,236 lb)
Max T-O and landing weight	2,717 kg (5,990 lb)
Max ramp weight	2,733 kg (6,025 lb)
Max zero-fuel weight	2,554 kg (5,630 lb)
Max wing loading	158·9 kg/m² (32·55 lb/sq ft)
Max power loading	5·88 kg/kW (9·66 lb/hp)

Performance (at max T-O weight, except speeds are those at mid-cruise weight):

Max level speed at 6,100 m (20,000 ft)
244 knots (452 km/h; 281 mph)

Max cruising speed, 74·8% power:
at 7,470 m (24,500 ft)
229 knots (425 km/h; 264 mph)
at 3,050 m (10,000 ft)
198 knots (367 km/h; 228 mph)

Econ cruising speed:
at 7,620 m (25,000 ft) with 272 kg (600 lb) usable fuel
184 knots (341 km/h; 212 mph)
at 7,620 m (25,000 ft) with 552 kg (1,218 lb) usable fuel
179 knots (332 km/h; 206 mph)

Stalling speed, flaps up, power off
79 knots (146 km/h; 91 mph) CAS

Stalling speed, flaps down, power off
71 knots (132 km/h; 82 mph) CAS

Max rate of climb at S/L	503 m (1,650 ft)/min
Rate of climb at S/L, one engine out	96 m (315 ft)/min
Service ceiling	9,085 m (29,800 ft)
Service ceiling, one engine out	4,815 m (15,800 ft)
T-O run	492 m (1,615 ft)
T-O to 15 m (50 ft)	663 m (2,175 ft)
Landing from 15 m (50 ft)	564 m (1,850 ft)
Landing run	235 m (770 ft)

Range, recommended lean mixture, with allowances for start, taxi, T-O, climb, descent and 45 min reserves at 45% power:

74·8% power at 7,470 m (24,500 ft) with 272 kg (600 lb) usable fuel 479 nm (888 km; 552 miles)

74·8% power at 7,470 m (24,500 ft) with 552 kg (1,218 lb) usable fuel
1,168 nm (2,165 km; 1,345 miles)

74·8% power at 3,050 m (10,000 ft) with 272 kg (600 lb) usable fuel 444 nm (822 km; 511 miles)

74·8% power at 3,050 m (10,000 ft) with 552 kg (1,218 lb) usable fuel
1,039 nm (1,925 km; 1,196 miles)

Econ cruising power at 7,620 m (25,000 ft) with 272 kg (600 lb) usable fuel
531 nm (983 km; 611 miles)

Econ cruising power at 7,620 m (25,000 ft) with 552 kg (1,218 lb) usable fuel
1,372 nm (2,543 km; 1,580 miles)

Econ cruising power at 3,050 m (10,000 ft) with 272 kg (600 lb) usable fuel
558 nm (1,035 km; 643 miles)

Econ cruising power at 3,050 m (10,000 ft) with 552 kg (1,218 lb) usable fuel
1,377 nm (2,552 km; 1,586 miles)

CESSNA MODEL 402C, 402C II and 402C III

The original Model 402 was intended for the third-level airline market, with a convertible cabin and reinforced cabin floor of bonded crushed honeycomb construction, enabling it to be changed quickly from a ten-seat commuter to a light cargo transport. On 8 December 1971 Cessna renamed the original Model 402 as the Model 402 Utililiner and introduced a version designated Model 402 Businessliner. On 29 October 1975 Mk II versions of both aircraft were made available, each including a package of factory-installed equipment and avionics as standard; Model 402 III versions of both aircraft were introduced for 1978.

For 1979 considerable changes have been made in this aircraft, which is known now as the Model 402C, and incorporates many of the improvements introduced in the Model 414A Chancellor in 1978. They include a new bonded 'wet' wing of increased span (without tip-tanks), improved landing gear, more powerful engines, and many detail changes. Five versions of the Model 402C are available for 1979:

Model 402C Utililiner. Basic version, as described in detail.

Model 402C Businessliner. As basic version, except six/eight seats and optional side-hinged door, next to standard cabin door, to provide a total loading door width of 1·02 m (3 ft 4 in). Other options include folding business desks, stereo equipment, refreshment centre and cabin dividers.

Model 402C II Utililiner. As basic version, plus the following factory-installed equipment and avionics as

Photograph and three-view drawing *(Pilot Press)* **of the Cessna Model 402C, latest version of the Businessliner/Utiliner**

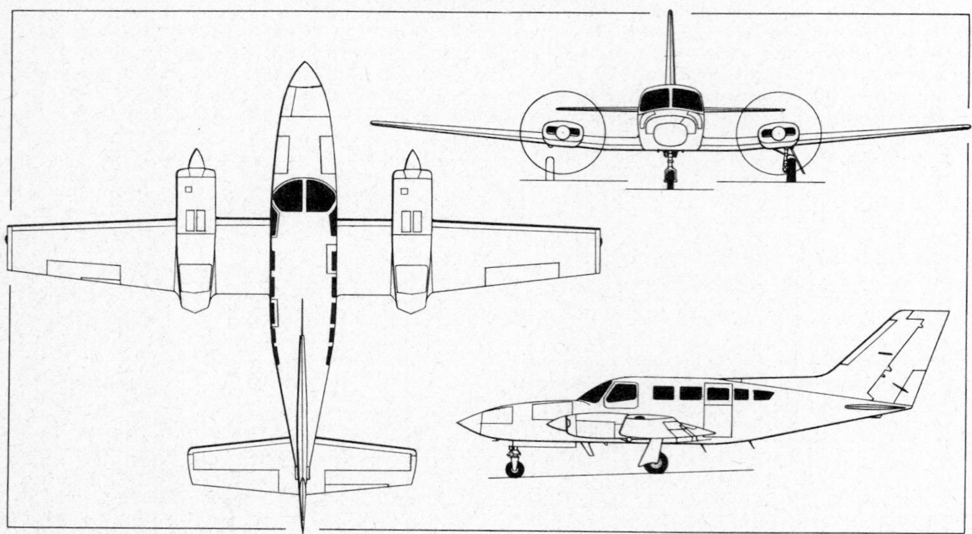

standard: dual controls, flight hour recorder, economy mixture indicator, cabin hand fire extinguisher, starboard landing light, taxi light, locator beacon, external power socket, static dischargers, dual Cessna Series 300 nav/com with 720-channel com, 200-channel nav and VOR/ILS and VOR/LOC indicators, Series 300 ADF, Series 400 marker beacon, glideslope and transponder, Series 400B Nav-O-Matic autopilot, and basic avionics kit comprising antennae, avionics cooling kit and audio system.

Model 402C II Businessliner. As Model 402C Businessliner, plus standard factory-installed equipment and avionics detailed for Model 402C II Utiliner.

Model 402C III Businessliner. As Model 402C II Businessliner, except that standard equipment includes 100A instead of 50A engine-driven alternators, and the avionics package comprises Series 400 nav/com with HSI; second Series 400 nav/com with VOR/ILS; dual Series 400 glideslope; Series 400 ADF, DME, marker beacon, RNAV, transponder; Series 800 encoding altimeter and altitude alerter; Series 1000 RMI; Bendix RDR-160 weather radar; Series 400B IFCS; yaw damper; and basic avionics kit, audio system, avionics cooling and antennae.

All 1979 versions of the Model 402C introduced a number of improvements as standard, including provision of a recirculating air control, provision of a pressure gauge to check state of landing gear emergency blowdown bottle, improved navigation and strobe light mountings, instrument panel changes to simplify equipment installation, resiting of the outside air temperature gauge, better access for maintenance of landing gear hydraulic filters and nose compartment avionics, a more corrosion-resistant exhaust system, and changes in the cabin airflow distribution system. New optional equipment includes a lightweight air-conditioning motor, a 2 in (5 cm) turn and bank indicator for the co-pilot, and an improved rudder lock.

The same prototype served for Models 401 and 402, and the FAA Type Certificate, awarded on 20 September 1966, also covered both types. A total of 1,053 Model 402s had been built by 1 January 1979. Twelve Model 402s were delivered in 1975 to the Royal Malaysian Air Force, which uses ten of them for multi-engine training and the other two for photographic and liaison missions.

TYPE: Ten-seat (optional nine-seat) convertible passenger/freight transport (Utiliner) or six/eight-seat business aircraft (Businessliner).

WINGS: Cantilever low-wing monoplane. Wing section NACA 23018 (modified) at aircraft centreline, NACA 23015 (modified) at centre-section/outer wing junction, NACA 23009 (modified) at tip. All-metal two-spar structure of light alloy with stamped ribs and surface skins reinforced with spanwise stringers. Outer wing panels of bonded construction. All-metal ailerons and electrically-actuated split flaps. Trim tab in port aileron. Optional pneumatic de-icing system.

FUSELAGE: All-metal semi-monocoque structure.

TAIL UNIT: Cantilever all-metal structure, with 40° sweepback on fin at quarter-chord. Fixed-incidence tailplane. Trim tabs in rudder and starboard elevator. Electrical operation of trim tabs optional. Optional pneumatic de-icing system.

LANDING GEAR: Hydraulically-retractable tricycle type. Main units retract inward into wings, nosewheel unit rearward. No doors over main wheels when retracted. Emergency extension system. Oleo-pneumatic shock-absorbers. Steerable nosewheel. Cleveland heavy-duty wheels. Main-wheel tyres size 6·50-10, nosewheel tyre size 6·00-6. Cleveland heavy-duty hydraulic brakes. Parking brakes.

POWER PLANT: Two 242 kW (325 hp) Continental TSIO-520-VB flat-six turbocharged engines, each driving a three-blade constant-speed fully-feathering metal propeller. Propeller synchronisation, automatic unfeathering and electrical de-icing optional. Integral wing fuel tanks with total capacity of 806 litres (213 US gallons), of which 772 litres (204 US gallons) are usable. Oil capacity 24·6 litres (6·5 US gallons).

ACCOMMODATION: Two seats side by side in pilot's compartment. Dual controls standard on Model 402C II/III versions, optional for Model 402C versions. The Utiliner cabin has four individual seats in pairs and two double seats. Passenger seats are 'Enviro-form' moulded honeycomb seats, glassfibre reinforced. Businessliner has four individual seats as standard, two additional seats optional, in the main cabin. Refreshment centre at aft end of cabin. Passenger reading lights standard on Businessliner, optional on Utiliner. Door with built-in airstair on port side of cabin at centre. Storm windows for pilot and co-pilot. Tinted cabin windows. An emergency escape hatch is provided on the starboard side of the cabin. Optional cargo door and crew access door available. Baggage contained in area at rear of cabin, nose compartment, and wing lockers at rear of each engine nacelle, with combined capacity of 680 kg (1,500 lb). Cabin heated and ventilated. Windscreen defrosting standard. Electric anti-icing of pilot's window or alcohol anti-icing of pilot's and co-pilot's windows optional.

SYSTEMS: Electrical system powered by two 24V 50A alternators. 24V 25Ah battery. Battery can be sited optionally in nose baggage area. 100A alternators optional, standard on 402C III version. Hydraulic system for brakes only. Vacuum system provided by two engine-driven pumps. Oxygen system of 1·25 m³ (44 cu ft) or 3·25 m³ (114·9 cu ft) capacity optional. Air-conditioning system optional. Heating and ventilation system with 45,000 BTU gasoline heater standard.

AVIONICS AND EQUIPMENT: Optional avionics as detailed for Model 310, plus radio telephone and CCC CIR-10 emergency locator transmitter. Standard equipment includes sensitive altimeter, quartz crystal clock, variable intensity floodlight, outside air temperature gauge, full blind-flying instrumentation, audible stall warning and landing gear indicators, cabin door 'Not Locked' light, map light, heater overheat warning light, alternator failure lights, navigation light detectors, variable intensity instrument post lights, aileron and elevator control lock, sun visors, armrests, pilot and co-pilot safety belt system, super soundproofing, cabin radio speaker, adjustable cabin air ventilators, courtesy lights, retractable landing light, navigation lights, two rotating beacons, all-over paint scheme and towbar. Optional equipment, unless part of Model 402C II or III packages, includes digital clock, inertial shoulder restraint system for pilot and co-pilot, co-pilot's blind-flying instrumentation, economy mixture indicator, instantaneous rate of climb indicator, true airspeed indicator, rudder lock, flight hour recorder, turn co-ordinator, cabin hand fire extinguisher, 'total flood' cabin fire extinguisher, Utiliner or Businessliner interiors (including flight deck divider curtains, window curtains, headrests, reading lights, 'Seat Belt' and 'No Smoking' signs and various arrangements of seats, tables, refreshment units and toilets), internal corrosion proofing, external power socket, ice detection light, second retractable landing light, taxi light, three-light strobe system, propeller synchrophaser, photographic provisions, dual heated static source and static dischargers.

DIMENSIONS, EXTERNAL:	
Wing span	13·45 m (44 ft 1½ in)
Wing chord at root	1·77 m (5 ft 9¾ in)
Wing chord at tip	1·05 m (3 ft 5½ in)
Length overall	11·09 m (36 ft 4½ in)
Height overall	3·49 m (11 ft 5½ in)
Tailplane span	5·18 m (17 ft 0 in)
Wheel track	5·48 m (17 ft 11½ in)
Wheelbase	3·19 m (10 ft 5½ in)
Propeller diameter	1·94 m (6 ft 4½ in)
Passenger door (standard):	
Height	1·24 m (4 ft 1 in)
Width	0·58 m (1 ft 11 in)
Cargo door (optional): Height	1·26 m (4 ft 1½ in)
Width	1·00 m (3 ft 3½ in)
Nose baggage doors (each):	
Height	0·51 m (1 ft 8 in)
Width	0·80 m (2 ft 7½ in)
Nacelle baggage doors (each):	
Length	0·61 m (2 ft 0 in)
Width	0·62 m (2 ft 0½ in)
DIMENSIONS, INTERNAL:	
Cabin: Length	4·83 m (15 ft 10 in)
Max width	1·42 m (4 ft 8 in)
Max height	1·30 m (4 ft 3 in)
Volume	6·30 m³ (222·4 cu ft)
AREAS:	
Wings, gross	20·98 m² (225·8 sq ft)
Fin	3·52 m² (37·89 sq ft)
Rudder, incl tab	1·65 m² (17·77 sq ft)
Tailplane	5·64 m² (60·70 sq ft)
Elevators, incl tab	1·64 m² (17·63 sq ft)
WEIGHTS AND LOADINGS:	
Weight empty: Businessliner	1,849 kg (4,077 lb)
Utiliner	1,862 kg (4,105 lb)
Businessliner II	1,914 kg (4,219 lb)
Utiliner II	1,924 kg (4,241 lb)
Businessliner III	1,967 kg (4,336 lb)
Max T-O and landing weight	3,107 kg (6,850 lb)
Max ramp weight	3,123 kg (6,885 lb)
Max zero-fuel weight	2,955 kg (6,515 lb)
Max wing loading	148·1 kg/m² (30·3 lb/sq ft)
Max power loading	6·42 kg/kW (10·5 lb/hp)

PERFORMANCE (at max T-O weight, except speeds are those at mid-cruise weight):

Max level speed at 4,875 m (16,000 ft) 231 knots (428 km/h; 266 mph)

Max cruising speed, 72% power:
- at 6,100 m (20,000 ft) 213 knots (394 km/h; 245 mph)
- at 3,050 m (10,000 ft) 194 knots (359 km/h; 223 mph)

Econ cruising speed:
- at 6,100 m (20,000 ft) 172 knots (318 km/h; 198 mph)
- at 3,050 m (10,000 ft) 146 knots (270 km/h; 168 mph)

Stalling speed, flaps up, power off
78 knots (145 km/h; 90 mph) CAS
Stalling speed, flaps down, power off
68 knots (126 km/h; 78 mph) CAS
Max rate of climb at S/L 442 m (1,450 ft)/min
Rate of climb at S/L, one engine out
92 m (301 ft)/min
Service ceiling 8,200 m (26,900 ft)
Service ceiling, one engine out 450 m (1,480 ft)
T-O run 537 m (1,763 ft)
T-O to 15 m (50 ft) 669 m (2,195 ft)
Landing from 15 m (50 ft) 757 m (2,485 ft)
Landing run 322 m (1,055 ft)
Range, recommended lean mixture, allowances for start, taxi, T-O, climb, descent and 45 min reserves at 45% power:
72% power at 6,100 m (20,000 ft) with 272 kg (600 lb) usable fuel 419 nm (776 km; 482 miles)
72% power at 6,100 m (20,000 ft) with 555 kg (1,224 lb) usable fuel 1,029 nm (1,907 km; 1,185 miles)
72% power at 3,050 m (10,000 ft) with 272 kg (600 lb) usable fuel 401 nm (744 km; 462 miles)
72% power at 3,050 m (10,000 ft) with 555 kg (1,224 lb) usable fuel 957 nm (1,773 km; 1,102 miles)
Econ cruising power at 6,100 m (20,000 ft) with 272 kg (600 lb) usable fuel 461 nm (855 km; 531 miles)
Econ cruising power at 6,100 m (20,000 ft) with 555 kg (1,224 lb) usable fuel
1,212 nm (2,247 km; 1,396 miles)
Econ cruising power at 3,050 m (10,000 ft) with 272 kg (600 lb) usable fuel 484 nm (896 km; 557 miles)
Econ cruising power at 3,050 m (10,000 ft) with 555 kg (1,224 lb) usable fuel
1,234 nm (2,287 km; 1,421 miles)

CESSNA MODEL 414A CHANCELLOR

Cessna introduced the pressurised twin-engined Model 414 on 10 December 1969 as a 'step-up' aircraft for owners of Cessna or other light unpressurised twins. It combined the basic fuselage and tail unit of the Model 421 with the wing of the Model 402 and had 231 kW (310 hp) turbocharged Continental engines.

It was replaced in 1978 by the similar but much improved Model 414A Chancellor. Major changes included a new bonded 'wet' wing of increased span, extended nose and baggage area, and introduction of an external access door to the tailcone.

Three versions of the Chancellor are available for 1979, as follows:

Model 414A Chancellor. Standard version, as described in detail.

Model 414A Chancellor II. As Model 414A above, but with the following avionics and equipment as standard: dual Series 400 nav/com, with ARC, VOR/ILS and VOR/LOC; Series 400 ADF, DME, transponder, glideslope, marker beacon; 400B Nav-O-Matic autopilot; basic avionics kit, cooling kit, audio system, and all essential antennae; variable cabin pressure control system, economy mixture indicator, flight hour recorder, co-pilot's blind-flying instrumentation, cabin hand fire extinguisher, starboard landing light, taxi light, high intensity strobe light, emergency locator beacon, external power socket, nosewheel fender and static dischargers.

Model 414A Chancellor III. As standard Model 414A, with standard equipment of 414A II plus cabin air-conditioning system and 100A alternators, and an all-weather avionics package which includes dual Series 1000 com, 1000 nav with HSI, 1000 nav with ARC, dual 1000 glideslope, 1000 ADF, RMI, Series 800 DME, RNAV, transponder, encoding altimeter and altitude alerter; 800B IFCS; Series 400 marker beacon; AA-100 radio altimeter; Bendix RDR-160 weather radar; Series 1000 audio panel, basic avionics kit, cooling kit, and all essential antennae.

The Model 414A introduced the following improvements as standard for 1979: relocation of the tail position light, a redesigned cabin door latch, better accessibility to avionics, revised radio panel, repositioned outside air temperature gauge, easier access to landing gear hydraulic filters, and an improved fuel pickup valve.

A total of 513 of the original Model 414s were built before introduction of the more advanced Model 414A. A total of 129 Model 414As had been delivered by 1 January 1979.

Type: Six/eight-seat pressurised light transport.

Wings: Cantilever low-wing monoplane. Wing section NACA 23018 (modified) at aircraft centreline, NACA 23015 (modified) at centre-section/outer wing junction, NACA 23009 (modified) at tip. Dihedral 5° on outer panels. Incidence 2°30′ at root, —0°30′ at tip. All-metal two-spar structure of light alloy with stamped ribs and surface skins reinforced with spanwise stringers. Outer wing panels of bonded construction. All-metal ailerons and electrically-actuated split flaps. Trim tab in port aileron. Optional pneumatic de-icing system.

Fuselage: Conventional all-metal semi-monocoque structure, with fail-safe structure in the pressurised section.

Tail Unit: Cantilever all-metal structure, with sweptback vertical surfaces. Fixed-incidence tailplane. Trim tabs in rudder and starboard elevator. Optional pneumatic de-icing system.

Landing Gear: Hydraulically-retractable tricycle type, main units retracting inward, nosewheel unit aft. Emergency extension by means of a 138 bar (2,000 lb/sq in) rechargeable nitrogen bottle. Oleo-pneumatic shock-absorbers. Steerable nosewheel. Main-wheel tyres size 6·50-10 (8-ply), nosewheel tyre size 6·00-6 (6-ply). Goodyear single-disc hydraulic brakes. Parking brakes.

Power Plant: Two 231 kW (310 hp) Continental TSIO-520-NB flat-six turbocharged engines, each driving a McCauley 3AF32C93M/82NC-5·5 three-blade constant-speed fully-feathering metal propeller. Unfeathering pressure accumulator and electrical blade de-icing system optional. Fuel system with max usable capacity of 806 litres (213 US gallons). Oil capacity 24·6 litres (6·5 US gallons).

Accommodation: Two seats side by side in pilot's compartment. Optional curtain, or solid divider with curtain, to separate pilot's compartment from main cabin. Standard seating arrangement for four forward-facing passenger seats. Optional arrangements provide for front passenger seats to face aft and forward-facing seventh and eighth seats. Individual consoles each include reading light and ventilator. Optional items include executive writing desk, tables, hat shelf, stereo equipment, electrically-adjustable pilot's and co-pilot's seats, refreshment and Thermos units, fore and aft cabin dividers, electric shaver converter, all-leather seats, passenger instrument console (clock, true airspeed indicator and altimeter) and intercom. Door is two-piece type with built-in airstairs in bottom portion, on port side of cabin at rear. Plug-type emergency escape hatch on starboard side of cabin. Double-pane cabin windows. Foul-weather windows for pilot and co-pilot, on each side of fuselage. Electrically de-iced windscreen optional. Baggage accommodated in nose compartment with external access doors, capacity 159 kg (350 lb), two wing lockers, capacity 54·5 kg (120 lb) each, and in rear cabin area, capacity 226 kg (500 lb). Total baggage capacity 494 kg (1,090 lb). External access door to tailcone on starboard side.

Systems: Cabin pressurisation system, max differential 0·34 bars (5·0 lb/sq in), maintains sea level cabin conditions to an altitude of 3,350 m (11,000 ft), and a 3,050 m (10,000 ft) cabin altitude to a height of 8,075 m (26,500 ft). Electrical system powered by two engine-driven 28V 50A alternators. 24V 25Ah battery. 28V 100A alternators optional, standard on 414A III versions. Hydraulic system for brakes only. Vacuum system for blind-flying instrumentation and optional wing and tail unit de-icing system. Oxygen system of 3·25 m³ (114·9 cu ft) capacity, or emergency oxygen system of 0·31 m³ (11·0 cu ft) capacity optional. Air-conditioning system optional, standard on 414A III.

Avionics and Equipment: The various versions of the Model 414A have avionics as detailed in the model listings. Optional avionics available for the basic 414A include those detailed for the 414A II/III, and alternative items from the Cessna Series 400, 800 and 1000 range are available for all versions. Standard equipment includes sensitive altimeter, quartz crystal clock, dual controls, windscreen defroster, outside air temperature gauge, blind-flying instrumentation, audible stall warning device, instrument post lights, alternator failure lights, aileron and elevator control lock, aircraft systems monitoring device, heater overheat light, cabin door 'Not Locked' light, sun visors, navigation light detectors, armrests, aft cabin light, adjustable cabin air ventilators, window curtains, courtesy lights, reading lights, super soundproofing, non-congealing oil coolers, quick-drain fuel valves, heated stall warning transmitter, pitot and fuel vents, retractable landing light, overall paint scheme, propeller synchronisers, full-flow oil filters, navigation lights, rotating beacons and towbar. Optional equipment for Model 414A includes blind-flying instrumentation for co-pilot, economy mixture indicator, flight hour recorder, variable cabin pressure control system, cabin hand fire extinguisher, air-

Cessna Model 414A Chancellor light transport with turbocharged engines

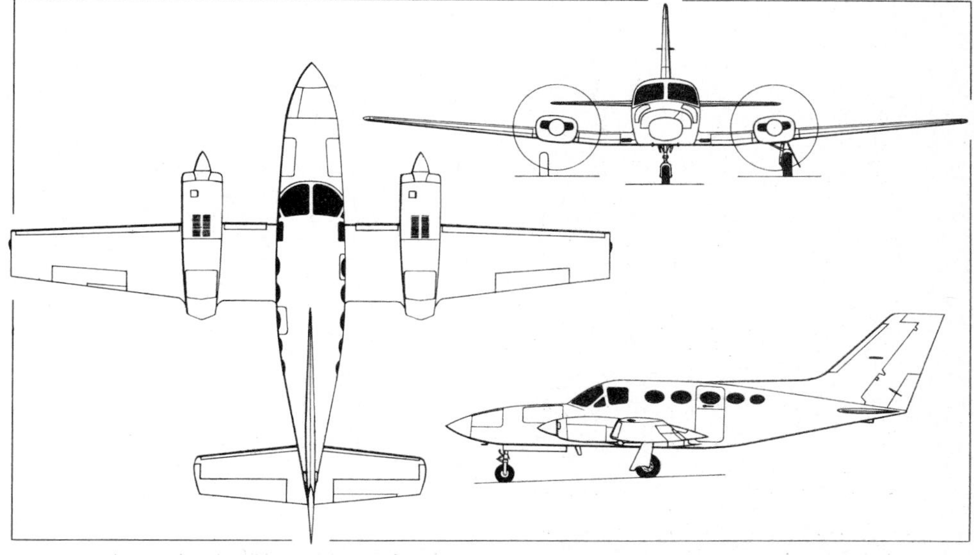

Cessna Model 414A Chancellor six/eight-seat pressurised light transport *(Pilot Press)*

conditioning system, 100A alternators, locator beacon, starboard landing light, strobe lights, taxi light, static dischargers, external power socket, and nosewheel fender. Optional for the Model 414A II are 100A alternators and cabin air-conditioning system. Optional equipment for all versions includes electric elevator trim, angle of attack indicator, digital clock, true airspeed indicator, instantaneous rate of climb indicators, digital fuel flow gauge with computer, rudder pedal lock, boom microphone, turn co-ordinator, electric or alcohol windscreen anti-icing, 'total flood' cabin fire extinguishing system, 7th and 8th seats, 'Fasten seat belt' and 'Oxygen' signs, toilet with privacy curtain, flight deck/cabin divider or curtain, executive table, refreshment centre, 8-track stereo installation, automatic timer to control courtesy lights, ventilating fan system, tinted windows, internal corrosion proofing, fuselage ice impact panels, ice detection lights, dual pitot system, radome nose, engine nacelle fire detection and extinguishing system and heavy-duty brakes.

DIMENSIONS, EXTERNAL:
- Wing span — 13·45 m (44 ft 1½ in)
- Wing chord at root — 1·77 m (5 ft 9¾ in)
- Wing chord at tip — 1·05 m (3 ft 5½ in)
- Length overall — 11·09 m (36 ft 4½ in)
- Height overall — 3·49 m (11 ft 5½ in)
- Tailplane span — 5·18 m (17 ft 0 in)
- Wheel track — 5·47 m (17 ft 11¾ in)
- Wheelbase — 3·18 m (10 ft 5¼ in)
- Propeller diameter — 1·94 m (6 ft 4½ in)
- Passenger door: Height — 1·21 m (3 ft 11½ in)
  - Width — 0·58 m (1 ft 11 in)
  - Height to sill — 1·21 m (3 ft 11½ in)

DIMENSIONS, INTERNAL:
- Cabin: Length — 4·42 m (14 ft 6 in)
  - Max width — 1·40 m (4 ft 7 in)
  - Max height — 1·29 m (4 ft 3 in)
  - Volume — 6·11 m³ (215·6 cu ft)

AREAS:
- Wings, gross — 20·98 m² (225·8 sq ft)
- Fin — 3·52 m² (37·89 sq ft)
- Rudder, incl tab — 1·65 m² (17·77 sq ft)
- Tailplane — 5·64 m² (60·70 sq ft)
- Elevators, incl tab — 1·64 m² (17·63 sq ft)

WEIGHTS AND LOADINGS:
- Weight empty: 414A — 1,975 kg (4,354 lb)
  - 414A II — 2,052 kg (4,523 lb)
  - 414A III — 2,161 kg (4,764 lb)
- Max T-O and landing weight — 3,062 kg (6,750 lb)
- Max ramp weight — 3,078 kg (6,785 lb)
- Max zero-fuel weight — 2,955 kg (6,515 lb)
- Max wing loading — 145·94 kg/m² (29·89 lb/sq ft)
- Max power loading — 6·63 kg/kW (10·89 lb/hp)

PERFORMANCE (at max T-O weight, except speeds are those at mid-cruise weight):
- Max level speed at 6,100 m (20,000 ft) — 239 knots (443 km/h; 275 mph)
- Cruising speed, 74·8% power at 7,470 m (24,500 ft) — 224 knots (415 km/h; 258 mph)
- Cruising speed, 74·8% power at 3,050 m (10,000 ft) — 193 knots (357 km/h; 222 mph)
- Econ cruising speed at 7,620 m (25,000 ft) — 185 knots (342 km/h; 213 mph)
- Econ cruising speed at 3,050 m (10,000 ft) — 144 knots (266 km/h; 166 mph)
- Stalling speed, flaps up, power off:
  - All versions — 82 knots (152 km/h; 95 mph) CAS
- Stalling speed, flaps down, power off:
  - All versions — 72 knots (133 km/h; 83 mph) CAS
- Max rate of climb at S/L — 482 m (1,580 ft)/min
- Rate of climb at S/L, one engine out — 88 m (290 ft)/min
- Service ceiling — 9,555 m (31,350 ft)
- Service ceiling, one engine out — 6,050 m (19,850 ft)
- T-O run — 666 m (2,185 ft)
- T-O to 15 m (50 ft) — 791 m (2,595 ft)
- Landing from 15 m (50 ft) at max landing weight — 729 m (2,393 ft)
- Landing run at max landing weight — 309 m (1,013 ft)
- Range, recommended lean mixture, with allowances for start, taxi, T-O, climb, descent and 45 min reserves at 45% power:
  - 74·8% power at 7,470 m (24,500 ft) with 272 kg (600 lb) usable fuel — 465 nm (861 km; 535 miles)
  - 74·8% power at 7,470 m (24,500 ft) with 555 kg (1,224 lb) usable fuel — 1,147 nm (2,126 km; 1,321 miles)
  - 74·8% power at 3,050 m (10,000 ft) with 272 kg (600 lb) usable fuel — 434 nm (805 km; 500 miles)
  - 74·8% power at 3,050 m (10,000 ft) with 555 kg (1,224 lb) usable fuel — 1,026 nm (1,901 km; 1,181 miles)
  - Econ cruising power at 7,620 m (25,000 ft) with 272 kg (600 lb) usable fuel — 496 nm (917 km; 571 miles)
  - Econ cruising power at 7,620 m (25,000 ft) with 555 kg (1,224 lb) usable fuel — 1,286 nm (2,383 km; 1,481 miles)
  - Econ cruising power at 3,050 m (10,000 ft) with 272 kg (600 lb) usable fuel — 522 nm (967 km; 601 miles)
  - Econ cruising power at 3,050 m (10,000 ft) with 555 kg (1,224 lb) usable fuel — 1,294 nm (2,398 km; 1,490 miles)

CESSNA MODEL 421

On 28 October 1965, Cessna announced a pressurised twin-engined business aircraft designated Model 421, the prototype of which had flown for the first time on 14 October 1965. FAA type approval was received on 1 May 1967 and deliveries began in the same month.

Two developed versions of the Model 421 were produced subsequently as the 421B Golden Eagle and 421B Executive Commuter, remaining in production until replaced by the Model 421C in 1976.

Three versions of the Model 421C Golden Eagle are available for 1979, as follows:

Model 421C Golden Eagle. Standard version, as described in detail.

Model 421C Golden Eagle II. As Model 421C above, but with the following avionics and equipment as standard: dual Series 400 nav/com, one with VOR/ILS, the other with VOR/LOC, ADF, transponder, DME, glideslope, marker beacon, 400B Nav-O-Matic, basic avionics and avionics cooling kits, associated antennae and slaved compass; variable cabin pressure control system, co-pilot's blind-flying instrumentation, economy mixture indicator, flight hour recorder, propeller synchroniser, cabin hand fire extinguisher, 100A alternators, starboard landing light, taxi light, high intensity strobe lights, emergency locator beacon, external power socket, static dischargers and nosewheel fender.

Model 421C Golden Eagle III. As standard Model 421C, with standard equipment of 421C II, plus cabin air-conditioning system and 100A alternators, and an all-weather avionics package which includes dual Series 1000 com and glideslope, Series 1000 nav with HSI, nav with ARC, ADF, RMI and audio panel; Series 800 DME, RNAV, transponder, encoding altimeter and altitude alerter; 800B IFCS; Series 400 marker beacon; AA-100 radio altimeter; RDR-160 weather radar; basic avionics and cooling kits, and all associated antennae.

The 1979 versions of the Golden Eagle introduced as standard the improvements detailed for the Model 414A, plus a more corrosion-resistant exhaust system, redesigned wing lockers, and new interior and exterior styling. New options include an improved rudder lock, new lighter-weight 100A alternators (standard on Golden Eagle II/III), a 2 in (5 cm) turn and bank indicator for the co-pilot's panel, and a lightweight motor for the optional (standard on Golden Eagle III) air-conditioning system.

A total of 1,500 Model 421s had been delivered by 1 January 1979.

The description which follows applies to the Model 421C Golden Eagle:

TYPE: Six/eight-seat pressurised light transport.

WINGS, FUSELAGE: As for Model 414A.

TAIL UNIT: As for Model 414A, except area of fin and rudder increased.

LANDING GEAR: Hydraulically-retractable tricycle type, main units retracting inward, nosewheel unit aft. Emergency extension by means of a 138 bar (2,000 lb/sq in) rechargeable nitrogen bottle. Oleo-pneumatic shock-absorbers. Steerable nosewheel. Main-wheel tyres size 6·50-10 (8-ply), nosewheel tyre 6·00-6 (6-ply). Goodyear single-disc hydraulic brakes. Parking brake.

POWER PLANT: Two 280 kW (375 hp) Continental GTSIO-520-L flat-six geared and turbocharged engines, each driving a McCauley three-blade fully-feathering constant-speed metal propeller. Standard total fuel capacity is 806 litres (213 US gallons), of which 780 litres (206 US gallons) are usable, contained in wet wing. Optional wing locker tanks provide a maximum usable capacity of 991 litres (262 US gallons). Oil capacity 24·6 litres (6·5 US gallons).

ACCOMMODATION: Generally the same as for Model 414A; seats have tapered backs and headrests. The nose compartment can contain a total of 272 kg (600 lb) of baggage and electronics, and two wing lockers an additional 91 kg (200 lb) each, plus 226 kg (500 lb) in the rear cabin area, making a total capacity of 680 kg (1,500 lb).

SYSTEMS, AVIONICS AND EQUIPMENT: Generally as for Model 414A. Hydraulic system for landing gear operation supplied by dual engine-driven pumps, pressure 103·5 bars (1,500 lb/sq in). Rechargeable nitrogen bottle for emergency extension of landing gear, pressure 138 bars (2,000 lb/sq in).

DIMENSIONS, EXTERNAL:
- Wing span — 12·53 m (41 ft 1½ in)
- Wing chord at root — 1·77 m (5 ft 9¾ in)
- Wing chord at tip — 1·14 m (3 ft 8½ in)
- Length overall — 11·09 m (36 ft 4½ in)
- Height overall — 3·49 m (11 ft 5½ in)
- Tailplane span — 5·18 m (17 ft 0 in)
- Wheel track — 5·48 m (17 ft 11¾ in)
- Wheelbase — 3·18 m (10 ft 5¼ in)

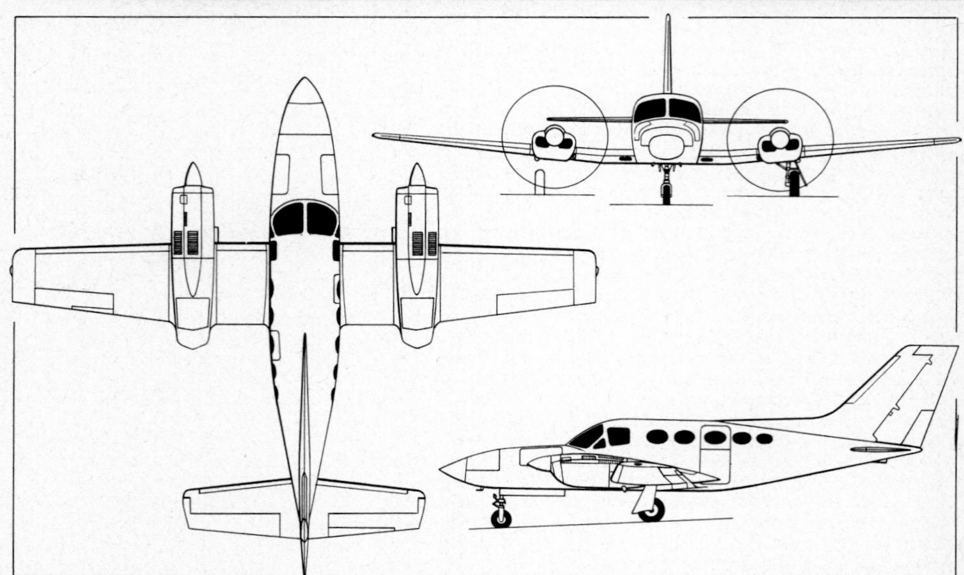

Photograph and three-view drawing *(Pilot Press)* **of the Cessna Model 421C Golden Eagle pressurised light transport**

Propeller diameter 2·29 m (7 ft 6 in)
AREA:
Wings, gross 19·97 m^2 (215 sq ft)
WEIGHTS AND LOADINGS:
Weight empty:
421C Golden Eagle 2,077 kg (4,578 lb)
421C II Golden Eagle 2,160 kg (4,763 lb)
421C III Golden Eagle 2,258 kg (4,979 lb)
Max T-O weight 3,379 kg (7,450 lb)
Max ramp weight 3,402 kg (7,500 lb)
Max zero-fuel weight 3,054 kg (6,733 lb)
Max landing weight 3,266 kg (7,200 lb)
Max wing loading 169·4 kg/m^2 (34·7 lb/sq ft)
Max power loading 6·03 kg/kW (9·9 lb/hp)
PERFORMANCE (at max T-O weight, except speeds are those at mid-cruise weight):
Max level speed at 6,100 m (20,000 ft) 258 knots (478 km/h; 297 mph)
Max cruising speed, 73·5% power at 7,620 m (25,000 ft) 241 knots (447 km/h; 278 mph)
Max cruising speed, 73·5% power at 3,050 m (10,000 ft) 208 knots (386 km/h; 240 mph)
Econ cruising speed at 7,620 m (25,000 ft) 195 knots (361 km/h; 224 mph)
Econ cruising speed at 3,050 m (10,000 ft) 155 knots (287 km/h; 178 mph)
Stalling speed, flaps up, power off:
All versions 83 knots (154 km/h; 96 mph) CAS
Stalling speed, flaps down, power off:
All versions 74 knots (137 km/h; 85 mph) CAS
Max rate of climb at S/L 591 m (1,940 ft)/min
Rate of climb at S/L, one engine out 107 m (350 ft)/min
Service ceiling 9,205 m (30,200 ft)
Service ceiling, one engine out 4,540 m (14,900 ft)
T-O run 544 m (1,786 ft)
T-O to 15 m (50 ft) 708 m (2,323 ft)
Landing from 15 m (50 ft) 699 m (2,293 ft)
Landing run 219 m (720 ft)
Range, recommended lean mixture, with allowances for start, taxi, T-O, climb, descent and 45 min reserves at 45% power:
73·5% power at 7,620 m (25,000 ft) with 561 kg (1,236 lb) usable fuel 955 nm (1,770 km; 1,100 miles)
73·5% power at 7,620 m (25,000 ft) with 713 kg (1,572 lb) usable fuel 1,271 nm (2,356 km; 1,464 miles)
73·5% power at 3,050 m (10,000 ft) with 561 kg (1,236 lb) usable fuel 853 nm (1,580 km; 982 miles)
73·5% power at 3,050 m (10,000 ft) with 713 kg (1,572 lb) usable fuel 1,123 nm (2,081 km; 1,293 miles)
Econ cruising power at 7,620 m (25,000 ft) with 561 kg (1,236 lb) usable fuel 1,092 nm (2,023 km; 1,257 miles)
Econ cruising power at 7,620 m (25,000 ft) with 713 kg (1,572 lb) usable fuel 1,487 nm (2,755 km; 1,712 miles)
Econ cruising power at 3,050 m (10,000 ft) with 561 kg (1,236 lb) usable fuel 1,088 nm (2,017 km; 1,253 miles)
Econ cruising power at 3,050 m (10,000 ft) with 713 kg (1,572 lb) usable fuel 1,464 nm (2,713 km; 1,686 miles)

CESSNA MODEL 425

Under development in 1979, the Model 425 is a pressurised twin-turboprop transport based on the Model 421. Power plant comprises two Pratt & Whitney Aircraft of Canada PT6A-112 turboprop engines.

CESSNA TITAN

On 16 July 1975 Cessna Aircraft Company announced that it was developing a new twin-engined business/commuter/cargo aircraft, designated Model 404 Titan. The model number was deleted subsequently, and the aircraft is known currently as the Cessna Titan. It was designed to carry a nominal 1,588 kg (3,500 lb) useful load out of a 771 m (2,530 ft) airstrip. A prototype flew for the first time on 26 February 1975. Deliveries began in October 1976, and a total of 185 had been delivered by 1 January 1979.

The Titan offers an increase of more than 30% in ton-miles per gallon by comparison with the Cessna 402. Its cabin, which is almost 5·79 m (19 ft 0 in) long, is designed for rapid conversion to satisfy cargo, commuter and executive transport roles.

The Cessna Titan is available in seven versions for 1979, as follows:

Titan Ambassador. Standard version, configured and equipped for passenger carrying, as described in detail.

Titan Ambassador II. As standard version, but with the following avionics and equipment: dual Series 300 nav/com with VOR/ILS and VOR/LOC; Series 300 ADF; Series 400 transponder, glideslope, marker beacon; 400B Nav-O-Matic; basic avionics kit, audio system, avionics cooling, and all associated antennae; dual controls, economy mixture indicator, flight hour recorder, cabin hand fire extinguisher, emergency locator beacon, starboard landing light, taxi light, external power socket, static dischargers, and nosewheel fender.

Cessna Titan business/commuter/cargo transport

Titan Ambassador III. As Titan Ambassador, with standard equipment of Ambassador II plus heavy duty brakes and 100A alternators, and an avionics package which includes dual Series 400 nav/com with HSI; 400 nav/com with ARC; dual 400 glideslope; 400 ADF, DME, marker beacon, RNAV, transponder; Series 800 encoding altimeter and altitude alert; Series 1000 RMI; 400B IFCS; Bendix RDR-160 weather radar; yaw damper, basic avionics kit, audio system, avionics cooling, and all associated antennae.

Titan Courier. Standard utility version for passenger/cargo role.

Titan Courier II. As standard Courier, but with the avionics and equipment detailed for the Ambassador II.

Titan Freighter. Cargo version with specially designed cabin walls and ceiling of impact resistant polycarbonate material and floor stressed to withstand loading of 976 kg/m^2 (200 lb/sq ft). Cargo handling facilities include the retention of floor tracks to provide tiedown attachment points, floor pallets to provide durable flooring flush with the tracks, five high-capacity cargo retaining nets. Cargo door 1·26 m (4 ft 1½ in) high and 1·24 m (4 ft 1 in) wide replaces normal cabin door on port side, and crew door is provided on port side over wing.

Titan Freighter II. As Titan Freighter, but with avionics and equipment detailed for Ambassador II.

The 1979 versions of the Titan introduce a number of improvements as standard, including relocation of the tail position light, better accessibility to avionics, revised radio panel, repositioned outside air temperature gauge, larger inspection gauge for landing gear emergency blowdown bottle, and an improved fuel pickup valve. New options include an improved rudder lock, new lighter-weight 100A alternators (standard in Ambassador III), a 2 in (5 cm) turn and bank indicator for the co-pilot's panel, and a lightweight motor for the optional air-conditioning system.

TYPE: Two/ten-seat passenger/executive/cargo transport.

WINGS: Cantilever low-wing monoplane. Wing section NACA 23018 at root, NACA 23012 at tip. Dihedral 3° 30′ on wing centre-section, 4° 55′ on outer panels. Incidence 2° at root, −1° at construction tip. All-metal three-spar centre-section structure to meet FAR 23 fail-safe requirements: two-spar structure for outer wing panels. Hydraulically-operated Fowler-type trailing-edge flaps of light alloy construction. Plain ailerons of light alloy construction. Trim tab in port aileron. Pneumatic de-icing system optional.

FUSELAGE: All-metal semi-monocoque structure.

TAIL UNIT: Cantilever structure of light alloy with swept surfaces. Fixed-incidence tailplane, with dihedral of 12°. Trim tab in rudder and each elevator. Electrical operation of trim tabs, and pneumatic de-icing system, optional.

LANDING GEAR: Hydraulically-retractable tricycle type with single wheel on each unit. Main units retract inward into wing, nosewheel aft. Emergency extension by means of a 138 bar (2,000 lb/sq in) rechargeable nitrogen bottle. Cessna oleo-pneumatic shock-absorbers. All legs of articulated (trailing-link) type. Cleveland main wheels with tyres size 22 × 7·75-10, pressure 4·83 bars (70 lb/sq in). Cleveland nosewheel with tyre size 6·00-6, pressure 3·45 bars (50 lb/sq in). Cleveland single-disc hydraulic brakes. Heavy duty brakes optional, standard on Ambassador III. Parking brake.

POWER PLANT: Two 280 kW (375 hp) Continental GTSIO-520-M flat-six engines, each driving a McCauley three-blade metal constant-speed fully-feathering propeller. Integral fuel tanks in wings, with combined usable capacity of 1,287 litres (340 US gallons). Oil capacity 26·5 litres (7 US gallons). Manifold pressure relief valves to prevent overboosting are standard. Propeller synchrophaser, automatic unfeathering system and electrical de-icing system optional.

ACCOMMODATION: Two seats side by side for pilot and co-pilot. Titan Courier has six individual seats and a two-passenger bench seat as standard; Titan Ambassador as Courier, except bench seat is optional. Passenger seats are 'Enviro-form' moulded honeycomb with glassfibre reinforcement. Passenger reading lights standard for Ambassador, optional for Courier. Door with built-in airstair on port side of fuselage, aft of wing. Emergency escape hatch on starboard side of cabin. Storm windows for pilot and co-pilot. Tinted cabin windows. Cargo door and crew access door optional for Courier, standard for Freighter. Baggage area at rear of cabin, capacity 227 kg (500 lb). Nose baggage compartment, with optional carpeting, can accommodate articles up to 1·96 m (6 ft 5 in) in length and has capacity of 159 kg (350 lb), accessible from each side. Avionics/baggage compartment in nose, separate from above baggage compartment and accessible through an 'over the top' 180° cam-lock door, has a capacity of 113 kg (250 lb); side access door optional. Wing lockers, at rear of each engine nacelle, each have capacity of 91 kg (200 lb). If no electronics carried in forward nose compartment, total baggage capacity is 680 kg (1,500 lb). Dual controls optional, standard on Titan II versions. Cabin heated and ventilated; air-conditioning optional. Windscreen defrosting standard. Electrical anti-icing of pilot's window, or alcohol anti-icing of pilot's and co-pilot's windows, optional.

SYSTEMS: Electrical system powered by two 28V 50A alternators; 100A alternators optional, standard on III versions. Battery, 24V 25Ah, can be sited optionally in nose baggage compartment. Hydraulic system for landing gear and flap operation, and for wheel brakes. Vacuum system provided by two engine-driven pumps. Oxygen system, capacity 1·25 m^3 (44 cu ft) or 3·25 m^3 (114·9 cu ft), optional. Heating and ventilation system standard, with 45,000 BTU gasoline heater. Air-conditioning system optional.

AVIONICS AND EQUIPMENT: The various versions of the Titan have avionics as detailed in the model listings. Optional avionics available for the basic Titan versions include those detailed for the II and III versions, and alternative items from the Cessna Series 400, 800 and 1000 are available for all versions. Standard equipment includes electric clock, variable intensity floodlight, sensitive altimeter, outside air temperature gauge, full blind-flying instrumentation, audible stall warning and landing gear indicators, navigation light detectors, cabin door 'Not Locked' light, map light, heater overheat warning light, alternator failure lights, variable intensity instrument post lights, aileron and elevator control locks, sun visors, pilot and co-pilot safety belt system, armrests, shoulder restraint system, super soundproofing, cabin radio speaker, adjustable cabin air ventilators, courtesy lights, retractable landing light, navigation lights, three-light strobe system, two rotating beacons, all-over paint scheme utilising polyurethane paint, and towbar. Optional equipment for all versions includes GMT clock, high-efficiency exhaust gas temperature gauges, instantaneous rate of climb indicator, true airspeed indicator, turn co-ordinator, internal corrosion proofing, ice detector light, anti-icing kit, dual heated static source, digital fuel flow gauge with computer, courtesy light timer, 'total flood' cabin fire extinguishing system; items detailed as standard for II and III versions are also available optionally as required.

DIMENSIONS, EXTERNAL:
Wing span 14·12 m (46 ft 4 in)
Wing chord at root 1·78 m (5 ft 10 in)
Wing chord at tip 1·22 m (4 ft 0 in)
Wing aspect ratio 8·74
Length overall 12·04 m (39 ft 6¼ in)
Height overall 4·04 m (13 ft 3 in)
Tailplane span 5·82 m (19 ft 1 in)
Wheel track 4·27 m (14 ft 0½ in)
Wheelbase 3·81 m (12 ft 6 in)

Propeller diameter 2·29 m (7 ft 6 in)
Passenger door (port): Height 1·24 m (4 ft 1 in)
Width 0·61 m (2 ft 0 in)
Height to sill 1·24 m (4 ft 1 in)
Cargo door (optional, port; standard Freighter):
Height 1·26 m (4 ft 1½ in)
Width 1·24 m (4 ft 1 in)
Height to sill 1·26 m (4 ft 1½ in)
Nose baggage doors (each):
Height 0·41 m (1 ft 4 in)
Width 0·86 m (2 ft 9¾ in)
Nacelle baggage doors (each):
Length 0·62 m (2 ft 0¼ in)
Width 0·64 m (2 ft 1 in)

DIMENSIONS, INTERNAL:
Cabin: Length 5·72 m (18 ft 9 in)
Max width 1·42 m (4 ft 8 in)
Max height 1·31 m (4 ft 3¼ in)
Volume 8·97 m³ (316·6 cu ft)

AREAS:
Wings, gross 22·48 m² (242 sq ft)
Horizontal tail surfaces (total) 5·89 m² (63·38 sq ft)
Vertical tail surfaces (total) 4·05 m² (43·60 sq ft)

WEIGHTS AND LOADINGS:
Weight empty: Ambassador 2,180 kg (4,807 lb)
Ambassador II 2,245 kg (4,950 lb)
Ambassador III 2,291 kg (5,050 lb)
Courier 2,190 kg (4,828 lb)
Courier II 2,252 kg (4,965 lb)
Freighter 2,119 kg (4,672 lb)
Freighter II 2,181 kg (4,808 lb)
Max T-O weight 3,810 kg (8,400 lb)
Max ramp weight 3,833 kg (8,450 lb)
Max zero-fuel and landing weight 3,674 kg (8,100 lb)
Max wing loading 169·5 kg/m² (34·71 lb/sq ft)
Max power loading 6·8 kg/kW (11·2 lb/hp)

PERFORMANCE (at max T-O weight unless otherwise indicated, except speeds are those at mid-cruise weight):
Max level speed at 4,875 m (16,000 ft) 232 knots (430 km/h; 267 mph)
Max cruising speed, 74·5% power at 6,100 m (20,000 ft) 217 knots (402 km/h; 250 mph)
Max cruising speed, 75·5% power at 3,050 m (10,000 ft) 199 knots (369 km/h; 229 mph)
Econ cruising speed at 6,100 m (20,000 ft) 163 knots (302 km/h; 188 mph)
Econ cruising speed at 3,050 m (10,000 ft) 141 knots (261 km/h; 162 mph)
Stalling speed, all versions:
Flaps up, power off 83 knots (154 km/h; 96 mph) CAS
Flaps down, power off, at max landing weight 70 knots (130 km/h; 81 mph) CAS
Max rate of climb at S/L 480 m (1,575 ft)/min
Rate of climb at S/L, one engine out 70 m (230 ft)/min
Service ceiling 7,925 m (26,000 ft)
Service ceiling, one engine out 3,080 m (10,100 ft)
T-O run 545 m (1,788 ft)
T-O to 15 m (50 ft) 721 m (2,367 ft)
Landing from 15 m (50 ft) at max landing weight 649 m (2,130 ft)
Landing run at max landing weight 335 m (1,100 ft)
Range, recommended lean mixture, allowances for start, taxi, T-O, climb, descent, and 45 min reserves at 45% power:
74·5% power at 6,100 m (20,000 ft) with 454 kg (1,000 lb) usable fuel 642 nm (1,189 km; 739 miles)
74·5% power at 6,100 m (20,000 ft) with 936 kg (2,064 lb) usable fuel 1,525 nm (2,826 km; 1,756 miles)
75·5% power at 3,050 m (10,000 ft) with 454 kg (1,000 lb) usable fuel 607 nm (1,125 km; 699 miles)
75·5% power at 3,050 m (10,000 ft) with 936 kg (2,064 lb) usable fuel 1,406 nm (2,606 km; 1,619 miles)
Econ cruising power at 6,100 m (20,000 ft) with 454 kg (1,000 lb) usable fuel 728 nm (1,349 km; 838 miles)
Econ cruising power at 6,100 m (20,000 ft) with 936 kg (2,064 lb) usable fuel 1,836 nm (3,402 km; 2,114 miles)
Econ cruising power at 3,050 m (10,000 ft) with 454 kg (1,000 lb) usable fuel 742 nm (1,374 km; 854 miles)
Econ cruising power at 3,050 m (10,000 ft) with 936 kg (2,064 lb) usable fuel 1,818 nm (3,368 km; 2,093 miles)

CESSNA CONQUEST

Cessna announced on 15 November 1974 that it was developing a twin-turboprop business aircraft designated Model 441, with initial deliveries scheduled for 1977. This type is designed to slot into the market gap between existing twin piston-engined aircraft and turbofan-powered business aircraft.

Redesignated officially as the Cessna Conquest, this aircraft is powered by two Garrett-AiResearch TPE 331-8-401 turboprop engines, which have been developed specially to meet the high-altitude high-speed requirements set by Cessna for this aircraft. Its high performance stems in part from use of a new high aspect ratio bonded wing, and from the high-strength trailing-link-type hydraulically retractable tricycle landing gear.

Production aircraft for 1979 introduce a number of improvements as standard, including a more durable door cable covering and attachment, redesigned vinyl headliner, several interior styling changes, relocation of the tail position light, better accessibility to avionics, larger inspection gauge for landing gear emergency blowdown bottle, an improved rudder lock, new upper cabin door inner handle latch mechanism, and new exterior styling.

Cessna Conquest (two Garrett-AiResearch TPE 331-8-401S turboprops)

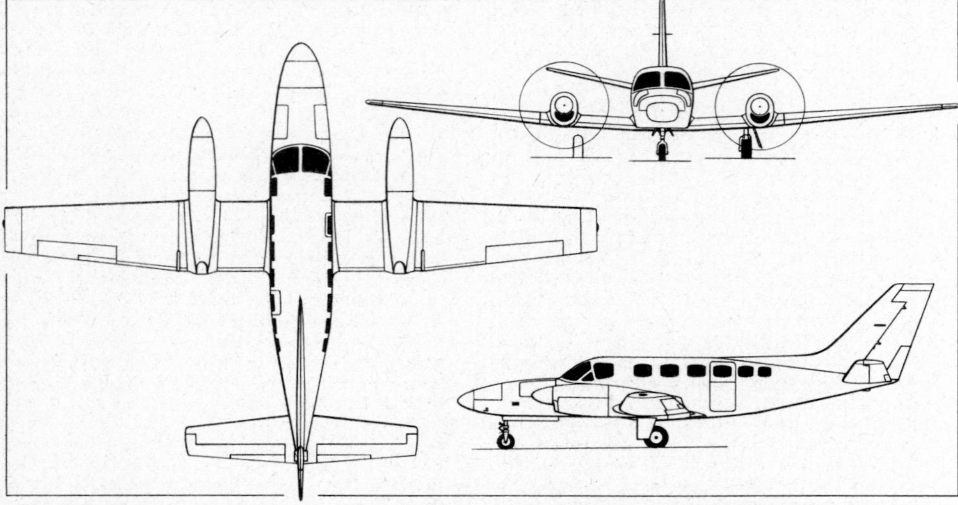

Cessna Conquest five/eleven-seat pressurised, turboprop-powered executive transport *(Pilot Press)*

The prototype of the Conquest flew for the first time on 26 August 1975 and 73 aircraft had been delivered by 1 January 1979.

TYPE: Five/eleven-seat pressurised executive transport.

WINGS: As Cessna Titan, except wing span and area increased by addition of wingtip extensions.

TAIL UNIT: Cantilever structure with sweptback vertical surfaces. Dihedral 12° on horizontal surfaces. Large tab in each elevator and rudder.

LANDING GEAR: As Cessna Titan.

POWER PLANT: Two Garrett-AiResearch TPE 331-8-401S turboprop engines, each flat rated at 474 kW (635·5 shp) to 4,875 m (16,000 ft). Hartzell constant-speed fully-feathering and reversible-pitch three-blade propellers. Total usable fuel capacity 1,798 litres (475 US gallons).

ACCOMMODATION: Seats for four to ten persons, and pilot, in pressurised and air-conditioned cabin. Various optional seating arrangements. Door aft of wing on port side, with upward-hinged top portion and downward-hinged lower portion with integral airstairs. Emergency exit over wing on starboard side. Baggage door on each side of nose. Max baggage capacity 680 kg (1,500 lb). Optional items include aft cabin divider, refreshment centre, toilet, writing tables and stereo system.

SYSTEMS: Pressurisation system max differential 0·43 bars (6·3 lb/sq in). Hydraulic system for operation of flaps, landing gear and brakes, pressure 103·5 bars (1,500 lb/sq in). Emergency extension of landing gear by means of 138 bar (2,000 lb/sq in) rechargeable gas bottle. Electrical power supplied by two 28V 200A starter/generators; two 24V 22Ah nickel-cadmium batteries housed in nose compartment. Electronic fuel control system.

AVIONICS: Standard avionics of Cessna manufacture include dual 1038A com, dual 1048A nav, dual 1043A glideslope, 1046A ADF, 402A marker beacon, 876A DME, 859A transponder, RMI, 400 encoding altimeter, Bendix RDR-160 weather radar, basic avionics kit. Collins avionics package optional.

DIMENSIONS, EXTERNAL:
Wing span, over tip-lights 15·04 m (49 ft 4 in)
Wing chord at root 1·78 m (5 ft 10 in)
Wing chord at tip 1·22 m (4 ft 0 in)
Wing aspect ratio 9·47
Length overall 11·89 m (39 ft 0¼ in)
Height overall 3·99 m (13 ft 1¼ in)
Tailplane span 5·81 m (19 ft 1 in)
Wheel track 4·28 m (14 ft 0¾ in)
Wheelbase 3·81 m (12 ft 5⅞ in)
Propeller diameter 2·29 m (7 ft 6 in)

DIMENSIONS, INTERNAL:
Cabin: Length 5·71 m (18 ft 9 in)
Max width 1·41 m (4 ft 7½ in)
Max height 1·29 m (4 ft 3 in)

AREAS:
Wings, gross 23·56 m² (253·6 sq ft)
Vertical tail surfaces 4·05 m² (43·6 sq ft)
Horizontal tail surfaces 5·89 m² (63·38 sq ft)

WEIGHTS AND LOADINGS:
Weight empty 2,535 kg (5,589 lb)
Max fuel 1,444 kg (3,183 lb)
Max ramp weight 4,502 kg (9,925 lb)
Max T-O weight 4,468 kg (9,850 lb)
Max landing weight 4,246 kg (9,360 lb)
Max zero-fuel weight 3,674 kg (8,100 lb)
Max wing loading 189·6 kg/m² (38·8 lb/sq ft)
Max power loading 4·79 kg/kW (7·88 lb/shp)

PERFORMANCE (at max T-O weight unless otherwise indicated, except speeds are those at mid-cruise weight):
Never-exceed speed Mach 0·55 (245 knots; 453 km/h; 282 mph) CAS
Max level speed at 4,875 m (16,000 ft) 295 knots (547 km/h; 340 mph)
Max cruising speed at 7,315 m (24,000 ft) 293 knots (543 km/h; 337 mph)
Stalling speed, gear and flaps up, power off 90 knots (167 km/h;104 mph) CAS
Stalling speed, gear and flaps down, power off 76 knots (141 km/h; 87·5 mph) CAS
Stalling speed, gear and flaps down, power off, at max landing weight 75 knots (139 km/h; 86·5 mph) CAS
Max rate of climb at S/L 742 m (2,435 ft)/min
Rate of climb at S/L, one engine out 218 m (715 ft)/min
Service ceiling 11,275 m (37,000 ft)
Service ceiling, one engine out 6,515 m (21,380 ft)
Max certificated operating altitude 10,060 m (33,000 ft)
T-O run 544 m (1,785 ft)
T-O to 15 m (50 ft) 751 m (2,465 ft)
Landing from 15 m (50 ft) at max landing weight 572 m (1,875 ft)
Landing run 334 m (1,095 ft)
Range, at max T-O weight with 11 persons, at max cruising power, allowances for engine start, taxi, T-O, climb, descent and 45 min reserves:
at 5,180 m (17,000 ft) 816 nm (1,511 km; 939 miles)
at 7,620 m (25,000 ft) 1,025 nm (1,899 km; 1,180 miles)

at 10,060 m (33,000 ft)
1,294 nm (2,398 km; 1,490 miles)
Range, at max T-O weight with 6 persons, at max cruising power, allowances as above:
at 5,180 m (17,000 ft)
1,274 nm (2,359 km; 1,466 miles)
at 7,620 m (25,000 ft)
1,617 nm (2,995 km; 1,860 miles)
at 10,060 m (33,000 ft)
2,070 nm (3,833 km; 2,382 miles)

CESSNA CITATION I

On 7 October 1968 Cessna announced that it was developing a new eight-seat pressurised executive turbofan aircraft named Fanjet 500, which would be able to operate from most airfields used by light and medium twin-engined aircraft.

After the first flight of the prototype, on 15 September 1969, it was announced that the aircraft's name had been changed to Citation. Subsequently, the gross weight was increased from 4,309 kg (9,500 lb) to 4,695 kg (10,350 lb) and several other changes were made. These included a lengthened front fuselage, movement of the engine nacelles further aft, larger vertical tail, and resiting of, and introduction of dihedral on, the tailplane.

On 1 July 1971 Cessna announced that the first production Citation 0001 (N502CC) had made its first flight. Final FAA certification under FAR Part 25 was awarded on 9 September 1971.

The Citation was designed to fly from runways as little as 762 m (2,500 ft) in length, and to fly into and out of many unpaved airfields which are not suitable for other commercial jet aircraft. Official tests have shown that the Citation has noise levels at take-off, sideline and approach which are at least 15 EPNdB below the allowable values specified by the FAA's FAR Part 36 noise certification requirements. The Citation is offered on a direct company-to-customer basis in the basic standard configuration or as a complete business aircraft package, including factory-installed interior and avionics, ground and flight training, and one year of computerised maintenance service. Cessna states that factory installation of interior and avionics allows greater payload and also ensures that proper attention is given to the weight distribution of installed equipment.

In February 1972 the Citation was certificated at a maximum T-O weight of 4,921 kg (10,850 lb), and it was subsequently announced, on 30 June 1972, that beginning with production aircraft No. 71, the certificated max ramp weight would be 5,284 kg (11,650 lb), with a max T-O weight of 5,215 kg (11,500 lb). Certification at this max T-O weight was granted on 17 January 1973, and Cessna made available a modification kit to provide the new gross weight capability for production aircraft prior to No. 71.

Certification in other countries includes a West German LBA type certificate issued on 21 June 1972, French SGAC type certificate issued on 27 March 1974 and UK type certificate issued on 30 August 1974. The Citation has also satisfied the requirements for registration in Australia, Austria, Belgium, Canada, Denmark, Japan, Italy, the Netherlands, Spain, Sweden, Switzerland, Yugoslavia and Zambia.

An increase in take-off gross weight to a maximum of 5,375 kg (11,850 lb) and the use of optional Rohr Industries thrust reversers received FAA certification in February 1976. The improved Citation I became available in December 1976, with a wing of increased span and JT15D-1A turbofan engines. It superseded the earlier model on the production line from c/n 350 onward and was certificated on 15 December 1976. The first Citation I was delivered on 21 December 1976. Two versions are currently available:

Citation I. Basic version, as described in detail.

Citation I/SP Model 501. Basically the same as the Citation I, but certificated to FAR 23 for single-pilot operation. Type Certification granted on 7 January 1977, first aircraft delivered on 25 January 1977.

A total of 118 Citation Is, of both models, had been delivered by 1 January 1979.

TYPE: Seven/eight-seat twin-turbofan executive transport.

WINGS: Cantilever low-wing monoplane without sweepback. Wing section at c/l NACA 23014 (modified), at wing station 247·95 NACA 23012. Incidence at c/l 2° 30′, at wing station 247·95 —0° 30′. Dihedral 4°. All-metal fail-safe structure with two primary spars, an auxiliary spar, three fuselage attachment points and conventional ribs and stringers. Manually-operated ailerons, with manual trim on port aileron. Electrically-operated single-slotted trailing-edge flaps. Hydraulically-operated aerodynamic speed brakes.

FUSELAGE: All-metal pressurised structure of circular section. Fail-safe design, providing multiple load paths.

TAIL UNIT: Cantilever all-metal structure. Horizontal surfaces have dihedral of 9°. Large dorsal fin and smaller ventral fin. Manually-operated control surfaces. Electric elevator trim with manual override; manual rudder trim.

LANDING GEAR: Hydraulically-retractable tricycle type with single wheel on each unit. Main units retract inward into the wing, nose gear forward into fuselage nose. Free-fall and pneumatic emergency extension systems.

Cessna Citation I seven/eight-seat twin-turbofan executive transport

Goodyear main wheels and tyres of 559 mm (22 in) diameter, pressure 6·21 bars (90 lb/sq in) on first 70 production aircraft; 71st and subsequent production aircraft have 22 in diameter main-wheel tyres, pressure 6·90 bars (100 lb/sq in). Steerable nosewheel with Goodyear wheel and tyre of 457 mm (18 in) diameter, pressure 8·27 bars (120 lb/sq in). Goodyear hydraulic brakes. Parking brake and pneumatic emergency brake system. Skid warning system optional.

POWER PLANT: Two Pratt & Whitney JT15D-1A turbofan engines, each rated at 9·77 kN (2,200 lb st) for take-off, mounted in pod on each side of rear fuselage. Rohr thrust reversers optional. Integral fuel tanks in wings, with capacity of 1,720 kg (3,793 lb).

ACCOMMODATION: Crew of two on separate flight deck. Fully-carpeted main cabin equipped with two individual forward-facing seats aft, one single forward-facing seat centre port, one single aft-facing seat centre starboard and a fifth aft-facing corner lounge chair at front of cabin on starboard side, all with headrests. Toilet compartment and main baggage area at rear of cabin. Refreshment unit at front of cabin. Second baggage area in nose. Cabin is pressurised, heated and air-conditioned. Individual reading lights and air inlets for each passenger. Drop-out constant-flow oxygen system for emergency use. Plug-type door with integral airstair at front on port side and one emergency exit on starboard side. Doors on each side of nose baggage compartment. Tinted windows, each with curtains. Optional eight-seat layout for crew of two and six passengers, executive table, flush toilet replacing standard toilet, electric razor socket and 110V converter and choice of interior trims.

SYSTEMS: Pressurisation system supplied with engine bleed air, max pressure differential 0·59 bars (8·5 lb/sq in). Hydraulic system, pressure 103·5 bars (1,500 lb/sq in), with two pumps to operate landing gear and speed brakes. Electrical system supplied by two 400A 28V DC starter/generators, with two 600VA inverters and 24V 39Ah nickel-cadmium battery. Oxygen system of 0·62 m³ (22 cu ft) capacity includes two crew demand masks and five drop-out constant-flow masks for passengers.

AVIONICS AND EQUIPMENT: Standard avionics equipment included in the fully-equipped standard Citation (up to c/n 275) comprises Bendix FGS-70 autopilot/flight director; King KDF 800 ADF; dual RCA AVC-110A VHF transceivers; dual RCA AVN-220A nav receivers, VOR, localiser, glideslope and marker beacon; dual RCA AVI-200 RMI; dual Avtech audio amplifiers; Bendix CB-70 compass system; Collins PN-101 HSI and compass system; RCA AVQ-21 radar; RCA AVQ-85 DME; RCA AVQ-95 transponder; Intercontinental Dynamics altitude alerting and reporting; and all related antennae and equipment. Standard Category II avionics package on aircraft subsequent to c/n 275 comprises Sperry SPZ 5200 flight control system with choice of single or double-cue command bars, including Sperry 500 autopilot, Sperry altimeter with altitude alerting and reporting functions, complete vertical navigation capability, air data computer, Sperry Model 600 (port)/Model 044 (starboard) horizontal situation indicator, Sperry ADI Model 300 or Model 600 command and control computer and autopilot servos, Bendix RDR 1200 (RDR 1100 subsequent to construction number 349) continuous vision weather radar, dual Collins VHF-20 com transceivers, dual Collins VIR-30 nav receivers, Collins TDR-90 transponder, DME-40, 332-CIO radio magnetic indicator, and ARC-846A ADF. Provision for advanced instrumentation and avionics to customer's specification. Standard equipment includes stall warning system, instrument standby lights, map light, internally lighted instruments, audible high Mach/airspeed warning, audible landing gear warning, generator load ammeters, standby magnetic compass, foul weather window, low fuel level and battery temperature warning lights, full blind-flying instrumentation, birdproof windscreen with de-fog system, windscreen anti-icing with standby alcohol de-icing system, gust locks, 'No Smoking, Fasten Seat Belts' sign, individual life vests, baggage tiedown kit, cabin fire extinguisher, two anti-collision beacons, entry light, emergency exit lights, storm lights, tailcone compartment light; wing ice, taxi, navigation and landing lights, external power socket, emergency battery pack, automatic engine start system, engine fire warning and extinguishing system, and inlet anti-icing. Optional items include high-capacity oxygen system, thrust reverser, gravel runway kit, drag chute, radio telephone (Flitefone), HF com transceiver, locator beacon, anti-skid system, surface de-icing system, skid warning system, strobe lights, angle of attack indicator, engine fan synchroniser, navigation chart case, hatrack/storage shelf, nose baggage compartment light, electric razor light, refreshment cabinets, storage drawers, executive tables and flush toilets.

DIMENSIONS, EXTERNAL:
Wing span 14·35 m (47 ft 1 in)
Wing aspect ratio 6·6
Length overall 13·26 m (43 ft 6 in)
Height overall 4·36 m (14 ft 3¾ in)
Tailplane span 5·74 m (18 ft 10 in)
Wheel track 3·84 m (12 ft 7 in)
Wheelbase 4·78 m (15 ft 8¼ in)
Cabin door (port): Height 1·29 m (4 ft 2¾ in)
Width 0·60 m (1 ft 11½ in)
Emergency exit (starboard):
Height 0·95 m (3 ft 1¼ in)
Width 0·56 m (1 ft 10 in)

DIMENSIONS, INTERNAL:
Cabin:
Length, front to rear bulkhead 5·33 m (17 ft 6 in)
Max width 1·50 m (4 ft 11 in)
Max height 1·32 m (4 ft 4 in)
Baggage space: Cabin 1·22 m³ (43 cu ft)
Nose 0·48 m³ (17 cu ft)

AREAS:
Horizontal tail surfaces 6·56 m² (70·6 sq ft)
Vertical tail surfaces 4·73 m² (50·9 sq ft)

WEIGHTS (from aircraft No. 350 onward):
Weight empty (incl electronics) 2,935 kg (6,470 lb)
Max T-O weight 555t,,375 kg (11,850 lb)
Max landing weight 5,148 kg (11,350 lb)
Max zero-fuel weight 3,810 kg (8,400 lb)
Optional max zero-fuel weight 4,309 kg (9,500 lb)

PERFORMANCE (at max T-O weight, except where indicated):
Cruising speed at average cruising weight
351 knots (649 km/h; 403 mph) TAS
Stalling speed at max landing weight
82 knots (152 km/h; 94·5 mph) CAS
Max rate of climb at S/L 829 m (2,719 ft)/min
Rate of climb at S/L, one engine out
251 m (825 ft)/min
Max certificated altitude 12,495 m (41,000 ft)
Service ceiling, one engine out 6,400 m (21,000 ft)
T-O to 10·7 m (35 ft) 896 m (2,940 ft)
Landing run at max landing weight 692 m (2,270 ft)
Range with 6 passengers, 45 min reserves
1,335 nm (2,474 km; 1,537 miles)

CESSNA CITATION II

First announced on 14 September 1976, this version of the Citation introduced several new features, including a fuselage lengthened by 1·14 m (3 ft 9 in), an increased-span high aspect ratio wing, increased fuel and baggage capacity, and the installation of Pratt & Whitney Aircraft of Canada JT15D-4 turbofan engines. The prototype (N550CC) flew for the first time on 31 January 1977, and certification was received in late March 1978; deliveries began immediately afterwards and a total oi 38 had been delivered by 1 January 1979.

Cessna Citation II 10/12-seat twin-turbofan business aircraft (Pratt & Whitney Aircraft of Canada JT15D-4 engines)

In addition to the standard Model 550 Citation II, which is certificated for a crew of two, the Model 551 Citation II/SP is available for single-pilot operation at a max T-O weight of 5,670 kg (12,500 lb).

In October 1977, the US Customs Service ordered a special-purpose Citation II, fitted with government-furnished radar and sensing equipment. Follow-on orders are expected.

The description of the Citation I applies basically to the Citation II, except as follows:

POWER PLANT: Two Pratt & Whitney Aircraft of Canada JT15D-4 turbofan engines, each rated at 11·12 kN (2,500 lb st) for take-off, mounted in pod on each side of rear fuselage. Integral fuel tanks in wings, with usable capacity of 2,703 litres (714 US gallons).

ACCOMMODATION: As for Citation I, except seating for 8-10 passengers in main cabin, with toilet and increased baggage capacity.

DIMENSIONS, EXTERNAL:

Wing span	15·75 m (51 ft 8 in)
Wing aspect ratio	8·3
Length overall	14·38 m (47 ft 2 in)
Height overall	4·50 m (14 ft 9 in)
Tailplane span	5·74 m (18 ft 10 in)
Wheel track	5·36 m (17 ft 7 in)
Wheelbase	5·54 m (18 ft 2 in)

DIMENSIONS, INTERNAL:

Cabin: Length, front to rear bulkhead	6·38 m (20 ft 11 in)
Max width	1·50 m (4 ft 11 in)
Max height	1·45 m (4 ft 9 in)
Baggage capacity	2·58 m³ (91 cu ft)

WEIGHTS:

Weight empty (incl electronics)	3,161 kg (6,969 lb)
Max ramp weight	6,123 kg (13,500 lb)
Max T-O weight	6,033 kg (13,300 lb)
Max landing weight	5,761 kg (12,700 lb)
Max zero-fuel weight	4,309 kg (9,500 lb)
Optional max zero-fuel weight	4,989 kg (11,000 lb)

PERFORMANCE (at max T-O weight except where indicated):

Cruising speed at average cruising weight at 7,620 m (25,000 ft)	365 knots (675 km/h; 420 mph)
Stalling speed at max landing weight	83 knots (154 km/h; 96 mph) CAS
Max rate of climb at S/L	991 m (3,250 ft)/min
Rate of climb at S/L, one engine out	277 m (910 ft)/min
Max certificated altitude	13,105 m (43,000 ft)
Service ceiling, one engine out	7,010 m (23,000 ft)
Balanced field length (FAR 25)	968 m (3,175 ft)
Landing run at max landing weight	739 m (2,426 ft)
Range with 8 persons, 45 min reserves	1,710 nm (3,167 km; 1,968 miles)

CESSNA CITATION III

While retaining some general similarity to earlier members of the Citation family, the Citation III is a very different aeroplane. The original design underwent major refinement during 1978. In particular, a T-tail was introduced, and the basic Citation III will now be supplemented by an extended-range version with an added fuel tank in the rear fuselage.

First flight of the prototype (N650CC) was made on 30 May 1979. Deliveries are scheduled to begin in mid-1981.

TYPE: Twin-turbofan 10/15-seat long-range executive transport.

WINGS: Cantilever low-wing monoplane. NASA-developed supercritical section. Sweepback at quarter-chord 25°. Conventional two-spar structure of light alloy, utilising bonded and riveted construction. Anti-icing of wing leading-edges. Hydraulically-actuated trailing-edge flaps and spoilers.

FUSELAGE: Conventional semi-monocoque light alloy structure of circular cross-section. Fail-safe in pressurised area.

TAIL UNIT: Cantilever T-tail structure of light alloy, with swept horizontal and vertical surfaces. Anti-icing of tailplane leading-edges.

LANDING GEAR: Hydraulically-retractable tricycle type. Twin wheels on each main unit, single wheel on hydraulically-steerable nose unit. Oleo-pneumatic shock-absorbers. Hydraulic anti-skid braking system with pneumatic backup.

POWER PLANT: Two Garrett-AiResearch TFE 731-3-100 S turbofan engines, each rated at 16·24 kN (3,650 lb st) for take-off, mounted in pod on each side of rear fuselage. Hydraulically-operated thrust reversers optional. Two independent fuel systems, with integral tanks in each wing; max usable capacity 3,034 kg (6,690 lb). Additional fuel cell available optionally, behind aft fuselage bulkhead. Single-point pressure refuelling optional. Fuel heaters optional. Engine intake anti-icing system.

ACCOMMODATION: Crew of two on separate flight deck. Eight to thirteen passengers. Standard interior has four forward-facing and four aft-facing individual seats, with toilet at rear of cabin. Storage in fuselage nose for crew baggage. Main baggage space in tailcone. Airstair door forward of wing on port side. Overwing emergency escape hatch on starboard side. Cabin is pressurised, heated and air-conditioned. Extended-range option provides a fuel cell aft of the cabin's rear pressure bulkhead, reducing baggage space by 0·425 m³ (15 cu ft), and has single-point pressure refuelling as standard. Windscreen anti-icing.

SYSTEMS: Environmental control system, with separate control of flight deck and cabin conditions. Direct engine bleed pressurisation system, with nominal pressure differential of 0·66 bars (9·5 lb/sq in), provides 2,440 m (8,000 ft) cabin altitude to max certificated altitude. Dual parallel electrical buses. Hydraulic system of 207 bars (3,000 lb/sq in) with backup system to provide emergency power. Oxygen systems for crew and passengers.

AVIONICS: Standard avionics package provides full Category 2 capability, and includes a Sperry SPZ-650A automatic flight control system, digital central air data computer, vertical navigation (VNAV) system with dual waypoints, AA-215 radio altimeter, dual C-14 slaved compass system and VG-14A vertical gyro; dual nav/com and RMI, transponder, DME and weather radar. A wide range of optional avionics is available to customer's requirements.

DIMENSIONS, EXTERNAL:

Wing span	16·26 m (53 ft 4¼ in)
Wing aspect ratio	8·94
Length overall	16·90 m (55 ft 5½ in)
Height overall	5·27 m (17 ft 3½ in)
Tailplane span	5·60 m (18 ft 4½ in)
Wheel track	2·86 m (9 ft 4½ in)
Wheelbase	6·48 m (21 ft 3 in)

DIMENSIONS, INTERNAL:

Cabin: Length, front to rear bulkhead	7·01 m (23 ft 0 in)
Length, aft of cockpit divider	5·49 m (18 ft 0 in)
Max width	1·73 m (5 ft 8 in)
Max height	1·78 m (5 ft 10 in)
Baggage capacity (aft)	2·10 m³ (74 cu ft)
Crew baggage compartment (nose)	0·28 m³ (10 cu ft)

AREA:

Wings, gross	29·00 m² (312 sq ft)

WEIGHTS (estimated; A: basic aircraft; B: with extended range option):

Weight empty: A	4,230 kg (9,325 lb)
B	4,264 kg (9,400 lb)
Max fuel: A	3,035 kg (6,690 lb)
B	3,590 kg (7,915 lb)
Max T-O weight: A	7,711 kg (17,000 lb)
B	8,301 kg (18,300 lb)
Max ramp weight: A	7,802 kg (17,200 lb)
B	8,391 kg (18,500 lb)
Max zero-fuel weight: A, B	5,897 kg (13,000 lb)
Max landing weight: A, B	7,121 kg (15,700 lb)

PERFORMANCE (estimated, at max T-O weight of 7,711 kg; 17,000 lb, unless stated otherwise):

Max level speed at average cruise weight of 6,214 kg (13,700 lb):

at 10,060 m (33,000 ft) Mach 0·81 (471 knots; 872 km/h; 542 mph)

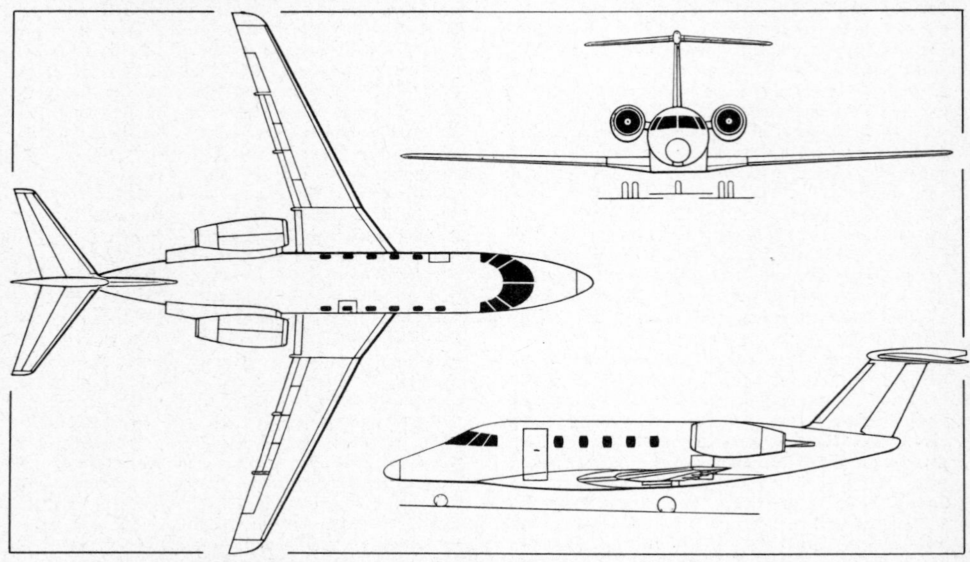

Cessna Citation III (two Garrett-AiResearch TFE-731-3-100S turbofan engines) *(Pilot Press)*

Prototype Cessna Citation III ten/fifteen-seat executive transport

Max cruising speed at average cruise weight of 6,214 kg (13,700 lb):
at 10,060 m (33,000 ft) 469 knots (869 km/h; 540 mph)
at 12,500 m (41,000 ft) Mach 0·8 (459 knots; 850 km/h; 528 mph)
at 13,715 m (45,000 ft) Mach 0·77 (442 knots; 818 km/h; 509 mph)
at 14,325 m (47,000 ft) 420 knots (779 km/h; 484 mph)
at 14,935 m (49,000 ft) 384 knots (711 km/h; 442 mph)
Stalling speed, flaps and gear down, at max landing weight 88 knots (164 km/h; 102 mph) CAS
Max rate of climb at S/L 1,615 m (5,300 ft)/min
Rate of climb at S/L, one engine out:
A 495 m (1,625 ft)/min
B 445 m (1,460 ft)/min
Time to 12,500 m (41,000 ft): A 18 min
B 20 min
Certificated ceiling 15,545 m (51,000 ft)
Ceiling, one engine out: A 9,525 m (31,250 ft)
B 8,990 m (29,500 ft)
FAA T-O field length at S/L: A 1,189 m (3,900 ft)
B 1,327 m (4,355 ft)
Landing distance at max landing weight 945 m (3,100 ft)
Range with two crew and four passengers, standard fuel, allowances for T-O, climb, descent and 45 min reserves 2,496 nm (4,626 km; 2,875 miles)
Range with two crew and ten passengers, standard fuel, allowances as above 1,902 km (3,524 km; 2,190 miles)
Range, two crew and four passengers, with rear-fuselage fuel tank, at T-O weight of 8,301 kg (18,300 lb), allowances as above 3,000 nm (5,555 km; 3,450 miles)
Range, two crew and ten passengers, with rear-fuselage fuel tank, at T-O weight of 8,301 kg (18,300 lb), allowances as above 2,400 nm (4,425 km; 2,750 miles)

COMPOSITE AIRCRAFT CORPORATION

c/o DIETRICK SALES AND SERVICE

ADDRESS: 523 Ridgeview Drive, Florence, Kentucky 41042

Telephone: (606) 371 7247

Mr Gerald P. Dietrick, the owner of Dietrick Sales and Service, has acquired the type certificate, the plant to manufacture non-woven unidirectional glassfibre fabric, moulds and engineering data, for construction of the Windecker Eagle 1, designed and developed from 1959 by Drs L. J. and F. M. Windecker. He has acquired also two of the five production Eagle 1s built by Windecker Industries Inc, and has an exclusive lease on a third aircraft. With these aircraft he is currently developing minor modifications, and plans to put the Eagle back into production. A company named Composite Aircraft Corporation has been registered for this purpose.

The five production Eagle 1s built by Windecker Industries had accumulated in excess of 8,000 flight hours by mid-January 1978: the last production aircraft (N4198G) had a total of 1,875 hours at that date. Details of the development of these aircraft can be found under the Windecker Industries entry in the 1974-75 *Jane's*.

In early 1979, aircraft N4198G was equipped with an autopilot, additional fuel tankage and navigation equipment, prior to being flown nonstop from Gander, Newfoundland, to Paris to participate in the 1979 Paris Air Show. Time taken for the 3,622 nm (6,708 km; 4,168 mile) flight, originating in Cincinnati, was 21 h 58 min.

Dietrick/Windecker Eagle four-seat cabin monoplane of GRP construction, at 1979 Paris Air Show *(Brian M. Service)*

DIETRICK/WINDECKER EAGLE

TYPE: Four-seat cabin monoplane.

WINGS: Cantilever low-wing monoplane. NACA 64_2415 wing section. Dihedral 4° 30′. Incidence 2° 30′. No sweepback. Fail-safe structure of GRP. Frise-type ailerons of GRP with pilot-controlled bungee trimming. Plain trailing-edge flaps constructed of GRP.

FUSELAGE: Fail-safe monocoque structure of GRP.

TAIL UNIT: Conventional cantilever structure of GRP. Fixed-incidence tailplane. Trim tabs on starboard elevator and rudder.

LANDING GEAR: Retractable tricycle type with single wheel on each unit. Electro-hydraulic retraction, main wheels inward, nosewheel rearward. Main wheels faired by landing gear doors when retracted. Nosewheel door functions as a cowl flap when the gear is retracted. Windecker oleo-pneumatic shock-absorbers. Cleveland 6·00-6 main wheels, 5·00-5 nosewheel; all tyre pressures 3·09 bars (45 lb/sq in). Cleveland hydraulic disc brakes. Parking brake.

POWER PLANT: One 212·5 kW (285 hp) Continental IO-520-C flat-six engine, driving a McCauley two-blade constant-speed propeller. Fuel capacity 318 litres (84 US gallons), in two 159 litre (42 US gallon) integral wing tanks. Refuelling point outboard on upper surface of each wing. Oil capacity 11·4 litres (3 US gallons).

ACCOMMODATION: Four persons in pairs in enclosed cabin. Forward-hinged door on each side of cabin. Compartment aft of rear seats for 54 kg (120 lb) baggage with external access door on port side; hatshelf on bulkhead at rear of cabin. Cabin ventilated and heated by ram air over exhaust.

SYSTEMS: Hydraulic system, pressure 103 bars (1,500 lb/sq in), for landing gear. Vacuum system for instruments. 12V 70A alternator. 12V 35Ah battery.

AVIONICS AND EQUIPMENT: Standard avionics comprise one Narco MK-16 VHF, one Narco VOA-40 VOR/LOC converter-indicator and an antennae package which includes VOR, communications, ADF sense, transponder, DME, glideslope and marker beacon antennae, headset, microphone and all wiring harnesses. Standard equipment includes full blind-flying instrumentation, 8-day clock, outside air temperature gauge, vacuum system and gauge, two anti-collision beacons, navigation lights, landing and taxi light, dome light, map light, instrument panel floodlights, radio lights, external power socket, fully-reclining track-mounted seats with seat belt, headrest, fresh-air outlet and map or magazine storage pocket for each seat, floor console between front seats for map and pencil storage, openable storm window on pilot's side, baggage net and attachments, retractable steps, hand holds, ultra-violet absorbent windscreen, windscreen defrosting system, tinted cabin windows, soundproofing, towbar, control jack, jack pads, shoulder harness for front seats and alternate static source. Four interior and exterior trims are available as standard, the latter consisting of polyurethane paint finish. Optional avionics include a wide range of Narco units, available singly or as a complete package, and one- and two-axis autopilots. Optional equipment includes cargo tiedown kit, engine winterisation kit, heated pitot, heated stall warning, instrument post lights, control wheel mounted chronograph, electric elevator trim, glider tow provisions, four-outlet oxygen system, engine primer, fire extinguisher, reading lights for rear seats and white strobe lights.

DIMENSIONS, EXTERNAL:
Wing span 9·75 m (32 ft 0 in)
Wing chord, constant 1·68 m (5 ft 6 in)
Wing aspect ratio 5·82
Length overall 8·69 m (28 ft 6 in)
Height overall 2·90 m (9 ft 6 in)
Tailplane span 3·42 m (11 ft 3 in)
Wheel track 2·13 m (7 ft 0 in)
Wheelbase 1·98 m (6 ft 6 in)
Propeller diameter 2·13 m (7 ft 0 in)
Propeller ground clearance 0·28 m (11 in)
Cabin doors: Height 0·89 m (2 ft 11 in)
Width 0·97 m (3 ft 2 in)
Height to sill 0·40 m (1 ft 4 in)
Baggage door (port side):
Height 0·60 m (1 ft 11½ in)
Width 0·39 m (1 ft 3½ in)

DIMENSIONS, INTERNAL:
Cabin: Length 3·30 m (10 ft 10 in)
Max width 1·28 m (4 ft 2⅜ in)
Max height 1·07 m (3 ft 6 in)

AREAS:
Wings, gross 15·51 m² (167 sq ft)
Ailerons (total) 1·42 m² (15·28 sq ft)
Trailing-edge flaps (total) 1·50 m² (16·1 sq ft)
Fin 0·93 m² (9·97 sq ft)
Rudder 0·59 m² (6·31 sq ft)
Tailplane 1·70 m² (18·3 sq ft)
Elevators, incl tab 1·48 m² (15·97 sq ft)

WEIGHTS AND LOADINGS:
Weight empty 975 kg (2,150 lb)
Max T-O and landing weight 1,542 kg (3,400 lb)
Max wing loading 94·7 kg/m² (19·3 lb/sq ft)
Max power loading 7·26 kg/kW (11·9 lb/hp)

PERFORMANCE (at max T-O weight):
Max level speed at S/L more than 182 knots (338 km/h; 210 mph)
Cruising speed, 75% power at 2,135 m (7,000 ft) 177 knots (328 km/h; 204 mph)

Cruising speed, 65% power at 3,660 m (12,000 ft) 175 knots (325 km/h; 202 mph)
Stalling speed, flaps and landing gear up, power off 61·5 knots (114 km/h; 71 mph)
Stalling speed, flaps and landing gear down, power off 57·5 knots (106 km/h; 66 mph)
Max rate of climb at S/L 372 m (1,220 ft)/min
Service ceiling 5,485 m (18,000 ft)
T-O run 261 m (855 ft)
T-O to 15 m (50 ft) 515 m (1,690 ft)
Range with max fuel at 3,050 m (10,000 ft), 45 min reserves 1,068 nm (1,979 km; 1,230 miles)

CONTINENTAL COPTERS

CONTINENTAL COPTERS INC

ADDRESS: PO Box 18284, Cardinal Road, Fort Worth, Texas 76118
Telephone: (817) 281 2330
Telex: 758-426
PRESIDENT: John L. Scott

Continental Copters has developed and is producing a series of specialised single-seat agricultural conversions of various versions of the Bell Model 47 helicopter, under the name El Tomcat. Design work on the original conversion began in 1959 and the prototype El Tomcat Mk II flew in April of that year, receiving an FAA Supplemental Type Certificate shortly afterwards. Improved Mk III, IIIA, IIIB and IIIC versions followed, and current conversions embrace the Mk V and VI versions.

The Mk V of 1968 was succeeded subsequently by the Mk V-A, based on the Model 47G-2, with a 194 kW (260 hp) Lycoming VO-435-A1F engine and a 24V electrical system; and the Mk V-B, with a 198 kW (265 hp) Lycoming VO-435-B1A and 24V electrical system. Subsequently, production of both the Mk IIIC and MK V-B was terminated in favour of the Mk V-A.

Next came the El Tomcat Mk VI, based on the Bell Model 47G-3B with turbocharged engine. Variants are the Mks VI-A and VI-B.

During 1977, five helicopters were completed, and by the beginning of 1979 the company had delivered approximately 80 Tomcats. These are in service with customers in the USA, Panama, Portugal, Puerto Rico, Switzerland and Turkey.

In addition, Continental Copters has for some years been producing passenger helicopters conforming to the Bell 47G and G-2 types. These are assembled from spare and/or surplus parts and are listed in the FAA Helicopter Specification H-1. Other helicopters, not included in this list, have been delivered to Latin America.

Continental Copters El Tomcat Mk V-A with new 3-piece centre frame

CONTINENTAL COPTERS JC-1 JET-CAT

In early 1975 the company began work on modifications to develop a special-purpose agricultural aircraft from the airframe of the Bell JetRanger. However, this was deferred in 1977 so that the company could concentrate on conversion of a Bell Model 204 (military UH-1) into a new type of single-seat agricultural aircraft. Work on the JetRanger project was resumed in late 1977, and in early 1978 the prototype, designated provisionally JC-1 JetCat, began load testing. Intended both for agricultural and utility operations, provision is made for the use of a cargo hook. The single-place cabin is similar in configuration to that of El Tomcat.

CONTINENTAL COPTERS EL TOMCAT Mk V-A

Each version of the El Tomcat is basically a Bell Model 47G-2 helicopter which has been converted into a specialised single-seat agricultural aircraft. Payload is increased by deletion of unnecessary structure and equipment. In particular, the original cabin is replaced by a simple functional cab for the pilot. This was improved during 1974 by the development of a strengthened 'cage' for the pilot, consisting of a rigid forward frame to the cockpit, constructed from 254 mm (1 in) square steel tube. Additionally, a wire deflector installation has been developed for this aircraft, consisting of a steel tube above and below the nose, mounted on the aircraft centreline. This would deflect any wires or cables to sharpened jaws mounted on the steel tubes.

Power plant consists of a 194 kW (260 hp) Lycoming VO-435-A1F engine. Standard Bell Model 47D-1 fuel system with a capacity of 109 litres (29 US gallons). Oil capacity 11 litres (3 US gallons). A 24V electrical system is standard.

In the current El Tomcat Mk V-A, which was awarded a full Type Certificate by the FAA in May 1973, the windscreen has been further reduced in area and moved closer to the pilot compared with earlier versions: in addition, the new strengthened forward frame serves as the windscreen mounting. The glassfibre nose has been modified to ensure easy accessibility to all instruments, the battery and other equipment. It provides a flush mounting for two 600W landing lights which are controllable in elevation by the pilot during flight, landing-light switches being mounted on the collective stick, immediately below the throttle. The cabin roof is of glassfibre, lower than on earlier versions of El Tomcat, and incorporates wraparound side windows for rear-quarter view. An FAA-approved folding jump-seat has been developed to permit carriage of a flagman to distant work sites when large fields are being sprayed. Standard equipment includes pilot's shoulder harness.

Improvements introduced in 1978 include a three-piece centre frame to simplify air transit, repair and engine replacement; wider nose to provide more foot space for pilot; modified pilot's seat; raised and separated shoulder straps; and use of high compression pistons in the Lycoming VO-435 engine.

El Tomcat has a revised control system. The collective control has been altered to conform to standard collective geometry, but Continental retains ball bearings in the collective jack shaft, instead of brass bushings, to provide smoother operation. A Harley Davidson throttle control is fitted. The flying controls are hydraulically-boosted.

The chemical hoppers take the form of two streamlined blister tanks which fit flush against the sides of the fuselage immediately aft of the cabin. A fan-driven pump is mounted adjacent to each tank, aft of the spraybar supports. A filtered ventilation system for the cockpit minimises toxic spray ingress during spraying operations. Types of spraygear fitted include the Bell Agmaster, Simplex Lo-Profile and special designs developed by customers.

Apart from the changes noted, the basic structural description of the standard Bell Model 47 (which can be found under the Agusta entry in the Italian section of the 1976-77 *Jane's*) applies also to El Tomcat.

DIMENSIONS: As for standard Bell Model 47G-2

WEIGHTS:
Weight empty, less specialised equipment 623 kg (1,375 lb)
Max T-O weight 1,111 kg (2,450 lb)

PERFORMANCE:
As for standard Bell Model 47G-2 except:
Range (with fuel reserve for 30 min) 86 nm (160 km; 100 miles)

CONTINENTAL COPTERS EL TOMCAT Mk VI-B

The original El Tomcat Mk VI was a conversion of the Bell Model 47G-3B, with a turbocharged Lycoming TVO-435 engine, developing 201 kW (270 hp), and Bell 47-110-250-23 main rotor blades. The increased length of these blades made it necessary to extend the basic Mk V-A centre frame both fore and aft. The extension aft (as on later production Bell 47s) was needed to provide adequate clearance between main and tail rotor blades, and extension forward to compensate for the resulting rearward movement of the CG.

As in the Mk V-A, the battery was accommodated in the nose of the cab. In addition, the engine oil tank was placed in the nose; an airscoop on top of and an outlet on the bottom of the nose were installed to allow ram air to carry away the heat radiated by the tank. The standard El Tomcat in-flight-adjustable landing lights were installed.

Only this prototype of the El Tomcat Mk VI was completed; it was supplied to an operator in the Rocky Mountain area for spraying operations at high altitude. FAA certification was not obtained prior to delivery.

The prototype was claimed to be very stable, and flight tests demonstrated its ability to hover directly into the wind with the pilot's hands and feet off the controls.

A prototype of the Mk VI-B, which has a component similarity to the Bell Model 47G-5, was subsequently completed and flown, and was awarded an FAA Supplemental Type Certificate in the Standard category; this is now the production version. The FAA required installation of a compass and altimeter to meet certification standards, and Continental Copters anticipated that instrument panel and windscreen changes would be required on subsequent aircraft to facilitate installation of these instruments. This has been catered for when carrying out the pilot's 'cage' modification as described for the Mk V-A. A new instrument panel, to bring engine speed and airspeed indicators closer to the pilot's line of vision and reduce reflections, was introduced for 1978: this has resulted in a changed fuselage nose with improved streamlining. Mk VI El Tomcats also have the three-piece centre frame of the Mk V-A.

The hydraulic reservoir/regulator unit for the Simplex Lo-Profile sprayer system fitted to the Mk VI-B has been mounted forward on the port side of the centre frame instead of in the usual rear position. This enables the pilot to see the hydraulic pressure gauge easily and also offsets the normal aft CG condition of the El Tomcat.

Empty weight of the El Tomcat Mk VI-B is 674 kg (1,487 lb) and max T-O weight 1,293 kg (2,850 lb). Maximum permissible speed has been limited to 61 knots (113 km/h; 70 mph) to minimise the airspeed calibration test. In other respects the flight envelope of the Mk VI-B is identical to that of the Bell 47G-5. Three examples of the Mk VI-B have been exported to Portugal.

Conversion kits for the Mk VI-B installation are available, and Continental Copters states that by using the data gained from this programme Supplemental Type Certification of conversions of Bell Model 47G-2A, -2B and -4 helicopters can be carried out with a minimum of FAA testing.

A Mk VI-C prototype with VO-435-A1F engine, which has high-compression pistons, and with the oil tank relocated in the nose, between instruments and battery, has received FAA approval.

Modified nose of current El Tomcat Mk VI-B

DOMINION

DOMINION AIRCRAFT CORPORATION LTD

ADDRESS: 1005 West Perimeter Road, Renton, Washington 98055
Telephone: (206) 228 3536
PRESIDENT: Lawrence Matanski

DOMINION SKYTRADER 800

The Skytrader 800 is a twin-engined STOL transport and general-purpose aircraft. Much of the design was carried out by former members of The Boeing Company's staff at Renton, Washington. The first flight of the Skytrader 800 was made in the Spring of 1975.

A full description of this aircraft can be found in the 1978-79 *Jane's*. There has been no recent news of its continued development, or of production plans.

EAGLE

EAGLE AIRCRAFT COMPANY

ADDRESS: PO Box 4127, Boise, Idaho 83704
Telephone: (208) 376 6700

EAGLE AIRCRAFT EAGLE

Eagle Aircraft Company has designed and built the prototype of a new agricultural aircraft, with large-span narrow-chord wings based on advanced glider technology, to which it has given the name Eagle. In addition to the biplane wings, other innovations include spraybooms built internally into the trailing-edge of the lower wings, spoilers for roll control mounted outboard on each lower wing, and a charcoal filtered cockpit ventilation system, as well as a choice of five power plants.

The company announced on 7 June 1979 the signature of an agreement with Bellanca Aircraft Corporation (which see), to manufacture the Eagle on its behalf. Initial deliveries of production aircraft were scheduled for 1 October 1979.

TYPE: Single-seat agricultural aircraft.

WINGS: Wire-braced single-bay biplane, with N-type interplane and centre-section struts. Narrow-chord wings of advanced design, with spraybooms built into the trailing-edges of the lower wings. Spoilers in upper surface of outboard section of each lower wing. Conventional ailerons with booster tabs on upper wings. Dacron fabric covering, with butyrate dope and polyurethane finish.

FUSELAGE: Conventional welded steel tube structure; rear part covered by Dacron fabric, and the remainder by quickly-removable side panels.

TAIL UNIT: Conventional wire-braced structure, with Dacron fabric covering, butyrate dope and polyurethane finish. Booster tab in elevator. Wire deflector cable between tip of fin and centre-section of upper wing.

LANDING GEAR: Non-retractable tailwheel type. Two side Vs and half-axles. Rubber-in-compression shock-absorbers. Cleveland main wheels and high-flotation tyres size 7·50-10. Hydraulically-operated disc brakes. Parking brake. Wire cutter on leading-edge of each main gear V.

POWER PLANT: Alternative power plants include one 179 kW (240 hp) Gulf Coast conversion of the Continental W670 radial engine, driving a Hartzell two-blade adjustable-pitch propeller; 205 kW (275 hp) Page-Jacobs R-755-B1, or 224 kW (300 hp) Page-Jacobs R-755 fuel-injection, or 261 kW (350 hp) Page-Jacobs R-755S radial engine, driving a Hartzell two-blade adjustable-pitch propeller (Hartzell constant-speed or Pacific Prop propeller type 2B20 optional); or a 298 kW (400 hp) Lycoming flat-eight engine, driving a Hartzell three-blade constant-speed propeller. Gravity-feed fuel tank in centre-section of upper wing, capacity 157·5 litres (41·6 US gallons). Wingtip fuel tanks for upper wing optional, with combined capacity of 113·5 litres (30 US gallons). Maximum fuel capacity 271 litres (71·6 US gallons). Refuelling point on top surface of upper wing.

ACCOMMODATION: Pilot only, beneath one-piece quick-release transparent canopy which is sealed against ingress of toxic chemicals. Canopy can be hinged to port or starboard by single lever, or can be removed entirely for open-cockpit flight. Pilot's seat has shoulder harness with inertia reel. Cockpit ventilated by ram air passed through charcoal filters. Chemical hopper, capacity 946 litres (250 US gallons) in front fuselage, with lightweight bottom loading valve. Baggage compartment for pilot, with external access door.

SYSTEMS: Electrical system powered by 24V 50A alternator. Hydraulic system for brakes only.

EQUIPMENT: Standard equipment includes recording tachometer, boom pressure gauge, stall warning light and horn, windscreen cleaning access windows, cockpit entry step, handholds, stainless steel rudder cables, non-glare paint on forward fuselage, corrosion-proof urethane paint on exterior metal surfaces and interior of removable panels, and tiedown rings. Optional equipment includes manifold and fuel pressure gauges, and electrically operated auxiliary fuel pump for R-755S engine, heavy-duty generator, navigation lights, instrument lights with dimming control, rotating beacons, and hopper light.

Eagle Aircraft Eagle agricultural aircraft as built by Bellanca Aircraft Corporation

DIMENSIONS, EXTERNAL (A: 240 hp; B: 275 hp; C: 300 hp; D: 350 hp; and E: 400 hp engine):

Wing span, all versions	16·76 m (55 ft 0 in)
Length overall: A, C, D	7·92 m (26 ft 0 in)
B	7·95 m (26 ft 1 in)
E	8·23 m (27 ft 0 in)
Height overall, all versions	3·23 m (10 ft 7 in)

AREA:

Wings, gross	35·86 m² (386 sq ft)

WEIGHTS AND LOADINGS:

Weight empty: A, B, C	1,156 kg (2,549 lb)
D	1,204 kg (2,655 lb)
E	1,197 kg (2,639 lb)
Max T-O weight, all versions	2,364 kg (5,211 lb)
Max wing loading, Restricted category	65·9 kg/m² (13·5 lb/sq ft)
Max power loading, Restricted category:	
A	13·21 kg/kW (21·7 lb/hp)
B	11·53 kg/kW (18·9 lb/hp)
C	10·55 kg/kW (17·4 lb/hp)
D	9·06 kg/kW (14·9 lb/hp)
E	7·93 kg/kW (13·0 lb/hp)

PERFORMANCE (at max T-O weight, Restricted category):

Max working speed:	
A	83 knots (153 km/h; 95 mph)
B	85 knots (158 km/h; 98 mph)
C	88 knots (163 km/h; 101 mph)
D	93 knots (172 km/h; 107 mph)
E	104 knots (193 km/h; 120 mph)
Min working speed, all versions	56·5 knots (105 km/h; 65 mph)
Stalling speed, power off, all versions	48 knots (88·5 km/h; 55 mph)
Stalling speed, power on, all versions	44 knots (82 km/h; 51 mph)

ECTOR

ECTOR AIRCRAFT COMPANY

ADDRESS: 414 East Hillmont Road, Odessa, Texas 79762
Telephone: (915) 362 1841
PRESIDENT: Alvin H. Parker

ECTOR L-19 MOUNTAINEER and SUPER MOUNTAINEER

The Ector Aircraft Company has in production a civil version of the Cessna L-19 Bird Dog (last described in the 1964-65 *Jane's*), to which it has given the name Mountaineer. This is available in two models:

Mountaineer. Standard model, with 159 kW (213 hp) Continental O-470-11 engine and fixed-pitch propeller. Continental O-470-11-13 (cruising speed increased to 108 knots; 201 km/h; 125 mph at 55% power) or O-470-11-13-15 engine and constant-speed propeller (104 knots; 193 km/h; 120 mph at 57% power) optional.

Super Mountaineer. More powerful version with a 179 kW (240 hp) Lycoming O-540-A4B5 engine, driving a Hartzell Type HC-C2YK-1B two-blade metal constant-speed propeller, and with additional equipment as standard. In 1978 Ector obtained a Supplementary Type Certificate for the Super Mountaineer at a maximum T-O weight of 1,270 kg (2,800 lb), and delivered an aircraft for operation at this weight.

Generally similar to the original Cessna L-19, Ector's Mountaineers are rebuilt completely from new off-the-shelf or serviceable components. The entire airframe is corrosion-proofed with zinc chromate before assembly; mounting brackets for floats are built into the basic airframe; and all four side windows can be opened in flight. The rear seat is removable to permit the carriage of cargo.

More than 30 Mountaineers have been produced for service with various organisations as glider tugs and for patrol and general-purpose duties. Others are flown as sporting aircraft.

TYPE: Two-seat lightweight cabin monoplane.

Ector Super Mountaineer, a civil version of the Cessna L-19 Bird Dog

WINGS: Braced high-wing monoplane. Single streamline-section bracing strut each side. Wing section NACA 2412. Dihedral 2° 8′. Incidence 1° 30′ at root, −1° 30′ at tip. All-metal single-spar structure, with metal skin. Frise-type all-metal ailerons. Fowler all-metal trailing-edge flaps. No tabs.

FUSELAGE: Conventional all-metal semi-monocoque structure.

TAIL UNIT: Cantilever all-metal structure. Trim tab in elevator. Small auxiliary fins are attached to tailplane tips of floatplane version.

LANDING GEAR: Non-retractable tailwheel type. Cantilever spring steel main legs. Goodyear main wheels with tyres size 6·00-6. Scott steerable tailwheel. Single-disc hydraulic brakes. Floats, skis or tandem landing gear for rough terrain optional.

POWER PLANT: One Continental or Lycoming flat-six engine as detailed in model listings, driving a two-blade fixed-pitch or constant-speed propeller. One fuel tank in each wing root, total capacity 151·4 litres (40 US gallons). Optionally, fuel cells in each wing with a total capacity of 246 litres (65 US gallons). Refuelling points on wing upper surface. Oil capacity 9·4 litres (2·5 US gallons).

ACCOMMODATION: Two seats in tandem in enclosed cabin with 360° field of vision. Door on starboard side. All four cabin side windows can be opened fully. Six skylights in roof. Space for baggage behind rear seats. With rear seat removed, 0·85 m³ (30 cu ft) of space is available for freight. Cabin heated and ventilated.

SYSTEMS: Hydraulic system for brakes only. Electrical system powered by 24V 50A engine-driven generator.

Super Mountaineer has a 12V electrical system.

Avionics and Equipment: Radio equipment available to customer's requirements. Navigation and landing lights, and heated pitot, standard. External power socket optional. Stall warning indicator, Hobbs hour meter and Whelen three-light strobe system standard on Super Mountaineer. Wing racks optional. Underfuselage cargo rack being certificated.

Dimensions, external:

Wing span	10·97 m (36 ft 0 in)
Wing chord at root	1·63 m (5 ft 4 in)
Wing chord at tip	1·09 m (3 ft 7 in)
Wing aspect ratio	7·35
Length overall	7·86 m (25 ft 9½ in)
Height overall	2·29 m (7 ft 6 in)
Tailplane span	3·21 m (10 ft 6½ in)
Propeller diameter	2·29 m (7 ft 6 in)
Propeller ground clearance	0·23 m (9 in)
Door: Height	0·64 m (2 ft 1 in)
Width	0·81 m (2 ft 8 in)
Height to sill	1·12 m (3 ft 8 in)

Weights (A: Mountaineer with O-470-11 engine and fixed-pitch propeller; B: Super Mountaineer):

Weight empty, equipped: A	658 kg (1,450 lb)
B	673 kg (1,483 lb)
Max T-O weight: A	1,043 kg (2,300 lb)
B	1,270 kg (2,800 lb)

Performance (at max T-O weight):

Max level speed at S/L:

A 87 knots (161 km/h; 100 mph) TAS

B 112 knots (208 km/h; 129 mph) IAS

Max cruising speed: B at 2,135 m (7,000 ft)

139 knots (257 km/h; 160 mph) TAS

Econ cruising speed: B at 2,895 m (9,500 ft)

109 knots (201 km/h; 125 mph) IAS

Stalling speed, flaps down:

B 45·5 knots (84 km/h; 52 mph)

Max rate of climb at S/L: A	366 m (1,200 ft)/min
B	549 m (1,800 ft)/min
Service ceiling: A	6,980 m (22,900 ft)
T-O run: A	122 m (400 ft)
Landing run: A	98 m (320 ft)

Range with max fuel, no reserves:

A 651 nm (1,207 km; 750 miles)

EMAIR

EMAIR (a division of Emroth Co)

Address: Hangar 38, Industrial Airpark, Harlingen, Texas 78550

Telephone: (512) 425 6363

President: George A. Roth

The development history of the original Emair MA-1, of which 25 were built before production ended in January 1976, can be found in earlier editions of *Jane's*. Flight testing of the more powerful MA-1B began in August 1975, and this version received FAA Type Approval in May 1976. By early 1979, approximately 30 MA-1Bs had been delivered.

EMAIR MA-1B DIABLO 1200

The MA-1B was designed specifically for agricultural use. For ease of maintenance and repair the fuselage comprises four bolt-together sections, covered by removable glassfibre side panels. Greater than average gap and stagger of the biplane wings improves pilot view and ensures easy access to the hopper; the wide-track main landing gear ensures adequate stability for operations from rough fields. The cockpit is fully enclosed, and sealed against the entry of dust and sprays.

The hopper, which forms an integral part of the front fuselage, has two outlets on which are mounted liquid-tight gates or doors. For granular dispersal the gates are controlled by a cockpit lever, the distribution of the granules being effected by a low-drag wing-type spreader mounted in the slipstream beneath the aircraft. For the distribution of liquids the gates remain closed, serving only as an emergency jettison device. Dispersal is accomplished by an easily-removable wind-driven spraypump, supplying spraybooms mounted in a low-drag area at the trailing-edge of each lower wing. A cockpit-controlled stop valve is located between the hopper and spraypump.

The MA-1B has an 895 kW (1,200 hp) Wright R-1820 engine, derated to 671 kW (900 hp). This is claimed to make it the most powerful agricultural aircraft in current production in the west, and permits the carriage of very heavy payloads, especially under high-altitude conditions and from short or muddy fields. The geared engine drives a slow-turning, large-diameter propeller with broad blades, resulting in good propulsive efficiency and low noise levels.

Type: Single-seat agricultural biplane.

Wings: Strut-braced biplane with forward-staggered wings of unequal span. NACA 4412 (modified) wing section. Dihedral 1° 30′ on upper wing, 3° on lower wings. Incidence 4° 30′ on upper wing, 4° on lower wings. No sweepback. Stagger 31°. Upper wing carried on streamline steel tube struts. Conventional two-spar structure. Centre-section of upper wing is of aluminium construction. Outer panels of top wing, and both lower wing panels, have spruce laminated spars and ribs, with duralumin channel-section compression struts and steel tie-rod internal bracing, and fabric covering. Ailerons, of aluminium construction with fabric covering, on both upper and lower wings, linked by struts. No trim tabs or slats. Butt fittings and inboard compression members of lower wings are stainless steel. Glassfibre wingtips.

Fuselage: Rectangular welded chrome-molybdenum steel tube framework in four separate bolt-together sections, with glassfibre side panels.

Emair MA-1B Diablo 1200 heavy-duty agricultural aircraft

Tail Unit: Conventional single fin and rudder, of welded chrome-molybdenum steel tube with fabric covering. Wire-braced fixed-incidence tailplane and fin. Trim tab in each elevator. Trim/balance tab in rudder.

Landing Gear: Non-retractable tailwheel type. Oleo-pneumatic shock-absorbers on main and nosewheel units. Main legs enclosed in streamlined glassfibre fairings. Main-wheel tyres size 29 × 11·00-10. Steerable tailwheel, with tyre size 12·5 × 4·5, becomes free-swivelling when rudder is at near full deflection. Cleveland single-disc hydraulic main-wheel brakes. Parking brakes.

Power Plant: One 895 kW (1,200 hp) Wright R-1820 radial engine, derated to 671 kW (900 hp) and driving a Hamilton Standard three-blade metal constant-speed Hydromatic propeller. Fuel tank in upper wing centre-section, capacity 408 litres (108 US gallons). Refuelling point above upper wing. Max oil capacity 75·7 litres (20 US gallons).

Accommodation: Pilot only, on adjustable seat. Fully enclosed, sealed and ventilated cockpit in centre of fuselage, with reinforced overturn structure aft of cockpit. Sliding side-screens of cockpit canopy retract into cockpit wall; overhead section of canopy hinges to either port or starboard.

Systems: Hydraulic system for brakes only. Electrical system supplied by 24V engine-driven alternator and 24V 25Ah battery.

Operational Equipment: Between the cockpit and the engine is mounted a glassfibre hopper for dust or liquid, with a capacity of 1·80 m³ (63·5 cu ft) or 1,798 litres (475 US gallons). It is built around the fuselage tubing, which in this area is of stainless steel to resist chemical corrosion. A window in the rear wall of the hopper allows in-flight inspection of the contents, and sight gauges are provided on each side of the hopper.

Dimensions, external:

Wing span (upper)	12·70 m (41 ft 8 in)
Wing span (lower)	10·67 m (35 ft 0 in)
Wing chord (both, constant)	1·60 m (5 ft 3 in)
Wing aspect ratio (upper)	7·9
Wing aspect ratio (lower)	6·7
Wing stagger	1·19 m (3 ft 11 in)
Wing gap	1·98 m (6 ft 6 in)
Length overall (tail up)	9·14 m (30 ft 0 in)
Height overall (tail down)	3·58 m (11 ft 9 in)
Propeller diameter	3·02 m (9 ft 11 in)
Propeller ground clearance (tail up)	0·25 m (10 in)
Tailplane span	3·81 m (12 ft 6 in)
Wheel track	2·59 m (8 ft 6 in)
Wheelbase	6·71 m (22 ft 0 in)
Hopper opening, above fuselage:	
Length	0·61 m (2 ft 0 in)
Width	0·46 m (1 ft 6 in)

Areas:

Wings, gross	37·16 m² (400 sq ft)
Ailerons (total)	5·13 m² (55·2 sq ft)
Fin	0·29 m² (3·14 sq ft)
Rudder	1·10 m² (11·83 sq ft)
Tailplane	1·97 m² (21·16 sq ft)
Elevators, incl tabs	1·31 m² (14·14 sq ft)

Weights and Loadings:

Weight empty	1,928 kg (4,250 lb)
Hopper load	1,360 kg (3,000 lb)
Certificated T-O and landing weight	2,834 kg (6,250 lb)
Max T-O weight (CAM.8)	3,810 kg (8,400 lb)
Max wing loading	102·53 kg/m² (21·0 lb/sq ft)
Max power loading	5·68 kg/kW (9·33 lb/hp)

Performance (at certificated T-O weight):

Never-exceed speed

128 knots (238 km/h; 148 mph) CAS

Max cruising and manoeuvring speed

102 knots (188 km/h; 117 mph) CAS

Stalling speed, power off

54 knots (100 km/h; 62 mph)

Stalling speed, power on

46 knots (85·5 km/h; 53 mph)

Max rate of climb at S/L	518 m (1,700 ft)/min
Min ground turning radius	9·14 m (30 ft)

ENSTROM

THE ENSTROM HELICOPTER CORPORATION

Head Office and Works: PO Box 277, Twin County Airport, Menominee, Michigan 49858

Telephone: (906) 863 9971

Telex: 26-3451

President: F. Lee Bailey

Senior Vice-President: Paul L. Shultz

Executive Vice-President: J. F. Hansen

Vice-Presidents:

D. E. Brandt (Engineering)

Robert Kroll (Quality Control)

Curt Larsen (Finance)

In its original form, as the R. J. Enstrom Corporation, this company began in 1959 to develop an experimental light helicopter built by Rudolph J. Enstrom, which flew for the first time on 12 November 1960. There followed a design and development programme on a new helicopter, designated F-28, and this flew for the first time in May 1962. A limited number of F-28s were built, and were followed by the improved Model F-28A in 1968.

The company was acquired by the Purex Corporation in October 1968 and was operated for a time as part of the Pacific Airmotive Aerospace group. Under this ownership, a turbocharged F-28B version was developed, as well as a Model T-28 turbine-powered version.

The activities of this group ended in February 1970; but in January 1971 the present company resumed manufacture of the Model F-28A. A total of 620 Enstrom helicopters had been built by 1 February 1979.

ENSTROM MODELS F-28 and 280

Production of the basic Model F-28A and the Model 280 Shark ended during 1978; details of these can be found in the 1978-79 *Jane's*. Turbocharged versions of both models remain in production, under the designations F-28C and 280C respectively. These received FAA certification on 8 December 1975.

Models available in 1979 were as follows:

F-28C. Basic version, with Lycoming HIO-360 engine and turbocharger.

F-28C-2. As F-28C, but with one-piece windscreen and centre instrument console.

Model 280C. Improved version of F-28C, with changed aerodynamic contours; tail stabilising surfaces which include a small dorsal fin, larger ventral fin, and small fixed horizontal surfaces; and increased fuel capacity.

In addition, the following versions are under development:

F-28F Falcon. Utility version of F-28C with 10·36 m (34 ft) diameter main rotor, wide one-piece windscreen and pedestal type instrument panel for improved view.

New detail design to improve accessibility and simplify maintenance. Powered by a 167·7 kW (225 hp) Lycoming flat-four engine. Type approval anticipated during 1979.

Model 280L Hawk. Four-seat version of Model 280C, first flown on 27 December 1978. Described separately.

Model 480 Eagle. Version of the 280L Hawk powered by an Allison 250-C20B turboshaft engine and with accommodation for five persons.

An Enstrom wet or dry dispersal agricultural kit is available for fitment to the F-28C/280C. It comprises two side-mounted hoppers with large quick-fill openings, and spraybooms with a normal span of 9·04 m (29 ft 8 in), extendable to 11·07 m (36 ft 4 in). A manually operated clutch provides positive control of the centrifugal pump, which has a liquid capacity of 227 litres (60 US gallons)/min. Dry discharge rate is variable from 0 to 272 kg (600 lb)/min. Weight of the entire quickly-removable dispersal system is 48 kg (105 lb). Hopper capacity is 340 litres (90 US gallons) of liquid or 0·5 m^3 (17·4 cu ft) of dry chemicals.

The following description applies to the current production versions:

TYPE: Three-seat light helicopter.

ROTOR SYSTEM: Fully-articulated metal three-blade main rotor. Blades are of bonded light alloy construction, each attached to rotor hub by retention pin and drag link. Blade section NACA 0013·5. Two-blade teetering tail rotor, with blades of bonded light alloy construction. Tail rotor on port side. Blades do not fold. No rotor brake.

ROTOR DRIVE: Poly V-belt drive system. Right-angle drive reduction gearbox. Main rotor/engine rpm ratio 1 : 7·154; tail rotor/engine rpm ratio 1 : 1·156.

FUSELAGE: Glassfibre and light alloy cab structure, with welded steel tube centre-section. Semi-monocoque aluminium tailcone structure.

LANDING GEAR: Skids carried on Enstrom oleo-pneumatic shock-absorbers. Air Cruiser inflatable floats available optionally.

POWER PLANT: One 153 kW (205 hp) Lycoming HIO-360-E1AD flat-four engine with Rajay 301 E-10-2 turbocharger. Two fuel tanks, each of 75·7 litres (20 US gallons). Total fuel capacity 151·4 litres (40 US gallons). Oil capacity 7·5 litres (2 US gallons).

ACCOMMODATION: Pilot and two passengers, side by side on bench seat; centre place removable. Fully-transparent removable door on each side of cabin. Baggage space aft of engine compartment, with external access door. Cabin heated and ventilated.

SYSTEMS: Electrical power provided by 12V 70A engine-driven alternator.

AVIONICS AND EQUIPMENT: Nav/com to customer's requirements. Cargo hook, floats, spraygear and litters optional.

DIMENSIONS, EXTERNAL:
- Diameter of main rotor: 9·75 m (32 ft 0 in)
- Diameter of tail rotor: 1·42 m (4 ft 8 in)
- Distance between rotor centres: 5·56 m (18 ft 3 in)
- Main rotor blade chord: 0·24 m (9½ in)
- Length overall: 8·94 m (29 ft 4 in)
- Height to top of rotor hub: 2·79 m (9 ft 2 in)
- Skid track: 2·36 m (7 ft 9 in)
- Cabin doors (each): Height: 1·04 m (3 ft 5 in)
  - Width: 0·84 m (2 ft 9 in)
  - Height to sill: 0·64 m (2 ft 1 in)
- Baggage door: Height: 0·55 m (1 ft 9½ in)
  - Width: 0·39 m (1 ft 3½ in)
  - Height to sill: 0·86 m (2 ft 10 in)

DIMENSIONS, INTERNAL:
- Max width of cabin: 1·47 m (4 ft 10 in)
- Volume of baggage hold: 0·20 m^3 (7 cu ft)

AREAS:
- Main rotor disc: 74·69 m^2 (804 sq ft)
- Tail rotor disc: 1·58 m^2 (17·06 sq ft)

WEIGHTS AND LOADINGS (A: F-28C; B: 280C):
- Weight empty: A, B: 678 kg (1,495 lb)
- Max T-O weight:
  - A (normal), B: 998 kg (2,200 lb)
  - A (agricultural): 1,179 kg (2,600 lb)
- Max landing weight:
  - A (agricultural): 1,066 kg (2,350 lb)
- Max disc loading: A, B: 13·38 kg/m^2 (2·74 lb/sq ft)
- Max power loading: A, B: 6·52 kg/kW (10·73 lb/hp)

PERFORMANCE (at max T-O weight, A: F-28C, B: 280C):
- Never-exceed speed at S/L:
  - A (normal): 97 knots (180 km/h; 112 mph) IAS
  - A (agricultural): 65 knots (120 km/h; 75 mph)
  - B: 102 knots (188 km/h; 117 mph)
- Max cruising speed at S/L:
  - A, B: 87 knots (161 km/h; 100 mph)
- Max rate of climb at S/L:
  - A, B: 396 m (1,300 ft)/min
- Service ceiling: A, B: 5,485 m (18,000 ft)
- Hovering ceiling OGE: A, B: 2,530 m (8,300 ft)
- Hovering ceiling IGE: A, B: 3,475 m (11,400 ft)
- Range with max fuel:
  - A, B: 205 nm (381 km; 237 miles)

Enstrom F-28C-2, latest version of the basic F-28 helicopter

Enstrom Model 280C Shark, with a Lycoming HIO-360-E1AD turbocharged engine

Prototype of the Enstrom Model 280L Hawk four-seat light helicopter *(Howard Levy)*

ENSTROM MODEL 280L HAWK

Design of the Model 280L Hawk, a four-seat version of the Model 280C, began in January 1978; construction of two prototypes started in August. The first flight was made on 27 December 1978, and the first production examples, of which 61 had been ordered by February 1979, are scheduled for delivery in April 1980.

The Model 280L is generally similar to the Model 280C, except as follows:

TYPE: Four-seat light helicopter.

ROTOR SYSTEM: As for Model 280C, except for increased-diameter main rotor blades, with sheet metal tabs at tip and mid-span.

ROTOR DRIVE: As Model 280C.

FUSELAGE: Glassfibre and light alloy cab structure, with welded steel tube and light alloy centre-section. Semi-monocoque tailcone structure of light alloy. Fail-safe construction in major areas.

TAIL UNIT: Fixed horizontal surface of light alloy, with small endplate fins.

LANDING GEAR: As Model 280C.

POWER PLANT: One 168 kW (225 hp) Lycoming HIO-360-F1AD flat-four engine with Rajay turbocharger. Two fuel tanks, one each side of main transmission, with combined capacity of 170 litres (45 US gallons). Refuelling point on each side of fuselage upper surface. Oil capacity 7·5 litres (2 US gallons).

ACCOMMODATION: Bench-type seats for pilot and co-pilot forward, two passengers aft, with baggage hold at rear of cabin. Double doors on each side of cabin. Accommodation is heated and ventilated as standard. Air-conditioning optional.

SYSTEM: Electrical system powered by 12V 70A engine-driven alternator.

AVIONICS AND EQUIPMENT: As for Model 280C.

DIMENSIONS, EXTERNAL:
- Diameter of main rotor: 10·36 m (34 ft 0 in)
- Diameter of tail rotor: 1·42 m (4 ft 8 in)
- Distance between rotor centres: 5·87 m (19 ft 3 in)
- Main rotor blade chord: 0·24 m (9½ in)
- Length overall: 9·86 m (32 ft 4 in)
- Height overall: 2·79 m (9 ft 2 in)
- Cabin doors (each): Height: 0·97 m (3 ft 2 in)
  - Width: 1·30 m (4 ft 2 in)
  - Height to sill: 0·71 m (2 ft 4 in)
- Baggage door: Height: 0·48 m (1 ft 7 in)
  - Width: 0·58 m (1 ft 11 in)
  - Height to sill: 0·71 m (2 ft 4 in)

DIMENSIONS, INTERNAL:
- Cabin: Length: 1·78 m (5 ft 10 in)
  - Max width: 1·47 m (4 ft 10 in)
  - Max height: 1·22 m (4 ft 0 in)
  - Floor area: 2·60 m^2 (28 sq ft)
  - Volume: 3·06 m^3 (108 cu ft)
  - Volume of baggage hold: 0·34 m^3 (12 cu ft)

AREAS:
- Main rotor disc: 84·35 m^2 (908 sq ft)
- Tail rotor disc: 1·58 m^2 (17·06 sq ft)

WEIGHTS AND LOADINGS:
- Weight empty, basic: 708 kg (1,560 lb)
- Max T-O and landing weight: 1,179 kg (2,600 lb)
- Max disc loading: 13·98 kg/m^2 (2·86 lb/sq ft)
- Max power loading: 7·02 kg/kW (11·56 lb/hp)

PERFORMANCE (at max T-O weight):
- Never-exceed speed: 104 knots (193 km/h; 120 mph)
- Max level and cruising speed at S/L: 95·5 knots (177 km/h; 110 mph)
- Max rate of climb at S/L: 349 m (1,144 ft)/min
- Service ceiling: 3,660 m (12,000 ft)
- Hovering ceiling IGE: 3,110 m (10,200 ft)
- Hovering ceiling OGE: 1,890 m (6,200 ft)
- Range with max fuel at 1,220 m (4,000 ft): 263 nm (488 km; 303 miles)

EXCALIBUR

EXCALIBUR AVIATION COMPANY

ADDRESS: PO Box 32007, San Antonio, Texas 78216
Telephone: (512) 927 6201 or (512) 696 4221
PRESIDENT: William C. Hickey

Excalibur Aviation, which for some time was responsible for production of the improved versions of the Beechcraft Queen Air and Twin-Bonanza marketed by Swearingen Aircraft, acquired all rights of this conversion programme on 1 October 1970, and has continued to produce these aircraft at Stinson Municipal Airport, San Antonio, Texas. The only change brought about by the new ownership is use of the name Queenaire 800 for the former Swearingen 800.

EXCALIBUR QUEENAIRE 800 and 8800

The Excalibur modification of Queen Air 65s and 80s includes installation of two 298 kW (400 hp) Lycoming IO-720-A1B eight-cylinder engines, each driving a Hartzell three-blade metal constant-speed and fully-feathering propeller; new engine mountings; new exhaust system; new low-drag engine nacelles; new (or zero-time overhauled and certificated) accessories; and Excalibur fully-enclosed wheel-well doors. Modifications of the Beechcraft Queen Air 65, A65 and 80 of all serial numbers are designated Queenaire 800; similar modifications to the Queen Air A80 and B80 of all serial numbers have the designation Queenaire 8800.

Weight and performance data are given after the Excalibur and Excalibur 800 description which follows.

EXCALIBUR EXCALIBUR and EXCALIBUR 800

The Excalibur modification of all Beechcraft Twin-Bonanzas except the 1954 B50, and including the installation of new 283 kW (380 hp) Lycoming IGSO-540-A1A engines, is designated Excalibur. The modification of all Twin-Bonanzas except the early B50 and C50, and including the installation of new 298 kW (400 hp) Lycoming IO-720-A1B engines, has the designation Excalibur 800.

As with the Queenaire conversions, the new engines (with Hartzell constant-speed and fully-feathering propellers) are installed in low-drag nacelles; the other modifications detailed for Queenaires are also embodied. If the Twin-Bonanza is one which had a fuel capacity of 681 litres (180 US gallons) as standard, the outer wing panels are removed from the aircraft and converted to receive new Beechcraft fuel cells to provide a total fuel capacity of 870 litres (230 US gallons). Depending upon the particular model, several changes may be necessary to cater for the increase in maximum take-off weight. These include, if and as necessary, installation of new nose gear casting, main gear trunnions, fuselage doubler on port side below the pilot's side windows, and structural reinforcement of the wing rear spar in the centre-section area (Excalibur 800 only).

WEIGHTS (A: Excalibur; B: Excalibur 800; C: Queenaire 800; D: Queenaire 8800):
Weight empty, equipped (average):
A, B 2,313 kg (5,100 lb)
C 2,449 kg (5,400 lb)
D 2,631 kg (5,800 lb)
Max T-O weight: A 3,311 kg (7,300 lb)
B 3,447 kg (7,600 lb)
C 3,628 kg (8,000 lb)
D 3,991 kg (8,800 lb)
Max landing weight: A 3,175 kg (7,000 lb)
B 3,284 kg (7,240 lb)
C 3,447 kg (7,600 lb)
D 3,792 kg (8,360 lb)

PERFORMANCE (at max T-O weight):
Cruising speed, 75% power:
A at 4,115 m (13,500 ft) 226 knots (418 km/h; 260 mph)
B at 2,530 m (8,300 ft) 204 knots (378 km/h; 235 mph)
C, D at 2,530 m (8,300 ft) 201 knots (372 km/h; 231 mph)
Cruising speed, 65% power:
A at 5,180 m (17,000 ft) 223 knots (414 km/h; 257 mph)
B at 3,050 m (10,000 ft) 198 knots (367 km/h; 228 mph)
C, D at 3,050 m (10,000 ft) 195 knots (362 km/h; 225 mph)
Cruising speed, 45% power at 3,050 m (10,000 ft):
A 187 knots (346 km/h; 215 mph)
B 174 knots (322 km/h; 200 mph)
C, D 172 knots (319 km/h; 198 mph)
Stalling speed, gear and flaps up:
A 78·5 knots (145 km/h; 90 mph)
B, C 80 knots (148 km/h; 92 mph)
D 86 knots (160 km/h; 99 mph)
Stalling speed, gear and flaps down:
A, B 71·5 knots (132 km/h; 82 mph)
C 68 knots (126 km/h; 78 mph)
D 70 knots (129 km/h; 80 mph)
Max rate of climb at S/L: A 579 m (1,900 ft)/min
B 570 m (1,870 ft)/min
C 468 m (1,535 ft)/min
D 454 m (1,490 ft)/min
Rate of climb at S/L, one engine out:
A 104 m (340 ft)/min
B 134 m (440 ft)/min
C 110 m (360 ft)/min
D 76 m (250 ft)/min
Service ceiling: A 9,145 m (30,000 ft)
B 6,765 m (22,200 ft)
C 6,005 m (19,700 ft)
D 5,700 m (18,700 ft)
Service ceiling, one engine out:
A 5,335 m (17,500 ft)
B, C 3,595 m (11,800 ft)
D 3,110 m (10,200 ft)
T-O to 15 m (50 ft): A 381 m (1,250 ft)
B 465 m (1,525 ft)
C 520 m (1,706 ft)
D 625 m (2,050 ft)
Landing from 15 m (50 ft): A 561 m (1,840 ft)
B 591 m (1,940 ft)
C 663 m (2,176 ft)
D 747 m (2,450 ft)
Range with max fuel at 3,050 m (10,000 ft), A with 30 min reserves, B, C, D with 113·6 litres (30 US gallons) reserves:
A 2,032 nm (3,765 km; 2,340 miles)
B 1,335 nm (2,475 km; 1,538 miles)
C 1,322 nm (2,451 km; 1,523 miles)
D 1,547 nm (2,867 km; 1,782 miles)

Typical Excalibur Queenaire 800/8800 conversion (two Lycoming IO-720-A1B engines)

Excalibur Excalibur conversion of Beechcraft Twin-Bonanza (two Lycoming IGSO-540-A1A engines)

FAIRCHILD INDUSTRIES

FAIRCHILD INDUSTRIES INC

CORPORATE OFFICES: 20301 Century Boulevard, Germantown, Maryland 20767
Telephone: (301) 428 6000
CHAIRMAN OF THE BOARD AND CHIEF EXECUTIVE OFFICER: Edward G. Uhl
PRESIDENT AND CHIEF OPERATING OFFICER: John F. Dealy
EXECUTIVE VICE-PRESIDENT: Charles Collis
CORPORATE VICE-PRESIDENTS:
George S. Attridge (Comptroller)
William R. Beckert (General Manager, Fairchild Stratos Division)
Robert J. Dixon (President, Fairchild Republic Company)
Harry Dornbrand (Management Systems)
James J. Foody (Aerospace Development)
Emanuel Fthenakis (Chairman & Chief Executive Officer, Fairchild Space & Electronics Company; President, American Satellite Corporation)
Dr Norman Grossman (Chairman, Fairchild Republic Company)
Richard R. Molleur (Secretary and General Counsel)
J. Gilbert Nettleton Jr (Marketing)
Joseph F. O'Connell (General Manager, Fairchild Burns Company and Fairchild Aircraft Service Division)
Richard G. Orr (General Manager, Fairchild Industrial Products Division)
Constantine Stathis (President, Swearingen Aviation Corporation)
James R. Wilson (Treasurer & Chief Financial Officer)
Robert C. Woods

Fairchild Republic Company
DIVISIONAL OFFICE AND WORKS: Farmingdale, Long Island, New York 11735
CHAIRMAN: Dr Norman Grossman
PRESIDENT: Robert J. Dixon
HAGERSTOWN, MARYLAND 21740 FACILITY:
SITE ADMINISTRATOR: Michael L. Hansen

Fairchild Aircraft Service Division
DIVISIONAL OFFICE AND WORKS: Crestview, Florida 32536
GENERAL MANAGER: Joseph F. O'Connell

Fairchild Space and Electronics Company
Germantown, Maryland 20767
PRESIDENT: Dr John W. Townsend Jr

Swearingen Aviation Corporation
San Antonio, Texas 78284
PRESIDENT: Constantine Stathis

Fairchild Stratos Division
Manhattan Beach, California 90266
GENERAL MANAGER: William R. Beckert

Fairchild Industrial Products Division
Winston-Salem, North Carolina 27105
GENERAL MANAGER: Richard G. Orr

Fairchild Burns Company
Winston-Salem, North Carolina 27105
GENERAL MANAGER: Joseph F. O'Connell

American Satellite Corporation
Germantown, Maryland 20767
PRESIDENT: Emanuel Fthenakis

S. J. Industries Inc
Alexandria, Virginia 22304
PRESIDENT: Richard F. Julius

Fairchild KLIF Inc
Radio Station KLIF, Dallas, Texas 75201
STATION MANAGER: Charles A. Macatee

Fairchild Industries is a diversified aerospace and communications company which builds and services military and civilian aircraft, manufactures spacecraft and aircraft subsystems, industrial and electronic products, operates a domestic satellite communications system, and is engaged in commercial radio broadcasting.

The Fairchild Republic Company (see following entry) combines all of Fairchild's military aircraft research, design, manufacture and personnel into one division. Facilities are located at Farmingdale, Long Island, New York; and Hagerstown, Maryland.

Based at the Crestview, Florida, facility, Fairchild Aircraft Service Division is an aircraft maintenance, repair, modification and support centre. Current programmes of this division include modification work to T-38 and A-10 aircraft under USAF contract, production of fire-retardant fuel tank foam for the Fairchild A-10, and seats for military helicopters.

The Fairchild Space and Electronics Company directs the company's efforts in the design, development and manufacture of spacecraft, spacecraft subsystems, rocket payload projects, and electronic systems; details of this work can be found in the Spaceflight section.

Fairchild Space and Electronics Company also builds electronics systems, including an armament control subsystem for the Fairchild A-10, a weapon control system for the Grumman F-14A Tomcat, a stores management system for the General Dynamics F-111, and a weapons control system for the US Navy's Light Airborne Multi-Purpose System (LAMPS) helicopter programme.

The Fairchild Stratos Division specialises in the development and manufacture of aerospace and commercial aircraft subsystems, accessories and components. It is now manufacturing valves and the ammonia boiler cooling system for the Space Shuttle, engine power turbines for Boeing 747 aircraft, aviation cooling packages, and beverage and food carts for commercial passenger aircraft.

Swearingen Aviation Corporation (which see), a subsidiary in which Fairchild Industries has a 100 per cent holding, manufactures the Merlin and Metro series of executive and commuter aircraft.

Fairchild Burns Company manufactures aircraft passenger seating used by more than 50 airlines worldwide, including the Airest line of lightweight seats.

FAIRCHILD REPUBLIC COMPANY

Farmingdale, Long Island, New York 11735
CHAIRMAN: Dr Norman Grossman

Founded on 17 February 1931, as the Seversky Aircraft Company, Republic operated as Republic Aviation Corporation from 1939 until September 1965, when it became a division of Fairchild Hiller Corporation, now Fairchild Industries Inc.

Fairchild Republic Company is proceeding with full-scale production of the A-10 close-support aircraft for the USAF. It is also manufacturing under subcontract aft fuselages, fin and tailcone assemblies, rudders, tailplanes and engine access doors for the McDonnell Douglas F/RF-4 Phantom II tactical fighter as well as the twin vertical fins for the Grumman F-14A Tomcat fighter. The company is a major subcontractor in the Boeing 747 programme, manufacturing ailerons, spoilers, and wing trailing-edge and leading-edge flaps. This work is performed at the Farmingdale and Hagerstown facilities.

Wing structures for Swearingen Aviation Corporation's Merlin and Metro series are manufactured at Hagerstown. This facility also provides support for the F-27 and F-227 twin-turboprop transport aircraft that were manufactured under licence from Fokker-VFW, as well as the FH-1100 five-passenger turbine-powered helicopter, the Porter STOL aircraft and its military version, the Peacemaker.

Fairchild Republic Company is also responsible for the vertical tail assembly for the Rockwell International Space Shuttle Orbiter Vehicle.

FAIRCHILD REPUBLIC THUNDERBOLT II

USAF designation: A-10A

On 18 December 1970, Fairchild Republic and Northrop were selected as the two companies that were each to build two prototypes for evaluation under the USAF's A-X programme, initiated in 1967, for a close-support aircraft. The first Fairchild Republic prototype (71-1369), designated YA-10A, flew for the first time on 10 May 1972, followed by the second prototype (71-1370) on 21 July 1972. On 18 January 1973 it was announced that the Fairchild A-10A had been selected as the winner, and the company later received a contract for ten pre-production aircraft (six for development test and evaluation and four for initial operational test and evaluation). The contract was reduced later to six DT and E aircraft, the first of which first flew on 15 February 1975. (Details of these six aircraft can be found in the 1977-78 *Jane's*.) Static and fatigue test airframes were also completed.

An initial order for 22 production A-10As for the USAF was confirmed on 20 December 1974, with the allocation of $99 million in the FY 1975 budget, and delivery of these, to the 333rd Tactical Fighter Training Squadron at Davis-Monthan AFB, Arizona, began in the Spring of 1976, following the first flight by a production A-10A (75-00258) on 21 October 1975. By the Autumn of 1977, funds had been approved for the procurement of a total of 195 production A-10As, and FY 1978 funding for a further 144 aircraft had been approved. Production of a total of 739 aircraft is planned (including the six DT and E aircraft), with 144 funded in FY 1979, 144 scheduled in FY 1980, and 106 in FY 1981. Maximum production rate will rise to 14 aircraft per month in FY 1980, with completion of the USAF's requirement scheduled for January 1983. The 200th production A-10A was delivered in April 1979.

The first combat-ready A-10A wing was the 354th Tactical Fighter Wing, based at Myrtle Beach, South Carolina, to which deliveries began in March 1977. The 354th TFW began in early 1978 to operate A-10As equipped with the Martin Marietta AN/AAS-35 Pave Penny laser target designation pod, now approved as a standard fit for the aircraft. In May 1977 several A-10As were assigned to the 422nd Fighter Weapons Squadron of the 57th Tactical Training Wing at Nellis AFB, Nevada, for operational training and testing purposes. On 15 October 1977 the 356th Tactical Fighter Squadron of 354 TFW became the first combat-ready A-10 squadron.

In May 1977, four A-10As were operated from a dry lake bed at Bicycle Lake, during exercise Red Flag 77-6 in support of Army troops in the Mojave Desert at Fort Irwin, California. In June 1977, two A-10As from Davis-Monthan AFB made a nine-day tour of the Pacific. At about the same time, two aircraft were flown from Davis-Monthan to Europe for the Paris Air Show and a follow-on deployment for tactics validation in various NATO countries. In August 1977, six A-10As flew to Europe for the first live firing of the aircraft's 30 mm Gatling gun and the anti-armour Maverick air-to-ground missile in the NATO theatre, expending 7·5 tons of conventional 500 lb bombs and 9,000 rounds of 30 mm ammunition during 117 close support sorties. Beginning in September 1977, A-10As from the 66th Fighter Weapons Squadron at Nellis AFB, Nevada, joined Army AH-1 HueyCobra helicopter gunships at Fort Hunter-Liggett, California, to participate in the Joint Attack Weapons Systems (JAWS) exercises, designed to develop and evaluate tactical co-ordination between the two types of aircraft. During the exercises, the A-10As and helicopters attacked simulated aggressor columns of tanks, armoured personnel carriers and missile launchers supported by artillery and aircraft as evaluations were made of tactics, pilot stress and camouflage effectiveness. These combined operations have continued as Joint Air Attack Team (JAAT) exercises, at Fort Bragg, North Carolina, with Cobra team leaders flying in OH-58 scout helicopters.

The first overseas deployment of the A-10 was made on 25 January 1979, with the arrival of 14 Thunderbolt IIs at RAF stations Bentwaters and Woodbridge in the UK, to equip the USAF's 81st Tactical Fighter Wing. A total of 72 aircraft were scheduled for delivery by September 1979, with an additional 36 aircraft to be delivered in 1980. Six squadrons will eventually be based at the two UK stations.

Deliveries of new production A-10As to four Tactical Fighter Groups of the Air National Guard are also under way.

European deployment of the A-10 calls for small numbers of aircraft to transfer on a rotational basis to various forward operating locations in NATO's central region, for deployment close to Allied defence positions. Sembach Air Base, which is a US installation, and the West German Air Force bases at Leipheim, Alhorn and Noervenich, have been named as initial forward operating locations.

A **two-seat night/adverse weather attack version** of the A-10A is described separately.

TYPE: Single-seat close-support aircraft.

WINGS: Cantilever low-wing monoplane, with wide-chord, deep aerofoil section (NACA 6716 on centre-section and at start of outer panel, NACA 6713 at tip) to provide low wing loading. Incidence −1°. Dihedral 7° on outer panels. Aluminium alloy three-spar structure, consisting of one-piece constant-chord centre-section and tapered outer panels with integrally stiffened skins and drooped (cambered) wingtips. Outer panel leading-edges and cores of trailing-edges are of honeycomb sandwich. Four-point attachment of wings to fuselage, at front and rear spars. Two-segment, three-position trailing-edge slotted flaps, interchangeable right with left. Wide-span ailerons, made up of dual upper and lower surfaces that separate to serve as airbrakes. Flaps, airbrakes and ailerons actuated hydraulically. Ailerons pilot-controlled by servo tab during manual reversion. Small leading-edge slat inboard of each main-wheel fairing. Redundant and armour-protected flight control system.

FUSELAGE: Semi-monocoque structure of aluminium alloy (chiefly 2024 and 7075), with four main longerons, multiple frames, and lap-jointed and riveted skins. Built in front, centre and aft portions. Single-curvature components aft of nose portion, interchangeable right with left. Centre portion incorporates wing box carry-through structure.

TAIL UNIT: Cantilever aluminium alloy structure, with twin fins and interchangeable rudders mounted at the tips of constant-chord tailplane. Interchangeable elevators, each with an electrically-operated trim tab. Rudders and elevators actuated hydraulically. Redundant and armour-protected flight control system.

LANDING GEAR: Menasco retractable tricycle type with single wheel on each unit. All units retract forward, and have provision for emergency gravity extension. Interchangeable main-wheel units retract into non-structural pod fairings attached to the lower surface of the wings. When fully retracted approximately half of each wheel protrudes from the fairing. Steerable nosewheel is offset to starboard to clear firing barrel of gun. Main wheels size 36 × 11, Type VII; nosewheel size 24 × 7·7-10, Type VII.

POWER PLANT: Two General Electric TF34-GE-100 high bypass ratio turbofan engines, each rated at 40·3 kN (9,065 lb st), enclosed in separate pods, each pylon-mounted to the upper rear fuselage at a point approximately midway between the wing trailing-edges and the tailplane leading-edges. Fuel is contained in two tear-resistant and self-sealing cells in the fuselage, and two smaller, adjacent integral cells in the wing centre-section. Maximum internal fuel capacity 4,853 kg (10,700 lb). All fuel cells are internally filled with reticulated foam, and all fuel systems pipework is contained within the cells except for the feeds to the engines, which have self-sealing covers. Three 2,271 litre (600 US gallon) jettisonable auxiliary tanks can be carried on underwing and fuselage centreline pylons. Provision for in-flight refuelling using universal aerial refuelling receptacle slipway installation (UARRSI).

ACCOMMODATION: Single-seat enclosed cockpit, well forward of wings, with large transparent bubble canopy to provide all-round view. Bulletproof windscreen.

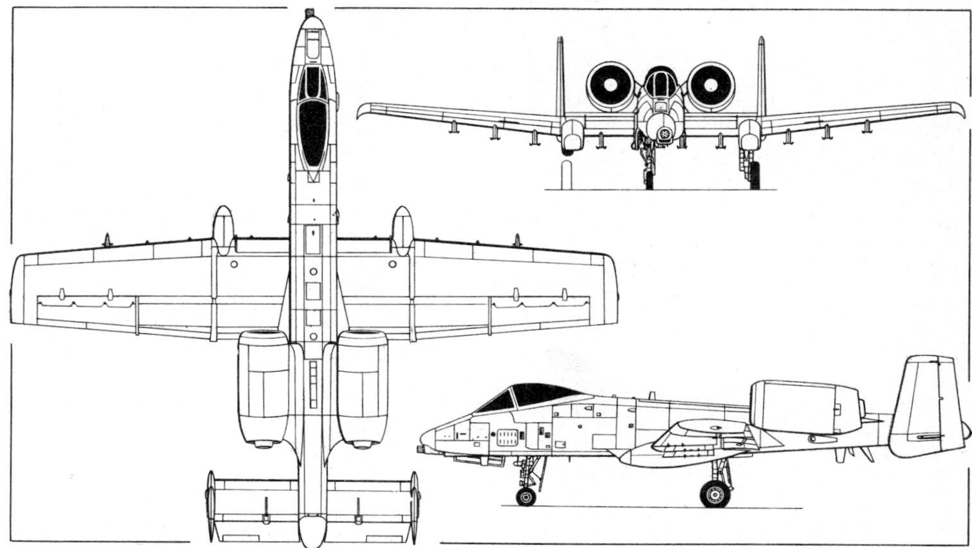

Fairchild Republic A-10A single-seat twin-engined close-support aircraft *(Pilot Press)*

Fairchild Republic A-10A Thunderbolt II, showing GAU-8/A cannon and underwing weapon pylons

Canopy is hinged at rear and opens upward. Douglas ejection seat operable at speeds from 450 knots (834 km/h; 518 mph) down to zero speed at zero height. Entire cockpit area is protected by an armoured 'bathtub' structure of titanium, capable of withstanding projectiles of up to 23 mm calibre.

SYSTEMS: Redundant control system incorporates two 207 bar (3,000 lb/sq in) primary hydraulic flight control systems, each powered by an engine-driven pump, and a manual backup. Hydraulic systems actuate flaps, flying control surfaces, landing gear, brakes and nosewheel steering. Two independent hydraulic motors, either of which is sufficient to sustain half-rate firing, supply drive for 30 mm gun barrel rotation. Electrical system includes two 30/40kVA 115/200V AC engine-driven generators and a standby battery and inverter. Auxiliary power unit. Environmental control system, using engine bleed air for cockpit pressurisation and air-conditioning, pressurisation of pilot's *g* suit, windscreen anti-icing and rain clearance, fuel transfer, gun compartment purging, and other services.

AVIONICS AND EQUIPMENT: Head-up display giving airspeed, altitude and dive angle; weapons delivery package with dual reticle optical sight for use in conjunction with underfuselage Pave Penny laser target seeker pod; target penetration aids; associated equipment for Maverick and other missile systems; IFF/SIF (AIMS); UHF/AM; VHF/AM; VHF/FM; Tacan; UHF/ADF; VOR/ILS; X-band transponder; all-altitude heading and attitude reference system (HARS); radar homing and warning (RHAW); secure voice communications; active or passive electronic countermeasures (ECM); armament control panel; and gun camera. Space provisions for HF/SSB, ILS/FDS, Loran C/D, ECM pod, chaff/flare dispenser and other 'growth' avionics and equipment.

ARMAMENT: General Electric GAU-8/A Avenger 30 mm seven-barrel cannon, mounted in nose with 2° depression and offset slightly to port so that as the barrels rotate the firing barrel is always on the aircraft's centreline. Gun and handling system for the linkless ammunition are mechanically synchronised and driven by two motors fed from the aircraft's hydraulic system. The single-drum magazine has a capacity of 1,350 rounds, and has a dual firing rate of either 2,100 or 4,200 rds/min. Four stores pylons under each wing (one inboard and three outboard of each main-wheel fairing), and three under fuselage, for max external load of 7,250 kg (16,000 lb). External load with full internal fuel is 6,640 kg (14,638 lb). The centreline pylon and the two flanking fuselage pylons cannot be occupied simultaneously. The centreline pylon has a capacity of 2,268 kg (5,000 lb); the two fuselage outer pylons and two centre-section underwing pylons 1,587 kg (3,500 lb) each; the two innermost outer-wing pylons 1,134 kg (2,500 lb) each; and the four outermost wing pylons 453 kg (1,000 lb) each. These allow carriage of a wide range of stores, including twenty-eight 500 lb Mk-82 LDGP or Mk-82 retarded bombs; six 2,000 lb Mk-84 general-purpose bombs; eight BLU-1 or BLU-27/B incendiary bombs; four SUU-25 flare launchers; twenty Rockeye II cluster bombs, sixteen CBU-52/71, ten CBU-38, or sixteen CBU-70 dispenser weapons; six AGM-65A Maverick missiles; Mk-82 and Mk-84 laser-guided bombs; Mk-84 electro-optically-guided bombs; two SUU-23 gun pods; chaff, ALE-37 and ALQ-119 ECM pods, or other jammer pods; or up to three drop-tanks.

DIMENSIONS, EXTERNAL:

Wing span	17·53 m (57 ft 6 in)
Wing chord at root	3·04 m (9 ft 11½ in)
Wing chord (mean)	2·73 m (8 ft 11·32 in)
Wing chord at tip	1·99 m (6 ft 6·4 in)
Wing aspect ratio	6·54
Length overall	16·26 m (53 ft 4 in)
Height overall	4·47 m (14 ft 8 in)
Tailplane span	5·74 m (18 ft 10 in)
Wheel track	5·25 m (17 ft 2½ in)
Wheelbase	5·40 m (17 ft 8¾ in)

AREAS:

Wings, gross	47·01 m² (506·0 sq ft)
Ailerons (total, incl tabs)	4·42 m² (47·54 sq ft)
Trailing-edge flaps (total)	7·99 m² (85·99 sq ft)
Leading-edge slats (total)	0·98 m² (10·56 sq ft)
Airbrakes (total)	8·06 m² (86·78 sq ft)
Fins (total)	7·80 m² (83·96 sq ft)
Rudders (total)	2·18 m² (23·50 sq ft)
Tailplane	8·31 m² (89·40 sq ft)
Elevators (total, incl tabs)	2·69 m² (29·00 sq ft)

WEIGHTS AND LOADINGS:

Manufacturer's empty weight	9,433 kg (20,796 lb)
Basic equipped weight, 'clean'	10,850 kg (23,920 lb)
Operating weight empty	10,977 kg (24,200 lb)
*Basic design weight, equipped	14,038 kg (30,950 lb)
**Forward airstrip weight	14,395 kg (31,735 lb)
Internal fuel load	4,853 kg (10,700 lb)
Max external ordnance	7,250 kg (16,000 lb)
Max external ordnance with full internal fuel	6,640 kg (14,638 lb)
Max T-O weight	22,680 kg (50,000 lb)
Max wing loading	457·4 kg/m² (93·68 lb/sq ft)
Max power loading	266·7 kg/kN (2·61 lb/lb st)
Thrust/weight ratio	0·4

**incl six 500 lb bombs, 750 rds of ammunition, and fuel for 300 nm (555 km; 345 miles) with 20 min reserves*

***with four Mk-82 bombs and 750 rds*

PERFORMANCE: (at max T-O weight except where indicated):

Never-exceed speed	450 knots (834 km/h; 518 mph)
Max level speed	368 knots (681 km/h; 423 mph)
Combat speed at 1,525 m (5,000 ft), with six Mk-82 bombs	385 knots (713 km/h; 443 mph)
Cruising speed at S/L	300 knots (555 km/h; 345 mph)
Cruising speed at 1,525 m (5,000 ft)	336 knots (623 km/h; 387 mph)
Stabilised 45° dive speed below 2,440 m (8,000 ft), AUW of 15,932 kg (35,125 lb)	260 knots (481 km/h; 299 mph)
Max rate of climb at S/L at basic design weight	1,828 m (6,000 ft)/min
T-O distance:	
at max T-O weight	1,372 m (4,500 ft)
at forward airstrip weight	610 m (2,000 ft)
Landing distance:	
at max T-O weight	762 m (2,500 ft)
at forward airstrip weight	610 m (2,000 ft)
Operational radius, 20 min reserve:	
close air support, 2 h loiter	250 nm (463 km; 288 miles)
escort, 1 h loiter	250 nm (463 km; 288 miles)
reconnaissance	400 nm (740 km; 460 miles)
deep strike	540 nm (1,000 km; 620 miles)
Ferry range, zero wind	2,620 nm (4,850 km; 3,015 miles)

FAIRCHILD REPUBLIC NIGHT/ADVERSE WEATHER A-10

The two-seat version of the A-10A Thunderbolt II is intended as a night/adverse weather (N/AW) attack aircraft, with secondary use as a trainer retaining operational capability. The company-funded prototype was converted under a lease agreement from one of the six single-seat DT & E A-10s built for the USAF in 1975, and made its first flight as a two-seater from Edwards AFB, California, on 4 May 1979. The Fairchild test programme was expected to continue until the end of September 1979. If, as a result of this, and subsequent USAF tests and evaluation, it is decided to procure the N/AW A-10 in quantity, it has been suggested that it could be deployed effectively on a one-to-one basis alongside in-service A-10As. Alternatively, if considered expedient, it would be possible to retrofit single-seat A-10As to N/AW A-10 standard.

The N/AW version of the A-10 carries, in addition to the pilot, a weapons system officer (WSO) in the aft cockpit, who is responsible for ECM, navigation and target or threat acquisition and designation. This enables the pilot to concentrate on control of the aircraft, with a far higher likelihood of success when attacking targets in darkness or adverse weather.

Generally similar to the single-seat A-10A, the N/AW version differs by having a second, aft, cockpit with raised seat to provide the WSO with virtually the same over-the-nose view as the pilot. His cockpit duplicates that of the pilot, except that it has a cathode ray tube (CRT) in lieu of a head-up display, and no flight controls or titanium armour. Other changes include forward extensions of the port and starboard landing gear housings to accommodate radar and FLIR respectively, and lengthened twin fins to increase their effective area, thus maintaining the same directional stability factor as the single-seat A-10A. In the construction of the N/AW A-10, Fairchild has introduced welded/bonded fuselage panels and graphite composite tailplane leading-edges for test purposes.

To provide the two-seat A-10 with its essential night/adverse weather capability, there are changes to the avionics equipment. New equipment includes a modified version of the Westinghouse WX-50 multimode radar, which is used as a ground moving target indicator, for ground mapping, terrain following/avoidance, and threat detection; a modified version of the Texas Instruments AAR-42 FLIR; Ferranti Type 105 laser rangefinder; Litton LN-39 INS; Honeywell radar altimeter; a changed Kaiser HUD for the pilot and Hartmann CRT for the WSO; and General Electric low-light-level TV (included for comparison with FLIR). The N/AW A-10 retains the Martin Marietta AN/AAS-35 Pave Penny laser target designation pod, which is standard equipment of in-service A-10As.

The description of the A-10A Thunderbolt II applies also to the N/AW A-10, except as described above. Available specification and performance figures are as follows:

Fairchild Republic two-seat night/adverse weather version of the A-10

DIMENSIONS, EXTERNAL: As for A-10A except:
- Height overall — 4·98 m (16 ft 4 in)

WEIGHTS (estimated):
- Operating weight empty — 11,908 kg (26,253 lb)
- Mission T-O weight, with 4,853 kg (10,700 lb) fuel — 20,032 kg (44,162 lb)

PERFORMANCE (estimated at mission T-O weight):
- Max level speed — 365 knots (676 km/h; 420 mph)
- T-O run — 860 m (2,820 ft)
- Landing run — 372 m (1,220 ft)
- Mission radius — 250 nm (463 km; 288 miles)

FOXJET

FOXJET INTERNATIONAL INC (a subsidiary of Fox Industries Inc)

HEAD OFFICE: 6701 West 110th Street, Minneapolis, Minnesota 55438

Telephone: (612) 941 8870

PRESIDENT: Tony Fox

VICE-PRESIDENT AND CHIEF PROJECT ENGINEER: N. Anderson

In the Spring of 1977, details were released of a lightweight four-seat twin-turbofan transport named Foxjet ST-600 which was expected to operate at 20 per cent of the fuel costs of the most economical business jet then in service. Since that time, the design has undergone considerable development. In particular, the type of Williams Research turbofan now specified to power the Foxjet develops 40 per cent more thrust than the WR19-3 originally chosen. This has made possible a scale-up of the overall dimensions, and the cabin will now accommodate up to six people in comfort.

A new wing, with reduced sweepback and higher aspect ratio, has been designed for the Foxjet by Branson Aircraft Corporation. Known as the Foxjet Super-Flow wing, this can be modified easily to supercritical form when required by future power increase, and is claimed to improve stability and low-speed control. Performance is generally improved by these changes. Fuel cost was claimed to be less than 10 US cents per mile at mid-1978 prices.

The company announced on 26 March 1979 the formation of Foxjet Austral-Asia by four Australian businessmen to sell and lease the Foxjet ST600-S in that area.

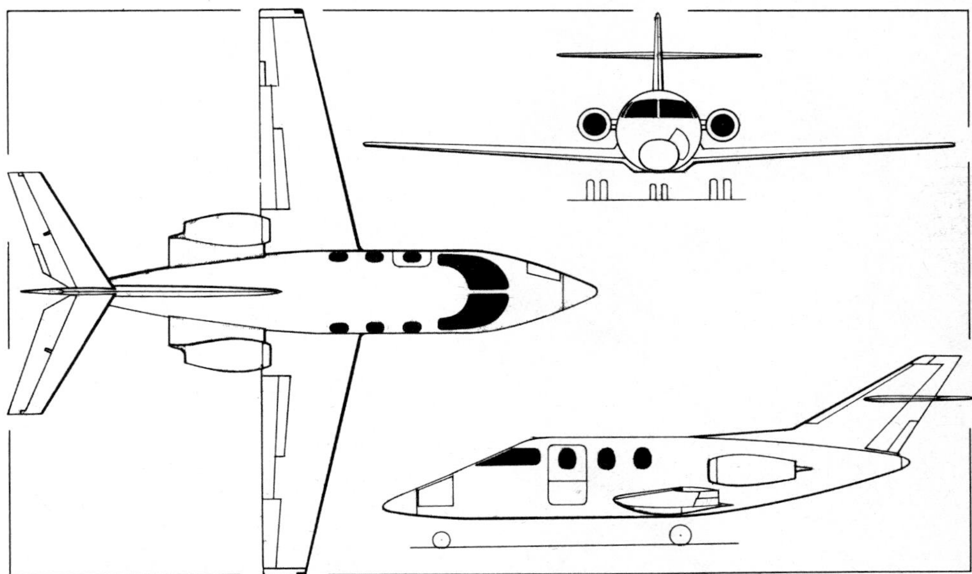

Foxjet ST600-S/8 four/six-seat twin-turbofan transport *(Pilot Press)*

Mockup of the Foxjet ST600-S/8 lightweight transport aircraft *(Erik Simonsen)*

FOXJET ST600-S/8

The prototype of this lightweight twin-turbofan transport is expected to fly in 1980. Firm orders for 73 aircraft, backed by deposits, were in hand in mid-1978, and Foxjet International envisages eventual manufacture of 44 Foxjet ST600s per month. Engine development is expected to uprate the present turbofan to 5·35 kN (1,200 lb st), with a subsequent refanned version rated at 6·24 kN (1,400 lb st).

TYPE: Four/six-seat twin-turbofan transport.

WINGS: Cantilever low-wing monoplane. NACA 65 Series laminar-flow section. Moderate leading-edge sweepback; straight trailing-edge. All-metal fail-safe structure, primarily of light alloy. Electrically-operated modified Fowler type single-slotted light alloy trailing-edge flaps. Manually-operated ailerons. Hydraulically-operated spoilers, forward of flaps, serve also as airbrakes. Trim tab in port aileron. Electrical anti-icing of each wing leading-edge at root; optional pneumatic de-icing boots for remainder of leading-edges.

FUSELAGE: Semi-monocoque light alloy fail-safe structure of circular cross-section. Light alloy honeycomb pressure bulkheads and baggage deck.

TAIL UNIT: Cantilever multi-spar light alloy structure with swept vertical and horizontal surfaces. Tailplane mounted approximately midway up fin. Manually-operated control surfaces, with tabs in rudder and port elevator. Leading-edges fitted with de-icing system.

LANDING GEAR: Hydraulically-retractable tricycle type, manufactured by Wiebel Tool Company, with twin wheels on each unit. Main units retract inward, nose unit aft. Oleo-pneumatic shock-absorbers. Main wheels have low-pressure tyres size 5·00-5. Hydraulically-steerable nosewheel unit, with water-chine tyres size 11 × 4·00-5. Hydraulic disc brakes on main wheels.

POWER PLANT: Two 3·78 kN (850 lb st) Williams Research WR44-800 turbofan engines, pod-mounted on each side of rear fuselage. Integral wing fuel tanks, total capacity 825 litres (218 US gallons).

ACCOMMODATION: Pilot and three to five passengers, in pairs. Two-piece door (upward-hinged portion, and downward-hinged portion with integral steps) on port side forward of wing. Emergency exit on starboard side. Accommodation air-conditioned and pressurised. Birdproof windscreen with pneumatic system for rain removal, defogging and defrosting. Equipment access door on port side of nose. Baggage hold aft of cabin.

SYSTEMS: Pressurisation system with max differential of 0·58 bars (8·4 lb/sq in), providing a cabin altitude of 2,440 m (8,000 ft) to 12,200 m (40,000 ft). Electrical system. Hydraulic system, with hydraulic backup. Pneumatic system.

AVIONICS AND EQUIPMENT: Standard avionics include dual nav/com, autopilot/flight director, ADF, DME and transponder. Weather radar optional. Blind-flying instrumentation standard. Optional equipment includes electrically-powered one-man towing system, stowed on board.

DIMENSIONS, EXTERNAL:
- Wing span — 9·64 m (31 ft 7½ in)
- Wing aspect ratio — 8
- Length overall — 9·70 m (31 ft 10 in)
- Height overall — 3·12 m (10 ft 2¾ in)
- Diameter of centre-fuselage — 1·40 m (4 ft 7 in)
- Tailplane span — 4·06 m (13 ft 4 in)
- Door: Width — 0·76 m (2 ft 6 in)

DIMENSIONS, INTERNAL:
- Cabin: Length — 3·66 m (12 ft 0 in)
- Baggage space (pilot and 3 passengers) — 1·13 m³ (39·8 cu ft)

AREA:
- Wings, gross — 11·61 m² (125·0 sq ft)

WEIGHTS AND LOADINGS (estimated):
- Weight empty — 1,092 kg (2,408 lb)
- Max T-O weight — 2,064 kg (4,550 lb)
- Max wing loading — 177·8 kg/m² (36·4 lb/sq ft)
- Max power loading — 273·0 kg/kN (2·68 lb/lb st)

PERFORMANCE (estimated, at max T-O weight):
- Max cruising speed at 11,000 m (36,000 ft) — 356 knots (659 km/h; 410 mph)

Recommended cruising speed at 11,000 m (36,000 ft) 286 knots (529 km/h; 329 mph)
Stalling speed, flaps up 85 knots (158 km/h; 98 mph)
Stalling speed, flaps down 74 knots (137 km/h; 85 mph)
Max rate of climb at S/L 1,035 m (3,400 ft)/min
Rate of climb at S/L, one engine out 305 m (1,000 ft)/min
Time to 11,000 m (36,000 ft) 22 min
Service ceiling 12,495 m (41,000 ft)
Service ceiling, one engine out 7,620 m (25,000 ft)
T-O run 488 m (1,600 ft)
T-O to 15 m (50 ft) 823 m (2,700 ft)
Landing from 15 m (50 ft) 567 m (1,860 ft)
Landing run 299 m (980 ft)
Range at recommended cruising speed, 45 min reserves 955 nm (1,768 km; 1,099 miles)

GACC

GULFSTREAM AMERICAN CORPORATION OF CALIFORNIA (a subsidiary of Gulfstream American Corporation)

HEAD OFFICE AND WORKS: 7701 Woodley Avenue, Van Nuys, California 91406
Telephone: (213) 988 9900
Telex: 662461

This is the former American Jet Industries Inc, which was renamed following its acquisition of Grumman American Corporation. GACC plans to transfer all tooling and materials for the Hustler 500 to the Gulfstream American Corporation works at Savannah, Georgia, and current details of the Hustler appear under that company's entry.

At Van Nuys, California, GACC will continue to carry out cargo conversions of civil transport aircraft, and will become also the western support centre for Gulfstream II and III executive transports. In addition, the programme involving retrofit of the new Gulfstream III wing to Gulfstream II aircraft will be carried out by GACC at Van Nuys.

GULFSTREAM AMERICAN CV-880 AIRLIFTER

Current programmes at Gulfstream American's Van Nuys plant include the conversion of ex-airline Convair 880 passenger transports for operation as freighters. This involves the installation of a freight door in the port side of the fuselage, forward of the wing, and a cargo floor stressed to 9*g*. The converted aircraft, known as the Airlifter, will carry its maximum payload of 23,133 kg (51,000 lb) over a range of 1,800 nm (3,336 km; 2,073 miles) at a block speed of 450 knots (833 km/h; 518 mph). Maximum range with reduced payload is 3,000 nm (5,555 km; 3,450 miles).

The first of two initial conversions was nearing completion in Spring 1979, with 22 more CV-880s available for conversion.

Details of the standard Convair 880 can be found in the 1965-66 *Jane's*.

GATES LEARJET

GATES LEARJET CORPORATION

CORPORATE OFFICES, AIRCRAFT DIVISION: Mid-Continent Airport, PO Box 7707, Wichita, Kansas 67277
Telephone: (316) 946 2000
Telex: 417441
MARKETING HEADQUARTERS, COMPLETION & SERVICE CENTRE: Tucson International Airport, PO Box 11186, Tucson, Arizona 85734
COMBS-GATES FIXED BASE OPERATIONS: Hangar 7, Stapleton International Airport, Denver, Colorado 80207
JET ELECTRONICS AND TECHNOLOGY INC: 5353 52nd Street, Grand Rapids, Michigan 49508
CHAIRMAN OF THE BOARD: Charles C. Gates
PRESIDENT: Harry B. Combs
EXECUTIVE VICE-PRESIDENT AND GENERAL MANAGER, AIRCRAFT DIVISION: L. S. Blue
EXECUTIVE VICE-PRESIDENTS:
A. J. Brizzolara (J.E.T.)
R. E. Cloughley (Combs-Gates)
SENIOR VICE-PRESIDENTS:
B. S. Stillwell (Marketing)
R. C. Scott (Operations)
VICE-PRESIDENTS:
L. C. Barry (Industrial Relations)
W. C. Bracas (Manufacturing)
C. E. Dyas (Marketing Support)
G. D. Gilmore (Governmental Marketing)
A. F. Green (General Manager, Tucson Operations)
J. R. Greenwood (Corporate Affairs)
D. J. Grommesh (Engineering & Research)
F. I. Hedlund (International Marketing)
Phillip F. Lovett (Domestic Marketing)
E. C. Mandenberg (Materiel)
M. F. Mastin (Marketing Programmes)
D. B. Norton (Product Support)
TREASURER: W. H. Webster
CONTROLLER: A. F. Hain
SECRETARY: R. C. Troll
MANAGER, INFORMATION SERVICES: J. M. Gregory

Founded in 1960 by the late William P. Lear Sr, this company was known originally as the Swiss American Aviation Corporation, which was formed to manufacture a high-speed twin-jet executive aircraft known as the Learjet 23 (formerly SAAC-23). Most of the tooling for production of this aircraft was completed in Europe and then, in 1962, all company activities were relocated at Wichita, Kansas; shortly afterwards the company became known as Lear Jet Corporation. In 1967 all of Mr Lear's interests in the company (approximately 60 per cent) were acquired by The Gates Rubber Company of Denver, Colorado, and in January 1970 the company name was changed to Gates Learjet Corporation.

On 28 October 1975 Gates Learjet announced improved models of its Learjets, under the designation Century III series. All Century III Learjets incorporate a cambered wing and other changes to reduce stall and approach speeds and balanced field length. This wing has a new contour, extending from the leading-edge aft to the second wing spar, and, coupled with other advances including an improved stall warning/prevention system, improves lateral stability and handling qualities in the slower flight regimes. Performance increases from Century III improvements include approach speed reductions of 16-18 knots (30-34 km/h; 18·5-21 mph), and increases in cruise range of as much as seven per cent. Century III improvements are available as a factory retrofit modification for earlier Learjet 24, 25, 35 and 36 models, and can be completed in approximately one week.

From 1 July 1979, all newly-delivered Learjets have embodied a 'Softflite' handling package to improve stall characteristics. Available for retrospective fit on earlier Century III series aircraft, this comprises a full-chord shallow fence on each wing, small devices on the inboard leading-edge, and two rows of boundary-layer energisers forward of each aileron, to energise the airflow and delay the onset of compressibility. Vortex generators are removed; the stick shaker/pusher is retained but unlikely to be required.

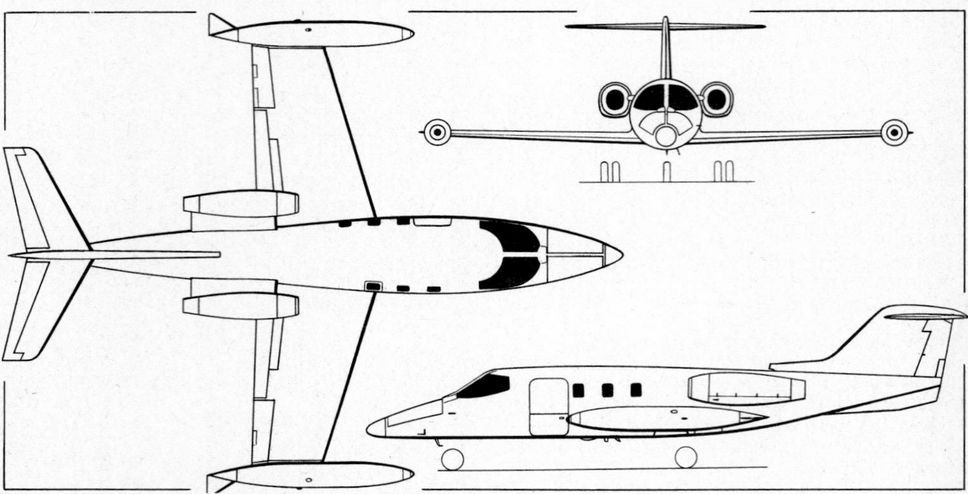

Gates Learjet 24 Series twin-jet light executive transport *(Pilot Press)*

During May 1976 a Learjet 36, captained by golf professional/pilot Arnold Palmer, established a business jet round-the-world speed record in an elapsed time of 57 h 25 min 42 s. The flight of 19,960·24 nm (36,989·96 km; 22,984·55 miles) was flown at an average speed of 347·57 knots (644·107 km/h; 400·23 mph).

In June and September 1977 Gates Learjet gave provisional details of advanced models, with wings of increased span provided with supercritical winglets. These are designated Learjet 28/29 Longhorn and Learjet 54/55/56 Longhorn.

During 1978 a total of 102 Learjets were delivered (69 to customers in the USA, the balance for export), making this the 14th consecutive year in which Gates Learjet has led in cumulative deliveries of business jet aircraft. Of this total, 31 were Model 24/25s and 71 were Model 35/36s. The company delivered its 900th Learjet, a Model 35A for McDonnell Douglas Corporation, on 27 April 1979.

Learjets are produced at the company's main facility at Wichita, Kansas. A new completion centre at Tucson, Arizona, was opened in 1976, and a new Customer Service Center was opened in 1978. Other fixed-base operations, under the name of Combs-Gates, are located at Denver, Colorado; Indianapolis, Indiana; and Palm Springs, California. A new assembly plant, for production of the Learjet 54/55/56 Longhorn, was scheduled for completion at Tucson in the Spring of 1979.

In January 1979 employees at the company's Aircraft Division facilities numbered approximately 3,450. Combined operations employment, including a wholly-owned subsidiary, Jet Electronics and Technology Inc, totals 4,250. Facilities include 60,385 m² (650,000 sq ft) on a 64-acre site at Wichita and an additional 55,740 m² (600,000 sq ft) throughout the USA.

GATES LEARJET 24F

The prototype Lear Jet twin-jet executive transport flew for the first time on 7 October 1963 and deliveries of production Learjet 23 aircraft began on 13 October 1964. After a total of 104 of this version had been delivered, it was superseded by the Learjet 24, which was certificated under Federal Air Regulations Part 25 (formerly CAR 4B), as have been all subsequent models produced by the company. Deliveries of the Learjet 24 began in March 1966, and a total of 80 were built. This was replaced by a developed version with more powerful engines, known as the Learjet 24B, which received FAA certification on 17 December 1968, and then by the 24D (see 1975-76 *Jane's*) and 24E (see 1978-79 *Jane's*).

The current Learjet 24F, with Century III modifications (see introductory notes), replaced the Learjet 24D and 24D/A in 1976. These latter aircraft were the first to feature a tail unit design in which the non-structural bullet at the junction of the tailplane and fin was deleted. The 'Softflite' handling package (introductory notes) was awaiting certification on the Learjet 24F in September 1979.

TYPE: Twin-jet light executive transport.

WINGS: Cantilever low-wing monoplane. Wing section NACA 64A 109. Dihedral 2° 30'. Incidence 1°. Sweepback 13° at quarter-chord. All-metal eight-spar structure with milled alloy skins. Manually-operated, aerodynamically-balanced all-metal ailerons. Hydraulically-actuated all-metal single-slotted flaps. Hydraulically-actuated all-metal spoilers mounted on trailing-edge ahead of flaps. Electrically-operated trim tab in port aileron. Balance tab in each aileron. Anti-icing by engine bleed air ducted into leading-edges.

FUSELAGE: All-metal flush-riveted semi-monocoque fail-safe structure.

TAIL UNIT: Cantilever all-metal sweptback structure, with electrically-actuated variable-incidence T-tailplane and small ventral fin. Conventional manually-operated control surfaces. Electrically-operated trim tab in rudder. Electrically-heated de-icing of tailplane leading-edges.

LANDING GEAR: Retractable tricycle type, with twin wheels on each main unit and single steerable nose-wheel. Hydraulic actuation, with backup pneumatic extension. Oleo-pneumatic shock-absorbers. Main wheels fitted with Goodyear 18 × 5·50 10-ply tyres, pressure 7·93 bars (115 lb/sq in). Nosewheel fitted with Goodyear Dual Chine tyre size 18 × 4·40 10-ply rating, pressure 7·24 bars (105 lb/sq in).Goodyear multiple-disc hydraulic brakes. Pneumatic emergency braking system. Parking brakes. Fully-modulated anti-skid system.

POWER PLANT: Two General Electric CJ610-8A turbojet engines, each rated at 13·1 kN (2,950 lb st), mounted in pod on each side of fuselage aft of wings. Fuel in integral wing and wingtip tanks, and a bladder-type cell in the fuselage, with a total standard fuel capacity of 3,180 litres (840 US gallons). Oil capacity 3·75 litres (1 US gallon) per engine. Engine inlet anti-icing by bleed air.

ACCOMMODATION: Two seats side by side on flight deck, with dual controls. Up to six passengers in cabin, with one on inward-facing bench seat on starboard side at front, then two on forward or aft-facing armchairs with centre aisle, and three on forward-facing couch. Toilet and stowage space under front inward-facing seat, which can be screened from remainder of cabin by curtain. Refreshment cabinet opposite this seat. Baggage compartment aft of cabin. With back of rear bench seat folded down, baggage compartment and rear of cabin can be used to carry cargo or stretchers. Table at rear. In full cargo version, the rearward-facing armchair seats are also removed. Two-piece door, with upward-hinged portion and downward-hinged portion with integral steps, on port side of cabin at front. Emergency exit on starboard side. Cargo door optional. Windscreen anti-icing by engine bleed air with liquid methyl alcohol backup.

SYSTEMS: Air-conditioning by Freon R12 vapour cycle system, supplemented by ram-air heat exchanger during pressurised flight. Cabin pressurisation, by engine bleed air, has max differential of 0·65 bars (9·4 lb/sq in). Electrical system powered by dual 400A 30V DC starter/generators with AC power supplied from dual 1,000 VA solid-state inverters. Dual 24V 41Ah lead-acid batteries; nickel-cadmium batteries optional. Emergency battery pack optional. Dual engine-driven hydraulic pumps, each capable of maintaining full system pressure of 103·5 bars (1,500 lb/sq in). Auxiliary electrically-driven hydraulic pump. Pneumatic system at pressure of 124-207 bars (1,800-3,000 lb/sq in) for emergency extension of landing gear and operation of wheel brakes. Engine fire detection and extinguishing system. Oxygen system for emergency use has crew demand masks and passenger dropout masks. Alcohol anti-icing system for radome.

AVIONICS AND EQUIPMENT: Complete nav/com systems, to full airline standard, are available to customer's requirements, comprising Collins, Bendix, Sperry or export equipment. All have Learjet autopilot as standard. A typical standard avionics package for the Learjet 24F includes dual Collins VHF-20A com, dual Collins VIR-30A VOR/ILS, dual marker lamps, dual Avtech audio heads, Collins DME-40, Collins TDR-90 transponder, Bendix RDR-1200 radar, Collins ADF-60 ADF, dual Allen 3137 RMI, Collins FD112V flight director, FC-110 flight control system, Collins/J.E.T. PN-101/5-4000 flight indicator (co-pilot), dual J.E.T. VG-206A vertical gyros, dual J.E.T. DN-101D directional gyros, and IDC electric-encoding altimeter with altitude alerter and static defect correction module. Standard equipment includes birdproof windscreen; instrument panel flood, depressurisation warning and engine fire warning lights; Mach warning and Alpha Dot stall warning system; dual clocks; control locks; cabin dome, reading and entry lights; cabin fire extinguisher; stereo system; ice detector, landing/taxi, navigation, strobe and baggage compartment lights; anti-collision beacons; heated pitot tubes and static ports; lightning protection; and fire axe.

DIMENSIONS, EXTERNAL:
- Span over tip-tanks: 10·84 m (35 ft 7 in)
- Wing chord at root: 2·74 m (9 ft 0 in)
- Wing chord at tip: 1·40 m (4 ft 7 in)
- Wing aspect ratio: 5·01
- Length overall: 13·18 m (43 ft 3 in)
- Length of fuselage: 12·50 m (41 ft 0 in)
- Height overall: 3·73 m (12 ft 3 in)
- Tailplane span: 4·47 m (14 ft 8 in)
- Wheel track (c/l shock-absorbers): 2·51 m (8 ft 3 in)
- Wheelbase: 4·93 m (16 ft 2 in)
- Cabin door: Height: 1·57 m (5 ft 2 in)
  - Standard width: 0·61 m (2 ft 0 in)
  - Optional width: 0·91 m (3 ft 0 in)
- Emergency exit: Height: 0·71 m (2 ft 4 in)
  - Width: 0·48 m (1 ft 7 in)

DIMENSIONS, INTERNAL:
- Cabin, between pressure bulkheads:
  - Length: 5·28 m (17 ft 4 in)
  - Max width: 1·50 m (4 ft 11 in)
  - Max height: 1·32 m (4 ft 4 in)
  - Volume, incl baggage compartment: 6·97 m³ (246·0 cu ft)
- Baggage compartment: 1·13 m³ (40·0 cu ft)

AREAS:
- Wings, gross: 21·53 m² (231·77 sq ft)
- Ailerons (total): 1·08 m² (11·70 sq ft)
- Trailing-edge flaps (total): 3·42 m² (36·85 sq ft)
- Spoilers: 0·66 m² (7·05 sq ft)
- Fin: 3·47 m² (37·37 sq ft)
- Rudder, incl tab: 0·67 m² (7·18 sq ft)
- Tailplane: 5·02 m² (54·00 sq ft)
- Elevators: 1·31 m² (14·13 sq ft)

WEIGHTS AND LOADINGS:
- Weight empty, equipped: 3,234 kg (7,130 lb)
- Operating weight empty: 3,415 kg (7,530 lb)
- Max payload: 1,542 kg (3,400 lb)
- Max T-O weight: 6,123 kg (13,500 lb)
- Max ramp weight: 6,259 kg (13,800 lb)
- Max wing bending weight: 5,171 kg (11,400 lb)
- Max landing weight: 5,388 kg (11,880 lb)
- Max wing loading: 284·4 kg/m² (58·25 lb/sq ft)
- Max power loading: 233·7 kg/kN (2·29 lb/lb st)

PERFORMANCE (at max T-O weight, unless stated otherwise):
- Never-exceed speed: Mach 0·81
- Max operating speed at 9,450 m (31,000 ft): 473 knots (877 km/h; 545 mph)
- Max operating speed at 13,715 m (45,000 ft): 464 knots (859 km/h; 534 mph)
- Econ cruising speed at 13,715 m (45,000 ft): 418 knots (774 km/h; 481 mph)
- Stalling speed, 'clean': 111 knots (206 km/h; 128 mph) IAS
- Stalling speed at max landing weight, wheels and flaps down: 88 knots (162·5 km/h; 101 mph) IAS
- Max rate of climb at S/L: 2,164 m (7,100 ft)/min
- Service ceiling: 15,545 m (51,000 ft)
- Service ceiling, one engine out: 8,230 m (27,000 ft)
- Min ground turning radius: 10·46 m (34 ft 4 in)
- T-O run: 703 m (2,305 ft)
- T-O to 10·7 m (35 ft), FAA balanced field length: 1,005 m (3,297 ft)
- Landing from 15 m (50 ft) at typical landing weight: 700 m (2,295 ft)
- Landing run at max landing weight: 419 m (1,375 ft)
- Range with 4 passengers, max fuel and 45 min reserves: 1,355 nm (2,512 km; 1,561 miles)

OPERATIONAL NOISE CHARACTERISTICS (FAR Pt 36):
- T-O noise level: 85·8 EPNdB
- Approach noise level: 95·3 EPNdB
- Sideline noise level: 103·7 EPNdB

Gates Learjet 25C with twin camera installation in specially modified fuselage

GATES LEARJET 25D

First flown on 12 August 1966 as the Learjet 25, this version is 1·27 m (4 ft 2 in) longer than the series 24 aircraft, and will accommodate eight passengers and a crew of two. FAA certification in the air transport category (FAR 25) was obtained on 10 October 1967 and the initial delivery was made in November 1967. British CAA certification was received on 26 June 1974.

The current version has the designation Learjet 25D, and in 1976 this introduced the same Century III improvements as the Learjet 24 series. The 'Softflite' handling package (see introductory notes) has also been standard on this model since 1 July 1979. In addition, 8° flap settings for take-off are approved for this version, improving the high altitude/hot day take-off performance. Factory-installed thrust reversers for the General Electric CJ610-8A turbojet engines are optional.

Two Learjet 25Bs supplied to the Peruvian Air Force in 1974 are each fitted with an underbelly pack containing two Wild RC-10 aerial survey cameras. An accompanying illustration shows a civil-registered Learjet 25C of Cruzeiro do Sul, Brazil, with a similar installation, which leaves the cabin interior quickly convertible for passenger or cargo transport duties.

The description of the Learjet 24F applies also to the Model 25D, except in the following details:

DIMENSIONS, EXTERNAL: As for Learjet 24F except:
- Length overall: 14·50 m (47 ft 7 in)
- Wheelbase: 5·84 m (19 ft 2 in)

DIMENSIONS, INTERNAL: As for Learjet 24F except:
- Cabin, between pressure bulkheads:
  - Length: 6·27 m (20 ft 7 in)
  - Volume, incl baggage compartment: 8·47 m³ (299 cu ft)

WEIGHTS AND LOADINGS:
- Weight empty, equipped: 3,465 kg (7,640 lb)
- Operating weight empty: 3,647 kg (8,040 lb)
- Max payload: 1,524 kg (3,360 lb)
- Max T-O weight: 6,804 kg (15,000 lb)
- Max ramp weight: 7,030 kg (15,500 lb)
- Max landing weight: 6,033 kg (13,300 lb)
- Max wing loading: 315·9 kg/m² (64·7 lb/sq ft)
- Max power loading: 259·7 kg/kN (2·54 lb/lb st)

PERFORMANCE (at max T-O weight, unless stated otherwise):
As for Learjet 24F, except:
- Max cruising speed at 12,500 m (41,000 ft): Mach 0·81 (464 knots; 859 km/h; 534 mph)
- Stalling speed, wheels and flaps down, at max landing weight: 93 knots (172 km/h; 107 mph) IAS
- Max rate of climb at S/L: 1,920 m (6,300 ft)/min
- Rate of climb at S/L, one engine out: 526 m (1,725 ft)/min
- Service ceiling, one engine out: 7,165 m (23,500 ft)
- Min ground turning radius: 11·43 m (37 ft 6 in)
- T-O run: 843 m (2,765 ft)
- T-O to 10·7 m (35 ft), FAA balanced field length: 1,200 m (3,937 ft)
- Landing from 15 m (50 ft) at typical landing weight: 686 m (2,250 ft)
- Landing run at max landing weight: 448 m (1,470 ft)
- Range with 4 passengers, max fuel and 45 min reserves: 1,437 nm (2,663 km; 1,655 miles)

OPERATIONAL NOISE CHARACTERISTICS (FAR Pt 36):
- T-O noise level: 90·9 EPNdB
- Approach noise level: 103·7 EPNdB
- Sideline noise level: 95·2 EPNdB

GATES LEARJET 28 and 29 LONGHORN

Displayed for the first time at the US National Business Aircraft Association's annual convention on 27-29 September 1977, the prototype of the Learjet 28/29 series was generally similar to the 10-seat Learjet 25D, except that it introduced a wing of much increased span, fitted with supercritical winglets. Combined with a cambered leading-edge, this is claimed to improve climb performance, reduce drag, offer improved high-altitude cruise efficiency, reduce runway requirements and reduce approach speed. The 'Softflite' handling package (see introductory notes) has been standard since 1 July 1979. No wingtip fuel tanks are fitted.

Like the Learjet 25D the 28/29 is powered by two General Electric CJ610-8A turbojet engines, each rated at 13·1 kN (2,950 lb st). Total usable fuel capacity of the Model 28 is 2,657 litres (702 US gallons), and of the Model 29 is 3,035 litres (802 US gallons). The Model 28 will accommodate a crew of two and ten passengers, the Model 29 a crew of two and eight passengers. In other respects the 28/29 are similar to the 25D.

FAA certification of the Learjet 28/29 was received on 30 January 1979, and the first production deliveries were scheduled to be made two months later.

On 19-20 February 1979, former astronaut Neil A. Armstrong set five new records for jet aircraft in FAI categories C1f (6,000-8,000 kg) and C1e (3,000-6,000 kg), subject to confirmation. They were for altitude and sustained altitude of 15,545 m (51,000 ft) in each category, and climb to that height in 12 min 26 s.

DIMENSIONS, EXTERNAL:
- Wing span: 13·35 m (43 ft 9·5 in)
- Length overall: 14·51 m (47 ft 7·6 in)
- Height overall: 3·73 m (12 ft 3·1 in)

DIMENSIONS, INTERNAL:
- Cabin, excl flight deck: Length:
  - 28: 4·37 m (14 ft 4 in)
  - 29: 3·86 m (12 ft 8 in)
  - Max width: 1·49 m (4 ft 11 in)
  - Max height: 1·32 m (4 ft 4 in)
  - Volume: 28: 5·80 m³ (205 cu ft)
  - 29: 4·67 m³ (165 cu ft)

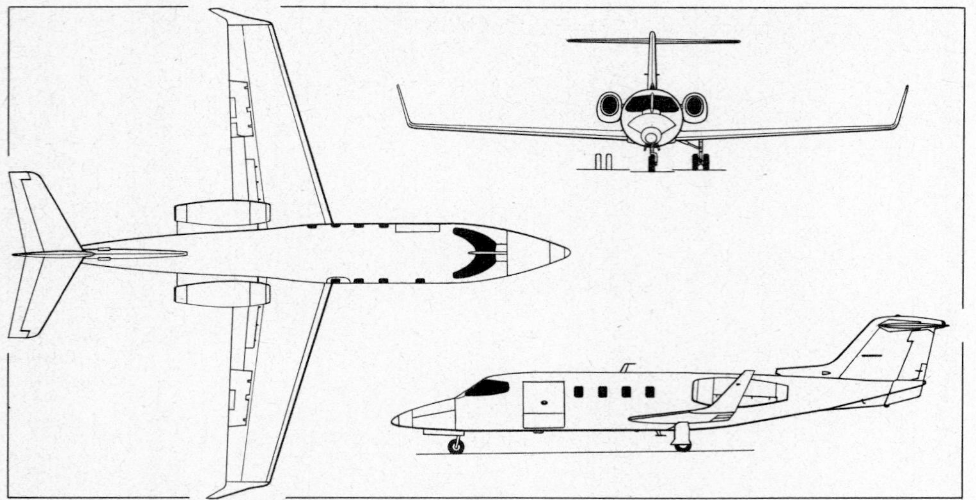

Gates Learjet 28/29 Longhorn, with supercritical winglets *(Pilot Press)*

Prototype of Gates Learjet 28/29 Longhorn series, with newly developed wing

Baggage compartment: 28 — 0·85 m³ (30 cu ft)
29 — 0·76 m³ (27 cu ft)

AREA:
Wings, gross — 24·57 m² (264·5 sq ft)

WEIGHTS AND LOADINGS:
Weight empty: 28 — 3,717 kg (8,195 lb)
29 — 3,700 kg (8,157 lb)
Max T-O weight — 6,804 kg (15,000 lb)
Max ramp weight — 7,030 kg (15,500 lb)
Max landing weight — 6,033 kg (13,300 lb)
Max wing loading — 276·9 kg/m² (56·71 lb/sq ft)
Max power loading — 246·52 kg/kN (2·42 lb/lb st)

PERFORMANCE (at max T-O weight, except where indicated):
Max level speed from S/L to 4,265 m (14,000 ft) — 300 knots (555 km/h; 345 mph) IAS
Max level speed above 4,265 m (14,000 ft) — 350 knots (648 km/h; 403 mph) IAS
Max cruising speed at 12,500 m (41,000 ft) at 5,443 kg (12,000 lb) AUW — 464 knots (859 km/h; 534 mph)
Stalling speed, flaps down — 79 knots (147 km/h; 91 mph)
Max rate of climb at S/L:
28 — 1,888 m (6,195 ft)/min
29 — 1,838 m (6,030 ft)/min
Rate of climb at S/L, one engine out — 610 m (2,000 ft)/min
Max certificated ceiling — 15,545 m (51,000 ft)
Balanced field length — 912 m (2,993 ft)
Landing from 15 m (50 ft) — 792 m (2,600 ft)
Range with max fuel and 544 kg (1,200 lb) payload:
28 — 1,370 nm (2,538 km; 1,577 miles)
29 — 1,580 nm (2,927 km; 1,819 miles)

GATES LEARJET 35A and 36A

Although generally similar in basic configuration to the Learjet 25, the Learjet 35 and 36 are slightly larger in size and powered by turbofan engines. A prototype (known originally as the Learjet Model 26) made its first flight with Garrett-AiResearch TFE 731-2 engines on 4 January 1973. The production 35 and 36, announced in May 1973, are almost identical, differing in fuel capacity and accommodation. FAA certification was awarded in July 1974, and customer deliveries began later that year.

Century III improvements, the 'Softflite' handling package (see introductory notes) and engine synchronisers are standard for both models; options include high-energy brakes and an Aeronca Inc thrust reverser package, available both as a retrofit kit and on new production aircraft.

A special-mission version known as the **Learjet Sea Patrol**, is available (see Addenda).

The description of the Learjet 24F applies also to the Learjet 35A and 36A, except in the following details:

TYPE: Twin-turbofan light executive transport.

WINGS: As for Learjet 24F, except span increased.

FUSELAGE: As for Learjet 24F, except length increased.

TAIL UNIT AND LANDING GEAR: As for Learjet 24F.

POWER PLANT: Two Garrett-AiResearch TFE 731-2-2B turbofan engines, each rated at 15·6 kN (3,500 lb st), mounted in pod on each side of rear fuselage. Fuel in integral wing and wingtip tanks and a fuselage tank, with a combined usable capacity (Learjet 35A) of 3,524 litres (931 US gallons). Learjet 36A has a larger fuselage tank, giving a combined usable total of 4,201 litres (1,110 US gallons). Refuelling point on upper surface of each wingtip tank. Fuel jettison system. Engine nacelle leading-edges anti-iced by engine bleed air.

ACCOMMODATION: Crew of two on flight deck, with dual controls. Up to eight passengers in Learjet 35A; one on inward-facing bench seat on starboard side at front, then two pairs of forward-facing armchairs with centre aisle, and three on forward-facing couch at rear of cabin. Learjet 36A can accommodate up to six passengers, one pair of forward-facing armchairs being removed. Toilet and stowage space under front inward-facing seat which can be screened from remainder of cabin. Refreshment cabinet opposite this seat, aft of passenger door. Baggage compartment with capacity of 226 kg (500 lb) aft of cabin. Two-piece clamshell door at forward end of cabin on port side, with integral steps built into lower half. Emergency exit on starboard side of cabin. Birdproof windscreens.

SYSTEMS: Environmental control system comprises cabin pressurisation, ventilation, heating and cooling. Heating and pressurisation are provided by engine bleed air, with a maximum pressure differential of 0·65 bars (9·4 lb/sq in), maintaining a cabin altitude of 1,980 m (6,500 ft) to an actual altitude of 13,715 m (45,000 ft). Freon R12 vapour cycle cooling system supplemented by a ram-air heat exchanger. Flight control system includes dual yaw dampers, dual stick pushers, dual stick shakers and Mach trim. Anti-icing system includes distribution of engine bleed air for wing, tailplane and engine nacelle leading-edges and windscreen; electrical heating of pitot heads, stall warning vanes and static ports; and alcohol spray on windscreen and nose radome. Hydraulic system supplied by two engine-driven pumps, each pump capable of maintaining alone the full system pressure of 103·5 bars (1,500 lb/sq in), for operation of landing gear, brakes, flaps and spoilers. Electrically-driven hydraulic pump for emergency operation of all hydraulic services. Pneumatic system of 124 to 207 bars (1,800 to 3,000 lb/sq in) pressure for emergency extension of landing gear and operation of brakes. Electrical system powered by two 30V 400A brushless generators, two 1kVA solid-state inverters to provide AC power, and two 24V 41Ah lead-acid batteries. Oxygen system for emergency use, with crew demand masks and drop-out masks for each passenger.

AVIONICS: A standard avionics package is available, comprising two Collins VHF-20A transceivers, two Collins VIR-30A VOR/ILS receivers, dual marker lamps, dual Avtech audio controls, Collins DME-40 with 339F-12A indicator and readout on pilot's HSI, dual Collins TDR-90 transponders, Bendix RDR-1200B radar, Collins ADF-60 ADF with pre-select control, dual Allen 3137 RMIs, Collins FD-108Y flight director indicator, integrated with Collins FC-200 flight control system for pilot, Collins/J.E.T. PN-101/5-4000 co-pilot's flight indicator, two J.E.T. VG-206A vertical gyros, two J.E.T. DN-101D directional gyros, IDC electric-encoding altimeter with altitude alerter and static defect correction module, IDC barometric altimeter for co-pilot, Collins ALT-50A radio altimeter, J.E.T. PS-823B and AI-804 emergency battery and attitude gyro, IDC electric ROC for pilot, and Gables controls for navs, coms, XPDRs and DME. Alternatively, customers may select avionics to meet specific requirements.

EQUIPMENT: Standard equipment includes dual battery overheat warning systems, two anti-collision beacons, landing/taxi lights, navigation lights, map lights, instrument panel and floodlights, baggage compartment lights, cabin reading lights, cabin entry light, strobe lights, recognition light, engine fire warning lights, dual engine fire extinguishing systems, fire extinguishing system armed lights, Mach warning system, cabin pressure warning system, dual stall warning systems, engine synchroniser, internal corrosion protection, polyurethane soundproofing, dual angle of attack indicators, dual battery temperature, exhaust gas temperature and turbine temperature gauges, engine synchronisation meter, cabin differential pressure gauge, cabin rate of climb indicator, dual clocks, wing temperature indicator,

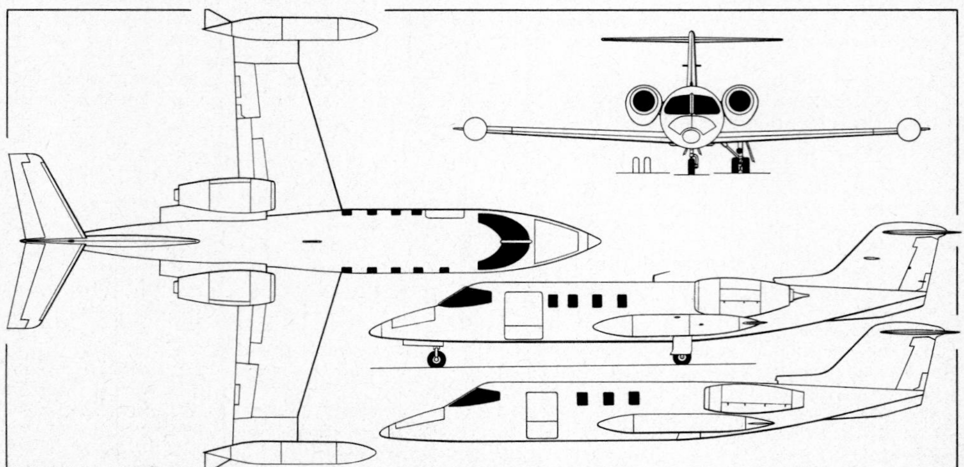

Gates Learjet 35A with optional cargo door. Additional side view (bottom) shows Learjet 25D *(Pilot Press)*

lightning protection, hand fire extinguisher, fire axe, flotation jackets for crew and passengers, control lock, alternate static source, and external power socket.

DIMENSIONS, EXTERNAL:

Wing span over tip-tanks	12·04 m (39 ft 6 in)
Wing chord at root	2·74 m (9 ft 0 in)
Wing chord at tip	1·55 m (5 ft 1 in)
Wing aspect ratio	5·74
Length overall	14·83 m (48 ft 8 in)
Height overall	3·73 m (12 ft 3 in)
Tailplane span	4·47 m (14 ft 8 in)
Wheel track	2·51 m (8 ft 3 in)
Passenger door:	
Standard: Height	1·57 m (5 ft 2 in)
Width	0·61 m (2 ft 0 in)
Optional: Height	1·57 m (5 ft 2 in)
Width	0·91 m (3 ft 0 in)
Emergency exit: Height	0·71 m (2 ft 4 in)
Width	0·48 m (1 ft 7 in)

DIMENSIONS, INTERNAL (A: Learjet 35A; B: Learjet 36A):

Cabin: Length, incl flight deck:	
A	6·60 m (21 ft 8 in)
B	5·77 m (18 ft 11 in)
Max width	1·50 m (4 ft 11 in)
Max height	1·32 m (4 ft 4 in)
Volume incl flight deck: A	7·99 m³ (282 cu ft)
B	6·49 m³ (229 cu ft)
Baggage compartment: A	1·13 m³ (40 cu ft)
B	0·76 m³ (27 cu ft)

AREA:

Wings, gross	23·53 m² (253·3 sq ft)

WEIGHTS AND LOADINGS (A: Learjet 35A; B: Learjet 36A):

Weight empty, equipped: A	4,132 kg (9,110 lb)
B	4,152 kg (9,154 lb)
Max payload: A	1,810 kg (3,990 lb)
B	1,790 kg (3,946 lb)
Max T-O weight: A	7,711 kg (17,000 lb)
B	8,164 kg (18,000 lb)
Max wing bending weight: A, B	6,123 kg (13,500 lb)
Max landing weight: A, B	6,486 kg (14,300 lb)
Max wing loading: A	327·6 kg/m² (67·1 lb/sq ft)
B	347·1 kg/m² (71·1 lb/sq ft)
Max power loading: A	247·1 kg/kN (2·43 lb/lb st)
B	261·7 kg/kN (2·57 lb/lb st)

PERFORMANCE (at max T-O weight, except where indicated otherwise, A: Learjet 35A; B: Learjet 36A):

Never-exceed speed: A, B	Mach 0·83
Max cruising speed:	
A, B	464 knots (859 km/h; 534 mph)
Normal cruising speed:	
A, B	441 knots (817 km/h; 508 mph)
Econ cruising speed:	
A, B	418 knots (774 km/h; 481 mph)
Stalling speed, wheels and flaps down:	
A, B	96 knots (178 km/h; 111 mph) IAS
Max rate of climb at S/L: A	1,494 m (4,900 ft)/min
B	1,379 m (4,525 ft)/min
Rate of climb at S/L, one engine out:	
A	457 m (1,500 ft)/min
B	404 m (1,325 ft)/min
Service ceiling: A, B	13,715 m (45,000 ft)
Service ceiling, one engine out:	
A	7,710 m (25,300 ft)
B	7,165 m (23,500 ft)
T-O to 15 m (50 ft): A	1,287 m (4,224 ft)
B	1,458 m (4,784 ft)
Landing from 15 m (50 ft), at typical landing weight of 5,080 kg (11,200 lb): A	753 m (2,470 ft)
B	754 m (2,475 ft)
Range with 4 passengers, max fuel and 45 min reserves:	
A	2,307 nm (4,276 km; 2,657 miles)
B	2,736 nm (5,071 km; 3,151 miles)

OPERATIONAL NOISE CHARACTERISTICS (FAR Pt 36):

T-O noise level: A	83·7 EPNdB
B	83·6 EPNdB
Approach noise level: A	91·2 EPNdB
B	91·3 EPNdB
Sideline noise level: A	86·9 EPNdB
B	87·4 EPNdB

GATES LEARJET 54, 55 and 56 LONGHORN

Gates Learjet announced, at the Paris Air Show in June 1977, the company's decision to develop a new series of business aircraft known as the Learjet 54, 55 and 56. Stemming from exhaustive engineering and marketing studies, these new aircraft will supplement the existing range of Learjets, providing a more spacious 'stand-up' cabin, and having accommodation for a maximum of eleven passengers in the Learjet 54 and 55, and eight passengers in the Learjet 56.

The first of two Learjet 55 prototypes (N551GL) was rolled out on 2 February 1979, and flew for the first time on 19 April 1979. Certification and first deliveries of the 54/55/56 series are scheduled for mid-1980.

TYPE: Twin-turbofan light executive transport.

WINGS: Cantilever low-wing monoplane. Sweepback 13° at quarter-chord. All-metal multi-spar structure with cavity-milled wing skins. Wing upper surface skin tapers in thickness from wing root to wingtip to save weight. The design incorporates an advanced cambered leading-edge, the 'Softflite' handling package (see introductory notes to Learjet entry) and supercritical winglets. Manually-operated ailerons. Electrically-operated trim tab in port aileron. Hydraulically-operated all-metal single-slotted trailing-edge flaps. Hydraulically-operated all-metal spoilers mounted on wing upper surface just forward of flaps. Anti-icing by engine bleed air ducted into leading-edges.

Gates Learjet 35A ten-seat twin-turbofan light executive transport

FUSELAGE: All-metal flush-riveted semi-monocoque fail-safe structure.

TAIL UNIT: Cantilever all-metal sweptback structure, with electrically-actuated variable-incidence T-tailplane. Small ventral fin. Electrically-heated de-icing of tailplane leading-edge.

LANDING GEAR: Hydraulically-retractable tricycle type, with twin wheels on each main unit and single steerable nosewheel. High-pressure pneumatic system for emergency extension. Oleo-pneumatic shock-absorbers. Chined nosewheel tyre. High-energy hydraulic braking system, with pneumatic backup. Fully-modulated anti-skid units.

POWER PLANT: Two Garrett-AiResearch TFE 731-3A turbofan engines, each rated at 16·24 kN (3,650 lb st), mounted in pod on each side of fuselage aft of wing. Fuel in integral wing tanks and a bladder type fuselage tank, with a combined capacity of (Model 54) 3,282 litres (867 US gallons), (Model 55) 3,846 litres (1,016 US gallons), (Model 56) 4,636 litres (1,225 US gallons). Refuelling point on upper surface of each outer wing. Engine nacelle leading-edges and fan hubs anti-iced by engine bleed air.

ACCOMMODATION: Crew of two on flight deck, with dual controls. Models 54 and 55 can seat from six to eleven passengers in differing interior layouts, all with an aft toilet, and all but the 10/11-seat versions with a galley cabinet. Model 56 seats six to eight passengers. Baggage space at rear of cabin, and in fuselage nose and tailcone. Two-piece clamshell door at forward end of cabin on port side, with integral steps built into the lower section. Emergency exit on starboard side of cabin.

SYSTEMS: Environmental control system comprises cabin pressurisation, ventilation, heating and cooling. Heating and pressurisation are provided by engine bleed air, with a maximum pressure differential of 0·65 bars (9·4 lb/sq in), maintaining a cabin altitude of 2,440 m (8,000 ft) to an actual altitude of 15,545 m (51,000 ft). Freon vapour-cycle cooling system, supplemented by a ram-air system. Anti-icing system includes distribution of engine bleed air to wing leading-edges, engine nacelle leading-edges and fan hubs, and pilot and co-pilot windscreens; electrical anti-icing of tailplane leading-edge, pitot heads, stall warning vanes and static ports; and alcohol anti-icing of windscreens and radome. Hydraulic system supplied by two engine-driven variable-volume constant-pressure pumps, one on each engine, each capable of maintaining alone the full system pressure of 103·5 bars (1,500 lb/sq in) for operation of landing gear, brakes, flaps and spoilers. Electrically-driven hydraulic pump for emergency operation of all hydraulic services. Pneumatic system of 124 to 207 bars (1,800 to 3,000 lb/sq in) pressure for emergency extension of landing gear and operation of brakes. Electrical system powered by two 28V 400A engine-driven brushless generators, either of which is capable of maintaining adequate DC power to operate all electrical services; two 1kVA solid-state inverters to provide AC power; and two 24V 40Ah nickel-cadmium batteries. Oxygen system of 1·08 m³ (38 cu ft) capacity, with crew demand masks; dropout mask for each passenger, which is presented automatically if cabin altitude exceeds 4,265 m (14,000 ft).

AVIONICS (provisional): Standard package will comprise dual Collins VIR-30A nav receivers, dual Collins VHF-20A com transceivers, dual Collins TDR-90 transponders, dual Allen 3137 RMIs, dual J.E.T. VG-206D vertical gyros, dual J.E.T. DN-104A directional gyros, Collins DME-40 DME, Collins ADF-60 ADF, Collins ALT-50A radio altimeter, Bendix RDR-1200B weather radar, and fully integrated autopilot/flight director with dual Collins FD-108Y flight indicators integrated with a J.E.T. FC-200 flight control system.

EQUIPMENT: Standard equipment includes six swivel/reclining seats on Models 54 and 55, five on Model 56, galley cabinet, two folding tables, electric flushing toilet, reading lights, air vents, indirect lighting, window shades, refreshment cabinet, entrance step light, cabin fire extinguisher and axe.

DIMENSIONS, EXTERNAL:

Wing span	13·35 m (43 ft 9½ in)
Length overall	16·80 m (55 ft 1¼ in)
Height overall	4·48 m (14 ft 8¼ in)
Wheelbase	2·51 m (8 ft 3 in)

DIMENSIONS, INTERNAL (A: Model 54; B: Model 55; C: Model 56):

Cabin: Length, excl flight deck: A	5·56 m (18 ft 3 in)
B	5·08 m (16 ft 8 in)
C	4·39 m (14 ft 5 in)
Max width	1·80 m (5 ft 11 in)
Max height	1·74 m (5 ft 8½ in)

Prototype of the Gates Learjet 55 Longhorn, first flown in April 1979

Volume, incl flight deck: A 14·00 m³ (495 cu ft)
B 13·35 m³ (472 cu ft)
C 12·70 m³ (449 cu ft)
Baggage capacity, total: A 2·24 m³ (79 cu ft)
B 1·70 m³ (60 cu ft)
C 1·41 m³ (50 cu ft)
AREA:
Wings, gross 24·57 m² (264·5 sq ft)
WEIGHTS (estimated):
Weight empty: A 4,675 kg (10,307 lb)
B 4,686 kg (10,331 lb)
C 4,848 kg (10,687 lb)
Max T-O weight: A 8,391 kg (18,500 lb)
B 8,618 kg (19,000 lb)
C 9,299 kg (20,500 lb)
Max ramp weight: A 8,505 kg (18,750 lb)
B 8,732 kg (19,250 lb)
C 9,412 kg (20,750 lb)
Max landing weight: A, B, C 7,257 kg (16,000 lb)
PERFORMANCE (estimated, at max T-O weight except where indicated):
Max level speed at 12,495 m (41,000 ft) at AUW of 6,350 kg (14,000 lb):
A, B, C 464 knots (859 km/h; 534 mph)
FAR 25 balanced field length:
A 1,217 m (3,994 ft)
B 1,292 m (4,240 ft)
C 1,448 m (4,750 ft)
FAR 91 landing distance:
A, B, C 899 m (2,950 ft)
Max range, incl allowances for warm-up, T-O, climb, cruise at long-range cruise setting, descent and land, with 45 min reserves at last cruise altitude:
A 2,172 nm (4,025 km; 2,501 miles)
B 2,605 nm (4,828 km; 3,000 miles)
C 3,012 nm (5,578 km; 3,466 miles)

GENERAL DYNAMICS
GENERAL DYNAMICS CORPORATION

HEAD OFFICE: Pierre Laclede Center, St Louis, Missouri 63105
Telephone: (314) 862 2440
CHAIRMAN, PRESIDENT AND CHIEF EXECUTIVE OFFICER:
David S. Lewis
EXECUTIVE VICE-PRESIDENTS:
James M. Beggs (Aerospace)
Lester Crown
Guy W. Fiske (Commercial)
Gorden E. MacDonald (Finance)
VICE-PRESIDENTS:
Richard E. Adams (General Manager, Fort Worth Division)
Leonard F. Buchanan (General Manager, Convair Division)
Otto J. Glasser (International, Washington)
Max Golden (Contracts)
Lyman C. Josephs (International)
E. J. LeFevre (Government Relations)
Edward E. Lynn (General Counsel)
Warren G. Sullivan (Industrial Relations)
P. Takis Veliotis (General Manager, Electric Boat Division)
Wayne Wells (Treasurer)
Robert H. Widmer (Science and Engineering)
Convair Division:
PO Box 80847, San Diego, California 92138
VICE-PRESIDENTS:
James M. Adamson (Programme Director, Aircraft)
G. E. Blackshaw (Research Engineering)
Leonard F. Buchanan (General Manager)
R. G. Daly (Operations)
Jay E. Hawley (Contracts and Estimating)
Ralph S. MacKenzie (Programme Director, Tomahawk)
J. A. Robertson (Marketing)
Fort Worth Division:
PO Box 748, Fort Worth, Texas 76101
VICE-PRESIDENTS:
Richard E. Adams (General Manager)
Forrest E. Armstrong (111 Programmes)
P. R. Cowen (Deputy General Manager)
Edward E. Hatchett (Finance)
D. R. Kent (F-16 Engineering)
Julius Y. McClure (Quality Assurance)
Robert W. McGuffee (Logistics and Support)
Herbert F. Rogers (Deputy General Manager and F-16 Programme Director)
Sterling V. Starr (Marketing)
Sidney C. Wilkinson (Operations)
Theodore S. Webb Jr (Research and Engineering)

General Dynamics conducts its US aerospace activities at four divisions: Convair Division, with operations at San Diego, California; Fort Worth Division, with operations at Fort Worth, Texas; Pomona Division, at Pomona, California; and Electronics Division, with headquarters in San Diego. Convair Division is responsible for the design, development and production of commercial aircraft and of systems for space exploration. Current programmes include development of four variants of the Tomahawk cruise missile, two for the US Navy and two for the USAF. Fort Worth Division is engaged in the design, development and production of military aircraft and electronics. Pomona Division is engaged in tactical missile and other ordnance programmes. Electronics Division is a leader in new technology to support the development and production of advanced electronics systems. Major programmes include sophisticated navigation positioning systems, tactical data and command control systems, automatic test equipment for high performance aircraft, and range measuring systems.

Fort Worth is currently responsible for production of the F-16 multi-role fighter; spares, support and modification/update for the F-111 fighter-bomber; and various ground-based radar systems. Convair Division is responsible for production of a major portion of the fuselage for the McDonnell Douglas DC-10 commercial transport aircraft and the KC-10A tanker/cargo aircraft, the mid-fuselage section of the Space Shuttle Orbiter vehicle, the Atlas-Centaur launch vehicle used to boost unmanned spacecraft and satellites, and the Tomahawk cruise missile.

Convair Division also retains detailed tooling for high-usage spares for the Convair-Liner 240/340/440 series of piston-engined transports, and Convair 880 and 990 jet transports, and is manufacturing components for operators of these types.

First of four RAAF aircraft converted to RF-111C configuration for electronic reconnaissance duties

GENERAL DYNAMICS F-111

Production of this two-seat variable-geometry tactical fighter was completed in 1976, but the various versions described in the 1978-79 and earlier editions of *Jane's* will remain important elements of USAF and Royal Australian Air Force strength for many more years, as will Strategic Air Command's FB-111A medium-range bomber variant.

Important avionics update programmes are continuing to maintain the effectiveness of Tactical Air Command F-111s. Details of some of those programmes follow:

F-111A/E. Current effort, scheduled to continue in RDT & E phases through FY 1981, involves replacement of current analogue bombing and navigation systems with digital equipment. This will provide capacity to handle modern guided munitions and advanced sensors, as well as growth potential for future systems such as the Navstar global positioning system and JTIDS (Joint Tactical Information Distribution System).

F-111F. Two F-111Fs fitted with Pave Tack pods were delivered to TAC's 4485th Test Squadron in 1977, and this 585 kg (1,290 lb) pack is expected to be deployed eventually throughout the F-111 force. Pave Tack, for which Ford Aerospace is prime contractor, is carried inside the aircraft's weapon bay on a cradle which rotates 180° in 5 s to expose it for use. Embodying a data link for stand-off delivery, Pave Tack provides a day/night all-weather capability to acquire, track and designate ground targets for laser, infra-red and electro-optically guided weapons, from very low altitudes if necessary.

Six more to be converted to ECM jamming aircraft under USAF contract of April 1979 (see description of EF-111A below and under Grumman entry).

EF-111A. ECM jamming version. Developed by Grumman, which converted two F-111As to this configuration for evaluation. Details under Grumman entry.

RF-111C. Four of the RAAF's 21 remaining F-111C strike aircraft have been allocated to an electronic/photographic reconnaissance role. An accompanying illustration shows the first of them, which was modified at Fort Worth and returned to Australia in the second quarter of 1979. Reconnaissance kits for the other three aircraft are being installed by RAAF personnel They include a Fairchild KA-56E low-altitude panoramic camera, Fairchild KS-87C split vertical camera, Honeywell AN/AAD-5 infra-red linescan and Cardion Electronics TV.

FB-111. The 1978-79 *Jane's* contained details of the FB-111H, a projected manned penetration bomber that could be evolved from the FB-111A to meet SAC requirements following cancellation of the Rockwell B-1. A simpler conversion of approximately 150 F-111Ds and FB-111As was proposed in early 1979, under the tentative designation **FB-111B.** Apart from an increase in wing span, modifications would be concentrated mainly on the rear fuselage, to house new engines (probably General Electric F101s as developed for the B-1) and additional fuel. GD believes that converted aircraft could be operational by 1983-84.

The following abbreviated description applies to the F-111F, which was described fully in the 1978-79 *Jane's*:

TYPE: Two-seat variable-geometry multi-purpose fighter.

POWER PLANT: Two Pratt & Whitney TF30-P-100 turbofan engines, each giving 111·5 kN (25,100 lb st) with afterburning. Fuel tanks in wings and fuselage.

ACCOMMODATION: Crew of two side by side in air-conditioned and pressurised cabin. Portion of canopy over each seat is hinged on aircraft centreline and opens upward. Zero-speed, zero-altitude (including underwater) emergency escape module developed by McDonnell Douglas Corpn and utilising a 178 kN (40,000 lb st) Rocket Power Inc rocket motor. Emergency procedure calls for both crew members to remain in capsule cabin section, which is propelled away from aircraft by rocket motor and lowered to ground by parachute. Airbags cushion impact and form flotation gear in water. Entire capsule forms survival shelter.

ARMAMENT: One M61 multi-barrel 20 mm gun plus one B43 bomb, or two B43s, in internal weapon bay. External stores are carried on three attachments under each wing. The two inboard pylons on each side pivot as the wings sweep back, to keep the stores parallel with the fuselage. The outboard pylon on each wing is jettisonable and non-swivelling.

DIMENSIONS, EXTERNAL:
Wing span: spread 19·20 m (63 ft 0 in)
fully swept 9·74 m (31 ft 11·4 in)
Length overall 22·40 m (73 ft 6 in)
Height overall 5·22 m (17 ft 1·4 in)
WEIGHTS:
Weight empty 21,537 kg (47,481 lb)
Max T-O weight 45,359 kg (100,000 lb)
PERFORMANCE:
Max speed at height Mach 2·5
Max speed at S/L Mach 1·2
Service ceiling over 18,000 m (59,000 ft)
T-O and landing run under 915 m (3,000 ft)
Range with max internal fuel
over 2,540 nm (4,707 km; 2,925 miles)

GENERAL DYNAMICS F-16

USAF designations: F-16A and F-16B

The F-16 had its origin in the USAF's Lightweight Fighter (LWF) prototype programme, in 1972. The history of this programme and a description of the YF-16 prototypes can be found in the 1978-79 and 1977-78 editions of *Jane's* respectively.

The first of two YF-16 prototypes (72-01567) made its official first flight on 2 February 1974. A level speed of Mach 2 at 12,200 m (40,000 ft) was attained on 11 March 1974. The second YF-16 (72-01568) flew for the first time on 9 May 1974. During subsequent weapon trials, this aircraft extended the planned operational capability of the design by completing successfully the initial launch of Sparrow missiles on 6 October 1977 and of a Sky Flash missile in November 1978.

On 13 January 1975 the Secretary of the USAF announced that the F-16 had been selected for full-scale engineering development. The original YF-16 requirement for an air superiority day fighter was expanded, to give equal emphasis to the air-to-surface role, including provision of radar and all-weather navigation capabilities. Finalised contracts covered the manufacture of eight pre-production aircraft, comprising six single-seat **F-16As** and two two-seat **F-16Bs,** construction of which began in July 1975.

The first development F-16A made its first flight on 8 December 1976, and the first F-16B on 8 August 1977. The last of the eight development aircraft was the second two-seater, which made its first flight in June 1978. Meanwhile, the USAF had indicated its intention to procure a total of 1,388 F-16s, including 204 two-seaters.

On 7 June 1975 a joint announcement by the four NATO countries of Belgium, Denmark, the Netherlands and Norway confirmed their selection of the F-16 to replace F-104s in current service. The initial order was for 348 aircraft (Belgium 116, Denmark 58, the Netherlands 102 and Norway 72), of which 58 will be two-seaters. Under co-production agreements, final assembly lines for these aircraft have been established in Belgium and the Netherlands. About 30 European companies are producing F-16 components, avionics and equipment.

In August 1977 Israel announced plans to acquire a minimum of 75 F-16s, of which deliveries are scheduled to begin in January 1980.

A $1·9 billion programme announced in the Spring of 1978 authorised the start of production by General Dynamics of 105 aircraft for the USAF, 192 of the 348 for Europe, and 55 of the 160 that had been ordered by Iran, but which were cancelled in January 1979. The first production F-16A (78-0001) flew for the first time on 7 August 1978 and was delivered formally to the USAF ten days later; five had been delivered by the end of 1978, with deliveries planned of a further 55 in 1979. First F-16 to enter operational service was delivered to the USAF's 388th Tactical Fighter Wing on 6 January 1979. The first F-16 for Europe was delivered to the Belgian Air Force on 26 January 1979.

General Dynamics announced on 7 April 1978 that company-funded preliminary design work had begun to evolve a sophisticated two-seat 'Wild Weasel' version of the F-16. This would be able to operate in an autonomous hunter-killer mode, or in direct support of strike aircraft. The USAF has no current requirement for such a version of the F-16, but allied nations have expressed an interest. Weapons under consideration for this version include AGM-45 Shrike anti-radiation missiles on wing stations 2 and 8, and either AGM-78 'F' Standard ARM, AGM-65 Maverick or AGM-88 HARM missiles on wing stations 3 and 7. The Wild Weasel F-16 can also carry 1,400 litre (370 US gallon) external fuel tanks on wing stations 4 and 6, and an electronic countermeasures pod on the fuselage centreline.

In late 1978 an F-16 prototype, fitted with a Martin Marietta ATLIS II (Automatic Tracking Laser Illumination System) pod, became the first single-seat fighter to hit ground targets with GBU-10 and GBU-16 laser-guided bombs, without assistance from air/ground locators. In December 1978 the USAF selected the F-16 as a testbed to explore promising new fighter aircraft technologies, under the Advanced Fighter Technology Integration (AFTI-16) programme.

The following description applies to the F-16A and F-16B, as indicated:

Type: Single-seat lightweight air combat fighter (F-16A) and two-seat fighter/trainer (F-16B).

Wings: Cantilever mid-wing monoplane, of blended wing/body design and cropped-delta planform. The blended wing/body concept is achieved by flaring the wing/body intersection, thus not only providing lift from the body at high angles of attack but also giving less wetted area and increased internal fuel volume. In addition, thickening of the wing root gives a more rigid structure, with a weight saving of some 113 kg (250 lb). Basic wing is of NACA 64A-204 section, with 40° sweepback on leading-edges. Structure is mainly of aluminium alloy, with 11 spars, 5 ribs and single upper and lower skins, and is attached to fuselage by machined aluminium fittings. Vortex lift and control is provided by sharp, highly-swept strakes extending along the fuselage forebody. This permits significant reduction in wing area. Variable wing camber is achieved by the use of leading-edge manoeuvring flaps that are programmed automatically as a function of Mach number and angle of attack. The increased wing camber maintains effective lift coefficients at high angles of attack. These flaps are one-piece bonded aluminium honeycomb sandwich structures, actuated by an AiResearch drive system using rotary actuators. The trailing-edges carry large flaperons (flaps/ailerons), which are interchangeable left with right and are actuated by National Water Lift integrated servo-actuators. The maximum rate of flaperon movement is 80°/s.

Fuselage: Semi-monocoque all-metal structure of frames and longerons, built in three main modules: forward (to just aft of cockpit), centre and aft. Nose radome built by Brunswick Corporation. Highly-swept vortex control strakes along the fuselage forebody.

Tail Unit: Cantilever structure with sweptback surfaces. Fin is multi-spar multi-rib aluminium structure with graphite-epoxy skins, aluminium tip, and glassfibre dorsal fin and root fairing. Interchangeable all-moving tailplane halves, constructed of graphite-epoxy composite laminate skins with full-depth bonded aluminium honeycomb sandwich core, titanium spar, steel leading-edge caps and aluminium tips. Ventral fins are bonded aluminium honeycomb core with aluminium skins. Split speed-brake inboard of rear portion of each horizontal tail surface to each side of nozzle, each deflecting 60° from the closed position. National Water Lift servo-actuators for rudder and tailplane.

The first production example of the General Dynamics F-16A multi-role fighter

First production example of the General Dynamics F-16B two-seat fighter/trainer

Landing Gear: Menasco hydraulically-retractable type, nose unit retracting aft and main units forward into fuselage. Nosewheel is located aft of intake, to reduce the risk of foreign objects being drawn into the engine during ground operation, and rotates 90° during retraction to lie horizontally under engine air intake duct. Oleo-pneumatic struts on all units. Goodyear main wheels and brakes; B. F. Goodrich main-wheel tyres, size 25·5 × 8-14. Steerable nosewheel with B. F. Goodrich tyre, size 18 × 5·5-8. All but two main unit components interchangeable. Brake-by-wire system on main gear, with Goodyear anti-skid units. Runway arrester hook under rear fuselage.

Power Plant: One Pratt & Whitney F100-PW-100(3) turbofan engine, rated at approx 111·2 kN (25,000 lb st) with afterburning, mounted within the rear fuselage. Fixed-geometry intake, with boundary layer splitter plate, beneath fuselage. A variable-geometry intake can be fitted later, without difficulty, if desirable to improve high-speed performance. The underfuselage intake position was chosen because here the airflow suffers least disturbance throughout the entire range of aircraft manoeuvres, and because it eliminates the problem of gun gas ingestion. Foreign object damage is avoided by placing the nose gear aft of the inlet lip. Standard fuel contained in wing and five fuselage cells which function as two tanks; internal fuel weight is 3,162 kg (6,972 lb) in F-16A, and approx 17% less in F-16B. In-flight refuelling receptacle in top of centre-fuselage, aft of cockpit. Auxiliary fuel can be carried in drop-tanks on underwing and underfuselage hardpoints.

Accommodation: Pilot only in F-16A, in air-conditioned cockpit. McDonnell Douglas Aces II zero-zero ejection seat. Texstar transparent bubble canopy, made of polycarbonate, an advanced plastics material. The windscreen and forward canopy are an integral unit without a forward bow-frame, and are separated from the aft canopy by a simple support structure which serves also as the break-point where the forward section pivots upward and aft to give access to the cockpit. A redundant safety-lock feature prevents canopy loss. Windscreen/canopy design provides 360° all-round view, 195° fore and aft, 40° down over the side, and 15° down over the nose. Supersonic drag penalty is considered to be more than offset by the improved rearward view afforded to the pilot. To enable the pilot to sustain high-*g* forces, and for pilot comfort, the seat is inclined 30° aft and the heel-line is raised. In normal operation the canopy is pivoted upward and aft by electrical power; the pilot is also able to unlatch the canopy manually and open it with a backup handcrank. Emergency jettison is provided by explosive unlatching devices and two forward-mounted rockets. A limited-displacement, force-sensing control stick is provided on the right hand console, with a suitable armrest, to provide precise control inputs during combat manoeuvres. The F-16B has two cockpits arranged in tandem and equipped with all controls, displays, instruments, electronics and life-support systems required to perform both training and combat missions. The layout of the F-16B second station is essentially the same as that of the F-16A, and is fully systems-operational. A single-enclosure polycarbonate transparency, made in two pieces and spliced aft of the forward seat with a metal bow-frame and lateral support member, provides outstanding view from both cockpits.

Systems: Regenerative bootstrap air-cycle environmental control system by United Technologies' Hamilton Standard Division, using engine bleed air, for pressurisation and cooling. Two separate and independent hydraulic systems supply power for operation of the primary flight control surfaces and the utility functions. Electrical system powered by engine-driven Westinghouse 40kVA and Lear Siegler 5kVA generators and ground control units, with Sundstrand constant-speed drive. Four dedicated, sealed-cell batteries provide transient electrical power protection for the fly-by-wire flight control system. Application of the control configured vehicle (CCV) principle of relaxed static stability produces a significant reduction in trim drag, especially at high load factors and supersonic speeds. The aircraft centre of gravity is allowed to move aft, reducing both the tail drag and the change in drag on the wing due to changes in lift required to balance the down-load on the tail. Relaxed static stability imposes a requirement for a highly-reliable, full-time-operating, stability augmentation system, including reliable electronic, electrical and hydraulic provisions. The signal paths in this quad-redundant system are used to control the aircraft, replacing the usual mechanical linkages. Direct electrical control is employed from pilot controls to surface actuators. An onboard Sundstrand/Solar jet fuel starter is provided for engine self-start capability. Hamilton Standard turbine compressor, and Sundstrand accessory drive gearbox. Simmonds fuel measuring system. AiResearch emergency power unit automatically drives a standby generator and pump to provide uninterrupted electrical and hydraulic power for control in the event of the engine or primary power systems becoming inoperative.

Avionics and Equipment: Westinghouse pulse-Doppler range and angle track radar, with planar array in nose. The radar has a lookdown range, in ground clutter, of 20-30 nm (37-56 km; 23-35 miles), and a lookup range of 25-40 nm (46-74 km; 29-46 miles). Forward avionics bay, immediately forward of cockpit, contains radar, air data equipment, inertial navigation system and flight control computer; rear avionics bay contains ILS, Tacan and IFF. A Dalmo Victor ALR-69 radar warning system, with AEL antennae, is installed. Communications equipment includes Magnavox AN/ARC-164 UHF transceiver; provisions for a Magnavox KY-58 secure

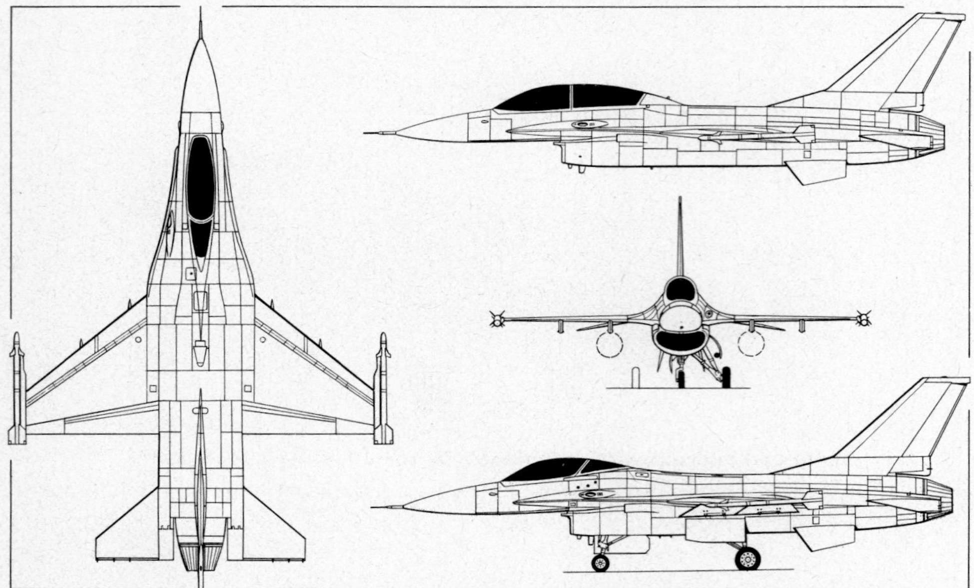

General Dynamics F-16A, with additional side view (top) of F-16B *(Pilot Press)*

voice system; Memcor AN/ARC-115 VHF transceiver; government furnished AN/AIC-18/25 intercom; and Novatronics interference blanker. Sperry Flight Systems central air data computer. Singer-Kearfott modified SKN-2400 inertial navigation system; Collins AN/ARN-108 ILS; Collins AN/ARN-118 Tacan; Teledyne Electronics AN/APX-101 air-to-ground IFF transponder with a government furnished IFF control; government furnished National Security Agency KIT-2A/TSEC cryptographic equipment; Lear Siegler stick force sensors; Marconi Avionics electronic head-up display set; a government-furnished horizontal situation indicator; Teledyne Avionics angle of attack transmitter; Gull Airborne angle of attack indicator; Clifton Precision attitude director indicator; Delco fire control computer; Photo-Sonics gun camera; Kaiser radar electro-optical display. Landing/taxying light on each main landing gear strut.

ARMAMENT: General Electric M61A-1 20 mm multi-barrel cannon in the port-side wing/body fairing, equipped with a General Electric ammunition handling system and a 'snapshoot' gunsight (part of the head-up display system) and 500 rounds of ammunition. There is a mounting for an infra-red air-to-air missile at each wingtip, one underfuselage hardpoint and six underwing hardpoints for the carriage of additional stores. The underfuselage station is stressed for a load of up to 1,000 kg (2,200 lb), the two inboard underwing stations for 1,587 kg (3,500 lb) each, the two centre underwing stations for 1,134 kg (2,500 lb) each, all at 5·5*g*; the two outboard underwing stations and the two wingtip stations 113 kg (250 lb) each, all at 9·0*g*. Total possible external weapon load, with reduced internal fuel, is 6,894 kg (15,200 lb), and a total load of approximately 4,763 kg (10,500 lb) can be carried with full internal fuel. Typical stores loads can include two wingtip-mounted AIM-9J/L Sidewinders, with up to four more on the outer underwing stations; Sargent-Fletcher 1,400 litre (370 US gallon; 308 Imp gallon) drop-tanks on the inboard underwing stations; a 1,136 litre (300 US gallon; 250 Imp gallon) drop-tank or a 2,200 lb bomb on the underfuselage station; a Martin Marietta Pave Penny laser tracker pod along the starboard side of the nacelle; and single or cluster bombs, air-to-surface missiles, or flare pods, on the four inner underwing stations. Stores can be launched from Aircraft Hydro-Forming MAU-12C/A bomb ejector racks, Hughes LAU-88 launchers, or Orgen triple or multiple ejector racks. Westinghouse AN/ALQ-119 ECM (jammer) pods and pod control system have been listed among probable equipment, and can be carried on the centreline and two underwing stations. Modified Tracor ALE-40 internal pyrotechnic/chaff dispensers have been specified. Weapon delivery capabilities include air-to-air combat with gun and Sidewinder missiles, and air-to-ground attack with gun, rockets, conventional bombs, special weapons, laser-guided and electro-optical weapons. Weapons already launched successfully from F-16s include radar-guided Sparrow and Sky Flash air-to-air missiles and TV-guided Maverick air-to-surface missiles.

DIMENSIONS, EXTERNAL:
- Wing span over missile launchers 9·45 m (31 ft 0 in)
- Wing span over missiles 10·01 m (32 ft 10 in)
- Wing aspect ratio 3·0
- Length overall, excl probe 14·52 m (47 ft 7·7 in)
- Height overall 5·01 m (16 ft 5·2 in)
- Tailplane span 5·495 m (18 ft 0·34 in)
- Wheel track 2·36 m (7 ft 9 in)
- Wheelbase 4·00 m (13 ft 1·44 in)

AREA:
- Wings, gross 27·87 m² (300·0 sq ft)

WEIGHTS AND LOADINGS:
- Operational weight empty:
  - F-16A 6,607 kg (14,567 lb)
  - F-16B 6,868 kg (15,141 lb)
- Internal fuel load: F-16A 3,162 kg (6,972 lb)
  - F-16B 2,624 kg (5,785 lb)
- Max external load (F-16A) 6,894 kg (15,200 lb)
- Structural design gross weight (9·0*g*) with full internal fuel (F-16A) 10,205 kg (22,500 lb)
- Maximum symmetric design load factor with full internal fuel at 10,205 kg (22,500 lb) gross weight (F-16A) 9·0
- Max T-O weight:
  - F-16A, air-to-air, no external tanks 10,335 kg (22,785 lb)
  - F-16B, air-to-air, no external tanks 10,051 kg (22,160 lb)
  - F-16A with external load 16,057 kg (35,400 lb)
- Wing loading:
  - at 10,070 kg (22,200 lb) AUW 361 kg/m² (74 lb/sq ft)
  - at 14,968 kg (33,000 lb) AUW 537 kg/m² (110 lb/sq ft)
- Thrust/weight ratio ('clean') 1·1 to 1

PERFORMANCE (F-16A):
- Max level speed at 12,200 m (40,000 ft) above Mach 2·0
- Service ceiling more than 15,240 m (50,000 ft)
- Radius of action more than 500 nm (925 km; 575 miles)
- Ferry range, with drop-tanks more than 2,100 nm (3,890 km; 2,415 miles)

GREAT LAKES
GREAT LAKES AIRCRAFT COMPANY

HEAD OFFICE: PO Box 11132, Wichita, Kansas 67202
Telephone: (316) 265 0786

PRESIDENT: Douglas L. Champlin

There has been no recent news from this company, but US press reports suggest that production of the Great Lakes Sport Trainer Model 2T-1A-2 was terminated at the end of 1978. Great Lakes Aircraft Company is believed to continue providing parts for the 126 Sport Trainers still in service. Details of the aircraft can be found in the 1978-79 *Jane's*.

GRUMMAN
GRUMMAN CORPORATION

HEAD OFFICE: 1111 Stewart Avenue, Bethpage, New York 11714
Telephone: (516) 575 0574

CHAIRMAN OF THE BOARD AND CHIEF EXECUTIVE OFFICER: John C. Bierwirth

PRESIDENT AND CHIEF OPERATING OFFICER: Joseph G. Gavin Jr

VICE-CHAIRMAN OF THE BOARD: John F. Carr

VICE-PRESIDENTS:
- Nat P.Busi (Controller)
- Robert G. Freese (Treasurer)
- Weyman B. Jones (Public Affairs)
- Robert G. Landon (Investment Management)
- Ross S. Mickey (Offset Activities)
- Lawrence M. Pierce (General Counsel)
- John B. Rettaliata (Community Affairs)
- Peter E. Viemeister (Development)

SECRETARY: Robert W. Bradshaw

GRUMMAN AEROSPACE CORPORATION

See below

GRUMMAN ALLIED INDUSTRIES INC

HEAD OFFICE AND WORKS: 600 Old Country Road, Garden City, New York 11530
Telephone: (516) 741 3500

CHAIRMAN OF THE BOARD AND CHIEF EXECUTIVE OFFICER: Robert G. Freese

PRESIDENT AND CHIEF OPERATING OFFICER: Robert W. Somerville

GRUMMAN DATA SYSTEMS CORPORATION

HEAD OFFICE AND WORKS: Bethpage, New York 11714
Telephone: (516) 575 0574

CHAIRMAN OF THE BOARD: John F. Carr

PRESIDENT: Robert A. Nafis

GRUMMAN ENERGY SYSTEMS INC

HEAD OFFICE AND WORKS: Bethpage, New York 11714
Telephone: (516) 575 0574

CHAIRMAN OF THE BOARD: Joseph G. Gavin Jr

PRESIDENT: Ronald B. Peterson

GRUMMAN INTERNATIONAL COMPANY

HEAD OFFICE: Bethpage, New York 11714
Telephone: (516) 575 1101

PRESIDENT: Peter B. Oram

The Grumman Aircraft Engineering Corporation was incorporated on 6 December 1929. Important changes in the corporate structure of the company were announced in 1969, resulting in the formation of Grumman Corporation, a small holding company, with Grumman Aerospace Corporation, Grumman Allied Industries Inc and Grumman Data Systems Corporation. A new organisation known as Grumman Ecosystems Corporation (now Grumman Energy Systems Inc) was brought into operation in January 1971, and on 2 January 1973 a merger took place with American Aviation Corporation of Cleveland, Ohio, to create Grumman American Aviation Corporation as a new subsidiary of Grumman Corporation. In 1978, Grumman Corporation's holding in Grumman American Aviation was purchased by AJI, which renamed the latter company Gulfstream American Corporation (which see).

GRUMMAN AEROSPACE CORPORATION

HEAD OFFICE AND WORKS: 1111 Stewart Avenue, Bethpage, New York 11714
Telephone: (516) 575 0574

CHAIRMAN OF THE BOARD AND PRESIDENT: George M. Skurla

EXECUTIVE VICE-PRESIDENTS:
- Ralph H. Tripp (Operations)
- John P. O'Brien (Internal Operations)
- Michael Pelehach (Business Development, Marketing and Advanced Systems)

SENIOR VICE-PRESIDENTS:
- Ira G. Hedrick (Presidential Asst for Corporate Technology)
- Lawrence M. Mead Jr (Departmental Operations)
- Ross S. Mickey

VICE-PRESIDENTS:
- Alexander D. Alexandrovich (Asst to Executive Vice-President)
- John M. Buxton (President, Grumman Houston Corporation)
- Edward Dalva (Stuart Operations)
- Thomas A. Guarino (Aerospace Programmes)
- Thomas J. Kane Jr (Business Development)
- Thomas J. Kelly (Engineering)
- Robert C. Miller (Presidential Asst for Corporate Development)
- Gordon H. Ochenrider (Washington Office)
- Carl A. Paladino (Treasurer)
- G.Thomas Rozzi (Security and Personnel Services)
- Philip S. Vassallo (Corporate Procurement Operations)
- William M. Zarkowsky (Milledgeville Operations)

SECRETARY AND GENERAL COUNSEL: Raphael Mur

Current products of this subsidiary of Grumman Corporation include versions of the A-6 Intruder, EA-6B Prowler, E-2C Hawkeye and F-14 Tomcat for the US Navy, and a tactical jamming version of the General Dynamics F-111, designated EF-111A, for the USAF. The Milledgeville plant manufactures wing skins and glassfibre wingtips for the Fairchild A-10A Thunderbolt II attack aircraft. A contract for Grumman Aerospace to build major components for the Sikorsky CH-53E heavy-lift helicopter was announced in the Spring of 1978. Grumman has since received a contract to manufacture the wing centre-section of the new Model 767 civil transport from The Boeing Company.

GRUMMAN HAWKEYE

US Navy designation: E-2

The E-2 Hawkeye was evolved as a carrier-borne early-warning aircraft, but is suitable also for land-based operations from unimproved fields. The prototype flew for the first time on 21 October 1960, since when the following versions have been built:

E-2A (formerly W2F-1). Initial production version. First flight on 19 April 1961, and first delivery to US Navy on 19 January 1964. Total of 62 built, including three prototypes.

E-2B. Prototype flew for the first time on 20 February 1969. Differs from E-2A by having a Litton Industries L-304 microelectronic general-purpose computer and reliability improvements. A retrofit programme, completed in December 1971, updated all operational E-2As to E-2B standard.

E-2C. First of two E-2C prototypes flew on 20 January 1971. Production began in mid-1971 and the first flight of a production aircraft was made on 23 September 1972; 41 had been delivered by the end of 1977. Firm orders exist for a total of 47 aircraft, with procurement of 36 more by the end of 1985, with a planned delivery of six aircraft per year. Israel has four; and in Summer 1979 Japan released funds for the first four of an eventual total of about 15 for the JASDF.

The E-2C has an advanced radar that is capable of detecting airborne targets anywhere in a three million cubic mile surveillance envelope. Improvements compared with earlier radars provide increased reliability and easier maintenance. The E-2C first entered service, with airborne early-warning squadron VAW-123 at NAS Norfolk, Va, in November 1973, and went to sea on board the USS *Saratoga* in late 1974. Squadrons which have since received E-2C aircraft include VAW-113, -114, -115, 120, -121, -123, -124 and -126. Training version is **TE-2C**.

Teams of Hawkeyes are able to maintain patrols on naval task force defence perimeters in all weathers, at an operating height of about 9,150 m (30,000 ft), and are capable of detecting and assessing any threat from approaching high-Mach-number enemy aircraft over ranges approaching 260 nm (480 km; 300 miles). The radar also monitors movement of enemy ships and land vehicles. It enables each E-2C to track, automatically and simultaneously, more than 250 targets and to control more than 30 airborne intercepts. To make this possible highly sophisticated equipment is carried by the aircraft, including a Randtron Systems AN/APA-171 antenna system housed in a 7·32 m (24 ft) diameter saucer-shaped rotodome mounted above the rear fuselage of the aircraft. The rotodome revolves in flight at 6 rpm, and can be lowered 0·64 m (1 ft 10¼ in) to facilitate aircraft stowage on board ship. The Yagi type radar arrays within the rotodome are interfaced to the onboard avionic systems, providing radar sum and difference signals plus IFF.

An Advanced Radar Processing System (ARPS), designated AN/APS-125, developed for the E-2C, has detection capability over land and water, even under conditions of intentional jamming. The first production aircraft to include ARPS was No. 34, delivered in December 1976. Earlier E-2Cs have been retrofitted with the AN/APS-125. This gives automatic detection, target acquisition, and both overland and overwater tracking, and can detect targets as small as a cruise missile at ranges in excess of 100 nm (185 km; 115 miles). The system is able to operate independently, in co-operation with other aircraft, or in concert with ground environments. Operating as an addition to the radar system, a Passive Detection System (PDS) alerts operators to the presence of electronic emitters at distances up to twice the detection range of the radar system, thus expanding significantly the surveillance capability of the E-2C.

To provide the Combat Information Center (CIC) staff with the essential man/machine interface, the Hazeltine Corporation's AN/APA-172 control indicator group consists of three identical display stations, each with a 0·25 m (10 in) main and a 0·13 m (5 in) auxiliary display. The main display shows target track information, while the auxiliary provides alpha-numeric information with random-write capability. Station controls allow each of the three CIC operators to select independently specific information for their displays, so that each may have the same or a different perspective on any tactical situation. Other Hazeltine equipment includes an OL-76/AP IFF detector processor, providing automatic Mk X SIF processing capability in a single integrated system. Signals generated by the OL-76/AP enable the CIC operators to obtain instant range, azimuth and altitude positions of a friendly target. In order to identify that target as friend or foe, an RT-988/A IFF interrogator 'challenges' and identifies the aircraft, feeding its information direct to the OL-76/AP for processing.

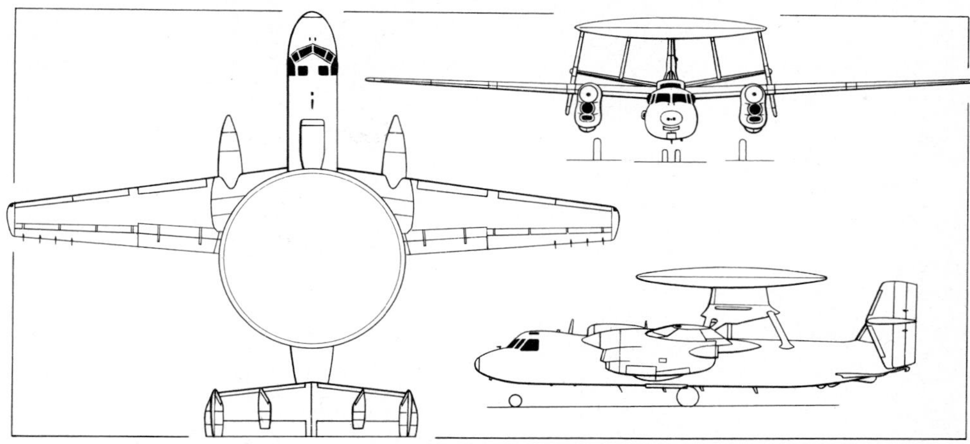

Grumman E-2C Hawkeye twin-turboprop airborne early-warning aircraft *(Pilot Press)*

Other equipment includes Litton Industries' AN/ASN-92 (LN-15C) carrier aircraft inertial navigation system (CAINS), an important feature of which is its capability of rapid alignment and orientation following take-off from a rolling and pitching carrier deck. Litton's Amecom division's AN/ALR-59 passive detection system provides early-warning capability.

Linking all this equipment is Litton Data Systems division's L-304 computer, which processes radar, Link 4 and Link 11 communications, navigation and passive detection data in real time. It computes automatically simultaneous intercept solutions. These can be transmitted automatically to interceptor aircraft, or all acquired information can be transmitted to ground control if desired. In addition, the E-2C has a Conrac Corporation CP-1085/AS air data computer (ADC).

The following details apply to the E-2C Hawkeye:

Type: Airborne early-warning aircraft.

Wings: Cantilever high-wing monoplane of all-metal construction. Centre-section is a structural box consisting of three beams, ribs and machined skins. Hinged leading-edge is non-structural and provides access to flying and engine controls. The outer panels fold rearward about skewed-axis hinge fittings mounted on the rear beams, to stow parallel with the rear fuselage on each side. Folding is done through a double-acting hydraulic cylinder. Trailing-edges of outer panels and part of centre-section consist of long-span ailerons and hydraulically-actuated Fowler flaps. When flaps are lowered, ailerons are drooped automatically. All control surfaces of E-2C are power-operated and incorporate devices to produce artificial feel forces. Automatic flight control system (AFCS) can be assigned sole control of the system hydraulic actuators, or AFCS signals can be superimposed on the pilot's mechanical inputs for stability augmentation. Pneumatically-inflated rubber de-icing boots on leading-edges.

Fuselage: Conventional all-metal semi-monocoque structure.

Tail Unit: Cantilever structure, with four fins and three double-hinged rudders. Tailplane dihedral 11°. Portions of tail unit made of glassfibre to reduce radar reflection. Power control and artificial feel systems as for ailerons. Pneumatically-inflated rubber de-icing boots on all leading-edges.

Landing Gear: Hydraulically-retractable tricycle type. Pneumatic emergency extension. Steerable nosewheel unit retracts rearward. Main wheels retract forward, and rotate to lie flat in bottom of nacelles. Twin wheels on nose unit only. Oleo-pneumatic shock-absorbers. Main wheel tyres size 36 × 11 Type VII 24-ply, pressure 17·93 bars (260 lb/sq in) on ship, 14·48 bars (210 lb/sq in) ashore. Hydraulic brakes. Hydraulically-operated retractable tailskid. A-frame arrester hook under tail.

Power Plant: Two 3,661 kW (4,910 ehp) Allison T56-A-425 turboprop engines, driving Hamilton Standard type 54460-1 four-blade fully-feathering reversible-pitch constant-speed propellers. These have foam-filled blades which have a steel spar and glassfibre shell which cause minimum interference to the radar equipment. Spinners and blades incorporate electrical anti-icers. Provision for auxiliary fuel tanks in outer wings, and for addition of flight refuelling capability.

Accommodation: Normal crew of five on flight deck and in ATDS compartment in main cabin, consisting of pilot, co-pilot, combat information centre officer, air control officer and radar operator. Provision for additional operator for long-endurance missions with auxiliary fuel. Downward-hinged doors, with built-in steps, on port side of centre-fuselage.

Avionics: AN/APA-171 rotodome (radar and IFF antennae), AN/APS-125 search radar, RT-988/A IFF interrogator with OL-76/AP IFF detector processor, AN/ALR-59 passive detection system, AN/APA-172 control indicator group, OL-77/ASQ computer programmer (L-304), ARC-158 UHF data link, ARQ-34 HF data link, ASM-440 in-flight performance monitor, ARC-51A UHF com, ARQ-34 HF com, AIC-14A intercom, AN/ASN-92 (LN-15C) CAINS carrier aircraft inertial navigation system, CP-1085/AS air data computer, APN-153 (V) Doppler, ASN-50 heading and attitude reference system, ARN-52 (V) Tacan, ARA-50 UHF ADF, ASW-25B ACLS and APN-171 (V) radar altimeter.

Dimensions, external:

Wing span	24·56 m (80 ft 7 in)
Length overall	17·55 m (57 ft 7 in)
Height overall	5·59 m (18 ft 4 in)
Diameter of rotodome	7·32 m (24 ft 0 in)
Propeller diameter	4·11 m (13 ft 6 in)

Area:

Wings, gross	65·03 m² (700 sq ft)

Weights (A current E-2C; B with auxiliary fuel):

Weight empty: A	17,241 kg (38,009 lb)
B	17,504 kg (38,589 lb)

Grumman E-2C Hawkeye airborne early-warning aircraft from USS *Constellation*

Max fuel (internal): A 5,624 kg (12,400 lb)
B 8,981 kg (19,800 lb)
Max T-O weight: A 23,541 kg (51,900 lb)
B 27,161 kg (59,880 lb)

PERFORMANCE (at max T-O weight. A, current E-2C; B, with auxiliary fuel):
Max level speed:
A, B 325 knots (602 km/h; 374 mph)
Cruising speed (ferry):
A 269 knots (499 km/h; 310 mph)
B 270 knots (500 km/h; 310 mph)
Approach speed:
A, B 100 knots (185 km/h; 115 mph)
Stalling speed (landing configuration):
A 74 knots (138 km/h; 85·5 mph)
Service ceiling: A 9,390 m (30,800 ft)
B 8,840 m (29,000 ft)
T-O run: A 580 m (1,900 ft)
B 884 m (2,900 ft)
T-O to 15 m (50 ft): A 793 m (2,600 ft)
B 1,128 m (3,700 ft)
Ferry range: A 1,394 nm (2,583 km; 1,605 miles)
B 2,170 nm (4,018 km; 2,497 miles)
Time on station, 175 nm (320 km; 200 miles) from base:
A 4 h
B over 6 h
Endurance with max fuel: A 6 h 6 min
B 9 h 18 min

GRUMMAN INTRUDER

US Navy designations: A-6, EA-6 and KA-6

The basic A-6A (originally A2F-1) Intruder was conceived as a carrier-borne low-level attack bomber equipped specifically to deliver nuclear or conventional weapons on targets completely obscured by weather or darkness. Later versions currently equip 17 operational US Navy/Marine Corps squadrons, and three readiness training squadrons.

Competition for the original A-6 contract was conducted from May to December 1957, Grumman's contender being selected on 31 December 1957. Seven variants of the basic design have been built, of which the A-6A, A-6B and A-6C (described in 1978-79 *Jane's*) are no longer operational. The current versions are as follows:

EA-6A. First flown in prototype form in 1963, this version retains partial strike capability, but is equipped primarily to support strike aircraft and ground forces by suppressing enemy electronic activity and obtaining tactical electronic intelligence within a combat area. Elements of the A-6A's bombing/navigation system are deleted and the EA-6A carries more than 30 different antennae to detect, locate, classify, record and jam enemy radiation. Externally-evident features include a radome at the top of the tail-fin, and attachment points under the wings and fuselage for ECM pods, fuel tanks and/or weapons. A total of 27 EA-6As were built for the US Marine Corps, including six A-6As modified into EA-6As.

EA-6B Prowler. Advanced electronics development of the EA-6A, described separately.

KA-6D Intruder. An A-6A was modified into a prototype flight refuelling tanker, with hose and reel in the rear fuselage, and flew for the first time on 23 May 1966. The KA-6D production model is fitted with Tacan and can transfer more than 9,500 kg (21,000 lb) of fuel immediately after take-off or 6,800 kg (15,000 lb) at a distance of 250 nm (463 km; 288 miles) from its carrier base. In addition, the KA-6D could act as a control aircraft for air-sea rescue operations or as a day bomber. A total of 62 A-6As were modified to KA-6D configuration.

A-6E Intruder. An advanced conversion of the A-6A with multi-mode radar and an IBM computer similar to that first tested in the EA-6B. First flight of an A-6E was made on 27 February 1970. First squadron deployment was made in September 1972, and the A-6E was approved officially for service use in December 1972. By the end of that month 24 A-6Es had been delivered to the US Navy, and a total procurement of 318 of these aircraft is planned.

An **A-6E/TRAM** (target recognition and attack multi-sensor) version of the A-6E flew for the first time on 22 March 1974 without sensors, and on 22 October 1974 with sensors. The initial flight test programme was carried out by converting this single aircraft, loaned by the Navy, but three other aircraft were converted and began flight testing in 1975. The conversion adds an undernose precision-stabilised turret, containing both infra-red and laser equipment, to a full-system Intruder, updates the inertial navigation system with AN/ASN-92 CAINS, provides a new communications-navigation-identification (CNI) system and automatic carrier landing capability. The sensor package is integrated with the multi-mode radar, providing the capability of detecting, identifying and attacking a wide range of targets (as well as viewing the terrain) under adverse weather conditions, and with an improved degree of accuracy, using either conventional or laser-guided weapons. The bombardier/navigator of the A-6E operates the TRAM system by first acquiring the target on his radar screen. He then switches to the Hughes Aircraft FLIR (forward-looking infra-red) system, using an optical zoom to enlarge the target's image. After identifying and selecting his targets, the bombardier uses a laser designator to mark the target with a laser spot, on which his own laser-guided weapons, or those from another aircraft, will home. Using TRAM's laser spot detector, the A-6E can also acquire a target that is being illuminated from another aircraft, or designated by a forward air controller on the ground. The first Intruder squadron to re-equip with the A-6E/TRAM version, VA-165, was deployed on board the USS *Constellation* in 1977. At that stage, the aircraft were complete except for the undernose detection and ranging set (DRS). The first production-equivalent DRS systems were installed in two A-6Es in 1977, and by early 1979 had accumulated more than 953 h of ground and airborne testing, including 260 flights in A-6Es. Production contracts for 60 complete TRAM systems had been placed by that time, with an option on 11 more. Delivery of production DRS began in February 1979, but squadron deployment had not started by Summer 1979.

CCW A-6A. Under a US Navy contract awarded in 1977, Grumman carried out the engineering development work and construction of a circulation control wing (CCW) which it installed on a US Navy A-6A. In this particular application, bleed air tapped from the J52 turbojets was ducted through a manifold and discharged through a longitudinal slot machined in a titanium and steel structure of circular cross-section which was mounted on the trailing-edge of each wing, from the wing root to the outboard end of the flap. This lift enhancement concept relied on the Coanda effect to increase the overall air circulation around the wing. Testing of the aircraft by Grumman showed significant reductions in landing speed and ground run. Touchdowns at speeds as low as 78 knots (145 km/h; 90 mph) were recorded, compared with about 120 knots (222 km/h; 138 mph) for a standard A-6A. After the final flight, landing run was 328 m (1,075 ft) at a weight of 15,150 kg (33,400 lb), compared with a normal 518 m (1,700 ft) at that landing weight. The overall results of the test programme were being evaluated by the Naval Ship Research and Development Center in early 1979.

Intruder training is carried out using Grumman TC-4C (modified Gulfstream I) aircraft, eight of which are in USN/USMC service. In mid-1978, two of these had been updated to A-6E/TRAM configuration, four others to A-6A and two to A-6E standard; Grumman planned to update all eight to A-6E/TRAM standard during 1978-79.

The following description applies to the standard A-6E:

TYPE: Two-seat carrier-based attack bomber.

WINGS: Cantilever mid-wing monoplane, with 25° sweepback at quarter-chord. All-metal structure. Hydraulically-operated almost-full-span leading-edge and trailing-edge flaps, with inset spoilers (flaperons) of same span as flaps forward of trailing-edge flaps. Trailing-edge of each wingtip, outboard of flap, splits to form speed-brakes which project above and below wing when extended. Two short fences above each wing. Outer panels fold upward and inward.

FUSELAGE: Conventional all-metal semi-monocoque structure. Bottom is recessed between engines to carry semi-exposed store.

TAIL UNIT: Cantilever all-metal structure. All-moving tailplane, without separate elevators. Electronic antenna in rear part of fin, immediately above rudder.

LANDING GEAR: Hydraulically-retractable tricycle type. Twin-wheel nose unit retracts rearward. Single-wheel main units retract forward and inward into air intake fairings. A-frame arrester hook under rear fuselage.

POWER PLANT: Two 41·4 kN (9,300 lb st) Pratt & Whitney J52-P-8A turbojet engines. Max internal fuel 7,230 kg (15,940 lb), 9,028 litres (2,385 US gallons). Provision for up to four external fuel tanks under wings, each of 1,136 litres (300 US gallons) capacity. Removable flight refuelling probe projects upward immediately forward of windscreen.

ACCOMMODATION: Crew of two on Martin-Baker Mk GRU7 ejection seats, which can be reclined to reduce fatigue during low-level operations. Bombar-

Grumman KA-6D Intruder tanker from a squadron on the USS *John F. Kennedy (Brian M. Service)*

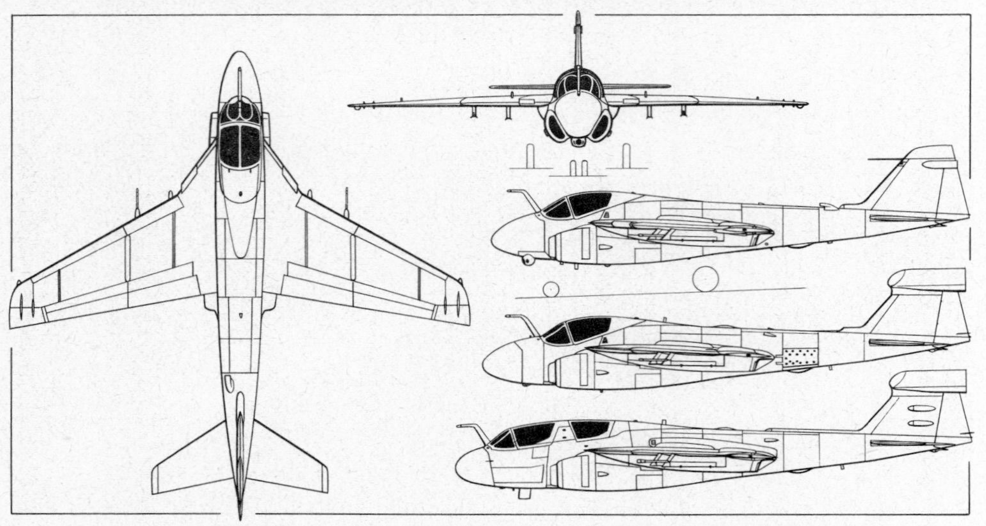

Grumman A-6E/TRAM, with additional side views of EA-6A (centre) and EA-6B (bottom) *(Pilot Press)*

dier/navigator slightly behind and below pilot to starboard. Hydraulically-operated rearward-sliding canopy.

SYSTEMS: AiResearch environmental control system for cockpit and avionics bay. Dual hydraulic systems for operation of flight controls, leading-edge and trailing-edge flaps, wingtip speedbrakes, landing gear brakes and cockpit canopy. One electrically-driven hydraulic pump provides restricted flight capability by supplying the tailplane and rudder actuators only. Electrical system powered by two AiResearch constant-speed drive starters that combine engine starting and electrical power generation, each delivering 30kVA. An AiResearch ram-air turbine, mounted so that it can be projected into the airstream above the port wing-root, provides in-flight emergency electrical power for essential equipment.

AVIONICS AND EQUIPMENT: Development of the A-6E began with the substitution of a single simultaneous multi-mode navigation and attack radar, developed by the Norden Division of UAC for the two earlier radar systems in the A-6A. Following the concepts of the EA-6B, the IBM Corporation and Fairchild Camera and Instrument Corporation have supplied a new attack and navigation computer system and an interfacing data converter. Conrac Corporation has designed an armament control unit and RCA has developed a video tape recorder for post-strike assessment of attacks.

The Norden Division's AN/APQ-148 multi-mode radar provides simultaneous ground mapping; identification, tracking, and rangefinding of fixed or moving targets; and terrain-clearance or terrain-following manoeuvres. It can also detect, locate and track radar beacons used by forward air controllers when providing close support for ground forces. The APQ-148 has mechanical scanning in azimuth and utilises a newly-developed avionics system for simultaneous vertical scanning. There are two cockpit displays, one for the pilot and one for the bombardier/navigator, and terrain data is also presented on a vertical display indicator ahead of the pilot.

IBM's AN/ASQ-133 solid-state digital computer is coupled to the A-6E's radar, inertial and Doppler navigational equipment, communications and automatic flight control system. As mission data is measured in flight by onboard aerodynamic and electronic sensors, the computer compares the data with the programmed information, computes any differences, and provides corrective data that can be used to alter the parameters of the mission.

Fairchild Camera and Instrument Corporation's signal data converter for the A-6E accepts analogue input data from up to sixty sensors, and converts that information to a digital output that is fed into the computer of the navigation and attack system.

Conrac Corporation's armament control unit (ACU) for the A-6E provides in a single unit all the inputs and outputs necessary to select and release the Intruder's weapons. The master arming switch has a 'practice' position that allows the ACU to be cycled up to the point of firing command.

The multi-mode AN/AVA-1 display developed by Kaiser Aerospace and Electronics Corporation serves as a primary flight aid for navigation, approach, landing and weapons delivery. The basic vertical display indicator (VDI) is a 0·20 m (8 in) cathode-ray tube which shows a synthetic landscape, sky, and electronically-generated command flight path that move to simulate the motion of these features as they would be seen by the pilot through the windscreen of the aircraft. Symbols are superimposed to augment the basic attitude data, and for attack a second set of superimposed information provides a target symbol, steering symbol, and release and pull-up markers. A solid-state radar data scan converter can provide on the same display an apparent real-world perspective of terrain, ten shades of grey defining terrain elevation at ten different segmented contour intervals up to 8·7 nm (16 km; 10 miles) ahead of the aircraft. This makes it possible for the pilot to fly the Intruder in either a terrain-following or terrain-avoidance mode at low altitude. Flight path and attack symbols can be superimposed over the terrain elevation data on the VDI, enabling the pilot to make his attack while avoiding or following terrain in the target area. Kaiser has also developed a micromesh filter to prevent 'washout' of the data displayed on the VDI in sunlight conditions. Naval pilots use the VDI as a primary flight instrument, for precise steering in navigation, and for weapons cues, progress, and status information during an attack. For carrier landing the unit is used as a flight director and, linked to the APQ-148 radar, it presents steering information, allowing the pilot to select a descent angle for the final approach.

ARMAMENT: Five weapon attachment points, each with a 1,633 kg (3,600 lb) capacity (max external stores load 8,165 kg; 18,000 lb). Typical weapon loads are thirty 500 lb bombs in clusters of six, or three 2,000 lb general purpose bombs plus two 1,135 litre (300 US gallon) drop-tanks.

DIMENSIONS, EXTERNAL:
Wing span 16·15 m (53 ft 0 in)

Grumman A-6E/TRAM (target recognition attack multisensor) version of the A-6E Intruder

Wing mean aerodynamic chord 3·32 m (10 ft 10¾ in)
Width folded 7·72 m (25 ft 4 in)
Length overall 16·69 m (54 ft 9 in)
Height overall 4·93 m (16 ft 2 in)
Tailplane span 6·21 m (20 ft 4½ in)
Wheel track 3·32 m (10 ft 10½ in)

AREAS:
Wings, gross 49·1 m² (528·9 sq ft)
Flaperons (total) 3·81 m² (41·0 sq ft)
Trailing-edge flaps (total) 9·66 m² (104·0 sq ft)
Leading-edge slats (total) 4·63 m² (49·8 sq ft)
Fin 5·85 m² (62·93 sq ft)
Rudder 1·52 m² (16·32 sq ft)

WEIGHTS AND LOADING:
Weight empty 11,675 kg (25,740 lb)
Fuel load: Internal 7,230 kg (15,940 lb)
external (four tanks) 3,638 kg (8,020 lb)
Max payload 7,838 kg (17,280 lb)
Max T-O weight:
catapult 26,580 kg (58,600 lb)
field 27,397 kg (60,400 lb)
Max zero-fuel weight 20,166 kg (44,460 lb)
Max landing weight:
carrier 16,329 kg (36,000 lb)
field 20,411 kg (45,000 lb)
Max wing loading 557·6 kg/m² (114·2 lb/sq ft)

PERFORMANCE (no stores):
Never-exceed speed 689 knots (1,276 km/h; 793 mph)
Max level speed at S/L 563 knots (1,043 km/h; 648 mph)
Cruising speed at optimum altitude 414 knots (767 km/h; 477 mph)
Stalling speed, flaps up 121 knots (225 km/h; 140 mph)
Stalling speed, flaps down 84 knots (156 km/h; 97 mph)
Max rate of climb at S/L 2,804 m (9,200 ft)/min
Rate of climb at S/L, one engine out 945 m (3,100 ft)/min
Service ceiling 14,480 m (47,500 ft)
Service ceiling, one engine out 9,083 m (29,800 ft)
Min T-O run 610 m (2,000 ft)
T-O run to 15 m (50 ft) 795 m (2,610 ft)
Landing from 15 m (50 ft) 689 m (2,260 ft)
Min landing run 579 m (1,900 ft)
Combat range with max external fuel 2,365 nm (4,382 km; 2,723 miles)
Range with max payload, 5% reserves plus 20 min at S/L 1,671 nm (3,096 km; 1,924 miles)
Ferry range 2,530 nm (4,688 km; 2,913 miles)

GRUMMAN EA-6B PROWLER

The EA-6B is an advanced electronics development of the EA-6A for which Grumman received a prototype design and development contract in the Autumn of 1966. Except for a 1·37 m (4 ft 6 in) longer nose section and large fin pod, the external configuration of this version is the same as that of the basic A-6A.

The longer nose section provides accommodation for a total crew of four, the two additional crewmen being necessary to operate the more advanced ECM equipment. This comprises high-powered electronic jammers and modern computer-directed receivers, which provided the US Navy with its first aircraft designed and built specifically for tactical electronic warfare. The prototype EA-6B flew for the first time on 25 May 1968; deliveries of production aircraft began in January 1971.

The US Administration Fiscal 1969 defence budget allocated a sum of $139 million for the initial purchase of eight EA-6Bs, and the total programme is expected to cover the supply of 96 aircraft (this including the four pre-production and one R and D aircraft), to equip Navy and Marine Corps squadrons.

An ICAP (Increased Capability) version of the EA-6B, which increases substantially the jamming efficiency of the aircraft, has been developed. Current production aircraft are delivered with ICAP as standard, and the first 21 production EA-6Bs have been modified by Grumman to ICAP configuration. Modifications include an expanded onboard tactical jamming system with eight frequency bands, reduced response time, and a new multi-format display. In addition, an automatic carrier landing system (ACLS) to permit carrier recovery in zero-zero weather, a new defensive electronic countermeasures system (DECM) and new communications-navigation-identification (CNI) equipment are installed.

Ten US Navy squadrons (VAQ-129, 130, 131, 132, 133, 134, 135, 136, 137 and 138) were equipped with the Prowler in mid-1977. The first detachment of US Marine Corps Prowler squadron VMAQ-2 began training on the EA-6B in September 1977 at NAS Whidbey Island, Washington, and the detachment deployed in late 1978. Two further detachments are scheduled for training, with the programme running into 1980.

Under a $4·8 million contract awarded in 1978, Norden Systems is to supply for the EA-6B an advanced navigation radar system designated AN/APS-130. The contract calls for one prototype and three pre-production systems before the start of full production. This is expected to run to approximately 100 systems.

The description of the standard A-6E Intruder applies also to the EA-6B, except as follows:

TYPE: Four-seat carrier- or land-based advanced ECM aircraft.

WINGS: As for A-6E, but reinforced to cater for increased gross weight, fatigue life and 5·5g load factor.

FUSELAGE: As for A-6E, but reinforcement of underfuselage structure in areas of arrester hook and landing gear attachments, and lengthened by 1·37 m (4 ft 6 in).

TAIL UNIT: As for A-6E, except for provision of a large fin-tip pod to house ECM equipment.

LANDING GEAR: As for A-6E, except for reinforcement of attachments, A-frame arrester hook, and upgrading of structure to cater for increased gross weight.

POWER PLANT: Two 50 kN (11,200 lb st) Pratt & Whitney J52-P-408 turbojet engines, each rated at 49·8 kN (11,200 lb st). Fuel capacity increased compared with A-6E.

ACCOMMODATION: Crew of four under two separate upward-opening canopies. The two additional crewmen are ECM Officers to operate the ALQ-99 equipment

Grumman EA-6B Prowler of Squadron VAQ-134 landing on the USS ***Enterprise***

from the rear cockpit. Either ECMO can independently detect, assign, adjust and monitor the jammers. The ECMO in the starboard front seat is responsible for communications, navigation, defensive ECM and chaff dispensing.

SYSTEMS: Generally as for A-6E.

AVIONICS: ALQ-99 advanced electronic countermeasures (ECM) to enable the EA-6B to fulfil a tactical electronic warfare role. Five integrally powered pods, with a total of 10 jamming transmitters, can be carried. Each pod covers one of seven frequency bands. Sensitive surveillance receivers in the fin-tip pod for long-range detection of radars; emitter information is fed to a central digital computer that processes the signals for display and recording. Detection, identification, direction-finding and jammer-set-on sequence can be performed automatically or with manual assistance from crew.

DIMENSIONS, EXTERNAL:
As for A-6E, except:
Width folded 7·87 m (25 ft 10 in)
Length overall 18·11 m (59 ft 5 in)
Height overall 4·95 m (16 ft 3 in)
Wheelbase 5·26 m (17 ft 3 in)

AREAS:
As for A-6E

WEIGHTS AND LOADING:
Weight empty 14,588 kg (32,162 lb)
Internal fuel load 6,995 kg (15,422 lb)
Max external fuel load 4,547 kg (10,025 lb)
T-O weight in stand-off jamming configuration 24,703 kg (54,461 lb)
T-O weight in ferry range configuration 27,492 kg (60,610 lb)
Max T-O weight, catapult or field 29,483 kg (65,000 lb)
Max zero-fuel weight 17,708 kg (39,039 lb)
Max landing weight, carrier or field 20,638 kg (45,500 lb)
Max wing loading 600·5 kg/m² (123 lb/sq ft)

PERFORMANCE (no stores):
Never-exceed speed 710 knots (1,315 km/h; 817 mph)
Max level speed at S/L 566 knots (1,048 km/h; 651 mph)
Cruising speed at optimum altitude 418 knots (774 km/h; 481 mph)
Stalling speed, flaps up, max power 124 knots (230 km/h; 143 mph)
Stalling speed, flaps down, max power 84 knots (156 km/h; 97 mph)
Max rate of climb at S/L 3,932 m (12,900 ft)/min
Rate of climb at S/L, one engine out 1,189 m (3,900 ft)/min
Service ceiling 13,565 m (44,500 ft)
Service ceiling, one engine out 8,930 m (29,300 ft)
T-O to 15 m (50 ft) 869 m (2,850 ft)
Landing from 15 m (50 ft) 823 m (2,700 ft)
Landing run 579 m (1,900 ft)
Combat range with max external fuel 2,083 nm (3,861 km; 2,399 miles)
Range with max payload, 5% reserves plus 20 min at S/L 955 nm (1,769 km; 1,099 miles)

GRUMMAN TOMCAT

US Navy designation: F-14

Grumman announced on 15 January 1969 that it had been selected as winner of the design competition for a new carrier-based fighter for the US Navy. Known as the VFX during the competitive phase of the programme, this aircraft was later designated F-14. First flight of the F-14A Tomcat prototype took place on 21 December 1970. It was lost in a non-fatal accident, and flight testing was resumed on 24 May 1971 with the second aircraft.

The F-14 is designed to fulfil three primary missions. The first of these, fighter sweep/escort, involves clearing contested airspace of enemy fighters and protecting the strike force, with support from early-warning aircraft, surface ships and communications networks to co-ordinate penetration and escape. Second mission is to defend carrier task forces via Combat Air Patrol (CAP) and Deck

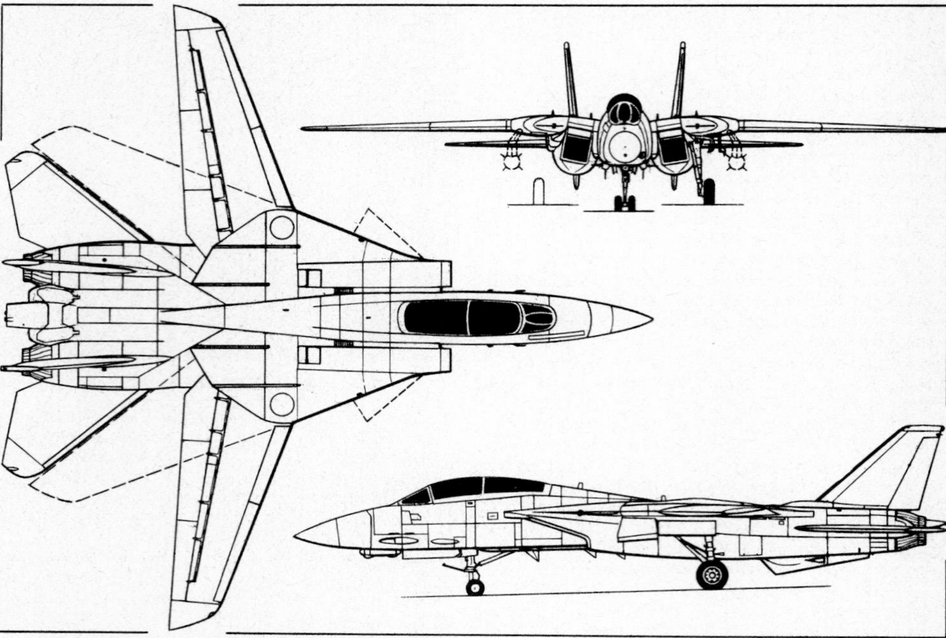

Grumman F-14A Tomcat carrier-based multi-mission fighter *(Pilot Press)*

Launched Intercept (DLI) operations. Third role is secondary attack of tactical targets on the ground, supported by electronic countermeasures and fighter escort.

The configuration of the F-14 is unique, with variable-geometry wings, small foreplanes (glove vanes) which are extended automatically at supersonic speeds to control centre-of-pressure shift, manoeuvring slats and flaps to create a lower effective wing loading, and twin outward-canted fins and rudders. Optimum sweep of the wing is controlled automatically by a Mach sweep programmer, which relates sweep to Mach number and altitude.

Under the initial contracts, Grumman was required to provide the US Navy with a mockup of the F-14A in May 1969, and to build 12 research and development aircraft. Subsequently, the US Navy ordered an initial series of 26 production F-14As, and is expected to acquire a total of 521 Tomcats, including the 12 development aircraft. Carrier trials were started in June 1972, and initial deployment with the fleet began in October 1972. Replacement Training Squadron (RTS) VF-124 at Miramar NAS, San Diego, California, was responsible for working up ground and air crews for the new aircraft, and the first two operational squadrons, VF-1 and VF-2, were serving on board the USS *Enterprise* in the Western Pacific in September 1974. A total of 306 F-14As had been delivered by 1 January 1979, with 36 more scheduled for delivery in 1979 and 36 in 1980.

The Naval Air Test Center at Patuxent River, Maryland, has completed test and evaluation of a 748 kg (1,650 lb) reconnaissance pod for the F-14. Designated **TARPS** (Tactical Air Reconnaissance Pod System), the pod is designed to be mounted 0·38 m (1 ft 3 in) off the centreline of the F-14's underfuselage, in the tunnel between the two engine nacelles. The pod has four main compartments: the nose carries a CAI KS-87B frame camera for either forward oblique or vertical photographs; the second contains a Fairchild KA-99 low/medium-altitude horizon-to-horizon panoramic camera; the third has a Honeywell AN/AAD-5 infra-red reconnaissance set; and the fourth is an equipment bay containing the ground check maintenance panel and a sensor control data display set.

Without the TARPS pod installed, the F-14 retains its full weapon system capability. The F-14/TARPS aircraft will fulfil an important tactical reconnaissance role pending the evolution of new photo-reconnaissance aircraft.

The Imperial Iranian Air Force ordered 80 F-14As, all of which had been delivered by the end of 1978; first flight by one of these aircraft was made on 5 December 1975, and the first three aircraft were ferried to Khatami AFB, Isfahan, in January 1976. Iranian F-14As retain the Phoenix weapon system, but have slightly different ECM equipment from US Navy aircraft.

Grumman F-14A Tomcat carrier-based multi-role fighter on the USS *Nimitz*

TYPE: Two-seat carrier-based multi-role fighter.

WINGS: Variable-geometry mid-wing monoplane, with 20° of leading-edge sweep in the fully-forward position and 68° when fully swept. Oversweep position of 75° for carrier stowage. Wing position is programmed automatically for optimum performance throughout the flight regime, but manual override is provided. A short movable wing outer panel, needing only a comparatively light pivot structure, results from the wide fuselage and fixed centre-section 'glove', with pivot points 2·72 m (8 ft 11 in) from the centreline of the airframe. The inboard wing sections, adjacent to the fuselage, arc upward slightly to minimise cross-sectional area and wave-drag, and consist basically of a one-piece electron beam-welded titanium assembly, 6·70 m (22 ft) in span, made from Ti-6A1-4V titanium alloy. Small canard surfaces, known as glove vanes, swing out from the leading-edge of the fixed portion of the wing, to a maximum of 15° in relation to the leading-edge, as sweep of outer panels is increased. Spoilers on upper surfaces of wing. Stabilisation in pitch, provided by the canard surfaces, leaves the differential tailplane free to perform its primary control function. Trailing-edge control surfaces extend over almost entire span. Leading-edge slats.

FUSELAGE: The centre-fuselage section is a simple, fuel-carrying box structure; forward fuselage section comprises cockpit and nose. The aft section has a tapered aerofoil shape to minimise drag, with a fuel dump pipe projecting from the rear. Speed brakes located on the upper and lower surfaces, between the bases of the vertical tail fins.

TAIL UNIT: Twin vertical fins, mounted at the rear of each engine nacelle. Outward-canted ventral fin under each nacelle. The all-flying horizontal surfaces have skins of boron-epoxy composite material.

LANDING GEAR: Retractable tricycle type. Twin-wheel nose unit and single-wheel main units retract forward and upward. Existing beryllium brakes to be replaced with Goodyear lightweight carbon brakes from Spring 1981. Arrester hook under rear fuselage, housed in small ventral fairing. Nose-tow catapult attachment on nose unit.

ENGINE INTAKES: Straight two-dimensional external compression inlets. A double-hinged ramp extends down from the top of each intake, and these are programmed to provide the correct airflow to the engines automatically under all flight conditions. Each intake is canted slightly away from the fuselage, from which it is separated by some 0·25 m (10 in) to allow sufficient clearance for the turbulent fuselage boundary layer to pass between fuselage and intake without causing turbulence within the intake. Engine inlet ducts and aft nacelle structures are manufactured by Rohr Corporation. The inlet duct, constructed largely of aluminium honeycomb, is about 4·27 m (14 ft) long, while the aft nacelle structure, of bonded aluminium honeycomb and conventional aluminium, is about 4·88 m (16 ft) in length.

POWER PLANT: Two Pratt & Whitney TF30-P-412A turbofan engines of 93 kN (20,900 lb st) with afterburning, mounted in ducts which open to provide 180° access for ease of maintenance. AiResearch ATS200-50 air-turbine starter. Two external fuel tanks can be carried under engine intake trunks.

ACCOMMODATION: Pilot and naval flight officer seated in tandem on Martin-Baker GRU-7A rocket-assisted zero-zero ejection seats, under a one-piece bubble canopy, hinged at the rear and offering all-round view.

ARMAMENT: One General Electric M61A-1 Vulcan 20 mm gun mounted in the port side of forward fuselage. Four Sparrow air-to-air missiles mounted partially sub-merged in the underfuselage, or four Phoenix missiles carried on special pallets which attach to the bottom of the fuselage. Two wing pylons, one under each fixed wing section, can carry four Sidewinder missiles or two additional Sparrow or Phoenix missiles with two Sidewinders. Various combinations of missiles and bombs to a max external weapon load of 6,577 kg (14,500 lb). A tactical reconnaissance pod has been developed by Grumman. This can accommodate a number of high- or low-altitude cameras and advanced electro-optical sensors. ECM equipment includes Goodyear AN/ALE-39 chaff and flare dispensers, with integral jammers.

AVIONICS: Hughes AN/AWG-9 weapons control system, with ability to track 24 enemy targets and attack six of them simultaneously at varied altitudes and distances. Kaiser Aerospace AN/AVG-12 vertical and head-up display system.

DIMENSIONS, EXTERNAL:

Wing span: unswept	19·45 m (64 ft 1½ in)
swept	11·65 m (38 ft 2½ in)
overswept	10·15 m (33 ft 3½ in)
Wing aspect ratio	7·28
Length overall	18·89 m (61 ft 11·9 in)
Height overall	4·88 m (16 ft 0 in)
Tailplane span	9·97 m (32 ft 8½ in)
Distance between fin tips	3·25 m (10 ft 8 in)
Wheel track	5·00 m (16 ft 5 in)
Wheelbase	7·02 m (23 ft 0½ in)

AREAS:

Wings, gross	52·49 m² (565·0 sq ft)
Horizontal tail surfaces (total)	13·01 m² (140·0 sq ft)
Vertical tail surfaces (total)	10·96 m² (118·0 sq ft)

WEIGHTS:

Weight empty	17,830 kg (39,310 lb)
Fuel (usable): internal	7,348 kg (16,200 lb)
external	1,724 kg (3,800 lb)
Normal T-O weight	26,553 kg (58,539 lb)
Max useful load (overload)	8,255 kg (18,200 lb)
T-O weight with 4 Sparrow	26,718 kg (58,904 lb)
T-O weight with 6 Phoenix	31,656 kg (69,790 lb)
Max T-O weight	33,724 kg (74,348 lb)
Design landing weight	23,510 kg (51,830 lb)

PERFORMANCE:

Max design speed	Mach 2·4
Max cruising speed	400-550 knots (741-1,019 km/h; 460-633 mph)
Landing speed	120 knots (222 km/h; 138 mph)
Service ceiling	above 15,240 m (50,000 ft)
Min T-O distance	214 m (700 ft)
Min T-O distance at 26,533 kg (58,495 lb) AUW	366 m (1,200 ft)
Min landing distance	488 m (1,600 ft)

GRUMMAN (GENERAL DYNAMICS) EF-111A

The programme to convert General Dynamics F-111As into EF-111A electronic warfare prototypes, and to evaluate their ability to provide ECM jamming coverage for air attack forces, was initiated in 1972-73. Operational deployment of the F-111A in Southeast Asia, from March 1968, had revealed shortcomings, despite special preparation under the Harvest Reaper programme to provide these aircraft with advanced ECM equipment that would facilitate penetration of enemy airspace. Subsequent enquiry revealed that many factors contributed to the limited success of the F-111A in Southeast Asia; lack of adequate and effective ECM jamming was responsible for many of its problems, as well as those of all other types of combat aircraft in that theatre of operations.

Because of the growing potential of Soviet-built air defence systems, which stretch across Eastern Europe, NATO anti-invasion forces must have the capability of suppressing literally thousands of radar 'eyes', able to locate precisely the route and speed of counter-attacking air strikes. In addition, updated SAM systems and new interceptors with sophisticated ECM equipment are being introduced regularly by the Soviet Union, providing its armed forces with a now-acknowledged lead in electronic warfare, both ground and airborne.

Senior USAF officials consider that utilisation of the EF-111 as a tactical jamming system, in combination with the E-3 AWACS, is vital to help offset this Soviet lead. Because of its vast masking power, the EF-111 is essential to provide cover for air-to-ground operations along the forward lines, and for support of penetrating allied strike forces. Should some future circumstances make it necessary to launch a counter-strike against Soviet penetration of NATO territory, EF-111s operating on the friendly side of the FEBA (forward edge of the battle area) could blind the other side's electronic 'eyes', making it possible for NATO strike forces to attack the armoured spearhead, as well as resupply areas, reserves and SAM installations

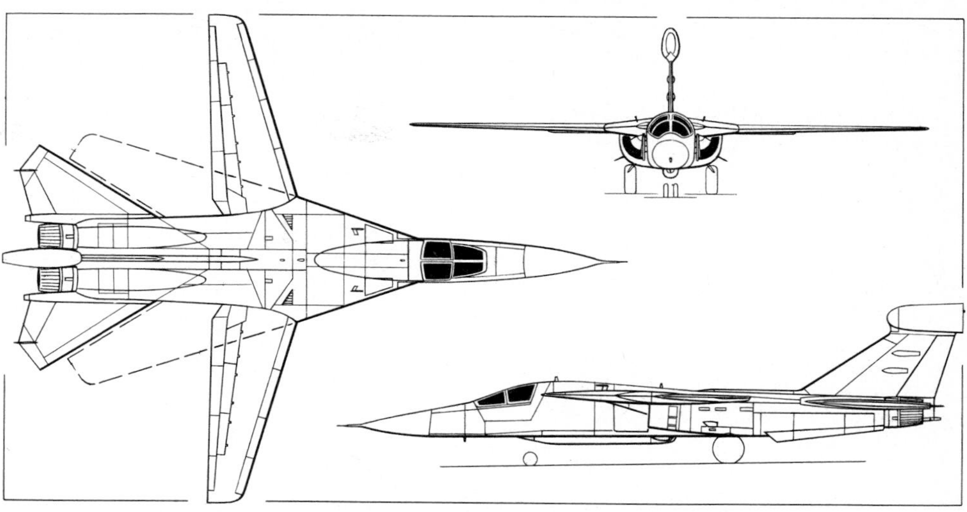

Grumman (General Dynamics) EF-111A electronic warfare aircraft *(Pilot Press)*

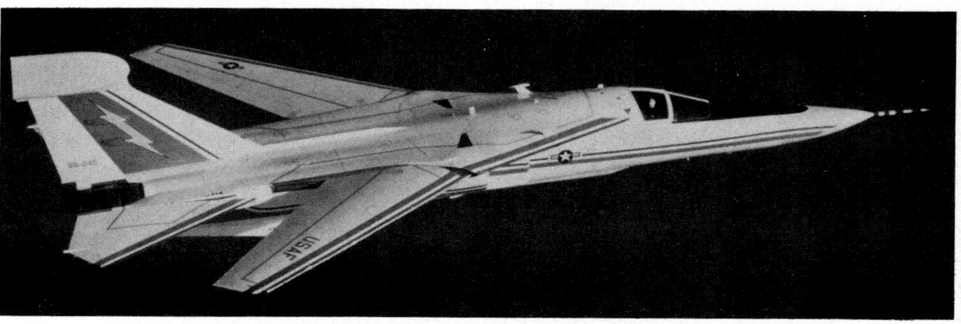

Prototype of the Grumman-modified EF-111A tactical jamming aircraft

17-35 nm (32-64 km; 20-40 miles) behind the opposing lines, with something less than half the anticipated losses that could be expected without use of the EF-111s' jamming systems.

Three basic modes of deployment are foreseen for the EF-111: Standoff, Penetration, and Close Air Support. In the Standoff role, jamming aircraft would operate within their own airspace, at the FEBA. Out of range of the enemy's ground-based weapons, orbiting EF-111s would use their jamming systems to screen the routes of friendly strike aircraft. In the Penetration role, the EF-111s would accompany strike aircraft to high-priority targets, their Mach 2 capability making them ideal escort aircraft for such a task. The Close Air Support requirement calls for EF-111 escorts to neutralise anti-air radars while the strike force delivers its attack on enemy armour.

Design study contracts were awarded to General Dynamics and Grumman by the USAF in 1974. and in January 1975 it was announced that Grumman had been awarded an $85·9 million contract to convert two existing F-111As to EF-111A prototype configuration. Basic equipment of these prototypes comprises the Raytheon AN/ALQ-99E tactical jamming system, comprising ten transmitters, five exciters and one RF calibrator per aircraft. In addition, each has a modified AN/ALQ-137 Self Protection System, and a modified AN/ALR-62 Terminal Threat Warning System. The ALQ-99E jammers are mounted in the weapons bay, with their antennae covered by a 4·9 m (16 ft) long canoe-shape radome. The fin-tip pod, similar in shape to that of the EA-6B Prowler, houses the receiver system and antennae. Total weight of the new equipment is about three tons.

The two-man crew of an EF-111 comprises a pilot and an electronic warfare officer (EWO). All tactical jamming functions are managed by the EWO who can, through computer management, handle a tactical electronic warfare workload which required previously several operators and more equipment. In addition, the automated system of the EF-111 has exceptional capability for locating, identifying, and assigning jammers to enemy emitters over a wide range of frequencies.

The first flight of an aerodynamic prototype was made on 10 March 1977, and the complete system was flown for the first time on 17 May 1977, on the second prototype. Subsequent Grumman flight testing of the jamming system involved 84 flights totalling 215 flight hours, completed by the two aircraft during a period of 3½ months. USAF flight testing involved 78 flights totalling 258 flight hours during a six-month test programme. The USAF tests verified various mission operational concepts, flight formations, and the jammer's electromagnetic compatibility with other strike aircraft. These latter tests dispelled an earlier concern that the friendly strike force, as well as enemy threats, might be jammed by the powerful signals emanating from the EF-111. Structural flight tests under all operating conditions demonstrated an 'infinite' life for all modified areas of the aircraft's structure, and flying qualities were considered virtually identical to those of the F-111 strike aircraft.

USAF plans envisage the conversion of 42 F-111Fs as ECM jamming aircraft. The production contract for the first six was signed in April 1979, with deliveries to begin in July 1981.

The description of the F-111A in the 1976-77 *Jane's* applies also to the EF-111A, except for the following additional or amended details:

TYPE: ECM tactical jamming aircraft.

WINGS: As detailed for F-111A. Wing section NACA 64A210.68 modified at pivot point, NACA 64A209.80 with modified leading-edge at tip. Dihedral, at 16° sweep, 1°. Incidence, at 16° sweep, 1° at root, −3° at tip.

POWER PLANT: As detailed for F-111A. Fuel capacity 19,010 litres (5,022 US gallons). Oil capacity 30·3 litres (8 US gallons).

AVIONICS: AN/ALQ-99E tactical jamming system; AN/ARC-109 UHF command, AN/AJQ-20A INS, AN/APQ-160 attack radar, AN/APN-167 radar altimeter, AN/APQ-110 terrain-following radar, AN/ARN-58 ILS, AN/ARC-112 HF transceiver, AN/AIC-25 intercom, AN/APX-64 IFF(AIMS), AN/ARN-52 Tacan, AN/ARA-50 UHF/DF, AN/ALQ-137 (modified) SPS, AN/ALR-62 (modified) TTWS, AN/ALR-23 CMRS, and AN/ALE-28 CMDS.

ARMAMENT: None.

DIMENSIONS, EXTERNAL:

Wing span, spread	19·20 m (63 ft 0 in)
Wing span, fully swept	9·74 m (31 ft 11·4 in)
Wing mean aerodynamic chord	2·76 m (9 ft 0 in)
Wing aspect ratio (16° sweep)	7·56
Length overall	23·51 m (77 ft 1·6 in)
Height overall	6·10 m (20 ft 0 in)
Wheel track	3·19 m (10 ft 0·4 in)
Wheelbase	7·44 m (24 ft 4·8 in)

AREA:

Wings, gross (16° sweep)	48·77 m² (525 sq ft)

WEIGHTS:

Weight empty (estimated)	24,230 kg (53,418 lb)
Design T-O weight	33,000 kg (72,750 lb)
Combat T-O weight	28,000 kg (61,729 lb)
Max T-O weight	39,680 kg (87,478 lb)
Max landing weight	36,287 kg (80,000 lb)

PERFORMANCE (estimated for typical mission, A: basic standoff; B: penetration; C: close air support. At max T-O weight unless detailed otherwise):

Max combat speed at combat T-O weight:	
A, B, C	1,007 knots (1,865 km/h; 1,160 mph)
Average speed, outbound:	
A	450 knots (834 km/h; 518 mph)
B	496 knots (919 km/h; 571 mph)
C	448 knots (830 km/h; 516 mph)
Average speed over combat area:	
A	321 knots (595 km/h; 370 mph)
B	336 knots (623 km/h; 387 mph)
C	318 knots (589 km/h; 366 mph)

Average speed, inbound:
  A 436 knots (808 km/h; 502 mph)
  B 496 knots (919 km/h; 571 mph)
  C 438 knots (811 km/h; 504 mph)
Stalling speed, power off:
  A, B, C 135·1 knots (250·4 km/h; 155·6 mph)
Rate of climb at S/L, intermediate power:
  A, B, C 1,095 m (3,592 ft)/min
Rate of climb at S/L, one engine out, with afterburning:
  A, B, C 986 m (3,234 ft)/min
Service ceiling with afterburning, at combat weight:
  A 16,670 m (54,700 ft)
  B 15,450 m (50,700 ft)
  C 16,185 m (53,100 ft)
T-O run: A, B, C 991 m (3,250 ft)
T-O to 15 m (50 ft): A, B, C 1,250 m (4,100 ft)
Landing from 15 m (50 ft):
  A, C, at 26,623 kg (58,693 lb) 853 m (2,800 ft)
  B, at 32,863 kg (72,451 lb) 1,245 m (4,085 ft)
Landing run:
  A, C, at 26,623 kg (58,693 lb) 539 m (1,770 ft)
  B, at 32,863 kg (72,451 lb) 759 m (2,490 ft)
Combat radius, with reserves:
  A 200 nm (370 km; 230 miles)
  B 250 nm (463 km; 287 miles)
  C 897 nm (1,661 km; 1,032 miles)
Ferry range 2,157 nm (3,998 km; 2,484 miles)

GULFSTREAM AMERICAN

GULFSTREAM AMERICAN CORPORATION

HEAD OFFICE AND WORKS: PO Box 2206, Savannah, Georgia 31402
Telephone: (912) 964 3000
Telex: 54-6470
CHAIRMAN, PRESIDENT AND CHIEF EXECUTIVE OFFICER: Allen E. Paulson
VICE-CHAIRMAN: Mario P. Borini
EXECUTIVE VICE-PRESIDENTS: Alan B. Lemlein
  Frank W. Wisekal (Corporate Development)
SENIOR VICE-PRESIDENTS:
  Roy C. Garrison (Commercial Light Aircraft Marketing)
  Charles G. Vogeley (Commercial Jet Aircraft Marketing)
VICE-PRESIDENTS:
  Robert H. Cooper (Marketing)
  Charles N. Coppi (Engineering)
  Albert H. Glenn (General Manager, Savannah Operations)
  Richard Kemper (Quality Control; New Products)
SECRETARY AND GENERAL COUNSEL: John P. Innes

On 1 September 1978 it was announced that American Jet Industries had purchased the 80% holding in Grumman American Aviation Corporation held by Grumman Corporation, and had made a cash offer to the holders of the remaining 20% stock. The company is now known as Gulfstream American Corporation. Under the terms of the transfer of ownership, Grumman is continuing to develop the Gulfstream III executive jet transport under contract with Gulfstream American, and to provide support for both the Gulfstream II and III. It was to receive a royalty on all sales made after 31 December 1979.

Gulfstream American builds the Cheetah, Tiger, Cougar and Gulfstream II and III; is responsible for manufacture and marketing of the Grumman-designed Super Ag-Cat and the turbine-powered Turbo Ag-Cat D; and is continuing development of the Hustler 500 designed by the former American Jet Industries, now known as Gulfstream American Corporation of California (which see).

Sales in 1978 included 20 Gulfstream IIs, 203 Super Ag-Cats, 96 two-seat Lynx/T-cats, 226 four-seat Cheetahs, 321 four-seat Tigers, and 70 twin-engined Cougars. Manufacture of the T-cat and Lynx has now ended; that of the Gulfstream II was scheduled to end in December 1979.

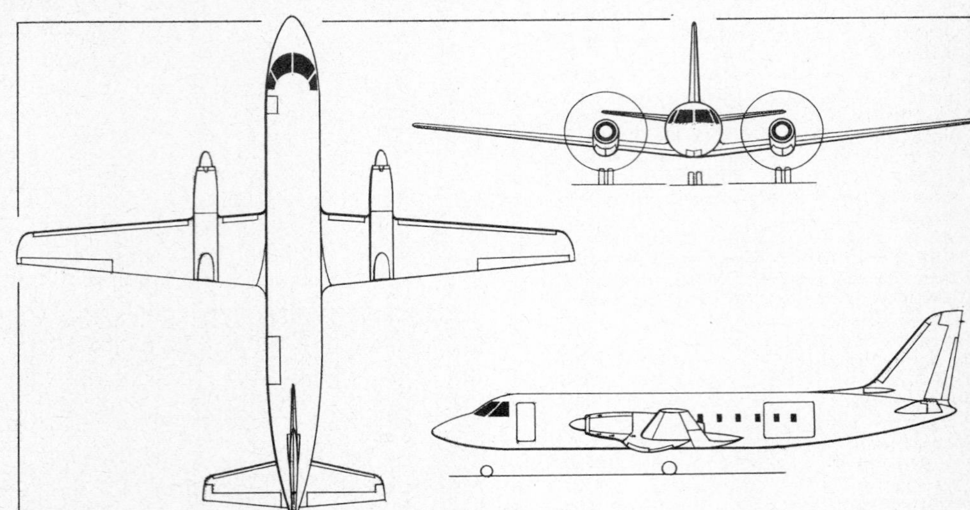

Gulfstream American commuter version of the Gulfstream I, with optional cargo door *(Pilot Press)*

GULFSTREAM AMERICAN GAC 159-C GULFSTREAM I COMMUTER

During the first half of 1979, Gulfstream American conducted marketing and engineering studies to determine the feasibility of putting into production a 32/38-seat commuter version of the twin-turboprop G-159 Gulfstream I, which Grumman Corporation designed as a 19-seat executive aircraft and marketed from 1958 to 1969. A total of 200 Gulfstream Is had been built when production was then terminated in favour of the twin-turbofan Gulfstream II. Gulfstream American acquired the tooling and fixtures for Gulfstream I production when it purchased the former Grumman American Aviation Corporation in September 1978.

Design changes planned for the Gulfstream I Commuter include lengthening the fuselage by 2·90 m (9 ft 6 in), to accommodate a maximum of 38 passengers, three-abreast at 74 cm (29 in) pitch, or 32 passengers at 86 cm (34 in) pitch. This leaves room for a toilet and carry-on baggage compartment at the front of the 40·21 m³ (1,420 cu ft) cabin, and a 4·08 m³ (144 cu ft) baggage compartment at the rear. The Commuter will also introduce rectangular cabin windows, and will have a reshaped nose and wraparound windscreen of the type designed for the Gulfstream III. Maximum payload will be 3,447 kg (7,600 lb) in passenger configuration, or up to 3,856 kg (8,500 lb) in an optional all-cargo layout with large freight door on the port side of the rear fuselage.

As a first stage, Gulfstream American was lengthening the fuselage of an existing Gulfstream I in Summer 1979, for flight testing and demonstration. This aircraft will retain its original Rolls-Royce Dart turboprop engines; but General Electric CT64 and Avco Lycoming T55 turboprops are under consideration as alternatives for future production Gulfstream I Commuters. Details of the original Grumman G-159 Gulfstream I can be found in the 1968-69 *Jane's*.

DIMENSIONS, EXTERNAL:
  Wing span 23·88 m (78 ft 4 in)
  Length overall 22·63 m (74 ft 3 in)
  Height overall 6·99 m (22 ft 11 in)
  Cargo door (optional): Width 2·08 m (6 ft 10 in)
    Height 1·63 m (5 ft 4 in)
WEIGHTS (Dart engines):
  Basic operating weight:
    passenger 10,682 kg (23,550 lb)
    cargo 10,773 kg (23,750 lb)
  Max T-O weight 16,330 kg (36,000 lb)
  Max landing weight 15,550 kg (34,285 lb)
  Max zero-fuel weight 14,625 kg (32,250 lb)
PERFORMANCE (estimated, at max T-O weight, Dart engines):
  Max cruising speed 309 knots (572 km/h; 356 mph)
  T-O field length 1,440 m (4,720 ft)
  Landing field length 1,385 m (4,540 ft)
  Range with max payload:
    passenger 621 nm (1,150 km; 715 miles)
    cargo 382 nm (707 km; 440 miles)
  Ferry range 1,850 nm (3,428 km; 2,130 miles)

GULFSTREAM AMERICAN GULFSTREAM II

US Coast Guard designation: VC-11A

The decision to start production of this twin-turbofan

Gulfstream American Gulfstream II executive transport with new wingtip tanks

executive transport was announced by Grumman on 17 May 1965. The first production Gulfstream II (no prototype was built) flew for the first time on 2 October 1966. FAA certification was gained on 19 October 1967, and the first production aircraft was delivered to National Distillers & Chemical Corporation on 6 December 1967.

Custom interiors and avionics, with the exception of the Sperry SP-50G automatic flight control system, which is standard, are installed by specialist agencies.

Deliveries totalled more than 240 by 1 January 1979, including a single Gulfstream II operated by the US Coast Guard under the designation **VC-11A**. Two other Gulfstream IIs were converted as flying simulators for the Space Shuttle Orbiter vehicle. Production was due to end in December 1979, after the sale of 256 aircraft.

From aircraft No. 166, delivered in July 1975, production aircraft incorporate an engine 'hush-kit', for which Grumman American received FAA certification on 2 May 1975; this modification can be retrofitted to earlier Gulfstream IIs if required.

Flight testing began in 1975 of a Gulfstream II with wingtip tanks, increasing the total fuel capacity to 12,156 kg (26,800 lb). This version has a max ramp weight of 29,937 kg (66,000 lb) and max T-O weight of 29,711 kg (65,500 lb). Increased fuel, amounting to 1,415 kg (3,120 lb), is carried in the wingtip tanks which serve as an extension of the main integral wing tanks. Wind tunnel tests showed that tne tip-tanks do not affect high-speed handling, that they offer a slight improvement in aircraft stability and lateral control, and that cruise performance penalty is approximately 5 per cent against max fuel range improvements of 12 per cent at long-range cruising speed, 11 per cent at 0·72 constant Mach, and 7 per cent at 0·80 constant Mach. This version is certificated for an NBAA IFR range of 3,180 nm (5,893 km; 3,662 miles) with a 200 nm (370 km; 230 mile) alternate.

The description which follows applies to the standard version:

TYPE: Twin-turbofan executive transport.

WINGS: Cantilever low-wing monoplane of all-metal construction. Thickness/chord ratio 12% at wing station 50, 9·5% at wing station 145 and 8·5% at wing station 414. Dihedral 3°. Incidence 3° 30′ at wing station 50, 1° 30′ at wing station 145 and −0° 30′ at wing station 414. Sweepback 25° at quarter-chord. One-piece single-slotted Fowler-type trailing-edge flaps. Spoilers forward of flaps assist in lateral control and can be extended for use as airbrakes. All control surfaces actuated hydraulically. Trim tab in port aileron. Anti-icing by engine bleed air.

FUSELAGE: Conventional all-metal semi-monocoque structure. Glassfibre nosecone hinged for access to radar, etc.

TAIL UNIT: Cantilever all-metal T-tail. All surfaces swept-back. Trim tab in rudder and each elevator. Powered controls (see under 'Systems' paragraph).

LANDING GEAR: Retractable tricycle type, with twin wheels on each unit. Inward-retracting main units, with tyres size 34 × 8·25-32, pressure 10·34 bars (150 lb/sq in). Forward-retracting steerable nose unit. Nosewheel tyres size 21 × 7·25-22, pressure 6·55 bars (95 lb/sq in). Goodyear aircooled brakes with Goodyear fully-modulating anti-skid units.

POWER PLANT: Two Rolls-Royce Spey Mk 511-8 turbofan engines, each 50·7 kN (11,400 lb st), mounted in pod on each side of rear fuselage. Rohr target-type thrust reversers form aft portions of nacelles when in stowed position. All fuel in integral tanks in wings, capacity 10,568 kg (23,300 lb). Provision for wingtip tanks, to increase fuel capacity to 12,156 kg (26,800 lb).

ACCOMMODATION: Crew of two or three. Certificated for 19 passengers in pressurised and air-conditioned cabin. Large baggage compartment at rear of cabin, capacity 907 kg (2,000 lb). Integral airstair door at front of cabin on port side. Electrically heated windscreen.

SYSTEMS: Cabin pressurisation system, with max differential of 0·65 bars (9·45 lb/sq in). Two independent hydraulic systems, each 103·5 bars (1,500 lb/sq in). All flying controls hydraulically powered, with manual reversion. APU in tail compartment. Basic 28V DC electrical system, using two 300A generators and a 200A transformer-rectifier. Two 20kVA alternators provide AC power for secondary and auxiliary systems. Third (APU-driven) 20kVA alternator for on-ground power. Three 2·5kVA inverters, powered by the transformer-rectifiers, provide 400Hz fixed-frequency power. Two 24V batteries.

DIMENSIONS, EXTERNAL:

Wing span	20·98 m (68 ft 10 in)
Wing span over tip-tanks	21·87 m (71 ft 9 in)
Length overall	24·36 m (79 ft 11 in)
Length of fuselage	21·74 m (71 ft 4 in)
Height overall	7·47 m (24 ft 6 in)
Tailplane span	8·23 m (27 ft 0 in)
Wheel track	4·16 m (13 ft 8 in)
Wheelbase	10·16 m (33 ft 4 in)
Passenger door: Height	1·57 m (5 ft 2 in)
Width	0·91 m (3 ft 0 in)
Baggage door: Height	0·72 m (2 ft 4½ in)
Width	0·91 m (2 ft 11¾ in)
Ventral door: Width	0·46 m (1 ft 6 in)
Length	0·71 m (2 ft 4 in)

DIMENSIONS, INTERNAL:

Cabin: Length	11·99 m (39 ft 4 in)
Width	2·24 m (7 ft 4 in)
Height	1·85 m (6 ft 1 in)
Volume	40·41 m³ (1,427 cu ft)
Baggage compartment	4·44 m³ (156·85 cu ft)

AREA:

Wings, gross	75·21 m² (809·6 sq ft)

WEIGHTS AND LOADINGS:

Manufacturer's weight empty:	
without tip-tanks	13,772 kg (30,363 lb)
with tip-tanks	14,053 kg (30,938 lb)
Typical operating weight empty:	
without tip-tanks	16,576 kg (36,544 lb)
with tip-tanks	16,867 kg (37,186 lb)
Max T-O weight	29,711 kg (65,500 lb)
Max ramp weight	29,937 kg (66,000 lb)
Max landing weight	26,535 kg (58,500 lb)
Max zero-fuel weight	19,050 kg (42,000 lb)
Max wing loading	394·8 kg/m² (80·9 lb/sq ft)
Max power loading	293 kg/kN (2·87 lb/lb st)

PERFORMANCE (at max T-O weight except where indicated):

Max cruising speed at 7,620 m (25,000 ft)
Mach 0·85 (505 knots; 936 km/h; 581 mph)

Econ cruising speed at 13,105 m (43,000 ft)
Mach 0·72 (420 knots; 778 km/h; 483 mph)

Approach speed at max landing weight
142 knots (263 km/h; 164 mph)

Max rate of climb at S/L 1,262 m (4,140 ft)/min

Rate of climb at S/L with tip-tanks
1,219 m (4,000 ft)/min

Rate of climb at S/L, one engine out
427 m (1,400 ft)/min

Rate of climb at S/L with tip-tanks, one engine out
366 m (1,200 ft)/min

Service ceiling 13,100 m (43,000 ft)

Service ceiling, one engine out 8,230 m (27,000 ft)

Service ceiling with tip-tanks, one engine out
7,405 m (24,300 ft)

FAA T-O field length 1,707 m (5,600 ft)

FAA T-O field length, with tip-tanks
1,737 m (5,700 ft)

FAA landing field length 1,067 m (3,500 ft)

NBAA IFR range with 200 nm (370 km; 230 mile) alternate, crew of three, plus 907 kg (2,000 lb) 'passenger payload' 2,859 nm (5,298 km; 3,292 miles)

Range, conditions as above, with tip-tanks
3,180 nm (5,893 km; 3,662 miles)

NBAA VFR range with 30 min reserves, crew of three, plus 907 kg (2,000 lb) 'passenger payload'
3,252 nm (6,025 km; 3,744 miles)

Range, conditions as above, with tip-tanks
3,581 nm (6,635 km; 4,123 miles)

OPERATIONAL NOISE CHARACTERISTICS (FAR Pt 36):

Approach noise level	98·41 EPNdB
Sideline noise level	102·98 EPNdB

GULFSTREAM AMERICAN GULFSTREAM III

Grumman (now Gulfstream) American announced the resumption of the Gulfstream III programme in the Spring of 1978. It differs from the Gulfstream II primarily in having redesigned wings, with 'winglets' at the tips, a lengthened fuselage, and increased fuel capacity combined with an increase of some 18% in fuel economy and efficiency.

A prototype, converted from a production-line Gulf-

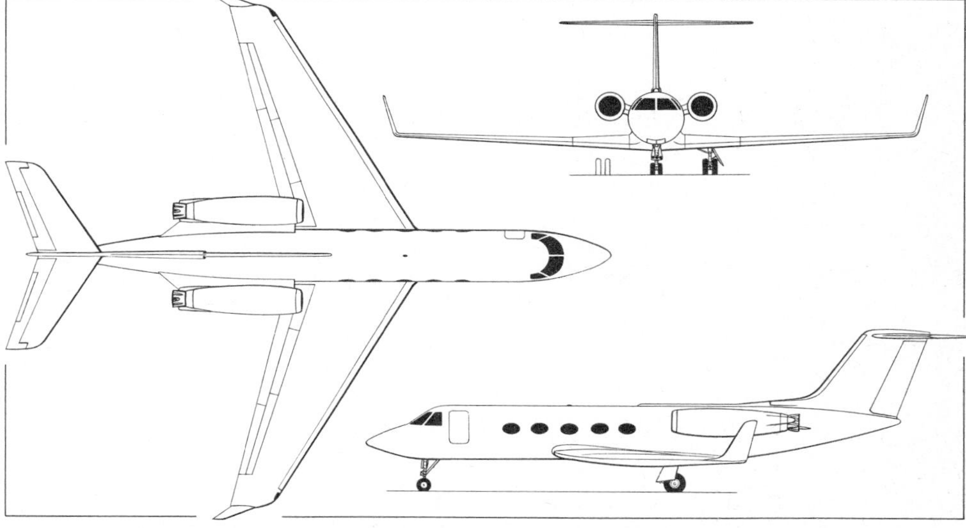

Gulfstream American Gulfstream III executive transport aircraft *(Pilot Press)*

Prototype Gulfstream American Gulfstream III, rolled out on 21 September 1979

stream II (c/n 249), was rolled out on 21 September 1979, and was scheduled to fly in November 1979, with first deliveries anticipated in mid-1980. Customers include the Royal Danish Air Force, which will use three for fishing surveillance, search and rescue and personnel transport duties.

TYPE: Twin-turbofan executive transport.

WINGS: Cantilever low-wing monoplane of conventional light alloy construction. By comparison with the wings of the Gulfstream II, these have slightly increased sweepback at quarter-chord (27° 40′), increased span, and extended-chord leading-edges (0·76 m; 2 ft 6 in at root, 0·13 m; 5 in at tip). Additional fuel tankage; NASA (Whitcomb) wingtip 'winglets'.

FUSELAGE: Generally as for Gulfstream II, but lengthened by 0·61 m (2 ft) plug aft of flight deck, and longer, more streamlined, nose radome.

TAIL UNIT AND LANDING GEAR: Generally as for Gulfstream II. Carbon brakes on production version.

POWER PLANT: As for Gulfstream II, but fuel capacity increased by additional 2,086 kg; 4,600 lb in enlarged wings to a total of approx 16,656 litres (4,400 US gallons). No wingtip tanks.

ACCOMMODATION: As for Gulfstream II, but flight deck has improved crew accommodation and new wraparound windscreen. Cabin seating for 19 passengers, with more space per passenger than in Gulfstream II. Max capacity of aft baggage compartment 907 kg (2,000 lb).

AVIONICS AND EQUIPMENT: Standard avionics include three Collins VHF com; two Collins VIR-31B VHF nav; two Collins ADF-60A; two Collins transponders; two Collins DME-40; cockpit voice recorders, Sperry SP2-800 or Collins automatic flight guidance and control system; and Collins WXR-250, Bendix RDR-1200 or RCA Primus 40 or 400 weather radar.

DIMENSIONS, EXTERNAL:
Wing span 23·72 m (77 ft 10 in)
Wing area, gross 86·83 m² (934·6 sq ft)
Length overall 25·27 m (82 ft 11 in)
Fuselage length 22·66 m (74 ft 4 in)
Height overall 7·21 m (23 ft 8 in)
Passenger door (fwd, port) as Gulfstream II
Baggage compartment door (aft) as Gulfstream II

DIMENSIONS, INTERNAL:
Cabin: Length 10·97 m (36 ft 0 in)
Width 2·24 m (7 ft 4 in)
Height 1·85 m (6 ft 1 in)
Volume 38·20 m³ (1,349 cu ft)
Aft baggage compartment volume 4·44 m³ (157 cu ft)

WEIGHTS (estimated):
Manufacturer's bare weight 14,742 kg (32,500 lb)
Typical operating weight empty 17,372 kg (38,300 lb)
Max fuel load 12,655 kg (27,900 lb)
Typical payload 726 kg (1,600 lb)
Max T-O weight 30,935 kg (68,200 lb)
Max ramp weight 31,162 kg (68,700 lb)
Max zero-fuel weight 19,050 kg (42,000 lb)
Max landing weight 26,535 kg (58,500 lb)

PERFORMANCE (estimated):
Max cruising speed Mach 0·85
Long-range cruising speed Mach 0·775
Approach speed 136 knots (252 km/h; 156 mph)
Stalling speed at max landing weight 105 knots (195 km/h; 121 mph)
Max operating altitude 13,720 m (45,000 ft)
FAA T-O field length 1,783 m (5,850 ft)
FAA landing distance 1,040 m (3,400 ft)
Range with 726 kg (1,600 lb) payload at long-range cruising speed, IFR reserves 3,760 nm (6,968 km; 4,330 miles)
Max range (VFR), 30 min reserves 4,045 nm (7,495 km; 4,660 miles)

GULFSTREAM AMERICAN AA-1C, T-CAT AND LYNX

Production of these two-seat light aircraft has ended. They were described and illustrated in the 1978-79 *Jane's*.

GULFSTREAM AMERICAN AA-5A and CHEETAH

The first flight of the original AA-5 was made on 21 August 1970, and FAA certification was awarded on 12 November 1971. Then named Traveler, the aircraft remained basically unchanged until it was redesignated AA-5A to indicate the introduction of redesigned tail surfaces and engine cowling, together with other standard improvements. In this form the aircraft was recertificated on 28 July 1975. Soon afterwards, the original Traveler de luxe was renamed Cheetah.

Differences in the two versions are as follows:

AA-5A. Standard version, to which the detailed description applies.

Cheetah. De luxe version; as standard model, plus the following additional equipment: electric clock, omni-flash beacon, dual controls, gyro system, landing light, outside air temperature gauge, sensitive altimeter, heated pitot, tinted windows, turn co-ordinator and vertical speed indicators, towbar, Narco Com 10A/Nav 10 nav/com transceiver with VOR/LOC indicator and Option 1 (Narco M-700 microphone, headset, speaker and antenna), and radio cooling kit.

Cheetah de luxe version of the Gulfstream American AA-5A four-seat lightplane

TYPE: Four-seat cabin monoplane.

WINGS: Cantilever low-wing monoplane. Wing section NACA 64_2415 (modified). Dihedral 5°. Incidence 3° 30′. No sweepback. Alclad light alloy skin and ribs, attached to tube-type circular-section main spar by adhesive bonding. Plain ailerons of bonded construction, with honeycomb ribs and Alclad light alloy skin. Electrically-actuated plain trailing-edge flaps of bonded construction, with honeycomb ribs and light alloy skin. Commercial Aircraft Products flap actuators. Hoerner type wingtips. Ground-adjustable trim tab on each aileron.

FUSELAGE: Light alloy honeycomb cabin section and light alloy semi-monocoque rear fuselage, utilising adhesive bonding. The use of honeycomb eliminates false floors, resulting in greater usable cabin space relative to cross-sectional area.

TAIL UNIT: Cantilever structure of adhesive-bonded light alloy. Movable surfaces built up of honeycomb ribs bonded to light alloy sheet. Combined trim and anti-servo tabs in both elevators. Ground-adjustable trim tab on rudder.

LANDING GEAR: Non-retractable tricycle type. Nose unit is flex-torque tube of 4340 steel, with dual shock-absorbers and large free-swivelling fork. Main legs are cantilever springs of laminated glassfibre. Main-wheel tyres size 17 × 6·00-6, pressure 1·66 bars (24 lb/sq in). Nosewheel tyre size 5·00-5, pressure 1·45 bars (21 lb/sq in). Toe-operated single-disc hydraulic brakes. Parking brake.

POWER PLANT: One 112 kW (150 hp) Lycoming O-320-E2G flat-four engine, driving a McCauley fixed-pitch two-blade metal propeller with spinner. Two integral fuel tanks in wings, with a total capacity of 144 litres (38 US gallons), of which 140 litres (37 US gallons) are usable. Optionally, two integral fuel tanks in wings with total capacity of 199 litres (52·6 US gallons), of which 193 litres (51 US gallons) are usable. Refuelling point in upper surface of each wing. Oil capacity 7·5 litres (2 US gallons).

ACCOMMODATION: Pilot and three passengers in enclosed cabin, with sliding canopy, on four separate seats, in pairs. Baggage area aft of rear seats, which may be folded forward when unoccupied to increase baggage space. Max normal baggage load 54·4 kg (120 lb). External baggage door. Cabin heated and ventilated, Windscreen defrosters.

SYSTEMS: Hydraulic system for brakes only. Electrical system includes 60A 14V engine-driven alternator, 12V 60A voltage regulator and 12V 25Ah battery.

AVIONICS AND EQUIPMENT: Standard avionics for the Cheetah, optional for the AA-5A, as detailed in model listings. A wide range of optional avionics and autopilots by Collins, Edo-Aire Mitchell, King and Narco is available to customer's requirements. Standard equipment includes armrests, carpeted floor and side panels, chart holders, coat hook, fold-down rear seat, instrument panel glareshield, glove compartment, hat shelf, soundproofing, de luxe interior, adjustable front seats, seat belts, shoulder harnesses, baggage tiedown rings, baggage straps, air ventilators, control locks, cabin dome light, variable-intensity instrument lights, navigation lights, quick fuel drains, audible stall warning, and recording tachometer. Optional equipment for AA-5A includes items standard on Cheetah, plus hour recorder, true airspeed indicator, turn and bank indicator, external power socket, tailplane abrasion boots, internal corrosion proofing, stainless steel control cables, emergency locator transmitter, cabin fire extinguisher, intercom, adjustable map light, alternate static source, rear seat ventilation, steps, strobe lights, sun visors, oil quick-drain valve, shock-mounted wheel fairings and wing levelling system.

DIMENSIONS, EXTERNAL:
Wing span 9·60 m (31 ft 6 in)
Wing chord (constant) 1·35 m (4 ft 5¼ in)
Wing aspect ratio 7·10
Length overall 6·71 m (22 ft 0 in)
Height overall 2·29 m (7 ft 6 in)
Tailplane span 3·86 m (12 ft 8 in)
Wheel track 2·51 m (8 ft 3 in)
Wheelbase 1·64 m (5 ft 4½ in)
Propeller diameter 1·85 m (6 ft 1 in)
Propeller ground clearance 0·27 m (10·6 in)

DIMENSIONS, INTERNAL:
Cabin: Length 1·98 m (6 ft 6 in)
Max width 1·02 m (3 ft 4 in)
Max height 1·12 m (3 ft 8 in)
Floor area 2·18 m² (23·5 sq ft)
Baggage space 0·34 m³ (12 cu ft)

AREAS:
Wings, gross 12·98 m² (139·7 sq ft)
Ailerons (total) 0·72 m² (7·74 sq ft)
Trailing-edge flaps (total) 1·51 m² (16·26 sq ft)
Fin 0·44 m² (4·76 sq ft)
Rudder 0·33 m² (3·55 sq ft)
Elevators, incl tabs 0·99 m² (10·68 sq ft)

WEIGHTS AND LOADINGS:
Weight empty 600 kg (1,323 lb)
Max T-O weight 998 kg (2,200 lb)
Max wing loading 76·6 kg/m² (15·7 lb/sq ft)
Max power loading 8·91 kg/kW (14·7 lb/hp)

PERFORMANCE (at max T-O weight):
Max level speed at S/L 136 knots (253 km/h; 157 mph)
Max cruising speed, 75% power at 2,590 m (8,500 ft) 127 knots (235 km/h; 146 mph)
Econ cruising speed, 65% power at 2,590 m (8,500 ft) 118 knots (219 km/h; 136 mph)
Stalling speed, flaps up 54 knots (100 km/h; 62 mph)
Stalling speed, flaps down 52 knots (97 km/h; 60 mph)
Max rate of climb at S/L 201 m (660 ft)/min
Service ceiling 3,855 m (12,650 ft)
T-O run 268 m (880 ft)
T-O to 15 m (50 ft) 488 m (1,600 ft)
Landing from 15 m (50 ft) 335 m (1,100 ft)
Landing run 116 m (380 ft)
Range at 2,590 m (8,500 ft), including allowances for start, taxi, T-O, climb to cruising altitude and 45 min reserves at 50% power:
max cruising speed with standard fuel 448 nm (830 km; 516 miles)
max cruising speed with optional fuel 657 nm (1,218 km; 757 miles)
econ cruising speed (55% power) with standard fuel 499 nm (925 km; 575 miles)
econ cruising speed (55% power) with optional fuel 733 nm (1,358 km; 844 miles)

GULFSTREAM AMERICAN AA-5B and TIGER

In late 1974 Grumman American announced the introduction of the AA-5B to its range of single-engined light aircraft. This differs from the AA-5A by having a more powerful engine and increased fuel capacity as standard.

Two versions of the AA-5B are available, as follows:

AA-5B. Standard version, to which the detailed description applies.

Tiger. De luxe version; as standard model, plus the additional equipment detailed for the Cheetah. The 1,000th Tiger was delivered on 21 November 1978.

The description of the AA-5A and Cheetah applies also to the AA-5B and Tiger, except as follows:

POWER PLANT: One 134 kW (180 hp) Lycoming O-360-A4K flat-four engine, driving a McCauley two-blade fixed-pitch metal propeller with spinner. Two integral fuel tanks in wings with total capacity of 199 litres (52·6 US gallons), of which 193 litres (51 US gallons) are usable. Refuelling point in upper surface of each wing. Oil capacity 7·5 litres (2 US gallons).

WEIGHTS AND LOADINGS:
Weight empty 617 kg (1,360 lb)
Max T-O weight 1,088 kg (2,400 lb)
Max wing loading 83·5 kg/m² (17·1 lb/sq ft)
Max power loading 8·12 kg/kW (13·3 lb/hp)

PERFORMANCE (at max T-O weight):
Max level speed at S/L 148 knots (274 km/h; 170 mph)

Max cruising speed, 75% power at 2,590 m (8,500 ft) 139 knots (257 km/h; 160 mph)
Econ cruising speed, 65% power at 2,590 m (8,500 ft) 129 knots (238 km/h; 148 mph)
Stalling speed, flaps up 56 knots (104 km/h; 64 mph)
Stalling speed, flaps down 53 knots (98 km/h; 61 mph)
Max rate of climb at S/L 259 m (850 ft)/min
Service ceiling 4,205 m (13,800 ft)
T-O run 264 m (865 ft)
T-O to 15 m (50 ft) 472 m (1,550 ft)
Landing from 15 m (50 ft) 341 m (1,120 ft)
Landing run 125 m (410 ft)
Range at 2,590 m (8,500 ft), including allowances for start, taxi, T-O, climb to cruising altitude and reserves for 45 min at 45% power:
max cruising speed with max fuel 554 nm (1,027 km; 638 miles)
econ cruising speed (55% power) with max fuel 588 nm (1,090 km; 677 miles)

GULFSTREAM AMERICAN GA-7 and COUGAR

Grumman (now Gulfstream) American announced on 20 December 1974 the first flight of a twin-engined light aircraft (N777GA) now known as the Model GA-7/Cougar. Representing the company's first entry into the lightweight twin-engined market, it is intended primarily for business use and for private pilots already possessing IFR experience in high-powered single-engined aircraft. It can also be used as an economical trainer for conversion to twin-engined flight. The production prototype (N877X) flew for the first time on 14 January 1977, and delivery of production aircraft began in February 1978.

Two versions are available:

GA-7. Basic version, as described in detail.

Cougar. A de luxe version of the GA-7, which has the following additional avionics and equipment as standard: Narco Com 120/Nav 121 with M-700B microphone and Option 1 (antennae, Telex headset, speaker, jacks, wiring, and radio cooling kit); electric clock ; direction and horizon gyros with pressure system; turn co-ordinator; vertical speed indicator; outside air temperature gauge; dual controls; glove box; tinted windscreen and windows; landing light; strobe lights; heated pitot; quick oil drain valves; and towbar.

TYPE: Four-seat lightweight cabin monoplane.

WINGS: Cantilever low-wing monoplane. Dihedral 5°. Wing section NACA 63A-415 (modified). All-metal two-spar structure of light alloy with wing skins attached to ribs and spars by metal to metal bonding techniques. Electrically-operated single-slotted Fowler-type trailing-edge flaps of light alloy. Plain ailerons of light alloy construction. Aileron trim system. Conical camber wingtips.

FUSELAGE: Cabin area of aluminium honeycomb construction; semi-monocoque rear fuselage structure of light alloy, using metal to metal bonding construction.

TAIL UNIT: Conventional cantilever structure of light alloy, with swept vertical surfaces. Trim tabs in rudder and each elevator.

LANDING GEAR: Hydraulically-retractable tricycle type with single wheel on each unit. Steerable nosewheel retracts forward, main units outward into undersurface of wing. Oleo-pneumatic shock-absorbers. Free-fall emergency extension system. Main wheels have 17 × 6·00-6 six-ply tyres, nosewheel has 15 × 6·00-6 four-ply tyre. Toe-operated hydraulic brakes. Parking brake.

POWER PLANT: Two 119·3 kW (160 hp) Lycoming O-320-D1D flat-four engines, each driving a Hartzell two-blade constant-speed fully-feathering metal propeller, Type HC-F2YL-2UF/FC7663D-3, with spinner. Integral fuel tank in each wing, with a combined capacity of 447 litres (118 US gallons). Refuelling point on upper surface of each wing. Oil capacity 15 litres (4 US gallons).

ACCOMMODATION: Four seats, in two side-by-side pairs, in enclosed cabin. Dual controls optional for GA-7, standard in Cougar. Overwing door on starboard side of fuselage. Baggage space aft of rear seats with external access door on starboard side. Door on starboard side of nose section to give access to battery and electronics, as well as an additional 0·34 m³ (12 cu ft) of baggage space. Provision for lightweight radar antenna in nosecone. Heating, ventilation, and windscreen defrosters standard.

SYSTEMS: Hydraulic system for landing gear actuation and operation of brakes. Electrical system includes 14V 60A engine-driven alternators, 14V voltage regulators and a 12V battery.

AVIONICS AND EQUIPMENT: Narco Com 120/Nav 121 and associated equipment optional for GA-7, standard on Cougar. A wide range of optional avionics and autopilots by Collins, Edo-Aire Mitchell, King and Narco is available to customer's requirements. Standard equipment includes lap belts and shoulder harnesses, front seats with inertia reel; front seat armrests; carpeted floor; instrument panel glareshield; hatshelf; map compartment and storage pockets; pilot's storm window; fold-down rear seat; soundproofing; controllable instrument panel lighting; cabin dome lights; indirect instrument panel lighting; navigation lights with detectors; audible stall warning device; sensitive altimeter; dual manifold pressure gauge; alternate static source; cabin step; tiedown rings; elevator and aileron gust locks; and polyurethane external paint scheme. Optional equipment for GA-7 includes items standard on Cougar, plus encoding altimeter, sensitive altimeter, hour recorder, true airspeed indicator, turn and bank indicator, external power socket, nose baggage compartment, control wheel microphone, internal corrosion proofing, stainless steel control cables, exhaust gas temperature gauge, map light, lighting package including rear reading, baggage compartment, exterior step and wing lights, propeller unfeathering accumulator, and rear-seat ventilation system.

DIMENSIONS, EXTERNAL:

Wing span	11·23 m (36 ft 10¼ in)
Wing chord (constant)	1·45 m (4 ft 9 in)
Wing aspect ratio	7·44
Length overall	9·09 m (29 ft 10 in)
Height overall	3·16 m (10 ft 4¼ in)
Tailplane span	4·24 m (13 ft 11 in)
Wheel track	2·03 m (6 ft 8 in)
Wheelbase	3·30 m (10 ft 10 in)

Gulfstream American Tiger (Lycoming O-360-A4K engine)

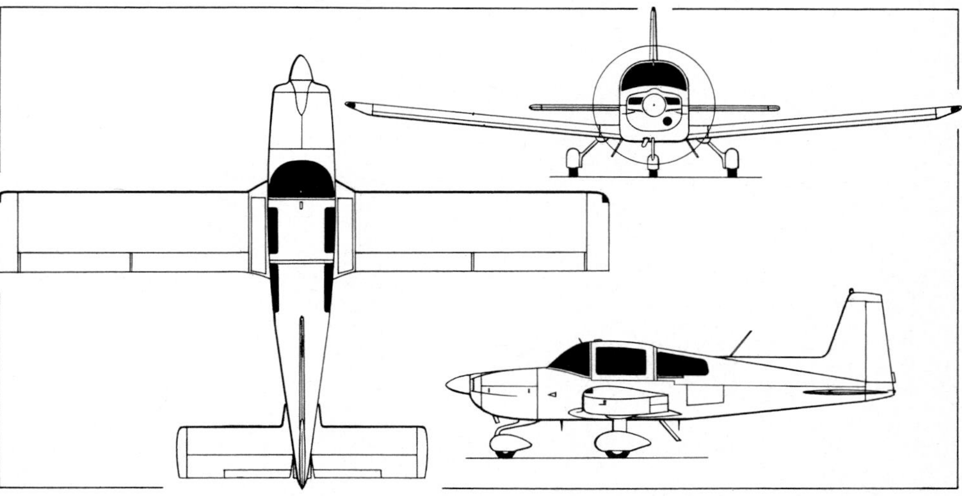

Gulfstream American Tiger four-seat light aircraft *(Pilot Press)*

Gulfstream American GA-7/Cougar four-seat lightweight cabin monoplane

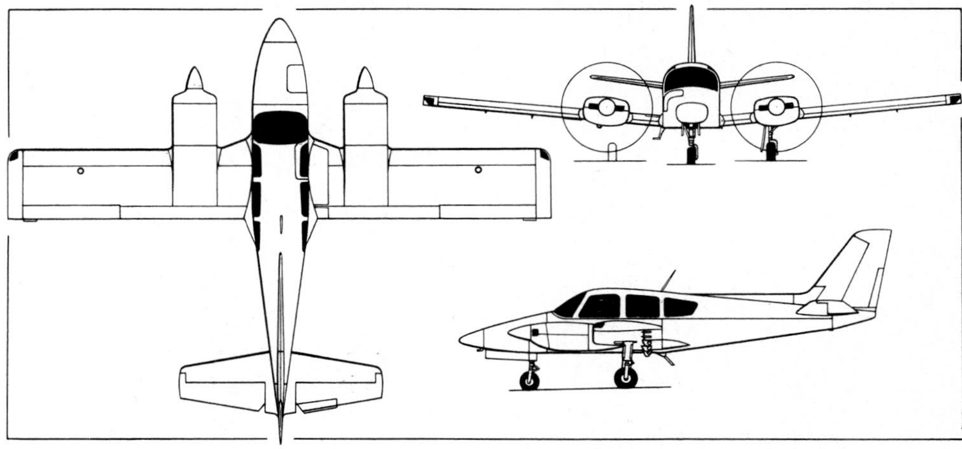

Gulfstream American Cougar (two Lycoming O-320-D1D engines) *(Pilot Press)*

Propeller diameter 1·85 m (6 ft 1 in)

AREAS:
- Wings, gross 17·09 m² (184 sq ft)
- Vertical tail surfaces (total) 1·86 m² (20 sq ft)
- Horizontal tail surfaces (total) 4·46 m² (48 sq ft)

WEIGHTS AND LOADINGS (A: GA-7; B: Cougar):
- Basic empty weight: A 1,174 kg (2,588 lb)
- Max T-O weight: A, B 1,724 kg (3,800 lb)
- Max wing loading:
  - A, B 100·8 kg/m² (20·65 lb/sq ft)
- Max power loading:
  - A, B 7·23 kg/kW (11·88 lb/hp)

PERFORMANCE (at max T-O weight):
- Max level speed at S/L 168 knots (311 km/h; 193 mph)
- Max cruising speed, 75% power at 2,590 m (8,500 ft) 160 knots (296 km/h; 184 mph)
- Econ cruising speed, 45% power at 2,590 m (8,500 ft) 109 knots (203 km/h; 126 mph)
- Stalling speed, flaps up, power off 71 knots (132 km/h; 82 mph)
- Stalling speed, flaps down, power off 63 knots (117 km/h; 72·5 mph)
- Min control speed, single engine 61 knots (113 km/h; 70·5 mph)
- Max rate of climb at S/L 354 m (1,160 ft)/min
- Rate of climb at S/L, one engine out 61 m (200 ft)/min
- Service ceiling 5,305 m (17,400 ft)
- Service ceiling, one engine out 1,295 m (4,250 ft)
- T-O run 305 m (1,000 ft)
- T-O to 15 m (50 ft) 564 m (1,850 ft)
- Landing from 15 m (50 ft) 405 m (1,330 ft)
- Landing run 216 m (710 ft)
- Range at 2,590 m (8,500 ft), including allowances for start, taxi, T-O, climb, cruise, descent, and reserves for 45 min at 45% power:
  - max cruising speed with max fuel 840 nm (1,556 km; 967 miles)
  - econ cruising speed (45% power) with max fuel 1,170 nm (2,168 km; 1,347 miles)

GULFSTREAM AMERICAN SUPER AG-CAT

The prototype of the original Ag-Cat agricultural biplane flew for the first time on 27 May 1957. Series production was entrusted to Schweizer, under subcontract from Grumman. First deliveries were made in 1959, and 2,280 Ag-Cats (including 2,250 of the A and B models) had been built by 1 January 1979, when the type was in service in 34 countries.

The Ag-Cat was certificated in the Restricted (agricultural) category on 20 January 1959, with a 106 kW (220 hp) Continental engine, and received additional approval in this category for patrolling and surveying on 9 April 1962. Other engines for which FAA Type Approval was received were the 179 kW (240 hp) Gulf Coast W-670-240, 183 kW (245 hp) Jacobs L-4M or L-4MB, 205-224 kW (275-300 hp) Jacobs R-755, and 335·5 kW (450 hp) Pratt & Whitney R-985.

The Super Ag-Cat A was certificated in the Restricted (agricultural) category on 4 March 1966 and was FAA approved with the 335·5 kW (450 hp) Pratt & Whitney R-985, and 447·5 kW (600 hp) Pratt & Whitney R-1340 engines; production of this model ended in December 1977.

The Super Ag-Cat B was certificated in the Restricted (agricultural) category on 18 November 1975. Although generally similar to the Super Ag-Cat A, it has greater wing span and longer spraybooms. Engines approved by the FAA for installation in this version include the two approved for the Super Ag-Cat A, plus the 391·5 kW (525 hp) Continental/Page R-975.

The Super Ag-Cat C was first flown on 27 February 1976, and received certification in the Restricted (agricultural) category on 23 November 1977. This model has a longer and deeper fuselage to accommodate a 1,893 litre (500 US gallon) hopper. Four versions of the Super Ag-Cat were therefore available in 1979:

Super Ag-Cat B/450. Basic version, powered by a 335·5 kW (450 hp) Pratt & Whitney R-985 nine-cylinder radial aircooled engine, driving a Hamilton Standard two-blade constant-speed metal propeller with type 2D30 hub and AG-100-2 blades.

Super Ag-Cat B/525. As Ag-Cat B/450, but with 391·5 kW (525 hp) Continental/Page R-975 nine-cylinder radial aircooled engine, driving a Hamilton Standard two-blade metal constant-speed propeller with type 2D30 hub and AG-100 blades.

Super Ag-Cat C/600. As Super Ag-Cat B/450, but with 447·5 kW (600 hp) Pratt & Whitney R-1340 nine-cylinder radial aircooled engine, driving a Hamilton Standard two-blade metal constant-speed propeller with Type 12D40 hub and AG-100 blades. Larger-capacity hopper.

Turbo Ag-Cat D. As Super Ag-Cat C/600 generally, but with a Pratt & Whitney Aircraft of Canada PT6A series turboprop engine. Described separately.

In addition, Gulfstream American sent to the 1979 Paris Air Show an example converted to carry a second pilot in an open cockpit in place of the hopper. Intended for pilot training, this aircraft is shown in an accompanying illustration.

TYPE: Single-seat agricultural biplane.

WINGS: Single-bay staggered biplane. NACA 4412 (modified) wing section. Dihedral 3°. Incidence 6°. Aluminium alloy (6061-T6) two-spar structure with 6061-T6 skins on entire top surface, around leading-edge and back to front spar on undersurface. Remainder of undersurface fabric-covered. Each D leading-edge is made of five separate sections to facilitate replacement if damaged. Glassfibre wingtips. N-type interplane struts. Ailerons of light alloy construction, with fabric covering, on all four wings. Ground-adjustable tab in both ailerons of lower wing. No flaps.

FUSELAGE: Welded 4130 chrome-molybdenum steel tube structure, covered with duralumin sheet. Removable side panels.

TAIL UNIT: Welded 4130 chrome-molybdenum steel tube structure, covered with fabric and wire-braced. Cable deflector wire from tip of fin to top of cockpit canopy. Controllable trim tab in port elevator. Ground-adjustable tabs on rudder and starboard elevator.

LANDING GEAR: Non-retractable tailwheel type. Cantilever spring steel legs. Cleveland wheels with tyres size 8·50-10 6-ply, pressure 2·42 bars (35 lb/sq in), on the Super Ag-Cat B; size 29 × 11-10 10-ply rated at the same pressure on the Super Ag-Cat C. Steerable tailwheel with tyre size 12·4-4·5, pressure 3·45 bars (50 lb/sq in). Cleveland heavy duty aircooled disc brakes, Parking brake.

POWER PLANT: One Pratt & Whitney or Continental/Page nine-cylinder aircooled radial engine with Hamilton Standard constant-speed propeller, as detailed in model listings. Fuel tank in upper centre-section with standard usable capacity of 174 litres (46 US gallons). Optional tanks, installed in wings on one or both sides of centre-section, are available for total usable capacities of 241 or 303 litres (64 or 80 US gallons) on the Super Ag-Cat B; 303 litres (80 US gallons) standard on Super Ag-Cat C. Single-point refuelling on upper surface of upper wing centre-section. Oil capacity 32·2 litres (8·5 US gallons).

ACCOMMODATION: Single seat beneath enclosed cockpit canopy. Reinforced fairing aft of cockpit for turnover protection. Canopy side panels open outward and down, canopy top upward and to starboard, to provide access. Baggage compartment. Cockpit pressurised against dust ingress and ventilated by ram air. Air-conditioning optional. Safety-padded instrsment panel. Air-conditioning by J.B. Systems optional.

SYSTEMS: Hydraulic system for brakes only. Optional electrical system with 24V alternator, external power socket, navigation lights and/or strobe lights and electric engine starter.

EQUIPMENT: Radio installation optional. Standard equipment includes refuelling steps and assist handles, tie-down rings, control column lock, instrument glareshield, seat belt and shoulder harness, stall warning light, tinted windshield and urethane paint in high-visibility yellow.

AGRICULTURAL EQUIPMENT: Forward of cockpit, over CG, is a 1·13 m³ (40 cu ft) glassfibre hopper, capacity (Super Ag-Cat B) 1,136 litres (300 US gallons) of agricultural chemicals (dry or liquid) with distributor beneath fuselage. Low-volume, ULV or high-volume spray system, with leading- or trailing-edge booms. Super Ag-Cat C has 1,893 litre (500 US gallon) capacity hopper. Spray or dust distribution systems available. Emergency dump system for hopper load; can be used also for water-bomber operations.

DIMENSIONS, EXTERNAL (A: Super Ag-Cat B/450; B: Super Ag-Cat B/525; C: Super Ag-Cat C/600):
- Wing span: A, B, C 12·88 m (42 ft 3 in)
- Wing chord (constant): A, B, C 1·47 m (4 ft 10 in)
- Wing aspect ratio, upper wing: A, B, C 8·74
  - Biplane, effective mean: A, B, C 5·46
- Length overall: A, B 7·90 m (25 ft 11 in)
  - C 9·14 m (30 ft 0 in)
- Height overall: A, B 3·35 m (11 ft 0 in)
  - C 3·48 m (11 ft 5 in)
- Tailplane span: A, B, C 3·96 m (13 ft 0 in)
- Wheel track: A, B 2·44 m (8 ft 0 in)
  - C 2·54 m (8 ft 4 in)
- Wheelbase: A, B 5·59 m (18 ft 4 in)
  - C 6·96 m (22 ft 10 in)
- Propeller diameter (max):
  - A, B, C 2·74 m (9 ft 0 in)
- Propeller ground clearance: A, B 0·27 m (10·8 in)
  - C 0·47 m (1 ft 6·7 in)

AREAS:
- Wings, gross: A, B, C 36·42 m² (392 sq ft)
- Ailerons (total): A, B, C 2·93 m² (31·5 sq ft)
- Fin: A, B 1·67 m² (17·97 sq ft)
  - C 0·84 m² (9·0 sq ft)
- Rudder: A, B, C 1·12 m² (12·0 sq ft)
- Tailplane: A, B, C 2·12 m² (22·8 sq ft)
- Elevators: A, B, C 2·06 m² (22·2 sq ft)

WEIGHTS AND LOADINGS:
- Weight empty equipped, spray version:
  - A 1,404 kg (3,095 lb)
  - B 1,424 kg (3,140 lb)
  - C 1,746 kg (3,850 lb)
- Weight empty equipped, duster version:
  - A 1,315 kg (2,900 lb)
  - B 1,338 kg (2,950 lb)
  - C 1,692 kg (3,730 lb)
- Max T-O weight (CAM.8):
  - A, B 2,755 kg (6,075 lb)
  - C (by formula) 3,855 kg (8,500 lb)
  - C (recommended) 3,629 kg (8,000 lb)
- Max wing loading: A, B 75·68 kg/m² (15·50 lb/sq ft)
  - C 99·65 kg/m² (20·41 lb/sq ft)

Gulfstream American Super Ag-Cat C loading spray chemicals

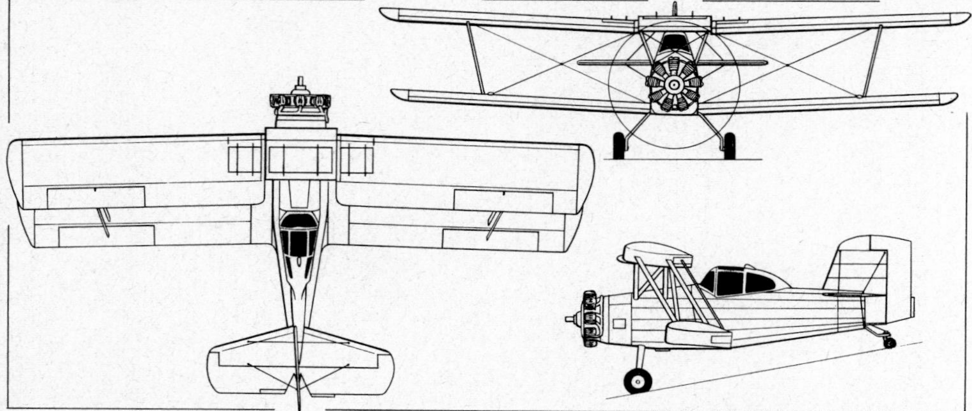

Three-view drawing of the Gulfstream American Super Ag-Cat B *(Pilot Press)*

Max power loading: A 8·21 kg/kW (13·5 lb/hp)
B 7·04 kg/kW (11·75 lb/hp)
C 8·11 kg/kW (13·33 lb/hp)

PERFORMANCE (at CAM.8 T-O weight):
Never-exceed speed:
A, B, C 128 knots (237 km/h; 147 mph)
Max cruising speed, 75% power at 1,525 m (5,000 ft):
A, B 102 knots (188 km/h; 117 mph)
Econ cruising speed, 50% power at 1,525 m (5,000 ft):
A, B 85 knots (158 km/h; 98 mph)
Stalling speed, power off:
A, B 52 knots (96 km/h; 60 mph) CAS
C 60 knots (111 km/h; 69 mph) CAS
Max rate of climb at S/L: A 323 m (1,060 ft)/min
B 411 m (1,350 ft)/min
T-O run: A 178 m (585 ft)
B 165 m (540 ft)
C 329 m (1,080 ft)
T-O to 15 m (50 ft): A 332 m (1,090 ft)
B 305 m (1,000 ft)
C 634 m (2,080 ft)
Landing from 15 m (50 ft): A, B 351 m (1,150 ft)
C 363 m (1,190 ft)
Landing run: A, B 172 m (565 ft)
C 180 m (590 ft)
Range with max standard fuel at 50% power:
A, B 216 nm (401 km; 249 miles)

GULFSTREAM AMERICAN MODEL G-164D TURBO AG-CAT D

This turboprop-powered version of the Ag-Cat is generally similar to the Super Ag-Cat C/600, but has a Pratt & Whitney Aircraft of Canada PT6A turboprop engine. It is available in three versions, as follows:

Turbo Ag-Cat D/T. With 507 kW (680 shp) PT6A-15 engine and 1,893 litre (500 US gallon) hopper/tank.

Turbo Ag-Cat D/ST. As D/T, but with 559 kW (750 shp) PT6A-34 engine.

Turbo Ag-Cat D/SST. As D/T, but with 634 kW (850 shp) PT6A-41 engine.

Gulfstream American began construction of a prototype in February 1978, and this flew for the first time on 19 July 1978. Construction of the first pre-production aircraft began in September 1978 and FAA certification under CAM 8 was anticipated in early 1979, with production deliveries beginning shortly after.

The description of the Super Ag-Cat applies also to the Turbo Ag-Cat D except as follows:

WINGS AND FUSELAGE: As Super Ag-Cat.

TAIL UNIT: As for Super Ag-Cat, except ground-adjustable trim tab on rudder only.

LANDING GEAR: Non-retractable tailwheel type. Cantilever spring steel main-gear legs. Main-wheel tyres size 29 × 11-10, pressure 2·42 bars (35 lb/sq in). Steerable tailwheel with tyre size 12·5-4·5, pressure 3·80 bars (55 lb/sq in). Cleveland heavy-duty aircooled disc brakes. Parking brake.

POWER PLANT: One 507 kW (680 shp) Pratt & Whitney Aircraft of Canada PT6A-15AG turboprop engine, driving a Hartzell HC-B3TN-3D/T10282A+4 constant-speed fully-feathering reversible-pitch three-blade metal propeller with Beta control and spinner. Optional power plants as detailed in model listings. Fuel contained in upper centre-section and two wing tanks, with combined capacity of 303 litres (80 US gallons). Single-point refuelling on top surface of upper wing centre-section. Oil capacity 8·7 litres (2·3 US gallons).

ACCOMMODATION: As for Super Ag-Cat, except no optional air-conditioning system.

SYSTEMS: Hydraulic system for brakes only. Electrical system standard, with 24V 250A starter/generator and two 12V 85Ah batteries.

EQUIPMENT: Standard equipment includes adjustable rudder pedals, control column lock, stainless steel control cables, adjustable seat with seat belt and shoulder harness, tinted windscreen, internal corrosion proofing, sensitive altimeter, engine oil chip detector with warning light, stall warning light, urethane paint and yellow paint scheme. Optional equipment includes external power socket, navigation lights, strobe/navigation light system, and stall warning horn.

AGRICULTURAL EQUIPMENT: This equipment, which includes a variety of options, is generally similar to that described for Super Ag-Cat.

DIMENSIONS, EXTERNAL: As for Super Ag-Cat C, except:
Length overall 10·46 m (34 ft 4 in)
Propeller diameter 2·71 m (8 ft 10½ in)

DIMENSIONS, INTERNAL:
Max width 0·81 m (2 ft 8 in)
Max height 1·37 m (4 ft 6 in)

AREAS: As for Super Ag-Cat C

WEIGHTS AND LOADINGS (A: liquid dispersal; B: dust dispersal):
Weight empty, equipped: A 1,565 kg (3,450 lb)
B 1,520 kg (3,350 lb)
Max payload (CAM.8): A 2,291 kg (5,050 lb)
B 2,336 kg (5,150 lb)
Design T-O weight 2,857 kg (6,300 lb)
Max T-O weight (CAM.8): A, B 3,856 kg (8,500 lb)
Max wing loading 105·9 kg/m² (21·68 lb/sq ft)
Max power loading 9·85 kg/kW (16·19 lb/shp)

The occupant of the open front cockpit identifies the pilot training version of the Ag-Cat *(Brian M. Service)*

Gulfstream American Turbo Ag-Cat D, latest version of this agricultural aircraft

PERFORMANCE (D/T version with PT6A-15AG engine):
Max level speed 135 knots (249 km/h; 155 mph)
Typical working speed
82·5-117 knots (153-217 km/h; 95-135 mph)
Stalling speed at AUW of 2,857 kg (6,300 lb)
60 knots (110 km/h; 69 mph)
Stalling speed at usual landing weight
49 knots (90 km/h; 56 mph)
T-O run 223 m (730 ft)
T-O to 15 m (50 ft) 411 m (1,350 ft)
Landing from 15 m (50 ft) fully loaded
509 m (1,670 ft)
Landing from 15 m (50 ft) at usual landing weight
411 m (1,350 ft)
Landing run, fully loaded 259 m (850 ft)
Landing run at usual landing weight 150 m (490 ft)

GULFSTREAM AMERICAN HUSTLER MODEL 500

Before acquiring Grumman's holding in Grumman American Aviation Corporation, and redesignation of this company as Gulfstream American Corporation, American Jet Industries announced on 24 October 1975 its plans to build a new general aviation aircraft. The design included a pressurised cabin, to permit cruising altitudes of up to 10,670 m (35,000 ft). STOL characteristics were to be provided by the use of a supercritical wing with full-span Fowler trailing-edge flaps, and spoilers, instead of ailerons, for lateral control. Most unusual feature was the power plant, comprising a nose-mounted Pratt & Whitney Aircraft of Canada PT6A turboprop, with a small Williams Research turbofan standby engine mounted in the aft fuselage. Designated Hustler Model 400, details of this aircraft can be found in the 1977-78 *Jane's*. The prototype, registered N400AJ, made its first flight on 11 January 1978 and had accumulated more than 250 hours' flying by mid-1979.

The desirability of obtaining certification of the Hustler as a twin-engined aircraft, coupled with a delay of some two years before the Williams Research standby turbofan would be available, brought the decision to change to a Pratt & Whitney JT15D-1 turbofan in the aft fuselage. This, in turn, made necessary further design changes, including lengthening the fuselage by insertion of a new 0·81 m (2 ft 8 in) section forward of the wing; resiting the cabin entrance door forward, instead of aft, of the wing; the provision of wingtip tanks to augment fuel capacity; and the replacement of spoilers by conventional ailerons, thus requiring the full-span flaps to be reduced to two-thirds span. The redesigned aircraft was designated Hustler 500.

Gulfstream American announced on 20 April 1979 that the Model 500 is to have a Garrett-AiResearch TPE 331-10 turboprop engine installed in lieu of the Pratt & Whitney PT6A-41; the former engine has a single under-fuselage exhaust outlet which will minimise exhaust gas ingression by the rear engine. The Model 500 was scheduled to fly with this new forward engine in Autumn 1979. A third prototype was built for static proof load testing at the Los Angeles Division of Rockwell International.

The following description applies to the Model 500:

TYPE: Twin-engined business/utility aircraft.

WINGS: Cantilever mid-wing monoplane. Supercritical wing section GAW Mod 4. Thickness/chord ratio 12·5%. Dihedral 2°. Incidence 0°. Sweepback at quarter-chord 15°. Conventional light alloy two-spar fail-safe structure with ribs, stringers and chemically-milled skins, flush riveted. Double-slotted hydraulically actuated light alloy Fowler trailing-edge flaps extending over two-thirds span. Conventional ailerons of light alloy construction. B. F. Goodrich pneumatic de-icing boots on wing leading-edges.

FUSELAGE: Semi-monocoque light alloy structure of circu-

Prototype Gulfstream American Hustler Model 400 twin-engined business/utility aircraft

Gulfstream American Hustler Model 500 with original Pratt & Whitney twin-engine power plant *(Pilot Press)*

lar cross-section, with fail-safe construction in the pressurised section extending between the firewall and aft pressure bulkhead.

TAIL UNIT: Cantilever light alloy structure with swept vertical surfaces. Manually-operated trim tab in rudder. Trim tabs in elevators. B. F. Goodrich pneumatic de-icing boots on fin and tailplane leading-edges. Ventral fin.

LANDING GEAR: Hydraulically-retractable tricycle type. Main units retract inward, nose unit aft. Oleo-pneumatic shock-absorbers. Single B. F. Goodrich wheel and tyre on each unit. Main wheels and tyres size 22 × 9·00, pressure 3·10 bars (45 lb/sq in); nosewheel size 17·50 × 6·00, pressure 2·41 bars (35 lb/sq in). B. F. Goodrich toe-operated hydraulic brakes.

POWER PLANT: One 671 kW (900 shp) Garrett-AiResearch TPE 331-10-501 turboprop engine, driving a Hartzell four-blade metal constant-speed reversible-pitch propeller with Beta control, mounted conventionally in the fuselage nose, and one 9·77 kN (2,200 lb st) Pratt & Whitney Aircraft of Canada JT15D-1 turbofan engine mounted in the rear fuselage. Fuel in integral wing and wingtip tanks with combined capacity of 1,828 litres (483 US gallons). Refuelling point on upper surface of each wingtip tank. Electrical propeller de-icing. Anti-icing of engine air intake by engine bleed air.

ACCOMMODATION: Two crew, and five or seven seats in passenger cabin. Refreshment centre; private toilet; folding tables. Baggage space at rear of cabin, capacity 91 kg (200 lb). Two-part door on port side, forward of wing, with airstairs in lower section. Hinged emergency exit on starboard side of cabin, between aft- and forward-facing seats. Access door to rear engine compartment aft of wing on port side. Accommodation heated, ventilated, air-conditioned and pressurised. Electrical windscreen de-icing.

SYSTEMS: AiResearch air cycle heating and cooling with pressurisation at a differential of 0·55 bars (8·0 lb/sq in). Hydraulic system for flaps, landing gear and brakes. Electrical system at 24V DC supplied by starter/generator. Nickel-cadmium storage battery. Oxygen system for emergency use.

AVIONICS AND EQUIPMENT: A range of avionics is available to customer's requirements, including dual nav/com, flight director, autopilot and weather radar. Blind-flying instrumentation standard. Optional weather radar in nose of starboard wingtip tank; landing light in nose of port wingtip tank.

DIMENSIONS, EXTERNAL:
Wing span 10·49 m (34 ft 5 in)
Wing chord at root 2·03 m (6 ft 8 in)
Length overall 12·57 m (41 ft 3 in)
Height overall 4·03 m (13 ft 2½ in)
Tailplane span 4·67 m (15 ft 4 in)
Wheel track 3·90 m (12 ft 9·6 in)
Wheelbase 3·66 m (12 ft 0¼ in)
Propeller diameter 2·35 m (7 ft 8½ in)
Passenger door: Height 1·17 m (3 ft 10 in)
Width 0·76 m (2 ft 6 in)
Emergency exit: Height 0·86 m (2 ft 10 in)
Width 0·71 m (2 ft 4 in)
Baggage door: Height 0·76 m (2 ft 6 in)
Width 0·58 m (1 ft 11 in)

DIMENSIONS, INTERNAL:
Cabin, aft of firewall: Length 5·59 m (18 ft 4 in)
Max width 1·22 m (4 ft 0 in)
Max height 1·27 m (4 ft 2 in)
Volume, incl cockpit area 7·36 m³ (260 cu ft)
Baggage compartment 0·74 m³ (26 cu ft)

AREA:
Wings, gross 17·72 m² (190·71 sq ft)

WEIGHTS AND LOADING:
Weight empty 2,463 kg (5,430 lb)
Max T-O weight 4,536 kg (10,000 lb)
Max ramp weight 4,572 kg (10,080 lb)
Max landing weight 4,309 kg (9,500 lb)
Max wing loading 256 kg/m² (52·4 lb/sq ft)

PERFORMANCE (estimated, at max T-O weight, ISA, except where indicated):
Max cruising speed at 7,620 m (25,000 ft) 400 knots (741 km/h; 461 mph)
Normal cruising speed, both engines, at 11,600 m (38,000 ft) 350 knots (648 km/h; 402 mph)
Approach speed at normal landing weight 103 knots (191 km/h; 119 mph)
Rotation speed 95 knots (176 km/h; 109 mph)
Stalling speed at normal landing weight 79 knots (146 km/h; 91 mph)
Max rate of climb at S/L 1,052 m (3,450 ft)/min
Operational ceiling 11,580 m (38,000 ft)
Operational ceiling, fwd engine only 6,705 m (22,000 ft)
Operational ceiling, aft engine only 8,990 m (29,500 ft)
T-O run (15° flap) 471 m (1,545 ft)
T-O to 15 m (50 ft) 532 m (1,745 ft)
Landing from 15 m (50 ft) 640 m (2,100 ft)
Landing from 15 m (50 ft), with propeller reversal 488 m (1,600 ft)
Range with max fuel, max cruising speed at 7,620 m (25,000 ft), 45 min reserves 1,120 nm (2,075 km; 1,289 miles)
Max range at normal cruising speed, 45 min reserves 2,000 nm (3,706 km; 2,303 miles)
Max range, aft engine shut down after 1·2 h at cruising altitude, 45 min reserves 2,400 nm (4,448 km; 2,764 miles)

GULFSTREAM AMERICAN PEREGRINE 600

On 25 July 1979, Gulfstream American announced its intention to build a prototype of the Peregrine 600 two-seat military trainer, based on its Hustler 500 design. The trainer will differ primarily by deletion of the forward engine and wingtip tanks of the Hustler. Seating will be side by side in the prototype, which will be powered by a single 13·34 kN (3,000 lb st) Pratt & Whitney Aircraft of Canada JT15D-5 turbofan engine, mounted in the rear fuselage. Options available for production Peregrines will include a different power plant, consisting of two Williams Research WR44 turbofans (each rated at 5·34 kN; 1,200 lb st), and tandem seating, which will involve further changes to the forward fuselage, transparent cockpit canopy and windscreen. In most other respects, the Peregrine 600 will be similar to the Hustler 500.

The following preliminary specification details have been made available:

DIMENSIONS, EXTERNAL:
Wing span 10·49 m (34 ft 5 in)
Length overall 11·66 m (38 ft 3 in)
Height overall 4·09 m (13 ft 5 in)
Tailplane span 4·65 m (15 ft 3 in)

WEIGHTS (estimated, A: JT15D-5; B: Williams Research 44s):
Max T-O weight: A 2,812 kg (6,200 lb)
B 2,903 kg (6,400 lb)
Mission weight: A, B 2,383 kg (5,254 lb)
Max landing weight: A 2,410 kg (5,313 lb)
B 2,486 kg (5,480 lb)
Normal landing weight: A 1,997 kg (4,402 lb)
B 2,124 kg (4,683 lb)

PERFORMANCE (estimated, at max T-O weight unless otherwise detailed):
Max level speed at 6,100 m (20,000 ft):
A 394 knots (730 km/h; 454 mph)
B 374 knots (693 km/h; 431 mph)
Stalling speed, power off:
A 66 knots (122 km/h; 76 mph)
B 67 knots (124 km/h; 77 mph)
Max rate of climb at S/L: A 1,585 m (5,200 ft)/min
B 1,204 m (3,950 ft)/min
Service ceiling: A 14,630 m (48,000 ft)
B 12,040 m (39,500 ft)
T-O run: A 307 m (1,008 ft)
B 361 m (1,186 ft)
T-O to 15 m (50 ft): A 489 m (1,604 ft)
B 592 m (1,943 ft)
Landing from 15 m (50 ft), at max landing weight:
A 799 m (2,621 ft)
B 880 m (2,888 ft)
Landing from 15 m (50 ft), at normal landing weight:
A 639 m (2,095 ft)
B 814 m (2,670 ft)
Landing run at max landing weight:
A 442 m (1,450 ft)
B 473 m (1,552 ft)
Landing run at normal landing weight:
A 366 m (1,202 ft)
B 437 m (1,435 ft)
Mission range at 12,190 m (40,000 ft):
A at 369 knots (683 km/h; 424 mph) 1,080 nm (2,001 km; 1,243 miles)
B at 319 knots (590 km/h; 367 mph) 1,315 nm (2,437 km; 1,514 miles)

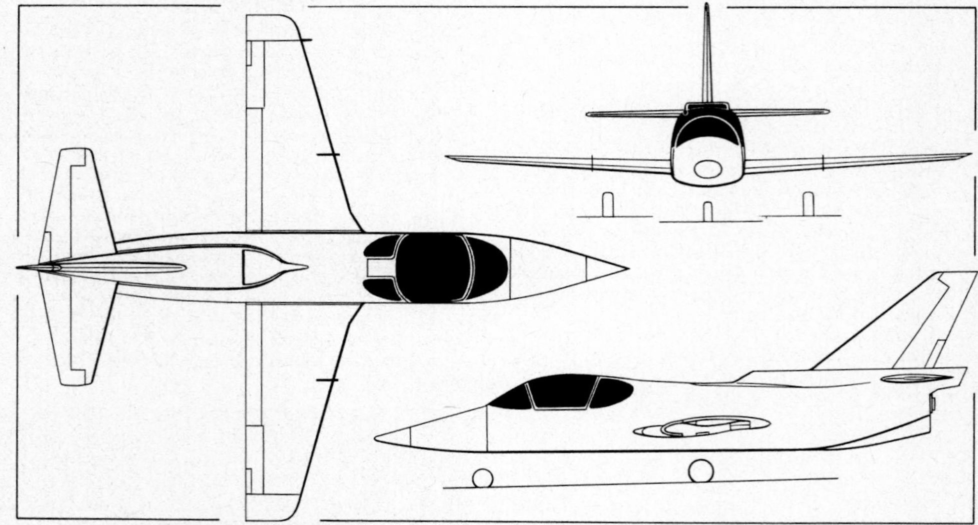

Prototype Gulfstream American Peregrine 600 trainer, with side-by-side seating *(Pilot Press)*

HAMILTON

HAMILTON AVIATION

HEAD OFFICE: PO Box 11746, Tucson, Arizona 85734
Telephone: (602) 294 3481
PRESIDENT: Gordon B. Hamilton
CHIEF ENGINEER: Clayton C. Hamilton

Hamilton Aviation, which is engaged primarily in the procurement and overhaul of various types of military aircraft for foreign governments, is also building and marketing turboprop conversions of the Beech Model 18 (last described in the 1969-70 *Jane's*). Three versions are available, known as the Westwind III, Westwind II STD and Westwind IV.

HAMILTON WESTWIND III

The Westwind III is a passenger/cargo aircraft, in which the passenger seats can be removed easily to make the whole cabin space available for cargo. Design began in

1961 and the prototype flew for the first time in 1963. FAA certification under CAR Part 3 was awarded in 1964.

The Westwind III can have agricultural or military applications.

Type: Utility passenger/cargo commuter airliner.

Wings, Fuselage, Tail Unit: As for Beech Model 18.

Landing Gear: Electrically-retractable tailwheel type. Oleo-pneumatic shock-absorbers on all units. Main wheels retract aft. Main-wheel tyre pressure 4·14 bars (60 lb/sq in). Tailwheel tyre pressure 5·52 bars (80 lb/sq in). Goodyear single-disc multi-puck hydraulic brakes. Main wheels fully enclosed by wheel-well doors when retracted.

Power Plant: Two 432 kW (579 ehp) Pratt & Whitney Aircraft of Canada PT6A-20 turboprop engines standard. Optional power plants include two 533 kW (715 ehp) (derated to 470 kW; 630 ehp) PT6A-27s, two 533 kW (715 ehp) (derated to 470 kW; 630 ehp) PT6A-28s or two 455 kW (610 ehp) Avco Lycoming LTP 101s. Hartzell three-blade fully-feathering constant-speed metal propellers. Standard fuel capacity 1,544 litres (408 US gallons), contained in outer wing, inner wing and centre-section tanks. Optional total fuel in larger-capacity tanks 2,801 litres (740 US gallons). Refuelling points on wing upper surface. Engine air intakes have an inertial separator system, including foreign object and hail bypass and heating of the leading-edges by engine bleed air.

Accommodation: Pilot and co-pilot on flight deck, with cabin seating eight passengers. Door on port side, aft of wing, with built-in airstair, can be replaced by larger cargo door. Separate door to flight deck, on port side of fuselage, is optional. Emergency exit (push-out type) on starboard side of cabin. Passenger seating quickly removable for conversion to all-cargo role. Baggage or cargo space aft of cabin and in extended fuselage nose. Cabin is heated by bleed air, and can be cooled by a bleed air converter. Windscreen de-icing standard.

Systems: Cabin cooling by AiResearch engine bleed air converter. Cabin heater manufactured by Hamilton Aviation. Pneumatic system, for flight instruments and wing and tail unit de-icing, supplied by engine bleed air. Electrical system powered by two 200A starter/generators and nickel-cadmium battery. Oxygen system optional.

Avionics and Equipment: Radio com/nav and radar to customer's requirements. Blind-flying instrumentation standard.

Armament: Optional armament for military versions includes a cargo pod containing two General Electric Miniguns, and hardpoints on the wings for the carriage of bombs or rockets.

Dimensions, external:
- Wing span: 14·02 m (46 ft 0 in)
- Wing chord at root: 4·19 m (13 ft 9 in)
- Wing chord at tip: 1·07 m (3 ft 6 in)
- Wing aspect ratio: 6·5
- Length overall: 10·85 m (35 ft 7¼ in)
- Tailplane span: 4·56 m (14 ft 11½ in)
- Passenger door (port, aft): Height 1·22 m (4 ft 0 in)
  - Width: 0·56 m (1 ft 10 in)
  - Height to sill: 0·79 m (2 ft 7 in)
- Cargo door (port, aft, optional):
  - Max height (forward edge): 1·52 m (4 ft 11¾ in)
  - Min height (rear edge): 1·19 m (3 ft 11 in)
  - Width: 1·47 m (4 ft 9¾ in)
  - Height to sill: 0·79 m (2 ft 7 in)
- Emergency exit (stbd): Height 0·64 m (2 ft 1 in)
  - Width: 0·48 m (1 ft 7 in)

Dimensions, internal:
- Cabin (bare cargo configuration):
  - Length: 4·57 m (15 ft 0 in)
  - Max width: 1·32 m (4 ft 4 in)
  - Max height: 1·55 m (5 ft 1 in)
  - Floor area: 7·80 m² (84 sq ft)
- Baggage/cargo hold (aft cabin): 0·85 m³ (30 cu ft)
- Baggage/cargo hold (fuselage nose) 1·53 m³ (54 cu ft)

Areas:
- Wings, gross: 30·32 m² (326·4 sq ft)
- Ailerons (total): 2·47 m² (26·6 sq ft)
- Trailing-edge flaps (total): 3·49 m² (37·6 sq ft)
- Fins (total): 3·03 m² (32·6 sq ft)
- Rudders (total): 3·21 m² (34·56 sq ft)
- Tailplane: 6·08 m² (65·4 sq ft)
- Elevator: 2·53 m² (27·22 sq ft)

Weights and Loadings:
- Weight empty: 2,495 kg (5,500 lb)
- Max payload: 1,814 kg (4,000 lb)
- Max T-O weight: 5,094 kg (11,230 lb)
- Max zero-fuel weight: 4,854 kg (10,700 lb)
- Max landing weight: 4,763 kg (10,500 lb)
- Max wing loading: 167·9 kg/m² (34·4 lb/sq ft)
- Max power loading: 5·90 kg/kW (19·4 lb/ehp)

Performance (at max T-O weight. A: PT6A-20 engines; B: PT6A-27):
- Max level speed at 3,660 m (12,000 ft):
  - A: 234 knots (435 km/h; 270 mph)
  - B: 269 knots (499 km/h; 310 mph)
- Max cruising speed at 3,660 m (12,000 ft):
  - A: 217 knots (402 km/h; 250 mph)
  - B: 252 knots (467 km/h; 290 mph)

Hamilton Westwind III conversion of the Beech Model 18 (two Pratt & Whitney Aircraft of Canada PT6A-27 derated turboprop engines)

- Econ cruising speed at 3,050 m (10,000 ft):
  - A: 204 knots (378 km/h; 235 mph)
  - B: 234 knots (435 km/h; 270 mph)
- Max rate of climb at S/L: A 549 m (1,800 ft)/min
  - B: 823 m (2,700 ft)/min
- Rate of climb at S/L, one engine out:
  - A: 183 m (600 ft)/min
  - B: 335 m (1,100 ft)/min
- Service ceiling: A 7,315 m (24,000 ft)
  - B: 8,535 m (28,000 ft)
- Service ceiling, one engine out:
  - A: 2,745 m (9,000 ft)
  - B: 3,960 m (13,000 ft)
- T-O run: A 549 m (1,800 ft)
  - B: 366 m (1,200 ft)
- T-O to 15 m (50 ft): A 1,005 m (3,300 ft)
  - B: 731 m (2,400 ft)
- Landing from 15 m (50 ft): A, B 549 m (1,800 ft)
- Landing run: A, B 366 m (1,200 ft)
- Range with max optional fuel:
  - A: 3,240 nm (6,004 km; 3,731 miles)
- Range with max payload:
  - A: 810 nm (1,501 km; 933 miles)

HAMILTON WESTWIND II STD

The Westwind II STD is a 'stretched' version of the Beech 18, providing accommodation for a maximum of 17 passengers. Otherwise it is generally similar to the Westwind III except that a version with tricycle landing gear is available optionally. The Westwind II STD is intended primarily as a commuter airliner, but is convertible for freight carrying or military uses. Hamilton announced plans to develop a new tail unit with single fin and rudder for this model.

The description of the Westwind III applies also to the Westwind II STD, except as follows:

Landing Gear: Retractable tricycle type available optionally.

Power Plant: Two 626 kW (840 ehp) Pratt & Whitney Aircraft of Canada PT6A-34 turboprop engines, derated to 470 kW (630 ehp), are standard, each driving a Hartzell constant-speed fully-feathering and reversible-pitch propeller. Two 579 kW (776 ehp) Garrett-AiResearch TPE 331-6-251 turboprop engines, derated to 470 kW (630 ehp), are available optionally.

Accommodation: Pilot and co-pilot or passenger on flight deck, with seating in main cabin for a maximum of 17 passengers. Two emergency exits on starboard side of fuselage.

Dimensions, external: As for Westwind III, except:
- Length overall (standard): 13·72 m (45 ft 0 in)
- Length overall (tricycle landing gear): 13·46 m (44 ft 2 in)

Dimensions, internal: As for Westwind III, except:
- Cabin: Length: 6·10 m (20 ft 0 in)

Weights and Loading (estimated):
- Weight empty: 2,712 kg (6,000 lb)
- Max payload: 2,041 kg (4,500 lb)
- Max T-O weight: 5,667 kg (12,495 lb)
- Max zero-fuel weight: 5,217 kg (11,500 lb)
- Max landing weight: 5,217 kg (11,500 lb)
- Max wing loading: 186·9 kg/m² (38·3 lb/sq ft)

Performance (at max T-O weight):
- Max level speed at 4,265 m (14,000 ft): 278 knots (515 km/h; 320 mph)
- Max cruising speed at 3,660 m (12,000 ft): 261 knots (483 km/h; 300 mph)
- Econ cruising speed at 6,705 m (22,000 ft): 234 knots (435 km/h; 270 mph)
- Stalling speed, flaps up: 87 knots (161 km/h; 100 mph)
- Stalling speed, flaps down: 74 knots (137 km/h; 85 mph)
- Max rate of climb at S/L: 945 m (3,100 ft)/min
- Rate of climb at S/L, one engine out: 274 m (900 ft)/min
- Service ceiling: 9,755 m (32,000 ft)
- Service ceiling, one engine out: 5,485 m (18,000 ft)
- T-O run: 427 m (1,400 ft)
- T-O to 15 m (50 ft): 1,036 m (3,400 ft)
- Landing from 15 m (50 ft):
  - without propeller reversal: 671 m (2,200 ft)
  - with propeller reversal: 335 m (1,100 ft)
- Range with max optional fuel: 3,240 nm (6,004 km; 3,731 miles)
- Range with max payload: 810 nm (1,501 km; 933 miles)

Hamilton Westwind II STD, a longer-fuselage conversion of the Beech Model 18

HAMILTON WESTWIND IV

Latest conversion of the Beech Model 18 by Hamilton Aviation is the Westwind IV. It is generally similar to the Westwind III but has the fuselage lengthened by 0·76 m (2 ft 6 in) and is available with six alternative power plants and a large cargo door.

TYPE: Twin-engined utility aircraft.

WINGS: Standard Beech Model 18 wings with Hamilton spar modification and crack detector system. Pneumatic de-icing boots on wing leading-edges.

FUSELAGE: Beech Model 18 fuselage lengthened 0·76 m (2 ft 6 in) aft of the wing. Heavier gauge skins and strengthened structure to fit aircraft for cargo role.

TAIL UNIT: Standard Beech Model 18 structure. Pneumatic de-icing boots on fin and tailplane leading-edges.

LANDING GEAR: Electrically-retractable tailwheel type. Main units retract aft. Oleo-pneumatic shock-absorbers. Goodyear wheels and tyres with single wheel on each unit. Single-disc hydraulic brakes.

POWER PLANT: Optional turboprop power plants include 429 kW (575 shp) Avco Lycoming LTP 101; 507 kW (680 shp), 559 kW (750 shp) and 761 kW (1,020 shp) Pratt & Whitney Aircraft of Canada PT6A-28, -34 and -45 respectively; and 526 kW (705 shp) and 626 kW (840 shp) Garrett-AiResearch TPE 331-101 and TPE 331-251 respectively. Standard fuel in wing tanks with capacity of 1,219 litres (322 US gallons). Optional auxiliary header tanks for PT6 engine installations with capacity of 416 litres (110 US gallons). Alternatively, optional integral outer panel tanks with capacity of 1,279 litres (338 US gallons). Max fuel capacity (all models) 2,498 litres (660 US gallons).

ACCOMMODATION: Large cargo door on port side of fuselage, aft of wing, able to accept standard 'D'-type cargo containers. Cargo hold in nose with volume of 1·98 m³ (70 cu ft). Accommodation air-conditioned and heated.

SYSTEMS: Garrett-AiResearch air-conditioning. Cabin heated by engine bleed air. Hydraulic system for brakes only. Electrical system supplied from starter/generators and storage battery. Pneumatic system for wing and tail unit de-icing and for flight instruments. Oxygen system optional.

AVIONICS AND EQUIPMENT: To customer's requirements.

DIMENSIONS, EXTERNAL:
- Cargo door (port, aft): Max width 2·16 m (7 ft 1 in)
- Max height 1·52 m (5 ft 0 in)

DIMENSIONS, INTERNAL:
- Cabin volume 9·77 m³ (345 cu ft)
- Nose hold volume 1·98 m³ (70 cu ft)

WEIGHTS:
- Weight empty, equipped 2,767 kg (6,100 lb)
- Max payload 2,222 kg (4,900 lb)
- Max T-O and ramp weight 5,670 kg (12,500 lb)
- Max zero-fuel weight 4,990 kg (11,000 lb)
- Max landing weight 5,216 kg (11,500 lb)

PERFORMANCE (estimated):
- Max cruising speed, depending on power plant 213-282 knots (394-523 km/h; 245-325 mph)
- Max range with 1,635 litres (432 US gallons) fuel, 1,452 kg (3,202 lb) payload and 30 min reserves 1,302 nm (2,414 km; 1,500 miles)
- Max range with 2,498 litres (660 US gallons) fuel, 785 kg (1,731 lb) payload and 30 min reserves 2,010 nm (3,724 km; 2,314 miles)

HAMMER-HUNT
ROBERT HAMMER and RICHARD HUNT

Mr Hammer, an engineer with Boeing, and Mr Hunt, an engineer and test pilot, designed, built and flew from Paine Field, Everett, Washington, a lightweight high-altitude reconnaissance aircraft known as the HH-1 Zipper. It was intended as a lower-cost substitute for the Lockheed U-2s which have operated civilian missions on behalf of US government agencies such as the Agriculture Department, Bureau of Land Management and US Geological Survey.

HAMMER-HUNT HH-1 ZIPPER

The Zipper, which flew for the first time in July 1979, originated as a preliminary design by Mr Hunt, who subsequently formed a partnership with Mr Hammer. It embodied a number of components bought from surplus stocks, including the wings of a Teledyne Ryan reconnaissance RPV and a General Electric turbojet.

On 15 August 1979, the Zipper crashed into Puget Sound, near Mukilteo, Washington, after Mr Hunt reported that it was breaking up at about 4,250 m (14,000 ft). Mr Hunt lost his life in the accident.

TYPE: Two-seat high-altitude reconnaissance aircraft.

WINGS: Cantilever low-wing monoplane, built originally for a Teledyne Ryan RPV.

FUSELAGE: Semi-monocoque structure of basically circular section.

TAIL UNIT: Cantilever V-tail. Small ventral fin.

LANDING GEAR: Retractable nosewheel and main unit in tandem on aircraft centreline. Small non-retractable balancer wheel under each wing at about mid-span (to be retractable on later aircraft).

POWER PLANT: One 12·7 kN (2,850 lb st) General Electric J85-17 turbojet engine, produced by removing afterburner from a surplus J85-5 and pod-mounted above centre-fuselage. Provision for a slipper fuel tank to be mounted on leading-edge of each wing.

ACCOMMODATION: Two seats in tandem in pressurised cockpit, with dual controls, under a long constant-section canopy. Max pressure differential 0·38 bars (5·5 lb/sq in).

EQUIPMENT: Equipment bays in nose and in fuselage aft of wings, for avionics and cameras. Provision for removing rear seat to make room for a large camera on a stabilised mounting.

WEIGHT (estimated for production aircraft):
- Max T-O weight 1,450 kg (3,200 lb)

PERFORMANCE (estimated):
- Max level speed at operating height Mach 0·9
- Max rate of climb at S/L 4,570 m (15,000 ft)/min
- Service ceiling 18,275 m (60,000 ft)
- Endurance with internal fuel, 45 min reserves 1 h
- Endurance with added slipper tanks, 45 min reserves 2 h 30 min

HELIO
HELIO COURIER LTD
Helio International

HEAD OFFICE: PO Box 130, Cross Anchor, South Carolina 29331

The original Helio Aircraft Corporation was founded in 1948 by Dr Lynn L. Bollinger of the Harvard Graduate School of Business Administration and Professor Otto C. Koppen of the Massachusetts Institute of Technology, to develop a light aircraft in the STOL category. In 1969 this company became a division of General Aircraft Corporation and was renamed Helio Aircraft Company.

The entire assets of the Helio Aircraft Company were acquired in 1974 by a new group named Helio Courier Ltd. In April 1977 spares were being produced for all Helio aircraft in service, totalling some 600 units; but production of Couriers and Stallions had been suspended.

There has been no subsequent news of the company or its products. A full description of the Helio Super Courier and Trigear Courier can be found in the 1978-79 *Jane's*.

HELITEC
HELITEC CORPORATION

HEAD OFFICE: 4930 East Falcon Drive, Falcon Field, Mesa, Arizona 85205
Telephone: (602) 832 0600
Telex: 668-446

EXECUTIVE VICE-PRESIDENT AND MARKETING MANAGER: James C. Jefferies

Aviation Specialties developed a turbine-powered conversion of the Sikorsky S-55 helicopter which was awarded FAA certification in the Transport Category on 19 January 1971. Subsequently, Helitec Corporation was formed to carry out the conversions and market them in the USA, and production of at least 100 of these conversions was anticipated. Details of the programme can be found in the 1978-79 *Jane's*.

HILLER
HILLER AVIATION (Division of Heli-Parts Inc)

ADDRESS: 2075 West Scranton Avenue, Porterville, California 93257
Telephone: (209) 781 2261
Telex: 682454

PRESIDENT: Edwin L. Trupe

Hiller Aviation, formed in January 1973, acquired from Fairchild Industries the design rights, production tooling and spares of the Hiller 12E piston-engined light helicopter. Initially, the company provided product support for UH-12 helicopters in service throughout the world, a total then estimated as being in excess of 2,200 aircraft. Service and repair facilities were added as a first move to expand the company's business. It was then decided to begin the manufacture of new aircraft from existing components, incorporating all modifications approved for the type since closure of the production line in the late 1960s.

It was planned also to develop a turbine-powered version of the UH-12, and in conjunction with Soloy Conversions of Chehalis, Washington, the company has evolved such an aircraft, with the power plant not only being suitable for new production aircraft, but one which can be installed retrospectively in existing UH-12s.

HILLER AVIATION UH-12E and UH-12E-4

Following the provision of a turbine power plant for the UH-12, two versions are available currently:

UH-12E. Basic model, as described, with accommodation for a pilot and two passengers.

UH-12E-4. Turbine-powered version of the UH-12E, with accommodation for three passengers side by side on a bench seat, the pilot on a single seat forward. Power plant comprises one 298 kW (400 shp) Allison 250-C20 turboshaft engine, derated to 224 kW (301 shp). Certification of this model was achieved by Soloy Conversions in January 1976.

Hiller UH-12E three-seat utility helicopter

The description which follows applies to both the UH-12E and UH-12E-4:

TYPE: Three-seat (UH-12E) or four-seat (UH-12E-4) utility helicopter.

ROTOR SYSTEM: Two-blade main rotor mounted universally on driveshaft, with small servo rotor; the latter is connected directly to the pilot's cyclic control stick, through a universally-mounted transfer bearing and simple linkage. Movement of the control stick introduces positive or negative pitch changes to the servo rotor paddles. The resulting aerodynamic forces tilt the rotor head and produce cyclic pitch changes to the rotor blades. Each main rotor blade has a steel spar and leading-edge, with light alloy trailing-edge skin, extrusion and channels. Blades are interchangeable individually and are bolted to forks which are retained at the rotor head by tension-torsion bars. Blades do not fold. Rotor brake optional. Two-blade tail rotor of light alloy construction, mounted on port side of tailboom.

ROTOR DRIVE: Mechanical drive through two-stage planetary main transmission. Bevel gear drive to auxiliaries. Tail rotor gearbox and fan gearbox. Main rotor/engine rpm ratio 1 : 8·64. Tail rotor/engine rpm ratio 1 : 1·45.

FUSELAGE: Light alloy fully-stressed semi-monocoque platform structure supporting the non-stressed cabin enclosure, engine mounting and landing gear. Tailboom of beaded light alloy sheet with no internal stiffeners.

TAIL UNIT: Horizontal stabiliser on starboard side of tailboom, with steel tube spar, light alloy ribs and skin. Incidence ground-adjustable.

LANDING GEAR: Wide-track light alloy tube skids carried on spring steel cross members. Ground handling wheels standard. Optional 'zip-on' pontoons, attached above the skids, permit water or land operations.

POWER PLANT: (UH-12E), one 253·5 kW (340 hp) Lycoming VO-540 flat-six engine, installed vertically and derated to 227·5 kW (305 hp). (UH-12E-4), one turboshaft engine as detailed in model listing, mounted diagonally aft of rotor pylon. Single bladder fuel cell, capacity 174 litres (46 US gallons), mounted in lower portion of rear fuselage, beneath engine. Two optional 75·7 litre (20 US gallon) auxiliary fuel tanks, mounted in fuselage on each side of engine. Oil capacity 12·5 litres (3·3 US gallons).

ACCOMMODATION: (UH-12E), three persons side by side on bench seat. (UH-12E-4), pilot on single forward seat, three passengers side by side on bench seat. Dual controls optional. Forward-hinged door on each side. Baggage compartment immediately aft of engine. Heater-defroster optional.

AVIONICS AND EQUIPMENT: A range of optional avionics is available. Standard equipment includes engine hour meter, edge-lighted instrument panel, outside air temperature gauge, eight-day clock, seat belts, provisions for shoulder harness, standard or extended landing gear legs, cargo hook hardpoint, electrically controlled trim system, and polyurethane paint finish. Optional equipment includes dual controls, inertia-reel shoulder harness, Mason cyclic control grip, fire extinguisher, first aid kit, night lighting equipment, 454 kg (1,000 lb) capacity cargo hook, twin heavy-duty cargo racks, auxiliary fuel tanks, agricultural spray equipment, loudspeaker/siren, searchlight, tropical doors, heater/defroster system, and twin litters.

DIMENSIONS, EXTERNAL (UH-12E):
- Diameter of main rotor: 10·80 m (35 ft 5 in)

Hiller UH-12E-4, with an Allison 250-C20 turboshaft engine

- Diameter of tail rotor: 1·68 m (5 ft 6 in)
- Distance between rotor centres: 6·17 m (20 ft 3 in)
- Length overall, rotors turning: 12·41 m (40 ft 8½ in)
- Length of fuselage: 8·69 m (28 ft 6 in)
- Height to top of rotor hub: 3·08 m (10 ft 1¼ in)
- Skid track: 2·29 m (7 ft 6 in)
- Cabin doors (each): Height: 1·13 m (3 ft 8½ in)
  - Max width: 0·76 m (2 ft 6 in)
  - Height to sill: 0·58 m (1 ft 11 in)

DIMENSIONS, INTERNAL:
- Cabin: Length: 1·52 m (5 ft 0 in)
  - Max width: 1·50 m (4 ft 11 in)
  - Max height: 1·35 m (4 ft 5 in)
  - Floor area: 1·16 m^2 (12·5 sq ft)

AREAS:
- Main rotor blades (each): 1·51 m^2 (16·3 sq ft)
- Tail rotor blades (each): 0·094 m^2 (1·01 sq ft)
- Main rotor disc: 91·97 m^2 (990 sq ft)
- Tail rotor disc: 2·57 m^2 (27·7 sq ft)

WEIGHTS AND LOADINGS (A: UH-12E; B: UH-12E-4):
- Weight empty: A: 798 kg (1,759 lb)
  - *B: 833 kg (1,836 lb)
- Max T-O weight: A: 1,270 kg (2,800 lb)
  - B: 1,406 kg (3,100 lb)
- Max disc loading: A: 13·82 kg/m^2 (2·83 lb/sq ft)
  - B: 15·28 kg/m^2 (3·13 lb/sq ft)
- Max power loading: A: 5·58 kg/kW (9·2 lb/hp)
  - B: 6·28 kg/kW (10·3 lb/shp)

**Empty weight includes radio, fire extinguisher and first aid kit*

PERFORMANCE (at T-O weight of 1,270 kg; 2,800 lb):
- Never-exceed speed and max level speed: 83 knots (154 km/h; 96 mph)
- Cruising speed: A: 78 knots (145 km/h; 90 mph)
  - B: 83 knots (154 km/h; 96 mph)
- Max rate of climb at S/L: A: 393 m (1,290 ft)/min
  - B: 520 m (1,706 ft)/min
- Vertical rate of climb at S/L: A: 226 m (740 ft)/min
  - B: 446 m (1,463 ft)/min
- Service ceiling: A: 4,940 m (16,200 ft)
- Hovering ceiling IGE: A: 3,290 m (10,800 ft)
- Hovering ceiling OGE: A: 2,195 m (7,200 ft)
- Range with standard fuel:
  - A: 187 nm (346 km; 215 miles)
  - B: 163 nm (303 km; 188 miles)
- Range with max auxiliary fuel:
  - A: 364 nm (676 km; 420 miles)
  - B: 305 nm (565 km; 351 miles)

HUGHES

HUGHES HELICOPTERS (Division of Summa Corporation)

HEAD OFFICE AND WORKS: Culver City, California 90230
Telephone: (213) 390 4451
Telex: 67-222

PRESIDENT AND CHIEF EXECUTIVE OFFICER:
J. G. Real

VICE-PRESIDENTS:
W. J. Blackburn (Manufacturing Operations)
R. E. Brix (Ordnance)
M. F. Gerardis (Finance and Administration)
J. N. Kerr (Advanced Attack Helicopter Programme)
C. D. Perry (Marketing)
C. E. Schaaf (Legal)
L. P. Sonsini (Product Assurance and Flight Operations)
F. C. Strible (Commercial Helicopters)

PUBLIC RELATIONS MANAGER: Anthony J. Longo

Following reorganisation of Hughes Tool Company as the Summa Corporation, its former Aircraft Division became known as Hughes Helicopters. Its current products are described in this entry. Research activities include work on composite rotor blades and tailbooms, metal insulation and IR suppression systems, and chain gun and lockless ordnance systems for air or ground applications.

Kawasaki Heavy Industries Ltd in Japan (which see) has assembled Model 369HM helicopters, this being the designation of the uprated version of the Hughes OH-6 available to foreign military customers. Other licence manufacture is undertaken by RACA in Argentina, Kawasaki in Japan, KAL in the Republic of Korea and BredaNardi in Italy.

Hughes Model 300C two/three-seat light helicopter equipped for agricultural spraying duties

HUGHES MODEL 300C

This is a developed version of the Model 300 (1976-77 *Jane's*), with improvements to allow a 45% increase in payload. The prototype made its first flight in August 1969, followed by the first production model in December 1969. FAA certification was received in May 1970. More than 550 Model 300Cs had been delivered by 1 January 1979.

The Model 300C is also manufactured in Italy by BredaNardi (which see).

A specially equipped 300C is available for police patrol. Known as the **Sky Knight**, it has as standard equipment safety mesh seats with inertia-reel shoulder harness, ballistic glassfibre armour beneath each seat, a high-power public address/siren system, a high-intensity controllable searchlight system, an integrated communications system based on the King KY 195 VHF transceiver, a heavy-duty 28V 100A electrical system, cabin heater, night lights with strobe beacons, cabin utility light, external power socket, fire extinguisher, first aid kit and map case.

Following the research that produced a modified version of the OH-6A known as 'The Quiet One', Hughes used similar techniques to develop and obtain full FAA certification of a quiet version of the Model 300, and this has the designation Model **300CQ**. In this configuration, emission of audible sound is 75% less than with earlier models, and the necessary modifications can be retrofitted to existing 300Cs. Max T-O weight of the 300CQ for quiet operation is 873 kg (1,925 lb), with a useful load of 397 kg (875 lb), and there is little change in range and endurance by comparison with the standard Model 300C.

TYPE: Two- or three-seat light helicopter.

ROTOR SYSTEM: Fully-articulated metal three-blade main rotor. Blades are of bonded construction, with constant-section extruded aluminium spar, wraparound skin and a trailing-edge section. Blade section NACA 0015. Tracking tabs on blades at three-quarters radius. Electric cyclic trim. Two-blade teetering tail rotor, each blade comprising a steel tube spar with glassfibre skin.

Limited blade folding. No rotor brake.

Rotor Drive: Combination Vee-belt/pulley and reduction gear drive system. Main rotor and tail rotor gearbox have spiral bevel right-angle drive. Main rotor/engine rpm ratio 1 : 6·8. Tail rotor/engine rpm ratio 0·97 : 1.

Fuselage: Welded steel tube structure, with light alloy and Plexiglas cabin and one-piece light alloy tube tailboom.

Tail Unit: Horizontal and vertical fixed stabilising surfaces, made of light alloy ribs and skins.

Landing Gear: Skids carried on Hughes oleo-pneumatic shock-absorbers. Two cast magnesium ground handling wheels with 0·25 m (10 in) balloon tyres, pressure 4·14-5·17 bars (60-75 lb/sq in). Available optionally on floats made of polyurethane coated nylon fabric, 4·70 m (15 ft 5 in) long and with a total installed weight of 27·2 kg (60 lb).

Power Plant: One 142 kW (190 hp) Lycoming HIO-360-D1A flat-four engine, mounted horizontally below seats. Aluminium fuel tank, capacity 103·5 litres (30 US gallons) mounted externally aft of cockpit. Crash-resistant fuel tank optional. Provision for aluminium auxiliary fuel tank, capacity 72 litres (19 US gallons), mounted opposite standard tank. Oil capacity 9·5 litres (2·5 US gallons).

Accommodation: Three persons seated side by side on sculptured and cushioned bench seat, in Plexiglas-enclosed cabin. Carpet and tinted canopy standard. Door on each side. Dual controls optional. Baggage capacity 45 kg (100 lb). Exhaust muff, or gasoline, heating and ventilation kits available.

Systems: Standard electrical system includes 28V 70A alternator, battery, starter and external power receptacle; 28V 100A alternator is optional.

Avionics and Equipment: Optional avionics include Collins VHF-251 or Bertea ML360 com transceiver and headsets. Standard equipment includes mapcase, first aid kit, fire extinguisher, engine hour meter, and main rotor blade tiedown kit. Optional equipment includes amphibious floats, litter kits, cargo racks with combined capacity of 91 kg (200 lb), external load sling of 408 kg (900 lb) capacity, agricultural spray or dry powder dispersion kits, 72 litre (19 US gallon) auxiliary fuel tank, night flying kit, dual controls, all-weather cover, heavy-duty skid plates, single or dual exhaust mufflers, door lock, dual oil coolers, tinted glass for cabin windows, gasoline or exhaust manifold cabin heating.

Dimensions, external:
Diameter of main rotor 8·18 m (26 ft 10 in)
Main rotor blade chord 0·171 m (6¾ in)
Diameter of tail rotor 1·30 m (4 ft 3 in)
Length overall, rotor blades fore and aft 9·40 m (30 ft 10 in)
Height over rotor hub 2·67 m (8 ft 9 in)
Width, rotor partially folded 2·44 m (8 ft 0 in)
Skid track 1·98 m (6 ft 6 in)
Passenger doors (each): Height 1·09 m (3 ft 7 in)
Width 0·97 m (3 ft 2 in)
Height to sill 0·91 m (3 ft 0 in)

Areas:
Main rotor blades (each) 0·70 m² (7·55 sq ft)
Tail rotor blades (each) 0·08 m² (0·86 sq ft)
Main rotor disc 52·5 m² (565·5 sq ft)
Tail rotor disc 1·32 m² (14·2 sq ft)
Fin 0·26 m² (2·8 sq ft)
Horizontal stabiliser 0·32 m² (3·44 sq ft)

Weights and Loadings (A: 300C; B: 300CQ):
Weight empty 476 kg (1,050 lb)
Max T-O weight: A 930 kg (2,050 lb)
B 921 kg (2,030 lb)
Max disc loading: A 17·67 kg/m² (3·62 lb/sq ft)
B 17·48 kg/m² (3·58 lb/sq ft)

Performance (at max T-O weight, ISA. A: 300C; B: 300CQ normal operation; C: 300CQ quiet operation at AUW of 873 kg; 1,925 lb):
Never-exceed speed:
A, B, C 91 knots (169 km/h; 105 mph)
Max cruising speed at S/L:
A, B 78 knots (145 km/h; 90 mph)
Max level speed at S/L:
C 61 knots (113 km/h; 70 mph)
Max cruising speed at 1,220 m (4,000 ft):
A 82 knots (153 km/h; 95 mph)
B 78 knots (145 km/h; 90 mph)
Max level speed at 1,220 m (4,000 ft):
C 62·5 knots (116 km/h; 72 mph)
Speed for max range, at 1,220 m (4,000 ft):
A, B 67 knots (124 km/h; 77 mph)
Max rate of climb at S/L: A 229 m (750 ft)/min
C 113 m (370 ft)/min
Service ceiling: A 3,110 m (10,200 ft)
B 3,050 m (10,000 ft)
C 2,440 m (8,000 ft)
Hovering ceiling IGE: A 1,830 m (6,000 ft)
B 1,220 m (4,000 ft)
Hovering ceiling OGE: A 823 m (2,700 ft)
Range at 1,220 m (4,000 ft), 2 min warm-up, max fuel, no reserves 200 nm (370 km; 230 miles)

HUGHES MODEL 500, 500C, 500D and 500M

These are the commercial and foreign military counterparts of the OH-6A military helicopter last described in the 1977-78 *Jane's*. Full-scale production began in November 1968. The following versions have been announced:

Model 500. Basic commercial version, as described in detail.

Model 500C. As Model 500, except for installation of 298 kW (400 shp) engine for improved hot-day/altitude performance.

Model 500D and **500 M-D Defender.** Commercial and foreign military versions respectively, with five-blade main rotor and Allison 250-C20B engine; described separately.

Model 500M. Uprated version of OH-6A, available to foreign military customers. First deliveries to Colombian Air Force in April 1968. Now in service also in Japan, Argentina, Denmark, Spain, Mexico and the Philippines. The Model 500Ms delivered to the Spanish Navy for ASW duties have an AN/ASQ-81 magnetic anomaly detector installed on the starboard side of the fuselage, and can carry two Mk 44 torpedoes beneath the fuselage. Control boxes for the MAD equipment are mounted on the instrument panel and centre pedestal, and special instrumentation includes a 6 in attitude indicator and radar altimeter.

Licence manufacture of the Model 500 Series is undertaken by RACA in Argentina, Kawasaki in Japan and BredaNardi in Italy (which see).

The following description applies to the basic commercial Model 500:

Type: Turbine-powered light helicopter.

Rotor System: Four-blade fully-articulated main rotor, with blades attached to laminated strap retention system by means of folding quick-disconnect pins. Each blade consists of an extruded aluminium spar hot-bonded to one-piece wraparound aluminium skin. Trim tab outboard on each blade. Main rotor blades can be folded. Two-blade tail rotor, each blade comprising a swaged steel tube spar and glassfibre skin covering. No rotor brake.

Rotor Drive: Three sets of bevel gears, three drive-shafts and one overrunning clutch. Main rotor/engine rpm ratio 1 : 12·806. Tail rotor/engine rpm ratio 1 : 1·987.

Hughes Model 500D one/seven-seat commercial helicopter *(Brian M. Service)*

Fuselage: Aluminium semi-monocoque structure of pod and boom type. Clamshell doors at rear of pod give access to engine and accessories.

Tail Unit: Fixed fin, horizontal stabiliser and ventral fin.

Landing Gear: Tubular skids carried on Hughes single-acting shock-absorbers.

Power Plant: The 236·5 kW (317 shp) Allison Model 250-C18A turbine engine (civil version of the T63-A-5A), installed in the 500 and 500M, is derated to 207 kW (278 shp) for T-O and has a max continuous rating of 181 kW (243 shp). The Model 500C is powered by a 298 kW (400 shp) Allison Model 250-C20 turboshaft engine; this also is derated to 207 kW (278 shp) for T-O and has a max continuous rating of 181 kW (243 shp). The Models 500 and 500C have a fuel capacity of 242 litres (64 US gallons); Model 500M has a capacity of 227 litres (60 US gallons). A crashworthy auxiliary tank of 132·5 litres (35 US gallons) is available optionally.

Accommodation (500/500C): Pilot and four passengers or equivalent freight. Optional accommodation for seven with litter kit in use or with four in passenger compartment.

Equipment (500/500C): Optional equipment includes shatterproof glass, heating system, radios and intercom, attitude and directional gyros, rate of climb indicator, inertia reels and shoulder harnesses for pilot and co-pilot, fire extinguisher, dual controls, cargo hook, hoist, auxiliary fuel system, heated pitot tube, extended landing gear, blade storage rack, litter kit, emergency inflatable floats, inflated utility floats, rotor brake, seating for four in passenger compartment, and first aid kit. Standard equipment includes engine hour meter, navigation lights, clock and ground handling wheels.

Dimensions, external:
Diameter of main rotor 8·03 m (26 ft 4 in)
Main rotor blade chord 0·171 m (6¾ in)
Diameter of tail rotor 1·30 m (4 ft 3 in)
Distance between rotor centres 4·58 m (15 ft 0¼ in)
Length overall, rotors fore and aft 9·24 m (30 ft 3¾ in)
Length of fuselage 7·01 m (23 ft 0 in)
Height to top of rotor hub 2·48 m (8 ft 1½ in)
Skid track 2·06 m (6 ft 9 in)
Cabin doors (fwd, each): Height 1·19 m (3 ft 11 in)
Width 0·89 m (2 ft 11 in)
Cargo compartment doors (each):
Height 1·04 m (3 ft 5 in)
Width 0·88 m (2 ft 10½ in)
Height to sill 0·57 m (1 ft 10½ in)

Dimensions, internal:
Cabin: Length 2·44 m (8 ft 0 in)
Max width 1·37 m (4 ft 6 in)
Max height 1·31 m (4 ft 3½ in)

Areas:
Main rotor blades (each) 0·69 m² (7·41 sq ft)
Tail rotor blades (each) 0·079 m² (0·85 sq ft)
Main rotor disc 50·60 m² (544·63 sq ft)
Tail rotor disc 1·32 m² (14·19 sq ft)
Fin 0·52 m² (5·65 sq ft)
Horizontal stabiliser 0·72 m² (7·70 sq ft)

Weights:
Weight empty: 500 493 kg (1,088 lb)
500C 501 kg (1,105 lb)
500M 512 kg (1,130 lb)
Max normal T-O weight 1,157 kg (2,550 lb)
Max overload T-O weight 1,360 kg (3,000 lb)

Performance (at max T-O weight):
Max level speed at 305 m (1,000 ft):
500, 500M 132 knots (244 km/h; 152 mph)
Max cruising speed at S/L:
500C 125 knots (232 km/h; 144 mph)
Max cruising speed at 1,220 m (4,000 ft):
500C 126 knots (233 km/h; 145 mph)
Cruising speed for max range at S/L:
500, 500M 117 knots (217 km/h; 135 mph)
500C 124 knots (230 km/h; 143 mph)
Max rate of climb at S/L:
500, 500C, 500M 518 m (1,700 ft)/min
Service ceiling: 500, 500M 4,390 m (14,400 ft)
500C 4,420 m (14,500 ft)
Hovering ceiling IGE:
500, 500M 2,500 m (8,200 ft)
500C 3,960 m (13,000 ft)
Hovering ceiling OGE:
500, 500M 1,615 m (5,300 ft)
500C 2,040 m (6,700 ft)
Range at 1,220 m (4,000 ft):
500 327 nm (606 km; 377 miles)
500M 318 nm (589 km; 366 miles)
Range at 1,220 m (4,000 ft), 2 min warm-up with max fuel, no reserves:
500C 325 nm (603 km; 375 miles)

HUGHES MODEL 500D

Announced in February 1975, the Model 500D is similar in size and general appearance to the Hughes Model 500C. It differs in having a 313 kW (420 shp) Allison 250-C20B engine, plus the modifications applied to 'The Quiet One' OH-6A and which were developed and test-flown extensively on that aircraft. It introduced also a small T-tail which gives greater flight stability in both high

Hughes 500M-D Defender firing TOW missiles during demonstration for US Army

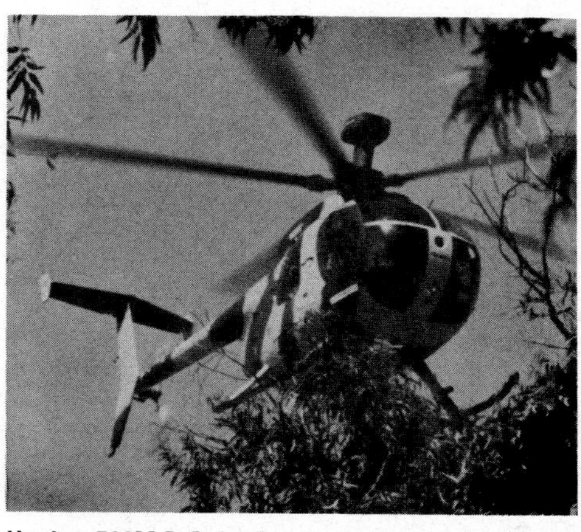

Hughes 500M-D Quiet Advanced Scout, with Martin Marietta mast-mounted sight

and low speed regimes, as well as better handling characteristics in abnormal manoeuvres. Construction of the prototype and its first flight took place in August 1974, and the first flight of a production aircraft was made on 9 October 1975.

Two versions are available:

Model 500D. Basic commercial version, of which description follows. Awarded FAA production certification on 8 December 1976, and deliveries began immediately. By February 1977 more than 250 had been ordered, and production was at the rate of 15 per month.

Model 500M-D Defender. Multi-role military version of the Model 500D, available to military customers. Described separately.

TYPE: Turbine-powered light commercial helicopter.

ROTOR SYSTEM: Generally the same as for Model 500C, except five-blade main rotor and two-blade teetering tail rotor with light alloy blades. Rotor brake optional.

ROTOR DRIVE: Generally the same as for Model 500C, but entire drive train strengthened to give longer service life. Main rotor/engine rpm ratio 0·0794; tail rotor/engine rpm ratio 0·5111.

FUSELAGE: As for Model 500C.

TAIL UNIT: T-tail, with horizontal stabiliser at tip of narrow-chord sweptback fin. Small auxiliary fin at tip of tailplane on each side. Narrow-chord sweptback ventral fin with integral tailskid to protect tail rotor in taildown attitude near ground.

LANDING GEAR: Tubular skids carried on Hughes oleo-pneumatic shock-absorbers. Utility floats, snow skis and emergency inflatable floats optional.

POWER PLANT: One 313 kW (420 shp) Allison 250-C20B turboshaft engine. Two interconnected bladder fuel tanks with combined usable capacity of 240 litres (63·4 US gallons). Self-sealing fuel tank optional. Refuelling point on starboard side of fuselage. Auxiliary fuel system with 132 litre (35 US gallon) crashworthy internal fuel tank, or two external glassfibre fuel cells with combined capacity of 167 litres (44 US gallons) optional. Oil capacity 5·7 litres (1·5 US gallons).

ACCOMMODATION: Forward bench seat for pilot and two passengers, with two or four passengers, or two litter patients and two medical attendants, in aft portion of cabin. Baggage space, capacity 0·31 m³ (11 cu ft), under and behind rear seat in five-seat form. Clear space for 1·19 m³ (42 cu ft) of cargo or baggage with only three front seats in place. Two doors on each side.

SYSTEM: Electrical system includes a 150A engine-driven generator and a nickel-cadmium battery.

AVIONICS AND EQUIPMENT: Optional avionics include dual King KY 195 com, KX 175 nav/com, KR 85 ADF, and KT 76 transponder; dual Collins VHF-251 com, VHF-251/351 nav/com, IND-350 nav indicator, ADF-650 ADF, and TDR-950 transponder; Sunair ASB 125; intercom system, headsets, microphones; public address system; stereo tape system; and flight management computer system. Standard equipment includes outside air temperature gauge, 8-day clock, engine hour meter, five sets inertia-reel shoulder harness, cargo tiedown fittings, fire extinguisher, first aid kit, passenger steps, external power socket, landing light, skid-tip position light, anti-collision strobe lights, cockpit utility light, aft cabin light, and instrument lights. Optional equipment includes dual controls, blind-flying instrumentation, electric hoist, cargo hook, external luggage pods, cargo racks, underfuselage cargo pod, nylon mesh seats, dual-strap shoulder harnesses, and heating/demisting system.

DIMENSIONS, EXTERNAL: As for Model 500C, except:

Diameter of main rotor	8·08 m (26 ft 6 in)
Distance between rotor centres	4·62 m (15 ft 2 in)
Length overall, rotors fore and aft	9·30 m (30 ft 6 in)
Height to top of rotor hub	2·59 m (8 ft 6 in)
Cabin doors (each): Height	1·16 m (3 ft 9½ in)
Width	0·76 m (2 ft 6 in)
Height to sill	0·76 m (2 ft 6 in)

DIMENSIONS, INTERNAL:

As for Model 500C, except:

Max width	1·31 m (4 ft 3½ in)
Max height	1·52 m (5 ft 0 in)

AREAS:

Main rotor blades (each)	0·69 m² (7·43 sq ft)
Tail rotor blades (each)	0·09 m² (0·94 sq ft)
Main rotor disc	50·89 m² (547·81 sq ft)
Tail rotor disc	1·32 m² (14·19 sq ft)
Fin	0·56 m² (6·05 sq ft)
Tailplane	0·61 m² (6·52 sq ft)

WEIGHTS AND LOADINGS:

Weight empty	598 kg (1,320 lb)
Fuel load	181 kg (400 lb)
Max T-O and landing weight	1,360 kg (3,000 lb)
Max disc loading	26·76 kg/m² (5·48 lb/sq ft)
Max power loading	4·35 kg/kW (7·14 lb/shp)

PERFORMANCE (at max T-O weight, ISA):

Never-exceed speed	152 knots (282 km/h; 175 mph)
Max cruising speed at S/L	139 knots (258 km/h; 160 mph)
Max cruising speed at 1,525 m (5,000 ft)	135 knots (249 km/h; 155 mph)
Econ cruising speed at S/L	130 knots (241 km/h; 150 mph)
Econ cruising speed at 1,525 m (5,000 ft)	126 knots (233 km/h; 145 mph)
Max rate of climb at S/L	579 m (1,900 ft)/min
Service ceiling	4,570 m (15,000 ft)
Hovering ceiling IGE: ISA	2,590 m (8,500 ft)
ISA +20°C	1,830 m (6,000 ft)
Hovering ceiling OGE: ISA	2,285 m (7,500 ft)
ISA +20°C	1,370 m (4,500 ft)
Range, 2 min warm-up, standard fuel, no reserves:	
S/L	260 nm (482 km; 300 miles)
at 1,525 m (5,000 ft)	287 nm (531 km; 330 miles)

HUGHES MODEL 500M-D DEFENDER

Structurally the military Defender is generally similar to the commercial Model 500M. It differs in having as standard or optional equipment self-sealing fuel cells, armour protection, Hughes 'Black Hole Ocarina' infra-red suppressor, and provisions for the carriage and deployment of a variety of weapons, including TOW missiles. Its diverse capabilities include training, command and control, scout, light attack, ASW, troop lift, and logistical support duties. It can carry up to seven people, including the pilot; or, in ambulance configuration, two stretcher patients with attendants in addition to a flight crew of two.

The four versions now available are identified as follows:

500 M-D Standard Scout. Basic military version, able to carry a variety of alternative weapons including fourteen 2·75 in rockets and either a 7·62 mm Minigun with 2,000 rounds of ammunition, a 40 mm grenade launcher or a 7·62 mm chain gun; or a 30 mm chain gun with 600 rounds of ammunition.

500 M-D/TOW. Anti-tank version armed with four TOW air-to-ground missiles. The TOW installation comprises four weapon pods, mounted two each side on a tubular mount carried through the lower aft fuselage, a telescopic sight mounted on the port side of the nose, sight control and arm rest for the gunner, and a steering indicator for the pilot.

500M-D Quiet Advanced Scout. Basically similar to Standard Scout, but with added quietening kit and Martin Marietta mast-mounted sight. Quietening kit features a slower-turning four-blade tail rotor, which imposes no reduction of performance. The sight, mounted on a unique static mast 61 cm (2 ft) above the main rotor, includes a multiple field of view silicon vidicon TV lens, a laser rangefinder/designator and a high-accuracy stabilisation system, with future night vision capability. This enables the crew to hover behind cover, and use the small sight as a periscope to scan a large area out to a range of 3,000 m (9,840 ft). If employed to spot enemy armour, it is envisaged that Scouts would call in TOW Defenders to attack the targets.

500M-D/ASW. Version for anti-submarine warfare and surface search missions, with two crew, search radar on nose, AN/ASQ-81 towed MAD, smoke marker launchers, hauldown gear, emergency 'popout' floats and armament of two Mk 44 or Mk 46 homing torpedoes. Max T-O weight 1,610 kg (3,550 lb). Can remain on station for 1 h 48 min when operated at a typical ASW mission radius of 22-87 nm (40-160 km; 25-100 miles) from ship or shore base. Using its radar, 500M-D/ASW could locate enemy destroyers and gunboats up to 150 nm (275 km; 172 miles) from its base-ship during a two-hour patrol.

Standard lightweight avionics equipment (SLAE) as developed for the OH-6A has been adapted for the 500M-D with minimal changes. This equipment comprises AN/ARC-164 UHF/AM, AN/ARC-115 UHF/AM, AN/ARC-114 VHF/FM, ARN-89 ADF, APX-72 IFF transponder, AN/ASN-43 directional gyro, ID-1351 heading and bearing indicator, and C-6533/ARC intercom.

The Model 500M-D is the subject of a building programme in South Korea (which see). By mid-June 1979, a total of 75 Scouts and 25 TOW-equipped Defenders had been delivered, with the local content progressing from

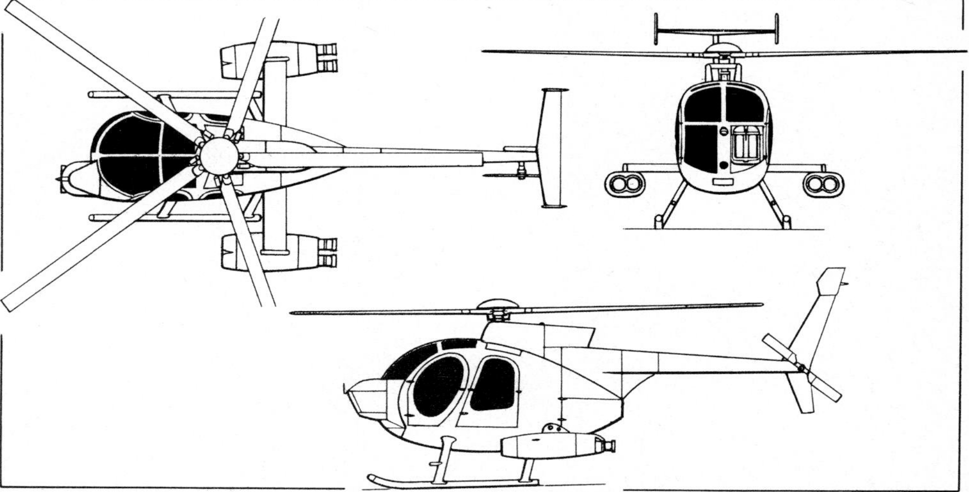

Hughes 500M-D Defender with TOW missile launchers *(Pilot Press)*

assembly to full manufacture. Another 48 were then in production, with the likelihood of a further order for 150 to follow. Israel has ordered 30 of the TOW version, and Kenya is to receive 32 Defenders, of which 15 will be equipped to fire TOW missiles. Deliveries to the Taiwanese Navy of 12 Defenders, equipped with search radar and torpedoes, began in May 1979.

HUGHES MODEL 77

US Army designation: AH-64

The Model 77 was proposed by Hughes to meet the US Army's requirement for an Advanced Attack Helicopter (AAH) capable of undertaking a full day/night/adverse weather anti-armour mission, and of fighting, surviving and 'living with' troops in a front-line environment. The Army announced on 22 June 1973 the award to Hughes of a $70·3 million contract to build two flight test prototypes and a ground test vehicle, for competitive evaluation against Bell's YAH-63. The Hughes contract covered, in addition, development of the XM-230 chain gun for installation in the Model 77 prototypes, which had been assigned the US Army designation YAH-64. The Defense Department emphasised that final unit costs and overall programme costs for the selected helicopter were more important than those for prototype development. The recurring flyaway cost per unit had to remain within a target figure, in 1972 dollars, of $1·6 million, based on a stated US Army requirement for 472 AAHs; this requirement was increased subsequently to 536. Delivery of the first production aircraft is planned for December 1982, production deliveries extending until March 1989.

The YAH-64 ground test vehicle began ground running in late June 1975. It was followed by the first flights of the first prototype (22248) at Palomar Airport, California, on 30 September and the second on 22 November 1975. By the time these two aircraft were handed over to the US Army in May 1976, a total of 850 hours of flight and ground testing had been completed. The ground test programme included static test, rotor flutter and vibration; firing tests of the XM-230 gun, rockets and TOW missiles were also completed.

Selection of the Hughes YAH-64 as winner of the competition was announced on 10 December 1976. This was followed by initiation of Phase 2 of the programme, which involved fitting the prototypes with advanced avionics, electro-optical equipment and weapon fire control systems, for further evaluation; continued development of the airframe; and the manufacture of three more aircraft.

Under separate contracts, Martin Marietta and Northrop are developing competitive equipment to fulfil the TADS (Target Acquisition and Designation System) and PNVS (Pilot's Night Vision System) tasks in the production AH-64.

In early 1978 the two helicopters used for the Phase 2 programme began a new series of tests to evaluate planned design modifications known as Mod 1. The changes include provision of swept tips on the main rotor blades; the addition of a Hughes-developed 'Black Hole' IR suppressor for each engine exhaust; a redesigned T-tail; and a 76 mm (3 in) increase in tail rotor diameter. A Mod 2 programme started later in that year, introduced final airframe improvements, as well as all mission equipment including armament, fire control and nav/com systems. These include cockpit windows of modified shape, with single-curvature side panels; and extending aft, to a point below the wing leading-edges, the fuselage side fairings over the forward electronics bay. Upon completion of the modifications the two prototype helicopters began a programme to confirm the airworthiness of the Mod 2 airframe changes. This was carried through on schedule, and initial tests of the weapon system, including the Hellfire missile, 2·75 in rocket, 30 mm chain gun, and the fire control system, were next completed, with no major problems. By mid-June 1979 five ballistic Hellfire missiles had been fired, without guidance system.

The three development aircraft are identified as AVO.1 to AVO.3. In June 1979 the first of these was being used by the US Army for continuing evaluation. AVO.3 was transferred to the Army's Yuma Proving Ground, Arizona, on 4 June, equipped with the Northrop TADS/PNVS. AVO.2, with the Martin Marietta TADS/PNVS, followed at the end of the same month. Company R & D with these two aircraft was expected to continue until the end of the year, with Army testing to follow in 1980 and to be completed in August 1981.

Flight testing carried out to June 1979 demonstrated the effectiveness of the efforts made to limit maintenance to a minimum: at that date maintenance was averaging 8 man-hours per flight hour.

Three additional development aircraft were then under construction, designated AVO.4 to AVO.6. All were scheduled to be delivered before the end of 1979, as total systems aircraft.

The following description applies to the YAH-64 prototypes, except where indicated:

TYPE: Prototype armed helicopter.

ROTOR SYSTEM: Four-blade fully-articulated main rotor and four-blade tail rotor, with blades manufactured by Tool Research and Engineering Corpn (Advance Structures Division). Main rotor blades are of high-camber aerofoil section and broad chord. Each blade has five stainless steel spars, a laminated stainless steel skin and a composite aft section. Blades are attached to hub by a laminated strap retention system similar to that of the OH-6A, and are fitted with elastomeric lead/lag dampers and offset flapping hinges. Four-blade tail rotor comprises two sets of two blades, mounted on port side of pylon/fin support structure at optimum quiet setting of approx 60°/120° to each other. Rotor mast similar to that of OH-6A, with driveshaft turning within a hollow, fixed outer shaft. Entire system capable of flight in negative *g* conditions.

ROTOR DRIVE: Transmission to main rotor via Litton (Precision Gear Division) engine nose gearboxes, and to tail rotor via Aircraft Gear Corpn intermediate and grease-lubricated tail rotor gearboxes, with Bendix driveshafts and couplings. Garrett cooling fan for tail rotor gearbox. Redundant flight control system for both rotors. Selected dynamic components constructed of 70/49 aluminium and electro-slag remelt (ESR) steel; critical parts of transmission (eg, bearings) have ESR collars for protection against hits by 12·7 mm or 23 mm ammunition. Rotor/engine rpm ratios approx 66·7 for main rotor, approx 14·3 for tail rotor.

WINGS: Cantilever mid-wing monoplane, of low aspect ratio, aft of cockpit. Trailing-edge flaps deploy automatically as function of control attitude and airspeed (max deflection 20°), and can be deflected 45° upward to offload wings in an emergency autorotative landing. Wings are removable, and attach to sides of cabin for transport and storage. Two hardpoints beneath each wing for the carriage of mixed ordnance.

FUSELAGE: Conventional semi-monocoque aluminium structure, built by Teledyne Ryan Aeronautical. Designed to survive hits by 12·7 mm and 23 mm ammunition.

TAIL UNIT: Fixed fin and cantilever movable T tailplane.

LANDING GEAR: Menasco tailwheel type, with single wheel on each unit. Main legs fold rearward to reduce overall height for storage and transportation. Fully-castoring, self-centering tailwheel. Main-wheel tyres size 22 × 8; tailwheel tyre size 13 × 5. Hydraulic brakes.

POWER PLANT: Two 1,145 kW (1,536 shp) General Electric T700-GE-700 turboshaft engines, derated for normal operations to provide reserve power for combat emergencies. Engines mounted one on each side of fuselage, above wings. Two crashproof fuel cells, capacity 1,366 litres (361 US gallons).

ACCOMMODATION: Crew of two in tandem, co-pilot/gunner in front and pilot aft on 483 mm (19 in) elevated seat. Large, shaped transparent cockpit enclosure for optimum field of view. Lightweight boron armour shields in cockpit floor and sides. Cockpits separated by armour plating and an anti-23 mm inner plastics shield.

SYSTEMS AND EQUIPMENT: Large avionics bay adjacent to gunner's position, in lower fuselage. Bertea hydraulic control system, with hydraulic actuators ballistic tolerant to direct 12·7 mm hits. In the event of hydraulic control system failure, the system adjusts to secondary fly-by-wire control. Bendix electrical power system, with two fully-redundant engine-driven generators and standby DC battery. Sperry Flight Systems automatic stabilisation equipment. Singer Kearfott lightweight Doppler navigation system. Garrett APU, and integrated pneumatic air systems. Sperry Flight Systems all-raster symbol generator is under development to process TV data from IR and other sensors, superimpose symbology and distribute the combination to CRT and helmet-mounted displays in the aircraft. BITE fault detection/location system.

ARMAMENT AND OPERATIONAL EQUIPMENT: Flexible armament consists of a Hughes-developed XM230E1 30 mm chain gun, mounted in an underfuselage turret between the main-wheel legs, and having a normal rate of fire of 800 rds/min. Ammunition max load is 1,200 rds, and is interoperable with NATO Aden/DEFA rounds. Turret designed to collapse into fuselage between pilots in the event of a crash-landing. Four underwing hardpoints, on which can be carried up to sixteen Hellfire anti-tank missiles; or up to seventy-six 2·75 in folding-fin rockets in their launchers; or a combination of Hellfire missiles and rockets. CPG stabilised sight in forward fuselage, ahead of cockpit, incorporates day and night (FLIR: forward-looking infra-red) sighting equipment, laser ranger and target designator, and laser tracker equipment. Co-pilot/gunner has primary responsibility for firing guns and missiles, but pilot can override his controls to fire gun or launch missiles. Pilot's night vision system (PNVS) in extreme tip of nose. Integrated Helmet And Display Sighting System (IHADSS) by Honeywell Avionics Division will enhance speed and flexibility of target acquisition. Forward bay includes electronics for stabilised sight, missiles and fire control computer provided by Teledyne Systems Inc.

DIMENSIONS, EXTERNAL:

Diameter of main rotor	14·63 m (48 ft 0 in)
Diameter of tail rotor	2·54 m (8 ft 4 in)
Main rotor blade chord	0·53 m (1 ft 9 in)
Length of fuselage	15·06 m (49 ft 5 in)
Length overall, rotors turning	17·60 m (57 ft 9 in)
Wing span	4·98 m (16 ft 4 in)
Height to top of rotor hub	3·83 m (12 ft 6⅞ in)

Hughes YAH-64 firing a Hellfire missile during initial compatibility trials

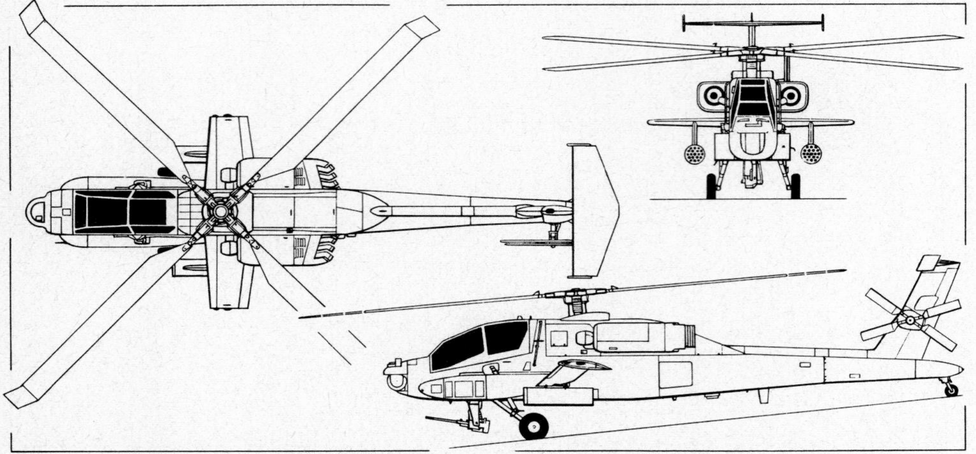

Hughes AH-64 tandem two-seat advanced attack helicopter *(Pilot Press)*

Tailplane span 3·15 m (10 ft 4 in)
Wheel track 2·03 m (6 ft 8 in)
AREA:
Main rotor disc 168·06 m² (1,809 sq ft)
WEIGHTS:
Weight empty 4,657 kg (10,268 lb)
Primary mission gross weight 6,271 kg (13,825 lb)
Structural design gross weight 6,650 kg (14,660 lb)
Max T-O weight 8,006 kg (17,650 lb)

PERFORMANCE (at 6,316 kg; 13,925 lb AUW, ISA except where indicated):
Never-exceed speed 204 knots (378 km/h; 235 mph)
Max level speed 167 knots (309 km/h; 192 mph)
Max cruising speed 158 knots (293 km/h; 182 mph)
Max vertical rate of climb at S/L 878 m (2,880 ft)/min
Max vertical rate of climb at 1,220 m (4,000 ft) at 35°C 259 m (850 ft)/min
Service ceiling 6,250 m (20,500 ft)
Service ceiling, one engine out 3,505 m (11,500 ft)
Hovering ceiling IGE 4,633 m (15,200 ft)
Hovering ceiling OGE 3,780 m (12,400 ft)
Max range, internal fuel 330 nm (611 km; 380 miles)
Ferry range, max internal and external fuel, still air 974 nm (1,804 km; 1,121 miles)
Endurance at 1,220 m (4,000 ft) at 35°C 1 h 50 min
Max endurance, internal fuel 3 h 23 min

ICX

ICX AVIATION INC

ADDRESS: 1101 Connecticut Avenue NW, Washington, DC 20036
PRESIDENT: Dale P. Lewis

This company announced in 1978 the conclusion of a preliminary agreement with Aviaexport of the USSR for licence manufacture in the USA of the Yakovlev Yak-40 three-turbofan light transport aircraft. A facility was then being established at Youngston, Ohio, for production of this aircraft, which has been given the name X-Avia.

ICX AVIATION X-AVIA

ICX Aviation began adapting the design of the Yak-40 for production in the USA in December 1976. Work on a demonstrator, converted from a Soviet-built Yak-40, began in October 1978, and the first flight of this aircraft was planned for May 1979. Construction of two prototypes of what will be marketed as the X-Avia was planned to begin in January 1979, with the first flight of a production aircraft anticipated in September 1981.

In early 1979, almost all work was being concentrated on the X-Avia A version, to carry 30 passengers or 3,400 kg (7,500 lb) of freight, and the 40-passenger X-Avia B version. An all-cargo C version will carry a payload of 4,535 kg (10,000 lb).

TYPE: Three-turbofan short-range transport.

WINGS: Cantilever low-wing monoplane. Dihedral 5° 30′. Incidence 3°. No sweepback. Light alloy structure with main spar, fore and aft auxiliary spars, ribs and stringers, covered with skin of varying thickness for which chemical milling is utilised. Wing made in two sections, joined at aircraft centreline. Manually-operated ailerons, each in two sections. Trim tab in port aileron. Hydraulically-actuated Fowler-type trailing-edge flaps, in three sections on each wing. De-icing of wing leading-edges by engine bleed air.

FUSELAGE: Semi-monocoque fail-safe light alloy structure of frames, longerons, stringers and skins.

TAIL UNIT: Conventional cantilever T-tail of light alloy. Variable-incidence tailplane. Trim tab in rudder. Anti-icing system being redesigned for US manufacture.

LANDING GEAR: Hydraulically-retractable tricycle type with single wheel on each unit. Main units retract inward, nose unit forward. Hydraulically-steerable nosewheel. Main-wheel tyres size 1,120 × 450 mm; nosewheel tyre size 720 × 310 mm. Brakes and anti-skid units being redesigned for US manufacture. Preliminary design study being made for optional amphibious floatplane version.

POWER PLANT: Three Garrett-AiResearch TFE 731-3 turbofan engines, each rated at 16·5 kN (3,700 lb st). Centre engine has S-duct air intake and thrust reversal. Outboard engines are mounted in pod on each side of rear fuselage. Fuel in integral wing tanks with combined capacity of 4,000 kg (8,818 lb). Single-point pressure refuelling and overwing gravity refuelling points.

ACCOMMODATION: Pilot and co-pilot side by side on flight deck. Cabin will accommodate 30 or 40 passengers and a cabin attendant in alternative layouts. Cargo version proposed with 2·18 m wide × 1·66 m high (7 ft 1¾ in × 5 ft 5¼ in) cargo door. Main door with airstairs in underfuselage, beneath centre engine air intake. Service door/emergency exit at forward end of cabin on port side. Two emergency exits overwing; one above flight deck. Baggage compartments at forward end of cabin on starboard side, and aft end of cabin on port side. Galley and toilet at aft end of cabin on starboard side. Accommodation is pressurised, air-conditioned, heated and ventilated.

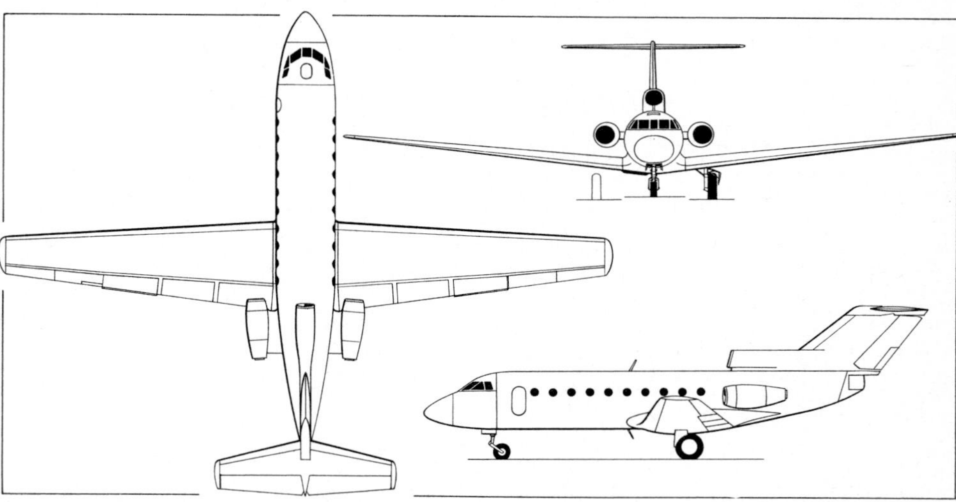

ICX Aviation X-Avia, a re-engined version of the Soviet Yak-40 light transport *(Pilot Press)*

SYSTEMS: Garrett-AiResearch pressurisation system, air conditioning and APU. Hydraulic, pneumatic, electrical, oxygen and de-icing systems being redesigned for US manufacture.

AVIONICS AND EQUIPMENT: Collins communications transceiver and navigation receiver. Blind-flying instrumentation standard. Sperry Flight Systems flight director and SPZ-600 autopilot.

DIMENSIONS, EXTERNAL:
Wing span 25·00 m (82 ft 0¼ in)
Wing chord at root 3·80 m (12 ft 5½ in)
Wing chord at tip 1·55 m (5 ft 1 in)
Wing aspect ratio 8·9
Length overall 20·36 m (66 ft 9½ in)
Diameter of fuselage 2·40 m (7 ft 10½ in)
Height overall 6·50 m (21 ft 4 in)
Tailplane span 7·50 m (24 ft 7¼ in)
Wheel track 4·52 m (14 ft 10 in)
Wheelbase 7·47 m (24 ft 6 in)
Service door (fwd, port):
Height 1·20 m (3 ft 11¼ in)
Width 0·55 m (1 ft 9½ in)

DIMENSIONS, INTERNAL (X-Avia A version):
Cabin, excl flight deck, incl toilet, baggage storage and galley: Length 10·11 m (33 ft 2 in)
Max width 2·24 m (7 ft 4¼ in)
Max height 1·85 m (6 ft 0¾ in)
Floor area 17·4 m² (187·3 sq ft)
Volume 33·88 m³ (1,196 cu ft)

AREAS:
Wings, gross 70·00 m² (753·50 sq ft)
Ailerons (total) 3·70 m² (39·83 sq ft)
Trailing-edge flaps (total) 16·50 m² (177·61 sq ft)
Fin 10·48 m² (112·81 sq ft)
Rudder (incl tab) 2·64 m² (28·42 sq ft)
Tailplane 13·03 m² (140·26 sq ft)
Elevators 4·91 m² (52·85 sq ft)

WEIGHTS AND LOADINGS (estimated):
Max T-O weight 16,450 kg (36,266 lb)
Max ramp weight 16,535 kg (36,453 lb)
Max zero-fuel weight 12,450 kg (27,448 lb)
Max landing weight 15,000 kg (33,069 lb)
Max wing loading 235 kg/m² (48·13 lb/sq ft)
Max power loading 332·3 kg/kN (3·27 lb/lb st)

PERFORMANCE (estimated, at max T-O weight):
Never-exceed speed Mach 0·6
Max level speed at 9,145 m (30,000 ft) 354 knots (657 km/h; 408 mph)
Max cruising speed at 10,970 m (36,000 ft) 315 knots (584 km/h; 363 mph)
Econ cruising speed at 10,970 m (36,000 ft) 300 knots (555 km/h; 345 mph)
Stalling speed, flaps up, power off 98 knots (182 km/h; 113 mph)
Stalling speed, flaps down, power off 84 knots (156 km/h; 97 mph)
Max rate of climb at S/L 914 m (3,000 ft)/min
Max rate of climb at S/L, one engine out 427 m (1,400 ft)/min
Service ceiling 12,190 m (40,000 ft)
Service ceiling, one engine out 7,620 m (25,000 ft)
Range with 3,400 kg (7,500 lb) cargo payload 850 nm (1,574 km; 978 miles)

INTERCEPTOR COMPANY—*See 'Prop-Jets Inc'*

ISHAM

ISHAM AIRCRAFT

ADDRESS: PO Box 12172, Mid Continent Airport, Wichita, Kansas 67277
Telephone: (316) 755 0713
PRESIDENT: Brad E. Isham

ISHAM (PIPER) PA-28 CHEROKEE and (CESSNA) R172K SKYHAWK CONVERSIONS

Isham AirCraft is marketing, with FAA approval, modification kits for various models of the Piper Cherokee which are designed to improve the aircraft's performance and handling during approach and landing. They are also claimed to make slight improvements in take-off distance, rate of climb and cruising speeds.

Kits are available for the Piper PA-28-140, -150, -160 and -180, to provide light alloy wing and tailplane exten-

Piper PA-28R-180 Cherokee with Isham AirCraft wing and fin modifications

sions, Hoerner-type wingtips, dorsal fins of ABS plastics, and a third window on each side. The third-window kit is available also for the Piper PA-28-235. A kit to provide the retractable-gear Piper PA-28R-180 and -200 with wing extensions, Hoerner wingtips and dorsal fin can be obtained from Isham AirCraft, as well as a kit to re-rate the Continental IO-360-K power plant of the Cessna R172K from 145 kW (195 hp) to 157 kW (210 hp) at take-off.

Performance and specification details of aircraft to which these kits have been applied are given in the accompanying table. By the beginning of 1979, Isham had sold 54 complete Cherokee wing/tail unit kits, 14 dorsal fin kits and 17 window kits; 7 wing/tail kits for the retractable-gear Cherokee Arrow; and 3 R172K engine uprate kits.

Dimensions/Performance	PA-28-140 PA-28-150	PA-28-180	PA-28R-180 PA-28R-200	R172K	Units
Wing span	9·81 (32·2)	9·81 (32·2)	9·81 (32·2)	N/C	m (ft)
Tailplane span	3·91 (12·83)	3·91 (12·83)	N/C	N/C	m (ft)
Wing area	15·7 (169)	15·7 (169)	15·7 (169)	N/C	m² (sq ft)
Max wing loading	62·1 (12·72)	69·3 (14·2)	72·2 (14·79)	N/A	kg/m² (lb/sq ft)
Max level speed	124 (230; 143)	135 (249; 155)	150 (278; 173)	N/A	knots (km/h; mph)
Max cruising speed (75% power)	119 (220; 137)	127 (235; 146)	143 (266; 165)	N/A	knots (km/h; mph)
Stalling speed	N/C	N/C	N/C	N/A	knots (km/h; mph)
Max rate of climb at S/L	247 (810)	274 (900)	302 (990)	351 (1,150)	m (ft)/min
T-O to 15 m (50 ft)	472 (1,547)	450 (1,477)	477 (1,565)	302 (990)	m (ft)
Landing from 15 m (50 ft)	N/C	N/C	N/C	N/A	m (ft)
Range, max fuel	687 (1,273; 791)	643 (1,191; 740)	757 (1,403; 872)	N/A	nm (km; miles)
Reduction in sink rate	27	26·4	27	N/A	%

Figures quoted are for S/L ISA at max T-O weight.
N/A: not available. N/C: no change.

JETCRAFTERS
JETCRAFTERS INCORPORATED

Address: PO Box 4640, Waco, Texas 76705
Telephone: (817) 799 6231
President: E. J. Swearingen
Vice-Presidents:
O. L. Anderson
E. A. Banks (San Antonio Operations)
A. S. Hess (Waco Operations)

Well-known as the designer of the Merlin and Metro twin-turboprop executive transports, 'Ed' J. Swearingen established Jetcrafters Inc to initiate a modification programme to enhance the performance and operating economy of the Beechcraft King Air 90 models. This work is carried out at James Connally Airport, Waco, Texas.

The company's facility at San Antonio, Texas, is manufacturing engine nacelles for AiResearch Aviation Company's 731 JetStar conversions.

Jetcrafters Taurus modification of the Beechcraft Model 90 King Air

JETCRAFTERS TAURUS MODIFICATION

Any model of the Beechcraft King Air 90 series is suitable for incorporation of the Jetcrafters Taurus modification. This involves replacing the existing engines with Pratt & Whitney Aircraft of Canada PT6A-135 turboprop engines, each flat rated at 522 kW (700 shp); modification of the existing engine nacelles to reduce their height and cross-sectional area; provision of new cowls, engine air inlets, inertial water/ice separators, a new low-profile exhaust system to reduce drag and increase thrust, new oil cooler airflow control system, and a new integral nacelle fuel tank with full lightning strike protection; removal of the existing engine-driven cabin supercharger and provision of a new flow control system to provide dual bleed air pressurisation; and the supply of new engine torque indicators.

After embodiment of the Taurus modification, the King Air 90, A90, B90, C90 and E90 are redesignated respectively Taurus 90, A90, B90, C90 and E90.

Brief details of performance improvements follow:

Performance (A: Taurus 90; B: A90; C: B90; D: C90; and E: E90):
Max cruising speed at optimum altitude:
A, B, C, D, E 278 knots (515 km/h; 320 mph)
Stalling speed, flaps down:
A, B, C, D, E 69 knots (127 km/h; 79 mph)
Max rate of climb at S/L: A 913 m (2,995 ft)/min
B 884 m (2,900 ft)/min
C, D 852 m (2,795 ft)/min
E 814 m (2,670 ft)/min
Service ceiling: A, B, C, D, E 11,430 m (37,500 ft)
T-O to 15 m (50 ft): A, B 625 m (2,050 ft)
C 533 m (1,750 ft)
D 689 m (2,261 ft)
E 617 m (2,024 ft)
Landing from 15 m (50 ft): A, B 716 m (2,350 ft)
C, D 613 m (2,010 ft)
E 643 m (2,110 ft)

KAMAN
KAMAN AEROSPACE CORPORATION
(a subsidiary of Kaman Corporation)

Head Office: Old Windsor Road, Bloomfield, Connecticut 06002
Telephone: (203) 242 4461
President and Chief Executive: Fred L. Smith
Vice-Presidents:
Wayne D. Hudson (Manufacturing)
Eamon N. Kelly (Contracts)
Walter R. Kozlow (Finance)
Cornelia V. Lynn (Personnel)
Donald W. Robinson (Marketing)
Llewellyn C. Schuler (Engineering)
Secretary: J. S. Murtha
Manager, Washington Operations: Owen F. Polleys

The original Kaman Aircraft Corporation was founded in 1945 by Mr Charles H. Kaman, who continues as President and Chairman of the Board of Kaman Corporation. Its initial programme was to develop and test a novel servo-flap control system for helicopter rotors, and the Kaman K-125 of 1947 was the first in a series of 'synchropter' designs with intermeshing contra-rotating rotors and the servo-flap control system. The later H-2 Seasprite naval helicopter utilises the servo-flap control system on a conventional single main rotor.

Kaman Aerospace operates two plants in Connecticut,

Kaman Circulation Control Rotor (CCR) during wind tunnel testing in 1978 at NASA-Ames

located at Bloomfield and Moosup. Its capabilities include major production work in the fields of airframe structures, sheet metal, glassfibre, composites, and reinforced honeycomb bonding. It is also a leading company in the field of helicopter dynamics, research and development, and in the application of new materials and technology.

Kamatics Corporation (formerly Kacarb Products Corporation), a subsidiary of Kaman Aerospace Corporation, was reorganised in January 1973 to reflect its developing potential in the industry. Products include bearings and couplings for a variety of aerospace applications.

In research and development, Kaman Aerospace is working on several advanced concepts. One of the most promising programmes is the development of a Circulation Control Rotor (CCR) technology demonstrator aircraft for the Naval Air Systems Command. In this concept a thin jet of air is ejected from a slot near the trailing-edge of each rotor blade, inducing a circulation which results in lift augmentation. Since conventional cyclic pitch is eliminated, the rotor hub and controls are simplified considerably. Full-scale whirl tests and wind tunnel tests were completed successfully in early 1978, with flight tests on a Kaman NHH-2D helicopter scheduled for early 1979.

Several other R & D programmes are under sponsorship of the US Army Research and Technology Laboratories, Applied Technology Laboratory, Fort Eustis, Virginia. They include a controllable twist rotor (CTR); dynamic anti-resonant vibration isolator; composite rotor hub; repairable/expendable main rotor blade concept; new concepts in structural dynamic testing; maintainability of major helicopter components; elastic pitch beam tail rotor; and new design, fabrication and inspection techniques for helicopter structures. Kaman modified the CTR hardware to incorporate a multicyclic flap system at the request of NASA's Ames Research Center, Moffett Field, California, and testing in the 12 × 24 m (40 × 80 ft) wind tunnel has been completed. Flight testing of the CTR on NASA's Sikorsky-built Rotor Systems Research Aircraft (RSRA) is scheduled for 1983.

For the Office of Naval Research, Kaman is under contract to design, build and demonstrate the feasibility of the Ship Tethered Aerial Platform (STAPL), a ship-towed drone autogyro with automatic flight controls and data recording equipment, which is visualised as an elevated sensor or instrument platform.

In addition to its R & D programmes related directly to aerospace technology, Kaman is involved in new wind energy programmes. Among these are a composite rotor blade for a 91·44 m (300 ft) diameter wind turbine; development of a smaller wind turbine rated at 40 kW; and a set of composite blades for NASA's 60·96 m (200 ft) diameter MOD-1 wind turbine.

Kaman Aerospace is engaged in several major airframe programmes as a subcontractor, including the construction of flaps, slats, spoilers and cove doors for the US Navy's F-14 Tomcat fighter; engine access, tailpipe, and landing gear doors for the USN's A-6E and EA-6B attack aircraft; various detail parts and tools on the USAF's A-10A Thunderbolt II close support aircraft; components of the external fuel tank and solid rocket boosters of NASA's Space Shuttle programme; acoustic structural components for jet engines; and structural components for various business and commercial aircraft.

Kaman Aerospace is also the supplier of bonded components for the C-130, B-52 and UH-1 aircraft for Army and Air Force government agencies. Kaman designed and is producing a new all-composite rotor blade for the Bell AH-1 HueyCobra in service with the US Army, funded by the Army. The first AH-1 fitted with the new blades made its first flight on 26 July 1976. Contractor development testing was completed in 1976, and initial production began in mid-1977. Improved performance, life and operational features have been demonstrated.

In May 1971 Kaman was awarded a contract by the USAF's Electronic Systems Division, Air Force Systems Command, for the design, fabrication and testing of the Airborne Weather Reconnaissance System (AWRS). Intended to improve collection, measurement, analysis, recording and communication of meteorological data, to increase the accuracy of predicting the force and direction of hurricanes, typhoons and lesser storms, AWRS was fitted in two Hercules aircraft delivered to the USAF Air Weather Service and the US Commerce Department's National Oceanic and Atmospheric Administration (NOAA) Research Flight Facility. AWRS may be installed in additional Air Weather Service C-130s for worldwide coverage of weather phenomena. Details can be found in the 1975-76 *Jane's*.

Kaman Sciences Corporation, with headquarters at Colorado Springs, Colorado, is engaged in nuclear research, weapons studies, advanced aerodynamics, computer programming and time sharing, neutron generators, advanced materials, measuring devices, systems analysis and solar energy. Kaman's general aviation subsidiaries comprise AirKaman Inc, a fixed-base operator at Bradley International Airport, Windsor Locks, Connecticut; Air Kaman of Omaha, Nebraska, and AirKaman of Jacksonville, Florida, all of which provide sales and service of light and twin-engined business aircraft, repairs, fuel sales, charter service, flight training and airline services.

At the beginning of 1979 total corporate employment was 3,562, of whom 1,050 were engaged in aerospace activities.

Kaman SH-2F LAMPS ASW helicopter, showing optional increased-capacity external fuel tank

KAMAN SEASPRITE

US Navy designations: UH-2 (formerly HU2K-1), HH-2 and SH-2

The prototype Seasprite flew for the first time on 2 July 1959, and many versions (described in previous editions of *Jane's*) were produced subsequently for the US Navy.

From 1967, all of the original UH-2A/B Seasprites were converted progressively to UH-2C twin-engined configuration, with two 932 kW (1,250 shp) General Electric T58-GE-8B turboshaft engines in place of the former single T58. They have since undergone further modification, under the US Navy's important LAMPS (Light Airborne Multi-Purpose System) programme, to provide helicopters for ASW (Anti-Submarine Warfare) and ASMD (Anti-Ship Missile Defence) operations.

The following versions remained available in early 1979:

HH-2D. Three aircraft, without LAMPS modifications, assigned to Coast and Geodetic Survey work.

NHH-2D. Test aircraft assigned to the circulation control rotor (CCR) programme.

SH-2D. LAMPS version, for ASW, ASMD and a utility role. The first of 20 SH-2Ds, modified from HH-2D unarmed search and rescue helicopters, made its first flight on 16 March 1971, and by March 1972 Kaman completed the modification of all of these aircraft. This involved the installation of Canadian Marconi LN-66 high-power surface search radar in a glassfibre honeycomb dome under the chin; ASQ-81 MAD deployed by winch from a pylon on the starboard side of the fuselage; 15 AN/SSQ-47 active or AN/SSQ-41 passive sonobuoys launched by a small explosive charge from a removable rack on the port side; ALR-54 electronic support measure; eight Mk 25 marine flares/smoke markers; data link; tactical navigation system, and associated command/control units, recorders, displays and antennae. Auxiliary fuel tank mounts on each side of the fuselage were hardened for the added purpose of launching Mk 44 and Mk 46 ASW homing torpedoes.

As the LAMPS helicopters became operational, the Navy organised squadrons to provide detachments to fleet units and to train additional personnel to operate and maintain them.

In early 1979 there were eight HSL LAMPS squadrons. Operational deployment began on 7 December 1971. By January 1979, 145 LAMPS SH-2D/F detachments had been deployed (not simultaneously) on long cruises, primarily in the Mediterranean and Pacific, on the following ship classes: DD-963, FFG-1, FF-1052, FF-1040, CGN-11, CG-35 and CG-26. The new DD-963 and FFG-7 classes are designed to operate with two LAMPS helicopters per ship.

SH-2F. Deliveries of this further-developed Mk I LAMPS version began in May 1973 and the first unit became operational with squadron HSL-33, deployed to the Pacific, on 11 September 1973. A total of 87 SH-2Fs has been delivered. The earlier SH-2Ds and HH-2Ds are being uprated to SH-2F configuration.

The SH-2F is fitted with Kaman's '101' rotor, which provides substantially increased performance in all flight regimes, while practically eliminating rotor vibrations at all speeds and weights, thus improving system reliability and maintainability. The new simplified rotor system utilises titanium hub and retention assemblies, reduces the number of control elements by two-thirds, and offers increased life for the entire rotor system.

Other features of the SH-2F include increased-strength landing gear; a shortened wheelbase by relocation of the tailwheel; and twin 1,007 kW (1,350 shp) General Electric T58-GE-8F turboshaft engines. It is planned in the near future to make improvements to the LN-66HP radar, tactical navigation system, ESM, sonobuoys and data link In January-February 1973 Kaman flight-tested the prototype for flight qualification to a maximum gross weight of 6,033 kg (13,300 lb), which is 227 kg (500 lb) more than the current SH-2F. This may be utilised as increased payload, or in the form of additional fuel in larger auxiliary tanks to provide extended range and endurance in a new production version of the SH-2. US Navy tests have proved the SH-2 suitable for dipping sonar operations, air-to-surface missile firing, and equipment with various guns and rockets. These are available to international customers as alternative configurations.

The following details apply to the SH-2F version of the Seasprite:

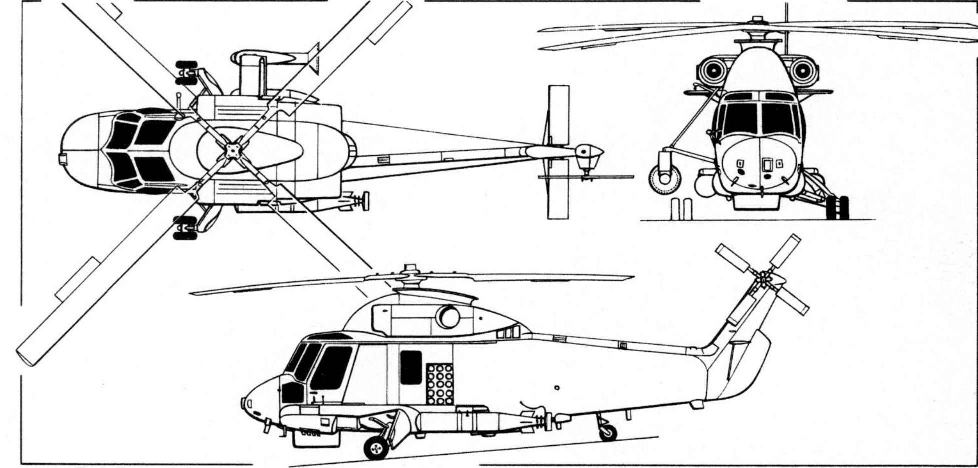

Kaman SH-2F Seasprite Light Airborne Multi-Purpose System (LAMPS) helicopter *(Pilot Press)*

TYPE: Naval anti-submarine warfare and anti-ship missile defence helicopter, with secondary capability for search and rescue, observation and utility missions.

ROTOR SYSTEM: Four-blade main and tail rotors. Blades of aluminium and glassfibre construction, with servo-flap controls. Blades folded manually. Main rotor rpm 287.

FUSELAGE: All-metal semi-monocoque structure, with flotation hull housing main fuel tanks. Nose split on centreline, to fold rearward on each side to reduce stowage space required. Fixed horizontal stabiliser on tail rotor pylon.

LANDING GEAR: Tailwheel type, with forward-retracting dual main wheels and non-retractable tailwheel. Liquid spring shock-absorbers in main gear legs; oleo-pneumatic shock-absorber in tailwheel unit, which is fully-castoring for taxying but locked fore and aft for T-O and landing. Main wheels have 8-ply tubeless tyres size 17·5 × 6·25-11, pressure 17·25 bars (250 lb/sq in); tailwheel tyre 10-ply tubeless size 5·00-5, pressure 11·04 bars (160 lb/sq in).

POWER PLANT: Two 1,007 kW (1,350 shp) General Electric T58-GE-8F turboshaft engines, mounted on each side of rotor pylon structure. Normal fuel capacity of 1,499 litres (396 US gallons), including external auxiliary tanks with a capacity of 454·6 litres (120 US gallons).

ACCOMMODATION: Crew of three, consisting of pilot, co-pilot and sensor operator. One passenger or litter patient with LAMPS equipment installed; four passengers or two litters with sonobuoy launcher removed. Provision for transportation of internal or external cargo.

AVIONICS AND EQUIPMENT: Include Canadian Marconi LN-66HP surveillance radar; ASQ-81 magnetic anomaly detector; ALR-54 passive radiation detection receivers (to be replaced by ALR-66); SSQ-41 passive and SSQ-47 active sonobuoys; smoke markers; one or two torpedoes; PT-429 plotting board system (to be replaced by Teledyne Systems ASN-123 tactical navigation system with computer and CRT display); APN-182 Doppler radar; and AYK-2 analogue navigation computer. Cargo hook for external loads, capacity 1,814 kg (4,000 lb). Rescue hoist with capacity of 272 kg (600 lb).

DIMENSIONS, EXTERNAL:

Diameter of main rotor	13·41 m (44 ft 0 in)
Main rotor blade chord	0·55 m (21·6 in)
Diameter of tail rotor	2·49 m (8 ft 2 in)
Tail rotor blade chord	0·236 m (9·3 in)
Length overall (rotors turning)	16·03 m (52 ft 7 in)
Length overall, nose and blades folded	11·68 m (38 ft 4 in)
Height overall (rotors turning)	4·72 m (15 ft 6 in)
Height to top of rotor head	4·14 m (13 ft 7 in)
Stabiliser span	2·97 m (9 ft 9 in)
Wheel track (outer wheels)	3·30 m (10 ft 10 in)
Wheelbase	5·11 m (16 ft 9 in)

WEIGHTS:

Weight empty	3,193 kg (7,040 lb)
*Normal T-O weight	5,805 kg (12,800 lb)

**Although not yet certificated for a T-O gross weight of 6,033 kg (13,300 lb), all testing has been accomplished at that weight*

PERFORMANCE (at normal T-O weight, except where indicated):

Max level speed at S/L	143 knots (265 km/h; 165 mph)
Normal cruising speed	130 knots (241 km/h; 150 mph)
Max rate of climb at S/L	744 m (2,440 ft)/min
Service ceiling	6,860 m (22,500 ft)
Hovering ceiling IGE	5,670 m (18,600 ft)
Hovering ceiling OGE	4,695 m (15,400 ft)
Normal range with max fuel	367 nm (679 km; 422 miles)

LAKE

LAKE AIRCRAFT DIVISION OF CONSOLIDATED AERONAUTICS INC

EXECUTIVE OFFICES: PO Box 399, Tomball, Texas 77375
SALES OFFICES: David Hooks Memorial Airport, Tomball, Texas 77375
Telephone: (713) 376 5421
Telex: 76-2054 Lake Air Hou
PRESIDENT: John J. O'Toole
EXECUTIVE VICE-PRESIDENT: M. L. Alson
VICE-PRESIDENT: Laurin Darrell (Marketing)
SECRETARY: B. A. Sigsbee
TREASURER: Herbert P. Lindblad

In 1962 Consolidated Aeronautics merged with Lake Aircraft Corporation of Sandford, Maine, as a result of which it operates Lake Aircraft as a division.

It is continuing production of the LA-4 amphibian, which Lake Aircraft developed from the original Colonial C-2 Skimmer IV after purchasing manufacturing rights from Colonial Aircraft Corporation in October 1959.

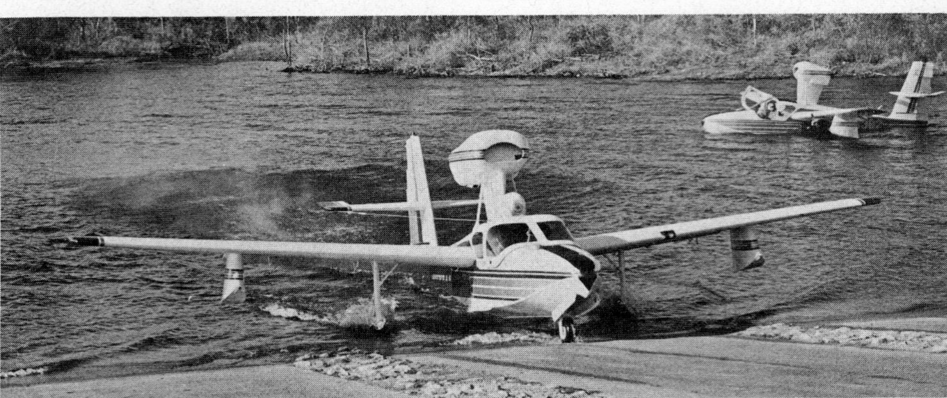

Lake LA-4-200 Buccaneer four-seat light amphibian (Lycoming IO-360-A1B flat-four engine)

LAKE LA-4-200 BUCCANEER

Design of the original C-1 Skimmer was started in August 1946. Construction of the prototype began in January 1947 and it flew for the first time in May 1948. Versions of the Lake LA-4 developed from the improved C-2 Skimmer IV have included the LA-4, LA-4A, LA-4P, LA-4S and LA-4T, as described in previous editions of *Jane's*.

The LA-4-200 current production version, described here, received FAA certification in 1970.

A total of 946 LA-4s of all versions had been built by 1 January 1979.

TYPE: Single-engined four-seat amphibian.

WINGS: Cantilever shoulder-wing monoplane with tapered wing panels attached directly to sides of hull. Wing section NACA 4415 at root, NACA 4409 at tip. Dihedral 5° 30′. Incidence 3° 15′. Structure consists of duralumin leading- and trailing-edge torsion boxes separated by a single duralumin main spar. All-metal ailerons and hydraulically-operated slotted flaps over 80% of span. Ground-adjustable trim tabs on ailerons. Wing balancer floats are light alloy monocoque structures.

HULL: Single-step all-metal structure, with double-sealed boat hull. Alodined and zinc chromated inside and out against corrosion, with polyurethane paint exterior finish.

TAIL UNIT: Cantilever all-metal structure. Outboard elevator section separate from inboard section and actuated hydraulically for trimming. Retractable water rudder in base of aerodynamic rudder.

LANDING GEAR: Hydraulically-retractable tricycle type. Consolidated oleo-pneumatic shock-absorbers on main gear, which retracts inward into wings. Long-stroke nosewheel oleo retracts forward. Gerdes main wheels with Goodyear tyres, size 6·00-6, pressure 2·41 bars (35 lb/sq in). Gerdes nosewheel with Goodyear tyre size 5·00-5, pressure 1·38 bars (20 lb/sq in). Gerdes disc brakes. Parking brake. Nosewheel is free to swivel 30° each side.

POWER PLANT: One 149 kW (200 hp) Lycoming IO-360-A1B flat-four engine, mounted on pylon above hull and driving a Hartzell two-blade metal constant-speed pusher propeller. US Rubber DL10 fuel tank in hull, capacity 151 litres (40 US gallons). Refuelling point above hull. Auxiliary fuel in stabilising floats, 28·4 litres (7·5 US gallons) each, optional. Total fuel capacity with optional tanks 208 litres (55 US gallons). Oil capacity 7·5 litres (2 US gallons).

ACCOMMODATION: Enclosed cabin seating pilot and three passengers. Dual controls. Entry through two forward-hinged windscreen sections. Baggage compartment, capacity 90·5 kg (200 lb), aft of cabin. Dual windscreen defroster system.

SYSTEMS: Vacuum system for flight instruments. Hydraulic system, pressure 86·2 bars (1,250 lb/sq in), for flaps, horizontal trim and landing gear actuation. Engine-driven 12V 60A alternator and 12V 35Ah battery. Stewart Warner 20,000 BTU heater optional.

AVIONICS AND EQUIPMENT: Basic avionics installation includes com and nav antennae, cabin speaker, microphone and circuit breakers. Three basic avionics packages comprise (i) Narco Com 120 720-channel com transceiver, Narco Nav 121 200-channel nav receiver with VOR/LOC, Narco AT 150 transponder with 4096 code capability, and ELT; (ii) King KX 170B 720-channel com transceiver, KI 208 200-channel nav receiver with VOR/LOC, KT 78A transponder with 4096 code capability, and ELT; (iii) Collins VHF-251 720-channel micro line com transceiver, VIR-351 200-channel nav receiver with VOR/LOC and IND-350 indicator, TDR-950L transponder with 4096 code capability, and ELT. A wide range of alternative avionics equipment is available to customers' requirements. Standard equipment includes full blind-flying instrumentation, electric clock, manifold pressure gauge, outside air temperature gauge, stall warning device, control locks, instrument panel lighting, carpeted floor, four fresh air vents, tinted glass for all windows, map pocket on front seats, baggage tiedown straps, landing and taxi lights, navigation lights, strobe light, heated pitot, fuselage nose bumper, wing float bumpers, paddle, cleat, line, full-flow oil filter, quick fuel drains, and inboard and outboard tiedown rings.

DIMENSIONS, EXTERNAL:

Wing span	11·58 m (38 ft 0 in)
Wing chord, mean	1·35 m (4 ft 5·1 in)
Wing aspect ratio	8·67
Length overall	7·60 m (24 ft 11 in)
Height overall	2·84 m (9 ft 4 in)
Tailplane span	3·05 m (10 ft 0 in)
Wheel track	3·40 m (11 ft 2 in)
Wheelbase	2·69 m (8 ft 10 in)
Propeller diameter	1·88 m (6 ft 2 in)

DIMENSIONS, INTERNAL:

Cabin: Length	1·57 m (5 ft 2 in)
Max width	1·05 m (3 ft 5½ in)
Max height	1·32 m (3 ft 11½ in)
Floor area	approx 1·53 m² (16·5 sq ft)
Volume	approx 1·70 m³ (60·0 cu ft)
Baggage hold	0·24 m³ (8·5 cu ft)

AREAS:

Wings, gross	15·8 m² (170 sq ft)
Ailerons (total)	1·16 m² (12·5 sq ft)
Trailing-edge flaps (total)	2·28 m² (24·5 sq ft)
Fin	1·25 m² (13·5 sq ft)
Rudder	0·79 m² (8·5 sq ft)
Tailplane	1·45 m² (15·6 sq ft)
Elevators	0·78 m² (8·4 sq ft)

WEIGHTS AND LOADINGS:

Weight empty, equipped	705 kg (1,555 lb)
Max T-O and landing weight	1,220 kg (2,690 lb)
Max wing loading	74·2 kg/m² (15·2 lb/sq ft)
Max power loading	8·19 kg/kW (13·45 lb/hp)

PERFORMANCE (at max T-O weight):

Max level speed at S/L	126·5 knots (235 km/h; 146 mph)
Max cruising speed, 75% power at 2,440 m (8,000 ft)	130 knots (241 km/h; 150 mph)
Stalling speed	39 knots (72·5 km/h; 45 mph)
Max rate of climb at S/L	366 m (1,200 ft)/min
Service ceiling	4,480 m (14,700 ft)
T-O run on land	183 m (600 ft)
T-O run on water	335 m (1,100 ft)
Landing run on land	145 m (475 ft)
Alighting run on water	183 m (600 ft)
Range with max fuel, at normal cruising speed, with reserves	564 nm (1,046 km; 650 miles)
Max range with max fuel, with reserves	716 nm (1,327 km; 825 miles)

LAS

LOCKHEED AIRCRAFT SERVICE COMPANY (Division of Lockheed Corporation)

HEAD OFFICE AND WORKS: Ontario International Airport, Ontario, California 91761
Telephone: (714) 988 2411
BASE: Luke Air Force Base, Arizona
SPECIAL DEVICES DIVISION: Ontario, California
LOCKHEED CENTER FOR MARINE RESEARCH: Carlsbad, California
JETPLAN AVIATION SERVICES: Los Gatos, California
PRESIDENT: Robert L. Vader
EXECUTIVE VICE-PRESIDENTS:
M. H. Greene (Administration)
C. M. Schnepp (Operations)

VICE-PRESIDENTS:
D. K. McKinley (New Business Development)
K. E. Neudoerffer (Operations)
D. C. Shea (Operations)
DIRECTOR OF PUBLIC RELATIONS: John R. Dailey

Lockheed Aircraft Service Company is claimed to be the world's largest independent aircraft maintenance and modification company. It has designed and installed major modifications for such aircraft as the Boeing KC-135 and 707; Douglas DC-8; and Lockheed C-130, C-141, L-188 Electra, C-121, L-1649, L-1011 and P-3. In particular, LAS delivered 41 Electras in a cargo configuration; details of this conversion can be found in the 1970-71 *Jane's*. It has also designed and installed interiors for various transport aircraft.

LAS has diversified into many other fields, including aircraft maintenance training devices, aircraft maintenance recording systems and airborne integrated data systems, marine anti-corrosion systems, aircraft ground support equipment and water pollution monitoring. In addition, under a contract awarded to LAS and three other US companies in November 1975, construction of a modern maintenance and manufacturing base for the Hellenic Aerospace Industry (HAI, which see) is under way at Tanagra, some 60 km (37 miles) from Athens. This will provide airlines operating in the Mediterranean area with a base for contract maintenance and manufacturing facilities, and will also offer depot level maintenance for the Greek Air Force and state services.

In June 1976 LAS began work on a 40-month programme to develop a modern air traffic control system for the kingdom of Saudi Arabia. In 1977 LAS initiated two major programmes in Iran: firstly, under a USAF contract, to provide a complete logistics programme to support the Imperial Iranian Air Force, including the training of personnel; secondly, following receipt of a funded letter of intent from Iran Aircraft Industries (IACI), the expansion of IACI's aircraft overhaul and maintenance capabilities. However, as a result of other internal priorities in Iran, work on the IACI programme was suspended in January 1979.

Lockheed L-1011 TriStar modified by LAS for service with AeroPeru

In 1974 LAS began delivery of its new Model 280 maintenance recorder, which records 50 hours of flight data on an easily accessible cassette. LAS has also developed JETPLAN, a computerised flight planning and worldwide weather service for airlines and corporate jet operations, and this became available on a worldwide basis in 1971.

Brief details of the company's latest conversion programmes follow.

LOCKHEED C-130 and L-1011 CONVERSIONS

LAS specialises in complex aircraft modifications of all types, both of military aircraft such as the C-130 Hercules, and of commercial transports like the L-1011 TriStar. Recent C-130 work included conversion of an HC-130H to DC-130H drone launch configuration for the USAF; and installation and flight testing of an in-flight refuelling system for the C-130, as described briefly in the 1978-79 *Jane's*. LAS also modified C-130A and C-130E cargo aircraft to DC-130A and DC-130E drone launch configurations, for USAF's Tactical Air Command.

LAS completed in 1978 the modification of two L-1011s, operated formerly by Pacific Southwest Airlines and leased currently to AeroPeru for its New York—Miami—Lima routes. The work included conversion of a carry-on baggage compartment into a galley, complete with galley lifts; and provision of wider first class seating, a video entertainment system, and navigation and radar equipment suited to AeroPeru's overwater routes.

LEARAVIA
LEARAVIA CORPORATION

HEAD OFFICE: PO Box 60000, Reno, Nevada 89506
Telephone: (702) 972 0711
Telex: 35 4463
CHAIRMAN: Moya Olsen Lear
PRESIDENT: Samuel H. Auld
VICE-PRESIDENT: J. Sheldon Lewis

LEARAVIA LEAR FAN MODEL 2100

The last aeroplane designed by Mr William P. Lear Sr, before his death on 14 May 1978, was a small twin-turbine business aircraft of advanced design, known originally as the Futura. Since that time it has undergone considerable modification and is known now as the Lear Fan Model 2100.

Of extremely clean appearance, the Model 2100 is built largely of graphite/epoxy composite materials, with other components made of boron, glassfibre, Kevlar and various resins. Design of this aircraft began in June 1977, and construction of the first prototype started in November 1978, with its first flight scheduled at the end of 1979.

TYPE: Twin-turbine business aircraft.

WINGS: Cantilever low-wing monoplane. Thickness/chord ratio 13·5%. Dihedral 4°. Incidence 1° 30′. No sweepback. Three-spar bonded stressed-skin fail-safe structure of advanced graphite/epoxy composite materials. Hydraulically-actuated plain trailing-edge flaps, and manually-operated ailerons, of graphite/epoxy composites. Small hydraulically-actuated airbrakes. Pneumatic de-icing boots on wing leading-edges.

FUSELAGE: Semi-monocoque fail-safe pressurised structure of graphite/epoxy composites, comprising frames and longerons bonded to the outer skin.

TAIL UNIT: Cantilever Y-shaped structure of graphite/epoxy composites, comprising single-spar V-tail and two-spar underfin, the latter stressed to withstand ground impact. Manually-operated elevators with trim tab in V-tail, and rudder with trim tab on underfin. Pneumatic de-icing boots on V-tail and fin leading-edges.

LANDING GEAR: Hydraulically-retractable tricycle type with single wheel on each unit. Nosewheel steering from rudder pedals. Oleo-pneumatic shock-absorbers. Main units retract inward. Main wheels size 6·50 × 8. Hydraulically-actuated brakes, with optional anti-skid system.

POWER PLANT: Two 634 kW (850 shp) Pratt & Whitney Aircraft of Canada PT6B-35F turboshaft engines, each flat-rated to 485 kW (650 shp), mounted in rear of fuselage and driving, via extension shafts and a combining/reduction gearbox with separate clutches, a Hartzell three-blade metal constant-speed and reversible-pitch slow-turning pusher propeller. Fuel in integral wing tanks with a usable capacity of 946 litres (250 US gallons). Refuelling points on wing upper surface.

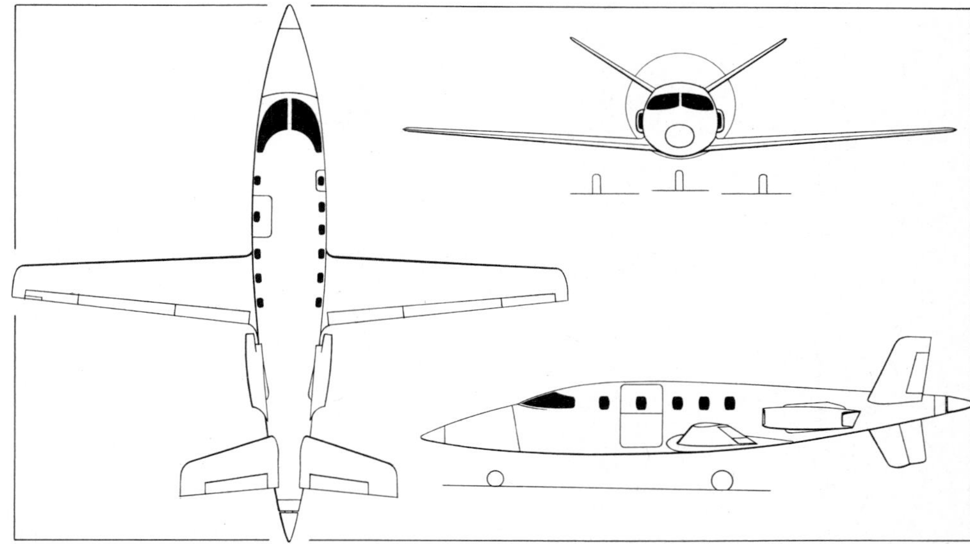

Learavia Lear Fan Model 2100 twin-turbine business aircraft *(Pilot Press)*

ACCOMMODATION: Two pilots and seven passengers, or one pilot and eight passengers, in a variety of seating arrangements, with refreshment cabinet and toilet. Seat tracks on each side of cabin simplify changes to interior layout, or removal of seats for use in a cargo role. Special optional ambulance version can accommodate two stretcher cases, each with attendant, and has biomedical facilities, therapeutic oxygen and toilet Clamshell type door, with integral airstairs in lower half, on port side of cabin, forward of wing. Emergency exit on starboard side. Baggage space at rear of cabin, accessible in flight. Entire accommodation pressurised and air-conditioned. Windscreen defrosting and anti-icing.

SYSTEMS: Cabin pressurisation by engine bleed air, with max pressure differential of 0·57 bars (8·3 lb/sq in), can maintain a 2,440 m (8,000 ft) cabin altitude to max certificated altitude. Freon vapour-cycle cooling system. Electrical system of 24V with dual parallel buses. Hydraulic system of 103·5 bars (1,500 lb/sq in) pressure, provided by two engine-driven hydraulic pumps, either of which is capable of maintaining full system function for operation of trailing-edge flaps, airbrakes and landing gear. Oxygen system for emergency use by crew and passengers. Anti-icing system includes pneumatic de-icing of wing and tail unit leading-edges, and electrical or bleed air anti-icing of engine inlets, pitot tubes, propeller leading-edges, static ports and windscreen.

AVIONICS: Standard Collins/Sperry avionics package includes dual nav/com, dual transponders, DME, ADF, weather radar, air data system, radar altimeter, and SPZ-650L fully integrated flight director/autopilot with RNAV. Optional avionics include VLF Omega, HF com and a second flight director installation for co-pilot.

DIMENSIONS, EXTERNAL:

Wing span	11·99 m (39 ft 4 in)
Wing aspect ratio	9·5
Length overall	11·79 m (38 ft 8 in)
Height overall	3·51 m (11 ft 6 in)
Wheel track	3·45 m (11 ft 4 in)
Wheelbase	4·65 m (15 ft 3 in)
Propeller diameter	2·29 m (7 ft 6 in)

DIMENSIONS, INTERNAL:

Cabin: Length, cockpit divider to rear pressure bulkhead	3·91 m (12 ft 10 in)
Max width	1·47 m (4 ft 10 in)
Max height	1·42 m (4 ft 8 in)
Baggage compartment volume	1·42 m³ (50 cu ft)

AREA:

Wings, gross	15·13 m² (162·9 sq ft)

WEIGHTS AND LOADINGS (estimated):

Weight empty	1,656 kg (3,650 lb)

Max T-O weight 3,266 kg (7,200 lb)
Max zero-fuel weight 2,676 kg (5,900 lb)
Max landing weight 3,107 kg (6,850 lb)
Max wing loading 215·9 kg/m² (44·2 lb/sq ft)
Max power loading 3·65 kg/kW (6 lb/shp)

PERFORMANCE (estimated, at max T-O weight, unless indicated):
Max level speed at 9,450 m (31,000 ft) over 347 knots (643 km/h; 400 mph)
Max cruising speed at 9,145 m (30,000 ft) 347 knots (643 km/h; 400 mph)
Econ cruising speed at 12,495 m (41,000 ft) 304 knots (563 km/h; 350 mph)
Stalling speed, flaps down, power off 78 knots (145 km/h; 90 mph)
Max rate of climb at S/L 1,082 m (3,550 ft)/min
Rate of climb at S/L, one engine out 579 m (1,900 ft)/min
Service ceiling 12,500 m (41,000 ft)
Service ceiling, one engine out 8,840 m (29,000 ft)
T-O run 762 m (2,500 ft)
Balanced field length 823 m (2,700 ft)
Balanced field length at 2,722 kg (6,000 lb) AUW 579 m (1,900 ft)
Landing from 15 m (50 ft), at max landing weight 701 m (2,300 ft)
Range at max cruising speed with max payload and max fuel, 45 min reserves 1,415 nm (2,620 km; 1,630 miles)
Range at econ cruising speed with max payload and max fuel, 45 min reserves 2,000 nm (3,700 km; 2,300 miles)

LOCKHEED
LOCKHEED CORPORATION

HEAD OFFICE: Burbank, California 91520
Telephone: (213) 847 6121
CHAIRMAN OF THE BOARD AND CHIEF EXECUTIVE: Roy A. Anderson
PRESIDENT AND CHIEF OPERATING OFFICER: L. O. Kitchen
DIRECTORS:
Roy A. Anderson
Michael Berberian
Edward W. Carter
Joseph P. Downer
Gilbert R. Ellis
Houston I. Flournoy
John T. Gurash
J. K. Horton
C. L. Johnson
L. O. Kitchen
Joseph R. Rensch
Leslie N. Shaw
John E. Swearingen
Fred M. Vinson Jr
CORPORATE SENIOR VICE-PRESIDENTS:
J. J. Catton (Business Development)
John E. Cavanagh (General Counsel)
E. M. Cortright (President, Lockheed-California Company)
Robert A. Fuhrman (President, Lockheed Missiles and Space Co Inc)
V. N. Marafino (Finance)
Robert B. Ormsby Jr (President, Lockheed-Georgia Company)
Thomas J. Raleigh (Human Resources)
W. B. Rieke (Group Vice-President, Lockheed Electronics Co Inc, Lockheed Petroleum Services Ltd, and Lockheed Shipbuilding and Construction Co)
R. L. Vader (President, Lockheed Aircraft Service Co)
W. R. Wilson (Strategic Planning)
CORPORATE VICE-PRESIDENTS:
F. A. Cleveland (Engineering)
R. F. Conley (International Marketing)
Richard K. Cook (Washington Area)
James Everington (Industrial Relations)
L. E. Frisbee (Vice-President and General Manager, Engineering and Operations, Lockheed-California Co)
M. H. Greene (Executive Vice-President, Administration, Lockheed Aircraft Service Co)
R. R. Heppe (Vice-President and General Manager, Government Programmes, Lockheed-California Co)
Dr H. Potter Kerfoot (Vice-President and General Manager, Research and Development Division of Lockheed Missiles and Space Co Inc)
A. H. Lorch (Executive Vice-President, Lockheed-Georgia Co)
R. R. McKirahan (Treasurer)
R. H. Northcutt, Jr (Controller)
Dr F. C. E. Oder (Vice-President and General Manager, Space Systems Division of Lockheed Missiles and Space Co Inc)
Thomas J. O'Hara (Contracts and Pricing)
W. D. Perreault Snr (Public Relations)
James W. Plummer (Executive Vice-President, Lockheed Missiles and Space Co Inc)
Ben R. Rich (Vice-President, Advanced Development Projects, Lockheed-California Co)
James J. Ryan (Secretary and Assistant General Counsel)
C. M. Schnepp (Executive Vice-President, Operations, Lockheed Aircraft Service Co)
William A. Stevenson (President, Lockheed Electronics Co Inc)
Dr D. A. Stuart (Vice-President and General Manager, Missile Systems Division, Lockheed Missiles and Space Co Inc)
R. W. Taylor (Vice-President and General Manager, Commercial Programmes, Lockheed-California Co)
J. G. Twomey (Chief Counsel)
G. G. Whipple (President, Lockheed Shipbuilding and Construction Co)

DIVISIONS:
Lockheed-California Company:
Burbank, California 91520
PRESIDENT: E. M. Cortright
Lockheed-Georgia Company:
Marietta, Georgia 30063
PRESIDENT: R. B. Ormsby Jr
Lockheed Aircraft Service Company:
Ontario, California 91761
PRESIDENT: Robert L. Vader

SUBSIDIARIES:
LOCKHEED AIR TERMINAL INC: Burbank, California 91505
PRESIDENT: D. M. Simmons
LOCKHEED ELECTRONICS COMPANY INC: Plainfield, New Jersey 07061
PRESIDENT: W. A. Stevenson
LOCKHEED MISSILES AND SPACE COMPANY INC: Sunnyvale, California 94088
PRESIDENT: Robert A. Fuhrman
LOCKHEED PETROLEUM SERVICES LTD:
New Westminster, British Columbia, Canada
PRESIDENT: Walter L. Weber
LOCKHEED SHIPBUILDING AND CONSTRUCTION COMPANY: Seattle, Washington 98134
PRESIDENT: G. G. Whipple
MURDOCK MACHINE & ENGINEERING CO OF TEXAS: Irving, Texas 75060
PRESIDENT: Paul R. Holmes

Built by the brothers Allan and Malcolm Lockheed, the first Lockheed aircraft, a tractor seaplane, first flew in 1913. Three years later the brothers established a company at Santa Barbara, California, to manufacture a twin-engined flying-boat, two seaplanes for the Navy and a small sport biplane that was a forerunner of the true streamlined aeroplane. Lockheed Aircraft Co, formed in 1926, moved to Burbank, California, in 1928 and was reorganised as Lockheed Aircraft Corporation in 1932.

On 30 November 1943, the Vega Aircraft Corporation, which had been formed in 1937 as an affiliate and in 1941 became a wholly-owned subsidiary of the Lockheed Aircraft Corporation, was absorbed and the name Vega abandoned. In September 1977 the title Lockheed Aircraft Corporation was changed to Lockheed Corporation, to reflect the company's diversified activities.

Lockheed's aircraft and missile activities are now handled by three separate companies, which were evolved from the former California, Georgia and Missiles and Space Divisions in the Summer of 1961.

The current products of the Lockheed-California and Lockheed-Georgia Companies are described hereafter under the individual company headings.

Lockheed has diversified into many fields of industry since 1959. Following the acquisition of Stavid Engineering Inc, it combined this company and its own Electronics and Avionics Division into Lockheed Electronics Company Inc.

Lockheed Air Terminal Inc (LAT), a wholly-owned subsidiary, operates and maintains the Hollywood-Burbank Airport, which now belongs to the cities of Burbank, Glendale and Pasadena, and provides fuelling and related services at 20 other locations in 11 states. Lockheed Aircraft Service Co (LAS) designs and manufactures products for the aerospace and marine industries, and Lockheed International Company provides international marketing services to all other Lockheed units; it coordinates efforts outside of the USA, and assists the development of new international marketing opportunities.

Since April 1959 Lockheed has also had an interest in shipbuilding and heavy construction, following its purchase of the Puget Sound Bridge and Dry Dock Company (now Lockheed Shipbuilding and Construction Co).

LOCKHEED-CALIFORNIA COMPANY

Burbank, California 91520

Lockheed-California has responsibility for production of the land-based P-3 Orion, CP-140 Aurora, developed from the P-3, L-1011 TriStar three-turbofan transport and a new high-altitude tactical surveillance and reconnaissance aircraft designated TR-1. This is a variant of the U-2R, which may itself go back into production to meet the USAF's PLSS programme requirements.

LOCKHEED F-104 STARFIGHTER

The Starfighter continues in production, under licence, by Aeritalia of Italy (which see).

LOCKHEED 'PROJECT STEALTH'

In the so-called 'Skunk Works' at Burbank, Lockheed-California is reported to be building, under an ARPA-funded contract from the USAF's Flight Dynamics Laboratory, a single-seat reconnaissance/strike aircraft, of which a primary feature is low radar, infra-red and optical signatures. The aircraft is said to be powered by two 53·4 kN (12,000 lb st) turbojet engines, and is believed to have flown for the first time in 1977.

Lockheed P-3C Orion production aircraft with Update II avionics *(see page 370)*

LOCKHEED U-2 and TR-1

Development of the U-2 began in the Spring of 1954 to meet a joint CIA/USAF requirement for a high-altitude strategic reconnaissance and special-purpose research aircraft. It took place in the Lockheed 'Skunk Works' at Burbank, California, where, after acceptance of the design in late 1954, two prototypes were hand-built in great secrecy by a small team of engineers. The aircraft's true purpose was cloaked under the USAF U-for-Utility designation U-2, and the first flight, by Lockheed test pilot Tony LeVier, took place on or about 1 August 1955 at Watertown Strip in the Nevada desert.

The configuration of the U-2 is basically that of a powered sailplane, which explains its unusual 'bicycle' landing gear, combined with underwing balancer units which provide stability during take-off and are then jettisoned. Range can, if necessary, be extended by shutting off the engine and gliding. Because of its configuration the U-2 requires unusually precise handling during take-off and landing—particularly the latter, since there is an

Lockheed U-2C electronic intelligence aircraft

U-2CT dual-control conversion trainer

extremely small margin between approach speed and stalling speed. After touchdown, the aircraft comes to rest on one of the down-turned wingtips, which serve as landing skids.

Initial quantities of 48 single-seat and five two-seat U-2s were ordered in FY 1956, but after about 30 of these had been completed the increasing weight of special equipment which the aircraft was required to carry had degraded performance to such an extent that a more powerful engine became necessary, and this was installed from 1959 onwards. At the same time a substantial increase in fuel capacity made possible a considerably greater range. In FY 1968 the U-2 was put back into production, to replace some of the two dozen or more aircraft lost over hostile territory or in accidents, and the production line is now to be reopened again to manufacture a new, tactical reconnaissance version, the TR-1.

In service, the U-2 was flown at first by CIA pilots, ostensibly in USAF units known as the 1st, 2nd and 3rd Weather Reconnaissance Squadrons (Provisional). These were based initially at Lakenheath in England, Adana in Turkey, and Edwards AFB, California, with detachments respectively in Germany, Pakistan and Okinawa. From here, and from bases in Cyprus, the south-west Pacific, Alaska and elsewhere, they were employed for photographic and electronic intelligence (elint) overflights of Eastern Europe, the USSR, the Middle East, China, Cuba and other sensitive areas. These operations, which began in January 1956, were 'blown' when a U-2B flown by Lt Francis Gary Powers was brought down near Sverdlovsk in the Soviet Union on 1 May 1960, during an overflight from Peshawar, Pakistan, to Bodö, Norway.

Deliveries to already-established USAF units began in early 1957, these including the 4028th and 4080th Strategic Reconnaissance Squadrons of Strategic Air Command, and Air Research and Development Command. In addition to their strategic reconnaissance role, they carried out much valuable high-altitude research work, including the monitoring of radioactivity levels in the atmosphere. Two-seat U-2Ds of the 6512th Test Squadron, USAF Systems Command, were also used for atmospheric sampling, for development of equipment for the Midas and Samos satellites, and to track and assist recovery of Discoverer spacecraft. At least six U-2s were transferred from the USAF to the Chinese Nationalist Air Force in the 1960s, most or all of which were subsequently lost.

From 1964, US Air Force U-2s began to operate from Bien Hoa in Viet-Nam, and later from detached bases at Osan, South Korea, and U-Tapao, Thailand. Overflights of mainland China, which had been made from bases in Taiwan, were halted after a Sino-American agreement in 1974, and the U-2s concerned were recalled to the USA. It is often (and wrongly) stated that the Lockheed SR-71 was a 'U-2 replacement', but such is not the case. In 1976 the 349th (formerly the 4080th) Strategic Reconnaissance Squadron was transferred to Beale AFB, California, and redesignated the 99th SRS. It shares this base with the 1st SRS, which flies the SR-71, the two units forming the 9th Strategic Reconnaissance Wing and illustrating that the two types are complementary. In recent years SAC U-2s have, in addition to their usual duties, flown photo-reconnaissance missions on behalf of the US Ministry of Agriculture, Society of Engineers and other agencies, and have been employed to monitor hurricanes, earthquakes and other natural disasters.

The other major operator of the U-2 has been the National Aeronautics and Space Administration and its predecessor, NACA. The first aircraft to appear in NASA markings was NASA 55741, which was shown to the press in June 1960, a month after the Powers incident. It has been suggested that this untypical registration may have been an attempt to disguise a USAF serial number, 55-5741, presumably indicating a prototype aircraft. At least four other U-2s have been operated by NASA (NASA 320,432,708 and 709), the last two of these being of the U-2C version. Work undertaken for NASA has been extensive and varied, and has included flights over ecological test areas, in support of various Earth resources programmes; investigations into clear air turbulence (HI-CAT programme); a NASA/USAF high-altitude atmospheric sampling programme (HASP); and observations in astronomy, atmospheric physics, and geophysics. One NASA U-2, fitted with a microwave radio-meter, was due to undertake a series of flights from Jorge Chavez Airport near Lima, Peru, in Spring 1979, in a programme to measure the speed at which the Earth travels through space.

In view of the continuing classified nature of much of its work, it is not possible to confirm officially many details concerning the U-2; but the list of variants and general description which follow are believed to be substantially correct. It should also be noted that there have been numerous conversions between one model and another during the aircraft's operational career, and that there may be differences between individual aircraft of the same model.

U-2A. Single-seat initial production version, powered by a 49·8 kN (11,200 lb st) Pratt & Whitney J57-P-37A turbojet engine with special wide-chord compressor blades for flight at very high altitudes. Approximately 30 built, of which most later converted to U-2B, others to WU-2A and U-2D. Deliveries to 1st, 2nd and 3rd Weather Reconnaissance Squadrons (Provisional) began in January 1956, and to 4028th and 4080th Strategic Reconnaissance Squadrons in early 1957.

WU-2A. Designation of small number of U-2As converted for atmospheric research. Bulged fairing on underside of fuselage, below air intakes. Used for weather reconnaissance flights over Europe, Turkey, Japan, Australia, the USA and Argentina. Took part in HI-CAT and HASP programmes, and in radioactivity sampling on behalf of SAC.

U-2B. Single-seat improved version of U-2A with strengthened airframe, more powerful J75 engine, and fully 'wet' wing. Total of 48 U-2A/Bs ordered (USAF serial numbers 56-6675 to 56-6722); from 1959 the last 18 (approx) of these, and most existing U-2As, were completed or re-engined to U-2B standard. Two supplied to Chinese Nationalist Air Force in July 1960, and at least four others later.

U-2C. Single-seat electronic intelligence (elint) version, converted from U-2B in early/middle 1960s and having similar performance. Bulged air intakes, and long dorsal spine fairing containing various additional avionics and other equipment. Two (NASA 708 and 709) delivered to NASA in April 1971 and used, *inter alia,* for Earth resources monitoring on behalf of Ames Research Center.

WU-2C. Original designation of U-2R (which see).

U-2CT. Two-seat dual-control conversion trainer, with elevated rear cockpit for instructor. Dorsal spine fairing and bulged intakes, as U-2C. Two examples known, one converted from U-2C and one from U-2D. On training flights, underwing balancer wheels are not jettisoned, to facilitate landings.

U-2D. Tandem two-seat development of U-2B for training and special duties, first displayed publicly at Wright-Patterson AFB in mid-1961. Five production aircraft (serials 56-6951 to 56-6955) built as U-2D; others converted from earlier models. Twin fairings above fuselage, one between cockpits and one above second cockpit, house antennae for infra-red, radioactivity or other sensors; these fairings vary in shape between individual aircraft.

U-2EPX. Proposed ocean surveillance version for US Navy (EPX = electronics patrol experimental). Two aircraft, converted to carry AN/APS-116 radar similar to that in Lockheed S-3A Viking, test-flown by Lockheed in 1973 to evaluate use of U-2 as an airborne relay aircraft for surveillance data. Not adopted by USN.

U-2R. Additional batch of 12 single-seat aircraft, ordered for strategic reconnaissance in FY 1968, by which time approx half of original U-2s had been lost through various causes. Serial numbers 68-10329 to 68-10340. Originally designated WU-2C. Bulged intakes, as on U-2C, but longer nose and fuselage, without dorsal spine fairing: increased wing span and internal fuel capacity: rear fuselage slightly bulged on top, just forward of fin; mainwheel unit further aft, tailwheel unit further forward, than on earlier models. Non-US bases have included Mildenhall, England. The U-2R has been selected as the preferred airborne relay vehicle for the Lockheed PLSS (Precision Location Strike System), intended to locate and identify enemy radar emitters, and to direct strike aircraft against them.

TR-1. Tactical reconnaissance version, described officially by the Department of Defense as "to be equipped with a variety of electronic sensors to provide continuously available, day or night, all-weather surveillance of the battle area in direct support of the US and Allied ground and air forces during peace, crises, and war situations". Tooling for the U-2 has been kept in store at the USAF-owned Plant 42 at Palmdale, California, and the FY 1979 defence budget included $10·2 million to reopen the production line in FY 1980. It is understood that the TR-1 will be based on the U-2R, still with the J75-P-13 engine, but with the significant addition of an 'advanced synthetic aperture' radar system (ASARS) in the form of a UPD-X side-looking airborne radar (SLAR) and modern electronic countermeasures (ECM). Seen as a replacement for the now-abandoned Compass Cope RPV (see 1977-78 *Jane's*), the TR-1 is intended primarily for use in Europe, where its SLAR will provide the capability to 'see' approximately 30 nm (55 km; 35 miles) into hostile territory without the need to overfly an actual or potential battle area. An initial $10·2 million was included in the FY 1979 budget for airframe and engine development. A further $43 million was requested by the USAF in FY 1980 for 25 TR-1s. The first two of these will be two-seat **TR-1Bs**, for training.

The following description applies primarily to the single-seat U-2B, C, and R versions, except where indicated otherwise:

TYPE: High-altitude reconnaissance and research aircraft.

WINGS: Cantilever mid-wing monoplane, with wingtips turned down 90° for use as skids during landing. All-metal structure. Trailing-edge flaps occupy approx 60% of each half-span, with ailerons outboard. Small tubular fairing between each flap and aileron: on U-2C/CT/R these are larger and project beyond trailing-edge. Small plate-type spoiler forward of outer portion of each flap. Some aircraft fitted with trim tab on each aileron.

FUSELAGE: All-metal semi-monocoque structure of circular cross-section, with thin-gauge skin. Fineness ratio approx 10:1. Forward-opening door-type airbrake on each side of fuselage aft of wings, used mainly as a landing aid. Large airscoop fairing on fuselage beneath rear of wing root: generally on starboard side, but some-

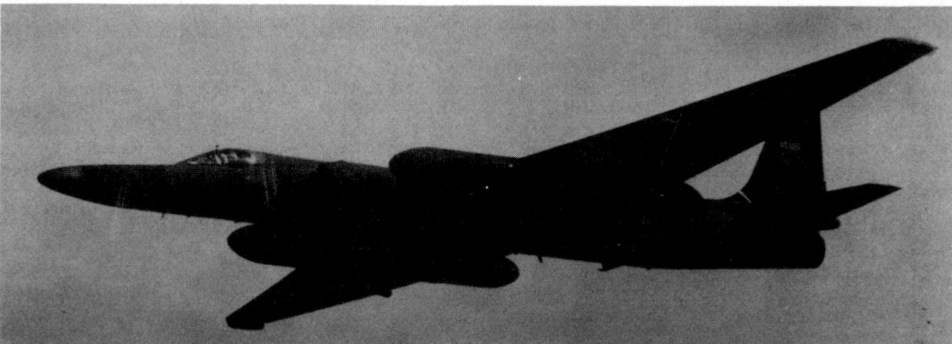

The new Lockheed TR-1 will resemble closely the U-2R high-altitude strategic reconnaissance aircraft shown here

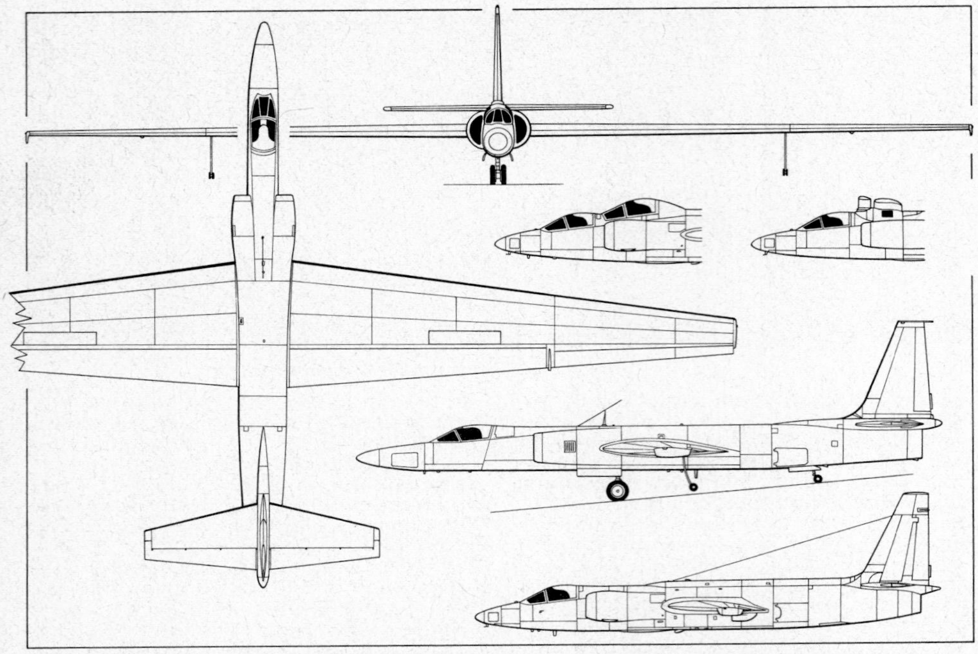

Lockheed U-2R, with additional side view of the U-2C (bottom) and scrap views of the U-2CT (top left) and U-2D (top right) *(Michael A. Badrocke)*

times on port side and sometimes on both. Since about 1974 some aircraft have had a modified tailpipe, to reduce the infra-red signature from the engine.

TAIL UNIT: Cantilever all-metal structure. Trim tab on rudder and in each elevator. Ventral fin under fuselage of U-2A and WU-2A, immediately aft of wings.

LANDING GEAR: Retractable bicycle type, with twin main wheels and twin small tailwheels in tandem, each unit retracting forward into fuselage. Balancer units under outer wings, each with twin small wheels, are jettisoned on take-off (except on U-2CT). Tailwheels and underwing wheels have solid tyres; castoring tailwheel unit aids manoeuvring on ground. Brakes on main wheels. Braking parachute in container under rudder.

POWER PLANT (except U-2A): One 75·6 kN (17,000 lb st) Pratt & Whitney J75-P-13 turbojet engine. Normal internal fuel capacity 2,970 litres (785 US gallons) in U-2A, approx 4,315 litres (1,140 US gallons) in U-2B, approx 4,448 litres (1,175 US gallons) in U-2C. Provision for two 397·5 litre (105 US gallon) non-jettisonable auxiliary slipper tanks on wing leading-edges; these were designed originally to extend range of U-2A, but may be seen on other models.

ACCOMMODATION: Pilot only in U-2A/B/C/R, on ejection seat (except in early U-2As before 1957). Rearward-sliding transparent canopy, protected internally against ultra-violet radiation. Accommodation is not pressurised. Tandem ejection seats and dual controls in U-2CT and U-2D, the rear cockpit in the U-2CT being 'stepped' above the upper line of the fuselage. Rearview periscope on most aircraft (positions vary).

AVIONICS AND EQUIPMENT: Typical standard avionics in U-2B include Magnavox ARC-34 UHF com, Tacan, ILS, Lear A-10 autopilot, Bendix ARN-6 ADF, MA-1 compass, and (for night flying) astro-compass. Equipment includes one vertical and two lateral cameras for training flights, or up to five 70 mm cameras (U-2) or side-looking airborne radar (TR-1) for operational missions. Panoramic camera(s) originally of Land Polaroid type, but more usually Model 73B or Perkin-Elmer Model 501 in U-2B, with ventral periscopic sight. The U-2B shot down over Sverdlovsk on 1 May 1960 reportedly carried also an electromagnetic receiver for monitoring and recording radio and radar transmissions from the ground, made by Huggins Laboratories, Hewlett-Packard and Raytheon.

DIMENSIONS, EXTERNAL:
Wing span: except U-2R — 24·38 m (80 ft 0 in)
U-2R — 31·39 m (103 ft 0 in)
Wing area, net: except U-2R — 52·49 m² (565 sq ft)
Wing aspect ratio — approx 10·2
Length overall: except U-2R — 15·11 m (49 ft 7 in)
U-2R — 19·20 m (63 ft 0 in)
Height overall: except U-2R — 3·96 m (13 ft 0 in)
U-2R — 4·88 m (16 ft 0 in)
Wheel track (c/l of wing balancer units):
except U-2R — approx 15·24 m (50 ft 0 in)
Wheelbase: except U-2R — approx 6·10 m (20 ft 0 in)

WEIGHTS:
Weight empty, without equipment:
U-2C — 6,259 kg (13,800 lb)
Fuel and equipment payload:
U-2B — approx 1,360 kg (3,000 lb)
U-2R — approx 5,443 kg (12,000 lb)
T-O weight without slipper tanks:
U-2A — 7,189 kg (15,850 lb)
Max T-O weight with slipper tanks:
U-2A — 7,833 kg (17,270 lb)
U-2B/C — 9,003 kg (19,850 lb)
U-2R — 13,154 kg (29,000 lb)

PERFORMANCE (estimated for TR-1):
Max level speed:
U-2A at approx 18,290 m (60,000 ft) — 429 knots (795 km/h; 494 mph)
U-2B/C at 19,810 m (65,000 ft) — 458 knots (850 km/h; 528 mph)
TR-1 at 18,290 m (60,000 ft) — 373 knots (692 km/h; 430 mph)
U-2C at low altitude — 174 knots (320 km/h; 200 mph)
Max cruising speed: U-2A at approx 18,290 m (60,000 ft) — 399 knots (741 km/h; 460 mph)
Max rate of climb at S/L:
U-2C — more than 3,000 m (9,845 ft)/min
Time to 21,330 m (70,000 ft), with fuel for 6 h 30 min mission: U-2C — 18 min
Operational ceiling: U-2A — 21,330 m (70,000 ft)
U-2B/C — 25,900 m (85,000 ft)
TR-1 — 27,430 m (90,000 ft)
T-O run: U-2C — 240 m (787 ft)
Range without slipper tanks, 378·5 litres (100 US gallons) reserves:
U-2A — 1,910 nm (3,540 km; 2,200 miles)
Range with slipper tanks:
U-2A, 378·5 litres (100 US gallons) reserves — 2,260 nm (4,185 km; 2,600 miles)
U-2B/C approx — 3,475 nm (6,435 km; 4,000 miles)
Max range: TR-1 — more than 2,605 nm (4,830 km; 3,000 miles)
Max endurance: U-2C, U-2R, TR-1 — 12 h

LOCKHEED MODEL 185/285 ORION

US Navy designation: P-3
CAF designation: CP-140 Aurora

In April 1958 it was announced that Lockheed had been successful in winning with a developed version of the civil Electra four-turboprop airliner a US Navy competition for an 'off-the-shelf' ASW aircraft. The two original contracts provided for initial research, development and pre-production activities; further contracts provided for purchase by the Navy of a standard commercial Electra and its modification, development and testing as a tactical testbed for anti-submarine warfare systems.

An aerodynamic prototype, produced by modifying the airframe of the third civil Electra, flew for the first time on 19 August 1958. A second aircraft, designated YP-3A (formerly YP3V-1), with full electronics, flew on 25 November 1959.

Details of the P-3A (retired from operational use by active-duty USN patrol squadrons on 13 November 1978) and WP-3A can be found in the 1978-79 *Jane's*. Subsequent production versions are as follows:

P-3B. Follow-on production version with 3,661 kW (4,910 ehp) Allison T56-A-14 turboprop engines, which do not need water-alcohol injection. USN contracts covered 124 P-3Bs. In addition, five P-3Bs were delivered to the Royal New Zealand Air Force in 1966, ten to the Royal Australian Air Force during 1968 and five to Norway in the Spring of 1969. USN P-3Bs were modified retrospectively to carry Bullpup missiles. Others became **EP-3Bs.** The US Navy and Lear Siegler developed in 1976 a modification kit for retrofitting to P-3B aircraft. This includes a 32K Rom computer, ASN-84 inertial navigation system, Omega, ASA-66 displays and ASN-124 navigation controller, together with the necessary controls and equipment to integrate the new and existing systems. Kits have been made available for the above installation.

P-3C. Advanced version with the A-NEW system of sensors and control equipment, built around a Univac digital computer that integrates all ASW information and permits retrieval, display and transmission of tactical data in order to eliminate routine log-keeping functions. This increases crew effectiveness by allowing them sufficient time to consider all tactical data and devise the best action to resolve problems. First flight of this version was made on 18 September 1968 and the P-3C entered service in 1969. A total of 143 of this version had been delivered to the US Navy by early 1978.

Under a programme designated **P-3C Update**, new avionics, and electronics software, were developed to enhance the effectiveness of this aircraft. Equipment includes a magnetic drum that gives a sevenfold increase in computer memory capacity, a new versatile computer language, Omega navigation system, improved acoustic processing sensitivity, a tactical display for two of the sensor stations, and an improved magnetic tape transport. A prototype with this equipment was handed over to the US Navy on 29 April 1974, and the first production aircraft was delivered in January 1975. All subsequent production aircraft for the US Navy have this equipment.

Ten P-3Cs with Update modifications were ordered for the Royal Australian Air Force, for delivery in 1978-79 for service with No. 10 Squadron. Japan has ordered 45 P-3Cs, of which four will be assembled and 38 licence-built in Japan by Kawasaki (which see).

The US Navy and Lockheed continued in 1976 with a further electronics improvement programme for the P-3C. Known as **Update II**, this added an infra-red detection system (IRDS) and a sonobuoy reference system (SRS). The Harpoon missile and control system are included in Update II, which was incorporated into production aircraft from August 1977. The first Update II P-3C was delivered to the Naval Air Development Center in that same month. The Royal Netherlands Navy has ordered 13 P-3Cs, and these will have Update II equipment. The first is scheduled for delivery in late 1981.

Update III, of which development began in February 1978, chiefly involves ASW avionics, including a new acoustic processor to analyse signals picked up from the

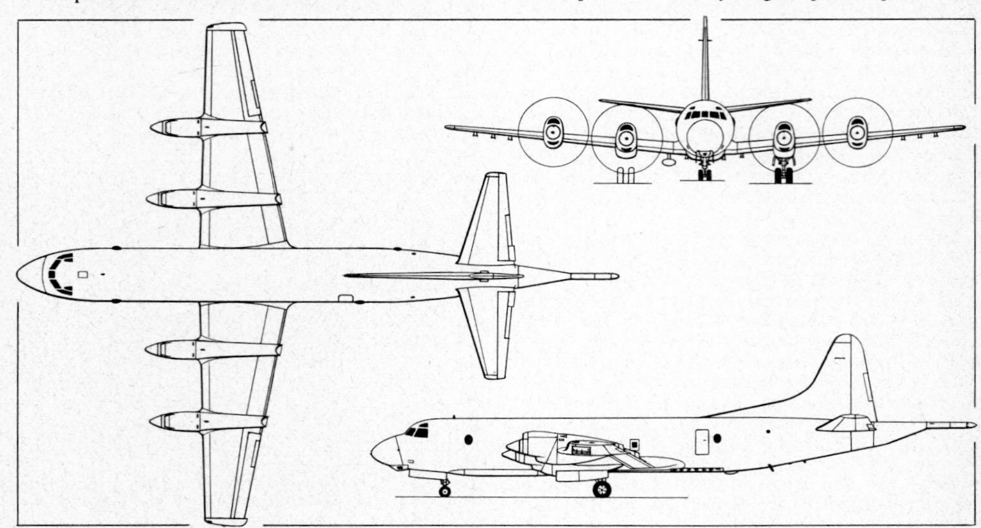

Lockheed P-3C Orion four-turboprop anti-submarine aircraft *(Pilot Press)*

sea, a new sonobuoy receiver which replaces DIFAR, an improved APU, and environmental controls to cater for increased heat from the avionics and to further improve crew comfort. A prototype Update III P-3C is scheduled for delivery in March 1980, with full production from the following September.

Two of the eight international records for turboprop aircraft set up in a P-3C by Cdr Donald H. Lilienthal, in early 1971, had not been beaten by mid-1979. They were a speed of 434·97 knots (806·10 km/h; 500·89 mph) over a 15/25 km course; and a time-to-height record, to 12,000 m in 19 min 42·24 s.

RP-3D. One P-3C was reconfigured during manufacture for a five-year mission to map the Earth's magnetic field, under Project Magnet, controlled by the US Naval Oceanographic Office. Crew of 17. Range increased to more than 5,000 nm (9,265 km; 5,755 miles) by installation of 4,545 litre (1,200 US gallon) fuel tank in weapons bay. Details of other changes in 1977-78 *Jane's*. Operated by US Navy's Oceanographic Development Squadron 8 (VXN-8) based at the Naval Air Test Center, Patuxent River, Maryland. On 4 November 1972, Cdr Philip R. Hite used it to set up an international closed-circuit distance record for turboprop aircraft, covering 5,451·97 nm (10,103·51 km; 6,278·03 miles).

WP-3D. Two aircraft equipped as airborne research centres, ordered by the US National Oceanic and Atmospheric Administration. Equipped to carry out atmospheric research and weather modification experiments. Pitot static boom on port wingtip; gust probe on fuselage; C-band range heading indicator (RHI) dish antenna in belly radome; and X-band antenna in radome at tail. These aircraft became operational during the Summer of 1976.

EP-3E. Ten P-3As and two EP-3Bs were converted to EP-3E configuration to replace Lockheed EC-121s in service with VQ-1 and VQ-2 squadrons. Identified by large canoe radars on upper and lower surfaces of fuselage and ventral radome forward of wing.

P-3F. Six aircraft, similar to the US Navy's P-3Cs, for the Imperial Iranian Air Force. Used initially for long-range surface surveillance and subsequently also for ASW missions. Delivery completed in January 1975.

CP-140 Aurora. Version for Canadian Armed Forces. Described separately.

By the beginning of 1979 Lockheed-California had delivered 483 P-3s of all versions. The following data refer to the P-3C, but are generally applicable to other versions, except for the details noted:

TYPE: Four-turboprop ASW aircraft.

WINGS: Cantilever low-wing monoplane. Wing section NACA 0014 (modified) at root, NACA 0012 (modified) at tip. Dihedral 6°. Incidence 3° at root, 0° 30' at tip. Fail-safe box beam structure of extruded integrally-stiffened aluminium alloy. Lockheed-Fowler trailing-edge flaps. Hydraulically-boosted aluminium ailerons. Anti-icing by engine bleed air ducted into leading-edges.

FUSELAGE: Conventional aluminium alloy semi-monocoque fail-safe structure.

TAIL UNIT: Cantilever aluminium alloy structure with dihedral tailplane and dorsal fin. Fixed-incidence tailplane. Hydraulically-boosted rudder and elevators. Leading-edges of fin and tailplane have electric anti-icing system.

LANDING GEAR: Hydraulically-retractable tricycle type, with twin wheels on each unit. All units retract forward, main wheels into inner engine nacelles. Oleo-pneumatic shock-absorbers. Main wheels have size 40-14 type VII 26-ply tubeless tyres. Nosewheels have size 28-7·7 type VII tubeless tyres. Hydraulic brakes. No anti-skid units.

POWER PLANT: Four 3,661 kW (4,910 ehp) Allison T56-A-14 turboprop engines, each driving a Hamilton Standard 54H60 four-blade constant-speed propeller. Fuel in one tank in fuselage and four wing integral tanks, with total usable capacity of 34,826 litres (9,200 US gallons). Four overwing gravity fuelling points and central pressure refuelling point. Oil capacity (min usable) 111 litres (29·4 US gallons) in four tanks. Electrically de-iced propeller spinners.

ACCOMMODATION: Normal ten-man crew. Flight deck has wide-vision windows, and circular windows for observers are provided fore and aft in the main cabin, each bulged to give 180° view. Main cabin is fitted out as a five-man tactical compartment containing advanced electronic, magnetic and sonic detection equipment, an all-electric galley and large crew rest area.

SYSTEMS: Air-conditioning and pressurisation system supplied by two engine-driven compressors. Pressure differential 0·37 bars (5·4 lb/sq in). Hydraulic system, pressure 207 bars (3,000 lb/sq in), for flaps, control surface boosters, landing gear actuation, brakes and bomb bay doors. Pneumatic system, pressure 207/83 bars (3,000/1,200 lb/sq in), for ASW store launchers (P-3A/B only). Electrical system utilises three 60kVA generators for 120/208V 400Hz AC supply. 24V DC supply. Integral APU with 60kVA generator for ground air-conditioning and electrical supply and engine starting.

AVIONICS AND EQUIPMENT: The ASQ-114 general-purpose digital computer is the heart of the P-3C system. Together with the AYA-8 data processing equipment and computer-controlled display systems, it permits rapid analysis and utilisation of electronic, magnetic and sonic data. Nav/com system comprises two ASN-84 inertial navigation systems, with latitude and longitude indicators; APN-187 Doppler; ARN-81 Loran A and C; ARN-84 Tacan; two ARN-87 VOR receivers; ARN-32 marker beacon receiver; ARN-83 LF-ADF; ARA-50 UHF direction finder; AJN-15 flight director indicator for tactical directions; HSI for long-range flight directions; glideslope indicator; on-top position indicator; two ARC-161 HF transceivers; two ARC-143 UHF transceivers; ARC-101 VHF receiver/transmitter; AGC-6 teletype and high-speed printer; HF and UHF secure communication units; ACQ-5 data link communication set and AIC-22 interphone set; APX-72 IFF transponder and APX-76 SIF interrogator. Electronic computer-controlled display equipment includes ASA-70 tactical display; ASA-66 pilot's display; ASA-70 radar display and two auxiliary readout (computer-stored data) displays. ASW equipment includes two ARR-72 sono receivers; two AQA-7 DIFAR sonobuoy indicator sets; hyperbolic fix unit; acoustic source signal generator; time code generator and AQH-4(V) sonar tape recorder; ASQ-81 magnetic anomaly detector; ASA-64 submarine anomaly detector; ASA-65 magnetic compensator; ALQ-78 electronic countermeasures set; APS-115 radar set (360° coverage); ASA-69 radar scan converter; KA-74 forward computer-assisted camera; KB-18A automatic strike assessment camera with horizon-to-horizon coverage; RO-308 bathythermograph recorder. Additional equipment includes APN-141(V) radar altimeter; two APQ-107 radar altimeter warning systems; A/A24G-9 true airspeed computer and ASW-31 automatic flight control system. P-3Cs delivered from 1975 have the avionics/electronics package updated by addition of an extra 393K memory drum and fourth logic unit, Omega navigation, new magnetic tape transport, and an ASA-66 tactical display for the sonar operators. To accommodate the new systems a new operational software computer programme will be written in CMS-2 language. Marconi Avionics AQS-901 acoustic signal processing and display system in RAAF P-3Cs.

ARMAMENT: Bomb bay, 2·03 m wide, 0·88 m deep and 3·91 m long (80 in × 34·5 in × 154 in), forward of wing, can accommodate a 2,000 lb MK 25/39/55/56 mine, three 1,000 lb MK 36/52 mines, three MK 57 depth bombs, eight MK 54 depth bombs, eight MK 43/44/46 torpedoes or a combination of two MK 101 nuclear depth bombs and four MK 43/44/46 torpedoes. Ten under-wing pylons for stores: two under centre-section each side can carry torpedoes or 2,000 lb mines; three under outer wing each side can carry respectively (inboard to outboard) a torpedo or 2,000 lb mine (or searchlight on starboard wing), a torpedo or 1,000 lb mine or rockets singly or in pods; a torpedo or 500 lb mine or rockets singly or in pods. Torpedoes can be carried underwing only for ferrying; mines can be carried and released. Search stores, such as sonobuoys and sound signals, are launched from inside cabin area in the P-3A/B. In the P-3C sonobuoys are loaded and launched externally and internally. Max total weapon load includes six 2,000 lb mines under wings and a 3,290 kg (7,252 lb) internal load made up of two MK 101 depth bombs, four MK 44 torpedoes, pyrotechnic pistol and 12 signals, 87 sonobuoys, 100 MK 50 underwater sound signals (P-3A/B), 18 MK 3A marine markers (P-3A/B), 42 MK 7 marine markers, two B.T. buoys, and two MK 5 parachute flares. Sonobuoys are ejected from P-3C aircraft with explosive cartridge actuating devices (CAD), eliminating the need for a pneumatic system. Australian P-3Cs use BARRA sonobuoys.

DIMENSIONS, EXTERNAL:

Wing span	30·37 m (99 ft 8 in)
Wing chord at root	5·77 m (18 ft 11 in)
Wing chord at tip	2·31 m (7 ft 7 in)
Wing aspect ratio	7·5
Length overall	35·61 m (116 ft 10 in)
Height overall	10·29 m (33 ft 8½ in)
Fuselage diameter	3·45 m (11 ft 4 in)
Tailplane span	13·06 m (42 ft 10 in)
Wheel track (c/l shock-absorbers)	9·50 m (31 ft 2 in)
Wheelbase	9·07 m (29 ft 9 in)
Propeller diameter	4·11 m (13 ft 6 in)
Cabin door: Height	1·83 m (6 ft 0 in)
Width	0·69 m (2 ft 3 in)

DIMENSIONS, INTERNAL:

Cabin, excl flight deck and electrical load centre:

Length	21·06 m (69 ft 1 in)
Max width	3·30 m (10 ft 10 in)
Max height	2·29 m (7 ft 6 in)
Floor area	61·13 m² (658 sq ft)
Volume	120·6 m³ (4,260 cu ft)

AREAS:

Wings, gross	120·77 m² (1,300 sq ft)
Ailerons (total)	8·36 m² (90 sq ft)
Trailing-edge flaps (total)	19·32 m² (208 sq ft)
Fin, incl dorsal fin	10·78 m² (116 sq ft)
Rudder, incl tab	5·57 m² (60 sq ft)
Tailplane	22·39 m² (241 sq ft)
Elevators, incl tabs	7·53 m² (81 sq ft)

WEIGHTS (P-3B/C):

Weight empty	27,890 kg (61,491 lb)
Max expendable load	9,071 kg (20,000 lb)
Max normal T-O weight	61,235 kg (135,000 lb)
Max permissible weight	64,410 kg (142,000 lb)
Design zero-fuel weight	35,017 kg (77,200 lb)
Max landing weight	47,119 kg (103,880 lb)

PERFORMANCE (P-3B/C, at max T-O weight, except where indicated otherwise):

Max level speed at 4,570 m (15,000 ft) at AUW of 47,625 kg (105,000 lb)
411 knots (761 km/h; 473 mph)

Econ cruising speed at 7,620 m (25,000 ft) at AUW of 49,895 kg (110,000 lb)
328 knots (608 km/h; 378 mph)

Patrol speed at 457 m (1,500 ft) at AUW of 49,895 kg (110,000 lb) 206 knots (381 km/h; 237 mph)

Stalling speed, flaps up
133 knots (248 km/h; 154 mph)

Stalling speed, flaps down
112 knots (208 km/h; 129 mph)

Max rate of climb at 457 m (1,500 ft)
594 m (1,950 ft)/min

Service ceiling	8,625 m (28,300 ft)
Service ceiling, one engine out	5,790 m (19,000 ft)
T-O run	1,290 m (4,240 ft)
T-O to 15 m (50 ft)	1,673 m (5,490 ft)

Landing from 15 m (50 ft) at design landing weight
845 m (2,770 ft)

Max mission radius (no time on station) at 61,235 kg (135,000 lb) 2,070 nm (3,835 km; 2,383 miles)

Mission radius (3 h on station at 457 m; 1,500 ft)
1,346 nm (2,494 km; 1,550 miles)

LOCKHEED CP-140 AURORA

The purchase of 18 special variants of the Lockheed P-3 Orion maritime patrol aircraft for the Canadian Armed Forces was announced on 21 July 1976. This marked the terminal phase of a procurement programme that originated in 1972, when Air Specification 15-14 defined the Canadian government's requirements for a Long-Range Patrol Aircraft (LRPA) to replace the CP-107 Argus maritime reconnaissance aircraft serving currently with the CAF.

Designated subsequently as the CP-140 Aurora, this new aircraft combines the P-3 Orion's airframe, power plant and basic aircraft systems with the avionics systems and data processing capability of the US Navy's carrier-based Lockheed S-3A Viking. It is able to perform missions involving a range of more than 4,000 nm (7,400 km; 4,600 miles), or flights of up to 17 hours' duration, and will be deployed initially for ASW duties; national sovereignty patrols; shipping, fisheries and Arctic surveillance; ice reconnaissance; and search and rescue. By the addition of a weapons bay sensors canister at a later date, the CP-140 will be able to undertake additional civilian tasks such as resources location, pollution control and aerial survey.

The cabin interior of the P-3C has been changed extensively to meet Canadian requirements: immediately aft of the flight deck are an observer's station on the port side and crew rest bunks on the starboard side. Moving aft, the tactical compartment comes next, with accommodation for the Tactical Navigator (TACNAV), Navigator/Communicator (NAVCOM), two Acoustic Sensor Operators (ASO), and two Non-Acoustic Sensor Operators (NASO), all on the port side. Aft of the tactical compartment is the search stores and camera bay, with two more observer stations, one on each side. At the rear of the cabin are a galley, on the port side, a dinette area, and an airborne maintenance station on the starboard side. A toilet is located on the port side of the cabin, immediately aft of the forward observer's position.

On the flight deck, an ASA-82 Multi-Purpose Display (MPD) provides the pilots with a real-time presentation of the tactical situation and sensor information; directions from the TACNAV and NAVCOM are fed through the computer for display on both the MPD and the Flight Director Indicators (FDIs). Cues and alerts, indicating required sequences of action, are displayed on the periphery of the MPD.

An AJN-15 Flight Director system supplies attitude, heading and fly-to-point references. For long-range navigation, data from the Horizontal Situation Indicator are normally adequate. For precise, close-in tactical manoeuvring the FDI is used, and the automatic flight control system includes full-time attitude control and proportional control-wheel steering.

The three observer stations each have a fully-swivelling seat and are provided with intercom. Each of the observation windows gives full hemispherical view, and there are power and storage provisions for a hand-held camera. Each position is provided with isolation curtains, to screen observer and window from cabin lighting during night visual search. A fourth station can be made available on the starboard side, by removal of the crew rest bunks.

The TACNAV has a console which includes an ASA-82 MPD, an ASQ-147 keyset and trackball, and armament controls. With his keyset the TACNAV can control, via the computer, the Sonobuoy Reference System (SRS), and can call up and display FLIR and other radar data on

The first CP-140 Aurora version of the Lockheed Orion for the Canadian Armed Forces, bearing a US civil registration during its early test flying

his MPD. The NAVCOM also has an ASA-82 and ASQ-147, plus HF, VHF (FM) and UHF transceivers; inertial, VLF (Omega) and Doppler navigation sets; LF and UHF ADF, and VHF homer; a high-speed teleprinter and teletype keyboard; provisions for Tactical Satellite Communications (TACSATCOM); data link; control of reconnaissance photography; provisions for control of survey photography; and provisions for secure communications. The NAVCOM's MPD and keyset serve as a backup for the TACNAV in the event of equipment failure.

The two ASOs share a dual console and each has an ASA-82 MPD and ASQ-147 keyset and trackball. They share also an ASA-82 Auxiliary Readout Unit (ARU), a time code generator, and an AN/ASH-27 28-track tape recorder. Their MPDs can display acoustic data or the tactical plot, but the ARU is a dedicated acoustic display. The acoustic functions of receiving, processing, display and recording are controlled by the keysets through the computer.

The two NASOs also have a dual console, each with an ASA-82 MPD and ASQ-147 keyset and trackball, the keysets being used to control radar, electronic support measures (ESM) and FLIR through the computer. Principal controls shared by these two operators, or available to only one of them, include ASQ-501 MAD, OA-5150/ASQ(FACS II) MAD compensator, video tape recorder, SIF and provisions for SLAR.

The heart of the entire control system is a Univac AN/AYK-10 Navigation/Tactical computer. Its two central processors function independently; both have co-ordinated access to a core memory of 65,536 words. There is growth capacity for an additional 32,000 words, and space has been allocated for a 127,000-word auxiliary memory in the acoustic system processor for the computer.

The search stores and camera bay has stowage for 'A' size sonobuoys, large and small marine markers, Signals Underwater Sound (SUS) and flares. Intercom controls and an ordnance status panel are provided for the ordnance crew member. The computer-controlled electrically-fired cartridge-actuated A-size launchers can all be operated with the aircraft pressurised. They comprise 36 underfloor launchers, loadable only on the ground, and three which can be loaded from the cabin with the aircraft pressurised or unpressurised. A C-size chute, just aft of the three cabin launch tubes, allows free-fall launch (with the aircraft unpressurised) of flares, small marine markers, SUS and mail, and air drops to remote ships or stations.

A KA-107A day/night reconnaissance camera is installed beneath the floor in this area, and is accessible in flight through a floor hatch. The illuminator for night reconnaissance photography is located beneath the floor of the in-flight maintenance station. This position has a bench with 28V DC and 115V 400Hz AC power outlets, and there are provisions for a microfiche reader.

Aircraft operational support equipment for the CP-140 includes the ground-based Data Interpretation and Analysis Center (DIAC), and a Ground Support Computer Complex (GSCC). The former provides operational support for the operating squadrons; the latter provides technical support for the operational software, and maintains software configuration records.

The aircraft's weapon bay, which has a maximum capacity of 2,177 kg (4,800 lb) on eight stations, can accommodate and drop the Canadian SKAD/BR search and rescue kit, as well as a variety of ordnance. There are ten underwing hardpoints, with an individual capacity ranging from 277 kg (611 lb) to 1,111 kg (2,450 lb).

Canadair Ltd is manufacturing forward and aft radomes, rear fuselage sections, centre and outer wing sections, and main electrical load centres, both for the Aurora and for Lockheed-built P-3Cs.

The first CP-140 was rolled out on 25 January 1979, and this aircraft completed a successful five-hour first flight on 22 March 1979. Delivery of the first and last of these 18 Canadian aircraft is scheduled for May 1980 and March 1981 respectively. Because of the growth potential of this aircraft's equipment, it is expected to serve into the next century.

Type: Four-turboprop long-range ASW and maritime patrol aircraft.

Wings: As P-3C, with ailerons operated by dual hydraulic boosters, supplied from two independent hydraulic systems.

Fuselage: As for P-3C.

Tail Unit: As P-3C, with rudder and elevators each operated by dual hydraulic boosters, supplied from two independent hydraulic systems. Trim tabs in elevators and rudder.

Landing Gear: Hydraulically-retractable tricycle type with twin wheels on each unit. All units retract forward, main wheels into inner engine nacelles. Oleo-pneumatic shock-absorbers. All units can free-fall to the down and locked position in emergency. Hydraulically-powered steerable nose unit, controlled by handwheel on the pilot's side console. Hydraulically-operated dual segmented-disc brakes. Pneumatic emergency braking system.

Power Plant: Four 3,661 kW (4,910 ehp) Allison T56-A-14 turboprop engines, each driving a four-blade metal constant-speed fully-feathering and reversible propeller. Fuel in one fuselage and four wing integral tanks, with total usable capacity of 34,826 litres (9,200 US gallons). Single-point pressure refuelling, and four overwing gravity refuelling points, are provided. Fuel dump system. Propeller blade cuffs and spinners de-iced by electrical heating.

Accommodation: Normal eleven-man crew, with seating for five additional passengers. Dual controls standard. Flight deck has wide-vision windows, and circular windows for up to four observers are provided in the main cabin, each bulged to give 180° visibility. Main cabin fitted out as detailed in introductory paragraphs. Door on port side, aft of wing. Overwing emergency exit on each side of cabin; others in side and ceiling of flight deck. De-fogging and anti-icing of windscreens by electrical heating; windscreens have mechanical wipers, a washing system for the removal of salt deposits, and a rain-repellent spray system. Stowage for clothing, life jackets and parachute harness. Four floor tiedown areas have a combined baggage/cargo capacity of 442 kg (975 lb).

Systems: Air-conditioning and pressurisation system supplied by two engine-driven compressors, maintaining cabin temperatures between 15·6°C and 26·7°C (60°F and 80°F), and a cabin altitude of 2,440 m (8,000 ft) to a height of 9,145 m (30,000 ft). Two independent hydraulic systems, each at a pressure of 207 bars (3,000 lb/sq in) are powered by three interchangeable electrically-driven pumps, any two of which can maintain full hydraulic services. Pneumatic system at pressure of 207 bars (3,000 lb/sq in) for emergency braking. Electrical system of 120/208V 400Hz AC supplied by three 60/90kVA engine-driven generators, any one of which can maintain full normal load. DC power supplied by three 200A 24V transformer-rectifiers and one 31Ah storage battery. APU drives a 60/90kVA generator and provides power and bleed air for ground air-conditioning, weapons bay heating and engine starting; it can also provide emergency electrical power in flight. Oxygen system for crew of three on flight deck with 3·5 hour capacity. Individual portable chemical oxygen generators for emergency use by all crew members. Automatic flight control system (AFCS) with dual-channel fail-safe autopilot; includes tactical and airways nav modes and proportional control wheel steering.

Avionics and Equipment: Univac AN/AYK-10 navigation/tactical computer; digital magnetic tape units; teleprinter; display generator units; APS-116 search radar; OR-89/AA (modified) FLIR; video recorder for FLIR imagery; ARS-2 sonobuoy reference system; OL-82 (modified) acoustics data processor; RD-348, ASQ-147 and ASA-82 displays; LN-33 inertial navigation system; APN-208 Doppler; ARN-115 Omega; Tacan; revised airways/approach nav aids; dual VOR/ILS; communications sets comprising HF, UHF, VHF (AM), VHF guard receiver, VHF(FM); HF SIMOPS filters; RCVR homing; USH 502 crash position indicator/flight data recorder; ASW-31 AFCS; ALR-47 ESM; AN/ASH-27 28-track tape recorder; ASQ-501 MAD; OA-5150/ASQ (FACSII) MAD compensator; SLAR provisions; IFF; data link: Airborne Radiation Thermometer (ART) provisions; and time coding generator. Equipment includes KA-107A day/night reconnaissance camera and night illuminator; provisions for civil sensors canister; galley with refrigerator and sink; white edge lighting for all console-mounted control panels; white cabin lighting; reading lights at all crew positions; white overhead lights; and aisle lights.

Performance (with mission payload of 2,540 kg; 5,600 lb except where stated otherwise):
- Max transit speed at optimum altitude 395 knots (732 km/h; 455 mph)
- Max level speed below cruise ceiling 375 knots (695 km/h; 432 mph)
- FAR balanced field length 2,408 m (7,900 ft)
- T-O to 15 m (50 ft) 1,829 m (6,000 ft)
- Landing from 15 m (50 ft) at 51,714 kg (114,000 lb) landing weight 975 m (3,200 ft)
- Endurance on station at 1,000 nm (1,853 km; 1,151 miles) radius 8·2 h
- Ferry range 4,500 nm (8,339 km; 5,182 miles)

LOCKHEED S-3A VIKING

US Navy designation: S-3A

On 4 August 1969 Lockheed announced the receipt of a $461 million contract from the US Navy to develop an anti-submarine aircraft under the designation S-3A. Development was carried out by Lockheed in partnership with Vought Systems Division of LTV and Univac Federal Systems Division of Sperry Rand. Vought designed and built the wing, engine pods, tail unit and landing gear, and Univac was responsible for the digital computer, the heart of the weapon system, which provides high-speed processing of data essential for the S-3A's ASW role. Lockheed built the fuselage, integrated the avionics, and was responsible for final assembly at Burbank, California, from where the first prototype flew on 21 January 1972.

Production of the 187 S-3As called for under successive US Navy contracts ended in mid-1978. All tooling has been placed in storage at Burbank pending a US Navy decision on further orders. Details of the S-3A Viking can be found in the 1978-79 *Jane's*.

LOCKHEED L-1011 (MODEL 385) TRISTAR

In January 1966, Lockheed-California began a study of future requirements in the short/medium-haul airliner market. The design which emerged, known as the L-1011 (Lockheed Model 385 TriStar), was influenced by the published requirements of American Airlines, which specified optimum payload/range performance over the Chicago-Los Angeles route, coupled with an ability to take off from comparatively short runways with full payload.

The original design centred around a twin-turbofan configuration. Discussions which followed with American domestic carriers led to the eventual selection of a three-engined configuration, and the Rolls-Royce RB.211 high bypass ratio turbofan was chosen as power plant.

In June 1968 the L-1011 TriStar moved to the production design stage. Construction of the first aircraft began in March 1969, and this was rolled out in September 1970. The first flight was made on 16 November 1970. On 22 December 1971 class II provisional Type Certification was received, permitting delivery of aircraft to customers for route proving and demonstration purposes. In mid-1978 the prototype TriStar was being fitted with a 1·37 m (4 ft 6 in) extension to each wingtip, to flight test a new 'active' aileron control system already evaluated on the standard TriStar wing.

The original version of the TriStar is now known as the L-1011-1. Four other versions were available in early 1977, and Lockheed announced on 15 March 1977 that the company was holding discussions with major airlines throughout the world regarding new versions for service on short/medium-range routes in the 1980s. Details of current production versions, and available information on proposed new versions, follow:

L-1011-1. Basic TriStar, as described in detail. Initial delivery of the L-1011-1, to Eastern Air Lines for crew training, made on 6 April 1972, followed by a similar delivery to TWA. FAA certification was granted in the same month and the first passenger service with the TriStar was flown by Eastern on 15 April. Scheduled services began eleven days later.

L-1011-100. Longer-range version. Outward configuration identical with that of L-1011-1. Available with RB.211-22B engines (each 187 kN; 42,000 lb st) or RB.211-22F engines (each 193·5 kN; 43,500 lb st). Max T-O weight of 204,120 kg (450,000 lb) can be increased to 211,375 kg (466,000 lb) with additional 8,165 kg (18,000 lb) of fuel in new centre-section tanks. Ordered by Cathay Pacific, Gulf Air and Saudi Arabian Airlines.

L-1011-200. Longer-range version, with improved take-off and climb performance, offering particular benefits to operators serving 'hot or high' areas. Outward configuration identical with that of L-1011-1. Powered by RB.211-524 engines (each 213·5 kN; 48,000 lb st). Optional max T-O weights of 204,120 kg (450,000 lb) or 211,375 kg (466,000 lb) according to whether new centre-section tankage is fitted. First flight of TriStar test-bed with RB.211-524 (one only) made on 10 April 1976. L-1011-200 certificated by FAA on 26 April 1977. Ordered by British Airways, Gulf Air and Saudi Arabian Airlines.

L-1011-250. Long-range version, with further increase in max T-O weight to 224,980 kg (496,000 lb) and max fuel capacity of 96,160 kg (212,000 lb), through added centre-section tankage. Outward configuration identical with that of L-1011-1. Wings, fuselage and fin front spar web reinforced to cater for higher design loads. New nosewheel unit and strengthened main landing gear axles. Larger tyres with increased ply rating on all units. Braking capacity increased. Powered by RB.211-524B engines (each 213·5 kN; 48,000 lb st). Galley can be below-deck, as on other versions, or dispersed on main deck, which doubles available space in forward cargo hold. Expanded forward hold accommodates 16 LD-3 half-width containers or 5 pallets, each measuring 2·23 m × 3·17 m (88 in × 125 in). For pallet loading, the forward cargo door is replaced by a 1·72 m × 2·64 m (68 in × 104 in) power-operated upward-opening door. Main-deck galleys reduce passenger accommodation from typical 273 to 253 in eight-abreast coach configuration, and from typical 302 to 284 in nine-abreast coach configuration, in each case with 10 per cent first class forward.

L-1011-400A. Proposed short/medium-range version, with overall dimensions similar to those of the L-1011-500, except for an increase of wing span to 50·09 m (164 ft 4 in). Introduction of active aileron control system (in which the aircraft's control surfaces are moved automatically to counter manoeuvre or gust loads, without action by the pilot) would permit increased span, to provide drag reduction and consequent fuel savings, without other structural modifications to the wing. Powered by three RB. 211-22E turbofan engines, each rated at 187 kN (42,000 lb st); derating would be possible if automatic take-off thrust control (ATTC) system were installed. Accommodation for 251 passengers; range of 4,200 nm (7,783 km; 4,836 miles). Maximum T-O weight 195,045 kg (430,000 lb). Galleys located on the main deck, to permit increased cargo capacity.

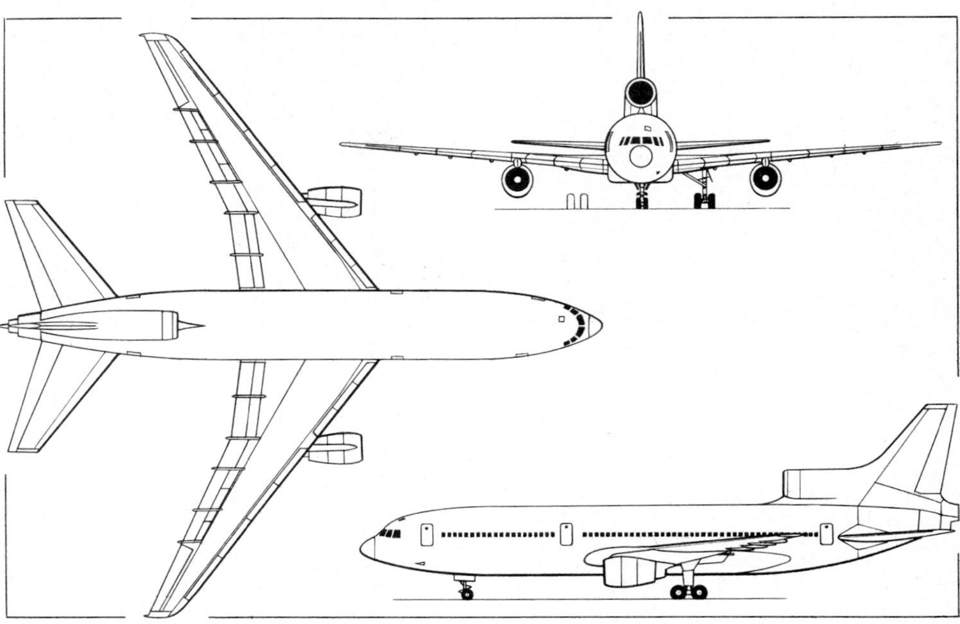
Lockheed L-1011-500 TriStar extended-range wide-bodied transport *(Pilot Press)*

L-1011-400A MP. Multi-purpose version of the -400A, with identical external dimensions. The -400A MP would have the same power plant, but increased fuel capacity and a max T-O weight of 211,375 kg (466,000 lb), providing international range. Accommodation for 241 passengers, with three main-deck galleys. Cargo capacity as for 400A. Range with full passenger payload 4,600 nm (8,525 km; 5,297 miles).

L-1011-500. Extended-range version, with a max T-O weight of 224,980 kg (496,000 lb) and max fuel capacity of 96,160 kg (212,000 lb) through added centre-section tankage. Fuselage is shortened by 4·11 m (13 ft 6 in); all other external dimensions are the same as for L-1011-1. Three RB.211-524B engines (each 222·4 kN; 50,000 lb st). Galley located on main deck. Forward cargo hold accommodates 12 LD-3 containers or four pallets each measuring 2·24 m × 3·17 m (88 in × 125 in). Centre hold takes 7 LD-3 containers. In a mixed class configuration, with 24 first class passengers in six-abreast seating and 222 economy passengers in nine-abreast seating, the aircraft carries 246 passengers. Max accommodation for 300 passengers. Ordered by AeroPeru, Air Canada, British Airways, BWIA, Delta Air Lines, LTU (Germany), PanAm and TAP/Air Portugal. New fuselage/centre engine fairing, installed first on the -500, may be adopted as standard for all TriStar models. Flight testing of this version began in October 1978, and -500s entered service with British Airways on 7 May 1979. Extended wingtips and active aileron system (with 2° low-speed aileron droop for 1% range improvement) will be introduced on Delta, Pan Am, LTU and Air Canada -500s during 1980-81, and will also be standard on the TAP aircraft.

L-1011-600. Proposed short/medium-range version with a fuselage 6·48 m (21 ft 3 in) shorter than that of the L-1011-500, new wing centre-section but retaining the outer wing panels of the L-1011-1, a new tail unit which eliminates the mounting for the third engine but retains the tailplane-elevator and fin-rudder assemblies of the L-1011-1, and two RB.211-524B engines the same as those which power the L-1011-500. Max T-O weight would vary between 119,750 kg (264,000 lb) and 134,715 kg (297,000 lb), providing accommodation for 174-200 passengers over ranges of up to 2,700 nm (5,000 km; 3,107 miles).

L-1011-600A. Proposed version of the L-1011-600, with a new supercritical wing, advanced high-lift system, and new tail unit, all constructed from high technology materials. Power plant and accommodation as for -600, but max T-O weight 119,750 kg (264,000 lb). Changed external dimensions include: wing span 43·51 m (142 ft 9 in); length overall 42·98 m (141 ft 0 in); height overall 16·15 m (53 ft 0 in); wing area 210·3 m² (2,264 sq ft).

Advanced TriStar. The original TriStar prototype (N1011) continues in use by Lockheed, under the name Advanced TriStar, to test and develop new ideas and systems that are under consideration for inclusion in future versions of this aircraft. In early 1979, N1011 was powered by three of the latest 222·4 kN (50,000 lb st) Rolls-Royce RB.211-524 turbofan engines. Its equipment included automatic brakes, automatic take-off thrust control, a flight management system, extended wingtips, active aileron control, Autoland, direct lift control, all-moving tailplane, an area navigation system and moving map display. It was intended to install during 1979 a new digital autopilot.

Automatic brakes operating in conjunction with anti-skid units ensure that braking is optimum at all times, in

Lockheed L-1011-500 TriStar extended-range transport in the insignia of British Airways

The original prototype TriStar, now flying as the Advanced TriStar testbed for new-technology equipment and techniques

relation to load, speed and weather conditions. Automatic take-off thrust control allows the pilot to use reduced take-off power settings, and to operate from shorter field lengths than would be normal for such settings. With the throttles set to provide the requisite take-off power, in relation to field length, altitude and aircraft gross weight, failure of an engine during take-off would be offset by automatic advance of the remaining two engines to rated take-off thrust, or to a pre-set emergency power rating limit, thus minimising any time lag that might be experienced due to slow crew response.

Each wing of the Advanced TriStar has been extended at the tip by 1·37 m (4 ft 6 in), resulting in a significant reduction of induced drag, and producing fuel savings in the order of 3 per cent. However, the added span generates an increased wing lift increment which would be unacceptable under certain manoeuvre or gust loads. This required the introduction of an active control system, to provide automatic aileron deflection to offset such loads, thus eliminating the need for wing structural redesign.

By 1 December 1978, Lockheed had delivered 156 L-1011 TriStars to Air Canada, All Nippon Airways, British Airways, Cathay Pacific Airways, Court Line, Delta Air Lines, Eastern Air Lines, Gulf Air, Lufttransport Unternehmen, Pacific Southwest Airlines, Saudi Arabian Airlines and Trans World Airlines. Sales totalled 230, with options on 71 more, by 13 September 1979.

The description which follows applies to the L-1011-1 TriStar in its initial operational form, except where indicated. The basic structural details apply to all current production derivatives:

Type: Three-turbofan commercial transport.

Wings: Cantilever low-wing monoplane. Special Lockheed aerofoil sections. Dihedral at trailing-edge 7° 31′ on inner wings, 5° 30′ outboard. Sweepback at quarter-chord 35°. The wing consists of a centre-section, passing through the lower fuselage, and an outer wing panel on each side. It is of conventional fail-safe construction, with aluminium alloy surfaces, ribs and spars, and integral fuel tanks. Hydraulically-powered aluminium alloy ailerons of conventional two-spar box construction, with aluminium alloy honeycomb trailing-edge, in inboard and outboard sections on each wing, operate in conjunction with flight spoilers. The low-speed ailerons extend from approximately 80% of semi-span to within 0·25 m (10 in) of the wingtips, the high-speed ailerons extend from approximately WBL 387 to WBL 480 on each wing. Double-slotted Fowler trailing-edge flaps, constructed of aluminium alloy and aluminium alloy honeycomb. Each flap segment consists of a honeycomb trailing-edge, a front spar, ribs, skin panels, carriages, and tracks mounted on the forward segment to provide for extension and rotation of the aft segment. A sheet metal vane surface, actuated by a linkage system during flap rotation, forms the forward section of the extended flap. Four aluminium alloy leading-edge slats outboard of engine pylon on each wing. Each segment is mounted to two roller-supported tracks and extends in a circular motion down and forward for take-off and landing. Three leading-edge slats inboard of engine pylon on each wing, made of aluminium alloy honeycomb and sheet metal fairings. Six spoilers on the upper surface of each wing, two inboard and four outboard of the inboard aileron, constructed from bonded aluminium alloy tapered honeycomb. No trim tabs. Flight controls fully powered. Each control surface system is controlled by a multiple redundant servo actuator system that is powered by four independent and separate hydraulic sources. Thermal de-icing of outboard wing leading-edge slats by engine bleed air.

Fuselage: Semi-monocoque structure of aluminium alloy. Constant cross-sectional diameter of 5·97 m (19 ft 7 in) for most of the length. Bonding utilised in skin joints, for attaching skin-doublers at joints and around openings to improve fatigue life. Skins and stringers supported by frames spaced at 0·51 m (20 in) intervals, with fail-safe straps midway between frames. These frames, with the exception of main frames and door-edge members, are 0·076 m (3 in) deep at the sides of the cabin, increasing progressively to a depth of 0·15 m (6 in) at the top of the fuselage and below the floor. Fuselage length reduced on L-1011-500.

Tail Unit: Conventional cantilever structure, consisting of variable-incidence horizontal tailplane-elevator assembly and vertical fin and rudder. Primary loads of the fin are carried by a conventional box-beam structure, with ribs spaced at approx 0·51 m (20 in) centres. The rudder comprises forward and aft spars, glassfibre trailing-edges, hinge and actuator backup ribs, sheet metal formers, box surface panels and leading-edge fairings. Elevators are of similar construction. Truss members for the tailplane centre-section are built up from forged and extruded sections. Outboard of the centre-section, construction is similar to that of the fin box-beam, leading- and trailing-edges, except that the surface structure is integrally stiffened. The elevators are linked mechanically to the tailplane actuation gear, to modify its camber and improve its effectiveness. No trim tabs. Controls are fully powered, the hydraulic servo actuators receiving power from four independent hydraulic sources, under control of electronic flight control system. Control feel is provided, with the force gradient scheduled as a function of flight condition. No de-icing equipment.

Landing Gear: Hydraulically-retractable tricycle type, produced by Menasco Manufacturing. Twin-wheel units in tandem on each main gear; twin wheels on nose gear, which is steerable 65° on each side. Nosewheels retract forward into fuselage. Main wheels retract inward into fuselage wheel-wells. Oleo-pneumatic shock-absorbers on all units. B. F. Goodrich forged aluminium alloy wheels of split construction. Main wheels have tubeless tyres size 50 × 20-20, Type VIII, pressure 10·34-11·38 bars (150-165 lb/sq in) for short- to medium-range operational weights, 12·41 bars (180 lb/sq in) for max-range weight. Nosewheels have tubeless tyres size 36 × 11-16, Type VII, pressure 12·76 bars (185 lb/sq in). Hydraulically-operated brakes, controlled by the rudder pedals. Anti-skid units, with individual wheel skid and modulated control, installed in the normal and alternative braking systems.

Power Plant (L-1011-1): Three Rolls-Royce RB.211-22B turbofan engines, each rated at 187 kN (42,000 lb st). Two engines mounted in pods on pylons under the wings, the third mounted in the rear fuselage at the base of the fin. Engine bleed air is used to anti-ice the engine inlet lips. Two integral fuel tanks in each wing; inboard tank capacity 30,581 litres (8,079 US gallons), outboard tank capacity 14,489 litres (3,828 US gallons). Total fuel capacity 90,140 litres (23,814 US gallons). Pressure refuelling points in wing leading-edges. Oil capacity approx 34 litres (9 US gallons) per engine. A detachable pylon can be fitted between the starboard engine nacelle and fuselage to permit carriage of a replacement engine for another TriStar. Alternative power plants for -100, -200, -250 and -500 detailed under model listings. These four models each have provision for additional centre-section tankage, raising total fuel capacity to 100,317 litres (26,502 US gallons) in -100 and -200, and 119,774 litres (31,642 US gallons) in -250 and -500.

Accommodation: Crew of 13. First class and coach mixed accommodation for 256 passengers, with a maximum of 400 in all-economy configuration. Alternative intermediate seating capacities are provided by using eight seat-tracks which permit 6, 8, 9 or 10-abreast seating, with two full-length aisles. Underfloor galley. Seven lavatories are provided, two forward and five aft. Three Type A passenger doors of the upward-opening plug type on each side of the fuselage, one pair immediately aft of flight deck, one pair forward of wing, one pair aft of wing. Two Type I emergency exit doors, one each side of fuselage, at rear of cabin, replaced by two Type A doors for 10-abreast seating. Baggage and freight compartments beneath the floor able to accommodate 16 containers, totalling 71·58 m³ (2,528 cu ft), and 19·8 m³ (700 cu ft) bulk cargo (19 containers and 14·2 m³; 500 cu ft in -500).

Systems: Air-conditioning and pressurisation system, using engine bleed air or APU air combined with air-cycle refrigeration. Pressurisation system maintains equivalent of 2,440 m (8,000 ft) conditions to 12,800 m (42,000 ft). Normal cabin pressure differential 0·582 bars (8·44 lb/sq in). Four independent 207 bar (3,000 lb/sq in) hydraulic systems provide power for primary flight control surfaces, normal brake power, landing gear retraction and nosewheel steering, etc. Electrical system includes four 120/208V 400Hz alternators, one on each engine and one driven by the APU, which is sited in the aft fuselage. APU provides ground and in-flight power, to an altitude of 9,145 m (30,000 ft), producing both shaft and pneumatic power for utilisation by the electrical, environmental control and hydraulic systems. Integral electric heaters to anti-ice windscreens, pitot masts and total temperature probes.

Avionics and Equipment: Standard equipment includes two ARINC 546 VHF communication transceivers, two ARINC 547 VHF navigation systems, two ARINC 568 interrogator units, an ARINC 564 weather radar system, two ARINC 572 air traffic control transponders, partial provision for a dual collision system, three vertical gyros, and full blind-flying instrumentation. Space is provided for installation of two ARINC 533A HF transceivers and a dual SATCOM system.

Dimensions, external:
Wing span 47·34 m (155 ft 4 in)
Wing chord at root 10·46 m (34 ft 4 in)
Wing chord at tip 3·12 m (10 ft 3 in)
Wing aspect ratio 6·95
Length overall:
-1, -100, -200, -250 54·17 m (177 ft 8½ in)
-500 50·05 m (164 ft 2½ in)
Height overall 16·87 m (55 ft 4 in)
Tailplane span 21·82 m (71 ft 7 in)
Wheel track 10·97 m (36 ft 0 in)
Wheelbase:
-1, -100, -200, -250 21·34 m (70 ft 0 in)
-500 19·71 m (64 ft 8 in)
Passenger doors (each): Height 1·93 m (6 ft 4 in)
Width 1·07 m (3 ft 6 in)
Height to sill 4·60 m (15 ft 1 in)
Emergency passenger doors (each):
Height 1·52 m (5 ft 0 in)
Width 0·61 m (2 ft 0 in)
Height to sill 4·60 m (15 ft 1 in)
Baggage and freight compartment doors (forward and centre): Height 1·73 m (5 ft 8 in)
Width 1·78 m (5 ft 10 in)
Height to sill 2·72 m (8 ft 11 in)
Baggage and freight compartment doors (aft):
Height 1·22 m (4 ft 0 in)
Width 1·12 m (3 ft 8 in)
Height to sill 2·92 m (9 ft 7 in)

Dimensions, internal:
Cabin, excl flight deck and underfloor galley:
Length 41·43 m (135 ft 11 in)
Max width 5·77 m (18 ft 11 in)
Max height 2·41 m (7 ft 11 in)
Floor area:
-1, -100, -200, -250 215·5 m² (2,320 sq ft)
-500 192·6 m² (2,073 sq ft)
Volume 453 m³ (16,000 cu ft)
Baggage/cargo holds, bulk capacity:
-1, -100, -200, -250 110·4 m³ (3,900 cu ft)
-500 118·9 m³ (4,200 cu ft)

Areas:
Wings, gross 320·0 m² (3,456 sq ft)
Ailerons (total) 14·86 m² (160 sq ft)
Trailing-edge flaps (total) 49·80 m² (536 sq ft)
Leading-edge slats (total):
inboard slats 11·52 m² (124 sq ft)
outboard slats 21·93 m² (236 sq ft)
Spoilers (total) 19·88 m² (214 sq ft)
Fin 51·10 m² (550 sq ft)
Rudder 11·89 m² (128 sq ft)
Tailplane 119·10 m² (1,282 sq ft)

Weights:
Operating weight empty:
-1 109,045 kg (240,400 lb)
-100 110,720 kg (244,100 lb)
-200 111,495 kg (245,800 lb)
-250 112,969 kg (249,054 lb)
-500 109,298 kg (240,963 lb)
Max payload: -1 38,373 kg (84,600 lb)
-100 34,427 kg (75,900 lb)
-200 33,020 kg (72,800 lb)
-250 40,345 kg (88,946 lb)
-500 44,015 kg (97,037 lb)
Max T-O weight: -1 195,045 kg (430,000 lb)
-100 211,375 kg (466,000 lb)
-200 216,363 kg (477,000 lb)
-250, -500 224,980 kg (496,000 lb)
Max zero-fuel weight: -1 147,417 kg (325,000 lb)
-100, -200 145,150 kg (320,000 lb)
-250, -500 153,315 kg (338,000 lb)
Max landing weight: -1 162,385 kg (358,000 lb)
-100, -200, -250, -500 166,920 kg (368,000 lb)

Performance (A: L-1011-1 at max T-O weight of 195,045 kg: 430,000 lb; B and C: L-1011-100 and L-1011-200 respectively at max T-O weight of 211,375 kg: 466,000 lb; D and E: L-1011-250 and L-1011-500 respectively at max T-O weight of 224,980 kg: 496,000 lb, except where indicated):
Never-exceed speed, all versions
Mach 0·95 (435 knots; 806 km/h; 501 mph) CAS
Max cruising speed, mid-cruise weight at 9,145 m (30,000 ft): A 520 knots (964 km/h; 599 mph)

B	515 knots (954 km/h; 593 mph)
C	530 knots (982 km/h; 610 mph)
D, E	525 knots (973 km/h; 605 mph)
Econ cruising speed, mid-cruise weight at 10,670 m (35,000 ft): A, B	480 knots (890 km/h; 553 mph)
C, D, E	485 knots (899 km/h; 558 mph)
Stalling speed at max landing weight, flaps and gear up:	
A	148 knots (274 km/h; 170 mph)
B, C, D, E	151 knots (280 km/h; 174 mph)
Stalling speed at max landing weight, flaps and gear down: A	108 knots (200 km/h; 124 mph)
B, C, D	109 knots (202 km/h; 126 mph)
E	111 knots (206 km/h; 128 mph)
Max rate of climb at S/L: A	856 m (2,810 ft)/min
B	765 m (2,510 ft)/min
C	847 m (2,780 ft)/min
D, E	777 m (2,550 ft)/min
Service ceiling, all versions	12,800 m (42,000 ft)
FAR T-O field length: A	2,426 m (7,960 ft)
B	3,243 m (10,640 ft)
C	2,460 m (8,070 ft)
D	2,838 m (9,310 ft)
E	2,975 m (9,760 ft)
FAR landing field length, at max landing weight:	
A	1,734 m (5,690 ft)
B, C, D	1,768 m (5,800 ft)
E	1,957 m (6,420 ft)

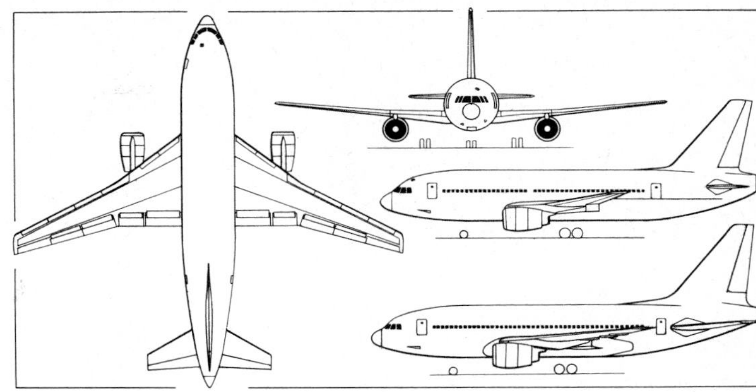

The projected twin-engined L-1011-600A, with additional side elevation (bottom) of L-1011-600 *(Pilot Press)*

Range with max passengers and baggage, international reserves: A	2,870 nm (5,319 km; 3,305 miles)
B	3,660 nm (6,783 km; 4,215 miles)
C	3,680 nm (6,820 km; 4,238 miles)
D	4,520 nm (8,376 km; 5,205 miles)
E	5,209 nm (9,653 km; 5,998 miles)
Range with max fuel, international reserves:	
A	4,360 nm (8,080 km; 5,021 miles)
B	4,820 nm (8,932 km; 5,550 miles)
C	4,880 nm (9,044 km; 5,619 miles)
D	5,900 nm (10,934 km; 6,794 miles)
E	6,150 nm (11,397 km; 7,082 miles)

Operational Noise Characteristics (FAR Pt 36):	
T-O noise level	97 EPNdB
Approach noise level	103 EPNdB
Sideline noise level	95 EPNdB

LOCKHEED-GEORGIA COMPANY

86 South Cobb Drive, Marietta, Georgia 30063

Lockheed-Georgia's main building at Marietta is one of the world's largest aircraft production plants under a single roof. Aircraft in current production on its assembly lines are the C-130 Hercules turboprop transport and its commercial counterpart, the L 100.

Lockheed-Georgia had a total of approximately 9,000 employees at the beginning of 1979.

LOCKHEED MODEL 382 HERCULES

USAF designations: C-130, AC-130, DC-130, HC-130, JC-130, RC-130 and WC-130
US Navy designations: C-130, DC-130, EC-130 and LC-130
US Marine Corps designation: KC-130
US Coast Guard designations: EC-130 and HC-130
Canadian Armed Forces designation: CC-130
RAF designations: Hercules C.Mk 1 and W.Mk 2

The C-130 was designed to a specification issued by the USAF Tactical Air Command in 1951. Lockheed was awarded its first production contract for the C-130A in September 1952, and a total of 461 C-130As and C-130Bs was manufactured. Details of these basic versions and of many variants for special duties can be found in the 1967-68 and 1975-76 *Jane's*. Later military versions of the C-130 are as follows:

C-130E (Lockheed Model 382-44). Extended-range development of C-130B, with four 3,020 kW (4,050 ehp) T56-A-7 turboprop engines and two 5,145 litre (1,360 US gallon) underwing fuel tanks. Deliveries began in April 1962, and by February 1975 the planned production of a total of 503 C-130Es had been completed. Details of the basic C-130E can be found in the 1973-74 *Jane's*.

EC-130E. Electronic surveillance version for USAF to replace Lockheed EC-121s. Large blade antennae added above dorsal fin and under each outer wing. Smaller antennae include horizontal blade on each side of rear fuselage. Bullet-shape canisters outboard of each underwing antenna and at extreme tail of aircraft house trailing wire antennae which extend several hundred feet behind the EC-130E in flight.

EC-130G. Redesignation of four C-130Gs acquired by US Navy. Equipped with VLF radio to relay emergency action messages to Fleet Ballistic Missile submarines anywhere in the world.

C-130H. Similar to earlier Hercules models except for more powerful engines: T56-A-15 turboprops rated at 3,661 kW (4,910 ehp) for take-off, but limited to 3,362 kW (4,508 ehp). Deliveries to USAF began in April 1975.

HC-130H. Lockheed was awarded two initial contracts in September 1963 for this extended-range air search, rescue and recovery version to be utilised by the Aerospace Rescue and Recovery Service of the USAF for aerial recovery of personnel or equipment and other duties. The US Coast Guard subsequently ordered seven. A folding nose-mounted recovery system makes possible repeated pickups from ground of persons or objects weighing up to 227 kg (500 lb) including the recoverable gear. Four 3,661 kW (4,910 ehp) (limited to 3,356 kW; 4,500 ehp) Allison T56-A-15 turboprop engines, each driving a Hamilton Standard 54H60-91 four-blade constant-speed propeller. Normal fuel tankage as for C-130H. Provision for installing two 6,184 litre (1,800 US gallon) tanks in cargo compartment. Normal crew of 10, consisting of pilot, co-pilot, navigator, 2 flight mechanics, radio operator, 2 loadmasters and 2 para-rescue technicians, with provision for additional pilot and navigator for long missions. Standard equipment includes four 6-man rafts, two litters, bunks, 16 personnel kits, recovery winches, 10 flare launchers. Total of 66 delivered, of which the first one flew on 8 December 1964. Four modified as **JHC-130H** with added equipment for aerial recovery of re-entering space capsules. One modified by LAS to **DC-130H**.

Lockheed C-130H Hercules of the Egyptian Air Force flying near the Pyramids

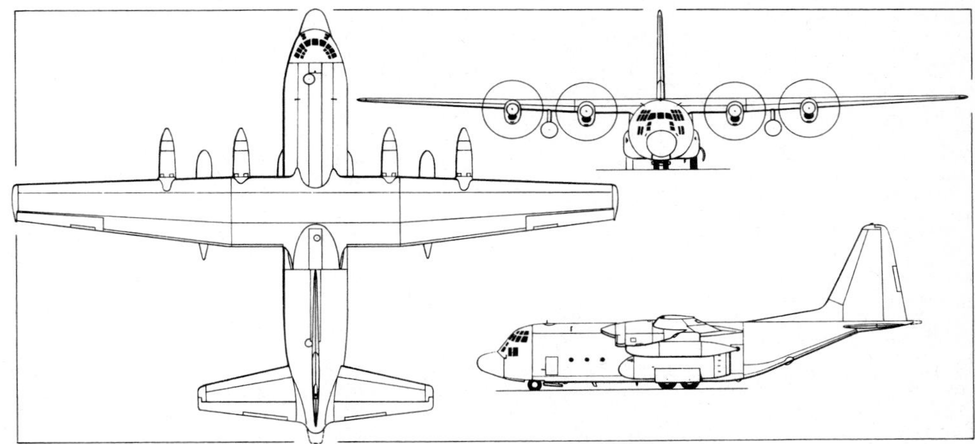

Lockheed C-130E Hercules four-turboprop medium/long-range combat transport *(Pilot Press)*

Large fairings forward of the fin and under each wing, plus antennae canisters, distinguish the new EC-130E

KC-130H. A tanker version of the C-130H, very similar to the KC-130R. Exported to Argentina (2), Brazil (2), Israel (2), Saudi Arabia (6) and Spain (3).

C-130K. This is basically a C-130H, modified for use by the Royal Air Force. Much of the electronics and instrumentation is of UK manufacture. Sixty-six delivered as **Hercules C. Mk 1**, of which the first flew on 19 October 1966. One modified by Marshall of Cambridge (Engineering) Ltd in the UK for use by the RAF Meteorological Research Flight, under the designation **Hercules W. Mk 2**. Thirty are each being lengthened by 4·58 m (15 ft 0 in), equivalent to commercial L 100-30 standard, during 1978-82. This will increase payload capacity to seven cargo pallets instead of five, or 128 troops instead of 92, or 92 fully-equipped paratroops instead of 64, or 93 stretcher patients (and six attendants) instead of 70. After modification, these aircraft will be redesignated **Hercules C. Mk 3.**

HC-130N. Search and rescue version for recovery of aircrew and retrieval of space capsules after re-entry, using advanced direction-finding equipment. Fifteen ordered for USAF in 1969.

HC-130P. Twenty HC-130Hs were modified into HC-130Ps with capability of refuelling helicopters in flight, and for mid-air retrieval of parachute-borne payloads. Modification involved the addition of refuelling drogue pods and associated plumbing. Typical helicopter refuelling mission involves taking off at an AUW of 70,310 kg (155,000 lb), with 33,385 kg (73,600 lb) of fuel on board, meeting up with the helicopters at a radius of 500 nm (925 km; 575 miles), transferring 22,000 kg (48,500 lb) of fuel to the helicopters and returning 500 nm to the point of origin.

EC-130Q. Eleven aircraft similar to EC-130G but with improved equipment and crew accommodation, for USN command communications duties.

KC-130R. Tanker version of the C-130H for US Marine Corps. Major changes from the earlier KC-130F include engines of 3,362 kW (4,508 ehp), increased T-O and landing weights, pylon-mounted fuel tanks to provide an additional 10,296 litres (2,720 US gallons) of fuel, plus a removable 13,627 litre (3,600 US gallon) fuel tank located in the cargo compartment. Four ordered in early 1974; ten more subsequently.

LC-130R. Basically a C-130H with wheel-ski gear for US Navy. Main skis each approximately 6·10 m (20 ft 0 in) long by 1·68 m (5 ft 6 in) wide. The nose ski is approximately 3·05 m (10 ft 0 in) long by 1·68 m (5 ft 6 in) wide. The total ski installation weighs approximately 2,540 kg (5,600 lb). The main skis have 8° nose-up and nose-down pitch and the nose skis have 15° nose-up and nose-down pitch, to enable them to follow uneven terrain. The load-bearing surfaces of the skis are coated with Teflon plastics to reduce friction and resist ice adhesion. Provision is made for fitting JATO units. Four converted, for service in the Antarctic. Two more aircraft in this configuration were ordered in late 1975 by the National Science Foundation, for use in the Antarctic.

Advanced versions. The Lockheed-Georgia company has studied several versions of the Hercules which would have improved capabilities. The C-130SS Stretch STOL version features a 2·54 m (8 ft 4 in) cargo compartment stretch, greater payload and better short-field capabilities than the C-130H. The C-130HS offers the above-mentioned fuselage stretch without the improved STOL features. The C-130WBS is a wide-body, stretched STOL version.

Commercial versions of the Hercules are described separately.

The C-130 is able to deliver single loads of up to 11,340 kg (25,000 lb) by the ground proximity extraction method. This involves making a fly-past 1·2-1·5 m (4-5 ft) above the ground with the rear loading ramp open. The aircraft trails a hook which is attached by cable to the palletised cargo. The hook engages a steel cable on the ground and the cargo is extracted from the aircraft and brought to a stop on the ground in about 30 m (100 ft) by an energy absorption system manufactured by All American Engineering of Wilmington, Delaware. An alternative extraction technique involves deploying a 6·70 m (22 ft) ribbon parachute to drag the pallet from the cabin. Loads of up to 22,680 kg (50,000 lb) have been delivered by this method.

By February 1979 firm orders for all versions of the C-130 totalled 1,553 for 44 nations. This total comprised 1,011 C-130s for the US services, 471 for foreign military operators, and 71 commercial Hercules. The 1,500th Hercules, a C-130H for the Sudan Air Force, was delivered on 13 March 1978. Production rate for 1979 was set at three aircraft per month.

The following details refer specifically to the C-130H, except where indicated otherwise:

TYPE: Medium/long-range combat transport.

WINGS: Cantilever high-wing monoplane. Wing section NACA 64A318 at root, NACA 64A412 at tip. Dihedral 2° 30′. Incidence 3° at root, 0° at tip. Sweepback at quarter-chord 0°. All-metal two-spar stressed-skin structure, with integrally-stiffened tapered machined skin panels up to 14·63 m (48 ft 0 in) long. Conventional aluminium alloy ailerons have tandem-piston hydraulic boost, operated by either of two independent hydraulic systems. Lockheed-Fowler aluminium alloy trailing-edge flaps. Trim tabs in ailerons. Leading-edge anti-iced by hot air bled from engines.

FUSELAGE: Semi-monocoque structure of aluminium and magnesium alloys.

TAIL UNIT: Cantilever all-metal stressed-skin structure. Fixed-incidence tailplane. Trim tabs in elevators and rudder. Elevator tabs use AC electrical power as primary source and DC as emergency source. Control surfaces have tandem-piston hydraulic boost. Hot-air anti-icing of tailplane leading-edge, by engine bleed air.

LANDING GEAR: Hydraulically-retractable tricycle type. Each main unit has two wheels in tandem, retracting into fairings built on to the sides of the fuselage. Nose unit has twin wheels and is steerable through 60° each side of centre. Oleo shock-absorbers. Main-wheel tyres size 56 × 20-20, pressure 5·52 bars (80 lb/sq in). Nose-wheel tyres size 39 × 13-16, pressure 4·14 bars (60 lb/sq in). Goodyear aircooled hydraulic brakes with anti-skid units. Retractable combination wheel-skis available.

POWER PLANT: Four 3,362 kW (4,508 ehp) Allison T56-A-15 turboprop engines, each driving a Hamilton Standard type 54H60 four-blade constant-speed fully-feathering reversible-pitch propeller. Eight Aerojet-General 15KS-1000 JATO units (each 4·45 kN; 1,000 lb st for 15 sec) can be carried. Fuel in six integral tanks in wings, with total capacity of 26,344 litres (6,960 US gallons) and two underwing pylon tanks, each with capacity of 5,146 litres (1,360 US gallons). Total fuel capacity 36,636 litres (9,680 US gallons). Single pressure refuelling point in starboard wheel well. Fillers for overwing gravity fuelling. Oil capacity 182 litres (48 US gallons).

ACCOMMODATION: Crew of four on flight deck, comprising pilot, co-pilot, navigator and systems manager. Provision for fifth man to supervise loading. Sleeping quarters for relief crew, and galley. Flight deck and main cabin pressurised and air-conditioned. Standard complements are as follows: troops (max) 92, paratroops (max) 64, litters 74 and 2 attendants. As a cargo carrier, loads can include heavy equipment such as a 12,080 kg (26,640 lb) type F.6 refuelling trailer or a 155 mm howitzer and its high-speed tractor. Up to six preloaded pallets of freight can be carried. Hydraulically-operated main loading door and ramp at rear of cabin. Paratroop door on each side aft of landing gear fairing.

SYSTEMS: Air-conditioning and pressurisation system max pressure differential 0·52 bars (7·5 lb/sq in). Two independent hydraulic systems, pressure 207 bars (3,000 lb/sq in). Electrical system supplied by four 40kVA AC generators, plus one 40kVA auxiliary generator driven by APU. Current production aircraft incorporate many systems and component design changes for increased reliability. There are differences between the installed components for US government and export versions.

DIMENSIONS, EXTERNAL:
- Wing span: 40·41 m (132 ft 7 in)
- Wing chord at root: 4·88 m (16 ft 0 in)
- Wing chord, mean: 4·16 m (13 ft 8½ in)
- Wing aspect ratio: 10·09
- Length overall:
  - all except HC-130H: 29·79 m (97 ft 9 in)
  - HC-130H, recovery system folded: 30·10 m (98 ft 9 in)
  - HC-130H, recovery system spread: 32·41 m (106 ft 4 in)
- Height overall: 11·66 m (38 ft 3 in)
- Tailplane span: 16·05 m (52 ft 8 in)
- Wheel track: 4·35 m (14 ft 3 in)
- Wheelbase: 9·77 m (32 ft 0¾ in)
- Propeller diameter: 4·11 m (13 ft 6 in)
- Main cargo door (rear of cabin):
  - Height: 2·77 m (9 ft 1 in)
  - Width: 3·05 m (10 ft 0 in)
  - Height to sill: 1·03 m (3 ft 5 in)
- Paratroop doors (each): Height: 1·83 m (6 ft 0 in)
  - Width: 0·91 m (3 ft 0 in)
  - Height to sill: 1·03 m (3 ft 5 in)

DIMENSIONS, INTERNAL:
- Cabin, excl flight deck:
  - Length without ramp: 12·60 m (41 ft 5 in)
  - Length with ramp: 15·73 m (51 ft 8½ in)
  - Max width: 3·13 m (10 ft 3 in)
  - Max height: 2·81 m (9 ft 2¾ in)
  - Floor area, excl ramp: 39·5 m² (425 sq ft)
  - Volume, incl ramp: 127·4 m³ (4,500 cu ft)

AREAS:
- Wings, gross: 162·12 m² (1,745 sq ft)
- Ailerons (total): 10·22 m² (110 sq ft)
- Trailing-edge flaps (total): 31·77 m² (342 sq ft)
- Fin: 20·90 m² (225 sq ft)
- Rudder, incl tab: 6·97 m² (75 sq ft)
- Tailplane: 35·40 m² (381 sq ft)
- Elevators, incl tabs: 14·40 m² (155 sq ft)

WEIGHTS AND LOADINGS:
- Operating weight empty: 34,169 kg (75,331 lb)
- Max payload: 19,872 kg (43,811 lb)
- Max normal T-O weight: 70,310 kg (155,000 lb)
- Max overload T-O weight: 79,380 kg (175,000 lb)
- Max landing weight: 58,970 kg (130,000 lb)
- Max zero-fuel weight, 2·5 *g*: 54,040 kg (119,142 lb)
- Max wing loading: 434·5 kg/m² (89 lb/sq ft)
- Max power loading: 5·23 kg/kW (8·6 lb/ehp)

Lockheed L 100-30 Hercules commercial transport in service with Safair Freighters of South Africa

PERFORMANCE (at max T-O weight, unless indicated otherwise):
- Max cruising speed:
  - C-130H: 335 knots (621 km/h; 386 mph)
  - HC-130H: 318 knots (589 km/h; 366 mph)
- Econ cruising speed: 300 knots (556 km/h; 345 mph)
- Stalling speed: 100 knots (185 km/h; 115 mph)
- Max rate of climb at S/L:
  - C-130H: 579 m (1,900 ft)/min
  - HC-130H: 555 m (1,820 ft)/min
- Service ceiling at 58,970 kg (130,000 lb) AUW: 10,060 m (33,000 ft)
- Service ceiling, one engine out, at 58,970 kg (130,000 lb) AUW: 8,075 m (26,500 ft)
- Min ground turning radius: 19·2 m (63 ft)
- Runway LCN at 70,310 kg (155,000 lb) AUW:
  - asphalt: 37
  - concrete: 42
- T-O run: 1,091 m (3,580 ft)
- T-O to 15 m (50 ft): 1,573 m (5,160 ft)
- Landing from 15 m (50 ft) at 45,360 kg (100,000 lb) AUW: 741 m (2,430 ft)
- Landing from 15 m (50 ft) at max landing weight: 838 m (2,750 ft)
- Landing run at max landing weight: 533 m (1,750 ft)
- Range with max payload, with 5% reserves and allowance for 30 min at S/L: 2,160 nm (4,002 km; 2,487 miles)
- Range with max fuel, incl external tanks, 9,070 kg (20,000 lb) payload and reserves of 5% initial fuel plus 30 min at S/L: 4,460 nm (8,264 km; 5,135 miles)

LOCKHEED L 100 SERIES COMMERCIAL HERCULES

Details of initial versions of the commercial Hercules have appeared in previous editions of *Jane's;* current models are as follows:

Model 382E (L 100-20). Certificated on 4 October 1968, this 'stretched' version of the Hercules has a 2·54 m (100 in) fuselage extension. A 1·52 m (60 in) fuselage plug is inserted aft of the forward crew door and a 1·02 m (40 in) plug aft of the paratroop doors. Allison 501-D22A engines. Operators have included Alaska International Air, Delta Air Lines, Saturn Airways and Southern Air Transport in the USA; Pacific Western Airlines in Canada; SATCO in Peru; Safair Freighters in the Republic of South Africa; the Kuwait Air Force (2); the Peruvian Air Force (5); Philippine Aerotransport; the Philippine Air Force (4); and the Republic of Gabon (2).

Model 382G (L 100-30). Generally similar to the Model 382E, but with the fuselage extended a further 2·03 m (80 in). Rear cargo windows, paratroop doors and provision for JATO eliminated. Saturn Airways was the first operator of this model, with services beginning in December 1970. Alaska International Air, Safair Freighters, the Republic of Gabon, the Republic of Uganda, SCIBE and Southern Air are among those who have operated the Model 382G.

A total of 71 commercial Hercules (all versions) had been delivered by January 1979. Details given for the C-130H apply also to the L 100-20 and L 100-30, except as follows:

TYPE: Medium/long-range transport.

LANDING GEAR: As for C-130H, except main-wheel tyre pressure 3·24-7·38 bars (47-107 lb/sq in) and nose-wheel tyre pressure 4·14 bars (60 lb/sq in).

POWER PLANT: Either four 3,020 kW (4,050 ehp) Allison 501-D22 or four 3,362 kW (4,508 ehp) Allison 501-D22A turboprop engines.

DIMENSIONS, EXTERNAL:
- Length overall: L 100-20: 32·33 m (106 ft 1 in)
  - L 100-30: 34·37 m (112 ft 9 in)
- Wheelbase: L 100-20: 11·30 m (37 ft 1 in)
  - L 100-30: 12·32 m (40 ft 5 in)
- Crew door (integral steps):
  - Height: 1·14 m (3 ft 9 in)
  - Width: 0·76 m (2 ft 6 in)
  - Height to sill: 1·04 m (3 ft 5 in)

DIMENSIONS, INTERNAL:
- Cabin, excl flight deck:
  - Length: L 100-20: 15·04 m (49 ft 4 in)
    - L 100-30: 17·07 m (56 ft 0 in)
  - Max height: 2·74 m (9 ft 0 in)
- Floor area, excl ramp:
  - L 100-20: 46·36 m² (499 sq ft)
  - L 100-30: 52·30 m² (563 sq ft)
- Floor area, ramp: 9·57 m² (103 sq ft)
- Volume, incl ramp:
  - L 100-20: 150·28 m³ (5,307 cu ft)
  - L 100-30: 171·5 m³ (6,057 cu ft)

WEIGHTS AND LOADINGS:
- Operating weight empty:
  - L 100-20: 33,299 kg (73,412 lb)
  - L 100-30: 33,685 kg (74,262 lb)
- Max payload: L 100-20: 21,132 kg (46,588 lb)
  - L 100-30: 23,014 kg (50,738 lb)
- Max ramp weight: 70,670 kg (155,800 lb)
- Max T-O weight: 70,308 kg (155,000 lb)
- Max landing weight:
  - L 100-20: 58,970 kg (130,000 lb)
  - L 100-30: 61,235 kg (135,000 lb)
- Max zero-fuel weight:
  - L 100-20: 54,430 kg (120,000 lb)
  - L 100-30: 56,700 kg (125,000 lb)
- Max wing loading: 433·5 kg/m² (88·8 lb/sq ft)
- Max power loading: 5·23 kg/kW (8·6 lb/ehp)

PERFORMANCE (at max T-O weight):
- Max cruising speed at 6,100 m (20,000 ft) at 54,430 kg (120,000 lb) AUW: 314 knots (581 km/h; 361 mph)
- Landing speed:
  - L 100-20: 126 knots (233 km/h; 145 mph)
  - L 100-30: 128 knots (237 km/h; 147 mph)
- Max rate of climb at S/L: 579 m (1,900 ft)/min
- Min ground turning radius: L 100-20: 26·8 m (88 ft)
  - L 100-30: 27·5 m (90 ft)
- Runway LCN: asphalt: 37
  - concrete: 42
- FAR T-O field length: 1,830 m (6,000 ft)
- FAR landing field length, at max landing weight:
  - L 100-20: 1,450 m (4,760 ft)
  - L 100-30: 1,472 m (4,830 ft)
- Range with max payload, 45 min reserves:
  - L 100-20: 2,220 nm (4,113 km; 2,556 miles)
  - L 100-30: 1,584 nm (2,935 km; 1,824 miles)
- Range with zero payload, 45 min reserves:
  - L 100-20: 3,660 nm (6,783 km; 4,215 miles)
  - L 100-30: 3,840 nm (7,117 km; 4,422 miles)

OPERATIONAL NOISE CHARACTERISTICS (FAR Pt 36):
- T-O noise level: 98·4 EPNdB
- Approach noise level: 99·1 EPNdB
- Sideline noise level: 93·9 EPNdB

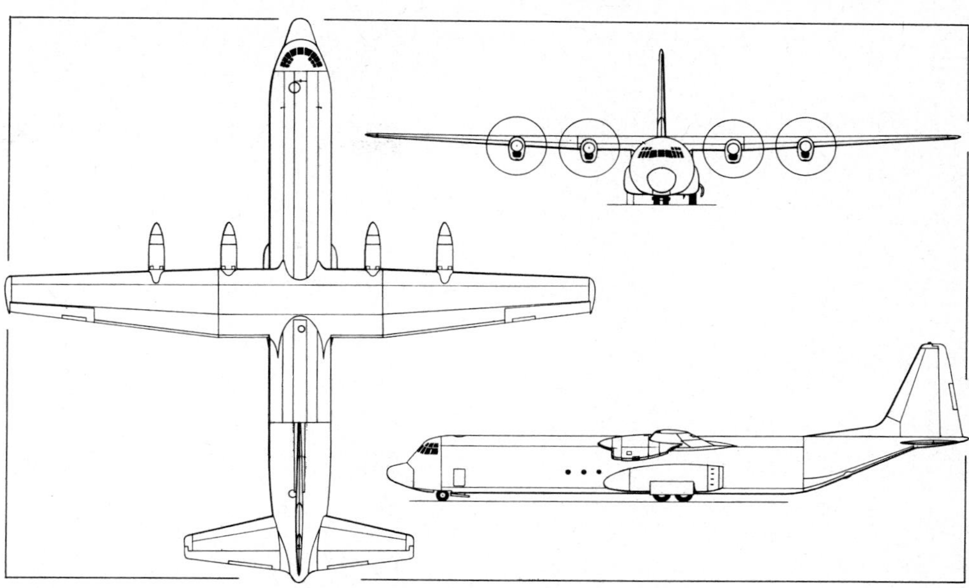

Lockheed L 100-50 commercial Hercules *(Pilot Press)*

LOCKHEED MODEL L 100-50 HERCULES

Lockheed-Georgia announced on 5 September 1976 that it had completed preliminary design work on a new high-capacity version of the Hercules, designated L 100-50. Extra capacity results from 'stretching' the L 100 basic airframe by an additional 10·67 m (35 ft 0 in), with a plug 6·10 m (20 ft 0 in) long forward of the wing and another 4·57 m (15 ft 0 in) long aft of the wing. This would provide a cargo compartment length of 26·03 m (85 ft 4¾ in), offering a bulk capacity of 229·4 m³ (8,100 cu ft). To cater for the proposed maximum take-off weight of 77,110 kg (170,000 lb), strengthening of the wing and landing gear structure is included in the design.

This new version of the commercial L 100 Hercules offers a maximum payload of 27,215 kg (60,000 lb), which could be carried over a range of 1,184 nm (2,193 km; 1,363 miles). For palletised cargo operations this represents a 40 per cent improvement in revenue payload capability by comparison with the current production L 100-30 Hercules. The cargo compartment would be able to accommodate nine 2·44 × 3·00 × 2·69 m (96 × 118 × 106 in) pallets, plus a smaller tenth pallet on the ramp, providing a total palletised volume of 180·32 m³ (6,368 cu ft).

LOCKHEED L 400 TWIN HERCULES

Lockheed announced on 25 January 1977 that the company had designed a twin-engined derivative of the C-130 Hercules. This resulted from a preliminary canvass in 30 countries which indicated a potential demand for a freight aircraft in this category.

Designated L 400, this aircraft would have a hold the same size as that of a C-130, and would be able to carry 10,206 kg (22,500 lb) of cargo over a range of 550 nm (1,018 km; 633 miles). Structural changes by comparison with the C-130 would affect parts of the wings, the power plant and main landing gear; the new aircraft would also have simplified systems and instrumentation. Many components and spares would be common to both versions, and the L 400 would be able to use C-130 ground handling and test equipment, as well as training programmes. Fuselage and tail unit would be substantially the same as those of the C-130, except that the flight deck would be similar to that of the Model L 100 series.

Changes to the wing would include a reduction of 6·70 m (22 ft 0 in) in the span of the centre-section. The existing outer wing panels would be retained and a new constant-chord wingtip, 1·37 m (4 ft 6 in) long, fitted outboard of each aileron. Considerably lower gross weight allows simplification of the landing gear, and the two tandem wheels on each side of the C-130 would be replaced by a single wheel on each main unit. Requiring a crew of only two, instead of four, it has been estimated that the cost of the L 400 would be approximately 25 per cent less than that of the four-engined C-130.

The description of the C-130H applies also to the proposed L 400, except as detailed below:

TYPE: Short-range civil or military transport.

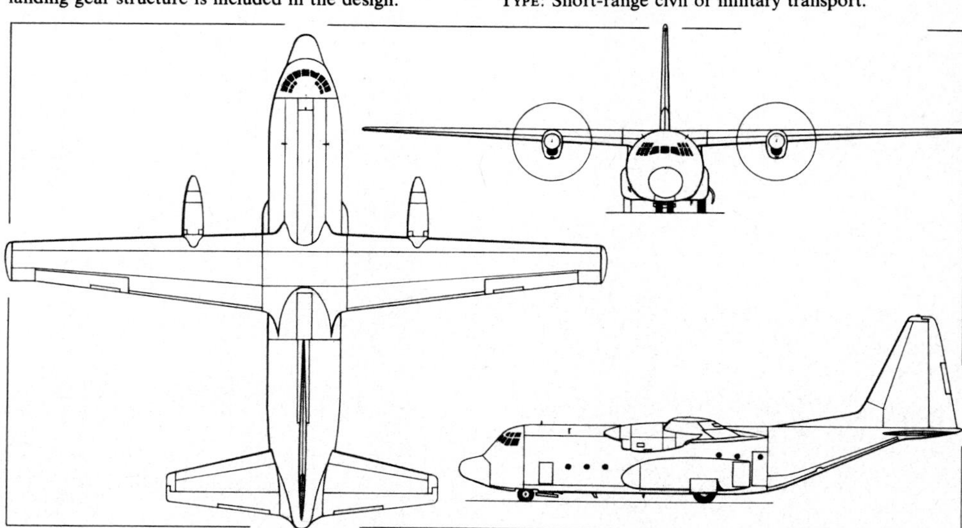

Lockheed L 400 Twin Hercules short-range transport *(Pilot Press)*

Wings: Generally as for C-130H, except span of centre-section reduced and new constant-chord wingtips fitted.

Fuselage and Tail Unit: Generally as for C-130H, except for changes in flight deck.

Landing Gear: As for C-130H, except single wheel on each main unit.

Power Plant: Two 3,424 kW (4,591 shp) Allison 501-D22D turboprop engines, each driving a Hamilton Standard four-blade metal constant-speed fully-feathering reversible-pitch propeller. Water-alcohol injection system. Fuel in two main and two auxiliary integral wing tanks with total capacity of 13,472 kg (29,700 lb).

Accommodation: Generally the same as C-130H, except crew of two on flight deck. Flight deck and main cabin pressurised and air-conditioned. Standard loads could include 2½-ton truck and 105 mm howitzer; 155 mm howitzer and its high-speed tractor; five pallets each 1,814 kg (4,000 lb); four containers each 2·4 × 2·4 × 3·0 m (8 × 8 × 10 ft); troops (max) 92; paratroops (max) 64; litters 74 and 2 attendants.

Systems: Air-conditioning and pressurisation systems. Two independent hydraulic systems, powered by engine-driven pumps, each with an electrically-operated auxiliary backup pump. Electrical system supplied by two engine-driven 60/90kVA generators. Auxiliary generator driven by APU, which can be operated in flight.

Avionics: Standard avionics include radar, flight director, gyro/magnetic compass, VHF nav/com. A wide range of options available to customer's requirements.

Dimensions, external:
- Wing span: 36·48 m (119 ft 8¼ in)
- Wing chord at root: 4·88 m (16 ft 0 in)
- Wing chord, mean: 3·93 m (12 ft 10¾ in)
- Wing aspect ratio: 9·63
- Length overall: 29·81 m (97 ft 9½ in)
- Height overall: approx 11·58 m (38 ft 0 in)
- Tailplane span: 16·05 m (52 ft 8 in)
- Wheel track: 4·36 m (14 ft 3½ in)
- Wheelbase: 10·55 m (34 ft 7¼ in)
- Propeller diameter: 4·27 m (14 ft 0 in)
- Propeller ground clearance: 1·89 m (6 ft 2½ in)

Dimensions, internal:
- Cargo compartment:
  - Length excl ramp: 12·50 m (41 ft 0 in)
  - Length incl ramp: 15·55 m (51 ft 0 in)
  - Max width: 3·05 m (10 ft 0 in)
  - Max height: 2·74 m (9 ft 0 in)
  - Floor area, incl ramp: 49·54 m² (533 sq ft)
  - Volume, incl ramp: 127·4 m³ (4,500 cu ft)

Areas:
- Wings, gross: 136·81 m² (1,472 sq ft)
- Fin: 20·90 m² (225 sq ft)
- Rudder, incl tab: 6·97 m² (75 sq ft)
- Tailplane: 35·40 m² (381 sq ft)
- Elevators, incl tabs: 14·40 m² (155 sq ft)

Weights and Loadings (estimated):
- Weight empty: 23,971 kg (52,847 lb)
- Operating weight empty: 24,449 kg (53,900 lb)
- Max payload: 11,385 kg (25,100 lb)
- Max ramp weight: 38,329 kg (84,500 lb)
- Max T-O weight: 38,102 kg (84,000 lb)
- Max landing weight: 37,648 kg (83,000 lb)
- Max wing loading: 278·6 kg/m² (57·07 lb/sq ft)
- Max power loading: 5·56 kg/kW (9·15 lb/shp)

Performance (estimated, at max T-O weight):
- Cruising speed: 250 knots (463 km/h; 288 mph)
- Max rate of climb at S/L: 488 m (1,600 ft)/min
- Rate of climb at S/L, one engine out: 114 m (375 ft)/min
- Service ceiling: 8,230 m (27,000 ft)
- Service ceiling, one engine out: 3,960 m (13,000 ft)
- Min ground turning radius: 21·18 m (69 ft 6 in)
- T-O run: 1,018 m (3,340 ft)
- Landing run: 915 m (3,000 ft)
- Range with 10,206 kg (22,500 lb) payload, 5% fuel reserve plus 30 min loiter: 550 nm (1,018 km; 633 miles)
- Ferry range with max fuel, 408 kg (900 lb) payload, 5% fuel reserve plus 30 min loiter: 3,050 nm (5,649 km; 3,510 miles)

LOCKHEED MODEL 1329-25 JETSTAR II

The Lockheed JetStar II, which was first announced in the Summer of 1973, has an airframe generally similar to that of the original JetStar (1973-74 *Jane's*), but with detail changes in configuration and equipment.

Design of the Model 1329-25 began in October 1972. The major change involved the installation of four Garrett-AiResearch TFE 731-3 turbofan engines, each flat rated at 16·5 kN (3,700 lb st) to 24·4°C (76°F), to replace the 14·7 kN (3,300 lb st) Pratt & Whitney JT12 turbojet engines of the earlier JetStar. This power plant offers significant improvement in both range and noise levels, as well as allowing an increase in maximum take-off weight.

Production of the JetStar II, at Lockheed-Georgia's Marietta plant, began in the Spring of 1975, and the first aircraft off the line flew on 18 August 1976. FAA certification of the JetStar II was granted on 14 December 1976. By January 1979, a total of 31 JetStar IIs had been built by Lockheed-Georgia. It was intended to complete nine more during 1979 and then to suspend production. It is unlikely that Lockheed will resume JetStar II manufacture, but Garrett-AiResearch will continue to offer its re-engining scheme to convert early JetStars to TFE 731 turbofan power. The first AiResearch Aviation Company 731 JetStar conversion flew for the first time on 10 July 1974, and the first production conversion on 18 March 1976.

The following abbreviated description applies to new-build JetStar IIs; a full structural description can be found in the 1978-79 *Jane's*.

Type: Four-turbofan light utility transport.

Power Plant: Four Garrett-AiResearch TFE 731-3 turbofan engines, flat rated at 16·5 kN (3,700 lb st) to 24·4°C (76°F), mounted in lateral pairs on sides of rear fuselage. Thrust reversers fitted. Air intake anti-icing provided by engine bleed air. Fuel in four integral wing tanks and two non-removable external auxiliary tanks glove-mounted on the wings. Capacity of numbers 1 and 4 internal tanks each 1,420 litres (375 US gallons); numbers 2 and 3 internal tanks each 1,476 litres (390 US gallons), auxiliary tanks each 2,188 litres (578 US gallons). Total fuel capacity 10,168 litres (2,686 US gallons). Gravity refuelling point above each tank, or single-point pressure refuelling from starboard wing root. Oil capacity 24·2 litres (6·4 US gallons).

Accommodation: Normal accommodation for crew of two and ten passengers, with wardrobe, galley and toilet aft of cabin and baggage compartments fore and aft. Layout and furnishing can be varied to suit customer's requirements. Optional jump-seat available for crew compartment. Door at forward end of fuselage, on port side, opens by moving inward and sliding aft. The fourth window aft on each side of the cabin is a CAR Type IV emegency exit, of plug type and removed inward. Accommodation heated, ventilated, air-conditioned and pressurised. High-pressure oxygen system for passengers and crew standard. Integral electric heaters for winscreen anti-icing and demisting.

Dimensions, external:
- Wing span: 16·60 m (54 ft 5 in)
- Wing chord at root: 4·16 m (13 ft 7¾ in)
- Wing chord at tip: 1·55 m (5 ft 1 in)
- Wing aspect ratio: 5·27
- Length overall: 18·42 m (60 ft 5 in)
- Length of fuselage: 17·92 m (58 ft 9½ in)
- Height overall: 6·23 m (20 ft 5 in)
- Tailplane span: 7·55 m (24 ft 9 in)
- Wheel track: 3·75 m (12 ft 3½ in)
- Wheelbase: 6·28 m (20 ft 7 in)
- Cabin door: Height: 1·50 m (4 ft 11 in)
  - Width: 0·67 m (2 ft 2½ in)
  - Height to sill: approx 1·37 m (4 ft 6 in)
- Servicing door (underfuselage), diameter: 0·61 m (2 ft 0 in)
- Emergency exits, each: Height: 0·49 m (1 ft 7¼ in)
  - Width: 0·66 m (2 ft 2½ in)

Dimensions, internal:
- Cabin, excl flight deck:
  - Length: 8·59 m (28 ft 2½ in)
  - Max width: 1·89 m (6 ft 2½ in)
  - Max height: 1·85 m (6 ft 1 in)
  - Volume: 24·07 m³ (850 cu ft)
- Baggage hold volume:
  - stbd forward: 1·25 m³ (43·1 cu ft)
  - port forward: 0·70 m³ (24·8 cu ft)
  - centre aft: 1·05 m³ (37·0 cu ft)

Weights and Loadings:
- Basic operating weight: 11,226 kg (24,750 lb)
- Max payload: 1,247 kg (2,750 lb)
- Max ramp weight: 20,298 kg (44,750 lb)
- Max T-O weight: 20,185 kg (44,500 lb)
- Max landing weight: 16,329 kg (36,000 lb)
- Max zero-fuel weight: 12,473 kg (27,500 lb)
- Max wing loading: 400·4 kg/m² (82·0 lb/sq ft)
- Max power loading: 305·8 kg/kN (3·01 lb/lb st)

Performance (at max T-O weight except where indicated):
- Never-exceed speed: Mach 0·87
- Max level and cruising speed at 9,145 m (30,000 ft): 475 knots (880 km/h; 547 mph)
- Econ cruising speed at 10,670 m (35,000 ft): 438 knots (811 km/h; 504 mph)
- Stalling speed, T-O flap setting: 125 knots (232 km/h; 144 mph)
- Max rate of climb at S/L: 1,265 m (4,150 ft)/min
- Rate of climb at S/L, one engine out: 686 m (2,250 ft)/min
- Service ceiling: 13,105 m (43,000 ft)
- Service ceiling, one engine out: 11,580 m (38,000 ft)
- T-O to 15 m (50 ft): 1,570 m (5,150 ft)
- Landing from 15 m (50 ft) at max landing weight: 1,271 m (4,170 ft)
- Range with max fuel, 30 min reserves: 2,770 nm (5,132 km; 3,189 miles)
- Range with max payload, 30 min reserves: 2,600 nm (4,818 km; 2,994 miles)

Operational Noise Characteristics (FAR Pt 36):
- Take-off noise level: 93·1 EPNdB
- Approach noise level: 97·4 EPNdB
- Sideline noise level: 87·7 EPNdB

LOCKHEED C-141B STARLIFTER

Operational experience with the Lockheed C-141 StarLifter by the USAF's Military Airlift Command emphasised the need to provide these aircraft with flight refuelling capability. Additionally, it had been found that on many occasions the cargo compartment was physically packed to capacity without the aircraft's maximum weight limitation being reached. As a result, the USAF awarded Lockheed-Georgia a $24·3 million contract in mid-1976

Lockheed Model 1329-25 JetStar II twelve-seat executive transport

Lockheed YC-141B 'stretched' StarLifter about to refuel in flight from a Boeing KC-135A over Edwards AFB, California

to extend the fuselage of an existing C-141 and, at the same time, to provide this aircraft with in-flight refuelling equipment.

Designated YC-141B, the prototype conversion was rolled out on 8 January 1977 and made its first flight on 24 March. It was fitted with flight refuelling equipment, and lengthened by the insertion of a 4·06 m (13 ft 4 in) fuselage plug immediately forward of the wing, and by a similar 3·05 m (10 ft 0 in) plug immediately aft of the wing. In addition, the YC-141B has improved wing root fairings to decrease drag, so providing higher speed and reducing fuel consumption. These fairings also change lift distribution, permitting the carriage of increased payload without affecting the fatigue life of the wing. The cargo compartment has its floor area increased by 21·65 m² (233 sq ft) and its volume increased by 59·47 m³ (2,100 cu ft). In it can be accommodated thirteen standard 463L pallets, instead of the ten carried by an unmodified C-141. The four 93·4 kN (21,000 lb st) Pratt & Whitney TF33-P-7 turbofan engines are unchanged.

The first flight of the YC-141B was made a month ahead of schedule, at a cost $4 million below budget. A flight test programme was completed in July 1977, after 79 flights totalling 155 h 56 min.

In June 1978 Lockheed received the first instalment of a USAF contract aimed at converting all 272 C-141A StarLifters at present operational to C-141B standard. In addition to the prototype conversion, the programme covers work on 27 aircraft in FY 1978, 85 in FY 1979, 124 in FY 1980 and 35 in FY 1981. The last modification, undertaken at Lockheed's Marietta, Georgia, factory, is scheduled to be completed by July 1982.

The USAF's C-141A fleet logged its 5,000,000th flying hour in February 1978.

DIMENSIONS, EXTERNAL:
- Wing span: 48·74 m (159 ft 11 in)
- Wing sweepback: 25°
- Length overall: 51·29 m (168 ft 3½ in)
- Height overall: 11·96 m (39 ft 3 in)

DIMENSIONS, INTERNAL:
- Cargo compartment: Length: 28·44 m (93 ft 3½ in)
  - Max height: 2·77 m (9 ft 1 in)
  - Max width: 3·11 m (10 ft 2½ in)
  - Usable cargo volume: 322·71 m³ (11,399 cu ft)

WEIGHTS:
- Max ramp weight (2·25*g*): 156,444 kg (344,900 lb)
- Max ramp weight (2·5*g*): 147,418 kg (325,000 lb)

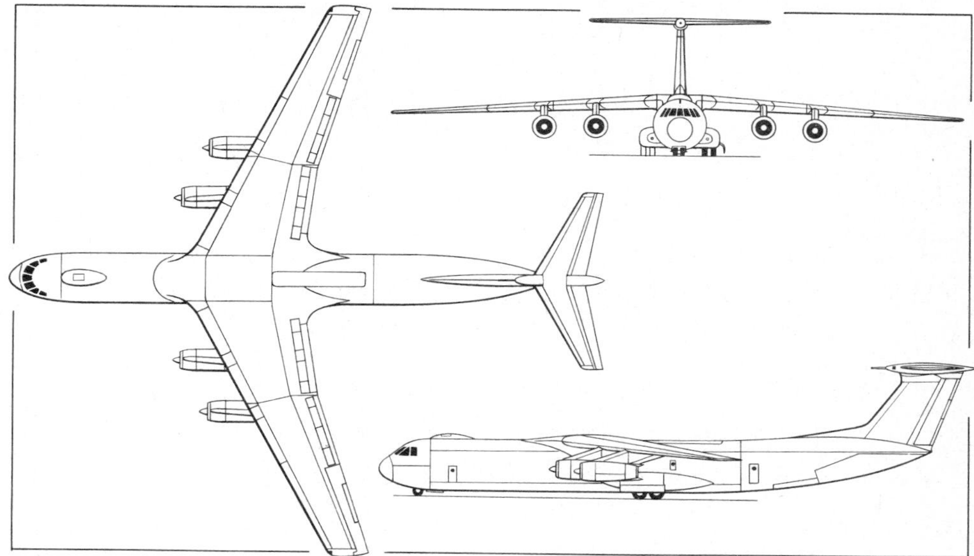

Lockheed YC-141B lengthened version of the StarLifter logistics transport *(Pilot Press)*

- Max payload (2·25*g*): 40,439 kg (89,152 lb)
- Max MAC payload (2·5*g*): 31,242 kg (68,877 lb)
- Operating weight (MAC): 67,970 kg (149,848 lb)
- Design landing weight: 116,800 kg (257,500 lb)
- Max landing weight: 153,224 kg (337,800 lb)

PERFORMANCE (at max T-O weight, except where indicated):
- Max cruising speed: 495 knots (916 km/h; 569 mph)
- Long-range cruising speed: 445 knots (824 km/h; 512 mph)
- Max rate of climb at S/L: 890 m (2,920 ft)/min
- T-O run: 1,829 m (6,000 ft)
- Landing run at design landing weight: 1,174 m (3,850 ft)
- Range with max payload: 2,780 nm (5,148 km; 3,200 miles)
- Ferry range: 5,550 nm (10,278 km; 6,386 miles)

LOCKHEED C-5 GALAXY

USAF designation: C-5A

In early 1978 Lockheed received a $24·3 million USAF contract to manufacture two new sets of wings for the C-5A, of a design intended to reduce stress and increase service life to 30,000 h. Apart from the moving surfaces, these wings are of virtually new design, using 7175-T73511 aluminium alloy for greater strength and increased resistance to corrosion. One set is for ground testing, and one for flight trials in 1980. If these tests are successful it is planned to fit them to the 77 Galaxies still in operational service with the USAF, between 1982 and 1987.

Full structural and specification details of the C-5A can be found in the 1975-76 *Jane's*. An abbreviated entry, with illustrations, appeared in the 1978-79 edition.

MARSH

MARSH AVIATION COMPANY

ADDRESS: 5060 East Falcon Drive, Mesa, Arizona 85205
Telephone: (602) 832 3770
VICE-PRESIDENT: William G. Walker Jr

MARSH/ROCKWELL S2R-T TURBO THRUSH

Marsh Aviation Company has converted the piston-engined Rockwell Thrush Commander to turbine power by the installation of a Garrett-AiResearch TPE 331-1-101 turboprop engine. Derated to 447 kW (600 shp) for this conversion, the full 580 kW (778 shp) output of the TPE 331 is available in emergency. This engine drives a Hartzell constant-speed fully-feathering and reversible-pitch propeller. Single-cycle air-conditioning and cockpit heating provided by engine bleed air, and agricultural spraypump is also operated by bleed air. The empty weight of the Turbo Thrush is 227 kg (500 lb) less than that of the Rockwell Thrush Commander, providing increased payload capability and improved speed and performance. For agricultural operators working in remote areas the TPE 331 installation has the advantage that ordinary automotive diesel fuel can be used if jet fuel is not available.

Following more than 600 hours of flight by two prototypes, an FAA Supplemental Type Certificate was issued. The first production conversion was handed over in September 1976. Orders for conversions totalled 56 by 1 January 1979, of which 34 had been delivered to operators in the USA, Europe and the Middle East.

Marsh Turbo Thrush, a turbine-engined conversion of the Rockwell International Thrush Commander

DIMENSIONS, EXTERNAL: As for Thrush Commander except:
- Length overall: 9·27 m (30 ft 5 in)

WEIGHTS AND LOADINGS: As for Thrush Commander except:
- Weight empty: 1,633 kg (3,600 lb)

Typical operating weight (CAR Pt 8) 3,538 kg (7,800 lb)

Performance (at 2,721 kg; 6,000 lb T-O weight, except where indicated):

Never-exceed speed	138 knots (256 km/h; 159 mph) IAS
Max level speed at 4,420 m (14,500 ft)	178 knots (330 km/h; 205 mph)
Econ cruising speed at 4,420 m (14,500 ft)	139 knots (257 km/h; 160 mph)
Cruising speed, 50% power	127 knots (235 km/h; 146 mph)
Working speed, 50% power	108·5 knots (201 km/h; 125 mph)
Stalling speed, flaps up	41·5 knots (77 km/h; 48 mph)
Stalling speed, flaps down	38 knots (71 km/h; 44 mph)
Stalling speed, flaps up at normal landing weight	39 knots (72·5 km/h; 45 mph)
Stalling speed, flaps down at normal landing weight	37 knots (69 km/h; 43 mph)
Max rate of climb at S/L	915 m (3,000 ft)/min
Service ceiling	7,620 m (25,000 ft)
T-O run	183 m (600 ft)
Landing run	91 m (300 ft)
Range with max payload	278 nm (515 km; 320 miles)
Ferry range, at 60% power	521 nm (966 km; 600 miles)

MAULE

MAULE AIRCRAFT CORPORATION

Head Office and Works: Spence Air Base, Moultrie, Georgia 31768

Telephone: (912) 985 2045

President: B. D. Maule

Vice-President: Mrs B. D. (June) Maule (Treasurer)

Engineering Manager: Lewis E. Blomeley

Sales Manager: Brenda Corbin

This company was formed to manufacture the Maule M-4 four-seat light aircraft, production of which ended in 1975. It transferred to new facilities in Moultrie, Georgia, in September 1968, and is now concentrating on production of the uprated M-5 Lunar Rocket.

The company has also designed auxiliary fuel transfer tanks for installation in the outboard wing bays of M-4 and M-5 aircraft. Providing a total usable additional fuel capacity of 87 litres (23 US gallons), these tanks offer owners of the M-4 or M-5 a minimum-payload range of 650 nm (1,200 km; 750 miles). FAA approval of the modification was given on 31 October 1973.

Maule M-5 Lunar Rocket four-seat light aircraft

MAULE M-5 LUNAR ROCKET

Developed from the M-4 Strata-Rocket, the M-5 Lunar Rocket series has a 30% increase in flap area and enlarged tail surfaces to improve short-field performance and rate of climb. Two prototypes were built originally. First to fly, on 1 November 1971, was the M-5-220C prototype, powered by a 164 kW (220 hp) Franklin 6A-350-C1 engine. Manufacture of this version has since been discontinued as the Franklin engine is no longer in production in the USA.

Versions available currently are as follows:

M-5-180C. With 134 kW (180 hp) Lycoming O-360-C1F flat-four engine, driving a Hartzell two-blade constant-speed metal propeller. Prototype first flown on 18 May 1978.

M-5-210C. Basic model with 156·5 kW (210 hp) Continental IO-360-D flat-six engine, driving a McCauley two-blade constant-speed metal propeller. Second prototype Lunar Rocket, flown on 16 October 1973, was of this version; FAA certification awarded on 28 December 1973.

M-5-210TC. Cargo version with 156·5 kW (210 hp) Lycoming TO-360-C1A6D flat-four turbocharged engine, driving a Hartzell two-blade constant-speed metal propeller. Prototype first flown on 9 August 1978.

M-5-235C. Version with the more powerful 175 kW (235 hp) Lycoming O-540-J1A5D flat-six engine, driving a larger-diameter Hartzell two-blade constant-speed metal propeller. Certification programme completed on 6 April 1976.

Maule Patroller. Civil patrol version of Lunar Rocket (any power plant), with any or all of the following modifications: Plexiglas-covered doors for improved view; port side rear observation window; 3·5 million candlepower belly-mounted manually-controlled searchlight; 100/200W siren and public address system; 28V electrical system; specialised radios to customer's requirements.

The M-5-210C/M-5-235C is a STOL aircraft, the 'C' in its designation implying that it has double aft doors on the starboard side to facilitate the loading of cargo.

Type: Four-seat light aircraft.

Wings: Braced high-wing monoplane. Streamline-section V bracing strut each side. USA 35B (modified) wing section. Dihedral 1°. Incidence 0° 30′. All-metal two-spar structure with metal covering and glassfibre tips. All-metal ailerons and two-position flaps. Ailerons linked with rudder tab, so that aircraft can be controlled in flight by using only the control wheel in the cockpit. Cambered wingtips standard.

Fuselage: Welded 4130 steel tube structure. Covered with glassfibre, except for metal doors and aluminium skin around cabin.

Tail Unit: Braced steel tube structure with glassfibre covering. Trim tab in port elevator. Servo tab in rudder linked to aileron movement. Starboard rudder trim via spring to starboard rudder pedal.

Landing Gear: Non-retractable tailwheel type. Maule oleo-pneumatic shock-absorbers on main units. Maule steerable tailwheel. Cleveland main wheels with Goodyear or McCreary tyres size 17 × 6·00-6, pressure 1·79 bars (26 lb/sq in). Tailwheel tyre size 8 × 3·50-4, pressure 1·03-1·38 bars (15-20 lb/sq in). Cleveland hydraulic disc brakes. Parking brake. Oversize tyres, size 20 × 8·50-6 (pressure 1·24 bars; 18 lb/sq in), and fairings aft of main wheels optional. Provisions for fitting optional Edo Model 248B2440, Pee Kay Model 2300 or Aqua Model 2400 floats, or Federal skis Model C2200H or C3000H.

Power Plant: One flat-four or flat-six engine, driving a constant-speed propeller, as detailed in model listings. Two fuel tanks in wings with total usable capacity of 151 litres (40 US gallons). Optional auxiliary fuel tanks in outer wings, each with usable capacity of 43·5 litres (11·5 US gallons). Maximum usable fuel capacity 238 litres (63 US gallons). Refuelling points on wing upper surface. Oil capacity: M-5-210C 9·5 litres (2·5 US gallons); M-5-235C 11·4 litres (3·0 US gallons).

Accommodation: Pilot and three passengers on two front bucket seats and rear bench seat, or optional quickly-removed rear sling seat. One door on port side of fuselage, hinged at front edge and opening forward. Three doors on starboard side of fuselage, the forward and centre doors hinged at the front edge, the rear baggage door hinged at the rear edge. The centre and aft doors can be opened together to provide an opening 1·24 m (4 ft 1 in) wide to facilitate loading of bulky cargo. Accommodation heated and ventilated.

Systems: Hydraulic system for brakes only. Electrical system powered by 60A engine-driven alternator. 28V electrical system optional.

Avionics and Equipment: A wide range of Collins Micro Line, King, Genave and Narco communication and navigation equipment is available to customer's requirements. Blind-flying instrumentation, autopilot, wing levelling system and automatic glideslope optional.

Dimensions, external:

Wing span	9·40 m (30 ft 10 in)
Wing chord, constant	1·60 m (5 ft 3 in)
Wing aspect ratio	5·71
Length overall:	
M-5-180C, M-5-210C	6·93 m (22 ft 9 in)
M-5-210TC	7·26 m (23 ft 10 in)
M-5-235C	7·16 m (23 ft 6 in)
Height overall	1·89 m (6 ft 2½ in)
Tailplane span	3·28 m (10 ft 9 in)
Wheel track	1·83 m (6 ft 0 in)
Wheelbase	4·82 m (15 ft 10 in)
Propeller diameter: M-5-210C	1·88 m (6 ft 2 in)
M-5-235C	1·98 m (6 ft 6 in)
Cabin doors (fwd, each): Height	0·84 m (2 ft 9 in)
Width	0·76 m (2 ft 6 in)
Height to sill	0·94 m (3 ft 1 in)
Cabin door (centre, stbd):	
Height	0·75 m (2 ft 5½ in)
Width	0·69 m (2 ft 3 in)
Height to sill	0·76 m (2 ft 6 in)
Baggage door (aft, stbd): Height	0·58 m (1 ft 11 in)
Width	0·56 m (1 ft 10 in)
Height to sill	0·61 m (2 ft 0 in)

Areas:

Wings, gross	14·67 m² (157·9 sq ft)
Ailerons (total)	1·19 m² (12·8 sq ft)
Trailing-edge flaps (total)	1·75 m² (18·8 sq ft)
Fin	1·22 m² (13·14 sq ft)
Rudder, incl tab	0·54 m² (5·83 sq ft)
Tailplane	1·32 m² (14·2 sq ft)
Elevators, incl tab	1·58 m² (17·0 sq ft)

Weights and Loadings (A: M-5-180C; B: M-5-210C; C: M-5-210TC); D: M-5-235C):

Basic operating weight: B	601 kg (1,325 lb)
Weight empty: A	601 kg (1,325 lb)
B	612 kg (1,350 lb)
C, D	635 kg (1,400 lb)
Max T-O and landing weight:	
All versions	1,043 kg (2,300 lb)
Max wing loading: All versions	71·3 kg/m² (14·6 lb/sq ft)
Max power loading: A	7·78 kg/kW (12·78 lb/hp)
B, C	6·66 kg/kW (10·95 lb/hp)
D	5·96 kg/kW (9·79 lb/hp)

Performance (at max T-O weight. A: M-5-180C; B: M-5-210C; C: M-5-210TC; D: M-5-235C):

Never-exceed speed:	
B, D	156 knots (290 km/h; 180 mph)

Maule Patroller special-purpose version of the M-5, with underbelly searchlight, as operated by Monroe, Louisiana, Police Department

Max level speed at optimum altitude:
A 117 knots (217 km/h; 135 mph)
B 137 knots (254 km/h; 158 mph)
C 165 knots (306 km/h; 190 mph)
D 149 knots (277 km/h; 172 mph)
Max cruising speed at optimum altitude:
A 110 knots (204 km/h; 127 mph)
B 137 knots (254 km/h; 158 mph)
C 148 knots (274 km/h; 170 mph)
D 149 knots (277 km/h; 172 mph)
Econ cruising speed, 65% power at 2,440 m (8,000 ft):
A 106 knots (196 km/h; 122 mph)
B 130 knots (241 km/h; 150 mph) CAS
C 135 knots (251 km/h; 156 mph)
D 139 knots (257 km/h; 160 mph) CAS
Stalling speed, flaps up:
B 53 knots (98 km/h; 61 mph)
Stalling speed, flaps down:
B 49 knots (90 km/h; 56 mph)
Max rate of climb at S/L: A 229 m (750 ft)/min
B 380 m (1,250 ft)/min
C, D 411 m (1,350 ft)/min
Service ceiling: A 4,570 m (15,000 ft)
B 5,485 m (18,000 ft)
C 7,620 m (25,000 ft)
D 6,100 m (20,000 ft)
T-O and landing run: B, D 122 m (400 ft)
T-O to and landing from 15 m (50 ft):
B, D 183 m (600 ft)
Range with max standard fuel:
A 426 nm (789 km; 490 miles)
B 521 nm (966 km; 600 miles)
C 391 nm (724 km; 450 miles)
D 478 nm (885 km; 550 miles)
Range with max fuel, 30 min reserves:
A 651 nm (1,207 km; 750 miles)
B 760 nm (1,408 km; 875 miles)
C 625 nm (1,159 km; 720 miles)
D 695 nm (1,287 km; 800 miles)

MCDONNELL DOUGLAS
MCDONNELL DOUGLAS CORPORATION

Head Office and Works: Box 516, St Louis, Missouri 63166
Telephone: (314) 232 0232
Telex: 44-857
Directors:
John C. Brizendine
George H. Capps
William H. Danforth
Donald W. Douglas Jr
George S. Graff
Robert L. Johnson
Edwin S. Jones
Robert C. Little
Donald S. Macdonald
James S. McDonnell (Chairman)
James S. McDonnell III
John F. McDonnell
Sanford N. McDonnell (President)
James T. McMillan
William R. Orthwein Jr
John T. Sant
Chairman: James S. McDonnell
President and Chief Executive Officer: Sanford N. McDonnell
Corporate Executive Vice-President: John F. McDonnell
Corporate Officers:
Harold D. Altis (Vice-President, Engineering and Research)
David C. Arnold (Vice-President)
Alvin L. Boyd (Vice-President)
Erwin F. Branahl (Vice-President)
John C. Brizendine (Vice-President)
Ben G. Bromberg (Vice-President)
Jerry G. Brown (Vice-President, Treasurer)
Robert F. Cortinovis (Vice-President, Operations)
John E. Crosthwait (Vice-President, Far East)
Richard J. Davis (Vice-President, External Relations)
Walter E. Diggs Jr (Secretary and Counsel)
John E. Forry (Vice-President)
Charles M. Forsyth (Vice-President)
George S. Graff (Vice-President)
Gordon M. Graham (Vice-President, Washington)
Robert L. Harmon (Vice-President)
Robert L. Johnson (Vice-President)
Ray J. Kleinberg (Asst Controller Financial Services)
Warren E. Kraemer (Vice-President, Europe)
Robert C. Krone (Vice-President, Personnel)
Robert C. Little (Vice-President, Engineering and Marketing)
James S. McDonnell III (Vice-President, Marketing)
James T. McMillan (Vice-President)
Donald Malvern (Vice-President)
William R. Orthwein Jr (Vice-President)
A. Joseph Quackenbush (Vice-President)
Albert J. Redway Jr (Vice-President, Eastern Region)
John T. Sant (Vice-President and General Counsel)
Stanley J. Sheinbein (Asst Treasurer)
Harry I. Sieferman (Tax Officer)
Albert H. Smith Jr (Vice-President, Contracts, and Controller)
John W. Walbran (Asst General Counsel)

Staff Officers:
R. Joseph Alagna (Vice-President, Material)
Donald P. Ames (Vice-President, McDonnell Douglas Research Laboratories)
Charles A. Gaskill (Vice-President, Properties and Facilities)
Arthur W. Hyland (Vice-President, Accounting)
Leo I. Mirowitz (Vice-President, Corporate Diversification)
William E. Schowengerdt (Vice-President, Auditing)
Howard C. Todt (Vice-President, Quality Assurance)
Michael Witunski (Vice-President)

McDonnell Douglas Research Laboratories
Box 516, St Louis, Missouri 63166
Director: Dr Donald P. Ames

McDonnell Douglas Corporation was formed on 28 April 1967, by the merger of the former Douglas Aircraft Company Inc and McDonnell Company. It encompasses both of the original companies and their subsidiaries.

There are six major operating components of McDonnell Douglas Corporation, as follows:

Douglas Aircraft Company
See pages 386-392 of this section
McDonnell Douglas Astronautics Company
See Missiles and Spaceflight sections
McDonnell Aircraft Company
See following entry
McDonnell Douglas Automation Company
Box 516, St Louis, Missouri 63166
President: William R. Orthwein Jr
McDonnell Douglas Electronics Company
St Charles, Missouri
President: David C. Arnold
McDonnell Douglas—Tulsa
Tulsa, Oklahoma
Vice-President and General Manager: O. Lee Howser
Subsidiaries:

Subsidiaries of McDonnell Douglas Corporation include McDonnell Douglas Canada Ltd, Malton, Ontario; McDonnell Douglas (Japan) Ltd, Tokyo; McDonnell Douglas International Sales Corporation, St Louis, Missouri; MDC Realty Company, Long Beach, California; and McDonnell Douglas Finance Corporation, Long Beach, California.

At 1 July 1979, McDonnell Douglas employed a total of 76,028 people, working in 72 communities in 29 states, the District of Columbia, Kwajalein in the Pacific Ocean, and eleven nations including Australia, Canada, England, West Germany and Japan. Total office, engineering, laboratory and manufacturing floor area was 2,379,392 m² (25,612,403 sq ft).

MCDONNELL AIRCRAFT COMPANY (A Division of McDonnell Douglas Corporation)

Headquarters: Box 516, St Louis, Missouri 63166
Telephone: (314) 232 0232
President: George S. Graff
Executive Vice-President: Donald Malvern
Vice-Presidents:
Aksel R. Andersen (Avionics Engineering)
Robert C. Bartz (Material)
William J. Blatz (Engineering Technology)
Alvin L. Boyd (Fiscal Management)
Chester V. Braun (General Manager F-15)
John J. Burns (Advanced Programmes)
Denver D. Clark (Marketing)
Paul T. Homsher (F-15 Saudi Operations)
Robert H. Koenig (Controller)
Edward B. Kuhlmann (Quality Assurance)
Richard A. Noyes (Aircraft Engineering)
Herbert Perlmutter (Manufacturing)
Madison L. Ramey (Engineering)
William S. Ross (Flight and Laboratory Development)
John N. Schuler (Contracts and Pricing)
John F. Sutherland (Product Support)
Joseph C. Waldner (General Manager F-18)
Darrel F. Waters (Personnel, East)

Development and production at St Louis continues to be concentrated on versions of the F-15 Eagle air superiority fighter, AV-8B Advanced Harrier and F-18 Hornet naval strike fighter.

MCDONNELL DOUGLAS PHANTOM II
US Navy and USAF designations: F-4 and RF-4

The Phantom II was developed initially as a twin-engined two-seat long-range all-weather fleet air defence fighter for service with the US Navy. A letter of intent to order two prototypes was issued on 18 October 1954, at which time the aircraft was designated AH-1. The designation was changed to F4H-1 on 23 June 1955, with change of mission to missile fighter, and the prototype F4H-1 flew for the first time on 27 May 1958. The first production Phantom II was delivered to US Navy Squadron VF-121 on 29 December 1960. Trials in a ground attack role led to USAF orders, and the basic USN and USAF versions became the F-4B and F-4C respectively. Many other variants have appeared, as follows:

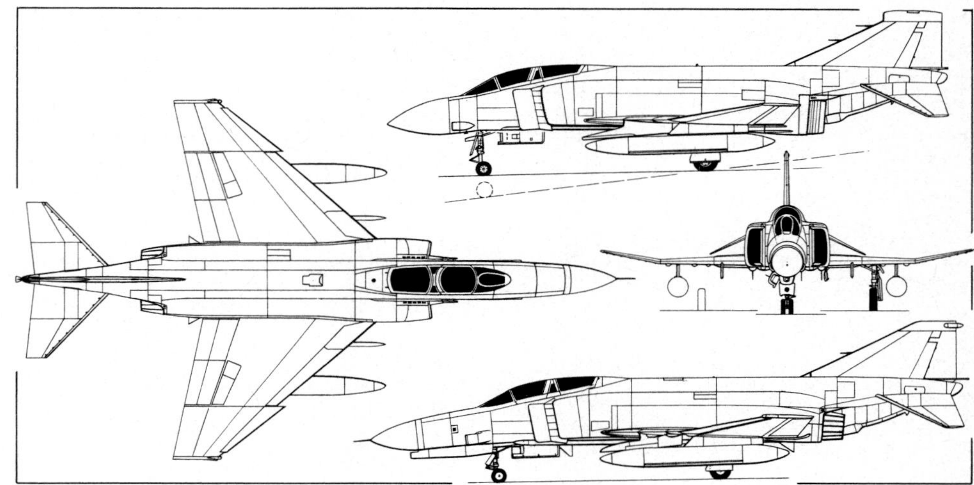
McDonnell Douglas F-4E Phantom II tactical fighter, with additional side view (top) of Phantom FGR. Mk 2 (F-4M) *(Pilot Press)*

F-4A (formerly F4H-1F). Two General Electric J79-GE-2 turbojet engines, with afterburning. Total of 21 pre-production and 24 production aircraft built. After evaluation of this version, the USAF decided to order land-based versions of the F-4B under the designation F-4C. Some converted to **TF-4A** for shore-based training, with carrier equipment deleted.

F-4B (formerly F4H-1). All-weather fighter for US Navy and Marine Corps, powered by two General Electric J79-GE-8 turbojet engines. Total of 649 built, including 12 F-4G. (See F-4G and F-4N.)

DF-4B. Conversion of F-4B for drone director duties.

QF-4B. See under US Navy entry in RPVs and Targets section.

RF-4B (formerly F4H-1P). Multi-sensor reconnaissance version of F-4B for US Marine Corps. No dual controls or armament. Reconnaissance system as for RF-4C. J79-GE-8 engines. High-frequency single sideband radio. First flown on 12 March 1965. Overall length increased to 19·2 m (63 ft). Total of 46 built. Thirty being updated from late 1978 by addition of Honeywell AN/AAD-5 infra-red linescan equipment, AN/APD-10 side-looking radar, AN/ASN-92 carrier inertial navigation system and AN/ASW-25 carrier automatic landing system. Prototype updated to this configuration in 1977.

F-4C (formerly F-110A). Variant of F-4B for USAF, with J79-GE-15 turbojets, cartridge starting, wider-tread low-pressure tyres size 30 × 11·5, larger brakes, Litton type LN-12A/B (ASN-48) inertial navigation system, APQ-100 radar, APQ-100 PPI scope, LADD timer, Lear Siegler AJB-7 bombing system, GAM-83 controls, dual controls and boom flight refuelling instead of drogue (receptacle in top of fuselage, aft of cockpit). Folding wings and arrester gear retained. For close support and attack duties with Tactical Air Command, PACAF and USAFE, and with the Air National Guard (ANG) from

January 1972. First F-4C flew on 27 May 1963; 36 supplied to Spanish Air Force, which designates them **C.12**. The last of 583 was delivered to TAC on 4 May 1966. Replaced in production by F-4D.

EF-4C. Sufficient F-4Cs were modified to equip two squadrons for a defence suppression role under the USAF's **Wild Weasel** programme. These aircraft carry ECM warning sensors, jamming pods, chaff dispensers and anti-radiation missiles.

RF-4C (formerly RF-110A). Multi-sensor reconnaissance version of F-4C for USAF, with radar and photographic systems in modified nose which increases overall length by 0·84 m (2 ft 9 in). Three basic reconnaissance systems are: side-looking radar to record high-definition radar picture of terrain on each side of flight path on film; infra-red detector to locate enemy forces under cover or at night by detecting exhaust gases and other heat sources; forward and side-looking cameras, including panoramic models with moving-lens elements for horizon-to-horizon pictures. Systems are operated from rear seat. HF single sideband radio. YRF-4C flew on 8 August 1963; first production RF-4C on 18 May 1964. Taken into service with ANG on 22 February 1971. Production ended December 1973. Total of 505 built, including two YRF-4C prototypes.

F-4CCV. Designation of one experimental aircraft, illustrated in the 1976-77 *Jane's*, fitted with experimental canard foreplanes to evaluate CCV (Control Configured Vehicle) techniques for combat aircraft.

F-4D. Development of F-4C for USAF, with J79-GE-15 turbojets, APQ-109 fire control radar, ASG-22 servoed sight, ASQ-91 weapon release computer, ASG-22 lead computing amplifier, ASG-22 lead computing gyro, 30kVA generators, and ASN-63 inertial navigation system. First production F-4D flew on 8 December 1965; total of 793 supplied to USAF. To be equipped with Compass Tie ECM system. Two squadrons of F-4Ds (32 aircraft) delivered to the Imperial Iranian Air Force and 36 to the Republic of Korea. Production completed. Total of 825 built, plus two prototypes converted from earlier models.

EF-4D. Conversion of two F-4Ds to qualify equipment for F-4G (Wild Weasel). First flight 6 December 1975.

F-4E. Multi-role fighter for air superiority, close support and interdiction missions with USAF. Has leading-edge manoeuvring slats, an internally-mounted M61A-1 20 mm multi-barrel gun, improved (AN/APQ-120) fire-control system and J79-GE-17 turbojets (each 79·6 kN; 17,900 lb st). Additional fuselage fuel cell. First production F-4E flown on 30 June 1967 and delivered to USAF on 3 October 1967. Total of 949 supplied to USAF, including many for MAP supply to other countries. To be equipped with Compass Tie ECM system. Supplied to Federal Germany for the Luftwaffe (10), the Israeli Air Force (204), Hellenic Air Force (56), Japan Air Self-Defence Force (13), Turkish Air Force (72), Republic of Korea Air Force (37) and Imperial Iranian Air Force (177). Thirty-five ex-USAF aircraft being supplied to Egypt. In addition, 24 were supplied on a two-year lease to the Royal Australian Air Force in 1970-72.

In early 1973 F-4Es began to be fitted with Northrop's target identification system electro-optical (TISEO). Essentially a vidicon TV camera with a zoom lens, it aids positive visual identification of airborne or ground targets at long range. The ASX-1 TISEO is mounted in a cylindrical housing on the leading-edge of the port wing of the F-4E.

A total of 116 F-4Es are being modified to F-4G 'Advanced Wild Weasel' configuration, as described in a later paragraph.

F-4EJ. On 1 November 1968, the Japan Defence Agency selected the F-4E as the main fighter for the JASDF. Except for the first two, these aircraft were built in Japan under a licence agreement, with some components being supplied from St Louis. The first US-built F-4EJ flew on 14 January 1971. Equipment includes tail warning radar and launchers for Mitsubishi AAM-2 air-to-air missiles. Total of 127 built.

RF-4E. Multi-sensor reconnaissance version in service with the air forces of the Federal Republic of Germany (which ordered 88), Greece (8), Iran (16), Israel (12), Japan (14) and Turkey (8). Generally similar to the RF-4C, it differs by having the J79-GE-17 turbojets of the F-4E and changed reconnaissance equipment. First flight 15 September 1970. Delivery of those for Germany completed by December 1971; they are in service with Luftwaffe units AG 51 and 52.

F-4F. Two-seat fighter, with leading-edge slats to improve manoeuvrability and modified electronics. 175 ordered by Federal Germany for the Luftwaffe. First flown on 18 May 1973; last was delivered in April 1976. In service with JG 71, JG 74, Jabo G 35 and Jabo G 36.

F-4G (Navy; no longer operational). Development of F-4B for US Navy, with AN/ASW-21 data link communications equipment, first flown on 20 March 1963. In service over Viet-Nam with Squadron VF-213 from USS *Kitty Hawk* from October 1965 to June 1966. Only 12 were built and these are included in the total quoted for F-4B production. Most were restored later to F-4B configuration.

F-4G (Advanced Wild Weasel). The USAF's Wild Weasel programme is concerned with the suppression of hostile weapon radar guidance systems. The provision of airborne equipment able to fulfil such a role, and modification of the necessary aircraft to create an effective force for deployment against such targets, had first priority in tactical Air Force planning in the Spring of 1975. The requirement for such a weapon system had been appreciated by Tactical Air Command as early as 1968, and feasibility studies were initiated in September of that year, following which eight sets of equipment were acquired for development, qualification testing and flight testing in two EF-4D aircraft. In the interests of force standardisation and airframe life, the F-4E Phantom was selected for modification to fulfil the Advanced Wild Weasel role. Technical studies of the F-4D and F-4E showed the latter aircraft to be easier to modify, resulting in a more satisfactory installation. This includes the addition of a torpedo-shape fairing to the top of the tail fin to carry APR-38 antennae, with other APR-38 antennae installed on the side of the fin and along the upper surface of the fuselage. Other modifications include changes to the LCOSS amplifier in the upper equipment bay, APR-38 CIS installation in the aft cockpit, APR-38 CIS installation in the forward cockpit, removal of the M61A-1 gun system to allow sufficient room for installation of APR-38 subsystems (receiver, HAWC, CIS), and the provision of suitable cockpit displays. The changes give the F-4G Wild Weasel the capability to detect, identify and locate hostile electromagnetic emitters, and to deploy against them suitable weapons for their suppression or destruction. Such aircraft would be able to operate independently in a hunter-killer role, but their main utilisation is likely to be as a component of a strike force where they would provide warning and suppression of hostile emitters, and have the capability of deploying their weapons against such targets.

The USAF sought funding in FY 1976 for the Advanced Wild Weasel concept, which would provide an expansion in the memory of the airborne processor and extended low-frequency emission coverage. The programme provided for the first F-4G operational kit installation in the Spring of 1976 and the second in the Autumn of that year, followed by 15 installations in 1977, 60 in 1978 and 39 in 1979, to provide a force of 116 aircraft (96 for combat units; 20 for training and testing). First F-4G delivered on 28 April 1978. Entered service with 35th Tactical Fighter Wing at George AFB, California, in October 1978. First two of 24 for 81st TF Squadron, USAFE, at Spangdahlem, Federal Republic of Germany, delivered in Spring 1979.

(F-4H designation not used, to avoid confusion with original F4H.)

F-4J. Development of F-4B for US Navy and Marine Corps, primarily as interceptor but with full ground attack capability. J79-GE-10 turbojets. Use of 16½° drooping ailerons and slotted tail gives reduced approach speed in spite of increased landing weight. Westinghouse AN/AWG-10 pulse Doppler fire-control system. Lear Siegler AJB-7 bombing system; 30kVA generators. First flight of a production F-4J was made on 27 May 1966. Production of 522 completed in January 1972.

F-4K. Development of F-4B, originally for Royal Navy, with improvements evolved for F-4J plus other changes. Westinghouse AN/AWG-10 pulse Doppler fire-control radar system modified to allow the antenna to swing around with the radome. This 'foldable radome' reduced the length of the aircraft, making it compatible with the deck elevators then in use on British aircraft carriers. Two Rolls-Royce Spey RB.168-25R Mk 201 turbofans initially (each rated at 55·6 kN; 12,500 lb st dry) with 70% afterburning; later the Mks 202/203 became standard, developing 91·25 kN (20,515 lb st) with afterburning. Air intake ducts 0·15 m (6 in) wider than on US models to cater for more powerful engines. Drooped ailerons. Tailplane has leading-edge fixed slot. Strengthened main landing gear. Nose landing gear strut extended to 1·02 m (40 in), compared to 0·51 m (20 in) on the F-4J, to permit optimum-incidence catapulting. Martin-Baker ejection seats. Weapons include Sparrow and Martel air-to-air missiles. Initial contracts for two YF-4Ks and two F-4Ks; ordered as Phantom FG. Mk 1. First flight (YF-4K) 27 June 1966. First operational Phantom unit, No. 892 Squadron, commissioned at RNAS Yeovilton on 31 March 1969. Now operated by Royal Air Force. Total of 52 built, including YF-4K prototypes.

F-4M. For Royal Air Force. Generally similar to F-4K, but with larger brakes and low-pressure tyres of F-4C, and no tailplane leading-edge slot. Folding wings and arrester gear retained. Up to 50% of the components manufactured in the UK. First YF-4M flew on 17 February 1967. Deliveries began on 23 August 1968. RAF designation is Phantom FGR. Mk 2. Total of 118 built, including two YF-4M prototypes. Some delivered with dual controls for use as conversion trainers.

F-4N. The US Navy updated 226 F-4Bs under this designation. The first (153034) was flown for the first time on 4 June 1972, and the initial delivery was made on 21 February 1973, the last in December 1978.

F-4S. The US Navy plans to modify up to 265 F-4Js under this designation, with structural strengthening to increase operational life, improvements to the electrical system, replacement of the original wing leading-edge flaps by highly-cambered, bulbous nosed leading-edge slats, and an improved AN/AWG-10A digital weapon control system. Delivery of modified aircraft from the Naval Air Rework Facility, North Island, California, began with F-4S No. 155565 on 26 May 1978.

F-4T. Improved air defence/interceptor version projected in 1978. Generally similar to F-4E, but with strike/bombing capability deleted. Armament of six Sparrow missiles and 20 mm gun; or four Sparrows, four Sidewinders and gun. Digital computer to define missile launch parameters. None built up to Summer 1979.

A total of 5,031 Phantoms had been delivered from St Louis by 1 January 1979; the 5,000th was delivered on 24 May 1978, only three days before the 20th anniversary of the prototype's first flight. The total included 2,640 for the US Air Force, 1,264 for the US Navy/Marine Corps, and 1,127 for foreign customers.

Production of the Phantom ended in the late Summer of 1979, with delivery of the 5,057th US-built aircraft.

A full description of the Phantom airframe and systems can be found in the 1978-79 *Jane's*. The following shortened description applies to the F-4E:

TYPE: Twin-engined two-seat all-weather fighter.

POWER PLANT: Two General Electric J79-GE-17A turbojet engines (each 79·6 kN; 17,900 lb st with afterburning). Variable-area inlet ducts monitored by air data computer. Integral fuel tankage in wings, between front and main spars, and in seven fuselage tanks, with total capacity of 7,022 litres (1,855 US gallons). Provision for one 2,270 litre (600 US gallon) external tank under fuselage and two 1,400 litre (370 US gallon) underwing tanks. Equipment for probe-and-drogue and 'buddy tank' flight refuelling, with retractable probe in starboard side of fuselage. Oil capacity 39 litres (10·3 US gallons).

ACCOMMODATION: Crew of two in tandem on Martin-Baker Mk H7 ejection seats, under individual rearward-hinged canopies. Optional dual controls.

AVIONICS AND EQUIPMENT: CPK-92A/A24G-34 central air data computer; AN/ASQ-19(B) com-nav-ident; MS25447/MS25448 counting accelerometer; AN/APN-155 radar altimeter; AN/AJB-7 all-altitude bomb system; AN/ASN-46A navigational computer; AN/ASN-63 INS; AN/ASQ-91 (MOD) weapons release system; AN/ASG-26 (MOD) lead computing optical sight; AN/APR-36, -37 RHAWS; AN/ASA-32 AFCS; AN/APQ-120 fire control system radar; AN/ARW-77 AGM-12 control system; TD-709/AJB-7 sequential timer; ID-1755/A standby attitude reference system; KB-25A gunsight camera; and Compass Tie ECM system, including Westinghouse AN/ALQ-119 (V) countermeasures system and Itek Applied Technology/Dalmo-Victor AN/ALR-69 radar warning system.

ARMAMENT: Four Falcon, Sparrow, Sidewinder, Shrike or Walleye missiles, or two Bullpup missiles, on four semi-submerged mountings under fuselage and four underwing mountings. Provision for carrying alternative loads of up to about 7,250 kg (16,000 lb) of nuclear or conventional bombs and stores on seven attachments under wings and fuselage. Stores which can be carried include B-28, -43, -57, -61 nuclear bombs; M117, M118, M129, MC-1, Mk 36, Mk 81, Mk 82, Mk 83 and Mk 84 bombs; MLU-10 land mine; BLU-1, -27, -52 and -76 fire bombs; cluster bombs; practice bombs; flares; rocket packs; ECM pods; gun pods; spray tanks; tow targets; Pave Knife pod; and AAVS IV camera pod. One M61A-1 nose-mounted gun.

McDonnell Douglas F-4G Advanced Wild Weasel. AN/APR-38 9 in beam receivers are visible in nose and sides of chin pod and on the fin-tip, facing aft

DIMENSIONS, EXTERNAL:
Wing span 11·77 m (38 ft 7½ in)
Wing mean aerodynamic chord 4·89 m (16 ft 0½ in)
Wing aspect ratio 2·82
Width, wings folded 8·41 m (27 ft 7 in)
Length overall 19·20 m (63 ft 0 in)
Height overall 5·02 m (16 ft 5½ in)
Wheel track 5·45 m (17 ft 10½ in)

AREA:
Wings, gross 49·2 m² (530 sq ft)

WEIGHTS AND LOADINGS:
Weight empty 13,757 kg (30,328 lb)
Weight empty, basic mission 14,448 kg (31,853 lb)
Combat T-O weight 18,818 kg (41,487 lb)
Design T-O weight 26,308 kg (58,000 lb)
Max T-O weight 28,030 kg (61,795 lb)
Max landing weight 20,865 kg (46,000 lb)
Max wing loading 569·2 kg/m² (116·59 lb/sq ft)
Max power loading 176·1 kg/kN (1·73 lb/lb st)

PERFORMANCE (A at 24,410 kg: 53,814 lb; B at 24,572 kg: 54,171 lb; C at 25,397 kg: 55,991 lb; D at 27,954 kg: 61,629 lb; and E at 28,030 kg: 61,795 lb T-O weight, except where indicated):
Max level speed with external stores over Mach 2
Average speed:
A, B 504 knots (934 km/h; 580 mph)
C 506 knots (938 km/h; 583 mph)
D 502 knots (930 km/h; 578 mph)
E 496 knots (919 km/h; 571 mph)
Stalling speed, approach power with BLC:
A 148 knots (273·5 km/h; 170 mph)
B 148·5 knots (275 km/h; 171 mph)
C 151 knots (280 km/h; 174 mph)
D 158·4 knots (294 km/h; 182·5 mph)
E 158·6 knots (294·5 km/h; 183 mph)
Max rate of climb at S/L: A 2,847 m (9,340 ft)/min
B 2,816 m (9,240 ft)/min
C 2,621 m (8,600 ft)/min
D 2,003 m (6,570 ft)/min
E 1,881 m (6,170 ft)/min
Rate of climb at S/L, one engine out:
A 1,731 m (5,680 ft)/min
B 1,713 m (5,620 ft)/min
C 1,591 m (5,220 ft)/min
D 1,167 m (3,830 ft)/min
E 1,067 m (3,500 ft)/min
Service ceiling (supersonic) 16,580 m (54,400 ft)
Service ceiling, one engine out:
A 9,905 m (32,500 ft)
B 9,860 m (32,350 ft)
C 9,340 m (30,650 ft)
D 7,055 m (23,150 ft)
E 6,490 m (21,300 ft)
T-O run: A 969 m (3,180 ft)
B 985 m (3,230 ft)
C 1,064 m (3,490 ft)
D 1,329 m (4,360 ft)
E 1,338 m (4,390 ft)
T-O to 15 m (50 ft): A 1,369 m (4,490 ft)
B 1,384 m (4,540 ft)
C 1,478 m (4,850 ft)
D 1,780 m (5,840 ft)
E 1,792 m (5,880 ft)
Landing run (A at landing weight of 16,706 kg: 36,831 lb; B and C at 15,937 kg: 35,134 lb; D at 17,155 kg: 37,821 lb; and E at 17,211 kg: 37,944 lb):
A 1,122 m (3,680 ft)
B, C 1,073 m (3,520 ft)
D 1,146 m (3,760 ft)
E 1,152 m (3,780 ft)
Landing run, with parabrake: A 927 m (3,040 ft)
B, C 887 m (2,910 ft)
D 948 m (3,110 ft)
E 951 m (3,120 ft)
Landing from 15 m (50 ft): A 1,704 m (5,590 ft)
B, C 1,655 m (5,430 ft)
D 1,728 m (5,670 ft)
E 1,734 m (5,690 ft)
Landing from 15 m (50 ft), with parabrake:
A 1,509 m (4,950 ft)
B, C 1,469 m (4,820 ft)
D 1,530 m (5,020 ft)
E 1,533 m (5,030 ft)
Combat radius:
Area intercept 683 nm (1,266 km; 786 miles)
Defensive counter-air 429 nm (795 km; 494 miles)
Interdiction 618 nm (1,145 km; 712 miles)
Ferry range 1,718 nm (3,184 km; 1,978 miles)

MCDONNELL DOUGLAS F-15 EAGLE

The USAF requested development funding for a new air superiority fighter in 1965, and in due course design proposals were sought from three airframe manufacturers: Fairchild Hiller Corporation, McDonnell Douglas Corporation, and North American Rockwell Corporation. On 23 December 1969 it was announced that McDonnell Douglas had been selected as prime airframe contractor. The contract called for the design and manufacture of 20 aircraft for development testing, these to comprise 18 single-seat **F-15As** and two **TF-15A** two-seat trainers, with production scheduled at a rate of one aircraft every other month.

RAF Phantom used for transatlantic flight on 60th anniversary of first non-stop flight by Alcock and Brown in 1919 *(Rolls-Royce)*

First flight of the F-15A was made on 27 July 1972, and the first flight of a two-seat TF-15A trainer, designated subsequently **F-15B**, on 7 July 1973.

A production go-ahead for the first 30 operational aircraft (FY 1973 funds) was announced on 1 March 1973. The FY 1974 Defense Procurement Bill authorised production of 62 aircraft, and the Defense Procurement Bills for FY 1975, 1976/7T, 1977, 1978 and 1979 authorised further production of 72, 135, 108, 97 and 78 aircraft respectively. The FY 1973-74 production contracts included 13 of the two-seat F-15B version; one of these (the 21st Eagle built) was the first Eagle delivered to the USAF, on 14 November 1974. Structural weight of the F-15B is approx 363 kg (800 lb) more than that of the single-seater. Eagles delivered from mid-1979 are to **F-15C** and **F-15D** standard, which provides for an additional 907 kg (2,000 lb) of internal fuel, and the ability to carry FAST Packs (see later paragraphs). Beginning in mid-1980 the APG-63 radar of these aircraft will be equipped with programmable signal processors, providing for future software changes and increased computer capability. F-15C and F-15D aircraft delivered prior to the availability of the programmable signal processor and expanded computer will be retrofitted subsequently to bring them up to standard.

The first F-15C (78-468) flew for the first time on 26 February 1979.

By 1 July 1979 a total of 444 Eagles had been delivered, and were in operational service with the 57th TTW at Nellis AFB, Nevada, the 58th TTW at Luke AFB, Arizona, the 1st TFW at Langley AFB, Virginia, the 36th TFW, which was deployed to Bitburg, Germany, with F-15s in April 1977, and the 49th TFW at Holloman AFB, New Mexico, in October 1977. In 1979 the F-15 also equipped the 33rd TFW at Eglin AFB, Florida, and the 32nd Tactical Fighter Squadron based at Soesterburg, The Netherlands. Production was at a rate of ten per month in January 1979. It is planned to procure 749 for the USAF by 1983, including the 20 R & D models. Thirty-five were ordered under an initial contract from the Israeli Air Force, and 60 by Saudi Arabia. The JASDF plans to purchase 100 **F-15Js,** of which all except eight will be licence-built in Japan, with Mitsubishi as the prime contractor.

Designed specifically as an air superiority fighter, the F-15A Eagle has proved equally suitable for air-to-ground missions without degradation of its primary role. It is able to carry a variety of air-to-air and air-to-ground weapons.

A large increase in the normal ferry range of a 'clean' F-15 can be achieved by the use of two low-drag fuel pallets known as FAST Packs (Fuel And Sensor Tactical Packs) developed specially for the F-15 by McDonnell Aircraft Company. Each FAST Pack contains approximately 3,228 litres (114 cu ft) of usable volume, which can accommodate 2,268 kg (5,000 lb) of JP-4 fuel. It attaches to the side of either the port or starboard engine air intake trunk (being made in handed pairs), is designed to the same load factors and airspeed limits as the basic aircraft, and can be removed in 15 minutes. FAST Packs can accommodate avionics such as reconnaissance sensors, radar detection and jamming equipment, a laser designator, low-light-level TV system, and reconnaissance cameras, in addition to fuel. All external stores stations remain available with the pallets in use. AIM-7F missiles

McDonnell Douglas F-15A Eagle single-seat fighter and attack aircraft with airbrake deployed

The first McDonnell Douglas F-15C Eagle overflying St Louis

and air-to-ground weapons can be attached to the corners of the FAST Packs.

The programmable signal processor for the F-15C/D will enable changes to be incorporated in the radar earlier and more cheaply. An updated radar data processor will be fitted which will increase memory capability from 24K to 96K. These added features will enable the radar to operate in a high-resolution rate assessment mode which can identify clustered targets individually. The PEP-2000 (Production Eagle Package-2,000 lb; 907 kg of additional fuel) expands the fighter's combat endurance considerably, and includes attachment points and fuel plumbing to accommodate FAST Packs.

Minor changes have been made to tyres, wheels and brakes to allow for an increased maximum T-O weight, which could be as high as 30,844 kg (68,000 lb) with full internal fuel, FAST Packs and external tanks. Landing gear and fuel system changes have added about 227 kg (500 lb) to the aircraft's dry weight.

Under a programme dubbed 'Streak Eagle', the F-15 demonstrated its climb capability by capturing eight time-to-height records, between 16 January and 1 February 1975. Three USAF pilots were involved: Majors Willard Macfarlane, David Peterson and Roger Smith. The new records were:

Altitude (metres)	*Previous record time to height*	*New record time to height*
3,000	34·5 s	27·57 s
6,000	48·8 s	39·33 s
9,000	1 min 1·7 s	48·86 s
12,000	1 min 17·1 s	59·38 s
15,000	1 min 54·5 s	1 min 17·04 s
20,000	2 min 49·8 s	2 min 2·94 s
25,000*	3 min 12·6 s	2 min 41·02 s
30,000*	4 min 3·9 s	3 min 27·80 s

*These two records have since been reclaimed by the E-266M version of the Soviet MiG-25 (which see).

The following description applies to the F-15A:

TYPE: Single-seat twin-turbofan air superiority fighter, with secondary attack role.

WINGS: Cantilever shoulder-wing monoplane. Leading-edge swept back at approximately 45°. Outboard aileron actuators by Ozone Metal Products.

FUSELAGE: All-metal semi-monocoque structure.

TAIL UNIT: Cantilever structure with twin fins and rudders. All-moving horizontal tail surfaces outboard of fins, with extended chord on outer leading-edges. Rudder servo actuators by Ronson Hydraulic Units Corporation. Actuators for horizontal surfaces by National Water Lift Company. Boost and pitch compensator for control stick by Moog Inc, Controls Division.

LANDING GEAR: Hydraulically-retractable tricycle type, with single wheel on each unit. Nose and main landing gear by Cleveland Pneumatic Tool Company. Wheels and carbon brake assemblies by Goodyear Tire and Rubber Company. Main and nosewheel tyres by B. F. Goodrich Company. Wheel braking skid control system by Hydro-Aire Division of Crane Company. All units retract forward.

POWER PLANT: Two Pratt & Whitney F100-PW-100 turbofan engines of approximately 111·2 kN (25,000 lb st). Internal fuel load 5,260 kg (11,600 lb). Fuel tanks by Goodyear Aviation Products Division. Fuel gauge system by Simmonds Precision Products Inc. FAST Pack conformal fuel pallets attached to side of engine air intakes, beneath wing, can be removed within 15 min. Each has usable volume of 3·23 m³ (114 cu ft) and can contain 2,268 kg (5,000 lb) of JP-4 fuel.

ENGINE INTAKES: Straight two-dimensional external compression inlets, on each side of the fuselage. Air inlet controllers by Hamilton Standard. Air inlet actuators by National Water Lift Company.

ACCOMMODATION: Pilot only, on Aces II ejection seat developed by Douglas. Stretched acrylic canopy and windscreen. Windscreen anti-icing valve by Dynasciences Corporation.

SYSTEMS: Electric power generating system by Lear Siegler Power Equipment Division; transformer-rectifiers by Electro Development Corporation; 40/50kVA generator constant-speed drive units by Sundstrand Corporation, Aviation Division. Three independent hydraulic systems (each 207 bars; 3,000 lb/sq in) powered by Abex engine-driven pumps; modular hydraulic packages by Hydraulic Research and Manufacturing Company. The oxygen system includes a liquid oxygen indicator by Simmonds Precision Products Inc. Air-conditioning system by AiResearch Manufacturing Company. Automatic flight control system by General Electric, Aircraft Equipment Division. Auxiliary power unit for engine starting, and for the provision of electric or hydraulic power on the ground independently of the main engines, supplied by AiResearch Manufacturing Company.

AVIONICS: Lightweight APG-63 pulse-Doppler radar developed by Hughes Aircraft Company provides long-range detection and tracking of small high-speed targets operating at all altitudes down to treetop level, and feeds accurate tracking information to the airborne central computer to ensure effective launch of the aircraft's missiles or the firing of its internal gun. For close-in dogfights, the radar automatically acquires the target on a head-up display. International Business Machines, Electronic Systems Center, is subcontractor for the central computer, and McDonnell Douglas Electronics Company for the head-up display. This latter unit projects all essential flight information in the form of symbols on to a combining glass positioned above the instrument panel at pilot's eye level. The display presents the pilot with all the information required to intercept and destroy an enemy aircraft without need for him to remove his eyes from the target. The display also provides navigation and other steering control information under all flight conditions. A transponder for the IFF system, developed by Teledyne Electronics Company, informs ground stations and other suitably equipped aircraft that the F-15 is a friendly aircraft. It also supplies data on the F-15's range, azimuth, altitude and identification to air traffic controllers. The F-15 carries an AN/APX-76 interrogator receiver-transmitter, built by Hazeltine Corporation, to inform the pilot if an aircraft seen visually or on radar is friendly. A reply evaluator for the IFF system, which operates with the AN/APX-76, was developed by Litton Systems Inc, Van Nuys. A vertical situation display set, that uses a cathode-ray tube to present radar, electro-optical identification and attitude director indicator formats to the pilot, has been developed by Sperry Rand Corporation, Sperry Flight Systems Division. This permits inputs received from the aircraft's sensors and the central computer to be visible to the pilot under any light conditions. This company has also developed an air data computer for the F-15, as well as an attitude and heading reference set to provide information on the aircraft's pitch, roll and magnetic heading that is fed to cockpit displays. This latter unit also serves as a backup to the inertial navigation set developed by Litton Guidance and Control Systems Division. This provides the basic navigation data and is the aircraft's primary attitude reference, enabling the F-15 to navigate anywhere in the world. In addition to giving the aircraft's position at all times, the inertial navigation system provides pitch, roll, heading, acceleration and speed information.

Other specialised equipment for flight control, navigation and communications includes a micro-miniaturised Tacan system by Collins Radio Company; a horizontal situation indicator to present aircraft navigation information on a symbolic pictorial display, by Collins Radio Company, which is also responsible for the ADF and ILS receivers. Magnavox provides the UHF transceiver and UHF auxiliary transceiver. The communications sets have cryptographic capability. Dorne and Margolin Aviation Products is responsible for the glideslope localiser antenna, and Teledyne Avionics Company for angle of attack sensors. A special nose radome has been developed by Brunswick Corporation, Technical Products Division. This is fabricated from syntactic foam material sandwiched between outer skins, and offers a weight saving of 35% by comparison with conventional radome structures, as well as providing heat resistance up to 500°F (260°C), undistorted passage for signals from the nose radar, and the strength of a primary structure.

An internal countermeasures set, designated AN/ALQ-135, which provides automatic jamming of enemy radar signals, is supplied by Northrop's Defense Systems Division; radar warning systems by Loral Electronic Systems; and an electronic warfare warning set by Magnavox.

EQUIPMENT: Tachometer, fuel and oil indicators by Bendix Corporation, Flight and Engine Instrument Division. Feel trim actuators by Plessey Airborne Corporation.

ARMAMENT: Provision for carriage and launch of a variety of air-to-air weapons over short and medium ranges, including four AIM-9L Sidewinders, four AIM-7F Sparrows, and a 20 mm M61A-1 six-barrel gun with 940 rounds of ammunition. A lead-computing gyro has been developed by the General Electric Co. To keep the pilot informed of the status of his weapons and provide for their management, an armament control set has been developed by Dynamic Controls Corporation. Five weapon stations allow for the carriage of up to 7,257 kg (16,000 lb) of bombs, rockets or additional ECM equipment.

DIMENSIONS, EXTERNAL:

Wing span	13·05 m (42 ft 9¾ in)
Length overall	19·43 m (63 ft 9 in)
Height overall	5·63 m (18 ft 5½ in)
Tailplane span	8·61 m (28 ft 3 in)
Wheel track	2·75 m (9 ft 0¼ in)
Wheelbase	5·42 m (17 ft 9½ in)

AREA:

Wings, gross	56·5 m² (608 sq ft)

WEIGHTS:

T-O weight (interceptor, full internal fuel and 4 Sparrows)	18,824 kg (41,500 lb)
T-O weight (incl three 600 US gallon drop-tanks)	24,675 kg (54,400 lb)
Max T-O weight	25,401 kg (56,000 lb)

PERFORMANCE:

Max level speed	more than Mach 2·5 (800 knots; 1,482 km/h; 921 mph CAS)
Approach speed	125 knots (232 km/h; 144 mph) CAS
T-O run (interceptor)	274 m (900 ft)
Landing run (interceptor), without braking parachute	762 m (2,500 ft)
Absolute ceiling	30,500 m (100,000 ft)
Ferry range: without FAST Pack	more than 2,500 nm (4,631 km; 2,878 miles)
with FAST Pack	more than 3,000 nm (5,560 km; 3,450 miles)
g limits	+9·0; −3·0

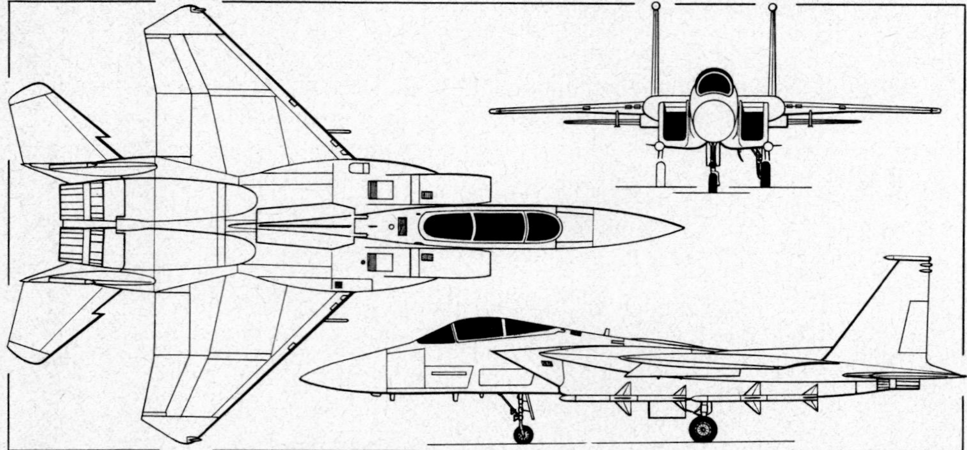

McDonnell Douglas F-15A Eagle twin-turbofan air superiority fighter *(Pilot Press)*

McDonnell Douglas F-15B Eagle two-seat trainer, fitted with FAST Packs

AV-8B ADVANCED HARRIER

In late 1973 and early 1974 the British and US governments received for approval various proposals for an advanced version of the BAe (HS) Harrier (see UK section). Subsequent to this came the announcement, on 15 May 1975, of the first British order for Sea Harrier FRS. Mk 1s for the Royal Navy.

Two months before the announcement of this order, the British Secretary of State for Defence, Mr Roy Mason, had stated that there was "not enough common ground on the Advanced Harrier for us to join in the programme with the US", and development studies for a US version have therefore been continued primarily by McDonnell Douglas to meet requirements of the US Navy and Marine Corps.

Essentially, the objective of the Advanced Harrier programme is to evolve a version which, without too much of a departure from the existing Harrier airframe, would virtually double the aircraft's weapons payload/combat radius.

The USMC has stated a requirement for 336 Advanced Harriers, and initially McDonnell Douglas and the USMC modified two AV-8As as prototype **YAV-8Bs**. The first of these flew for the first time on 9 November 1978, and the second in February 1979. Prototype demonstration was completed in Summer 1979, in 185 test flights totalling 173 flying hours, during which the two aircraft met or exceeded all performance requirements specified by the Marine Corps and Naval Air Systems Command.

Aim of the AV-8B is to achieve the improved performance capability required of the original AV-16A proposal by aerodynamic means, while retaining the same basic F402-RR-402 (Pegasus 11) engine, thus saving the cost of developing the Pegasus 15 engine that was originally considered necessary for the advanced version.

Aerodynamic changes include use of a supercritical wing; the addition of under-gun-pod strakes and a movable flap panel forward of the pods, to increase lift for vertical take-off; the use of larger wing trailing-edge flaps and drooped ailerons; and redesigned engine air intakes. The landing gear is strengthened to cater for the higher operating weights and greater external stores loads made possible by these changes.

Four full-scale development aircraft are to be built next; the first of these is scheduled to fly in mid-1981, with Navy BIS (Bureau of Inspection and Survey) trials following in Spring 1983. The operational date planned for the AV-8B is mid-1985, should production be approved. McDonnell Douglas would be prime contractor for the airframe, with British Aerospace as subcontractor; prime engine contractor would be either Pratt & Whitney or Rolls-Royce, with the other as subcontractor.

Wings: Cantilever shoulder-wing monoplane, of broadly similar planform to Harrier/AV-8A but of supercritical section, approx 20% greater in span and 14% greater in area. Thickness/chord ratio 11·5% at root, 7·5% at tip. 10° less sweepback on leading-edges, and non-swept inboard trailing-edges. Composite construction, making extensive use of graphite epoxy in the main multi-spar torsion box, ribs, skins, outrigger fairings and wingtips. Trailing-edge single-slotted flaps, of substantially greater chord than those of AV-8A, and drooping ailerons, also of graphite epoxy construction.

Fuselage: Generally similar to AV-8A. New forward fuselage, with raised cockpit, constructed from graphite epoxy composite material, and additional lift-augmenting surfaces. These comprise a fixed strake on each of the two underfuselage gun packs, and a retractable forward flap just aft of the nosewheel unit. During VTOL modes the 'box' formed by the ventral strakes and the lowered nose flap augment lift by trapping the cushion of air bounced off the ground by the engine exhaust. This additional lift allows the AV-8B to take off vertically at a gross weight equal to its maximum hovering gross weight.

Landing Gear: Main landing gear strengthened to cater for higher operating weights. Dowty Rotol/Cleveland outrigger wheels and fairings, moved inboard to approx mid-span beneath each wing between flaps and ailerons.

Power Plant: One Rolls-Royce Pegasus (F402-RR-404) vectored-thrust turbofan engine rated at 95·64 kN (21,500 lb st). Engine air intakes redesigned, with elliptical lip shape and double instead of single row of suction relief doors. Increased fuel tankage available in wings, raising total internal fuel capacity (fuselage and wing tanks) from approx 2,268 kg (5,000 lb) in the AV-8A to 3,402 kg (7,500 lb) in the AV-8B. Each of the four inner underwing stations capable of carrying an auxiliary fuel tank.

Avionics and Equipment: Improved attitude and heading reference system, AN/ARN-84 Tacan, AN/ARC-159 UHF, AN/APX-100 IFF, visual landing aids, inertial navigation system, dual combining glass head-up display, and CRT multi-purpose display. Marconi Avionics self-contained pitch and roll autostabilisation computer, with built-in rate gyroscopes and added electronic package to interface with new forward reaction control motor.

Armament and Operational Equipment: Twin underfuselage gun/ammunition packs, as in AV-8A, each mounting a US 20 mm cannon or a 30 mm Aden gun. Single 454 kg (1,000 lb) stores point on fuselage centreline, between gun packs. Three stores stations under each wing, the inner one capable of carrying a 907 kg (2,000 lb) store, the centre one 454 kg (1,000 lb), and the outer one 286 kg (630 lb). The four inner wing stations are 'wet', permitting the carriage of auxiliary fuel tanks. Including fuel, stores, weapons and ammunition, and water injection for the engine, the maximum useful load for vertical take-off is approximately 3,175 kg (7,000 lb), and for short take-off nearly 7,710 kg (17,000 lb). Typical weapons include Mk 82 Snakeye bombs, and laser or electro-optical guided weapons. Main weapon delivery by Angle Rate Bombing System (ARBS), comprising a dual-mode (TV and laser) target seeker linked to a Marconi head-up display via an IBM digital computer. Passive ECM equipment.

Prototype of McDonnell Douglas AV-8B Advanced Harrier in hovering flight

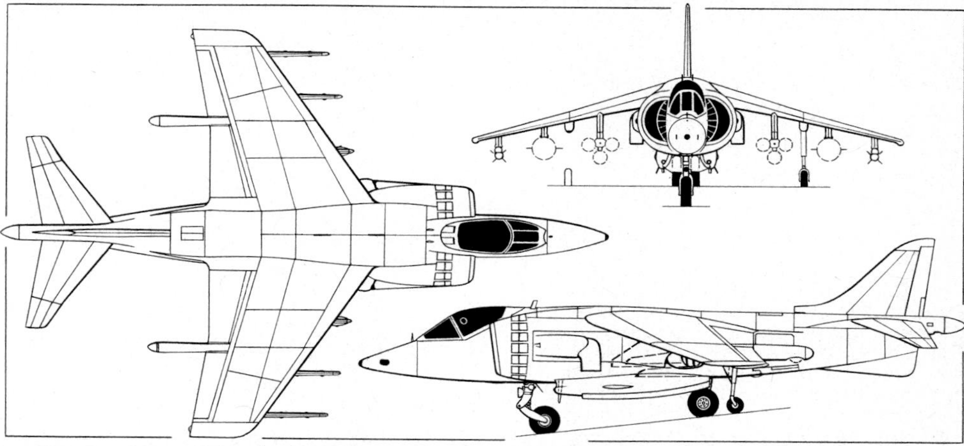

AV-8B Advanced Harrier under development by McDonnell Douglas for the US Marine Corps *(Pilot Press)*

Dimensions, external:

Wing span: AV-8A — 7·70 m (25 ft 3 in)
AV-8B — approx 9·23 m (30 ft 3½ in)
Length overall: AV-8A — 13·87 m (45 ft 6 in)
AV-8B — 14·11 m (46 ft 3½ in)
Height overall: AV-8A — 3·43 m (11 ft 3 in)
AV-8B — 3·54 m (11 ft 7¼ in)
Wing area (gross): AV-8A — 18·68 m² (201·1 sq ft)
AV-8B — approx 21·37 m² (230 sq ft)

Weights:

Basic operating weight, empty:
AV-8A — 5,533 kg (12,200 lb)
AV-8B — 5,693 kg (12,550 lb)
Max T-O weight:
AV-8A (STO) — over 11,340 kg (25,000 lb)
AV-8B (STO) — 13,403 kg (29,550 lb)
AV-8B (VTO) — 8,550 kg (18,850 lb)
Design landing weight: AV-8B — 8,799 kg (19,400 lb)

Performance (AV-8B data estimated):

AV-8A operational radius with external loads shown:
vertical T-O, 1,360 kg (3,000 lb) — 50 nm (92 km; 57 miles)
short T-O (185 m; 600 ft), 2,268 kg (5,000 lb) — 125 nm (231 km; 144 miles)
short T-O (457 m; 1,500 ft), 3,630 kg (8,000 lb) — 222 nm (411 km; 255 miles)
short T-O (305 m; 1,000 ft), 1,360 kg (3,000 lb) — 360 nm (667 km; 414 miles)
AV-8B operational radius with external loads shown:
vertical T-O, 3,538 kg (7,800 lb) — 100 nm (185 km; 115 miles)
short T-O (305 m; 1,000 ft), twelve Mk 82 Snakeye bombs, internal fuel, 1 h loiter — more than 150 nm (278 km; 172 miles)
short T-O (305 m; 1,000 ft), seven Mk 82 Snakeye bombs, external fuel tanks, no loiter — more than 650 nm (1,204 km; 748 miles)

MCDONNELL DOUGLAS F/A-18 HORNET

In the Spring of 1974 the US Department of Defense accepted a proposal from the US Navy to study a low-cost lightweight multi-mission fighter, then identified as the VFAX. In June 1974 the USN approached the US aircraft industry to submit critiques and comments on such an aircraft. Six companies responded, including McDonnell Aircraft Company; but in August of that year Congress terminated the VFAX concept, directing instead that the Navy should investigate versions of the General Dynamics YF-16 and Northrop YF-17 lightweight fighter prototypes then under evaluation for the USAF.

McDonnell Douglas made a study of the configuration of these two aircraft and concluded that Northrop's contender not only met most nearly the Navy's requirements, but would also prove the easier to convert to a combat fighter suitable for operation from aircraft carriers.

As a result of this review, McDonnell Douglas teamed with Northrop to propose a derivative of the YF-17 to meet the Navy's requirement, with McDonnell Douglas as the prime contractor. Identified as the Navy Air Combat Fighter (NACF), this received the designation F-18 Hornet when selected for further development.

On 22 January 1976 it was announced that full-scale development had been initiated by the US Navy, with initial funding of $16 million. Total cost of the development programme is expected to be about $1·4 billion, including the production of 11 YF-18s for the flight test programme.

The first Hornet (160775) was rolled out on 13 September 1978, and made its first flight on 18 November 1978; the second flew on 12 March 1979, and five aircraft had flown by mid-year. The first batch of nine production Hornets was authorised in FY 1979. The F-18 is due to become operational in 1982.

The Hornet derives from development work carried out by Northrop during recent years, which formed the basis of the company's YF-17 prototype. The Hornet airframe differs from that of the latter aircraft by having increased wing area, a wider and longer fuselage to provide greater internal fuel capacity, an enlarged nose to accommodate the 0·71 m (28 in) radar dish to meet the Navy's search range requirement of over 30 nm (56 km; 35 miles), and strengthening of the airframe structure to cater for the increased loads caused by catapult launches and arrested landings. Approximately 2,000 kg (4,400 lb) of additional fuel will be carried to meet Navy mission range requirements.

Ease of maintenance has been given most careful consideration in formulation of the F-18's design. Servicing points are disposed so that essential maintenance personnel can work simultaneously without getting in each other's way. An engine change can be effected within approximately 20 minutes, and radar equipment is track-mounted so that it can be rolled out for maintenance. Electronics equipment is housed behind quick-release doors at chest height, and the windscreen is hinged to permit easy access behind the instrument panel. A built-in test panel mounted within the nosewheel well will pinpoint system failures, and when the indicated access door is opened the assembly which has failed will 'flag' confirmation that it needs repair or replacement. Groundcrew will have access to a 'go, no go' panel for rapid pre-flight check, and this will confirm levels of essential liquids, such as engine oil, hydraulic fluid, radar coolant, APU oil and oxygen. Safety features include self-sealing fuel tanks and fuel lines, fire suppressant foam within the fuel tanks, built-in fire extinguishers, filler foam in the fuselage for fire suppression, and a system which detects hydraulic fluid leaks and then isolates the relative section.

Conventional instrumentation has almost disappeared from the cockpit, replaced by three cathode ray tubes and an information control panel directly in front of the pilot. All essential flight and target information is projected on to the eye-level head-up display so that, without taking his eyes from the target, the pilot is kept constantly aware of the changing situation. So that he will not be distracted by

McDonnell Douglas Hornet prototype, first flown on 18 November 1978

having to move his hands to different controls, every critical switch for air-to-air and air-to-surface engagements is either in the throttle in his left hand, or on the control stick in his right hand. During air-to-air combat the Hughes AN/APG-65 radar can track multiple targets, displaying up to eight target tracks while retaining up to ten in its memory. A raid assessment mode enables the pilot to discriminate between closely spaced targets. The radar information is displayed on a clutter-free scope in either lookup or lookdown attitude; it provides also range-while-search capability, long-range search and track, and several modes for close-in combat. Doppler beam sharpening (DBS) achieves greater resolution of radar signal returns during air-to-surface mapping.

McDonnell Douglas is prime contractor for the Hornet, with the centre of activities at St Louis, Missouri. Northrop builds the centre and aft fuselage, which is delivered totally assembled to McDonnell Douglas. Assembly is completed at St Louis and flight testing is carried out at NATC Patuxent River, Maryland.

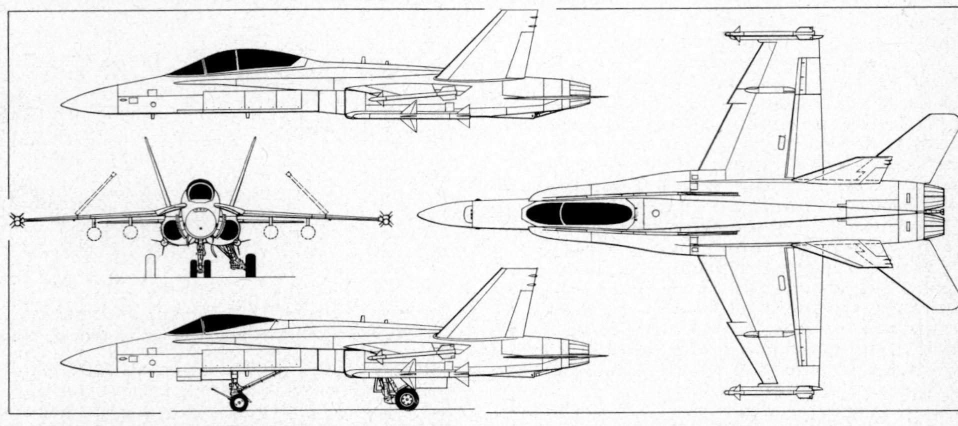

McDonnell Douglas F-18 Hornet, with additional side view (top) of the two-seat training version *(Pilot Press)*

A total of 1,377 Hornets, including the 11 development aircraft, is planned for construction by the end of the 1980s, as the Hornet is required to replace both USN and US Marine Corps F-4 Phantoms for the primary missions of fighter escort and interdiction. About 7 per cent of those built will be two-seat trainers, and the attack version of the Hornet will replace the Navy's A-7 Corsair II aircraft in the mid-1980s, under the designation **A-18**. This is identical to the F-18 except that FLIR and a laser tracker, which are being developed as part of the Hornet programme, will take the place of fuselage-mounted Sparrows for attack missions.

Type: Single-seat carrier-based naval strike fighter.

Wings: Cantilever mid-wing monoplane. Moderate-sweep multi-spar structure, primarily of light alloy and graphite/epoxy. Boundary layer control achieved by wing-root slots. Full-span leading-edge manoeuvring flaps have a maximum extension angle of 30°. Single-slotted trailing-edge flaps, actuated by Bertea hydraulic cylinders, deploy to a maximum of 45°. Ailerons, with Hydraulic Research actuators, can be drooped to 45°, providing the advantages of full-span flaps for low approach speeds. Leading- and trailing-edge flaps are computer programmed to deflect for optimum lift and drag in both manoeuvring and cruise conditions. Notched sections on outer wing leading-edge to enhance aileron effectiveness. Wing-root leading-edge extensions (LEX) permit flight at angles of attack exceeding 60°. Wings fold, by means of AiResearch mechanical drive, at the inboard end of each aileron.

Fuselage: Semi-monocoque basic structure, primarily of light alloy, with graphite/epoxy used for access doors/panels. Airbrake in upper surface of fuselage between tail fins. Pressurised cockpit section of fail-safe construction. Arrester hook for carrier landings under rear fuselage.

Tail Unit: Cantilever structure with swept vertical and horizontal surfaces. Twin outward-canted fins and rudders, mounted forward of all-moving tailplane, which is actuated by National Water Lift servo-cylinder hydraulic units.

Landing Gear: Retractable tricycle type, manufactured by Cleveland, with twin-wheel nose and single-wheel main units. Nose unit retracts forward, main wheels aft, turning 90° to stow horizontally inside the lower surface of the engine air ducts. Bendix wheels and brakes. Ozone nosewheel steering unit. Nose unit towbar for catapult launch.

Power Plant: Two General Electric F404-GE-400 low bypass turbofan engines, each producing approx 71·2 kN (16,000 lb thrust). Internal fuel load approx 4,990 kg (11,000 lb); provision for up to three external tanks, increasing total fuel capacity to approx 7,257 kg (16,000 lb). Simmonds fuel gauging system.

Accommodation: Pilot only, on Martin-Baker Mk 10 ejection seat in pressurised, heated and air-conditioned cockpit. Upward-opening two-part canopy, both sections hinged individually.

Systems: Fly-by-wire flight control system, with mechanical backup. Garrett-AiResearch air-conditioning system. GEC electrical power system. Oxygen system.

Avionics and Equipment: Will include an automatic carrier landing system (ACLS) for all-weather carrier operations; a Hughes AN/APG-65 multi-mode digital air-to-air and air-to-ground tracking radar, with air-to-air modes which include Velocity Search (VS), Range While Search (RWS), Track While Scan (TWS), which can track ten targets and display eight to the pilot, and Raid Assessment Mode (RAM). Itek ALR-67 radar warning receiver; General Electric quadruple-redundant flight control system with two AYK-14 digital computers; Litton inertial navigation system; Kaiser multi-purpose cockpit display, including head-up display and three CRTs; Conrac communications system control; Normalair-Garrett digital data recorder for Bendix maintenance recording system; Smiths standby altimeter; and Kearflex standby airspeed indicator, standby vertical speed indicator, and cockpit pressure altimeter. Garrett-AiResearch APU for engine starting and ground pneumatic, electrical and hydraulic power.

Armament: Nine external weapon stations with a combined capacity of 8,165 kg (18,000 lb) of mixed ordnance at high *g*. These comprise two wingtip stations for AIM-9 Sidewinder air-to-air missiles; two outboard wing stations for an assortment of air-to-ground or air-to-air weapons, including AIM-7 Sparrows; two inboard wing stations for external fuel tanks or air-to-ground weapons; two nacelle fuselage stations for Sparrows or Martin Marietta sensor pods; and a centreline fuselage station for external fuel or weapons. An M61 20 mm six-barrel gun, with 540 rounds, is mounted in the nose and will have a McDonnell Douglas director gunsight, with a conventional sight as backup. Pod-mounted Ford forward-looking infra-red (FLIR) and Ferranti/Bendix laser spot tracker to be developed for A-18.

Dimensions, external:

Wing span	11·43 m (37 ft 6 in)
Wing span over missiles	12·31 m (40 ft 4¾ in)
Width, wings folded	8·38 m (27 ft 6 in)
Length overall	17·07 m (56 ft 0 in)
Height overall	4·66 m (15 ft 3½ in)
Tailplane span	6·58 m (21 ft 7¼ in)
Wheel track	3·11 m (10 ft 2½ in)
Wheelbase	5·42 m (17 ft 9½ in)

Area:

Wings, gross	37·16 m² (400 sq ft)

Weights:

Fighter mission T-O weight	15,234 kg (33,585 lb)
Attack mission T-O weight	21,319 kg (47,000 lb)

Performance (estimated):

Max level speed	more than Mach 1·8
Max speed, intermediate power	more than Mach 1·0
Approach speed	130 knots (240 km/h; 150 mph)
Combat ceiling	approx 15,240 m (50,000 ft)
T-O run	less than 305 m (1,000 ft)
Combat radius, fighter mission	400 nm (740 km; 460 miles)
Combat radius, attack mission	550 nm (1,019 km; 633 miles)
Ferry range, unrefuelled	more than 2,000 nm (3,706 km; 2,303 miles)

DOUGLAS AIRCRAFT COMPANY (a Division of McDonnell Douglas Corporation)

Headquarters: 3855 Lakewood Boulevard, Long Beach, California 90846

Telephone: (213) 593 5511

President: John C. Brizendine

Executive Vice-Presidents:
- Charles M. Forsyth
- John E. Forry (Finance and Administration)

Vice-Presidents:
- Ray E. Bates (Advanced Programmes)
- Harold Bayer (Product Support)
- Richard A. Bibee (Operations Control Division)
- Jerald D. Burns (Commercial Contracts)
- Charles Conrad Jr (Marketing)
- Edward Curtis (Contracts and Pricing)
- Larry S. Dickenson (Commercial Sales, Europe, Africa and Middle East)
- Eugene F. Dubil (Engineering)
- Joseph S. Dunning (Administration)
- William T. Gross (Programme Management)
- N. Douglas Ingebretsen (Personnel, West)
- Robert C. P. Jackson (Plans)
- Ray J. Kleinberg (Controller)
- Donald J. Krokus (Commercial Sales, Pacific and Asia)
- Marvin D. Marks (Government Marketing and Programme Manager AMST)
- Victor R. Saliture (Manufacturing)
- John W. Stillwell (Quality Assurance)
- Howell L. Walker (Commercial Sales, Americas)
- Lupton A. Wilkinson Jr (Manufacturing Support)
- William R. Worrell (Material)

Chief Counsel: John H. Carroll Jr

Director, External Relations: Raymond L. Towne

The Douglas Aircraft Company operates plants at Long Beach, Palmdale and Torrance, California.

MCDONNELL DOUGLAS DC-8 FREIGHTER CONVERSION

Under a programme launched at Tulsa works in February 1976, McDonnell Douglas is modifying DC-8 passenger transports into specialised freighters at a current rate of up to nine aircraft per year. First to be converted were two DC-8-43 series airliners, which were also re-engined with Pratt & Whitney JT3D turbofans, under contract from Frederick B. Ayer and Associates. Subsequent orders for a total of eight conversions have been received from Intercontinental Airways, International Air Leases Inc, International Air Service, Overseas National Airways and Transmeridian Air Cargo.

Modification includes removal of passenger installations and fitting a production freighter seven-track floor, and a 2·16 m × 3·56 m (85 × 140 in) main deck cargo door. Cabin windows are replaced by metal plugs, and a cargo loading system is installed. Conversion to turbofan power is optional for turbojet models.

MCDONNELL DOUGLAS DC-8 SRS 71, 72 and 73

These new series of DC-8 four-turbofan transports were announced by McDonnell Douglas in the Spring of 1979. The Srs 71, 72 and 73 are, respectively, re-engined Srs 61, 62 and 63 aircraft. The same designations apply whether the customer chooses CFM56 or Pratt & Whitney JT8D-209 engines to replace the original JT3D-3B/7s.

First customer was United Air Lines, which is having 30 DC-8 Srs 61s converted to Srs 71 standard, with CFM56 engines, each flat rated at 98·1 kN (22,050 lb st). Deliveries of the re-engined aircraft will begin in 1981.

MCDONNELL DOUGLAS DC-9

USAF designations: C-9A and VC-9C
US Navy designation: C-9B

Design study data on the DC-9, then known as the Douglas Model 2086, were released in 1962. Preliminary design work began during that year. Fabrication was started on 26 July 1963 and assembly of the first airframe began on 6 March 1964. It flew for the first time on 25 February 1965 and five DC-9s were flying by the end of June 1965. These were of the basic version, known as the DC-9 Series 10, of which production has ended; details can be found in the 1978-79 *Jane's*. Other variants are as follows:

Series 20. For operation in hot climate/high-altitude conditions, combining long-span wings of Series 30 with short fuselage of original Series 10. Up to 90 passengers. Two 64·5 kN (14,500 lb st) JT8D-9 turbofans. The Series 20 flew for the first time on 18 September 1968, and was certificated on 11 December 1968. The first Series 20 was delivered to SAS on the same day and entered commercial service on 23 January 1969. Described in 1977-78 *Jane's*.

Series 30. Developed version, initially with 62·3 kN (14,000 lb st) JT8D-7s, increased wing span, longer fuselage accommodating up to 105 passengers (normal) or 119 (with reduced facilities), and new high-lift devices including full-span leading-edge slats and double-slotted flaps. First Srs 30 flew for first time on 1 August 1966. First delivery, to Eastern Air Lines, was made on 27 January 1967 and scheduled services began on 1 February 1967. Engine options available include JT8D-9 of 64·5 kN (14,500 lb st); JT8D-11 of 66·7 kN (15,000 lb st); JT8D-15 of 69 kN (15,500 lb st); and JT8D-17 of 71·2 kN (16,000 lb st). Newer engines have sound-treated nacelles that comply with FAA FAR Pt 36 noise regulations.

Series 40. As Series 30, but with 64·5 kN (14,500 lb st) JT8D-9, 69 kN (15,500 lb st) JT8D-15 or 71·2 kN (16,000 lb st) JT8D-17 turbofans, increased fuel capacity, longer fuselage accommodating up to 132 passengers, and greater AUW. First flight was made on 28 November 1967 and FAA certification was received on 27 February 1968. The first Series 40 was delivered to SAS on 29 February 1968 and entered commercial service with that airline on 12 March 1968.

Series 50. 'Stretched' short/medium-range development of the Series 30, announced on 5 July 1973. High-density seating for up to 139 passengers made possible by a 4·34 m (14 ft 3 in) fuselage extension. A 'new look' interior features enclosed overhead racks for carry-on baggage, sculptured wall panels, acoustically-treated ceiling panels and indirect lighting. Available with either Pratt & Whitney JT8D-15 or -17 turbofan engines, rated at 69 kN (15,500 lb st) and 71·2 kN (16,000 lb st) respectively, and embodying sound-absorption materials as developed for the engines and nacelles of the DC-10, the Series 50 meets FAR Pt 36 noise requirements. The engines are smokeless and have thrust reversers rotated 17° from the vertical to reduce the possibility of exhaust gas ingestion. The landing gear is fitted with an improved anti-skid braking system. First flight of a Series 50 was made on 17 December 1974. First deliveries were made to Swissair, with whom it entered service in August 1975.

Super 80. Increased capacity short/medium-range version of the DC-9, with accommodation for a maximum of 172 passengers. Described separately.

Current versions are offered in passenger, cargo (**DC-9F**), convertible (**DC-9CF**) or passenger-cargo (**DC-9RC**) configurations. The cargo and convertible models have a main cabin cargo door measuring 3·45 m (11 ft 4 in) wide and 2·06 m (6 ft 9 in) high. An executive transport version is also offered, with increased fuel, enabling up to 15 persons to be carried nonstop over 2,865 nm (5,300 km; 3,300 mile) transcontinental or transocean stages. First delivery of an all-cargo model, a DC-9 Srs 30F, was made to Alitalia on 13 May 1968. This model has 122·1 m³ (4,313 cu ft) of cargo space in main cabin, plus the underfloor hold, enabling it to carry eight full cargo pallets and two half-pallets with total weight of nearly 18,144 kg (40,000 lb).

There are also three military versions of the DC-9, as follows:

C-9A Nightingale. Aeromedical airlift transport, based on DC-9 Srs 30; 21 delivered to USAF between 1968-73. Details in 1977-78 *Jane's*.

C-9B Skytrain II. Fleet logistic support transport, of which 15 were ordered by the USN and two by Kuwait. Described separately.

VC-9C. DC-9-30 type aircraft with special configuration, ordered in December 1973 by the USAF for service in the Special Air Missions Wing based at Andrews AFB, Maryland, near Washington, DC. Three delivered in 1975.

Orders for the DC-9 totalled 1,028, including 41 military versions, by 1 July 1979. These included:

Series 10	137
Series 20	10
Series 30	611
Series 40	71
Series 50	95
Super 80	64

A total of 911 DC-9s (including 21 C-9As, 17 C-9Bs and 3 VC-9Cs) had been delivered by 1 July 1979, at which time there were 53 operators of DC-9 aircraft.

In June 1966, the FAA certificated three Category 2 all-weather landing systems for the DC-9, comprising the Collins FD-108 flight director system, Sperry AD-200 flight director system, and coupled approach utilising the Sperry SP-50A autopilot.

The following structural details apply to the DC-9 Series 30:

TYPE: Twin-turbofan short/medium-range airliner.

WINGS: Cantilever low-wing monoplane. Mean thickness/chord ratio 11·0%. Dihedral 3°. Sweepback 24° 30′ at quarter-chord. All-metal construction, with three spars inboard, two spars outboard and spanwise stringers riveted to skin. Glassfibre trailing-edges on wings, ailerons and flaps. Manually-controlled aileron on each wing. Wing-mounted speed brakes. Full-span leading-edge slats (also on Srs 20/40/50). Hydraulically-actuated double-slotted trailing-edge flaps over 67% of semi-span. Single boundary-layer fence (vortillon) under each wing. Detachable wingtips. Thermal anti-icing of leading-edges.

FUSELAGE: Conventional all-metal semi-monocoque structure.

TAIL UNIT: Cantilever all-metal structure with electrically-actuated variable-incidence T-tailplane. Manually-controlled elevators with servo tabs. Hydraulically-controlled rudder with manual override. Glassfibre trailing-edges on control surfaces.

LANDING GEAR: Retractable tricycle type of Menasco manufacture, with steerable nosewheel. Hydraulic retraction, nose unit forward, main units inward. Twin Goodyear wheels on each unit. Main-wheel tyres size 40 × 14. Nosewheel tyres size 26 × 6·60. Goodyear brakes. Hydro-Aire Hytrol anti-skid units.

POWER PLANT: Two Pratt & Whitney JT8D turbofan engines (details given under individual model listings), pod-mounted on each side of rear fuselage. Engines fitted with 40% target-type thrust reversers for ground operation only. Standard fuel capacity 13,937 litres (3,682 US gallons), also in Srs 10 and 20; 16,122 litres (4,259 US gallons) in Srs 40; and up to 19,074 litres (5,039 US gallons) in Srs 50. In Srs 30, 40 and 50 aircraft an additional 8,517 litres (2,250 US gallons) can be stored in auxiliary tanks.

ACCOMMODATION: Crew of two on flight deck, plus cabin attendants. Normal accommodation in main cabin is for 105 passengers, with seating for maximum of 119 with reduced facilities. Fully pressurised and air-conditioned. Toilets at rear of cabin. Provision for galley. Passenger door at front of cabin on port side, with electrically-operated built-in airstairs. Optional ventral stairway. Servicing and emergency exit door opposite on starboard side. Underfloor freight and baggage holds, with forward and rear doors on starboard side.

DIMENSIONS, EXTERNAL:	
Wing span: Srs 30, 40, 50	28·47 m (93 ft 5 in)
Wing aspect ratio: Srs 30, 40, 50	8·71
Length overall: Srs 30	36·37 m (119 ft 3½ in)
Srs 40	38·28 m (125 ft 7¼ in)
Srs 50	40·72 m (133 ft 7¼ in)
Height overall: Srs 30	8·38 m (27 ft 6 in)
Srs 40, 50	8·53 m (28 ft 0 in)
Tailplane span:	
Srs 30, 40, 50	11·23 m (36 ft 10¼ in)
Wheel track: Srs 30, 40, 50	5·03 m (16 ft 6 in)
Wheelbase: Srs 30	16·22 m (53 ft 2½ in)
Srs 40	17·10 m (56 ft 1¼ in)
Srs 50	18·56 m (60 ft 11 in)
Passenger door (port, fwd):	
Height	1·83 m (6 ft 0 in)
Width	0·85 m (2 ft 9½ in)
Height to sill	2·13 m (7 ft 2 in)
Servicing door (stbd, fwd): Height	1·22 m (4 ft 0 in)
Width	0·69 m (2 ft 3 in)
Height to sill	2·18 m (7 ft 2 in)
Freight and baggage hold doors:	
Height	1·27 m (4 ft 2 in)
Width: fwd	1·35 m (4 ft 5 in)
rear	0·91 m (3 ft 0 in)
Height to sill	1·07 m (3 ft 6 in)
DIMENSIONS, INTERNAL:	
Cabin: Max width	3·07 m (10 ft 1 in)
Floor width	2·87 m (9 ft 5 in)
Max height	2·06 m (6 ft 9 in)
Freight hold (underfloor):	
Srs 30	25·3 m³ (895 cu ft)
Srs 40	28·9 m³ (1,019 cu ft)
Srs 50	33·24 m³ (1,174 cu ft)
AREAS:	
Wings, gross:	
Srs 30, 40, 50	92·97 m² (1,000·7 sq ft)
Ailerons (total): All versions	3·53 m² (38·0 sq ft)
Trailing-edge flaps (total):	
All versions	19·58 m² (210·8 sq ft)
Leading-edge slats (total):	
Srs 50	11·22 m² (120·8 sq ft)
Spoilers (total): All versions	3·22 m² (34·7 sq ft)
Fin: All versions	14·96 m² (161·0 sq ft)
Rudder: All versions	6·07 m² (65·3 sq ft)
Tailplane: All versions	25·60 m² (275·6 sq ft)
Elevators, incl tabs: All versions	9·83 m² (105·8 sq ft)
WEIGHTS:	
Manufacturer's empty weight:	
Srs 30	25,940 kg (57,190 lb)
Srs 40	26,612 kg (58,670 lb)
Srs 50	28,068 kg (61,880 lb)

McDonnell Douglas DC-9 Series 50 in the insignia of Hawaiian Air

Max space-limited payload:
Srs 30 14,118 kg (31,125 lb)
Srs 40 15,610 kg (34,415 lb)
Max weight-limited payload:
Srs 30 12,743 kg (28,094 lb)
Srs 40 14,363 kg (31,665 lb)
Srs 50 15,617 kg (34,430 lb)
Max T-O weight:
Srs 30, 40, 50 54,885 kg (121,000 lb)
Max ramp weight:
Srs 30, 40, 50 55,338 kg (122,000 lb)
Max zero-fuel weight:
Srs 30, 40, 50 44,678 kg (98,500 lb)
Max landing weight:
Srs 30, 40, 50 49,895 kg (110,000 lb)

Performance (at max T-O weight, except where indicated):
Never-exceed speed:
Srs 50 537 knots (995 km/h; 618 mph)
Max level speed:
All versions 500 knots (926 km/h; 575 mph)
Max cruising speed at 7,620 m (25,000 ft):
Srs 30 490 knots (907 km/h; 564 mph)
Srs 40, 50 485 knots (898 km/h; 558 mph)
Average long-range cruising speed at 9,145-10,675 m (30,000-35,000 ft) 443 knots (821 km/h; 510 mph)
Max rate of climb at S/L:
Srs 30 885 m (2,900 ft)/min
Srs 40 865 m (2,850 ft)/min
Srs 50 792 m (2,600 ft)/min
FAA T-O field length: Srs 30 1,685 m (5,530 ft)
Srs 40 2,088 m (6,850 ft)
FAA landing field length: Srs 30 1,425 m (4,680 ft)
Srs 40 1,440 m (4,720 ft)
Srs 50 1,485 m (4,880 ft)
Range at Mach 0·8, with reserves for 200 nm (370 km; 230 mile) flight to alternate and 60 min hold at 3,050 m (10,000 ft):
Srs 30 at 9,150 m (30,000 ft) with 64 passengers and baggage 1,160 nm (2,148 km; 1,335 miles)
Srs 40 at 7,620 m (25,000 ft) with 70 passengers and baggage 930 nm (1,723 km; 1,071 miles)
Range at long-range cruising speed at 9,150 m (30,000 ft), reserves for 200 nm (370 km; 230 mile) flight to alternate and 45 min continued cruise at 9,150 m (30,000 ft):
Srs 30 with 80 passengers and baggage 1,670 nm (3,095 km; 1,923 miles)
Srs 40 with 87 passengers and baggage 1,555 nm (2,880 km; 1,790 miles)
Srs 50 with 97 passengers and baggage 1,795 nm (3,326 km; 2,067 miles)
Ferry range, reserves as above:
Srs 30 1,980 nm (3,669 km; 2,280 miles)
Srs 40 1,850 nm (3,428 km; 2,130 miles)
Srs 50 2,185 nm (4,049 km; 2,516 miles)

MCDONNELL DOUGLAS DC-9 SUPER 80

The McDonnell Douglas DC-9 Super 80 has been evolved specifically to meet the needs of operators on short/medium-range routes who require an aircraft of increased capacity, and the basic design has been modified to offer improved economy in operation, reduced fuel consumption, and far quieter engines. Contributing to the operational advantages are a lengthened fuselage to accommodate a maximum of 172 passengers in a five-abreast commuter layout, a new wing of increased area, and a refanned Pratt & Whitney JT8D engine which provides increased thrust and a lower specific fuel consumption.

The new wing is increased in span to 32·87 m (107 ft 10 in) by the insertion of wing root plugs and by a 0·61 m (2 ft 0 in) wingtip extension on each wing, giving a wing area 28% greater than that of the DC-9 Srs 50. Full-span leading-edge slats have three position settings.

The fuselage is extended in length by 4·34 m (14 ft 3 in), achieved by the insertion of a 3·86 m (12 ft 8 in) plug forward of the wing, and by an 0·48 m (1 ft 7 in) segment aft of the wing. This will allow a typical cabin arrangement of 12 first class and 125 coach seats, but there are several alternative options. The cabin will have 'wide look' decor, with large enclosed overhead baggage compartments, acoustical ceiling and soft fluorescent lighting. The increase in fuselage length provides also underfloor cargo holds of increased capacity; an additional cargo door is provided in the starboard side of the new forward fuselage plug, and the existing aft cargo door is increased in size and relocated. A new servicing door is installed in the port side of the fuselage, forward of the engine. The landing gear track is increased, the wheelbase extended, and the landing gear strengthened to cater for the new higher maximum T-O weight.

Basic power plant of the Srs 80 comprises two Pratt & Whitney JT8D-209 turbofan engines, each rated at 82·3 kN (18,500 lb st) for take-off, and having an emergency thrust reserve of 3·3 kN (750 lb st) which becomes available automatically in an engine-out situation. Refanned with a larger-diameter single-stage fan, this version of the JT8D engine has a bypass ratio of 1·68, by comparison with 1·00 of earlier versions, resulting in a lower specific fuel consumption and reduced noise emission. In addition, sound suppression materials applied to the inlet, fan duct and tailpipe duct of each nacelle, plus a cold/hot-stream exhaust mixer, will reduce engine noise to new low levels. Predicted noise levels for the Super 80 are significantly below the requirements of FAR Pt 36, and will also satisfy the more stringent requirements of ICAO CAN 5 established recently for new aircraft designs. Standard fuel capacity is increased by 5,754 litres (1,520 US gallons) as a result of the larger wing.

On 16 April 1979, McDonnell Douglas announced a further version of the DC-9 Super 80 which, subject to the receipt of sufficient orders, could be available for service in 1981. The proposal is for a more powerful variant, equipped with Pratt & Whitney JT8D-217 turbofan engines, which are derived from the JT8D-17. The -217 is rated at 89 kN (20,000 lb st), and has an emergency thrust reserve of 3·8 kN (850 lb st). This makes it particularly attractive for use in aircraft operating from airports located at high altitude, or with relatively high prevailing temperatures; but the higher thrust of the JT8D-217 engines would also make possible for the DC-9 an increased maximum take-off weight of 66,678 kg (147,000 lb), with increased payload and range, when operating from standard airports. At an airport such as Denver, Colorado, which is 1,525 m (5,000 ft) above sea level, the Super 80 with -217 engines would be able to take off with 155 passengers and their baggage, and have a nonstop range of approximately 1,300 nm (2,415 km; 1,500 miles). Generally similar to the basic Super 80 except for the changed power plant, it would have the same fuel capacity and max landing weight.

A **Super 80SF** short-field version is also under consideration, based on the DC-9 Series 40.

Systems improvements in the Super 80 include a new digital electronics integrated flight guidance and control system; a 'dial-a-flap' system to permit more accurate selection of flap angle for optimum take-off and landing performance; flow-through cooling of the aircraft's avionics compartment; a larger capacity APU; a new recirculating system for ventilation air; and an advanced digital fuel quantity gauging system. In addition, structural modifications are to be introduced to extend the airframe life to 50,000 landings.

In October 1977, Swissair placed a firm order for 15 Super 80 aircraft, delivery of which is scheduled between March 1980 and March 1981. By 1 July 1979 firm orders totalled 64 aircraft, plus conditional firm orders and options for 32 more aircraft, to serve with eight airlines. First order (for three aircraft) for the version with JT8D-217 engines was placed by Aeromexico in September 1979.

The description of the DC-9 Srs 30 applies also to the Super 80, except as follows:

Wings: As for Srs 30, except: Dihedral 3°. Incidence 1° 15′. Sweepback at quarter-chord 24° 30′. Three spoilers per wing; two outboard panels act as flight and ground spoilers, inboard panel is ground spoiler only.

Fuselage: All-metal semi-monocoque fail-safe structure of heat-treated light alloy. Majority of cabin floor constructed of balsa or Nomex core composite. Engine pylons built by Calcor, fuselage panels by Aeritalia.

Landing Gear: As for Srs 30, except gear of Cleveland Pneumatic manufacture. Twin Goodyear wheels and tyres on each unit. Main-wheel tyres size 44·5 × 16·5-20, pressure 11·38 bars (165 lb/sq in). Nosewheel tyres size 26 × 6·6-14, pressure 10·34 bars (150 lb/sq in). Goodyear disc brakes. Hydro-Aire Mk IIIA anti-skid units. Douglas ram-air brake cooling.

Power Plant (basic version): Two Pratt & Whitney JT8D-209 turbofan engines, each rated at 82·3 kN (18,500 lb st), with emergency thrust reserve of 3·3 kN (750 lb st). Standard fuel capacity 21,876 litres (5,779 US gallons). Pressure refuelling point in starboard wing leading-edge. Overwing gravity refuelling points.

Accommodation: As for Srs 30, except accommodation is for a maximum of 172 passengers. Servicing and emergency exit doors at starboard forward end and aft port end of cabin. Three cargo doors for underfloor holds on starboard side. Overwing emergency exits, two each side.

Systems: AiResearch dual air cycle air-conditioning and pressurisation system utilising engine bleed air, max differential 0·536 bars (7·77 lb/sq in). Two separate 207 bar (3,000 lb/sq in) hydraulic systems for operation of

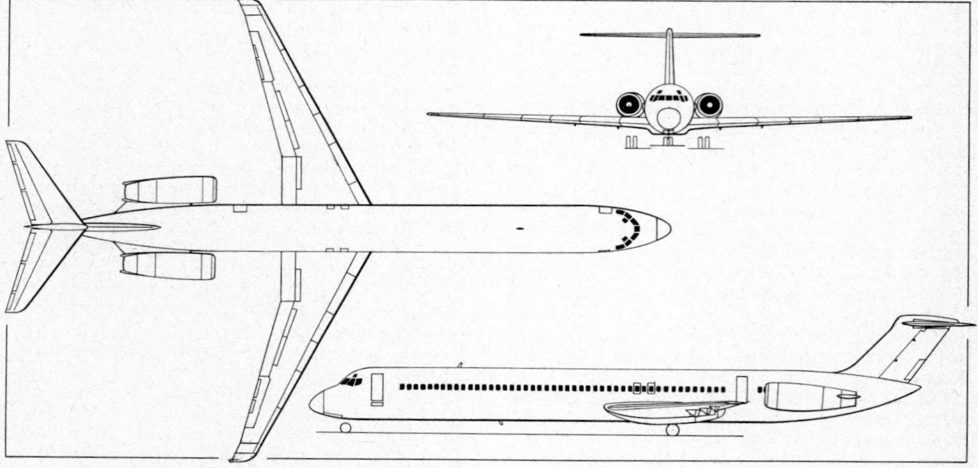

McDonnell Douglas DC-9 Super 80 'stretched' version of this twin-turbofan transport *(Pilot Press)*

First McDonnell Douglas DC-9 Super 80 undergoing fuel system tests in September 1979, prior to first flight

spoilers, flaps, slats, rudder, landing gear, nosewheel steering, brakes, rotated thrust reversers and ventral stairway. Pneumatic system, for air-conditioning/pressurisation, engine starting and ice protection, utilises 8th or 13th stage engine bleed and/or APU. Electrical system includes three 40kVA 120/208V three-phase 400Hz alternators, two engine-driven, one driven by APU. Oxygen system of diluter-demand type for crew on flight deck; continuous-flow type with automatic mask presentation for cabin passengers. Anti-icing of wing and engine inlets, and de-icing of tailplane, by engine bleed air. Electrical de-icing of windscreen. APU provides pneumatic and electrical power on ground, and electrical power in flight.

AVIONICS AND EQUIPMENT: All-digital avionics, including dual Sperry integrated flight systems; Sperry Cat IIIA autoland; autopilot and stability augmentation system; speed command with digital autothrottles; rat/thrust rating indicator system; dual air data systems; automatic reserve thrust; tune ADF system; and weather radar display. Sundstrand head-up display.

DIMENSIONS, EXTERNAL:
- Wing span: 32·87 m (107 ft 10 in)
- Wing chord at root: 7·05 m (23 ft 1½ in)
- Wing chord at tip: 1·10 m (3 ft 7½ in)
- Wing aspect ratio: 9·62
- Length overall: 45·06 m (147 ft 10 in)
- Height overall: 9·04 m (29 ft 8 in)
- Tailplane span: 12·24 m (40 ft 2 in)
- Wheel track: 5·08 m (16 ft 8 in)
- Wheelbase: 22·07 m (72 ft 5 in)
- Passenger door (port, fwd):
  - Height: 1·83 m (6 ft 0 in)
  - Width: 0·86 m (2 ft 10 in)
  - Height to sill: 2·24 m (7 ft 4 in)
- Servicing door (stbd, fwd): Height 1·22 m (4 ft 0 in)
  - Width: 0·69 m (2 ft 3 in)
  - Height to sill: 2·24 m (7 ft 4 in)
- Servicing door (port, rear): Height 1·52 m (5 ft 0 in)
  - Width: 0·69 m (2 ft 3 in)
  - Height to sill: 2·67 m (8 ft 9 in)
- Freight and baggage hold doors:
  - Height: 1·27 m (4 ft 2 in)
  - Width: 1·35 m (4 ft 5 in)
  - Height to sill: fwd 1·17 m (3 ft 10 in)
    - centre: 1·30 m (4 ft 3 in)
    - aft: 1·52 m (5 ft 0 in)
- Emergency exits (overwing, port and stbd):
  - Height: 0·91 m (3 ft 0 in)
  - Width: 0·51 m (1 ft 8 in)

DIMENSIONS, INTERNAL:
- Cabin, excl flight deck, incl toilets:
  - Length: 30·78 m (101 ft 0 in)
  - Max width: 3·07 m (10 ft 1 in)
  - Max height: 2·06 m (6 ft 9 in)
  - Floor area: 89·65 m² (965 sq ft)
  - Volume: 191·9 m³ (6,778 cu ft)
- Freight holds (underfloor):
  - fwd: 13·14 m³ (464 cu ft)
  - centre: 9·80 m³ (346 cu ft)
  - aft: 12·54 m³ (443 cu ft)

AREAS:
- Wings, gross: 118·8 m² (1,279 sq ft)
- Ailerons (total): 3·53 m² (38·0 sq ft)
- Fin: 14·96 m² (161·0 sq ft)
- Rudder: 6·07 m² (65·3 sq ft)
- Tailplane: 29·17 m² (314·0 sq ft)

WEIGHTS AND LOADING (JT8D-209 engines):
- Weight empty: 35,288 kg (77,797 lb)
- Max payload: 18,236 kg (40,203 lb)
- Max T-O weight: 63,502 kg (140,000 lb)
- Max ramp weight: 63,956 kg (141,000 lb)
- Max zero-fuel weight: 53,524 kg (118,000 lb)
- Max landing weight: 58,060 kg (128,000 lb)
- Max wing loading: 565·4 kg/m² (115·8 lb/sq ft)

PERFORMANCE (JT8D-209 engines, estimated, at max T-O weight unless indicated otherwise):
- Never-exceed speed: 537 knots (994 km/h; 618 mph)
- Max level speed: 500 knots (927 km/h; 576 mph)
- Max cruising speed at 7,620 m (25,000 ft): 485 knots (898 km/h; 558 mph)
- Econ cruising speed at 9,144-10,670 m (30-35,000 ft): 443 knots (821 km/h; 510 mph)
- Stalling speed, flaps up: 160 knots (298 km/h; 185 mph)
- Stalling speed, flaps down, at max landing weight: 102 knots (190 km/h; 118 mph)
- Max rate of climb at S/L: 732 m (2,400 ft)/min
- T-O to 10·7 m (35 ft): 2,195 m (7,200 ft)
- FAA dry runway landing field length: 1,402 m (4,600 ft)
- Range with max fuel, 70% load factor, domestic reserves, 200 nm (370 km; 230 mile) alternate: 2,390 nm (4,429 km; 2,752 miles)
- Range with max payload, allowances as above: 2,060 nm (3,817 km; 2,372 miles)

MCDONNELL DOUGLAS C-9B SKYTRAIN II

The US Navy's C-9B Skytrain II is a special convertible passenger/cargo version of the DC-9 Series 30 commercial transport. The contract for five (increased subsequently to eight) was signed by Naval Air Systems Command on 24 April 1972, and the first of these aircraft made its initial flight on 7 February 1973, two months ahead of schedule. The first two aircraft were delivered on 8 May 1973, to Fleet Tactical Support Squadrons 1 (VR-1) at NAS Norfolk, Virginia, and 30 (VR-30) at NAS Alameda, California. All eight were delivered during 1973. A further six C-9Bs were ordered in late 1974, and delivery of these was completed by mid-1976. One more was ordered for the Navy in FY 1979; two were sold to the Kuwait Air Force.

Accommodation in the C-9B was described in the 1977-78 *Jane's*. Normal passenger access is by means of forward port and aft ventral doors, each with electrically-actuated ventral airstairs to make the C-9B independent of ground facilities.

WEIGHTS:
- Operating weight, empty:
  - passenger configuration: 29,612 kg (65,283 lb)
  - cargo configuration: 27,082 kg (59,706 lb)
- Max ramp weight: 50,350 kg (111,000 lb)
- Max T-O weight: 49,900 kg (110,000 lb)
- Max landing weight: 44,906 kg (99,000 lb)

PERFORMANCE (at max T-O weight unless otherwise specified):
- Max cruising speed: 500 knots (927 km/h; 576 mph)
- Long-range cruising speed: 38 knots (811 km/h; 504 mph)
- Military critical field length: 2,259 m (7,410 ft)
- Landing distance, at max landing weight: 786 m (2,580 ft)
- Range, long-range cruising speed at 9,145 m (30,000 ft) with 4,535 kg (10,000 lb) payload: 2,538 nm (4,704 km; 2,923 miles)

MCDONNELL DOUGLAS DC-10

In April 1966, American Airlines circulated to seven airframe manufacturers a statement of the company's future requirements, based on traffic forecasts. It appreciated that increasing airport congestion would be alleviated by the introduction of commercial transport aircraft of greater passenger-carrying capacity, but considered it essential that such aircraft should not be restricted to operation from those airports with very long runways. At that time, it visualised a twin-turbofan aircraft with dimensions and performance tailored specifically for operation from smaller airports. During the evolutionary period, the major change was a decision to use three instead of two turbofan engines.

The aircraft which McDonnell Douglas evolved to meet this specification was designated DC-10, an all-purpose commercial transport able to operate economically over ranges from 260 nm to 5,300 nm (480 to 9,815 km; 300 to 6,100 miles), according to Series, and able to carry 270 mixed class passengers, or a maximum of 380 passengers in an all-economy configuration.

It has since been produced in four versions, as follows:

Series 10. Initial version, powered by three General Electric CF6-6D or -6D1 turbofan engines, each rated at 178 kN (40,000 lb st) or 182·4 kN (41,000 lb st) respectively. Intended for service on domestic routes of 260-3,125 nm (480-5,795 km; 300-3,600 miles). First ordered by American Airlines on 19 February 1968. The first DC-10 Srs 10 made its first flight on 29 August 1970, and 124 had been ordered by 1 January 1979.

On 29 July 1971 simultaneous deliveries of the first two McDonnell Douglas DC-10 Srs 10 commercial transport aircraft were made to American Airlines and United Air Lines at Long Beach, California. The FAA awarded the company a type certificate for the Srs 10 on the same day.

First scheduled passenger flight of the DC-10 Srs 10 was made on 5 August 1971, when American Airlines began a daily DC-10 service between Los Angeles and Chicago.

Series 15. Basically as Series 10, but with General Electric CF6-45B2 engines, each rated at 206·8 kN (46,500 lb st). Two each ordered by Aeromexico and Mexicana in Summer 1979, for delivery in 1981.

Series 30. Extended-range version for intercontinental operations, powered by three General Electric CF6-50A or -50C turbofan engines, each rated at 218 kN (49,000 lb st) and 227 kN (51,000 lb st) respectively. Later versions have CF6-50C1 or C2 engines rated at 233·5 kN (52,500 lb st). Increased fuel capacity. Wing span increased by 3·05 m (10 ft 0 in). Landing gear supplemented by additional dual-wheel unit, mounted on the fuselage centreline between the four-wheel bogie main units.

First flight of the Series 30 was made on 21 June 1972. FAA certification was granted on 21 November 1972, simultaneously with the first deliveries of production aircraft to KLM and Swissair. Total of 163 ordered by 1 January 1979.

Series 40. Extended-range version for intercontinental operations, powered by three Pratt & Whitney turbofan engines. Twenty-two early models, built for Northwest Orient Airlines, had JT9D-20 turbofans, each rated at 220 kN (49,400 lb st) with water injection. First flight of the Series 40 (known originally as the Series 20) was made on 28 February 1972, and FAA certification was received on 20 October 1972. Later versions of the Series 40, built for Japan Air Lines, are equipped with JT9D-59A turbofans, each rated at 236 kN (53,000 lb st). First flight of a Series 40 aircraft with this latter power plant was made on 25 July 1975. A total of 31 Series 40 DC-10s had been ordered by 1 January 1979.

There are also convertible cargo versions designated Model **10CF** and **30CF**, of which the latter is described separately. On 19 December 1977 the USAF announced selection of the DC-10 Srs 30CF as its **Advanced Tanker Cargo Aircraft (ATCA)**, and this version also is described separately (see entry for KC-10A Extender).

Under consideration for possible future production are domestic and intercontinental versions with fuselages lengthened by 7·92 to 12·19 m (26 to 40 ft) compared with current series. The largest of the new models would accommodate a total of 395 passengers in mixed first class/coach seating, with improved seat/mile costs and reduced fuel consumption per seat.

The DC-10 manufacturing plan calls for subassemblies and components to be brought together at Long Beach for final assembly. Certain major subassemblies are produced at other divisions of McDonnell Douglas, and Convair Division of General Dynamics Corporation at San Diego, California, is subcontractor for the fuselage, being responsible for five sections totalling 39·01 m (128 ft).

By 24 September 1979, McDonnell Douglas had received firm orders for 346 DC-10s, plus conditional firm orders and options on 53 more, making a total of 397, of which 289 had been delivered. At that date, 46 airlines, plus the USAF, had ordered DC-10s: the worldwide fleet had then carried 233 million passengers and had amassed more than 1,564 million nm (2,897 million km; 1,800 million miles).

TYPE: Three-turbofan commercial transport.

WINGS: Cantilever low-wing monoplane of all-metal fail-safe construction. Several different wing sections of Douglas design are used between wing root and tip. Thickness/chord ratio varies from slightly more than 12·2% at root to less than 8·4% at tip. Dihedral 5° 14·4′ inboard, 3° 1·8′ outboard. Incidence ranges from positive at wing root to negative at tip. Sweepback at quarter-chord 35°. All-metal inboard and outboard ailerons, the former used conventionally, the latter only when the leading-edge slats are extended. Double-slotted all-metal trailing-edge flaps mounted on external hinges, with an inboard and outboard flap panel on each wing. Five all-metal spoiler panels on each wing, at the rear edge of the fixed wing structure, forward of the flaps. All spoilers operate in unison as lateral control, speed brake and ground spoilers. Full-span three-position all-metal leading-edge slats. Ailerons are powered by hydraulic actuators manufactured by Bertea Corporation, spoilers by hydraulic actuators manufactured by Parker-Hannifin Corporation. Each aileron is powered by either of two hydraulic systems; each spoiler is powered by a single system. All leading-edge slat segments outboard of the engines are anti-iced with engine bleed air.

FUSELAGE: Aluminium alloy semi-monocoque fail-safe structure of circular cross-section. Except for auxiliary areas the entire fuselage is pressurised.

TAIL UNIT: Cantilever all-metal structure. Variable-incidence tailplane, actuated by Vickers hydraulic motors. Longitudinal and directional controls are fully powered and comprise inboard and outboard elevators, each segment powered by a Bertea tandem actuator; upper and lower rudder each powered by a Bertea actuator. Rudder standby power supplied by two transfer motor pumps manufactured by Abex Corporation.

LANDING GEAR (Srs 10): Hydraulically-retractable tricycle type, with gravity free-fall for emergency extension. Nosewheel unit retracts forward, main units inward into fuselage. Twin-wheel steerable nose unit. Main gear comprises two four-wheel bogies. Oleo-pneumatic shock-absorbers on all units. Goodyear nosewheels and tyres size 37 × 14-14, pressure 11·03 bars (160 lb/sq in). Goodyear main wheels and tyres size 50 × 20-20, pressure 11·72 bars (170 lb/sq in). Goodyear disc brakes and anti-skid system, with individual wheel control.

LANDING GEAR (Srs 30 and 40): These versions have an additional dual-wheel main unit mounted on the fuselage centreline between the four-wheel bogie units, and this retracts forward. Goodyear nosewheels and tyres size 40 × 15·5-16, pressure 12·41 bars (180 lb/sq in). Four-wheel bogie main units and centreline unit have Goodyear wheels and tyres size 52 × 20·5-23. The former have a pressure of 11·38 bars (165 lb/sq in), the latter 9·65 bars (140 lb/sq in). Otherwise as Srs 10.

POWER PLANT: Three turbofan engines (details under Series descriptions), two of which are mounted on underwing pylons, the third above the rear fuselage at the base of the fin. All engines are fitted with thrust reversers for ground operation. Engine air inlets have load-carrying acoustically-treated panels for noise attenuation, and each engine fan case and fan exhaust is similarly treated. Three integral wing fuel tanks with a total capacity of approximately 82,142 litres (21,700 US gallons). Four standard pressure refuelling adapters, two in each wing outboard of the engine pylons. Series 30 and 40 aircraft have four integral wing fuel tanks and an auxiliary tank in the wing centre-section with a con-

McDonnell Douglas DC-10 Series 40 in the insignia of Japan Air Lines

nected structural compartment fitted with a bladder cell, giving increased total capacity of approximately 138,165 litres (36,500 US gallons). Oil capacity, Series 10 and 30: 34·1 litres (9 usable US gallons); Series 40: 56·8 litres (15 usable US gallons).

Accommodation: Crew of three (pilot, first officer, flight engineer), with seating for two observers, plus cabin attendants. Standard seating for 255 or 270 in mixed class versions, with a maximum of 380 passengers in an economy class arrangement. Two aisles run the length of the cabin, which is separated into sections by cloakroom dividers. In the first class section, with three pairs of reclining seats abreast, the aisles are 0·78 m (2 ft 7 in) wide. In the coach class section, four pairs of seats, with a table between the centre pairs, also have two aisles, these being 0·51 m (1 ft 8 in) wide. One pair of seats is exchanged for a three-seat unit in the nine-abreast high-density layout. Up to nine lavatories located throughout the passenger cabin. Cloakrooms of standard and elevating type distributed throughout the cabin. Cabin windows, 0·28 × 0·41 m (11 in × 16 in), are spaced at 0·51 m (20 in) centres. Overhead stowage modules, fully enclosed and providing stowage for passengers' personal effects, are located on the sidewalls and extend the full length of the cabin. Optional centreline overhead baggage racks available. Eight passenger doors, four on each side, open by sliding inward and upward into the above-ceiling area. Containerised or bulk cargo compartments located immediately forward and aft of the wing, with outward-opening doors on the starboard side. A bulk cargo compartment is located in the lower aft section of the fuselage, with its door on the port side. Entire accommodation is fully air-conditioned, with five separate control zones for the standard below-floor galley configuration. Series 30 and 40 aircraft have an optional main cabin galley to replace the lower galley, and in this configuration there are four separate control zones for the air-conditioning. The lower-deck galley is provided with five to eight high-temperature ovens, and with refrigerators, storage space for linen, china and other accessories. Serving carts are taken to cabin level by two electric elevators, to a buffet service centre, from where stewardesses serve passengers. To permit quick turnround at terminals, without interference to passenger movement in the main cabin, the kitchen is provisioned through the cargo doors at ground level.

Systems: Three parallel continuously-operating and completely separate hydraulic systems supply the fully-powered flight controls and wheel brakes. Normally, one of the systems supplies power for landing gear actuation. Two reversible motor pumps, each sized to deliver power from one of the other two systems for standby operation of landing gear, can also power any other hydraulically operated unit. Each hydraulic system is powered by two identical engine-driven pumps, capable of delivering a total of 265 litres (70 US gallons)/min at 207 bars (3,000 lb/sq in) at take-off. All three hydraulic systems are applied to each primary control axis in a manner which ensures maximum control effectiveness in the event of single or dual hydraulic system failures. An AiResearch TSCP-700-4 APU provides ground electrical and pneumatic power, including main engine starting, and auxiliary electric power in flight.

Avionics and Equipment: A dual fail-operative landing system is installed to meet Category IIIA weather minima. Digital air data computer meeting ARINC 576 requirements on Srs 10. Triple inertial navigation system meeting ARINC 561 requirements on Srs 30 and 40, with optional dual area navigation system capability.

Dimensions, external:
- Wing span: Series 10, 15 — 47·34 m (155 ft 4 in)
  - Series 30, 40 — 50·41 m (165 ft 4·4 in)
- Wing chord at root — 10·71 m (35 ft 1·8 in)
- Wing chord at tip: Series 10 — 3·21 m (10 ft 6½ in)
  - Series 30, 40 — 2·73 m (8 ft 11½ in)
- Wing aspect ratio: Series 10 — 6·8
  - Series 30, 40 — 7·5
- Length overall: Series 10 — 55·30 m (181 ft 5 in)
  - Series 15, 30, 40 — 55·50 m (182 ft 1 in)
- Length of fuselage — 51·97 m (170 ft 6 in)
- Height overall — 17·70 m (58 ft 1 in)
- Tailplane span — 21·69 m (71 ft 2 in)
- Wheel track — 10·67 m (35 ft 0 in)
- Wheelbase: Series 10, 40 — 22·07 m (72 ft 5 in)
  - Series 30 — 22·05 m (72 ft 4 in)

Dimensions, internal:
- Cabin: Length, from aft bulkhead of flight deck to aft cabin bulkhead — approx 41·45 m (136 ft 0 in)
  - Max width — 5·72 m (18 ft 9 in)
  - Height (basic) — 2·41 m (7 ft 11 in)
- Series 10, 30, 40 in lower-galley configuration:
  - Forward baggage and/or freight hold (forward of wing):
    - Containerised volume — 27·2 m³ (960 cu ft)
    - Bulk volume — 37·9 m³ (1,339 cu ft)
  - Centre baggage and/or freight hold (aft of wing):
    - Containerised volume — 36·2 m³ (1,280 cu ft)
    - Bulk volume — 43·9 m³ (1,552 cu ft)
  - Aft hold:
    - Bulk volume — 22·8 m³ (805 cu ft)
- Series 30, 40 in upper-galley configuration:
  - Forward baggage and/or freight hold (forward of wing):
    - Containerised volume — 72·5 m³ (2,560 cu ft)
    - Bulk volume — 86·2 m³ (3,045 cu ft)
  - Centre baggage and/or freight hold (aft of wing):
    - Containerised volume — 45·3 m³ (1,600 cu ft)
    - Bulk volume — 54·8 m³ (1,935 cu ft)
  - Aft hold:
    - Bulk volume — 14·4 m³ (510 cu ft)

Areas:
- Wings, gross: Series 10 — 358·7 m² (3,861 sq ft)
  - Series 30, 40 — 367·7 m² (3,958 sq ft)
- Ailerons, inboard (total) — 7·68 m² (82·7 sq ft)
- Ailerons, outboard (total) — 9·76 m² (105·1 sq ft)
- Trailing-edge flaps (total) — 62·1 m² (668·2 sq ft)
- Leading-edge slats (total):
  - Series 10 — 42·05 m² (452·6 sq ft)
  - Series 30, 40 — 43·84 m² (471·9 sq ft)
- Spoilers (total) — 12·73 m² (137·0 sq ft)
- Fin — 45·92 m² (494·29 sq ft)
- Rudders (total) — 10·29 m² (110·71 sq ft)
- Tailplane — 96·6 m² (1,040·2 sq ft)
- Elevators (total) — 27·7 m² (298·1 sq ft)

Weights and Loadings:
- Basic empty weight:
  - Series 10 — 109,438 kg (241,270 lb)
  - Series 30 — 120,914 kg (266,570 lb)
  - Series 40 — 122,737 kg (270,590 lb)
- Max payload:
  - Series 10 — 44,678 kg (98,500 lb)
  - Series 30 — 48,330 kg (106,550 lb)
  - Series 40 — 46,243 kg (101,950 lb)
- Max T-O weight:
  - Series 10 — 206,384 kg (455,000 lb)
  - Series 30 — 259,450 kg (572,000 lb)
  - Series 40 (-20 engines) — 251,744 kg (555,000 lb)
  - Series 40 (-59A engines) — 259,450 kg (572,000 lb)
- Max ramp weight:
  - Series 10 — 207,745 kg (458,000 lb)
  - Series 30 — 260,815 kg (575,000 lb)
  - Series 40 (-20 engines) — 253,105 kg (558,000 lb)
  - Series 40 (-59A engines) — 260,815 kg (575,000 lb)
- Max zero-fuel weight:
  - Series 10 — 151,953 kg (335,000 lb)
  - Series 30, 40 — 166,922 kg (368,000 lb)
- Max landing weight:
  - Series 10 — 164,880 kg (363,500 lb)
  - Series 30, 40 — 182,798 kg (403,000 lb)
- Max wing loading:
  - Series 10 — 575·4 kg/m² (117·8 lb/sq ft)
  - Series 30 — 705·6 kg/m² (144·5 lb/sq ft)
  - Series 40 (-20 engines) — 684·6 kg/m² (140·2 lb/sq ft)
  - Series 40 (-59A engines) — 705·6 kg/m² (144·5 lb/sq ft)

Performance (at max T-O weight unless specified):
- Never-exceed speed — Mach 0·95
- Max level speed at 7,620 m (25,000 ft) — Mach 0·88 (530 knots; 982 km/h; 610 mph)

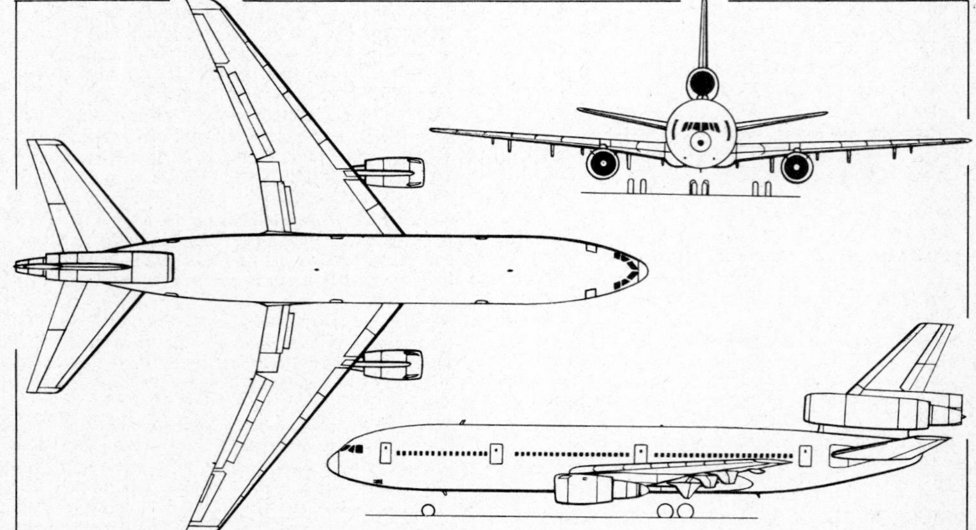

McDonnell Douglas DC-10 Series 30 high-capacity three-engined transport *(Pilot Press)*

Max cruising speed at 9,145 m (30,000 ft):
- Series 10 (-6D engines) 499 knots (925 km/h; 575 mph)
- Series 10 (-6D1 engines) 501 knots (928 km/h; 577 mph)
- Series 30 490 knots (908 km/h; 564 mph)
- Series 40 (-20 engines) 489 knots (906 km/h; 563 mph)
- Series 40 (-59A engines) 498 knots (922 km/h; 573 mph)

T-O speed (V_2):
- Series 10 (-6D engines) 181 knots (335 km/h; 208 mph)
- Series 10 (-6D1 engines) 175 knots (325 km/h; 202 mph)
- Series 30 (-50C engines) 189 knots (351 km/h; 218 mph)
- Series 40 (-20 engines) 187 knots (346 km/h; 215 mph)
- Series 40 (-59A engines) 178 knots (330 km/h; 205 mph)

Landing speed (at max landing weight unless specified):
- Series 10, at 151,953 kg (335,000 lb) 136 knots (252 km/h; 157 mph)
- Series 30 145 knots (269 km/h; 167 mph)
- Series 40 (-20 engines) 146·5 knots (271 km/h; 168·5 mph)
- Series 40 (-59A engines) 143·5 knots (265·5 km/h; 165 mph)

Max rate of climb at S/L:
- Series 10 (-6D engines) 817 m (2,680 ft)/min
- Series 10 (-6D1 engines) 838 m (2,750 ft)/min
- Series 30 884 m (2,900 ft)/min
- Series 40 (-20 engines) 829 m (2,720 ft)/min
- Series 40 (-59A engines) 762 m (2,500 ft)/min

Service ceiling:
- Series 10 (-6D engines) at 192,775 kg (425,000 lb) AUW 10,605 m (34,800 ft)
- Series 10 (-6D1 engines) at 192,775 kg (425,000 lb) AUW 10,730 m (35,200 ft)
- Series 30 at 249,475 kg (550,000 lb) AUW 10,180 m (33,400 ft)
- Series 40 (-20 engines) at 242,670 kg (535,000 lb) AUW 9,660 m (31,700 ft)
- Series 40 (-59A engines) 9,965 m (32,700 ft)

En-route climb altitude, one engine out:
- Series 10 at 195,045 kg (430,000 lb) AUW 4,145 m (13,600 ft)
- Series 30 at 251,744 kg (555,000 lb) AUW 4,360 m (14,300 ft)
- Series 40 (-20 engines) at 247,205 kg (545,000 lb) AUW 3,565 m (11,700 ft)
- Series 40 (-59A engines) at 254,010 kg (560,000 lb) AUW 5,135 m (16,850 ft)

FAR T-O distance to 10·7 m (35 ft):
- Series 10 (-6D engines) 3,505 m (11,500 ft)
- Series 10 (-6D1 engines) 3,200 m (10,500 ft)
- Series 30 (-50C engines) 3,581 m (11,750 ft)
- Series 40 (-20 engines) 3,734 m (12,250 ft)
- Series 40 (-59A engines) 3,124 m (10,250 ft)

FAR landing distance from 15 m (50 ft) at max landing weight:
- Series 10 1,777 m (5,830 ft)
- Series 30 1,817 m (5,960 ft)
- Series 40 1,780 m (5,840 ft)

Range with max fuel, no payload, international reserves:
- Series 10 5,150 nm (9,543 km; 5,930 miles)
- Series 30 6,250 nm (11,580 km; 7,197 miles)
- Series 40 (-20 engines) 5,850 nm (10,840 km; 6,736 miles)
- Series 40 (-59A engines) 6,100 nm (11,305 km; 7,024 miles)

Range with max payload at max zero-fuel weight:
- Series 10 2,350 nm (4,355 km; 2,706 miles)
- Series 30 4,000 nm (7,413 km; 4,606 miles)
- Series 40 (-20 engines) 3,500 nm (6,485 km; 4,030 miles)
- Series 40 (-59A engines) 4,050 nm (7,505 km; 4,663 miles)

MCDONNELL DOUGLAS DC-10 SERIES 30CF

The Series 30CF is a convertible freighter version of the McDonnell Douglas DC-10 transport. Generally similar to the basic DC-10 Series 30 and 40, it is designed for easy conversion to either passenger or cargo configuration. Its payload can consist of 380 passengers and baggage or 64,860 kg (143,000 lb) of cargo over full intercontinental range; or up to 70,626 kg (155,700 lb) of cargo on domestic transcontinental routes.

The first Series 30CF was powered by three General Electric CF6-50A turbofans. It flew for the first time on 28 February 1973 and initial deliveries were made to Overseas National Airways and Trans International Airlines on 17 April 1973. In June 1977, Overseas National Airways took delivery of two of the later DC-10 Srs 30CFs, powered by General Electric CF6-50C1 engines rated at 233·5 kN (52,500 lb st).

In the passenger configuration, interior layout is generally similar to that of the DC-10, but the Series 30CF was designed to permit overnight conversion to an all-cargo configuration. This entails removal of seats, overhead baggage racks, forward food service centre, cloakrooms and carpeting from the main cabin, and installation of freight loading tracks and rollers, a cargo tiedown system and restraint nets. Coffee service fixtures and lavatories in the aft cabin may also be removed but are retained normally for regular cargo flights.

The cargo loading system for the Series 30CF is based on that in use in the DC-8 Super Sixty Series freighters. A two-channel network of roller conveyors, adjustable guide rails and pallet restraint fittings is installed in the seat tracks in the cabin floor by use of simple stud and locking pin devices. A 2·59 m high × 3·56 m wide (8 ft 6 in × 11 ft 8 in) cargo door in the side of the fuselage swings upward and allows easy loading of bulky freight.

A total of 30 standard 2·24 m × 2·74 m (7 ft 4 in × 9 ft) cargo pallets, or 22 larger pallets measuring 2·24 m × 3·18 m (7 ft 4 in × 10 ft 5 in) or 2·44 m × 3·05 m (8 ft × 10 ft), can be accommodated in the main cabin. The Series 30CF with upstairs galleys also has 132·2 m³ (4,670 cu ft) of cargo space in the two lower cargo compartments for bulk freight, or for 26 half-size containers, or for five full-size pallets and 16 half-size containers.

A DC-10 Series 30CF delivered to Sabena Belgian World Airlines in 1973 is certificated for carrying combination loads of freight and passengers in the main cabin. Other DC-10 series aircraft are also offered in convertible versions. Continental Air Lines is operating the DC-10 Series 10CF. A total of 31 CF models had been ordered by 1 January 1979.

MCDONNELL DOUGLAS EXTENDER

US Air Force designation: KC-10A

The USAF announced on 19 December 1977 that, following evaluation of the Boeing 747 and McDonnell Douglas DC-10 to meet its requirement for an Advanced Tanker/Cargo Aircraft (ATCA), the DC-10 ATCA was selected to fulfil this role. Subsequently, the aircraft was designated KC-10A and named Extender.

A force of KC-10As will greatly enhance the ability of the USAF to deploy combat aircraft, men and supplies on a global scale. This point was emphasised in a USAF submission to Congress in which the spokesman commented that 40 Boeing KC-135 tankers and a number of cargo aircraft would be needed to fuel an F-4 fighter squadron and carry its personnel and equipment from the USA to the Middle East. Just 17 of the proposed KC-10As could fulfil the same task, more economically and efficiently. USAF Military Airlift Command's (MAC) need for support by such aircraft was highlighted during the 1973 Arab-Israeli war, when many countries denied landing rights to MAC aircraft. From these circumstances came the decision to develop an ATCA to support the strategic airlift fleet, under the operational control of the USAF Strategic Air Command.

The initial $28 million contract awarded to McDonnell Douglas covered the funding for initial production planning, engineering and tooling. A second $429,000 contract was for initial planning of a logistics support programme covering the entire KC-10A military tanker fleet.

On 20 November 1978, the USAF authorised McDonnell Douglas to begin production of the KC-10A. The contract calls for an expenditure of $132·5 million by the USAF, for the acquisition of two KC-10As, and in payment of the balance of the non-recurring engineering costs. In addition, under a separate $15·5 million contract, McDonnell Douglas was authorised to purchase the initial spare parts and support equipment for the KC-10A system. Quantities of KC-10As to be procured over the next five years will be determined by available funding, but it is anticipated that up to 20 KC-10As may be procured eventually by the USAF. The FY 1980 budget requested funding for four, to be delivered in 1981. The first KC-10A is scheduled for delivery to Barksdale AFB, Louisiana, for operation by SAC, in October 1980.

The commercial DC-10 Series 30CF convertible freighter, the basic airframe chosen for conversion to the ATCA role, is currently certificated for operation at a max T-O weight of 267,620 kg (590,000 lb).

The modifications necessary to convert the DC-10-30CF to the ATCA configuration include the installation

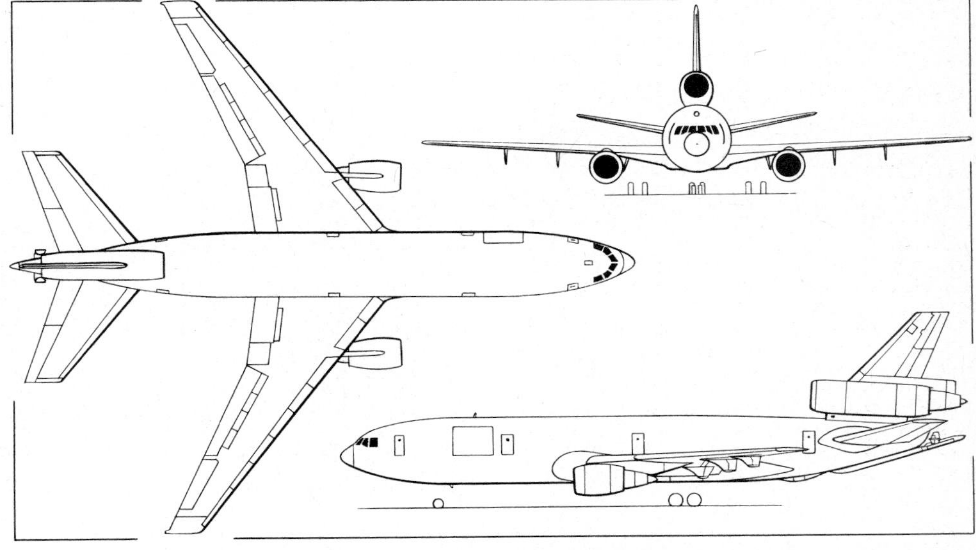

McDonnell Douglas KC-10A Extender Advanced Tanker/Cargo Aircraft for the USAF *(Pilot Press)*

McDonnell Douglas DC-10 Series 30CF convertible freighter in the insignia of World Airways

of fuel cells in the lower fuselage compartment; the provision of a boom operator station, an aerial refuelling boom, a refuelling receptacle, an improved cargo handling system, and some military electronics systems. Various seating layouts will be available in the forward area to permit the transport of a fighter squadron's essential support personnel. Seven bladder fuel cells are to be installed in the lower fuselage compartments, three forward and four aft of the wing, mounted within framework that will restrain and support the cells. These will contain a total of 53,446 kg (117,829 lb) of fuel, equivalent to approx 68,610 litres (18,125 US gallons), which will be interconnected with the aircraft's basic fuel system, comprising 108,062 kg (238,236 lb). All can then be used for extended range, or fuel from the lower deck cells and the aircraft's basic fuel system can be used for in-flight refuelling.

The aerial refuelling operator's station, with access from the upper main deck, will be sited in the lower aft fuselage and can accommodate the boom operator, an instructor and an observer, although only the boom operator is needed for a refuelling mission. The station will have a rear window and a periscope observation system to give a wide field of view, and will be pressurised and air-conditioned. The advanced aerial refuelling boom, which is the production version of a boom developed and tested in prototype form by McDonnell Douglas, provides greater capability than the type installed in the KC-135; in particular, it has a greater transfer flow rate, being rated at 5,678 litres (1,500 US gallons)/min. The boom operator 'flies' it by means of a digital fly-by-wire control system supplied by Sperry Flight Systems. A hose/reel unit for probe and drogue refuelling will also be installed, so that the ATCA can service USN, USMC and NATO aircraft, as well as older types of fighter still serving with Reserve and ANG units.

The provision of a refuelling receptacle, above the flight deck of the KC-10A, will allow greater flexibility on long-range cargo or refuelling operations, extending the range beyond the nominal 6,000 nm (11,112 km; 6,905 miles) with a 45,400 kg (100,000 lb) payload. The improved cargo handling system, by comparison with the basic DC-10-30CF, will include an increased floor area covered by omni-directional rollers, installation of power rollers, and a portable winch to move cargo fore and aft.

Changes to the avionics are concerned chiefly with the deletion of equipment intended specifically for commercial operations, and the addition of UHF and secure com systems, Tacan, IFF, beacon transponder and a radar beacon mode.

The description of the DC-10 Series 30CF applies to the KC-10A, except as follows:

Type: Military flight refuelling/cargo aircraft.

Wings, Fuselage, Tail Unit: As for DC-10-30CF.

Landing Gear: As for DC-10-30CF, except Goodyear nosewheels and tyres size 40 × 15·5-16, pressure 13·10 bars (190 lb/sq in). Four-wheel bogie main units and centreline unit have Goodyear wheels and tyres size 52 × 20·5-23. The former have a pressure of 13·79 bars (200 lb/sq in), the latter 10·69 bars (155 lb/sq in). Goodyear disc brakes and anti-skid system, with individual wheel control.

Power Plant: Generally as for later models of DC-10-30CF. Basic aircraft fuel system comprises three integral main wing fuel tanks, and an integral auxiliary tank in the wing centre-section with a connected structural compartment fitted with a bladder cell, giving a total capacity of approximately 135,510 litres (36,650 US gallons). Oil capacity 34·1 litres (9 US gallons).

Accommodation: Three crew on flight deck. Various seating arrangements for a limited number of essential support personnel at forward end of main cabin. Aerial refuelling station, with accommodation for boom operator, instructor and a student observer at aft end of lower fuselage compartment. Five passenger doors on main deck. A 2·59 m × 3·56 m (8 ft 6 in × 11 ft 8 in) cargo door on the port side of the fuselage will permit loading of standard USAF 463L pallets, bulk cargo or wheeled vehicles. Maximum capacity will be 25 pallets with access from both sides of the compartment, or 27 pallets with a single aisle on the starboard side.

Systems: As for DC-10-30CF.

Avionics and Equipment: Will include some additional military avionics comprising navigation, communication, Tacan, IFF transponder, and modified commercial weather radar. Seven Goodyear Aerospace rubberised fabric fuel cells mounted in the lower fuselage compartments, with combined capacity of 53,446 kg (117,829 lb) fuel, equivalent to approx 68,610 litres (18,125 US gallons), which are interconnected into the aircraft's basic fuel system. Flight refuelling boom mounted under rear fuselage, plus hose/reel unit for probe and drogue refuelling. Flight refuelling receptacle mounted on fuselage upper surface above flight deck.

Dimensions, external: As for DC-10-30CF except:
- Length overall: 55·35 m (181 ft 7 in)
- Height overall: 17·70 m (58 ft 1 in)
- Wheel track: 10·57 m (34 ft 8 in)

Areas: As for DC-10-30CF

Weights and Loading (estimated):
- Operating weight empty:
  - tanker: 108,747 kg (239,747 lb)
  - cargo: 110,664 kg (243,973 lb)
- Max cargo payload: 77,123 kg (170,027 lb)
- Design max T-O weight: 267,620 kg (590,000 lb)
- Max wing loading: 727·8 kg/m² (149·06 lb/sq ft)

Performance (estimated):
- Critical field length: 3,353 m (11,000 ft)
- Max range with max cargo: 3,300 nm (6,115 km; 3,800 miles)

MCDONNELL DOUGLAS YC-15

Two prototypes of the YC-15 were built as McDonnell Douglas contenders for the USAF's AMST prototype fly-off programme, which was terminated in 1978 for economic reasons. Full details of the aircraft and their test programme can be found in the 1978-79 *Jane's*.

MCDONNELL DOUGLAS SKYHAWK

US Navy designation: A-4

Designed originally to provide the US Navy and Marine Corps with a simple low-cost lightweight attack and ground suppport aircraft, the Skyhawk was based on experience gained during the Korean War. Since the initial requirement called for operation by the US Navy, special design consideration was given to providing low-speed control and stability during take-off and landing, added strength for catapult launch and arrested landings, and dimensions that would permit it to negotiate standard aircraft carrier lifts without the complexity of folding wings.

Construction of the XA-4A (originally XA4D-1) prototype Skyhawk began in September 1953 and the first flight of this aircraft, powered by a Wright J65-W-2 engine (32 kN; 7,200 lb st), took place on 22 June 1954.

Early Skyhawk versions included the A-4A, -4B, -4C and -4E, of which 1,845 examples were built. These were described in the 1973-74 *Jane's*; a description of the later TA-4E, A-4F, TA-4F, A-4G, TA-4G, A-4H and TA-4H can be found in the 1977-78 edition; details of the TA-4J, A-4K, A-4KU, TA-4K, TA-4KU, A-4L, A-4M, A-4N, A-4P, A-4Q, A-4S, TA-4S and A-4Y can be found in the 1978-79 *Jane's*. The following additional version has been reported:

OA-4M. Forward air control version for US Marine Corps, converted from TA-4F. Total of 23 being converted by Naval Air Rework Facility at Pensacola, Florida. Avionics and weapons capability similar to those of A-4M. First OA-4M (154294) began flight testing at NATC Patuxent River in July 1978. Due to enter service in Autumn 1979 with H & MS 32 at Cherry Point, North Carolina.

Production of the A-4 ended on 27 February 1979, when the US Navy took delivery of the final aircraft off the assembly line, an A-4M for the US Marine Corps. Delivered to Marine Attack Squadron VMA-331, it was the 2,960th Skyhawk manufactured by McDonnell Douglas in 26 years of continuous production. The total was made up of 2,405 attack aircraft and 555 trainers.

McKINNON—*See Canadian section*

MEYERS

MEYERS AIRCRAFT MANUFACTURING COMPANY (a division of Branson Aircraft Corporation)

Head Office: 4275 Broadway, Denver, Colorado 80216
Telephone: (303) 825 3529
President: Carl F. Branson

Meyers Aircraft Manufacturing Company was formed to manufacture the Meyers 200D four-seat light monoplane. Designed and produced originally by the Meyers Aircraft Company of Tecumseh, Michigan, the prototype Model 200 flew for the first time on 8 September 1953. It was produced subsequently by Aero Commander's Albany Division.

MEYERS 200D

Type: Four-seat cabin monoplane.

Wings: Cantilever low-wing monoplane. Dihedral 6°. Root section of welded 4130 chrome-molybdenum steel tube. Flush-riveted outer wing panels of conventional two-spar light alloy construction, with removable wingtips. Spring-loaded ailerons with controllable trim. Hydraulically-operated semi-Fowler type track-guided trailing-edge flaps of light alloy construction.

Fuselage: Cabin section of welded 4130 chrome-molybdenum steel tube, with overturn structure and light alloy covering. Semi-monocoque rear fuselage of light alloy construction, with flush-riveted pre-formed skin. Light alloy engine cowling in upper and lower sections.

Tail Unit: Cantilever structure of light alloy. Fixed-incidence tailplane. Trim tab in each elevator.

Landing Gear: Hydraulically-retractable tricycle type, main units retracting inboard, nosewheel aft. Two independent emergency extension systems. Meyers oleo-pneumatic shock-absorber in each unit. Cleveland wheels with Goodyear tyres; main wheels 7·00-6, nosewheel 6·00-6. Cleveland hydraulic disc brakes.

Power Plant: One 212·5 kW (285 hp) Continental IO-520 flat-six engine, driving a McCauley two-blade constant-speed metal propeller. Fuel contained in two 75·5 litre (20 US gallon) wing tanks and one 151 litre (40 US gallon) fuselage tank, with total combined capacity of 302 litres (80 US gallons). Refuelling points on upper surface of wings. Oil capacity 11·4 litres (3 US gallons).

Meyers Aircraft Meyers 200D four-seat lightweight cabin monoplane

Accommodation: Four seats in pairs in enclosed cabin. Door on starboard side. Space for up to 90 kg (200 lb) of baggage aft of rear seats, with external access door on starboard side. Cabin heated and ventilated. Rear seats and starboard front seat removable for cargo carrying or use as air ambulance.

Systems: Hydraulic system for landing gear, flaps and brakes. Electrical system powered by 60A engine-driven alternator. Carry-on oxygen supply optional.

Avionics and Equipment: A range of avionics equipment by Bendix, Collins, Edo-Aire and King available to customer's requirements. Dual controls and blind-flying instrumentation optional.

Dimensions, external:
- Wing span: 9·30 m (30 ft 6 in)
- Wing chord, outer panel at root: 1·47 m (4 ft 10 in)
- Length overall: 7·42 m (24 ft 4 in)
- Height overall: 2·24 m (7 ft 4 in)
- Tailplane span: 3·73 m (12 ft 3 in)
- Wheel track: 2·67 m (8 ft 9 in)
- Wheelbase: 2·11 m (6 ft 11 in)
- Propeller diameter: 2·08 m (6 ft 10 in)
- Propeller ground clearance: 0·30 m (1 ft 0 in)
- Passenger door (stbd): Height: 0·94 m (3 ft 1 in)
  - Width: 0·97 m (3 ft 2 in)
- Baggage door (stbd): Height: 0·61 m (2 ft 0 in)
  - Width: 0·51 m (1 ft 8 in)

Dimensions, internal:
- Cabin: Length: 2·84 m (9 ft 4 in)
  - Max width: 1·12 m (3 ft 8 in)
  - Max height: 1·27 m (4 ft 2 in)

Area:
- Wings, gross: 15·00 m² (161·5 sq ft)

Weights and Loadings:
- Weight empty: 878 kg (1,940 lb)
- Max T-O and landing weight: 1,542 kg (3,400 lb)
- Max wing loading: 102·8 kg/m² (21·05 lb/sq ft)
- Max power loading: 7·26 kg/kW (11·93 lb/hp)

Performance (at max T-O weight):
- Never-exceed speed: 205 knots (380 km/h; 236 mph)
- Max level speed: 187 knots (346 km/h; 215 mph)

Cruising speed at 75% power at 2,440 m (8,000 ft) 184 knots (341 km/h; 212 mph)
Cruising speed at 65% power at 2,440 m (8,000 ft) 175 knots (325 km/h; 202 mph)
Stalling speed, flaps up 58 knots (108 km/h; 67 mph)
Stalling speed, flaps down 47 knots (87 km/h; 54 mph)
Max rate of climb at S/L 341 m (1,120 ft)/min
Service ceiling 5,640 m (18,500 ft)
T-O to 15 m (50 ft) 482 m (1,580 ft)
Landing from 15 m (50 ft) 396 m (1,300 ft)
Range with max fuel, 75% power at 2,440 m (8,000 ft), 45 min reserves 790 nm (1,464 km; 910 miles)
Range with max fuel, 65% power at 2,440 m (8,000 ft), 45 min reserves 900 nm (1,667 km; 1,036 miles)

MID-CONTINENT

MID-CONTINENT AIRCRAFT CORPORATION

Address: Hayti, Missouri

MID-CONTINENT KING CAT

Mid-Continent Aircraft Corporation, an operator and distributor of Gulfstream American/Grumman Ag-Cats, has obtained an FAA Supplementary Type Certificate for an Ag-Cat re-engined with an 895 kW (1,200 hp) Wright R-1820-202A radial engine, driving a three-blade metal propeller. The engineering work for this STC was carried out by Serv-Aero Engineering Inc (which see). After modification, the aircraft is known as a King Cat.

Based on the airframe of the Super Ag-Cat C, which has a hopper accommodating 1,893 litres (500 US gallons) of spray or 1,814 kg (4,000 lb) of dry chemicals, the King Cat offers improved high-altitude/high-temperature performance. It is available as a conversion of a new Super Ag-Cat C, or a kit is obtainable for installation by the customer or his maintenance organisation.

Performance (at max T-O weight):
Working speed 87-113 knots (161-209 km/h; 100-130 mph)
Ferry speed 117 knots (217 km/h; 135 mph)
T-O run, 32°C less than 365 m (1,200 ft)

Mid-Continent King Cat, a Wright-engined conversion of the Grumman Super Ag-Cat C *(Howard Levy)*

MITSUBISHI

MITSUBISHI AIRCRAFT INTERNATIONAL INC

Corporate Headquarters: Park Central III, 12700 Park Central Drive, Suite 1310, Box 57, Dallas, Texas 75251
Telephone: (214) 387 5600
Telex: 73-2575
Works: PO Box 3848, San Angelo, Texas 76901
Telephone: (915) 944-1511
Telex: 73-9438
President: Takeshi Iwatsuki

This wholly-owned subsidiary of Mitsubishi Heavy Industries Ltd was established at San Angelo in 1967, to assemble and equip the MU-2 twin-turboprop utility STOL transport designed by the parent company. Wings, fuselage and tail unit components are manufactured in Japan and shipped to the USA. At San Angelo they go back on to an assembly production line, where American-built components which include engines, avionics, tyres, brakes and interiors are installed. A description of current versions of the MU-2 can be found in the Japanese aircraft section of this edition.

Mitsubishi Aircraft International in Dallas has worldwide marketing responsibility for the MU-2. Aircraft of this type produced at San Angelo are in service in Africa, Canada, Europe, Mexico, the Middle East, South America and in the USA.

MOONEY

MOONEY AIRCRAFT CORPORATION (Subsidiary of Republic Steel Corporation)

Head Office and Works: PO Box 72, Kerrville, Texas 78028
Telephone: (512) 896 6000
President: T. J. Smith
Vice-Presidents:
Don K. Cox (Marketing)
L. P. Lopresti (Engineering)
D. R. White (Finance)

The original Mooney Aircraft Inc was formed in June 1948, in Wichita, Kansas, from where the single-seat Model M-18 Mooney Mite was produced until 1952. The company transferred to Kerrville, Texas, in 1953 and completed a merger with Alon Inc of McPherson, Kansas, in October 1967. Subsequently, in late 1969, Butler Aviation International acquired 100 per cent stock ownership of Mooney Aircraft, the company name being changed to Aerostar Aircraft Corporation on 1 July 1970. Production of Aerostar aircraft was suspended in early 1972. On 4 October 1973 came news that the Republic Steel Corporation of Cleveland, Ohio, had assumed control of the company, once again named Mooney Aircraft.

MOONEY RANGER

The prototype Ranger (known initially as Mark 21) flew on 23 September 1961 and the first production model on 7 November 1961. FAA Type Approval was received on 7 November 1961. A total of 2,191 Rangers had been produced by 1 December 1978.

Type: Four-seat cabin monoplane.

Wings: Cantilever low-wing monoplane. Wing section NACA 63_2-215 at root, NACA 64_1-412 at tip. Dihedral 5° 30'. Incidence 2° 30' at root, 1° at tip. Sweepforward 2° 29'. Light alloy structure with flush-riveted stretch-formed wraparound skins. Full-span main spar; rear spar terminates at mid-span of flaps. Sealed-gap differentially-operated light alloy ailerons. Electrically-operated single-slotted light alloy flaps over 70% of trailing-edge. No tabs.

Fuselage: Composite all-metal structure. Cabin section is of welded 4130 chrome-molybdenum steel tube with sheet light alloy covering. Rear section is of semi-monocoque construction, with sheet light alloy bulkheads and skin and extruded alloy stringers.

Tail Unit: Cantilever light alloy structure, with variable-incidence tailplane. All surfaces covered with wraparound metal skin.

Landing Gear: Electrically-retractable levered-suspension tricycle type. Nosewheel retracts rearward, main units inward into wings. Rubber disc shock-absorbers on main units. Delco hydraulic shock-absorber on nose unit. Cleveland main wheels, size 6·00-6, and steerable nosewheel, size 5·00-5. Tyre pressure (all units) 2·07 bars (30 lb/sq in). Cleveland hydraulic single-disc brakes on main wheels. Parking brakes.

Power Plant: One 134 kW (180 hp) Lycoming O-360-A1D flat-four engine, driving a Hartzell HC-C2YK-1F/F7662-2 two-blade metal constant-speed propeller. Two integral fuel tanks in wing roots, with total usable capacity of 197 litres (52 US gallons). Flush refuelling point above each tank. Oil capacity 7·5 litres (2 US gallons).

Accommodation: Cabin accommodates four in two individual front seats and one side-by-side rear bench seat; front seats have reclining backs. Dual controls standard. Standard rudder pedals optionally removable to allow more leg room for passenger. Overhead ventilation system. Cabin heating and cooling system, with adjustable outlets and illuminated control. One-piece wraparound windscreen. Tinted Plexiglas windows. Starboard front and entire rear seat removable for freight stowage. Single door on starboard side. Compartment for 54 kg (120 lb) baggage behind cabin, with access from cabin or through door on starboard side. Windscreen defrosting system standard.

Systems: Hydraulic system for brakes only. Electrical system includes 60A alternator, 12V 35Ah battery, voltage regulator and warning light, together with protective circuit breakers.

Avionics: An extensive range of optional avionics is available to customer's requirements, manufactured by Bendix, Collins, Edo-Aire Mitchell, King and Narco.

Equipment: Standard equipment includes sensitive altimeter, annunciator lights, glareshield, sun visors, dual controls, cabin lights, navigation lights, landing/taxi lights, full flow oil filter, quick oil drain, streamlined spinner and zinc chromate anti-corrosion treatment. An operational package includes turn co-ordinator, directional gyro, pictorial artificial horizon, vertical speed indicator, electric clock, microphone jacks, cabin speaker, emergency locator transmitter, wingtip strobe lights, heated pitot, alternate static source and nav and com antennae. Other optional equipment includes dual brakes, exhaust gas temperature gauge, hour meter, encoding altimeter, de luxe control wheel with map light and microphone button, knots-only airspeed indicator, headrests, inertia reel shoulder harness, all-leather interior, cabin fire extinguisher, rotating beacon and external power socket.

Dimensions, external:
Wing span 10·67 m (35 ft 0 in)
Wing chord, mean 1·45 m (4 ft 9¼ in)
Wing aspect ratio 7·338
Length overall 7·06 m (23 ft 2 in)
Height overall 2·54 m (8 ft 4 in)
Tailplane span 3·58 m (11 ft 9 in)
Wheel track 2·76 m (9 ft 0¾ in)
Wheelbase 1·68 m (5 ft 6½ in)
Propeller diameter 1·88 m (6 ft 2 in)
Cabin door: Height 0·95 m (3 ft 1¼ in)
Width 0·78 m (2 ft 6½ in)
Height to sill 0·34 m (1 ft 1½ in)
Baggage compartment door:
Height 0·52 m (1 ft 8½ in)
Width 0·43 m (1 ft 5 in)

Dimensions, internal:
Cabin: Length 2·64 m (8 ft 8 in)
Max width 1·10 m (3 ft 7½ in)
Max height 1·13 m (3 ft 8½ in)
Baggage compartment 0·38 m³ (13·5 cu ft)

Areas:
Wings, gross 15·51 m² (167·00 sq ft)
Ailerons (total) 1·07 m² (11·50 sq ft)
Trailing-edge flaps (total) 1·63 m² (17·50 sq ft)
Fin 0·74 m² (7·92 sq ft)
Rudder 0·58 m² (6·23 sq ft)
Tailplane 2·00 m² (21·50 sq ft)
Elevators 1·12 m² (12·05 sq ft)

Weights and Loadings:
Weight empty 691 kg (1,525 lb)
Max T-O and landing weight 1,168 kg (2,575 lb)
Max wing loading 75·2 kg/m² (15·4 lb/sq ft)
Max power loading 8·72 kg/kW (14·3 lb/hp)

Performance:
Max level speed at S/L 147 knots (272 km/h; 169 mph)
Stalling speed (flaps and wheels down, power off) 49 knots (90 km/h; 56 mph) IAS
Rate of climb at S/L 244 m (800 ft)/min
Service ceiling 5,030 m (16,500 ft)
T-O run, zero wind, ISA 248 m (815 ft)
Landing run, zero wind, ISA 291 m (955 ft)
Range, 75% power, no reserves 761 nm (1,410 km; 876 miles)

MOONEY 201 (M20J)

The Mooney 201, a faster development of the now discontinued Executive (last described in the 1977-78 *Jane's*), first flew in June 1976 and received FAA certification in September 1976. A total of 763 had been produced by 1 December 1978.

The description of the Ranger applies also to the Mooney 201, except as follows:

Landing Gear: Nosewheel tyre pressure 3·38 bars (49 lb/sq in).

Power Plant: One 149 kW (200 hp) Lycoming IO-360-A3B6D flat-four engine, driving a McCauley two-blade metal constant-speed propeller. Two integral fuel tanks in wings, with combined usable capacity of 242 litres (64

Mooney 201 four-seat cabin monoplane (Lycoming IO-360-A3B6D engine)

US gallons). Refuelling points in wing upper surface. Oil capacity 7·5 litres (2 US gallons).

DIMENSIONS, EXTERNAL: As for Ranger, except:

Length overall	7·52 m (24 ft 8 in)
Height overall	2·54 m (8 ft 4 in)
Wheelbase	1·82 m (5 ft 11½ in)
Propeller diameter	1·88 m (6 ft 2 in)
Propeller ground clearance	0·24 m (9½ in)

WEIGHTS AND LOADINGS:

Weight empty	743 kg (1,640 lb)
Max T-O and landing weight	1,243 kg (2,740 lb)
Max wing loading	80·07 kg/m² (16·4 lb/sq ft)
Max power loading	8·34 kg/kW (13·7 lb/hp)

PERFORMANCE (at max T-O weight):

Never-exceed speed	196 knots (364 km/h; 226 mph)
Max level speed at S/L	175 knots (325 km/h; 202 mph)
Max cruising speed, 75% power at 2,470 m (8,100 ft)	169 knots (314 km/h; 195 mph)
Econ cruising speed, 55% power at 2,470 m (8,100 ft)	145 knots (269 km/h; 167 mph)
Stalling speed, flaps up	63 knots (117 km/h; 72·5 mph) IAS
Stalling speed, flaps down	55 knots (102 km/h; 63·5 mph) IAS
Max rate of climb at S/L	314 m (1,030 ft)/min
Service ceiling	5,730 m (18,800 ft)
T-O to 15 m (50 ft)	475 m (1,559 ft)
Landing from 15 m (50 ft)	491 m (1,610 ft)
Landing run	235 m (770 ft)
Range, 75% power, no reserves	974 nm (1,804 km; 1,121 miles)

TURBO MOONEY 231 (M20K)

Mooney began the design of this turbocharged version of the Ranger in May 1976. Construction of the prototype began in the following month, and the first flight was recorded in October 1976. Certification in the Normal category was awarded by the FAA on 16 November 1978.

Generally similar to the Ranger, the Turbo Mooney 231 differs mainly in having a turbocharged engine and increased wing span.

TYPE: Four-seat cabin monoplane.

WINGS: Cantilever low-wing monoplane. Wing section NACA 63₂-215 at root, NACA 64₁-412 at tip. Dihedral 5° 30′. Incidence 2° 30′. No sweepback. Conventional structure of light alloy. Plain ailerons and trailing-edge flaps of light alloy construction. No tabs.

FUSELAGE AND TAIL UNIT: As for Ranger.

LANDING GEAR: Electrically-retractable tricycle type. Nosewheel retracts rearward, main units inward into wings. All wheels faired by doors when retracted. Shock-absorption of nosewheel and main-wheel units by Lord rubber discs. Cleveland wheels, with main-wheel tyres size 6·00-6 6-ply, pressure 2·90 bars (42 lb/sq in). Nosewheel tyre size 5·00-5 6-ply, pressure 3·38 bars (49 lb/sq in). Cleveland hydraulic brakes on main wheels. Parking brake.

POWER PLANT: One 156·5 kW (210 hp) Continental TSIO-360-GB flat-six turbocharged engine, driving a McCauley constant-speed metal propeller. Two integral fuel tanks in inner wings, with combined capacity of 303 litres (80 US gallons), of which 272·5 litres (72 US gallons) are usable. Refuelling points in upper surface of the inboard section of each wing. Oil capacity 7·5 litres (2 US gallons).

ACCOMMODATION: Cabin accommodates four on two individual front seats and a rear bench seat. Cabin door on starboard side. Baggage space aft of rear seat, accessible from cabin and via baggage door on starboard side. Accommodation heated and ventilated.

SYSTEMS: Hydraulic system for brakes only. Electrical system powered by a 64A engine-driven alternator. Portable oxygen supply optional.

AVIONICS: Nav/coms by Bendix, Collins, King and Narco, autopilot, flight director and RNAV optional.

DIMENSIONS, EXTERNAL:

Wing span	11·00 m (36 ft 1 in)
Wing aspect ratio	7·448
Length overall	7·75 m (25 ft 5 in)
Height overall	2·51 m (8 ft 3 in)
Tailplane span	3·58 m (11 ft 9 in)
Wheel track	2·76 m (9 ft 0¾ in)
Wheelbase	1·82 m (5 ft 11½ in)
Propeller diameter	1·88 m (6 ft 2 in)
Propeller ground clearance	0·24 m (9½ in)
Cabin door (stbd, over wing):	
Height	1·13 m (3 ft 8½ in)
Width	0·74 m (2 ft 5 in)
Baggage door (stbd, aft):	
Height	0·52 m (1 ft 8½ in)
Width	0·43 m (1 ft 5 in)
Height to sill	1·17 m (3 ft 10 in)

DIMENSIONS, INTERNAL:

Cabin: Length	2·90 m (9 ft 6 in)
Max width	1·10 m (3 ft 7½ in)
Max height	1·13 m (3 ft 8½ in)
Baggage compartment	0·48 m³ (17 cu ft)

AREAS:

Wings, gross	16·24 m² (174·8 sq ft)
Ailerons (total)	1·06 m² (11·4 sq ft)
Trailing-edge flaps (total)	1·66 m² (17·9 sq ft)
Fin	0·72 m² (7·7 sq ft)
Tailplane	1·99 m² (21·42 sq ft)
Elevators	1·21 m² (13·0 sq ft)

WEIGHTS AND LOADINGS:

Weight empty	816 kg (1,800 lb)
Max T-O and landing weight	1,315 kg (2,900 lb)
Max zero-fuel weight	1,119 kg (2,468 lb)
Max wing loading	80·97 kg/m² (16·6 lb/sq ft)
Max power loading	8·4 kg/kW (13·8 lb/hp)

PERFORMANCE (at max T-O weight):

Never-exceed speed	195 knots (362 km/h; 225 mph)
Max level speed	182 knots (338 km/h; 210 mph)
Max cruising speed, 75% power at 5,485 m (18,000 ft)	174 knots (322 km/h; 200 mph)
Econ cruising speed, 55% power at 7,315 m (24,000 ft)	162 knots (301 km/h; 187 mph)
Stalling speed, flaps down, idling power	57 knots (106 km/h; 66 mph)
Max rate of climb at S/L	329 m (1,080 ft)/min
Certificated ceiling	7,315 m (24,000 ft)
T-O to 15 m (50 ft)	628 m (2,060 ft)
Landing from 15 m (50 ft)	695 m (2,280 ft)
Landing run	350 m (1,147 ft)
Range with max fuel, 55% power, no reserves	1,182 nm (2,190 km; 1,361 miles)

NASA

NATIONAL AERONAUTICS AND SPACE ADMINISTRATION

HEADQUARTERS: 400 Maryland Avenue SW, Washington, DC 20546

Telephone: (202) 755 2320

NASA has several research programmes of general aviation interest, including an augmentor wing jet STOL research aircraft, digital fly-by-wire techniques, continuing evaluation of the supercritical wing, conversion of a Lockheed JetStar to fulfil a General Purpose Airborne Simulator role, implementation of a Terminal Configured Vehicle programme, testing of a Quiet Short-haul Research Aircraft (QSRA), and development and testing of the Space Shuttle Orbiter.

NASA / DITC AUGMENTOR WING JET STOL RESEARCH AIRCRAFT

In a co-operative venture between NASA and the Canadian government, as represented by the Department of Industry, Trade and Commerce (DITC), a de Havilland Canada C-8A Buffalo transport aircraft was modified extensively to serve as an augmentor wing research aircraft. The modified Buffalo made its first flight on 1 May 1972; details of this aircraft can be found in the 1978-79 and earlier editions of *Jane's*.

NASA/BOEING QSRA

Under a $21 million contract, Boeing carried out for NASA the conversion of a DHC C-8A Buffalo into a Quiet Short-Haul Research Aircraft (QSRA). This aircraft is being used to develop the technology for quiet short-haul commercial airliners of the future, with short take-off and landing capabilities, as well as to explore the operating procedures of such aircraft in the airport terminal environment. Additionally, the QSRA provides NASA with an alternative powered-lift system for comparison with the results of the programme carried out with the NASA/DITC C-8A augmentor wing jet STOL research aircraft. Boeing was responsible for construction of the new wing; new engine nacelles to provide for Upper Surface Blowing (USB) of the inboard Coanda flaps; cross-ducting to supply Boundary Layer Control (BLC) air to the wing leading-edge and ailerons; construction of a new tail, similar in configuration to that of the original; and the installation of new instrumentation. The first flight of

NASA/Boeing Quiet Short-haul Research Aircraft (four Avco Lycoming YF102 turbofan engines)

NASA's converted Boeing 747 Shuttle Carrier Aircraft mated with Shuttle Orbiter OV-102 *Columbia*

the QSRA aircraft took place on 6 July 1978; subsequently, it was flown in a series of tests from Boeing's Seattle facility, during which Boeing and NASA research pilots demonstrated steady-state flight at speeds of 50-190 knots (93-352 km/h; 58-219 mph), shutdown and restart of all four engines in flight, three-engine take-off and landing, a rate of climb of 1,067 m (3,500 ft)/min, operation at altitudes up to 4,570 m (15,000 ft), and high-performance T-O with a run of only 247 m (810 ft). On 3 August 1978 NASA announced that the QSRA had been delivered to its Ames Research Center, at Moffett Field, California, where a 'proof of concept' flight test programme was to be undertaken. Upon completion of this initial programme, the aircraft was to be used for an advanced flight research programme, to be followed by a series of flight experiment activities.

Of primary importance in this project is that the noise shielding inherent in the upper surface blowing concept, combined with the high climb and descent angles which stem from the advanced techniques being explored, is expected to result in a 90 EPNdB 'footprint' area of only three-tenths of a square mile (0·78 km²). This means that the noise level would be unobtrusive even at small, secondary airports.

The description of the QSRA which appeared in the 1977-78 *Jane's* is amended in the following respects:

WINGS: Hydraulically-actuated ailerons, of light alloy honeycomb construction, operate differentially for roll control, and can be drooped symmetrically to augment the trailing-edge flaps for take-off and landing. Leading-edge variable-camber type flaps, fixed in the high-lift position. USB Coanda type trailing-edge flaps aft of the engine nacelles; double-slotted trailing-edge flaps between the USB flaps and ailerons; all of light alloy construction. Two spoiler panels of light alloy construction on each wing forward of double-slotted flaps, for use as speed brakes or for roll control; pilot-selectable for lift dumping after touchdown and for initiation of Direct Lift Control (DLC). All trailing-edge control surfaces, including the spoilers, are independently hydraulically-operated, but are controlled by electrical (fly-by-wire) techniques. No anti-icing provisions.

LANDING GEAR: Tricycle type, as described in 1977-78 edition, but non-retractable.

POWER PLANT: As described in 1977-78 edition, but JP-5 fuel capacity of 4,627 kg (10,200 lb).

DIMENSIONS, EXTERNAL: As given in 1977-78 edition, except:
- Height overall — 8·43 m (27 ft 8 in)

WEIGHTS AND LOADINGS (estimated):
- Operational weight empty — 16,692 kg (36,800 lb)
- Max T-O weight: normal — 22,680 kg (50,000 lb)
- overload (external ballast) — 27,215 kg (60,000 lb)
- Mission zero-fuel weight — 18,053 kg (39,800 lb)
- Max landing weight — 21,772 kg (48,000 lb)
- Max wing loading: normal — 406·7 kg/m² (83·3 lb/sq ft)
- overload — 488·2 kg/m² (100 lb/sq ft)

PERFORMANCE (estimated):
- Design max diving speed — 190 knots (352 km/h; 219 mph)
- Design cruising speed — 160 knots (296 km/h; 184 mph)
- Approach speed — 65·5 knots (121 km/h; 75 mph)
- T-O field length (at AUW of 22,680 kg; 50,000 lb) — 404-1,219 m (1,325-4,000 ft)
- Landing field length — 434-1,219 m (1,425-4,000 ft)
- Ferry range — 315 nm (583 km; 363 miles)

OPERATIONAL NOISE CHARACTERISTICS (estimated at 152 m; 500 ft sideline):
- T-O — 91 EPNdB
- Approach — 89 EPNdB

Gulfstream American Gulfstream II converted as a Shuttle Training Aircraft (STA) for NASA

NASA YF-12 PROGRAMME

NASA has been operating two Lockheed YF-12 aircraft in the second phase of a joint USAF/NASA research programme. Basic purpose was to obtain information from sustained cruising flight at a speed of Mach 3 (approximately 1,735 knots; 3,220 km/h; 2,000 mph) at altitudes of around 22,860 m (75,000 ft), to assist in the development and operation of future supersonic aircraft and the Space Shuttle. One of the YF-12s was returned to the USAF on 27 October 1978, following the termination of its part in the programme. The second aircraft then had about six more flights to complete, and the programme was scheduled to end in early 1979; details can be found in the 1977-78 *Jane's*.

During the period to the end of October 1978, NASA completed 224 flights with these two aircraft. An unexpected discovery was that inlet noise emanating from the YF-12s during static and fly-over tests was much lower than that coming from other aircraft. In an effort to learn the reason for this, a series of test flights was conducted with a YF-12 in July/August 1979, with microphones inside the inlets and on the ground to monitor noise levels.

SHUTTLE CARRIER AIRCRAFT

In July 1974 NASA acquired from American Airlines a Boeing 747-123 primarily to be modified for use as a Space Shuttle Orbiter ferry aircraft. Before the aircraft was returned to Boeing for modification, in April 1976, it was used by NASA's Dryden Flight Research Center to investigate the problems associated with wake vortex flow from wide-body jet transports.

On 14 January 1977 the Shuttle Carrier Aircraft (SCA) was handed over to NASA, following completion of the modifications carried out by The Boeing Company to fit the Model 747 for its new SCA role. Details of these can be found in the 1977-78 *Jane's*.

Take-off weight of the SCA with fuel and the Shuttle Orbiter was 264,898 kg (584,000 lb) when the combination flew for the first time on 18 February 1977. The second flight, on 22 February, was made at a T-O weight of 283,722 kg (625,500 lb). Maximum altitude of the initial flight was 4,875 m (16,000 ft), and a speed of 250 knots (463 km/h; 288 mph) was attained.

The planned test programme called for six mated flights with the Orbiter unmanned and inert, followed by a series of flights with the Orbiter manned. The first free flight, when the Orbiter was launched from the SCA at approximately 6,950 m (22,800 ft) to glide to an unpowered landing at Edwards AFB, was achieved successfully on 13 August 1977.

The Shuttle Orbiter is described under the Rockwell International heading in the spaceflight section.

NASA SHUTTLE TRAINING AIRCRAFT

To help train astronauts for Space Shuttle Orbiter landings, NASA acquired two Gulfstream American Gulfstream II twin-jet executive aircraft which had been specially modified for this role. The first of the training aircraft made its first flight at Bethpage, New York, on 29 September 1975. Both were delivered for use in mid-1976, and are based at NASA's Johnson Space Center, Houston, Texas, where astronauts are trained for Space Shuttle operations.

Known as Shuttle Training Aircraft (STA), these Gulfstream IIs have been converted by the addition of special equipment, and modified aerodynamic and engine controls have been added to the conventional controls. By using the special controls and displays, an astronaut can pilot the STA to simulate the Shuttle Orbiter in various control modes during approach and landing.

The STA is fitted with aerodynamic controls which provide complete and independent control of each translational and rotational motion. Special direct-lift flaps are moved up or down to control lift; the side force surfaces on the underside of the STA are pivoted left or right to control lateral acceleration; and the engine throttles control thrust.

The engines are fitted with special thrust reverser systems to allow operation in reverse thrust in flight. In the simulation mode the engines actually provide drag rather than thrust, to simulate the unpowered Orbiter.

The STA provides realistic simulation of the Orbiter flight characteristics by commanding all the special and conventional control surfaces and the engines through a process called 'model following'.

A digital computer on board the aircraft contains a

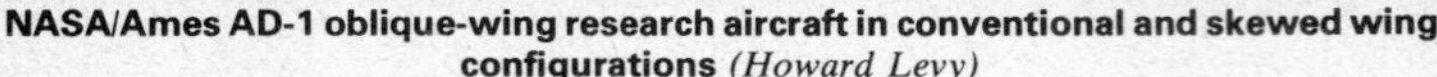

NASA/Ames AD-1 oblique-wing research aircraft in conventional and skewed wing configurations *(Howard Levy)*

complete mathematical model of the Orbiter. The model receives commands from the pilot's rotational hand controller, as well as information from other controls and sensors, and interprets the Orbiter's response to those commands. The computer then sends commands to the STA control surfaces and engines which cause the STA to respond with the same motion as that predicted for the Orbiter.

The simulation pilot occupies the port seat on the STA flight deck. This station is equipped with the rotational hand controller, speed brake control, flight instruments and miscellaneous switches and indicators required to fly the Orbiter. Using these controls and displays, the pilot can fly the STA to simulate the Orbiter in various flight control modes, including control stick steering, backup, direct (unaugmented) and automatic. Even the windows are masked to simulate the Orbiter's field of view.

The instructor pilot, in the starboard seat, has all the controls and displays required to fly the aircraft in its normal Gulfstream II mode. The instructor flies the aircraft to the simulation entry point, switches control to the simulation pilot, then monitors progress of the flight to ensure that the operation is proceeding safely and within limits.

The Orbiter touchdown is simulated. It occurs when the pilot's eye is at the same height above the runway as it would be in the Orbiter. Because the STA is much smaller than the Orbiter, it is actually about 6 m (20 ft) in the air when the simulated touchdown occurs. At the end of the simulation, which normally occurs at touchdown, the instructor again assumes control and performs a climbout to begin another simulation run.

The flight simulation engineer, seated behind and between the two pilots, operates the simulator computer and associated systems, and assists the instructor in monitoring the aircraft and the trajectory. The passenger cabin is bare except for the small computer.

The two STAs are based at Houston, but because of the rapid descent of the STA during the simulation runs, a restricted airspace is required. Thus, training flights take place at either Holloman AFB, Mexico, or Edwards AFB, California.

Basic dimensions and performance are similar to those of the standard Gulfstream II. Empty weight is 18,144 kg (40,000 lb) and max T-O weight 28,350 kg (62,500 lb).

NASA AD-1 OBLIQUE-WING AIRCRAFT

On 20 February 1978, NASA announced the award of a $218,000 fixed-price contract to the Ames Industrial Corporation of Bohemia, New York, for the development and construction of a small oblique-wing aircraft, which has been allocated the designation AD-1 (Ames/Dryden-1). Emanating from NASA's Dryden Flight Research Center, Edwards, California, this pivoting oblique-wing concept is a significant change from conventional aircraft design, and NASA has initiated a low-cost exploratory programme to study the fundamental aspects of piloting such an aircraft.

At low flight speeds the wing is positioned conventionally, providing efficient operation for take-off and landing and in low-speed flight. The concept offers good low-speed stability and control characteristics, and does not require complex high-lift systems. Engine power required for take-off is reduced substantially, and could result in lower noise levels during take-off and landing.

For high-speed flight the wing is pivoted to form an oblique angle of up to 60° with the aircraft's fuselage, reducing drag, and permitting increased speed and range for the same fuel expenditure. Analytical and wind tunnel studies indicate that an oblique-wing civil transport flying at 868 knots (1,610 km/h; 1,000 mph) might achieve twice the fuel economy of the Anglo-French Concorde or Russian Tu-144; at the same time, this wing configuration may alleviate the effects of sonic boom.

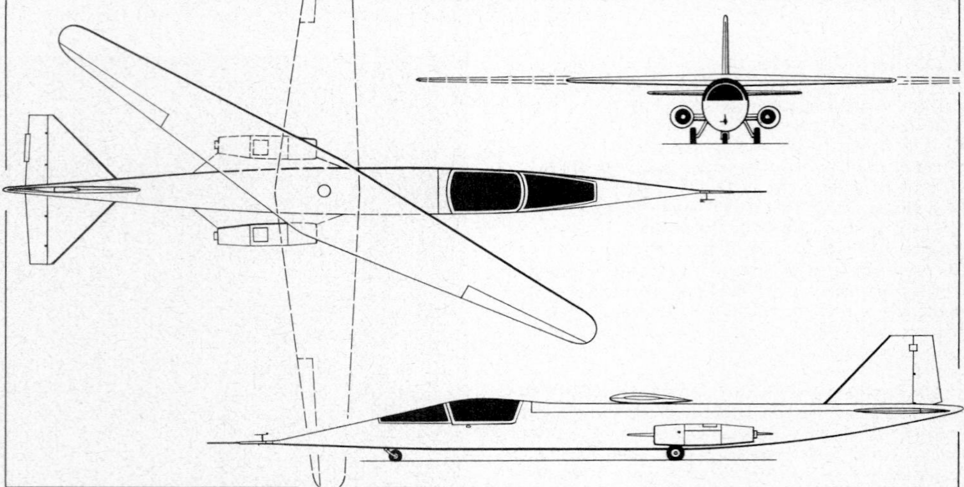

NASA/Ames AD-1 (two Microturbo TRS 18 turbojets) *(Pilot Press)*

NASA provided the design to Ames Industrial, which constructed the AD-1. Delivery of the aircraft to Dryden Center was made in March 1979.

TRANSONIC AIRCRAFT TECHNOLOGY

As a second application of the NASA supercritical wing concept, a General Dynamics F-111 variable-geometry aircraft has been flown with a supercritical wing to evaluate the application of such a wing to a highly manoeuvrable advanced aircraft. In a joint NASA/USAF programme, known as Transonic Aircraft Technology (TACT), flight tests with the F-111 aircraft are being made to evaluate the effects of the new wing shape on aircraft performance in the transonic speed range. The supercritical wing permits the aircraft to increase its manoeuvrability capabilities in this speed range as well as providing an increase in the aircraft's subsonic cruise performance.

General Dynamics F-111 TACT aircraft with supercritical wing

GENERAL PURPOSE AIRBORNE SIMULATOR

NASA's Dryden Flight Research Center is using a specially modified Lockheed JetStar subsonic jet transport as a General Purpose Airborne Simulator (GPAS). Equipped with an electronic variable stability and control system, it is able to carry out airborne simulation of a wide variety of advanced aircraft. Its advantage over ground-based simulators is that it can provide motion and visual cues to the pilot while he is in the actual flight environment. It has been used also to study aircraft ride qualities in flight, and to test wing coatings and wing cleaning devices, the aim being to ensure that the aerodynamic performance of the wing is maintained at the optimum.

NASA TERMINAL CONFIGURED VEHICLE

The Terminal Configured Vehicle (TCV) programme has been established to conduct research, and to develop and evaluate aircraft and flight management technology, that will benefit conventional take-off and landing operations in the terminal area.

The objectives and programme elements are:

1. To improve terminal area capacity and efficiency by:
   Systems and procedures for ATC evolution.
   Systems and procedures for runway capacity.
   Profiles and procedures for fuel conservation.
2. To improve approach and landing capability in adverse weather using:
   Human factor elements for effective flight management.
   Systems and information to minimise wind-shear hazard.
   Airborne sensors for weather penetration.
3. To reduce noise impact through:
   Development of profiles and configuration for noise reduction.

The research programme involves analyses, simulation, and flight studies with a modified Boeing 737 aircraft, provided with highly flexible display and control equipment, and an aft flight deck for research purposes. A series of development and demonstration activities is being conducted to evolve practical systems and to solicit and encourage acceptance by flight crews and the airlines.

A Boeing 737-100 was obtained and a second (aft) flight deck and an array of computers and monitors were installed in the passenger cabin. The aircraft is designed to be flown from the forward flight deck with the conventional controls, and from the aft flight deck using a fly-by-wire, triple-redundant digital computer system. From the aft flight deck, the aircraft can be flown with advanced electronic displays and pilot selectable automatic navigation, guidance and control systems in simulated Cat III operations. Safety is assured through monitoring, and by takeover capability of the forward flight deck crew.

NASA AGRICULTURAL AIRCRAFT

NASA is undertaking studies, using an Ayres Thrush Commander 800, to improve the aerodynamics and application equipment and techniques of future agricultural aircraft.

NASA ELECTRICALLY-POWERED LIGHT AIRCRAFT

In collaboration with the Jet Propulsion Laboratory, NASA's Dryden Research Center is studying a possible future electrically-powered light aircraft which will derive its power from a ground-transmitted microwave beam. A Schweizer SGS 1-26E sailplane will be modified to flight test the concept.

NASA AIRCRAFT NOISE MONITORING PROGRAMME

NASA's Ames Research Center was in 1977-78 modifying a Lockheed YO-3A to act as a flying platform for equipment designed to monitor noise made by other aircraft.

NATURAL LAMINAR FLOW AIRCRAFT

In April 1979 it was reported that NASA had been gathering performance data on General Dynamics F-111 aircraft, prior to carrying out natural laminar flow testing of an F-111 at Dryden Flight Research Center in the late Summer of 1979. Study has proved that it will be possible to fly the aircraft without flaps at safe take-off and landing speeds, and this is essential for the flight tests which are to be made.

Under the joint NASA/USAF programme, the wings of the F-111 are to be fitted with aerofoil shapes known as 'gloves', to determine the effect on cruise efficiency. Wind tunnel tests have already shown that the selected 'glove' maintains a favourable pressure gradient over most of the wing chord. It is suggested that if the airflow over the 'gloves' is predominantly laminar, turbulence will be reduced, thus increasing cruise efficiency and at the same time reducing fuel consumption.

NASA's GPAS research aircraft, a specially equipped Lockheed JetStar

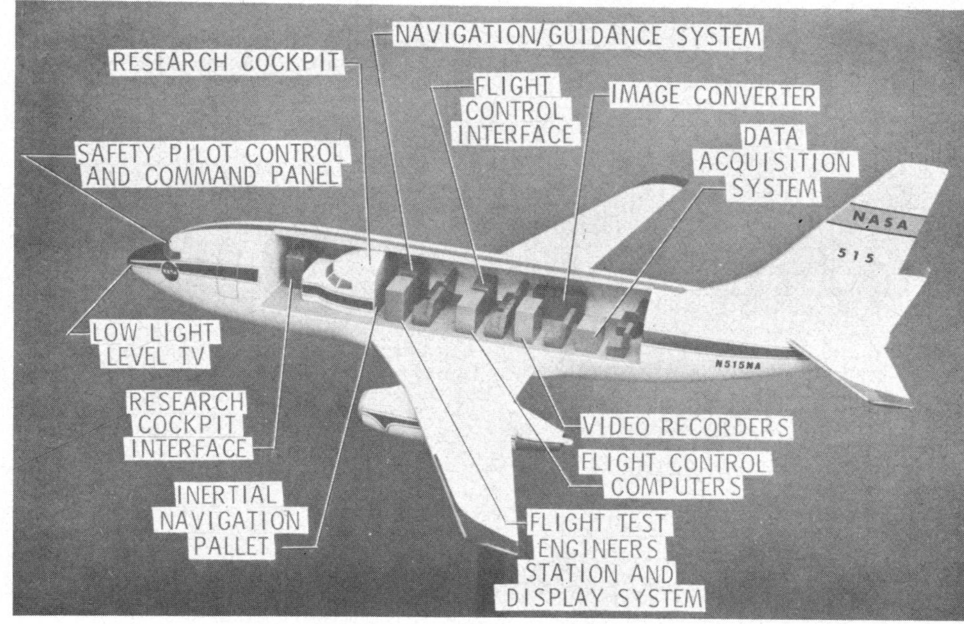

Cutaway model of NASA's TCV Boeing 737, showing internal layout

Boeing KC-135 fitted with NASA winglets, to evaluate their fuel-saving potential

NASA/USAF KC-135 WINGLET TESTS

In February 1978 a USAF KC-135 cargo/tanker aircraft was delivered to NASA's Dryden Flight Research Center, where it was modified by the installation of NASA winglets and is being test flown to evaluate the fuel-saving potential of these supplementary aerofoil surfaces. They are expected to improve overall performance by some 8%. According to the USAF's Flight Dynamics Laboratory, this could represent annual fuel savings of about 140 million litres (37 million US gallons) for the KC-135 fleet of aircraft, as well as improving take-off performance, and slightly improving fuel offload capability.

Under a USAF contract worth approximately $3 million, The Boeing Company constructed the winglets. Each has a chord of 0·61 m (2 ft 0 in) at the tip, 1·83 m (6 ft 0 in) at the base, and is 2·74 m (9 ft 0 in) in length. Constructed of light alloy, they weigh approximately 68 kg (150 lb) each. Boeing installed them on outer wing panels. These outer panels with winglets were then installed on the KC-135 by NASA personnel at Dryden, where the modified aircraft flew for the first time on 24 July 1979. It is possible to make adjustments to the incidence and cant angle of the winglets between flights, so that the optimum setting can be established.

Data from the fully instrumented KC-135 will be compared with data that was gathered from flight testing prior to installation of the winglets, allowing a direct comparison to be made.

The winglet concept was developed in wind tunnels at NASA's Langley Research Center by Dr Richard T. Whitcomb, who was also responsible for the NASA supercritical wing.

NAVION

NAVION RANGEMASTER AIRCRAFT CORPORATION

Head Office: PO Box 311, Wharton, Texas 77488
Telephone: (713) 532 4444
Chairman of the Board and Chief Executive Officer:
John C. Dalton Jr

President: Cedric Kotowicz

In late 1972 Mr Kotowicz purchased the assets of the bankrupt Navion Aircraft Corporation, including jigs, machine tools and a large parts inventory, and these were moved to a facility at Wharton, Texas. Navion Rangemaster Aircraft started by providing support for the 1,800 Navion aircraft which then remained in operation throughout the world. In November 1973 it was announced that the Navion would be put back into production.

The first production Navion Rangemaster Model G made its first flight on 16 November 1974, but due to economic problems only one other Rangemaster was produced before control of the company passed to Consolidated Holding Inc in late 1975. Subsequently five more aircraft were built and, following an exclusive distributor arrangement with Two Jacks Inc of Olive Branch, Mississippi, it was planned to produce one improved Rangemaster Model H per week from late 1976.

No recent news has been received from the company. Details of the Rangemaster Model H can be found in the 1978-79 *Jane's*.

NORTHROP

NORTHROP CORPORATION

Corporate Office: 1800 Century Park East, Century City, Los Angeles, California 90067
Telephone: (213) 553 6262
Chairman of the Board and Chief Executive Officer: Thomas V. Jones
President and Chief Operating Officer, and Group Executive, Communications and Electronics: Dr Thomas O. Paine
Vice-Chairman of the Board: Richard W. Millar
Senior Vice-Presidents and Group Executives:
Frank W. Lynch (Tactical Systems Group)
Ross F. Miller (Aircraft Group)
Frederick Stevens (Construction Group)
Senior Vice-Presidents:
William M. Elliott (General Counsel)
Welko E. Gasich (Advanced Projects)
Donald A. Hicks (Marketing and Technology)
James V. Holcombe (Asst to Chief Executive Officer for Government Relations)
James D. Willson (Finance)
Division Vice-Presidents:
David N. Ferguson (Electronics)
Kent Kresa (Ventura)
R. H. Madeira (Aircraft Services)
James M. Ricketts (Electro-Mechanical)
Wallace C. Solberg (Defense Systems Division)
W. E. Woolwine (Aircraft)
Joseph Yamron (Precision Products)
Subsidiary Presidents:
L. Kaufold (Wilcox Electric Inc)
F. J. Manzella (Page Communications Engineers)
D. A. McInnis (Northrop Services Inc)
James E. Ware (Northrop Architectural Systems Inc)
Other Vice-Presidents:
J. R. Alison (Customer Relations)
C. H. Bernstein (Asst to Chief Executive Officer for Analysis)
D. A. Burchinal (Europe, Middle East, Near East and Africa)
Henry A. Byroade (Saudi Arabia Operations)
J. B. Campbell (Controller)
William J. Chalmers (Manager, Northrop Research and Technology Center)
L. Daly (Public Affairs)
W. B. Dennis (Forward Planning)
C. R. Gates (Northrop International)
Felix Gerace (Middle East)
D. G. Head (President, George A. Fuller Company)
R. P. Jackson (Programme Management)
J. C. Jones (Asst to Chief Executive Officer for Aeronautical Systems)
D. L. Lewis (Business Analysis and Management Services)
T. A. McDougall (International Business Operations)
John J. Richardson (Industrial Relations)
Donald D. Warner (Administration and Services)
G. Ronald Wenninger (Advanced Systems)
Paul O. Wierk (Northrop Data Processing)
Corporate Secretary: R. B. Watts Jr
Corporate Treasurer: Richard B. Lohrer
Asst to Chairman—Community Relations: W. H. Habblett
Executive Asst to Chairman: W. H. Gurnee
Director of Public Affairs—Europe: J. K. Corfield
Director of Information: A. W. Cantafio

This company was formed in 1939 by John K. Northrop and others to undertake the design and manufacture of military aircraft. During the second World War it built 1,131 aircraft of its own design and was engaged in extensive subcontract work. It also devoted considerable attention to the design and construction of aircraft of the 'Flying Wing' type.

Although continuing its activities in the design, development and production of aircraft, missiles and target drone systems, Northrop has broadened its scope of operation to include electronics, space technology, communications, construction, support services and commercial products. To reflect this changing character of its business, the company changed its name from Northrop Aircraft Inc to Northrop Corporation in 1959.

In October 1976 Northrop established an Aircraft Group, comprising its existing Aircraft Division and a new organisation, the Aircraft Services Division, to give greater attention to aircraft design, development and production, as well as to programmes of training, support and service. The company had established previously an Electronics and Communications Group, and a Construction Group. The company established a Tactical Systems Group in January 1978, comprising the Electro-Mechanical and Ventura Divisions, and Northrop Services Inc (a subsidiary). A corporate office of advanced projects was established in May 1979.

Divisions of Northrop now include Aircraft Division, specialising in the research, development, production and sale of military aircraft, commercial airframe assemblies and subassemblies; Aircraft Services Division, engaged primarily in worldwide total air base systems support, requirement analysis and planning, programme management, facilities development and maintenance, training, logistics, aircraft maintenance and overhaul, and base operation; Electronics Division, which handles the company's activities in electronics research, development, and manufacturing of navigation and guidance systems; Electro-Mechanical Division, which handles advanced missile programmes, electro-optical systems for target identification and target designation; Defense Systems Division, designer and manufacturer of electronics countermeasures systems, including the Internal Countermeasures Set (ICS) for the USAF's F-15 Eagle; Precision Products Division, a leading supplier of precision gyroscopes and related guidance and control systems for communication and weather satellites, in key missile programmes, and on aircraft, submarines and ships; Ventura Division, designer and manufacturer of remotely piloted vehicles, target systems for anti-aircraft gunnery, surface-to-air and air-to-air missile crew training and weapons system evaluation, recoverable and expendable target aircraft, operation, maintenance and target range support services, torpedo modification kits, and mobile underwater targets; and George A. Fuller Company, a leading construction and construction-management company.

Northrop's communications activities are handled by two subsidiaries: Wilcox Electric Inc of Kansas City, Missouri, designers and producers of a wide range of ground-based navigation equipment, and Page Communications Engineers, Vienna, Virginia, which designs, engineers, installs and maintains total communications systems.

To further expand its research and development work, Northrop has divided its Research and Technology Center into three organisations: the Corporate Laboratories, Laser System Laboratories and Laser Technology Laboratories. Current programmes include research and development in such fields as information sciences, electronic devices and materials, nuclear radiation effects, high-energy laser development and laser systems applications.

The number of employees of Northrop Corporation totalled about 30,000 in early 1979.

NORTHROP CORPORATION AIRCRAFT GROUP

Address: 3901 West Broadway, Hawthorne, California 90250
Telephone: (213) 970 2000
Senior Vice-President and Group Executive: Welko E. Gasich
Corporate Vice-President: R. P. Jackson (Manager, F-18 Programme)
Senior Vice-President: M. G. Gonzalez (Business Operations)
Vice-Presidents:
R. A. Graham (Marketing)
M. Kuska (General Manager Aircraft Programmes)
J. Mannion (Public Affairs)
G. S. Shackelford (Contracts and Pricing)
S. R. Smith (Iran Operations)
R. S. Taylor (Finance)
Robert W. Young (Administration)
Assts to V-P Finance:
W. G. Niemann
S. Zitter

Aircraft Division:
Corporate Vice-President and General Manager: Woodrum E. Woolwine
Vice-Presidents:
C. W. Benson (Materiel)
R. D. Lovell (Manufacturing)
J. L. McCoy (Product Support)
B. T. Moser (Production Operations)
Thomas R. Rooney (Technical)

Aircraft Services Division:
Corporate Vice-President and General Manager: Grif B. Doyle
Vice-Presidents:
H. B. Gunther (Construction Operations)
L. J. Hunt Jr (Manager, Saudi Arabia Programme)
R. H. Madeira (Support Services)

Current production at Northrop's Aircraft Group is centred on the F-5E Tiger II, F-5F two-seat fighter/trainer, and major Boeing 747 subcontract work, which includes the main fuselage section and the extra-large side-loading cargo door.

Northrop F-5E Tiger II for service with the Swiss Air Force

Northrop's share of work on development and production of the US Navy's F/A-18 Hornet multi-mission fighter is proceeding on schedule. Northrop builds the centre and aft fuselage and the twin vertical tails on the Navy version of the Hornet. The company is responsible also for integration of all internal systems such as the environmental control system and auxiliary power system. McDonnell Douglas (which see) is prime contractor to the USN for the carrier-based Hornet, with Northrop responsible for about 40 per cent of production. The Navy has stated a requirement for 1,366 operational Hornets, to replace its existing A-7 and F-4 aircraft. Northrop's land-based version of the F-18 is known as the F-18L. As prime contractor for the land-based F-18, Northrop would carry out approximately 60 per cent of its production, McDonnell Douglas 40 per cent. Both carrier- and land-based versions use the same General Electric engines, and they are 80-90 per cent identical in high-usage spare parts. Design modifications to convert the carrier-designed F-18 airframe for land-based operation are intended to simplify it, and reduce the cost.

In addition to its main factory at Hawthorne, the Aircraft Division has facilities at El Segundo, Carson, Torrance, Palmdale and Edwards Air Force Base, California.

NORTHROP TIGER II

USAF designations: F-5E and F-5F

The F-5E was selected in November 1970 by the US government as the winner of a competition to determine the International Fighter Aircraft (IFA) which was to succeed Northrop's F-5A aircraft.

The F-5E design places particular emphasis on manoeuvrability rather than high speed, notably by the incorporation of manoeuvring flaps, based on the design of a similar system for the Netherlands Air Force's NF-5A/Bs. Full-span leading-edge flaps work in conjunction with conventional trailing-edge flaps, and are operated by a control on the pilot's throttle quadrant.

Wing loading on the F-5E is maintained at approximately the same value as on the F-5A, as the result of an increase in wing area to 17·30 m² (186 sq ft). This is due principally to the widened fuselage, which also increases wing span. The tapered wing leading-edge extension, between the inboard leading-edge and fuselage, was modified to enhance airflow over the wing at high angles of attack.

The F-5E incorporates other features developed for the Canadian, Dutch and Norwegian F-5s. These include two-position nosewheel gear, which increases wing angle of attack on the ground by 3° 22' and which, in conjunction with the more powerful engines, has improved F-5E take-off performance some 30% by comparison with earlier F-5s. Arrester gear permits operation from short runways. It is qualified to carry two 1,040 litre (275 US gallon) underwing fuel tanks, in addition to the centreline 1,040 litre (275 US gallon) tank, and up to seven 500 lb MK-82 bombs, following the addition of a Multiple Ejector Rack (MER) on the centreline stores station.

The first F-5E was rolled out on 23 June 1972, and made its first flight on 11 August 1972. USAF Tactical Air Command, with assistance from Air Training Command, was assigned responsibility for training pilots and technicians of user countries. First deliveries of the F-5E, to the USAF's 425th Tactical Fighter Squadron, were made in the Spring of 1973. Twenty aircraft had been supplied for the USAF training programme by the end of September 1973, and deliveries to foreign countries began in late 1973. The 1,000th F-5E was delivered to the Republic of Korea in August 1979, when production of the F-5E and two-seat F-5F was continuing at the rate of 10 a month. Customers to date include the USAF (112 F-5Es), US Navy (10 F-5Es and 3 F-5Fs), Brazil, Chile, Republic of China, Iran, Jordan, Kenya, South Korea, Malaysia, Saudi Arabia, Singapore, Sudan, Switzerland, Thailand and the Yemen Arab Republic.

In addition to their use as tactical fighters, F-5Es are operated by the USAF and US Navy in the 'aggressor' role, to simulate 'enemy' aircraft at major air combat training schools in the USA, England and the Philippines.

Details of the 1979 production versions of the Tiger II are as follows:

F-5E. Standard production version, to which the detailed description applies. In production also, under licence, by AIDC in Taiwan (which see). Can be fitted with an R-843A/ARN-58 localiser receiver and a reconnaissance nose containing four KS-121A 70 mm framing cameras and related equipment. Intended for low/medium-altitude photo-reconnaissance, the nose is similar to that of the RF-5A.

To extend the range of armament options, an F-5E completed a technology flying demonstration with a 30 mm underbelly gun pod developed by General Electric. More than 800 rounds of 30 mm GAU-8 type ammunition were fired on USAF test ranges at Edwards AFB, California.

The F-5Es for the Royal Saudi Air Force (RSAF) have a Litton LN-33 inertial navigation system, capable of accuracy exceeding 1·5 nm (2·7 km; 1·7 miles) CEP per flight hour, which provides attitude reference, range and bearing to ten pre-set destinations, as well as true ground track steering. The system is self-aligning in 10 min in the gyro compass mode, and can be aligned in 3 min to a stored heading. In-flight refuelling capability.

F-5Es of the Brazilian Air Force have a large dorsal fin to accommodate an ADF antenna.

F-5F. Tandem two-seat version of F-5E, with fuselage lengthened by 1·08 m (3 ft 6½ in). Fire control system retained, enabling aircraft to be used for both training and combat duties, but one M-39 gun deleted. Development approved by USAF in early 1974. First flight was made on 25 September 1974. Two F-5Fs completed flight test and qualification in early 1976. Total of 118 ordered; deliveries began in the Summer of 1976.

On 31 March 1978, Northrop announced receipt of US government approval for a company-funded development and flight demonstration programme of an **RF-5E** specialised reconnaissance version of the F-5E. This has a modified forward fuselage with quick-change capabilities to accommodate a wide variety of reconnaissance equipment. Both day and night photo missions were demonstrated during the subsequent test programme. Modification of a production F-5E made possible the first flight of the RF-5E prototype in January 1979, and a brief description of this aircraft is given separately.

The following details refer specifically to the F-5E, but are generally applicable to both versions except for details noted under model listings:

Type: Single-seat light tactical fighter.

Wings: Cantilever low-wing monoplane. Wing section NACA 65A004·8 (modified). No dihedral. No incidence. Sweepback at quarter-chord 24°. Multi-spar light alloy structure with heavy plate machined skins. Hydraulically-powered sealed-gap ailerons at approximately mid-span. Electrically-operated light alloy single-slotted trailing-edge flaps inboard of ailerons. Electrically-operated leading-edge manoeuvring flaps. No de-icing system.

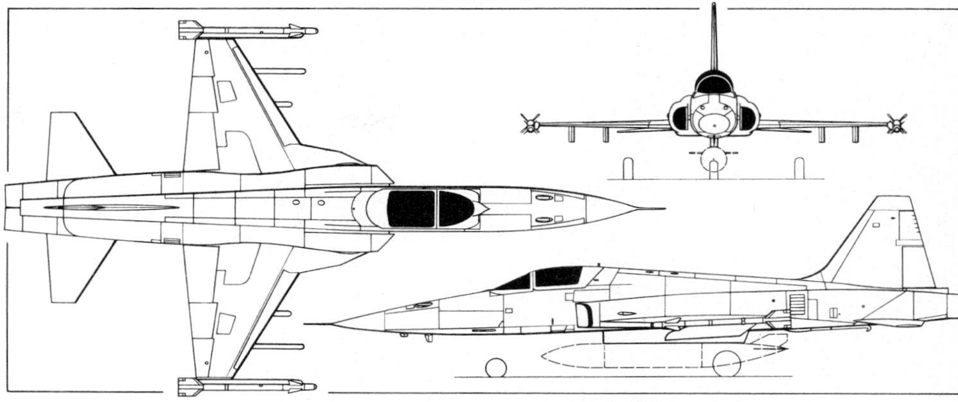

Northrop F-5E Tiger II single-seat twin-jet tactical fighter aircraft *(Pilot Press)*

Fuselage: Light alloy semi-monocoque basic structure, with steel, magnesium and titanium used in certain areas. Two hydraulically-actuated airbrakes of magnesium alloy construction, mounted on underside of fuselage forward of main-wheel wells. Electronics bay and cockpit pressurised; fail-safe structure in pressurised sections.

Tail Unit: Cantilever all-metal structure, with hydraulically-powered rudder and one-piece all-moving tailplane. Tailplane incidence varied by hydraulic actuators. No trim tabs. Dual hydraulic actuators of Northrop design for control of rudder and tailplane.

Landing Gear: Hydraulically-retractable tricycle type, main units retracting inward into fuselage, nosewheel forward. Oleo-pneumatic struts of Northrop design on all units. Two-position extending nose unit increases static angle of attack by 3° 22′ to reduce T-O distance, and is shortened automatically during the retraction cycle. Gravity-operated emergency extension. Main wheels and tyres size 24 × 8·00-13, pressure 14·48 bars (210 lb/sq in). Steerable nose unit with wheel and tyre size 18 × 6·50-8, pressure 8·27 bars (120 lb/sq in). All-metal multiple-disc brakes of Northrop design.

Power Plant: Two General Electric J85-GE-21A turbojet engines, each rated at 22·24 kN (5,000 lb st) with afterburning. Two independent fuel systems, one for each engine. Fuel for starboard engine supplied from two rubber-impregnated bladder-type nylon fabric cells, comprising a centre-fuselage cell of 803 litre (212 US gallon) capacity, and an aft-fuselage cell of 640 litre (169 US gallon) capacity. Port engine supplied from a forward fuselage cell of 1,120 litre (296 US gallon) capacity. Total fuel capacity 2,563 litres (677 US gallons). No fuel is carried in the wings. Fuel crossfeed system allows fuel from either or both cell systems to be fed to either or both engines. Auxiliary jettisonable fuel tanks of 568 or 1,040 litres (150 or 275 US gallons) can be carried on the fuselage centreline pylon and the inboard underwing pylons. Single refuelling point on lower fuselage for fuselage fuel cell and external tank installation. Provision for in-flight refuelling by means of a detachable probe. Oil capacity 4·5 litres (1·2 US gallons) per engine.

Engine Intakes: Intakes are supplemented with auxiliary air inlet doors for use during T-O and low-speed flight, to improve compressor face pressure recovery and to decrease distortion. Each door consists of a set of six pivot-mounted louvres in removable panels on each side of the fuselage. The doors are actuated by the pilot at T-O, and controlled automatically in flight by Mach sensor switches, and are maintained in the open position at airspeeds below Mach 0·35-0·4.

Accommodation: Pilot only in pressurised, heated and air-conditioned cockpit, on rocket-powered ejection seat. Upward-opening canopy, hinged at rear.

Systems: Cockpit and electronics bay pressurised, heated and air-conditioned by engine bleed air, maximum pressure differential 0·34 bars (5 lb/sq in). Hydraulic power supplied by two independent systems at a pressure of 207 bars (3,000 lb/sq in). Flight control system provides power solely for operation of primary flight control surfaces. Utility system provides hydraulic backup power for the primary flight control surfaces and operating power for the landing gear, landing gear doors, airbrakes, wheel brakes, nosewheel steering, gun bay purge doors, gun gas deflectors and stability augmentation system. Electrical power supplied by two 13/15kVA 115/200V three-phase 320-480Hz non-paralleled engine-driven alternators. Each alternator has the capacity to accept full aircraft power load via an automatic transfer function. 250VA 115V 400Hz single-phase solid-state static inverter provides secondary AC source for engine starting. Two 33A 26-32V transformer-rectifiers and a 24V 11Ah nickel-cadmium battery provide DC power. Liquid oxygen system with capacity of 5 litres.

Avionics and Equipment (F-5E): AN/ARC-164 UHF command radio, 3,500-channel with 50kHz spacing. Emerson Electric AN/APQ-159 lightweight micro-miniature X-band pulse radar for air-to-air search and range tracking; target information, at a range of up to 20 nm (37 km; 23 miles), is displayed on a 0·13 m (5 in) DVST in cockpit. AN/ARA-50 UHF ADF; AN/AIC-18 intercom system; AN/APX-101 IFF/SIF system; AN/ARN-118 Tacan; attitude and heading reference system; angle of attack system; and central air data computer. Full blind-flying instrumentation. Optional avionics include LN-33 inertial navigation system; AN/ARN-108 instrument landing system; CPU-129/A flight director computer; VHF; VOR/ILS with DME; LF ADF; CRT with scan converter for radar or electro-optical weapon (AGM-65 Maverick); and radar warning receiver.

Avionics and Equipment (F-5F): AN/ARC-164 UHF/AM command radio, AN/AIC-18 or -25 interphone set, AN/APX-101 IFF/SIF transponder, TS1843/APX transponder test set, AN/ARN-118 Tacan, AN/APQ-159 fire control radar, AN/ASG-29 lead computing optical sight, and AN/ARA-50 UHF/DF. Optional equipment includes photo-reconnaissance nose; in-flight refuelling system; pylon jettison conversion kits; anti-skid brakes; and chaff/flare countermeasures package.

Armament (F-5E): Two AIM-9 Sidewinder missiles on wingtip launchers. Two M-39A2 20 mm cannon mounted in fuselage nose, with 280 rounds per gun. Up to 3,175 kg (7,000 lb) of mixed ordnance can be carried on one underfuselage and four underwing stations, including M129 leaflet bombs; MK-82 GP and Snakeye 500 lb bombs; MK-36 destructors; MK-84 2,000 lb bomb; BLU-1, -27 or -32 U or F napalm; LAU-68 (7) 2·75 in rockets; LAU-3 (19) 2·75 in rockets; CBU-24, 49, -52 or -58 cluster bomb units; SUU-20 bomb and rocket packs; SUU-25 flare dispensers; TDU-10 tow targets (Dart); and RMU-10 reel (Dart). Lead-computing optical gunsight uses inputs from airborne radar for air-to-air missiles and cannon, and provides a roll-stabilised manually-depressible reticle aiming reference for air-to-ground delivery. A 'snapshoot' capability is included for attack on violently manoeuvring and fleeting targets. The gunsight incorporates also a detachable 16 mm reticle camera with 15 m (50 ft) film magazine. Optional ordnance capability includes the AGM-65 Maverick; centreline multiple ejector rack; and laser guided bombs.

Armament (F-5F): Two AIM-9J Sidewinder missiles on wingtip launchers. One M-39 20 mm cannon in port side of nose with 140 rounds. Underfuselage and underwing stores as detailed for the F-5E. Optional ordnance includes a laser designator in the rear cockpit.

Dimensions, external:

Wing span	8·13 m (26 ft 8 in)
Span over missiles	8·53 m (27 ft 11⅞ in)
Wing chord at root	3·57 m (11 ft 8⅝ in)
Wing chord at tip	0·68 m (2 ft 2⅞ in)
Wing aspect ratio	3·82
Length overall (incl nose-probe):	
F-5E	14·68 m (48 ft 2 in)

Northrop F-5F tandem two-seat fighter-trainer, armed with wingtip-mounted Sidewinder missiles

F-5F 15·72 m (51 ft 7 in)
Height overall: F-5E 4·06 m (13 ft 4 in)
F-5F 4·01 m (13 ft 1¾ in)
Tailplane span 4·31 m (14 ft 1½ in)
Wheel track 3·80 m (12 ft 5½ in)
Wheelbase 5·17 m (16 ft 11½ in)

AREAS:
Wings, gross 17·3 m² (186 sq ft)
Ailerons (total) 0·86 m² (9·24 sq ft)
Trailing-edge flaps (total) 1·95 m² (21·0 sq ft)
Leading-edge flaps (total) 1·14 m² (12·3 sq ft)
Fin 3·85 m² (41·42 sq ft)
Rudder 0·57 m² (6·10 sq ft)
Tailplane 5·48 m² (59·0 sq ft)

WEIGHTS AND LOADINGS:
Weight empty: F-5E 4,392 kg (9,683 lb)
F-5F 4,793 kg (10,567 lb)
Max T-O weight: F-5E 11,193 kg (24,676 lb)
F-5F 11,442 kg (25,225 lb)
Max landing weight: F-5F 11,406 kg (25,147 lb)
Max zero-fuel weight: F-5E 7,953 kg (17,534 lb)
Max wing loading: F-5E 649·4 kg/m² (133 lb/sq ft)
Max power loading: F-5E 251·6 kg/kN (2·5 lb/lb st)

PERFORMANCE (F-5E at combat weight of 6,055 kg; 13,350 lb, F-5F at combat weight of 6,375 kg; 14,055 lb, unless stated otherwise):
Never-exceed speed
710 knots (1,314 km/h; 817 mph) EAS
Max level speed:
F-5E at 10,975 m (36,000 ft) Mach 1·63
F-5F at 11,000 m (36,090 ft) Mach 1·55
Max cruising speed:
F-5E at 10,975 m (36,000 ft) Mach 0·98
Econ cruising speed Mach 0·80
Stalling speed, flaps down, power off:
F-5E 124 knots (230 km/h; 143 mph)
F-5F 136 knots (253 km/h; 157 mph)
Max rate of climb at S/L:
F-5E 10,516 m (34,500 ft)/min
F-5F 10,030 m (32,900 ft)/min
Service ceiling: F-5E 15,790 m (51,800 ft)
F-5F 15,484 m (50,800 ft)
Service ceiling, one engine out:
F-5E over 12,495 m (41,000 ft)
F-5F 12,285 m (40,300 ft)
T-O run:
F-5E at 7,053 kg (15,550 lb) 610 m (2,000 ft)
F-5F at 7,371 kg (16,250 lb) 701 m (2,300 ft)
T-O run at max T-O weight:
F-5E 1,737 m (5,700 ft)
F-5F 1,829 m (6,000 ft)
T-O to 15 m (50 ft):
F-5E at 7,053 kg (15,550 lb) 884 m (2,900 ft)
F-5F at 7,371 kg (16,250 lb) 975 m (3,200 ft)
Landing from 15 m (50 ft):
F-5E at 5,230 kg (11,530 lb), without brake chute
1,417 m (4,650 ft)
F-5F at 5,554 kg (12,245 lb), without brake chute
1,524 m (5,000 ft)
Landing run with brake chute:
F-5E at 5,230 kg (11,530 lb) 762 m (2,500 ft)
F-5F at 5,554 kg (12,245 lb) 792 m (2,600 ft)
Range, F-5E:
with max fuel and reserves for 20 min max endurance at S/L: tanks retained
1,340 nm (2,483 km; 1,543 miles)
tanks dropped
1,545 nm (2,863 km; 1,779 miles)
Combat radius, F-5E:
with max fuel, two Sidewinder missiles, allowances as above and 5 min combat with max afterburning power at 4,570 m (15,000 ft)
570 nm (1,056 km; 656 miles)
with 2,358 kg (5,200 lb) ordnance load, two Sidewinder missiles, max fuel, allowances as above and 5 min combat at military power at S/L, lo-lo-lo mission 120 nm (222 km; 138 miles)
with max fuel, two Sidewinder missiles and two 530 lb bombs, allowances as above and 5 min combat at military power at S/L, hi-lo-hi mission
480 nm (890 km; 553 miles)
Range, F-5F:
ferry range with max fuel, allowances comprising 5 min at normal thrust, 1 min at max thrust, 20 min loiter at S/L, plus reserve of 5 per cent of initial fuel: crew of two 1,270 nm (2,353 km; 1,462 miles)
Combat radius, F-5F:
with max internal fuel, and allowances comprising 2 min at normal thrust, 1 min at max thrust, 5 min max thrust for combat at 4,570 m (15,000 ft), 20 min loiter at S/L, plus reserve of 5 per cent of initial fuel 520 nm (964 km; 599 miles)
with max fuel, two Sidewinder missiles and two 530 lb bombs, allowances as above, and 5 min combat at military power at S/L, hi-lo-hi mission
450 nm (834 km; 518 miles)

NORTHROP RF-5E

Northrop's RF-5E prototype made its international debut at the 1979 Paris Air Show, following a flight from Edwards AFB, California. First flown in January 1979, this prototype had completed more than 60 test and demonstration flights by the beginning of June 1979, during which missions had been flown at heights between 61 m (200 ft) and 14,325 m (47,000 ft), by day and night, at speeds of up to 600 knots (1,112 km/h; 691 mph).

Basically similar to the F-5E Tiger II, the RF-5E differs by having a modified forward fuselage, and specialised equipment to enable it to fulfil a highly efficient reconnaissance role. The modified forward fuselage extends the overall length by 0·20 m (8 in), and provides 0·74 m³ (26 cu ft) of space to accommodate reconnaissance equipment. To allow maximum flexibility for differing reconnaissance roles, Northrop decided to group the various combinations of proposed cameras/sensors on portable pallets, any one of which could be loaded easily and quickly into this forward fuselage compartment. In addition to the selected pallet, a KS-87B oblique frame camera is mounted in a forward nose compartment and provided with lenses of 6 in and 12 in focal length.

Four pallets have been developed to date for the RF-5E, the first comprising a KA-95 medium/high-altitude panoramic camera, KA-56E low-altitude panoramic camera, and an RS-702 infra-red linescanner. Pallet 2 also has the KA-56E panoramic camera, with a KA-93 panoramic camera which is intended for horizon-to-horizon coverage at heights of 3,050-15,240 m (10,000-50,000 ft). Pallet 3 is configured for long-range oblique photo (LOROP) missions, and carries a single LOROP camera of 48 in or 66 in focal length. Pallet 4 provides night reconnaissance capability, equipped with a KA-98 covert laser linescanner and an RS-702 infra-red linescanner. Optionally available for use with Pallet 4 is a special nosecone accommodating the AN/APQ-146 terrain-following radar system which equips B-1 and F-111 aircraft.

The pilot has available advanced nav/com systems to complement the reconnaissance equipment, plus a video viewfinder system which enables him to view the terrain below the aircraft on a cathode ray tube (CRT) display in the cockpit. Using this system, the pilot can monitor and correct his line-of-flight during mapping runs, and can also update the INS when passing over recognisable terrain features. In addition, there is an integrated sensor control system (ISCS), which handles many operations automatically, thus reducing the pilot's workload. The ISCS takes inputs from the radar altimeter and INS to compute the angular velocity (V/H) for the terrain passing below the aircraft. V/H signals and the camera cycle rates are directed to individual cameras, with the appropriate scaling factor required for that particular sensor. The ISCS can cater for a wide variety of additional growth sensors.

The RF-5E retains the external stores stations of the F-5E, permitting the carriage of up to three external fuel tanks (each 1,040 litres; 275 US gallons) for maximum range and speed performance. It has essentially the same performance and armament capabilities as the F-5E tactical fighter, and on all missions is able to carry one M-39 20 mm gun with 280 rounds, plus two AIM-9 missiles.

Pilots of four nations had made flights in the RF-5E by the time it was shown at the 1979 Paris Air Show, and many of the 25 nations then flying F-5s had expressed their interest in evaluating the RF-5E.

PERFORMANCE:
Mission radius (A, with one external fuel tank and two AIM-9s; B, with three external fuel tanks and two AIM-9s):
Low altitude throughout:
A 250 nm (463 km; 287 miles)
B 365 nm (676 km; 420 miles)
Hi-lo-hi: A 410 nm (759 km; 471 miles)
B 560 nm (1,037 km; 644 miles)
Hi-lo-lo-hi: A 365 nm (676 km; 420 miles)
B 520 nm (963 km; 598 miles)
High altitude throughout:
A 495 nm (916 km; 569 miles)
B 630 nm (1,166 km; 725 miles)

NORTHROP F/A-18L

The F/A-18L is a multi-role land-based version of the US Navy's F/A-18 Hornet carrier-suitable combat aircraft, for which McDonnell Douglas (which see) is prime contractor. Both aircraft are derivatives of the YF-17 twin-engined fighter prototypes, which represented Northrop's submission in the USAF's Lightweight Fighter (LWF) prototype programme. In the case of the F/A-18 Hornet production programme, Northrop's share of the work is approximately 40 per cent, that of McDonnell Douglas approximately 60 per cent. The percentages are reversed in the F/A-18L programme, for which Northrop is prime contractor.

The land-based F/A-18L and carrier-suitable F/A-18 Hornet are about 80-90 per cent common in high-value/high-usage spare parts, with the same General Electric F404 engines. The F/A-18L is, however, considerably lighter in terms of empty weight as a result of the deletion of specifically-naval equipment and requirements, such as the heavy-duty landing gear and arrester hook needed for deck operations.

A two-seat version of the F/A-18L is also available, and would be capable of both transitional training and full tactical employment.

The description and dimensions given for the F/A-18 Hornet apply generally to the F/A-18L.

Sensor windows are visible beneath the forward fuselage of Northrop's RF-5E reconnaissance aircraft

Mockup of two-seat version of F/A-18L at 1979 Paris Air Show

PERFORMANCE: (estimated, F-18L in basic air-to-air interception configuration):
Max level speed, with afterburning in Mach 2 class
Max level speed, without afterburning, with two Sidewinders above Mach 1
Approach speed 115 knots (213 km/h; 132 mph)
Stalling speed at air-to-air landing weight 92 knots (171 km/h; 106 mph)
Max rate of climb at S/L (50% fuel, two Sidewinders) more than 18,290 m (60,000 ft)/min
T-O run (two Sidewinders):
with afterburning 275 m (900 ft)
without afterburning 396 m (1,300 ft)
T-O run (7,257 kg; 16,000 lb external load), with afterburning 670 m (2,200 ft)
Landing run (without brake chute) 518 m (1,700 ft)
Combat radius more than 700 nm (1,295 km; 805 miles)
Ferry range more than 2,500 nm (4,630 km; 2,875 miles)
g limit (60% fuel) +9

A Northrop F-18L prototype takes off at Edwards AFB on an evaluation flight by a Spanish Air Force pilot

OMAC
OMAC INC

ADDRESS: Stead Airport, Reno, Nevada 89506
PRESIDENT: Larry Heuberger

This relatively new company has been founded by Larry Heuberger, who was William Lear's chief engineer in the early days of the Learjet 23 and 24, and industrialist Carl Parise. Their aim is to develop a new low-cost high-performance and economical 6/8-seat turboprop-powered business aircraft of canard configuration. It was planned to exhibit a full-size mockup at the NBAA display at Atlanta, Georgia, in October 1979. A prototype is scheduled for rollout in the Spring of 1980, with type certification and initial deliveries following in early 1981. All components and assemblies will be contracted out, leaving OMAC responsible for final assembly and flight testing. All available details of this aircraft follow:

OMAC I

TYPE: Lightweight business aircraft.
WINGS: Cantilever high-wing monoplane, with 45° swept inboard leading-edge and unswept constant-chord outer panels. Aerofoil section NACA 641-212 (Mod B). Conventional two-spar structure of light alloy, with H-section extruded front spar. Hydraulically-operated half-span trailing-edge plain flaps. Half-span cable-actuated ailerons. Trim tab in port aileron. Winglets fitted at wingtips, each carrying a rudder with 25° of movement.
FUSELAGE: Conventional light alloy semi-monocoque pressurised structure.
FOREPLANE: Low-set constant-chord cantilever monoplane. Aerofoil section NACA 641-212 (Mod B). Conventional two-spar light alloy structure. Both spars of extruded H-section. Full-span elevator each side. Trim tab in each elevator, electrically and manually actuated, and spring-interlocked with flaps for automatic trimming.
LANDING GEAR: Hydraulically-retractable tricycle type. Steerable nosewheel retracts forward. Oleo-pneumatic shock-absorber with shimmy damper on nosewheel. Main units have tubular spring steel legs. Nosewheel tyre size 6·00-6. Main wheels have heavy-duty tyres size 17·5-6·25 × 6. Heavy-duty brakes.

Model of OMAC I lightweight turboprop-powered business aircraft *(Howard Levy)*

POWER PLANT: One 522 kW (700 shp) Lycoming LTP 101-700A-A1 turboprop engine, driving a four-blade reversible-pitch metal pusher propeller, with 'Q' tips and Beta control. Fuel in wing leading-edge and centre-section tanks, and aft-fuselage main feed tank, with combined capacity of 1,090 litres (288 US gallons). Refuelling points on wing upper surface.
ACCOMMODATION: Three alternative layouts for a pilot and one, six or seven passengers. Two forward-facing seats for pilot and co-pilot/passenger, with two or three individual reclining and swivelling seats, and three-seat bench at rear of cabin. Baggage compartment aft of rear seats, with space for toilet with privacy curtain. Split-type airstair door on port side. Emergency exit on starboard side.
SYSTEMS: Max cabin pressure differential 0·38 bars (5·5 lb/sq in). Hydraulic system with electrically-powered pump for operation of flaps, landing gear and brakes. Electrical system. Oxygen system.
AVIONICS: Bendix BX 2000 and RDR 160 radar standard.
DIMENSIONS, EXTERNAL:
Wing span 9·14 m (30 ft 0 in)
Foreplane span 4·57 m (15 ft 0 in)
Length overall 8·08 m (26 ft 6 in)
Height overall 3·25 m (10 ft 8 in)
Wheelbase 4·18 m (13 ft 8½ in)
Propeller diameter 2·16 m (7 ft 1 in)
DIMENSIONS, INTERNAL:
Cabin: Length 3·99 m (13 ft 1 in)
Max height 1·37 m (4 ft 6 in)
Max width 1·42 m (4 ft 8 in)
PERFORMANCE (estimated, at max T-O weight)
Max cruising speed at 6,100 m (20,000 ft) 261 knots (483 km/h; 300 mph)
Econ cruising speed at 9,145 m (30,000 ft) 217 knots (402 km/h; 250 mph)
Max range with max fuel, 1 h hold 2,944 nm (5,456 km; 3,390 miles)

OMNIONICS

ADDRESS: Meritt Island, Florida

In 1965, Omnionics began development of an all-glassfibre amphibian for commuter and business transport operation. This has evolved as the Dolphinair, of which available details follow:

OMNIONICS DOLPHINAIR

The general configuration of this unique transport amphibian is shown in the accompanying photograph of a model displayed in 1979. The sweptback high-mounted wings carry at each wingtip a large fixed float/fuel tank, with an aerofoil, similar to a large NASA winglet, mounted on the upper surface. Outboard of this is a smaller winglet at the tip of a wing extension which can retract into or extend from the main wing structure, to give a variable span and area. Wing section will be a 12% NACA aerofoil.

The Dolphinair is to be powered by two Garrett-AiResearch ATF3 turbofan engines (each 22·7 kN; 5,100 lb st), each pod-mounted above the side of the rear fuselage. The cabin is nearly 7·3 m (24 ft) long, with a max headroom and width of 1·83 m (6 ft), to accommodate up to 12 passengers in executive layout or 20 commuters.

In mid-1979, moulds were being made for construction of Kevlar, carbon fibre and glassfibre airframe components. The prototype Dolphinair is expected to be completed in mid-1981, and to fly for the first time at the beginning of 1982.

Model of Omnionics Dolphinair variable-span amphibian *(Howard Levy)*

DIMENSIONS, EXTERNAL:
Wing span: extensions out 24·38 m (80 ft 0 in)
extensions in 13·56 m (44 ft 6 in)
Wing aspect ratio: extensions out 11·3
extensions in 4·5
WEIGHT:
Max T-O weight 11,340 kg (25,000 lb)
PERFORMANCE (estimated):
Max cruising speed Mach 0·85
Approach speed 90 knots (167 km/h; 104 mph)

Max rate of climb at S/L	2,750 m (9,000 ft)/min
Service ceiling	18,275 m (60,000 ft)
Service ceiling, one engine out	9,150 m (30,000 ft)
Landing run, ashore	610 m (2,000 ft)
Range with max fuel, 45 min reserves	3,000 nm (5,550 km; 3,450 miles)

PIASECKI
PIASECKI AIRCRAFT CORPORATION

Head Office and Works: Island Road, International Airport, Philadelphia, Pennsylvania 19153
Telephone: (215) 365 2222
Directors:
Virgil Kauffman
Donald N. Meyers
Arthur J. Kania
J. Mecallef
F. N. Piasecki
President: Frank N. Piasecki
Vice-President: Donald N. Meyers (Engineering)
Secretary: Arthur J. Kania
Industrial Engineering: K. R. Meenen

The Piasecki Aircraft Corporation was formed in 1955 by Mr Frank Piasecki, who was formerly Chairman of the Board and President of the Piasecki Helicopter Corporation (now the Boeing Vertol Company).

PIASECKI HELI-STAT

Recent work carried out by Piasecki, some of it under contract to the US Navy, is concerned with the investigation of a hybrid VTOL vehicle, named a Heli-Stat. This concept links the envelope of a lighter-than-air craft with current-technology helicopters, the aerostat providing static lift to support approximately the full empty weight of the entire assembly. The helicopters furnish the lift to support the payload, as well as providing propulsion and control, with adequate control forces to enable the Heli-Stat to hover with precision, a characteristic with which conventional airships cannot comply.

Details of an early Heli-Stat project can be found in the 1977-78 *Jane's*. By 1979 Piasecki had started engineering work on a prototype, designated **Model 97-34J** and named **Logger**, which is intended to demonstrate the advantages of such a vehicle for tasks such as the economic transportation of otherwise inaccessible timber over distances of up to 8·7 nm (16 km; 10 miles). The envelope of the aerostat will be 74·07 m (243 ft) long, with a maximum diameter of 26·06 m (85 ft 6 in). Lifting of the 23,794 kg (52,456 lb) payload, propulsion, and control of the low-cost demonstrator, will be provided by four Sikorsky S-58 helicopters, each fitted with a 1,137 kW (1,525 hp) Wright R-1820-84A radial aircooled engine.

Artist's impression of a Heli-Stat hauling timber

PIPER
PIPER AIRCRAFT CORPORATION (Subsidiary of Bangor Punta Corporation)

Head Office and Works: Lock Haven, Pennsylvania 17745
Telephone: (717) 748 6711
Telex: 841425
Other Works:
Vero Beach, Florida 32960
Lakeland, Florida 33801
Piper, Pennsylvania 16845
Renovo, Pennsylvania 17764
Santa Maria, California 93454
Board of Directors:
Max E. Bleck
Stephen Galle
Thomas W. Gillespie
J. Lynn Helms
Sheldon Kaplan
Alfred J. Koontz Jr (Finance)
Jonathan Lushing
John J. Martin (Secretary)
David L. Ottenstein
Dudley C. Phillips (General Counsel)
James E. Stewart
David W. Wallace
President and Chief Executive Officer: Max E. Bleck
Chairman of the Board: J. Lynn Helms
Senior Vice-Presidents:
Thomas W. Gillespie Jr (Marketing and Sales)
Dudley C. Phillips (General Counsel)
Group Vice-Presidents:
Vincent J. Montuoro
Harry M. Graham (Lakeland and Lock Haven Divisions)
Vice-Presidents:
Marion J. Dees Jr (Engineering)
Findley A. Estlick (Plant Facilities & Foreign Assembly Operations)
C. Raymond Johnson (Sales)
Alfred J. Koontz Jr (Finance)
John J. Martin (Secretary)
Controller: Jack J. Cattoni
Treasurer: John R. Leeson
Administrator, Corporate Communications:
John W. Alter

In April 1976, Piper produced its 100,000th aircraft, a twin-turboprop Cheyenne.

Vero Beach is responsible for the experimental development of Piper aircraft and also houses one of the company's Plastics Divisions. Lock Haven also has R & D facilities for aircraft built at Lock Haven.

Piper operates also four other plants. The first two are at Piper, Pennsylvania, where sheet metal parts are formed, and Renovo, Pennsylvania, which makes plastics components; the third is at Lakeland, Florida, where PA-31 aircraft are in production; the fourth, at Santa Maria, California, is the former Ted Smith Aerostar Corporation, which Piper acquired in 1978.

Optional equipment on several current models includes a choice of four automatic flight systems. Simplest of these is the Piper-developed AutoFlite II, a solid-state system which holds the wings level and has turn-command capability for up to standard rate turns. This flight system is integrated with the pictorial turn rate indicator, which serves as the sensing element. If the Nav Tracker II is added to the AutoFlite II, it allows automatic tracking to and from Omni stations and is equipped with a two-position sensitivity switch.

Latest version of the established two-control autopilot is the Piper AutoControl III, which features positive heading lock and course selector, and is available with automatic VOR/ILS radio coupling.

A full three-control system, the Piper AltiMatic III-C, provides course preselection and positive heading lock; altitude preselection and hold, with automatic pitch trim. It is also available with automatic VOR/ILS radio coupling.

The fourth of the range of flight systems is the FCS 810 AP/FD, an autopilot and flight director system, replacing the model V/FD-1 which was offered previously as an option for Aztecs, Navajos and Pressurised Navajos only. It consists of three basic panel components: a horizontal situation indicator, a steering horizon and a compact flight programmer console. The FCS 810 AP autopilot unit is available without the flight director unit.

The horizontal situation indicator combines directional gyro, VOR/LOC and glideslope information in a single instrument. The electrically-driven directional gyro unit is magnetically slaved. A fast-slaving function is automatic and conventional flag alarms are provided.

The steering horizon replaces the standard gyro horizon, providing normal attitude information in pictorial form. Computed information, required to direct the aircraft on its proper course, appears in the form of a command disc at each wingtip of a miniature aircraft in the gyro horizon indicator. To follow a programmed flight sequence the discs are held in alignment with the wingtips of the miniature aircraft, either by autopilot or by manual control.

The flight programmer console, which has seven push-buttons, annunciator lights and a pitch attitude control disc, can be programmed for autopilot action and/or flight director display. Once a sequence, such as an ILS approach, is initiated, logic circuits automatically execute sequential mode switching and dynamic response changes as required. Altitude is set by pushing the 'ALT' button on the flight programmer console when reaching the desired altitude, which is then held plus or minus 6 m (20 ft).

In 1971, 1974, 1977 and 1979 respectively, Piper announced agreements with Chincul SA (which see) for the manufacture of a broad range of Piper products in Argentina; with EMBRAER (which see) for the development, production and marketing of Piper aircraft in Brazil; with PZL Mielec (which see) of Poland to assemble, manufacture and distribute the Piper Seneca II light twin-engined aircraft in that country; and with Short Brothers Ltd (which see) for production of the Piper Tomahawk in the UK.

PIPER (PA-18) SUPER CUB

The original PA-18 with 67 kW (90 hp) Continental C90-12F engine received FAA Type Approval on 18 November 1949. The PA-18-150, PA-18A-150 agricultural aircraft and PA-18S and PA-18AS seaplanes were all approved on 1 October 1954.

The current international height record in Class C1b (aircraft with T-O weight of 500-1,000 kg) is held by Miss C. Bayley of the USA, who climbed to a height of 9,206 m (30,203 ft) in a Super Cub with 93·2 kW (125 hp) Lycoming engine, on 4 January 1951.

The following factory-installed avionics packages are available optionally for the Super Cub:

Group KS-1-SC. King KX 145 nav/com, King KI 205 VOR/LOC indicator, Telex 100T noise cancelling microphone, Telex headset, cabin speaker, com and VOR antennae.

Group KS-2-SC. As above, except KX 145 and KI 205 deleted, and replaced by King KX 170B com and KI 208 VOR/LOC converter/indicator.

Group NC-1-SC. As KS-1-SC, except KX 145 and KI 205 deleted, and replaced by Narco COMM 120 com and Narco NAV 121 nav with VOR/LOC converter/indicator.

Group EA-1-SC. As KS-1-SC, except KX 145 and KI 205 deleted, and replaced by Edo-Aire RT-563 nav/com with built-in VOR/LOC converter/indicator.

Group CTM-1-SC. As KS-1-SC, except KX 145 and KI 205 deleted, and replaced by Collins VHF-250 com, Collins VIR-350 nav with VOR/LOC converter, and Collins IND-350 VOR/LOC indicator.

In addition, other optional avionics are available to customer's requirements.

By mid-February 1978 more than 40,000 examples of the PA-18 Cub and its predecessors had been delivered.

Type: Two-seat light cabin monoplane.

Wings: Braced high-wing monoplane, with steel tube Vee bracing struts each side. Wing section USA 35B. Thickness/chord ratio 12%. Dihedral 1°. No incidence at mean aerodynamic chord. Total washout of 3° 18′. Aluminium spars and ribs, aluminium sheet leading-edge and aileron false spar, wingtip bow of ash, with fabric covering overall and fire-resistant Duraclad plastic finish. Plain ailerons and trailing-edge flaps of light alloy construction.

Fuselage: Rectangular welded steel tube structure covered with fabric. Fire-resistant Duraclad plastic finish.

Tail Unit: Wire-braced structure of welded steel tubes and channels, covered with fabric. Fire-resistant Duraclad plastic finish. Tailplane incidence variable for trimming. Balanced rudder and elevators.

Landing Gear: Non-retractable tailwheel type. Two side Vs and half axles hinged to bottom of fuselage. Rubber cord shock-absorption. Main-wheel tyres size 6·00-6 four-ply, with 7·00-6, six-ply or 8·00-6, four-ply, optional. Steerable leaf-spring tailwheel. Dual expanding brakes. Parking brake.

Power Plant: One 112 kW (150 hp) Lycoming O-320 flat-four engine, driving a Sensenich two-blade fixed-pitch metal propeller with spinner. Steel tube engine mounting is hinged at firewall, allowing it to be swung to port for access to rear of engine. One 68 litre (18 US gallon) metal fuel tank in each wing. Total fuel capacity 136 litres (36 US gallons), of which 135·5 litres (35·8 US gallons) are usable. Refuelling points on top of wing.

Accommodation: Enclosed cabin seating two in tandem with dual controls. Adjustable front seat. Rear seat quickly removable for cargo carrying. Inertia-reel shoulder harness and seat belts standard for front and rear seats. Heater and adjustable cool-air vent. Downward-hinged door on starboard side, and upward-hinged window above, can be opened in flight. Sliding windows on port side. Baggage compartments aft of rear seat, capacity 22 kg (50 lb).

Systems: Electrical system, comprising 14V 60A alternator, 12V 35Ah battery, optional. Vacuum system for gyro driven instruments optional.

Avionics and Equipment: Stall warning device, sensitive altimeter, control locks and tiedown rings standard. Optional extras include Narco Com 120/Nav 121, AT 150 transponder; Edo-Aire RT-563 nav/com, RT-777 transponder; King KX 170B nav/com with KI 201C nav indicator, or KX 145 nav/com with KI 205 nav indicator, KT 78A transponder; and United encoding altimeter; automatic locator beacon, blind-flying instruments, vacuum system, outside air temperature gauge, dome light, radio speaker, electric fuel gauge, metal fuselage bottom panels, cabin fire extinguisher, 8-day clock, landing light, metallising, polyurethane finish for steel components, tail strobe light, and stainless steel control cables.

Dimensions, external:

Wing span	10·76 m (35 ft 3½ in)
Wing chord (constant)	1·60 m (5 ft 3 in)
Wing aspect ratio	7
Length overall	6·86 m (22 ft 6 in)
Height overall	2·04 m (6 ft 8½ in)
Tailplane span	3·20 m (10 ft 6 in)
Wheel track	1·84 m (6 ft 0½ in)

Dimension, internal:

Baggage compartment	0·51 m³ (18 cu ft)

Areas:

Wings, gross	16·58 m² (178·5 sq ft)
Ailerons (total)	1·75 m² (18·80 sq ft)
Trailing-edge flaps (total)	1·07 m² (11·50 sq ft)
Fin	0·43 m² (4·66 sq ft)
Rudder	0·63 m² (6·76 sq ft)
Tailplane	1·40 m² (15·10 sq ft)
Elevators	1·09 m² (11·70 sq ft)

Weights and Loadings (N: Normal category; R: Restricted, agricultural, category):

Weight empty: N, R	429 kg (946 lb)
Max T-O and landing weight: N	794 kg (1,750 lb)
R	939 kg (2,070 lb)
Max wing loading: N	48·8 kg/m² (10·0 lb/sq ft)
R	56·64 kg/m² (11·6 lb/sq ft)
Max power loading: N	7·09 kg/kW (11·6 lb/hp)
R	8·38 kg/kW (13·8 lb/hp)

Performance (at max T-O weight: N: Normal category; R: Restricted, agricultural, category):

Never-exceed speed:	
N, R	132 knots (246 km/h; 153 mph)
Max cruising speed, 75% power at 1,525 m (5,000 ft)	
N	100 knots (185 km/h; 115 mph)
R	91 knots (169 km/h; 105 mph)
Stalling speed, flaps down:	
N	37 knots (69 km/h; 43 mph)
R	39 knots (73 km/h; 45 mph)
Max rate of climb at S/L: N	293 m (960 ft)/min
R	232 m (760 ft)/min
Service ceiling: N	5,795 m (19,000 ft)
R	5,180 m (17,000 ft)
Absolute ceiling: N	6,492 m (21,300 ft)
T-O run: N	61 m (200 ft)
R	92 m (300 ft)
T-O to 15 m (50 ft): N	153 m (500 ft)
R	290 m (950 ft)
Landing from 15 m (50 ft): N	270 m (885 ft)
R	267 m (875 ft)
Landing run: N	107 m (350 ft)
R	125 m (410 ft)
Range with max fuel and max payload, 75% power at optimum altitude: N	400 nm (742 km; 461 miles)
R	312 nm (580 km; 360 miles)

PIPER (PA-23-250) AZTEC F

The current version of the Aztec, designated Model F, has a number of improvements as standard. These include interconnection of the all-moving tailplane with the flaps, to eliminate need for pitch re-trim when flaps are operated, redesigned wingtips, dual engine-driven hydraulic pumps and new external paint schemes. The Aztec is available in several configurations, as follows:

Custom Aztec. Basic model, as described in detail.

Sportsman Aztec. As Custom model, with addition of Piper external power socket and de luxe interior; adding total of 3·08 kg (6·8 lb) to basic empty weight.

Professional Aztec. As Sportsman model, with addition of electrically heated windscreen panel, electrical propeller de-icing and pneumatic de-icing boots on wings and tail; adding a total of 22·14 kg (48·8 lb) to basic empty weight.

Turbo Aztec. Turbocharged version, described separately.

Each of the above versions can be fitted with one of six avionics packages, as follows:

Group NC-1-23. Two Narco Com 120 360-channel VHF transceivers; Narco Nav 121 200-channel VOR/LOC receiver with converter indicator; Narco Nav 122 200-channel VOR/LOC receiver with glideslope deviation and indicator; glideslope receiver; ADF-141 with Narco ADF-101 indicator; AT-150 transponder; Narco marker beacon receiver and marker beacon light; CP-135 audio panel; Piper AutoControl IIIB; Edo-Aire electric trim; Edo-Aire VOR/LOC coupler to autopilot; Piper static discharge wicks, Telex headset, 100T noise-cancelling microphone, and all associated antennae; adding total of 23·45 kg (51·7 lb) to basic empty weight.

Group NC-2-23. As Group NC-1-23, with deletion of Narco Nav 122 and Piper AutoControl IIIB. Replaced by VOR/LOC receiver with glideslope deviation indicator and HSI; Nav 124 VOR receiver; DME-195; Piper AltiMatic IIIC autopilot with VOR/LOC/GS coupling and electric trim; adding 30·4 kg (67 lb) to basic empty weight.

Group KS 1-23. Dual King KX 170B nav/com transceivers with 720-channel com and 200-channel nav; KI 209 VOR/LOC/glideslope indicator with VOR/LOC converter; KI 208 VOR/LOC converter indicator; KN 75 glidescope receiver; KR 86 ADF; KT 76A transponder; KMA 20 audio panel; marker beacon receiver with indicator lights; Piper AutoControl IIIB; Edo-Aire VOR/LOC coupler to AutoControl IIIB, with electric trim; Telex 100T microphone; and Piper anti-static kit; adding 24·81 kg (54·7 lb) to basic empty weight.

Group KTS 2-23. Dual King KX 175B nav/com transceivers with 720-channel com and 200-channel nav; King KCS 55A HSI VOR/LOC/GS indicator; KI 203 VOR/LOC indicator; KN 72 VOR/LOC converter; KN 75 glideslope receiver; KR 85 ADF with KI 225 indicator; KT 76A transponder; KMA 20 audio selector panel with marker beacon lights; KI 266 DME, KAP 200 AFS with electric trim and VOR/LOC/GS coupling; Telex 100T noise cancelling microphone; headset; Piper static discharge wicks; avionics master switch; and all associated antennae; adding 43·1 kg (95 lb) to basic empty weight.

Group CTM-1-23. Dual Collins VHF-250 720-channel com transceivers, with Telex 100T noise-cancelling microphone and headset; dual Collins VIR-350 nav receivers with VOR/LOC converter; Collins IND-351 VOR/LOC/GS indicator No. 1; Collins GLS-350 glideslope receiver; Collins IND-350 VOR/LOC indicator No. 2; Collins AMR-350 audio selector panel, audio amplifier, marker beacon lights and marker beacon receiver; Collins ADF-650 and IND-650 indicator; Collins TDR-950 transponder with 4096 code capability; Piper AutoControl IIIB; Edo-Aire VOR/LOC coupling to AutoControl with electric trim; Piper avionics master switch; Piper static discharge wicks; and dual Collins PWC-150 power converters to supply 14V DC for dual com/nav systems; adding 40·3 kg (88·9 lb) to basic empty weight.

Group CTM-2-23. As Group CTM-1-23, except for deletion of dual Collins VHF-250 and VIR-350, Piper AutoControl IIIB, and Edo-Aire VOR/LOC coupling with electric trim. Replaced by dual Collins VHF-251 and VIR-351; King KN 65A DME with tuning adapter and digital display indicator; and Piper AltiMatic IIIC AFS with VOR/LOC/GS coupling and electric trim; adding 40·3 kg (88·9 lb) to basic empty weight.

The Aztec received FAA Type Approval as a five-seat aircraft on 18 September 1959, and with six seats on 15 December 1961.

The prototype of a floatplane version of the Aztec was produced as a joint project by Melridge Aviation of Vancouver, Washington, and Jobmaster Company Inc of Seattle. Fitted with Edo 4930 floats, this aircraft can take off from calm water in 20 seconds at max T-O weight of 2,360 kg (5,200 lb). Useful load is 816 kg (1,800 lb), permitting a six-passenger load with 455 litres (120 US gallons) of fuel. To simplify docking and loading from either side, a door was designed for installation on the port side, by the pilot's seat, and is part of the kit offered by Melridge Aviation to permit conversion in the field.

Piper Super Cub two-seat light cabin monoplane (Lycoming O-320 engine)

Type: Six-seat twin-engined executive transport.

Wings: Cantilever low-wing monoplane. Wing section USA 35-B (modified). Thickness/chord ratio 14%. Dihedral 5°. Incidence 0° at root, −1° 12′ at mean chord. All-metal stressed-skin structure, with heavy stepped-down main spar, front and rear auxiliary spars, ribs, stringers and detachable wingtips. Plain all-metal ailerons and hydraulically-actuated flaps. Optional Goodrich de-icing system.

Fuselage: Basic aluminium semi-monocoque structure with welded steel tube truss around cabin.

Tail Unit: Cantilever all-metal structure with swept fin and all-moving horizontal surfaces which interconnect mechanically with the flap system to avoid need for pitch re-trim when flaps are lowered. Trim tab in rudder. Geared anti-servo tab in horizontal surfaces. Optional Goodrich de-icing system.

Landing Gear: Retractable tricycle type. Hydraulic retraction, with CO_2 emergency extension system. Nosewheel retracts rearward, main wheels forward. Wheel doors enclose landing gear fully when retracted. Electrol oleo shock-absorber struts. Cleveland main wheels, size 6·00-6, with size 7·00-6 8-ply tyres. Cleveland steerable nosewheel, size 6·00-6, with 6·00-6 4-ply tyre. Hydraulic disc brakes. Parking brake.

Power Plant: Two 186·5 kW (250 hp) Lycoming IO-540-C4B5 flat-six engines, each driving a Hartzell HC-E2YK-2RB two-blade constant-speed fully-feathering metal propeller. Two rubber fuel cells in each wing with NACA type anti-icing non-siphoning vents. Total standard fuel capacity 544 litres (144 US gallons); 519 litres (137·2 US gallons) usable. Refuelling points above wings. Two internal wingtip fuel tanks optional, with total capacity of 151 litres (40 US gallons). Oil capacity 22·7 litres (6 US gallons). Propeller synchroniser and electrical de-icing system optional.

Accommodation: Six persons on two pairs of adjustable individual seats and rear bench seat. Shoulder harnesses for pilot's and co-pilot's seat; seat belts for all seats. Dual controls standard. Individual seat lights and controllable overhead ventilation. 35,000 BTU heater with four adjustable cool/warm air outlets and two windscreen defrosters. Heated windscreen optional. Double windows. Passenger step. Door at front of cabin on starboard side. Emergency exit at rear on port side. Centre and rear seats removable to provide space for stretcher, survey camera or up to 725 kg (1,600 lb) of freight. Rear cabin bulkhead removable for stretcher and cargo loading via rear baggage door. Baggage compartments at rear of cabin and in nose, with tie-down fittings, each with capacity of 68 kg (150 lb). Baggage doors on starboard side; rear one enlarged on current aircraft, for stretcher loading. Armrests, cabin dome light, individual reading lights, coat hooks, complete soundproofing and two sun visors. Seat headrests and leather upholstery optional.

Systems: Hydraulic system with dual engine-driven pumps, pressure 79 bars (1,150 lb/sq in), for landing gear and flaps. Two 70A 28V alternators. 24V 17Ah battery. 24V 25Ah battery optional.

Avionics and Equipment: Standard equipment includes full blind-flying instrumentation with 3 in pictorial rate of turn indicator, artificial horizon and directional gyro (flight instruments arranged in 'T' configuration), sensitive altimeter, Piper TruSpeed Indicator, alternate static source, clock, gyro air filter, outside air temperature gauge, dual vacuum gauges, stall warning horn, dual recording tachometers/hour meters, oil pressure, oil temperature, cylinder head temperature and fuel quantity gauges, dual fuel flow and manifold pressure gauges, flap position indicator, navigation lights, landing light,

Piper Turbo Aztec F six-seat cabin monoplane (two Lycoming TIO-540-C1A engines)

taxi light, white wingtip anti-collision lights, four map lights, glare-ban instrument lights, individual reading lights, cabin dome light, two door-ajar indicator lights, baggage compartment courtesy lights, heated pitot tube, two quick oil drains, towbar, tiedown rings, jack pads, nosewheel safety mirror, cabin and baggage door locks, cabin curtains and a wide choice of exterior trims. Optional items listed under descriptions of individual models and under electronic groups, plus altimeter and toe-brakes for co-pilot, fire extinguisher, blind-flying instrumentation for co-pilot, oxygen system with 3·23 m³ (114 cu ft) bottle and six outlets, Piper exhaust gas temperature gauge, wing ice inspection light, red tail strobe light, zinc chromate treatment, tinted windows, Piper automatic locator beacon, and propeller ice protection shields.

DIMENSIONS, EXTERNAL:
Wing span 11·37 m (37 ft 3½ in)
Wing chord (constant) 1·70 m (5 ft 7 in)
Wing aspect ratio 6·8
Length overall 9·51 m (31 ft 2½ in)
Height overall 3·08 m (10 ft 1¼ in)
Tailplane span 3·81 m (12 ft 6 in)
Wheel track 3·45 m (11 ft 4 in)
Wheelbase 2·29 m (7 ft 6 in)
Propeller diameter 1·96 m (6 ft 5 in)
Cabin door: Height 0·97 m (3 ft 2 in)
Width 0·84 m (2 ft 9 in)
Baggage compartment door (front):
Height 0·51 m (1 ft 8 in)
Width 0·76 m (2 ft 6 in)
Baggage compartment door (rear):
Height 0·76 m (2 ft 6 in)
Width 0·79 m (2 ft 7 in)

DIMENSIONS, INTERNAL:
Baggage compartments: front 0·60 m³ (21·3 cu ft)
rear 0·72 m³ (25·4 cu ft)
Max cargo space, incl baggage compartments 3·45 m³ (122 cu ft)

AREAS:
Wings, gross 19·23 m² (207·0 sq ft)
Ailerons (total) 0·77 m² (8·38 sq ft)
Trailing-edge flaps (total) 1·54 m² (16·60 sq ft)
Fin 1·37 m² (14·80 sq ft)
Rudder 0·96 m² (10·30 sq ft)
Horizontal surfaces (total) 3·70 m² (39·80 sq ft)

WEIGHTS AND LOADINGS:
Weight empty 1,461 kg (3,221 lb)
Max T-O and ramp weight 2,360 kg (5,200 lb)
Max landing weight 2,241 kg (4,940 lb)
Max wing loading 122·7 kg/m² (25·12 lb/sq ft)
Max power loading 6·33 kg/kW (10·4 lb/hp)

PERFORMANCE (at max T-O weight):
Never-exceed speed 240 knots (446 km/h; 277 mph)
Max level speed 187 knots (346 km/h; 215 mph)
Normal cruising speed at 1,175 m (3,850 ft) 179 knots (332 km/h; 206 mph)
Intermediate cruising speed at 1,830 m (6,000 ft) 176 knots (327 km/h; 203 mph)
Econ cruising speed at 1,905 m (6,250 ft) 170 knots (315 km/h; 196 mph)
Long-range cruising speed at 3,290 m (10,800 ft) 162 knots (301 km/h; 187 mph)
Stalling speed, flaps up 61 knots (113 km/h; 70 mph)
Stalling speed, flaps down 54·5 knots (101 km/h; 63 mph)
Max rate of climb at S/L 426 m (1,400 ft)/min
Rate of climb at S/L, one engine out 72 m (235 ft)/min
Service ceiling 5,365 m (17,600 ft)
Service ceiling, one engine out 1,465 m (4,800 ft)
T-O run, normal 302 m (990 ft)
T-O run, short-field 288 m (945 ft)
T-O to 15 m (50 ft), normal 604 m (1,980 ft)
T-O to 15 m (50 ft), short-field 517 m (1,695 ft)
Landing from 15 m (50 ft), normal 483 m (1,585 ft)
Landing from 15 m (50 ft), short run 399 m (1,310 ft)
Landing run, normal 232 m (760 ft)
Landing run, short-field 204 m (670 ft)
Range with standard max fuel, allowances for start, taxi, T-O, climb, and 45 min reserves at long-range cruise power:
Intermediate cruise power 790 nm (1,464 km; 910 miles)
Econ cruise power 830 nm (1,538 km; 956 miles)
Long-range cruise power at 2,135 m (7,000 ft) 985 nm (1,825 km; 1,134 miles)
Range with optional max fuel, allowances as above:
Intermediate cruise power 1,060 nm (1,963 km; 1,220 miles)
Econ cruise power 1,110 nm (2,055 km; 1,277 miles)
Long-range cruise power at 2,135 m (7,000 ft) 1,320 nm (2,444 km; 1,519 miles)

PIPER (PA-23-250) TURBO AZTEC F

The Turbo Aztec F is identical in every way with the Aztec F, except that it has 186·5 kW (250 hp) Lycoming TIO-540-C1A engines, fitted with the AiResearch turbocharging system. These specially modified engines allow a turbo cruise setting at 2,400 rpm, providing a constant manifold pressure from sea level to 6,705 m (22,000 ft), and result in considerably improved performance.

Standard equipment includes a density controller to prevent inadvertent overboost of the engines at full throttle, and a differential pressure controller to provide constant manifold pressure during cruising flight. An oxygen system with 3·23 m³ (114 cu ft) bottle and six outlets is optional.

WEIGHTS AND LOADINGS:
As for Aztec F, except:
Weight empty (standard) 1,523 kg (3,357 lb)

PERFORMANCE (at max T-O weight):
As for Aztec F, except:
Max level speed at 5,640 m (18,500 ft) 220 knots (407 km/h; 253 mph)
Turbo cruising speed at 6,705 m (22,000 ft) 210 knots (389 km/h; 241 mph)
Intermediate cruising speed at 7,315 m (24,000 ft) 203 knots (376 km/h; 233 mph)
Econ cruising speed at 7,315 m (24,000 ft) 193 knots (357 km/h; 222 mph)
Long-range cruising speed at 6,100 m (20,000 ft) 165 knots (305 km/h; 190 mph)
Max rate of climb at S/L 448 m (1,470 ft)/min
Rate of climb at S/L, one engine out 68 m (225 ft)/min
Service ceiling over 7,315 m (24,000 ft)
Service ceiling, one engine out 5,180 m (17,000 ft)
Range with standard max fuel, allowances for start, taxi, T-O, climb, and 45 min reserves at long-range cruise power:
Turbo cruising speed at 6,705 m (22,000 ft) 695 nm (1,287 km; 800 miles)
Intermediate cruising speed at 7,315 m (24,000 ft) 740 nm (1,371 km; 852 miles)
Econ cruising speed at 7,315 m (24,000 ft) 780 nm (1,445 km; 898 miles)
Long-range cruising speed at 6,100 m (20,000 ft) 835 nm (1,548 km; 962 miles)
Range with optional max fuel, allowances as above:
Turbo cruising speed 947 nm (1,753 km; 1,089 miles)
Intermediate cruising speed 1,020 nm (1,889 km; 1,173 miles)
Econ cruising speed 1,075 nm (1,990 km; 1,237 miles)
Long-range cruising speed 1,145 nm (2,120 km; 1,317 miles)

PIPER (PA-25) PAWNEE D

The current version of the Pawnee D is available with the following optional factory-installed avionics packages:

Group KS-1-AG. King KX 145 nav/com with shared receiver, KI 205 VOR/LOC indicator, Telex 100T noise cancelling microphone, cabin speaker, headset, and necessary antennae; adding 3·6 kg (8·0 lb) to basic empty weight.

Group KS-2-AG. As Group KS-1-AG, except KX 145 and KI 205 deleted and replaced by King KX 170B nav/com with independent nav receiver, and KI 208 VOR/LOC converter/indicator; adding 6·4 kg (14·0 lb) to basic empty weight.

Group NC-1-AG. As Group KS-1-AG, except KX 145 and KI 205 deleted and replaced by Narco COMM 120 com transceiver, and NAV 121 nav receiver with VOR/LOC convertor/indicator; adding 4·9 kg (10·7 lb) to basic empty weight.

Group EA-1-AG. As Group KS-1-AG, except KX 145 and KI 205 deleted and replaced by Edo-Aire RT-563 nav/com having independent nav receiver with VOR/LOC converter/indicator; adding 5·4 kg (11·9 lb) to basic empty weight.

Group CTM-1-AG. As Group KS-1-AG, except KX 145 and KI 205 deleted and replaced by Collins VHF-250 com and VIR-350 nav with VOR/LOC converter/indicator; adding 3·9 kg (8·7 lb) to basic empty weight.

TYPE: Single-seat agricultural monoplane.

WINGS: Braced low-wing monoplane. Streamlined Vee bracing struts on each side of fuselage, with additional short support struts. Wing section USA 35B (modified). Thickness/chord ratio 12%. Dihedral 7°. Incidence 1° 18′ at mean aerodynamic chord. Wings are of fabric-covered aluminium construction, with fire-resistant Duraclad plastic finish. Trailing-edge flaps and ailerons of light alloy construction. No trim tabs.

FUSELAGE: Basically rectangular-section welded steel tube structure, with fabric covering and Duraclad plastic finish, except for removable metal underskin and removable metal top of rear fuselage. Glassfibre engine cowling.

TAIL UNIT: Wire-braced steel tube structure with fabric covering and Duraclad plastic finish. Fixed-incidence tailplane. Balanced rudder and elevators. No trim tabs. Cable from top of cockpit to top of rudder to deflect wires and cables.

LANDING GEAR: Non-retractable tailwheel type. Bungee rubber shock-absorbers. Main gear has two side Vs and half-axles hinged to centreline of underside of fuselage. Cleveland 40-84A main wheels, with 8·00-6 4-ply tyres. Cleveland type 30-41 toe-actuated hydraulic brakes. Parking brake. Wire-cutters on leading-edge of each side V. Scott 200 mm (8 in) steerable tailwheel.

POWER PLANT: One 175 kW (235 hp) (derated) Lycoming O-540 flat-six engine, driving a McCauley Type 1A200/FA84 two-blade fixed-pitch metal propeller with spinner. Fuel tank in each wing, with combined capacity of 145·7 litres (38·5 US gallons), of which 136 litres (36 US gallons) are usable. Oil capacity 11·4 litres (3 US gallons).

ACCOMMODATION: Pilot on adjustable seat in specially-strengthened enclosed cockpit, with steel tube overturn structure. Heavy-duty safety belt and shoulder harness with inertia reel. Wire-cutter mounted on centre of windscreen. Combined window and door on each side, hinged at bottom. Window assemblies jettisonable for emergency exit. Cabin is heated and ventilated. Adjustable cool air vents. Utility compartment under seat.

SYSTEMS: Electrical system includes a 14V 60A alternator, 12V 35Ah battery and a battery charging diode. Hydraulic system for brakes only.

AVIONICS AND EQUIPMENT: Optional avionics as detailed in standard factory-installed packages, plus optional transponder by each manufacturer. Standard equipment includes a non-corrosive hopper/tank, installed forward of cockpit and approximately on CG, volume of which is 0·59 m³ (21 cu ft) or 568 litres (150 US gallons), with capacity for 544 kg (1,200 lb) of dust; quick-change boom brackets, quick-drain gascolator, low-quantity fuel warning light, full-flow oil filter, quick-drain oil sump, quick-dump valve to jettison hopper contents in emergency, quick-release hinge pins in side windows, tiedown rings, top-deck loading door, sensitive altimeter, recording tachometer, engine bay fire extinguisher and provision for automatic locator beacon. Optional high and low volume spray system uses Simplex centrifugal pump similar to that on PA-18A, with spraybars. The venturi distributor used for dry chemicals gives a total effective swath width of up to 18·3 m (60 ft). Changeover from dust to spray, and vice versa, takes less than five minutes. Optional side loading nozzle for liquid chemicals. Optional equipment includes multi-directional inertia-reel shoulder harness (exchange), automatic locator beacon, control lock, hand fire extinguisher, landing lights, navigation lights, rotating beacon, and electric turn and bank indicator.

DIMENSIONS, EXTERNAL:
Wing span 11·02 m (36 ft 2 in)
Wing chord (constant) 1·60 m (5 ft 3 in)
Wing aspect ratio 7·15
Length overall 7·53 m (24 ft 8½ in)
Height overall 2·21 m (7 ft 3 in)
Tailplane span 2·90 m (9 ft 6 in)
Wheel track 2·13 m (7 ft 0 in)

Wheelbase	5·52 m (18 ft 1¼ in)
Propeller diameter	2·13 m (7 ft 0 in)

AREAS:

Wings, gross	17·0 m² (183 sq ft)
Ailerons (total)	1·78 m² (19·2 sq ft)
Trailing-edge flaps (total)	0·78 m² (8·4 sq ft)
Fin	0·35 m² (3·8 sq ft)
Rudder	0·64 m² (6·9 sq ft)
Tailplane	1·21 m² (13·0 sq ft)
Elevators	1·27 m² (13·7 sq ft)

WEIGHTS AND LOADINGS:

Weight empty:	
no dispersal equipment	715 kg (1,576 lb)
duster	736 kg (1,623 lb)
sprayer	743 kg (1,638 lb)
Max T-O and landing weight	1,315 kg (2,900 lb)
Max wing loading	77·15 kg/m² (15·8 lb/sq ft)
Max power loading	7·51 kg/kW (12·3 lb/hp)

PERFORMANCE (at max T-O weight, except where indicated):

Never-exceed speed	135 knots (251 km/h; 156 mph)
Max level speed at S/L:	
no dispersal equipment	108 knots (200 km/h; 124 mph)
duster	96 knots (177 km/h; 110 mph)
sprayer	102 knots (188 km/h; 117 mph)
Max cruising speed (75% power):	
no dispersal equipment	99 knots (183 km/h; 114 mph)
duster	87 knots (161 km/h; 100 mph)
sprayer	91 knots (169 km/h; 105 mph)
Stalling speed, flaps down	53 knots (98 km/h; 61 mph)
Stalling speed at normal landing weight of 771 kg (1,700 lb)	40 knots (74 km/h; 46 mph)
Max rate of climb at S/L:	
no dispersal equipment	213 m (700 ft)/min
duster	152 m (500 ft)/min
sprayer	192 m (630 ft)/min
T-O run: no dispersal equipment	239 m (785 ft)
duster	291 m (956 ft)
sprayer	244 m (800 ft)
T-O to 15 m (50 ft):	
no dispersal equipment	411 m (1,350 ft)
duster	428 m (1,470 ft)
sprayer	418 m (1,370 ft)
Max landing run	259 m (850 ft)
Range (75% power) with max fuel:	
no dispersal equipment	251 nm (467 km; 290 miles)
duster	221 nm (410 km; 255 miles)
sprayer	234 nm (434 km; 270 miles)

Piper Pawnee D agricultural aircraft (Lycoming O-540 flat-six engine)

PIPER (PA-28-161) WARRIOR II

Design of the Warrior began in June 1972, an important feature of this version being the increased-span tapered wing. As a result of its introduction the Warrior, which at that time had essentially the same 112 kW (150 hp) engine as the discontinued Cherokee Cruiser, was certificated at a maximum T-O weight 79 kg (175 lb) greater. First flight of a prototype was made on 17 October 1972, and FAA certification of the original Model PA-28-151 was granted on 9 August 1973.

The 1977 version, first flown on 27 August 1976, was re-engined with a 119 kW (160 hp) engine which operates on 100 octane low-lead fuel, and this model was re-designated PA-28-161 Cherokee Warrior II.

Two groups of optional equipment are available for the current Warrior II as basic packages.

Custom. Comprises Piper TruSpeed indicator; advanced instrument panel with 3 in pictorial gyro horizon, 3 in directional gyro, pictorial turn rate indicator, rate of climb indicator, outside air temperature gauge and electric clock; engine-driven vacuum pump with indicator, regulator, filter and annunciator light; instrument panel white backlighting and overhead red spotlight, cabin dome, navigation, landing/taxi, and radio dimming lights; high performance wheel speed fairings; rotating beacon; assist strap; aircraft step; engine primer system; quick oil-drain; towbar and de luxe carpet; adding 25·6 kg (56·4 lb) to basic empty weight.

Executive. As Custom package, plus pilot's vertically-adjustable seat, sun visors, wing and tail strobe lights replacing rotating beacon, alternate static source, 35Ah battery, automatic locator beacon, heated pitot, external power socket; adding 38·4 kg (84·6 lb) to basic empty weight.

In addition, eight optional avionics groups are available for installation in the Warrior II, as well as in the related PA-28 and PA-32 models of the Cherokee family, as follows:

Group N-1-28. Narco COMM-120 com transceiver, NAV-121 nav receiver with VOR/LOC indicator, AT-150 transponder, all associated antennae, Piper M-700B noise cancelling microphone, headset and radio speaker; adding 6·8 kg (15·0 lb) to basic empty weight.

Group N-2-28. Dual Narco COMM-120 com transceivers, dual NAV-121 nav receivers, each with VOR/LOC indicators and VOR/LOC converters, CP-135M audio selector panel with marker beacon receiver, ADF-141 ADF, AT-150 transponder, all associated antennae, Piper AutoControl IIIB autopilot with VOR/LOC coupler, longitudinal electric trim, M-700B noise cancelling microphone, headset and radio speaker; adding 22·2 kg (49·0 lb) to basic empty weight.

Group N-3-28. As Group N-2-28, with deletion of dual NAV-121 receivers and marker beacon receiver from CP-135M, and addition of Narco NAV-124A nav receiver with integral marker beacon receiver, ID-124 VOR/LOC/GS indicator with VOR/LOC converter, NAV-122 nav receiver with VOR/LOC indicator and VOR/LOC converter, and UGR-2A glideslope receiver; adding 24·9 kg (55·0 lb) to basic empty weight.

Group KS-1-28. King KX 170B combined com transceiver and nav receiver, KI 208 VOR/LOC indicator, KT 78A transponder, Piper 66C microphone, headset, radio speaker, and all associated antennae; adding 8·6 kg (19·0 lb) to basic empty weight.

Group KS-2-28. Dual King KX 170B combined com transceiver and nav receiver; dual KI 208 VOR/LOC indicators with VOR/LOC converters; KMA 20 audio selector panel including amplifier, marker beacon receiver and marker beacon lights; KR 86 ADF; KT 78A transponder; Piper AutoControl IIIB autopilot with VOR/LOC coupler; longitudinal electric trim; Piper 66C microphone, headset, radio speaker, and all associated antennae; adding 26·3 kg (58·0 lb) to basic empty weight.

Group KS-3-28. Dual King KX 175B combined com transceiver and nav receiver; KI 204 VOR/LOC/GS indicator and VOR/LOC converter; KI 203 VOR/LOC indicator and VOR/LOC converter; KN 75 glideslope receiver; KMA 20 audio selector panel including amplifier, marker beacon receiver and marker beacon lights; KR 85 ADF; KT 76A transponder; Piper AutoControl IIIB with VOR/LOC coupler; longitudinal electric trim; Piper 100T microphone, headset, radio speaker, and all associated antennae; adding 30·8 kg (68·0 lb) to basic empty weight.

Group CTM-1-28. Collins VHF-250 com transceiver; VIR-350 nav receiver with VOR/LOC converter; IND-350 VOR/LOC indicator; TDR-950 transponder; Piper 100T microphone, headset, radio speaker, and all associated antennae; adding 7·7 kg (16·9 lb) to basic empty weight.

Group CTM-2-28. As Group CTM-1-28, plus an additional VHF-250 and VIR-350; AMR-350 audio selector panel including amplifier, marker beacon receiver and marker beacon lights; ADF-650 ADF; and Piper AutoControl IIIB with VOR/LOC coupling and longitudinal electric trim; adding 24·7 kg (54·5 lb) to basic empty weight.

TYPE: Four-seat cabin monoplane.

WINGS: Cantilever low-wing monoplane. Wing section NACA 65_2-415 on inboard panels; outboard leading-edge incorporates modification No. 5 of NACA TN 2228. Dihedral 7°. Incidence 2° at root, −1° at tip. Sweepback at quarter-chord 5°. Light alloy single-spar structure with glassfibre wingtips. Plain ailerons of light alloy construction. Trailing-edge flaps constructed of light alloy with ribbed skins.

FUSELAGE: Light alloy semi-monocoque structure with glassfibre nose cowl and tailcone.

TAIL UNIT: Cantilever structure of light alloy, except for glassfibre tips on fin and tailplane. Fin and rudder have ribbed light alloy skins. One-piece all-moving tailplane, with combined anti-servo and trim tab. Rudder trimmable, but no trim tab in rudder.

LANDING GEAR: Non-retractable tricycle type. Steerable nosewheel. Piper oleo-pneumatic shock-absorbers; single wheel on each unit. Cleveland wheels with 4-ply tyres size 6·00-6 on main units, pressure 1·65 bars (24 lb/sq in). Cleveland nosewheel and 4-ply tyre size 5·00-5, pressure 1·65 bars (24 lb/sq in). Cleveland disc brakes. Parking brake. Wheel fairings optional.

POWER PLANT: One 119 kW (160 hp) Lycoming O-320-D3G flat-four engine, driving a Sensenich two-blade fixed-pitch metal propeller type 74DM6-0-60. Fuel in two wing tanks, with total capacity of 189 litres (50 US gallons), of which 181·5 litres (48 US gallons) are usable. Refuelling point on upper surface of each wing. Oil capacity 7·5 litres (2 US gallons).

ACCOMMODATION: Four persons in pairs in enclosed cabin. Individual adjustable front seats, bench type rear seat. Shoulder harnesses with inertia reel on two front seats. Dual controls standard. Large door on starboard side. Baggage compartment at rear of cabin, with volume of 0·74 m³ (26 cu ft) and capacity of 90 kg (200 lb). External access door on starboard side. Heating, ventilation and windscreen defrosting standard.

SYSTEMS: Hydraulic system for brakes only. Electrical system powered by 60A engine-driven alternator. 12V 25Ah battery standard, 12V 35Ah battery optional. Vacuum system for blind-flying instrumentation optional.

AVIONICS AND EQUIPMENT: Collins, King and Narco avionics in eight optional groups, or an extensive range of King, Narco, Bendix and Piper avionics. Optional equipment includes items listed in Custom and Executive packages, plus cabin soundproofing, stainless steel control cables, front seat headrests, overhead air vent system or Piper Aire air-conditioning system, rear seat air vents, rear seat shoulder harnesses with inertia reels, tinted windows, ventilation fan, co-pilot's vertically adjustable front seat, zinc chromate finish, engine hour recorder, red strobe light for tail, cabin fire extinguisher, and external power cable.

DIMENSIONS, EXTERNAL:

Wing span	10·67 m (35 ft 0 in)
Wing chord at root	1·60 m (5 ft 3 in)
Wing chord at tip	1·07 m (3 ft 6¼ in)
Wing aspect ratio	7·24
Length overall	7·25 m (23 ft 9½ in)
Height overall	2·22 m (7 ft 3½ in)
Tailplane span	3·92 m (12 ft 10½ in)
Wheel track	3·05 m (10 ft 0 in)
Wheelbase	2·03 m (6 ft 8 in)
Propeller diameter	1·88 m (6 ft 2 in)
Propeller ground clearance	0·21 m (8¼ in)

Piper Warrior II four-seat cabin monoplane

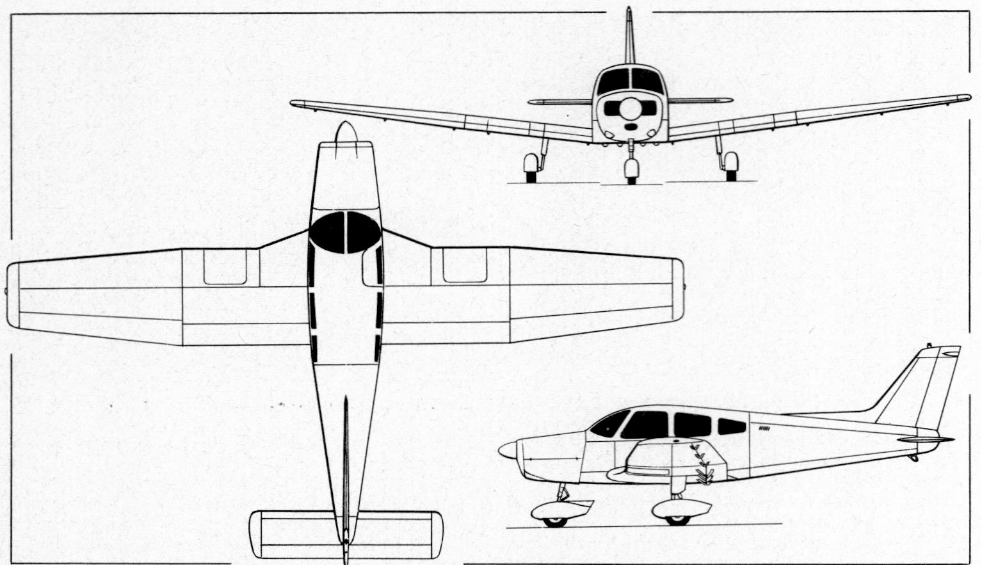

Piper Warrior II (Lycoming O-320-D3G engine) *(Pilot Press)*

Cabin door: Height 0·89 m (2 ft 11 in)
Width 0·99 m (3 ft 3 in)
Baggage door: Height 0·48 m (1 ft 7 in)
Max width 0·66 m (2 ft 2 in)
Height to sill 0·71 m (2 ft 4 in)

DIMENSIONS, INTERNAL:
Cabin: Length 2·74 m (9 ft 0 in)
Max width 1·07 m (3 ft 6 in)
Max height 1·22 m (4 ft 0 in)
Floor area 2·28 m² (24·5 sq ft)
Volume 2·61 m³ (92 cu ft)

AREAS:
Wings, gross 15·8 m² (170 sq ft)
Ailerons (total) 1·23 m² (13·2 sq ft)
Trailing-edge flaps (total) 1·36 m² (14·6 sq ft)
Fin 0·69 m² (7·4 sq ft)
Rudder 0·38 m² (4·1 sq ft)
Tailplane, incl tab 2·46 m² (26·5 sq ft)

WEIGHTS AND LOADINGS:
Weight empty, standard 610 kg (1,344 lb)
Max T-O and landing weight 1,054 kg (2,325 lb)
Max wing loading 66·74 kg/m² (13·67 lb/sq ft)
Max power loading 8·86 kg/kW (14·53 lb/hp)

PERFORMANCE (at max T-O weight):
Never-exceed speed
153 knots (282 km/h; 176 mph)
*Max level speed at S/L
126 knots (233 km/h; 145 mph)
*Best power cruising speed, 75% power at 2,745 m (9,000 ft) 127 knots (235 km/h; 146 mph)
*Best power cruising speed, 65% power at 3,810 m (12,500 ft) 118 knots (219 km/h; 136 mph)
*Best power cruising speed, 55% power at 3,810 m (12,500 ft) 107 knots (198 km/h; 123 mph)
*Best econ cruising speed, 75% power at 2,745 m (9,000 ft) 122 knots (225 km/h; 140 mph)
*Best econ cruising speed, 65% power at 3,810 m (12,500 ft) 116 knots (215 km/h; 134 mph)
*Best econ cruising speed, 55% power at 3,810 m (12,500 ft) 103 knots (191 km/h; 119 mph)
Stalling speed, flaps up
56 knots (104 km/h; 65 mph) CAS
Stalling speed, flaps down
50 knots (93 km/h; 57·5 mph) CAS
Max rate of climb at S/L 216 m (710 ft)/min
Service ceiling 4,265 m (14,000 ft)
Absolute ceiling 4,600 m (15,100 ft)
T-O run 297 m (975 ft)
T-O to 15 m (50 ft) 454 m (1,490 ft)
Landing from 15 m (50 ft) 340 m (1,115 ft)
Landing run 181 m (595 ft)
*Range with max fuel, with allowances for taxi, T-O, climb, and descent, and 45 min reserves at max range power:
At best power settings
75%power at 2,745 m (9,000 ft)
520 nm (964 km; 599 miles)
65% power at 3,810 m (12,500 ft)
545 nm (1,011 km; 628 miles)
55% power at 3,810 m (12,500 ft)
560 nm (1,038 km; 645 miles)
At best econ power settings
75% power at 2,745 m (9,000 ft)
589 nm (1,091 km; 678 miles)
65% power at 3,810 m (12,500 ft)
624 nm (1,157 km; 719 miles)
55% power at 3,810 m (12,500 ft)
635 nm (1,176 km; 731 miles)

**With optional wheel fairings*

PIPER (PA-28-181) ARCHER II

On 9 October 1972 Piper introduced the Cherokee Challenger as successor to the Cherokee 180. In 1974 this was superseded by the Cherokee Archer, with the same basic airframe and power plant, but introducing many new equipment and avionics options. In 1976 this aircraft was redesignated PA-28-181 Cherokee Archer II, and in 1978 introduced the tapered wings of the Warrior II.

The Archer II can be fitted with generally similar optional Custom and Executive equipment packages, as well as the eight optional avionics packages, which are available for the Warrior II. The equipment packages vary as follows:

Custom. As for Warrior II, except for deletion of tow-bar and engine primer system.

Executive. As for Warrior II, plus rotating beacon and sun visors, strobe lights for wings only, and deletion of tow-bar and engine primer system.

TYPE: Four-seat cabin monoplane.

WINGS: Cantilever low-wing monoplane. Wing section NACA 65_2-415 on inboard panels; outboard leading-edge has modification No. 5 of NACA TN 2228. Dihedral 7°. Incidence 2° at root, −1° at tip. Sweepback at quarter-chord 5°. Light alloy single-spar structure with glassfibre wingtips. Plain ailerons of light alloy construction. Trailing-edge flaps constructed of light alloy with ribbed skins.

FUSELAGE: Aluminium alloy semi-monocoque structure. Glassfibre engine cowling.

TAIL UNIT: Cantilever structure of aluminium alloy, except for glassfibre tips on fin and tailplane. Fin and rudder have corrugated metal skin. One-piece all-moving horizontal surface with combined anti-servo and trim tab. Trim tab in rudder.

LANDING GEAR: Non-retractable tricycle type. Steerable nosewheel. Piper oleo-pneumatic shock-absorbers. Cleveland wheels and Schenuit tyres, size 6·00-6, 4-ply rating, on all three wheels. Cleveland high capacity disc brakes. Parking brake. Wheel speed fairings optional.

POWER PLANT: One 134 kW (180 hp) Lycoming O-360-A4M flat-four engine, driving a Sensenich two-blade fixed-pitch metal propeller with spinner. Fuel in two tanks in wing leading-edges, with total capacity of 189 litres (50 US gallons), of which 181·5 litres (48 US gallons) are usable.

ACCOMMODATION: Four persons in pairs in enclosed cabin. Individual adjustable front seats, with dual controls; individual rear seats. Large door on starboard side. Baggage compartment aft of cabin, with volume of 0·68 m³ (24 cu ft) and capacity of 90 kg (200 lb); door on starboard side. Rear seats removable to provide 1·25 m³ (44 cu ft) cargo space. Accommodation heated and ventilated. Windscreen defrosting.

SYSTEMS: Optional Piper Aire air-conditioning system. Electrical system includes 60A alternator and 12V 25Ah battery. Hydraulic system for brakes only. Vacuum system optional.

AVIONICS AND EQUIPMENT: A variety of optional factory-installed avionics packages is available, as well as a wide range of other avionics equipment to customer's requirements. Standard equipment includes sensitive altimeter, stall warning horn, annunciator warning lights, quick oil drain, full-flow oil filter, engine primer system, fuel tank quick drains, soundproofing, map pockets, sun visors, luggage tiedown straps, external tiedown points, wing jack points, towbar, and provisions for Piper automatic locator. Optional equipment includes items detailed under Custom and Executive groups, plus fire extinguisher, inertia-reel shoulder harness for rear seats, adjustable front seat for co-pilot, overhead vent system and ventilation fan for air vent system, or Piper Aire air-conditioning, super soundproofing, headrests, zinc chromate application, stainless steel control cables, engine hour recorder, tinted windows, and external power cable.

DIMENSIONS, EXTERNAL:
Wing span 10·67 m (35 ft 0 in)
Wing chord at root 1·60 m (5 ft 3 in)
Wing chord at tip 1·07 m (3 ft 6¼ in)
Length overall 7·25 m (23 ft 9½ in)
Height overall 2·23 m (7 ft 3½ in)
Tailplane span 3·92 m (12 ft 10½ in)
Wheel track 3·05 m (10 ft 0 in)
Wheelbase 2·00 m (6 ft 7 in)
Propeller diameter 1·93 m (6 ft 4 in)

AREAS:
Wings, gross 15·79 m² (170 sq ft)
Ailerons (total) 1·23 m² (13·20 sq ft)
Trailing-edge flaps (total) 1·36 m² (14·60 sq ft)
Fin 0·70 m² (7·50 sq ft)
Rudder 0·38 m² (4·10 sq ft)
Tailplane 2·46 m² (26·50 sq ft)

WEIGHTS AND LOADINGS:
Weight empty, equipped (standard) 640 kg (1,412 lb)
Max T-O and landing weight 1,156 kg (2,550 lb)
Max wing loading 73·2 kg/m² (15·0 lb/sq ft)
Max power loading 8·63 kg/kW (14·17 lb/hp)

PERFORMANCE (at max T-O weight):
Never-exceed speed
148 knots (275 km/h; 171 mph) CAS
*Max level speed at S/L
133 knots (246 km/h; 153 mph)
*Best power cruising speed, 75% power at 2,745 m (9,000 ft) 131 knots (243 km/h; 151 mph)
*Best power cruising speed, 65% power at 3,660 m (12,000 ft) 125 knots (231 km/h; 144 mph)
*Best power cruising speed, 55% power at 3,810 m (12,500 ft) 111 knots (206 km/h; 128 mph)
*Best econ cruising speed, 75% power at 2,745 m (9,000 ft) 128 knots (237 km/h; 147 mph)
*Best econ cruising speed, 65% power at 3,660 m (12,000 ft) 122 knots (225 km/h; 140 mph)
*Best econ cruising speed, 55% power at 3,810 m (12.500 ft) 107 knots (198 km/h; 123 mph)
Stalling speed, flaps up
59 knots (109 km/h; 68 mph) CAS
Stalling speed, flaps down
53 knots (98 km/h; 61 mph) CAS
Max rate of climb at S/L 224 m (735 ft)/min
Service ceiling 4,570 m (15,000 ft)
Absolute ceiling 4,800 m (15,750 ft)
T-O run 265 m (870 ft)
T-O to 15 m (50 ft) 495 m (1,625 ft)
Landing from 15 m (50 ft) 427 m (1,400 ft)
Landing run 285 m (935 ft)

Piper Archer II, which has the tapered wings introduced on the Cherokee Warrior

*Range with max fuel, allowances for taxi, T-O, climb and descent, and 45 min reserves at max range power:
At best power settings
75% power at 2,745 m (9,000 ft) 515 nm (954 km; 593 miles)
65% power at 3,660 m (12,000 ft) 565 nm (1,048 km; 651 miles)
55% power at 3,810 m (12,500 ft) 580 nm (1,075 km; 668 miles)
At best econ power settings
75% power at 2,745 m (9,000 ft) 598 nm (1,109 km; 689 miles)
65% power at 3,660 m (12,000 ft) 645 nm (1,196 km; 743 miles)
55% power at 3,810 m (12,500 ft) 670 nm (1,242 km; 772 miles)

**With optional wheel fairings*

Piper Arrow IV retractable-gear four-seat cabin monoplane with T-tail

PIPER (PA-28RT-201) ARROW IV

The Piper Arrow IV, introduced for 1979, derives from the Cherokee Arrow II, which was generally similar to the Cherokee Archer II, but had a retractable landing gear, more powerful engine, and the untapered wing of the 1975 PA-28-180 Archer. In 1977, Piper updated this model by fitting long-span tapered wings identical with those of the Archer II, but with increased fuel capacity, giving improved performance; the 1978 version of this aircraft was named Arrow III, the prototype of which flew for the first time on 16 September 1975, followed by the first production aircraft on 7 January 1977. Piper designation was **PA-28R-201.** The Turbo Arrow III differed by having a turbocharged engine, mounted in a streamline cowling, and the first production example of this version flew on 1 December 1976. Piper designation was **PA-28R-201T.**

For 1979 Piper has introduced an improved model with an all-moving T tailplane. Two versions are available:

Arrow IV. Basic model, as described, which has the Piper designation **PA-28RT-201.**

Turbo Arrow IV. As Arrow IV, but power plant comprises one 149 kW (200 hp) Continental TSIO-360-F flat-six turbocharged engine, mounted in a streamline cowling, and driving a Hartzell two-blade constant-speed metal propeller with spinner. A three-blade propeller is optional.

Two groups of optional equipment are available for the Arrow IV as recommended packages:

Custom. Comprises Piper TruSpeed indicator; basic lighting package comprising instrument panel white backlighting with overhead red lighting, cabin dome, navigation, landing/taxi, and radio dimming lights; wing strobe lights; assist strap; entrance step; engine-driven vacuum pump with filter; advanced instrument panel with 3 in pictorial gyro horizon, 3 in directional gyro, pictorial turn rate indicator, rate of climb indicator, outside air temperature gauge and electric clock; adding 13·0 kg (28·7 lb) to aircraft basic weight.

Executive. As Custom package, plus alternate static source, 12V 35Ah battery, automatic locator beacon, heated pitot head/landing gear sensor, external power socket, and vertically adjustable seat for pilot; adding 22·1 kg (48·7 lb) to aircraft basic weight.

In addition to the above equipment, the avionics packages which are available for the Warrior II are also available optionally for the Turbo Arrow IV.

The tricycle landing gear of both versions is retracted hydraulically, with an electrically-operated pump supplying the hydraulic pressure. In addition to the usual 'gear up' warning horn and red light, both Arrow IVs have an automatic extension system which drops the landing gear automatically if power is reduced and airspeed drops below 91 knots (169 km/h; 105 mph). The sensing system consists of a small probe mounted on the port side of the fuselage. Being located in the propeller slipstream, it can differentiate between a climb with power on and an approach to land with power reduced. A free-fall emergency extension system is also fitted. An 'anti-retraction' system guards against premature retraction of the landing gear below an airspeed of 74 knots (137 km/h; 85 mph) at take-off, or accidental retraction on the ground. There is also a manual override lever by which the pilot can hold the landing gear retracted as airspeed falls below 91 knots (169 km/h; 105 mph).

The description of the Archer II applies also to the Arrow IV, except for the following details:

Tail Unit: Cantilever T-tail of light alloy construction. All-moving tailplane with trim tab. Rudder trim.

Landing Gear: Retractable tricycle type, with single wheel on each unit. Hydraulic retraction, main units inward into wings, nose unit rearward. Free-fall emergency extension system. All units fitted with oleo-pneumatic shock-absorbers. Main wheels and tyres size 6·00-6, 6-ply rating. Nosewheel and tyre size 5·00-5, 4-ply rating. High-capacity dual hydraulic disc brakes and parking brake.

Power Plant: Arrow IV has one 149 kW (200 hp) Lycoming IO-360-C1C6 flat-four engine, driving a McCauley 90 DHA-6 B2D34C213 or Hartzell HC-C2YK-1/F7666A-2R two-blade constant-speed metal propeller with spinner. Turbo Arrow IV as detailed in model listing. Both versions have fuel tanks in wing leading-edges with total capacity of 291 litres (77 US gallons), of which 272·5 litres (72 US gallons) are usable. Oil capacity 7·5 litres (2 US gallons).

Avionics and Equipment: Optional avionics and standard equipment generally as detailed for Warrior II, plus cylinder head temperature gauge, exhaust gas temperature gauge, electric engine priming system standard on Turbo Arrow IV. Optional equipment as listed in 'Custom' and 'Executive' paragraphs.

Dimensions, external:
Wing span 10·67 m (35 ft 0 in)
Wing chord at root 1·60 m (5 ft 3 in)
Wing chord at tip 1·07 m (3 ft 6¼ in)
Length overall 7·62 m (25 ft 0 in)
Height overall 2·44 m (8 ft 0 in)
Wheel track 3·19 m (10 ft 5½ in)
Wheelbase 2·40 m (7 ft 10½ in)
Propeller diameter: Arrow IV 1·88 m (6 ft 2 in)
Turbo Arrow IV 1·93 m (6 ft 4 in)
Cabin door (stbd): Width 0·91 m (3 ft 0 in)
Height 0·89 m (2 ft 11 in)
Baggage door (stbd): Width 0·56 m (1 ft 10 in)
Height 0·51 m (1 ft 8 in)

Piper Turbo Arrow IV (Continental TSIO-360-F engine) *(Pilot Press)*

Dimensions, internal:
Cabin:
Length, panel to rear bulkhead 2·41 m (7 ft 11 in)
Max width 1·05 m (3 ft 5½ in)
Max height 1·24 m (4 ft 1 in)
Volume (incl baggage area) 3·00 m³ (106 cu ft)

Area:
Wings, gross 15·79 m² (170 sq ft)

Weights and Loadings (A: Arrow IV; B: Turbo Arrow IV):
Weight empty: A 723 kg (1,593 lb)
B 743 kg (1,638 lb)
Max T-O weight: A 1,247 kg (2,750 lb)
B 1,315 kg (2,900 lb)
Max wing loading: A 79·0 kg/m² (16·18 lb/sq ft)
B 83·29 kg/m² (17·06 lb/sq ft)
Max power loading: A 8·37 kg/kW (13·75 lb/hp)
B 8·83 kg/kW (14·5 lb/hp)

Performance (at max T-O weight):
Never-exceed speed 186 knots (344 km/h; 214 mph) CAS
Max level speed:
A at S/L 152 knots (282 km/h; 175 mph)
B at 4,265 m (14,000 ft) 178 knots (330 km/h; 205 mph)
Best power cruising speed, 75% power at optimum altitude: A 143 knots (265 km/h; 165 mph)
B 172 knots (319 km/h; 198 mph)
Best power cruising speed, 65% power at optimum altitude: A 138 knots (256 km/h; 159 mph)
B 167 knots (309 km/h; 192 mph)
Best power cruising speed, 55% power at optimum altitude: A 131 knots (243 km/h; 151 mph)
B 158 knots (293 km/h; 182 mph)
Best econ cruising speed, 75% power at optimum altitude: A 139 knots (257 km/h; 160 mph)
B 167 knots (309 km/h; 192 mph)
Best econ cruising speed, 65% power at optimum altitude: A 133 knots (246 km/h; 153 mph)
B 164 knots (304 km/h; 189 mph)
Best econ cruising speed, 55% power at optimum altitude: A 122 knots (226 km/h; 140 mph)
B 154 knots (285 km/h; 177 mph)
Stalling speed, flaps up:
A 59 knots (109 km/h; 68 mph) CAS
B 63 knots (117 km/h; 72 mph) CAS
Stalling speed, flaps down:
A 55 knots (102 km/h; 63·5 mph) CAS
B 58 knots (107·5 km/h; 67 mph) CAS
Max rate of climb at S/L: A 253 m (831 ft)/min
B 287 m (940 ft)/min
Service ceiling: A 5,180 m (17,000 ft)
*B 6,100 m (20,000 ft)
Absolute ceiling: A 5,610 m (18,400 ft)
*B 6,100 m (20,000 ft)
T-O run: A 312 m (1,025 ft)
B 338 m (1,110 ft)
T-O to 15 m (50 ft): A 488 m (1,600 ft)
B 494 m (1,620 ft)
Landing from 15 m (50 ft): A 465 m (1,525 ft)
B 474 m (1,555 ft)
Landing run: A 188 m (615 ft)
B 197 m (645 ft)
Range with max fuel, allowances for taxi, T-O, climb and descent, and 45 min reserves at max range power:
At best power settings:
At 75% power:
A 720 nm (1,334 km; 829 miles)
B 675 nm (1,250 km; 777 miles)

**Max operating altitude*

At 65% power:
A 770 nm (1,427 km; 887 miles)
B 705 nm (1,307 km; 812 miles)
At 55% power:
A 795 nm (1,473 km; 915 miles)
B 740 nm (1,371 km; 852 miles)
At best econ power settings:
At 75% power:
A 810 nm (1,502 km; 933 miles)
B 780 nm (1,445 km; 898 miles)
At 65% power:
A 845 nm (1,566 km; 973 miles)
B 830 nm (1,539 km; 956 miles)
At 55% power:
A 875 nm (1,622 km; 1,008 miles)
B 860 nm (1,593 km; 990 miles)

PIPER CHEROKEE PATHFINDER

Production of this aircraft was transferred to EMBRAER in Brazil (which see), by whom it was built as the EMB-710C Carioca. Brazilian production was due to end in 1979.

PIPER (PA-28-236) DAKOTA

Piper introduced in 1978 an addition to the Warrior, Archer, Arrow line known as the PA-28-236 Dakota, which differs primarily by having a 175 kW (235 hp) Lycoming engine to provide increased performance, and increased capacity fuel tanks to cater for this power plant. Like the related aircraft mentioned earlier, it is available with a variety of optional factory-installed avionics packages, and also two Operational Groups as follows:

Custom. As detailed for Warrior II, with addition of pilot's vertically adjustable seat, and deletion of engine primer system, de luxe carpet and towbar; adding 24·4 kg (53·8 lb) to basic empty weight.

Executive. As detailed for Warrior II, plus rotating beacon, exhaust gas temperature gauge, and deletion of engine primer system, de luxe carpet, towbar and sun visors; adding 35·2 kg (77·7 lb) to basic empty weight.

The description of the Archer II applies also to the Dakota, except as follows:

Power Plant: One 175 kW (235 hp) Lycoming O-540-J3A5D flat-six engine, driving a Hartzell two-blade metal constant-speed propeller with spinner. Two integral fuel tanks in each wing, with a total capacity of 291·5 litres (77 US gallons), of which 272·5 litres (72 US gallons) are usable. Refuelling points on upper surface of each wing. Oil capacity 11·4 litres (3 US gallons).

Avionics and Equipment: A variety of optional factory-installed avionics packages is available, as well as a wide range of other avionics equipment to customer's requirements. Standard equipment includes sensitive altimeter, manifold pressure gauge, annunciator warning lights, stall warning horn, cabin soundproofing, map pockets, armrests, sun visors, shoulder safety belts for front seats with inertia reel restraint, seat belts, fuel tank quick drains, full-flow oil filter, external tiedown points, towbar, and provisions for emergency locator beacon. Optional equipment includes items detailed in Custom and Executive packages, plus engine hour recorder, cabin fire extinguisher, Piper Aire air-conditioning, tinted windows, external power cable, super soundproofing, stainless steel control cables, headrests, shoulder harness and inertia reel for third and fourth seats, vertically adjustable seat for co-pilot, zinc chromate finish, and ventilation fan when air-conditioning is not installed.

Dimensions, external: as for Archer II except:
Length overall 7·32 m (24 ft 0 in)
Height overall 2·26 m (7 ft 4¾ in)
Wheelbase 1·98 m (6 ft 6 in)
Cabin door (stbd): Height 0·91 m (3 ft 0 in)
Width 0·89 m (2 ft 11 in)

Dimensions, internal:
Cabin: Length 2·46 m (8 ft 1 in)
Max width 1·05 m (3 ft 5½ in)
Max height 1·24 m (4 ft 1 in)
Volume 3 m³ (106 cu ft)

Weights and Loadings:
Weight empty 741 kg (1,633 lb)
Max T-O weight 1,361 kg (3,000 lb)
Max wing loading 85·93 kg/m² (17·6 lb/sq ft)
Max power loading 7·78 kg/kW (12·8 lb/hp)

Performance (at max T-O weight):
Max level speed at S/L
148 knots (274 km/h; 170 mph)
Max cruising speed, 75% power at optimum altitude
144 knots (267 km/h; 166 mph)
Cruising speed, 65% power at optimum altitude
138 knots (256 km/h; 159 mph)
Cruising speed, 55% power at optimum altitude
131 knots (243 km/h; 151 mph)
Stalling speed, flaps up
63 knots (117 km/h; 72·5 mph) CAS
Stalling speed, flaps down
56 knots (104 km/h; 64·5 mph) CAS
Max rate of climb at S/L 294 m (965 ft)/min
Service ceiling 5,455 m (17,900 ft)
Absolute ceiling 5,790 m (19,000 ft)
T-O run 247 m (810 ft)
T-O to 15 m (50 ft) 396 m (1,300 ft)
Landing from 15 m (50 ft) 530 m (1,740 ft)
Landing run 317 m (1,040 ft)
Range with max fuel, allowances for taxi, T-O, climb, cruise, descent, and 45 min reserves at max range power:
75% power, optimum altitude
696 nm (1,289 km; 801 miles)
65% power, optimum altitude
769 nm (1,426 km; 886 miles)
55% power, optimum altitude
862 nm (1,596 km; 992 miles)

PIPER (PA-28-201T) TURBO DAKOTA

Piper introduced for 1979 a low-cost four-seat turbocharged aircraft with fixed landing gear. First announced on 8 March 1979, the company claims that it is the first aircraft to enter production in this specific class. Named Turbo Dakota, it nevertheless has the company designation PA-28-201T which links it more directly with the Arrow, rather than the PA-28-236 Dakota.

The Turbo Dakota is available with a wide variety of optional avionics to meet customer's requirements, as well as a number of optional factory-installed avionics packages. Two groups of optional equipment are also available for the Turbo Dakota as basic packages:

Custom. As described for the Dakota.

Executive. As described for the Dakota, less exhaust gas temperature gauge.

Type: Four-seat cabin monoplane.

Wings, Fuselage and Tail Unit: Generally as for Arrow IV.

Landing Gear: Non-retractable tricycle type with single wheel on each unit. Piper oleo-pneumatic shock-absorbers. Main-wheel tyres size 6·00-6, 6-ply rating. Steerable nosewheel with tyre size 5·00-5, 6-ply rating. High capacity disc brakes. Parking brake.

Power Plant: One 149 kW (200 hp) Continental TSIO-360-FB flat-six turbocharged engine, driving a two-blade constant-speed metal propeller with spinner. Two fuel tanks in wings, with combined capacity of 291 litres (77 US gallons), of which 273 litres (72 US gallons) are usable. Refuelling point on upper surface of each wing. Oil capacity 7·5 litres (2 US gallons).

Accommodation: As described for Archer II.

Systems: Electrical system includes 14V 65A alternator and 12V 25Ah battery. 12V 35Ah battery optional. Hydraulic system for brakes only. Air-conditioning system, vacuum system and oxygen system optional.

Avionics and Equipment: A number of factory-installed avionics packages and a wide range of additional avionics items are available to customer's requirements. Standard equipment includes sensitive altimeter, stall warning horn, annunciator warning lights, cylinder head temperature gauge, exhaust gas temperature gauge, full-flow oil filter, quick fuel drains, electric engine priming system, soundproofing, map pockets, armrests, sun visors, shoulder harnesses with inertia reel for front seats, external tiedown points, towbar, and provisions for automatic locator beacon. Optional equipment as for Custom and Executive packages, plus engine hour recorder, oxygen system, cabin fire extinguisher, Piper Aire air-conditioning system, external power cable, cold weather starting kit, super soundproofing, stainless steel control cables, headrests, shoulder harnesses and inertia reel for third and fourth seats, ventilation fan when no air-conditioning installed, vertically adjustable seat for co-pilot, zinc chromate finish, and interior group which includes curtains, de luxe seat fabrics, headrests and carpet.

Dimensions, external: As for Arrow IV, except:
Height overall 2·32 m (7 ft 7¼ in)
Wheel track 3·05 m (10 ft 0 in)
Wheelbase 2·22 m (7 ft 3½ in)
Propeller diameter 1·88 m (6 ft 2 in)

Dimensions, internal: As for Arrow IV, except:
Cabin:
Length, panel to rear bulkhead 2·46 m (8 ft 1 in)

Area:
Wings, gross 15·79 m² (170 sq ft)

Weights and Loadings:
Weight empty 709 kg (1,563 lb)
Max T-O weight 1,315 kg (2,900 lb)
Max wing loading 83·3 kg/m² (17·06 lb/sq ft)
Max power loading 8·83 kg/kW (14·5 lb/hp)

Performance (at max T-O weight):
Max level speed at 4,570 m (15,000 ft)
162 knots (300 km/h; 186 mph)
Best power cruising speed:
75% power at 5,730 m (18,800 ft)
156 knots (290 km/h; 180 mph)
65% power at 6,100 m (20,000 ft)
151 knots (280 km/h; 174 mph)
55% power at 6,100 m (20,000 ft)
142 knots (264 km/h; 164 mph)
Best econ cruising speed:
75% power at 5,730 m (18,800 ft)
154 knots (285 km/h; 177 mph)
65% power at 6,100 m (20,000 ft)
148 knots (274 km/h; 170 mph)
55% power at 6,100 m (20,000 ft)
139 knots (257 km/h; 160 mph)
Stalling speed, flaps up
65 knots (121 km/h; 75 mph) CAS
Stalling speed, flaps down
58 knots (108 km/h; 67 mph) CAS
Max rate of climb at S/L 275 m (902 ft)/min
*Service ceiling 6,100 m (20,000 ft)
T-O run 294 m (963 ft)
T-O to 15 m (50 ft) 427 m (1,402 ft)
Landing from 15 m (50 ft) 517 m (1,697 ft)
Landing run 262 m (861 ft)
Range at 3,660 m (12,000 ft) with max fuel, allowances for taxi, T-O, climb, descent, and 45 min reserves at max range power:
At best power settings:
75% power 633 nm (1,173 km; 729 miles)
65% power 660 nm (1,223 km; 760 miles)
55% power 690 nm (1,279 km; 795 miles)
At best econ power settings:
75% power 729 nm (1,350 km; 839 miles)
65% power 766 nm (1,419 km; 882 miles)
55% power 795 nm (1,473 km; 915 miles)

Max certificated altitude

PIPER PA-32-300 SIX 300

The prototype of the PA-32 Cherokee SIX (N9999W) was flown for the first time on 6 December 1963, followed by the first production model (N9998W) on 17 September 1964. FAA Type Approval was received on 4 March 1965 (SIX 260) and 27 May 1966 (SIX 300).

The original version was a six-seater, but the model introduced in October 1966 (FAA Type Approval 15 November 1966) offered an optional seventh seat. The 1969 Cherokee SIX B introduced increased cabin space, achieved by moving the instrument panel forward. Additional shoulder, hip and leg room was provided by moving the seats one inch away from the fuselage walls. Two versions were available in 1978, but the Cherokee SIX 260, of which details can be found in the 1978-79 *Jane's*, has now been discontinued. The more powerful Six 300 (formerly Cherokee SIX 300) continues in production, and has been improved by embodiment of the Lance's higher-capacity integral fuel tanks.

The following interior group packages are available as options for the SIX 300:

De luxe. Comprises curtains, de luxe seat fabrics, oversize headrests, and plush carpet; adding 13·7 kg (30·2 lb) to basic empty weight.

De luxe conference. As De luxe, plus a club seating arrangement; adding 20·1 kg (44·4 lb) to basic empty weight.

Piper Turbo Dakota, a low-cost turbocharged aircraft with fixed landing gear

De luxe lounge. As De luxe conference, plus refreshment console and fold-down armrest (5th & 6th seat); adding 24·5 kg (54·0 lb) to basic empty weight.

The following optional equipment packages are also available for the Six 300:

Custom. Includes Piper TruSpeed indicator; basic lighting package comprising instrument panel white lighting and overhead red lighting, navigation, landing/taxi, two map lights, four individual reading lights, forward baggage compartment light, radio dimming and waterfall switch panel lighting; rotating beacon; two assist straps; entrance step; high performance wheel speed fairings; engine-driven vacuum pump with annunciator light and filter; advanced instrument panel with 3 in pictorial gyro horizon, 3 in directional gyro, pictorial turn rate indicator, rate of climb indicator, outside air temperature gauge and electric clock; and quick oil drain.

Executive. As Custom group, less rotating beacon, plus the addition of a courtesy lighting package comprising forward baggage compartment light with automatic switch, cabin door entrance light, and rear cabin light switch for aft cabin door entrance; wing and tail strobe lights; alternate static source; 12V 35Ah battery; automatic locator beacon; heated pitot head; external power socket; and pilot's vertically adjustable seat.

Overall dimensions are increased by comparison with the two/four- and four-seat versions of the Cherokee, but the basic structural description of the Archer II applies generally to the Six 300 also. It is available with similar equipment and with the same optional avionics packages. The optional range of autopilots is extended by availability of the Piper AltiMatic IIIC, a full three-axis system. The Six 300 can also be fitted with the new RCA Weather Scout I weather radar, with antennae built into the outboard leading-edge of the starboard wing.

POWER PLANT: One 224 kW (300 hp) Lycoming IO-540-K1G5D flat-six engine, driving a two-blade constant-speed metal propeller with spinner. Four integral fuel tanks in wings with combined capacity of 371 litres (98 US gallons), of which 356 litres (94 US gallons) are usable. Refuelling point above each tank. Oil capacity 11·5 litres (3 US gallons).

ACCOMMODATION: Enclosed cabin, seating six people in pairs. Optional seventh seat between two centre seats. Dual controls standard. Two forward-hinged doors, one on starboard side at front and other on port side at rear. Space for 45 kg (100 lb) baggage at rear of cabin, and another 45 kg (100 lb) forward, between engine and instrument panel. Passenger seats easily removable to provide up to 3·11 m³ (110 cu ft) of cargo space inside cabin, or room for stretcher and one or two attendants. Large upward-hinged utility door adjacent to rear door provides loading entrance nearly 1·5 m (5 ft) wide. Ten silent fresh air outlets, cabin heater with eight warm air outlets including two defrosters, and cabin air exhaust vent are standard.

DIMENSIONS, EXTERNAL:
- Wing span: 9·99 m (32 ft 9½ in)
- Length overall: 8·45 m (27 ft 8¾ in)
- Height overall: 2·50 m (8 ft 2½ in)
- Tailplane span: 3·92 m (12 ft 10½ in)
- Wheel track: 3·22 m (10 ft 7 in)
- Wheelbase: 2·39 m (7 ft 10 in)
- Propeller diameter: 2·03 m (6 ft 8 in)
- Cabin door (fwd, stbd): Height: 0·89 m (2 ft 11 in)
  - Width: 0·91 m (3 ft 0 in)
- Cabin door (rear, port): Height: 0·84 m (2 ft 9 in)
  - Width: 0·74 m (2 ft 5 in)
- Baggage door (fwd): Height: 0·46 m (1 ft 6 in)
  - Width: 0·61 m (2 ft 0 in)
- Baggage/utility door (aft): Height: 0·51 m (1 ft 8 in)
  - Width: 0·71 m (2 ft 4 in)

DIMENSIONS, INTERNAL:
- Cabin:
  - Length, panel to rear wall: 3·17 m (10 ft 5 in)
  - Max width: 1·24 m (4 ft 1 in)
  - Max height: 1·24 m (4 ft 1 in)
- Baggage compartment volume:
  - forward: 0·20 m³ (7 cu ft)
  - aft: 0·49 m³ (17·3 cu ft)

AREA:
- Wings, gross: 16·21 m² (174·5 sq ft)

WEIGHTS AND LOADINGS:
- Weight empty, equipped: 833 kg (1,837 lb)
- Max T-O weight: 1,542 kg (3,400 lb)
- Max wing loading: 95 kg/m² (19·5 lb/sq ft)
- Max power loading: 6·88 kg/kW (11·3 lb/hp)

PERFORMANCE (at max T-O weight):
- Max level speed at S/L 156 knots (289 km/h; 179 mph)
- Best power cruising speed at optimum altitude:
  - 75% power: 152 knots (282 km/h; 175 mph)
  - 65% power: 145 knots (268 km/h; 167 mph)
  - 55% power: 132 knots (244 km/h; 152 mph)
- Best econ cruising speed at optimum altitude:
  - 75% power: 148 knots (274 km/h; 170 mph)
  - 65% power: 141 knots (261 km/h; 162 mph)
  - 55% power: 125 knots (231 km/h; 144 mph)
- Stalling speed, flaps up: 62 knots (114 km/h; 71 mph) CAS
- Stalling speed, flaps down: 55 knots (101 km/h; 63 mph) CAS

Piper Six 300 six/seven-seat cabin monoplane

- Max rate of climb at S/L: 320 m (1,050 ft)/min
- Service ceiling: 5,210 m (17,100 ft)
- Absolute ceiling: 5,485 m (18,000 ft)
- T-O run: 274 m (900 ft)
- T-O to 15 m (50 ft): 411 m (1,350 ft)
- Landing from 15 m (50 ft): 305 m (1,000 ft)
- Landing run: 192 m (630 ft)
- Range with max fuel, allowances for taxi, T-O, climb, descent, and 45 min reserves at max range power:
  - At best power settings:
    - 75% power at 2,440 m (8,000 ft): 679 nm (1,259 km; 782 miles)
    - 65% power at 3,050 m (10,000 ft): 715 nm (1,324 km; 823 miles)
    - 55% power at 3,660 m (12,000 ft): 733 nm (1,358 km; 844 miles)
  - At best econ power settings:
    - 75% power at 2,440 m (8,000 ft): 744 nm (1,379 km; 857 miles)
    - 65% power at 3,050 m (10,000 ft): 802 nm (1,487 km; 924 miles)
    - 55% power at 3,660 m (12,000 ft): 835 nm (1,548 km; 962 miles)

PIPER (PA-32RT-300) LANCE II

On 30 August 1974 Piper flew the prototype of a new 6/7-seat single-engined aircraft, included in the Cherokee range with the designation PA-32R-300 (the R indicating retractable landing gear) and the name Lance. It combined a fuselage basically the same as that of the Cherokee SIX 300 with Seneca II main landing gear, Arrow II/III nose gear, and Seneca II fuel tanks. FAA certification in the CAR 3-8 Normal category was granted on 25 February 1975, and the first production aircraft made its first flight on 17 July 1975.

The 1978 version of the Lance introduced a T-tail to replace the conventional tail unit of the Cherokee SIX; being some 23% smaller in area, there is a reduction in drag and an improvement in performance and stability. This newly-configured Lance was given the company designation PA-32RT-300 (the T indicating T-tail) and the name Lance II. Two versions are currently available:

Lance II. Basic version, as described in detail.

Turbo Lance II. Turbocharged version, described separately.

Both versions are available with optional factory-installed avionics packages, as well as a wide range of avionics equipment to customer's requirements, plus the interior group options described for the Six 300. There are variations in the optional equipment packages, as follows:

Custom: As for Six 300, with deletion of rotating beacon, wheel speed fairings, and quick oil drain; and with addition of white wingtip strobe lights.

Executive: As for Six 300, with deletions noted above.

TYPE: Six/seven-seat cabin monoplane.

WINGS: Structure similar to wing of Archer II, but with constant chord and Seneca II single spar and fuel tanks.

FUSELAGE: As for Six 300.

TAIL UNIT: Cantilever T-tail of light alloy construction. All-moving tailplane with trim tab. Rudder trim tab. Small ventral fin.

LANDING GEAR: Hydraulically-retractable tricycle type, with integrated automatic system which extends the landing gear at 102 knots (189 km/h; 117 mph), unless overridden by pilot. Steerable nosewheel. Emergency free-fall extension system. Piper oleo-pneumatic shock-absorber in each unit. Main-wheel tyre size 6·00-6, 8-ply rating; nosewheel tyre size 5·00-5, 6-ply rating. High-capacity disc brakes. Parking brake. Heavy-duty tyres and brakes optional.

POWER PLANT: One 224 kW (300 hp) Lycoming IO-540-K1G5D flat-six engine, driving a Hartzell two-blade constant-speed metal propeller. Two interconnected metal fuel tanks in the leading-edge of each wing with a total capacity of 371 litres (98 US gallons) of which 356 litres (94 US gallons) are usable. Fuel system features external wing sight gauges. Refuelling points in upper surface of outboard wing panels. Oil capacity 11·5 litres (3 US gallons).

ACCOMMODATION, SYSTEMS, AVIONICS AND EQUIPMENT: As for Six 300.

DIMENSIONS, EXTERNAL: As for Six 300, except:
- Wing chord (constant): 1·60 m (5 ft 3 in)
- Length overall: 8·62 m (28 ft 3½ in)
- Height overall: 2·90 m (9 ft 6 in)
- Wheel track: 3·38 m (11 ft 0⅞ in)
- Wheelbase: 2·42 m (7 ft 11⅜ in)

WEIGHTS AND LOADINGS:
- Weight empty: 893 kg (1,968 lb)
- Max T-O and landing weight: 1,633 kg (3,600 lb)
- Max wing loading: 100·6 kg/m² (20·6 lb/sq ft)
- Max power loading: 7·29 kg/kW (12·0 lb/hp)

PERFORMANCE (at max T-O weight):
- Never-exceed speed: 188 knots (349 km/h; 217 mph)
- Max level speed at S/L: 166 knots (307 km/h; 191 mph)
- Best power cruising speed, 75% power at optimum altitude: 158 knots (293 km/h; 182 mph)
- Best power cruising speed, 65% power at optimum altitude: 149 knots (276 km/h; 172 mph)
- Best power cruising speed, 55% power at optimum altitude: 139 knots (258 km/h; 160 mph)
- Best econ cruising speed, 75% power at optimum altitude: 156 knots (289 km/h; 180 mph)
- Best econ cruising speed, 65% power at optimum altitude: 146 knots (270 km/h; 168 mph)
- Best econ cruising speed, 55% power at optimum altitude: 138 knots (256 km/h; 159 mph)
- Stalling speed, flaps up: 64 knots (119 km/h; 74 mph) CAS
- Stalling speed, flaps down: 60 knots (111 km/h; 69 mph) CAS
- Max rate of climb at S/L: 305 m (1,000 ft)/min
- Service ceiling: 4,695 m (15,400 ft)
- Absolute ceiling: 4,940 m (16,200 ft)
- T-O run: 442 m (1,450 ft)
- T-O to 15 m (50 ft): 719 m (2,360 ft)
- Landing from 15 m (50 ft): 521 m (1,710 ft)
- Landing run: 268 m (880 ft)
- Range with max fuel, allowances for taxi, T-O, climb, descent, and 45 min reserves at max range power:
  - Best power settings at optimum altitude:
    - 75% power: 656 nm (1,215 km; 755 miles)
    - 65% power: 685 nm (1,270 km; 789 miles)
    - 55% power: 714 nm (1,323 km; 822 miles)
  - Best econ power settings at optimum altitude:
    - 75% power: 780 nm (1,445 km; 898 miles)
    - 65% power: 825 nm (1,529 km; 950 miles)
    - 55% power: 870 nm (1,613 km; 1,002 miles)

PIPER (PA-32RT-300T) TURBO LANCE II

The Turbo Lance II is identical in every way with the Lance II, except for the installation of a 224 kW (300 hp) Lycoming TIO-540-S1AD turbocharged flat-six engine, driving a Hartzell two-blade constant-speed metal propeller with spinner. Changes associated with the installation of this engine include provision of a low-slung elliptical air intake, dual controllable cowl flaps, and an automatic interconnect control to provide a single lever power control for engine throttle and turbocharging system. A two-bottle oxygen system with six outlets is available as an option for this version of the Lance II. FAA certification of the Turbo Lance II was granted on 20 April 1978.

WEIGHTS AND LOADINGS: As for Lance II, except:
- Weight empty: 937 kg (2,065 lb)

PERFORMANCE (at max T-O weight):
- Max level speed at optimum altitude: 189 knots (351 km/h; 218 mph)

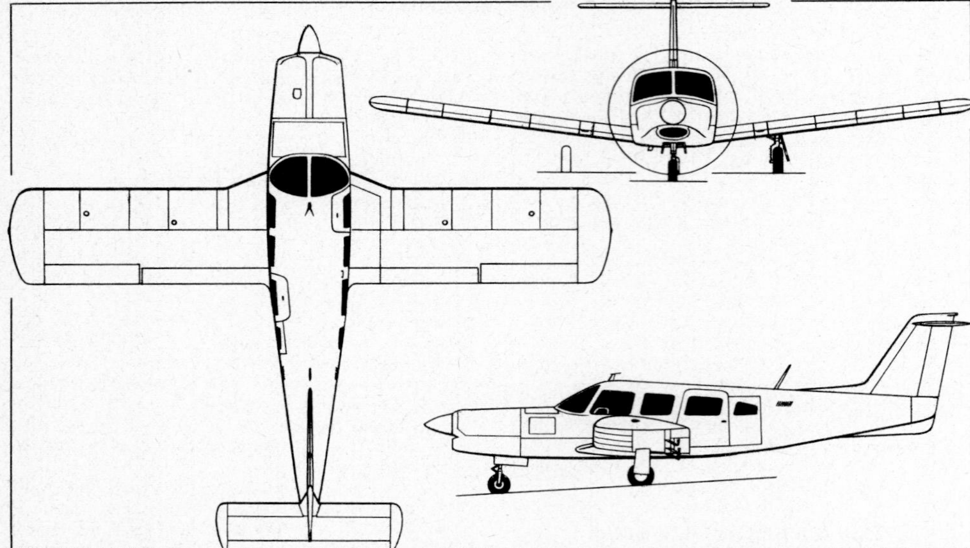

Three-view drawing *(Pilot Press)* **and photograph of the Piper Turbo Lance II, showing T-tail and inlet for turbocharged engine**

Best power cruising speed at optimum altitude:
- 81% power 183 knots (339 km/h; 211 mph)
- 75% power 176 knots (327 km/h; 203 mph)
- 65% power 160 knots (296 km/h; 184 mph)
- 55% power 142 knots (264 km/h; 164 mph)

Best econ cruising speed at optimum altitude:
- 75% power 173 knots (320 km/h; 199 mph)
- 65% power 158 knots (293 km/h; 182 mph)
- 55% power 139 knots (257 km/h; 160 mph)

Stalling speed, flaps up 67 knots (125 km/h; 78 mph) CAS
Stalling speed, flaps down 60 knots (112 km/h; 69·5 mph) CAS
Max rate of climb at S/L 320 m (1,050 ft)/min
Max certificated ceiling 6,100 m (20,000 ft)
T-O run 430 m (1,410 ft)
T-O to 15 m (50 ft) 572 m (1,875 ft)
Landing from 15 m (50 ft) 536 m (1,760 ft)
Landing run 320 m (1,050 ft)
Range with max fuel, allowances for taxi, T-O, climb, cruise, descent and 45 min reserves at max range power:

Best power settings at optimum altitude:
- 81% power 577 nm (1,069 km; 664 miles)
- 75% power 597 nm (1,106 km; 687 miles)
- 65% power 609 nm (1,128 km; 701 miles)
- 55% power 623 nm (1,154 km; 717 miles)

Best econ power settings at optimum altitude:
- 75% power 712 nm (1,320 km; 820 miles)
- 65% power 720 nm (1,334 km; 829 miles)
- 55% power 730 nm (1,353 km; 841 miles)

PIPER (PA-31) NAVAJO

On 30 September 1964 Piper flew the first of what it described as a new series of larger executive aircraft for corporate and commuter airline service. Named Navajo, it was then available with normally-aspirated or turbocharged engines, the latter being known as the Turbo Navajo. Subsequently, three additional versions were introduced, the Navajo C/R, the Pressurised Navajo and Navajo Chieftain. The Pressurised Navajo has been discontinued but details can be found in the 1977-78 *Jane's*. The Navajo C/R and Chieftain are described separately.

Five optional factory-installed avionics packages are available for the Navajo; there are, in addition, two optional equipment groups, and details of these follow:

Group KTS-1-31. Dual King KX 175B nav/com; KI 525A VOR/LOC/GS indicator; KI 206 VOR/LOC indicator; dual KM 72 VOR/LOC converters; KN 75 glideslope receiver; KR 85 ADF; KI 225 ADF indicator; KT 76A transponder; KMA 20 audio selector panel and amplifier, marker beacon receiver and lights; KN 65A DME with KI 266 indicator; KAP 200 AFS; KCS 55A slaved compass system; dual KA 39 power converters; Piper passenger address system, static discharge wicks, and avionics master switch; Telex 100T noise-cancelling microphone and headset; and all associated antennae.

Group KTG-3-31. Dual King KTR 905 com; KNR 630 nav 1; KNR 632 nav 2; KI 525A VOR/LOC/GS indicator; KI 206 VOR/LOC indicator, with VOR/LOC converter and glideslope receiver; KMR 675 marker beacon receiver; KA 35A marker beacon lights; KDF 805 ADF with KNI 580 indicator; KXP 755 transponder; KAA 445 audio amplifier; KDM 705A DME with KDI 571 indicator; Gables master control panel with avionics master switch; then as Group KTS-1-31, from and including KAP 200 AFS.

Group CT-1-31. Dual Collins VHF-20A com; dual VIR-30M nav; King 525A VOR/LOC indicator; Collins 331H-3G VOR/LOC indicator with VOR/LOC converter, glideslope and marker beacon receiver; Collins ADF-60A ADF, with King KNI 580 indicator; Collins TDR-90 transponder; King KA 35A marker beacon lights; Collins DME-40 DME, with 339F-12 indicator; Collins 346B-3 audio amplifier; Gables master control panel with avionics master switch; then as Group KTS-1-31, from and including KAP 200 AFS.

Group CTM-1-31. Dual Collins VHF-251 com; dual VIR-351 nav with VOR/LOC converter; King KI 525A VOR/LOC/GS indicator; Collins GLS-350 glideslope receiver; IND-350 VOR/LOC indicator; AMR-350 audio selector panel/audio amplifier/marker beacon receiver/marker beacon lights; ADF-650 digital ADF; IND-650 ADF indicator; TDR-950 transponder; King KN 65A DME, with KA 43 tuning adaptor, and KI 266 digital display; dual Collins PWC-150 power converters; then as Group KTS-1-31, from and including KAP 200 AFS.

Group NC-1-31. Dual Narco COMM 120 com; dual NAV 124A nav; King KI 525A VOR/LOC/GS indicator; ID-124 VOR/LOC indicator with VOR/LOC converter; UGR-2A glideslope receiver; ADF-141 ADF; ADF-101 ADF indicator; AT-150 transponder; CP-136TM audio selector panel/amplifier, with marker beacon receiver and lights; DME-195 DME; CP-136TM passenger address system; four Narco MP-10 and two MP-11 power converters; Piper anti-precipitation ADF sense antenna; then as Group KTS-1-31, from and including KAP 200 AFS.

Co-pilot Flight Instrument Group. Includes Piper TruSpeed indicator; Piper pictorial turn rate indicator; sensitive altimeter; 3 in attitude gyro and directional gyro; 8-day clock; rate of climb indicator; heated pitot tube; and separate static system and individual rheostat controlled lighting; adding 5·6 kg (12·4 lb) to basic empty weight. Electrical gyros or vacuum gyros optional.

De-icing Group. Pneumatic de-icing boot installation for wing and tail unit leading-edges; electrical propeller de-icing; ice inspection light; and electrical windscreen de-icing and windscreen wiper port side; adding 28·1 kg (62·0 lb) to basic empty weight.

Other combinations of the above equipment are available optionally, together with an extensive range of radio and radar equipment by Bendix, Collins, King, Narco and RCA.

The description which follows applies to the Navajo:

Type: Six/eight-seat corporate and commuter airline transport.

Wings: Cantilever low-wing monoplane. Wing section NACA 63_2415 at root, NACA 63_1212 at tip. 1° aerodynamic twist. 2° 30′ geometric twist. All-metal structure, with heavy stepped-down main spar, front and rear spars, lateral stringers, ribs and stressed skin. Wings spliced on centreline with heavy steel plates. Flush riveted forward of main spar. Wing-root leading-edge extended forward between nacelle and fuselage. Glassfibre wingtips. Balanced ailerons are interconnected with rudder. Trim tab in starboard aileron. Electrically-operated flaps. Pneumatic de-icing boots optional.

Fuselage: Conventional all-metal semi-monocoque structure.

Tail Unit: Cantilever all-metal structure, with sweptback vertical surfaces. Variable-incidence tailplane. Trim tabs in rudder and starboard elevator. Optional pneumatic de-icing boots.

Landing Gear: Hydraulically-actuated retractable tricycle type, with single wheel on each unit. Manual hydraulic emergency extension. Main wheels and tyres size 6·50-10, eight-ply rating, pressure 4·14 bars (60 lb/sq in). Steerable nosewheel and tyre size 6·00-6, six-ply rating, pressure 2·90 bars (42 lb/sq in). Toe-controlled hydraulic disc brakes. Heavy duty brakes and toe-operated brakes for co-pilot optional. Parking brake. Main-wheel doors close when gear is fully extended.

Power Plant: Two 231 kW (310 hp) Lycoming TIO-540-A2C flat-six turbocharged engines. Hartzell three-blade fully-feathering metal propellers with spinners. Propeller de-icing optional. Four rubber fuel cells in wings; inboard cells each contain 212 litres (56 US gallons), outboard cells 151·5 litres (40 US gallons) each. Total fuel capacity 727 litres (192 US gallons), of which 709 litres (187·3 US gallons) are usable. Fuel cells equipped with NACA-type anti-icing non-siphoning fuel vents. Oil capacity 22·7 litres (6 US gallons). Two-piece glassfibre engine nacelles.

Accommodation: Six individual seats, with headrests and armrests, in pairs with centre aisle. Seventh and eighth seats optional. Dual controls standard. Thermostatically-controlled Janitrol 35,000 BTU combustion heater, windscreen defrosters and fresh air system standard. Double-glazed windows. Electrical de-icing and windscreen wiper for port side of windscreen optional. 'Dutch' door at rear of cabin on port side. Top half hinges upward; lower half hinges down and has built-in steps. Pilot's and co-pilot's storm windows. Super soundproofing. Window curtains. Emergency exit. Baggage compartments in nose, capacity 68 kg (150 lb), and in rear of cabin, capacity 91 kg (200 lb). Cargo door and cockpit door optional.

Systems: Hydraulic system utilises two engine-driven pumps. 24V electrical system supplied by two engine-driven 28V 70A alternators and 24V 17Ah battery; 25Ah battery optional. External power socket standard. Oxygen system optional.

Avionics and Equipment: A wide range of optional avionics, including factory-installed packages, available to customer's requirements. Blind-flying instrumentation standard, with optional dual installation for co-pilot. Standard equipment includes fore, aft, and vertically adjustable and tilting seats for pilot and co-pilot, with headrests, folding armrests, shoulder safety belts and inertia reels, and oxygen mask storage beneath each seat. Four adjustable and reclining passenger seats in club arrangement, with headrests and folding armrests, seat belts, oxygen mask storage beneath each seat, magazine storage pockets, 'No smoking, Fasten seat belt' sign, curtain cockpit divider and a choice of five interior colour schemes, Piper TruSpeed indicator, sensitive altimeter, outside air temperature gauge, annunciator panel, engine hour recorder, alternate static source, stall warning horn, external power socket, sun visors, corrosion proofing, tiedown rings, and stowable towbar. Optional equipment includes cabin ground ventilation fan, cabin fire extinguisher, cold-weather heater for rear cabin, propeller synchroniser, aft cabin divider with curtain and shelf, fuselage ice protection shields, beverage dispensers, folding tables, forward cabin divider with curtain and magazine racks, automatic locator beacon, ice inspection light, toilet, utility door, tinted windows, toe-brakes for co-pilot, and pilot's windscreen wiper. Standard electrical equipment includes navigation, landing, taxying, cockpit, cabin dome and passenger reading lights, wingtip and tail anti-collision lights, stall warning light, courtesy lights, cabin and cockpit speakers and heated pitot tube.

DIMENSIONS, EXTERNAL:
- Wing span: 12·40 m (40 ft 8 in)
- Length overall: 9·94 m (32 ft 7½ in)
- Height overall: 3·96 m (13 ft 0 in)
- Tailplane span: 5·52 m (18 ft 1½ in)
- Wheel track: 4·19 m (13 ft 9 in)
- Wheelbase: 2·64 m (8 ft 8 in)
- Propeller diameter: 2·03 m (6 ft 8 in)
- Cabin door (port, aft): Height 1·14 m (3 ft 9 in)
  - Width: 0·70 m (2 ft 3½ in)

DIMENSIONS, INTERNAL:
- Cabin: Length 3·33 m (10 ft 11 in)
  - Max width: 1·27 m (4 ft 2 in)
  - Max height: 1·31 m (4 ft 3½ in)
- Baggage compartments: Nose 0·40 m³ (14 cu ft)
  - Aft: 0·62 m³ (22 cu ft)

AREA:
- Wings, gross: 21·3 m² (229 sq ft)

WEIGHTS AND LOADINGS:
- Weight empty: 1,816 kg (4,003 lb)
- Max T-O and landing weight: 2,948 kg (6,500 lb)
- Max ramp weight: 2,965 kg (6,536 lb)
- Max zero-fuel weight: 2,812 kg (6,200 lb)
- Max wing loading: 138·7 kg/m² (28·4 lb/sq ft)
- Max power loading: 6·38 kg/kW (10·5 lb/hp)

PERFORMANCE (at max T-O weight):
- Cruising speed at average cruise weight:
  - 75% power at 6,705 m (22,000 ft): 215 knots (399 km/h; 248 mph)
  - 75% power at 3,660 m (12,000 ft): 195 knots (362 km/h; 225 mph)
  - 65% power at 7,320 m (24,000 ft): 204 knots (378 km/h; 235 mph)
  - 65% power at 3,660 m (12,000 ft): 183 knots (340 km/h; 211 mph)
  - 55% power at 7,320 m (24,000 ft): 186 knots (344 km/h; 214 mph)
  - 55% power at 3,660 m (12,000 ft): 169 knots (314 km/h; 195 mph)
- Stalling speed, flaps down: 70 knots (130 km/h; 81 mph) IAS
- Max rate of climb at S/L: 440 m (1,445 ft)/min
- Rate of climb at S/L, one engine out: 75 m (245 ft)/min
- Service ceiling: 8,015 m (26,300 ft)
- Service ceiling, one engine out: 4,635 m (15,200 ft)
- Normal T-O run: 314 m (1,030 ft)
- Short-field T-O run: 262 m (860 ft)
- Normal T-O to 15 m (50 ft): 668 m (2,190 ft)
- Short-field T-O to 15 m (50 ft): 518 m (1,700 ft)
- *Normal landing from 15 m (50 ft) at max landing weight: 554 m (1,818 ft)
- *Short-field landing from 15 m (50 ft): 464 m (1,521 ft)
- *Normal landing run: 276 m (906 ft)
- *Short-field landing run: 274 m (900 ft)
- Range with max fuel, allowances for start, taxi, T-O, climb, and 45 min reserves at long-range cruise power:
  - 75% power at 6,100 m (20,000 ft): 1,005 nm (1,862 km; 1,157 miles)
  - 75% power at 3,660 m (12,000 ft): 995 nm (1,844 km; 1,146 miles)
  - 65% power at 6,100 m (20,000 ft): 1,055 nm (1,955 km; 1,215 miles)
  - 65% power at 3,660 m (12,000 ft): 1,045 nm (1,936 km; 1,203 miles)
  - 55% power at 6,100 m (20,000 ft): 1,065 nm (1,973 km; 1,226 miles)
  - 55% power at 3,660 m (12,000 ft): 1,060 nm (1,965 km; 1,221 miles)

**With optional heavy duty brakes*

PIPER (PA-31-325) NAVAJO C/R

Identical to the PA-31 Navajo except for having counter-rotating engines and nacelle baggage compartments, as introduced on the Navajo Chieftain in 1972, the Navajo C/R is available in the same optional versions, and with the same optional avionics and operational package options, as the Navajo.

POWER PLANT: One 242·5 kW (325 hp) Lycoming LTIO-540-F2BD and one 242·5 kW (325 hp) Lycoming TIO-540-F2BD flat-six turbocharged counter-rotating engines.

WEIGHTS AND LOADINGS: As for Navajo, except:
- Weight empty: 1,859 kg (4,099 lb)
- Max ramp weight: 2,966 kg (6,540 lb)

Piper Navajo six/eight-seat light transport, basic version of the Navajo series

PERFORMANCE (at max T-O weight):
- Cruising speed at average cruise weight:
  - 75% power at 6,100 m (20,000 ft): 220 knots (407 km/h; 253 mph)
  - 75% power at 3,660 m (12,000 ft): 202 knots (375 km/h; 233 mph)
  - 65% power at 6,100 m (20,000 ft): 208 knots (386 km/h; 240 mph)
  - 65% power at 3,660 m (12,000 ft): 190 knots (352 km/h; 219 mph)
  - 55% power at 4,875 m (16,000 ft): 180 knots (333 km/h; 207 mph)
  - 55% power at 3,660 m (12,000 ft): 175 knots (325 km/h; 202 mph)
- Max rate of climb at S/L: 457 m (1,500 ft)/min
- Rate of climb at S/L, one engine out: 78 m (255 ft)/min
- Service ceiling: 8,045 m (26,400 ft)
- Service ceiling, one engine out: 4,665 m (15,300 ft)
- Normal T-O run: 302 m (990 ft)
- Short-field T-O run: 256 m (840 ft)
- Normal T-O to 15 m (50 ft): 634 m (2,080 ft)
- Short-field T-O to 15 m (50 ft): 497 m (1,630 ft)
- *Normal landing from 15 m (50 ft): 554 m (1,818 ft)
- *Short-field landing from 15 m (50 ft): 464 m (1,521 ft)
- *Normal landing run: 276 m (906 ft)
- *Short-field landing run: 274 m (900 ft)
- Range with max fuel, allowances for start, taxi, T-O, climb, and 45 min reserves at long-range cruise power:
  - 75% power at 6,100 m (20,000 ft): 940 nm (1,741 km; 1,082 miles)
  - 75% power at 3,660 m (12,000 ft): 910 nm (1,687 km; 1,048 miles)
  - 65% power at 6,100 m (20,000 ft): 1,000 nm (1,854 km; 1,152 miles)
  - 65% power at 3,660 m (12,000 ft): 970 nm (1,798 km; 1,117 miles)
  - 55% power at 4,875 m (16,000 ft): 1,040 nm (1,928 km; 1,198 miles)
  - 55% power at 3,660 m (12,000 ft): 1,025 nm (1,899 km; 1,180 miles)

**With optional heavy duty brakes*

PIPER (PA-31-350) CHIEFTAIN

First announced on 11 September 1972, the PA-31-350 Chieftain is a lengthened version of the Navajo, with the fuselage extended by 0·61 m (2 ft 0 in) and with 261 kW (350 hp) counter-rotating turbocharged engines.

The main cabin floor is designed to carry heavy concentrated loads of up to 976 kg/m² (200 lb/sq ft) and, in addition to the 6·14 m³ (217 cu ft) of cargo space in the main cabin, 91 kg (200 lb) of cargo or baggage can be carried in the forward nose compartment, and 68 kg (150 lb) in the rear of each engine nacelle.

Two optional interior groups of equipment are available, depending upon the proposed use of the aircraft:

Standard Interior Group. Comprises six adjustable seats. Passenger seats in club arrangement with headrests, folding armrests, seat belts, oxygen mask stowage beneath each seat, and magazine storage pockets on each seat back. 'No smoking/Fasten seat belt' sign. Pull-curtain cockpit divider. Choice of five interior colour schemes.

Commuter Interior Group. Comprises ten forward-facing seats. Eight adjustable and reclining passenger seats with oxygen mask stowage and magazine storage as above. 'No smoking/Fasten seat belt' sign. Pull-curtain cockpit divider. Adds 39·5 kg (87 lb) to basic empty weight.

Operational groups, comprising Co-pilot Instrument Group and De-icing Group, and avionics groups as detailed for the Navajo, are available for the Chieftain, as well as a wide range of optional avionics.

The description of the Navajo applies also to the Chieftain, except as follows:

FUSELAGE: As for Navajo, except length increased by 0·61 m (2 ft 0 in).

POWER PLANT: Two 261 kW (350 hp) Lycoming flat-six turbocharged engines, one TIO-540-J2BD and one LTIO-540-J2BD, each driving a three-blade fully-feathering metal propeller. Four rubber fuel cells in wings; inboard cells each contain 212 litres (56 US gallons), outboard cells each 151·5 litres (40 US gallons). Total fuel capacity 727 litres (192 US gallons), of which 689 litres (182 US gallons) are usable. Oil capacity 22·7 litres (6 US gallons).

ACCOMMODATION: Pilot and co-pilot on individually adjustable and reclining seats. Dual controls standard. Interior seating and equipment as detailed in optional interior groups. Cabin heated by thermostatically-controlled Janitrol 50,000 BTU combustion heater. Piper Aire 16,000 BTU air-conditioning system optional. Baggage/cargo compartments in nose, capacity 91 kg (200 lb), and in the rear of each engine nacelle, each 68 kg (150 lb).

AVIONICS AND EQUIPMENT: A wide range of optional avionics is available, as well as full dual instrumentation, a flight director system integrated with autopilot, weather radar, pneumatic wing and tail unit de-icing, and electric propeller and windscreen anti-icing. Standard and optional equipment is generally similar to that available for the Navajo. Also available optionally for all interior groups is a cargo kit which includes cargo barrier, tiedown rings and net, eight seat-track tiedown rings, four plug-in tiedown rings, and four tiedown straps.

DIMENSIONS, EXTERNAL:
- Wing span: 12·40 m (40 ft 8 in)
- Length overall: 10·55 m (34 ft 7½ in)
- Height overall: 3·96 m (13 ft 0 in)
- Tailplane span: 5·52 m (18 ft 1½ in)
- Wheel track: 4·19 m (13 ft 9 in)
- Wheelbase: 3·24 m (10 ft 7½ in)
- Propeller diameter: 2·03 m (6 ft 8 in)

DIMENSIONS, INTERNAL:
- Cabin: Length 3·84 m (12 ft 7 in)
  - Width: 1·27 m (4 ft 2 in)
  - Height: 1·31 m (4 ft 3½ in)
- Baggage/cargo compartments:
  - Nose: 0·40 m³ (14 cu ft)
  - Aft: 0·62 m³ (22 cu ft)
  - Engine nacelles (each): 0·37 m³ (13·25 cu ft)

AREA:
- Wings, gross: 21·3 m² (229 sq ft)

WEIGHTS AND LOADINGS:
- Weight empty (standard): 1,915 kg (4,221 lb)
- Max T-O and landing weight: 3,175 kg (7,000 lb)
- Max ramp weight: 3,196 kg (7,045 lb)
- Max wing loading: 149·4 kg/m² (30·6 lb/sq ft)
- Max power loading: 6·08 kg/kW (10·0 lb/hp)

PERFORMANCE (at max T-O weight):
- Cruising speed at average cruise weight
  - 75% power at 6,100 m (20,000 ft): 221 knots (409 km/h; 254 mph)
  - 75% power at 3,660 m (12,000 ft): 205 knots (380 km/h; 236 mph)
  - 65% power at 6,100 m (20,000 ft): 210 knots (389 km/h; 242 mph)
  - 65% power at 3,660 m (12,000 ft): 191 knots (354 km/h; 220 mph)
  - 55% power at 4,570 m (15,000 ft): 177 knots (328 km/h; 204 mph)
  - 55% power at 3,660 m (12,000 ft): 173 knots (320 km/h; 199 mph)
- Stalling speed, flaps up: 80 knots (148 km/h; 92 mph)
- Stalling speed, flaps down: 74 knots (137 km/h; 85 mph)
- Max rate of climb at S/L: 424 m (1,390 ft)/min
- Rate of climb at S/L, one engine out: 70 m (230 ft)/min
- Service ceiling: 8,290 m (27,200 ft)
- Service ceiling, one engine out: 4,175 m (13,700 ft)
- Normal T-O run: 415 m (1,360 ft)

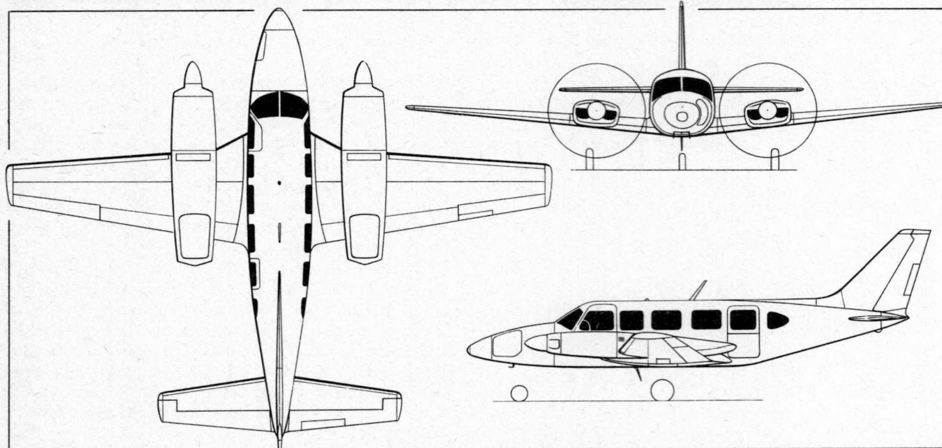

Photograph *(Austin J. Brown)* **and three-view drawing** *(Pilot Press)* **of the Piper Chieftain six/ten-seat executive/commuter/cargo aircraft**

Short-field T-O run 320 m (1,050 ft)
Normal T-O to 15 m (50 ft) 759 m (2,490 ft)
Short-field T-O to 15 m (50 ft) 543 m (1,780 ft)
Normal landing from 15 m (50 ft) 573 m (1,880 ft)
Short-field landing from 15 m (50 ft) 491 m (1,610 ft)
Normal landing run 319 m (1,045 ft)
Short-field landing run 297 m (975 ft)
Accelerate/stop distance 640 m (2,100 ft)
Range with max fuel, allowances for start, taxi, T-O, climb, and 45 min reserves at long-range cruise power:
75% power at 6,100 m (20,000 ft) 885 nm (1,640 km; 1,019 miles)
75% power at 3,660 m (12,000 ft) 855 nm (1,585 km; 985 miles)
65% power at 6,100 m (20,000 ft) 925 nm (1,714 km; 1,065 miles)
65% power at 3,660 m (12,000 ft) 900 nm (1,667 km; 1,036 miles)
55% power at 4,570 m (15,000 ft) 950 nm (1,761 km; 1,094 miles)
55% power at 3,660 m (12,000 ft) 950 nm (1,761 km; 1,094 miles)

PIPER (PA-31T-1) CHEYENNE I

Introduced in 1978, the Cheyenne I is a low-cost version of the established Cheyenne PA-31T, which has now been redesignated Cheyenne II, and which is described separately. It differs primarily by having less powerful engines. It is available with the optional Standard and Executive interiors, De-icing Group and Co-pilot Flight Group as detailed for the Cheyenne II. Also available optionally as factory-installed packages are the KTS-4-31T-II and CTM-3-31T-II avionics groups detailed for the Cheyenne II, under the respective designations KTS-1-31T-I and CTM-1-31T-I. Both substitute the King KFC 250 AFCS/FD for the Bendix M-4D integrated AP/FD system, and the King KCS 55A VOR/LOC/GS indicator for the Bendix IN 863A.

FAA certification was received on 23 March 1978, and deliveries began at the end of April 1978.

The description of the Cheyenne II applies also to the Cheyenne I, except as follows:

Landing Gear: As Cheyenne II except: Cleveland Type 40-106 main wheels, with 6·50 × 10 10-ply tyres, pressure 5·52 bars (80 lb/sq in). Cleveland Type 40-120A nosewheel, with 17·5 × 6·25 10-ply tyres, pressure 5·52 bars (80 lb/sq in). Cleveland Type 40-120A nosewheel, with 17·5 × 6·25 10-ply tyre, pressure 5·52 bars (80 lb/sq in). Cleveland Type 30-106 brakes.

Power Plant: Two 372·6 kW (500 shp) Pratt & Whitney Aircraft of Canada PT6A-11 turboprop engines, each driving a Hartzell three-blade constant-speed reversible pitch and fully-feathering metal propeller. Each wing has three interconnected fuel cells, with total capacity of 1,211 litres (320 US gallons), of which 1,136 litres (300 US gallons) are usable. Optional wingtip tanks, each of 113·6 litres (30 US gallons) capacity, provide a maximum total usable capacity of 1,363 litres (360 US gallons). Refuelling points on top of engine nacelles and on upper surface of each tip-tank. Oil capacity 24·6 litres (6·5 US gallons).

Dimensions, external: As for Cheyenne II, except:
Wing span over optional tip-tanks 13·01 m (42 ft 8¼ in)
Wing chord at root 2·61 m (8 ft 6¾ in)
Wing chord at tip 0·97 m (3 ft 2 in)
Wing aspect ratio 7·37
Passenger door (port, aft):
Height to sill 0·97 m (3 ft 2 in)
Baggage door (port, fwd):
Width 0·51 m (1 ft 8 in)

Dimensions, Internal: As for Cheyenne II, except:
Cabin (excl flight deck): Length 2·57 m (8 ft 5 in)
Max width 1·27 m (4 ft 2 in)
Max height 1·31 m (4 ft 3½ in)

Areas: As for Cheyenne II, except:
Fin 1·37 m² (14·72 sq ft)
Rudder, incl tab 1·20 m² (12·88 sq ft)

Weights and Loadings:
Weight empty 2,222 kg (4,900 lb)
Max T-O and landing weight 3,946 kg (8,700 lb)
Max ramp weight 3,969 kg (8,750 lb)
Max zero-fuel weight 3,266 kg (7,200 lb)
Max wing loading 185·5 kg/m² (38·0 lb/sq ft)
Max power loading 5·30 kg/kW (8·7 lb/shp)

Performance (at max T-O weight and without optional wingtip tanks installed, unless specified otherwise):
Cruising speed, max cruise power, average cruise weight at:
3,660 m (12,000 ft) 249 knots (461 km/h; 287 mph)
4,875 m (16,000 ft) 248 knots (460 km/h; 286 mph)
6,100 m (20,000 ft) 244 knots (452 km/h; 281 mph)
7,620 m (25,000 ft) 236 knots (437 km/h; 272 mph)
Stalling speed, flaps up 84 knots (155 km/h; 97 mph) IAS
Stalling speed, flaps down 72 knots (133 km/h; 83 mph) IAS
Rotation speed 90 knots (167 km/h; 104 mph)
Approach speed 101 knots (187 km/h; 116 mph)
Max rate of climb at S/L 533 m (1,750 ft)/min
Rate of climb at S/L, one engine out 126 m (413 ft)/min
Service ceiling 8,595 m (28,200 ft)
Service ceiling, one engine out 3,810 m (12,500 ft)
T-O run 522 m (1,712 ft)
T-O to 15 m (50 ft) 774 m (2,541 ft)
Landing from 15 m (50 ft) 777 m (2,548 ft)
Landing from 15 m (50 ft) with propeller reversal 650 m (2,131 ft)
Landing run 517 m (1,695 ft)
Landing run with propeller reversal 364 m (1,193 ft)
Accelerate/stop distance 1,006 m (3,300 ft)
Range with standard fuel, allowances for start, taxi, T-O, climb, descent, and 45 min reserves at max range cruising power:
Max cruising power at:
3,660 m (12,000 ft) 715 nm (1,325 km; 823 miles)
4,875 m (16,000 ft) 780 nm (1,445 km; 897 miles)
6,100 m (20,000 ft) 850 nm (1,575 km; 978 miles)
7,620 m (25,000 ft) 940 nm (1,742 km; 1,081 miles)
Range with max optional fuel, allowances as above:
Max cruising power at:
3,660 m (12,000 ft) 955 nm (1,770 km; 1,100 miles)
4,875 m (16,000 ft) 1,040 nm (1,927 km; 1,198 miles)
6,100 m (20,000 ft) 1,130 nm (2,094 km; 1,301 miles)
7,620 m (25,000 ft) 1,260 nm (2,335 km; 1,451 miles)

PIPER (PA-31T) CHEYENNE II

Design of the PA-31T began at the end of 1965. First flight of the prototype was made on 20 August 1969, with FAA certification being granted on 3 May 1972. The first production aircraft flew for the first time on 22 October 1973. Following the introduction of the low-cost Cheyenne I and 6/11-seat Cheyenne III, both of which are described separately, the original version was redesignated Cheyenne II.

It is available with Standard and Executive interior options and two operational group options as follows:

Standard. Six individual seats in pairs, with headrests and armrests. Pilot/co-pilot seats four-way adjustable with shoulder harness inertia reels; third and fourth cabin seats aft facing; and all cabin seats with seat belts; window curtains and wall to wall carpet. Rear cabin divider with clothes bar and baggage security net. Forward cabin divider curtain. 'No smoking/Fasten seat belt' sign. Oxygen outlets and masks at each seat position. Options available include pneumatic door extender; forward cabin combination unit; storage cabinets; folding tables; aft cabin combination unit, which includes side-facing seventh seat/toilet; seventh and eighth seats; tinted cabin windows; cabin fire extinguisher; stereo system; and all-leather seat covering.

Executive. Six individual seats, comprising two crew seats and four reclining chairs in the Standard arrange-

Piper Cheyenne I pressurised six/eight-seat cabin monoplane, low-cost model of the Cheyenne range

ment. Other standard equipment as described, plus forward cabin combination unit which includes cabin dividers and curtain, electrically-heated Thermos unit, cup dispenser, storage for ice, beverages and manuals; two folding tables; pneumatic door extender and aft cabin combination unit which includes side-facing seventh seat/toilet, cabin divider with mirror, privacy curtain, refreshment centre; AC power outlet for electric razor. Options include cabin fire extinguisher, storage cabinets, eighth seat, tinted cabin windows, stereo system and all-leather seat covering.

De-icing Group. Pneumatic de-icing boots for wing and tail unit leading-edges, and wing ice inspection light; adding 17·9 kg (39·4 lb) to basic empty weight.

Co-pilot Flight Group. Airspeed and rate of climb indicator, altimeter, electric turn rate indicator, attitude and directional gyro, clock, heated pitot, static system with alternate source, co-pilot's toe-brakes and windscreen wiper; adding 8·9 kg (19·7 lb) to basic empty weight.

Seven optional factory-installed avionics packages are available:

Group KTG/D-1-31T-II. King KCU 565A keyboard and display; dual KTR 905 720-channel com transceivers with KCU 591 control and display units and broad band antennae; KNR 665 digital VOR/LOC/GS receiver/converter with RNAV computer; KNR 615 standby digital VOR/LOC/GS receiver/converter, without RNAV computer; KPI 553 pictorial navigation indicator with DME readout and KDA 335 display data adapter; KDM 705A DME; KCU 561 control/display unit; KPI 552 VOR/LOC/GS indicator; KMR 675 marker beacon receiver with dual KA 35A marker beacon light displays; KDF 805 ADF with King KNI 581 RMI ADF indicator; KXP 775 transponder; KCU 578 ADF and transponder control unit; KAA 455 audio amplifier with KA 37 selector panel; Bendix RDR-1200B Weathervision radar; Bendix M-4D integrated AP/FD system with 4 in displays; Piper electronics master switch, PA system, static discharge wicks, ramp hailer, external microphone and phone jack, 100T noise-cancelling microphone, headset and insulated ADF sense antenna; adding 131 kg (288·7 lb) to basic empty weight.

Group KTG-2-31T-II. As KTG/D-1-31T-II except for deletion of KNR 615, KPI 552, KCU 561 and one unit KA 35A, and addition of KNR 630 analogue VOR/LOC/GS receiver/converter with KPI 533 HSI with DME readout, KDA 335 data adaptor, KI 206 VOR/LOC/GS indicator, KFS 560B manual tuner; KFS 580B manual ADF tuner and KFS 570B manual transponder tuner; adding 126·9 kg (279·8 lb) to basic empty weight.

Group KTG-3-31T-II. As KTG-2-31T-II, except for deletion of KFS 560B, KFS 570B and KFS 580B tuners, KNR 665/KCU 565 and KPI 553/KDA 335; and addition of second KNR 630; FD/HSI VOR/LOC indicator; KDI 571 digital DME readout; and Gables master control panel; adding 123·6 kg (272·4 lb) to basic empty weight.

Group KTS-4-31T-II. Dual King KX 175B nav/com; Bendix IN 863A VOR/LOC/GS indicator; King KI 203 VOR/LOC indicator; dual KN 72 VOR/LOC converters; KN 75 glideslope receiver; KR 85 ADF; KI 226 RMI with Nav 1/Nav 2 VOR switching; KT 76A transponder; KMA 20 audio selector panel and amplifier; marker beacon receiver and lights; Bendix RDR-150 weather radar; KN 65A DME with KI 266 indicator; Bendix M-4D integrated AP/FD system with DH866A director horizon; Telex 100T noise cancelling microphone and pilot's headset; Piper passenger address system, static wicks and electronics master switch; Sperry VG and DG gyro system; adding 102·8 kg (226·7 lb) to basic empty weight.

Group CT-1-31T-II. Gables master control panel; dual Collins VHF-20 com transceivers with broad band antennae; dual VIR-30 nav receivers with 200-channel VOR/LOC and 40-channel GS; Bendix IN 863A HSI and Collins 331H-3G VOR/LOC indicators with VOR/LOC converters, glideslope and marker beacon receivers; Collins ADF-60A ADF and Collins 332C-10 ADF indicator; TDR-90 transponder; KA 35A marker beacon lights; DME-40 DME; Collins 332C-10 RMI and dual VOR and ADF displays; Collins 346B-3 audio amplifier; Bendix RDR-1200B Weathervision radar; Bendix M-4D integrated AP/FD system with 4 in displays; Piper electronics master switch, PA system, ramp hailer, external mike and phone jack, static discharge wicks, insulated ADF sense antenna, 100T noise-cancelling microphone and headset; adding 126 kg (277·8 lb) to basic empty weight.

Group CTD-2-31T-II. As Group CT-1-31T-II, except for deletion of Gables master control panel, Collins 332C-10 ADF indicator and Piper PA system; and addition of Collins NCS-31 navigation control RNAV system with digital keyboard control; and hard-wired thumb wheel backup controls; adding 125·7 kg (277·2 lb) to basic empty weight.

Group CTM-3-31T-II. Dual Collins VHF-251 com; dual VIR-351 nav with VOR/LOC converter; Bendix IN 863A HSI with VOR/LOC/GS indicator; Collins IND-350 VOR/LOC indicator; GLS-350 glideslope receiver; AMR-350 audio selector panel, with amplifier, marker beacon receiver and lights, and passenger address system; ADF-650 digital ADF; King KI 226 RMI with Nav 1/Nav 2 VOR switching; Collins TDR-950 transponder; King KN 65A DME with KI 266 indicator; Bendix RDR-150 weather radar; Bendix M-4D integrated AP/FD system; Telex 100T noise cancelling microphone and pilot's headset; Piper static wicks and electronics master switch, and dual Collins PWC 150 power converters; adding 92·7 kg (204·3 lb) to basic empty weight.

Piper Cheyenne II six/eight-seat cabin monoplane (two P&WC PT6A-28 turboprop engines)

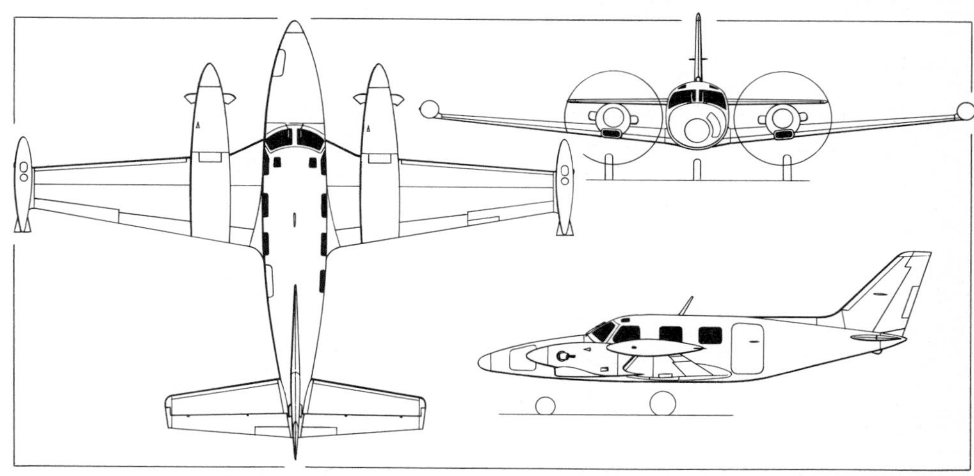

Original version of the Piper Cheyenne pressurised six/eight-seat cabin monoplane which has been redesignated Cheyenne II *(Pilot Press)*

An extensive range of other optional avionics is available to customer's requirements, including the full variety of equipment needed for maritime surveillance duties.

TYPE: Six/eight-seat cabin monoplane.

WINGS: Cantilever low-wing monoplane. Wing section NACA 63_2A415 at root, NACA 63_1A212 at tip. Dihedral 5°. Incidence 1° 30′ at root, −1° at tip. Sweepback 0° at 30% chord. Three-spar structure of 2024ST light alloy. Balanced ailerons and single-slotted trailing-edge flaps of 2024ST light alloy. Trim tab in starboard aileron. Pneumatic de-icing boots on wing leading-edges optional.

FUSELAGE: Semi-monocoque structure of 2024ST light alloy, with fail-safe structure in the pressurised areas.

TAIL UNIT: Cantilever structure of 2024ST light alloy with sweptback vertical surfaces. Fixed-incidence tailplane. Trim tabs in elevators and rudder. Pneumatic de-icing of fin and tailplane leading-edges optional.

LANDING GEAR: Hydraulically-retractable tricycle type with single wheel on each unit, main units retracting inward and nosewheel aft. Nosewheel safety mirror. Piper oleo-pneumatic shock-absorbers. Main wheels and tyres size 6·50-10, 10-ply rating. Steerable nosewheel with Type VII tyre size 18 × 4·4, 6-ply rating. Goodyear disc-type hydraulic brakes. Parking brake.

POWER PLANT: Two 462 kW (620 ehp) Pratt & Whitney Aircraft of Canada PT6A-28 turboprop engines, each driving a Hartzell three-blade constant-speed reversible-pitch fully-feathering metal propeller type HC-BTN-3B. Each wing has three interconnected fuel cells and a tip-tank, with combined total capacity of 1,476 litres (390 US gallons), of which 1,446 litres (382 US gallons) are usable. Refuelling points in engine nacelles and on upper surface of each tip-tank. NACA type anti-icing non-siphoning fuel tank vents with flame arresters. Oil capacity 24·6 litres (6·5 US gallons). Electrically heated air intake anti-icing boot, air intake ice deflection and air bypass doors. Electrical propeller de-icing.

ACCOMMODATION: Pilot and co-pilot on two individual adjustable seats. Dual controls standard. Pilot's storm window. Heated windscreen and windscreen wiper for pilot, optional for co-pilot. Cabin seating for four to six passengers on individual seats. Door with built-in airstair on port side, which has seven locking pins and inflatable pressurisation seal. Dual-pane windows. Emergency exit window on starboard side. Cabin heated and air-conditioned. Forward and aft cabin dividers. A wide range of options for cabin includes folding tables, beverage dispensers, pneumatic door extender, storage cabinets and tinted windows. Baggage compartments in nose and rear of cabin, each with 91 kg (200 lb) capacity. External access door to nose compartment.

SYSTEMS: Air-conditioning and pressurisation, with pressure differential of 0·38 bars (5·5 lb/sq in). Freon-type air-conditioner of 23,000 BTU capacity. Janitrol combustion heater of 35,000 BTU capacity with automatic windscreen defroster. Hydraulic system supplied by dual engine-driven pumps for landing gear retraction and brakes. Pneumatic system and vacuum system provided by engine bleed air. Electrical system supplied by two 28V 200A starter/generators and 24V 43Ah nickel-cadmium battery. External power socket standard. Oxygen system of 1·37 m³ (48·3 cu ft) capacity. De-icing system comprises electric anti-icing boots for air intakes, heated pitot and electric propeller de-icing. Fire detection system with six sensors; engine fire extinguishing system optional.

AVIONICS: In addition to the seven optional factory-installed packages, an extensive range of optional avionics is available, including radar, communications, area navigation, autopilot and flight director systems by Bendix, Collins, King, Piper and Sperry.

EQUIPMENT: Installed standard equipment is extensive, and optional items include flight instrument group, toe brakes, heated windscreen and windscreen wiper for co-pilot; wing and tail pneumatic de-icing boots, engine fire-extinguisher system, emergency electrical power supply system, fuselage ice protection plates, ice inspection lights, propeller synchronisers, and automatic locator beacon.

DIMENSIONS, EXTERNAL:

Wing span over tip-tanks	13·01 m (42 ft 8¼ in)
Length overall	10·57 m (34 ft 8 in)
Height overall	3·89 m (12 ft 9 in)
Tailplane span	6·05 m (19 ft 10 in)
Wheel track	4·19 m (13 ft 9 in)
Wheelbase	2·64 m (8 ft 8 in)
Propeller diameter	2·36 m (7 ft 9 in)
Propeller ground clearance	0·27 m (10½ in)
Passenger door (port, aft):	
Height	1·17 m (3 ft 10 in)
Width	0·71 m (2 ft 4 in)
Height to sill	0·94 m (3 ft 1 in)
Baggage door (fwd): Height	0·53 m (1 ft 9 in)
Width	0·66 m (2 ft 2 in)
Height to sill	1·10 m (3 ft 7½ in)

Emergency exit (stbd, fwd):
 Height 0·64 m (2 ft 1 in)
 Width 0·48 m (1 ft 7 in)

DIMENSIONS, INTERNAL:
 Cabin (incl flight deck): Length 4·90 m (16 ft 1 in)
 Max width 1·27 m (4 ft 2 in)
 Max height 1·31 m (4 ft 3½ in)
 Floor area 4·37 m^2 (47 sq ft)
 Volume 6·29 m^3 (222 cu ft)
 Forward baggage compartment 0·57 m^3 (20 cu ft)
 Aft baggage compartment 0·62 m^3 (22 cu ft)

AREAS:
 Wings, gross 21·3 m^2 (229 sq ft)
 Ailerons (total) 1·21 m^2 (13 sq ft)
 Trailing-edge flaps (total) 3·12 m^2 (33·6 sq ft)
 Fin 1·48 m^2 (15·9 sq ft)
 Rudder, incl tab 0·98 m^2 (10·6 sq ft)
 Tailplane 3·92 m^2 (42·2 sq ft)
 Elevators, incl tab 2·63 m^2 (28·3 sq ft)

WEIGHTS AND LOADINGS:
 Weight empty, standard, equipped 2,257 kg (4,976 lb)
 Max T-O and landing weight 4,082 kg (9,000 lb)
 Max ramp weight 4,105 kg (9,050 lb)
 Max zero-fuel weight 3,265 kg (7,200 lb)
 Max wing loading 191·9 kg/m^2 (39·3 lb/sq ft)
 Max power loading 4·42 kg/kW (7·26 lb/ehp)

PERFORMANCE (at max T-O weight, unless specified otherwise):
 Cruising speed, max cruise power, average cruise weight of 3,493 kg (7,700 lb) at:
  3,350 m (11,000 ft) 283 knots (524 km/h; 326 mph)
  4,875 m (16,000 ft) 277 knots (513 km/h; 319 mph)
  6,400 m (21,000 ft) 268 knots (497 km/h; 309 mph)
  8,840 m (29,000 ft) 250 knots (463 km/h; 288 mph)
 Stalling speed, flaps up 86 knots (159 km/h; 99 mph) IAS
 Stalling speed, flaps down 75 knots (139 km/h; 96 mph) IAS
 Rotation speed 91 knots (167 km/h; 105 mph) IAS
 Approach speed 98 knots (182 km/h; 113 mph)
 Max rate of climb at S/L 853 m (2,800 ft)/min
 Rate of climb at S/L, one engine out 201 m (660 ft)/min
 Service ceiling 9,630 m (31,600 ft)
 Service ceiling, one engine out 4,450 m (14,600 ft)
 T-O run 430 m (1,410 ft)
 T-O to 15 m (50 ft) 604 m (1,980 ft)
 Landing from 15 m (50 ft) 756 m (2,480 ft)
 Landing from 15 m (50 ft), with propeller reversal 567 m (1,860 ft)
 Landing run 436 m (1,430 ft)
 Landing run with propeller reversal 291 m (955 ft)
 Accelerate/stop distance 1,006 m (3,300 ft)
 Range with max fuel at max cruise power, with allowances for start, taxi, T-O, climb, descent, and 45 min reserves at long-range cruise power at:
  3,660 m (12,000 ft) 905 nm (1,677 km; 1,042 miles)
  4,875 m (16,000 ft) 1,020 nm (1,890 km; 1,175 miles)
  6,400 m (21,000 ft) 1,155 nm (2,140 km; 1,330 miles)
  8,840 m (29,000 ft) 1,380 nm (2,557 km; 1,589 miles)
 Range at max range power, fuel and allowances as above, at:
  3,660 m (12,000 ft) 1,090 nm (2,020 km; 1,255 miles)
  4,875 m (16,000 ft) 1,195 nm (2,215 km; 1,376 miles)
  6,400 m (21,000 ft) 1,330 nm (2,465 km; 1,532 miles)
  8,840 m (29,000 ft) 1,510 nm (2,798 km; 1,739 miles)

PIPER PA-42 CHEYENNE III

Piper announced on 26 September 1977 the introduction of a third member of the Cheyenne family of twin-turboprop aircraft. Designated Cheyenne III, it differs from the I and II by having increased wing span, a lengthened fuselage, a T-tail and more powerful PT6A-41 engines. By the beginning of April 1979, the engineering test programme had accumulated 1,000 flight hours. The production prototype flew for the first time on 18 May 1979; FAA certification was expected in December 1979, with deliveries of the first production aircraft following shortly afterwards.

The Cheyenne III will be available with Standard and Executive interior options, De-icing and Co-pilot Flight Groups, and the seven optional factory-installed avionics packages detailed for the Cheyenne II.

TYPE: Six/eleven-seat corporate and commuter airline transport.

WINGS: Cantilever low-wing monoplane. Wing section NACA 63_2A415, modified, at root, NACA 63_1A212 at tip. Dihedral 5°. Incidence 1° 30′. No sweepback. Three-spar fail-safe structure of light alloy. Ailerons and trailing-edge flaps as for Cheyenne II. B.F. Goodrich pneumatic de-icing boots for wing leading-edges are standard.

FUSELAGE: Conventional semi-monocoque structure of light alloy, with fail-safe structure in the pressurised areas.

TAIL UNIT: Cantilever T-tail of light alloy construction, with sweptback vertical surfaces. Fixed-incidence tailplane. Elevators and rudder of light alloy. Servo tab in rudder; anti-servo tab in elevator. B.F. Goodrich de-icing equipment standard for leading-edge of tailplane.

LANDING GEAR: Hydraulically-retractable tricycle type with single wheel on each unit. Main units retract inward, nosewheel aft. Piper oleo-pneumatic shock-absorbers. Cleveland main wheels with tyres size 6·50-10 12-ply Type III, pressure 6·90 bars (100 lb/sq in). Cleveland nosewheel with tyre size 6·00-6 8-ply rating Type III, pressure 4·83 bars (70 lb/sq in). Cleveland hydraulically-operated disc brakes. Parking brake.

POWER PLANT: Two Pratt & Whitney Aircraft of Canada PT6A-41 turboprop engines, each flat rated to 507 kW (680 shp) and driving a Hartzell three-blade constant-speed feathering and reversible-pitch metal propeller. Each wing has three interconnected fuel cells and a tip-tank, with a combined total capacity of 1,514 litres (400 US gallons). Optional fuel tanks in each engine nacelle, capacity 284 litres (75 US gallons), to provide total capacity of 2,082 litres (550 US gallons). Refuel-

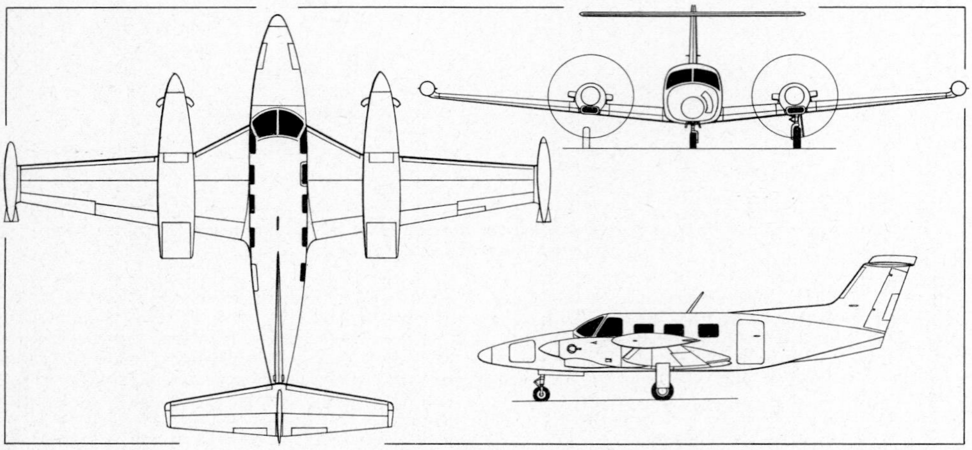

Photograph and three-view drawing *(Pilot Press)* **of Piper's T-tailed Cheyenne III**

ling points on upper surface of each tip-tank and engine nacelle. Oil capacity 24·6 litres (6·5 US gallons). Electrical intake anti-icing and propeller de-icing.

ACCOMMODATION: Pilot and co-pilot on two individual adjustable seats. To be certificated for single-pilot operation. Dual controls standard. Pilot's storm window. Cabin seats up to nine passengers in individual reclinable seats. Door with built-in airstair on port side, with seven locking pins and inflatable pressurisation seal. Emergency exit window on starboard side. Forward and aft cabin dividers. A wide range of options for cabin furnishing. Baggage compartments in nose and aft cabin, each with capacity of 136 kg (300 lb). When aircraft is operated without engine nacelle fuel tank option, an additional 68 kg (150 lb) of baggage can be accommodated in each nacelle locker to give a maximum total baggage capacity of 408 kg (900 lb). Accommodation is pressurised, heated and air-conditioned. Pilot's windscreen heated; provisions for heating co-pilot's windscreen.

SYSTEMS: AiResearch pressurisation system with max differential of 0·43 bars (6·3 lb/sq in). Freon-type air conditioner of 24,000 BTU capacity. Heating system of 45,000 BTU capacity. Hydraulic system supplied by dual engine-driven pumps. Pneumatic system supplied by engine bleed air. Electrical system includes two 28V 250A engine-driven generators. Oxygen system of 0·62 m³ (22 cu ft) capacity with ten outlets. De-icing system includes pneumatic wing and tailplane de-icing boots, electric anti-icing of engine air intakes, heated pitots, electrical propeller de-icing, and windscreen heating.

AVIONICS AND EQUIPMENT: Generally as for Cheyenne II.

DIMENSIONS, EXTERNAL: As for Cheyenne II, except:

Wing span over tip-tanks	14·53 m (47 ft 8⅛ in)
Wing chord at root	3·12 m (10 ft 3 in)
Wing chord at tip	0·97 m (3 ft 2 in)
Wing aspect ratio	7·82
Length overall	11·94 m (39 ft 2 in)
Height overall	3·84 m (12 ft 7¼ in)
Tailplane span	5·49 m (18 ft 0 in)
Wheel track	5·72 m (18 ft 9 in)
Wheelbase	3·23 m (10 ft 7¼ in)
Propeller diameter	2·41 m (7 ft 11 in)

DIMENSIONS, INTERNAL:

Cabin (from instrument panel to rear of aft baggage area): Length	5·59 m (18 ft 4 in)
Max width	1·30 m (4 ft 3 in)
Max height	1·35 m (4 ft 5 in)
Volume	approx 9·91 m³ (350 cu ft)
Nose baggage compartment	0·57 m³ (20 cu ft)
Aft baggage compartment	0·88 m³ (31 cu ft)
Nacelle baggage locker (two, each)	0·41 m³ (14·5 cu ft)

AREAS:

Wings, gross	27·22 m² (293 sq ft)
Ailerons (total)	1·25 m² (13·5 sq ft)
Trailing-edge flaps (total)	3·98 m² (42·8 sq ft)
Fin	2·17 m² (23·36 sq ft)
Rudder, incl tab	1·88 m² (20·2 sq ft)
Tailplane	3·48 m² (37·5 sq ft)
Elevators, incl tab	2·26 m² (24·3 sq ft)

WEIGHTS AND LOADINGS:

Basic empty weight	2,608 kg (5,750 lb)
Max T-O weight	4,763 kg (10,500 lb)
Max ramp weight	4,785 kg (10,550 lb)
Max zero-fuel weight	3,928 kg (8,660 lb)
Max landing weight	4,524 kg (9,975 lb)
Max wing loading	174·8 kg/m² (35·8 lb/sq ft)
Max power loading	4·70 kg/kW (7·72 lb/shp)

PERFORMANCE (at max T-O weight, unless stated otherwise):

Never-exceed speed	246 knots (455 km/h; 283 mph) IAS
Max level speed and max cruising speed at 5,880 m (19,300 ft)	300 knots (555 km/h; 345 mph)
Econ cruising speed at 9,600 m (31,500 ft)	221 knots (409 km/h; 254 mph)
Stalling speed, flaps up	90 knots (167 km/h; 104 mph) CAS
Stalling speed, flaps down	78 knots (145 km/h; 90 mph) CAS
Max rate of climb at S/L	732 m (2,400 ft)/min
Rate of climb at S/L, one engine out	168 m (550 ft)/min
Service ceiling	10,285 m (33,750 ft)
Service ceiling, one engine out	5,210 m (17,100 ft)
T-O run	495 m (1,625 ft)
T-O to 15 m (50 ft)	707 m (2,320 ft)
Landing from 15 m (50 ft)	654 m (2,145 ft)
Landing run	491 m (1,610 ft)
Range with max standard plus optional fuel, with allowances for start, taxi, T-O, climb, cruise, descent, and 45 min reserves at max range cruising power	over 2,135 nm (3,954 km; 2,457 miles)
Range with max payload, allowances as above	1,030 nm (1,908 km; 1,186 miles)

PIPER PA-34 SENECA II

On 23 September 1971, Piper announced a new twin-engined light aircraft which had the company designation PA-34 and, following Piper tradition, had the Indian name Seneca. Built at Piper's Vero Beach, Florida, factory, the 1975 version of this aircraft was redesignated Seneca II.

The Seneca II has a counter-rotating (C/R) engine and propeller installation. The retractable landing gear is operated by an electro-hydraulic system and includes an emergency extension system which allows the wheels to free-fall into the down and locked position. A dual-vane stall warning system provides warning by horn well in advance of the stall in either 'clean' or gear/flaps-down configuration.

The 1978 Seneca II introduced the standard improvements and options detailed for the Warrior II, plus Bendix RDR-160 weather radar which is available optionally for the Seneca II.

It was announced on 3 January 1977 that Piper had signed an agreement with Pezetel, the Polish foreign trade organisation, whereby PZL Mielec will assemble, manufacture and distribute the Seneca II in Eastern Europe. These aircraft (several hundred are involved in the agreement) will be powered by 164 kW (220 hp) PZL-Franklin engines and will be known as the **M-20 Mewa** (Gull).

The extensive range of avionics available for the Seneca II includes many options, plus five groups as follows:

Group N-2-34. Dual Narco Com 120 720-channel VHF transceivers; Nav 121 and 122 200-channel VOR/LOC receivers with VOR/LOC/GS indicator, VOR/LOC converter indicators, marker beacon receiver, lights, and glideslope receiver; ADF-141 ADF; AT-150 transponder; CP-135 audio panel; Piper AutoControl IIIB autopilot, VOR/LOC coupler, electric trim; M-700B noise cancelling microphone, headset, and all associated antennae; adding 26·8 kg (59 lb) to basic empty weight.

Group NT-3-34. Dual Narco Com 120 720-channel VHF transceivers; Nav 124A 200-channel VOR/LOC receiver with 40-channel localiser and ID-124 VOR/LOC/GS indicator, VOR/LOC converter and marker beacon receiver; NAV-122A nav with VOR/LOC indicator and converter; dual UGR-2A glideslope receivers; CP-135 audio panel with amplifier and marker beacon lights; ADF-141 ADF; AT-150 transponder; Piper AltiMatic IIIC autopilot; Piper VOR/LOC coupler; Piper electric trim; Piper dual broad band com antennae, static wicks, M-700B noise-cancelling microphone and headset; adding 34 kg (75 lb) to basic empty weight.

Group KS-2-34. Dual King KX 170B 720-channel nav/com transceivers with 200-channel nav; KI 209 VOR/LOC/GS indicator and VOR/LOC converters; KI 208 VOR/LOC indicator and converter; KN 75 glideslope receiver; KR 86 ADF; KT 76A transponder; VOR/LOC coupler; KMA 20 audio panel and amplifier with marker beacon receiver and lights; Piper AutoControl IIIB autopilot; Piper electric trim; and Piper 66C microphone and headset; adding 29·9 kg (66 lb) to basic empty weight.

Group KTS-3-34. Dual King KX 175B nav/com transceivers with 720-channel com and 200-channel nav; KI 204 VOR/LOC/GS indicator and VOR/LOC converter; KI 203 VOR/LOC indicator and converter; KN 75 glideslope receiver; KMA 20 audio panel with marker beacon receiver and indicator lights; KR 85 ADF with KI 225 indicator; KT 76A transponder; Piper AltiMatic IIIC autopilot with VOR/LOC coupler; Piper electric trim; Piper dual broad band antennae and static discharge wicks; Piper 100T noise-cancelling microphone, headset and speaker; adding 40 kg (88 lb) to basic empty weight.

Group CTM-1-34. Dual Collins VHF 250 com transceivers, dual VIR 350 nav receivers with VOR/LOC converters, dual IND 350 VOR/LOC indicators, AMR 350 audio selector panel/amplifier/lights, incl marker beacon receiver, ADF 650 ADF with indicator, TDR 950 transponder, Piper VOR antenna, dual broad band com antennae, AltiMatic IIIC, VOR/LOC coupler, electric trim, static discharge wicks, Piper 100T microphone, headset and radio speaker; adding 27·1 kg (59·7 lb) to basic empty weight.

Two operational groups are also available:

Executive. Comprising Piper TruSpeed indicator, instrument panel white backlighting and overhead red lighting, navigation lights, landing/taxi light, dual map lights, four individual reading lights, forward baggage compartment light, radio dimming and switch panel lighting, wingtip strobe lights, dual vacuum system and advanced instrument panel with 3 in pictorial gyro horizon, 3 in directional gyro, Piper turn rate indicator, rate of climb indicator, outside air temperature gauge and electric clock, heated pitot head/stall warning, and aircraft towbar; adding 14·3 kg (31·5 lb) to basic empty weight.

Sportsman. As Executive group, plus inertia-reel safety belts for rear seats, tinted windows and windscreen, external power socket, courtesy lighting package comprising forward baggage compartment and cabin door entrance lights and switching, automatic locator beacon, vertically-adjustable pilot's seat, and quick oil drains; adding 22 kg (48·5 lb) to basic empty weight.

Piper Seneca II, powered by two Continental TSIO-360-E turbocharged counter-rotating engines

TYPE: Six/seven-seat twin-engined light aircraft.

WINGS: Cantilever low-wing monoplane. Single-spar wings, Frise ailerons, and wide-span slotted flaps, of light alloy construction. Glassfibre wingtips. Flaps manually operated.

FUSELAGE: Light alloy semi-monocoque structure.

TAIL UNIT: Cantilever structure of light alloy. One-piece all-moving horizontal surface with combined anti-balance and trim tab. Anti-servo tab in rudder.

LANDING GEAR: Hydraulically-retractable tricycle type. Steerable nosewheel. Emergency free-fall extension system. Main wheels with tyre size 6·00-6, 8-ply rating; nosewheel and tyre size 6·00-6, 6-ply rating. Nosewheel safety mirror. High-capacity disc brakes. Parking brake. Heavy-duty tyres and brakes optional.

POWER PLANT: Two 149 kW (200 hp) Continental TSIO-360-E flat-four turbocharged counter-rotating engines, driving Hartzell two-blade constant-speed fully-feathering metal propellers. Three-blade propellers optional. Fuel in two tanks in wings, with a total capacity of 371 litres (98 US gallons) of which 352 litres (93 US gallons) are usable. Optional 57 litre (15 US gallon) auxiliary tank in each wing to provide a max capacity of 485 litres (128 US gallons) of which 466 litres (123 US gallons) are usable. Oil capacity 7·5 litres (2 US gallons). Glassfibre engine cowlings. Electrical propeller de-icing optional.

ACCOMMODATION: Enclosed cabin, seating six people in pairs on individual seats with 0·25 m (10 in) centre aisle. Optional seventh seat between two centre seats. Dual controls standard. Pilot's storm window. Two forward-hinged doors, one on starboard side at front, the other on port side at rear. Large optional door adjacent to rear cabin door provides an extra-wide opening for loading bulky items. Passenger seats removable easily to provide different seating/baggage/cargo combinations. Space for 45 kg (100 lb) baggage at rear of cabin, and for 45 kg (100 lb) in nose compartment with external access door on port side. Cabin heated and ventilated. Electrically de-iced windscreen for pilot, and ice inspection light, optional.

SYSTEMS: Electro-hydraulic system for landing gear retraction. Electrical system powered by dual 12V 65A alternators. 12V 35Ah battery. Oxygen system with six outlets optional. Dual engine-driven vacuum pumps for flight instruments optional. Piper Aire air-conditioning system optional. Janitrol 45,000 BTU combustion heater.

AVIONICS AND EQUIPMENT: Factory-installed avionics packages as group listing in introductory copy, plus a wide range of additional items available to customer's requirements. Standard equipment includes sensitive altimeter, alternate static source, exhaust gas temperature gauge, dual recording tachometers, stall warning device, full-flow oil filters, red strobe light on fin, fuel quick drains, electrical engine priming system, soundproofing, sun visors, tiedown rings and aircraft step. Optional items include individual reading lights, zinc chromate finish, stainless steel cables, cabin fire extinguisher, headrests, inertia-reel safety belts for centre and rear seats, seventh seat, solar control windows, advanced instrument panel for co-pilot, engine hour recorder, external power cable, cold weather starting kit, nose radome installation, a complete de-icing group, anti-collision lights, ventilation fan, super soundproofing, and automatic locator beacon.

DIMENSIONS, EXTERNAL:
Wing span 11·85 m (38 ft 10¾ in)
Length overall 8·69 m (28 ft 6 in)
Height overall 3·02 m (9 ft 10¾ in)
Wheel track 3·38 m (11 ft 1¼ in)
Wheelbase 2·13 m (7 ft 0 in)
Propeller diameter 1·93 m (6 ft 4 in)
Cabin door (stbd, fwd): Height 0·89 m (2 ft 11 in)
Width 0·91 m (3 ft 0 in)
Cabin door (port, aft): Height 0·84 m (2 ft 9 in)
Width 0·74 m (2 ft 5 in)
Baggage door (stbd, aft): Height 0·51 m (1 ft 8 in)
Width 0·71 m (2 ft 4 in)
Baggage door (port, fwd): Height 0·46 m (1 ft 6 in)
Width 0·61 m (2 ft 0 in)

DIMENSIONS, INTERNAL:
Cabin (incl flight deck):
Length 3·17 m (10 ft 5 in)
Max width and height 1·24 m (4 ft 1 in)
Volume 5·53 m³ (195·3 cu ft)
Forward baggage compartment 0·43 m³ (15·3 cu ft)
Aft baggage compartment 0·49 m³ (17·3 cu ft)

AREA:
Wings, gross 19·39 m² (208·7 sq ft)

WEIGHTS AND LOADINGS:
Weight empty 1,292 kg (2,848 lb)
Max T-O weight 2,073 kg (4,570 lb)
Max landing weight 1,969 kg (4,342 lb)
Max wing loading 107·4 kg/m² (22 lb/sq ft)
Max power loading 6·96 kg/kW (11·4 lb/hp)

PERFORMANCE (at max T-O weight, except where indicated):
Max level speed at 3,660 m (12,000 ft)
195 knots (361 km/h; 225 mph)
Cruising speed:
75% power at 6,100 m (20,000 ft)
190 knots (352 km/h; 219 mph)
75% power at 3,050 m (10,000 ft)
178 knots (330 km/h; 205 mph)
65% power at 7,315 m (24,000 ft)
181 knots (335 km/h; 208 mph)
65% power at 3,050 m (10,000 ft)
166 knots (308 km/h; 191 mph)
55% power at 7,620 m (25,000 ft)
165 knots (306 km/h; 190 mph)
55% power at 3,050 m (10,000 ft)
154 knots (285 km/h; 177 mph)
Stalling speed, flaps up
66 knots (122 km/h; 76 mph) CAS
Stalling speed, flaps down
61 knots (113 km/h; 70 mph) CAS
Max rate of climb at S/L 408 m (1,340 ft)/min
Rate of climb at S/L, one engine out
69 m (225 ft)/min
Certificated operating ceiling 7,620 m (25,000 ft)
Service ceiling, one engine out 4,080 m (13,400 ft)
T-O run 274 m (900 ft)
T-O to 15 m (50 ft) 378 m (1,240 ft)
Landing from 15 m (50 ft) 637 m (2,090 ft)
*Landing from 15 m (50 ft) 567 m (1,860 ft)
Landing run 421 m (1,380 ft)
*Landing run 320 m (1,050 ft)
Accelerate/stop distance 768 m (2,520 ft)
*Accelerate/stop distance 690 m (2,264 ft)
Range with standard fuel, allowances for taxi, T-O, climb, descent, and 45 min reserves at long-range cruise power:
75% power at 6,100 m (20,000 ft)
546 nm (1,012 km; 629 miles)
65% power at 6,550 m (21,500 ft)
585 nm (1,084 km; 674 miles)
55% power at 6,100 m (20,000 ft)
609 nm (1,129 km; 701 miles)
Range with max optional fuel, allowances as above:
75% power at 6,100 m (20,000 ft)
783 nm (1,451 km; 902 miles)
65% power at 6,550 m (21,500 ft)
843 nm (1,562 km; 971 miles)
55% power at 6,100 m (20,000 ft)
882 nm (1,635 km; 1,016 miles)

**With optional heavy duty brakes*

PIPER (PA-36) BRAVE

On 9 October 1972 Piper Aircraft Corporation released details of a new agricultural aircraft named the Pawnee Brave, which had a more powerful engine than the PA-25 Pawnee D and was larger, with increased capacity for either liquid or dry chemicals.

Experience gained by Piper in the construction, progressive refinement, and operation of several thousand PA-25 Pawnees led to design of the Brave. Primary consideration was to provide an aircraft able to offer high standards of safety and comfort for the pilot.

The basic configuration seats the pilot well aft. The long nose is designed to collapse progressively in an emergency. The fuselage is a welded truss structure of chrome-molybdenum steel, which is graded in strength to provide excellent energy absorption and progressive collapse. A sturdy overturn pylon is an integral part of the fuselage structure. The wing is of conventional cantilever construction, with laminated spars to provide structural redundancy. The wing leading-edges each comprise two glassfibre sections, reinforced by a foam insert beam running spanwise. Normal impacts are absorbed by the leading-edge, more serious contacts by ribs designed to collapse with minimal impact transference to the basic wing structure.

The pilot is located in an isolated cockpit capsule which keeps him well clear of main structural members. The floor, for example, is 0·30 m (1 ft 0 in) above the lower longerons, and a cockpit width of 0·97 m (3 ft 2 in) allows for substantial deformation of the fuselage structure without hazard to the pilot. The seat is attached to the overturn pylon, and is articulated to allow the pilot's position to change with fuselage deformation. The cockpit capsule is sealed to prevent the ingress of toxic chemicals; and all protrusions, knobs and levers which might cause injury have been eliminated. The instrument panel is equipped with a large energy-absorbing crash roll.

Ventilation of the cockpit capsule is provided by an airscoop in the top of the canopy, which filters the incoming air before discharge through two adjustable diffusers. A heating system is standard, and the inflow of ventilating and/or heated air has the effect of pressurising the cockpit, further discouraging any inflow of toxic fumes or chemicals.

Several fire suppression provisions have been introduced which are unique for an agricultural aircraft. The fuel tanks, located in the wing roots, are filled with reticulated polyurethane foam to serve both as a fire suppressant and as a constant baffle to reduce fuel surge. Fire-resistant fuel pipes are wire-reinforced at potential rupture points.

To meet varying requirements, two hopper sizes are available. The larger hopper has a maximum dry chemicals capacity of 862 kg (1,900 lb), and is compatible with applicators designed to spread chemicals at rates of up to 181 kg (400 lb) per acre.

Spray equipment for the Brave has a capability of up to 863 litres (228 US gallons) per minute, which is the equivalent of 64 litres (17 US gallons) per acre at 117 knots (217 km/h; 135 mph) and with a 15·25 m (50 ft) swath width. The spray equipment consists of a quickly-removable pylon-mounted wind-driven spraypump, and spraybooms located just aft of the wing trailing-edges. This location reduces drag and allows the pilot to make visual checks of their operation.

All parts of the Brave's airframe are treated to prevent corrosion damage, with extensive use of polyurethane coating, selection of stainless steel for cables and other moving components in vulnerable areas, and internal oiling of lower truss sections. The design eliminates dust traps and inaccessible areas, and fuselage covering is spaced away from the frame to permit thorough hosing down. To facilitate washing, inspection and maintenance, the plastics side panels and entire belly covering are attached by quick-release fasteners.

Two versions of the Brave are available:

Brave 300. Basic version, equipped with one 224 kW (300 hp) Lycoming IO-540-K1G5 flat-six engine, driving a Hartzell HC-C2YK-1BF two-blade constant-speed metal propeller. Three-blade propeller optional.

Brave 375. Introduced in 1978: basically as Brave 300, but equipped with 279·5 kW (375 hp) Lycoming IO-720-D1CD flat-eight engine, driving a Hartzell three-blade constant-speed metal propeller, and with the 862 kg (1,900 lb) hopper as standard. FAA certification in Normal and Restricted categories was awarded on 4 October 1977.

The following description applies to both versions of the Brave:

TYPE: Single-seat agricultural aircraft.

WINGS: Cantilever low-wing monoplane. Wing section NACA 63_3-618. Dihedral 6°. Incidence 2° 30′ at root, 0° 30′ at tip. Conventional two-spar metal structure. Light alloy laminated spars with two-bolt main spar attachment to fuselage structure. Light alloy covering, except for detachable leading-edges of glassfibre, reinforced by foam inserts, and glassfibre wingtips. Conventional ailerons and trailing-edge flaps. Landing lights in wing leading-edges.

FUSELAGE: Welded chrome-molybdenum steel tube structure. Removable metal underskin and removable side panels of plastics material. Glassfibre engine cowling.

TAIL UNIT: Cantilever all-metal structure. Tailplane has glassfibre tips. Tab on rudder and in each elevator. Cable from top of cockpit structure to tip of fin to deflect cables.

LANDING GEAR: Non-retractable tailwheel type. Interchangeable cantilever spring steel main-gear struts, with wire-cutters on leading-edges. Cleveland main wheels type 40-101 with tyres size 8·50-10, 6-ply rating, pressure 1·93-2·21 bars (28-32 lb/sq in). Scott steerable tailwheel type 3450-21 with tyre of 0·25 m (10 in) diameter, pressure 2·41-3·10 bars (35-45 lb/sq in). Cleveland type 30-67B hydraulic brakes. Parking brakes.

POWER PLANT: One engine as detailed in model listings. Three-blade constant-speed propeller optional for Brave 300. One fuel tank in each wing root, capacity 170·3 litres (45 US gallons). Total fuel capacity for both versions 348 litres (92 US gallons), of which 325·5 litres (86 US gallons) are usable. Refuelling point on upper surface of each wing. Fuel tanks filled with reticulated polyurethane safety foam (Safom). Oil capacity of Brave 300, 11·4 litres (3 US gallons); Brave 375, 16·1 litres (4·25 US gallons).

ACCOMMODATION: Pilot only, on adjustable seat in an isolated cockpit capsule, with steel tube overturn structure. Seat, equipped with double shoulder harness and inertia reel, is attached to overturn structure. Wire-cutter mounted in centre of windscreen. Combined window and door on each side, hinged at bottom. Cockpit capsule is ventilated and can be heated optionally.

SYSTEMS: Electrical system of Brave 300 supplied by 28V 70A alternator, with 24V 17Ah battery. Brave 375 has 28V 70A alternator with two 12V 25Ah batteries in series. Hydraulic system for brakes only.

AVIONICS: The optional factory-installed avionics pack-

Chincul Argentinian built example of the Piper Brave 300 agricultural aircraft

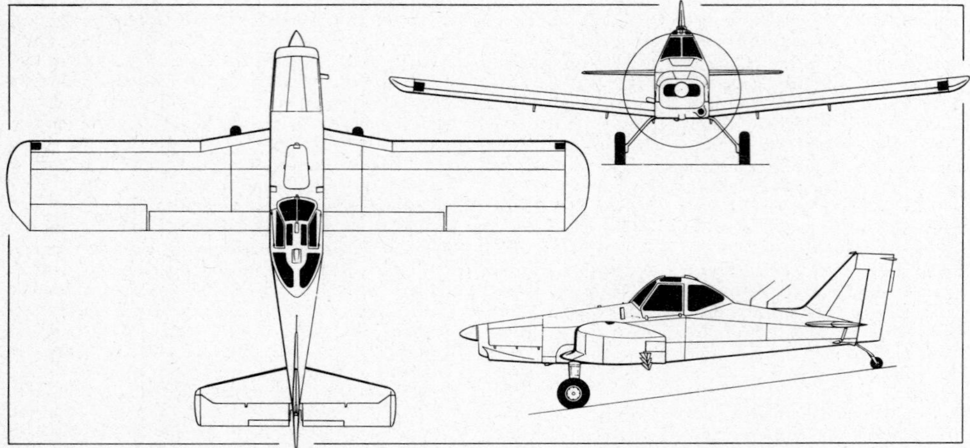

Piper Brave single-seat agricultural aircraft *(Pilot Press)*

ages detailed for the Pawnee D are available also for the Brave, as well as a range of transponders.

EQUIPMENT: Standard on Brave 300 is a non-corrosive hopper/tank of translucent glassfibre-reinforced plastics, installed forward of cockpit and approximately on CG, of 0·85 m^3 (30 cu ft) capacity, containing 852 litres (225 US gallons). Hopper/tank of 1·08 m^3 (38 cu ft) capacity, containing 1,041 litres (275 US gallons) optional for Brave 300, standard for Brave 375. The latter has a maximum capacity for dry chemicals of 862 kg (1,900 lb). Venturi-type dry material spreaders of either stainless steel or aluminium available, including a basic design capable of application rates of 2·3 to 91 kg (5 to 200 lb) per acre. Spray system comprises an easily-removable wind-driven spraypump and 38 mm (1½ in) diameter sprayblooms equipped with 60 nozzles. Other optional equipment includes 8-day clock; turn co-ordinator; landing and taxi lights; navigation, instrument panel and anti-collision lights; cockpit fire extinguisher; and heater.

DIMENSIONS, EXTERNAL:
Wing span 11·82 m (38 ft 9½ in)
Wing chord at root: Brave 375 2·03 m (6 ft 8 in)
Wing chord at tip: Brave 375 1·75 m (5 ft 9 in)
Wing aspect ratio: Brave 375 6·66
Length overall: Brave 300 8·17 m (26 ft 9½ in)
Brave 375 8·38 m (27 ft 6 in)
Height overall 2·29 m (7 ft 6 in)
Tailplane span: Brave 375 4·01 m (13 ft 1¾ in)
Wheel track: Brave 375 2·65 m (8 ft 8⅜ in)
Wheelbase: Brave 375 5·91 m (19 ft 4¾ in)
Propeller diameter: Brave 300 2·41 m (7 ft 11 in)
Brave 375 2·18 m (7 ft 2 in)
Propeller ground clearance:
Brave 300 0·25 m (10 in)
Brave 375 0·23 m (9 in)
Access doors:
Both versions: Height 0·76 m (2 ft 6 in)
Width 0·71 m (2 ft 4 in)
Height to sill 1·57 m (5 ft 2 in)
Hopper loading door, Brave 375:
Length 1·27 m (4 ft 2 in)
Width 0·48 m (1 ft 7 in)

DIMENSIONS, INTERNAL:
Cabin: Max width 0·97 m (3 ft 2 in)
Max height 1·32 m (4 ft 4 in)

AREAS:
Wings, gross 20·96 m^2 (225·65 sq ft)
Ailerons (total) 2·01 m^2 (21·6 sq ft)
Trailing-edge flaps (total) 2·32 m^2 (25·0 sq ft)
Fin 0·95 m^2 (10·2 sq ft)
Rudder 0·90 m^2 (9·7 sq ft)
Tailplane 2·11 m^2 (22·67 sq ft)
Elevators (incl tabs) 1·92 m^2 (20·66 sq ft)

WEIGHTS AND LOADINGS (A: Brave 300; B: Brave 375):
Weight empty: No dispersal equipment:
A 989 kg (2,180 lb)
B 1,104 kg (2,434 lb)
Sprayer: A 1,039 kg (2,290 lb)
B 1,140 kg (2,514 lb)
Duster: A 1,039 kg (2,290 lb)
B 1,139 kg (2,510 lb)
Max T-O weight, Normal category:
A, B 1,769 kg (3,900 lb)
Max T-O weight, Restricted category:
A 1,996 kg (4,400 lb)
B 2,177 kg (4,800 lb)
Max landing weight, Normal and Restricted categories:
A, B 1,769 kg (3,900 lb)
Max wing loading, Normal category:
A, B 84·4 kg/m^2 (17·3 lb/sq ft)
Max wing loading, Restricted category:
A 95·2 kg/m^2 (19·5 lb/sq ft)
B 103·9 kg/m^2 (21·3 lb/sq ft)
Max power loading, Normal category:
A 7·90 kg/kW (13·0 lb/hp)
B 6·33 kg/kW (10·4 lb/hp)
Max power loading, Restricted category:
A 8·91 kg/kW (14·7 lb/hp)
B 7·79 kg/kW (12·8 lb/hp)

PERFORMANCE (at Normal category max T-O weight, no dispersal equipment installed; A: Brave 300; B: Brave 375):
Max level speed at optimum altitude:
A 129 knots (238 km/h; 148 mph)
B 139 knots (257 km/h; 160 mph)
Cruising speed, best power mixture:
A, 75% power at 1,675 m (5,500 ft)
123 knots (229 km/h; 142 mph)
B, 75% power at 1,705 m (5,600 ft)
129 knots (240 km/h; 149 mph)
A, 65% power at 2,835 m (9,300 ft)
120 knots (222 km/h; 138 mph)
B, 65% power at 2,895 m (9,500 ft)
126 knots (233 km/h; 145 mph)
A, 55% power at 3,415 m (11,200 ft)
109 knots (203 km/h; 126 mph)
B, 55% power at 4,265 m (14,000 ft)
119 knots (220 km/h; 137 mph)
Stalling speed, flaps up:
A 62·5 knots (116 km/h; 72 mph) CAS

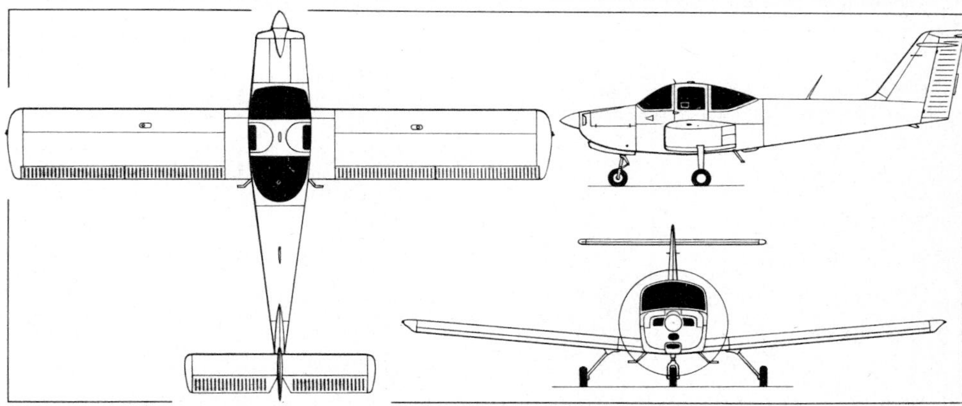

Photograph and three-view drawing *(Pilot Press)* **of the Piper Tomahawk two-seat trainer/utility aircraft**

B 61·5 knots (114 km/h; 71 mph) CAS
Stalling speed, flaps down:
A 54 knots (100 km/h; 62 mph) CAS
B 56 knots (105 km/h; 65 mph) CAS
Max rate of climb at S/L: A 235 m (770 ft)/min
B 323 m (1,060 ft)/min
T-O run: A 293 m (960 ft)
B 213 m (700 ft)
T-O to 15 m (50 ft): A 465 m (1,525 ft)
B 351 m (1,150 ft)
Landing from 15 m (50 ft): A 503 m (1,650 ft)
B 524 m (1,720 ft)
Landing run: A 213 m (700 ft)
B 235 m (770 ft)
Range with max fuel, best econ mixture, with allowances for start, taxi, T-O, climb, descent and 45 min reserves:
A 75% power at 1,675 m (5,500 ft)
556 nm (1,030 km; 640 miles)
B 75% power at 1,705 m (5,600 ft)
465 nm (861 km; 535 miles)
A 65% power at 2,835 m (9,300 ft)
586 nm (1,086 km; 675 miles)
B 65% power at 2,895 m (9,500 ft)
495 nm (917 km; 570 miles)
A 55% power at 3,415 m (11,200 ft)
612 nm (1,135 km; 705 miles)
B 55% power at 4,265 m (14,000 ft)
525 nm (974 km; 605 miles)

PIPER (PA-38-112) TOMAHAWK

Piper introduced a completely new trainer in 1978, under the name of Tomahawk. It provides side-by-side seating in a roomy cabin with all-round view, has a T-tail and wide-track landing gear, and is available with an optional factory-installed Special Training Package or an optional factory-installed avionics package in lieu:

Special Training Package. Comprises advanced instrument package, true airspeed indicator, sun visors, tinted windscreen and side windows, dual toe-operated brakes, night lighting, entrance steps each side, towbar, and avionics including King KX 170B 720-channel transceiver with 200-channel nav, King KI 208 indicator with VOR/LOC converter, Telex 66C microphone, Telex headset, and Poly Planar cabin speaker; adding 21·5 kg (47·5 lb) to basic empty weight.

Group KS-1-38. Comprising King KX 170B 720-channel com transceiver and 200-channel nav receiver, King KI 208 VOR/LOC indicator with VOR/LOC converter, Telex 66C microphone, Telex headset, and Poly Planar cabin speaker; adding 7·21 kg (15·9 lb) to basic empty weight.

The STP and avionics packages include all associated antennae.

FAA certification of the Tomahawk was granted on 20 December 1977, and the 1,000th production example was delivered in November 1978. Second-source production of the Tomahawk is undertaken for Piper by Short Brothers in the UK.

TYPE: Two-seat trainer/utility aircraft.

WINGS: Cantilever low-wing monoplane. NASA GAW-1 aerofoil section. Thickness/chord ratio 17%. Dihedral 5°. Incidence 2° at root, 0° at tip. No sweepback. Conventional structure of light alloy with plastics wingtips. Plain ailerons of light alloy construction. Plain trailing-edge flaps of light alloy construction. No trim tabs.

FUSELAGE: Conventional semi-monocoque structure, primarily of light alloy, but with some components of steel or plastics. High strength roll-over structure.

TAIL UNIT: Cantilever T-tail of light alloy construction, with plastics fin and tailplane tips. Fixed-incidence tailplane. Spring-loaded elevator trim. Ground-adjustable trim tab on rudder.

LANDING GEAR: Non-retractable tricycle type. Main wheels carried on interchangeable cantilever steel leaf springs. Nose unit has Piper oleo-pneumatic shock-absorber. Cleveland main wheels Type 40-78B and nosewheel Type 40-77B, all fitted with 5·00-5 4-ply tyres and tubes, pressure 1·79 bars (26 lb/sq in). Cleveland Type 30-9 toe-operated brakes. Dual toe-operated brakes optional. Parking brake.

POWER PLANT: One 83·5 kW (112 hp) Lycoming O-235-L2C flat-four engine, driving a Sensenich two-blade fixed-pitch metal propeller with spinner. One integral fuel tank in each wing, total capacity 121 litres (32 US gallons), of which 113·5 litres (30 US gallons) are usable. Refuelling point in upper surface of each wing. Oil capacity 5·7 litres (1·5 US gallons).

ACCOMMODATION: Enclosed cabin seating two, side by side, with dual controls standard. High strength roll-over support structure in cabin area. Door on each side. Fore, aft, and vertically adjustable seats with safety belts and shoulder harnesses. Baggage space, capacity 45·4 kg (100 lb), behind seats. Accommodation heated and ventilated. Sun visors, tinted windscreen and side windows optional. Windscreen defroster standard.

SYSTEMS: Electrical system includes a 14V 60A alternator and 12V 25Ah battery. Hydraulic system for brakes only.

AVIONICS AND EQUIPMENT: Standard equipment includes sensitive altimeter, recording tachometer, alternate static source, audible stall warning device, chart holders, coat hooks, baggage tiedown straps, carpeted floor, interior soundproofing, quick oil-drain valve, full-flow oil filter, and wing and tail tiedown rings. In addition to the electronics and equipment detailed in the optional STP and avionics group packages, a wide range of optional avionics and equipment is available to customers' requirements.

DIMENSIONS, EXTERNAL:
Wing span 10·36 m (34 ft 0 in)

Wing chord, constant 1·12 m (3 ft 8 in)
Wing aspect ratio 9·27
Length overall 7·04 m (23 ft 1¼ in)
Height overall 2·76 m (9 ft 0¾ in)
Tailplane span 3·20 m (10 ft 6 in)
Wheel track 3·05 m (10 ft 0 in)
Wheelbase 1·45 m (4 ft 9 in)
Propeller diameter 1·83 m (6 ft 0 in)
Propeller ground clearance 0·18 m (7 in)
Doors (port and stbd, each):
Height 0·74 m (2 ft 5 in)
Width 0·58 m (1 ft 11 in)
Height to sill 1·02 m (3 ft 4 in)

DIMENSIONS, INTERNAL:
Cabin, from instrument panel to rear bulkhead:
Length 1·74 m (5 ft 8½ in)
Max width 1·07 m (3 ft 6 in)
Max height 1·28 m (4 ft 2½ in)
Baggage space 0·57 m³ (20 cu ft)

AREAS:
Wings, gross 11·59 m² (124·7 sq ft)
Ailerons (total) 1·02 m² (11·0 sq ft)
Trailing-edge flaps (total) 1·01 m² (10·9 sq ft)
Vertical tail surfaces (total) 1·42 m² (15·3 sq ft)
Horizontal tail surfaces (total) 2·03 m² (21·9 sq ft)

WEIGHTS AND LOADINGS:
Weight empty 494 kg (1,088 lb)
Max T-O and landing weight 757 kg (1,670 lb)
Max wing loading 65·42 kg/m² (13·4 lb/sq ft)
Max power loading 9·07 kg/kW (14·9 lb/hp)

PERFORMANCE (at max T-O weight):
Never-exceed speed
138 knots (256 km/h; 159 mph) IAS
Max level speed at S/L
109 knots (202 km/h; 126 mph)
Max cruising speed, 75% power at 2,165 m (7,100 ft)
108 knots (200 km/h; 124 mph)
Cruising speed, 65% power at 3,200 m (10,500 ft)
100 knots (185 km/h; 115 mph)
Stalling speed, flaps up
48 knots (89·5 km/h; 55·5 mph) IAS
Stalling speed, flaps down
47 knots (88 km/h; 54·5 mph) IAS
Max rate of climb at S/L 219 m (718 ft)/min
Service ceiling 3,660 m (12,000 ft)
Absolute ceiling 4,265 m (14,000 ft)
T-O run 250 m (820 ft)
T-O to 15 m (50 ft) 445 m (1,460 ft)
Landing from 15 m (50 ft) 447 m (1,465 ft)
Landing run 191 m (625 ft)
Range with max fuel, allowances for taxi, T-O, climb, descent, with 45 min reserves at 55% power:
75% power at 2,135 m (7,000 ft)
452 nm (838 km; 520 miles)
65% power at 3,200 m (10,500 ft)
468 nm (867 km; 539 miles)

PIPER (PA-44-180) SEMINOLE

A new lightweight twin-engined four-seat cabin monoplane named Seminole was announced by Piper on 21 February 1978. Features of this economically-priced aircraft (first flown in prototype form in May 1976) are the T-tail for improved controllability and stability, counter-rotating engines, a new fuel drain sump system with only two drain valves for the entire system, and a one-piece glassfibre nosecone to give easy access to the landing gear mechanism, combustion heater, battery and landing light.

Two optional equipment packages are available for the Seminole:

Custom. Comprising Piper TruSpeed indicator; basic lighting package including instrument panel white backlighting and overhead red lighting, navigation, landing/taxi, dual map, cabin dome, radio dimming, and waterfall switch panel lights; wingtip strobe lights; assist strap; entrance step; dual engine-driven vacuum pumps with annunciator light; advanced instrument panel comprising 3 in pictorial gyro horizon, 3 in directional gyro, pictorial turn rate indicator, rate of climb indicator, outside air temperature gauge and electric clock; and dual quick oil drains; adding 15·7 kg (34·6 lb) to basic empty weight.

Executive. As Custom group, plus alternate static source, automatic locator beacon, exhaust gas temperature gauge, heated pitot head/stall warning sensor, external power socket, and pilot's vertically adjustable seat; adding 21·4 kg (47·2 lb) to basic empty weight.

TYPE: Twin-engined lightweight four-seat cabin monoplane.

WINGS: Cantilever low-wing monoplane. Conventional structure of light alloy. Plain ailerons and trailing-edge flaps of light alloy construction.

FUSELAGE: Conventional semi-monocoque structure, primarily of light alloy.

TAIL UNIT: Cantilever T-tail of light alloy construction. All-moving tailplane with full-span tab. Rudder anti-servo tab.

LANDING GEAR: Hydraulically-retractable tricycle type. Piper oleo-pneumatic shock-absorbers. Main-wheel tyres size 6·00-6, 8-ply, with tubes. Steerable nosewheel with 5·00-5 (4-ply) tyre and tube. Nosewheel safety mirror. Dual toe-operated high-capacity disc brakes. Parking brake. Heavy duty brakes and tyres optional.

POWER PLANT: Two 134 kW (180 hp) Lycoming flat-four counter-rotating engines (one O-360-E1AD and one LO-360-E1AD), each driving a Hartzell two-blade constant-speed fully-feathering metal propeller with spinner. Three-blade propellers optional. One bladder-type fuel tank in each engine nacelle, with total capacity of 416 litres (110 US gallons), of which 409 litres (108 US gallons) are usable. Refuelling point on upper surface of each nacelle. Oil capacity 11·4 litres (3 US gallons).

ACCOMMODATION: Cabin seats four in two pairs of individual seats. Pilot and co-pilot seats horizontally adjustable, and fitted with seat belts and shoulder harness, with inertia reels. Dual controls standard. Rear seats have safety belts and are reclinable. Cabin door on starboard side. Emergency exit on port side. Pilot's storm window. Baggage compartment at rear of cabin, capacity 91 kg (200 lb). Accommodation heated and ventilated. Windscreen defrosters.

SYSTEMS: Hydraulic system for landing gear actuation and brakes. Electrical system includes dual engine-driven 14V 60A alternators and 12V 35Ah battery. Combustion heater of 45,000 BTU capacity.

AVIONICS AND EQUIPMENT: A wide range of optional avionics is available to customer's requirements, including eight avionics packages based on dual nav/com, glideslope receiver, ADF and transponder from Narco, King or Collins; encoding altimeter, radar altimeter, DME, RNAV and HSI. Standard equipment includes sensitive altimeter, dual recording tachometers, full flow oil filters, stall warning horn, tiedown rings, soundproofing, sun visors, map pockets and headrest provisions. Optional equipment includes engine hour recorder, cabin fire extinguisher, external power cable, super soundproofing, headrests, shoulder harnesses with inertia reels for third and fourth seats, tinted windows and windscreen, ventilation fan, vertically adjustable seats for pilot and co-pilot; de luxe interior group with curtains and choice of seat fabrics, oversize headrests and carpet; polyurethane exterior finish, and stainless steel control cables.

DIMENSIONS, EXTERNAL:
Wing span 11·75 m (38 ft 6⅝ in)
Length overall 8·41 m (27 ft 7¼ in)
Height overall 2·59 m (8 ft 6 in)
Wheel track 3·19 m (10 ft 5¾ in)
Wheelbase 2·59 m (8 ft 5¾ in)
Propeller diameter 1·88 m (6 ft 2 in)
Cabin door (stbd): Width 0·91 m (3 ft 0 in)
Height 0·89 m (2 ft 11 in)

DIMENSIONS, INTERNAL:
Cabin, instrument panel to rear bulkhead:
Length 2·46 m (8 ft 1 in)
Max width 1·05 m (3 ft 5½ in)
Max height 1·245 m (4 ft 1 in)
Volume 3·00 m³ (106 cu ft)

AREA:
Wings, gross 16·72 m² (180 sq ft)

WEIGHTS AND LOADINGS:
Weight empty 1,091 kg (2,406 lb)
Max T-O weight 1,723 kg (3,800 lb)
Max wing loading 103·1 kg/m² (21·11 lb/sq ft)
Max power loading 6·43 kg/kW (10·55 lb/hp)

PERFORMANCE (at max T-O weight):
Max level speed at S/L
168 knots (311 km/h; 193 mph)
Cruising speed, best power settings:
75% power at 2,440 m (8,000 ft)
166 knots (308 km/h; 191 mph)
65% power at 3,630 m (11,900 ft)
162 knots (300 km/h; 187 mph)
55% power at 4,875 m (16,000 ft)
153 knots (284 km/h; 176 mph)
Cruising speed, best econ power settings:
75% power at 2,135 m (7,000 ft)
161 knots (298 km/h; 185 mph)
65% power at 3,260 m (10,700 ft)
157 knots (291 km/h; 181 mph)
55% power at 4,420 m (14,500 ft)
149 knots (276 km/h; 171 mph)
Stalling speed, flaps up
64 knots (119 km/h; 74 mph) CAS
Stalling speed, flaps down
59 knots (109 km/h; 68 mph) CAS
Max rate of climb at S/L 408 m (1,340 ft)/min
Rate of climb at S/L, one engine out
66 m (217 ft)/min
Service ceiling 5,210 m (17,100 ft)

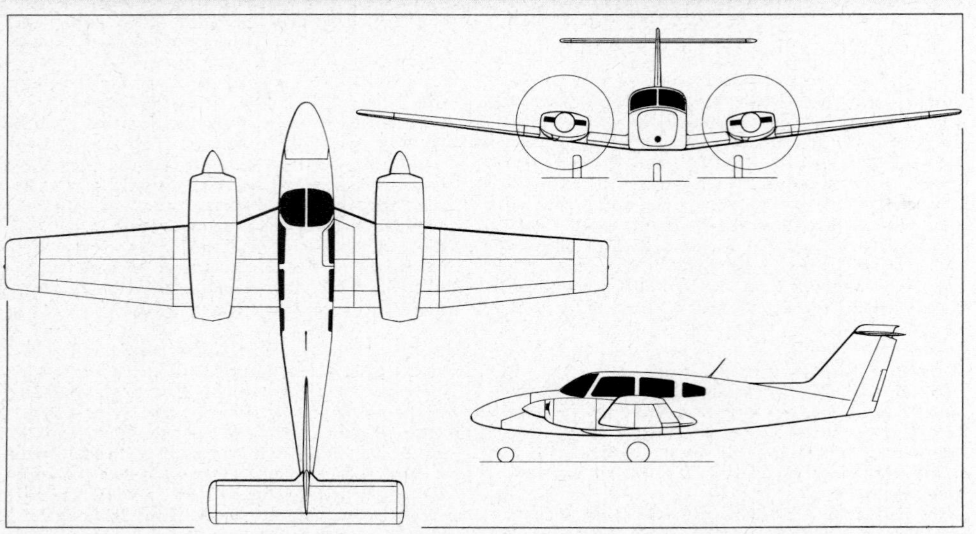

Photograph and three-view drawing *(Pilot Press)* **of the Piper Seminole lightweight twin-engined four-seat cabin monoplane**

Service ceiling, one engine out 1,250 m (4,100 ft)
Absolute ceiling 5,670 m (18,600 ft)
Absolute ceiling, one engine out 1,600 m (5,250 ft)
T-O run 268 m (880 ft)
T-O to 15 m (50 ft) 427 m (1,400 ft)
Landing from 15 m (50 ft) 363 m (1,190 ft)
Landing run 117 m (383 ft)
Accelerate/stop distance, with heavy-duty brakes 631 m (2,070 ft)
Range with max fuel at best power settings, allowances for taxi, T-O, climb, descent, and 45 min reserves at max range power:
75% power at 2,135 m (7,000 ft) 690 nm (1,279 km; 795 miles)
65% power at 3,260 m (10,700 ft) 725 nm (1,344 km; 835 miles)
55% power at 4,420 m (14,500 ft) 730 nm (1,353 km; 841 miles)
Range with max fuel at econ power settings, allowances as above:
75% power at 2,135 m (7,000 ft) 790 nm (1,464 km; 910 miles)
65% power at 3,260 m (10,700 ft) 850 nm (1,575 km; 979 miles)
55% power at 4,420 m (14,500 ft) 880 nm (1,631 km; 1,013 miles)

SANTA MARIA DIVISION

ADDRESS: 2560 Skyway Drive, Santa Maria, California 93454
Telephone: (805) 922 8411
GENERAL MANAGER: Ron W. Smith

On 27 March 1978, Piper Aircraft Corporation and Ted Smith Aerostar Corporation announced jointly the acquisition by Piper of all of the assets and business of Aerostar with effect from 24 March 1978. The existing Aerostar facility has become Piper's Santa Maria Division with Ron W. Smith, formerly President of Aerostar, remaining with the Division in the capacity of General Manager. Piper is not only continuing to manufacture the Aerostar 600, 601 and 601P, but is increasing production at Santa Maria to satisfy the demand for these aircraft. On 12 April 1978, Piper received the FAA Production Certificate for these three aircraft. The earlier history of Ted Smith Aerostar Corporation can be found under that company's entry in the 1977-78 *Jane's*.

PIPER AEROSTAR 600/601/601P

Design work on this series was started by the Ted Smith Aircraft Company in November 1964 and the first Model 600/601 prototype made its first flight in October 1967. FAA Type Approval of the Model 600 was awarded in March 1968, and of the Model 601 in November 1968.

It is claimed that the Aerostar airframe contains only 50% as many components as are used in other designs of comparable size. Construction involves extensive use of monocoque assemblies, in which unstiffened sections of heavy-gauge skin carry loads. The horizontal and vertical fixed tail surfaces, together with their related control surfaces, are interchangeable.

On 6 August 1975, an Aerostar 601A piloted by Jack F. Chrysler set a Class C1d 2,000 km closed-circuit speed record for piston-engined landplanes of 237·08 knots (439·07 km/h; 272·83 mph). On 21 January 1975, a 601A flown by Capt Barry Schiff captured the 500 km closed-circuit record with a speed of 264·77 knots (490·36 km/h; 304·70 mph).

On 8 November 1977, an Aerostar 601P piloted by Philander Claxton III and Jack Cink recorded a new round-the-world speed record for piston-engined aircraft, completing the 19,974 nm (37,015 km; 23,000 mile) flight in 104 h 5 min, and so beating the previous record of 122 h set by two Australians in a Beechcraft Duke.

Current production versions of the Aerostar comprise:

Model 600A. Powered by two 216 kW (290 hp) Lycoming IO-540-K1J5 flat-six engines. European models designated 600AE.

Model 601B. As Model 600A, but with increased wing span and powered by two 216 kW (290 hp) Lycoming IO-540-S1A5 flat-six turbocharged engines. Certificated for a max T-O and landing weight of 2,722 kg (6,000 lb). European models designated 601BE.

Model 601P. As Model 601B, but with higher flow-rate turbochargers to supply bleed air for cabin pressurisation. European models designated 601PE.

An optional group of factory-installed de-icing equipment is available for all three versions, and comprises de-icing boots for wing and tail unit leading-edges, electrically heated propeller boots, alcohol de-icing system for windscreen, and wing ice inspection light; adding 33·5 kg (73·9 lb) to basic empty weight.

TYPE: Twin-engined light transport aircraft.

WINGS: Cantilever mid-wing monoplane. Wing section NACA 64₁A212. Dihedral 2°. Incidence 1°. No sweepback. All-metal structure using heavy gauge skins attached to three spars, several bulkheads and stringers. Entire wing assembly, excluding attachments for ailerons and flaps, contains fewer than 50 detail parts. Ailerons and flaps each comprise a spar, ribs, nose skin and one-piece wraparound light alloy skin aft of spar. No trim tabs. Models 601B and 601P have increased wing span. De-icing for wing leading-edges optional.

FUSELAGE: All-metal fail-safe monocoque structure. Skin composed of large segments of light alloy sheet over stringers and frames. Entire fuselage contains fewer than 100 parts, including skin panels. All fuselage assemblies designed basically for pressurisation.

TAIL UNIT: Cantilever all-metal structure, with swept vertical and horizontal surfaces. Both fixed and control surfaces are interchangeable. Electrically-operated trim tab in rudder and each elevator. De-icing boots for fin and tailplane leading-edges optional.

LANDING GEAR: Hydraulically-retractable tricycle type. Main units retract inward, nosewheel forward. Steerable nosewheel. Hydraulically-operated dual caliper brakes. Parking brake.

POWER PLANT: Two Lycoming engines, as detailed in model listings, each driving a Hartzell three-blade constant-speed and fully-feathering metal propeller with spinner. Fuel in integral wing tanks and fuselage tank with total capacity of 669 litres (177 US gallons), of which 660·5 litres (174·5 US gallons) are usable. Oil capacity 22·7 litres (6 US gallons).

Piper Aerostar Model 601B light transport (two Lycoming IO-540-S1A5 engines)

ACCOMMODATION: Cabin seats six people on track-mounted individual reclining seats, in pairs. Dual controls standard. Door on port side by pilot's seat; top half hinges upward, bottom half downward. Emergency escape windows at rear of cabin. Tinted windscreen and dual pane tinted cabin windows. Large utility shelf in aft cabin. Baggage compartment, capacity 109 kg (240 lb), aft of cabin, with external access. Individual air vents and reading lights for each seat. Cabin heated/ventilated in 600A/601B, and also pressurised in 601P. Control locks. Windscreen defrosting; alcohol de-icing system optional.

SYSTEMS: Heating/ventilation system includes a Janitrol 35,000 BTU heater. Pressurisation system for Model 601P supplied by engine bleed air; pressure differential 0·29 bars (4·25 lb/sq in). Hydraulic system for landing gear actuation, wheel brakes and flaps, powered by an engine-driven pump, pressure 69 bars (1,000 lb/sq in). Dual pneumatic systems for instrument gyros and optional de-icing boots. Electrical system powered by two 28V 70A engine-driven alternators with failure warning lights. Two 12V 24Ah batteries. External power socket. Models 601B and 601P each have an oxygen system, with individual outlets at each seat, as standard; capacity 601B 3·26 m³ (115 cu ft), 601P 0·31 m³ (11 cu ft).

AVIONICS AND EQUIPMENT: Standard avionics by King for Models 600A and 601B include dual KX 175B nav/coms, KI 204 VOR/ILS/glideslope indicator and VOR/LOC converter, KI 203 VOR/ILS indicator and VOR/LOC converter, KN 73 glideslope receiver, KR 85 ADF receiver and KI 225 ADF indicator with rotating azimuth (601B only), KN 61 DME unit with KI 261 indicator and Nav 1/Nav 2 switching, KT 76 transponder, KMA 20 control console including audio amplifier and marker beacon receiver, and associated antennae, filters, microphone and cabin speaker. Standard avionics for Model 601P include dual Collins VHF-250 com transceivers and antennae, dual VIR-350 nav receivers with VOR/LOC converters and antenna, GLS-350 glideslope with antenna, IND-351 course deviation indicator with glideslope indicator, IND-350 course deviation indicator, ADF-650 ADF system with indicator and antennae, TDR-950 transponder, AMR-350 marker/audio panel, dual PWC-150 power converters, radio master switch, Narco DME-195, Narco AR-500 altitude encoder, dual cabin speakers, microphones and associated equipment. A wide range of optional avionics is available to customer's requirements. Standard equipment includes map lights, red and white instrument panel lights, baggage compartment light, dual taxi and landing lights, navigation lights, strobe lights, full blind-flying instrumentation, eight-day clock, outside air temperature gauge, flight hour recorder, emergency locator transmitter, heated pitot, full flow oil filters, control locks, sun visors, jack pads and towbar. 601P has in addition as standard an alternate static source.

DIMENSIONS, EXTERNAL:
Wing span: 600A 10·41 m (34 ft 2 in)
601B, 601P 11·18 m (36 ft 8 in)
Wing chord at root 2·18 m (7 ft 2 in)
Wing chord at tip: 600A 0·87 m (2 ft 10⅜ in)
601B, 601P 0·76 m (2 ft 6 in)
Wing aspect ratio: 600A 6·83
601B, 601P 7·55
Length overall 10·61 m (34 ft 9¾ in)
Height overall 3·70 m (12 ft 1½ in)
Tailplane span 4·37 m (14 ft 4 in)
Wheel track 3·11 m (10 ft 2½ in)
Propeller diameter 1·98 m (6 ft 6 in)
Passenger door: Height 1·14 m (3 ft 9 in)
Width 0·71 m (2 ft 4 in)
Baggage compartment door:
Height 0·61 m (2 ft 0 in)
Width 0·56 m (1 ft 10 in)

DIMENSIONS, INTERNAL:
Cabin: Length 3·81 m (12 ft 6 in)
Width 1·17 m (3 ft 10 in)
Height 1·22 m (4 ft 0 in)
Baggage space 0·85 m³ (30 cu ft)

AREAS:
Wings, gross: 600A 15·79 m² (170 sq ft)
601B, 601P 16·54 m² (178 sq ft)
Tailplane 4·20 m² (45·2 sq ft)

WEIGHTS AND LOADINGS:
Weight empty, equipped: 600A 1,715 kg (3,780 lb)
601B 1,808 kg (3,985 lb)
601P 1,857 kg (4,095 lb)
Max T-O and landing weight:
600A 2,495 kg (5,500 lb)
601B, 601P 2,721 kg (6,000 lb)
Max wing loading: 600A 158·2 kg/m² (32·4 lb/sq ft)
601B, 601P 164·5 kg/m² (33·7 lb/sq ft)
Max power loading: 600A 5·77 kg/kW (9·5 lb/hp)
601B, 601P 6·29 kg/kW (10·34 lb/hp)

PERFORMANCE (at max T-O weight, A: 600A; B: 601B; C: 601P):
Cruising speed at average cruise weight:
A 75% power at 2,285 m (7,500 ft) 220 knots (408 km/h; 253 mph)
B, C 75% power at 7,620 m (25,000 ft) 257 knots (476 km/h; 296 mph)
A 65% power at 3,050 m (10,000 ft) 213 knots (395 km/h; 245 mph)
B, C 65% power at 7,620 m (25,000 ft) 238 knots (441 km/h; 274 mph)
A 55% power at 3,050 m (10,000 ft) 200 knots (371 km/h; 230 mph)
B, C 55% power at 7,620 m (25,000 ft) 218 knots (404 km/h; 251 mph)
Stalling speed, flaps down:
A 74 knots (137 km/h; 85 mph) IAS
B, C 77 knots (143 km/h; 89 mph) IAS
Max rate of climb at S/L: A 549 m (1,800 ft)/min
B, C 466 m (1,530 ft)/min
Rate of climb at S/L, one engine out:
A 137 m (450 ft)/min
B, C 77 m (254 ft)/min
Service ceiling: A 6,460 m (21,200 ft)
B 9,145 m (30,000 ft)
C 7,620 m (25,000 ft)
Service ceiling, one engine out:
A 1,875 m (6,150 ft)
B, C 2,835 m (9,300 ft)
T-O run: A 307 m (1,008 ft)
B, C 579 m (1,900 ft)
T-O to 15 m (50 ft): A 427 m (1,400 ft)
B, C 759 m (2,490 ft)
Landing from 15 m (50 ft): A 735 m (2,410 ft)
B, C 619 m (2,030 ft)
Landing run: A 272 m (892 ft)
B, C 375 m (1,230 ft)

Range with max fuel, allowances for start, taxi, T-O, climb, and 45 min reserves at long-range cruise power:
A 75% power at 1,830 m (6,000 ft) 1,103 nm (2,044 km; 1,270 miles)
A 65% power at 2,745 m (9,000 ft) 1,223 nm (2,266 km; 1,408 miles)
B 65% power at 4,570 m (15,000 ft) 1,063 nm (1,970 km; 1,224 miles)
C 65% power at 4,570 m (15,000 ft) 1,086 nm (2,013 km; 1,251 miles)
A 55% power at 3,050 m (10,000 ft) 1,320 nm (2,446 km; 1,520 miles)
B 55% power at 4,570 m (15,000 ft) 1,244 nm (2,305 km; 1,432 miles)
C 55% power at 6,100 m (20,000 ft) 1,271 nm (2,355 km; 1,464 miles)

PITTS

PITTS AEROBATICS

ADDRESS: PO Box 547, Afton, Wyoming 83110
Telephone: (307) 886 3151
GENERAL MANAGER: E. H. Andersen Jr

One of the best-known US designers of high-performance sporting aircraft, Mr Curtis Pitts, announced on 1 January 1977 that he had sold the manufacturing, engineering, and sales rights of the Pitts S-1 and S-2 aircraft to Doyle Child of Afton, Wyoming. A new company, Pitts Aerobatics, was formed to continue engineering and sales activities, being based at the same location as Aerotek Inc, which formerly produced the S-2 for Pitts Aviation Enterprises.

Detailed construction drawings for the single-seat S-1 version are available to amateur constructors (see Homebuilts section). For pilots who do not wish to build their own aircraft, Aerotek Inc can supply a ready-to-fly single-seater designated S-1S. The two-seat S-2 is available both as a factory-built aircraft and in kit form, and is produced by Aerotek for Pitts Aerobatics. The single-seat S-2S, of which the first production examples became available in late 1978, is also being marketed in kit form for amateur construction. Production S-2S aircraft are certificated currently in the Experimental-Exhibition category, but it is planned to gain full type certification.

PITTS S-1 SPECIAL

The original single-seat Pitts Special was designed in 1943-44. Construction of a prototype began in 1944 and it flew in September of that year. One of the most successful early models was *Little Stinker,* powered by a 67 kW (90 hp) Continental engine, and built by Mr Pitts in 1947 for Miss Betty Skelton, then an internationally-known aerobatic display pilot. The *Black Beauty* biplane, built by Pitts for Miss Caro Bailey, was of similar design, but powered by a 93 kW (125 hp) Lycoming O-290-D engine.

Since then even more powerful engines have been installed in Pitts Specials built by both the designer and other people, and those versions of the single-seat Special for which drawings are available are designed to take a Lycoming engine of up to 134 kW (180 hp), as noted in the Homebuilts section.

Current versions of the S-1 are as follows:

S-1D. Intended for homebuilders only, with plans available. Generally similar to the S-1S.

S-1E. Intended for homebuilders only; has wings of symmetrical aerofoil section. Plans available.

S-1S. Production aircraft, FAA type certificated and built at rate of 25 aircraft per year. It is available also in kit form, parts, materials and components being produced under an FAA Approved Production Certificate.

There is also an S-1C version, but Pitts can no longer supply plans for its construction.

Details of some of the major successes achieved by US pilots of Pitts Specials in national and international aerobatic competitions, since 1966, have been given in the 1972-73 and later *Jane's*.

The details which follow apply to the S-1S factory-built aircraft with 134 kW (180 hp) engine, but engines of 74·5-134 kW (100-180 hp) can be fitted to the S-1 Special.

TYPE: Single-seat sporting biplane.

WINGS: Braced biplane type, with single faired interplane strut each side and N-type cabane struts. Dual streamline flying and landing wires. Wing section M6. Thickness/chord ratio 12%. Dihedral 0° on upper wing, 3° on lower wings. Incidence 1° 30′ on upper wing, 0° on lower wings. Sweepback at quarter-chord 6° 40′ on upper wing only. Wooden structure, with fabric covering. Frise-type ailerons on both upper and lower wings, of similar construction to wings. No flaps or tabs.

FUSELAGE: Welded steel tube structure, fabric covered.

TAIL UNIT: Wire-braced steel tube structure, fabric-covered. Fixed-incidence tailplane. Trim tab in each elevator.

LANDING GEAR: Non-retractable tailwheel type. Rubber-cord shock-absorption. Cleveland main wheels with 6-ply tyres, size 5·00-5, pressure 2·07 bars (30 lb/sq in). Cleveland hydraulic disc brakes. Steerable tailwheel. Glassfibre fairings on main wheels.

POWER PLANT: One 134 kW (180 hp) Lycoming IO-360-B4A flat-four engine, driving a Sensenich type 76EM8-O-56/62 two-blade fixed-pitch metal propeller. Fuel tank aft of firewall, capacity 75 litres (20 US gallons). Refuelling point on upper surface of fuselage, forward of windscreen. Oil capacity 7·5 litres (2 US gallons). Inverted fuel and oil systems standard.

ACCOMMODATION: Single seat in open cockpit.

DIMENSIONS, EXTERNAL:
Wing span, upper 5·28 m (17 ft 4 in)
Wing chord (constant, both) 0·91 m (3 ft 0 in)
Wing aspect ratio 5·77
Length overall 4·71 m (15 ft 5½ in)
Height overall 1·92 m (6 ft 3½ in)
Tailplane span 1·98 m (6 ft 6 in)
Propeller diameter 1·93 m (6 ft 4 in)

AREA:
Wings, gross 9·15 m² (98·5 sq ft)

WEIGHTS AND LOADING:
Weight empty 326 kg (720 lb)
Max T-O weight 521 kg (1,150 lb)
Max power loading 3·89 kg/kW (6·38 lb/hp)

PERFORMANCE (at max T-O weight):
Never-exceed speed 176 knots (326 km/h; 203 mph)
Max level speed at S/L 153 knots (283 km/h; 176 mph)
Max cruising speed at S/L 122 knots (227 km/h; 141 mph)
Stalling speed 54 knots (100 km/h; 62 mph)
Max rate of climb at S/L 792 m (2,600 ft)/min
Service ceiling 6,795 m (22,300 ft)
T-O to 15 m (50 ft) 331 m (1,085 ft)
Range with max fuel, no reserves 273 nm (507 km; 315 miles)

Pitts S-2A Special, a factory-built two-seater with enclosed rear cockpit *(Antonio Camarasa)*

PITTS S-2A SPECIAL

First flown in 1967, the S-2A is a two-seat version of the Pitts Special. It is similar to the single-seat S-1 in basic configuration and construction, but is slightly larger in overall dimensions, with no attempt at commonality of components. The increased size and power, coupled with aerodynamic changes, give the two-seater improved aerobatic and landing characteristics, and make it extremely stable in rough air conditions. Control responses are better than on the S-1. The ailerons are aerodynamically balanced for higher rate of roll at low speeds, and full vertical rolls can be made with ease. The different wing sections used on the S-2A provide inverted performance equal to conventional flight, and facilitate outside loops.

The S-2A is FAA type certificated in the Normal and Aerobatic categories. It is a production aeroplane, not intended for the homebuilder, and plans are not available.

Five S-2As, each fitted with a 149 kW (200 hp) Lycoming engine, were supplied in early 1973 to the British aerobatic display team then financed by the Rothman Tobacco Company. During displays, the front cockpit of each aircraft was covered by a removable panel. Five similar aircraft were supplied to the Carling Black Label aerobatic team operating from Toronto, Canada.

S-2As have been exported to Australia, Brazil, Sweden and Venezuela. In mid-1976, the Peruvian Air Force announced the order of six Pitts Specials, for 'an unspecified training role'.

TYPE: Two-seat aerobatic biplane.

WINGS: Braced biplane type, with single faired interplane strut each side and N-type cabane. Wing section NACA 6400 series on upper wing, 00 series on bottom wings. Two-spar wooden (spruce) structure with fabric covering. Aerodynamically-balanced ailerons on both upper and lower wings. No flaps or tabs.

FUSELAGE: Welded steel tube structure with wooden stringers, covered with Dacron fabric except for metal top-decking.

TAIL UNIT: Wire-braced welded steel tube structure. Fixed surfaces metal-covered, control surfaces fabric-covered. Trim tab in each elevator.

LANDING GEAR: Non-retractable tailwheel type. Rubber-cord shock-absorption. Steerable tailwheel. Fairings on main wheels.

POWER PLANT: One 149 kW (200 hp) Lycoming IO-360-A1A flat-four engine, driving a Hartzell type HC-C2YK-4/C7666A-2 two-blade constant-speed metal propeller with spinner. Fuel tank in fuselage, immediately aft of firewall, capacity 90·5 litres (24 US gallons). Refuelling point on fuselage upper surface forward of front windscreen. Oil capacity 7·5 litres (2·0 US gallons). Inverted fuel and oil systems standard.

ACCOMMODATION: Two seats in tandem cockpits with dual controls. Rear cockpit can be enclosed by a transparent canopy, if required. Space for 9 kg (20 lb) baggage aft of rear cockpit when flown in non-aerobatic category.

SYSTEM: Electrical system powered by 12V 40A alternator and non-spill 12V battery.

DIMENSIONS, EXTERNAL:
Wing span, upper 6·10 m (20 ft 0 in)
Wing span, lower 5·79 m (19 ft 0 in)
Wing chord (constant, both) 1·02 m (3 ft 4 in)
Length overall 5·41 m (17 ft 9 in)
Height overall 1·94 m (6 ft 4½ in)

Pitts Model S-2S single-seat biplane (Lycoming AEIO-540-D4A5 engine)

AREA:
Wings, gross 11·6 m² (125 sq ft)
WEIGHTS AND LOADINGS (A: Aerobatic; B: Normal category):
Weight empty: A, B 453 kg (1,000 lb)
Max T-O weight: A 680 kg (1,500 lb)
B 714 kg (1,575 lb)
Max wing loading: A 58·6 kg/m² (12·0 lb/sq ft)
B 61·5 kg/m² (12·6 lb/sq ft)
Max power loading: A 4·56 kg/kW (7·5 lb/hp)
B 5·33 kg/kW (7·87 lb/hp)

PERFORMANCE (at max T-O weight. A: Aerobatic; B: Normal category):
Never-exceed speed:
A, B 176 knots (326 km/h; 203 mph)
Max level speed at S/L:
A, B 136 knots (253 km/h; 157 mph)
Max cruising speed at S/L:
A, B 132 knots (245 km/h; 152 mph)
Stalling speed: A 51 knots (94 km/h; 58 mph)
B 51·5 knots (95 km/h; 59 mph)
Max rate of climb at S/L: A 579 m (1,900 ft)/min
B 549 m (1,800 ft)/min
Service ceiling: A 6,125 m (20,100 ft)
B 4,875 m (16,000 ft)
T-O to 15 m (50 ft): A 351 m (1,150 ft)
Range with max fuel:
A 297 nm (552 km; 343 miles)

PITTS MODEL S-2S

Pitts Aerobatics began production in late 1978 of this single-seat version of the S-2A. It has a modified forward fuselage to permit the installation of a 194 kW (260 hp) Lycoming AEIO-540-D4A5 flat-six engine, driving a McCauley Type 1A/200 two-blade fixed-pitch metal propeller with spinner. The first flight of the prototype was made on 9 December 1977. Maximum level speed is 157 knots (291 km/h; 181 mph), max rate of climb at S/L 915 m (3,000 ft)/min. The Model S-2S is available either as a factory-built aircraft, or in kit form for amateur construction.

In early 1979 the S-2S was available only with Experimental category certification, but the company intends to obtain FAA type certification at an early date.

PROP-JETS

PROP-JETS INC

ADDRESS: 2950 Pearl Street, Boulder, Colorado 80301
Telephone: (303) 442 3877
PARTNERS:
Ted D. Malpass
Peter Paul Luce

A company named Interceptor Corporation was formed on 18 November 1968 for the purpose of designing, manufacturing, distributing and servicing aircraft for the general aviation market. The first aircraft that it produced was the Interceptor 400, an advanced turbine-engined development of what was known originally as the Meyers 200C and was produced subsequently by Aero Commander as its Model 200D. Interceptor Corporation acquired all design drawings, production jigs and tools for this latter aircraft and redesigned the fuselage for pressurisation, the new power plant and a revised tail unit. Construction of the prototype Interceptor 400 started in January 1969 and the first flight was made on 27 June 1969. FAA certification was received on 20 August 1971.

The first Interceptor 400 (c/n 401) was sold to a Mr F. Lee Bailey who leased it back to the company for demonstration flights. Following a forced landing by this aircraft the company ran into financial difficulties, but was sold subsequently to a new Interceptor Company with Mr Ted Malpass and Mr Peter Luce as partners.

The Type Certificate for the Interceptor 400 was transferred to a corporate entity named Prop-Jets Inc on 1 July 1977, under the same partners, who were seeking finance in early 1979 to put the aircraft into production. Details of the Interceptor 400 can be found in the 1978-79 and earlier editions of *Jane's*.

RAISBECK

THE RAISBECK GROUP

CORPORATE OFFICES: 7777 Perimeter Road S, Seattle, Washington 98108
Telephone: (206) 762 5156
Telex: Aeroamerica 32 0233
PRESIDENT AND BOARD CHAIRMAN: James D. Raisbeck
EXECUTIVE VICE-PRESIDENT—FINANCE:
Dwight D. Christy Jr
SENIOR VICE-PRESIDENT:
R. Kim Frinell (Experimental Operations)
VICE-PRESIDENT:
Thomas P. May (Contract Administration)

The Raisbeck Group was formed in 1974 by many of the team members who had developed high-lift systems for Boeing, McDonnell Douglas and Robertson Aircraft Corporation. Its aim is to improve the overall productivity of business and commercial jet aircraft by the infusion of current and advanced technology into existing airframes. Heavy emphasis is placed on aerodynamic refinements to reduce cruise drag at normal operating speeds, and to reduce required runway field length through an associated reduction in certificated stalling speeds in take-off and landing configurations.

Rockwell Sabreliner 60 fitted with increased-span Raisbeck supercritical wing

HOWARD/RAISBECK MARK II SYSTEM

The first programme by The Raisbeck Group involved the Gates Learjet family of aircraft. Work on a 'Mark II System' began in late 1973. Subsequent flight test and development, initially in conjunction with Gates Learjet Corporation and completed later through a joint effort with The Dee Howard Company of San Antonio, Texas, has brought to the market an advanced technology high-lift system for Learjet aircraft. This makes the following contribution to the aircraft's performance:

(i) Reduction in T-O and approach speeds of 16-23 knots (30-43 km/h; 18·5-26·5 mph), depending on configuration and the specific model.

(ii) Reduction in the aircraft's cruise drag of measurably significant proportions.

(iii) Certification of the turbojet versions of the Learjet Models 23, 24 and 25 to FAR Part 36 acoustic requirements without the use of sound suppressors or any change to the engine nacelle configuration.

(iv) Elimination of the stick-pusher as a performance-limiting item.

(v) Aircraft has inherent aerodynamic stall-warning characteristics.

Certification of the Mark II System was received by the Howard/Raisbeck joint venture in October 1975, and production of retrofit systems for the Learjet family of aircraft was launched immediately. By May 1979 approximately 250 production Mark II Systems had been delivered for retrofit to existing Learjet 23/24/25 aircraft, and production was continuing.

Features of the Mark II System include the installation of full-span supercritical wing leading-edges over the first 5% of wing chord, while retaining the standard Learjet anti-icing system; addition of strakes inboard of the wing-tip tanks to enhance aileron response during slow-speed and engine-out operation; removal of vortex generators; provision of new aileron gap seals; extension of the upper surface of the basic wing to cover the existing trailing-edge flap, combined with new flap tracks, to allow a significant increase in aft flap travel prior to downward deflection; addition of stall turbulators on wing leading-edges; provision of a flap-actuated pitch trim system which puts an 'up' pre-load on the elevators automatically as the flaps are deflected; installation of improved angle of attack indicator and new flap position sensor/indicator systems; and resetting of the stick shaker and pusher to conform with enhanced aerodynamic stall characteristics. A new trailing-edge flap preselect system, as part of the Mark II System for all Learjet Models 23, 24 and 25 aircraft, was announced on 18 August 1976 following certification under FAR 25. This allows easy preselection of all flap settings from full up to 10° T-O; 20° T-O, approach and go-around; and full down landing position. Announced subsequently, on 17 January 1977, was the certification of

	LEARJET 24B/24D		LEARJET 25/25B/25C	
	Basic Aircraft knots-km/h-mph	Mk II System knots-km/h-mph	Basic Aircraft knots-km/h-mph	Mk II System knots-km/h-mph
T-O speed at max T-O weight, 10° flap	*	123-229-142	*	130-241-150
T-O speed at max T-O weight, 20° flap	131-243-151	115-212-132	144-267-166	121-224-139
Minimum control speed (VMC)	108-200-124	80-148-92	102-188-117	Below stall speed
Normal cruising speed	441-816-507	458-848-527	441-816-507	458-848-527
Long range cruising speed	405-750-466	430-797-495	408-756-470	434-805-500
Approach speed at max landing weight, flaps down	133-246-153	115-212-132	139-257-160	122-225-140
Approach speed at 120% of empty weight, flaps down	114-211-131	95-175-109	118-219-136	101-187-116
Stalling speed at max T-O weight, flaps up	126-233-145	106-196-122	137-254-158	112-208-129
Stalling speed at max T-O weight, 10° flap	*	101-187-116	*	106-196-122
Stalling speed at max T-O weight, 20° flap	109-203-126	94-174-108	118-219-136	99-183-114
Stalling speed at max landing weight, flaps down	100-185-115	85-158-98	107-198-123	91-169-105

NOTE: Figures quoted are indicated airspeeds (IAS) and are stated by Howard/Raisbeck to be typical of the improvements under all operating conditions. *Indicates new capability in this configuration.

the Teledyne angle of attack system for Model 23 and 24 Learjets.

The new system provides precise stall warning capability, using existing Learjet shaker and pusher equipment which is controlled by a new computer. This also drives flap-position compensated and normalised angle of attack indicators, to provide a lift situation display which is valid for the entire flight regime.

A summary of Howard/Raisbeck Mark II System performance improvements for Gates Learjet aircraft is given in the accompanying table.

Flight testing of the Raisbeck Mark Five System on a Rockwell Sabreliner 60A

Raisbeck Mark Four Learjet, embodying stall characteristics improvement system

RAISBECK MARK FOUR LEARJET CENTURY III STALL CHARACTERISTICS IMPROVEMENT SYSTEM

The Raisbeck Group announced on 4 May 1979 the completion of certification of a new aerodynamic system designed specifically for the Learjet Century III series of aircraft. Intended to increase the performance margin during take-off and landing, and to reduce the cruise drag of the aircraft, production installation of the system on in-service Learjet 35A/36A aircraft began on 7 May 1979.

Known as the Raisbeck Stall Characteristics Improvement System, it includes the addition of four stall fences (two on the leading-edge of each wing), and is fitted by the Raisbeck Group at its works at Boeing Field International. It provides a reduction of several knots in certificated stalling speeds; natural aerodynamic buffet warning; good stall characteristics without the need for a highly sensitive stick pusher; and a 7% to 10% reduction in cruise drag by removal of the wing vortex generators. The system has been tested with ice shapes across the entire span of the wing leading-edge, and the aircraft has proved to be insensitive in stall characteristics to these ice formations during approach to a stall.

Available as optional extras to the above system are a flap preselect system, and an automatic flap pitch trim compensator, which eliminates the need for large changes in tailplane trim during flap operation.

ROCKWELL/RAISBECK MARK FIVE SYSTEM

The Raisbeck Group's goals for an advanced technology aerodynamic system suitable for the Rockwell family of Sabreliners comprised enhanced payload, increased range, more efficient cruise, improved take-off and landing performance, and lower operating costs.

The initial development flight testing was carried out on a Sabreliner 60, and three different leading-edges incorporating elements of supercritical technology were investigated.

The finalised Mark Five System for the Sabreliner comprises the Raisbeck Group's new supercritical wing; 1·83 m (6 ft) wing span extension; fully decambered wing root; extended chord and span Fowler-type trailing-edge flaps; aileron seals; flight and automatic ground spoilers on wings; Hydro-Aire Mk III anti-skid braking system; Teledyne angle of attack system; new landing gear barrels, metering pins, pistons, wheels and tyres, as necessary; larger tailplane and elevator; automatic pitch trim system; full-span blunt wing leading-edge with integral fuel tank, and thermal anti-icing capability; and smaller items developed specifically for the Sabreliner Mark Five System.

Performance of the Mark Five System Sabreliners includes a reduction in take-off field length without reduction of range; up to 0·05 increase in cruise Mach number at max cruise thrust setting and unchanged weights; higher initial cruise altitude at unchanged weight; 4-10% increase in nautical air miles per pound of fuel, depending on cruise Mach number; a 590 kg (1,300 lb) increase in usable wing fuel; increase in range, depending on take-off limitations, fuel reserves and cruise Mach number; reduction in landing distance for the same payload; full 30,000 hour/30,000 mission fatigue life for the Mark Five modified Sabreliner wing, tailplane and aft fuselage; elimination of the fuselage speed-brake through incorporation of wing lift spoilers (cleared for the entire flight envelope, flaps up, and used as automatic ground spoilers during landing); full certification for flight into known icing, through incorporation of the thermal anti-icing Mark Five wing leading-edge, without fin and tailplane de-icing boots; and, in the case of the Sabreliner 60, expanded CG envelope by incorporation of the Model 75A tail planform.

The FAA's Supplemental Type Certificate for the Sabreliner 60 with the full Raisbeck Mark Five System was awarded on 15 November 1978, and the reconfigured aircraft is designated Sabreliner 60A Mark Five. Similar conversion schemes for the Sabreliner 75A and Sabreliner 40A will result in the respective designations of Sabreliner 80A Mark Five and Sabreliner 40B Mark Five. It was anticipated that the STC for the former would be awarded in September 1979, with that for the 40B following soon after. The Raisbeck system is also being delivered in kit form to Rockwell International for standard installation on all new production Sabreliner 65 aircraft.

The first Sabreliner modified to full 60A Mark Five production standard (N605RG) was flown for the first time on 8 September 1978, and was flown nonstop from Seattle to St Louis five days later for static display in connection with the NBAA Convention. The first customer conversion was completed for Hanna Mining of Cleveland, Ohio, this aircraft (N168H) being handed over on 20 December 1978. Production rate was 3·4 per month in Spring 1979, with 26 deliveries scheduled for 1979 and 41 for 1980.

The accompanying table provides a rapid comparison of Sabreliner 40A, 60 and 75A aircraft with and without the Mark Five System modifications.

Feature	Sabreliner 40A	Sabreliner 40B Mark Five	Sabreliner 60	Sabreliner 60A Mark Five	Sabreliner 75A	Sabreliner 80A Mark Five
Max ramp weight	8,634 kg (19,035 lb)	9,707 kg (21,400 lb)	9,241 kg (20,372 lb)	10,387 kg (22,900 lb)	10,659 kg (23,500 lb)	11,566 kg (25,500 lb)
Max T-O weight	8,459 kg (18,650 lb)	9,707 kg (21,400 lb)	9,150 kg (20,172 lb)	10,297 kg (22,700 lb)	10,569 kg (23,300 lb)	11,566 kg (25,500 lb)
Design landing weight	7,938 kg (17,500 lb)	9,344 kg (20,600 lb)	7,938 kg (17,500 lb)	9,344 kg (20,600 lb)	9,979 kg (22,000 lb)	9,979 kg (22,000 lb)
Max zero-fuel weight	6,260 kg (13,800 lb)	7,099 kg (15,650 lb)	6,260 kg (13,800 lb)	7,053 kg (15,550 lb)	7,085 kg (15,620 lb)	8,255 kg (18,200 lb)
Flaps up wing area	31·77 m² (342 sq ft)	35·30 m² (380 sq ft)	31·77 m² (342 sq ft)	35·30 m² (380 sq ft)	31·77 m² (342 sq ft)	35·30 m² (380 sq ft)
Flaps down wing area	32·61 m² (351 sq ft)	39·11 m² (421 sq ft)	32·61 m² (351 sq ft)	39·11 m² (421 sq ft)	32·61 m² (351 sq ft)	39·11 m² (421 sq ft)
Wing aspect ratio	5·57	6·70	5·57	6·70	5·57	6·70
T-O flap settings	0°	0°, 10°, 20°	0°	0°, 10°, 20°	0°, 15°	0°, 10°, 20°
Landing flap settings	25°	36°	25°	36°	25°	36°
Wing lift spoilers	None	26% span	None	26% span	None	26% span
Nacelle inlet	Splitters	Clean	Splitters	Clean	—	—
Anti-skid system	On/off	Fully-modulated	On/off	Fully-modulated	Fully-modulated	Fully-modulated

RILEY

RILEY AIRCRAFT CORPORATION

ADDRESS: 2016 Palomar Airport Road, Carlsbad, California 92008
Telephone: (714) 438 0660
Telex: 69 7936 Riley Jet
PRESIDENT: Jack M. Riley

Mr J. Riley was responsible for the Riley 55 Twin-Navion conversion scheme in 1952 and the Riley Rocket conversion of the Cessna 310 in 1962, as well as for Dove, Heron and Cessna 310/320 conversions known respectively as the Riley Turbo-Exec 400, Turbo Skyliner and Turbostream. His company is marketing currently a Cessna 310/320 conversion known as the Riley Super 310; three Cessna 340 conversions which are designated Riley Super 340, Riley Rocket 340 and Riley Jet Prop 340; a conversion of the Cessna 414 designated Riley Rocket Power 414, and a Cessna 421 conversion designated Riley Turbine Rocket 421.

FAA approved export conversion kits are available for the six aircraft in the current production programme, and assistance is available if required to gain approval by the civil aviation authority in the country to which the kit has been exported.

RILEY SUPER 310

The Super 310 represents a similar conversion to that of the Super 340, the existing power plants in the Cessna 310/320 being replaced by 231 kW (310 hp) Continental TSIO-520-Js. The conversion is FAA approved for the Cessna 310I to 310R, 320B to 320F and T310P to T310R. Installation of the complete kit requires 12 working days.

A description of the current Cessna Model 310 appears under the Cessna entry in this edition. It applies also to the Riley Super 310, except as follows:

Power Plant: As described for Riley Super 340.

Weights and Loading: As for the appropriate Cessna 310/320 model except as follows:
- Weight empty — increased by 10 kg (22 lb)
- Max payload — reduced by 10 kg (22 lb)
- Max power loading — 5·11 kg/kW (8·4 lb/hp)

Performance (at max T-O weight):
- Max level speed at 7,315 m (24,000 ft) — 270 knots (500 km/h; 311 mph)
- Max cruising speed at 7,315 m (24,000 ft) — 255 knots (473 km/h; 294 mph)
- Max cruising speed at 3,660 m (12,000 ft) — 225 knots (417 km/h; 259 mph)
- Econ cruising speed at 3,660 m (12,000 ft) — 200 knots (370 km/h; 230 mph)
- Max rate of climb at S/L — 671 m (2,200 ft)/min
- Cruise rate of climb at max cruising power — 457 m (1,500 ft)/min
- Rate of climb at S/L, one engine out — 152 m (500 ft)/min
- Service ceiling — 10,980 m (36,000 ft)
- Service ceiling, one engine out — 7,315 m (24,000 ft)
- T-O run — 335 m (1,100 ft)
- T-O to 15 m (50 ft) — 472 m (1,550 ft)
- Landing from 15 m (50 ft) — 546 m (1,790 ft)
- Range with 757 litres (200 US gallons) fuel, max cruising speed at 7,315 m (24,000 ft), no reserves — 1,476 nm (2,735 km; 1,700 miles)
- Range with 757 litres (200 US gallons) fuel, econ cruising speed at 7,315 m (24,000 ft), no reserves — 1,815 nm (3,363 km; 2,090 miles)

RILEY SUPER 340

The Riley Super 340 differs from the standard Cessna 340 primarily through replacement of the latter's TSIO-520-K engines by TSIO-520-Js. The most important change associated with this new engine installation is the addition of an intercooler which allows a higher power output and also improves specific fuel consumption, critical altitude, engine life and reliability.

The prototype Super 340 received FAA certification in June 1974 and 177 aircraft had been modified by January 1978. The standard Cessna 340A for 1976 was updated in a manner similar to that of the Riley Super 340. Consequently, only Cessna 340 aircraft constructed from 1972 until the last of the 1975 models were completed are suitable for this conversion, which is completed by Riley engineers in five working days.

A description of the current Cessna Model 340A appears under the Cessna entry in this edition. It applies also to the Riley Super 340, except as follows:

Power Plant: Two 231 kW (310 hp) Continental TSIO-520-N flat-six turbocharged and intercooled engines, each driving a McCauley three-blade propeller. Engine installation upgraded from Cessna 340 to Cessna 414 configuration. Fuel system as for Cessna 340. Optional aft nacelle fuel tanks, each of 75·7 litres (20 US gallons), provide max optional fuel capacity of 920 litres (243 US gallons) when used in conjunction with the Cessna optional 768 litre (203 US gallon) system.

Weights and Loading:
- Weight empty — 1,754 kg (3,868 lb)
- Max payload — 904 kg (1,993 lb)
- Max T-O weight — 2,710 kg (5,975 lb)
- Max power loading — 5·87 kg/kW (9·64 lb/hp)

Performance (at max T-O weight):
- Max level speed at 7,315 m (24,000 ft) — 252 knots (467 km/h; 290 mph)
- Max cruising speed at 7,315 m (24,000 ft) — 234 knots (435 km/h; 270 mph)
- Max cruising speed at 5,485 m (18,000 ft) — 226 knots (418 km/h; 260 mph)
- Max cruising speed at 4,265 m (14,000 ft) — 217 knots (402 km/h; 250 mph)
- Econ cruising speed at 7,315 m (24,000 ft) — 208 knots (386 km/h; 240 mph)
- Max rate of climb at S/L — 549 m (1,800 ft)/min
- Cruise rate of climb at max cruising power — 305 m (1,000 ft)/min
- Rate of climb at S/L, one engine out — 107 m (350 ft)/min
- Service ceiling — 9,755 m (32,000 ft)
- Service ceiling, one engine out — 4,875 m (16,000 ft)
- T-O run — 457 m (1,500 ft)
- T-O to 15 m (50 ft) — 594 m (1,950 ft)
- Landing from 15 m (50 ft) — 561 m (1,840 ft)
- Landing run — 233 m (765 ft)
- Range with 768 litres (203 US gallons) fuel, max cruising speed at 7,315 m (24,000 ft), no reserves — 1,302 nm (2,415 km; 1,500 miles)
- Range with 920 litres (243 US gallons) fuel, econ cruising speed at 7,315 m (24,000 ft), no reserves — 2,170 nm (4,025 km; 2,500 miles)
- Range with pilot, co-pilot, four passengers, 91 kg (200 lb) baggage, fuelled to max T-O weight, econ cruising speed at 7,315 m (24,000 ft), no reserves — 868 nm (1,610 km; 1,000 miles)

Riley Rocket 340 conversion of the Cessna Model 340 (Lycoming TIO-540-R engines)

RILEY ROCKET 340

This Riley conversion of the Cessna 340 is, like the Super 340 conversion, concerned primarily with the installation of a different power plant to improve performance. Thus, the Continental TSIO-520-J engines of the Super 340 are replaced by counter-rotating Lycoming TIO-540-Rs of increased power. These engines feature the latest Garrett-AiResearch turbocharger system, with the wastegate and automatic manifold pressure controller integral with the engine turbocharger. First flight of a Rocket 340 was made in December 1977.

A description of the current Cessna Model 340A appears under the Cessna entry in this edition. It applies to also to the Riley Rocket 340, except as follows:

Power Plant: One Lycoming TIO-540-R and one LTIO-540-R flat-six engine, each rated at 254 kW (340 hp) for take-off and driving a Hartzell propeller with spinner. Fuel system as for Riley Super 340. Intake air intercoolers standard.

Equipment: Standard equipment includes a propeller synchrophaser. Optional equipment includes wing and tailplane de-icing boots, Cleveland heavy duty wheels and brakes, super soundproofing of nose baggage area adjacent to propeller arc, custom interior, seventh cabin seat, automatic in-line fuel boost pumps, J.B. Systems electrically-driven air-conditioner, polyurethane exterior paint, and a range of avionics to customers' requirements.

Weight and Loadings:
- Max T-O weight — 2,853 kg (6,290 lb)
- Max wing loading — 158·7 kg/m² (32·5 lb/sq ft)
- Max power loading — 5·62 kg/kW (9·25 lb/hp)

Performance (at max T-O weight, ISA):
- Max cruising speed at 7,315 m (24,000 ft) — 261 knots (483 km/h; 300 mph)
- Cruising speed, 65% power at 7,315 m (24,000 ft) — 240 knots (444 km/h; 276 mph)
- Max rate of climb at S/L — 655 m (2,150 ft)/min
- Rate of climb at S/L, one engine out — 152 m (500 ft)/min
- Service ceiling — over 9,145 m (30,000 ft)
- Service ceiling, one engine out — 6,310 m (20,700 ft)
- Minimum field length — 561 m (1,840 ft)
- Max range, 45 min reserves:
  - 444 kg (978 lb) fuel — 960 nm (1,778 km; 1,105 miles)
  - 552 kg (1,218 lb) fuel — 1,260 nm (2,335 km; 1,451 miles)

RILEY JET PROP 340

Generally similar to the Riley Super 340 and Rocket 340 conversions, the Jet Prop 340 has two Lycoming LTP 101 turboprop engines which are flat rated to provide first class performance over a wide range of operating conditions. The description of the Cessna 340A which appears under the Cessna entry in this edition applies also to the Riley Jet Prop 340, except as follows:

Power Plant: Two Lycoming LTP 101 turboprop engines, flat rated at approximately 60% of normal T-O power, each driving a Hartzell three-blade constant-speed metal propeller with spinner.

Weight and Loadings (estimated):
- Max T-O weight — 2,717 kg (5,990 lb)
- Max wing loading — 158·9 kg/m² (32·55 lb/sq ft)
- Max power loading — 4·57 kg/kW (7·50 lb/shp)

Performance (estimated, at max T-O weight, ISA):
- Max cruising speed at 6,100 m (20,000 ft) — 300 knots (555 km/h; 345 mph)
- Econ cruising speed at 7,620 m (25,000 ft) — 240 knots (444 km/h; 276 mph)
- Econ cruising speed at 4,875 m (16,000 ft) — 235 knots (436 km/h; 271 mph)
- Max rate of climb at S/L — 762 m (2,500 ft)/min
- Rate of climb at S/L, one engine out — 229 m (750 ft)/min
- Service ceiling — 9,145 m (30,000 ft)
- Service ceiling, one engine out — 6,100 m (20,000 ft)
- Min landing field length — 564 m (1,850 ft)
- Max range — 1,200 nm (2,224 km; 1,382 miles)

RILEY TURBINE ROCKET 421

This Riley conversion of the pressurised Cessna 421 involves installation of Lycoming turboprop engines of the type used in the Riley Jet Prop 340, except that in this case the LTP 101-700s are flat rated to approximately 70% of normal T-O power. First flight of a Turbine Rocket 421 was made on 10 January 1978, followed by the first production conversion on 4 June 1978.

The description of the Cessna 421 Golden Eagle which appears under the Cessna entry in this edition applies also to the Riley Turbine Rocket 421, except that the landing gear is equipped with Cleveland 199-76 heavy-duty brakes; each engine drives a Hartzell propeller with Q-tips and Beta propeller reversal; and optional wing fuel tanks are available to add 363 litres (96 US gallons) to the max total capacity. Six Turbine Rocket 421s had been delivered by 1 February 1979, with 29 more on order.

Weight and Loadings:
- Max T-O weight — 3,379 kg (7,450 lb)
- Max wing loading — 171·9 kg/m² (35·20 lb/sq ft)
- Max power loading — 4·77 kg/kW (7·84 lb/shp)

Performance (estimated, at max T-O weight, ISA):
- Max cruising speed at 6,100 m (20,000 ft) — 260 knots (481 km/h; 299 mph)
- Econ cruising speed at 7,620 m (25,000 ft) — 225 knots (417 km/h; 259 mph)
- Econ cruising speed at 4,875 m (16,000 ft) — 222 knots (412 km/h; 256 mph)
- Max rate of climb at S/L — 762 m (2,500 ft)/min
- Rate of climb at S/L, one engine out — 225 m (737 ft)/min
- Service ceiling — 9,145 m (30,000 ft)

Riley Turbine Rocket 421 turboprop conversion of the Cessna 421

Riley Rocket Power 414, a conversion of the Cessna 414 (two Lycoming IO-720 engines)

Service ceiling, one engine out 5,485 m (18,000 ft)
Min landing field length 686 m (2,250 ft)
Landing run with propeller reversal 152 m (500 ft)
Max range 1,301 nm (2,410 km; 1,498 miles)

RILEY ROCKET POWER 414

This Riley conversion of the Cessna 414 involves installation of Lycoming IO-720 flat-eight engines to provide improved performance. It moves the empty aircraft CG forward, allowing more flexibility in loading, and introduces also Hartzell automatic propeller synchrophasing, an Aerosonic electronic fuel management system, and heavy-duty Cleveland brakes. The engines are mounted in new glassfibre cowlings which have louvres for engine cooling, making redundant the cowl flaps which were provided originally, and these are removed.

A description of the current Cessna Model 414 appears under the Cessna entry in this edition. It applies also to the Riley Rocket Power 414, except as follows:

Power Plant: Two 298 kW (400 hp) Lycoming IO-720 flat-eight engines, each driving a Hartzell four-blade constant-speed metal propeller. Riley intake air intercoolers standard. Fuel system as for Cessna 414, except an Aerosonic fuel management system is provided. Hartzell automatic propeller synchrophasers standard.

Weight and Loadings:
Max T-O and landing weight 3,096 kg (6,825 lb)
Max wing loading 170·0 kg/m² (34·82 lb/sq ft)
Max power loading 5·19 kg/kW (8·53 lb/hp)

Performance (at max T-O weight, ISA):
Max level speed, turbo cruise power:
At 7,315 m (24,000 ft) 261 knots (483 km/h; 300 mph)
At 3,660 m (12,000 ft) 217 knots (402 km/h; 250 mph)
Speed at intermediate cruise power:
At 7,315 m (24,000 ft) 243 knots (451 km/h; 280 mph)
At 3,660 m (12,000 ft) 200 knots (370 km/h; 230 mph)
Max rate of climb at S/L 686 m (2,250 ft)/min
Rate of climb at S/L, one engine out 122 m (400 ft)/min
Service ceiling 9,145 m (30,000 ft)
Service ceiling, one engine out 7,620 m (25,000 ft)
Max range, 45 min reserves:
490 kg (1,080 lb) fuel 771 nm (1,429 km; 888 miles)
653 kg (1,440 lb) fuel 1,136 nm (2,105 km; 1,308 miles)

ROBERTSON

ROBERTSON AIRCRAFT CORPORATION

Headquarters: 839 West Perimeter Road, Renton Municipal Airport, Renton, Washington 98055
Telephone: (206) 228 5000
Telex: 910-423-1555
President: Leland R. Lynch
Vice-President (Marketing) and Chief Pilot: Henry I. McKay
Chief Engineer: Roy D. Carter
Sales Manager: Edward D. Stiller

Robertson Aircraft Corporation was formed by the late Mr James L. Robertson, who had long been a pioneer in the development of STOL aircraft, having been responsible for the Skycraft Skyshark, Wren 460 and STOL modifications to the IMCO CallAir A-9 and B-1. It has designed, built and certificated a series of Hi-Lift advanced technology safety and performance systems for standard single- and twin-engined Beech, Cessna and Piper aircraft.

Three additional aircraft programmes were engineered and completed in 1978. These include a new Fowler-type flap and actuation system for the Cessna 421C, the provision of Hi-lift systems for the Cessna Models 310 and 340, and the first modification of a Beechcraft model with the design of a full-span flap and a spoiler system for the V-tail Bonanza.

Research contracts with Kansas University and NASA were completed in 1974, covering the design of an Advanced Technology Light Twin (ATLIT). A standard Piper Seneca fuselage was fitted with an experimental wing that had a new aerofoil section and 30% chord full-span Fowler flaps. There were no ailerons and roll control was achieved by the use of upper-surface spoilers. Construction of the aircraft was completed by Piper Aircraft Corporation and the first flight was recorded in late 1974.

Following completion of the ATLIT research programme, Robertson embarked on a development project to evolve spoilers and full-span flaps suitable for retrofit on the standard Piper Seneca I. FAA certification of the resulting system represented the first approval of spoilers for use on general aviation aircraft manufactured in the USA (see full description under this entry).

The most recent Robertson development has provided a high-differential aileron-droop Hi-Lift system for high-performance single-engined aircraft, such as the Cessna Model 210 Pressurised Centurion.

ROBERTSON / CESSNA and ROBERTSON / PIPER SAFETY and STOL CONVERSIONS

Continuous product improvement has been made on Robertson's line of Hi-Lift systems for Cessna and Piper single-engined and smaller twin-engined aircraft. The Robertson modification, first applied to a Cessna 182, comprises full-span wing leading-edge and trailing-edge high-lift systems which greatly reduce the take-off and landing distances normally required by such aircraft.

The existing ailerons are used as an integral part of the full-span trailing-edge flap system. When the conventional inboard flaps are lowered for take-off or landing, the ailerons droop with them, virtually doubling the wing lift at low speeds. The ailerons retain their differential operation for roll control when drooped.

Robertson STOL-equipped Cessna 182RG with Hi-Lift system

Beechcraft V 35 Bonanza, with Robertson full-span flaps extended, makes approach for short-field landing

In addition, the wing is fitted with a full-span distributed-camber leading-edge to provide an optimum spanwise lift distribution for maximum cruise efficiency. The cambered leading-edge also reduces the aerofoil leading-edge pressure peak at high angles of attack, to impart maximum resistance to stall and to provide highly-responsive manoeuvrability at low airspeeds. Some types of Cessna single-engined aircraft built since 1972 include this Robertson leading-edge as a standard production feature.

The full-span flap system, in combination with Robertson's conical-cambered wingtips, dorsal and ventral fins, belly-mounted vortex generators, and flap/elevator automatic trim system, are combined in various models to offer increased performance.

To improve controllability at low speeds, stall fences are provided between flaps and ailerons, and to complete the Hi-Lift modification the aileron gap is sealed with a strip of aluminium sheet or rubberised canvas. These modifications permit safe STOL landings and take-offs by even novice pilots, and cruising speed and range are increased by 2-4%.

Maximum gross weight increases have accompanied the certification of Robertson modifications of twin-engined aircraft such as the Cessna Super Skymaster and Piper Twin Comanche. This is due primarily to their increased climb performance and slower take-off and landing speeds.

Development of a Hi-Lift system for the Cessna 400 series of twin-engined business aircraft entailed complete redesign of the wings from the rear spar aft to allow installation of 100% Fowler flaps and flap-actuated drooping ailerons. This system, in combination with Robertson's automatic pitch trim system and double-hinged rudder, led to FAA-certificated decreases in take-off and landing field lengths of approximately 40%.

In 1974, the FAA certificated the Robertson-equipped Piper Seneca I, with wing upper-surface spoilers for roll control, full-span slotted flaps, cambered wingtips and an anti-servo rudder tab. These modifications allow shorter take-off and landing distances; minimum control speed is reduced by 16%, the best rate of climb speed is lowered by 19%, single-engine service ceiling is raised by 213 m (700 ft) and roll response is increased greatly at all speeds and configurations. A similar modification of the Seneca II was certificated during 1976.

More recent activities have entailed fitting full-span trailing-edge flaps and spoilers for roll control on a Piper Cherokee SIX; and developing a high-differential aileron-droop Hi-Lift system for high-performance single-engined aircraft, such as the Cessna Model P210 Pressurised Centurion. In this application a new and improved control mechanism droops both ailerons symmetrically to 15° 30′ when the trailing-edge flaps are extended to 20° for take-off. For roll control the ailerons travel up and down in high-ratio differential: thus, with the control wheel fully to starboard, the starboard aileron moves up 40° to act as a spoiler (25° up from its normal faired position); at the same time the port aileron is deflected downward an additional 10° to a total of 25° 30′. Ailerons are also drooped symmetrically by 15° when the trailing-edge flaps are extended to 40° for approach and landing.

Benefits from this advanced Hi-Lift system include a greatly-reduced adverse yaw tendency in turns, and a higher roll rate for more precise control when flaps are down and speed low. Control wheel forces are significantly less than with unmodified aircraft from zero deflection to about 10° of aileron movement; slightly higher than normal wheel forces are experienced when ailerons are deflected more than 10°. The resulting full-span flap effect produces a noticeable increase in lift at low speeds, improving short-field performance beyond that achieved by earlier aileron-droop Hi-Lift systems.

Four stall strips, two on each wing, retain the desirable stall characteristics common to all Robertson Hi-Lift systems. For aircraft fitted with wing leading-edge de-icing boots, rubber strips are cemented to the rubber boots; when these are not fitted, aluminium stall strips are riveted to the wing leading-edge. A strip 0·13 m (5 in) long, close to the wing root, initiates an early-warning signal that the aircraft is approaching the stall. A longer strip, mounted further outboard and lower than the first, initiates the stall of the inboard and centre wing sections, while the outboard section and the wingtip are still unaffected by stall conditions. When the aircraft stalls it noses forward and down, under the complete control of ailerons which remain unstalled and effective for roll control.

The Robertson integrated high-lift and safety systems have been designed for easy field maintenance. They are designed to be applicable to almost the entire range of Cessna and Piper aircraft, as detailed in the accompanying tables.

Full details of the basic Cessna and Piper airframes are given under the appropriate company headings in this and earlier editions of *Jane's*, and apply also to the Robertson versions, except for the added Hi-Lift systems as described. Weights and performance details of the entire range of Hi-Lift modifications are given in the accompanying tables. The conversions can be fitted as a retrospective modification to any of the models listed, irrespective of year.

The complete line of Robertson STOL systems is available throughout the world from 23 installation centres and more than 60 dealers.

R/STOL Cessna 310 on landing approach with Fowler flaps extended

R/STOL Cessna 421C on approach for short-field landing with Fowler flaps extended and ailerons drooped

Robertson STOL conversion of the Cessna 414; the Fowler-type trailing-edge flaps add 14 per cent to wing area

R/STOL VERSION OF BEECH MODEL

	Weight empty equipped kg (lb)	Weight gross kg (lb)	Max level speed knots (km/h; mph)	Max cruising speed knots (km/h; mph)	Stalling speed, wheels and flaps down knots (km/h; mph)	Max rate of climb at S/L m (ft)/min	Single-engine rate of climb at S/L m (ft)/min	Service ceiling m (ft)	T-O run m (ft)	T-O to 15 m (50 ft) m (ft)	Landing from 15 m (50 ft) m (ft)	Landing run m (ft)	Max range** nm (km; miles)
V-35B Bonanza	987 (2,176)	1,542 (3,400)	181 (335; 208)	176 (325; 202)	53 (98; 61)	343 (1,125)	—	5,443 (17,858)	B 239 (785)	B 420 (1,377)	B 279 (914)	B 146 (478)	875 (1,620; 11,007)

B: Robertson Normal operation. **With optional long-range tanks fitted, if available.

R/STOL VERSIONS OF CESSNA MODELS

	Weight empty equipped kg (lb)	Weight gross kg (lb)	Max level speed knots (km/h; mph)	Max cruising speed knots (km/h; mph)	Stalling speed, wheels and flaps down knots (km/h; mph)	Max rate of climb at S/L m (ft)/min	Single-engine rate of climb at S/L m (ft)/min	Service ceiling m (ft)	T-O run m (ft)	T-O to 15 m (50 ft) m (ft)	Landing from 15 m (50 ft) m (ft)	Landing run m (ft)	Max range** nm (km; miles)
Model 150 and Commuter	449 (990)	725 (1,600)	110 (204; 127)	105 (195; 121)	20 (48·3; 30)	213 (700)		3,930 (12,900)	A 129 (422) B 161 (527)	A 248 (815) B 273 (895)	A 193 (632) B 230 (755)	A 90 (295) B 106 (348)	790 (1,464; 910)
Model 172 and Skyhawk†	572 (1,263)	1,043 (2,300)	126 (233; 145)	118 (219; 136)	28 (51·5; 32)	206 (675)		4,150 (13,600)	A 140 (460) B 175 (575)	A 274 (900) B 302 (990)	A 223 (730) B 267 (875)	A 92 (302) B 109 (356)	738 (1,367; 850)
Model 172 and Skyhawk floatplane*	646 (1,425)	1,007 (2,220)	97 (180; 112)	94 (174; 108)	28 (51·5; 32)	191 (625)		3,765 (12,350)	A 256 (840) B 320 (1,050)	A 405 (1,330) B 451 (1,480)	A 267 (875) B 296 (970)	A 145 (475) B 171 (560)	477 (885; 550)
Model 180 Skywagon†	707 (1,560)	1,270 (2,800)	152 (282; 175)	144 (267; 166)	32·2 (60; 37)	364 (1,195)		6,215 (20,400)	A 110 (360) B 137 (450)	A 216 (710) B 239 (785)	A 207 (680) B 254 (835)	A 88 (290) B 104 (342)	1,098 (2,035; 1,265)
Model 180 Skywagon floatplane	850 (1,875)	1,338 (2,950)	142 (264; 164)	133 (246; 153)	32·2 (60; 37)	332 (1,090)		5,425 (17,800)	A 245 (805) B 307 (1,006)	A 369 (1,210) B 402 (1,320)	A 254 (832) B 308 (1,010)	A 145 (475) B 171 (560)	1,063 (1,971; 1,225)
Model 182 and Skylane†	725 (1,599)	1,338 (2,950)	150 (278; 173)	143 (266; 165)	33 (62; 38)	288 (945)		5,610 (18,400)	A 131 (430) B 164 (537)	A 248 (815) B 270 (885)	A 237 (777) B 280 (920)	A 99 (325) B 117 (384)	1,050 (1,947; 1,210)
Model 182 RG	800 (1,764)	1,412 (3,112)	187 (347; 215)	173 (321; 199)	42 (80; 48)	317 (1,040)		6,100 (20,000)	A 133 (435)	A 248 (815)	A 237 (777)	A 119 (389)	1,030 (1,909; 1,186)
Model 185 Skywagon†	721 (1,590)	1,519 (3,350)	159 (295; 183)	149 (277; 172)	34 (63; 39)	320 (1,050)		5,440 (17,850)	A 114 (375) B 143 (469)	A 233 (763) B 265 (870)	A 230 (755) B 271 (890)	A 95 (310) B 111 (365)	972 (1,802; 1,120)
Model 185 Skywagon floatplane	866 (1,910)	1,505 (3,320)	149 (277; 172)	140 (259; 161)	34 (63; 39)	311 (1,020)		5,210 (17,100)	A 182 (596) B 227 (745)	A 332 (1,090) B 364 (1,195)	A 265 (870) B 326 (1,070)	A 146 (480) B 173 (566)	903 (1,673; 1,040)
Model 188 AGwagon 230	836 (1,844)	1,723 (3,800)	124 (230; 143)	116 (214; 133)	38·5 (71; 44)	245 (805)		4,330 (14,200)	A 207 (680) B 259 (850)	A 338 (1,110) B 431 (1,420)	A 186 (610) B 256 (840)	A 94 (308) B 111 (363)	303 (563; 350)
Model A188 AGwagon 300†	843 (1,859)	1,814 (4,000)	135 (251; 156)	127 (235; 146)	40 (74; 46)	302 (990)		4,905 (16,100)	A 183 (600) B 229 (750)	A 293 (960) B 381 (1,250)	A 186 (610) B 256 (840)	A 94 (308) B 111 (363)	390 (724; 450)
Model 206 Stationair 6†	785 (1,732)	1,633 (3,600)	155 (288; 179)	148 (274; 170)	36 (66; 41)	296 (970)		4,695 (15,400)	A 147 (482) B 184 (603)	A 302 (990) B 352 (1,155)	A 226 (740) B 270 (885)	A 92 (301) B 108 (355)	916 (1,697; 1,055)
Model 206 Stationair 6 floatplane	943 (2,080)	1,587 (3,500)	144 (267; 166)	136 (253; 157)	36 (66; 41)	276 (905)		4,450 (14,600)	A 248 (815) B 311 (1,019)	A 454 (1,490) B 486 (1,595)	A 280 (917) B 343 (1,125)	A 148 (485) B 174 (572)	833 (1,544; 960)
Model T206 Turbo Stationair 6	831 (1,832)	1,633 (3,600)	178 (330; 205)	163 (303; 188)	36 (66; 41)	322 (1,055)		8,260 (27,100)	A 148 (485) B 185 (606)	A 303 (995) B 358 (1,175)	A 226 (740) B 270 (885)	A 92 (301) B 108 (355)	963 (1,786; 1,110)
Model T206 Turbo Stationair 6 floatplane	979 (2,160)	1,633 (3,600)	164 (304; 189)	148 (274; 170)	36 (66; 41)	311 (1,020)		7,650 (25,100)	A 241 (790) B 301 (987)	A 442 (1,450) B 475 (1,560)	A 283 (928) B 344 (1,130)	A 151 (495) B 178 (584)	911 (1,690; 1,050)
Model 207 Skywagon and Stationair 7	862 (1,902)	1,723 (3,800)	150 (278; 173)	142 (264; 164)	38·5 (71; 44)	262 (860)		4,205 (13,800)	A 155 (510) B 194 (637)	A 332 (1,090) B 390 (1,280)	A 244 (800) B 298 (975)	A 97 (318) B 114 (375)	829 (1,536; 955)
Model T207 Turbo Skywagon and Turbo Stationair 7	908 (2,002)	1,723 (3,800)	168 (312; 194)	156 (290; 180)	38·5 (71; 44)	277 (910)		7,650 (25,100)	A 155 (510) B 194 (637)	A 332 (1,090) B 390 (1,280)	A 244 (800) B 298 (975)	A 97 (318) B 114 (375)	812 (1,504; 935)
Model 210 Centurion II	953 (2,102)	1,723 (3,800)	178 (330; 205)	167 (309 192)	38·5 (71; 44)	274 (900)		4,905 (16,100)	A 155 (510) B 194 (637)	A 326 (1,070) B 376 (1,232)	A 239 (783) B 293 (960)	A 93 (305) B 110 (360)	1,137 (2,108; 1,310)
Model T210 Turbo Centurion II	998 (2,202)	1,723 (3,800)	204 (378; 235)	192 (356; 221)	38·5 (71; 44)	293 (960)		9,020 (29,600)	A 160 (525) B 200 (656)	A 328 (1,075) B 401 (1,318)	A 239 (783) B 293 (960)	A 93 (305) B 110 (360)	1,133 (2,100; 1,305)

A, B, *, **, † see notes under Cessna table on page 427.

CESSNA MODELS—*continued*

	Weight empty equipped kg (lb)	Weight gross kg (lb)	Max level speed knots (km/h; mph)	Max cruising speed knots (km/h; mph)	Stalling speed, wheels and flaps down knots (km/h; mph)	Max rate of climb at S/L m (ft)/min	Single-engine rate of climb at S/L m (ft)/min	Service ceiling m (ft)	T-O run m (ft)	T-O to 15 m (50 ft) m (ft)	Landing from 15 m (50 ft) m (ft)	Landing run m (ft)	Max range** nm (km; miles)	Min control speed knots (km/h; mph)
Model P210 Pressurised Centurion	1,064 (2,345)	1,822 (4,016)	206 (381; 237)		55 (102; 63)	283 (930)		7,010 (23,000)	366 (1,200)	607 (1,990)	271 (890)	424 (1,390)	925 (1,714; 1,065)	
Model 310R	1,701 (3,750)	2,495 (5,500)	237 (439; 273)	223 (414; 257)	64 (119; 74)	518 (1,700)	119 (390)	8,350 (27,400)	B 290 (950)	B 448 (1,470)	B 355 (1,165)	B 219 (720)	1,242 (2,301; 1,430)	69 (129; 80) CAS
Model 337 Super Skymaster	1,196 (2,638)	2,100 (4,630)	177 (328; 204)	168 (312; 194)	39 (72·5; 45)	369 (1,210)	99 (325)	6,125 (20,100)	A 130 (428) B 163 (535)	A 265 (870) B 322 (1,055)	A 273 (895) B 323 (1,060)	A 105 (343) B 123 (405)	1,207 (2,236; 1,390)	
Model T337 Turbo Super Skymaster	1,289 (2,843)	2,131 (4,700)	204 (378; 235)	200 (370; 230)	40 (74; 46)	353 (1,160)	93 (305)	9,265 (30,400)	A 136 (445) B 169 (556)	A 280 (920) B 332 (1,088)	A 273 (895) B 323 (1,060)	A 107 (352) B 126 (415)	1,406 (2,607; 1,620)	
Model T337 Pressurised Super Skymaster	1,315 (2,900)	2,132 (4,700)	217 (402; 250)	208 (385; 239)	40 (74; 46)	353 (1,160)	126 (415)	6,100 (20,000)	A 126 (413) B 157 (516)	A 280 (920) B 332 (1,088)	A 273 (895) B 323 (1,060)	A 107 (352) B 126 (415)	1,307 (2,422; 1,505)	
Model 340	1,878 (4,140)	2,717 (5,990)	242 (447; 278)	228 (421; 262)	61 (114; 71)	503 (1,650)	96 (315)	9,085 (29,800)					1,372 (2,542; 1,580)	75 (140; 87) CAS
Model 401	1,673 (3,690)	2,858 (6,300)	226 (420; 261)	208 (386; 240)	65·5 (121; 75)	491 (1,610)	69 (225)	7,980 (26,180)	A 240 (786) B 300 (983)	A 378 (1,240) B 472 (1,550)	A 354 (1,160) B 442 (1,450)	A 155 (510) B 183 (600)	1,263 (2,340; 1,454)	72 (134; 83)
Model 402	1,673 (3,690)	2,858 (6,300)	226 (420; 261)	208 (386; 240)	65·5 (121; 75)	491 (1,610)	69 (225)	7,980 (26,180)	A 240 (786) B 300 (983)	A 378 (1,240) B 472 (1,550)	A 354 (1,160) B 442 (1,450)	A 155 (510) B 183 (600)	1,263 (2,340; 1,454)	72 (134; 83)
Model 411	1,764 (3,890)	2,948 (6,500)	233 (431; 268)	212 (393; 244)	61·5 (114; 71)	579 (1,900)	98 (320)	7,925 (26,000)	A 278 (912) B 347 (1,140)	A 372 (1,220) B 465 (1,525)	A 340 (1,115) B 425 (1,395)	A 183 (600) B 276 (905)	1,303 (2,414; 1,500)	76 (142; 88)
Model 414	1,764 (3,890)	2,880 (6,350)	236 (438; 272)	217 (402; 250)	68·5 (126·5; 78·4)	482 (1,580)	73 (240)	9,175 (30,100)	A 271 (888) B 338 (1,110)	A 397 (1,304) B 497 (1,630)	A 354 (1,160) B 442 (1,450)	A 145 (476) B 171 (560)	1,402 (2,599; 1,615)	74 (137; 85)
Model 421A	1,932 (4,260)	3,102 (6,840)	240 (444; 276)	224 (414; 258)	69 (128; 79)	512 (1,680)	88 (290)	8,230 (27,000)	A 307 (1,008) B 384 (1,260)	A 443 (1,452) B 553 (1,815)	A 419 (1,375) B 524 (1,720)	A 208 (683) B 245 (804)	1,488 (2,756; 1,713)	83 (153; 95)
Model 421B	2,011 (4,435)	3,379 (7,450)	245 (454; 282)	230 (426; 265)	71 (132; 81·8)	564 (1,850)	93 (305)	9,450 (31,000)	A 313 (1,028) B 365 (1,196)	A 428 (1,403) B 535 (1,754)	A 427 (1,400) B 534 (1,752)	A 134 (440) B 158 (517)	1,490 (2,762; 1,716)	78 (145; 90)
Model 421C	2,173 (4,790)	3,379 (7,450)	256 (475; 295)	240 (444; 276)	71 (132; 82)	591 (1,940)	107 (350)	9,200 (30,200)	B 396 (1,300)	B 558 (1,830)	B 518 (1,700)	B 317 (1,040)	1,487 (2,755; 1,712)	77 (143; 89) CAS

A: Robertson STOL operation. B: Robertson Normal operation. *Available also with engines of increased horsepower. **With optional long-range tanks fitted, if available. †Leading-edge already installed by Cessna on current models.

R/STOL VERSIONS OF PIPER MODELS

PA-28-140 Cherokee	558 (1,232)	975 (2,150)	126 (223; 145)	120 (222; 138)	29 (53·2; 33)	206 (675)		4,480 (14,700)	A 171 (560) B 189 (620)	A 354 (1,160) B 404 (1,325)	A 192 (630) B 221 (725)	A 94 (310) B 110 (360)	825 (1,529; 950)	
PA-28-160 Cherokee	576 (1,270)	997 (2,200)	128 (237; 147)	121 (224; 139)	31 (56·5; 35)	216 (710)		4,970 (16,300)	A 152 (500) B 177 (580)	A 341 (1,120) B 390 (1,280)	A 204 (670) B 226 (740)	A 104 (340) B 114 (375)	838 (1,553; 965)	
PA-28-180 Cherokee	638 (1,406)	1,111 (2,450)	129 (238; 148)	122 (227; 141)	36 (66; 41)	221 (725)		4,313 (14,510)	A 165 (540) B 186 (610)	A 351 (1,150) B 399 (1,310)	A 238 (780) B 262 (860)	A 131 (430) B 146 (480)	596 (1,104; 686)	
PA-28R-180 Cherokee Arrow II	611 (1,349)	1,134 (2,500)	149 (275; 171)	142 (262; 163)	35 (64·5; 40)	270 (885)		4,695 (15,400)	A 171 (560) B 195 (640)	A 347 (1,140) B 396 (1,300)	A 259 (850) B 299 (980)	A 145 (475) B 168 (550)	911 (1,690; 1,050)	
PA-28R-200 Cherokee Arrow II	693 (1,528)	1,202 (2,650)	152 (282; 175)	143 (266; 165)	37 (69; 43)	274 (900)		4,570 (15,000)	A 175 (575) B 198 (650)	A 344 (1,130) B 393 (1,290)	A 283 (930) B 319 (1,045)	A 168 (550) B 187 (615)	782 (1,448; 900)	

A: Robertson STOL operation. B: Robertson Normal operation.
**With optional long-range tanks fitted, if available.

PIPER MODELS—*continued*

	Weight empty equipped	Weight gross	Max level speed	Max cruising speed	Stalling speed, wheels and flaps down	Max rate of climb at S/L	Single-engine rate of climb at S/L	Service ceiling	T-O run	T-O to 15 m (50 ft)	Landing from 15 m (50 ft)	Landing run	Max range**	Min control speed
	kg (lb)	kg (lb)	knots (km/h; mph)	knots (km/h; mph)	knots (km/h; mph)	m (ft)/min	m (ft)/min	m (ft)	m (ft)	m (ft)	m (ft)	m (ft)	nm (km; miles)	knots (km/h; mph)
PA-28-235 Cherokee 235	712 (1,570)	1,361 (3,000)	140 (259; 161)	132 (245; 152)	39 (72; 45)	244 (800)		3,660 (12,000)	A 168 (550) B 191 (625)	A 265 (870) B 302 (990)	A 274 (900) B 312 (1,025)	A 149 (490) B 171 (560)	926 (1,716; 1,066)	
PA-32-260 Cherokee SIX	783 (1,726)	1,542 (3,400)	144 (267; 166)	137 (254; 158)	38 (71; 44)	259 (850)		4,420 (14,500)	A 180 (590) B 238 (780)	A 317 (1,040) B 341 (1,120)	A 247 (810) B 267 (875)	A 155 (510) B 171 (560)	964 (1,786; 1,110)	
PA-32-300 Cherokee SIX	825 (1,819)	1,542 (3,400)	151 (280; 174)	146 (270; 168)	38 (71; 44)	320 (1,050)		4,955 (16,250)	A 171 (560) B 226 (740)	A 299 (980) B 320 (1,050)	A 247 (810) B 267 (875)	A 158 (520) B 168 (550)	921 (1,706; 1,060)	
PA-24-180 Comanche	694 (1,530)	1,157 (2,550)	149 (277; 172)	143 (266; 165)	35 (64; 40)	293 (960)		5,850 (19,200)	A 183 (600) B 302 (990)	A 324 (1,065) B475 (1,560)	A 262 (860) B 326 (1,070)	A 128 (420) B 149 (490)	868 (1,609; 1,000)	
PA-24-250 Comanche	776 (1,710)	1,315 (2,900)	168 (311; 193)	161 (298; 185)	35·5 (66; 41)	427 (1,400)		6,310 (20,700)	A 187 (615) B 290 (950)	A 296 (970) B 389 (1,275)	A 256 (840) B 347 (1,140)	A 140 (460) B 213 (700)	1,537 (2,848; 1,770)	
PA-24-260 Comanche	812 (1,792)	1,451 (3,200)	174 (322; 200)	164 (304; 189)	36 (66; 41)	410 (1,345)		6,355 (20,850)	A 200 (655) B 302 (990)	A 338 (1,110) B 401 (1,315)	A 268 (880) B 360 (1,180)	A 152 (500) B 226 (740)	1,137 (2,108; 1,310)	
PA-24-260 Turbo Comanche	821 (1,810)	1,451 (3,200)	213 (394; 245)	201 (372; 231)	36 (66; 41)	410 (1,345)		7,620 (25,000)	A 200 (655) B 302 (990)	A 338 (1,110) B 401 (1,315)	A 268 (880) B 360 (1,180)	A 152 (500) B 226 (740)	1,306 (2,422; 1,505)	
PA-24-400 Comanche	966 (2,130)	1,633 (3,600)	196 (364; 226)	189 (351; 218)	39 (72; 45)	506 (1,660)		6,155 (20,200)	A 126 (415) B 168 (550)	A 233 (765) B 271 (890)	A 303 (995) B 379 (1,245)	A 184 (605) B 216 (710)	1,568 (2,905; 1,805)	
PA-30 Twin Comanche*	1,022 (2,253)	1,724 (3,800)	158 (293; 182)	153 (283; 176)	45 (84; 52)	427 (1,400)	79 (260)	6,100 (20,000)	B 206 (675)	B 341 (1,120)	B 355 (1,165)	B 186 (610)	1,481 (2,744; 1,705)	69 (129; 80)
PA-30 Turbo Twin Comanche*	1,088 (2,399)	1,724 (3,800)	213 (394; 245)	197 (365; 227)	45 (84; 52)	427 (1,400)	69 (225)	7,620 (25,000)	B 206 (675)	B 341 (1,120)	B 355 (1,165)	B 186 (610)	1,528 (2,832; 1,760)	69 (129; 80)
PA-39 Twin Comanche C/R*	1,022 (2,253)	1,724 (3,800)	181 (336; 209)	174 (322; 200)	45 (84; 52)	445 (1,460)	79 (260)	6,100 (20,000)	B 206 (675)	B 320 (1,050)	B 355 (1,165)	B 186 (610)	1,468 (2,720; 1,690)	65 (121; 75)
PA-39 Turbo Twin Comanche C/R*	1,088 (2,399)	1,724 (3,800)	212 (393; 244)	197 (365; 227)	45 (84; 52)	427 (1,400)	69 (225)	7,620 (25,000)	B158 (520)	B 323 (1,060)	B 355 (1,165)	B 189 (620)	1,515 (2,808; 1,745)	65 (121; 75)
PA-23-235 Aztec	1,241 (2,735)	2,177 (4,800)	182 (338; 210)	175 (325; 202)	40 (74; 46)	465 (1,525)	62 (205)	5,515 (18,100)	B 210 (690)	B 331 (1,085)	B 381 (1,250)	B 195 (640)	1,090 (2,020; 1,255)	54 (98; 62)
PA-E23-250 Aztec	1,339 (2,953)	2,266 (4,995)	197 (365; 227)	191 (354; 220)	41 (76; 47)	509 (1,670)	99 (325)	6,615 (21,700)	B 190 (625)	B 315 (1,035)	B 395 (1,295)	B 203 (665)	1,112 (2,060; 1,80)	56 (103; 64)
PA-23-250 Aztec	1,326 (2,925)	2,359 (5,200)	188 (348; 216)	179 (332; 206)	45·5 (84; 52)	491 (1,610)	85 (280)	6,035 (19,800)	B 195 (640)	B 323 (1,060)	B 395 (1,295)	B 203 (665)	916 (1,697; 1,055)	56 (105; 65)
PA-23-250 Turbo Aztec	1,397 (3,080)	2,359 (5,200)	222 (412; 256)	182 (388; 210)	43 (79; 49)	372 (1,220)	64 (210)	9,145 (30,000)	B 195 (640)	B 323 (1,060)	B 395 (1,295)	B 203 (665)	1,050 (1,947; 1,210)	56 (105; 65)
PA-34 Seneca I	1,160 (2,557)	1,905 (4,200)	170 (315; 196)	162 (300; 187)	58 (106; 66)	414 (1,360)	57 (190)	5,730 (18,800)	B 195 (640)	B 320 (1,050)	B 381 (1,250)	B 196 (645)	743 (1,378; 856)	57 (106; 65)
PA-34 Seneca I	1,280 (2,823)	2,073 (4,570)	195 (361; 225)	190 (352; 219)	66 (122; 76)	421 (1,380)	67 (220)	7,620 (25,000)	B 198 (650)	B 332 (1,090)	B 573 (1,880)	B 213 (700)	882 (1,633; 1,015)†	57 (106; 65)

A: Robertson STOL operation. B: Robertson Normal operation. *Available also with engines of increased horsepower.
**With optional long-range tanks fitted, if available. †1,192 (2,207; 1,371) with optional long range tanks.

ROBINSON

ROBINSON HELICOPTER COMPANY INC

Head Office and Works: 24747 Crenshaw Boulevard, Torrance, California 90505
Telephone: (213) 539 0508
Chairman of the Board: C. K. LeFiell
President: Franklin D. Robinson
Vice-President: C. K. LeFiell
Marketing Co-ordinator: Karen L. Walling

Robinson Helicopter Company was formed to design and manufacture a lightweight helicopter which could be competitive in price with current two/four-seat fixed-wing light aircraft. The design of this aircraft, the Robinson R22, began in June 1973 with emphasis on efficiency, low noise emission and minimum maintenance. The first prototype flew for the first time on 28 August 1975, and the second was completed in early 1977. Both were employed in the programme which led to FAA certification on 16 March 1979.

Orders for a total of 524 R22s had been received by 1 January 1979, and initial deliveries of production helicopters were scheduled to be made in April/May 1979. Production is intended to be at the rate of 40 helicopters a month by mid-1980.

ROBINSON MODEL R22

Type: Two-seat lightweight helicopter.

Rotor System: Two-blade main rotor, with a tri-hinged underslung rotor hub to reduce blade flexing, rotor vibration and control force feedback. Main rotor blade section NACA 63-015 (modified). Rigid-in-plane, and free to flap, these blades are of bonded all-metal construction, with a stainless steel spar and leading-edge, light alloy skin and light alloy honeycomb core. One fixed trim tab on main rotor blades. The two-blade tail rotor, mounted on the port side, is of light alloy bonded construction.

Rotor Drive: V-belt drive with sprag-type overrunning clutch. The main and tail gearboxes each utilise spiral bevel gears. Maintenance-free flexible couplings of proprietary manufacture are used in both the main and tail rotor drive systems. Main rotor/engine rpm ratio 1:5. Tail rotor/engine rpm ratio 1·28:1.

Fuselage: Welded steel tube and light alloy primary structure for cabin, rotor pylon and engine mounting, with full monocoque tailcone. Cabin skins of light alloy and glassfibre.

Tail Unit: Cruciform light alloy structure with fixed horizontal stabiliser and vertical fin. Small spring skid beneath lower half of fin to give protection in a tail-down landing.

Landing Gear: Welded steel tube and light alloy skid landing gear, with energy-absorbing crosstubes.

POWER PLANT: One 112 kW (150 hp) Lycoming O-320-A2B flat-four engine (derated to 92·5 kW; 124 hp), mounted in the lower aft section of the main fuselage, and partially exposed to improve cooling and simplify maintenance. Light alloy fuel tank in upper rear section of the fuselage on port side, capacity 75·5 litres (20 US gallons). Oil capacity 7·5 litres (2 US gallons).

ACCOMMODATION: Two seats side by side in enclosed cabin. Cyclic control stick mounted between seats, with dual grips on yoke so that aircraft can be flown from either seat. Conventional dual collective and throttle controls mounted at the port side of each seat. Cyclic control pivots to either side to simplify entry and exit. Curved two-panel windscreen. Door, with window, on each side. Baggage space beneath each seat. Cabin heated and ventilated.

SYSTEM: Electrical system powered by 12V DC generator.

AVIONICS AND EQUIPMENT: Optional avionics include Narco COM 11A com transceiver, NAV 11 Omni receiver and AT 504 transponder, and Narco ADF, or similar avionics by King. Standard equipment includes sensitive altimeter, low rotor rpm warning horn, temperature and chip warning lights for main gearbox and chip warning light for tail gearbox, and soundproofing. Optional equipment includes anti-collision, navigation, panel and landing lights; and ground handling wheels.

DIMENSIONS, EXTERNAL:

Diameter of main rotor	7·67 m (25 ft 2 in)
Diameter of tail rotor	1·07 m (3 ft 6 in)
Main rotor blade chord	0·18 m (7·2 in)
Distance between rotor centres	4·39 m (14 ft 5 in)
Length overall (rotors turning)	8·76 m (28 ft 9 in)
Length of fuselage	6·30 m (20 ft 8 in)
Height overall	2·67 m (8 ft 9 in)
Skid track	1·93 m (6 ft 4 in)

DIMENSION, INTERNAL:

Cabin: Max width	1·12 m (3 ft 8 in)

AREAS:

Main rotor blades (each)	0·70 m² (7·55 sq ft)
Tail rotor blades (each)	0·037 m² (0·40 sq ft)
Main rotor disc	46·21 m² (497·4 sq ft)
Tail rotor disc	0·89 m² (9·63 sq ft)
Fin	0·21 m² (2·28 sq ft)
Stabiliser	0·14 m² (1·53 sq ft)

Second prototype Robinson Model R22 two-seat lightweight helicopter (Lycoming O-320-A2B engine)

WEIGHTS AND LOADINGS:

Weight empty	347 kg (764 lb)
Max T-O and landing weight	590 kg (1,300 lb)
Max zero-fuel weight	535 kg (1,180 lb)
Max disc loading	12·77 kg/m² (2·61 lb/sq ft)
Max power loading	6·38 kg/kW (10·48 lb/hp)

PERFORMANCE (at max T-O weight):

Never-exceed speed	101 knots (188 km/h; 117 mph)
Max level speed	97 knots (180 km/h; 112 mph)
Max cruising speed	94 knots (174 km/h; 108 mph)
Econ cruising speed	76 knots (142 km/h; 88 mph)
Max rate of climb at S/L	366 m (1,200 ft)/min
Service ceiling	4,265 m (14,000 ft)
Hovering ceiling IGE	1,950 m (6,400 ft)
Hovering ceiling OGE	1,370 m (4,500 ft)
Range with max fuel and max payload, no reserves	208 nm (386 km; 240 miles)

ROCKWELL INTERNATIONAL

ROCKWELL INTERNATIONAL CORPORATION

CORPORATE OFFICES: 2230 East Imperial Highway, El Segundo, California 90245
600 Grant Street, Pittsburgh, Pennsylvania 15219

CHAIRMAN OF THE BOARD AND CHIEF EXECUTIVE OFFICER: Robert Anderson

PRESIDENT AND CHIEF OPERATING OFFICER: Donald R. Beall

CORPORATE VICE-PRESIDENTS:
Robert De Palma (Finance and Chief Financial Officer)
J. A. Earley (Corporate Development)
Charles Fazio (General Products Operations)
Richard W. Foxen (Strategic Management)
Kenneth B. Gay (Purchasing)
George W. Jeffs (President, North American Aerospace Operations)
Samuel Petok (Communications)
A. B. Kight (International)
Edward A. Loeser (Operations)
Donald S. MacLeod (Public Affairs)
William L. Neely (Treasurer)
Carl J. Oles (Personnel)
John J. Roscia (General Counsel)
C. E. Ryker (Controller)
W. F. Swanson Jr (Secretary)
Martin D. Walker (President Automotive Operations)

North American Aviation Inc, incorporated in Delaware in 1928 and a manufacturer of aircraft of various kinds from 1934, and Rockwell-Standard Corporation of Pittsburgh, Pennsylvania, a manufacturer of automotive components and builder of the Aero Commander line of civilian aircraft, merged on 22 September 1967 to form North American Rockwell Corporation.

During 1971 the Corporation was reorganised into four principal parts: the North American Aerospace Group (formerly the Aerospace and Systems Office); the Industrial Products Group (formerly the Commercial Products Group); the Automotive Group; and the Electronics Group. There is, in addition, a further component known as the Utility and Consumer Products Group. The constitution of the Corporation was changed on 16 February 1973, when North American Rockwell and Rockwell Manufacturing Company merged to become Rockwell International Corporation.

In September 1978, as the culmination of a succession of organisational changes, the company's aerospace activities were consolidated into one organisation, North American Aerospace Operations, comprising the North American Aircraft Group, the Space Systems Group and the Energy Systems Group. Details of this regrouping follow:

NORTH AMERICAN AEROSPACE OPERATIONS

EXECUTIVE OFFICES: 2230 East Imperial Highway, El Segundo, California 90245
Telephone: (213) 647 5000
PRESIDENT: George W. Jeffs

Rocketdyne Division

6633 Canoga Avenue, Canoga Park, California 91304
Telephone: (213) 334 4000
PRESIDENT: Norman J. Ryker

NORTH AMERICAN AIRCRAFT GROUP

2230 East Imperial Highway, El Segundo, California 90245
Telephone: (213) 647 5000
PRESIDENT: Bastian J. Hello

Columbus Aircraft Division

4300 East Fifth Avenue, Columbus, Ohio 43216
Telephone: (614) 239 3344
PRESIDENT: J. P. Fosness

General Aviation Division

5001 North Rockwell Avenue, Bethany, Oklahoma 73008
Telephone: (405) 789 5000
PRESIDENT: Cornell J. Slivinsky

Los Angeles Division

815 Lapham Street, Los Angeles, California 90045
Telephone: (213) 670 9151
PRESIDENT: C. E. Blalock

Sabreliner Division

6161 Aviation Drive, St Louis, Missouri 63134
Telephone: (314) 731 2260
PRESIDENT: James J. Edwards Jr

Tulsa Division

2000 North Memorial Drive, Tulsa, Oklahoma 74151
Telephone: (918) 835 3111
PRESIDENT: E. H. Ricketts

SPACE SYSTEMS GROUP

EXECUTIVE OFFICES: 12214 Lakewood Boulevard, Downey, California 90241
Telephone: (213) 922 2111
PRESIDENT: George B. Merrick

Satellite Systems Division

12214 Lakewood Boulevard, Downey, California 90241
Telephone: (213) 922 2111
VICE-PRESIDENT: Richard Schwartz

Shuttle Orbiter Division

12214 Lakewood Boulevard, Downey, California 90241
Telephone: (213) 922 2111
VICE-PRESIDENT: Edward P. Smith

Space Transportation System Integration and Operations Division

12214 Lakewood Boulevard, Downey, California 90241
Telephone: (213) 922 2111
VICE-PRESIDENT: William E. Dean

ENERGY SYSTEMS GROUP

8900 De Soto Avenue, Canoga Park, California 91304
Telephone: (213) 341 1000
PRESIDENT: Sam F. Iacobellis

NORTH AMERICAN AIRCRAFT GROUP

Latest aircraft products of North American Aircraft Group are as follows:

ROCKWELL INTERNATIONAL BUCKEYE

US Navy designation: T-2

After a design competition among several leading US manufacturers, what was then North American's Columbus Division was awarded a contract in 1956 to develop and build a jet training aircraft for the US Navy. The first T2J-1 flew on 31 January 1958. Five versions of the aircraft were produced subsequently, of which the T-2A (217 built) and T-2B (97 built) were described in the 1977-78 and earlier editions of *Jane's*. More recent versions are as follows:

T-2C. Generally similar to T-2B, but with General Electric J85-GE-4 instead of Westinghouse (T-2A) and Pratt & Whitney (T-2B) engines. Entered production in late 1968, following extensive evaluation of J85-GE-4 engines in a T-2B which was redesignated T-2C No. 1. First production T-2C flew on 10 December 1968. Deliveries of 231 ordered by Naval Air Training Command were completed in 1975.

Rockwell International T-2E Buckeye in Hellenic Air Force camouflage

T-2D. Differs from T-2C only in avionics and by deletion of carrier landing capability. Twenty-four delivered to Venezuelan Air Force as advanced jet trainers for student pilots.

T-2E. Generally similar to T-2C, except for new avionics and an accessory kit which permits utilisation in attack role. The accessory kit provides six wing store stations with a combined capacity of 1,588 kg (3,500 lb), and protection against small arms fire for the fuel tanks. Forty supplied to Hellenic Air Force Training Command as advanced and tactical jet trainers for student pilots in their final stages of training. Delivery completed in January 1977.

Although the Buckeye was not in production in mid-1979, tooling remains in place in anticipation of further foreign sales. The following abbreviated description applies to the standard T-2C; a full structural description can be found in the 1977-78 edition.

TYPE: Two-seat general-purpose jet trainer.

POWER PLANT: Two 13·12 kN (2,950 lb st) General Electric J85-GE-4 turbojet engines, with jet outlets under rear fuselage. Fuel in main tanks over engines with capacity of 1,465 litres (387 US gallons), two wingtip tanks each of 386 litres (102 US gallons) capacity, and two tanks in the inboard sections of the wings. Total fuel capacity 2,616 litres (691 US gallons).

ACCOMMODATION: Pupil and instructor in tandem in enclosed cabin, on rocket-powered LS-1 ejection seats, under clamshell canopy. Instructor is raised 0·25 m (10 in) above level of pupil.

ARMAMENT: Optional packaged installations of guns, target-towing gear, 100 lb practice bombs, M-5 or MK 76 practice bomb clusters, Aero 4B practice bomb containers, 2·25 in rocket launchers or seven 2·75 in rockets in Aero 6A-1 rocket containers, can be carried on two store stations, one beneath each wing, with a combined capacity of 290 kg (640 lb). Alternative option includes above package, plus four additional wing store stations, to provide a total underwing ordnance capacity of 1,588 kg (3,500 lb), and protection against small arms fire for the fuel tanks.

DIMENSIONS, EXTERNAL:

Wing span over tip-tanks	11·62 m (38 ft 1½ in)
Length overall	11·67 m (38 ft 3½ in)
Height overall	4·51 m (14 ft 9½ in)
Tailplane span	5·46 m (17 ft 11 in)
Wheel track	5·61 m (18 ft 4¾ in)

AREA:

Wings, gross	23·69 m² (255 sq ft)

WEIGHTS:

Weight empty	3,680 kg (8,115 lb)
Max T-O weight	5,983 kg (13,191 lb)

PERFORMANCE (at max T-O weight):

Max level speed at 7,620 m (25,000 ft)	460 knots (852 km/h; 530 mph)
Stalling speed	87 knots (161 km/h; 100 mph)
Max rate of climb at S/L	1,800 m (5,900 ft)/min
Service ceiling	13,870 m (45,500 ft)
Max range	930 nm (1,722 km; 1,070 miles)

ROCKWELL INTERNATIONAL BRONCO

US military designation: OV-10

The development history of the Bronco and a detailed structural description can be found in the 1978-79 and earlier editions of *Jane's*. The type was no longer in production in mid-1979, but tooling remains in place in anticipation of further foreign sales.

The following versions were built:

OV-10A. Initial production version ordered in October 1966 and first flown on 6 August 1967. US Marine Corps had 114 in service in September 1969, of which 18 were on loan to the USN; used for light armed reconnaissance, helicopter escort and forward air control duties. At the same date the USAF had 157 OV-10As for use in the forward air control role, and for limited quick-response ground support pending the arrival of tactical fighters. Production ended in April 1969.

OV-10B. Generally similar to the OV-10A; six supplied to Federal German government for target towing.

OV-10B(Z). Structurally similar to OV-10B. Provision for General Electric J85-GE-4 turbojet of 13·12 kN (2,950 lb st) to be mounted above wing, on a pylon attached to existing hoisting points, to increase performance for target towing. First of 12 for Federal German government flown 21 September 1970. Delivery completed November 1970. The jet pods were fitted by RFB, in Germany, following the prototype installation by Rockwell.

OV-10C. Version of OV-10A for Royal Thai Air Force. Deliveries of 32 completed in September 1973.

YOV-10D/OV-10D. Two YOV-10Ds were OV-10As modified under a 1970 contract from the US Navy, to provide a new concept in night operational capability for the US Marine Corps. The first one flew for the first time on 9 June 1970 and both were combat tested in Viet-Nam in 1971. Distinguishing features of the YOV-10D Night Observation/Gunship System were a 20 mm gun turret beneath the aft fuselage and a forward-looking infra-red (FLIR) sensor beneath the extended nose. A laser target designator was incorporated within the FLIR sensor turret. Two wing pylons were installed at the Sidewinder missile stations, capable of carrying rocket pods, flare pods and free-fall stores.

In 1974, Rockwell received a US Navy contract to establish and test a production OV-10D configuration. This led to delivery of 17 US Marine Corps OV-10As to Rockwell's Columbus Aircraft Division, beginning in the Spring of 1978, for conversion to the Night Observation Surveillance (NOS) role. In addition to the NOS systems and the retention of basic OV-10A fuselage stores and external fuel capability, the OV-10D NOS has uprated (775·5 kW; 1,040 shp) engines, wing pylons capable of carrying rocket pods, flare pods, free-fall stores and 378 litre (100 US gallon) external fuel tanks when extended radius/loiter time is required. The Texas Instruments FLIR sensor and laser target designator are installed in a rotating ball turret in the nose. The sensor turret can be linked to a turret-mounted General Electric M-97 20 mm cannon, mounted beneath the fuselage, in lieu of normal operation with standard OV-10A armament sponsons and centreline station. First-phase testing of the FLIR system and uprated engines was completed by a pre-production OV-10D in 1978. First deliveries of modified aircraft were scheduled for Spring 1979.

OV-10E. Version of OV-10A for Venezuelan Air Force. Sixteen delivered.

OV-10F. Version of OV-10A for Indonesia. Sixteen delivered.

The following abbreviated description applies to the standard OV-10A, except where stated:

TYPE: Two-seat multi-purpose counter-insurgency aircraft.

POWER PLANT: Two 533 kW (715 ehp) Garrett-AiResearch T76-G-416/417 turboprop engines, each driving a Hamilton Standard three-blade constant-speed reversible-pitch and fully-feathering metal propeller. (OV-10D has 775·5 kW; 1,040 shp T76-G-420/421 engines, each driving a similar Hamilton Standard propeller but with glassfibre blades.) Five self-sealing bladder-type fuel tanks in wings, with combined capacity of 954 litres (252 US gallons). Gravity refuelling point above each tank on wing upper surface. Provision for carrying one 568 litre (150 US gallon) drop-tank on underfuselage pylon; OV-10D also has provisions for carrying one 378 litre (100 US gallon) drop-tank on each wing pylon. Oil capacity 11·4 litres (3 US gallons).

ACCOMMODATION: Crew of two in tandem, on LW-3B zero-zero ejection seats, under canopy with two large upward-opening transparent door panels on each side. Dual controls optional. Cargo compartment aft of rear seat, with rear-loading door at end of fuselage pod. Rear seat removable to provide increased space for up to 1,452 kg (3,200 lb) of freight, or for carriage of five paratroops, or two stretcher patients and attendant.

SYSTEMS: Heating and ventilation system combines engine bleed air and cold ram air to provide temperature controlled conditions. Engine bleed air is used also for windscreen defrosting and to supply crew's anti-*g* suits. Hydraulic system of intermittent-duty type powered by an electrically-driven hydraulic pump at a pressure of 103·5 bars (1,500 lb/sq in), for actuation of trailing-edge flaps, landing gear and nosewheel steering. Wheel brakes, which have two independent manually-driven brake units, are fed directly from the hydraulic system reservoir. Electrical system powered by two 30V 300A starter/generators and two 24V 22Ah nickel-cadmium batteries. (OV-10D has two 30V 400A starter/generators and two 24V 30Ah aircooled batteries.) AC power derived from two 750VA inverters which supply 115V at 400Hz three-phase; single-phase AC of 115V or 26V at 400Hz can be tapped from the bus system. (An additional 3,000VA inverter is installed in the OV-10D.) External power sockets for engine starting and utility services; the latter can be used to provide 28V DC to other aircraft for engine starting or servicing. Demand-regulated oxygen system supplied from two 0·008 m³ (0·3 cu ft) oxygen cylinders at a pressure of 124·2 bars (1,800 lb/sq in). Independent fire warning system for each engine, comprising control unit, sensing elements, and warning lights. USAF aircraft only have an electrically-fired fire extinguishing system installed in each engine nacelle. No pneumatic system.

AVIONICS: USAF aircraft are equipped with AN/AIC-18 intercom; AN/ARC-51BX UHF, Wilcox 807A VHF, dual FM-622A VHF, and HF-103 HF com radios; nav system includes AN/ASN-75 compass, AN/ARN-52(V) Tacan, AN/ARA-50 UHF-ADF, AN/ARN-83 LF-ADF, 51R-6 VOR, and 51V-4A ILS glideslope; identification system includes AN/APX-64(V) IFF/SIF, and SST-181-X radar beacon. USMC aircraft are equipped with AN/AIC-18 intercom; AN/ARC-51AX VHF, AN/ARC-54 VHF, and AN/ARC-120 HF com radios; nav system includes AN/ASN-75 compass,

Rockwell International OV-10D, with production-configuration Night Observation Surveillance (NOS) equipment

AN/APN-171 radar altimeter, AN/ARN-52(V) Tacan, and AN/ARA-50 UHF-ADF; AN/APX-64(V) IFF/SIF for identification. (OV-10D NOS aircraft have a FLIR sensor system package, comprising FLIR, a laser target designator, and an automatic video tracker.)

ARMAMENT: Four weapon attachment points, each with capacity of 272 kg (600 lb), under short sponsons extending from bottom of fuselage on each side, under wings. Fifth attachment point, capacity 544 kg (1,200 lb), under centre-fuselage. Two 7·62 mm M-60C machine-guns, each with 500 rounds of ammunition, carried in each sponson. USMC OV-10A has provision also for carrying one AIM-9D Sidewinder missile under each wing. Stores which can be carried on the under-fuselage and sponson stations include Mk 81, 82 and 83 GP bombs, Mk 81 and 82 GP (Snakeye) bombs; Mk 77 Mod 2 and Mod 4 fire bombs; LAU-3/A, LAU-10/A, LAU-32/A, LAU-59/A, LAU-60/A, LAU-61/A, LAU-68/A and LAU-69/A rocket packages; SUU-11A/A (7·62 mm Minigun), Mk 4 Mod 0 (20 mm), and GPU-2/A (20 mm) gun pods; SUU-40/A and SUU-44/A with Mk 24 and Mk 45 flares; Mk 12 Mod 0 (Podeye) smoke tank; Mk 86A/A37B-3 MBR with Mk 76 and Mk 106 practice bombs; CBU-55/B cluster bomb. Max weapon load on fuselage stations 1,633 kg (3,600 lb). (OV-10D aircraft have wing pylons with stores capacity of 272 kg; 600 lb each, which can carry CBU-55/B cluster bombs; LAU-10/A, LAU-68/A and LAU-69/A rocket packages; SUU-40/A and SUU-44/A with Mk 24 and Mk 45 flares. In lieu of sponsons and fuselage centreline load, the OV-10D can accommodate a 20 mm gun turret kit installed on centreline station hardpoints.)

DIMENSIONS, EXTERNAL:
- Wing span: 12·19 m (40 ft 0 in)
- Length overall: 12·67 m (41 ft 7 in)
- Height overall: 4·62 m (15 ft 2 in)
- Tailplane span: 4·45 m (14 ft 7 in)
- Wheel track: 4·52 m (14 ft 10 in)
- Wheelbase: 3·56 m (11 ft 8 in)
- Propeller diameter: 2·59 m (8 ft 6 in)
- Rear loading door: Height 0·99 m (3 ft 3 in)
  - Width 0·76 m (2 ft 6 in)

AREA:
- Wings, gross: 27·03 m² (291 sq ft)

WEIGHTS AND LOADING:
- Weight empty: 3,127 kg (6,893 lb)
- Normal T-O weight: 4,494 kg (9,908 lb)
- Overload T-O weight: 6,552 kg (14,444 lb)
- Max wing loading: 242·4 kg/m² (49·6 lb/sq ft)

PERFORMANCE (at weights stated. A: OV-10A/C/E/F; B: OV-10B(Z)):
- Max level speed at S/L, without weapons:
  - A: 244 knots (452 km/h; 281 mph)
- Max level speed at 3,050 m (10,000 ft) at AUW of 4,536 kg (10,000 lb):
  - B: 341 knots (632 km/h; 393 mph)
- Max rate of climb at S/L at max T-O weight:
  - A: 790 m (2,600 ft)/min
- Max rate of climb at S/L at AUW of 5,443 kg (12,000 lb): B 2,073 m (6,800 ft)/min
- T-O run:
  - A, at normal T-O weight: 226 m (740 ft)
  - B, at 5,443 kg (12,000 lb) AUW: 168 m (550 ft)
- T-O to 15 m (50 ft):
  - A, at normal T-O weight: 341 m (1,120 ft)
  - A, at max T-O weight: 853 m (2,800 ft)
- Landing from 15 m (50 ft):
  - A, at normal T-O weight: 372 m (1,220 ft)
- Landing run:
  - A, at normal T-O weight: 226 m (740 ft)
  - A, at max T-O weight: 381 m (1,250 ft)
- Combat radius with max weapon load, no loiter:
  - A: 198 nm (367 km; 228 miles)
- Ferry range with auxiliary fuel:
  - A: 1,200 nm (2,224 km; 1,382 miles)

ROCKWELL INTERNATIONAL B-1

The B-1 was the outcome of a succession of defence studies, begun in 1962 and leading to the AMSA (Advanced Manned Strategic Aircraft) requirement of 1965, for a low-altitude penetration bomber to replace the Boeing B-52s of USAF Strategic Air Command by 1980. It was to be the third and most flexible component of the US Triad defence system, comprising also land-based and submarine-launched ballistic missiles.

To meet the B-1 requirement, the Department of Defense issued RFPs (Requests For Proposals) to the US aerospace industry on 3 November 1969, and from three airframe and two engine finalists it awarded research, development, test and evaluation contracts on 5 June 1970 to North American Rockwell's Los Angeles Division for the airframe and to the General Electric Company for the F101 turbofan engine. The original cost-plus-incentive contracts were for five flying prototypes, two structural test airframes and 40 engines; in January 1971, in which month the essential design of the B-1 was frozen, these quantities were reduced to three flight test aircraft, one ground test aircraft and 27 engines. Procurement of a fourth flight test aircraft, as a pre-production prototype, was approved under the FY 1976 budget. The USAF hoped to order 244 B-1s, including prototypes, to replace B-52s now in service.

The B-1 prototypes were assembled in USAF facilities known as Plant 42 at Palmdale, California. Assembly of the first aircraft began in late 1972; this aircraft (74-0158) made its first flight, at Palmdale, on 23 December 1974. This occasion was also the first flight of the YF101 engine. The third B-1, used as a testbed for the avionics systems, made its first flight on 1 April 1976, and was followed by the first flight of the second B-1 on 14 June 1976. The second aircraft had been used for proof loads testing; these tests occupied approximately eight months during 1975, after which No. 2 was converted to a flight test aircraft. By 1 January 1979 the three aircraft involved in the test programme had accumulated a total of over 1,200 hours in more than 200 test missions.

The fourth B-1 (76-0174) flew for the first time on 14 February 1979, and is the only example fitted with the complete B-1 offensive and defensive weapons systems. The first prototype was retired in 1978 and the second in 1979, in order to utilise limited funding in tests of the most advanced aircraft, following the 30 June 1977 announcement by President Carter that production of the B-1 would be cancelled and priority given instead to the cruise missile development programme. Authority was given for the test and development programme to continue, in order to provide the needed technical base in the event that the alternative systems should run into difficulty.

In 1978 B-1 derivative designs were included in continuing Department of Defense studies to evaluate various types of aircraft as cruise missile carriers.

A full description of the B-1 can be found in the 1977-78 *Jane's*.

DIMENSIONS, EXTERNAL:
- Wing span: fully spread 41·67 m (136 ft 8½ in)
  - fully swept 23·84 m (78 ft 2½ in)
- Wing area, gross: approx 181·2 m² (1,950 sq ft)
- Length overall: incl nose probe 45·78 m (150 ft 2½ in)
  - excl nose probe 44·70 m (146 ft 8 in)
- Height overall: 10·24 m (33 ft 7¼ in)
- Wheel track (c/l of shock-absorbers): 4·42 m (14 ft 6 in)
- Wheelbase: 17·53 m (57 ft 6 in)

WEIGHTS:
- Design max T-O weight: 179,170 kg (395,000 lb)
- Max landing weight: approx 158,755 kg (350,000 lb)

PERFORMANCE (estimated, with VG inlets):
- Max level speed at 15,240 m (50,000 ft): approx Mach 2·2 (1,260 knots; 2,335 km/h; 1,451 mph)
- Max level speed at 152 m (500 ft): approx 650 knots (1,205 km/h; 750 mph)
- Cruising speed at 15,240 m (50,000 ft): Mach 0·85 (562 knots; 1,042 km/h; 648 mph)
- Max range without refuelling: Intercontinental

ROCKWELL INTERNATIONAL XFV-12A

The US Navy initiated the XFV-12A V/STOL Fighter/Attack Technology Prototype programme to develop the capability of V/STOL operation from comparatively small carrier decks that would have neither catapult nor arrester gear.

The prototype aircraft is roughly the size of a McDonnell Douglas A-4 Skyhawk. It employs an augmentor-wing concept with forward canard and aft semi-delta wings, and is powered by a single, special version of the Pratt & Whitney F401-PW-400 advanced-technology turbofan engine.

The augmentor system has a diverter valve to block off

Fourth and final Rockwell International B-1 strategic bomber, with its wings in the forward position

Rockwell International XFV-12A prototype during tethered testing in the hover mode

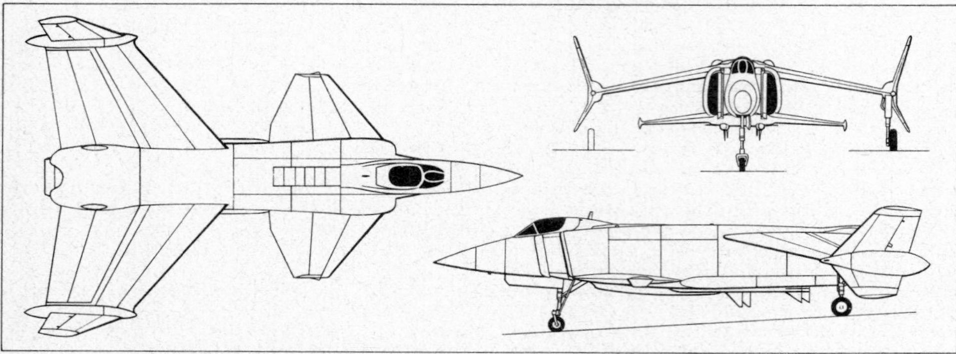

Rockwell International XFV-12A single-seat V/STOL fighter/attack prototype *(Pilot Press)*

the turbofan nozzle and divert the exhaust gases through ducts to nozzles in the wings and canards for V/STOL operations. A full-span ejector-flap system on each wing and canard allows ambient air to be drawn in over the flaps and ejected downward, mixed with the primary exhaust flow in a 7 : 1 ratio to provide the required jet-lift, which is considerably greater than the engine thrust.

The thrust from each of the four augmentors is modulated by flap movement to provide lift and attitude control with no change in engine setting. As the flaps are closed from their maximum lift position, the amount of entrained airflow is reduced. Simultaneous operation of all four augmentors provides height control; differential movement between wing and canard augmentors provides pitch control; while roll control is achieved by differential operation of the port and starboard wing augmentors. Control in yaw is obtained by moving one set of wing flaps forward and the other set aft. All lift is under control at all times and no reaction control is required.

The large amounts of entrained air increase greatly the circulation lift on the aerodynamic surfaces during short take-off and conversion from hover to conventional flight. Take-off gross weight can be increased by 25 per cent with a 91 m (300 ft) T-O run.

Cost considerations have limited the amount of test hardware associated with the development programme. To evaluate thrust augmentor components, a complete flight wing and canard with diffuser flaps were mounted on a rotary test rig. An F401 engine with thrust diverter was incorporated in the rig in January 1974. This allows engine exhaust air to be ducted along the rig and exhausted through the augmentor components for static lift measurements, or while the rig is rotated at high speed.

The NASA Langley Lunar Lander gantry has been used for tethered testing of the aircraft in the hover mode, both in and out of ground effect. Initial testing was conducted during the first half of 1978. Although the desired lift was not achieved, precise manoeuvring capability was demonstrated with the hover control system. Lift improvement testing is being conducted in the company's test rig, and the wing and canard ducting is being modified, to provide lift levels in aircraft-compatible hardware which had been achieved previously during individual wing and canard tests. Funding limitations continue to constrain severely the progress of this programme.

Type: Single-seat all-weather V/STOL fighter/attack prototype.

Wings: Cantilever shoulder-wing monoplane. Wing section NACA 64 series (modified). Thickness/chord ratio 0·076 at root, 0·045 at tip. Anhedral 10°. Incidence 1° 30′. Sweepback at quarter-chord 35°. Light alloy structure of semi-delta configuration, forward portion of wing structure embodying an F-4 wing box. Titanium honeycomb is used for construction of the ejector flaps. Hydraulically-powered controls with irreversible actuators of Rockwell design and manufacture. Full-span trailing-edge flaps provide a lifting force for manoeuvrability in high-speed flight. Vertical endplate surfaces are mounted at each wingtip, comprising a fixed fin below the wing, outward-canted at 35°, and a fixed fin and rudder above the wing, outward-canted at 19°. Wing augmentor (ejector) flaps extend almost full span. They provide control of the vertical lift propulsion, acting as thrust vectors and so giving attitude and height control in hover and low-speed flight. The aft ejector flaps (together with those in the canard surfaces) serve as conventional flight controls in cruising flight. The fore and aft ejector flaps can be used together as speed brakes.

Canard Surfaces: Cantilever low-wing monoplane. Anhedral 5°. Full-span trailing-edge flaps provide a lifting force for manoeuvrability in high-speed flight. Full-span augmentor (ejector) flaps function in combination with those on wings.

Fuselage: Forward fuselage, to aft of cockpit, is that of an A-4. Broad-section fuselage aft of cockpit, to house engine intake ducts and augmentor system ducting, is of light alloy semi-monocoque construction. Engine mounted in aft fuselage, which incorporates titanium material in its structure.

Landing Gear: Hydraulically-retractable tricycle type. Main units retract rearward into wingtip fairings, nosewheel unit forward. Oleo-pneumatic shock-absorption. Hydraulic nosewheel steering. All units as for McDonnell Douglas A-4. Main wheels with tyres size 24 × 5·5-14, pressure 20·7 bars (300 lb/sq in). Nosewheel with tyre size 18 × 5·7-8, pressure 14·82 bars (215 lb/sq in). Goodyear dual disc brakes.

Power Plant: One modified Pratt & Whitney F401-PW-400 afterburning turbofan engine in the 133·4 kN (30,000 lb) thrust class. Engine inlet ducts are modified from the F-4. Auxiliary inlet in fuselage upper surface, aft of cockpit, augments air mass flow when aircraft is operating in vertical mode. A special electro-hydraulically actuated diverter valve, designed by Pratt & Whitney, will be installed in the tailpipe of the engine. When open, in the horizontal flight mode, it will allow free passage of engine exhaust gases for conventional propulsion. When closed, for vertical flight, the exhaust gases will be diverted to the ducts that feed the wing and canard augmentor nozzles. Fuel contained in two fuselage bladder tanks, capacity 1,590 litres (420 US gallons), and integral wing tanks, capacity 1,173 litres (310 US gallons). Total fuel capacity 2,763 litres (730 US gallons). Single-point refuelling. Oil capacity 11·4 litres (3 US gallons).

Accommodation: Pilot only, on McDonnell Douglas Escapac zero-zero ejection seat. Cockpit pressurised and air-conditioned.

Systems: AiResearch air cycle air-conditioning and pressurisation system, maintaining sea level cockpit altitude to 2,440 m (8,000 ft). Two independent and simultaneously operating hydraulic systems, at a pressure of 207 bars (3,000 lb/sq in), to operate flight controls, landing gear, ejector flaps and inlet ramps. Primary power source of the electrical system is a 30kVA integrated drive generator, the system providing 115/200V 400Hz AC power and 28V DC power. Emergency oxygen system with capacity of 5 litres (0·18 cu ft) of liquid oxygen, with converter. Anti-icing by engine bleed air.

Avionics and Equipment: Collins AV/ARC-159 UHF radio. Radar system under study. Bendix RN-242A VOR; King KN65 DME. Blind-flying instrumentation standard.

Armament: Ability to carry air-to-air and air-to-ground weapons. Space for internal gun in lower fuselage. Associated equipment is under study.

Dimensions, external:	
Wing span	8·69 m (28 ft 6¼ in)
Wing chord at root	4·98 m (16 ft 4¼ in)
Wing chord at tip	2·25 m (7 ft 4½ in)
Wing aspect ratio	2·09
Length overall	13·39 m (43 ft 11 in)
Height overall	3·15 m (10 ft 4 in)
Canard surfaces span	3·69 m (12 ft 1¼ in)
Wheel track	7·34 m (24 ft 1 in)
Wheelbase	7·62 m (25 ft 0 in)
Areas:	
Wings, gross	27·2 m² (293 sq ft)
Elevons (total)	1·91 m² (20·57 sq ft)
Fins (total)	5·08 m² (54·64 sq ft)
Rudders (total)	1·23 m² (13·20 sq ft)
Canard surfaces, gross	7·72 m² (83·05 sq ft)
Elevators (total)	2·75 m² (29·62 sq ft)
Weights (estimated):	
Basic operating weight	6,259 kg (13,800 lb)
Max vertical T-O weight	8,845 kg (19,500 lb)
Max short-field T-O weight	11,000 kg (24,250 lb)
Performance (estimated, at max T-O weight):	
Max level speed	in excess of Mach 2
T-O run at 11,000 kg (24,250 lb)	91 m (300 ft)

SABRELINER DIVISION

Executive Offices: 6161 Aviation Drive, St Louis, Missouri 63134

Telephone: (314) 731 2260

Telex: 44-7227

President: James J. Edwards Jr

Executives:

E. J. Brandreth Jr (Vice-President, Marketing and Customer Service)
C. Castillo (Manager, Public Relations)
D. Denison (Manager, Pre-Owned Aircraft Sales)
H. L. Humble (Manager, Western Regional Sales)
J. Medeiros (Manager, Sales Administration)
P. Picciano (Manager, Customer Support)
R. H. Reid (Vice-President, Finance, and Controller)
T. Reilly (Manager, Eastern Regional Sales)
F. Smith (Director, US Government Sales)
P. Wickham (Chief Engineer)
T. R. Young (Manager, Marketing Services)
Carl G. Ziegler (Manager, International Sales)

On 4 March 1977 Rockwell International announced the intention to consolidate Sabreliner activities in St Louis, Missouri. Structures and components continue to be manufactured in Los Angeles and are shipped to Perryville Municipal Airport, Missouri, for final assembly and flight test.

Delivery of the 500th Sabreliner, a Model 75A, was made in July 1977. Production of this version, and of the Sabreliner 60, was completed in Spring 1979, since when manufacture has concentrated on the new Sabreliner 65. Preliminary development of the intercontinental Sabreliner 85 has started.

ROCKWELL SABRELINER 40, 60 and 75A

USAF and US Navy designation: T-39

Production of the Sabreliner 60 ended in April 1979, after 146 had been built; the last of 72 Sabreliner 75 As was completed in the following month. Detailed descriptions of both models can be found in the 1978-79 *Jane's*.

Mark Five retrofit improvements for these aircraft, and for the Sabreliner 40 (described in 1974-75 *Jane's*), are available only from the Raisbeck Group (which see).

The Rockwell T-39A Sabreliner shown in an accompanying illustration is fitted with the Hughes APG-65 nose-mounted radar and other avionics of the McDonnell Douglas F-18 Hornet, including the latter's mission computer, displays and inertial navigation system. Conversion was undertaken in 1978, when initial testbed flying of the radar was performed at Hughes Aircraft facilities. In March 1979, the Sabreliner transferred to the McDonnell airfield at St Louis and began a series of 10 flights for US Navy preliminary assessment of the Hornet radar and avionics. These flights, completed in July 1979, included intercept missions against F-15 Eagle and F-4 Phantom fighters, evaluation of ground mapping capability and other air-to-surface missions.

By 27 July, radar and avionics integration testing on

board the Sabreliner totalled more than 70 h in 47 flights. Most current flights include three or four intercepts, long-range and close-in. Real-beam radar and Doppler-beam radar maps produced during return flights have revealed resolution 20 to 60 times better than those possible with conventional radars. Subjects have included an Illinois bridge and lake, Scott AFB near St Louis, downtown St Louis and St Charles, Missouri.

Crew of this testbed Sabreliner consists normally of a pilot, radar operator and two engineers.

ROCKWELL SABRELINER 65

Construction of a prototype of Rockwell's Sabreliner 65, which has the company Model number NA-265-65, began in January 1977, and this aircraft made its first flight on 29 June 1977. Construction of a pre-production aircraft began in December 1977, and this entered the certification programme in February 1979. Certification was planned for June 1979, with initial deliveries of production aircraft scheduled for July 1979.

The Sabreliner 65 embodies the Mark Five advanced technology features developed jointly by Rockwell International and the Raisbeck Group (which see).

TYPE: Twin-turbofan business transport.

WINGS: Cantilever low-wing monoplane. Supercritical wing with dihedral. Incidence 1·68° at root, —4·64° at tip. Sweepback at quarter-chord 32·79°. Integrally stiffened milled skin light alloy structure. Conventional ailerons with single spar and ribbed skins of light alloy. Electrically-operated Fowler-type trailing-edge flaps of light alloy construction. Hydraulically-operated spoilers of light alloy construction, two on upper surface of each wing, forward of flaps, are operable in flight and on the ground. Electrically-operated trim tab in port aileron. Anti-icing of wing leading-edges by engine bleed air.

FUSELAGE: Conventional semi-monocoque safe-life structure of light alloy.

TAIL UNIT: Cantilever structure of light alloy. Electrically-operated variable-incidence tailplane. Electrically-operated trim tab in rudder.

LANDING GEAR: Hydraulically-retractable tricycle type, with single wheel on each main unit and twin nosewheels. Main units retract outward, nose unit forward; all wheels enclosed by fairings when retracted. Oleo-pneumatic shock-absorbers on all units. Main wheels have tyres size 26 × 6·75, 16-ply rating, pressure 17·86 bars (259 lb/sq in). Nosewheel tyres size 18 × 4·4 Type VII, 10-ply rating, pressure 5·17 bars (75 lb/sq in). Nose unit steerable. Hydraulically-operated disc brakes. Parking brake. Electrically-controlled hydraulically-actuated fully-modulating anti-skid units.

POWER PLANT: Two Garrett-AiResearch TFE731-3-1D turbofan engines, each 16·46 kN (3,700 lb st), mounted in pod on each side of rear fuselage. Hydraulically-actuated target-type thrust reversers. Integral fuel tanks in wings, with capacity of 4,124 litres (1,089·5 US gallons), one aft fuselage bladder tank, capacity 607·5 litres (160·5 US gallons), and one forward fuselage bladder tank, beneath cabin floor, with capacity of 254·4 litres (67·2 US gallons), providing total fuel capacity of 4,985·9 litres (1,317·2 US gallons). Single-point refuelling standard. Gravity refuelling points on wing upper surface, and on starboard side of fuselage, above engine.

ACCOMMODATION: Crew of two and 8-10 passengers in pressurised and air-conditioned cabin with a variety of seating layouts, all with galley, toilet and baggage compartment. Dual controls standard. Bottom-hinged downward-opening door with built-in airstairs forward of wing on port side. Overwing emergency exit on each side of cabin, FAA Type IV, removable from inside or outside. Baggage compartment at forward end of cabin on starboard side; baggage space in aft toilet compartment; total baggage capacity 247 kg (545 lb).

SYSTEMS: Air-conditioning and pressurisation by engine bleed air, max differential 0·61 bars (8·8 lb/sq in) to provide cabin altitude of 2,440 m (8,000 ft) to a height of 13,715 m (45,000 ft); separate ducting and temperature controls for cabin and flight deck. Hydraulic system supplied by a single electrically-driven pump, pressure 207 bars (3,000 lb/sq in). Auxiliary hydraulic accumulator for emergency use provides through separate lines a limited number of cycles for anti-skid units, wheel brakes, nosewheel steering and spoilers. Electrical system includes two 400A engine-driven generators. Oxygen system comprising one 2·10 m³ (74 cu ft) cylinder in aft cabin, with quick-donning crew masks and automatic dropout masks for passengers. Anti-icing of wing leading-edges and engine air intakes by engine bleed air; electrical de-icing of pitots, stall-warning vanes and windscreens. APU optional for air-conditioning and electrical/hydraulic power on the ground and for electrical/hydraulic power when airborne.

AVIONICS: Include dual Collins VHF com, dual VHF nav with VOR/ILS, dual FD 109 flight directors, APS-80 autopilot, WXR-250 weather radar, DME-40, ADF-60A, TRD-90 transponder, and dual MC-103 compasses. Full blind-flying instrumentation is standard.

Rockwell T-39A Sabreliner, with nose-mounted APG-65 radar

DIMENSIONS, EXTERNAL:
- Wing span: 15·37 m (50 ft 5⅛ in)
- Length overall: 14·30 m (46 ft 11 in)
- Height overall: 4·88 m (16 ft 0 in)
- Tailplane span: 5·91 m (19 ft 4⅝ in)
- Wheel track: 2·20 m (7 ft 2½ in)
- Wheelbase: 4·85 m (15 ft 10¾ in)
- Cabin door (port, fwd): Height: 1·19 m (3 ft 11 in)
  - Width: 0·71 m (2 ft 4 in)
- Emergency exits (port, stbd, each):
  - Height: 0·66 m (2 ft 2 in)
  - Width: 0·51 m (1 ft 8 in)

DIMENSIONS, INTERNAL:
- Cabin (excl flight deck): Length: 5·79 m (19 ft 0 in)
  - Max width: 1·60 m (5 ft 3 in)
  - Max height: 1·60 m (5 ft 3 in)
  - Volume: 13·59 m³ (480 cu ft)
- Baggage compartments (fore and aft):
  - Volume: 1·22 m³ (43 cu ft)

AREAS:
- Wings, gross: 35·30 m² (380 sq ft)
- Ailerons (total): 1·53 m² (16·42 sq ft)
- Trailing-edge flaps (total): 3·87 m² (41·67 sq ft)
- Spoilers (total): 1·11 m² (11·92 sq ft)
- Fin: 3·86 m² (41·58 sq ft)
- Rudder, incl tab: 0·83 m² (8·95 sq ft)
- Tailplane: 8·37 m² (90·08 sq ft)
- Elevators: 1·80 m² (19·43 sq ft)

WEIGHTS AND LOADINGS:
- Weight empty, basic (incl 2 crew): 6,237 kg (13,750 lb)
- Max T-O weight: 10,886 kg (24,000 lb)
- Max zero-fuel weight: 7,371 kg (16,250 lb)
- Max landing weight: 9,868 kg (21,755 lb)
- Max wing loading: 308·4 kg/m² (63·2 lb/sq ft)
- Max power loading: 330·7 kg/kN (3·24 lb/lb st)

PERFORMANCE (provisional, at max T-O weight, unless specified otherwise):
- Max operating speed: Mach 0·85
- Stalling speed, flaps up 115 knots (212 km/h; 132 mph)
- Stalling speed, full flap, operating weight empty, plus 4 passengers and reserve fuel: 81 knots (150 km/h; 93 mph)
- Max rate of climb at S/L: 1,079 m (3,540 ft)/min

Rockwell Sabreliner 65 with supercritical wing and other aerodynamic improvements

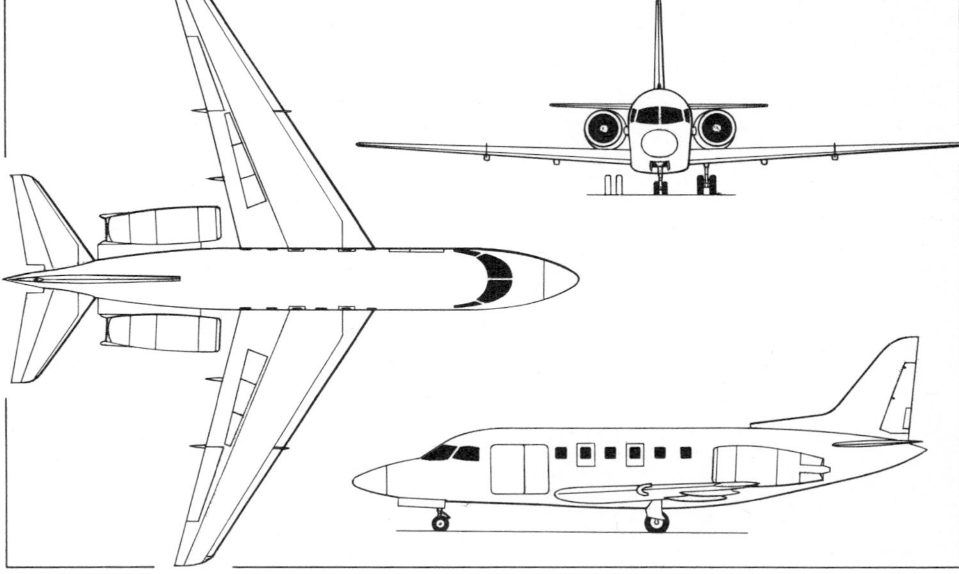

Rockwell Sabreliner 85 twin-turbofan intercontinental business transport *(Pilot Press)*

Rate of climb at S/L, one engine out
290 m (950 ft)/min
Service ceiling 13,715 m (45,000 ft)
Service ceiling, one engine out 6,100 m (20,000 ft)
FAA T-O field length 1,615 m (5,300 ft)
FAA landing field length 790 m (2,590 ft)
Range with 907 kg; 2,000 lb payload, NBAA VFR reserves 2,600 nm (4,818 km; 2,994 miles)
Range with max fuel, NBAA VFR reserves
2,910 nm (5,393 km; 3,351 miles)

ROCKWELL SABRELINER 85

Rockwell announced on 11 September 1978 that its Sabreliner Division had started preliminary design of a new model designated Sabreliner 85. Intended to offer true intercontinental range, this aircraft will have a supercritical wing, advanced technology turbofan engines, and a cabin 7·62 m (25 ft 0 in) long to provide the spaciousness and facilities essential on long-range flights. Engines being considered for installation in the Sabreliner 85 are the 33·4 kN (7,500 lb st) Avco Lycoming ALF-502L, and the 24·7 kN (5,540 lb st) Rolls-Royce RB.401-07. Max usable fuel capacity will be 6,214 kg (13,700 lb). Computer analysis has produced the following specification/performance estimates:

Dimensions, external:
Wing span 16·99 m (55 ft 9 in)
Length overall 16·29 m (53 ft 5½ in)
Height overall 5·64 m (18 ft 6 in)

Weights (A: Rolls-Royce RB.401-07; B: Avco Lycoming ALF-502L turbofans):
Operating weight empty, incl crew:
A 7,938 kg (17,500 lb)
B 8,165 kg (18,000 lb)
Payload with max fuel 590 kg (1,300 lb)
Max ramp/T-O weight: A 14,742 kg (32,500 lb)
B 14,969 kg (33,000 lb)
Max landing weight: A 14,515 kg (32,000 lb)
B 14,742 kg (32,500 lb)

Performance (at max T-O weight, unless specified otherwise):
Max operating speed: A Mach 0·85
B Mach 0·88
Max cruising speed: A Mach 0·84
B Mach 0·87
Econ cruising speed: A, B Mach 0·74
FAA T-O field length: A 1,646 m (5,400 ft)
B 1,204 m (3,950 ft)
FAA landing distance at AUW of 10,886 kg (24,000 lb): A 1,036 m (3,400 ft)
B 1,189 m (3,900 ft)
Max range with NBAA VFR reserves, 30 min hold at 1,525 m (5,000 ft):
A 4,400 nm (8,155 km; 5,067 miles)
B 3,900 nm (7,228 km; 4,491 miles)
Max range with NBAA IFR reserves, missed approach, 200 nm (370 km; 230 mile) alternate, 30 min hold at 1,525 m (5,000 ft):
A 3,950 nm (7,319 km; 4,548 miles)
B 3,450 nm (6,394 km; 3,973 miles)

GENERAL AVIATION DIVISION

Executive Offices: 5001 North Rockwell Avenue, Bethany, Oklahoma 73008
Telephone: (405) 789 5000
President: Cornell J. Slivinsky
Executive Vice-President: Alan Kehlet
Executives:
A. F. Balaban (Manager, Public Relations)
J. Cobb (Director, Industrial Relations)
Herbert B. Franck (Manager, Multi-engine Sales)
Gary Glancy (Manager, Single-engine Sales)
Larry L. McHughes (Director, Engineering)
C. J. Slivinsky (Acting Director, Marketing)

Rockwell International's General Aviation Division is a part of North American Aerospace Operations, and incorporates the Corporation's manufacturing, marketing and servicing of general aviation aircraft. It manufactures and markets Rockwell Commander turboprop and piston-engined multi-engine aircraft and single-engine personal and business aircraft.

Rockwell Alpine Commander four-seat turbocharged cabin monoplane

ROCKWELL ALPINE COMMANDER

Following extensive consumer research in the lightplane market, Rockwell initiated design of the original Commander 112 in December 1969. Construction of the first of five prototypes began in February 1970 and the first flight was made on 17 December 1970. Deliveries of the Model 112 began in 1972.

The current version, known as the Alpine Commander, has a turbocharged engine, blind-flying instrumentation, luxury interior and many detail improvements including double-pane side windows, thicker windscreens, structural stiffeners and new soundproofing materials to enhance the cabin environment; full 90° opening cabin access doors; changes in the aileron rigging; more accurate engine gauge readings; better avionics cooling; and an improved battery solenoid switch.

Type: Four-seat turbocharged cabin monoplane.

Wings: Cantilever low-wing monoplane. Wing section NACA 63.415 (modified). Dihedral 7°. Incidence at root 2°. Sweepforward at quarter-chord 2° 30′. Conventional light alloy structure. Ailerons of light alloy construction, using a channel spar and one-piece beaded skin. Electrically-operated light alloy single-slotted trailing-edge flaps, extending from wing station 25 to 121.20 with chord of 0·33 m (1 ft 1 in). Ground-adjustable trim tab on port aileron.

Fuselage: Conventional semi-monocoque light alloy structure.

Tail Unit: Cantilever light alloy structure with swept vertical surfaces. Dorsal fin faired into fuselage. Fixed-incidence tailplane. Elevator and rudder trim control, with indicators.

Landing Gear: Hydraulically-retractable tricycle type. Main wheels retract inward, nosewheel aft. Trailing-beam type main units, with oleo-pneumatic shock-absorbers. Steerable nosewheel. Cleveland main-wheel assemblies type 40-75H with tyres size 6·00-6, 6-ply, pressure 2·62 bars (38 lb/sq in). Nosewheel tyre size 5·00-5, 6-ply, pressure 3·45 bars (50 lb/sq in). Cleveland type 30-52H hydraulic brakes. Parking brake.

Power Plant: One 156·6 kW (210 hp) Lycoming TO-360-C1A6D turbocharged flat-four engine, driving a Hartzell Type HC-E2YR-1BF/F8467-7R two-blade constant-speed metal propeller. Two integral fuel tanks in the wing leading-edges, capacity of each 94·5 litres (25 US gallons) standard, 132·5 litres (35 US gallons) optional. Total usable fuel capacity 182 litres (48 US gallons) standard, 257 litres (68 US gallons) optional. Refuelling point in upper surface of each wing. Oil capacity 7·5 litres (2 US gallons).

Accommodation: Pilot and three passengers seated in pairs in enclosed and fully carpeted cabin. Dual controls standard. Passenger door on each side of cabin, over wing, hinged at forward edge. External baggage door on port side of fuselage aft of wing. Baggage capacity 91 kg (200 lb). Cabin heated and ventilated. Windscreen defrosting.

Systems: Hydraulic system powered by a single electrically-driven hydraulic pump. Electrical system supplied by 12V 60A engine-driven alternator and 12V 35Ah battery. Vacuum system with gauge.

Avionics and Equipment: Standard King avionics comprise dual KX170B com/nav, KI204 VOR/LOC/glideslope converter indicator, KN75 glideslope, KI203 VOR/LOC converter indicator, KMA20 audio control with marker receiver, KR85 digital ADF, KT76A transponder and KN65A digital DME, with Mitchell Century III autopilot and VOR/LOC and GS couplers. Optional additions include dual KX175B com/nav in exchange for KX170Bs and a second altimeter. Collins avionics are available as optional alternative to King series. Standard equipment includes adjustable front seats with seat belts, shoulder harness with inertia reels and headrests, adjustable backrests and shoulder harness for rear seats, armrests, baggage tiedown rings, cargo net, storm windows, sun visors, overhead reading lights, tinted double-pane windows, instrument panel lights, landing/taxi light, map light, navigation lights, step lights, alternate static source, sensitive altimeter, true airspeed indicator, artificial horizon, directional gyro, rate of climb indicator, compass, clock, outside air temperature gauge, encoding altimeter, cylinder head temperature gauge, exhaust gas temperature gauge, heated pitot, carburettor air temperature gauge, audible stall warning device, anti-collision light, three-light strobe system, baggage compartment light, control lock, emergency locator beacon, external power socket, internal corrosion proofing, tiedown rings and towbar.

Dimensions, external:
Wing span 10·85 m (35 ft 7·2 in)
Wing chord at centreline 2·39 m (7 ft 10·2 in)
Wing chord at tip 0·813 m (2 ft 8·1 in)
Wing mean aerodynamic chord 1·52 m (4 ft 11·8 in)
Wing aspect ratio 7·9
Length overall 7·63 m (25 ft 0½ in)
Height overall 2·57 m (8 ft 5 in)
Tailplane span 4·10 m (13 ft 5½ in)
Wheel track 3·34 m (10 ft 11·4 in)
Wheelbase 2·11 m (6 ft 11 in)
Propeller diameter 1·96 m (6 ft 5 in)
Propeller ground clearance 0·19 m (7·4 in)
Passenger doors (each): Height 0·91 m (3 ft 0 in)
Width 0·86 m (2 ft 10 in)
Baggage door: Height 0·46 m (1 ft 6 in)
Width 0·64 m (2 ft 1 in)

Dimensions, internal:
Cabin: Length 1·91 m (6 ft 3 in)
Max width 1·19 m (3 ft 11 in)
Max height 1·24 m (4 ft 1 in)
Baggage compartment 0·62 m³ (22 cu ft)

Areas:
Wings, gross 15·22 m² (163·8 sq ft)
Ailerons (total) 1·02 m² (11 sq ft)
Trailing-edge flaps (total) 1·67 m² (18 sq ft)
Fin 1·58 m² (17 sq ft)

Weights and Loadings:
Weight empty 923 kg (2,035 lb)
Max T-O weight 1,338 kg (2,950 lb)
Max ramp weight 1,344 kg (2,962 lb)
Max zero-fuel weight 1,234 kg (2,720 lb)
Max wing loading 87·9 kg/m² (18·0 lb/sq ft)
Max power loading 8·54 kg/kW (14·05 lb/hp)

Performance (at max T-O weight):
Never-exceed speed 180 knots (333 km/h; 207 mph)
Max level speed at 6,100 m (20,000 ft)
170 knots (315 km/h; 196 mph)
Max cruising speed, 75% power at 6,100 m (20,000 ft)
163 knots (302 km/h; 188 mph)
Stalling speed, flaps up
58 knots (107·5 km/h; 67 mph) CAS
Stalling speed, flaps down
54 knots (100 km/h; 62·5 mph) CAS
Max rate of climb at S/L 279 m (914 ft)/min
Max operating altitude 6,100 m (20,000 ft)
T-O run 363 m (1,190 ft)
T-O to 15 m (50 ft) 533 m (1,750 ft)
Landing from 15 m (50 ft) 389 m (1,275 ft)
Landing run 220 m (723 ft)
Range with standard fuel at 4,570 m (15,000 ft), 45 min reserves at 45% power:
75% power 460 nm (853 km; 530 miles)
55% power 597 nm (1,106 km; 687 miles)
Range with optional fuel, reserves as above:
75% power at 6,100 m (20,000 ft)
664 nm (1,231 km; 765 miles)
55% power at 4,570 m (15,000 ft)
901 nm (1,670 km; 1,038 miles)

ROCKWELL GRAN TURISMO COMMANDER

The Gran Turismo Commander, known as the Commander 114 when introduced in 1976, is basically similar to the Alpine Commander, but has a Lycoming IO-540 flat-six engine and certain equipment changes. The 1979 model introduced the improvements detailed for the Alpine Commander and the description of this latter aircraft applies also to the Gran Turismo, except as follows:

Power Plant: One 194 kW (260 hp) Lycoming IO-540-T4B5D flat-four engine, driving a McCauley three-blade constant-speed metal propeller with spinner. Two integral fuel tanks in the wing leading-edges, capacity of each 132·5 litres (35 US gallons), providing a total usable capacity of 257 litres (68 US gallons). Refuelling point in upper surface of each wing.

Systems: As for Alpine, except electrical system powered by a 12V 70A engine-driven alternator.

Avionics: An additional option is the King KFC200 autopilot with KI256 V-bar flight director and KCS55A compass system.

Weights and Loadings:
Weight empty 939 kg (2,070 lb)

Max T-O weight	1,479 kg (3,260 lb)
Max ramp weight	1,484 kg (3,272 lb)
Max wing loading	97·2 kg/m² (19·9 lb/sq ft)
Max power loading	7·62 kg/kW (12·5 lb/hp)

PERFORMANCE (at 1,424 kg: 3,140 lb AUW unless detailed otherwise):

Never-exceed speed	186 knots (344 km/h; 214 mph)
Max level speed at S/L	166 knots (308 km/h; 191 mph)
Max cruising speed, 75% power at 2,135 m (7,000 ft)	157 knots (291 km/h; 181 mph)
Stalling speed, flaps up	60 knots (111 km/h; 69 mph) CAS
Stalling speed, flaps down	54 knots (100 km/h; 62·5 mph) CAS
Max rate of climb at S/L	314 m (1,030 ft)/min
Service ceiling at 1,304 kg (2,875 lb) AUW	5,030 m (16,500 ft)
T-O to 15 m (50 ft)	655 m (2,150 ft)
Landing from 15 m (50 ft)	366 m (1,200 ft)
Range with max fuel, 45 min reserves at 45% power:	
75% power	628 nm (1,164 km; 723 miles)
55% power	706 nm (1,308 km; 813 miles)

ROCKWELL SHRIKE COMMANDER 500S

The Rockwell Shrike Commander is a twin-engined aircraft designed for the businessman-pilot and certificated for Utility category operation.

TYPE: Twin-engined light transport.

WINGS: Cantilever high-wing monoplane. Wing section NACA 23012 (modified). Dihedral 4°. Incidence 3° at root, −3° 30′ at tip. All-metal two-spar flush-riveted structure. Frise statically-balanced all-metal ailerons. Hydraulically-operated all-metal slotted flaps. Ground-adjustable tab in starboard aileron. Pneumatic de-icing boots optional.

FUSELAGE: All-metal semi-monocoque structure with flush-riveted skin.

TAIL UNIT: Cantilever all-metal structure with 10° dihedral on tailplane. Trim tabs in each elevator and rudder. Pneumatic de-icing boots optional.

LANDING GEAR: Retractable tricycle type, with single wheel on each unit. All wheels retract rearward hydraulically, main wheels turning through 90° to stow horizontally in nacelles. Oleo-pneumatic shock-absorbers. Hydraulically-steerable nosewheel. Goodyear main wheels with 8-ply tyres size 25·65 × 8·70-10, pressure 3·79 bars (55 lb/sq in). Nosewheel with 6-ply tyre size 17·5 × 6·30-6, pressure 2·90 bars (42 lb/sq in). Goodyear aircooled hydraulic disc brakes.

POWER PLANT: Two 216 kW (290 hp) Lycoming IO-540-E1B5 flat-six engines, each driving a Hartzell HC-C3YR-2/C8468-6R three-blade constant-speed fully-feathering metal propeller. Bag-type fuel tanks in wings, with usable capacity of 590 litres (156 US gallons). Overwing refuelling. Oil capacity 22·7 litres (6 US gallons) total. Electrically-heated fuel vents and propeller anti-icing boots optional.

ACCOMMODATION: Four individual seats: two in front with inertia-reel and shoulder harness, and two at rear. Dual controls. Curtains divide pilot's compartment from cabin. Swivel-mounted fresh air vents above each seat, window curtains, emergency exit, announcement signs, adjustable heating and fresh air ventilation ports at cabin floor level, double-glazed windows in cabin and a hatbox shelf in aft cabin bulkhead are standard. Optional seating layouts for up to seven persons, some with rear bench seat for three. Optional refreshment cabinet for hot and cold drinks. Forward-opening passenger door under wing on port side. Forward-opening door by pilot's seat at front of cabin on port side. All equipment can be removed to permit cabin to be used for freight carrying. Compartment for 227 kg (500 lb) baggage aft of cabin, with outside door. Windscreen wiper and alcohol de-icing system for port side optional.

SYSTEMS: Hydraulic system, pressure 86 bars (1,250 lb/sq in), for landing gear, flaps, brakes and nosewheel steering. Electrical hydraulic pump emergency system for brakes. Electrical system includes two 70A alternators and two 35 Ah batteries. 100A alternators optional. Vacuum system for flight instruments.

Rockwell Gran Turismo Commander (one Lycoming IO-540-T4B5D flat-four engine)

AVIONICS AND EQUIPMENT: Standard equipment includes blind-flying and engine instrumentation, clock, Janitrol 35,000 BTU cabin heater, anti-collision light, landing lights, reading lights, position lights, vacuum warning lights, instrument lighting system, dual air filters for vacuum instruments, dual vacuum pumps, electrically-adjustable cowl flap, external power socket, stall warning horn and alternative static source. Optional equipment includes more advanced instruments, and extensive range of avionics which are available in package form or as individual items, underfuselage rotating beacon, three-light strobe system, heated stall warning sensor, heated pitot, pilot and co-pilot vertically-adjustable seats, blind-flying instrumentation for co-pilot, storage drawers under aft couch, cockpit fire extinguisher, low-fuel warning light, glass-holders, seat headrests, lavatory chair for starboard side of aft cabin, complete with curtain, 1·37 m³ (48·3 cu ft) or 2·74 m³ (96·6 cu ft) oxygen system, propeller synchronising equipment, propeller unfeathering pump, dual relief tubes, sidewall-mounted stereo console, extra seat tracks, polished spinners, cabin table, tinted cabin windows, sun visors, storm window for co-pilot, static discharge wicks, emergency locator transmitter, fuselage ice shields and wing ice lights.

DIMENSIONS, EXTERNAL:

Wing span	14·95 m (49 ft 0½ in)
Wing chord at root	2·54 m (8 ft 4 in)
Wing chord at tip	0·65 m (2 ft 1½ in)
Wing aspect ratio	9·45
Length overall	11·22 m (36 ft 9¾ in)
Height overall	4·42 m (14 ft 6 in)
Tailplane span	5·10 m (16 ft 9 in)
Wheel track	3·95 m (12 ft 11 in)
Wheelbase	4·26 m (13 ft 11¾ in)
Propeller diameter	2·03 m (6 ft 8 in)
Crew door (fwd): Height	1·17 m (3 ft 10 in)
Width	0·58 m (1 ft 11 in)
Passenger door (aft): Height	1·14 m (3 ft 9 in)
Width	0·71 m (2 ft 4 in)
Baggage door: Height	0·60 m (1 ft 11½ in)
Width	0·48 m (1 ft 7 in)

DIMENSIONS, INTERNAL:

Cabin: Length	3·24 m (10 ft 7½ in)
Max width	1·32 m (4 ft 4 in)
Max height	1·35 m (4 ft 5 in)
Volume	5·01 m³ (177 cu ft)
Baggage hold	0·91 m³ (32 cu ft)

AREAS:

Wings, gross	23·69 m² (255 sq ft)
Ailerons (total)	1·90 m² (20·52 sq ft)
Trailing-edge flaps (total)	1·97 m² (21·20 sq ft)
Fin	2·23 m² (24·00 sq ft)
Rudder, incl tab	1·43 m² (15·40 sq ft)
Tailplane	3·07 m² (33·06 sq ft)
Elevators, incl tabs	1·91 m² (20·54 sq ft)

WEIGHTS AND LOADINGS:

Weight empty, equipped	2,102 kg (4,635 lb)
Max T-O and landing weight	3,062 kg (6,750 lb)
Max wing loading	129·2 kg/m² (26·47 lb/sq ft)
Max power loading	7·09 kg/kW (11·64 lb/hp)

PERFORMANCE (at max T-O weight):

Max cruising speed at S/L	187 knots (346 km/h; 215 mph)
Max cruising speed (75% power) at 2,745 m (9,000 ft)	176 knots (326 km/h; 203 mph)
Stalling speed, flaps and landing gear up	68 knots (126 km/h; 78 mph) CAS
Stalling speed, flaps and landing gear down	59 knots (109 km/h; 68 mph) CAS
Min single-engine control speed	65·5 knots (121 km/h; 75 mph)
Max rate of climb at S/L	408 m (1,340 ft)/min
Rate of climb at S/L, one engine out	81 m (266 ft)/min
Service ceiling	5,915 m (19,400 ft)
Service ceiling, one engine out	1,980 m (6,500 ft)
Min ground turning radius	11·63 m (38 ft 2 in)
T-O to 15 m (50 ft)	584 m (1,915 ft)
Landing from 15 m (50 ft)	681 m (2,235 ft)
Range with standard fuel at 2,745 m (9,000 ft) at 178 knots (330 km/h; 205 mph), 45 min reserves	693 nm (1,282 km; 797 miles)
Range, conditions as above, no reserves	824 nm (1,525 km; 948 miles)
Absolute range, standard fuel, at 4,570 m (15,000 ft) at 45% power and cruising speed of 118 knots (262 km/h; 163 mph), 45 min reserves	1,033 nm (1,915 km; 1,190 miles)

ROCKWELL TURBO COMMANDER 690B

The Rockwell Turbo Commander 690B is a pressurised transport aircraft, powered by two Garrett-AiResearch turboprop engines, which was developed from the Turbo Commander 690.

The prototype of the Turbo Commander 690B was flown for the first time in January 1976; FAA certification was awarded on 5 October 1976. Although certification was granted under CAR Part 3, many portions of the systems and structure exceed the requirements of CAR Part 4, SR422B and FAR 25.

Two versions were available for 1979, but were scheduled to be superseded by the new Jetprop Commander 840 and 980 before the end of the year:

Executive I. Version which has as standard factory-installed equipment everything needed for basic IFR operation. Anti-icing and de-icing package comprises windscreen demister, heated windscreens, windscreen wipers, heated stall warning sensor, heated fuel vents, heated pitots and alternate static source, heaters for general air inlets, rudder horn slots and rudder tab, propeller de-icing, fuselage ice shields, wing and tail unit de-icing boots, and wing ice lights. Standard seven-seat interior, curtain between cabin and flight compartment, sun visors, individual air vents for crew and passengers, reading lights, oxygen masks for all occupants, map pockets, folding table, storage/refreshment console, 'No smoking-Fasten seat belt' sign and warning chime, tinted cabin windows, entrance courtesy light, and choice of four interior finish schemes. Standard avionics include a foundation kit comprising edge-lighted audio panels, marker receiver display for pilot and co-pilot panels, dual King KAA455 audio systems with dual microphones, headsets and speakers, boom microphone/headset provisions for pilot and co-pilot, all necessary antennae, dual DC power feeder circuits, noise suppression system, and static discharge wicks. King avionics package comprising dual KTR905 VHF com transceivers, dual KNR630 nav receivers with glideslope, KMR675 marker receiver, Bendix M-4D autopilot with DH-866A and IN-863A flight director and Sperry C-14 compass system, King KI206 Nav 2 indicator, KDM705A DME with KDI571 indicator, KXP755 transponder, KDF805 ADF with Collins 332C-10 RMI, Bendix RDR-1200 radar, Collins ALT-50 radar altimeter, dual 250VA inverters and an IDC 571-25005-012 non-servoed encoding altimeter.

Executive II. Version with standard seven-seat interior (all seats facing forward) and anti-icing and de-icing kit as described for Executive I. Other equipment is to customer's specification.

On 7 April 1972, a Turbo Commander 690 set two

Rockwell Shrike Commander 500S twin-engined light transport aircraft

Rockwell Turbo Commander 690B business aircraft (two AiResearch TPE 331-5-251K turboprop engines)

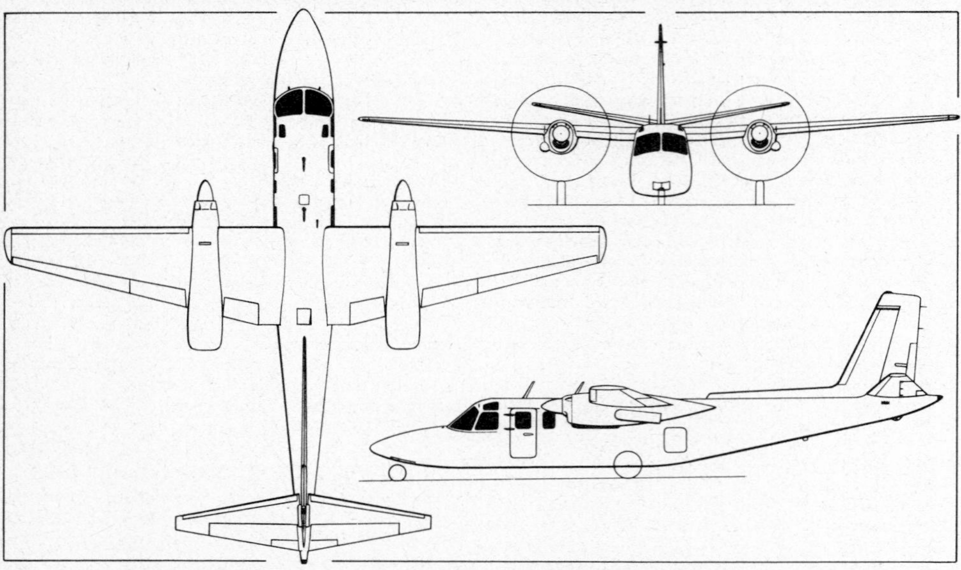

Rockwell Turbo Commander 690B seven/ten-seat twin-turboprop transport *(Pilot Press)*

speed records in FAI Class C1e, Group II, for turboprop aircraft in the 3,000-5,999 kg (6,614-13,225 lb) weight category. The first was established over a 500 km triangular course, at a speed of 293·20 knots (543·36 km/h; 337·63 mph); the second was a straight and level speed record of 328·67 knots (609·08 km/h; 378·47 mph). On 27 April 1978 five more records were established in a Turbo Commander 690B. The first three, achieved by Robert A. Hoover, were for climb to 3,000 m in 2 min 20·8 s, to 6,000 m in 5 min 15·8 s, and to 9,000 m in 9 min 42·6 s. The remaining two records were set on the same day, in the same 690B, by West German businessman/pilot Jo Blumschein. These were for sustained altitude of 12,567·5 m (41,232 ft) in horizontal flight, and an absolute height record of 12,925 m (42,405 ft).

Type: Twin engined light transport

Wings: Cantilever high-wing monoplane. Wing section NACA 23012 modified. Dihedral 4°. Incidence 3° at root, −1° at tip. All-metal two-spar flush-riveted structure. Frise statically-balanced all-metal ailerons. Hydraulically-operated all-metal slotted flaps. Electrically-operated trim tab in starboard aileron. Pneumatic de-icing boots optional.

Fuselage: All-metal semi-monocoque structure with flush-riveted skin.

Tail Unit: Cantilever all-metal structure with 10° dihedral on tailplane. Trim tabs in each elevator and rudder. Pneumatic de-icing boots optional.

Landing Gear: Retractable tricycle type, with single wheel on each unit. All wheels retract rearward hydraulically, main wheels turning through 90° to stow horizontally in nacelles. Oleo-pneumatic shock-absorbers. Hydraulically-steerable nosewheel. Goodyear main wheels with tyres size 25·65 × 8·70-10, pressure 4·83 bars (70 lb/sq in). Nosewheel tyre size 17·5 × 6·30-6, pressure 2·90 bars (42 lb/sq in). Goodyear aircooled hydraulic disc brakes.

Power Plant: Two 522 kW (700 shp) Garrett-AiResearch TPE 331-5-251K turboprop engines, each driving a Hartzell HC-B3TN-5FL/LT 10282H+4 three-blade constant-speed fully-feathering and reversible-pitch propeller. Fuel contained in bag-type wing tanks with a total usable capacity of 1,453 litres (384 US gallons). Refuelling points on upper surface of each wing. Oil capacity 11·5 litres (3 US gallons).

Accommodation (Executive I): Standard seating for pilot and six passengers, on two adjustable seats on flight deck, two aft-facing single seats and a three-place forward-facing bench seat in main cabin. Optional arrangement offers two forward-facing seats instead of the port aft-facing seat. (In Executive II, a variety of optional seating layouts offers accommodation for up to 10 persons.) Cabin pressurised, heated and air-conditioned. Forward-hinged outward-opening cabin door on port side, with retractable cabin step. Emergency exit on starboard side of fuselage. Baggage compartment of 1·32 m³ (46·5 cu ft) with 272 kg (600 lb) capacity aft of rear pressure bulkhead with external access door on port side of fuselage.

Systems: Cabin pressurisation, heating and air-conditioning by engine bleed air; max pressure differential 0·36 bars (5·2 lb/sq in). Hydraulic system supplied by two pumps at 86 bars (1,250 lb/sq in), with hydraulic reservoir for emergency use. Electrical system powered by two 300A starter/generators. Two 40Ah lead-acid batteries (48Ah in Executive II). Scott constant-flow emergency oxygen system of 0·62 m³ (22 cu ft) capacity, with individual outlets. Vacuum system for operation of flight instruments.

Avionics and Equipment: Avionics and equipment detailed as standard for Executive I version are available optionally for the Executive II. In addition, a wide range of avionics by Bendix, Collins, King and Sperry, and additional equipment, are available for both versions.

Dimensions, external:

Wing span	14·23 m (46 ft 8 in)
Wing chord at root	2·64 m (8 ft 7¾ in)
Wing chord at tip	0·84 m (2 ft 9 in)
Wing aspect ratio	8·19
Length overall	13·52 m (44 ft 4¼ in)
Height overall	4·56 m (14 ft 11½ in)
Tailplane span	6·03 m (19 ft 9¼ in)
Wheel track	4·70 m (15 ft 5 in)
Wheelbase	5·38 m (17 ft 7¾ in)
Propeller diameter	2·69 m (8 ft 10 in)
Propeller ground clearance	0·36 m (1 ft 2¼ in)
Cabin door: Height	1·19 m (3 ft 11 in)
Width	0·67 m (2 ft 2½ in)
Height to sill	0·47 m (1 ft 6½ in)
Baggage door: Height	0·79 m (2 ft 7¼ in)
Width	0·50 m (1 ft 7½ in)
Height to sill	0·52 m (1 ft 8½ in)
Emergency exit: Height	0·48 m (1 ft 7 in)
Width	0·68 m (2 ft 2¾ in)

Dimensions, internal:

Cabin: Length	4·34 m (14 ft 3 in)
Max width	1·22 m (4 ft 0¼ in)
Max height	1·36 m (4 ft 5⅝ in)
Volume	6·34 m³ (224 cu ft)

Areas:

Wings, gross	24·7 m² (266·0 sq ft)
Ailerons (total)	1·83 m² (19·74 sq ft)
Trailing-edge flaps (total)	1·65 m² (17·74 sq ft)
Fin	2·25 m² (24·23 sq ft)
Rudder (incl tab)	1·92 m² (20·66 sq ft)
Tailplane	3·51 m² (37·80 sq ft)
Elevators (incl tab)	1·91 m² (20·57 sq ft)

Weights and Loadings:

Weight empty, standard:	
Executive I	3,054 kg (6,733 lb)
Executive II	2,810 kg (6,195 lb)
Max T-O weight	4,683 kg (10,325 lb)
Max ramp weight	4,706 kg (10,375 lb)
Max zero-fuel weight	3,969 kg (8,750 lb)
Max landing weight	4,389 kg (9,675 lb)
Max wing loading	189·5 kg/m² (38·82 lb/sq ft)
Max power loading	4·49 kg/kW (7·38 lb/ehp)

Performance (at max T-O weight, unless specified otherwise):

Max cruising speed, 96% power at 5,335 m (17,500 ft)	284 knots (526 km/h; 327 mph)
Normal cruising speed, 96% power at 6,100 m (20,000 ft)	283 knots (525 km/h; 326 mph)
Long-range cruising speed at 9,450 m (31,000 ft)	250 knots (463 km/h; 288 mph)
Min control speed	86 knots (159 km/h; 99 mph) CAS
Stalling speed, flaps and wheels up	82 knots (151 km/h; 94 mph) CAS
Stalling speed, flaps and wheels down	77 knots (143 km/h; 89 mph) CAS
Max rate of climb at S/L	860 m (2,821 ft)/min
Rate of climb at S/L, one engine out	268 m (878 ft)/min
Service ceiling	9,995 m (32,800 ft)
Service ceiling, one engine out	5,975 m (19,600 ft)
FAA operational ceiling	9,450 m (31,000 ft)
Min ground turning radius	12·47 m (40 ft 11 in)
Normal T-O run	444 m (1,458 ft)
Short-field T-O run	364 m (1,194 ft)
Normal T-O to 15 m (50 ft)	689 m (2,259 ft)
Short-field T-O to 15 m (50 ft)	512 m (1,680 ft)
Landing from 15 m (50 ft) with propeller reversal, at max landing weight	492 m (1,613 ft)
Landing from 15 m (50 ft) without propeller reversal, at max landing weight	640 m (2,100 ft)
Landing run with propeller reversal, at max landing weight	276 m (906 ft)
Landing run without propeller reversal, at max landing weight	427 m (1,402 ft)
Range with max fuel, long-range cruise power at 9,450 m (31,000 ft), 45 min reserves	1,467 nm (2,718 km; 1,689 miles)
Range with max fuel, high-speed cruise power at 5,485 m (18,000 ft), 45 min reserves	1,036 nm (1,920 km; 1,193 miles)

ROCKWELL COMMANDER 700

This twin-engined six/eight-seat light transport aircraft was developed and is being produced in collaboration with Fuji in Japan. Design began in Japan, under the designation **FA-300**, in the latter half of 1971, following more than two years of market research. Fuji and Rockwell International signed the agreement which established further development as a collaborative venture on 28 June 1974.

Five flying prototypes were built, the first of which made its first flight at Utsunomiya, Japan, on 13 November 1975. The second (N9901S), assembled by Rockwell, flew for the first time, at Bethany, on 25 February 1976. By the time JCAB certification was received, on 19 May 1977, two Japanese and three US assembled prototypes had accumulated 800 hours of flight testing. US certification, to FAR 23 Amendment 14 standards, was awarded on 31 October 1977, and the first delivery of a production aircraft was made on 21 August 1978. Production was at the rate of three aircraft per month in early 1979.

Airframe sub- and major assemblies for the Commander 700 are manufactured in Japan, and assembly by Rockwell's General Aviation Division utilises US manufactured electronics, power plant, brakes, wheels and tyres.

Three factory-installed packages of operational equipment are available as options:

Engine Group. Comprising propeller synchroniser, propeller unfeathering accumulator, and a visual synchronising tachometer; adding 11·25 kg (24·8 lb) to the basic empty weight.

Utility Group. Comprising flight hour meter, external

power socket and relay, wingtip recognition lights, and dual windscreen wipers; adding 5·6 kg (12·3 lb) to the basic empty weight.

Anti-icing/De-icing Equipment. Comprising electrically heated pilot's windscreen, electrical propeller de-icing, ice light, wing, tailplane and fin leading-edge de-icing boots, fuselage ice shields, and large capacity engine-driven pneumatic pump for airframe de-icing; adding 35·5 kg (78·2 lb) to basic empty weight.

TYPE: Twin-engined six/seven-seat pressurised cabin monoplane.

WINGS: Cantilever low-wing monoplane, with exclusive Fuji-developed aerofoil sections. Dihedral 7°. Sealed box-beam structure, forming integral fuel tank. Trim tab in each aileron. Pneumatic de-icing of leading-edges optional.

FUSELAGE: Conventional semi-monocoque structure, with rather more frames and fewer stringers than comparable types of aircraft. All-metal construction, primarily of 2024 aluminium alloy, with 7075 aluminium alloy for high-stress members.

TAIL UNIT: Cantilever all-metal structure, with sweptback vertical surfaces and shallow dorsal fin. Fixed-incidence non-swept tailplane, mounted part-way up fin. Balanced elevators and rudder, each with trim tab. Pneumatic de-icing system optional.

LANDING GEAR: Hydraulically-retractable tricycle type, all units retracting forward. Free-fall emergency extension. Oleo-pneumatic shock-absorbers. Main-wheel tyres size 6·50-8 (8-ply rating); nosewheel tyre size 6·00-6 (6-ply rating). Heavy duty disc brakes. Parking brake.

POWER PLANT: Two 253 kW (340 hp) Lycoming TIO-540-R2AD turbocharged flat-six engines, each driving a Hartzell three-blade constant-speed fully-feathering but non-reversible metal propeller with spinner. Electrical propeller de-icing system optional. Integral fuel tanks in wings, total capacity 795 litres (210 US gallons). Oil capacity 11·5 litres (3 US gallons).

ACCOMMODATION: Pilot and co-pilot on individual adjustable and reclining seats with seat belts and shoulder harnesses. Dual controls standard. Pilot's storm window. Heated windscreen and windscreen wipers optional. Normal accommodation for four passengers in pairs. Optional private toilet at rear on starboard side, can double as extra seat. Forward and aft cabin dividers optional. Baggage compartments in nose and rear of pressurised cabin, capacity 136 kg (300 lb). Door with built-in airstair on port side; emergency exit on starboard side. Cabin heated, air-conditioned and pressurised. Windscreen defroster.

SYSTEMS: Air-conditioning and pressurisation system (differential 0·38 bars; 5·5 lb/sq in). Freon-type 16,000 BTU air-conditioner optional. 45,000 BTU capacity combustion heater, with windscreen defroster. Hydraulic system supplied by electro-hydraulic power package. Pressure pumps, driven by each engine, supply air pressure to gyro instruments, cabin door seal, and (when fitted) to wing and tail de-icing systems. Oxygen system of 0·31 m³ (11 cu ft) capacity. Electrical system supplied by two 28V 70A alternators and 24V 25Ah lead-acid battery. 28V 90A alternators optional.

AVIONICS AND EQUIPMENT: Installed standard equipment includes full blind-flying instrumentation, outside air temperature gauge, 8-day clock, heated pitot, heated static air source, dual exhaust temperature gauges, audible stall warning device, navigation lights, landing light, anti-collision strobe lights, instrument post lights, map light, taxi light, sun visors, pilot's storm window, reading lights, carpeted cabin, window curtains, baggage retention net, entrance door light, baggage compartment lights, cockpit floodlight and towbar. Wide range of optional avionics available, including four factory-installed packages, plus an extensive range of options. Other optional items include emergency locator transmitter, large-capacity oxygen system, tinted inner cabin windows, stereo unit, cabin fire extinguisher, adjustable height pilot's seat, cabin tables, cockpit curtain, lavatory with partition and curtain, refreshment console, and 'No Smoking/Fasten seat belts' sign.

DIMENSIONS, EXTERNAL:

Wing span	12·94 m (42 ft 5½ in)
Length overall	12·03 m (39 ft 5¾ in)
Height overall	4·05 m (13 ft 3½ in)
Tailplane span	4·92 m (16 ft 1¾ in)
Wheel track	5·05 m (16 ft 6½ in)
Wheelbase	3·15 m (10 ft 4¼ in)
Propeller diameter	2·06 m (6 ft 9 in)
Distance between propeller centres	4·75 m (15 ft 7 in)
Propeller/fuselage clearance	0·57 m (1 ft 10 ½ in)
Propeller ground clearance	0·30 m (11¾ in)
Cabin door (port, aft): Height	1·21 m (3 ft 11½ in)
Width	0·71 m (2 ft 4 in)
Baggage door (nose, port): Height	0·43 m (1 ft 5 in)
Width	0·86 m (2 ft 10 in)

DIMENSIONS, INTERNAL:

Cabin (incl rear baggage compartment):	
Length	5·00 m (16 ft 5 in)
Max width	1·43 m (4 ft 8¼ in)
Max height	1·44 m (4 ft 8¾ in)
Volume	8·44 m³ (298·0 cu ft)

Rockwell Commander 700 pressurised light transport (Lycoming TIO-540-R2AD engines)

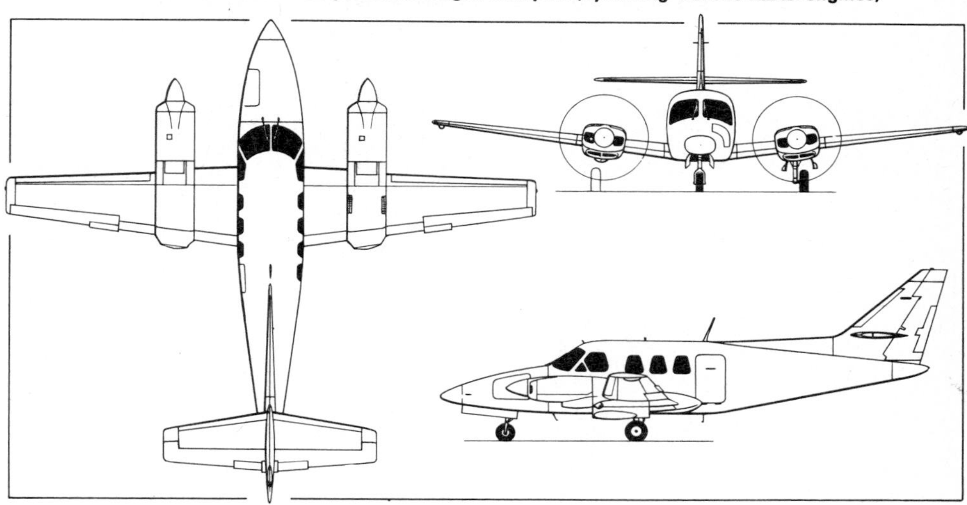

Rockwell Commander 700 six/seven-seat pressurised transport *(Pilot Press)*

Baggage volume (nose and rear of cabin, total)	1·42 m³ (50·0 cu ft)

AREAS:

Wings, gross	18·60 m² (200·2 sq ft)
Fin	3·71 m² (39·9 sq ft)
Tailplane	5·51 m² (55·4 sq ft)

WEIGHTS AND LOADINGS:

Weight empty, standard	2,134 kg (4,704 lb)
Max T-O weight	3,151 kg (6,947 lb)
Max ramp weight	3,170 kg (6,987 lb)
Max landing weight	2,994 kg (6,600 lb)
Max wing loading	169·4 kg/m² (34·7 lb/sq ft)
Max power loading	6·23 kg/kW (10·2 lb/hp)

PERFORMANCE (at max T-O weight unless specified otherwise):

Max level speed, AUW of 2,880 kg (6,350 lb) at 5,180 m (17,000 ft) 221 knots (409 km/h; 254 mph)

Cruising speed, AUW of 2,880 kg (6,350 lb) at 6,555 m (21,500 ft) 212 knots (393 km/h; 244 mph)

Min control speed 78 knots (145 km/h; 90 mph) CAS

Stalling speed, flaps up 86 knots (159 km/h; 99 mph) CAS

Stalling speed, flaps down 68 knots (126 km/h; 78 mph) CAS

Max rate of climb at S/L	481 m (1,578 ft)/min
Service ceiling	8,350 m (27,400 ft)
Service ceiling, one engine out	3,230 m (10,600 ft)
FAA operational ceiling	7,620 m (25,000 ft)
T-O run	489 m (1,604 ft)
T-O to 15 m (50 ft)	690 m (2,264 ft)
Landing from 15 m (50 ft)	657 m (2,154 ft)

Range with max fuel, 65% power, with allowances for start, taxi, T-O, climb and descent 1,056 nm (1,956 km; 1,216 miles)

Range with max fuel, 45% power, allowances as above, 45 min reserves 1,202 nm (2,226 km; 1,384 miles)

ROCKWELL COMMANDER 710

Second of a new series of aircraft being developed jointly by Rockwell and Fuji in Japan (which see), this

Rockwell Jetprop Commander 980 (two Garrett-AiResearch TPE 331-10 turboprop engines)

twin-engined pressurised aircraft made its first flight on 22 December 1976. No specification details are available except that the Commander 710 has 335 kW (450 hp) engines). It was being test-flown in 1979 with NASA (Whitcomb) type winglets.

ROCKWELL JETPROP COMMANDER 840 and 980

Little information on these replacements for the Turbo Commander 690B had been released until the prototypes were shown to those attending the 32nd US National Business Aircraft Association Convention in late September 1979. Details available as these pages closed for press were as follows:

Jetprop Commander 840. Business transport seating 7, 8 or up to 11 people, including pilot. Powered by two Garrett-AiResearch TPE331-5 turboprop engines, driving Dowty Rotol R.306 'supercritical' three-blade propellers which offer improved performance, lower installed weight and reduced operating noise levels. Redesigned wings, with shallow winglets above tips and partial integral tankage for increased fuel capacity; span increased to 15·9 m (52 ft 1¼ in). Flight deck improvements include new instrument panels and vertically-adjustable reclining seats. Lighted, insulated and optionally heated baggage compartment, capacity 2m³ (70 cu ft), separate from passenger cabin.

Jetprop Commander 980. Generally similar to Jetprop Commander 840, but with TPE331-10 engines.

A commuter version is under development.

SCENIC

SCENIC AVIATION SERVICES

ADDRESS: 241 East Reno Avenue, Las Vegas, Nevada 89119
Telephone: (702) 739 5611
Telex: 684476
PRESIDENT: Karl A. Fahr

Scenic Air Lines acquired from American Jet Industries of Van Nuys, California, in early 1977, all engineering and manufacturing rights for the turboprop conversions of Cessna Model 402 and 414 aircraft designed by AJI. Of these, the former continued in production in 1979; a description of the Turbo Star Pressurised 414 appeared in the 1977-78 *Jane's*. Scenic Aviation Services had completed three 402 conversions and one 414 by the end of 1978.

SCENIC/AJI TURBO STAR 402

In November 1969, American Jet Industries began conversion of a standard Cessna 402 to turbine power. This involved removal of its Continental piston engines and their replacement by two 298 kW (400 shp) Allison 250-B17 turboprop engines, each driving a Hartzell Type HCa3VF-7 three-blade constant-speed fully-feathering reversible-pitch metal propeller with Beta control.

The conversion offered an overall saving of 229 kg (505 lb) in terms of empty weight, giving increased performance, range and payload by comparison with the standard Cessna 402.

The first flight of the Turbo Star 402, as AJI named the conversion, was made on 10 June 1970. Subsequently, a number of additional modifications were introduced. Gross weight was increased to 2,959 kg (6,525 lb), an automatic propeller feathering system added, minimum control speed reduced by 12·6%, and fuel capacity increased from 477 litres (126 US gallons) to 757 litres (200 US gallons). Recertification of the Turbo Star 402 in this form became effective in January 1974.

Scenic/AJI Turbo Star 402, a turbine-powered conversion of the Cessna Model 402

WEIGHTS AND LOADINGS:

Weight empty	1,458 kg (3,214 lb)
Max T-O weight	2,959 kg (6,525 lb)
Max zero-fuel weight	2,857 kg (6,300 lb)
Max landing weight	2,812 kg (6,200 lb)
Max wing loading	163·6 kg/m² (33·5 lb/sq ft)
Max power loading	4·96 kg/kW (8·16 lb/shp)

PERFORMANCE (at max T-O weight):

Max level speed at 2,895 m (9,500 ft)	233 knots (431 km/h; 268 mph)
Max cruising speed at 3,660 m (12,000 ft)	223 knots (414 km/h; 257 mph)
Econ cruising speed at 6,100 m (20,000 ft)	208 knots (386 km/h; 240 mph)
Approach speed	90·5 knots (167 km/h; 104 mph) CAS
Min control speed, one engine out	77·5 knots (144 km/h; 89 mph) CAS
Max rate of climb at S/L	639 m (2,095 ft)/min
Rate of climb, one engine out	148 m (485 ft)/min
Operational ceiling	7,620 m (25,000 ft)
Service ceiling, one engine out	3,870 m (12,700 ft)
T-O run	254 m (832 ft)
T-O to 15 m (50 ft)	440 m (1,445 ft)
Accelerate/stop distance	605 m (1,984 ft)
Balanced field length	605 m (1,984 ft)
Landing from 15 m (50 ft), with propeller reversal, at max landing weight	336 m (1,104 ft)
Landing run, with propeller reversal, at max landing weight	137 m (450 ft)
Range at max cruising speed, no reserves	1,149 nm (2,130 km; 1,324 miles)
Max range at econ cruising speed, no reserves	1,397 nm (2,589 km; 1,609 miles)

SCHAPEL

SCHAPEL AIRCRAFT COMPANY

ADDRESS: PO Box 60039, Reno, Nevada 89506
Telephone: (702) 972 8937
PRESIDENT: Rodney E. Schapel

SCHAPEL S-525 SUPER SWAT

Believing that present-day agricultural aircraft designs are many years behind their potential, having regard to current technological advances in aerodynamics and structural materials, Schapel Aircraft Company began studies in 1977 which it was hoped would lead to the design of an advanced agricultural aircraft. By the Spring of 1979, wind tunnel testing of a model had been completed successfully. Construction of a prototype began in July 1979, and this aircraft is scheduled to make its first flight in January 1980.

Known as the S-525 Super Swat, it is of unconventional configuration and is constructed primarily of composites. Liquids are sprayed from a full-span manifold with more than 100 nozzles. Alternatively, dry chemicals can be dispensed by means of an applicator spanning 13·41 m (44 ft 0 in). The hopper has a capacity of 1,893 litres (500 US gallons), and standard equipment includes an Agrinautics hydraulic drive and control system which will allow the Super Swat to dispense a swath of liquid chemicals 30% greater than that of any US agricultural aircraft in current use. In the case of dry chemicals, the standard applicator will provide a swath up to 24·4 m (80 ft 0 in) wide. The hopper is mounted within the fuselage nacelle, aft of the pilot; this places it close to the aircraft's CG, and minimises the effects of varying chemical loads. Liquid can be dispensed at a rate of 30·6 litres/hectare (20 US gallons/acre), and dry chemicals at 73·4 kg/hectare (400 lb/acre).

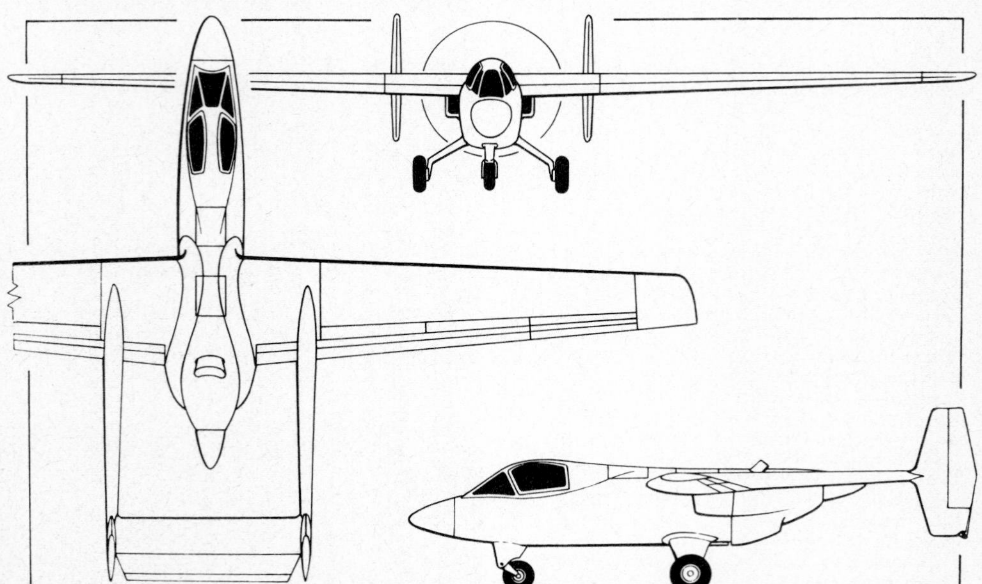
Schapel S-525 Super Swat (P&WC PT6A-15AG turboprop engine) *(Michael A. Badrocke)*

TYPE: Advanced-design agricultural aircraft.

WINGS: Cantilever shoulder-wing monoplane. Aerofoil section NASA (Whitcomb) GAW-1. Thickness/chord ratio 17%. Dihedral 1° 30′. Incidence 3°. No sweepback. Fail-safe plate stringer structure of carbon fibre/epoxy. Slot-lip ailerons of glassfibre, Kevlar 49 (R) and honeycomb/epoxy sandwich. Full-span electrically-actuated Fowler-type trailing-edge flaps of similar construction. Trim tab in starboard aileron.

FUSELAGE: Welded steel tube structure, with skins of composite materials. Tailbooms of carbon fibre/epoxy construction.

TAIL UNIT: Twin endplate fins with rudders, mounted on tailbooms, with fixed incidence tailplane between, forming a rigid box structure. One piece elevator. Construction of glassfibre, Kevlar 49 (R) and honeycomb/epoxy sandwich. Trim tabs in elevator and rudder.

LANDING GEAR: Non-retractable tricycle type, with single wheel on each unit. Main wheels carried on cantilever units. Shock-absorption by rubber in compression. Cleveland main wheels with tyres of 685 mm (27·00 in) diameter. Nosewheel tyre 585 mm (23·00 in) diameter. Cleveland brakes.

POWER PLANT: One 507 kW (680 shp) Pratt & Whitney Aircraft of Canada PT6A-15AG turboprop engine, driving a Hartzell constant-speed three-blade metal pusher propeller. Fuel in two wing tanks with combined capacity of 378·5 litres (100 US gallons). Single-point pressure refuelling in side of fuselage. Gravity refuelling point on upper surface of each wing.

ACCOMMODATION: Single seat for pilot. Cockpit canopy hinged at top, and openable upward on each side. Accommodation heated, ventilated and air-conditioned.

SYSTEMS: Air-conditioning and electrical systems.
EQUIPMENT: Hopper in fuselage for liquid spray or dry chemicals, volume 1·93 m³ (68 cu ft), capacity 1,893 litres (500 US gallons).

DIMENSIONS, EXTERNAL:

Wing span	16·46 m (54 ft 0 in)
Wing aspect ratio	10·33
Length overall	9·66 m (31 ft 8½ in)
Height overall	3·26 m (10 ft 8½ in)
Tailplane span	3·66 m (12 ft 0 in)
Wheel track	2·44 m (8 ft 0 in)
Wheelbase	2·96 m (9 ft 8½ in)
Propeller diameter	2·44 m (8 ft 0 in)
Propeller ground clearance	0·15 m (6 in)

AREA:

Wings, gross	26·48 m² (285 sq ft)

WEIGHTS AND LOADINGS (estimated):

Weight empty	1,270 kg (2,800 lb)
Max T-O and landing weight	3,629 kg (8,000 lb)
Max zero-fuel weight	3,342 kg (7,367 lb)
Max wing loading	126·2 kg/m² (28·07 lb/sq ft)
Max power loading	6·59 kg/kW (11·76 lb/shp)

PERFORMANCE (estimated at max T-O weight):

Never-exceed speed	250 knots (463 km/h; 288 mph)
Max level speed at S/L	177 knots (328 km/h; 204 mph)
Cruising speed at 7,620 m (25,000 ft)	175 knots (324 km/h; 202 mph)
Stalling speed, flaps up	74·9 knots (139 km/h; 86 mph)
Stalling speed, flaps down	50·4 knots (93 km/h; 58 mph)
Max rate of climb at S/L	503 m (1,650 ft)/min
Service ceiling	7,620 m (25,000 ft)
T-O run	238 m (780 ft)
T-O to 15 m (50 ft)	511 m (1,677 ft)
Landing from 15 m (50 ft)	233 m (765 ft)
Landing run	140 m (460 ft)
Range with max fuel, no payload	890 nm (1,649 km; 1,025 miles)

Wind tunnel model of Schapel S-525 Super Swat agricultural aircraft *(Howard Levy)*

SEAPLANE FLYING
SEAPLANE FLYING INC

ADDRESS: PO Box 2164, Pearson Air Park, Vancouver, Washington 98661
Telephone: (206) 694 6287
PRESIDENT: L. W. Soukup

Seaplane Flying Inc is carrying out STOL and/or performance improvements to a variety of lightplanes manufactured by Cessna, Maule, Piper, Stinson and Waco. Performance increases result largely from replacing the original power plant by a Franklin engine of increased power, but the company has also designed a STOL kit for installation on Cessna 170B, 172 and 175 aircraft. This comprises a wing fence, leading-edge cuff, new wingtips, and trailing-edge flap and aileron gap seals, which improve take-off and landing performance by approximately 7 per cent.

Power plant replacements involve removal of the existing engine from Cessna 170B, 172 and 175, and Stinson 108 aircraft, and the installation of a 164 kW (220 hp) Franklin flat-six engine. The 186 kW (250 hp) turbocharged Franklin can also be installed in the Cessna 172, 175 and Stinson 108, and this power plant is used also for installation in the Maule M-5 Lunar Rocket in lieu of a 157 kW (210 hp) Continental or 164 kW (220 hp) Franklin engine. Conversion of the Piper Cherokee and Waco Vela to use a 164 kW (220 hp) and 186 kW (250 hp) Franklin engine respectively was being carried out in early 1979.

Performance figures for Seaplane Flying's conversions certificated by early 1979 are given in the accompanying table.

	Max level speed knots (km/h; mph)	Max cruising speed at 2,135 m (7,000 ft) knots (km/h; mph)	Max rate of climb at S/L m (ft)/min	Service ceiling m (ft)	T-O run m (ft)	Range nm (km; miles)
Cessna 170B	A 148 (274; 170)	A 137 (254; 158)	A 457 (1,500)	A 5,485 (18,000)	A 91 (300)	A 434 (804; 500)
Cessna 172	A 145 (269; 167)	A 135 (251; 156)	A 427 (1,400)	A 5,485 (18,000)	A 91 (300)	A 521 (966; 600)
	B 148 (274; 170)*	B 148+ (274; 170)	B 549 (1,800)	B 9,145 (30,000)	B 84 (275)	B 521 (966; 600)
Cessna 175	A 145 (269; 167)	A 135 (251; 156)	A 427 (1,400)	A 5,485 (18,000)	A 91 (300)	A 521 (966; 600)
	B 148 (274; 170)*	B 148+ (274; 170)	B 549 (1,800)	B 9,145 (30,000)	B 84 (275)	B 521 (966; 600)
Stinson 108	A 139 (258; 160)	A 131 (243; 151)	A 488 (1,600)	A 5,485 (18,000)	A 91 (300)	A 521 (966; 600)
	B 139 (258; 160)*	B 139 (258; 160)	B 579 (1,900)	B 9,145 (30,000)	B 84 (275)	B 521 (966; 600)
Maule M-5	B 152 (282; 175)	B 142 (263; 164)	B 549 (1,800)	B 9,145 (30,000)	B 84 (275)	B 564 (1,045; 650)

A: 164 kW (220 hp) Franklin 6A-350-C2 normally aspirated engine
B: 186 kW (250 hp) Franklin 6AS-350-A1 turbocharged engine
*: max certificated speed

Seaplane Flying modification of Cessna 170B with Franklin 6A-350-C2 engine

SERV-AERO
SERV-AERO ENGINEERING INC

ADDRESS: Municipal Airport, Salinas, California 93901
Telephone: (408) 422 7866/7

Serv-Aero Engineering is one of a number of companies involved in programmes to re-engine standard types of agricultural aircraft which are powered by Pratt & Whitney radial engines. The R-1340 radial, in particular, has been out of production since the mid-fifties, and spare parts for this engine have become difficult to obtain. In addition to the conversions of which details follow, Serv-Aero has been working on a programme to equip an Ayres Turbo-Thrush S-2R with a 1,893 litre (500 US gallon) hopper. This involved major changes to the engine installation and the forward fuselage, and it was planned to flight test a mockup installation before fitting the new hopper into the prototype aircraft.

AG-CAT/LEONIDES and THRUSH COMMANDER/LEONIDES

Serv-Aero was recently responsible for the installation of 417 kW (560 hp) Alvis Leonides radial engines in a

Gulfstream American Ag-Cat with Alvis Leonides engine, following conversion by Serv-Aero

Grumman Ag-Cat and a Rockwell Thrush Commander. In each case, the engine drives a Dowty Rotol R289 three-blade propeller.

Despite the slightly lower power of the Leonides, by comparison with the R-1340 that was fitted originally to each aircraft, its reduced drag and increased propeller efficiency have improved overall performance.

The Leonides is out of production, but the Scottish Division of British Aerospace acquired and is overhauling a number of engines of this type, removed from retired airframes.

THRUSH COMMANDER/R-1820

Servo-Aero has developed a conversion of the Thrush Commander which involves removal of the Pratt & Whitney R-1340 or Wright R-1300, and its replacement by an 895 kW (1,200 hp) Wright R-1820-71 radial piston engine, driving a slow-turning large-diameter three-blade Hamilton Standard propeller. A Supplemental Type Certificate covering this airframe/engine combination was received on 8 October 1977, followed subsequently by Parts Manufacturing Approval covering the production of conversion kits.

It is reported that this engine installation provides a 396 m (1,300 ft) T-O run with full hopper (1,476-1,514 litres; 390-400 US gallons) at S/L in zero-wind ISA conditions. Working speed is 117-126 knots (217-233 km/h; 135-145 mph), resulting in a lower fuel consumption per acre worked. The slower-turning, quieter propeller permits operators to work closer to inhabited areas without creating noise problems.

AG-CAT G-164C/R-1820

On behalf of Mid-Continent Aircraft Corporation of Hayti, Missouri, Serv-Aero produced a prototype conversion of a Gulfstream American Ag-Cat G-164C with a Wright R-1820 engine replacing the original Pratt & Whitney R-1340.

SIKORSKY

SIKORSKY AIRCRAFT, DIVISION OF UNITED TECHNOLOGIES CORPORATION

HEAD OFFICE AND WORKS: Stratford, Connecticut 06602
Telephone: (203) 378 6361
OTHER WORKS: South Avenue, Bridgeport, Connecticut; Sikorsky Memorial Airport, Stratford, Connecticut; and Development Flight Test Center, West Palm Beach, Florida
PRESIDENT: Gerald J. Tobias
EXECUTIVE VICE-PRESIDENTS: Fred W. Carroll (Operations)
Robert F. Daniell (Engineering & Programmes)
SENIOR VICE-PRESIDENTS:
John R. Graham (Finance and Administration)
William F. Paul (Engineering & Development)
Robert J. Torok (Production Programmes)
VICE-PRESIDENTS:
Eugene Buckley (UTTAS Programme)
James W. Dunn (Manufacturing)
William M. Flaherty
J. Colin Green (Planning and Analysis)
Willard E. Lewis (Finance)
Philip Locke (Contracts and Counsel)
Porter D. Lyke (Personnel and Industrial Relations)
Stephen Percy (Government & International Business)
Allan K. Poole (Product Support—Government Programmes)
David O. Smith (Commercial Marketing)
Eugene J. Tallia (Government Relations)
Harvey I. White (Material)
DIVISIONAL AUDITOR: H. W. Engstrom
DIRECTOR OF PUBLIC RELATIONS: Robert G. H. Carroll III

Founded on 5 March 1923 by the late Igor I. Sikorsky as the Sikorsky Aero Engineering Corporation, this company has been a division of United Technologies since 1929. Its main plant at Stratford, which has 120,775 m² (1,300,000 sq ft) of working space, produces the S-61 twin-turbine amphibious transport helicopter and its military counterparts, and the CH-53E, a large multi-purpose military transport. It houses also the production line for the US Army's new twin-turbine UH-60A Black Hawk helicopter. The Bridgeport facility, which has 55,740 m² (600,000 sq ft) of working space, houses the production line for the new S-76 Spirit twin-turbine commercial helicopter, and is used for detail fabrication, overhaul and repair. The Development Flight Test Center is in Florida. The total number of employees was expected to increase from 8,800 to 10,000 during 1979.

Sikorsky is involved in a number of important development programmes. Its ABC (advancing blade concept) helicopter, the S-69, has successfully completed flight tests in its pure helicopter configuration and is now undergoing tests using auxiliary propulsion for flight at speeds up to 300 knots (556 km/h; 345 mph). Also under development are two high-speed multi-purpose research helicopters for NASA and the US Army, known as Rotor Systems Research Aircraft (RSRA).

Sikorsky licensees include Westland of Great Britain, Agusta of Italy, Aérospatiale of France, VFW-Fokker in Germany, Mitsubishi of Japan, and Pratt & Whitney Aircraft of Canada Ltd.

SIKORSKY S-61A and S-61B

US military designations: SH-3 Sea King, HH-3A, VH-3

CAF designation: CH-124

The first version of the S-61 ordered into production was the SH-3A (formerly HSS-2) Sea King amphibious anti-submarine helicopter. The original US Navy contract for this aircraft was received on 23 September 1957, the prototype flew for the first time on 11 March 1959 and deliveries to the Fleet began in September 1961. On 11 March 1979, Sikorsky drew attention to the 20th anniversary of the prototype's first flight, since when more than 900 military S-61s had accumulated over 3 million flight hours, and 130 commercial S-61s had logged a total of more than 815,000 hours.

The S-61 series includes the following military and commercial variants:

SH-3A Sea King. Initial anti-submarine version for the US Navy, powered by 932 kW (1,250 shp) General Electric T58-GE-8B turboshaft engines. A total of 255 were produced by Sikorsky. Also standard equipment in the Japan Maritime Self-Defence Force (see entry for Mitsubishi, which also converted two SH-3As to S-61A standard for use during Antarctic expeditions).

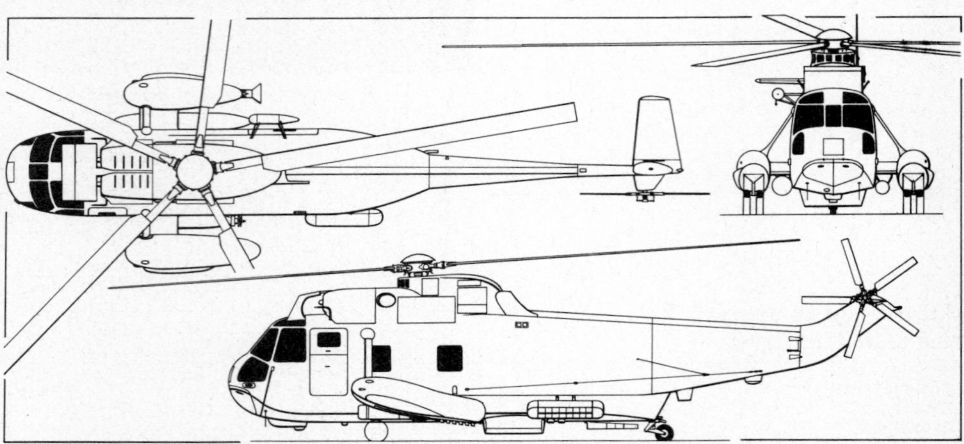

Sikorsky SH-3H twin-engined multi-purpose amphibious helicopter *(Pilot Press)*

CH-124. Designation of 41 aircraft, similar to SH-3A, ordered for the Canadian Armed Forces. First of these was delivered in May 1963: fifth and subsequent aircraft were assembled by United Aircraft of Canada Ltd. Originally designated CHSS-2.

S-61A. Amphibious transport, generally similar to the US Navy's SH-3A. Accommodates 26 troops, 15 litters, cargo, or 12 passengers in VIP configuration. Rolls-Royce Gnome H.1200 turboshafts available as alternative to standard General Electric T58 engines. Nine delivered to Royal Danish Air Force for long-range air-sea rescue duties, with additional fuel tankage. The Decca Navigator Co in the UK received a £100,000 contract in 1973 to supply Mk 19 Decca Navigator airborne receivers, Danac computers and pictorial displays for the Royal Danish Air Force S-61A fleet. One S-61A delivered to Construction Helicopters.

S-61A-4 Nuri. Thirty-eight aircraft for the Royal Malaysian Air Force, each with 31 seats, rescue hoists and auxiliary fuel tanks as standard equipment. These aircraft are used for troop transport, cargo carrying and rescue.

HH-3A. Variant of SH-3A, for search and rescue duties with US Navy. HH-3A conversion kits were supplied to the Navy's overhaul and repair base at Quonset Point, Rhode Island, where 12 conversions were carried out. Changes included installation of two electrically-powered Minigun turrets behind the sponsons, T58-GE-8F turbine engines, a high-speed refuelling and fuel dumping system, a high-speed rescue hoist, modified electronics package, external auxiliary fuel tanks and complete armour installation. The SH-3A's sonar well is covered and a reinforced cabin floor substituted.

SH-3D Sea King. Standard anti-submarine helicopter of the US Navy, with T58-GE-10 engines and more fuel than SH-3A. First SH-3D, delivered in June 1966, was one of 10 for the Spanish Navy, which later ordered 12 more. Four were delivered to the Brazilian Navy and 72 to the US Navy. Versions with Rolls-Royce Gnome turboshaft engines and British anti-submarine equipment are manufactured by Westland Helicopters Ltd (which see). SH-3Ds are also manufactured under licence by Agusta in Italy.

S-61D-4. Four for Argentine Navy, similar to SH-3D.

VH-3D. Eleven delivered to replace VH-3As of Executive Flight Detachment.

SH-3G. US Navy conversion of 105 SH-3As into utility helicopters, by removing anti-submarine warfare equipment. Six equipped with Minigun pods for search and rescue missions in combat conditions.

SH-3H. Multi-purpose version of the SH-3G. Contracts from the US Navy, awarded since 1971, call for conversion of 163 existing aircraft, to increase fleet helicopter capability against submarines and low-flying enemy missiles. This programme will continue into 1980. New ASW equipment includes lightweight sonar, active and passive sonobuoys, and magnetic anomaly detection equipment. Electronic surveillance measures (ESM) equipment enables the SH-3H to make an important contribution to the missile defence of the fleet. General Electric T58-GE-10 engines are fitted.

S-61L. Non-amphibious civil transport with longer fuselage than S-61A/B. Described separately.

S-61N. Amphibious counterpart of S-61L, with which it is described.

S-61R. Development of S-61B for transport duties with USAF, under the designations **CH-3C** and **E.** Described separately.

The following details apply to the SH-3D Sea King, but are generally applicable to other versions except for accommodation and equipment:

TYPE: Twin-engined amphibious all-weather anti-submarine helicopter.

ROTOR SYSTEM: Five-blade main and tail rotors. All-metal fully-articulated oil-lubricated main rotor. Flanged cuffs on blades bolted to matching flanges on all-steel rotor head. Main rotor blades are interchangeable and are provided with an automatic powered folding system. Rotor brake standard. All-metal tail rotor.

ROTOR DRIVE: Both engines drive through freewheel units and rotor brake to main gearbox. Steel drive-shafts. Tail rotor shaft-driven through intermediate and tail gearboxes. Accessories driven by power take-off on tail rotor shaft. Additional freewheel units between accessories and port engine, and between accessories and tail rotor shaft. Main rotor/engine rpm ratio 1 : 93·43. Tail rotor/engine rpm ratio 1 : 16·7.

FUSELAGE: Boat hull of all-metal semi-monocoque construction. Single step. Tail section folds to reduce stowage requirements.

TAIL SURFACE: Fixed stabiliser on starboard side of tail section.

LANDING GEAR: Amphibious. Land gear consists of two twin-wheel main units, which are retracted rearward hydraulically into stabilising floats, and non-retractable tailwheel. Oleo-pneumatic shock-absorbers. Goodyear main wheels and tubeless tyres size 6·50-10 type III, pressure 4·83 bars (70 lb/sq in). Goodyear tailwheel and tyre size 6·00-6. Goodyear hydraulic disc brakes. Boat hull and pop-out flotation bags in stabilising floats permit emergency operation from water.

POWER PLANT: Two 1,044 kW (1,400 shp) General Electric T58-GE-10 turboshaft engines. Three bladder-type fuel tanks in hull; forward tank capacity 1,314 litres (347 US gallons), centre tank capacity 530 litres (140 US gallons), rear tank capacity 1,336 litres (353 US gallons). Total fuel capacity 3,180 litres (840 US gallons). Refuelling point on port side of fuselage. Oil capacity 26·5 litres (7 US gallons).

ACCOMMODATION: Pilot and co-pilot on flight deck, two sonar operators in main cabin. Dual controls. Crew door at rear of flight deck on port side. Large loading door at rear of cabin on starboard side.

SYSTEMS: Primary and auxiliary hydraulic systems, pressure 103·5 bars (1,500 lb/sq in), for flying controls. Utility hydraulic system, pressure 207 bars (3,000 lb/sq in), for landing gear, winches and blade folding. Pneumatic system, pressure 207 bars (3,000 lb/sq in), for blow-down emergency landing gear extension. Electrical system includes one 300A DC generator, two

Sikorsky SH-3H multi-purpose helicopter for ASW and fleet missile defence

20kVA 115A AC generators and 24V 22Ah battery. APU optional.

Avionics and Equipment: Bendix AQS-13 sonar with 180° search beam width. Hamilton Standard auto-stabilisation equipment. Automatic transition into hover. Sonar coupler holds altitude automatically in conjunction with Teledyne APN-130 Doppler radar (Litton AN/APS-503 in CH-124) and radar altimeter. Provision for 272 kg (600 lb) capacity rescue hoist and 3,630 kg (8,000 lb) capacity automatic touchdown-release low-response cargo sling for external loads.

Armament: Provision for 381 kg (840 lb) of weapons, including homing torpedoes.

Dimensions, external:

Diameter of main rotor	18·90 m (62 ft 0 in)
Main rotor blade chord	0·46 m (1 ft 6¼ in)
Diameter of tail rotor	3·23 m (10 ft 7 in)
Distance between rotor centres	11·10 m (36 ft 5 in)
Length overall	22·15 m (72 ft 8 in)
Length of fuselage	16·69 m (54 ft 9 in)
Length, tail pylon folded	14·40 m (47 ft 3 in)
Width, rotors folded	4·98 m (16 ft 4 in)
Height to top of rotor hub	4·72 m (15 ft 6 in)
Height overall	5·13 m (16 ft 10 in)
Wheel track	3·96 m (13 ft 0 in)
Wheelbase	7·18 m (23 ft 6½ in)
Crew door (fwd, port): Height	1·68 m (5 ft 6 in)
Width	0·91 m (3 ft 0 in)
Height to sill	1·14 m (3 ft 9 in)
Main cabin door (stbd): Height	1·52 m (5 ft 0 in)
Width	1·73 m (5 ft 8 in)
Height to sill	1·14 m (3 ft 9 in)

Dimensions, internal (S-61A):

Cabin: Length	7·60 m (24 ft 11 in)
Max width	1·98 m (6 ft 6 in)
Max height	1·92 m (6 ft 3½ in)
Floor area	15·1 m^2 (162 sq ft)
Volume	28·9 m^3 (1,020 cu ft)

Areas:

Main rotor blades (each)	4·14 m^2 (44·54 sq ft)
Tail rotor blades (each)	0·22 m^2 (2·38 sq ft)
Main rotor disc	280·5 m^2 (3,019 sq ft)
Tail rotor disc	8·20 m^2 (88·30 sq ft)
Stabiliser	1·86 m^2 (20·00 sq ft)

Weights:

Weight empty: S-61A	4,428 kg (9,763 lb)
S-61B	5,382 kg (11,865 lb)
Normal T-O weight: S-61A	9,300 kg (20,500 lb)
SH-3A (ASW)	8,185 kg (18,044 lb)
SH-3D (ASW)	8,449 kg (18,626 lb)
Max T-O weight: S-61A	9,750 kg (21,500 lb)
S-61B	9,300 kg (20,500 lb)
SH-3H	9,525 kg (21,000 lb)

Performance (at 9,300 kg; 20,500 lb AUW):

Max level speed	144 knots (267 km/h; 166 mph)
Cruising speed for max range	118 knots (219 km/h; 136 mph)
Max rate of climb at S/L	670 m (2,200 ft)/min
Service ceiling	4,480 m (14,700 ft)
Hovering ceiling IGE	3,200 m (10,500 ft)
Hovering ceiling OGE	2,500 m (8,200 ft)
Range with max fuel, 10% reserves	542 nm (1,005 km; 625 miles)

SIKORSKY S-61L and S-61N

Although basically similar to the S-61A and B, the S-61L and N commercial transports incorporate a number of changes, including a longer fuselage. Other details are as follows:

S-61L. Non-amphibious configuration. Modified landing gear, rotor head and stabiliser. Accommodation for up to 30 passengers. First flight of the prototype S-61L was made on 6 December 1960, and it received FAA Type Approval on 2 November 1961. Production completed.

S-61N. Similar to S-61L, but with sealed hull for amphibious operation and stabilising floats as on SH-3. Accommodation for 26-28 passengers. First flown on 7 August 1962. Now available also in Mark II form, with General Electric CT58-140-1 or -2 turboshaft engines (earlier aircraft have 1,007 kW; 1,350 shp engines), enabling it to carry 22 passengers on an 86°F (30°C) day, compared with the former 10. Six individual cargo bins to speed baggage handling. Other changes include improved vibration damping. In production.

Payloader. Stripped-down version of S-61N, weighing nearly 907 kg (2,000 lb) less than standard version but capable of lifting a payload of more than 4,990 kg (11,000 lb). Intended for logging, general construction, powerline installation and similar operations. Sponsons replaced by fixed main-wheel landing gear; sealed-off rear airstair door.

On 6 October 1964 the S-61L and S-61N became the first transport helicopters to receive FAA approval for IFR operations.

A total of 116 commercial S-61s had been delivered by 8 June 1979.

Type: Twin-turbine all-weather helicopter airliners.

Rotor System and Rotor Drive: As for SH-3A/D, S-61A and S-61B, except blades do not fold.

Fuselage: All-metal semi-monocoque structure of boat-hull form.

Tail Surface: Stabiliser on starboard side of tail section.

Landing Gear (S-61L): Non-amphibious non-retractable tailwheel type with twin wheels on main units. Oleo-pneumatic shock-absorbers. Goodyear main wheels and tubeless tyres, size 22·1 × 6·50-10 Type III, pressure 6·55 bars (95 lb/sq in). Goodyear tailwheel with tyre size 18·3 × 6·00-10, pressure 5·17 bars (75 lb/sq in). Goodyear hydraulic disc brakes.

Landing Gear (S-61N): Amphibious hydraulically-retractable type. Twin wheels on main units, which retract rearward into stabilising floats. Non-retractable tailwheel. Each float provides 1,506 kg (3,320 lb) buoyancy and, with the sealed hull, permits operation

Sikorsky S-61N, used on the Airlink shuttle between London's Heathrow and Gatwick Airports *(Brian M. Service)*

from water. Shock-absorbers, wheels, tyres and brakes as for S-61L.

Power Plant (S-61N Mk II): Two 1,118 kW (1,500 shp) General Electric CT58-140-1/-2 turboshaft engines. Two bladder-type fuel tanks in hull; forward tank capacity 796 litres (210 US gallons), rear tank capacity 757 litres (200 US gallons). Total fuel capacity 1,553 litres (410 US gallons). Additional 924 litre (244 US gallon) tank optionally available for S-61N. Refuelling point on port side of fuselage. Oil capacity 26·5 litres (7 US gallons).

Accommodation: Crew of three: pilot, co-pilot and flight attendant. Main cabin accommodates up to 30 passengers (22 at 86°F; 30°C). Standard arrangement has eight single seats and one double seat on port side of cabin, seven double seats on starboard side and one double seat at rear. Rear seat may be replaced by a toilet. Galley may be installed in forward baggage compartment area on starboard side. Forward half of cabin may be provided with folding seats and tiedown rings for convertible passenger/freight operations. Two doors on starboard side of cabin: main cabin door of airstair type. Baggage space above and below floor at front, on starboard side of cabin, and below floor in area of airstair door (aft, starboard side).

Systems: As for SH-3A, S-61A and S-61B.

Avionics and Equipment: Radio and radar to customer's specification. Blind-flying instrumentation standard.

Dimensions, external:
- Diameter of main rotor: 18·90 m (62 ft 0 in)
- Diameter of tail rotor: 3·23 m (10 ft 7 in)
- Distance between rotor centres:
  - S-61L: 11·10 m (36 ft 5 in)
  - S-61N: 11·17 m (36 ft 8 in)
- Length overall (rotors fore and aft):
  - S-61L: 22·21 m (72 ft 10½ in)
  - S-61N: 22·20 m (72 ft 10 in)
- Width, over landing gear: S-61L: 4·47 m (14 ft 8 in)
  - S-61N: 6·02 m (19 ft 9 in)
- Height to top of rotor hub pitot head:
  - S-61L: 5·18 m (17 ft 0 in)
  - S-61N: 5·32 m (17 ft 5½ in)
- Height overall: S-61L: 5·18 m (17 ft 0 in)
  - S-61N: 5·63 m (18 ft 5½ in)
- Wheel track: S-61L: 3·96 m (13 ft 0 in)
  - S-61N: 4·27 m (14 ft 0 in)
- Wheelbase: S-61L: 7·15 m (23 ft 5½ in)
  - S-61N: 7·30 m (23 ft 11½ in)
- Cabin door (airstair): Height: 1·68 m (5 ft 6 in)
  - Width: 0·81 m (2 ft 8 in)
  - Height to sill: 1·14 m (3 ft 9 in)
- Cargo door: Height: 1·68 m (5 ft 6 in)
  - Width: 1·27 m (4 ft 2 in)
  - Height to sill: 1·14 m (3 ft 9 in)

Dimensions, internal:
- Cabin: Length: 9·73 m (31 ft 11 in)
  - Max width: 1·98 m (6 ft 6 in)
  - Max height: 1·92 m (6 ft 3½ in)
  - Floor area: approx 20·16 m² (217 sq ft)
  - Volume: approx 36·95 m³ (1,305 cu ft)
- Freight hold (above floor): approx 3·54 m³ (125 cu ft)
- Freight hold (underfloor): approx 0·71 m³ (25 cu ft)

Areas:
- Main rotor blades (each): 3·75 m² (40·4 sq ft)
- Tail rotor blades (each): 0·22 m² (2·38 sq ft)
- Main rotor disc: 280·5 m² (3,019 sq ft)
- Tail rotor disc: 8·20 m² (88·3 sq ft)
- Stabiliser: 2·51 m² (27·0 sq ft)

Weights and Loadings:
- Weight empty: S-61L: 5,308 kg (11,704 lb)
  - S-61N: 5,674 kg (12,510 lb)
- Max T-O weight (S-61N):
  - FAA, CAA: 9,300 kg (20,500 lb)
  - FAA with external load: 9,980 kg (22,000 lb)
- Max disc loading: 35·59 kg/m² (7·29 lb/sq ft)
- Max power loading: 4·46 kg/kW (7·33 lb/shp)

Performance (at max T-O weight):
- Max cruising speed:
  - S-61N: 130 knots (241 km/h; 150 mph)
- Average cruising speed: 120 knots (222 km/h; 138 mph)
- Max rate of climb at S/L: 395 m (1,300 ft)/min
- Rate of climb, one engine out:
  - S-61N: 91 m (300 ft)/min
- Service ceiling: 3,810 m (12,500 ft)
- Hovering ceiling IGE: S-61L: 2,743 m (9,000 ft)
  - S-61N: 2,652 m (8,700 ft)
- Hovering ceiling OGE: S-61L: 1,189 m (3,900 ft)
  - S-61N: 1,158 m (3,800 ft)
- Min ground turning radius:
  - S-61L: 13·70 m (44 ft 11½ in)
  - S-61N: 13·93 m (45 ft 8½ in)
- Runway LCN at max T-O weight: approx 4·4
- Range with standard fuel, 30 min reserves:
  - S-61L: 230 nm (426 km; 265 miles)
  - S-61N: 245 nm (453 km; 282 miles)
- Range with auxiliary fuel, 30 min reserves:
  - S-61N: 430 nm (796 km; 495 miles)

SIKORSKY S-61R

US military designations: CH-3 and HH-3 Jolly Green Giant

Although based on the SH-3A, this amphibious transport helicopter introduced many important design changes. They include provision of a hydraulically-operated rear ramp for straight-in loading of wheeled vehicles, a 907 kg (2,000 lb) capacity winch for internal cargo handling, retractable tricycle-type landing gear, pressurised rotor blades for quick and easy inspection, gas-turbine auxiliary power supply for independent field operations, self-lubricating main and tail rotors, and built-in equipment for the removal and replacement of all major components in remote areas.

The first S-61R flew on 17 June 1963, followed by the first CH-3C a few weeks later. FAA Type Approval was received on 30 December 1963, and the first delivery of an operational CH-3C was made on the same day, for drone recovery duties at Tyndall AFB, Florida. Subsequent deliveries made to USAF Aerospace Defense Command, Air Training Command, Tactical Air Command, Strategic Air Command and Aerospace Rescue and Recovery Service.

Production by Sikorsky has ended, but S-61R variants continue to be available from Agusta in Italy (which see).

There have been four Sikorsky-built versions, as follows:

CH-3C. Two 969·5 kW (1,300 shp) T58-GE-1 turboshaft engines. After a total of 41 had been built for the USAF, production was switched to the CH-3E. All aircraft delivered as CH-3Cs were modified to CH-3E standard.

CH-3E. Designation applicable since February 1966, following introduction of uprated engines (1,118 kW; 1,500 shp T58-GE-5s). A total of 42 were built as new aircraft to this standard.

HH-3E. For USAF Aerospace Rescue and Recovery Service. Additional equipment comprises armour, self-sealing fuel tanks, retractable flight refuelling probe, defensive armament and rescue hoist. Two 1,118 kW (1,500 shp) T58-GE-5 turboshafts. A total of 50 HH-3Es were converted from CH-3Es, and are known as **Jolly Green Giants**.

On 31 May-1 June 1967, two HH-3Es made the first non-stop transatlantic flights by helicopters, en route to the Paris Air Show. Nine aerial refuellings were made by each aircraft. The 3,708 nm (6,870 km; 4,270 miles) from New York to Paris were flown in 30 h 46 min.

HH-3F. Similar to HH-3E, for US Coast Guard, which has given them the name **Pelican**. Advanced electronic equipment for search and rescue duties. No armour plate, armament or self-sealing tanks. First order announced in August 1965. Deliveries began in 1968 and a total of 40 were built.

The following details apply to the CH-3E:

Type: Twin-engined amphibious transport helicopter.

Rotor System: Five-blade fully-articulated main rotor of all-metal construction. Flanged cuffs on blades bolted to matching flanges on rotor head. Control by rotating and stationary swashplates. Blades do not fold. Rotor brake standard. Conventional tail rotor with five aluminium blades.

Rotor Drive: Twin turbines drive through freewheeling units and rotor brake to main gearbox. Steel drive-shafts. Tail rotor shaft-driven through intermediate gearbox and tail gearbox. Main rotor/engine rpm ratio 1 : 93·43. Tail rotor/engine rpm ratio 1 : 16·7.

Fuselage: All-metal semi-monocoque structure of pod and boom type. Cabin of basic square section.

Tail Surface: Horizontal stabiliser on starboard side of tail rotor pylon.

Landing Gear: Hydraulically-retractable tricycle type, with twin wheels on each unit. Main wheels retract forward into sponsons, each of which provides 2,176 kg (4,797 lb) of buoyancy and, with boat hull, permits amphibious operation. Oleo-pneumatic shock-absorbers. All wheels and tyres tubeless Type III rib, size 22·1 × 6·50-10, manufactured by Goodyear. Tyre pressure 6·55 bars (95 lb/sq in). Goodyear hydraulic disc brakes.

Power Plant: Two 1,118 kW (1,500 shp) General Elec-

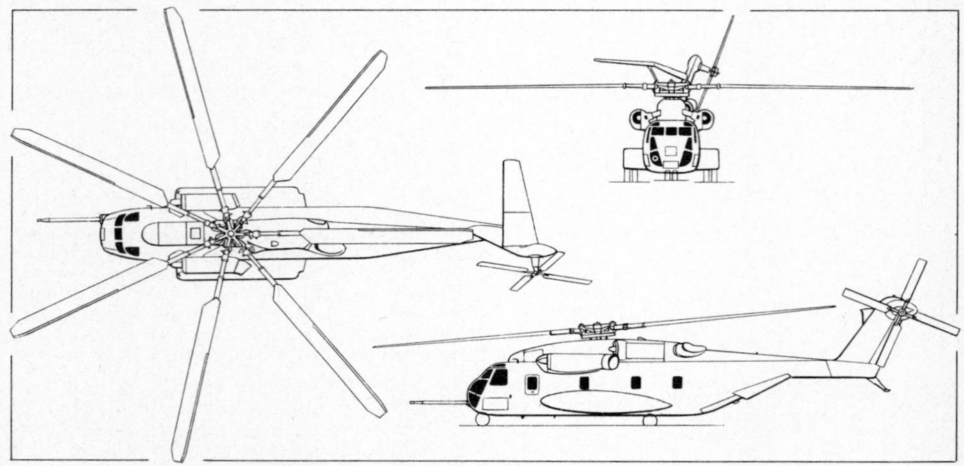

Sikorsky CH-53E heavy-duty multi-purpose helicopter *(Pilot Press)*

Sikorsky CH-53E heavy-lift helicopter (three General Electric T64-GE-415 turboshaft engines)

tric T58-GE-5 turboshaft engines, mounted side by side above cabin, immediately forward of main transmission. Fuel in two bladder-type tanks beneath cabin floor; forward tank capacity 1,204 litres (318 US gallons), rear tank capacity 1,226 litres (324 US gallons). Total fuel capacity 2,430 litres (642 US gallons). Refuelling point on port side of fuselage. Total oil capacity 26·5 litres (7 US gallons).

Accommodation: Crew of two side by side on flight deck, with dual controls. Provision for flight engineer or attendant. Normal accommodation for 25 fully-equipped troops. Alternative arrangements for 30 troops, 15 stretchers or 2,270 kg (5,000 lb) of cargo. Jettisonable sliding door on starboard side at front of cabin. Internal door between cabin and flight deck. Hydraulically-operated rear loading ramp for vehicles, in two hinged sections, giving opening with minimum width of 1·73 m (5 ft 8 in) and headroom of up to 2·21 m (7 ft 3 in).

Systems: Primary and auxiliary hydraulic systems, pressure 103·5 bars (1,500 lb/sq in), for flying control servos. Utility hydraulic system, pressure 207 bars (3,000 lb/sq in), for landing gear, rear ramp and winches. Pneumatic system, pressure 207 bars (3,000 lb/sq in), for emergency blow-down landing gear extension. Electrical system includes 24V 22Ah battery, two 20kVA 115V AC generators and one 300A DC generator. APU standard.

Dimensions, external:
Diameter of main rotor 18·90 m (62 ft 0 in)
Main rotor blade chord 0·46 m (1 ft 6¼ in)
Diameter of tail rotor 3·15 m (10 ft 4 in)
Distance between rotor centres 11·22 m (36 ft 10 in)
Length overall 22·25 m (73 ft 0 in)
Length of fuselage 17·45 m (57 ft 3 in)
Width, over landing gear 4·82 m (15 ft 10 in)
Height to top of rotor hub 4·90 m (16 ft 1 in)
Height overall 5·51 m (18 ft 1 in)
Wheel track 4·06 m (13 ft 4 in)
Wheelbase 5·21 m (17 ft 1 in)
Cabin door (fwd, stbd): Height 1·65 m (5 ft 4¾ in)
Width 1·22 m (4 ft 0 in)
Height to sill 1·27 m (4 ft 2 in)
Rear ramp: Length 4·29 m (14 ft 1 in)
Width 1·85 m (6 ft 1 in)

Dimensions, internal:
Cabin (excl flight deck):
Length 7·89 m (25 ft 10½ in)
Max width 1·98 m (6 ft 6 in)
Max height 1·91 m (6 ft 3 in)
Floor area approx 15·61 m² (168 sq ft)
Volume approx 29·73 m³ (1,050 cu ft)

Areas:
Main rotor blades (each) 3·71 m² (39·9 sq ft)
Tail rotor blades (each) 0·22 m² (2·35 sq ft)
Main rotor disc 280·5 m² (3,019 sq ft)
Tail rotor disc 7·80 m² (83·9 sq ft)
Stabiliser 2·51 m² (27·0 sq ft)

Weights:
Weight empty 6,010 kg (13,255 lb)
Normal T-O weight 9,635 kg (21,247 lb)
Max T-O weight 10,000 kg (22,050 lb)

Performance (at normal T-O weight):
Max level speed at S/L
141 knots (261 km/h; 162 mph)
Cruising speed for max range
125 knots (232 km/h; 144 mph)
Max rate of climb at S/L 400 m (1,310 ft)/min
Service ceiling 3,385 m (11,100 ft)
Hovering ceiling IGE 1,250 m (4,100 ft)
Min ground turning radius 11·29 m (37 ft 0½ in)
Runway LCN at max T-O weight approx 4·75
Range with max fuel, 10% reserves
404 nm (748 km; 465 miles)

SIKORSKY S-65A

US Navy designation: CH-53A Sea Stallion
USAF designations: HH-53B/C
US Marine Corps designations: CH-53A/D

Although no longer in production, this large twin-turboshaft helicopter continues in first-line service in the several versions described in the 1978-79 *Jane's*.

Eight HH-53Cs are being modified for night search and rescue operations under the USAF's Pave Low 3 programme, following evaluation of a prototype conversion which flew for the first time in June 1975. The work is being done at the US Naval Air Rework Facility (NARF), Naval Air Station, Pensacola, Florida, on behalf of Military Airlift Command's Aerospace Rescue and Recovery Service.

The **Pave Low 3 HH-53C** has a stabilised Texas Instruments FLIR (forward-looking infra-red) installation mounted below the refuelling boom; a Litton inertial navigation system; a Canadian Marconi Doppler navigation system; an IBM computer; Systems Research symbol generator; and Texas Instruments terrain following/avoidance radar in an offset (to port) 'thimble' fairing on the nose.

The USAF accepted the first production Pave Low 3 HH-53C at Pensacola on 13 March 1979. All eight conversions are scheduled for completion by Spring 1980.

Sikorsky HH-53 modified under the USAF's Pave Low 3 programme

SIKORSKY CH-53E

The Sikorsky S-65 was chosen in 1973 for development with three engines to provide the US Navy and Marine Corps with a heavy-duty multi-purpose helicopter. Other changes to increase performance included installation of a new seven-blade main rotor of increased diameter, with blades of titanium/glassfibre construction, and an uprated transmission of 9,798 kW (13,140 shp) capacity to cater for future development.

Development was initiated by the award of a $1·7 million US Navy cost-plus-fixed-fee contract; in May 1973 Sikorsky announced that construction of two prototypes was to go ahead, with the objective of a first flight in April 1974. Bettering this by a month, the first of these two helicopters, with the designation YCH-53E, made a successful half-hour flight on 1 March 1974, during which low-altitude hovering and limited manoeuvres were carried out. It was lost subsequently in an accident on the ground, but the programme was resumed on 24 January 1975 with the second YCH-53E. This aircraft has flown at an AUW of 33,793 kg (74,500 lb), the highest gross weight achieved by any helicopter outside the USSR. It has been used for preliminary evaluation and testing under Phase I of the development programme. Phase II covered the construction of a static test vehicle and two preproduction prototypes, the first of which flew on 8 December 1975. Both have been involved in flight testing since early 1976, and by May 1978 had completed more than 1,000 hours of flight testing, including shipboard suitability trials at sea. In February 1978 Sikorsky was awarded a contract to begin full-scale production, with initial approval for six aircraft. Later in that same year, on 15 November, the US Navy exercised an option for the supply of an additional 14 CH-53Es.

The US Navy plans to use the CH-53E for vertical on-board delivery operations, to support mobile construction battalions, and for the removal of battle-damaged aircraft from carrier decks. In amphibious operations, it would be able to airlift 93 per cent of a US Marine division's combat items, and would be able to retrieve 98 per cent of the Marine Corps' tactical aircraft without disassembly. Features include extended-range fuel tanks, in-flight refuelling capability, an onboard all-weather navigation system, and an advanced dual digital automatic flight control system.

The CH-53E is the largest helicopter capable of full operation from the Navy's existing and planned ships, requiring only 10 per cent more deck space than the twin-turbine H-53. It offers double the lift of the latter aircraft with an increase of only 50 per cent in engine power.

It is anticipated that CH-53Es will begin to join the US fleet in late 1980. The current Navy/Marine programme is for 49 aircraft, but the eventual production total may exceed 100.

Type: Triple-turbine heavy-duty multi-purpose helicopter.

Rotor System and Transmission: Seven-blade main rotor with blades of titanium/glassfibre construction. Titanium and steel main rotor head. Main rotor blades fold. Four-blade tail rotor mounted on pylon canted 20° to port. Rotor transmission, manufactured by Indiana Gear Works, is rated at 9,798 kW (13,140 shp) for 10 s, 8,628 kW (11,570 shp) for 30 min. Tail rotor pylon folds on starboard side of fuselage.

Fuselage: Conventional semi-monocoque structure of light alloy, steel and titanium.

Tail Surface: Initial fixed tailplane on undersurface of fuselage, superseded successively by single high-mounted stabiliser on starboard side and lightweight gull-wing type. Surface folds when tail rotor pylon is folded.

Landing Gear: Retractable tricycle type, with twin wheels on each unit. Main units retract into rear of sponsons on each side of fuselage.

Power Plant: Three General Electric T64-GE-415 turboshaft engines, each with a max rating of 3,266 kW (4,380 shp) for 10 min, intermediate rating of 3,091 kW (4,145 shp) for 30 min and max continuous power rating of 2,756 kW (3,696 shp).

Accommodation: Crew of three. Main cabin will accommodate up to 55 troops in a high-density seating arrangement.

Dimensions, external:
Main rotor diameter 24·08 m (79 ft 0 in)
Tail rotor diameter 6·10 m (20 ft 0 in)
Length overall 30·20 m (99 ft 1 in)
Length, rotor and tail pylon folded
18·44 m (60 ft 6 in)
Length of fuselage 22·48 m (73 ft 9 in)
Width of fuselage 2·69 m (8 ft 10 in)
Width, rotor and tail pylon folded
8·41 m (27 ft 7 in)
Height overall 8·46 m (27 ft 9 in)
Height, rotor and tail pylon folded
5·74 m (18 ft 10 in)
Wheel track 3·96 m (13 ft 0 in)
Wheelbase 8·31 m (27 ft 3 in)

Dimensions, internal:
Cabin: Length 9·14 m (30 ft 0 in)
Max width 2·29 m (7 ft 6 in)
Max height 2·01 m (6 ft 6 in)

Weights:
Weight empty 15,071 kg (33,226 lb)
Internal payload (100 nm; 185 km; 115 miles radius) 13,607 kg (30,000 lb)
External payload (50 nm; 92·5 km; 57·5 miles radius) 14,605 kg (32,200 lb)
Max T-O weight 33,339 kg (73,500 lb)

Performance (ISA, at T-O weight of 25,400 kg; 56,000 lb):
Max level speed at S/L
170 knots (315 km/h; 196 mph)
Cruising speed at S/L
150 knots (278 km/h; 173 mph)
Max rate of climb at S/L 838 m (2,750 ft)/min
Hovering ceiling IGE, at max power
3,520 m (11,550 ft)
Hovering ceiling OGE, at max power
2,895 m (9,500 ft)
Service ceiling, at max continuous power
5,640 m (18,500 ft)
Range, at optimum cruise condition for best range
1,120 nm (2,075 km; 1,290 miles)

SIKORSKY S-69

US Army designation: XH-59A

On 7 February 1972 Sikorsky announced that the company was designing and building a research aircraft, designated S-69, to flight test the Advancing Blade Concept (ABC) rotor system, under a contract awarded by the Eustis Directorate, US Army Air Mobility Research and Development Laboratory, Fort Eustis, Virginia. Subsequently, the value of the contract was increased to cover detail design changes and the construction of two demon-

Sikorsky S-69 (XH-59A) prototype for evaluation of the ABC rotor system

strator aircraft under the Army designation XH-59A.

The ABC rotor system, consisting of two co-axial counter-rotating rigid rotors, takes advantage of the aerodynamic lift potential of the advancing blades. At high speed, the retreating blades are unloaded, the majority of the load being carried on the advancing sides of both rotors, and the usual penalties of retreating blade stall are eliminated. This removes the need for a wing to supplement the rotor to provide speed and agility, even at high density altitude. Another advantage of the concept is the elimination of a conventional anti-torque tail rotor and its drive system.

The purpose of this research aircraft programme is to evaluate the performance of the ABC system in flight, following successful full-scale wind tunnel tests of a 12·2 m (40 ft) diameter rotor at NASA's Ames Research Center. The first aircraft (21941) made its first flight on 26 July 1973, as a pure helicopter, but was damaged in a flight accident at Sikorsky's Stratford works in the following month. Detailed investigation led to a number of design changes and the installation of a modified control system. The test programme was resumed on 21 July 1975, with the second aircraft (21942), also flying as a pure helicopter.

Task II flight testing of the XH-59A began in November 1975, and the two-year programme was concerned with continued expansion of the flight envelope. The aircraft was flown to a height of 4,265 m (14,000 ft), and demonstrated full autorotation at 60, 80 and 100 knots (111, 148 and 185 km/h; 69, 92 and 115 mph). Hard-over tests of the stability augmentation system were carried out at speeds ranging from 40 to 150 knots (74 to 278 km/h; 46 to 173 mph), and single engine cuts were made at 80 to 150 knots (148 to 278 km/h; 92 to 173 mph). By March 1977 the demonstrator had attained a speed of 160 knots (296 km/h; 184 mph) in level flight at sea level; 194·5 knots (360·5 km/h; 224 mph) in a shallow dive; up to 156 knots (290 km/h; 180 mph) at 3,050 m (10,000 ft); up to 40 knots (74 km/h; 46 mph) in sideways flight; up to 30 knots (56 km/h; 35 mph) in rearward flight; and a load factor of over 2·2*g*.

Following completion of flight tests in the pure helicopter configuration in March 1977, a new phase of testing, with two Pratt & Whitney J60 turbojet engines added for auxiliary forward thrust in a high-speed configuration, was authorised and funded jointly by the US Army. USN and NASA. Installation of the J60-P-3A turbojets was carried out during 1978, and low-speed testing with these auxiliary engines was completed before the end of that year. The high-speed envelope was being investigated in early 1979 at United Technologies Division's Development Flight Test Center near West Palm Beach, Florida. It was reported from there on 12 April 1979 that the S-69 had attained a speed of 204 knots (378 km/h; 235 mph) in level flight. Its maximum design speed is 300 knots (555 km/h; 345 mph) at a 2*g* load factor.

Under NASA contract, the first S-59 is being rebuilt and modified as a full-scale wind-tunnel vehicle for testing in NASA's 40 × 80 ft tunnel at Moffett Field, California.

Type: Two-seat research helicopter.

Rotor System: Two contra-rotating three-blade main rotors mounted co-axially. No tail rotor. Blade tip speed (PT6T-3 only) 198 m (650 ft)/s; reduced to 137 m (450 ft)/s above 225 knots (416 km/h; 259 mph) with turbojets fitted.

Fuselage: All-metal semi-monocoque structure of circular cross-section.

Tail Unit: Cantilever all-metal structure of conventional fixed-wing aircraft type. Twin endplate fins and rudders.

Landing Gear: Retractable tricycle type, with twin wheels on nose unit and single wheels on main units. Nosewheels retract aft into fuselage nose, main wheels inward into fuselage.

Power Plant: One 1,360 kW (1,825 shp) Pratt & Whitney Aircraft of Canada PT6T-3 Turbo Twin Pac mounted within the fuselage, and two Pratt & Whitney J60-P-3A turbojet engines (each 13·35 kN; 3,000 lb st) in pod on each side of the fuselage.

Accommodation: Crew of two on flight deck, with door on each side. Fuselage access door on port side of fuselage, aft of flight deck.

Dimensions, external:
- Diameter of rotors (each) 10·97 m (36 ft 0 in)
- Mean rotor blade chord 0·44 m (1 ft 5¼ in)
- Length overall, rotors fore and aft 12·62 m (41 ft 5 in)
- Length of fuselage 12·42 m (40 ft 9 in)
- Height over fins 3·94 m (12 ft 11 in)
- Tailplane span 4·72 m (15 ft 6 in)
- Wheel track 2·44 m (8 ft 0 in)

Weights (A, PT6T-3 only; B, with J60 engines):
- Design max T-O weight: A 4,082 kg (9,000 lb)
- B 5,035 kg (11,100 lb)

Performance:
- Max diving speed: A 196 knots (363 km/h; 225 mph)
- Max level speed at S/L:
  - A 160 knots (296 km/h; 184 mph)
  - B 280 knots (518 km/h; 322 mph)
- Hovering ceiling IGE: A 2,042 m (6,700 ft)
  - B 183 m (600 ft)
- *g* limits: A +2·5
  - B +2·0

SIKORSKY S-70

US Army designations: UH-60A and EH-60A/B Black Hawk

At the end of August 1972, the US Army selected Sikorsky and Boeing Vertol as competitors to build three prototypes each, plus one ground test vehicle, of their submissions for the Utility Tactical Transport Aircraft System (UTTAS) requirement. Sikorsky's $61 million contract called for flight trials to begin in November 1974, but the first YUH-60A flew on 17 October 1974, six weeks ahead of schedule. The second prototype flew on 21 January 1975, followed by the third on 28 February 1975. Fly-off evaluation against Boeing Vertol's YUH-61A prototypes began in early 1976 and occupied a period of seven months. On 23 December 1976 Sikorsky's design was declared the winner.

Designed to carry 11 fully-equipped troops plus a crew of three, the UH-60A has a large cabin which enables it to be used without modification for medical evacuation, reconnaissance, command and control purposes or troop resupply. For external lift missions its cargo hook has a capacity of up to 3,630 kg (8,000 lb). Design is compact, so that the helicopter itself can be airlifted over long ranges. One can be accommodated in a C-130, two in a C-141 and six in a C-5A.

The UH-60A, now named Black Hawk, is intended to serve as the US Army's primary combat assault helicopter, and the Army plans to procure a total of 1,107 by the mid-eighties. The basic production contract awarded to Sikorsky, plus options exercised by mid-1979, cover the construction of 200 aircraft during the first three years of production, which began in the Autumn of 1977. The first flight of a production aircraft was made in October 1978, and Black Hawks were delivered for pilot training to the US Army Aviation Center, Fort Rucker, Alabama, in April 1979. The first delivery of production aircraft to an operational unit was made on 19 June 1979, when four Black Hawks were handed over to the 101st Airborne Division at Fort Campbell, Kentucky. They were to be used initially by this unit in an extensive Force Development Test and Experimentation (FDTE) programme under field conditions. Later in 1979 it was planned to deploy Black Hawks to jungle areas of Panama, to desert regions in the southwest USA, and to the Arctic, for testing under a wide variety of temperatures and conditions.

In tests carried out during early 1979, the Black Hawk demonstrated its ability to sustain heavy landing impacts without damage. In a series of such tests, the helicopter sustained drop rates of 3·5 m (11·5 ft)/s at a forward speed of 63 knots (117 km/h; 73 mph) and gross weight of 7,632 kg (16,825 lb). Another aircraft, flown under artificial icing conditions, confirmed that safe flight can be made in moderate icing conditions by use of a specially developed de-icing kit.

Two special variants of the Black Hawk were reported in 1979, as follows:

EH-60A. ECM variant. US Army requested $14·5 million in FY 1980 and $2·3 million in FY 1981, to begin the integration of Quick Fix II equipment into the Black Hawk.

EH-60B. Eight prototypes being produced under a $36·6 million US Army contract, announced in September 1979, for SOTAS (Stand-Off Target Acquisition System) missions. Each will be equipped with a rotating underbelly antenna and a data terminal in the main cabin, to detect the movement of enemy forces on the battlefield and relay the information to a ground station. Electronics packages to be supplied by Motorola. First prototype scheduled to fly in late 1980. Army plans envisage eventual production of more than 100 SOTAS helicopters.

Type: Twin-turbine combat assault squad transport.

Rotor System: Four-blade main rotor. Sikorsky SC-1095 blade section, with thickness/chord ratio of 9·5%. Middle section has leading-edge droop and trailing-edge tab to overcome vortex impingement from preceding blade

Production example of the Sikorsky UH-60A Black Hawk combat assault helicopter

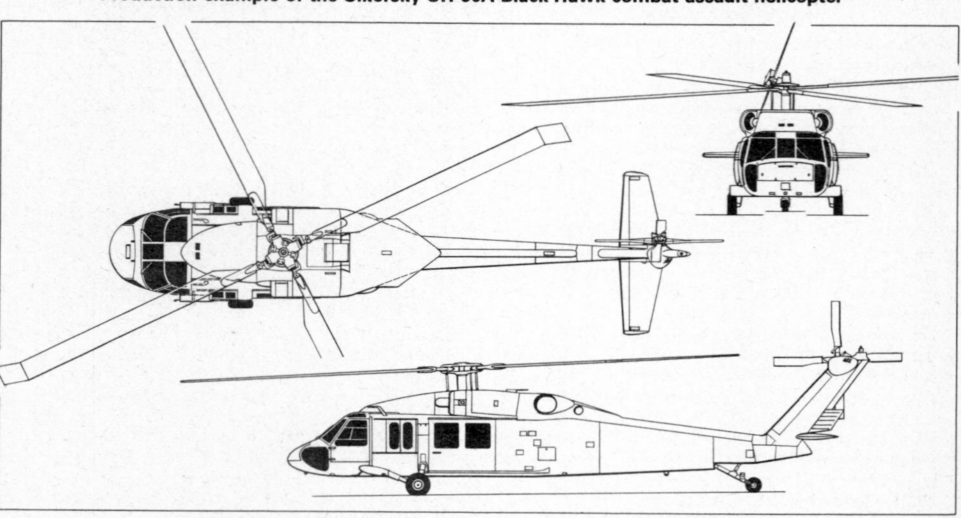

Sikorsky UH-60A Black Hawk combat assault helicopter *(Pilot Press)*

in cruising flight. Blade twist 18°. Blade tip swept back 20°. Each blade consists of an oval titanium spar, Nomex honeycomb core, graphite trailing-edge and root, covered with glassfibre, and with plastics leading-edge counterweight and titanium leading-edge sheath. Blades are tolerant to small arms damage, and are pressurised and equipped with gauges providing fail-safe confirmation of blade structural integrity. Electrically-heated de-icing mat in leading-edge of each blade. C/R Industries elastomeric rotor hub bearings require no lubrication, reduce hub maintenance by 60%. Bifilar self-tuning vibration absorbers on rotor head. Manual blade folding. Canting of tail rotor (20° to port) increases vertical lift and allows greater CG travel. 'Cross beam' four-blade tail rotor of composite materials, eliminating all rotor head bearings.

ROTOR DRIVE: Conventional transmission system with both turbines driving through freewheeling units to main gearbox. This is of modular construction to simplify maintenance. Transmission can operate for 30 min following total oil loss. Intermediate and tail rotor gearboxes oil lubricated.

FUSELAGE: Conventional semi-monocoque light alloy crashworthy structure.

TAIL UNIT: Pylon structure with port-canted tail rotor mounted on starboard side. Large variable-incidence tailplane has a control system which senses airspeed, collective-lever position, pitch-attitude rate and lateral acceleration. Tailplane is set at about +34° incidence in the hover, and −6° for autorotation. Tailplane moved by dual electric actuators, with manual backup.

LANDING GEAR: Non-retractable tailwheel type with single wheel on each unit. Energy-absorbing main gear with a tailwheel which gives protection for the tail rotor in taxying over rough terrain or during a high-flare landing. Axle assembly and main gear shock-absorbers by General Mechatronics.

POWER PLANT: Two 1,151 kW (1,543 shp) General Electric T700-GE-700 advanced technology turboshaft engines; combined transmission rating 2,109 kW (2,828 shp). Two crashworthy, bulletproof fuel tanks, with combined capacity of 1,340 litres (354 US gallons), aft of cabin.

ACCOMMODATION: Pilot and co-pilot on armour protected seats. Main cabin area open to cockpit to provide good communication with flight crew and forward view for squad commander. Accommodation for 11 troops and crew of three. Eight troop seats can be removed and replaced by four litters for medivac missions, or to make room for internal cargo. Cabin heated and ventilated. External cargo hook, having a 3,630 kg (8,000 lb) lift capability. Large aft-sliding door on each side of fuselage for rapid entry and exit. Electrical windscreen de-icing.

SYSTEMS: Solar T-62T-40-1 APU; AiResearch engine start system; Bendix 30/40kVA and 20/30kVA electric power generators; 17Ah nickel-cadmium battery. Engine fire extinguishing system.

AVIONICS: Include VHF/AM, VHF/FM and UHF/AM com, Singer Doppler, LF/ADF, AN/APR-39 radar warning receiver, SIF/IFF, and TSEC/KY-28 secure speech.

ARMAMENT AND OPERATIONAL EQUIPMENT: Provision for one or two M-60 side-firing machine-guns in forward area of cabin, infra-red jamming flares and XM-130 chaff dispenser.

DIMENSIONS, EXTERNAL:

Main rotor diameter	16·36 m (53 ft 8 in)
Tail rotor diameter	3·35 m (11 ft 0 in)
Length overall (rotors turning)	19·76 m (64 ft 10 in)
Fuselage length	15·26 m (50 ft 0¾ in)
Fuselage width	2·36 m (7 ft 9 in)
Height overall	5·13 m (16 ft 10 in)
Tailplane span	4·38 m (14 ft 4½ in)
Wheel track	2·70 m (8 ft 10¼ in)
Wheelbase	8·83 m (28 ft 11¾ in)
Cabin doors (each): Height	1·37 m (4 ft 6 in)
Width	1·75 m (5 ft 9 in)

DIMENSION, INTERNAL:

Cabin: Volume	10·90 m^3 (385 cu ft)

AREAS:

Main rotor blades (each)	4·34 m^2 (46·70 sq ft)
Tail rotor blades (each)	0·41 m^2 (4·45 sq ft)
Main rotor disc	210·05 m^2 (2,261 sq ft)
Tail rotor disc	8·83 m^2 (95·0 sq ft)

WEIGHTS:

Weight empty	4,955 kg (10,924 lb)
Mission T-O weight	7,474 kg (16,478 lb)
Max alternative T-O weight	9,185 kg (20,250 lb)

PERFORMANCE (at mission T-O weight, except where indicated):

Never-exceed speed	195 knots (361 km/h; 224 mph)
Max level speed at S/L	160 knots (296 km/h; 184 mph)
Max level speed at max T-O weight	158 knots (293 km/h; 182 mph)
Max cruising speed at 1,220 m (4,000 ft)	145 knots (269 km/h; 167 mph)
Single-engine cruising speed	109 knots (201 km/h; 125 mph)
Vertical rate of climb at S/L	over 137 m (450 ft)/min
Service ceiling	5,790 m (19,000 ft)
Hovering ceiling IGE (35°C)	2,895 m (9,500 ft)
Hovering ceiling OGE: ISA	3,170 m (10,400 ft)
35°C	1,705 m (5,600 ft)
Range at max T-O weight, 30 min reserves	324 nm (600 km; 373 miles)
Endurance	2·3 h

Artist's impression of Sikorsky EH-60B SOTAS variant of the Black Hawk

SIKORSKY S-70L

US Navy designation: SH-60B Seahawk

The S-70L, since designated SH-60B Seahawk, was Sikorsky's submission for the US Navy's LAMPS (Light Airborne Multi-Purpose System) Mk III competition, and was selected as the winner in September 1977 in preference to Boeing Vertol's Model 237.

Detail design of the Seahawk was initiated by a US Navy award to Sikorsky of a $2·7 million sustaining engineering contract. At the same time, General Electric was given a $547,000 contract for further development of the T700 advanced turboshaft engine to provide increased power and improved corrosion resistance, while a $17·9 million contract went to IBM Federal Systems to continue development of the avionics essential for the SH-60B to fulfil the LAMPS Mk III role. On 28 February 1978, it was announced that the US Department of Defense had authorised full-scale development of the SH-60B, and had awarded Sikorsky a $109·3 million contract for the development, manufacture and flight testing of five prototypes, plus a further airframe for ground testing.

Earlier, Sikorsky had updated the original UH-60A Black Hawk mockup to SH-60B configuration, and this was formally reviewed just prior to announcement of the contract award. In July and August 1978, this mockup was used for shipboard compatibility trials on board the frigate USS *Oliver Hazard Perry* (FFG-7) and the Spruance class destroyer USS *Arthur W. Radford* (DD-968). On 29 March 1979 it was announced that final assembly of the first Seahawk prototype had begun. Rollout took place on 30 August 1979; first flight was anticipated during December 1979. The second prototype was scheduled to start final assembly in July, with parts and major components for the remaining prototypes already in production.

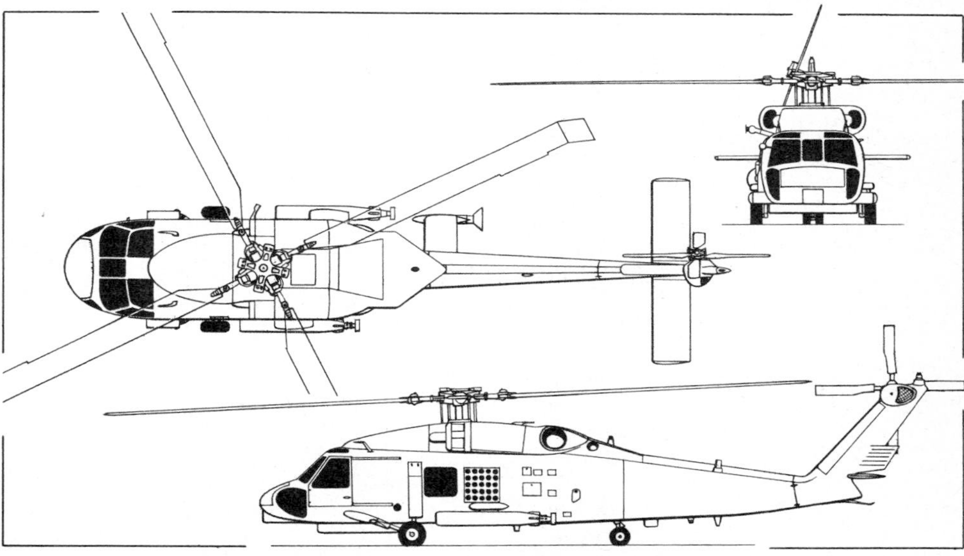

Sikorsky SH-60B Seahawk twin-turbine ASW/ASST helicopter *(Pilot Press)*

Prototype of the Sikorsky SH-60B Seahawk, developed to meet the US Navy's LAMPS Mk III requirement

In February 1979, the main transmission completed qualification testing, during which it was run at up to 2,685 kW (3,600 shp). This is 447 kW (600 shp) in excess of the Navy's mission performance specification. Aircraft lighting was reviewed in April by a team of contractor and US Navy engineers, with production equipment and instrumentation installed in the mockup. Fatigue testing of major dynamic components was scheduled for July 1979, followed by the start of fatigue testing of the airframe in September, completion of the static test aircraft also in September, and completion of the main rotor whirl test in October.

The US Navy has indicated a requirement for 204 of these helicopters for deployment on board Spruance class ASW destroyers, Aegis-equipped guided missile destroyers, and guided missile frigates in the class of the FFG-7 USS *Oliver Hazard Perry*. In addition to the LAMPS MK III primary missions of anti-submarine warfare (ASW) and anti-ship surveillance and targeting (ASST), the Seahawk is required also to perform secondary missions which include search and rescue (SAR), medical evacuation (Medevac) and vertical replenishment (Vertrep). It is intended for operational deployment in 1984.

Generally similar to the UH-60A Black Hawk, the Seahawk differs in the modifications necessary for shipboard compatibility and in the provision of avionics and equipment suitable for the naval mission. The former includes a rotor brake, automatic blade folding, folding tailplane and tail rotor pylon, a simplified short-wheelbase landing gear, sliding cabin door, and the introduction of recovery assist, secure and traversing (RAST) equipment for rapid hauldown of the helicopter on to a small deck in rough sea conditions, hovering in-flight refuelling capability, and buoyancy features. Modifications necessary for the mission requrement include the provision of a sensor operator's station, rescue hoist, chin-mounted pods for ESM equipment, pylons for two Mk 46 torpedoes or auxiliary fuel tanks, a pylon on the starboard side to carry MAD equipment, a sonobuoy launcher on the port side, an increased capacity fuel system, and deletion of armour for the pilot's and co-pilot's seats.

Type: Twin turbine ASW/ASST helicopter.

Rotor System: As for UH-60A, except that main rotor blades can be folded by electrical power, and a rotor brake is provided.

Rotor Drive: As for UH-60A.

Fuselage: As for UH-60A, except for inclusion of flotation bags and sealing of tailboom to provide buoyancy.

Tail Unit: As for UH-60A, except that the pylon structure can be folded to port pneumatically, eliminating the necessity to fold the tail rotor, and the tailplane folds upward.

Landing Gear: Non-retractable tailwheel type, with single wheels on main units and twin wheels on tail unit. Wheelbase shortened by 46·6%. Landing gear structure is less complex, since the SH-60B's vertical impact requirement is 71·5% below that of the UH-60A. Main-wheel tyres size 26 × 10·0-11; tailwheel tyres size 17·5 × 6·00-6. Multiple disc brakes.

Power Plant: Two 1,260 kW (1,690 shp) General Electric T700-GE-401 advanced technology turboshaft engines. Crash-resistant twin-cell fuel system in rear fuselage with total capacity of 2,241 litres (592 US gallons). Lower one-third of fuel cells is self-sealing. Single-point refuelling connection on port side. Hovering in-flight refuelling capability. Two auxiliary fuel tanks can be carried on fuselage pylons.

Accommodation: Pilot and co-pilot/ATO in cockpit, sensor operator in specially-equipped station. Sliding door with jettisonable window on starboard side. Accommodation is heated, ventilated and air-conditioned.

Systems: Generally as for UH-60A.

Avionics and Equipment: Avionics includes Collins AN/ARC-159 UHF and AN/ARC-174 HF com, Hazeltine AN/APX-76A active IFF, IBM AN/UYS-1 acoustic processor, Raytheon AN/ALQ-142 ESM, Teledyne Ryan AN/APN-217 Doppler, Texas Instruments AN/ASQ-81 MAD and AN/APS-124 search radar. Equipment includes a 25 tube pneumatic launcher for sonobuoys, and a rescue hoist for SAR operations.

Armament: Includes two Mk 46 torpedoes.

Dimensions, external:

Main rotor diameter	16·36 m (53 ft 8 in)
Tail rotor diameter	3·75 m (11 ft 0 in)
Blade chord, main rotor	0·53 m (1 ft 8·75 in)
Length overall (rotors turning)	19·76 m (64 ft 10 in)
Length overall (rotors and pylon folded)	12·51 m (41 ft 0·6 in)
Fuselage length	15·26 m (50 ft 0·75 in)
Width (rotors folded)	3·26 m (10 ft 8·5 in)
Height to top of rotor hub	3·79 m (12 ft 5·4 in)
Height overall	5·18 m (17 ft 0 in)
Height overall (pylon folded)	4·00 m (13 ft 1·5 in)
Tailplane span	4·37 m (14 ft 4 in)
Wheel track	2·79 m (9 ft 2 in)
Wheelbase	4·72 m (15 ft 5·7 in)

Areas:

Main rotor blades (each)	4·34 m² (46·70 sq ft)
Tail rotor blades (each)	0·41 m² (4·46 sq ft)
Main rotor disc	210·05 m² (2,261 sq ft)
Tail rotor disc	8·83 m² (95 sq ft)

Weights (estimated. A, ASW mission; B, ASST mission):

Weight empty, equipped: A, B	6,191 kg (13,648 lb)
Desired mission T-O weight: A	8,983 kg (19,804 lb)
B	8,148 kg (17,963 lb)
Max T-O weight: A	9,908 kg (21,844 lb)
B	9,926 kg (21,884 lb)

Performance (estimated, at mission T-O weight):

Max cruising speed at 1,525 m (5,000 ft), tropical conditions: A 135 knots (249 km/h; 155 mph)

Vertical rate of climb at S/L:

A 363 m (1,192 ft)/min

Rate of climb at S/L, one engine out:

A, B 235 m (770 ft)/min

SIKORSKY S-72 (RSRA)

Sikorsky announced in October 1973 that, following a design competition in which Bell Helicopter Textron also took part, it had been selected by NASA/US Army as prime contractor for a high-speed multi-purpose research helicopter which received the company designation S-72. A contract for the construction of two prototypes, one set of removable wings and a pair of podded turbofan engines was awarded to Sikorsky by NASA/US Army in January 1974. Known officially as Rotor Systems Research Aircraft (RSRA), these prototypes will be used by NASA and the US Army to develop and test a wide variety of rotor systems and integrated propulsion systems. They will provide test facilities that cannot be met in existing aircraft or wind tunnels, and will serve as a standardised base for comparing the various rotor systems. NASA and Army plans may call for the evaluation of composite bearingless, variable-geometry, gimballed, articulated, hingeless, circulation control, reverse velocity and jet flap rotors.

The fuselage of the S-72 is entirely new, designed to meet the unique requirements of the RSRA. It includes tail surfaces like those of a fixed-wing aircraft. The vertical surfaces are swept; conventional rudder and elevators are fitted, and there is a large ventral fin which carries the tailwheel. The five-blade anti-torque tail rotor is mounted on the port side of the fin.

Each S-72 is powered by two 1,044 kW (1,400 shp) General Electric T58-GE-5 turboshaft engines, driving initially a standard Sikorsky S-61 rotor system. Conversion from pure helicopter to compound form is achieved by fitting the set of full-length cantilever low-mounted wings, of NACA 63_2-415 section, and two 41·26 kN (9,275 lb st) General Electric TF34-GE-400A turbofan cruise engines in Lockheed S-3A Viking pods. The wings are fitted with conventional ailerons and flaps, and have adjustable incidence, over the range of −9° to +15°.

The wings and auxiliary engines are intended to permit the S-72 to test rotor systems that might be too small to support the aircraft, and will provide an extra margin of safety for the crew, comprising two pilots, side by side, and a flight engineer. In the event of trouble with a rotor system, the crew would be able to jettison the main blades by means of explosives and return to base by flying the S-72 as a conventional aircraft.

The S-72 is also equipped with a crew escape system that first severs the rotor blades and then extracts the three crewmen by igniting rockets on the backs of their Stanley Aviation extraction seats. This is an independent system that does not rely upon the aircraft for power.

Other features of the S-72 include accurate measuring systems to measure forces and moments on the rotor, wing, tail rotor and auxiliary engines; a fly-by-wire control system that operates through a mechanical backup system; an active vibration isolation system; and an electronic flight control system with an on-board digital computer to control the aircraft during research missions and carry out automatic, pre-programmed manoeuvres.

First flight of the first S-72 took place on 12 October 1976, in pure helicopter form, without wings or auxiliary turbofans. It completed its initial flight test phase in February 1977, after logging 14 hours in 21 flights, and was flown to NASA's Wallops Island Flight Center in Virginia on 21 July 1977. There it completed additional flight testing and was then delivered to NASA's Ames Research Center, Moffett Field, California, in February 1979. During 1979 it was undergoing its initial government research

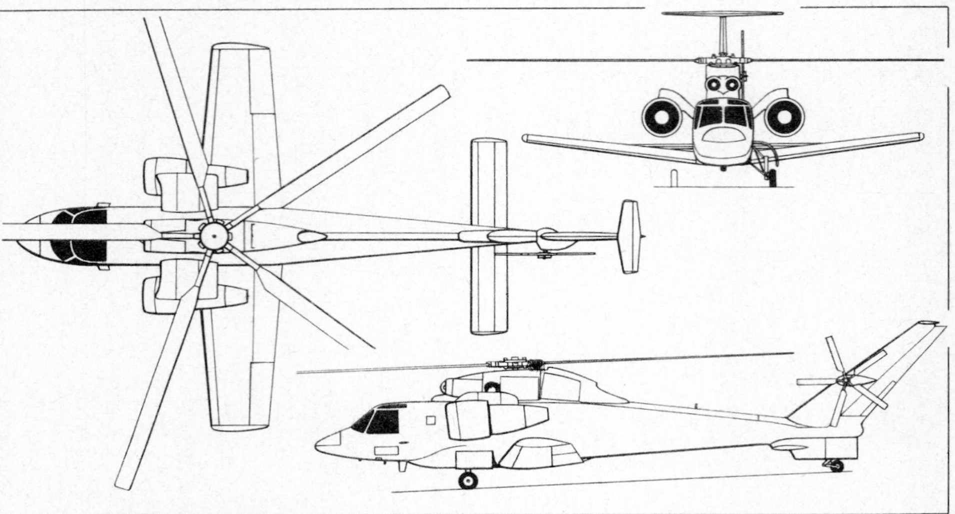

Compound version of Sikorsky S-72 research helicopter *(Pilot Press)*

S-72 in compound helicopter form, with auxiliary turbofans and fixed wings

programmes, in pure helicopter form. Meanwhile, the second S-72, in compound helicopter configuration, spent the first part of 1979 completing its contractor testing at NASA's Wallops Flight Center before joining the first aircraft at Moffett Field. The first flight of an S-72 as a compound helicopter, with two auxiliary turbofan engines and a full-span wing, was made on 10 April 1978. The aircraft have a potential service life of 12 years, and will be able to fly as pure helicopters, compound helicopters or fixed-wing aircraft, as required.

DIMENSIONS, EXTERNAL:
- Diameter of main rotor — 18·90 m (62 ft 0 in)
- Diameter of tail rotor — 3·25 m (10 ft 8 in)
- Main rotor blade chord — 0·46 m (1 ft 6¼ in)
- Wing span — 13·74 m (45 ft 1 in)
- Fuselage length — 21·51 m (70 ft 7 in)
- Height to top of rotor hub — 4·42 m (14 ft 6 in)
- Wheel track — 3·30 m (10 ft 10 in)

AREAS:
- Main rotor disc — 280·5 m² (3,019 sq ft)
- Tail rotor disc — 8·29 m² (89·2 sq ft)
- Wings, gross — 34·37 m² (370 sq ft)
- Upper tailplane:
  - helicopter — 3·29 m² (35·4 sq ft)
  - compound — 1·60 m² (17·2 sq ft)

WEIGHTS (estimated):
- Weight empty, helicopter configuration 6,572 kg (14,490 lb)
- Weight empty, compound configuration 9,535 kg (21,022 lb)
- Design T-O weight, helicopter configuration 8,346 kg (18,400 lb)
- Design T-O weight, compound configuration 11,884 kg (26,200 lb)

PERFORMANCE (estimated):
- Max level speed:
  - as pure helicopter 160 knots (296 km/h; 184 mph)
  - as compound helicopter 300 knots (555 km/h; 345 mph)

SIKORSKY S-76 SPIRIT

Sikorsky Aircraft announced on 19 January 1975 the company's decision to build a new 12-passenger twin-turbine commercial helicopter, as the first stage of a programme intended to give the company a bigger share of the civil aircraft market. The go-ahead for prototype construction followed a period of market research during which firm contracts were signed with numerous commercial operators, both in the USA and abroad.

Construction of four prototypes began in May 1976, and the first flight was made, by the No. 2 aircraft (N762SA), on 13 March 1977. Second prototype to fly, in late April 1977, was the No. 3 aircraft, and a further prototype was flown about a month later.

Designated Sikorsky S-76, the design conforms with FAR Part 29 Category A IFR. By designing and building to this standard, Sikorsky has produced a rugged and reliable civil helicopter, and one which can be taken 'off the shelf' to satisfy a wide variety of air transport missions. A version of the S-76 was proposed to meet the US Coast Guard requirement for an SRR (Short Range Recovery) helicopter, but Sikorsky announced on 26 March 1979 that the company was withdrawing from this competition.

The S-76 benefits from the design, research and development work carried out on the dynamic system of Sikorsky's UH-60A Black Hawk. The main rotor, for example, is a scaled-down version of that developed for the UH-60A. The power plant consists of two Allison 250-C30 turboshaft engines, a growth version of the current production Model 250-C20 which powers a number of important helicopters.

By 25 September 1979, a total of 265 Spirits had been ordered by approx 65 operators in 22 countries, half of them for offshore duties. Initial deliveries of fully certificated IFR production aircraft were made to Air Logistics of Lafayette, Louisiana, on 27 February 1979. It was anticipated that 40 Spirits would enter service during 1979.

TYPE: Twin-turbine general-purpose all-weather helicopter.

ROTOR SYSTEM: Four-blade main rotor. Each blade consists of a titanium spar, titanium leading-edge cover, nickel leading-edge abrasion strip, and glassfibre/nylon honeycomb trailing-edge. Blades have swept tips (30° on leading-edges, 10° on trailing-edges). Elastomeric rotor hub bearings which need no lubrication. Bifilar vibration absorbers on rotor head. Cross-beam four-blade tail rotor of composite materials. Rotor brake optional.

ROTOR DRIVE: Conventional transmission system, with both turbines driving through freewheeling units to main gearbox. Intermediate and tail rotor gearboxes are oil lubricated.

FUSELAGE: Composite structure, comprising glassfibre nose, light alloy honeycomb cabin, semi-monocoque light alloy tailcone and Kevlar fairings.

Sikorsky S-76 Spirit general-purpose commercial helicopter in service with Okanagan Helicopters

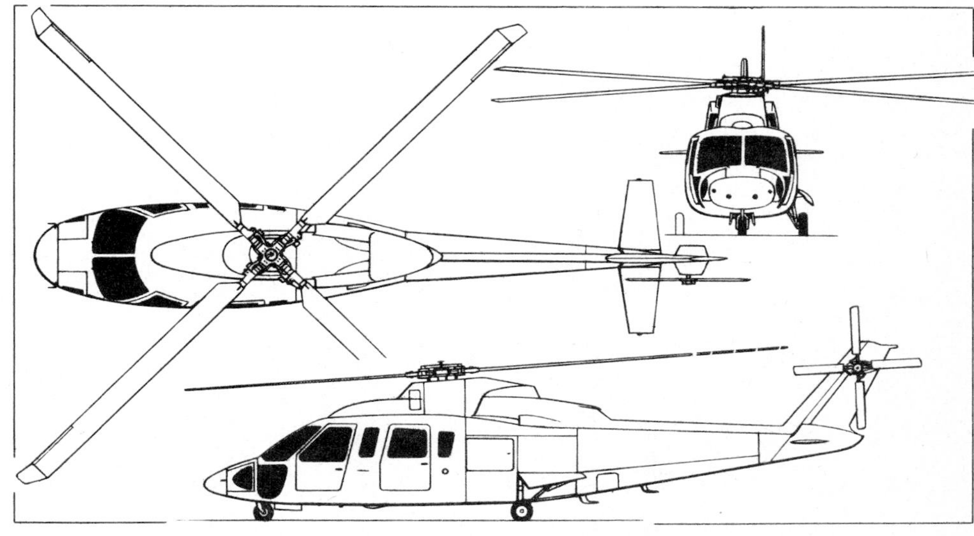

Sikorsky S-76 eight/twelve-passenger commercial transport helicopter *(Pilot Press)*

TAIL UNIT: Pylon structure with tail rotor on port side. All-moving tailplane, which serves also to protect passengers or ground crew from contact with tail rotor.

LANDING GEAR: Hydraulically-retractable tricycle type, with single wheel on each unit. Nosewheel retracts aft, main units inward into rear fuselage; all three units are enclosed by wheel doors when retracted. Main-wheel tyres size 14·5 × 5·5-6, nosewheel tyre size 13 × 5·00-4. Hydraulic brakes; hydraulic main-wheel parking brake.

POWER PLANT: Two 485 kW (650 shp) Allison 250-C30 turboshaft engines, mounted above the cabin aft of the main rotor shaft. Standard fuel system has a capacity of 1,060 litres (280 US gallons). Extended range fuel tanks and closed circuit refuelling optional.

ACCOMMODATION: Pilot and co-pilot plus a maximum of 12 passengers. In this configuration passengers are seated on three four-abreast rows of seats, floor-mounted at a pitch of 79 cm (31 in). A number of executive layouts are available, including a four-passenger 'Office-in-the-Sky' configuration. Executive versions will have luxurious interior trim, full carpeting, special soundproofing, radio-telephone, and co-ordinated furniture. Dual controls optional. Two large doors on each side of fuselage, hinged at their forward edges. Baggage hold aft of cabin, with external access door on each side of the fuselage. Cabin heated and ventilated. Windscreen demisting and dual windscreen wipers. Windscreen heating optional. Optional external cargo hook with capacity of 1,814 kg (4,000 lb).

SYSTEMS: Hydraulic system at pressure of 207 bars (3,000 lb/sq in) supplied by two pumps driven from main gearbox. Electrical system comprises one Lucas 7·5kVA gearbox-driven generator, two 200A starter/generators, one 115V 600VA 400Hz static inverter and 24V 17Ah nickel-cadmium battery. Engine fire detection and extinguishing system.

AVIONICS AND EQUIPMENT: Standard equipment includes provision for dual controls; cabin fire extinguishers; cockpit, cabin, instrument, navigation and anti-collision lights; landing light; external power socket; first aid kit; and utility soundproofing. VHF com transceiver and intercom system standard. Optional equipment includes air-conditioning, cargo hook, rescue hoist, emergency flotation gear, engine air particle separators, full IFR instrumentation, litter installation and stability augmentation system. Wide range of optional avionics available, according to configuration, including VHF nav receivers, transponder, compass system, weather radar, flight director system, radar altimeter, ADF, DME, VLF nav system and ELT and sonic transmitters.

DIMENSIONS, EXTERNAL:
- Diameter of main rotor — 13·41 m (44 ft 0 in)
- Main rotor blade chord — 0·39 m (1 ft 3½ in)
- Diameter of tail rotor — 2·44 m (8 ft 0 in)
- Tail rotor blade chord — 0·16 m (6½ in)
- Length overall, rotors turning — 16·00 m (52 ft 6 in)
- Height overall — 4·41 m (14 ft 5¾ in)
- Tailplane span — 2·95 m (9 ft 8 in)
- Length of fuselage — 13·44 m (44 ft 1 in)
- Width of fuselage — 2·13 m (7 ft 0 in)
- Wheel track — 2·44 m (8 ft 0 in)
- Wheelbase — 5·00 m (16 ft 5 in)

DIMENSIONS, INTERNAL:
- Cabin: Length — 2·46 m (8 ft 1 in)
  - Max width — 1·93 m (6 ft 4 in)
  - Max height — 1·35 m (4 ft 5 in)
  - Floor area — 5·30 m² (57 sq ft)
  - Volume — 5·78 m³ (204 cu ft)
- Baggage compartment volume — 1·08 m³ (38 cu ft)

AREAS:
- Main rotor disc — 116·77 m² (1,257 sq ft)
- Tail rotor disc — 4·67 m² (50·27 sq ft)
- Tailplane — 2·00 m² (21·5 sq ft)

WEIGHTS AND LOADING:
- Weight empty, standard equipment 2,392 kg (5,273 lb)
- Max T-O weight — 4,536 kg (10,000 lb)
- Max disc loading — 38·9 kg/m² (7·96 lb/sq ft)

PERFORMANCE (A: at gross weight of 4,536 kg; 10,000 lb. B: at gross weight of 3,810 kg; 8,400 lb):
- Max cruising speed:
  - A — 145 knots (269 km/h; 167 mph)
  - B — 155 knots (286 km/h; 178 mph)
- Cruising speed for max range:
  - A — 125 knots (232 km/h; 144 mph)
- Max rate of climb at S/L — 411 m (1,350 ft)/min
- Service ceiling: A — 4,570 m (15,000 ft)
- Service ceiling, one engine out:
  - A — 1,890 m (6,200 ft)
  - B — 3,445 m (11,300 ft)
- Hovering ceiling IGE: A — 1,890 m (6,200 ft)
  - B — 3,415 m (11,200 ft)
- Range with 12 passengers, standard fuel, 30 min reserves 404 nm (748 km; 465 miles)
- Range with 8 passengers, auxiliary fuel and offshore equipment 600 nm (1,112 km; 691 miles)

SPECIALIZED AIRCRAFT—*See Tri Turbo Corporation*

SPITFIRE
SPITFIRE HELICOPTER COMPANY LTD

Address: PO Box 61, Media, Pennsylvania 19063
Telephone: (215) 565 2986
Telex: 831750
President: John J. Fetsko

Spitfire Helicopter Company began in January 1975 the design of a new lightweight helicopter known as the Spitfire Mark I. Evolved from the basic design of the Enstrom F-28A, this has a turbine power plant instead of the Lycoming piston engine of the original aircraft. The drive from the turbine passes via a reduction gear, instead of through multiple vee belts, showing a weight saving of 91 kg (200 lb), as well as freeing space which can be utilised for additional cargo or auxiliary fuel. Construction of the prototype began in January 1976, and of pre-production aircraft in February 1977.

The company has designed, and is building, the prototype of an improved four-seat version designated Spitfire Mark II. It has also projected a completely new four-seat helicopter with stub wings, designated Spitfire Mark III; and an advanced version of the same design with stub wings of increased span and area, and with an auxiliary propulsion engine mounted at the rear of the fuselage. In this version reversible ducted fans, mounted at the tip of each stub wing, will replace the tail rotor for torque control. This design has the designation Spitfire Mark IV.

On 12 August 1978, Spitfire concluded an agreement with the Polish aircraft marketing organisation Pezetel, under which Spitfire received limited rights to distribute the WSK-PZL Swidnik (Mil) Mi-2 twin-turbine helicopter in western markets. Spitfire refers to this aircraft as the Taurus 2, although this name is not approved by PZL Swidnik.

SPITFIRE MARK I

Type: Three-seat turbine-powered light helicopter.

Rotor System: Fully-articulated metal three-blade main rotor. Blades of bonded light alloy construction, each attached to rotor hub by retention pin and drag link. Blade section NACA 00135. Two-blade teetering tail rotor, with blades of bonded light alloy construction. Blades do not fold. Rotor brake optional.

Rotor Drive: Shaft drive to both main and tail rotors through reduction gear. Main rotor/engine rpm ratio 1 : 18·2. Tail rotor/engine rpm ratio 1 : 2·54.

Fuselage: Glassfibre and light alloy cab structure, with welded steel tube centre-section. Semi-monocoque light alloy tailcone structure.

Landing Gear: Skids, carried on oleo-pneumatic shock-absorbers.

Power Plant: One 313 kW (420 shp) Allison 250-C20B turboshaft engine, derated to 179 kW (240 shp) for take-off. Total standard fuel capacity 265 litres (70 US gallons).

Accommodation: Pilot and two passengers, side by side on bench seat. Fully-transparent removable door on each side of cabin. Baggage compartment of 0·57 m³ (20 cu ft) capacity forward of engine compartment, with external access door on each side of fuselage. Helicopter can be operated with these doors removed to permit loading of outsize cargo. Cabin heated and ventilated.

System: Electrical system is supplied by a 28V DC engine-driven generator and 24V nickel-cadmium battery.

Avionics and Equipment: Various nav/com systems available to customer's requirements. IFR provisions. Cargo hook and litters optional. It is intended to make available survey and agricultural equipment.

Dimensions, external:
Diameter of main rotor	9·75 m (32 ft 0 in)
Diameter of tail rotor	1·42 m (4 ft 8 in)
Distance between rotor centres	5·56 m (18 ft 3 in)
Main rotor blade chord	0·241 m (9½ in)
Length overall	8·96 m (29 ft 4¾ in)
Height overall	2·79 m (9 ft 2 in)
Skid track	2·36 m (7 ft 9 in)
Cabin doors (each): Height	1·09 m (3 ft 7 in)
Width	1·02 m (3 ft 4 in)
Height to sill	0·61 m (2 ft 0 in)

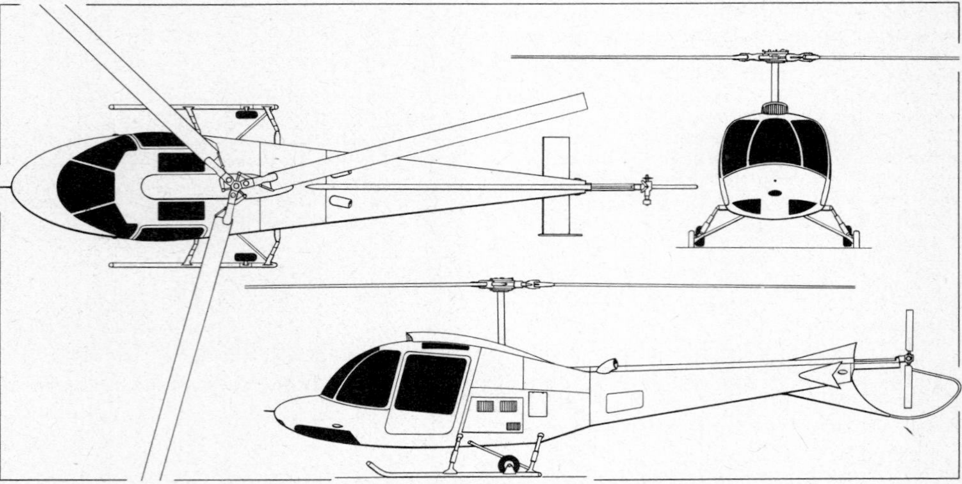

Spitfire Mark II four-seat light helicopter *(Pilot Press)*

Artist's impression of close support version of the Spitfire Mark IV helicopter *(Howard Levy)*

Areas:
Main rotor blades (each)	2·22 m² (23·94 sq ft)
Main rotor disc	74·69 m² (804 sq ft)
Tail rotor disc	1·59 m² (17·1 sq ft)

Weights and Loadings:
Weight empty	567 kg (1,250 lb)
Max T-O weight	1,043 kg (2,300 lb)
Max disc loading	13·97 kg/m² (2·86 lb/sq ft)
Max power loading	5·83 kg/kW (9·58 lb/shp)

Performance (at max T-O weight):
Never-exceed speed	112 knots (208 km/h; 129 mph)
Max level speed	112 knots (208 km/h; 129 mph)
Cruising speed	95·5 knots (177 km/h; 110 mph)
Max rate of climb at S/L	472 m (1,550 ft)/min
Service ceiling	4,570 m (15,000 ft)
Hovering ceiling IGE	4,085 m (13,400 ft)
Hovering ceiling OGE	2,440 m (8,000 ft)
Range with max fuel	390 nm (724 km; 450 miles)

SPITFIRE MARK II

Information available indicates that the Mark II version of the Spitfire helicopter is generally similar to the production Mark I, except that more power is available at take-off from the derated Allison turboshaft engine, and that fuselage dimensions have been increased to cater for an additional seat.

The description of the Spitfire Mark I applies also to the Mark II, except as follows:

Type: Four-seat turbine-powered light helicopter.

Landing Gear: As for Mark I, except that ground handling wheels are provided.

Accommodation: Pilot at front and three passengers side by side on rear bench seat. Cabin door on starboard side of fuselage. Baggage space in fuselage, aft of cabin, with external access door on each side; baggage volume 0·57 m³ (20 cu ft). Cabin heated and ventilated.

Dimensions, external: As for Spitfire Mk I, except:
Length overall	9·30 m (30 ft 6 in)

Weights and Loading (estimated):
Weight empty	601 kg (1,325 lb)
Max T-O weight	1,134 kg (2,500 lb)
Max disc loading	13·96 kg/m² (3·11 lb/sq ft)

Performance (estimated, at max T-O weight):
Max level speed	117 knots (217 km/h; 135 mph)
Cruising speed	104 knots (193 km/h; 120 mph)
Max rate of climb at S/L	472 m (1,550 ft)/min
Service ceiling	4,570 m (15,000 ft)
Hovering ceiling IGE	4,085 m (13,400 ft)
Hovering ceiling OGE	2,440 m (8,000 ft)
Max endurance	4 h

SPITFIRE MARK IV

The accompanying illustration shows a projected military version of the Spitfire Mark IV, of which first details were given by Spitfire Helicopter Company at the Helicopter Association of America's 1979 convention in Las Vegas. The aircraft would be powered by two Allison 250-C20B turboshaft engines, driving both the four-blade rotor and a pair of reversible ducted fans, mounted at the tips of stub-wings and dispensing with the need for a tail rotor for torque control. Armament is intended to comprise an underfuselage gun turret and four air-to-surface guided missiles.

SUMMIT
SUMMIT AVIATION INC

Address: Middletown, Delaware 19709
Telephone: (302) 834 5400
Telex: 83-5499

SUMMIT SENTRY O2-337

Summit Aviation is producing for sale to military customers a version of the Cessna Model T337 which is suitable for a wide range of missions. These include forward air control, helicopter escort, light air-to-ground attack, convoy protection, maritime patrol, six-seat personnel carrier, light cargo transport, aerial photography, psychological warfare and airborne discharge. Special configurations are available for VIP transport, medevac, and high-altitude missions. In all configurations day or night capability can be provided.

Summit's modifications, to fit this aircraft for the specific role required by the customer, begin with the purchase of a new Model T337 from the Cessna Aircraft Company. Power plant of this version comprises two 168 kW (225 hp) Continental TSIO-360 turbocharged flat-six engines, and details of the basic airframe can be found under the Cessna entry in this edition.

With four standard NATO MALL-4A pylons mounted beneath the wings, each able to carry a max load of 159 kg (350 lb), the Summit Sentry can carry weapons which include SUU-11A/A 7·62 mm gun pods; FFV UNI 12·75 mm gun pods; LAU-32A/A, 32B/A, 59A, 68A and 68B/A rocket launchers; CBU-14, SUU-14/A containers and bombs, LUU 1B, 5B, and Mod 6 Mk 3 markers; Mk 24 flares; ADSID; and a combined search radar and speaker system.

Available specification and performance details are as follows:

Weights:
Weight empty, approx	1,433 kg (3,160 lb)
Max T-O weight	2,359 kg (5,200 lb)
Max landing weight	2,200 kg (4,850 lb)

Performance (at max T-O weight):
Max level speed at S/L	163 knots (302 km/h; 188 mph)
Max level speed at 3,050 m (10,000 ft)	179 knots (332 km/h; 206 mph)
Max cruising speed at S/L	150 knots (278 km/h; 173 mph)
Max cruising speed at 1,525 m (5,000 ft)	155 knots (287 km/h; 178 mph)
Max cruising speed at 3,050 m (10,000 ft)	165 knots (306 km/h; 190 mph)
Max rate of climb at S/L	335 m (1,100 ft)/min
Service ceiling	8,690 m (28,500 ft)
T-O run	164 m (538 ft)
Landing run	137 m (449 ft)
Range, at 75% power with 560 litres (148 US gallons) usable fuel	955 nm (1,770 km; 1,100 miles)
Max range, long range cruise power, fuel as above	1,175 nm (2,177 km; 1,353 miles)

SWEARINGEN

SWEARINGEN AVIATION CORPORATION (a subsidiary of Fairchild Industries)

ADDRESS: PO Box 32486, San Antonio, Texas 78284
Telephone: (512) 824 9421
Telex: 767-315
CHAIRMAN: E. J. Swearingen
PRESIDENT: C. J. Stathis
EXECUTIVE VICE-PRESIDENT: W. Daniel Heidt
VICE-PRESIDENTS:
R. D. Busey (Treasurer)
Don Howard (Operations)
R. E. McKelvey (Engineering)
Salvatore J. Mira (Contracts)
Richard N. Robinson (Marketing)

In a joint announcement, made on 2 November 1971, Fairchild Industries and Swearingen Aircraft gave details of an agreement under which a new subsidiary of Fairchild, to be known as Swearingen Aviation Corporation, would acquire the assets of Swearingen Aircraft. Mr Edward J. Swearingen, founder and Chief Executive Officer of Swearingen Aircraft, became Chairman of the new company.

At that stage, 90% of the stock was owned by Fairchild Industries. On 4 January 1979, Fairchild announced the acquisition of the remaining 10% interest in Swearingen Aviation Corporation, making this latter company a wholly-owned subsidiary.

Since 1966 Swearingen has been engaged in the manufacture of the Merlin series of twin-turboprop pressurised executive transport aircraft and the Metro airliner. A total of 354 Merlins and Metros of all models had been delivered throughout the world by January 1979. Production was then at a rate of six aircraft per month.

Over the next two years this rate is to be doubled to 12 a month, and the company's manufacturing facilities are being increased by about 50% to permit this.

SWEARINGEN MERLIN IIIB

The Merlin IIIB eight/eleven-seat all-weather pressurised executive transport differs from the earlier Merlin III by having additional windows, major system and flight deck improvements and a wide selection of new interiors. The original Merlin III received FAA certification on 27 July 1970, and was described in the 1974-75 *Jane's*. The later Merlin IIIA was described in the 1977-78 edition.

A total of 92 Merlin IIIs and IIIAs had been delivered by 1 January 1979, by which time production had ended, following introduction of the Merlin IIIB. Customers included the Belgian Air Force, and the Argentine Army and Air Force.

The Merlin IIIB, which received FAA Type Approval on 3 November 1978, has interior and exterior refinements and is powered by uprated TPE 331 engines. Exterior improvements include reshaped wing root/fuselage fairings, new tailplane leading-edge contours, new rudder bias system, and large-diameter four-blade propellers fitted with a noise-reducing synchrophaser system. Internally, cabin comfort is improved by movable seating and a new environmental control system. Significant performance improvements were announced in September 1979, as a result of further test flying, together with an increase in max landing weight.

Delivery of the first Merlin IIIB was made on 1 December 1978. The first example exported to Europe (D-IBBB) set a class C1e distance record of 3,298 nm (6,108 km; 3,795 miles), subject to confirmation, during delivery, from Teterboro, New Jersey, to Cologne-Bonn Airport, Germany, on 5-6 January 1979.

TYPE: Eight/eleven-seat twin-turboprop executive transport.

WINGS: As for Metro II, but with improved wing root/fuselage fairings.

FUSELAGE: Cylindrical all-metal fail-safe structure, flush-riveted throughout. Glassfibre honeycomb nose-cap will accommodate a 0·38 m (15 in) weather radar antenna.

TAIL UNIT: Cantilever all-metal structure with sweptback vertical and horizontal surfaces. Dorsal fin, with tailplane mounted approximately one-third up from base of fin. Small ventral fin. Pneumatic de-icing boots on tailplane leading-edges.

LANDING GEAR: As for Metro II.

POWER PLANT: Two 671 kW (900 shp) Garrett-AiResearch TPE 331-10U-501G turboprop engines, each driving a Hartzell four-blade fully-feathering and reversible-pitch metal propeller fitted with synchrophaser. Continuous alcohol/water injection system optional. Integral fuel tank in each wing, each with a usable capacity of 1,226 litres (324 US gallons): total usable fuel capacity 2,452 litres (648 US gallons). Refuelling points in each outer wing panel. Engine inlet de-icing by bleed air.

ACCOMMODATION: Crew of two on flight deck, with dual controls. Bulkhead with sliding door divides flight deck from cabin. Standard accommodation for six to nine passengers with seats disposed on each side of a central aisle. Rapid relocation of seats and couches is made possible by continuous tracks recessed into floor, permitting layout to be varied according to mission. Large 360° rotating chairs, with retracting arms and reclining backs, are optional; these chairs track laterally and fore and aft. Passenger door at rear of cabin on port side, with integral airstair. Emergency exit on starboard side of cabin.

SYSTEMS: Electronic temperature control system. Dual, totally redundant cooling/heating systems. Cabin pressure differential 0·48 bars (7·0 lb/sq in). Conrac stall avoidance system, with nose-mounted stall vane. Otherwise generally similar to Metro II except that automatic water-methanol system is not installed.

Swearingen Merlin IIIB eight/eleven-seat twin-turboprop executive transport

DIMENSIONS, EXTERNAL:
Wing span 14·10 m (46 ft 3 in)
Wing chord at root 2·62 m (8 ft 7 in)
Wing chord at tip 1·04 m (3 ft 5 in)
Wing aspect ratio 7·71
Length overall 12·85 m (42 ft 1·9 in)
Height overall 5·12 m (16 ft 9½ in)
Tailplane span 4·61 m (15 ft 1½ in)
Wheel track 4·57 m (15 ft 0 in)
Wheelbase 3·23 m (10 ft 7 in)
Propeller diameter 2·69 m (8 ft 10 in)
Propeller ground clearance 0·305 m (1 ft 0 in)
Passenger door: Height 1·35 m (4 ft 5 in)
Width 0·64 m (2 ft 1 in)

DIMENSIONS, INTERNAL:
Length, incl flight deck and rear utility section 6·93 m (22 ft 9 in)
Passenger cabin:
Length, incl rear utility section 5·31 m (17 ft 5 in)
Width 1·57 m (5 ft 2 in)
Height 1·45 m (4 ft 9 in)
Volume, incl rear utility section 9·09 m³ (321 cu ft)
Baggage volume (total) 2·97 m³ (105 cu ft)

AREA:
Wings, gross 25·78 m² (277·50 sq ft)

WEIGHTS AND LOADINGS:
Weight empty, equipped 3,538 kg (7,800 lb)
Fuel load 1,969 kg (4,342 lb)
Max T-O weight 5,670 kg (12,500 lb)
Max ramp weight 5,715 kg (12,600 lb)
Max zero-fuel weight 4,535 kg (10,000 lb)
Max landing weight 5,670 kg (12,500 lb)
Max wing loading 219·7 kg/m² (45·0 lb/sq ft)
Max power loading 4·22 kg/kW (6·94 lb/shp)

PERFORMANCE (at max T-O weight except where indicated):
Max cruising speed at 3,660 m (12,000 ft), and at AUW of 4,535 kg (10,000 lb) 309 knots (571 km/h; 355 mph)
Stalling speed, flaps and wheels up 103 knots (191 km/h; 119 mph) IAS
Stalling speed, flaps and wheels down 89 knots (164 km/h; 102 mph) IAS
Max rate of climb at S/L 848 m (2,782 ft)/min
Service ceiling 9,570 m (31,400 ft)
Max operating altitude 9,450 m (31,000 ft)
T-O to 15 m (50 ft) at S/L, ISA 904 m (2,965 ft)
Landing from 15 m (50 ft) at S/L, ISA 996 m (3,266 ft)
Range with max fuel at econ cruising speed, IFR reserves 2,464 nm (4,567 km; 2,838 miles)

SWEARINGEN MERLIN IVA

The Merlin IVA is a corporate version of the Metro II commuter airliner, to which it is generally similar. It differs principally in its internal configuration, which provides accommodation for 12 to 15 passengers, with a private toilet and a baggage volume of 4·05 m³ (143 cu ft). Initial deliveries of the earlier Merlin IV (1974-75 *Jane's*) were made in 1970, following FAA certification on 23 September that year. A total of 50 Merlin IV/IVAs had been delivered by 1 January 1979.

The description of the Metro applies also to the Merlin IVA, except for some variation in the systems. In particular, usable fuel capacity is 2,096 litres (554 US gallons).

DIMENSIONS, EXTERNAL: As for Metro II

DIMENSIONS, INTERNAL:
Cabin, excl flight deck and aft baggage compartment:
Length 7·75 m (25 ft 5 in)
Baggage compartment: Length 2·34 m (7 ft 8 in)
Volume 4·05 m³ (143 cu ft)

AREAS: As for Metro II

WEIGHTS AND LOADINGS:
Weight empty, equipped 3,719 kg (8,200 lb)
Max T-O, landing and zero-fuel weight 5,670 kg (12,500 lb)
Max ramp weight 5,715 kg (12,600 lb)
Max wing loading 219·7 kg/m² (45·0 lb/sq ft)
Max power loading 4·53 kg/kW (7·44 lb/shp)

PERFORMANCE (at max T-O weight): As for Metro II, except:
Max cruising speed at 4,875 m (16,000 ft) 269 knots (499 km/h; 310 mph)
Econ cruising speed at 8,535 m (28,000 ft) 240 knots (444 km/h; 276 mph)
Range with max fuel at max cruising speed, 45 min reserves 1,367 nm (2,534 km; 1,575 miles)
Ferry range with max fuel at econ cruising speed, 45 min reserves 1,819 nm (3,371 km; 2,095 miles)

SWEARINGEN MERLIN MARITIME SURVEILLANCE AIRCRAFT

Swearingen announced on 6 August 1979 the availability of a new multi-mission aircraft, configured specifically for maritime surveillance, which has been developed from the Metro II commuter airliner. FAA certification in the Restricted category for operation of the Metro II or Merlin IVA as special mission aircraft, at a max T-O weight of 6,350 kg (14,000 lb), was announced as long ago as 9 March 1978, and since that time the company has been developing this maritime surveillance version. Its basic structure is generally similar to that of the Metro II, but is readily identifiable externally by the addition of a rotatable searchlight in the fuselage nose, a blister radome housing the search radar antenna beneath the centre-fuselage, and a large bubble window for an observer mounted on the starboard side of the rear fuselage.

The pressurised cabin of this aircraft provides ample accommodation for a crew of seven and all avionics/surveillance equipment essential for the maritime mission, but is designed also for quick conversion for passenger,

Swearingen Merlin IVA, a corporate version of the Metro II commuter airliner

cargo, or other roles. All special mission equipment can be removed or exchanged when the aircraft is used for other applications.

The basic description of the Metro II applies also to this aircraft, except as detailed below:

TYPE: Twin-turboprop multi-mission aircraft.

WINGS: As for Metro II.

FUSELAGE: As for Metro II, except rotatable searchlight mounted in nose.

TAIL UNIT, LANDING GEAR, POWER PLANT: As for Metro II.

ACCOMMODATION: Crew of seven, comprising pilot and co-pilot; navigator/flight co-ordinator, seated on starboard side of cabin, just forward of the wing; two observers, one on starboard side adjacent to bubble window, one at camera position on fuselage centreline, slightly forward of first observer; and two relief crew on port side, one seated overwing and one just aft of the wing. Dual controls standard. Navigator's console on port side, forward of wing. Scanner console and other avionics equipment on starboard side, aft of wing. Camera installation on fuselage centreline. Toilet compartment at rear of cabin on starboard side. Integral-step passenger door on port side of fuselage, immediately aft of pilot's position. Large outward-opening cargo door on port side of fuselage at rear of cabin, hinged at top, and with inward opening drop door forming the centre of cargo door. Two emergency exits overwing, one on each side. Cabin air-conditioned and pressurised. Electrical windscreen de-icing. Windscreen wipers.

SYSTEMS: Generally as for Metro II.

EQUIPMENT: Includes Wild NF-2 or Zeiss NT-2 navigation sight; Zeiss RMKA 8·5/23 camera, or Wild RC-10 camera, with 0·61 × 0·61 m (2 ft × 2 ft) optical glass; Agiflite hand-held camera; Locator Model B or Radiation Corporation rotatable searchlight; and 15-man droppable liferaft.

AVIONICS: Includes Litton AN/APS-504 (V) search radar, with 1·07 × 0·46 m (3 ft 6 in × 1 ft 6 in) flat-plate antenna; Bendix M²S modular multiband scanner, or Daedalus DS-1220 infra-red scanner; thermal reference unit, signal processing unit, power supply, and stabilising gyro for M²S system, or film recorder, scanner control, tape machine, and power supply for DS-1220 system; Decca ground speed and drift meter; Decca TANS computer display; Decca 72 Doppler; Collins VHF 20-B transceiver; Collins 718U-5 HF transceiver; Collins ARC-159-V-1 UHF transceiver; Global Navigation Inc GNS-500A-VLF/Omega navigation system, or Litton LTN-72 INS; ground stabilisation interface unit; control and display unit for VLF/Omega or INS; azimuth/range indicator; and radar control unit.

DIMENSIONS, AREAS: As for Metro II.

WEIGHT:
Max T-O weight 6,350 kg (14,000 lb)

PERFORMANCE (at max T-O weight):
Max cruising speed 250 knots (463 km/h; 288 mph)
Low altitude loiter speed 133 knots (246 km/h; 153 mph)
Range with max fuel 1,758 nm (3,257 km; 2,024 miles)

SWEARINGEN MODEL SA-226TC METRO II

The Metro II is a 19/20-passenger all-weather pressurised, air-conditioned airliner, certificated under Special Federal Air Regulation 23. The standard aircraft has an easily convertible passenger/cargo interior with special kits available for conversion to an executive interior, air ambulance with up to 10 litters, hospital equipped for on-board emergency operations, and single or dual camera photographic configuration. An all-cargo configuration is available, with 286 kg (630 lb) additional payload and without windows and passenger amenities.

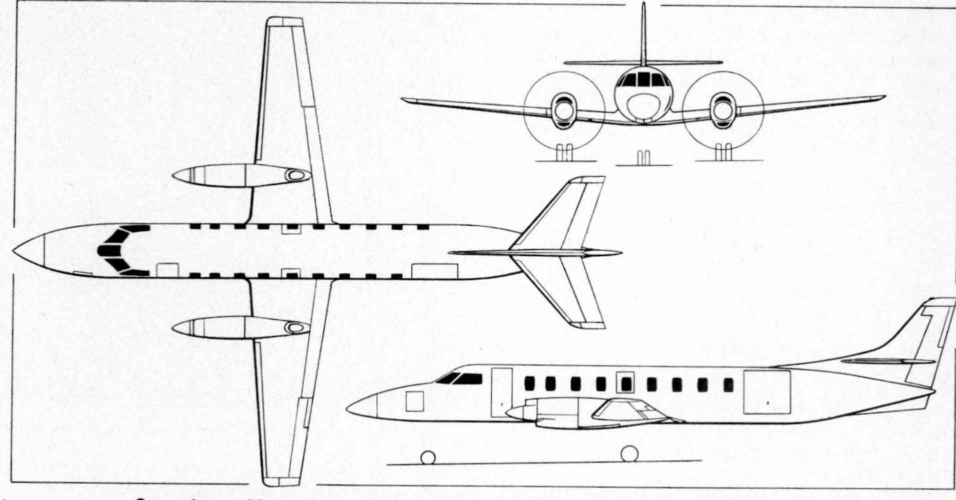

Swearingen Metro II nineteen/twenty-passenger commuter airliner *(Pilot Press)*

The Metro II differs from the earlier Metro (1974-75 *Jane's*) by the introduction of larger windows and major systems and flight deck improvements.

A total of 86 Metros/Metro IIs had been delivered by 1 January 1979. Total number in service or on order on 10 September 1979 was more than 160, for 21 airlines in the USA and 12 in Canada, Australia, Europe, the Middle East and South America.

TYPE: Twin-turboprop 19/20-passenger commuter airliner.

WINGS: Cantilever low-wing monoplane. Wing section NACA 65_2A215 at root, NACA 64_2A415 at tip. Dihedral 5°. Incidence 1° at root, −1° at tip. Sweepback at quarter-chord 0·9°. All-metal two-spar semi-monocoque fail-safe structure of aluminium alloy. Hydraulically-operated double-slotted trailing-edge flaps. Manually-controlled trim tab in port aileron. Goodrich pneumatic de-icing boots on wing leading-edges, with automatic bleed air cycling system.

FUSELAGE: All-metal cylindrical semi-monocoque fail-safe structure of aluminium alloy. Glassfibre honeycomb nose cap can accommodate a 0·45 m (18 in) weather radar antenna.

TAIL UNIT: Cantilever all-metal structure with sweptback vertical surfaces and dorsal fin. Electrically-adjustable variable-incidence tailplane. Manually-controlled rudder trim. Goodrich pneumatic de-icing boots on tailplane leading-edges, with automatic bleed air cycling system.

LANDING GEAR: Retractable tricycle type with twin wheels on each unit. Hydraulic retraction, with dual actuators on each unit. All wheels retract forward, main gear into engine nacelles, nosewheels into fuselage. Ozone Aircraft Systems oleo-pneumatic shock-absorber struts. Nosewheel steerable. Free-fall emergency extension system, with backup of hand-operated hydraulic pump. B.F. Goodrich main wheels and tyres, size 18 × 5·50, type VII, pressure 6·90 bars (100 lb/sq in). Jay-Em nosewheels and Goodyear tyres, size 16 × 4·40, type VII, pressure 5·86 bars (85 lb/sq in). Low-pressure tyres optional. Goodrich self-adjusting hydraulically-operated disc brakes. Heavy duty brakes and anti-skid system optional.

POWER PLANT: Two 701 kW (940 shp) Garrett-AiResearch TPE 331-3UW-303G turboprop engines with automatic emergency water-methanol system, each driving a Hartzell three-blade fully-feathering and reversible-pitch propeller with automatic synchronisation. Integral fuel tank in each wing, each with a usable capacity of 1,226 litres (324 US gallons). Total usable fuel capacity 2,452 litres (648 US gallons). Refuelling point on each outer wing panel. Oil capacity 15·1 litres (4 US gallons). Engine inlet de-icing by bleed air. Oil cooler inlet anti-icing by hot oil. Electrical propeller de-icing. Automatic fuel heating system to prevent filter icing. Flush-mounted fuel vents. Single-point rapid drain provisions. Optional JATO (single 1·56 kN; 350 lb st rocket) and continuous alcohol and water injection for 'hot and high' operations.

ACCOMMODATION: Crew of two on flight deck, separated from passenger/cargo area by arm-level curtain. Dual controls standard. Bulkhead between cabin and flight deck optional. Standard accommodation for 19-20 passengers seated two abreast, on each side of centre aisle. Double pane windows. 'No Smoking' and 'Fasten seat belt' signs. Stowing fold-up seats for rapid conversion to cargo or mixed passenger/cargo configuration. Movable bulkhead between passenger and cargo sections. Snap-in carpeting. Self-stowing aisle filler. Tiedown fittings for cargo at 0·76 m (30 in) spacing. Integral-step passenger door on port side of fuselage, immediately aft of flight deck. Large cargo loading door on port side of fuselage at rear of cabin, hinged at top. Three window emergency exits, one on the port, two on the starboard side. Forward baggage compartment in nose, capacity 1·27 m³ (45 cu ft). Pressurised rear cargo compartment in passenger version, capacity 3·85 m³ (136 cu ft). Cabin air-conditioned and pressurised. Electrical windscreen de-icing. Windscreen wipers.

SYSTEMS: AiResearch automatic cabin pressure control system maintains a differential of 0·48 bars (7·0 lb/sq in). Engine bleed air heating, dual air-cycle cooling system, with automatic temperature control. Air blower system for on-ground ventilation. Independent hydraulic system for brakes. Dual engine-driven hydraulic pumps, using fire-resistant MIL-H-83282 hydraulic fluid, provide 138 bars (2,000 lb/sq in) to operate flaps and landing gear. Electrical system supplied by two 300A 28V DC starter/generators. Fail-safe system with overload and over-voltage protection. Redundant cir-

Swearingen Metro II 19/20-passenger commuter airliner in service with Tejas Airlines

cuits for essential systems. Two 250VA solid-state inverters supply 115V and 26V AC. Two 25Ah nickel-cadmium batteries for main services. One small nickel-cadmium battery for utility lights only. Engine fire detection system standard. Engine fire extinguisher systems optional. Oxygen system of 1·39 m³ (49 cu ft) capacity with flush outlets at each seat; system with capacity of 3·26 m³ (115 cu ft) optional. Stall avoidance system comprising angle indicator, visual and aural warning and stick pusher.

Avionics and Equipment: Standard equipment includes individual reading lights and air vents for each passenger, electrically-heated pitot heads, external power socket, automatic engine start cycle, static wicks, internally-operated control locks, pilot and co-pilot foot warmers, navigation lights, retractable landing lights, taxi light, ice inspection light, rotating beacon, instrument and map lights, baggage compartment light, cargo compartment lights and entrance lights, ice-free instrument static sources. Provisions for installation of remotely-mounted or panel-mounted avionics, customer-furnished antennae, weather radar and autopilot. Two flight deck and four cabin speakers standard.

Dimensions, external:
- Wing span 14·10 m (46 ft 3 in)
- Wing chord at root 2·62 m (8 ft 7 in)
- Wing chord at tip 1·04 m (3 ft 5 in)
- Wing aspect ratio 7·71
- Length overall 18·10 m (59 ft 4¾ in)
- Height overall 5·12 m (16 ft 9¾ in)
- Tailplane span 4·61 m (15 ft 1½ in)
- Wheel track 4·57 m (15 ft 0 in)
- Wheelbase 5·83 m (19 ft 1½ in)
- Propeller diameter 2·59 m (8 ft 6 in)
- Propeller ground clearance 0·254 m (10 in)
- Passenger door (fwd): Height 1·35 m (4 ft 5 in)
  - Width 0·64 m (2 ft 1 in)
- Cargo door (aft): Height 1·30 m (4 ft 3¼ in)
  - Width 1·35 m (4 ft 5 in)
  - Height to sill 1·30 m (4 ft 3¼ in)

Dimensions, internal:
- Cabin, excl flight deck and aft cargo compartment:
  - Length 7·75 m (25 ft 5 in)
  - Max width 1·57 m (5 ft 2 in)
  - Max height (aisle) 1·45 m (4 ft 9 in)
  - Floor area 13·01 m² (140 sq ft)
  - Volume 13·88 m³ (490 cu ft)
- Aft cargo compartment (pressurised):
  - Length 2·34 m (7 ft 8 in)
  - Max width 1·57 m (5 ft 2 in)
  - Max height 1·32 m (4 ft 4 in)
  - Volume 3·85 m³ (136 cu ft)
- Nose cargo compartment (unpressurised):
  - Length 1·75 m (5 ft 9 in)
  - Volume 1·27 m³ (45 cu ft)

Areas:
- Wings, gross 25·78 m² (277·50 sq ft)
- Ailerons (total) 1·31 m² (14·12 sq ft)
- Trailing-edge flaps (total) 3·78 m² (40·66 sq ft)
- Fin 5·20 m² (56·00 sq ft)
- Rudder, incl tab 1·80 m² (19·38 sq ft)
- Tailplane 7·06 m² (75·97 sq ft)
- Elevators 1·98 m² (21·27 sq ft)

Weights and Loadings:
- Weight empty 3,379 kg (7,450 lb)
- Max T-O and landing weight 5,670 kg (12,500 lb)
- Max ramp weight 5,715 kg (12,600 lb)
- Max wing loading 219·7 kg/m² (45·0 lb/sq ft)
- Max power loading 4·04 kg/kW (6·65 lb/shp)

Performance (at max T-O weight except where indicated):
- Max cruising speed at 3,050 m (10,000 ft), at 5,445 kg (12,000 lb) AUW 255 knots (473 km/h; 294 mph)
- Long range cruising speed at 6,100 m (20,000 ft), at 5,445 kg (12,000 lb) AUW 242 knots (449 km/h; 279 mph)
- Max speed, flaps and wheels down 153 knots (283 km/h; 176 mph)
- Stalling speed, flaps and wheels up 97 knots (180 km/h; 112 mph)
- Stalling speed, flaps and wheels down 86 knots (160 km/h; 99 mph)
- Max rate of climb at S/L 732 m (2,400 ft)/min
- Rate of climb at S/L, one engine out 198 m (650 ft)/min
- Service ceiling at 5,445 kg (12,000 lb) 8,230 m (27,000 ft)
- Service ceiling at 5,445 kg (12,000 lb), one engine out 4,480 m (14,700 ft)
- T-O to 15 m (50 ft) 799 m (2,620 ft)
- Landing from 15 m (50 ft) 1,082 m (3,550 ft)
- Range at max cruising speed, with 19 passengers and 45 min reserves 187 nm (346 km; 215 miles)
- Range at max cruising speed, with 15 passengers and 45 min reserves 595 nm (1,102 km; 685 miles)
- Max ferry range (allowance for taxi, T-O, climb, cruise, descent and 45 min reserves) 2,132 nm (3,952 km; 2,456 miles)

TAC
TEAL AIRCRAFT CORPORATION

Works: PO Drawer 499, St Augustine, Florida 32084
Telephone: (904) 892 3402
President: D. S. McIntosh

Teal Aircraft Corporation of Markham, Ontario, Canada (which see) acquired production facilities at St Augustine, Florida, in which to produce Teal II and III amphibians. These aircraft represent improved versions of the Teal amphibian, designed by Mr David B. Thurston and produced originally at Sanford, Maine, and subsequently by Schweizer Aircraft Corporation of Elmira, New York. The Teal programme and all production tooling and fixtures were acquired by TAC in the Spring of 1976, and the first aircraft from the St Augustine facility was rolled out in August 1977.

By the Spring of 1979, seven aircraft had been built, of which four had been delivered. Production was then reported to have ceased, pending additional financing.

A full description of the Teal can be found in the 1978-79 *Jane's*.

TAYLORCRAFT
TAYLORCRAFT AVIATION CORPORATION

Address: 14600 Commerce Avenue NE, Alliance, Ohio 44601
Telephone: (216) 823 6675
President: Dorothy A. Feris

Taylorcraft Aviation Corporation, which was re-formed on 1 April 1968 primarily to provide product support, has in production a two-seat trainer/sporting aircraft which has the designation Model F-19 Sportsman 100. Design originated in August 1967, based on the well-known Taylorcraft Model B of second World War origin; but it was not until 1973 that construction of pre-production and production aircraft started. More than 120 had been completed by early 1979.

Taylorcraft Model F-19 Sportsman 100 two-seat trainer/sports aircraft

TAYLORCRAFT MODEL F-19 SPORTSMAN 100

Type: Two-seat trainer/sporting aircraft.

Wings: Braced high-wing monoplane with V bracing struts each side. Wing section NACA 23012. Dihedral 1°. Composite structure with spruce spars, stamped metal ribs and fabric covering. Plain wide-span ailerons of similar construction. No flaps. No trim tabs.

Fuselage: Welded structure of 4130 steel tube with fabric covering.

Tail Unit: Wire-braced welded steel tube structure with fabric covering. Trim tab in port elevator.

Landing Gear: Non-retractable tailwheel type. Two side Vs and half-axles. Main wheels fitted with 6·00-6 4-ply tyres. Cleveland heavy-duty caliper brakes. Parking brake. Float and ski landing gear to be made available optionally.

Power Plant: One 74·5 kW (100 hp) Continental O-200-A flat-four engine, driving a McCauley Type 1A105SCM two-blade fixed-pitch metal propeller with spinner. One fuel tank in each wing, with combined capacity of 45·4 litres (12 US gallons), and one fuel tank in fuselage, immediately aft of firewall, with capacity of 45·4 litres (12 US gallons). Total fuel capacity 90·8 litres (24 US gallons). Oil capacity 5·7 litres (1·5 US gallons).

Accommodation: Two seats side by side in enclosed cabin. Dual controls standard. Seat belts, carpeted floor. Metal door each side with sliding windows. Baggage compartment aft of seats, capacity 32·7 kg (72 lb). Accommodation heated and ventilated.

System: Electrical system powered by engine-driven generator, with storage battery. Wiring provisions for landing and anti-collision light. Engine-driven vacuum pump for optional blind-flying instrumentation.

Avionics and Equipment: Optional avionics include Genave Alpha 200B com transceiver, King KX 145 com transceiver, KR 86 ADF and KT 76 transponder, EBC-102A emergency locator transmitter, microphone, headsets, speakers and com antenna. Standard equipment includes navigation lights, wiring for landing and anti-collision lights, cargo tiedown straps, sensitive altimeter and glove compartment. Optional equipment includes full blind-flying instrumentation, with vacuum system; rate of climb indicator; 8-day clock; co-pilot brake assembly; cockpit, landing and anti-collision lights; streamlined fairings for main landing gear legs, streamlined wheel fairings, skis, tiedown rings, and grade A cotton or Ceconite covering.

Dimensions, external:
- Wing span 10·97 m (36 ft 0 in)
- Wing chord (constant) 1·60 m (5 ft 3 in)
- Length overall 6·74 m (22 ft 1¼ in)
- Height overall 1·98 m (6 ft 6 in)
- Tailplane span 3·05 m (10 ft 0 in)
- Wheel track 1·83 m (6 ft 0 in)

Areas:
- Wings, gross 17·07 m² (183·71 sq ft)
- Ailerons (total) 1·86 m² (20·0 sq ft)
- Fin 0·34 m² (3·7 sq ft)
- Rudder 0·59 m² (6·3 sq ft)
- Tailplane 1·21 m² (13·0 sq ft)
- Elevators, incl tab 0·99 m² (10·66 sq ft)

Weights and Loadings:
- Weight empty 408 kg (900 lb)
- Max T-O weight 680 kg (1,500 lb)
- Max wing loading 39·9 kg/m² (8·17 lb/sq ft)
- Max power loading 9·12 kg/kW (15 lb/hp)

Performance (at max T-O weight):
- Max level speed 110 knots (204 km/h; 127 mph)
- Cruising speed, 75% power at optimum altitude 103 knots (190 km/h; 118 mph)
- Cruising speed, 65% power at optimum altitude 97 knots (180 km/h; 112 mph)
- Stalling speed 37·5 knots (69·5 km/h; 43 mph)
- Max rate of climb at S/L 236 m (775 ft)/min
- Service ceiling 5,485 m (18,000 ft)
- T-O run 91·5 m (300 ft)
- T-O to, and landing from, 15 m (50 ft) 114 m (375 ft)
- Range with max fuel:
  - 75% power at optimum altitude 347 nm (643 km; 400 miles)
  - 65% power at optimum altitude 391 nm (724 km; 450 miles)

TEXAS HELICOPTER
TEXAS HELICOPTER CORPORATION

Address: 1336 South Irving Heights Drive, Irving, Texas 75060
President: Gifton McCreary

TEXAS HELICOPTER WASP

Texas Helicopter has developed a high-performance agricultural/utility helicopter which is based on the Bell 47G. Early examples of this aircraft, which has the name Wasp, have a refurbished engine, transmission and tail rotor gearbox. It is planned, however, to use all-new components in the construction of later production aircraft. A lightweight spray system has been developed by the company for the Wasp, which is available in three versions:

M-74. Version with wooden main rotor blades, as used

on some Bell 47G2s; certificated in July 1976.

M-74A. Available with metal main rotor blades in two versions, with and without the main rotor stabilisation bar; certificated in August and December 1977 respectively. Removal of the stabilisation bar provides a weight saving of 11·3 kg (25 lb).

Empty weight of the single-seat Wasp is 644 kg (1,420 lb) and maximum T-O weight 1,247 kg (2,750 lb). It is claimed that maintenance costs are the lowest for any helicopter, with the tail rotor blades certificated for 2,500 hours and the engine mounting for 3,000 hours. Sales totalled 76 M-74s and M-74As by February 1979, including one each for export customers in Guatemala and Nicaragua.

The company has produced also a two-seat version of this helicopter with the designation M79S Tandem-Wasp, the prototype of which was flown for the first time on 6 January 1979.

For further details see Addenda.

Texas Helicopter Tandem-Wasp, a two-seat conversion of the Bell 47G *(Helicopter Magazine)*

TRI TURBO
TRI TURBO CORPORATION

ADDRESS: PO Box 217, Hangar No. 3, Camarillo Airport, Camarillo, California 93010
Telephone: (805) 484 4394 and 482 5576
PRESIDENT: Jack M. Conroy

This company is now responsible for the Tri Turbo-3 conversion of the DC-3, produced originally for Specialized Aircraft Co.

TRI TURBO-3

Aircraft Technical Service Corporation of Van Nuys, California, undertook on behalf of Specialized Aircraft Co the conversion of a Douglas DC-3 to utilise a power plant comprising three 875·5 kW (1,174 ehp) Pratt & Whitney Aircraft of Canada PT6A-45 turboprop engines. The aircraft so converted was formerly the twin-Dart-engined Conroy Super Turbo-Three, last described in the 1972-73 *Jane's*.

The first flight of this prototype installation was made on 2 November 1977, and it was hoped to obtain FAA certification in the transport category by the end of 1979, with power plant installation and performance complying with the current FAR Part 25 requirements.

It is planned to offer two alternative conversions, using 673 kW (903 ehp) PT6A-41 engines driving four-blade propellers, or 583 kW (783 ehp) PT6A-34 engines, driving three-blade propellers. The prototype installation, with the PT6A-45 engines driving Hartzell five-blade metal constant-speed propellers, reduces the aircraft basic weight by approximately 1,134 kg (2,500 lb), permitting operation under more arduous temperature/altitude conditions, or operation with heavier payload. New outboard wing fuel tanks enable the Tri Turbo-3 to be operated with a maximum payload of 5,443 kg (12,000 lb).

Present plans are for Tri Turbo Corporation to market completely modified aircraft, to convert customer's own aircraft, or to provide kits for installation by the owner/operator. Kit installation will require approximately 3,000 man-hours per aircraft.

Tri Turbo-3, a Douglas DC-3 conversion, in latest form with wheel-ski landing gear *(Brian M. Service)*

The prototype was exhibited at the Farnborough International air show in September 1978 in maritime patrol configuration, with a Litton search radar in an underfuselage fairing below the wing trailing-edge, and additional fuel in outboard wing tanks. It was then taken on a demonstration flight around the world before being used by the Polar Research Laboratory, under the operating name Polair, on scientific research and oceanographic survey duties for the US Office of Naval Research. Operating on skis, it helped to establish, and then supplied over a three-month period, camps on ice floes for the US Navy's Arctic East 79 project. It flew directly from the Arctic to Paris, to participate in the 1979 Paris Air Show.

WEIGHTS:
- Weight empty, cargo configuration 6,350 kg (14,000 lb)
- Operating weight, empty 6,577 kg (14,500 lb)
- Payload with standard fuel 4,145 kg (9,140 lb)
- Max T-O weight 13,150 kg (29,000 lb)

PERFORMANCE (prototype):
- Cruising speed at 1,525 m (5,000 ft) 191 knots (354 km/h; 220 mph)
- Cruising speed at 3,050 m (10,000 ft) 200 knots (370 km/h; 230 mph)
- Cruising speed (two outboard engines only, at optimum altitude) 156 knots (290 km/h; 180 mph)
- Range, standard fuel, no reserves:
  - Three-engine cruise 985 nm (1,826 km; 1,135 miles)
  - Two-engine cruise 1,159 nm (2,148 km; 1,335 miles)
- Range, long-range fuel, no reserves:
  - Three-engine cruise 2,345 nm (4,345 km; 2,700 miles)
  - Two-engine cruise 2,779 nm (5,150 km; 3,200 miles)

UNIVAIR
UNIVAIR AIRCRAFT CORPORATION

HEAD OFFICE AND WORKS: Route 3, PO Box 59, Aurora, Colorado 80011
Telephone: (303) 364 7661
CHAIRMAN OF THE BOARD: Veda Dyer Williams
PRESIDENT: Stephen E. Dyer
VICE-PRESIDENTS:
F. A. King (Sales)
Robert M. Williams (Production)
SECRETARY: Janice M. Dyer

Univair Aircraft Corporation, founded in 1946, is a company specialising in the manufacture of propellers and components for light aircraft. It holds 19 Type Certificates and 12 Supplemental Type Certificates, drawings, production tooling and rights to manufacture aircraft which include the Globe and Temco Swift Models GC-1A and GC-1B; the Ercoupe, Alon, Forney and Mooney M-10 Cadet series; and the Stinson 108. Details of these aircraft have appeared in earlier editions of *Jane's*, under their original manufacturers. The company also holds 224 Parts Manufacture Approvals (PMAs), covering 444 items for various models of classic or older aircraft. Wing lift struts for fabric-wing Cessna 120 and 140 aircraft are but a single example of the parts being manufactured for older designs by such companies as Aeronca, Cessna, Luscombe, Navion, Piper and Taylorcraft.

Propellers produced by Univair under Type Certificate include Flottorp wooden fixed-pitch, Flottorp variable-pitch (of Beech-Roby design), Flottorp F1 fixed-pitch and F12 constant-speed metal, Flottorp F200 and Aeromatic 220 automatic propellers.

Univair Stinson 108-5 four-seat cabin monoplane (Franklin 6A-335-B1 engine)

Univair has completed rebuilding a Piper J3 Cub in which has been installed a Continental O-200 engine. Certification tests were completed in 1977 and the company was awarded a multiple Supplemental Type Certificate by the FAA for O-200 engine installations in clipped-wing J3 Cubs. Either an Aeromatic automatically adjustable propeller, or a McCauley fixed-pitch metal propeller can be used with this STC.

The company has built to order an updated version of the Stinson 108, which has the designation Univair Stinson 108-5.

UNIVAIR STINSON 108-5

Design of Univair's version of the Stinson 108 began in November 1962, and the first flight of the prototype was made on 21 April 1964; FAA certification was granted almost three months later, on 14 July. Subject to availability of 134 kW (180 hp) Franklin engines, Univair markets a kit to convert the earlier Stinson Model 108-3 to Univair Stinson standard.

TYPE: Four-seat cabin monoplane.

WINGS: Braced high-wing monoplane, with light alloy V bracing struts each side. Wing section NACA 4412.

Dihedral 2° 30′. Incidence 1° 31′ at root, 0° 7′ at tip. No sweepback. Constant-chord two-spar structure of light alloy with fabric covering. Plain ailerons of light alloy and fabric covering, with a fixed slot forward of each aileron. Plain trailing-edge flaps of light alloy stressed-skin construction. Ground-adjustable tab on each aileron.

Fuselage: Welded steel tube structure, with fabric covering.

Tail Unit: Cantilever all-metal structure of light alloy. Fixed-incidence tailplane with horn-balanced elevators. Servo tab in port elevator. Horn-balanced rudder with servo tab.

Landing Gear: Non-retractable tailwheel type. Cantilever main units with spring/hydraulic shock-absorbers. Cleveland main wheels with tyres size 7·00-6, pressure 1·38 bars (20 lb/sq in). Maule P8 steerable tailwheel, with tyre size 2·80 × 2·50-4, pressure 1·72 bars (25 lb/sq in). Cleveland hydraulic shoe or disc brakes.

Power Plant: One 134 kW (180 hp) Franklin 6A-335-B1 flat-six engine, driving a McCauley two-blade constant-speed metal propeller type 2A31C21/84S with spinner. One fuel tank in each wing; total capacity 189·3 litres (50 US gallons). Refuelling point on inboard upper surface of each wing. Oil capacity 8·5 litres (2·25 US gallons).

Accommodation: Standard seating for four in two pairs, with rear seats easily removable to accommodate cargo or extra baggage. Door, with window, on each side of cabin. Accommodation heated and ventilated. Space for 45 kg (100 lb) baggage, with external access door.

Systems: Electrical system powered by 12V DC engine-driven generator, with storage battery. Scott Mark II oxygen system.

Avionics and Equipment: Narco Mark 12 VHF nav/com with VOR. Blind-flying instrumentation standard.

Dimensions, external:

Wing span	10·34 m (33 ft 11 in)
Wing chord, constant	1·45 m (4 ft 9 in)
Wing aspect ratio	6·8
Length overall	7·67 m (25 ft 2 in)
Height overall	2·29 m (7 ft 6 in)
Tailplane span	3·40 m (11 ft 2 in)
Wheel track	2·16 m (7 ft 1 in)
Wheelbase	5·66 m (18 ft 7 in)
Propeller diameter	1·93 m (6 ft 4 in)
Propeller ground clearance	0·23 m (9·14 in)
Passenger doors (each): Height	1·22 m (4 ft 0 in)
Width	0·76 m (2 ft 6 in)
Height to sill	0·81 m (2 ft 8 in)
Baggage door: Height	0·61 m (2 ft 0 in)
Width	0·56 m (1 ft 10 in)
Height to sill	0·99 m (3 ft 3 in)

Dimensions, internal:

Cabin: Length	1·75 m (5 ft 9 in)
Max width	0·97 m (3 ft 2 in)
Max height	1·42 m (4 ft 8 in)

Areas:

Wings, gross	14·4 m² (155 sq ft)
Ailerons (total)	1·675 m² (18·02 sq ft)
Trailing-edge flaps (total)	1·14 m² (12·22 sq ft)
Fin	1·33 m² (14·28 sq ft)
Rudder, incl tab	0·63 m² (6·78 sq ft)
Tailplane	1·36 m² (14·66 sq ft)
Elevators, incl tab	1·60 m² (17·24 sq ft)

Weights and Loadings:

Weight empty, equipped	590 kg (1,300 lb)
Max T-O and landing weight	1,088 kg (2,400 lb)
Max wing loading	75·7 kg/m² (15·5 lb/sq ft)
Max power loading	8·12 kg/kW (13·3 lb/hp)

Performance (at max T-O weight):

Never-exceed speed	147 knots (273 km/h; 170 mph)
Max level speed at S/L	132 knots (245 km/h; 152 mph)
Max cruising speed, 75% power at 1,525 m (5,000 ft)	117 knots (217 km/h; 135 mph)
Econ cruising speed at 2,285 m (7,500 ft)	115 knots (212 km/h; 132 mph)
Stalling speed, flaps up	56·5 knots (105 km/h; 65 mph)
Stalling speed, flaps down	53 knots (98·5 km/h; 61 mph)
Max rate of climb at S/L	305 m (1,000 ft)/min
Service ceiling	5,790 m (19,000 ft)
T-O run	122 m (400 ft)
T-O to 15 m (50 ft)	213 m (700 ft)
Landing from 15 m (50 ft)	198 m (650 ft)
Landing run	91·5 m (300 ft)
Range with max payload, 45 min reserves	412 nm (764 km; 475 miles)

UTC
UNITED TECHNOLOGIES CORPORATION

Head Office: United Technologies Building, Hartford, Connecticut 06101

Telephone: (203) 728 7000

Directors:
Hubert Faure
T. Mitchell Ford
Harry J. Gray
Edward L. Hennessy Jr
David C. Hewitt
Howard C. Kauffman
Paul W. O'Malley
Walter F. Probst
Arthur E. Smith
Olcott D. Smith
Richard S. Smith
William I. Spencer
Robert L. Sproull
Alfred W. Van Sinderen
Mrs Jacqueline Grennan Wexler
Roger C. Wilkins

Chairman, President and Chief Executive Officer:
Harry J. Gray

Executives:
Raymond D'Argenio (Senior V-P, Communications)
Robert J. Carlson (Group V-P Power; President, Pratt & Whitney Aircraft Group)
Hubert Faure (Group V-P; President, Otis Group)
Edward L. Hennessy Jr (Executive V-P, Chief Financial Officer; Group Vice-President, Systems and Equipment Group)
Paul W. O'Malley (Group V-P)
Peter L. Scott (Group V-P; President, Essex Group; President, Norden Systems)

Vice-Presidents:
Rolf D. Bibow (International)
Joseph A. Biernat (Treasurer)
Stillman B. Brown (Finance)
Robert L. Cole
William J. Evans
Wesley A. Kuhrt (Technology)
Edward W. Large (General Counsel)
Clark MacGregor
N. B. Morse (Industrial Relations)
Francis L. Murphy (Public Relations and Advertising)
Charles B. Preston (Controller)
Dale W. Van Winkle
Ralph A. Weller
George E. Williams

Secretary and Deputy General Counsel: Martin R. Lewis Jr

Divisions and Subsidiaries:
Pratt & Whitney Aircraft Group (see Engines section, Canada and USA):
Commercial Products Division
Government Products Division
Manufacturing Division
Pratt & Whitney Aircraft of Canada Ltd (see Engines section)
Otis Group
Essex Group
Sikorsky Aircraft (see this section)
Hamilton Standard
Power Systems
Norden Systems
Chemical Systems (see Engines section)
United Technologies Research Center

VARGA
VARGA AIRCRAFT CORPORATION

Address: 12250 East Queen Creek Road, Chandler, Arizona 85224

Telephone: (602) 963 4914

President: George Varga Jr

Varga Aircraft Corporation purchased from Shinn Engineering Inc in 1965 the full manufacturing rights, tooling and spare parts inventory for the Shinn Model 2150A. This entered production by Varga as the Model 2150A Kachina. Its design originated in the plywood Morrisey Nifty of 1957, built by a former Douglas Aircraft chief test pilot. Ten examples of an improved all-metal version, designated Morrisey Model 2150, were produced by Morrisey Aviation Inc, and this version was described in the 1959-60 *Jane's*. Production rights were acquired subsequently by Shinn Engineering Inc, which put into production a further improved version designated Shinn Model 2150A, with changes to the engine installation, landing gear and interior arrangement. This version was certificated by the FAA on 31 July 1961 and was last described in the 1964-65 *Jane's*. The Varga Kachina is basically the same as the Shinn 2150A.

Varga Model 2150A Kachina, a direct descendant of the Morrisey Nifty

VARGA MODEL 2150A KACHINA

Type: Two-seat lightweight sporting/training aircraft.

Wings: Cantilever low-wing monoplane. Wing section NACA 43015. Dihedral 7°. Incidence 3°. No sweepback. Conventional two-spar stressed-skin structure of light alloy. Plain ailerons and two-position trailing-edge flaps of light alloy construction. Ground-adjustable trim tab in starboard aileron. Glassfibre wingtips.

Fuselage: Forward fuselage of welded 4130 steel tube with light alloy covering. Semi-monocoque light alloy structure aft of cockpit. Nose cowl and tailcone of glassfibre.

Tail Unit: Cantilever structure of light alloy. Fixed-incidence tailplane. Fin and tailplane have glassfibre tips. Ground-adjustable trim tab in rudder.

Landing Gear: Non-retractable tricycle type. Oleo-pneumatic shock-absorbers on all units. Main units attached directly to rear spar of wing. Steerable nosewheel. Main wheel tyre pressure 1·66 bars (24 lb/sq in). Nosewheel tyre pressure 1·52 bars (22 lb/sq in). Cleveland hydraulic disc brakes. Parking brake.

Power Plant: One 112 kW (150 hp) Lycoming O-320-A2C flat-four engine, driving a Sensenich two-blade metal fixed-pitch propeller type M74DM. Fuel tank in each wing, total capacity 132·5 litres (35 US gallons). Refuelling points in upper surface of wings. Oil capacity 7·5 litres (2 US gallons).

Accommodation: Two seats in tandem under sideways-opening cockpit canopy, hinged on starboard side. Tinted windscreen and windows. Rear window of canopy completes 360° unrestricted view. Dual controls standard. Baggage space aft of rear seat, capacity 22·7 kg (50 lb). Utility shelf. Accommodation heated and ventilated.

Systems: Electrical system powered by 60A engine-driven alternator and 12V 25Ah battery. Hydraulic system for brakes only.

Avionics and Equipment: Optional avionics equipment by Edo-Aire, King and Narco. Standard equipment includes sensitive altimeter, recording tachometer, stall warning device, carpet, soundproofing, navigation lights, landing light in nose cowl, electric starter, quick gascolator drain, and tiedown rings.

Dimensions, external:

Wing span	9·14 m (30 ft 0 in)
Wing chord at root	1·52 m (5 ft 0 in)
Wing chord at tip	1·14 m (3 ft 9 in)
Length overall	6·45 m (21 ft 2 in)
Height overall	2·13 m (7 ft 0 in)
Tailplane span	2·79 m (9 ft 2 in)
Propeller diameter	1·88 m (6 ft 2 in)

Areas:

Wings, gross	13·38 m² (144 sq ft)

Ailerons (total, incl tab) 2·60 m² (28 sq ft)
Trailing-edge flaps (total) 2·42 m² (26 sq ft)
Fin 0·33 m² (3·6 sq ft)
Rudder (incl tab) 0·53 m² (5·7 sq ft)
Tailplane 1·34 m² (14·4 sq ft)
Elevators 0·62 m² (6·7 sq ft)

WEIGHTS AND LOADINGS:
Weight empty 510 kg (1,125 lb)
Max T-O weight, Utility category 712 kg (1,570 lb)
Max T-O weight, Normal category 824 kg (1,817 lb)
Max wing loading 61·6 kg/m² (12·6 lb/sq ft)
Max power loading 7·36 kg/kW (12·1 lb/hp)

PERFORMANCE (at max T-O weight):
Never-exceed speed 147·5 knots (273 km/h; 170 mph)
Max level speed at S/L 128 knots (238 km/h; 148 mph)
Cruising speed, 75% power at optimum altitude 117 knots (217 km/h; 135 mph)
Cruising speed, 65% power at optimum altitude 110 knots (204 km/h; 127 mph)
Stalling speed, flaps up 49·5 knots (92 km/h; 57 mph)
Stalling speed, flaps down 45 knots (84 km/h; 52 mph)
Max rate of climb at S/L 442 m (1,450 ft)/min
Service ceiling 6,705 m (22,000 ft)
T-O to 15 m (50 ft) 134 m (440 ft)
Landing from 15 m (50 ft) 137 m (450 ft)
Range with max fuel 455 nm (845 km; 525 miles)

VOLPAR

VOLPAR INC

HEAD OFFICE AND WORKS: 7929 Hayvenhurst Avenue, Van Nuys, California 91406
Telephone: (213) 787 4393 and 873 5599
Telex: 65-1419
PRESIDENT: Frank V. Nixon Jr
GENERAL MANAGER: Albert B. Seed
CHIEF ENGINEER: James Roberts
MANUFACTURING SUPERVISOR: Robert E. Nixon
CHIEF INSPECTOR: F. F. Taylor
PURCHASING AGENT: Carl Jones
PUBLIC RELATIONS MANAGER: R. M. Byrne

Volpar Inc was formed in 1960 by Volitan Aviation Inc, a modification and repair company, and Paragon Tool, Die and Engineering, an established manufacturer of turbine engine components and other precision machined parts. Its original purpose was to design, develop and manufacture tricycle landing gear kits for the Beech Model 18, while Volitan was to install the kits. In 1968, however, Volitan was merged into Volpar, which continued all of the aviation activities. The Volpar landing gear kit was certificated in 1960, becoming original equipment on new Beech aircraft, and by late 1978 more than 400 kits had been sold.

As a follow-up to this modification, Volpar produces kits to convert the Model 18 to turboprop power, using Garrett-AiResearch TPE 331 engines. The basic converted aircraft is known as the Turbo 18. After wide acceptance of this, Volpar introduced a 'stretched' version known as the Turboliner, and then the Turboliner II which is approved under SFAR 23 for commuter airline operation.

Using the nacelles that were developed for the Turbo 18 and Turboliner, Volpar next produced an engine installation which it markets under the name of Packaged Power. This is available with any of the Garrett-AiResearch TPE 331 series of turboprop engines, with either over-engine or under-engine air intake as required by the particular installation. Packaged Power units have been fitted to such aircraft as the Beechcraft Model 18, de Havilland Dove, Grumman Goose and de Havilland Beaver. It is understood that they are being considered for installation in several aircraft currently in the development stage.

Since February 1976 Volpar, in conjunction with Century Aircraft Corporation of Amarillo, Texas, has been engaged in the installation of Garrett-AiResearch TPE 331-3U-303 turboprop engines in Handley Page H.P.137 Jetstream aircraft. Other programmes have included modification of Cessna Model 402B and 421C aircraft to accept Wild camera systems and navigational sights, under contract to foreign governments.

As a further development of its Packaged Power programme, Volpar acquired in January 1978 a piston-engined Beechcraft T-34B into which it has installed a Garrett-AiResearch TPE 331-1-101B turboprop engine. The converted aircraft is identified as the Volpar Model T-34V Turbotrainer.

Volpar 'Packaged Power' units, embodying AiResearch TPE 331-2U-203 engines, in a Grumman Goose

VOLPAR (BEECHCRAFT) MODEL 18

The basic Volpar modification converts the Beechcraft Model 18 to a tricycle landing gear configuration, offering substantially lower approach speeds, greatly improved braking and easier ground handling. Cruising speed is improved, as all three wheels retract completely in flight. Futhermore, the aircraft can be kept in hangars with a lower roof clearance, since the overall height is reduced to 2·79 m (9 ft 2 in).

The Volpar kit, which passed all FAA static tests for a maximum landing weight of 4,433 kg (9,772 lb), utilises basic components of the existing main landing gear. The new nose gear is connected to the existing retraction system, where the tailwheel connection was removed. The complete modification can be made without removing the wings or stripping any of the wing skin. All cockpit controls and emergency procedures are unchanged, including the instrument panel wheel position indicator. Existing airstair doors can be retained with only minor modification.

Basically, the modification moves the main landing gear 1·22 m (4 ft 0 in) aft of the original position, attaching it to a welded tube truss that increases the torsional strength of the centre wing structure by 60% in landing configuration. The nose assembly is completely new and includes a streamlined nose fairing which adds 0·67 m (2 ft 2½ in) to the fuselage length. Space inside the fairing can be used for additional equipment, including a weather radar dish of up to 0·305 m (12 in) diameter.

All three wheels are of aluminium and can be fitted with either Goodrich or Goodyear tubed or tubeless tyres, size 8·50-10, ten-ply rating. Main-wheel tyre pressure 4·48 bars (65 lb/sq in), nosewheel tyre pressure 3·10 bars (45 lb/sq in). Shock-absorption is provided by hydraulic oleo struts of Volpar manufacture. Goodrich multiple disc brakes. All three wheels retract forward in less than eight seconds. On the ground the cabin floor is only 1·07 m (3 ft 6 in) off the ground at the door. Wheelbase is 2·62 m (8 ft 7 in). The aircraft will turn on a 1·22 m (4 ft) radius of the inside wheel and a centering device is incorporated on the shimmy damper for take-off and landing.

The current Mk IV Volpar conversion incorporates Goodrich nine-piston full-circle brakes with twice the braking energy and three times the service life of the two-piston type fitted formerly. The new brakes fit on the original gear and are obtainable from either Volpar or Goodrich.

More than 400 sets of Volpar tri-gear have been delivered.

VOLPAR (BEECHCRAFT) TURBO 18

The Volpar Turbo 18 is a Beechcraft Model 18 fitted with the Volpar Mk IV tricycle landing gear and re-engined with two 526 kW (705 ehp) Garrett-AiResearch TPE 331-1-101B turboprop engines, flat rated to 451 kW (605 ehp). The wing planform is changed, by extending forward the entire leading-edge inboard of each engine nacelle and carrying the new leading-edge line past the nacelle, so increasing the chord and sweepback to a point outboard of the nacelle. The rectangular wingtip panels of the standard Super 18 are replaced by smaller tips which decrease the wing span and maintain the normal leading-edge sweep to the tip.

Installation of TPE 331 engines and Hartzell Model HC-B3TN-5 three-blade reversible-pitch propellers reduces the empty weight, permitting an increase in fuel or payload. Internal fuel capacity is increased by 379 litres (100 US gallons) by installing new integral tanks in the leading-edge immediately outboard of each engine nacelle. These become the main tanks, each delivering fuel directly to the adjacent engine. They increase the maximum fuel capacity to 2,385 litres (630 US gallons), with a normal capacity of 1,159 litres (306 US gallons).

Air-conditioning and heating installations are available, using engine bleed air. A large cargo door, 1·57 m (5 ft 2 in) wide, with a max height of 1·09 m (3 ft 7 in), can be provided, incorporating the existing airstair door.

The detailed description of the Turboliner (which follows), applies also to the Turbo 18, except that the Turbo 18 does not have the 'stretched' fuselage.

FAA Supplemental Type Approval of the Turbo 18 was received on 17 February 1966. Two aircraft were delivered to the US Environmental Protection Agency in 1966, and production of conversion kits was initiated. Customers include Air Asia of Taiwan, which converted 15 C-45H aircraft for the US government. These aircraft were acquired in 1977 by Ciba Pilatus Aerial Spraying Co Ltd of Switzerland.

In April 1977, Volpar received FAA Supplemental

Volpar Turbo 18 conversion of the Beechcraft Model 18, operated by the Environmental Protection Agency of the US government

Type Approval to increase the max T-O weight of the Turbo 18 from 4,666 kg (10,286 lb) to 5,216 kg (11,500 lb). The required modification includes strengthening of the centre wing structure and replacement of some landing gear components, involving an increase of only 13·6 kg (30 lb) in the aircraft's structural weight.

DIMENSIONS, EXTERNAL:

Wing span	14·02 m (46 ft 0 in)
Length overall	11·40 m (37 ft 5 in)
Height overall	2·92 m (9 ft 7 in)
Wheelbase	2·62 m (8 ft 7 in)

DIMENSIONS, INTERNAL:

Cabin, excl flight deck:	
Length	3·87 m (12 ft 8½ in)
Max width	1·32 m (4 ft 4 in)
Max height	1·68 m (5 ft 6 in)
Volume	7·36 m³ (260 cu ft)

WEIGHTS AND LOADINGS (A: basic Turbo 18; B Turbo 18 with Volpar increased gross weight conversion):

Weight empty, basic: A	2,495 kg (5,500 lb)
B	2,508 kg (5,530 lb)
Max payload: A	2,171 kg (4,786 lb)
B	2,708 kg (5,970 lb)
Max T-O weight: A	4,666 kg (10,286 lb)
B	5,216 kg (11,500 lb)
Max zero-fuel weight: A	4,082 kg (9,000 lb)
Max landing weight: A	4,433 kg (9,772 lb)
Max wing loading: A	134·3 kg/m² (27·51 lb/sq ft)
B	150·2 kg/m² (30·76 lb/sq ft)
Max power loading: A	5·17 kg/kW (8·50 lb/ehp)
B	5·78 kg/kW (9·50 lb/ehp)

PERFORMANCE (A, at max T-O weight):

Max cruising speed at 3,050 m (10,000 ft)
243 knots (451 km/h; 280 mph)

Econ cruising speed at 3,050 m (10,000 ft)
222 knots (412 km/h; 256 mph)

Stalling speed, wheels and flaps up, power off
80 knots (148 km/h; 92 mph)

Stalling speed, wheels and flaps down, power off
77 knots (142 km/h; 88 mph)

Max rate of climb at S/L	521 m (1,710 ft)/min
Service ceiling	7,925 m (26,000 ft)
Service ceiling, one engine out	4,265 m (14,000 ft)
T-O run	507 m (1,665 ft)
T-O to 15 m (50 ft)	725 m (2,380 ft)
Landing from 15 m (50 ft)	642 m (2,107 ft)
Landing run with reverse thrust	265 m (870 ft)

Range with max fuel at 222 knots (412 km/h; 256 mph), 45 min reserves 1,884 nm (3,492 km; 2,170 miles)

Range with max payload, 45 min reserves
400 nm (741 km; 461 miles)

VOLPAR (BEECHCRAFT) TURBOLINER

This is a 15-passenger version of the Volpar (Beechcraft) Turbo 18, with lengthened fuselage, intended for the third-level airline market. Design was started in August 1966 and construction of the prototype began in December 1966. This aircraft flew for the first time on 12 April 1967 and FAA certification was granted on 29 March 1968, the Turboliner being approved for operation at a gross weight of 5,216 kg (11,500 lb).

By the beginning of 1979 a total of 27 Turboliners had been delivered and were in service with small airlines throughout the world. In March 1970 a Turboliner (N353V), on a delivery flight from Los Angeles to Singapore, set six official international speed records. It carried on board during the flight all necessary spares for one year's normal operation, together with a 1,515 litre (400 US gallon) ferry tank in the fuselage, and was in operation with a commuter airline two days after arrival in Singapore.

TYPE: Twin-turboprop light transport aircraft.

WINGS: Cantilever low-wing monoplane. Wing section NACA 63-015 at station 28·0, NACA 23014 at station 144·5, NACA 23012 at station 260·4. Dihedral 6°. Incidence 5° 20′ at root, 1° at tip. Sweepback 16° 21′ on inner wings, 8° 23′ on outer panels. Steel truss centre-section spar; remainder of structure aluminium semi-monocoque. Plain differential ailerons and plain trailing-edge flaps of conventional aluminium construction. Trim tab in port aileron. Optional Goodrich pneumatic de-icing boots on leading-edges.

FUSELAGE: Conventional aluminium semi-monocoque structure.

TAIL UNIT: Cantilever aluminium semi-monocoque structure with twin endplate fins and rudders. Fixed-incidence tailplane. Trim tabs in rudder and elevators. Optional Goodrich pneumatic de-icing boots on leading-edges.

LANDING GEAR: Volpar electrically-retractable tricycle type. All units retract forward, main wheels into engine nacelles. Volpar hydraulic shock-absorbers. All three wheels size 8·50-10 with Goodrich or Goodyear tubeless or tube-type tyres. Main-wheel tyre pressure 5·52 bars (80 lb/sq in); nosewheel tyre pressure 3·10 bars (45 lb/sq in). Goodrich multiple-disc brakes.

POWER PLANT: Two 526 kW (705 ehp) Garrett-AiResearch TPE 331-1-101B turboprop engines, each driving a Hartzell HC-B3TN-5 three-blade reversible-pitch propeller with T10176H blades. Four to eight fuel tanks in wings, including new integral main tanks in wing leading-edges outboard of nacelles. Normal fuel capacity 1,159 litres (306 US gallons); max capacity 2,385 litres (630 US gallons). Refuelling points in upper surface of wings. Total oil capacity 11·4 litres (3 US gallons).

ACCOMMODATION: Crew of two and up to 15 passengers. Downward-hinged airstair door on port side at rear of cabin. Optional double-door for freight loading. Seats removable to enable aircraft to be used for freight-carrying. Heating and air-conditioning optional. Baggage space aft of cabin and in each wing.

SYSTEMS: Hydraulic system for brakes only. Electrical supply from two 200A starter/generators and two 24V batteries, for landing gear and flap operation, propeller anti-icing, landing lights, radio and lighting.

AVIONICS AND EQUIPMENT: Blind-flying instrumentation, radio and radar to customer's specification.

DIMENSIONS, EXTERNAL:

Wing span	14·02 m (46 ft 0 in)
Wing chord at root	4·15 m (13 ft 7·36 in)
Wing chord at tip	1·14 m (3 ft 8·94 in)
Wing aspect ratio	5·67
Length overall	13·47 m (44 ft 2½ in)
Height overall	2·92 m (9 ft 7 in)
Tailplane span	4·57 m (15 ft 0 in)
Wheel track	3·94 m (12 ft 11 in)
Wheelbase	3·84 m (12 ft 7 in)
Propeller diameter	2·46 to 2·57 m (8 ft 0⅜ in to 8 ft 5⅜ in)
Passenger door: Height	1·22 m (4 ft 0 in)
Width	0·69 m (2 ft 3 in)
Height to sill	1·07 m (3 ft 6 in)

DIMENSIONS, INTERNAL:

Cabin, excl flight deck: Length	5·94 m (19 ft 6 in)
Max width	1·32 m (4 ft 4 in)
Max height	1·68 m (5 ft 6 in)
Floor area	7·43 m² (80 sq ft)
Volume	11·16 m³ (394 cu ft)
Freight hold (aft of cabin) volume	0·65 m³ (23 cu ft)
Freight holds (wings) volume (total)	0·91 m³ (32 cu ft)

AREAS:

Wings, gross	34·75 m² (374 sq ft)
Ailerons (total)	2·47 m² (26·6 sq ft)
Trailing-edge flaps (total)	2·62 m² (28·2 sq ft)
Fins (total)	1·51 m² (16·3 sq ft)
Rudders (total)	16·05 m² (17·28 sq ft)
Tailplane	35·49 m² (38·2 sq ft)
Elevators, incl tab	25·28 m² (27·22 sq ft)

WEIGHTS AND LOADINGS:

Weight empty: Cargo version	2,676 kg (5,900 lb)
Airliner	2,993 kg (6,600 lb)
Max T-O weight	5,216 kg (11,500 lb)
Max zero-fuel weight	4,762 kg (10,500 lb)
Max landing weight	4,989 kg (11,000 lb)
Max wing loading	150·1 kg/m² (30·75 lb/sq ft)
Max power loading	4·96 kg/kW (8·15 lb/ehp)

PERFORMANCE (at max T-O weight):

Max level and cruising speed at 3,050 m (10,000 ft)
243 knots (451 km/h; 280 mph)

Econ cruising speed at 3,050 m (10,000 ft)
222 knots (412 km/h; 256 mph)

Stalling speed, wheels and flaps up, power off
84 knots (154·5 km/h; 96 mph)

Stalling speed, wheels and flaps down, power off
80 knots (148·5 km/h; 92 mph)

Max rate of climb at S/L	463 m (1,520 ft)/min
Service ceiling	7,315 m (24,000 ft)
Service ceiling, one engine out	3,960 m (13,000 ft)
T-O run	570 m (1,870 ft)
T-O to 15 m (50 ft)	989 m (3,245 ft)
Landing from 15 m (50 ft)	762 m (2,500 ft)
Landing run	317 m (1,040 ft)

Range with max fuel, 45 min reserves
1,802 nm (3,340 km; 2,076 miles)

Range with max payload, 45 min reserves
300 nm (556 km; 346 miles)

VOLPAR (BEECHCRAFT) TURBOLINER II

The Turboliner II is basically a Turboliner that has been modified to meet the new requirements of SFAR 23. The prototype was completed in February 1970 and received certification in July 1970. Dimensions and performance are the same as those given for the Turboliner.

Recent conversions incorporate a number of improvements, including battery temperature indicators, a fail-safe Hydro-Aire Hytrol anti-skid braking system, installation of a 38,000 BTU Janitrol heater in the nose for ground heating of cockpit and engine nacelles, and modification to the standard Volpar side-opening cargo door. This now incorporates an inward-opening door 0·66 m (2 ft 2 in) in width and with a minimum height of 1·16 m (3 ft 9½ in), which may be opened in flight to permit the air drop of firefighting personnel or cargo. During 1974 Volpar, in conjunction with Sierracin Manufacturing Company, developed electrically heated windscreens for the Turboliner II. Complete installation kits are available also for other Volpar conversions.

During 1977 Volpar developed and delivered a specially modified long-range Turboliner II to Société Interthon of Port Peche, France. This aircraft is identified as the 'Asterix' series VLR Turboliner, and is designed for long-range maritime reconnaissance. It can carry a complement of observers. offshore nav/com systems, proprietary marine search equipment and ocean survival gear. The standard 'Asterix' aircraft has 2,385 litres (630 US gallons) of fuel in wing tanks, plus 757 litres (200 US gallons) in two removable cabin fuel tanks; total capacity 3,142 litres (830 US gallons), providing an endurance of almost 12 hours and range of 2,200 nm (4,076 km; 2,533 miles) with reserves. Special bubble-type windows are provided for both pilots; other equipment includes an inward/outward opening cargo door for air drops to surface vessels, lavatory, navigation tables, refreshment console, and provisions for camera and special search equipment. Certification by the FAA and French DGAC was awarded in December 1977.

VOLPAR (BEECHCRAFT) T-34V TURBOTRAINER

Volpar acquired a piston-engined Beech T-34B aircraft which it has re-engined with a Garrett-AiResearch TPE 331-1-101B turboprop, flat rated at 298 kW (400 shp) to provide an easily maintained and economical trainer. Flight testing was scheduled to begin in May 1979, with

Volpar 'Asterix' series VLR Turboliner II long-range maritime reconnaissance aircraft operated by Société Interthon

initial delivery of conversion kits in August 1979. These kits allow conversion in the field of existing T-34A and T-34B aircraft to T-34V standard.

Volpar provided the following preliminary specification details for the T-34V in early 1979:

WEIGHTS (estimated):
- Weight empty 1,089 kg (2,400 lb)
- Max T-O and landing weight 1,769 kg (3,900 lb)

PERFORMANCE (estimated, at max T-O weight):
- Never-exceed speed 250 knots (463 km/h; 288 mph)
- Max level speed at 5,335 m (17,500 ft) 230 knots (426 km/h; 265 mph)
- Cruising speed at 5,335 m (17,500 ft) 220 knots (354 km/h; 253 mph)
- Stalling speed, flaps up 65 knots (121 km/h; 75 mph)
- Stalling speed, flaps down 55 knots (101 km/h; 63 mph)
- Max rate of climb at S/L 914 m (3,000 ft)/min
- Service ceiling over 9,145 m (30,000 ft)
- T-O run 183 m (600 ft)
- T-O to 15 m (50 ft) 305 m (1,000 ft)
- Landing from 15 m (50 ft) 274 m (900 ft)
- Range with max fuel (492 litres; 130 US gallons) at 6,100 m (20,000 ft) 680 nm (1,260 km; 783 miles)
- Mission endurance 4·0 h
- *g* limits +6; −3

VOLPAR (CENTURY) JETSTREAM III

In 1976 Volpar was engaged by Century Aircraft Corporation of Amarillo, Texas, to re-engine the Handley Page H.P.137 Jetstream with Garrett-AiResearch TPE 331-3U-303 turboprop engines. Flight testing of the prototype conversion began in August 1976, and FAA certification under FAR 23 for Part 135 operation was awarded in June 1977.

Known as the Century Jetstream III, this aircraft was offered in both executive and 18-passenger commuter configurations. Conversions of aircraft and the production of modification kits continued at Volpar during 1978, with four conversions for Air Illinois, and two for Air US of Denver, Colorado. It is likely that this completed the programme, as there appear to be no more Jetstreams available for conversion.

The primary objective of this programme was to replace the original Astazou XIV engines by 626 kW (840 shp) Garrett-AiResearch TPE 331-3U-303 engines to provide operators with the increased TBO and reliability of the TPE 331 engine series. In addition to a reduction in aircraft empty weight, overall aircraft performance has been improved significantly. The power plant installation uses the basic Volpar TPE 331 power package, forward of the firewall. A new aft nacelle has been faired to the Handley Page wing, with overwing exhaust. The propeller plane, wing station location and thrust line are unchanged from the original Astazou installation. The Volpar nacelle is supported by a new tubular truss mounted to six wing attachment points to provide a fully fail-safe structure.

The original AC electrical system is replaced by a new DC system powered by two 250A engine-driven starter/generators. AC power for the instruments and heated windscreens is provided by four 750VA solid-state inverters. Dual DC-powered fuel pumps to feed each engine, and a DC cabin air recirculation fan, have been installed to use the ample DC power. The resulting electrical system is totally redundant and features Lear Siegler solid-state voltage control and overcurrent protection. Other aircraft systems are unchanged, except that a later model Vickers pump is substituted in the hydraulic system to provide increased reliability.

WEIGHTS:
- Weight empty, fully equipped commuter configuration 3,719 kg (8,200 lb)
- Max ramp weight 5,692 kg (12,500 lb)
- Max T-O and landing weight 5,670 kg (12,550 lb)

PERFORMANCE (at max T-O weight):
- Max cruising speed at 4,570 m (15,000 ft) 262 knots (486 km/h; 302 mph)
- T-O to 15 m (50 ft) 762 m (2,500 ft)
- Landing from 15 m (50 ft) 704 m (2,310 ft)
- Accelerate/stop distance 1,088 m (3,570 ft)
- Range at max cruising power, no reserves 1,303 nm (2,414 km; 1,500 miles)

Volpar T-34V conversion in progress to provide the Beech T-34 Mentor with turboprop power

Volpar (Century) Jetstream III conversion, with TPE 331 engines, in service with Air Illinois

VOUGHT

VOUGHT CORPORATION (a subsidiary of THE LTV CORPORATION)

HEAD OFFICE: PO Box 225907, Dallas, Texas 75265

Telephone: (214) 266 4765

PRESIDENT AND CHIEF EXECUTIVE OFFICER: R. L. Kirk

SENIOR VICE-PRESIDENTS:
- R. S. Buzard
- E. F. Cvetko (Operations)
- R. N. Parker (Research and Engineering)
- B. M. Smith
- J. J. Welch Jr (Marketing)

VICE-PRESIDENTS:
- D. P. Appleby (Materials)
- J. W. Casey (Logistics)
- K. R. Chapman (Planning)
- Felix Fenter (Research & Advanced Technology)
- D. R. Hagler (General Counsel)
- P. W. Hare (A-7 Programmes)
- W. R. Kiefer (Manufacturing)
- G. F. Montry (Finance)
- F. W. Randall (Subcontracts)
- W. L. Shepard (Strategic Defense)
- C. E. Snyder (Human Resources)
- G. T. Upton (V/STOL Programme)
- J. P. Woolnough (International)

CORPORATE DIRECTOR OF PUBLIC RELATIONS AND ADVERTISING: Beal Box

Michigan Plant

HEADQUARTERS: 38111 Van Dyke, Sterling Heights, Michigan 48077

VICE-PRESIDENT AND GENERAL MANAGER: J. J. Ryan

Prototype of the Vought TA-7C tandem two-seat trainer conversion

The former Chance Vought Aircraft Inc, founded in 1917 and a leading producer of aircraft for the US Navy throughout its history, became the Chance Vought Corporation on 31 December 1960. On 31 August 1961, Chance Vought Corporation merged with Ling-Temco Electronics Inc, to form a combined company known as Ling-Temco-Vought Inc (now The LTV Corporation).

After a succession of reorganisations, what is now known as Vought Corporation took over responsibility for all LTV's aircraft and space activities, aerospace support and training equipment from 1 January 1976, including current construction of Boeing 747 tail assemblies, McDonnell Douglas DC-10 tailplanes and elevators, and Lockheed C-130 control surfaces.

On 23 February 1979 the company announced receipt of a multi-million dollar contract from The Boeing Company covering the construction of up to 300 complete tailplane assemblies for the Boeing Model 767. Initial

A-7D with Pave Penny laser target designation pod under air intake lip

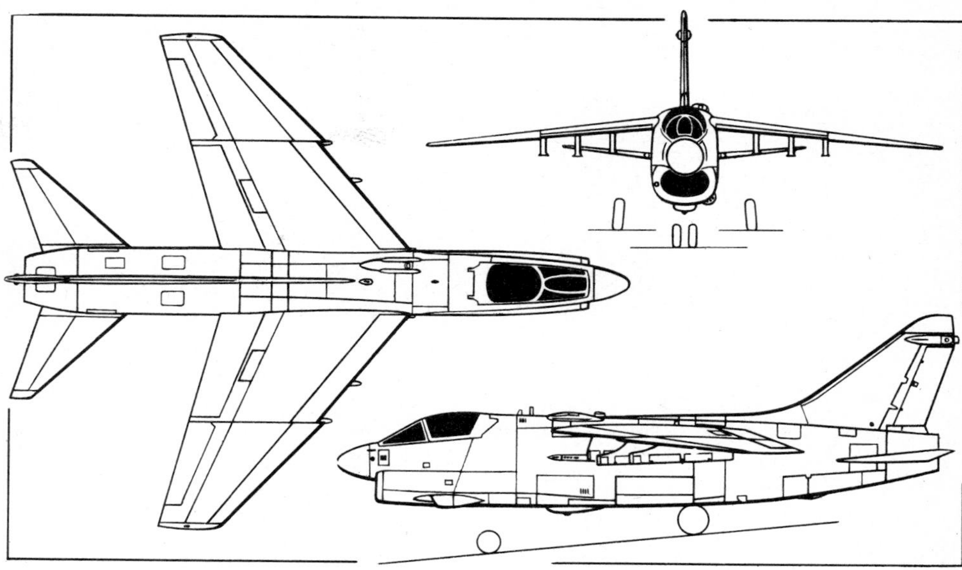

Vought A-7D tactical fighter version of the Corsair II for the USAF *(Pilot Press)*

delivery is scheduled for November 1980, with continuing production until June 1985 of six to nine units per month.

Vought has in production the A-7E attack aircraft and TA-7C two-seat trainer for the USN. It is overhauling 25 F-8H Crusaders for the Philippine Air Force, and is providing five TA-7H two-seat trainers for the Hellenic Air Force. In addition, Congress has appropriated FY 1979 funds for procurement of A-7K two-seat trainers for the US Air National Guard. Other current products include the Scout launch vehicle for NASA; components for manned and unmanned space vehicles; advanced missile, guidance, control and environmental systems; Airtrans automatic transit systems; and advanced thermal protection systems.

In December 1974, Vought's Low Volume RamJet (LVRJ) propulsion system test vehicle made a successful first flight, covering a distance of more than 30 nm (56 km; 35 miles) and attaining a speed in excess of 1,259 knots (2,334 km/h; 1,450 mph). In four subsequent flights, extending into 1976, the vehicle demonstrated speeds well above 1,476 knots (2,736 km/h; 1,700 mph) and a range of more than 87 nm (161 km; 100 miles). Under development for the US Navy, the LVRJ is regarded as a highly promising propulsion system for a new generation of higher-performance tactical missiles. Air-launched from a US Navy A-7 Corsair II, the flight test vehicle is 4·57 m (15 ft) long and 0·38 m (1 ft 3 in) in diameter. It can be scaled up or down for air-to-air, surface-to-air or surface-to-surface applications.

The Michigan Plant of Vought Corporation is prime contractor for the US Army's Lance battlefield missile system. This manufacturing centre will close when Lance production ends in October 1980.

VOUGHT CORSAIR II

US military designation: A-7

On 11 February 1964 the US Navy named the former LTV Aerospace Corporation winner of a design competition for a single-seat carrier-based light attack aircraft. The requirement was for a subsonic aircraft able to carry a greater load of non-nuclear weapons than the A-4E Skyhawk. To keep costs to a minimum and speed delivery it had been stipulated by the Navy that the new aircraft should be based on an existing design; the LTV design study was based, therefore, on the F-8 Crusader. An initial contract to develop and build three aircraft, under the designation A-7A, was awarded on 19 March 1964; first flight was made on 27 September 1965.

Since that time several versions of the A-7 have been evolved as Corsair IIs, for the US Navy, the USAF and the Hellenic Air Force, as follows:

A-7A. Initial attack version for the US Navy, powered by a non-afterburning Pratt & Whitney TF30-P-6 turbofan engine, rated at 50·5 kN (11,350 lb st). Delivery of 199 to the Navy was completed in Spring 1968.

A-7B. Developed version for the US Navy with non-afterburning TF30-P-8 engine, rated at 54·3 kN (12,200 lb st). Engine was modified later to TF30-P-408 configuration which provides 59·6 kN (13,400 lb st). Last of 196 was delivered to the Navy on 7 May 1969.

A-7C. Designation applied in late 1971 to the first 67 TF30-engined A-7Es (which see) to eliminate confusion with subsequent Allison-powered A-7Es.

TA-7C. Sixty-five A-7Bs and A-7Cs are being converted into tandem two-seat trainers, with operational capability, under this designation. The first of them (154477) flew for the first time on 17 December 1976. Flight refuelling capability, gun and weapon pylons retained. Configuration similar to YA-7E, but powered by the non-afterburning 54·3 kN (12,200 lb st) Pratt & Whitney TF30-P-8 engine. Entered service with VA-122 and VA-174 in 1978.

A-7D. Tactical fighter for the USAF, with a non-afterburning Allison TF41-A-1 (Spey) turbofan engine of 64·5 kN (14,500 lb st). Production of 459 was completed in December 1976. Details can be found in 1976-77 *Jane's*.

From mid-1978, 383 A-7Ds are being modified at the USAF's Oklahoma City Air Logistics Center to carry a Martin Marietta Pave Penny laser target designation pod mounted under the air duct lip.

A-7E. Developed version for the US Navy equipped as a light attack/close air support/interdiction aircraft. First 67 aircraft (since redesignated A-7C, as indicated) powered by TF30-P-408 non-afterburning turbofan engine, which provides 59·6 kN (13,400 lb st); 68th and subsequent aircraft by Allison TF41-A-2 (Spey) non-afterburning turbofan engine, which provides 66·8 kN (15,000 lb st). First flight of an A-7E was made on 25 November 1968 and deliveries began on 14 July 1969. The A-7E entered combat service in Southeast Asia with Attack Squadrons 146 and 147 in May 1970, operating from the aircraft carrier USS *America*. During this conflict USAF and USN A-7 Corsairs of all types flew more than 100,000 combat missions. Production continues at a rate of about one a month.

In early 1977 production began of an A-7E FLIR version, called formerly TRAM (target recognition and attack multi-sensor system). This has a pod under the starboard wing to house equipment which includes a Texas Instruments FLIR sensor, and a Marconi raster-HUD cockpit display, to provide improved night capability. Deliveries of new-production FLIR-equipped A-7Es to the Navy began on 15 September 1978. Several hundred aircraft are to receive the system, mostly by retrofit.

YA-7E. Two-seat version. Described separately.

A-7H. Land-based version of A-7E, retaining the folding wings. First A-7H flew for first time on 6 May 1975. Total of 60 delivered to the Hellenic Air Force.

TA-7H. Two-seat version for the Hellenic Air Force, with an Allison TF41-A-400 engine. Configuration similar to TA-7C, but no in-flight refuelling capability. Five ordered; delivery scheduled to begin in May 1980.

A-7K. Two-seat version of the USAF's A-7D. Congress appropriated funds in FY 1979 for the first 12 of a planned procurement of 42 for service with the US Air National Guard from 1981. Basically two-seat trainers, these aircraft will retain combat capability.

Deliveries of all versions totalled 1,477 by 1 January 1979.

The following description, which applies in particular to the A-7E, is generally applicable to other versions of the A-7 except as detailed under the individual model listings:

Type: Subsonic single-seat tactical fighter.

Wings: Cantilever high-wing monoplane. Wing section NACA 65A007. Anhedral 5°. Incidence −1°. Wing sweepback at quarter-chord 35°. Outer wing sections fold upward for carrier parking, and in the A-7D and A-7H to allow best utilisation of revetments at combat airfields. All-metal multi-spar structure with integrally-stiffened aluminium alloy upper and lower skins. Plain sealed inset aluminium ailerons, outboard of wing fold, are actuated by fully-triplicated hydraulic system. Leading-edge flaps. Large single-slotted trailing-edge flaps. Spoiler above each wing forward of flaps.

Fuselage: All-metal semi-monocoque structure. Large door-type ventral speed-brake under centre-fuselage.

Tail Unit: Large vertical fin and rudder, swept back 44·28° at quarter-chord. One-piece all-moving tailplane, swept back 45° at quarter-chord and set at dihedral angle of 5° 25′. Tailplane is operated by triplicated hydraulic systems, and the rudder powered by two systems.

Landing Gear: Hydraulically-retractable tricycle type, with single wheel on each main unit and twin-wheel nose unit. Main wheels retract forward into fuselage, nosewheels aft. Main wheels and tyres size 28 × 9-12; nosewheels and tyres size 22 × 5·50. Nose gear launch bar for carrier catapulting. Sting-type arrester hook under rear fuselage for carrier landings, emergency landings or aborted take-offs. Anti-skid brake system.

Power Plant: One Allison TF41-A-2 (Rolls-Royce Spey) non-afterburning turbofan engine, rated at 66·7 kN (15,000 lb st). The A-7E has a pneumatic starter requiring ground air supply; A-7D, A-7H and TA-7H engines have self-start capability through the medium of battery-powered electric motor that spins an air turbine starter, and the A-7K will also have this capability. The engine has self-contained ignition for start/airstart, automatic relight and selective ignition. Integral fuel tanks in wings and additional fuselage tanks. Maximum internal fuel 5,678 litres (1,500 US gallons). Maximum external fuel 4,542 litres (1,200 US gallons). The A-7D has all fuel tanks filled with polyurethane fire-suppressing foam. In the A-7E/H only the fuselage sump tank is filled with foam. Some fuselage tanks and fuel lines self-sealing. The A-7D has an alternate fuel feed system. Flight refuelling capability of first 26 A-7Ds and all A-7Es provided by a probe and drogue system; 27th and subsequent A-7Ds have (and A-7K will have) boom receptacle above fuselage on port side in line with wing leading-edge. The A-7H and TA-7H do not have an air refuelling capability. Boron carbide (HFC) engine armour.

Accommodation: Pilot on McDonnell Douglas Escapac rocket-powered ejection system, complete with USAF life support system on the A-7D, and a USN life support system on the A-7A/B/C/E/H. Escape system provides

Vought A-7E Corsair II close air support/interdiction aircraft of the US Navy

Vought A-7D tactical fighters of the USAF's 23rd Tactical Fighter Wing

a fully-inflated parachute three seconds after sequence initiation; positive seat/man separation and stabilisation of the ejected seat and pilot. Boron carbide (HFC) cockpit armour.

Systems: Triple-redundant hydraulic system for flight controls; double-redundant system for flaps, brakes and landing gear retraction. Liquid oxygen system. An air-conditioning unit using engine bleed air provides pressurisation and cooling for the cockpit and cooling for certain electronics components. Automatic flight control system provides control-stick steering, altitude hold, heading hold, heading pre-select and attitude hold, which is coupled for automatic carrier landings. Ram-air turbine provides hydraulic pressure and electrical power down to airspeeds below those used in normal landing approaches.

Avionics and Equipment: The navigation/weapon delivery system is the heart of the A-7D/E/H light attack aircraft. It performs continuously the computations needed for greatly increased delivery accuracy, and for manoeuvring freedom during navigation to a target and the attack, weapon release, pull up, and safe return phases of the mission. The system not only provides the pilot with a number of options during navigation and weapon delivery, but also relieves him of much of his work load. The AN/ASN-91(V) navigation/weapon delivery computer is the primary element of the system, in constant 'conversation' with basic electronic sensors, and computes and displays continuously present position, using computed position and stored data to calculate navigation and weapon delivery solutions, and monitors the reliability of data inputs and outputs. An AN/ASN-90(V) inertial measurement set is the basic three-axis reference system for navigation and weapon delivery. AN/APN-190(V) Doppler measures groundspeed and drift angle. AN/APQ-126(V) forward-looking radar provides the pilot with ten modes of operation: air-to-ground ranging; terrain following; terrain avoidance; ground mapping, shaped beam; ground mapping, pencil beam; beacon; cross-scan terrain avoidance; cross-scan ground mapping, pencil; TV; and SIDS. An AN/AVQ-7(V) HUD receives and displays computed attack, navigation and landing data from the tactical computer; aircraft performance data from flight sensors: and discrete signals from various aircraft systems. CP-953A/AJQ air data computer is a solid-state servomechanical analogue computer which measures and computes continuously required altitude and airspeed information. The Armament Station Control unit integrates and controls the weapon release system; it supplies electrical signals to arm and release or jettison external stores; controls and fires the Vulcan cannon; furnishes store-type information to the tactical computer; supplies weapon status information to the pilot; determines weapon release according to priority of stations; and determines compatibility of selected release mode with the stores on selected stations. Standard aeronautical charts reproduced on 35 mm film in full colour are stored in an AN/ASN-99 Projected Map Display Set which, as a subsystem of the tactical computer, provides a continuous display of the aircraft's geographical position. Other avionics include AN/ASN-54 approach power compensator; AN/ASW-30 AFCS; ARA-63 ACLS; dual AN/ARC-159 UHF com; AN/ARN-84 Tacan; AN/APX-72 IFF transponder; AN/AN-154 radar beacon; AN/ASW-25 data link; AN/ARA-50 ADF; and AN/AIC-25 audio system. ECM equipment includes ALR-45/50 internal homing and warning systems; ALQ-126 active ECM; chaff/flare dispensers; and external pod-mounted systems compatible with the aircraft's internal sytems.

Armament: A wide range of stores, to a total weight of more than 6,805 kg (15,000 lb), can be carried on six underwing pylons and two fuselage weapon stations, the latter suitable for Sidewinder air-to-air missiles. Two outboard pylons on each wing can each accommodate a load of 1,587 kg (3,500 lb). Inboard pylon on each wing can carry 1,134 kg (2,500 lb). Two fuselage weapon stations, one on each side, can each carry load of 227 kg (500 lb). Weapons carried include air-to-air and air-to-ground (anti-tank and anti-radar missiles); electro-optical (TV) and laser guided weapons; general-purpose bombs; bomblet dispensers; rockets; gun pods; Pave Penny AN/AAS-35 laser target designation pod (A-7D); and auxiliary fuel tanks. In addition, an M61A-1 Vulcan 20 mm cannon is mounted in the port side of the fuselage. This has 1,000-round ammunition storage and selected firing rates of 4,000 or 6,000 rds/min. Strike camera in lower rear fuselage for damage assessment.

Dimensions, external:

Wing span	11·80 m (38 ft 9 in)
Width, wings folded	7·24 m (23 ft 9 in)
Wing chord at root	4·72 m (15 ft 6 in)
Wing chord at tip	1·18 m (3 ft 10¼ in)
Wing aspect ratio	4
Length overall	14·06 m (46 ft 1½ in)
Height overall	4·90 m (16 ft 0¾ in)
Tailplane span	5·52 m (18 ft 1½ in)
Wheel track	2·90 m (9 ft 6 in)

Areas:

Wings, gross	34·83 m² (375 sq ft)
Ailerons (total)	1·85 m² (19·94 sq ft)
Trailing-edge flaps (total)	4·04 m² (43·48 sq ft)
Leading-edge flaps (total)	4·53 m² (48·74 sq ft)
Spoiler	0·43 m² (4·60 sq ft)
Deflector	0·32 m² (3·44 sq ft)
Fin	10·33 m² (111·20 sq ft)
Rudder	1·40 m² (15·04 sq ft)
Horizontal tail surfaces	5·24 m² (56·39 sq ft)
Speed-brake	2·32 m² (25·00 sq ft)

Weights:

Weight empty	8,668 kg (19,111 lb)
Max T-O weight	19,050 kg (42,000 lb)

Performance:

Max level speed at S/L
600 knots (1,112 km/h; 691 mph)

Max level speed at 1,525 m (5,000 ft):
with 12 Mk 82 bombs
562 knots (1,040 km/h; 646 mph)
after dropping bombs
595 knots (1,102 km/h; 685 mph)

Sustained manoeuvring performance at 1,525 m (5,000 ft), at AUW of 13,047 kg (28,765 lb) with 6 pylons and 2 Sidewinder missiles
1,770 m (5,800 ft) turning radius at 4g and 500 knots (925 km/h; 575 mph)

T-O run at max T-O weight 1,830 m (6,000 ft)

Ferry range:
max internal fuel
1,981 nm (3,671 km; 2,281 miles)
max internal and external fuel
2,485 nm (4,604 km; 2,861 miles)

VOUGHT CORSAIR II₂

US military designation: YA-7E

Under a project funded partially by the company, and by modification of an aircraft furnished by the US Navy, Vought designed and built the prototype of a two-seat version of the A-7 Corsair II. Envisaged as an advanced trainer, or as a new operational configuration for tactical duties such as electronic countermeasures, it was known originally as the Vought Project V-159, and later as the YA-7H, but now has the designation YA-7E to avoid confusion with the single-seat A-7H and two-seat TA-7H ordered by the Hellenic Air Force.

The YA-7E has the same basic structure and equipment as the A-7, with a 0·41 m (1 ft 4 in) longer nose section to make room for the second cockpit. A 0·46 m (1 ft 6 in) section is inserted in the rear fuselage, in line with the trailing-edge of the wing, and the overwing fairing is modified to maintain the fuselage profile. The aft fuselage is also modified to cant upward 1° 19′, so making possible approach and landing attitudes identical to those of other A-7s, despite the longer fuselage.

The new cockpit section has two McDonnell Douglas Escapac ejection seats in tandem, under an electrically-actuated sideways-opening (to starboard) cockpit canopy. Ejection is through the canopy, with the aid of a centreline explosive canopy fracturing system, but the seat headrests include strikers to further shatter the canopy and assure a clear egress. Each cockpit has full flying controls, communications and navigation equipment. The rear cockpit, occupied by an instructor or check pilot, has a repeater-type head-up display, and the seat is raised slightly above the level of the front seat to enhance forward view. A brake parachute is installed to permit short-field operations.

The YA-7E, which was converted from the first production A-7E fitted with the Allison TF41-A-2 (Spey) turbofan engine, was modified at the Vought works in Dallas. It was not fitted with an in-flight refuelling probe or gun, but is able to accept such equipment if required.

First flight of the YA-7E was made on 29 August 1972. Despite an increase in empty weight, there is little difference in performance between the YA-7E and the A-7E. The TA-7C Corsair II trainers undergoing conversion from A-7B/C are similar in configuration to the YA-7E.

Dimensions, external:

Wing span	11·80 m (38 ft 9 in)
Length overall	14·68 m (48 ft 2 in)
Height overall	5·00 m (16 ft 5 in)

Weights:

Weight empty 8,938 kg (19,705 lb)

Normal T-O weight (no military stores)
13,725 kg (30,259 lb)

Performance (at T-O weight of 15,450 kg; 34,062 lb):

Max level speed at S/L
598 knots (1,108 km/h; 689 mph)

Catapult T-O speed 142 knots (264 km/h; 164 mph)

T-O run 1,097 m (3,600 ft)

Landing run:
without brake parachute 960 m (3,150 ft)
with brake parachute 670 m (2,200 ft)

Radius of action 405 nm (750 km; 466 miles)

Ferry range (no external stores)
1,900 nm (3,521 km; 2,188 miles)

VOUGHT V-529D

Vought has proposed a twin-engined development of the A-7E to the US Navy. The single TF41 engine of the current A-7E would be replaced by two non-afterburning General Electric F404 turbojets, each producing approx 44·5 kN (10,000 lb st). Structural changes to accommodate this new power plant would include an increase of 0·51 m (1 ft 8 in) in fuselage length to provide static balance, a local fuselage width increase of 0·74 m (2 ft 5 in), and a new aft fuselage structure with bifurcated duct. Empty weight of such an aircraft would be 9,068 kg (19,992 lb), and internal fuel capacity would be increased from 4,552 kg (10,036 lb) to 5,749 kg (12,674 lb). It is anticipated that the use of the engines, and other components, being developed of the F-18 Hornet, would not only improve present A-7E survivability, but would raise this aircraft's operational readiness well above existing fleet standards.

Artist's impression of Vought V-529D twin-engined A-7 proposal

WEATHERLY

WEATHERLY AVIATION COMPANY INC

ADDRESS: 2304 San Felipe Road, Hollister, California 95023
Telephone: (408) 637 5534
PRESIDENT: John C. Weatherly

Between January 1961 and the Autumn of 1965, Weatherly Aviation produced 19 Model WM-62C agricultural aircraft. These were conversions of Fairchild M-62 airframes and most were powered by a Continental W670 radial engine, although a few were delivered with Pratt & Whitney R-985 engines.

Weatherly then developed a new agricultural monoplane, known as the Model 201, which was an outgrowth of the conversion programme. Somewhat larger than the M-62, and with many improvements, the prototype received FAA certification in early 1967. The current production version, designated Model 201C, received FAA certification in December 1975. More than 100 Model 201s of all versions had been built by 1 April 1979.

Weatherly has developed small sweptback vanes which can be attached to, or removed easily from, each wingtip, and these have two primary functions: to increase the effective swath width; and to reduce the amount of spray materials lost from the swath area. With the vanes installed the swath width is increased by 1·80 to 2·75 m (6 to 9 ft), but because of reduced outboard airflow the vanes are not used when dispersing dust or other solid material. Normal flight characteristics are not impaired with the vanes installed. Take-off run is reduced by a few feet, and cruising speed is increased approximately 1·7 knots (3·2 km/h; 2 mph), due to a reduction in induced drag.

Weatherly Model 201C agricultural aircraft with wingtip vanes for increase of swath width

WEATHERLY MODEL 201C

TYPE: Single-seat agricultural aircraft.

WINGS: Cantilever low-wing monoplane. Wing section NACA 4215 (modified). Dihedral, on outer panels, 6°. Incidence 3° 30′. Conventional structure of light alloy, with removable leading-edge sections. Ailerons of light alloy construction. Ground-adjustable tab on starboard aileron. Wingtip vanes for increased swath width optional (see introductory paragraph to this entry).

FUSELAGE: Forward fuselage has welded structure of chrome-molybdenum steel tube, covered by removable light alloy panels. Rear fuselage, aft of cockpit, is a conventional semi-monocoque structure of light alloy.

TAIL UNIT: Cantilever structure of light alloy. Controllable trim tab in port elevator. Horn-balanced control surfaces. Ground-adjustable tab on rudder.

LANDING GEAR: Non-retractable tailwheel type. Wide-track main gear embodies spring-oil type shock-absorbers, attached to wing main spar. Cleveland main wheels, with tyres size 8·50 × 10. Tailwheel tyre size 12·5 × 4·5. Hydraulic brakes. Parking brake.

POWER PLANT: One 335·6 kW (450 hp) Pratt & Whitney R-985 nine-cylinder aircooled radial engine, driving a Hamilton Standard Type 2D30 two-blade constant-speed metal propeller. Fuel in two wing tanks with total usable capacity of 246 litres (65 US gallons). Refuelling points in upper surface of wing. Oil capacity 26·5 litres (7 US gallons).

ACCOMMODATION: Pilot only, in enclosed cabin. Shoulder harness on seat. Combined window/door on each side, hinged at bottom. Wire-cutter forward of windscreen. Cable from top of cockpit structure to tip of fin to deflect cables.

SYSTEMS: 24V electrical system. Hydraulic system for brakes only.

EQUIPMENT: Heavy-walled glassfibre hopper in forward fuselage, capacity 1,022 litres (270 US gallons), for liquid or dry chemicals. Standard equipment includes spray system, bottom loading tube, stall warning light and control locks. Optional equipment includes wingtip vanes and solids dispersal system.

DIMENSIONS, EXTERNAL:
- Wing span: 11·89 m (39 ft 0 in)
- Wing chord at root: 1·93 m (6 ft 4 in)
- Wing aspect ratio: 6·04
- Length overall: 8·29 m (27 ft 2½ in)
- Height overall: 2·48 m (8 ft 1½ in)
- Wheel track: 3·18 m (10 ft 5 in)
- Propeller diameter: 2·41 m (7 ft 11 in)

AREA:
- Wings, gross: 23·36 m² (251·5 sq ft)

WEIGHTS AND LOADINGS:
- Weight empty, equipped: 1,157 kg (2,550 lb)
- Design T-O weight: 1,588 kg (3,500 lb)
- Max T-O weight (Restricted category): 2,177 kg (4,800 lb)
- Max wing loading: 93·2 kg/m² (19·1 lb/sq ft)
- Max power loading: 6·49 kg/kW (10·67 lb/hp)

PERFORMANCE:
- Never-exceed speed: 126 knots (233 km/h; 145 mph)
- Max level speed at max continuous power: 111 knots (206 km/h; 128 mph)
- Manoeuvring speed: 100 knots (185 km/h; 115 mph)
- Cruising speed: 91 knots (169 km/h; 105 mph)
- Stalling speed at AUW of 2,177 kg (4,800 lb): 60 knots (111 km/h; 69 mph)
- Stalling speed at design T-O weight: 49 knots (92 km/h; 57 mph)
- Stalling speed, no chemical load: 46 knots (85 km/h; 53 mph)
- Max rate of climb at S/L at AUW of 2,177 kg (4,800 lb): 293 m (960 ft)/min

YUGOSLAVIA

SOKO

'SOKO' METALOPRERADIVACKA INDUSTRIJA SA OGRANICENOM SOLIDARNOM ODGOVORNOSCU OOUR-A OOUR FABRIKA VAZDUHOPLOVA

ADDRESS: 79000 Mostar
Telephone: 22-121)125, 22-139, 22-156/157, 22-183
Telex: 46-180
DIRECTOR, AIRCRAFT DIVISION: Dr Krsto Draca
DIRECTOR, AIRCRAFT FACTORY: Zijo Kreso, BSc
DIRECTOR, MARKETING: Novica Djurica, BSc
DIRECTOR, RESEARCH: Dipl Ing S. Gosto

Founded in 1951, this company is manufacturing several aircraft of its own design and is participating, with Romania, in developing the Orao strike aircraft described under the SOKO/CIAR heading in the International section.

Soko is also building under licence the Aérospatiale/Westland Gazelle helicopter, on behalf of the Yugoslav government.

SOKO G2-A GALEB (SEAGULL)

Design of the Galeb was started in 1957. Construction of two prototypes began in 1959 and the first of these flew for the first time in May 1961. Development was carried out in collaboration with the Yugoslav Aeronautical Research Establishments and construction is in accordance with current military airworthiness requirements. Production began in 1963 for the Yugoslav Air Force and has continued to fulfil repeat Yugoslav and export orders. First overseas operator was the Zambian Air Force, in early 1971.

There are two current versions of the Galeb:

G2-A. Standard version for Yugoslav Air Force. Progressive design improvements include availability of optional cockpit air-conditioning system.

G-2A-E. Export version, with updated equipment. First flown in late 1974. Series production began in 1975, reportedly for the Libyan Arab Air Force, and was continuing through 1979.

Soko G2-A Galeb two-seat basic training aircraft (Rolls-Royce Viper 11 turbojet engine)

TYPE: Two-seat armed jet basic trainer, designed for load factors of +8*g* and −4*g*.

WINGS: Cantilever low-wing monoplane. Wing section NACA 64A213·5 at root, NACA 64A212·0 at tip. Dihedral 1° 30′. No incidence. Sweepback at quarter-chord 4° 19′. Conventional light alloy two-spar stressed-skin structure, consisting of a centre-section, integral with the fuselage, and two outer panels which can be removed easily. Manually-operated light alloy ailerons. Trim tab on port aileron. Hydraulically-actuated Fowler flaps. No de-icing system.

FUSELAGE: Light alloy semi-monocoque structure in two portions, joined together by four bolts at frame aft of wing trailing-edge. Rear portion removable for engine servicing. Two hydraulically-actuated door-type air-brakes under centre-fuselage.

TAIL UNIT: Cantilever light alloy stressed-skin structure. Fixed-incidence tailplane. Rudder and elevators statically and dynamically balanced and manually operated. Manually-operated trim tab in each elevator. VHF radio aerial forms tip of fin.

LANDING GEAR: Hydraulically-retractable tricycle type,

with single wheel on each unit. Nosewheel retracts forward, main units inward into wings. Oleo-pneumatic shock-absorbers manufactured by Prva Petoletka of Trstenik. Dunlop main wheels and tyres size 23 × 7·25-10, pressure 4·41 bars (64 lb/sq in). Dunlop nosewheel and tyre size 6·50-5·5 TC, pressure 3·43 bars (49·8 lb/sq in). Prva Petoletka hydraulic differential disc brakes, toe-operated from both cockpits.

POWER PLANT: One Rolls-Royce Viper 11 Mk 22-6 turbojet engine, rated at 11·12 kN (2,500 lb st). Two flexible fuel tanks aft of cockpits, with total capacity of 780 kg (1,720 lb). Two jettisonable wingtip tanks, each with capacity of 170 kg (375 lb). Refuelling point on upper part of fuselage aft of cockpits. Fuel system designed to permit up to 15 seconds of inverted flight. Oil capacity 6·25 litres (1·4 Imp gallons).

ACCOMMODATION: Crew of two in tandem on HSA (Folland) Type 1-B fully-automatic lightweight ejection seats. Separate sideways-hinged (to starboard) jettisonable canopy over each cockpit. Cockpit air-conditioning to special order only.

SYSTEMS: Hydraulic system, pressure 58·5-69 bars (850-1,000 lb/sq in), for landing gear, airbrakes and flaps. Separate system for wheel brakes. Pneumatic system for armament cocking. Electrical system includes 6kW 24V generator, 24V battery, and inverter to provide 115V 400Hz AC supply for instruments. G2-A has low-pressure oxygen system, capacity 1,450 litres. G-2A-E has high-pressure oxygen system.

AVIONICS AND EQUIPMENT (G2-A): Blind-flying instrumentation, Marconi radio compass (licence-built by Rudi Cajavec), intercom and STR-9Z1 VHF radio transceiver standard. Standard electrical equipment includes navigation lights, 250W landing lamp in nose, and 50W taxying lamp on nose landing gear. Camera, with focal length of 178 mm (7 in) and 125-exposure magazine, can be fitted in fuselage, under rear cockpit floor. Flares can be carried on the underwing bomb racks for night photography. Target towing hook under centre-fuselage.

AVIONICS AND EQUIPMENT (G-2A-E): Full IFR instrumentation. Electronique Aérospatiale (EAS) Type TVU-740 VHF/UHF com radio transceiver, Marconi AD 370B radio compass, EAS RNA-720 VOR/LOC and ILS, Iskra 75R4 marker beacon receiver, and intercom. Vinten Type 360/140A camera with 3 in automatic exposure-control lens. Otherwise as G2-A.

ARMAMENT: All production aircraft have two 0·50 in machine-guns in nose (with 80 rds/gun); and underwing pylons for two 50 kg or 100 kg bombs and four 57 mm rockets or two 127 mm rockets; or clusters of small bombs and expendable bomblet containers of up to 150 kg (330 lb) weight (300 kg; 660 lb total).

DIMENSIONS, EXTERNAL:

Wing span	10·47 m (34 ft 4½ in)
Wing span over tip-tanks	11·62 m (38 ft 1½ in)
Wing chord at root	2·36 m (7 ft 9 in)
Wing chord at tip	1·40 m (4 ft 7 in)
Wing aspect ratio	5·55
Length overall	10·34 m (33 ft 11 in)
Height overall	3·28 m (10 ft 9 in)
Tailplane span	4·27 m (14 ft 0 in)
Wheel track	3·89 m (12 ft 9 in)
Wheelbase	3·59 m (11 ft 9½ in)

AREAS:

Wings, gross	19·43 m² (209·14 sq ft)
Ailerons (total)	2·36 m² (25·40 sq ft)
Trailing-edge flaps (total)	2·02 m² (21·75 sq ft)
Airbrake	0·34 m² (3·66 sq ft)
Fin	1·34 m² (14·42 sq ft)
Rudder, incl tab	0·56 m² (6·03 sq ft)
Tailplane	3·66 m² (39·40 sq ft)
Elevators, incl tabs	0·83 m² (8·93 sq ft)

WEIGHTS:

Weight empty, equipped	2,620 kg (5,775 lb)
Max T-O weight:	
Fully-aerobatic trainer ('clean')	3,374 kg (7,438 lb)
Basic trainer (no tip-tanks)	3,488 kg (7,690 lb)
Navigational trainer (with tip-tanks)	3,828 kg (8,439 lb)
Weapons trainer	3,988 kg (8,792 lb)
Strike version	4,300 kg (9,480 lb)

PERFORMANCE (at normal T-O weight):

Max level speed at S/L	408 knots (756 km/h; 470 mph)
Max level speed at 6,200 m (20,350 ft)	438 knots (812 km/h; 505 mph)
Max cruising speed at 6,000 m (19,680 ft)	394 knots (730 km/h; 453 mph)
Stalling speed:	
flaps and airbrakes down	85 knots (158 km/h; 98 mph)
flaps and airbrakes up	97 knots (180 km/h; 112 mph)
Max rate of climb at S/L	1,370 m (4,500 ft)/min
Time to 3,000 m (9,840 ft)	2·4 min
Time to 6,000 m (19,680 ft)	5·5 min
Time to 9,000 m (29,520 ft)	10·2 min
Service ceiling	12,000 m (39,375 ft)
T-O run on grass	490 m (1,610 ft)
T-O to 15 m (50 ft)	640 m (2,100 ft)
Landing from 15 m (50 ft)	710 m (2,330 ft)
Landing run on grass	400 m (1,310 ft)
Max range at 9,000 m (29,520 ft), with tip-tanks full	669 nm (1,240 km; 770 miles)
Max endurance at 7,000 m (23,000 ft)	2 h 30 min

Soko J-1 Jastreb single-seat light attack aircraft, developed from the Galeb

SOKO J-1/RJ-1 JASTREB (HAWK)

The basic J-1 Jastreb is a single-seat light attack version of the G2-A Galeb, developed and produced for service with the Yugoslav Air Force. An export version is available, and the first overseas operator was the Zambian Air Force, which received four Jastrebs in early 1971.

In the J-1 Jastreb, the front cockpit of the G2-A Galeb trainer, with sideways-hinged (to starboard) canopy, is retained, a metal fairing replacing the rear canopy. The engine is the more powerful Rolls-Royce Bristol Viper 531. Other changes include the installation of improved day and night reconnaissance equipment, navigation and communications equipment, and self-contained engine starting. In other respects the airframe and power plant remain essentially unchanged except for some local strengthening and the provision of strongpoints for heavier underwing stores.

Currently in production and service are two attack versions and two tactical reconnaissance versions of the Jastreb, as follows:

J-1. Standard attack version for Yugoslav Air Force.

J-1-E. Export attack version with updated equipment. Ordered by unnamed foreign operators.

RJ-1. Tactical reconnaissance version for Yugoslav Air Force.

RJ-1-E. Export reconnaissance version with updated equipment.

In addition, there is a two-seat operational conversion and pilot proficiency training version, designated TJ-1. This is described separately.

The details given for the G2-A Galeb apply equally to the J-1, J-1-E, RJ-1 and RJ-1-E Jastreb, with the following exceptions:

TYPE: Single-seat light attack and tactical reconnaissance aircraft.

POWER PLANT: One Rolls-Royce Viper 531 turbojet engine, rated at 13·32 kN (3,000 lb st). Capacity of each wingtip tank 220 kg (485 lb). Provision for attaching two 4·44 kN (1,000 lb st) JATO rockets under fuselage for use at take-off or in flight.

ACCOMMODATION: Pilot only, on HSA (Folland) Type 1-B fully-automatic lightweight ejection seat. Cockpit air-conditioning to special order only.

SYSTEMS: Electrical system includes 6kW 24V generator and second battery, permitting independent engine starting without ground electrical supply. Two oxygen bottles supply high-pressure oxygen system of nominal 1,900 litres (67 cu ft) capacity, at a pressure of 138 bars (2,000 lb/sq in).

AVIONICS AND EQUIPMENT (J-1 and RJ-1): Full IFR instrumentation. Standard Telephones & Cables STR-9Z1 VHF com transceiver and Marconi AD 370B radio compass. The fuselage camera of the RJ-1 is supplemented by two further cameras in nose of tip-tanks, which are also available for the J-1 and J-1-E attack versions. An aerial target can be towed from a hook under the centre-fuselage. Brake parachute housed in fairing above jet nozzle.

AVIONICS AND EQUIPMENT (J-1-E and RJ-1-E): Nav/com equipment same as for G-2A-E Galeb export version. Photo-reconnaissance equipment of RJ-1-E consists of a daylight reconnaissance system comprising two Vinten 360/140A cameras with 3 in AEC lenses in nose of tip-tanks (also available on J-1-E attack version), and a third camera of the same type in the fuselage, with interchangeable lens units; and a night reconnaissance system comprising one Vinten 1025/527 camera at the fuselage station.

ARMAMENT (J-1 and J-1-E): Three 0·50 in Colt-Browning machine-guns in nose (with 135 rds/gun). Total of eight underwing weapon attachments. Two inboard attachments can carry two bombs of up to 250 kg each, two clusters of small bombs, two 200 litre napalm tanks, two pods each with twelve or sixteen 57 mm or four 128 mm rockets, two multiple carriers each with three 50 kg bombs, two bomblet containers, or two 45 kg photo flares. Other attachments can each carry a 127 mm rocket. Semi-automatic gyro gunsight and camera gun standard.

ARMAMENT (RJ-1 and RJ-1-E): Four underwing attachments, intended basically for carrying flash bombs for night photography, can be used also for carrying high-explosive or other types of bombs. The inboard pylons can each carry a single bomb of up to 250 kg, the outboard pylons up to 150 kg. No rocket armament. Otherwise same as for J-1 and J-1-E.

DIMENSIONS, EXTERNAL: As for Galeb, except:

Wing span over tip-tanks	11·68 m (38 ft 4 in)
Length overall	10·88 m (35 ft 8½ in)
Height overall	3·64 m (11 ft 11½ in)
Wheelbase	3·61 m (11 ft 10 in)

AREAS: As for Galeb

WEIGHTS:

Weight empty, equipped	2,820 kg (6,217 lb)
Max ramp weight	5,287 kg (11,655 lb)
Max T-O weight	5,100 kg (11,243 lb)
Max landing weight	3,750 kg (8,267 lb)

PERFORMANCE (T-O and landing runs on concrete):

Max level speed at 6,000 m (19,680 ft) at AUW of 3,968 kg (8,748 lb)	442 knots (820 km/h; 510 mph)
Max cruising speed at 5,000 m (16,400 ft), at AUW of 3,968 kg (8,748 lb)	399 knots (740 km/h; 460 mph)
Stalling speed, wheels down:	
flaps and airbrakes down	82 knots (152 km/h; 95 mph)
flaps and airbrakes up	94 knots (174 km/h; 108 mph)
Max rate of climb at S/L, at AUW of 3,968 kg (8,748 lb)	1,260 m (4,135 ft)/min
Service ceiling at AUW of 3,968 kg (8,748 lb)	12,000 m (39,375 ft)
T-O run at AUW of 3,968 kg (8,748 lb)	700 m (2,300 ft)
T-O run, rocket-assisted, at max T-O weight	404 m (1,325 ft)
T-O to 15 m (50 ft) at AUW of 3,968 kg (8,748 lb)	960 m (3,150 ft)
T-O to 15 m (50 ft), rocket-assisted, at max T-O weight	593 m (1,945 ft)
Landing from 15 m (50 ft)	1,100 m (3,610 ft)
Landing run	600 m (1,970 ft)
Max range at 9,000 m (29,520 ft), with tip-tanks full	820 nm (1,520 km; 945 miles)

SOKO TJ-1 JASTREB TRAINER

This two-seat operational conversion and pilot proficiency training version of the Jastreb is designed for maximum commonality with the J-1, retaining the full operational capability of the ground attack version. The prototype TJ-1 flew for the first time in mid-1974. Deliveries of production aircraft began in January 1975, to fulfil Yugoslav and export orders.

The details given for the J-1 Jastreb apply equally to the TJ-1 Jastreb Trainer, with the following exceptions:

TYPE: Two-seat operational conversion trainer.

ACCOMMODATION: Crew of two in tandem on HSA (Folland) Type 1-B ejection seats. Separate sideways-hinged (to starboard) jettisonable canopy over each cockpit.

AVIONICS AND EQUIPMENT: Same as for J-1 Jastreb, plus intercom and Iskra 75R4 marker beacon receiver. Only two cameras, in tip-tank nosecones.

WEIGHTS:

Weight empty, equipped	2,980 kg (6,570 lb)
Typical training mission T-O weight	4,350 kg (9,590 lb)
Max landing weight	3,950 kg (8,708 lb)

Cockpit section of the Jastreb Trainer

UTVA

FABRIKA AVIONA

Head Office and Works: Utva Zlatokrila 9, Pancevo
Telephone: 013 44 755
Telex: 131-16
General Manager: Marko Saranović
Manager of Aircraft Division: Zdravko Rapaić
Manager of Aircraft Development: Dragoslav Dimić

UTVA-75

The UTVA-75 is a side-by-side two-seat training, glider towing and utility lightplane, which was projected, designed and built in partnership by UTVA-Pancevo, Prva Petoletka-Trstenik, Vazduhoplovnotehnicki Institut and Institut Masinskog Fakulteta of Belgrade. Design was started in 1974. Construction of two prototypes was undertaken in 1975; the first of these flew for the first time on 20 May 1976 and the second on 18 December 1976. Series production began immediately and is continuing.

Type: Two-seat light aircraft.

Wings: Cantilever low-wing monoplane, with short-span centre-section and two constant-chord outer panels. Wing section NACA 65_2415. Dihedral 0° on centre-section, 6° on outer panels. Conventional all-metal structure. Ailerons and flaps along entire trailing-edge of outer panels, except for tips. Flettner trim tab on each aileron.

Fuselage: Conventional all-metal semi-monocoque structure.

Tail Unit: Cantilever all-metal structure, with sweptback vertical surfaces. Fluted skin on fin and rudder. Elevator and rudder horn-balanced. Trim tab in elevator. Flettner trim tab on rudder.

Landing Gear: Non-retractable tricycle type, with single wheel on each unit, and small tail bumper. Prva Petoletka-Trstenik oleo-pneumatic shock-absorbers. Dunlop tyres, size 6·00-6 on main wheels, 5·00-5 on nosewheel. Prva Petoletka-Trstenik hydraulic brakes.

Power Plant: One 134 kW (180 hp) Lycoming IO-360-B1F flat-four engine, driving a Hartzell HC-C2YK-1BF/F7666A two-blade metal variable-pitch propeller. Two integral fuel tanks in wings, total capacity 160 litres (35 Imp gallons). Provision for carrying two 100 litre (22 Imp gallon) drop-tanks under wings, raising max total capacity to 360 litres (79 Imp gallons). Oil capacity 10 litres (2·2 Imp gallons).

Accommodation: Two seats side-by-side in enclosed cabin, with large upward-opening canopy door over each seat, hinged on centreline. Cabin heated and ventilated.

Systems: Dual hydraulic systems. 12V electrical system, with 35Ah battery, navigation lights, rotating beacon and landing lights as standard equipment.

Avionics and Equipment: King KY 195B radio optional. Standard equipment includes radio compass.

Armament and Military Equipment: Standard fittings for light weapon loads underwing.

Dimensions, external:

Wing span	9·73 m (31 ft 11 in)
Wing chord (constant)	1·55 m (5 ft 1 in)
Length overall	7·11 m (23 ft 4 in)
Height overall	3·15 m (10 ft 4 in)
Tailplane span	3·80 m (12 ft 5½ in)
Wheel track	2·58 m (8 ft 5½ in)
Wheelbase	1·99 m (6 ft 6¼ in)
Propeller diameter	1·93 m (6 ft 4 in)
Propeller ground clearance	0·295 m (11¾ in)

Area:

Wings, gross	14·63 m² (157·5 sq ft)

Weights:

Weight empty, equipped	650 kg (1,433 lb)
Max T-O weight	960 kg (2,116 lb)

Performance (at max T-O weight):

Max level speed	118 knots (220 km/h; 136 mph)
Econ cruising speed	89 knots (165 km/h; 102 mph)
Stalling speed, engine idling:	
flaps up	51·5 knots (95 km/h; 59 mph)
25° flap	43 knots (80 km/h; 50 mph)
Max rate of climb at S/L	270 m (885 ft)/min
Service ceiling	4,500 m (14,760 ft)
T-O run	125 m (410 ft)
T-O to 15 m (50 ft)	250 m (820 ft)
Landing from 15 m (50 ft)	350 m (1,150 ft)
Range with drop-tanks, no reserves	1,078 nm (2,000 km; 1,242 miles)

The nearer of these UTVA-75 two-seat training and utility aircraft is armed with four underwing rocket launchers

HOMEBUILT AIRCRAFT
(including Man-powered and Racing Aircraft)

ARGENTINA

AVEX
ASOCIACION ARGENTINA DE CONSTRUCTORES DE AVIONES EXPERIMENTALES

Acassuso 1640, Olivos-FCNGBM, Buenos Aires
Telephone: 797-1629
PRESIDENT: Yves Arrambide
SECRETARY: Norberto Marino

AVEX is an Argentine light aircraft association for amateur constructors, similar in concept to the Experimental Aircraft Association in the USA. It was formed in 1968 and its members include many people well known among the Argentine aircraft industry, including specialists in most aspects of materials and construction, including the use of glassfibre and plastics.

AVEX activities have been described in the 1971-72 and subsequent editions of *Jane's*. Of many recent aircraft projects by AVEX members, those that have flown include two Armar I Gorrions, the Yakstas racer, and examples of the Evans VP-1, Jodel D.9 and Mignet H-14.

GHINASSI HELICOPTERS

Sr Sesto Ghinassi is a specialist in, and racer of, motorcycles. He built a small single-seat helicopter, using unapproved materials and a 22·4 kW (30 hp) engine developed by himself.

This aircraft (described and illustrated in the 1973-74 *Jane's*) was later scrapped, but Sr Ghinassi currently has a new helicopter under construction, for which he is using aircraft quality materials. Available details follow:

ROTOR SYSTEM AND DRIVE: Variable-pitch main and tail rotors, the former driven by chain drive from engine. Symmetrical-section blades, with 7% thickness/chord ratio, of wooden construction with aluminium skin. Max rpm of main rotor 400.

FUSELAGE: Welded steel tube structure.

POWER PLANT: One 22·4 kW (30 hp) 470 cc two-cylinder four-stroke turbine-cooled engine of Ghinassi design; max rpm 6,300. Fuel tank capacity 20 litres (4·4 Imp gallons).

ACCOMMODATION: Single seat.

DIMENSIONS, EXTERNAL:
- Main rotor diameter: 6·00 m (19 ft 8¼ in)
- Tail rotor diameter: 0·60 m (1 ft 11¾ in)
- Main rotor blade chord: 0·22 m (8¾ in)
- Fuselage length: 4·00 m (13 ft 1½ in)
- Fuselage width: 1·00 m (3 ft 3¼ in)
- Height overall: 1·55 m (5 ft 1 in)

PERFORMANCE (estimated):
- Range: 162 nm (300 km; 186 miles)

AUSTRALIA

CORBY
JOHN C. CORBY

86 Eton Street, Sutherland, NSW 2232

Mr Corby, a consultant aero engineer, has designed and is marketing plans for a single-seat wooden ultra-light aircraft known as the Starlet. By March 1979 at least nine Starlets had been completed and a further 40 were known to be under construction in Australia, Tasmania and New Zealand, including a metal version.

CORBY CJ-1 STARLET

The first Starlet (VH-ULV) was built by a group of about ten members of the Latrobe Valley division of the Australian Ultra Light Aircraft Association. Mr Erle Jones (Secretary and former President of the ULAA, Latrobe Valley Aero Club) was responsible for test flying the completed aircraft, with Mr John Brown acting as instructor in building techniques. Details of this aircraft were given in the 1974-75 *Jane's*.

The following description applies to the standard Starlet, as built to current plans:

TYPE: Single-seat ultra-light homebuilt aircraft.

WINGS: Cantilever low-wing monoplane of wooden construction. Wing section NACA 43012A. Dihedral 6°. Incidence 2° 30′ at root, −1° at tip. Laminated main spar of solid spruce, subspars of spruce, built-up girder-type ribs and D-shaped nose section. Plywood covering from leading-edge to main spar, remainder fabric covered. Provision for dismantling into two equal halves. Ailerons, of spruce with birch plywood covering, deflect 15° up and down.

FUSELAGE: Plywood-covered spruce structure.

TAIL UNIT: Cantilever type, of similar construction to wings. Fixed-incidence tailplane. Plywood-covered fixed surfaces; fabric-covered rudder and elevators. Elevators deflect 30° up, 20° down; rudder deflects 25° to left and right.

LANDING GEAR: Non-retractable two-wheel type standard. Separate spring steel leaf-type shock-absorbing main legs, attached directly to fuselage via a solid spruce/ash beam which also serves as the wing leading-edge attachment member. Wheels, tyres and brakes of customer's choice, subject to main wheels of 89 mm (3½ in) minimum diameter with 4·00-4 tyres and Olympic go-kart hubs. Sturmey Archer cycle drum/shoe brakes may be used. Leaf-spring tailskid, or tailwheel at customer's option. Wheel fairings optional.

POWER PLANT: Any suitable engine of up to 56 kW (75 hp) and 72 kg (160 lb) weight, driving a two-blade propeller. Fuel tank, capacity 36-45 litres (8-10 Imp gallons), aft of engine firewall. Oil capacity 2·25 kg (5 lb).

ACCOMMODATION: Single seat. Sliding canopy optional. Baggage locker behind seat.

DIMENSIONS, EXTERNAL:
- Wing span: 5·64 m (18 ft 6 in)
- Wing chord at root: 1·32 m (4 ft 4 in)
- Wing area, gross: 6·36 m² (68·50 sq ft)
- Length overall: 4·50 m (14 ft 9 in)
- Fuselage: Max width: 0·55 m (1 ft 9¾ in)
- Height overall: 1·47 m (4 ft 10 in)
- Tailplane span: 1·98 m (6 ft 6 in)
- Wheel track: 1·37 m (4 ft 6 in)
- Propeller diameter: 1·37 m (4 ft 6 in)
- Propeller ground clearance: 0·255 m (10 in)

WEIGHTS:
- Weight empty: 183-190 kg (405-420 lb)
- Max T-O weight (semi-aerobatic): 295 kg (650 lb)

PERFORMANCE (prototype, with 36·5 kW; 49 hp engine, at 295 kg; 650 lb AUW):
- Never-exceed speed: 138 knots (255 km/h; 159 mph) IAS
- Max level speed: 117 knots (217 km/h; 135 mph)
- Max cruising speed: 107 knots (198 km/h; 123 mph)
- Stalling speed, power off: 42 knots (79 km/h; 49 mph); 30 knots (57 km/h; 35 mph) IAS
- Typical rate of climb at S/L: 213-259 m (700-850 ft)/min
- Service ceiling: 4,420 m (14,500 ft)
- T-O to, and landing from, 15 m (50 ft): 305-335 m (1,000-1,100 ft)
- *g* limits: ±4·5

TODHUNTER
R. W. TODHUNTER

5 Leemon Street, Condell Park, NSW 2200

In 1963, Mr Reg Todhunter began the design of a man-powered aircraft named the Skycycle. His brother Ern shared in its construction, which required approximately 4,000 man-hours of work over a six-year period, beginning in 1970. Following an accident during testing in January 1977, which broke the port wing, the original upper-surface spoiler system was replaced by a new system for lateral and yaw control. This involved replacement of the original wingtips by new tapered tips set at a nominal (but adjustable) anhedral of 30°, embodying controllable trailing-edge flaps and with small balancer wheels in the extreme tips. The flaps are intended to provide some aileron control, with extended 'up' travel to provide yaw control. The tips are also expected to reduce induced drag. Other refinements have also been incorporated into the rebuilt Skycycle.

The first flight test of the modified aircraft had not been undertaken by January 1979, as construction of the new transporter-trailer had not been completed.

Mr Todhunter has also begun building an ultra lightweight powered sailplane, which was expected to be completed by October 1979. No details of this aircraft are available at the present time.

TODHUNTER SKYCYCLE

TYPE: Single-seat canard man-powered aircraft.

WINGS: Cantilever high-wing monoplane, made in five parts: a long-span centre-section and two outer panels of constant chord, and two tapered wingtips. Abrial reflexed section. Thickness/chord ratio 15%. Dihedral 3° on outer panels. Anhedral on tips nominally 30° but adjustable. Incidence 12° 30′. No sweepback. Spars have spruce booms and balsa shear webs at 45°. Styrene foam ribs with balsa capstrips. D-type leading-edge of balsa construction. Light alloy (2024-T3) fittings. 0·005 in. Melinex plastics film covering overall. Wingtip trailing-edge flaps have travel of 10° down and 50° up. All-moving foreplane of similar construction to fin, actuated by wooden tube pushrod from hand controls.

FUSELAGE: Sugar pine box girder structure, with balsa stringers and styrene foam fairings, all covered by 0·001 in Mylar film. Drive box constructed from 0·02 in aluminium sheet.

TAIL UNIT: Fin only, constructed of sugar pine with plywood spars, styrene foam ribs and balsa leading-edge. Mylar film covering overall.

LANDING GEAR: Non-retractable and unpowered main-wheel, diameter 0·31 m (12·5 in), in tandem with nose-wheel of 0·13 m (5 in) diameter. Wingtip wheels of 0·102 m (4 in) diameter. Pneumatic tyres.

POWER SYSTEM: Pilot drives two-blade propeller via bicycle pedals and chain, producing approx 0·25 kW (0·32 hp). Propeller, mounted in pusher configuration at top of tail fin, consists of an aluminium tube spar embedded in solid styrene foam, covered with glass cloth and epoxy resin, and finished in polyurethane paint. Propeller rpm 210 in cruising flight.

ACCOMMODATION: Pilot only, reclined at 35° under removable canopy.

DIMENSIONS, EXTERNAL:
- Wing span: 20·27 m (66 ft 6 in)
- Wing chord, constant, except for anhedral tip sections: 0·99 m (3 ft 3 in)
- Wing chord at tips: 0·15 m (6 in)
- Wing aspect ratio: 20·85
- Length overall: 4·11 m (13 ft 6 in)
- Foreplane span: 3·66 m (12 ft 0 in)
- Propeller diameter: 2·74 m (9 ft 0 in)

AREAS:
- Wings, gross, projected: 19·7 m² (212 sq ft)
- Foreplane: 1·21 m² (13 sq ft)

WEIGHTS:
- Weight empty: 40 kg (88 lb)
- Max T-O weight: 107 kg (235 lb)

PERFORMANCE:
- Estimated flying speed 18·2 knots (34 km/h; 21 mph)

Todhunter Skycycle man-powered aircraft before the latest modifications, with all-moving foreplane and without rudder or anhedral wingtips

Corby Starlet single-seat homebuilt aircraft

CANADA

FRIZZLE

JAMES R. FRIZZLE

Allen Heights, RR 3 Armdale, Nova Scotia B3L 4T3

Mr J. R. Frizzle, a retired RCAF Group Captain, built a small two-seat amphibian called the Drake, which had been designed by Mr J. Eut Tileston of Carmichael, California, USA. Construction began in 1971 and the first flight was made in May 1977. After logging four flying hours, Mr Frizzle sold the Drake. The new owner had a fatal accident in the aircraft, following a stall, on 15 October 1978, after a further 20 flying hours had been accumulated.

FRIZZLE (TILESTON) DRAKE

Type: Two-seat light amphibian.

Wings: Cantilever shoulder-wing monoplane. Wing section 9155. Dihedral 3° on outer wing panels. Incidence 2° 30'. Laminated sitka spruce spars; birch plywood covering. Ailerons and flaps of plywood construction. Ailerons drooped with flaps. Stabilising floats beneath wings.

Fuselage: Conventional flying-boat hull of wooden construction; sitka spruce frames, covered with birch plywood.

Tail Unit: Cantilever tail unit of similar construction to wings. Sweptback vertical surfaces. Tailplane had inverted camber. Adjustable tabs on elevators.

Landing Gear: Retractable tricycle type. Main units retracted manually into stabilising floats, with spring-loaded assist mechanism. Cord-type shock absorption. Tyres size 5·00-5. Hydraulic disc brakes.

Power Plant: One 97 kW (130 hp) Franklin Sport 4 flat-four engine, driving a three-blade adjustable-pitch wooden propeller. Two fuel tanks in wings, total capacity 83·2 litres (22 US gallons). Refuelling point on top of wing, near root.

Accommodation: Two persons in tandem beneath rearward-hinged transparent canopy. Dual controls. Baggage area aft of seats.

System: 40A alternator for electrical supply.

Electronics: Genave 100B Alpha nav/com.

Dimensions, external:

Wing span	8·23 m (27 ft 0 in)
Wing area, gross	12·08 m² (130 sq ft)
Wing chord, constant	1·40 m (4 ft 7 in)
Length overall	6·86 m (22 ft 6 in)
Height overall	2·13 m (7 ft 0 in)
Tailplane span	3·05 m (10 ft 0 in)
Wheel track	2·18 m (7 ft 2 in)
Wheelbase	1·78 m (5 ft 10 in)

Weights:

Weight empty	454 kg (1,000 lb)
Max T-O weight	726 kg (1,600 lb)

Performance:

Max level speed	122 knots (225 km/h; 140 mph)
Max cruising speed	113 knots (209 km/h; 130 mph)
Econ cruising speed	104 knots (193 km/h; 120 mph)

JEAN ST-GERMAIN

CENTRE DE RECHERCHES JEAN ST-GERMAIN INC

924 St-Pierre, Drummondville, PQ
Telephone: (819) 477 1221
Designer: Jean Saint-Germain
General Manager: Gilbert Lapointe

JEAN ST-GERMAIN RAZ-MUT

The Raz-Mut was designed by Jean Saint-Germain as an easy-to-build and easy-to-fly ultra-light aircraft, suitable for home construction, for sport flying by amateurs, and for a variety of utility applications including agricultural spraying and survey work. Design of the aircraft was started in May 1976 and the original prototype, built at Mr Saint-Germain's research centre, flew for the first time in September 1976, powered by a 33 kW (44 hp) Kohler K-440-2AS-M aircooled two-stroke engine. It proved to be underpowered, and the third Raz-Mut, demonstrated at the 1977 EAA Fly-in at Oshkosh and shown in the accompanying illustration, has a 1,700 cc Volkswagen engine. Also at the Fly-in was a then-unflown version with the alternative McCulloch MC-431 engine. Both embodied a number of aerodynamic refinements compared with the first Raz-Mut, including a drooped wing leading-edge, upper-surface fences and wide fairings over the wing bracing struts.

Kit production began in December 1976; by Autumn 1977 a total of 39 kits had been delivered and seven amateur-built Raz-Muts were flying in Canada.

The basic kit contains all raw materials and components needed to build the Raz-Mut, including the engine and propeller but excluding instruments, battery and seat cushion. A more expensive kit offers the materials and components in pre-finished state, so that only a simple tool kit is required to complete the aircraft. As an alternative, building and servicing instructions, and a list of materials, are available to those who are willing to purchase their own materials and perform all the machining and other work.

Type: Single-seat ultra-light aircraft.

Wings: Strut-braced high-wing monoplane, with single wide aerofoil-section bracing strut each side. Modified NACA 4400 wing section. Constant chord. Some dihedral. Plain aileron and three-position flap form entire trailing-edge of each wing. Entire wing and control surfaces of aluminium, including covering. Shallow fence above each wing between aileron and flap. End-plates standard.

Fuselage: Open structure of square-section aluminium tube, bolted together.

Tail Unit: All-moving horizontal surface with ground-adjustable tab at centre of trailing-edge. Small fin and large-area horn-balanced rudder with ground adjustable tab. All control surfaces cable-actuated. Entire structure of aluminium with fabric covering.

Landing Gear: Non-retractable tricycle type. Brake on nosewheel. Small tail bumper wheel in rear end of keel member. Skis and floats optional.

Power Plant: One 52 kW (70 hp) 1,700 cc Volkswagen flat-four four-stroke or 53·5 kW (72 hp) McCulloch MC-431 flat-four two-stroke engine, driving a two-blade fixed-pitch wooden pusher propeller through multiple belts. Fuel tank, capacity 23 litres (6 US gallons), aft of seat. Provision for second, similar, tank. Manual or electric engine starting.

Accommodation: Pilot only, on open seat. Glassfibre cabin enclosure optional.

Dimensions, external:

Wing span	7·01 m (23 ft 0 in)
Wing area, gross	8·55 m² (92 sq ft)
Wing chord, constant	1·22 m (4 ft 0 in)
Length overall	5·58 m (18 ft 3½ in)
Height overall	1·77 m (5 ft 9½ in)
Propeller diameter	1·09 m (3 ft 7 in)

Weights (VW engine):

Weight empty	204 kg (450 lb)
Max T-O weight	363 kg (800 lb)

Performance (VW engine):

Max level speed	74 knots (136 km/h; 85 mph)
Max cruising speed	61 knots (112 km/h; 70 mph)
Landing speed	39 knots (73 km/h; 45 mph)
Max rate of climb at S/L	198 m (650 ft)/min
Service ceiling	2,745 m (9,000 ft)
T-O run	61 m (200 ft)
Landing run	54 m (175 ft)
Range with standard fuel	130 nm (240 km; 150 miles)

REPLICA PLANS

REPLICA PLANS

PO Box 94248, Richmond, BC V6Y 2A6

The SE-5A replica was designed to be an easy-to-build and inexpensive 85% scale representation of the famous First World War fighter, although exact reproduction was waived in favour of making the aircraft simple to construct, using modern and more readily available materials.

Design of the aircraft began in 1969, in which year construction of the first prototype also started. The SE-5A prototypes were designed for Continental engines ranging from 48·5 to 74·5 kW (65-100 hp), but larger engines can be installed to the individual homebuilder's preference. The first prototype flew for the first time in 1970 and certification has been granted by the FAA in the Experimental (homebuilt) category.

Plans are available to amateur builders, and more than 300 sets had been sold by early 1979.

REPLICA PLANS SE-5A REPLICA

Type: Single-seat sporting biplane.

Wings: Braced biplane wings of Clark CYH section. Dihedral 3°. Incidence 3°. Ailerons on lower wings only. Centre-section of upper wing houses a small tank which can be used as an auxiliary fuel tank or smoke tank, or can be left out at building stage. The centre-section is carried on four spruce cabane struts and is braced with stainless steel cables and turnbuckles. Spruce interplane struts, with 4130 steel end fittings. Stainless steel flying, landing and incidence wires. Wing ribs of mahogany plywood, with cap strips; spruce spars. From the front spar forward, the leading-edge is covered with glassfibre or aluminium. Wings are fabric-covered.

Fuselage: Ply-skinned box structure, with fabric-covered turtledeck and aluminium-covered forward top decking. Dummy Vickers machine-gun in housing on port side of fuselage, and gunsights on decking forward of windscreen.

Tail Unit: Tail surfaces built on spruce spars, with structure similar to that of wings except for drag bracing. Pushrod-operated elevators. Cable-operated rudder, with a horn for tailwheel steering.

Landing Gear: Non-retractable tailwheel type. Bungee cord shock-absorption. Converted motorcycle wheels on main units, size 3·25-16. Size 6·00-2 tailwheel. Mechanical brakes.

Power Plant: Various engines can be installed. Performance figures quoted relate to aircraft with 63·5 kW (85 hp) Continental C85 flat-four engine, driving a two-blade fixed-pitch wooden propeller. Fuel capacity 72 litres (19 US gallons). Oil capacity 3·8 litres (1 US gallon).

Accommodation: Single seat in open cockpit.

Frizzle Drake light amphibian

Jean St-Germain Raz-Mut (1,700 cc Volkswagen engine) *(Howard Levy)*

Replica Plans SE-5A, an 85% scale representation of a First World War fighter *(Tony Swain)*

Prototype PGK-1 Hirondelle two-seat light aircraft

Dimensions, external:
- Wing span 6·96 m (22 ft 10 in)
- Wing chord, constant 1·27 m (4 ft 2 in)
- Wing area, gross 13·01 m² (140 sq ft)
- Height overall 2·18 m (7 ft 2 in)
- Wheel track 1·52 m (5 ft 0 in)
- Propeller diameter 1·83 m (6 ft 0 in)

Weights:
- Weight empty 358 kg (790 lb)
- Max T-O weight 499 kg (1,100 lb)

Performance:
- Max level speed at S/L 78 knots (145 km/h; 90 mph)
- Max cruising speed 74 knots (137 km/h; 85 mph)
- Stalling speed 30·5 knots (57 km/h; 35 mph)
- Max rate of climb at S/L 152 m (500 ft)/min

WESTERN

WESTERN AIRCRAFT SUPPLIES

623 Markerville Road NE, Calgary, Alberta T2E SX1
Telephone: (403) 276 3087
Director: Jean J. Peters

Western Aircraft Supplies markets materials for amateur aircraft constructors, and has sold plans for construction of the RL-3 Monsoon, a two-seat light aircraft originally designed in India. At least 12 sets of plans for the Monsoon and five kits of materials were sold. Details of this aircraft can be found in the 1977-78 *Jane's*.

Western has developed another aircraft, of basic wooden construction, known as the PGK-1 Hirondelle. Plans and wood kits are available to amateur constructors, as well as preformed engine cowlings, windscreens and fuel tanks.

PGK-1 HIRONDELLE

Design of the PGK-1 Hirondelle began in 1969 and construction of a prototype (C-GWYL) started in July 1970. First flight was achieved on 27 June 1976. It is said to be suited for cross-country and recreational flying, and simple enough for first-time constructors to build. All fabric covering is glued in place, rather than stitched.

Type: Two-seat light aircraft.

Wings: Cantilever low-wing monoplane of constant chord. Wing section NACA 23012. Dihedral 4° from roots. Incidence 4° at root, 2° at tip. No sweepback. Wooden box spar and plank-type auxiliary rear spar. Plywood ribs. Dacron fabric covered, with dope and polyurethane finish. Ailerons of wood and fabric construction. No flaps or tabs.

Fuselage: Conventional structure of spruce bulkheads and spruce longerons, plywood covered to rear of cabin, with outer covering of Dacron. Cabin constructed of wood formers with polystyrene foam infill and glassfibre top. Rounded corners of turtledeck formed from foam and glassfibre. Rear fuselage Dacron-covered, with dope and polyurethane finish.

Tail Unit: Cantilever structure of capped spars and plywood ribs, all plywood-covered and with outer covering of Dacron. Tab in starboard elevator.

Landing Gear: Non-retractable tailwheel type. Tapered spring steel main struts; 5·00-5 tyres on main wheels. Industrial Dynamics brakes. Cessna 150 main-wheel fairings.

Power Plant: One 86 kW (115 hp) Lycoming O-235-C1B flat-four engine, driving a Warnke three-blade ground-adjustable propeller. Two glassfibre fuel tanks in leading-edges of wings, each 54·5 litres (12 Imp gallons) capacity. Oil capacity 5·7 litres (1·25 Imp gallons).

Accommodation: Two seats side by side in enclosed cabin. Dual controls and heater standard.

System: Electrical system includes 12V 20A generator for lights, radio and fuel pump.

Electronics: Genave Alpha 200B radio and VOR.

Dimensions, external:
- Wing span 7·92 m (26 ft 0 in)
- Wing chord, constant 1·40 m (4 ft 7 in)
- Wing area, gross 10·96 m² (118 sq ft)
- Wing aspect ratio 5·7
- Length overall 6·27 m (20 ft 7 in)
- Height overall 2·29 m (7 ft 6 in)
- Wheel track 2·03 m (6 ft 8 in)
- Wheelbase 4·39 m (14 ft 5 in)
- Propeller diameter 1·68 m (5 ft 6 in)
- Propeller ground clearance 0·20 m (8 in)

Weights:
- Weight empty, equipped 428 kg (944 lb)
- Max T-O weight 669 kg (1,475 lb)

Performance (at max T-O weight):
- Never-exceed speed 160 knots (297 km/h; 185 mph)
- Max level speed 123 knots (228 km/h; 142 mph)
- Max cruising speed 117 knots (217 km/h; 135 mph)
- Stalling speed 52·5 knots (96·5 km/h; 60 mph)
- Max rate of climb at S/L over 305 m (1,000 ft)/min
- Service ceiling 3,840 m (12,600 ft)
- T-O run approx 228 m (750 ft)
- Endurance, with 45 min reserves 3 h 36 min

ZENAIR

ZENAIR LTD

236 Richmond Street, Richmond Hill, Ontario L4C 3Y8
Telephone: (416) 884 9044
President and Designer: Christophe Heintz

M Heintz, a professional aeronautical engineer, participated in the design of several of the aircraft produced by Avions Pierre Robin. While in France, he also designed and built the prototype of a two-seat light aircraft named the Zénith, intended for amateur construction.

Many Zéniths are now flying, and others are under construction, including single-seat and three-seat models, as described in this entry. In addition, Mr Heintz' Zenair company is developing the four-seat Zénith-CH 400 for factory production (see main Aircraft section).

Zenair Ltd has ten full-time employees, producing on average one kit per week.

ZÉNITH-CH 200

Work on the Zénith-CH 200 began in October 1968; the prototype, registered F-WPZY (later C-FEYC), flew for the first time on 22 March 1970 and was granted French CNRA (homebuilt experimental aircraft) certification. In October 1970 the original wing of NACA 64A315 (modified) section was replaced by one offering improved low-speed characteristics.

In 1974 the Zénith-CH 200 was granted the National Association of Sport Aircraft Designers (NASAD, USA) 'seal of quality' No. 108.

Sets of plans and a constructional manual for the Zénith-CH 200 are available to amateur builders, as follows:

French manual and metric measurements from D. Triques, 23 Ave Edouard Belin, Fontaine d'Ouche, F21 Dijon.

English manual and drawings to US standards, with English and metric measurements, from Zenair, which offers materials, parts and complete kits for all current Heintz designs. Zenair also designs and manufactures wooden propellers for engines of up to 134 kW (180 hp).

By 1979 more than 700 sets of plans had been sold in all parts of the world, and over 40 aircraft were flying.

The Zénith-CH 200 is approved by the Australian DCA and the New Zealand airworthiness authorities. Several kits have been exported to these countries, as well as to South Africa, Belgium, Sweden, the UK and Switzerland.

During the 1976 eight-day EAA Fly-in at Oshkosh, Chris Heintz, assisted by volunteer experienced metal workers, built a Zénith-CH 200 from standard prefabricated kit components (as available to the homebuilder) and flew it on the last day of the meeting.

The single-seat Mono Z-CH 100 and three-seat Tri-Z-CH 300 are variations of the basic design and are described separately. Several optional items are available for all three aircraft, including tailwheel landing gear, a forward-sliding canopy, dual control column (not on CH 100) and detachable wings.

The following description applies to the standard Zénith-CH 200, of which Zenair was producing five complete kits each month in early 1978:

Type: Two-seat all-metal homebuilt light aircraft, with ultimate stress factor of 9*g*.

Wings: Cantilever low-wing monoplane. Constant-chord

wings, of NACA 64A515 (modified) section. Dihedral 6° from roots. Single-spar aluminium alloy structure, with blind riveted aluminium alloy skin. Hoerner wing-tips. Aluminium alloy piano-hinged ailerons and electrically-actuated plain flaps on trailing-edge.

FUSELAGE: Conventional aluminium alloy stressed-skin structure, of basically rectangular section with rounded top-decking.

TAIL UNIT: Rectangular one-piece all-moving tailplane, with combined trim and anti-servo tabs. Plans show rudder only, with slight sweepback. Conventional fin and rudder can be fitted if desired. Tailplane and rudder are both single-spar structures with ribs and skin of aluminium alloy.

LANDING GEAR: Non-retractable tricycle type, with rubber-block shock-absorbers. Manual locking of steerable nosewheel. All three Cleveland wheels and tyres size 6·00-6. Hydraulically-actuated disc brakes on main units. Streamlined glassfibre fairings over all three wheels and legs. At least one aircraft is fitted with twin floats in summer and skis in winter.

POWER PLANT: Design suitable for engines from 63·5 kW (85 hp) to 119 kW (160 hp). Fuel tank in fuselage, aft of seats, capacity 90 litres (20 Imp gallons). Optional fuel tanks in wing leading-edges, total capacity 72·5 litres (16 Imp gallons). Refuelling point aft of canopy on port side.

ACCOMMODATION: Side-by-side seating for pilot and one passenger under sideways-opening (to starboard) Plexiglas canopy. Dual controls, with single control column located centrally between seats. Space for 35 kg (77 lb) of baggage aft of seats. Cabin heated and ventilated.

SYSTEMS: 12V battery and generator provide power for engine starting, fuel pump and flap actuation. VHF radio.

DIMENSIONS, EXTERNAL:

Wing span	7·00 m (22 ft 11¾ in)
Wing chord, constant	1·40 m (4 ft 7 in)
Wing area, gross	9·80 m² (105·9 sq ft)
Wing aspect ratio	5
Length overall	6·30 m (20 ft 8 in)
Height overall	1·85 m (6 ft 0¾ in)
Tailplane span	2·30 m (7 ft 6½ in)
Wheel track	2·25 m (7 ft 4½ in)
Wheelbase	1·42 m (4 ft 8 in)
Min ground turning radius	4·00 m (13 ft 1¾ in)
Propeller diameter	1·83 m (6 ft 0 in)
Propeller ground clearance	0·25 m (9¾ in)

DIMENSION, INTERNAL:

Cabin: Max width	1·01 m (3 ft 3¾ in)

WEIGHTS (with 74·5 kW; 100 hp engine):

Weight empty, equipped	400 kg (881 lb)
Normal T-O and landing weight	650 kg (1,433 lb)
Max T-O weight	680 kg (1,499 lb)

PERFORMANCE (at max T-O weight. A: 74·5 kW; 100 hp engine, B: 112 kW; 150 hp engine):

Max level speed at S/L:	
A	126 knots (233 km/h; 145 mph)
B	143 knots (266 km/h; 165 mph)
Cruising speed (75% power) at S/L:	
A	110 knots (205 km/h; 127 mph)
B	132 knots (245 km/h; 152 mph)
Cruising speed (75% power) at 2,750 m (9,000 ft):	
A	116 knots (215 km/h; 134 mph)
B	135 knots (251 km/h; 156 mph)
Stalling speed, flaps down:	
A, B	46 knots (85 km/h; 53 mph)
Max rate of climb at S/L:	
A	240 m (787 ft)/min
B	426 m (1,400 ft)/min
Service ceiling:	
A	4,600 m (15,100 ft)
B	over 4,875 m (16,000 ft)
Range with max fuel, no reserves (75% power)	
A	432 nm (800 km; 497 miles)
B	451 nm (836 km; 520 miles)

MONO Z-CH 100

The single-seat Mono Z-CH 100 is of generally similar all-metal construction to the two-seat Zénith, but is slightly smaller overall and is designed to be powered by engines in the 37·25 to 74·5 kW (50 to 100 hp) range. The prototype (C-GNYM), which has a Volkswagen engine, made its first flight on 8 May 1975. Like the two-seat Zénith, it is stressed to ± 9*g* ultimate at normal max T-O weight.

Construction drawings and manual, materials, parts and complete kits to build the Mono Zénith are available from Zenair and 40 sets had been sold by early 1979.

TYPE: Single-seat homebuilt light aircraft.

WINGS: Cantilever low-wing monoplane. Wing section GA(PC) 1. Thickness/chord ratio 15%. Dihedral 6°. Incidence 7° 30′. Single-spar aluminium alloy structure, with aluminium alloy skin, blind riveted. Aluminium alloy piano-hinged ailerons. Wings easily removable.

FUSELAGE: Conventional aluminium alloy stressed-skin structure, of basically rectangular section, with rounded top-decking.

TAIL UNIT: Rectangular one-piece all-moving tailplane, with automatic and controllable trim tab. Single-spar structures, with ribs and skins of aluminium.

LANDING GEAR: Non-retractable tricycle type, with rubber-block shock-absorbers. Tailwheel gear optional. All three Cleveland wheels and tyres size 5·00-5. Hydraulically-actuated disc brakes.

POWER PLANT: One 41 kW (55 hp) 1,700 cc converted Volkswagen motor-car engine in prototype, driving a Zenair wooden propeller. Continental engine optional. Fuel tank in fuselage, capacity 54·5 litres (12 Imp gallons).

ACCOMMODATION: Single seat under Plexiglas canopy. Baggage compartment aft of seat, capacity 11·3 kg (25 lb).

DIMENSIONS, EXTERNAL:

Wing span	6·71 m (22 ft 0 in)
Wing chord, constant	1·27 m (4 ft 2 in)
Wing area, gross	8·50 m² (91·5 sq ft)
Wing aspect ratio	5·27
Length overall	5·94 m (19 ft 6 in)
Tailplane span	2·26 m (7 ft 5 in)
Wheel track	2·13 m (7 ft 0 in)
Wheelbase	1·27 m (4 ft 2 in)
Propeller diameter	1·47 m (4 ft 10 in)

WEIGHTS:

Weight empty	263 kg (580 lb)
Max T-O weight:	
VW engine	413 kg (910 lb)
74·5 kW; 100 hp engine	444 kg (980 lb)

PERFORMANCE (A: 1,700 cc Volkswagen, B: 48·5 kW; 65 hp, C: 74·5 kW; 100 hp engine):

Max level speed:	
A	103 knots (190 km/h; 118 mph)
B	109 knots (200 km/h; 125 mph)
C	130 knots (240 km/h; 150 mph)
Cruising speed (75% power):	
A	91 knots (170 km/h; 105 mph)
B	97 knots (180 km/h; 112 mph)
C	118 knots (218 km/h; 135 mph)
Stalling speed:	
A, B, C	41 knots (76 km/h; 47 mph)
Max rate of climb at S/L:	
A	200 m (610 ft)/min
B	220 m (720 ft)/min
C	490 m (1,500 ft)/min
Service ceiling: A	3,050 m (10,000 ft)
T-O run: A	183 m (600 ft)
T-O to 15 m (50 ft): A	335 m (1,100 ft)
Landing run: A	152 m (500 ft)
Range with 55 litres (12 Imp gallons) fuel:	
A, B	350 nm (645 km; 400 miles)
C	312 nm (580 km; 360 miles)
Endurance with 55 litres (12 Imp gallons) fuel:	
A, B	4 h 0 min
C	2 h 30 min

TRI-Z-CH 300

The three-seat Tri-Z-CH 300 is a 'stretched' version of the two-seat CH 200, with a longer fuselage and enlarged cabin, to provide room for a rear bench seat able to carry a third adult, two children or 95 kg (210 lb) of baggage. It has a greater wing span and larger tailplane; a fin and rudder assembly is standard. The ailerons are aerodynamically balanced, and electrically-actuated slotted flaps are fitted. Recommended power is in the 93-134 kW (125-180 hp) range. Fuel is carried in two 65 litre (14 Imp gallon) tanks, one in each wing leading-edge. Extra fuel can be carried in similar tanks installed in the outer wing sections. A forward-sliding canopy is standard. Limiting load factors are ±5·7*g* ultimate.

The prototype (C-GQTR), built by Harold Allsop of Toronto and powered by a 112 kW (150 hp) Lycoming O-320 engine, made its first flight on 9 July 1977.

Sets of plans and a constructional manual for the Tri-Z-CH 300 are available to amateur builders (180 sold by early 1979), as are materials, prefabricated component parts and complete kits.

The Tri-Z-CH 300 illustrated (C-GOVK) was built by Robin 'Red' Morris, Gerry Boudreau and Doug Holtby in a little over six months, including modifications to the fuel system to provide 773 litres (170 Imp gallons) of fuel in two fuselage and six wing tanks. Max T-O weight 1,134 kg (2,500 lb). Power plant is a 134 hp (180 hp) Lycoming O-360-2F, and full IFR equipment is installed. It was flown non-stop by 'Red' Morris from Vancouver International Airport to Halifax International Airport between 1 July and 2 July 1978, covering approximately 2,397 nm (4,440 km; 2,759 miles) in a flying time of 22 h 44 min. This set FAI Class C1c records between Vancouver and North Bay (103·831 knots; 192·295 km/h; 119·487 mph); Vancouver and Winnipeg (109·977 knots; 203·678 km/h; 126·560 mph); and Vancouver and Halifax (105·344 knots; 195·097 km/h; 121·228 mph).

DIMENSIONS, EXTERNAL:

Wing span	8·10 m (26 ft 6¾ in)
Wing chord, constant	1·48 m (4 ft 10½ in)
Wing area, gross	12·00 m² (129·2 sq ft)
Wing aspect ratio	5·48
Length overall	6·85 m (22 ft 5¾ in)
Tailplane span	2·60 m (8 ft 6¼ in)
Wheel track	2·25 m (7 ft 4½ in)
Wheelbase	1·45 m (4 ft 9 in)

WEIGHTS :

Weight empty	498 kg (1,100 lb)
Max T-O weight	840 kg (1,850 lb)

PERFORMANCE (at max T-O weight, with 112 kW; 150 hp engine):

Max level speed	137 knots (254 km/h; 158 mph)
Max cruising speed (75% power)	126 knots (233 km/h; 145 mph)
Stalling speed, flaps down	46 knots (85 km/h; 53 mph)
Max rate of climb at S/L	305 m (1,000 ft)/min
Range at max cruising speed	434 nm (804 km; 500 miles)
Endurance at max cruising speed	3 h 30 min

CH 50 MINI Z

Construction began in February 1978 of this small single-seat monoplane, of which the first flight was scheduled for July 1979.

TYPE: Single-seat light aircraft.

WINGS: Cantilever low-wing monoplane. Wing section NACA 4415. Dihedral 6°. Incidence 6°. Single-spar aluminium alloy structure. Elastic-hinged plain ailerons. No flaps. Wings removable.

FUSELAGE: Conventional aluminium alloy stressed-skin structure, of basically rectangular section with rounded top-decking.

TAIL UNIT: One-piece all-moving tailplane, with combined trim and anti-servo tabs. Vertical surfaces comprise rudder only. Tailplane and rudder are single-spar structures with ribs and skin of aluminium alloy.

LANDING GEAR: Non-retractable tailskid type. Aluminium spring shock-absorption. Main wheels and tyres size 4·10 ×3·50-4. Tyre pressure 1·24 bars (18 lb/sq in).

POWER PLANT: One 22·4 kW (30 hp) Mazda RX 7 rotating-combustion engine, driving a Zenair fixed-pitch wooden propeller. Single fuel tank in fuselage, capacity 35 litres (7·7 Imp gallons). Refuelling point on top of fuselage.

ACCOMMODATION: Single seat in open cockpit. Space for 10 kg (22 lb) of baggage, aft of cockpit.

DIMENSIONS, EXTERNAL:

Wing span	5·70 m (18 ft 8¼ in)
Wing area	6·20 m² (66·74 sq ft)
Wing chord, constant	1·10 m (3 ft 7¼ in)
Wing aspect ratio	5·2
Height overall	approx 1·60 m (5 ft 3 in)
Tailplane span	2·00 m (6 ft 7 in)
Wheel track	3·50 m (11 ft 5¾ in)
Wheelbase	1·35 m (4 ft 5 in)
Propeller diameter	1·32 m (4 ft 4 in)
Propeller ground clearance	0·30 m (1 ft 0 in)

WEIGHTS:

Weight empty	160 kg (352 lb)
Max T-O weight	270 kg (595 lb)

PERFORMANCE (estimated):

Max level speed at S/L	97 knots (180 km/h; 112 mph)
Max cruising speed at S/L	89 knots (165 km/h; 103 mph)
Stalling speed	43·5 knots (80 km/h; 50 mph)
Max rate of climb at S/L	120 m (394 ft)/min
T-O run	183 m (600 ft)
T-O to, and landing from, 15 m (50 ft)	305 m (1,000 ft)
Range with max fuel	188 nm (350 km; 217 miles)

DENMARK

SEREMET

W. VINCENT SEREMET

Godsparken 50, 2670 Greve Strand
Telephone: (01) 90 29 49

Since 1962, Mr W. Vincent Seremet, a Danish engineer and amateur constructor, has designed and built a series of small rotating-wing aircraft of which details have appeared annually in *Jane's*. Two of his latest designs are shown in the accompanying illustrations, but few technical details of these types may yet be published.

SEREMET W.S.9 AUTOGYROCOPTER

TYPE: Single-seat light autogyro.

ROTOR SYSTEM: Two-blade main rotor of laminated wood construction. Blade section NACA 8-H 12.

Zénith-CH 200 with 74·5 kW (100 hp) engine

Mono Z-CH-100 (41 kW; 55 hp Volkswagen engine)

Seremet W.S.12 powered parawing

Tri-Z-CH 300 *Challenger* **flown by Mr 'Red' Morris non-stop across Canada** *(Howard Levy)*

Seremet W.S.9 Autogyrocopters

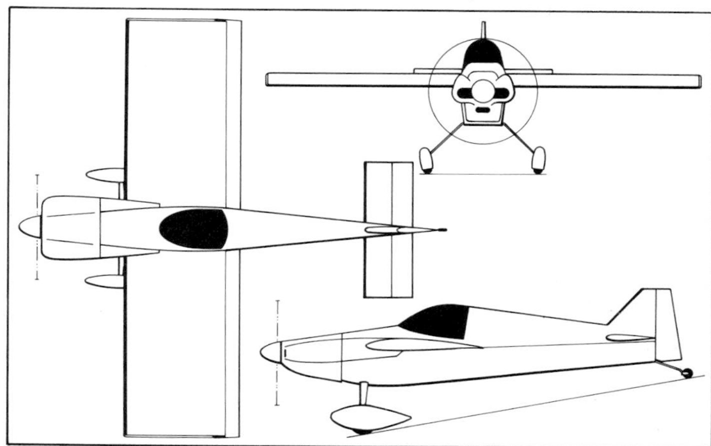

PIK-21 Super Sytky single-seat racing aircraft *(Roy J. Grainge)*

FUSELAGE: Built from aluminium tubes, bolted together. Faired cockpit with small windscreen.

TAIL UNIT: Conventional fin and rudder only.

LANDING GEAR: Non-retractable tricycle type. Steerable nosewheel.

POWER PLANT: One 53·5 kW (72 hp) McCulloch flat-four two-stroke engine, driving a two-blade wooden pusher propeller.

ACCOMMODATION: Pilot only, in open cockpit.

DIMENSIONS:

Diameter of main rotor	6·30 m (20 ft 8 in)
Length of fuselage	3·00 m (9 ft 10 in)
Height overall	1·80 m (5 ft 11 in)
Propeller diameter	1·05 m (3 ft 5¼ in)

SEREMET W.S.12

This powered parawing appears to have much in common with an aircraft illustrated in the 1974-75 *Jane's*. This was described as combining "a strap-on small jet engine with an aluminium tube and nylon Rogallo-type wing. For take-off, the pilot inclines the wing 50° upward and the engine exhaust nozzles 60° downward, and runs forward for a few paces in order to acquire the necessary lift. Once in the air, the wing is realigned to a 30° angle and the exhaust nozzles to 20° for flight. The process is reversed in order to land. Steering is by means of a grip held in each hand. The wing can be folded for portability."

The W.S.12 can be assumed to embody similar characteristics.

FINLAND

PIK
POLYTEKNIKKOJEN ILMAILUKERHO

(The Flying Club of the Helsinki University of Technology)

Lepolantie 69D, 00660 Helsinki

PROJECT ENGINEER: Kai Mellén

Mr K. Mellén, an engineer with Finnair, has designed and is building, under the auspices of the Polyteknikkojen Ilmailukerho, a Formula V racing aircraft known as the Super Sytky. Design work started at the end of 1973, and construction of the prototype began on 15 March 1975.

The Super Sytky was about 85% complete by early 1979, and the first flight was expected to take place before the end of the year.

PIK-21 SUPER SYTKY

TYPE: Single-seat racing monoplane.

WINGS: Cantilever constant-chord wooden wings, with no anhedral or dihedral. Wing section NACA $64_1$212. Single box spar and truss ribs, plywood covered. Full-span narrow-chord ailerons of plywood-covered wood construction. No tabs.

FUSELAGE: Conventional semi-monocoque wooden structure, plywood covered.

TAIL UNIT: Cantilever wooden structure, plywood covered. Constant-chord tailplane and elevators. Fin integral with rear fuselage. Ground-adjustable trim tabs in rudder and elevator.

LANDING GEAR: Non-retractable tailwheel type. Steel leaf spring main legs, carrying Azuza wheels, with tyres size 5·00-5. Tapered rod tailspring with 12·7 cm (5 in) tailwheel. Reinforced plastics main-wheel fairings. Azuza mechanical brakes.

POWER PLANT: One 1,600 cc modified Volkswagen motor car engine, producing 37·25 kW (50 hp) at 3,400 rpm and driving a Ray Hegy two-blade wooden fixed-pitch propeller, with large spinner. One fuel tank in fuselage, capacity 40 litres (8·8 Imp gallons). Refuelling point in front of windscreen. Oil capacity 2·5 litres (0·55 Imp gallons).

ACCOMMODATION: Enclosed cabin seating pilot only. One-piece jettisonable windscreen/canopy, hinged on starboard side.

ELECTRONICS: Radio fitted.
DIMENSIONS, EXTERNAL:

Wing span	5·30 m (17 ft 4¾ in)
Wing area, gross	7·20 m² (77·5 sq ft)
Wing chord, constant	1·37 m (4 ft 6 in)
Wing aspect ratio	3·87
Length overall	5·16 m (16 ft 11¼ in)
Tailplane span	1·70 m (5 ft 7 in)
Wheel track	1·32 m (4 ft 4 in)
Wheelbase	3·93 m (12 ft 10¾ in)
Propeller diameter	1·32 m (4 ft 4 in)

WEIGHTS (estimated):

Weight empty, equipped	200 kg (441 lb)
Max T-O weight	320 kg (705 lb)

PERFORMANCE: No data available.

TERVAMÄKI

JUKKA TERVAMÄKI

Aidasmäentie 16-20E, 00650 Helsinki 65

Mr Tervamäki, former Technical Manager of Wihuri-Yhtymä Oy, Lentohuolto, Finland's largest private aviation company, and currently Technical Manager of a medical instrument company, first became interested in autogyros in 1956. In 1959 he worked briefly for the Bensen Aircraft Corporation in the USA. He obtained a Diploma in Aeronautical Engineering at the Helsinki Institute of Technology in 1963, and later served in the helicopter section of the Finnish Air Force. He was for two years project manager and chief designer of the PIK-19 Muhinu glider-towing aircraft. More recently, he modified a Schleicher ASK 14 powered sailplane to make it capable of taxying on large airports; and designed the engine installation for the JT-6 prototype powered sailplane, which is in production as the PIK-20E (see Sailplanes section).

Early autogyros designed by Mr Tervamäki were completed in 1958 (JT-1) and 1965 (JT-2). More recent designs are the Tervamäki-Eerola ATE-3 (see 1977-78 *Jane's*) and Tervamäki JT-5.

TERVAMÄKI JT-5

The JT-5 is a development of the ATE-3, the major visible differences being the use of a triple tail assembly, to improve static and dynamic stability; a fully-enclosed cockpit; improved, low-drag fuselage contours; and extensive use of plastics materials in the basic structure and main components. Other features include an upward-directed exhaust, to reduce engine noise, and a simplified carburettor installation and heating system of Tervamäki design.

The prototype JT-5 (OH-XYS) was flown for the first time on 7 January 1973. It was later sold, together with all production rights, tools and moulds, to Sr Vittorio Magni of Italy (see 1975-76 *Jane's*). There has been no recent news of Sr Magni's intentions for marketing the JT-5; but about 30 sets of plans had been sold by Mr Tervamäki by early 1979, when three more JT-5s were under construction by homebuilders in Finland, of which one was nearing completion.

One of the latest JT-5s to be completed is that built by Mr Matti Värelä of Raisio, shown in the accompanying illustration. This is being test flown with an open cockpit, although a Plexiglas canopy is being fabricated for it, as per drawings. About 30 flying hours had been completed in this aircraft by early 1979.

With minor modifications, glassfibre rotor blades of the type fitted to the JT-5 can be installed on other autogyros and rotor head designs, and several sets are already flying on aircraft built in Scandinavia.

TYPE: Single-seat light autogyro.

ROTOR SYSTEM: Two-blade semi-rigid rotor of glassfibre-reinforced epoxy resin, with polyurethane plastics foam core. Blades, of constant chord and NACA 8-H-12 section, are each attached to hub by two bolts. A lead bar in each blade leading-edge forms the chordwise balance weight. Rotor mast of streamlined SAE 4130 steel tubing. Rotor head is of a compact offset-gimbal type with centrifugal teeter stops and rotor brake installed. There are two spiral springs for trim adjustment, which is effected via the control stick twist-grip handle. Normal rotor rpm is 400, maximum 600. Designed for the JT-5, but not yet fitted, is a modified Cierva-type inclined drag hinge which would allow the blades to move to zero pitch when pre-rotation torque is applied, permitting an increase of 100 rpm in pre-spin speed and, consequently, a shorter take-off.

ROTOR DRIVE: Rotor spin-up by Vee-belt, clutch, 90° gearbox, sliding universal shaft and inertia-operated Bendix drive. Overall reduction ratio 8. Rotor spin-up of 300 rpm can be achieved.

FUSELAGE: Basic structure of welded 4130 steel tubing with a glassfibre/HFB honeycomb sandwich cockpit. All internal cockpit structures of glassfibre-reinforced epoxy resin. One-piece aluminium engine cowling.

TAIL UNIT: Central main fin and rudder, of glassfibre-reinforced epoxy resin, with rigid PVC foam ribs and Courtauld carbon fibre stiffeners. Horizontal tail and auxiliary endplate fins of glassfibre sandwich construction with honeycomb core. Tail assembly attached to fuselage by a single streamlined steel tube. Small tail-wheel beneath base of fin.

LANDING GEAR: Non-retractable tricycle type. Main gear legs consist of 4 × 4 cm (1·6 × 1·6 in) glassfibre-reinforced epoxy resin springs, encased in streamlined fairings of the same material. Cables inside these fairings to main gear drum brakes. Main-wheel tyres size 300 × 100. Compression rubber shock-absorption in nose gear. Nosewheel tyre size 260 × 80. Nosewheel steerable by rudder pedals.

POWER PLANT: One 56 kW (75 hp) 1·7 litre Volkswagen engine, converted for autogyro use by Limbach Motorenbau. No oil cooler, generator or electric starter. Two-blade pusher propeller, of glassfibre-reinforced epoxy. Glassfibre fuel tank, integrally built into fuselage aft of pilot's seat, capacity 50 litres (11 Imp gallons).

ACCOMMODATION: Single seat under sideways-opening Plexiglas canopy. Instrument panel cover and pilot's seat back (the latter also forming a firewall to the engine compartment) open together with the canopy.

EQUIPMENT: Standard equipment and controls are as listed in the 1974-75 *Jane's*. A 6-channel radio is installed.

DIMENSIONS, EXTERNAL:

Rotor diameter	7·00 m (22 ft 11½ in)
Rotor blade chord (constant, each)	0·18 m (7·1 in)
Length of fuselage	3·50 m (11 ft 5¾ in)
Height overall	2·00 m (6 ft 6¾ in)
Wheel track	1·70 m (5 ft 7 in)
Propeller diameter	1·20 m (3 ft 11¼ in)

AREAS:

Rotor blades (each)	0·63 m² (6·78 sq ft)
Rotor disc	38·50 m² (414·4 sq ft)

WEIGHTS:

Weight empty, equipped	167 kg (368 lb)
Max T-O weight	290 kg (639 lb)

PERFORMANCE (at max T-O weight):

Never-exceed speed	97 knots (180 km/h; 111·5 mph)
Max level speed at S/L	92 knots (170 km/h; 106 mph)
Max cruising speed at S/L	81 knots (150 km/h; 93 mph)
Econ cruising speed	70 knots (130 km/h; 81 mph)
Min level speed	19 knots (35 km/h; 22 mph)
Max rate of climb at S/L	180 m (590 ft)/min
Service ceiling	4,000 m (13,125 ft)
T-O run	70 m (230 ft)
T-O to 15 m (50 ft)	120 m (394 ft)
Landing from 15 m (50 ft)	50 m (165 ft)
Landing run	5 m (16 ft)
Range with max fuel, no reserves	189 nm (350 km; 217 miles)

FRANCE

CHAGNES

M CHAGNES

In February 1979, a photograph was received showing a variant of the Rutan VariViggen two-seat canard delta powered by two Microturbo TRS 18-046 turbojets (each 0·898 kN; 202 lb st) in place of the usual rear-mounted 112 kW (150 hp) piston engine. Built at Toulouse, in France, by M Chagnes, the airframe was built to Rutan plans and is similar to that of the standard VariViggen described in the US section of this edition. The installation of the two TRS 18-046 engines was undertaken with the cooperation of Microturbo SA. Because of the light weight of these turbojets, which are positioned one above the other at the rear of the fuselage, no CG problem was encountered.

Taxi tests of this jet-powered VariViggen had begun by February 1979. First flight of the aircraft was expected to take place in late March or early April.

CHASLE

YVES CHASLE

M Chasle, a stress engineer with Aérospatiale, designed and built a light aircraft named the YC-12 Tourbillon, the dimensions of which were governed by the maximum size that could be accommodated in his garage workshop. First flight was made on 9 October 1965. As a result of the flight tests leading to its restricted C of A, the height of the vertical tail surfaces was later increased slightly. Plans are available to amateur constructors.

Subsequently, M Chasle designed a tandem two-seat light aircraft known as the YC-20, of which details can be found in the 1972-73 *Jane's*. He also designed the LMC-1 side-by-side two-seater, of which a prototype was built by members of the Aero Club Léon Morane, and which was described in the 1977-78 *Jane's*.

CHASLE YC-12 TOURBILLON (WHIRLWIND)

The Tourbillon can be built in a variety of forms, differing mainly in the type of engine fitted, as follows:

YC-121. With 48·5 kW (65 hp) Continental A65 engine. Generally similar to prototype (see 1970-71 *Jane's*) except for detail changes.

YC-122. Similar to YC-121, but with 71 kW (95 hp) Continental C90 or 74·5 kW (100 hp) Rolls-Royce Continental O-200-A engine.

YC-123. Similar to YC-121, but with 78·3 kW (105 hp) Potez 4E-20b engine.

Construction of YC-12s has been undertaken in several countries, including France, Canada, the USA, New Zealand and the UK. Marketing of the YC-12 in North America is by E. Littner, 546 83rd Avenue, Laval-Chomedey, Quebec, Canada.

TYPE: Single-seat amateur-built light aircraft.

WINGS: Cantilever low-wing monoplane. Wing section NACA Srs 7. Dihedral 6°. Incidence 3° 30′. All-wood structure, with main box spar of spruce and okoumé, spruce plank rear spar, girder-type ribs and okoumé plywood covering. All-wood ailerons and three-position slotted flaps.

FUSELAGE: Conventional plywood-covered wood structure, built around four spruce longerons, four main frames, five secondary frames and stringers.

TAIL UNIT: Cantilever all-wood structure, with swept vertical surfaces. Fixed tailplane and conventional elevators.

LANDING GEAR: Non-retractable tailwheel type. Steerable tailwheel linked with rudder. Main units have ERAM oleo-pneumatic suspension. Vespa wheels, size 400-100, mounted on L-shape legs. Independent mechanical brakes. Tailwheel carried on leaf spring. Provision for changing to a tricycle configuration, by switching main legs port and starboard, with lower arm of L facing rearward, and mounting nose unit on firewall.

POWER PLANT: One flat-four engine (see introductory copy) driving an EVRA two-blade propeller. Fuel tank, capacity 60·5 litres (13·3 Imp gallons), aft of firewall. Oil capacity 3·75 litres (0·83 Imp gallons).

ACCOMMODATION: Single seat under large transparent rearward-sliding canopy. Baggage space aft of seat.

ELECTRONICS AND EQUIPMENT: Optional items include Radiomaster radio, generator, starter, and night-flying equipment.

DIMENSIONS, EXTERNAL:

Wing span	6·70 m (22 ft 0 in)
Wing chord at root	1·40 m (4 ft 7¼ in)
Wing chord at tip	0·79 m (2 ft 7¼ in)
Wing area, gross	7·50 m² (80·7 sq ft)
Wing aspect ratio	6·0
Length overall:	
YC-121	5·95 m (19 ft 6 in)
YC-122, YC-123	5·85 m (19 ft 2¼ in)
Height overall	2·40 m (7 ft 10½ in)
Tailplane span	2·00 m (6 ft 6¾ in)
Wheel track	1·60 m (5 ft 3 in)
Wheelbase	3·65 m (11 ft 11¾ in)
Propeller diameter	1·75 m (5 ft 9 in)

WEIGHTS:

Weight empty:	
YC-121	285 kg (628 lb)
YC-122, YC-123	313 kg (690 lb)
Max T-O weight, without radio:	
YC-121	432 kg (952 lb)
YC-122, YC-123	460 kg (1,015 lb)

PERFORMANCE (estimated):

Max level speed at S/L:	
YC-121	127 knots (235 km/h; 146 mph)
YC-122	146 knots (270 km/h; 168 mph)
YC-123	151 knots (280 km/h; 174 mph)
Max cruising speed (70% power):	
YC-121	110 knots (205 km/h; 127 mph)
YC-122	129 knots (240 km/h; 149 mph)
YC-123	135 knots (250 km/h; 155 mph)

Tervamäki JT-5 built by Mr Matti Värelä of Raisio, Finland. This is being test flown with an open cockpit

VariViggen built by M Chagnes, with two Microturbo TRS 18-046 turbojet engines

Prototype Chasle YC-12 Tourbillon single-seat light aircraft (Continental A65 engine)

MC 10 Cricri No. 4 (two 125 cc McCulloch two-stroke engines) built by Gérard Constant of Dreux

Stalling speed:
- YC-121: 41 knots (75 km/h; 47 mph)
- YC-122, YC-123: 44 knots (80 km/h; 50 mph)

Max rate of climb at S/L:
- YC-121: 276 m (905 ft)/min
- YC-122: 420 m (1,380 ft)/min
- YC-123: 480 m (1,575 ft)/min

T-O run:
- YC-121: 260 m (855 ft)
- YC-122: 200 m (660 ft)
- YC-123: 180 m (593 ft)

Max range:
- YC-121: 434 nm (800 km; 500 miles)
- YC-122, YC-123: 377 nm (700 km; 435 miles)

COLOMBAN
MICHEL COLOMBAN

37*bis* rue Lakanal, 92500-Rueil-Malmaison
Telephone: 967-88-76

Formerly with the Morane and Potez companies, and now an aerodynamicist with Aérospatiale, M Colomban designed and built a very small and unique twin-engined lightplane named the Cricri. Its construction required some 1,200 hours of work and cost only 5,000 francs (1971-72 prices), including the engines.

It is intended to market plans of an improved version of the Cricri; but these will not be made available until testing of the aircraft has been completed, and until definitive drawings and a constructional manual are ready for distribution.

COLOMBAN MC 10 CRICRI (CRICKET)

The prototype Cricri was powered by two Rowena 6507J single-cylinder two-stroke engines of 137cc, each giving 6·7 kW (9 hp) and weighing 6·5 kg (14·3 lb). It was claimed to be the smallest twin-engined aeroplane then flying, and the only one able to lift a useful load equivalent to 170 per cent of its own empty weight. Special constructional features permitted assembly or disassembly in only five minutes. Its light weight and small size made it particularly easy to transport on a trailer towed by car and to store in a garage or shed.

The Cricri was flown for the first time on 19 July 1973 by Robert Buisson, a 68-year-old pilot who had already logged 12,000 flying hours. A number of design refinements were made later that year, after which testing was resumed. Within fifteen days the Cricri had logged a total of 13 trouble-free flying hours, including rolls, reversements, 'split S' manoeuvres and inverted flight, made possible by its Tillotson diaphragm carburettor. Flight tests at up to 135 knots (250 km/h; 155 mph) confirmed that no special piloting skills were needed to fly the aircraft.

In particular, the Cricri handled like a single-engined design. This resulted from the fact that the two small engines were mounted close together, and from the carefully-conceived shape of the cockpit canopy which deflected the propeller slipstream over the tail surfaces in such a way that the failure of one engine would produce no dangerous handling problems. If one engine was throttled back fiercely, with hands and feet off the controls, the Cricri was said to do no more than begin a gentle turn.

A number of improved and re-engined Cricris are being built by friends of M Colomban, and one of these (No. 4, built by M Gérard Constant of Dreux) was exhibited in the static park at the 1977 Paris Salon. This aircraft flew for the first time in July 1978 and has since performed entirely satisfactorily. Take-off, in particular, is achieved in 80 m (263 ft), in a time of 7 s, in zero wind, followed by a stabilised climb at a rate of 360 m (1,180 ft)/min. On the other hand, the 125 cc McCulloch MC-101 single-cylinder two-stroke engines (each 8·9 kW; 12 hp) specified originally for the Cricri, and fitted to this aircraft, are now considered too sophisticated for this application. So, although they have proved generally satisfactory, they will be superseded by two Valmet engines, which might prove more reliable as standard power plants for such aircraft. Meanwhile, development continues.

TYPE: Twin-engined single-seat ultra-light aircraft, stressed to $+10g$ and $-5g$.

WINGS: Cantilever low-wing monoplane of constant chord. Laminar-flow aerofoil derived from a Wortmann section. Thickness/chord ratio 21·7%. Dihedral 4° from roots. Incidence 1° at root, −30′ at tip. No sweep. Single-spar box structure. Spar comprises a web riveted to AU4G angle-section booms. Inboard end of spar in each wing is of 'forked-tongue' form, like that of many sailplanes, to permit rapid assembly and disassembly of wings (2 minutes). Closely-spaced Klégécel ribs are bonded fore and aft of the spar. Skin consists of a single sheet of AU4G, bonded to structure under pressure after its leading-edge has been formed. No rear spar. Wing box is closed at each end by a riveted metal rib. Entire trailing-edge is occupied by two-section external flaps of the kind fitted to many wartime Junkers aircraft, operating collectively as high-lift devices and differentially as ailerons. Flaps are spar-less, consisting of a metal monocoque structure, with four metal ribs per section (at each tip and each pivot point), filled with Klégécel over the entire span and over 20% of the chord. Flaps are each actuated via a ball-joint at the root. No controls pass through the wing box, which contains only an AU4G tube as provision for any future installation of fuel tanks on wingtips.

FUSELAGE: Simple metal box structure of AU4G sheet made in two parts to reduce space required for manufacture. Rear portion is of inverted triangular section. Rectangular-section forward portion is riveted together with four angle sections at the corners. Structure is stiffened by Klégécel stringers, bonded in place. AU4G frames riveted in position in line with the attachments for the wings, landing gear, tail unit and engine mountings.

TAIL UNIT: Cantilever T type, with sweptback vertical surfaces and all-moving constant-chord horizontal surface. Construction similar to that of wings. No tabs. Tailplane actuated by control rods, rudder by cables. Tailplane provided with artificial loading by bungee cord.

LANDING GEAR: Non-retractable tricycle type. Nosewheel fitted with bungee shock-absorption and linked to rudder bar for steering. Each main wheel carried on cantilever leg of glassfibre/epoxy laminations. Main-wheel tyres size 210-70, pressure 1·80 bars (28 lb/sq in). Nosewheel tyre size 200-50, pressure 0·80 bars (11·6 lb/sq in). Colomban disc brakes. Provision for fairing on all three wheels.

POWER PLANT: Two modified 160 cc Valmet SM 160J single-cylinder two-stroke engines, each giving 8·9 kW (12 hp) at 6,500 rpm. Tillotson diaphragm carburettors for all-attitude flight. Each engine drives an MCH 700-18 two-blade propeller, made of laminated wood and sheathed in plastics. Plastics fuel tank in fuselage, capacity 20 litres (4·4 Imp gallons). Provision for tank on each wingtip, total capacity 24 litres (5·25 Imp gallons).

ACCOMMODATION: Single seat under large transparent canopy, hinged to open sideways, to starboard. Ventilation through port in side of fuselage. No heating.

DIMENSIONS, EXTERNAL:

Wing span, with or without tip-tanks	4·90 m (16 ft 0¾ in)
Wing chord, incl flap (constant)	0·63 m (2 ft 0¾ in)
Wing chord, excl flap (constant)	0·48 m (1 ft 6¾ in)
Wing area, gross	3·10 m² (33·4 sq ft)
Wing aspect ratio	7·75
Length overall	3·91 m (12 ft 10 in)
Height overall	1·20 m (3 ft 11¼ in)
Tailplane span	1·55 m (5 ft 1 in)
Wheel track	1·10 m (3 ft 7¼ in)
Wheelbase	1·15 m (3 ft 9¼ in)
Propeller diameter	0·68 m (2 ft 2¾ in)
Distance between propeller centres	0·95 m (3 ft 1½ in)

DIMENSIONS, INTERNAL:
Cabin: Length 1·30 m (4 ft 3¼ in)
Max width 0·55 m (1 ft 9½ in)
Max height 0·82 m (2 ft 8¼ in)
WEIGHTS:
Weight empty 70 kg (154 lb)
Max T-O and landing weight 170 kg (375 lb)
PERFORMANCE (estimated, at AUW of 160 kg; 352 lb):
Never-exceed speed 158 knots (293 km/h; 182 mph)
Max level speed 118 knots (220 km/h; 136 mph)
Max cruising speed (75% power) 105 knots (195 km/h; 121 mph)
Stalling speed, flaps down 42 knots (77 km/h; 48 mph)
Stalling speed, flaps up 50 knots (93 km/h; 58 mph)
Best glide ratio, engines off and T-O configuration, at 60 knots (110 km/h; 69 mph) 11
Max rate of climb at S/L 336 m (1,100 ft)/min
Rate of climb at S/L, one engine out 80 m (262 ft)/min
Service ceiling 4,600 m (15,090 ft)
T-O run 110 m (360 ft)
T-O to 15 m (50 ft) 310 m (1,020 ft)
Landing from 15 m (50 ft) 350 m (1,150 ft)
Landing run 150 m (495 ft)
Range with max fuel 430 nm (800 km; 496 miles)

JACQUES COUPÉ
AVIONS JACQUES COUPÉ

La Trute, 37270 Azay-sur-Cher

AVIONS JACQUES COUPÉ JC-01

The accompanying photograph of this aircraft was taken shortly after its first flight on 16 March 1976; it has since been registered F-PXKV. Few details are available, except that the JC-01 carries a pilot and one passenger, and is powered by a 48·5 kW (65 hp) Continental A65-8F flat-four engine.

CROSES
EMILIEN CROSES

Route de Davayé (Aérodrome), 71000-Charnay les Macon
Telephone: (85) 38-07-31

Since M Emilien Croses began work as a designer/constructor in 1947, he has been responsible for nine different prototypes, all of which have been certificated. Addition of the initial 'B' in the designation of some of these reflects assistance given to M Croses by M R. Bujon, a specialist metal worker. Other assistance is given by MM J. Mottez with stressing and aerodynamics; Alain Croses with aerodynamic studies; and Y. Croses, an engineer specialising in applications of high-strength plastics and glassfibre.

CROSES EAC-3 POUPLUME

As in the familiar Mignet designs, the Pouplume single-seat tandem-wing biplane has a fixed rear wing and a pivoted forward wing which dispenses with the need for ailerons and elevators. A conventional rudder is fitted, with a large tailwheel built into its lower edge.

Construction is conventional, with spruce wing structure and a square-section spruce fuselage covered with okoumé ply. The main landing gear consists of Vespa scooter wheels carried on a wooden cross-member.

The power unit in the prototype (EAC-3-01) is a 7·8 kW (10·5 hp) Moto 232 cc two-stroke motorcycle engine, with chain reduction drive to the propeller shaft. The reduction ratio is 3·5 : 1, giving a propeller speed of 1,300 rpm. Fuel capacity is 10 litres (2·2 Imp gallons).

The EAC-3-01 Pouplume took 600 hours to build and flew for the first time in June 1961. This machine was followed, in 1967, by a second prototype (EAC-3-02), with a 20 cm (8 in) longer fuselage. M Croses is offering sets of plans to other constructors, and at least 12 Pouplumes had flown by early 1979. The one shown in the accompanying illustration was built in France by an amateur constructor.

A version known as the Pouplume Sport differs in having a 1500 cc Volkswagen engine and reduced span of 6·40 m (21 ft 0 in). About 55 Pouplume Sports were under construction in early 1979.

The following data apply to the standard Moto-powered Pouplume:

DIMENSIONS, EXTERNAL:
Span of forward wing 7·8 m (25 ft 7 in)
Span of rear wing 7·0 m (23 ft 0 in)
Wing area, gross 16·0 m² (172 sq ft)
Length overall 4·7 m (15 ft 3 in)
Height overall 1·8 m (5 ft 11 in)
WEIGHTS:
Weight empty 110-140 kg (243-310 lb)
Max T-O weight 220-260 kg (485-573 lb)
PERFORMANCE (A: 7·8 kW; 10·5 hp engine. B: 13·4 kW; 18 hp engine):
Max level speed:
A 38 knots (70 km/h; 43·5 mph)
B 65 knots (120 km/h; 75 mph)
Econ cruising speed:
A 27 knots (50 km/h; 31 mph)
B 38 knots (70 km/h; 43·5 mph)
T-O speed:
A 13·5 knots (25 km/h; 15·5 mph)
Landing speed:
A 9·7 knots (18 km/h; 11 mph)
T-O run:
A 60 m (200 ft)
B 40 m (131 ft)
Landing run:
A 24 m (80 ft)
Fuel consumption:
A 4·5 litres (1 Imp gallon)/h

CROSES EC-6 CRIQUET (LOCUST)

This design by Emilien Croses is a development of his earlier EC-1-02 prototype and is a side-by-side two-seater based on the familiar Mignet tandem-wing formula. Construction was started in March 1964 and the EC-6-01 flew for the first time on 6 July 1965.

Plans of the wooden version of the Criquet, of which details follow, are available to amateur constructors. At least seven examples were flying by early 1979, with about 60 more under construction.

An all-plastics version, known as the LC-10, was described briefly in the 1977-78 *Jane's*. Plans of this are not available.

TYPE: Two-seat tandem-wing light aircraft.

WINGS: Forward wing built in one piece and pivoted on two streamlined supports, giving variable incidence between −2° and +12°. Fixed rear (lower) wing. Wing section NACA 23012 (modified). Both wings have two-spar wooden structure, with plywood leading-edge, overall fabric covering and some components of glassfibre. No ailerons.

FUSELAGE: Spruce structure, covered with plywood. Glassfibre engine cowling.

TAIL UNIT: Plywood-covered spruce fin and rudder. No tailplane or elevators.

LANDING GEAR: Non-retractable tailwheel type. Main wheels, size 420-150, carried on single cantilever arch structure made from ash wood on a forme and covered with glassfibre. Tailwheel, size 420-150, semi-enclosed in bottom of rudder.

POWER PLANT: One 67 kW (90 hp) Continental flat-four engine, driving a modified SIPA two-blade propeller. Fuel capacity originally 60 litres (13 Imp gallons); planned to be increased to 90 litres (20 Imp gallons).

ACCOMMODATION: Two seats side by side in enclosed cabin. Door on starboard side. Constructors can utilise either the special Mignet type of control system or a conventional system with ailerons and rudder bar.

DIMENSIONS, EXTERNAL:
Span of forward wing 7·80 m (25 ft 7 in)
Span of rear wing 7·00 m (22 ft 11½ in)
Wing chord (constant, each) 1·20 m (3 ft 11¼ in)
Wing area, gross 16·0 m² (172 sq ft)
Length overall 4·65 m (15 ft 3 in)
WEIGHTS:
Weight empty 290 kg (639 lb)
Max T-O weight 550 kg (1,213 lb)
PERFORMANCE (officially certificated, at max T-O weight):
Max level speed at S/L 115 knots (213 km/h; 132 mph)
Max cruising speed 92 knots (170 km/h; 106 mph)
Econ cruising speed 86 knots (160 km/h; 99 mph)
Min flying speed 22 knots (40 km/h; 25 mph)
Will not stall
T-O time (max) 6 s
Climb to 2,000 m (6,560 ft) 6 min 14 s

CROSES EC-8 TOURISME

This three-seat touring aircraft is generally similar to the standard wooden Criquet but has an 'all-terrain' landing gear comprising two tandem pairs of main wheels. Two EC-8s were flying in 1977.

CROSES B-EC-9 PARAS-CARGO

Unique in being a cargo transport for construction and operation by amateurs, the B-EC-9 employs the same Mignet tandem-wing configuration and simple wood construction as earlier Croses designs. Like them, it can be built with conventional three-axis controls or the special two-control system devised by Henri Mignet, with large 'tab' control surfaces on the trailing-edge of the rear wing.

It is intended to certificate the prototype, following tests of the aircraft's suitability as a transport for parachutists. It will be offered to amateur constructors and clubs in the form of both plans and kits of components.

TYPE: Light cargo transport and utility aircraft for amateur construction.

WINGS: Tandem-wing configuration of Mignet type, with forward wing supported, parasol-fashion, at three pivot points. Fixed cantilever aft wing mounted at top of rear fuselage. Both wings have same constant chord, with round and slightly upswept tips. No dihedral. No sweep. Wood structure, with fabric covering aft of main spar. Large inset tab in trailing-edge of each rear wing, but no ailerons, on prototype, which has Mignet two-control system.

FUSELAGE: Large-volume plywood box structure, with unobstructed interior.

TAIL UNIT: Fin, integral with fuselage, and rudder only, of plywood-covered wood construction. No tabs.

LANDING GEAR: Croses 'tous terrains' type. Two pairs of main wheels in tandem, carried on one-piece cantilever arch structure of wood covered with glassfibre. Two forward wheels larger than rear wheels. Large tailwheel semi-enclosed in base of rudder.

POWER PLANT: One 134 kW (180 hp) Lycoming flat-four engine, driving a two-blade fixed-pitch propeller without spinner.

ACCOMMODATION: Crew of two side by side on flight deck, connected by a passage to the square-section main cabin. Accommodation for freight, four parachutists, two stretcher patients and seats for two attendants, or agricultural equipment. Very low floor for easy loading. Large door on port side of cabin opens inward and upward to permit airdropping of parachutists or cargo. Separate forward-hinged crew door on port side of flight deck. Use of a door at the rear of the cabin would permit the carriage of items such as metal tubes, boards or helicopter rotor blades up to 5·50 m (18 ft 0 in) long.

DIMENSIONS, EXTERNAL:
Wing span:
front wing 9·60 m (31 ft 6 in)
rear wing 8·80 m (28 ft 10½ in)
Wing chord, constant 1·60 m (5 ft 3 in)
Wing gap (projected) 0·94 m (3 ft 1 in)
Length overall 7·50 m (24 ft 7¼ in)
DIMENSIONS, INTERNAL:
Cabin: Length 2·60 m (8 ft 6¼ in)
Max width 1·35 m (4 ft 5 in)
Max height 1·45 m (4 ft 9 in)
Usable volume 5 m³ (176 cu ft)
WEIGHTS:
Weight empty 650 kg (1,433 lb)
Max payload 450 kg (992 lb)
PERFORMANCE:
Normal cruising speed 94 knots (175 km/h; 108 mph)
Econ cruising speed 86 knots (160 km/h; 99 mph)
Speed for airdropping 32 knots (60 km/h; 37 mph)
Rate of climb at S/L 240 m (785 ft)/min
T-O run 150 m (490 ft)

DURUBLE
ROLAND DURUBLE

40 rue du Paradis, Les Essarts, 76530-Grand-Couronne
Telephone: 92-20-63

M Roland Duruble, with MM Guy Chanut and Legrand, of Rouen, designed and built a two-seat all-metal light aircraft named the RD-02 Edelweiss, which flew for the first time on 7 July 1962. Full details of this aircraft can be found in the 1972-73 *Jane's*.

Plans of an enlarged and improved version, known as the RD-03 Edelweiss, are available to other constructors.

DURUBLE RD-03 EDELWEISS

The RD-03 Edelweiss is designed to AIR 2052 (CAR 3) standards, in three versions, as follows:

RD-03A. With 74·5 kW (100 hp) Continental O-200 flat-four engine and fuel capacity of 100 litres (22 Imp gallons) in two wing tanks. Can be fitted with 67 kW (90 hp) engine or 100·5 kW (135 hp) Lycoming O-320 engine. Side-by-side seats for pilot and one passenger (total weight 172 kg; 380 lb) in cabin.

RD-03B. With 100·5 kW (135 hp) Lycoming O-320 or Franklin Sport 4B engine and same fuel capacity as RD-03A. Seating as RD-03A for Utility category operation, or in '2 + 2' arrangement for pilot and three passengers (154 kg; 340 lb on front seats, 110 kg; 240 lb on rear seats) in Normal category.

RD-03C. With 112 kW (150 hp) Lycoming engine and additional wing tanks, increasing total fuel capacity to 150

Avions Jacques Coupé JC-01 *(R. Kunert)*

Croses B-EC-9 Paras-Cargo light utility/cargo transport *(Geoffrey P. Jones)*

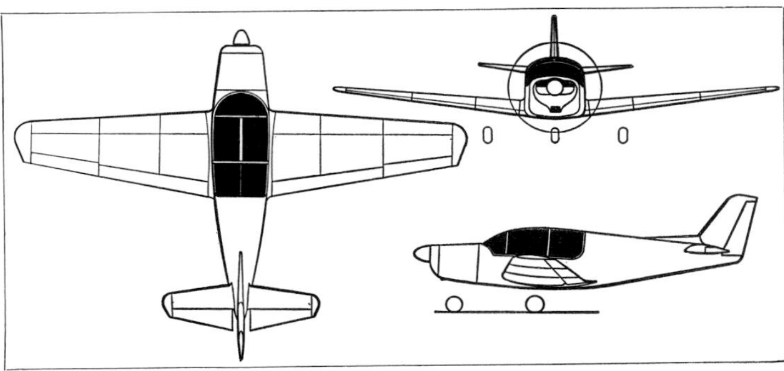

Durable RD-03C Edelweiss two/four-seat light aircraft

Croses EAC-3 Pouplume light aircraft (Moto engine)

Croses EC-6 Criquet built by M Cuesuin of Belfort

The RD-02 Edelweiss prototype (Walter Mikron III engine)

litres (33 Imp gallons). In Utility two-seat form (as RD-03A) or with seating for a pilot and three passengers (total weight 308 kg; 680 lb) in Normal category.

Plans of the RD-03 have been available since the Autumn of 1970. By early 1979, a total of 47 sets of plans had been sold. Nine Edelweiss are known to be under construction in France, two in Belgium, eleven in Canada and the USA, and one in New Zealand. The first of these was not expected to fly until 1978/79.

TYPE: Two/four-seat light aircraft.

WINGS: Cantilever low-wing monoplane. Wing section NACA 23000 series. Thickness/chord ratio 18% at root, 12% at tip. Dihedral 6° 5′ from roots. Incidence 3° at root, 0° at tip. No sweepback. All-metal two-spar duralumin structure, with metal slotted trailing-edge flaps and slotted ailerons. No trim tabs.

FUSELAGE: Conventional semi-monocoque duralumin structure.

TAIL UNIT: Cantilever all-metal structure, with sweptback vertical surfaces. Fixed-incidence tailplane. Trim tab in each elevator, one actuated by flap linkage and the other manually.

LANDING GEAR: Retractable tricycle type. Hydraulic retraction, nosewheel rearward, main units inward into wings. Duruble hydro-air shock-absorbers on all three units. Main-wheel tyres size 355 × 150, nosewheel tyre size 330 × 130. Pressure (all tyres) 1·24 bars (18 lb/sq in). Hydraulic disc brakes.

POWER PLANT: One 67, 74·5, 100·5 or 112 kW (90, 100, 135 or 150 hp) flat-four engine (details under individual model listings). Refuelling point above wing.

ACCOMMODATION: Side-by-side seats for two, three or four persons (details under individual model listings) in fully-enclosed cabin.

SYSTEMS: Hydraulic system, pressure 69 bars (1,000 lb/sq in), for flap and landing gear actuation.

ELECTRONICS AND EQUIPMENT: Radio optional. Blind-flying instrumentation not fitted.

DIMENSIONS, EXTERNAL:
- Wing span: 8·82 m (28 ft 11¼ in)
- Wing chord at root: 1·70 m (5 ft 7 in)
- Wing chord at tip: 0·86 m (2 ft 10 in)
- Wing area, gross: 11·07 m² (119·2 sq ft)
- Wing aspect ratio: 7·05
- Length overall (RD-03A): 6·875 m (22 ft 6¾ in)
- Height overall: 2·60 m (8 ft 6¼ in)
- Tailplane span: 3·05 m (10 ft 0 in)

DIMENSIONS, INTERNAL:
- Cabin: Max length: 2·44 m (8 ft 0 in)
- Max width: 1·10 m (3 ft 7¼ in)

WEIGHTS (estimated. A: RD-03A; B: RD-03B; C: RD-03C):
- Weight empty, equipped:
  - A: 416·5 kg (918 lb)
  - B: 426·5 kg (940 lb)
  - C: 433 kg (955 lb)
- Max T-O and landing weight:
  - A (Utility): 679 kg (1,497 lb)
  - B (Utility): 695 kg (1,532 lb)
  - B (Normal): 806 kg (1,777 lb)
  - C (Utility): 722 kg (1,592 lb)
  - C (Normal): 878 kg (1,936 lb)

PERFORMANCE (estimated, at max T-O weight):
- Never-exceed speed:
  - A (Utility), B (Utility), C (Utility): 170 knots (316 km/h; 196 mph)
  - B (Normal), C (Normal): 182 knots (339 km/h; 210 mph)
- Max level speed at S/L:
  - A (Utility): 139 knots (257 km/h; 160 mph)
  - B (Utility): 143 knots (265 km/h; 165 mph)
  - B (Normal): 141 knots (262 km/h; 163 mph)
  - C (Utility): 149 knots (277 km/h; 172 mph)
  - C (Normal): 146 knots (270 km/h; 168 mph)
- Max cruising speed at S/L:
  - A (Utility): 126·5 knots (234 km/h; 145·5 mph)
  - B (Utility): 129 knots (240 km/h; 149 mph)
  - B (Normal): 128 knots (238 km/h; 148 mph)
  - C (Utility): 136 knots (252 km/h; 157 mph)
  - C (Normal): 133 knots (246 km/h; 153 mph)
- Econ cruising speed at S/L:
  - A (Utility), B (Utility): 121 knots (224 km/h; 139 mph)
  - B (Normal): 120 knots (222 km/h; 138 mph)
  - C (Utility): 128 knots (237 km/h; 147·5 mph)
  - C (Normal): 125 knots (233 km/h; 144·5 mph)
- Stalling speed, flaps up:
  - A (Utility), B (Utility): 50 knots (92 km/h; 57·5 mph)
  - B (Normal), C (Utility): 56 knots (104 km/h; 65 mph)
  - C (Normal): 59 knots (109 km/h; 68 mph)
- Stalling speed, flaps down:
  - A (Utility), B (Utility): 43 knots (79 km/h; 49·5 mph)
  - B (Normal): 48 knots (88 km/h; 55 mph)
  - C (Utility): 45 knots (83 km/h; 51·5 mph)
  - C (Normal): 48 knots (89 km/h; 55·5 mph)
- Max rate of climb at S/L:
  - A: 198 m (650 ft)/min
  - B: 213 m (700 ft)/min
  - C: 300 m (985 ft)/min
- Service ceiling:
  - A, B: 4,570 m (15,000 ft)
  - C: 5,030 m (16,500 ft)
- T-O to 15 m (50 ft):
  - A, B: 450 m (1,475 ft)
  - C: 510 m (1,675 ft)
- Landing from 15 m (50 ft):
  - A: 500 m (1,640 ft)
  - B, C: 515 m (1,690 ft)
- Range with max fuel, 30 min reserves:
  - A, C: 502 nm (930 km; 578 miles)
  - B: 512 nm (950 km; 590 miles)

FAUVEL

CHARLES FAUVEL

72 Boulevard Carnot, 06400-Cannes (AM)
Telephone: (93) 68-26-24

In addition to the sailplanes and self-launching sailplanes described in the relevant section of this edition, Charles Fauvel has designed several powered lightplanes. Plans of these are available to amateur constructors.

M Fauvel is also perfecting a unique form of wooden integral fuel tank for potential embodiment in all of his powered designs and other aeroplanes.

FAUVEL AV.44

The general appearance of this all-wood side-by-side two-seat, or three-seat, tail-less monoplane can be seen in the accompanying illustration. It is a direct development of M Fauvel's AV.10 aircraft which flew for the first time in 1935, with a 56 kW (75 hp) Pobjoy R engine, and subsequently set up altitude records in single-seat and two-seat categories, in competition with aircraft of considerably greater power. The AV.10 was the only tail-less aeroplane in the world to obtain a full normal certificate of airworthiness before the second World War by meeting requirements laid down for conventional designs.

The AV.44 can be powered by a variety of engines in the 67-97 kW (90-130 hp) range, and is classed as a STOL (ADAC) type. Alternatively, it can be powered by two engines of 41-52 kW (55-70 hp), mounted in the nose and driving two co-axial propellers. This would involve no penalties in terms of drag or dissymmetry; nor would it require any additional 'twin-engine' training for the pilot.

Examples of the AV.44 are being built by five amateur constructors. All available details follow:

DIMENSIONS, EXTERNAL:
- Wing span: 10·70 m (35 ft 1¼ in)
- Wing area, gross: 19·8 m² (213·1 sq ft)
- Wing aspect ratio: 5·8
- Length overall: 5·00 m (16 ft 4¾ in)

WEIGHTS:
- Weight empty: 340 kg (749 lb)
- Fuel and oil: 90 kg (198 lb)
- Normal T-O weight, two-seat: 604 kg (1,331 lb)
- Max T-O weight, three-seat: 681 kg (1,501 lb)

PERFORMANCE (74·5 kW; 100 hp Continental engine):
- Max level speed at S/L: 113 knots (210 km/h; 130 mph)
- Max cruising speed at S/L: 102 knots (190 km/h; 118 mph)
- Max rate of climb at S/L: 294 m (965 ft)/min
- Endurance with max fuel at econ cruising speed: 5½ h

FAUVEL AV.50 (61) LUTIN (ELF)

The AV.50 (61) is a single-seat all-wood light aircraft of tailless configuration. Its wing section can be either Fauvel F2 or a special Wortmann FX-66-H-159 laminar aerofoil. Suitable power plants include modified Volkswagen motor car engines developing 30 kW (40 hp) to 50 kW (67 hp), and the Austrian Rotax engine of 37·25 kW (50 hp) with dual ignition. A tandem-wheel, tailwheel or tricycle landing gear can be fitted.

Predecessor of the AV.50 (61) was the AV.60 Leprechaun, of which an example built and flown in the USA was illustrated in the 1975-76 *Jane's*. No AV.50 had been completed by mid-1978, when the most advanced aircraft was that under construction in Australia. Its wing section, originally intended to be thinner, has now reverted to the thickness of the F2 section. Some control components are identical with those of the AV.45. In general, the constructional principles are the same as those of the AV.60.

Only details of the AV.50 (61) available in 1979 were the following:

DIMENSIONS, EXTERNAL:
- Wing span: 7·50 m (24 ft 7¼ in)
- Wing area, gross: 10·80 m² (116·25 sq ft)
- Wing aspect ratio: 5·2
- Length overall:
  - VW engine: 4·10 m (13 ft 5½ in)

WEIGHTS (with VW engine):
- Weight empty, equipped: 190 kg (419 lb)
- Fuel: 45 kg (99 lb)
- Max T-O weight: 329 kg (725 lb)

PERFORMANCE (estimated, with VW engine, at max T-O weight):
- Max level speed:
  - tandem landing gear: 102 knots (190 km/h; 118 mph)
  - tailwheel landing gear: 98 knots (182 km/h; 113 mph)
  - tricycle landing gear: 92 knots (170 km/h; 106 mph)
- Max rate of climb at S/L: 216 m (710 ft)/min
- T-O run: 100 m (330 ft)
- Endurance with max fuel: 5 h

GATARD

AVIONS A. GATARD

52 route de Jonzac, 17130-Montendre
Telephone: 46.49.4276

M Albert Gatard has developed a control system for aeroplanes which involves the use of a variable-incidence lifting tailplane of large area, and has built a series of aircraft, including the Alouette, Poussin and Pigeon, incorporating his ideas. The Alouette (described in the 1959-60 *Jane's*) was purely experimental, but plans of the Poussin are available to amateur constructors.

Instead of altering the wing angle of attack to increase lift on these aircraft, the pilot lowers full-span slotted aileron/flaps and adjusts the tailplane to maintain pitching equilibrium. In consequence, the aircraft climb with the fuselage datum at no more than 4° to the horizontal, which preserves a good forward view and low body drag.

GATARD STATOPLAN AG 02 POUSSIN (CHICK)

M Gatard built two prototypes of the Poussin and the detailed description applies to the second of these, which introduced a number of design improvements, in its original form. Flight tests revealed excellent aerobatic qualities and the power plant is modified to permit up to 20 seconds of inverted flying.

This prototype was extensively flight-tested at the Centre d'Essais en Vol at Istres, and the performance figures quoted are those which were obtained during the tests. As a result of recommendations by the CEV, a 27 kW (36 hp) Rectimo (modified Volkswagen VW 1200) engine is suggested as the most suitable power plant for use by amateur constructors of the Poussin. The second prototype has been re-engined with a 1,200 cc Volkswagen, by M Mathevet of Mollard-Chateauneuf (Loirs), on behalf of M Gatard. Installation of this engine was expected to improve the CG position and make possible a max speed of approx 92 knots (170 km/h; 106 mph), a max cruising speed of approx 83 knots (155 km/h; 96 mph) and a rate of climb at S/L of 210 m (690 ft)/min.

Several Poussins are being built by amateur constructors, and three of these had been completed and flown by March 1979, one (F-PYBS) with a non-standard tricycle landing gear. Another of them is shown in an accompanying illustration.

The plans have been refined during 1978-79, and the version of the Poussin now offered for amateur construction is designated **AG 02Sp**. The wingtips are now more rounded, with inset ailerons. The wing structure has been modified to permit an increased max T-O weight of 305 kg (672 lb); and the landing gear has been refined to give an increase of about 5% in cruising speed.

The following details apply to the standard Poussins now flying:

TYPE: Single-seat ultra-light monoplane.

WINGS: Cantilever low-wing monoplane. NACA 23012 wing section. Dihedral 4°. Incidence 3° 30' at root, 2° at tip. Plywood-covered single-spar all-wood structure. Full-span slotted aileron/flaps, each in two sections which are moved together but at different angles (inboard sections up to 35°, outboard up to 20°) to give the effect of increased aerodynamic twist of the complete wing/aileron/flap assemblies. Aileron/flaps are linked with the variable-incidence tailplane.

FUSELAGE: Plywood-covered wood structure. Perforated airbrake, under fuselage, operates automatically when the main aileron/flaps are lowered at large angles, as during landing.

TAIL UNIT: Braced all-wood structure, with variable-incidence all-moving tailplane of NACA 2309 section. Endplates fitted to tailplane to increase vertical fin area and effective tailplane span. No elevators. Rudder trim tab actuated by lateral movement of control column, permitting full control by means of the control column alone in normal flight.

LANDING GEAR: Non-retractable tailwheel type. Cantilever levered-suspension main units with rubber-band shock-absorption. Modified Dunlop brakes. Steerable tailwheel.

POWER PLANT: One 18 kW (24 hp) modified Volkswagen flat-four engine, driving a Gatard two-blade fixed-pitch wooden propeller. Provision for fitting any alternative engine of up to 30 kW (40 hp) weighing between 50 and 60 kg (110-132 lb). Fuel tank aft of firewall, capacity 30 litres (6·6 Imp gallons). Oil capacity 2 litres (0·45 Imp gallons).

ACCOMMODATION: Single seat under large rearward-sliding transparent canopy. Baggage space aft of seat. Two map pockets.

DIMENSIONS, EXTERNAL:
- Wing span: 6·40 m (21 ft 0 in)
- Wing chord, constant: 1·00 m (3 ft 3¼ in)
- Wing area, gross: 6·15 m² (66·2 sq ft)
- Length overall: 4·53 m (14 ft 10½ in)
- Height overall: 1·50 m (4 ft 11 in)
- Wheel track: 1·50 m (4 ft 11 in)
- Wheelbase: 3·20 m (10 ft 6 in)

WEIGHTS:
- Weight empty: 170 kg (375 lb)
- Max T-O weight: 280 kg (617 lb)

PERFORMANCE (at max T-O weight):
- Never-exceed speed: 116 knots (216 km/h; 134 mph)
- Max cruising speed: 77 knots (144 km/h; 89 mph)
- Max speed for aerobatics: 69 knots (130 km/h; 80 mph)
- Stalling speed: 35 knots (65 km/h; 40·5 mph)
- Max rate of climb at S/L: 132 m (435 ft)/min
- T-O run: 190 m (625 ft)
- T-O to 15 m (50 ft): 435 m (1,425 ft)
- Landing from 15 m (50 ft): 320 m (1,050 ft)
- Landing run: 200 m (655 ft)

GATARD STATOPLAN AG 04 PIGEON

The AG 04 Pigeon is a two/three-seat high-wing monoplane, powered by a 67 kW (90 hp) Continental engine. It utilises the same type of control system as its predecessors, except that the Statoplan aileron/flaps are in three sections on each wing. As on the Poussin, they move together but through different angles (successively 45°, 30° and 20°) to give the effect of increased aerodynamic twist of the complete wing/aileron/flap assemblies.

The wings are braced by a single streamline-section strut each side and can be folded by two people in seven or eight minutes, to permit the aircraft to be towed along roads behind M Gatard's 6 cv Peugeot 204 motor car, on its own wheels, at 70 km/h (43 mph). Overall dimensions under tow are: length 6·00 m (19 ft 8¼ in), width 2·10 m (6 ft 10¾ in) and height 3·00 m (9 ft 10 in).

A non-retractable tailwheel-type landing gear is fitted, with long-stroke rubber-ring shock-absorbers on all three units. Both manual and toe-operated brakes are specified, the former serving also as a parking brake.

The two front seats are adjustable fore and aft and tilt forward to facilitate access to the rear of the cabin. All controls are so mounted that the main cabin area is completely clear, with a suspended control column. Full control is possible in normal flight by means of this control column alone, as on the Poussin. Dual controls are provided for a second pilot, but can be disconnected easily. Entry is via a two-section door on each side; the lower section opens forward, the top section upward under the wing. The top section can be opened to a mid-position for additional ventilation while taxying. An optional door on the starboard side permits loading of a stretcher 1·80 m long by 0·45 m wide (5 ft 11 in by 1 ft 6 in) when the aircraft is used in an ambulance role. The rear seat on this side can be folded down to make room for the stretcher.

Fuel is carried in two completely independent tanks, with capacities of 70 litres (15·4 Imp gallons) and 14 litres (3·08 Imp gallons) respectively. Should the fuel pump fail, a special cock enables the engine to be supplied by gravity feed.

The prototype Pigeon was flying by mid-1976 and had logged 60 flying hours in about 180 flights by March 1979.

DIMENSIONS, EXTERNAL:
- Wing span: 9·00 m (29 ft 6¼ in)
- Wing area, gross: 11·75 m² (126·5 sq ft)
- Length overall: 6·00 m (19 ft 8¼ in)

WEIGHTS:
- Weight empty: 398 kg (878 lb)
- Max T-O weight: 715 kg (1,576 lb)

PERFORMANCE:
- Max level speed: 94 knots (175 km/h; 108 mph)
- Max cruising speed, three persons: 81 knots (150 km/h; 93 mph)
- Stalling speed: 35 knots (65 km/h; 41 mph)
- Max rate of climb at S/L: 210 m (690 ft)/min
- T-O run: 100 m (328 ft)
- T-O to 15 m (50 ft): 280 m (920 ft)
- Landing from 15 m (50 ft): 260 m (855 ft)
- Landing run: 150 m (493 ft)
- Range with max fuel: 297 nm (550 km; 341 miles)
- Range with max payload: 243 nm (450 km; 280 miles)

JODEL

AVIONS JODEL SA

HEAD OFFICE: 36 Route de Seurre, 21-Beaune
DESIGN OFFICE: 21-Darois
PRESIDENT-DIRECTOR GENERAL: J. Delemontez

The Société des Avions Jodel was formed in March 1946, by MM Jean Delemontez and Edouard Joly, with the former acting as business and technical manager and the latter as test pilot.

Its first activities were concerned with the repair of gliders and light aircraft of the Service d'Aviation Légère et Sportive, on behalf of the State. Simultaneously, the company designed and built the D.9 Bébé Jodel single-seat light monoplane, which made its first flight in January 1948. This aeroplane, which is certificated with various power plants, proved ideal for amateur construction and can be built in as little as 500 man-hours.

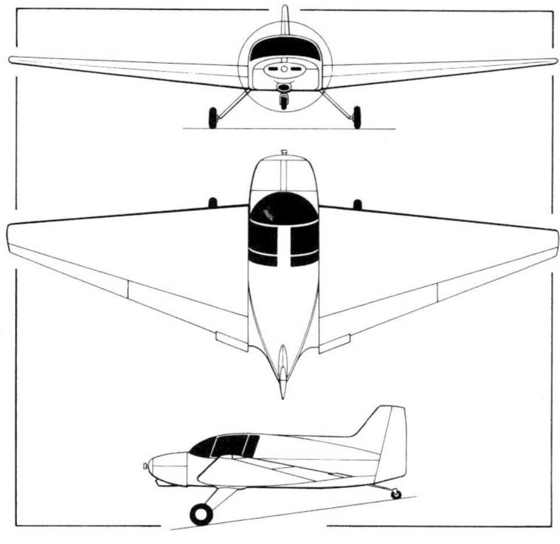

Fauvel AV.44 *(Michael A. Badrocke)*

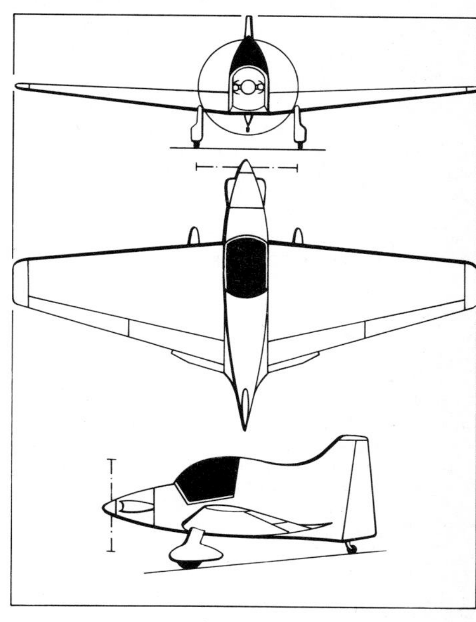

Fauvel AV.50 (61) Lutin *(Tony Mitchell)*

Gatard AG 02 Poussin No. 19, built by M A. Hézard of Dijon

Gatard Statoplan AG 04 Pigeon with wings and tailplane folded

Jodel F.11, a Canadian example of the D.11 built by Mr Anatel Yaremchuk of Vernon, BC *(Phil Hanson)*

Jodel D.9 single-seat homebuilt aircraft (Volkswagen engine) *(Peter J. Bish)*

As the result of official tests with the D.9, the French authorities placed an order for the development and construction of two prototypes of a two-seat model, the D.11 fitted with a 33·6 kW (45 hp) Salmson, and the D.111 with a 56 kW (75 hp) Minié engine. Subsequent developments of the D.11 are the D.112 and D.117, which have a 48·5 kW and 67 kW (65 hp and 90 hp) Continental engine respectively. These designs also have been built in large numbers, both commercially and by amateurs.

Avions Jodel now devotes its activities mainly to designing advanced developments of its established types and to acting as a consultant to those building and developing its designs.

JODEL D.9 and D.92 BÉBÉ

The type designation of the Bébé varies according to the type of engine fitted. The original version, with 18·6 kW (25 hp) Poinsard engine, was designated D.9; the D.92 has a modified Volkswagen engine.

The following details refer to all standard versions of the Bébé:

TYPE: Single-seat light monoplane.

WINGS: Cantilever low-wing monoplane. Single-spar one-piece wing with wide-span centre-section of constant chord and thickness and two tapering outer portions set at a coarse dihedral angle (14°). Spar and ribs of spruce and plywood, with fabric covering. Ailerons similar in construction.

FUSELAGE: Rectangular spruce and plywood structure.

TAIL UNIT: Cantilever structure of spruce and plywood, with plywood covering on tailplane and fabric-covered rudder and elevators. No fin.

LANDING GEAR: Non-retractable cantilever main legs with rubber-in-compression springing. Leaf-spring tailskid or tailwheel. Cable brakes.

POWER PLANT: One 18·6 kW (25 hp) Poinsard (D.9) or modified Volkswagen (D.92) flat-four engine, but other engines of 18·5 to 48·5 kW (25 to 65 hp) may be fitted, including the 27 kW (36 hp) Aeronca JAP and Continental A40. Fuel tank in fuselage, capacity 25 litres (5·5 Imp gallons).

ACCOMMODATION: Single seat in open cockpit.

DIMENSIONS, EXTERNAL:

Wing span	7·00 m (22 ft 11 in)
Wing chord (centre-section, constant)	1·40 m (4 ft 7 in)
Wing area, gross	9·0 m² (96·8 sq ft)
Wing aspect ratio	5·45
Length overall	5·45 m (17 ft 10½ in)

WEIGHTS:

Weight empty	190 kg (420 lb)
Max T-O weight	320 kg (705 lb)

PERFORMANCE (30 kW; 40 hp engine, at max T-O weight):

Max level speed at S/L	87 knots (160 km/h; 100 mph)
Cruising speed	74 knots (137 km/h; 85 mph)
Stalling speed	35 knots (65 km/h; 40 mph)
Max rate of climb at S/L	180 m (590 ft)/min
T-O run	110 m (360 ft)
Landing run	100 m (330 ft)
Range with max fuel	217 nm (400 km; 250 miles)

JODEL D.11 and D.119

The original D.11, with 33·5 kW (45 hp) Salmson engine, was the basic model in the series of Jodel two-seaters for amateur and commercial production.

The version for amateur construction with 67 kW (90 hp) Continental engine is designated D.119.

A typical D.11 was built over an eight-year period by Wayne Nelson, an aeronautical engineer of Bountiful, Utah, at a cost of $2,000. The wing is of wood, covered with Dacron, the fuselage and tail unit of wood covered with glassfibre. Changes from the standard design include the fitting of a fixed tail-fin forward of the rudder, and of cantilever spring main landing gear legs. This D.11 spans 8·23 m (27 ft 0 in), has an empty weight of 340 kg (750 lb) and loaded weight of 562 kg (1,240 lb), and is powered by a 48·5 kW (65 hp) Continental A65-8 flat-four engine. Performance is as follows:

PERFORMANCE:

Max level speed at S/L	93 knots (173 km/h; 108 mph)
Cruising speed	86 knots (161 km/h; 100 mph)
Landing speed	35 knots (64·5 km/h; 40 mph)
Max rate of climb at S/L	152 m (500 ft)/min
Service ceiling	4,875 m (16,000 ft)
T-O run	152 m (500 ft)
Landing run	244 m (800 ft)
Range with max fuel	260 nm (482 km; 300 miles)

JODEL D.112 CLUB

The D.112 is a two-seat dual-control version of the D.9. Except for increased overall dimensions, a wider fuselage and enclosed side-by-side cockpit, the D.112 conforms in layout and structure to the D.9, but is fitted normally with a 48·5 kW (65 hp) Continental flat-four engine. Fuel capacity is 60 litres (13 Imp gallons).

DIMENSIONS, EXTERNAL:

Wing span	8·2 m (26 ft 10 in)
Wing area, gross	12·72 m² (137 sq ft)
Length overall	6·36 m (20 ft 10 in)
Dihedral on outer wings	19°

WEIGHTS:

Weight empty	270 kg (600 lb)
Max T-O weight	520 kg (1,145 lb)

PERFORMANCE (at max T-O weight):

Max level speed at S/L	102 knots (190 km/h; 118 mph)
Max cruising speed	92 knots (170 km/h; 105·5 mph)
Econ cruising speed	81 knots (150 km/h; 93 mph)
Stalling speed	38 knots (70 km/h; 43 mph)
Max rate of climb at S/L	193 m (632 ft)/min
T-O run	137 m (450 ft)
Landing run	120 m (395 ft)
Range with max fuel	323 nm (600 km; 373 miles)

JURCA
MARCEL JURCA

2, rue des Champs Philippe, 92-La Garenne-Colombes (Seine)
Telephone: 242.9633 and 551.6306

M Marcel Jurca, an ex-military pilot and hydraulics engineer, has designed a series of high-performance light aircraft of which plans are available to amateur constructors.

A prototype of his first design, the M.J.1, was built but did not fly. To gain experience, M Jurca next built a two-seat Jodel light aircraft, with the help of members of the Aéro Club of Courbevoie, and this flew for the first time in 1954.

The same team then built a prototype of M Jurca's second design, the M.J.2 Tempête single-seat light aircraft; incorporating many Jodel components. It proved so successful that sets of plans were offered to amateur constructors and many Tempêtes are now flying or under assembly throughout the world.

M Jurca developed from the Tempête the two-seat M.J.5 Sirocco and the M.J.51 Sperocco, and has produced a further series of designs by scaling down the basic airframes of second World War fighters to two-thirds or three-quarters of the original size.

For the North American market, Jurca plans are available from Mr Ken Heit, 581 Helen Street, Mt Morris, Michigan 48458, USA. Representative for Australia and New Zealand is Mr Steve Rankin, RD 9, Whangarei, New Zealand.

JURCA M.J.2 and M.J.20 TEMPÊTE

The prototype Tempête was flown for the first time, by its designer, on 27 June 1956. It obtained its certificate of airworthiness very quickly, and a total of at least 28 Tempêtes are now flying, with 20 more under construction, in France, Denmark, Luxembourg, Portugal, the UK, the United States and Canada, all amateur built.

The type of engine fitted to a particular aircraft is indicated by a suffix letter in its designation. Suffix letters are A for the 48·5 kW (65 hp) Continental A65, B for the 56 kW (75 hp) Continental A75, C for the 63·5 kW (85 hp) Continental C85, D for the 67 kW (90 hp) Continental C90-14F, E for the 74·5 kW (100 hp) Continental O-200-A, F for the 78·5 kW (105 hp) Potez 4 E-20, G for the 86 kW (115 hp) Potez 4 E-30, and H for the 93 kW (125 hp) Lycoming.

The standard version is the M.J.2A with A65 engine. The M.J.2D, with 67 kW (90 hp) C90-14F, cruises at 105 knots (195 km/h; 121 mph) and climbs to 1,000 m (3,280 ft) in 3 minutes. It can also perform aerobatics without loss of height. The Tempête built in Portugal is an M.J.2D with 67 kW (90 hp) Continental.

A version known as the **M.J.20** was under construction in Denmark with a 134 kW (180 hp) engine and strengthened airframe. It has been abandoned and its role as a prototype has been taken by a 112 kW (150 hp) Tempête being built in the Rouen area of France by M Yves Chopart.

The Tempête is basically a single-seat aircraft, but the 112 and 134 kW (150 and 180 hp) versions have provision for carrying behind the pilot on cross-country flights a second person weighing not more than 55 kg (121 lb). This is not permitted by the DGAC in France; but a two-seater has already flown in the USA, built by Mr Don Kerkhof of Mankato, Minnesota.

The 112 and 134 kW versions are intended to have an aerobatic capability adequate to compete with the American Pitts Specials in international competitions.

The following details apply generally to all basic single-seat M.J.2 models:

TYPE: Single-seat light monoplane.

WINGS: Cantilever low-wing monoplane. NACA 23012 wing section. Incidence varies according to engine power. The 48·5 kW (65 hp) version has an incidence of 4° at root, 2° at tip. No dihedral. All-wood one-piece single-spar structure with fabric covering. Fabric-covered wooden ailerons.

FUSELAGE: All-wood structure of basic rectangular section, plywood-covered.

TAIL UNIT: Cantilever all-wood structure. Tailplane and fin plywood-covered, elevators and rudder fabric-covered. Trim tab on starboard elevator.

LANDING GEAR: Non-retractable tailwheel type. Jodel D.112 cantilever legs with rubber-in-compression springing. Jodel D.112 wheels and Dunlop 420 × 150 tyres. Jodel D.112 tailskid or tailwheel.

POWER PLANT: One 48·5 kW (65 hp) Continental A65 flat-four engine, driving a Ratier two-blade wooden propeller with ground-adjustable pitch. Provision for fitting 56, 63·5, 67, or 74·5 kW (75, 85, 90 or 100 hp) Continental, 78·5 or 86 kW (105 or 115 hp) Potez or 93 kW (125 hp) Lycoming engine. Jodel engine mounting and cowling. Jodel fuel tank, capacity 60 litres (13·2 Imp gallons), aft of firewall in fuselage.

ACCOMMODATION: Single seat under long rearward-sliding transparent canopy.

DIMENSIONS, EXTERNAL:

Wing span	6·00 m (19 ft 8 in)
Wing chord (basic)	1·40 m (4 ft 7 in)
Wing area, gross	7·98 m² (85·90 sq ft)
Wing aspect ratio	4·5
Length overall	5·855 m (19 ft 2½ in)
Height overall	2·40 m (7 ft 10 in)
Tailplane span	2·50 m (8 ft 2 in)
Wheel track	2·30 m (7 ft 6½ in)

WEIGHTS:

Weight empty	90 kg (639 lb)
Max T-O weight	430 kg (950 lb)

PERFORMANCE (48·5 kW; 65 hp engine):

Max level speed	104 knots (193 km/h; 120 mph)
Cruising speed	89 knots (165 km/h; 102 mph)
Landing speed	43 knots (80 km/h; 50 mph)
Max rate of climb at S/L	170 m (555 ft)/min
Service ceiling	3,500 m (11,500 ft)
T-O run	250 m (820 ft)
Endurance	3 h 20 min

JURCA M.J.3H DART

The M.J.3H Dart is a single-seat all-wood monoplane, with the fuselage of the M.J.2 Tempête and the wings of the M.J.5 Sirocco. The prototype, built by Denis Jacobs of Dayton, Ohio, made its first flight in 1977.

TYPE: Single-seat sporting aircraft.

WINGS: As for M.J.5 Sirocco. Wing section NACA 23012. No dihedral. Incidence 3°. Washout 2° at half-span. Wood construction, including three-position split flaps and ailerons.

FUSELAGE: As for M.J.2 Tempête. All-wooden semi-monocoque structure.

TAIL UNIT: Conventional cantilever all-wooden structure, comprising fin and rudder, tailplane and elevators with trim tab on starboard side.

LANDING GEAR: Retractable tailwheel type. Main wheels retract inward.

POWER PLANT: One 86 kW (115 hp) Lycoming O-235-C1 flat-four engine, driving a two-blade propeller. Fuel tanks in front and rear fuselage, total capacity 75·7 litres (16·6 Imp gallons).

ACCOMMODATION: Single seat under sliding transparent canopy.

DIMENSIONS, EXTERNAL:

Wing span	6·35 m (20 ft 10 in)
Wing chord at tip	1·40 m (4 ft 7 in)
Wing area, gross	9·66 m² (104 sq ft)
Wing aspect ratio	4·25
Length overall	6·248 m (20 ft 6 in)
Tailplane span	2·54 m (8 ft 4 in)
Wheel track	2·44 m (8 ft 0 in)

WEIGHTS:

Weight empty	476 kg (1,050 lb)
Max T-O weight	612 kg (1,350 lb)

PERFORMANCE (48·5 kW; 65 hp engine):

Never-exceed speed	173 knots (322 km/h; 200 mph)
Max level speed at 1,525 m (5,000 ft)	134 knots (248 km/h; 154 mph)
Max cruising speed (75% power) at 1,525 m (5,000 ft)	123 knots (229 km/h; 142 mph)
Econ cruising speed	117 knots (217 km/h; 135 mph)
Stalling speed, landing gear and flaps up	52 knots (97 km/h; 60 mph)
Stalling speed, landing gear and flaps down	48 knots (88·5 km/h; 55 mph)
Time to 1,000 m (3,280 ft)	3 min 15 s
Service ceiling (estimated)	3,660 m (12,000 ft)
T-O run, 15·5°C	229 m (750 ft)
Landing run	305 m (1,000 ft)
Endurance	2 h 45 min
Load factors	+9*g*, −4·5*g* (ultimate)

JURCA M.J.5 SIROCCO

The M.J.5 Sirocco is a tandem two-seat monoplane, developed from the M.J.2 Tempête as a potential club training and touring aircraft. It is fully aerobatic when flown as a two-seater.

The longer-span wings have an extended leading-edge inboard of the fence on each side and a completely new tip shape. A sweptback fin and rudder are standard.

The prototype M.J.5 flew for the first time on 3 August 1962, powered by a 78·5 kW (105 hp) Potez 4 E-20 engine. It was fitted originally with a non-retractable landing gear, but retractable landing gear and a 119·5 kW (160 hp) Lycoming O-320 engine were fitted in 1966, followed by a 134 kW (180 hp) Lycoming engine later. Its fuel capacity is 116 litres (25·5 Imp gallons).

By mid-February 1967, five more Siroccos were flying, one of them factory-built at Nancy. This aircraft, powered by a 74·5 kW (100 hp) Continental engine, concluded tests at Istres in January 1969. The French government then concluded an agreement with Constructions Aéronautiques Lorraines, François et Cie of Nancy, which built an airframe for static tests, in March 1971. These were required in view of the fact that the Sirocco is regarded as a basic trainer suitable for amateur construction; and it was awarded subsequently a certificate of airworthiness in the Utility category. Supplementary tests were conducted at the CEV with another Sirocco, powered by a 100·5 kW (135 hp) Lycoming O-320 engine.

A full C of A, covering Aerobatic requirements and unlimited spinning, is applicable only when a power plant of 112 kW (150 hp) minimum rating is installed.

The version of the Sirocco for amateur construction is generally similar to the factory-built version, with optional retractable landing gear.

At least 40 Siroccos are reported to be flying or under construction by amateurs in France, Canada, Germany, Switzerland, England and the USA, with various engines.

The type of engine fitted to a particular aircraft is indicated by a suffix letter in its designation. Suffix letters are A for the 67 kW (90 hp) Continental C90-8 or -14F, B for the 74·5 kW (100 hp) Continental O-200-A, C for the 78·5 kW (105 hp) Potez 4 E-20, D for the Potez 4 E-30, E for the 78·5 kW (105 hp) Hirth, F for the 93 kW (125 hp) Lycoming, G for the 100·5 kW (135 hp) Regnier, H for the 119·5 kW (160 hp) Lycoming, K for the 134 kW (180 hp) Lycoming and L for the 164 kW (220 hp) Franklin. Addition of the numeral 1 indicates a non-retractable landing gear and the numeral 2 indicates a retractable landing gear. Thus, the designation of the original prototype in its current form is M.J.5K2. The example built at Nancy for certification has a 74·5 kW (100 hp) Continental engine and so is designated M.J.5B1.

Two examples of the M.J.5K, flying in Vichy and Montelimar, France, are each fitted with a 134 kW (180 hp) Lycoming engine and Christen inverted fuel system. Work on two M.J.5L Siroccos, with 164 kW (220 hp) Franklin engine, was started in 1975, in the USA and France, for use in international aerobatic championships.

A Sirocco with 86 kW (115 hp) Lycoming O-235-C2B engine and 1·85 m (6 ft 0¾ in) diameter propeller was constructed by Luftsportgruppe Liebherr-Aero-Technik (LAT) in Germany. This has a modified rudder of reduced height and greater chord, and a jettisonable, sideways-hinged cockpit canopy, and is intended for certification for aerobatic flying. The details which follow apply to this aircraft, but are generally typical of all versions.

A developed version, known as the M.J.51 Sperocco, is described separately.

DIMENSIONS, EXTERNAL:

Wing span	7·00 m (23 ft 0 in)
Wing area, gross	10·00 m² (107·64 sq ft)
Wing aspect ratio	4·9
Length overall	6·15 m (20 ft 2 in)
Height overall, tail up:	
standard model	2·80 m (9 ft 2¼ in)
LAT version	2·60 m (8 ft 6¼ in)
Tailplane span	3·24 m (10 ft 7½ in)
Wheel track	2·80 m (9 ft 2¼ in)

WEIGHTS:

Weight empty	430 kg (947 lb)
Max T-O weight	680 kg (1,499 lb)

PERFORMANCE (at max T-O weight):

Max level speed	127 knots (235 km/h; 146 mph)
Cruising speed	116 knots (215 km/h; 134 mph)
Stalling speed	44 knots (80 km/h; 50 mph)
Climb to 1,000 m (3,280 ft)	4 min
Service ceiling	5,000 m (16,400 ft)
T-O run	250 m (820 ft)
Landing run	200 m (655 ft)
Endurance	4 h 20 min

JURCA M.J.5 SIROCCO (SPORT WING)

A special version of the Sirocco, with 86 kW (115 hp) engine and increased wing span, has been evolved for the New Zealand and Australian market. Known as a 'Sport' wing, the wing of this aircraft embodies one additional rib and inter-rib bay each side. The modification is available in the English-language set of Sirocco plans.

JURCA M.J.51 SPEROCCO

Using knowledge gained from flight experience with the M.J.5 and the Canadian prototype M.J.7, M Jurca evolved, with the assistance of M J. Lecarme, a design incorporating features of each aircraft. It is known as the M.J.51 Sperocco, the name being a contraction of 'Special Sirocco', and is intended for high-performance aerobatic and competition flying. Like other Jurca designs, the M.J.51 is suitable for amateur construction.

The wings, of Habib 64000 748 laminar-flow profile, are essentially those of the M.J.7 Gnatsum. They are without dihedral, and the angle of incidence varies according to the rating of the engine that is installed, as in the Tempête. The fuselage is of completely new design, with a basically triangular cross-section, but is of similar construction to the M.J.5. The tail unit consists of M.J.7 horizontal surfaces with a shorter and wider-chord fin and rudder. Landing gear is of the M.J.5 type and is fully retractable.

Any horizontally-opposed engine of 112-179 kW (150-240 hp) may be installed. Fuel is contained in two wing tanks, each of 55 litres (12 Imp gallons) capacity, and one fuselage tank of 45 or 100 litres (10 or 22 Imp gallons) capacity.

The M.J.51 seats two persons in tandem under a one-piece sliding canopy, the rear seat being 10 cm (3·9 in) higher than the front seat.

The first M.J.51, powered by a 134 kW (180 hp) Lycoming AIO-360 engine, is under construction by M Serge Brilliant at Melun.

DIMENSIONS, EXTERNAL:

Wing span	7·623 m (25 ft 0 in)
Wing area, gross	11·00 m² (118 sq ft)
Length overall	7·24 m (23 ft 9 in)

Jurca M.J.2D Tempête built by M Sire of Pons *(Michel Bernard)*

Prototype M.J.3H Dart, built by Mr Denis Jacobs of Dayton, Ohio

Jurca M.J.5H2 Sirocco, with Lycoming IO-320-B engine and retractable landing gear, built by M Cavagna of Remoulins

Jurca M.J.7H Gnatsum built in Canada by Capt W. T. Foster, CAF

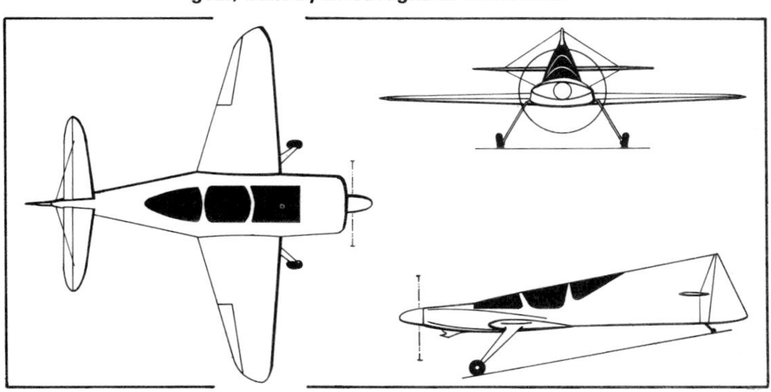
Jurca M.J.14 Fourtouna single-seat racing aircraft *(Roy J. Grainge)*

Jurca M.J.8 1-Nine-O built by Mr Joseph Kiska of Connecticut

WEIGHT:
Max T-O weight 730 kg (1,653 lb)
PERFORMANCE (estimated, with 112 kW; 150 hp Lycoming engine):
Max level speed 149 knots (275 km/h; 171 mph)
Max cruising speed (75% power) 135 knots (250 km/h; 155 mph)
Stalling speed 49 knots (90 km/h; 56 mph)
Time to 1,000 m (3,280 ft) 1 min 30 s

JURCA M.J.7 and M.J.77 GNATSUM

The Gnatsum is a scale replica, for amateur construction, of the North American P-51 Mustang single-seat fighter of the second World War. Its name 'Gnatsum' is 'Mustang' reversed.

Initially, M Jurca designed the wings, fuselage, tail surfaces and manually-retractable landing gear. The engine installation was deliberately not designed, to permit constructors to utilise any of the suitable Lycoming, Continental, Ranger or other power plants that are available.

During construction of the M.J.7 prototype in Canada (see below), a number of modifications and improvements were made to the basic design. These were embodied in the drawings, which are available from M Jurca in two forms, as follows:

M.J.7. To two-thirds scale. Prototype (CF-XZI, now N51HR) built in the works of Falconar Aircraft Ltd on the Industrial Airport, Edmonton, Alberta, Canada, and first flown on 31 July 1969. Granted DoT type approval by early 1970. Described under the 'SAL' entry in the Canadian section of the 1973-74 *Jane's*. The second M.J.7 built in Canada was the one constructed by Captain W. T. Foster, to which the data given at the end of this entry apply. Two other Gnatsums were flown in 1977, under the SAL designation, built by Mr Bill Slater and Mr Ross Grady of the USA. The first example built in the UK, by Mr W. E. Wilks, was illustrated in the 1978-79 *Jane's*. Plastics fuselage shells for the M.J.7 are available from Boeve Brothers of Holland, Michigan, USA.

M.J.77. To three-quarters scale. Examples under construction by Mr Bob Aughton in Michigan, M Glorieux of Pau, M Piazola of Egletons and M Semenadisse of Hyères, near Toulon, France.

Unlike previous small-scale replicas of this aircraft, the Gnatsum is scaled down precisely. Use of an in-line engine, such as the 134 kW (180 hp) or 149 kW (200 hp) Ranger, permits the fuselage cowling lines to follow closely those of the original. Alternative installation of a 149 kW (200 hp) Lycoming horizontally-opposed air-cooled engine requires fairing blisters over the cylinders.

M Jurca's plans provide for alternative plywood-covered semi-monocoque fuselage construction or a square wooden box structure covered with two plastics shells.

DIMENSIONS, EXTERNAL:
Wing span 7·52 m (24 ft 8¼ in)
Wing area, gross 10·41 m² (112 sq ft)
Length overall 6·55 m (21 ft 6 in)
WEIGHTS (Capt Foster's M.J.7 with 149 kW; 200 hp Ranger engine):
Weight empty 673 kg (1,485 lb)
Max T-O weight 850 kg (1,875 lb)
PERFORMANCE (Capt Foster's M.J.7 with 149 kW; 200 hp Ranger engine):
Max level speed 190 knots (351 km/h; 218 mph)
Cruising speed at 2,133 m (7,000 ft) 175 knots (325 km/h; 202 mph)
Stalling speed (flaps down) 57 knots (106 km/h; 66 mph)
Take-off speed (flaps up) 70-75 knots (131-139 km/h; 81-86·5 mph)
Landing speed (flaps up) 65-70 knots (121-130 km/h; 75-81 mph)
Landing speed (flaps down) 63 knots (117 km/h; 72·5 mph)
Max rate of climb at S/L 305 m (1,000 ft)/min
T-O run 457 m (1,500 ft)
Landing run 610-762 m (2,000-2,500 ft)

JURCA M.J.7S SOLO

Intended as a single-seat advanced trainer, the M.J.7S Solo is basically similiar to the M.J.7 Gnatsum but does not retain the underbelly scoop which the latter inherited from the original P-51 Mustang design. A prototype is under construction by M Duhamel of Strasbourg, with a 134 kW (180 hp) Lycoming AIO-360 flat-four engine.

The wing section of the M.J.7S is quoted as Habib 64-000 748-MJ7-104.

DIMENSIONS, EXTERNAL:
Wing span 7·523 m (24 ft 8½ in)
Wing area, gross 10·8 m² (116·2 sq ft)
Length overall, tail up 6·664 m (21 ft 10 in)
Tailplane span 3·00 m (9 ft 10 in)

JURCA M.J.8 and M.J.80 1-NINE-O

The M.J.8 is a single-seat sporting aircraft which has been designed by M Jurca by scaling down to three-quarters of the original dimensions the airframe of the Focke-Wulf Fw 190 fighter. Its general appearance is shown in the accompanying illustration.

This prototype, built by Mr Ronald Kitchen of Carson City, Nevada, flew for the first time on 30 March 1975. A second example was built by Mr J. Kiska of Norwalk, Connecticut; and Mr Evan Wolfe of California is constructing an enlarged M.J.8, in an attempt to produce a full-size 'Fw 190'. This has been designated **M.J.80.**

The M.J.8 prototype has a 216 kW (290 hp) Lycoming IO-540 engine, but the design is suitable for the alternative use of any horizontally-opposed or radial engine in the 74·5-149 kW (100-200 hp) range. The landing gear is retractable.

DIMENSIONS, EXTERNAL (M.J.8):
Wing span 7·87 m (25 ft 10 in)
Wing chord at root 1·70 m (5 ft 7 in)
Wing chord at tip 0·90 m (2 ft 11½ in)
Wing area, gross 10·2 m² (109·8 sq ft)
Length overall 6·63 m (21 ft 9 in)
Tailplane span 2·84 m (9 ft 4 in)
WEIGHTS (M.J.8, 119·5 kW; 160 hp engine):
Weight empty 400 kg (880 lb)
Max T-O weight 626 kg (1,380 lb)
PERFORMANCE (M.J.8, estimated, with 119·5 kW; 160 hp engine):
Max level speed at S/L 139 knots (257 km/h; 160 mph)
Max cruising speed 124 knots (230 km/h; 143 mph)
Stalling speed 49 knots (90 km/h; 56 mph)
Max rate of climb at S/L 503 m (1,650 ft)/min

JURCA M.J.9 ONE-OH-NINE

A prototype three-quarter scale Messerschmitt Bf 109 fighter of the second World War is being constructed by

Mr Werner Hohn of Carson City, Nevada. This has been designated M.J.9. A second example is being built by Mr Heyser of Tustin, California.

JURCA M.J.10 SPIT

The M.J.10 is a single-seat, three-quarter scale representation of the Supermarine Spitfire which can also be modified as a two-seater. It is suitable for any horizontally-opposed or in-line engine of 89·5-164 kW (120-220 hp), although some slight variations from the Spitfire's contours are necessary in the former case. Construction is entirely of wood, except for the glassfibre engine cowling and fabric covering on the control surfaces. The single-spar wing is similar in construction to that of the Sirocco. The manually-operated retractable landing gear is fitted with helicoidal spring shock-absorbers.

The basic plans adopted the Spitfire Mk IX as the standard M.J.10 version, but alternative detail plans are available for representing both Merlin- and Griffon-engined models, including the Mks VC and XIV, and for clipped, standard or extended-span wings.

A prototype is under construction by Mr Pendlebury of the Chesterfield Air Touring Group at West Bridgford, Nottingham, England. Another is being built by Mr Ed Storo of New York, USA.

DIMENSIONS, EXTERNAL:
- Wing span:
  - standard: 8·40 m (27 ft 6¾ in)
  - clipped: 7·46 m (24 ft 5½ in)
- Wing area, gross: 12·60 m² (135·6 sq ft)
- Length overall: 7·125 m (23 ft 4½ in)

WEIGHTS (119·5 kW; 160 hp engine):
- Weight empty: 658 kg (1,450 lb)
- Max T-O weight: 907 kg (2,000 lb)

PERFORMANCE (estimated, with 119·5 kW; 160 hp engine):
- Max level speed at S/L: 139 knots (257 km/h; 160 mph)
- Cruising speed: 124 knots (230 km/h; 143 mph)
- Stalling speed: 49 knots (90 km/h; 56 mph)
- Max rate of climb at S/L: 503 m (1,650 ft)/min
- T-O run: 200 m (660 ft)

JURCA M.J.12 PEE-40

The M.J.12 is a three-quarter scale representation of the Curtiss P-40 single-seat fighter of the second World War. It spans 8·524 m (27 ft 11½ in) and has an overall length (tail up) of 7·62 m (25 ft 0 in)

Two M.J.12s are under construction in the USA, one by Mr Ron Kitchen of Carson City, Nevada, who built the prototype M.J.8.

JURCA M.J.14 FOURTOUNA

Designed in 1971, the M.J.14 Fourtouna (Tempête in Romanian) will be a small single-seat racing aircraft of unorthodox configuration, with a semi-reclining seat for the pilot. Construction of a prototype was undertaken by M Beliard in Coutances, France, and was well advanced in the Spring of 1978. Its general appearance is shown in the accompanying three-view drawing.

The standard tapered wings can be replaced by constant-chord wings of the same span if the aircraft is intended for 'rapid liaison'. Tailplane incidence is adjustable on the ground. The following data apply to the aircraft as illustrated, with a 67 kW (90 hp) Continental C90-8F flat-four engine. Fuel capacity is 70 litres (15·5 Imp gallons).

DIMENSIONS, EXTERNAL:
- Wing span: 6·00 m (19 ft 8½ in)
- Wing area, gross: 6·1 m² (65·66 sq ft)
- Length overall: 5·68 m (18 ft 7½ in)
- Tailplane span: 2·97 m (9 ft 9 in)

WEIGHTS:
- Weight empty: 250 kg (550 lb)
- Max T-O weight: 420 kg (925 lb)

LEDERLIN

FRANÇOIS LEDERLIN

2 rue Charles Peguy, 38-Grenoble

M Lederlin, an architect, designed and built a two-seat light aeroplane based on the familiar Mignet 'Pou-du-Ciel' formula. Although derived from the Mignet HM-380 and designated 380-L, it retains little of the original except for the wing section. First flight was made on 14 September 1965, a restricted C of A being granted in the following month.

Plans of the 380-L, annotated in English and with both English and metric measurements, are available to amateur constructors, and several examples are under construction or already flying.

LEDERLIN 380-L

TYPE: Two-seat amateur-built light aircraft.

WINGS: Tandem-wing biplane. Wing section 3-40-13. Dihedral 3° 30′ on outer sections only (both wings). Incidence variable from 0° to 12° (forward wing). Incidence of rear wing 6°. No sweepback. Each wing is made in two parts, bolted together at the centreline. Construction is conventional, with wooden box-spar and trellis ribs, plywood leading-edge and overall fabric covering. The variable-incidence front wing is pivoted on the cabane structure by ball-joints and on the bracing struts (one each side) by cardan-joints. No ailerons or flaps. Long-span tab on trailing-edge of rear wing, controllable in flight.

FUSELAGE: Welded steel tube structure, covered with light alloy to front of cabin and with fabric on rear fuselage, over light spruce formers.

TAIL UNIT: Fin and rudder only. Spruce and ply structure, covered with fabric. Ground-adjustable tab in rudder.

LANDING GEAR: Non-retractable tailwheel type. Cantilever main legs consist of conical spring steel rods, inclined rearward. Fournier main wheels and tyres, size 380 × 150, with mechanical brakes. Large tailwheel, carried on telescopic leg with spring shock-absorber, can be steered by the rudder controls through a linkage engaged by the pilot.

POWER PLANT: One 67 kW (90 hp) Continental C90-14F flat-four engine, driving a McCauley two-blade metal fixed-pitch propeller. Single fuel tank, capacity 85 litres (18·75 Imp gallons). Oil capacity 4·5 litres (1 Imp gallon).

ACCOMMODATION: Two seats side by side in enclosed cabin. Forward-hinged door on each side. Controls comprise a rudder bar for directional control and a stick, suspended from the roof of the cabin and free laterally, to control the incidence of the forward wing. A further lever, suspended from the roof, controls the tab on the rear wing. Baggage space aft of seats.

DIMENSIONS, EXTERNAL:
- Wing span:
  - forward: 7·92 m (26 ft 0 in)
  - rear: 6·00 m (19 ft 8¼ in)
- Wing chord (constant, each): 1·30 m (4 ft 3¼ in)
- Wing area, gross:
  - forward: 9·92 m² (106·8 sq ft)
  - rear: 7·43 m² (80·0 sq ft)
- Length overall: 4·77 m (15 ft 7¾ in)
- Height overall: 2·08 m (6 ft 10 in)
- Wheel track: 2·05 m (6 ft 8¾ in)
- Wheelbase: 3·10 m (10 ft 2 in)
- Propeller diameter: 1·83 m (6 ft 0 in)
- Doors (each): Height: 0·90 m (2 ft 11½ in)
  - Width: 0·75 m (2 ft 5½ in)
  - Height to sill: 0·50 m (1 ft 7½ in)

DIMENSIONS, INTERNAL:
- Cabin:
  - Max width: 1·07 m (3 ft 6 in)
  - Max height: 1·03 m (3 ft 4 in)
  - Baggage space: 0·20 m³ (7 cu ft)

WEIGHTS:
- Weight empty: 360 kg (794 lb)
- Max T-O weight: 600 kg (1,323 lb)

PERFORMANCE (at max T-O weight):
- Never-exceed speed: 126 knots (233 km/h; 145 mph)
- Max level speed at 305 m (1,000 ft): 109 knots (201 km/h; 125 mph)
- Max cruising speed: 97 knots (180 km/h; 112 mph)
- Econ cruising speed at 610 m (2,000 ft): 87 knots (161 km/h; 100 mph)
- Stalling speed, power off: 26 knots (49 km/h; 30 mph)
- Max rate of climb at S/L: 275 m (900 ft)/min
- Service ceiling: over 3,660 m (12,000 ft)
- T-O run: 122 m (400 ft)
- Landing run: 153 m (500 ft)
- Range at econ cruising speed: 477 nm (885 km; 550 miles)

LEFEBVRE

ROBERT LEFEBVRE

CES A. Camus, rue Adeline, 76100-Rouen

M Lefebvre has built and flown a small single-seat racing aircraft named the Busard, assisted by pupils of the A. Camus technical school at Rouen. Basis of the design was the MP.204 prototype racer with 56 kW (75 hp) Minié engine, designed by Max Plan and first flown on 5 June 1952. By comparison with the MP.204, the Busard has been lightened, and simplified for construction by amateurs.

LEFEBVRE MP.205 BUSARD

The description below applies to the prototype Busard (F-PTXT) built and flown by M. Lefebvre. This aircraft was powered originally with a 48·5 kW (65 hp) Continental engine and was illustrated in this form in the 1974-75 *Jane's*. After 20 flying hours it was re-engined with a 67 kW (90 hp) Continental and underwent several refinements, including the fitting of main-wheel fairings.

At least fifteen sets of plans have been sold to amateur constructors. One Busard is being built with a 48·5 kW (65 hp) Walter engine, two with versions of the Volkswagen, and the remainder with Continentals.

TYPE: Single-seat amateur-built racing aircraft.

WINGS: Cantilever low-wing monoplane. Wing section NACA 23012. Constant incidence of 1°. Slight dihedral. Conventional single-spar wood structure, covered entirely with plywood. Fabric-covered wooden slotted ailerons, operated by control rods. Fabric-covered wooden slotted three-position trailing-edge flaps.

FUSELAGE: Conventional wooden structure, covered with plywood. Domed plywood decking. Plastics engine cowling, built in top and bottom sections.

TAIL UNIT: Cantilever wood structure. Fixed surfaces plywood-covered; control surfaces fabric-covered. Neither rudder nor elevators are aerodynamically balanced. Flettner tab in starboard elevator. Rudder is cable-operated.

LANDING GEAR: Non-retractable tailwheel type. Cessna-type aluminium leaf-spring cantilever main legs, with plastics wheel fairings. Steerable tailwheel. Brakes on main wheels.

POWER PLANT: One 67 kW (90 hp) Continental flat-four engine, driving a two-blade fixed-pitch propeller. Light alloy fuel tank aft of firewall in fuselage, capacity 40 litres (8·8 Imp gallons).

ACCOMMODATION: Single seat in enclosed cabin, with max width of 0·58 m (1 ft 10¾ in). Sideways-opening canopy, hinged on starboard side. Baggage space aft of seat.

DIMENSIONS, EXTERNAL:
- Wing span: 6·00 m (19 ft 8¼ in)
- Wing chord at root: 1·50 m (4 ft 11 in)
- Wing chord at tip: 0·75 m (2 ft 5½ in)
- Wing area, gross: 6·00 m² (64·6 sq ft)
- Wing aspect ratio: 6·00
- Length overall:
  - Continental: 5·35 m (17 ft 6¾ in)
  - Volkswagen: 5·20 m (17 ft 0¾ in)
- Height overall: 1·50 m (4 ft 11 in)

WEIGHTS (A, 48·5 kW; 65 hp Continental; B, 67 kW; 90 hp Continental):
- Weight empty:
  - A: 233 kg (514 lb)
  - B: 239 kg (527 lb)
- Max T-O weight:
  - A: 339 kg (747 lb)
  - B: 345 kg (760 lb)

PERFORMANCE (A, 48·5 kW; 65 hp Continental; B, 67 kW; 90 hp Continental; C, 1,600 cc Volkswagen):
- Max level speed at S/L:
  - A: 127 knots (235 km/h; 146 mph)
  - B: 156 knots (290 km/h; 180 mph)
  - C: 113 knots (210 km/h; 130 mph)
- Landing speed:
  - A: 43 knots (80 km/h; 50 mph)
- Range with max fuel:
  - A: 242 nm (450 km; 279 miles)

LUCAS

EMILE LUCAS

3 rue Paul Doumer, 59990-Estreux
Telephone: (20) 30-40-50

Emile Lucas has built a two-seat light aircraft designated Lucas L5. Design began in 1969, and construction of the prototype was undertaken in the designer's living room. First flight was made on 13 August 1976. Three more L5s are under construction.

LUCAS L5

TYPE: Two-seat light monoplane.

WINGS: Cantilever low-wing monoplane. Dihedral 3°. Incidence 3°. No sweepback. All-metal construction of AU2G and AU4G light alloy, including metal ailerons and two-position flaps. Chord sharply reduced at each wingtip by curved trailing-edge. Leading-edge of each wing extended forward at root to house main landing gear leg when retractable landing gear is fitted. No tabs.

FUSELAGE: Conventional all-metal structure of AU2G and AU4G light alloy.

TAIL UNIT: Cantilever structure of AU4G light alloy. Constant-chord tailplane, with one-piece elevator, horn-balanced at tips. Sweptback fin and horn-balanced rudder. No tabs.

LANDING GEAR: Non-retractable tricycle or mechanically-retractable tailwheel type, both having been fitted to prototype during development. Rubber

Lederlin 380-L two-seat light aircraft (Continental C90-14F engine) *(Peter J. Bish)*

Lefebvre MP.205 Busard (67 kW; 90 hp Continental engine) *(J. M. G. Gradidge)*

Two views of the Lucas L5 prototype, with non-retractable tricycle (left) and retractable tailwheel landing gear respectively

Piel Super Diamant (112 kW; 150 hp Lycoming engine) built by Mr Eric R. Glew of Agincourt, Ontario, Canada *(Neil A. Macdougall)*

Piel Emeraude (93 kW; 125 hp Lycoming O-290-D) built by Mr Ted Hendrickson *(Howard Levy)*

shock-absorption. Wheel size 420 × 150 on all three units (both versions). Hydraulic brakes.

POWER PLANT: One 85·75 kW (115 hp) Lycoming O-235 flat-four engine, driving an EVRA two-blade fixed-pitch propeller with spinner. One fuel tank standard in fuselage. Total fuel capacity 75 or 115 litres (16·5 or 25·3 Imp gallons).

ACCOMMODATION: Two seats side by side under transparent canopy. Baggage hold, capacity 30 kg (66 lb).

ELECTRONICS: Jolliet ER400 VHF radio.

DIMENSIONS, EXTERNAL:
- Wing span: 9·20 m (30 ft 2¼ in)
- Wing area, gross: 11·90 m² (128·1 sq ft)
- Wing aspect ratio: 7·2
- Length overall: 6·30 m (20 ft 8 in)
- Height overall: 2·10 m (6 ft 10¾ in)
- Propeller diameter: 1·70 m (5 ft 7 in)
- Propeller ground clearance: 0·30 m (11¾ in)

WEIGHTS:
- Weight empty, equipped: 505 kg (1,113 lb)
- Max T-O weight: 746 kg (1,644 lb)

PERFORMANCE:
- Never-exceed speed: 161 knots (300 km/h; 186 mph)
- Max level speed:
  - retractable landing gear: 140 knots (260 km/h; 162 mph)
  - fixed gear: 127 knots (235 km/h; 146 mph)
- Max cruising speed:
  - retractable landing gear: 129 knots (240 km/h; 149 mph)
  - fixed gear: 108 knots (200 km/h; 124 mph)
- Econ cruising speed:
  - retractable landing gear: 108 knots (200 km/h; 124 mph)
  - fixed gear: 97 knots (180 km/h; 112 mph)
- Max rate of climb at S/L: 300 m (985 ft)/min
- T-O to 15 m (50 ft): 280 m (920 ft)
- Landing from 15 m (50 ft): 380 m (1,245 ft)
- Range with max fuel: 539 nm (1,000 km; 621 miles)

PIEL

AVIONS CLAUDE PIEL

104 côte de Beulle, 78580-Maule
Telephone: 478.82.49

M Claude Piel has designed several light aircraft, including the Emeraude, Diamant and Beryl, of which sets of plans are available to amateur constructors. In addition, M Piel granted licence rights for their manufacture by several commercial concerns (see 1977-78 *Jane's*).

The authorised distributor for plans of all Piel designs available to amateur constructors is:

E. Littner, CP 272, Saint Laurent, Montreal, Quebec H4L 4V6, Canada.

PIEL EMERAUDE and SUPER EMERAUDE

There have been several factory-built versions of the Emeraude and Super Emeraude, but the aircraft are no longer being produced in this form. The designs continue to be available for amateur construction, and the following amateur-built versions have flown:

C.P.301. With 67 kW (90 hp) Continental engine.

C.P.304. With 63·4 kW (85 hp) Continental C85-12F engine and wing flaps.

C.P.305. With 86 kW (115 hp) Lycoming engine.

C.P.308. With 56 kW (75 hp) Continental engine.

C.P.320. With Super Emeraude wings and 74·5 kW (100 hp) Continental engine. **C.P.320A** has sweptback fin.

C.P.321. As C.P.320, with 78·5 kW (105 hp) Potez engine.

C.P.323A. With 112 kW (150 hp) Lycoming engine and sweptback fin. **C.P.323AB** has tricycle landing gear.

The Emeraude is one of the types approved by the Popular Flying Association for amateur construction in the United Kingdom.

The following details refer to the basic C.P.301 Emeraude and C.P.320 Super Emeraude, but are generally applicable to all versions:

TYPE: Two-seat light monoplane.

WINGS: Cantilever low-wing monoplane. NACA 23012 wing section. Dihedral 5° 40′. Incidence 4° 10′. Inner half of each wing is rectangular in plan, outer half semi-elliptical. All-wood single-spar structure with fabric covering overall. Slotted ailerons and flaps.

FUSELAGE: Conventional wood structure, covered with fabric.

TAIL UNIT: Cantilever wood structure. Fin integral with fuselage. Single-piece all-wood tailplane. Elevators and rudder fabric-covered. Trim tab in starboard elevator.

LANDING GEAR: Non-retractable tailwheel type. Cantilever main legs have rubber-in-compression springing. Hydraulic brakes.

POWER PLANT (C.P.301): One 67 kW (90 hp) Continental C90-12F flat-four engine. Two-blade fixed-pitch wooden propeller. Fuel tank in fuselage, behind fireproof bulkhead, capacity 80 litres (17·6 Imp gallons). Provision for auxiliary tank, capacity 40 litres (8·8 Imp gallons).

POWER PLANT (C.P.320): One 74·5 kW (100 hp) Continental O-200 flat-four engine, driving a two-blade fixed-pitch wooden propeller. Fuel as for C.P.301.

ACCOMMODATION: Enclosed cockpit seating two side by side with dual controls. Sides of canopy hinge forward for access and exit. Heating and ventilation.

DIMENSIONS, EXTERNAL:
- Wing span: 8·04 m (26 ft 4½ in)
- Wing chord at root: 1·50 m (4 ft 11 in)
- Wing chord at tip: 0·55 m (1 ft 9½ in)
- Wing area, gross: 10·85 m² (116·7 sq ft)
- Wing aspect ratio: 5·95
- Length overall:
  - C.P.301: 6·30 m (20 ft 8 in)
  - C.P.320: 6·45 m (21 ft 2 in)
- Height overall:
  - C.P.301: 1·85 m (6 ft 0¾ in)
  - C.P.320: 1·90 m (6 ft 2¾ in)
- Wheel track: 2·05 m (6 ft 8¾ in)
- Propeller diameter:
  - C.P.301: 1·80 m (5 ft 11 in)
  - C.P.320: 1·78 m (5 ft 10 in)

WEIGHTS:
- Weight empty:
  - C.P.301: 380 kg (838 lb)
  - C.P.320: 410 kg (903 lb)
- Max T-O weight:
  - C.P.301: 650 kg (1,433 lb)
  - C.P.320: 700 kg (1,543 lb)

PERFORMANCE (at max T-O weight):
- Never-exceed speed:
  - C.P.301: 118·5 knots (220 km/h; 136·5 mph)
  - C.P.320: 149 knots (277 km/h; 172 mph)
- Max level speed:
  - C.P.301: 110 knots (205 km/h; 127 mph)
  - C.P.320: 124 knots (230 km/h; 143 mph)
- Max cruising speed (75% power) at 1,200 m (3,940 ft):
  - C.P.301: 108 knots (200 km/h; 124 mph)
  - C.P.320: 119 knots (220 km/h; 137 mph)
- Econ cruising speed (65% power) at 1,200 m (3,940 ft):
  - C.P.301: 101 knots (187 km/h; 116 mph)
  - C.P.320: 110 knots (205 km/h; 127 mph)
- Approach speed, flaps down:
  - C.P.301, C.P.320: 65 knots (120 km/h; 75 mph)
- Stalling speed, flaps up:
  - C.P.301: 51 knots (92 km/h; 58 mph)
  - C.P.320: 53 knots (97 km/h; 61 mph)

Stalling speed, flaps down:
C.P.301 46 knots (85 km/h; 53 mph)
C.P.320 49 knots (90 km/h; 56 mph)
Max rate of climb at S/L:
C.P.301 168 m (551 ft)/min
C.P.320 240 m (787 ft)/min
Service ceiling:
C.P.301 4,000 m (13,125 ft)
C.P.320 4,300 m (14,100 ft)
T-O run:
C.P.301 250 m (820 ft)
C.P.320 230 m (755 ft)
T-O to 15 m (50 ft):
C.P.301 440 m (1,443 ft)
C.P.320 400 m (1,312 ft)
Landing from 15 m (50 ft):
C.P.301 475 m (1,558 ft)
C.P.320 490 m (1,608 ft)
Landing run:
C.P.301 250 m (820 ft)
C.P.320 260 m (853 ft)
Range at econ cruising speed:
C.P.301, C.P.320 538 nm (1,000 km; 620 miles)

PIEL C.P.1320

This aircraft combines the general characteristics of the Super Emeraude with the Diamant's three-seat cabin and fuel tanks in the wings. It can be fitted with engines of 112 kW (150 hp) to 149 kW (200 hp) and the prototype, built by Mr Lascoutounas of Blanquefort, near Bordeaux, will have a 119·5 kW (160 hp) Lycoming. Design started in January 1977 and construction of the prototype began in September of the same year. Although plans for amateur construction of the C.P.1320 had not been completed by January 1979, six sets had already been sold and work on several aircraft had been started.

Normal load factors will be $+5g$ and $-2·5g$. For aerobatics in two-seat form at a T-O weight of 720 kg (1,585 lb), the permissible load factors will be $+6g$ and $-3g$.

Type: Three-seat light monoplane.

Wings: Cantilever low-wing monoplane. NACA 23012 wing section. Dihedral 3°. Incidence 2°. Conventional all-wood structure. Slotted ailerons and slotted flaps of wood construction.

Fuselage: Conventional wooden semi-monocoque structure.

Tail Unit: Cantilever wooden structure. Sweptback fin and long dorsal fin integral with fuselage. All-wood constant-chord tailplane and elevator. Tab in elevator trailing-edge.

Landing Gear: Tailwheel type. Main units retract inward. Electrical retraction. Non-retractable tailwheel. Drum brakes on main wheels.

Power Plant: Prototype has one 119·5 kW (160 hp) Lycoming engine, driving a two-blade Evra wooden fixed-pitch propeller. Single fuel tank in fuselage, capacity 70 litres (15·4 Imp gallons), and two fuel tanks in wings with total capacity of 70 litres (15·4 Imp gallons). Max fuel capacity 140 litres (30·8 Imp gallons).

Accommodation: Three seats, under rearward-sliding transparent canopy.

Dimensions, external:
Wing span 7·90 m (25 ft 11 in)
Wing area, gross 11·10 m² (119·48 sq ft)
Wing chord, at root 1·64 m (5 ft 4½ in)
Wing chord, at tip 1·14 m (3 ft 9 in)
Wing aspect ratio 5·62
Length overall 6·60 m (21 ft 8 in)
Height overall 1·80 m (5 ft 11 in)
Tailplane span 2·50 m (8 ft 2½ in)
Wheel track 2·20 m (7 ft 2½ in)
Propeller diameter 1·80 m (5 ft 11 in)

Weights:
Weight empty 470 kg (1,036 lb)
Max T-O weight 800 kg (1,764 lb)

Performance:
Never-exceed speed 183 knots (340 km/h; 211 mph)
Max level speed 162 knots (300 km/h; 186 mph)
Max cruising speed (75% power) 145 knots (270 km/h; 167 mph)
Econ cruising speed (65% power) 132 knots (245 km/h; 152 mph)
Approach speed, flaps down 70 knots (130 km/h; 81 mph)
Stalling speed, flaps up 54 knots (100 km/h; 62 mph)
Stalling speed, flaps down 51·5 knots (95 km/h; 59 mph)
Max rate of climb at S/L 600 m (1,968 ft)/min
Service ceiling 5,000 m (16,400 ft)
T-O run 200 m (657 ft)
T-O to 15 m (50 ft) 420 m (1,378 ft)
Landing from 15 m (50 ft) 600 m (1,968 ft)
Landing run 300 m (984 ft)
Range with max fuel (65% power) 593 nm (1,100 km; 683 miles)

PIEL SUPER DIAMANT

The Super Diamant is essentially a three/four-seat version of the Emeraude. It is fully certificated for commercial production and is available also in plan form for construction by amateurs. By early 1979, 42 sets of plans had been sold. Current versions are as follows:

C.P.604. Prototype (F-PMEC) flown in Summer of 1964, with a 108 kW (145 hp) Continental engine. Current version has swept vertical tail surfaces.

C.P.605. Much-modified four-seat ('2+2') version, with 112 kW (150 hp) Lycoming O-320-E2A engine. Fully certificated for commercial production, as well as for amateur construction. Details in 1973-74 *Jane's*.

C.P.605B. Version of C.P.605 with retractable tricycle landing gear.

Type: Three/four-seat light monoplane.

Wings: Cantilever low-wing monoplane. Wing section NACA 23012. Dihedral 5° 40'. Incidence 4° 10'. All-wood single-spar structure, made in one piece, with fabric covering. Slotted ailerons and slotted flaps of wood construction, with fabric covering.

Fuselage: Wood structure, covered with fabric.

Tail Unit: Cantilever wood structure, with sweptback fin and rudder. Fixed surfaces plywood-covered. Control surfaces fabric-covered. Ground-adjustable tab on each elevator.

Landing Gear (C.P.604): Non-retractable tailwheel type. Main wheels size 420 × 150. Hydraulic brakes. Wheel spats. Steerable tailwheel, size 155 × 50.

Landing Gear (C.P.605B): Retractable tricycle type. Main wheels retract inward. All three wheels and tyres size 400 × 100.

Power Plant: One flat-four engine, driving an EVRA two-blade fixed-pitch wooden propeller. Fuel tank in fuselage, capacity 85 litres (18·7 Imp gallons). Provision for additional tankage to give total capacity of 160 litres (35 Imp gallons). Oil capacity 4 litres (0·9 Imp gallons).

Accommodation: Four seats ('2+2') in enclosed cabin under large rearward-sliding transparent canopy.

Dimensions, external (C.P.605B):
Wing span 9·20 m (30 ft 2¼ in)
Wing chord at root 1·50 m (4 ft 11 in)
Wing area, gross 13·30 m² (143·2 sq ft)
Wing aspect ratio 6·4
Length overall 7·00 m (22 ft 11¾ in)
Height overall 2·00 m (6 ft 6¾ in)
Wheel track 3·00 m (9 ft 10 in)
Propeller diameter 1·80 m (5 ft 11 in)

Weights (C.P.605B):
Weight empty 520 kg (1,146 lb)
Max T-O weight 850 kg (1,873 lb)

Performance (C.P.605B, at max T-O weight):
Never-exceed speed 151 knots (280 km/h; 174 mph)
Max level speed 141 knots (260 km/h; 162 mph)
Max cruising speed (75% power) at 1,200 m (3,940 ft) 132 knots (245 km/h; 152 mph)
Econ cruising speed (65% power) at 1,200 m (3,940 ft) 124 knots (230 km/h; 143 mph)
Approach speed, flaps down 68 knots (125 km/h; 78 mph)
Stalling speed, flaps up 49 knots (90 km/h; 56 mph)
Stalling speed, flaps down 45 knots (82 km/h; 51 mph)
Max rate of climb at S/L 330 m (1,082 ft)/min
Service ceiling 5,000 m (16,400 ft)
T-O run 160 m (525 ft)
T-O to 15 m (50 ft) 380 m (1,247 ft)
Landing from 15 m (50 ft) 600 m (1,969 ft)
Landing run 270 m (886 ft)
Range at econ cruising speed 620 nm (1,150 km; 714 miles)

PIEL C.P.70 and C.P.750 BERYL

The prototype **C.P.70 Beryl** was displayed publicly for the first time in August 1965. It combines the wing of the C.P.30 Emeraude, virtually unchanged, with a fuselage containing two seats in tandem, and with non-retractable tricycle landing gear.

Intended for aerobatic flying, the **C.P.750 Beryl** is also similar in general appearance to the Emeraude but has a longer, steel tube fuselage seating two persons in tandem, slightly reduced span, a non-retractable tailwheel-type landing gear and other changes.

The C.P.750 has so far been built principally by amateur constructors in Canada, but may also be built in France through the facilities offered by M Choisel at Abbeville. By early 1979, fifteen sets of plans had been sold.

The example (N7NT) shown in an accompanying illustration was built by Mr Norman Taylor of Ontario, Oregon, over a period of 4 years and 10 months, at a cost of $8,000. Constructed according to plans, with a 119·5 kW (160 hp) Lycoming O-320 engine, it has an empty weight of 605 kg (1,332 lb), max take-off weight of 905 kg (1,996 lb), cruising speed of 139 knots (257 km/h; 160 mph), landing speed of 52 knots (97 km/h; 60 mph), rate of climb of 457 m (1,500 ft)/min at sea level, take-off and landing run of 145 m (475 ft), and range of 390 nm (725 km; 450 miles) with max fuel.

Type: Two-seat aerobatic monoplane.

Wings: Cantilever low-wing monoplane. Wing section NACA 23012. Dihedral 5° 40'. Incidence 4° 10'. All-wood single-spar structure, made in one piece, with fabric covering. Slotted ailerons and slotted flaps of wood construction with fabric covering.

Fuselage: Fabric-covered structure of wood (C.P.70) or welded steel tube (C.P.750).

Tail Unit: Cantilever wood structure. Fixed surfaces plywood-covered, control surfaces fabric-covered. Ground-adjustable tab on each elevator.

Landing Gear (C.P.70): Non-retractable tricycle type.

Landing Gear (C.P.750): Non-retractable tailwheel type. Main wheels size 420 × 150, pressure 1·65 bars (24 lb/sq in). Hydraulic brakes. Wheel fairings. Steerable tailwheel.

Power Plant (C.P.70): One 48·5 kW (65 hp) Continental C65-8F flat-four engine, driving a two-blade wooden propeller. Fuel tank in fuselage, capacity 70 litres (15·4 Imp gallons).

Power Plant (C.P.750): One 112 kW (150 hp) Lycoming O-320-E2A flat-four engine, driving an EVRA two-blade fixed-pitch wooden propeller. Fuel tank in fuselage, capacity 70 litres (15·4 Imp gallons), with provision for two auxiliary tanks in wings to give total capacity of 140 litres (30·75 Imp gallons). Oil capacity 5 litres (1·0 Imp gallon).

Accommodation: Two seats in tandem under rearward-sliding transparent canopy. Rear seat of C.P.70 is wide enough to accommodate one adult and a child, or two children.

Dimensions, external:
Wing span:
C.P.70 8·25 m (27 ft 0¾ in)
C.P.750 8·04 m (26 ft 4½ in)
Wing chord at root 1·50 m (4 ft 11 in)
Wing area, gross:
C.P.70 10·85 m² (116·8 sq ft)
C.P.750 11·00 m² (118 sq ft)
Wing aspect ratio:
C.P.70 5·95
C.P.750 5·85
Length overall:
C.P.70 6·45 m (21 ft 2 in)
C.P.750 6·90 m (22 ft 7¾ in)
Height overall:
C.P.70 1·60 m (5 ft 3 in)
C.P.750 2·10 m (6 ft 10¾ in)
Wheel track:
C.P.70 2·00 m (6 ft 6¾ in)
C.P.750 2·40 m (7 ft 10½ in)
Propeller diameter 1·80 m (5 ft 11 in)

Weights:
Weight empty:
C.P.70 320 kg (705 lb)
C.P.750 480 kg (1,058 lb)
Max T-O weight:
C.P.70 540 kg (1,190 lb)
C.P.750 760 kg (1,675 lb)

Performance (at max T-O weight):
Never-exceed speed:
C.P.70 118·5 knots (220 km/h; 136·5 mph)
C.P.750 183 knots (340 km/h; 211 mph)
Max level speed:
C.P.70 95 knots (175 km/h; 109 mph)
C.P.750 151 knots (280 km/h; 174 mph)
Max cruising speed (75% power) at 1,200 m (3,940 ft):
C.P.70 84 knots (156 km/h; 97 mph)
C.P.750 143 knots (265 km/h; 165 mph)
Econ cruising speed (65% power) at 1,200 m (3,940 ft):
C.P.70 78 knots (145 km/h; 90 mph)
C.P.750 135 knots (250 km/h; 155 mph)
Approach speed, flaps down:
C.P.70 54 knots (100 km/h; 62·5 mph)
C.P.750 70 knots (130 km/h; 81 mph)
Stalling speed, flaps up:
C.P.70 41 knots (75 km/h; 47 mph)
C.P.750 54 knots (100 km/h; 62·5 mph)
Stalling speed, flaps down:
C.P.70 39 knots (70 km/h; 44 mph)
C.P.750 52 knots (95 km/h; 59 mph)
Max rate of climb at S/L:
C.P.70 120 m (394 ft)/min
C.P.750 390 m (1,280 ft)/min
Service ceiling:
C.P.70 3,000 m (9,850 ft)
C.P.750 5,200 m (17,060 ft)
T-O run:
C.P.70 280 m (919 ft)
C.P.750 190 m (623 ft)
T-O to 15 m (50 ft):
C.P.70 420 m (1,378 ft)
C.P.750 350 m (1,148 ft)
Landing from 15 m (50 ft):
C.P.70 280 m (919 ft)
C.P.750 520 m (1,706 ft)
Landing run:
C.P.70 140 m (459 ft)
C.P.750 280 m (919 ft)
Range at econ cruising speed:
C.P.70 323 nm (600 km; 372 miles)
C.P.750 593 nm (1,100 km; 683 miles)

PIEL C.P.80

The C.P.80 was designed as a single-seat racing aircraft for amateur construction. The basic version is made of wood, as described; but M Calvel of l'Hospitalet du Larzac adapted the design to enable his C.P.80 Zef to be constructed of laminated plastics. This was the first C.P.80 to fly, followed in July 1974 by the C.P.80 Racer No. 01 (F-PVQF) built by M Claude Piel.

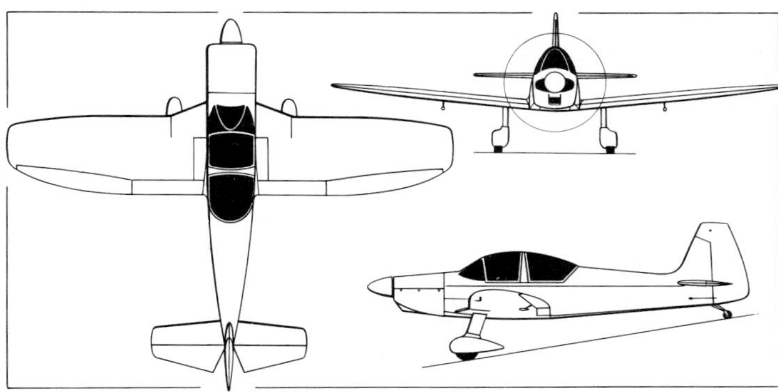

Piel C.P.750 Beryl two-seat light aircraft (Lycoming O-320-E2A engine) *(Pilot Press)*

Piel C.P.750 Beryl (Lycoming O-320 engine) built by Mr Norman Taylor of Ontario, Oregon *(Howard Levy)*

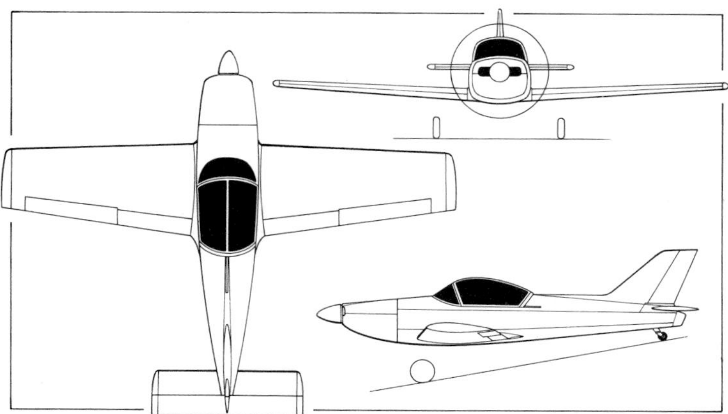

Piel C.P.1320 three-seat light aircraft *(Michael A. Badrocke)*

Piel C.P.90 Pinocchio single-seat light sporting aircraft *(Pilot Press)*

C.P.80 No. 01 single-seat racing aircraft built by M Claude Piel

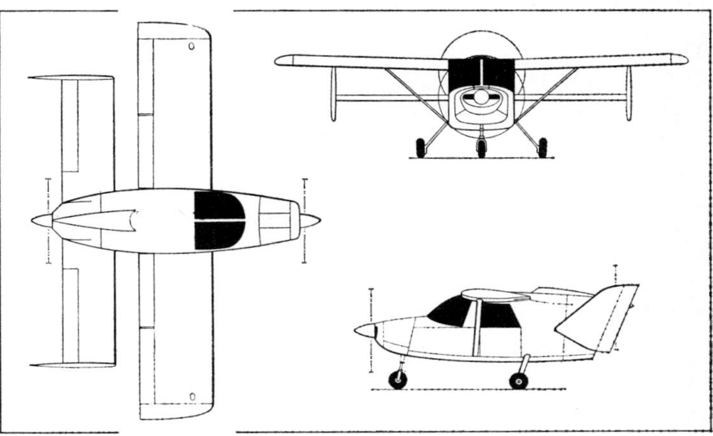

Piel C.P.500 tandem-wing twin-engined light aircraft *(Roy J. Grainge)*

About 61 wooden C.P.80s are under construction by amateurs. The general appearance of the aircraft is shown in the accompanying illustration.

M Piel's prototype has confirmed the accuracy of the estimated weight and performance figures quoted. It has attained a maximum level speed of 162 knots (300 km/h; 186 mph) without main wheel fairings, suggesting an eventual maximum level speed of 172 knots (320 km/h; 199 mph) when these are fitted and development is completed.

TYPE: Single-seat amateur-built racing aircraft.

WINGS: Cantilever low-wing monoplane. Wing section NACA 23012. Dihedral 3°. Incidence 2° (constant). No sweep at quarter-chord. Conventional single-spar wood structure, plywood-covered and with polyester plastics tips. Ailerons mass-balanced and cable-actuated. No flaps or tabs.

FUSELAGE: Conventional plywood-covered wood structure of basic rectangular section, with four longerons, nine frames and domed rear decking. Polyester plastics engine cowling. Steel tube engine mounting attached to fireproof bulkhead.

TAIL UNIT: Cantilever plywood-covered all-wood structure, with vertical surfaces swept back at 50° on leading-edge. All-moving constant-chord horizontal surfaces, with centrally-positioned anti-balance and trim tab, and with mass-balance arm projecting forward inside fuselage. Horn-balanced rudder. Control surfaces cable-operated.

LANDING GEAR: Non-retractable tailwheel type. Main wheels carried on cantilever spring legs of treated AU4SG alloy. Steerable tailwheel carried on steel spring. Hydraulic brakes on main wheels.

POWER PLANT: One 67 kW (90 hp) Continental C90-8F flat-four engine, driving through a short extension shaft a two-blade fixed-pitch wooden propeller. Provision for other engines, including 48·5 kW (65 hp) Continental. Fuel tank of AG-3 alloy, capacity 40 litres (8·8 Imp gallons) aft of firewall, with refuelling point in top-decking.

ACCOMMODATION: Pilot only, in enclosed cockpit, under sideways-hinged transparent canopy.

DIMENSIONS, EXTERNAL:
- Wing span: 6·00 m (19 ft 8¼ in)
- Wing chord at aircraft centreline: 1·35 m (4 ft 5¼ in)
- Wing chord at tip: 0·90 m (2 ft 11½ in)
- Wing area, gross: 6·20 m^2 (66·7 sq ft)
- Wing aspect ratio: 5·8
- Length overall: 5·30 m (17 ft 4¾ in)
- Height overall: 1·70 m (5 ft 7 in)
- Tailplane span: 1·58 m (5 ft 2¼ in)
- Wheel track: 1·60 m (5 ft 3 in)
- Wheelbase: 3·50 m (11 ft 5¾ in)
- Propeller diameter: 1·52 m (5 ft 0 in)

WEIGHTS (67 kW; 90 hp engine):
- Weight empty: 260 kg (573 lb)
- Max T-O weight: 380 kg (837 lb)

PERFORMANCE (estimated, with 67 kW; 90 hp engine, at max T-O weight):
- Never-exceed speed: 205 knots (380 km/h; 236 mph)
- Max level speed: 167 knots (310 km/h; 193 mph)
- Max cruising speed (75% power) at 1,200 m (3,940 ft): 151 knots (280 km/h; 174 mph)
- Econ cruising speed (65% power) at 1,200 m (3,940 ft): 129·5 knots (240 km/h; 149 mph)
- Approach speed: 70 knots (130 km/h; 81 mph)
- Stalling speed: 51·5 knots (95 km/h; 59 mph)
- Max rate of climb at S/L: 720 m (2,360 ft)/min
- Service ceiling: 6,000 m (19,685 ft)
- T-O run: 200 m (656 ft)
- T-O to 15 m (50 ft): 400 m (1,312 ft)
- Landing from 15 m (50 ft): 360 m (1,181 ft)
- Landing run: 200 m (656 ft)
- Range at econ cruising speed: 243 nm (450 km; 280 miles)
- *g* limits: +8; −6

PIEL C.P.90 PINOCCHIO

The C.P.90 Pinocchio is essentially a smaller, single-seat development of the basic Emeraude, intended for aerobatic and general sporting flying. Six sets of plans had been sold by early 1979.

WINGS: Cantilever low-wing monoplane, of similar general planform and construction to Emeraude. Dihedral 5° 40′. Incidence 3°. Ailerons only, no flaps.

FUSELAGE: Fabric-covered wooden structure of basically rectangular cross-section with domed decking.

TAIL UNIT: Cantilever fabric-covered wooden structure, similar to that of Emeraude.

LANDING GEAR: Non-retractable tailwheel type. Streamlined leg and wheel fairings on main units.

POWER PLANT: One 74·5 kW (100 hp) Continental O-200 flat-four engine, driving a two-blade wooden propeller. Fuel capacity 60 litres (13·2 Imp gallons).

ACCOMMODATION: Single seat under fully-transparent canopy.

DIMENSIONS, EXTERNAL:
- Wing span: 7·20 m (23 ft 7½ in)
- Wing area, gross: 9·65 m^2 (103·9 sq ft)
- Wing aspect ratio: 5·4
- Length overall: 6·00 m (19 ft 8¼ in)
- Height overall: 1·80 m (5 ft 11 in)
- Wheel track: 1·60 m (5 ft 3 in)
- Propeller diameter: 1·80 m (5 ft 11 in)

WEIGHTS:
- Weight empty: 335 kg (738 lb)
- Max T-O weight: 460 kg (1,014 lb)

PERFORMANCE (estimated, at max T-O weight):
- Never-exceed speed: 171 knots (320 km/h; 198 mph)
- Max level speed: 141 knots (260 km/h; 162 mph)
- Max cruising speed (75% power) at 1,200 m (3,940 ft): 132 knots (245 km/h; 152 mph)
- Econ cruising speed (65% power) at 1,200 m (3,940 ft): 124 knots (230 km/h; 143 mph)
- Approach speed: 59 knots (110 km/h; 68 mph)
- Stalling speed: 41 knots (75 km/h; 47 mph)
- Max rate of climb at S/L: 480 m (1,575 ft)/min
- Service ceiling: 6,000 m (19,685 ft)
- T-O run: 180 m (590 ft)
- T-O to 15 m (50 ft): 400 m (1,312 ft)

Landing from 15 m (50 ft) 300 m (984 ft)
Landing run 160 m (525 ft)
Range at econ cruising speed 296 nm (550 km; 341 miles)

PIEL C.P.500

As can be seen in the accompanying illustration, the C.P.500 is a 'push and pull' twin-engined aircraft of staggered tandem-wing configuration. Although this gives it some similarity to the Mignet formula, the wings are fixed, and the pilot's controls conventional.

The strut-braced forward wing has four-section slotted trailing-edge flaps over 75% of the span and 25% of the chord, actuated electrically through 35°. The rear wing carries two elevons, actuated by control rods from 40° up to 35° down; these function differentially for roll control and collectively for pitch control. Endplate fins and rudders on the rear wing provide yaw control. The relative position of the wings is expected to permit steep 'parachute' descents of the kind possible with Mignet designs.

Wing section is NACA 23015. The front wing has a dihedral of 1° 30′ and incidence of 2° 30′ constant; the rear wing has a constant incidence of 4° 30′ but no dihedral.

Construction of the prototype C.P.500 has been started by the Aero Club Jean Bertin. Although it was intended originally to be built of wood, this aircraft is now basically of metal construction, as specified for any future series production of the type. The engine cowlings, wingtips and fairings are of laminated plastics. Two 112/119·5 kW (150/160 hp) Lycoming O-320 flat-four engines are specified, with the rear engine driving its propeller through an extension shaft, 15 cm (5·9 in) long. Fuel tanks in the tips of the forward wing have a combined capacity of 300 litres (66 Imp gallons).

A non-retractable tricycle landing gear is standard, with Wittman-type cantilever steel spring main legs and a steerable nosewheel. Each main wheel is fitted with a hydraulic brake.

Basic accommodation is for two persons side by side in front, with optional dual controls, and three passengers on a rear bench seat. Aft of the rear seat is space for a sixth person or a considerable quantity of baggage.

Dimensions, external:
Wing span:
front 8·80 m (28 ft 10½ in)
rear 6·43 m (21 ft 1¼ in)
Wing chord (constant):
front 1·50 m (4 ft 11 in)
rear 1·10 m (3 ft 7¼ in)
Wing area, gross:
front 13·20 m² (142·1 sq ft)
rear 7·10 m² (76·42 sq ft)
Wing aspect ratio:
front 5·85
rear 5·88
Wing stagger 0·46 m (1 ft 6 in)
Length overall 6·10 m (20 ft 0 in)
Height overall 2·25 m (7 ft 4½ in)
Fuselage depth (max) 1·56 m (5 ft 1½ in)
Fuselage width (max) 1·40 m (4 ft 7 in)
Wheel track 2·56 m (8 ft 4¾ in)
Wheelbase 2·60 m (8 ft 6¼ in)

Weights:
Weight empty 866 kg (1,909 lb)
Max T-O weight 1,500 kg (3,307 lb)

Performance (estimated):
Max level speed 162 knots (300 km/h; 186 mph)
Max level speed, one engine out 129 knots (240 km/h; 149 mph)
Max cruising speed (75% power) 143 knots (265 km/h; 165 mph)
Max cruising speed, one engine out (75% power) 108 knots (200 km/h; 124 mph)
Stalling speed, flaps down 49 knots (90 km/h; 56 mph)
Max rate of climb at S/L 540 m (1,770 ft)/min
Max rate of climb at S/L, one engine out 180 m (590 ft)/min
Service ceiling 6,800 m (22,300 ft)
Service ceiling, one engine out 3,000 m (9,850 ft)
Range with max fuel 647 nm (1,200 km; 745 miles)

POTTIER

JEAN POTTIER

4 rue de Poissy, 78130 Les Mureaux
Telephone: 099 13-85

In addition to the light aircraft and sailplanes that he designed jointly with M Robert Jacquet, during his period as technical director at Société CARMAM, M Pottier is responsible for the purely amateur projects of which details follow.

POTTIER P.50 BOUVREUIL (BULLFINCH)

Designed by M Jean Pottier, the Bouvreuil is a single-seat racing monoplane, intended for construction by amateurs. Construction is entirely of wood, except for the plastics engine cowling and main-wheel fairings.

The Bouvreuil can be fitted with a variety of engines in the 48·5-86 kW (65-115 hp) category. It has also been designed from the start to have either a non-retractable (P.50) or retractable (P.50R) landing gear. Design load factors are ± 10.

The first Bouvreuil to be completed will be number 04, built in Switzerland, with a 67 kW (90 hp) Continental C90 engine and a retractable landing gear, which offers a 10% improvement in overall performance. This aircraft was expected to fly for the first time in 1979. The French-built 02 has a 48·5 kW (65 hp) Continental and non-retractable landing gear.

Type: Single-seat racing monoplane.

Wings: Cantilever low-wing monoplane. Wing section NACA 23015 at root, NACA 23012 at tip. Dihedral from roots. All-wood structure, with full-span ailerons and flaps. No tabs.

Fuselage: Conventional wood semi-monocoque structure, with plastics engine cowling.

Tail Unit: Cantilever all-wood structure, with swept vertical surfaces. Trim tab in each elevator.

Landing Gear: Alternative retractable or non-retractable tailwheel type. Wheel fairings standard on non-retractable main wheels. Steerable tailwheel. Independent main-wheel brakes.

Power Plant: Standard power plant is a 67 kW (90 hp) Continental C90 flat-four engine, driving a two-blade fixed-pitch propeller with spinner. Other engines of 48·5 to 86 kW (65-115 hp) are optional. Fuel capacity 60 litres (13 Imp gallons) for racing, 100 litres (22 Imp gallons) for touring. Provision for carrying one removable auxiliary fuel tank under each wing.

Accommodation: Single seat in enclosed cabin, under large rearward-sliding transparent canopy.

Dimensions, external:
Wing span 6·20 m (20 ft 4 in)
Wing area, gross 7·50 m² (80·7 sq ft)
Wing aspect ratio 5·10
Length overall 5·65 m (18 ft 6½ in)

Weights (67 kW; 90 hp engine):
Weight empty 270 kg (595 lb)
Max T-O weight 400 kg (882 lb)

Performance (estimated, with 67 kW; 90 hp engine and non-retractable landing gear):
Max level speed 167 knots (310 km/h; 192 mph)
Max cruising speed (75% power) 151 knots (280 km/h; 174 mph)
Min speed 43 knots (80 km/h; 50 mph)

POTTIER P.70S

This small sporting aircraft is derived from the P.70B, designed by M Pottier and built by M Alain Besneux (see 1976-77 *Jane's*). Design of the P.70S was started in January 1974, and by 1979 at least 20 were being or had been constructed by amateur builders. First to fly, in 1977, was No. 23, powered by a 30 kW (40 hp) Volkswagen 1,500 cc engine and embodying some design changes, including a tailwheel-type landing gear (illustrated in 1978-79 *Jane's*).

The following details apply to the standard P.70S:

Type: Single-seat sporting aircraft.

Wings: Cantilever mid-wing monoplane. Wing section NACA 4415. No dihedral. Incidence 2°. No sweep. Constant-chord all-metal structure of 2024 alloy, with I-beam main spar and channel-section rear spar. Entire trailing-edge of each wing formed by aileron hinged to upper surface and plain flap hinged to bottom surface. No tabs.

Fuselage: All-metal structure of 2024 alloy, built up on five frames.

Tail Unit: Cantilever all-metal structure, with sweptback vertical surfaces. Minimal fixed fin. No tabs.

Landing Gear: Non-retractable tricycle type. Cantilever main legs.

Power Plant: One 30/37·3 kW (40/50 hp) Volkswagen converted motor car engine, driving a two-blade fixed-pitch propeller. Single fuel tank in fuselage, aft of firewall, capacity 40 litres (8·75 Imp gallons).

Accommodation: Pilot only, in enclosed cockpit.

Dimensions, external:
Wing span 5·90 m (19 ft 4¼ in)
Wing chord, constant 1·25 m (4 ft 1¼ in)
Wing area, gross 7·2 m² (77·5 sq ft)
Wing aspect ratio 4·8
Length overall 5·00 m (16 ft 4¾ in)
Height overall 1·60 m (5 ft 3 in)
Tailplane span 2·10 m (6 ft 10¾ in)
Wheel track 1·20 m (3 ft 11¼ in)
Propeller diameter 1·30 m (4 ft 3¼ in)
Propeller ground clearance 0·20 m (8 in)

Weights (No. 23):
Weight empty, equipped 215 kg (474 lb)
Max T-O and landing weight 325 kg (716 lb)

Performance (standard P.70S with 30 kW; 40 hp engine, at max T-O weight, except where indicated):
Never-exceed speed at S/L 129 knots (240 km/h; 149 mph)
Max level speed at S/L:
Standard 97 knots (180 km/h; 112 mph)
No. 23 110 knots (205 km/h; 127 mph)
Max cruising speed at S/L:
Standard 89 knots (165 km/h; 103 mph)
No. 23 100 knots (185 km/h; 115 mph)
Econ cruising speed at S/L 65 knots (120 km/h; 75 mph)
Stalling speed, flaps down 38 knots (70 km/h; 44 mph)
Max rate of climb at S/L 300 m (985 ft)/min
Service ceiling 4,500 m (14,775 ft)
T-O to 15 m (50 ft) 320 m (1,050 ft)
Range with max fuel 270 nm (500 km; 310 miles)

POTTIER P.80S

The Pottier P.80S is a small single-seat sporting aircraft derived from the P.70S. Overall dimensions and structures are unchanged, but the P.80S is a low-wing monoplane and has a restyled cockpit hood. The prototype is powered by a 30 kW (40 hp) Rectimo 4 AR 1200 engine, itself a derivative of the Volkswagen motor car engine, but engines of 18·6-37·25 kW (25-50 hp) can be fitted. Fuel capacity is 50 litres (11 Imp gallons).

Design of the P.80S began in January 1977 and construction of the prototype (F-PYEB) started in June 1977 at the Paris Air Show. Roll-out was achieved at the Show on 12 June. By early 1979, fourteen more were under construction by amateur builders.

Dimensions, external:
As for P.70S, except:
Wing span 5·80 m (19 ft 0¼ in)
Length overall 5·10 m (16 ft 9 in)

Weights:
Weight empty 180 kg (397 lb)
Max T-O weight 320 kg (705 lb)

Performance (with 30 kW; 40 hp engine):
Max level speed 97 knots (180 km/h; 112 mph)
Max cruising speed 89 knots (165 km/h; 103 mph)
Stalling speed 38 knots (70 km/h; 44 mph)
Max rate of climb at S/L 300 m (985 ft)/min
T-O run from grass 320 m (1,050 ft)
Range 270 nm (500 km; 310 miles)

POTTIER P.100S and P.110S

The P.100S and P.110S are small high-wing monoplanes of generally similar configuration, accommodating two and three persons respectively. Two examples of each are under construction, but plans are not available to amateur builders at the present time. Both aircraft have an NACA 4415 wing section. The P.100S can be fitted with engines of 48·5-74·5 kW (65-100 hp), the P.110S with engines of 74·5-97 kW (100-130 hp). Fuel capacity of each aircraft is 90 litres (19·8 Imp gallons).

Types: Two-seat (P.100S) and three-seat (P.110S) light monoplanes.

Dimensions, external (A: P.100S, B: P.110S):
Wing span: A 6·70 m (21 ft 11¾ in)
B 7·70 m (25 ft 3 in)
Wing area, gross: A 8·70 m² (93·65 sq ft)
B 10·00 m² (107·64 sq ft)
Wing aspect ratio: A 5·2
B 5·9
Length overall: A 6·50 m (21 ft 4 in)
B 7·00 m (23 ft 0 in)
Height overall: A 2·20 m (7 ft 2½ in)
B 2·25 m (7 ft 4½ in)

Weights (A: P.100S with 67 kW; 90 hp engine, B: P.110S):
Weight empty: A 315 kg (694 lb)
B 360 kg (794 lb)
Max baggage: A 33 kg (72·7 lb)
B 46 kg (101·4 lb)
Max T-O weight: A 565 kg (1,245 lb)
B 700 kg (1,543 lb)

Performance (A: P.100S with 67 kW; 90 hp engine, B: P.110S with 85·7 kW; 115 hp engine):
Max cruising speed
A 108 knots (200 km/h; 124 mph)
B 116 knots (215 km/h; 134 mph)
Stalling speed
A, B 43·5 knots (80 km/h; 50 mph)
Max rate of climb at S/L
A, B 270 m (885 ft)/min
Range with max fuel
A 378 nm (700 km; 435 miles)
B 350 nm (650 km; 403 miles)
Endurance, with 45 min reserves
A 3 h 30 min
B 3 h
g limits +6·6 (ultimate)

POTTIER P.170S

The P.170S is a tandem two-seat version of the P.70S. It is of all-metal (AU4G) construction and has a retractable tricycle landing gear. Power is provided by a 44·7 kW (60 hp) 1,700 cc Volkswagen modified motor car engine. Plans are available to amateur constructors, and by early 1979 seven P.170S were being built.

Type: Two-seat sporting aircraft.

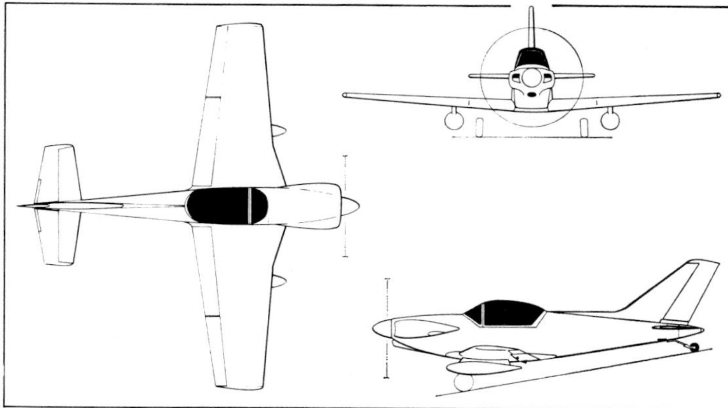

Pottier P.50R Bouvreuil single-seat racing aircraft *(Roy J. Grainge)*

Pottier P.70S with standard tricycle landing gear *(M. J. Hooks)*

The prototype Pottier P.80S, constructed at the 1977 Paris Air Show *(Geoffrey P. Jones)*

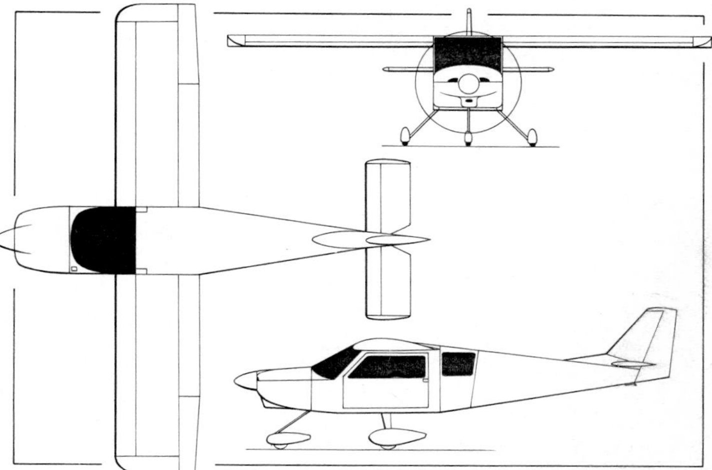

Pottier P.110S three-seat light aircraft *(Michael A. Badrocke)*

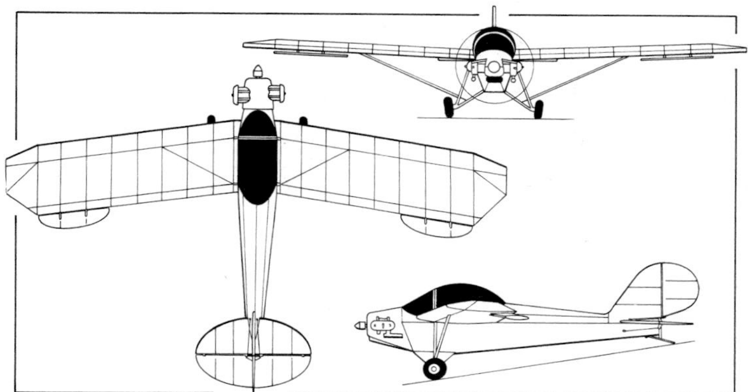

Starck Super New Look ultra-light monoplane *(Michael A. Badrocke)*

Starck AS-37A of M Rudy Nickel as originally flown *(Geoffrey P. Jones)*

DIMENSIONS, EXTERNAL:
- Wing span: 5·95 m (19 ft 6¼ in)
- Wing chord, constant: 1·25 m (4 ft 1¼ in)
- Wing area, gross: 7·40 m² (79·65 sq ft)
- Wing aspect ratio: 4·8
- Length overall: 5·60 m (18 ft 4½ in)
- Height overall: 1·65 m (5 ft 5 in)

WEIGHTS:
- Weight empty: 218 kg (481 lb)
- Max baggage: 12 kg (26·5 lb)
- Max T-O weight: 430 kg (948 lb)

PERFORMANCE:
- Max level speed: 108 knots (200 km/h; 124 mph)
- Max cruising speed: 97 knots (180 km/h; 112 mph)
- Stalling speed: 41 knots (75 km/h; 47 mph)
- Max rate of climb at S/L: 240 m (785 ft)/min
- T-O run: 350 m (1,150 ft)
- Landing from 15 m (50 ft): 350 m (1,150 ft)
- Range with standard 50 litres (11 Imp gallons) of fuel, 45 min reserves: 269 nm (500 km; 310 miles)
- *g* limits: +5·7 (ultimate)

POTTIER P.180S

The P.180S is a side-by-side two-seat version of the P.80S. It is of all-metal (AU4G) construction and has a non-retractable tricycle landing gear with fairings over the wheels. Power is provided by a 47 kW (63 hp) 1,700 cc Volkswagen modified motor car engine. Plans are available to amateur constructors and by early 1979 twelve P.180S were being built.

TYPE: Two-seat sporting aircraft.

DIMENSIONS, EXTERNAL:
- Wing span: 6·40 m (21 ft 0 in)
- Wing chord, constant: 1·25 m (4 ft 1¼ in)
- Wing area, gross: 8·00 m² (86·1 sq ft)
- Wing aspect ratio: 5·1
- Length overall: 5·30 m (18 ft 1¾ in)
- Height overall: 1·70 m (5 ft 7 in)

WEIGHTS:
- Weight empty: 225 kg (496 lb)
- Max baggage: 18 kg (40 lb)
- Max T-O weight: 440 kg (970 lb)

PERFORMANCE:
- Max level speed: 102 knots (190 km/h; 118 mph)
- Max cruising speed: 92 knots (170 km/h; 106 mph)
- Stalling speed: 41 knots (75 km/h; 47 mph)
- Max rate of climb at S/L: 240 m (785 ft)/min
- T-O run: 250 m (820 ft)
- Landing from 15 m (50 ft): 350 m (1,150 ft)
- Range with standard 60 litres (13·2 Imp gallons) fuel, 45 min reserves: 350 nm (650 km; 404 miles)
- *g* limits: ±5·7 (ultimate)

STARCK

ANDRÉ STARCK

M André Starck has been flying since 1927, when he first left the ground in a Chanute-type hang glider. He next built a Mignet Pou-du-Ciel, followed by the first of his own designs, the AS-10. This was a tandem two-seat biplane, and led to the AS-20, first flown on 23 October 1942, with the sharply staggered narrow-gap biplane wing arrangement first conceived by an aerodynamicist named Nenadovitch.

Five fairly conventional monoplane designs were next, designated AS-70 Jac, AS-71, AS-57, AS-80 Holiday and AS-90 New-Look. In the AS-27 Starcky (see 1978-79 *Jane's*) and AS-37, described briefly below, M Starck reverted to the narrow-gap staggered biplane formula.

STARCK AS-37

As can be seen in the accompanying illustration, this design by M André Starck embodies the narrow-gap, sharply staggered biplane wing configuration that characterised several of his earlier products. The power plant is also unusual, as the engine is mounted behind the side-by-side two-seat cabin and drives, through timing belts, two pusher propellers mounted in the gap between the wings, on each side. This is claimed to enhance, by means of the propeller slipstream, the slot effect produced by the wing arrangement.

The prototype (F-WYBQ), built by M Rudy Nickel of Romans, flew for the first time on 13 January 1977. It was powered at that time by a 48·5 kW (65 hp) Citroën GS 1220 aircooled four-cylinder engine, with a 1:2 reduction in the belt drive, so that each propeller turned at 2,200 rpm in cruising flight. Wingtip 'curtains', inclined at 45° to join the wingtips, stiffened the overall structure, making dihedral unnecessary on the main wings, and were claimed to improve stall characteristics and lateral control; the ailerons were attached to their trailing-edges. Construction of the aircraft was all-wooden, with spruce structure and acajou ply covering. Disc brakes were fitted to the main wheels of the non-retractable tricycle landing gear. Dual controls were fitted.

In that original form, as the **AS-37A**, M Nickel's aircraft logged 100 flying hours and 300 flights by October 1977. A second AS-37A (F-WXDU) was built and flown by M Léon Knoepfli of Sélestat, also with a GS 1220 engine. After a short period of flight testing, this was modified to

AS-37B standard. The wingtip 'curtains' were removed and replaced by wide cantilever interplane struts, some distance inboard from extended wingtips. Conventional ailerons were installed on the upper wings, and flaps on the lower wings. Other changes included replacement of the original main landing gear legs, comprising side Vs and half-axles, with new cantilever legs of laminated glassfibre, with streamlined fairings over all three wheels.

Flight trials of the AS.37B soon confirmed its stability in yaw and roll, as well as its manoeuvrability. However, the increase in empty weight, to 451 kg (995 lb), suggested that a more powerful engine might be desirable. Both the AS-37A of M Nickel and AS-37B of M Knoepfli have therefore been re-engined with a 74·5 kW (100 hp) Porsche 2 flat-four engine, with dual electronic ignition on the AS-37A. Other AS-37s, under construction by M Boucher of Saint-Marcellin and M Bourdreux of Cadarache, will have a 67 kW (90 hp) Renault 843-01 engine and a SACMA engine respectively. M Nickel's aircraft is also being tested with three-blade ground-adjustable wooden propellers.

Twenty-three sets of plans for the AS.37 had been sold to amateur constructors by Spring 1978.

The following data apply to the AS-37A as originally flown:

Dimensions, external:
- Wing span: 6·30 m (20 ft 8 in)
- Wing aspect ratio: 3·0
- Wing area, gross: 13·60 m² (146·4 sq ft)
- Length overall: 6·00 m (19 ft 8 in)
- Height overall: 1·60 m (5 ft 3 in)

Weights:
- Weight empty: 400 kg (882 lb)
- Max T-O weight: 620 kg (1,366 lb)

Performance (estimated):
- Max level speed at S/L: 100 knots (185 km/h; 115 mph)
- Cruising speed at S/L: 91 knots (170 km/h; 105 mph)
- Landing speed: 38 knots (70 km/h; 43·5 mph)
- Rate of climb at S/L: 210 m (690 ft)/min
- Service ceiling: 4,500 m (14,750 ft)
- T-O run: 200 m (655 ft)
- Landing run: 140 m (460 ft)
- Range with 90 litres (19·75 Imp gallons) fuel: 810 nm (1,500 km; 930 miles)

STARCK SUPER NEW LOOK

This simple, low-cost, single-seat light aircraft had its origin in André Starck's AS-90 New Look, the first example of which was flown on 11 June 1950. At the request of French amateur constructors, he has updated the design, with a strut-braced wing of new section and powered by any one of a variety of modified motor car engines. A prototype is under construction by M Parent of Cannes.

Type: Single-seat ultra-light monoplane.

Wings: Braced mid-wing monoplane. Single bracing strut each side, from main landing gear struts. Wing section GAW 1. Thickness/chord ratio 17%. Dihedral 3° from roots. Incidence 4°. Sweepback on leading-edge 6°. Constant-chord wood structure, with single plank-like main spar and trellis ribs, fabric-covered. Elliptical aileron articulated under each wingtip trailing-edge. No flaps.

Fuselage: Welded tube girder structure, fabric-covered.

Tail Unit: Cantilever structure of welded tube, fabric-covered. No tabs.

Landing Gear: Non-retractable two-wheel type, with tailskid. Each main wheel carried on a faired, welded tube V and a strut from the wing root.

Power Plant: One 24·5 kW (33 hp) Citroën Ami 6 converted motor car engine (alternative engines from Volkswagen and DAF suitable). Provision for 20 kg (44 lb) of fuel.

Accommodation: Single seat in enclosed cockpit, under sideways hinged fully transparent canopy.

Dimensions, external:
- Wing span: 8·00 m (26 ft 3 in)
- Wing chord, constant: 1·20 m (3 ft 11¼ in)
- Wing aspect ratio: 7
- Wing area, excl ailerons: 8·46 m² (27 ft 9 in)
- Length overall: 5·50 m (18 ft 0½ in)
- Height overall: 1·40 m (4 ft 7¼ in)

Weights:
- Weight empty: 154 kg (340 lb)
- Max T-O weight: 262 kg (578 lb)

Performance (estimated, with Citroën Ami 6 engine):
- Max level speed at S/L: 81 knots (150 km/h; 93 mph)
- Cruising speed: 73 knots (135 km/h; 84 mph)
- Landing speed: 27 knots (50 km/h; 31 mph)
- Service ceiling: 3,500 m (11,500 ft)

GERMANY
(FEDERAL REPUBLIC)

BECKER
HORST BECKER

Herr Becker, an architect and member of the Oskar-Ursinus-Vereinigung (OUV) association of amateur constructors, has built a two-seat touring aircraft known as the Mistral CP 310. This is based on the airframe of the Binder Aviatik Smaragd (Emerald), described in the 1966-67 *Jane's*. The Smaragd was itself a licence-manufactured de luxe version of the Piel Emeraude, of which full details can be found in the French pages of this section.

BECKER MISTRAL CP 301

Major changes by comparison with the Smaragd include the installation of a 112 kW (150 hp) Lycoming O-320-E2A flat-four engine, in place of the latter's 74·5 kW (100 hp) O-200; addition of streamlined wingtip fuel tanks, to increase total fuel capacity by nearly 25%, to 104 kg (230 lb); introduction of a new canopy giving a 360° field of view; and an increase in the height of the vertical tail surfaces; in addition to certain detail refinements. This involved some airframe strengthening, notably to the engine mounting and wing spar, which was done with the help of Ing Hermann Stützle, a stress engineer who has led the OUV project staff for many years.

The Mistral CP 301 flew for the first time in 1978, after some 4,000 man-hours of work had gone into its design and construction.

Dimensions, external:
- Wing span over tip-tanks: 8·98 m (29 ft 5½ in)
- Wing area: 12·35 m² (132·9 sq ft)
- Wing aspect ratio: 6·52
- Length overall: 6·52 m (21 ft 4¾ in)
- Height overall: 2·16 m (7 ft 1 in)

Weights:
- Weight empty: 540 kg (1,190 lb)
- Max T-O weight: 790 kg (1,742 lb)

Performance:
- Max level speed: 162 knots (300 km/h; 186 mph)
- Cruising speed: 122 knots (226 km/h; 140 mph)
- Landing speed: 46 knots (85 km/h; 53 mph)
- Max rate of climb at S/L: 336 m (1,102 ft)/min
- T-O run: 160 m (525 ft)
- T-O to 15 m (50 ft): 370 m (1,214 ft)
- Landing from 15 m (50 ft): 350 m (1,150 ft)
- Range with max fuel: 464 nm (860 km; 534 miles)

BINDER
HELLMUTH BINDER

7000 Stuttgart 61, Weinklinge 24
Telephone: (0711) 424912

BINDER Bi 20

Information has been received concerning a four/five-seat homebuilt aircraft of unusual design, known as the Binder Bi 20. It is not known when design of the Bi 20 was started or whether construction of a prototype has begun; but a 1·80 m (5 ft 11 in) span scale model has been flight tested.

Type: Four/five-seat light aircraft.

Wings: Cantilever mid-wing monoplane, positioned to rear of fuselage. Wing section NACA 23015/23009. Dihedral 3°. Incidence 3°. Sweepback 15° at quarter-chord. All-wood construction. Ailerons and trailing-edge slotted flaps.

Foreplane: Canard foreplane carried above forward fuselage by tapered vertical fin, which incorporates a rudder. Foreplane has straight leading-edge and tapered elevators, each with horn balance.

Fuselage: Rounded fuselage, tapering towards rear. Steel tube structure, possibly wood covered.

Tail Unit: Large cantilever dorsal and ventral fins.

Landing Gear: Retractable tricycle type, mechanically actuated. Nosewheel tyre, size 350 × 135, remains semi-exposed when retracted to reduce damage in a wheels-up landing. Main wheel tyre size 420 × 150.

Power Plant: One 156 kW (210 hp) engine, driving three-blade variable-pitch shrouded propeller at tail. One fuel tank in fuselage, capacity 160 litres (35 Imp gallons). Refuelling point in port side of fuselage. Oil capacity 15 litres (3·3 Imp gallons).

Accommodation: Four seats, in pairs, in heavily glazed cabin, with provision for a fifth person on rear bench seat. Two upward-hinged doors. Heating and ventilation standard.

Dimensions, external:
- Wing span: 9·00 m (29 ft 6¼ in)
- Wing chord at root: 1·90 m (6 ft 2¾ in)
- Wing chord at tip: 1·10 m (3 ft 7¼ in)
- Wing area, gross: 13·00 m² (140·0 sq ft)
- Length overall: 6·00 m (19 ft 8¼ in)
- Height overall: 2·30 m (7 ft 6½ in)
- Foreplane span: 3·20 m (10 ft 6 in)
- Wheel track: 3·00 m (9 ft 10 in)
- Wheelbase: 2·65 m (8 ft 8¼ in)
- Propeller diameter: 1·25 m (4 ft 1¼ in)

Dimensions, internal:
- Cabin: Length: 2·40 m (7 ft 10½ in)
  - Max width: 1·30 m (4 ft 3¼ in)
  - Max height: 1·12 m (3 ft 8 in)

Weights:
- Weight empty: 530 kg (1,168 lb)
- Max payload: 340 kg (750 lb)
- Max T-O weight: 1,000 kg (2,205 lb)

Performance (estimated):
- Max level speed: 189 knots (350 km/h; 217 mph)
- Max cruising speed: 175 knots (325 km/h; 202 mph)
- Econ cruising speed: 162 knots (300 km/h; 186 mph)
- Stalling speed, flaps down: 38 knots (70 km/h; 43·5 mph)
- Range with max fuel and max payload: 836 nm (1,550 km; 963 miles)

FREBEL
HERMANN FREBEL

Mr Frebel, who died on 15 November 1978, was an engineer with Wolf Hirth GmbH and a well-known personality in German sailplane and light aircraft circles. An accompanying illustration shows the F5, an aircraft of Mignet Pou-du-Ciel form, which he built and flew successfully during the last year of his life.

FREBEL F-5

Type: Single-seat tandem-wing light aircraft.

Wings: Tandem-wing biplane. Wing section NACA 23015. Each wing made in three panels, comprising a wide-span centre-section without dihedral and two outer panels with dihedral. Incidence of forward wing variable to +11° by control column. No sweepback. D-spar leading-edge torsion box of balsa/Gfk sandwich with double-T spar. Ribs of Conticell stiffened with balsa. Overall fabric covering. Front wing pivoted on two streamlined cabane struts. Large tab under trailing-edge of front wing centre-section. Combined aileron/elevator in trailing-edge of each rear wing.

Fuselage: Conventional box structure of spruce frames and stringers covered with Gfk-stiffened balsa sheet.

Tail Unit: Vertical surfaces only, of similar construction to wings. Fin integral with fuselage. Rudder fabric-covered.

Landing Gear: Non-retractable tricycle type, with steerable nosewheel. Main wheels carried on one-piece cantilever Gfk beam. Brakes on main wheels.

Power Plant: One 33 kW (45 hp) Stark Stamo 1500/1 flat-four engine, driving a two-blade wooden fixed-pitch propeller made by Nicolas Down. Fuel tank, capacity 30·5 litres (6·7 Imp gallons), between cockpit and engine.

Accommodation: Single seat in enclosed cockpit, with rearward-hinged fully-transparent one-piece windscreen-canopy. Cabin heated.

Dimensions, external:
- Wing span: forward: 7·80 m (25 ft 7 in)
  - rear: 7·20 m (23 ft 7½ in)
- Wing area, gross: 14·80 m² (159·3 sq ft)
- Wing aspect ratio: forward: 7·9
  - rear: 7·3
- Length overall: 4·20 m (13 ft 9½ in)
- Height overall: 1·95 m (6 ft 4¾ in)
- Wheel track: 1·80 m (5 ft 10¾ in)
- Wheelbase: 1·20 m (3 ft 11¼ in)
- Propeller diameter: 1·50 m (4 ft 11 in)

Weights:
- Weight empty: 227 kg (500 lb)
- Max T-O weight: 345 kg (760 lb)

Performance:
- Max level speed at S/L: 101 knots (187 km/h; 116 mph)
- Cruising speed at S/L: 70 knots (130 km/h; 80 mph)
- Max rate of climb at S/L: 360 m (1,180 ft)/min
- Service ceiling: 4,200 m (13,775 ft)
- T-O run: 50 m (164 ft)
- Landing run: 40 m (131 ft)
- Range with max fuel: 270 nm (500 km; 310 miles)

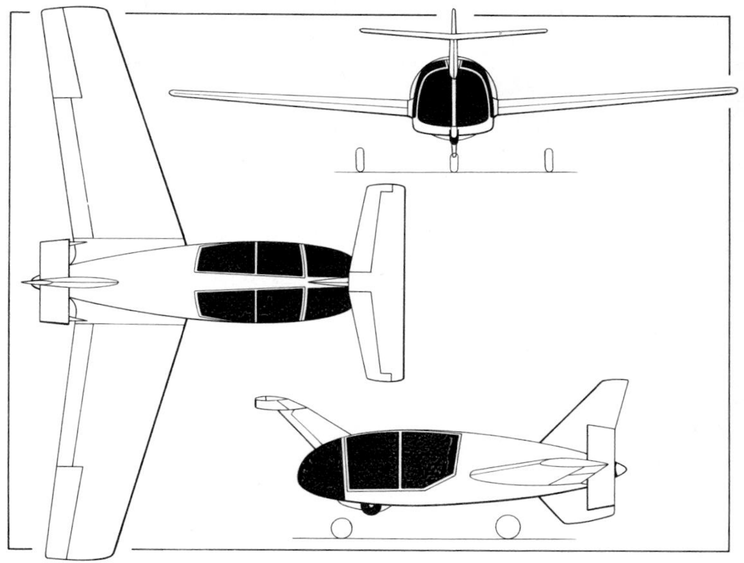

Binder Bi 20 four/five-seat light aircraft *(Michael A. Badrocke)*

Frebel F-5 single-seat tandem-wing light aircraft *(Wolfgang Wagner)*

Wallerkowski Hornisse single-seat monoplane

Schilling HSX-3 light autogyro *(Avicentra-Archiv)*

HELLBACH

WALTER HELLBACH

Ortenbergerstrasse 3, 6471-Bergheim/Kr Rueding

Mr Hellbach built a single-seat ultra-light autogyro, designated HW 03, of which all available details were given in the 1978-79 *Jane's*. There has been no news concerning flight trials of this aircraft.

SCHILLING

ING HORST SCHILLING

Hanaunerstrasse 8 PF 13, 6463-Freigericht

The HSX-3 single-seat light autogyro constructed by Ing Schilling was first seen in public at an OUV meeting in the summer of 1976. It has since made a number of short flights.

SCHILLING HSX-3

TYPE: Single-seat light autogyro.

ROTOR SYSTEM: Two-blade semi-rigid all-metal rotor on a conventional tilting head, activated by the pilot's control column. Head runs on two tensioned taper roller bearings with a wide angle of cone. No drive from engine to rotor. Blades are foldable.

FUSELAGE: Built up of two glass-reinforced plastics (GfK) half-shells and a two-piece cabin fairing.

TAIL UNIT: All-moving horizontal trim surface (elevator) is a GfK-balsa wood shell, with a core of Styropor expanded polystyrene, and is activated by a lever on the port side of the cockpit, forward of the pilot. Fin is a GfK shell with polyurethane core. Rear part of rudder is fabric covered. Conventional rudder pedals control rudder movement.

LANDING GEAR: Non-retractable tricycle type, with tail-skid for protection in tail-down landing or take-off. Cantilever main legs consist of a GfK spring into which layers of wood are laminated, with roving stiffeners. Tailskid spring is of similar construction. Brakes on main wheels, and parking brake.

POWER PLANT: One 44 kW (60 hp) converted Volkswagen motor car engine, mounted behind rotor mast and controlled by twist-grip throttle on elevator lever. Two-blade fixed-pitch pusher propeller. Single fuel tank, capacity 20 kg (44 lb), with engine-driven fuel pump. Oil capacity 4 kg (8·8 lb).

ACCOMMODATION: Single seat in open cockpit.

DIMENSIONS, EXTERNAL:

Rotor diameter	6·80 m (22 ft 3¾ in)
Rotor disc area	36·30 m² (390·7 sq ft)
Length overall, excl rotor	4·40 m (14 ft 5¼ in)
Height overall	2·35 m (7 ft 8½ in)

WEIGHTS:

Weight empty	200 kg (441 lb)
Max T-O weight	320 kg (705 lb)

PERFORMANCE:

No details available

SCHOLZ-SCHMITZ

MANFRED SCHOLZ

Fine Frau Strasse 18, 4640-Wattenscheid

Flugkapitän Manfred Scholz, in partnership with Mr Wolfgang Schmitz, designed a long-distance racing aircraft designated SS-1, of which details were given in the 1978-79 *Jane's*. The aim was to produce an aircraft of exceptional aerodynamic quality, in order to cover long distances with much less power than is required by the average Formula 1 racer. To achieve this objective, while providing high fuel capacity, the designers decided to build the SS-1 almost entirely of glassfibre-reinforced plastics (GfK) or carbon fibre-reinforced plastics (KfK).

Construction of the SS-1 was started; but there is no news of its approaching completion.

WALLERKOWSKI

HEINZ WALLERKOWSKI

Rablstrasse 16, 8000 Munich 80
Telephone: (089) 486678

Heinz Wallerkowski is an airline captain with Bavaria-Germanair. He began the design of the Hornisse (D-EBXG) in January 1974; construction of the prototype was initiated one year later, and the first flight took place on 30 June 1978. By December 1978, twenty-seven flying hours had been logged during 65 flights. A streamlining programme was underway at that time, affecting the landing gear and canopy. Captain Wallerkowski is a member of the Oskar-Ursinus-Vereinigung, the German Chapter of the EAA.

WALLERKOWSKI HORNISSE (HORNET)

TYPE: Single-seat monoplane.

WINGS: Cantilever low-wing monoplane. NACA 23012 wing section. Dihedral 3° 30′. Incidence 1°. No sweepback. All-metal (2024-T3) construction, flush-riveted. All-metal Frise-type ailerons and all-metal flaps. No tabs.

FUSELAGE: All-metal semi-monocoque structure, flush-riveted.

TAIL UNIT: Conventional cantilever assembly of all-metal construction. Two-spar tailplane, with only two ribs each side and heavy skin. Flettner-type trim tabs in elevators.

LANDING GEAR: Non-retractable tailwheel type. Cantilever steel-tube main legs, with streamline fairings. Main wheels size 5·00-5. Wheel fairings. Steerable tail-wheel. Gerdes hydraulic brakes.

POWER PLANT: One 112 kW (150 hp) Lycoming O-320-E1C flat-four engine, driving a Hoffmann three-blade ground-adjustable propeller. Two fuel tanks in wings, total capacity 90 litres (20 Imp gallons).

ACCOMMODATION: Single seat under starboard-hinged transparent canopy. Baggage space behind seat.

SYSTEM: 12V battery for engine starting.

DIMENSIONS, EXTERNAL:

Wing span	6·14 m (20 ft 1¾ in)
Wing chord, constant	1·38 m (4 ft 6¼ in)
Wing area, gross	8·4 m² (90·4 sq ft)
Wing aspect ratio	4·45
Length overall	5·80 m (19 ft 1 in)
Height overall	1·60 m (5 ft 3 in)
Tailplane span	2·22 m (7 ft 3½ in)
Wheel track	1·80 m (5 ft 11 in)
Wheelbase	4·70 m (15 ft 5 in)
Propeller diameter	1·55 m (5 ft 1 in)

DIMENSIONS, INTERNAL:

Cockpit: Length	1·20 m (3 ft 11¼ in)
Max width	0·64 m (2 ft 1¼ in)
Max height	1·04 m (3 ft 5 in)

WEIGHTS:

Weight empty	334 kg (736 lb)
Max payload	95 kg (210 lb)
Max T-O weight: normal	500 kg (1,102 lb)
aerobatic	460 kg (1,014 lb)

Performance (estimated, at max T-O weight, without wheel fairings):
Never-exceed speed 188 knots (350 km/h; 217 mph)
Max level speed at 2,440 m (8,000 ft) 179 knots (332 km/h; 206 mph)
Max cruising speed at 2,440 m (8,000 ft) 166 knots (308 km/h; 191 mph)
Econ cruising speed at 2,440 m (8,000 ft) 151 knots (280 km/h; 174 mph)
Stalling speed, flaps down, power off 45 knots (82 km/h; 51 mph)
Stalling speed, flaps up, power off 48 knots (88 km/h; 55 mph)
Max rate of climb at S/L 561 m (1,840 ft)/min
Service ceiling over 6,100 m (20,000 ft)
T-O run 150 m (490 ft)
T-O to 15 m (50 ft) 300 m (985 ft)
Landing from 15 m (50 ft) 300 m (985 ft)
Landing run 200 m (655 ft)
Range with max fuel, 45 min reserves 432 nm (800 km; 497 miles)

JAPAN

ABE

KEICHI ABE

17-11-4 Cho-me, Masuura, Kushiro-Shi, Hokaido

Mr Keichi Abe has designed and is building a lightweight single-seat monoplane known as the Mizzet (Midget) No. III. Design work began in September 1977, and construction of the prototype was started in November of the same year. By early 1979 the aircraft was about 85% complete. First flight was scheduled for August 1979.

ABE MIZZET No. III

Type: Single-seat lightweight monoplane.

Wings: Strut-braced low-wing monoplane. Göttingen 387 wing section. Constant chord. Marked dihedral from roots. All-wood structure, with two box-spars, fabric covered. Ailerons, but no flaps.

Fuselage: Main structure of 6063T rectangular metal beams and tubes. Plywood and urethane used for sides of cockpit and nose, and to give form to rear fuselage. Fabric covering overall.

Tail Unit: Cantilever wooden structure, fabric covered. Constant-chord tailplane, with elevators. Small dorsal fin and large horn-balanced rudder.

Landing Gear: Non-retractable nosewheel type.

Power Plant: One 30 kW (40 hp) 1,210 cc modified Volkswagen motor car engine, driving a two-blade wooden propeller. Glassfibre fuel tank in wing leading-edge, capacity 15 litres (3·3 Imp gallons). Oil capacity 2·5 litres (0·55 Imp gallons).

Accommodation: Single seat in open cockpit.

Dimensions, external:
Wing span 7·30 m (23 ft 11½ in)
Wing area, gross 8·75 m² (94·2 sq ft)
Wing chord, constant 1·20 m (3 ft 11¼ in)
Wing aspect ratio 6·1
Length overall 5·26 m (17 ft 3 in)
Height overall 2·05 m (6 ft 8¾ in)
Tailplane span 2·40 m (7 ft 10½ in)
Propeller diameter 1·35 m (4 ft 5 in)

Weights:
Weight empty 200 kg (441 lb)
Max T-O weight 288 kg (635 lb)

Performance (estimated):
Max level speed 81 knots (150 km/h; 93 mph)
Max cruising speed 65 knots (120 km/h; 74·5 mph)
Stalling speed 38 knots (70 km/h; 43·5 mph)
Max rate of climb at S/L 252 m (826 ft)/min
Range with max fuel 146 nm (270 km; 168 miles)
Max endurance 3h

JAPAN AMATEUR BUILT AIRCRAFT LEAGUE

% JAA (Japan Aeronautical Association), 1-18-2 Shimbashi, Minato-ku, Tokyo

Telephone: (03) 502 1203

This new organisation came into being in April 1978, superseding the former Japan Experimental Aircraft Association. Various fixed- and rotating-wing aircraft have been designed and/or built and flown by its members, and several of these have been described and illustrated in recent editions of *Jane's*. Others are examples of US homebuilt types such as the Baby Great Lakes, Flaglor Scooter, Hovey Whing Ding II, Stolp Starduster and Bensen Gyro-Copter as described in the US section.

HAMAO SHIOKARATOMBO

This small single-seat biplane, designed and built by Mr Y. Hamao, is powered by a 112 kW (150 hp) Lycoming O-320 engine.

The Shiokaratombo is of wooden construction, fabric covered, and its general layout can be seen in the accompanying photograph. The wing section is NACA 4218.

Dimensions, external:
Wing span (upper) 6·40 m (21 ft 0 in)
Wing span (lower) 5·60 m (18 ft 4½ in)
Wing chord, mean 0·90 m (2 ft 11½ in)
Wing area, gross 10 m² (107·6 sq ft)
Length overall 5·70 m (18 ft 8¼ in)
Height overall 2·40 m (7 ft 10½ in)
Tailplane span 2·40 m (7 ft 10½ in)
Propeller diameter 1·88 m (6 ft 2 in)

Weights:
Weight empty 380 kg (838 lb)
Max T-O weight 500 kg (1,102 lb)

Performance: No details available

KAKO

TERUO KAKO

15 Futsuginda, Ichijogi, Hidari-Kyo-ku, Kyoto-Shi T606

TERUO KAKO TK-1

Mr T. Kako began design of the TK-1 in 1971; construction started in April 1973, with the assistance of Mr K. Kubota. The prototype was completed in December 1975, as a seaplane, with a single large wooden float under the fuselage and two small underwing floats. Taxying trials on water were undertaken before modification started in January 1977 to convert the TK-1 into a landplane. The original 33·6 kW (45 hp) Volkswagen engine has also been replaced by a more powerful Corvair engine.

Type: Single-seat sporting aircraft.

Wings: Cantilever low-wing monoplane, made up of centre-section and two outer panels. RAF 48 wing section, with 16% thickness/chord ratio. Dihedral 7°. Incidence 3° 30′. Wood single-spar structure, with D-type leading-edge torsion box; plywood and fabric covering. No flaps.

Fuselage: Wooden semi-monocoque structure, with plywood covering and fabric overall.

Tail Unit: Fabric-covered wooden cantilever structure.

Landing Gear: Non-retractable tailwheel type, with steerable tailwheel of 200 mm diameter. Balloon tyres on main wheels, diameter 600 mm. No shock-absorbers.

Power Plant: One 89·5 kW (120 hp) 2,600 cc modified Chevrolet Corvair motor car engine, driving a two-blade fixed-pitch laminated wood propeller. Fuel capacity 30 litres (6·6 Imp gallons); oil capacity 3 litres (0·66 Imp gallons).

Accommodation: Single seat in open cockpit.

Dimensions, external:
Wing span 9·90 m (32 ft 5¾ in)
Wing chord, constant 1·51 m (4 ft 11½ in)
Wing area, gross 14·85 m² (159·8 sq ft)
Wing aspect ratio 6·6
Length overall 6·36 m (20 ft 10½ in)
Height overall 2·70 m (8 ft 10¼ in)
Tailplane span 3·20 m (10 ft 6 in)
Wheel track 1·50 m (4 ft 11 in)
Propeller diameter 1·40 m (4 ft 7 in)

Weights:
Weight empty 375 kg (827 lb)
Max T-O weight 465 kg (1,025 lb)

Performance (estimated):
Max level speed 74·5 knots (138 km/h; 86 mph)
Max cruising speed 54 knots (100 km/h; 62 mph)
Stalling speed 38 knots (70 km/h; 43·5 mph)
Max rate of climb at S/L 150 m (490 ft)/min
T-O run 70 m (230 ft)
Landing run 120 m (395 ft)

MUKAI

ISAO MUKAI

KO 4, No. 1, Kisho, Utsumi-Machi, Shozu-Gun, Kagawa Prefecture

MUKAI OLIVE No. 2

The Olive No. 2 is Mr Mukai's second aircraft project. Design began in 1972 and the prototype was completed in March of the following year. Taxying trials started in July 1976, followed shortly afterwards by the first flight. At least one other Olive had been constructed by Spring 1979.

Type: Single-seat light seaplane.

Wings: Braced high-wing monoplane. Constant chord. Clark Y wing section. No dihedral on centre-section; slight dihedral on outer wings. Two-spar all-wooden structure, fabric covered, with dope and enamel finish. Vee main bracing struts. Large-span wooden ailerons. No flaps.

Fuselage: Welded metal tube truss structure, fabric covered.

Tail Unit: Braced all-wood structure, fabric covered. Horizontal surfaces of constant chord. Ground-adjustable tab on starboard elevator. All-moving vertical tail surface.

Landing Gear: Twin floats of all-wooden construction, plywood covered.

Power Plant: One 48·5 kW (65 hp) 1,834 cc modified Volkswagen motor car engine, driving a two-blade propeller. One fuel tank, aft of pilot's seat, capacity 50 litres (11 Imp gallons).

Accommodation: Single seat in enclosed cabin. Upward-hinged door on port side of fuselage. Space for baggage aft of pilot's seat.

Dimensions, external:
Wing span 12·00 m (39 ft 4½ in)
Wing chord, constant 1·40 m (4 ft 7 in)
Wing area, gross 16·80 m² (180·8 sq ft)
Wing aspect ratio 8·6
Length overall 7·30 m (23 ft 11½ in)
Height overall 2·98 m (9 ft 9¼ in)
Tailplane span 3·20 m (10 ft 6 in)
Propeller diameter 1·35 m (4 ft 5 in)

Dimensions, internal:
Cabin: Length 1·30 m (4 ft 3 in)
Max width 0·80 m (2 ft 7½ in)
Max height 1·00 m (3 ft 3½ in)

Weights:
Weight empty, incl oil and fuel 295 kg (650 lb)
Max T-O weight 365 kg (805 lb)

Performance:
Max level speed at 1,000 m (3,050 ft) 59·5 knots (110 km/h; 68·5 mph)
Max cruising speed 49 knots (90 km/h; 56 mph)
Econ cruising speed 43·5 knots (80 km/h; 50 mph)
Stalling speed 24·5 knots (45 km/h; 28 mph)
Max rate of climb at S/L 150 m (490 ft)/min
T-O run 150 m (490 ft)
T-O to 15 m (50 ft) 300 m (980 ft)
Landing from 15 m (50 ft) 180 m (590 ft)
Range with max fuel 215 nm (400 km; 248 miles)

MUKAI OLIVE SMG III

Latest of Mr Mukai's aircraft is the Olive SMG III flying-boat motor-glider. Design began on 3 May 1978, and construction of the prototype started on 10 October 1978. By early 1979 it was only 10% complete, and first flight is not expected until October 1980.

Type: Two-seat flying-boat motor-glider.

Wings: Strut-braced high-wing monoplane. Göttingen 549 wing section. Slight dihedral. Wooden box-spar and ribs, fabric covered. Large-span wooden ailerons. Airbrakes standard.

Fuselage: Conventional flying-boat hull. Welded stainless steel tube truss structure, glassfibre-covered on lower surface and Dacron fabric-covered on upper surface.

Tail Unit: Braced all-wood structure, fabric covered. High-mounted tailplane. Tab in starboard elevator. Fin integral with fuselage. Horn-balanced rudder, with water-rudder beneath.

Landing Gear: Hull, with stabilising floats under wings.

Power Plant: One 45 kW (60 hp) modified Volkswagen motor car engine, mounted on struts above wing and driving a two-blade propeller. Two fuel tanks, total capacity 30 litres (6·6 Imp gallons). Oil capacity 2·5 litres (0·55 Imp gallons).

Accommodation: Two seats in fully enclosed cabin.

Dimensions, external:
Wing span 14·00 m (46 ft 0 in)
Wing area, gross 16·80 m² (180·83 sq ft)
Wing chord, at root 1·40 m (4 ft 7 in)

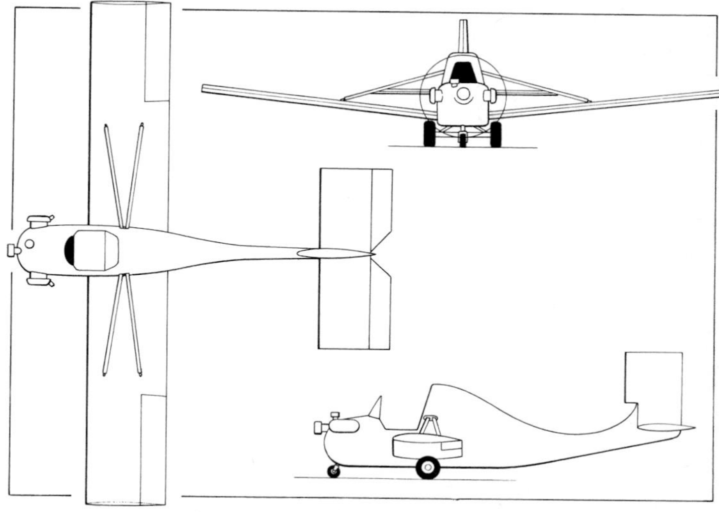

Abe Mizzet No. III *(Michael A. Badrocke)*

Abe Mizzet No. III under construction

Shiokaratombo single-seat biplane designed by Mr Y. Hamao (Lycoming O-320 engine)

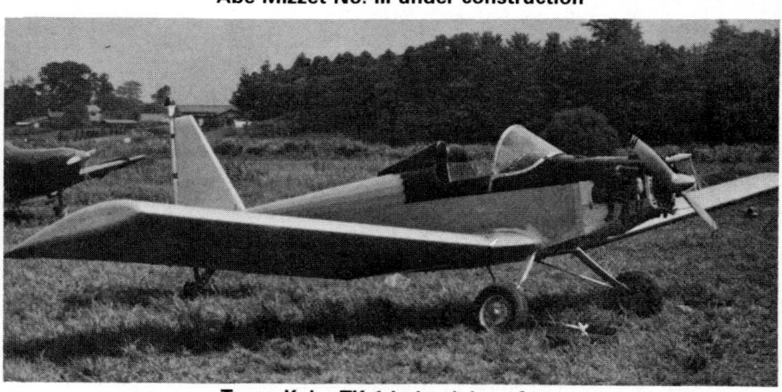

Teruo Kako TK-1 in landplane form

Mukai Olive No. 2 seaplane

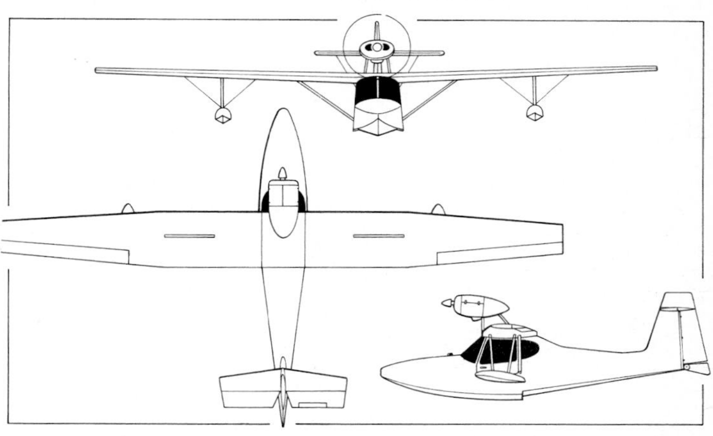

Mukai Olive SMG III *(Michael A. Badrocke)*

Wing chord, at tip	0·80 m (2 ft 7½ in)
Wing aspect ratio	11·7
Length overall	7·80 m (25 ft 7 in)
Height overall	2·85 m (9 ft 4¼ in)
Tailplane span	3·20 m (10 ft 6 in)
WEIGHTS:	
Weight empty	430 kg (948 lb)
Max T-O weight	575 kg (1,268 lb)
PERFORMANCE (estimated):	
Best glide ratio	20
Max level speed	81 knots (150 km/h; 93 mph)
Max cruising speed	54 knots (100 km/h; 62 mph)
Stalling speed	30 knots (55 km/h; 34 mph)
Max rate of climb at S/L	150 m (492 ft)/min
Range with max fuel	215 nm (400 km; 248 miles)

NIHON UNIVERSITY

COLLEGE OF SCIENCE AND ENGINEERING (DEPARTMENT OF AEROSPACE ENGINEERING), NIHON UNIVERSITY

1-8 Kanda-Surugadai, 1-chome, Chiyoda-ku, Tokyo 101
Telephone: Tokyo (03) 293 3251
CHIEF PROFESSOR: Dr Hidemasa Kimura

Under the leadership of Dr Kimura, students of Nihon University have designed and built several aircraft, including the Okamura N-52 and N-58 Cygnet lightplanes and a STOL lightplane designated N-62, in collaboration with the Itoh company, which built the prototype. The N-62 was put into production by Itoh, as the Eaglet, and was described in the 1968-69 *Jane's*.

This design team has also built a series of successful man-powered aircraft named Linnet, Egret, Stork and Ibis A, all of which have been described fully in previous editions of *Jane's*. A motor-glider, the N-70 Cygnus, was described in the 1974-75 edition; a new motor-glider, known as N-75 Cygnus II, is currently under construction.

SAWANO

SHIRO SAWANO

6-147 Isezaki-cho, Naka-ku, Yokohama, Kanagawa Prefecture
Telephone: (045) 251 2580

SAWANO MR SMOOTHIE

Built by Mr Shiro Sawano, this modified Bowers Fly Baby was described and illustrated in the 1978-79 *Jane's*. Design began in 1967 and construction was started in the following year. By May 1975 the aircraft had been completed, but test flying did not begin until one year later. In early 1978 Mr Sawano reported his intention to modify the aircraft into a tandem two-seater, with an engine of greater power and increased wing area. No details of this conversion have yet been received.

YAMATO

SAWAZO YAMATO

1-5-27 Imaike Machi, Sakai-Shi, Osaka Prefecture
Telephone: 0722 38 7510

YAMATO SY MOTOR GLIDER

Design of the SY motor glider began in April 1976 and construction was started in March 1977. By January 1979 the aircraft was 90% complete, and first flight was scheduled for April 1979.

TYPE: Single-seat ultra-light monoplane.

WINGS: Strut-braced parasol monoplane. Rear section of wing rests on raised fuselage turtleback. Wing section NACA 4412. Dihedral 1°. Incidence 3°. All-wood structure, with two spruce box-spars, fabric-covered and dope-finished. Plain half-span ailerons of spruce. Vee bracing struts. No tabs.

FUSELAGE: Conventional structure with four spruce longerons, 1·5 mm plywood-covered.

TAIL UNIT: Conventional all-wood (spruce) structure, fabric-covered and dope-finished. No tabs.

LANDING GEAR: Non-retractable tailwheel type. Main gear carried on side Vees and half-axles. Main wheels size 340 × 110, with brakes. Piper Cub type bungee shock-absorption.

POWER PLANT: One 30 kW (40 hp) modified Volkswagen 1,600 cc motor car engine, driving a fixed-pitch wooden propeller of home construction. Fuel tank aft of firewall, capacity 20 litres (4·4 Imp gallons). Oil capacity 3 litres (0·66 Imp gallons).

ACCOMMODATION: Single seat in open cockpit.

DIMENSIONS, EXTERNAL:

Wing span	12·22 m (40 ft 1 in)
Wing chord, constant	1·40 m (4 ft 7 in)
Wing area, gross	17·00 m² (183·0 sq ft)
Wing aspect ratio	8·7
Length overall	6·77 m (22 ft 2½ in)
Height overall	2·40 m (7 ft 10½ in)
Tailplane span	3·20 m (10 ft 6 in)
Wheel track	1·60 m (5 ft 3 in)
Wheelbase	5·30 m (17 ft 4½ in)
Propeller diameter	1·35 m (4 ft 5¼ in)

WEIGHTS:

Weight empty	280 kg (617 lb)
Max T-O weight	380 kg (837 lb)

PERFORMANCE (estimated):

Never-exceed speed	80·5 knots (150 km/h; 93 mph)
Max level speed	57 knots (105 km/h; 66 mph)
Max cruising speed	38 knots (70 km/h; 44 mph)
Stalling speed	29 knots (53 km/h; 33 mph)

YAMAZAKI
TAKASHI YAMAZAKI

1305-5 Kokubu, Nangoku-Shi, Kochi Prefecture

YAMAZAKI VP-1

Mr Takashi Yamazaki has built a seaplane version of the Evans VP-1 single-seat monoplane. Design of the modifications began in December 1974, and construction was started on 10 January 1975. By early 1979 the aircraft had been completed. Details are generally similar to those listed under the Evans VP-1 entry in the US section, except for the following:

TYPE: Single-seat light seaplane.

WINGS: Reinforced wing spars, through fuselage, to take float landing gear struts.

LANDING GEAR: Twin floats of Polyestel foam, with Dynel fabric covering. Total weight of floats, struts and fittings 47·6 kg (105 lb).

POWER PLANT: One 44·5 kW (60 hp) 1,800 cc modified Volkswagen motor car engine. Fuel capacity 32 litres (7 Imp gallons). Oil capacity 2·2 litres (0·5 Imp gallons).

DIMENSIONS, EXTERNAL:

Length overall	7·00 m (22 ft 11½ in)
Height overall	2·23 m (7 ft 3¾ in)

WEIGHTS:

Weight empty	272 kg (600 lb)
Max T-O weight	369·2 kg (814 lb)

PERFORMANCE:
No details yet available.

NEW ZEALAND

ARDC of NZ
AERONAUTICAL RESEARCH and DEVELOPMENT COMPANY OF NEW ZEALAND LTD

PO Box 11542, Wellington

PRESIDENT: James Lobet

TECHNICAL DIRECTOR: George Jacquemin

The original Ganagobie was designed and built by the brothers William and James Lobet at Lille, France, and made its first flight in 1953, powered by an old Clerget engine. After modification and redesignation as Ganagobie 02 it flew for a further 30 hours before being grounded by engine failure in 1954, and later became Ganagobie 2 when fitted with a two-stroke target drone engine.

Construction of the second aircraft, Ganagobie 03, was started in Alberta, Canada, by Mr La Rue Smith and completed by Mr Pierre Descamps. Built of birch plywood, it was somewhat heavier than the first aircraft and was powered by a 26 kW (35 hp) Poinsard engine. Engines fitted to later Ganagobie 03s were a 53·7 kW (72 hp) McCulloch and a 30 kW (40 hp) Continental; this version is also suitable for converted Volkswagen engines of 1,500 cc and above. The 'ultra-light' version, known as the Ganagobie 04, is suitable for 35·8 kW (48 hp) Nelson and other small two-stroke engines. Very light okoumé mahogany, and other weight-saving features, may be used in its construction. Latest version is the Ganagobie 05, of which the prototype is being completed in New Zealand. Plans of the Ganagobie 03 and 05 are available to amateur constructors.

Mr Lobet decided to establish the present company in New Zealand for financial reasons, as it had proved difficult to produce kits at a competitive price in Australia, which had been the home of the Ganagobie programme for a number of years.

ARDC of NZ may develop a variety of aeronautical and engineering products suitable for home assembly or construction, and will market plans and kits for a number of aircraft in addition to the Ganagobies. The exact types have not been chosen, but those being considered include Fauvel designs, the Potez 60 and Lederlin 380 L, gliders and sailplanes that could be produced under licence in the form of kits and subassemblies.

GANAGOBIE 05

The Ganagobie 05 is a small, high-wing single-seat aircraft, designed primarily for amateur construction. The basic homebuilt model is all-wooden; but production versions are under consideration, either in kit form with a fabric-covered steel tube fuselage and wooden wings and tail, or in factory-built form with all-metal fabric-covered wing and tail control surfaces. The following description applies to the all-wood homebuilt version, of which a prototype (the property of ARDC of NZ) was expected to fly in New Zealand in 1979:

TYPE: Single-seat light aircraft.

WINGS: Braced high-wing monoplane. Wing section NACA 23012. Constant-chord wings, with main and auxiliary spars and semi-circular tips. Centre-section integral with top of fuselage. Main panels have dihedral and can be detached for storage and transit, being carried in frames attached to the landing gear and cabane fittings on each side of the fuselage. A special frame fits over the rear of the fuselage to provide added support. Wooden spars and ribs, with non-structural plywood or aluminium leading-edge and fabric covering. Cable-operated plain ailerons. No flaps. Wings braced to fuselage by streamline-section steel tube Vee strut assembly on each side.

FUSELAGE: Basically wooden structure, of diamond-shaped cross-section, consisting of spruce longerons, 12 bulkheads and formers, and plywood covering. Steel tube engine mounting frame and wing root cabane structure.

TAIL UNIT: Plywood-covered wooden fin and strut-braced tailplane; fabric-covered wooden elevators and horn-balanced rudder. Struts detachable to permit horizontal surfaces to fold upwards for storage and transit. Rudder and elevators cable-operated. Trim tab on port elevator.

LANDING GEAR: Non-retractable main wheels and tailskid or tailwheel. Main wheels are mounted on tripod struts, the main legs of which have rubber-in-compression shock-absorption, and are of 203 mm (8 in) diameter with 8·00-4 tyres. Normally, spoon-type tailskid mounted at end of flat spring beneath rear fuselage. Front-wheel brakes are necessary if a tailwheel is fitted.

POWER PLANT: Aircraft is designed for a modified VW engine of at least 26 kW (35 hp), with direct-drive two-blade propeller; a typical engine is the Limbach SL 1700 D. Alternatively, geared-down VW engines with either Vee-belt or gear reduction drive may be installed, provided that aircraft does not exceed its weight and CG range limitations. Fuel in two wing tanks between main and auxiliary spars; almost all of fuel load is usable.

ACCOMMODATION: Single seat in fully-enclosed cabin, with upward-opening door on each side. Ventilation devices in each transparent door panel. Seat belt attached to bulkhead.

DIMENSIONS, EXTERNAL:

Wing span	7·40 m (24 ft 3¼ in)
Wing chord, constant	1·20 m (3 ft 11¼ in)
Wing area, gross	8·57 m² (92·25 sq ft)
Wing aspect ratio	6·25
Length overall	4·92 m (16 ft 1¾ in)
Height overall	1·83 m (6 ft 0 in)
Tailplane span	2·38 m (7 ft 9¾ in)
Wheel track	1·50 m (4 ft 11 in)
Propeller diameter (direct drive)	1·50 m (4 ft 11 in)

WEIGHTS:

Weight empty	285 kg (630 lb)
Max T-O weight	362 kg (800 lb)

PERFORMANCE (at max T-O weight, estimated, with SL 1700 D engine):

Max level speed	98 knots (182 km/h; 113 mph)
Max cruising speed (75% power)	87 knots (161 km/h; 100 mph)
Stalling speed	41 knots (76 km/h; 47 mph)
Service ceiling	3,050 m (10,000 ft)

POLAND

JANOWSKI
JAROSLAW JANOWSKI

ul. Nowomiejska 2M29, 91-061 Lodz

Mr Janowski, assisted by Mr Witold Kalita, designed a light single-seat aircraft named the J-1 Don Kichot, in the latter 1960s. Its power plant, the 17 kW (23 hp) Saturn two-cylinder engine, was also designed by Mr Janowski, and built by Mr S. Polawski. Plans of the aircraft in J-1B form (which has also been referred to by the Polish name Przasniczka), are available to amateur builders in the West from Mr Andrew J. Baracz, 56 Signal Hill Trail, Sparta, NJ 07871, USA.

A smaller development of the J-1 is known as the J-2 Polonez.

JANOWSKI J-1B DON KICHOT (DON QUIXOTE)

Design and construction of the prototype J-1 was started in 1967, and it flew for the first time in 1970. The engine originally fitted to this aircraft (as in detailed description) proved adequate, but it was decided to allow for more powerful engines of 18·6-37·25 kW (25-50 hp) on the plans that have since become available to other amateur constructors. This necessitated some strengthening of the structure. At the same time, the design was modified to eliminate all welding from the fuselage, except for the engine mounting, and to offer a fuselage of polyurethane foam and glassfibre as an alternative to the more conventional fabric-covered wood of the prototype. The aircraft now covered by plans is designated J-1B. Design coefficients are +4/−2*g* for the wood and fabric version; +6/−3*g* for the foam/glassfibre design, with an ultimate load factor of +9/−4·5*g* for the latter.

TYPE: Single-seat ultra-light monoplane.

WINGS: Strut-braced high-wing monoplane. Clark Y wing section. Thickness/chord ratio 13%. Single-spar wooden structure, with plywood D-section leading-edge, fabric covering and additional glassfibre covering on centre-section. Alternative plastics spar version with polyurethane ribs, glassfibre covered. Braced by single steel strut on each side. Fabric-covered wooden, or polyurethane foam and glassfibre, ailerons. No flaps.

FUSELAGE: Pod-and-boom type. Prototype J-1 was of plywood-covered wood construction, except for welded steel tube central fuselage structure. J-1B plans offer alternative plywood-covered wood structure or a fuselage of polyurethane foam and glassfibre.

TAIL UNIT: Wooden or polyurethane foam and glassfibre structure, with non-swept constant-chord horizontal surfaces and sweptback vertical surfaces. All fixed surfaces in wooden version plywood-covered, movable surfaces fabric-covered. Trim tab in elevator.

LANDING GEAR: Non-retractable tailwheel type. Cantilever spring steel or glassfibre and epoxy resin main legs, each with single wheel and 300-125 low pressure tyre. Castering tailwheel, diameter 4·72 in (120 mm). Mechanical brakes.

POWER PLANT: Prototype has one 17 kW (23 hp) Janowski Saturn two-stroke two-cylinder horizontally-opposed aircooled engine, mounted at top of fuselage aft of cabin and driving a two-blade fixed-pitch wooden pusher propeller designed by Mr Janowski. Engines (such as converted Volkswagen) in 18·6 -37·25 kW (25-50 hp) range suitable for aircraft built by amateur constructors. Fuel capacity of prototype 20 litres (4·4 Imp gallons).

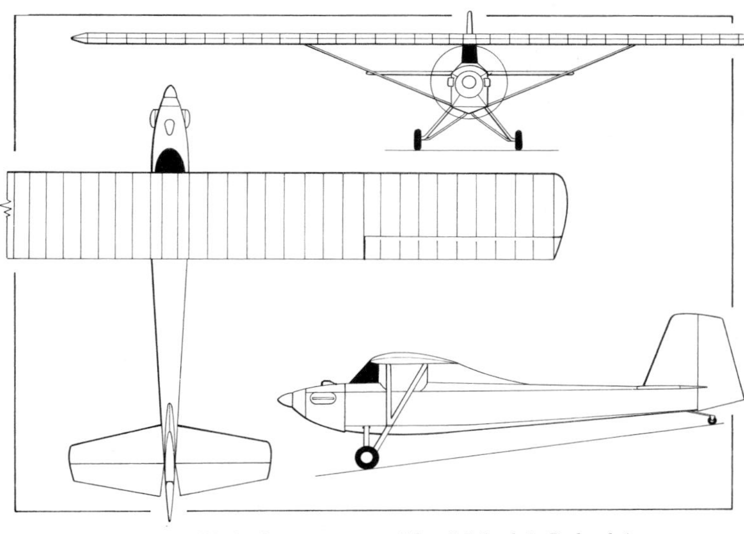

Yamato SY single-seat motor glider *(Michael A. Badrocke)*

Mr Takashi Yamazaki's seaplane version of the Evans VP-1

Model of the Janowski J-2 Polonez light aircraft

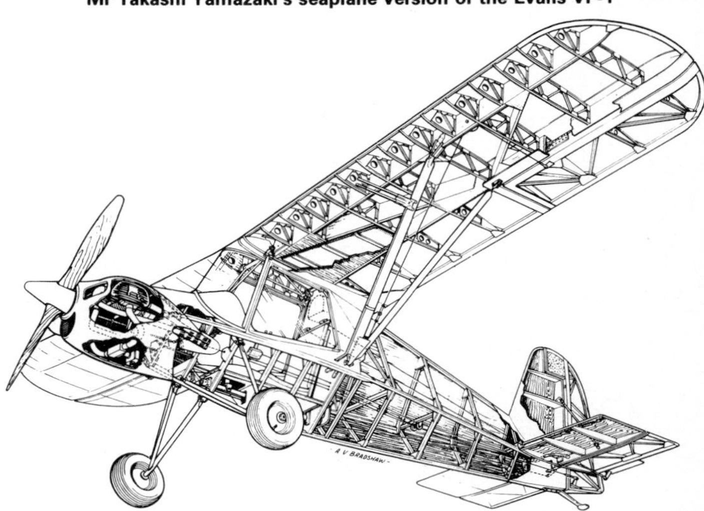

Cutaway drawing of Ganagobie 05 *(A. V. Bradshaw)*

Increased capacity fuel tank of glassfibre version in wing leading-edge.

ACCOMMODATION: Single seat in enclosed cabin formed from flat panels of Plexiglas sheet.

DIMENSIONS, EXTERNAL:

Wing span	7·19 m (23 ft 7¼ in)
Wing chord, constant	1·00 m (3 ft 3¼ in)
Wing area, gross	7·10 m² (76·4 sq ft)
Length overall	4·88 m (16 ft 0 in)
Height overall	1·40 m (4 ft 7¼ in)

WEIGHTS (A: prototype, B: 18·6 kW; 25 hp engine, C: 37·25 kW; 50 hp engine):

Weight empty: A	130 kg (286 lb)
B	154 kg (340 lb)
C	177 kg (390 lb)
Max T-O weight: A	250 kg (551 lb)
B	272 kg (600 lb)
C	295 kg (650 lb)

PERFORMANCE (A: prototype, B: 18·6 kW; 25 hp engine, C: 37·25 kW; 50 hp engine):

Max level speed: A	89 knots (165 km/h; 103 mph)
B	73 knots (135 km/h; 84 mph)
C	108 knots (200 km/h; 124 mph)
Cruising speed: A	65 knots (120 km/h; 75 mph)
B	59 knots (109 km/h; 68 mph)
C	97 knots (180 km/h; 112 mph)
Stalling speed: A	36 knots (66 km/h; 41 mph)
B	32 knots (60 km/h; 37 mph)
C	36 knots (66 km/h; 41 mph)
Max rate of climb at S/L: A	120 m (394 ft)/min
B	78 m (255 ft)/min
C	240 m (785 ft)/min
Service ceiling: A	2,500 m (8,200 ft)
B	2,100 m (6,900 ft)
C	3,960 m (13,000 ft)
T-O run: A	100 m (328 ft)
Landing run: A	50 m (164 ft)
Range: A	215 nm (400 km; 248 miles)
B	269 nm (499 km; 310 miles)
C	538 nm (998 km; 620 miles)

JANOWSKI J-2 POLONEZ

Mr Janowski designed in 1971 an amateur-built single-seat aircraft known as the J-2 Polonez. This is smaller than the J-1, but is of generally similar configuration except for its mid-mounted wings and a T tail. A prototype flew for the first time on 22 August 1977.

TYPE: Single-seat ultra-light aircraft.

WINGS: Cantilever mid-wing monoplane. Wing section NACA 23012. Constant-chord wings. All-wood single-spar structure. Leading-edge plywood-covered, rest of wing fabric-covered. Fabric-covered ailerons. No tabs.

FUSELAGE: Pod and boom type. Enclosed cabin faired into front fuselage. Wooden single-boom structure supporting tail unit.

TAIL UNIT: Cantilever wooden structure, with T tailplane. Fin plywood-covered; remainder fabric-covered. Sweptback vertical surfaces and constant-chord non-swept horizontal surfaces. Tab in trailing-edge of horizontal surfaces, plus two mass balance arms projecting forward of leading-edge.

LANDING GEAR: Non-retractable single main wheel, with tyre size 350-135, and tailwheel.

POWER PLANT: One 22·5 kW (30 hp) Trabant aircooled two-stroke two-cylinder motor car engine, mounted at top of fuselage aft of cabin and driving a two-blade fixed-pitch wooden pusher propeller. The aircraft may be fitted with any other suitable engine of 18·5-30 kW (25-40 hp).

DIMENSIONS, EXTERNAL:

Wing span	7·00 m (23 ft 0 in)
Wing chord, constant	1·06 m (3 ft 6 in)
Wing area, gross	7·00 m² (75·35 sq ft)
Length overall	4·84 m (15 ft 10½ in)
Height overall	1·35 m (4 ft 5¼ in)
Tailplane span	2·00 m (6 ft 6¾ in)
Propeller diameter	1·06 m (3 ft 6 in)

WEIGHTS:

Weight empty	105 kg (231 lb)
Normal T-O weight	235 kg (518 lb)

PERFORMANCE:

Max level speed	86 knots (160 km/h; 99 mph)
Cruising speed	65 knots (120 km/h; 74·5 mph)
Stalling speed	32·5 knots (60 km/h; 37·5 mph)
Max rate of climb at S/L	180 m (590 ft)/min
Endurance	3h

SOUTH AFRICA

CRUTCHLEY

S. CRUTCHLEY

PO Box 616, Plettenberg Bay 6600

CRUTCHLEY SPECIAL

The Crutchley Special was designed by Mr S. Crutchley as an easy-to-build all-metal aircraft that could be powered by a modified Volkswagen engine. Its angular shape reflected the fact that all work had to be carried out with hand tools. Design of the Special was started in June 1970 and construction began two months later. The first flight took place on 28 November 1975, and by early 1979 the Crutchley Special had completed 150 flying hours. Although no passenger had flown in the aircraft at that time (a stipulation of the permit to fly), the equivalent weight in sandbag ballast had been carried. The aircraft is designed to 6*g* limit load factor at maximum weight; but this was mainly to provide additional safety as it is intended to gain certification at 3·8*g* in the Normal category.

The details that follow include references to a number of refinements made to the aircraft during the past year. There is no intention at this stage of building any more Crutchley Specials. The hang glider project mentioned in the 1978-79 *Jane's* has been shelved due to Mr Crutchley's business commitments.

TYPE: Two-seat light monoplane.

WINGS: Cantilever low-wing monoplane. NACA 4415 wing section. No dihedral. Incidence 3°. Main spar fabricated as I-beam with flanges of B51S-TF extruded light alloy angle sections and web of 2024-T3 Alclad. Ribs and skins of Alclad. Rod-actuated plain ailerons, with B51S-TF spars and Alclad ribs and skins. Plain flaps of similar construction are now fixed in 'up' position.

FUSELAGE: Rectangular-section four-longeron box. B51S-TF extruded angle-sections, with formers and skins of 2024-T3 Alclad.

TAIL UNIT: Cantilever assembly, of similar construction to

ailerons. Glassfibre reinforced plastics tips fitted to tailplane and fin to improve appearance. New 2024-T3 Alclad dorsal fin fitted forward of fin to aid stability. Rudder cable-operated. Elevator actuated by pushrods. Fixed tab on elevator.

LANDING GEAR: Non-retractable tricycle type. Helical spring shock-absorbers in telescopic units of steel tube construction. German Continental go-kart steerable nosewheel, with tyre size 10 × 3·00-5, pressure 1·72 bars (25 lb/sq in). Swedish Varnamo industrial main wheels, each with tyre size 12 × 4·00-4, pressure 1·72 bars (25 lb/sq in). Aircooled Yamaha motorcycle drum brakes on main wheels and special disc brake for parking on nosewheel.

POWER PLANT: One 2,100 cc Volkswagen/Revmaster 2100S engine, developing 55 kW (74 hp) at 3,500 rpm and driving a Hegy wooden propeller of 0·97 m (3 ft 2 in) pitch. Fuel tank between instrument panel and firewall with capacity of 50 litres (11 Imp gallons). Refuelling point forward of windscreen on starboard side. Oil capacity 2·5 litres (0·55 Imp gallons). Engine fitted with Posa low-pressure injector carburettor.

ACCOMMODATION: Two seats side by side under rearward-hinged Perspex canopy, the inside roof of which has been sprayed with metallic-coated plastic film to reflect the Sun's heat. Ventilated by adjustable ram-air scoop.

SYSTEM: 12V 5Ah Yuasa motorcycle battery for radio and emergency electric fuel pump.

ELECTRONICS AND EQUIPMENT: Genave Alpha 10 transceiver.

DIMENSIONS, EXTERNAL:

Wing span	6·00 m (19 ft 8 in)
Wing chord, constant	1·32 m (4 ft 4 in)
Wing area, gross	7·90 m² (85 sq ft)
Wing aspect ratio	4·5
Length overall	5·64 m (18 ft 6 in)
Height overall	2·00 m (6 ft 7 in)
Tailplane span	2·20 m (7 ft 2½ in)
Wheel track	1·70 m (5 ft 7 in)
Wheelbase	1·12 m (3 ft 8 in)
Propeller diameter	1·52 m (5 ft 0 in)

DIMENSION, INTERNAL:

Cabin:	
Max width	1·02 m (3 ft 4 in)

WEIGHTS:

Weight empty	264 kg (581 lb)
Max T-O weight	450 kg (992 lb)

PERFORMANCE (at max T-O weight):

Never-exceed speed	113 knots (209 km/h; 130 mph)
Max level speed at 915 m (3,000 ft)	92 knots (171 km/h; 106 mph)
Max cruising speed at 915 m (3,000 ft)	78 knots (145 km/h; 90 mph)
Econ cruising speed at 915 m (3,000 ft)	73 knots (135 km/h; 84 mph)
Stalling speed	50·5 knots (94 km/h; 58 mph)
Max rate of climb at S/L	183 m (600 ft)/min
Service ceiling	3,660 m (12,000 ft)
T-O run	244 m (800 ft)
Landing run	274 m (900 ft)
Range with max fuel and max payload	269 nm (500 km; 310 miles)

C. H. J. VAN ASWEGEN

Box 88, Plettenberg Bay 6600

Details follow of a single-seat light aircraft named the Bergwind, designed by Mr van Aswegen. A second aircraft of his design was scheduled to fly by March 1979. No details are yet available, except that it is different from the Bergwind.

VAN ASWEGEN BERGWIND

Mr van Aswegen has designed and built a single-seat light aircraft named Bergwind. Design started in April 1976 and construction of the aircraft began in the following month. First flight was achieved on 17 April 1977. Bergwind plans will not be made available to amateur constructors.

TYPE: Single-seat light monoplane.

WINGS: Cantilever low-wing monoplane. Wing section NACA 2412. Dihedral 3°. Incidence 1° 30′. No sweepback. Constant chord. All-metal structure, with ribs, I-beam spar and skin of Alclad 2024-T3 aluminium alloy. Constant-chord ailerons of Alclad 2024-T3 light alloy. No flaps or tabs.

FUSELAGE: Conventional semi-monocoque structure of Alclad 2024-T3.

TAIL UNIT: Cantilever structure, of Alclad 2024-T3 light alloy. Slightly-sweptback fin and rudder. All-moving tailplane with ground-adjustable tab and spring bias trim.

LANDING GEAR: Non-retractable tricycle type. Oleo shock-absorber on fully-castoring nosewheel unit; cantilever spring steel rod main legs. Nosewheel tyre size 10 × 3·50-4, pressure 1·03 bars (15 lb/sq in). Main-wheel tyres size 12 × 5·00-4, pressure 1·15 bars (17 lb/sq in). Hydraulic drum-type brakes.

POWER PLANT: One 48·5 kW (65 hp) Lycoming O-145-B2 flat-four engine, driving a three-blade fixed-pitch wooden propeller of Van Aswegen manufacture. One fuel tank in fuselage, capacity 50 litres (11 Imp gallons). Refuelling point in front of windscreen. Oil capacity 5·7 litres (1·25 Imp gallons).

ACCOMMODATION: Single seat beneath sideways-opening (to starboard) canopy. Cockpit heated and ventilated. Baggage space aft of seat.

SYSTEM: 13·5V dry-cell storage battery for Genave Alpha 100 transceiver.

DIMENSIONS, EXTERNAL:

Wing span	6·25 m (20 ft 6 in)
Wing chord, constant	1·30 m (4 ft 3 in)
Wing area, gross	8·08 m² (87 sq ft)
Wing aspect ratio	4·8
Length overall	5·11 m (16 ft 9 in)
Tailplane span	2·13 m (7 ft 0 in)
Wheel track	1·63 m (5 ft 4 in)
Wheelbase	1·14 m (3 ft 9 in)
Propeller diameter	1·42 m (4 ft 8 in)

DIMENSIONS, INTERNAL:

Cabin: Length	1·40 m (4 ft 7 in)
Max width	0·56 m (1 ft 10 in)
Max height	0·91 m (3 ft 0 in)
Baggage hold volume	0·028 m² (1 cu ft)

WEIGHTS:

Weight empty	269 kg (594 lb)
Max T-O weight	390 kg (860 lb)

PERFORMANCE:

Never-exceed speed	126 knots (233 km/h; 145 mph)
Max level speed	100 knots (185 km/h; 115 mph)
Max cruising speed at 1,000 m (3,280 ft)	95·5 knots (177 km/h; 110 mph)
Econ cruising speed at 1,000 m (3,280 ft)	82·5 knots (152 km/h; 95 mph)
Stalling speed	45·5 knots (84 km/h; 52 mph)
Max rate of climb at S/L	183 m (600 ft)/min
Service ceiling	3,660 m (12,000 ft)
T-O and landing run	300 m (985 ft)
T-O to, and landing from, 15 m (50 ft)	700 m (2,295 ft)
Range with max fuel, 45 min reserves	260 nm (483 km; 300 miles)

SWEDEN

ANDREASSON
BJÖRN ANDREASSON

c/o Saab-Scania, Box 463, S-201 24, Malmö 1

Mr Andreasson has designed eleven different types of light aircraft. Of these, the BA-7 was built in series by AB Malmö Flygindustri as the MFI-9B Trainer/Militrainer and by MBB in Germany as the BO 208 C Junior (see 1970-71 *Jane's*).

An earlier design, the BA-4 biplane, was modernised by Mr Andreasson for members of the Swedish branch of the Experimental Aircraft Association, and a prototype was built by apprentices of the MFI apprentice school as part of their training programme. To distinguish it from the original BA-4, it is designated BA-4B.

Mr Andreasson's latest design is the BA-11.

ANDREASSON BA-4B

The prototype BA-4B, built by MFI apprentices, was of all-metal construction. The design provides for alternative all-wooden wings.

World manufacturing rights in the BA-4B are held by Mr P. J. C. Phillips of Down House, Cocking, Midhurst, Sussex, and the aircraft has been built in small numbers in the UK by Crosby Aviation Ltd (which see). Plans for homebuilders continue to be available from Mr Andreasson.

Two amateur-built BA-4Bs were flying in Sweden in 1978, with one more under construction.

TYPE: Single-seat fully-aerobatic light biplane.

WINGS: Braced biplane type, with a single streamline-section interplane strut each side. A streamline-section bracing strut runs from the bottom fuselage longeron on each side to the top of the interplane strut, and an N-type cabane structure supports the centre-section. Incidence, upper wing 3°, lower wings 4°. Stagger 20°. Dihedral, upper wing 2°, lower wings 4°. Alternative all-metal structure or all-wood structure, with solid spars, covered with heavy plywood skin. Pop-riveted ailerons, of simplified sheet metal construction, on lower wings only. No flaps. Provision for fitting detachable plastics wingtips.

FUSELAGE: Sheet metal structure, with external stringers, making extensive use of pop-riveting. Turtledeck either sheet metal or reinforced plastics.

TAIL UNIT: Cantilever structure of pop-riveted sheet metal construction.

LANDING GEAR: Non-retractable tailwheel type. Cantilever spring steel main legs. Main wheels size 5·00-4 or 5·00-5. Hydraulic brakes. Steerable tailwheel carried on leaf spring.

POWER PLANT: Prototype has 74·5 kW (100 hp) Rolls-Royce Continental O-200-A flat-four engine. Provision for other engines, including Volkswagen conversions. Standard fuel tank, capacity 50 litres (11 Imp gallons), forward of cockpit. Provision for carrying external 'bullet' tank of 50 litres (11 Imp gallons) capacity under fuselage.

ACCOMMODATION: Single seat in open cockpit.

ELECTRONICS AND EQUIPMENT: Provision for battery, VHF radio and IFR instrumentation.

DIMENSIONS, EXTERNAL:

Wing span:	
upper	5·34 m (17 ft 7 in)
lower	5·14 m (16 ft 11 in)
Wing chord (upper and lower, constant)	0·80 m (2 ft 7½ in)
Wing area, gross	8·3 m² (90 sq ft)
Wing aspect ratio (upper and lower)	6
Length overall	4·60 m (15 ft 0 in)
Tailplane span	2·00 m (6 ft 6¾ in)

WEIGHT:

Max T-O weight	375 kg (827 lb)

PERFORMANCE (prototype, at max T-O weight):

Max level speed	122 knots (225 km/h; 140 mph)
Max cruising speed	104 knots (193 km/h; 120 mph)
Min flying speed	35 knots (64 km/h; 40 mph)
Max rate of climb at S/L	610 m (2,000 ft)/min
T-O and landing run	less than 100 m (330 ft)
Range with standard fuel	152 nm (280 km; 175 miles)

ANDREASSON BA-11

The BA-11 is an all-metal biplane, intended for single-seat aerobatic, two-seat training or competition flying. It is designed generally to FAR Pt 23 Appendix A category A (Aerobatic) requirements, but has enhanced limiting load factors of +9 to −6*g* as a single-seater, and in excess of +6 to −3*g* as a two-seater.

TYPE: Two-seat training and competition biplane.

WINGS: Biplane type, braced with dual sets of streamlined tie-rods. Ailerons, of simplified pop-riveted sheet metal construction, on both upper and lower wings. Positive stagger.

FUSELAGE: Metal structure, with one-piece moulded glassfibre turtledeck.

TAIL UNIT: All-metal structure. Control surfaces of similar construction to ailerons.

LANDING GEAR: Non-retractable tailwheel type. Main legs consist of two steel leaf springs attached to bottom of fuselage. Size 5·50-5 main wheels, with hydraulic disc brakes. Tailwheel also uses leaf spring and is steerable.

POWER PLANT: Designed for one 149 kW (200 hp) Lycoming fuel-injection engine, driving a 1·88 m (6 ft 2 in) diameter Hartzell constant-speed propeller. Main fuel tank in upper front fuselage, capacity approx 60 litres (13 Imp gallons). Auxiliary fuel tank, capacity approx 50 litres (11 Imp gallons), in upper wing centre-section.

ACCOMMODATION: Two seats in tandem, each designed to accommodate a back-type parachute. Prototype has enclosed cockpits, but open cockpits are optional. Basic instrumentation only in forward cockpit. Instrument panel of rear cockpit is large enough to accommodate a limited IFR panel in addition to the normal engine instruments. Electrical equipment, including starter, alternator and battery, can be fitted.

DIMENSIONS, WEIGHTS AND PERFORMANCE:
No details received for publication

EKSTRÖM
STAFFAN W. EKSTRÖM

Tivedsvägen 1, S-181 64 Lidingö
Telephone: (08) 7663448

EKSTRÖM HUMLAN 2

Mr Ekström began the design of this single-seat autogyro in June 1971. Construction began in April 1972, and it flew for the first time in June 1973. Three more Humlans had been completed and flown in Sweden by Autumn 1978, with four more under construction.

The prototype (SE-HXE) was fitted initially with the standard tricycle landing gear, as described. It now has

Crutchley Special being flown by its designer/builder

van Aswegen Bergwind single-seat light aircraft

Andreasson BA-4B single-seat fully-aerobatic homebuilt biplane

Andreasson BA-11 tandem two-seat biplane *(Hans Strömberg)*

Berger BX-50A single-seat helicopter, with canopy open

Ekström Humlan 2 built by Mr Ingvar Arvidsson

twin floats, each weighing 16 kg (35 lb), as illustrated in the 1978-79 *Jane's*.

Type: Single-seat homebuilt autogyro.

Rotor System: Single two-blade semi-rigid rotor, attached to hub by a single bolt. Ztan Zee rotor blades. Rotor brake added 1975.

Rotor Drive: Flexible shaft for rotor spin-up only, via gearbox and two Vee-belts.

Fuselage: Cruciform chassis of 6061 T6 square-section aluminium tube, on which is mounted a pod-type nacelle.

Tail Unit: Conventional single fin and rudder, and fixed tailplane with dihedral, built of 0·4 mm and 0·8 mm aluminium sheet.

Landing Gear: Non-retractable tricycle type, with additional small wheel beneath tail. Rubber shock-absorption on tailwheel only. Go-kart wheels on main and nose units, tyre pressure 0·88 bars (12·8 lb/sq in). Nosewheel is steerable, self-centering, and is fitted with cycle-type brake.

Power Plant: One 67 kW (90 hp) McCulloch AF 100-X3 four-cylinder engine, driving a two-blade fixed-pitch pusher propeller. Fuel tank, capacity 32 litres (7 Imp gallons), behind pilot's seat. Fuel is a petrol/oil mixture, with 5% oil.

Accommodation: Single seat in open cockpit. One-piece curved windscreen. Shoulder harness fitted.

Dimensions, external (wheel landing gear):

Rotor diameter	6·80 m (22 ft 3¾ in)
Length overall	3·42 m (11 ft 2¾ in)
Height overall	1·98 m (6 ft 6 in)
Width over wheels	1·65 m (5 ft 5 in)
Propeller diameter	1·20 m (3 ft 11¼ in)

Weights (A: wheel landing gear, B: floats):

Weight empty:	
A	145 kg (320 lb)
B	182 kg (401 lb)
Normal max T-O weight:	
A	260 kg (573 lb)
B	285 kg (628 lb)
Max T-O weight:	
A	295 kg (650 lb)

Performance (A: wheel landing gear, B: floats, at 260 kg; 573 lb AUW):

Never-exceed speed	
A, B	97 knots (180 km/h; 111·5 mph)
Max cruising speed:	
A	81 knots (150 km/h; 93 mph)
B	65 knots (120 km/h; 74 mph)
Econ cruising speed:	
A	64·5 knots (120 km/h; 74·5 mph)
B	54-59 knots (100-110 km/h; 62-68 mph)
Max rate of climb at S/L:	
A	300 m (984 ft)/min
B	180 m (590 ft)/min
T-O run:	
A	60 m (197 ft)
B	200 m (656 ft)
T-O to 15 m (50 ft):	
A	100 m (328 ft)
B	400 m (1,312 ft)
Landing from 15 m (50 ft), zero wind:	
A	30 m (98 ft)
Landing run, zero wind:	
A	5 m (16 ft)
Max range, no reserves:	
A	97 nm (180 km; 112 miles)
B	75 nm (140 km; 87 miles)

SWITZERLAND

BERGER

BERGER-HELIKOPTER

CH-6573 Magadino TI

Telephone: (092) 64 21 71

Director: Hans Berger

Mr Berger has built and flown prototypes of two light helicopters, of which available details follow:

BERGER BX-50A

Type: Single-seat light helicopter.

Rotor System: Two-blade main rotor and two-blade tail rotor.

Fuselage: All-metal frame of tubular alloy construction. Lower cabin fairing and forward-sliding transparent half-canopy.

Tail Unit: Small ventral fin.

Landing Gear: Skid-type.

Power Plant: One 67 kW (90 hp) Continental C90 flat-four engine. Fuel in one or two tanks mounted aft of pilot.

Accommodation: Semi-enclosed cockpit for pilot only.

Dimensions, external:

Diameter of main rotor	8·00 m (26 ft 3 in)
Diameter of tail rotor	1·10 m (3 ft 7¼ in)

Weights:

Weight empty	290 kg (639 lb)
Max T-O weight	410 kg (904 lb)

Performance:

Never-exceed speed	75 knots (140 km/h; 87 mph)
Max cruising speed	65 knots (120 km/h; 75 mph)

BERGER BX-110

The BX-110 (HB-YAK) is a two-seat homebuilt light helicopter, powered by a Wankel rotating-piston engine. It flew for the first time on 3 June 1974, and has been awarded a permit for experimental flying by the Swiss Board of Aviation.

TYPE: Two-seat light helicopter.

ROTOR SYSTEM: Three-blade semi-rigid main rotor and two-blade tail rotor. Main rotor blades are of NACA 0012 section, and are foldable. Max pitch of main rotor 12°. Main and tail rotors of alloy construction. No rotor brake.

ROTOR DRIVE: By toothed belt, from specially designed gearbox. Main rotor/engine rpm ratio 0·09 : 1; tail rotor/engine rpm ratio 0·6 : 1.

FUSELAGE: All-metal frame, of square and circular tubular alloy construction. Large 'goldfish bowl' cabin, with framed transparencies.

TAIL UNIT: Half-tailplane on starboard side of tailboom, forward of tail rotor, with approx 45° dihedral.

LANDING GEAR: Original skid-type replaced later by non-retractable tricycle wheeled gear, with main-wheel brakes.

POWER PLANT: One 134 kW (180 hp) Wankel rotating-piston engine. Fuel in two saddle tanks aft of cabin, total capacity 108 litres (23·75 Imp gallons). Refuelling point on top of each tank. Oil capacities: engine 4 litres (0·9 Imp gallons); gearbox 4 litres (0·9 Imp gallons); tail rotor 0·2 litres (0·04 Imp gallons).

ACCOMMODATION: Side-by-side seats for pilot and one passenger in 'goldfish bowl' cabin.

ELECTRICAL SYSTEM: 12V battery.

DIMENSIONS, EXTERNAL:

Diameter of main rotor	7·40 m (24 ft 3¼ in)
Diameter of tail rotor	1·20 m (3 ft 11¼ in)
Distance between rotor centres	4·35 m (14 ft 3¼ in)
Length overall	6·40 m (21 ft 0 in)
Height to top of rotor hub	2·52 m (8 ft 3¼ in)
Wheel track	1·85 m (6 ft 0¾ in)

DIMENSIONS, INTERNAL:

Cabin: Length	1·30 m (4 ft 3¼ in)
Max width	1·25 m (4 ft 1¼ in)
Max height	1·28 m (4 ft 2½ in)

AREAS:

Main rotor disc	43·00 m² (462·85 sq ft)
Tail rotor disc	1·13 m² (12·16 sq ft)

WEIGHTS:

Weight empty	460 kg (1,014 lb)
Max T-O weight	720 kg (1,587 lb)

PERFORMANCE (at max T-O weight):

Never-exceed speed	91 knots (170 km/h; 105 mph)
Max cruising speed	86 knots (160 km/h; 99 mph)
Max rate of climb at S/L	240 m (787 ft)/min

BRÜGGER

MAX BRÜGGER

CH- 1724 Zénauva
Telephone: (037) 33 29 20

Brief details of the Brügger Colibri 1 single-seat ultra-light aircraft, which flew for the first time on 30 October 1965, were given in the 1967-68 and 1971-72 *Jane's*.

More recent designs are the Colibri 2 and MB-3, of which details follow:

BRÜGGER MB-2 COLIBRI 2

Mr Brügger began design of the Colibri 2 in January 1966. Construction was started a year later, and the first of two prototypes flew for the first time on 1 May 1970. Plans are available to amateur constructors, and about 140 Colibri 2s were under construction or flying in Europe by early 1979.

TYPE: Single-seat light aircraft.

WINGS: Cantilever low-wing monoplane. Wing section NACA 23012. Dihedral from roots. Two-spar constant-chord wings. Wings and ailerons built of spruce with fabric covering. No flaps or tabs.

FUSELAGE: Plywood-covered wooden structure.

TAIL UNIT: Cantilever all-wood structure. Rudder only: no fin. All-moving horizontal surfaces, with Flettner-type elevators.

LANDING GEAR: Non-retractable tailwheel type, with coil spring shock-absorption on main units. Main wheels size 400 × 100, with streamline fairings. Tailwheel mounted on leaf spring. Mechanically-operated disc brakes.

POWER PLANT: One 30 kW (40 hp) 1,600 cc Volkswagen engine (Brügger modification), driving a Brügger two-blade fixed-pitch wooden propeller with plastics-coated blades. Fuel in single fuselage tank, capacity 33 litres (7·25 Imp gallons). Oil capacity 2·5 litres (0·55 Imp gallons).

ACCOMMODATION: Single seat under one-piece moulded transparent canopy, with quarter-lights to rear.

DIMENSIONS, EXTERNAL:

Wing span	6·00 m (19 ft 8¼ in)
Wing chord, constant	1·40 m (4 ft 7 in)
Wing area, gross	8·20 m² (88·25 sq ft)
Length overall	4·80 m (15 ft 9 in)
Height overall	1·60 m (5 ft 3 in)
Tailplane span	2·00 m (6 ft 6¾ in)
Wheel track	1·80 m (5 ft 11 in)
Propeller diameter	1·38 m (4 ft 6⅓ in)

WEIGHTS:

Weight empty	215 kg (474 lb)
Max T-O and landing weight	330 kg (727 lb)

PERFORMANCE (at max T-O weight):

Max speed at 1,000 m (3,280 ft)	97 knots (180 km/h; 111 mph)
Econ cruising speed (70% power) at 1,000 m (3,280 ft)	86 knots (160 km/h; 99 mph)
Stalling speed	32·5 knots (60 km/h; 37·5 mph)
Max rate of climb at S/L	180 m (590 ft)/min
Service ceiling	4,500 m (14,760 ft)
T-O and landing run	200 m (656 ft)
Range with max fuel	270 nm (500 km; 310 miles)

BRÜGGER MB-3

Design of this single-seat all-metal light aircraft (HB-YBB) was started in July 1974. Construction took from February 1975 until December 1976, and it flew for the first time on 19 March 1977. Plans are not available.

Among outstanding features are that the aircraft can be made ready for flight after transportation, or dismantled for transportation after flight, in only three minutes. It can be towed on its own wheels behind a small car.

Major differences by comparison with the all-wood Colibri are the MB-3's pop-riveted metal airframe; dismountable tail surfaces with anti-tabs; and 33·5 kW (45 hp) 1,600 cc Volkswagen engine, driving a two-blade fixed-pitch wooden propeller of Mr Brügger's own manufacture. The single fuselage fuel tank has a capacity of 46 litres (10 Imp gallons). Oil capacity is unchanged at 2·5 litres (0·55 Imp gallons).

DIMENSIONS, EXTERNAL:

Wing span	6·00 m (19 ft 8¼ in)
Wing area, gross	7·20 m² (77·5 sq ft)
Length overall	5·00 m (16 ft 4¾ in)
Height overall	1·56 m (5 ft 1½ in)
Tailplane span	1·91 m (6 ft 3¼ in)
Wheel track	1·57 m (5 ft 2 in)
Propeller diameter	1·36 m (4 ft 5½ in)

WEIGHTS:

Weight empty	236 kg (520 lb)
Max T-O weight	360 kg (793 lb)

PERFORMANCE (at max T-O weight):

Max level speed	108 knots (200 km/h; 124 mph)
Max cruising speed	97 knots (180 km/h; 112 mph)
Stalling speed	38 knots (70 km/h; 43·5 mph)
Max rate of climb at S/L	240 m (785 ft)/min
Service ceiling	4,000 m (13,125 ft)
T-O run	220 m (722 ft)
Landing run	250 m (820 ft)
Range with max fuel	432 nm (800 km; 497 miles)

GUEX

JEAN-CLAUDE GUEX

La Pierre-d'Yvonand, CH-1482 Bollion, Fribourg
Telephone: (024) 21 33 12

REKCUB

First flown in the Autumn of 1976, the Rekcub (HB-YAZ) is a diminutive all-metal single-seat homebuilt biplane of angular appearance. Its square-tipped wings are supported by N-type cabane struts and a single interplane strut each side. There are ailerons on only the lower wings. The wings are unswept, with dihedral on the lower planes only. Wing sections are NACA 4415 (upper wing) and NACA 2315 (lower wings). Other features include a conventional unswept cantilever tail unit, open cockpit and non-retractable tailwheel landing gear with curved cantilever main-wheel units.

Power plant of the Rekcub is a Porsche 1,600 cc air-cooled engine, driving a two-blade wooden fixed-pitch propeller through five belts and a reduction gear of 1:2¼ ratio. This produces a maximum propeller rpm of 1,750 and, in conjunction with a special exhaust system, makes the Rekcub quiet to operate. However, the engine does not allow aerobatics. Fuel capacity is 48 litres (10·5 Imp gallons).

DIMENSIONS:

Wing span	5·00 m (16 ft 4¾ in)
Wing area, gross	8·00 m² (86·1 sq ft)
Length overall	4·60 m (15 ft 1 in)
Height overall (approx)	1·70 m (5 ft 7 in)

WEIGHTS:

Weight empty	255 kg (562 lb)
Baggage	10 kg (22 lb)
Max T-O weight	380 kg (838 lb)

PERFORMANCE:

Max level speed	121 knots (225 km/h; 140 mph)
Cruising speed (75% power)	83 knots (153 km/h; 95 mph)
Stalling speed	48 knots (89 km/h; 55 mph)
Max rate of climb at 500 m (1,640 ft)	244 m (800 ft)/min
Max range	215 nm (400 km; 248 miles)

NEUKOM

ALBERT NEUKOM SEGELFLUGZEUGBAU

Flugplatz Schmerlat, CH-8213 Neuenkirch

Mr Albert Neukom, constructor of the Elfe series and AN-66C sailplanes (see Sailplanes section of this edition), has designed and built a single-seat sporting aircraft (HB-YAX). First flight was made on 9 September 1976, with Mr Neukom at the controls. Performance proved disappointing with the 31 kW (42 hp) converted Volkswagen motor car engine then installed, and this has since been replaced by a Continental engine, as described:

NEUKOM AN-100

TYPE: Single-seat light sporting monoplane.

WINGS: Cantilever low-wing monoplane. Eppler 441 section. GFK spar, four plywood ribs, and GFK sandwich skin. Plain trailing-edge flaps.

FUSELAGE: Conventional semi-monocoque structure of plywood frames and fir stringers, covered with laminated okoumé plywood and glassfibre.

TAIL UNIT: Cantilever structure of wood and glassfibre. Fin integral with fuselage. Narrow chord rudder. All-moving tailplane.

LANDING GEAR: Non-retractable tailwheel type. Cantilever spring steel main legs. Fairings over main wheels. Brakes on main wheels.

POWER PLANT: One 48·5 kW (65 hp) Continental A65-12F flat-four engine, driving a two-blade wooden propeller. Close cowling over engine. Fuel capacity 72 litres (15·75 Imp gallons), in wing and fuselage tanks.

ACCOMMODATION: Single-seat under rearward-hinging transparent canopy.

DIMENSIONS, EXTERNAL:

Wing span	7·80 m (25 ft 7 in)
Wing area	7·20 m² (77·5 sq ft)
Wing aspect ratio	8·2
Length overall	6·10 m (20 ft 0 in)
Height overall	1·50 m (4 ft 11 in)

WEIGHTS:

Weight empty	280 kg (617 lb)
Max T-O weight	420 kg (926 lb)

PERFORMANCE:

Max level speed	140 knots (260 km/h; 162 mph)
Max cruising speed	119 knots (220 km/h; 137 mph)
Approach speed	65-70 knots (120-130 km/h; 75-81 mph)
Stalling speed	49 knots (90 km/h; 56 mph)
Max rate of climb at S/L	240-300 m (785-985 ft)/min
T-O run	250 m (820 ft)
Range with max fuel	431 nm (800 km; 497 miles)

UNITED KINGDOM

CLUTTON-TABENOR

ERIC CLUTTON

92 Newlands Street, Shelton, Stoke-on-Trent, Staffordshire ST4 2RF

CLUTTON-TABENOR FRED SERIES 2

FRED (Flying Runabout Experimental Design) was designed as a powered aircraft that could be flown by any reasonably experienced glider pilot without further training. Other aims were that it should be able to operate from small, rough fields and be roadable.

First flight was made on 3 November 1963, with a 20 kW (27 hp) 500 cc Triumph 5T motorcycle engine; this

Berger BX-110 two-seat helicopter

Brügger MB-2 Colibri 2 single-seat light aircraft built in Sweden by Mr L. E. Karlsson *(Kjell Franzen)*

Prototype of the all-metal Brügger MB-3 *(Roland Eichenberger)*

Rekcub all-metal single-seat biplane *(Roland Eichenberger)*

Neukom AN-100 light sporting monoplane *(Roland Eichenberger)*

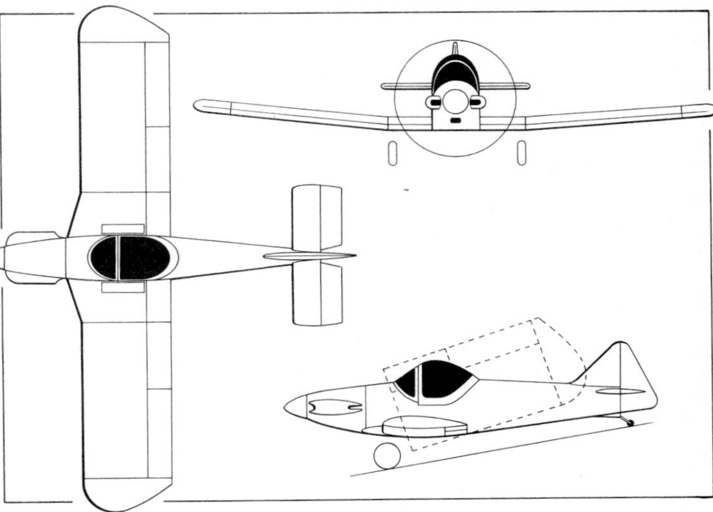

E.C.2 Easy Too, designed by Eric Clutton *(Michael A. Badrocke)*

First 'plans-built' FRED Series 2, constructed by Mr Richard Yates

was replaced later by a Scott A2S engine, and later still (1966) by a converted American-built Lawrance radial engine from an APU.

Another change made after the first flights was replacement of the original bungee-in-tension landing gear shock-absorbers by steel springs.

During 1968 the Lawrance engine was replaced by a 49 kW (66 hp) Volkswagen 1,500 cc engine, modified by the provision of a toothed belt to drive the propeller at half engine speed. Early in 1970 it was running with a reduction ratio of 2 : 1, driving a 1·73 m (5 ft 8 in) American-style propeller. Ignition was by two Lucas SR4 magnetos, chain-driven from the clutch end of the crankshaft. Since then, FRED has again been re-engined, with a Franklin, as described below, although it flies well with a converted Volkswagen.

FRED is described by its builders as being virtually unstallable with power on or off. Wings can be folded by one person unaided, and the tail unit is quickly detachable for easy transportation. Folded and tail-less width of FRED is 1·22 m (4 ft).

Plans for FRED have been available to amateur constructors since February 1970. Approximately 140 sets had been sold by early 1979, when four aircraft were flying, including one in New Zealand. At least two are powered by direct-drive 1,500 cc Volkswagen engines.

The FRED Series 2 illustrated was built by Mr Richard Yates in nine months. The rudder shape has been modified, and this restyling is now available on the plans. First flight was made in November 1976. Powered by a 1,600 cc Volkswagen engine, Mr Yates' FRED has a cruising speed of 61·5 knots (114 km/h; 71mph) at 2,900 rpm and can take off to 61 m (200 ft) in 274 m (900 ft). Maximum nose-up attitude, power off, gives 35 knots (64 km/h; 40 mph) with no stall.

TYPE: Single-seat light aircraft.

WINGS: Wire-braced parasol monoplane. Wing section Göttingen 535. Thickness/chord ratio 17·2%. No dihedral or incidence. 1° washout on tips. Spruce and plywood structure, with torsion-box leading-edge, auxiliary rear spar and drag spar, fabric-covered. Non-differential ailerons. No flaps or trim tabs.

FUSELAGE: Spruce longerons. Plywood covered to rear of cockpit, except for aluminium top decking. Fabric covering on rear fuselage, except for plywood top decking, front portion of which is removable for access to baggage locker.

TAIL UNIT: Cantilever structure of spruce and plywood. No fixed fin. Tailplane incidence adjustable on ground. Pushrod-operated elevators. No tabs.

LANDING GEAR: Non-retractable main wheels and tailskid. Main units sprung with motorcycle rear suspension springs. Industrial truck wheels. Tyre pressure 1·79 bars (26 lb/sq in). No brakes.

POWER PLANT: One 37·25 kW (50 hp) Franklin 4AC-150 engine in prototype, giving performance roughly equivalent to a geared 1,600 cc Volkswagen modified motor car engine, driving a two-blade fixed-pitch propeller. Single fuel tank in centre-section, capacity 34 litres (7·5 Imp gallons). Provision for second centre-section tank. Oil capacity 3·5 litres (0·75 Imp gallons).

ACCOMMODATION: Single seat in open cockpit.

DIMENSIONS, EXTERNAL:

Wing span	6·86 m (22 ft 6 in)
Wing chord, constant	1·52 m (5 ft 0 in)
Wing area, gross	10·22 m² (110 sq ft)
Wing aspect ratio	4·4
Length overall	5·18 m (17 ft 0 in)
Height overall	1·83 m (6 ft 0 in)
Tailplane span	2·74 m (9 ft 0 in)
Wheel track	1·22 m (4 ft 0 in)
Wheelbase	3·20 m (10 ft 6 in)
Propeller diameter	1·83 m (6 ft 0 in)

WEIGHTS:

Weight empty	242 kg (533 lb)
Max T-O weight	350 kg (773 lb)

PERFORMANCE (at max T-O weight):

Max cruising speed	70 knots (130 km/h; 81 mph)
Econ cruising speed	55 knots (101 km/h; 63 mph)
Approach speed	40-45 knots (74-84 km/h; 46-52 mph)
Stalling speed	approx 35 knots (63 km/h; 40 mph)
Range with max fuel	173 nm (320 km; 200 miles)

CLUTTON-TABENOR E.C.2 EASY TOO

The Easy Too design was started in 1969 to utilise a geared Volkswagen power plant developed by Mr Clutton and Mr Tabenor. It is a single-seat all-wooden folding-wing aircraft, plywood-covered with a polyester resin finish, and is stressed for aerobatics. A full centre-section flap is fitted.

Completion of the prototype was delayed by other work, and in 1976-77 the Easy Too underwent some redesign, to enable it to qualify as an entrant for a PFA competition, on the lines of the Light Aeroplane Competitions organised at Lympne in the 1920s. By early 1978, only the wing outer panels were awaiting assembly; but completion has been delayed by repair work on FRED after a heavy landing, and by continued propeller research.

The general appearance of the redesigned Easy Too can be seen in the accompanying three-view drawing. The prototype has a direct-drive 1,600 cc Volkswagen engine, but the aircraft is equally suited to 1,500 cc or larger-bore Volkswagen engines. Fuel capacity is 41 litres (9 Imp gallons).

The decision to use a direct-drive 1,600 cc VW engine meant that the engine mounting had to be lengthened by comparison with the original design (see 1976-77 *Jane's*), altering the aircraft's appearance considerably. The new engine drives a four-blade propeller. A further design change has been the adoption of a mechanically-retractable landing gear in place of the original fixed and trousered type.

The outer wing panels can be folded back by one person, by withdrawing pins and replacing them by an irreversible screwjack arrangement which locks them in position. The ailerons and flaps are coupled automatically. The folding hinge and support are entirely separate from the flying fittings, and the aeroplane can be towed on the road behind a motor car. The wingtips, of glassfibre, are of similar type and size to those fitted to the Druine Turbulent and the Taylor Monoplane. A one-piece sliding cockpit canopy is fitted. It is intended to make plans of the aircraft available after the conclusion of flight testing.

DIMENSIONS, EXTERNAL:
- Wing span: 7·11 m (23 ft 4 in)
- Length overall: 5·08 m (16 ft 8 in)
- Height overall: 1·37 m (4 ft 6 in)

WEIGHTS (estimated):
- Weight empty: 254 kg (560 lb)
- Max T-O weight: 363 kg (800 lb)

PERFORMANCE (estimated):
- Normal cruising speed: 100 knots (185 km/h; 115 mph)
- Range with max fuel: 347 nm (644 km; 400 miles)

COATES

J. R. COATES

The Spinney, Breachwood Green, Hitchin, Hertfordshire SG4 8PL

Mr Coates designed and built a two-seat light aircraft known as the S.A.II Swalesong, which was described fully in the 1975-76 *Jane's*. Drawings for amateur construction are not available, but a simplified version, the S.A.III, is under development and will be suitable for homebuilding.

COATES S.A.III SWALESONG

This aircraft (G-BAAH) is a development of the S.A.II, and the best features of that aircraft have been maintained. Changes include a fuselage of more rounded form, a simplified wing of constant chord, and a vertical tail unit of reduced height. All control surfaces are mass and aerodynamically balanced.

The prototype S.A.III is being built in all-wood form. Following flight development, some parts may be changed to metal or structural foam, the latter being preferred as it enables weight reductions to be achieved and allows engines like the Volkswagen to be considered as adequate power sources.

First flight is expected to take place in late 1979 or early 1980.

TYPE: Two-seat light aircraft.

WINGS: Cantilever low-wing monoplane. Wing section NACA 63415. Dihedral 4°. Incidence 1° 30′. All-wood (spruce) structure with plywood covering, built in three pieces. All-wood slotted ailerons. Slotted all-wood flaps.

FUSELAGE: Semi-monocoque spruce structure with plywood covering.

TAIL UNIT: Cantilever structure, with sweptback vertical surfaces. Tailplane incidence adjustable on ground. One-piece fabric-covered wooden elevator, with tab.

LANDING GEAR: Non-retractable tricycle type. Cantilever light alloy main legs. Steerable nosewheel, with motor car shock-absorber and glassfibre fairing. Size 5·00-5 tyres on main wheels; 130-1300 tyre on nosewheel. Disc brakes.

POWER PLANT: One 63·4-80·5 kW (85-108 hp) Continental or Lycoming flat-four engine, driving a fixed-pitch wooden propeller. Fuel capacity 72·7 litres (16 Imp gallons).

ACCOMMODATION: Two seats side by side in enclosed cockpit, with sliding one-piece hood. Baggage space aft of seats. Cockpit heated and ventilated.

DIMENSIONS, EXTERNAL:
- Wing span: 7·62 m (25 ft 0 in)
- Wing chord, constant: 1·37 m (4 ft 6 in)
- Wing area, gross: 10·41 m² (112 sq ft)
- Wing aspect ratio: 5·6
- Length overall: 5·64 m (18 ft 6 in)
- Width, wings folded: 1·73 m (5 ft 8 in)
- Height overall: 2·08 m (6 ft 10 in)
- Tailplane span: 2·44 m (8 ft 0 in)
- Wheel track: 1·68 m (5 ft 6 in)
- Wheelbase: 1·30 m (4 ft 3 in)
- Propeller diameter: 1·63 m (5 ft 4 in)

DIMENSION, INTERNAL:
- Cockpit: Max width: 1·07 m (3 ft 6 in)

WEIGHTS:
- Weight empty: 317 kg (700 lb)
- Max T-O and landing weight: 544 kg (1,200 lb)

PERFORMANCE (estimated):
- Never-exceed speed at 305 m (1,000 ft): 165 knots (305 km/h; 190 mph)
- Max level speed at 305 m (1,000 ft): 130 knots (241 km/h; 150 mph)
- Max cruising speed at 305 m (1,000 ft): 113 knots (209 km/h; 130 mph)
- Econ cruising speed at 305 m (1,000 ft): 95·5 knots (177 km/h; 110 mph)
- Stalling speed, flaps down: 44 knots (81 km/h; 50 mph)
- Max rate of climb at S/L: 260 m (850 ft)/min

CROSBY

CROSBY AVIATION LTD

Archery House, Leycester Road, Knutsford, Cheshire
Telephone: 0565 4254

DIRECTORS:
John Crosby
P. J. C. Phillips

CROSBY (ANDREASSON) BA-4B

The Andreasson BA-4B single-seat biplane, described in the Swedish section, is available in the UK from Crosby Aviation. Mr P. J. C. Phillips holds the world rights for commercially-manufactured examples of this aircraft, and has vested these rights in Crosby Aviation, of which he is a director. Crosby markets plans and kits for amateur constructors wishing to build their own aircraft, and approximately 50 sets of plans had been sold by early 1979. Plans (only) can also be obtained from the BA-4B's Swedish designer, Mr Björn Andreasson.

Five versions are available from Crosby Aviation; examples of three of these had flown by 1979:

BA-4B. Basic model with 74·5 kW (100 hp) Rolls-Royce Continental O-200-A flat-four engine. Standard fuel capacity 56·3 litres (12·4 Imp gallons). Provision for carrying an external 'bullet' tank of 50 litres (11 Imp gallons) capacity.

Super BA-4B. Structurally identical to BA-4B, but powered by a 97 kW (130 hp) Rolls-Royce Continental O-240-A flat-four engine. The Super BA-4B is able to tow a modern two-seat sailplane to 610 m (2,000 ft) in 4½ minutes.

Super BA-4B Srs 2. Identical to Super BA-4B except for having modified fuel and oil systems for inverted flight; full IFR equipment, including VOR; and an enclosed cockpit.

Prototypes of the remaining variants were still under construction in 1979. One has a 119 kW (160 hp) Lycoming AEIO-320-D1A flat-four engine, on a dynafocal mounting, and Christen inverted fuel and oil systems. The other has a 112 kW (150 hp) Lycoming O-320 engine.

The description of the BA-4B given in the Swedish section applies also to the aircraft produced in the UK, except in the following details:

ELECTRONICS AND EQUIPMENT: Aircraft can be equipped with electric starter for engine, engine-driven alternator, battery, 360-channel VHF com radio, cabin heater, disc brakes, fully-castoring tailwheel, corrosion proofing and *g*-meter.

DIMENSIONS, EXTERNAL (A: BA-4B; B: Super BA-4B):
- Wing span: 5·64 m (18 ft 6 in)
- Wing area, gross: 8·36 m² (90 sq ft)
- Length overall:
  - A: 4·67 m (15 ft 4 in)
  - B: 4·72 m (15 ft 6 in)

WEIGHTS (A: BA-4B; B: Super BA-4B):
- Weight empty, basic:
  - A: 295 kg (650 lb)
  - B: 304 kg (670 lb)
- T-O weight, aerobatic: 451 kg (996 lb)
- Max T-O weight: 460 kg (1,014 lb)

PERFORMANCE (at max T-O weight. A: BA-4B; B: Super BA-4B):
- Never-exceed speed:
  - A, B: 161 knots (299 km/h; 186 mph)
- Max level speed at S/L:
  - A: 130 knots (241 km/h; 150 mph)
  - B: 139 knots (257 km/h; 160 mph)
- Max cruising speed, 75% power at 2,135 m (7,000 ft):
  - A: 117 knots (217 km/h; 135 mph)
  - B: 126 knots (233 km/h; 145 mph)
- Stalling speed, power off:
  - A,B: 51 knots (94 km/h; 58 mph)
- Stalling speed, power on:
  - A, B: 39 knots (73 km/h; 45 mph)
- Max rate of climb at S/L:
  - A: 366 m (1,200 ft)/min
  - B: 549 m (1,800 ft)/min
- Range, standard fuel, 75% power:
  - A: 282 nm (523 km; 325 miles)
  - B: 273 nm (507 km; 315 miles)
- Range, max optional fuel, 75% power:
  - A: 529 nm (981 km; 610 miles)
  - B: 521 nm (965 km; 600 miles)

HPA

HERTFORDSHIRE PEDAL AERONAUTS

26 Rose Walk, Marshalswick, St Albans, Hertfordshire

OFFICERS:
M. S. Pressnell, BSc, CEng, MRAeS (Chairman)
P. R. Sladden, BSc (Vice-Chairman)
R. E. Harris, BSc (Treasurer)
P. L. Jones, BSc, CEng, MRAeS (Hon Secretary)

The Hertfordshire Pedal Aeronauts group was formed in September 1965, mainly from engineers of the former Handley Page Ltd, to design and build a man-powered aircraft to compete for the Kremer prizes. With the aid of a grant from the Royal Aeronautical Society, construction of the group's first aircraft was completed in mid-1972. This aircraft (named Toucan, the pun being deliberate) made its first flight at Radlett on 23 December 1972. Its longest flight, of 640 m (2,100 ft), was made on 3 July 1973.

This original version was the largest man-powered aircraft then to have flown, and also the first two-man-powered aircraft to fly.

HPA TOUCAN Mk 2

This is a modified version of the Toucan Mk 1 (1974-75 *Jane's*), with a 4·88 m (16 ft 0 in) greater wing span, and remains the largest man-powered aircraft yet constructed. Early flight testing began in October and November 1975, the best flight being one of 261 m (855 ft). The aircraft was then damaged when an outrigger wheel struck the ground heavily during a landing, causing a torsional drag failure of the inboard section of the starboard wing. Repairs were put in hand during 1977, and flight trials were resumed in early 1978. The use of the group's workshop at Radlett airfield was terminated in September 1978, when the land was sold. Toucan Mk 2 was than transferred to the Shuttleworth Collection at Old Warden, where it is now on display to the public.

Full details of the Toucan Mk 2 can be found in the 1977-78 *Jane's*.

ISAACS

JOHN O. ISAACS

23 Linden Grove, Chandler's Ford, Hampshire SO5 1LE
Telephone: 042 15 60885

Mr Isaacs designed and built a single-seat light aircraft, the airframe of which is basically a 7/10th scale wooden version of that of the Hawker Fury fighter of the 1930s. Constructional drawings are available to amateur builders.

He has also designed and built an all-wood scaled-down version of the Supermarine Spitfire single-seat fighter of the Second World War.

ISAACS FURY II

Design of the Isaacs Fury was started in January 1961 and construction of the aircraft began in April 1961. It flew for the first time on 30 August 1963, powered by a 48·5 kW (65 hp) Walter Mikron engine (see 1965-66 *Jane's*).

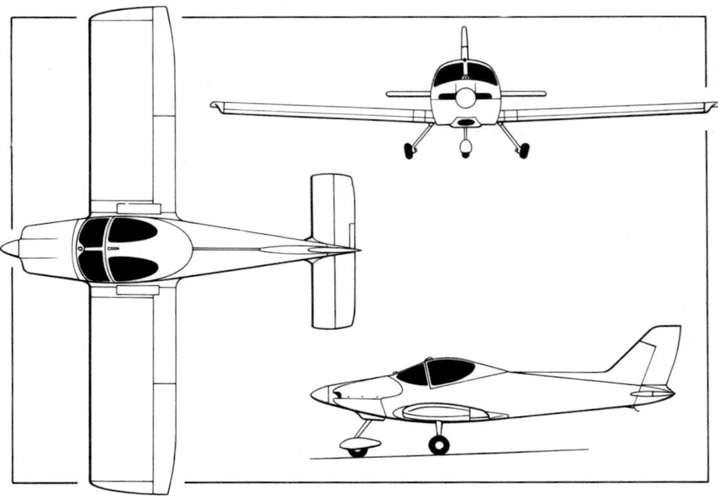

Coates S.A.III Swalesong *(Michael A. Badrocke)*

Crosby (Andreasson) BA-4B (Rolls-Royce Continental O-200-A engine)

HPA Toucan Mk 2 man-powered aircraft making its last flight at Radlett in September 1978

Prototype Isaacs Spitfire single-seat light sporting aircraft

Isaacs Fury built by John B. Bergeson of Mt Pleasant, Michigan

In 1966-67 Mr Isaacs modified the Fury prototype to Mk II standard, by re-stressing the airframe and installing a 93 kW (125 hp) Lycoming O-290 engine, and flew the aircraft in this form in the Summer of 1967. It was acquired subsequently by Mr W. Raper of Wrotham, Kent, who made further refinements, including the addition of blister fairings over the engine cylinders. It has since changed hands again, and is now based at Land's End airfield.

The aircraft illustrated (N37896) was built by Mr John B. Bergeson of Mount Pleasant, Michigan, and is owned by Mr Charles A. Whitmore of Ottawa, Illinois. This aircraft has an extra fuel tank in the wing centre-section, approx capacity 38 litres (8·3 Imp gallons).

Furies are under construction in the UK, New Zealand, Jersey, the USA, Canada and Finland. In addition to the prototype, one Fury is flying in the UK, one in New Zealand, one in Canada and two in the USA.

TYPE: Single-seat ultra-light biplane, stressed to 9*g* for aerobatics.

WINGS: Staggered biplane, with N type interplane strut each side and two N strut assemblies supporting centre-section of top wing above fuselage. Conventional wire bracing. Wing section RAF 28. Thickness/chord ratio 9·75%. Dihedral 1° on top wing, 3° 30′ on bottom wings. Incidence 3° 20′ on top wing, 3° 50′ on bottom wings. Spruce 'plank' spars and Warren girder ribs, with fabric covering. Fabric-covered spruce ailerons on top wing only. No flaps.

FUSELAGE: Spruce structure, covered with birch plywood.

TAIL UNIT: Strut-braced spruce structure of 'plank' spars and girder ribs, fabric-covered. Ground-adjustable tab in port elevator.

LANDING GEAR: Non-retractable type, with tailskid. Cross-axle tied to Vees with rubber-cord shock-absorption. Main wheels consist of WM.2 355 mm (14 in) rims spoked to home-made hubs. Dunlop tyre, size 3·25-14, pressure approx 2·28 bars (33 lb/sq in). Brakes optional.

POWER PLANT (prototype): One 93 kW (125 hp) Lycoming O-290 flat-four engine. Two-blade fixed-pitch propeller. Fuel tank in fuselage, aft of fireproof bulkhead, capacity 45·5 litres (10 Imp gallons) or 54·5 litres (12 Imp gallons).

ACCOMMODATION: Single seat in open cockpit. Small door above top longeron on port side opens downward. Space for light baggage aft of seat. Radio optional.

DIMENSIONS, EXTERNAL:

Wing span:	
upper	6·40 m (21 ft 0 in)
lower	5·54 m (18 ft 2 in)
Wing chord (both, constant)	1·07 m (3 ft 6 in)
Wing area (total)	11·50 m² (123·8 sq ft)
Wing aspect ratio (upper)	6
Length overall	5·87 m (19 ft 3 in)
Height over tail (flying attitude)	2·16 m (7 ft 1 in)
Tailplane span	2·13 m (7 ft 0 in)
Wheel track	1·27 m (4 ft 2 in)

WEIGHTS (93 kW; 125 hp Lycoming):

Weight empty	322 kg (710 lb)
Max permissible T-O weight	450 kg (1,000 lb)

PERFORMANCE (with uncowled 93kW; 125 hp engine):

Max level speed	100 knots (185 km/h; 115 mph)
Stalling speed	33 knots (61 km/h; 38 mph)
Max rate of climb at S/L	488 m (1,600 ft)/min

ISAACS SPITFIRE

Construction of this prototype 6/10-scale Spitfire (G-BBJI) began in the Summer of 1969, and it flew for the first time on 5 May 1975. The airframe is stressed to meet the aerobatic requirements of +9*g* and −4·5*g* (factored) as laid down in BCAR. Plans for the Isaacs Spitfire are available to homebuilders, and two sets had been sold by early 1979.

TYPE: Single-seat sporting aircraft.

WINGS: Cantilever low-wing monoplane of semi-elliptical planform. Wing section NACA 2200 series. Thickness/chord ratio 13·2% at root, 6% at tip. Dihedral 6°. Incidence 2° at root, −30′ at tip. Two-spar wing built in one piece, mainly of spruce, with birch plywood covering, except for ailerons which are fabric-covered.

FUSELAGE: Spruce structure, covered with birch plywood.

TAIL UNIT: Cantilever structure of plywood-covered spruce.

LANDING GEAR: Non-retractable tailwheel type on prototype. Cantilever main legs. Dunlop 5·00-5 tyres, wheels and hydraulic disc brakes.

POWER PLANT: One 74·5 kW (100 hp) Continental O-200 flat-four engine, or alternative engine in same category. Two-blade ground-adjustable Ratier metal propeller. Fuel tank in fuselage, aft of fireproof bulkhead, capacity 45·5 litres (10 Imp gallons).

ACCOMMODATION: Single seat under blister-type transparent canopy. Space for light baggage aft of seat.

DIMENSIONS, EXTERNAL:

Wing span	6·75 m (22 ft 1½ in)
Wing chord at root	1·52 m (5 ft 0 in)
Wing area, gross	8·08 m² (87 sq ft)
Length overall	5·88 m (19 ft 3 in)
Height overall	1·73 m (5 ft 8 in)
Tailplane span	1·92 m (6 ft 3½ in)
Wheel track	1·80 m (5 ft 11 in)

WEIGHTS:

Weight empty	366 kg (805 lb)
Max T-O weight	499 kg (1,100 lb)

PERFORMANCE (at max T-O weight):

Max level speed	130 knots (240 km/h; 150 mph)
Cruising speed	116 knots (215 km/h; 134 mph)
Stalling speed, 'clean'	45-47 knots (84-87 km/h; 52-54 mph)
Stalling speed, with optional fuselage airbrake extended	41 knots (76 km/h; 47 mph)
Max rate of climb at S/L	336 m (1,100 ft)/min

KNOWLES

GP CAPT A. S. KNOWLES

17 East Meads, Guildford, Surrey GU2 5SW

Telephone: 0483 4242

KNOWLES DUET

The Duet, known originally as the Minor III, is a version of the Luton L.A.4a Minor (see description under PFA heading in this section) with side-by-side seating for two persons, and was developed originally by Gp Capt A. S. Knowles in association with the former Phoenix Aircraft Ltd. Design began in 1968 and the prototype Duet (registration G-AYTT) flew for the first time on 22 June 1973. A special category C of A was granted on 24 June 1974.

During 1976 shaped wingtips were developed for the Duet, and flight testing with these began in early 1977. The new tips increased the wing span by 0·71 m (2 ft 4 in), and resulted in reduced stalling speed, increased rate of climb and improved gliding angle.

Final plans for the Duet, to allow home construction by amateurs, are being prepared and at least one other Duet is known to be under construction.

TYPE: Two-seat light aircraft.

WINGS: Strut-braced parasol monoplane. Fabric-covered

Knowles Duet, adapted from Luton Minor *(M. D. West)*

Replica de Havilland (Airco) D.H.2 fighter *(Leisure Sport)*

Replica Albatros D.Va fighter *(Leisure Sport)*

Replica SPAD XIII fighter *(Leisure Sport)*

wooden wings, braced with steel tube struts, as described for L.A.4a.

FUSELAGE: Wood- and fabric-covered wooden structure, as L.A.4a except for widened cockpit.

TAIL UNIT: Cantilever fabric-covered wooden structure, as L.A.4a. Plain tab on elevator.

LANDING GEAR: Non-retractable tailwheel type, as L.A.4a, with rubber-block shock-absorption. Mainwheel tyres size 6 in × 6 in, pressure 0·83 bars (12 lb/sq in). Goodyear caliper brakes. Solid tailwheel.

POWER PLANT: One 71 kW (95 hp) Continental C90 flat-four engine, driving a two-blade fixed-pitch propeller. Single fuel tank in upper forward fuselage, capacity 63·6 litres (14 Imp gallons). Refuelling point above tank. Oil capacity 4·5 litres (1 Imp gallon).

ACCOMMODATION: Side-by-side seats for two persons, with dual controls, in open cockpit under wing centre-section. Baggage locker aft of seats.

ELECTRONICS AND EQUIPMENT: Venturi-driven full blind-flying panel. Avionic Systems (Heathrow) Ltd 360-channel VHF radio.

DIMENSIONS, EXTERNAL:

Wing span with new tips	8·89 m (29 ft 2 in)
Wing chord, constant	1·60 m (5 ft 3 in)
Wing aspect ratio with new tips	5·37
Wing area, gross, with new tips	13·75 m² (148·0 sq ft)
Length overall	6·55 m (21 ft 6 in)
Height overall	2·01 m (6 ft 7 in)
Tailplane span	2·44 m (8 ft 0 in)
Wheel track	1·68 m (5 ft 6 in)
Wheelbase	4·50 m (14 ft 9 in)
Propeller diameter	1·75 m (5 ft 9 in)

DIMENSIONS, INTERNAL:

Cockpit: Max width	1·07 m (3 ft 6 in)
Baggage compartment volume	0·06 m³ (2·0 cu ft)

WEIGHTS:

Max payload	170 kg (375 lb)
Max T-O and landing weight	544 kg (1,200 lb)

PERFORMANCE (at max T-O weight):

Never-exceed speed	130 knots (240 km/h; 149 mph)
Max cruising speed at S/L	85 knots (157 km/h; 98 mph)
Econ cruising speed at S/L	70 knots (130 km/h; 81 mph)
Stalling speed	32 knots (60 km/h; 37 mph)
Max rate of climb at S/L	146 m (480 ft)/min
Service ceiling	2,440 m (8,000 ft)
T-O run	128 m (420 ft)
Landing run	110 m (360 ft)
Max range with 9·1 litres (2 Imp gallons) reserve fuel	185 nm (342 km; 213 miles)

LEISURE SPORT

LEISURE SPORT LTD (Member Company of the Ready Mixed Concrete Ltd Group)

Thorpe Park, Staines Lane, Chertsey, Surrey KT16 8PN
Telephone: 09328 62633

Since building and flying a full-size reproduction of the Supermarine S.5 Schneider Trophy seaplane of 1927 (see 1977-78 *Jane's*), Leisure Sport has completed and flown replicas of several first World War fighters, including two Sopwith Camel F.1s (one with 97 kW; 130 hp Clerget and one with 123 kW; 165 hp Warner Scarab engine), a Fokker Dr.I triplane (123 kW; 165 hp Warner Scarab engine), Fokker D.VII (149 kW, 200 hp Ranger engine), Albatros D.Va (149 kW; 200 hp Ranger engine), SPAD XIII (149 kW; 200 hp Lycoming engine) and de Havilland (Airco) D.H.2 (67 kW; 90 hp Pobjoy engine). A Sopwith 1½-Strutter (97 kW; 130 hp Clerget engine) and a Fokker D.VIII (123 kW; 165 hp Warner Scarab engine) were to be completed in 1979. Other aircraft to be built include the Macchi M.39 and Curtiss R3C-2 Schneider Trophy seaplanes of 1926 and 1925 respectively.

LIVESEY

DAVID M. LIVESEY

'Rawhiti', 12 Kenwood Drive, Burwood Park, Walton on Thames, Surrey KT12 5AU

There has been no recent news of the D.L.5 single-seat ultra-light aircraft, designed by Mr David Livesey. Details of the project can be found in the 1978-79 *Jane's.*

NIPPER

NIPPER KITS AND COMPONENTS LTD

1 Ridgeway Drive, Bromley, Kent BR1 5DG
Telephone: 01-857 7821

DIRECTORS:
D. P. L. Antill (Chairman)
A. F. Ayles
R. Marshall
A. S. Pearcey

Complete worldwide rights for the Nipper aircraft were purchased from Belgium in 1966, and the aircraft was marketed in both factory-built form and in the form of several stages of kits for amateur construction.

The former Nipper Aircraft Ltd went into receivership in May 1971. Prior to this Mr D. P. L. Antill, formerly Managing Director of Nipper Aircraft Ltd, acquired all rights in the Nipper aircraft, and on 20 October 1971 formed a new company, Nipper Kits and Components Ltd, to supply spares for existing aircraft and to encourage and support amateur construction of the Nipper. Plans and an advisory service for amateur constructors continue to be available.

Four Nipper kits were ordered in 1977. Construction of three of the aircraft was nearing completion in early 1979, and they were expected to fly that year.

NIPPER Mk III and IIIA

The Mk III Nipper is powered by a 1·5 litre Rollason Ardem engine; when fitted with the 1·6 litre Ardem engine it is known as the Mk IIIA. The Nipper may also be fitted with wingtip fuel tanks which almost double the standard fuel capacity. With these tanks fitted, but empty, the aircraft remains aerobatic. Flutter tests have been completed satisfactorily at speeds up to 156 knots (290 km/h; 180 mph).

TYPE: Single-seat ultra-light monoplane.

WINGS: Cantilever mid-wing monoplane. Modified NACA 43012A wing section. Dihedral 5° 30′. Incidence 2°. All-wood one-piece single-spar structure, with plywood-covered leading-edge and overall fabric covering. Wooden ailerons with fabric covering. No flaps. Portion of port wing-root trailing-edge is made of light alloy and hinged, with built-in foot-rest, so that it can be folded down to assist access to cockpit. Wing is quickly removable, to permit aircraft to be towed behind a motor car.

FUSELAGE: Welded steel tube structure. Underfuselage fairing of glassfibre. Rear fuselage fabric-covered.

TAIL UNIT: Braced tailplane and elevators of wood construction. No fin. Rudder of steel tube construction with fabric covering.

LANDING GEAR: Non-retractable tricycle type. Nieman transverse rubber-ring shock-absorbers. Steerable nosewheel. Continental tyres, size 4·00-4, pressure 1·79 bars (26 lb/sq in). Disc brakes.

POWER PLANT: Standard power plant is one 41 kW (55 hp) Rollason Ardem XI flat-four engine, driving a two-blade fixed-pitch wooden propeller with glassfibre spinner. More powerful versions of Ardem engine can be fitted optionally. Fuel tank between engine and cockpit, capacity 34 litres (7·5 Imp gallons). Provision for two 16·5 litre (3·6 Imp gallon) wingtip fuel tanks. Oil capacity 3·5 litres (0·77 Imp gallons).

ACCOMMODATION: Single seat under blown Perspex canopy which hinges sideways to starboard. Small baggage space aft of seat.

ELECTRONICS: Pye Bantam, Bayside BEI 990P and various other radio installations available.

DIMENSIONS, EXTERNAL:

Wing span (without tip-tanks)	6·00 m (19 ft 8 in)
Wing span (with tip-tanks)	6·25 m (20 ft 6 in)
Wing chord at c/l	1·40 m (4 ft 7¼ in)
Wing chord at tip	1·10 m (3 ft 7¼ in)
Wing area, gross	7·50 m² (80·70 sq ft)
Wing aspect ratio	4·8

Replica Fokker D.VII *(Leisure Sport)*

Replica Fokker Dr.I *(Leisure Sport)*

Replica Sopwith Camel F.1 (Warner Scarab engine) *(Leisure Sport)*

Nipper Mk III single-seat ultra-light aircraft

Ord-Hume GY-201 Minicab built at Niton, Isle of Wight, by Mr Barry Evans

Length overall 4·56 m (15 ft 0 in)
Height overall 1·91 m (6 ft 3 in)
Tailplane span 2·14 m (7 ft 0 in)
Wheel track 1·40 m (4 ft 7 in)
Wheelbase 1·13 m (3 ft 8 in)
WEIGHTS:
Weight empty 210 kg (465 lb)
Max T-O weight:
Aerobatic 310 kg (685 lb)
Normal 340 kg (750 lb)
PERFORMANCE (at max T-O weight):
Never-exceed speed 126 knots (235 km/h; 146 mph)
Max level speed at S/L:
without tip-tanks 93 knots (173 km/h; 107 mph)
with tip-tanks 83 knots (155 km/h; 96 mph)
Max cruising speed (75% power) at S/L:
without tip-tanks 81 knots (150 km/h; 93 mph)
Econ cruising speed at S/L
78 knots (145 km/h; 90 mph)
Stalling speed, power off 33 knots (61 km/h; 38 mph)
Max rate of climb at S/L 198 m (650 ft)/min
Service ceiling 3,660 m (12,000 ft)
T-O run 85 m (280 ft)
T-O to 15 m (50 ft) 338 m (1,110 ft)
Landing from 15 m (50 ft) 457 m (1,500 ft)
Landing run 110 m (360 ft)
Range with max internal fuel, 30 min reserves
173 nm (320 km; 200 miles)
Range with tip-tanks 390 nm (720 km; 450 miles)

ORD-HUME

ARTHUR W. J. G. ORD-HUME

14 Elmwood Road, Chiswick, London W4
Telephone: 01-994 3292

Mr Ord-Hume was a co-founder and (until 1962) a director of the former Phoenix Aircraft Ltd. During this time he was responsible for redesigning the pre-war Luton Minor and Luton Major aircraft. As an amateur aircraft constructor, he was one of the first in the UK to construct his own aircraft after the second World War and has since built or restored 11 aeroplanes.

ORD-HUME GY-201 MINICAB

The original two-seat GY-20 Minicab was designed in France by M Yves Gardan and flew for the first time in February 1949. A small number of production aircraft were built by Constructions Aéronautiques du Béarn (see 1956-57 *Jane's*). Mr Ord-Hume subsequently acquired original drawings for both the Minicab and its precursor, the Babyclub, and redesigned and redrafted the plans to make the aircraft suitable for amateur construction in the UK, United States and Australia. The resulting variant was first introduced in 1963, and amateur construction of the Ord-Hume GY-201 Minicab, for which Mr Ord-Hume holds the sole and exclusive rights, is approved in the USA, Canada, Australia, New Zealand, France, Germany and the UK. At least nine examples built to the English plans have flown in the UK and others are under construction. A large number are flying in the USA, and also in Australia, where the Minicab was one of the first aircraft of post-war design to gain DCA approval for amateur construction.

Owing to non-availability of Sitka spruce in Australia and New Zealand, aircraft built in that part of the world from local materials are unable to conform to the normal max T-O weight of 560 kg (1,235 lb). For these countries only, the design has been re-stressed for a max T-O weight of 635 kg (1,400 lb), for which weight a 74·5 kW (100 hp) Continental engine is mandatory.

The standard Ord-Hume GY-201 Minicab may be powered by engines of 48·5 to 89·5 kW (65 to 120 hp), although for practical operation at optimum weight 67 kW (90 hp) is strongly advised as a minimum.

TYPE: Two-seat light monoplane.

POWER PLANT: One 48·5 kW (65 hp) Continental flat-four engine; or one 67 kW (90 hp) (recommended minimum), 74·5 kW (100 hp) (Australian/New Zealand minimum), or 89·5 kW (120 hp) Continental engine. Standard fuel capacity 50 litres (11 Imp gallons) in fuselage tank aft of engine firewall. Provision for 23 litre (5 Imp gallon) internal slipper tank in baggage compartment.

ACCOMMODATION: Side-by-side seating for two persons under forward-hinged canopy. Space for 11 kg (25 lb) of baggage aft of seats. Dual controls optional.

DIMENSIONS, EXTERNAL:
Wing span 7·62 m (25 ft 0 in)
Wing area, gross 10·0 m² (107·6 sq ft)
Length overall 5·44 m (17 ft 10 in)
Height overall 1·65 m (5 ft 5 in)
WEIGHTS:
Weight empty 270 kg (595 lb)
Max T-O weight (except Australia and NZ)
560 kg (1,235 lb)
Max T-O weight (Australia and NZ only)
635 kg (1,400 lb)
*PERFORMANCE (at max T-O weight):
Max level speed at S/L, fixed-pitch propeller
108 knots (200 km/h; 124 mph)
Max level speed at S/L, 74·5 kW; 100 hp engine, fixed-pitch propeller 112 knots (208 km/h; 129 mph)
Cruising speed at S/L, fixed-pitch propeller
97 knots (180 km/h; 112 mph)
Stalling speed, flaps up 41 knots (76 km/h; 47 mph)
Max rate of climb at S/L 207 m (680 ft)/min
Max rate of climb at S/L, 74·5 kW (100 hp) engine
366 m (1,200 ft)/min
Service ceiling 4,000 m (13,100 ft)
Range with normal fuel capacity
404 nm (750 km; 466 miles)

**Minimum performance: a number of examples have demonstrated considerably more favourable speeds, and much depends on the engine/propeller combination used*

ORD-HUME O-H4B MINOR

The pre-war Luton Minor light aircraft was redesigned by Mr Ord-Hume for post-war use and was for many years marketed by the former Phoenix company, of which he was a director and co-founder. It is described under the 'PFA' heading in this edition.

A development of the Ord-Hume version of the L.A.4a Minor, known as the O-H4B Minor, was announced at the end of August 1975, and production drawings for this were first offered in 1976.

There has been no recent news of the project. Details can be found in the 1978-79 *Jane's*.

PFA
POPULAR FLYING ASSOCIATION

Terminal Building, Shoreham Airport, Shoreham-by-Sea, Sussex BN4 5FF
Telephone: 079 17 61616

Following the collapse of Phoenix Aircraft Ltd, the PFA assumed responsibility for marketing plans of the Luton L.A.4a Minor. Other types of which plans are obtainable from the Association include the Isaacs Fury, Evans VP-1 and Pazmany PL-4, described under their designers' names in this section of *Jane's*, and the Currie Wot and Druine Turbulent, described below with the L.A.4a Minor.

CURRIE WOT

This aircraft was designed originally by Mr J. R. Currie in 1937. Two examples were built at Lympne in that year, but were destroyed in a wartime bombing raid. Mr V. H. Bellamy took over the design after the war, at the Hampshire Aeroplane Club, and the first Wot built by members of this club (G-APNT) flew for the first time on 11 September 1958. The second example built at the club (G-APWT) was powered by a 45 kW (60 hp) Walter Mikron flat-four engine. Both aircraft were described in earlier editions of *Jane's*.

Further Wots have since been completed, including G-ARZW with a 48·5 kW (65 hp) Walter Mikron III engine, built by Dr J. H. B. Urmston.

Dr Urmston purchased all rights in the design from Mr Bellamy, and the following details refer to G-ARZW, built to standard plans, as obtainable from the PFA. Data on the versions with Aeronca-JAP and Mikron engines can be found in the 1961-62 *Jane's*.

TYPE: Single-seat fully-aerobatic light biplane.

WINGS: Braced biplane type, with two parallel interplane struts each side and N-type centre-section support struts. Wing section Clark Y. Dihedral (both wings) 3°. No incidence. Conventional spruce and plywood structure, with fabric covering. Fabric-covered ailerons on lower wings only. No flaps.

FUSELAGE: All-wood structure. Plywood-box construction, with overall fabric covering.

TAIL UNIT: Cantilever structure of spruce and plywood, with fabric covering. Fixed-incidence tailplane. Adjustable tab on rudder. Trim tab in port elevator.

LANDING GEAR: Non-retractable two-wheel type. Rubber-cord shock-absorption. Main wheels fitted with Dunlop tyres, size 400 × 8, pressure 1·24 bars (18 lb/sq in). No brakes.

POWER PLANT: One 48·5 kW (65 hp) Walter Mikron III flat-four engine, driving a two-blade fixed-pitch wooden propeller. Fuel tank aft of firewall, capacity 54·5 litres (12 Imp gallons). Oil capacity 7 litres (1·5 Imp gallons).

ACCOMMODATION: Single seat in open cockpit.

DIMENSIONS, EXTERNAL:
Wing span (both) 6·73 m (22 ft 1 in)
Wing chord (both), constant 1·07 m (3 ft 6 in)
Wing area, gross 13·0 m² (140 sq ft)
Wing aspect ratio 6·3
Length overall 5·58 m (18 ft 3½in)
Height overall 2·06 m (6 ft 9 in)
Wheel track 1·38 m (4 ft 6½ in)

WEIGHTS:
Weight empty 250 kg (550 lb)
Max T-O weight 408 kg (900 lb)

PERFORMANCE (at max T-O weight):
Never-exceed speed 112 knots (209 km/h; 130 mph)
Max level speed at 610 m (2,000 ft) 83 knots (153 km/h; 95 mph)
Max cruising speed at 610 m (2,000 ft) 78 knots (145 km/h; 90 mph)
Econ cruising speed at 610 m (2,000 ft)) 69 knots (129 km/h; 80 mph)
Stalling speed 35 knots (65 km/h; 40 mph)
Max rate of climb at S/L 183 m (600 ft)/min
Range with max fuel 208 nm (385 km; 240 miles)

DRUINE D31 TURBULENT

The following data apply to the D31 Turbulent as factory-built in the UK for many years by Rollason Aircraft and Engines Ltd. Rollason's version was generally similar to the standard Druine design. Main differences were that it had wheels of slightly greater size and a tailskid instead of a tailwheel, although a tailwheel was available optionally.

The fitting of optional wheel spats and a sliding canopy increases speed by about 7 knots (13 km/h; 8 mph).

TYPE: Single-seat ultra-light monoplane.

WINGS: Cantilever low-wing monoplane. Wing section NACA 23012. Dihedral 4°. Incidence 3° 40'. All-wood two-spar structure, covered with fabric. Built-in leading-edge slot on outer 45% of half-span. Wooden slotted ailerons with fabric covering. No flaps or tabs.

FUSELAGE: Conventional rectangular four-longeron wood structure with domed decking. Plywood-covered.

TAIL UNIT: Cantilever wooden structure. Fixed surfaces plywood-covered, movable surfaces fabric-covered. No tabs.

LANDING GEAR: Non-retractable tailwheel type (optional tailskid). Compression-spring shock-absorbers. Dunlop or Goodyear main wheels and tyres, size 14 × 3, pressure 1·95 bars (28 lb/sq in). Vespa mechanical brakes. Wheel spats, taxying and parking brakes optional. Skis or floats may be fitted as alternative to wheels.

POWER PLANT: One 33·5 kW (45 hp) Rollason Ardem 4CO2 Mk IV or 41 kW (55 hp) Ardem Mk V flat-four engine, driving a two-blade fixed-pitch wooden propeller. Fuel tank in fuselage forward of cockpit, capacity 39 litres (8·5 Imp gallons). Oil capacity 2·25 litres (0·5 Imp gallons).

ACCOMMODATION: Pilot only, in open cockpit (sliding canopy optional). Baggage locker aft of seat, capacity 11·5 kg (25 lb).

ELECTRONICS: Provision for lightweight radio.

DIMENSIONS, EXTERNAL:
Wing span 6·58 m (21 ft 7 in)
Wing chord, constant 1·90 m (3 ft 11 in)
Wing area, gross 7·20 m² (77·5 sq ft)
Wing aspect ratio 5·4
Length overall 5·33 m (17 ft 6 in)
Height overall 1·52 m (5 ft 0 in)
Tailplane span 1·98 m (6 ft 6 in)
Wheel track 1·73 m (5 ft 8 in)
Wheel/tailskid base 3·81 m (12 ft 6 in)

WEIGHTS:
Weight empty 179 kg (395 lb)
Max T-O weight 281 kg (620 lb)

PERFORMANCE (with 33·5 kW; 45 hp engine, at max T-O weight):
Never-exceed speed 108 knots (202 km/h; 125 mph)
Max level speed 95 knots (176 km/h; 109 mph)
Max cruising speed 87 knots (161 km/h; 100 mph)
Econ cruising speed 76 knots (141 km/h; 87 mph)
Stalling speed 39 knots (71 km/h; 44 mph)
Max rate of climb at S/L 137 m (450 ft)/min
Service ceiling 2,740 m (9,000 ft)
T-O run from grass 95 m (310 ft)
T-O to 15 m (50 ft) from grass 125 m (410 ft)
Landing from 15 m (50 ft) on grass 98 m (320 ft)
Landing run on grass 52 m (170 ft)
Range with max fuel, normal allowances 217 nm (400 km; 250 miles)

LUTON L.A.4a MINOR

The first Luton Minor flew in 1936 and proved entirely suitable for construction and operation by amateur builders and pilots. Examples were built pre-war in England and other parts of the world.

In 1960, the design was modernised and restressed completely to the latest British Airworthiness Requirements, allowing for a power increase to 41 kW (55 hp) and a maximum flying weight of 340 kg (750 lb).

Minors are under construction in many parts of the world, and a considerable number of amateur-built examples have been completed and flown successfully since mid-1962. At least one of them, built in Australia by R. A. Pearman and H. Nash, obtained a full Certificate of Airworthiness.

The following description applies to the aircraft in the form previously marketed by Phoenix.

TYPE: Single-seat light monoplane.

WINGS: Strut-braced parasol monoplane. Wing section RAF 48. No dihedral. Wooden two-spar structure in two halves, attached to the fuselage by tubular centre-section pylons and braced by parallel lift struts of streamline-section steel tubing. Wings removable for ground transport and storage. Leading-edge and tips plywood-covered, remainder fabric-covered. Plain ailerons of wood construction, fabric-covered, hinged directly from rear spar. No flaps.

FUSELAGE: Rectangular all-wood structure. Sides and bottom plywood-covered. Curved decking aft of cockpit fabric-covered.

TAIL UNIT: Cantilever all-wood structure, fabric-covered. Fixed fin. Aerodynamically-balanced rudder.

LANDING GEAR: Non-retractable tailwheel type with divided main legs of tubular steel construction. Rubber disc shock-absorbers. Brakes and wheel fairings optional. Fully-castoring tailwheel.

POWER PLANT: One aircooled engine in the 27·5-41 kW (37-55 hp) range, driving a two-blade fixed-pitch wooden propeller. Fuel tank forward of cockpit, capacity 29·5 litres (6·5 Imp gallons). Provision for additional tanks in wings.

ACCOMMODATION: Single seat in open cockpit. Coupé top optional. Baggage space aft of seat.

DIMENSIONS, EXTERNAL:
Wing span 7·62 m (25 ft 0 in)
Wing chord, constant 1·60 m (5 ft 3 in)
Wing area, gross 11·6 m² (125 sq ft)
Wing aspect ratio 5
Length overall 6·32 m (20 ft 9 in)
Height overall 2·29 m (7 ft 6 in)

WEIGHTS:
Weight empty 177 kg (390 lb)
Max T-O weight 340 kg (750 lb)

PERFORMANCE (27·5 kW; 37 hp Aeronca-JAP J.99 engine, at normal T-O weight):
Max level speed at 450 m (1,500 ft) 60 knots (111 km/h; 69 mph)
Normal cruising speed 55 knots (102 km/h; 63 mph)
Stalling speed 25 knots (45 km/h; 28 mph)
Max rate of climb at S/L 76 m (250 ft)/min
T-O run 92 m (300 ft)
Landing run 36·5 m (120 ft)
Range with standard fuel 155 nm (290 km; 180 miles)
Range with auxiliary tanks 340 nm (645 km; 400 miles)

PRACTAVIA
PRACTAVIA LTD

Wycombe Air Park, Booker, near Marlow, Buckinghamshire
Telephone: 0494 35342
MANAGING DIRECTOR: C. B. Healey

This company was formed to market plans and kits of a two-seat all-metal aerobatic aircraft known as the Sprite, the design of which was initiated by *Pilot* magazine.

PRACTAVIA SPRITE/BANDIT

Initial design work on the Sprite was started by the staff of *Pilot* magazine in early 1968, after consultation with many experienced light aircraft constructors, and a design and development panel was set up to foster the project. Detailed design began in November 1968 and construction of the first Sprite was started in 1969. Mr Brian Healey, former editor of *Pilot* magazine, is project executive, and Mr Lloyd Jenkinson and Mr Peter Sharman, lecturers at Loughborough University, are the designers.

First flight of a Sprite, built by Mr Peter Burril of Snape, Yorkshire, took place on 16 June 1976. This aircraft was lost in an accident; but several more Sprites are nearing completion or already flying, including that shown in an accompanying illustration, which flew for the first time on 18 June 1978. Plans are available for amateur construction, and 150 Sprites were under construction in early 1979. Kits are also available.

A version named **Bandit** is offered for military training and other duties.

TYPE: Two-seat all-metal aerobatic aircraft, suitable for amateur construction.

WINGS: Cantilever low-wing monoplane. Wing section NACA 64315. Dihedral 6° on outer panels only. No incidence or sweepback. All-metal structure of aluminium alloy, built in three equal-length sections. Single main spar with light rear spar forming central torsion box. Skins and ribs of L72 alloy, extrusions of L65 alloy and spar caps of L73 alloy. Single-slotted flaps and plain ailerons of L72 alloy extend over full span. No trim tabs. Outer wing panels detachable for transit.

FUSELAGE: All-metal semi-monocoque structure, with no double curvature. Longerons of L65 aluminium alloy, skins and frames of L72 alloy. Sides and top curved to avoid drumming.

TAIL UNIT: Cantilever all-metal structure with swept vertical surfaces, constructed of L72 alloy. Fixed-incidence tailplane. Trim tab in centre of elevator trailing-edge, of one-third span; outer one-third on each side comprises anti-balance tab.

LANDING GEAR: Non-retractable tricycle type standard, although design of wing structure will allow for retractable gear as a future development. Shock-absorption by rubber in compression. Wheels and tyres size 5·00-5. Hydraulic disc brakes.

POWER PLANT: One 97 kW (130 hp) Rolls-Royce Continental O-240-A flat-four engine (now standard), driving a two-blade fixed-pitch propeller. Fuel contained in one fuselage tank, aft of firewall, capacity 54·5 litres (12 Imp gallons), and standard wingtip fuel tanks, capacity 54·5 litres (12 Imp gallons) each. Maximum total capacity 163·5 litres (36 Imp gallons). Oil capacity 4·5 litres (1 Imp gallon)

ACCOMMODATION: Two seats, side by side, in enclosed cockpit, with rearward-sliding transparent canopy. Space for baggage behind seats.

SYSTEMS: Hydraulic system for brakes only. 12V electrical system.

ELECTRONICS AND EQUIPMENT: Radio, blind-flying instrumentation and special equipment to individual builder's requirements.

DIMENSIONS, EXTERNAL:
Wing span over tip-tanks 8·23 m (27 ft 0 in)
Wing chord, constant 1·22 m (4 ft 0 in)
Wing area, gross 8·92 m² (96 sq ft)
Wing aspect ratio 6
Length overall 6·10 m (20 ft 0 in)
Width, outer panels removed 2·44 m (8 ft 0 in)
Height overall 2·51 m (8 ft 3 in)
Tailplane span 2·44 m (8 ft 0 in)
Wheel track 2·29 m (7 ft 6 in)
Wheelbase 1·40 m (4 ft 7 in)

Currie Wot, described under PFA entry

Druine D31 Turbulent, described under PFA entry *(David Partington)*

Practavia Sprite built by Mr G. B. Castle and Mr F. Rycroft

Luton L.A.4a Minor, described under PFA entry *(Peter R. March)*

Procter Petrel two-seat light aircraft built by British Aerospace apprentices

DIMENSION, INTERNAL:
 Cabin:
  Max width 1·17 m (3 ft 10 in)

WEIGHTS (74·5 kW; 100 hp engine):
 Weight empty 385 kg (850 lb)
 Max T-O weight 635 kg (1,400 lb)

PERFORMANCE (at max T-O weight with 93 kW; 125 hp engine):
 Never-exceed speed 212 knots (394 km/h; 245 mph)
 Max cruising speed 120 knots (222 km/h; 138 mph)
 Econ cruising speed 111 knots (206 km/h; 128 mph)
 Stalling speed, flaps down 48 knots (89 km/h; 55 mph)

PROCTER

PROCTER AIRCRAFT ASSOCIATES LTD

c/o Kinetrol Ltd, Trading Estate, Farnham, Surrey
Telephone: 0252 723688

DIRECTORS:
 Alan R. B. Nash, BSc, CEng, MICE, MRAeS
 Richard C. Nash, BA (Cantab)
 Roy G. Procter, CEng, MRAeS

In early 1978 a controlling interest in this company was obtained by Mr Alan Nash. It remains the intention of Procter Aircraft Associates to exploit the commercial potential of both the single-seat Kittiwake (see 1978-79 *Jane's*) and the two-seat Petrel. However, Mr Nash's main interest is in using the aircraft as the basis for a manufacturing programme rather than in the amateur plans/kits market, although sympathetic to the latter.

PROCTER PETREL

This two-seat light aircraft is based upon the Kittiwake I single-seat lightplane (see 1978-79 *Jane's*), with many components in common, but has increased wing area and has been optimised for glider towing. It has a number of improvements and simplifications to the detail mechanical design, compared with Kittiwake I. Materials used throughout are L72 clad dural and S510 mild steel.

Completion of the company's prototype Petrel is being undertaken by Mr Alan Nash. Another Petrel has been built by British Aerospace apprentices at Preston.

At the present time, Mr Nash does not consider the existing drawings of Petrel to be complete or sufficiently definitive for sale to amateurs.

TYPE: Two-seat light aircraft.

WINGS: Cantilever low-wing monoplane. Wing section NACA 3415. Dihedral 5° on outer panels. No sweepback or washout. All-metal constant-chord structure, built in three sections: centre-section, integral with fuselage, to which outer panels are each attached with three bolts. Single main spar at 30% chord and lightweight auxiliary spar at 66% chord. Multiple ribs, with no spanwise stiffeners. All-metal NACA slotted flaps and ailerons. Flaps are operated manually by pushrod and torque tube; ailerons are mass-balanced and operated by cables.

FUSELAGE: All-metal structure. Four-longeron basic structure, with flat sides and bottom and single-curvature top-decking. Integral wing centre-section forms seat and main landing gear attachment structure.

TAIL UNIT: Cantilever all-metal structure. Fixed-incidence tailplane. Manually-operated tab in starboard elevator. Tab on rudder. Control surfaces mass-balanced and operated by cables.

LANDING GEAR: Non-retractable tricycle type. Nose unit is an oleo-pneumatic strut with Goodyear 5·00-6 wheel, and is steerable from the rudder pedals. Main gear is of cantilever spring type, with Goodyear 6·00-6 wheels and hydraulic disc brakes. Tyre pressure (all) 1·72 bars (25 lb/sq in).

POWER PLANT: One 97 kW (130 hp) Rolls-Royce Continental O-240 flat-four engine, driving a McCauley fixed-pitch two-blade metal propeller. Fuel capacity 73 litres (16 Imp gallons).

ACCOMMODATION: Two persons side by side, on seats with individually adjustable backs. Baggage space aft of seats.

EQUIPMENT: Starter, generator and basic instrumentation. Radio, navigation and other equipment to builder's requirements.

DIMENSIONS, EXTERNAL:
 Wing span 9·14 m (30 ft 0 in)
 Wing chord, constant 1·38 m (4 ft 6½ in)
 Wing area, gross 12·5 m² (135·0 sq ft)
 Wing aspect ratio 6·6
 Length overall 6·30 m (20 ft 8 in)
 Height overall 2·33 m (7 ft 8 in)
 Tailplane span 2·79 m (9 ft 2 in)
 Wheel track 2·24 m (7 ft 4 in)
 Wheelbase 1·52 m (5 ft 0 in)

WEIGHTS:
 Weight empty 515·5 kg (1,137 lb)
 Max T-O weight 762 kg (1,680 lb)

PERFORMANCE (at max T-O weight: estimated, based on measured performance of Kittiwake I):
 Max level speed 113 knots (209 km/h; 130 mph)
 Cruising speed 104 knots (193 km/h; 120 mph)
 Max rate of climb at S/L 305 m (1,000 ft)/min

TAYLOR

Mrs JOHN F. TAYLOR

25, Chesterfield Crescent, Leigh-on-Sea, Essex SS9 5PD
Telephone: 0702 521063

The late Mr John Taylor, AMIED, an amateur constructor, designed and built the prototype of a single-seat ultra-light sporting monoplane, designated J.T.1. His object was to produce the airframe for not more than £100. Construction took about 14 months, and it flew for the first time on 4 July 1959.

A second design by Mr Taylor, the J.T.2 Titch, was awarded second prize in the Midget Racer Design Competition organised by Mr Norman Jones of the Rollason company in 1964. A prototype was built and flown successfully, but crashed on 16 May 1967, killing its designer.

Mrs J. F. Taylor is continuing to market plans of both of these aircraft to amateur constructors.

TAYLOR J.T.1 MONOPLANE

Plans of the Taylor monoplane have been sold to amateur constructors in the United Kingdom and about 20 other countries in all parts of the world. More than 70 J.T.1s are known to be flying in the UK, Canada, USA, Australia and New Zealand, including ten completed in these countries during 1978.

Aircraft currently flying or under construction are fitted with a variety of engines, including the 30 kW (40 hp) Aeronca E 113, 48·5 kW (65 hp) Continental A65, 48·5 kW (65 hp) Lycoming, 53·7 kW (72 hp) two-stroke McCulloch and the modified Volkswagen series. Aircraft with the 48·5 kW (65 hp) engines have a 10 cm (4 in) longer nose and 25 cm (10 in) longer rear fuselage to maintain the correct CG position.

TYPE: Single-seat fully-aerobatic ultra-light monoplane.

WINGS: Cantilever low-wing monoplane. Wing section RAF 48. Constant chord. Dihedral on outer panels 4°. Incidence 3°. Wooden two-spar structure, comprising centre-section and outer panels. Plywood and fabric covering. Differential ailerons. Split trailing-edge flaps. No tabs.

FUSELAGE: Conventional plywood-covered wood structure of four main longerons and curved formers. Centre-section integral with fuselage.

TAIL UNIT: Cantilever fin and fixed-incidence tailplane are plywood-covered wood structures. Elevators and rudder are fabric-covered wood structures.

LANDING GEAR: Non-retractable two-wheel type. Cantilever main legs, with coil spring shock-absorption. Size 5 × 4 (305 mm; 12 in) main wheels, tyre pressure 1·65 bars (24 lb/sq in). Leaf spring tailskid with steerable skid-pad. One example, built by Mr R. Ladd in the US (see 1972-73 *Jane's*), has manually-actuated inward-retracting main gear.

POWER PLANT (prototype): One 28·3 kW (38 hp) JAP two-cylinder engine, driving a modified Flottorp two-blade wooden fixed-pitch propeller. Fuel tank aft of firewall, capacity 27 litres (6 Imp gallons).

ACCOMMODATION: Single seat under transparent Perspex canopy. Aerobatic harness. Small locker aft of seat.

DIMENSIONS, EXTERNAL:

Wing span	6·40 m (21 ft 0 in)
Wing area, gross	7·06 m² (76 sq ft)
Wing aspect ratio	6
Length overall	4·57 m (15 ft 0 in)
Height over tail	1·47 m (4 ft 10 in)
Tailplane span	1·98 m (6 ft 6 in)
Wheel track	1·52 m (5 ft 0 in)

WEIGHTS:

Weight empty	186 kg (410 lb)
Max T-O weight	276 kg (610 lb)

PERFORMANCE:

Never-exceed speed	113 knots (209 km/h; 130 mph)
Max level speed at S/L	91 knots (169 km/h; 105 mph)
Econ cruising speed	78 knots (145 km/h; 90 mph)
Never-exceed speed with flaps down	56 knots (105 km/h; 65 mph)
Stalling speed, flaps up	40 knots (75 km/h; 46 mph)
Stalling speed, flaps down	33 knots (62 km/h; 38 mph)
Max rate of climb at S/L	305 m (1,000 ft)/min
Range	200 nm (370 km; 230 miles)
g limits	+9; −9

TAYLOR J.T.2 TITCH

Construction of the prototype Titch was started in February 1965 and it flew for the first time on 22 January 1967.

Nineteen Titches are known to be flying, including 12 in the USA, two in New Zealand, one in France, one in Rhodesia and three in England; plans have also been supplied to amateur constructors in Alaska, Argentina, Brazil, Iceland, Ireland, Japan, Italy, Kenya, Mexico and Spain.

The Titch illustrated was built by Jim Miller of Missouri, USA. Maximum speed is 139 knots (257 km/h; 160 mph) at 2,700 rpm and cruising speed 122 knots (225 km/h; 140 mph) at 2,600 rpm with a metal propeller. When fitted with a wooden propeller, the rate of climb is stated to be 700 m (2,300 ft)/min. Empty weight is 255 kg (562 lb).

The following description refers to the prototype:

TYPE: Single-seat light monoplane.

WINGS: Cantilever low-wing monoplane. Taylor-modified NACA 23012 wing section. Dihedral 5° on top surface. Incidence 3°. Spruce structure with main box-spar and 'plank' auxiliary spar. Plywood and fabric covering. Plain manually-operated ply-covered flaps over half-span and fabric-covered differential ailerons.

FUSELAGE: All-wood structure, with four main longerons, four secondary longerons and double-curvature ply covering. Aluminium cockpit side panels.

TAIL UNIT: All-wood structure, with fixed-incidence tailplane. Fixed surfaces plywood-covered, control surfaces fabric-covered.

LANDING GEAR: Non-retractable tailwheel type. Steerable tailwheel. Chrome-vanadium compression coil-spring shock-absorbers. Wheels of constructor's manufacture with 4-ply tyres size 5·00-4 and drum brakes.

POWER PLANT: One 63·5 kW (85 hp) Continental C85 flat-four engine, driving a Hegy wooden two-blade scimitar propeller. Glassfibre fuel tank between firewall and instrument panel, capacity 45·5 litres (10 Imp gallons).

ACCOMMODATION: Single seat, with aerobatic harness, under bubble canopy hinged along starboard side.

DIMENSIONS, EXTERNAL:

Wing span	5·72 m (18 ft 9 in)
Wing chord at root	1·37 m (4 ft 6 in)
Wing chord at tip	0·91 m (3 ft 0 in)
Wing area, gross	6·32 m² (68 sq ft)
Wing aspect ratio	5·14
Length overall	4·91 m (16 ft 1½ in)
Height overall	1·42 m (4 ft 8 in)
Tailplane span	1·98 m (6 ft 6 in)
Wheel track	1·52 m (5 ft 0 in)
Propeller diameter	1·52 m (5 ft 0 in)

WEIGHTS (A: 63·5 kW; 85 hp Continental engine; B: Volkswagen engine):

Weight empty: A	227 kg (500 lb)
B	185 kg (410 lb)
Max T-O weight: A	338 kg (745 lb)
B	290 kg (640 lb)

PERFORMANCE (prototype, at max T-O weight except where indicated):

Never-exceed speed	195 knots (362 km/h; 225 mph)
Max level speed	174 knots (322 km/h; 200 mph)
Normal cruising speed	135 knots (250 km/h; 155 mph)
Econ cruising speed	95·5 knots (177 km/h; 110 mph)
Best approach speed	65 knots (121 km/h; 75 mph)
Stalling speed, flaps up: A	50·5 knots (93·5 km/h; 58 mph)
B	46 knots (86 km/h; 53 mph)
Stalling speed, flaps down: A	43·5 knots (80·5 km/h; 50 mph)
B	40 knots (74 km/h; 46 mph)
T-O speed	54 knots (100 km/h; 62 mph)
Touchdown speed	48 knots (89 km/h; 55 mph)
Max rate of climb at S/L	335 m (1,100 ft)/min

TRAGO MILLS
TRAGO MILLS LTD

AIRCRAFT DIVISION: Treswithick Farm, Cardinham, Bodmin, Cornwall
Telephone: 020882 485

Trago Mills sponsored and owns the prototype of a single-seat ultra-light aircraft known as the MW2 Excalibur, with a ducted propulsion unit, designed by Mr Michael Whittaker. Further development of this aircraft (see 1977-78 *Jane's*) was deferred pending availability of a larger, lower-speed fan.

In September 1977, Trago Mills began design of a more conventional two-seat light aircraft, designated SAH.1 There has been no recent news of this project, of which details can be found in the 1978-79 *Jane's*.

WHITTAKER
MICHAEL W. J. WHITTAKER

Dawlish Cottage, Pincots Lane, Wickwar, Wotton under Edge, Gloucestershire

Following his work on the prototype MW2 Excalibur, Michael Whittaker has designed a new aircraft which he has named the MW3 Airkart. Design began in October 1976 and construction of the prototype started on 4 January 1977. By February 1978 the assembly of major components had begun. A notable modification to the design was made during 1977, when the engine and propeller were changed from pusher to tractor configuration.

WHITTAKER MW3 AIRKART

TYPE: Single-seat ultra-light aircraft.

WINGS: Cantilever low-wing monoplane. Wing section NACA 63418. Dihedral 5° from roots. Incidence 3° 30′. Foam core, with glassfibre spar and skins. Wings fold for transportation. Foam and glassfibre ailerons. No flaps or tabs.

FUSELAGE: Pod-type nacelle of foam and glassfibre construction. Stressed-skin tailboom, made up of aluminium angle longerons and aluminium skins with pressed-in stiffeners.

TAIL UNIT: Vee tail of foam and glassfibre. Spring bias on elevator.

LANDING GEAR: Non-retractable tailwheel type. Cantilever glassfibre spring legs. Go-kart wheels and tyres size 13 × 4·00-5 on main units. Solid rubber tyre, diameter 10·2 cm (4 in), on castoring tailwheel. Go-kart internally expanding brakes.

POWER PLANT: One 33·5 kW (45 hp) 1,600 cc Volkswagen engine, driving a fixed-pitch propeller. One metal fuel tank behind pilot's seat, capacity 32 litres (7 Imp gallons). Oil capacity 2·27 litres (0·5 Imp gallons).

ACCOMMODATION: Single seat in open cockpit. Baggage area aft of seat.

DIMENSIONS, EXTERNAL:

Wing span	6·71 m (22 ft 0 in)
Wing chord, constant	1·07 m (3 ft 6 in)
Wing area, gross	7·15 m² (77 sq ft)
Wing aspect ratio	6·28
Length overall	4·42 m (14 ft 6 in)
Width, wings folded	2·29 m (7 ft 6 in)
Height overall	1·52 m (5 ft 0 in)
Tailplane span	2·29 m (7 ft 6 in)
Wheel track	1·22 m (4 ft 0 in)
Wheelbase	3·05 m (10 ft 0 in)
Propeller diameter	1·37 m (4 ft 6 in)

DIMENSIONS, INTERNAL:

Cabin: Length	1·22 m (4 ft 0 in)
Max width	0·56 m (1 ft 10 in)

WEIGHTS:

Weight empty	182 kg (400 lb)
Max T-O weight	317 kg (700 lb)

PERFORMANCE (estimated):

Never-exceed speed	108 knots (201 km/h; 125 mph)
Max level speed	65 knots (120 km/h; 75 mph)
Max cruising speed	61 knots (113 km/h; 70 mph)
Econ cruising speed	56 knots (105 km/h; 65 mph)
Stalling speed	37 knots (68 km/h; 42 mph)
Max rate of climb at S/L	152 m (500 ft)/min
Service ceiling	3,660 m (12,000 ft)
T-O run	152 m (500 ft)
Landing from 15 m (50 ft)	274 m (900 ft)
Landing run	122 m (400 ft)
Range with max fuel	173 nm (322 km; 200 miles)

UNITED STATES OF AMERICA

ACE
ACE AIRCRAFT MANUFACTURING CO

106 Arthur Road, Asheville, North Carolina 28806
Telephone: (704) 252 4325
OWNER: Thurman G. Baird
SALES AND PUBLIC RELATIONS MANAGER: V. P. Baird

This company is a successor to the original Corben Aircraft Company, which was established in 1923 and began manufacturing the Baby Ace single-seat ultra-light monoplane in kit form in 1931. All rights in the current updated design were purchased by the present owner in 1965. Plans, kits and parts of the Baby Ace and Junior Ace are available to amateur builders from Ace Aircraft, together with plans of the Flaglor Scooter, described in this section of *Jane's*.

Ace Aircraft also has full rights in the American Flea Ship and Heath Parasol light aircraft, of which plans are available; descriptions of these two aircraft last appeared in the 1970-71 *Jane's*.

BABY ACE MODEL D

The prototype of the redesigned Baby Ace Model D flew for the first time on 15 November 1956. Large numbers have since been built by amateurs, some of whom have introduced authorised refinements to the basic design. At least one Baby Ace is flying with a float landing gear, and was illustrated in the 1975-76 *Jane's*. The floats were constructed of glassfibre, using a wood pattern and glassfibre mould, and have spruce struts wrapped in glassfibre, with cast aluminium end fittings. Twin water rudders are fitted for surface handling, and performance is claimed to be comparable with that of a Piper Cub seaplane with 48·5 kW (65 hp) engine.

TYPE: Single-seat ultra-light monoplane.

WINGS: Braced parasol monoplane. Wing section Clark Y (modified). Dihedral 1°. Incidence 1°. Fabric-covered two-spar wood structure. Fabric-covered wood ailerons. No flaps.

FUSELAGE: Welded steel tube structure, fabric-covered.

TAIL UNIT: Wire-braced steel tube structure, fabric-covered.

LANDING GEAR: Non-retractable tailwheel type. Combination special tubing and spring shock-absorption. Goodrich 8·00-4 main wheels. Scott hydraulic brakes. Wheel spats optional. Steerable tailwheel. Edo 1140 floats on seaplane version.

Taylor J.T.1 monoplane built in Australia

Taylor J.T.2 Titch built by Jim Miller of Missouri

Side-by-side two-seat Junior Ace Model E *(J. M. G. Gradidge)*

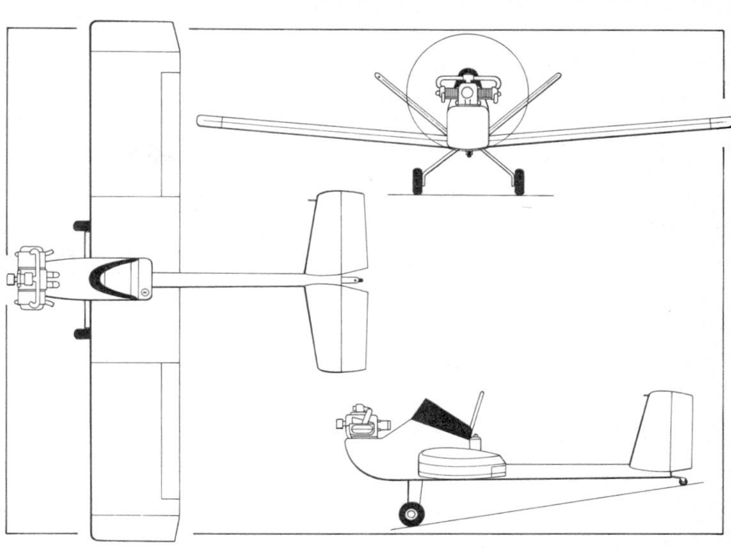
Whittaker MW3 Airkart, now with forward-mounted engine *(Michael A. Badrocke)*

Baby Ace Model D (Continental A65 engine) built by Capt Lloyd Windh of Air Canada *(Neil A. Macdougall)*

POWER PLANT: One Continental A65, A85, C65 or C85 flat-four engine of 48·5-63·5 kW (65-85 hp), driving a two-blade wooden fixed-pitch propeller. Fuel in tank aft of firewall with capacity of 63·6 litres (16·8 US gallons). Oil capacity 3·8 litres (1 US gallon).

ACCOMMODATION: Single seat in open cockpit. Wide door on starboard side. Space for 4·5 kg (10 lb) baggage.

DIMENSIONS, EXTERNAL:

Wing span	8·05 m (26 ft 5 in)
Wing chord, constant	1·37 m (4 ft 6 in)
Wing area, gross	10·43 m² (112·3 sq ft)
Wing aspect ratio	5·95
Length overall	5·40 m (17 ft 8¾ in)
Height overall	2·02 m (6 ft 7¾ in)
Tailplane span	2·13 m (7 ft 0 in)
Wheel track	1·83 m (6 ft 0 in)
Wheelbase	3·96 m (13 ft 0 in)

WEIGHTS:

Weight empty, equipped	261 kg (575 lb)
Max T-O weight:	
48·5 kW (65 hp)	431 kg (950 lb)
63·5 kW (85 hp) landplane or seaplane	522 kg (1,150 lb)

PERFORMANCE (48·5 kW; 65 hp engine, at max T-O weight):

Max level speed at S/L	96 knots (177 km/h; 110 mph)
Max cruising speed	87-91 knots (160-169 km/h; 100-105 mph)
Stalling speed	30 knots (54·7 km/h; 34 mph)
Max rate of climb at S/L	365 m (1,200 ft)/min
Service ceiling	4,875 m (16,000 ft)
T-O run	60 m (200 ft)
Landing run	76 m (250 ft)
Range with max fuel	303·5 nm (560 km; 350 miles)

JUNIOR ACE MODEL E

The Junior Ace Model E differs from the Baby Ace Model D in being a side-by-side two-seater. It is powered usually by a 63·5 kW (85 hp) Continental C85 flat-four engine, and the details refer to an aircraft with this power plant that was built by Mr Louis C. Seno of Melrose Park, Illinois.

First flown on 2 August 1966, it has a cockpit 7·5 cm (3 in) wider and 10 cm (4 in) deeper than that of the standard Model E, a full electrical system and increased fuel capacity of 85 litres (22·5 US gallons).

DIMENSIONS, EXTERNAL:

Wing span	7·92 m (26 ft 0 in)
Wing chord, constant	1·37 m (4 ft 6 in)
Wing aspect ratio	5·95
Length overall	5·50 m (18 ft 0 in)
Height overall	2·00 m (6 ft 7 in)

WEIGHTS:

Weight empty	367 kg (809 lb)
Max T-O weight	606 kg (1,335 lb)

PERFORMANCE:

Max level speed at S/L	113 knots (209 km/h; 130 mph)
Cruising speed	91 knots (169 km/h; 105 mph)
Landing speed	57 knots (105 km/h; 65 mph)
Service ceiling	3,050 m (10,000 ft)
T-O run	122 m (400 ft)
Landing run	183 m (600 ft)
Range with max fuel	303·5 nm (560 km; 350 miles)

AEROCAR

AEROCAR INC

PO Box 1171, Longview, Washington 98632

Telephone: (206) 423 8260

PRESIDENT AND GENERAL MANAGER: Moulton B. Taylor

In February 1948 Aerocar Inc began developing a flying automobile designed by Mr M. B. Taylor. The prototype Aerocar, with a Lycoming O-290 engine, was completed in October 1949. It was followed by a pre-production Aerocar Model I, with Lycoming O-320 engine, and this was used for tests which led to FAA airworthiness certification of the Aerocar on 13 December 1956. Four additional Model I Aerocars were completed subsequently for demonstration tours of the United States and for sale to customers.

The accumulated road travel on the six Model I Aerocars is well over 200,000 miles and they have logged a total of more than 5,000 flying hours. No further production of this model is planned, but development of the Aerocar has continued. The prototype of a refined Model III Aerocar was built and many changes have been made to the hand-built Model Is, enhancing both the flight performance and the road operation.

It seemed for a number of years that any Aerocar able to conform with current and projected US government safety and environmental requirements for automobiles would be so heavy and expensive that it could be neither practical nor economical. There have been indications that the concerned government agencies might be willing to relax for vehicles of this kind the regulations which govern the operation of automobiles. However, even if such relaxation became law, the problem of finding suitable production capital for such a major programme would remain to be solved. As a consequence, Aerocar Inc, which is basically a three-person operation, has continued to devote most of its activity to other projects, notably the single-seat Mini-Imp, which embodies features of the Aerocar and is suitable for amateur construction.

In 1966 Aerocar built the prototype of a light flying-boat for a private customer. It was followed by two further aircraft, named Coot, on similar lines but provided with tricycle landing gear for amphibious operation. Many sets of plans for this aircraft, now known as the Sooper-Coot, have been sold to amateur constructors.

Aerocar is also devoting much effort to the development of a low-cost and low-power aircraft engine, based on a Kawasaki motorcycle engine, which would be suitable for powering many types of light aircraft of the future. It originally flight tested for over 100 hours a 900 cc Kawasaki engine in a 1937 Taylorcraft. This was then replaced by a 1,000 cc Kawasaki engine, which had completed 160 flight hours by early 1979, prior to being modified further and turbocharged. Hand-made engines to a comparable standard are being offered to amateur constructors by Aerocar. Flight testing of the latest engine began in January 1978.

AEROCAR SOOPER-COOT MODEL A

The prototype of this aircraft flew for the first time in February 1971. It logged approximately 100 hours powered by an 89·5 kW (120 hp) Franklin 225 engine, driving a Sensenich fixed-pitch metal propeller. This was subsequently replaced by a 134 kW (180 hp) Franklin 335 engine, driving a Hartzell constant-speed metal propeller, and the aircraft has been flown extensively since 1972 with this more powerful engine.

The 'float-wing' configuration of the Sooper-Coot permits rough-water operation and, since the close proximity of the wings to the water forms a 'pressure wedge', unusually low take-off and landing speeds are possible without recourse to flaps or other lift-enhancing devices.

The structure is basically of wood, but the tailboom and

tail unit can be of steel tube and fabric, wood monocoque or all-metal construction. The rearward-folding wings, of NACA 4415 section, can be folded by one person. The fabric-covered ailerons are of metal construction and statically balanced. There are no tip floats. Construction of the hull, which has only seven bulkheads, is straightforward, without the complication of wheel-well doors. Tailplane and elevators also fold and the elevators have trim tabs. All control surfaces are statically balanced. The tricycle-type landing gear is manually retractable into the wings, but an alternative powered retraction system is shown on the plans.

Recommended power plant for the Sooper-Coot is a Franklin flat-six engine of either 134 or 164 kW (180 or 220 hp). However, many builders of the Sooper-Coot are fitting a 157 kW (210 hp) Continental IO-360. To minimise expenditure, others are fitting Lycoming O-320 and O-320-B engines of 119 kW (160 hp). These are reported to be satisfactory if only a limited weight of optional equipment is installed in the aircraft. However, a constant-speed propeller has proved essential to maintain reasonable performance with the O-320/320-B. Maximum fuel capacity is 189 litres (50 US gallons).

Certain component parts (including the glassfibre engine cowls, glassfibre hull shell, foredeck, instrument panel, tail fairings, engine cooling-fan blades and spring steel main landing gear legs), and plans, are available to amateur constructors. The company also maintains a list of recommended suppliers of welded assemblies and machined components. More than 400 Sooper-Coots were under construction in early 1979, with 50 already flying in the USA and other countries.

Dimensions, external:
- Wing span: 10·97 m (36 ft 0 in)
- Wing chord, constant: 1·52 m (5 ft 0 in)
- Wing area, gross: 16·72 m² (180 sq ft)
- Length overall: 6·10 to 6·71 m (20 ft 0 in to 22 ft 0 in)
- Height overall: 2·44 m (8 ft 0 in)
- Width folded: 2·44 m (8 ft 0 in)
- Tailplane span: 3·04 m (10 ft 0 in)

Weights:
- Weight empty: 499 kg (1,100 lb)
- Max T-O weight: 884 kg (1,950 lb)

Performance (134 kW; 180 hp engine, at max T-O weight):
- Never-exceed speed: 120 knots (223 km/h; 139 mph)
- Max cruising speed: 113 knots (209 km/h; 130 mph)
- Econ cruising speed at 50% power: 95·5 knots (177 km/h; 110 mph)
- Max rate of climb at S/L: 381 m (1,250 ft)/min
- T-O run (land): 61 m (200 ft)
- T-O (water): 6-8 s

AEROCAR IMP

Design of the Imp (an acronym derived from Independently Made Plane) began in January 1972. Many design features of the Aerocar were embodied, including folding wings and a pusher propeller aft of the tail unit. All-metal construction, using pop-rivets, bolt-together assemblies and limited welding, was specified to reduce building time.

Construction of a two-seat prototype Imp began in August 1972, but completion of the test programme was delayed by the need for further investigation into many aspects of the design. Subsequent non-availability of the Franklin engine which was intended to power the aircraft led to the decision to give priority instead to the single-seat Mini-Imp (which see).

More recently, it was decided to resume the Imp programme by converting the original prototype to two-plus-two configuration, with the pilot and one passenger seated side by side at the front of the cabin and two folding seats at the rear for children. The necessary new skins for the modification had been built by early 1977. However, the aircraft was transferred to another builder in St Louis, Missouri, in 1978, and he is carrying out the conversion. It is not clear whether the modified prototype will incorporate all changes shown on the current Imp information sheet supplied by Aerocar, such as use of the GA (PC)-1 aerofoil section, Kawasaki engine and a lengthened fuselage. Therefore, the modified details below may refer to subsequent Imps and not the prototype, which Aerocar hoped to display at the 1979 EAA Fly-in, at Oshkosh.

The future of the Imp programme will be determined largely by the outcome of Aerocar's work to evolve a low-cost and low-power aero-engine from the Kawasaki motorcycle engine. Two 1,000 cc 74·5 kW (100 hp) four-cylinder engines of this type might be geared to drive a single propeller, with centreline thrust and 'either/or' engine drive capability, via a chain drive.

Type: Four-seat light aircraft.

Wings: Cantilever high-wing monoplane. Wing section GA(PC)-1. No dihedral. Incidence 4°. No sweepback. All-metal structure of constant chord. Wings fold aft, alongside fuselage, for towing or storage. All-metal ailerons, each with trim tab. No flaps.

Fuselage: All-metal structure with glassfibre shell.

Tail Unit: Inverted 'V' type, of all-metal construction, with variable-incidence tailplane surfaces.

Landing Gear: Electrically-retractable tricycle type, main units retracting outward. Special highway-type wheels and 6-ply tyres suitable for road towing. Tyre pressure 2·76 bars (40 lb/sq in). Rosenhan wheel brakes. Nosewheel retracts separately from main wheels for road towing.

Power Plant: Prototype may be powered by the existing 93 kW (125 hp) Franklin engine or a new 149 kW (200 hp) Franklin engine. Plans show installation of the Kawasaki twin-engine arrangement. One fuel tank of 53 litres (14 US gallons) capacity in each wing root. Total fuel capacity 106 litres (28 US gallons). Refuelling points in upper surface of wings, inboard of wing fold. Oil capacity 7·5 litres (2 US gallons).

Accommodation: Two seats, side by side, at front of enclosed cabin, with two folding seats at rear. Large baggage space if rear seats folded against bulkhead. Airstair doors.

System: Electrical system powered by 12V 60A engine-driven alternator.

Electronics: Narco Escort 110 radio and Type 50A transponder.

Dimensions, external:
- Wing span: 8·84 m (29 ft 0 in)
- Wing chord, constant: 1·22 m (4 ft 0 in)
- Wing area, gross: 10·41 m² (112 sq ft)
- Wing aspect ratio: 7
- Length overall: 6·71 m (22 ft 0 in)
- Width, wings folded: 2·13 m (7 ft 0 in)
- Height overall (propeller blades horizontal): 1·68 m (5 ft 6 in)
- Tailplane span: 2·44 m (8 ft 0 in)
- Wheel track: 1·78 m (5 ft 10 in)
- Wheelbase: 2·67 m (8 ft 9 in)
- Propeller diameter: 1·83 m (6 ft 0 in)

Dimension, internal:
- Cockpit: Max width: 1·12 m (3 ft 8 in)

Weights (estimated):
- Weight empty: 499 kg (1,100 lb)
- Max T-O and landing weight: 703 kg (1,550 lb)

Performance (estimated):
- Max cruising speed: more than 130 knots (241 km/h; 150 mph)
- Stalling speed: 44 knots (81 km/h; 50 mph)
- Max rate of climb at S/L: 244 m (800 ft)/min

AEROCAR MINI-IMP

The Mini-Imp is a single-seat version of the Aerocar Imp, to which it is generally similar. The basic structure, which is stressed to ±9g, is all metal and is assembled with bolts and pop-rivets, thereby eliminating the need for welding skill. It is claimed that only a bench drill, sander and bandsaw are needed for home construction of the Mini-Imp, in addition to the usual hand tools and a pop-riveter. Average time taken for construction is 700 working hours, at a cost of $5,000, excluding engine, instruments and electronics.

By early 1979 the Mini-Imp prototype had completed about 190 flying hours, powered by a 51 kW (68 hp) Limbach 1,900 cc flat-four engine, driving a Hoffmann propeller. During the Winter of 1975/76 Aerocar built a folding wing for this aircraft, which folds in a similar way to that of the Imp. This permits the builder to construct the aircraft in small areas, and is a standard feature on the plans for the aircraft.

All drawings for the Mini-Imp were available by early 1978, and parts kits were being delivered. More than 100 amateur-built examples were being built by early 1979 and several Mini-Imps are already flying. Recommended power plant is the turbocharged Revmaster 2100D, driving a Maloof metal constant-speed propeller; Aerocar has built a prototype fitted with this propeller, and this is 30 cm (12 in) longer overall than the original prototype. Individual builders are fitting a variety of engines, including the 74·5 kW (100 hp) Continental O-200, 86 kW (115 hp) Lycoming O-235, and two-cylinder 44·5 kW (60 hp) Franklin. Another Aerocar-built Mini-Imp will be fitted with the turbocharged Kawasaki engine and Maloof propeller, after testing in the Taylorcraft has been completed.

The description of the Imp applies also to the Mini-Imp, except as follows:

Type: Single-seat light sporting aircraft.

Wings: As for Imp. Wing pivots 90° to a fore and aft position for towing by motor car.

Fuselage, Tail Unit and Landing Gear: As for Imp.

Power Plant: Recommended engine is the turbocharged Revmaster 2100D, driving a Maloof constant-speed metal propeller via the standard extended drive shaft incorporating a Flexidyne dry fluid coupling. Alternative engines in the 44·5-74·5 kW (60-100 hp) range may be installed. Fuel tank in wing centre-section, capacity 45·4 litres (12 US gallons), plus tip-tanks, each of 34 litres (9 US gallons) capacity. Refuelling point on wing upper surface.

Accommodation: Single semi-reclining moulded glassfibre bucket seat beneath sideways-opening (to port) transparent canopy. Seat folds forward to provide access to space for 46 kg (100 lb) of baggage.

Dimensions, external:
- Wing span: 7·77 m (25 ft 6 in)
- Wing chord, constant: 0·91 m (3 ft 0 in)
- Length overall: 4·88 m (16 ft 0 in)
- Height over fuselage: 1·24 m (4 ft 1 in)
- Height over propeller: 1·89 m (6 ft 2½ in)
- Tailplane span: 1·98 m (6 ft 6 in)
- Propeller diameter: 1·45 m (4 ft 9 in)

Weights:
- Weight empty: 236 kg (520 lb)
- Max T-O weight: 362 kg (800 lb)

Performance (Limbach engine, except where indicated):
- Never-exceed speed: 260 knots (482 km/h; 300 mph)
- Max cruising speed at S/L: 130 knots (241 km/h; 150 mph)
- Max cruising speed (Revmaster engine and Maloof propeller, estimated): over 173 knots (322 km/h; 200 mph)
- Stalling speed: 43·5 knots (80·5 km/h; 50 mph)
- Max rate of climb at S/L: 366 m (1,200 ft)/min
- T-O run: 183 m (600 ft)
- Range: over 434 nm (804 km; 500 miles)

AEROCAR MICRO-IMP

The Micro-Imp is of similar configuration to the Mini-Imp, but is constructed primarily of glassfibre-reinforced paper. Design began in August 1978, and construction of the prototype was started in December 1978. No date has been suggested for the first flight.

Type: Single-seat light sporting aircraft.

Wings: Cantilever high-wing monoplane. Wing section GA (PC)-1. Thickness/chord ratio 15%. No anhedral or dihedral. Incidence 3°. Glassfibre-reinforced paper construction. Full-span constant-chord ailerons of similar construction to wings. Ailerons droop for flap function.

Fuselage: Glassfibre-reinforced paper structure. Non-structural and removable nosecone of moulded glassfibre.

Tail Unit: Inverted 'V' type, of glassfibre-reinforced paper, with variable-incidence tailplane surfaces.

Landing Gear: Manually-retractable tricycle type. Main units retract vertically. Cantilever spring steel tube main legs. Three plastics wheels, diameter 25·4 cm (10 in). Tyres size 3·00-4, pressure 3·45 bars (50 lb/sq in). Aerocar mechanical brakes.

Power Plant: One 18·6 kW (25 hp) Onan Model NHC-S horizontally-opposed two-cylinder four-stroke engine, driving a tail-mounted Hendrickson two-blade wooden pusher propeller. One fuel tank aft of seat, capacity 19 litres (5 US gallons). Refuelling point on side of fuselage. NASA flush air intake ducts, plus cooling fan.

Accommodation: Single semi-reclining seat under sideways-hinged (to port) transparent canopy. Baggage space aft of seat.

Avionics: Radair 10A 10-channel radio, operated by nickel-cadmium battery.

Dimensions, external:
- Wing span: 8·23 m (27 ft 0 in)
- Wing chord, constant: 0·91 m (3 ft 0 in)
- Wing aspect ratio: 9
- Length overall: 4·57 m (15 ft 0 in)
- Max width of fuselage: 0·69 m (2 ft 3 in)
- Height overall: 1·22 m (4 ft 0 in)
- Tailplane span: 2·13 m (7 ft 0 in)
- Wheel track: 1·22 m (4 ft 0 in)
- Wheelbase: 1·37 m (4 ft 6 in)
- Propeller diameter: 1·07 m (3 ft 6 in)
- Propeller ground clearance: 0·61 m (2 ft 0 in)

Weights:
- Weight empty: 113 kg (250 lb)
- Max T-O weight: 238 kg (525 lb)

Performance (estimated):
- Never-exceed speed: 120 knots (223 km/h; 139 mph)
- Max level speed: 104 knots (193 km/h; 120 mph)
- Max cruising speed: 91 knots (169 km/h; 105 mph)
- Econ cruising speed: 87 knots (161 km/h; 100 mph)
- Stalling speed: 42 knots (78 km/h; 48 mph)
- Max rate of climb at S/L: 152 m (500 ft)/min
- Service ceiling: 3,050 m (10,000 ft)
- T-O run: 152 m (500 ft)
- T-O to 15 m (50 ft): 290 m (950 ft)
- Landing from 15 m (50 ft): 274 m (900 ft)
- Landing run: 122 m (400 ft)

AERO DESIGN

AERO DESIGN ASSOCIATES

Hangar One, Building 147, Opa-Locka Airport, Opa-Locka, Florida 33054
Telephone: (305) 685 8128
President: David Garber

AERO DESIGN DG-1

This unorthodox monoplane is the first custom-built Unlimited Class racing aircraft constructed in the United States since the 1930s. Designated DG-1, it is intended to compete directly with the highly modified P-51 Mustangs, F8F Bearcats and Hawker Sea Furies, and also to be capable of breaking the existing world speed record for propeller-driven aircraft, which stands at 419·249 knots (776·449 km/h; 482·463 mph).

The DG-1 has a cigar-shaped fuselage embodying a flush cockpit canopy. It is powered by two engines—one at each end of the fuselage—with respective tractor and

Aerocar Sooper-Coot Model A lightweight homebuilt amphibian

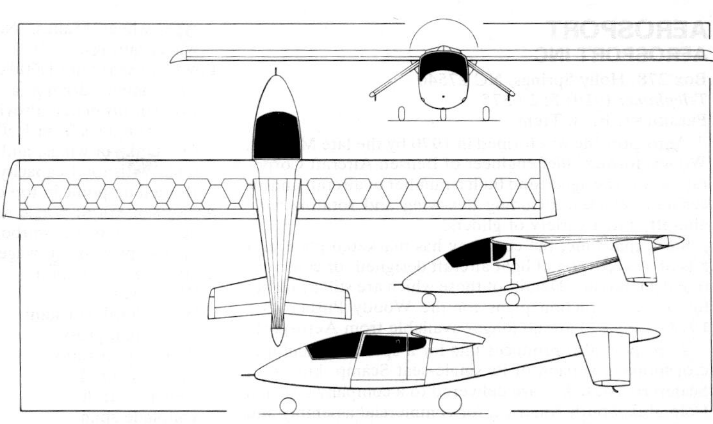
Aerocar Micro-Imp, with additional side elevation (bottom) of four-seat Imp *(Michael A. Badrocke)*

Aerocar Mini-Imp single-seat homebuilt aircraft (1,900 cc Limbach engine)

Aero Design DG-1 in revised form with underfuselage airscoop

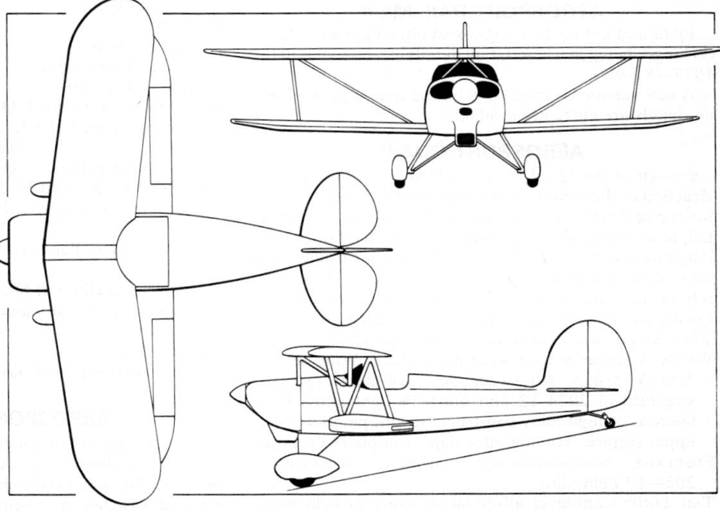
Miller Lil' Rascal, for construction by schools *(Michael A. Badrocke)*

pusher propellers. The tailplane has marked anhedral and both dorsal and ventral tail fins are fitted. Stress limits are ±12*g*.

The President of Aero Design Associates, Mr David Garber, a pilot with Pan American World Airways, has several years' experience of racing in the Sport Biplane Class in modified Pitts Specials.

Design of the DG-1 was started in 1973 and construction began in late 1974. The aircraft made its first brief flight on 25 July 1977, when the port landing gear broke. Repairs were put in hand and at the same time the airscoop was moved to an underfuselage position, between the main landing gear legs. Flying resumed on 4 June 1978, and by early 1979 ten test flights had been made. Although the aircraft is reported to fly well, it was experiencing oil cooling problems at that time.

TYPE: Single-seat racing monoplane.

WINGS: Cantilever monoplane. NACA 065 wing section. Thickness/chord ratio 12%. No dihedral or anhedral. Incidence 0° 30'. Glassfibre-reinforced spar; foam-filled wing interior and glassfibre covering. Ailerons of similar construction to wings.

FUSELAGE: Steel tube (4130) structure, covered with 2·4 mm (3/32 in) plywood and glassfibre.

TAIL UNIT: All-moving tailplane with 10° anhedral, dorsal fin, and ventral fin and rudder, all constructed of foam and glassfibre.

LANDING GEAR: Fully retractable tricycle type, with single 0·25 m (10 in) diameter wheel on each unit. Tyre pressure 4·14 bars (60 lb/sq in). All three wheels retract rearward hydraulically into fuselage. Nosewheel lock coupled to control stick. Gerides brakes.

POWER PLANT: Two Mazda RX-3 rotary-combustion motor car engines, modified to produce an estimated 243 kW (330 hp) each at more than 8,000 rpm. Engines have fuel injection, and custom-built Air Research turbochargers. Each drives a Hartzell three-blade constant-speed propeller. Usable fuel capacity 208 litres (55 US gallons) plus externally-carried 113·5 litre (30 US gallon) optional tank. Oil capacity of each engine 7·5 litres (2 US gallons).

ACCOMMODATION: Single semi-reclining seat under two-section Plexiglas canopy.

SYSTEMS: 14V DC electrical system, with AC for electric gyros. Full blind-flying, high-altitude capability, including oxygen system.

DIMENSIONS, EXTERNAL:

Wing span	6·10 m (20 ft 0 in)
Wing chord at root	1·07 m (3 ft 6 in)
Wing chord at tip	0·53 m (1 ft 9 in)
Wing area, gross	4·88 m² (52·5 sq ft)
Wing aspect ratio	7·6
Length overall	6·25 m (20 ft 6 in)
Height overall	1·68 m (5 ft 6 in)
Tailplane span	2·13 m (7 ft 0 in)
Wheel track	1·22 m (4 ft 0 in)
Wheelbase	2·24 m (7 ft 4 in)
Propeller diameter	1·73 m (5 ft 8 in)
Propeller ground clearance	0·25 m (10 in)

WEIGHTS:

Weight empty	816 kg (1,800 lb)
Max T-O weight, racing	1,043 kg (2,300 lb)
Max T-O weight	1,088 kg (2,400 lb)
Max landing weight	998 kg (2,200 lb)

PERFORMANCE (estimated):

Never-exceed speed	Mach 0·75
Max level speed at S/L with racing wing	391 knots (724 km/h; 450 mph)
Max level speed with special speed record wing	over 434 knots (804 km/h; 500 mph)
Normal cruising speed at 5,180 m (17,000 ft)	304 knots (563 km/h; 350 mph)
Stalling speed, flaps down	85 knots (158 km/h; 98 mph)
Max rate of climb at S/L	914 m (3,000 ft)/min
Service ceiling	7,315 m (24,000 ft)
Service ceiling, one engine out	5,180 m (17,000 ft)
Range with max fuel, 15 min reserves, at 60% power	600 nm (1,112 km; 691 miles)
Range with internal fuel, 15 min reserves, at 60% power	400 nm (740 km; 460 miles)
Range, 100% power, no reserves	290 nm (537 km; 334 miles)

AERONEERING
AERONEERING INC

PO Box 8, Claxton-Evans County Airport, Claxton, Georgia 30417
Telephone: (912) 739 1930
PRESIDENT: Merle B. Miller

Mr Miller designed and built a lightweight sporting aircraft known as the Red Bare-un, of which plans were made available to amateur constructors. Design began in June 1970, and the prototype flew for the first time on 3 June 1971. Details of the Red Bare-un, in its original form, can be found in the 1974-75 *Jane's*.

A second aircraft has been designed by Mr Miller, and details of this follow:

MILLER LIL' RASCAL

This aircraft has been designed primarily for construction by amateurs and by schools. Work on the prototype was started in November 1975, by a class of 15 students, under the direction of Mr B. G. Tippins of Claxton High School, specially formed for this project under the sponsorship of Chapter 330 of the Experimental Aircraft Association (Savannah, Georgia).

TYPE: Two-seat sporting aircraft.

WINGS: Strut-braced biplane wings of Clark Y section. Sweepback 9° at quarter-chord on upper wing only. Conventional structure of spruce and plywood, covered with Stits Poly-Fiber Dacron. Wire-braced internally. No landing or flying wires. Wooden ailerons. No flaps.

FUSELAGE: Conventional 4130 steel tube structure, with wooden stringers, covered with Stits Poly-Fiber Dacron.

TAIL UNIT: Structure of 4130 steel tube, covered with Stits Poly-Fiber Dacron. Elevators fitted. No tabs.

LANDING GEAR: Non-retractable tailwheel type. Main units of 4130 steel tube, with steel coil spring suspension; wheel size 5·00-5. Wheel fairings optional. Disc brakes.

POWER PLANT: One 63·5 kW (85 hp) Continental C85-8 flat-four engine, driving a two-blade fixed-pitch propeller. Alternatively, a 67 kW (90 hp) Franklin engine can be installed. Main fuel tank forward of cockpit; auxiliary tanks in upper-wing roots. Oil capacity 4·75 litres (1·25 US gallons).

ACCOMMODATION: Two seats side by side in open cockpit.

DIMENSIONS, EXTERNAL:

Wing span (upper wing)	6·30 m (20 ft 8 in)
Wing chord, constant	1·07 m (3 ft 6 in)
Wing area, gross	11·71 m² (126 sq ft)
Length overall	4·65 m (15 ft 3 in)
Height overall	1·66 m (5 ft 5½ in)
Propeller diameter	1·75 m (5 ft 9 in)
Propeller ground clearance	0·203 m (8 in)

DIMENSION, INTERNAL:

Cockpit: Max width	0·85 m (2 ft 9⅜ in)

WEIGHTS:

Weight empty (approx)	295 kg (650 lb)
Max T-O weight	499 kg (1,100 lb)

PERFORMANCE (estimated):

Max level speed	87 knots (161 km/h; 100 mph)
Max cruising speed	78 knots (145 km/h; 90 mph)
Stalling speed	48 knots (88·5 km/h; 55 mph)

AEROSPORT

AEROSPORT INC

Box 278, Holly Springs, NC 27540
Telephone: (919) 552 6375
President: E. B. Trent

Aerosport Inc was formed in 1970 by the late Mr H. L. Woods, former chief engineer of Bensen Aircraft Corporation, who designed and built a number of aircraft and air cushion vehicles, including flex-wing and rotating-wing aircraft, and a variety of gliders.

Since that time, the company has marketed plans and kits of a succession of light aircraft designed for construction by amateurs. Details of those which are still available follow. Construction plans for the Woody Pusher (see 1978-79 *Jane's*) are no longer available from Aerosport.

Aerosport also produces kits for a special agricultural cropspraying version of its single-seat Scamp, known as Scamp B. These kits are delivered to a company based in Colombia, South America, for commercial assembly and sale as completed aircraft. Details can be found in the main Aircraft section of this edition.

AEROSPORT RAIL Mk II

Plans and kits for this single-seat ultra-light aircraft are no longer being marketed. Full details can be found in the 1977-78 *Jane's*.

A new version is expected to be announced in 1980, but no details are currently available.

AEROSPORT QUAIL

Design of the Quail began in January 1970, and construction of the prototype was started in July 1971. It flew for the first time in December 1971, with an all-moving tailplane; but the designers incorporated a fixed-incidence tailplane with elevators before plans and construction kits were made available to amateur constructors. About 375 sets of plans had been sold by 1979. Approximately 26 Quails are under construction and about ten are flying.

Type: Single-seat lightweight cabin monoplane.

Wings: Cantilever high-wing monoplane. Wing section NACA 23015. No sweepback. All-metal two-spar structure of 2024-T3 and 6061-T6 light alloy. Plain ailerons of light alloy construction with piano hinge at upper surface. Trailing-edge flaps. Endplates optional.

Fuselage: Semi-monocoque all-metal structure of 2024-T3 light alloy.

Tail Unit: Cantilever all-metal structure of light alloy, with swept vertical surfaces. Fixed-incidence tailplane. Trim tab on rudder and elevator of prototype; optional for later aircraft.

Landing Gear: Non-retractable tricycle type. Cantilever spring main gear struts of light alloy. Nosewheel shock-absorption by rubber in compression. Main wheels and tyres size 5·30 × 4·50-6; nosewheel and tyre size 2·80 × 2·50-4. Tyre pressure 1·38 bars (20 lb/sq in). Barrel-type wheel brakes. Nosewheel steerable. Optional wheel fairings.

Power Plant: One 1,600 cc modified Volkswagen motor car engine, driving a 54-36 two-blade fixed-pitch wooden propeller. Provision for installation of Volkswagen engines from 1,500 cc to 1,800 cc capacity. Two fuel tanks in wings, and 7·5 litre (2 US gallon) meter tank, with total capacity of 38 litres (10 US gallons). Refuelling point in top of each wing.

Accommodation: Single seat in enclosed cabin, which is heated. Door on starboard side is hinged at top and opens upwards. Stowage for 9 kg (20 lb) baggage.

Dimensions, external:
- Wing span: 7·32 m (24 ft 0 in)
- Wing chord, constant: 1·07 m (3 ft 6 in)
- Wing area, gross: 7·8 m² (84 sq ft)
- Wing aspect ratio: 6·87
- Length overall: 4·85 m (15 ft 11 in)
- Height overall: 1·69 m (5 ft 6½ in)
- Tailplane span: 1·83 m (6 ft 0 in)
- Wheel track: 1·52 m (5 ft 0 in)
- Wheelbase: 1·22 m (4 ft 0 in)
- Propeller diameter: 1·37 m (4 ft 6 in)

Weights:
- Weight empty: 242 kg (534 lb)
- Normal T-O weight: 345 kg (762 lb)
- Max T-O weight: 359 kg (792 lb)

Performance (at max T-O weight):
- Max level speed at S/L: 113 knots (209 km/h; 130 mph)
- Max cruising speed: 100 knots (185 km/h; 115 mph)
- Econ cruising speed: 95·5 knots (177 km/h; 110 mph)
- Max manoeuvring speed: 78 knots (145 km/h; 90 mph)
- Stalling speed, flaps down: 42 knots (78 km/h; 48 mph)
- Max rate of climb at S/L: 259 m (850 ft)/min
- Service ceiling (estimated): 3,660 m (12,000 ft)
- T-O run: 91 m (300 ft)
- Landing run: 122 m (400 ft)
- Range with max fuel, no reserves: 200 nm (370 km; 230 miles)

AEROSPORT SCAMP A

The prototype of the single-seat all-metal Scamp A flew for the first time on 21 August 1973. It was intended primarily for operation from grass strips, and tricycle landing gear was chosen as being more rational for a generation of amateur pilots who had received their initial flight training on aircraft equipped with landing gear of this configuration. Stressed to +6*g* and −3*g*, the Scamp A can be used for limited aerobatics; and emphasis has been placed on simple construction techniques to make it an easy project for the homebuilder.

Plans and kits of parts, except for the engine, are available to amateur constructors. More than 640 sets of plans had been sold by 1979. At least 12 Scamps are flying and approximately 30 more are under construction from Aerosport kits.

An agricultural cropspraying version, known as Scamp B, is assembled in South America from Aerosport kits and marketed commercially (see under Colombia in main Aircraft section).

Type: Single-seat light aircraft.

Wings: Braced biplane structure, with Vee-type interplane strut each side. Flying and landing wires of streamline section. Single 5 cm by 12·5 cm (2 in by 5 in) extruded section of 6061-T6 light alloy forms a pylon to support the centre-section of the upper wing. Dihedral 3° on lower wings only. All-metal two-spar structures of light alloy. Plain ailerons of light alloy construction, with piano hinge at upper surface, on upper wing only. No flaps. No trim tabs.

Fuselage: Semi-monocoque all-metal structure of light alloy.

Tail Unit: Braced T-tail of light alloy construction. Single bracing strut on each side. Fixed-incidence tailplane. Ground-adjustable trim tab on rudder.

Landing Gear: Non-retractable tricycle type. Cantilever spring main-gear struts of light alloy. Wheel fairing on each unit optional.

Power Plant: Prototype has one 44·5 kW (60 hp) 1,834 cc Volkswagen modified motor car engine. Design suitable for Volkswagen engines of 1,700 cc to 2,100 cc, driving a 56-38 two-blade fixed-pitch wooden propeller. Fuel tank in fuselage nose, aft of firewall, capacity 30·5 litres (8 US gallons). Refuelling point on fuselage upper surface, forward of windscreen.

Accommodation: Single seat in open cockpit.

Dimensions, external:
- Wing span: 5·33 m (17 ft 6 in)
- Wing chord, constant: 0·91 m (3 ft 0 in)
- Wing area, gross: 9·52 m² (102·5 sq ft)
- Length overall: 4·27 m (14 ft 0 in)
- Height overall: 1·69 m (5 ft 6½ in)
- Wheel track: 1·52 m (5 ft 0 in)
- Wheelbase: 1·17 m (3 ft 10 in)

Weights (prototype):
- Weight empty: 236 kg (520 lb)
- Max T-O weight: 348 kg (768 lb)

Performance (prototype):
- Never-exceed speed: 108 knots (201 km/h; 125 mph)
- Max level speed: 82 knots (153 km/h; 95 mph)
- Cruising speed: 74 knots (137 km/h; 85 mph)
- Max manoeuvring speed: 72 knots (134 km/h; 83 mph)
- Stalling speed: 39 knots (73 km/h; 45 mph)
- Service ceiling (estimated): 3,660 m (12,000 ft)
- T-O run: 91 m (300 ft)
- Landing run: 122 m (400 ft)
- Range at cruising speed: 130 nm (241 km; 150 miles)

ANDERSON

ANDERSON AIRCRAFT CORPORATION

c/o E. K. Morice Jr, PO Box 2048, Delray Beach, Florida 33444
Telephone: (305) 276 5207

Mr Earl Anderson, a Boeing 747 captain flying for Pan American World Airways, designed and built an original light amphibian which he named EA-1 Kingfisher. The project occupied a period of nine years from start of design to completion, at a cost of around $5,500, and the first flight was made on 24 April 1969.

After a time, Mr Anderson replaced the original 74·5 kW (100 hp) Continental O-200 engine by an 86 kW (115 hp) Lycoming O-235-C1, driving a Sensenich M76AM-4-44 propeller. With this power plant the Kingfisher has an empty weight of 495 kg (1,092 lb), a max T-O weight of 725 kg (1,600 lb) and improved performance. By January 1975 the prototype had accumulated a total of more than 600 flying hours.

Plans available to amateur constructors cover the increase in weight. The Kingfisher was designed originally to accept alternative power plants up to a maximum of 104·4 kW (140 hp), but on the basis of experience with the 86 kW (115 hp) Lycoming engine, Mr Anderson is discouraging homebuilders from installing more powerful engines than this.

Mr Anderson formed Anderson Aircraft Corporation to market plans of the Kingfisher. By early 1979 well over 200 sets of plans had been sold, and more than 100 Kingfishers were under construction in the USA, Canada, Mexico, Sweden, Germany and Panama. At least ten homebuilt Kingfishers are known to be flying.

The following details apply to Mr Anderson's Kingfisher in its original configuration:

ANDERSON EA-1 KINGFISHER

Type: Two-seat light amphibian.

Wings: Braced high-wing monoplane with streamline-section Vee bracing struts each side (standard J3, PA-11 or PA-12 Piper Cub wing). Stabilising floats mounted beneath wings, adjacent to wingtips, are constructed of ⅜ in square mahogany stringers, covered with ¹/₁₆ in mahogany plywood coated with glassfibre. Each float weighs 4·1 kg (9 lb).

Fuselage: Conventional flying-boat hull of wooden construction with spruce frames and longerons, covered with ¹/₁₆ in and ¼ in mahogany plywood coated with glassfibre.

Tail Unit: Conventional strut-braced tail unit of steel tubing, fabric covered.

Landing Gear: Retractable tailwheel type. Each main unit is retracted forward, manually and individually, with spring-loaded assist mechanism. Bungee shock-absorption.

Power Plant: One 74·5 kW (100 hp) Continental O-200 flat-four engine, driving a fixed-pitch two-blade tractor propeller. Alternatively a Lycoming O-235-C1 of 86 kW (115 hp) or other engine of up to 112 kW (150 hp), can be fitted. Single fuel tank in hull, immediately forward of windscreen, capacity 76 litres (20 US gallons). Refuelling point on nose. Oil capacity 5·7 litres (1·5 US gallons).

Accommodation: Two seats, side by side, in enclosed cabin. Piper Tri-Pacer windscreen. Door on port side.

System: 30A alternator for radios, lights and starter.

Dimensions, external:
- Wing span: 11·00 m (36 ft 1 in)
- Length overall: 7·16 m (23 ft 6 in)
- Height overall: 2·44 m (8 ft 0 in)
- Wheel track: 1·52 m (5 ft 0 in)
- Propeller diameter: 1·83 m (6 ft 0 in)

Weights:
- Weight empty: 468 kg (1,032 lb)
- Max T-O weight: 680 kg (1,500 lb)

Performance (at max T-O weight):
- Never-exceed speed: 104 knots (193 km/h; 120 mph)
- Max level speed: 104 knots (193 km/h; 120 mph)
- Cruising speed at 305 m (1,000 ft): 74 knots (136 km/h; 85 mph)
- Stalling speed: 39 knots (72·5 km/h; 45 mph)
- Max rate of climb at S/L: 150-180 m (500-600 ft)/min
- Service ceiling: 3,050 m (10,000 ft)
- T-O run: 122-152 m (400-500 ft)
- T-O to 15 m (50 ft): 305 m (1,000 ft)
- Range with max fuel: 173 nm (322 km; 200 miles)

BAKENG

BAKENG AIRCRAFT

19025 92nd W, Edmonds, Washington 98020
Telephone: (206) 774 7846

BAKENG DUCE

Design and construction of the original Duce were started by Mr Gerald Bakeng in October 1969; it was completed six months later at a cost of approximately $1,500. The first flight was made on 2 April 1970. Plans are available to amateur constructors, and more than 200 sets have been sold.

The example illustrated was built by Mr Ray Hesselgrave of Henry, Illinois, and is known as the Baking Powder Special. Modifications from plans include use of a symmetrical wing section for higher cruising speed, a 10 cm (4 in) wider fuselage, redesigned tail unit and main landing gear mountings, and the addition of a large sliding canopy. First flight was made on 12 March 1977, with a 119 kW (160 hp) Lycoming IO-320 flat-four engine, propeller and cowling from a Piper Twin Comanche. Length is increased to 6·71 m (22 ft) and T-O weight to 862 kg (1,900 lb).

The following description applies to Mr Bakeng's prototype:

Type: Two-seat light sporting aircraft.

Wings: Braced parasol-wing monoplane, with Vee bracing struts each side. Streamline centre-section struts. Wing section Clark Y modified. Dihedral 1°. Incidence 3°. No sweepback. Composite structure of spruce and

Aerosport Scamp A single-seat biplane (56 kW; 75 hp Volkswagen 1,834 cc engine) built by Mr M. H. Sutherland *(Neil A. Macdougall)*

Aerosport Quail single-seat lightweight cabin monoplane

Anderson EA-1 Kingfisher amphibian *(Chris Reich)*

Mr Ray Hesselgrave's Baking Powder Special, a modified Bakeng Duce *(Howard Levy)*

Oldfield 'Baby' Lakes built by Mr Jerry Rodgers of Los Angeles (Continental A75 engine) *(Henry Artof)*

Bakeng Double Duce two-seat sporting biplane (Continental R-670 radial engine) *(Peter M. Bowers)*

4130 steel tube, fabric-covered. Frise-type ailerons of wooden construction, fabric-covered. Trailing-edge flaps of wooden construction, fabric-covered. Ground-adjustable tabs on ailerons.

FUSELAGE: Welded 4130 steel tube Warren truss structure, with fabric covering.

TAIL UNIT: Conventional wire-braced structure of welded 4130 steel tube, fabric-covered. Incidence of tailplane ground-adjustable. Ground-adjustable trim tab on rudder.

LANDING GEAR: Non-retractable tailwheel type. Cantilever spring steel main units. Main-wheel tyres size 6·00-6, pressure 0·34 bars (5 lb/sq in). Goodyear puck-type wheel brakes. Glassfibre wheel fairings on main units. Design may be adapted for float or ski landing gear.

POWER PLANT: One 93 kW (125 hp) Lycoming O-290-G (GPU) flat-four engine in prototype, driving a Sensenich two-blade fixed-pitch metal propeller with spinner. Design suitable for other engines in 56-93 kW (75-125 hp) range. One fuel tank in wing centre-section, capacity 42 litres (11 US gallons), and one tank in forward fuselage, immediately aft of firewall, capacity 64 litres (17 US gallons). Total fuel capacity 106 litres (28 US gallons). Refuelling points on upper surface of wing centre-section and front fuselage. Oil capacity 7·5 litres (2 US gallons).

ACCOMMODATION: Two persons in tandem in open cockpits. Fold-down doors on starboard side.

DIMENSIONS, EXTERNAL:
- Wing span: 9·25 m (30 ft 4 in)
- Wing chord, constant: 1·37 m (4 ft 6 in)
- Wing area, gross: 12·8 m² (138 sq ft)
- Length overall: 6·32 m (20 ft 9 in)
- Height overall: 2·44 m (8 ft 0 in)
- Tailplane span: 2·44 m (8 ft 0 in)
- Wheel track: 2·13 m (7 ft 0 in)
- Wheelbase: 4·88 m (16 ft 0 in)
- Propeller diameter: 1·88 m (6 ft 2 in)

DIMENSION, INTERNAL:
- Cockpit: Max width: 0·64 m (2 ft 1¼ in)

WEIGHTS:
- Weight empty: 407 kg (898 lb)
- Max T-O and landing weight: 680 kg (1,500 lb)

PERFORMANCE (at max T-O weight):
- Never-exceed speed: 130 knots (241 km/h; 150 mph)
- Max level speed at S/L: 126 knots (233 km/h; 145 mph)
- Max cruising speed at S/L: 122 knots (225 km/h; 140 mph)
- Econ cruising speed at S/L: 91 knots (169 km/h; 105 mph)
- Stalling speed, flaps down: 31·5 knots (58 km/h; 36 mph)
- Max rate of climb at S/L: 610 m (2,000 ft)/min
- Service ceiling: 5,180 m (17,000 ft)
- T-O run: 46 m (150 ft)
- Landing run: 46 m (150 ft)
- Range with max fuel: 260 nm (482 km; 300 miles)

BAKENG DOUBLE DUCE

The Double Duce is similar to the Duce in all respects except for its biplane configuration. It has a fabric-covered steel tube fuselage and wooden wings, braced with N-type interplane struts and with ailerons on all four wings. The power plant can be almost any horizontally-opposed or radial engine in the 93-164 kW (125-220 hp) range.

No additional details have been received from Mr Bakeng.

BARNEY OLDFIELD
BARNEY OLDFIELD AIRCRAFT COMPANY

PO Box 5974, Cleveland, Ohio 44101
Telephone: (216) 449 6300
PRESIDENT: Harvey R. Swack
TECHNICAL DIRECTOR: Richard M. Lane

Barney Oldfield Aircraft Co markets plans and material kits for the 'Baby' Lakes, a scaled down version of the Great Lakes Sport Trainer, the prototype of which was designed and built by Mr Andrew Oldfield, who died during 1970. Over 650 sets of drawings had been sold by early 1979, and many 'Baby' Lakes are under construction. About 40 were flying by 1979.

A variant of the 'Baby' Lakes is the 'Super Baby', with a more powerful engine and other modifications. Plans are available and 25 sets had been sold by January 1979. Another new variant of the design is the 'Buddy Baby', of which all known details can be found below.

Under development are inverted oil and fuel systems for the 'Baby' Lakes, so that it can be used as a low-cost aerobatic aircraft. It is stressed for ±9*g* at the recommended 385 kg (850 lb) gross weight.

OLDFIELD 'BABY' LAKES

TYPE: Single-seat sporting biplane.

WINGS: Braced biplane, with N-type interplane struts, double landing and flying wires and N-type centre-section support struts. Wing section modified M6, tapering to USA 27 46 cm (18 in) from tips. Incidence 2° 30′ on top wing, 1° 30′ on bottom wing. Wood structure of spruce spars and Warren truss ribs, with overall fabric covering. Ailerons on lower wings only. No flaps.

FUSELAGE: Welded steel tube structure, fabric-covered.

TAIL UNIT: Wire-braced welded steel tube structure, fabric-covered.

LANDING GEAR: Non-retractable tailwheel type. Oleo main legs with size 5·00-4 wheels. Steerable tailwheel.

POWER PLANT: One 59·5 kW (80 hp) Continental A80 flat-four engine, driving a two-blade fixed-pitch propeller. Provision for alternative engines of between 37·25 and 74·5 kW (50 and 100 hp), and several aircraft now under construction will have 1,500 and 1,600 cc Volkswagen engines. Fuel tank in front fuselage, capacity 45 litres (12 US gallons).

ACCOMMODATION: Single seat, normally in open cockpit. Cockpit canopy optional.

DIMENSIONS, EXTERNAL:
- Wing span: top: 5·08 m (16 ft 8 in)
- Wing chord (both wings, constant): 0·91 m (3 ft 0 in)
- Wing area, gross: 7·99 m² (86 sq ft)
- Length overall: 4·19 m (13 ft 9 in)
- Height overall: 1·37 m (4 ft 6 in)

WEIGHTS (A80 engine):
- Weight empty: 215 kg (475 lb)
- Max T-O weight: 385 kg (850 lb)

PERFORMANCE (A80 engine, at max T-O weight):
- Max level speed at S/L: 117 knots (217 km/h; 135 mph)
- Cruising speed at S/L: 102 knots (190 km/h; 118 mph)

Stalling speed 43·5 knots (81 km/h; 50 mph)
Max rate of climb at S/L 610 m (2,000 ft)/min
Service ceiling 5,200 m (17,000 ft)
T-O run 91 m (300 ft)
Landing run (no brakes) 122 m (400 ft)
Max range 217 nm (400 km; 250 miles)

OLDFIELD 'SUPER BABY' LAKES

Since 1976, a prototype 'Super Baby' Lakes (N362RB), based on the 'Baby' Lakes but with an 85·75 kW (115 hp) Lycoming O-235 flat-four engine, has been under test by its constructors, Mr Ray Ball, Mr Alan Lane and Mr Richard Lane. Following completion of more than 100 flying hours by early 1977, plans were made available to other constructors, with provision for fitting Lycoming engines of 80·5 to 93 kW (108-125 hp). At least two other plans-built 'Super Babies' were flying by early 1979.

The O-235 engine of the prototype drives a 69-54 Met-L-Prop two-blade metal propeller. Other modifications compared with the 'Baby' Lakes include use of a Burtch die spring landing gear, and routed wing spars which allow installation of wing fuel tanks without any appreciable increase in the empty weight by comparison with the wings of a standard 'Baby'. To prevent the possibility of fuel starvation, due to the high acceleration at take-off interupting forward fuel flow from the main tank, a 0·95 litre (1 US quart) header tank is installed forward of the carburettor. Covering is Dacron, finished with Stits Poly-Fiber and Imeron polyurethane colour.

Take-off distances are reduced by 20-25% compared with the 'Baby'. Other data measured with the prototype 'Super Baby' are as follows:

DIMENSIONS, EXTERNAL:
As for 'Baby' Lakes, except:
Length overall 4·34 m (14 ft 3 in)
WEIGHT:
Weight empty 218 kg (480 lb)
Max T-O weight 385 kg (850 lb)
PERFORMANCE:
Max level speed 135 knots (249 km/h; 155 mph) IAS
Cruising speed (75% power) 117 knots (217 km/h; 135 mph) IAS
Stalling speed 48 knots (88·5 km/h; 55 mph) IAS
Max rate of climb at S/L 915 m (3,000 ft)/min
T-O run 69 m (225 ft)
Landing run 130 m (425 ft)
Max range, with wing tanks 260 nm (483 km; 300 miles)

OLDFIELD 'BUDDY BABY' LAKES

Prototype construction and testing of the two-seat 'Buddy Baby' was under way in the first half of 1979, after a one-year delay due to relocation of the technical personnel and construction facilities from New York to Ohio. Flight testing was expected to be completed by the late Summer of 1979.

The 'Buddy Baby' utilises standard 'Baby' wings and tail unit. To prevent a significant increase in wing loading, a 41 cm (16 in) upper wing centre-section has been introduced, together with short stub-wings built integrally with the fuselage to increase the lower span by a similar amount.

The fuselage is a completely new design, which has been widened and stretched only enough to permit seating positions for two average-sized (77 kg; 170 lb) people in a configuration much like that of a 'buddy seat' on a motorcycle. Dual throttle and rudder pedals are provided, with a single dual-position joystick. The aircraft is flown solo from the rear seat and dual from the front position.

BARTON
WAYNE F. BARTON

11145 Cherokee Street, Northglenn, Colorado 80234
Telephone: (303) 452 8784

BARTON SYLKIE ONE MODEL B-1

Mr Wayne Barton, a pattern maker, has built a light aircraft known as the Sylkie One. Design and construction began in September 1966, and total cost of building was $6,600. First flight was made in April 1975. Plans are expected to be available to amateur builders in late 1979.

TYPE: Two-seat light aircraft.

WINGS: Cantilever tapered low-wing monoplane. Wing section NACA 23015 at root, NACA 23010 at tip. Dihedral from roots. Incidence 3° at root, 1° at tip. Spruce and mahogany structure, birch plywood and Dacron covered, with Butarae dope finish. Frise-type slotted ailerons and slotted flaps, of similar construction to wings. Trim tab on aileron.

FUSELAGE: Conventional spruce and mahogany truss structure, Dacron covered and dope finished.

TAIL UNIT: Cantilever structure, of similar construction to wings. Fin integral with fuselage. All-moving tailplane, with full-span trim/anti-servo tabs.

LANDING GEAR: Tricycle type, with spring-assisted mechanical retraction. Main wheels retract inward, nosewheel rearward. Steerable nosewheel. Shock-absorption by steel spring, with oil damping. Single Cleveland wheel on each unit, size 5·00-5, with 36 cm (14·2 in) diameter tyre. Tyre pressure: Main wheels 2·41 bars (35 lb/sq in), nosewheel 1·72 bars (25 lb/sq in). Cleveland hydraulic brakes.

POWER PLANT: One 112 kW (150 hp) Lycoming O-320 flat-four engine, driving a two-blade wooden fixed-pitch propeller. Two fuel tanks forward of instrument panel, each with capacity of 26·5 litres (7 US gallons), and one glassfibre fuel tank aft of seat, capacity 106 litres (28 US gallons). Refuelling point on starboard side of fuselage. Oil capacity 7·5 litres (2 US gallons).

ACCOMMODATION: Two seats side by side under rearward-sliding transparent canopy. Baggage space aft of seat.

SYSTEM: 12V battery and 40A alternator.

AVIONICS: Genave 200B radio.

DIMENSIONS, EXTERNAL:
Wing span 7·57 m (24 ft 10 in)
Wing area, gross 10·22 m² (110 sq ft)
Wing chord at root 1·60 m (5 ft 3 in)
Wing chord at tip 0·76 m (2 ft 6 in)
Length overall 6·27 m (20 ft 7 in)
Height overall 2·14 m (7 ft 0½ in)
Tailplane span 2·67 m (8 ft 9 in)
Wheel track 2·43 m (7 ft 11¾ in)
Wheelbase 1·16 m (3 ft 9¾ in)
Propeller diameter 1·83 m (6 ft 0 in)
WEIGHTS:
Weight empty 463 kg (1,020 lb)
Max T-O weight 735 kg (1,620 lb)
PERFORMANCE:
Never-exceed speed 187 knots (346 km/h; 215 mph)
Max level speed at 2,440 m (8,000 ft) 184 knots (341 km/h; 212 mph)
Max cruising speed at 2,440 m (8,000 ft) 167 knots (309 km/h; 192 mph)
Econ cruising speed at 2,440 m (8,000 ft) 148 knots (273 km/h; 170 mph)
Stalling speed, flaps down 43·5 knots (81 km/h; 50 mph) IAS
Max rate of climb at S/L 488 m (1,600 ft)/min
Service ceiling over 5,790 m (19,000 ft)
T-O run at 1,735 m (5,700 ft) 564 m (1,850 ft)
T-O to 15 m (50 ft) at 1,735 m (5,700 ft) 823 m (2,700 ft)
Landing from 15 m (50 ft) 700 m (2,300 ft)
Landing run 366 m (1,200 ft)
Range with max fuel, 30 min reserves 833 nm (1,545 km; 960 miles)

BEDE
BEDE AIRCRAFT INC

Details of the aircraft designed by Bede Aircraft Inc for amateur construction can be found in the 1977-78 *Jane's.*

BEETS
GLENN BEETS

Mr G. Beets of Riverside, California, designed a lightweight sporting aircraft which he named the G/B Special. Construction of the prototype occupied two years and cost approximately $2,500, the first flight being made on 25 July 1973. Plans of the G/B Special, kits of components and materials are available from Stolp Starduster Corporation (which see).

BEETS G/B SPECIAL

TYPE: Single-seat sporting aircraft.

WINGS: Braced parasol monoplane. Wing section Curtis 72. Vee bracing struts each side with auxiliary struts. N-type cabane struts. Conventional wood structure with spruce spars and truss ribs, Dacron covered. Plain ailerons of similar construction. No trim tabs. Cutout in wing trailing-edge.

FUSELAGE: Welded structure of 4130 steel tube with Dacron covering.

TAIL UNIT: Cantilever structure of wood, with foam filling and covering of $^1/_{16}$ in mahogany plywood.

LANDING GEAR: Non-retractable tailwheel type, with main wheels carried on braced tubular steel struts. Glassfibre wheel fairings on main wheels.

POWER PLANT: One 52 kW (70 hp) Volkswagen 1,641 cc modified motorcar engine, driving a two-blade fixed-pitch propeller through a 2½ : 1 reduction drive. Design will accept engines of 37·25-74·5 kW (50-100 hp).

ACCOMMODATION: Single seat in open cockpit.

DIMENSIONS, EXTERNAL:
Wing span 7·62 m (25 ft 0 in)
Wing chord 1·27 m (4 ft 2 in)
Length overall 4·98 m (16 ft 4 in)
Height overall 1·83 m (6 ft 0 in)
WEIGHTS:
Weight empty 274 kg (603 lb)
Max T-O weight 420 kg (925 lb)
PERFORMANCE (at max T-O weight with cruise performance propeller):
Max level speed at S/L 135 knots (251 km/h; 156 mph)
Cruising speed 104 knots (193 km/h; 120 mph)
Landing speed 30·5 knots (56 km/h; 35 mph)
Max rate of climb at S/L 610 m (2,000 ft)/min
T-O run 61 m (200 ft)
Landing run 92 m (300 ft)
Range 520 nm (965 km; 600 miles)

BENSEN
BENSEN AIRCRAFT CORPORATION

Box 31047, Raleigh-Durham Airport, Raleigh, North Carolina 27612
Telephone: (919) 787 4224/0945
PRESIDENT: Dr Igor B. Bensen, PE

The Bensen Aircraft Corporation was formed by Dr Igor B. Bensen, formerly Chief of Research of the Kaman company, to develop a series of lightweight helicopters and rotary-wing gliders suitable for production in kit form for amateur construction as well as in ready-to-fly condition. More than 2,000 were flying by 1979.

Production is centred on the B-8M/V and Super Bug Gyro-Copter powered autogyros, the twin-engined B-16S Gyro-Copter, and various land and waterborne versions of the B-8 rotor-kite. Research into new models and concepts continues, and Bensen has announced important new second-generation versions of the Gyro-Copter that are capable of 'jump' take-off and of hovering flight.

BENSEN MODEL B-8 GYRO-GLIDER

The Gyro-Glider is a simple unpowered rotor-kite which can be towed behind even a small motorcar and has achieved free gliding with the towline released. It is available as either a completed aircraft or kit of parts for amateur construction. Alternatively, would-be constructors can purchase a set of plans, with building and flying instructions. No pilot's licence is required to fly it in the United States and many hundreds of kits and plans have been sold.

The original Model B-7 Gyro-Glider was described in the 1958-59 *Jane's.* It was followed by the Model B-8, which is offered as either a single-seater or two-seater, the latter version being suitable for use as a pilot trainer.

The Model B-8 consists basically of an inverted square-section tubular aluminium T-frame structure, of which the forward arm supports the lightweight seat, towing arm, rudder bar and landing gear nosewheel. The rear arm supports a large stabilising fin and rudder, made normally of plywood, but optionally of metal. The main landing gear wheels are carried on a tubular axle near the junction of the T-frame. The free-turning two-blade rotor is universally-mounted at the top of the T-frame and is normally operated directly by a hanging-stick control. A floor-type control column is available as optional equipment. Pedal controls for the rudder are standard.

The Gyro-Glider rotor is made normally of laminated plywood, with a steel spar. Factory-built all-metal rotor blades are available as optional items.

The two-seat trainer version of the Gyro-Glider is fitted with castoring crosswind landing gear and has an extra-wide wheel track. It will maintain level flight down to 16·5 knots (30·5 km/h; 19 mph).

DIMENSIONS, EXTERNAL:
Diameter of rotor 6·10 m (20 ft 0 in)
Length of fuselage 3·45 m (11 ft 4 in)
Height overall 1·90 m (6 ft 3 in)

First Oldfield 'Super Baby' Lakes, built by Mr Ray Ball, Mr Alan Lane and Mr Richard Lane

Barton Sylkie One Model B-1 light aircraft

Beets G/B Special lightweight sporting aircraft (Volkswagen engine)
(Howard Levy)

Bensen B-8V Gyro-Copter built in Australia by Mr Bob Higgins
(The Herald & Weekly Times, Melbourne)

Bensen B-8MJ jump take-off Gyro-Copter

Bensen Model B-8W Hydro-Glider being towed by a motorboat

BENSEN MODEL B-8W HYDRO-GLIDER

The basic structure of this floatplane rotor-kite is similar to that of the B-8 Gyro-Glider and conversion from one to the other is simple. Main change is that the nosewheel landing gear is replaced by two floats. The original round-type floats have been superseded by flat-bottomed pontoons of polyurethane foam covered by glassfibre, which give better planing, with less spray.

The Hydro-Glider is towed by a motorboat.

BENSEN MODEL B-8M, B-8V and SUPER BUG GYRO-COPTERS and B-8MW HYDRO-COPTER

First flown on 6 December 1955, the Gyro-Copter is a powered autogyro conversion of the Gyro-Glider, designed for home construction from kits or plans. When fitted with floats it is known as a Hydro-Copter.

The current **B-8M** version of the Gyro-Copter has a more powerful engine than the original B-7M and can be equipped with an optional mechanical rotor drive. By engaging this drive, the rotor can be accelerated to flying speed while the aircraft is stationary. Then, by transferring the power to the pusher propeller, it is possible to take off in only 15 m (50 ft), with the rotor autorotating normally. Alternatively, a 1 hp Ohlsson & Rice Compact III two-stroke engine can be attached to the rotor for pre-rotation, automatically disengaging itself at take-off rpm.

Other non-standard items available optionally include a 67 kW (90 hp) engine instead of the normal 53·5 kW (72 hp) engine, a stronger aluminium bolted-together engine mounting, a larger-diameter rotor, an offset gimbal rotor head, a redundant mast consisting of a pair of closely matched alloy tubes instead of the normal square-tube mast, a floor-type control column instead of the normal overhead type of column, dual ignition, nosewheel arrester, Bensen-manufactured pontoons of polyurethane foam covered with glassfibre, and a detachable glassfibre open cabin nacelle for single-seat Gyro-Copters of 1976 or later type (only with redundant mast and aluminium engine mount of new design). All-metal rotor blades and tail surfaces are available as alternatives to the standard wooden components.

The prototype Model B-8M Gyro-Copter flew for the first time on 8 July 1957 and the first production model on 9 October 1957.

The B-8M is roadable, requiring no removal of, or changes in, its equipment for transition from air to ground travel. The rotor is merely stopped in a fore-and-aft position by a lock. Gyro-Copters have been driven on highways and have negotiated heavy city traffic with ease in a number of public demonstrations in the USA.

The **B-8V**, which flew for the first time in the Autumn of 1967, is basically a standard B-8M, but is powered by a 1,600 cc Volkswagen engine. In unmodified form the VW1600 yields just adequate flight performance at 272 kg (600 lb) gross weight. Since Bensen engineers considered that most Gyro-Copters would not have a gross weight as high as 600 lb, the VW engine justified inclusion as an alternative power plant to the standard McCulloch engine.

Kits and parts for the B-8V, excluding engine and mounting, are available, as are plans and an instruction manual for converting the B-8M to a B-8V, or for mounting a VW engine on a standard B-8 airframe.

In May 1971, Bensen announced introduction of the **Super Bug**, an advanced version of the standard Model B-8M. This features a twin-engine installation to spin up the rotor prior to take-off. Bensen claims this as an intermediate step towards full VTOL capability, as this more powerful pre-rotation enables the Super Bug to take off and clear a 15 m (50 ft) obstacle within 137 m (450 ft) of starting its T-O run in zero wind conditions at max T-O weight. Other standard equipment of the Super Bug includes rotor brake, parking brake on main wheels, single control of rudder and nosewheel steering, soft suspension of the auxiliary tailwheel and an increase of 45·5 kg (100 lb) in max T-O weight.

The following description applies to the Models B-8M and B-8V:

Type: Single-seat light autogyro.

Rotor System: B-8M has single two-blade rotor of laminated plywood construction, with steel spar (optional all-metal rotor). Blade section Bensen G2. Teetering hub, with no lag hinges or collective pitch control. A similar rotor, of all-metal construction, is provided for the B-8V. A larger-diameter rotor is not available as an alternative for this latter model. No anti-torque rotor. Rotor speed 400 rpm.

Rotor Drive (optional): An auxiliary 0·75 kW (1 hp) Ohlsson & Rice engine is available to spin up the rotor.

Fuselage: Square-section tubular 6061-T6 aluminium structure. Optional redundant twin rotor mast of alloy tubes.

Tail Surfaces: Vertical fin and rudder of ¼ in plywood. Optional all-metal tail surfaces.

Landing Gear: Non-retractable tricycle type, with auxiliary tailwheel. No shock-absorbers. Steerable nosewheel. General Tire wheels, size 30·5-10·15 cm (12-4 in). Tyre pressure 0·69 bars (10 lb/sq in). Brake on nosewheel. Optional skis.

Power Plant: One 53·5 kW (72 hp) McCulloch Model 4318AX flat-four two-stroke engine (or, optionally, a 67 kW; 90 hp McCulloch 4318GX engine of similar weight and dimensions), driving a two-blade wooden fixed-pitch Aero Prop Model BA 48-A2 pusher propeller with leading-edges covered with stainless steel. Alternatively, one 47·5 kW (64 hp) Volkswagen 1,600 cc flat-four four-stroke engine, driving a Troyer Model 50-24-65 two-blade wooden fixed-pitch pusher propeller. Fuel tank under pilot's seat, capacity 22·75 litres (6·0 US gallons). Can be fitted with auxiliary tank for ferrying. Optional plastics tank shaped as pilot's seat, replacing standard tank and seat and increasing fuel capacity to 36·5 litres (9·7 US gallons).

Accommodation: Open seat. Overhead azimuth stick and rudder pedal controls. Optional floor-type control column. Safety belt. Optional glassfibre open cabin nacelle.

Dimensions, external:

Diameter of rotor:	
standard	6·10 m (20 ft 0 in)
optional (on B-8M and B-8MW)	6·70 m (22 ft 0 in)
Rotor blade chord	0·18 m (7 in)
Length of fuselage	3·45 m (11 ft 4 in)
Height overall	1·90 m (6 ft 3 in)
Wheel track	1·52 m (5 ft 0 in)
Propeller diameter:	
53·5 kW (72 hp) McCulloch	1·22 m (4 ft 0 in)
47·5 kW (64 hp) Volkswagen	1·27 m (4 ft 2 in)

Areas (standard rotor):

Rotor blades (each)	0·54 m² (5·83 sq ft)
Rotor disc	29·17 m² (314 sq ft)

Weights (standard rotor):

Weight empty:	
B-8M	112 kg (247 lb)
B-8V	158 kg (348 lb)
Max T-O weight:	
B-8M	227 kg (500 lb)
B-8V	272 kg (600 lb)

Performance (at max T-O weight, with standard rotor):

Max level speed at S/L:	
B-8M	74 knots (137 km/h; 85 mph)
B-8V	52 knots (96·5 km/h; 60 mph)
Max cruising speed at S/L:	
B-8M	52 knots (96·5 km/h; 60 mph)
B-8V	43 knots (80·5 km/h; 50 mph)
Econ cruising speed:	
B-8M, B-8V	39 knots (72·5 km/h; 45 mph)
Min speed in level flight:	
B-8M	13 knots (24 km/h; 15 mph)
B-8V	17·5 knots (32 km/h; 20 mph)
T-O speed at S/L:	
B-8M	17·5 knots (32 km/h; 20 mph)
B-8V	22 knots (40 km/h; 25 mph)
Landing speed:	
B-8M	6 knots (11·5 km/h; 7 mph)
B-8V	9 knots (16 km/h; 10 mph)
Max rate of climb at S/L:	
B-8M	305 m (1,000 ft)/min
B-8V	198 m (650 ft)/min
Service ceiling:	
B-8M	3,800 m (12,500 ft)
B-8V	2,440 m (8,000 ft)
T-O run, unpowered rotor, zero wind:	
B-8M	92 m (300 ft)
B-8V	122 m (400 ft)
T-O run, powered rotor, zero wind:	
B-8M	15 m (50 ft)
Landing run in 9 knot (16 km/h; 10 mph) wind:	
B-8M, B-8V	0 ft
Landing run in zero wind:	
B-8M	6 m (20 ft)
B-8V	7·5 m (25 ft)
Normal range:	
B-8M	86 nm (160 km; 100 miles)
B-8V	130 nm (241 km; 150 miles)
Ferry range:	
B-8M	260 nm (482 km; 300 miles)
B-8V	345 nm (643 km; 400 miles)
Endurance:	
B-8M	1·5 h
B-8V	2·25 h

BENSEN MODEL B-8HD

This 1979 Bensen Gyro-Copter is based on the Super Bug design, but uses hydraulic drive (hence the HD designation) to feed about 3 kW (4 hp) from the main engine to the rotor, instead of having a separate engine for pre-rotation. The rotor is thus engaged continuously during all aspects of flight. This is reported to give the aircraft a take-off run of less than 61 m (200 ft), and to improve climb and range, while allowing an increase in payload. A near-vertical landing is also possible.

The hydraulic drive is expected to be marketed as a retrofit kit for the current B-8M.

BENSEN B-8MJ

Bensen Aircraft Corporation announced in early 1977 that it was to market a Power Head to fit any standard B-8M Gyro-Copter, enabling the aircraft to take off vertically, without any ground roll. The Power Head is claimed to provide a 30° angle of climb. Hovering cannot be achieved.

Power Heads are offered only to builders or owners of Gyro-Copters with 50 or more hours of solo flight. The resulting aircraft are designated B-8MJ (for 'Jump' take-off).

BENSEN MODEL B-8MH HOVER-GYRO

Demonstrated in public for the first time in 1976, the B-8MH is described as a 'Hovering Gyro-Copter', a capability reflected by the 'H' in its designation.

Development dates from 1973. On 29 June that year, Dr Igor Bensen piloted a Gyro-Glider with two two-blade co-axial rotors during its first flight at Raleigh-Durham Airport. Nineteen further flights followed, during which the aircraft executed a full range of flight manoeuvres.

In the B-8MH the lower two-blade rotor is driven by a vertically-mounted engine; the upper rotor autorotates. A small engine mounted immediately forward of the tail-fin drives a pusher propeller.

Able to be built as a conversion of the standard B-8M Gyro-Copter, the B-8MH can fly forwards, sideways and backwards, as well as being able to hover. It is claimed to be safer than either an aeroplane or a helicopter, as it will not stall or spin and does not need any special skill to land with the engine stopped. A detachable glassfibre cabin enclosure is optional on the standard single-seater. Conversion to a side-by-side two-seat configuration for pilot training is quick and easy.

Power Plant: One 52·2-82 kW (70-110 hp) modified watercooled outboard engine, driving the lower two-blade main rotor. Upper rotor autorotates. One 10·4 kW (14 hp) modified aircooled go-kart engine driving a two-blade pusher propeller mounted at rear. Fuel consumption at cruising speed, 19 litres (5 US gallons) per hour.

Dimensions, external:

Rotor diameter (each)	8·53 m (28 ft 0 in)
Height overall	2·74 m (9 ft 0 in)
Width overall	2·13 m (7 ft 0 in)

Weights:

Max T-O weight	408 kg (900 lb)
Useful load	136 kg (300 lb)

Performance:

Max cruising speed	56·5 knots (105 km/h; 65 mph)
Range at optimum cruising speed	104 nm (193 km; 120 miles)
Hovering endurance	45 min

BIRDMAN

BIRDMAN AIRCRAFT INC

480 Midway, Daytona Beach, Regional Airport, Daytona Beach, Florida 32014

Telephone: (904) 252 4053/2755

President: Leonard I. Roberts

Engineering: J. G. Ladesic

Production: R. Anderson

Sales: J. Roberts

Birdman Aircraft Inc has developed an ultra lightweight sporting aircraft which, despite a wing span of 10·36 m (34 ft 0 in), has an empty weight of only 55·5 kg (122 lb) in its current form. The company's aim was to design a strong, lightweight and inexpensive aircraft that could be assembled easily by a novice builder. In achieving this aim, it introduced some unusual ideas and construction materials. The covering, for example, consists of a bi-axially orientated synthetic film known as aircraft Monokote, and this offers the key to the combination of light weight and strength.

Design of what proved to be the world's lightest powered aircraft, known as the Birdman TL-1, with an empty weight of 45 kg (100 lb) in prototype form, began in April 1969. The first flight was recorded almost six years later, on 25 January 1975, after considerable structural research and testing. The company is marketing the aircraft in kit form, with all materials, components, engine and accessories provided, together with plans for its construction and a builder's manual. First orders were taken in June 1975 and by early 1979 over 300 kits were under construction.

BIRDMAN TL-1A

The prototype TL-1 (N111ET) had full-span trailing-edge flaps. These are deleted on the TL-1A production version, which also has a V-tail instead of the T-tail fitted to the prototype.

Type: Ultra lightweight sporting aircraft.

Wings: Cantilever monoplane, built in three sections, with detachable outer panels. Wing section USA 35B modified. Thickness/chord ratio 14%. Dihedral on outer wing panels 5°. Incidence 3°. No sweepback. Composite structure, with single built-up spruce spar, wooden ribs, leading-edge D cell of reinforced expanded synthetic foam and aircraft Monokote covering. No ailerons. Sequentially-operated spoilers, immediately aft of main spar, for both yaw and roll control; the more the stick is moved, the more panels come into operation.

Fuselage: Three-part structure: forward portion of riveted semi-monocoque 2024-T3 light alloy, centre section of spruce and plywood, and an aft section comprising a tapered plywood monocoque.

Tail Unit: Braced V-tail. Two-spar structure with laminated plywood ribs and aircraft Monokote covering. No rudders.

Landing Gear: Non-retractable main units only, sited at point of balance. Pilot's legs and feet substitute as retractable nose gear. Castor at aft end of fuselage to support aircraft on ground. Shock-absorption by rubber bungee. Main-wheel tyres size 12 × 1·25, pressure 3·10 bars (45 lb/sq in). No brakes.

Power Plant: One 8·5 kW (11·5 hp) McCulloch MC-101 DT single-cylinder aircooled two-stroke engine, pylon-mounted from centre-section structure aft of pilot, and driving a 28-9 two-blade wooden fixed-pitch pusher propeller. Fuel contained in one (normal) or two (auxiliary) aluminium tanks with combined capacity of 15 litres (4 US gallons). Lubricating oil mixed in fuel at ratio of 1 : 16.

Accommodation: Exposed seat of aluminium tube and cloth, with harness, adjustable to allow pilot to fly the aircraft in an upright or semi-reclining position.

Dimensions, external:

Wing span	10·36 m (34 ft 0 in)
Wing chord, constant	1·30 m (4 ft 3 in)
Wing area, gross	13·42 m² (144·5 sq ft)
Wing aspect ratio	8
Length overall	5·92 m (19 ft 5 in)
Height overall, tail up	2·18 m (7 ft 2 in)
Tailplane span	2·59 m (8 ft 6 in)
Wheel track	1·83 m (6 ft 0 in)
Propeller diameter	0·71 m (2 ft 4 in)

Weights:

Weight empty	55·5 kg (122 lb)
Normal T-O and landing weight	131 kg (288 lb)
Max T-O and landing weight	159 kg (350 lb)

Performance (at max T-O weight):

Never-exceed speed	60·5 knots (112 km/h; 70 mph)
Max level speed at S/L	43·5 knots (80·5 km/h; 50 mph)
Max cruising speed at 1,980 m (6,500 ft)	35 knots (64 km/h; 40 mph)
Econ cruising speed at 1,220 m (4,000 ft)	33 knots (61 km/h; 38 mph)
Stalling speed	12 knots (22·5 km/h; 14 mph)
Estimated rate of climb at S/L	61-92 m (200-300 ft)/min
Service ceiling	over 1,675 m (5,500 ft)
T-O run	26 m (85 ft)
T-O to 15 m (50 ft)	92 m (300 ft)
Landing from 15 m (50 ft)	30 m (100 ft)
Landing run	14 m (45 ft)
Min field length	92 m (300 ft)
Normal range	59·4 nm (110 km; 68·4 miles)

Bensen Hover-Gyro, with co-axial rotors, being flight tested

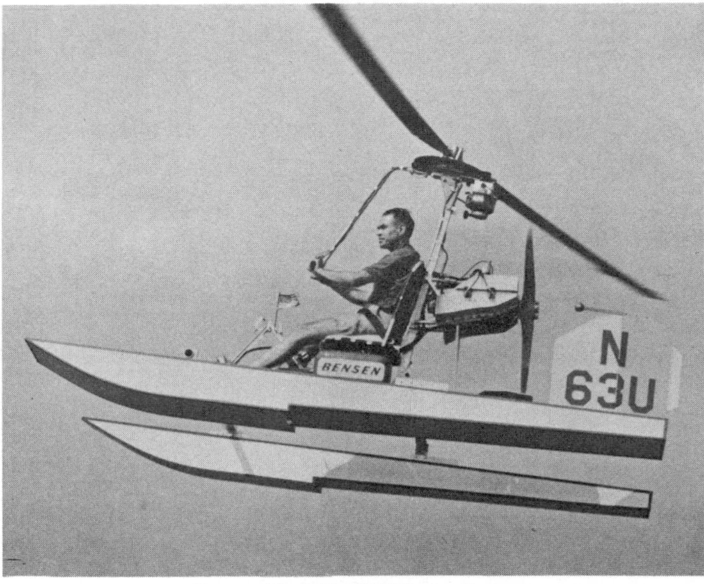

Bensen Model B-8MW Hydro-Copter

Bensen Model B-8HD hydraulic drive Gyro-Copter

Birdman TL-1A ultra-light homebuilt aircraft

Bowers Fly Baby 1-A (48·5 kW; 65 hp Continental engine) built by Don Enochs of Seattle *(Peter M. Bowers)*

Bowers Fly Baby 1-B converted from a standard 1-A monoplane by Ernest D. Harbin of Flushing, Michigan

Bowers Fly Baby 1-A (Continental A65) converted into a tandem two-seater by Mr Victor F. Meznarsic *(Howard Levy)*

BOWERS

PETER M. BOWERS

10458 16th Avenue South, Seattle, Washington 98168

Mr Peter Bowers, an aeronautical engineer with Boeing in Seattle, is a principal source of detailed information on vintage aircraft in the United States, and has provided much of the data for a number of replicas of first World War aircraft now under construction or flying.

Mr Bowers has built a number of aircraft himself. In particular, he designed and constructed prototypes of a single-seat light aircraft known as the Fly Baby, which is flying in both monoplane and biplane forms, and a side-by-side two-seat light monoplane named Namu II.

BOWERS FLY BABY 1-A

The prototype Fly Baby monoplane was produced to compete in an Experimental Aircraft Association design contest, organised to encourage the development of a simple, low-cost, easy-to-fly aeroplane that could be built by inexperienced amateurs for recreational flying. It was built in 720 working hours, at a cost of $1,050, and flew for the first time on 27 July 1960. As only one other aircraft was completed by the specified closing date, the contest was postponed for two years.

When the EAA contest was finally held in the Summer of 1962, Fly Baby was placed first and won a prize of $2,500. Home construction plans of the aircraft are available and 3,870 sets had been sold by May 1979. Construction of well over 670 Fly Babies is known to have been undertaken, of which about 350 had been completed and flown by 1979, including some based on detailed drawings and instructions published in *Sport Aviation,* journal of the EAA.

The Fly Baby monoplane has been tested as a twin-float seaplane, in which configuration it has a max AUW of 454 kg (1,000 lb) and cruising speed of 84 knots (156 km/h; 97 mph).

During 1968, Mr Bowers designed and built biplane wings for the Fly Baby, which are interchangeable with the monoplane wings. The monoplane version is known as the Fly Baby 1-A, and the biplane as the Fly Baby 1-B (described separately).

Mr Bowers amended his plans during 1973 to allow for construction of a two-seat version of the Fly Baby. The changes include a 0·97 m (3 ft 2 in) wide fuselage, a 1·52 m (5 ft 0 in) span wing centre-section to support a shock-absorbing landing gear similar to that of the Ryan ST/PT-22 of 1934-42, the use of heavier flying wires with swaged fork ends, a raised aft turtledeck to offset the drag of the larger cockpit and a recommendation to use an engine of 63·5 to 80 kW (85 to 107 hp). The outer wing panels are unchanged, giving the two-seat Fly Baby a span of 9·45 m (31 ft 0 in) and wing area of 12·4 m² (133·5 sq ft).

Mr Bowers feels that the use of side-by-side seating is a great performance handicap to the basic design, and approves the tandem arrangement worked out by Mr Victor F. Meznarsic (see accompanying illustration). At present, he is developing a stretched tandem two-seater, to be fitted with longer two-bay biplane wings, in a deliberate attempt to resemble a First World War type such as the B.E.2C. This will be a low-performance 'fun flier' on engines up to 74·5 kW (100 hp), and will not be aerobatic.

Because of the shortage of aircraft engines in the 48·5-63·5 kW (65-85 hp) range, Mr Bowers has been asked repeatedly by would-be builders about the suitability of Volkswagen conversions for the Fly Baby. He has consistently recommended against this, but now that a Finnish constructor has had some success, first with a 1,600 cc and later with an 1,800 cc conversion, Mr Bowers approves the use of VW engines of over 1,800 cc.

The following description applies to the original single-seat Fly Baby 1-A:

TYPE: Single-seat light monoplane.

WINGS: Wire-braced low-wing monoplane. Double ½ in 1 × 19 stainless steel bracing wires. Wing section NACA 4412. Wooden two-spar structure, covered with Dacron fabric and finished with two coats of nitrate dope and one coat of automotive enamel. Wings rotate about a special fitting to fold back alongside the fuselage for towing.

FUSELAGE: Conventional plywood-covered wood structure of rectangular section. Decking behind cockpit, including pilot's headrest, is removable and can be replaced with higher transparent section matched with a sliding transparent cockpit canopy for enclosed cockpit operation.

TAIL UNIT: Wire-braced wood structure, fabric-covered.

LANDING GEAR: Non-retractable tailwheel type. Main landing gear struts of laminated wood, braced by crossed steel wires. Steel tube straight-across axle faired with streamline-section steel tube. Ends of axles project beyond wheel hubs to serve as anchor points for wing bracing wires. Shock-absorption by low-pressure 8·00-4 tyres, carried on Piper Cub wheels, with hydraulic brakes.

POWER PLANT: One 63·5 kW (85 hp) Continental C75 flat-four engine, driving a two-blade fixed-pitch propeller. Fuel tank from Piper J-3 Cub, capacity 60·5 litres (16 US gallons).

ACCOMMODATION: Single seat in open or enclosed cockpit. Baggage in underfuselage 'tank' which can be removed and carried like a suitcase.

DIMENSIONS, EXTERNAL:
Wing span 8·53 m (28 ft 0 in)
Wing chord, constant 1·37 m (4 ft 6 in)
Length overall 5·64 m (18 ft 6 in)
Height, wings folded 1·98 m (6 ft 6 in)

WEIGHTS:
Weight empty 274 kg (605 lb)
Max T-O weight 419 kg (924 lb)

PERFORMANCE (at max T-O weight):
Max level speed at S/L over 104 knots (193 km/h; 120 mph)
Cruising speed 91-96 knots (169-177 km/h; 105-110 mph)
Landing speed 39 knots (72·5 km/h; 45 mph)
Max rate of climb at S/L 335 m (1,100 ft)/min
T-O and landing run 76 m (250 ft)
Range with max fuel 277 nm (515 km; 320 miles)

BOWERS FLY BABY 1-B

During 1968 Mr Bowers designed and built a set of interchangeable biplane wings for the original prototype Fly Baby and with these fitted it flew for the first time on 27 March 1969. About four more biplanes, designated Fly Baby 1-B, had been completed and flown by early 1979.

The new wings have the same aerofoil section and incidence as those of the monoplane version, but the rib webs are made of 1/16 in instead of ⅛ in plywood and the wingtip bows are formed from ½ in aluminium tube instead of laminated wood strips. This lightweight construction limits weight increase to only 21 kg (46 lb) for an increase of 2·79 m² (30 sq ft) in wing area. Span is reduced by 1·83 m (6 ft) and chord by 0·30 m (1 ft). Ailerons are fitted to the lower wings only.

To facilitate entry to the cockpit the upper wing has been located well forward, and in order to bring the new centre of lift in line with the original CG, both planes have been given 11° of sweepback. Changeover from monoplane to biplane configuration can be accomplished by two people in approximately one hour.

The biplane is intended to use the same engines as the monoplane, for which Mr Bowers does not recommend anything heavier than the Continental O-200. Since some biplane builders have desired to use the Lycoming O-290, a modification has been authorised for the biplane, whereby the wing sweep is decreased by 5° for CG reasons.

The description of the Fly Baby 1-A applies also to the 1-B, except in the following details:

TYPE: Single-seat light biplane.

WINGS: Forward-stagger single-bay biplane with N-type interplane and centre-section struts. Landing and flying bracing wires. Sweepback 11°. Wooden structure with Dacron covering. Rib webs constructed of 1/16 in plywood, wingtip bows formed of ½ in aluminium tube. Ailerons on lower wings only.

POWER PLANT: One 63·5 kW (85 hp) Continental C85 flat-four engine.

DIMENSIONS, EXTERNAL:
Wing span 6·71 m (22 ft 0 in)
Wing chord, both wings, constant 1·07 m (3 ft 6 in)
Wing area, gross 13·94 m² (150 sq ft)
Height overall 2·08 m (6 ft 10 in)

The description of the Fly Baby 1-A applies also to the 1-B, except in the following details:

WEIGHTS:
Weight empty 295 kg (651 lb)
Max T-O weight 440 kg (972 lb)

PERFORMANCE (at max T-O weight):
Cruising speed 75·5 knots (140 km/h; 87 mph)
Max rate of climb at S/L 267 m (875 ft)/min

BROKAW

BROKAW AVIATION INC

2625 Johnson Point, Leesburg, Florida 32748
Telephone: (904) 787 2329
PRESIDENT: Bergon F. Brokaw, MD, FACFP

BROKAW BULLET

Dr B. F. Brokaw, a former US Navy pilot, and Dr E. Jones, who has a PhD in aeronautical engineering, combined their talents to design and build a two-seat low-wing monoplane which was claimed to be the world's fastest homebuilt. Dr Brokaw was concerned primarily with overall design and construction, Dr Jones with stress analysis and structural design.

Basic intention was to evolve a high-speed all-weather two-seat homebuilt suitable for cross-country flying. Aerobatic potential was of secondary consideration, but the Bullet, which was known originally as the BJ-520, is stressed to ±6*g* for aerobatics and 9*g* ultimate.

Design began in August 1966 and construction of the prototype started six months later. First flight was made on 18 November 1972, and during the Summer of 1973 work was carried out to clean up the airframe to take better advantage of the design potential. This included the provision of wheel-well doors, and reduction of the drag of the engine cooling system, achieved by the use of baffles, ducts and direct ram-air cooling.

Further major redesign and modification were undertaken in 1976, and the prototype resumed flying in 1977 as the Bullet. The latest refinements include changes to the wing span and section, and power plant, as described below. (For performance and other data relating to the original version, powered by a 212·5 kW (285 hp) Continental TSIO-520-B turbocharged engine, see 1975-76 *Jane's*.) By early 1979 the aircraft had logged more than 600 flying hours and had been flown in all weather conditions, including light ice.

Dr Brokaw formed Brokaw Aviation Inc to market plans, a construction manual and pilot handbook to amateur constructors. Although full kits are not available, it is intended also to supply certain components such as the canopy, cowling and, possibly, bulkheads and ribs, to simplify the task of the homebuilder. By early 1979 ten sets of plans had been sold and three Bullets were under construction, one with a tailwheel landing gear and a 410 kW (550 hp) Ranger twelve-cylinder V engine.

TYPE: Two-seat sporting aircraft.

WINGS: Cantilever low-wing monoplane. Laminar-flow wing section: NACA 64A412 at root, NACA 64A410 at tip. Dihedral 4° 30′. Incidence 1° at root, −2° at tip. Conventional structure of 2024-T3 light alloy. Ailerons and trailing-edge flaps of light alloy. Ground-adjustable tabs on ailerons.

FUSELAGE: Semi-monocoque structure of light alloy.

TAIL UNIT: Cantilever light alloy structure. Fixed-incidence tailplane. Electrically-operated trim tabs in elevators and rudder.

LANDING GEAR: Hydraulically-retractable tricycle type. Main and nose units and associated hydraulic system are from a Navion aircraft. Main units retract inward and nosewheel rearward. Single wheel on each main unit, with 15 × 6·00-6 low-profile tyre, pressure 4·48 bars (65 lb/sq in). Nosewheel tyre size 14 × 5·00-4, pressure 3·10 bars (45 lb/sq in). Goodyear hydraulic brakes on main wheels.

POWER PLANT: One 283 kW (380 hp) Avco Lycoming TIO-541-E flat-six engine, driving a Sensenich three-blade metal constant-speed propeller with spinner. Alternative power plant is 213 kW (285 hp) Teledyne Continental TSIO-520-B flat-six engine, driving a McCauley three-blade metal constant-speed propeller with spinner, or other engine of 223-373 kW (300-500 hp). Four integral wing fuel tanks, with capacity of 363 litres (96 US gallons). Refuelling points at wingtips. Oil capacity 11·3 litres (3 US gallons).

ACCOMMODATION: Two seats in tandem beneath transparent individual canopies. Port half of each canopy hinged at centreline to open upwards. Baggage space, which accommodates 31·8 kg (70 lb), aft of rear seat. Cabin heated and ventilated.

SYSTEMS: Hydraulic system at 103·5 bars (1,500 lb/sq in) for landing gear retraction and brakes. 28V 70A alternator for electrical system. Oxygen system for pilot and passenger, with capacity of 5 hours.

ELECTRONICS AND EQUIPMENT: Full IFR instrumentation, including DGO 10, DME 70, dual Narco 360-channel transceivers and dual VORs, ADF, transponder, marker beacon and ILS. Landing gear warning lights, navigation lights and external power socket.

DIMENSIONS, EXTERNAL:
Wing span 7·16 m (23 ft 6 in)
Wing chord at root 1·52 m (5 ft 0 in)
Wing chord at tip 0·76 m (2 ft 6 in)
Wing area, gross 8·95 m² (96·3 sq ft)
Wing aspect ratio 6
Length overall 6·25 m (20 ft 6 in)
Height overall 2·69 m (8 ft 10 in)
Tailplane span 2·69 m (8 ft 10 in)
Wheel track 2·54 m (8 ft 4 in)
Wheelbase 1·80 m (5 ft 11 in)
Propeller diameter 1·98 m (6 ft 6 in)

DIMENSIONS, INTERNAL:
Length 2·54 m (8 ft 4 in)
Max width 0·91 m (3 ft 0 in)
Max height 1·37 m (4 ft 6 in)

WEIGHTS (TIO-541-E engine):
Weight empty 922 kg (2,033 lb)
Max T-O weight 1,425 kg (3,142 lb)

PERFORMANCE (TIO-541-E engine):
Max level speed at 7,315 m (24,000 ft) 290 knots (537 km/h; 334 mph)
Normal cruising speed (75% power) at 7,315 m (24,000 ft) 260 knots (481 km/h; 299 mph)
Econ cruising speed (55% power) at 7,315 m (24,000 ft) 245 knots (454 km/h; 282 mph)
Stalling speed, clean 79 knots (147 km/h; 91 mph)
Stalling speed, wheels and flaps down 76 knots (142 km/h; 88 mph)
Max rate of climb at S/L 762 m (2,500 ft)/min
Service ceiling over 8,535 m (28,000 ft)
T-O run 396 m (1,300 ft)
T-O to 15 m (50 ft) 610 m (2,000 ft)
Landing from 15 m (50 ft) 853 m (2,800 ft)
Landing run 488 m (1,600 ft)
Range at econ cruising speed, 45 min reserves 1,080 nm (2,000 km; 1,243 miles)

BUSHBY

BUSHBY AIRCRAFT INC

Route 1, PO Box 13B, Minooka, Illinois 60447
Telephone: (815) 462 2346

Mr Robert W. Bushby, a research engineer with Sinclair Oil Co, began by building a Midget Mustang single-seat sporting monoplane, using drawings, jigs and certain components produced by the aircraft's designer, the late David Long. He has since produced the aircraft in kit form and also offers sets of plans of the Midget Mustang and a two-seat derivative known as the Mustang II to amateur constructors.

BUSHBY/LONG MM-1 MIDGET MUSTANG

The prototype of the Midget Mustang was completed in 1948 by David Long, then chief engineer of the Piper company. He flew it in the National Air Races that year, and in 1949 was placed fourth in the Continental Trophy Race at Miami.

Two basic versions have been developed by Robert Bushby, as follows:

MM-1-85. Powered by 63·5 kW (85 hp) Continental C85-8FJ or -12 engine. Flew for the first time on 9 September 1959.

MM-1-125. Powered by 101 kW (135 hp) Lycoming O-290-D2 engine. Otherwise similar to MM-1-85. Flew for first time in July 1963. New propeller introduced during 1973 has improved max speed and cruising speed.

Ninety-five Midget Mustangs had been completed by the Spring of 1979, with 900 more under construction throughout the world. Several of those now flying have a 112 kW (150 hp) Lycoming O-320 engine, providing a cruising speed of 234 knots (435 km/h; 270 mph) at 2,440 m (8,000 ft). Some have been fitted with retractable main landing gear.

The following details apply to the two basic versions:

TYPE: Single-seat fully-aerobatic sporting monoplane.

WINGS: Cantilever low-wing monoplane. Wing section NACA 64A212 at root, NACA 64A210 at tip. Dihedral 5°. Incidence 1° 30′. Two-spar flush-riveted stressed-skin aluminium structure. Aluminium statically-balanced ailerons and plain trailing-edge flaps.

FUSELAGE: Aluminium flush-riveted stressed-skin monocoque structure.

TAIL UNIT: Cantilever all-metal structure. Controllable trim tab in port elevator.

LANDING GEAR: Non-retractable tailwheel type. Can-

Brokaw Bullet in its latest form

Bushby/Long Midget Mustang (Lycoming O-290-D2 engine) built by Mr Bill Johns and Mr Larry Haas of Osawatomie, Kansas *(Howard Levy)*

Bushby M-II Mustang II built by Mr Ray Crandall

tilever spring steel main legs. Steerable tailwheel. Goodyear wheels and tyres, size 5·00-5, pressure 1·24 bars (18 lb/sq in). Goodyear hydraulic disc brakes.

POWER PLANT (MM-1-85): One 63·5 kW (85 hp) Continental C85-8FJ or -12 flat-four engine, driving a McCauley two-blade metal fixed-pitch propeller. Fuel tank aft of firewall, capacity 57 litres (15 US gallons). Optional integral wing fuel tanks, each with capacity of 57 litres (15 US gallons). Optional wingtip tanks, each with capacity of 13 litres (3·5 US gallons). Oil capacity 3·75 litres (1 US gallon).

POWER PLANT (MM-1-125): One 101 kW (135 hp) Lycoming O-290-D2 flat-four engine, driving a Sensenich two-blade metal fixed-pitch propeller. Fuel tank aft of firewall, capacity 57 litres (15 US gallons). No provision for wingtip tanks. Oil capacity 5·75 litres (1·5 US gallons).

ACCOMMODATION: Single seat in enclosed cabin. Canopy hinged on starboard side. Space for 5·5 kg (12 lb) of baggage aft of seat. Room for back parachute.

ELECTRONICS AND EQUIPMENT: Radio optional. No provision for blind-flying instrumentation. Electrical system available on MM-1-85 only.

DIMENSIONS, EXTERNAL:
- Wing span 5·64 m (18 ft 6 in)
- Wing span over tip-tanks (MM-1-85) 5·99 m (19 ft 8 in)
- Wing chord at root 1·53 m (5 ft 0 in)
- Wing chord at tip 0·76 m (2 ft 6 in)
- Wing area, gross 6·32 m² (68 sq ft)
- Wing aspect ratio 4
- Length overall 5·00 m (16 ft 5 in)
- Height overall 1·37 m (4 ft 6 in)
- Tailplane span 1·98 m (6 ft 6 in)
- Wheel track 1·55 m (5 ft 1 in)

DIMENSIONS, INTERNAL:
- Cabin:
  - Max width 0·56 m (1 ft 10 in)
- Baggage space 0·057 m³ (2 cu ft)

WEIGHTS:
- Weight empty:
  - MM-1-85 261 kg (575 lb)
  - MM-1-125 268 kg (590 lb)
- Max T-O and landing weight:
  - MM-1-85 397 kg (875 lb)
  - MM-1-125 408 kg (900 lb)

PERFORMANCE (at max T-O weight):
- Never-exceed speed: 243 knots (450 km/h; 280 mph)
- Max level speed at S/L:
  - MM-1-85 165 knots (306 km/h; 190 mph)
  - MM-1-125 195 knots (362 km/h; 225 mph)
- Max cruising speed at 2,440 m (8,000 ft):
  - MM-1-85 171 knots (317 km/h; 197 mph)
  - MM-1-125 187 knots (346 km/h; 215 mph)
- Econ cruising speed:
  - MM-1-85 129 knots (238 km/h; 148 mph)
  - MM-1-125 143 knots (265 km/h; 165 mph)
- Stalling speed, flaps down:
  - MM-1-85 50 knots (92 km/h; 57 mph)
  - MM-1-125 53 knots (97 km/h; 60 mph)
- Max rate of climb at S/L:
  - MM-1-85 533 m (1,750 ft)/min
  - MM-1-125 670 m (2,200 ft)/min
- Service ceiling:
  - MM-1-85 over 4,875 m (16,000 ft)
  - MM-1-125 5,790 m (19,000 ft)
- T-O run:
  - MM-1-85 137 m (450 ft)
  - MM-1-125 122 m (400 ft)
- T-O to 15 m (50 ft):
  - MM-1-85 274 m (900 ft)
  - MM-1-125 213 m (700 ft)
- Landing from 15 m (50 ft) 365 m (1,200 ft)
- Landing run 152 m (500 ft)
- Range with max fuel:
  - MM-1-85 347 nm (640 km; 400 miles)
  - MM-1-125 325 nm (603 km; 375 miles)
- Range with max fuel and tip-tanks:
  - MM-1-85 651 nm (1,200 km; 750 miles)

BUSHBY M-II MUSTANG II

Design of this side-by-side two-seat derivative of the Midget Mustang was started in 1963. Construction of a prototype began in 1965 and it flew for the first time on 9 July 1966. During 1968 Mr Bushby designed an alternative non-retractable tricycle landing gear for the Mustang II, and amateur constructors have the option of either configuration. About 800 Mustang IIs were being built by amateurs in the Spring of 1979, at which time 60 were flying.

The Mustang II illustrated was built by Mr Ray Crandall. It is powered by a Lycoming O-290 engine, driving a Sensenich 74 DM6-2-63 propeller, which gives a max speed of 155 knots (286 km/h; 178 mph), stalling speed of 59 knots (110 km/h; 68 mph) and a rate of climb of 425 m (1,400 ft)/min.

The description applies to the de luxe model, and the empty weight quoted includes IFR instrumentation and nav/com equipment. The M-II can also be operated as an aerobatic aircraft in what Bushby Aircraft calls the 'Sport' configuration. This is identical to the de luxe model except that the electrical system, radio and additional IFR instrumentation are deleted. The 'Sport' model has an empty weight of 340 kg (750 lb) and T-O weight of 567 kg (1,250 lb).

A new Hartzell controllable-pitch propeller has now replaced the fixed-pitch propeller as standard, and the performance figures quoted for the 119 kW (160 hp) engine are obtained with this propeller. The figures for the 93 kW (125 hp) engine are those obtained with the fixed-pitch propeller.

TYPE: Two-seat light sporting aircraft.

WINGS: Cantilever low-wing monoplane. Outer wings similar to those of Midget Mustang, attached to new constant-chord centre-section of short span. Wing section NACA 64A212 at root, NACA 64A210 at tip. Dihedral 5° on outer wings only. Incidence 1° 30′. Two-spar flush-riveted stressed-skin aluminium structure. Aluminium statically-balanced ailerons and plain trailing-edge flaps. No trim tabs.

FUSELAGE: Aluminium flush-riveted stressed-skin monocoque structure.

TAIL UNIT: Cantilever all-metal structure. Fixed-incidence tailplane. Controllable trim tab in starboard elevator.

LANDING GEAR: Standard version has non-retractable tailwheel type. Cantilever spring steel main legs. Goodyear 5·00-5 main wheels and tyres, pressure 1·38 bars (20 lb/sq in). Goodyear hydraulic disc brakes. Steerable tailwheel. Alternatively, non-retractable tricycle type. Cantilever spring steel main legs. Cleveland or Goodyear main wheels and tyres size 5·00-5. Non-steerable nosewheel, mounted on oleo-pneumatic shock-strut and free to swivel up to 16° either side. Goodyear nosewheel and tyre size 5·00-5. Goodyear or Cleveland hydraulic disc brakes. Wheel fairings optional on either type of landing gear.

POWER PLANT: Normally one 119 kW (160 hp) Lycoming O-320 flat-four engine, driving a Hartzell two-blade controllable-pitch metal propeller. Provision for other engines including a 93 kW (125 hp) Lycoming O-290 engine, driving a two-blade fixed-pitch metal propeller. Fuel tank aft of firewall, capacity 94·6 litres (25 US gallons). Optional integral wing fuel tanks, each with a capacity of 45 litres (12 US gallons). Refuelling point on starboard side of fuselage aft of firewall. Provision for wingtip tanks. Oil capacity 7·5 litres (2 US gallons).

ACCOMMODATION: Two seats side by side, under large rearward-sliding transparent canopy. Dual controls. Baggage space aft of seats, capacity 34 kg (75 lb).

SYSTEMS: 12V electrical system, supplied by Delco-Remy 15A generator and Exide 33A battery.

ELECTRONICS AND EQUIPMENT: Provision for full IFR instrumentation and dual nav/com system.

DIMENSIONS, EXTERNAL:
- Wing span 7·37 m (24 ft 2 in)
- Wing chord at root 1·47 m (4 ft 10 in)
- Wing chord at tip 0·79 m (2 ft 7 in)
- Wing area, gross 9·02 m² (97·12 sq ft)
- Wing aspect ratio 5·5
- Length overall 5·94 m (19 ft 6 in)
- Height overall 1·60 m (5 ft 3 in)
- Tailplane span 2·29 m (7 ft 6 in)
- Wheel track 2·08 m (6 ft 10 in)
- Propeller diameter:
  - 93 kW (125 hp) 1·73 m (5 ft 8 in)
  - 119 kW (160 hp) 1·82 m (6 ft 0 in)

DIMENSIONS, INTERNAL:
- Cabin:
  - Max width 1·02 m (3 ft 4 in)
- Baggage space 0·16 m³ (5·5 cu ft)

WEIGHTS:
- Weight empty, equipped (N: nosewheel, T: tailwheel landing gear):
  - N 93 kW (125 hp) engine 413 kg (911 lb)
  - T 93 kW (125 hp) engine 408 kg (900 lb)
  - N 119 kW (160 hp) engine 425 kg (938 lb)
  - T 119 kW (160 hp) engine 420 kg (927 lb)
- *Max T-O and landing weight 680 kg (1,500 lb)

**Except for countries that restrict max wing loading to 73·2 kg/m² (15 lb/sq ft), where T-O weight of 658 kg (1,450 lb) applies*

PERFORMANCE (with tailwheel, at max T-O weight):
- Never-exceed speed:
  - 93 kW (125 hp) 173 knots (322 km/h; 200 mph)
  - 119 kW (160 hp) 211 knots (391 km/h; 243 mph)
- Max level speed at S/L:
  - 93 kW (125 hp) 156 knots (290 km/h; 180 mph)
  - 119 kW (160 hp) 182 knots (338 km/h; 210 mph)
- Max cruising speed at 2,285 m (7,500 ft):
  - 93 kW (125 hp) 152 knots (282 km/h; 175 mph)
  - 119 kW (160 hp) 181 knots (335 km/h; 208 mph)
- Stalling speed, flaps down:
  - 93 kW (125 hp) 47 knots (87 km/h; 54 mph)
  - 119 kW (160 hp) 51 knots (94 km/h; 58 mph)
- Stalling speed, flaps up:
  - 93 kW (125 hp) 51 knots (94 km/h; 58 mph)
  - 119 kW (160 hp) 53 knots (96 km/h; 60 mph)
- Max rate of climb at S/L:
  - 93 kW (125 hp) 305 m (1,000 ft)/min
  - 119 kW (160 hp) 670 m (2,200 ft)/min
- Service ceiling:
  - 93 kW (125 hp) 4,875 m (16,000 ft)
  - 119 kW (160 hp) 5,485 m (18,000 ft)
- T-O run
  - 93 kW (125 hp) 198 m (650 ft)
  - 119 kW (160 hp) 137 m (450 ft)
- T-O to 15 m (50 ft):
  - 93 kW (125 hp) 320 m (1,050 ft)

119 kW (160 hp)	198 m (650 ft)
Landing from 15 m (50 ft):	
93 kW (125 hp)	290 m (950 ft)
119 kW (160 hp)	259 m (850 ft)
Landing run:	
93 kW (125 hp)	215 m (700 ft)
119 kW (160 hp)	168 m (550 ft)
Range with standard fuel (75% power):	
93 kW (125 hp)	416 nm (770 km; 480 miles)
119 kW (160 hp)	373 nm (692 km; 430 miles)
Range with optional wingtip tanks:	
119 kW (160 hp)	542 nm (1,005 km; 625 miles)

BUTTERWORTH
G. N. BUTTERWORTH

Richmond Airport, Heaton Orchard Road, West Kingston, Rhode Island 02892
Telephone: (401) 789 0384

BUTTERWORTH WESTLAND WHIRLWIND MARK II

Mr G. N. Butterworth has designed and built a ⅔-scale representation of a second World War Westland Whirlwind single-seat fighter. Design began on 20 October 1976, and construction of the prototype started simultaneously. Based on the wings and horizontal tail surfaces of a Grumman American AA-1A Trainer, construction took 900-950 working hours over a nine-month period. Estimated cost of construction was $3,000-4,000. First flight was made in July 1977.

Plans are available to amateur constructors.

Type: Single-seat ⅔-scale replica fighter.

Wings: Cantilever low-wing monoplane, based on those of a Grumman American AA-1A Trainer. Dihedral 2°. Incidence 2°. Aluminium structure, except for outer wing panels which are made of 29 mm (1·125 in) sitka spruce spars and solid polyurethane foam filling, covered with Dynel and polyester resins. Outer wings removable in 15 minutes to permit road trailering. No flaps or tabs.

Fuselage: Conventional all-aluminium semi-monocoque structure, with ·02 in skins and ·03 in bulkheads.

Tail Unit: Cantilever aluminium structure. High-mounted horizontal surfaces based on those of a Grumman American AA-1A Trainer. Trim tab on starboard elevator.

Landing Gear: Hydraulically-retractable tailwheel type. Main wheels retract forward into engine nacelles. Cleveland wheels. Main-wheel tyres size 6·00-6. Tailwheel diameter 10 cm (4in). Oleo shock-absorbers. Cleveland disc brakes.

Power Plant: Two 48·5 kW (65 hp) 1,600 cc Volkswagen modified motor car engines, each driving a Hegy fixed-pitch two-blade propeller. Two fuel tanks, total capacity 76 litres (20 US gallons). Refuelling points in top of glassfibre engine cowlings. Oil capacity (total) 5·5 litres (1·5 US gallons).

Accommodation: Single seat under rearward-sliding transparent canopy. No heating or ventilation.

Dimensions, external:	
Wing span	8·53 m (28 ft 0 in)
Wing chord, constant	1·22 m (4 ft 0 in)
Length overall	5·94 m (19 ft 6 in)
Height overall	2·16 m (7 ft 1 in)
Tailplane span	2·49 m (8 ft 2 in)
Wheel track	2·44 m (8 ft 0 in)
Propeller diameter	1·35 m (4 ft 5 in)
Distance between propeller centres	2·13 m (7 ft 0 in)
Weights:	
Weight empty	472 kg (1,042 lb)
Max T-O weight	635 kg (1,400 lb)
Performance:	
Max level and cruising speed	126 knots (233 km/h; 145 mph)
Econ cruising speed	87 knots (161 km/h; 100 mph)
Stalling speed	55·5 knots (103 km/h; 64 mph)
Max rate of climb at S/L	229 m (750 ft)/min
Service ceiling	2,440 m (8,000 ft)
T-O run	366 m (1,200 ft)
T-O distance to 15 m (50 ft)	549 m (1,800 ft)
Landing distance from 15 m (50 ft)	549 m (1,800 ft)
Landing run	427 m (1,400 ft)
Range with max fuel	608 nm (1,126 km; 700 miles)

CASSUTT
THOMAS K. CASSUTT

11718 Persuasion Drive, San Antonio, Texas 78216

While employed as an airline pilot, Capt Tom Cassutt designed and built in 1954 a small single-seat racing monoplane known as the Cassutt Special I (No. 111), in which he won the 1958 National Air Racing Championships. In 1959, he completed a smaller aircraft on the same lines, known as the Cassutt Special II (No. 11).

Plans of both aircraft, and of a sporting version of No. 111 with a larger cockpit, are available to amateur constructors, and a total of about 2,000 sets of plans had been sold by early 1979. Many Cassutt Specials are flying or are under construction, in Australia, France, Germany, New Zealand, South Africa, Sweden, the UK and elsewhere. Brief details of a number of these were given in a table in the 1977-78 *Jane's*.

Following his retirement from airline flying, Tom Cassutt plans to develop a number of different aircraft to meet Formula I specifications. It is also his intention to modify the plans of the Special to show ways of improving performance, and possibly to evolve a tandem two-seat cockpit layout.

CASSUTT SPECIAL I

The Cassutt Special I illustrated, owned by Mr Charles Lemmond, has completed many hundreds of hours of cross-country and aerobatic flying in five years, powered by Continental C85 and O-200 engines.

The following description applies to the original Cassutt Special I (No. 111), named *Jersey Skeeter:*

Type: Single-seat racing monoplane.

Wings: Cantilever mid-wing monoplane. Wing section Cassutt 1107. No incidence or dihedral. All-wood two-spar structure with spruce ribs, solid spars and plywood skin, fabric-covered. Ailerons are of welded steel tube construction, fabric-covered. No flaps.

Fuselage: Steel tube structure, fabric-covered.

Tail Unit: Cantilever steel tube structure, with fabric covering.

Landing Gear: Non-retractable tailwheel type. Wittman cantilever spring steel main legs. Main-wheel tyres size 5·00-5. Wheel fairings standard.

Power Plant: Originally one Continental C85-8F flat-four engine, rated normally at 63·5 kW (85 hp) but capable of developing 83·5-85·75 kW (112-115 hp) in racing trim. Aircraft now fitted usually with a Lycoming engine. Sensenich two-blade fixed-pitch propeller. Fuel capacity 57 litres (15 US gallons). Oil capacity 3·8 litres (1 US gallon).

Accommodation: Single seat in enclosed cockpit.

Dimensions, external:	
Wing span	4·54 m (14 ft 11 in)
Wing chord (mean)	1·37 m (4 ft 6 in)
Wing area, gross	6·13 m² (66·0 sq ft)
Wing aspect ratio	3·37
Length overall	4·88 m (16 ft 0 in)
Height overall	1·30 m (4 ft 3 in)
Tailplane span	1·19 m (3 ft 11 in)
Wheel track	1·37 m (4 ft 6 in)
Weights (with Continental engine):	
Weight empty	234 kg (516 lb)
Max T-O weight	331 kg (730 lb)
Performance (Continental engine at max T-O weight):	
Max level speed	200 knots (370 km/h; 230 mph)
Max cruising speed	165 knots (306 km/h; 190 mph)
Stalling speed	61 knots (113 km/h; 70 mph)
Max rate of climb at S/L	610 m (2,000 ft)/min
Endurance with max fuel	3 h

CASSUTT SPECIAL II

Type: Single-seat racing monoplane.

Wings: Cantilever mid-wing monoplane. Wing section Cassutt 13106. No incidence or dihedral. All-wood structure. No flaps.

Fuselage: Steel tube structure, fabric-covered.

Tail Unit: Cantilever steel tube structure, fabric-covered. The prototype (No. 11) has small centre fin and auxiliary fins on the tailplane tips.

Landing Gear: Non-retractable tailwheel type. Wittman cantilever spring steel main legs. Main-wheel tyre size 5·00-5. Wheel fairings standard.

Power Plant and Accommodation: As for Cassutt Special I.

Dimensions, external:	
Wing span	4·16 m (13 ft 8 in)
Wing chord, constant	1·47 m (4 ft 10 in)
Wing area, gross	6·13 m² (66 sq ft)
Wing aspect ratio	2·83
Length overall	4·88 m (16 ft 0 in)
Height overall	1·16 m (3 ft 10 in)
Tailplane span	1·14 m (3 ft 9 in)
Wheel track	0·97 m (3 ft 2 in)
Weights:	
Weight empty	196 kg (433 lb)
Max T-O weight	363 kg (800 lb)
Performance (at max T-O weight):	
Max level speed at S/L	204 knots (378 km/h; 235 mph)
Max cruising speed	174 knots (322 km/h; 200 mph)
Stalling speed	54 knots (100 km/h; 62 mph)
Max rate of climb at S/L	915 m (3,000 ft)/min
Endurance with max fuel	3 h

CHRISTEN
CHRISTEN INDUSTRIES INC

1048 Santa Ana Valley Road, Hollister, California 95023
Telephone: (408) 637 7405
President: Frank Christensen

Two aircraft make up the current Christen Eagle series of aerobatic biplanes. The **Eagle I** is a special-purpose single-seater intended solely for unlimited class aerobatic competition and is structured to +9*g*, −6*g* operational. It is powered by a 194 kW (260 hp) Lycoming AEIO-540-D4B5 flat-six engine, driving a Sensenich fixed-pitch propeller. The **Eagle II** is a less-austere two-seat sporting biplane that can be used for unlimited class aerobatics as well as for advanced aerobatic training and comfortable cross-country flying. It has the same structural limits as the Eagle I. All Eagles have a roll rate of 187° a second.

The Eagle IF and IIF, to which reference was made in the 1978-79 *Jane's*, were discontinued on completion of flight testing. First version to become available was the Eagle II, which can be built by amateur constructors, using a series of 26 parts-kits supplied by Christen Industries. Each kit makes up a separate portion of the aircraft and is supported by a very detailed constructional manual. This allows the cost of building the aircraft to be spread over a period of time. Only common hand tools and power tools are required in construction, and no previous aircraft experience is thought necessary. Christen believes that a typical homebuilder could complete the aircraft in 1,400 to 1,600 man-hours.

Following completion of its flight test programme, the Eagle I also became available in kit form in the Summer of 1979.

The following description applies to the Eagle II:

CHRISTEN EAGLE II

Design began in June 1974 and construction of a prototype started in August 1975. First flight was achieved in February 1977, when construction of other pre-production Eagles began. Manufacture of kits was initiated by Christen Industries in October 1977 and by January 1979 a total of 184 had been ordered, of which 100 had been delivered.

Type: Two-seat unlimited class aerobatic biplane.

Wings: Braced biplane with steel tube I-type main interplane struts. Symmetrical sections. Thickness/chord ratio 15%. Dihedral 0° 30′ on lower wings, 0° on upper wing. Incidence 0°. Sweepback at quarter-chord 7° 30′ on upper wing, 0° on lower wings. Wooden spars and ribs; metal leading- and trailing-edges, polyester fabric covered. Conventional ailerons on upper and lower wings, of similar construction to wings. No flaps or tabs.

Fuselage: Conventional structure of welded 4130N steel tubing. Covered with removable light alloy panels from firewall to back of rear seat. Rear fuselage fabric covered.

Tail Unit: Conventional wire-braced structure, comprising a tailplane and elevators fitted with boost tabs, and fin and rudder, all of welded steel tube, polyester fabric covered.

Landing Gear: Non-retractable tailwheel type. Aluminium spring main legs. Main tyres size 5·00-5, pressure 1·52 bars (22 lb/sq in). Cleveland hydraulic disc brakes. Streamline wheel fairings.

Power Plant: One 149 kW (200 hp) Lycoming AEIO-360-A1D flat-four engine, driving a Hartzell HC-C2YK-4/C7666A-2 constant-speed propeller. One fuel tank in fuselage, capacity 98·4 litres (26 US gallons). Refuelling point in upper fuselage. Oil capacity 7·5 litres (2 US gallons). Fuel system allows unlimited inverted flight.

Accommodation: Two seats in tandem beneath one-piece side-hinged bubble canopy. Heated. Baggage hold in turtledeck, capacity 13·6 kg (30 lb).

Systems: 12V DC battery for starting and radio.

Electronics: Narco Escort 110 radio.

Dimensions, external:	
Wing span	6·07 m (19 ft 11 in)
Wing chord, constant	1·02 m (3 ft 4 in)
Wing area, gross	11·61 m² (125 sq ft)
Length overall	5·64 m (18 ft 6 in)
Height overall	1·98 m (6 ft 6 in)
Tailplane span	2·13 m (7 ft 0 in)
Wheel track	1·83 m (6 ft 0 in)
Wheelbase	3·96 m (13 ft 0 in)
Propeller diameter	1·93 m (6 ft 4 in)
Dimensions, internal:	
Cabin: Length	2·13 m (7 ft 0 in)
Max width	0·71 m (2 ft 4 in)
Max height	0·99 m (3 ft 3 in)

G. N. Butterworth's ⅔-scale replica of a Westland Whirlwind

Cassutt Special 111M, built in the UK *(J. M. G. Gradidge)*

Condor Shoestring *Yellow Jacket*, **built from current plans**

Christen Industries Eagle II two-seat aerobatic biplane

WEIGHTS:
- Weight empty 465 kg (1,025 lb)
- Max T-O and landing weight 716 kg (1,578 lb)

PERFORMANCE:
- Never-exceed speed 184 knots (341 km/h; 212 mph)
- Max level speed at 1,825 m (6,000 ft) 160 knots (296 km/h; 184 mph)
- Max cruising speed at 1,825 m (6,000 ft) 143 knots (265 km/h; 165 mph)
- Econ cruising speed at 1,825 m (6,000 ft) 137 knots (254 km/h; 158 mph)
- Stalling speed 50·5 knots (94 km/h; 58 mph)
- Max rate of climb at S/L 640 m (2,100 ft)/min
- Service ceiling 5,180 m (17,000 ft)
- T-O run 244 m (800 ft)
- T-O to 15 m (50 ft) 381 m (1,250 ft)
- Landing from 15 m (50 ft) 480 m (1,575 ft)
- Range with max fuel and max payload 330 nm (611 km; 380 miles)

CONDOR
CONDOR AERO INC

PO Box 762, Vero Beach, Florida 32960
PRESIDENT: Landis G. Ketner

CONDOR SHOESTRING

The original Shoestring was designed and built by the Mercury Air Group, consisting of Mr Vincent Ast, Mr Carl Ast and Mr Rodney Kreimendahl, in 1949. As a racing monoplane (No. 16) it first competed at Miami in 1950 where, piloted by Bob Downey, it achieved third place at a speed of 157·474 knots (291·844 km/h; 181·334 mph). At San Jose, California, in the same year it finished first in the hands of Vincent Ast, at 152 knots (282 km/h; 175 mph). By 1974, when a new wing was fitted to Shoestring, the aircraft had achieved fourteen first places in air races, three seconds and four thirds.

A full description of the original Shoestring appeared in the 1959-60 *Jane's*.

In 1965 Shoestring was purchased by John Anderson and taken to Miami, where a set of drawings of the aircraft was made. The first new racer to be built from these drawings was *Yellow Jacket*, constructed by Jim Strode, which flew for the first time on 15 July 1970. Although this aircraft was very similar to the original Shoestring, the fuselage structure was made 5 cm (2 in) wider and 10 cm (4 in) longer to provide a more comfortable cockpit. The power plant installation, canopy and fairings were also of Jim Strode's design.

Since then other Shoestrings have been built in modified form, and plans are available to amateur constructors.

TYPE: Single-seat Formula One racing monoplane.

WINGS: Cantilever shoulder-mounted monoplane of wood construction, built as one unit and fabric covered. Front spar built of three pieces of spruce bonded together. Rear spar can be cut from one piece of spruce or built up from several pieces. Plywood ribs with capstrips bonded to top and bottom. Skins bonded to spars and ribs. Ailerons built as part of wing and cut out after the top skin has been bonded in place.

FUSELAGE: Steel tube structure, with plywood formers and fabric covering from instrument panel aft. Thin-gauge aluminium skin forward of panel and on each side of cockpit above wing. Roll-over structure of heavy gauge steel.

TAIL UNIT: Conventional cantilever spruce structure, with fabric-covered plywood skin.

LANDING GEAR: Non-retractable tailwheel type. Main wheels carried on one-piece formed aluminium member bolted directly to bottom of fuselage. Sheet aluminium fairings over legs; aluminium wheel fairings. Solid rubber tailwheel. Brakes fitted.

POWER PLANT: Originally one 63·5 kW (85 hp) Continental flat-four engine. Alternative 74·5 kW (100 hp) engine to meet current PRPA regulations. Recommended engines are Continental C85, C90 and O-200 flat-fours. Fuel tank aft of firewall, capacity 38 litres (10 US gallons). Provision for auxiliary tank behind seat.

ACCOMMODATION: Single seat under blown Plexiglas canopy.

DIMENSIONS, EXTERNAL:
- Wing span 5·79 m (19 ft 0 in)
- Wing area, gross 6·13 m² (66 sq ft)
- Length overall 5·38 m (17 ft 7¾ in)
- Height overall 1·42 m (4 ft 8 in)

WEIGHT:
- Weight empty 256 kg (565 lb)
- Max T-O weight 362 kg (800 lb)

PERFORMANCE:
- Max level speed over 208 knots (386 km/h; 240 mph)
- Max cruising speed 156 knots (290 km/h; 180 mph)
- Stalling speed 57 knots (105 km/h; 65 mph)
- Max rate of climb at S/L 915 m (3,000 ft)/min
- T-O run 245 m (800 ft)

CVJETKOVIC
ANTON CVJETKOVIC

20111 Vintage Street, Chatsworth, California 91311
Telephone: (805) 498 3092

When living in Yugoslavia, Mr Anton Cvjetkovic designed a single-seat light aeroplane designated CA-51 and powered by a modified Volkswagen engine. A prototype was built by members of Zagreb Aeroclub in 1951, and was followed by five more aircraft of the same type.

After moving to the United States, Mr Cvjetkovic began work, in May 1960, on the design of an improved light aircraft which he designated CA-61. Construction of a prototype was started in February 1961 and it flew for the first time in August 1962. Plans of both single-seat and two-seat all-wood versions are available to amateur constructors, together with plans of a two-seat aircraft designated CA-65, of which the prototype was completed in 1965. Plans of an all-metal version of the CA-65, designated CA-65A, are also available.

By early 1979 more than 400 sets of plans of these aircraft had been sold, and completed aircraft were flying in Australia, Canada, South Africa and the United States.

CVJETKOVIC CA-61/-61R MINI ACE

The CA-61 can be built as a single-seat or side-by-side two-seat light aircraft, with any Continental engine of between 48·5 and 63·5 kW (65 and 85 hp). Alternatively, the single-seater can be fitted with a modified Volkswagen engine. Construction takes less than 1,000 hours.

The design was modified during 1973 to allow for installation of retractable landing gear; when constructed in this form, the aircraft is designated **CA-61R**.

The following details refer specifically to the single-seat CA-61 prototype:

TYPE: Single-seat light aircraft.

WINGS: Cantilever low-wing monoplane. Wing section NACA 4415. Dihedral 3°. No incidence. Structure consists of two spruce spars, each built in one piece, built-up spruce girder-type ribs and plywood-covered leading-edge torsion box, with fabric covering overall. Fabric-covered spruce ailerons. No flaps.

FUSELAGE: Conventional wooden structure of basic square section, plywood-covered.

TAIL UNIT: Cantilever wooden structure, covered with plywood. Fixed-incidence tailplane. Trim tab in elevator.

LANDING GEAR: Non-retractable tailwheel type. Cantilever main legs, with helical spring shock-absorption. Goodyear main wheels and tyres, size 5·00-5 Type III, and Model L5 brakes. Steerable tailwheel.

POWER PLANT: One 48·5 kW (65 hp) Continental A65

flat-four engine, driving a Flottorp 63-55 two-blade fixed-pitch propeller. Fuel in two steel tanks in fuselage, with capacities of 45 litres (12 US gallons) and 19 litres (5 US gallons) respectively. Total fuel capacity 64 litres (17 US gallons). Oil capacity 4·5 litres (1·25 US gallons).

ACCOMMODATION: Single seat in enclosed cockpit.

ELECTRONICS AND EQUIPMENT: Prototype fitted with Nova Star radio and Omni.

DIMENSIONS, EXTERNAL:

Wing span	8·38 m (27 ft 6 in)
Wing chord, constant	1·40 m (4 ft 7 in)
Wing area, gross	11·75 m² (126·5 sq ft)
Wing aspect ratio	6·0
Length overall	5·77 m (18 ft 11 in)
Height overall (in flying position)	2·08 m (6 ft 10 in)
Wheel track:	
Single-seat	2·49 m (8 ft 2 in)
Two-seat	2·62 m (8 ft 7 in)

WEIGHTS:

Weight empty:	
Single-seat	275 kg (606 lb)
Two-seat	363 kg (800 lb)
Max T-O weight:	
Single-seat	430 kg (950 lb)
Two-seat	590 kg (1,300 lb)

PERFORMANCE:

Max level speed at S/L	104 knots (193 km/h; 120 mph)
Normal cruising speed	87 knots (161 km/h; 100 mph)
Min flying speed:	
Single-seat	37 knots (67·5 km/h; 42 mph)
Two-seat	44 knots (80·5 km/h; 50 mph)
Range with max fuel:	
Single-seat	369 nm (685 km; 425 miles)
Two-seat	321 nm (595 km; 370 miles)

CVJETKOVIC CA-65

Design of this side-by-side two-seat light aircraft was started in September 1963. Construction of the prototype began in March 1964 and it flew for the first time in July 1965. Plans are available.

The CA-65 closely resembles the CA-61 in general appearance, but has a more powerful engine and retractable landing gear. A folding-wing version was introduced during 1967.

TYPE: Two-seat light aircraft.

WINGS: Cantilever low-wing monoplane. Modified NACA 4415 wing section. Dihedral 0° on centre-section, 3° on outer wings. Structure consists of two spruce spars, each built in one piece, and built-up spruce girder-type ribs, completely plywood-covered. Fabric-covered spruce ailerons. On the folding-wing version, the outer wings fold upward from their junction with the centre-section.

FUSELAGE: Conventional wooden structure of basically square section, plywood-covered. Manually-operated landing flap under fuselage.

TAIL UNIT: Cantilever wooden structure. Fixed surfaces covered with plywood. Elevator and rudder fabric-covered. Fixed-incidence tailplane.

LANDING GEAR: Mechanically-retractable tailwheel type. Main wheels retract inward. Goodyear main wheels and tyres, size 5·00-5 Type III. Goodyear type L5 brakes. Steerable tailwheel.

POWER PLANT: One 93 kW (125 hp) Lycoming O-290-G flat-four engine, driving a Sensenich 66-68 two-blade fixed-pitch propeller. Two aluminium fuel tanks in fuselage, each with capacity of 53 litres (14 US gallons). Total fuel capacity 106 litres (28 US gallons).

ACCOMMODATION: Two seats side by side in enclosed cockpit, with dual controls; although hydraulic brakes can be operated only by the pilot. Forward-opening canopy.

RADIO: Bayside BEI-990 radio fitted in prototype.

DIMENSIONS, EXTERNAL:

Wing span	7·62 m (25 ft 0 in)
Wing area, gross	10·03 m² (108 sq ft)
Width, wings folded	2·74 m (9 ft 0 in)
Length overall	5·79 m (19 ft 0 in)
Height overall (in flying position)	2·24 m (7 ft 4 in)
Height, wings folded	3·05 m (10 ft 0 in)
Wheel track	2·11 m (6 ft 11 in)
Propeller diameter	1·73 m (5 ft 8 in)

WEIGHTS:

Weight empty	408 kg (900 lb)
Max T-O weight	680 kg (1,500 lb)

PERFORMANCE (at max T-O weight):

Max level speed	139 knots (257 km/h; 160 mph)
Normal cruising speed	117 knots (217 km/h; 135 mph)
Stalling speed	48 knots (89 km/h; 55 mph)
Max rate of climb at S/L	305 m (1,000 ft)/min
Service ceiling	4,575 m (15,000 ft)
T-O run	137 m (450 ft)
Landing run	183 m (600 ft)
Range with max fuel	434 nm (804 km; 500 miles)

CVJETKOVIC CA-65A

This aircraft is an all-metal version of the wooden CA-65, with swept vertical tail surfaces. It is designed for +9*g* and −6*g* ultimate loading.

The general description of the CA-65 applies also to the CA-65A, except in the following details:

WINGS: The wing structure consists of a single main spar and an auxiliary wing spar, with aluminium sheet ribs and skin, riveted throughout. The main wing spar cap is made of extruded and bent-up sheet aluminium angles, tapered towards the tip to produce a wing of uniform bending strength. Ribs are formed from 0·025 in aluminium sheet. Wing skin is of 2024T-3 aluminium alloy sheet.

FUSELAGE: All-metal structure with four aluminium angle longerons and built-up frames. Fuselage skin is of 0·025-0·032 in 2024T-3 aluminium alloy sheet. To simplify formation of the curvature on the upper fuselage, the skins are broken up into small sections of flat panels.

TAIL UNIT: Cantilever all-metal structure, with swept vertical surfaces. Construction similar to that of the wings.

POWER PLANT: The structure is designed to accommodate a Lycoming engine of 80·5-112 kW (108-150 hp).

DIMENSIONS, EXTERNAL: As for Model CA-65 except:

Wing span	7·75 m (25 ft 5 in)
Wing area, gross	10·16 m² (109·4 sq ft)
Length overall	5·99 m (19 ft 8 in)
Height overall	2·29 m (7 ft 6 in)

PERFORMANCE (112 kW; 150 hp engine):

Max level speed	151 knots (280 km/h; 174 mph)
Normal cruising speed	130 knots (241 km/h; 150 mph)
Stalling speed	48 knots (89 km/h; 55 mph)
Max rate of climb at S/L	466 m (1,530 ft)/min
Service ceiling	4,570 m (15,000 ft)
T-O run	99 m (325 ft)
Landing run	183 m (600 ft)
Range with max fuel	460 nm (853 km; 530 miles)

D'APUZZO

NICHOLAS E. D'APUZZO

1029 Blue Rock Lane, Blue Bell, Pennsylvania 19422
Telephone: (215) 646 4792

Mr D'Apuzzo, who was formerly employed by the Naval Air Development Center, Warminster, Pennsylvania, as a project manager on specialised projects, retired from the Navy Department during 1973. He retains an association with the Navy on a consultant basis.

He has designed several sporting aircraft for amateur construction, among the best known of which are the Denight Special midget racer, described in the 1962-63 *Jane's,* and the PJ-260 single-seat aerobatic biplane described under the Parsons-Jocelyn heading in the 1974-75 *Jane's*. His other designs include the Senior Aero Sport, which is a two-seat version of the PJ-260, the smaller single-seat D-200 Freshman, and the D-201 Sportwing.

By early 1979 a total of 30 PJ-260s and Senior Aero Sports were known to have been completed by amateur constructors in the United States, with at least 32 more under construction. The latest to fly was a D-260(1) built by Merrill Vallender of Downer's Grove, Illinois, which took to the air in July 1978.

D'APUZZO D-260/D-295 SENIOR AERO SPORT

There are six versions of the Senior Aero Sport, as follows:

D-260(1). With Lycoming O-435 series engine.

D-260(2). With Continental O-470/E-185 series engine. Prototype first flown on 17 July 1965, with a 168 kW (225 hp) E-185 (modified) engine, driving an Aeromatic F-200H-O-85 propeller. Fuel in one 60·5 litre (16 US gallon) tank in fuselage and one 79·5 litre (21 US gallon) streamlined external tank under fuselage.

D-260(3). With Lycoming GO-435 series engine. Construction of prototype started by Mr G. A. Shallbetter of Minneapolis in April 1961 and first flight made on 17 July 1965, with a 194 kW (260 hp) GO-435-C2 engine, driving a Hartzell controllable-pitch propeller of 2·29 m (7 ft 6 in) diameter. Four fuel tanks in fuselage, with total capacity of 136 litres (36 US gallons). Second D-260(3), completed by Mr Alfred Fessenden of Lafayette, New York, is fitted with a Hartzell constant-speed propeller.

D-260(4). With Ranger 6-440-C six-cylinder inverted aircooled engine.

D-260(5). With 224 kW (300 hp) Lycoming R-680-E3 engine. Prototype built by Mr Henry Neys of Lake Stevens, Washington.

D-295. With 209 kW (280 hp) Lycoming GO-480-G1D6 engine. First example built by Mr Ed Mahler; D-295-2 (illustrated) completed in 1976 by Mr Geoffrey Geisz of Flint, Michigan.

TYPE: Two-seat sporting biplane.

WINGS: Conventional braced biplane type. Wing section NACA M-12 (modified). Dihedral 30′ on lower wings only. Incidence 2°. Sweepback 9° 15′ on upper wings. Two wood spars, metal ribs, fabric covering. Metal Frise ailerons on all four wings, with fabric covering. No flaps.

FUSELAGE: Steel tube structure, with aluminium alloy access panels forward of cockpit and fabric covering aft.

TAIL UNIT: Wire-braced fabric-covered steel tube structure. Trim tab in starboard elevator.

LANDING GEAR: Non-retractable tailwheel type. Cantilever spring steel main units. Goodyear 6·00-6 main wheels and tyres, pressure 1·38 bars (20 lb/sq in). Goodyear disc brakes.

POWER PLANT: One flat-six engine; details given under individual model listings. Fuel in 125 litre (33 US gallon) main tank and 41·5 litre (11 US gallon) aerobatic tank, both in fuselage. Total fuel capacity 166·5 litres (44 US gallons). Oil capacity 11 litres (3 US gallons).

ACCOMMODATION: Two seats in tandem in open cockpits. Baggage space behind headrest.

SYSTEM: 12V electrical system, with optional starter and navigation lights.

ELECTRONICS: Prototypes fitted with two-way radio and Omni.

DIMENSIONS, EXTERNAL:

Wing span	8·23 m (27 ft 0 in)
Wing chord, constant (both)	1·17 m (3 ft 10 in)
Wing area, gross	17·2 m² (185 sq ft)
Wing aspect ratio	4·22
Length overall	6·40 m (21 ft 0 in)
Height overall	2·32 m (7 ft 7½ in)
Tailplane span	3·10 m (10 ft 2 in)
Wheel track	2·57 m (8 ft 5 in)
Wheelbase	4·80 m (15 ft 9 in)

WEIGHTS:

Normal T-O weight:	
D-260 (2)	930 kg (2,050 lb)
D-260 (3)	975 kg (2,150 lb)
Max T-O and landing weight:	
All versions	975 kg (2,150 lb)

PERFORMANCE (D-260 (3) at max T-O weight. D-260 (2) comparable):

Never-exceed speed	165 knots (305 km/h; 190 mph)
Max level speed at 2,135 m (7,000 ft)	135 knots (250 km/h; 155 mph)
Max cruising speed at 2,135 m (7,000 ft)	122 knots (225 km/h; 140 mph)
Econ cruising speed at 2,135 m (7,000 ft)	113 knots (209 km/h; 130 mph)
Stalling speed	48 knots (89 km/h; 55 mph)
Max rate of climb at S/L	610 m (2,000 ft)/min
Service ceiling	6,100 m (20,000 ft)
T-O run	122 m (400 ft)
T-O to 15 m (50 ft)	213 m (700 ft)
Landing from 15 m (50 ft)	275 m (900 ft)
Landing run	183 m (600 ft)
Range with max fuel and max payload	434 nm (805 km; 500 miles)

D'APUZZO D-200 FRESHMAN

The D-200 Freshman (formerly Junior Aero Sport) is a smaller single-seat version of the PJ-260. Its design was started in September 1963 and construction of two prototypes began in September 1964. The first of these was almost completed in early 1973 when the building in which it was being constructed was destroyed by fire. The Freshman was not damaged severely, but due to the delay in obtaining new workshop premises completion of this prototype was not resumed until early 1975. The aircraft has been inspected and approved for final assembly, by the FAA; but, because of a shift of emphasis to two-seat biplanes, work on the Freshman has been retarded until after completion of the D-201 Sportwing (which see).

TYPE: Single-seat sporting biplane.

WINGS: Conventional braced biplane type. Wing section NACA M-12 (mod). Dihedral 0° on top wing, 0° 30′ on bottom wing. Incidence 2° on both wings. No sweepback. Spruce spars, wooden ribs and light alloy nose skin, with fabric covering. Fabric-covered aluminium alloy ailerons. No flaps.

FUSELAGE: Welded steel tube structure, with aluminium alloy panels forward of cockpit and fabric covering aft.

TAIL UNIT: Wire-braced welded steel tube structure with fabric covering. Fixed-incidence tailplane. Trim tab in each elevator.

LANDING GEAR: Non-retractable tailwheel type. Cantilever spring steel main legs. Goodrich-Hayes main wheels and tyres, size 5·00-4, pressure 1·38 bars (20 lb/sq in). Goodrich-Hayes brakes.

POWER PLANT: One 134 kW (180 hp) Lycoming O-360 flat-four engine, driving a Hartzell two-blade constant-speed metal propeller. Fuel tank in fuselage, capacity 75 litres (20 US gallons). Oil capacity 7·5 litres (2 US gallons).

ACCOMMODATION: Single seat in open cockpit.

DIMENSIONS, EXTERNAL:

Wing span (both)	6·60 m (21 ft 8 in)
Wing chord, constant	1·02 m (3 ft 4 in)
Wing area, gross	13·0 m² (140 sq ft)
Wing aspect ratio	4·2
Length overall	5·56 m (18 ft 3 in)
Height overall	1·93 m (6 ft 4 in)
Tailplane span	2·18 m (7 ft 2 in)
Wheel track	1·52 m (5 ft 0 in)
Wheelbase	4·11 m (13 ft 6 in)

The single-seat Cvjetkovic CA-61R (Continental A65 engine)

First folding-wing version of the Cvjetkovic CA-65, built by Graham Scarr of Duffy, Australia

Cvjetkovic CA-65 two-seat light aircraft (Lycoming O-290-G engine)

D'Apuzzo D-295-2 Senior Aero Sport built by Mr Geoffrey Geisz

Partially completed airframe of D'Apuzzo D-200 Freshman

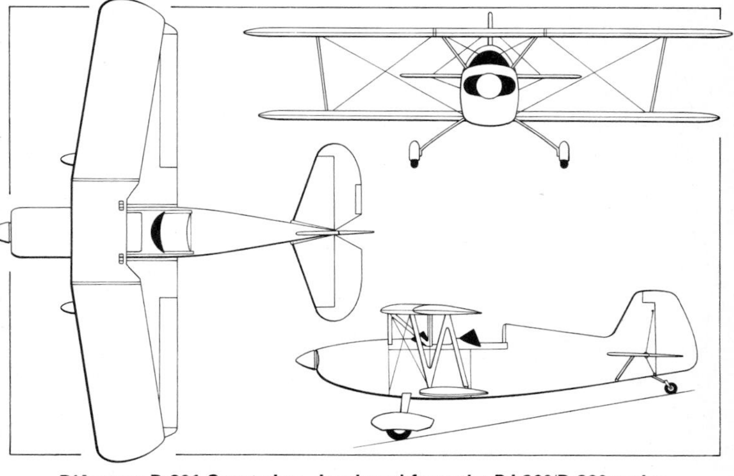

D'Apuzzo D-201 Sportwing, developed from the PJ-260/D-260 series *(Michael A. Badrocke)*

WEIGHTS:
- Weight empty 381 kg (840 lb)
- Max T-O and landing weight 578 kg (1,275 lb)

PERFORMANCE (estimated, at max T-O weight):
- Never-exceed speed 191 knots (354 km/h; 220 mph)
- Max level speed at 2,135 m (7,000 ft) 139 knots (257 km/h; 160 mph)
- Max cruising speed at 2,135 m (7,000 ft) 122 knots (225 km/h; 140 mph)
- Stalling speed 48 knots (89 km/h; 55 mph)
- Max rate of climb at S/L 762 m (2,500 ft)/min
- Service ceiling 6,100 m (20,000 ft)
- T-O run 122 m (400 ft)
- T-O to 15 m (50 ft) 198 m (650 ft)
- Landing from 15 m (50 ft) 260 m (850 ft)
- Landing run 168 m (550 ft)
- Range with max fuel 260 nm (480 km; 300 miles)

D'APUZZO D-201 SPORTWING

The D-201 is a completely redesigned development of the PJ-260/D-260 Senior Aero Sport series. Special attention has been given to reducing the cost and complexity of building the aircraft, while retaining the safety aspects of the previous models. The aircraft features long-span ailerons on the lower wings only, to reduce weight and to simplify construction; the front cockpit has been enlarged by 7·6 cm (3 in), without affecting the rear cockpit; and the wing panel structures and tailplane assembly have been redesigned. Many preformed parts are available to the homebuilder.

Construction of the prototype D-201 began in January 1977; by early 1979 it was about 75% complete, and it was hoped that the first flight could take place at the end of September 1979.

TYPE: Two-seat sporting biplane.

WINGS: Conventional braced biplane type. Wing section NACA M-12 (modified). Dihedral 0° on upper wings; 0° 30′ on lower wings. Incidence 2° on all wings. Sweepback 9° 15′ on upper wings only, outboard of centre-section. Long-span ailerons, on lower wings only. N-type interplane struts and cabane struts.

FUSELAGE: Conventional steel tube structure, with aluminium alloy panels forward of cockpit and fabric covering aft.

TAIL UNIT: Conventional wire-braced structure. Trim tab in starboard elevator. All control surfaces horn-balanced.

LANDING GEAR: Non-retractable tailwheel type. Cantilever spring steel main units. Wheel fairings.

POWER PLANT: One 119 kW (160 hp) Lycoming O-320 flat-four engine driving a Hartzell constant-speed propeller in prototype. Design suitable for any Lycoming engine from the 112 kW (150 hp) O-320 to the 149 kW (200 hp) O-360.

ACCOMMODATION: Two seats in tandem. Optional canopy over rear cockpit.

SYSTEM: Starter and generator standard.

DIMENSIONS, EXTERNAL:
- Wing span, upper 8·23 m (27 ft 0 in)
- Wing span, lower 7·86 m (25 ft 9½ in)
- Wing chord, constant 1·17 m (3 ft 10 in)
- Wing area, gross 17·14 m² (184·5 sq ft)
- Length overall, tail up 6·59 m (21 ft 7½ in)
- Height overall, tail down 2·34 m (7 ft 8 in)
- Elevator span 3·15 m (10 ft 4 in)
- Wheel track 2·57 m (8 ft 5 in)

WEIGHTS (estimated, with O-320 engine):
- Weight empty 537·5 kg (1,185 lb)
- Design max T-O weight 839 kg (1,850 lb)

PERFORMANCE:
- No details yet available

DAVIS
LEEON D. DAVIS

PO Box 207, 405 North St Paul, Stanton, Texas 79782
Telephone: (915) 756 2100

Details of the first light aircraft designed by Mr Davis, the DA-1A five-seat high-wing monoplane, can be found in the 1960-61 *Jane's*. He completed subsequently the prototype of a two-seat low-wing monoplane designated DA-2A, of which plans are available to other builders.

Until recently the prototype DA-3, a four-seat development of the DA-2A of which details appeared in the 1973-74 *Jane's*, had remained uncompleted since the late 1960s when the fuselage was put on display. It has since been completed and brief details of the aircraft can be found below. Despite the DA-3's unfinished state, Mr Davis and his son built a new single-seat sporting aircraft during 1974 and this has the designation DA-5A. It was constructed in only 67 working days.

DAVIS DA-2A

This side-by-side two-seat light aircraft was flown for the first time on 21 May 1966, after 18 months of spare-time work and an expenditure of $1,600. At the Experimental Aircraft Association's annual Fly-in a few weeks later, it gained the awards for both the most outstanding design and the most popular aircraft. Plans are available to other amateur constructors.

By early 1976 the prototype had flown a total of 860 hours, and the twenty DA-2As that were then flying had accumulated approximately 4,000 flying hours. It is believed that about 100 other DA-2As are under construction.

The DA-2A is of simple all-metal construction and has an all-moving Vee-tail (included angle 100°) like Mr Davis's earlier DA-1A. The wings are of constant chord, without flaps. Dihedral is 5°. The non-retractable tricycle landing gear has cantilever spring steel main legs and a steerable nosewheel. Power plant is a 48·5 kW (65 hp) Continental A65-8 flat-four engine; but the DA-2A is stressed for engines of up to 74·5 kW (100 hp). Total fuel capacity is 75 litres (20 US gallons) and oil capacity 3·75 litres (1 US gallon).

There is baggage space aft of the side-by-side seats or, alternatively, a child's seat may be located in this position.

DIMENSIONS, EXTERNAL:
- Wing span: 5·86 m (19 ft 2¾ in)
- Wing chord, constant: 1·31 m (4 ft 3½ in)
- Wing area, gross: 7·66 m² (82·5 sq ft)
- Wing aspect ratio: 4·48
- Length overall: 5·44 m (17 ft 10¼ in)
- Height overall: 1·65 m (5 ft 5 in)

DIMENSIONS, INTERNAL:
- Cabin: Length: 1·49 m (4 ft 6¾ in)
- Max width: 1·04 m (3 ft 5 in)
- Max height: 1·14 m (3 ft 8¾ in)

WEIGHTS:
- Weight empty: 277 kg (610 lb)
- Max T-O weight: 510 kg (1,125 lb)

PERFORMANCE (at max T-O weight):
- Max level speed at S/L: 104 knots (193 km/h; 120 mph)
- Cruising speed: 100 knots (185 km/h; 115 mph)
- Landing speed: 54 knots (100 km/h; 62 mph)
- Range with max fuel: 390 nm (725 km; 450 miles)

DAVIS DA-3

The DA-3 is a four-seat scaled-up development of the DA-2A. Work on the prototype began in the latter 1960s but was abandoned before the fuselage had been completed. Although stressed for engines of up to 74·5 kW (100 hp), the prototype was to be powered by a 48·5 kW (65 hp) Continental A65 flat-four engine. This aircraft has recently been completed, and has been joined by a three-seat DA-3 built by Mr Marcel DeWulf of Lake Bluff, Indiana, which first flew on 8 July 1978. The latter aircraft is powered by a 74·5 kW (100 hp) Continental O-200 flat-four engine, and has a wing span and length of 6·78 m (22 ft 2¾ in) and 5·97 m (19 ft 7¼ in) respectively. Max T-O weight is 726 kg (1,600 lb).

Plans are not being made available to homebuilders.

DAVIS DA-5A

Design of this aircraft began in October 1972, and Mr Davis and his son began construction of the prototype on 4 May 1974. It had been intended to power the aircraft with a two-cylinder Franklin Sport 2 engine, but non-availability of this power plant enforced a design change to utilise a 48·5 kW (65 hp) Continental A65. Despite the extra work involved, the first flight of the DA-5A was made on 22 July 1974. During 6-7 August 1976, a modified Davis DA-5A, with wing span increased by 0·91 m (3 ft 0 in) and with 318 litres (84 US gallons) of fuel on board, flew a distance of 1,966·36 nm (3,641·70 km; 2,262·85 miles), setting up a new FAI Class C1a closed circuit distance record for aircraft of under 500 kg empty weight. Total flying time was 21h 42 min, which included 26 nm (48 km; 30 miles) flying to and from the course. Pilot was Mr Leeon Davis.

Plans are available to amateur constructors.

TYPE: Single-seat sporting aircraft.

WINGS: Cantilever low-wing monoplane. Wing section Clark Y. Thickness/chord ratio 12%. Dihedral 5°. Incidence 0°. Light alloy structure with single spar, ribs of 2024T-3 alloy, and stressed skins. Plain ailerons of light alloy construction. No flaps. No trim tabs.

FUSELAGE: Light alloy stressed-skin structure with four frames and stainless steel firewall. Steel tube overturn structure aft of pilot's seat.

TAIL UNIT: All-moving Vee tail (included angle 100°) with steel tube spar and light alloy ribs and skins. Anti-servo tabs in trailing-edges.

LANDING GEAR: Non-retractable tricycle type. Mainwheel legs of light alloy streamline section mounted rigidly to wing spar. Shock-absorption by tyres and rubber grommets. Main wheels have tyres size 14 × 5-4, pressure 1·03 bars (15 lb/sq in). Steerable nosewheel with tyre size 10 × 3-4, pressure 1·03 bars (15 lb/sq in). Rosenhan drum brakes.

POWER PLANT: One 48·5 kW (65 hp) Continental A65 flat-four engine, driving a Hegy type 60-70 two-blade fixed-pitch wooden propeller with spinner. Fuel tank in fuselage, immediately aft of firewall, capacity 64·3 litres (17 US gallons). Refuelling point on fuselage upper surface forward of windscreen. Oil capacity 3·75 litres (1 US gallon).

ACCOMMODATION: Single seat beneath canopy hinged on port side.

DIMENSIONS, EXTERNAL:
- Wing span: 4·76 m (15 ft 7¼ in)
- Wing chord, constant: 1·12 m (3 ft 8 in)
- Wing area, gross: 5·31 m² (57·20 sq ft)
- Wing aspect ratio: 4·26
- Length overall: 4·80 m (15 ft 9 in)
- Height overall: 1·35 m (4 ft 5¼ in)
- Span over Vee tail: 1·60 m (5 ft 3 in)
- Wheel track: 1·55 m (5 ft 1 in)
- Wheelbase: 1·12 m (3 ft 8 in)
- Propeller diameter: 1·52 m (5 ft 0 in)
- Propeller ground clearance: 0·203 m (8 in)

DIMENSION, INTERNAL:
- Cockpit: Max width: 0·53 m (1 ft 9 in)

WEIGHTS:
- Weight empty: 208 kg (460 lb)
- Max T-O weight: 351 kg (775 lb)

PERFORMANCE (at max T-O weight):
- Never-exceed speed: 147 knots (273 km/h; 170 mph)
- Max level speed at S/L: 139 knots (257 km/h; 160 mph)
- Max cruising speed at S/L: 122 knots (225 km/h; 140 mph)
- Econ cruising speed at S/L: 104 knots (193 km/h; 120 mph)
- Stalling speed: 52·5 knots (97 km/h; 60 mph)
- Max rate of climb at S/L: 244 m (800 ft)/min
- Service ceiling: 4,420 m (14,500 ft)
- T-O run: 183 m (600 ft)
- T-O to 15 m (50 ft): 259 m (850 ft)
- Landing from 15 m (50 ft): 335 m (1,100 ft)
- Landing run: 183 m (600 ft)
- Range with max fuel: 390 nm (724 km; 450 miles)

DREWS

JOHN DREWS

107 Highland Road, Lake Mills, Wisconsin 53551

DREWS B-1-A

Mr John Drews has built a variant of the Bowers Fly Baby 1-B, modified to look like a first World War fighter. Changes from the standard single-seat Fly Baby 1-B include a new-shape tail unit and installation of an 86 kW (115 hp) Lycoming O-235-C1B engine in a new cowling. The materials used in construction remain the same. First flight was achieved in 1976, since when larger wheels have been fitted, as shown in illustration.

DIMENSIONS, EXTERNAL:
- Wing span: 7·32 m (24 ft 0 in)
- Wing chord (both wings), constant: 1·12 m (3 ft 8 in)
- Length overall: 5·79 m (19 ft 0 in)
- Height overall: 2·44 m (8 ft 0 in)

WEIGHTS:
- Weight empty: 358 kg (789 lb)
- Max T-O weight: 499 kg (1,100 lb)

PERFORMANCE:
- Max level speed: 91 knots (169 km/h; 105 mph)
- Cruising speed: 74 knots (137 km/h; 85 mph)
- Landing speed: 35 knots (64·5 km/h; 40 mph)
- Max rate of climb at S/L: 305 m (1,000 ft)/min
- Service ceiling: 2,440 m (8,000 ft)
- T-O run: 122 m (400 ft)
- Landing run: 152 m (500 ft)
- Range with max fuel: 173 nm (322 km; 200 miles)

DSK

DSK AIRMOTIVE INC

PO Box 629, Fort Walton Beach, Florida 32548
Telephone: (904) 651 1301
PRESIDENT: Sarah R. Killingsworth

Mr Richard Killingsworth, then a USAF Chief Master Sergeant, designed and built a single-seat sporting aircraft which he designated DSK-1 Hawk. It flew for the first time on 26 May 1973, and interest in the design was such that he formed DSK Airmotive Inc to market plans and partial kits to amateur constructors. The business is being carried on by Mrs Killingsworth following her husband's death on 12 April 1975, when the prototype Hawk crashed as the result of an engine failure at take-off.

The fuselage structure of the prototype was basically a surplus Air Force/Navy 200 US gallon drop-tank; but Mr Killingsworth's plans provide for alternative bulkhead/stressed-skin construction for builders unable to obtain a suitable drop-tank. In this form the aircraft is designated DSK-2 Golden Hawk and is described separately.

By early 1979, about 49 Hawks were thought to be under construction.

DSK AIRMOTIVE DSK-1 HAWK

TYPE: Single-seat sporting aircraft. Structure stressed to 9*g* ultimate.

WINGS: Cantilever low-wing monoplane. Clark Y section. Thickness/chord ratio 15%. Slight dihedral on outer panels. No incidence. Conventional two-spar structure of 2024T-3 light alloy. Wingtips are drooped, raked and conical. Trailing-edge flaps of light alloy construction extend from inner edge of ailerons and continue beneath fuselage. Plain ailerons of light alloy construction. Optional aileron droop. No tabs. Wings detach for trailering or stowage.

FUSELAGE: All-metal structure utilising a surplus military drop-tank as its basis, with 2024T-3 alloy sheet and 6061T-6 structural angle reinforcement.

TAIL UNIT: Cantilever all-metal structure with swept vertical surfaces. Incidence of tailplane ground-adjustable. Trim tab on elevator.

LANDING GEAR: Non-retractable tricycle type. All units have a tubular steel strut with compression springs for shock-absorption. Nosewheel and main-wheel tyres size 14 × 5·00-5, pressure 2·07 bars (30 lb/sq in). Steerable and self-centering nosewheel. Mechanical disc brakes. Parking brake. Wheel fairings optional.

POWER PLANT: Prototype has one 48·5 kW (65 hp) Lycoming O-145-B2 flat-four engine, driving a McCauley two-blade metal fixed-pitch propeller refurbished by Aero Prop. Provision for alternative engines of up to 93 kW (125 hp). Fuel contained in forward fuselage tank, capacity 34 litres (9 US gallons). Auxiliary tank, raising total fuel capacity to 68 litres (18 US gallons), optional. Refuelling point for front tank forward of windscreen, for rear tank in turtledeck aft of cockpit. Oil capacity 4·7 litres (1·25 US gallons).

ACCOMMODATION: Single seat in enclosed cockpit. Canopy slides aft for access. Baggage space aft of pilot's seat. Cockpit heated and ventilated. All control surfaces actuated by push-pull rods.

SYSTEM: Simple air-driven alternator under design by DSK Airmotive.

AVIONICS: Battery-powered Narco VHT-3 nav/com and Omni.

DIMENSIONS, EXTERNAL:
- Wing span: 6·21 m (20 ft 4½ in)
- Wing chord, constant: 0·97 m (3 ft 2 in)
- Wing area, gross: 5·95 m² (64 sq ft)
- Wing aspect ratio: 6·42
- Length overall: 4·57 m (15 ft 0 in)
- Height overall: 1·83 m (6 ft 0 in)
- Tailplane span: 1·88 m (6 ft 2 in)
- Wheel track: 1·63 m (5 ft 4 in)
- Wheelbase: 1·14 m (3 ft 9 in)
- Propeller diameter: 1·60 m (5 ft 3 in)

WEIGHTS:
- Weight empty: 238 kg (525 lb)
- Max T-O and landing weight: 405 kg (893 lb)

PERFORMANCE (at max T-O weight):
- Max level speed at 1,525 m (5,000 ft): 127 knots (235 km/h; 146 mph)
- Max cruising speed at 1,525 m (5,000 ft): 114 knots (211 km/h; 131 mph)
- Econ cruising speed at 1,525 m (5,000 ft): 96 knots (177 km/h; 110 mph)
- Stalling speed, flaps up: 52·5 knots (97 km/h; 60 mph)
- Stalling speed, flaps down: 39-44 knots (73-81 km/h; 45-50 mph)
- Max rate of climb at S/L: 457 m (1,500 ft)/min
- Service ceiling: 3,660 m (12,000 ft)
- T-O run: 122-183 m (400-600 ft)
- T-O to 15 m (50 ft): 244 m (800 ft)
- Landing from 15 m (50 ft): 229 m (750 ft)
- Landing run: 107-168 m (350-550 ft)
- Range with max fuel, 45 min reserves: 477 nm (885 km; 550 miles)

DSK AIRMOTIVE DSK-2 GOLDEN HAWK

Generally similar to the DSK-1 Hawk, the DSK-2 was designed to eliminate the use of a military drop-tank as the basic fuselage structure and is 0·46 m (1 ft 6 in) longer overall. Design began in January 1974 and construction of the prototype was started four months later. It was hoped originally to complete the flight testing in 1976; instead the prototype was placed into storage. Flying subsequently

Davis DA-5A single-seat lightweight sporting aircraft *(left)* and Davis DA-2A two-seat aircraft

DSK Airmotive DSK-1 Hawk single-seat sporting aircraft (Lycoming O-145-B2 engine)

DSK-2 Golden Hawk built by Mr Donald A. Kames of Chicago *(J. M. G. Gradidge)*

Drews B-1-A, a modified Bowers Fly Baby 1-B

Durand Mk V two-seat sporting biplane *(Howard Levy)*

resumed, and by early 1978 this DSK-2 had logged 29 flight hours. Two other Golden Hawks have been completed; that illustrated was constructed by Mr Don Kames of West Chicago and first flew in 1976.

TYPE: Single-seat sporting aircraft.

WINGS: As for DSK-1, with 6061T-6 light alloy structural angle reinforcement of spars. Ailerons droop collectively with flaps.

FUSELAGE: Light alloy semi-monocoque structure with five bulkheads, 6061T-6 structural angle longerons, and 2024T-3 alloy bulkheads and stressed skin.

TAIL UNIT: Cantilever structure of light alloy, with swept tail surfaces. Box-beam/rib/stressed-skin structure of 2024T-3 alloy. Incidence of tailplane ground-adjustable. Manually-adjustable trim tab on elevator.

LANDING GEAR: Non-retractable tricycle type, as on DSK-1 Hawk. Main legs of steel tube, with springs in compression. Corded neoprene for absorption of side loads. Self-centering steerable nosewheel. Main wheels and tyres size 14 × 5·50-5, pressure 2·07 bars (30 lb/sq in). Nosewheel and tyre size 13 × 5·00-5, 14 × 5·00-5 optional, pressure 2·07 bars (30 lb/sq in). Cleveland hydraulic brakes. Fairings on main legs.

POWER PLANT: As for DSK-1.

ACCOMMODATION: As for DSK-1, except new sliding canopy and seatback, and control column removable to provide room for pilot to sleep, between flights, during sporting trips. Aircraft can be flown with canopy open or closed. Tandem passenger seat can be installed. Baggage space.

SYSTEMS: Hydraulic system for brakes only. Power for electronics provided by rechargeable battery. DSK air-driven alternator optional.

AVIONICS: Prototype has, currently, Narco VHT-2 nav/com. It is intended to install a 90-channel nav/com.

DIMENSIONS, EXTERNAL:

As for DSK-1, except:

Wing area, gross	5·99 m² (64·5 sq ft)
Wing aspect ratio	6·43
Length overall	5·03 m (16 ft 6 in)
Height overall	1·91 m (6 ft 3 in)
Wheel track	1·64 m (5 ft 4½ in)

WEIGHTS (estimated):

Weight empty	251 kg (554 lb)
Max T-O weight	414 kg (914 lb)

PERFORMANCE (estimated, at max T-O weight):

Max level speed at 1,525 m (5,000 ft)	135 knots (251 km/h; 156 mph)
Max cruising speed at 1,525 m (5,000 ft)	122 knots (227 km/h; 141 mph)
Econ cruising speed	104 knots (193 km/h; 120 mph)
Stalling speed, flaps up	52·5 knots (97 km/h; 60 mph)
Stalling speed, flaps down	43·5 knots (81 km/h; 50 mph)
Max rate of climb at S/L	457 m (1,500 ft)/min
Service ceiling	3,660 m (12,000 ft)
T-O run	122-183 m (400-600 ft)
T-O to 15 m (50 ft)	320 m (1,050 ft)
Landing from 15 m (50 ft)	274-320 m (900-1,050 ft)
Landing run	168 m (550 ft)
Range with 53 litres (14 US gallons) fuel at econ cruising speed	416 nm (772 km; 480 miles)

DURAND

WILLIAM DURAND

84th and McKinley, Omaha, Nebraska 68122

DURAND Mk V

Mr William Durand, a professional engineer, has designed and built a two-seat all-metal high-performance biplane known as the Durand Mk V. Design began in the mid-1960s, and first flight was achieved on 28 June 1978. By 11 August 1978, the aircraft had logged 30 flying hours.

The Mk V is Mr Durand's fifth homebuilt aircraft. Previous designs were the Mk I wood and fabric glider of 1934; Mk II two-seat steel tube, wood and fabric monoplane of 1940, with a three-cylinder Szekely engine; Mk III single-seat shoulder-wing monoplane of 1942, with C40 engine; and Mark IV all-metal pusher design of 1948, with C85 engine and tricycle landing gear, which it was hoped would go into production but never did.

Plans of the Durand Mk V are available to amateur builders.

TYPE: Two-seat sporting biplane.

WINGS: Negative stagger biplane. Constant chord. Dihedral 0° upper wing, 2° 30′ lower wings. Incidence 3° both wings. Inverted V interplane struts. No wire bracing. All-metal construction. Full-span flaps on upper and lower wings. Spoilers in place of ailerons, forward of flaps on lower wings only.

FUSELAGE: Conventional all-metal structure.

TAIL UNIT: Cantilever all-metal type, with sweptback fin and large-area rudder. All-moving tailplane.

LANDING GEAR: Non-retractable tricycle type. Same-size wheels on all three units. Cantilever main legs. Steerable nosewheel.

POWER PLANT: One 112 kW (150 hp) Lycoming O-320-E2A flat-four engine, driving a two-blade propeller with spinner. Auxiliary wing fuel tanks optional.

ACCOMMODATION: Two seats side by side under forward-sliding canopy. Transparent rear-fuselage section aft of cockpit and upper wings. Dual, stick-type, controls.

DIMENSIONS, EXTERNAL:

Wing span	7·44 m (24 ft 5 in)
Wing chord, constant	0·914 m (3 ft 0 in)
Length overall	6·17 m (20 ft 3 in)
Height overall	2·06 m (6 ft 9 in)
Tailplane span	2·71 m (8 ft 10½ in)
Wheel track	2·13 m (7 ft 0 in)
Wheelbase	1·70 m (5 ft 7 in)

DIMENSION, INTERNAL:

Cabin: Max width	1·12 m (3 ft 8 in)

WEIGHTS:

Weight empty	549 kg (1,210 lb)
Max T-O weight	834 kg (1,840 lb)

PERFORMANCE:

Max cruising speed (75% power) at 2,285 m (7,500 ft)	122 knots (225 km/h; 140 mph)
Landing speed	40 knots (74 km/h; 46 mph)
Normal range	347 nm (644 km; 400 miles)
Max range with auxiliary tanks	521 nm (966 km; 600 miles)

DYKE

DYKE AIRCRAFT

2840 Old Yellow Springs Road, Fairborn, Ohio 45324
Telephone: (513) 878 9832

Mr John W. Dyke was the designer of a small delta-wing aircraft, designated JD-1 Delta, which he built with Mrs Jennie Dyke. This was described in the 1964-65 *Jane's*. Subsequently, Mr Dyke developed the design, and the first flight of the JD-2 Delta was made in July 1966.

DYKE AIRCRAFT JD-2 DELTA

Plans of the JD-2 are available to amateur constructors, and Mr Dyke has formed Dyke Aircraft to market them. A total of about 300 JD-2s were thought to be under construction in early 1979, in Australia, Brazil, Canada, France, Germany, Japan, New Zealand, South Africa, the United Kingdom and the United States. About eleven had been completed and flown by then.

As a help to the homebuilder, hardware and tubing kits are available.

A feature of the Dyke Delta is that the outer wing panels

can be folded flat above the cockpit for easy towing.

TYPE: Delta-winged sporting aircraft.

WINGS: Delta wing of modified NACA 63012 and 66015 wing section. No dihedral. No incidence. Sweepback of wing centre-section 61°. Sweepback of outer wing panels 31°. Welded steel tube structure, with stainless steel capstrips to which the laminated glassfibre skins are secured by Dupont explosive rivets. Aluminium skin optional; attached by aluminium pop rivets. Trailing-edge elevons extending from centreline to approximately two-thirds span. Elevons have a basic structure of metal but are fabric covered. Trim tab at inboard edge of each elevon. Wing outer panels fold upward and lay above the fuselage so that the JD-2 can be towed on the landing gear. Folding and unfolding can be carried out by one person.

FUSELAGE: Welded steel tube structure with stainless steel capstrips and glassfibre skins, except for fuselage undersurface which has 4130 steel tube capstrips and fabric covering.

TAIL UNIT: Welded steel tube structure with swept fin and rudder, both fabric covered. Optional all-moving T-tailplane, with steel tube main spar and aluminium skin, for improved low-speed trim when a heavier engine, such as the 149 kW (200 hp) Lycoming, is installed.

LANDING GEAR: Manually retractable tricycle type, all units retracting aft. Shock-absorption by torsion bars of 6150 heat-treated steel. Main wheels have tyres size 14 × 5-6, pressure 3·10 bars (45 lb/sq in). Nosewheel tyre size 12 × 5-4, pressure 2·07 bars (30 lb/sq in). Firestone hydraulic brakes.

POWER PLANT: Prototype has one 134 kW (180 hp) Lycoming O-360 flat-four engine, driving a McCauley two-blade fixed-pitch propeller with spinner. Constant-speed propeller and 149 kW (200 hp) engine installation optional. Glassfibre fuel tank in fuselage, immediately aft of cabin, capacity 178 litres (47 US gallons), with pilot and two passengers. Fuel capacity reduced to 87 litres (23 US gallons) as a four-seat aircraft. Refuelling point on port side of aft fuselage upper surface. Oil capacity 7·5 litres (2 US gallons).

ACCOMMODATION: Standard accommodation for pilot, on single forward seat, and three passengers on aft bench seat. Access by upward-opening canopy, hinged on starboard side. Accommodation is ventilated. Space for limited baggage in starboard wing centre-section.

SYSTEMS: Hydraulic system for brakes only. Vacuum system for instruments. Electrical supply from 12V DC generator; solid-state inverter provides 110V AC at 400Hz.

ELECTRONICS AND EQUIPMENT: Genave Series 200A 200-channel nav and com transceiver. Blind-flying instrumentation standard.

DIMENSIONS, EXTERNAL:
- Wing span: 6·87 m (22 ft 2½ in)
- Wing chord at root (centre-section): 4·27 m (14 ft 0 in)
- Wing chord at root (outer panels): 2·90 m (9 ft 6 in)
- Wing chord at tip: 0·51 m (1 ft 8 in)
- Wing area, gross: 17·00 m² (183 sq ft)
- Wing aspect ratio: 2·7
- Length overall: 5·79 m (19 ft 0 in)
- Width, wings folded: 2·24 m (7 ft 4 in)
- Height overall: 1·83 m (6 ft 0 in)
- Tailplane span (T-tail): 0·91 m (3 ft 0 in)
- Wheel track: 1·97 m (6 ft 5½ in)
- Wheelbase: 2·13 m (7 ft 0 in)
- Propeller diameter: 1·88 m (6 ft 2 in)

DIMENSIONS, INTERNAL:
- Cabin: Length: 1·88 m (6 ft 2 in)
  - Max width: 1·22 m (4 ft 0 in)
  - Max height: 1·02 m (3 ft 4 in)
  - Floor area: 1·67 m² (18 sq ft)
- Baggage space: 0·17 m³ (6 cu ft)

WEIGHTS (A: 134 kW; 180 hp, B: 149 kW; 200 hp engine):
- Weight empty, basic equipped:
  - A, B: 435 kg (960 lb)
- Weight empty, IFR equipped:
  - A, B: 483 kg (1,065 lb)
- Max T-O weight:
  - A, B: 862 kg (1,900 lb)
- Max landing weight:
  - A, B: 816 kg (1,800 lb)

PERFORMANCE (at max T-O weight with 134 kW; 180 hp engine, except where indicated):
- Never-exceed speed: 191 knots (354 km/h; 220 mph)
- Max level speed at 2,285 m (7,500 ft): 165 knots (306 km/h; 190 mph)
- Max cruising speed at 2,285 m (7,500 ft), fixed-pitch propeller: 156 knots (290 km/h; 180 mph)
- Max cruising speed, constant-speed propeller: 165 knots (306 km/h; 190 mph)
- Max cruising speed, with 149 kW (200 hp) engine and constant-speed propeller: 174 knots (322 km/h; 200 mph)
- Econ cruising speed at 2,285 m (7,500 ft): 135 knots (249 km/h; 155 mph)
- Max rate of climb at S/L: 610 m (2,000 ft)/min
- Service ceiling: 4,420 m (14,500 ft)
- Service ceiling, with 149 kW (200 hp) engine: 5,485 m (18,000 ft)
- T-O run: 213 m (700 ft)
- T-O to 15 m (50 ft): 488 m (1,600 ft)
- Landing from 15 m (50 ft): 549 m (1,800 ft)
- Landing run: 244-305 m (800-1,000 ft)
- Range with max fuel and pilot only: 625 nm (1,158 km; 720 miles)
- Range with max payload: 390 nm (724 km; 450 miles)

EAA

EXPERIMENTAL AIRCRAFT ASSOCIATION INC

PO Box 229, Hales Corners, Wisconsin 53130
Telephone: (414) 425 4860
PRESIDENT: Paul H. Poberezny
VICE-PRESIDENT: Ray Scholler
SECRETARY: S. H. Schmid
TREASURER: Arthur Kilps

As a service to its members, the EAA decided in 1955 to develop a modern single-seat sporting biplane suitable for home construction by amateurs. The design drawings were prepared by Mr J. D. Stewart and Mr T. Seely of the Allison Division, General Motors Corporation, with the assistance of Mr Paul H. Poberezny, President of the EAA, and this aircraft became known as the EAA Biplane. It was followed in 1972 by the Acro-Sport, an aerobatic aircraft designed by Mr Poberezny. These two designs were supplemented in 1973 by a more advanced aerobatic aircraft, the Super Acro-Sport.

Latest designs to emanate from the EAA President are the lightweight Pober P-9 Pixie, which flew for the first time in July 1974, and the Acro-Sport II.

EAA BIPLANE

The prototype of the EAA Biplane was built between 1957 and May 1960 as a classroom project by students of St Rita's High School, Chicago, under the supervision of Mr Robert Blacker. It flew for the first time on 10 June 1960, powered by a 48·5 kW (65 hp) Continental A65 engine.

After this prototype had been taken over by the EAA, a number of modifications were made, including installation of a 63·5 kW (85 hp) engine. Mr Poberezny subsequently introduced further changes, including lighter wing spars and fittings, which reduced the empty weight of the aircraft, together with increases in the area of the tail surfaces and many other improvements. This modified version was known as the EAA Biplane Model P. Subsequent changes led successively to Models P1 and P2, with successively thinner spars and, in the P2, movement of the cockpit to a slightly more forward position.

Over 7,000 sets of plans of the EAA Biplane have been sold by the EAA Museum Foundation, and many examples are flying and under construction.

The following details apply to the standard EAA Biplane Model P2:

TYPE: Single-seat sporting biplane.

WINGS: Braced biplane, with N-shape streamline-section cabane struts and interplane struts. Dihedral 0° on upper wing, 2° on lower wings. Incidence 2° on upper wing, 2° on lower wings. All-wood two-spar structure, with aluminium leading-edge and overall fabric covering. Spars 25·5 mm (1·0 in) thick. Ailerons of similar construction to wings, on lower wings only. No flaps.

FUSELAGE: Welded steel tube structure, fabric-covered.

TAIL UNIT: Wire-braced welded steel tube structure, fabric-covered.

LANDING GEAR: Non-retractable tailwheel type, modified from standard Piper J-3 components. Rubber cord shock-absorption. Brakes on main wheels. Wheel fairings optional. Piper J-3 steerable tailwheel.

POWER PLANT: Prototype Model P has a 63·5 kW (85 hp) Continental C85-8 flat-four engine, driving a two-blade metal fixed-pitch propeller. Provision for engines of up to 112 kW (150 hp); but most Model Ps have a 93 kW (125 hp) Lycoming. Piper J-3 fuel tank aft of firewall in fuselage, capacity 68 litres (18 US gallons).

ACCOMMODATION: Single seat in open cockpit.

DIMENSIONS, EXTERNAL:
- Wing span: 6·10 m (20 ft 0 in)
- Wing chord (both), constant: 0·91 m (3 ft 0 in)
- Wing area, gross: 10·03 m² (108 sq ft)
- Length overall: 5·18 m (17 ft 0 in)
- Height overall: 1·83 m (6 ft 0 in)
- Wheel track: 1·71 m (5 ft 7½ in)
- Propeller diameter:
  - 85 hp: 1·78 m (5 ft 10 in)
  - 150 hp: 1·88 m (6 ft 2 in)

WEIGHTS (63·5 kW; 85 hp engine):
- Weight empty: 322 kg (710 lb)
- Max T-O weight: 522 kg (1,150 lb)

PERFORMANCE (A, with 63·5 kW; 85 hp Continental engine; B, with 112 kW; 150 hp Lycoming engine, at max T-O weight):
- Max level speed at S/L:
  - A: 109 knots (201 km/h; 125 mph)
- Econ cruising speed:
  - A: 96 knots (177 km/h; 110 mph)
- Stalling speed: A: 48 knots (89 km/h; 55 mph)
  - B: 52 knots (97 km/h; 60 mph) CAS
- Max rate of climb at S/L: A: 305 m (1,000 ft)/min
  - B: 370 m (1,210 ft)/min
- Service ceiling: A: 3,500 m (11,500 ft)
- T-O run: A: 91 m (300 ft)
- Landing run: A: 245 m (800 ft)
- Range with max fuel:
  - A: 304 nm (560 km; 350 miles)
- *g* limits: normal ±6, ultimate ±9

EAA ACRO-SPORT I

The Acro-Sport I was designed by Mr Paul Poberezny, President of the EAA, specifically for construction by school students, as a pupils' project. The EAA considers that such a project enables those who participate to discover their capabilities and potential in the manual crafts necessary to build an aircraft, possibly helping the individual to choose a career more wisely.

First flight of the prototype Acro-Sport (N1AC) was made on 11 January 1972, only 352 days after its design was started, although it represented a completely new design, unrelated to the EAA Biplane.

Plans and construction manuals are available to homebuilders from Acro-Sport Inc (see Super Acro-Sport for address), and about 800 sets had been sold by January 1979.

The following details apply to the prototype:

TYPE: Single-seat aerobatic biplane.

WINGS: Braced single-bay biplane, with single streamline-section interplane strut each side. N-type centre-section struts. Double streamline-section flying and landing wires. Wing section M-6. Dihedral: upper 0°, lower 2°. Incidence (both) 1° 30′. Conventional two-spar structure, with spruce spars and ribs, single wire drag and anti-drag truss, fabric-covered. Glassfibre wingtips. Ailerons, on all four wings, of wood construction with fabric covering. No flaps. Cutout in trailing-edge of upper wing.

FUSELAGE: Composite structure of welded steel tube, with wooden stringers, fabric-covered. Glassfibre nose cowl and light alloy engine cowlings.

TAIL UNIT: Wire-braced welded steel tube structure with fabric covering. Controllable trim tab on port side of elevator, servo tab on starboard side.

LANDING GEAR: Non-retractable tailwheel type, modified from Piper J-3 components. Two side Vees and half axles. Rubber bungee shock-absorption. Main-wheel tyres size 5·00-5, pressure 1·86-1·93 bars (27-28 lb/sq in). Cleveland or Goodyear hydraulic brakes. Glassfibre wheel fairings. Steerable tailwheel. Parking brake.

POWER PLANT: Prototype has a 134 kW (180 hp) Lycoming engine, driving a Sensenich two-blade metal fixed-pitch propeller with spinner. Basic power plant is a 74·5 kW (100 hp) Continental O-200 flat-four engine. Single fuel tank immediately aft of firewall, capacity 104 litres (20 US gallons). Refuelling point on upper surface of fuselage. Small smoke oil tank, capacity 19 litres (5 US gallons), forward of instrument panel, could also be used for fuel.

ACCOMMODATION: Single seat in open cockpit, which is large enough to accommodate a pilot 1·95 m (6 ft 5 in) tall and weighing 115 kg (250 lb). Baggage space behind headrest, capacity 16 kg (35 lb).

DIMENSIONS, EXTERNAL:
- Wing span, upper: 5·97 m (19 ft 7 in)
- Wing span, lower: 5·82 m (19 ft 1 in)
- Wing chord (both), constant: 0·91 m (3 ft 0 in)
- Wing area, gross: 10·73 m² (115·5 sq ft)
- Wing aspect ratio, upper: 6·6
- Length overall: 5·33 m (17 ft 6 in)
- Height overall: 1·83 m (6 ft 0 in)
- Tailplane span: 2·16 m (7 ft 1 in)
- Wheel track: 1·78 m (5 ft 10 in)
- Propeller diameter: 1·93 m (6 ft 4 in)

WEIGHTS:
- Weight empty, equipped: 335 kg (739 lb)
- Max T-O and landing weight: 534 kg (1,178 lb)

PERFORMANCE (at max T-O weight):
- Never-exceed speed: 156 knots (289 km/h; 180 mph)
- Max level speed: 132 knots (245 km/h; 152 mph)
- Max cruising speed: 113 knots (209 km/h; 130 mph)
- Econ cruising speed: 91 knots (169 km/h; 105 mph)
- Stalling speed: 43·5 knots (80·5 km/h; 50 mph)
- Max rate of climb at S/L: 1,067 m (3,500 ft)/min
- T-O run: 46 m (150 ft)
- T-O to 15 m (50 ft): 107 m (350 ft)
- Landing from 15 m (50 ft): 267 m (875 ft)
- Landing run: 244 m (800 ft)
- Range with max fuel: 304 nm (563 km; 350 miles)

EAA SUPER ACRO-SPORT

Design of a developed version of the Acro-Sport was started in January 1971. Construction began in the follow-

Dyke Delta built by Avions Pierre Robin in France *(Brian M. Service)*

EAA Biplane single-seat sporting aircraft

EAA Acro-Sport II two-seat aerobatic biplane *(Lee Fray)*

EAA Acro-Sport I aerobatic biplane

EAA Pober P-9 Pixie *(Howard Levy)*

ing year and the first flight of this prototype was made on 28 March 1973. Known as the Super Acro-Sport, it is intended for unlimited International Class aerobatic competition at a world championship level. Generally similar in external appearance to the Acro-Sport, it has a more powerful engine, nearly symmetrical aerofoil sections, a better rate of climb, and improved outside (negative *g*) aerobatic capability.

The differences by comparison with the standard Acro-Sport are covered in a supplement to the basic plans which are available from Acro-Sport Inc, PO Box 462, Hales Corners, Wisconsin 53130. The description of the Acro-Sport applies also to the Super Acro-Sport, except as follows:

TYPE: Single-seat advanced aerobatic biplane.

WINGS: As Acro-Sport, except wing section NACA 23012.

TAIL UNIT: As Acro-Sport, except controllable trim tab on starboard side of elevator, servo tab on port side.

LANDING GEAR: As Acro-Sport, except Cleveland hydraulic brakes. Steerable tailwheel has a solid tyre.

POWER PLANT: Prototype has a 149 kW (200 hp) Lycoming IO-360-A2A flat-four engine, driving a Sensenich two-blade metal fixed-pitch propeller type 76EM8-0-60 with spinner. Fuel system and capacity as for Acro-Sport. Oil capacity 7·5 litres (2 US gallons).

DIMENSIONS, EXTERNAL: As for Acro-Sport, except:
- Length overall — 5·30 m (17 ft 4½ in)

WEIGHTS:
- Weight empty — 401 kg (884 lb)
- Max T-O weight — 612 kg (1,350 lb)

PERFORMANCE (at max T-O weight):
- Never-exceed speed — 156 knots (289 km/h; 180 mph)
- Max level speed at S/L — 135 knots (251 km/h; 156 mph)
- Max cruising speed — 117 knots (217 km/h; 135 mph)
- Stalling speed — 43·5 knots (80·5 km/h; 50 mph)
- Max rate of climb at S/L — 1,128 m (3,700 ft)/min
- Service ceiling — 4,570 m (15,000 ft)
- T-O run — 38 m (125 ft)
- T-O to 15 m (50 ft) — 91 m (300 ft)
- Landing from 15 m (50 ft) — 274 m (900 ft)
- Landing run — 244 m (800 ft)
- Range with max fuel — 260 nm (482 km; 300 miles)

EAA ACRO-SPORT II

The Acro-Sport II is a two-seat aerobatic biplane derived from the Acro-Sport I, by Mr Paul Poberezny, for the pilot with only a small number of flying hours to his credit. Design began in 1976 and construction started in 1977. The first flight was achieved on 9 July 1978. Plans are available to the homebuilder from Acro-Sport Inc (see Super Acro-Sport for address), and several hundred sets of plans have already been sold. Stress limits are $+6{\cdot}5g/-4{\cdot}5g$.

TYPE: Two-seat aerobatic biplane.

WINGS, FUSELAGE AND TAIL UNIT: As for Acro-Sport I.

LANDING GEAR: As for Acro-Sport I, except for main-wheel tyres size 6·00-6, pressure 1·86-1·93 bars (27-28 lb/sq in).

POWER PLANT: Prototype has one 134 kW (180 hp) Lycoming O-360-A4B engine, driving a Sensenich two-blade metal fixed-pitch propeller with spinner. Can be powered by engines of 93-149 kW (125-200 hp). Fuel capacity 98·4 litres (26 US gallons).

ACCOMMODATION: Two seats in tandem in separate cockpits. Baggage space, capacity 13·6 kg (30 lb).

DIMENSIONS, EXTERNAL:
- Wing span, upper — 6·60 m (21 ft 8 in)
- Wing span, lower — 6·32 m (20 ft 9 in)
- Wing chord, constant — 1·09 m (3 ft 7 in)
- Wing area, gross — 14·12 m² (152 sq ft)
- Length overall — 5·75 m (18 ft 10¼ in)
- Height overall — 2·03 m (6 ft 7¾ in)
- Wheel track — 1·85 m (6 ft 0¾ in)

WEIGHTS:
- Weight empty — 397 kg (875 lb)
- Max T-O weight — 689 kg (1,520 lb)

PERFORMANCE (prototype):
- Max cruising speed — 107 knots (198 km/h; 123 mph)
- Stalling speed — 46 knots (86 km/h; 53 mph)
- T-O run — 91 m (300 ft)

EAA POBER P-9 PIXIE

Design and construction of this lightweight sporting aircraft began simultaneously in January 1974, and the first flight was made in July 1974.

It was conceived under 'Project Econoplane' to be economical in operation; and the prototype was originally powered by a converted Volkswagen motor car engine. The Pixie made its public debut at the 1974 EAA Fly-in at Oshkosh, Wisconsin. Soon afterwards, the prototype was re-engined with a Limbach-VW engine, and a special pressure cowl was fitted to improve cooling and increase the cruising speed.

Plans are available to amateur constructors from Acro-Sport Inc (see Super Acro-Sport for address), and more than 300 sets had been sold by January 1979.

TYPE: Single-seat lightweight sporting aircraft.

WINGS: Braced parasol monoplane. Two streamline-section struts and wire bracing each side. Wing section Clark Y. Dihedral 2°. Incidence 2°. Conventional wooden structure utilising spruce spars, mahogany plywood and fabric covering. Full-span Frise-type ailerons. No flaps. No trim tabs.

FUSELAGE: Welded structure of 4130 chrome molybdenum steel tubing with wood formers and fabric covering.

TAIL UNIT: Wire-braced structure of welded 4130 chrome molybdenum steel tubing, fabric covered. Fixed-incidence tailplane. No trim tabs.

LANDING GEAR: Non-retractable tailwheel type. Side Vees with half-axles carry main wheels. Shock-absorption by rubber bungee. Main wheels with tyres size 5·00-5, pressure 2·07 bars (30 lb/sq in). Tailwheel tyre of solid type. Cleveland brakes. Glassfibre fairings over main wheels.

POWER PLANT: One 44·5 kW (60 hp) Limbach SL 1700 EA flat-four engine, driving a Sensenich two-blade fixed-pitch propeller. Equally suited to Monnett Volkswagen engine conversions. Fuel tank in wing centre-section, capacity 46·6 litres (12·3 US gallons). Refuelling point on wing upper surface. Oil capacity 2·84 litres (0·75 US gallons).

ACCOMMODATION: Single seat in open cockpit. Door on starboard side. Baggage capacity 9 kg (20 lb).

DIMENSIONS, EXTERNAL:
- Wing span — 9·09 m (29 ft 10 in)
- Wing chord, constant — 1·37 m (4 ft 6 in)
- Wing area, gross — 12·47 m² (134·25 sq ft)
- Length overall — 5·26 m (17 ft 3 in)
- Height overall — 1·88 m (6 ft 2 in)
- Wheel track — 1·60 m (5 ft 3 in)
- Propeller diameter — 1·35 m (4 ft 5 in)

WEIGHTS:
- Weight empty — 246 kg (543 lb)
- Max T-O weight — 408 kg (900 lb)

PERFORMANCE (at max T-O weight):
- Never-exceed speed — 113 knots (209 km/h; 130 mph)
- Max level speed at S/L — 89 knots (166 km/h; 103 mph)
- Max cruising speed — 72 knots (134 km/h; 83 mph)
- Stalling speed — 26 knots (49 km/h; 30 mph)
- Max rate of climb at S/L — 213 m (700 ft)/min
- Service ceiling — 3,810 m (12,500 ft)
- T-O and landing run — 91 m (300 ft)
- T-O to 15 m (50 ft) — 305 m (1,000 ft)
- Landing from 15 m (50 ft) — 152 m (500 ft)
- Range with max fuel — 251 nm (466 km; 290 miles)

EAA NESMITH COUGAR

The sale of plans for the Nesmith Cougar has been discontinued. Details of this aircraft can be found in the 1978-79 *Jane's*.

EAGLE

EAGLE HELICOPTER CORPORATION

Scottsdale, Arizona 85252

The Eagle Helicopter Corporation has developed and built prototypes of two lightweight helicopters. The Eagle II is a 'cold-jet' tip-driven helicopter (as illustrated) and the Eagle III is powered by two 0·178 kN (40 lb st) Gluhareff G8 pressure jet engines, mounted at the rotor tips and burning liquid propane. A 151 litre (40 US gallon) fuel tank is expected to give the Eagle III an endurance of about two hours.

EAGLE HELICOPTER EAGLE II

Type: Two-seat lightweight helicopter.

Rotor System: Two-blade rotor, driven by tip-mounted 'cold-jets' supplied with air from a bleed-air compressor. Rotor blades, which are hollow light alloy extrusions on prototype, are attached to the rotor hub by stainless steel torsion straps (production blades to be of stainless steel). Simple pylon structure immediately aft of cabin bulkhead. Max rotor speed 312 rpm. Normal rotor speed 212 rpm. No tail rotor. Cooling fan air is blown over rudder for control in hovering flight.

Fuselage: Rectangular-section forward fuselage, probably comprising basic steel tube structure and glassfibre shell.

Tail Unit: Small fin. Movable rudder, beneath fin, mounted centrally in efflux from compressor. Narrow-chord horizontal stabiliser mounted at base of fin trailing-edge.

Power Plant: One 175 kW (235 hp) Evinrude 200749 six-cylinder V engine. Compressor supplies air to cold-jets through hollow rotor mast and blades.

Accommodation: Two seats side by side in enclosed cabin. Probably conventional helicopter controls.

Dimensions, external:
- Rotor diameter — 10·97 m (36 ft 0 in)
- Rotor blade chord: prototype — 0·23 m (9¼ in)
- production — 0·36 m (1 ft 2 in)
- Length of fuselage — 3·69 m (12 ft 1 in)
- Width overall, less rotor — 1·66 m (5 ft 5¼ in)
- Height overall — 2·13 m (7 ft 0 in)

Weights:
- Weight empty — 340 kg (750 lb)
- Normal T-O weight — 703 kg (1,550 lb)

Performance (estimated):
- Max cruising speed — 78 knots (145 km/h; 90 mph)
- Normal cruising speed — 69·5 knots (129 km/h; 80 mph)
- Max rate of climb at S/L — 314 m (1,030 ft)/min
- Vertical rate of climb at S/L — 244 m (800 ft)/min
- Hovering ceiling IGE — 3,353 m (11,000 ft)
- Hovering ceiling OGE — 1,525 m (5,000 ft)
- Service ceiling — 4,575 m (15,000 ft)
- Range at 60 knots (113 km/h; 70 mph) — 173·5 nm (322 km; 200 miles)

EVANS

EVANS AIRCRAFT

PO Box 744, La Jolla, California 92038

Mr W. S. Evans, while employed as a design engineer with the Convair Division of General Dynamics Corporation, set out to design for the novice homebuilder an all-wood aircraft that would be easy to build and safe to fly. He was prepared to sacrifice both appearance and performance to achieve this aim. Two years of spare-time design and a year of construction produced a strut-braced low-wing monoplane with an all-moving tail unit, powered by a 30 kW (40 hp) Volkswagen engine, which Mr Evans named the Volksplane but which has since been designated VP-1.

The prototype was subsequently re-engined with a 39·5 kW (53 hp) Volkswagen, increasing the rate of climb to 183 m (600 ft)/min at sea level.

Mr Evans next developed a two-seat version of the VP-1, known as the VP-2. This is powered by a 44·5/48·5 kW (60/65 hp) Volkswagen engine, but in other respects has only minor constructional variations from the VP-1.

Plans of both models are available to amateur constructors, and the VP-1 is approved by the PFA for construction in the UK. VP-1 and VP-2 aircraft are currently flying in Australia, Belgium, Canada, France, Germany, Italy, Ireland, Japan, New Zealand, the UK and the USA.

EVANS VP-1

Type: Single-seat light aircraft.

Wings: Strut-braced low-wing monoplane. Two streamline-section bracing struts on each side. Wing section NACA 4412. Square tips. Dihedral 5°. Conventional wood structure with two rectangular spar beams, internal wooden compression struts and diagonal wire bracing, dispensing with the need for a complicated box spar. Fabric covering. Ailerons of wooden construction, fabric covered. No trim tabs. No flaps.

Fuselage: Rectangular-section all-wood stressed-skin structure, consisting essentially of three bulkheads, four longerons and plywood skin. Stressed-skin design eliminates the need for any diagonal bracing. Glassfibre fairing aft of pilot's seat.

Tail Unit: No fixed fin. The rudder is constructed of plywood ribs clamped to a 5·08 cm (2 in) aluminium tube which is mounted vertically through the rear fuselage and pivots in two nylon bushes. Leading- and trailing-edges are of wood and the whole unit is fabric-covered. The fabric-covered all-moving tailplane is a wooden cantilever structure, comprising ply ribs blocked and glued to a simple constant-section box spar. Both rudder and tailplane have anti-servo tabs.

Landing Gear: Non-retractable main wheels and tailskid. Main wheels carried on a bent section of heavy-gauge 24ST-3 aluminium bar, wire-braced by diagonal cables. Shock-absorption by low-pressure tyres. Main wheels and tyres size 6·00-6. Tyre pressure 0·83 bars (12 lb/sq in). Hydraulic brakes operated by single hand lever.

Power Plant: One 30 kW, 39·5 kW or 44·5 kW (40 hp, 53 hp or 60 hp) modified Volkswagen motor car engine, driving a Hegy two-blade propeller, with pitch of 0·61 m (24 in) for 30 kW (40 hp) engine, 0·76 m (30 in) for 39·5 kW (53 hp) and 0·91 m (36 in) for 44·5 kW (60 hp). Glassfibre fuel tank aft of firewall and integral with the forward fuselage cowling, capacity 30 litres (8 US gallons). Filling point on top of fuselage, forward of windscreen.

Accommodation: Single seat in open cockpit. No baggage stowage.

Dimensions, external:
- Wing span — 7·32 m (24 ft 0 in)
- Wing chord, constant — 1·27 m (4 ft 2 in)
- Wing area, gross — 9·29 m² (100 sq ft)
- Length overall — 5·49 m (18 ft 0 in)
- Height overall — 1·56 m (5 ft 1½ in)
- Tailplane span — 2·13 m (7 ft 0 in)
- Wheel track — 1·50 m (4 ft 11 in)
- Propeller diameter — 1·37 m (4 ft 6 in)

Weights:
- Weight empty — 200 kg (440 lb)
- Max T-O weight — 340 kg (750 lb)

Performance (with 30 kW; 40 hp engine, at T-O weight of 295 kg; 650 lb):
- Never-exceed speed — 104 knots (193 km/h; 120 mph)
- Cruising speed — 65 knots (121 km/h; 75 mph)
- Stalling speed — 35 knots (65 km/h; 40 mph)
- Max rate of climb at S/L — 122 m (400 ft)/min
- T-O run (average breeze) — 137 m (450 ft)
- Landing run (average breeze) — 61 m (200 ft)

EVANS VP-2

Type: Two-seat light aircraft.

Wings: Generally similar to VP-1, except for NACA 4415 wing section and increased wing span and chord.

Fuselage: Similar to VP-1, but width increased by 0·305 m (1 ft 0 in).

Tail Unit: Similar to VP-1. No fin. Increased rudder area; all-moving tailplane of increased span and chord.

Landing Gear: Similar to VP-1. Wheel track increased by 0·23 m (9 in).

Power Plant: One 44·5 kW (60 hp) 1,834 cc or 48·5 kW (65 hp) 2,100 cc modified Volkswagen motor car engine, driving a two-blade propeller. Glassfibre fuel tank aft of firewall, capacity 53 litres (14 US gallons).

Accommodation: Two seats side by side in open cockpit.

Dimensions, external:
- Wing span — 8·23 m (27 ft 0 in)
- Wing chord, constant — 1·47 m (4 ft 10 in)
- Wing area, gross — 12·08 m² (130 sq ft)
- Length overall — 5·87 m (19 ft 3 in)
- Tailplane span — 2·44 m (8 ft 0 in)
- Wheel track — 1·73 m (5 ft 8 in)
- Propeller diameter — 1·52 m (5 ft 0 in)

Weights:
- Weight empty — 290 kg (640 lb)
- Max T-O weight — 471 kg (1,040 lb)

Performance (44·5 kW; 60 hp engine, at max T-O weight):
- Never-exceed speed — 104 knots (193 km/h; 120 mph)
- Max level speed — 87 knots (161 km/h; 100 mph)
- Max cruising speed — 65 knots (121 km/h; 75 mph)
- Stalling speed — 35 knots (64·5 km/h; 40 mph)
- Max rate of climb at S/L (pilot only) — 213 m (700 ft)/min
- Max rate of climb at S/L (pilot and passenger) — 122 m (400 ft)/min

FIKE

WILLIAM J. FIKE

PO Box 683, Anchorage, Alaska 99510
Telephone: (907) 272 7069

Mr W. J. Fike, whose 16,000 hours logged as a pilot include thousands of hours of 'bush flying' in Alaska, has designed and built five light aircraft since 1929. His Model 'B' of 1935 was a tiny parasol-wing single-seat monoplane, powered by a 26 kW (35 hp) Long Harlequin engine and with an empty weight of only 136 kg (300 lb). In the following year he produced the Model 'C' of similar configuration. A later design was the single- or two-seat Model 'D' high-wing cabin monoplane, of which details follow. By January 1979, about 3,000 copies of the book containing plans of this aircraft had been sold.

The 'D' was followed by the Model 'E', completed in 1970. In early 1979 Mr Fike had almost completed construction of a new lightweight cabin monoplane which he has designated Model 'F'. This needed only covering and a few minor details before flight testing could begin. The 'F' is a braced sweptwing monoplane which may be powered by engines of 30-74·5 kW (40-100 hp). A 48·5 kW (65 hp) Continental A65-8 has been installed in the prototype.

Mr Fike is also working on a special high-altitude wing for high-wing Piper aircraft, known as the 'Astro Wing'. The accompanying illustration of the wing, on an experimental aircraft, shows that it includes full-span flaps and drooping ailerons.

Plans of the Model 'D' and Model 'E' are available to amateur constructors.

FIKE MODEL 'D'

The Fike Model 'D' first flew in October 1950. A unique feature of the aircraft is the overhead control system.

Type: Single- or two-seat light monoplane.

Wings: Braced high-wing monoplane. Wing section NACA 4409. Constant chord. No dihedral. Incidence 1° 15′. All-wood construction, except for aluminium-covered leading- and trailing-edges and internal steel wire bracing; fabric covered. No flaps.

Fuselage: Welded steel tube structure, fabric-covered.

Tail Unit: Wire-braced welded-steel tube structure with fabric covering.

Landing Gear: Standard Piper J-3 gear of non-retractable tailwheel type, with rubber-cord shock-absorption. Interchangeable wheels and skis. Hydraulic brakes.

Power Plant: One 48·5 kW (65 hp) Continental A65-8 flat-four engine, driving a Sensenich 72-C-44 two-blade fixed-pitch wooden propeller. Fuel tank in fuselage, capacity 45 litres (12 US gallons). Oil capacity 3·8 litres (1 US gallon).

Accommodation: Pilot, with provision for passenger seated in tandem, in enclosed cabin. Baggage compartment, capacity 0·17 m³ (6 cu ft).

Dimensions, external:
- Wing span — 8·86 m (29 ft 1 in)
- Wing chord, constant — 1·52 m (5 ft 0 in)
- Wing area, gross — 12·26 m² (132 sq ft)
- Length overall — 5·69 m (18 ft 8 in)
- Height overall — 1·65 m (5 ft 5 in)
- Tailplane span — 2·39 m (7 ft 10 in)

Weights:
- Weight empty — 277 kg (611 lb)
- Normal T-O weight — 472 kg (1,040 lb)
- Max T-O weight — 485 kg (1,070 lb)

Performance:
- Max level speed — 93 knots (172 km/h; 107 mph)
- Max cruising speed — 78 knots (145 km/h; 90 mph)
- Stalling speed — 35 knots (64 km/h; 40 mph)
- Max rate of climb at S/L — 245 m (800 ft)/min
- Service ceiling — over 3,050 m (10,000 ft)
- T-O run — 76 m (250 ft)
- Landing run, with brakes — 45 m (150 ft)
- Range — 234 nm (435 km; 270 miles)

FIKE MODEL 'E'

In 1953 Mr Fike began design of an aircraft to evaluate the flight characteristics of a low aspect ratio (3·0) wing of only 9% thickness/chord ratio when applied to a low-power monoplane of high-wing configuration. The wing, of wooden geodetic construction, is so designed that various wingtips may be installed for evaluation. A standard Piper J-3 tail unit is utilised, but this is modified by keeping the tailplane span within the 2·44 m (8 ft) limit allowed by US highway regulations for towed vehicles.

A secondary objective of the Model 'E' project was to develop a low-cost easy-to-build two-seat lightplane. The wing can be removed within ten minutes to enable the aircraft to be towed by a motor vehicle or for storage in an ordinary garage.

Mr Fike's former heavy commitments as an airline pilot were responsible for the extended construction time, over a period of seven years; but construction was completed in early 1970 and the first flight was made on 22 March 1970.

During 1971 Mr Fike re-engined the Model 'E' with a 63·5 kW (85 hp) Continental C85-8 engine, and it was first flown with this power plant in July 1971. It had accumulated a total of more than 250 flight hours by early 1979.

During 1974 Mr Fike added 0·36 m (1 ft 2 in) wingtip extensions and, at a later stage of flight testing, flat endplates were added to the wingtips. The extensions to the wing have been shown to enhance performance but the effect of the endplates has proved negligible.

At least one plans-built Model 'E' was also flying in

Prototype Eagle II 'cold-jet' helicopter *(Howard Levy)*

Evans VP-1 single-seat light aircraft *(J. M. G. Gradidge)*

Evans VP-2 two-seat monoplane

Fike experimental aircraft with high-altitude 'Astro Wing'

Fike Model 'D' single/two-seat light aircraft

First plans-built Fike Model 'E' built by Mr R. A. Marczi of Welland, Ontario, Canada *(Howard Levy)*

early 1979. This aircraft, built by Mr Marczi of Welland, Ontario, Canada, was first flown in September 1975, about 30 months after plans were received. It incorporates several refinements compared with the prototype 'E', including those recommended by Mr Fike. They include a deeper fuselage in the cockpit area, to improve comfort and visibility, and a floor-mounted control stick. A radio, battery, wind-driven generator and complete wiring system have also been installed. As a result, empty weight is increased by 45·5 kg (100 lb), and the maximum T-O weight is currently 567 kg (1,250 lb). The extra weight is reported to make little difference to overall performance, except that the take-off run needs to be a little longer, climb is slower, and the aircraft has a slightly higher sink rate with power off.

The following description applies to Mr Fike's prototype:

TYPE: High-wing sporting monoplane.

WINGS: Cantilever high-wing monoplane. Wing section NACA 4409. No dihedral. Incidence 1° 15'. No sweepback. All-wood geodetic structure, fabric-covered. Conventional wooden ailerons. No flaps. No trim tabs.

FUSELAGE: Welded steel tube structure; fabric-covered. Piper PA-11 engine cowling.

TAIL UNIT: Cantilever welded steel tube structure with fabric covering. Adjustable-incidence tailplane. No trim tabs.

LANDING GEAR: Standard Piper J-3 gear of non-retractable tailwheel type, with rubber-cord shock-absorption. Main wheels and tyres size 8·00-4, pressure 1·03-1·38 bars (15-20 lb/sq in). Max speed can be increased by 7 knots (13 km/h; 8 mph) by fitting 5·00-4 wheels, tyres and tubes. Goodrich toe-operated hydraulic brakes. Federal A-1500 skis available optionally.

POWER PLANT: One 63·5 kW (85 hp) Continental C85-8 flat-four engine, driving a Sensenich Type 76AK two-blade fixed-pitch metal propeller. One fuel tank in each wing. Total fuel capacity 56·75 litres (15 US gallons). Refuelling point on top of each wing. Oil capacity 3·8 litres (1 US gallon).

ACCOMMODATION: Pilot (with provision for passenger seated in tandem) in enclosed cabin. Door on each side of fuselage, hinged at forward edge. Cabin heated and ventilated. Baggage compartment aft of cabin. Overhead control assembly permits sleeping in the cabin after removing or collapsing seat.

EQUIPMENT: Radair 10 10-channel VHF communications transceiver.

DIMENSIONS, EXTERNAL:
- Wing span: 6·82 m (22 ft 4½ in)
- Wing chord (constant, except for tips): 2·03 m (6 ft 8 in)
- Wing chord at tip: 1·37 m (4 ft 6 in)
- Wing area, gross: 13·29 m² (143·10 sq ft)
- Wing aspect ratio: 3·0
- Length overall: 5·84 m (19 ft 2 in)
- Height overall: 1·73 m (5 ft 8 in)
- Tailplane span: 2·39 m (7 ft 10 in)
- Wheel track: 1·83 m (6 ft 0 in)
- Wheelbase: 4·32 m (14 ft 2 in)
- Propeller diameter: 1·88 m (6 ft 2 in)

DIMENSIONS, INTERNAL:
- Cabin: Max width: 0·61 m (2 ft 0 in)
- Volume: 0·99 m³ (35 cu ft)
- Baggage compartment: 0·34 m³ (12 cu ft)

WEIGHTS:
- Weight empty: 313 kg (690 lb)
- Normal T-O weight: 522 kg (1,150 lb)

PERFORMANCE (with 63·5 kW; 85 hp engine and 5·00-4 wheels, at normal T-O weight):
- Max level speed at S/L: 96 knots (177 km/h; 110 mph)
- Max cruising speed: 87 knots (161 km/h; 100 mph)
- Landing speed: 32 knots (59·5 km/h; 37 mph)
- Max rate of climb at S/L: 244 m (800 ft)/min
- Service ceiling: over 3,050 m (10,000 ft)
- T-O run: 76-92 m (250-300 ft)
- Landing run: under 92 m (300 ft)
- Normal range, standard tanks: 243 nm (450 km; 280 miles)

FLAGLOR

FLAGLOR AIRCRAFT

1550A Sanders Road, Northbrook, Illinois 60062

The latest of a series of light aircraft designed and built in prototype form by Mr K. Flaglor is an ultra-light sporting monoplane named the Scooter. Design work began in July 1965, and construction was started in November of the same year.

The prototype Scooter was powered originally by a 13·5 kW (18 hp) Cushman golf-kart engine, and it was with this power plant that the first flight was made in June 1967. Performance was marginal and, as a result, Mr Flaglor replaced the Cushman with an 18·5-21 kW (25-28 hp) Volkswagen engine. Current power plant is a 1,500 cc Volkswagen engine developing 30 kW (40 hp). When flown to the 1967 EAA meet at Rockford, Illinois, the prototype Scooter won the 'Outstanding Ultra-light' and 'Outstanding Volkswagen-Powered Airplane' awards.

Plans are available to amateur constructors from Ace Aircraft Manufacturing Company (which see), and many Scooters are flying.

FLAGLOR SCOOTER

The following description applies to the prototype Scooter in its current form:

TYPE: Ultra-light sporting monoplane.

WINGS: High-wing monoplane, braced by wires attached

to fuselage and to kingpost mounted above centre-section. Wing section NACA 23012. Dihedral 2°. Incidence 3°. Two-spar all-wood structure with wood drag and anti-drag bracing. Aluminium leading-edge and plywood covering. Conventional wooden ailerons. No flaps. No trim tabs.

Fuselage: Wooden structure, plywood-covered in the forward cockpit area, fabric-covered aft. Fuselage of triangular section aft of the wing. Wing centre-section and engine mounting constructed of 4130 steel tube.

Tail Unit: All-wood construction with strut bracing. No fixed fin. No trim tabs.

Landing Gear: Non-retractable tailwheel type. Fixed spring steel main units. Steerable tailwheel. Main wheels of go-kart type, size 4·10 × 3·50-5. Tyre pressure 1·38 bars (20 lb/sq in). Vespa or Sears motor scooter brakes.

Power Plant: One 30 kW (40 hp) Volkswagen 1,500 cc flat-four engine, driving a two-blade Troyer 54-28 propeller. Single fuel tank in fuselage nose, capacity 19 litres (5 US gallons). Refuelling point on top of fuselage forward of windscreen. Oil capacity 2·37 litres (2·5 US quarts).

Accommodation: Single seat in cockpit protected by deep windscreen.

Dimensions, external:
- Wing span: 8·64 m (28 ft 0 in)
- Wing chord, constant: 1·27 m (4 ft 2 in)
- Wing area, gross: 10·68 m² (115 sq ft)
- Wing aspect ratio: 6·7
- Length overall: 4·78 m (15 ft 8 in)
- Height overall: 2·13 m (7 ft 0 in)
- Tailplane span: 2·18 m (7 ft 2 in)
- Wheel track: 1·37 m (4 ft 6 in)

Weights:
- Weight empty: 177 kg (390 lb)
- Max T-O and landing weight: 295 kg (650 lb)

Performance:
- Never-exceed speed: 82 knots (153 km/h; 95 mph)
- Max level speed: 78 knots (145 km/h; 90 mph)
- Max cruising speed: 69 knots (129 km/h; 80 mph)
- Econ cruising speed: 56 knots (105 km/h; 65 mph)
- Stalling speed: 30 knots (55 km/h; 34 mph)
- Max rate of climb at S/L: 183 m (600 ft)/min
- T-O and landing run: 76 m (250 ft)
- Range with max fuel: 152 nm (282 km; 175 miles)

FREDERICK-AMES

FREDERICK-AMES RESEARCH CORPORATION

Novi, Michigan

President: Frederick Smith

FREDERICK-AMES EOS

Mr Fred Smith, president of Frederick-Ames Research Corporation, designed a small single-seat sporting aircraft called the EOS, which first appeared in an incomplete form at the 1973 EAA Fly-in at Oshkosh. After the meeting the EOS was completed; but on its maiden flight the Hirth engine seized and the aircraft crash landed, causing extensive damage. Although some restoration work was carried out, the aircraft was subsequently abandoned through lack of finance. In early 1978 the project was revived, with a Volkswagen modified motor car engine in place of the original engine. First flight of the reworked aircraft was in mid-1978, piloted by Mr Robert Bishop. By August 1978 the EOS had completed about ten flying hours, and further modifications to the aircraft had been made. Changes still to be made at that time included fitting new ailerons, and re-contouring the fin and rudder.

Kits to build the EOS will be made available to amateur constructors in due course. All aluminium sheet is bent and flat wrapped, with no complicated forming. Structures are pop riveted and bonded, requiring no welding.

Type: Single-seat light sporting aircraft.

Wings: Cantilever tapered low-wing monoplane. Wing section NACA 651212. Light alloy all-metal structure, except for glassfibre wing fillets, pop riveted and epoxy resin bonded.

Fuselage: Conventional light alloy semi-monocoque structure, pop riveted and epoxy resin bonded. Glassfibre engine cowling.

Tail Unit: Cantilever light alloy structure, comprising triangular fin, integral with rear fuselage, rudder, and all-moving tailplane with projecting balance arms at roots. Tailplane actuated via servo tabs.

Landing Gear: Manually-retractable tricycle type. Main units retract inwards. Fully-castoring and steerable nosewheel. Rubber-in-compression shock-absorption. Disc brakes.

Power Plant: One 52 kW (70 hp) 1,834 cc Volkswagen modified motor car engine, driving through a 178 mm (7 in) extension shaft a Rand Robinson three-blade ground-adjustable propeller, with Mooney 201 spinner. Fuel capacity 56·75 litres (15 US gallons).

Accommodation: Single glassfibre seat under large transparent canopy.

System: Electrical system includes 45A alternator and starter.

Dimensions, external:
- Wing span: 7·92 m (26 ft 0 in)
- Wing area, gross: 6·97 m² (75 sq ft)
- Wing aspect ratio: 9
- Length overall: 5·05 m (16 ft 7 in)
- Height overall: 1·98 m (6 ft 6 in)
- Propeller diameter: 1·27 m (4 ft 2 in)

Weights:
- Weight empty: 304 kg (670 lb)
- Max T-O weight: 442 kg (975 lb)

Performance (as tested by early 1979):
- Max level speed (estimated): 174 knots (322 km/h; 200 mph)
- Cruising speed (70% power) at 1,525 m (5,000 ft): 152 knots (281 km/h; 175 mph)
- Stalling speed at 1,370 m (4,500 ft): 50 knots (92 km/h; 57 mph) IAS
- Max rate of climb at S/L: 305 m (1,000 ft)/min
- T-O run: 305 m (1,000 ft)

GREAT LAKES

GREAT LAKES AIRCRAFT COMPANY

PO Box 11132, Wichita, Kansas 67202

In addition to marketing factory-built **Great Lakes Sport Trainers,** this company offered certificated components and assemblies, but not plans, to amateur constructors. The aircraft was described fully in the main US Aircraft section of the 1978-79 *Jane's*.

GREGA

JOHN W. GREGA

355 Grand Boulevard, Bedford, Ohio 44146

In addition to the standard Aircamper design, of which plans are available from Mr Bernard H. Pietenpol (see under 'Pietenpol'), a modernised version has been evolved by Mr John Grega. Plans of this are available to homebuilders.

GN-1 AIRCAMPER

The prototype of this modernised version of the Aircamper two-seat light monoplane flew for the first time in November 1965. It uses cut-down Piper J-3 Cub wings and bracing struts and J-3 Cub landing gear. Other differences compared with the standard Aircamper (which see) are as follows:

Power Plant: One 48·5 kW (65 hp) Continental A65-8 flat-four engine in prototype, driving a two-blade 72/41 metal fixed-pitch propeller. Other engines of up to 63·5 kW (85 hp) can be installed. Fuel tanks aft of firewall, capacity 45 litres (12 US gallons), and in wing centre-section, capacity 22·5 litres (6 US gallons). Oil capacity 3·75 litres (1 US gallon).

Dimensions, external:
- Wing span: 8·84 m (29 ft 0 in)
- Wing chord, constant: 1·52 m (5 ft 0 in)
- Wing area, gross: 13·94 m² (150 sq ft)
- Wing aspect ratio: 6
- Length overall: 5·51 m (18 ft 1 in)
- Height overall: 2·06 m (6 ft 9 in)
- Tailplane span: 2·29 m (7 ft 6 in)
- Wheel track: 1·60 m (5 ft 3 in)

Weight:
- Max T-O weight: 499 kg (1,100 lb)

Performance (at max T-O weight):
- Max level speed at S/L: 100 knots (185 km/h; 115 mph)
- Max cruising speed at S/L: 78 knots (145 km/h; 90 mph)
- Stalling speed: 31 knots (56 km/h; 35 mph)
- Max rate of climb at S/L: 152 m (500 ft)/min
- T-O run: 122 m (400 ft)
- Landing run: 76 m (250 ft)
- Range with max fuel: 347 nm (640 km; 400 miles)

HARMON

HARMON ENGINEERING COMPANY

Box 227, Rt 4, Sherman, Texas 75090

Telephone: (214) 893 2682

President: James B. Harmon

Harmon Engineering Company designed and built the prototype of a single-seat sporting aircraft named Der Donnerschlag (The Thunderclap). Design began in December 1972, and construction of the prototype started six months later. The first flight of this aircraft took place in June 1974.

Four months later, the aircraft suffered an engine failure while being flown by Mr James Harmon. He hit the ground at 52 knots (96 km/h; 60 mph) at a 45° impact angle, but was able to walk away from the accident. The aircraft was so little damaged that the decision was made to rebuild it as the prototype of a variant of Der Donnerschlag named Mister America. Design of the variant was started in November 1974, simultaneously with the rebuilding, and first flight of Mister America took place on 31 October 1975.

Plans of Der Donnerschlag are no longer available, but full details of the aircraft can be found in the 1978-79 *Jane's*. Those for Mister America remain available, and Mr Harmon is currently working on a number of new projects; no details of these were available at the time of going to press.

HARMON 1-2 MISTER AMERICA

Type: Single-seat lightweight sporting aircraft.

Wings: Wire-braced shoulder-wing monoplane. Original wing section, with thickness/chord ratio of 14·5%. Dihedral 1°-2°. Incidence 0°. Wooden structure with fabric covering. Two simple beam spars; built-up ribs. Plain ailerons of similar construction. No flaps. Provision for ground-adjustable tabs in ailerons, if required. Dual flying and landing wires each side, landing wires attached to cabane structure at forward end of fuselage, which also forms windscreen support.

Fuselage: Welded structure of 4130 chrome-molybdenum steel tube with fabric covering. Wooden stringer turtledeck, with fabric covering. Aluminium and glassfibre engine cowling.

Tail Unit: Wire-braced welded structure of 4130 chrome-molybdenum steel tube with fabric covering. Tailplane incidence ground-adjustable. Elevators fitted. Provision for ground-adjustable trim tabs, if required.

Landing Gear: Non-retractable tailwheel type. Main units consist of two Vees, attached to fuselage structure, wire-braced and with a through axle. Shock-absorption by rubber bungee. Cleveland 5·00-5 main wheels and tyres, pressure 1·03 bars (15 lb/sq in). Aviation Products 10 cm (4 in) steerable tailwheel. Cleveland disc brakes with air cooling. Faired main legs and wheels.

Power Plant: One 44·7-48·5 kW (60-65 hp) 1,650 cc Volkswagen modified motor car engine, driving a two-blade fixed-pitch 54-36 propeller. Fuel tank aft of engine firewall, capacity 34 litres (9 US gallons). Refuelling point forward of windscreen.

Accommodation: Single seat in open cockpit.

Dimensions, external:
- Wing span: 5·99 m (19 ft 8 in)
- Wing chord, constant: 1·22 m (4 ft 0 in)
- Wing area, gross: 7·06 m² (76·0 sq ft)
- Wing aspect ratio: 4·916
- Length overall: 4·62 m (15 ft 2 in)
- Height overall: 1·52 m (5 ft 0 in)
- Tailplane span: 1·78 m (5 ft 10 in)
- Wheel track: 1·52 m (5 ft 0 in)
- Wheelbase: 3·51 m (11 ft 6 in)
- Propeller diameter: 1·37 m (4 ft 6 in)

Dimensions, internal:
- Cockpit: Max width: 0·52 m (1 ft 8½ in)

Weights:
- Weight empty: 195 kg (430 lb)
- Max T-O weight: 295 kg (650 lb)

Performance:
- Never-exceed speed: 143 knots (265 km/h; 165 mph)
- Max level speed at S/L: 109 knots (201 km/h; 125 mph)
- Max cruising speed at S/L: 95·5 knots (177 km/h; 110 mph)
- Econ cruising speed at S/L: 87 knots (161 km/h; 100 mph)
- Stalling speed: 42 knots (77·5 km/h; 48 mph)
- Max rate of climb at S/L: 244 m (800 ft)/min
- Service ceiling: 3,660 m (12,000 ft)
- T-O run: 61 m (200 ft)
- T-O to 15 m (50 ft): 122 m (400 ft)
- Landing from 15 m (50 ft): 152 m (500 ft)
- Landing run: 92 m (300 ft)
- Range with max fuel: 347 nm (643 km; 400 miles)

Flaglor Scooter built by Japanese students of Tokyo Aeronautical College

Frederick-Ames EOS single-seat sporting aircraft *(Howard Levy)*

GN-1 Aircamper built by Mr J. Nickerson of Pittsburgh, Pennsylvania *(Howard Levy)*

Harmon Mister America sporting aircraft

Hatz CB-1 biplane built by Mr Bob Shindler of Gardner, Kansas (85·7 kW; 115 hp Lycoming O-235 engine)

Hill Hummer ultralight monoplane *(Howard Levy)*

HATZ

HATZ AIRPLANE SHOP

Rt 2, Gleason, Wisconsin 54435

INFORMATION: Dudley Kelley, Rt 4, Versailles, Kentucky 40383

Mr John D. Hatz designed and built the prototype of a two-seat lightweight biplane, designated CB-1, of which plans are available to amateur constructors. Design and construction started in September 1959, and the first flight of the CB-1 was made on 19 April 1968. It was then powered by a 63·5 kW (85 hp) Continental C85-12 engine, but this has since been replaced by a 112 kW (150 hp) Lycoming O-320. Many more CB-1s are under construction, and six were flying by early 1979.

HATZ CB-1 BIPLANE

TYPE: Two-seat lightweight biplane.

WINGS: Braced single-bay biplane, with N-type interplane struts each side. N-type centre-section struts and streamline-section flying and landing wires. Wing section Clark Y. Dihedral 2°, on lower wings only. Incidence (both wings) 2°. Wooden two-spar structure with fabric covering. Cutout in trailing-edge of upper wing. Plain unbalanced ailerons of wood construction, with fabric covering, on both wings. No flaps. No trim tabs.

FUSELAGE: Welded steel tube structure, with fabric covering.

TAIL UNIT: Wire-braced welded steel tube structure, with fabric covering. Tailplane incidence adjustable by screwjack.

LANDING GEAR: Non-retractable tailwheel type. Two side Vees and half-axles hinged to fuselage structure. No shock-absorption. Main wheels from Piper J-3 Cub, with Goodyear tyres size 8·00-4, pressure 1·03 bars (15 lb/sq in). Wheel brakes from J-3 Cub. Glassfibre fairings on main wheels.

POWER PLANT: One 112 kW (150 hp) Lycoming O-320 flat-four engine, driving a Sensenich Type M74DM two-blade metal fixed-pitch propeller. Two fuel tanks in centre-section of upper wing, each with capacity of 60·5 litres (16 US gallons). Total fuel capacity 121 litres (32 US gallons). Refuelling points on upper surface of upper wing centre-section. Oil capacity 7·5 litres (2 US gallons).

ACCOMMODATION: Two seats in tandem in open cockpits.

SYSTEM: Electrical system, with 12V 12A DC engine-driven generator and 12V battery, for engine starting, navigation and instrument lights.

DIMENSIONS, EXTERNAL:

Wing span (both)	7·92 m (26 ft 0 in)
Wing chord, constant (both)	1·37 m (4 ft 6 in)
Wing area, gross	17·65 m² (190 sq ft)
Wing aspect ratio	5·77
Length overall	5·64 m (18 ft 6 in)
Height overall	2·39 m (7 ft 10 in)
Tailplane span	2·74 m (9 ft 0 in)
Wheel track	1·83 m (6 ft 0 in)
Propeller diameter	1·88 m (6 ft 2 in)

WEIGHTS:

Weight empty	438 kg (966 lb)
Max T-O weight	726 kg (1,600 lb)

PERFORMANCE (at max T-O weight):

Never-exceed speed	130 knots (241 km/h; 150 mph)
Max cruising speed	87 knots (161 km/h; 100 mph)
Stalling speed	39 knots (72·5 km/h; 45 mph)
Max rate of climb at S/L	366 m (1,200 ft)/min
T-O run	approx 122 m (400 ft)
Range with max fuel, 30 min reserves	234 nm (434 km; 270 miles)

HILL

KLAUS HILL

Box 1655, Salt Lake City, Utah 84110

Telephone: (801) 532 2555

HILL HUMMER

Mr Klaus Hill has designed and built a single-seat ultralight aircraft known as the Hummer. Design began in August 1977 and construction of the first prototype started in October of the same year. Construction took just 50 working hours and cost $2,000. First flight was achieved in November 1977. The Hummer is basically a powered version of Mr Hill's Superfloater glider, itself a follow-on to earlier non-powered aircraft designed and built by Mr Hill. These have included two sailplanes, a Rogallo-type and the Voyager hang gliders, and the Fledgling hang glider currently in production by Manta Products Inc (see Hang Glider section). Kits of parts, as well as plans to construct the Hummer, will be made available to amateur builders, the component parts produced either by an outside company or by Mr Hill himself. By March 1979 twelve Hummers had been completed.

TYPE: Single-seat ultralight monoplane.

WINGS: Wire-braced high-wing monoplane. Dihedral 45·7 cm (18 in) from horizontal at tips. Leading-edge spar of 4·4 cm (1¾ in) diameter aluminium tube; trailing-edge spar of 3·8 cm (1½ in) diameter aluminium tube. Eleven ribs of 1·3 cm (½ in) diameter aluminium tubing. Structure bolted together. Dacron fabric covering sewn into shape and slipped over wing structure, avoiding use of dope, glue or rib stitching. No ailerons or spoilers. Wings fold back and attach to tail for transportation. Assembly and disassembly takes one man 15-20 mins.

FUSELAGE: Prototype has 12·7 cm (5 in) diameter irrigation pipe main boom, to which wing and engine supporting truss structures are attached. 6061-T6 tubing will be used for main boom in kits.

TAIL UNIT: Strut-braced V tail, with tailplane and elevators/rudders set at dihedral angle of about 33°. Construction similar to wings. Control by cables.

LANDING GEAR: Non-retractable tailwheel type, with fully-castoring (optionally steerable) tailwheel. Formed sheet metal main legs with two steel cross-tubes. Go-Kart wheels. No brakes.

POWER PLANT: Prototype has one 16·4 kW (22 hp) 250 cc Chaparral snowmobile two-stroke engine, driving a two-blade laminated wood pusher propeller. Plastics fuel tank aft of seat, capacity 19 litres (5 US gallons). Fuel consumption 5·7 litres (1½ US gallons)/h.

ACCOMMODATION: Single seat in open position.

DIMENSIONS, EXTERNAL:

Wing span	10·06 m (33 ft 0 in)
Wing area, gross	11·89 m² (128 sq ft)
Wing chord, constant	1·32 m (4 ft 4 in)
Length overall	5·49 m (18 ft 0 in)
Height overall	2·51 m (8 ft 3 in)
Tailplane span	2·49 m (8 ft 2 in)
Wheel track	1·07 m (3 ft 6 in)
Propeller diameter	0·84 m (2 ft 9 in)

WEIGHTS:

Weight empty	82 kg (180 lb)
Max T-O weight	172 kg (380 lb)

PERFORMANCE:

Max level speed	39-43·5 knots (72·5-80·5 km/h; 45-50 mph)
Cruising speed	26 knots (48 km/h; 30 mph)
T-O and landing speed	22-24·5 knots (40·5-45 km/h; 25-28 mph)
Stalling speed	19·5-21 knots (35·5-39 km/h; 22-24 mph)
Max rate of climb at S/L	122 m (400 ft)/min
T-O run	91-122 m (300-400 ft)
Landing distance	18-46 m (60-150 ft)

HOLLMANN

HOLLMANN AIRCRAFT

7917 Festival Court, Cupertino, California 95014
Telephone: (408) 255 2194

The HA-2M Sportster two-seat gyroplane has been developed by Mr Martin Hollmann, a senior design engineer in the aerospace industry. It is claimed to be the first aircraft of its type designed for the homebuilder who has access to a minimum of power tools. About 90% of the structure is bolted and riveted together, and a minimum of machined parts are used.

Two average-size people can fly in the Sportster, which is suitable for pilot training and for flying on short cross-country journeys of up to 78 nm (145 km; 90 miles). It has been designed for towing behind a car, with the rotor stowed in a box attached to the car's roof. From the towed condition, the Sportster can be ready for its pre-flight walk-round inspection in ten minutes.

Plans, materials and many components are available to amateur constructors, and a network of distributors has been organised.

HOLLMANN HA-2M SPORTSTER

Design of this gyroplane began in June 1969, and construction of the first prototype was started in December 1972. The first flight of the prototype was made in October 1974, with FAA certification in the Experimental category. The first passenger was Dr Tom Butler, Vice-President Engineering and Research of AMF Incorporated, who flew in October 1975; test flying was completed by January 1976. The same year the prototype won a 'Best Original Design' award at the EAA Oshkosh meeting and an 'Outstanding New Design' award at the PRA Fly-in at Rockford. In 1977 it received the 'Best Autogyro' award at the EAA's Annual Antique Fly-in and air show at Watsonville, California. The prototype Sportster had logged over 160 flying hours by early 1979.

The Sportster utilises a collective pitch mechanism and a mechanical pre-rotator which engages the engine, via a clutch, prior to take-off to pre-spin the rotor to 300 rpm. This allows the aircraft to take off after a very short run, and is expected to permit jump starts after brief further development. A rotor brake is utilised to slow down the rotor after landing and to stop the blades for taxying. A tension spring is adjusted from within the cockpit to trim the control stick in pitch.

By early 1979 more than 50 Sportsters were under construction in the USA, Canada, New Zealand and Sweden. Most of these will be powered by a Lycoming O-320 engine, rated at 112 kW (150 hp). Several Sportsters are flying.

TYPE: Two-seat gyroplane.

ROTOR SYSTEM: Two-blade rotor of NACA 8-H-12 section. Solidity ratio 0·035. Pre-cone angle 2°. Blade pitch +2½°. Metal blades, each made up of a 2024-T8511 leading-edge extrusion, aluminium formed ribs and Alclad skin, riveted and bonded together. Rotor rpm 380.

FUSELAGE: Square-tube 6061-T6 aluminium structure, bolted together. Aluminium skin. Glassfibre fairings. Two mast tubes. Large rear window for 360° view.

TAIL UNIT: Twin fins and balanced rudders carried on short tailbooms. Aluminium structure, with 2024-T3 Alclad skins pop-riveted in place. Glassfibre tips. Fixed horizontal surface between fins.

LANDING GEAR: Non-retractable tricycle type, with single wheel on each unit. Two small tailwheels. Main-wheel tyres size 18 × 6, pressure 1·8 bars (26 lb/sq in). Nosewheel tyre of 0·25 m (10 in) diameter, pressure 1·8 bars (26 lb/sq in). Mechanical drum brake on nosewheel only.

POWER PLANT: One 97 kW (130 hp) Franklin Sport 4B flat-four engine, driving a Troyer 6635 pusher propeller, on prototype. One fuel tank of 45·4 litres (12 US gallons) capacity, with refuelling point inside cockpit. Oil capacity 5·7 litres (1·5 US gallons). Most other aircraft fitted with one Lycoming O-320 engine, rated at 112 kW (150 hp), driving a Troyer 6648 propeller.

ACCOMMODATION: Two seats side by side in cabin with open sides.

SYSTEMS: Standard aircraft instruments and Narco Mk IV radio in prototype. 12V battery. Rotor pre-rotation and collective pitch system to spin rotor to 300 rpm.

DIMENSIONS, EXTERNAL:

Rotor diameter	8·53 m (28 ft 0 in)
Blade chord, constant	0·23 m (9 in)
Length overall	3·66 m (12 ft 0 in)
Height to top of rotor hub	2·34 m (7 ft 8 in)
Tailplane span	1·17 m (3 ft 10 in)
Wheel track	2·06 m (6 ft 9 in)
Wheelbase	1·42 m (4 ft 8 in)
Propeller diameter	1·68 m (5 ft 6 in)

DIMENSIONS, INTERNAL:

Max width	0·914 m (3 ft 0 in)
Max height	1·45 m (4 ft 9 in)

WEIGHTS (A: prototype, B: 112 kW; 150 hp engine):

Weight empty, equipped: A	281 kg (620 lb)
Max T-O and landing weight: A	476 kg (1,050 lb)
B	500 kg (1,100 lb)

PERFORMANCE (A: prototype, B: 112 kW; 150 hp engine):

Never-exceed speed at S/L	
A	78 knots (145 km/h; 90 mph)
Max cruising speed at S/L	
A	65 knots (121 km/h; 75 mph)
Econ cruising speed at S/L	
A	52 knots (97 km/h; 60 mph)
Stalling speed: A	24·5 knots (45 km/h; 28 mph)
Max rate of climb at S/L: A	152 m (500 ft)/min
B	213 m (700 ft)/min
Service ceiling	2,135 m (7,000 ft)
T-O run	107 m (350 ft)
Landing run	0-6 m (0-20 ft)
Range with max fuel	78 nm (145 km; 90 miles)
Range with max payload	61 nm (112 km; 70 miles)

HOVEY

ROBERT W. HOVEY

Aircraft Specialties Co, PO Box 1074, Canyon Country, California 91351
Telephone: (805) 252 4054

Mr Hovey has designed and built an ultra-lightweight biplane of which plans are available to amateur constructors. His objective was to produce an aircraft which would require minimal construction time and have STOL performance, and which could be quickly disassembled for transportation. To achieve these ends the design has some unusual features, such as wing warping for roll control and use of an aluminium tube tailboom which has high-strength light alloy sheet and urethane foam stiffening. The original tail surfaces of craft paper over a styrofoam core have, however, been superseded by new horizontal and vertical tail surfaces of fabric-covered spruce construction.

Design began in October 1970, construction starting in the following month. First flight was made in February 1971, at which time the aircraft, known as Whing Ding II, received FAA certification in the Experimental category.

The original prototype was sold in Japan, where considerable interest was aroused among homebuilders. A second prototype was completed subsequently. Over 6,000 sets of plans had been sold and many Whing Dings were under construction or flying by early 1979.

Mr Hovey's latest design is a monoplane derivative of the WD-II, known as the Beta Bird (originally Bushwacker). Powered by a 1,600 cc Volkswagen converted motor car engine, this aircraft has wings which fold aft about a pin-joint in the rear spar; full-span flaperons and a large slow-turning propeller will suit it for off-airport STOL operations. First flight was expected to take place at Mojave in February 1979.

HOVEY WHING DING II (WD-II)

TYPE: Single-seat ultra-lightweight biplane.

WINGS: Braced single-bay biplane with parallel streamline-section interplane struts. Aircraft's fuselage, into which wing spars are socketed, gives location of inboard ends of wings. Landing and flying wires, the rear flying wires being used to control warping of upper wing. Wing section Hovey-10. Thickness/chord ratio 10%. Dihedral, both 1°. Incidence, both 4°. No sweepback. Wooden two-spar structure with ribs formed of 9·5 mm (⅜ in) light alloy tube. Wingtip bows of 9·5 mm (⅜ in) light alloy tube. Leading-edge faired in with rigid urethane foam. Wing structure fabric covered, tension of which retains the ribs in position. A plasticised fabric dope is used to ensure adequate flexibility for wing warping. No ailerons. No flaps. No trim tabs.

FUSELAGE: A closed box structure of 3·2 mm (⅛ in) mahogany plywood glued to 12·7 mm (½ in) square pine stringers, which is filled with urethane foam to stiffen and stabilise the plywood skin. This narrow fuselage provides attachment points for the seat, rudder bar and controls, and sockets for the wing spars. A reinforced extension at the top of the fuselage carries the engine. Aluminium tube tailboom is reinforced by high-strength alloy sheet at the forward end, this being wrapped around the tube and bonded with epoxy resin. The entire tube is filled with free-foam urethane.

TAIL UNIT: Strut-braced structure. Horizontal and vertical surfaces constructed of 12·7 mm (½ in) square-section spruce, with fabric covering. All-moving tailplane, attached to tailboom by piano hinge. Rudder attached to fin by cloth hinges. No trim tabs.

LANDING GEAR: Non-retractable tailwheel type. Main wheels carried on spring-type strut of laminated fir covered with a layer of polyester glassfibre. Go-kart type main wheels with 28 cm (11 in) diameter tyres. Tyre pressure 1·38 bars (20 lb/sq in). Tailwheel has solid rubber tyre. Alternative steel tube landing gear available.

POWER PLANT: One 10·44 kW (14 hp) McCulloch MC-101A single-cylinder two-stroke aircooled go-kart engine, driving a two-blade hand-carved laminated birch or beechwood fixed-pitch pusher propeller. Original chain-drive reduction system now replaced by a double 'V' belt drive. Fuel tank integral with engine, capacity 1·9 litres (0·5 US gallons).

ACCOMMODATION: Pilot only on open seat.

EQUIPMENT: Basic instrumentation only, comprising airspeed and engine speed indicators and cylinder head temperature gauge.

DIMENSIONS, EXTERNAL:

Wing span (both)	5·18 m (17 ft 0 in)
Wing chord (both), constant	0·91 m (3 ft 0 in)
Wing area, gross	9·10 m² (98 sq ft)
Wing aspect ratio	5·66
Length overall	4·27 m (14 ft 0 in)
Height overall	1·68 m (5 ft 6 in)
Tailplane span	1·93 m (6 ft 4 in)
Wheel track	1·22 m (4 ft 0 in)
Wheelbase	2·97 m (9 ft 9 in)
Propeller diameter	1·22 m (4 ft 0 in)

WEIGHTS:

Weight empty, incl fuel	55·5 kg (123 lb)
Max T-O weight	140 kg (310 lb)

PERFORMANCE (at max T-O weight):

Never-exceed speed	52 knots (96·5 km/h; 60 mph)
Max level speed at S/L	43·5 knots (80·5 km/h; 50 mph)
Econ cruising speed at S/L	35 knots (64·5 km/h; 40 mph)
Stalling speed	23 knots (42 km/h; 26 mph)
Service ceiling	1,220 m (4,000 ft)
T-O run	76 m (250 ft)
T-O to 15 m (50 ft)	107 m (350 ft)
Landing from 15 m (50 ft)	76 m (250 ft)
Landing run	46 m (150 ft)
Range	17 nm (32 km; 20 miles)

JAMES-DENNIS

JAMES-DENNIS ENTERPRISES INC

1601 North-West 29 Street, Miami, Florida 33142
Telephone: (305) 633 9961
DESIGNER: Mike Melfa

JAMES-DENNIS VCA-1

Mr Mike Melfa has designed and built a small single-seat aircraft designated VCA-1. Design started in February 1970 and construction of the aircraft began in July of the following year. First flight was achieved in October 1976. It is not the intention of James-Dennis Enterprises to produce any further aircraft or, presumably, to sell plans or kits.

TYPE: Single-seat light monoplane.

WINGS: Cantilever low-wing monoplane. Wing section

Hollmann HA-2M Sportster two-seat gyroplane

Hovey Whing Ding II built by Mr Lin Bruty of Mt Emu Farm, Australia
(The Herald & Weekly Times, Melbourne)

James-Dennis VCA-1, designed and built by Mr Mike Melfa

Amateur-built Javelin Wichawk (Continental O-470-R engine)

NASA (Whitcomb) GA(W)-1. Thickness/chord ratio 17%. Dihedral 3°. Incidence 0° 30′. No sweepback. Constant-chord all-metal structure of 2024-T3 aluminium alloy. Plain ailerons and electrically-actuated flaps, of 2024-T3 aluminium alloy. No tabs.

FUSELAGE: Conventional all-metal semi-monocoque structure of 2024-T3 aluminium alloy.

TAIL UNIT: All-metal (2024-T3) structure, comprising a fin of basically triangular shape, constant-chord large-area rudder and constant-chord T-tailplane with elevators. Adjustable tab in port elevator.

LANDING GEAR: Non-retractable tricycle type. Rigid 2024-T3 aluminium alloy cantilever legs. Nosewheel diameter 20·3 cm (8 in). Main wheel diameter 33 cm (13 in). Streamline wheel fairings. Cleveland brakes.

POWER PLANT: One 74·5 kW (100 hp) Continental O-200-A flat-four engine, driving a two-blade Sensenich fixed-pitch propeller. Two fuel tanks in wings, one in fuselage; total capacity 93 litres (24·5 US gallons). Oil capacity 5·7 litres (1·5 US gallons).

ACCOMMODATION: Single seat under sideways-opening (to starboard) canopy.

SYSTEMS: Electrical system includes 60A alternator for Genave 200B com/nav radio.

DIMENSIONS, EXTERNAL:

Wing span	6·10 m (20 ft 0 in)
Wing chord, constant	1·02 m (3 ft 4 in)
Wing area, gross	6·50 m² (70 sq ft)
Wing aspect ratio	6
Length overall	5·49 m (18 ft 0 in)
Height overall	1·73 m (5 ft 8 in)
Wheel track	1·45 m (4 ft 9 in)
Wheelbase	1·45 m (4 ft 9 in)
Propeller diameter	1·83 m (6 ft 0 in)

WEIGHTS:

Weight empty	322 kg (710 lb)
Max T-O weight	499 kg (1,100 lb)

PERFORMANCE:

Never-exceed speed at S/L	156 knots (290 km/h; 180 mph)
Max level speed at S/L	130 knots (241 km/h; 150 mph)
Max cruising speed at S/L	113 knots (209 km/h; 130 mph)
Econ cruising speed at S/L	95·5 knots (177 km/h; 110 mph)
Stalling speed, flaps up	55 knots (102 km/h; 63 mph)
Stalling speed, flaps down	49·5 knots (92 km/h; 57 mph)
Max rate of climb at S/L	335 m (1,100 ft)/min
Range with max fuel	174 nm (322 km; 200 miles)

JAVELIN

JAVELIN AIRCRAFT COMPANY INC

1979 Easy Street, Wichita, Kansas 67230
Telephone: (316) 733 1011
PRESIDENT AND CHIEF ENGINEER: David D. Blanton

Javelin Aircraft Company was founded on 1 March 1953 to manufacture a low-cost automatic pilot for small aircraft; this was followed by equipment manufacture, and aircraft development work. Following restoration of a Curtiss Robin between 1957 and 1961, which won the National Championship award for the best restored antique aircraft in 1961, Javelin sought an Arrow Sport biplane for similar treatment. Unable to find a suitable aircraft, the company began design and development of a new biplane on 1 January 1964.

The resulting aircraft, named Wichawk, has structural geometry similar to a Stearman biplane, as well as some of its aerodynamic features, and is stressed for +12 and −6g. It flew for the first time on 24 May 1971 and had accumulated 420 flying hours by early 1979.

Javelin Aircraft does not produce any assembled Wichawks, but plans, wing ribs and fuel tanks are available to amateur constructors. Eventually, Javelin Aircraft intends to sell complete kits for amateur construction of the aircraft, and it has been reported that the type may go into production in a foreign country as a primary trainer. A total of 225 sets of plans had been sold by early 1979, and more than 100 Wichawks were under construction, including several in Canada and Australia, and one in Argentina. Seven aircraft built to Javelin plans were known to be flying. The first of these (N29JC), built by Mr Jim Crawford, a retired airline captain, made its first flight on 2 August 1975. A 168 kW (225 hp) Continental O-470-11 flat-six engine gives this aircraft maximum and cruising speeds very similar to those of the Lycoming-engined prototype; max rate of climb is increased to 762 m (2,500 ft)/min.

Two other Wichawks are powered by 134 kW (180 hp) Lycoming O-360 engines, one with a Continental E-225-8 (ex-Beechcraft Bonanza) engine, and one with a 172 kW (230 hp) Continental O-470-R engine taken from a Cessna 182. This last aircraft (illustrated) has a three-blade propeller. It is said to be very smooth to fly, and can take off in 2½ seconds, climb at 762 m (2,500 ft)/min, cruise on 65% power at 113 knots (209 km/h; 130 mph) IAS, and perform well aerobatically.

The main current production work of Javelin Aircraft involves manufacture of 190 litre (50·2 US gallon) glassfibre slipper fuel tanks for the Rockwell Commander and Turbo-Commander 680/690 series. The company is also flight testing a turbocharged Ford Pinto motor car engine in a 1956 Cessna 172; this develops 134 kW (180 hp), and Javelin will eventually sell plans for the conversion to amateur constructors.

JAVELIN WICHAWK

TYPE: Two/three-seat sporting biplane.

WINGS: Braced single-bay biplane, with N-shape streamline-section cabane and interplane struts. Streamline-section landing and flying wires. Wing section NACA 23015. 2° dihedral on lower wings only. Incidence 0°. No sweepback. Composite structure, with two wooden spars and 2024T3 light alloy ribs, fabric-covered. Simple sealed ailerons on lower wings only. No flaps. Geared trim tab.

FUSELAGE: Welded structure of 4130 chrome-molybdenum steel tube with light alloy tubular stringers, fabric-covered.

TAIL UNIT: Wire-braced welded structure of 4130 chrome-molybdenum steel tube with fabric covering. Fixed-incidence tailplane. Trim tab in starboard elevator.

LANDING GEAR: Non-retractable tailwheel type. Main wheels carried on side Vees hinged to lower fuselage longerons. Shock-absorption by automotive-type shock-struts, similar to those of Piper PA-20, and rubber shock cord. Main wheels and tyres size 6·00-6. Cleveland toe brakes. Steerable tailwheel.

POWER PLANT: Prototype has one 134 kW (180 hp) Lycoming O-360 flat-four engine, driving a Sensenich two-blade fixed-pitch propeller type 76EM8-0-56. McCauley propellers optional. Provision for alternative horizontally-opposed or radial engines from 112 kW (150 hp) to 224 kW (300 hp), for which Javelin can provide installation drawings. Other engines currently being installed, other than those previously mentioned, include the 175 kW (235 hp) Lycoming O-435, 224 kW (300 hp) Lycoming O-540 and 224 kW (300 hp) Continental O-520. Fuel tank of 94·5 litre (25 US gallon) capacity in upper wing centre-section, and one of 56·8 litre (15 US gallon) capacity in fuselage aft of firewall. Refuelling points above tanks. Oil capacity of prototype 7·5 litres (2 US gallons).

ACCOMMODATION: Two seats, side by side, in open cockpit. Provision for tandem two-seat or three-seat configurations. Drawings available for rearward-sliding transparent cockpit canopy. Dual controls standard. Baggage compartment aft of seats, capacity 45·4 kg (100 lb). Baggage locker, in turtleback, capacity 9 kg (20 lb).

SYSTEMS: Electrical system powered by 12V 50A engine-driven generator. Hydraulic system for brakes only.

DIMENSIONS, EXTERNAL:

Wing span (upper)	7·32 m (24 ft 0 in)
Wing chord (both), constant	1·27 m (4 ft 2 in)
Wing area, gross	17·2 m² (185 sq ft)
Wing aspect ratio	5·76
Length overall	5·87 m (19 ft 3 in)
Height overall	2·18 m (7 ft 2 in)
Tailplane span	2·44 m (8 ft 0 in)
Wheel track	1·87 m (6 ft 1½ in)
Propeller diameter	1·93 m (6 ft 4 in)

DIMENSIONS, INTERNAL:

Cockpit: Max width	0·93 m (3 ft 0½ in)
Baggage compartment	0·34 m³ (12 cu ft)

WEIGHTS (prototype with 134 kW; 180 hp engine):

Weight empty	580 kg (1,280 lb)
*Max T-O weight	907 kg (2,000 lb)

** Max T-O weight is increased to 998 kg (2,200 lb) with high-powered engines.*

PERFORMANCE (prototype with 134 kW; 180 hp engine):

Never-exceed speed	156 knots (289 km/h; 180 mph)
Max level speed at S/L	121·5 knots (225 km/h; 140 mph)
Max cruising speed	110 knots (204 km/h; 127 mph)
Landing speed	39 knots (72·5 km/h; 45 mph)
Max rate of climb at S/L	518 m (1,700 ft)/min
T-O run	46 m (150 ft)
Load factors at max AUW	+12*g*, −6*g*

JEFFAIR

JEFFAIR CORPORATION

PO Box 975, Renton, Washington 98055
Telephone: (206) 863 7992
PRESIDENT: Geoffrey L. Siers

This company was formed by Mr Geoffrey Siers, a former RAF fighter pilot and design engineer with BAC, who emigrated to the USA in 1964. In 1966 he began designing a high-performance all-wooden two-seat light aircraft, of which construction was started in June 1969. Now known as the Barracuda, this aircraft (N19GS) flew for the first time on 29 June 1975, and is certificated in the FAA's Experimental category. At the EAA Fly-in at Oshkosh in 1976, the Barracuda won the 'Most Outstanding New Design' award. Plans are available to amateur constructors, and about 220 Barracudas were being built by January 1979.

JEFFAIR BARRACUDA

TYPE: Two-seat all-wooden sporting monoplane.

WINGS: Cantilever low-wing monoplane, made in three pieces: two constant-chord outer panels and a centre-section which is integral with the fuselage. Wing section NACA 64_2415. Upper surface of centre-section each side has slight anhedral, but bottom surface has neither anhedral nor dihedral. Dihedral of 5° on outer panels. No incidence. Basic structure of spruce, with mahogany and birch plywood covering. Box-section main spar with spruce booms and ply webs; truss-type ribs of spruce. Frise-type ailerons of wood and glassfibre. Electrically-actuated wooden plain flap on entire centre-section trailing-edge, extending under fuselage.

FUSELAGE: Conventional spruce structure, covered with birch plywood stressed skin.

TAIL UNIT: Cantilever spruce structure, plywood-covered. Glassfibre tips. Electrically-actuated trim tab in port elevator. Rudder has bungee trim.

LANDING GEAR: Retractable tricycle type. Electro-hydraulic retraction, main wheels inward, nosewheel rearward; all wheels fully enclosed by doors when retracted. Emergency extension by gravity. Legs made from 4130 steel tubing, with steel coil spring shock-absorption. Cleveland wheels, size 5·00-5, with 0·36 m (14 in) diameter tyres. Cleveland aircooled brakes.

POWER PLANT: One 164 kW (220 hp) Lycoming GO-435-2 flat-six engine, driving a Hartzell three-blade controllable-pitch propeller. Two glassfibre fuel tanks in centre-section forward of spar, total capacity 166·5 litres (44 US gallons). Oil capacity 11·5 litres (3 US gallons).

ACCOMMODATION: Two armchair seats, with thigh support, side by side under upward-hinged individual 'gull-wing' canopy doors. Dual controls. Baggage space behind seats. Cabin heated and ventilated.

SYSTEMS: Electric pump supplies hydraulic system. Electrical supply via 12V DC system.

ELECTRONICS: Edo-Air 360-channel nav/com.

DIMENSIONS, EXTERNAL:

Wing span	7·54 m (24 ft 9 in)
Wing chord at root	2·11 m (6 ft 11 in)
Wing chord, outer panels, constant	1·45 m (4 ft 9 in)
Wing area, gross	11·15 m² (120 sq ft)
Length overall	6·55 m (21 ft 6 in)
Wheel track	2·54 m (8 ft 4 in)
Propeller diameter	2·18 m (7 ft 2 in)

DIMENSION, INTERNAL:

Cabin: Max width	1·07 m (3 ft 6 in)

WEIGHTS:

Weight empty	678 kg (1,495 lb)
Baggage hold capacity	18 kg (40 lb)
Max T-O weight	1,043 kg (2,300 lb)

PERFORMANCE:

Never-exceed speed	260 knots (482 km/h; 300 mph)
Max level speed at 2,135 m (7,000 ft)	189 knots (351 km/h; 218 mph)
Max cruising speed at 2,135 m (7,000 ft)	174 knots (322 km/h; 200 mph)
Cruising speed (62% power) at 2,750 m (9,000 ft)	156 knots (290 km/h; 180 mph)
Stalling speed, flaps down	54 knots (100 km/h; 62 mph)
Max rate of climb at S/L	670 m (2,200 ft)/min
Range at max T-O weight, 65% power, with 30 min reserves	390 nm (724 km; 450 miles)

JONAS

GERALD JONAS

San Francisco, California

JONAS HUMMINGBIRD

Mr Gerald Jonas, an architect, has designed a light two-seat aircraft known as the Hummingbird. By July 1977, about 75% of the airframe and mechanical parts had been built, with the help of two other constructors, on a part-time basis. First flight was then scheduled for October of the same year.

The design features a moulded glassfibre lifting fuselage and boundary layer control, with a symmetrical aerofoil. The rear-mounted narrow-chord tapering wings are also constructed of moulded glassfibre, with spars of graphite, and have full-span electrically-actuated flaps, with spoilers for roll control. The constant-chord canard foreplane is of similar construction. Power is provided by a rear-mounted 58 kW (78 hp) Revmaster Volkswagen 2,000 cc modified motor car engine, driving a Maloof two-speed aluminium propeller. The tricycle landing gear is fully retractable and the graphite main legs fold scissor-like into the under-fuselage.

Plans and kits are expected to be made available to amateur constructors.

DIMENSIONS, EXTERNAL:

Wing span	6·10 m (20 ft 0 in)
Wing area, gross (incl canard foreplane)	3·81 m² (41 sq ft)
Length overall	3·05 m (10 ft 0 in)

WEIGHTS:

Weight empty	197 kg (435 lb)
Max T-O weight	385 kg (850 lb)

PERFORMANCE (estimated):

Max cruising speed	191 knots (354 km/h; 220 mph)
Stalling speed	56 knots (103 km/h; 64 mph)
Range with max fuel	955 nm (1,770 km; 1,100 miles)

KELEHER

JAMES J. KELEHER

4321 Ogden Drive, Fremont, California 94538

In the early 1960s Mr J. Keleher designed and built a mid-wing sporting monoplane which he called the Lark. The design was revised in 1963, and the current model, for which plans are available to amateur constructors, is designated Lark-1B.

KELEHER LARK-1B

The following description applies to the Lark-1B with a 48·5 kW (65 hp) Continental engine. Examples are flying with 56 kW (75 hp) A75-8 and 74·5 kW (100 hp) O-200 Continental engines.

TYPE: Single-seat sporting monoplane.

WINGS: Braced mid-wing monoplane with streamline-section Vee bracing struts each side. Wing section NACA $2R_212$. No dihedral. Incidence 4° at root, 2° 30′ at tip. All-wood structure of Sitka spruce, with built-up I beam front spar and ribs, fabric-covered. Stressed to 6*g* plus. Fabric-covered wooden ailerons; no trim tabs or flaps.

FUSELAGE: Welded steel tube structure, fabric-covered, stressed to 6*g* plus.

TAIL UNIT: Wire-braced welded steel tube structure with sheet steel ribs and fabric covering. Adjustable-incidence tailplane. Swept fin. No trim tabs.

LANDING GEAR: Non-retractable tailwheel type. Divided main landing gear with shock-absorption by rubber cord in fuselage. Cleveland main wheels and tyres size 5·00-5, pressure 1·38-1·72 bars (20-25 lb/sq in). Cleveland disc brakes. Wheel fairings optional.

POWER PLANT: Provision for alternative flat-four engines of 48·5-74·5 kW (65-100 hp), driving a two-blade metal fixed-pitch propeller. One galvanised steel fuel tank in the fuselage, aft of the firewall, capacity 56 litres (15 US gallons). Refuelling point on top of cowl, forward of windscreen. Oil capacity 5·7 litres (1·5 US gallons).

ACCOMMODATION: Single seat in enclosed cockpit under sliding canopy. Lowered turtledeck and bubble canopy optional. Stowage for 9 kg (20 lb) baggage aft of seat.

DIMENSIONS, EXTERNAL:

Wing span	7·01 m (23 ft 0 in)
Wing chord, constant	1·22 m (4 ft 0 in)
Wing area, gross	7·48 m² (80·5 sq ft)
Wing aspect ratio	5·75
Length overall	5·18 m (17 ft 0 in)
Height overall	1·65 m (5 ft 5 in)
Tailplane span	2·03 m (6 ft 8 in)
Wheel track	1·57 m (5 ft 2 in)
Propeller diameter:	
A65-8	1·70 m (5 ft 7 in)
A75-8	1·66 m (5 ft 5½ in)

WEIGHTS (48·5 kW: 65 hp engine):

Weight empty	249 kg (550 lb)
Max T-O and landing weight	387 kg (855 lb)

PERFORMANCE (with 48·5 kW; 65 hp engine, at max T-O weight):

Never-exceed speed	160 knots (297·5 km/h; 185 mph)
Max level speed	115 knots (212 km/h; 132 mph)
Max cruising speed	103 knots (192 km/h; 119 mph)
Stalling speed	48 knots (89 km/h; 55 mph)
Max rate of climb at S/L	274 m (900 ft)/min
Service ceiling	5,950 m (19,500 ft)
T-O run	183 m (600 ft)
Range with max payload, with reserves	303 nm (563 km; 350 miles)

KINMAN

DUANE KINMAN

Rubidoux, California

KINMAN SUPER SIMPLE I

As its name suggests, the Super Simple I was designed by Mr Duane Kinman to be easy to construct. It is a small single-seater, the prototype of which was built in three weeks, at a cost of $2,680, from six sheets of 1·22 × 3·66 m (4 × 12 ft) aluminium. There are no compound curves, except in the glassfibre nose cowl, and no welding because of the extensive use of glue and pop rivets. Plans will be made available to amateur builders.

TYPE: Single-seat light monoplane.

WINGS: Cantilever low-wing monoplane. Wing section NACA 64212. Slight dihedral. No sweepback. Constant chord. Structure of 2024 T3 aluminium, bonded by Hysol 9410 glue. Full-span drooping ailerons. No tabs.

FUSELAGE: Conventional 2024 T3 aluminium structure, pop riveted. Tailcone is a 30 cm (12 in) propeller spinner.

TAIL UNIT: Conventional cantilever 2024 T3 aluminium structure, pop riveted. Constant-chord tailplane with full-span elevators. No tabs.

LANDING GEAR: Non-retractable tailwheel type. Cantilever main legs made from 1·9 cm (¾ in) thick 2024 T3 aluminium strip. Main wheels size 2·80-4. Hydraulic disc brakes.

POWER PLANT: One 42·5 kW (57 hp) 1,800 cc modified Volkswagen motor car engine, driving a Bob Mende four-blade wooden propeller, with spinner. Fuel tank in nose, capacity 38 litres (10 US gallons).

ACCOMMODATION: Single semi-reclining seat under a bubble canopy.

DIMENSIONS, EXTERNAL:

Wing span	5·54 m (18 ft 2 in)
Wing chord, constant	1·27 m (4 ft 2 in)
Length overall	4·88 m (16 ft 0 in)
Propeller diameter	1·27 m (4 ft 2 in)

DIMENSIONS, INTERNAL:

Cockpit: max width	0·51 m (1 ft 8 in)
max height	0·76 m (2 ft 6 in)

Jeffair Barracuda with modified windows, built by Mr J. Yoder of Midland, Michigan *(Howard Levy)*

Uncompleted Hummingbird two-seat light aircraft, designed by Mr Gerald Jonas of San Francisco *(Howard Levy)*

Keleher Lark-1B single-seat sporting monoplane *(J. M. G. Gradidge)*

Kinman Super Simple I single-seat monoplane *(Howard Levy)*

Kraft Super Fli aerobatic monoplane *(Howard Levy)*

Prototype Larkin KC-3 Skylark (1,600 cc Volkswagen engine)

WEIGHTS:
- Weight empty 201 kg (443 lb)
- Max T-O weight 306 kg (675 lb)

PERFORMANCE (estimated):
- Max level speed over 139 knots (257 km/h; 160 mph)
- Max cruising speed 130 knots (241 km/h; 150 mph)
- Landing speed 39-42 knots (72·5-77 km/h; 45-48 mph)
- T-O run 152 m (500 ft)
- Range with max fuel 174 nm (322 km; 200 miles)

KRAFT

KRAFT SYSTEMS INC

450 West California Avenue, PO Box 1268, Vista, California 92083
Telephone: (714) 724 7146

KRAFT K-1 SUPER FLI

Designed and built by Phil Kraft, with help from Paul White, the Super Fli was produced to model aircraft standards in terms of wing design, areas and moments, as Phil Kraft is a world champion model aircraft builder. After 1½ years of work, the Super Fli was first flown in December 1974 and was taken to the EAA Fly-in at Oshkosh in 1975. Aerobatic pilots at Oshkosh who flew the aircraft found it most satisfactory, and the prototype had logged more than 350 hours of almost continuous unlimited aerobatics by the Spring of 1977. Plans of the Super Fli are available to amateur constructors.

TYPE: Single-seat aerobatic monoplane.

WINGS: Cantilever low-wing monoplane. Spruce spars, plywood ribs and plywood covering. Horn-balanced ailerons.

FUSELAGE: Oval section fuselage of steel tube construction, aluminium covered.

TAIL UNIT: Wire-braced steel tube structure, fabric covered.

LANDING GEAR: Non-retractable tailwheel type. Faired main legs and faired wheels. Steerable tailwheel.

POWER PLANT: One 149 kW (200 hp) Lycoming IO-360-A1D flat-four engine. Provision for fitting 134 kW (180 hp) Lycoming.

ACCOMMODATION: Single seat under transparent canopy, hinged on starboard side.

DIMENSION, EXTERNAL:
- Wing span 7·32 m (24 ft 0 in)

WEIGHTS:
- Weight empty 445 kg (980 lb)
- Max T-O weight 635 kg (1,400 lb)

PERFORMANCE:
- Max level speed 174 knots (322 km/h; 200 mph)
- Cruising speed 143 knots (265 km/h; 165 mph)
- Landing speed 35 knots (65 km/h; 40 mph)
- Max rate of climb at S/L 914 m (3,000 ft)/min
- Service ceiling 3,660 m (12,000 ft)
- Range with max fuel 260 nm (483 km; 300 miles)

LARKIN

LARKIN AIRCRAFT COMPANY

PO Box 66899, 4865 Scotts Valley Drive, Scotts Valley, California 95066
Telephone: (408) 438 3883
PRESIDENT: Keith Larkin

Larkin Aircraft Corporation, a subsidiary of ACS Communications Inc, designed and built the prototype of a two-seat light aircraft known as the Model KC-3 Skylark. Design began in 1961 and prototype construction started in 1970, with the first flight on 8 June 1972. The first public showing was at the Watsonville Fly-in in May 1973. Emphasis was placed on producing a robust structure suitable for homebuilders, the primary skill necessary to build a Skylark being that of sheet metal riveting.

Plans and material kits are available to amateur constructors, who may also order from the company any part or parts which they consider beyond their ability to fabricate. At least one further Skylark has been constructed, in addition to the prototype.

In early 1977, the right to licence-build the Skylark in kit form was negotiated with another company, as well as possible licence manufacture in Australia. The outcome of these negotiations is not known.

LARKIN KC-3 SKYLARK

TYPE: Two-seat light aircraft.

WINGS: Cantilever shoulder-wing monoplane. Wing section NACA 4415. Light alloy two-spar structure, with metal ribs and skins. Cambered wingtips of glassfibre. Ailerons of aluminium construction. No flaps or tabs.

FUSELAGE: Light alloy square-section tubular keel, mast and triangular support structure. Mast carries engine, drive and propeller. Support structure carries wings and tailbooms. Keel supports landing gear and seats. Glassfibre lower and upper fairings. Optional Vee-shaped stepped lower hull of glassfibre for amphibious operations.

TAIL UNIT: Twin-boom structure of rectangular-section light alloy, attached to wings, with twin fins and rudders. Large trim tab in centre of elevator trailing-edge.

LANDING GEAR: Non-retractable tricycle type. Shock-absorption by low-pressure tyres. Nosewheel steerable. Goodyear main wheels with tyres size 6·00-6, pressure 1·38 bars (20 lb/sq in). Nosewheel tyre size 14 × 6·00-5, pressure 1·38 bars (20 lb/sq in). Goodyear disc brakes. Large glassfibre main-wheel fairings.

POWER PLANT: One 50 kW (67 hp) 1,679 cc Volkswagen LA-1700 modified motor car engine as standard, driving a Fahlin two-blade fixed-pitch wooden pusher propeller via Larkin seven-belt V-drive reduction gearing. Glassfibre spinner. Fuel tank aft of pilot's seat, capacity 57 litres (15 US gallons). Refuelling point on tank's upper surface. Oil capacity 1·9 litres (0·5 US gallons).

ACCOMMODATION: Two seats, side by side, in enclosed cockpit. Dual controls standard. Port side of transparent canopy is hinged on centreline to provide access. Cockpit heating optional.

SYSTEM: Electrical system standard, comprising engine-driven generator and storage battery for engine starting.

ELECTRONICS AND EQUIPMENT: Navigation lights, radio and additional electronics optional.

DIMENSIONS, EXTERNAL:

Wing span	8·08 m (26 ft 6 in)
Wing chord, constant	1·27 m (4 ft 2 in)
Wing area, gross	10·59 m² (114 sq ft)
Wing aspect ratio	7·0
Length overall	5·55 m (18 ft 2½ in)
Height overall	1·89 m (6 ft 2½ in)
Tailplane span	2·54 m (8 ft 4 in)
Wheel track	1·57 m (5 ft 2 in)
Wheelbase	1·55 m (5 ft 1 in)
Propeller diameter	1·75 m (5 ft 9 in)

DIMENSION, INTERNAL:

Cabin: Max width	1·04 m (3 ft 5 in)

WEIGHTS:

Weight empty	358 kg (790 lb)
Baggage capacity	45 kg (100 lb)
Max T-O weight	565 kg (1,246 lb)

PERFORMANCE:

Never-exceed speed	156 knots (289 km/h; 180 mph)
Max level speed	100 knots (185 km/h; 115 mph)
Max cruising speed	91 knots (169 km/h; 105 mph)
Econ cruising speed	87 knots (161 km/h; 100 mph)
Stalling speed	37 knots (68 km/h; 42 mph)
Max rate of climb at S/L	168 m (550 ft)/min
Service ceiling (estimated)	3,660 m (12,000 ft)
T-O run	183 m (600 ft)
T-O to 15 m (50 ft)	225 m (740 ft)
Landing from 15 m (50 ft)	168 m (550 ft)
Landing run	122 m (400 ft)
Range	347 nm (644 km; 400 miles)

LASHER

LASHER

LASHER RENEGADE I

The Lasher-designed Renegade I Formula V racer (N73RL) was built by Mr M. Ricketts. Construction took 18 months and cost $4,000. First flight was made in 1974. It is currently owned by Mr Vernon Willingham from Sparta, Illinois. Construction is conventional, with all-wood wings, and fabric-covered tubular steel fuselage and tail unit. Power is provided by a 41 kW (55 hp) modified Volkswagen motor car engine.

DIMENSIONS, EXTERNAL:

Wing span	5·18 m (17 ft 0 in)
Wing chord, constant	1·52 m (5 ft 0 in)
Length overall	4·57 m (15 ft 0 in)
Height overall	1·30 m (4 ft 3 in)

WEIGHTS:

Weight empty	204·5 kg (451 lb)
Max T-O weight	304 kg (670 lb)

PERFORMANCE:

Max level speed	over 148 knots (273 km/h; 170 mph)
Max cruising speed	126 knots (233 km/h; 145 mph)
Landing speed	43·5 knots (80·5 km/h; 50 mph)
Max rate of climb at S/L	259 m (850 ft)/min
Service ceiling	3,660 m (12,000 ft)
Range with max fuel	195 nm (362 km; 225 miles)

MacCREADY

DR PAUL MacCREADY

AeroVironment Inc, 145 Vista Avenue, Pasadena, California 91107

Telephone: (213) 449 4392

On 23 August 1977, the Gossamer Condor man-powered aircraft designed under the leadership of Dr Paul MacCready won the £50,000 Kremer Prize by becoming the first aircraft propelled entirely by a man to complete a figure-of-eight flight around two pylons half a mile apart. Pilot on the 7 min 27·5 s flight, at Shafter, California, was racing cyclist Bryan Allen.

A full description and illustration of the Gossamer Condor appeared in the 1978-79 *Jane's*.

A new man-powered aircraft named the Gossamer Albatross, also designed under the leadership of Dr Paul MacCready, is currently being tested. Generally similar to the Gossamer Condor in design, it is intended to attempt a crossing of the English Channel, and is designed to allow cruising flight on about half the power needed by the Condor. The most up-to-date details of the Gossamer Albatross available at the time of closing for press are given in the Addenda.

MacDONALD

MacDONALD AIRCRAFT COMPANY

1282 Fowler Creek Road, Sonoma, California 95476

Telephone: (707) 996 7897

PROPRIETOR: Robert A. MacDonald

Mr MacDonald, an aircraft engineer, has designed and built a single-seat lightweight sporting aircraft of which plans are available to amateur constructors. It is of all-metal construction, and fabrication is simplified by extensive use of pop rivets.

Design and construction of the aircraft, which is designated MacDonald S-20, began simultaneously in March 1969. First flight was made on 9 March 1972.

The designation S-20 applies to the prototype, which is described. Aircraft built to Mr MacDonald's plans have the designation **S-21**. Sales of plans totalled around 100 sets by early 1976, and the first aircraft to be built from the plans was expected to make its first flight during that year. There has been no recent news from the company.

MacDONALD S-20

TYPE: Single-seat lightweight sporting aircraft.

WINGS: Cantilever low-wing monoplane. Wing section NACA 747A315. Small centre-section without dihedral. Dihedral on outer wing panels 5°. Incidence 1°. No sweepback. Constant-chord light alloy structure, with main and auxiliary spars and skins of 2024-T3 aluminium. Modified Frise-type ailerons of 2024-T3 light alloy. No flaps. No trim tabs.

FUSELAGE: Forward fuselage of welded steel tube truss construction. Aft fuselage has light alloy bulkheads and longerons. Skin is of 2024-T3 light alloy.

TAIL UNIT: Cantilever light alloy structure of 2024-T3 aluminium, with two spars in both fin and tailplane. Fixed-incidence tailplane. Combination trim and anti-servo tab on starboard elevator. Ground-adjustable tab on rudder (integral with port-side skin on S-21).

LANDING GEAR: Non-retractable tailwheel type. Shock-absorption of main-gear struts by neoprene discs in compression. Go-kart wheels with tyres size 4·00-5. Mechanical caliper wheel brakes.

POWER PLANT: One 1,500 cc Volkswagen modified motor car engine, developing 39·5 kW (53 hp) and driving a Hegy two-blade wooden fixed-pitch propeller. Aluminium fuel tank in fuselage, immediately aft of firewall, capacity 37 litres (9·8 US gallons). Refuelling point on fuselage upper surface, forward of windscreen. Oil capacity 1·27 litres (0·34 US gallons).

ACCOMMODATION: Single seat for pilot in open cockpit. Space for baggage aft of seat, nominally 9 kg (20 lb) capacity, but prototype has storage battery and radio weighing 5 kg (11 lb) stowed in this area.

ELECTRONICS: Battery-powered Genave Alpha 100 com transceiver in prototype.

DIMENSIONS, EXTERNAL:

Wing span	7·62 m (25 ft 0 in)
Wing chord, constant	1·14 m (3 ft 9 in)
Wing area, gross	8·73 m² (94 sq ft)
Wing aspect ratio	6·65
Length overall	5·64 m (18 ft 6 in)
Height overall	1·60 m (5 ft 3 in)
Tailplane span	2·13 m (7 ft 0 in)
Wheel track	1·57 m (5 ft 2 in)
Wheelbase	4·70 m (15 ft 5 in)
Propeller diameter	1·35 m (4 ft 5 in)

WEIGHTS:

Weight empty	206 kg (456 lb)
Design T-O weight	326 kg (720 lb)

PERFORMANCE (at T-O weight of 313 kg; 690 lb):

Never-exceed speed	140 knots (260 km/h; 162 mph)
Max level speed, from S/L to 610 m (2,000 ft)	96 knots (177 km/h; 110 mph)
Max cruising speed, from S/L to 610 m (2,000 ft)	78 knots (145 km/h; 90 mph)
Econ cruising speed, from S/L to 610 m (2,000 ft)	69·5 knots (129 km/h; 80 mph)
Stalling speed	33 knots (61·5 km/h; 38 mph)
Max rate of climb at S/L	259 m (850 ft)/min
T-O run	91 m (300 ft)
Landing run	approx 91 m (300 ft)
Range with max fuel, no reserves	218 nm (404 km; 251 miles)

MaHUGH

G. IRVIN MaHUGH

Baker, Oregon

MaHUGH FLYING BATHTUB

Mr G. Irvin MaHugh has built a single-seat monoplane known as the Flying Bathtub, using plans that he modified from those which appeared in a 1932 edition of *Flying and Glider Manual,* recently republished by the EAA. Compared with the original, the Flying Bathtub has been structurally strengthened and is powered by a 56 kW (75 hp) Continental A75-8F flat-four engine, against only 22·5 kW (30 hp) in the original aircraft. Construction took 2½ years and cost $4,000. First flight was made on 15 May 1978.

The Flying Bathtub's general configuration can be seen in the accompanying illustration. The high-mounted wing has spruce spars and spruce/mahogany ribs, Dacron-covered, and is braced by 4130 steel struts each side. The remainder of the airframe is also built from 4130 steel tubing, in parts Dacron-covered.

DIMENSIONS, EXTERNAL:

Wing span	10·64 m (34 ft 11 in)
Wing chord, constant	1·60 m (5 ft 3 in)
Length overall	6·71 m (22 ft 0 in)
Height overall	1·78 m (5 ft 10 in)

WEIGHTS:

Weight empty	355 kg (782 lb)
Max T-O weight	590 kg (1,300 lb)

PERFORMANCE:

Max level speed	over 74 knots (137 km/h; 85 mph)
Max cruising speed	65 knots (121 km/h; 75 mph)
Landing speed	35 knots (64·5 km/h; 40 mph)
Max rate of climb at S/L	152 m (500 ft)/min
Service ceiling	2,590 m (8,500 ft)
T-O run	91 m (300 ft)
Landing run	122-152 m (400-500 ft)
Range with max fuel	208 nm (386 km; 240 miles)

McCARLEY

Mrs CHARLES E. McCARLEY

1129 27 Avenue, Hueytown, Alabama 35020

McCARLEY MINI-MAC

Designed by the late Mr Charles E. McCarley, the prototype Mini-Mac took 1,600 working hours to build, at a cost of $1,800, and first flew in July 1970. It was totally destroyed, and Mr McCarley was fatally injured, in an accident on 28 October 1978. The aircraft was reportedly operating normally up to the time of the crash; Mr McCarley apparently was blinded by the sun and failed to see a powerline.

A modified version of the Mini-Mac (N75GH), built by George M. Harrison, was completed on 4 July 1974 and accumulated 122 flying hours in its first year. As well as having a shortened wing span, N75GH has 10° drooping ailerons.

The Mini-Mac is capable of limited aerobatics , and has a number of optional features, including a cockpit canopy, radio and an electrical system. Plans are available to amateur constructors and three more Mini-Macs were known to be under construction in January 1979.

The following description generally applies to both aircraft mentioned above, except where indicated:

TYPE: Single-seat limited aerobatic monoplane.

WINGS: Cantilever low-wing monoplane. Clark Y wing section. All-metal construction. 10° drooping ailerons fitted to N75GH. Folding wings.

FUSELAGE: Conventional all-metal structure.

TAIL UNIT: Conventional cantilever all-metal structure. Tab in elevators.

LANDING GEAR: Non-retractable tricycle type. Wheels enclosed in streamline fairings. Small tail bumper skid.

POWER PLANT: One 1,834 cc (N152CM prototype) or 1,600 cc (N75GH) modified Volkswagen motor car engine, driving a two-blade propeller. Conventional fuel and oil systems, not modified for inverted flight.

ACCOMMODATION: Single seat in open or enclosed cockpit, latter with rearward-sliding canopy.

DIMENSIONS, EXTERNAL (A: prototype; B: N75GH):

Wing span:	
A	6·25 m (20 ft 6 in)
B	5·79 m (19 ft 0 in)

Lasher Renegade I Formula V single-seat racer *(Howard Levy)*

MacDonald S-20 lightweight single-seat sporting aircraft

MaHugh Flying Bathtub single-seat monoplane *(Howard Levy)*

The late Mr Charles E. McCarley and the prototype Mini-Mac

Prototype WM-2 sport aircraft built by Mr William Miller

Prototype of production version of powered Mitchell Wing, before installation of engine *(Howard Levy)*

Wing chord:	
A	1·02 m (3 ft 4 in)
B	1·04 m (3 ft 5 in)
Length overall:	
A	4·47 m (14 ft 8 in)
B	4·39 m (14 ft 5 in)
Height overall:	
A and B	1·73 m (5 ft 8 in)
WEIGHTS:	
Weight empty:	
A	233 kg (514 lb)
B	208 kg (458 lb)
Max T-O weight:	
A	363 kg (800 lb)
B	318 kg (700 lb)
PERFORMANCE:	
Max level speed:	
A and B	139 knots (257 km/h; 160 mph)
Cruising speed:	
A	109 knots (201 km/h; 125 mph)
B	95 knots (177 km/h; 110 mph)
Landing speed:	
A	44 knots (81 km/h; 50 mph)
B	48 knots (89 km/h; 55 mph)
Max rate of climb at S/L:	
A	305 m (1,000 ft)/min
B	213 m (700 ft)/min
Service ceiling:	
A and B	2,440 m (8,000 ft)
T-O run:	
A	152 m (500 ft)
B	183 m (600 ft)
Landing run:	
A and B	152 m (500 ft)
Range with max fuel:	
A	434 nm (804 km; 500 miles)
B	260 nm (483 km; 300 miles)

M COMPANY

M COMPANY

1900 S Newcomb, Porterville, California 93257
Telephone: (209) 781 0778

M COMPANY MITCHELL WING

M Company, which produces the Mitchell Wing hang glider, is also marketing two versions of an ultra-light powered aircraft which uses the wing of the hang glider. The powered Mitchell Wing is available with an open cockpit for the pilof, or with a fuselage pod, either structure being attached to the wing brackets provided originally for the hang glider cage. Controls are conventional. Kits to build either version are available to amateur constructors, the price varying according to the type of engine selected and to choice of the open or pod-type cockpit. By early 1979 approximately 300 hang glider kits and plans had been sold (with 40 Mitchell Wings flying), plus five of the new power kits.

The illustration shows the prototype of a future production version of the powered Mitchell Wing, minus engine, with wingtip 'draggers' in place of the usual spoilers.

TYPE: Single-seat ultra-light monoplane.

WINGS: Tapered parasol-wing monoplane. Wing section NACA 23015. Dihedral on outer wing panels, which fold over centre-section for transportation. Spar of 6061 T6 aluminium tube, with spruce ribs, and birch plywood and fabric covering. Small uncovered section of wing immediately above cockpit, to ease access to seat. Mitchell-patented stabilators, moving 4° downwards and 35° upwards, for differential control.

FUSELAGE: Open aluminium-tube truss structure, or pod-type structure with cabane struts, beneath wing.

TAIL UNIT: Wingtip rudders provided in kits. (At least one powered Mitchell Wing is not fitted with rudders.)

LANDING GEAR: Non-retractable tricycle type, with similar wheels and tyres on all units. Steerable nosewheel.

POWER PLANT: One 9 kW (12 hp) 125 cc McCulloch MC-101 engine, driving a two-blade pusher propeller, or one West Bend engine. Fuel tank aft of seat.

ACCOMMODATION: Single open seat, with belt, or pod-type cockpit. Conventional control column and foot pedal controls.

DIMENSION, EXTERNAL:	
Wing span	10·36 m (34 ft 0 in)
WEIGHTS:	
Weight empty	56·7 kg (125 lb)
Max T-O weight	159 kg (350 lb)
PERFORMANCE:	
Max level speed	43·5 knots (80·5 km/h; 50 mph)
Cruising speed	31·5 knots (58 km/h; 36 mph)
Stalling speed	17·5 knots (32·5 km/h; 20 mph)
Max rate of climb at S/L	137 m (450 ft)/min
Sinking rate (unpowered) at 22·5 knots (42 km/h; 26 mph)	68·6 m (225 ft)/min
T-O run, no wind	53·5 m (175 ft)
Landing distance	30·5 m (100 ft)

MILLER

WILLIAM Y. MILLER

1439 West Second Street, Mesa, Arizona 85201

Mr William Y. Miller built the prototype of the WM-2 sporting aircraft, which had been designed by Mr W. Terry Miller for amateur construction.

MILLER WM-2

The WM-2 is a low-powered, high-performance aircraft, conceived originally for the exploration of wave soaring conditions, thermal soaring with the engine stopped, and high-altitude, economical powered sport flying. The prototype (N24832) was built by Mr William Miller between 1969 and 1972, and made its first flight in August 1972. Flight testing was undertaken during 1973-74, and by January 1978 the aircraft had completed 430 flying hours. Plans are available to amateur constructors, and approximately ten WM-2s were under construction by January 1978, the first of which was expected to fly in the late Summer of that year.

TYPE: Single-seat sport aircraft.

WINGS: Cantilever low-wing monoplane. Modified NACA laminar-flow series wing sections. Thickness/chord ratio 15%. Dihedral 4°. Incidence 1°. Sweepback 0° 53′ at quarter-chord. Conventional structure of spruce spars, with birch plywood, glassfibre and fabric covering. Wooden ailerons. No flaps or tabs. Metal spoiler in each upper surface.

FUSELAGE: Conventional spruce structure, with birch plywood and glassfibre covering.

TAIL UNIT: Plywood- and fabric-covered spruce cantilever structure.

LANDING GEAR: Manually-retractable monowheel (wheel and tyre size 6·00-6) and tailskid. Hydraulic brake.

POWER PLANT: One 48·5 kW (65 hp) Continental flat-four engine, driving a two-blade fixed-pitch metal propeller. Fuel tank, capacity 37·8 litres (10 US gallons), aft of firewall. Fuel consumption at an econ cruising speed of 69·5 knots (129 km/h; 80 mph) is less than 7·5 litres (2 US gallons)/hour.

ACCOMMODATION: Single seat under one-piece sideways-opening bubble canopy.

DIMENSIONS, EXTERNAL:

Wing span	12·19 m (40 ft 0 in)
Wing chord at root	1·37 m (4 ft 6 in)
Wing chord at tip	0·76 m (2 ft 6 in)
Wing area, gross	13·38 m² (144·0 sq ft)
Wing aspect ratio	11·11
Length overall	6·10 m (20 ft 0 in)
Height over tail	1·60 m (5 ft 3 in)
Tailplane span	2·44 m (8 ft 0 in)
Propeller diameter	1·88 m (6 ft 2 in)

WEIGHTS:

Weight empty, equipped	351 kg (775 lb)
Max T-O weight	476 kg (1,050 lb)

PERFORMANCE (at max T-O weight):

Never-exceed speed	130 knots (241 km/h; 150 mph)
Max level speed at S/L	118 knots (219 km/h; 136 mph)
Normal cruising speed at 3,050 m (10,000 ft), 50% power	109 knots (203 km/h; 126 mph)
Stalling speed	39·5 knots (72·5 km/h; 45 mph)
Max rate of climb at S/L	271 m (890 ft)/min
Rate of climb at 4,575 m (15,000 ft)	152 m (500 ft)/min
Service ceiling (computed)	7,315 m (24,000 ft)
Range at normal cruising speed at 3,050 m (10,000 ft) with 30 min reserves	291 nm (540 km; 336 miles)
Best glide ratio at 54 knots (100 km/h; 62 mph), power off	15

MINI-HAWK

MINI-HAWK INTERNATIONAL INC

1930 Stewart Street, Santa Monica, California 90404
Telephone: (213) 828 4078
DIRECTOR OF MARKETING: E. Y. Treffinger

Mini-Hawk International was formed to market plans and kits for construction of an all-metal single-seat monoplane known as the Mini-Hawk TH.E.01 Tiger-Hawk. Three officers of the corporation, designer William B. Taylor, engineer Thomas E. Maloney and pilot E. Y. Treffinger, combined their efforts to design and construct the prototype. This aircraft flew for the first time during 1974 and the test programme was completed in 1976.

Mini-Hawk offers amateur constructors a complete set of plans and a construction manual or a complete kit package with or without an engine; by early 1979 at least five sets had been sold.

MINI-HAWK TH.E.01 TIGER-HAWK

TYPE: Single-seat lightweight aircraft.

WINGS: Cantilever low-wing monoplane of all-metal construction. Constant-chord wing. Dihedral 4° on outer panels. Full-span ailerons of all-metal construction, operated by push/pull rods. All-metal trailing-edge flaps. Wings removable in 10 min for towing or storage.

FUSELAGE: Built-up structure of light alloy.

TAIL UNIT: Cantilever all-metal structure. Fixed-incidence tailplane. Elevator of light alloy construction. No trim tabs.

LANDING GEAR: Non-retractable tricycle type with steerable nosewheel. Hurst/Airheart hydraulic disc brakes. Single wheel with speed fairing on each unit.

POWER PLANT: One 53·5 kW (72 hp) Revmaster Model 1831D modified Volkswagen motor car engine, with dual ignition, driving an Eng. Duplicating 54/42 two-blade fixed-pitch propeller with spinner. Fuel tank in fuselage with capacity of 45·4 litres (12 US gallons). Suitable for Volkswagen engines of up to 67 kW (90 hp). Oil capacity 2·35 litres (5 US pints).

ACCOMMODATION: Single seat under transparent canopy.

EQUIPMENT: Genave radio optional.

DIMENSIONS, EXTERNAL:

Wing span	5·49 m (18 ft 0 in)
Wing chord, constant	0·99 m (3 ft 3 in)
Wing area, gross	5·30 m² (57 sq ft)
Length overall	4·04 m (13 ft 3 in)
Width overall, wings removed	1·83 m (6 ft 0 in)
Height overall	2·08 m (6 ft 10 in)
Tailplane span	1·83 m (6 ft 0 in)
Wheel track	1·78 m (5 ft 10 in)
Wheelbase	1·93 m (6 ft 4 in)
Propeller diameter	1·37 m (4 ft 6 in)

WEIGHTS:

Weight empty	238 kg (525 lb)
Max T-O weight	362 kg (800 lb)

PERFORMANCE (at max T-O weight):

Never-exceed speed	173 knots (321 km/h; 200 mph)
Max level speed	152 knots (282 km/h; 175 mph)
Max cruising speed	139 knots (257 km/h; 160 mph)
Stalling speed, flaps up	54 knots (100 km/h; 62 mph)
Stalling speed, flaps down	44 knots (81 km/h; 50 mph)
Max rate of climb at S/L	275-305 m (900-1,000 ft)/min
Service ceiling	3,050 m (10,000 ft)
Absolute ceiling	3,660 m (12,000 ft)
T-O and landing run	122 m (400 ft)
Range with max fuel	608 nm (1,126 km; 700 miles)

MONNETT

MONNETT EXPERIMENTAL AIRCRAFT INC

955 Grace Street, Elgin, Illinois 60120
Telephone: (312) 741 2223

Mr John T. Monnett formed this company to market plans and certain components of an original-design Formula V racer. Known originally as the Monnett II Sonerai, this received the Best in Class Formula V Racer award at the EAA Fly-in at Oshkosh in 1971, as well as an award for its outstanding contribution to low-cost flying. Since that time Mr Monnett has designed a two-seat version of the Sonerai, with the result that the original single-seat model is now known simply as Sonerai, the two-seat model as Sonerai II.

Other products available from Monnett Experimental Aircraft include the company's Aero Vee light aero-engines. The two current models are the E-V and Super-Vee, supplied as either 1,600 cc or 1,700 cc units, with or without alternator. Both are stock Volkswagen direct-drive engines, producing 44·7-48·5 kW (60-65 hp) at 4,000 rpm. Customers can purchase either a conversion kit for any Volkswagen Type 3 case of 1969 or newer, or a ready-to-run engine.

MONNETT SONERAI

Mr Monnett began design of the Sonerai in September 1970, construction starting two months later. First flight was made in July 1971, with FAA certification in the Experimental category. Plans and certain components are available to amateur constructors, including glassfibre engine cowlings, clear or tinted Plexiglas cockpit canopy, main landing gear struts, formed aluminium ribs, tapered rod tail spring, fuel tanks, spar kits, instruments, injector carburettor and wheels and brakes. Estimated building time is 850 working hours. The aircraft is stressed to $\pm 6g$.

Approximately 500 sets of plans are known to have been sold, and more than 300 Sonerais are under construction or flying.

TYPE: Single-seat Formula V racing aircraft.

WINGS: Cantilever mid-wing monoplane. Wing section NACA 64212. No dihedral, incidence or sweepback. Conventional light alloy structure. Full-span light alloy ailerons. No flaps or tabs. Wings fold on each side of the fuselage to allow the aircraft to be towed tail-first.

FUSELAGE: Welded chrome-molybdenum steel tube structure with fabric covering. Glassfibre engine cowling.

TAIL UNIT: Cantilever structure of welded chrome-molybdenum steel tube with fabric covering. Tailplane incidence ground-adjustable. No trim tabs.

LANDING GEAR: Non-retractable tailwheel type. Cantilever spring main gear of light alloy. Main wheels and tyres size 5·00-5. Caliper type wheel-brakes. Glassfibre fairings on main wheels.

POWER PLANT: One 44·7 kW (60 hp) Volkswagen 1,600 cc modified motor car engine, driving a Hegy two-blade propeller with spinner. Fuel tank in fuselage, immediately aft of firewall, capacity 37·8 litres (10 US gallons). Refuelling point on fuselage upper surface forward of canopy. Oil capacity 2·82 litres (0·75 US gallons).

ACCOMMODATION: Single seat under jettisonable Plexiglas bubble canopy, hinged at the starboard side.

ELECTRONICS: Battery-powered 100-channel com transceiver.

DIMENSIONS, EXTERNAL:

Wing span	5·08 m (16 ft 8 in)
Wing chord, constant	1·37 m (4 ft 6 in)
Wing area, gross	6·97 m² (75 sq ft)
Length overall	5·08 m (16 ft 8 in)
Height overall	1·52 m (5 ft 0 in)
Tailplane span	1·98 m (6 ft 6 in)
Wheel track	1·22 m (4 ft 0 in)
Propeller diameter	1·27 m (4 ft 2 in)

WEIGHTS:

Weight empty	199 kg (440 lb)
Max T-O weight	340 kg (750 lb)

PERFORMANCE (at max T-O weight):

Max level speed at S/L	152 knots (281 km/h; 175 mph)
Max cruising speed	130 knots (241 km/h; 150 mph)
Econ cruising speed	109 knots (201 km/h; 125 mph)
Stalling speed	35 knots (64·5 km/h; 40 mph)
Max rate of climb at S/L	305 m (1,000 ft)/min
T-O run	183 m (600 ft)
Landing run	183 m (600 ft)
Range, with reserves	260 nm (482 km; 300 miles)

MONNETT SONERAI II

The success of the Sonerai encouraged Mr Monnett to begin the design and construction of a two-seat version in December 1972. Generally similar to the Sonerai, it differs by being slightly larger and by having a more powerful Volkswagen engine. It is stressed to $\pm 4{\cdot}4g$ in the Utility category and to $\pm 6g$ in a single-seat Aerobatic category. The prototype made its first flight in July 1973. Orders had been received for 690 sets of plans and at least 140 Sonerai IIs were flying by early 1979. Many components, complete kits for fuselage and wings, and materials, are available to amateur constructors. Estimated building time is 850 working hours.

The description of the Sonerai applies also to Sonerai II, except as follows:

TYPE: Two-seat high-performance sporting aircraft.

WINGS: As for Sonerai, except span increased.

FUSELAGE: As for Sonerai, except length increased.

TAIL UNIT: As for Sonerai, except tailplane has fixed incidence and reduced span.

POWER PLANT: One 1,700 cc Volkswagen modified motor car engine, developing 48·5-52·2 kW (65-70 hp), driving a two-blade wooden ground-adjustable propeller. Fuel capacity 37·8 litres (10 US gallons); oil as for Sonerai.

ACCOMMODATION: Two seats in tandem beneath transparent bubble canopy, hinged on starboard side.

ELECTRONICS: Prototype has alternator-powered 100-channel radio.

DIMENSIONS, EXTERNAL: As Sonerai, except:

Wing span	5·69 m (18 ft 8 in)
Wing area, gross	7·80 m² (84 sq ft)
Length overall	5·74 m (18 ft 10 in)
Tailplane span	1·83 m (6 ft 0 in)
Propeller diameter	1·32-1·37 m (4 ft 4 in to 4 ft 6 in)

DIMENSION, INTERNAL:

Cockpit: Max width	0·61 m (2 ft 0 in)

WEIGHTS:

Weight empty	230 kg (506 lb)
Max T-O weight	419 kg (925 lb)

PERFORMANCE (at max T-O weight):

Max level speed at S/L	approx 143 knots (266 km/h; 165 mph)
Max cruising speed at S/L	122 knots (225 km/h; 140 mph)
Econ cruising speed at S/L	113 knots (209 km/h; 130 mph)
Stalling speed	39 knots (73 km/h; 45 mph)
Max rate of climb at S/L	229 m (750 ft)/min
T-O run, ISA	274 m (900 ft)
Landing run	152 m (500 ft)
Range, with reserves	217 nm (402 km; 250 miles)

MOONEY MITE

MOONEY MITE AIRCRAFT CORPORATION

PO Box 3999, Charlottesville, Virginia 22903

Mooney Mite Aircraft Corporation was formed to market to amateur constructors plans of the Mooney Mite, a version of the Mooney M-18 first designed and built as a production aircraft by Mooney Aircraft Inc.

Mini-Hawk TH.E.01 Tiger-Hawk with current, revised canopy

Monnett Sonerai (1,850 cc Volkswagen engine) built by Mr Zig Bergins of Montreal, Canada *(Neil A. Macdougall)*

Monnett Sonerai II two-seat sporting aircraft *(Howard Levy)*

Mooney Mite single-seat light aircraft

Murphy VM-7 Competitor Unlimited class aerobatic monoplane *(Howard Levy)*

MOONEY MITE

TYPE: Single-seat sporting aircraft.

WINGS: Cantilever low-wing monoplane. Wing section NACA 63215 at root, NACA 64415 at tip. Dihedral 5° 30′ from roots. Incidence 4°. Conventional single-spar structure of wood, with plywood D-type leading-edge torsion box, and fabric covering aft of the spar. Ailerons and trailing-edge flaps of welded steel tube construction with fabric covering.

FUSELAGE: Forward section to aft of cockpit of welded steel tube with light alloy skins. Aft fuselage of wood monocoque construction with fabric covering.

TAIL UNIT: Cantilever welded steel tube structure, fabric-covered. Tailplane incidence variable by 'Safe-Trim' system that interconnects tail trim with trailing-edge flaps to establish automatically the correct settings for take-off, climb, approach and landing.

LANDING GEAR: Manually retractable tricycle type. Shock-absorption of main units by rubber-in-compression. Nosewheel steerable. Main wheels of Cleveland, Firestone or Goodyear manufacture, with tyres size 5·00-5. Hydraulic brakes.

POWER PLANT: One 48·5 kW (65 hp) Lycoming O-145-B2 flat-four aircooled engine, driving a Sensenich Type 66CB-54 two-blade fixed-pitch propeller with spinner. Fuel tank in fuselage, capacity 41·5 litres (11 US gallons). Provision for auxiliary tank, capacity 23 litres (6 US gallons). Oil capacity 3·75 litres (1 US gallon).

ACCOMMODATION: Single seat beneath aft-sliding transparent canopy. Space for 18 kg (40 lb) baggage aft of seat.

SYSTEM: Electric power supplied by wind-driven generator mounted on pylon on upper surface of aft fuselage.

DIMENSIONS, EXTERNAL:

Wing span	8·19 m (26 ft 10½ in)
Wing area	8·83 m² (95 sq ft)
Length overall	5·37 m (17 ft 7¼ in)
Height overall	1·89 m (6 ft 2½ in)
Tailplane span	2·54 m (8 ft 4 in)
Wheel track	1·55 m (5 ft 1 in)
Wheelbase	1·22 m (4 ft 0 in)
Propeller diameter	1·60 m (5 ft 3 in)

WEIGHTS:

Weight empty	229 kg (505 lb)
Max T-O weight	353 kg (780 lb)

PERFORMANCE (at max T-O weight):

Max level speed at S/L	124 knots (230 km/h; 143 mph)
Econ cruising speed, 50% power at S/L	99 knots (183 km/h; 114 mph)
Min controllable speed, power on	33 knots (61·5 km/h; 38 mph)
Landing speed, power off	39 knots (72 km/h; 45 mph)
Stalling speed, power off	37·5 knots (69·5 km/h; 43 mph)
Max rate of climb at S/L	332 m (1,090 ft)/min
Service ceiling	5,915 m (19,400 ft)
T-O run	213 m (698 ft)
T-O to 15 m (50 ft)	305 m (1,000 ft)
Landing from 15 m (50 ft)	366 m (1,200 ft)
Landing run	73 m (240 ft)
Range at econ cruising speed, standard fuel	382 nm (708 km; 440 miles)
Range with auxiliary fuel	521 nm (965 km; 600 miles)

MURPHY

R. L. MURPHY

90 Pebble Woods Drive, Doylestown, Pennsylvania 18901

Mr Dick Murphy, a First Officer with American Airlines, with 22 years of military and civil flying and engineering experience, has designed and built a single-seat Unlimited class aerobatic aircraft known as the VM-7 Competitor (N5P). He had previously constructed a Van's RV-3, which was flown competitively during 1976; the VM-7 Competitor owes much to this aircraft and to ideas and suggestions from other designers and pilots. Design objectives for the VM-7 were that it should be easy to construct, should cost under $10,000, and should have good performance. Without the engine and propeller, it cost $6,000 and took 2,000 working hours to build. Plans may be made available to amateur builders when the prototype has proved its capability in competitive aerobatics.

MURPHY VM-7 COMPETITOR

TYPE: Single-seat Unlimited class aerobatic monoplane.

WINGS: Cantilever mid-wing monoplane. Wing section NACA 23015. Constant chord. Light alloy structure, comprising a laminated main spar, passing through fuselage under pilot's knees, and twenty hydroformed ribs, covered with light alloy skin panels, bonded and pop-riveted in place. Symmetrical, balanced and sealed ailerons.

FUSELAGE: Semi-monocoque structure, with pop-riveted light alloy skin and frames.

TAIL UNIT: Conventional wire-braced light alloy structure. Fin integral with rear fuselage. Trim tab in port elevator.

LANDING GEAR: Non-retractable tailwheel type. Wittman cantilever spring steel main legs. Brakes fitted. Streamline fairings over main wheels. Steerable tailwheel.

POWER PLANT: One 134-149 kW (180-200 hp) Lycoming O-360 flat-four engine, driving a two-blade constant-speed propeller, with spinner. Engine fitted with IO-360 sump, manifold and fuel injector. Main and auxiliary fuel tanks in forward fuselage; total capacity 64·4 litres (17 US gallons). Second auxiliary tank optional.

ACCOMMODATION: Single seat, inclined at about 15°, under forward-sliding canopy.

DIMENSIONS, EXTERNAL:

Wing span	5·94 m (19 ft 6 in)
Length overall	6·02 m (19 ft 9 in)
Propeller diameter	1·93 m (6 ft 4 in)

WEIGHTS:

Weight empty, with starter and battery	361·5 kg (797 lb)
Max T-O weight	567 kg (1,250 lb)

PERFORMANCE:

Never-exceed speed	186 knots (346 km/h; 215 mph)
Max level speed at S/L	174 knots (322 km/h; 200 mph)
Max cruising speed (75% power)	152 knots (282 km/h; 175 mph)
Econ cruising speed (50% power)	130 knots (241 km/h; 150 mph)
Stalling speed, power off	43·5 knots (80·5 km/h; 50 mph)
T-O time	4s
Landing run	366 m (1,200 ft)
g limits: normal	±9
ultimate	±14

OSPREY

OSPREY AIRCRAFT

3741 El Ricon Way, Sacramento, California 95825
Telephone: (917) 483 3004

Osprey Aircraft was formed originally to market to amateur constructors plans of the Osprey I aircraft designed and built by Mr George Pereira. This was an unusual project for the homebuilder, being a flying-boat, intended for operation on and from enclosed waters rather than the open sea. The plans drawn up by Mr Pereira included drawings of a special trailer for carriage of the aircraft, which allowed the pilot to launch and recover the Osprey unassisted. Details of this aircraft can be found in the 1974-75 *Jane's*.

Mr Pereira subsequently completed the prototype of a two-seat amphibian version designated Osprey II.

PEREIRA GP3 OSPREY II

Design and construction of the Osprey II, a two-seat amphibian development of the Osprey I, began in January 1972.

Mr Pereira evolved an unusual form of hull construction for this aircraft. When the all-wood fuselage structure had been completed and controls installed, the undersurface was given a deep coating of polyurethane foam. This was then sculptured to the requisite hull form before being covered with several protective layers of glassfibre cloth bonded with resin. The resulting structure is light, but extremely strong, with good shock resisting characteristics.

First flight of the Osprey II from water was made in April 1973, the amphibian becoming airborne in less than 244 m (800 ft), with no tendency to porpoise at any speed. In later tests from land it was found that with the landing gear retracted, and at a speed of about 104 knots (193 km/h; 120 mph), there was slight buffet aft of the cabin and the noise level was unacceptably high. Modifications carried out in early 1974 included lengthening of the cabin by 0·18 m (7 in), and installation of a Lycoming O-320 engine in place of the original Franklin Sport, in a new cowling. Testing was resumed and completed satisfactorily during 1974, since when the shape of the tail fin has been changed. Sets of plans are available to amateur constructors, and the accompanying illustration shows an Osprey II built by Mr Carl McCain of Peru, Indiana. This departs from plans only in having additional cockpit upholstery.

TYPE: Two-seat lightweight amphibian.

WINGS: Cantilever mid-wing monoplane, of constant chord. Wing section NACA 23012. Dihedral 4° 30′. Incidence 5°. All-wood structure, with single box spar and auxiliary rear spar for aileron attachment. Forward of the main spar the wing is plywood-covered to form a rigid 'D' section. Aft of the spar the wing is fabric-covered. Conventional ailerons, 100% mass-balanced, will be fitted with a ground-adjustable tab if this proves desirable. No trailing-edge flaps. Wingtip stabilising floats of polyurethane foam covered with glassfibre.

HULL: All-wood structure of longerons and frames, covered with 2·5 mm (3/32 in) marine plywood. Hull undersurface contours formed from polyurethane foam, protected by several layers of glassfibre cloth bonded with resin.

TAIL UNIT: Cantilever all-wood structure, with swept vertical surfaces; tailplane mounted high on fin, which is integral with hull. Incidence of tailplane ground-adjustable. Controllable trim tab in starboard elevator. Water rudder, contained within the base of the aerodynamic rudder, is spring-loaded in the down position and retracted by cable.

LANDING GEAR: Retractable tricycle type, with single wheel on each unit. Main units retract inward into the wing roots, the wheel wells being covered by doors in the retracted position. Nosewheel retracts forward into the nosecone and is also enclosed by a door. Manual retraction system. Shock-absorption by coil springs. Cleveland main wheels and tyres size 5·00-5. Nosewheel, of industrial type with roller bearings, has a tyre of 10 in diameter. Cleveland hydraulic disc brakes.

POWER PLANT: One 112 kW (150 hp) Lycoming O-320 flat-four engine, mounted on a steel tube pylon structure which is bolted to the wing truss. Hendrickson 66 × 52 three-blade fixed-pitch wooden pusher propeller. One glassfibre fuel tank mounted beneath the main spar at the wing centre-section, usable capacity 98·4 litres (26 US gallons). Refuelling point on starboard side of hull, just aft of cabin.

ACCOMMODATION: Two seats side by side beneath transparent canopy, which is hinged at rear and swings upward. Dual controls standard; but toe-operated wheel brakes on starboard side only. Baggage compartment aft of seats, capacity 41 kg (90 lb).

SYSTEMS: Hydraulic system for brakes only. Electrical system powered by engine-driven generator.

DIMENSIONS, EXTERNAL:

Wing span	7·92 m (26 ft 0 in)
Wing chord, constant	1·52 m (5 ft 0 in)
Wing area, gross	12·08 m² (130 sq ft)
Wing aspect ratio	5·2
Length overall	6·25 m (20 ft 6 in)
Height overall (wheels down)	1·83 m (6 ft 0 in)
Tailplane span	2·44 m (8 ft 0 in)
Wheel track	2·59 m (8 ft 6 in)
Wheelbase	2·13 m (7 ft 0 in)
Propeller diameter	1·68 m (5 ft 6 in)

WEIGHTS:

Weight empty	440 kg (970 lb)
Max T-O weight	707 kg (1,560 lb)

PERFORMANCE (at max T-O weight unless specified otherwise):

Never-exceed speed	130 knots (241 km/h; 150 mph)
Max cruising speed at 75% power	113 knots (209 km/h; 130 mph)
Econ cruising speed at 55% power	94 knots (175 km/h; 109 mph)
Stalling speed	53 knots (97 km/h; 60 mph)
Max rate of climb at S/L, with pilot only	365 m (1,200 ft)/min
Rate of climb at S/L	305 m (1,000 ft)/min
T-O run, land	122 m (400 ft)
T-O run, water	159 m (520 ft)

OWL

GEORGE A. OWL Jr

17700 S. Western Avenue, Apartment 195, Gardena, California 90248
Telephone: (213) 323 3385

Mr George Owl, a member of the preliminary design staff of Rockwell International, is also the designer of two Formula One racing aircraft known as the Owl Racers OR-70 and OR-71. The former was designed to order for Bernadine and Jim Stevenson, both racing pilots, and was built by them (see 1977-78 *Jane's*). The OR-71 was produced in co-operation with Mr Vince DeLuca, proprietor of Vin-Del Aircraft, who has built a prototype and is making plans available to amateur constructors.

Prototypes of a version of the OR-71 with a new wing have been under construction since 1975. This wing, of all-wood construction and utilising a special laminar flow aerofoil section, is calculated to raise the maximum speed of the OR-71 by 5 knots (10 km/h; 6 mph). The designation of these aircraft will be OR-71B.

Vin-Del Aircraft

ADDRESS:
29718 Knollview Drive, Miraleste, California 90732

Mr Vince DeLuca, proprietor of Vin-Del Aircraft, built the prototype of a Formula One racer of Mr Owl's design which he designated OR-71 *Lil Quickie*. Construction began on 2 December 1971 and the first flight was made on 6 June 1972. Plans are available to amateur constructors.

VIN-DEL/OWL OR-71 LIL QUICKIE

Limit load factor of the OR-71 is ±7·33*g*, ultimate load factor ±11·0*g*.

TYPE: Single-seat Formula One racing aircraft.

WINGS: Cantilever mid-wing monoplane. Owl laminar flow aerofoil section, tapered in chord. Dihedral 0° 51′. Incidence 0°. Non-linear thickness distribution. Thickness/chord ratio is 13·7% at root, 10% on outer 60% of wing. All-wood structure. Laminated spruce one-piece main spar, plywood ribs with spruce caps, and plywood skins. Ailerons of spruce and plywood construction, mass-balanced at tip. No flaps. No trim tabs. Plans show optional high-lift leading-edge of larger radius and increased camber.

FUSELAGE: Welded steel tube structure, with light alloy fairings and Dacron covering. Glassfibre nose cowl incorporates an annular cooling inlet. Engine cowl has controllable air exit flap.

TAIL UNIT: Cantilever wooden structure, with spruce spars and mahogany plywood ribs and skins. Fixed-incidence tailplane. No trim tabs.

LANDING GEAR: Non-retractable tailwheel type. Prototype has cantilever light alloy main legs. Spring steel legs optional. Main wheels and tyres size 5·00-5, pressure 2·41 bars (35 lb/sq in). Cleveland hydraulic disc brakes. Glassfibre fairings on main wheels. Tailwheel is a ball-bearing castor.

POWER PLANT: One 74·5 kW (100 hp) Continental O-200 flat-four engine, driving an Anderson, McCauley or Sensenich two-blade fixed-pitch propeller. Fuel tank in fuselage, immediately aft of firewall, capacity 34 litres (9 US gallons). Auxiliary integral fuel tank in each wing leading-edge, with combined capacity of 22·7 litres (6 US gallons). Total fuel capacity 56·7 litres (15 US gallons). Refuelling point on upper surface of fuselage, forward of windscreen. Oil capacity 5·7 litres (1·5 US gallons).

ACCOMMODATION: Single seat beneath small transparent canopy, hinged on starboard side, opening upwards and to starboard.

DIMENSIONS, EXTERNAL:

Wing span	6·10 m (20 ft 0 in)
Wing chord at root	1·27 m (4 ft 2 in)
Wing chord at tip	0·76 m (2 ft 6 in)
Wing area, gross	6·13 m² (66 sq ft)
Wing aspect ratio	6
Length overall	4·98 m (16 ft 4 in)
Height overall	1·40 m (4 ft 7 in)
Wheel track	1·30 m (4 ft 3 in)
Wheelbase	3·63 m (11 ft 11 in)
Propeller diameter (max)	1·52 m (5 ft 0 in)

WEIGHTS:

Weight empty	251 kg (553 lb)
Max T-O weight	386 kg (850 lb)

PERFORMANCE (at max T-O weight):

Never-exceed speed	260 knots (482 km/h; 300 mph) IAS
Max level speed	more than 221 knots (410 km/h; 255 mph)
Stalling speed	60 knots (111 km/h; 69 mph)

PARKER

C. Y. PARKER

PO Box 625, Coolidge, Arizona 85228
Telephone: (602) 723 5660

PARKER TEENIE TWO

Mr Cal Parker completed and flew in 1969 the prototype of an improved version of the small lightweight all-metal homebuilt aircraft which he had designated Jeanie's Teenie. With completion of the new prototype, the original model became known as Teenie One. Plans for the Jeanie's Teenie were available for three years prior to Teenie Two plans being marketed.

Mr Parker's original aim was to build an aircraft specifically to utilise the Volkswagen motor car engine and, at the same time, to evolve an all-metal design that would present few constructional problems even to homebuilders with virtually no metal-working experience. This has been achieved, and no special tools or jigs are needed beyond a tool to close and form the cadmium-plated steel pop rivets that are used for practically all assembly. One gauge of aluminium sheet and one size of light alloy angle section is used for almost all of the structure, except for chromoly steel tube and sheet which are used for construction of the landing gear and control actuation tubes respectively. For simplicity and economy, push/pull tubes are used for all flying controls.

Teenie One conformed to these ideas, but the Teenie Two was considerably refined to produce a much cleaner aeroplane. The prototype cost approximately $650 to build, over a period of six months. Its structure is stressed for full aerobatics, but the fuel and oil systems are not suitable for inverted flight.

Teenie Two has been tested with various propellers, but a computer-designed propeller is available in the parts kit which gives optimum performance for take-off, climb and cruise.

Plans, complete kits of parts, and details of modifications for the Volkswagen engine are available to amateur constructors; approximately 3,500 sets of plans and 500 kits had been sold by early 1979. Some Teenie Twos built from plans had completed well over 750 flying hours by that time.

A two-seat version of the Teenie, named **Double Teenie,** is under construction and was expected to fly in 1979.

The following details apply to the standard Teenie Two:

TYPE: Single-seat light aircraft.

WINGS: Cantilever low-wing monoplane. Wing section NACA 4415. All-metal two-spar structure, with detachable outer wing panels. Light alloy ribs and skin. Plain ailerons of metal construction. No flaps.

FUSELAGE: All-metal semi-monocoque structure with longerons of light alloy angle, three built-up bulkheads and light alloy skin.

TAIL UNIT: Cantilever all-metal structure with swept vertical surfaces. Small dorsal fin eliminates the need for a fourth bulkhead by carrying loads from fin leading-edge to centre bulkhead. Conventional rudder and elevators of metal construction.

LANDING GEAR: Non-retractable tricycle type. Shock-absorption provided by springs in compression and rubber hose. All three wheels same size, with tyres size 10·5 × 4·00-4, pressure 1·72 bars (25 lb/sq in). Mechanically-actuated wheel brakes.

POWER PLANT: One 31·5 kW (42 hp) 1,600 cc or 30 kW (40 hp) 1,500 cc Volkswagen modified motor car engine (conversion parts sold by Parker), driving a two-blade fixed-pitch wooden propeller. Single fuselage fuel tank, immediately aft of firewall, capacity 34 litres (9 US gallons). Refuelling point on top of fuselage, forward of windscreen. Oil capacity 2·5 litres (0·66 US gallons).

ACCOMMODATION: Single seat in open cockpit. Drawings of optional canopy available; this increases max level speed to 122 knots (225 km/h; 140 mph).

Osprey II built from plans, by Mr Carl McCain, with Mr Pereira's prototype in background *(Howard Levy)*

Vin-Del/Owl OR-71 *Lil Quickie* Formula One racing aircraft

Knight Twister (Lycoming O-235-C1 engine) built by Robert Ubel *(Howard Levy)*

Parker Teenie Two powered by a modified Volkswagen engine

SYSTEM: Prototype now fitted with alternator, starter and battery to power lights and radio, giving an increase in empty weight of 18 kg (40 lb).

DIMENSIONS, EXTERNAL:
- Wing span 5·49 m (18 ft 0 in)
- Wing chord, constant 1·02 m (3 ft 4 in)
- Width, wings detached 1·83 m (6 ft 0 in)
- Length overall 3·91 m (12 ft 10 in)

WEIGHTS:
- Weight empty 140 kg (310 lb)
- Max T-O weight 267 kg (590 lb)

PERFORMANCE (at max T-O weight, 1,600 cc engine):
- Max level speed 104 knots (193 km/h; 120 mph)
- Max cruising speed (75% power) 95·5 knots (177 km/h; 110 mph)
- Landing speed 43·5 knots (80·5 km/h; 50 mph)
- Max rate of climb at S/L (standard propeller) 244 m (800 ft)/min
- Max rate of climb at S/L (52 × 37 propeller) 305 m (1,000 ft)/min
- Service ceiling 4,575 m (15,000 ft)
- Range 347 nm (643 km; 400 miles)

PAYNE

VERNON W. PAYNE

Route No. 4, PO Box 319M, Escondido, California 92025
Telephone: (714) 746 4465

Mr Vernon Payne is the designer of the Knight Twister, a light sporting biplane of which plans and kits are available for amateur construction. It exists in several versions.

KNIGHT TWISTER KT-85

The original prototype of the Knight Twister KT-85 single-seat sporting biplane flew in 1933. Considerable refinement of the design since that time has improved both the appearance and the performance of later models, which have been built in substantial numbers by amateur constructors in the United States and elsewhere.

Standard power plant is a Continental flat-four engine of 63·5-67 kW (85-90 hp), but alternative engines have been fitted by some constructors. Most powerful Knight Twister flown to date is one owned by Mr Charles Williams of Mount Prospect, Illinois, which has a 134 kW (180 hp) Lycoming O-360 engine installed.

The following details refer to the standard Knight Twister built from Mr Payne's plans:

TYPE: Single-seat light biplane.

WINGS: Braced biplane type. Wing section NACA M-6. No dihedral. Incidence 1° 30'. All-wood two-spar structure, plywood-covered and with fabric covering overall. Ailerons on lower wings only, of fabric-covered wood construction. No flaps.

FUSELAGE: Steel tube truss structure with wood stringers and fabric covering.

TAIL UNIT: Cantilever type. Vertical surfaces have fabric-covered steel tube structure. Horizontal surfaces have plywood-covered wood structure, with fabric covering overall.

LANDING GEAR: Non-retractable tailwheel type. Cantilever main units. Rubber cord or hydraulic shock-absorption. Wheels size 6·00-6 with Goodyear tyres, pressure 0·345-0·69 bars (5-10 lb/sq in). Goodyear disc brakes.

POWER PLANT: One 67 kW (90 hp) Continental C90 flat-four engine, driving a two-blade wood or metal fixed-pitch propeller. Alternatively any other Continental or Lycoming flat-four engine of 63·5-108 kW (85-145 hp). Fuel tank aft of engine firewall, capacity 68 litres (18 US gallons). Oil capacity 3·7-5·7 litres (1-1·5 US gallons).

ACCOMMODATION: Single seat, normally in open cockpit. Baggage compartment capacity 9 kg (20 lb). Radio optional.

DIMENSIONS, EXTERNAL:
- Wing span: upper 4·57 m (15 ft 0 in)
- lower 3·96 m (13 ft 0 in)
- Wing chord (mean, both) 0·65 m (2 ft 1·6 in)
- Wing area, gross 5·57 m² (60 sq ft)
- Wing aspect ratio: upper 6·87
- lower 6·13
- Length overall 4·27 m (14 ft 0 in)
- Height overall 1·60 m (5 ft 3 in)
- Tailplane span 2·13 m (7 ft 0 in)
- Wheel track 1·52 m (5 ft 0 in)
- Wheelbase 5·23 m (17 ft 2 in)

DIMENSION, INTERNAL:
- Cockpit: Width 0·53 m (1 ft 9 in)

WEIGHTS (67 kW; 90 hp engine):
- Weight empty 243 kg (535 lb)
- Max T-O weight 435 kg (960 lb)

PERFORMANCE (67 kW; 90 hp engine, at max T-O weight):
- Max level speed at S/L 139 knots (257 km/h; 160 mph)
- Max cruising speed 122 knots (225 km/h; 140 mph)
- Econ cruising speed 109 knots (201 km/h; 125 mph)
- Stalling speed 53 knots (97 km/h; 60 mph)
- Max rate of climb at S/L 275 m (900 ft)/min
- T-O run 125 m (410 ft)
- T-O to 15 m (50 ft) 305 m (1,000 ft)
- Landing from 15 m (50 ft) 366 m (1,200 ft)
- Landing run 205 m (670 ft)
- Range with max fuel 338 nm (625 km; 390 miles)

SUNDAY KNIGHT TWISTER SKT-125

This developed version of the Knight Twister has a 93 kW (125 hp) Lycoming engine. Increased wing area makes it easier to fly and its name is meant to imply that it is for the 'Sunday flyer'.

A fully aerobatic Sunday Knight Twister, with a 134 kW (180 hp) engine, has been built by Mr J. F. Carter of Drewry, Alabama.

DIMENSIONS, EXTERNAL:
- Wing span 5·94 m (19 ft 6 in)
- Wing area, gross 7·71 m² (83 sq ft)
- Length overall 4·72 m (15 ft 6 in)
- Height overall 1·68 m (5 ft 6 in)

WEIGHTS:
- Weight empty 318 kg (700 lb)
- Max T-O weight 461 kg (1,016 lb)

PERFORMANCE (at max T-O weight):
- Max level speed at S/L 146 knots (270 km/h; 168 mph)
- Max cruising speed 144 knots (267 km/h; 166 mph)
- Econ cruising speed 126 knots (233 km/h; 145 mph)
- Stalling speed 43·5 knots (80·5 km/h; 50 mph)
- Max rate of climb at S/L 366 m (1,200 ft)/min
- T-O run 113 m (370 ft)
- T-O to 15 m (50 ft) 232 m (760 ft)
- Landing run 265 m (870 ft)
- Range at max cruising speed with max fuel 307 nm (570 km; 354 miles)

KNIGHT TWISTER JUNIOR KT-75

The Knight Twister Junior has the same fuselage, tail unit and landing gear as the KT-85, but its tapered wings have a larger area. The prototype flew in 1947. Details are as for the KT-85, except for the following:

WINGS: Incidence 2°.

POWER PLANT: One Continental or Lycoming flat-four engine of 56-93 kW (75-125 hp). Fuel capacity with 56 kW (75 hp) engine 45 litres (12 US gallons).

DIMENSIONS, EXTERNAL:
- Wing span: upper 5·33 m (17 ft 6 in)
- lower 4·11 m (13 ft 6 in)
- Wing area, gross 6·76 m² (72·8 sq ft)
- Wing aspect ratio: upper 7·78
- lower 7·10

WEIGHTS (56 kW; 75 hp engine):
- Weight empty 227 kg (500 lb)
- Max T-O weight 404 kg (890 lb)

PERFORMANCE (56 kW; 75 hp engine, at max T-O weight):
- Max level speed at S/L 117 knots (217 km/h; 135 mph)
- Max cruising speed 109 knots (201 km/h; 125 mph)
- Econ cruising speed 97 knots (180 km/h; 112 mph)
- Stalling speed 42 knots (77·5 km/h; 48 mph)
- Max rate of climb at S/L 275 m (900 ft)/min
- T-O run 114 m (375 ft)
- T-O to 15 m (50 ft) 277 m (910 ft)
- Landing from 15 m (50 ft) 311 m (1,020 ft)
- Landing run 190 m (625 ft)
- Range with max fuel 247 nm (460 km; 285 miles)

PAZMANY

PAZMANY AIRCRAFT CORPORATION

Box 80051, San Diego, California 92138
Telephone: (714) 276 0424

This company was formed by Mr Ladislao Pazmany, designer of a two-seat light aircraft known as the PL-1 Laminar. A prototype, constructed by Mr John Green and Mr Keith Fowler, was flown for the first time on 23 March 1962, the test pilots being Cdr Paul Hayek, USN, and Lieut Richard Gordon, who is best known as one of the Gemini/Apollo astronauts.

Some 5,000 design hours and 4,000 hours of construction went into the prototype PL-1, which has logged more than 1,500 flying hours.

Pazmany Aircraft Corporation is no longer marketing plans of the PL-1: instead, plans and instructions for building the improved PL-2 and a lightweight, low-cost single-seat monoplane designated PL-4A are available to amateur constructors and many aircraft of these types are being built. Mr Pazmany also contributed to the design of the Ryson Aviation Cloudster two-seat motor-glider, of which details can be found in the 'Sailplanes' section of this edition.

PAZMANY PL-1 LAMINAR

A total of about 375 sets of plans and instructions for building the PL-1 have been sold, and PL-1s are being built and flown in the USA, Canada, Australia, Norway and other countries.

In early 1968 the Aeronautical Research Laboratory of the Chinese Nationalist Air Force, at Taichung, Taiwan, acquired a set of PL-1 drawings. Under the supervision of General K. F. Ku and Colonel C. Y. Lee, personnel of the ARL built a PL-1 in a record time of 100 days. It was flown for the first time on 26 October 1968 and on 30 October was presented to Generalissimo Chiang Kai-Shek. Extensive flight testing resulted in the decision to utilise the PL-1 as a basic trainer for CAF cadets, and 58 additional aircraft, designated PL-1B, were constructed between 1970 and 1974, powered by the 112 kW (150 hp) Lycoming O-320 engine.

The description applies to the prototype PL-1, which was stressed to 9*g* (ultimate) for aerobatics and to permit the fitting of more powerful engines.

Type: Two-seat light aircraft.

Wings: Cantilever low-wing monoplane. Wing section NACA 63_2615. Dihedral 3°. Incidence −1° 20′. All-metal single-spar structure in one piece, with leading-edge torsion box. Plain piano-hinged ailerons and flaps of all-metal construction. No trim tabs.

Fuselage: Conventional all-metal semi-monocoque structure, with flat or single-curvature skins.

Tail Unit: Cantilever all-metal structure. One-piece horizontal surface, with anti-servo tab which serves also as a trim tab.

Landing Gear: Non-retractable tricycle type, with all three oleo-pneumatic shock-absorbers interchangeable. Goodyear wheels and tyres, size 5·00-5. Tyre pressure 2·14 bars (31 lb/sq in). Goodyear brakes. Steerable nosewheel.

Power Plant: One 71 kW (95 hp) Continental C90-12F flat-four engine, driving a McCauley Model IA100/MCM 6663 two-blade metal fixed-pitch propeller. Fuel in two glassfibre wingtip tanks, each of 47 litres (12·5 US gallons) capacity. Total fuel capacity 94 litres (25 US gallons). Oil capacity 4·5 litres (5 US quarts).

Accommodation: Two seats side by side under rearward-sliding transparent canopy. Dual controls. Space for 18 kg (40 lb) baggage aft of seats. Heater and airscoops for ventilation. VHF radio.

Dimensions, external:

Wing span	8·53 m (28 ft 0 in)
Wing chord, constant	1·27 m (4 ft 2 in)
Wing area, gross	10·78 m² (116 sq ft)
Wing aspect ratio	6·7
Length overall	5·77 m (18 ft 11 in)
Height overall	2·64 m (8 ft 8 in)
Tailplane span	2·44 m (8 ft 0 in)
Wheel track	2·50 m (8 ft 2½ in)
Wheelbase	1·30 m (4 ft 3 in)

Dimensions, internal:

Cabin: Length	1·27 m (4 ft 2 in)
Width	1·02 m (3 ft 4 in)
Height	1·02 m (3 ft 4 in)

Weights:

Weight empty, equipped	363 kg (800 lb)
Max T-O weight	602 kg (1,326 lb)

Performance (at max T-O weight):

Never-exceed speed	178 knots (330 km/h; 205 mph)
Max level speed at S/L	104 knots (193 km/h; 120 mph)
Max cruising speed at S/L	100 knots (185 km/h; 115 mph)
Econ cruising speed at S/L	91 knots (169 km/h; 105 mph)
Stalling speed, flaps down	44 knots (82 km/h; 51 mph)
Max rate of climb at S/L	305 m (1,000 ft)/min
Service ceiling	5,500 m (18,000 ft)
T-O run	168 m (550 ft)
T-O to 15 m (50 ft)	239 m (784 ft)
Landing from 15 m (50 ft)	335 m (1,100 ft)
Landing run	54 m (175 ft)
Range with max fuel	521 nm (965 km; 600 miles)

PAZMANY PL-1B

This is the version of the PL-1 that was built in Taiwan. It differs from the basic PL-1 mainly in having a 112 kW (150 hp) Lycoming O-320 engine.

PAZMANY PL-2

Shortly after flight trials of the PL-1 began, Mr Pazmany initiated a complete redesign of the aircraft. The developed design, known as the PL-2, is almost identical with the PL-1 in external configuration. Cockpit width is increased by 5 cm (2 in) and wing dihedral is increased from 3° to 5°. The internal structure is extensively changed, to simplify construction and reduce weight. Suitable Lycoming power plants are the 80·5 kW (108 hp) O-235-C1, 93 kW (125 hp) O-290-G (ground power unit), 101 kW (135 hp) O-290-D2B or 112 kW (150 hp) O-320-A.

Static tests of every major assembly up to ultimate loads had been made by early 1967. The first PL-2 to be completed was built by Mr H. Pio of Ramona, California, and this aircraft made its first flight on 4 April 1969, piloted by Mr Pio. It has an O-290-G engine. A total of 350 sets of plans had been sold by early 1979. Aircraft built and flown include several examples for evaluation and use by foreign military training centres (see 1977-78 *Jane's*).

Dimensions, external:

As for PL-1, except:

Length overall	5·90 m (19 ft 3½ in)
Height overall	2·44 m (8 ft 0 in)
Wheel track	2·60 m (8 ft 5½ in)

Weights (A with 80·5 kW; 108 hp engine, B with 93 kW; 125 hp, C with 101 kW; 135 hp, D with 112 kW; 150 hp):

Weight empty:	
A	396 kg (875 lb)
B, C	408 kg (900 lb)
D	409 kg (902 lb)
Max T-O weight:	
A	642 kg (1,416 lb)
B, C	655 kg (1,445 lb)
D	656 kg (1,447 lb)

Performance (at max T-O weight):

Max level speed at S/L:	
A	120 knots (222 km/h; 138 mph)
B	125 knots (232 km/h; 144 mph)
C	128 knots (238 km/h; 148 mph)
D	133 knots (246 km/h; 153 mph)
Econ cruising speed:	
A	103 knots (192 km/h; 119 mph)
B	111 knots (206 km/h; 128 mph)
C	113 knots (209 km/h; 130 mph)
D	118 knots (219 km/h; 136 mph)
Stalling speed (flaps down):	
A	45·5 knots (84 km/h; 52 mph)
B, C, D	47 knots (87 km/h; 54 mph)
Max rate of climb at S/L:	
A	390 m (1,280 ft)/min
B	457 m (1,500 ft)/min
C	488 m (1,600 ft)/min
D	518 m (1,700 ft)/min
Range at econ cruising speed:	
A	427 nm (790 km; 492 miles)
B	422 nm (780 km; 486 miles)
C	428 nm (792 km; 493 miles)
D	330 nm (610 km; 381 miles)

PAZMANY PL-4A

The prototype of a lightweight single-seat low-wing monoplane designated PL-4A flew for the first time on 12 July 1972. It was designed specifically for easy low-cost construction by amateur builders, to provide a safe aircraft that would be economical in operation. The prototype had completed 335 hours of flight by January 1978. Sets of plans, kits of prefabricated components, glassfibre wing-tips and fuel tank and transparent cockpit canopy are available to amateur constructors.

By the beginning of 1979 more than 600 sets of plans had been sold, and the PL-4A had received approval in Australia for construction by amateurs.

Two aircraft were built to evaluate three different power plant installations, comprising a Volkswagen engine with 2¼ : 1 Vee-belt reduction; a Limbach SL 1700 E Volkswagen with direct drive to the propeller; and a Continental A65 aircooled engine.

Type: Single-seat lightweight sporting aircraft.

Wings: Cantilever low-wing monoplane. Wing section NACA 63_3418. Dihedral 5°. Incidence 3°. No sweep-back. All-metal structure, with main spar, 'Z' section rear beam, sheet metal ribs and skins. Wings fold along-side fuselage for towing or storage. Plain piano-hinged ailerons of all-metal construction. Glassfibre wingtips, which are cambered on many aircraft now flying. No flaps. No trim tabs.

Fuselage: All-metal structure, with bulkheads built up from bent sheet metal channels and standard extruded angles for longerons, and with sheet metal skins.

Tail Unit: All-metal cantilever T-tail. All-moving tail-plane with large anti-servo tab which serves also as a trim tab.

Landing Gear: Non-retractable tailwheel type. Spring steel cantilever main legs. Single go-kart type wheel on each main unit, with 4·10 × 3·50-6 four-ply tyre, pressure 4·48 bars (65 lb/sq in). Steerable and castoring tailwheel with solid tyre size 5 × 1·5-1·5. Go-kart type hydraulic disc brakes by Hurst-Airheart.

Power Plant: One 1,600 cc modified Volkswagen motor car engine with Becar V-belt reduction of 2¼ : 1, developing approximately 37·5 kW (50 hp) and driving a two-blade fixed-pitch wooden propeller of Pazmany design, manufactured by Ted Hendricksen. Glassfibre fuel tank immediately aft of firewall, usable capacity 45 litres (12 US gallons). Refuelling point on upper fuselage forward of windscreen. Oil capacity 2·8 litres (0·75 US gallons).

Accommodation: Single seat under transparent Plexiglas canopy, hinged on starboard side. Compartment aft of seat for 9 kg (20 lb) baggage. Cabin heated and ventilated.

Systems: Hydraulic system for brakes only. Electrical system powered by 12V 25Ah battery situated in baggage compartment.

Dimensions, external:

Wing span	8·13 m (26 ft 8 in)
Wing chord, constant	1·02 m (3 ft 4 in)
Wing area, gross	8·27 m² (89·0 sq ft)
Wing aspect ratio	8·0
Length overall	5·04 m (16 ft 6½ in)
Width, wings folded	2·44 m (8 ft 0 in)
Height overall	1·73 m (5 ft 8 in)
Tailplane span	2·29 m (7 ft 6 in)
Wheel track	2·06 m (6 ft 9 in)
Wheelbase	3·56 m (11 ft 8 in)
Propeller diameter	1·73 m (5 ft 8 in)
Propeller ground clearance	0·25 m (10 in)

Weights:

Weight empty	262 kg (578 lb)
Max T-O and landing weight	385 kg (850 lb)

Performance (at max T-O weight):

Never-exceed speed	161 knots (299 km/h; 186 mph)
Max level speed at S/L	109 knots (201 km/h; 125 mph)
Max cruising speed at S/L	85 knots (158 km/h; 98 mph)
Econ cruising speed at S/L	78 knots (145 km/h; 90 mph)
Stalling speed, power on	40 knots (74 km/h; 46 mph)
Stalling speed, power off	42 knots (77·5 km/h; 48 mph)
Max rate of climb at S/L	198 m (650 ft)/min
Service ceiling	3,960 m (13,000 ft)
Min ground turning radius	3·05 m (10 ft 0 in)
T-O run	148 m (486 ft)
Landing run	133 m (436 ft)
Range with max fuel, no allowances	295 nm (545 km; 340 miles)

PDQ

PDQ AIRCRAFT PRODUCTS

28975 Alpine Lane, Elkhart, Indiana 46514
Telephone: (219) 264 2906

Mr Wayne Ison formed this company to market plans of the PDQ-2 lightweight sporting aircraft which he had designed and built. The PDQ-2 is intended to provide a cheap, robust, easily and quickly built aircraft which is easy for an average pilot to fly.

Design of the prototype had begun in September 1972, and construction was started on 5 January 1973. Excluding the 27 kW (36 hp) Rockwell (Venture) JLO-LB-600-2 engine that was originally fitted, the cost of construction was only $350, and the first flight was made on 30 May 1973.

During 1975 it became clear that an alternative power plant was needed, owing to the increasing scarcity of the JLO engine. One amateur constructor has fitted a BMW motorcycle engine; but Mr Ison decided to test the prototype PDQ-2 with a converted Volkswagen motor car engine, a type of power plant which is readily available and inexpensive. The increased engine weight required a number of structural modifications, notably to the engine mounting, wing spars and landing gear; but flight testing proved satisfactory, and details of the new engine installation have been sent to over 2,000 purchasers of sets of plans, in 35 countries. About 50 to 60 PDQ-2s were flying by early 1979.

PDQ AIRCRAFT PRODUCTS PDQ-2

The version of this aircraft described below is the **PDQ-2 Model C** (unless otherwise stated), which has wings and tail constructed of wood and polyurethane foam. The

Pazmany PL-1 built by Mr Dieter Bochmann *(Neil A. Macdougall)*

Pazmany PL-2 built by Mr Kenneth Arnold *(Howard Levy)*

Pazmany PL-4A with cambered wingtips built by Mr John Pollock of Red Deer, Alberta, Canada

PDQ-2 Model E all-metal lightweight sporting aircraft

Mr Pietenpol's current B4 Aircamper with Corvair engine

Model D differs from the C only in having wings and tail of wood, with fabric covering; while the **Model E** (illustrated) has all-metal wings and tail, constructed from aluminium sheet. At least two aircraft have been fitted with wings of NASA GAW-1 section.

TYPE: Lightweight sporting aircraft.

WINGS: Wire-braced monoplane. Wing section NACA 63_2A615. Dihedral 5°. Incidence 3°. Composite structure with spruce spars, polyurethane foam ribs, sheet foam skins, covered with Sharkskin fabric. Full-span plain ailerons. No flaps or trim tabs. Wings quickly removable for towing and storage.

FUSELAGE: Basic structure consists of 0·05 m (2 in) square tubes of 6061-T6 light alloy. A lower forward tube carries the landing gear; attached to it is a vertical kingpost, to which the wing is attached and wire-braced. An aft horizontal tube attached to the kingpost carries the T-tail.

TAIL UNIT: Strut-braced T-tail, with swept vertical surfaces. Fixed-incidence tailplane. No trim tabs. Composite structure of polyurethane foam, spruce strips, plywood and Sharkskin fabric covering.

LANDING GEAR: Non-retractable tricycle type. Shock-absorption by spring steel leaf mounting struts. Go-kart type main wheels, diameter 0·28 m (11 in); steerable nosewheel, diameter 0·15 m (6 in). Go-kart type brakes.

POWER PLANT: Prototype flew originally with Rockwell (Venture) JLO-LB-600-2 engine, mounted on top of the kingpost and driving a two-blade fixed-pitch wooden pusher propeller. This engine remains suitable, but prototype now has a 1,385 cc converted Volkswagen motor car engine, developing 30 kW (40 hp), and this is recommended for amateur-built PDQ-2s. Plastics fuel tank mounted alongside pilot's seat on port side, capacity 22·7 litres (6 US gallons). Refuelling point on tank upper surface.

ACCOMMODATION: Single open seat mounted immediately forward of kingpost.

DIMENSIONS, EXTERNAL:

Wing span	7·44 m (24 ft 5 in)
Wing chord, constant	1·07 m (3 ft 6 in)
Wing area, gross	7·90 m² (85 sq ft)
Length overall	4·42 m (14 ft 6 in)
Height overall	1·27 m (4 ft 2 in)
Tailplane span	1·83 m (6 ft 0 in)
Wheel track	1·27 m (4 ft 2 in)

WEIGHTS (Volkswagen engine):

Weight empty: Model C	164 kg (360 lb)
Model D	145 kg (320 lb)
Normal T-O weight:	
Model C	257 kg (566 lb)
Model D	239 kg (526 lb)
Max T-O weight:	
Model C	281 kg (620 lb)
Model D	263 kg (580 lb)

PERFORMANCE (Model C and D, at max T-O weight, Volkswagen engine):

Never-exceed speed	78 knots (145 km/h; 90 mph)
Max level speed at S/L	69 knots (129 km/h; 80 mph)
Max cruising speed at S/L	61 knots (113 km/h; 70 mph)
Stalling speed:	
Model C	37·5 knots (69·5 km/h; 43 mph)
Model D	35 knots (65 km/h; 40 mph)
Max rate of climb at S/L	152 m (500 ft)/min
Service ceiling	3,050 m (10,000 ft)
T-O run	107 m (350 ft)
Landing run	122 m (400 ft)
Range with max fuel	173 nm (321 km; 200 miles)

PIETENPOL
DON PIETENPOL

215, 21st Street SE, Rochester, Minnesota 55901

The prototype of Mr Bernard H. Pietenpol's Aircamper two-seat parasol monoplane flew for the first time in 1929, powered by a 30 kW (40 hp) Ford Model A engine. Plans were published in the magazine *Modern Mechanics and Inventions* in the following year and large numbers of Aircampers, with a wide variety of power plants, were built by amateurs, either from the magazine plans or from kits of parts marketed by Mr Pietenpol.

The original Aircamper was of all-wood construction, with fabric covering, but some examples completed recently or currently being built have a steel tube fuselage and tail unit.

The accompanying illustration shows Mr Pietenpol's Aircamper, which he modified by extending the fuselage by 9 in (23 cm), fitting modified Piper J-3 Cub landing gear, strengthening the wings, and installing two 15 litre (4 US gallon) fuselage fuel tanks and a 38 litre (10 US gallon) fuel tank in the wing centre-section. This aircraft, which now has a converted Chevrolet Corvair motor car engine, rated at 45 kW (60 hp), has completed over 600 flying hours.

Another version of the Aircamper, embodying many Piper Cub components, is described under the Grega entry in this section.

PIETENPOL B4 AIRCAMPER

TYPE: Single-seat light aircraft. (Basic design makes provision for second seat.)

WINGS: Parasol monoplane, with two parallel bracing struts each side and centre-section cabane structure. Pietenpol special wing section. Thickness/chord ratio 16·6%. No dihedral. Incidence 2°. Fabric-covered two-spar wood structure. Tips may be rounded or square. Plain wooden ailerons with fabric covering. No flaps.

FUSELAGE: Wooden de Havilland truss structure of Sitka spruce, covered with birch plywood to back of rear cockpit and fabric on rear fuselage.

TAIL UNIT: Wire-braced wood and steel tube structure, covered with fabric.

LANDING GEAR: Divided main gear, with spring shock-absorption, modified from Piper J-3 Cub gear. Mainwheel tyres size 8·00-4, pressure 1·03 bars (15 lb/sq in). Piper hydraulic brakes. Steerable tailwheel.

POWER PLANT (Mr Pietenpol's aircraft): One 45 kW (60 hp) Chevrolet Corvair converted motor car engine, driving a two-blade wooden propeller. A variety of other engines have been fitted in amateur-built Aircampers. One fuel tank in wing, capacity 38 litres (10 US gallons); two tanks in fuselage, total capacity 30 litres (8 US gallons). Oil capacity 4·75 litres (1·25 US gallons).

ACCOMMODATION: Single seat in open cockpit in Mr Pietenpol's Aircamper *N7533U*. Second seat is optional in basic design.

DIMENSIONS, EXTERNAL:

Wing span	8·84 m (29 ft 0 in)
Wing chord, constant	1·52 m (5 ft 0 in)
Wing area, gross	13·47 m² (145 sq ft)
Wing aspect ratio	6
Propeller diameter	1·52 m (5 ft 0 in)

WEIGHT:

Weight empty	282 kg (622 lb)

PERFORMANCE:

Max level and never-exceed speed	95·5 knots (177 km/h; 110 mph)
Max cruising speed	74 knots (137 km/h; 85 mph)
Econ cruising speed	69 knots (129 km/h; 80 mph)
Stalling speed	33 knots (61·5 km/h; 38 mph)
Max rate of climb at S/L	152 m (500 ft)/min
T-O and landing run	76 m (250 ft)
Range, with 30 min reserves	330 nm (611 km; 380 miles)

PITTS

PITTS AEROBATICS

PO Box 547, Afton, Wyoming 83110
Telephone: (307) 886 3151
GENERAL MANAGER: E. H. Andersen Jr

In addition to marketing factory-built examples of the single-seat and two-seat Pitts Special biplanes, Pitts Aerobatics, which bought all rights to this range of aircraft from Mr Curtis Pitts, supplies plans of the S-1D single-seater to amateur constructors. It also began, in 1977, to supply kits for both single-seat and two-seat versions as the S-1E and S-2E respectively. No plans are available separately for the S-2.

PITTS S-1D SPECIAL

The version of the single-seat S-1 for which plans are currently available is designated S-1D. Details are generally similar to those given for the factory-built S-1S in the main US Aircraft section of this edition.

There is also an S-1C version, but Pitts Aerobatics does not supply plans for its construction. By comparison with earlier models, this has flat-bottomed wings, and ailerons on the lower wings only, and is suitable for the installation of engines of between 74·5 and 134 kW (100 to 180 hp).

POLLIWAGEN

POLLIWAGEN INC

8782 Hewitt Place, Garden Grove, California 92644
Telephone: (714) 897 9852
PRESIDENT: Joseph P. Alvarez

POLLIWAGEN

The Polliwagen is a side-by-side two-seat sporting aircraft, stressed for aerobatics and designed for amateur construction. The prototype flew for the first time in July 1977. Plans are now available, together with a wide range of component parts, including pre-moulded glassfibre cowlings, landing gear fairings, canopy and ribs, landing gear assemblies, brakes and instrument panel.

TYPE: Two-seat light sporting aircraft.

WINGS: Cantilever low-wing monoplane. Wortmann FX-67-K-150 wing section; full-span trailing-edge flaps and ailerons reflex upward for higher cruising speed. Dihedral 4°. No sweepback or washout. Composite structure of glassfibre and foam, embodying sailplane technology. Wingtip tanks increase effective span by reducing induced drag.

FUSELAGE: Glassfibre and foam structure, consisting basically of one bottom and two side D-spars, designed in such a way that the cockpit would break outward if subjected to impact loads.

TAIL UNIT: Cantilever T-tail of similar construction to wings, with sweepback on all surfaces. Fin integral with fuselage. All-moving horizontal surfaces.

LANDING GEAR: Retractable tricycle type. Main units retract forward, nosewheel rearward. Main wheels remain semi-exposed to reduce damage in a wheels-up landing.

POWER PLANT: One 60 kW (81 hp) turbocharged Revmaster-developed Volkswagen 2,100 cc engine, driving a Maloof two-blade oil-controlled two-position metal propeller. Total of 76 litres (20 US gallons) of fuel in two wingtip tanks (each 34 litres; 9 US gallons) and a small gravity-feed tank in the fuselage nose. Fuel capacity can be augmented up to 152 litres (40 US gallons).

ACCOMMODATION: Two seats side by side under rearward-articulating transparent canopy.

SYSTEMS: All flying controls actuated through pushrods and bearings. Full electrical system, with provision for three-axis electric trim adaptable to an autopilot.

DIMENSIONS, EXTERNAL:

Wing span	7·92 m (26 ft 0 in)
Wing chord, constant	1·07 m (3 ft 6 in)
Wing area, gross	8·36 m² (90 sq ft)
Length overall	4·88 m (16 ft 0 in)
Height overall	1·70 m (5 ft 7 in)
Wheel track	1·60 m (5 ft 3 in)
Wheelbase	1·09 m (3 ft 7 in)
Propeller diameter	1·42 m (4 ft 8 in)

WEIGHTS:

Weight empty	254 kg (560 lb)
Max T-O weight	499 kg (1,100 lb)

PERFORMANCE (at max T-O weight, except when stated otherwise):

Max cruising speed at 5,790 m (19,000 ft), 75% power	200 knots (370 km/h; 230 mph)
Max cruising speed at 2,590 m (8,500 ft), 75% power	146 knots (270 km/h; 168 mph)
Landing speed	39 knots (72·5 km/h; 45 mph)
Stalling speed, 12° flaps	33 knots (61 km/h; 38 mph)
Max rate of climb at S/L	213 m (700 ft)/min
Max rate of climb at S/L, pilot only	366 m (1,200 ft)/min
Service ceiling	8,535 m (28,000 ft)
T-O run	137 m (450 ft)
Landing run	168 m (550 ft)
Range with max fuel	868 nm (1,609 km; 1,000 miles)

POWELL

JOHN C. POWELL

4 Donald Drive, Middletown, Rhode Island 02840

John Powell, formerly a Commander in the US Navy, designed and built a two-seat parasol-wing monoplane, of which plans are available to amateur constructors. Known as the P-70 Acey Deucy, its design was started in 1966 and construction began during 1967. FAA certification in the Experimental homebuilt category was awarded on 19 June 1970 and the first flight was recorded on the following day. By the beginning of 1979 this prototype had accumulated 573 hours' flying time.

More than 140 sets of plans have been sold, and the first aircraft built from plans was flying by the Autumn of 1973. At least seven Acey Deucys were flying by early 1979, with many more under construction.

POWELL P-70 ACEY DEUCY

TYPE: Two-seat light monoplane.

WINGS: Braced parasol-wing monoplane with steel tube Vee bracing struts on each side, auxiliary bracing struts and N-type centre-section struts. Wing section NACA 4412. Dihedral 1° on outer panels. Incidence 2°. No sweepback. Composite structure of steel tube and wood, fabric covered. Frise-type ailerons of wooden construction, fabric covered. No flaps. No trim tabs.

FUSELAGE: Welded 4130 steel tube structure with wooden stringers, fabric covered.

TAIL UNIT: Wire-braced welded steel tube structure with 'U' channel ribs. Tailplane incidence adjustable by screwjack at leading-edge. No trim tabs.

LANDING GEAR: Non-retractable tailwheel type. Two side Vees and half axles hinged to fuselage structure. Shock-absorption by springs in compression. Goodyear main wheels and tyres size 8·00-4, pressure 0·83 bars (12 lb/sq in). Motor scooter type caliper brakes.

POWER PLANT: Suitable for installation of engines from 48·5-67 kW (65 to 90 hp). Prototype has one 48·5 kW (65 hp) Continental A65 flat-four engine, driving a McCauley two-blade metal fixed-pitch propeller. One fuel tank in fuselage, immediately aft of firewall, capacity 53 litres (14 US gallons). Refuelling point on top of fuselage, forward of front cockpit. Oil capacity 3·75 litres (1 US gallon).

ACCOMMODATION: Two persons in tandem, normally in open cockpits. Sliding canopy available. Small door by front cockpit on starboard side.

DIMENSIONS, EXTERNAL:

Wing span	9·91 m (32 ft 6 in)
Wing chord, constant	1·52 m (5 ft 0 in)
Wing area, gross	14·4 m² (155 sq ft)
Wing aspect ratio	6·5
Length overall	6·32 m (20 ft 9 in)
Height overall	2·06 m (6 ft 9 in)
Tailplane span	2·59 m (8 ft 6 in)
Wheel track	1·83 m (6 ft 0 in)

WEIGHTS (prototype):

Weight empty	340 kg (750 lb)
Max T-O weight	578 kg (1,275 lb)

PERFORMANCE (prototype):

Never-exceed speed	126 knots (233 km/h; 145 mph)
Max level speed at S/L	90 knots (167 km/h; 104 mph)
Max cruising speed at 610 m (2,000 ft)	80 knots (148 km/h; 92 mph)
Stalling speed	23·5-26 knots (44-48·5 km/h; 27-30 mph)
Max rate of climb at S/L	190·5 m (625 ft)/min
Service ceiling (approx)	3,050-3,355 m (10,000-11,000 ft)
T-O run	76 m (250 ft)
T-O to 15 m (50 ft)	approx 213 m (700 ft)
Landing run	approx 76 m (250 ft)
Range, with 30 min reserves	217 nm (402 km; 250 miles)

QUICKIE

QUICKIE AIRCRAFT CORPORATION

PO Box 786, Mojave, California 93501 and Building 68, Mojave Airport, Mojave, California 93501
Telephone: (805) 824 4313

Quickie Aircraft Corporation is a company formed by Gene Sheehan and Tom Jewett to develop the Quickie aircraft and then to sell complete kits, including engine, to amateur constructors who wish to build this type. Gene Sheehan has worked in the aerospace industry since 1964 and has been involved in several previous homebuilt projects; Tom Jewett's career has been devoted to flight testing, and he was a Flight Test Engineer on board the Rockwell International B-1 supersonic bomber.

QUICKIE AIRCRAFT CORPORATION QUICKIE

The Quickie is a new single-seat aircraft of unusual configuration. The project began in 1975 when Mr Sheehan and Mr Jewett started looking for a low-power engine that could be installed in a highly-efficient single-seat sporting aircraft, the design of which had not then been initiated. Not until 1977 was the Onan engine found and tested. Having proved its reliability, Burt Rutan of VariViggen fame was contacted to assist in designing an aircraft that would make optimum use of the engine. Having established the basic configuration, Tom Jewett and Burt Rutan began detailed design work, while Gene Sheehan continued engine development.

On 13 August 1977 construction of the prototype Quickie was started, and it was completed in 400 working-hours over a three-month period. First flight was achieved on 15 November 1977. Fifteen flights were made by the three designer/pilots during the first five days of the test programme.

The Quickie design was frozen on 14 April 1978, after 125 hours of flight testing. The full programme of air and ground testing included investigation of performance, stability and control, flutter testing to156 knots (290 km/h; 180 mph) TAS, static load testing and landing gear drop testing to FAA Pt 23 certificated aircraft standards, fuel economy measurements, and taxying, take-off and landing in surface winds of over 50 knots. Extensive stall/departure/spin testing revealed that the Quickie could not be made to spin.

In August 1978, the Quickie was flown to the Experimental Aircraft Association's Fly-in at Oshkosh, Wisconsin, where it subsequently received the 'Outstanding New Design' award for 1978. The 3,650 nm (6,760 km; 4,200 mile) journey to and from Oshkosh was accomplished without incident, averaging 95 knots (177 km/h; 110 mph) and 27·5 km/litre (65 miles/US gallon), while costing only $55 in fuel and oil costs.

Complete kits, including engines, have been available since June 1978. Each includes prefabricated cowling, canopy, all machined parts, all welded parts, and some of the tools, in order to reduce the building time to 400 man-hours for the inexperienced builder.

By January 1979, more than 180 kits had been sold and several homebuilt versions were flying. The Quickie prototype logged over 225 hours of flying time within its first year, and cost only $3·25 per hour to operate, including fuel, oil, maintenance and insurance.

TYPE: Single-seat light sporting aircraft of canard configuration.

WINGS: Tapered cantilever shoulder-wing monoplane. Dihedral from roots. Two unidirectional glassfibre spars and shaped low-density rigid foam core, covered with glassfibre. Constant-chord inboard ailerons. No flaps.

FOREPLANE: Tapered and slightly sweptback cantilever foreplane, mounted low on forward fuselage. Marked anhedral. Construction similar to that of wings. Main-wheel housings attached to tips. Full-span tapered elevator/flaps.

FUSELAGE: Semi-monocoque structure of banana shape, formed from 25 mm (1 in) thick foam, with glassfibre covering inside and out, and tapering towards rear. Foam/glassfibre sandwich bulkheads.

TAIL UNIT: Cantilever sweptback vertical fin and narrow-chord rudder of similar construction to wings.

LANDING GEAR: Non-retractable tailwheel type. Main wheels positioned at tips of canard foreplane in swept fairings. Steerable tailwheel aft of fuselage.

POWER PLANT: One modified Onan horizontally-opposed two-cylinder four-stroke engine, developing 13·5 kW (18 hp) at 3,600 rpm and driving a two-blade wooden fixed-pitch propeller. Fuel capacity 30·3 litres (8 US gallons). Fuel consumption approx 44·2 km/litre (104 miles/gallon).

ACCOMMODATION: Single seat under one-piece side-hinged canopy. Cockpit suitable for pilot up to 1·98 m (6 ft 6 in) tall and weighing up to 95 kg (210 lb). Max baggage capacity with lighter pilot 13·6 kg (30 lb).

DIMENSIONS, EXTERNAL:

Wing span	5·08 m (16 ft 8 in)
Wing area, gross	2·52 m² (27·08 sq ft)
Canard wing span	4·67 m (15 ft 4 in)
Canard wing area	2·47 m² (26·57 sq ft)
Length overall	5·28 m (17 ft 4 in)

DIMENSIONS, INTERNAL:

Cockpit: Length	1·63 m (5 ft 4 in)
Width	0·56 m (1 ft 10 in)
Height	0·86 m (2 ft 10 in)

WEIGHTS:

Weight empty	109 kg (240 lb)

Polliwagen two-seat light sporting aircraft

Powell P-70 Acey Deucy with new sliding canopy

Quickie Aircraft Corporation Quickie prototype *(Don Dwiggins)*

Rand Robinson KR-1 built by Mr F. Keller *(J. M. G. Gradidge)*

Max T-O weight 218 kg (480 lb)
PERFORMANCE:
Max level speed 109 knots (202 km/h; 126 mph)
Max cruising speed 105 knots (195 km/h; 121 mph)
Stalling speed, power off
46 knots (86 km/h; 53 mph)
Stalling speed, power on
43 knots (79 km/h; 49 mph)
Normal rate of climb at S/L 130 m (425 ft)/min
Max rate of climb at 1,525 m (5,000 ft)
110 m (360 ft)/min
Service ceiling 3,750 m (12,300 ft)
T-O run 201 m (660 ft)
Landing run 255 m (835 ft)
Range at normal cruising speed
477 nm (885 km; 550 miles)
Range at econ cruising speed
712 nm (1,320 km; 820 miles)

RAND ROBINSON
RAND ROBINSON ENGINEERING INC

5842 K McFadden Avenue, Huntington Beach, California 92649
Telephone: (714) 898 3811

In 1974, the late Mr Kenneth Rand formed Rand Robinson Engineering Inc to market plans for the KR-1 single-seat lightweight sporting aircraft, and of a slightly larger two-seat version, designated KR-2. His last design was the KR-3 light amphibian, described in the 1978-79 *Jane's*.

RAND ROBINSON KR-1

Mr Kenneth Rand designed and built the prototype of a single-seat lightweight sporting aircraft known as the Rand KR-1. The design originated in 1969; construction of the prototype was started in 1970 and the first flight was made in February 1972. Plans are available to amateur constructors; 6,000 sets had been sold by the beginning of 1979 and about 200 KR-1s were known to be flying.

The performance figures that are quoted relate generally to the re-engined prototype fitted with a 67 kW (90 hp) 2,074 cc Volkswagen engine. Performance figures with the original 27 kW (36 hp) 1,200 cc VW engine can be found in the 1975-76 *Jane's*.

TYPE: Single-seat lightweight sporting aircraft.

WINGS: Cantilever low-wing monoplane. Wing section RAF 48. Thickness/chord ratio 15%. Dihedral 5°. Incidence 5° at root, 2° at tip. No sweepback. Composite two-spar structure. Front spar of spruce; rear spar built of spruce and plywood. Most ribs formed from polyurethane foam, spaces between ribs being filled with polyurethane foam slab. Structure covered with Dynel reinforced epoxy. Outer wing panels removable for storage. Ailerons of polyurethane foam, with Dynel reinforced epoxy covering, over full span of outer panels. Trailing-edge flaps standard.

FUSELAGE: Composite structure, lower half of spruce longerons with plywood skin, upper surface of carved Styrofoam covered with Dynel epoxy. Firewall is a plywood, asbestos and stainless steel lamination.

TAIL UNIT: Cantilever structure with spruce spars, the remainder of the structure being carved polyurethane foam, Dynel epoxy covered. Fixed-incidence tailplane. Trim tabs in rudder and elevator.

LANDING GEAR: Tailwheel type. Main units retract aft manually into wing centre-section. Shock-absorption by flat spring crossbar to which main units are attached. Main-wheel tyres size 10½ × 4·00-5, pressure 2·07 bars (30 lb/sq in). Steerable tailwheel with solid tyre of 7·6 cm (3 in) diameter. Manual drum brakes.

POWER PLANT: One Volkswagen modified motor car engine, driving a Maloof metal two-blade two-position propeller with spinner. Prototype has been re-engined with a Rajay-turbocharged 67 kW (90 hp) 2,074 cc VW. Fuel tankage with larger engine comprises one tank immediately aft of firewall, capacity 38 litres (10 US gallons), and one 76 litre (20 US gallon) tank in each wing, giving total capacity of 190 litres (50 US gallons). Refuelling point on fuselage upper surface, forward of windscreen. Oil capacity 2·8 litres (0·75 US gallons).

ACCOMMODATION: Pilot only, beneath rearward-sliding transparent cockpit canopy. Baggage space aft of seat.

SYSTEM: Electrical power supplied by 20A alternator and 12V 14Ah storage battery. Bosch electric starter.

AVIONICS AND EQUIPMENT: Edo-Aire 720-channel transceiver with 200-channel Auto Omni. Full blind-flying panel.

DIMENSIONS, EXTERNAL:
Wing span 5·18 m (17 ft 0 in)
Wing chord at root 1·22 m (4 ft 0 in)
Wing chord at tip 0·91 m (3 ft 0 in)
Wing area, gross 5·76 m² (62 sq ft)
Wing aspect ratio 4·5
Length overall 3·89 m (12 ft 9 in)
Width, wings removed 1·52 m (5 ft 0 in)
Height overall 1·07 m (3 ft 6 in)
Tailplane span 1·52 m (5 ft 0 in)
Wheel track 1·27 m (4 ft 2 in)
Propeller diameter 1·35 m (4 ft 5 in)

DIMENSIONS, INTERNAL:
Cockpit: Length 1·22 m (4 ft 0 in)
Max width 0·51 m (1 ft 8 in)
Max height 0·76 m (2 ft 6 in)
Baggage hold 0·11 m³ (4 cu ft)

WEIGHTS (A: 27 kW; 36 hp. B: 67 kW; 90 hp):
Weight empty, equipped: A 154 kg (340 lb)
B 218 kg (480 lb)
Max T-O and landing weight: A 272 kg (600 lb)
B 408 kg (900 lb)

PERFORMANCE (A: 27 kW; 36 hp. B: 67 kW; 90 hp, at max T-O weight):
Never-exceed speed:
A 140 knots (259 km/h; 161 mph)
B 217 knots (402 km/h; 250 mph)
Max level speed at S/L:
A 130 knots (241 km/h; 150 mph)
B 191 knots (354 km/h; 220 mph)
Max cruising speed at 1,525 m (5,000 ft):
A 130 knots (241 km/h; 150 mph)
B 191 knots (354 km/h; 220 mph)
Econ cruising speed at 5,485 m (18,000 ft):
B 217 knots (402 km/h; 250 mph)
Stalling speed: A, B 39 knots (73 km/h; 45 mph)
Max rate of climb at S/L: A 182 m (600 ft)/min
B 457 m (1,500 ft)/min
Service ceiling: A 3,660 m (12,000 ft)
B 9,145 m (30,000 ft)
T-O run: A, B 122 m (400 ft)
T-O to 15 m (50 ft): A, B 244 m (800 ft)
Landing from 15 m (50 ft): A, B 305 m (1,000 ft)
Landing run: A, B 152 m (500 ft)
Range with max fuel:
B 2,600 nm (4,825 km; 3,000 miles)

RAND ROBINSON KR-2

The KR-2 is a slightly larger two-seat version of the KR-1, to which it is generally similar in construction. Design began in 1973 and the prototype flew for the first time in July 1974. Construction occupied approximately 800 man hours, at a cost of about $2,000. Plans and kits of parts are available to amateur constructors.

By February 1979, a total of 4,500 sets of plans and 2,800 kits had been sold; about 350 KR-2s were flying at that time.

TYPE: Two-seat lightweight sporting aircraft.

WINGS: As for KR-1, except span increased by 1·07 m (3 ft 6 in).

FUSELAGE: As for KR-1, except dimensions increased.

TAIL UNIT AND LANDING GEAR: As for KR-1, except wheel track increased.

POWER PLANT: Airframe designed to accept Volkswagen modified motor car engines of 1,600 to 2,200 cc. Prototype has a Rajay turbocharged 2,074 cc Volkswagen engine, driving a Maloof two-position propeller with spinner. Fuel tank immediately aft of firewall, capacity 38 litres (10 US gallons). One fuel tank in each wing, capacity 53 litres (14 US gallons). Total fuel capacity 144 litres (38 US gallons). Refuelling point on fuselage upper surface, forward of windscreen.

ACCOMMODATION: Two persons, side by side, beneath transparent cockpit canopy.

AVIONICS AND EQUIPMENT: Provision for wide range of electronics and blind flying instruments. Prototype has full IFR panel, dual nav/com transceivers, glideslope receiver, three-light marker beacon receiver, and radar transponder with altitude reporting.

DIMENSIONS, EXTERNAL:
Wing span 6·30 m (20 ft 8 in)
Wing chord at root 1·22 m (4 ft 0 in)
Wing chord at tip 0·91 m (3 ft 0 in)
Wing area, gross 7·43 m² (80 sq ft)
Wing aspect ratio 5·5
Length overall 4·42 m (14 ft 6 in)
Height overall 1·07 m (3 ft 6 in)
Tailplane span 1·52 m (5 ft 0 in)
Wheel track 1·52 m (5 ft 0 in)
Propeller diameter 1·32 m (4 ft 4 in)

DIMENSIONS, INTERNAL:
Cockpit: Length 1·22 m (4 ft 0 in)
Max width 0·91 m (3 ft 0 in)
Max height 0·76 m (2 ft 6 in)
Baggage hold 0·11 m³ (4 cu ft)

WEIGHTS (prototype, A: without turbocharger, B: with turbocharger):
Weight empty, equipped: A 200 kg (440 lb)
B, with IFR and electrics 263 kg (580 lb)

Max T-O and landing weight: A 363 kg (800 lb)
B 499 kg (1,100 lb)
Performance (prototype, at max T-O weight. A: without turbocharger, B: with turbocharger):
Never-exceed speed:
A, B 186 knots (346 km/h; 215 mph)
Max level speed at S/L:
A 156 knots (290 km/h; 180 mph)
B 161 knots (298 km/h; 185 mph)
Max cruising speed:
A at 1,525 m (5,000 ft) 156 knots (290 km/h; 180 mph)
B at 5,485 m (18,000 ft) 191 knots (354 km/h; 220 mph)
Econ cruising speed at 3,660 m (12,000 ft):
A 148 knots (274 km/h; 170 mph)
Stalling speed: A 39 knots (73 km/h; 45 mph)
Max rate of climb: A at S/L 244 m (800 ft)/min
B at 5,500 m (18,000 ft) 244 m (800 ft)/min
Service ceiling: A 4,875 m (16,000 ft)
B 7,925 m (26,000 ft)
T-O run: A, B 122 m (400 ft)
T-O to 15 m (50 ft): A, B 244 m (800 ft)
Landing from 15 m (50 ft): A, B 305 m (1,000 ft)
Landing run: A, B 152 m (500 ft)
Range with max fuel:
B 1,735 nm (3,215 km; 2,000 miles)

REPLOGLE

E. H. REPLOGLE

23 Wayside Court, Buffalo, New York 14226

Mr Replogle, an experienced sailplane pilot, designed and built a two-seat light aircraft, designated REP-2, which flew for the first time on 6 June 1977 and was then flown from Buffalo to Oshkosh, Wisconsin, to take part in the 1977 EAA Fly-in.

REPLOGLE REP-2

Type: Two-seat light aircraft.

Wings: Cantilever low-wing monoplane. Wortmann wing section, utilising flaperons which are reflexed to 6° for cruising flight. Dihedral from roots. Light alloy tubular spar, over which a foam and glassfibre wing is built up.

Fuselage: All-wood box structure of basically rectangular section.

Tail Unit: Cantilever structure. All-moving horizontal surfaces with large tabs, and projecting balance arm forward of each tip.

Landing Gear: Retractable tricycle type of own design. Main wheels retract rearward and remain semi-exposed under wings to reduce damage in a wheels-up landing. Steerable nosewheel.

Power Plant: One 2,100 cc Revmaster flat-four engine, driving a Warnke two-blade ground-adjustable propeller. Fuel tankage inside wing spar, with filler at port wingtip.

Accommodation: Two seats side by side under forward-hinged canopy with 360° field of view.

Dimensions and Weights: No details available

Performance (provisional):
Max level speed 128 knots (238 km/h; 148 mph)
Stalling speed approx 51 knots (94 km/h; 58 mph)
Max rate of climb at S/L 135-150 m (450-500 ft)/min

RLU

CHARLES ROLOFF, ROBERT LIPOSKY and CARL UNGER

c/o Charles B. Roloff, PO Box 358, Palos Park, Illinois 60464

Telephone: (312) 598 6210

Three professional pilots designed and built a unique light aircraft known as the Breezy Model RLU-1, the designation being made up of the initial letters of the surnames of the designers. Well over 700 sets of plans for the Breezy have since been sold, and many examples are flying, including some built in Australia, Canada, South Africa and Switzerland.

BREEZY MODEL RLU-1

Described as being of vintage configuration with all modern facilities, such as full radio, instruments and hydraulic brakes, the prototype Breezy is an open three-seat light aircraft powered by a 67 kW (90 hp) Continental engine. Construction took six months, at a cost of $3,400, including radio. First flight was made on 7 August 1964.

First Breezy to be built from the published plans was that constructed by Airpark Aero of Santa Rosa, California, for Mr Jack Gardiner of Pandora, Ohio. It differed from the prototype only by having two bucket seats, one of these replacing the usual two-place bench seat behind the pilot.

The following description applies to the prototype Breezy:

Type: Three-seat parasol-wing monoplane.

Wings: Strut-braced parasol-wing monoplane. Standard Piper PA-12 wing, with Vee streamline-section bracing struts each side.

Fuselage: Triangular-section welded chrome-molybdenum steel tube structure, without any covering.

Tail Unit: Welded chrome-molybdenum steel tube braced structure; all surfaces fabric-covered.

Landing Gear: Non-retractable tricycle type. Main wheels and tyres size 6·00-6, 4-ply; nosewheel and tyre size 5·00-5. Cleveland hydraulic brakes.

Power Plant: One 67 kW (90 hp) Continental C90-8F-P flat-four engine, driving a Flottorp 72A50 two-blade pusher propeller. Single fuel tank, capacity 68 litres (18 US gallons), in wing centre-section. Oil capacity 4·5 litres (1·25 US gallons).

Accommodation: Seats for three in tandem. Pilot on single seat forward, two passengers on bench seat aft.

Dimensions, external:
Wing span 10·06 m (33 ft 0 in)
Wing area, gross 15·3 m² (165 sq ft)
Length overall 6·86 m (22 ft 6 in)
Height overall 2·59 m (8 ft 6 in)
Wheel track 1·83 m (6 ft 0 in)
Wheelbase 3·05 m (10 ft 0 in)

Weights:
Weight empty 317 kg (700 lb)
Max T-O weight 544 kg (1,200 lb)

Performance:
Never-exceed speed 91 knots (168·5 km/h; 105 mph)
Cruising speed, 70% power 65 knots (121 km/h; 75 mph)
Stalling speed 26 knots (49 km/h; 30 mph)
Service ceiling 4,572 m (15,000 ft)
T-O run (grass) 137 m (450 ft)
T-O to 15 m (50 ft) 335 m (1,100 ft)
Landing from 15 m (50 ft) 335 m (1,100 ft)
Landing run (grass) 91 m (300 ft)
Range with max fuel 217 nm (402 km; 250 miles)

ROBERTS

DON E. ROBERTS

Noblesville Senior High School, 300 North 17th Street, Noblesville, Indiana 46060

ROBERTS DOUGLAS SBD-3 DAUNTLESS

Mr Don Roberts, an aviation instructor, and approximately 75 students of Noblesville High School, Indiana, designed and built a three-quarter scale replica of the second World War Douglas Dauntless carrier-based dive bomber. The design was based on a set of model aeroplane plans.

Construction began in Autumn 1972 and the prototype was completed in mid-May 1977. The first flight was recorded on 27 May 1977. It is stated that the aircraft is 99% accurate in every respect compared with the original bomber, except for actual size and power plant. No plans are available to amateur builders.

Type: Three-quarter scale replica bomber.

Wings: Cantilever low-wing monoplane. Rectangular centre-section with outer sections tapering in chord and thickness. All-metal construction. Perforated metal split dive-brakes, forming upper and lower surfaces of mid-wing trailing-edge. Ailerons.

Fuselage: Conventional structure with welded steel tube framework, aluminium formers and skins. Dummy arrester hook.

Tail Unit: Cantilever type. All-metal tailplane. Rudder and elevators have metal frames, aluminium-covered. Trim tab on rudder.

Landing Gear: Retractable tailwheel type. Steerable tailwheel.

Power Plant: One 142 kW (190 hp) Lycoming O-435-1 flat-six engine, driving a three-blade propeller. Annular engine cowling, as original SBD-3.

Accommodation: Crew of two in tandem beneath glasshouse-type canopy. Cabin heated and ventilated. Intercom system.

Systems: Narco nav-com radio. Landing gear position indicators.

'Armament': Dummy machine-guns and underfuselage 'bomb'.

Dimensions, external:
Wing span 9·75 m (32 ft 0 in)
Length overall 7·24 m (23 ft 9 in)
Height overall 2·64 m (8 ft 8 in)

Weights:
Weight empty 837 kg (1,845 lb)
Max T-O weight 1,088 kg (2,400 lb)

Performance (estimated):
Max level speed 138 knots (256 km/h; 159 mph)
Max cruising speed 128 knots (238 km/h; 148 mph)
Landing speed 61 knots (113 km/h; 70 mph)
Rate of climb at S/L 305 m (1,000 ft)/min
Service ceiling 3,960 m (13,000 ft)
T-O and landing run 550 m (1,800 ft)
Range with max fuel 400 nm (740 km; 460 miles)

ROTOR MASTER

ROTOR MASTER AIRCRAFT

PO Box 81769, San Diego, California 92108

President: R. W. Hively

This company is advertising a small rotorcraft named the Boomerang for which plans and kits are available.

ROTOR MASTER BOOMERANG

The Boomerang is offered to amateur constructors in single-seat or two-seat form. Configuration appears to be conventional, with a two-blade teetering rotor, pusher power plant mounted to the rear of the rotor mast, a faired open cockpit, and non-retractable tricycle landing gear. Twin tailbooms each carry a large fin and rudder assembly.

Construction is all-aluminium, and engines of 48·5 to 134 kW (65-180 hp) may be fitted to the Boomerang. No other details, or a photograph, are available.

ROTORWAY

ROTORWAY AIRCRAFT INC

14805 S. Interstate 10, Tempe, Arizona 85284

Telephone: (602) 963 6652

Mr B. J. Schramm formed the Schramm Aircraft Company to market, in both ready-to-fly and prefabricated component form, a single-seat helicopter of his own design, named the Javelin. Details of this aircraft, which flew for the first time in August 1965, can be found in the 1967-68 *Jane's*.

Subsequently, a new company named RotorWay Aircraft Inc was formed to market to amateur constructors plans and kits of components to build Mr Schramm's Scorpion helicopter, described as a production version of the Javelin (see 1972-73 *Jane's*). After a period this aircraft was superseded by the two-seat Scorpion Too, now known as the Scorpion 133.

RotorWay currently offers a package deal which includes Scorpion 133 construction kits, a RotorWay RW 133 engine, and a complete training programme for the constructor/pilot which covers flight training, operation and theory, and maintenance. Plans by themselves are no longer available.

During 1978, a turbocharged version of the RW 133 engine became available as an alternative to the basic, normally aspirated model, for owners who require improved performance at altitude.

ROTORWAY SCORPION 133

Type: Two-seat light helicopter.

Rotor System: Two-blade semi-rigid main rotor, incorporating Schramm Tractable Control rotor system. Blade section NACA 0015. All-metal D-spar thermal-bonded blades, which do not fold, are attached to aluminium teetering rotor hub by retention straps. Two-blade aluminium teetering tail rotor. Swashplate for cyclic pitch control. Cable through rotor shaft to blades for collective pitch control.

Rotor Drive: Drive from engine to vertical shaft via four power bands. Drive from vertical shaft to main rotor shaft via sprocketed triple-row chain. Tail rotor driven by Vee-belt from first stage of reduction pulleys.

Fuselage: Basic 4130 steel tube structure of simplified form. Removable glassfibre body fairing.

Tail Unit: Braced steel tube tailboom only, to carry tail rotor.

Landing Gear: Tubular skid type.

Power Plant: One 99 kW (133 hp) RotorWay RW 133 watercooled flat-four engine, designed and produced for the Scorpion 133 by RotorWay and mounted aft of cabin area. Turbocharged version available, giving 119

The two-seat Rand Robinson KR-2

Replogle REP-2 two-seat light aircraft *(Howard Levy)*

Breezy Model RLU-1 built by Mr R. J. Weller *(J. M. G. Gradidge)*

Three-quarter scale replica of a Douglas Dauntless bomber, built by Mr Don Roberts and students of the Noblesville High School *(Howard Levy)*

RotorWay Scorpion 133 with turbocharged engine

Rutan Defiant four-seat twin-engined lightplane

kW (160 hp) at 70% boost. Standard fuel capacity 37·5 litres (10 US gallons) in tank mounted above drive chain, aft of main rotor shaft.

ACCOMMODATION: Two individual bucket seats, side by side, in enclosed cabin.

DIMENSIONS, EXTERNAL:
- Diameter of main rotor: 7·62 m (25 ft 0 in)
- Diameter of tail rotor: 1·10 m (3 ft 7¼ in)
- Length, nose to tail rotor axis: 6·26 m (20 ft 6½ in)
- Height to top of main rotor: 2·22 m (7 ft 3½ in)
- Width of cabin: 1·22 m (4 ft 0 in)
- Landing skid track: 1·64 m (5 ft 4¾ in)

WEIGHTS (A without turbocharger, B with turbocharger):
- Weight empty: A 365 kg (805 lb)
- B 372 kg (820 lb)
- Max T-O weight: A, B 560 kg (1,235 lb)

PERFORMANCE (at max T-O weight. A without turbocharger, B with turbocharger):
- Cruising speed: A, B 69·5 knots (129 km/h; 80 mph)
- Max rate of climb at S/L: A 244 m (800 ft)/min
- B 366 m (1,200 ft)/min
- Service ceiling: A 3,050 m (10,000 ft)
- B 4,875 m (16,000 ft)
- Hovering ceiling IGE: A 1,675 m (5,500 ft)
- B 2,745 m (9,000 ft)
- Range with max fuel: A 104 nm (193 km; 120 miles)
- B 100 nm (185 km; 115 miles)

RUTAN

RUTAN AIRCRAFT FACTORY

Building 13, Mojave Airport, Box 656, Mojave, California 93501

Telephone: (805) 824 2645

PRESIDENT: Elbert L. Rutan

RUTAN VARIVIGGEN

The prototype of a light aircraft known as the VariViggen (N27VV) was rolled out on 27 February 1972. Mr Rutan had begun its design in 1963 and its configuration was developed via a low-cost automobile-mounted test system. This involved construction of a one-fifth scale model which was mounted on a specially-built test rig attached to the roof of a motor car. Ailerons, rudders and canard elevators were operated by remote control from within the car, and transducers in the test rig allowed measurement of airspeed, angle of attack, lift, drag, sideslip, side force, roll moment and elevator/aileron/rudder positions. An extra data channel provided for measurement of stick forces and structural load.

A one-fifth scale radio-controlled model was used to confirm the design's spin-proof characteristics. Construction of the prototype began during 1968, and the first flight was made in May 1972. By early 1976 the VariViggen had accumulated a total flying time of nearly 600 hours, and flight testing had confirmed the spin-free characteristics demonstrated by the free-flying scale model. The prototype had no conventional stall in its original form, and could climb, cruise, glide, turn and land with continuous full aft stick, giving a stable speed of 45 knots (83·5 km/h; 52 mph) throughout. Rate of climb at this speed is 152 m (500 ft)/min. The full-span ailerons provide a high rate of roll, and a 360° roll can be accomplished at a speed of only 80 knots (148 km/h; 92 mph) without loss of height. Manoeuvrability is such that the aircraft's turn radius is less than 61 m (200 ft) at speeds of 60-110 knots (111-204 km/h; 69-127 mph). Nosewheel rotation on take-off occurs at 50 knots (93 km/h; 58 mph), at which speed the aircraft will enter an immediate stable climb.

The full-span ailerons are described as 'reflexerons', since they serve both as ailerons and as an adjustable 'reflex' control for the main wing. Differential aileron motion is related mechanically to the stick, but the collective 'reflex' is electrically controlled. This is achieved by electrically controlled aileron droop, which causes the resulting nose-down trim to be countered by a nose-up deflection of the elevators on the forward canard surface. Thus both ailerons and elevators serve also as flaps. The ailerons are also adjusted at cruising speed to minimise trim drag and optimise the lift/drag ratio. Trim is achieved by an electrically-controlled bungee device on the mechanical elevator system.

In 1975 Mr Rutan began experimenting with a new SP (special performance) wing outer panel, constructed from urethane foam and unidirectional glassfibre, and with a Wortmann FX-60-126 section. With an increase of wing span to 7·23 m (23 ft 8½ in), and of area to 11·61 m² (125 sq ft), it was anticipated that this would provide a 25% increase in the max rate of climb and give a cruising speed 4·5-6 knots (8-11 km/h; 5-7 mph) greater than with the standard wing. Tests showed that the new wing increased rate of climb, but that the former 'no stall' characteristic had been sacrificed. With the SP wing, the VariViggen will 'roll off' if uncoordinated at full aft stick. It is, however, easier to build and stronger than the aluminium outer panel, and is covered on sets of plans currently available to amateur constructors.

A further refinement on the SP wing is the addition of NASA-developed 'winglets', designed by Dr Whitcomb, to enhance directional stability at no cost in performance.

The SP wing panels attach to the standard inboard wing panels, without modification. Each SP outer wing houses a 28·4 litre (7·5 US gallon) fuel tank, giving an additional 56·8 litres (15 US gallons) of auxiliary fuel.

About 900 sets of VariViggen plans have been sold; it is believed that approximately 300 aircraft are being built and three homebuilt examples were flying by early 1979. One aircraft assembled in France by M Chagnes is powered by two Microturbo TRS 18 turbojet engines (see French section).

The following details apply to the VariViggen with the original type of outer wing panels:

TYPE: Two-seat (or 2+2) light aircraft.

WINGS: Cantilever low-wing monoplane of cropped delta configuration. Rutan wing section. Thickness/chord ratio 7% at root, 9% at tip. Dihedral 3° on outer wing panels. Incidence 0°. Sweepback at quarter-chord 27°. Composite structure with spruce spars, plywood ribs and skin, Ceconite-covered, except for outboard aft wing panels which are of flush-riveted metal construction. Inward-canted fin and rudder each side at approximately one-third span. Full-span ailerons, extending between fins and wingtips, constructed as a shell of 0·016 in aluminium with foam filling. Cutout in inboard trailing-edges to accommodate pusher propeller.

CANARD SURFACES: Cantilever structure mounted high on the nose, forward of the windscreen. Aerofoil section NACA 4414 (modified). Slotted flap-type elevator in trailing-edge.

FUSELAGE: Basically square-section fuselage of wooden construction, Ceconite-covered. Landing light in nosecone, which is hinged at top and opens upwards for access to equipment. Engine mounted in aft end of fuselage.

Landing Gear: Electrically-retractable tricycle type. Nosewheel retracts forward, main wheels inward into wings. Nosewheel mounted on oleo-pneumatic shock-strut. Shock-absorption of main units by rubber discs in compression. Goodyear main wheels, with tyres size 14 × 5·00-5, pressure 2·07 bars (30 lb/sq in). Scott nosewheel with 228 mm (9 in) diameter tyre, pressure 2·07 bars (30 lb/sq in). Goodyear caliper brakes.

Power Plant: One 112 kW (150 hp) Lycoming O-320-A2A flat-four engine, mounted in rear fuselage and driving a Hegy two-blade wooden fixed-pitch propeller. One fuel tank in fuselage, capacity 87 litres (23 US gallons) and one external fuel tank, mounted on aircraft centreline under fuselage, capacity 45 litres (12 US gallons). Total capacity 132 litres (35 US gallons). Refuelling point on fuselage upper surface. Oil capacity 7·5 litres (2 US gallons).

Accommodation: Two seats in tandem in individual cockpits, beneath transparent canopies which are hinged on the starboard side. Space for two children, each weighing not more than 22·5 kg (50 lb), or 45 kg (100 lb) of baggage aft of rear seat.

Systems: Dual 12V electrical systems. Storage battery. Hydraulic system for brakes only.

Electronics and Equipment: ARC 360-channel VHF com transceiver, ARC 200-channel VHF nav receiver. Edo Air transponder. Angle of attack indicator.

Dimensions, external:

Wing span	5·79 m (19 ft 0 in)
Wing chord at root	2·26 m (7 ft 5 in)
Wing chord at tip	0·89 m (2 ft 11 in)
Wing area, gross	11·06 m² (119 sq ft)
Wing aspect ratio	3
Length overall	5·79 m (19 ft 0 in)
Canard surface span	2·44 m (8 ft 0 in)
Wheel track	2·20 m (7 ft 2½ in)
Wheelbase	2·44 m (8 ft 0 in)
Propeller diameter	1·78 m (5 ft 10 in)
Propeller ground clearance	0·41 m (1 ft 4 in)

Dimensions, internal:

Cabin: Length	2·54 m (8 ft 4 in)
Max width	0·64 m (2 ft 1 in)

Weights:

Weight empty, equipped	431 kg (950 lb)
Max T-O and landing weight	771 kg (1,700 lb)

Performance (A: standard wing; B: SP wing, at max T-O weight, except as indicated):

Never-exceed speed:
A 156 knots (289 km/h; 180 mph)

Max level speed at S/L:
A 142 knots (262 km/h; 163 mph)

Max cruising speed at 2,135 m (7,000 ft):
A 130 knots (241 km/h; 150 mph)
B 137 knots (254 km/h; 158 mph)

Econ cruising speed at 2,135 m (7,000 ft):
A 109 knots (201 km/h; 125 mph)

Max rate of climb at S/L: A 244 m (800 ft)/min
B 305 m (1,000 ft)/min

Service ceiling: A 4,265 m (14,000 ft)

T-O run: A 259 m (850 ft)

T-O to 15 m (50 ft): A 290 m (950 ft)

Landing from 15 m (50 ft) at max landing weight
A 183 m (600 ft)

Landing run at max landing weight: A 152 m (500 ft)

Range with max fuel, 30 min reserves
A 347 nm (643 km; 400 miles)

RUTAN VARIEZE

Mr Rutan designed and built two prototypes of a high-performance two-seat aircraft of canard configuration, named the VariEze, of which plans are available. The name stems from its simplicity of construction, the entire structure being a composite of high-strength, primarily unidirectional glassfibre with rigid foam as core material.

The configuration of the VariEze is based on that of the VariViggen, with canard foreplanes; but the cropped-delta wings of that aircraft are replaced by more conventional swept wings of high aspect ratio. At the tip of each wing is a vertical fin, known as a 'winglet'. Developed by Dr Richard Whitcomb at NASA's Langley Research Center, each 'winglet' consists of large above-wing and small below-wing surfaces. That beneath the wing extends aft from the leading-edge to 33% of the tip chord, is cambered inward and inclined outward at 30° from vertical. The above-wing surface, extending aft from 33% of the tip chord, is cambered outward and also inclined outward at 15° from vertical. This 'winglet' system has been shown to 'unwind' the wingtip vortex to a maximum, limiting induced drag and resulting in a fuel saving of 6%; the inclination of the upper and lower surfaces also offsets 40% of the parasite drag of the vertical fins. These vertical surfaces include rudders, which are moved outward individually by single cables and centralised by return springs. The rudder control cables include in their run slotted bellcranks, so that extended movement of either rudder pedal causes the bellcrank to actuate its respective wheel-brake master cylinder. A conventional control column operates elevators mounted on the trailing-edges of the canard foreplanes and ailerons on the trailing-edges of the rear wings.

The tricycle landing gear has another unusual feature: the main units are fixed but the nosegear retracts both on the ground and in the air. Retracting the nose unit on the ground, termed kneeled parking, not only facilitates access to the cockpits but raises the propeller at a convenient height for hand-swinging and, at the same time, dispenses with a need for wheel chocks.

Designed in late 1974, the first VariEze (N7EZ) was built over a ten-week period in the Spring of 1975 and made its first flight on 21 May, powered by a 47 kW (63 hp; 1,834 cc) Volkswagen engine. By early 1977 it had logged approximately 260 flying hours. Optimum economy cruise performance was a primary design aim, so that the prototype could be used to attack existing world distance records in the under 500 kg gross weight class C1a. On 4 August 1975 the aircraft set a new closed-circuit distance record in this class, by covering 1,415·119 nm (2,620·80 km; 1,628·49 miles). In 1979 the aircraft was being prepared for an attempt to raise the record to around 2,780 nm (5,150 km; 3,200 miles).

A second prototype (N4EZ), embodying some modifications and powered by a Continental O-200 engine, was built during the Winter of 1975-76. It represents the prototype of the version for which plans are available, and is described in detail below.

All raw materials and certain component parts of the VariEze are also available to homebuilders, including the Plexiglas canopy, moulded glassfibre nosewheel and main landing gear struts, and glassfibre cowling.

A large underfuselage drag device has been added to the VariEze to enable it to land in shorter distances. About 2,000 VariEzes are being constructed by homebuilders in many countries, and 100 were flying by early 1979.

Type: Two-seat sporting aircraft.

Wings: Cantilever mid-wing monoplane with sweptback surfaces. Single-spar structure of unidirectional glassfibre with rigid foam core. Inboard ailerons. Vertical above-wing 'winglet' surface at each wingtip includes rudder.

Canard Foreplane: Cantilever structure of unidirectional glassfibre with rigid foam core. Trailing-edge elevators of similar construction.

Fuselage: Composite structure comprising large sheets of rigid urethane foam, with wood strips as corner fillers, and internal and external covering of unidirectional glassfibre. A standard-size light alloy extrusion is used for engine, landing gear, and control stick mounts, as well as for canopy latches and other parts.

Landing Gear: Tricycle landing gear, with fixed main units and mechanically-retractable nosewheel which is carried on a glassfibre strut moulded to conform to the outside contour of the fuselage, so eliminating need for a fairing door. Nose gear retracted by hand-lever. Main wheels carried on one-piece moulded glassfibre strut. Fairings on main wheels. Hydraulically-operated brakes.

Power Plant; One 74·5 kW (100 hp) Continental O-200-B flat-four engine, mounted in the aft fuselage and driving a two-blade fixed-pitch pusher propeller with spinner. Provision for Continental C65, C75, C85 or C90 engines. Fuel tanks, of glassfibre/foam/glassfibre sandwich construction, form strakes on each side of the fuselage that fair the wing roots; total capacity 91 litres (24 US gallons). A small fuselage tank is also available. Refuelling points on each side of fuselage, on the upper surface of tanks.

Accommodation: Pilot and passenger on semi-reclining seats in individual cockpits. Side-stick controls. Dual controls limited to control stick at rear position. One-piece bubble canopy of moulded Plexiglas covers both cockpits and is hinged on starboard side. Roll-over structure. Space for 14 kg (30 lb) baggage in two specially designed suitcases which fit in rear seat area.

Systems: Hydraulic system for wheel brakes only. Can have simple electrical system with a single nav/com and gyro instrument.

Dimensions, external:

Wing span	6·77 m (22 ft 2½ in)
Wing chord at root	0·91 m (3 ft 0 in)
Wing chord at tip	0·41 m (1 ft 4 in)
Wing area, gross	4·98 m² (53·6 sq ft)
Foreplane span	3·81 m (12 ft 6 in)
Foreplane chord, constant	0·32 m (1 ft 0½ in)
Foreplane area	1·21 m² (13 sq ft)
Wing area, gross	6·22 m² (67 sq ft)
Length overall	4·32 m (14 ft 2 in)

Weights (Continental O-200 engine):

Weight empty	254 kg (560 lb)
Max T-O weight	476 kg (1,050 lb)

Performance (at max T-O weight, Continental O-200 engine):

Max cruising speed	170 knots (313 km/h; 195 mph)
Econ cruising speed	143 knots (265 km/h; 165 mph)
Landing speed	60 knots (112 km/h; 70 mph)
Stalling speed	48 knots (90 km/h; 55·5 mph)
Max rate of climb at S/L	487 m (1,600 ft)/min
T-O and landing run	275 m (900 ft)
Range at 75% power	607 nm (1,126 km; 700 miles)
Range at econ cruising speed	738 nm (1,368 km; 850 miles)

RUTAN DEFIANT

The Rutan Defiant (N78RA), which made its first flight in proof-of-concept prototype form on 30 June 1978, is a four-seat twin-engined light aircraft of unconventional design. Benefiting from experience gained with the smaller two-seat VariEze, it retains the latter's rear-mounted swept cantilever wings with winglet surfaces, canard foreplane and retractable nosewheel/fixed main-wheel type of landing gear, but is powered by two 119 kW (160 hp) Lycoming O-320 engines which are installed at the front and rear of the fuselage in tractor and pusher configurations. One 170 litre (45 US gallon) fuel tank is provided for each engine. The aircraft also has two simple separate electrical systems, each with a battery and alternator. An IFR system is installed, with the avionics split between both electrical systems to provide additional safety in the event of one failing.

The Defiant is claimed to be a very basic aircraft with no flaps, fixed-pitch propellers and few complex systems, but to provide greater leg room and comfort than other twin-engined lightplanes of larger overall size. It is also claimed that the Defiant will have no minimum control speed, will require no pilot action or configuration changes in order to continue a climb if an engine fails, and will be able to climb at its minimum full-aft-stick speed, at maximum weight, with one propeller windmilling and the nosewheel down.

By early 1979, the Defiant prototype had accumulated about 220 flying hours. It has been found, however, that the aircraft has certain minor deficiencies in design. In particular, boarding is difficult because the canopy opens only to one side and the sill is 1·27 m (4 ft 2 in) from the ground, with no wing on which to stand. Also, the baggage area has no loading door. If the decision is taken to certificate a production version, this will be modified to have a large door on each side of the cabin, opening upwards to allow step-in boarding and easy baggage loading. It will also have a more square upper fuselage section, to increase lateral headroom and baggage area.

Dimensions, external:

Wing span	8·89 m (29 ft 2 in)
Wing area, gross	11·83 m² (127·3 sq ft)
Propeller diameter	1·75 m (5 ft 9 in)

Dimensions, internal:

Cabin width, forward	1·17 m (3 ft 10 in)
Cabin width, aft	1·09 m (3 ft 7 in)

Weights:

Weight empty (IFR)	730 kg (1,610 lb)
Max T-O weight	1,315 kg (2,900 lb)

Performance:

Max cruising speed (70% power)
186 knots (344 km/h; 214 mph)

Normal cruising speed (65% power)
182 knots (337 km/h; 210 mph)

Stalling speed, nosewheel down
65 knots (121 km/h; 75 mph)

Econ cruising speed 170 knots (315 km/h; 196 mph)

Max rate of climb at S/L 488 m (1,600 ft)/min

Max rate of climb, one engine out 94 m (310 ft)/min

Range with max fuel, four adults and 36 kg (80 lb) baggage, 45 min reserves
980 nm (1,815 km; 1,128 miles)

SEQUOIA

SEQUOIA AIRCRAFT CORPORATION

900 West Franklin Street, Richmond, Virginia 23220

President: Alfred P. Scott

Sequoia Aircraft Corporation was formed by Mr Alfred P. Scott to develop the Sequoia cabin monoplane. Work on this aircraft was begun in July 1975, with all design and engineering by Mr David B. Thurston, a consultant whose other designs have included the Colonial Skimmer (now the Lake amphibian), the Teal and Marlin amphibians, and the TA-16 Trojan amphibian.

Three variations on the basic Sequoia design are available. The Model 300 Sequoia is a side-by-side two-seat aircraft, with two aft-facing rear seats optional and a sliding bubble canopy. The Model 301 (no name assigned) is a tandem two-seat aircraft with a sliding bubble canopy. The Model 302 Kodiak is a four-seat aircraft with an enclosed cabin.

The three aircraft have a high degree of commonality of parts. Kits consisting of formed and machined parts have been produced and delivered to amateur constructors who are building the first examples of the aircraft. In January 1979, twelve aircraft were under construction. Ten kits had been delivered and a further ten kits had been completed; 30 sets of plans had been sold.

In addition to marketing plans and kits to amateur aircraft builders, Sequoia Aircraft Corporation has offered the aircraft as military trainers to countries that wish to assemble their own aircraft, using local labour. Meanwhile, Aeronics (Pty) Ltd of the Republic of South Africa has signed an exclusive production agreement for manufacture of the aircraft for civilian use in South Africa. In January 1979, no date had been set for beginning production, and it was estimated that it would take about nine months to complete the necessary financing.

Rutan VariEze two-seat high-performance tail-first monoplane (foreground) flying with the Rutan VariViggen two-seat canard delta; both aircraft are now fitted with NASA 'winglets' *(Don Dwiggens)*

Artist's impression of Sequoia Models 300 *(top)* **and 301**

Sindlinger ⅝-scale replica of a Hawker Hurricane IIC

MODEL 300 SEQUOIA

Type: Two-seat utility and aerobatic monoplane.

Wings: Cantilever low-wing monoplane. Wing section NACA 64_2A215 at root, NACA 64A210 at tip. Dihedral 3° from roots. Incidence 3° 30′ at root. Washout 2°. All-metal flush-riveted structure with single I-beam spar, 2024-T4 Alclad ribs and 2024-T3 Alclad skin. Glassfibre tips. Frise balanced ailerons of aluminium construction with rubber seals. Slotted aluminium flaps.

Fuselage: Welded 4130 steel tube structure. Entire fuselage, including wing fillets, covered with lightweight shell of glassfibre/PVC foam/glassfibre sandwich, attached to tubing with glassfibre and epoxy resin. Kevlar is optional alternative to glassfibre.

Tail Unit: Conventional cantilever unit of flush-riveted aluminium alloy construction. Elevators fitted, each with trim tab. Rudder trim is bungee system.

Landing Gear: Retractable tricycle type. Electro-hydraulic retraction. Oleo-pneumatic shock-absorbers.

Power Plant: One 224 kW (300 hp) Lycoming TIO-540-S1AD flat-six engine, driving a Hartzell two-blade constant-speed propeller. Other Lycoming engines of 175-224 kW (235-300 hp) may be used. Two integral fuel tanks in wings, with total capacity of 291·5 litres (77 US gallons). Provision for tip-tanks of approximately 75 litres (20 US gallons) capacity each; and two underwing attachment points for additional fuel tanks, radar or stores of up to 272 kg (600 lb) combined weight. Refuelling points in wingtips.

Accommodation: Two seats side by side, beneath sliding Plexiglas canopy. An aft-facing rear seat can be installed to provide a two-plus-two layout. Baggage compartment, capacity 45·4 kg (100 lb).

Systems: A completely flush antenna system is being designed. The nav antennae will be in the glassfibre wingtips and the remainder will be under the fuselage shell.

Dimensions, external:
- Wing span 9·14 m (30 ft 0 in)
- Wing chord at root 1·68 m (5 ft 6 in)
- Wing chord at tip 0·91 m (3 ft 0 in)
- Wing area, gross 12·08 m² (130 sq ft)
- Wing aspect ratio 6·92
- Length overall 7·62 m (25 ft 0 in)
- Height overall 2·90 m (9 ft 6 in)
- Propeller diameter 2·03 m (6 ft 8 in)

Weights:
- Weight empty 816 kg (1,800 lb)
- Max T-O weight, utility 1,270 kg (2,800 lb)
- Max T-O weight, aerobatic 1,088 kg (2,400 lb)

Performance (estimated):
- Never-exceed speed 243 knots (450 km/h; 280 mph)
- Max level speed at S/L 195 knots (362 km/h; 225 mph)
- Max cruising speed at 2,440 m (8,000 ft) 185 knots (343 km/h; 213 mph)
- Stalling speed 'clean' 75 knots (139 km/h; 86 mph)
- Stalling speed, flaps and wheels down 60 knots (111 km/h; 69 mph)
- Max rate of climb at S/L 664 m (2,180 ft)/min
- Service ceiling 7,620 m (25,000 ft)
- T-O run 457 m (1,500 ft)
- T-O to 15 m (50 ft) 610 m (2,000 ft)
- Landing run 548 m (1,800 ft)
- Range at max cruising speed, with 45 min reserves 868 nm (1,609 km; 1,000 miles)

MODEL 301

This tandem two-seat version of the Model 300 Sequoia differs only in the following dimensional changes. Estimated performance is increased by about 8·5 knots (16 km/h; 10 mph).

Dimensions, external:
- Wing span 8·89 m (29 ft 2 in)
- Wing area 11·61 m² (125 sq ft)
- Wing aspect ratio 6·81

SEQUOIA MODEL 302 KODIAK

The Kodiak, of which a prototype is scheduled to fly before the end of 1979, is a four-seat development of the Model 300 Sequoia, using the same wing assembly, tail unit, landing gear, power plant and mount, engine cowling, firewall, control system, instrument panel and windscreen. Wingtip fuel tanks can be fitted to increase range; gull-wing doors provide access to the enclosed cabin; and the aircraft is designed to be fully aerobatic.

Power plant will be in the 186-224 kW (250-300 hp) Lycoming IO-540/TIO-540-S1AD range, driving a Hartzell two-blade constant-speed propeller with a diameter of 2·03 m (6 ft 8 in). Empty weight will be 839 kg (1,850 lb); Max T-O weight 1,451 kg (3,200 lb); fuel capacity 341 litres (90 US gallons).

SINDLINGER

SINDLINGER AIRCRAFT

37030 204th Avenue SE, Auburn, Washington 98002

Mr Fred G. Sindlinger began the design of a ⅝-scale replica of the second World War Hawker Hurricane IIC fighter in April 1969. Construction of the prototype was started three months later and the first flight was made in January 1972. By February 1977, this aircraft had accumulated a total of approximately 400 flying hours; it has since been sold.

Plans and certain component parts are available to amateur constructors; by early 1979 about 50 sets of drawings had been sold, and about 17 Sindlinger Hurricanes were under construction, including examples being built in Australia, France, Germany and the United Kingdom. The first plans-built aircraft to fly was constructed in South Africa and was flown in 1978.

SINDLINGER HH-1 HAWKER HURRICANE

Type: Single-seat sporting aircraft.

Wings: Cantilever low-wing monoplane. Wing section NACA 2418 in centre-section, with progressive change to NACA 2412 at tip. Dihedral 3° 30′ on outer panels only. Incidence 0° 36′. Sweepback at quarter-chord 3°. Two-spar structure of wood. Front spar is of I-beam construction in the centre-section and of built-up box section in the outer panels. Rear spar is an I-beam in the centre-section, and of U-channel form in the outer panels. Built-up truss ribs and 2·4 mm (3/32 in) plywood skin, fabric-covered overall. Frise-type ailerons of wood construction, fabric-covered and statically balanced. Split trailing-edge flaps of wood.

Fuselage: All-wood monocoque structure of 3·2 mm (1/8 in) plywood from firewall to aft of cockpit. Rear fuselage is a built-up box truss frame, with formers and stringers. Entire structure fabric-covered.

Tail Unit: All-wood cantilever structure. Two-spar tailplane and fin have plywood skins, covered with fabric overall. Rudder and elevators are of wood construction with fabric covering. Elevator trimmed by internal spring tension. Ground-adjustable trim tab on rudder.

Landing Gear: Manually-retractable tailwheel type. Main wheels retract inward. Shock-absorption of main and tail units by coil spring inside steel tubes. Tailwheel steerable. Goodyear main wheels and tyres size 5·00-5. Goodyear hydraulic brakes.

Power Plant: One 112 kW (150 hp) Lycoming O-320 flat-four engine, driving a Hartzell two-blade metal constant-speed propeller with spinner. Up to three fuel tanks: one in fuselage aft of firewall with capacity of 54 litres (14 US gallons) and, optionally, one in each wing root, with capacity of 38 litres (10 US gallons) each. Max total fuel capacity 130 litres (34 US gallons). Refuelling point in fuselage upper surface, forward of windscreen. Oil capacity 7·5 litres (2 US gallons). Glassfibre engine cowlings.

Accommodation: Pilot only, beneath rearward-sliding transparent canopy. Cockpit heated and ventilated. Space for 18 kg (40 lb) baggage aft of pilot's seat.

Systems: Hydraulic system for brakes only. Electrical system powered by 12V DC engine-driven generator. 12V 35Ah battery.

Electronics and Equipment: 90-channel VHF com transceiver, VOR Omni nav receiver. Partial IFR instrumentation. Wooden imitation cannon or machine-guns in wing leading-edges.

Dimensions, external:
- Wing span 7·65 m (25 ft 1 in)
- Wing chord on centre-section, constant 1·52 m (5 ft 0 in)
- Wing chord at tip 0·91 m (3 ft 0 in)
- Wing area, gross 9·38 m² (101 sq ft)
- Wing aspect ratio 6·2
- Length overall 5·99 m (19 ft 8 in)
- Height overall, tail up 1·78 m (5 ft 10 in)
- Tailplane span 2·24 m (7 ft 4 in)
- Wheel track 1·83 m (6 ft 0 in)
- Propeller diameter 1·93 m (6 ft 4 in)

Dimension, internal:
- Cockpit: Max width 0·66 m (2 ft 2 in)

WEIGHTS:
- Weight empty: 446 kg (984 lb)
- Max T-O weight: 624 kg (1,375 lb)

PERFORMANCE (at max T-O weight):
- Never-exceed speed: 208 knots (386 km/h; 240 mph)
- Max level speed at S/L: 174 knots (322 km/h; 200 mph)
- Max cruising speed, 65% power at 1,830 m (6,000 ft): 148 knots (273 km/h; 170 mph)
- Econ cruising speed, 60% power at 2,745 m (9,000 ft): 135 knots (249 km/h; 155 mph)
- Stalling speed, flaps up: 58 knots (108 km/h; 67 mph)
- Stalling speed, flaps down: 54 knots (100 km/h; 62 mph)
- Max rate of climb at S/L: 564 m (1,850 ft)/min
- Service ceiling: 6,400 m (21,000 ft)
- T-O run: 150 m (490 ft)
- Landing run: 168 m (550 ft)
- Range, 65% power, 30 min reserves: 500 nm (925 km; 575 miles)
- Max range, no reserves: 542 nm (1,005 km; 625 miles)
- *g* limits: +4·4 utility, +6·6 ultimate

SINFIELD

ROLAND A. SINFIELD

PO Box 513, Morgan, Utah 84050
Telephone: (801) 829 6726

SINFIELD HONEYBEE

The Honeybee ultra-light aircraft was designed by Mr Roland Sinfield and built with the help of Mr Klaus Hill and Mr Larry Hall. The main design aims were to produce an aircraft that was simple and inexpensive to construct, and that had a low flying speed while still being fun to fly. Because of its low speed and light weight, the Honeybee should be flown only in calm conditions, although if caught in an unexpected wind the aircraft can land in a small field. Another important point is that small variations in the weight of the pilot can be tolerated, but any major weight difference must be compensated by adding weight to either the nose or tail of the aircraft to maintain an acceptable centre of gravity location. The aircraft can be broken down into small components for storage.

The prototype Honeybee had accumulated approximately 5 hours of flying by January 1978. It had been taken to an altitude of 1,980 m (6,500 ft) above sea level, at which it was still climbing well. Development had not reached a stage where it was appropriate to sell plans to amateur constructors; but an information booklet containing construction details, photographs of components, suggestions about starting similar projects, and addresses of component suppliers is available. This also gives current news about the Honeybee and of a second aircraft, built by Mr Klaus Hill and called the Hummer, which is similar to the Honeybee but has a double-surface wing, smoother-running engine, a Vee-tail and an aluminium tube fuselage.

The following details refer to the Honeybee:

TYPE: Single-seat ultra-light aircraft.

WINGS: Wire-braced parasol wing. Dihedral 9°. Incidence 3° 30′ at root, 2° 30′ at tip. Aluminium tube structure with hang glider-type cloth covering on upper surface only. No wing control surfaces.

FUSELAGE: Four wooden stringers with plywood covering, forming box girder-type structure to which the pilot's seat, wing mounts, tail unit, engine mounts and landing gear are attached.

TAIL UNIT: Conventional wire-braced unit comprising tailplane and elevators, and vertical fin and rudder. Elevators and rudder represent the only control surfaces of the aircraft. Aluminium tube structure, fabric covered.

LANDING GEAR: Non-retractable tailskid type. Main units consist of two side Vees, attached to fuselage structure, wire-braced and with a single horizontal stay.

POWER PLANT: One 15 kW (20 hp) JLO 395 cc single-cylinder engine, driving a two-blade Banks Maxwell 42 × 20 wooden pusher propeller. Fuel capacity 3·8 litres (1 US gallon).

ACCOMMODATION: Single seat in open position.

DIMENSIONS, EXTERNAL:
- Wing span: 9·14 m (30 ft 0 in)
- Wing chord, constant: 1·52 m (5 ft 0 in)
- Wing area, gross: 13·94 m² (150 sq ft)
- Length overall: 5·44 m (17 ft 10 in)

WEIGHT:
- Weight empty: 84 kg (185 lb)

PERFORMANCE:
- Max level speed: 39 knots (72 km/h; 45 mph)
- Cruising speed: 35 knots (64 km/h; 40 mph)
- Stalling speed: 26 knots (48·5 km/h; 30 mph)
- T-O speed: 17·5 knots (32 km/h; 20 mph)
- Endurance, at full throttle: 45 min

SISLER

SISLER AIRCRAFT COMPANY

Box 20219, Bloomington, Minnesota 55420

Captain Bert Sisler is an airline pilot who had logged more than 15,000 flying hours on 67 types of aircraft by the beginning of 1979. During his flying career, he has piloted seaplanes and sailplanes, instructed on single-engined and multi-engined aircraft, and served five years as a test pilot.

The first aircraft he designed and built was the Pipit two-seater, now owned by another pilot. It was followed by the SF-2 Whistler, which gained the 'Outstanding Design Contribution' award at the 1973 EAA Fly-in at Oshkosh. Capt Sisler has subsequently improved this design, making it easier to build, aerodynamically cleaner and 23 kg (50 lb) lighter. Plans of the improved version, now known as the SF-2A Cygnet, are available to other constructors.

SISLER SF-2A CYGNET

TYPE: Two-seat light aircraft.

WINGS: Strut-braced shoulder-wing monoplane of all-wood construction, swept forward 5° from roots. Wing section NACA 3413. Dihedral 3° 30′. Each wing consists of a main spar, light front and rear auxiliary spars, six plywood ribs, some stringers, geodetic upper and lower coverings of spruce strips, and an overall Dacron covering. Fabric-covered wooden ailerons, without tabs. No flaps.

FUSELAGE: Conventional welded chrome molybdenum steel tube structure, Dacron-covered.

TAIL UNIT: Conventional strut-braced unit, comprising tailplane and elevators, vertical fin and rudder. Structure similar to that of fuselage. Trim tab in port elevator. Ground-adjustable tab on rudder.

LANDING GEAR: Non-retractable tailwheel type. Two side Vs and half axles of welded steel tube. Bungee shock-absorption. Main-wheel tyres size 5·00-5 on prototype; size 6·00-6 tyres or skis optional. Steerable tailwheel.

POWER PLANT: One 46 kW (62 hp) 1,834 cc Volkswagen modified motor car engine, driving a two-blade propeller. Fuel capacity 57 litres (15 US gallons).

ACCOMMODATION: Two seats side by side in enclosed cockpit. Windscreen made up of two door panels, hinged on centreline. Baggage capacity 23 kg (50 lb).

SYSTEM: Prototype has no electrical system, but light-weight alternator and battery are optional.

DIMENSIONS, EXTERNAL:
- Wing span: 9·14 m (30 ft 0 in)
- Wing chord, constant: 1·27 m (4 ft 2 in)
- Wing area: 11·60 m² (124·8 sq ft)
- Wing aspect ratio: 7·1
- Length overall: 5·79 m (19 ft 0 in)
- Height overall: 1·78 m (5 ft 10 in)
- Tailplane span: 2·39 m (7 ft 10 in)
- Propeller diameter: 1·47 m (4 ft 10 in)

DIMENSION, INTERNAL:
- Cockpit width: 0·99 m (3 ft 3 in)

WEIGHTS:
- Weight empty: 265 kg (585 lb)
- Max T-O weight: 499 kg (1,100 lb)

PERFORMANCE (at max T-O weight):
- Max level speed: 94 knots (174 km/h; 108 mph)
- Cruising speed at 2,440 m (8,000 ft): 87 knots (161 km/h; 100 mph)
- Stalling speed: 42 knots (78 km/h; 48 mph)
- Max rate of climb: 177 m (580 ft)/min
- T-O and landing run: 213 m (700 ft)
- *g* limit: + 4

SKYOTE

SKYOTE AEROMARINE LTD

PO Box 142, Boulder, Colorado 80306
PRESIDENT: O. E. Bartoe Jr

This company was formed to produce components for an aerobatic biplane named Skyote, which is intended for amateur construction. Its President is also President of Ball-Bartoe Aircraft Corporation (see main Aircraft section).

SKYOTE AEROMARINE SKYOTE

Construction of the prototype Skyote (N8XX), with a 67 kW (90 hp) Continental C90F engine, began in March 1975 and the first flight of this aircraft took place on 23 April 1976. FAA certification in the Aerobatic category was applied for on 17 February 1977. At that time, components for five other aircraft were being produced, the first of which was completed by Mr Duane Burnett of Boulder, and first flew in Summer 1978. This Skyote took 2,500 working hours to build. It is powered by a 74·5 kW (100 hp) Continental O-200 engine, which gives the aircraft a max cruising speed of 97 knots (180 km/h; 112 mph); a max rate of climb of 564 m (1,850 ft)/min; T-O run of 107 m (350 ft); and landing run of 168 m (550 ft). Plans are available to amateur constructors, and Univair is reportedly selling wing kits.

TYPE: Single-seat aerobatic biplane.

WINGS: Braced biplane, with two parallel interplane struts each side and two pairs of centre-section support struts. Wing section NACA (1.8)412. No anhedral or dihedral. Incidence 2°. Sweepback on all wings at quarter-chord 7° 12′. Forward-staggered upper wing. All structure of 2024 aluminium, with hydroformed ribs, fabric covered. Plain ailerons on upper and lower wings, torque tube actuated.

FUSELAGE: Truss structure of welded 4130N chrome-molybdenum steel tubing, fabric covered.

TAIL UNIT: Wire-braced unit of 4130N steel tube, fabric covered. Ground-adjustable tailplane incidence. No tabs.

LANDING GEAR: Non-retractable tailwheel type. Main wheels carried on side Vees and half-axles. Type 1280HD bungee cord shock-absorption. Cleveland main wheels and tyres size 18 × 7-6. Tyre pressure 1·24 bars (18 lb/sq in). Cleveland hydraulically-actuated disc brakes.

POWER PLANT: Aircraft used for FAA certification programme has one 88 kW (118 hp) Lycoming O-235-K2A flat-four engine, driving a Sensenich two-blade fixed-pitch propeller. Other engines can be installed, including 67 kW (90 hp) Continental C85 or C90 flat-four. Fuel tanks in wing centre-section and fuselage, each with capacity of 24·6 litres (6·5 US gallons). Total fuel capacity 49·2 litres (13 US gallons). Refuelling points in top of wing centre-section and top of fuselage. Oil capacity 7·5 litres (2 US gallons).

ACCOMMODATION: Single seat in open cockpit. Baggage compartment behind seat.

DIMENSIONS, EXTERNAL:
- Wing span: 6·10 m (20 ft 0 in)
- Wing chord, constant: 0·97 m (3 ft 2 in)
- Wing area, gross: 11·43 m² (123 sq ft)
- Wing aspect ratio: 4·22
- Length overall: 4·95 m (16 ft 3 in)
- Height overall: 2·03 m (6 ft 8 in)
- Tailplane span: 2·03 m (6 ft 8 in)
- Wheel track: 1·22 m (4 ft 0 in)
- Wheelbase: 3·66 m (12 ft 0 in)
- Propeller diameter: 1·88 m (6 ft 2 in)

WEIGHTS:
- Weight empty: 270 kg (595 lb)
- Max T-O weight: 406 kg (895 lb)

PERFORMANCE (prototype):
- Never-exceed speed: 137 knots (253 km/h; 157 mph)
- Max cruising speed, at 2,135 m (7,000 ft): 100 knots (185 km/h; 115 mph)
- Stalling speed: 38 knots (71 km/h; 44 mph)
- Max rate of climb at S/L: 579 m (1,900 ft)/min
- Service ceiling: 5,180 m (17,000 ft)
- Range with max fuel: 180 nm (333 km; 207 miles)

SMITH

MRS FRANK W. (DOROTHY) SMITH

3502 Sunny Hills Drive, Norco, California 91760

The late Frank W. Smith built and flew in October 1956 the prototype of a single-seat fully-aerobatic sporting biplane which he designated the DSA-1 (Darn Small Aeroplane) Miniplane. This aircraft (N90P) is now in the EAA Museum. Plans continue to be marketed by Mrs Smith, and about 450 sets have been sold to constructors in several countries. Many Miniplanes have been completed and flown.

Mrs Smith's son designed a two-seat version of the DSA-1, which was provisionally designated Miniplane + 1; all available details of this aircraft appeared in the 1974-75 *Jane's*. It was expected to make its first flight in Summer 1979, with a 93 kW (125 hp) Lycoming engine.

SMITH DSA-1 MINIPLANE

The following details refer to the standard Miniplane, built according to Frank Smith's original plans:

TYPE: Single-seat sporting biplane.

Sinfield Honeybee ultra-light aircraft

SF-2A Cygnet, designed and built by Bert Sisler of Bloomington, Minnesota *(Howard Levy)*

Skyote Aeromarine Skyote aerobatic biplane built by Mr Duane Burnett *(Howard Levy)*

Smith DSA-1 Miniplane built by Mr W. R. Edwards of Troy, Alabama

Smyth Sidewinder built by Mr John M. Lee of Beaumont, Texas *(Howard Levy)*

WINGS: Braced biplane with N-type interplane struts each side and two N-type strut assemblies supporting centre of top wing above fuselage. NACA 4412 wing section. Dihedral 2° on lower wings only. Incidence 0° on top wing, 2° on lower wings. All-wood structure, fabric-covered. Fabric-covered wooden ailerons on lower wings only. No flaps.

FUSELAGE: Welded steel tube structure, fabric-covered.

TAIL UNIT: Wire-braced welded steel tube structure, fabric-covered. Adjustable-incidence tailplane.

LANDING GEAR: Non-retractable tailwheel type. Tripod streamlined-tube main legs. Compression-spring shock-absorbers optional (now fitted on prototype). Goodyear main wheels and tyres, size 7·00-4, pressure 1·38 bars (20 lb/sq in). Goodyear shoe-type brakes. Scott tailwheel.

POWER PLANT: Designed to take any engine in 48·5-93 kW (65-125 hp) category. Prototype has 80·5 kW (108 hp) Lycoming O-235-C flat-four engine, driving a Sensenich two-blade metal fixed-pitch propeller. Most aircraft have a 48·5 kW (65 hp) Continental A65, 56 kW (75 hp) Continental A75 or 93 kW (125 hp) Lycoming flat-four engine. Fuel in tank in fuselage, capacity 64·5 litres (17 US gallons). Oil capacity 5·7 litres (1·5 US gallons).

ACCOMMODATION: Single seat in open cockpit. Space for 27 kg (60 lb) baggage.

DIMENSIONS, EXTERNAL:

Wing span (upper)	5·18 m (17 ft 0 in)
Wing span (lower)	4·80 m (15 ft 9 in)
Wing chord, constant (both)	0·91 m (3 ft 0 in)
Wing area, gross	9·29 m² (100 sq ft)
Length overall	4·65 m (15 ft 3 in)
Height overall	1·52 m (5 ft 0 in)
Wheel track	1·52 m (5 ft 0 in)
Propeller diameter	1·80 m (5 ft 11 in)

WEIGHTS (prototype):

Weight empty, equipped	279 kg (616 lb)
Max T-O weight	454 kg (1,000 lb)

PERFORMANCE (prototype, at max T-O weight):

Max level speed at S/L	117 knots (217 km/h; 135 mph)
Max cruising speed	102 knots (190 km/h; 118 mph)
Econ cruising speed	96 knots (177 km/h; 110 mph)
Stalling speed	48 knots (88·5 km/h; 55 mph)
Max rate of climb at S/L	380 m (1,250 ft)/min
Service ceiling	3,960 m (13,000 ft)
T-O run	107 m (350 ft)
Landing run	152 m (500 ft)
Endurance with max fuel	2 h 30 min

SMYTH

JERRY SMYTH

ADDRESS FOR PLANS AND KITS: George Blair, PO Box 815, Newbury Park, California 91320

In February 1958 Mr Smyth began the design of a sporting monoplane, setting out to evolve an aircraft that would be reasonably easy to construct, easy to fly, stressed to 9*g* for limited aerobatics, of good appearance and offering economic operation. Construction of the prototype began in January 1967, and occupied two years before completion, at a cost of around $2,500. First flight of what Mr Smyth named the Model 'S' Sidewinder was made on 21 February 1969, and this aircraft received the 'Outstanding Design' award at the EAA Fly-in at Rockford, Illinois, in 1969. Plans and kits of parts are available to amateur constructors.

An illustration in the 1975-76 *Jane's* showed a Sidewinder with retractable landing gear, built by Mr Donald Adams of Columbia City, Indiana. Powered, like the prototype, by a 93 kW (125 hp) Lycoming O-290-G engine, the retractable gear allows a max cruising speed of 156 knots (290 km/h; 180 mph), an increase of 17 knots (32 km/h; 20 mph) by comparison with Mr Smyth's prototype.

The Sidewinder illustrated was built over a five-year period by Mr John M. Lee of Beaumont, Texas. Powered by a 112 kW (150 hp) Lycoming O-320 flat-four engine, it has a maximum T-O weight of 680 kg (1,500 lb). Other specification and performance figures are similar to those of the prototype Sidewinder. It is stressed to ± 6*g*.

SMYTH MODEL 'S' SIDEWINDER

The following description applies to Mr Smyth's prototype:

TYPE: Two-seat sporting monoplane.

WINGS: Cantilever low-wing monoplane. Wing section NACA 64-612 at root, NACA 64-210 at tip. Dihedral 4°. Incidence 1° 30′. No sweepback. All-metal structure comprising a centre-section and two outer wing panels. Built-up main spar of ·040 in 2024-T3 aluminium 'U'-sections, to which flat aluminium capstrips are riveted; secondary spar is of formed sections. Eleven equally-spaced ribs in each wing panel are made of ·025 in 6061-T4 aluminium. The wing skin, of ·025 in 2024-T3 aluminium, is in three sections: leading-edge, lower and upper skin, and is flush-riveted. Wings filled with epoxy. Simple sealed-gap ailerons of aluminium construction, attached to secondary spar by piano-type hinge. No trim tabs. No flaps.

FUSELAGE: Welded steel tube structure with aluminium formers and skin. Electrically-operated speed brake may be fitted on lower fuselage.

TAIL UNIT: Cantilever all-metal structure with swept vertical surfaces. All-moving horizontal surface with electrically-operated anti-servo tab.

LANDING GEAR: Non-retractable nosewheel type. Wittman cantilever spring steel main gear. Main wheels and tyres size 5·00-5, pressure 1·72 bars (25 lb/sq in). Nose unit carries a 25·4 cm (10 in) diameter tailwheel and smooth tyre, free-castoring and non-steerable, pressure 1·72 bars (25 lb/sq in). Cleveland hydraulic brakes. Glassfibre fairings on all wheels.

POWER PLANT: Provision for installation of engines from 67-134 kW (90-180 hp). Prototype has a 93 kW (125 hp) Lycoming O-290-G flat-four engine, driving a two-blade fixed-pitch aluminium propeller with spinner. Fuel tank in fuselage, forward of instrument panel, capacity 66·2 litres (17·5 US gallons). Refuelling point on top of fuselage, forward of windscreen. Provision for wingtip tanks. Oil capacity 7·5 litres (2 US gallons).

ACCOMMODATION: Pilot and passenger, seated side by side under rearward-sliding bubble canopy. Compartment for 40·8 kg (90 lb) of baggage aft of seats. Cabin heated and ventilated.

SYSTEMS: Hydraulic system for brakes and, optionally, for operation of aerodynamic speed brake. Engine-driven generator provides 35A 12V DC for instruments, lights, electrically-operated stabilator tab and optional electrically-driven hydraulic pump to operate aerodynamic speed brake.

ELECTRONICS: Simple 10-channel VHF communications transceiver.

DIMENSIONS, EXTERNAL:

Wing span	7·57 m (24 ft 10 in)
Wing chord at root	1·52 m (5 ft 0 in)
Wing chord at tip	0·91 m (3 ft 0 in)
Wing area, gross	8·92 m² (96 sq ft)

Wing aspect ratio 6·85
Length overall 5·89 m (19 ft 4 in)
Height overall 1·66 m (5 ft 5½ in)
Tailplane span 2·33 m (7 ft 7¾ in)
Wheel track 1·70 m (5 ft 7 in)
Wheelbase 1·30 m (4 ft 3 in)
Propeller diameter 1·70 m (5 ft 7 in)
DIMENSIONS, INTERNAL:
Cabin: Max width 0·97 m (3 ft 2 in)
Baggage compartment 0·25 m³ (9 cu ft)
WEIGHTS:
Weight empty 393 kg (867 lb)
Max T-O and landing weight 657 kg (1,450 lb)
PERFORMANCE (at max T-O weight):
Never-exceed speed 173 knots (321 km/h; 200 mph)
Max level speed at 610 m (2,000 ft) 161 knots (298 km/h; 185 mph)
Max cruising speed, 75% power at 610 m (2,000 ft) 139 knots (257 km/h; 160 mph)
Stalling speed 48 knots (89 km/h; 55 mph)
Max rate of climb at S/L:
at 0°C 366 m (1,200 ft)/min
at 24°C 274 m (900 ft)/min
Service ceiling 4,570 m (15,000 ft)
T-O run 244 m (800 ft)
T-O to and landing from 15 m (50 ft) 610 m (2,000 ft)
Landing run 457 m (1,500 ft)
Range with max fuel, no reserves 369 nm (684 km; 425 miles)

SORRELL

SORRELL AVIATION

Route 1, Box 660, Tenino, Washington 98589
Telephone: (206) 264 2866

Sorrell Aviation designed and built a two-seat aerobatic biplane named the SNS-6 Hiperbipe, with the intention of providing a true HIgh PERformance BIPlane that would be suitable for construction by amateurs. Flight testing confirmed that the aircraft had an outstanding aerobatic performance and, when demonstrated and displayed at the EAA 1973 Fly-in at Oshkosh, it received the Outstanding New Design of 1973 award. Plans for the fully-developed SNS-7 'production' version are not sold separately; but a basic kit package, containing construction drawings for the aircraft and certain completed components, is available.

SORRELL SNS-7 HIPERBIPE

Design of the Hiperbipe began in 1964; construction of the SNS-6 first prototype started in June 1971. This aircraft made its initial flight in March 1973; a second prototype, modified to the SNS-7 standard offered to homebuilders, followed in March 1975.

The following details refer to the second prototype:

TYPE: Two-seat aerobatic biplane.

WINGS: Braced single-bay biplane, of modified NACA 0012 wing sections. Dihedral 1° 30′ on lower wings only. Incidence 1° 30′ on upper wing, 2° 30′ on lower wings. Sweepback 4° 30′ on lower wings only. Wide-chord welded 4130 steel I-type interplane struts and dual streamline-section landing and flying wires. Conventional structure of spruce spars, web ribs and stressed plywood skin, fabric covered overall. Centre-section of upper wing is skinned with transparent plastics to allow improved view for aerobatics. Cambered wingtips. Four full-span 'flaperons' of aluminium alloy sheet pop-riveted to aluminium torque tubes. No tabs.

FUSELAGE: Conventional structure of welded 4130 chrome-molybdenum steel tube, fabric-covered. Glassfibre engine cowling.

TAIL UNIT: Wire-braced structure of welded 4130 chrome-molybdenum steel tube, fabric-covered. Large dorsal fin. Tailplane and inset elevator extend aft of rudder trailing-edge. No tabs.

LANDING GEAR: Non-retractable tailwheel type. Wittman-type tapered spring steel rod main gear, with single wheel, glassfibre wheel fairing, and leg fairing on each unit. Cleveland 6·00-6 main wheels, with low-profile tyres. Maule 0·15 m (6 in) steerable tailwheel. Cleveland hydraulic spot disc brakes.

POWER PLANT: One 134 kW (180 hp) Lycoming IO-360-B1E flat-four engine, driving a Hartzell HC-C2YK-4AF two-blade metal constant-speed propeller with spinner. Fuel tank in fuselage, capacity 147·5 litres (39 US gallons). Christen 801 inverted oil system, capacity 7·5 litres (2 US gallons).

ACCOMMODATION: Two seats side by side in enclosed cabin. Dual controls standard. Forward-hinged door on each side. Baggage capacity 36 kg (80 lb). Cabin heated and ventilated.

SYSTEM: Full electrical system, with lights.

ELECTRONICS AND EQUIPMENT: Narco Com 11A 360-channel radio.

DIMENSIONS, EXTERNAL:
Wing span 6·96 m (22 ft 10 in)
Wing chord, constant 1·016 m (3 ft 3·9 in)
Wing area (projected) 13·9 m² (150 sq ft)
Length overall 6·35 m (20 ft 10 in)
Height overall 1·80 m (5 ft 10¾ in)
Tailplane span 2·87 m (9 ft 5 in)
Wheel track 2·16 m (7 ft 1 in)
Propeller diameter 1·93 m (6 ft 4 in)
DIMENSIONS, INTERNAL:
Cabin: Length 1·40 m (4 ft 7 in)
Max width 1·07 m (3 ft 6 in)
WEIGHTS:
Weight empty 561 kg (1,236 lb)
Max T-O weight:
Aerobatic 766 kg (1,690 lb)
Normal 867 kg (1,911 lb)
PERFORMANCE (at max T-O weight):
Never-exceed speed 195 knots (362 km/h; 225 mph)
Max level speed at S/L 149 knots (277 km/h; 172 mph)
Max cruising speed at S/L 139 knots (257 km/h; 160 mph)
Econ cruising speed 130 knots (241 km/h; 150 mph)
Stalling speed, flaperons down 43 knots (79 km/h; 49 mph)
Stalling speed, flaperons up 51 knots (94 km/h; 58 mph)
Max rate of climb at S/L 457 m (1,500 ft)/min
Service ceiling, estimated 6,100 m (20,000 ft)
T-O run 122 m (400 ft)
Landing run 181 m (595 ft)
Range 436 nm (807 km; 502 miles)

SPENCER

P. H. SPENCER

12780 Pierce Street, Pacoima, California 91331
Telephone: (213) 899 1010

Mr P. H. Spencer, who made his first solo flight in a powered aircraft on 15 May 1914, has been associated with the design of several single-engined amphibians, dating back to 1930, when Amphibians Inc of Garden City, Long Island, NY, put the Privateer amphibian into production. This was followed by the Spencer-Larsen, Spencer Air Car S-12, Republic Seabee RC 1, RC 2 and RC 3.

All of these designs, as well as the Trident TR-1 amphibian prototype (see entry in main Canadian section), are variations of Mr Spencer's basic Air Car configuration, on which he was granted a patent on 3 January 1950. This was originally a two-seat amphibian powered by an 82 kW (110 hp) engine, and was developed into a four-seat version, known as the S-12-C. Mr Spencer then completed the design of the more advanced S-12-D, of which plans are available to homebuilders as well as certain glassfibre mouldings and metal assemblies. Since that time development has continued, the installation of a Teledyne Continental Tiara 6-285-B engine resulting in a change of designation to S-12-E for the prototype. This had accumulated a total of 800 hours' flying time by early 1978, 450 of them with the Tiara engine. The wing sweepback has also been increased, from 3° to 5°.

By early 1979 at least 36 Air Cars were known to be under construction, with a variety of power plants ranging from 149 to 212·5 kW (200 to 285 hp), and 140 sets of plans had been sold. Air Car parts are currently being produced at a new facility at the address quoted.

The first S-12-E Air Car to be completed from Mr Spencer's plans made its first flight on 1 August 1974. Built by Mr Peter Breinig of Sausalito, California, it had logged 200 flying hours by early 1976. Four more Air Cars flew for the first time in 1975, three in 1976, at least two in 1977, and a further two or three in 1978. Five are S-12-Es, with 212·5 kW (285 hp) Tiara engine, and five aircraft soon to fly are also powered by Tiara engines.

Mr Spencer has also designed a new biplane hydro-glider named Drag-N-Fly. This aircraft made its first flight at the hands of Mr Spencer in 1977, on his 80th birthday, towed behind a motorboat. The Drag-N-Fly is not available for homebuilding; deliveries of completed aircraft began in 1979 (see Sailplanes section).

SPENCER AMPHIBIAN AIR CAR MODEL S-12-E

TYPE: Four-seat amphibian.

WINGS: Braced high-wing monoplane with single streamline-section bracing strut on each side. Specially-designed STOL wing section. Thickness/chord ratio 15%. Dihedral 1°. Incidence 2°. Sweepback at quarter-chord 5°. Conventional two-spar structure of wood, steel and glassfibre. Frise-type ailerons of wooden construction. Electrically-operated trailing-edge flaps. Glassfibre stabilising float mounted on strut beneath each wing at approximately two-thirds span.

HULL: Conventional single-stepped hull with wood frames, longerons and skin. Welded steel tube structure to provide wing and engine mounting and attachment points for landing gear.

TAIL UNIT: Cantilever structure, comprising conventional fin and rudder, and all-moving tailplane set approximately midway up fin. Combined anti-servo and trim tab in tailplane. Retractable water rudder in base of aerodynamic rudder.

LANDING GEAR: Manually-retractable tricycle type. Main wheels retract aft to take up a near-vertical position on each side of the cabin. Nosewheel retracts forward through almost 180° and is partially housed in the nose of the hull, above the waterline, to form a nose fender. Cantilever spring steel main gear. Main wheels and tyres size 7·00-6. Nosewheel and tyre size 6·00-6. Cleveland hydraulic disc brakes.

POWER PLANT: One 212·5 kW (285 hp) Teledyne Continental Tiara 6-285-B flat-six engine, driving a Hartzell three-blade metal constant-speed reversible-pitch pusher propeller. Fuel tanks in fuselage and wing stabilising floats. Total fuel capacity 355 litres (94 US gallons). Oil capacity 8·5 litres (2·25 US gallons).

ACCOMMODATION: Four seats in pairs in enclosed cabin. Backs of front seats fold forward to improve access. Rear seats fold back against bulkhead to provide cargo or baggage space. Baggage space in rear fuselage, aft of rear cabin bulkhead. Door on each side of fuselage, hinged at forward edge. Bow access door on starboard side, hinged on centreline and opening upward. Dual controls standard. Accommodation heated and ventilated.

SYSTEMS: Hydraulic system for brakes only. Electrical system supplied by 24V 50A engine-driven alternator.

ELECTRONICS AND EQUIPMENT: Complete IFR instrumentation. Bendix 360 nav/com transceiver.

DIMENSIONS, EXTERNAL:
Wing span 11·38 m (37 ft 4 in)
Wing chord, constant 1·52 m (5 ft 0 in)
Wing area, gross 17·1 m² (184 sq ft)
Wing aspect ratio 7·4
Length overall 8·05 m (26 ft 5 in)
Height overall 2·90 m (9 ft 6 in)
Tailplane span 3·66 m (12 ft 0 in)
Wheel track 2·54 m (8 ft 4 in)
Wheelbase 3·10 m (10 ft 2 in)
Propeller diameter 2·13 m (7 ft 0 in)
Cabin doors (port and starboard, each):
Height 0·97 m (3 ft 2 in)
Width 1·02 m (3 ft 4 in)
Height to sill 0·86 m (2 ft 10 in)
Cabin door (bow, starboard):
Length 0·89 m (2 ft 11 in)
Width 0·51 m (1 ft 8 in)
DIMENSIONS, INTERNAL:
Cabin: Length 2·59 m (8 ft 6 in)
Max width 1·14 m (3 ft 9 in)
WEIGHTS:
Weight empty 993 kg (2,190 lb)
Max T-O weight 1,451 kg (3,200 lb)
PERFORMANCE (at max T-O weight):
Max level speed at S/L 128 knots (237 km/h; 147 mph)
Max cruising speed at 1,675 m (5,500 ft) 122 knots (225 km/h; 140 mph)
Econ cruising speed, 65% power at 2,315 m (7,600 ft) 117 knots (217 km/h; 135 mph)
Stalling speed, flaps up 46 knots (86 km/h; 53 mph)
Stalling speed, 35° flap 37·5 knots (70 km/h; 43 mph)
Max rate of climb at S/L 305 m (1,000 ft)/min
T-O time from calm water at S/L 16 s
Range, 65% power at 2,375 m (7,800 ft), 20 min reserves 695 nm (1,285 km; 800 miles)

SPEZIO

WILLIAM EDWARDS

25 Madison Avenue, Northampton, Massachusetts 01060

Tony and Dorothy Spezio designed and built a two-seat light aircraft named the Tuholer, all rights of which were acquired by Mr Edwards in August 1973. He is continuing to market plans of the Tuholer to amateur constructors.

SPEZIO DAL-1 TUHOLER

Named Tuholer because of its two open cockpits, the prototype flew for the first time on 2 May 1961.

Folding wings enable the Tuholer to be kept in a normal home garage and it is towed behind a car on its own landing gear. It can be made ready for flight by two people in about 10 minutes or by one person in 20 minutes.

The following description applies to the Tuholer built by Mr Edwards to the current plans:

Sorrell Hiperbipe two-seat aerobatic biplane *(Peter M. Bowers)*

Spencer Amphibian Air Car built from plans *(Peter M. Bowers)*

Spezio Tuholer two-seat sporting aircraft

Sport Air Craft Mini Coupe single-seat sporting aircraft

TYPE: Two-seat sporting aircraft.

WINGS: Strut-braced low-wing monoplane, with streamline-section Vee bracing struts each side. Jury struts brace centre of these struts. Clark Y wing section. Dihedral 3°. Incidence 1°. Washout at wingtips 1°. Two-spar spruce structure, with plywood leading-edge and overall fabric covering. Conventional wooden ailerons. Drawings for Frise type ailerons are available. No flaps. Wings fold back along sides of fuselage for stowage.

FUSELAGE: Steel tube structure with wood or light alloy stringers and fabric covering.

TAIL UNIT: Braced steel tube structure, fabric covered. Tailplane incidence adjustable by screwjack.

LANDING GEAR: Non-retractable tailwheel type. Coil spring shock-absorption. Main units fitted with Cleveland wheels and tyres, size 6·00-6. Cleveland brakes. Tyre pressure 2·76 bars (40 lb/sq in). Steerable tailwheel. Wheel fairings optional.

POWER PLANT: One 112 kW (150 hp) Lycoming O-320 flat-four engine. Sensenich two-blade metal fixed-pitch propeller. Glassfibre fuel tank aft of firewall, capacity 90·5 litres (24 US gallons). Oil capacity 7·5 litres (2 US gallons).

ACCOMMODATION: Two persons in tandem in open cockpits. Small baggage compartment aft of rear seat.

EQUIPMENT: Nova-Tech TR-102 radio.

DIMENSIONS, EXTERNAL:
- Wing span: 7·55 m (24 ft 9 in)
- Wing chord, constant: 1·52 m (5 ft 0 in)
- Wing area, gross: 11·21 m² (120·7 sq ft)
- Wing aspect ratio: 5
- Length overall: 5·56 m (18 ft 3 in)
- Height overall: 1·57 m (5 ft 2 in)
- Tailplane span: 2·26 m (7 ft 5 in)
- Wheel track: 1·57 m (5 ft 2 in)

WEIGHTS:
- Weight empty: 408 kg (900 lb)
- Max T-O weight: 680 kg (1,500 lb)

PERFORMANCE (at max T-O weight):
- Max level speed at S/L: 130 knots (241 km/h; 150 mph)
- Cruising speed: 109-117 knots (201-217 km/h; 125-135 mph)
- Stalling speed: 48 knots (89 km/h; 55 mph)
- Max rate of climb at S/L: 732 m (2,400 ft)/min
- T-O and landing run: 61 m (200 ft)
- Endurance with max fuel: 3 h

SPORT AIR CRAFT

SPORT AIR CRAFT INTERNATIONAL

PO Box 1, Hillsboro, Oregon 97123
Telephone: (503) 985 7612
PROPRIETOR: Bill W. Johnson

Known originally as Chris Tena Aircraft Association, this concern is responsible for a lightweight all-metal single-seat sporting aircraft known as the Mini Coupe. Design originated in June 1968, and construction of the first prototype began in July 1970. This aircraft made its first flight in September 1971 and FAA certification in the Experimental category was awarded on 2 June 1972. Kits of components and materials for two alternative versions, less engine, are available to amateur constructors. Building of the Mini Coupe has now been approved also in Australia and Switzerland, where aircraft are being constructed.

SPORT AIR CRAFT MINI COUPE

Glassfibre wingtips have been added to the Mini Coupe since its early testing, to increase the wing area by 0·47 m² (5·1 sq ft). This improves the glide ratio, makes the aircraft more stable during banks, and has reduced stalling speed. A total of 256 sets of plans of the Mini Coupe had been sold by early 1979, when 27 aircraft were known to be flying.

There are two versions, as follows:

Mini Coupe. Basic model, similar to prototype, with tricycle landing gear and twin-fin tail unit. Most amateur-built Mini Coupes are of this type.

Mini Coupe TD. Generally similar to basic model, but with tailwheel landing gear and single fin and rudder. First TD was completed by Mr E. Argence of New Orleans, Louisiana, on 1 June 1977.

TYPE: Single-seat lightweight sporting aircraft.

WINGS: Cantilever low-wing monoplane. Wing section modified Clark Y. Thickness/chord ratio 7%. Incidence 0°. Conventional metal stressed-skin structure of constant chord, with glassfibre wingtips. Plain all-metal ailerons. No flaps. No trim tabs.

FUSELAGE: All-metal semi-monocoque structure.

TAIL UNIT: Cantilever all-metal structure with twin endplate fins and rudders of constant chord. Fixed-incidence tailplane. Manually controlled trim tab in centre of elevator. Alternative single fin and rudder configuration available on Mini-Coupe TG.

LANDING GEAR: Non-retractable tricycle type. Shock-absorption on all units depends on use of oversize tyres. Main wheels with tyres size 14 × 6·00-6, pressure 0·55 bars (8 lb/sq in). Nosewheel tyre size 12 × 6·00-5, pressure 0·34 bars (5 lb/sq in). Asuze drum and band brakes. Alternative non-retractable tailwheel type, with faired main wheels, on Mini Coupe TG.

POWER PLANT: One 48·5 kW (65 hp) modified Volkswagen 1,600 cc motor car engine, driving a Reese-Shores two-blade fixed-pitch wooden propeller. (Two aircraft fitted with 48·5 kW; 65 hp Continental.) One metal fuel tank in fuselage, immediately aft of firewall, capacity 49 litres (13 US gallons). Refuelling point on fuselage upper surface, forward of windscreen.

ACCOMMODATION: Single seat for pilot in open cockpit. Transparent cockpit canopy optional. Baggage compartment aft of headrest, volume 0·085 m³ (3 cu ft).

SYSTEM: Provision for electrical system, for engine starter and radio.

DIMENSIONS, EXTERNAL:
- Wing span: 7·32 m (24 ft 0 in)
- Wing chord, constant: 1·07 m (3 ft 6 in)
- Wing area, gross: 7·76 m² (83·5 sq ft)
- Length overall: 4·98 m (16 ft 4 in)
- Height overall: 1·80 m (5 ft 11 in)
- Tailplane span: 1·83 m (6 ft 0 in)
- Wheel track: 1·83 m (6 ft 0 in)
- Wheelbase (tricycle landing gear): 0·97 m (3 ft 2 in)
- Propeller diameter: 1·37 m (4 ft 6 in)

WEIGHTS (A: tricycle landing gear; B: tailwheel landing gear):
- Weight empty: A: 225 kg (497 lb)
- B: 241 kg (532 lb)
- Max T-O weight: A: 385 kg (850 lb)
- B: 408 kg (900 lb)

PERFORMANCE (at max T-O weight with 1,600 cc engine; A and B as above):
- Never-exceed speed:
  - A, B: 125 knots (231 km/h; 145 mph)
- Max level speed at 610 m (2,000 ft):
  - A: 91 knots (169 km/h; 105 mph)
  - B: 118 knots (219 km/h; 136 mph)
- Max cruising speed at 610 m (2,000 ft):
  - A: 78 knots (145 km/h; 90 mph)
  - B: 100 knots (185 km/h; 115 mph)
- Stalling speed, power off:
  - A: 42 knots (78 km/h; 48 mph)
  - B: 50·5 knots (94 km/h; 58 mph)
- Stalling speed, power on:
  - A, B: 38 knots (70 km/h; 43 mph)
- Max rate of climb at S/L: A: 229 m (750 ft)/min
  - B: 305 m (1,000 ft)/min
- Service ceiling: A, B: 3,810 m (12,500 ft)
- T-O run: A, B: 122 m (400 ft)
- T-O to 15 m (50 ft): A, B: 274 m (900 ft)
- Landing from 15 m (50 ft): A, B: 274 m (900 ft)
- Landing run: A, B: 152 m (500 ft)
- Range with max fuel, 20 min reserves:
  - A, B: 260 nm (482 km; 300 miles)

SPRATT

SPRATT AND COMPANY INC

PO Box 351, Media, Pennsylvania 19063

Mr George G. Spratt, formerly a design engineer with The Boeing Company and Consolidated Vultee (now Convair Division of General Dynamics), has completed more than 30 years' work on developing a two-piece movable-wing control system, which he claims provides improved safety factors compared with the conventional aileron, elevator and rudder control system.

While he was with Consolidated Vultee, Mr Spratt designed a roadable aircraft which featured an earlier version of his wing control system, but this did not enter production. Since that time Mr Spratt has concentrated on perfecting his idea as a private venture.

To flight test his movable-wing control system, Mr Spratt built a lightweight experimental flying-boat (N910Z) constructed almost entirely of moulded plastics; details of this can be found in the 1974-75 *Jane's*. Two further designs have followed:

SPRATT MODEL 107

Following construction and flight testing of his first experimental flying-boat, Mr Spratt designed and constructed a more advanced prototype known as the Model 107 (N2236) for public demonstration. Dimensions and weights are essentially the same as those of the test vehicle, but construction has been simplified to facilitate fabrication. The Mercury 800 modified outboard marine engine of the Model 107 is of slightly increased capacity, and produces greater horsepower with better fuel economy as a result of improved combustion chamber and inlet port design.

Mr Spratt claims that the Model 107 will neither stall nor spin, and displays 75% less reaction to turbulence than a conventional design.

Plans of this aircraft are available to amateur constructors. By early 1979 more than 80 sets had been sold, and the first amateur-built Model 107 flew in the Autumn of 1975.

Details have been received of a new hull that has been constructed for the Model 107. It is made from PVC foam, with Kevlar skin, coated with epoxy resin. Flight testing began in Spring 1979. Power for the new Model 107 is being provided by a Mercury 850 modified outboard marine engine.

The following data apply to the original version:

TYPE: Two-seat lightweight flying-boat.

WINGS: Pivoted controllable parasol wings, with inverted Vee bracing struts each side. Wing section NACA 23112. No dihedral. No sweepback. Reinforced plastics structure. No ailerons, flaps or trim tabs. Flying controls so arranged that the wings are allowed to move freely and collectively in incidence, while their incidence is controlled differentially by a steering wheel. The wings' angle of attack can be adjusted by a separate control.

HULL: Structure of polyurethane foam with reinforced plastics skin. Small water rudder interconnected with the control wheel.

TAIL UNIT: Butterfly-type tail unit, with no movable surfaces, constructed of reinforced plastics.

POWER PLANT: One 59·7 kW (80 hp) Mercury 800 modified outboard two-stroke marine engine, driving a two-blade plastics pusher propeller through an extended drive shaft, which locates the propeller between the butterfly tail surfaces. The pitch of the propeller, which is of Mr Spratt's design, is adjustable on the ground. Outboard engine type of fuel tank.

ACCOMMODATION: Two persons side by side, in open cockpit.

DIMENSIONS, EXTERNAL:

Wing span	7·32 m (24 ft 0 in)
Wing chord, constant	1·22 m (4 ft 0 in)
Wing area, gross	8·92 m² (96 sq ft)
Wing aspect ratio	6
Length overall	5·18 m (17 ft 0 in)
Height overall	1·52 m (5 ft 0 in)
Propeller diameter	1·52 m (5 ft 0 in)

WEIGHTS:

Weight empty	226 kg (500 lb)
Max T-O weight	453 kg (1,000 lb)

SPRATT MODEL 105

Mr Spratt has designed a landplane version of the movable-wing flying-boats already described, and a prototype of this aircraft (N49888) has been built by Mr Robert Quaintance of Coatsville, Pennsylvania, as the Spratt Controlwing or Model 105.

Since it first flew, several refinements have been made to the aircraft, aimed at improving its structural simplicity and its aerodynamic efficiency by reduction of fuselage drag.

Few details of the Model 105 are known, but all available information follows:

TYPE: Two-seat lightweight experimental landplane.

WINGS: As described for Model 107, except wings can be folded alongside fuselage for towing or storage.

FUSELAGE: Primarily a composite structure of polyurethane foam and glassfibre.

TAIL UNIT: Fixed vertical surface only, of polyurethane foam and glassfibre. No movable surfaces.

LANDING GEAR: Non-retractable tricycle type. Steerable nosewheel is of conventional aircraft type. Main wheels are of the automotive type to allow extensive road towing, and are fitted with fairings. Nosewheel designed to attach to a trailer hitch for road towing.

POWER PLANT: One Subaru modified motor car engine mounted in a mid-fuselage position. Two-blade fixed-pitch pusher propeller driven via an extended shaft.

ACCOMMODATION: Two seats side by side in enclosed cockpit.

DIMENSIONS, EXTERNAL:

As for Model 107 except:

Wing span	6·71 m (22 ft 0 in)
Length overall	3·81 m (12 ft 6 in)

WEIGHT:

Weight empty	249 kg (550 lb)

STATLER

WILLIAM H. STATLER

9300 Encino Avenue, Northridge, California 91325
Telephone: (213) 886 1854

While employed as an aeronautical engineer with Lockheed, from 1940 to 1972, Mr Statler built his first two homebuilt aircraft, Formula One racers known as *Ginny* and *Skeeter*. Following his retirement from Lockheed, he began work, in January 1973, on a two-seat homebuilt aircraft capable of limited aerobatic flying. Construction of what became the Firefly started in June 1973, with the help of Byrl Robinson and Claude Fiske. The Firefly was rolled out in May 1976, when taxying trials began. The first flight, piloted by Al Foss, took place on 8 October 1976.

Plans and a construction manual are available to amateur builders and 28 sets had been sold by early 1979. Meantime, work has begun on an Unlimited Class racing aircraft, of which no details are currently available.

STATLER FIREFLY

TYPE: Two-seat light monoplane.

WINGS: Cantilever low-wing monoplane. Wing section NACA 2412. Dihedral 5°. Incidence 2°. No sweepback. All-metal construction, with aluminium ribs and skins, flush-riveted. Glassfibre wingtips. All-metal ailerons and electrically-actuated plain trailing-edge flaps. Ground-adjustable tab on starboard aileron. Wings detachable for transportation.

FUSELAGE: All-metal semi-monocoque structure, with flush-riveted aluminium skin. Glassfibre engine cowl.

TAIL UNIT: Cantilever all-metal structure, with swept vertical surfaces. Fixed tailplane set at −3° incidence. Trim tab on elevator, controllable from either cockpit.

LANDING GEAR: Non-retractable tricycle type. Cantilever spring main units made from a single piece of aluminium. Ercoupe nosewheel, on oleo strut. Mainwheel tyres size 12 × 6·00-6, pressure 1·93 bars (28 lb/sq in). Nosewheel tyre size 10 × 5·00-5, pressure 1·93 bars (28 lb/sq in). Gerdes hydraulic brakes. Glassfibre wheel fairings.

POWER PLANT: One 63·5 kW (85 hp) Continental C85-12F flat-four engine, driving two-blade Wayne's Woodcraft fixed-pitch 62 × 54 propeller. Two interconnected fuel tanks in fuselage, total capacity 68 litres (18 US gallons). Refuelling point on forward tank. Oil capacity 5·7 litres (6 US quarts).

ACCOMMODATION: Two seats in tandem, under Gee Bee bubble canopy which is hinged on starboard side. Baggage compartment, capacity 22·6 kg (60 lb), in turtleback aft of rear cockpit.

SYSTEMS: Hydraulic system for brakes. 12V 35Ah battery and generator for engine starting, wing flap actuation and instruments.

ELECTRONICS: Bayside portable transceiver.

DIMENSIONS, EXTERNAL:

Wing span	5·84 m (19 ft 2 in)
Wing chord, constant	1·27 m (4 ft 2 in)
Wing area, gross	7·43 m² (80 sq ft)
Wing aspect ratio	4·6
Length overall	5·77 m (18 ft 11 in)
Height overall	2·15 m (7 ft 0½ in)
Tailplane span	2·82 m (9 ft 3 in)
Wheel track	1·37 m (4 ft 6 in)
Wheelbase	1·50 m (4 ft 11 in)
Propeller diameter	1·57 m (5 ft 2 in)

WEIGHTS:

Weight empty	379 kg (835 lb)
Max T-O weight	590 kg (1,300 lb)

PERFORMANCE:

Never-exceed speed	208 knots (386 km/h; 240 mph)
Max cruising speed at S/L	139 knots (257 km/h; 160 mph)
Econ cruising speed at 1,980 m (6,500 ft)	124 knots (230 km/h; 143 mph)
Stalling speed, flaps up	55 knots (102 km/h; 63 mph)
Max rate of climb at S/L	244 m (800 ft)/min
Service ceiling	4,875 m (16,000 ft)
T-O run	283 m (930 ft)
T-O to 15 m (50 ft)	354 m (1,160 ft)
Landing from 15 m (50 ft)	488 m (1,600 ft)
Landing run	152 m (500 ft)
Range with max fuel, no reserves	347 nm (643 km; 400 miles)

STEEN

STEEN AERO LAB INC

15623 De Gaulle Circle, Brighton, Colorado 80601
Telephone: (303) 659 7182

Mr Lamar Steen, an aerospace teacher in a Denver, Colorado, high school, designed a two-seat fully-aerobatic biplane named Skybolt which was built as a class project in the school. Simplicity of construction was a primary aim of the design, begun in June 1968, and it is stressed to +12 and −10*g*. Construction began on 19 August 1969, costing approximately $5,000, and the first flight was made in October 1970. The Skybolt received an EAA award for Best School Project. Plans are available to amateur constructors, together with fuselage and wing kits; over 2,000 sets of plans have been sold and many Skybolts are flying.

STEEN SKYBOLT

The following description applies to the prototype with 134 kW (180 hp) Lycoming engine, built under Mr Steen's supervision:

TYPE: Two-seat aerobatic biplane.

WINGS: Braced biplane with single interplane strut each side. N-type centre-section struts. Streamline-section landing and flying wires. Wing sections: upper wing NACA 63₂A015, lower wing NACA 0012. Dihedral 0° on upper wing, 2° 30′ on lower wings. Incidence (both) 1° 30′. Sweepback 6° on upper wing only. Wooden two-spar structures with spruce spars, built-up ribs and fabric covering. Fabric-covered Frise-type ailerons on upper and lower wings. Cutout in centre-section trailing-edge of upper wing.

FUSELAGE: Welded structure of 4130 chrome-molybdenum steel tube, with fabric covering.

TAIL UNIT: Wire-braced welded structure of 4130 chrome-molybdenum steel tube, with fabric covering. Adjustable trim tab in port elevator.

LANDING GEAR: Non-retractable main wheels and tailwheel. Two side Vees and half axles hinged to fuselage structure. Shock-absorption by rubber bungee. Cleveland wheels with tyres size 6·00-6, pressure 1·72 bars (25 lb/sq in). Cleveland hydraulic disc brakes. Glassfibre fairings for main wheels.

POWER PLANT: One 134 kW (180 hp) Lycoming HO-360-B1B flat-four engine, driving a McCauley two-blade fixed-pitch propeller with spinner. Provision for alternative engines of 93-194 kW (125-260 hp). Fuselage fuel tank, immediately aft of firewall, capacity 110 litres (29 US gallons). Optional tank of 37·8 litres (10 US gallons) capacity can be installed in centre-section of upper wing. Total optional fuel capacity 151·2 litres (40 US gallons). Refuelling points on fuselage upper surface, forward of windscreen, and on top surface of upper wing. Oil capacity 7·5 litres (2 US gallons).

ACCOMMODATION: Two seats in open cockpits. Provision for canopy over rear cockpit. Space for 13·6 kg (30 lb) baggage aft of rear seat.

SYSTEM: Hydraulic system for brakes only.

ELECTRONICS: Battery-powered Alpha 200 nav/com transceiver.

DIMENSIONS, EXTERNAL:

Wing span, upper	7·32 m (24 ft 0 in)
Wing span, lower	7·01 m (23 ft 0 in)
Wing chord, constant (both)	1·07 m (3 ft 6 in)
Wing area, gross	14·2 m² (152·7 sq ft)
Length overall	5·79 m (19 ft 0 in)
Height overall	2·13 m (7 ft 0 in)
Propeller diameter	1·88 m (6 ft 2 in)

WEIGHTS:

Weight empty	490 kg (1,080 lb)
Max T-O weight	748 kg (1,650 lb)

PERFORMANCE (at max T-O weight):

Max level speed	126 knots (233 km/h; 145 mph)
Cruising speed	113 knots (209 km/h; 130 mph)
Landing speed	43 knots (80·5 km/h; 50 mph)
Max rate of climb at S/L	762 m (2,500 ft)/min
Service ceiling	5,500 m (18,000 ft)
T-O run	122 m (400 ft)
Range with max fuel	390 nm (720 km; 450 miles)

STEPHENS

STEPHENS AIRCRAFT

ADDRESS FOR PLANS: Gerry Zimmerman, 8563 West Sixty-Eighth Place, Arvada, Colorado 80004

Mr C. L. Stephens designed a single-seat aerobatic monoplane specifically for homebuilders who wish to own an aircraft for competitive aerobatics. The prototype, designated Model A, was designed for Margaret Ritchie, US National Women's Aerobatic Champion in 1966, and the second aircraft, the Model B, for Dean S. Engelhardt of Garden Grove, California.

Stressed to +12*g* and −11*g*, it was the first US aircraft known to be designed around the Aresti Aerocriptografic System for competitive aerobatics. All control surfaces are fully static-balanced and the entire aircraft comes very close to being aerodynamically symmetrical. Design of the **Model A** started in July 1966 and construction of the prototype began a month later. First flight of this version was made on 27 July 1967, and of the **Model B**, with wings and ailerons of increased area and reduced fuel tankage, on 9 July 1969. Plans of the Stephens Akro are available to amateur constructors.

Spratt Model 107 two-seat movable-wing flying-boat

Spratt Model 105 two-seat landplane

Statler Firefly homebuilt two-seat light monoplane

Steen Skybolt built by Capt John Watt of Air Canada, with starboard engine cowling open *(Howard Levy)*

Stephens Akro Model B flown by Mr Dean S. Engelhardt *(Peter M. Bowers)*

Stewart Headwind built by Mr Richard F. Geide Jr of Wichita, Kansas (Volkswagen modified motor car engine)

STEPHENS AKRO

The following description applies to the prototype with 134 kW (180 hp) Lycoming engine:

TYPE: Single-seat sporting monoplane.

WINGS: Cantilever mid-wing monoplane. Wing section NACA 23012. No dihedral, incidence or sweepback. All-wood two-spar structure. One-piece wing, with solid spar passing through fuselage and positioned by means of removable top longeron sections. Rear spar in two pieces. No internal wires or compression struts. Wing covered with mahogany skin. Plain ailerons have a 4130 steel spar, and spruce ribs and trailing-edge, and are fabric-covered. Ground-adjustable trim tabs on ailerons, which are statically balanced. No flaps.

FUSELAGE: Welded 4130 steel tube structure, mostly of 0·75 in outside diameter tubing, with Ceconite covering.

TAIL UNIT: Wire-braced welded 4130 steel tube structure with swept surfaces, fabric-covered. Tailplane has variable incidence. Ground-adjustable trim tab on rudder; controllable trim tab in elevator. All control surfaces statically balanced.

LANDING GEAR: Non-retractable tailwheel type. Cantilever spring steel main gear. Goodyear main wheels and tyres size 5·00-5, pressure 1·93 bars (28 lb/sq in). Cleveland disc brakes. Maule steerable tailwheel. Glassfibre fairings on main wheels.

POWER PLANT: One 134 kW (180 hp) Lycoming AIO-360-A1A flat-four engine, driving a Sensenich Type 7660 two-blade fixed-pitch metal propeller. Model A has fuel system for prolonged inverted flight, Model B has both fuel and oil system so modified. Model B can also have optional constant-speed propeller. Fuel tank in fuselage, forward of instrument panel. Model A has fuel capacity of 121 litres (32 US gallons), Model B has capacity of 102 litres (27 US gallons). Refuelling point on top of fuselage, forward of windscreen. Oil capacity 7·5 litres (2 US gallons).

ACCOMMODATION: Single seat for pilot under rearward-sliding bubble canopy. Large window in underfuselage, forward of control column. Model B has, in addition, a quarter window in each side of the fuselage, beneath the wings. Forced-air ventilation.

SYSTEM: Hydraulic system for brakes only.

ELECTRONICS: Battery-operated Bayside transceiver.

DIMENSIONS, EXTERNAL:

Wing span	7·47 m (24 ft 6 in)
Wing chord at root	1·60 m (5 ft 3 in)
Wing chord at tip: Model A	0·76 m (2 ft 6 in)
Model B	0·91 m (3 ft 0 in)
Wing area, gross: Model A	8·73 m^2 (94 sq ft)
Model B	9·29 m^2 (100 sq ft)
Length overall	5·82 m (19 ft 1 in)
Height overall	1·73 m (5 ft 8 in)
Tailplane span	2·44 m (8 ft 0 in)
Wheel track	1·37 m (4 ft 6 in)
Propeller diameter	1·93 m (6 ft 4 in)

WEIGHTS:

Weight empty: Model A	385 kg (850 lb)
Model B	431 kg (950 lb)
Max T-O weight: Model A	544 kg (1,200 lb)
Model B	589 kg (1,300 lb)

PERFORMANCE (at 544 kg; 1,200 lb T-O weight):

Never-exceed speed	191 knots (354 km/h; 220 mph)
Max level speed at 610 m (2,000 ft)	148 knots (274 km/h; 170 mph)
Max cruising speed at 610 m (2,000 ft)	139 knots (257 km/h; 160 mph)
Econ cruising speed at 610 m (2,000 ft)	109 knots (201 km/h; 125 mph)
Stalling speed	48 knots (89 km/h; 55 mph)
Max rate of climb at S/L	1,220 m (4,000 ft)/min
Service ceiling	6,705 m (22,000 ft)
T-O run	61 m (200 ft)
T-O to 15 m (50 ft)	122 m (400 ft)
Landing from 15 m (50 ft)	457 m (1,500 ft)
Landing run	183 m (600 ft)
Range with max fuel	303 nm (563 km; 350 miles)

STEWART

STEWART AIRCRAFT CORPORATION

11420 State Route 165, Salem, Ohio 44460
Telephone: (216) 332 0865

Mr Donald Stewart formed this company to market plans of a simple single-seat light aircraft named the Headwind, of which he designed and built a prototype. During 1969 he designed a new wing for the Headwind and this is an integral part of the plans available to homebuilders. A two-seat version is under construction, and by early 1979 the wings, ailerons, fuselage and vertical tail surfaces had been completed. Mr Stewart expects to power this aircraft with either a 44·5 kW (60 hp) Franklin or 1,600 cc Volkswagen modified motor car engine with Maximizer.

Work on the original single-seat Headwind was followed by design and construction of the JD$_2$FF Foo Fighter, which is described separately.

Latest of Mr Stewart's projects is a foot-launched ultralight aircraft, with wings that can be dismounted in 5 minutes, without tools. Power will be provided by a 7·45 kW (10 hp) Chrysler engine with Maximizer. Empty weight will be 43·5 kg (96 lb), max T-O weight 159 kg (350 lb), cruising speed 43·5-48 knots (80·5-88·5 km/h; 50-55 mph) and landing speed 10·5-13 knots (19·5-24 km/h; 12-15 mph).

STEWART JD$_1$ HW 1·7 HEADWIND

Built in only five months, the prototype Headwind flew for the first time on 28 March 1962, and has since undergone considerable refinement. Plans are available to amateur constructors, who can build the aircraft with either an open or enclosed cockpit. The wings can be removed or fitted in about 20 minutes by two people.

The power plant of the prototype Headwind has a belt-driven propeller reduction drive designed by Mr Stewart. Given the name Maximizer, this unit was put into production in the Spring of 1972 and is available to amateur constructors for use with Volkswagen power plants.

Several thousand sets of plans for the Headwind have been sold. About 250 aircraft are believed to be under construction, with approximately 30 already flying, including examples in Mexico and South Africa.

TYPE: Single-seat light aircraft.

WINGS: Strut-braced high-wing monoplane, with streamline-section Vee bracing strut each side. Wing section NACA 4412. Dihedral 2°. Incidence 2°. Two spruce spars, steel tube compression members, drag and anti-drag wires, plywood ribs, fabric covering. Frise-type ailerons of similar construction to wings. No flaps.

FUSELAGE: Welded steel tube structure, fabric-covered.

TAIL UNIT: Braced steel tube structure, fabric-covered. Ground-adjustable tailplane incidence. Fixed tabs on rudder and starboard elevator.

LANDING GEAR: Non-retractable tailwheel type. Shock-absorption by low-pressure tyres. Hayes main wheels with Goodyear tyres size 8·00-4. Tyre pressure 0·83 bars (12 lb/sq in). Alternatively, rubber-in-compression shock-struts, with Cleveland or Goodyear wheels and tyres size 6·00-6, tyre pressure 1·24 bars (18 lb/sq in). No brakes. Steerable tailwheel.

POWER PLANT: One 27 kW (36 hp) modified Volkswagen 1,192 cc motor car engine, driving a special Stewart/Kirk two-blade fixed-pitch propeller via a

Stewart belt-driven reduction unit, ratio 1·6 : 1. Engines weighing up to 84 kg (185 lb) can be utilised. Fuel tank aft of firewall, capacity 19 litres (5 US gallons). Oil capacity 2·4 litres (5 US pints).

ACCOMMODATION: Single seat in open or enclosed cockpit, with door on starboard side. Provision for up to 4·5 kg (10 lb) baggage in net, directly aft of cockpit.

DIMENSIONS, EXTERNAL:

Wing span	8·61 m (28 ft 3 in)
Wing chord, constant	1·22 m (4 ft 0 in)
Wing area, gross	10·3 m² (110·95 sq ft)
Wing aspect ratio	7
Length overall	5·41 m (17 ft 9 in)
Height overall	1·68 m (5 ft 6 in)
Tailplane span	2·13 m (7 ft 0 in)
Wheel track	1·52 m (5 ft 0 in)
Wheelbase	4·11 m (13 ft 6 in)
Propeller diameter	1·57 m (5 ft 2 in)

WEIGHTS:

Weight empty	198 kg (437 lb)
Max T-O and landing weight	317 kg (700 lb)

PERFORMANCE (at max T-O weight):

Never-exceed speed	95·5 knots (177 km/h; 110 mph)
Max level speed at S/L	69·5 knots (129 km/h; 80 mph)
Cruising speed	65 knots (121 km/h; 75 mph)
Stalling speed	32-33 knots (58-61 km/h; 36-38 mph)
Max rate of climb at S/L	122 m (400 ft)/min
Absolute ceiling	3,355 m (11,000 ft)
T-O run	91 m (300 ft)
T-O to 15 m (50 ft)	365 m (1,200 ft)
Landing from 15 m (50 ft)	490 m (1,600 ft)
Landing run	137 m (450 ft)
Endurance with max fuel, no reserves	2½ h

STEWART JD₂FF FOO FIGHTER

Design of Mr Stewart's Foo Fighter began in October 1967 and the first prototype (N2123) made its first flight in June 1971 powered by a six-cylinder Ford Falcon motorcar engine developing 89·5 kW (120 hp) at 3,800 rpm. This engine was replaced subsequently by a 93 kW (125 hp) Franklin Sport 4.

A second prototype of the Foo Fighter (N2124), with a 93 kW (125 hp) Lycoming engine, was sold for exhibition flights at Lafayette Escadrille '76 in Pennsylvania. During 1972, Mr Stewart designed new wings for the Foo Fighter, of increased span and chord. Since that time he has modified the design to allow for installation of Lycoming flat-four engines of up to 112 kW (150 hp), and has made refinements to the fuselage, tail unit and landing gear. Sets of plans of the Foo Fighter are available to amateur constructors. About 85 examples are thought to be under construction, and one Foo Fighter has been completed in Connecticut, reportedly with a Continental C90 flat-four engine.

The following description is applicable to the aircraft in fully-updated form:

TYPE: Single-seat lightweight sporting biplane.

WINGS: Braced single-bay biplane. Wing section NACA 4412. Dihedral 0° upper wing, 1° lower wing. Incidence 2° upper wing, 0° lower wing. Conventional structure with two wooden spars and wooden truss ribs, fabric-covered. N-type interplane struts each side; two N-type struts, joined at their upper ends, support the centre of the upper wing above fuselage. The lower wing extends below the fuselage, being attached to a cabane, and is faired over with light gauge light alloy sheet. Streamline-section landing and flying wires. Cutout in trailing-edges of both wings. Frise-type ailerons of similar construction to wings. No flaps. No trim tabs.

FUSELAGE: Welded steel tube structure with wood formers and stringers, fabric-covered.

TAIL UNIT: Wire-braced welded steel tube structure with fabric covering. Tailplane incidence adjustable on ground or, optionally, controllable in flight. Fixed tab in starboard elevator.

LANDING GEAR: Non-retractable tailwheel type, with steerable tailwheel or tailskid. Two side Vees with half-axles attached to fuselage structure. Shock-absorption by rubber cords in tension. Stewart wheels with tyres size 3·00-16, pressure 2·76 bars (40 lb/sq in). Stewart mechanical band brakes.

POWER PLANT: One 93 kW (125 hp) Franklin Sport 4 flat-four engine, driving a two-blade wooden fixed-pitch propeller. Provision for Lycoming flat-four engine of up to 112 kW (150 hp). Fuel contained in aluminium tank mounted in fuselage immediately aft of firewall, capacity 72 litres (19 US gallons). Refuelling point on fuselage upper surface. Oil capacity 3·75 litres (1 US gallon).

ACCOMMODATION: Single seat in open cockpit. Space for 4·5 kg (10 lb) baggage aft of seat.

DIMENSIONS, EXTERNAL:

Wing span (both)	6·30 m (20 ft 8 in)
Wing chord, constant (both)	1·02 m (3 ft 4 in)
Wing area, gross	12·08 m² (130 sq ft)
Wing aspect ratio	6·075
Length overall	5·72 m (18 ft 9 in)
Height overall	2·13 m (7 ft 0 in)
Tailplane span	1·93 m (6 ft 4 in)
Wheel track	1·75 m (5 ft 9 in)
Wheelbase	3·76 m (12 ft 4 in)
Propeller diameter	1·83 m (6 ft 0 in)

WEIGHTS:

Weight empty	328 kg (725 lb)
Max T-O weight	499 kg (1,100 lb)

PERFORMANCE (at max T-O weight):

Never-exceed speed	126 knots (233 km/h; 145 mph)
Max cruising speed	100 knots (185 km/h; 115 mph)
Stalling speed	42 knots (77·5 km/h; 48 mph)
Max rate of climb at S/L	366 m (1,200 ft)/min
T-O run	137 m (450 ft)
Landing run	168 m (550 ft)

STOLP

STOLP STARDUSTER CORPORATION

4301 Twining, Riverside, California 92509
Telephone: (714) 686 7943
PRESIDENT: Jim Osborne
GENERAL MANAGER: Eric Shilling
SECRETARY-TREASURER: Hanako Osborne

Mr Louis A. Stolp and Mr George M. Adams designed and built a light single-seat sporting biplane known as the Starduster, which flew for the first time in November 1957; and founded Stolp Starduster Corporation to market to amateur constructors plans, components and basic materials for the Starduster and subsequent designs. On 1 May 1972 this company was acquired by Jim and Hanako Osborne, who continue to trade under the original name.

Plans of the SA-100 Starduster are no longer available; but the company continues to market plans, kits and materials for the two-seat Starduster Too, single-seat Starlet, aerobatic V-Star, Acroduster 1 and Acroduster Too. In addition, it is marketing plans for a replica of the Fokker D.VII, the G/B Special designed by Glenn Beets and the Knight Twister designed by Vernon Payne.

STOLP SA-300 STARDUSTER TOO

The SA-300 Starduster Too is an enlarged two-seat version of the original SA-100 Starduster, and is suitable for engines of 93-194 kW (125-260 hp). The weight and performance figures quoted apply to the example illustrated (N2MR), which won the Grand Champion award at the 1977 EAA Fly-in at Oshkosh. It has a 149 kW (200 hp) Lycoming HIO-360-A1A engine, driving a McCauley constant-speed propeller.

TYPE: Two-seat sporting biplane.

WINGS: Biplane wings of unequal span with a single interplane strut each side. Multiple centre-section bracing struts. Streamline section landing and flying wires. Wing section M-6 modified. Dihedral 1° 30′ on lower wings only. Incidence 1° on lower wings only. Sweepback on leading-edge of upper wing 6°. All-wood structure with spruce spars and ribs of 6·5 mm (¼ in) plywood, fabric-covered. Ailerons of wooden construction, fabric-covered, on both upper and lower wings. No trailing-edge flaps.

FUSELAGE: Welded 4130 steel tube structure with fabric covering. Glassfibre turtleback.

TAIL UNIT: Welded 4130 steel tube structure with fabric covering. Wire-braced fixed-incidence tailplane.

LANDING GEAR: Non-retractable tailwheel type. Rubber cord shock-absorption. Wheel fairings on main units. Hydraulic brakes.

POWER PLANT (prototype): One 134 kW (180 hp) Lycoming O-360-A1A flat-four engine, driving a two-blade fixed-pitch propeller with spinner. Fuel tank in fuselage, immediately aft of firewall.

ACCOMMODATION: Two seats in tandem open cockpits.

The specification and performance details which follow apply to the radial-engined Starduster Too with a 123 kW (165 hp) Warner Super Scarab engine, built by Mr Jack Mills of Zionsville, Indiana, which was illustrated in the 1973-74 *Jane's:*

DIMENSIONS, EXTERNAL:

Wing span, upper	7·32 m (24 ft 0 in)
Wing chord, constant (both)	1·22 m (4 ft 0 in)
Length overall	6·63 m (21 ft 9 in)
Height overall	2·21 m (7 ft 3 in)

WEIGHTS:

Weight empty	517 kg (1,139 lb)
Max T-O weight	907 kg (2,000 lb)

PERFORMANCE (at max T-O weight, except where stated):

Max level speed	174 knots (322 km/h; 200 mph)
Max cruising speed	133 knots (246 km/h; 153 mph)
Econ cruising speed	100 knots (185 km/h; 115 mph)
Stalling speed	51 knots (94 km/h; 58 mph)
Sustained rate of climb, pilot only	548 m (1,800 ft)/min

STOLP SA-500 STARLET

The SA-500 Starlet is a single-seat swept parasol-wing monoplane. The wing is of wooden construction with spruce spars, plywood web and capstrip ribs, with Dacron covering. It has a Clark YH section; sweepback is 9° and incidence 3° 30′. The fuselage is of welded 4130 steel tube with Dacron covering, and the tail unit is a braced structure of the same materials. The non-retractable tailwheel-type landing gear has cantilever main legs with wheel fairings. Power plant in the prototype consists of a 1,500 cc Volkswagen flat-four engine, driving a fixed-pitch two-blade propeller with spinner. Other engines of 63·5-93 kW (85-125 hp) may be fitted, the 80·5 kW (108 hp) Lycoming being recommended.

Construction of the prototype occupied three months and cost $1,500. First flight was made on 1 June 1969.

The following details refer to the prototype:

DIMENSIONS, EXTERNAL:

Wing span	7·62 m (25 ft 0 in)
Wing chord	0·91 m (3 ft 0 in)
Wing area, gross	7·71 m² (83 sq ft)
Length overall	5·18 m (17 ft 0 in)
Height overall	2·03 m (6 ft 8 in)

WEIGHT:

Max T-O weight	340 kg (750 lb)

PERFORMANCE (at max T-O weight):

Cruising speed	78 knots (145 km/h; 90 mph)
Landing speed	48-52 knots (89-97 km/h; 55-60 mph)

STOLP SA-700 ACRODUSTER 1

Introduced in 1973, the SA-700 is a single-seat fully-aerobatic biplane. Ailerons on both wings produce a roll rate in excess of 240° a second, and an interesting design feature is that the four ailerons are raised slightly when the control column is pulled back. This helps maintain aileron control when the aircraft is stalled in a normal attitude. Conversely, the ailerons are drooped slightly when the control column is pushed forward, which helps to maintain aileron control in an inverted stall. Plans and kits of components are available to amateur constructors.

TYPE: Single-seat aerobatic biplane.

WINGS: Braced single-bay biplane. Single I-type interplane strut each side. N-type centre-section struts. Streamline-section flying and landing wires. Aerofoil section Osborne A-1. Upper wing swept back 6°. Conventional two-spar structure. Spruce spars, plywood ribs and fabric covering. Ailerons on both wings. Upper wing built as two separate panels, joined by bolts at the centre. Stressed to $\pm 9g$ ultimate.

FUSELAGE: All-metal semi-monocoque structure of light alloy.

TAIL UNIT: Cantilever structure of light alloy.

LANDING GEAR: Non-retractable tailwheel type. Main wheels carried on sprung cantilever legs of 2024-0 T-4 light alloy. Fairings for main wheels.

POWER PLANT: Prototype had originally a 149 kW (200 hp) Lycoming flat-four engine, driving a two-blade fixed-pitch propeller with spinner, but was re-engined subsequently with a 134 kW (180 hp) engine. Design is suitable for engines of 93-149 kW (125-200 hp). Fuel tank in fuselage, aft of firewall, capacity 94·5 litres (25 US gallons). Refuelling point on upper fuselage forward of windscreen.

ACCOMMODATION: Single seat in open cockpit. Space for 23 kg (50 lb) of baggage in turtledeck compartment.

DIMENSIONS, EXTERNAL:

Wing span, upper	5·79 m (19 ft 0 in)
Wing area, gross	9·75 m² (105 sq ft)
Length overall	4·80 m (15 ft 9 in)
Height overall	1·91 m (6 ft 3 in)

WEIGHTS (prototype with 149 kW; 200 hp engine):

Weight empty	335 kg (740 lb)
Aerobatic T-O weight	476 kg (1,050 lb)
Max T-O weight	539 kg (1,190 lb)

PERFORMANCE (prototype with 149 kW; 200 hp engine, at AUW of 476 kg; 1,050 lb):

Max level speed	156 knots (290 km/h; 180 mph)
Cruising speed	143 knots (266 km/h; 165 mph)
Stalling speed	61 knots (113 km/h; 70 mph)
Max rate of climb at S/L	more than 914 m (3,000 ft)/min
Endurance at cruising speed, with reserves	2 h

STOLP SA-750 ACRODUSTER TOO

The SA-750 is basically a two-seat aerobatic biplane generally similar to the Starduster Too. Stressed to $\pm 9g$, it has symmetrical wings, the upper wing being swept back 6°, and is powered by a 149 kW (200 hp) Lycoming IO-360 engine driving a two-blade constant-speed propeller. The front cockpit is open and has a small windscreen. A bubble canopy for the rear cockpit is faired neatly to the turtleback.

DIMENSIONS, EXTERNAL:

Wing span, upper	6·53 m (21 ft 5 in)
Wing area, gross	12·1 m² (130 sq ft)
Length overall	5·64 m (18 ft 6 in)
Height overall	2·08 m (6 ft 10 in)

PERFORMANCE (at max T-O weight):

Cruising speed	139 knots (257 km/h; 160 mph)
Stalling speed	48 knots (88·5 km/h; 55 mph)
Max rate of climb at S/L	701 m (2,300 ft)/min

STOLP SA-900 V-STAR

To meet the demand for low-cost, low-horsepower aircraft with aerobatic capability, Stolp has introduced the

Stewart JD₂FF Foo Fighter (Franklin Sport 4 engine) *(Howard Levy)*

Stolp SA-300 Starduster Too built by Mr Roger Rourke of Culver City *(Howard Levy)*

Stolp SA-900 V-Star (Lycoming O-290-D2 engine) *(Howard Levy)*

Stolp SA-500 Starlet built in England by Mr S. S. Miles *(Air Portraits)*

SA-750 Acroduster Too built by Mr Jim Osborne, President of Stolp Starduster Corporation (Lycoming IO-540-N1A5 engine) *(Howard Levy)*

Stolp SA-700 Acroduster 1 (Lycoming IO-360-A1A engine) *(Howard Levy)*

SA-900 V-Star, which is essentially a biplane version of the single-seat SA-500 Starlet.

It is stressed to ±9*g*. The wings, of Clark YH section, have N centre-section and I interplane struts. Incidence of the upper wing is 2° 30′ and that of the lower wings 2°. The upper wing is swept back 6°.

The prototype has a 48·5 kW (65 hp) Continental flat-four engine, driving a two-blade fixed-pitch propeller, but engines of 44·5-93 kW (60-125 hp) may be installed.

DIMENSIONS, EXTERNAL:
- Wing span, upper: 7·01 m (23 ft 0 in)
- Wing area, gross: 13·1 m² (141 sq ft)
- Length overall: 5·23 m (17 ft 2 in)
- Height overall: 2·26 m (7 ft 5 in)

PERFORMANCE (prototype, at max T-O weight):
- Cruising speed: 65 knots (121 km/h; 75 mph)
- Stalling speed: 30·5 knots (56·5 km/h; 35 mph)
- Max rate of climb at S/L: 183 m (600 ft)/min

TAYLOR

C. GILBERT TAYLOR

Aero Industries, Camareo, California

TAYLOR BIRD

In 1976 Mr C. Gilbert Taylor, founder of the original Taylor Aircraft (Taylorcraft) Company and creator of the Cub design, unveiled his latest aircraft. Named the Bird, this is a two-seat lightplane of unusual configuration, designed for operation from small fields.

Materials and component parts, such as the main load-bearing member and pre-formed graphite-epoxy fairings, are available from Aero Industries.

At the 1976 Oshkosh meeting, the Taylor Bird received the EAA award for the 'Best New Design or Innovation'.

TYPE: Two-seat ultra-light aircraft.

WINGS: Cantilever shoulder-wing monoplane. Wing section NACA 23015. Small dihedral. Conventional aluminium alloy structure, with rectangular box-type main spar, drawn ribs and pop-riveted Alclad T3 skin. Plastics composite root section, which remains attached to fuselage when wings are removed for towing or storage. Double-canted endplates at tips. Full-span metal ailerons, each with slot on outboard 20%. No flaps or tabs.

FUSELAGE: Main load-bearing member comprises a 5·4 m (17 ft 8½ in) long, 150 mm (6 in) diameter 6061-T6 aluminium alloy tube, to which are bolted two pylons for the cabin/landing gear/engine/wing group and the tail unit assembly. All fairings, including cabin enclosures, of graphite-epoxy.

TAIL UNIT: Cantilever structure of aluminium alloy honeycomb, with plastics leading-edges. Constant-chord horizontal surfaces, with one-piece elevator.

LANDING GEAR: Non-retractable tailwheel type. Cantilever aluminium alloy main units, with solid industrial wheels and toe-operated disc brakes. Steerable tailwheel.

POWER PLANT: One 48·5 kW (65 hp) watercooled Subaru 1,400 cc converted motor car engine, driving a two-blade pusher propeller via a timing belt speed reduction.

ACCOMMODATION: Two seats in tandem in fully-enclosed cabin. Access by sliding forward entire nose fairing and windscreen assembly.

DIMENSIONS, EXTERNAL:
- Wing span: 7·92 m (26 ft 0 in)
- Wing chord, constant: 1·27 m (4 ft 2 in)
- Length overall: 5·33 m (17 ft 6 in)
- Height overall: 1·68 m (5 ft 6 in)

WEIGHTS:
- Weight empty: 209 kg (460 lb)
- Max T-O weight: 408 kg (900 lb)

PERFORMANCE (estimated):
- Max level speed: 109 knots (201 km/h; 125 mph)
- Max cruising speed: 100 knots (185 km/h; 115 mph)
- Landing speed: 35 knots (64·5 km/h; 40 mph)
- T-O run: 61 m (200 ft)
- Endurance: 4 h

TEDDE

TURNER EDUCATIONAL DEVELOPMENT ENTERPRISES

3717 Ruth Road, Fort Worth, Texas 76118
Telephone: (817) 284 8038
PRESIDENT: Ray Kendall

The 1966-67 *Jane's* contained details of a single-seat sporting aircraft designated T-40, which was designed and built by Mr E. L. Turner and flew for the first time on 3 April 1961. This aircraft was modified by Mr Turner and his son into a prototype of the two-seat T-40A and has since formed the basis of a succession of developed versions of the same general design.

Plans are now distributed by Turner Educational Development Enterprises (TEDDE), which is also responsible for continued design and development of the series of aircraft, with Mr Turner available as a consultant. A total of 412 sets of plans had been sold by January 1979.

Unfinished prototype of the Bird two-seat lightplane, designed by Mr C. Gilbert Taylor *(Howard Levy)*

Turner Super T-40A built by Dr Jim Mandley

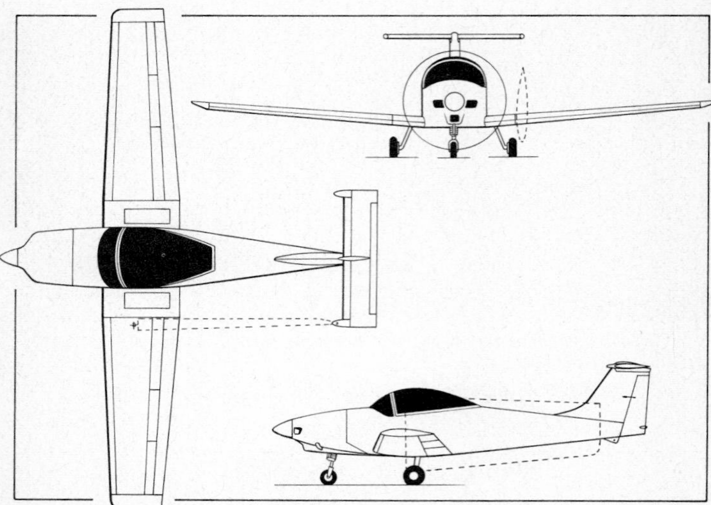

Turner T-40C two-seat sporting and aerobatic aircraft with non-retractable landing gear *(Roy J. Grainge)*

The latest version of the basic T-40 design is the T-40C, utilising the NASA GAW general aviation wing section; spoilers without ailerons for roll control; and aerodynamically-operated leading-edge slats. The T-40C will undergo flight testing and development as a testbed for a new series of single-engined sporting aircraft, beginning with a four-seater.

All Turner aircraft have folding wings, for reduced hangar space requirements and for transport by trailer. Approval for construction by amateur builders is being sought in Australia, England and South Africa.

TURNER T-40A

The prototype T-40A was produced by conversion of the original T-40. Modification took about four months and the aircraft flew for the first time in this form on 29 July 1966.

The T-40A is small enough to fit in a single-car garage and is transported on a small trailer. It has built-in skids in the fuselage, to protect the pilot in a minor crash landing, and an overturn structure.

TYPE: Two-seat sporting aircraft.

WINGS: Cantilever low-wing monoplane. Wing section NACA 65-215. Dihedral 4°. Incidence 1° 30′. All-wood (fir) two-spar structure with mahogany plywood covering. Hoerner low-drag tips. Plain ailerons. Large plain flaps. Wings fold rearward for stowage.

FUSELAGE: All-wood (fir) structure, covered with mahogany plywood. Glassfibre engine cowling.

TAIL UNIT: Cantilever all-wood (fir) structure with mahogany plywood covering. Horizontal surface of all-flying type with anti-servo tabs. Glassfibre dorsal fin.

LANDING GEAR: Non-retractable tailwheel type. Cantilever spring steel main units attached to front spar. Cleveland main wheels and tyres, size 5·00-5, pressure 3·10 bars (45 lb/sq in). Cleveland brakes.

POWER PLANT: One Continental flat-four engine of 63·5-74·5 kW (85 to 100 hp), driving a McCauley two-blade fixed-pitch propeller, type 65/57. Fuel tank in front fuselage, capacity 75 litres (20 US gallons). Oil capacity 3·75 litres (1 US gallon).

ACCOMMODATION: Pilot and passenger side by side. Each half of transparent canopy is hinged on centreline of aircraft to form a door, folding in two as it opens upward. Space for 11·5 kg (25 lb) baggage aft of seats.

EQUIPMENT: Prototype had Narco Mark III radio.

DIMENSIONS, EXTERNAL:
Wing span 7·67 m (25 ft 2 in)
Wing chord, constant 1·08 m (3 ft 6½ in)
Wing area, gross 8·35 m² (89·9 sq ft)
Wing aspect ratio 7·2
Length overall 6·02 m (19 ft 9 in)
Width, wings folded 2·39 m (7 ft 10 in)
Height overall 1·83 m (6 ft 0 in)
Tailplane span 1·96 m (6 ft 5 in)
Wheel track 2·24 m (7 ft 4 in)

DIMENSION, INTERNAL:
Cabin: Max width 1·02 m (3 ft 4 in)

WEIGHTS:
Weight empty 376 kg (828 lb)
Max T-O and landing weight 640 kg (1,410 lb)

PERFORMANCE (63·5 kW; 85 hp engine, at max T-O weight):
Never-exceed speed 191 knots (354 km/h; 220 mph)
Max level speed at S/L
130 knots (241 km/h; 150 mph)
Max cruising speed at S/L
113 knots (209 km/h; 130 mph)
Econ cruising speed at S/L
104 knots (193 km/h; 120 mph)
Stalling speed, flaps up
51·5 knots (95 km/h; 59 mph)
Stalling speed, flaps down
47 knots (87 km/h; 54 mph)
Max rate of climb at S/L 229 m (750 ft)/min
Service ceiling 3,660 m (12,000 ft)
T-O run 380 m (1,250 ft)
T-O to 15 m (50 ft) 730 m (2,400 ft)
Landing from 15 m (50 ft) 520 m (1,700 ft)
Landing run 305 m (1,000 ft)
Range with max payload, 20 min reserves
412 nm (756 km; 475 miles)

TURNER SUPER T-40A

The Super T-40A differs from the standard T-40A by having a larger wing, more powerful engine, swept tail, bubble canopy and other improvements. The prototype made its first flight in early 1972.

WINGS: As for T-40A, except span and chord increased.

TAIL UNIT: As for T-40A, except swept vertical surfaces, and vertical and horizontal surfaces of increased area.

LANDING GEAR: Non-retractable tailwheel type standard, with optional non-retractable or retractable tricycle type.

POWER PLANT: One 93 kW (125 hp) flat-four engine standard; provision for engines of up to 112 kW (150 hp).

ACCOMMODATION: As for T-40A, except for having a bubble canopy.

DIMENSIONS, EXTERNAL:
Wing span 8·13 m (26 ft 8 in)
Wing chord, constant 1·17 m (3 ft 10 in)
Wing area, gross 9·5 m² (102·5 sq ft)
Wing aspect ratio 6·98
Length overall 6·12 m (20 ft 1 in)

WEIGHTS:
Weight empty 445 kg (980 lb)
Max T-O weight 703 kg (1,550 lb)

PERFORMANCE (at max T-O weight):
Max level speed at S/L
152 knots (282 km/h; 175 mph)
Max cruising speed 135 knots (249 km/h; 155 mph)
Stalling speed, flaps down
43·5 knots (81 km/h; 50 mph)
Max rate of climb at S/L 425 m (1,400 ft)/min

TURNER T-40C

The T-40C utilises the T-40A fuselage and incorporates simplified model aeroplane type construction. The wing has a highly modified and computer-developed version of the NASA GAW general aviation section and incorporates a quick-folding mechanism. A retractable tandem-type landing gear was intended to be fitted; but in order to get the aircraft completed without further delay, a non-retractable gear has been substituted initially.

In January 1979 the prototype T-40C was expected to fly within three months.

TYPE: Two-seat sporting aircraft.

WINGS: Cantilever low-wing monoplane. NASA GAW-2 general aviation wing section. All-wood (fir) two-spar structure, with mahogany plywood covering. Hoerner low-drag tips. Aerodynamically-operated leading-edge slats. Hydraulically-actuated, single-slotted, full-span Fowler flaps. Spoilers without supplemental ailerons, in six sections, for roll control, and ground spoilers. Wings fold rearward, incorporating a quick-folding mechanism.

FUSELAGE: All-wood (fir) structure, covered with mahogany plywood. Glassfibre engine cowling. Central section embodies the wing centre-section structure, landing gear, engine mounting and cockpits. Rear fuselage carries the tail unit.

TAIL UNIT: Cantilever all-wood (fir) T-tail structure with mahogany plywood covering. Horizontal surface of all-flying type with anti-servo tab, which serves also as a trim tab. Glassfibre dorsal fin.

LANDING GEAR: Non-retractable tricycle type fitted initially. Electrically-retractable tandem type, with retractable balancer wheels at mid-span, is being considered. Cantilever main units attached to front spar. Cleveland main wheels and tyres, size 5·00-5, pressure 3·10 bars (45 lb/sq in). Cleveland brakes.

POWER PLANT: One 112 kW (150 hp) Lycoming flat-four engine, driving a McCauley two-blade fixed-pitch propeller, type 65/57. Fuel tanks in front fuselage, capacity 95 litres (25 US gallons), and in centre-section, capacity 60 litres (16 US gallons). Oil capacity 3·75 litres (1 US gallon).

ACCOMMODATION: Pilot and passenger side by side under rearward-sliding transparent canopy. Space for 22·5 kg (50 lb) baggage aft of seats.

EQUIPMENT: Prototype has Narco Mark III, Com III, Nav II, transponder, AM/FM radio receiver and CB transceiver.

DIMENSIONS, EXTERNAL:
Wing span 8·53 m (28 ft 0 in)
Wing chord 1·08 m (3 ft 6½ in)
Wing area, gross 9·48 m² (102 sq ft)
Wing aspect ratio 9·2
Length overall 6·12 m (20 ft 1 in)
Width, wings folded 2·39 m (7 ft 10 in)
Height overall 1·83 m (6 ft 0 in)
Tailplane span 1·96 m (6 ft 5 in)

DIMENSIONS, INTERNAL:
Cabin: Length 1·78 m (5 ft 10 in)
Max width 1·02 m (3 ft 4 in)

WEIGHTS:
Weight empty 376 kg (828 lb)
Max T-O and landing weight 748 kg (1,650 lb)

PERFORMANCE (112 kW; 150 hp engine, at max T-O weight):
Never-exceed speed 225 knots (418 km/h; 260 mph)
Max ɪevel speed at S/L
165 knots (306 km/h; 190 mph)
Max cruising speed at S/L
152 knots (282 km/h; 175 mph)
Econ cruising speed at S/L
122 knots (225 km/h; 140 mph)
Stalling speed, flaps up 51 knots (94 km/h; 58 mph)
Stalling speed, flaps down
41 knots (76 km/h; 47 mph)
Max rate of climb at S/L 457 m (1,500 ft)/min
Estimated service ceiling 6,400 m (21,000 ft)
T-O run 152 m (500 ft)
T-O to 15 m (50 ft) 305 m (1,000 ft)
Landing run 91 m (300 ft)
Range, max payload, 20 min reserves
521 nm (965 km; 600 miles)

Thompson Boxmoth (one two-cylinder snowmobile engine)

Thompson Boxmoth with wing panels folded

Thompson Special high-speed monoplane (Lycoming TIO-540 engine)
(Howard Levy)

Metal Hurlant two-seat monoplane designed and built by Dr Norman Thompson
(Henry Artof)

THOMPSON
THOMPSON AIRCRAFT

336 Fitzwater Street, Philadelphia, Pennsylvania 19147
Telephone: (215) 925 8942
PRESIDENT: Richard R. Thompson

THOMPSON BOXMOTH

Mr Richard R. Thompson has designed and built the prototype of a unique light aircraft known as the Thompson Boxmoth. Intended as an easy-to-build low-speed ultra-light type for the homebuilder, its construction requires no welding, machining, sheet metal, woodwork, or conventional fabric or dope. All materials and components can be purchased from local hardware and farm supply stores and from distributors of recreational vehicles. Any high-performance, lightweight snowmobile, motorcycle or outboard engine can be fitted. The wings fold against the main frame for towing behind a car or for storage in a one-car garage.

Licences to build the Boxmoth are available, together with three-view drawings, detail photos, notes and progress reports of the development and flight testing of the prototype; but it is not intended to sell completed aircraft or certificated plans at present. Estimated time to build a Boxmoth, by bolting together and wire-bracing the strong but flexible rhomboidal and triangular structure that supports the eight wing panels, seat, power plant and landing gear, is 134 man-hours; estimated cost of the aircraft is $1,555. By early 1979 about 16 licences had been issued.

Development of the Boxmoth began in October 1968; construction of the prototype was started in January 1970. It flew for the first time in November 1975 and had made approximately a dozen flights by early 1978. An FAA Experimental Airworthiness Certificate was granted on 18 May 1978.

Patent rights in the Boxmoth are reserved by Mr Richard R. Thompson, and no unauthorised production, use or sale of the Boxmoth concept is permitted without authorisation.

During the Autumn of 1978 Mr Thompson increased the span of the forward wing by 20%, adding 3·72 m² (40 sq ft) to the area and decreasing the dihedral/anhedral angles of the wing cell panels. The modification required changing only four wing spars and adding small extension panels laced to the tips of the original fabric panels. This decreased the power needed for take-off from 6,000 rpm to 4,500 rpm, at an airspeed of 22-26 knots (40-48 km/h; 25-30 mph).

The following details refer to the Boxmoth prototype without the forward wing modification, although this will be standard on future aircraft:

TYPE: Single-seat tandem biplane type.

WINGS: Rhomboidal wings at front and rear of aircraft. The four panels making up each wing assembly consist of aluminium leading-edge spars of irrigation pipe and single-surface sail-type panels of Mothsilk nylon-reinforced vinyl, with curved ribs of lightweight aluminium tubing sewn into the fabric. Each pair of top and bottom spars is pivoted to the centre-frame and bolted together at the tip, to form a triangular structure. Spars of forward wing fold backward, spars of rear wing fold forward for stowage, with fabric panels furled and lashed to centre frame. Lateral control by ailerons made of Mothsilk on aluminium frame, supplemented at low speed by differential flexing of the trailing-edges of the forward wing cells, by means of struts and cables.

FUSELAGE FRAME: Wire-braced open frame, mainly of 50 mm (2 in) aluminium tubing, bolted together. Vertical centre-frame comprises a pair of bottom longerons supporting the pilot's seat, controls and engine; an upper longeron carried on a forward N structure and two forward-sloping parallel members at rear. A further longeron extends the full length of the aircraft on each side, from the leading-edge of the forward wing to the trailing-edge of the rear wing, providing wingtip attachments for both sets of spars and for the flexible trailing-edges of the Mothsilk panels. A further cross-stay extends between the side longerons in line with the trailing-edge of the front wing.

TAIL UNIT: All-moving elevator pivoted at mid-point of rearmost vertical frame member. Rudder between this member and the parallel member forward of it. Both surfaces made of Mothsilk on aluminium frame. Elevator is supplemented by collective flexing of trailing-edges of rear wing panels in low-speed flight.

LANDING GEAR: Non-retractable tailwheel type. Main legs of nylon-braced Tuf-Rod plastic. Utility type tyres. No brakes required.

POWER PLANT: Prototype has one 41 kW (55 hp) 650 cc two-cylinder two-stroke snowmobile engine, driving a Thompson Aircraft two-blade variable-pitch propeller via two-strand chain drive 3:1 reduction gearing. Provision for variety of alternative engines. One 9·5 litre (2·5 US gallon) translucent plastics utility container serves as fuel tank. Provision for larger tankage.

ACCOMMODATION: Underslung PVC seat for pilot, mounted between two bottom longerons.

DIMENSIONS, EXTERNAL:

Wing span (original panels)	approx 6·10 m (20 ft 0 in)
Wing span (current long span panels)	approx 7·32 m (24 ft 0 in)
Wing chord, front	1·83 m (6 ft 0 in)
Wing chord, rear	1·22 m (4 ft 0 in)
Wing area, gross (original panels)	37·16 m² (400 sq ft)
Wing aspect ratio (original panels)	3·3
Length overall	7·92 m (26 ft 0 in)
Width, wings folded	1·37 m (4 ft 6 in)
Height overall	3·35 m (11 ft 0 in)
Tailplane span	3·05 m (10 ft 0 in)
Wheel track	1·37 m (4 ft 6 in)
Wheelbase	3·66 m (12 ft 0 in)
Propeller diameter	1·83 m (6 ft 0 in)

WEIGHTS:

Weight empty	159 kg (350 lb)
Max T-O weight	249 kg (550 lb)

PERFORMANCE:

Never-exceed speed	48 knots (88 km/h; 55 mph)
Max level and cruising speed	39 knots (72 km/h; 45 mph)
Econ cruising speed	35 knots (64·5 km/h; 40 mph)
Stalling speed	26 knots (48·5 km/h; 30 mph)
Max rate of climb (estimated)	152 m (500 ft)/min
Service ceiling (estimated)	3,050 m (10,000 ft)
T-O run	61 m (200 ft)
T-O run to 15 m (50 ft)	91 m (300 ft)
Landing from 15 m (50 ft)	91 m (300 ft)
Landing run	30·5 m (100 ft)
Range, with 38 litres (10 US gallons) of fuel	173 nm (321 km; 200 miles)

THOMPSON
JOHN A. THOMPSON

4940 East 22nd Street, Tucson, Arizona 85711

THOMPSON SPECIAL

Mr John A. Thompson has designed and built a single-seat high-speed all-metal monoplane based loosely on the Bushby M-II Mustang II. Construction took a year and cost $10,000. First flight was made in September 1977. Power is provided by a 231 kW (310 hp) Lycoming TIO-540 engine, taken from a Piper Navajo and driving a three-blade propeller with spinner.

Other aircraft built by Mr Thompson have included a Dyke Delta and a Bede BD-4 with a Mazda engine. The following data refer to the Thompson Special, of which plans are not available to amateur builders.

DIMENSIONS, EXTERNAL:

Wing span	7·32 m (24 ft 0 in)
Length overall	6·58 m (21 ft 7 in)
Height to top of fin	1·55 m (5 ft 1 in)

WEIGHTS:

Weight empty	687 kg (1,515 lb)
Max T-O weight	1,089 kg (2,400 lb)

PERFORMANCE:

Max cruising speed	304 knots (563 km/h; 350 mph)
Landing speed	87 knots (161 km/h; 100 mph)
Max rate of climb at S/L	over 914 m (3,000 ft)/min
Service ceiling	9,145 m (30,000 ft)
T-O run	244 m (800 ft)
Landing run	457 m (1,500 ft)
Range with max fuel	1,302 nm (2,414 km; 1,500 miles)

THOMPSON

DR NORMAN THOMPSON

Torrance, California

THOMPSON METAL HURLANT

Dr Norman Thompson, a dentist, has designed and built a tandem two-seat all-metal strut-braced high-wing monoplane known as the Metal Hurlant. Construction required 2,300 working hours over a ten-year period. Cost of building, presumably minus the 48·5 kW (65 hp) Lycoming O-145-B2 engine, was $950, due mainly to the use of surplus materials. The Metal Hurlant reportedly has a complex and strong structure, with design limits of ±10g, and made its first flight on 9 July 1978. Its general configuration can be seen in the accompanying illustration. No flaps are fitted.

DIMENSIONS, EXTERNAL:
- Wing span: 7·01 m (23 ft 0 in)
- Wing chord, constant: 0·99 m (3 ft 3 in)
- Length overall: 4·88 m (16 ft 0 in)
- Height overall: 1·37 m (4 ft 6 in)

WEIGHTS:
- Weight empty: 312 kg (688 lb)
- Max T-O weight: 544 kg (1,200 lb)

PERFORMANCE:
- Max level speed: 104 knots (193 km/h; 120 mph)
- Max cruising speed: 91 knots (169 km/h; 105 mph)
- Landing speed: 61 knots (113 km/h; 70 mph)
- Max rate of climb at S/L: 183 m (600 ft)/min
- T-O run: 244 m (800 ft)
- Landing run: 274 m (900 ft)
- Range with max fuel: 304 nm (563 km; 350 miles)

THORP

THORP ENGINEERING COMPANY

PO Box 516, Sun Valley, California 91352

This company was founded by Mr John W. Thorp, who is well known as a designer of light aircraft. It markets plans of the T-18 Tiger two-seat all-metal sporting aircraft. More than 1,300 sets of drawings had been sold and over 200 T-18s were flying by early 1979.

For a number of years there have been more T-18s in attendance at the annual EAA Fly-in at Oshkosh, Wisconsin, than any other type of homebuilt.

THORP T-18 TIGER

First T-18 to be completed was N9675Z with a 134 kW (180 hp) Lycoming O-360 engine. Built by Mr W. Warwick, it flew for the first time on 12 May 1964 and was illustrated in the 1964-65 *Jane's*.

More than 160 of the T-18s under construction and flying in 1979 are T-18Cs, with folding wings designed by Mr Luther Sunderland of Apalachin, NY. These wings can be folded back on each side of the fuselage, for road transport, in less than five minutes.

Between 1 August and 30 September 1976, a T-18 piloted by Mr Don Taylor became the first homebuilt aircraft to circumnavigate the world, covering more than 21,400 nm (39,633 km; 24,627 miles) in 171·5 flying hours.

The aircraft illustrated was built by Mr Paul White and took three years to construct at a cost of $17,000. It won for Mr White awards for 'Outstanding Innovations on a T-18' and 'Reserve Grand Champion' at the 1978 EAA Oshkosh Fly-in. It has full IFR equipment, added aileron gap seals, balanced control surfaces, split wheel fairings, flush engine exhaust pipes, a NASA injector air inlet and strobes. The Hartzell constant-speed propeller has swept-back tips to reduce noise. Modifications to the fuselage include added stringers, and heavier gauge metal skins are used on the inner wing sections. Power is provided by a 149 kW (200 hp) Lycoming HIO-360 modified helicopter engine. First flight was made in December 1977. Because of the modifications, empty weight is increased to 499 kg (1,100 lb). Max T-O weight is 862 kg (1,900 lb), max level speed 204 knots (378 km/h; 235 mph), max cruising speed 182 knots (338 km/h; 210 mph), landing speed 78 knots (145 km/h; 90 mph), max rate of climb 910 m (3,000 ft)/min and range 738 nm (1,368 km; 850 miles).

The following details apply to the standard Thorp T-18:

TYPE: Two-seat high-performance sporting aircraft.

WINGS: Cantilever low-wing monoplane, with 8° dihedral on outer panels only. All-metal two-spar structure. Normally no flaps, but a flap installation is under design. Folding wings optional. With these, the centre-section span is reduced but the outer panels are lengthened to give an overall wing span of 7·67 m (25 ft 2 in).

FUSELAGE: All-metal structure, without double curvature.

TAIL UNIT: Cantilever all-metal structure.

LANDING GEAR: Non-retractable tailwheel type. Cantilever main legs. Steerable tailwheel. Main-wheel tyres size 5·00-5.

POWER PLANT: One Lycoming or Continental flat-four engine in 80·5-149 kW (108-200 hp) category, driving a two-blade fixed-pitch propeller. Fuel tank aft of firewall, capacity 110 litres (29 US gallons).

ACCOMMODATION: Two seats side by side in open cockpit, with dual controls. Space for 36 kg (80 lb) baggage. Canopy optional.

DIMENSIONS, EXTERNAL:
- Wing span (non-folding): 6·35 m (20 ft 10 in)
- Wing chord, constant: 1·27 m (4 ft 2 in)
- Wing area, gross: 8·0 m² (86 sq ft)
- Length overall: 5·54 m (18 ft 2 in)
- Height overall: 1·47 m (4 ft 10 in)
- Tailplane span: 2·10 m (6 ft 11 in)
- Propeller diameter: 1·60 m (5 ft 3 in)

WEIGHTS (134 kW; 180 hp Lycoming):
- Weight empty: 408 kg (900 lb)
- Max T-O weight: 683 kg (1,506 lb)

PERFORMANCE (134 kW; 180 hp Lycoming):
- Max level speed at S/L: 174 knots (321 km/h; 200 mph)
- Max cruising speed: 152 knots (282 km/h; 175 mph)
- Stalling speed: 57 knots (105 km/h; 65 mph)
- Max rate of climb at S/L: 610 m (2,000 ft)/min
- Service ceiling: 6,100 m (20,000 ft)
- T-O run: 91 m (300 ft)
- Landing run: 275 m (900 ft)
- Range with max fuel: 434 nm (805 km; 500 miles)

VAN'S

VAN'S AIRCRAFT

22730 SW Francis, Beaverton, Oregon 97005
Telephone: (503) 649 5378

Mr Richard VanGrunsven designed and built a single-seat all-metal sporting aircraft known as Van's RV-3. It was built over a 2½-year period, from 1968, at a cost of approximately $2,000, and won its designer the Best Aerodynamic Detailing award at the 1972 EAA Fly-in. In addition to trailing-edge flaps, it has drooping ailerons to improve low-speed control.

After the RV-3's first flight, and subsequent EAA award, Mr VanGrunsven formed Van's Aircraft to market plans to amateur constructors. By early 1979 at least 650 sets of plans had been sold, with about 200 aircraft under construction and at least 32 RV-3s flying, including the prototype.

VAN'S RV-3

The RV-3 illustrated set the current FAI Class C1a speed record of 172·40 knots (319·28 km/h; 198·39 mph) over a 3 km course on 11 July 1976. Its builder and pilot was Mr William M. Pomeroy of Norval, Ontario, Canada. It is powered by a 119 kW (160 hp) Lycoming O-320 flat-four engine.

The following data apply to the basic plans-built RV-3:

TYPE: Single-seat sporting monoplane.

WINGS: Cantilever low-wing monoplane. Wing section NACA 23012. Dihedral 3° 30′. Incidence 1°. Conventional 2024-T3 light alloy structure of constant chord, with I-beam main spar, light rear spar, pressed ribs and moulded glassfibre tips. All-metal bottom-hinged plain trailing-edge flaps. All-metal Frise-type ailerons, which can be drooped to augment flaps. No tabs.

FUSELAGE: All-metal semi-monocoque structure of 2024-T3 light alloy. Glassfibre engine cowling.

TAIL UNIT: Cantilever structure of light alloy, with glassfibre tips. Trim tab in port elevator.

LANDING GEAR: Non-retractable tailwheel type. Cantilever tapered steel-spring main gear struts, with streamline fairings. Cleveland main wheels with tyres size 14 × 5·00-5, pressure 1·38 bars (20 lb/sq in). Steerable tailwheel with 0·15 m (6 in) diameter tyre. Cleveland brakes. Glassfibre streamlined fairings on main wheels.

POWER PLANT: One 93 kW (125 hp) Lycoming O-290-G (GPU) flat-four engine, driving a Sensenich two-blade fixed-pitch propeller with spinner. Fuel capacity 91 litres (24 US gallons).

ACCOMMODATION: Pilot only, beneath rearward-sliding Plexiglas bubble canopy. Baggage space aft of seat, capacity 0·23 m³ (8 cu ft).

DIMENSIONS, EXTERNAL:
- Wing span: 6·07 m (19 ft 11 in)
- Wing chord, constant: 1·37 m (4 ft 6 in)
- Wing area, gross: 8·36 m² (90 sq ft)
- Wing aspect ratio: 4·43
- Length overall: 5·79 m (19 ft 0 in)
- Height overall: 1·55 m (5 ft 1 in)
- Tailplane span: 2·13 m (7 ft 0 in)
- Wheel track: 1·73 m (5 ft 8 in)
- Wheelbase: 4·29 m (14 ft 1 in)
- Propeller diameter: 1·73 m (5 ft 8 in)

DIMENSION, INTERNAL:
- Cabin: Width: 0·64 m (2 ft 1 in)

WEIGHTS:
- Weight empty: 315 kg (695 lb)
- Max T-O weight: 476 kg (1,050 lb)

PERFORMANCE (at max T-O weight):
- Never-exceed speed: 191 knots (354 km/h; 220 mph)
- Max level speed at S/L: 169 knots (314 km/h; 195 mph)
- Max cruising speed at 2,440 m (8,000 ft): 161 knots (298 km/h; 185 mph)
- Econ cruising speed at 3,050 m (10,000 ft): 139 knots (257 km/h; 160 mph)
- Stalling speed, flaps up: 45·5 knots (84 km/h; 52 mph)
- Stalling speed, flaps down: 42 knots (78 km/h; 48 mph)
- Max rate of climb at S/L: 579 m (1,900 ft)/min
- Service ceiling: 6,400 m (21,000 ft)
- T-O run: 61 m (200 ft)
- Landing run: 91·5 m (300 ft)
- Range, no reserves: 520 nm (965 km; 600 miles)

VAN'S RV-6

This side-by-side two-seat light aircraft was designed by Mr VanGrunsven at the request of Mr Art Chard of Bronson, Missouri, who built it in 15 months. First flight was made on 26 April 1977. Like the RV-3, it is of all-metal construction, with glassfibre cowlings, tips and fairings. Power plant is a 112 kW (150 hp) Lycoming O-320 flat-four engine.

Plans of the RV-6 are not currently available.

DIMENSIONS, EXTERNAL:
- Wing span: 7·32 m (24 ft 0 in)
- Wing chord, constant: 1·47 m (4 ft 10 in)
- Length overall: 6·10 m (20 ft 0 in)

WEIGHTS:
- Weight empty: 454 kg (1,000 lb)
- Max T-O weight: 680 kg (1,500 lb)

PERFORMANCE:
- Max level speed: 152 knots (281 km/h; 175 mph)
- Max cruising speed: 139 knots (257 km/h; 160 mph)
- Landing speed: 44 knots (81 km/h; 50 mph)
- Range with max fuel: 347 nm (643 km; 400 miles)

VOLMER

VOLMER AIRCRAFT

Box 5222, Glendale, California 91201
Telephone: (213) 247 8718

Mr Volmer Jensen, well known as a designer of sailplanes and gliders, also designed and built a two-seat light amphibian named the Sportsman. Construction of the prototype began in September 1957 and this aircraft flew for the first time on 22 December 1958. It has since logged more than 1,600 flying hours.

Plans of the Sportsman are available to amateur constructors. About 800 sets had been sold by early 1979 and approximately 100 Sportsman amphibians are flying. Some have tractor propellers, but this modification is not recommended by Mr Jensen.

VOLMER VJ-22 SPORTSMAN

The following details refer to Mr Jensen's prototype:

TYPE: Two-seat light amphibian.

WINGS: Braced high-wing monoplane. Dihedral 1°. Incidence 3°. Wings are standard Aeronca Chief or Champion assemblies with wooden spars, light alloy ribs and fabric covering, and carry stabilising floats under the tips. Plans of newly-designed wing, with wooden ribs and spars, available. Streamline V bracing struts each side.

FUSELAGE: Conventional flying-boat hull of wooden construction, covered with mahogany plywood and coated with glassfibre.

TAIL UNIT: Strut-braced steel tube structure, fabric-covered.

LANDING GEAR: Retractable tailwheel type. Rubber-cord shock-absorption. Manual retraction. Cleveland wheels and mechanical brakes. Tyre pressure 1·38 bars (20 lb/sq in). Castoring retractable tailwheel with integral water rudder.

POWER PLANT: 63·5 kW (85 hp) Continental C85, 67 kW (90 hp) or 74·5 kW (100 hp) Continental O-200-B flat-four engine, driving a Sensenich two-blade fixed-pitch pusher propeller. Fuel in a single tank, capacity 76 litres (20 US gallons). Oil capacity 4·25 litres (4·5 US quarts).

ACCOMMODATION: Two seats side by side in enclosed cabin with dual controls.

DIMENSIONS, EXTERNAL:
- Wing span: 11·12 m (36 ft 6 in)

Thorp T-18 built by Mr Paul White *(Howard Levy)*

Van's RV-3 built by Mr William Pomeroy *(Neil A. Macdougall)*

Van's RV-6, a two-seat development of the RV-3

The original Volmer VJ-22 Sportsman, named *Chubasco*

Watson GW-1 Windwagon (half an 1,800 cc Volkswagen modified motor car engine) *(Howard Levy)*

Wag-Aero CUBy Sport Trainer, an updated version of the Piper Cub for construction by homebuilders

Wing chord	1·52 m (5 ft 0 in)
Wing area, gross	16·3 m² (175 sq ft)
Wing aspect ratio	7·2
Length overall	7·32 m (24 ft 0 in)
Height overall	2·44 m (8 ft 0 in)

WEIGHTS (63·5 kW; 85 hp):

Weight empty	454 kg (1,000 lb)
Max T-O weight	680 kg (1,500 lb)

PERFORMANCE (63·5 kW; 85 hp, at max T-O weight):

Max level speed at S/L	83 knots (153 km/h; 95 mph)
Max cruising speed	74 knots (137 km/h; 85 mph)
Stalling speed	39 knots (72 km/h; 45 mph)
Max rate of climb at S/L	183 m (600 ft)/min
Service ceiling	3,960 m (13,000 ft)
Range with max fuel, no reserves	260 nm (480 km; 300 miles)

WAG-AERO

WAG-AERO INC

PO Box 181, 1216 North Road, Lyons, Wisconsin 53148
Telephone: (414) 763 9588
PRESIDENT: Richard H. Wagner

Wag-Aero supplies plans and kits of parts which enable amateur constructors to build modern versions of the Piper Cub and Vagabond light aircraft.

WAG-AERO CUBy

Wag-Aero plans and kits offer homebuilders the choice of four different modern versions of the famous Piper Cub. Known as the CUBy Sport Trainer, the basic two-seat sporting aircraft follows the original design, but benefits by utilising up-to-date constructional techniques. The wing has a wooden main spar and ribs, light alloy leading-edge and fabric covering. The fuselage and tail unit are of welded 4130 chrome molybdenum steel tube with fabric covering. The CUBy can be powered by any flat-four Continental, Franklin or Lycoming engine of between 48·5 and 93 kW (65 and 125 hp).

Also available are the CUBy Acro Trainer which differs from the standard version by having a strengthened fuselage, shortened wings, modified lift struts, improved wing fittings and rib spacing, and a new leading-edge; the CUBy Observer which is a replica L-4 military liaison aircraft; and the Super-CUBy with structural modifications to accept engines of up to 112 kW (150 hp), making it suitable for glider towing, bush operations, or for operation as a floatplane.

Design of the CUBy began in 1974 and construction of a prototype started in December of that year. First flight took place on 12 March 1975. By February 1979 plans for approximately 610 CUBys had been ordered.

The following details apply to the standard CUBy Sport Trainer:

DIMENSIONS, EXTERNAL:

Wing span	10·73 m (35 ft 2½ in)
Wing chord, constant	1·60 m (5 ft 3 in)
Wing area, gross	16·58 m² (178·5 sq ft)
Wing aspect ratio	6·96
Length overall	6·82 m (22 ft 4½ in)
Height overall	2·03 m (6 ft 8 in)

WEIGHTS:

Weight empty	327 kg (720 lb)
Max T-O weight	635 kg (1,400 lb)

PERFORMANCE (at max T-O weight):

Max level speed at S/L	89 knots (164 km/h; 102 mph)
Cruising speed	82 knots (151 km/h; 94 mph)
Stalling speed	34 knots (63 km/h; 39 mph)
Max rate of climb at S/L	149 m (490 ft)/min
Service ceiling	over 3,660 m (12,000 ft)
T-O run	114 m (375 ft)
Range at cruising speed with standard fuel (45 litres; 12 US gallons)	191 nm (354 km; 220 miles)
Range with auxiliary fuel (98 litres; 26 US gallons)	395 nm (732 km; 455 miles)

WAG-AERO WAG-A-BOND

The name Wag-A-Bond covers two aircraft which can be built by amateur constructors: a replica of the Piper PA-15 Vagabond, known as the Classic, and the Traveler. The latter is a modified and updated version of the Vagabond with port and starboard doors, overhead skylight window, extended sleeping deck (conversion from aircraft to camper interior taking about two minutes and accommodating two persons), extended baggage area, engine of up to 85·7 kW (115 hp), and provision for a full electrical system.

A prototype Wag-A-Bond was completed by Wag-Aero in May 1978 and has been test flown successfully. The following details apply to both versions, unless stated otherwise:

TYPE: Two-seat light monoplane.

WINGS: Strut-braced high-wing monoplane. Fabric-covered all-wood structure of spruce spar and ribs, with mahogany plywood gussets. Fabric-covered aluminium ailerons. V bracing struts. Steel drag and anti-drag wires.

FUSELAGE: Welded 4130 steel tube and flat plate structure, fabric-covered.

TAIL UNIT: Wire-braced structure, comprising tailplane with elevators, vertical fin and rudder, all of welded 4130 steel tube, fabric-covered.

LANDING GEAR: Non-retractable tailwheel type. Welded steel tube side Vs and half-axles. Bungee shock-absorption. Cleveland wheels, size 6·00-6, and 7·00-6 tyres, covered by fairings. Cleveland brakes. Skis optional.

Power Plant: Traveler can be powered by a Lycoming engine of 80·5-85·7 kW (108-115 hp), driving a two-blade wooden or metal propeller. Classic can be powered by a Continental engine of 48·5-74·5 kW (65-100 hp) driving a similar propeller. Fuel capacity of Traveler 98·5 litres (26 US gallons). Fuel capacity of Classic 45·5 litres (12 US gallons).

Accommodation: Two persons side by side in enclosed cabin. Baggage area, capacity 27·2 kg (60 lb) for Traveler, 18 kg (40 lb) for Classic.

Systems: Traveler has provision for full electrical system.

Dimensions, external:

Wing span	8·32 m (29 ft 3½ in)
Wing area, gross	13·70 m² (147·5 sq ft)
Length overall	5·70 m (18 ft 8½ in)
Height overall	1·83 m (6 ft 0 in)

Weights (A: Traveler, B: Classic):

Weight empty: A	329 kg (725 lb)
B	290 kg (640 lb)
Max T-O weight: A	658 kg (1,450 lb)
B	567 kg (1,250 lb)

Performance (A: Traveler with 80·5 kW; 108 hp engine, B: Classic):

Max level speed: A	106 knots (196 km/h; 122 mph)
B	91 knots (169 km/h; 105 mph)
Cruising speed: A	100 knots (185 km/h; 115 mph)
B	83 knots (153 km/h; 95 mph)
Stalling speed: A, B	39 knots (72·5 km/h; 45 mph)
Max rate of climb at S/L: A	259 m (850 ft)/min
B	190 m (625 ft)/min

WAR

WAR AIRCRAFT REPLICAS

348 South Eighth Street, Santa Paula, California 93060

President: Kenneth L. Thoms

War Aircraft Replicas is a company formed to market plans and kits from which amateur constructors can build ½-scale replicas of a series of second World War aircraft. The term '½-scale' is not strictly accurate, but refers to the general overall dimensions of the aircraft. For example, to provide adequate accommodation for the pilot, the cockpit is considerably larger than ½-scale, and the area of the horizontal and vertical tail surfaces has been increased beyond scale to ensure adequate stability.

The basic concept involves the use of a common-design wooden fuselage box and spar structure. The desired contours to duplicate a particular aircraft are obtained by using carved polyurethane foam, covered with high-strength laminating fabric and epoxy resin to form a light-weight and rigid structure that is stressed to ±6g, allowing for aerobatic manoeuvres. By changing fuselage contours, using different engine cowlings and wingtips, and by shape changes to tail unit surfaces, it was considered that a number of different aircraft could be copied with reasonable similarity to the full-scale combat types.

The Focke-Wulf 190 was chosen as the first prototype to be completed, its design starting in July 1973 and construction in February 1974. The first flight of this aircraft was made on 21 August 1974 and it had logged a total of 200 flying hours by 20 February 1976. At least 197 sets of plans of the WAR Focke-Wulf 190 had been sold by early 1979. A prototype replica of the Vought F4U Corsair was being completed at that time, and well over 200 sets of plans for this aircraft have been sold. Approximately 100 sets of plans have been sold for the construction of replica Republic P-47 Thunderbolts. A prototype replica of the Hawker Sea Fury has been completed; a replica of the North American P-51 Mustang was awaiting its engine in December 1978 and was expected to fly in the first months of 1979. Prototype replicas of the Mitsubishi Zero and P-40 Warhawk were under construction at that time. Development continues on a P-38 Lightning replica.

The description which follows applies specifically to the Focke-Wulf 190 replica, but will be applicable generally to the range of aircraft for which the company is producing plans, components and kits.

WAR AIRCRAFT REPLICAS FOCKE-WULF 190

Type: Half-scale combat aircraft replica.

Wings: Cantilever low-wing monoplane, built in three sections: nominal 2·44 m (8 ft) centre-section, integral with fuselage box, and two nominally 1·83 m (6 ft) outer panels. Wing section NACA 23015 at root, 23012 at tip. Dihedral 5°. Incidence 2°. Washout 2°. Primary structure of wood, with a laminated hollow plywood-covered front spar and solid laminated rear spar. Plywood ribs are used at the root, both faces of the centre-section joints and at the tip sections, with intermediate ribs of polyurethane foam. Aerofoil contours built up with carved polyurethane foam, bonded in place. High-strength laminating fabric and epoxy resin used for covering and for internal strengthening. Frise-type ailerons with wooden front spar bonded to a shaped form of urethane foam with fabric/epoxy covering. No flaps. Ground-adjustable tab on each aileron.

Fuselage: Of similar general construction to wings, with a standard four-longeron box built from ¾ in fir stringers, ¾ in by ½ in diagonals and cross pieces, ¹⁄₁₆ in birch plywood covering and a metal-faced ⅛ in plywood firewall. Fuselage contoured by carved polyurethane foam with fabric/epoxy covering.

Tail Unit: Cantilever wooden structure, utilising the same construction technique as for the wings. Fixed tailplane with elevators. Ground-adjustable trim tab on rudder and each elevator.

Landing Gear: Electrically-retractable tailwheel type, with manual emergency retraction system. Main wheels retract inward into wings. Fixed tailwheel. Oleo-pneumatic shock-struts on main units. Main wheels and tyres size 3·50 × 4·10-6. Cleveland hydraulic disc brakes.

Power Plant: One 74·5 kW (100 hp) Continental O-200 flat-four engine, driving a three-blade fixed-pitch wooden propeller with spinner. Fuel tank in fuselage, immediately aft of firewall, with capacity of 45·5 litres (12 US gallons). Refuelling point on upper surface of fuselage, forward of windscreen.

Accommodation: Single seat beneath rearward-sliding cockpit canopy. Accommodation heated and ventilated.

Systems: Hydraulic system for brakes only. Electrical system powered by 12V engine-driven alternator.

Dimensions, external:

Wing span	6·10 m (20 ft 0 in)
Wing chord at root	1·37 m (4 ft 6 in)
Wing chord at tip	0·94 m (3 ft 1 in)
Wing area, gross	6·50 m² (70 sq ft)
Wing aspect ratio	5·7
Length overall	5·05 m (16 ft 7 in)
Height overall	2·13 m (7 ft 0 in)
Tailplane span	2·29 m (7 ft 6 in)
Wheel track	2·03 m (6 ft 8 in)
Wheelbase	3·25 m (10 ft 8 in)
Propeller diameter	1·52 m (5 ft 0 in)

Weights:

Weight empty	286 kg (630 lb)
Max T-O weight	408 kg (900 lb)

Performance (at max T-O weight):

Max level speed at 1,065 m (3,500 ft)	169 knots (314 km/h; 195 mph)
Max cruising speed at 1,065 m (3,500 ft)	126 knots (233 km/h; 145 mph)
Econ cruising speed at 1,065 m (3,500 ft)	108 knots (201 km/h; 125 mph)
Stalling speed	48 knots (89 km/h; 55 mph)
Max rate of climb at S/L	305 m (1,000 ft)/min
Service ceiling	3,810 m (12,500 ft)
T-O run	305 m (1,000 ft)
Landing from 15 m (50 ft)	550 m (1,800 ft)
Landing run	365 m (1,200 ft)
Range with max fuel	347 nm (643 km; 400 miles)

WATSON

GARY WATSON

Rt 1, Newcastle, Texas 76372

WATSON GW-1 WINDWAGON

Mr Gary Watson has designed and built a diminutive single-seat all-metal monoplane known as the GW-1 Windwagon (N64614). Although this is Mr Watson's first design, he was previously a member of a team that constructed a Parker Teenie Two.

Construction of the prototype Windwagon took six months and cost $1,222·74, including the engine taken from a derelict Volkswagen 'Beetle' cut in half and reworked. First flight was made on 19 April 1977.

Plans to build the Windwagon are available to amateur builders, and by Autumn 1978 approximately 67 sets had been sold (including details for modifying the VW engine).

Type: Single-seat light monoplane.

Wings: Cantilever low-wing monoplane. Wing section Clark Y. Constant chord. All-metal pop-riveted structure of aluminium alloy, built in three 1·83 m (6 ft 0 in) sections, the outer wing sections being removable for trailering. Conventional ailerons. No flaps.

Fuselage: Conventional pop-riveted aluminium alloy semi-monocoque structure.

Tail Unit: Cantilever all-metal structure of aluminium alloy, comprising constant-chord tailplane with elevators, slightly swept fin and rudder. No tabs.

Landing Gear: Non-retractable tricycle type, employing tubular legs. No shock-absorbers. Hydraulic brakes.

Power Plant: One 22·4 kW (30 hp) 900 cc half-Volkswagen modified motor car engine, driving normally a four-blade propeller made by Dick Bohls, with spinner. A 1·27 m (4 ft 2 in) two-blade propeller was fitted initially. Fuel capacity 15·14 litres (4 US gallons). Oil capacity 1·4 litres (1·5 US quarts).

Accommodation: Single semi-reclining seat in open cockpit. Large windscreen.

Dimensions, external:

Wing span	5·49 m (18 ft 0 in)
Wing chord, constant	0·91 m (3 ft 0 in)
Length overall	3·96 m (13 ft 0 in)
Height overall	1·07 m (3 ft 6 in)
Propeller diameter (four blade)	1·02 m (3 ft 4 in)

Weights:

Weight empty	124 kg (273 lb)
Max T-O weight	220 kg (485 lb)

Performance:

Max level speed	117 knots (217 km/h; 135 mph)
Normal cruising speed	82·5 knots (153 km/h; 95 mph)
Landing speed	39 knots (72·5 km/h; 45 mph)
Max rate of climb at S/L	137 m (450 ft)/min
T-O run	76 m (250 ft)
Landing run	91 m (300 ft)
Range with max fuel	260 nm (483 km; 300 miles)

WEEDHOPPER

WEEDHOPPER OF UTAH INC

1965 S, 1100 West Ogden, Utah 84404

Telephone: (801) 621 3941

WEEDHOPPER JC-2-1 WEEDHOPPER

Mr John F. Chotia designed and built a light monoplane known as the Weedhopper. This represented Mr Chotia's 23rd design; others comprised 18 hang-gliders and four powered lightplanes.

Design of the Weedhopper (which is reminiscent in configuration of the 1909 Demoiselle built by Alberto Santos-Dumont) began in August 1977, the main aims being to produce an ultra-light aircraft with good manoeuvrability which was also easy to handle. Construction of the first of two prototypes started in February 1978, and this aircraft made its first flight in the following month. Kits of parts to build the aircraft became available to amateur builders in July 1978. By January 1979, 73 kits had been ordered, of which 53 had been delivered, and 20 Weedhoppers were flying. Construction is said to take about 40 working hours.

It is claimed that the Weedhopper will complete a 360° turn in under 18 seconds, and that recovery from a stall, with power on, can be completed within an altitude loss of 3 m (10 ft). As no ailerons are fitted, bank and roll control are effected by using the rudder.

Type: Single-seat light monoplane.

Wings: Strut-braced high-wing monoplane. Dihedral 12°. Incidence 0°. Washout 4° 30′. Sweepback 4°. Aluminium tube structure, covered on top surface only with Dacron fabric. Aluminium tube V bracing struts each side, from landing gear axle to wing leading- and trailing-edges.

Fuselage: Open triangulated structure of aluminium tubing. Upper fuselage tube supports wing roots, tailplane and engine.

Tail Unit: Cantilever structure, comprising tailplane with elevators, ventral fin and rudder. Aluminium tube structure, Dacron fabric covered.

Landing Gear: Non-retractable tricycle type. Steerable nosewheel. All three tyres size 3·50-4. Brake on nosewheel.

Power Plant: One Chotia 460 two-stroke engine, developing 13·75 kW (18·5 hp) at 3,500 rpm, and driving a Weedhopper-built two-blade wooden propeller. Single fuel tank of standard 3·8 litre (1 US gallon) capacity, or optional 13·25 litre (3·5 US gallon) capacity.

Accommodation: Single semi-reclined open seat.

Systems: Battery for ignition system.

Dimensions, external:

Wing span	8·53 m (28 ft 0 in)
Wing area, gross	15·61 m² (168 sq ft)
Wing chord at root	2·44 m (8 ft 0 in)
Wing chord at tip	1·22 m (4 ft 0 in)
Wing aspect ratio	4·7
Length overall	5·64 m (18 ft 6 in)
Height overall	1·98 m (6 ft 6 in)
Tailplane span	2·44 m (8 ft 0 in)
Wheel track	1·30 m (4 ft 3 in)
Wheelbase	0·99 m (3 ft 3 in)
Propeller diameter	1·14 m (3 ft 9 in)

Weights:

Weight empty	72·5 kg (160 lb)
Max T-O weight	172 kg (380 lb)

WAR half-scale replica of the F4U Corsair (Continental O-200 engine) *(J. M. G. Gradidge)*

Half-scale replicas of Focke-Wulf 190 built to WAR plans *(Peter M. Bowers)*

Weedhopper JC-2-1 Weedhopper light open monoplane

Wendt WH-1 Traveler two-seat homebuilt aircraft

PERFORMANCE:
- Never-exceed speed 43·5 knots (80·5 km/h; 50 mph)
- Max level speed 43·5 knots (80·5 km/h; 50 mph)
- Max cruising speed 30·5 knots (56·5 km/h; 35 mph)
- Econ cruising speed 26 knots (48·5 km/h; 30 mph)
- Stalling speed 16 knots (29 km/h; 18 mph) IAS
- Max rate of climb at S/L 183 m (600 ft)/min
- Service ceiling over 3,050 m (10,000 ft)
- T-O run 30·5 m (100 ft)
- T-O distance to 15 m (50 ft) 91 m (300 ft)
- Landing run 18 m (60 ft)
- Range with optional fuel 78 nm (145 km; 90 miles)

WENDT
WENDT AIRCRAFT ENGINEERING

9900 Alto Drive, La Mesa, California 92041

Wendt Aircraft Engineering designed and built the prototype of a two-seat sporting monoplane which is known as the WH-1 Traveler. The design originated on 4 September 1969, and construction of the prototype began on 26 November of the same year. The first flight was made on 15 March 1972, and FAA certification in the Experimental category was awarded on 30 May 1972. Plans of the Traveler are available to amateur constructors, and at least 50 sets had been sold by early 1979, at which time eight aircraft were under construction and at least one completed.

WENDT WH-1 TRAVELER

TYPE: Two-seat sporting aircraft.

WINGS: Cantilever low-wing monoplane. Wing section NACA 64_3A-418. Dihedral 5° 30′. Incidence 2°. No sweepback. Constant-chord two-spar structure. Spruce spars, marine plywood ribs, pine leading- and trailing-edges and 3/32 in mahogany plywood skin from leading-edge to 37% chord. Aft of main spar, wing is Dacron-covered. Plain ailerons, hinged at upper surface, made of spruce with plywood ribs, and Dacron-covered. No flaps. Bungee trim on control column. Glassfibre wing-tips.

FUSELAGE: Conventional structure of spruce frames and longerons, plywood formers and tension ties, with steel tube overturn structure in the cockpit section. Fuselage undersurface and sides covered with 1/8 in mahogany plywood. Upper surface Dacron-covered. Glassfibre nose cowl.

TAIL UNIT: Cantilever wooden structure with swept vertical surfaces and all-moving tailplane. Each surface has a spruce spar, spruce and plywood ribs, and a 1/16 in mahogany plywood torsion box. All surfaces Dacron-covered. Static balance weights near tips of tailplane leading-edge. Tailplane has a half-span trim and anti-balance tab. Tailplane tips of glassfibre.

LANDING GEAR: Non-retractable tricycle type. Cantilever spring steel main gear. Steerable nosewheel has coil spring shock-absorption. Cleveland 5·00-5 wheels with Armstrong tyres, pressure 2·07 bars (30 lb/sq in). Cleveland caliper-type brakes. Glassfibre wheel fairings.

POWER PLANT: Prototype has one 56 kW (75 hp) Continental A75 flat-four engine, driving a McCauley Type 1C90 two-blade metal fixed-pitch propeller with glassfibre spinner. Design is suitable for installation of engines from 48·5-74·5 kW (65 to 100 hp). One aerofoil-shaped glassfibre fuel tank at each wingtip, capacity 41·5 litres (11 US gallons). Total fuel capacity 83 litres (22 US gallons). Refuelling points on upper surface of each wingtip. Oil capacity 3·8 litres (1·0 US gallon).

ACCOMMODATION: Pilot and passenger in tandem, beneath canopy which has large transparent panels at each side. Canopy hinged on port side. Dual controls standard. Stowage for 23 kg (50 lb) baggage aft of rear seat.

SYSTEM: Electrical system powered by 30A engine-driven alternator. 12V 25Ah storage battery in glassfibre battery box in aft fuselage.

ELECTRONICS: Prototype has a Narco Escort 110 com transceiver.

DIMENSIONS, EXTERNAL:
- Wing span 9·14 m (30 ft 0 in)
- Wing chord, constant 1·20 m (3 ft 11¼ in)
- Wing area, gross 10·96 m² (118 sq ft)
- Wing aspect ratio 7·63
- Length overall 5·94 m (19 ft 6 in)
- Height overall 2·08 m (6 ft 10 in)
- Tailplane span 2·44 m (8 ft 0 in)
- Wheel track 1·93 m (6 ft 4 in)
- Wheelbase 1·45 m (4 ft 9 in)
- Propeller diameter 1·80 m (5 ft 11 in)

DIMENSION, INTERNAL:
- Max width 0·71 m (2 ft 4 in)

WEIGHTS:
- Weight empty, equipped 408 kg (900 lb)
- Max T-O and landing weight 635 kg (1,400 lb)

PERFORMANCE (at max T-O weight):
- Never-exceed speed 142 knots (264 km/h; 164 mph)
- Max level speed at 1,220 m (4,000 ft) 114 knots (211 km/h; 131 mph)
- Max cruising speed at 1,220 m (4,000 ft) 107 knots (198 km/h; 123 mph)
- Econ cruising speed at 1,220 m (4,000 ft) 100 knots (185 km/h; 115 mph)
- Stalling speed 50 knots (92 km/h; 57 mph)
- Max rate of climb at S/L (no passenger) 229 m (750 ft)/min
- Max rate of climb at S/L (with passenger) 152 m (500 ft)/min
- Service ceiling 3,960 m (13,000 ft)
- T-O run 244 m (800 ft)
- Landing run 213 m (700 ft)
- Range with max fuel, no reserves 503 nm (933 km; 580 miles)
- Range with max payload, no reserves 416 nm (772 km; 480 miles)

WHITE
E. MARSHALL WHITE

Meadowlark Airport, 5141 Warner Avenue, Huntington Beach, California 92649
Telephone: (714) 846 2409

WHITE WW-1 DER JÄGER D.IX

Mr Marshall White, a staff engineer of TRW Systems at Redondo Beach, California, designed an unusual homebuilt aircraft named Der Jäger D.IX, which is reminiscent of several German designs, mainly of first World War vintage. The wings are patterned on those of an Albatros D.Va, with the landing gear fairings of the Focke-Wulf Stösser and tail unit of the Fokker D.VII.

Design and construction of the prototype started simultaneously at the beginning of 1969, as Mr White's fifth homebuilt, and first flight of the prototype was made on 7 September 1969.

Plans and kits of materials, as well as some of the more difficult-to-construct parts in finished form, are available to amateur constructors, and at least 75 Der Jäger D.IXs are under construction. The first completed aircraft to be seen at an EAA Fly-in at Oshkosh, in 1974, was N1007, built by Mr Ray D. Fulwiler of Algoma, Wisconsin, with a 112 kW (150 hp) Lycoming engine.

The following details apply to the prototype in its original form. It has since been re-engined with a 112 kW (150 hp) Lycoming, but no details have been received of performance with this more powerful engine.

TYPE: Single-seat sporting biplane.

WINGS: Forward-stagger single-bay biplane with N-type interplane and centre-section struts. Single streamlined lift strut from each side of lower fuselage to attachment point of forward interplane strut on upper wing. No flying or landing wires. Aerofoil section M-6. Incidence 3° upper wing, 2° lower wings. Spruce spars and plywood ribs, fabric covered. Internal steel tube bracing. Ailerons in both top and bottom wings. Scalloped trailing-edge to both wings.

FUSELAGE: Welded 4130 steel tube structure, fabric covered. Aluminium engine cowling.

TAIL UNIT: Wire-braced welded 4130 steel tube structure,

White Der Jäger D.IX homebuilt biplane (Lycoming O-235-C1 engine)

Wittman W-10 powered by the Oldsmobile F85 engine

Wittman W-8 Tailwind (Lycoming O-235 engine) built by Mr Ed Graham *(Peter M. Bowers)*

with sheet metal ribs, fabric covered. Balanced rudder and elevator. Ground-adjustable trim tabs in elevator.

Landing Gear: Non-retractable tailwheel type. Main legs each consist of an 'A' frame, welded into the fuselage, with tension springs in the centre-fuselage to cushion landing shock. Main wheels and tyres size 5·00-5. Glassfibre wheel fairings.

Power Plant: One 86 kW (115 hp) Lycoming O-235-C1 flat-four engine, driving a McCauley two-blade propeller. Structure suitable for alternative power plants from 1,600 cc Volkswagen up to 112 kW (150 hp). Fuel contained in two tanks, one in upper wing centre-section, capacity 53 litres (14 US gallons), one in fuselage, capacity 38 litres (10 US gallons); total 91 litres (24 US gallons).

Accommodation: Single seat in open cockpit, with headrest faired into wood or glassfibre fuselage turtleback.

Equipment: Two dummy machine-guns mounted on top of fuselage, forward of cockpit. Dummy bomb, carried between legs of main landing gear, can be adapted as oil tank for smoke discharge system.

Dimensions, external:

Wing span, upper	6·10 m (20 ft 0 in)
Wing span, lower	4·88 m (16 ft 0 in)
Wing chord, upper at root	1·07 m (3 ft 6 in)
Wing chord, upper at tip	1·22 m (4 ft 0 in)
Wing chord, lower, constant	0·91 m (3 ft 0 in)
Wing area, gross	10·68 m² (115 sq ft)
Length overall	5·18 m (17 ft 0 in)
Tailplane span	2·44 m (8 ft 0 in)
Wheel track	1·52 m (5 ft 0 in)
Propeller diameter	1·68 m (5 ft 6 in)

Weights:

Weight empty	242 kg (534 lb)
Max T-O weight	403 kg (888 lb)

Performance (at max T-O weight):

Never-exceed speed	152 knots (282 km/h; 175 mph)
Max level speed at 610 m (2,000 ft)	126 knots (233 km/h; 145 mph)
Max cruising speed at 610 m (2,000 ft)	116 knots (214 km/h; 133 mph)
Stalling speed	47 knots (87 km/h; 54 mph)
Max rate of climb at S/L	732 m (2,400 ft)/min
T-O run	46 m (150 ft)

WITTMAN

S. J. WITTMAN

Box 2672, Oshkosh, Wisconsin 54901

Famous as a racing pilot since 1926, Steve Wittman has designed and built a large number of different racing and touring aeroplanes at Winnebago County Airport, of which he became manager in 1931.

Most popular current Wittman design is the W-8 Tailwind side-by-side two-seat light aeroplane. The prototype was built in 1952-53 and proved so successful that sets of plans and prefabricated components were made available to amateur builders. By early 1979 there were more than 325 Model W-8 Tailwinds flying, including a number built in foreign countries, and more than 100 were known to be under construction. In January 1968 Mr Wittman's plans were approved by the Australian Department of Civil Aviation.

In 1966, a more powerful six-cylinder Continental engine was installed in a Tailwind redesigned to take the added weight and power. This version is designated W-9 and was described in the 1978-79 *Jane's*. Also flying is a Tailwind Model W-10 with a converted Oldsmobile motor car engine.

WITTMAN TAILWIND MODEL W-8

Some Tailwinds have been built with tricycle landing gear, retractable main wheels and other design changes. The following data refer to the standard W-8 Tailwind built to Mr Wittman's plans:

Type: Two-seat cabin monoplane.

Wings: Braced high-wing monoplane. Wing section is a combination of NACA 4309 (upper surface) and NACA 0006 (lower surface). Thickness/chord ratio 11·5%. No dihedral. Incidence 1°. Wooden structure with plywood and fabric covering. Single bracing strut each side. Ailerons and flaps of steel and stainless steel construction.

Fuselage: Steel tube structure, fabric-covered.

Tail Unit: Cantilever structure of steel and stainless steel. Ground-adjustable trim tabs in control surfaces.

Landing Gear: Non-retractable tailwheel type. Spring steel cantilever main legs. Goodyear 15 × 5 main wheels and tyres, pressure 2·21 bars (32 lb/sq in). Goodyear brakes.

Power Plant: Normally one 67 kW (90 hp) Continental C90-12F flat-four engine, driving a Sensenich or Flottorp two-blade wood fixed-pitch propeller. Alternative engines are the 63·5 kW (85 hp) Continental C85, 74·5 kW (100 hp) Continental O-200, 86 kW (115 hp) Lycoming O-235 or 104·5 kW (140 hp) Lycoming O-290. One fuel tank of 94·5 litres (25 US gallons) capacity in fuselage. Oil capacity 1·85-2·8 litres (4-6 US quarts).

Accommodation: Two seats side by side in enclosed cabin, with door on each side. Space for 27 kg (60 lb) baggage.

Dimensions, external:

Wing span	6·86 m (22 ft 6 in)
Wing chord, constant	1·22 m (4 ft 0 in)
Wing area, gross	8·36 m² (90 sq ft)
Wing aspect ratio	5·5
Length overall	5·87 m (19 ft 3 in)
Height overall	1·73 m (5 ft 8 in)
Tailplane span	2·03 m (6 ft 8 in)
Wheel track	1·65 m (5 ft 5 in)
Propeller diameter	1·63 m (5 ft 4 in)

Weights (74·5 kW; 100 hp Continental engine):

Weight empty	318 kg (700 lb)
Max T-O weight	590 kg (1,300 lb)

Performance (74·5 kW; 100 hp Continental engine at max T-O weight):

Never-exceed speed	160 knots (297 km/h; 185 mph)
Max level speed at S/L	143 knots (265 km/h; 165 mph)
Max cruising speed	139 knots (257 km/h; 160 mph)
Econ cruising speed	113 knots (209 km/h; 130 mph)
Stalling speed, flaps down	48 knots (89 km/h; 55 mph)
Max rate of climb at S/L	275 m (900 ft)/min
Service ceiling	4,876 m (16,000 ft)
T-O run	245 m (800 ft)
T-O to 15 m (50 ft)	405 m (1,325 ft)
Landing from 15 m (50 ft)	350 m (1,150 ft)
Landing run	183 m (600 ft)

Range with max payload at 3,050 m (10,000 ft), no reserves:

at 139 knots (257 km/h; 160 mph)	521 nm (965 km; 600 miles)
at 122 knots (225 km/h; 140 mph)	607 nm (1,125 km; 700 miles)

WITTMAN TAILWIND MODEL W-10

Built and first flown in the mid-1950s, the W-10 is generally similar to the W-8, but has been fitted with several different power plants and has been used as a testbed for design refinements. Earlier Continental O-300 and Lycoming O-320 flat-six engines were followed a few years ago by the currently-installed Oldsmobile F85 converted motor car engine, driving a propeller of 1·57 m (5 ft 2 in) diameter. The W-10 had logged 276 flying hours with this power plant by early 1979. It also has new wingtips which improve the rate of climb, glide ratio and service ceiling.

Performance (A: Oldsmobile F85 engine, B: Continental O-300):

Max level speed: B	174 knots (322 km/h; 200 mph)
Max cruising speed: A	156 knots (290 km/h; 180 mph)
B	165 knots (306 km/h; 190 mph)
Landing speed: A	48 knots (89 km/h; 55 mph)
B	50·5 knots (93·5 km/h; 58 mph)
Max rate of climb at S/L: A	425 m (1,400 ft)/min
Service ceiling: A	5,180 m (17,000 ft)
T-O run: A	183 m (600 ft)
Range with max fuel: A	564 nm (1,045 km; 650 miles)

SAILPLANES

(For specification data, see tables at end of section)

ARGENTINA

AS

AERO SALADILLO

Casilla Correo 24, 7260 Saladillo, Provincia de Buenos Aires

Telephone: 41 5260 (Comodoro A. R. Mantel, in Buenos Aires)

This company was formed in 1973 to build aircraft of GRP.

AS LENTICULAR 15 S

Production of the Lenticular single-seat Standard Class sailplane has been suspended. A description and illustration can be found in the 1978-79 *Jane's*.

AUSTRALIA

SUNDERLAND

GARY SUNDERLAND

1 Nicholas Grove, Heatherton, Victoria 3202

Telephone: 551 2564

Mr Sunderland is building a 15 metre sailplane known as the MOBA-2C.

SUNDERLAND MOBA-2C

The original 2A version of the MOBA was one of two 13 metre sailplanes which competed with one another in 1972 in a design competition held by the Australian Gliding Federation. The MOBA-2B was a 15 metre version of the 2A, and the MOBA-2C represents an improved version of both earlier models.

Construction of the MOBA-2C began in 1975, and was well advanced by the beginning of 1979. It was hoped to make the first flight later that year. Series production is not intended.

TYPE: Single-seat 15 metre Standard Class sailplane; *g* limits +4; −1·5.

AIRFRAME: Cantilever high-wing monoplane, with T tail. Box-spar wings, of Wortmann FX-67-K-150 section, built in three pieces. Dihedral 1° at tips. Plywood ribs, with urethane foam infill; spar of pop-riveted aluminium alloy sheet. Epoxy-resin glasscloth skin. Aluminium alloy plain flaps on trailing-edges, serving also as airbrakes; GRP-covered wooden ailerons. Nose and central fuselage are riveted aluminium alloy box structures, with sliding nose of balsa/GRP sandwich; centre fairing of foam with GRP skin; tailboom is of flush-riveted aluminium alloy sheet. Tail unit of wood, with foam infill and GRP skin. Elevator has spring trim. Manually retractable Standard Libelle twin wheels, side by side; non-retractable tailskid. No water ballast provision.

AUSTRIA

ALPLA

ALPLA-WERKE Alwin Lechner OHG

A-6971 Hard, Lochbachstrasse 6/7

ALPLA AVO 68V SAMBURO

This motor glider flew for the first time in 1977; production ended in January 1979.

All known details were given in the 1978-79 *Jane's*.

BRDITSCHKA

H. W. BRDITSCHKA OHG

A-4053 Haid, Dr Schärfstrasse 42, Postfach 12

Telephone: 07229/8355

Telex: 21909

DIRECTOR: Heinz W. Brditschka

BRDITSCHKA HB-21

The HB-21, which first flew on 22 March 1974, is essentially an enlarged version of the HB-3 (1977-78 *Jane's*), with increased-span wings, tandem seating for two persons, and a Volkswagen engine. Four prototypes were built. Certification was granted in February 1978, and 15 HB-21s had been built by early 1979.

TYPE: Two-seat motor glider; *g* limits +5·3; −2·7.

AIRFRAME: Fabric-covered wooden wings, with Wortmann sections (FX-61-184 at root, FX-60-126 at tip). Dihedral 2°. Incidence 3°. All-wood ailerons and upper-surface spoilers. Steel tube fuselage with glassfibre covering. Fixed-incidence all-wood tailplane. Non-retractable tricycle landing gear, with Tost mechanical main-wheel brakes.

POWER PLANT: One 44·75 kW (60 hp) VW-Westermayer 1600G flat-four piston engine, driving a Hoffmann HO 14-175 B 117 LD two-blade fixed-pitch pusher propeller. Aluminium fuel tank in wing, capacity 54 litres (11·9 Imp gallons). Fuel is a 75/25% petrol/oil mixture.

BRAZIL

CTA

CENTRO TÉCNICO AEROESPACIAL

São José dos Campos, São Paulo State

IPD (Instituto de Pesquisas e Desenvolvimento)/PAR (Divisão de Aeronaves)

The IPD is the aeronautical research and development institute of the CTA (see Aircraft section). The PAR is its Aircraft Division, having responsibility for flight testing, evaluating, certificating and developing new aircraft projects. One of these is the Urubu, a new two-seat all-metal training sailplane.

IPD/PAR PE-80367 URUBU

The PE-80367 programme is intended to develop a modern training sailplane which, after testing and certification, will be handed over to private industry for series production. One static test prototype, and one for flight test and certification, are being built; first flight was scheduled to take place in the second half of 1979.

TYPE: Tandem two-seat training sailplane; *g* limits: semi-aerobatic, +6·2/−3·4; fully aerobatic, +6·5/−3·5.

AIRFRAME: Cantilever shoulder-wing monoplane. Wing section NACA 63_2A-615 at root, NACA 63_1A-412 at tip. Dihedral 2° 12′. Sweepforward 1° 51′ at quarter-chord. Incidence 3° at root. All-metal two-spar wings, with light alloy airbrakes in upper and lower surfaces, and all-metal ailerons. All-metal semi-monocoque oval-section fuselage. All-metal tail unit, with fixed-incidence tailplane; controllable trim tab in each elevator. Non-retractable rubber-sprung monowheel, with mechanical brake; non-retractable tailwheel.

EEUFMG (CEA)

ESCOLA DE ENGENHARIA DA UNIVERSIDADE FEDERAL DE MINAS GERAIS (Centro de Estudos Aeronáuticos)

Rua Espirito Santo 35, 30.000 Belo Horizonte, Minas Gerais State

Telephone: 222 4011

HEAD OF CEA: Prof Cláudio Pinto de Barros

CB-2/B MINUANO

The Air Research Centre of the Engineering School at Minas Gerais Federal University began the design of this single-seat sailplane in 1969. Its designation indicates that it is the second design by Professor Cláudio Barros; his first, the CB-1 Gaivota, was completed when he was an engineering student. The CB-2 prototype (PP-ZPZ) flew for the first time on 20 December 1975 and was described in the 1977-78 *Jane's*.

A further four Minuanos have been ordered, and the second aircraft was scheduled for completion by the end of 1979. This incorporates several modifications, and is designated CB-2/B; the description applies to this version. The Minuano is named after a strong, cold wind in southern Brazil.

TYPE: Single-seat high-performance sailplane; *g* limits (at safety factor of 1·72): normal, +5·3/−3·0; ultimate, +9·14/−5·19.

AIRFRAME: High-wing monoplane, with Wortmann FX-67-K-170/17 (root) and FX-60-126 (tip) wing sections. Single aluminium alloy main spar; wing skin of plywood/glassfibre honeycomb sandwich. Flaps and ailerons, similar except for wooden spars, are interconnected; flaps can be used also as airbrakes. Provision for 80 kg (176 lb) of water ballast. All-wood semi-monocoque fuselage. Plywood-covered tail surfaces, stiffened with foam plastics. All-moving tailplane, with trim tab in each half. Retractable unsprung monowheel (tyre pressure 2·45 bars; 35·5 lb/sq in), with internal shoe brake, and sprung tailskid.

IPE

INDÚSTRIA PARANAENSE DE ESTRUTURAS

Av Igúaçu 808, Caixa Postal 2621, 80.000 Curitiba, Paraná State

IPE is building the KW 1 b 2 Quero Quero II single-seat training sailplane, and is developing a two-seat training sailplane known as the IPE 02.

IPE KW 1 b 2 QUERO QUERO II

Development of the original KW 1 designed by Ing Kuno Wiedmaier has been described in previous editions

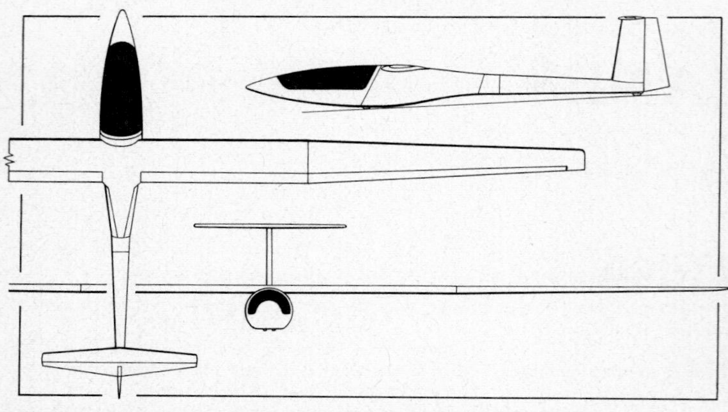
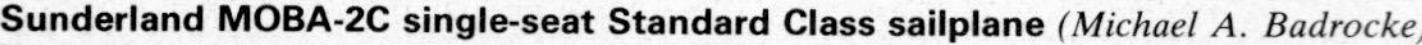

Sunderland MOBA-2C single-seat Standard Class sailplane *(Michael A. Badrocke)*

Brditschka HB-21 two-seat motor glider

of *Jane's*. The KW 1 b 2 made its first flight on 1 October 1972. CTA certification, in the semi-aerobatic category with an extension for cloud flying, was awarded in December 1976.

By 31 March 1979, IPE had completed one static and three flying prototypes, four first-series production aircraft (one of which was lost in a non-fatal accident), and a second-series batch of 20. These are in service with various Brazilian flying clubs.

TYPE: Single-seat training glider; *g* limit +8.

AIRFRAME: High-wing monoplane, with Scheibe Spatz wing section, built of wood and plywood (Brazilian pine). Upper/lower-surface spoilers. Non-retractable monowheel and tailwheel.

IPE 02

The general appearance of this aircraft can be seen from the accompanying illustration. It flew for the first time on 24 May 1979.

TYPE: Tandem two-seat training sailplane.

AIRFRAME: Shoulder-wing monoplane with Scheibe Spatz (modified) wing section. Ailerons and upper/lower surface spoilers. Non-retractable monowheel in streamlined fairing, and tailwheel.

IPE 03

The IPE 03, under development for completion in the Spring of 1980, is a two-seat motor glider powered by a 44·7-67 kW (60-90 hp) Volkswagen engine. It is of low-wing monoplane layout, and has a tailwheel-type landing gear.

SIDOU
ENG ANTONIO MENEZES SIDOU

Rua Luciana de Abreu, 184 Moinhos de Vento, 90.000 Porto Alegre, RS

SIDOU JOÃO GRANDE (STORK)

Eng Sidou hoped to begin building the João Grande at Passo Fundo, Rio Grande do Sul, in 1979. For general appearance, see accompanying three-view drawing.

TYPE: Tandem two-seat Open Class and advanced training sailplane (OSTIV aerobatic category A); *g* limits +9·75; −6·00 (ultimate).

AIRFRAME: Cantilever mid-wing monoplane, with cambered wingtips and T tail. Wortmann wing sections: FX-61-184 (modified) at root, FX-60-126 (modified) at tip. Dihedral 3° 36′. All-wood single-spar structure, with plywood covering and abrasion-resistant plastics finish. Wide-span ailerons and upper/lower surface Schempp-Hirth airbrakes. All wing and tail control surfaces statically and dynamically balanced. Wooden semi-monocoque fuselage. Jettisonable cockpit canopy. Retractable rubber-sprung monowheel, with mechanical brake, and tail bumper.

CANADA

MARSDEN
DR DAVID J. MARSDEN

c/o Dept of Mechanical Engineering, University of Alberta, Edmonton, Alberta T6G 2G8
Telephone: (403) 432 3705

Prof Marsden of the University of Alberta has acquired from Operation Sigma Ltd the Sigma variable-geometry sailplane last described in the 1974-75 *Jane's*. He has replaced the former area-increasing flap system by full-span slotted flaps similar to those used on the Gemini, a two-seat sailplane of his own design. Modification work was carried out at the Cranfield Institute of Technology in the UK, where Prof Marsden was spending a sabbatical year during 1977-78. Two half-hour test flights were made at Cranfield before his return to Canada. Development flight testing was due to be continued in Alberta during the Winter of 1978-79.

MARSDEN GEMINI

Construction of this successful variable-geometry sailplane began in 1970, and it flew for the first time in October 1973.

The full-span slotted-flap configuration has a number of advantages over the chord-extending type as used originally on Sigma. Apart from the obvious advantage of simpler flap extension mechanisms, it is possible to achieve higher overall lift coefficient; even more significant is the excellent aileron effectiveness when the flaps are extended. Climb capability is similar to that of unballasted 15 metre sailplanes, and high-speed glide performance is comparable to that of Open Class sailplanes when the Gemini is flown at its normal wing loading of just over 43·9 kg/m² (9 lb/sq ft) with two occupants.

The performance figures given in the Table are those measured in October 1978, but Gemini is expected to improve upon these after air leaks between the fuselage and wing, and around the canopy joints and wheel-well doors, have been sealed.

TYPE: Two-seat variable-geometry sailplane; *g* limits +6·0; −6·0.

AIRFRAME: Cantilever mid-wing monoplane, with T tail. Wing section Wortmann FX-61-163, modified for slotted flap. Dihedral 3°. Incidence 0°. All-metal single box-spar structure, built in four portions, with metal skins providing torsional stiffness. Full-span all-metal (2024-T3 aluminium alloy) slotted flap system, outer segments of which function also as ailerons. No spoilers or airbrakes. Forward fuselage has a structural glassfibre shell, with a steel tube frame to carry wing loads, and sheet metal internal bulkheads. Tailcone is a monocoque of aluminium alloy sheet. All-metal tail unit, with full-span anti-balance tab on all-moving tailplane. Mechanically retractable oleo-sprung monowheel, with hydraulic disc brake; tyre pressure 2·76 bars (40 lb/sq in). Non-retractable tailwheel, tyre pressure 2·07 bars (30 lb/sq in). Side-by-side seating for two persons in cockpit.

CZECHOSLOVAKIA

OMNIPOL
OMNIPOL FOREIGN TRADE CORPORATION

Washingtonova 11, Prague 1
Telephone: 2126
Telex: 121489, 121808 and 121077
SALES MANAGER: Ing Miloslav Branný

Omnipol handles all exports of products of the Czechoslovak aircraft industry.

LET
LET NÁRODNÍPODNIK (Let National Corporation)

Uherské Hradiste-Kunovice

In addition to its work on powered aircraft, Let National Corporation manufactured the L-13 Blaník sailplane.

LET L-13 BLANÍK

The Blanik was designed for training in all categories from elementary to 'blind' flying and for high-performance flight. It is fully aerobatic when flown solo and capable of basic aerobatic manoeuvres when carrying a crew of two.

Design started in January 1955, and construction of two prototypes began in August 1955. First flight was made in March 1956.

Up to the end of 1978, when production terminated, more than 2,600 Blaniks had been sold. Of these, over 2,000 had been exported to customers in more than 40 countries, including more than 1,000 to the USSR, approx 200 to the USA, approx 150 to the UK and more than 100 each to Australia and Canada.

A description of the standard Blanik can be found in the 1978-79 *Jane's*. During the course of its career, a number of Blaniks were converted into motor gliders, not all of which have been recorded before in *Jane's*. These, in chronological order, included the following:

XL-13M. 1964 conversion, with 19·5 kW (26 hp) Walter engine on non-retractable mounting aft of cockpit.

L-13J. With 31 kW (42 hp) Motorlet M-150 engine on non-retractable mounting aft of cockpit. First flown (OK-9821) on 26 March 1968.

XL-13T. With 26 kW (35 hp) Motorlet M-151 engine on non-retractable mounting aft of cockpit. First flown (OK-62) in 1970.

L-13-2M. 1971 conversion by Sigmund Flugtechnik of Germany, with two 33 kW (44 hp) Lloyd LS-400 engines mounted in overwing nacelles.

LAK-6. 1975 Soviet conversion, with 51 kW (68 hp) Limbach SL 1700 EI engine mounted in nose. Illustrated in USSR section of 1977-78 *Jane's*.

L-13 Wankel. 1976 conversion, with 37 kW (50 hp) Wankel rotating-piston engine on non-retractable mounting aft of cockpit.

L-13SV. With 48·5 kW (65 hp) Walter Mikron IIIA engine mounted in nose. First flown (OK-068) on 10 May 1978.

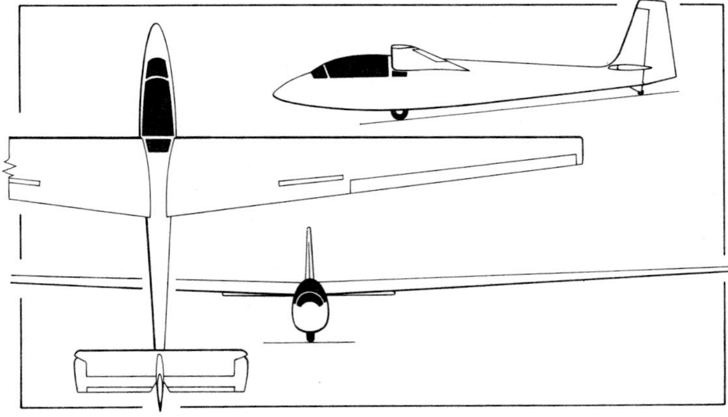

CTA (IPD/PAR) PE-80367 Urubu *(Michael A. Badrocke)*

Prototype EEUFMG CB-2 Minuano single-seat sailplane

IPE Quero Quero II single-seat sailplanes

IPE 02 two-seat training sailplane, currently under development

Marsden Gemini two-seat variable-geometry sailplane

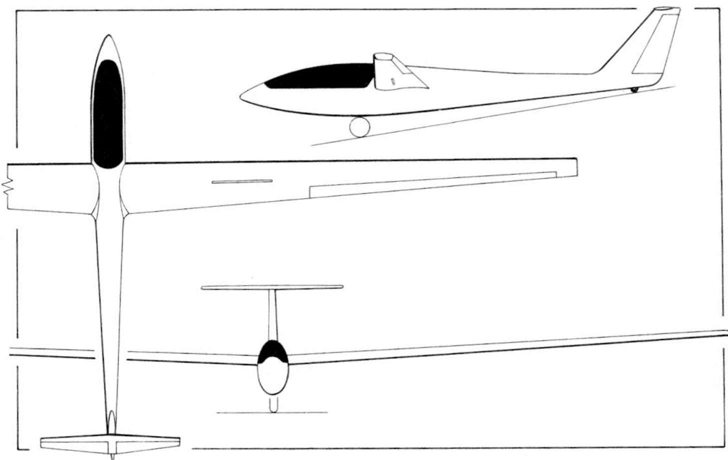

Sidou João Grande *(Michael A. Badrocke)*

VSO 10 single-seat high-performance sailplane

VSO

VYVOJOVÁ SKUPINA ORLICAN

c/o Orlican Národní Podnik, 565 37 Chocen

Telephone: Chocen 70 and 80
Telex: 0 196 210
Chief Designer: Dipl Ing Jan Janovec

This group was formed by members of the former VSB (1973-74 *Jane's*) and some of the design staff of the Orlican National Works. Its first product is the VSO 10.

VSO 10

Design of the VSO 10 began in March 1972. Construction of three prototypes (one for structural test and two for flight test) began in 1975, and the first flight took place on 26 October 1976. Series production began in December 1978, with first deliveries being made to the Aeroclub of the Czechoslovakian SSR.

Type: Single-seat high-performance sailplane; *g* limits +5·3/−3·5.

Airframe: Cantilever shoulder-wing monoplane, with Wortmann wing sections: FX-61-163 at root, FX-60-126 at tip. Dihedral 3°. All-wood single-spar forward-swept wings with sandwich skin. All-metal DFS air-brakes on upper surfaces. All-wood slotted ailerons. Glassfibre monocoque front and centre fuselage sections, latter reinforced by steel tube frame. Monocoque rear fuselage of aluminium alloy sheet. Metal T tail with fabric-covered elevators and rudder. Fixed-incidence tailplane. Retractable rubber-sprung monowheel (tyre pressure approx 2·45 bars; 35·5 lb/sq in), with drum brake. Semi-recessed unsprung tailwheel. Detachable cockpit canopy.

DENMARK

PROJEKT 8

PROJEKT 8 I/S

Fynsvej 56, DK-4000 Roskilde

DOLPHIN

The Projekt 8 I/S company, formed by Helge Petersen and 10 other glider pilots, is building a two-seat motor glider known as the Dolphin. Construction is taking place at three separate sites near Copenhagen. It was anticipated that the first flight would be made in late 1979.

Type: Tandem two-seat motor glider; *g* limits +6; −4.

Airframe: Cantilever mid-wing monoplane with T tail. Wortmann and NACA wing sections: FX-67-K-170 on centre-section; outer panels vary through FX-67-K-150 to NACA 64-212 at tip. Dihedral 4°. Aluminium wing centre-section; outer panels, including flaps and ailerons, of wood and glassfibre. Aluminium upper-surface airbrakes. Welded steel tube forward fuselage, covered by light glassfibre shell; wooden rear fuselage, reinforced by glassfibre. Wooden tail unit, with fixed-incidence tailplane. Central trim tab in elevator, inset tab at base of rudder. Semi-retractable rubber-sprung Tost main wheel; Tost nosewheel; steerable solid-tyre tailwheel; retractable wingtip balancer wheels. Cockpit canopy opens sideways.

POWER PLANT: One 40·25 kW (54 hp) VW 1600 engine, driving a two-blade pusher propeller, mounted on pylon which retracts rearward into top of fuselage when not in use.

FINLAND

ALANNE

PENTTI ALANNE

Orapihlajantie 6, 02620 Espoo 62

Mr Pentti Alanne has been concerned with a number of motor glider conversions since the second World War. In 1949, with Mr Vilho Swahn, he modified a Grunau Baby glider by installing a Poinsard engine in the nose and fitting a landing gear similar to that of a Piper Cub. The Motorlerche, described hereafter, is a Rhönlerche II glider fitted with similar landing gear and a modified Volkswagen engine. Currently, Mr Alanne is converting a Czechoslovak Blanik sailplane to receive a dorsally-mounted VW engine; this was expected to make its first flight in the Summer of 1979.

ALANNE MOTORLERCHE

The Motorlerche, which flew for the first time on 10 August 1973, is a conversion of the Rhönlerche II, a former training glider now readily obtainable at a low cost. The forward section of the fuselage is removed, and attachments welded on for a modified Volkswagen 1,500 cc engine. Landing gear consists of main-wheel and tail-wheel units similar to those of a Piper Cub, and the complete conversion can be accomplished in approx 200 h.

By the Spring of 1979, six Motorlerche were flying and five more were under construction.

TYPE: Side-by-side two-seat motor glider. Aerobatics prohibited.

AIRFRAME: As for Rhönlerche II, except for modifications necessary to install power plant and non-retractable landing gear.

POWER PLANT: One 37·2 kW (50 hp) modified Volkswagen 1,500 cc engine (Ted Barker conversion), driving a two-blade propeller. Usable fuel capacity 26 litres (5·7 Imp gallons). Oil capacity 2·5 litres (0·5 Imp gallons).

EIRI

EIRIAVION OY

Kisällinkatu 8, SF-15170, Lahti 17
Telephone: (918) 334 280
Telex: 16165 eiri sf
SALES: Hannu Riihelä

Technical Dept and Works: 38800 Jämijärvi
Telephone: (930) 71 200
Telex: 26254 eiri sf
TECHNICAL DIRECTOR: Stefan Nyström

EIRI PIK-20

Design of the PIK-20 began on 1 May 1971 at Helsinki University of Technology. The first of two prototypes flew for the first time on 10 October 1973.

The original PIK-20, described in the 1975-76 *Jane's*, was followed by the PIK-20B with higher gross weight, increased water ballast, and interconnected flaps and ailerons for improved performance. Carbon fibre spars became available as an option from c/n 20100, reducing empty weight to 225 kg (496 lb).

Finnish certification of the PIK-20 was granted on 20 June 1974. FAA certification was granted on 20 June 1975, being extended to cover the PIK-20B on 15 January 1976 and the PIK-20D on 13 January 1977.

Versions of the PIK-20 so far announced are as follows:

PIK-20B. First major production version (149 built); described in 1976-77 *Jane's*. Superseded in production by PIK-20D.

PIK-20D. Current production version, first flown on 19 April 1976. Schempp-Hirth airbrakes and improved flaps ('flaperons') for enhanced performance. Carbon fibre wing spar standard; fuselage also reinforced with carbon fibre. Enlarged cockpit, with improved layout. Total of 150 built by January 1979.

PIK-20E. Experimental powered prototype flown for first time on 2 October 1976; described in 1977-78 *Jane's*. Production prototype, based on PIK-20D and powered by manually retractable Rotax 503 engine, made its first (aero-tow) flight on 16 March 1978, and its first powered flight two days later. Production version has Rotax 501 engine, steerable rubber-sprung tailwheel and fixed wingtip wheels. Wing sweepback 1° 21·6'; longer nose; 25% more tailplane area than PIK-20D. Series production began in late 1978.

The following description applies primarily to the PIK-20D, except where indicated otherwise:

TYPE: Single-seat 15 metre Contest Class sailplane; *g* limits (manoeuvring) +5·3/−2·65, (gust at max weight) +6·6/−4·6.

AIRFRAME: Cantilever shoulder-wing monoplane with T tail. Wortmann wing sections: FX-67-K-170 at root, FX-67-K-150 at tip. Dihedral 3°. Glassfibre/epoxy/PVC foam sandwich wings. Spars of carbon fibre reinforced epoxy. Schempp-Hirth airbrakes standard. Plain flaps ('flaperons') function as both flaps and ailerons. Provision for 140 litres (30·8 Imp gallons) of water ballast (120 litres; 26·4 Imp gallons in PIK-20E). Glassfibre/epoxy monocoque fuselage, reinforced with ribs and carbon fibre. Optional Tost towing hook on PIK-20E. T-tail of similar construction to wings. Fixed-incidence tailplane, with one-piece elevator. Retractable Tost monowheel with drum brake. Continental tail-wheel. Cockpit canopy opens sideways.

POWER PLANT (PIK-20E): One 32 kW (43 hp) Rotax 501 two-cylinder two-stroke engine, driving a Hoffmann two-blade fixed-pitch wooden propeller, retracting manually into fuselage aft of cockpit when not in use. Electric starter. Fuel tank capacity 30 litres (6·6 Imp gallons).

FRANCE

CARMAM

CARMAM SOCIÉTÉ ANONYME

Aérodrome de Moulins, BP 201, 03001 Moulins Cédex
Telephone: (70) 44 36 18
PRESIDENT-DIRECTOR GENERAL: Jean Pottier
TECHNICAL DIRECTOR: Christian Rocheteau

CARMAM is currently responsible for the J.P.15-36, designed by M Robert Jacquet and M Jean Pottier, and the CARMAM 15-38. It is also producing the Pottier P.A. 15-34 Kit-Club (which see) in factory-built form.

CARMAM J.P.15-36A AIGLON (EAGLET)

The Aiglon was designed as a private venture by M Robert Jacquet and M Jean Pottier. Design began in September 1971, and prototype construction started at the end of 1972. The prototype (F-WCAP) made its first flight on 14 June 1974.

Series production, in the CARMAM works, began in 1976, and the first production **J.P.15-36A** flew for the first time on 16 October 1976. With retractable monowheel, the aircraft is designated **J.P.15-36AR**.

A total of 36 J.P.15-36A and J.P.15-36AR Aiglons had been built by April 1979.

TYPE: Single-seat Standard Class sailplane; *g* limit +5·3.

AIRFRAME: Cantilever mid-wing monoplane, with Wortmann wing sections: FX-67-K-170 at root, FX-60-126 at tip. Dihedral 3°. Single glassfibre wing spar, with glassfibre/Rohacell/epoxy sandwich skin and steel-tipped wingtip 'salmons'. Plastics plain ailerons, which can be operated differentially or in unison. Schempp-Hirth upper/lower surface airbrakes. Provision for 55 kg (121 lb) water ballast. Semi-monocoque glassfibre fuselage, moulded in two halves and joined at centre-line. Single bulkhead forms cockpit backrest and shock-absorbing structure for monowheel. Sweptback fin, integral with fuselage, with fabric-covered wooden rudder. All-moving plastics tailplane. Non-retractable monowheel, with brake, and tail bumper on J.P.15-36A. Retractable monowheel on J.P.15-36AR. Detachable cockpit canopy.

CARMAM 15-38

Construction of this single-seat Standard Class sailplane began in February 1977, and the prototype flew for the first time on 17 January 1979. It utilises the same wings as the J.P.15-36A, but with provision for 100 kg (220 lb) water ballast; the fuselage is of new design, but of similar construction to the J.P.15-36A; it has a T tail, with elevator spring trim, and a mechanically retractable unsprung monowheel.

ENSAE

ÉCOLE NATIONALE SUPÉRIEURE DE L'AÉRONAUTIQUE ET DE L'ESPACE

Complexe Aéro-spatial, 10 avenue Edouard-Belin, BP 4032, 31055 Toulouse Cédex
Telephone: (61) 53 21 21
Telex: 510647 Aerosup

Construction by ENSAE students of the two-seat Farfelu training glider, described in the 1978-79 *Jane's*, has been abandoned.

The group has, however, begun the construction of an alternative project, though no details of this had been received at the time of closing for press.

ENSMA

ÉCOLE NATIONALE SUPÉRIEURE DE MÉCANIQUE ET D'AÉROTECHNIQUE

1 rue Guillaume-VII-le-Troubadour, 86034 Poitiers
Telephone: 41 37 11

ENSMA MODIFIED FS-25 CUERVO

Led by MM Gauthier and Piquereau, students of the ENSMA are building at Poitiers a single-seat sailplane. This is based upon the Akaflieg Stuttgart FS-25 Cuervo, described and illustrated in the 1973-74 *Jane's*, but has a retractable monowheel and modifications to the internal structure and wing/fuselage attachments. Dimensions, weights and performance are the same as those for the German-built FS-25. The aircraft was expected to fly in the second half of 1979.

FAUVEL

CHARLES FAUVEL

72 boulevard Carnot, 06400 Cannes AM
Telephone: (93) 68 26 24

M Charles Fauvel has been developing and producing tail-less sailplanes for many years. The original AV.36 Monobloc single-seater first flew in 1951 and more than 100 were sold to customers in 14 countries before this design was superseded by the improved AV.361. Several powered versions of M Fauvel's sailplanes have flown, and the prototype AV.45 has flight tested a lightweight turbojet power plant.

Plans of the AV.361, AV.45 and AV.222 are currently available from M Fauvel for amateur construction. In addition, glassfibre component moulds for the AV.45, and cockpit transparency moulds for the AV.222, can be supplied if required. Formers or moulds for certain components of the AV.44 and AV.50 powered aircraft (see Homebuilt Aircraft section) are also available.

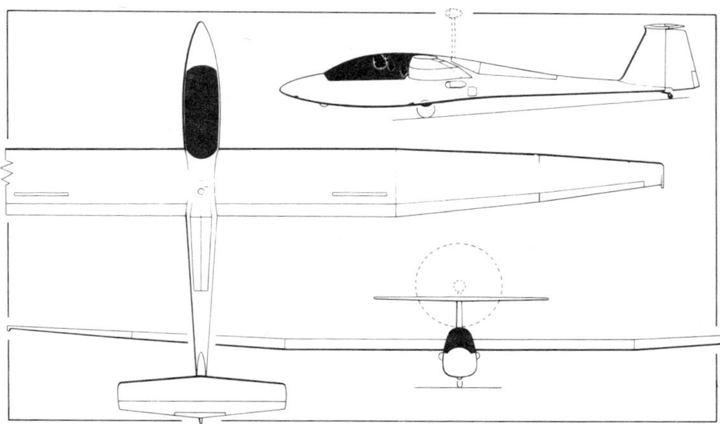
Projekt 8 Dolphin tandem two-seat motor glider *(Michael A. Badrocke)*

Alanne Motorlerche motor glider (modified VW engine)

Eiri PIK-20D single-seat glassfibre 15 m Contest Class sailplane

Eiri PIK-20E motor glider, with retractable power plant

CARMAM J.P.15-36A Aiglon Standard Class sailplane

Fauvel AV.221 side-by-side two-seat motor glider

FAUVEL AV.361

Well over 100 AV.36 and AV.361 sailplanes are flying in 17 countries. Plans are available in French and English, and construction by amateurs continues, especially in the USA and Spain.

Details of this single-seat general-purpose sailplane may be found in the 1970-71 *Jane's*. The standard F2 section wing can, at builder's option, be replaced in the AV.361 by one with a Wortmann FX-66-H-159 laminar-flow section, which increases the best glide ratio to 30 at a speed of 46 knots (85 km/h; 53 mph).

Details of an AV.361 completed by the Escuela de Aeromodelismo at Alicante, Spain, can be found in the 1977-78 *Jane's*.

FAUVEL AV.45 and AV.451

The AV.45 single-seat tail-less motor glider first flew on 4 May 1960 with a 26 kW (35 hp) Nelson engine. A second, slightly modified prototype, with 16·5 kW (22 hp) SOLO engine, was built by Société Aéronautique Normande (SAN). More recently, the protoype AV.45 has been fitted with a 22·4 kW (30 hp) Rockwell-JLO engine by an amateur constructor; a CNA (certificat de navigabilité amateur) has been issued for this aircraft in this form. The standard engines recommended are the 30-41 kW (40-55 hp) modified Hirth O-280R or Rotax. Fuel is contained in integral wooden tanks in the wing leading-edges.

As with the AV.361, the AV.45 may also be fitted with a Wortmann laminar-flow wing, with which the best glide ratio is increased to 30.

For several years a French homebuilt AV.45 with Nelson engine has been flying, and a Japanese homebuilt AV.45 with SOLO engine is flying in South Africa. In early 1978 four other AV.45s were under construction in France, three in the USA, and one each in Finland, Germany, Martinique and Spain. The German example is fitted with a SOLO engine.

An improved version, the **AV.451,** has a laminar-flow wing, of Wortmann FX-66H-159 section, with the span extended to 15·00 m (49 ft 2½ in); a more tapered nose; more streamlined wheel fairings; and vertical tail surfaces of Wortmann symmetrical section. The first example, built in France by MM François and Roger Gross at Baccarat, has a 30 kW (40 hp) Rotax engine and was flown for the first time in early September 1978. A glide ratio of 32 at 47 knots (87 km/h; 54 mph) was expected with propeller folded and stowed. Plans of this version are not yet generally available.

FAUVEL AV.222

This motor glider was developed from the AV.22 tailless sailplane, described in the 1960-61 *Jane's*. It first flew on 8 April 1965. Brief details of the AV.221 prototype were given in the 1970-71 *Jane's*.

Plans are available to amateur constructors of a lighter and simplified version of the AV.221, designated AV.222, of which examples are being built in France, Germany, Italy, Sweden, the UK and the USA.

Type: Side-by-side two-seat motor glider.

Airframe: Wings are built in three sections, and a conventional twin-main-wheel landing gear was fitted successfully to both the AV.221 prototype and the AV.222. This consisted of cantilever self-sprung laminated glassfibre legs, and Duruble 330 × 130 wheels with hydraulic brakes and streamlined wheel fairings, in place of the underfuselage monowheel and its fairing. For amateur construction, however, the monowheel landing gear is recommended as being lighter, cheaper and easier to install.

Power Plant: Suitable power plants include the 30 kW (40 hp) Rectimo or 45 kW (60 hp) Limbach Volkswagen conversions, or the 30 or 37·25 kW (40 or 50 hp) Rotax. Fuel capacity 30 litres (6·6 Imp gallons) standard, 45 litres (9·9 Imp gallons) optional.

FOURNIER
FOURNIER AVIATION

Aérodrome de Nitray, 37270-Montlouis
Telephone: (47) 50 68 30
Managing Director: René Caillet
Consultant: René Fournier

This company was formed in the Spring of 1978 as a successor to Avions Fournier (see 1977-78 *Jane's*).

FOURNIER RF-9

The prototype RF-9 (F-WARF) flew for the first time on 20 January 1977. A second prototype was scheduled to fly in April 1979; this aircraft has a lighter-weight landing gear, new airbrakes, and no trailing-edge flaps. In this form the RF-9 was expected to enter production during the Summer of 1979.

Type: Side-by-side two-seat training motor glider.

Airframe: Cantilever low-wing monoplane, of all-wood construction. NACA 64_3-618 section wings, with dihedral from roots. Ailerons and upper-surface airbrakes. (Electrically actuated trailing-edge flaps on first prototype only.) Outer portion of each wing can be folded inward for stowage (span folded 10·00 m; 32 ft

9½ in), with connect/disconnect aileron controls. Semi-monocoque fuselage, slightly-swept fin and rudder, and small dorsal fin. Retractable main wheels and steerable tailwheel. One-piece cockpit canopy opens upward and rearward.

POWER PLANT: One 50 kW (68 hp) Limbach SL 1700 E flat-four engine, driving a Hoffmann two-blade constant-speed (optionally variable-pitch) propeller. Fuel capacity 30 litres (6·6 Imp gallons).

GEP
GROUPE D'ÉTUDES GEORGES PAYRE

2 rue Abel, 75012 Paris
Telephone: 522 30 31

GEP TCV-03 TRUCAVAYSSE

Design of the TCV-03 began in October 1968, and prototype construction started in February 1969. This aircraft (F-CRRH), built by the Aéro Club de Norois, flew for the first time on 14 July 1973; others, under construction by amateur builders, are believed to include one in Germany.

No news of GEP has been received for several years. A description and illustration of the TCV-03 can be found in the 1978-79 *Jane's*.

GEP TCV-04

Under development in 1977, the TCV-04 is essentially a TCV-03 fuselage, modified and mated with the wings of a Siren C-30 Edelweiss. The general appearance can be seen in the accompanying three-view drawing; no other details have been received for publication.

GEPAS
GROUPE D'ÉTUDES POUR L'AVIATION SPORTIVE

Allée Gabriel Voisin, BP No. 3, 78370 Plaisir

GEPAS COMPACT

M B. de Lagarde of GEPAS has designed and built this single-seat sailplane. The prototype (F-CRRL) was flown for the first time on 9 June 1978.

TYPE: Single-seat homebuilt sailplane.

AIRFRAME: Cantilever mid-wing monoplane, built of glassfibre and epoxy resin. Trailing-edge flaps/airbrakes. Non-retractable monowheel. Flush-fitting one-piece cockpit canopy.

ISSOIRE
ISSOIRE-AVIATION SA

Aérodrome d'Issoire-le-Broc (Puy-de-Dôme), BP No. 7, 63501 Issoire Cédex
Telephone: (73) 89 01 54
Telex: ISSAVIA 990 185 F
PRESIDENT-DIRECTOR GENERAL: Xavier Laguette
TECHNICAL DIRECTOR: Philippe Moniot
DESIGNER: Bruno Boulnois

This company was formed in late 1977 by the President of Siren SA, following the bankruptcy of Wassmer Aviation. It is now responsible for production of the Siren (formerly CERVA CE 75) Silène and the Siren D 77 Iris sailplanes.

ISSOIRE (SIREN) D 77 IRIS

Design of the Iris began in 1973, and the prototype (F-WAQA) flew for the first time on 26 February 1977.

French certification was granted in early February 1979, at which time approx 50 Iris had been ordered. Production, at the rate of two per month, was then about to begin. The D 77 is also available in kit form for amateur construction.

TYPE: Single-seat training sailplane; *g* limits +5·3/−2·65 (normal), +8·0/−4·0 (ultimate).

AIRFRAME: Cantilever mid-wing monoplane. Bertin E55-166 wing section. Dihedral 3°. Glassfibre/polyester/PMC sandwich construction, with glassfibre ailerons and Schempp-Hirth metal airbrakes on upper surfaces. Glassfibre/polyester monocoque fuselage, built in two halves. Cantilever tail unit, of similar construction to wings. Fixed-incidence tailplane. Spring tab in each elevator. Non-retractable unsprung monowheel, tyre size 330 × 130, pressure 1·8 bars (26 lb/sq in); tailskid. Siren hydraulic brake. Cockpit canopy opens sideways to starboard.

ISSOIRE (SIREN) E 78 SILÈNE

Design of the original E 75 Silène (by Siren SA) began on 1 January 1972. Construction by CERVA of a CE 75 prototype started on 1 February 1973, and this aircraft (F-CCFF) made its first flight at Argenton on 2 July 1974. French certification was granted on 3 February 1978.

By January 1979 six Silènes had been delivered, of approx 20 then on order, including examples for customers in Australia, Germany, the UK and the USA. Fuselages are built by Siren SA.

Current versions of the Silène are designated as follows:

E 78. Cockpit improvements by comparison with E 75 include a larger canopy, lowered seats, increased width at shoulder level, and repositioned starboard rudder pedals. Retractable monowheel. Certificated 1 August 1978. In production.

E 78B. Basic version, with non-retractable monowheel. Certificated 1 August 1978.

I 79. Advanced version, with wing flaps and water ballast. Under development in 1979. Fuselage as for E 78, but modified wings incorporating carbon-fibre components; Bertin E55-166 V.M2 wing section; aspect ratio 20. Monowheel, wing flaps and airbrakes actuated hydraulically.

The following description applies to the E 78 and E 78B:

TYPE: Side-by-side two-seat training sailplane; *g* limits +5·3/−2·65 (normal), +8·0/−4·0 (ultimate).

AIRFRAME: Cantilever mid-wing monoplane, built entirely of glassfibre/polyester/PMC sandwich. Bertin E55-166 wing section. Dihedral 2°. Sweepforward 2° at quarter-chord. Two-section ailerons, with spring tabs. Schempp-Hirth airbrakes above and below each wing. Semi-monocoque fuselage. Cantilever tail unit, with fixed-incidence tailplane. Spring tab in each elevator. Retractable or non-retractable rubber-sprung monowheel, tyre size 330 × 130, pressure 2·4 bars (35 lb/sq in). Siren hydraulic brake optional. Tailskid.

LORAVIA
LORRAINE AVIATION

Aérodrome de Thionville, 57110 Yutz, Moselle
Telephone: (87) 88 56 87
EXECUTIVES: M. Schmitt and R. Kieger

This company took over from SLCA (1974-75 *Jane's*) continued production of the Scheibe SF-27 under licence in France, where it is known as the Topaze. German production of the SF-27 ended several years ago.

LA-11 TOPAZE

The Topaze is the Scheibe SF-27 Zugvogel V built under licence in France. It received a French certificate of airworthiness on 25 April 1972.

SLCA built nine SF-27s under the French designation SLCA-10 (now LA-10). The LA-11 has the monowheel lowered 80 mm (3·15 in). It flew for the first time on 15 October 1973; six were completed by SLCA in 1973, and 12 in 1974. In early 1976, Loravia had completed 30 of 33 then on order; no later news has been received.

A description and illustration of the Topaze can be found in the 1978-79 *Jane's*.

POTTIER
JEAN POTTIER

4 rue de Poissy, 78130 Les Mureaux
Telephone: 099 13 85

POTTIER P.A. 15-34 KIT-CLUB

This is essentially the same sailplane as the CARMAM J.P.15-36A Aiglon (which see), with some constructional simplification to make it suitable for amateur builders.

Prototype construction began in November 1975; first flight was made on 6 November 1976.

French certification was received on 15 February 1979. First kits for homebuilders became available in mid-March 1979, and by mid-April two Kit-Clubs had been completed, both by M Jean Magne of Livry Gargan.

The P.A.15-34 is also produced in factory-built form by CARMAM (which see).

The description of the Aiglon applies also to the P.A.15-34, except in the following respects:

TYPE: Single-seat homebuilt sailplane; *g* limits +8·3/−4·0.

AIRFRAME: As Aiglon, but of plywood-covered spruce construction except for glassfibre nosecone. Provision for 80 kg (176 lb) of water ballast. Rudder and rear part of tailplane fabric-covered. Non-retractable unsprung monowheel, with cable-operated drum brake for production aircraft.

SCAP
SOCIÉTÉ DE COMMERCIALISATION AÉRONAUTIQUE DU PLESSIS, SàRL

Aérodrome de Bailleau-Armenonville, 28320 Gallardon
Telephone: (37) 23 43 74 and 23 54 32

SCAP is marketing, as the Cirrus 78L, the former Schempp-Hirth Standard Cirrus, and has developed the SL-2 two-seat all-plastics sailplane.

SCAP CIRRUS 78L

The Cirrus 78L is a current version of the Standard Cirrus sailplane produced originally by Schempp-Hirth in Germany. It is manufactured in France by the holding company Dubigeon-Normandie, and distributed by SCAP. Thirty had been completed by 1 January 1979.

TYPE: Single-seat high-performance Standard Class sailplane; *g* limit +10.

AIRFRAME: Cantilever mid-wing monoplane with T tail. Wortmann wing section. Dihedral 3°. Sweepback 1°18′ at leading-edge. Glassfibre/foam sandwich wings, ailerons and tail surfaces. Schempp-Hirth glassfibre airbrakes on wing upper surface. Provision for 130 litres (28·6 Imp gallons) of water ballast. Glassfibre fuselage shell, stiffened with bonded-in foam rings. Fixed tailplane, with elevator. Retractable monowheel standard. Non-retractable faired monowheel optional. Tost wheel with drum brake and Continental tyre, pressure 3·45 bars (50 lb/sq in). New-design canopy, opening sideways to starboard.

SCAP-LANAVERRE SL-2

First flown on 15 October 1977, the SL-2 is a development of the Schempp-Hirth Janus (which see), from which it differs chiefly in having a fixed tailplane with elevators instead of a one-piece all-moving tailplane. There is provision for 200 litres (44 Imp gallons) of water ballast in the wings, and a more comfortable cockpit for both occupants, with provision for back-type parachutes.

SIREN
SIREN SA

Route des Chambons, BP 42, 36200 Argenton-sur-Creuse
Telephone: (54) 04 14 47
Telex: 750534 Chamco-Châteauroux Siren 200-1
DIRECTOR: Xavier Laguette

Well known as a manufacturer of aircraft components and equipment, Siren built the C.30S Edelweiss single-seat Standard Class sailplane and the Open Class Edelweiss IV, both described in the 1971-72 *Jane's*.

Two later designs, the **E 78 Silène** and **D 77 Iris**, are described under the Issoire heading in this section. Siren is building fuselages for the E 78.

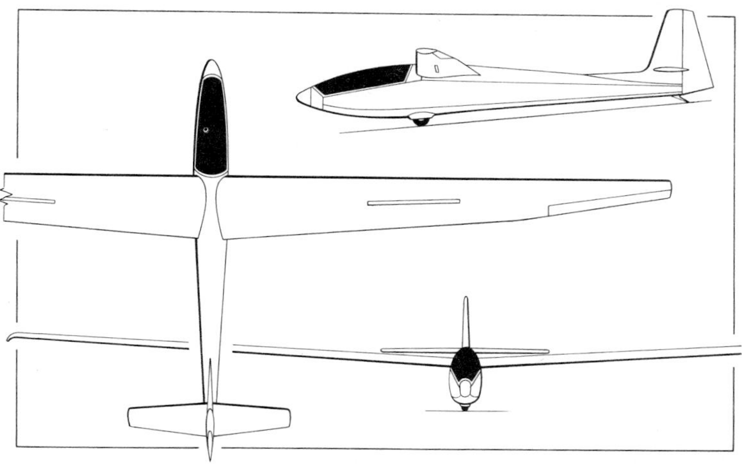

GEP TCV-04 proposal for a homebuilt sailplane using the wings of a Siren Edelweiss *(Michael A. Badrocke)*

Issoire (Siren) E 75 Silène side-by-side two-seat training sailplane

GEPAS Compact homebuilt sailplane

Issoire (Siren) D 77 Iris single-seat training sailplane

Pottier P.A.15-34 Kit-Club prototype homebuilt sailplane *(Geoffrey P. Jones)*

Prototype Fournier RF-9 two-seat training motor glider

Two views of the Akaflieg Braunschweig SB-11 Antares variable-geometry sailplane, winner of the unlimited 15 metre Class competition at the 1978 World Gliding Championships *(Peter F. Selinger)*

GERMANY
(FEDERAL REPUBLIC)

AKAFLIEG BRAUNSCHWEIG
AKADEMISCHE FLIEGERGRUPPE BRAUNSCHWEIG EV

3300 Braunschweig, Flughafen Akafliegheim
Telephone: 0531 3952149
Director: Martin Hansen

The students of Brunswick University have built a series of high-performance sailplanes (see 1977-78 and earlier editions of *Jane's*). The latest product of Akaflieg Braunschweig is the SB-11.

AKAFLIEG BRAUNSCHWEIG SB-11 ANTARES

The SB-11 has been built primarily to evaluate the use of carbon fibre reinforced epoxy resin for construction of all parts of a glider, and for testing a new variable-geometry flap system for sailplanes. Categorised in the FAI Unlimited Standard Class, its design was started in the Spring of 1974 and construction of the one and only prototype began in April 1976.

This aircraft (D-1177) flew for the first time on 14 May 1978. Six weeks later, at the World Gliding Championships at Châteauroux, France, it won the unlimited 15 metre Class contest, piloted by Dr Helmut Reichmann, who thus became the only person to win the title of World Champion three times. In November 1978 the SB-11 was named Antares, and received the 1978 Wolf Hirth prize for the best development in light aircraft and gliding.

In order to achieve a high average cross-country speed without the operating inconveniences of excessive wing span, a telescopic wing or a slotless Fowler flap wing, Akaflieg Braunschweig designed an aircraft that would accomplish this while retaining the flying and handling characteristics of a conventional sailplane. It decided that a constant-thickness Fowler flap would avoid the necessity to open a flexible lip at the lower surface of the wing and would also avoid friction between wing and flap. With the assistance of Prof Wortmann, a special SB-11 wing section was evolved and was flight tested on the fuselage of a Kranich III glider. The results encouraged Akaflieg Braunschweig to believe that, with flaps out, the SB-11 would outclimb any other Standard Class sailplane; and that, with flaps in, it would perform as a conventional Standard Class type.

Type: Single-seat high-performance research sailplane; *g* limit (flaps in or out) +5·3.

Airframe: Cantilever mid-wing monoplane. Specially-designed Wortmann SB-11 wing section. Dihedral 2° 15′. Incidence 0° 30′ (flaps in), 7° 30′ (flaps out). No sweepback. Single carbon fibre spar, and roving spar flanges, and carbon fibre/plastics foam sandwich outer shell. Entire trailing-edge of each wing is made up of a 25% chord slotless Fowler flap (inboard) and (outboard) a flaperon of 22% chord (in) and 17% chord (extended). Flaps and flaperons of carbon fibre/plastics foam sandwich. Schempp-Hirth airbrakes, of carbon fibre/balsa wood sandwich, on upper surfaces. Wing tanks for 130 kg (286 lb) of releasable water ballast. Carbon fibre monocoque fuselage (not sandwich). Cantilever T tail, of carbon fibre/plastics foam sandwich except for rudder, which is of glassfibre/plastics foam sandwich. All-moving tailplane, with spring trim. Retractable unsprung monowheel, tyre pressure 2·5 bars (36·25 lb/sq in), with Tost internal drum brake. Rubber-sprung tailskid.

AKAFLIEG DARMSTADT
AKADEMISCHE FLIEGERGRUPPE DARMSTADT EV

6100 Darmstadt, Technische Hochschule, Hochschulestrasse

Telephone: 06151 162790

The Fliegergruppe of Darmstadt University has been designing, building and flying sailplanes since 1921. Its postwar products have been described in previous editions of *Jane's*. The D-38 is currently in production, in slightly modified form, as the Glaser-Dirks DG-100 (which see).

AKAFLIEG DARMSTADT D-39

The D-39 motor glider utilises the basic D-38 airframe, except for a low-mounted wing and a nose-mounted power plant.

The prototype was expected to make its first flight in May 1979.

Type: Single-seat motor glider; *g* limits +5·3/−3·6.

Airframe: Cantilever low-wing monoplane with T tail. Wortmann wing sections: FX-61-184 at centreline, FX-60-126 at tip. Dihedral 4° from roots. Glassfibre/balsa sandwich wings, tail and monocoque fuselage, with glassfibre/Klégécel foam sandwich ailerons. All-moving one-piece swept tailplane, with half-span Flettner tab. Retractable sprung monowheel, with Tost drum brake, and small tailwheel.

Power Plant: One 37·5 kW (50 hp) Hirth O-28 engine, driving a two-blade foldable wood and glassfibre propeller.

AKAFLIEG KARLSRUHE
AKADEMISCHE FLIEGERGRUPPE KARLSRUHE EV

Technische Hochschule, 75 Karlsruhe, Postfach 6380, Kaiserstrasse 12

Telephone: 0721 6081

Public Relations: Adolf Herlitzka

AKAFLIEG KARLSRUHE AK 2

A prototype of the AK 2 is under construction. All known details are given hereafter; appearance of the AK 2 can be seen in the accompanying three-view drawing.

Type: Single-seat motor glider.

Airframe: Cantilever mid-wing monoplane with upper-surface airbrakes, trailing-edge flaps and ailerons. GFK wings. Cantilever T-tail. Monowheel and tailwheel.

Power Plant: One 41 kW (55 hp) Hirth O-28 two-cylinder two-stroke engine, driving a tractor propeller and retractable into fuselage when not in use.

AKAFLIEG MÜNCHEN
AKADEMISCHE FLIEGERGRUPPE MÜNCHEN EV

8000 München 2, Arcisstrasse 21, Postfach 20 24 20

Telephone: 28 61 11

Director: Klaus Raeder

Design Manager: Johannes Ehrhardt

Recent designs by students at Munich University have included the Mü 26 (1973-74 *Jane's*) and Mü 27.

AKAFLIEG MÜNCHEN Mü 27

A prototype of the Mü 27 is under construction, and was expected to fly for the first time in the Spring of 1979.

Type: Tandem two-seat high-performance sailplane.

Airframe: Cantilever shoulder-wing monoplane with T tail. Wortmann FX-67-VC-170/136 section, with Fowler-type flaps which increase wing area by 36% when fully extended. Aluminium alloy wing spar and metal webs, with glassfibre/foam sandwich wing and tail skins; all-glassfibre semi-monocoque fuselage. Double ailerons, linked to flaps when latter are extended. Airbrakes on wing upper surfaces. Retractable monowheel and fixed tailwheel. Canopy opens sideways to starboard.

AKAFLIEG STUTTGART
AKADEMISCHE FLIEGERGRUPPE STUTTGART EV

7000 Stuttgart 80, Pfaffenwaldring 35

Telephone: (0711) 784 2442 and 784 2443

President: Harald Joos

The Akaflieg Stuttgart has been engaged since the mid-1920s in aerodynamic research and experimental aircraft construction, mainly in the field of sailplane development, and it was in the wind tunnels at Stuttgart that the well-known Eppler and Wortmann wing sections were first developed. In more recent years Akaflieg Stuttgart has been in the forefront in developing the use of glassfibre in sailplane construction, and flew its first glassfibre sailplane, the FS-24 Phönix, on 25 November 1957. Akaflieg Stuttgart's latest known design, the FS-29, was described in the 1976-77 *Jane's*.

BLESSING
GERHARD BLESSING

205 Hamburg 80, Ochsenwerder Landstrasse 33

BLESSING REBELL

The Rebell is a single-seat homebuilt motor glider, with provision for a second occupant. The prototype (D-KEBO) first flew on 3 June 1973 and was powered originally by a 40·5 kW (54 hp) Hirth engine driving a pusher propeller; it was subsequently flown with a modified VW power plant.

The Rebell is no longer available in its 'pusher-engined' form. Herr Blessing plans to fly it again in 1980, with a front-mounted engine and tractor propeller.

GLASER-DIRKS
GLASER-DIRKS FLUGZEUGBAU GmbH

7520 Bruchsal 4, Postfach 47, Im Schollengarten 19-20

Telephone: 07257 (1071)

Directors: Gerhard Glaser and Dipl-Ing Wilhelm Dirks

GLASER-DIRKS DG-100

Manufacture of the DG-100 series is now carried out under licence by Elan in Yugoslavia, under whose entry a description and illustration can be found. By the end of 1978, production by Glaser-Dirks and Elan totalled 105 DG-100 Standard Class sailplanes and 16 examples of the generally similar DG-100G.

GLASER-DIRKS DG-200

The DG-200 (D-8200), which flew for the first time in prototype form on 22 April 1977, is an improved DG-100 fitted with wing flaps, and was developed for unlimited international competition.

Three versions were available for 1979, as follows:

DG-200. High-performance 15 metre Class standard version. Total of 20 delivered by early 1978.

DG-200A Acroracer. As DG-200, but with detachable wingtips to reduce span for aerobatics. No water ballast. First flown in October 1978.

DG-200/17. As DG-200, but with insertable wingtips to extend span for Open Class competition. Ten ordered by early 1979; first flight scheduled for March 1979.

Type: Single-seat high-performance sailplane.

Airframe: Cantilever shoulder-wing monoplane. Wing section Wortmann FX-67K-170-17 from root to tip. Dihedral 3° from roots. Incidence 0°. Glassfibre roving main spar. Glassfibre/Conticell/foam sandwich wings, with glassfibre flaps and carbon-fibre ailerons. All-glassfibre semi-monocoque fuselage, fin and rudder. Glassfibre/foam sandwich T tailplane, with all-glassfibre elevator. Schempp-Hirth aluminium airbrakes on upper wing surfaces. Water ballast tank in each wing (except Acroracer), combined capacity 130 kg (286 lb). Manually-retractable monowheel, size 5·00-5, with Tost drum brake; size 200 × 50 tailwheel.

GLASFLÜGEL
HOLIGHAUS & HILLENBRAND GmbH & Co KG

7318 Lenningen, Württ 1

Telephone: 07026 855

The present company was formed following the death on 5 October 1975 of Ing Eugen Hänle, former Director of the Glasflügel company. Glasflügel was responsible for the Standard Libelle, a description of which can be found in the 1974-75 *Jane's*. Glasflügel also built a developed version of Björn Stender's BS 1, utilising the same type of all-glassfibre construction as in the Libelle; and 10 examples of the Glasflügel 604 (1974-75 *Jane's*).

Current production is of the Glasflügel Kestrel, Hornet, Mosquito and Mosquito B.

GLASFLÜGEL KESTREL

The Glasflügel Kestrel was known originally as the 17 metre Libelle. In addition to proven Libelle features, the Kestrel has a larger cockpit canopy, a new fuselage and wing profile, and a T tail.

The 17 metre version holds the single-seat 100 km closed-circuit glider speed record of 89·22 knots (165·348 km/h; 102·74 mph), set by K. B. Briegleb of the USA on 18 July 1974.

Deliveries of production Kestrels began in 1969, and by the end of 1978 at least 129 had been delivered.

Type: Single-seat high-performance Open Class sailplane.

Airframe: Cantilever shoulder-wing monoplane, with T tail. Two-piece glassfibre and balsa and/or foam sandwich wings, with unidirectional glassfibre spar caps produced by the HH method. Glassfibre and balsa sandwich shear web. Ailerons linked differentially with high-lift camber-changing flaps, all partially mass-balanced. Flush-fitting dive brakes. Glassfibre (not sandwich) monocoque fuselage, with tail unit of similar construction to wings. Tail control surfaces mass-balanced. Retractable monowheel, with internally-expanding brake. Interchangeable tailwheel or skid.

GLASFLÜGEL HORNET

The Hornet is a derivative of the Club Libelle (1977-78 *Jane's*), from which it differs principally in having a retractable monowheel, provision for water ballast, and an enlarged flush-fitting canopy. The prototype (D-9432) flew for the first time on 21 December 1974. At least 88 Hornets had been delivered by the end of 1978.

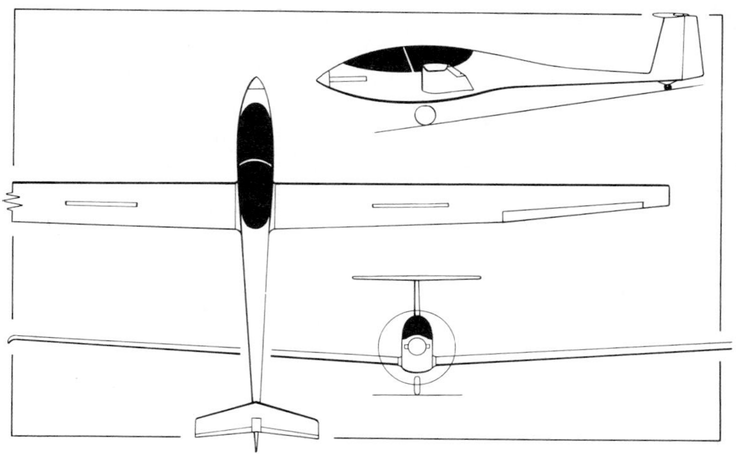

Akaflieg Darmstadt D-39 single-seat motor glider *(Michael A. Badrocke)*

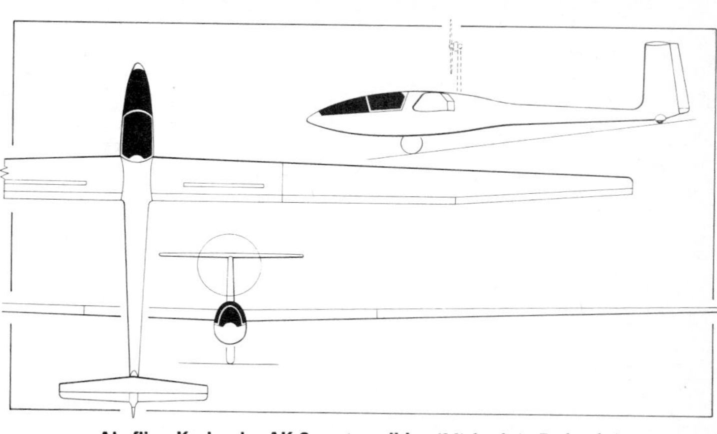

Akaflieg Karlsruhe AK 2 motor glider *(Michael A. Badrocke)*

Glaser-Dirks DG-200A Acroracer aerobatic sailplane

Partially-completed prototype of the Akaflieg München Mü 27

Prototype Glasflügel Hornet 15 metre competition sailplane

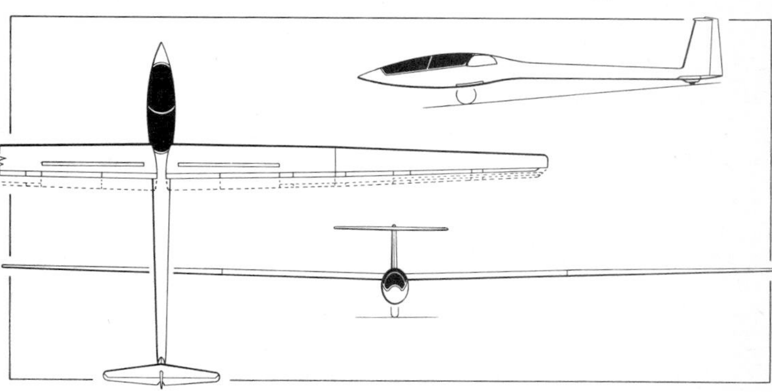

Akaflieg München Mü 27 two-seat sailplane *(Michael A. Badrocke)*

Glasflügel Kestrel 17 metre single-seat Open Class sailplane

Glasflügel Mosquito B single-seat 15 m Contest Class sailplane

The **Hornet C**, due to fly in April 1979, has a wing of carbon-fibre construction, reducing the empty weight to 210 kg (463 lb). Delivery of this version was expected to begin by the Summer of 1979.

TYPE: Single-seat Standard Class sailplane; *g* limits +5·3/−3·25 (safety factor 1·5).

AIRFRAME: Cantilever shoulder-wing monoplane with T tail. Wortmann wing section. Entire structure of glassfibre monocoque and glassfibre/foam sandwich. Rotating airbrakes and partially mass-balanced ailerons on wing trailing-edges. Elevator spring trim. Retractable unsprung monowheel, tyre pressure 3·45 bars (50 lb/sq in), with internally-expanding brake; non-retractable tailwheel. Provision for 75 kg (165 lb) water ballast.

GLASFLÜGEL MOSQUITO

The Mosquito design was started in the Summer of 1975. The prototype flew for the first time in March 1976, and LBA certification in the Utility category was awarded on 26 January 1977. A total of 100 Mosquitos had been delivered by January 1979.

TYPE: Single-seat 15 metre Contest Class sailplane.

AIRFRAME: Cantilever mid-wing monoplane with T tail. Wortmann FX-67-K-150 wing section. Dihedral 3° on wing upper surface; sweepback 0° 9′ at quarter-chord. Construction generally similar to Hornet, but with carbon fibre mass-balanced ailerons. Camber-changing trailing-edge flaps; spoiler forward of each flap combines with flap to act as trailing-edge airbrake. Flap, aileron and airbrake controls linked automatically. Fixed-incidence tailplane; elevator has spring trim. Retractable unsprung monowheel, tyre pressure 3·5 bars (50·75 lb/sq in), with internally-expanding brake; non-retractable semi-recessed tailwheel. Provision for 120 kg (265 lb) water ballast.

GLASFLÜGEL MOSQUITO B

Glasflügel began building a prototype of this Mosquito version in September 1977. It differs from the standard Mosquito in having GRP ailerons, no fuselage/wing fairings, reduced wing span (still with provision for 120 kg; 265 lb water ballast), and slimmer horizontal tail surfaces.

The Mosquito B is in production, about 60 having been delivered by January 1979.

GROB
GROB FLUGZEUGBAU

Flugplatz Mindelheim-Mattsies, 8939 Mattsies
Telephone: 08268 411
Telex: 53 96 14

This company built the Schempp-Hirth Standard Cirrus under licence between 1972 and 1975. It is now manufacturing the Astir series of sailplanes of its own design.

GROB ASTIR

Prototype construction of the Astir CS (Club Standard) single-seat Standard Class sailplane began in March 1974, and this aircraft (D-6102) made its first flight on 19 December 1974. German certification by the LBA was awarded in September 1975. The Astir CS77, first flown on 26 March 1977, introduced modified tailplane actuation.

The Astir is produced currently in two forms: the **Standard Astir**, and the **Club Astir**, the latter having a non-retractable monowheel and no water ballast provision. By Spring 1978, a total of more than 550 of the successive versions had been delivered, and 160 more were on order; these figures included 110 and 140 respectively of the Club version.

Type: Single-seat Standard and Club Class sailplanes.

Airframe: Cantilever mid-wing monoplane with T tail. Eppler E 603 wing section. Wing sweepback 1°. Glassfibre roving main spar; wings and tail surfaces have glassfibre/epoxy resin sandwich skin, except ailerons which are of glassfibre sandwich. Schempp-Hirth upper-surface aluminium airbrakes. Glassfibre semi-monocoque fuselage, with towing/launching hook. Retractable Tost monowheel standard (non-retractable on Club version), tyre pressure 2·5 bars (36·3 lb/sq in), with internally-expanding drum brake; rubber-sprung tailwheel. Canopy opens sideways to starboard. Provision for 100 litres (22 Imp gallons) water ballast.

GROB TWIN ASTIR

The Twin Astir is essentially a tandem two-seat development of the Standard Astir, from which it differs principally in having an enlarged cockpit and swept-forward wings of greater span.

Design and prototype construction began in September 1974 and March 1976 respectively, and this aircraft (D-7398) flew for the first time on 31 December 1976.

By early 1978 more than 250 Twin Astirs had been ordered, and approx 120 had been delivered. A **Twin Astir Trainer** version, with non-retractable monowheel and no water ballast, is also available.

Type: Tandem two-seat training and competition sailplane.

Airframe: Generally similar to Standard Astir but with 3° 18′ of forward sweep. Provision for 90 kg (198 lb) water ballast.

GROB SPEED ASTIR II

The prototype of the Speed Astir II made its first flight in mid-April 1978. More than 50 were then on order; deliveries were scheduled to begin in early 1979.

An extended-span version, the **Speed Astir II-17·5**, was due to become available from October 1979.

Type: Single-seat Open Class sailplane.

Airframe: Cantilever mid-wing monoplane with T tail. Generally similar to Standard Astir except for wings, which are of reduced area, Eppler E 662 section, and fitted with so-called 'elastic flaps' (ie, the gaps are elastically sealed), which can be deflected upward or downward. Ailerons actuated by a similar system. Provision for 150 litres (33 Imp gallons) water ballast.

ISF
INGENIEUR-BÜRO DIPL-ING STRAUBER — FROMMHOLD GmbH & Co KG

6140 Bensheim 3-Auerbach, Wilhelm-Leuschner-Strasse 13
Telephone: 06251/74561

ISF MODEL 2 MISTRAL-C

The original Mistral was described and illustrated under the Strauber heading in the 1976-77 *Jane's*. Design of a second model, known as the ISF Mistral-C, was started in October 1974, and this made its first flight on 21 October 1976. A total of 20 had been completed by the beginning of 1979.

Type: Single-seat Club Class sailplane; *g* limits +5·8/−3·8.

Airframe: Cantilever shoulder-wing monoplane with T tail. Wortmann wing sections: FX-61-163 at root, FX-60-126 at tip. Dihedral 4° 18′. Sweepforward 1° at quarter-chord. Structure: main wings and tail of GRP/foam/Conticell CC60 sandwich, ailerons of GRP. Schempp-Hirth aluminium airbrakes on upper wing surfaces. GRP monocoque fuselage. Fixed-incidence tailplane, with spring trim. Non-retractable monowheel, tyre pressure 2·5 bars (36·25 lb/sq in), with Tost brake; tailskid.

KORTENBACH & RAUH
KORTENBACH & RAUH KG

5650 Solingen 15, Postfach 150121, Weyerstrasse 277
Telephone: (02122) 312031
Telex: 8514848 kora d

KORTENBACH & RAUH KORA 1

The Kora 1 first prototype flew for the first time on 13 September 1973. It was designed by Herren Schultes, Seidel and Putz, and was described in the 1977-78 *Jane's*.

The second prototype, which made its first flight on 9 April 1976, differs in having a non-retractable main landing gear. The following description applies to this aircraft.

Flight testing of the second prototype was expected to be completed during 1979. A decision on whether to initiate production had not been made up to the beginning of 1979.

Type: Side-by-side two-seat training motor glider.

Airframe: Cantilever high-wing monoplane, of all-wood construction. Wortmann wing sections: FX-66-S-196 at root, FX-66-S-161 at tip. Schempp-Hirth airbrakes on upper wing surfaces. Pod-type fuselage nacelle, with twin tailbooms supporting twin fins and rudders topped by horizontal tail surfaces. Forward-retracting nose-wheel. Main units are non-retractable, are cantilevered from the fuselage nacelle, and have streamlined wheel fairings. Canopy opens sideways to starboard.

Power Plant: One 48·5 kW (65 hp) Limbach SL 1700 ECI engine, driving a Hoffmann two-blade variable-pitch feathering pusher propeller.

KUFFNER
LEICHTFLUGZEUGBAU KUFFNER GmbH & Co KG

5485 Sinzig/Koisdorf, Postfach 1233

KUFFNER WK-1

The design of this all-metal motor glider was started by Werner Kuffner in 1973, and a prototype is under construction. It was hoped that flight testing would begin in 1978.

The general appearance of the WK-1 can be seen in the accompanying illustration. Features of the design are the mounting of the engine at the CG, in the fuselage beneath the wing/fuselage junction, and the staggered side-by-side cockpit seating.

Type: Side-by-side two-seat motor glider; *g* limits +5·3/−3·3.

Airframe: Cantilever shoulder-wing monoplane, with Wortmann wing sections. Dihedral on outer panels, which have cambered tips. Ailerons and trailing-edge flaps/airbrakes. No spoilers. All-metal pod and boom fuselage. Cantilever cruciform tail unit. Retractable monowheel and tailwheel. Retractable outrigger wheels under wings.

Power Plant: One 50 kW (67 hp) BMW 1,000 cc motorcycle engine, installed in fuselage under wings and driving a three-blade pusher propeller. Propeller blades retract rearward into fuselage when not in use.

LCF
LUFTSPORTCLUB DER ZEPPELINSTADT FRIEDRICHSHAFEN

7990 Friedrichshafen/Bodensee, Postfach 644

LCF II

A description and illustration of this Club Class sailplane appeared in the 1978-79 *Jane's*. Series production is not now intended.

LVD
SCHÜLERFLUGGEMEINSCHAFT DER LUFTSPORTVEREIN DETMOLD EV

℅ Heinrich Hennigs, 4930 Detmold 19, Talstrasse 7
Telephone: 05231/58267

The Flying Training School of the Detmold Aero Club converted a Scheibe Bergfalke-IV into a two-seat motor glider, as described and illustrated in the 1978-79 *Jane's*.

A new project was being developed in 1979, but no details of this were received before closing for press.

PFLUMM & RICHTER
MANFRED PFLUMM and K. J. RICHTER

Öschwende 17, 7900 Ulm-Lehr

Herr Pflumm of Stuttgart and Herr Richter of Ulm have produced a small, ultralight collapsible motor glider known as the **Faltente**, designed to be carried on the roof rack of a motor-car. General appearance can be seen in the accompanying three-view drawing; all known details are given in the Table at the end of this section. Power plant is a 7·5 kW (10 hp) Sachs-Wankel KM 48 piston engine.

ROLLADEN-SCHNEIDER
ROLLADEN-SCHNEIDER FLUGZEUGBAU GmbH

6073 Egelsbach, Mühlstrasse 10 (Schliessfach 1130)
Telephone: Langen (06103) 4126
Officers: Walter Schneider and Dipl-Ing Wolf Lemke

Rolladen-Schneider is producing the LS3 sailplane, and is developing the Standard Class LS4.

ROLLADEN-SCHNEIDER LS3

The LS3 was developed from the LS1-f. Design and construction began in 1975, and the prototype flew for the first time on 4 February 1976. A total of 270 of all versions had been ordered by early 1979, of which 256 had been completed.

Three versions have been built, as follows:

LS3. Standard FAI 15 metre Class sailplane, as described in detail. Total of 155 built by early 1979.

LS3a. Similar to LS3, but with horizontal and vertical tail surfaces of greater area and different aerofoil sections, and reduced empty weight. First flown on 18 February 1978; deliveries began in Spring 1978. Total of 100 built by early 1979.

LS3-17. Extended-span (17 metre) version of LS3; due to fly for the first time at the end of January 1979.

Type: Single-seat FAI 15 metre Class sailplane.

Airframe: Cantilever mid-wing monoplane, with modified Wortmann wing section. Dihedral 4°. Ailerons and flaps over entire trailing-edge. Schempp-Hirth airbrakes on upper wing surfaces. Semi-monocoque fuselage. Cantilever T tailplane, with elevator. Entire structure of Gfk sandwich. Retractable Tost rubber-sprung monowheel, tyre pressure 2·94 bars (43 lb/sq in), with drum brake; tailskid. Provision for 120 kg (265 lb) water ballast.

ROLLADEN-SCHNEIDER LS4

Design of this new Standard Class sailplane began in the Winter of 1978, and construction of the prototype at the beginning of 1979; it was due to make its first flight during the following Summer. No further details had been received at the time of closing for press.

Grob Astir CS single-seat Standard Class sailplane

Grob Twin Astir tandem two-seat sailplane

ISF Mistral-C single-seat Club Class sailplane

Second prototype Kortenbach & Rauh Kora 1 motor glider

Model of the Kuffner WK-1 two-seat motor glider

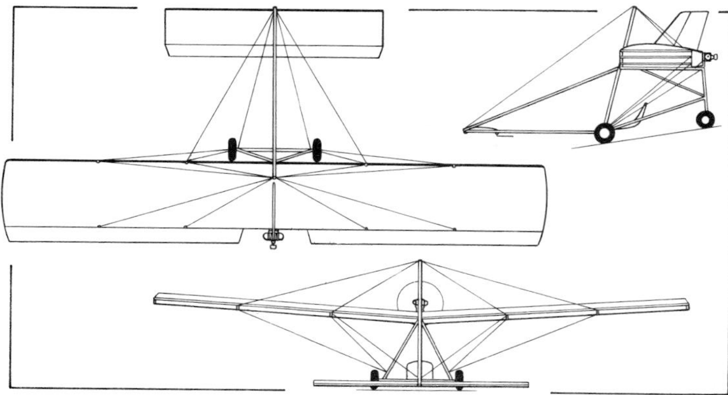

Pflumm & Richter Faltente ultralight motor glider *(Michael A. Badrocke)*

Rolladen-Schneider LS3 single-seat FAI 15 metre Class sailplane

Rolladen-Schneider LS3a, a lighter-weight version of the LS3

LS1-C Club Class version of the Rolladen-Schneider LS1, not illustrated previously in *Jane's*

SCHEIBE

SCHEIBE FLUGZEUGBAU GmbH

HEAD OFFICE AND WORKS: D-8060 Dachau, August-Pfaltz-Strasse 23, Postfach 1829, near Munich
Telephone: Dachau 4047, 6813 and 81886
MANAGERS: Dipl-Ing Egon Scheibe and Ing Christian Gad

Scheibe Flugzeugbau GmbH was founded at the end of 1951 by Dipl-Ing Scheibe; its first type produced in quantity was the Mü-13E Bergfalke I.

Subsequently, Scheibe has built many new types of sailplane, and since 1957 has become the major producer of motor gliders in Germany. Currently in production or under development are the SF-25C and C-S Falke, SF-25E Super-Falke and SF-28 Tandem-Falke motor gliders, in addition to the Bergfalke-IV and SF-H34 sailplanes.

Production of the SF-32 and SF-33 motor gliders, described in the 1977-78 and 1978-79 editions of *Jane's* respectively, has not been undertaken.

Scheibe has built more than 2,000 aircraft of various types, in addition to many kits for home construction by amateurs. Gliders of Scheibe design are being built under licence by gliding clubs as well as by foreign companies.

SCHEIBE BERGFALKE-IV

The Bergfalke-IV is a developed version of the Bergfalke-III, with a new wing which provides improved performance. Construction of the prototype began in early 1969 and first flight was accomplished a few months later. A total of 70 had been built by the beginning of 1979 and production is continuing.

TYPE: Tandem two-seat training and competition sailplane; *g* limit +8 (ultimate).

AIRFRAME: Cantilever mid-wing monoplane, primarily of plywood-covered wooden construction except for welded steel tube fuselage, which is covered with moulded glassfibre shell (nose section) and fabric. Wortmann wing sections: SO 2 at root, SO 2/1 at tip. Dihedral 3°. Wooden ailerons and Schempp-Hirth airbrakes. Flettner trim tab on starboard elevator. Non-retractable monowheel and tailwheel.

SCHEIBE SF-25C and C-S FALKE '76 (FALCON)

The SF-25C is an improved version of the SF-25B Falke, to which it is structurally similar. The primary difference is in the use of a more powerful engine, giving an enhanced performance.

By January 1979 a total of 265 SF-25C Falkes had been built by Scheibe; a further 50 were built under licence by Sportavia in Germany. Type certification was granted in September 1972.

With a Hoffmann feathering propeller, adjustable engine cowl flap and slightly modified fuselage, the aircraft is known as the **SF-25C-S** and has a best glide ratio of 25 at 43·5 knots (80 km/h; 50 mph). Twenty of this version had been built by January 1979.

Optional features include an additional exhaust outlet and a slower-turning propeller. With this installation the nominal noise level is reduced to less than 60 dB. In addition, Scheibe has developed an optional folding wing, which reduces the span to 9·50 m (31 ft 2 in) for easier hangar storage.

Current models, known as **Falke '76**, introduced a number of design improvements, as listed in the 1977-78 *Jane's*.

TYPE: Side-by-side two-seat motor glider, particularly suitable for basic and advanced training.

AIRFRAME: Cantilever low-wing monoplane. Forward-swept wooden wings, with airbrakes and aerodynamically balanced ailerons. Wing folding optional. Fabric-covered welded steel tube fuselage; forward section coated with laminated glassfibre. Tow hitch optional. Wooden tail unit. Non-retractable unsprung monowheel with brake and aerodynamic fairing; steerable tailwheel; sprung outrigger stabilising wheel under each wing. Rubber-sprung monowheel optional. Alternative twin-wheel main gear available optionally, with streamlined wheel fairings.

POWER PLANT: One 48·5 kW (65 hp) Limbach SL 1700 EA I modified Volkswagen engine, driving a two-blade propeller. Electric starter. Fuel in single fuselage tank, capacity 45 litres (9·9 Imp gallons) standard, 55 litres (12·1 Imp gallons) optional.

SCHEIBE SF-25E SUPER-FALKE

Developed from the SF-25C-S, the Super-Falke has an increased wing span and a rubber-sprung monowheel; a cabin heater is fitted as standard. Production aircraft have a tailwheel, and upper-surface Schempp-Hirth airbrakes.

A 48·5 kW (65 hp) Limbach SL 1700 EA 1 engine is fitted, with a 12V battery and alternator for electrical engine starting. Fuel capacity is 45 litres (9·9 Imp gallons). Optionally, the outer wing panels can be made foldable to facilitate transportation and storage.

The Super-Falke was flown for the first time in the Summer of 1974; 44 had been delivered by January 1979.

SCHEIBE SF-28A TANDEM-FALKE

The Tandem-Falke, as its name implies, is a further development of the Falke series of motor gliders in which the two seats are arranged in tandem. Design began in 1970, and the prototype (D-KAFJ) flew for the first time in May 1971, powered by a 33·5 kW (45 hp) Stamo MS 1500 engine. Details apply to the production version, of which 103 had been built by January 1979.

TYPE: Tandem two-seat motor glider.

AIRFRAME: Cantilever low-wing monoplane. Wing section Gö 533. Single-spar wooden wings, with wooden ailerons. No flaps. Spoiler on upper surface of each wing. Fabric-covered steel tube fuselage. Wooden tail unit, with trim tab in elevator. Non-retractable monowheel, with internal brake, and steerable tailwheel. Nylon leg with outrigger stabilising wheel under each wing. Can be flown solo from front seat, with space for 90 kg (198 lb) of baggage on rear seat.

POWER PLANT: One 48·5 kW (65 hp) Limbach SL 1700 EAI engine, driving a Hoffmann two-blade feathering (optionally, fixed-pitch) propeller. 12V alternator standard, for engine starting. Fuel capacity 40 litres (8·8 Imp gallons).

SCHEIBE SF-H34

Design of the SF-H34 sailplane began in 1978, and it flew for the first time on 28 October that year. Production began in early 1979.

TYPE: Tandem two-seat training and sporting sailplane.

AIRFRAME: Cantilever mid-wing monoplane. Wortmann wing sections: FX-61-184 at root, FX-60-126 at tip. Glassfibre roving main spar. Wings and tail unit of Gfk honeycomb sandwich construction; fuselage is a Gfk shell. Schempp-Hirth airbrake in upper surface of each wing. Non-retractable semi-exposed monowheel and nosewheel, tyre sizes 5·00-4 and 265 × 85 respectively; tailskid. Tandem seats under frameless one-piece flush canopy. Towing hooks under nose and at CG.

SCHEMPP-HIRTH

SCHEMPP-HIRTH GmbH & Co KG

7312 Kirchheim-Teck, Krebenstrasse 25, Postfach 143
Telephone: (07021) 2441 and 6097
Telex: 7267817 hate
DIRECTOR: Dipl-Ing Klaus Holighaus

Schempp-Hirth specialises in the production of high-performance Open Class and Standard Class sailplanes. In 1970 Dipl-Ing Klaus Holighaus became a 50% shareholder of Schempp-Hirth KG, later becoming its director following the retirement of Herr Martin Schempp.

Production by Schempp-Hirth of the original Cirrus ended in late 1971, after 120 had been built; but manufacture has continued since early 1972 by VTC in Yugoslavia, under which heading the description of the Cirrus can now be found.

SCHEMPP-HIRTH NIMBUS 2

Generally similar to the HS-3 Nimbus (1972-73 *Jane's*), from which it was developed, the Nimbus 2 differs principally by having reduced span and a wing built in four pieces to limit weight and dimensions for rigging, storage and trailer transport.

Design was initiated by Dipl-Ing Holighaus in January 1970 and construction of the prototype began in April of the same year. The first flight was made in April 1971; a Nimbus 2 took first place in the Open Class at the 1972 and 1974 World Championships at Vrsac, Yugoslavia, and Waikerie, Australia; and in the 1976 World Championships at Räyskälä, Finland, Nimbus 2s took no fewer than 14 of the first 25 places. On 15 February 1977, a Nimbus 2 flown by R. J. Rowe of Australia set a speed record of 72·354 knots (134·000 km/h; 83·264 mph) over a 750 km course. A similar record over 500 km was set in a Nimbus 2 on 27 November 1976 by Edward Pearson of Rhodesia at 77·235 knots (143·04 km/h; 88·881 mph). The world distance record to a goal, for single-seat gliders, was set by a group of three Nimbus 2s flown by S. H. Georgeson, B. L. Drake and D. N. Speight, who covered 677·25 nm (1,254·26 km; 779·36 miles) in New Zealand on 14 January 1978.

By 1 January 1979 a total of 185 Nimbus 2s, 2Bs and 2Cs had been delivered, with production continuing. Aircraft with a fixed-incidence, instead of all-moving, T-tailplane are designated **Nimbus 2B**. The **Nimbus 2C** is similar, but has a new brake/flap system, higher gross weight and (optionally) wings and horizontal tail surfaces of carbon-fibre construction.

The following description applies primarily to the Nimbus 2B:

TYPE: Single-seat Open Class sailplane; *g* limit +10·5.

AIRFRAME: Cantilever mid-wing monoplane. Wortmann wing section. Dihedral 2°. Sweepback at leading-edge 1° on inner panels, 2° on outer panels. Glassfibre/foam sandwich wings and tail. Ailerons and interconnected trailing-edge flaps are glassfibre shells. Schempp-Hirth glassfibre airbrake on each upper wing surface. Central tubular steel fuselage framework. Glassfibre shell, stiffened with bonded-in foam bulkheads. Cantilever T tail, with all-moving tailplane on first 132 aircraft (Nimbus 2); fixed-incidence T-tailplane from 133rd onward (Nimbus 2B/C). Retractable rubber-sprung monowheel, tyre pressure 3·45 bars (50 lb/sq in). Tost drum brake. Tailskid. Provision for up to 160 kg (353 lb) of water ballast (250 kg; 550 lb in Nimbus 2C).

SCHEMPP-HIRTH HS-7 MINI-NIMBUS

As its name implies, the Mini-Nimbus is a scaled-down version of the Nimbus 2, the chief differences being a shorter wing, fitted with trailing-edge flaps/airbrakes, designed to qualify under the new FAI regulations for 15 metre Standard Class sailplanes. With optional fixed-incidence tailplane it is known as the **Mini-Nimbus B**; with the same new features as listed for the Nimbus 2C, it is known as the **Mini-Nimbus C**.

The prototype Mini-Nimbus (D-3119) flew for the first time on 18 September 1976. A total of 104 Mini-Nimbus had been delivered by 1 January 1979. The following details apply primarily to the Mini-Nimbus and Mini-Nimbus B:

TYPE: Single-seat 15 metre Contest Class sailplane.

AIRFRAME: Cantilever mid-wing monoplane. Wortmann wing section. Dihedral 3°. Glassfibre/foam sandwich wings; flaps/airbrakes and ailerons are glassfibre shells. Glassfibre fuselage shell, stiffened with bonded foam rings and a central tubular steel frame. All-moving glassfibre/foam sandwich T tailplane (fixed-incidence tailplane on Mini-Nimbus B/C); fin integral with fuselage. Manually-retractable rubber-sprung monowheel, tyre pressure 3·45 bars (50 lb/sq in), with Tost drum brake. Provision for up to 190 kg (418 lb) of water ballast.

SCHEMPP-HIRTH JANUS

The Janus is of all-glassfibre construction. Original design work, begun by Dipl-Ing Holighaus in 1969, was continued from early 1972 onward, and the prototype made its first flight in the Spring of 1974.

A Janus flown by E. Mouat Biggs and S. Murray set three speed records over triangular courses in South Africa in November 1977. On 16 November, it averaged 73·171 knots (135·513 km/h; 84·204 mph) over 300 km; next day it achieved 75·631 knots (140·068 km/h; 87·034 mph) over 500 km; on 21 November it averaged 79·476 knots (147·19 km/h; 91·46 mph) over 100 km.

Production began in January 1975 with the second, improved aircraft; a **Janus B** version became available in March 1978, with fixed-incidence tailplane. A total of 80 Janus and Janus B had been delivered by 1 January 1979. One aircraft (D-KIBO), designated **Janus M**, was flown as a motor glider in 1978. This was powered by a 41 kW (55 hp) Hirth O-28 engine, pylon-mounted aft of the cockpit and retracting into the top of the fuselage when not in use.

TYPE: Tandem two-seat high-performance training sailplane; *g* limit +9.

AIRFRAME: Cantilever mid-wing monoplane. Wortmann wing sections: FX-67-K-170 at root, FX-67-K-15 at tip. Dihedral 4°. Sweepforward 2° on leading-edge. Glassfibre/foam sandwich wings, with glassfibre monocoque ailerons, trailing-edge flaps and Schempp-Hirth upper-surface airbrakes. Glassfibre monocoque fuselage with bonded-in foam bulkheads. Cantilever glassfibre/foam sandwich T tailplane, of all-moving or (on Janus B) fixed-incidence type. Non-retractable monowheel and nosewheel. Continental tyres: pressure 2·69 bars (39 lb/sq in) on main wheel; pressure 0·79 bars (11·5 lb/sq in) on nosewheel. Tost drum brake on main wheel. Bumper under rear fuselage. Tail drag 'chute.

SCHLEICHER

ALEXANDER SCHLEICHER SEGEL-FLUGZEUGBAU

HEAD OFFICE AND WORKS: D-6416 Poppenhausen/Wasserkuppe
Telephone: (06658) 225

This company is one of the oldest manufacturers of sailplanes in the world. Its founder, Alexander Schleicher, was himself winner of the contest for training sailplanes at the 1927 meeting at the famous Wasserkuppe gliding centre. In the same year he built at Poppenhausen a small factory for manufacturing gliders, two of his best-known pre-war products being the Rhönbussard and Rhönadler, designed by Hans Jacobs.

During the second World War, the factory was engaged in the repair of Baby IIb sailplanes. For a time afterwards it became a furniture factory; but it began producing sailplanes once more in 1951.

Scheibe Bergfalke-IV two-seat training and competition sailplane

Scheibe SF-H34 two-seat training and sporting sailplane

Scheibe SF-25C Falke '76, showing bulged canopy and modified vertical tail

British-registered Scheibe SF-28A Tandem-Falke motor glider

Scheibe SF-25E Super-Falke motor glider, with increased wing span

Schempp-Hirth Janus two-seat all-glassfibre training sailplane

Schempp-Hirth Nimbus 2C high-performance Open Class sailplane

Schempp-Hirth HS-7 Mini-Nimbus C single-seat 15 metre sailplane

Descriptions of the sailplanes in current production follow. In addition, the ASK 13 is available in kit form for amateur constructors. Schleicher also manufactures and markets spare parts, constructional materials and dust- and weatherproof covers for sailplanes.

SCHLEICHER ASK 13

This tandem-seat sailplane was developed from the K 7, which is in worldwide use by gliding clubs.

The prototype first flew in July 1966; production was continuing in 1979.

TYPE: Tandem two-seat training and high-performance sailplane; *g* limit +4·0 (safety factor of 2).

AIRFRAME: Cantilever mid-wing monoplane. Wing section developed from Göttingen 535 and 549. Sweepforward at quarter-chord 6°. Dihedral 5°. Single-spar wooden wings, with fabric covering. Wooden ailerons, with plywood covering; Schempp-Hirth metal airbrakes above and below each wing. Welded steel tube fuselage with spruce formers and fabric main covering. Nose made of glassfibre. Turtledeck aft of canopy is plywood shell. Cantilever wooden tail unit, plywood-covered except for fabric-covered rear portion of rudder and elevators. Flettner tab in starboard elevator. Non-retractable sprung monowheel, with Tost drum brake; skid in front of wheel; steel tailskid. Canopy opens sideways to starboard.

SCHLEICHER ASW 19 B

This Standard Class sailplane, which flew for the first time on 23 November 1975, is essentially an improved version of the ASW 15 B (1977-78 *Jane's*), from which it differs in having a T tail unit. Production began in the Spring of 1976. The ASW 19 took 1st place in the Standard Class at the 1978 World Championships at Châteauroux, France.

Current production aircraft are designated ASW 19 B.

TYPE: Single-seat Standard Class sailplane.

AIRFRAME: Cantilever mid-wing monoplane. Wortmann wing sections: FX-61-163 at root, FX-60-126 at tip. Dihedral 2°. Glassfibre roving wing main spar. Wings and tail surfaces of glassfibre/foam sandwich, with Schempp-Hirth metal upper-surface airbrakes. Glassfibre/honeycomb sandwich fuselage, with reinforced keel. T tailplane with elevator. Retractable monowheel, size 5·00-5, with internal drum brake; rubber tailskid. Canopy hinged at front and opens upward. Provision for 100 kg (220 lb) water ballast. Towing hook at CG; optional second hook in nose.

SCHLEICHER ASW 20

The ASW 20 was designed by Gerhard Waibel. It is intended to take advantage of the March 1975 CIVV regulations for Open Class 15 metre sailplanes, and is fitted with trailing-edge flaps. The ASW 20 has an additional high-drag flap range incorporating a special mechanism to eliminate pitch and airspeed changes when changing flap position between 30° and 55°. A new device automatically co-ordinates and optimises flap position to the prevailing airspeed. This eliminates the need for conventional underwing airbrakes, but large upper-surface spoilers are fitted.

The prototype ASW 20 made its first flight on 29 January 1977, and aircraft of this type won 2nd, 3rd, 4th, 6th and 7th places in their class at the 1978 World Championships. A version designated **ASW 20F** is being built under licence in France by Centrair; this received French certification on 31 March 1978.

TYPE: Single-seat 15 metre Contest Class sailplane.

AIRFRAME: As described for ASW 19 B, except for addition of wing flaps, no option for nose towing hook, and max water ballast increased to 120 kg (265 lb).

SCHLEICHER ASW 20 L

This version of the ASW 20 (L for Lang: long) has a 16·50 m (54 ft 1½ in) span wing. A prototype, with carbon fibre reinforced fuselage, has been flown and was undergoing LBA certification trials in early 1979. A best glide ratio of 45 is estimated.

SCHLEICHER ASK 21

Latest design by Ing Kaiser, the ASK 21 prototype was expected to fly for the first time in early 1979.

TYPE: Tandem two-seat competition and training sailplane.

AIRFRAME: Cantilever mid-wing monoplane. Two-piece wings, primarily of GRP/foam sandwich construction with GRP roving spar. Wortmann wing sections: FX S 02-196 from root to inboard of ailerons, FX-60-126 at tip. Dihedral 4°. Schempp-Hirth upper-surface airbrakes. Fixed T tailplane and separate elevator. Non-retractable semi-recessed nosewheel (size 4·00-4) and sprung monowheel (size 5·00-5), the latter with internal drum brake; steel-shod rubber tailskid. Front and rear canopies open forward and rearward respectively.

SPORTAVIA

SPORTAVIA-PÜTZER GmbH u Co KG

HEAD OFFICE AND WORKS: D-5377 Dahlem-Schmidtheim, Flugplatz Dahlemer Binz

Telephone: (02447) 277/8

Telex: 08 33 602 spkg

This company was formed in 1966 by Comte Antoine d'Assche, director of the French company Alpavia SA, and Herr Alfons Pützer, to take over from Alpavia manufacture of the Avion-Planeur series of motor gliders designed by M René Fournier.

In 1969, RFB (see Aircraft section), a subsidiary of VFW-Fokker GmbH, acquired a percentage holding in Sportavia.

Current Sportavia products are certificated as motor gliders with the exception of the RS 180, described in the Aircraft section of this edition.

SPORTAVIA AVION-PLANEUR RF5

Construction of the prototype RF5 (D-KOLT) started in the Summer of 1967, and this aircraft flew for the first time in January 1968. Production began in late 1968. The RF5 was certificated by the LBA in the motor glider category in March 1969. A total of 145 RF5s had been delivered by the end of 1978; production ended in the Spring of 1979.

Data for the RF5 are given in the Table at the end of this section; a description of the airframe and power plant can be found in the 1978-79 *Jane's*.

SPORTAVIA RF5B SPERBER

The RF5B Sperber is an improved, high-performance development of the RF5, differing chiefly in having increased wing span/area and reduced fuselage side area. Construction began in early 1971, and the first flight was made in May of that year. The Sperber was certificated in the motor glider category by the LBA in March 1972, and by the end of 1978 a total of about 35 had been delivered. Production rate has now been reduced, and from 1979 the Sperber is available only to firm order.

Modifications introduced in 1973 included an improved cabin heating system; engine muffler to decrease exterior and cabin noise levels; adjustable ventilation system; optional disc brakes; and a wider range of equipment options which include artificial horizon, electric compass and flight data computer.

TYPE: Tandem two-seat motor glider.

AIRFRAME: Cantilever low-wing monoplane. Wing section NACA 23015 at root, NACA 23012 at tip. Dihedral 3° 30′ at main spar centreline. Plywood and fabric covered wooden structure with metal-skinned spoilers on each wing upper surface inboard of ailerons. Outer wing panels fold inward to facilitate hangarage. Fabric covered wooden ailerons. No flaps or tabs. Wooden fuselage and tail unit, plywood and fabric covered. Fuselage cut down at rear to reduce side area and improve rearward view. Fixed-incidence tailplane. Flettner trim tab in port elevator. Entire tail unit detachable for transportation. Retractable Tost monowheel, with twin oleo-pneumatic shock-absorbers; tyre pressure 1·96 bars (28·4 lb/sq in); manually-operated brake. Steerable tailwheel; outriggers beneath each wing, just inboard of fold line.

POWER PLANT: One 50·7 kW (68 hp) (max continuous rating 47 kW; 63 hp) Limbach SL 1700 E Comet four-cylinder four-stroke engine, driving a Hoffmann HO-11-145-B80L two-blade fixed-pitch metal propeller. Fully-feathering and HO-V62R variable-pitch propellers available optionally. Fuel in single fuselage tank, capacity 39 litres (8·6 Imp gallons). Refuelling point on top of port wing. Oil capacity 2·5 litres (0·55 Imp gallons).

INDIA

CIVIL AVIATION DEPARTMENT

TECHNICAL CENTRE, CIVIL AVIATION DEPARTMENT

Civil Aviation Department, R. K. Puram, New Delhi 22

WORKS: Technical Centre, opposite Safdarjung Airport, New Delhi 110003

Telephone: 611504

DIRECTOR GENERAL: B. S. Gidwani

DEPUTY DIRECTOR GENERAL: K. B. Ganesan

DEPUTY DIRECTOR (R & D): P. R. Chandrasekhar

The Technical Centre is the research and development establishment of the Indian Civil Aviation Department. It is equipped with all facilities necessary for the development of design, airworthiness and operational standards, operational research, development testing and standardisation of indigenous aircraft materials, type certification of prototype aircraft and equipment, and the scientific investigation of accidents.

Since 1950 the Technical Centre has undertaken the design and development of gliders, under the leadership of S. Ramamritham, utilising predominantly indigenous materials. The first of these gliders, of the open-cockpit primary type, was flown in November 1950. Since then the Technical Centre has built gliders of eight types for service at civil gliding centres in India, as listed in the 1972-73 *Jane's*. Of these, five have been original designs.

The Technical Centre does not undertake quantity production of gliders. Drawings of designs developed at the Centre are supplied to interested organisations with permission to manufacture them in series.

HS-II MRIGASHEER

This single-seat Standard Class sailplane is the first to be designed and developed at the Technical Centre by the team of designers and engineers led by Mr K. B. Ganesan, Director of Research and Development. The original version, the HS-I, made its first flight in November 1970 and was described and illustrated in the 1973-74 *Jane's*.

The further-developed HS-II flew for the first time in April 1973. Based on the aerodynamic design of the first HS-II, a second prototype has been built. This has trailing-edge slotted flaps instead of airbrakes, and made its first flight in May 1977.

The following description applies to this second aircraft:

TYPE: Single-seat Standard Class sailplane.

AIRFRAME: Cantilever high-wing monoplane. Wortmann wing sections: FX-61-184 at root, varying through FX-61-163 to FX-60-126 at tip. Dihedral 1° 30′. Entire airframe is of plywood-covered wooden construction, with plain wooden ailerons and slotted trailing-edge flaps, except for rudder, which is fabric-covered. Retractable unsprung monowheel, tyre pressure 2·07 bars (30 lb/sq in), with drum-type brake. Rubber-sprung nose-skid with replaceable steel shoe. Rubber-sprung tailskid. Forward-opening jettisonable canopy.

TG-1 ARUDHRA

Design of the Arudhra was almost complete at the beginning of 1978, and the prototype was scheduled to fly during February 1979.

TYPE: Tandem two-seat advanced training sailplane; *g* limits +5·3/−2·65.

AIRFRAME: Cantilever shoulder-wing monoplane. Wortmann FX-61-184 wing section from root to tip. Dihedral 1° 30′. Incidence 3°. Sweepforward 3° at leading-edge. Plywood-covered multi-spar wooden wings, plywood covered on leading- and trailing-edges; plain wooden ailerons; wooden airbrakes in upper and lower wing surfaces. Tail unit of similar construction, but with rear portions of rudder and elevator fabric covered. Horn-balanced rudder. Plywood-covered tab in starboard elevator. Semi-monocoque wooden fuselage, with plywood covering. Nosecone of glassfibre. Non-retractable unsprung monowheel, tyre size 6·00-4, with drum brake. Rubber-sprung nose-skid, with replaceable steel shoe, and rubber-sprung tailskid.

ITALY

CAPRONI VIZZOLA

CAPRONI VIZZOLA COSTRUZIONI AERONAUTICHE SpA

20122 Milano, Via Durini 24

Telephone: (02) 700826 and 781975

WORKS: 21010 Vizzola Ticino (Varese)

Telephone: (0331) 230826 and 230727

Telex: Caproni 332554 CAVIZ I

PRESIDENT: Dott Giovanni Caproni di Taliedo

The Caproni company, formed in 1910, is the oldest Italian aircraft manufacturer. Its works at Vizzola Ticino have approx 30,000 m² (322,917 sq ft) of covered space, and are adjacent to Malpensa Airport. They are equipped to manufacture complete structural subassemblies for helicopters and medium-sized fixed-wing aircraft. Caproni Vizzola also produces ground support equipment for General Electric T64/CT64, J79, J85 and CF6 and Turbo Union RB.199 turbojet and turbofan engines.

In 1969 Caproni Vizzola began producing a series of Calif sailplanes designed by Carlo Ferrarin and Livio Sonzio. Details of the earlier A-10 (one built), A-12 (two built), A-14 (one built), A-15 (one built), A-20 and A-21 have been given in the 1972-73 and subsequent *Jane's*.

Development of an improved two-seat version of the A-20, designated A-20S, is at present in abeyance.

CAPRONI VIZZOLA CALIF A-21S

The original A-21 was a two-seat version of the A-14, from which it differed in having a wider (to accommodate two side-by-side seats) and slightly longer fuselage. This version (1975-76 *Jane's*) is no longer being built, its place having been taken by the A-21S which has been certificated by the RAI, FAA, LBA and DGAC.

It was in an A-21S that, on 18 August 1974, Adele Orsi and Franca Bellingeri set the current Class D2 speed record for women over a 300 km closed circuit at 52·742 knots (97·741 km/h; 60·733 mph).

Deliveries of the third series of 50 A-21S were under way in 1979.

Schleicher ASW 20 15 metre Contest Class sailplane

Schleicher ASW 19 B single-seat Standard Class sailplane

Model of the Schleicher ASK 21 tandem two-seat sailplane

Second prototype HS-II Mrigasheer single-seat Standard Class sailplane

Schleicher ASK 13 tandem two-seat training and high-performance sailplane

Sportavia RF5B Sperber, developed from the RF5, with cut-down rear fuselage

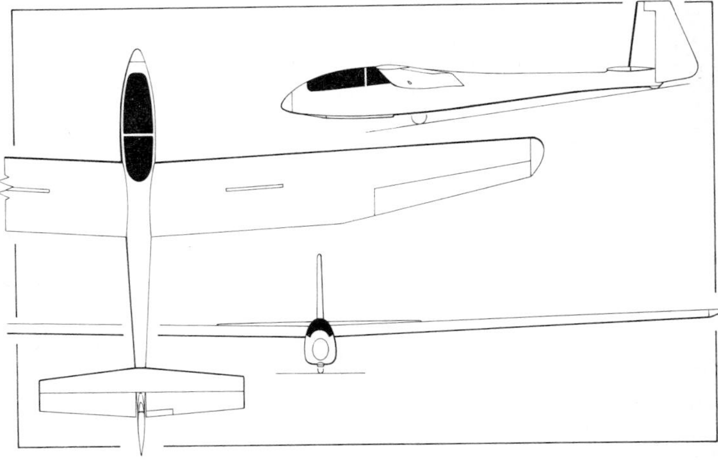

Civil Aviation Dept TG-1 Arudhra *(Michael A. Badrocke)*

TYPE: Side-by-side two-seat high-performance sailplane; g limit +5·0 (ultimate).

AIRFRAME: Cantilever mid-wing monoplane. Wing section Wortmann FX-67-K-170 at root, FX-60-126 at tip. Dihedral 0° at root, 1° 30′ on outer panels. All-metal multi-spar wings, with glassfibre wingtips. Chemically-milled trailing-edge flaps/spoilers and differentially-operated plain ailerons. Glassfibre/foam plastics semi-monocoque forward fuselage, with load-carrying light alloy frame; all-metal stressed-skin rear fuselage. All-metal T tail, with spring-adjusted tailplane trim and chemically-milled elevator. Mechanically retractable twin main wheels, with rubber-in-compression shock-absorbers, tyre pressure (each) 5·07 bars (73·5 lb/sq in), and Tost brake; non-retractable steerable tailwheel.

CAPRONI VIZZOLA CALIF A-21SJ

An A-21J jet-powered version of the A-21 two-seat sailplane, fitted with a 0·90 kN (202 lb st) Microturbo TRS 18 turbojet, flew for the first time at the end of January 1972. In 1976 this prototype was acquired by Lockheed-Georgia, USA, for use in a joint research programme with Mississippi State University. Details of this programme were given in the 1977-78 *Jane's*.

The version currently in production by Caproni Vizzola is based on the A-21S sailplane (which see), and is designated A-21SJ. Two had been completed by May 1979, at which time five others were under construction. One aircraft was being tested with a more powerful TRS 18 engine rated at 1·08 kN (242·5 lb st).

TYPE: Side-by-side two-seat jet-powered sailplane.

AIRFRAME: As A-21S, except for modifications necessary to incorporate power plant aft of cockpit.

POWER PLANT: One 0·88 kN (198 lb st) Microturbo TRS 18-046 turbojet engine, installed to rear of cockpit. Fuel load, in fuselage and wing tanks, 110 kg (242·5 lb). 24V/600W starter/generator and 24V 12Ah batteries for in-flight and ground starting.

GLASFASER

GLASFASER ITALIANA SrL

24030 Valbrembo (Bergamo), Via Locatelli 1
Telephone: (035) 612617
PRESIDENT: Dott Ing Sergio Aldo Capoferri
TECHNICAL DIRECTOR: Giampaolo Ghidotti

This company's factory occupies an area of 1,300 m² (13,993 sq ft) and is insulated and heated to maintain a controlled temperature of 20°C, essential for work on glassfibre structures.

Glasfaser holds RAI licences to build glassfibre sailplanes and to repair, maintain and modify sailplanes and training aircraft.

Glasfaser built 25 single-seat 17 metre Kestrel sailplanes, described under the Glasflügel entry in the German section of this edition. The company has built 130 complete fuselage assemblies for the Kestrel and assembled 10 Hornets. It has also completed 10 Glaser-Dirks DG-200s, and is an agency for Grob sailplanes (see German section).

Other activities include construction of glassfibre trailers for road transportation of sailplanes, the repair and maintenance of sailplanes of glassfibre, wood and metal construction, and installation and modification work on sailplanes of all types.

MAGGI

ANGELO MAGGI

c/o Club Aviazione Popolare, Via Dante 80, 21015 Lonate Pozzolo (Varese)

MAGGI MG3-15L CONDOR

This homebuilt sailplane, of which construction began in May 1975, was expected to make its first flight in February 1979. It is unusual in having NASA (Whitcomb) type winglets at the wingtips.

TYPE: Single-seat homebuilt sailplane.

AIRFRAME: Cantilever shoulder-wing monoplane. Wing section NACA 65_3-618. Dihedral 4°. Incidence 4°. Single light alloy main spar; wing leading-edges of PVC resin, coated with glassfibre. NASA (Whitcomb) winglets at each wingtip. Fiat light alloy ailerons; airbrakes and plain trailing-edge flaps, also of light alloy. Fuselage has light alloy structure with glassfibre/polyurethane foam covering. Cantilever tailplane of light alloy, leading-edges of which are of balsa with glassfibre coating; separate elevators, with spring trim. Retractable unsprung monowheel, tyre size 5·00-5, pressure 3·2 bars (46·4 lb/sq in), with drum brake; non-retractable tailskid.

JAPAN

NIPPI

NIHON HIKOKI KABUSHIKI KAISHA (Japan Aircraft Manufacturing Co Ltd)

HEAD OFFICE AND SUGITA PLANT: No. 3175 Showa-machi, Kanazawa-ku, Yokohama 236
Telephone: Yokohama (045) 771 1251
Telex: (3822) 267
SECTION CHIEF, SAILPLANE SALES: N. Kagata
OTHER OFFICERS: see Aircraft section

NIPPI NP-100A ALBATROSS

Nippi began the design of this motor glider in late 1973, and the prototype (NP-100) made its first flight on 25 December 1975. Flight testing was carried out during 1976, as a result of which several modifications were made. Principal point of interest in the NP-100A is the power plant, which is of the ducted-fan type and is fully buried within the fuselage aft of the main landing gear.

A secondary flight test programme took place between March and July 1978, to determine the final specification for a production version.

The following description applies to the first prototype in its current form:

TYPE: Side-by-side two-seat motor glider.

AIRFRAME: Cantilever shoulder-wing monoplane. Wing section Wortmann FX-67-K-170 (modified) from root to tip. No dihedral or sweepback. All-metal single-spar structure, with two-section metal-skinned flaps on each trailing-edge (designed for upward or downward deflection) and plain ailerons. No spoilers. All-metal semi-monocoque fuselage. All-metal tail unit, with conventional elevators and rudder. Forward-retracting twin-wheel main landing gear, operated mechanically with spring assistance. Steerable, non-retractable tailwheel, linked to rudder movement.

POWER PLANT (prototype): One modified 50·7 kW (68 hp at 6,000 rpm) M2 1,000 cc two-stroke aircooled flat-four engine, installed in centre of fuselage and driving a four-blade wooden ducted fan. Triple 'Venetian blind' air intake doors, on each side of fuselage, interconnected with engine starting circuit to prevent engine operating when doors are closed. Fuel in single fuselage tank, capacity 40 litres (8·8 Imp gallons).

NIPPI PILATUS B4-PC11AF

Pilatus Flugzeugwerke of Switzerland designed and built this single-seat Standard Class sailplane for multi-purpose training and aerobatics. Swiss certification was granted on 12 June 1972, and by March 1978 more than 330 had been delivered by Pilatus to customers in 30 countries in all parts of the world.

Production and marketing rights in the aircraft were transferred to Nippi in June 1978, and it is now known as the Nippi Pilatus B4-PC11AF. The first Nippi-built example was rolled out on 1 June 1979. Initial production, after JCAB certification, is to be at the rate of three per month.

TYPE: Single-seat Standard Class sailplane; g limits +6·32/−4·32 (Normal); +7·0/−4·79 (Aerobatic).

AIRFRAME: Cantilever shoulder-wing monoplane with T tail. Wing section NACA 64_3-618. Dihedral 1°. Conventional light alloy wings with single U spar and hard PVC foam ribs between metal ribs; conventional ailerons of similar construction. Light alloy spoilers at 60% chord on wing upper surfaces. Semi-monocoque light alloy fuselage, with flush-riveted skin. Rear fuselage consists of two half-shells, riveted together. Cantilever light alloy tail unit, with PVC ribs. Fixed-incidence tailplane. Elevator spring trim. Retractable (optionally non-retractable) unsprung Tost monowheel, and fixed tailwheel, in tandem. Main wheel faired by doors when retracted. Mechanical independent drum brakes. Canopy jettisonable in flight.

TAINAN

TAINAN INDUSTRY CO LTD (Tainan Kogyo KK)

5139-3 1-chome, Komatsubara, Zama-shi, Kanagawa-ken 228
Telephone: 0462 54 2332/3/4
PRESIDENT: H. Shinozaki
MANAGER, LIGHT AIRCRAFT DIVISION: Kakuichiro Harada

This company took over the manufacture of sailplanes from LADCO (see 1971-72 *Jane's*), and is continuing production, under licence, of the former company's Mita III two-seat sailplane. Its latest design is the TN-1.

TAINAN MITA III

By 1 January 1979, a total of 37 Mita IIIs had been built.

TYPE: Tandem two-seat training and sporting sailplane.

AIRFRAME: Cantilever shoulder-wing monoplane. Wing section NACA 63_3-618. All-wood monospar construction, plywood-covered. Ailerons fabric-covered. Schempp-Hirth airbrakes. Steel tube fuselage with wooden stringers and fabric covering. Nose of glassfibre. Aero-tow release in nose; winch release at CG. Wooden tail unit, with fabric-covered rudder and elevators. Non-retractable rubber-sprung monowheel, with brake, and tailskid. Canopy opens sideways to starboard.

TAINAN TN-1

The TN-1 (manufacturer's designation F5) was designed by Yukio Tanaka. Construction of a prototype began in August 1974, and this made its first flight in December 1976. Certification trials by the JCAB were under way in the Spring of 1978, and it was hoped to begin production in the following Summer. No later information had been received at the time of closing for press.

TYPE: Single-seat sailplane; g limits +5·3/−2·65.

AIRFRAME: Cantilever high-wing monoplane. Modified Göttingen wing sections. Dihedral 3°. Sweepforward 2° 4′ at quarter-chord. Single-spar wings of spruce and plywood, with fabric covering. Plywood-covered wooden ailerons. Schempp-Hirth airbrakes. Steel tube fuselage with wooden stringers and fabric covering. Glassfibre nose. Cantilever wooden tail unit, with fabric-covered elevators and rudder. Trim tab in starboard elevator. Non-retractable unsprung monowheel at CG, tyre pressure 2·94 bars (42·7 lb/sq in); Tainan band brake; tailskid.

POLAND

SZD

PRZEDSIEBIORSTWO DOSWIADCZALNO-PRODUKCYJNE SZYBOWNICTWA (Experimental and Production Concern for Gliders) PZL-BIELSKO

HEAD OFFICE AND WORKS: 43-300 Bielsko-Biala 1, ul. Cieszynska 325
Telephone: 250 21 to 250 26
Telex: 031-259 SZD PL
DIRECTOR: Ing Kazimierz Jasinski
SALES REPRESENTATIVE: Pezetel, 02-344 Warszawa, ul. Czestochowska 4a

The Instytut Szybownictwa (Gliding Institute), formed officially in January 1946 at Bielsko-Biala, has since undergone several changes of name, as detailed in the 1977-78 *Jane's*. The change to the present title took place in July 1975, but the well-known designation initials SZD are retained. This organisation is responsible for the design and development of all Polish gliders and sailplanes. Production plants are situated at Bielsko-Biala, Wroclaw and Jezów.

Caproni Vizzola Calif A-21S two-seat high-performance sailplane

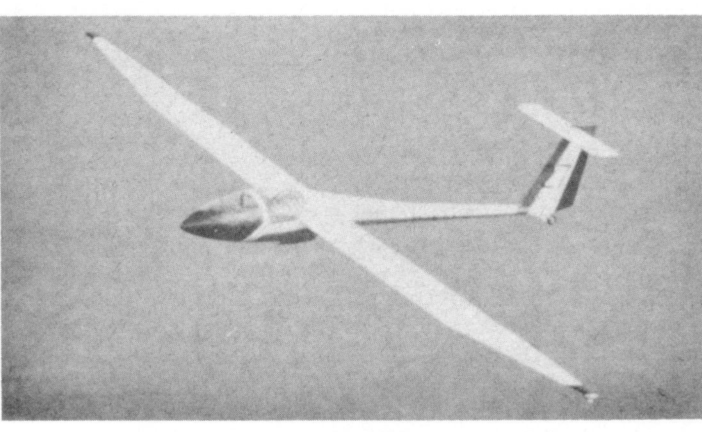

Caproni Vizzola Calif A-21SJ jet-powered sailplane

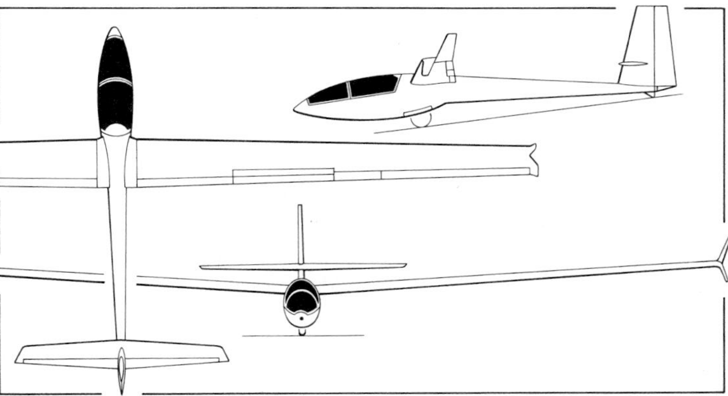

Maggi MG3-15L Condor homebuilt sailplane *(Michael A. Badrocke)*

Swiss-built Nippi Pilatus B4-PC11AF aerobatic Standard Class sailplanes

First prototype Nippi NP-100A, with original Kawasaki H2 engine

Tainan Mita III two-seat training and sporting sailplane

Tainan TN-1 (F5) single-seat sailplane

Between 1947 and 1978 the Polish aircraft industry produced 3,785 gliders of 100 different types, and SZD sailplanes have been exported all over the world in substantial numbers.

SZD-30C PIRAT

Designed by Ing Jerzy Smielkiewicz, the prototype of this single-seat Standard Class sailplane flew for the first time on 19 May 1966. It is suitable for the full range of duties from training to competition flying and is cleared for cloud flying, spinning and basic aerobatics.

Production of the Pirat started in 1967 and 764 had been built by the beginning of 1979, including 430 completed by the WSK-Swidnik works, where production was also undertaken until October 1977. Pirats have been exported to 24 countries, including Argentina, Australia, Austria, Canada, Denmark, Egypt, Finland, France, Germany (Democratic Republic), Germany (Federal Republic), Hungary, Italy, North Korea, the Netherlands, New Zealand, Norway, Spain, Sweden, Switzerland, UK, USA, USSR, Venezuela and Yugoslavia.

The SZD-30B Pirat 75 described in the 1977-78 *Jane's* was a prototype only. The improved version current from 1978 is the SZD-30C, to which the following description applies; the first SZD-30C was flown on 10 January 1978.

Type: Single-seat Standard Class sailplane; *g* limits +5·3/−2·65.

Airframe: Cantilever high-wing monoplane with T tail. Wortmann wing sections: FX-61-168 at root, FX-60-1261 at tip. Dihedral 2° 30′ on outer panels only. Plywood-covered wooden wings, comprising multi-spar rectangular centre-section and single-spar tapered outer panels. Epoxy/glassfibre, partially mass-balanced ailerons (smaller than on earlier Pirat models). Double-plate airbrakes. Plywood monocoque fuselage, with glassfibre nose and cockpit floor. Forward fuselage reinforced with thick layer of glassfibre, instead of original front skid. Towing hooks in nose and near CG. Wooden tail unit, with trim tab on elevator trailing-edge. Non-retractable monowheel, size 350 × 135 mm, with disc brake and roller bearings; tailwheel replaceable with rubber-sprung tailskid. Canopy opens sideways. Two cockpit baggage compartments.

SZD-41A JANTAR STANDARD (AMBER)

This single-seat Standard Class sailplane was designed by Ing W. Okarmus on the basis of the prototype Open Class SZD-38 Jantar-1. The fuselage and tail unit are the same for both types; the wings of the SZD-41A are designed to OSTIV Standard Class requirements.

The Jantar Standard was flown for the first time at Bielsko-Biala on 3 October 1973, piloted by A. Zientek. Polish pilots flying the SZD-41 in the 1974 World Championships at Waikerie, Australia, gained third and seventh places in the Standard Class competition. Jantar Standards gained fourth, sixth and eighteenth places in the World Championships at Räyskälä, Finland in June 1976. The current production version is designated SZD-41A.

A total of 137 Jantar Standards had been built by the beginning of 1979, for customers in Argentina, Australia, Austria, Belgium, Bulgaria, Canada, Denmark, Finland, Germany (Democratic Republic), Germany (Federal Republic), Hungary, Poland, Sweden, Switzerland, the UK, the USA, the USSR and Yugoslavia.

Type: Single-seat Standard Class sailplane; *g* limits +5·3/−2·65.

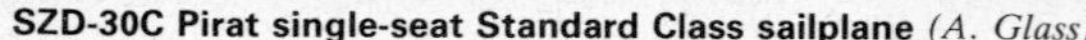

SZD-30C Pirat single-seat Standard Class sailplane *(A. Glass)*

SZD-41A Jantar Standard single-seat Standard Class sailplane

AIRFRAME: Cantilever mid-wing monoplane. Wing section NN-8. Dihedral 1° 30'. Sweepback 0° 30' at quarter-chord. Single-spar ribless wings with foam-filled glassfibre/epoxy resin sandwich skin. Multi-hinged ailerons; no flaps. DFS glassfibre airbrakes above and below each wing. All-glassfibre/epoxy resin shell fuselage; centre portion has a steel tube frame coupling together the wings, fuselage and landing gear. Cantilever T-tail, of glassfibre/epoxy resin. Elevator spring trim. Fin integral with fuselage. Retractable monowheel, tyre pressure 3·43 bars (49·8 lb/sq in), with disc brake; non-retractable tailwheel. Provision for 80 kg (176 lb) water ballast.

SZD-42-1 JANTAR 2 (AMBER)

This high-performance single-seat Open Class sailplane, originally designated SZD-42, was developed by Dipl-Ing Adam Kurbiel from the series-built all-plastics SZD-38A Jantar 1, and flew for the first time on 2 February 1976.

The first two examples were flown by the Polish team in the 1976 World Championships at Räyskälä, Finland, where they gained second and third places in the Open Class; these two aircraft had wings built in two sections. Series-built versions, to which the following description applies, have four-piece wings; one of these aircraft, flown by R. Johnson of the USA, gained seventh place in the 1976 World Championships.

A total of 23 Jantar 2s had been built by the beginning of 1979.

TYPE: Single-seat high-performance Open Class sailplane; *g* limits +4·0/−1·5 with water ballast, +5·3/−2·65 without water ballast.

AIRFRAME: Generally similar to SZD-41A, but wings have 2° dihedral and light alloy DFS-type airbrakes. Cantilever cruciform tail unit of glassfibre/epoxy resin. Monowheel tyre pressure 2·96 bars (43 lb/sq in); tailskid instead of tailwheel. Provision for 130 litres (28·6 Imp gallons) water ballast.

SZD-42-2 JANTAR 2B

Designed by Dipl-Ing Adam Kurbiel, the SZD-42-2 Open Class sailplane is based on the SZD-42-1. The prototype flew for the first time on 13 March 1978, and 14 Jantar 2Bs had been built by the beginning of 1979.

TYPE: Single-seat Open Class sailplane.

AIRFRAME: Generally similar to SZD-42-1, but with wings raised from mid-mounted to shoulder position and incidence reduced by 1° 30'. Water ballast provision is increased to 170 kg (375 lb). Improvements made to elevator spring trim, monowheel retraction system and cockpit comfort. Hinged canopy and provision for CG tow hook.

SZD-45A OGAR (GREYHOUND)

This two-seat school and training motor glider was designed by Dipl Ing Tadeusz Labuc, originally with a 33·5 kW (45 hp) Stamo engine and later with a 50·7 kW (68 hp) Sportavia Limbach engine. The first prototype (SP-0001) made its first flight on 29 May 1973, and was described in the 1973-74 *Jane's*.

A total of 59 Ogars had been built by the beginning of 1979, for customers in Germany (Democratic Republic), Germany (Federal Republic), Sweden, the UK and the USA.

The Ogar is to be flight tested with a 44·7 kW (60 hp) PZL-Franklin 2A-120C two-cylinder engine, which is planned to become the standard engine for production aircraft.

TYPE: Side-by-side two-seat school and training motor glider.

AIRFRAME: Cantilever shoulder-wing monoplane. Wortmann wing sections: FX-61-168 at root, FX-60-1261 at tip. Dihedral 1° 30'. Sweepback 1° at quarter-chord. Single-spar wooden wings, with moulded plywood stressed skin covered with glassfibre. Glassfibre sandwich slotless ailerons; airbrake above and below each wing. Pod and boom fuselage; main nacelle is glassfibre/epoxy resin shell built on two wooden frames which carry wings, engine mounting, fuel tank, and tubular duralumin boom which supports tail unit. Cantilever T-tail, fin being integral with tailboom. Semi-retractable monowheel with shock-absorber and disc-type brake. Fully-castoring tailwheel. For school use, outrigger legs and wheels are mounted adjacent to wingtips. Canopy opens upward. Dual controls standard.

POWER PLANT: One 50·7 kW (68 hp) Limbach SL 1700 EC four-cylinder four-stroke aircooled engine, mounted behind cabin and driving a two-blade Hoffmann pusher propeller. Fuel load 22 kg (48·5 lb).

SZD-48 JANTAR STANDARD 2

This Standard Class sailplane is a development of the SZD-41A Jantar Standard (which see), and was designed by Ing Wladyslaw Okarmus. The prototype flew for the first time on 10 December 1977, and 36 had been built by the beginning of 1979.

With simple modifications to the trim and speed measuring systems, the SZD-48 can be converted quickly to the **SZD-48-2** version, which has a never-exceed speed of 151 knots (280 km/h; 174 mph).

TYPE: Single-seat Standard Class sailplane.

AIRFRAME: Cantilever shoulder-wing monoplane, with NN-8 wing section. Dihedral 1° 30'. Single glassfibre roving main spar, with glassfibre/foam/glassfibre moulded skins (no ribs) and plain ailerons. Duralumin upper/lower surface airbrakes. Glassfibre fuselage, with steel tube central support structure, rear portion stiffened by half-frames and ribs. Cantilever T tail of similar construction to wings. Elevator spring trim. Retractable monowheel, with disc brake; semi-recessed tailwheel. Provision for 150 litres (33 Imp gallons) water ballast.

SZD-50-2 PUCHACZ (EAGLE OWL)

The Puchacz, designed by Dipl-Ing Adam Meus, is a high-performance sailplane intended particularly for training and performance flying. It has been modified and developed from a prototype, designated SZD-50-1 Dromader, which first flew on 21 December 1976.

A second prototype made its initial flight on 20 December 1977. Production was intended to begin during 1979.

TYPE: Tandem two-seat high-performance training sailplane; *g* limits +5·3/−2·65.

AIRFRAME: Cantilever mid-wing monoplane, mainly of glassfibre sandwich construction. Wortmann wing sections. Plain ailerons. Upper/lower surface airbrakes. Glassfibre fuselage, supported in central portion by two wooden frames. Glassfibre sandwich cruciform tail unit, with fabric-covered rudder. Non-retractable semi-recessed nosewheel and sprung monowheel (latter with disc brake), and tailskid. Canopy opens sideways.

ROMANIA

ICA-BRASOV

INTREPRINDEREA DE CONSTRUCTII AERONAUTICE (Aircraft Construction Factory)

HEAD OFFICE AND WORKS: Brasov

As detailed in the Aircraft section, the current activities of the Romanian aircraft industry are divided between two main industrial centres, IRMA in Bucharest and ICA at Brasov. In addition to its work on powered aircraft, the ICA is responsible for all sailplane development and production previously undertaken by URMV-3 (up to 1959) and IIL (Ghimbav) up to 1968. The principal Romanian designer of sailplanes is Dipl Ing Iosif Silimon, whose designs are prefixed with the letters IS. Details of his earlier designs appeared in the 1961-62, 1965-66 and 1972-73 *Jane's*.

IS-28B2

Despite its similar designation, this high-performance training sailplane represents a considerable advance over the IS-28 (1975-76 *Jane's*), from which it differs principally in having 17 m span all-metal wings, a longer and more slender fuselage, and reduced wing and tailplane dihedral. Design began in the Autumn of 1971, and the first IS-28B made its first flight on 26 April 1973.

There have been two production versions, as follows:

IS-28B1. Version without wing flaps. No longer in production. Described in 1976-77 *Jane's*.

IS-28B2. Current (1979) production version, with Schempp-Hirth type (instead of DFS type) airbrakes and trailing-edge split flaps. Description applies to this version, of which more than 100 have been sold, chiefly in Australia and the USA. Production is continuing at a rate of 70-100 per year, but is expected to be replaced from mid-1980 by the IS-30. The IS-28B2 has also been certificated in the UK and the Federal Republic of Germany.

TYPE: Tandem two-seat high-performance training sailplane; *g* limits (single-seat) +6·4/−4·2; (two-seat) +5·3/−2·65.

AIRFRAME: Cantilever mid-wing monoplane. Wortmann wing sections: FX-61-163 at root, FX-60-126 at tip. Forward-swept all-metal wings, with L-section main spar booms and dural web, dural auxiliary spar, and dural ribs. Schempp-Hirth metal airbrake above and below each wing. Ailerons and split trailing-edge flaps fabric-covered. No tabs. All-metal semi-monocoque forward and centre fuselage. Rear fuselage is duralumin monocoque. Cantilever T-tail, with moderate tailplane dihedral. Elevator trailing-edges and rudder fabric-covered. Trim tab in each elevator. Semi-retractable monowheel with oleo-pneumatic shock-absorber and disc brake; sprung tailskid. Canopy opens sideways (to starboard) and can be jettisoned in flight. Nose towing hook, with Tost cable release, is standard; CG towing hook optional.

IS-28M

Two motor glider versions of the IS-28B2 have been developed. The rear fuselage, tail unit and main wings are virtually unchanged from the IS-28B2, but the powered versions are of low-wing configuration and have redesigned forward fuselages, cockpit canopies and main landing gear. The wings of both versions can be folded from a point immediately inboard of the ailerons. Production was reportedly two per month in the Spring of 1978, with plans to increase to 10 per month.

The two versions are designated as follows:

IS-28M1. Tandem two-seater, with main landing gear comprising a retractable central monowheel, with balloon tyre, and underwing outrigger wheels. Otherwise generally similar to IS-28M2, except that wing span is increased. Reported that deliveries were due to begin in late 1979.

IS-28M2. Side-by-side two-seater, with main landing gear comprising two retractable wheels side by side under fuselage centre-section, with shock-absorbers. Steerable tailwheel. Prototype (YR-1013) flew for the first time on 26 June 1976. The first 10 aircraft of this type were allocated to the UK, where they are marketed by Morisonics Ltd of The Parade, Frimley, Surrey. Supplied also to customers in Canada and the USA. In production.

TYPE: Two-seat motor glider; *g* limits +4·0/−1·5 (M1), +5·3/−2·65 (M2).

AIRFRAME: Cantilever low-wing monoplane, of mainly metal construction. Wortmann wing sections: FX-61-163 at root, FX-60-126 at tip. Dihedral 2°. Sweepforward 2° 30' at quarter-chord. Single-spar wings, with aluminium ribs and skin, fabric-covered metal ailerons and (optionally) all-metal split flaps on trailing-edges. Flaps can be set to a negative position. All-metal two-section Hütter airbrakes on upper surfaces. Optional

SZD-50-2 Puchacz two-seat training sailplane

SZD-42-2 Jantar 2B single-seat Open Class sailplane

SZD-48-2 Jantar Standard 2 single-seat sailplane

SZD-42-1 Jantar 2 single-seat Open Class sailplane

Close-up of cabin and main landing gear of IS-28M1 *(Brian M. Service)*

SZD-45A Ogar side-by-side two-seat motorised training glider

ICA-Brasov IS-31(E3) single-seat Open Class sailplane

IS-28B2 tandem two-seat high-performance training sailplane
(The Age, Melbourne)

IS-28M2 side-by-side two-seat motor glider *(Brian M. Service)*

folding of outer wing panels, inward over inboard panels. Conventional fuselage, in three parts: metal front portion, built up on two longerons and cross-frames and having glassfibre fairings and engine cowling panels; aluminium alloy monocoque centre portion; and rear portion of aluminium alloy frames and skin. Cantilever aluminium alloy T-tail, with dihedral tailplane. Rudder and elevator trailing-edges fabric-covered. Trim tab in each elevator. Landing gear as described under model listings. Rearward-sliding canopy. Dual controls standard.

Power Plant: One 50·7 kW (68 hp) Limbach SL 1700 EI flat-four engine, driving a Hoffmann HO-V-62/R160T two-blade variable-pitch fully-feathering propeller. Single fuel tank aft of cockpit, capacity 40 litres (8·8 Imp gallons).

IS-29 and IS-33

The IS-29, designed under the leadership of Dipl Ing Iosif Silimon, can be adapted to suit a variety of requirements or weather conditions. All versions have an identical fuselage and tail unit, and a choice of wings is available. The versions so far announced are as follows:

IS-29B. Standard Class version, with 15 m all-wooden wings. First flown April 1970; certificated September 1970. Not now in production. See 1975-76 *Jane's*.

IS-29D. Standard Class version, with all-metal 15 m span wings. First flown in November 1970; certificated in 1971. Approx 30 built by 1974. Described in 1975-76 *Jane's*. Production version from 1976, designated **IS-29D2,** has improved cockpit and controls, Hütter airbrakes, separate tailplane and elevator, and improved rigging system. More than 60 sold in Australia and the USA. Production continuing in 1979 at rate of 10-15 a year. Club version is designated **IS-29D3**, 15 metre version **IS-29D4**. A version with 150 kg (300 lb) water ballast tanks is designated **IS-33;** it is estimated to have a best glide ratio of 41·5 at 61·5 knots (114 km/h; 71 mph) and is expected to fly before mid-1980.

IS-29E. Open Class version, having increased-span wings fitted with ailerons, flaps, Schempp-Hirth airbrakes and integral water ballast tanks. First flown in August 1971 with 17·60 m (57 ft 9 in) span wings, as described in 1975-76 *Jane's*. A 19 m version, the **IS-29E2,** has been developed. Further details of this, the 20 m span **IS-31(E3)** and 24 m span **IS-29(E4)** versions, can be found in the Addenda.

IS-29G. Club version, with all-metal 16·5 m span wings. Prototype completed in 1972. Described in 1975-76 *Jane's*.

The following description applies to the D and E models, except where a specific model is indicated:

Type: Single-seat Standard Class (D) and Open Class (E) sailplanes.

Airframe: Cantilever shoulder-wing monoplane, with T-tail. Wortmann wing sections: FX-61-165 at root, FX-61-124 at tip on D2; FX-K-170 (root) and FX-K-150 (tip) on E2 and E3. All-metal wings, with main spar, false rear spar and riveted dural skin. Full-span trailing-edge flaps and ailerons, coupled to operate in unison but can be disconnected for separate operation during landing. Airbrakes (see under model listings for type) in upper and lower surface of each wing (upper surface only on D2). All-metal semi-monocoque fuselage identical on all versions except for local variations at wing attachment points. Detachable glassfibre nosecap. Cantilever all-metal T-tail, with full-span elevator. Retractable monowheel, with brake; non-retractable tailwheel. Canopy hinges sideways to starboard and can be jettisoned in flight. Provision for water ballast in E2 and E3.

IS-29DM and EM

Motorised versions of D2 and E3 respectively, of which prototypes are flying. Further details in Addenda.

IS-30

The IS-30, undergoing flight testing in the Spring of 1978, is an Open Class development of the IS-28B2 with 18·00 m (59 ft 0¾ in) span wings, the redesigned tail of the IS-32, and no water ballast provision; *g* limits are the same as for the IS-28B2. The IS-30 is expected to become available from mid-1980 as a replacement for the IS-28B2.

IS-32

First shown publicly at the Paris Air Show in June 1977, the IS-32 tandem two-seat Open Class sailplane is developed from the IS-28B2. Of all-metal construction, it has 20 m wings of an improved Wortmann FX-K-170 (root) and FX-K-150 (tip) section, with interconnected flaps and ailerons and water ballast tanks, and redesigned tail surfaces; *g* limits are +4·0/1·5. Certification has been awarded, and deliveries are intended to begin in 1980. The IS-32 was expected to be displayed at Oshkosh in 1979.

SPAIN

CASES
FRANCISCO CASES

Benetuser, Valencia

CASES LIBEL-LULA

This lightweight homebuilt glider, built by an experienced aeromodeller and glider pilot, was awaiting a permit to fly in early 1979. Its general appearance can be seen in the accompanying three-view drawing. Future development plans include the fitting of a 9 kW (12 hp) engine.

Type: Single-seat homebuilt sailplane; *g* limits +4/−1·5.

Airframe: Braced high-wing monoplane. Wings of rectangular planform, with constant Wortmann FX-S-02-196 section except in area of ailerons; built in two halves and joined to fuselage upper beam. D-section torsion box formed from leading-edge and main spar; polyester/glassfibre moulded ribs; overall nylon covering (wings and ailerons). Single steel tube bracing strut each side. Fuselage comprises triangular-section beam to carry wings and tail unit, with pear-shaped glassfibre nacelle, moulded in two halves, below and forward of wings. Tail surfaces of plywood and glassfibre, with nylon covering. Rubber-sprung landing skid beneath nacelle; semi-recessed monowheel optional. Tip of underfin acts as tailskid. Single seat in open cockpit.

SWITZERLAND

AVIAFIBER
AVIAFIBER AG

Sagenrainstrasse 4, CH-8636 Wald
Telephone: (055) 952055
President: Dipl-Ing Hans U. Farner

AVIAFIBER CANARD-2 FL

First flown on 7 September 1977, the Canard-2 FL was designed by Dipl-Ing Hans U. Farner, who also designed the Colibri 1 SL canard motor glider described in a following entry. It can be bungee-launched in a conventional manner, foot-launched, or rolled downhill on wheels for take-off. Production of the Canard-2 FL began in 1978. A powered version was scheduled for completion in the Summer of 1979.

The following description applies to the production version:

Type: One-man ultralight sailplane; *g* limits +5·3 (limit)/+7·9 (ultimate).

Airframe: 'Parasol monoplane' configuration, with main wing at rear, supported by V-form pylons which act as both lifting surfaces and 'vertical' fins; fixed-incidence canard foreplane. Wings, pylons and canard surface have Wortmann FX-63-137 section. Wings have external aerofoil ailerons; trailing-edges of V-tail pylons movable to act as Venom-type airbrakes. Wing is a single-spar structure, with vacuum-formed shell of laminated resin (Du Pont Kevlar, CIBA-Geigy 2878) and glassfibre, and core of styrofoam plate; other structures have a similar shell, with cores of hard foam cells (ailerons) or solid hard foam (airbrakes). Leg and head doors for foot-launch, after which pilot swivels into prone position, on sliding board, and closes both doors. One-piece canopy/windscreen, open at rear. Retractable front skid for landing; monowheel, or jettisonable twin main- and tailwheels, optional for downhill rolling take-off.

FARNER
DIPL-ING ETH HANS ULRICH FARNER

c/o Aviafiber AG, Sagenrainstrasse 4, CH-8636 Wald
Telephone: (055) 952055

FARNER HF COLIBRI 1 SL

Herr Farner has designed, built and flown an unusual experimental motor glider, known as the HF Colibri 1 SL and registered HB-2036. Its general appearance can be seen in the accompanying illustration.

Type: Single-seat motor glider; two-seat version under development.

Airframe: Cantilever gull-wing monoplane, with canard foreplane. Main wing of very high aspect ratio, mounted on top of fuselage at rear. It has dihedral on constant-chord, constant-section (Wortmann FX-61-184) inner portions, and anhedral on the all-moving outer panels, which have leading-edge taper and a Wortmann FX-60-1261 section. No flaps or ailerons. Constant-chord, constant-section foreplane (Wortmann FX-60-1261), mounted on telescopic extension of long, tapering nose to vary moment arm, can be pivoted about fuselage longitudinal axis. Adjustment of telescopic nose also permits foreplane incidence to be varied. Very short, narrow fuselage, with telescopic nose tube permitting overall length to be varied in flight. Rear fuselage ends in split-wedge section which acts as vertical fin when closed and airbrake when opened. Retractable tricycle landing gear, of narrow track. Yaw control by pivoting canard surface about fuselage longitudinal axis; pitch control by varying canard moment arm; roll (bank) control by operating all-moving wingtips ('tiperons') with dynamically irreversible drive.

Power Plant: Two 10·14 kW (13·6 hp) McCulloch MC-101A 123 cc single-cylinder two-stroke engines, mounted aft of cabin and driving, via a reduction gear, a two-blade pusher propeller aft of the wing trailing-edge. Propeller blades are of Wortmann section, and can be folded to the rear when not in use. Fuel capacity 21 litres (4·6 Imp gallons).

MAHRER
FRITZ MAHRER

Buchgasse 1, CH-4126 Bettingen

MAHRER HB-1340 DELPHIN

This single-seat experimental variable-geometry sailplane was first flown by Herr Mahrer on 6 May 1977. It is, essentially, a modified Neukom S-4A, with Eppler wing sections similar to those of the Neukom AN-66C (1978-79 *Jane's*), and with a T tail unit similar to that of the Schempp-Hirth Cirrus. The 15 metre span wings are fitted with area-increasing Fowler-type flaps, actuated electrically. Construction is mainly of plastics materials.

NEUKOM
ALBERT NEUKOM SEGELFLUGZEUGBAU

Flugplatz Schmerlat, CH-8213 Neuenkirch

Sailplanes built by Mr Neukom and three fellow-workers are the Standard Elfe 15 and 17.

NEUKOM S-4A ELFE 15

The S-4A Elfe 15 is a developed version of the Standard Class S-3 (see 1974-75 *Jane's*). The prototype flew for the

ICA-Brasov IS-32 two-seat Open Class sailplane

IS-29D2 single-seat Standard Class sailplane produced by ICA-Brasov

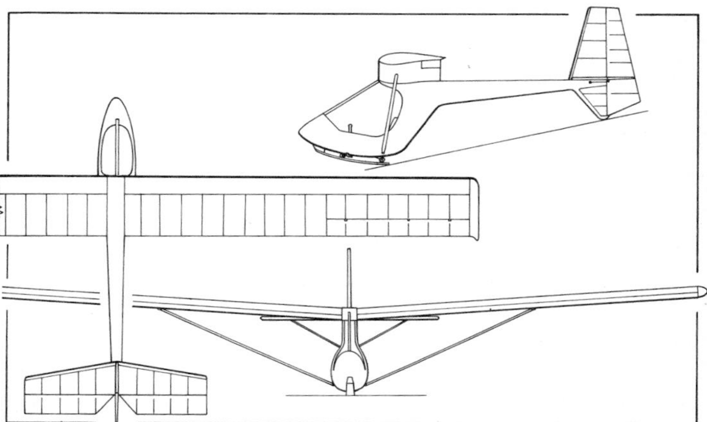

Cases Libel-lula single-seat homebuilt glider *(Michael A. Badrocke)*

Aviafiber Canard-2 FL ultralight sailplane with jettisonable four-wheel take-off gear

Farner HF Colibri 1 SL experimental motor glider *(J. Urech)*

Neukom S-4 Elfe 15 single-seat Standard Class sailplane *(Martin Fricke)*

first time in 1970, and 10 had been built by early 1973. Production continues, though at a relatively slow rate. The Elfe 15 is also available in kit form for amateur construction.

Type: Single-seat Standard Class sailplane.

Airframe: Cantilever high-wing monoplane. Wortmann wing sections: FX-61-163 at root, FX-60-126 at tip. Single wing spar of aluminium alloy, with plywood/foam sandwich skin. Plain ailerons. Schempp-Hirth airbrakes on upper surfaces. Forward fuselage of reinforced glassfibre; rear portion and tail unit of plywood/foam sandwich. Elevator spring trim. Retractable rubber-sprung monowheel, with brake. Detachable canopy. Universal aero-tow/winch coupling forward of monowheel.

NEUKOM ELFE 17

The Elfe 17 is an Open Class version of the S-4A, employing the same fuselage, but having a two-piece wing of 17 metres span with provision for a tank in each leading-edge to contain a total of 60 kg (132 lb) water ballast. A braking parachute is carried on this version.

A total of 10 Elfe 17s had been built by the Spring of 1973. Production continues, though at a relatively slow rate. The Elfe 17 is available also in kit form for amateur construction.

NEUKOM ELFE M 17

This motorised version of the Elfe 17 was flown for the first time in mid-March 1978.

Type: Single-seat motor glider.

Power Plant: One 33·5 kW (45 hp) Parodi HP 45 four-cylinder four-stroke engine, driving a Hoffmann two-blade propeller which is pylon-mounted aft of the cockpit and retracts into the fuselage when not in use. Electric starting. Fuel tank capacity 45 litres (10 Imp gallons).

NEUKOM SUPER-ELFE AN-66C

A description of this prototype sailplane can be found in the 1978-79 *Jane's*. For other details see Table.

UNION OF SOVIET SOCIALIST REPUBLICS

LAK

LITOVSKAYA AVIATSIONNAYA KONSTRUKTSIYA (Lithuanian Aircraft Construction)

Litovsk SSR (Lithuanian SSR)

Director: Vitautas Pakarskas

Chief Designer: Balis Karvyalis

This factory originated in the late 1960s with a 12-man 'initiative group', led by designers B. Oshkinis, B. Karvyalis and A. Paknis, and assisted by the Lithuanian branch of DOSAAF. Its primary objective was the evaluation of a plastics-construction sailplane. A workshop, opened in the Summer of 1969, began by building the Oshkinis BRO-11 elementary training glider. At that time it was known as the Experimentalnii Zavod Sportivnoi Aviatsii (Experimental Sports Aviation Factory). Its first plastics sailplane, designed by Balis Karvyalis, was the BK-7 Lietuva, which was first flown by Alexander Ionushas in December 1972 and was described and illustrated in the 1975-76 *Jane's*. This was followed by a small experimental production batch designated BK-7A, two of which took part in an international competition between Socialist countries at Kishinev in April 1976. As a result, a number of modifications were introduced in a developed version, the LAK-9, then under construction to participate in the 1976 World Championships in Finland.

In the early 1970s further experience was gained by repairing Czechoslovak Blanik sailplanes. More than 300 Blaniks had been overhauled by mid-1977, and LAK is now the sole overhaul centre in the USSR for this type of sailplane. Repairs were also undertaken of German MBB Phoebus and Schleicher ASW 15 plastics sailplanes. The factory has its own static test laboratory; design calculations and wind tunnel testing of LAK designs are carried out by the Central Aero-Hydrodynamic Institute (TsAGI) in Moscow. Branch factories now handle Blanik overhauls and BRO-11 production, and a new, larger, sports aviation factory is under construction.

Other recent activities have included the fitting of an engine to a standard L-13 Blanik, and this aircraft (the LAK-6, illustrated in the 1977-78 *Jane's*) serves as a flying testbed for a new plastics-construction motor glider, of which a prototype was under construction in 1977. The latest known LAK design is a new Standard Class sailplane, designed by Ionas Bankauskas and known as the LAK-11.

OSHKINIS BRO-11 ZILE (ACORN)

The BRO-11 was first built in 1954, and has since been built in considerable numbers as an elementary training glider for use by the DOSAAF. A modified version, designated BRO-11-M, was illustrated in the 1975-76 *Jane's;* the 1977-78 edition contained brief details of a biplane seaplane version, the **BRO-16,** first flown in August 1973, and a shorter-span (experimental?) version of this, known as the **BRO-17U Utochka.**

The BRO-11 is currently being manufactured by a branch factory of the LAK.

TYPE: Single-seat basic training glider.

AIRFRAME: Strut-braced high-wing monoplane, of fabric- and plywood-covered wooden construction. Towing hook under nose. Semi-recessed monowheel landing gear.

LAK-9 LIETUVA

As indicated in the introductory copy, the LAK-9 is a developed version of the Karvyalis BK-7/7A; its chief designer was Kestutis Gechas. The first LAK-9, registered CCCP-6301, was flown by O. Pasetsnik in the Open Class of the June 1976 World Championships at Räyskälä, Finland. It was not placed among the first 25 aircraft on that occasion, and it was reported that the three LAK-9s then built had not, at that time, fully completed flight testing.

The LAK-9 has since entered full production; the fourth series, begun in the Winter of 1976-77, is reported to have the designation LAK-9M, indicating 'Modernised'.

TYPE: Single-seat Open Class sailplane; *g* limits +6·0/−3·0.

AIRFRAME: Cantilever shoulder-wing monoplane. Single-spar wings, of Wortmann FX-67-K-170 section, with flaps and ailerons on trailing-edges. Glassfibre/epoxy construction. Retractable monowheel and tailwheel. Provision for 180 kg (397 lb) water ballast.

UNITED KINGDOM

SWALES

SWALES SAILPLANES

Long Street, Thirsk, North Yorkshire
Telephone: 0845 23096
OFFICERS:
Bryan Swales, MBIM, Eng Dip, MIMI
G. L. Kemp, BEM (Chief Inspector)

SWALES SD3-15T

Construction of the prototype SD3 started in September 1974, and it flew for the first time in March 1975. This aircraft was designated SD3-13V. Production aircraft were designated SD3-15V (first flight July 1975) and SD3-15T (first flight December 1976), the suffix letter denoting the tail configuration. By mid-1979, six SD3-15s had been built. Construction is now to order, and is restricted to the T-tail version, of which one was nearing completion at that time.

TYPE: Single-seat sailplane; *g* limits +3·5/−1·0.

AIRFRAME: Cantilever mid-wing monoplane. Wortmann FX-61-168 wing section. Dihedral 3°. Wings built mainly of metal, with metal and polystyrene ribs and GRP wingtips. All-metal trailing-edge flaps/airbrakes. Metal plain ailerons, with foam ribs. Semi-monocoque fuselage with metal skin and GRP nosecone. Cantilever T tail, of metal construction with 50% foam ribs. Full-span elevator with spring trim. Non-retractable monowheel, tyre pressure 2·41 bars (35 lb/sq in), with internally-expanding brake. Canopy opens sideways to starboard.

VICKERS-SLINGSBY

VICKERS-SLINGSBY (A Division of Vickers Limited Offshore Engineering Group)

HEAD OFFICE AND WORKS: Kirkbymoorside, York YO6 6EZ
Telephone: 0751 31751
Telex: 57911
MANAGING DIRECTOR: J. S. Tucker, BSc

Vickers-Slingsby was formed from the assets of the former Slingsby Aircraft Company, which went into liquidation in July 1969.

Present aircraft production is devoted to the Vickers-Slingsby Vega 15 metre Standard Class sailplane and the Vickers-Slingsby T.61E Venture, a 'military' version of the earlier T.61A built between 1971 and 1974. The Kestrel 22, described in the 1978-79 *Jane's*, is no longer being produced.

Vickers-Slingsby also manufactured parts of the Aerospace Developments AD-500 airship (see Lighter-Than-Air section).

VICKERS-SLINGSBY VEGA

The first sailplane entirely of Slingsby design to appear since the failure of the previous Slingsby company in 1969, the Vega was designed to take advantage of the change in the rules for Standard Class sailplanes permitting, after 1976, the installation of flaps in this class. Designed for optimum performance in its class, its wings have a unique flap and airbrake speed limiting system fitted to their trailing-edges, operated by a single control lever in the cockpit. The fuselage is gently 'waisted' to reduce the possibility of flow separation over the fuselage/wing junction.

The prototype Vega flew for the first time on 3 June 1977. Deliveries began in April 1978, at which time 48 had been ordered.

TYPE: Single-seat 15 metre Contest Class sailplane.

AIRFRAME: Cantilever mid-wing monoplane with T tail. Wing section Wortmann FX-67-K-150 from root to tip. Wings of foam plastics sandwich, with single carbon fibre main spar. Combined flaps/airbrakes inboard, ailerons outboard, on trailing-edges; ailerons can be operated independently or in conjunction with flaps. Turned-down wingtips. Conventional semi-monocoque plastics fuselage, with retractable tow hook. Cantilever T tail, with elevator spring trim. Tost monowheel, with brake, and tailwheel, both fully retractable. Canopy opens forward and upward, and is jettisonable. Provision for 100 kg (220 lb) water ballast.

VICKERS-SLINGSBY T.61E VENTURE

RAF name: Venture T.Mk 2

Slingsby began producing the Scheibe SF-25B Falke motor glider under licence in 1970, and completed a total of 35.

The Venture is a special version, of which 40 have been ordered by the Ministry of Defence (Air) for the Air Training Corps. It features a special glassfibre spar, encased in plywood, which simultaneously reduces the empty weight and increases the max permissible T-O weight of the aircraft. Many other glassfibre components are used in the aircraft, including a new seat designed to improve comfort and to reduce the hazard of loose articles slipping under the seat into the control area. The power plant is a Rollason-modified Volkswagen 33·5 kW (45 hp) 1,600 cc motor car engine, driving a two-blade fixed-pitch propeller.

First flight of a production Venture T.Mk 2 (XZ550) was made on 2 July 1977. Deliveries began in Autumn 1977, and 15 had been completed by November 1978. A prototype (XW983) was evaluated earlier under the designation Venture T.Mk 1.

UNITED STATES OF AMERICA

AERO TEK

New Mexico
DIRECTOR: George Applebay

AERO TEK MODEL V ZUNI

This sailplane made its first flight on 18 November 1976. Its appearance is shown in the accompanying three-view drawing.

TYPE: Single-seat 15 metre Contest Class sailplane.

AIRFRAME: Cantilever shoulder-wing monoplane, with T tail, of glassfibre construction. Wortmann wing section. Full-span camber-changing flaps/ailerons. One-piece all-moving tailplane. Retractable monowheel; non-retractable semi-recessed tailwheel. Provision for 109 kg (240 lb) water ballast.

AHRENS

AHRENS AIRCRAFT CORPORATION

PO Box 432, Ramey, Puerto Rico 00604
Telephone: (809) 891 2033
Telex: 385 9451 AHRENS PR
VICE-PRESIDENT, ENGINEERING: Kim K. Ahrens

This company built three prototypes of the AR 124 single-seat sailplane, as described in previous editions of *Jane's*, but for the moment its main activities are concerned with the AR 404 four-engined transport, described in the Aircraft section, and the AR 124 programme is dormant. A description and illustration of the AR 124 can be found in the 1978-79 *Jane's*.

AmEAGLE

AmEAGLE CORPORATION

841 Winslow Court, Muskegon, Michigan 49441
Telephone: (616) 780 4680
PRESIDENT: Larry Haig

This company was formed by Mr Larry Haig, a 1958 graduate engineer from Wayne State University, following seven years experience in gas turbine engine development with the research laboratories of General Motors; a further seven years in automotive and diesel engine design and application work for the Allison Division of General Motors and Teledyne Continental Motors; and two years experience with composite laminate structures with Brunswick Corporation.

Its first product is a homebuilt self-launching sailplane known as the American Eaglet.

AmEAGLE AMERICAN EAGLET

Design of the American Eaglet began in September 1974. Construction of the prototype started in June 1975, and this aircraft (N101EA) made its first flight on 19 November of that year.

A total of 350 kits had been ordered by early 1979, of which 15 had been completed.

TYPE: Single-seat homebuilt self-launching sailplane; *g* limits +4·4/−2·2 (safety factor 1·5).

AIRFRAME: Shoulder-wing monoplane, with single aluminium tube bracing strut on each side. Wing section Wortmann FX-61-184. Dihedral 1° 30′ from roots. Sparless stressed-skin structure with urethane foam core, moulded glassfibre leading-edges and wingtips, and epoxy-bonded pre-cured glassfibre skin. 'Spoilerons' (for both roll and glidepath control) at 30% chord on each upper surface. Pod-and-boom fuselage, the forward portion comprising two pre-formed glassfibre half-shells pop-riveted to tubular aluminium longerons. Tailboom is a thin-wall aluminium tube with a moulded glassfibre tailcone. Combined pitot tube/lifting handle in nose. Cantelever inverted-V tailplane and elevators, suspended from rear of tailboom. Tail surfaces have urethane foam core and epoxy/glassfibre skin. Manually-retractable monowheel, tyre pressure 2·41 bars (35 lb/sq in), with external friction-pad brake, forward of CG. Tailwheel under tip of each half-tailplane.

POWER PLANT: One 9 kW (12·2 hp at 8,000 rpm) McCulloch MC-101B single-cylinder two-stroke engine, installed aft of cockpit and driving a two-blade fixed-pitch pusher propeller with folding plastics blades. Recoil starting. Engine is for T-O and self-recovery only, and not for cross-country continuous operation. Fuel tank capacity 2 litres (0·5 US gallons). Normal fuel load of approx 1·81 kg (4 lb) (consumption at max power is 5·5 kg/h; 12 lb/h) is sufficient for one T-O and climb to 610 m (2,000 ft) and three airborne restarts and climbs from 150 m (500 ft) to 610 m (2,000 ft).

LAK-9 Lietuva single-seat Open Class sailplane (*reproduced from* Krilya Rodini)

Oshkinis (LAK) BRO-11 primary training glider (*reproduced from* Krilya Rodini)

Vickers-Slingsby Vega high-performance 15 metre sailplane

Swales SD3-15T single-seat sailplane

Vickers-Slingsby T.61E Venture T.Mk 2 in service with UK Air Cadets

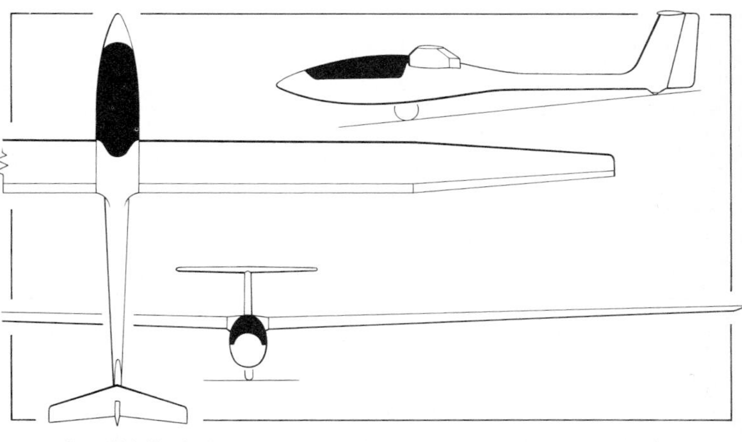

Aero Tek Zuni 15 metre Contest Class sailplane (*Michael A. Badrocke*)

Bryan (Schreder) HP-18 high-performance 15 metre Class sailplane

AmEagle American Eaglet single-seat self-launching sailplane (*J. M. G. Gradidge*)

BRYAN

BRYAN AIRCRAFT INC

Head Office and Works: Williams County Airport, PO Box 488, Bryan, Ohio 43506

Telephone: (419) 636 1340

Director: R. E. Schreder

This company markets plans and kits for the RS-15 and HP-18 high-performance Standard Class sailplanes, and is developing the more recent HP-19.

BRYAN (SCHREDER) RS-15

The RS-15 was designed by Mr Schreder to meet OSTIV Standard Class specifications. It is designed for simple, rapid assembly by the homebuilder and is licensed in the amateur-built Experimental category. No jigs are required, and most major components are prefabricated, to reduce assembly time to approx 500 man-hours for a builder with average mechanical aptitude.

Type: Single-seat Standard Class sailplane.

Airframe: Cantilever shoulder-wing monoplane. Wing section Wortmann FX-67-K-150. Dihedral 2° 18′. All-metal wings except for polyurethane foam plastics ribs. Main wing spar caps of aluminium plate. Water ballast carried inside wing box spars. Plain ailerons. Optional trailing-edge flaps/airbrakes, of aluminium sheet bonded to PVC foam ribs, which can be linked with ailerons. Monocoque fuselage: prefabricated glassfibre forward pod, complete with bulkheads, floorboards and finish; aluminium tube tailboom. All-metal V tail, which can be folded upward for towing or storage. Retractable monowheel, with hydraulic shock-absorber and brake, and non-retractable steerable tailwheel. Provision for 91 kg (200 lb) water ballast.

BRYAN (SCHREDER) HP-18

The HP-18 was flown for the first time in 1975. Approx 170 had been built or were under construction by early 1979. Assembly time is approx 700 man-hours.

Type: Single-seat Standard Class sailplane.

Airframe: Generally similar to the RS-15, the HP-18 has a slightly longer fuselage, with low profile circular instead of oval section, and other features designed to reduce drag and produce a superior competition aircraft; *g* limits are +12/−12. Improvements include better gap seals, new wingtips, faired tailwheel and better streamlining; ailerons and 90° flaps are coupled, to improve cross-country speed; use of full flap permits steeper approaches and slower landing speeds. NASA-type winglets can be added to increase glide ratio and improve aileron control. Fuselage comprises a prefabricated glassfibre pod and aluminium monocoque tailboom. The Tost monowheel has a tyre pressure of 2·07 bars (30 lb/sq in) and is fitted with a mechanically-expanding brake.

BRYAN (SCHREDER) HP-19

Expected to fly in mid-March 1979, the HP-19 is an improved version of the HP-18. A carbon-fibre main spar and other weight savings reduce wing weight by 32 kg (70 lb), while increasing water ballast capacity to 136 kg (300 lb). A new Schreder wing section with higher maximum lift coefficient, together with NASA-type winglets, decrease thermalling and landing speeds, decrease minimum sink rate, improve aileron control and increase glide ratios. Coupled flaps and ailerons improve performance at all speeds, while 90° flaps permit steeper approaches and slower landing speeds than were possible with conventional airbrakes. Simplified constructional materials and methods reduce assembly time to about 500 man-hours.

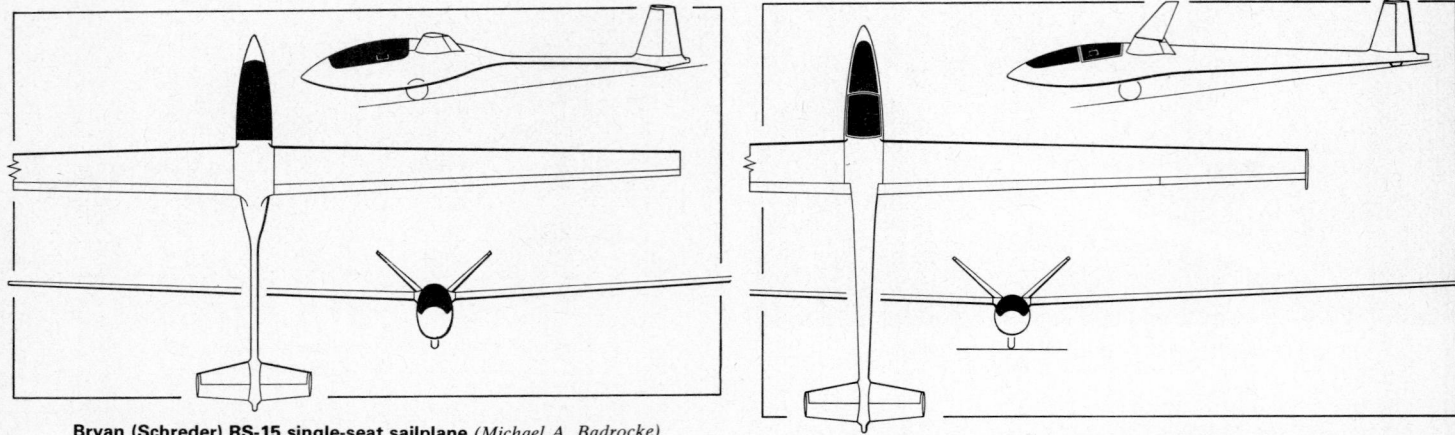

Bryan (Schreder) RS-15 single-seat sailplane *(Michael A. Badrocke)*

Bryan (Schreder) HP-19 high-performance sailplane *(Michael A. Badrocke)*

DSK

DSK AIRCRAFT CORPORATION

13161 Sherman Way, North Hollywood, California 91605
VICE-PRESIDENT, MARKETING: Rodney E. Gage

In addition to the well-established Duster homebuilt sailplane, DSK is developing an improved version known as the DS-1. It has also acquired all production and marketing rights in the Woodstock homebuilt sailplane designed and originally built by Mr Jim Maupin.

DSK BJ-1b DUSTER

The Duster is available in the form of plans and/or component kits for amateur construction. Average construction time is approx 600-700 hours.

TYPE: Single-seat homebuilt sailplane; *g* limits +5·3/−3·1.

AIRFRAME: Cantilever shoulder-wing monoplane. NACA 4415 (modified) wing section, with 2° washout at tips. Single wooden main spar, with plywood ribs and plywood covering. Wing built in three portions: two outer panels, and a 2·13 m (7 ft) span centre-section integral with fuselage. Trailing-edge flaps/airbrakes; top-hinged ailerons. Straight-sided plywood fuselage shell, having an elongated hexagonal cross-section in the cockpit area, changing to triangular section aft of wings. Ventral plywood keel, reinforced by two bulkheads shaped to seat contour and supporting floor-mounted seat. Glassfibre nosecone and fairings. Cantilever tail unit, with tailplane mounted on top of fuselage. Construction similar to that of wings. All tail surfaces plywood skinned. Non-retractable semi-recessed monowheel beneath keel, and tailwheel. Aircraft can be flown with one-piece flush-fitting canopy, or with open cockpit and windscreen only.

POWER PLANT: Auxiliary power package, using a 19·4 kW (26 hp) engine, under development. Plans will detail all hardware necessary to support an engine mount, which can be added at builder's option without further alteration of airframe.

EXPLORER

EXPLORER AIRCRAFT COMPANY INC

PO Box 60036 Reno, Nevada 89506
Telephone: (702) 972 7757

Explorer Aircraft markets plans of the biplane Aqua Glider. Designed by Colonel William L. Skliar, USAF (Ret'd), it is intended for tethered gliding by unlicensed pilots, towed behind any motor boat able to attain a speed of 30 knots (56 km/h; 35 mph). If the pilot has the necessary licence, he can cast off from the motor boat when airborne and make a free flight before landing back on the water.

EXPLORER PG-1 AQUA GLIDER

Design of the Aqua Glider began in September 1958, and the prototype made its first flight in July 1959. Plans are available to amateur constructors and approx 1,000 sets have been sold in more than 20 countries all over the world. About 12 Aqua Gliders are known to have flown, in the USA, the Bahamas, Brazil and Japan, and about 200 more are under construction.

The prototype, after making about 1,000 flights and being flown by about 60 pilots, was donated to the Experimental Aircraft Association Museum.

TYPE: Single-seat homebuilt waterborne glider; *g* limit +4·0.

AIRFRAME: Forward-stagger single-bay biplane with N interplane and parallel centre-section struts. Wing section (both) NACA 4412. Dihedral 2° 30′ on lower wing only. Conventional single-spar wooden structure with fabric covering. Spoiler-type light alloy ailerons on lower wing only, immediately aft of main spar. Balancer floats at lower wingtips. Unstepped watertight wooden hull of spruce with mahogany plywood bow, bottom skins and sides. Plywood is glassfibre-covered below waterline. Tow hook on nose. Wire-braced spruce tail unit, with plywood and fabric covering, carried on welded steel tube or wire-braced wooden boom. All-moving one-piece tailplane with bungee trim. Conventional rudder. Standard jumper skis, 1·83 m (6 ft) in length, attached to small wire-braced struts below hull. Open cockpit.

FLIGHT DYNAMICS

FLIGHT DYNAMICS INC

PO Box 5070, State University Station, Raleigh, North Carolina 27607
Telephone: (919) 834 6806 or 781 6138
PRESIDENT: Thomas H. Purcell Jr

FLIGHT DYNAMICS SEASPRITE

The Seasprite is the unpowered Stage I version of the aircraft which, in a fully-developed powered form, is known as the Flightsail VII. The Seasprite is of more simplified construction, and is available in plans form to amateur sailplane constructors.

Flight Dynamics has fitted a Seasprite with a twin tail unit; a 22·5 kW (30 hp) engine was to be added, in which form the aircraft was to undergo powered flight trials in the Summer of 1979.

The following description applies to the standard model:

TYPE: Single/two-seat homebuilt glider.

AIRFRAME: Fuselage, of aerofoil/hydrofoil cross-section, is built on a framework of aluminium tubing. Sides and top are covered with polyethylene foil, except for upper part of nose section, which has a transparent covering of polyester film and Plexiglas. Pilot sits in centre-section, to right of slender aluminium boom which carries the simple tail unit, his weight being balanced by a counterweight at port wingtip if a second occupant is not carried. Underside of fuselage/hull has catamaran-type twin floats, built of plastics with a plywood covering. For only a minimal weight increase, structure can be covered instead with aluminium foil, which has a much longer life. Wings are of triangular planform, and are of sailwing type, with aluminium tube leading-edge, wire trailing-edge, and polyethylene covering. They are braced to fuselage sides, and can be folded rearward when not in use. Wingtips pivot about their leading-edges, to provide roll control. Fin/tailplane is built as a single unit, pivoting only in vertical plane for control in pitch.

MARSKE

MARSKE AIRCRAFT CORPORATION

130 Crestwood Drive, Michigan City, Indiana 46360
Telephone: (219) 879 7039
PRESIDENT: James J. Marske

MARSKE MONARCH C

The first Monarch single-seat ultra-light glider was designed and built by Mr Jim Marske in 1973-74, and made its first flight on 4 July 1974. Plans and kits are available to amateur constructors. A total of 71 Monarchs were under construction by the beginning of 1979, of which four are known to have been completed.

Mr Marske has successfully test-flown the Monarch prototype with a 9 kW (12 hp) McCulloch engine installed behind the pilot's seat, driving a 0·635 m (2 ft 1 in) diameter pusher propeller. It is considered, however, that an engine of approx 15 kW (20 hp) should be fitted to homebuilt aircraft.

The earlier Monarch B was described in the 1977-78 *Jane's*; the following description applies to the current Monarch C version, which replaced it:

TYPE: Single-seat ultra-light homebuilt glider; *g* limits +8·0/−4·0 (ultimate).

AIRFRAME: Braced high-wing monoplane, with single steel strut each side. Wing section NACA 43012R or 43112. Dihedral 2°. Sweepforward 3° at quarter-chord. Moulded glassfibre D leading-edge, with glassfibre front spar web and booms, wood and foam plastics ribs, wooden rear spar and trailing-edge, and fabric covering. Ailerons (outboard) and elevators (inboard) have single Sitka spruce spars with foam plastics ribs. Fixed tab on each elevator. All control surfaces Dacron-covered. Aluminium spoiler above each wing. Simple minimal beam-type fuselage of laminated glassfibre, moulded in two halves and joined at centreline. Forward section supports pilot's seat, with nose fairing over instrument panel; rear section forms integral fin leading-edge. CG tow hook on each side of nose fairing. Fin and rudder, above and below level of wings. Glassfibre leading-edge (fin), wooden trailing-edge (rudder), foam ribs and fabric covering. No horizontal tail surfaces. Reinforced underfuselage landing skid. Single landing wheel, below pilot's open seat. Conventional floor-mounted control column.

MONNETT

MONNETT EXPERIMENTAL AIRCRAFT INC

955 Grace Street, Elgin, Illinois 60120
Telephone: (312) 741 2223
GENERAL MANAGER: Gregg Erikson

In addition to its Sonerai powered aircraft (see Homebuilts section), Monnett produces kits of parts for the Monerai single-seat homebuilt sailplane.

MONNETT MONERAI S

The Monerai, development of which began in 1976, was designed to fill a need for a low-cost homebuilt sailplane with better-than-average performance. It flew for the first time in March 1978. The kit includes many extruded or preformed components, to permit quick construction with a minimum of equipment or experience. Average construction time is 300 hours.

By mid-January 1979 more than 100 Monerai S kits had been sold, of which 50 had been delivered since 1 November 1978.

TYPE: Single-seat homebuilt sailplane; *g* limits +6/−6.

AIRFRAME: Cantilever mid-wing monoplane. Wing section Wortmann FX-61-192 (modified). Dihedral 4°. Aluminium main spar of extruded, modified I section; rear spar is an aluminium C channel. Constant chord

DSK BJ-1b Duster single-seat homebuilt sailplane

Flight Dynamics Seasprite single/two-seat homebuilt glider

Marske Monarch B single-seat ultralight glider

Explorer PG-1 Aqua Glider built by Sr Fernando de A. Botelho of São Paulo, Brazil

Monnett Monerai S single-seat homebuilt sailplane

Monnett Monerai P, powered version of the S for self-launch

allows all the preformed ribs to be identical, and single-piece aluminium skin to wrap around from trailing-edge to trailing-edge. Skin bonded to spars and ribs with Hysol epoxy. Glassfibre wingtips. Aileron and flap skins are preformed and ready for assembly. Fuselage is built up from chrome-molybdenum steel tube and is covered by a non-structural premoulded glassfibre shell. A 12·7 cm (5 in) diameter extruded aluminium tube is attached to the frame and extends 3·66 m (12 ft) to the rear where an upright, all-flying, all-aluminium V tail is attached. Non-retractable monowheel, with mechanical brake; tailskid. One-piece flush-fitting canopy. No provision for water ballast.

MONNETT MONERAI P

Exhibited at Oshkosh in 1978, the Monerai P is identical to the S version, but has a small auxiliary engine (7·5 kW; 10 hp West Bend two-stroke) to permit self-launch. A combination turnover structure and power pod mount, aft of the cockpit, allows the sailplane to be converted to the P version in only five minutes. The engine and propeller do not fold away when not in use, but a streamlined glassfibre fairing encloses the engine and pylon.

OLDERSHAW

VERNON W. OLDERSHAW

2508 Talisman Drive, Bakersfield, California 93304

OLDERSHAW O-3

Mr Oldershaw, who was involved in the construction of the Gossamer Condor man-powered aeroplane, designed and built the original O-3 in fifteen months. It flew for the first time in June 1967. He then began to develop a retractable power plant for the sailplane, which was added to a second O-3 completed in 1975. The engine is used primarily for T-O and climb to soaring altitude.

A description and illustration of the second O-3 can be found in the 1978-79 *Jane's*; a third was under construction in 1979 at Porterville, California. Despite numerous requests, Mr Oldershaw has not been able to produce and market plans of the aircraft, due to his heavy commitments to the development of man-powered flight.

RYSON

RYSON AVIATION CORPORATION

548 San Fernando Street, San Diego, California 92106
Telephone: (714) 278 4791
PRESIDENT: T. Claude Ryan
EXECUTIVE VICE-PRESIDENT AND OPERATIONS MANAGER: Jerome D. Ryan
CHIEF ENGINEER: L. Pazmany

Ryson Aviation Corporation was founded by Mr T. Claude Ryan, until 1969 Chairman and Chief Executive Officer of the Ryan Aeronautical Company (now Teledyne Ryan Aeronautical). Other executives include his son, Mr Jerry Ryan, and Mr Ladislao Pazmany. The aim of the Corporation is to develop aeronautical products and make them available for manufacture by other companies.

First new design to emanate from the Ryson company was a two-seat motor glider designated STP-1 Swallow, details of which appeared in the 1973-74 *Jane's*.

Since early 1975 the company has been working on a motor glider of completely new design, designated ST-100 (Soaring/Touring—100 hp).

RYSON ST-100 CLOUDSTER

Believed to be the first American motor glider designed for production, the ST-100 has the traditional tractor-propeller configuration of the most popular European powered sailplanes. Its design, which was started on 18 March 1974, incorporates all-metal construction, fully-folding wings, power-operated flaps for air braking, and ailerons which operate with the flaps. It is designed to be aerobatic and to meet the current FAR Pt 23 gust load requirements (15·25 m; 50 ft/s); is capable of performing as an aero-tow aircraft for unpowered sailplanes; and can be used as a conventional powered aircraft for cross-country flying.

Construction of the ST-100 prototype began on 11 July 1974, and this aircraft (N2RY) flew for the first time on 21 December 1976. By January 1979 it had accumulated about 600 hours of flight testing and demonstration, including an economy record flight from California to Oshkosh, Wisconsin (1,456 nm; 2,697 km; 1,676 miles), on 28 of the available 32 US gallons of fuel (106 of 121 litres); and a 5,214 nm (9,656 km; 6,000 mile) flight around the perimeter of the United States. FAA certification was expected in July 1979. A production programme by a licensee is planned.

TYPE: Tandem two-seat motor glider; *g* limits +6·75/−3·5.

AIRFRAME: Cantilever low-wing monoplane. Wing section Wortmann FX-67-K-170/17 throughout, with max thickness at 40% chord. Dihedral 4° from roots. All-metal safe-life structure, with some fail-safe features, built of extruded 2024-T4 and other alloys of aluminium, with sheet aluminium skin. Aluminium plain ailerons and plain trailing-edge flaps, with foam core. Flaps, powered by electrically-operated screw-jack, can be deflected downward for use as airbrakes. Ailerons operate with flaps. No spoilers or tabs. Wings fold back alongside fuselage for stowage or transportation. Conventional all-metal semi-monocoque fuselage, with extruded aluminium longerons, and sheet metal frames, bulkheads and skins. Cantilever T tail, with sweptback fin and rudder and non-swept horizontal surfaces, latter comprising fixed-incidence tailplane and one-piece balanced elevator. Rudder and elevator have riveted sheet aluminium primary ribs, bonded intermediate foam ribs, and bonded sheet aluminium skin. Elevator tips removable for transportation or storage. Anti-servo and trim tab, of similar construction, in centre of elevator. Two-wheel main gear and steerable tailwheel, all non-retractable. Ryson oleo-pneumatic shock-absorbers. Cleveland main wheels, with Cleveland hydraulic disc brakes, and Goodyear tailwheel. Streamlined glassfibre fairings on main gear legs, main wheels and tailwheel. Canopy opens sideways to starboard. Dual controls standard. Baggage space aft of rear seat.

POWER PLANT: One 74·5 kW (100 hp) Continental O-200 flat-four engine, driving a Hoffmann HO-V-62 variable-pitch fully-feathering propeller with two composite blades. Fuel in two integral tanks in leading-edges of wing centre-section, with combined capacity of 121 litres (26·6 Imp gallons; 32 US gallons). Oil capacity 5·7 litres (1·25 Imp gallons; 1·5 US gallons).

SCHWEIZER

SCHWEIZER AIRCRAFT CORPORATION

HEAD OFFICE AND WORKS: Box 147, Elmira, New York 14902
Telephone: (607) 739 3821
Telex: 932459
PRESIDENT AND CHIEF ENGINEER: Ernest Schweizer
SALES MANAGER: W. E. Doherty Jr

Schweizer Aircraft Corporation is the leading American designer and manufacturer of sailplanes. Its current products include the SGS 1-26E, SGS 2-33A and SGS 1-35 series.

By agreement with Gulfstream American, Schweizer also manufactures the Super Ag-Cat agricultural biplane, a description of which can be found under the Gulfstream heading in the Aircraft section. Other subcontract work includes production of fuselage assemblies for Piper Aircraft Corporation and major structures for Bell Helicopter Textron.

About 500 people were employed by Schweizer in 1979.

SCHWEIZER SGS 1-26

This relatively small sailplane was developed for one-design class activities. It was designed to be produced both complete and in kit form for the homebuilder. The prototype was first flown in January 1954, and with award of the FAA Type Certificate production of complete sailplanes and kits began in November of that year.

The current production version, the **SGS 1-26E**, introduced an all-metal semi-monocoque fuselage. More than 680 SGS 1-26 sailplanes had been produced by January 1979, of which approximately 200 were in kit form.

TYPE: Single-seat medium-performance sailplane.

AIRFRAME: Cantilever mid-wing monoplane. Dihedral 3° 30′. All-metal structure of aluminium alloy, with metal skin. Fabric-covered ailerons. Balanced airbrakes immediately aft of spar on each wing. Production SGS 1-26E has an all-metal semi-monocoque fuselage. Fabric-covered aluminium alloy tail unit. Non-retractable unsprung monowheel, with Schweizer brake, aft of rubber-sprung nose-skid. Small tailwheel.

SCHWEIZER SGS 2-32

The SGS 2-32 flew for the first time on 3 July 1962. FAA Type Approval was received in June 1964 and production began immediately. A total of 89 had been built by January 1978, when production was halted. A description and illustration can be found in the 1978-79 *Jane's*.

SCHWEIZER SGS 2-33A

The SGS 2-33 was developed to meet the demand for a medium-priced two-seat sailplane for training and general family soaring. The prototype was first flown in the Autumn of 1966 and received FAA Type Approval in February 1967. Production began in January 1967, and 540 SGS 2-33 sailplanes had been built by January 1979. The current 2-33A is also available in kit form.

TYPE: Tandem two-seat training sailplane.

AIRFRAME: Strut-braced high-wing monoplane. Aluminium alloy structure with metal skin and all-metal ailerons. Airbrakes fitted. Welded chrome-molybdenum steel tube fuselage. Nose covered with glassfibre, remainder with Ceconite fabric. Steel tube tail unit, covered with Ceconite fabric. Braced tailplane. Non-retractable Cleveland monowheel immediately aft of nose-skid. Rubber-block shock-absorption for skid. Wingtip wheels.

SCHWEIZER SGS 1-34B

Design of this single-seat high-performance Standard Class sailplane began in 1967 and construction of the prototype started in the following year. This flew for the first time in the Spring of 1969 and FAA type certification was awarded in September 1969. A total of 93 production models had been completed by January 1978, when production was halted. A description and illustration can be found in the 1978-79 *Jane's*.

SCHWEIZER SGS 1-35 SERIES

The SGS 1-35 is an all-metal single-seat high-performance 15 metre Class sailplane, the prototype of which was flown for the first time in April 1973. The FAA certification programme was completed in Spring 1974.

The 1-35 is claimed to have the widest wing loading range in the FAI 15 metre Class (28·22 to 43·75 kg/m²; 5·78 to 8·96 lb/sq ft), and carries 146·5 kg (323 lb) of water ballast. It can thus compete effectively in both light and strong soaring conditions. The 80° landing flaps are used instead of the more conventional airbrakes.

Two newer models are also available, as follows:

SGS 1-35A. Unrestricted 15 metre Class version. Monowheel forward of CG, large tailwheel and no nose-skid. Interconnected flaps and ailerons standard. Data as for standard 1-35 except for empty equipped weight of 222 kg (490 lb) and best glide ratio of 41.

SGS 1-35C (Club-35). Simplified, lower-cost version for club or syndicate ownership. Non-retractable Cleveland unsprung monowheel aft of CG, Cleveland hydraulic brake, nose-skid, and no water ballast provision. Flush rivets used on aft fuselage. Data as for standard 1-35 except for empty equipped weight of 192 kg (425 lb), max T-O weight of 310 kg (685 lb), max wing loading of 32·16 kg/m² (6·59 lb/sq ft), and best glide ratio of 36.

A total of 95 SGS 1-35s of all versions had been produced by January 1979. The following description applies to the standard SGS 1-35:

TYPE: Single-seat 15 metre Class sailplane; *g* limits +8·33/−5·33.

AIRFRAME: Cantilever shoulder-wing monoplane. Wortmann wing sections: FX-67-K-170 at root, FX-67-K-150 at tip. Dihedral 3° 30′. Aluminium stressed-skin and stringer wing structure. Bottom-hinged trailing-edge flaps and top-hinged ailerons of aluminium torque cell construction. No airbrakes or spoilers. All-aluminium monocoque fuselage. Cantilever aluminium T-tail, with fixed-incidence tailplane and fabric-covered elevator. No tabs. Mechanically-retractable unsprung monowheel, tyre pressure 2·41 bars (35 lb/sq in). Hydraulic brake. Nose-skid and tailwheel or tailskid. Detachable canopy. Provision for 146·5 kg (323 lb) water ballast.

VOLPAR

VOLPAR INC

7929 Hayvenhurst Avenue, Van Nuys, California 91406
Telephone: (213) 787-4393 and 873-5599
OFFICERS: See Aircraft section

Volpar Inc is engaged primarily in the conversion and manufacture of light/medium-sized turboprop-powered aircraft, as described in the Aircraft section.

In addition, in February 1977 the company retained Mr Percival H. Spencer to design a small but fully manoeuvrable water-based glider, utilising modern plastics and foam materials for high strength and low cost, and having simple controls that could be operated safely by an amateur or non-pilot. Mr Spencer is a pioneer pilot, amphibious aircraft designer and manufacturer of the Spencer Amphibian Air Car (see Homebuilts section).

VOLPAR-SPENCER DRAG-N-FLY

The Drag-N-Fly is intended to be towed in tethered flight by a conventional motor-boat. The tether may be disconnected by the pilot in an emergency, and will disconnect automatically if the glider tends to overrun the tow boat. An unusual feature is the hinged fuselage, which permits the glider to be transported on a light road trailer without exceeding a width of 2·44 m (8 ft 0 in).

The prototype was first flown, by Mr Spencer, on 20 April 1977. Development testing, continued throughout 1978, resulted in the addition of a 0·305 m (1 ft) tip extension on each wing in order to reduce tow-boat power requirements. Flight and water characteristics, including control response, are now entirely satisfactory, and in early 1979 the Drag-N-Fly was ready for production.

TYPE: Single-seat waterborne glider; *g* limit +6.

AIRFRAME: Strut-braced biplane. Aerofoil-shaped styrofoam blocks, with plywood spar caps bonded to styrofoam shear web with epoxy resin. Wooden blocks between capstrips at each end provide bolt attachments to join panels. Wings covered in glasscloth laminate, bonded with epoxy resin. Spoilers on outer panels of lower wing. Fuselage and floats built of plywood internal frames and bulkheads, covered in polyester resin-bonded moulded glassfibre cloth laminate. Cantilever tail unit with styrofoam core, wooden frame edges (vertical surfaces) and plywood spar caps (horizontal surfaces); glassfibre laminate covering. Horizontal tail is one-piece unit, hinged at fuselage aft bulkhead and statically balanced with bob-weight; bungee spring for trim adjustment. Water rudder, operated from cockpit, for towing control. Single open cockpit forward of wings.

Ryson ST-100 Cloudster (Continental O-200 engine)

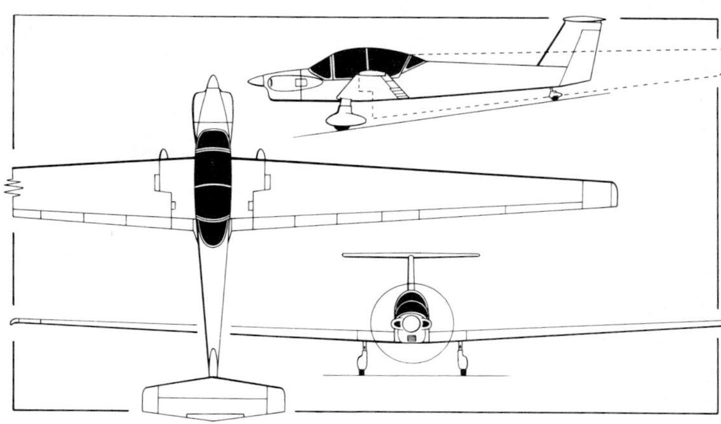
Ryson ST-100 Cloudster two-seat motor glider *(Michael A. Badrocke)*

Schweizer SGS 1-26E single-seat medium-performance sailplane

Schweizer SGS 2-33 two-seat general-purpose sailplane *(Peter M. Bowers)*

Schweizer SGS 1-35 single-seat 15 metre sailplane *(Neil A. Macdougall)*

German-built Glaser-Dirks DG-100s. This sailplane is now produced under licence by Elan in Yugoslavia

Volpar-Spencer single-seat Drag-N-Fly

YUGOSLAVIA

ELAN

Begunje

This factory has, since the beginning of 1979, assumed responsibility for licence production of the DG-100 sailplane formerly built by Glaser-Dirks of Germany (which see).

ELAN (GLASER-DIRKS) DG-100 ELAN

The DG-100 is a modified and lighter-weight development of the Akaflieg Darmstadt D-38 described in the 1973-74 *Jane's*. Its design, by Dipl-Ing Wilhelm Dirks, began in August 1973, and the prototype (D-7100) flew for the first time on 10 May 1974. By the end of 1978, Glaser-Dirks had completed 105 DG-100s and 16 examples of the DG-100G (first flight 11 June 1976), which differs in having a tailplane similar to that of the Glaser-Dirks DG-200. A Club version of the DG-100, without water ballast, is also available.

From early 1979, the DG-100 entered licence production in Yugoslavia, and the two versions are now known as the **DG-100 Elan** and **DG-100G Elan**. The following description applies to the former (standard) version:

TYPE: Single-seat Standard Class sailplane; *g* limit +6·1.

AIRFRAME: Cantilever shoulder-wing monoplane. Wortmann wing sections: FX-61-184 at centreline, FX-60-126 at tip. Dihedral 3° from roots. Glassfibre roving main spar. Glassfibre/Conticell/foam sandwich wings, ailerons and all-moving T tailplane; all-glassfibre semi-monocoque fuselage, fin and rudder. Schempp-Hirth duralumin airbrakes on wing upper surfaces. Water ballast tank in each wing (except on Club version), combined capacity 100 kg (220 lb). Full-span Flettner tab in tailplane. Manually-retractable monowheel, tyre pressure 2·0 bars (29 lb/sq in), with Tost drum brake, and tailwheel.

JASTREB

JASTREB AEROPLANE AND GLIDER FACTORY

Vrsac
Telephone: (013) 813157, 813051, 813639 and 815491

JASTREB SOLE-77

The Jastreb SOLE-77, illustrated in an accompanying three-view drawing, is a two-seat motor glider for elementary and advanced training, and can be used for basic aerobatics. Other applications include atmospheric sampling, photogrammetry, and study of air currents. The monowheel is said to be retractable; the tailwheel, linked to the rudder pedals, is fully castoring. The cockpit canopy, which opens forward, is jettisonable. Power off, the SOLE-77 has a best glide ratio of 29. The engine, of unknown type, develops 54 kW (72 hp) and drives a two-blade propeller; there is provision for an auxiliary fuel tank. Without this tank, standard fuel load is 50 kg (110 lb) and powered flight endurance 5 h.

All other known details are given in the Table.

MF

MASINSKI FAKULTET (Faculty of Mechanical Engineering, Aeronautical Institute ATI)

27 Marta 80, 11000 Belgrade
Telephone: (011) 329 362
SAILPLANE DESIGNER: Prof Dr Tomislav Dragovic, Dipl Eng

The Faculty of Mechanical Engineering at the University of Belgrade is the leading research and educational institution for aircraft engineering in Yugoslavia. It has tackled many important light aviation projects in recent years, and collaborates closely with the national aerospace industry. Among its recent designs was the UTVA-75, described in the Aircraft section.

MF VUK-T

The prototype of this single-seat all-plastics sailplane was designed and built at the MF in 1976, and made its first flight in 1977. It entered production in the Jastreb Aeroplane and Glider Factory at Vrsac (which see) in January 1979. At that time 110 had been ordered by the Yugoslav Aeronautical Union.

Chief features of the VUK-T are an entirely new technique of plastics stressed-skin construction and the use of a supercritical wing section. The sailplane is designed to OSTIV airworthiness requirements, and is cleared for cloud flying, aerobatics and spinning.

TYPE: Single-seat high-performance basic and advanced training sailplane; *g* limits +5·3/−2·65 (safety factor 1·5).

AIRFRAME: Cantilever mid-wing monoplane. NASA GAW-1 supercritical wing section from root to tip, with no twist. Thickness/chord ratio 17%. Dihedral 3°. Glassfibre roving main spar, integral with the upper and lower wing skins, which are of glassfibre/Conticell foam sandwich. Auxiliary rear spar carries the top-hinged plain ailerons. Schempp-Hirth airbrakes in upper surfaces at 50% chord. Fuselage is of glassfibre sandwich construction forward, glassfibre monocoque aft. Cantilever T tailplane, with separate elevator, of similar construction to wings. Retractable monowheel, with brake, and non-retractable tailwheel. Semi-reclining seat under one-piece flush-fitting jettisonable canopy. No water ballast provision.

VTC

VAZDUHOPLOVNO TEHNICKI CENTAR—VRSAC

Vrsac, 29 Novembra b.b. Guduricki put
Telephone: 80-111
DIRECTOR: Veselinovic Zivota
CHIEF DESIGNER: Dipl Ing Ivan Sostaric

The VTC at Vrsac is producing the Schempp-Hirth Cirrus and Standard Cirrus under licence. The first production Cirrus built at Vrsac was delivered in late 1971.

VTC (SCHEMPP-HIRTH) CIRRUS

This single-seat high-performance sailplane was designed in Germany by Dipl-Ing Klaus Holighaus, who utilised a thick Wortmann series wing section, without flaps, to achieve good low-speed and climb characteristics.

The first prototype Cirrus flew for the first time in January 1967 with a V tail unit. The second prototype had a conventional tail unit, as fitted to production models.

Schempp-Hirth built a total of 120 Cirrus sailplanes before ending production in late 1971. Since then the Cirrus has been produced under licence by VTC in Yugoslavia, which had completed about 60 by early 1979.

TYPE: Single-seat high-performance sailplane.

AIRFRAME: Cantilever mid-wing monoplane. Wortmann FX-66 series section. Dihedral 3° at spar centreline. Wing shell is a glassfibre/foam sandwich structure, with an all-glassfibre box spar. Hinged ailerons of glassfibre/balsa sandwich. No flaps. Schempp-Hirth

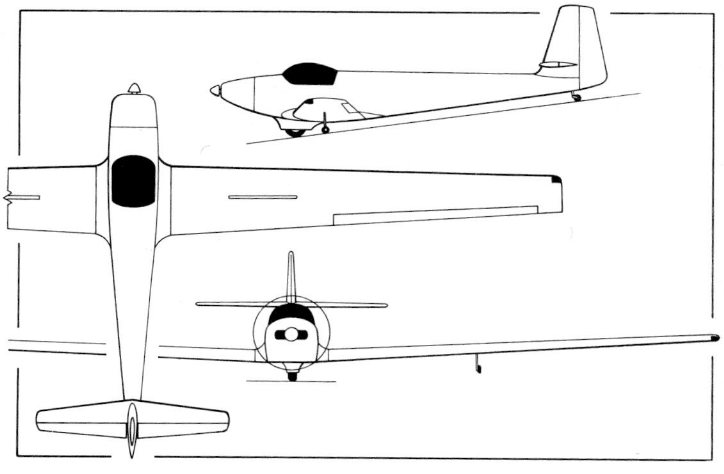

Jastreb SOLE-77 two-seat motor glider *(Michael A. Badrocke)*

VUK-T all-plastics training sailplane, designed by the Yugoslav Faculty of Mechanical Engineering

aluminium alloy airbrakes. Glassfibre fuselage shell, stiffened with foam rings, secured with resin. Cantilever tail unit of glassfibre/foam sandwich. Retractable rubber-sprung Tost monowheel, tyre pressure 3·38 bars (49 lb/sq in). Tost drum brake.

VTC (SCHEMPP-HIRTH) STANDARD CIRRUS 75-VTC

Designed by Dipl-Ing Klaus Holighaus, this Standard Class version of the Schempp-Hirth Cirrus entered production in Germany in the Summer of 1969, following the first flight of the prototype in March 1969.

By April 1977 a total of 700 Standard Cirrus had been built, including 200 under licence by Grob Flugzeugbau in Germany. Production by Grob ended in July 1975, and by Schempp-Hirth in April 1977. Since then licence manufacture has been undertaken by Lanaverre in France, and from January 1979 by VTC in Yugoslavia. VTC had built 14 Standard Cirrus by the Spring of 1979.

TYPE: Single-seat Standard and Club Class sailplane; *g* limit +10.

AIRFRAME: Cantilever mid-wing monoplane. Wortmann wing section. Dihedral 3°. Sweepback 1°18′ at leading-edge. Glassfibre/foam sandwich wings, ailerons and tail surfaces. Schempp-Hirth glassfibre airbrakes on upper surfaces. Glassfibre fuselage shell, stiffened with bonded-in foam rings. All-moving T tailplane. Retractable monowheel standard; non-retractable faired monowheel optional. Tost wheel with drum brake and Continental tyre, pressure 3·45 bars (50 lb/sq in). Canopy opens sideways to starboard. Provision for 60 kg (132 lb) of water ballast.

DATA: SAILPLANES AND MOTOR GLIDERS (POWER OFF)

Manufacturer and Model	Dimensions					Weights and Loading		
	Wing span: m; ft in	Wing aspect ratio	Wing area (gross): m²; sq ft	Length overall: m; ft in	Height over tail: m; ft in	Empty: kg; lb	Max T-O: kg; lb	Max wing loading: kg/m²; lb/sq ft
AUSTRALIA								
Sunderland MOBA-2C	14·99;	24·74	9·08;	6·78;	1·36;	220;	331;	36·5;
	49 2		97·7	22 3	4 5½	485	730	7·48
AUSTRIA								
Brditschka HB-21	16·24;	13·89	18·98;	8·10;	2·60;	505;	710;	37·4;
	53 3½		204·3	26 7	8 6¼	1,113	1,565	7·66
BRAZIL								
CTA PE-80367 Urubu	17·80;	15·1	20·92;	8·50;	2·53;	320;	500;	23·9;
	58 4¾		225·2	27 10¾	8 3½	705	1,102	4·89
EEUFMG (CEA) CB-2/B Minuano	15·00;	22	10·20;	7·00;	1·43;	230;	400;	39·22;
	49 2½		109·8	22 11¾	4 8¼	507	882	8·03
IPE KW 1 b 2 Quero Quero II	15·00;	18	11·70;	6·47;	1·34;	170;	270;	21·3;
	49 2½		125·9	21 2¾	4 4¾	374	595	4·36
IPE 02	17·20;	15·36	19·26;	8·40;	1·57;	360;	500;	25·9;
	56 5¼		207·3	27 6¾	5 1¾	793	1,102	5·32
Sidou João Grande	18·00;	25	12·96;	9·00;	2·52;	270;	450;	34·72;
	59 0¾		139·5	29 6¼	8 3¼	595	992	7·11
CANADA								
Marsden Gemini	18·45;	29·7	11·45;	7·60;	1·50;	357;	545;	47·6;
	60 6½		123·2	24 11¼	4 11	787	1,201	9·75
CZECHOSLOVAKIA								
VSO 10	15·00;	18·75	12·00;	7·00;	1·20;	250;	380;	31·67;
	49 2½		129·2	22 11¾	3 11¼	551	837	6·49
DENMARK								
Projekt 8 Dolphin	18·72;	16·8	20·80;	8·50;	1·30;	480;	750;	36·0;
	61 5		223·9	27 10¾	4 3¼	1,058	1,653	7·37
FINLAND								
Alanne Motorlerche	13·00;	10·3	16·34;	6·86;	n.k.	288;	400;	23·8;
	42 7¾		175·9	22 6		635	882	4·88
PIK-20D	15·00;	22·5	10·00;	6·45;	1·45;	220;	450;	45·0;
	49 2½		107·6	21 2	4 9	485	992	9·22
PIK-20E	15·00;	22·5	10·00;	6·53;	1·47;	300;	470;	47·0;
	49 2½		107·6	21 5	4 10	661	1,036	9·63
FRANCE								
CARMAM J.P. 15-36A Aiglon	15·00;	20·4	11·00;	6·18;	1·40;	229;	390;	35·0;
	49 2½		118·4	20 3¼	4 7	505	860	7·16
CARMAM 15-38	15·00;	20·6	11·00;	6·70;	1·45;	230;	440;	40·0;
	49 2½		118·4	21 11¾	4 9	507	970	8·19
Fauvel AV.45	13·74;	12	15·95;	3·59;	1·82;	216;	350;	22·0;
	45 1		171·7	11 9¼	5 11¾	476	771	4·51
Fauvel AV.222	16·40;	12	23·00;	5·22;	2·37;	325;	550;	23·9;
	53 9¾		247·6	17 1½	7 9¼	716	1,212	4·89
Fournier RF-9	17·00;	16	18·00;	7·86;	1·93;	530;	750;	41·67;
	55 9½		193·75	25 9½	6 4	1,168	1,653	8·53
GEPAS Compact	12·80;	17·2	9·50;	6·00;	1·30;	160;	266;	28·0;
	42 0		102·3	19 8¼	4 3¼	352	586	5·73
Issoire (Siren) D 77 Iris	13·50;	16	11·40;	6·37;	1·20;	220;	330;	28·9;
	44 3½		122·7	20 10¾	3 11¼	485	727	5·92
Issoire (Siren) E 78 Silène	18·00;	18	18·00;	7·95;	1·50;	365;	565;	31·3;
	59 0½		193·8	26 1	4 11	805	1,245	6·43
Pottier P.A.15-34 Kit-Club	15·00;	20·6	11·00;	6·25;	1·40;	225;	420;	39·0;
	49 2½		118·4	20 6	4 7	496	926	7·99
SCAP Cirrus 78L	15·00;	22·5	10·00;	6·41;	1·32;	218;	450;	45·0;
	49 2½		107·6	21 0½	4 4¾	480	992	9·22
SCAP-Lanaverre SL-2	18·20;	19·95	16·60;	8·57;	1·00;	370;	620;	37·3;
	59 8½		178·7	28 1½	3 3¼	815	1,366	7·64
GERMANY								
Akaflieg Braunschweig SB-11 Antares	15·00;	21·3	10·56;	7·40;	1·38;	260;	470;	44·5;
(flaps in)	49 2½		113·7	24 3¼	4 6¼	573	1,036	9·11
Akaflieg Braunschweig SB-11 Antares	15·00;	17	13·20;	7·40;	1·38;	260;	470;	35·6;
(flaps out)	49 2½		142·1	24 3¼	4 6¼	573	1,036	7·29
Akaflieg Darmstadt D-39	15·00;	20·5	11·00;	7·15;	*1·02;	320;	430;	39·1;
	49 2½		118·4	23 5½	3 4¼	705	948	8·01
Akaflieg Karlsruhe AK 2	20·00;	27·6	14·50;	7·60;	1·67;	n.k.	580;	40·0;
	65 7½		156·1	24 11¼	5 5¾		1,278	8·19
Akaflieg München Mü 27 (flaps in)	22·00;	27·5	17·60;	10·30;	2·10;	480;	700;	40·0;
	72 2¼		189·4	33 9½	6 10¾	1,058	1,543	8·19
Akaflieg München Mü 27 (flaps out)	22·00;	20·2	23·90;	10·30;	2·10;	480;	700;	29·3;
	72 2¼		257·3	33 9½	6 10¾	1,058	1,543	6·00
Glaser-Dirks DG-200	15·00;	22·5	10·00;	7·00;	1·40;	238;	450;	45·0;
	49 2½		107·6	22 11¾	4 7	525	992	9·22
Glaser-Dirks DG-200A Acroracer	13·10;	18·6	9·25;	7·00;	1·40;	237;	360;	38·9;
	42 11¾		99·6	22 11¾	4 7	522	793	7·97
Glaser-Dirks DG-200/17	17·00;	27·34	10·57;	7·00;	1·40;	246;	450;	42·5;
	55 9¼		113·8	22 11¾	4 7	542	992	8·71
Glasflügel Kestrel	17·00;	25	11·60;	6·72;	1·52;	260;	400;	34·5;
	55 9¼		124·8	22 0½	5 0	574	882	7·07

n.k. = not known

	Performance (at max T-O weight except where indicated)								
Best glide ratio	at (speed): knots; km/h; mph	Min sinking speed: m (ft)/s	at (speed): knots; km/h; mph	Stalling speed: knots; km/h; mph	Max speed (smooth air): knots; km/h; mph	Max speed (rough air): knots; km/h; mph	Max aero-tow speed: knots; km/h; mph	Max winch-launching speed: knots; km/h; mph	Remarks
38	55; 102; 48	0·64; 2·10	48; 89; 42	*45; 83·5; 39·5	117; 217; 102	88; 163; 101	88; 163; 101	75; 139; 86·5	*Flaps up. All performance estimated
24-26	56·5; 105; 65	1·20; 3·94	45; 84; 52	38; 70; 43·5	108; 200; 124	94; 174; 108	*	*	*Not applicable
30·6	46; 85; 53	0·70; 2·30	39; 72; 45	35; 64; 40	139; 257; 160	87; 161; 100	81; 150; 93	n.k.	
39	51; 95; 59	0·60; 1·97	45; 83; 51·5	35; 65; 40·5	140; 260; 161	86; 160; 99	86; 160; 99	*	*Not applicable
28	39; 73; 45	0·64; 2·10	33·5; 62; 38·5	32·5; 60; 37·5	81; 150; 93	81; 150; 93	65; 120; 75	*	*Not applicable
29	40·5; 75; 47	0·68; 2·23	37; 68; 42·5	30; 55; 35	108; 200; 124	81; 150; 93	65; 120; 75	*	*Not applicable
43·9	51; 95; 59	0·57; 1·87	44; 81; 50·5	38; 70; 43·5	162; 300; 186	97; 180; 112	97; 180; 112	59·5; 110; 68·5	
37	60; 111; 69	**0·72; 2·37	45; 83; 52	35; 65; 40·5	140; 260; 161	120; 222; 138	75; 139; 86	*	*Not applicable **Flaps extended
36·2	51; 94; 58·5	0·63; 2·07	39; 72; 45	37; 68; 42·5	140; 260; 161	88; 163; 101	86; 160; 99	65; 120; 75	
32	54; 100; 62	0·70; 2·30	43·5; 80; 50	38; 70; 43·5	141·5; 263; 163	141·5; 263; 163	67·5; 125; 77·5	59; 110; 68	
17	n.k.	1·00; 3·28	n.k.	n.k.	81; 150; 93	65; 120; 75	*	*	*Not applicable
42	63; 117; 73	0·66; 2·17	46·5; 86; 53·5	40; 74; 46	157; 292; 181	129; 240; 149	102; 190; 118	67; 125; 78	
41	63; 117; 73	0·70; 2·30	47·5; 88; 55	40·5; 75; 47	154; 285; 177	119; 220; 136	105; 195; 121	67; 125; 78	
36·9	43·5; 80; 50	0·62; 2·03	39; 72; 45	33·5; 62; 39	119; 220; 136	89; 166; 103	89; 166; 103	n.k.	
38	54; 100; 62	0·60; 1·97	40; 75; 46·5	35; 64; 40	119; 220; 136	89; 166; 103	119; 220; 136	89; 166; 103	
27	46; 85; 53	0·80; 2·62	40·5; 75; 47	*32; 59; 37	119; 220; 136	89; 165; 103	**	**	*Min flying speed: does not stall. **Not applicable
26	46; 85; 53	0·87; 2·85	40; 74; 46	*33·5; 62; 39	119; 220; 136	89; 165; 103	**	**	*Min flying speed: does not stall. **Not applicable
28	n.k.	0·80; 2·62	43·5; 80; 50	n.k.	n.k.	n.k.	n.k.	n.k.	
31	48·5; 90; 56	0·70; 2·30	38; 70; 43·5	32·5; 60; 37·5	113; 210; 130	81; 150; 93	76; 140; 87	65; 120; 75	
33	51; 95; 59	0·70; 2·30	43·5; 80; 50	35·5; 65; 40·5	121; 225; 140	91; 170; 105	91; 170; 105	*	*Details not yet available
38	51; 95; 59	0·67; 2·20	43·5; 80; 50	40·5; 75; 47	119; 220; 136	91; 170; 105	91; 170; 105	*	*Details not yet available
36	41·5; 77; 48	0·63; 2·07	39; 72; 45	34; 62; 39	135; 250; 155	135; 250; 155	135; 250; 155	n.k.	
38·5	48·5; 90; 56	0·60; 1·97	40·5; 75; 47	34; 62; 39	135; 250; 155	135; 250; 155	81; 150; 93	65; 120; 75	
40	55; 102; 63	0·65; 2·13	47; 87; 54	n.k.	119; 220; 136	91; 169; 105	81; 150; 93	n.k.	
41	56; 104; 64·5	0·62; 2·03	43; 80; 50	40·5; 75; 47	143; 265; 165	97; 180; 112	97; 180; 112	64·5; 120; 74·5	
36	46; 85; 53	0·62; 2·03	38; 70; 43·5	31·5; 58; 36	78; 145; 90	81; 150; 93	70·5; 130; 81	64·5; 120; 74·5	
**36	56·5; 105; 65	**0·70; 2·30	45; 84; 52	39; 72; 45	135; 250; 155	135; 250; 155	89; 165; 103	59; 110; 68	*Height over fuselage **With propeller folded
47	54; 100; 62	n.k.	n.k.	35; 64; 40	n.k.	n.k.	n.k.	n.k.	
47	54·5; 101; 63	0·57; 1·87	44; 91; 56·5	47; 87; 54·5	151; 280; 174	151; 280; 174	108; 200; 124	108; 200; 124	
39	47·5; 88; 54·5	0·56; 1·84	37; 69; 43	32·5; 60; 37·5	75·5; 140; 87	75·5; 140; 87	75·5; 140; 87	75·5; 140; 87	
42·5	59·5; 110; 68·5	0·59; 1·94	43; 80; 50	*34; 62; 39	146; 270; 168	146; 270; 168	102; 190; 118	70; 130; 80·5	*At 300 kg (661 lb) AUW; other performance at 420 kg (926 lb)
37	57; 106; 66	0·70; 2·30	46; 85; 53	35; 64; 40	156; 290; 180	n.k.	n.k.	n.k.	
44·6	59·5; 110; 68·5	0·53; 1·74	43; 80; 50	32·5; 60; 37·5	146; 270; 168	146; 270; 168	102; 190; 118	70; 130; 80·5	
43	52·5; 97; 60·5	0·55; 1·80	40; 74; 46	33·5; 62; 39	135; 250; 155	135; 250; 155	n.k.	n.k.	

Manufacturer and Model	Dimensions: Wing span: m; ft in	Wing aspect ratio	Wing area (gross): m²; sq ft	Length overall: m; ft in	Height over tail: m; ft in	Weights and Loading: Empty: kg; lb	Max T-O: kg; lb	Max wing loading: kg/m²; lb/sq ft
Glasflügel Hornet	15·00;	23	9·80;	6·40;	1·40;	227;	420;	42·9;
	49 2½		105·5	21 0	4 7	500	926	8·79
Glasflügel Hornet C	15·00;	23	9·80;	6·40;	1·40;	210;	450;	45·9;
	49 2½		105·5	21 0	4 7	463	992	9·40
Glasflügel Mosquito	15·00;	22·82	9·86;	6·40;	1·40;	235;	450;	46·0;
	49 2½		106·1	21 0	4 7	518	992	9·42
Glasflügel Mosquito B	15·00;	22·82	9·86;	6·40;	1·40;	235;	450;	46·0;
	49 2½		106·1	21 0	4 7	518	992	9·42
Grob Standard Astir	15·00;	18·2	12·40;	6·69;	1·40;	265;	450;	36·3;
	49 2½		133·5	21 11¼	4 7	584	992	7·43
Grob Club Astir	15·00;	18·2	12·40;	6·69;	1·40;	260;	380;	30·6;
	49 2½		133·5	21 11¼	4 7	573	837	6·27
Grob Twin Astir	17·50;	17·1	17·90;	8·10;	1·60;	395;	650;	36·3;
	57 5		192·7	26 8¾	5 3	870	1,433	7·43
Grob Twin Astir Trainer	17·50;	17·1	17·90;	8·10;	1·60;	390;	650;	36·3;
	57 5		192·7	26 8¾	5 3	860	1,433	7·43
Grob Speed Astir II	15·00;	19·6	11·50;	6·60;	1·27;	250;	515;	44·8;
	49 2½		123·8	21 7¾	4 2	551	1,135	9·18
Grob Speed Astir II-17·5	17·50;	24·2	12·60;	6·60;	1·27;	265;	515;	40·9;
	57 5		135·6	21 7¾	4 2	584	1,135	8·38
ISF Mistral-C	15·00;	20·7	10·85;	6·73;	1·45;	230;	350;	32·3;
	49 2½		116·8	22 1	4 9	507	771	6·62
Kortenbach & Rauh Kora 1	18·00;	16·65	19·44;	7·40;	1·85;	510;	750;	38·6;
(2nd prototype)	59 0¾		209·25	24 3¼	6 0¾	1,124	1,653	7·90
Kuffner WK-1	18·80;	17·72	19·95;	8·00;	1·95;	432;	660;	33·1;
	61 8¼		214·7	26 3	6 4¾	952	1,455	6·78
Rolladen-Schneider LS3	15·00;	21·4	10·50;	6·86;	1·20;	270;	470;	45·0;
	49 2½		113·0	22 6	3 11¼	595	1,036	9·22
Rolladen-Schneider LS3-a	15·00;	21·4	10·50;	6·84;	1·20;	240;	472;	45·0;
	49 2½		113·0	22 5¼	3 11¼	529	1,040	9·22
Scheibe Bergfalke-IV	17·20;	17·4	17·00;	8·00;	1·50;	300;	500;	29·4;
	56 5¼		183·0	26 3	4 11	661	1,102	6·02
Scheibe SF-25C and C-S Falke '76	15·25;	13·8	18·20;	7·55;	1·85;	375;	610;	33·5;
	50 0¼		195·9	24 9¼	6 0¾	826	1,345	6·86
Scheibe SF-25E Super-Falke	18·00;	17·8	18·20;	7·50;	1·85;	440;	650;	35·0;
	59 0¾		195·9	24 7¼	6 0¾	970	1,433	7·17
Scheibe SF-28A Tandem-Falke	16·30;	14·5	18·50;	8·10;	1·55;	410;	610;	33·0;
	53 5¾		199·1	26 7	5 1	904	1,345	6·76
Scheibe SF-H34	15·80;	16·9	14·80;	7·50;	n.k.	306;	500;	33·8;
	51 10		159·3	24 7¼		675	1,102	6·92
Schempp-Hirth Nimbus 2C	20·30;	28·62	14·40;	7·33;	1·45;	355;	650;	45·0;
	66 7¼		155·0	24 0½	4 9	782	1,433	9·22
Schempp-Hirth Mini-Nimbus C	15·00;	23	9·86;	6·41;	1·32;	235;	500;	51·0;
	49 2½		106·1	21 0½	4 4	518	1,102	10·45
Schempp-Hirth Janus B	18·20;	19·95	16·60;	8·62;	1·45;	370;	620;	37·0;
	59 8½		178·7	28 3¼	4 9	815	1,366	7·58
Schleicher ASK 13	16·00;	14·6	17·50;	8·18;	1·60;	290;	480;	26·8;
	52 6		188·4	26 9½	5 3	640	1,060	5·49
Schleicher ASW 19 B	15·00;	20·4	11·00;	6·82;	1·45;	240;	454;	41·3;
	49 2½		118·4	22 4½	4 9	529	1,000	8·46
Schleicher ASW 20	15·00;	21·43	10·50;	6·82;	1·45;	250;	454;	43·0;
	49 2½		113·0	22 4½	4 9	551	1,000	8·81
Schleicher ASK 21	17·00;	16·1	17·95;	8·35;	1·55;	350;	570;	30·6;
	55 9¼		193·2	27 4¾	5 1	772	1,256	6·27
Sportavia RF5	13·74;	12·25	15·12;	7·80;	1·96;	420;	650;	42·8;
	45 1		162·8	25 7¼	6 5	926	1,433	8·77
Sportavia RF5B Sperber	17·02;	15·25	19·00;	7·71;	1·96;	475;	680;	35·8;
	55 10		204·5	25 3½	6 5	1,047	1,499	7·33
INDIA								
Civil Aviation Dept HS-II Mrigasheer	15·00;	19·85	11·24;	7·59;	2·50;	237;	335;	29·55;
(2nd prototype)	49 2½		121·0	24 10¾	8 2½	522	738	6·05
Civil Aviation Dept TG-1 Arudhra	16·50;	12·46	21·83;	8·681;	2·464;	274;	454;	20·78;
	54 1½		235·0	28 3	8 1	604	1,000	4·25
ITALY								
Caproni Vizzola Calif A-21S	20·38;	25·65	16·19;	7·737;	1·615;	436;	644;	39·8;
	66 10¼		174·3	25 4½	5 3½	961	1,419	8·15
Maggi MG3-15L Condor	15·00;	20	11·25;	6·80;	1·56;	340;	510;	45·3;
	49 2½		121·1	22 3¾	5 1½	750	1,124	9·28
JAPAN								
Nippi NP-100A Albatross (1st prototype)	18·00;	18	18·00;	8·00;	2·02;	500;	680;	37·8;
	59 0¾		193·75	26 3	6 7½	1,102	1,499	7·74
Nippi Pilatus B4-PC11AF	15·00;	16	14·04;	6·57;	1·57;	230;	350;	25·0;
	49 2½		151·1	21 6¾	5 1¾	506	770	5·13
Tainan Mita III	16·00;	16·13	15·87;	7·96;	1·28;	300;	450;	28·4;
	52 5		170·8	26 1½	4 2½	661	992	5·82
Tainan TN-1	15·50;	15·03	15·98;	7·64;	2·203;	270;	380;	23·78;
	50 10½		172·0	25 0¾	7 2¾	595	837	4·87
POLAND								
SZD-30C Pirat	15·00;	16·3	13·80;	6·92;	1·67;	255;	370;	26·8;
	49 2½		148·5	22 8½	5 5¾	562	816	5·49
SZD-41A Jantar Standard	15·00;	21·1	10·66;	7·11;	1·60;	250;	440;	41·3;
	49 2½		114·7	23 4	5 3	551	970	8·46
SZD-42-1 Jantar 2	20·50;	29·5	14·25;	7·11;	1·76;	330;	593;	41·6;
	67 3		153·4	23 4	5 9¼	727	1,307	8·52

n.k. = not known

Performance (at max T-O weight except where indicated)									
Best glide ratio	at (speed): knots; km/h; mph	Min sinking speed: m (ft)/s	at (speed): knots; km/h; mph	Stalling speed: knots; km/h; mph	Max speed (smooth air): knots; km/h; mph	Max speed (rough air): knots; km/h; mph	Max aero-tow speed: knots; km/h; mph	Max winch-launching speed: knots; km/h; mph	Remarks
38	41; 75; 47	*0·60; 1·97	41; 75; 47	39; 72; 45	135; 250; 155	135; 250; 155	81; 150; 93	65; 120; 74·5	*At 345 kg (760 lb) AUW
38·2	58; 107; 66·5	0·55; 1·80	37; 68; 42·5	34·5; 64; 40	135; 250; 155	135; 250; 155	n.k.	n.k.	
42	61·5; 114; 71	0·67; 2·20	51; 94; 58·5	42·5; 78; 48·5	135; 250; 155	108; 200; 124	81; 150; 93	81; 150; 93	
42	59·5; 110; 68·5	0·67; 2·20	51; 95; 59	42·5; 78; 48·5	135; 250; 155	108; 200; 124	81; 150; 93	81; 150; 93	
37	51; 95; 59	0·60; 1·97	41; 75; 47	32·5; 60; 37·5	135; 250; 155	135; 250; 155	91; 170; 105	65; 120; 74·5	
35	49; 90; 56	0·60; 1·97	41; 75; 47	32·5; 60; 37·5	135; 250; 155	135; 250; 155	91; 170; 105	65; 120; 74·5	
38·5	59·5; 110; 68·5	0·62; 2·03	43; 80; 50	37; 68; 42·5	135; 250; 155	108; 200; 124	91; 170; 105	65; 120; 74·5	
38	56·5; 105; 65	0·64; 2·10	43; 80; 50	37; 68; 42·5	135; 250; 155	108; 200; 124	91; 170; 105	65; 120; 74·5	
41·5	64·5; 120; 74·5	0·57; 1·87	41; 75; 47	34·5; 64; 40	146; 270; 168	108; 200; 124	91; 170; 105	65; 120; 74·5	
45	62; 115; 71·5	0·54; 1·77	39; 72; 45	34; 62; 39	135; 250; 155	108; 200; 124	91; 170; 105	65; 120; 74·5	
37	50; 92; 57	0·66; 2·17	44·5; 82; 51	36·5; 67; 42	135; 250; 155	135; 250; 155	86; 160; 99·5	70; 130; 80·5	
30	51; 95; 59	0·85; 2·79	46; 85; 53	n.k.	n.k.	n.k.	n.k.	n.k.	
35	52·5; 97; 60·5	0·73; 2·40	43; 80; 50	38·5; 71; 44·5	121; 224; 139	88; 163; 101	n.k.	n.k.	
40	54; 100; 62	0·60; 1·97	38; 70; 43·5	35·5; 65; 40·5	146; 270; 168	102·5; 190; 118	102·5; 190; 118	70; 130; 80·5	
41·8	n.k.	0·60; 1·97	38; 70; 43·5	34; 62; 39	146; 270; 168	102·5; 190; 118	102·5; 190; 118	70; 130; 80·5	
34	51·5; 95; 59	0·75; 2·46	46; 85; 53	35·5; 65; 40·5	108; 200; 124	92; 170; 106	76; 140; 87	59·5; 110; 68·5	
23	41; 75; 47	1·00; 3·28	38; 70; 43·5	32·5; 60; 37·5	102·5; 190; 118	102·5; 190; 118	*	*	*Not applicable
28/29	46; 85; 53	0·85; 2·79	41; 75; 47	37; 68; 42·5	102·5; 190; 118	102·5; 190; 118	*	*	*Not applicable
26/27	51·5; 95; 59	0·90; 2·95	38; 70; 43·5	32·5; 60; 37·5	102·5; 190; 118	102·5; 190; 118	*	*	*Not applicable
35	51·5; 95; 59	0·70; 2·30	41; 75; 47	35·5; 65; 40·5	135; 250; 155	n.k.	n.k.	n.k.	
49	56·5; 105; 65	0·53; 1·74	49; 90; 56	38; 70; 43·5	146; 270; 168	146; 270; 168	97; 180; 112	81; 150; 93	Performance at 403 kg (888 lb) AUW
42	56·5; 105; 65	0·70; 2·30	51; 95; 59	43·5; 80; 50	135; 250; 155	135; 250; 155	97; 180; 112	81; 150; 93	
*39·5	*59·5; 110; 68·5	*0·70; 2·30	*48·5; 90; 56	*38; 70; 43·5	118; 220; 136	118; 220; 136	91; 170; 105	64·5; 120; 74·5	*At wing loading of 36·5 kg/m^2 (7·48 lb/sq ft)
28	48·5; 90; 56	0·80; 2·62	38; 70; 43·5	33; 61; 38	108; 200; 124	75·5; 140; 87	75·5; 140; 87	54; 100; 62	Performance at 470 kg (1,036 lb) AUW
38·5	60·5; 112; 70	0·73; 2·40	48·5; 90; 56	36·5; 67; 42	137; 255; 158	137; 255; 158	92; 170; 106	67·5; 125; 78	
42	n.k.	0·59; 1·94	45·5; 84; 52·5	35·5; 65; 40·5	143; 265; 165	97; 180; 112	97; 180; 112	67·5; 125; 78	
34	48·5; 90; 56	0·72; 2·36	39; 72; 45	35·5; 65; 40·5	135; 250; 155	135; 250; 155	94; 175; 109	70; 130; 80·5	
22	n.k.	1·40; 4·59	n.k.	n.k.	n.k.	n.k.	*	*	*Not applicable
26	53; 98; 61	0·95; 3·12	40·5; 75; 46·5	n.k.	n.k.	n.k.	*	*	*Not applicable
32	47; 87; 54	0·58; 1·90	37; 68·5; 42·5	36·5; 68; 42	115; 213; 132	80; 148; 92	62; 115; 71·5	53·5; 99; 61·5	
26	47; 87; 54	0·78; 2·56	39; 72; 45	30; 55; 34	116; 215; 133	68·5; 127; 79	67·5; 125; 77·5	59·5; 110; 68	
43	56·5; 105; 65	0·60; 1·97	46; 85; 53	34; 63; 39·5	136; 252; 156	136; 252; 156	75·5; 140; 87	70; 130; 81	
42	62; 115; 71·5	0·66; 2·16	47; 87; 54	40·5; 74·5; 46·5	137; 254; 158	137; 254; 158	n.k.	n.k.	
30	54; 100; 62	0·90; 2·95	49; 90; 56	35·5; 65; 40·5	n.k.	n.k.	n.k.	n.k.	
35	46; 85; 53	0·64; 2·10	39; 72; 45	33; 61; 38	129; 240; 149	129; 240; 149	88; 163; 101	70·5; 130; 81	
30	44; 82; 51	0·72; 2·36	41; 75; 47	34; 62·5; 39	102; 190; 118	n.k.	70; 130; 81	59·5; 110; 68	
26	42·5; 79; 49	0·79; 2·59	n.k.	31·5; 58; 36·5	102; 190; 118	70; 130; 81	70; 130; 81	59·5; 110; 68	
34	45·5; 84; 52	0·70; 2·30	41; 75; 47	32·5; 60; 37·5	135; 250; 155	78·5; 145; 90	75·5; 140; 87	64·5; 120; 74·5	
40	56·5; 105; 65	0·62; 2·03	42; 78; 48·5	37; 68; 42·5	135; 250; 155	86; 160; 99	81; 150; 93	59·5; 110; 68·5	Performance = without water ballast, at 360 kg (793 lb) AUW
48	55; 102; 63·5	0·55; 1·80	48·5; 90; 56	43·5; 80; 50	135; 250; 155	86; 160; 99	75·5; 140; 87	*	*Not applicable

	Dimensions					Weights and Loading		
Manufacturer and Model	Wing span: m; ft in	Wing aspect ratio	Wing area (gross): m²; sq ft	Length overall: m; ft in	Height over tail: m; ft in	Empty: kg; lb	Max T-O: kg; lb	Max wing loading: kg/m²; lb/sq ft
SZD-42-2 Jantar 2B	20·50; 67 3	29·2	14·25; 153·4	7·11; 23 4	1·56; 5 1½	355; 782	645; 1,422	45·3; 9·28
SZD-45A Ogar	17·53; 57 6¼	16·2	19·10; 205·6	7·95; 26 1	1·72; 5 7¾	473; 1,042	700; 1,543	36·6; 7·50
SZD-48 Jantar Standard 2	15·00; 49 2½	21·1	10·66; 114·7	6·71; 22 0¼	1·26; 4 1½	247; 544	520; 1,146	48·8; 9·99
SZD-50-2 Puchacz	16·67; 54 8¼	15·3	18·16; 195·5	8·38; 27 6	1·92; 6 3½	331; 729	550; 1,212	30·3; 6·20
ROMANIA								
IS-28B2	17·00; 55 9¼	15·8	18·24; 196·3	8·17; 26 9¾	1·80; 5 11	360; 793	590; 1,300	32·34; 6·62
IS-28M1	18·00; 59 0¾	17·1	18·95; 204·0	7·96; 26 1½	1·90; 6 2¾	485; 1,069	730; 1,609	38·52; 7·89
IS-28M2	17·00; 55 9¼	15·8	18·24; 196·3	7·50; 24 7¼	2·15; 7 0¾	495; 1,091	745; 1,642	40·8; 8·36
IS-29D2	15·00; 49 2½	21·6	10·40; 111·9	7·30; 29 2½	1·68; 5 6¼	230; 507	360; 794	34·62; 7·09
IS-29E2	19·00; 62 4	26·5	13·60; 146·4	7·30; 29 2½	1·68; 5 6¼	320; 705	500; 1,102	36·76; 7·53
IS-30	18·00; 59 0¾	17·1	18·92; 203·6	8·36; 27 5¼	1·90; 6 2¾	365; 804	590; 1,300	31·71; 6·49
IS-32	20·00; 65 7½	27·2	14·68; 158·0	8·36; 27 5¼	1·90; 6 2¾	390; 860	590; 1,300	40·6; 8·31
SPAIN								
Cases Libel-lula	10·50; 34 5½	11·7	9·45; 101·7	5·00; 16 4¾	2·26; 7 5	75; 165	160; 352	17; 3·48
SWITZERLAND								
Aviafiber Canard-2 FL	13·50; 44 3½	20	13·00; 139·9	4·94; 16 2½	1·80; 5 11	58; 128	170; 375	12·5; 2·56
Farner HF Colibri 1 SL	17·50; 57 5	31·7	9·65; 103·9	7·20; 23 7½	1·45; 4 9	255; 562	362; 798	32·8; 6·71
Mahrer (Neukom) HB-1340 Delphin (flaps in)	15·00; 49 2½	22·5	10·00; 107·6	7·10; 23 3½	1·50; 4 11	280; 617	n.k.	n.k.
Mahrer (Neukom) HB-1340 Delphin (flaps out)	15·00; 49 2½	19·9	11·30; 121·6	7·10; 23 3½	1·50; 4 11	280; 617	n.k.	n.k.
Neukom S-4A Elfe 15	15·00; 49 2½	19·1	11·80; 127·0	7·10; 23 3½	1·50; 4 11	230; 507	350; 771	29·6; 6·06
Neukom Elfe 17	17·00; 55 9¼	21·8	13·20; 142·1	7·10; 23 3½	1·50; 4 11	255; 562	380; 837	28·8; 5·90
Neukom AN-66C Super-Elfe (flaps in)	23·00; 75 5½	33·1	16·00; 172·2	8·10; 26 6¾	1·85; 6 0¾	420; 926	650; 1,433	40·6; 8·31
Neukom AN-66C Super-Elfe (flaps out)	23·00; 75 5½	27·6	19·20; 206·7	8·10; 26 6¾	1·85; 6 0¾	420; 926	650; 1,433	33·8; 6·92
USSR								
Oshkinis BRO-11 Zile	7·28; 23 10½	5·05	10·50; 113·0	5·17; 16 11½	n.k.	58; 128	118; 260	11·24; 2·30
LAK-9 Lietuva	20·02; 65 8¼	26·8	14·99; 161·35	7·27; 23 10¼	1·53; 5 0¼	382; 842	670; 1,477	44·7; 9·15
UK								
Swales SD3-15T	15·00; 49 2½	23·7	9·48; 102·0	6·10; 20 0	1·30; 4 3	218; 480	331; 730	34·96; 7·16
Vickers-Slingsby Vega	15·00; 49 2½	22·4	10·05; 108·2	6·72; 22 0½	1·50; 4 11	233; 515	440; 970	43·8; 8·97
Vickers-Slingsby Venture T.Mk 2	15·25; 50 0¼	13·8	18·20; 195·9	7·55; 24 9¼	1·85; 6 0¾	376·5; 830	612; 1,350	33·6; 6·88

n.k. = not known

Performance (at max T-O weight except where indicated)									
Best glide ratio	at (speed): knots; km/h; mph	Min sinking speed: m (ft)/s	at (speed): knots; km/h; mph	Stalling speed: knots; km/h; mph	Max speed (smooth air): knots; km/h; mph	Max speed (rough air): knots; km/h; mph	Max aero-tow speed: knots; km/h; mph	Max winch-launching speed: knots; km/h; mph	Remarks
48	56·5; 105; 65	0·56; 1·84	47; 87; 54	44·5; 82; 51	151; 280; 174	108; 200; 124	75·5; 140; 87	62; 115; 71·5	
22·6	51; 95; 59	1·10; 3·61	43·5; 80; 50	42·5; 78; 48·5	121; 225; 140	121; 225; 140	*	*	*Not applicable
39·5	70; 130; 81	0·77; 2·53	50; 92; 57	46; 85; 53	135; 250; 155	135; 250; 155	81; 150; 93	67·5; 125; 78	
30	52; 96; 60	0·70; 2·30	42; 78; 48·5	32·5; 60; 37·5	118; 220; 136	81; 150; 93	81; 150; 93	64·5; 120; 74·5	
34	54; 100; 62	0·67; 2·20	43·5; 80; 50	39; 72; 45	124; 230; 143	89; 136; 84·5	n.k.	n.k.	Performance at 540 kg (1,190 lb) AUW
32	54; 100; 62	0·81; 2·66	42; 78; 48·5	*35; 64; 40	113; 210; 130	n.k.	n.k.	n.k.	*Flaps down
29	54; 100; 62	0·87; 2·85	43·5; 80; 50	*36; 66; 41	113; 210; 130	n.k.	n.k.	n.k.	*Flaps down
37	50; 93; 58	0·58; 1·90	42; 78; 48·5	38; 70; 43·5	135; 250; 155	n.k.	n.k.	n.k.	
46	60·5; 112; 70	0·58; 1·90	47; 87; 54·5	40·5; 75; 47	121; 225; 140	n.k.	n.k.	n.k.	
36·5	54; 100; 62	0·62; 2·03	44; 82; 51	38; 70; 43·5	124; 230; 143	n.k.	n.k.	n.k.	
46	58; 107; 66·5	0·53; 1·74	47; 87; 54	40; 74; 46	124; 230; 143	n.k.	n.k.	n.k.	
19	n.k.	1·00; 3·28	n.k.	27; 50; 31·5	65; 120; 75	54; 100; 62	59; 110; 68·5	n.k.	
31	32; 60; 37·5	0·50; 1·64	27; 50; 31	21; 38; 24	54; 100; 62	54; 100; 62	*	*	*Not applicable
41-43	54·5; 101; 63	0·55; 1·80	42; 77; 48	37·6; 69·6; 43·3	119; 220; 137	97; 180; 112	*	*	*Not applicable
n.k.	n.k.	n.k.	n.k.	n.k.	n.k.	n.k.	n.k.	n.k.	
n.k.	n.k.	n.k.	n.k.	34; 63; 39·5	n.k.	n.k.	n.k.	n.k.	
37·5	48·5; 90; 56	0·60; 1·97	38; 70; 43·5	35·5; 65; 40·5	113; 210; 130	113; 210; 130	75·5; 140; 87	54; 100; 62	
40·5	48·5; 90; 56	0·56; 1·84	40·5; 75; 46·5	35·5; 65; 40·5	113; 210; 130	113; 210; 130	75·5; 140; 87	54; 100; 62	
48	48·5; 90; 56	0·55; 1·80	38; 70; 43·5	33·5; 62; 39	145·5; 270; 168	n.k.	n.k.	n.k.	
n.k.	n.k.	0·50; 1·64	40·5; 75; 46·5	32·5; 60; 37·5	135; 250; 155	135; 250; 155	n.k.	n.k.	
n.k.	n.k.	1·00; 3·28	n.k.	21·5; 30; 19	n.k.	n.k.	n.k.	n.k.	
48	55·5; 103; 64	0·51 1·67	40; 74; 46	35; 64; 40	n.k.	113; 210; 130	75·5; 140; 87	n.k.	
36	48; 88·5; 55	0·73; 2·40	42; 78; 48·5	34; 63·5; 39·5	109; 201; 125	86; 159; 99	78; 145; 90	65; 121; 75	
42	60; 111; 69	0·67; 2·21	44; 82; 51 (EAS)	41; 76·5; 47·5	135; 250; 155	105; 195; 121	80; 148; 92	70; 129; 80	
20·5	50·5; 93·5; 58	1·00; 3·30	43·5; 80·5; 50	37·5; 69·5; 43	100; 185; 115	80; 148; 92	*	*	*Not applicable

Manufacturer and Model	Dimensions: Wing span: m; ft in	Wing aspect ratio	Wing area (gross): m²; sq ft	Length overall: m; ft in	Height over tail: m; ft in	Weights and Loading: Empty: kg; lb	Max T-O: kg; lb	Max wing loading: kg/m²; lb/sq ft
USA								
Aero Tek Model V Zuni	15·00; 49 2½	22·2	10·13; 109·0	6·71; 22 0	1·30; 4 3	222; 490	431; 950	42·5; 8·71
AmEagle American Eaglet	10·97; 36 0	18	6·69; 72·0	4·88; 16 0	0·91; 3 0	72·5; 160	163; 360	24·41; 5·00
Bryan (Schreder) RS-15	15·00; 49 2½	21·4	10·50; 113·0	6·71; 22 0	1·17; 3 10	204; 450	431; 950	41·04; 8·41
Bryan (Schreder) HP-18	15·00; 49 2½	21·4	10·50; 113·0	7·06; 23 2	1·22; 4 0	213; 470	440; 970	41·87; 8·58
Bryan (Schreder) HP-19	15·00; 49 2½	21·4	10·50; 113·0	7·06; 23 2	1·22; 4 0	181; 400	453; 1,000	43·18; 8·85
DSK BJ-1b Duster	13·00; 42 7¾	17·4	9·72; 104·65	n.k.	n.k.	177; 390	281; 620	28·9; 5·92
Explorer PG-1 Aqua Glider	4·88; 16 0	5	8·73; 94·0	4·17; 13 8	1·52; 5 0	81; 180	181; 400	20·5; 4·20
Flight Dynamics Seasprite	10·36; 34 0	6·96	15·42; 166·0	6·10; 20 0	2·44; 8 0	75; 165	227; 500	14·68; 3·01
Marske Monarch C	12·80; 42 0	9·5	17·19; 185·0	3·51; 11 6	2·39; 7 10	100; 220	204; 450	11·72; 2·40
Monnett Monerai S	10·97; 36 0	16·6	7·25; 78·0	5·97; 19 7	1·32; 4 4	100; 220	204; 450	28·11; 5·76
Ryson ST-100 Cloudster	17·58; 57 8	15·61	19·79; 213·0	7·78; 25 6·4	1·78; 5 10	550; 1,212	748; 1,650	37·82; 7·75
Schweizer SGS 1-26	12·19; 40 0	10	14·87; 160·0	6·57; 21 6½	2·21; 7 2½	195; 430	317; 700	21·34; 4·37
Schweizer SGS 2-32	17·40; 57 1	18·05	16·70; 180·0	8·15; 26 9	2·10; 6 10½	385; 850	649; 1,430	38·77; 7·94
Schweizer SGS 2-33A	15·54; 51 0	11·85	20·39; 219·48	7·85; 25 9	2·83; 9 3½	272; 600	472; 1,040	23·14; 4·74
Schweizer SGS 1-34B	15·00; 49 2½	16·04	14·03; 151·0	7·85; 25 9	2·29; 7 6	249; 550	362; 800	25·9; 5·30
Schweizer SGS 1-35	15·00; 49 2½	23·29	9·64; 103·8	5·84; 19 2	1·35; 4 5	199; 440	422; 930	43·75; 8·96
Volpar-Spencer Drag-N-Fly	5·79; 19 0	5·57	11·24; 121·0	4·85; 15 11	1·75; 5 9	113; 250	204; 450	18·15; 3·72
YUGOSLAVIA								
Elan (Glaser-Dirks) DG-100/DG-100G Elan	15·00; 49 2½	20·5	11·00; 118·4	7·00; 22 11¾	1·40; 4 7	*230; 507	418; 921	38·0; 7·78
Elan (Glaser-Dirks) DG-100 Club Elan	15·00; 49 2½	20·5	11·00; 118·4	7·00; 22 11¾	1·40; 4 7	*225; 496	385; 848	35·0; 7·17
MF VUK-T	15·00; 49 2½	18·82	12·00; 129·2	6·50; 21 4	1·30; 4 3¼	245; 540	355; 783	29·7; 6·08
VTC (Schempp-Hirth) Cirrus	17·74; 58 2½	24·98	12·60; 135·6	7·20; 23 7¼	1·56; 5 1½	260; 573	400; 882	31·7; 6·49
VTC (Schempp-Hirth) Standard Cirrus 75	15·00; 49 2½	22·5	10·00; 107·6	6·41; 21 8½	1·32; 4 4¾	215; 474	330; 727	33·0; 6·76

n.k. = not known

Performance (at max T-O weight except where indicated)									
Best glide ratio	at (speed): knots; km/h; mph	Min sinking speed: m (ft)/s	at (speed): knots; km/h; mph	Stalling speed: knots; km/h; mph	Max speed (smooth air): knots; km/h; mph	Max speed (rough air): knots; km/h; mph	Max aero-tow speed: knots; km/h; mph	Max winch-launching speed: knots; km/h; mph	Remarks
n.k.	n.k.	0·51; 1·67	45; 84; 52	36·5; 68; 42	156; 290; 180	n.k.	n.k.	n.k.	
27	45; 84; 52	0·76; 2·50	35; 64·5; 40	33; 61·5; 38	100; 185; 115	69·5; 129; 80	69·5; 129; 80	*	*Not applicable
38	59; 109; 68	*0·64; 2·10	43·5; 80; 50	**40; 74; 46	130; 241; 150	104; 193; 120	104; 193; 120	78; 145; 90	*At 284 kg (626 lb) AUW; **at 335 kg (740 lb) AUW
40	59; 109; 68	*0·52; 1·70	39; 73; 45	**35; 64·5; 40	130; 241; 150	104; 193; 120	104; 193; 120	78; 145; 90	*At 275 kg (606 lb) AUW; **at 326 kg (720 lb) AUW
42	n.k.	*0·46 1.50	35; 64·5 40	*30·5; 56·5; 35	130; 241; 150	104; 193; 120	104; 193; 120	78; 145; 90	*At 266 kg (586 lb) AUW
n.k.	n.k.	n.k.	n.k.	n.k.	n.k.	n.k.	n.k.	n.k.	
6·5	39; 72·5; 45	**	**	*30·5; 56·5; 35	56·5; 104·5; 65	75; 105; 65	75; 105; 65	75; 105; 65	*At 149 kg (330 lb) AUW **Not applicable
6	35; 64; 40	1·77; 5·80	35; 64; 40	30; 56; 35	60; 111; 69	50; 93; 58	35; 64; 40	*	*Not applicable
19	35; 64; 40	0·82; 2·70	26; 48·5; 30	21; 39; 24	61; 113; 70	43·5; 80; 50	43·5; 80; 50	43·5; 80; 50	
28	52; 97; 60	0·85; 2·80	48; 88·5; 55	33; 61·5; 38	104; 193; 120	78; 145; 90	n.k.	n.k.	
28	52; 97; 60	0·90; 2·95	47; 87; 54	36·5; 68; 42	139; 258; 160	139; 258; 160	*	*	*Not applicable
23	46; 85; 53	0·79; 2·60	35; 64·5; 40	29; 54; 33	99; 183; 114	99; 183; 114	99; 183; 114	55; 101; 63	
34	51; 95; 59	0·72; 2·38	43·5; 80; 50	44; 81; 50	122; 225; 140	130; 241; 150	96; 177; 110	75; 138; 86	Performance = Utility Category at 544 kg (1,200 lb) AUW
22·25	45; 84; 52	0·91; 3·00	33; 61; 38	30·5; 57; 35	85; 158; 98	85; 158; 98	85; 158; 98	60; 111; 69	
34	45; 84; 52	0·64; 2·10	40; 74; 46	42·5; 61·5; 38	117; 217; 135	121; 223; 139	100; 185; 115	57·5; 106; 66	
39	46; 85; 53	0·61; 2·00	43; 79; 49	28; 51·5; 32	121; 223; 139	121; 223; 139	121; 223; 139	*	*Not applicable
n.k.	n.k.	n.k.	n.k.	n.k.	65; 120; 75	n.k.	n.k.	*35; 65; 40	*Required speed for T-O
39	56·5; 105; 65	0·59; 1·94	40; 74; 46	32·5; 60; 37·5	140; 260; 161	140; 260; 161	89; 165; 102·5	70; 130; 80·5	*With normal tailplane; 235 kg (518 lb) with all-moving tailplane
36	49; 90; 56	0·60; 1·97	40; 74; 46	32·5; 60; 37·5	n.k.	n.k.	n.k.	n.k.	*With normal tailplane; 230 kg (507 lb) with all-moving tailplane
37·5	51; 95; 59	0·65; 2·13	42; 78; 48·5	32; 59; 37	129; 240; 149	81; 150; 93	67·5; 125; 78	59; 110; 68	
44	46; 85; 53	0·50; 1·64	39; 73; 45	33·5; 62; 39	119; 220; 137	119; 220; 137	76; 140; 87	59; 110; 68	
38·5	48·5; 90; 56	0·60; 1·97	39·5; 75; 47	33·5; 62; 39	119; 220; 137	119; 220; 137	81; 150; 93	65; 120; 75	

DATA: MOTOR GLIDERS (POWER ON)

Manufacturer and Model	Dimensions Wing span: m; ft in	Wing aspect ratio	Wing area (gross): m²; sq ft	Length overall: m; ft in	Height over tail: m; ft in	Weights and Loading Empty: kg; lb	Max T-O: kg; lb	Max power loading: kg/kW; lb/hp
AUSTRIA								
Brditschka HB-21	16·24; 53 3½	13·89	18·98; 204·3	8·10; 26 7	2·60; 8 6¼	505; 1,113	710; 1,565	15·80; 26·00
BRAZIL								
IPE 03	16·00; 52 6	n.k.	n.k.	7·00; 22 11½	1·50; 4 11	n.k.	n.k.	n.k.
FINLAND								
Alanne Motorlerche	13·00; 42 7¾	10·3	16·34; 175·9	6·86; 22 6	n.k.	288; 635	400; 882	12·07; 19·84
PIK-20E	15·00; 49 2½	22·5	10·00; 107·6	6·53; 21 5	1·44; 4 8¾	300; 661	470; 1,036	14·62; 24·03
FRANCE								
Fournier RF-9	17·00; 55 9½	16	18·00; 193·75	7·86; 25 9½	1·93; 6 4	530; 1,168	750; 1,653	14·79; 24·31
GERMANY								
Akaflieg Darmstadt D-39	15·00; 49 2½	20·5	11·00; 118·4	7·15; 23 5½	†1·02; 3 4¼	320; 705	430; 948	5·76; 9·48
Akaflieg Karlsruhe AK 2	20·00; 65 7½	27·6	14·50; 156·1	7·60; 24 11¼	1·67; 5 5¾	n.k.	580; 1,278	14·14; 23·23
Kortenbach & Rauh Kora 1 (second prototype)	18·00; 59 0¾	16·65	19·44; 209·25	7·40; 24 3¼	1·85; 6 0¾	510; 1,124	750; 1,653	15·00; 24·67
Kuffner WK-1	18·80; 61 8¼	17·72	19·95; 214·7	8·00; 26 3	1·95; 6 4¾	432; 952	660; 1,455	13·21; 21·71
Pflumm and Richter Faltente	8·80; 28 10½	5·43	14·26; 153·5	4·05; 13 3½	n.k.	49·5; 109	134·5; 296·5	18·03; 29·65
Scheibe SF-25C and C-S Falke '76	15·25; 50 0¼	13·8	18·20; 195·9	7·55; 24 9¼	1·85; 6 0¾	375; 826	610; 1,345	12·58; 20·68
Scheibe SF-25E Super-Falke	18·00; 59 0¾	17·8	18·20; 195·9	7·50; 24 7¼	1·85; 6 0¾	440; 970	650; 1,433	13·41; 22·04
Scheibe SF-28A Tandem-Falke	16·30; 53 5¾	14·5	18·50; 199·1	8·10; 26 7	1·55; 5 1	410; 904	610; 1,345	12·58; 20·68
Sportavia RF5	13·74; 45 1	12·25	15·12; 162·8	7·80; 25 7¼	1·96; 6 5	420; 926	650; 1,433	13·0; 21·4
Sportavia RF5B Sperber	17·02; 55 10	15·25	19·00; 204·5	7·71; 25 3½	1·96; 6 5	475; 1,047	680; 1,499	13·6; 22·3
ITALY								
Caproni Vizzola Calif A-21SJ	20·38; 66 10¼	25·65	16·19; 174·3	7·737; 25 4½	1·615; 5 3½	528; 1,164	808; 1,781	915 kg/kN; 8·97 lb/lb st
JAPAN								
Nippi NP-100A Albatross (first prototype)	18·00; 59 0¾	18	18·00; 193·75	8·00; 26 3	2·02; 6 7½	500; 1,102	680; 1,499	13·4; 22·0
POLAND								
SZD-45A Ogar	17·53; 57 6¼	16·2	19·10; 205·6	7·95; 26 1	1·72; 5 7¾	473; 1,042	700; 1,543	13·8; 22·7
ROMANIA								
IS-28M1	18·00; 59 0¾	17·1	18·95; 204·0	7·96; 26 1½	1·90; 6 2¾	485; 1,069	730; 1,609	14·4; 23·6
IS-28M2	17·00; 55 9¼	15·8	18·24; 196·3	7·50; 24 7¼	2·15; 7 0¾	495; 1,091	745; 1,642	14·7; 24·1
SWITZERLAND								
Farner HF Colibri 1 SL	17·50; 57 5	31·7	9·65; 103·9	7·20; 23 7½	1·45; 4 9	255; 562	362; 798	17·8; 29·3
Neukom Elfe M 17	17·00; 55 9¼	21·8	13·20; 142·1	7·10; 23 3½	1·50; 4 11	350; 771	480; 1,058	14·3; 23·5
UK								
Vickers-Slingsby Venture T.Mk 2	15·25; 50 0¼	13·8	18·20; 195·9	7·55; 24 9¼	1·85; 6 0¾	376·5; 830	612; 1,350	18·3; 30·0
USA								
AmEagle American Eaglet	10·97; 36 0	18	6·69; 72·0	4·88; 16 0	0·91; 3 0	72·5; 160	163; 360	17·9; 29·5
Ryson ST-100 Cloudster	17·58; 57 8	15·61	19·79 213·0	7·78; 25 6·4	1·78; 5 10	550; 1,212	748; 1,650	10·0; 16·5
YUGOSLAVIA								
Jastreb SOLE-77	16·40; 53 9¾	n.k.	n.k.	7·67; 25 2	n.k.	500; 1,102	n.k.	n.k.

n.k. = not known

Performance at max T-O weight (powered)								
Max cruising speed: knots; km/h; mph	Econ cruising speed: knots; km/h; mph	Stalling speed: knots; km/h; mph	Max rate of climb at S/L: m; ft/min	Service ceiling: m; ft	T-O run: m; ft	Landing run: m; ft	Range with max fuel: nm; km; miles	Remarks
86; 160; 99	70·5; 130; 81	39·5; 75; 47	198; 650	6,300; 20,675	100; 330	80; 262	431; 800; 497	
n.k.	n.k.	n.k.	n.k.	n.k.	n.k.	n.k.	n.k.	
65; 120; 75	54; 100; 62	n.k.	150; 492	n.k.	n.k.	n.k.	162; 300; 186	
73; 135; 84	73; 135; 84	40·5; 75; 47	162; 531	5,200; 17,050	*500; 1,640	300; 985	156; 290; 180	*To 15 m (50 ft)
86; 160; 112	n.k.	35·5; 65; 40·5	180; 590	6,000; 19,685	n.k.	n.k.	n.k.	
*97; 180; 112	n.k.	39; 72; 45	270; 885	n.k.	n.k.	n.k.	269; 500; 310	†Height over fuselage *Max level speed
n.k.	n.k.	n.k.	n.k.	n.k.	n.k.	n.k.	n.k.	
*102; 190; 118	76; 140; 87	38; 70; 43·5	120; 394	n.k.	n.k.	n.k.	n.k.	*Max level speed
88; 163; 101	56; 104; 65	n.k.	228; 748	6,500; 21,325	*292; 958	129; 423	227; 420; 261	*To 15 m (50 ft)
*30; 55; 34	24; 45; 28	n.k.	30; 98	n.k.	n.k.	n.k.	n.k.	Wing loading 9·5 kg/m^2 (1·95 lb/sq ft) *Max level speed
86; 160; 99	70·5; 130; 81	35·5; 65; 40·5	138; 453	5,000; 16,400	180; 590	100; 328	404; 750; 466	
*97; 180; 112	81; 150; 93	37; 68; 42·5	150; 492	5,000; 16,400	150-200; 490-655	100; 328	323; 600; 372	*Max level speed
*97; 180 112	81; 150; 93	33·5; 62; 39	132; 435	5,000; 16,400	150-200; 490-655	150; 492	280; 520; 323	*Max level speed
97; 180; 112	65; 120; 75	41; 75; 47	180; 590	5,000; 16,400	200; 655	180; 590	410; 760; 472	
97; 180; 112	65; 120; 75	37; 68; 42·5	180; 590	5,000; 16,400	187; 615	204; 669	232; 430; 267	Performance with fully-feathering propeller
*124; 230; 143	102·5; 190; 118	34; 63; 39·5	240; 787	11,000; 36,100	300; 985	n.k.	189; 350; 217	Max wing loading 49·9 kg/m^2 (10·22 lb/sq ft) *Max level speed
65; 120; 74	48·5; 90; 56	35·5; 65; 40·5	120; 394	n.k.	365; 1,200	*400; 1,312	108; 200; 124	*From 15 m (50 ft)
*97·5; 180; 112	75·5; 140; 87	37; 68; 42·5	159; 522	3,100; 10,175	200; 656	155; 508	296; 550; 341	*Max level speed
95; 176; 109	86; 159; 99	38; 70; 44	192; 630	5,500; 18,050	180; 590	90; 295	242; 450; 280	
92; 170; 106	81; 150; 93	35·5; 65; 40·5	186; 610	5,000; 16,400	240; 788	90; 295	242; 450; 280	
65; 120; 75	51; 95; 59	37; 68; 42·5	240; 787	n.k.	120; 394	n.k.	n.k.	
89;165; 102·5	81; 150; 93	43·5; 80; 50	120; 394	n.k.	200; 656	n.k.	243; 450; 280	Max wing loading 36·3 kg/m^2 (7·44 lb/sq ft)
76; 140; 87	65; 121; 75	37·5; 69·5; 43	125; 410	n.k.	198; 650	100; 328	217; 402; 250	
n.k.	n.k.	n.k.	137; 450	n.k.	305; 1,000	90; 300	n.k.	Classified as self-launching sailplane. Max wing loading 24·4 kg/m^2 (5·00 lb/sq ft)
130; 241; 150	*69; 129; 80	37·5; 69·5; 43	256; 840	7,315; 24,000	290; 950	244; 800	595; 1,104; 686	*At 26% power
92; 170; 106	n.k.	39; 72; 45	186; 610	4,500; 14,760	*350; 1,148	n.k.	378; 700; 435	*To 15 m (50 ft)

HANG GLIDERS

CIVL
COMMISSION INTERNATIONALE DE VOL LIBRE

c/o Fédération Aéronautique Internationale, 6 rue Galilée, 75782 Paris, Cédex 16, France

President: Erwin Kjellerup (Sweden)

Honorary Presidents:
Daniel F. Poynter (USA)
Mrs Ann Welch (UK)

Vice-Presidents:
Tom Hudson (Ireland)
Harry W. Robb (USA)
Donald Wood (South Africa)

Secretary: Tom Hudson

International Representatives:

Australia: Roger Pullem, GPO Box 1706, Adelaide, South Australia 5001
Austria: Sepp Himberger, A-6345 Kössen
Belgium: Philippe Peetrons, Aéro-Club Royal de Belgique, 1 rue Montoyer, 1040 Brussels
Canada: Willi Müller, Hang Gliding Association of Canada, PO Box 4063, PSC, Calgary, Alberta
Denmark: Juan Garcia, Kalkbränderihavnsgade 22, 2100 Copenhagen O
France: René Coulon, 3 rue Ampère, 94200 Ivry-sur-Seine
Germany (Federal Republic): Eberhard Jehle, Bahnhofstrasse 65, D-8959 Seeg/Allgau
Ireland: Tom Hudson, 60 Hillcourt Road, Glenageary, Co Dublin
Italy: Heinz Kostner, 39033 Coruara
Japan: Asahi Miyahara, 2-27, Uehara Shibuya-ku, Tokyo 151
Korea: Kim Suk Whan (address not known)
Luxembourg: Jean Willems, 15 rue de la Sûre, Echternach
Mexico: A. Cruz y Celis Hernández (address not known)
Netherlands: Floor C. G. Gremmen, G. Doustraat 7, Assen
Norway: Stein Arne Fossum, Brendöyveien 21, 6900 Florö
Poland: Dr Jerzy Wolf, Instytut Lotnictwa, Al. Krakowska 110/114, 02-256 Warsaw
South Africa: Donald Wood, 19 Ena Street, Florida 1710
Spain: Roman Camps, Beethoven 12, Barcelona 6
Sweden: Erwin Kjellerup, Rullharvsgatan 1B, 431 40 Mölndal
UK: R. Spooner, Clifton House, Bath Road, Cowes, Isle of Wight
USA: Harry W. Robb, 2909 Gulf to Bay Q203, Clearwater, Florida 33515

The CIVL held its first meeting in June 1975. One of its first actions was to define a hang glider as "a heavier-than-air, fixed-wing (not rotating) glider, capable of being carried, foot-launched and landed solely by the energy and use of the pilot's legs". It has since defined three Competition classes of hang glider. Other tasks of the commission include safety and pilot ratings.

The listing which follows, while not complete, includes data for all hang gliders of which details had been received at the time this edition closed for press; however, many manufacturers have failed to supply information for the present edition.

ARGENTINA

JOHAN F. BYTTEBIER

San Martin 359, Las Heras, Mendoza

Sr Byttebier's 1978 models were the Johan S3 (for training), Johan S3B (max T-O weight 95 kg; 209 lb) and Johan 087 (max T-O weight 140 kg; 308 lb). They were produced in both free-flight and tow versions, the latter being designed specially for slow towing, even in zero-wind conditions. The airframe is of aluminium alloy tube, cables of stainless steel, and sail of Dacron. For details of **Johan 087**, see Table.

AUSTRALIA

FARRELLY HANG GLIDERS

Surfblanks Pty Ltd, c/o Post Office, Palm Beach, NSW 2108

For 1978 details see Table; no 1979 details received.

FREE FLIGHT HANG GLIDERS

8/3 First Avenue, Ascot Park, South Australia 5043

For 1978 details see Table; no 1979 details received.

HANG GLIDERS PTY LTD

16 Mills Road, Glenhaven, NSW 2154

Distributor in 1978 for **Wings Ranger, Javelin and Lynx**. Ranger airframe (leading-edges, spreader tubes and keel) is of aluminium alloy, with kingpost and stainless steel cables; it is stressed to $+6g$ and $-5g$. Javelin is of similar construction, and has pre-formed battens and deflexers. Lynx is also of similar construction to Ranger, but has a double-surface aerofoil with pre-formed battens and double deflexers; it is fully stressed for cross-country flight and thermalling. Lynx C is an advanced cross-country glider and incorporates latest refinements for safety, stability and performance. For other details see Table.

MOYES DELTA GLIDERS PTY LTD

173 Bronte Road, Waverley, Sydney, NSW 2024

Manufacturer of the Stinger range, of which seven basic models were available in 1979, as follows:

Maxi Stinger Mark III. Class 2 competition model, for expert pilots only; 1979 version has keel pocket battens and cambered sail; 700 sold by early 1979.

Moyes Maxi Stinger

Maxi Stinger SP. Similar to Maxi Mark III, but scaled down 5% for lighter-weight pilots; 45 sold by early 1979.

Mega Stinger. Competition model for advanced pilots. Features include feathered radial tip, pre-formed keel pocket battens, and deep fin floating keel pocket; 40 sold by early 1979.

Micro Stinger. Smallest, fastest and newest model, for intermediate or expert pilots. Features include feathered radial tip, pre-formed keel pocket battens, and deep fin keel with adjustable twist control and tip washout limiting tubes; 10 sold by early 1979.

Mini Stinger. New model, based on a scaling-down of Maxi; suitable for learner pilots and experts. Features include radial tip, pre-formed keel pocket battens and deep keel fin; 120 sold by early 1979.

Stinger. Basic Class 1 model, with single-batten roached tip and moderate speed range; easy to fly and suitable for learner pilots and experts; unchanged for 1979. Total of 300 sold by early 1979.

Stingray. Low-speed model, suitable for small ridge and sand-dune soaring, and for learner pilots. Produced in three sizes, the largest being also suitable for Class 1 competition flying. Total of 100 sold by early 1979.

For other details see Table.

ULTRALIGHT FLIGHT SYSTEMS

15 Grand Parade, Brighton le Sands, NSW 2216

For details see Table.

WINGS

PO Box 71, Pascoe Vale South, Victoria 3044

For 1978 details see Table and Hang Gliders Pty Ltd entry in this section; no 1979 details received.

CANADA

BIRDMAN ENTERPRISES LTD

8027 Argyll Road, Edmonton, Alberta T6C 4A9

Producer of the **Falcon I and II, MJ-5, MJ-6 and XC** hang gliders (see Table for details). All airframes are of aluminium alloy, with vinyl-coated stainless steel cables, single-thickness Dacron sail, and a kingpost as standard. All are stressed to a g limit of $+6{\cdot}5$. Both Falcon models are suitable for training; MJ-5, MJ-6 and XC are suitable for competition flying. Falcons have floating keel pocket, single deflexers and ribs, but no fin; and can be tow-launched. The two MJ models have a stabilising fin, floating keel pocket and ribs, but no deflexers; MJ-5 can be tow-launched. The XC has a fin, floating keel pocket, triple deflexers and ribs.

Birdman MJ-5 with engine

Birdman MJ-6

Birdman also markets power plant packs suitable for most high-performance hang gliders.

HIGH PERSPECTIVE INC

RR No. 2, Claremont, Ontario L0H 1E0

By early 1979, High Perspective had sold 50 examples of its **HP IV** Class 2 glider. Suitable for training or private flying, this has an aluminium alloy airframe with vinyl-coated stainless steel cables and a single-thickness Dacron sail. A kingpost is standard; other features include a floating keel pocket, pre-formed battens and double deflexers; and the glider can be tow-launched. Details in the Table are for the medium-sized model: smaller and larger models are available, for pilot weights of 32-54·5 kg (70-120 lb) and 72·5-100 kg (160-220 lb) respectively.

High Perspective's main activities in 1979 were training, and the manufacture of safety landing wheels, floats, tow frames and winches.

High Perspective HP IV

MÜLLER KITES LTD

c/o Hang Gliding Association of Canada, PO Box 4063, PSC, Calgary, Alberta

No details of this company's products were received in either 1978 or 1979. Details of its last known gliders can be found in the 1978-79 *Jane's*.

FRANCE

DAHU PLANE (ÉTABLISSEMENTS NOIN AÉRONAUTIQUE)

Le Logis-Neuf, RN85 Châteauvieux, 05130-Tallard

Models in production in 1979 were as follows:

Baby 18. For learner pilots. Airframe of duralumin, with anodised stainless steel cables and Dacron sail.

Nimbus. High-performance competition glider, for expert pilots; stressed to $+5/-2g$. Airframe materials as for Baby. Kingpost standard; other features include rudder, floating keel pocket, pre-formed battens, triple deflexers, and double-thickness sail over 85% of area.

Stratus IV. Class 1 glider, flown in several 1978 competitions in France. Airframe materials similar to Nimbus.

Dahu Plane Nimbus

Double-thickness sail forward of kingposts; shallow stabilising fin.

For other details see Table.

BERNARD DANIS

Manufacture d'Ailes Volantes B. Danis, 71 rue Roger-François, 94700 Maisons-Alfort

The popular **SK-1, 2 and 3** continued in production in 1978, and the more recent **X 9** was also available. All have an aluminium alloy frame, with stainless steel cables on the SK series, and a sail of Dacron or Torray. For SK and X 9 details see Table. No details for 1979 received.

FAVUL

20 rue du Tire-Pesseau, 21000 Dijon; or 55 bis avenue Jean-Jaurès, 21000 Dijon

Manufacturer in 1978 of the **Odyssée, Star** (two models) and **Viking**: aluminium alloy frames, stainless steel cables and Dacron sail. For other details see Table. No details for 1979 received.

LA MOUETTE

79 avenue du Drapeau, 21000 Dijon

Manufacturer of the **Atlas 14 and 16** (25 and 90 sold respectively by early 1979); **Lotus 15 and 17** (sales 5 and 5); and **Mouette 15, 17, 19 and 23B** (sales 25, 240, 780 and 90). Of these, the two Atlas models are suitable for competition flying; the Lotus 15 and all four Mouettes are suitable for training. All have duralumin frames (with kingpost as standard), vinyl-coated stainless steel cables, and Dacron sails (double thickness on both Atlas, single on Lotus and Mouette models); all are stressed to $+6/-4g$. All eight models have a floating keel pocket; Lotus and Mouette have ribs, Atlas models have pre-formed battens. For other details see Table.

La Mouette

MAV (MANUFACTURE D'AILES VOLANTES)

39300 La Joux-Supt

Manufacturer in 1978 of the generally similar **Demoisel, Eden** and **Tantal Sinusoide**: see Table for details. Airframes all of aluminium alloy, with stainless steel cables and Dacron sail. No details for 1979 received.

SOFREC 'VÉLIPLANE' (Société Française de Représentation et d'Échanges Commerciaux)

16 rue Georges-Appay, 92150 Surèsnes

The well-known **Strato** continues in production (two models), together with the more recent **Starga** (three models). Both types are suitable for training and competition flying; the Stargas are stressed to $+6/-4g$, Strato models to $+5/-4g$. Airframes are of duralumin, with vinyl-coated anodised stainless steel cables and single Dacron sail; kingpost standard on all models. All are fitted with fin, pre-formed battens and tips; Starga models have a floating keel pocket. For other details see Table.

Véliplane Starga

GERMANY (Federal Republic)

WOLF HIRTH GmbH

7312 Kirchheim/Teck-Nabern

Producer of the **W-17 Dracula** series, of which 22 had been built and 17 sold by early 1979. Current model (from mid-1978) is **W-17B**: see Table for details. Special features claimed are very quick assembly (one cable connection only), and curve steering with external slip (opposite control movements compared with conventional Rogallos). Marketed jointly with Peraves AG für Flugentwicklungen, Oberfeldstrasse 44A, CH-8408 Winterthur, Switzerland.

Suitable for training and competition flying, Dracula does not fit precisely into any FAI-defined class. It is fitted with a fin, rudder and damping elevator, and has an aluminium alloy frame, stainless steel cables and Dacron sail. The airframe is stressed to $+6/-3g$.

A motorised version is designated W-17BM.

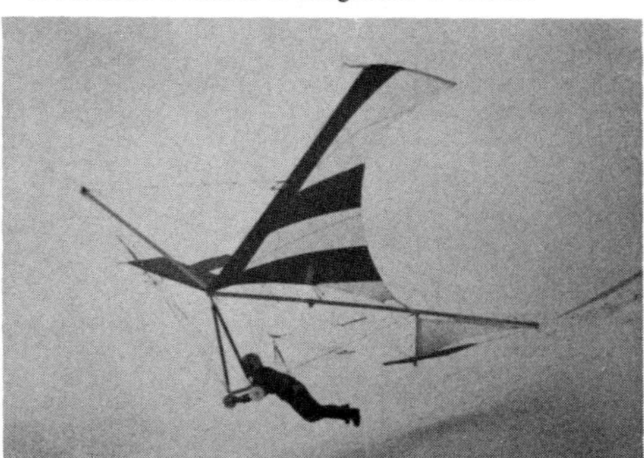

Hirth W-17B Dracula B

ENTWICKLUNG UND ERPROBUNG VON LEICHTFLUGZEUGEN

Fichtenstrasse 7, 8077 Reichertshofen

ULF-1

The ULF-1 (Ultra Leicht Flugzeug) is a one-man rigid-wing high-wing monoplane, designed by Dieter Reich and built by Heiner Neumann. It has a Wortmann FX-63-137 wing section, and is built of pinewood and balsa with fabric covering. After foot-launch, the pilot retracts his legs, to operate rudder pedals. Landing is made on a nose-skid and glassfibre tube tailskid. First flight was made in 1977, and certification flying was completed in the late Summer of 1979. Plans are available to amateur constructors, and 15 were being built by mid-1979.

DIMENSIONS:	
Wing span	10·40 m (34 ft 1½ in)
Wing aspect ratio	8
Wing area	13·40 m² (144·24 sq ft)
Length overall	5·55 m (18 ft 2½ in)
Height overall	2·55 m (8 ft 4½ in)
WEIGHTS AND LOADING:	
Weight of glider	45 kg (99 lb)
Pilot weight	60-90 kg (132-198 lb)
Max wing loading	9·7 kg/m² (1·99 lb/sq ft)
PERFORMANCE:	
Best glide ratio at 30 knots (55 km/h; 34 mph)	15
Min sinking speed at 19-21·5 knots (35-40 km/h; 22-25 mph)	48 m (157 ft)/min
Stalling speed	16·5 knots (30 km/h; 19 mph)
Max speed	38 knots (70 km/h; 43·5 mph)

Reich & Neumann ULF-1

JAPAN

JEAA

Yoshikatsu Tondokoro, 2166-13 Midorii Sato-cho, Hiroshima-shi, Hiroshima Prefecture

Mr Tondokoro successfully flew his first hang glider in early 1943. His latest design is the Class 3 rigid-aerofoil **No. II My Wing**, successfully flown for the first time in the Summer of 1977.

AIRFRAME: Sweptback (25°) flying wing configuration, with 124° nose angle and 4° anhedral. All-wood structure, stressed for 6g (ultimate), with single spar, ribs and fabric covering. Combined aileron/rudder control surface inset at tip of each wing. Suspended harness, with twist-grip controls; can be flown in seated or supine position.

Tondokoro No. II My Wing (JEAA) *(M. Hiratu)*

Japanese rigid hang glider built by Mr Hamao (no details known)

DIMENSIONS:	
Wing span	9·00 m (29 ft 6¼ in)
Wing aspect ratio	7·5
Wing area, gross	10·80 m² (116·25 sq ft)
Length overall	3·00 m (9 ft 10 in)
WEIGHTS:	
Weight empty	18 kg (40 lb)
Max T-O weight	93 kg (205 lb)
PERFORMANCE (pilot supine):	
Best glide ratio	15·5
Min sinking speed:	45 m (148 ft)/min

POLAND

VLADIMIR TALANCZUK

ul. Dubois 16a m 18, 50-207 Wroclaw

Mr Talanczuk, of the Aeroklub Wroclaw, is responsible for the **Mars-Agat WT-8** competition glider, of which eight had been built by early 1979. His previous designs have included the WT-6 Mars-S and WT-7 Mars-2S.

The WT-8 has a duralumin airframe, with kingpost, anodised cables and a single-thickness specially-sewn Dacron sail; it is stressed to $+5/-3g$. Other features include a floating keel pocket. For other details see Table.

Talanczuk Mars-Agat WT-8

PAWEL WIERZBOWSKI

ul. Wroblewskiego 25/506, 51-627 Wroclaw

Mr Wierzbowski's **Vega 106** is available in two models, the Uni and the Sport. Ten had been built and sold by early 1979; in addition, 50 sets of plans had been sold, and 30 Vega 106s were under construction by amateur builders.

Wierzbowski Vega 106 Uni

The Vega 106, which is suitable for training or private flying, has a duralumin airframe, with kingpost, and stainless steel cables; the single-thickness sail may be of Dacron, nylon or polyester material. Other features include pre-formed battens and a floating keel pocket. For other details see Table.

DR JERZY WOLF

Stepinska 6 m 63, 00-739 Warsaw

Dr Wolf, of the Instytut Lotnictwa (Aviation Institute) in Warsaw, has worked since 1970 on developing a stretched-membrane sailwing for various low-speed applications (including sailing applications: see *Jane's Surface Skimmers)*. The stretched membrane, or 'spring-wing', is an ultralight, highly flexible aerofoil of significant aspect ratio. The foldable elastic sail is fixed at the centreline and wingtips to the main structure, with considerable freedom for spanwise elastic deformation. Thin, flat profiled ribs are attached to the sail, and are stabilised by the tension of the sail fabric; this tension is altered by the elastic fittings attaching the tips of the sail to the 'wing spar' cross-tube. Under loaded conditions the elastic sail assumes a curvature depending upon the value of the loading force, without deforming the aerodynamic profile of the wing. The design features of the stretched membrane wing are protected by Polish patents.

Four types of hang glider embodying this feature have been built, of which the Spring Wing Z-75 and Z-75-7 were described and illustrated in the 1978-79 *Jane's*.

The two most recent designs are:

Spring Wing Z-76. Designed and built in 1976. First rectangular flexible and stretched membrane wing, intended for experimental purposes. Airframe skeleton has circular-section tubes and is simplified for quick assembly.

Elastic Wing Z-77. Experimental Class 2 glider; near-rectangular flexible wing has specially reflexed profiles and double-thickness covering over first 50% chord. Three examples built by early 1979, testing both cable and tubular leading-edges. Main frame is of duralumin, with anodised cables, Dacron sail, and kingpost; airframe is stressed to $+7/-2\cdot5g$. Other features include ribs, preformed battens and fin.

Further details of these two gliders are given in the Table.

Wolf Spring Wing Z-76

SOUTH AFRICA

FRANK MARSHALL

Details of Mr Marshall's most recent activities can now be found under the United Kingdom heading in this section.

SOLAR WINGS

No news of this company's activities has been received since 1977. Its last known products were listed in the 1978-79 *Jane's*.

UNITED HANG GLIDERS

No news of United's activities has been received since 1977. Its last known products were listed in the 1978-79 *Jane's*.

UNION OF SOVIET SOCIALIST REPUBLICS

A number of hang gliders have been portrayed in Soviet publications during the past year. One of these, apparently belonging to the Rostov aero club, is shown in an accompanying illustration; a very similar hang glider has the Soviet designation Sokol-2.

Soviet 'Rostov' hang glider

UNITED KINGDOM

BIRDMAN SPORTS LTD

Overtown House, Mildenhall, Marlborough, Wiltshire

Main details of this company's last known hang gliders were given in the 1977-78 *Jane's*; no 1978 or 1979 details were received.

CHARGUS GLIDING COMPANY

Wagland Engineering, Gawcott, Buckingham

No 1978 or 1979 details received.

DAVID COOK

Hillcrest, Aldeburgh Road, Aldringham, near Leiston, Suffolk

Mr David Cook acquired a Volmer VJ-23 Swingwing hang glider (which see) in the Spring of 1974, subsequently fitting it with a McCulloch MC-101B piston engine and two 5 litre (1·1 Imp gallon) fuel tanks. In this form, Mr Cook piloted the aircraft across the Channel from Walmer Castle, Deal, to Blériot Plage, France, on 9 May 1978 in a flying time of 1 h 15 min. The VJ-23E thus became the lowest-powered aeroplane to make a cross-Channel flight up to that time.

David Cook and the VJ-23E Swingwing powered glider on which he crossed the Channel in May 1978
(Dr Alan Beaumont)

ECLIPSE

7 Exbridge Road, Dulverton, Somerset

No details known.

FLEXI-FORM SKYSAILS

Unit 24, Nassau Mill, Cawdor Street, Patricroft, Manchester

Current models (1979) are **Skyline, Spirit** and **Vector,** sales of which had totalled 70,230 and 60 respectively by early 1979. Skyline is suitable for competition flying; Vector held the British cross-country record of 23·5 nm (43·5 km; 27 miles) in the Summer of 1978.

All models have an aluminium alloy airframe, with kingpost as standard, PVC-coated galvanised steel cables, flexible PVC battens and single-thickness Terylene sail. Skyline and Vector are stressed to $+6\cdot5/-5g$, Spirit to $+5/-5g$. Other features include floating keel pocket and a roached tip design with minimum fixed washout (Skyline); adjustable keel camber and adjustable double deflexers (Spirit); floating keel pocket, triple deflexers, and a truncated tip design with fully tensioned sail (Vector).

HIWAY HANG GLIDERS LTD

Sirhowy Hill, Tredegar, Gwent NP2 4XP

Current gliders (1979) are the **Gemini, Harrier** (two models), **Spectrum** (two models) and **Super Scorpion** (three models). All have an aluminium alloy frame, with kingpost as standard, vinyl-coated galvanised steel cables, and a single-thickness Dacron sail; and are stressed to $+6\cdot6/-3g$. Other features include adjustable sail camber, ribs, and a floating keel pocket. Gemini can carry two persons; Super Scorpion has small tip-struts, to facilitate quick recovery from a dive.

Hiway does not release performance figures, but all other known details are given in the Table.

FRANK MARSHALL

19 Station Road, Filton, Bristol BS12 7BZ

Mr Marshall, whose Fantail hang glider was described under the South African section in the 1978-79 *Jane's*, is now resident in the UK. His two latest designs are the Heatwave and Madcap, both powered hang gliders.

MARSHALL HEATWAVE

The Heatwave is of conventional semi-rigid design, but quick-folding for carriage on a car roof rack. The double-surface wing has a pre-sewn sail bag, with removable pre-formed battens in top and bottom surfaces. Tailplane and rudder are rigid, but easily detachable. Control in pitch is by weight shift, control for turning by a long vertical twist bar moving the rudder. Power plant is a Rowena 6424 210 cc engine driving a 0·91 m (3 ft) diameter propeller. First flight was made in January 1978.

DIMENSIONS:
- Wing span: 9·91 m (32 ft 6 in)
- Wing area, gross: 15·33 m² (165 sq ft)
- Wing aspect ratio: 6·4
- Length overall: 5·33 m (17 ft 6 in)

WEIGHTS:
- Weight of glider: 47·6 kg (105 lb)
- Pilot weight range: 54-77 kg (120-170 lb)

PERFORMANCE (with 63·5 kg; 140 lb pilot):
- Best rate of climb at S/L, at 22 knots (40 km/h; 25 mph): 70 m (230 ft)/min

Marshall Heatwave

MARSHALL MADCAP

The Madcap has a canard layout, chosen to provide static balance when using the Rowena 6424 engine in a 'pusher' installation. The fin forms the engine mount, and incorporates a 4·5 litre (1 Imp gallon) GRP fuel tank in its leading-edge. The wing uses the proven pre-stressed curved spar technique developed for the Fantail, resulting in only 2-3° washout while retaining the single-spar, flexible wing structure. Control is by weight shift in both axes. First flight took place in South Africa in May 1978.

DIMENSIONS:
- Wing span: 12·19 m (40 ft 0 in)
- Wing area, gross: 18·58 m² (200 sq ft)
- Wing aspect ratio: 8
- Length overall: 5·18 m (17 ft 0 in)

WEIGHTS:
- Weight of glider: 44 kg (97 lb)
- Pilot weight range: 79-104 kg (175-230 lb)

PERFORMANCE (with 86 kg; 190 lb pilot):
- Best rate of climb at S/L, at 20 knots (37 km/h; 23 mph): 91 m (300 ft)/min

Marshall Madcap

MILES WINGS (ENGINEERS) LTD

Unidev Works, Croydon Road, Elmers End, Beckenham, Kent BR3 4BP

Currently engaged in design and development only. Responsible for design of **Gryphon** now manufactured and marketed by Waspair (see Table).

SAILWINGS (SCOTLAND) LTD

Craigview, Comelybank Lane, Dumbarton G82 4JA

No 1978 or 1979 details received.

SCOT-KITES

19 Camphill Avenue, Glasgow G41 3AU

Was marketing US Electra Flyer Olympus in 1978; no 1979 details received.

SKYHOOKS SAILWINGS LTD

4 Thornlea Avenue, Oldham, Lancashire

No 1978 or 1979 details received. Current 1978 model was **Sunspot**.

WASPAIR LTD

Restmor Way, Hackbridge Road, Wallington, Surrey SM6 7AH

Current models (1979) are the **Falcon V, Gryphon G160** and **G180,** and **Laser L190**. All are suitable for private and competition flying; Falcon V is also suitable for training. Gryphons are latest developments of the Gryphon III (1978-79 *Jane's*) designed by Miles Wings. Falcon can be flown prone or seated; Gryphons prone or supine; Laser prone, seated or supine.

Airframes in all cases are of fully anodised aluminium alloy, with kingpost as standard, vinyl-coated stainless steel cables (galvanised steel on Falcon), and Dacron sail (single on Falcon and Laser, double on Gryphons); *g* limits are +6/−4 (Falcon), +7/−4 (Laser), +8/−4 (Gryphon). Falcon and Gryphons can carry two persons. All models have adjustable camber and a floating keel pocket; Gryphons, in addition, have pre-formed battens.

For other details, see Table.

Waspair Falcon V

Waspair Gryphon G160

Waspair Laser L190

UNITED STATES OF AMERICA

AA FLIGHT SYSTEMS

10 North Barton, New Buffalo, Michigan 49117

For details of 1978 **Streaker** see Table. No details for 1979 received.

CHUCK'S GLIDER SUPPLIES

4252 Pearl Road, Cleveland, Ohio 44109

PROPRIETOR: Chuck Slusarczyk

Details of the **Spitfire** (500 sold by 1978) and **Falcon** (1,000 sold) are included in the Table, and production of both types continued in 1978. Airframes are of anodised aluminium tubing, with anodised cables and a Dacron sail. lo details for 1979 received.

DELTA WING KITES AND GLIDERS INC

PO Box 483, Van Nuys, California 91408

No details of this company's hang gliders have been received since 1977. Details of its last known products can be found in the 1978-79 *Jane's*.

DSK (DUSTER SAILPLANE KITS)

13161 Sherman Way, North Hollywood, California 91605

In addition to its current sailplanes (which see), DSK also produces two powered rigid hang gliders, the Flatlander and Drifter.

DSK FLATLANDER

Available in fully prefabricated kit form for homebuilders, the Flatlander is an ultralight rigid hang glider designed specifically for powered operation. Deliveries were due to begin in the Spring of 1979. The airframe is stressed to *g* limits of +4·67/−2·33 (normal) and +7/−3·5 (ultimate), and meets FAA sailplane Utility category requirements.

AIRFRAME: Strut-braced high-wing monoplane. All-aluminium frame, assembled with bolts and pop-rivets. Full aerodynamic control in all three axes by ailerons, elevators and rudder. Foldaway seat for pilot. Single main wheel and steerable tailwheel. Wings and tail detachable for transportation.

POWER PLANT: One 7·5 kW (10 hp) Star/Tek 134 cc piston engine, with overhead starter; 9 kW (12 hp) engine available optionally.

DIMENSIONS:
- Wing span — 11·00 m (36 ft 1 in)
- Wing area, gross — 13·69 m² (147·34 sq ft)
- Wing aspect ratio — 8·84
- Propeller diameter — 1·07 m (3 ft 6 in)

WEIGHTS AND LOADING:
- Weight empty — 66·5 kg (147 lb)
- Max T-O weight — 168 kg (370 lb)
- Max wing loading — 12·28 kg/m² (2·52 lb/sq ft)

PERFORMANCE:
- Best glide ratio — 14·7
- Min sinking speed, power off — 49 m (162 ft)/min
- Never-exceed speed — 56 knots (104 km/h; 65 mph)
- Max level speed — more than 35 knots (64 km/h; 40 mph)
- Cruising speed — 31 knots (58 km/h; 36 mph)
- Stalling speed — 17·5 knots (32·5 km/h; 20 mph)
- Landing speed — 15 knots (27·5 km/h; 17 mph)
- Max rate of climb (77 kg; 170 lb pilot, 7·5 kW; 10 hp engine) — 65 m (215 ft)/min

DSK DRIFTER

Alternative version of Flatlander, but with structure of all flying surfaces built of epoxy bonded fir, spruce and plywood.

EIPPER-FORMANCE INC

PO Box 246, Lomita, California 90717

No details of Eipper-Formance hang gliders have been received since 1977. Its last known products were listed in the 1978-79 *Jane's*.

ELECTRA FLYER

700 Comanche NE, Albuquerque, New Mexico 87107

For details see Addenda.

TARAS KICENIUK JR

976 La Vuelta, Santa Paula, California 93060

For details of **Batso** hang glider, see Table. This Rogallo is built of bamboo, tape and plastics. Details below are for rigid-wing hang gliders:

KICENIUK ICARUS II

Mr Kiceniuk began design of the Icarus tail-less sweptwing biplane hang glider in May 1971. It made its first flight in August 1971. The improved Icarus II is approved by the FAA for amateur construction, and is available in kit form only.

TYPE: One-man amateur-built hang glider; *g* limit +3·0.

AIRFRAME: Sweptback, staggered flying-wing biplane. Modified Eiffel 32 wing section. Dihedral approx 8°. Incidence 2° 15′ upper wing, 0° lower wing. Sweepback approx 15°. Aluminium tube leading-edge and trailing-edge spars, wood and styrofoam ribs, and Dacron covering. Balsa and plywood vertical rudders, one attached to each outermost rear interplane strut, actuated independently to provide strong lateral control because of effects of sweep and dihedral angle. When actuated simultaneously, rudders act as airbrakes. No other control surfaces needed, pitch control being effected by pilot's body movement. Aircraft is inherently stable, and returns to straight and level flight when flown hands-off. No fuselage or tail surfaces.

DIMENSIONS:
- Wing span — 8·84 m (29 ft 0 in)
- Wing area, gross — 18·12 m² (195·0 sq ft)
- Wing aspect ratio (geometric) — 8·7
- Length overall — 2·74 m (9 ft 0 in)

WEIGHTS AND LOADING:
- Weight empty — 25 kg (55 lb)
- Max T-O weight — 115 kg (255 lb)
- Max wing loading — 6·34 kg/m² (1·3 lb/sq ft)

PERFORMANCE:
- Best glide ratio at 17 knots (32 km/h; 20 mph) — 8
- Min sinking speed at 17 knots (32 km/h; 20 mph) — 64 m (210 ft)/min
- Stalling speed — 15 knots (27 km/h; 17 mph)
- Max speed (smooth air) — 35 knots (64 km/h; 40 mph)

KICENIUK ICARUS V

The Icarus V is a monoplane hang glider, the prototype of which flew for the first time on 1 September 1973; it is suitable for both thermal soaring and cross-country flying.

TYPE: One-man amateur-built hang glider; *g* limit +6·0.

AIRFRAME: Constant-chord sweptback flying-wing monoplane. TK 7315 high-lift, low-moment wing section. Dihedral from roots. Sweepback 20°. No incidence. Aluminium tube frame, foam sheet leading-edge, doped fabric covering. Dependent fin and rudder at each wingtip. Yaw and roll control through independently-controlled rudders, pitch control by pilot weight shift. Aircraft can spiral continuously at bank angles of 60°, is extremely stable, and has a very gentle stall.

DIMENSIONS:
- Wing span — 9·75 m (32 ft 0 in)
- Wing area, gross — 14·86 m² (160·0 sq ft)
- Wing aspect ratio — 6·4
- Length overall — 3·81 m (12 ft 6 in)
- Height overall — 1·83 m (6 ft 0 in)

WEIGHTS AND LOADING:
- Weight empty — 29·5 kg (65 lb)
- Max T-O weight — 129 kg (285 lb)
- Max wing loading — 8·7 kg/m² (1·78 lb/sq ft)

PERFORMANCE:
- Best glide ratio at 17 knots (32 km/h; 20 mph) — 10
- Min sinking speed at 16 knots (29 km/h; 18 mph) — 64 m (210 ft)/min
- Stalling speed — 14 knots (26 km/h; 16 mph)
- Max speed (smooth air) — 43·5 knots (80·5 km/h; 50 mph)

MANTA PRODUCTS

1647 East 14th Street, Oakland, California 94606

Manta produces only the Fledgling rigid-wing hang gliders.

MANTA FLEDGLING

This rigid sweptwing tail-less monoplane can be flown from either a seated or prone position, and is suitable for training, private or competition flying. Total sales had reached 500 by early 1979.

It is produced as the Fledgling I and II, respectively with single-surface and double-surface wing covering; each model is available in two sizes, designated A and B.

Manta Fledgling II

TYPE: One-man rigid-wing hang glider; *g* limits +7·5/−7·5.

AIRFRAME: Sweptback flying-wing monoplane (18° on leading-edges). Each half-wing has two aluminium alloy spars, and compression struts; wings linked by vinyl-coated stainless steel sweep wires. Pre-formed ribs and Dacron covering. Kingpost standard. Drag rudder at each wingtip. Provision for power plant and landing gear.

DIMENSIONS:
- Wing span (included): A — 8·84 m (29 ft 0 in)
  - B — 10·06 m (33 ft 0 in)
- Wing leading-edge length: A — 4·42 m (14 ft 6 in)
  - B — 5·03 m (16 ft 6 in)
- Wing chord at root (keel length): A, B — 1·68 m (5 ft 6 in)
- Wing area, gross: A — 13·19 m² (142·0 sq ft)
  - B — 15·05 m² (162·0 sq ft)
- Wing aspect ratio: A — 6·0
  - B — 6·8
- Nose angle — 144°
- Billow angle — not applicable

WEIGHT:
- Weight empty: A — 22·6 kg (50 lb)
  - B — 25·4 kg (56 lb)
- Pilot weight: A — 59-72·5 kg (130-160 lb)
  - B — 77-100 kg (170-220 lb)

PERFORMANCE:

Best glide ratio	13
Min sinking speed	61 m (200 ft)/min
Maximum speed	35 knots (64·5 km/h; 40 mph)
Cruising speed	16-22 knots (29-40 km/h; 18-25 mph)
Stalling speed	12·5 knots (23 km/h; 14 mph)

PACIFIC GULL

150 H, Los Obreros Lane, San Clemente, California 92672

For details of current **Alpine** series, see Table. Airframes are of aluminium alloy tube, with kingpost as standard, and are stressed to *g* limits of +6·0 (+4·8 rolling) and −3·0. Cables are of vinyl-coated stainless steel, sails of Dacron. All have pre-formed battens, triple deflexers and a floating keel pocket. Alpine 2·5 can carry two persons in tandem; all models are suitable for private or competition flying.

Total sales had reached 159 by early 1979.

Pacific Gull Alpine 1·0

SEAGULL AIRCRAFT INC

3021 Airport Avenue, Santa Monica, California 90405

Details of earlier Seagull Rogallos can be found in the 1977-78 *Jane's*; those for current 1978 **Seagull** and **Seahawk** models are given in the Table. Airframes are of aluminium tube, with stainless steel cables and a Dacron sail. No 1979 details were received.

In addition, Seagull produces the rigid-wing Waterman & Seagull Flyer, for amateur construction.

WATERMAN & SEAGULL FLYER

The Seagull Flyer is a rigid-wing fabric-covered wooden biplane hang glider with rudder and elevator control.

DIMENSIONS:

Wing span	7·92 m (26 ft 0 in)
Length overall	4·27 m (14 ft 0 in)

WEIGHT:

Weight empty	27·2 kg (60 lb)

SKY SPORTS INC

PO Box 507, 394 Somers Road (Route 83), Ellington, Connecticut 06029

Current (1979) types (see Table for details) are the **Eaglet, Bobcat IV, Osprey II** and **Sirocco III,** all of which have aluminium tube airframes, stainless steel cables and double-surface Dacron sails. Bobcat has a two-position double billow wing; Sirocco has a buried cross-member.

For other details see Table. All models are available in other sizes; some have provision for power plant.

JIM SPURGEON

5590 Morro Way, La Mesa, California 92041

Was marketing plans in 1978 for replicas of several historic rigid-wing hang gliders, all suitable for amateur construction. No details of 1979 activities received.

1883 MONTGOMERY MONOPLANE GLIDER

First hang glider to make a successful, controlled and manned flight (see accompanying photograph).

DIMENSIONS:

Wing span	7·01 m (23 ft 0 in)
Wing chord	1·37 m (4 ft 6 in)

WEIGHT: 17·2 kg (38 lb)

Spurgeon scale model of 1883 Montgomery glider

1895 LILIENTHAL MONOPLANE GLIDER

Wood and fabric with wire bracing; foldable wings.

DIMENSIONS:

Wing span	5·79 m (19 ft 0 in)
Wing chord (max)	2·50 m (8 ft 2½ in)
Length overall	3·94 m (12 ft 11 in)

1896 CHANUTE BIPLANE GLIDER

Tailed boxkite design which made more than 1,000 successful flights near Lake Michigan. Also of wood and fabric, with wire bracing.

DIMENSIONS:

Wing span	4·78 m (15 ft 8 in)
Wing chord	1·50 m (4 ft 11 in)
Length overall	3·94 m (12 ft 11 in)

1920/21 PELZNER BIPLANE GLIDER

Leading German glider of 1920/21. Wood and fabric construction, with wire bracing and rudder control.

DIMENSIONS:

Wing span	5·38 m (17 ft 8 in)
Wing chord (max)	1·30 m (4 ft 3 in)
Length overall	5·23 m (17 ft 2 in)

SUNBIRD ULTRALIGHT GLIDERS

12501 Gladstone Avenue, No. A4, Sylmar, California 91342

For details of earlier Strato series, see 1978-79 *Jane's*. These are no longer in production. Current model in 1979 was the **Nova**, first flown in 1978 and now produced in four models. Suitable for private and competition flying, the Nova can be flown in a prone, seated or supine position. The airframe is of aluminium alloy, with kingpost as standard; cables are of vinyl-coated stainless steel, and sail of Dacron. Other features include a floating keel pocket, leading-edge without deflexers, and floating tips.

Sunbird Nova

ULTRALIGHT FLYING MACHINES OF WISCONSIN

PO Box 248, Kansasville, Wisconsin 53139

This company produces John Moody's **Easy Riser,** a rigid-wing powered hang glider stressed to +11/−5*g*. More than 250 had been delivered by mid-1978, many of them for construction by homebuilders. The general appearance of the Easy Riser can be seen in the accompanying photograph; all other known details follow:

AIRFRAME: Constant-chord sweptback flying-wing biplane, of unequal span. No fuselage. Drag rudder aft of wings on one or both sides, attached to outermost rear interplane strut(s). Landing gear optional.

POWER PLANT: One 9 kW (12 hp) go-kart engine. Fuel capacity 4·7 litres (1·25 US gallons).

PERFORMANCE:

Max rate of climb at S/L	61 m (200 ft)/min
Typical endurance	45 min

Ultralight (John Moody) powered Easy Riser, built by Herr Stockhausen in Germany (*J. M. G. Gradidge*)

UP INC (ULTRALITE PRODUCTS)

PO Box 582, 28011 Front Street, Rancho California, Temecula, California 92390

Producer of **Condor, Firefly** and **Spyder** series; see Table for details. Airframes are of anodised aluminium alloy tube, with kingpost as standard, and Dacron sail. Options include lightweight aluminium frame, applied leading-edge and keel pockets, soaring windows, swept tips (Condor only), and prone or supine flying position.

Spyder and Firefly prototypes have been tested with airframes built of Graftek graphite composite material, which is tougher and lighter than aluminium. It is hoped to make these available on production gliders in due course.

UP Condor

VOLMER AIRCRAFT

PO Box 5222, Glendale, California 91201

VOLMER VJ-23 SWINGWING

This monoplane hang glider was designed in 1971 by Volmer Jensen and Irving Culver, making its first flight towards the end of that year. Subsequent modifications made the aircraft safer and more controllable. Volmer Aircraft markets plans (but not kits or materials) for the VJ-23; several hundreds have been sold.

Following the success of David Cook in the UK (which see) in installing an engine in his Swingwing, drawings for a **VJ-23E** powered version are now also available from Volmer Aircraft.

Volmer VJ-23 Swingwing

Volmer VJ-23E powered Swingwing

The following details apply to the unpowered VJ-23:

AIRFRAME: Cantilever high-wing monoplane, constructed of steel tube, spruce, mahogany and plywood with fabric covering. Control by means of ailerons, elevators and rudder.

DIMENSIONS:

Wing span	9·93 m (32 ft 7 in)
Wing area, gross	16·63 m² (179·0 sq ft)
Length overall	5·31 m (17 ft 5 in)
Height overall	1·83 m (6 ft 0 in)

WEIGHTS:

Weight empty	45·5 kg (100 lb)
Max T-O weight	136 kg (300 lb)

PERFORMANCE:

Best glide ratio	9
Cruising speed	17 knots (32 km/h; 20 mph)
Stalling speed	13 knots (24 km/h; 15 mph)

VOLMER VJ-24 SUNFUN

The VJ-24 rigid-wing monoplane hang glider is essentially a simplified-construction version of the earlier VJ-23 Swingwing, from which it differs primarily in having wings and tail of fabric-covered aluminium tube instead of wooden spars and ribs; rectangular instead of tapered planform wings, of increased span, with V bracing struts; and a pair of ground handling wheels.

A **VJ-24E** is also available, with a 7·5 kW (10 hp) engine and fuel tank installed beneath the wing, aft of the pilot, to permit take-offs from level ground or uphill.

The following details apply to the unpowered VJ-24:

DIMENSIONS:

Wing span	11·13 m (36 ft 6 in)
Wing area, gross	15·14 m² (163·0 sq ft)
Length overall	5·54 m (18 ft 2 in)

Height over tail	1·73 m (5 ft 8 in)
WEIGHTS:	
Weight empty	50 kg (110 lb)
Max T-O weight	140·5 kg (310 lb)

PERFORMANCE: As for VJ-23

Volmer VJ-24E powered Sunfun

WILLS WING INC

1208-h, East Walnut, Santa Ana, California 92701

Formerly known as Sport Kites Inc, this company marketed the Wills Wing and Swallowtail gliders, as listed in the 1978-79 *Jane's*. Its current (1979) products are the **Alpha, Omega** and **Omni,** of which details are given in the Table; nearly 1,000 of these had been sold by early 1979. All are stressed to *g* limits of +7/−5, and are suitable for training, private and competition flying. Airframes are of aluminium alloy and composite materials, with a kingpost as standard; cables are of vinyl-coated stainless steel; single-surface sail is of Dacron. Other features include applied leading-edge pockets, floating keel pocket, adjustable camber, triple deflexers, foam/glassfibre battens (Alpha), pre-formed battens (Omega), and washout control tips. All are capable of tow launch, and the larger sizes are capable of carrying two persons.

WILLIAM H. WOLF

18703 S.E. 44th Place, Issaquah, Wichita 98027

WOLF VALKYRIE

The Valkyrie is a rigid, non-swept tail-less monoplane

Wolf Valkyrie

hang glider with a drag rudder near each wingtip. Construction is of aluminium alloy tube, with stainless steel cables and Dacron covering. Wings have 7° dihedral.

DIMENSIONS:	
Wing span	9·37 m (30 ft 9 in)
Wing chord (constant)	1·37 m (4 ft 6 in)
Wing area	12·82 m² (138·0 sq ft)
Wing aspect ratio	6·83
Length overall	1·91 m (6 ft 3 in)
Height overall	2·29 m (7 ft 6 in)
WEIGHT:	
Weight empty	21·8 kg (48 lb)
PERFORMANCE (at 95·25 kg; 210 lb gross weight):	
Best glide ratio at 15·5 knots (29 km/h; 18 mph)	8
Min sinking speed	60 m (197 ft)/min
Stalling speed	10·5 knots (19·5 km/h; 12 mph)

THE WRIGHT BROTHERS AEROPLANE CO

3501 Hollyslope Road, Altadena, California 91001

WBAC CA-14

The CA-14 is a rigid-wing monoplane hang glider, to which can be fitted, optionally, a power plant for take-offs from level ground or uphill, or for cross-country flight. Both the CA-14 and CA-15 are now in production. By early 1979 a total of 140 had been sold, of which 124 had been completed.

TYPE: One-man amateur-built hang glider; *g* limit +5·0.

AIRFRAME: Cantilever constant-chord sweptback flying-wing monoplane. Sweepback 17°. Dihedral 7° on outer panels. Washout at wingtips. Main spar and plywood-covered nose ribs are epoxy-bonded to form a D-section leading-edge; aft of this are a rear spar and truss-braced stamped aluminium ribs, covered with Dacron. Forward section is a pre-moulded, gel-coated two-layer glassfibre shell; rear section has a doped polyester fabric covering. Spoilers in upper surface. Reflexed (upturned) trailing-edge. Wingtips formed from aluminium tube. Stainless steel fittings and steel cables.

POWER PLANT (optional): One 9 kW (12 hp) two-stroke aircooled piston engine, driving a two-blade propeller. Fuel tank capacity 7·5 litres (2 US gallons).

DIMENSIONS:	
Wing span	9·14 m (30 ft 0 in)
Wing area	12·54 m² (135·0 sq ft)
Wing aspect ratio	6·7
WEIGHTS AND LOADINGS:	
Weight empty:	
unpowered	25 kg (55 lb)
powered	36 kg (80 lb)
Max pilot weight	91 kg (200 lb)
Max T-O weight:	
unpowered	116 kg (255 lb)
powered	127 kg (280 lb)
Max wing loading	9·03 kg/m² (1·85 lb/sq ft)
Max power loading	12·66 kg/kW (20·8 lb/hp)
PERFORMANCE (unpowered):	
Best glide ratio at 26·5 knots (49 km/h; 30·5 mph)	15
Min sinking speed at 22 knots (40 km/h; 25 mph)	49 m (160 ft)/min
PERFORMANCE (powered):	
Max level speed	52 knots (96 km/h; 60 mph)
Cruising speed	26 knots (48 km/h; 30 mph)
Stalling speed	15 knots (27·5 km/h; 17 mph)
Max rate of climb at S/L	142 m (466 ft)/min
Ceiling	3,050 m (10,000 ft)
T-O run	15 m (50 ft)
Landing run	3 m (10 ft)
Max range	52 nm (97 km; 60 miles)
Max endurance	2 h

Wright Brothers CA-14 in glide

WBAC CA-15

The CA-15 is essentially similar to the CA-14, except that the wings have a curving ('elliptical') dihedral and are covered with Mylar; and the aircraft is equipped with 'rudderons', which effectively combine the functions of rudder and ailerons.

FLEXIBLE WING HANG GLIDER DATA

Manufacturer and Model	FAI class	Span: m/ft-in	Leading-edge: m/ft-in	Keel: m/ft-in	Nose/Billow angle: degrees	Wing area: m²/sq ft	Wing aspect ratio	Weight: kg/lb	Glide ratio	Sink rate: m/ft per min	Remarks
ARGENTINA											
Byttebier *(1978: no 1979 details received)*											
Johan 087	3	n.k.	n.k.	n.k.	102/n.k.	23·23/250	n.k.	23·6/52	5	n.k.	Weighs 27·2 kg (60 lb) in tow configuration.
AUSTRALIA											
Farrelly *(1978: no 1979 details received)*											
Elektra	2	9·14/30-0	5·49/18-0	3·81/12-6	118/1·0	17·28/186	4·84	22·7/50	n.k.	n.k.	Four intermediate sizes available.
Elektra	2	12·19/40-0	6·71/22-0	3·73/12-3	131/1·0	20·44/220	7·27	27·2/60	n.k.	n.k.	
Free Flight *(1978: no 1979 details received)*											
Saturn IV	2	9·75/32-0	5·79/19-0	2·84/9-4	110/1·0	15·79/170	6·02	21·8/48	n.k.	n.k.	
Twister V	2	10·67/35-0	6·40/21-0	3·35/11-0	110/0·5	17·19/185	6·62	22·7/50	n.k.	n.k.	
Moyes											
Maxi-Stinger Mark III	2	10·40/34-1½	6·10/20-0	4·00/13-1½	117/0·0	20·00/215	5·40	28·0/61·7	8·5	58/190	Stall 10 knots (18 km/h; 11·5 mph).
Maxi Stinger SP	2	10·00/32-9¾	5·80/19-0½	4·00/13-1½	117/0·0	18·00/194	5·55	26·0/57·3	8·5	61/200	Stall 10 knots (18 km/h; 11·5 mph).
Mega Stinger	2	10·00/32-9¾	5·80/19·0½	4·00/13-1½	120/0·0	16·75/180	6·00	26·0/57·3	8·6	67/220	Stall 13·5 knots (25 km/h; 16 mph).
Micro Stinger	2	9·00/29-6½	5·00/16-4¾	3·00/9-10	115/0·0	14·00/151	5·75	24·0/52·9	7·5	85/280	Stall 12·5 knots (23 km/h; 14·5 mph)
Mini Stinger	2	9·00/29-6½	5·50/18-0½	4·00/13-1½	120/1·0	16·00/172	5·00	25·0/55·1	6·5	84/275	Stall 11 knots (20 km/h; 12·5 mph); max pilot weight 70 kg (154 lb).
Stinger	1	9·00/29-6½	5·50/18-0½	4·00/13-1½	109/1·5	18·50/199	4·40	25·0/55·1	5·5	87/285	Stall 10 knots (18 km/h; 11·5 mph); pilot weight 55-75 kg (121-165 lb).
Stingray (small)	1	8·50/27-10½	4·80/15-9	4·00/13-1½	120/1·0	16·25/175	4·50	23·0/50·7	5·5	73/240	Stall 10 knots (18 km/h; 11·5 mph).
Stingray (medium)	1	9·00/29-6½	5·00/16-4¾	4·00/13-1½	120/1·0	18·60/200	4·50	25·0/55·1	5·5	70/230	Stall 10 knots (18 km/h; 11·5 mph).
Stingray (large)	1	9·40/30-10	5·20/17-0¾	4·00/13-1½	115/1·0	20·00/215	4·50	26·0/57·3	5·5	67/220	Stall 10 knots (18 km/h; 11·5 mph).
Ultralight Flight Systems *(1978: no 1979 details received)*											
CB 3	2	8·84/29-0	5·49/18-0	3·66/12-0	107/n.k.	17·28/186	4·52	20·4/45	n.k.	n.k.	
Skydart I	2	8·99/29-6	5·18/17-0	2·90/9-6	120/n.k.	14·86/160	5·44	24·5/54	n.k.	n.k.	
Skydart II	2	9·30/30-6	5·49/18-0	2·90/9-6	116/n.k.	16·72/180	5·17	24·5/54	n.k.	n.k.	
Skyhook II	2	10·36/34-0	5·94/19-6	3·66/12-0	121/n.k.	19·97/215	5·38	24·5/54	n.k.	n.k.	
Wings *(1978: no 1979 details received)*											
Javelin	2	9·75/32-0	5·79/19-0	3·05/10-0	115/1·0	18·58/200	5·12	22·7/50	7·5	61/200	
Lynx B	3	9·86/32-4	5·79/19-0	2·74/9-0	120/0·5	17·19/185	5·65	23·6/52	9	61/200	
Lynx C	3	10·67/35-0	6·10/20-0	2·59/8-6	120/0·5	16·26/175	7·00	23·6/52	9+	61/200	
Ranger	2	9·14/30-0	5·33/17-6	3·66/12-0	110/1·5	18·58/200	4·50	21·8/48	7	70/230	
CANADA											
Birdman Enterprises											
Falcon I	n.k.	8·23/27-0	5·49/18-0	3·96/13-0	96/n.k.	15·33/165	4·40	20·4/45	6	87/285	Pilot weight 45-72·5 kg (100-160 lb); stall 10·5 knots (19·5 km/h; 12 mph).
Falcon II	n.k.	8·84/29-0	5·79/19-0	4·27/14-0	96/n.k.	16·72/180	4·60	20·4/45	6	87/285	Pilot weight 61-91 kg (135-200 lb); stall 10·5 knots (19·5 km/h; 12 mph).
MJ-5	n.k.	9·60/31-6	5·49/18-0	3·05/10-0	120/0·5	16·72/180	5·50	22·2/49	8+	68·5/225	Pilot weight 63·5-88·5 kg (140-195 lb); stall 9 knots (16·5 km/h; 10 mph).
MJ-6	n.k.	10·06/33-0	5·61/18-5	3·35/11-0	115/0·0	17·00/183	5·70	22·7/50	8·5	61/200	Pilot weight 63·5-95 kg (140-210 lb); stall 9 knots (16·5 km/h; 10 mph).
XC	n.k.	10·21/33-6	5·94/19-6	3·51/11-6	116/0·75	19·51/210	5·40	24·9/55	9+	61/200	Pilot weight 82-104 kg (180-230 lb); stall 9 knots (16·5 km/h; 10 mph).
High Perspective											
HP IV	2	8·53/28-0	5·49/18-0	3·66/12-0	100/2·0	14·86/160	5·00	15·9/35	6+	68·5/225	Pilot weight 50-72·5 kg (110-160 lb); stall 13 knots (24·5 km/h; 15 mph). Smaller and larger models available.
FRANCE											
Dahu Plane (Noin)											
Baby 18	n.k.	8·00/26-3	n.k.	4·50/14-9¼	92/n.k.	18·00/193·7	3·50	18·0/39·7	5-6	96/315	
Nimbus	2	10·40/34-1½	5·60/18-4½	3·00/9-10	122/0·0	13·40/144·2	8·10	26·0/57·3	10-11	59/194	Pilot weight 60-75 kg (132-165 lb); stall 14·5 knots (26 km/h; 16·5 mph).
Stratus IVB	1	8·35/27-4¾	n.k.	4·00/13-1½	100/n.k.	17·00/183·0	4·40	19·0/41·9	n.k.	84/276	Stall 11 knots (20 km/h; 12·5 mph).
Danis *(1978: no 1979 details received)*											
SK 1	1	9·00/29-6¼	4·90/16-1	3·40/11-1¾	120/2·0	15·00/161·5	5·40	19·0/41·9	n.k.	n.k.	
SK 2	1	n.k.	5·15/16-10¾	3·30/10-10	120/2·0	17·00/183·0	4·76	22·0/48·5	n.k.	n.k.	Pilot weight 60-85 kg (132-187 lb).
SK 3	1	10·50/34-5½	6·05/19-10¼	4·00/13-1½	120/2·0	20·50/220·7	5·38	25·0/55·1	n.k.	n.k.	
X 9	2	11·00/36-1	5·58/18-3¾	3·50/11-5¾	135/1·0-2·0	15·30/164·7	7·91	25·0/55·1	n.k.	n.k.	Pilot weight 60-100 kg (132-220 lb).
Favul *(1978: no 1979 details received)*											
Odyssée	2	9·00/29-6¼	5·20/17-0¾	3·20/10-6	118/1·0	17·00/183·0	4·76	19·0/41·9	n.k.	n.k.	Pilot weight (max) 80 kg (176 lb). Nose/billow angle variable from 117/1·5 to 119/1·0.
Star	2	8·85/29-0½	5·85/19-2¼	4·50/14-9¼	108/1·0-2·0	16·30/175·5	4·80	23·0/50·7	n.k.	n.k.	Pilot weight 65-80 kg (143-176 lb). Also available as 25 kg (55·1 lb) Star HR (Haute Résistance).
Viking	2	10·60/34-9¼	6·10/20-0	4·40/14-5¼	120/0·0	17·00/183·0	6·61	25·0/55·1	n.k.	n.k.	Pilot weight 60-85 kg (132-187 lb).

La Mouette											
Atlas 14	2	9·30/30-6¼	5·36/17-7	3·50/11-5¾	120/0·5	13·80/148·5	6·25	24·5/54·0	9	54/177	Pilot weight 65-75 kg (143-165 lb); stall 10 knots (18 km/h; 11·5 mph).
Atlas 16	2	9·80/32-1¾	5·70/18-8½	3·50/11-5¾	120/0·5	15·50/166·8	6·20	25·0/55·1	9	54/177	Pilot weight 65-100 kg (143-220 lb); stall 10 knots (18 km/h; 11·5 mph).
Lotus 15	2	9·45/31-0	5·40/17-8½	3·50/11-5¾	120/2·0	15·50/166·8	5·70	23·0/50·7	7·5	66/217	Pilot weight 40-75 kg (88-165 lb); stall 11 knots (20 km/h; 12·5 mph).
Lotus 17	2	9·80/32-1¾	5·70/18-8½	3·50/11-5¾	120/2·0	17·00/183·0	5·60	24·0/52·9	7·5	66/217	Pilot weight 65-95 kg (143-209 lb); stall 11 knots (20 km/h; 12·5 mph).
Mouette 15	1	8·00/26-3	5·00/16-4¾	3·80/12-5½	102/2·0	15·00/161·5	4·30	15·0/33·1	6·5	78/256	Pilot weight 40-55 kg (88-121 lb); stall 10 knots (18 km/h; 11·5 mph).
Mouette 17	1	8·50/27-10½	5·21/17-1	4·00/13-1½	102/2·0	17·00/183·0	4·30	17·0/37·5	6·5	78/256	Pilot weight 50-68 kg (110-150 lb); stall 10 knots (18 km/h; 11·5 mph).
Mouette 19	1	9·00/29-6¼	5·40/17-8½	4·20/13-9¼	102/2·0	19·00/204·5	4·30	19·0/41·9	6·5	78/256	Pilot weight 65-100 kg (143-220 lb); stall 10 knots (18 km/h; 11·5 mph).
Mouette 23B	1	10·60/34-9¼	5·40/17-8½	4·50/14-9¼	102/2·0	23·00/247·6	4·30	30·0/66·1	6·5	78/256	Pilot weight 100-180 kg (220-397 lb); stall 11 knots (20 km/h; 12·5 mph).
MAV *(1978: no 1979 details received)*											
Demoisel	1	7·76/25-5½	5·00/16-4¾	4·30/14-1¼	100/6·0	18·00/193·8	3·35	18·0/39·7	n.k.	n.k.	Pilot weight 46-65 kg (101-143 lb).
Eden	1	9·08/29-9½	5·84/19-2	5·00/16-4¾	100/6·0	18·50/199·1	4·46	21·0/46·3	n.k.	n.k.	Pilot weight 60-90 kg (132-198 lb).
Tantal Sinusoïde	n.k.	variable	5·50/18-0½	4·20/13-9½	variable	variable*	variable*	25·0/55·1	n.k.	n.k.	*Aspect ratio varies from 4·8 to 5·5; average wing area 16·80 m² (180·8 sq ft). Pilot weight 60-75 kg (132-165 lb).
SOFREC Véliplane											
Starga 15	2	9·14/30-0	4·85/15-11	3·60/11-9¾	140/1·0	15·00/161·5	5·60	25·0/55·1	10	66/217	Pilot weight 40-60 kg (88-132 lb); stall 12 knots (22 km/h; 14 mph).
Starga 16	2	10·00/32-9¾	4·85/15-11	3·60/11-9¾	140/1·0	16·00/172·2	6·25	25·0/55·1	10	66/217	Pilot weight 55-75 kg (121-165 lb); stall 12 knots (22 km/h; 14 mph).
Starga 17	2	10·00/32-9¾	4·85/15-11	3·60/11-9¾	140/1·0	17·00/183·0	5·88	25·0/55·1	10	66/217	Pilot weight 70-95 kg (154-209 lb); stall 12 knots (22 km/h; 14 mph).
Strato 16	2	9·20/30-2¼	4·80/15-9	4·80/15-9	123/0·0	16·30/175·5	5·19	25·0/55·1	9	75/246	Pilot weight 55-75 kg (121-165 lb); stall 13·5 knots (25 km/h; 16 mph).
Strato 18	2	9·20/30-2¼	4·80/15-9	4·80/15-9	123/0·0	17·30/186·2	4·89	25·0/55·1	9	75/246	Pilot weight 70-90 kg (154-198 lb); stall 13·5 knots (25 km/h; 16 mph).
GERMANY											
Hirth											
W-17B Dracula B	—	10·00/32-9¾	5·00/16-4¾	5·00/16-4¾	180/0·0	16·00/172·2	6·25	28·0/61·7	7-8	78/256	Pilot weight 65-95 kg (143-209 lb); stall 13·5 knots (25 km/h; 16 mph).
POLAND											
Talanczuk											
Mars-Agat WT-8	1	9·60/31-6	6·08/19-11½	2·80/9-2¼	105/3·0	21·50/231·4	4·30	25·0/55·1	9	54/177	Pilot weight 80-95 kg (176-209 lb); stall 5·5 knots (10 km/h; 6·5 mph).
Wierzbowski											
Vega 106 Sport	2	9·60/31-6	6·00/19-8¼	3·60/11-9¾	106/2·0	19·50/209·9	4·75	20·0/44·1	8·5	69/226	Pilot weight 60-95 kg (132-209 lb); stall 13 knots (24 km/h; 15 mph).
Vega 106 Uni	2	9·60/31-6	6·00/19-8¼	3·80/12-5½	106/4·0	19·20/206·7	4·80	20·0/44·1	7	75/246	Pilot weight 60-95 kg (132-209 lb); stall 14·5 knots (26 km/h; 16·5 mph).
Wolf											
Spring Wing Z-76	2	7·50/24-7¼	4·00/13-1½	2·75/10-9¼	130/1·5	13·00/139·9	4·33	15·0/33·1	5	n.k.	
Elastic Wing Z-77	2	12·00/39-4½	6·00/19-8¼	6·00/19-8¼	180/0·0	19·00/204·5	7·60	25·0/55·1	12	54/177	Pilot weight 60-85 kg (132-187 lb); stall 11 knots (20 km/h; 12·5 mph).
UNITED KINGDOM											
Flexi-form Skysails											
Skyline	n.k.	10·06/33-0	n.k.	2·44/8-0	114/1·0	15·79/170	6·40	20·9/46	7	61/200	Pilot weight 51-63·5 kg (112-140 lb); stall 14 knots (26 km/h; 16 mph).
Skyline	n.k.	10·26/33-8	n.k.	2·44/8-0	114/1·0	16·26/175	6·40	22·2/49	7	61/200	Pilot weight 63·5-76 kg (140-168 lb); stall 14 knots (26 km/h; 16 mph).
Skyline	n.k.	10·36/34-0	n.k.	2·59/8-6	114/1·0	18·12/195	6·00	24·0/53	7	61/200	Pilot weight 76-89 kg (168-196 lb); stall 14 knots (26 km/h; 16 mph).
Skyline	n.k.	10·82/35-6	n.k.	2·90/9-6	114/1·0	19·97/215	5·90	24·5/54	7	61/200	Pilot weight 89-102 kg (196-225 lb); stall 14 knots (26 km/h; 16 mph).
Spirit	n.k.	n.k.	6·25/20-6	n.k.	102/2·5	17·65/190	5·00	23·6/52	7	61/200	Pilot weight 59-77 kg (130-170 lb); stall 13·5 knots (24·5 km/h; 15 mph).
Spirit	n.k.	n.k.	6·71/22-0	n.k.	102/2·5	19·97/215	5·00	24·9/55	7	61/200	Pilot weight 77-102 kg (170-225 lb); stall 13·5 knots (24·5 km/h; 15 mph).
Vector	n.k.	10·67/35-0	6·25/20-6	2·26/7-5	114/0·0	15·79/170	7·30	24·0/53	8+	55/180	Pilot weight 59-77 kg (130-170 lb); stall 14 knots (26 km/h; 16 mph).
Vector	n.k.	11·10/36-5	6·48/21-3	2·26/7-5	114/0·0	16·72/180	7·40	24·0/53	8+	55/180	Pilot weight 77-102 kg (170-225 lb); stall 14 knots (26 km/h; 16 mph).
Hiway Hang Gliders											
Gemini	1	10·29/33-9	6·50/21-4	5·00/16-5	105/—	24·15/260	4·30	29·0/64	—	—	Two-man glider: can carry weight of up to 165 kg (364 lb); enlarged, strengthened version of Spectrum.
Harrier Standard	1	n.k.	5·49/18-0	3·96/13-0	100/n.k.	18·12/195	4·25	20·4/45	—	—	
Harrier Large	1	n.k.	6·10/20-0	4·27/14-0	100/n.k.	20·44/220	4·25	23·1/51	—	—	
Spectrum Small	1	8·18/26-10	5·18/17-0	4·04/13-3	105/n.k.	15·33/165	4·45	20·4/45	—	—	Pilot weight 50-76 kg (110-167 lb).
Spectrum Large	1	8·97/29-5	5·64/18-6	4·57/15-0	105/n.k.	17·93/193	4·45	23·1/51	—	—	Pilot weight 57-90 kg (125-198 lb).
Super Scorpion B	2	9·32/30-7	5·49/18-0	3·68/12-1	120/n.k.	16·07/173	5·60	20·9/46	—	—	Pilot weight 57-82 kg (125-181 lb).
Super Scorpion C	2	10·21/33-6	5·99/19-8	4·04/13-3	120/n.k.	18·39/198	5·70	23·6/52	—	—	Pilot weight 70-90 kg (154-198 lb.)
Super Scorpion C+	2	10·21/33-6	5·99/19-8	4·04/13-3	120/n.k.	18·39/198	5·70	n.k.	—	—	Pilot weight 89-98 kg (196-217 lb).
Waspair											
Falcon V	1	8·69/28-6	5·66/18-7	3·66/12-0	102/2·0	18·12/195	4·45	20/44·1	n.k.	n.k.	Pilot weight 50-80 kg (110-176 lb); stall 7-9 knots (13-16·5 km/h; 8-10 mph); 2 metre 'breakdown' version also available.
Gryphon G160	2/3	9·83/32-3	5·26/17-3	2·31/7-7	138/0·0	14·86/160	7·00	22·7/50	10	n.k.	Pilot weight 60-70 kg (132-154 lb); 3 metre 'breakdown' version also available.
Gryphon G180	2/3	10·52/34-6	5·51/18-1	2·44/8-0	138/0·0	16·72/180	7·00	23·6/52	10	n.k.	Pilot weight 70-100 kg (154-220 lb); 3 metre 'breakdown' version also available.
Laser L190	2	10·52/34-6	6·10/20-0	2·44/8-0	120/0·0	17·65/190	6·20	23·0/50·7	n.k.	n.k.	Pilot weight 60-100 kg (132-220 lb); 3 metre 'breakdown' version also available.

Manufacturer and Model	FAI class	Span: m/ ft-in	Leading-edge: m/ ft-in	Keel: m/ ft-in	Nose/ Billow angle: degrees	Wing area: m²/ sq ft	Wing aspect ratio	Weight: kg/lb	Glide ratio	Sink rate: m/ft per min	Remarks
UNITED STATES OF AMERICA											
AA Flight Systems *(1978: no 1979 details received)*											
Streaker	n.k.	7·16/23-6	5·49/18-0	5·49/18-0	81/n.k.	n.k.	n.k.	15·9/35	n.k.	n.k.	Also available with 4·27, 4·88 and 6·10 m (14, 16 and 20 ft) keels.
Chuck's Glider Supplies *(1978: no 1979 details received)*											
Falcon V	2	8·66/28-5	5·49/18-0	n.k.	105/1·65	14·31/154	5·24	17·7/39	8	61/200	Pilot weight 45-63·5 kg (100-140 lb).
Falcon V	2	9·63/31-7	6·10/20-0	n.k.	105/1·65	17·65/190	5·41	18·6/41	8	61/200	Pilot weight 61-84 kg (135-185 lb).
Falcon V	2	10·59/34-9	6·71/22-0	n.k.	105/1·65	21·18/228	5·30	19·5/43	8	61/200	Pilot weight 77-113 kg (170-250 lb).
Falcon V½	n.k.	8·88/29-1½	5·49/18-0	n.k.	108/0·0	14·40/155	n.k.	n.k.	9·5+	n.k.	
Falcon V½	n.k.	9·86/32-4¼	6·10/20-0	n.k.	108/0·0	16·26/175	n.k.	n.k.	9·5+	n.k.	
Falcon V½	n.k.	10·36/33-11¾	6·40/21-0	n.k.	108/0·0	17·65/190	n.k.	n.k.	9·5+	n.k.	
Spitfire	n.k.	7·01/23-0	5·18/17-0	4·57/15-0	90/3·5	13·94/150	3·53	16·8/37	6·5	61/200	Pilot weight 45-63·5 kg (100-140 lb).
Spitfire	n.k.	7·62/25-0	5·49/18-0	4·88/16-0	90/3·5	16·72/180	3·47	17·7/39	6·5	61/200	Pilot weight 61-79 kg (135-175 lb).
Spitfire	n.k.	8·53/28-1	6·10/20-0	5·49/18-0	90/3·5	20·95/225·5	3·50	19·5/43	6·5	61/200	Pilot weight 79 kg (175 lb) or heavier.
Kiceniuk											
Batso	n.k.	6·40/21-0	4·88/16-0	7·01/23-0	85/5·0	23·78/256	1·72	18·1/40	4	n.k.	
Pacific Gull											
Alpine 1·0	n.k.	9·91/32-6	5·79/19-0	2·74/9-0	115/1·0	15·79/170	6·21	23·1/51	9·5	63-66/205-215	Pilot weight 54-75 kg (120-165 lb); stall 8 knots (14·5 km/h; 9 mph).
Alpine 1·5	n.k.	9·91/32-6	5·79/19-0	2·74/9-0	115/1·0	16·54/178	6·21	23·4/51·5	9·5	63-66/205-215	Pilot weight 64-79 kg (140-175 lb); stall 8 knots (14·5 km/h; 9 mph).
Alpine 2·0	n.k.	10·36/34-0	6·10/20-0	3·05/10-0	115/1·0	17·28/186	6·22	23·6/52	9·5	63-66/205-215	Pilot weight 75-100 kg (166-220 lb); stall 8 knots (14·5 km/h; 9 mph).
Alpine 2·5	n.k.	10·36/34-0	6·10/20-0	3·05/10-0	115/1·0	19·14/206	6·22	24·0/53	9·5	63-66/205-215	Pilot weight 84-106 kg (185-235 lb); stall 8 knots (14·5 km/h; 9 mph).
Seagull Aircraft *(1978: no 1979 details received)*											
Seagull 10M	n.k.	10·29/33-9	6·10/20-0	2·44/8-0	110/0·0	16·17/174	6·55	n.k.	n.k.	n.k.	Pilot weight 59-79 kg (130-175 lb); stall 12·5 knots (23 km/h; 14 mph).
Seagull 10·5M	n.k.	10·44/34-3	6·40/21-0	2·44/8-0	110/0·0	18·21/196	5·99	n.k.	n.k.	n.k.	Pilot weight 77-100 kg (170-220 lb); stall 12·5 knots (23 km/h; 14 mph).
Seahawk 140	n.k.	7·92/26-0	5·18/17-0	3·05/10-0	100/1·5	12·29/132·34	5·11	n.k.	n.k.	n.k.	Stall 13·5 knots (24·5 km/h; 15 mph).
Seahawk 170	n.k.	9·35/30-8	5·79/19-0	3·66/12-0	100/1·5	16·70/179·76	5·23	n.k.	n.k.	n.k.	Stall 13·5 knots (24·5 km/h; 15 mph).
Seahawk 190	n.k.	9·45/31-0	6·10/20-0	3·96/13-0	100/1·5	18·59/200·14	4·80	n.k.	n.k.	n.k.	Stall 13·5 knots (24·5 km/h; 15 mph).
Sky Sports											
Bobcat IV	1	9·07/29-9	5·79/19-0	3·96/13-0	100/1·5	19·51/210	4·21	21·8/48	7	n.k.	All available in other sizes.
Eaglet	1	8·46/27-9	5·79/19-0	3·96/13-0	105/1·5	13·10/141	4·00	15·9/35	6	n.k.	
Osprey II	2	9·88/32-5	6·02/19-9	3·66/12-0	110/1·0	19·23/207	5·08	21·8/48	8	n.k.	
Sirocco III	2	10·67/35-0	6·40/21-0	2·74/9-0	120/0·0	17·19/185	6·62	24·5/54	10	n.k.	
Sunbird Ultralight Gliders											
Nova 150	n.k.	8·92/29-3	4·88/16-0	3·66/12-0	130/n.k.	13·94/150	5·70	n.k.	8·5	58/190	Pilot weight 45-64 kg (100-140 lb); stall 12·5 knots (23 km/h; 14 mph).
Nova 170	n.k.	9·45/31-0	5·18/17-0	3·81/12-6	130/n.k.	15·79/170	5·70	n.k.	8·5	58/190	Pilot weight 54-72 kg (120-160 lb); stall 12·5 knots (23 km/h; 14 mph).
Nova 190	n.k.	10·00/32-9¾	5·49/18-0	3·96/13-0	130/n.k.	17·65/190	5·70	n.k.	8·5	58/190	Pilot weight 64-86 kg (140-190 lb); stall 12·5 knots (23 km/h; 14 mph).
Nova 230	n.k.	10·97/36-0	6·10/20-0	4·42/14-6	130/n.k.	21·37/230	5·70	n.k.	8·5	58/190	Pilot weight 79-100 kg (175-220 lb); stall 12·5 knots (23 km/h; 14 mph).
UP Inc											
Condor 151	2	9·30/30-6	5·41/17-9	3·49/11-5½	118/0·75	14·03/151	6·20	20·4/45	9+	52/170	Pilot weight 48-79 kg (106-175 lb); stall 13·5 knots (24·5 km/h; 15 mph).
Condor 178	2	10·13/33-3	5·89/19-4	3·66/12-0	118/0·75	16·54/178	6·20	22·7/50	9+	52/170	Pilot weight 59-88 kg (130-195 lb); stall 13·5 knots (24·5 km/h; 15 mph).
Condor 194	2	10·57/34-8	6·17/20-3	3·96/13-0	118/0·75	18·03/194	6·20	24·5/54	9+	52/170	Pilot weight 66-95 kg (145-210 lb); stall 13·5 knots (24·5 km/h; 15 mph).
Condor 224	2	11·38/37-4	6·63/21-9	4·27/14-0	118/0·75	20·81/224	6·20	26·8/59	9+	52/170	Pilot weight 75-104 kg (165-230 lb); stall 13·5 knots (24·5 km/h; 15 mph).
Condor 269	2	12·45/40-10	7·26/23-10	4·60/15-1	118/0·75	24·99/269	6·20	35·4/78	9+	52/170	Pilot weight 87-122 kg (191-270 lb); stall 13·5 knots (24·5 km/h; 15 mph).
Firefly 2-149	2	8·72/28-7	5·56/18-2¾	2·87/9-5	107/1·5	13·84/149	5·50	20·9/46	7·5	61/199	Pilot weight 47-70 kg (103-155 lb); stall 15 knots (27·5 km/h; 17 mph).
Firefly 2-181	2	9·63/31-7	6·08/19-11¼	3·49/11-5½	107/1·5	16·82/181	5·50	23·1/51	7·5	61/199	Pilot weight 59-87 kg (130-193 lb); stall 15 knots (27·5 km/h; 17 mph).
Firefly 2-216	2	10·52/34-6	6·67/21-10⅝	4·17/13-8	107/1·5	20·07/216	5·50	25·4/56	7·5	61/199	Pilot weight 72-100 kg (160-220 lb); stall 15 knots (27·5 km/h; 17 mph).
Spyder 154	2	9·12/29-11	5·44/17-10	2·21/7-3	114/1·0	14·31/154	5·80	21·8/48	8·5+	63/208	Pilot weight 51-72 kg (113-160 lb); stall 17 knots (31 km/h; 19 mph).
Spyder 168	2	9·53/31-3	5·69/18-8	2·29/7-6	114/1·0	15·61/168	5·80	22·7/50	8·5+	63/208	Pilot weight 66-80 kg (145-177 lb); stall 17 knots (31 km/h; 19 mph).
Spyder 180	2	9·86/32-4	5·87/19-3	2·36/7-9	114/1·0	16·72/180	5·80	23·1/51	8·5+	63/208	Pilot weight 71-87 kg (156-192 lb); stall 17 knots (31 km/h; 19 mph).
Spyder 190	2	10·19/33-5	6·07/19-11	2·46/8-1	114/1·0	17·84/192	5·80	23·6/52	8·5+	63/208	Pilot weight 77-100 kg (170-220 lb); stall 17 knots (31 km/h; 19 mph).
Wills Wing											
Alpha 155	2	8·94/29-4	5·18/17-0	3·35/11-0	111/0·5	14·40/155	5·55	19·1/42	n.k.	n.k.	Pilot weight 50-66 kg (110-145 lb).
Alpha 185	2	9·70/31-10	5·64/18-6	3·66/12-0	111/0·5	17·19/185	5·50	20·4/45	n.k.	n.k.	Pilot weight 63-79 kg (140-175 lb).
Alpha 215	2	10·52/34-6	6·10/20-0	3·96/13-0	111/0·5	19·97/215	5·50	21·8/48	n.k.	n.k.	Pilot weight 75-93 kg (165-205 lb).
Alpha 245	2	11·28/37-0	6·55/21-6	4·27/14-0	111/0·5	22·76/245	5·60	25·0/55	n.k.	n.k.	Pilot weight 86-113 kg (190-250 lb).
Omega 180	2	10·82/35-6	6·17/20-3	3·58/11-9	120/0·5	16·72/180	7·00	23·6/52	n.k.	n.k.	Pilot weight 59-79 kg (130-175 lb).
Omega 220	2	11·58/38-0	6·68/21-11	3·78/12-5	120/0·5	20·44/220	6·60	25·4/56	n.k.	n.k.	Pilot weight 75-100 kg (165-220 lb).
Omega 260	2	12·34/40-6	7·14/23-5	3·99/13-1	120/0·5	24·15/260	6·30	27·2/60	n.k.	n.k.	Pilot weight 91-120 kg (200-265 lb).
Omni 170	2	10·21/33-6	5·64/18-6	3·35/11-0	120/0·2	15·79/170	6·60	22·7/50	n.k.	n.k.	Pilot weight 59-77 kg (130-170 lb).
Omni 200	2	10·97/36-0	6·10/20-0	3·66/12-0	120/0·2	18·58/200	6·50	24·5/54	n.k.	n.k.	Pilot weight 72-91 kg (160-200 lb).
Omni 230	2	11·73/38-6	6·55/21-6	3·96/13-0	120/0·2	21·37/230	6·40	26·3/58	n.k.	n.k.	Pilot weight 86-104 kg (190-230 lb).

n.k. = not known

LIGHTER-THAN-AIR: AIRSHIPS

AUSTRALIA

MANTAINER
MANTAINER PTY LTD

52 Hawker Street, Airport West, near Melbourne, Victoria 3042
Telephone: 338 2231

Managing Director: A. G. Norton

The Mantainer MA-1 airship (VH-PSE), the first to be designed and built in Australia, was flown for the first time on 8 July 1978. Details of this craft can be found in the 1978-79 *Jane's*.

JAPAN

FUJI
FUJI MANUFACTURING CO LTD

16 Hotoku-cho, Kita-ku, Nagoya
Telephone: (052) 991 8171

President: Yasushi Koizumi

In the Autumn of 1974 Fuji Manufacturing Co began construction of a small remotely controlled pilotless research airship (construction number 2) which flew for the first time on 23 December 1974. (It is believed that No. 1 was the airship built by members of the Japan Experimental Aircraft Association and described under the JEAA heading in the 1975-76 *Jane's*.)

Airship No. 3 flew on 28 July 1975, this being a modified version of No. 2. No details are known of Nos 4, 5 and 6; but No. 7, which first flew on 21 November 1975, has an overall length of 6·0 m (19 ft 7½ in) and was supplied to Tohoku University Geographical Laboratory. Airship No. 12 was under test at the end of 1978.

Latest radio-controlled research airship in the Fuji Model 500 Aero-Ship series

FUJI MODEL 500 AERO-SHIP

The word Aero-Ship, which forms a part of the designation of the Fuji Model 500, is an allusion to the unique aeroplane-type horizontal lifting surface which is attached to the lower structure of the gondola. The Aero-Ship's envelope is helium filled, and it is claimed that the wing not only provides additional lift but, in conjunction with the fairly large tail surfaces, ought to make the vessel highly manoeuvrable. Flown under radio control, it is suggested that the Aero-Ship could be utilised for such applications as aerial photography, various forms of meteorological and pollution measurement, seed and fertiliser distribution, and advertising.

The envelope of the Model 500 is of plastics, the gondola and cruciform tail surfaces of wood, with silk covering. Tailplane incidence is normally 3°, but is ground adjustable. Trim tabs in elevators. The wing is also of wood, with silk covering. Wing section is Göttingen Gö 535 and the wing is normally mounted without incidence. Two handling wheels, with tyres of 365 mm (14·4 in) diameter, are mounted beneath the wing, one at the aft end of the gondola and one beneath the lower fin. Two ENYA 60 IIIB aircooled engines, each developing 0·97 kW (1·3 hp), are mounted at the rear of the gondola, at each end of an outrigger. The forward part of the gondola is able to house a camera or other equipment. Radio control equipment and batteries are accommodated in the central area, and a fuel tank in the aft section.

Limited range of the radio control equipment used to date has prevented full evaluation of the Aero-Ship's performance, but a speed range of 5·4-43 knots (10-80 km/h; 6·2-50 mph) and ceiling of 1,000 m (3,280 ft) have been demonstrated.

Dimensions:	
Length overall	8·0 m (26 ft 3 in)
Wing span	3·26 m (10 ft 8½ in)
Wing chord, constant	0·68 m (2 ft 2¾ in)
Tailplane span	2·25 m (7 ft 4½ in)
Dimensions, envelope:	
Max diameter	1·90 m (6 ft 2¾ in)
Volume, gross	18·28 m³ (645 cu ft)
Areas:	
Wings, gross	1·01 m² (10·87 sq ft)
Rudders (total)	0·43 m² (4·63 sq ft)
Tailplane	0·86 m² (9·26 sq ft)
Elevators (incl tabs)	0·49 m² (5·27 sq ft)
Weights and Loading:	
Weight empty, equipped	22·7 kg (50 lb)
Weight, helium filled	4·0 kg (8·8 lb)
Max T-O weight	6·0 kg (13·2 lb)
Max wing loading	5·96 kg/m² (1·22 lb/sq ft)

UNITED KINGDOM

AEROSPACE DEVELOPMENTS
AEROSPACE DEVELOPMENTS (LONDON) LTD

19-21 Newbury Street, London EC1A 7HU
Telephone: (01) 606 5981/3
Telex: 884985 MTAAD

Aerospace Developments has designed and built the first of 22 non-rigid airships which its associated marketing organisation, Multimodal Transport Analysis Ltd, contracted in 1977 to supply to a Venezuelan customer, Aerovision. Two contracts were involved. The first covered the supply of a single airship, designated AD-500; the other provided for a further 21 airships to be delivered over the ensuing 10 years.

Five types of airship have been proposed, with payload capability respectively of 0·5, 2, 5, 10 and 20-25 tons. It is understood that other South American countries are interested in the potential of airships for transport to and from undeveloped and otherwise inaccessible areas. It is suggested that the cost of operation can be offset by using such vessels also in a night-time advertising role.

The AD-500 prototype (G-BECE), built under the first Venezuelan contract, was completed in early 1979 and made its first flight from RAF Cardington, Bedfordshire, on 3 February 1979. It was planned that, following minor modifications and flight trials, the vessel would be tested by the Royal Navy, and evaluated by the UK Ministry of Agriculture and Fisheries, before being dismantled in the late Summer for transport to the United States for US Navy trials. The interest of these bodies reflects the potential of an airship for such tasks as maritime patrol, fishery protection, and anti-submarine warfare. The AD-500 has been designed for, and is intended to obtain, a full Transport Category certificate of airworthiness.

Aerospace Developments AD-500 non-rigid airship at the time of its first flight

The prototype was damaged when unexpected force 9 winds caught it at its moorings. The programme is to be continued in Canada, under new sponsorship.

AEROSPACE DEVELOPMENTS AD-500

The envelope of the AD-500 is manufactured from a strong-in-weft single-ply polyester fabric, developed by Aerospace Developments, and coated with titanium dioxide polyurethane sealant to minimise loss of the helium lifting gas. The nose structure consists of a domed disc, moulded from Kevlar and carrying the fitting by which the airship is moored to its transportable mast. Two ballonets, which together comprise 25 per cent of the envelope volume, are installed fore and aft, so that differential inflation will provide some degree of fore and aft trim. Catenary curtains carry 12 main cables of Kevlar within the envelope for suspension of the gondola. The tail unit is of conventional cruciform layout, each surface being attached to the envelope at its root and braced by four wires on each side. All four surfaces are constructed from interlocking ribs and spars of Fibrelam and have GRP skins: their hinged rudder and elevator control surfaces are cable-operated and each has a trim tab.

The gondola is a one-piece moulding of Kevlar-reinforced plastics, with flooring and bulkheads of Fibrelam panels; those which form the engine compartment at the rear of the gondola are faced with stainless steel for fire protection. There is accommodation for a pilot and co-pilot, with dual controls, although the vessel is designed to be flown by a single pilot; there are seven individual seats for passengers. Door on port side, just aft of flight deck. Transparent plastics dome in ceiling of flight deck for visual internal inspection of envelope. Ballast in the form of lead shot is contained in a box situated below the crew seats, and water ballast totalling 513 kg (1,130 lb) is contained in tanks at the rear of the gondola. A single fully-castoring wheel with pneumatic tyre is mounted on an oleo-pneumatic strut beneath the gondola to ensure that the latter is not damaged by contact with the ground.

Power plant comprises two 149 kW (200 hp) Porsche six-cylinder aircooled motorcar engines. Each drives, via a modified Lynx helicopter tail rotor gearbox, a ducted propulsor designed by Aerospace Developments, consisting of a Hoffmann five-blade reversible-pitch metal propeller rotating within an annular duct constructed of GRP, reinforced with carbon fibre. Each propulsor can be rotated about its pylon attachment to the gondola through an arc of 210°: 90° upward and 120° downward. The 30° of movement past centre with the ducted propulsors facing downward is to maintain cable tension while the airship is being moored to its mast. The vectored thrust available throughout this range of 210° simplifies the tasks of take-off and landing. A fuel tank, capacity 536 litres (118 Imp gallons), is mounted at rear of engine compartment. Max fuel capacity is 1,577 litres (347 Imp gallons). Engine modifications include provision of automatic mixture control, fuel injection and electronic ignition. The 28V electrical system is supplied by engine-driven alternators. Avionics installed in the AD-500 prototype include Bendix 2000 series dual nav/com, ADF, VOR/ILS and Omega, Bendix 1400 weather radar, and Decca Doppler 80 nav system with PBDI and automatic chart display.

DIMENSIONS, ENVELOPE:
- Length overall: 50·00 m (164 ft 0½ in)
- Max diameter: 14·00 m (45 ft 11¼ in)
- Volume, gross: 5,130 m³ (181,160 cu ft)
- Volume, ballonets: 1,282·5 m³ (45,290 cu ft)

DIMENSIONS, GONDOLA:
- Length overall: 9·25 m (30 ft 4 in)
- Height: 2·26 m (7 ft 4⅞ in)
- Max width: 2·41 m (7 ft 10¾ in)

WEIGHT:
- Nominal payload to 610 m (2,000 ft): 2,540 kg (5,600 lb)

PERFORMANCE (estimated):
- Max level speed: 62 knots (114 km/h; 71 mph)
- Cruising speed: 49 knots (90 km/h; 56 mph)
- Pressure altitude: 3,050 m (10,000 ft)
- Range with 1,577 litres (347 Imp gallons) of fuel, 15% reserves:
  - at 15 knots (28 km/h; 17 mph): 6,375 nm (11,800 km; 7,335 miles)
  - at max speed: 600 nm (1,110 km; 690 miles)

CAMERON
CAMERON BALLOONS LTD

1 Cotham Park, Bristol BS6 6BZ
Telephone: (0272) 41455

DIRECTORS:
D. A. Cameron, BSc (Aero Eng), MIE, MRAeS
Kim Cameron
Tom Sage, ARPS, AIIP

Cameron Balloons Ltd, which designs and manufactures a wide range of hot-air balloons (which see), also designed and built the world's first hot-air airship, of which production versions are available. In early 1979 a new, higher-performance airship was being studied. It was anticipated that this would have a speed of 40 knots (74 km/h; 46 mph).

CAMERON D96 HOT-AIR AIRSHIP

First flight of the prototype (G-BAMK) was made at Wantage, Berkshire, on 7 January 1973. Since that time a considerable amount of work has been carried out to improve and develop the airship, and the current production model has two vertical and two horizontal stabilisers. An improved method of suspending the gondola has also been evolved, eliminating the distortion of the envelope which occurred in the early stages. During 1978, further development led to an increase in the length and volume of the envelope. Like the envelopes of Cameron hot-air balloons, this is made from a light but high-strength nylon fabric. A lightweight gondola carries the propane burner, gas supply, pilot, and power plant. A maximum of two passengers can be accommodated.

Power plant is a 33·5 kW (45 hp) 1,600 cc Volkswagen modified motor car engine, using propane as fuel and driving a large-diameter semi-shrouded pusher propeller.

The first production airship was completed for a customer in the United States; seven more have been constructed for customers in Australia, Belgium, France, the Netherlands, Sweden and UK.

Production Cameron D96 hot-air airship for C & A, the first of the 1978 modified design

The following data apply to the current version, with the envelope lengthened by 3·66 m (12 ft):

DIMENSIONS, ENVELOPE:
- Length overall: 34·14 m (112 ft 0 in)
- Max diameter: 13·72 m (45 ft 0 in)
- Volume, gross: 2,917 m³ (103,000 cu ft)

PERFORMANCE:
- Max speed: 13 knots (24 km/h; 15 mph)
- Turning radius at 8·7 knots (16 km/h; 10 mph): 30·5 m (100 ft)
- Endurance: 2 h

THUNDER
THUNDER BALLOONS LTD

75 Leonard Street, London EC2A 4QS
Telephone: (01) 729 0231/0206
Telex: 261234 reference H5758D

CHAIRMAN: K. F. Simonds

DIRECTORS:
T. M. Donnelly (Managing)
A. R. Wirth

Thunder Balloons has been involved in the design and development of a hot-air airship during the past two years. A one-fifth-scale radio controlled model has been flown successfully, confirming flight characteristics. The full-size airship was under construction in the Spring of 1979, and was scheduled for delivery to an English customer later in the year. Very few details had been released in early 1979: it was known only that the envelope length was approximately 38·10 m (125 ft), diameter 12·19 m (40 ft), and gross volume 3,965 m³ (140,000 cu ft). The gondola, with burner mounted above, will accommodate three persons. Design maximum speed is quoted as 25 knots (46 km/h; 29 mph).

UNITED STATES OF AMERICA

BOLAND
BOLAND BALLOON

Pine Drive, RD 2, Burlington, Connecticut 06013
Telephone: (203) 673 1307

BOLAND A-1 ALBATROSS

Mr Brian Boland, an art and photographic teacher at Farmington High School, Connecticut, has, with his wife Kathy, designed and built hot-air balloons, described in the Balloons section (which see), as well as a hot-air airship named *Albatross.* Construction began in January 1975 and it was flown for the first time on 11 October 1975. By January 1978 a total of 24 flying hours had been accumulated.

The envelope is made from 32 separate strips of polyurethane-coated rip-stop nylon. The gondola, which can accommodate four persons, has a basic structure of light alloy, around which wicker sidewalls have been woven. It has oak landing skids on its undersurface, and is mounted on a wheeled trailer for easy ground handling, this being left on the ground on lift-off. The gondola is suspended from the envelope by 28 flexible steel cables which run through its light alloy tubular framework and are attached to two catenary suspension curtains. The tubular framework of the gondola serves also as mounting

Boland A-1 *Albatross* in latest form, with ram-air inflated fin and rudder

for three 8 million BTU propane burners. The fuel supply comprises six low-pressure cylinders, with a combined capacity of 227 litres (60 US gallons) of liquid propane, and a 22·7 litre (6 US gallon) tank of fuel/oil mixture for the propulsion engine. This is a 29·8 kW (40 hp) Rockwell JLO two-stroke engine, driving a Banks Maxwell two-blade ducted pusher propeller.

On the basis of flight experience with *Albatross* Mr Boland designed a number of improvements, including shortening each of the original catenary cables by 2·29 m (7 ft 6 in); adding 7·32 m (24 ft) of catenary curtain aft of the original curtains; and improving the structural integrity of the gondola by heliarc welding of all metal fittings. The rigid-frame fabric-covered fin and rudder, with which *Albatross* was flown originally, has been replaced by a multi-chambered inflatable fin and rudder with three times the surface area.

A second hot-air airship was designed in 1978. This is believed to have a volume of about 1,699-1,982 m³ (60,000-70,000 cu ft) and is described as being ultra-lightweight, responsive and compact. Construction was expected to start in 1979.

The following details apply to *Albatross:*

DIMENSIONS, OVERALL:
- Length: 34·14 m (112 ft 0 in)
- Height: 19·81 m (65 ft 0 in)
- Width: 15·24 m (50 ft 0 in)
- Volume: 3,965 m³ (140,000 cu ft)

DIMENSIONS, GONDOLA:
- Length overall: 3·35 m (11 ft 0 in)
- Height: 3·05 m (10 ft 0 in)
- Width: 1·22 m (4 ft 0 in)

WEIGHTS:
- Flight weight, fuelled: 658 kg (1,450 lb)
- Max design gross weight: 1,089 kg (2,400 lb)

PERFORMANCE:
- Max speed: approx 8·7 knots (16 km/h; 10 mph)
- Turning radius: approx 91 m (300 ft)

CONRAD

CONRAD AIRSHIP CORPORATION

Chandler, Arizona

No further details have become available of this company's airship which was described briefly on page 632 of the 1977-78 *Jane's,* but a brief report has been received of an unusual new rigid airship being built in the USA, the shape and basic form of which can be seen in the adjacent photograph; this is assumed to be the Conrad airship. It is to be powered by three engines used normally as marine outboard motors, namely two 97 kW (130 hp) Evinrude engines, and one 112 kW (150 hp) Mercury engine. When completed the airship is intended to have a helium-filled envelope, and will provide accommodation for a pilot and seven passengers.

DIMENSIONS, EXTERNAL:
- Diameter: 24·38 m (80 ft 0 in)
- Height overall: 8·23 m (27 ft 0 in)

WEIGHTS (estimated):
- Weight empty: 1,361 kg (3,000 lb)
- Max T-O weight: 2,041 kg (4,500 lb)

PERFORMANCE (estimated):
- Cruising speed: 35 knots (64 km/h; 40 mph)

Overall view of basic structure of the Conrad airship *(Neil A. Macdougall)*

GOODYEAR

THE GOODYEAR TIRE & RUBBER COMPANY—AIRSHIP OPERATIONS

1144 East Market Street, Akron, Ohio 44316
Telephone: (216) 794 4045
CHAIRMAN OF THE BOARD AND CHIEF EXECUTIVE OFFICER: Charles J. Pilliod Jr
VICE-PRESIDENT PUBLIC RELATIONS: Robert H. Lane

Goodyear has built a total of 303 airships, more than any other company in the world. Of these, 261 were constructed under contract for the US Army and Navy, and included the USS *Akron* and USS *Macon,* the largest rigid airships constructed in the USA. The remaining 42 have been commercial airships, of which the first was the *Pilgrim,* launched in 1925.

Goodyear operates currently four non-rigid airships for public relations and sales promotion activities: *America, Columbia IV, Europa* and *Mayflower. Europa* is based near Rome, Italy, the other three airships in the USA. Details of the newly constructed *Mayflower* follow. In size, equipment and performance it is generally the same as the three other airships in the fleet. Details of a smaller version of the *Mayflower* (N38A), which was completed in 1976 and is no longer in service, can be found in the 1978-79 *Jane's.*

Goodyear has been studying the development of heavy-lift airships, and believes that existing technology can provide such a vehicle in the 1980s if adequate funding is available. The company suggests that a helium-filled airship, using helicopter-type rotors for lift and conventional propellers for forward flight, would prove more economical than helicopters in a flying-crane role, and would also have a very much greater lift capability. Studies indicate that by using such techniques a 73,625 m³ (2·6 million cu ft) airship would have a useful lifting capacity of 76·2 tonnes (75 tons).

The new *Mayflower,* **constructed by Goodyear during 1978**

Model of heavy-lift airship studied by the Goodyear company

MAYFLOWER

This latest *Mayflower* (N3A) was constructed during 1978 and erected at Houston, Texas, where it was flown for the first time in early November 1978. Some two weeks later it was flown to its base at Miami, Florida. Like its sister ships, it has a gross volume of 5,740 m³ (202,700 cu ft) and envelope surface area of 2,006 m² (21,600 sq ft). The envelope is made of two-ply Neoprene-coated Dacron and is helium-filled. On each side is a four-colour sign 32·00 m (105 ft 0 in) long and 7·47 m (24 ft 6 in) high, containing 3,780 lamps to flash static or animated messages. These can be read at a distance of 1·6 km (1 mile) when the airship is cruising at a height of 305 m (1,000 ft). A turbojet APU, mounted in a removable pod on the undersurface of the 'ship's gondola, drives a 500A 28V generator to supply electrical power for the signs and their control equipment. The turbojet is designed to operate without developing any appreciable amount of forward thrust for the airship.

The gondola, attached to the undersurface of the envelope, has accommodation for a pilot and six passengers, and has a single non-retractable landing wheel mounted beneath it.

Power plant consists of two 157 kW (210 hp) Continental IO-360-D flat-six engines, each driving a Hartzell two-blade metal reversible-pitch pusher propeller. Tankage is provided for 527 litres (138 US gallons) of fuel.

DIMENSIONS, OVERALL:
- Length: 58·67 m (192 ft 6 in)
- Width: 15·24 m (50 ft 0 in)
- Height: 18·14 m (59 ft 6 in)

DIMENSIONS, ENVELOPE:
- Length: 58·00 m (190 ft 3½ in)
- Max diameter: 14·00 m (45 ft 11½ in)
- Fineness ratio: 14·4
- Volume, gross: 5,740 m³ (202,700 cu ft)
- Volume, ballonets: 1,662·2 m³ (58,700 cu ft)

DIMENSIONS, GONDOLA:
- Length overall: 6·93 m (22 ft 9 in)
- Height: 2·47 m (8 ft 1¼ in)
- Height, incl landing gear: 3·59 m (11 ft 9½ in)
- Width at ceiling: 2·13 m (7 ft 0 in)
- Width at floor: 1·31 m (4 ft 3½ in)

WEIGHTS:
- Weight empty: 4,252 kg (9,375 lb)
- Max design gross weight: 5,824 kg (12,840 lb)

PERFORMANCE:
- Max speed: 43·5 knots (80 km/h; 50 mph)
- Normal cruising speed: 30-35 knots (56-64 km/h; 35-40 mph)
- Max rate of climb at S/L: 732 m (2,400 ft)/min
- Max rate of descent: 427 m (1,400 ft)/min
- Normal operational altitude: 305-915 m (1,000-3,000 ft)
- Service ceiling: 2,285 m (7,500 ft)
- Endurance at cruising speed: approx 10 h

HOV-AIR-SHIP

HOV-AIR-SHIP INC

ADDRESS: 1427 West 22nd Street, Miami Beach, Florida 33140
Telephone: (305) 531 8968/8969

HOV-AIR-SHIP HX-1

Designed by Mr Saul I. Slater, who formed Hov-Air-Ship Inc to hold the patents of this and other designs he has produced, the HX-1 is a small-scale remotely controlled airship 5·79 m (19 ft) long and 2·13 m (7 ft) in diameter, with cruciform tail surfaces. It has been test-flown tethered to a 110V electrical power source and piloted by a controller on the ground; a magnetic device is used to moor the airship, without any need for groundcrew assistance.

A feature which at the present time is unique to this airship is an ability to hover over a fixed point, and ascend or descend above that point. The HX-1 has been acquired by the US Navy, and was delivered on 16 October 1978 for extensive tests at the Naval Air Development Center, Warminster, Pennsylvania.

Mr Slater has proposed an enlarged HX-2 version to the US Navy and Coast Guard. This would be approx 41·15 m (135 ft) long, 10·67 m (35 ft) in diameter, have an envelope volume of 2,124 m³ (75,000 cu ft), and be powered by small turboshaft engines. Such an airship could, it is claimed, carry a two/three-man crew and 181 kg (400 lb) of equipment, plus enough fuel for a 24 h mission (4 h cruise at 50 knots; 93 km/h; 58 mph, a further 10 h at 20 knots; 37 km/h; 23 mph, and 10 h loiter). Alternatively, the HX-2 could be operated in remotely piloted form, untethered, as a cargo carrier.

Hov-Air-Ship's HX-1 small experimental airship, which was being tested by the US Navy in 1979

TUCKER

TUCKER AIRSHIP COMPANY

13218 Lake Street, Los Angeles, California 90066
Telephone: (213) 398 6907; (213) 354 6970
PRESIDENT: Curtis E. Tucker Jr

The Tucker Airship Company was founded in 1973 by Curtis Tucker Jr, with the object of building airships that would benefit from the latest technology and materials.

Production of three prototype airships was planned as follows:

TX-1. An experimental flight vehicle to validate the basic design, test materials and mooring system, and subsequently be used for research, pilot training and advertising. Funding for the TX-1 was reduced during 1977, but a decision was made to provide further funds during 1978 so that the vessel would become operational and available for company use. Following inflation in July 1978 for installation of finger patches and gas valve reinforcements, it was anticipated that the TX-1 would make its first flight by the late Summer of 1979.

Proposal 751. A non-rigid airship for enforcement of laws and treaties (ELT), aerial photography and advertising, with a crew of two plus one passenger. Low noise and vibration levels make such a vehicle an excellent platform for coastal surveillance and photography, providing, by comparison with a helicopter, long range and improved crew comfort. Early studies indicate that operating costs will be lower than those of a helicopter, although initial capital cost may be greater. Design parameters include length 41·15 m (135 ft), volume 2,265 m³ (80,000 cu ft), max speed 87 knots (160 km/h; 100 mph), ceiling 3,050 m (10,000 ft), range of approx 430 nm (800 km; 500 miles).

Proposal 761. A semi-rigid airship for geological exploration or as an experimental airship for naval use. In the former configuration this vessel would have quarters, facilities and laboratories for a crew of four and six passengers and would be able to remain airborne for periods of five to six days for exploration of remote areas. Initial applications in a naval role would be to appraise its potential for sea control and anti-submarine warfare. Reduced accommodation and the elimination of laboratories would provide for advanced avionics equipment to be carried over an extended range. Special features envisaged for this proposal include the provision of a small helipad on the upper surface of the envelope, artificial superheating and chilling to assist vessel trimming, ducted propellers, electronic control of subsystems and internal control runs for the operation of aerodynamic surfaces. Design parameters include length 106·68 m (350 ft), volume 28,317 m³ (1,000,000 cu ft), max speed 78 knots (145 km/h; 90 mph), ceiling 3,660 m (12,000 ft), pressure height 2,440 m (8,000 ft), range 4,165 nm (7,720 km; 4,800 miles).

TUCKER TX-1

Design of the TX-1 originated in October 1972 and construction began in May 1973. During 1976 the company encountered a problem with its envelope sealing process, but this was subsequently resolved. The TX-1 is very much an experimental vessel, intended to provide experience in design, construction and operation, and will be used to test new design ideas, materials and ground handling concepts. Should the future airship proposals develop, it is envisaged that the TX-1 type would serve as a low-cost primary trainer. It is intended to be available for research use by scientific, military and industrial organisations upon request.

Tucker TX-1 airship during inflation checks in August 1978

A semi-rigid design was chosen to provide for multi-mission roles, permitting the carriage of external loads; all of the superstructure, including the tail control surfaces, is located beneath the envelope. Oversize ballast and trim tanks are provided to keep the airship level irrespective of load disposition, and to provide additional safety during pilot training. A unique feature of the design is its modular construction. The TX-1 breaks down into twelve units for transportation or storage, and can be assembled and inflated in an open field. A portable mooring mast, which can be erected in 30 minutes, has been designed and built, and this accepts the company's Mk 1 pneumatic mooring spindle which requires only one man on the ground to carry out mooring and castoff operations. When broken down for transit, the entire vessel can be accommodated in a standard-width trailer, 4·57 m (15 ft) in length, and there is sufficient space in the trailer for a power generating unit, air to ground communication system, and other essential supplies and equipment. During 1978 a portable double-wall air-inflated hangar was developed to accommodate the TX-1. Measuring 33·5 × 12·2 × 10·7 m (110 × 40 × 35 ft), it has an air-operated upward-opening clamshell door.

The forward-mounted gondola of the TX-1 airship provides accommodation for the pilot and one passenger, seated in tandem. Excellent visibility is provided by a wide and deep windscreen, plus large sliding side windows. Standard airship controls are provided and equipment includes VFR instrumentation and communication radio. A monowheel is mounted beneath the gondola. Tail control surfaces comprise a large fin and rudder, with a wide-span horizontal tail surface and elevator. Power plant planned originally was a 67 kW (90 hp) McCulloch two-stroke four-cylinder engine, mounted beneath the keel structure at approximately its mid-point, and driving an AAF tractor propeller 1·12 m (3 ft 8 in) in diameter. However, during 1978 tests were made of a new power plant with an output of 89 kW (120 hp). Total fuel capacity is 227 litres (60 US gallons).

Three holds are provided within the keel structure, each with a capacity of 90·7 kg (200 lb), and are available for equipment or baggage. Hardpoints are provided for the carriage of external loads.

The envelope, which contains a single ballonet, is manufactured from a plastic laminate, coated with a special sealant developed by the company, and is intended to be hydrogen filled for short test flights. For operational use the envelope would be inflated with helium. Special equipment includes pneumatic ballast controls, and there are provisions for full IFR instrumentation.

DIMENSIONS, OVERALL:
- Length: 27·74 m (91 ft 0 in)
- Height: 7·92 m (26 ft 0 in)

DIMENSIONS, ENVELOPE:
- Length: 27·74 m (91 ft 0 in)
- Max diameter: 6·10 m (20 ft 0 in)
- Length of constant-diameter section: 13·11 m (43 ft 0 in)
- Volume: 580·5 m³ (20,500 cu ft)

DIMENSIONS, GONDOLA:
- Length overall: 2·74 m (9 ft 0 in)
- Height: 1·37 m (4 ft 6 in)
- Max width: 0·91 m (3 ft 0 in)

AREAS:
- Fin: 6·97 m² (75·0 sq ft)
- Rudder: 2·93 m² (31·5 sq ft)
- Tailplane: 7·43 m² (80·0 sq ft)
- Elevator: 5·39 m² (58·0 sq ft)

WEIGHTS (estimated):
- Weight empty: 295 kg (650 lb)
- Max design gross weight: 635 kg (1,400 lb)

PERFORMANCE (estimated, with 67 kW; 90 hp engine):
- Max speed: 48 knots (88 km/h; 55 mph)
- Service ceiling: 1,370 m (4,500 ft)
- Range with max fuel: 434 nm (804 km; 500 miles)
- Range with max payload: 43 nm (80 km; 50 miles)

LIGHTER-THAN-AIR: BALLOONS

FRANCE

CHAIZE
BALLONS CHAIZE

48 rue Balay, 42000 Saint-Étienne
Telephone: (77) 33 43 76

M Maurice Chaize was offering four hot-air balloons during 1978, one in the FAI AX-6 class, the others in the AX-7 class. The envelopes are made from high-strength nylon, with the lower panels in the throat made from Nomex flame-resistant fabric. They are supplied in a ready-to-fly state, complete with basket, burners, and gas cylinders, but without instruments.

The company holds the French Certificat de Navigabilité de Type for all four models, details of which can be found in the accompanying tables.

The prototype balloon was flown for the first time in December 1972. Deliveries began in the Summer of 1977, and totalled nine by February 1978; no information on subsequent production had been received by early 1979.

UNITED KINGDOM

CAMERON
CAMERON BALLOONS LTD

1 Cotham Park, Bristol BS6 6BZ
Telephone: (0272) 41455
Directors: See Airships sub-section

Cameron Balloons has been manufacturing hot-air balloons in Bristol since 1968. The company is the second largest manufacturer of hot-air balloons in the world, and has built the world's largest hot-air balloon, the *Gerard A. Heineken* of 14,158 m³ (500,000 cu ft). Cameron balloons hold the absolute altitude record for hot-air balloons of 13,971 m (45,836 ft) and the absolute duration record of 18 h 56 min. The company holds CAA, FAA, Certificat de Navigabilité de Type and the West German Musterzulassungsschein type certificates for its balloons. It constructed also the world's first hot-air airship (see Airships section).

Envelopes are made from rip-stop nylon which has been treated with a polyurethane sealant to reduce porosity. The lower section of the envelope is made from Nomex flame-resistant fabric. The envelopes are available with either a Velcro seal or parachute deflation system, and those with the Velcro seal have also a vertical flap-type vent. Cameron offers a wide range of balloons, details of which can be found in the accompanying table. Each is supplied complete with willow and cane basket, burner and gas cylinders and is ready to fly when delivered. Optional items include instrument pack, envelope thermometer, pressure scoop, Nomex skirt, rigid-suspension basket, trail rope and additional gas cylinders.

During 1976 the company initiated the design of specially shaped balloons for advertising purposes. Two new sporting balloons were introduced during 1977, one in the AX-4 and the other in the AX-7 class; 1978 saw introduction of a balloon in the AX-3 class.

THUNDER
THUNDER BALLOONS LTD

75 Leonard Street, London EC2A 4QS
Telephone: (01) 729 0231/0206
Telex: 261234 reference H5758D
Chairman: K. F. Simonds
Directors:
T. M. Donnelly (Managing)
A. R. Wirth

Thunder Balloons manufactures a range of ready-to-fly hot-air balloons, details of which can be found in the accompanying tables. In early 1979 there were four basic types, all of them incorporating a fail-safe plug-parachute deflation system.

Envelopes are made from coated polyamide or polyester fabrics, with lower panels of Nomex flame-resistant fabric. All balloons are supplied complete with basket, burner and fuel cylinders, and are certificated for use throughout the world. Series 1, 2 and Z balloons are available with an instrument dashboard which covers the fuel cylinders and provides more room within the basket. 'Bolt' type balloons, in a lower price range, were introduced during 1978. The British team competing in the World Championship events in 1979 flew Z-type Thunder balloons.

The company is developing also a hot-air airship, all available details of which are given in the Airships section.

UNITED STATES OF AMERICA

ADAMS
MIKE ADAMS' BALLOON LOFT INC

PO Box 12168, Atlanta, Georgia 30355
Telephone: (404) 261 5818

Mike Adams' Balloon Loft is manufacturing a range of hot-air balloons, of which details can be found in the accompanying tables.

Envelopes are made from rip-stop nylon, which may be coated optionally with a polyurethane or aluminised sealant to reduce porosity. Nomex flame-resistant fabric is used to protect the envelope throat. Two manoeuvring vents are located in the crown of the balloon and there is a duffle bag type of deflation system.

For 1978 Adams introduced the first two of a series of balloons, named 'Little Devil' models. These feature a deflation system which the company calls MultiVent, a single control line creating 16 diamond-shape openings which snap shut immediately the control line is released. MultiVent provides an improved measure of control, and is available optionally for all balloons manufactured by the company.

Adams balloons are supplied complete with a woven rattan basket, burner, aluminium fuel cylinders, and instruments which include a sensitive altimeter, rate-of-climb indicator, envelope temperature gauge, bubble type compass and fuel gauges. Optional items include tank-mounted pressure gauge, Nomex skirt, MultiVent deflation system, inflator fan and additional fuel cylinders.

Some new designs were under development in 1979.

AVIAN
AVIAN BALLOON

South 4323 Locust Road, Spokane, Washington 99206

Avian Balloon has completed FAA certification of two hot-air balloons: these are in FAI classes AX-7 and AX-8 and are named Falcon II and Skyhawk respectively. The company was working in early 1978 to complete the certification of a new, larger (2,973 m³; 105,000 cu ft) balloon in the AX-8 class which is named Eagle, and plans to introduce a larger basket which will include a fully gimballed burner. No further information on this project had been received in early 1979.

The balloon envelopes are made from rip-stop nylon, which can be treated with a sealant to reduce porosity, or can optionally be made from aluminised balloon fabric. A feature of the design is the incorporation of a mechanical rapid deflation system. The basket is of wicker and, in addition to the burner and gas cylinders, an instrument panel that includes an altimeter, rate-of-climb indicator, envelope temperature gauge and compass is standard. Options include an inflater fan, redundant burner system, night light, extra fuel line, ball variometer, and extra propane tank. Details of Avian's balloons are given in the accompanying tables.

BALLOON WORKS
THE BALLOON WORKS

Rhyne Aerodrome—RFD2, Statesville, North Carolina 28677
Telephone: (704) 873 0503
Directors:
Tracy Barnes
Dodds Meddock
Karl Stefan

The Balloon Works is currently marketing four category sizes of hot-air balloons, details of which are given in the accompanying tables.

The envelopes of this company's balloons are made of a polyester fabric, which tests have shown to be less affected by heat and sunlight exposure than other materials, and are coated with a urethane sealant to reduce porosity. Rapid deflation is made possible by use of a wide-diameter envelope valve, which is self-sealing immediately the valve line is released. Triangular wicker baskets are leather trimmed and are available in three sizes. One high-output burner is fitted.

Standard equipment includes the Barnes triple burner, one main tank and related fuel lines, apex handling line, thermometer, rate of climb indicator, sensitive altimeter, fuel pressure gauge and a hand-held compass.

Optional equipment includes Fire 2 supplementary quiet burner system, Nomex envelope skirt, electronic temperature and rate of climb indicators, autopilot, extra fuel tanks and tethering kit. A wide variety of envelope artwork can be provided.

Maurice Chaize CS.2000 balloon in FAI AX-7 class

Cameron O-84 balloon for the Bombard Society of New York

British team's Thunder balloons at Uppsala, Sweden

One of the Mike Adams' Balloon Loft range of hot-air balloons

Avian Balloon 20-gore envelope in the AX-7 class

Boland XXUS AX-1 class balloon

BOLAND

BOLAND BALLOON

Pine Drive, RD 2, Burlington, Connecticut 06013
Telephone: (203) 673 1307

Mr Brian Boland, designer and builder, with his wife Kathy, of the *Albatross* hot-air airship (described in the Airships section) has also designed and built a number of hot-air balloons. Early examples included the very small *Piccolo,* and the somewhat larger *Fred II* of which Mr Boland built six examples. A plan/construction manual and materials source book is available for *Fred II,* and details of both of these early balloons can be found in the 1978-79 *Jane's.*

During 1978 the Bolands built three new balloons, two of them in the lower-size FAI categories. First was the XXUS, with the model name Scooter, which is in the AX-1 class, and has an envelope weighing only 11 kg (24 lb). Fully-fuelled take-off weight is 41 kg (90 lb), and Mr Boland believes it to be the smallest certificated experimental hot-air balloon in the world. The construction of the XXUS is unusual in that its upper hemisphere contains two inner envelopes with dead air trapped between them, forming an insulated balloon that reduces heat loss. This balloon, piloted by Mrs Kathy Boland, who weighs only 50 kg (110 lb), set records in the AX-1 class for distance and duration, of 4·81 km (3 miles) and 30 min 5 s respectively, on 29 July 1978. A new class AX-1 altitude record of 3,477 m (11,407 ft) was established by Mrs Boland on 2 November 1978.

The second design is in the AX-3 class. Three examples named *High Fred, Fairplay* and *High Fred II,* were built during 1978, each with an insulated envelope of the type described above. A very light non-porous spun-bonded olifin material and 1·1 oz rip-stop nylon fabric were used to produce the envelope, which weighs only 29·5 kg (65 lb). On 27 August 1978 Mr Boland used one of these balloons to set new records for distance and duration in the AX-3 class, at figures of 57·3 km (35·6 miles) and 3 h 46 min respectively. On 1 November 1978 *High Fred II* was used to set an altitude record of 4,642 m (15,230 ft).

The third new Boland model is the 2,322 m³ (82,000 cu ft) *Spirit of Lake Garda,* in the FAI AX-8 class. Able to carry three or four people, this balloon has two 8 million BTU burners, either of which is capable of maintaining altitude with the full load of passengers, and only one burner is used normally. With four passengers, 113·5 litres (30 US gallons) of liquid propane can be carried to provide a duration of 2 h. With two passengers, 227 litres (60 US gallons) of propane can be carried to give increased endurance.

Available details of these balloons are given in the accompanying tables.

Boland *High Fred II,* used to set a new AX-3 class height record

HARE

HARE BALLOONS

056 Laguna Avenue, Los Angeles, California 90026

Hare Balloons is marketing six different sizes of hot-air balloons in kit form for construction by amateur enthusiasts. The kits are complete with all materials, burner system and gas cylinders, and all but the smallest balloon have a glassfibre gondola. Woven wicker baskets are available optionally. The smallest AX-4 balloon is supplied with a special harness and quick release in lieu of a gondola/basket.

It is claimed that an enthusiastic constructor should be able to make the largest in the series in approximately 330 hours. Details of the Hare balloons are given in the accompanying tables.

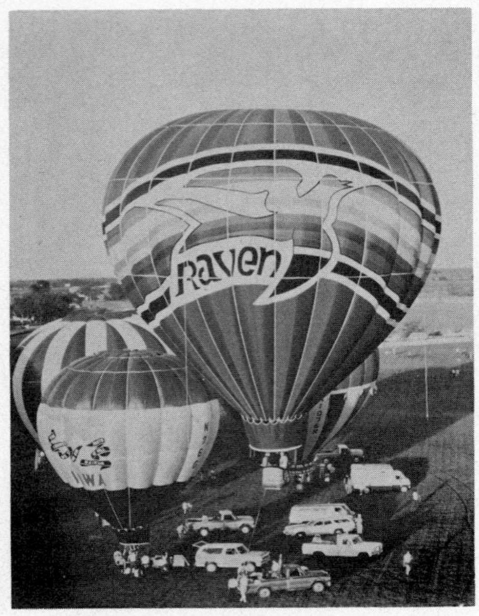

Group of balloons made by Raven Industries; largest is the new RX-7

Semco AX-6 balloon *(Peter J. Bish)*

RAVEN
RAVEN INDUSTRIES INC

Box 1007, Sioux Falls, South Dakota 57101
Telephone: (605) 336 2750

Raven Industries has been manufacturing hot-air balloons since the early 1960s, and also built the STAR hot-air airship of which details were given in the 1977-78 *Jane's*.

In 1979 Raven introduced a new balloon designated RX-7, which falls within the FAI class AX-7 and joins the RX-6 in Raven's Rally II economy balloon class. In addition, the company markets three sizes of custom design balloons. Details of these may be found in the accompanying tables.

Raven envelopes are made from rip-stop nylon treated with ultra-violet inhibitors to prolong fabric life. They embody to the customer's choice either a parachute-style deflation system or a Velcro rapid deflation port. All models have woven rattan wicker baskets. Standard equipment includes the burner, gas cylinders, and an instrument case which includes a sensitive altimeter, rate-of-climb indicator and envelope temperature gauge. A range of options includes fire retardant Kynol skirt liner, Kynol throat liner, stainless steel or additional aluminium gas cylinders, electric variometer, special colours, designs and decorations for the envelope, banners, bunting and repair fabrics.

SEMCO
SEMCO BALLOON

Route 3, PO Box 514, Aerodrome Way, Griffin, Georgia 30223
Telephone: (404) 228 4005

Semco Balloon is marketing currently four standard hot-air balloons, and details of these are given in the accompanying tables.

Envelopes are made from rip-stop nylon and have a rapid deflation system and manoeuvring vent. Aluminised interior coating and Nomex fire-resistant envelope throat lining optional. Burners and gas cylinders are standard, but models are available with either an aluminium gondola or woven wicker basket. An instrument panel is standard, and this includes a sensitive altimeter, rate-of-climb indicator, compass and envelope thermometer. A ground inflation fan, climb and descent indicator and additional gas cylinders are available as options.

HOT-AIR BALLOON DATA

Country	Company	Model	Volume m³/cu ft	Diameter m/ft	Height m/ft	Crew	Basket	Fuel Cylinders	Burners	Lift, S/L ISA kg/lb
FAI CLASS AX-1										
United States	Boland Balloon	XXUS	239/8,450	7·62/25	8·53/28	1	Harness seat	1	1	—
FAI CLASS AX-2										
United States	Boland Balloon	Piccolo	345/12,200	8·53/28	9·75/32	1	Harness seat	1	1	136/300
FAI CLASS AX-3										
United Kingdom	Cameron Balloons	O-20	566/20,000	—	—	1	Harness	2	1	—
United States	Boland Balloon	Fred II	566/20,000	10·4/34·25	12·2/40	1	Wicker	1	1	181/400
United States	Boland Balloon	High Fred	595/21,000	10·06/33	—	1	Harness seat	1	1	—
FAI CLASS AX-4										
United Kingdom	Cameron Balloons	N-31	890/31,430	—	—	1	Willow/Cane	2	1	—
United Kingdom	Cameron Balloons	O-31	890/31,430	—	—	1	Willow/Cane	2	1	—
United Kingdom	Cameron Balloons	V-31	890/31,430	—	—	1	Willow/Cane	2	1	—
United Kingdom	Thunder Balloons	31Z	890/31,430	—	—	1	Rattan	2	1	—
United States	Hare Balloons	AX-4	900/31,779	12·5/41	15·24/50	1	Harness Only	1	1	283/625
United States	Raven Industries	S-40	900/31,779	12·19/40	16·76/55	1	Aluminium Chair	1	1	299/660
United States	Semco Balloon	30-AL	850/30,000	12·19/40	18·29/60	1	Aluminium Chair	2	1	—
FAI CLASS AX-5										
United Kingdom	Cameron Balloons	O-42	1,190/42,024	—	—	2	Willow/Cane	2	1	—
United Kingdom	Thunder Balloons	42	1,190/42,024	13·4/44	14·1/46·4	2	Rattan	2	1	—
United Kingdom	Thunder Balloons	42 Bolt	1,190/42,024	—	—	2	Willow	2	1	—
United States	Adams' Balloon Loft	LD	964/34,029	12·95/42·5	15·54/51	1	Rattan	2	1	318/700
United States	Adams' Balloon Loft	LD-S	1,104/38,978	12·95/42·5	16·46/54	1-2	Rattan	2	1	318/700
United States	The Balloon Works	FireFly 5	1,182/41,742	13·9/45·6	14·8/48·4	2	Wicker	2	2	393/867
United States	Hare Balloons	AX-5	1,200/42,372	13·72/45	16·46/54	2	Glassfibre/Aluminium	2	1	378/834

HOT-AIR BALLOON DATA

Country	Company	Model	Volume m³/cu ft	Diameter m/ft	Height m/ft	Crew	Basket	Fuel Cylinders	Burners	Lift, S/L ISA kg/lb
FAI CLASS AX-6										
France	M. Chaize	CS. 1600	1,600/56,503	—	—	2	Rattan	2	—	—
United Kingdom	Cameron Balloons	O-56	1,590/56,150	—	—	3	Willow/Cane	2	1	—
United Kingdom	Cameron Balloons	Viva 56	1,590/56,150	—	—	3	Willow/Cane	2	1	—
United Kingdom	Cameron Balloons	N-56	1,590/56,150	—	—	3	Willow/Cane	2	1	—
United Kingdom	Thunder Balloons	56	1,590/56,150	14·8/48·4	15·5/50·9	3	Rattan	2	1	—
United Kingdom	Thunder Balloons	56Z	1,590/56,150	14·51/47·6	15·7/51·5	3	Rattan	2	1	—
United Kingdom	Thunder Balloons	56 Bolt	1,590/56,150	—	—	3	Willow	2	1	—
United States	Adams' Balloon Loft	A50	1,557/54,985	15·24/50	17·68/58	2	Rattan	4	1	544/1,200
United States	The Balloon Works	FireFly 6	1,576/55,656	15·3/50·1	16·1/52·8	3	Wicker	3	2	476/1,050
United States	Hare Balloons	AX-6	1,600/56,503	15·24/50	17·68/58	3	Glassfibre/Aluminium	2	1	504/1,112
United States	Raven Industries	S-50A	1,597/56,400	15·24/50	17·68/58	2-4	Wicker	3	1	635/1,400
United States	Raven Industries	RX-6	1,597/56,400	15·24/50	17·68/58	2-3	Wicker	2	1	—
United States	Semco Balloon	Model T	1,585/56,000	15·24/50	20·73/68	2	Aluminium or Wicker	2	2	—
FAI CLASS AX-7										
France	M. Chaize	CS. 1800	1,800/63,565	—	—	—	Rattan	2	—	—
France	M. Chaize	CS. 2000	2,000/70,629	—	—	3-4	Rattan	3	—	—
France	M. Chaize	CS. 2200	2,200/77,682	—	—	3-4	Rattan	3	—	—
United Kingdom	Cameron Balloons	O-65	1,840/64,980	—	—	3	Willow/Cane	3	1	—
United Kingdom	Cameron Balloons	O-77	2,190/77,339	—	—	4	Willow/Cane	4	1	—
United Kingdom	Cameron Balloons	V-77	2,190/77,339	—	—	4	Willow/Cane	2	1	—
United Kingdom	Cameron Balloons	N-77	2,190/77,339	—	—	4	Willow/Cane	4	1	—
United Kingdom	Thunder Balloons	65	1,840/64,980	15·5/50·8	16·3/53·5	3	Rattan	2	1	—
United Kingdom	Thunder Balloons	65Z	1,840/64,980	—	—	3	Rattan	2	1	—
United Kingdom	Thunder Balloons	65 Bolt	1,840/64,980	—	—	3	Willow	2	1	—
United Kingdom	Thunder Balloons	77	2,190/77,339	16·4/53·8	17·3/56·6	4	Rattan	2	1	—
United Kingdom	Thunder Balloons	77Z	2,190/77,339	15·97/52·38	16·66/54·66	4	Rattan	2	1	—
United Kingdom	Thunder Balloons	77 Bolt	2,190/77,339	—	—	4	Willow	2	1	—
United States	Adams' Balloon Loft	A50S	1,755/61,977	15·24/50	18·59/61	3	Rattan	4	1	544/1,200
United States	Adams' Balloon Loft	A55	2,123/74,973	16·76/55	19·51/64	3	Rattan	4	1	680/1,500
United States	Avian Balloon	Falcon II	1,700/60,000	15·39/50·5	20·42/67	1-2	Wicker	2	1/2	376/830
United States	The Balloon Works	FireFly 7	2,167/76,526	17·0/55·8	17·7/58·2	3	Wicker	3	2	753/1,660
United States	Hare Balloons	AX-7	2,200/77,682	17·07/56	19·2/63	4	Glassfibre/Aluminium	2	1	693/1,529
United States	Raven Industries	S-55A	2,195/77,500	16·76/55	19·2/63	3-4	Wicker	3	1	657/1,450
United States	Raven Industries	RX-7	2,195/77,500	16·76/55	19·2/63	3	Wicker	3	1	657/1,450
United States	Semco Balloon	Challenger	2,145/75,750	16·0/52·5	21·34/70	3	Wicker or Aluminium	2	3	—
FAI CLASS AX-8										
United Kingdom	Cameron Balloons	O-84	2,380/84,047	—	—	4	Willow/Cane	4	1	—
United Kingdom	Cameron Balloons	A-105	2,970/104,884	—	—	6	Willow/Cane	6	2	—
United Kingdom	Cameron Balloons	N-105	2,970/104,884	—	—	6	Willow/Cane	6	2	—
United Kingdom	Thunder Balloons	84	2,380/84,047	—	—	4	Rattan	2	1	—
United Kingdom	Thunder Balloons	90	2,550/90,050	17·5/57·5	17·5/57·5	5	Rattan	2	2	—
United Kingdom	Thunder Balloons	105	2,970/104,884	18·44/60·5	18·44/60·5	6	Rattan	2	2	—
United States	Adams' Balloon Loft	A55S	2,350/82,990	16·76/55	20·42/67	4	Rattan	4	1	680/1,500
United States	Avian Balloon	Skyhawk	2,265/80,000	16·46/54	22·56/74	3-4	Wicker	3	1/2	544/1,200
United States	Avian Balloon	Eagle	2,973/105,000	18·29/60	22·56/74	4-5	Wicker	4	1/2	680/1,500
United States	The Balloon Works	FireFly 8	2,956/104,400	18·8/61·8	19·5/64	4-5	Wicker	6	2	916/2,020
United States	Boland Balloons	*Spirit of Lake Garda*	2,322/82,000	—	—	4	Wicker	3/6	2	—
United States	Hare Balloons	AX-8	3,000/105,930	18·9/62	21·03/69	4-5	Glassfibre/Aluminium	3	1	—
United States	Raven Industries	S-60A	2,973/105,000	18·29/60	21·03/69	3-4	Wicker	3	1	680/1,500
United States	Semco Balloon	TC-4	2,577/91,000	16·76/55	24·99/82	4	Birch/Aluminium	4	3	—
FAI CLASS AX-9										
United Kingdom	Cameron Balloons	A-140	3,960/139,846	—	—	8	Willow/Cane	6	2	—
United Kingdom	Thunder Balloons	140	3,965/140,022	20·36/66·8	20·36/66·8	8	Rattan	2	2	—
United States	Hare Balloons	AX-9	4,000/141,240	20·73/68	23·16/76	6-7	Glassfibre/Aluminium	3	1	1,261/2,781
United States	Raven Industries	S-68	4,000/141,240	—	—	4-6	Wicker	2	2	998/2,200

RPVs AND TARGETS

ARGENTINA

FMA (AREA DE MATERIAL CÓRDOBA)

Instituto de Investigaciónes Aeronáuticas y Espacial (IIAE)

Avenida Fuerza Aérea Argentina Km 5½, Córdoba
Telephone: 45011, 37048 and 44732
DIRECTOR: Brigadier Fernando Rodriguez

FMA IA 59

Designed to Argentinian Air Force requirements by the IIAE (Aerospace Research Institute), the IA 59 target drone has a McCulloch piston engine of less than 15 kW (20 hp). Two prototypes had been built, of which one had flown, by the Autumn of 1978. The avionics and guidance system were also designed by the IIAE.

AUSTRALIA

GAF
GOVERNMENT AIRCRAFT FACTORIES

Fishermen's Bend, Private Bag No. 4, Post Office, Port Melbourne, Victoria 3207
Telephone: 64 0661
Telex: AA 34397
OFFICERS: see Aircraft section

Current GAF products include the Jindivik weapons target and a target drone version of the Ikara anti-submarine missile, known as the Turana.

GAF JINDIVIK Mk 3B

The Jindivik continues to be a standard weapons target in Australia and Great Britain.

Design began in March 1948 and construction of the prototype Jindivik Mk 1 started in December 1950. This prototype flew for the first time on 28 August 1952.

A total of 486 Jindiviks had been ordered by 1 January 1979, including 234 for the UK, 163 for a joint UK/Australia Weapons Project for use on the Woomera range, 42 for the US Navy, 37 for the Royal Australian Navy and 10 for Sweden. Of these, 466 had been delivered, including 360 earlier Marks (as listed in the 1977-78 *Jane's)* and 106 Mk 3Bs (first flight 22 January 1970). Those used in the UK are assembled and equipped to British operational standards; uses include towing targets for air-to-air missile firing practice, at the Missile Practice Camp at RAF Valley, Anglesey, by RAF Strike Command Lightnings (armed with Red Top and Firestreak) and Phantoms (Sparrows and Sidewinders).

One Jindivik was fitted with an ACLS (air cushion landing system); details of this can be found in the 1977-78 *Jane's*.

Only the 700 Series Mks 103BL and 203B versions are still in production; deliveries of these versions began in 1976. Customers include the UK (40 Mk 103BL) and Royal Australian Navy (12 Mk 203B). These models were designed to cater for low-level trials at speeds in excess of 500 knots (925 km/h; 575 mph). The autopilot is the improved Marconi L4 or L5, and system 'black boxes' incorporate printed-circuit techniques.

An improved Mk 4 Jindivik was in the design stage in 1979, and production of 40 of this version is due to begin in 1981. The Mk 4 has a rationalised electrical/electronic system, aimed at containing costs and increasing the manoeuvring capability to +6*g*.

For low-altitude work, the standard-span Jindivik can be fitted either with Mk 5 wingtip camera pods, or with larger Mk 8 pods each containing two cameras, a Luneberg lens and a small amount of fuel. For high-altitude work (also with a choice of Mk 5 or Mk 8 wing pods), constant-chord wing extension panels can be added outboard of the pods. For extra high altitude flying (with Mk 5 pods only), these panels can be replaced by increased-span panels, tapered on the leading-edge. A ventral tail fin is also fitted in this configuration.

Up to 1 January 1979, Jindiviks had flown more than 3,590 sorties at the RAE, Llanbedr, North Wales; one particular Mk 3A drone (WRE 418) was eventually destroyed after successfully completing 285 sorties at Woomera. Total sorties by all Jindiviks at that date amounted to more than 6,200.

TYPE: Pilotless target drone.

WINGS: Cantilever low/mid-wing monoplane. Wing section NACA 64A-106 with modified trailing-edge. Dihedral 2° 30′. Incidence 1°. Araldite-bonded multi-spar box structure of aluminium alloy. Interspar torsion box utilised as integral fuel tankage. Aluminium alloy monocoque flaps and ailerons. Ailerons fitted with inset geared tab and driven by GAF-designed twin-motor servo motor. Flaps operated pneumatically.

FUSELAGE: Aluminium alloy semi-monocoque structure, built in front, centre and rear sections. Front fuselage carries all control equipment, autopilot amd telemetry equipment. Pitot head and wave-guide boom mounted on permanent nose probe. Moulded glassfibre canopy, which lifts off for access to equipment, forms ram-type air intake. Rear end of front fuselage and front end of centre fuselage form bay for all special trials equipment. Centre-fuselage also houses landing skid. Rear fuselage carries engine and jetpipe.

TAIL UNIT: Cantilever multi-spar light alloy tailplane. Elevators driven by GAF-designed twin-motor servo motor. Inset geared tabs. Fin of light alloy skin bonded to two spars, stabilised by metal honeycomb filling. No rudder. Ventral fin on extra high altitude version.

LANDING GEAR: Pneumatically-extended, manually retracted (on ground) central skid. Pneumatic jack acts as shock-absorber. Steel auxiliary skids at wingtips. See also paragraph on 'Take-off and Landing'.

POWER PLANT: One Rolls-Royce Viper Mk 201 turbojet engine, rated at 11·1 kN (2,500 lb st). Engine relight capability available in the event of flameout. Flexible rubber main fuselage fuel tank, capacity 291 litres (64 Imp gallons), and two integral wing tanks, total capacity 173 litres (38 Imp gallons). Oil capacity 4·5 litres (1 Imp gallon).

TAKE-OFF AND LANDING: Take-off from aircraft trolley, steered by gyro and servo-controlled nosewheel which responds to signals from ground controller. Aircraft/trolley combination accelerates under normal jet power with flaps retracted and with aircraft set at negative incidence. When unstick speed (125 knots; 231 km/h; 144 mph) is reached, aircraft is rotated to take-off incidence and flaps are lowered rapidly. Rotation of aircraft initiates trolley release system and the aircraft climbs away. When Jindivik is in approach run, flaps and skid are selected down for landing. On touchdown, at approx 120 knots (222 km/h; 138 mph), a 'sting' extended below main skid rotates on impact and initiates rapid retraction of flaps. Fuel supply terminated by radio command.

REMOTE-CONTROL EQUIPMENT: Radio control equipment comprises two receivers and GAF relay receiving set. Telemetry equipment consists of NIC transducers and Australian-designed transmitter and junction box.

SYSTEMS: No hydraulic system. Non-regenerative pneumatic system: air stored at 138 bars (2,000 lb/sq in) in power pack which supplies air to flaps and landing skid reduced to 39·6 bars (575 lb/sq in). Engine-driven 11·5kVA alternator delivers 208V AC 3-phase electrical supply at 300-550Hz. In event of alternator failure, a 24V DC battery provides limited power for essential control functions. Automatic orbit and/or destruct systems provided, consistent with range safety requirements.

TRIALS EQUIPMENT: Transponders and microwave reflectors for trials of active, semi-active or beam-riding missiles. Heat sources, including infra-red flare packs mounted on rear of fuselage, can be fitted to provide low-frequency IR output. Transponders in X, S and C bands can be fitted for target acquisition and to enable Jindivik to be tracked at greater range. Provision for Tonic Beam under each wing, on which can be carried recoverable Tonic Tow Bodies. These Tow Bodies can carry either active radar, in-flight-commanded IR flares, or forward-looking Luneberg lens. They can be towed at 15-150 m (50-500 ft) behind aircraft; recovery by electric winch mounted in centre of fuselage. Other types of special tow may also be carried.

RECORDING EQUIPMENT: Cameras fitted with wide-angle lenses are carried in wingtip pods, with all-round viewing capability. Variants are Mk 5 pod with cameras only and Mk 8 with cameras, fuel and provision for fitment of microwave reflectors in leading-edge and trailing-edge radomes. By fitting rearward-looking prisms to the lower cameras they can be used to film and record missile performance when Tonic towed targets are used.

DIMENSIONS, EXTERNAL:
Wing span:
short span, low altitude 6·32 m (20 ft 8·99 in)
extended, high altitude 7·92 m (26 ft 6 in)
extended, extra high altitude 9·78 m (32 ft 1·4 in)
Wing area, gross: short span 7·06 m² (76·0 sq ft)
extended span, high altitude 9·48 m² (102·0 sq ft)
extended span, extra high altitude 10·68 m² (115·0 sq ft)
Length overall: incl nose probe 8·15 m (26 ft 8¾ in)
excl nose probe 7·11 m (23 ft 3¾ in)
Height overall, skid extended 2·08 m (6 ft 9·85 in)

WEIGHTS:
Weight empty, equipped (min) 1,315 kg (2,900 lb)
Max payload: short-span version 249 kg (550 lb)
extended-span versions 181 kg (400 lb)
Max T-O weight:
short span, Mk 5 wing pods 1,451 kg (3,200 lb)
short span, Mk 8 wing pods 1,655 kg (3,650 lb)
high altitude, Mk 5 wing pods 1,474 kg (3,250 lb)
high altitude, Mk 8 wing pods 1,655 kg (3,650 lb)
extra high altitude, Mk 5 wing pods 1,496 kg (3,300 lb)

PERFORMANCE (A: short span, Mk 5 pods; B: short span, Mk 8 pods; C: high altitude, Mk 5 pods; D: high altitude, Mk 8 pods; E: extra high altitude, Mk 5 pods):
Max level speed at max operational ceiling:
A, B, C, D Mach 0·86 (490 knots; 908 km/h; 564 mph)
E Mach 0·82 (470 knots; 871 km/h; 541 mph)
Min operating height: A, B 15 m (50 ft)
Max operational ceiling: A 17,375 m (57,000 ft)
B 16,460 m (54,000 ft)
C 19,200 m (63,000 ft)
D 18,595 m (61,000 ft)
E 20,420 m (67,000 ft)
Time to max operational ceiling: A 26 min
B, C 30 min
D, E 34 min
Typical max on-station endurance: A, C 1 h 6 min
B 1 h 38 min
D 1 h 52 min
E 1 h 3 min
Max range: A 430 nm (796 km; 495 miles)
B 670 nm (1,240 km; 771 miles)
C 540 nm (1,000 km; 621 miles)
D 900 nm (1,667 km; 1,036 miles)
E 700 nm (1,297 km; 806 miles)

GAF TURANA

The Turana is a target drone based on the Ikara missile. It was developed by the Dept of Productivity initially to meet a Royal Australian Navy Staff Requirement for a modern gunnery and guided weapons target. First flight was made on 12 March 1971.

The Turana is capable of demand turns of up to 3*g*, customer-specified manoeuvres of more than 10*g*, and demand heading changes of up to 26°. Construction ensures an average life of at least 10 flights per drone. Equipment is designed for at least 20 complete missions, including sea-water immersion. Guidance and rocket propulsion aspects of the project are subcontracted by GAF to the Weapons Research Establishment/EMI Electronics (Australia) and Weapons Research Establishment/Ordnance Factory and Explosives Factory, Maribyrnong, respectively.

IA 59 target drone, under development by FMA, on its launcher

Right: Shipboard launch of a GAF Turana target drone

GAF Jindivik Mk 203B target drone, with Mk 1 in background

Hawker de Havilland HDH-10 Enmoth target aircraft

The Concurrent Evaluation Phase (CEP), to ensure the target's readiness for entry into RAN service, was completed with 26 flights in the series up to early 1978. Operational evaluation by the RAN was continuing in early 1979. Performance aspects demonstrated during the CEP have included sea-skimming gunnery presentations from 25 nm (46 km; 28·8 miles) at 15·25 m (50 ft), low-altitude flight at 11·25 m (37 ft), and precision control during gunnery engagements by two ships. One Turana has flown 15 times.

TYPE: Pilotless target drone.

WINGS: Cantilever mid-wing tail-less monoplane of cropped-delta planform. Wing section modified NACA 64010. Spindle attachment to fuselage, spindle being also the main spar. Two metal ribs and metal rear spar; remainder of wing of foam-filled glassfibre. Full-span elevons operated via differential mechanical linkage by two electric actuators, one for pitch and one for roll control. Wings quickly detachable from fuselage.

FUSELAGE: Aluminium alloy torsion box, with removable glassfibre fairings, housing autopilot, fuel tank, engine and various miss-distance equipments and transponders. Main structural member consists of H-section structure of chemically-milled side skins, bulkheads and forgings, and a bottom diaphragm. Interface attachments identical with those of Ikara.

TAIL UNIT: Single vertical fin, of NACA 64010 section. Chemically-milled aluminium skins and aluminium ribs and spars, with glassfibre tip and trailing-edge.

POWER PLANT: One Microturbo Couguar 022 turbojet engine of 0·78 kN (176 lb st). Stainless steel/airbag fuel tank of 51·8 litres (11·4 Imp gallons) capacity. Airbag pressurised from engine compressor. Compressed-air starting. Engine speed controlled by electronic unit, which forms part of a speed demand loop.

BOOST: Single-nozzle PMD41 solid-propellant booster motor specially developed for Turana, attached to fuselage by swivelling links and two explosive bolts; jettisoned at end of boost phase. Nominal burning time 2 seconds; nominal thrust 26·7 kN (6,000 lb).

LAUNCH AND RECOVERY: Launch from standard Ikara ship launcher, or from lightweight portable launcher, at fixed elevation of 22° 30′. Command parachute recovery, activated automatically in event of engine, electrical power system or command link failure. Parachute housed in ejectable nose compartment. Short or long time delays can be included in command link failure mode to allow for momentary signal fades. Initial versions designed for water recovery. For use on land, a larger parachute and land recovery system can be developed.

GUIDANCE AND CONTROL: Initial guidance equipment adapted from Ikara system on board RAN ships. Navigation by Ikara tracking receiver and ship's plotting facilities. Guidance equipment housed in fin. Control by open loop demands from ground and closed loop sensing and autocontrol system in drone. Steering by autopilot and elevons. Elevons operated symmetrically or differentially by electric actuators. Autopilot includes displacement gyro sensing roll and pitch, rate gyro sensing yaw, air data unit with airspeed and altitude transducers, signal summing and shaping networks, and drive amplifiers for servo system. Radar altimeter option available, to allow automatic controlled flight at low altitudes. All control equipment in waterproof containers; electrical connections through waterproof connectors. Pitot-static tube fitted to tip of fin. Height lock and speed lock loops provided. If required, modified guidance equipment can be developed which is independent of ship facilities; alternative tracking and return data links are also possible.

SYSTEMS: All electric. Rechargeable silver/zinc battery pack, in compartment beneath centre of fuselage, provides power for all services for one hour. Pyrotechnic charge for ejection of nose section.

TRIALS EQUIPMENT: Smoke release system for visual augmentation. Forward-looking passive radar augmentation by 190 mm (7½ in) Luneberg lens in nose. Space and large weight-carrying capacity available for active augmentation or for other special equipment such as 465MHz 48-channel telemetry system. Pyrotechnic flares can be accommodated. Acoustic miss-distance indication system available. Short-tow system, to carry infra-red flares or a Luneberg lens radar reflector, can be developed.

DIMENSIONS, EXTERNAL:

Wing span	1·53 m (5 ft 0·2 in)
Wing area, gross	1·23 m² (13·2 sq ft)
Length overall	3·37 m (11 ft 0½ in)
Height (less boost motor)	1·02 m (3 ft 4 in)
Height (with boost motor)	1·19 m (3 ft 10·8 in)

DIMENSION, INTERNAL:

Special equipment capacity	0·028 m³ (1 cu ft)

WEIGHTS (excl special equipment):

Weight dry	196 kg (432 lb)
Weight at launch	293 kg (646 lb)
Weight excl booster	240 kg (529 lb)
Weight at recovery (empty)	187 kg (412 lb)
Fuel	41 kg (91 lb)
Special equipment	more than 45 kg (100 lb)

PERFORMANCE:

Max level speed	500 knots (927 km/h; 576 mph)
Boost acceleration (nominal)	10g
End-of-boost speed	170 m (560 ft)/s
Service ceiling	20,000 m (65,625 ft)
Max rate of climb at S/L	1,219 m (4,000 ft)/min
Range	174 nm (322 km; 200 miles)
Endurance	up to 34 min

HAWKER DE HAVILLAND

HAWKER DE HAVILLAND AUSTRALIA PTY LTD (Member Company of Hawker Siddeley Group)

PO Box 30, Bankstown, NSW 2200

Telephone: 772 8111

Telex: 20719

TECHNICAL DIRECTOR: S. S. Schaetzel

HAWKER DE HAVILLAND HDH-10 ENMOTH

Hawker de Havilland developed the Enmoth mini-RPV in 1975, to provide an aiming and scoring system for the Royal Australian Army's Redeye surface-to-air missiles. The complete system consists of a target aircraft, a transport container, and a self-contained ground support package.

Twelve Enmoths were ordered by the Australian Army in January 1977; deliveries began at the end of June in that year, and have been completed. A full description of the Enmoth can be found in the 1978-79 *Jane's*.

HAWKER DE HAVILLAND HDH-11 BEEMOTH

The HDH-11 Beemoth has a similar planform to the Promoth, but has double the linear dimensions, greatly increased payload capacity, and a pusher propeller.

HAWKER DE HAVILLAND HDH-12 PROMOTH

The Promoth mini-RPV is designed specifically as a rugged, low-cost expendable target for small-arms gunnery practice. Three prototypes have been flown, and development has been completed.

Airframe: Cropped-delta monoplane, with 'flat plate' section wings of glassfibre-covered foam. Elevon on each trailing-edge. Rectangular-section fuselage. Cropped-delta fin, also of 'flat plate' section. Skid landing gear.

Power Plant: One K & B 40 piston engine, driving a pusher propeller; 33 fl oz fuel in centre-section.

Launch and Recovery: Catapult launch and net recovery; skid landing on grass also possible. Both methods proved in flight trials.

Guidance and Control: Standard Futaba radio control link and actuators, providing pitch, roll and throttle control.

Dimensions, external:
- Wing span: 1·00 m (3 ft 3¼ in)
- Length overall: 1·12 m (3 ft 8 in)
- Height overall: 0·34 m (1 ft 1½ in)

Weights:
- Weight empty: 3·2 kg (7·05 lb)
- Max fuel: 0·73 kg (1·61 lb)

Performance (at average weight of 3·63 kg; 8 lb):
- Max level speed: more than 95 knots (175 km/h; 109 mph)
- Recommended net recovery speed: 30-35 knots (56-65 km/h; 34·5-40·5 mph)
- Max rate of climb at S/L: 823 m (2,700 ft)/min
- Rate of roll at 100 knots (185 km/h; 115 mph): approx 360°/s

BELGIUM

MBLE

MANUFACTURE BELGE DE LAMPES ET DE MATÉRIEL ELECTRONIQUE SA

Rue des Deux Gares 80, B-1070 Brussels
Telephone: (02) 523 00 00
Telex: 21 420
Marketing Manager: M. Broussier

This company, which employs 5,000 people, has contributed to a number of military programmes, is participating in the European F-16 programme, and in the Belgian Air Force Mirage ECM project. It developed battlefield surveillance systems named Épervier and Asmodée.

MBLE ÉPERVIER (SPARROWHAWK) and ASMODÉE

The Épervier battlefield reconnaissance system, developed and built entirely in Belgium, was described as fully as its classified nature allows in the 1978-79 *Jane's*.

An order for Éperviers for the Belgian Army was announced in 1974, and two complete squadrons were equipped in 1976. Since then, several demonstrations have been held of the Épervier for NATO delegations and of **Asmodée** for various non-NATO countries. The Asmodée system is identical to the Épervier except for codes and radio frequencies.

CANADA

CANADAIR

CANADAIR LTD

PO Box 6087, Montreal, Quebec H3C 3G9
Telephone: (514) 744 1511
Officers: see Aircraft section

In addition to its work on manned aircraft, Canadair is developing or producing various drone systems, including the CL-289 described in the International section.

CANADAIR CL-89

NATO designation: AN/USD-501
British Army name: Midge

The Canadair CL-89 (AN/USD-501) airborne surveillance drone system evolved from a need of the western Allied armed forces for an intelligence-gathering device for battlefield commanders; details of its early history can be found in the 1977-78 and earlier editions of *Jane's*.

With a very high probability of survival against all known air defence systems, the CL-89 can acquire timely and accurate battlefield intelligence using its photographic and infra-red line-scanning equipment. The system, consisting of the air vehicles plus the related ground support and operational maintenance equipment, is totally integrated, mobile, and independent of such external services as electrical power supplies.

The CL-89 system has been produced for Canada, the Federal Republic of Germany (five battalions, each with 12 drones and two launchers), Italy (jointly with Meteor, which see) and the UK. Well over 500 drones have been manufactured and by late 1978 had made more than 1,500 flights. An order from the French government was announced in August 1978; some subsystems for these drones will be supplied by Dornier GmbH.

Type: Recoverable airborne surveillance drone system.

Airframe: Cylindrical metal body, with curved nosecone and tapering tailcone. Three detachable dorsal packs for forward and rear landing bags and flare container; two detachable ventral packs for sensor equipment and parachute recovery system. Four rectangular stub-wings at rear of body, in cruciform arrangement at 45° to horizontal and vertical centrelines. Upper pair fold out of way when landing airbags are inflated. Ailerons on port upper and starboard lower stub-wings. Two pairs of canard foreplanes aft of nosecone on horizontal and vertical centrelines, for pitch and yaw trim respectively.

Power Plant: One 0·56 kN (125 lb st) Williams Research WR2-6 turbojet engine, with variable exhaust nozzle, installed in tailcone aft of wings. Air intake duct on each side of fuselage, forward of wings. Fuel and oil tanks in central body compartment, forward of air intakes. One 20·29 kN (4,550 lb st) average thrust Bristol Aerojet Wagtail booster rocket motor, attached to body of drone by three V-shaped thrust arms and cable.

Launch and Recovery: Launched from truck-mounted short ramp; booster separates automatically after 2·5 s of flight. For recovery, after final positioning by ground homing beacon, drone is slowed by drogue parachute until main parachute deploys. Drone is then inverted, and forward and rear airbags are inflated and deployed automatically to absorb landing impact.

Guidance and Control: Flight path, altitude and sensor on/off commands are controlled by preset programmer which receives information from onboard Air Distance Measuring Unit (ADMU) and combines this with preset programme to control flight path. Ground homing beacon positions drone in final stages of flight to ensure accuracy of landing.

Equipment: Engine-driven alternator for electrical power during flight. Two main sensor systems currently in use: Carl Zeiss KRb 8/24 camera system and British Aerospace Dynamics Type 201 infra-red linescan system. Aft of sensor pack is compartment for fuel and oil tanks. Compartment aft of tanks has ventral forward-hinged door providing access to engine start air connector, and dorsal pack containing 12 photoflares just forward of rear landing bag container. Final cylindrical compartment houses rear landing bag container and parachute recovery pack, between dorsal and ventral pairs of wings respectively. Other onboard equipment includes forward and rear landing airbags; Air Distance Measuring Unit (ADMU); programmer; static power converter; homing receiver; amplifier; flash detector; directional and vertical gyros; transponder antenna; and air bottle to inflate airbags.

Dimensions, external:
- Length overall, excl nose probe:
  - with booster: 3·73 m (12 ft 3 in)
  - without booster: 2·60 m (8 ft 6½ in)
- Body diameter: 0·33 m (1 ft 1 in)
- Span of wings: 0·94 m (3 ft 1 in)
- Span of foreplanes: 0·48 m (1 ft 7 in)

Weights:
- Weight dry (excl fuel, oil and payload): 78·2 kg (172·4 lb)
- Payload: 17-20 kg (37·5-44 lb)
- Max launching weight: with booster: 156 kg (343 lb)
  - without booster: 108 kg (238 lb)

Performance:
- Max speed: 400 knots (741 km/h; 460 mph)

CANADAIR CL-227

The CL-227 is designed as a highly survivable surveillance and target acquisition system for use at medium range. It has VTOL capability, and is launched and recovered using a 1·83 m (6 ft) diameter platform mounted on a truck or small ship.

It has a peanut-shaped body housing the power plant in the upper sphere, with the sensors and autopilot in the lower sphere. Two contra-rotating rigid propellers, mounted amidships, provide the lift and attitude control. Current power plant is a 15·7 kW (21 hp) Fichtel & Sachs Wankel-type rotating-piston engine, but a small turboshaft will power the production version of the CL-227.

First flight took place on 25 August 1978; the initial phase of the flight test programme, consisting of more than 200 tethered flights, was completed in November 1978. The accompanying photograph, taken during the tethered flight test programme, shows one of the landing configurations that were tested.

A unique characteristic of the CL-227 is the landing concept, in which the air vehicle is winched on to the landing platform to provide an automatic landing capability. This platform also acts as the transportation platform and minimises ground handling of the air vehicle between flights.

Dimensions:
- Height overall: 1·32 m (4 ft 4 in)
- Body diameter (max): 0·51 m (1 ft 8 in)
- Propeller diameter (approx): 2·29 m (7 ft 6 in)

*Weights:
- Payload: 15 kg (33 lb)
- Max T-O weight: 93 kg (205 lb)

*Performance (estimated):
- Max level speed: 70 knots (130 km/h; 81 mph)
- Max operating altitude: 2,500 m (8,200 ft)
- Typical operating radius: 27 nm (50 km; 31 miles)
- Typical mission endurance: 2 h

* *Larger-diameter propellers can be used for heavier payloads and longer endurance*

FRANCE

AÉROSPATIALE

SOCIÉTÉ NATIONALE INDUSTRIELLE AÉROSPATIALE

Division des Engins Tactiques

2-18 rue Béranger, BP 36, 92320 Châtillon-sous-Bagneux
Telephone: 655 54 00
Telex: AIRSPA 25881 F
Officers: see Aircraft section

Aérospatiale (Division des Engins Tactiques) is currently producing the CT.20 target drone for the French armed forces. Approx 50 examples of the C.20, referred to in the 1978-79 *Jane's*, were produced. Under development as a high-performance subsonic target is the C.22.

AÉROSPATIALE CT.20

The CT.20 is a turbojet-powered radio-controlled target of medium performance, which is also used as a tug for a towed target. Series production began in 1958; by 1 January 1979 a total of 1,466 had been built, including more than 300 for export to NATO and non-NATO countries. Recent customers include Egypt and Sweden. Rate of production in 1978 was approx seven to eight per month.

It is standard equipment for training military units in the use of air-to-air and surface-to-air missiles, in particular the Hawk. A version known as the **CT.20 TBA,** with very low altitude capability, is also operational.

The CT.20, fitted with a Thomson-CSF active homing radar, and with a warhead in place of the recovery system, also formed the basis of the M.20 anti-ship missile designed by Aérospatiale for the Swedish Navy and built by Saab-Scania as the RB08.

Type: Turbojet-powered radio-controlled target.

Airframe: Body in three main sections. Forward section, of aluminium alloy, contains command guidance, autopilot, batteries and principal recovery parachute.

Hawker de Havilland HDH-12 Promoth on its support equipment stand

Truck launch of an MBLE Épervier battlefield surveillance RPV

Canadair CL-89 airborne surveillance/target acquisition drone system

Aérospatiale CT.20 target drones on launching ramps

Aérospatiale C.22 variable-speed subsonic target drone

Canadair CL-227 surveillance/target acquisition drone

Central section consists of structural steel tank divided into two parts, one for fuel and one containing chemicals for tracking smoke. Rear fuselage, of aluminium alloy, contains engine and carries aluminium alloy V-tail. Braking parachute in cone above jet nozzle. Mid-mounted swept wings, of aluminium alloy, have wingtip spoilers for lateral control; elevators controlled simultaneously by single jack. Ventral fin.

Power Plant: One Turboméca Marboré II (3·92 kN; 880 lb st) turbojet engine in CT.20 Version IV; Marboré VI (4·7 kN; 1,056 lb st) turbojet in CT.20 Version VII.

Launch and Recovery: Launched by booster rockets from nearly-zero-length vehicle-mounted ramp. Recovery by parachute and impact-absorbing airbag, deployed after engine is stopped by transmission of landing signal. Can be recovered from land or water.

Guidance and Control: Radio command guidance system, operated by controller on ground or in airborne director aircraft. Nine basic signals can be transmitted: turn right; turn left; nose up; nose down; increase power; decrease power; trace smoke; operate cameras; and land.

Equipment: Can be used to tow Dornier target which is pylon-mounted under starboard wing at launch; or can be used with trailed target system developed for the Centre d'Essais des Landes, primarily for training in use of air-to-air missiles with electro-magnetic (BEY target) or infra-red homing (EMIR target) systems. CT.20 TBA version has TRT AVH-6 radio altimeter for very low (about 30 m; 100 ft) altitude capability, and an improved remote guidance system.

Dimensions, external (A: standard version; B: extended version with trailed target):

Wing span	3·16 m (10 ft 4½ in)
Wing area, gross	3·20 m² (33·34 sq ft)
Length overall:	
A	5·45 m (17 ft 10½ in)
B	5·60 m (18 ft 4½ in)
Body diameter (max)	0·66 m (2 ft 2 in)

Weights (A: standard version; B: extended version with trailed target):

Weight empty: A	490 kg (1,080 lb)
B	610 kg (1,344 lb)
Fuel load: A	164 kg (361 lb)
B	192 kg (423 lb)

Max launching weight: A 660 kg (1,455 lb)
B 800 kg (1,763 lb)

Performance (A: standard version; B: extended version with trailed target):

Max speed at 10,000 m (32,800 ft):
Marboré II 485 knots (900 km/h; 560 mph)
Marboré VI 512 knots (950 km/h; 590 mph)
Max Mach number (A, B) Mach 0·85
Service ceiling: Marboré II 12,000 m (39,375 ft)
Marboré VI 15,000 m (49,200 ft)
Max operating height: A 14,000 m (45,925 ft)
B 13,000 m (42,650 ft)
Time to max operating height: A, B 15 min
Time to 10,000 m (32,800 ft) 6 min
Endurance at max operating height: A 50 min
B 1 h 10 min
Min operating height: A, B 30 m (100 ft)
Practical range of command guidance and tracking system 135 nm (250 km; 155 miles)
Endurance at min operating height: A 15 min
B 21 min
Average endurance at 10,000 m (32,800 ft) 45 min

AÉROSPATIALE C.22

The C.22, which is currently under development, has been designed for use as a variable-speed target for anti-aircraft weapons and, especially, for training land or air force units equipped with conventional guns or surface-to-air or air-to-air missiles. Its dimensions, low radar signature and high performance enable it to perform equally realistically whether representing a bomber at 12,200 m (40,000 ft) or a sea-skimming anti-ship missile.

Type: High-performance variable-speed subsonic target.

Airframe: Moulded plastics wings, with symmetrical profile and no control surfaces. Fuselage of wound glassfibre, impregnated with epoxy resin, reinforced by metal inserts at attachment points. Nosecone and tailcone of moulded plastics. Cruciform light alloy tail-fins, with four control surfaces operated by electrical actuators.

Power Plant: One 3·4 kN (772 lb st) Microturbo TRI 60 turbojet engine, mounted in pod on top of fuselage; and two jettisonable solid-fuel booster rockets (each 28·3 kN; 6,360 lb st) attached beneath wings on sides of fuselage. Fuel tanks for TRI 60 in centre of fuselage, capacity 235 litres (52 Imp gallons).

Launch and Recovery: Launched by jettisonable rockets from ground or ship base. Parachute system for recovery from land or sea. Inflatable airbag beneath fuselage to absorb landing impact.

Guidance and Control: Radio command guidance system. Flight control, based upon a mini-computer, permits complex manoeuvres at more than 6*g*. Aerodynamic control by cruciform tail-fins indexed at 45° from vertical axis.

Special Equipment: Nose compartment available for equipment, including tow winch. Tail compartment includes smoke generator and recovery parachutes. Equipment/payload compartments for up to 75 kg (165 lb) of Luneberg lenses or 500W propane heat source for radar or infra-red augmentation respectively; active or passive countermeasures; or recording equipment for assessing the effectiveness of weapon systems during training; up to 2,000 m (6,560 ft) cables for towing one or two 30 kg (66 lb) towed targets at speeds of more than 485 knots (900 km/h; 559 mph).

Dimensions, external:
Wing span 2·50 m (8 ft 2½ in)
Span over tail-fins 1·20 m (3 ft 11¼ in)
Length overall 5·10 m (16 ft 8¾ in)
Height overall 1·15 m (3 ft 9¼ in)
Body diameter 0·40 m (1 ft 3¾ in)

Weights:
Weight empty 255 kg (562 lb)
Max launching weight 550 kg (1,212 lb)

Performance:
Max speed Mach 0·95
Time to 12,000 m (39,375 ft) less than 6 min
Service ceiling 14,000 m (45,950 ft)
Minimum operating altitude less than 30 m (100 ft)
Endurance at Mach 0·9 at 13,000 m (42,650 ft) 2 h
g limit more than +6

EERM
ÉTABLISSEMENT D'ÉTUDES ET DE RECHERCHES MÉTÉOROLOGIQUES (Direction de la Météorologie Nationale)

77 rue de Sèvres, 92106 Boulogne-Billancourt, Cédex
Telephone: (1) 604 91 51
Director: A. Villevieille

EERM SAM

The SAM (Sonde Aérologique Motorisée) has been used in considerable numbers by the EERM since 1976 as a pilotless atmospheric sounding vehicle. Two types have been built: SAM-B for low-altitude flights (up to 500 m; 1,640 ft) and SAM-C for work at higher altitudes, up to cloud level. Both have line-of-sight radio control, although an out-of-sight version, equipped with an autopilot, is envisaged.

First high-altitude (3,200-4,000 m; 10,500-13,125 ft) tests with a SAM-C were made in May 1978 at Deux-Alpes, and in the following month one was flown over the 3,300 m (10,825 ft) Mount Etna in Sicily, to measure thermal conditions in the vicinity of the volcano and to take gas samples to determine their chemical composition.

The following details refer to SAM-C:

Airframe: Cantilever shoulder-wing monoplane with marked wing dihedral and inverted-V tail surfaces. Cylindrical fuselage, with rounded nose and tapered tail section.

Power Plant: One 1·12 kW (1·5 hp) 10 cc piston engine, pod-mounted on pylon above centre-fuselage and driving a two-blade propeller.

Launch and Recovery: Launched by catapult from short ramp.

Equipment: Temperature, humidity and atmospheric pressure sensors.

Dimensions:
Wing span 3·15 m (10 ft 4 in)
Wing area 1·00 m² (10·76 sq ft)
Length overall 2·00 m (6 ft 6¾ in)

Weights:
Payload 2·5 kg (5·5 lb)
Max launching weight 9·0 kg (19·8 lb)

Performance:
Speed range 15·5-68 knots (29-126 km/h; 18-78 mph)
Endurance in level flight 1 h

FRANCE-ENGINS
SOCIÉTÉ ANONYME FRANCE-ENGINS

c/o Microturbo SA, BP 2089, Chemin du Pont-de-Rupé, 31019 Toulouse Cédex
Telephone: (61) 47 63 26
Telex: 531442 miturbo
President-Director General: André de Boysson

This company was formed, in early 1975, by Microturbo SA (see Aero-Engines section) and Société Soulé.

FRANCE-ENGINS MITSOUBAC

The Mitsoubac is a low-cost target drone for naval operation, designed for high-*g* manoeuvrability at medium altitude and very low-level flight over water. Maximum use of watertight equipment minimises refurbishing. Mitsoubac is intended to provide a target for ships' armament without the need for support by land-based installations.

A typical flight lasts 15 min; a long-range version with 45 min endurance is planned. Flight trials began in 1975 as a private venture, using a Bell 47 light helicopter as the launch aircraft, and continued in 1976-77 at Cazaux using an Alouette III helicopter. Evaluation was continuing in 1979.

Airframe: Tapered cylindrical body, with clipped-delta wings and sweptback fin, moulded in laminated polyester. No horizontal tail surfaces: control surfaces comprise two elevons, the electrical actuators of which are controlled by autopilot, with light-aircraft vertical gyro for reference.

Power Plant: One 0·98 kN (220 lb st) Microturbo TRS 18-056 turbojet. Fuel capacity 31 litres (6·8 Imp gallons).

Launch and Recovery: Launched by shipborne helicopter, with parachute descent and helicopter recovery.

Guidance and Control: Flight manoeuvres can be pre-programmed or radio controlled. Analogue-type autopilot (comprising gyroscopic attitude sensor; altimeter; analogue computer; and two electrically actuated servo controls) pilots the drone by control of the pitch and roll angles.

Dimensions, external:
Wing span 1·35 m (4 ft 5¼ in)
Length overall 2·86 m (9 ft 4½ in)
Height overall 0·72 m (2 ft 4½ in)

Weights:
Payload 15 kg (33 lb)
Launching weight 150 kg (330 lb)

Performance:
Max level speed at 100 m (330 ft) 437 knots (810 km/h; 503 mph)
Max cruising speed at 1,500 m (5,000 ft) 324 knots (600 km/h; 373 mph)
Range, no reserves:
at max level speed 71 nm (131 km; 81 miles)
at max cruising speed 93 nm (173 km; 107 miles)

GERMANY
(FEDERAL REPUBLIC)

DORNIER
DORNIER GmbH

Postfach 2160, 8000 München 66
Telephone: München 8715480
Telex: 05-23543
Officers: see Aircraft section

Current activities of Dornier GmbH include the development of drones, RPVs, reconnaissance systems, missiles and air target systems.

The Dornier Aerial Target System (DATS) can be adapted to a wide variety of aircraft and target drones, and was described briefly in the 1975-76 *Jane's*.

Dornier developed the Do 34 Kiebitz mobile drone system, based on the Do 32 K Experimental Kiebitz; and the Aerodyne unmanned VTOL research vehicle, described in previous editions of *Jane's*. It is currently developing the LA-RPV, and is active in the fields of tactical RPVs, stand-off missiles, mini-RPVs and helicopter drones.

Jointly with Canadair and SAT, Dornier is developing the AN/USD-502, details of which can be found in the International section.

DORNIER Do 34 KIEBITZ (PEEWIT)

In August 1972 Dornier announced the receipt of a DM 7 million contract from the Federal Ministry of Defence for the first development phase of a prototype of an operational Kiebitz system, to be used for reconnaissance, fire control, communications and traffic monitoring duties. This followed the completion in mid-1972 of the design of a Do 34 operational model as a sensor platform with a payload of 140 kg (308 lb). Full-scale mockups of the Do 34 were followed by the construction of two prototype flight vehicles and two ground stations. Under a bilateral agreement between the German and French governments, both flight vehicles are fitted with an advanced version of the French LCT Orphée II radar, to define, integrate and test a new battlefield reconnaissance system known as **Argus** (see International section). The first Argus prototype made its initial flight on 14 May 1979.

Flight testing of the first Do 34 Kiebitz (F 01) began on 1 February 1978, and on 3 March the maximum flight altitude of more than 300 m (985 ft) was reached, the Kiebitz staying aloft for 40 minutes. Further flights followed.

The following details apply to the basic Do 34 flight vehicle:

Airframe: Flight vehicle is roughly cone-shaped, to reduce radar signature. Approximately cylindrical payload compartment located beneath this, enabling sensors to be changed quickly and allowing space for large-volume radome. Two-blade rotor, with blades attached by straps and driven by cold air expelled through blade-tip nozzles. Air to nozzles supplied by MTU radial compressor driven by engine.

Power Plant: One 313 kW (420 shp) Allison 250-C50B turboshaft engine, installed at an angle to give good air intake position.

Launch and Recovery: Not applicable. Kiebitz is cable-tethered, housed in vehicle which incorporates its landing platform, winch, control post, fuel tank and auxiliary equipment.

Guidance and Control: After arrival on site, can be in position at operational height of 300 m (985 ft) in 8 min; limiting factors are wind speed of 14 m (46 ft)/s ± 8 m (26 ft)/s, available thrust reserves, and sensor requirements. Control system aligns drone according to airframe attitude and position in relation to ground. Electromagnetic sensor measures any drift from desired position.

Equipment: Appropriate payload packages for reconnaissance, target acquisition, fire control, communications relay or traffic monitoring.

Dimensions, external:
Diameter of rotor 8·00 m (26 ft 3 in)
Height overall 1·45 m (4 ft 9 in)
Body diameter at bottom edge 1·05 m (3 ft 5¼ in)

EERM SAM-B meteorological drone

EERM SAM-C atmospheric sounding vehicle

France-Engins Mitsoubac carried by Alouette III helicopter

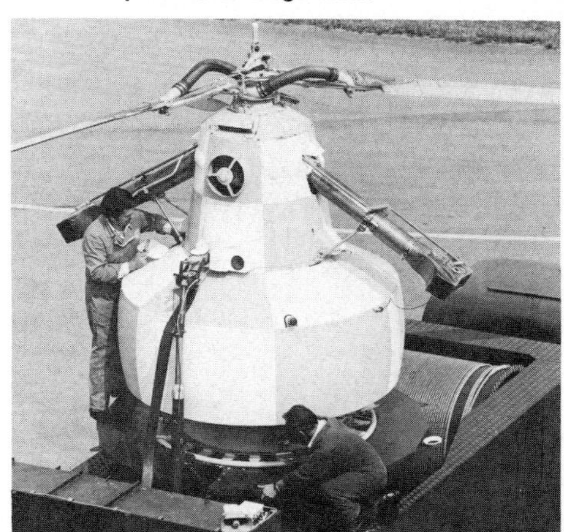

Dornier Do 34 Operational Kiebitz tethered rotor platform

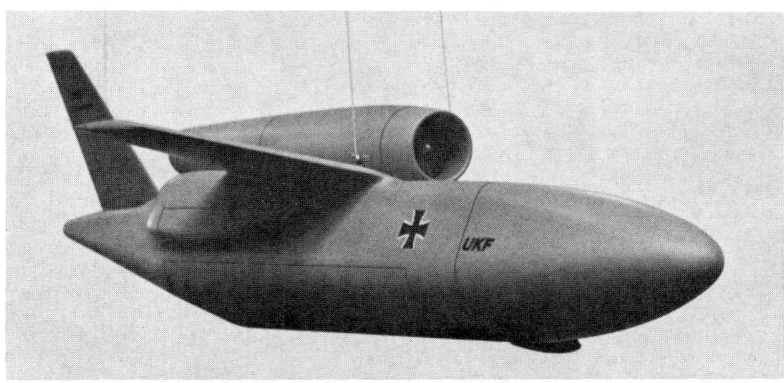

Model of possible Dornier LA-RPV strike RPV *(Brian M. Service)*

Underwing sensor pod on G91R test aircraft for Dornier LA-RPV programme

WEIGHTS:

Weight without tether or payload	280 kg (617 lb)
Max payload to 300 m (985 ft), ISA	150 kg (330 lb)

DESIGN PERFORMANCE:

Reel-in/reel-out speed	3 m (9·8 ft)/s
Operational ceiling	300 m (985 ft)
Mission endurance	24 h

DORNIER LA-RPV

Formerly known as the UKF, the LA (Luft-Angriffs: air attack) RPV has been proposed by Dornier, under the Federal Defence Ministry's Component Air Testing Programme, as a means of examining the basic problems of target acquisition, armament and flight guidance for ground support RPVs.

The principal tasks of the LA-RPV are seen as air strike (especially battlefield interdiction) against highly defended fixed and transient ground targets; tactical reconnaissance; and electronic warfare including air defence suppression. Several different possible configurations have been studied, the one most favoured in 1978-79 (see accompanying photograph) being a ground-launched re-usable vehicle with retractable landing gear, an internal weapon load, an externally-mounted turbojet engine, and inertial navigation updated by satellite data or terrain comparison. This would take off and land conventionally, having provision for booster-assisted take-off and an arrester system for landing.

Particular attention is being paid to accuracy of navigation and weapons delivery, with or without terminal guidance or with remote-based ground control. Since most missions will be against preselected targets, there will be no onboard detection sensors for an enemy to jam. Most missions will be undertaken at high speed and low altitude, and will be pre-programmed out and back, with provision for the ground controller to override the mission programme during the take-off, formation, flight monitoring and recovery phases. Target attack would be by means of 'scatter' weapons ejected from an onboard munitions container.

An Aeritalia (Fiat) G91R aircraft is serving as a multipurpose RPV testbed, and will be used in co-operation with VFW-Fokker in a remote target acquisition programme. This aircraft is manually piloted, and has been modified by Dornier to carry an AEG-Telefunken underwing television camera, an Eltro forward-looking infrared (FLIR) sensor, a two-axis stabilisation system, and a TV transmitter, all housed in an underwing pod. The TV/infra-red experiments were completed by the beginning of 1979, and the G91 is being used by the two companies in other programmes.

DIMENSIONS:

Wing span	3·80 m (12 ft 5½ in)
Length overall	6·50 m (21 ft 4 in)
Height overall	1·90 m (6 ft 2¾ in)

DORNIER MINI-RPV

Dornier has been studying for some years the development of mini-RPVs, and a vehicle of this type was displayed for the first time at the Paris Air Show in May/June 1977. A half-scale model has been flight-tested, as well as experimental full-scale prototypes during the flight test campaign for the concept phase of a programme known as Kleindrohne Antiradar (anti-radiation mini-drone).

Typical missions for which the vehicle is intended include electro-optical reconnaissance, target acquisition and fire control, anti-radar operations, anti-tank or point target attack, and target presentation. For the reconnaissance and target acquisition and fire control missions, the integration of a sensor package comprising a stabilised TV camera, with auto-track facility coupled with a laser illuminator, is under investigation. Anti-radar missions and attacks on tanks or point targets are 'kamikaze' missions in which the vehicle homes on to and attacks the target after a search flight using, for example, passive or active radar and/or infra-red seeker heads. For target missions, it can be fitted with various augmentation devices, including smoke cartridges, flares or Luneberg lenses. It can also be used to test missile proximity fuses or homing heads. The flight guidance, data transmission and ground control systems are adapted to suit specific mission requirements.

The Dornier mini-RPV is one of three designs (others are by MBB and VFW-Fokker, which see) competing in a joint US-German competition for the development of the **Locust** harassment weapon system.

AIRFRAME: Consists essentially of two glassfibre half-shells. Wings built integrally with fuselage, and fitted with elevons on trailing-edges. Tail surfaces comprise a main fin and an underfin, the latter also serving as a keel surface to protect the propeller during landing.

POWER PLANT: One 16·4 kW (22 hp) two-cylinder two-stroke piston engine, mounted in rear of fuselage and driving a four-blade pusher propeller. Fuel in two fuselage tanks; provision to install a third tank in centre of fuselage instead of main recovery parachute. Provision for booster engine for launch.

LAUNCH AND RECOVERY: During initial flight tests, drone was launched by catapult from hydraulically operated launching sled. When required for re-use, the RPV is fitted with an electro-mechanically deployed parachute recovery system (drogue parachute in fin-tip fairing, main parachute in centre-fuselage), activated by radio command, with automatic activation in the event of onboard systems failure. Inflatable airbags to absorb landing impact. For expendable missions, parachute can be replaced by an additional fuel tank or other equipment.

GUIDANCE AND CONTROL: Automatic or remote radio command guidance system. Aerodynamic control by elevons.

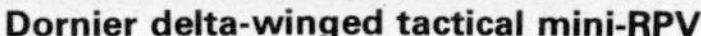
Dornier delta-winged tactical mini-RPV

Dornier Spähplattform unpowered camera-carrying device

DIMENSIONS, EXTERNAL:
- Wing span: 2·00 m (6 ft 6¾ in)
- Length overall: 2·10 m (6 ft 10½ in)

DIMENSIONS, INTERNAL:
- Payload compartment: Length 0·60 m (1 ft 11½ in)
- Diameter: 0·20 m (8 in)

WEIGHTS:
- Payload: 15 kg (33 lb)
- Max launching weight: 70 kg (154 lb)

PERFORMANCE:
- Max diving speed: 194 knots (360 km/h; 223 mph)
- Max level speed at S/L, ISA: 135 knots (250 km/h; 155 mph)
- Max operating height: 3,000 m (9,850 ft)
- Max endurance: 3 h

DORNIER SPÄHPLATTFORM

The Spähplattform (spotting platform) is an unpowered camera-carrying device being developed as a private venture for battlefield surveillance.

AIRFRAME: Small, domed payload compartment, mounted on top of an upper gyroscopic ring encircling a four-blade rotor, and a lower stationary ring, in which four control vanes are mounted.

POWER SOURCE: 25 kW (33·5 hp) is available for initial rotor spin-up; 90 N is required to maintain the hover mode.

LAUNCH AND RECOVERY: Not applicable. The Spähplattform is vehicle-mounted, and tethered to its control vehicle by an umbilical cable, via which drive from the parent vehicle is transmitted to spin up the four-blade flywheel rotor to 4,000 rpm for take-off. The blade-tips of the rotor are attached to the upper gyroscopic ring, in which the energy from spin-up is stored; the four control vanes, mounted on cruciform tubes within the stationary lower ring, can be actuated to control the platform in azimuth. A conventional cyclic pitch control of the rotor determines the platform's position, and gyroscopic effect stabilises its attitude. The Spähplattform is reeled out and hovers on the energy stored in the flywheel rotor.

GUIDANCE AND CONTROL: Control and sensor signals are transmitted via the tethering cable from the ground control vehicle.

SPECIAL EQUIPMENT: Still camera of 12·5 mm to 75 mm focal length, or TV camera, in payload compartment.

DIMENSION:
- Rotor diameter: 1·20 m (3 ft 11¼ in)

WEIGHTS:
- Weight of twin-ring assembly: 20 kg (44 lb)
- Weight of complete vehicle, without payload: 30 kg (66 lb)
- Payload: 5 kg (11 lb)
- Max T-O weight: 35 kg (77 lb)

PERFORMANCE:
- Reel-in/reel-out speed: 5 m (16·4 ft)/s
- Operational ceiling: 50 m (164 ft)
- Mission endurance: 55 s

MBB

MESSERSCHMITT-BÖLKOW-BLOHM GmbH

Ottobrunn bei München, 8 München 80, Postfach 801220

OFFICERS: see Aircraft section

MBB HARASSMENT DRONE

This miniature drone is being developed under Federal German Ministry of Defence contract, to combat the radar units of enemy air defence installations.

The drone is launched by means of a booster directly from its storage and transport container. When inside the container the wings, control surfaces and propeller are folded; they flip out for use immediately upon launch.

Designed to search for, and attack, enemy air defence radars, this small RPV was evolved in collaboration with Teledyne Brown Engineering of Huntsville, Alabama, USA. Components for the terminal guidance system are manufactured by Motorola.

VFW-FOKKER

VEREINIGTE FLUGTECHNISCHE WERKE-FOKKER GmbH

Hünefeldstrasse 1-5, 28 Bremen 1, Postfach 1206

VFW-FOKKER MINI-RPV

To meet a German Defence Ministry requirement, VFW-Fokker is developing a catapult-launched mini-RPV of canard configuration. The first prototype, designed in association with Northrop of the USA, had a tapered wing and was powered by a 1·5 kW (2 hp) piston engine, mounted at the extreme tail and driving a two-blade pusher propeller. This prototype carried no telemetry equipment and had a weight of only 5 kg (11 lb). After a period of training for the pilot, with the model in a wind tunnel, it made free flights at up to 52 knots (96 km/h; 60 mph) after take-off from a moving motorcar.

The second prototype, which was displayed at the 1978 Hanover Air Show, was described as the Mini-RPV 2012. It has constant-chord wings, a 4·5 kW (6 hp) single-cylinder piston engine and onboard telemetry equipment, increasing the take-off weight to 20 kg (44 lb). Its general configuration is shown in the accompanying illustration. The wing has a Wortmann section, and is fitted with spoilers. There are elevators on the canard foreplane, and a tail fin but no rudder.

VFW-Fokker hoped to progress to a pre-production version of this mini-RPV, weighing about 60 kg (132 lb). For anti-radar missions, such a vehicle could carry a warhead of about 8 kg (17·6 lb) weight and would be able to fly at 100 knots (185 km/h; 115 mph).

VFW-FOKKER VF-500

This larger RPV, of delta-winged aircraft configuration with twin fins and rudders, was displayed in model form at the 1978 Hanover Air Show.

DIMENSIONS, EXTERNAL:
- Wing span: 4·00 m (13 ft 1½ in)
- Length overall: 7·80 m (25 ft 7 in)
- Height overall: 1·95 m (6 ft 4¾ in)

WEIGHT:
- Max launching weight: 1,940 kg (4,277 lb)

INDONESIA

LAPAN

LEMBAGA PENERBANGAN DAN ANTARIKSA NASIONAL (National Aeronautics and Space Institute)

HEADQUARTERS: Jalan Pemuda Persil No. 1, PO Box 3048, Jakarta Timur

Telephone: (021) 465125, 482808 and 482653

Telex: 45675 LAPAN IA

OFFICERS: see Aircraft section

This Institute, established in 1963, has designed and built an experimental mini-RPV, known as the XTG-01.

LAPAN XTG-01

Test-flown for the first time at Rumpin airfield in FY 1977, the XTG-01 is being developed for such applications as aerial photography, emergency transmitter aerial, and flight research.

TYPE: Experimental mini-RPV.

AIRFRAME: High-wing monoplane configuration, built basically of balsa wood; wings have 2° dihedral, 2° incidence, and a flat-bottomed section. Balsa fuselage, laminated with synthetic fibres.

POWER PLANT: One 1·28 kW (1·71 hp) Hirtenberger HP 61 FS single-cylinder aircooled piston engine, driving a two-blade fixed-pitch wooden propeller. Fuel capacity 2·5 litres (0·55 Imp gallons).

LAUNCH AND RECOVERY: Conventional T-O and landing.

GUIDANCE AND CONTROL: Futaba FP-6FN six-channel radio command flight control system; transmitter and receiver operate in 27MHz band. Aerodynamic control by ailerons, elevators and rudder.

EQUIPMENT: 9·6V battery.

DIMENSIONS, EXTERNAL:
- Wing span: 2·43 m (7 ft 11¾ in)
- Wing area, gross: 0·814 m² (8·76 sq ft)
- Length overall: 1·60 m (5 ft 3 in)
- Height overall: 0·575 m (1 ft 10¾ in)

WEIGHTS:
- Weight empty: 5·3 kg (11·7 lb)
- Max payload: 2 kg (4·4 lb)
- Max T-O weight: 7·0 kg (15·4 lb)

PERFORMANCE:
- Speed: 60 knots (112 km/h; 70 mph)
- Endurance: 1 h

Launch of MBB Harassment Drone mini-RPV. After launch, wing and tail surfaces are extended

VFW-Fokker second prototype mini-RPV (No. 2012) *(Brian M. Service)*

LAPAN XTG-01 prototype experimental mini-RPV

Mockup of AN/USD-502/CL-289 reconnaissance drone and launcher

Dornier Do 34 Kiebitz in Argus configuration

INTERNATIONAL PROGRAMMES

AN/USD-502

PRIME CONTRACTORS:

Canadair Ltd, PO Box 6087, Montreal, Quebec H3C 3G9, Canada
Telephone: (514) 744 1511

Dornier GmbH, Postfach 2160, 8000 München 66, Federal Republic of Germany
Telephone: München 8715480
Telex: 05-23543

AN/USD-502/CL-289

The AN/USD-502 originated as a joint Canadair/Dornier programme, based on AN/USD-501 (Canadair CL-89, which see) technology, to meet a German military technical requirement for a longer-range drone for service from about 1983. It has the NATO designation AN/USD-502, and the Canadair designation **CL-289**.

The main contract was awarded in July 1976 to Canadair, as part of a shared-cost project between Canada and Germany. Dornier is subcontracted by Canadair for a substantial part of the work, and SAT of France joined the programme on 29 March 1977.

Resembling a scaled-up CL-89, the AN/USD-502 will have greater payload capacity and will be fitted with both Zeiss photographic and SAT Super Cyclope infra-red linescanning (IRLS) sensors; a real-time data transmission system for IRLS imagery; a Matra air-to-ground data link; Canadian Marconi Doppler navigation system; a Dornier MUDAS onboard digital computer. Integration, test and evaluation of the IRLS and other avionics, representing approx 10 per cent of the total programme, are the responsibility of SAT. Launch and recovery systems are basically similar to those of the CL-89. Power plant will consist of a KHD turbojet engine and a Bristol Aerospace booster rocket.

ARGUS

Dornier GmbH, Postfach 2160, 8000 München 66, eral Republic of Germany
Telephone: München 8715480
Telex: 05-23543

LCT (Laboratoire Central de Télécommunications), 18-20 Rue Grange-Dame-Rose, 78140 Vélizy-Villacoublay, BP 40, France
Telephone: 946 96 15
Telex: 690892

ARGUS

Argus (Autonomes Radar Gefechtsfeld Uberwachungs System) is a battlefield surveillance system being developed under a German-French government agreement signed on 6 March 1974. Dornier has the main contract for co-ordinating, integrating and testing the system, and the programme is administered by a board of directors representing the two governments.

The Argus prototypes consist of the two prototypes of the Dornier Do 34 Kiebitz, each fitted with an advanced version of the LCT Orphée II radar as the primary sensor. The first Argus prototype made its initial flight on 14 May 1979 and the second prototype was due to fly in September 1979. Ground and flight testing were to be followed by a presentation to the French and German armed forces in 1979.

The complete Argus system incorporates a mobile ground station and a tether cable. The ground station is installed in a container mounted on a cross-country 10 ton truck and provided with all equipment necessary for transportation and up to 24 h operation of the system. Operating height of the flight vehicle is 300 m (985 ft).

A description of the Kiebitz appears under the Dornier heading in the German section.

ISRAEL

TADIRAN

TADIRAN ISRAEL ELECTRONICS INDUSTRIES LTD

3 Hashalom Road, PO Box 648, Tel-Aviv 61000
Telephone: 267272
Telex: 03-3537
MANAGING DIRECTOR: E. Caspi
MARKETING AND INTERNATIONAL OPERATIONS: A. Leshem
PLANNING AND DEVELOPMENT: A. Mayer

TADIRAN MASTIFF

This mini-RPV completed over 100 test flights with great success, and is now in production for the Israeli armed forces and for export. No details are available of earlier products by this company, but the caption to the accompanying photograph described the Mastiff as Tadiran's "latest version" RPV.

Of high-wing monoplane configuration, the Mastiff has a low-set tailplane, non-retractable tailwheel landing gear, and a ventral payload compartment within the centre-fuselage. It is said to have a very low radar signature. Applications include photographic reconnaissance, real-time TV surveillance, target acquisition and artillery spotting.

POWER PLANT: One 7·5 kW (10 hp) two-cylinder piston engine, driving a two-blade propeller.

GUIDANCE AND CONTROL: Radio command guidance system.

EQUIPMENT: TV camera with real-time video link; ciné or panoramic camera; or other mission equipment.

DIMENSION:
Wing span 4·20 m (13 ft 9½ in)

WEIGHTS:
Payload 10-15 kg (22-33 lb)
Max launching weight 70 kg (154 lb)

PERFORMANCE:
Max level speed 80 knots (148 km/h; 92 mph)
Typical cruising speed 40-60 knots (74-111 km/h; 46-69 mph)
Max operating altitude 3,050 m (10,000 ft)
Endurance 4-6 h

ITALY

METEOR

METEOR SpA AIRCRAFT AND ELECTRONICS INDUSTRY

146 Via Nomentana, 00162 Rome
Telephone: (06) 8380232, 8391690, 8392145 and 8394200
Telex: 680136 Meteor
PRESIDENT AND GENERAL MANAGER: Comm Avv Furio Lauri
GENERAL AND ADMINISTRATIVE AFFAIRS SERVICE MANAGER: Mrs Luciana Bortolotti-Lauri
MARKET CO-ORDINATION PLANNING MANAGER: Capt Guido Borsari, ItN
TECHNICAL/OPERATIONAL SERVICE DEVELOPMENT MANAGER: Ing Carlo Spanò
PRODUCTION PLANT: 34074 Monfalcone, Stazioni F.S. Ronchi Nord
Telephone: (0481) 778001
Telex: 460288 METMON
PLANT MANAGER: Dott Antonio Castelli

Meteor was established in Trieste as a joint stock company in 1947. Its present head office is in Rome, supported by facilities at Monfalcone (Trieste) and Cagliari (Sardinia). The former is a production factory, the latter being equipped for flight operations and for technical assistance to the users of the tri-service range at Salto di Quirra.

Meteor is producing for the Italian and foreign armed forces various propeller-driven and turbojet-powered radio-controlled drones covering a speed range from 323 knots (600 km/h; 372 mph) up to Mach 2·8, and altitudes from 10 m (35 ft) to 25,000 m (82,000 ft) above sea level. It also co-produces the Northrop-Ventura Meteor 1 and 2, Northrop-Ventura Meteor/USD-1, Aérospatiale Meteor 20 (CT.20) target drones and the BM-1 (Beech Meteor 1) missile target system. Under licence from Canadair, Meteor produces 50% of the AN/USD-501 (CL-89) reconnaissance systems ordered by Italy.

METEOR ANDROMEDA/MIRACH SYSTEM

The Andromeda system is designed to meet a basic operational requirement which synthesises and integrates the requirements of most potential operators. Such a multi-role system, equipped with various types of RPV for combat or training use by air, land and naval forces in natural and operational environments, could reduce the attrition of conventional piloted aircraft used in conjunction with them and/or replaced by them in missions operationally suited to the use of RPVs.

The Andromeda system, which is characterised by completely independent operation, maximum utilisation and considerable mobility, is composed of the following subsystems:

1st Subsystem (Alamak). Ground station for accomplishing and/or controlling the mission by the ground crew (Standard and RID versions). Produced for foreign markets.

2nd Subsystem. Equipment for launch, recovery and maintenance of the aerial vehicles. Produced for foreign markets.

3rd Subsystem. Equipment for preparation, recovery, maintenance and operation and/or evaluation of the payload and/or its results. Produced for foreign markets.

4th Subsystem. The aerial vehicle system, configured in a range of five types of vehicle, known as **Mirach**, compatible with the Andromeda system to guarantee maximum effectiveness.

The Andromeda system can be adapted, with only slight modification, to use other types of air vehicle which operators may already have at their disposal. It is being developed in collaboration with Aerosystem Electronic AG of Switzerland.

The following versions of the Mirach flight vehicle are available:

Mirach-10. RPV for target acquisition, location and designation; surveillance; 'kamikaze' missions; and enemy defence saturation. Powered by single 11·2 kW (15 hp) piston engine. Meteor radio command guidance system. Equipped with real-time TV, photo-reconnaissance cameras and laser designator. Under development for foreign markets.

Mirach-70. Target, or RPV for surveillance, target acquisition, electronic warfare, or decoy saturation. Powered by single 52 kW (70 hp) McCulloch piston engine. Meteor radio command guidance system. Various combat or training payloads. In production for foreign markets.

Mirach-100. Target, or RPV for surveillance; reconnaissance; target acquisition, location and designation; electronic warfare strike; and defence saturation. Powered by single 1·11 kN (250 lb st) Microturbo TRS 18-076 turbojet engine. Meteor radio command guidance, or programmed guidance with real-time updating. Various combat or training payloads. In production for Italian Navy and foreign markets.

Mirach-300. Target, or RPV for surveillance, reconnaissance, target acquisition, location and designation, electronic warfare strike, and defence saturation. Powered by single 2·94 kN (660 lb st) Teledyne CAE 372-2A turbojet engine. Guidance as for Mirach-100. Various combat or training payloads. Under development for foreign markets.

Mirach-600. Target, or RPV for training and evaluation, area reconnaissance, electronic warfare strike, and defence suppression. Powered by two 2·94 kN (660 lb st) Teledyne CAE 372-2A turbojet engines. Guidance as for Mirach-100. Various combat or evaluation payloads.

DIMENSIONS, EXTERNAL:
Span overall (wings or fins):
10 2·71 m (8 ft 10¾ in)
70 3·57 m (11 ft 8½ in)
100 2·80 m (9 ft 2¼ in)
300 2·83 m (9 ft 3½ in)
600 3·60 m (11 ft 9¾ in)
Length overall (excl booster):
10 2·25 m (7 ft 4½ in)
70 3·66 m (12 ft 0 in)
100 3·91 m (12 ft 10 in)
300 4·88 m (16 ft 0 in)
600 6·10 m (20 ft 0 in)

WEIGHTS:
Weight empty: *10 50 kg (110 lb)
70 200 kg (441 lb)
100 210 kg (463 lb)
*300 320 kg (705 lb)
*600 680 kg (1,499 lb)
Combat payload (internal): 70 20 kg (44 lb)
100 30 kg (66 lb)
300 40 kg (88 lb)
600 100 kg (220 lb)
Max T-O weight (incl booster): *10 70 kg (154 lb)
70 260 kg (573 lb)
100 310 kg (683 lb)
*300 450 kg (992 lb)
*600 1,000 kg (2,204 lb)
**estimated*

PERFORMANCE:
Max level speed:
10 107 knots (200 km/h; 124 mph)
70 169 knots (314 km/h; 195 mph)
100 485 knots (900 km/h; 559 mph)
300, 600 Mach 0·9
Max endurance: 10 3 h 0 min
70 1 h 0 min
100 1 h 10 min

METEOR P-X

Details of this basic training drone, built for the armed forces of Italy and other countries, can be found in the 1978-79 *Jane's*.

METEOR GUFO

Details of the Gufo tactical reconnaissance system can be found in the 1978-79 *Jane's*.

JAPAN

FUJI

FUJI JUKOGYO KABUSHIKI KAISHA (Fuji Heavy Industries Ltd)

Subaru Building, 7-2, 1-chome, Nishi-Shinjuku, Shinjuku-ku, Tokyo
Telephone: Tokyo (03) 347 2505
Telex: 0-232-2268
OFFICERS: see Aircraft section

Under contract from the Japan Defence Agency, Fuji is building the Teledyne Ryan BQM-34A Firebee I subsonic target drone (see US section) for use in the training of Tartar missile and gunnery crews and for the evaluation of air-to-air missile systems. The first shipboard launch of a Fuji-built drone was carried out successfully in 1970, and 140 flights had been made by the beginning of 1979.

Fuji-built BQM-34As include one drone fitted with RALACS (Radar Altimeter Low Altitude Control System: see Teledyne Ryan entry in US section), for training the crews of defensive weapons against attack by anti-shipping missiles.

Twenty Fuji-built BQM-34As had been completed and delivered to the Japan Maritime Self-Defence Force, and two to the Technical Research and Development Institute of the Japan Defence Agency, by the end of FY 1977. A total of 26 were scheduled to be completed by the end of FY 1978 (March 1979).

NEC

NIPPON ELECTRIC CO LTD (Nippon Denki Kabushiki Kaisha)

33-1 Shiba Gochome, Minato-ku, Tokyo 108
Telephone: Tokyo (03) 454 1111
Telex: NECTOK A J22686
PRESIDENT: Tadao Tanaka
MANAGER, OVERSEAS RELATIONS: Kiyoshi Yamauchi

Under a technical aid agreement with Northrop Corporation, USA, NEC is responsible for production and repair of Northrop KD2R5 (Shelduck) target drones for the Japan Maritime Self-Defence Force and Ground Self-Defence Force. Delivery of these drones to the JMSDF and JGSDF began in 1961, and a total of 271 had been delivered by the end of 1978. Production was expected to continue at the rate of approx 15 per year.

Tadiran Mastiff mini-RPV

Mirach-70 RPV on its launch trailer

Model of the Mirach-10 multi-purpose RPV *(Brian M. Service)*

Mirach-100 target/RPV on launcher

Meteor Mirach-300 target/RPV with mobile launch trailer and ground control vehicle

Fuji-built BQM-34A Firebee target drone of the JMSDF

NEC-built Northrop Shelduck target drone

SAUDI ARABIA

MCS

MID-CONTINENT SCIENTIFIC CO (A subsidiary of Qutub International Ltd)

PO Box 3603, Riyadh

PRESIDENT: Dr Musa Qutub, PhD

MCS PL-60

The PL-60 is a twin-engined mini-RPV capable of use for surveillance and other military duties, border patrol, forest fire surveillance, aerial photography, traffic patrol, air pollution and weather monitoring, and similar applications. It is claimed that it cannot be detected by radar.

Design began, in the USA, in 1971; a prototype PL-60 was flown in 1972, and production began in the same year. By March 1979 a total of 1,580 had been ordered and built in two versions, designated **PL-60A** and **PL-60B**, the latter having a strengthened structure to carry a heavier payload.

POWER PLANT: Two 1·4 kW (1·9 hp) piston engines, mounted in overwing nacelles and each driving a two-blade propeller. Fuel capacity 1·9 litres (0·5 US gallons) standard, 7·6 litres (2 US gallons) optional.

LAUNCH AND RECOVERY: Conventional T-O, using tailwheel-type fixed landing gear. Wire recovery.

EQUIPMENT: Automatic navigation system, TV or other camera installations, optional.

DIMENSIONS, EXTERNAL:

Wing span	3·30 m (10 ft 10 in)
Wing area, gross	1·57 m² (16·94 sq ft)
Length overall	1·96 m (6 ft 5 in)
Height overall	0·58 m (1 ft 11 in)

WEIGHTS:

Payload: PL-60A	11·3 kg (25 lb)
PL-60B	22 kg (48 lb)
Max T-O weight	27·2 kg (60 lb)

PERFORMANCE:

Max level speed	65-87 knots (121-161 km/h; 75-100 mph)
Cruising speed	56·5 knots (105 km/h; 65 mph)
Max operating height	3,050 m (10,000 ft)
T-O run (hard surface)	99 m (325 ft)
Range: standard fuel	30·5 nm (56·5 km; 35 miles)
max optional fuel	121·5 nm (225 km; 140 miles)

SOUTH AFRICA

NATIONAL DYNAMICS
NATIONAL DYNAMICS (PTY) LTD

PO Box 20163, Virginia Airport, Durban North 4016
Telephone: Durban 845350
MANAGING DIRECTOR: S. J. Reed

In addition to its piloted aircraft programmes (see Aircraft section), National Dynamics is developing the Observer mini-RPV.

NATIONAL DYNAMICS ND-100 OBSERVER

The Observer low-cost multi-purpose mini-RPV has been built as a private venture for various military and civil applications, including real-time forest surveillance; aerial photography; search missions; flood, wildfire and shoreline pollution detection and mapping; powerline, pipeline and highway traffic observation and patrol; air sampling and storm research; fishing law enforcement and fishery spotting; and aerial survey.

TYPE: Multi-purpose mini-RPV.

AIRFRAME: High-wing monoplane, of near-delta planform, with special aerofoil section. Dihedral 0°. Sweepback 30° on leading-edges. Trailing-edge elevons, actuated by radio-controlled servos, function as both ailerons and elevators. NASA (Whitcomb) fixed 'winglet' at each wingtip; no vertical moving surfaces. Cylindrical fuselage, with wooden bulkheads, glassfibre/epoxy skin, and transparent hemispherical nose-cap. Low-density styrofoam and plywood also used in construction, to provide corrosion-resistant structure.

POWER PLANT: One 15 kW (20 hp) Herbrandson Dyad 280 piston engine, with electronic ignition, driving a four-blade fixed-pitch wooden pusher propeller. Single fuselage fuel tank (petrol/oil mixture), capacity 42·5 litres (9·35 Imp gallons).

LAUNCH AND RECOVERY: Self-powered launch from vehicle-mounted, controllable (in T-O speed and direction) rotary arm launcher which also acts as boom for low-speed parafoil/boom recovery. Alternative launch by catapult and net recovery.

GUIDANCE AND CONTROL: Tracking by onboard transponder and forward-looking video tracking subsystem, with associated X-Y plotter and TV monitor in two-man mobile ground control station. Target designation by separate downward-looking video subsystem. Guidance and control based upon command uplink plus antennae, command receiver, control servos, electrostatic autopilot with ionising units, telemetry channels to monitor airframe/engine states and RPV equipment, and data link and video transmitters. Landing after deployment of parafoil in response to command signal from ground is by standard non-tracking radio control link, using a portable transmitter. Rotating beacon fitted to assist recovery in poor visibility.

EQUIPMENT: Engine-driven alternator, rectifier/regulator and twin-battery pack provide electrical power to operate onboard receiver, servos, lightweight autopilot, telemetry and video equipment, and transmitters. Space for ample operational equipment payload, according to mission.

DIMENSIONS, EXTERNAL:

Wing span	4·34 m (14 ft 3 in)
Wing area, gross	4·13 m² (44·5 sq ft)
Length overall	2·54 m (8 ft 4 in)
Height overall	1·12 m (3 ft 8 in)
Body diameter	0·46 m (1 ft 6 in)
Propeller diameter	0·61 m (2 ft 0 in)

WEIGHTS AND LOADINGS:

Weight empty, equipped	50 kg (110 lb)
Max fuel load	32 kg (70 lb)
Max payload (avionics)	36 kg (80 lb)
Max launching weight	118 kg (260 lb)
Max wing loading	28·6 kg/m² (5·8 lb/sq ft)
Max power loading	7·87 kg/kW (13·0 lb/hp)

PERFORMANCE (at max T-O weight at S/L):

Max level speed	95·5 knots (177 km/h; 110 mph)
Cruising speed	65 knots (120 km/h; 75 mph)
Stalling speed	37·5 knots (69 km/h; 43 mph)
Max rate of climb	533 m (1,750 ft)/min
Service ceiling	approx 4,575 m (15,000 ft)
Endurance	more than 6 h
Range	Radio line of sight (or, out of line of sight, by use of two RPVs: one sensor and one relay)

UNION OF SOVIET SOCIALIST REPUBLICS

UR-1

According to press reports appearing in early 1979, and unconfirmed at the time of closing for press, the designation UR-1 applies to a target drone observed during tests of late-model MiG-25 'Foxbat' interceptors equipped with AA-X-9 radar-guided air-to-air missiles. These tests were said to have been successful against drones flying at low level, in ground clutter, and at altitudes up to approx 21,335 m (70,000 ft). The drones, used to simulate targets of some 25·00 m² (269 sq ft) gross area, are air-launched from Tu-16 carrier aircraft. They are said to operate normally between 19,810 m (65,000 ft) and 30,500 m (100,000 ft), but to be capable of flying as high as 39,625 m (130,000 ft).

UNITED KINGDOM

AEL
AERO ELECTRONICS (AEL) LTD

Gatwick House, Horley, Surrey RH6 9SU
Telephone: 02 934 5353
Telex: 877362 and 87116
MANAGING DIRECTOR: M. H. Nicholas
MANAGER, AERIAL TARGET DIVISION: T. Irlam

This company manufactures small, low-cost radio- and optically-guided systems for target drone, reconnaissance or other RPV applications.

AEL4111 SNIPE Mk II

The AEL Snipe aerial target system was developed as a dynamic target for use with air defence gun systems, of up to 40 mm calibre, and close-range missile systems. It combines simplicity of design with outstanding performance and ease of operation. Its high manoeuvrability enables it faithfully to reproduce any of the complex attack profiles which are normally executed by full-size, manned ground attack aircraft.

The Mk II Snipe is a development of the original aircraft (see 1978-79 *Jane's*) which is in service in six countries and is on order or under evaluation by several others.

AIRFRAME: High-wing monoplane configuration. Built of wood and plywood veneer covering a polystyrene foam core. Finish is to customer's specification, but is normally a high gloss red paint.

POWER PLANT: One 76 cc single-cylinder two-stroke air-cooled engine, with electronic ignition. Petrol/oil mixture (25:1), contained in a 2·3 litre (0·5 Imp gallon) tank.

LAUNCH AND RECOVERY: Launch by simple rubber bungee catapult mounted on two-wheel transporting trailer. Recovery by orthodox belly landing or by parachute. Fail-safe system automatically closes throttle and deploys parachute in event of loss of command signal, heavy radio interference or loss of internal power supplies.

GUIDANCE AND CONTROL: Radio control by modified commercial equipment operating in both VHF band (27-72MHz) and UHF band (400MHz). VHF equipment available with either AM or FM mode. Two transmitters normally supplied with each trailer, on frequencies specified by customer. Aerodynamic control by ailerons and elevators.

SPECIAL EQUIPMENT: For visual enhancement, underwing pylons can be fitted to carry four smoke flares which can be ignited sequentially. The 40 s burning time is adequate to allow full target engagement. For weapons employing infra-red homing techniques, heat from engine is normally sufficient to allow lock-on and full target engagement. For special applications, one infra-red flare with 25 s burning time can be fitted to each wingtip and fired sequentially. For radar enhancement, a special radar-reflective mesh is incorporated between foam core and skin of aircraft which is sufficient to provide a return on most radars operating between 2-10 GHz. For customers requiring a greater radar response, a corner reflector can be mounted in rear of fuselage. For special applications a robot camera can be supplied for aerial photography. Under development are a Doppler Miss Distance Indicating Equipment (by an associate company) and an airborne lightweight closed-circuit TV system. For naval air defence training, target aircraft are specially waterproofed for recovery from sea. GSE (ground support equipment) comprises trailer, launcher, and all ground-based stores needed to fly aircraft. Trailer is matched to standard Land-Rover truck with Avonride suspension. Trailer can carry two target aircraft and has built-in workbench for ease of maintenance. For naval air defence training, GSE can be supplied without trailer, for shipboard mounting.

DIMENSIONS, EXTERNAL:

Wing span	2·44 m (8 ft 0 in)
Wing area	0·99 m² (10·64 sq ft)
Length overall	2·13 m (7 ft 0 in)

WEIGHT:

Max launching weight	18 kg (40 lb)

PERFORMANCE:

Max speed	113 knots (209 km/h; 130 mph)
Average sortie	45 min

AEL4560 SMIDGE

This small arms target drone, described in the 1978-79 *Jane's*, has been discontinued.

FR
FLIGHT REFUELLING LTD

Wimborne, Dorset BH21 2BJ
Telephone: 020 125 2121
Telex: 41247
CHAIRMAN: M. J. Cobham, MA, FRAeS, Barrister

For more than 20 years, Flight Refuelling Ltd has been engaged, inter alia, in the design and manufacture of control systems for pilotless aircraft. It was responsible for the conversion of more than 250 Gloster Meteor aircraft to pilotless or drone configuration. Some of these aircraft are still in service use for missile development trials and practice firings.

Flight Refuelling is continuing its development work on target drones; details of one of these can be found in the Addenda.

FR UNIVERSAL DRONE PACK

Flight Refuelling has developed a Universal Drone Pack (UDP), providing a packaged system which enables most types of aircraft to be readily converted to drone or pilotless configuration with only minor modifications to their conventional flying control system inputs, and without degrading the aircraft's original manned performance envelope. The pack is designed for installation on the existing seat rail in the aircraft's cockpit. The first of a series of aircraft to be fitted with the UDP was a Hawker Siddeley Sea Vixen D. Mk 3.

MCS PL-60 twin-engined mini-RPV

National Dynamics Observer RPV, without heatshield and with parafoil compartment doors open

AEL Snipe Mk II miniature target aircraft

Mounted on its ground transporter, an FR Universal Drone Pack awaits installation in a Sea Vixen aircraft

RCS4020 Merlin miniature drone

RCS4024 Heron target drone, operated by the British Army

RCS Falcon mini-RPV and its ground control equipment

RCS

RCS GUIDED WEAPONS SYSTEMS (Division of Radio Control Specialists Ltd)

6 Wolsey Road, Ashford, Middlesex TW15 2RB
Telephone: 078 42 53661/2

DIRECTORS:
E. A. Falkner, CEng, MRAeS, FIED
P. R. Conway, BSc (Eng), CEng, MICE
K. E. Mackley, CEng, MIERE

This company manufactures a range of small, low-cost radio- and optically-guided systems for target drone, reconnaissance or other RPV applications. All types listed were in full-scale production at the beginning of 1979.

The standard systems offer payload capabilities of up to 13·6 kg (30 lb) and a visual control range of up to 2·7 nm (5 km; 3·1 miles). Non-standard systems can be produced with payload capabilities of up to 22·7 kg (50 lb). To simplify control, an autostabiliser is available, with options of height lock and heading lock. An autopilot is under development to permit automatic out-and-back sorties beyond, and returning to, visual control. All systems are controlled using a standard tripod-mounted transmitter, and each system operates in a slot with an approximate bandwidth of 25kHz and an ERP (effective radiated power) maximum of 10W.

Also available for the larger drones is an airborne RF television link, weighing 2·3 kg (5 lb) and having a line-of-sight range of up to 8 km (5 miles).

RCS MERLIN

The Merlin system consists of a delta-shaped flying-wing drone, built of polystyrene foam with a plywood skin, powered by a 10 cc piston engine and fitted with a tricycle landing gear. A six-function pulse width modulated VHF guidance system with RF output of 5W is used.

Three versions are available, as follows:

RCS4018 Target System. For training air defence weapon crews to acquire and track target aircraft. Can carry X- and S-band radar enhancement devices. A 2·13 m (7 ft) drogue target can be towed on a 152 m (500 ft) cable for live firing work.

RCS4019 Camera System. For short-range aerial reconnaissance with radio-triggered Robot f/2·8 35 mm camera at heights up to 915 m (3,000 ft). Optional kit for rapid film processing and printing.

RCS4020 Composite Target/Camera System. Combines facilities of RCS4018 and 4019.

LAUNCH AND RECOVERY: T-O from ground or launch from system launcher; orthodox landing.

DIMENSIONS, EXTERNAL:
Wing span 1·45 m (4 ft 9 in)
Length overall 1·22 m (4 ft 0 in)

WEIGHTS:
Payload 1·4 kg (3 lb)
Max launching weight 4·8 kg (10·5 lb)

PERFORMANCE:
Max speed 78 knots (145 km/h; 90 mph)
Max controllable range (optical) 1·6 nm (3 km; 1·9 miles)
Endurance 30 min

RCS FALCON

The Falcon is generally similar to the Merlin, but is larger, has a greater payload and longer endurance, and is powered by a 7·5 kW (10 hp) engine. Guidance, launch and recovery are as for the Merlin.

Three versions are available, as follows:

RCS4012 Target System. For training air defence weapon crews to acquire and track low-level high-speed aircraft. Can carry X- and S-band radar enhancement devices. Facility for trailing a 3·05 m (10 ft) towed target on a 152 m (500 ft) cable. Supplied to Libyan government in 1973-74.

RCS4015 Camera System. For short-range aerial reconnaissance; same equipment as Merlin, including optional processing/printing kit. Target location by photo/map comparison. Supplied to Libyan government 1973-74.

RCS4017 Composite Target/Camera System. Combines facilities of RCS 4012 and 4015.

Dimensions, external:
- Wing span: 2·13 m (7 ft 0 in)
- Length overall: 1·98 m (6 ft 6 in)

Weights:
- Payload: 5·4 kg (12 lb)
- Max launching weight: 16·3 kg (36 lb)

Performance:
- Max speed: 110 knots (204 km/h; 126·5 mph)
- Max controllable range (optical): 2·7 nm (5 km; 3·1 miles)
- Endurance: 45 min

RCS4024 HERON

This high-wing monoplane RPV is powered by a 7·5 kW (10 hp) engine. Fuel capacity is 4·5 litres (1 Imp gallon). Although designed specifically for target work, payload capability and 0·03 m³ (1 cu ft) payload bay make it equally suitable for other applications, and up to 5 kg (11 lb) of total payload may consist of pylon-mounted underwing stores such as flares or small bombs. A good X-band radar signature is provided for tracking. Guidance, launch and recovery as for Merlin system. Controllable in winds gusting up to 30 knots (56 km/h; 34·5 mph). Ordered by British Army.

Both Heron and Heron HS can be supplied with a laser gun hit simulating system, in which hits are recorded on an airframe counter and marked with a small flare or flash when a hit is made.

Dimensions, external:
- Wing span: 3·00 m (9 ft 10 in)
- Length overall: 2·13 m (7 ft 0 in)
- Fuselage: Max width: 0·254 m (10 in)

Weights:
- Max payload:
  - catapult launch: 6·8 kg (15 lb)
  - ground T-O: 13·6 kg (30 lb)
- Max weight:
  - catapult launch: 15·4 kg (34 lb)
  - ground T-O: 24 kg (53 lb)

Performance:
- Max speed: 104 knots (193 km/h; 120 mph)
- Max controllable range (optical): 2·7 nm (5 km; 3·1 miles)
- Endurance: 30 min

RCS HERON HS

High-speed version of standard Heron, improved aerodynamically by reducing wing thickness and area, introducing linear taper and eliminating wing struts and pylons. Wheeled landing gear replaced by sprung metal skid and catapult launching points; take-off dolly can be provided, permitting a 25% increase in payload. Dimensions as for standard Heron, except for 2·44 m (8 ft 0 in) wing span. Max payload is 4·5 kg (10 lb); max speed 121·5 knots (225 km/h; 140 mph).

RCS4030 TRAINING DRONE

Designed to train operators of operational drone/RPVs, RCS4030 is broadly similar externally to Heron, but slightly smaller and powered by a 10 cc engine. Six-channel proportional radio control, designed for use with standard RCS ground control system.

Dimensions, external:
- Wing span: 2·13 m (7 ft 0 in)
- Length overall: 1·83 m (6 ft 0 in)

Weights:
- Payload: 1·8 kg (4 lb)
- Weight dry: 5 kg (11 lb)

Performance:
- Max speed: 52·1 knots (96·6 km/h; 60 mph)
- Max controllable range: 0·9 nm (1·6 km; 1 mile)
- Endurance: 35 min

RCS SATS

SATS (Small Arms Target System) is used as live target for infantry anti-aircraft firing practice with rifles and sub-machine-guns. Controlled with hand-held transmitter.

Dimensions, external:
- Wing span: 2·21 m (7 ft 3 in)
- Length overall: 1·98 m (6 ft 6 in)

Weights:
- Payload: 0·68 kg (1·5 lb)
- T-O weight: 4·1 kg (9 lb)

Performance:
- Max speed: 74 knots (137 km/h; 85 mph)
- Endurance: 40 min

RCS SWIFT

Photographic or target drone, of sweptwing aircraft configuration. Glassfibre fuselage; plywood-covered wings with styrofoam core.

Launch and Recovery: Launched from specially designed toggle action catapult; flown along fixed heading at fixed climb angle, using optical tracking system.

Guidance and Control: Tripod-mounted high-power radio transmitter (range 5·4 nm; 10 km; 6·2 miles) and optical sight. Can be operated with 6-channel hand-held transmitter.

Special Equipment: 35 mm camera, barometric trip switch and marker flash.

Dimensions, external:
- Wing span: 1·83 m (6 ft 0 in)
- Length overall: 0·91 m (3 ft 0 in)

Weights:
- Payload: 0·9 kg (2 lb)
- Max T-O weight: 4·5 kg (10 lb)

Performance:
- Max speed: 100-120 knots (185-222 km/h; 115-138 mph)
- Range: 4·3 nm (8 km; 5 miles)
- Endurance: 30 min

RCS TELEDRONE II

Real-time TV reconnaissance drone. Airframe of glassfibre, plywood, expanded foam and duralumin. Powered by two 1·5 kW (2 hp) or one 4·5 kW (6 hp) piston engine. Launched from catapult or T-O dolly; skid landing or parachute recovery. Standard TV payload; options include chaff dispenser, ECM, radar augmentation or radar transponders. Radio guidance (8-channel VHF), with 20W power amplifier optional.

Dimensions, external:
- Wing span: 2·90 m (9 ft 6 in)
- Length overall: 1·98 m (6 ft 6 in)

Weights:
- Weight empty: 10 kg (22 lb)
- Fuel: 3·85 kg (8·5 lb)
- Normal payload (incl fuel): 9 kg (20 lb)
- Max launching weight: approx 20·4 kg (45 lb)

Performance:
- Max speed: 90 knots (167 km/h; 104 mph)
- Cruising speed: 65 knots (120 km/h; 75 mph)
- Max operating height: 3,050 m (10,000 ft)
- Max range: 5·4 nm (10 km; 6·2 miles)
- Endurance: up to 2 h

RCS SMALL ROTARY-WING DRONE

Small rigid-rotor target drone, intended primarily to train operators of radar-controlled missiles; powered by 0·9 kW (1·2 hp) 10 cc piston engine. Fuel capacity 0·5 litres (0·1 Imp gallons).

Launch and Recovery: Conventional helicopter T-O and landing, using non-retractable tricycle landing gear.

Guidance and Control: Six-channel proportional radio control system (four for pitch, roll, yaw and throttle control, and two for camera controls).

Special Equipment: Choice of half-frame (f/2·8) or full-frame (f/2·5) 35 mm camera, each with 18 exposures per wind and automatic film advance. Heavy-duty 12V electric starter optional.

Dimensions, external:
- Main rotor diameter: 1·63 m (5 ft 4 in)
- Tail rotor diameter: 0·36 m (1 ft 2 in)
- Length overall: 1·83 m (6 ft 0 in)

Weights:
- Payload: 0·9 kg (2 lb)
- Weight dry: 5 kg (11 lb)

Performance:
- Max speed: 61 knots (113 km/h; 70 mph)
- Range: 0·9 nm (1·6 km; 1 mile)
- Endurance: 20 min

RCS LARGE ROTARY-WING RPV

Surveillance mini-RPV, powered by 7·5 kW (10 hp) two-stroke piston engine; details apply to this version. Twin-engined version, capable of carrying 18 kg (40 lb) payload, has been tested.

Launch and Recovery: Conventional helicopter T-O and landing, using wide-track tubular skid landing gear.

Special Equipment: Standard payload comprises ground surveillance TV system, cameras, sensors and other equipment. Gyroscopic stabilisation optional.

Dimensions, external:
- Main rotor diameter: 2·29 m (7 ft 6 in)
- Length overall: 1·83 m (6 ft 0 in)

Weights:
- Payload: 8·5 kg (18·7 lb)
- Max T-O weight: 20 kg (44 lb)

Performance:
- Max speed: 32 knots (60 km/h; 37 mph)
- Guidance radius: 2·7 nm (5 km; 3·1 miles)
- Endurance: 1 h

SHORTS

SHORT BROTHERS LIMITED

PO Box 241, Airport Road, Belfast BT3 9DZ, Northern Ireland
Telephone: 0232 58444
Telex: 74688
Officers: see Aircraft section

SHORTS MATS-B

MATS-B (Military Aircraft Target System, Type B) is a compact, highly-manoeuvrable radio controlled aerial target for use in target tracking, training and practice firings of close-range missiles and guns. Acceptance trials were completed in January 1977, at the Royal Artillery range in the Hebrides, and the target is now in production against an MoD contract. Development of the design is being pursued.

Airframe: Modular construction cantilever high-wing monoplane. Fuselage of metal and GRP. Polyurethane foam-filled glassfibre wings, fin and tailplane.

Power Plant: One 8·6 kW (11·5 hp) McCulloch MC-101D 123 cc single-cylinder two-stroke aircooled engine.

Launch and Recovery: Launched pneumatically from simple two-wheel launcher having a capacity of eight launches from one charging. Recovery by parachute or by conventional landing, using fuselage underfairing as a skid. Launches can be carried out in headwinds of up to 25 knots (46 km/h; 29 mph).

Guidance and Control: Eight-channel (roll, pitch, throttle, ignition/fail-safe, smoke candle firing, and three spare) radio command guidance system (hand-held transmitter and 10W rf amplifier), in the 68MHz band. Automatic barometric height hold available. Visual control sight with binoculars to assist pilot in flying the aircraft visually to over 2·7 nm (5 km; 3·1 miles) range and to enable repeatable race tracks to be flown.

Special Equipment: Reflector in rear fuselage for radar signature enhancement. Four 40 s smoke candles fitted in landing skid. Parachute in forward fuselage, deployed either on demand by pilot or automatically in event of engine, power supply or radio-control failure.

Dimensions, external:
- Wing span: 3·35 m (11 ft 0 in)
- Wing area: 1·53 m² (16·5 sq ft)
- Length overall: 2·49 m (8 ft 2 in)

Weights:
- Payload: 6·8 kg (15 lb)
- Max launching weight: 48·5 kg (107 lb)

Performance:
- Max level speed: 110 knots (203 km/h; 126 mph)
- Stalling speed: 48 knots (89 km/h; 55 mph)
- Max in-sight range: over 2·7 nm (5 km; 3·1 miles)
- Endurance at full throttle: 45 min

SHORTS SKEET

The Skeet is a development of MATS-B combining the advantages of the original drone with higher speed, payload and endurance for the same range of tasks. Most of the major assemblies of Skeet and MATS-B are interchangeable.

Airframe: As described for MATS-B, except for shorter fuselage.

Power Plant: One 13·4 kW (18 hp) Weslake 274-6 274 cc two-cylinder two-stroke aircooled engine.

Launch and Recovery: As described for MATS-B.

Guidance and Control: As described for MATS-B.

Special Equipment: Reflector in rear fuselage, and parachute in forward fuselage, as described for MATS-B. Sixteen 40 s smoke candles fitted in landing skid. Two wing-mounted pods can carry such items as miss-distance indicator and Simflak, as required. Skeet can accept payloads of a non-target nature (eg, for surveillance and tactical aggression) according to customer's requirements.

Dimensions, external:
- Wing span: 3·35 m (11 ft 0 in)
- Wing area: 1·53 m² (16·5 sq ft)
- Length overall: 2·32 m (7 ft 7½ in)

Weights:
- Payload: 8 kg (17·6 lb)
- Max launching weight: 63 kg (139 lb)

Performance:
- Max level speed: 125 knots (232 km/h; 144 mph)
- Stalling speed: 50 knots (93 km/h; 58 mph)
- Max in-sight range: 2·7 nm (5 km; 3·1 miles)
- Max range under control: more than 5·4 nm (10 km; 6·2 miles)
- Endurance at full throttle: 1 h 30 min

RCS Small Arms Target System (SATS)

RCS small rotary-wing drone, of mini-helicopter configuration

RCS Teledrone II TV reconnaissance drone

Single-engined version of RCS's large rotary-wing surveillance RPV

Shorts MATS-B military target aircraft

RCS Swift photo-reconnaissance or target drone, on its catapult launcher

SKYLEADER

SKYLEADER RADIO CONTROL LTD

Airport House, Purley Way, Croydon CR0 0XZ, Surrey
Telephone: 01 686 6688 or 0700
MANAGING DIRECTOR: S. E. Uwins

This company designed and produced the **MATS-A** target system, in use for several years by the British Army. A further version, with sweptback wings and designed to simulate the Panavia Tornado, is under development; no details of this have been received for publication.

SKYLEADER MATS-A

AIRFRAME: Cantilever high-wing monoplane configuration. Fuselage built of glassfibre-reinforced resin material with additional strengthening. Wings have polystyrene foam core with veneer covering. Tail surfaces are of balsa. All flying surfaces further covered with tough vinyl.

POWER PLANT: One 10 cc single-cylinder piston engine, driving a two-blade propeller. Methanol/castor oil fuel mixture.

LAUNCH AND RECOVERY: Hand-launched. Normal belly landing on fuselage undersurface. Parachute recovery system optional.

GUIDANCE AND CONTROL: Line-of-sight radio command guidance system, using hand-held transmitter. Aerodynamic control by conventional flying surfaces.

EQUIPMENT: Onboard electronics comprise four-channel superhet receiver, operating on 27MHz bandwidth, within which 12 spot frequencies are available. Rechargeable nickel-cadmium battery pack and three or four proportional feedback servos provide outputs to control surfaces. Transmitter power (1W) is adequate for operating distance of up to 1·1 nm (2 km; 1·25 miles). Other frequencies available up to 72MHz.

DIMENSIONS, EXTERNAL:
Wing span 1·73 m (5 ft 8 in)
Length overall 1·22 m (4 ft 0 in)

WEIGHT:
Max launching weight 3·85 kg (8·5 lb)

PERFORMANCE:
Max level speed approx 78 knots (145 km/h; 90 mph)
Operating range approx 1·7 nm (3·2 km; 2 miles)
Endurance 15-20 min

WESTLAND

WESTLAND HELICOPTERS LTD

Yeovil, Somerset BA20 2YB
Telephone: 0935 5222
Telex: 46277
OFFICERS: see Aircraft section

Westland Helicopters Ltd began studies on RPHs (remotely piloted helicopters) in 1968. Experimental work began in 1972 using models for wind tunnel work and the measurement of radar, optical and infra-red signatures. At the same time simulated flights were made using a computer to check the stability and controllability of the RPH.

This ground work was followed in mid-1975 by the start of a flight development programme, using a small flying testbed aircraft known as the Mote to prove the aerodynamics and to continue development of the control system. This led to a Ministry of Defence development contract for the Wisp, a small RPH for the British Army. A description and illustration of the Wisp can be found in the 1978-79 *Jane's*.

By the Spring of 1976 Westland had been contracted to develop a second RPH, known as Wideye, for battlefield reconnaissance for the British Army.

WESTLAND WIDEYE/SUPERVISOR

The Wideye, which flew for the first time on 24 August 1978, is a remotely piloted rotorcraft developed by Westland from the earlier and smaller Wisp. When combined with a payload developed by Marconi Avionics, it forms the **Supervisor** surveillance system, capable of reconnaissance at distances up to 27 nm (50 km; 31 miles) beyond the forward edge of the battle area (FEBA). In early 1979

Wideye and the Supervisor system were undergoing evaluation to define the full operational system before it goes into full-scale production. The smaller Wisp (1978-79 *Jane's*) is also being used in the Wideye development programme. The system is scheduled to be ready for service with the British Army in the early 1980s. It includes also a ground station truck, on which a tracker antenna is mounted; Westland Helicopters and Marconi Avionics are jointly responsible for this vehicle.

Type: Battlefield surveillance RPV.

Airframe: Barrel-shaped glassfibre body containing power plant, fuel and payload. Retractable four-legged splayed landing gear on underside of body. Power plant drives a pair of two-blade co-axial counter-rotating rotors on top of body. Directional control by differential changing of collective pitch of rotors. Low radar, infra-red and noise signatures.

Power Plant: Two 13·5 kW (18 hp) Weslake 274-3 two-cylinder two-stroke aircooled piston engines.

Launch and Recovery: Conventional helicopter-type take-off and landing.

Guidance and Control: Two-way radio link to convey command data from ground to helicopter and video data to ground vehicle.

Special Equipment: Electronics payload, developed by Marconi Avionics Electro-Optical Surveillance Division, comprises a small, stabilised TV camera and two-way radio link.

Dimensions, external:

Diameter of rotors (each)	2·13 m (7 ft 0 in)
Body diameter (max)	0·74 m (2 ft 5 in)
Height overall, landing gear deployed	1·83 m (6 ft 0 in)
Height overall, landing gear retracted	1·52 m (5 ft 0 in)

Weight:

Max T-O weight	125 kg (275 lb)

Performance:

No details available for publication

UNITED STATES OF AMERICA

APL

APPLIED PHYSICS LABORATORY, THE JOHNS HOPKINS UNIVERSITY

Johns Hopkins Road, Laurel, Maryland 20810

Telephone: (301) 953 7100 and 792 7800

In addition to the RPD2, which is described briefly and illustrated, APL had under development in the Spring of 1979 a new drone of which testing was to begin in August 1979.

APL RPD2

This drone, developed by APL from an earlier US Army programme vehicle, first flew on 13 June 1975 at the US Naval Surface Weapons Center. It is a miniature target for evaluating improved shipboard fire control systems.

Four RPD2s were built, of which two were still operable in Summer 1979, when testing was to be resumed.

Power Plant: One 7·5 kW (10 hp) McCulloch MC-101A single-cylinder piston engine, driving two-blade pusher propeller at tail.

Launch and Recovery: Launch by catapult system. Parachute recovery system, with airbag impact absorbers stowed in each wing. Fin tip comes off for parachute release.

Guidance and Control: System includes autopilot which uses Earth's electrostatic field for pitch and roll stabilisation.

Special Equipment: Includes passive radar augmentation device in nose and Luneberg lens in fairing on fin trailing-edge. Pitch sensor above nose; roll sensors at wingtips.

Dimensions:

Wing span	2·083 m (6 ft 10 in)
Wing area	1·74 m² (18·75 sq ft)
Length overall	2·057 m (6 ft 9 in)
Height overall	0·72 m (2 ft 4¼ in)
Propeller diameter	0·51 m (1 ft 8 in)

Weights:

Weight empty	23 kg (50·5 lb)
Payload	12 kg (26·4 lb)
Max launching weight	46 kg (101 lb)

Performance:

Max level speed	150 knots (278 km/h; 173 mph)
Cruising speed	65 knots (120 km/h; 75 mph)
Service ceiling	5,500 m (18,000 ft)
Endurance	2 h 30 min

BEECHCRAFT

BEECH AIRCRAFT CORPORATION

Wichita, Kansas 67201

Telephone: (316) 689 7111

Officers: see Aircraft section

In addition to manufacturing piloted aircraft, Beech has been designing and producing pilotless target drones since 1955. By 1 January 1979 it had built a total of 5,940 target drones. This figure includes 293 MQM-61As for the US Army, and 3,417 AQM-37As.

Beech has also carried out design studies to examine the suitability of its range of light aircraft for operation under remote control.

BEECHCRAFT MODELS 1019, 1072, 1088, 1094, 1095 and 1102

US military designation: AQM-37A (Models 1019 and 1102)

UK designations: SD.2 Stiletto (Model 1072) and Model 1095

Italian designation: Model 1088

French designation: Vanneau (Model 1094)

Winner of a 1959 US Navy/Air Force design competition, the Beechcraft Model 1019 (US Navy AQM-37A, formerly KD2B-1) target system is designed to simulate aircraft and missile threats, and to provide defence weapon system evaluation and operational crew training.

The complete target system includes a launcher, test and checkout equipment, handling and servicing equipment and launch aircraft controls, as well as the target vehicle itself. The target is normally expendable and requires no recovery support. The only procedures required to ready the target for flight are decanning, battery servicing, pre-flight checking out, pressure cartridge inserting and nitrogen pressurising.

The AQM-37A was launched successfully for the first time on 31 May 1961, at the Naval Missile Center, Point Mugu, California. In subsequent development tests it flew higher and faster than any previous drone developed for target duties.

The AQM-37A has been operational with the US Navy since 1963 from shore installations and aircraft carriers and is being launched at present from three types of US Navy aircraft, the F-4, F-8 and A-4. A follow-on batch of 202 AQM-37A targets was completed for the USN in 1974.

In 1968, Beech modified 10 AQM-37As for evaluation by the USAF and three for the US Army, making their avionics and destruct systems compatible with current advanced weapon systems and range requirements of these services.

In 1975-76 Beech modified 20 AQM-37As to **Sea Skipper** configuration for the US Naval Air Systems Command. This classified Navy programme called for development and modification of missile targets capable of being air-launched over the sea at 366 m (1,200 ft) altitude and then flown as low as 15 m (50 ft) over predetermined points. The purpose of the programme was to demonstrate the feasibility of modifying AQM-37A targets for use in the evaluation of ship defence systems and the training of crews.

In 1976 the US Army received from Beech 20 government-furnished AQM-37As modified for weapon systems evaluation. Also in 1976 the Army ordered 28 recoverable AQM-37As (the first with such capability), fitted with a two-stage parachute system. Under this contract Beech produced two versions of the AQM-37A. One was a supersonic high-altitude target capable of operating at up to 1,181 knots (2,188 km/h; 1,360 mph) and 21,335 m (70,000 ft) altitude; the other a low-altitude modification which can be flown to within 55 m (180 ft) of the terrain. Deliveries were completed in March 1977.

Deliveries were also completed in 1977 of 100 AQM-37As ordered by the US Army under a $2 million contract in October 1976. These targets, designated Beechcraft **Model 1102,** incorporate a solid-state autopilot, improved wing design, and other technological improvements. A further 150 AQM-37As were ordered in June 1977; a follow-on contract for 165 targets, announced in March 1978, continues production until December 1979.

In addition to the AQM-37A variants built for the US services, four other models have been announced:

Model 1072 (Shorts SD.2 Stiletto). Version for UK, substantially re-engineered by Beech and Shorts to meet British requirements, including virtually complete replacement of radio and radar systems and control system changes. Total of 95 ordered, fitted by Beech with single-chamber rocket motor. Deliveries completed in 1977. Further details in 1978-79 *Jane's*.

Model 1088. Five targets supplied to Italy; for air-launch from Italian Air Force F-104S.

Model 1094 (Matra Vanneau: Lapwing). Forty-five targets ordered by French Air Force, deliveries of which began in 1974; these are modified to French requirements by Matra.

Model 1095. Twenty targets ordered by British Ministry of Defence and modified by Shorts to MoD specifications for crew training exercises. Deliveries completed in 1977.

Production of the drone was transferred from Wichita to Beech's Aerospace Division at Boulder, Colorado, in 1968. Total deliveries of this target, in all its versions, had reached 3,417 by January 1979.

Type: Air-launched expendable or recoverable target.

Airframe: Mid-wing monoplane, of canard configuration, with slim-delta main wings (of double-wedge section) at rear having 76° sweep on leading-edges, 0° dihedral, 0° incidence, and full-span ailerons. Movable canard foreplanes, of modified double-wedge section. Fixed endplate fin at tip of each main wing. Cylindrical centre-fuselage, with ogival nose section and tapering rear section over rocket chambers. Underbelly tunnel for rocket-engine cartridge-operated start valves, plumbing, infra-red flare and miss-distance scoring system antenna.

Power Plant: One Rocketdyne/AMF LR64 P-4 two-chamber liquid-propellant rocket engine (2·81 kN; 631 lb st). Three propellant tanks, for nitrogen pressurant, mixed amine fuel (MAF-4) and IRFNA oxidiser, form integral part of centre-fuselage.

Launch and Recovery: Air-launched from launcher which is adaptable to various fighter aircraft. Normally non-recoverable, but some US Army AQM-37As have parachute recovery system.

Guidance and Control: Programmed guidance system. Flight normally terminated by aerodynamic means, but explosive destructor system is available to provide additional range safety and operational flexibility.

Special Equipment: Target provides both active and passive radar augmentation for radar acquisition and lock-on. Chemical flare for missions requiring IR augmentation. Choice of two miss-distance scoring systems.

Dimensions, external:

Wing span	1·00 m (3 ft 3½ in)
Wing area (exposed)	0·87 m² (9·35 sq ft)
Length overall	3·82 m (12 ft 6½ in)
Height overall	0·51 m (1 ft 8 in)
Diameter of fuselage	0·33 m (1 ft 1 in)

Weight:

Max launching weight	256 kg (565 lb)

Performance (rated):

Operating speed	Mach 0·4 to Mach 3·0
Operating height	300-24,385 m (1,000-80,000 ft)
Endurance	5-15 min
Range	more than 100 nm (185 km; 115 miles)

BEECHCRAFT MODEL 1070 HAST

US Air Force designation: AQM-81A

Beech Aircraft developed the Model 1070 for the USAF Armament Laboratory at Eglin AFB, Florida, to provide a high-performance air-launched aerial target system for use by all three US Services. The HAST (High Altitude Supersonic Target) is a continuation of the former Sandpiper project, described in the 1970-71 *Jane's*. Twelve flight test units of the HAST and 13 refurbishment kits have been built; delivery of the former began in 1972.

The flight performance envelope of the HAST covers a range from Mach 1·2 at 12,200 m (40,000 ft) to Mach 4·0 at 30,500 m (100,000 ft). In August 1974 Beech and the US Air Force initiated a 28-month programme to demonstrate flight performance. By the end of 1975, the HAST had flown at up to Mach 3·0 at 24,400 m (80,000 ft). In 1976, during advanced development flight demonstrations at Eglin AFB, Florida, it demonstrated Mach 4·0 speed and 30,500 m (100,000 ft) altitude.

Three HASTs were fitted by Beech in 1977 with scoring equipment and radar augmentation devices, for trials by the US Navy with the RCA Aegis ship-based air defence system. Three successful flights under the programme were completed in May 1978.

Type: Supersonic air-launched recoverable target drone.

Airframe: Mid-wing monoplane, with slim-delta main wings swept 75° on leading-edges and of constant thickness except for leading-edges. Full-span aileron on each trailing-edge. Arrow-planform canard foreplanes for longitudinal control. Fixed endplate fin at tip of each main wing. Cylindrical body, with 3·5 calibre von Kármán nose section and conical boat-tail section.

Power Plant: CSD hybrid rocket engine. Propellant is polybutadiene and polymethyl-methacrylate, with IRFNA oxidiser. System is inherently safe, since propellants will not burn unless external ignition is applied. Engine is throttleable, with thrust variable from 0·53 to 5·34 kN (120 to 1,200 lb st). The 0·33 m (13 in) thrust chamber forms integral part of fuselage assembly. Oxidiser pressurisation and electrical power provided

Second prototype Westland Wideye

Beechcraft Model 1089, Swedish RB06 version

Beechcraft Model 1019 AQM-37A target drone

RPD2 naval weapons target, developed by APL, on its launch trolley

Beechcraft Model 1070 HAST under belly of Phantom launch aircraft

by ducted power unit. This unit, developed by Marquardt, is powered by ram-air turbine with air intake and exit on lower side of fuselage mid-section. Beech free siphon device provides uninterrupted oxidiser flow during manoeuvres. Manoeuvring requirements dictate positive expulsion system for oxidiser.

Launch and Recovery: Air-launched from carrier aircraft (initially, F-101, F-4, F-14 and F-15), at speeds between Mach 1·2 and 2·5. Recovery by 13·72 m (45 ft) diameter parachute from land, water or mid-air.

Guidance and Control: Manoeuvres can either be preprogrammed or initiated via ground command radio link. Manoeuvres of between 5*g* at 10,670 m (35,000 ft) and 1·15*g* at 27,400 m (90,000 ft) are part of flight test programme; vehicle also capable of 'S' and 180° turns in horizontal plane and altitude changes in vertical plane.

Special Equipment: Modular payloads, with a wide variety of options, for accurate simulation of aircraft or missile threats; various radar and IR augmentation devices, as well as a flare/chaff dispenser. Vector miss-distance scoring systems.

Dimensions, external:

Wing span	1·02 m (3 ft 4 in)
Wing area (total exposed)	0·97 m² (10·44 sq ft)
Length	5·08 m (16 ft 8 in)
Height (stabiliser)	0·66 m (2 ft 2 in)
Body diameter	0·33 m (1 ft 1 in)

Volume:

Payload volume	0·041 m³ (2,500 cu in)

Weights:

Launching weight	519 kg (1,145 lb)
Propellant	297 kg (655 lb)
Payload	38 kg (85 lb)

Performance:

Max level speed:	
at 21,350 m (70,000 ft)	Mach 2
at 24,400 m (80,000 ft)	Mach 3
at 30,500 m (100,000 ft)	Mach 4
Endurance at Mach 3	5 min

BEECHCRAFT MODEL 1089

US Army designation: MQM-107A Streaker
Swedish Air Force designation: RB06 Girun

Beech Aircraft Corporation took part, with Northrop, in a competition to design and develop a Variable-Speed Training Target (VSTT) for the US Army Material Missile Readiness Command. Beech was announced the winner of this competition in the Spring of 1975.

Production of the VSTT, now known as the MQM-107A Streaker, began in December 1975, and first flight of a production MQM-107A was made in April 1976. The US Army ordered 385 of these targets, with deliveries extending to March 1979. Some of the targets were for supply to Iran and Sweden by the US Army under its foreign military sales programme. The Swedish version, known as the RB06 Girun, has the original guidance system replaced by one made by Esterline, and is fitted also with radar augmentation, transponders and infra-red-reflecting tow targets.

The US Navy procured 10 MQM-107As, which were flown for fleet evaluation of the system between early 1977 and March 1978.

Airframe: Low-wing monoplane configuration, with sweptback wings and tail surfaces. Engine suspended on pylon beneath centre of fuselage. Modular design throughout, with flat-section wings and tail surfaces of bonded honeycomb and foam-filled aluminium ailerons and elevators. Cylindrical body, with ogival nose and tail cones.

Power Plant: One 2·85 kN (640 lb st) Teledyne CAE 372-2 (J402-CA-700) turbojet engine in underfuselage pod, with 242 litres (64 US gallons) of fuel. JATO bottle for launch boost. New solid-propellant rocket booster developed and qualified by Atlantic Research Corporation.

Launch and Recovery: Lightweight ground launcher and checkout system, easily transportable in two suitcase-size containers. Drogue and main parachute command recovery system.

Guidance and Control: Radio command guidance of manoeuvre and recovery, which can be either preprogrammed or maintained directly during flight. In flight, guidance and control system automatically stabilises about roll, yaw and pitch attitudes, and provides altitude and speed hold modes.

Special Equipment: Principal function is to tow a variety of tow targets for missile training and evaluation. Two TA-8 radar or IR augmentation targets can be carried on each mission and towed separately up to 2,440 m (8,000 ft) behind MQM-107A. Streaker serves as aerial target for such air defence systems as Chaparral, Redeye, Hawk, Roland and Stinger, and is expected to become primary subsonic missile training target for US Army. Internal payload capacity for avionics; wingtip payload capacity for decoy augmentation and additional avionics; capacity for up to 113 kg (250 lb) beneath each wing.

Dimensions, external:

Wing span	3·00 m (9 ft 10 in)

Wing area (total projected) 2·52 m² (27·16 sq ft)
Length 5·13 m (16 ft 10 in)
Height (total) 1·47 m (4 ft 10 in)
Body diameter 0·38 m (1 ft 3 in)

WEIGHTS:
Weight empty 295 kg (650 lb)
Usable fuel 173 kg (382 lb)
Launching weight (incl booster) 460 kg (1,014 lb)

PERFORMANCE:
Operating speed range 247-499 knots (459-925 km/h; 285-575 mph)
Operating height range S/L to 12,200 m (40,000 ft)
Endurance more than 3 h

BIG BIRD

c/o John E. Burkam, 571 Mount Alverno Road, Media, Pennsylvania 19063

BIG BIRD

Details and an illustration of this small radio-controlled helicopter appeared in the 1978-79 *Jane's*. Development has been terminated, and in 1979 the aircraft was available for outright purchase.

BRUNSWICK
BRUNSWICK DEFENSE DIVISION

3333 Harbor Boulevard, Costa Mesa, California 92626
Telephone: (714) 546 8030
MARKETING DIRECTOR: A. H. Bickel

On behalf of the USAF Avionics Laboratory, Brunswick developed the small Maxi-Decoy glider, and the larger rocket-powered Propelled Decoy, to be carried by US strike aircraft. Equivalent to an 'iron' bomb, the decoys are carried with wings folded on the aircraft external stores points. Shortly after release the wings are opened by internal command. Flight profiles and manoeuvres are pre-programmed.

BRUNSWICK MAXI-DECOY

Unpowered decoy glider, having a square-section body and flip-out sweptback wings. Capable of high subsonic speed. Under development by USAF primarily as active or passive ECM carrier, using F-4 Phantom carrier aircraft. Three Maxis can be accommodated in each of F-4's four underfuselage Sparrow missile recesses, and two on each 340 kg (750 lb) underwing hardpoint; several decoys can be deployed simultaneously. Electronic warfare payloads are designed and manufactured by Automated Systems Division of RCA. Series of payload test flights conducted at Eglin AFB during 1977. Typical payloads include a C-band jammer; or a G-band jammer combined with radar signature augmentation. Further details are classified.

DIMENSIONS:
Wing span approx 0·76 m (2 ft 6 in)
Body width 0·13 m (5 in)
Length 1·14 m (3 ft 9 in)
Payload volume 0·008 m³ (500 cu in)

WEIGHT:
Max launching weight 59 kg (130 lb)

PERFORMANCE:
Max speed Mach 0·8-0·9

BRUNSWICK PROPELLED DECOY

Larger than Maxi-Decoy, with circular-section body, flip-out sweptback wings and cruciform sweptback tail surfaces; powered by Atlantic Research solid-propellant rocket motor. Flight testing began in 1974. Two-axis (roll and heading/altitude) autopilot allows decoy to manoeuvre at high cruising speeds as well as performing in glide modes; unlike Maxi, Propelled Decoy can cruise at high subsonic speeds. Six successful launchings from F-4 carrier aircraft made at Eglin AFB in 1974. One Propelled Decoy can be carried on each of Phantom's 340 kg (750 lb) underwing hardpoints. Further details are classified.

DIMENSIONS:
Wing span 1·40 m (4 ft 7 in)
Body diameter 0·25 m (10 in)
Length 2·24 m (7 ft 4 in)
Payload volume 0·03 m³ (1,800 cu in)

WEIGHT:
Launch weight 136 kg (300 lb)

PERFORMANCE:
Burn time 5 min
Max speed Mach 0·8-0·9

DSI
DEVELOPMENTAL SCIENCES INC

15757 East Valley Boulevard, PO Box 1264, City of Industry, California 91749
Telephone: (213) 330 6865
PRESIDENT: Dr Gerald R. Seemann

DSI designed and built, under contract to NASA, a prototype oblique-wing RPRA which made its first flight in mid-1976 and was described and illustrated in the 1976-77 *Jane's*. The company also designed and built the Sky Eye and Scout mini-RPVs, and, for LMSC, the Aquila, based on the Sky Eye. In 1977 it undertook, for the US Army, a study of the feasibility of equipping mini-RPVs with 2·75 in FFAR rockets for attack duties. A further contract, for test and analysis of projectiles launched from small RPVs, was awarded in 1978 by the US Army Research and Technology Laboratories. Also in 1978, DSI completed, for the US Army, a recovery programme using LMSC Aquila drones fitted with a parachute and an inflatable airbag. Aquilas were recovered, without damage, from as low as 36·5 m (120 ft) at airspeeds of 60-90 knots (111-167 km/h; 69-104 mph).

DSI is currently engaged in several classified RPV programmes, and has undertaken a study for the Jet Propulsion Laboratory of an RPV suitable for transport to Mars, for deployment and data-gathering flight in the Martian atmosphere. It is also engaged, with All American Engineering Inc, in an overseas programme involving the Sky Eye R-4D.

DSI RPA-12 SKY EYE

The prototype Sky Eye first flew on 26 April 1973; details of this and early models can be found in previous editions of *Jane's*. The last two Sky Eye I-Bs, which were being flown as testbeds, were taken out of service in mid-1978.

Current models are as follows:

Sky Eye II-E. Expendable version of II-R, developed from Sky Eye I-B (1977-78 *Jane's*).

Sky Eye II-R. Recoverable version, 6% larger than II-E but with endplate fins at wingtips and lower radar signature. Basically similar to I-B, but of glassfibre/foam construction. Endplate fins later deleted and propeller duct added. Non-retractable tricycle landing gear. Orders for several Sky Eye IIs received, from the US Army and various aerospace companies.

Sky Eye R-4D. Upgraded version of II-R with improved wing; larger, flat-bottomed fuselage; no landing gear; and upgraded flight control system. More powerful engine, increased payload and higher gross weight. Endurance more than 8 h with 36 kg (80 lb) payload. By beginning of 1979 the Sky Eye R-4D was the version mainly in use and the only version being sold.

The following description applies to the Sky Eye R-4D:

AIRFRAME: Predominantly of Kevlar 49 honeycomb sandwich materials, giving a lightweight but robust vehicle capable of sustaining ±6*g* (normal) and 8*g* axial loading at max gross weight, and of surviving rough handling in operation. Sweptback high-wing monoplane, with servo-actuated trailing-edge elevons and turned-down wingtips. Wing section NACA 23-015 (modified). Incidence 3° at root. Aerodynamic twist (washout) 3°. Removal of wing and nosecone provides access to entire payload installation in nose and central bays. Fuselage consists of four basic components: nose fairing, central body, cowling and propeller shroud. Flat-bottomed fuselage has three quickly removable structural bottom panels, intended specifically for easy pallet-style installation and interchanging of a wide variety of payloads.

POWER PLANT: One 15 kW (20 hp) D & H or TCM piston engine, driving a two-blade wooden pusher propeller turning within a 0·69 m (2 ft 3 in) diameter annular duct.

LAUNCH AND RECOVERY: Ramp launch; parachute or net recovery.

GUIDANCE AND CONTROL: VHF radio command guidance system. Aerodynamic control by elevons.

AVIONICS AND EQUIPMENT: Autopilot and uplink. Equipped initially with 600W electrical system; 1,200W system under development. Flight control system built by LSI-AD, based on a DSI-LSI-AD design.

DIMENSIONS, EXTERNAL (R-4D):
Wing span 3·78 m (12 ft 4¾ in)
Wing area, gross 2·99 m² (32·2 sq ft)
Wing aspect ratio 4·75
Length overall 2·01 m (6 ft 7¼ in)
Body: Max diameter 0·356 m (1 ft 2 in)

WEIGHTS (R-4D):
Weight empty, dry 45·4 kg (100 lb)
Fuel load (standard tanks) 13·6 kg (30 lb)
Payload 31·7 kg (70 lb)
Launching weight 90·7 kg (200 lb)

PERFORMANCE (R-4D 'clean' at 90·7 kg; 200 lb gross weight):
Max level speed:
at S/L 130 knots (241 km/h; 150 mph)
at 3,050 m (10,000 ft) 128 knots (237 km/h; 147 mph)
at 6,100 m (20,000 ft) 125 knots (232 km/h; 144 mph)
at 9,150 m (30,000 ft) 113 knots (209 km/h; 130 mph)
Stalling speed 39 knots (72·5 km/h; 45 mph)
Max rate of climb:
at S/L 600 m (1,970 ft)/min
at 3,050 m (10,000 ft) 375 m (1,230 ft)/min
at 6,100 m (20,000 ft) 194 m (638 ft)/min
at 7,625 m (25,000 ft) 118 m (386 ft)/min
Service ceiling (46 m; 150 ft/min climb) 9,150 m (30,000 ft)
Endurance with 13·6 kg (30 lb) standard fuel 7 h 30 min

DSI RPA-9 SCOUT

For Northrop, under a US Air Force contract, DSI designed, built and flight tested an electrically-propelled mini-RPV named Scout. Development continued by DSI as a company-funded programme, with a new engine and autopilot. Experimental flights continued in 1978, when the Scout had flown with two different power plants. One was an electric motor powered by lithium batteries, using a small petrol engine for launch only; the other was a low-cost 3·7 kW (5 hp) two-stroke engine, installed for harassment RPV development.

AIRFRAME: Sweptback shoulder-wing monoplane, with servo-actuated trailing-edge elevons and sweptback endplate fin at each wingtip. Wings, elevons and fins have Kevlar skins, with partial urethane foam support. Tapered body, of super-elliptical cross-section, built of bulkheads and Kevlar skin and having detachable nose-cap. Non-retractable tricycle landing gear.

POWER PLANT: See introductory copy.

LAUNCH AND RECOVERY: Conventional wheeled T-O and landing standard.

GUIDANCE AND CONTROL: As for Sky Eye.

EQUIPMENT: DSI-PSA-WL-01 stability augmentation autopilot. Eight telemetry channels to monitor speed, altitude, autopilot functions and onboard sensors.

DIMENSIONS, EXTERNAL:
Wing span 2·715 m (8 ft 10·92 in)
Wing area, gross 1·38 m² (14·86 sq ft)
Length overall 0·91 m (3 ft 0 in)
Height overall 0·20 m (8·04 in)

WEIGHTS:
Weight empty, equipped 15·4 kg (34 lb)
Payload 6·8 kg (15 lb)
Max T-O weight 25 kg (55 lb)

PERFORMANCE (at max T-O weight):
Max level speed 60 knots (111 km/h; 69 mph)
Stalling speed 32·5 knots (60 km/h; 37 mph)
Max rate of climb at S/L 91 m (300 ft)/min
Range 43 nm (80 km; 50 miles)
Endurance 1 h 15 min

DSI RPMB

Details of DSI's original 4·88 m (16 ft) long RPMB (Remotely Piloted Mini-Blimp) appeared in the 1977-78 *Jane's*.

DSI subsequently built a larger RPMB, also helium-filled, by extensive modification of a Fulton Sky Hook air rescue tethered balloon. This RPMB has an envelope of 2 oz nylon/Mylar laminate, and is powered by a 2 cu in displacement Quadra piston engine; it also has three composite-material tail surfaces instead of the previous inflatable ones. The horizontal tail surfaces are fitted with elevators; 'rudder action' is provided by gimballing the engine.

This RPMB prototype, which was 7·92 m (26 ft 0 in) long and had a speed of just under 22 knots (41 km/h; 25 mph), was illustrated and briefly described in the 1978-79 *Jane's*.

For 1979, DSI has designed a third, larger RPMB to what it describes as a final configuration, and powered by a 15 kW (20 hp) D & H two-stroke engine driving a Sensenich two-blade wooden propeller. The envelope is of 6 oz Neoprene-coated Dacron. The following details apply to this version:

GUIDANCE AND CONTROL: Radio command guidance system. Pitch and yaw control provided by gimballing engine. If command link is lost, engine shuts down and helium is dumped (dumping 8·5 m³; 300 cu ft makes craft 9 kg; 20 lb 'heavy'). If engine fails, helium is dumped in same way; if altitude hold malfunctions, and vehicle escapes from 152 m (500 ft) to higher altitude, independent transducer triggers helium dump.

AVIONICS AND EQUIPMENT: Dufresne 28V 650W alternator for electrical power; guidance and control equipment; servo motors; data link; payload (camera, bullhorn and spotlight); transponder and running lights; ballast.

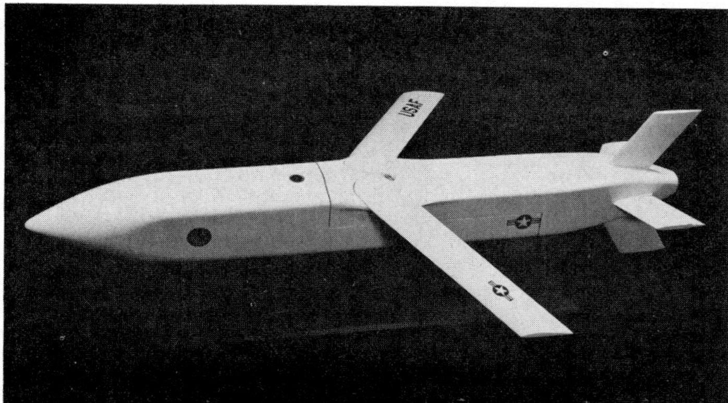

Brunswick Maxi-Decoy unpowered decoy, with flip-out wings

DSI Sky Eye II-R, with conventional nose and ducted propeller

DSI Sky Eye R-4D, enlarged development of the II-R

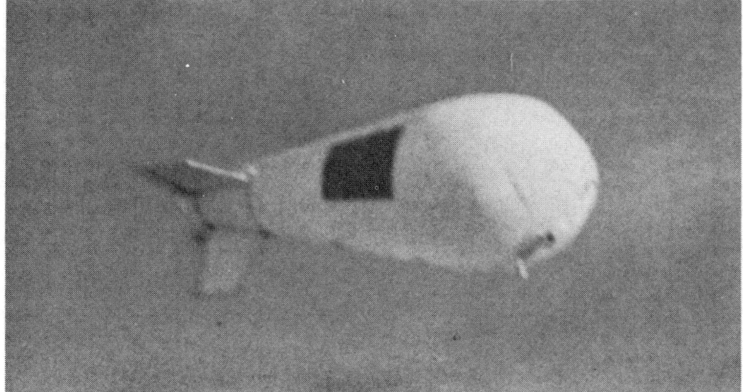

DSI RPMB airship drone, 7·92 m (26 ft) version

DSI RPA-9 Scout mini-RPV

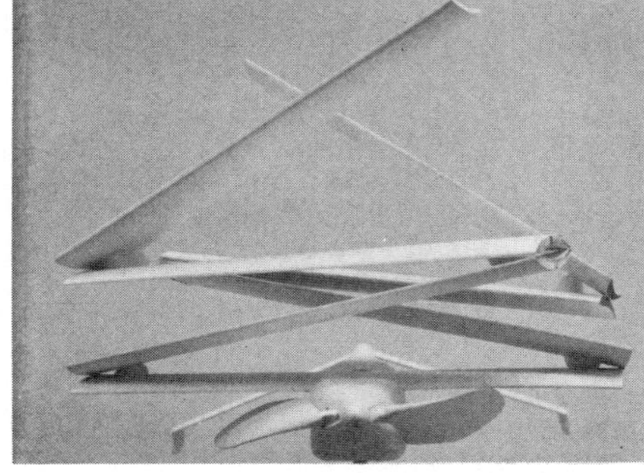

Model of the DSI Mars Astroplane, for pilotless survey of the planet Mars, in folded and deployed configurations

DIMENSIONS:	
Length overall	11·94 m (39 ft 2 in)
Envelope max diameter	3·40 m (11 ft 2 in)
Envelope fineness ratio	3·5
Envelope volume	85 m³ (3,000 cu ft)
WEIGHTS:	
Payload	20·5 kg (45 lb)
Fuel	11 kg (25 lb)
Max T-O weight	97·5 kg (215 lb)
PERFORMANCE (estimated):	
Max level speed	43 knots (80 km/h; 50 mph)
Min flying speed (full fuel)	4·3 knots (8 km/h; 5 mph)
Endurance at 17·5 knots (32 km/h; 20 mph)	24 h

DSI MARS ASTROPLANE

Among concepts being studied by NASA for future exploration of the planet Mars is one for a series of recoverable, remotely controlled small aircraft able to photograph terrain, take atmospheric soundings, and acquire other useful data. DSI has submitted proposals to NASA for an aircraft, the Mars Astroplane, capable of meeting such a requirement. A one-tenth-scale deployable model of the Astroplane has been built, together with a full-size fuselage section for demonstration of the potential payload capacity.

Applications for such an aircraft include:

(1) gathering widely-dispersed samples and delivering them to a central site for pickup;

(2) deploying seismometers, meteorology stations and other scientific apparatus at preselected sites within an accuracy of a few kilometres;

(3) performing high-resolution imaging, magnetic, gravity and geochemical aerial surveys;

(4) performing aerial search for subsurface water, geothermal fields and active volcanoes;

(5) soft-landing experiment packages for in situ elemental and mineral phase analysis or biological exploration at selected sites, within an accuracy of a few kilometres;

(6) performing atmospheric sounding for meteorology or air constituent analyses up to 7·5 km (4·7 miles) above the surface;

(7) soft-landing mini-rover vehicles;

(8) performing site selection surveys for Mars spacecraft; and

(9) deploying navigation aids at distributed points on the Martian surface.

The options for the aircraft are a vehicle which either performs aerial surveys, atmospheric sounding or deployment of network science, and then crashes; or one equipped with a variable-thrust rocket installation, like the Viking lander, so that it may soft-land itself and take off. The most important question is to define the role of an aeroplane in exploration of the planet. It is, clearly, a versatile means of transportation that can carry experiment packages or otherwise play an important support role in Mars exploration; the technological feasibility of the aircraft has been studied and found to be favourable, and it is as ready as any other current means of delivering payloads to Mars.

DSI's proposals to NASA include both cruiser and lander aircraft, each with a choice of power plant. Initial studies suggested that a hydrazine-burning engine would offer the best results, but further research has indicated that a specially-developed electrical power plant would provide a much superior performance.

The other basic elements of the technology required for the Mars Astroplane—ultralight airframe, flight control and navigation, engine, landing rockets and entry system—have already been developed in other military, space or aeronautical research programmes, and no new technology is required. A three-year plan of component evaluation, system design, prototype fabrication and flight test has been outlined; at the end of this period a prototype, fully flight-tested by balloon drops from a 33,525 m (110,000 ft) altitude above the Earth, could provide the basis for full-scale project design, manufacture and test.

Although still in the design definition stage, and thus liable to change, the following description applies to the Mars Astroplane prototype as envisaged by DSI in early 1979:

TYPE: Remotely controlled Mars exploration aircraft.

AIRFRAME: Cantilever high-wing monoplane, made largely of carbon-fibre composites. High aspect ratio wings of low Reynolds number and with zero dihedral. Ailerons at trailing-edges of tapered outer panels. Entire wing hinged at six points, at 3 m (9 ft 10 in) intervals, enabling it to fold for stowage inside a Viking-type aero-shell container. Fuselage also is hinged to fold for stowage, at mid-point and just forward of tail unit. Payload compartment in mid-fuselage, with access via door on underside. A 0·165 m (6½ in) radius transparent bubble protrudes from the bottom of this door, to provide a full hemispherical clear field of view for imaging while in flight or on the surface. The bottom of the payload bay is 0·61 m (2 ft) above the surface when the aircraft is on the ground. Instruments which require isolation from the fuselage, such as magnetometer sensors, can be mounted on or in the wings if of modest mass. Heavier instruments may also be mounted on the wings, but must be sufficiently inboard to avoid excessive structural loads on the wing, and mass unbalance. The payload compartment would be thermally controlled to acceptable limits for payload operation when the door is closed. When open, no compartment thermal control is provided, and instruments must be controlled individually. Tail surfaces comprise inverted-V fins and inset elevators/rudders, with included angle of 140°.

POWER PLANT: For cruising flight, a Sundstrand electric motor can be mounted in the nose, driving a large-diameter variable-pitch foldable propeller. This motor, comprising a lightweight samarium-cobalt magnet rotor motor, solid state inverter and planetary gearbox, has a rating of 15 kW (20 hp) at an operating voltage of 245V, and is powered by an Altus lithium battery. Alternatively, an 11·25 kW (15 hp) Akkerman non-air-breathing engine can be fitted, driving a smaller-diameter propeller. Hydrazine monopropellant for this engine is contained in two fuselage tanks. For soft-landing and take-off, two variable-thrust Viking lander rockets (0·27-2·85 kN; 60-640 lb st) can be mounted in the fuselage, one forward and one aft of the wing and each supplied by a 20 litre (4·4 Imp gallon; 5·3 US gallon) fuel tank.

Launch, Recovery, Guidance and Control: The basic mission concept for the Mars aeroplane is to de-orbit 12 aircraft from three spacecraft/aircraft carriers, from a 500 km (310 mile) altitude periapsis by 1 sol orbit, similar to that of Viking. Each spacecraft/aircraft carrier would carry four aeroplane/entry units; these would be de-orbited one at a time on successive orbits, or at will. After all aircraft were de-orbited, the spacecraft/aircraft carriers would be manoeuvred into 1 sol synchronous circular orbits, 120° apart in longitude and at 28° inclination, to form a Mars Comsat network with 100 per cent global coverage. These Comsats would have very long life, typical of Earth Comsats; they would serve as high-capacity communications relay satellites to Earth for all Mars vehicles. After release from its parent carrier, each Astroplane would descend by parachute at 3,600 m (11,810 ft)/min, unfold, detach from the parachute and fly off. The proposed flight control and navigation system consists of a strapdown inertial system, Doppler radar, radar altimeter and terrain avoidance radar. Outputs of the inertial and Doppler systems would be optimally mixed to provide navigation steering signals. Position fixes would be obtained by the range-range method, using turnaround ranging measurements to the Comsats. Specified navigation accuracy is 1% of the distance travelled from the last position fix. Communication between Astroplane and Comsats would be via a 60W UHF transmitter: the transmit antenna is a 0·8 × 3·1 m (2 ft 7½ in × 10 ft 2 in) 2 × 8 element microstrip steerable array, mounted on one wing panel. Broadside gain is 14 dB, and 9 dB at an elevation angle of 30°. With the Comsat overhead, the aircraft could transmit 5 Mbps imaging data, permitting a pixel resolution of 12·7 cm (5 in) if flying at 762 m (2,500 ft) altitude. A single-element 42 × 42 cm (16·5 × 16·5 in) patch antenna would provide hemispherical coverage for receiving from the Comsat. There would be no direct link with Earth.

Special Equipment: Typical mission equipment would include Apollo/LPO-type gamma ray spectrometer on port wing, 4 m (13 ft 1½ in) from fuselage; Earth Telescopes/LPO-type 400-channel reflectance spectrometer: Terrestrial Applications electromagnetic sounder, with 20 m (65 ft 7½ in) antenna on underside of wings; military/LPO-type gravity gradiometer; dual Pioneer Venus/LPO/Voyager-type magnetometers on starboard wing, one at two-thirds span and one at tip; MVM-73 infra-red radiometer; Viking-type gas chromatograph/mass spectrometer; Galileo-type f/1·8 multi-spectral camera/imager; and Viking/Surveyor-type deployable seismometer/meteorology package. Each instrument would have to provide its own data processing services. The aircraft would provide only a telemetry commutator to sample instrument bit streams periodically, and would have no data storage capability. Commands would be demodulated by the aircraft's radio subsystem and put into a common bus for transmission to, and decoding by, each instrument.

Dimensions, external:

Wing span	21·00 m (68 ft 10¾ in)
Wing chord (inboard, constant)	1·00 m (3 ft 3¼ in)
Wing chord at tip	0·655 m (2 ft 1¾ in)
Wing area	20·00 m² (215 sq ft)
Length overall	6·35 m (20 ft 10 in)
Tailplane span (projected)	3·40 m (11 ft 1¾ in)
Propeller diameter:	
electric motor	4·50 m (14 ft 9¼ in)
hydrazine engine	4·00 m (13 ft 1½ in)

Dimensions, internal:

Payload compartment (mid-fuselage):	
Length	1·00 m (3 ft 3¼ in)
Width	0·50 m (1 ft 7⅝ in)
Height	0·45 m (1 ft 5¾ in)
Volume	0·20 m³ (7·06 cu ft)
Avionics compartment (aft of wing), volume	0·03 m³ (1·06 cu ft)

Weights (A: electric motor; B: hydrazine engine):

Weight empty:	
cruiser (A)	120 kg (264 lb)
cruiser (B)	113 kg (249 lb)
lander (A)	155 kg (341 lb)
lander (B)	148 kg (326 lb)
Payload (all versions)	40-100 kg (88-220 lb)
Fuel load:	
cruiser (A)	nil
cruiser (B)	147 kg (324 lb)
lander (A)	50 kg (110 lb)
lander (B)	112 kg (247 lb)
Max all-up weight (all versions)	300 kg (661 lb)

Performance (cruiser, estimated, at 300 kg; 661 lb AUW and cruise altitude of 1,000 m; 3,280 ft. A: payload of 100 kg; 220 lb, B: payload of 40 kg; 88 lb):

Range:	
hydrazine engine (A)	1,215 nm (2,250 km; 1,400 miles)
hydrazine engine (B)	2,225 nm (4,125 km; 2,565 miles)
electric motor of 295Wh/lb (A)	1,685 nm (3,125 km; 1,940 miles)
electric motor of 295Wh/lb (B)	2,900 nm (5,375 km; 3,340 miles)
electric motor of 545Wh/lb (A)	3,100 nm (5,750 km; 3,575 miles)
electric motor of 545Wh/lb (B)	5,330 nm (9,875 km; 6,135 miles)
Endurance:	
hydrazine engine (A)	7 h 30 min
hydrazine engine (B)	15 h 0 min
electric motor of 295Wh/lb (A)	9 h 36 min
electric motor of 295Wh/lb (B)	16 h 51 min
electric motor of 545Wh/lb (A)	17 h 48 min
electric motor of 545Wh/lb (B)	31 h 6 min

E-SYSTEMS

E-SYSTEMS INC

PO Box 6030, Dallas, Texas 75222

Melpar Division: 7700 Arlington Boulevard, Falls Church, Virginia 22046

Telephone: (703) 560 5000

E-Systems Inc's activities lie predominantly in aerospace systems development and manufacture, in addition to which it has carried out specialised conversion work on nearly 400 C-135 and KC-135 series aircraft for the US Air Force. Its Greenville Division designed and built the L450F, a single-engined aircraft capable of manned or unmanned operation and described in previous editions of *Jane's*. Melpar Division has designed a number of mini-RPVs, of which details follow.

E-SYSTEMS E-55

The E-55 is an improved version of the E-45 mini-RPV (1978-79 *Jane's*), with a more powerful engine and higher gross weight. It is designed to carry a variety of electronic payloads for real-time reconnaissance, jamming, targeting, and homing missions. Several E-55s were employed successfully during the harassment weapons systems concept demonstration conducted at Meppen in the Federal Republic of Germany in early 1977. All existing E-45 vehicles have been upgraded to the E-55 configuration, a description of which follows:

Airframe: High-wing twin-tailboom monoplane, with pod-shaped central nacelle. Dihedral on outer wing panels. Twin endplate fins and rudders; enclosed tailplane with full-span elevator.

Power Plant: One 2·76 kW (3·7 hp) single-cylinder two-stroke Roper engine, mounted in rear of fuselage nacelle and driving a two-blade pusher propeller. Fuel capacity 3·4 litres (0·9 US gallons).

Launch and Recovery: Launch by vehicle-mounted launcher, using jettisonable take-off dolly, or by catapult. Recovery by conventional landing, on skid beneath central nacelle, or by net.

Guidance and Control: Either by real-time tracking radar mounted on top of two-man mobile van, or by standard non-tracking radio control link. Radar system can control RPV effectively for approx 43·5 nm (80·5 km; 50 miles). This can be extended to 130 nm (241 km; 150 miles) by pre-programming flight and using airborne relay for video downlink. Aircraft can be controlled either manually or by combination of pre-programmed flight and manual landing.

Equipment: Melpar-designed five-axis autopilot weighing 0·9 kg (2 lb), which can be used for dead reckoning or Omega navigation. Melpar TV surveillance system provides means for remote manual control, target identification, and navigational assistance away from launch site.

Dimensions, external:

Wing span	2·41 m (7 ft 11 in)
Wing area, gross	0·68 m² (7·36 sq ft)
Length overall	2·36 m (7 ft 9 in)
Height overall	0·51 m (1 ft 8 in)
Width over tailbooms	0·71 m (2 ft 4 in)
Fuselage diameter	0·20 m (8 in)

Weights:

Weight empty, equipped	11·3 kg (25 lb)
Payload	13·6 kg (30 lb)
Fuel	2·7 kg (6 lb)
T-O weight	25 kg (55 lb)

Performance:

Cruising speed	52 knots (97 km/h; 60 mph)
Stalling speed	39 knots (72 km/h; 45 mph)
Rate of climb at S/L	198 m (650 ft)/min
Service ceiling	3,050 m (10,000 ft)
Endurance	4 h

E-SYSTEMS E-90

The E-90 is a 41 kg (90 lb) version of the E-75 'harassment' vehicle (1978-79 *Jane's*). The use of a more powerful engine improves performance and allows an increase in payload weight. It was first flown in October 1977.

In addition to its potential mission as a passive radar homing system, future applications for the E-90 include loiter over enemy defences while carrying RV reconnaissance jamming, FLIR, or photographic payloads.

Airframe: High-wing single-boom monoplane. Glassfibre wings, with high/low-density foam core; moulded polyethylene fuselage; internal phenolic resin coated cardboard tubes to stiffen tailboom and tail surfaces.

Power Plant: One 8·2 kW (11 hp) Herbrandson DH-160 flat-twin two-stroke piston engine, driving a two-blade pusher propeller. Fuel capacity 5·7 litres (1·5 US gallons).

Equipment: Pre-programmed autonomous autopilot/navigation system using onboard microprocessor.

Dimensions, external:

Wing span	3·05 m (10 ft 0 in)
Wing area, gross	1·02 m² (11·0 sq ft)
Length overall	2·41 m (7 ft 11 in)
Height overall	0·51 m (1 ft 8 in)
Fuselage: Max width	0·25 m (10 in)

Weights:

Weight empty, equipped	22·7 kg (50 lb)
Payload	13·6 kg (30 lb)
Fuel	4·5 kg (10 lb)
T-O weight	41 kg (90 lb)

Performance (typical):

Max level speed	104 knots (193 km/h; 120 mph)
Cruising speed	87 knots (161 km/h; 100 mph)
Stalling speed	45 knots (84 km/h; 52 mph)
Rate of climb at S/L	488 m (1,600 ft)/min
Service ceiling	3,660 m (12,000 ft)
Endurance	3 h 30 min

E-SYSTEMS E-100X

Essentially, the E-100X is an enlarged development of the E-45 (1978-79 *Jane's*), having extended-span wings, greater engine power, and increased payload volume. It consists of three major assemblies (fuselage pod, wing, and booms and tail unit), designed for quick and simple assembly or dismantling. The wing contains a sealed fuel tank. The pod is a sealed unit accommodating the onboard avionics and power plant.

Some 0·085 m³ (3 cu ft) of volume and more than 22·7 kg (50 lb) of weight can be devoted to possible payloads such as a low-cost miniature TV reconnaissance system, similar to that developed for the E-45, or packages for photographic reconnaissance, electronic jamming, tactical strike support, communications relay, and remote communications interception.

Airframe: Similar to E-45.

Power Plant: One 6·7 kW (9 hp) Rosspower flat-four two-stroke piston engine, driving a two-blade fixed-pitch pusher propeller. Fuel in integral wing tank, capacity approx 11·4 litres (3 US gallons).

Launch, Recovery, Guidance and Control: Similar to E-45.

Equipment: According to mission (see introductory copy).

Dimensions, external (typical):

Wing span	3·28 m (10 ft 9 in)
Wing area, gross	1·33 m² (14·33 sq ft)
Length overall	2·74 m (9 ft 0 in)
Height overall	0·57 m (1 ft 10½ in)
Fuselage diameter	0·27 m (10¾ in)

Weights (typical):

Weight empty, equipped	18 kg (40 lb)
Payload	22·7-23·6 kg (50-55 lb)
Fuel	8·2 kg (18 lb)
T-O weight	49 kg (108 lb)

Performance (typical):

Max level speed	95 knots (175 km/h; 109 mph)
Cruising speed	75 knots (139 km/h; 86 mph)
Stalling speed	42 knots (78 km/h; 48·5 mph)
Rate of climb at S/L	305 m (1,000 ft)/min
Service ceiling	above 3,050 m (10,000 ft)
Endurance	more than 5 h

E-SYSTEMS E-150

The E-150, which flew for the first time on 4 August 1978, was designed to carry a 27·2 kg (60 lb) stabilised TV camera. It was constructed with as many standard Melpar parts as possible, but with new nose structure and fairings; extended wings, tailboom and horizontal tail; additional fin area; rudder control; and a new shock-absorbing landing gear.

Airframe: Derived from that of E-75 (1978-79 *Jane's*).

Power Plant: One 9·7 kW (13 hp) Herbrandson DH-174 horizontally-opposed two-stroke piston engine, driving a two-blade wooden pusher propeller. Fuel capacity 9·5 litres (2·5 US gallons).

Launch and Recovery: Launched from truck top, free in yaw and pitch. Lands on shock-absorbing, self-stabilising skid/castor gear.

Guidance and Control: Autopilot-guided, similar to E-45.

Dimensions, external:

Wing span	3·96 m (13 ft 0 in)
Wing area, gross	1·45 m² (15·6 sq ft)

E-Systems E-55 mini-RPV at a desert test site

E-Systems E-90 mini-RPV on truck-mounted launcher

E-Systems E-150 TV-carrying RPV

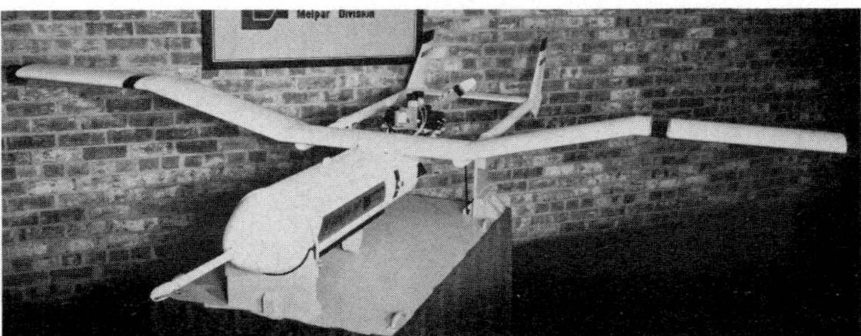
E-Systems E-100X multi-purpose mini-RPV

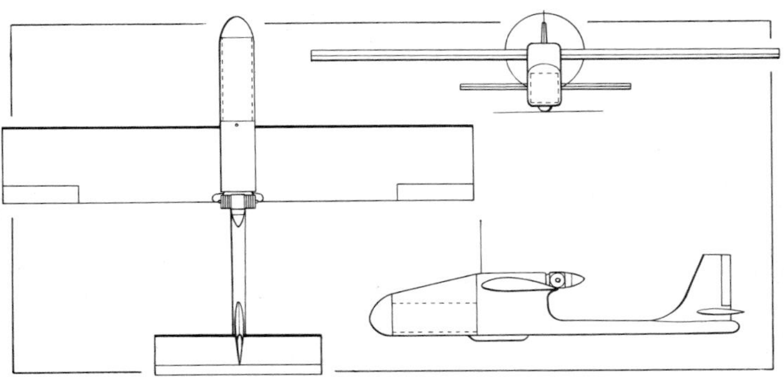
Provisional drawing of E-Systems E-200 testbed RPV *(Michael A. Badrocke)*

Eglen Falcon multi-purpose mini-RPV

Length overall 2·22 m (7 ft 3½ in)
Height overall 0·89 m (2 ft 11 in)
Fuselage width 0·25 m (10 in)

WEIGHTS:
Weight empty, equipped 37·6 kg (83 lb)
Payload 27·2 kg (60 lb)
Fuel 6·8 kg (15 lb)
Max T-O weight 71·6 kg (158 lb)

PERFORMANCE:
Max level speed 74 knots (137 km/h; 85 mph)
Cruising speed 56·5 knots (105 km/h; 65 mph)
Stalling speed 46 knots (86 km/h; 53 mph)
Endurance 2 h

E-SYSTEMS E-200

Due to begin flight testing in late 1979, the E-200 is a scaled-up derivative of the E-75 described in the 1978-79 *Jane's*. Its 91 kg (200 lb) take-off gross weight will allow a 31·75 kg (70 lb) payload to be flown at altitudes of up to 3,660 m (12,000 ft). The vehicle is configured for use as a flying testbed, permitting flight demonstration of airborne reconnaissance, jamming or navigation systems without incurring the costs of manned flight test programmes. Electrical power for the payload and the Melpar-designed digital autopilot/flight control system will be provided by a 0·5 kW engine-driven alternator.

AIRFRAME: A formed and machined aluminium backbone joins the firewall, propulsion unit, tailboom and wing spars. Fuselage structure and payload covered with cast plastics fairing. Firewall provides for structural mounting of payload. Wings and horizontal tail surfaces are shaped foam cores covered with glassfibre-reinforced skin. Wing spars and tailboom are structural tubes. Fin of cast plastics. Nosecone removable for ease of access to payload; wings and horizontal tail surfaces removable for transportation. Lifting yoke at CG.

POWER PLANT: One 13·4 kW (18 hp) Herbrandson DH-220 flat-twin two-stroke piston engine, driving a two-blade fixed-pitch pusher propeller. Fuel capacity 8·7 litres (2·3 US gallons).

LAUNCH AND RECOVERY: Vehicle-mounted launcher. Recovery by conventional landing on skid beneath central nacelle.

GUIDANCE AND CONTROL: Radio command control for launch and recovery. In-flight guidance by three-axis Melpar-designed autopilot. Aerodynamic control by ailerons, elevator and rudder.

EQUIPMENT: Volume of 0·06 m³ (2·08 cu ft) available for user-defined payload.

DIMENSIONS, EXTERNAL (provisional):
Wing span 4·27 m (14 ft 0 in)
Wing area, gross 3·07 m² (33·0 sq ft)
Length overall 3·35 m (11 ft 0 in)
Height overall 0·71 m (2 ft 4 in)
Fuselage: Max width 0·305 m (1 ft 0 in)

WEIGHTS (typical):
Weight empty, incl flight controls 52·1 kg (115 lb)
Payload 31·75 kg (70 lb)
Fuel 6·8 kg (15 lb)
Max T-O weight 91 kg (200 lb)

PERFORMANCE (estimated):
Max level speed 96 knots (177 km/h; 110 mph)
Cruising speed 82 knots (153 km/h; 95 mph)
Stalling speed 39 knots (73 km/h; 45 mph)
Rate of climb at S/L 610 m (2,000 ft)/min
Service ceiling 3,660 m (12,000 ft)
Endurance 2 h

EHI
EGLEN HOVERCRAFT INC (RPV Division)

PO Box 1671, Terre Haute, Indiana 47808
Telephone: (812) 234 4307
CHAIRMAN: Jan Alan Eglen

EHI currently produces two target RPVs: the Falcon, and the more recent Matador for RC/MATS programmes.

EGLEN FALCON-M

The Falcon mini-RPV is in service with NATO and other military and civil authorities for testing sensor and weapon systems and for weather monitoring. It was designed at the USAF Flight Dynamics Laboratory.

It is available in a target version. Other potential applications include reconnaissance, surveillance, electronic warfare or countermeasures, photography, search missions, flood or forestry survey, air sampling, traffic observation, infra-red or laser target designation, and air testing of autopilots, flight computers and other equipment.

AIRFRAME: High-wing monoplane, built mainly of glassfibre, foam plastics and plywood, with epoxy paint finish. Non-retractable tricycle landing gear, with steerable nosewheel, is standard, but can be replaced by skis for operation in snow or desert conditions.

POWER PLANT: One Homelite two-stroke piston engine, of 1·86 kW (2·5 hp), driving a two-blade pusher propeller. Fuselage fuel tank, capacity 1·9 litres (0·5 US gallons).

LAUNCH AND RECOVERY: Conventional T-O and landing; or catapult launch and net recovery.

GUIDANCE AND CONTROL: Radio command guidance system. Aerodynamic control by ailerons, elevators and rudder.

EQUIPMENT: Six-channel Proline radio control system standard (four channels for flight control and two for payload operation). Eight-channel system available optionally. Standard airborne TV payload package includes Conic 8W CTM UHF 408V S-band TV transmitter with antenna; Sony AVC 1400 TV camera and lens (modified for airborne use); and battery pack. Optional equipment includes miss-distance indicator, strobe light detection system, autopilot, underwing pods, retro-reflectors, 3·05 m (10 ft) span wings, and metallic reflection (chaff) for radar operations.

DIMENSIONS, EXTERNAL:

Wing span	2·44 m (8 ft 0 in) or 3·05 m (10 ft 0 in)
Wing area, gross	1·11 m² (12·00 sq ft) or 1·39 m² (15·00 sq ft)
Fuselage length	1·83 m (6 ft 0 in)
Height over fin	0·64 m (2 ft 1 in)

WEIGHTS:

Weight empty	11·3 kg (25 lb)
Max payload	11·3 kg (25 lb)
Balanced T-O weight	15·4 kg (34 lb)
Max T-O weight	22·7 kg (50 lb)

PERFORMANCE:

Max level speed	87 knots (161 km/h; 100 mph)
Service ceiling	approx 3,050 m (10,000 ft)
Normal radio range	approx 1·74 nm (3·2 km; 2 miles)
Max endurance	5 h

EGLEN MATADOR

First flown in February 1978, the Matador is being produced for RC/MATS (Radio Control/Military Air Target System) programmes. It is designed particularly for target use with Vulcan or Chaparral weapons, but can be used with any similar weapon system.

AIRFRAME: Delta-wing monoplane, of foam and balsa construction. Full-span flaps and ailerons on trailing-edge. Sweptback fin at each wingtip. Landing skids under nose and each wingtip.

POWER PLANT: One 0·75-3 kW (1-4 hp) K & B piston engine, driving a two-blade propeller. Centre-fuselage fuel tank, capacity 0·47 litres (1 US pint).

LAUNCH AND RECOVERY: Hand launch; skid landing.

GUIDANCE AND CONTROL: EK Logitrol four-channel radio command guidance system.

EQUIPMENT: Infra-red source or small payload.

DIMENSIONS, EXTERNAL:

Wing span	1·52 m (5 ft 0 in)
Length overall	1·37 m (4 ft 6 in)
Height overall	0·36 m (1 ft 2 in)

WEIGHTS:

Max payload	2·27 kg (5 lb)
Max launching weight	4·54 kg (10 lb)

PERFORMANCE:

Max level speed	78-87 knots (145-161 km/h; 90-100 mph)
Max cruising speed	69·5 knots (129 km/h; 80 mph)
Stalling speed	22 knots (40·5 km/h; 25 mph)
Service ceiling	3,050 m (10,000 ft)

FSI

FLIGHT SYSTEMS INC

4000 Westerly Place, PO Box 2400, Newport Beach, California 92663

Telephone: (714) 833 9661

DIRECTOR, AERIAL TARGETS: S. C. Warrick

FSI QF-86E SABRE

FSI demonstrated to the US Army in 1975 two remotely controlled North American F-86 Sabre jet fighters, the converted aircraft actually being Canadair-built Sabre 5s, structurally similar to the US-built F-86E.

Twenty-nine QF-86Es had been ordered by 1 January 1979; deliveries began in mid-1977. They are being produced to test and evaluate US Army air defence systems. Manoeuvres of up to 8*g* can be performed, and the QF-86Es can also deploy stores, initiate jamming and provide other countermeasures, all under remote control.

A description of the basic F-86 airframe can be found in the 1959-60 *Jane's;* the following details apply to the FSI QF-86E/Sabre 5:

POWER PLANT: One Orenda 10 turbojet engine, rated at 28·15 kN (6,325 lb st). Fuel capacity 1,571 litres (415 US gallons) internal, plus provision for two 454 or 757 litre (120 or 200 US gallon) underwing drop-tanks.

LAUNCH AND RECOVERY: Conventional runway T-O and landing, on retractable tricycle landing gear. Aircraft programmed to come to a halt, or continue and make safe T-O and climb-out, if ground control link is lost during T-O run.

GUIDANCE AND CONTROL: Radio command guidance system. Primary mode of operation is NOLO (No Local Operator), over full range of pre-programmed flight manoeuvres including T-O and landing; but provision for onboard human pilot is retained (eg for manned practice presentations, or maintenance or ferry flights). Remote control exercised from one fixed and one mobile ground station, both manufactured by Vega Precision Laboratories; or by the drone formation control system manufactured by IBM Corporation.

SPECIAL EQUIPMENT: Onboard avionics and instrumentation comprise three basic installations: autopilot, with FSI avionics; Vega Precision Laboratories command/telemetry data system; and FSI interface coupler for processing uplink command and downlink telemetry data to and from drone aircraft. A fourth installation, the IBM drone formation control system, is optional. Radar altimeter optional, for simulated low-level attack presentations. Ancillary equipment, according to mission, may include scoring gear, infra-red flare dispenser, chaff dispensers or ECM pods. Television has been added as an optional T-O and landing aid.

DIMENSIONS, EXTERNAL:

Wing span	11·31 m (37 ft 1·2 in)
Length overall	11·43 m (37 ft 6 in)
Height overall	4·48 m (14 ft 8·4 in)

WEIGHTS:

Basic weight empty	4,921 kg (10,850 lb)
T-O weight 'clean'	6,123 kg (13,500 lb)
T-O weight with two 454 litre (120 US gallon) drop-tanks	6,894 kg (15,200 lb)

PERFORMANCE:

Max level speed above 11,000 m (36,000 ft)	Mach 0·92 (527 knots; 977 km/h; 607 mph)
Service ceiling	13,715 m (45,000 ft)
Max range at 9,145 m (30,000 ft) with two 454 litre (120 US gallon) drop-tanks	600 nm (1,112 km; 691 miles)
Max endurance, conditions as above	2 h 0 min
g limit	+7·0

ILC

ILC INDUSTRIES INC

Dover Division

PO Box 266, Frederica, Delaware 19946

Telephone: (302) 674 4020

VICE-PRESIDENT AND GENERAL MANAGER: Homer D. Reihm

MANAGER, INFLATABLE PRODUCTS: George P. Durney

This company, which has for some years been a manufacturer of tethered balloons, has recently evaluated the application of inflatable surfaces to lightweight RPVs. Early experiments with winch- or tow-launched hang gliders have been followed by development of the Apteron, an inflatable-wing mini-RPV.

ILC APTERON

This small, lightweight RPV was built to prove the feasibility of a 'flying wing' vehicle using an inflatable aerofoil. It is claimed that the principle could be applied to much larger vehicles of up to 22·86 m (75 ft) wing span, capable of operation at altitudes of up to 21,340 m (70,000 ft).

AIRFRAME: 'Flying wing' monoplane. Moderate sweepback. Reflex-section fabric wing, inflated by compressed air prior to flight. To maintain inflation pressure irrespective of barometric or ambient temperature changes during flight, aircraft carries a small tank of Freon gas in fuselage. Wing is fitted with elevons, of Mylar-covered balsa construction. Aerofoil-shaped plywood fuselage. Non-retractable tricycle landing gear. Fabric wing has virtually no radar signature.

POWER PLANT: One 0·4 kW (0·5 hp) piston engine, driving a two-blade pusher propeller.

LAUNCH AND RECOVERY: Conventional T-O and landing.

GUIDANCE AND CONTROL: Radio command guidance system. Pitch and roll control by elevons.

DIMENSION, EXTERNAL:

Wing span	1·55 m (5 ft 1 in)

WEIGHTS:

Weight empty	1·8 kg (4 lb)
Payload	1·4 kg (3 lb)

KAMAN

KAMAN AEROSPACE CORPORATION

Old Windsor Road, Bloomfield, Connecticut 06002

Telephone: (203) 242 4461

OFFICERS: see Aircraft section

KAMAN STAPL

Kaman began design of the STAPL (Ship Tethered Aerial Platform) under contract to the US Office of Naval Research in September 1972, and construction of two prototypes began in the following month. Testing of the two aircraft and their mobile launch and recovery platform and control system began in 1974 and was continuing in 1979.

The prototypes are of autogyro configuration, and are equipped with automatic flight control systems and data recording equipment. A photograph of the first prototype appeared in the 1977-78 *Jane's;* since that time, modifications have been made to the rudder to accommodate a horizontal stabiliser. The self-contained AFCS, engineered by Kaman, provides three-axis stabilisation and automatic flight path control, and incorporates redundancy for mission reliability.

AIRFRAME: Welded steel tube fuselage and skid-type landing gear. Sheet metal vertical fin and aerodynamically balanced rudder. All-metal electrically actuated variable-incidence horizontal stabiliser. Two-blade Bensen G2 teetering and autorotating rotor, with metal blades bolted to hub. Blades do not fold. No rotor brake.

POWER PLANT: One 67 kW (90 hp) McCulloch 4318G piston engine, driving a Bensen BA-48-A8-70 two-blade fixed-pitch propeller. Single fuselage fuel tank, capacity 22·4 litres (6 US gallons).

LAUNCH AND RECOVERY: Tethered T-O and landing.

GUIDANCE AND CONTROL: Electrically-driven automatic flight control system (AFCS).

EQUIPMENT: Three 12V batteries to drive AFCS.

DIMENSIONS:

Rotor diameter	6·64 m (21 ft 9½ in)
Rotor blade chord	0·18 m (7 in)
Length overall (excl rotor)	3·02 m (9 ft 10½ in)
Width overall	1·47 m (4 ft 10 in)
Height to top of rotor hub	1·92 m (6 ft 3½ in)
Propeller diameter	1·22 m (4 ft 0 in)

AREAS:

Rotor blades (each)	0·59 m² (6·3 sq ft)
Rotor disc	34·56 m² (372 sq ft)
Fin	0·28 m² (3·0 sq ft)
Rudder	0·32 m² (3·4 sq ft)
Horizontal stabiliser	0·22 m² (2·4 sq ft)

WEIGHTS AND LOADING:

Weight empty	168 kg (370 lb)
Fuel load	17·7 kg (39 lb)
Max payload	34 kg (75 lb)
Max T-O weight	220 kg (484 lb)
Max disc loading	6·35 kg/m² (1·3 lb/sq ft)

PERFORMANCE: No details available

LMSC

LOCKHEED MISSILES AND SPACE COMPANY INC

1111 Lockheed Way, Sunnyvale, California 94088

Telephone: (408) 742 4321

PUBLIC RELATIONS: Paul J. Binder

The LMSC Aquila was in 1974 declared the winner of the US Army's competition for a battlefield surveillance mini-RPV. A harassment weapon system mini-RPV has also been undergoing development and flight testing since 1975; this was described and illustrated in the 1978-79 *Jane's*.

LOCKHEED GTD-21B

Brief details have become known concerning this drone vehicle, examples of which have been retired to store since August 1976 at the USAF's Military Aircraft Storage and Disposition Center at Davis-Monthan AFB, Arizona.

Its resemblance to the Lockheed YF-12/SR-71 (1974-75 *Jane's*) is self-evident, and it is believed to have been developed in parallel with the YF-12/SR-71 as an extension of the latter types' reconnaissance capabilities. A total of 38 are understood to have been built in 1964-67, and this is borne out by observed identification serial numbers. In addition, it is now known that 13 YF-12As were com-

Eglen Matador hand-launched delta-winged target

Flight Systems Inc QF-86E drone conversion of the Canadair Sabre 5

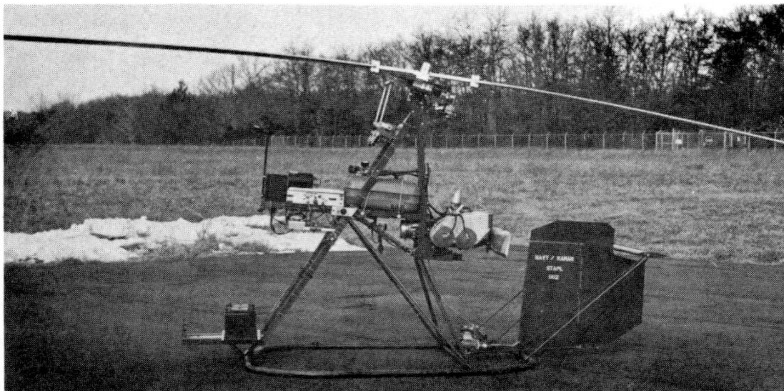
Kaman STAPL prototype in modified form, with all-moving horizontal tail surface

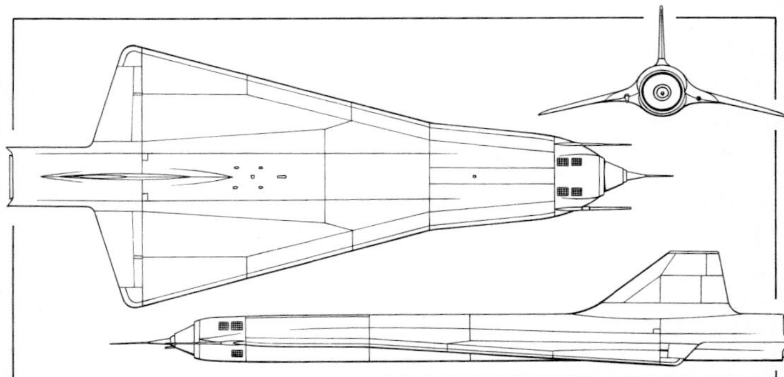
Provisional drawing of the LMSC GTD-21B *(Michael A. Badrocke)*

Parachute/airbag recovery system for LMSC Aquila, developed and tested by DSI

LMSC GTD-21B in storage at Davis-Monthan AFB, Arizona

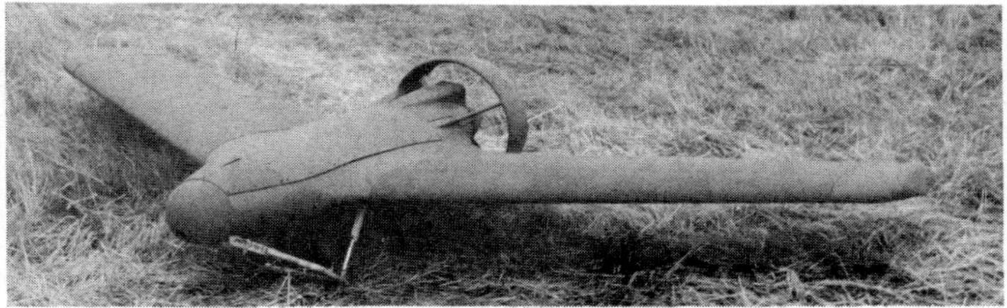
LMSC Aquila mini-RPV for US Army

pleted, not four as had been thought previously; it is reported that these aircraft, each carrying one all-black GTD-21B beneath the fuselage, performed an interim operational strategic reconnaissance role from 1964 until mid-1967, when the SR-71A became fully operational with the 9th Strategic Reconnaissance Wing at Beale AFB, California. Details of these missions have not been released, but presumably involved overflights of areas too sensitive for the use of a manned surveillance aircraft.

At least 17 GTD-21Bs were in store at Davis-Monthan AFB in the Autumn of 1977; at that time, nine YF-12As were in storage at Lockheed's Palmdale, California, facility. More GTD-21Bs have arrived at Davis-Monthan since then.

TYPE: Reconnaissance drone.

AIRFRAME: Low/mid-wing monoplane, of basically delta planform with inboard leading-edges extended forward in curve to lip of air intake; conical camber on outer leading-edges. Pitot boom on each leading-edge, near root. Blended wing/body design, similar to that of YF-12A/SR-71. Large conical centrebody in air intake. Single fin and inset rudder, well forward of exhaust nozzle; no horizontal tail surfaces. Construction probably makes extensive use of titanium and composite materials.

POWER PLANT: One turbojet (or turbo-ramjet) engine, of unknown type. Forward and rear rows of bypass doors, as in YF-12A/SR-71. Intake design, with large conical centrebody spike, also similar to that of YF-12/SR-71. Engine appears to be technically similar to Pratt & Whitney J58, but substantially smaller and with unusual exhaust nozzle. Latter is cone-shaped, of fixed geometry, and has a honeycomb-like plug inside, beyond the neck area.

LAUNCH AND RECOVERY: Air-launched from YF-12A or SR-71. Recovery method not known.

EQUIPMENT: Small air-conditioned bay for camera(s) under forward fuselage, aft of engine inlet.

DIMENSIONS:
- Wing span: 5·18 m (17 ft 0 in)
- Length overall: 12·19 m (40 ft 0 in)

PERFORMANCE (estimated):
- Max level speed: more than 2,171 knots (4,023 km/h; 2,500 mph)
- Absolute ceiling: well above 30,500 m (100,000 ft)
- Max range: approx 1,085 nm (2,010 km; 1,250 miles)

LMSC AQUILA

US Army designation: XMQM-105

The Aquila (Latin for 'eagle') mini-RPV was developed under US Army contract to demonstrate available technology for RPV use in surveillance, target acquisition, artillery adjustment, and laser designation for precision-guided munitions. One complete system consists of an RPV, a truck-mounted ground control station (GCS), pneumatic rail launcher and vertical-ribbon barrier retrieval system.

The GCS houses the system computer, TV displays, position plotters, automatic tracking system, command and data link equipment, and control consoles for the RPV and sensor operators. Design and development of the Aquila by LMSC utilised prior efforts by DSI (which see) with its Sky Eye RPV, and DSI supplied LMSC with technology demonstration airframe parts.

A total of 23 RPVs, and two each of the GCS, launchers and recovery systems were delivered, following the first flight of an Aquila in December 1975. More than 150 flights had been made by January 1978 in the US Army's demonstration programme to develop utilisation measures, doctrine and operational specifications. Flights were continued during 1978 at the White Sands Missile Range, New Mexico; Fort Bliss, Texas; and Fort Huachuca, Arizona.

During the 188th flight, on 3 June 1978, an Aquila demonstrated its laser designation capability by enabling a Martin Marietta Copperhead cannon-launched guided projectile to achieve a direct hit on a stationary tank. The RPV was at a height of 350 m (1,150 ft), 0·75 nm (1·40 km; 0·87 miles) from the target and 6·5 nm (12 km; 7·5 miles) from its control station when the hit occurred. The Copperhead was fired from 5·9 nm (11 km; 6·8 miles) and intentionally aimed 500 m (1,650 ft) short of the tank to test the performance of the seeker. In another US Army test, to determine RPV survivability, more than 3,000 rounds of 0·50 in and other ammunition were fired at an Aquila over ranges between 460 and 1,830 m (1,500-6,000 ft), without a single hit being registered.

In its production form, Aquila would have a more powerful engine, lower radar signature and ability to carry a variety of sensors.

AIRFRAME: Shoulder-wing monoplane of near-delta planform, built of Kevlar 49 honeycomb material, for low radar signature. Elevons on trailing-edges; turned-down wingtips. Airframe dismantles into four major components (centrebody, two wings, and propeller duct), and has quick-disconnect bladder fuel system.

POWER PLANT: One 8·2 kW (11 hp) McCulloch MC-101M/C single-cylinder piston engine, driving a two-blade pusher propeller mounted in an annular duct.

LAUNCH AND RECOVERY: Catapult-launched from mobile pneumatic-tube launcher at airspeed of 44 knots (81·5 km/h; 51 mph); recovered in vertical ribbon arrester net and parallel-strap retrieval net system. Parachute/air-bag recovery system tested successfully by DSI in 1978.

GUIDANCE AND CONTROL: Radio pre-programmed guidance system, with operator override capability.

SPECIAL EQUIPMENT: Lockheed autopilot, Aacom data link and Honeywell laser designator. Four different payloads being evaluated: for real-time surveillance (TV camera), target acquisition, laser target designation (Honeywell designator), and target location and artillery adjustment. Crash-resistant payload protection system standard.

DIMENSIONS, EXTERNAL:
- Wing span: 3·76 m (12 ft 4·2 in)
- Length: 1·83 m (6 ft 0 in)

WEIGHTS:
- Payload: 17·2 kg (38 lb)
- Max launching weight: 64·9 kg (143 lb)

PERFORMANCE:
- Max speed: 118 knots (219 km/h; 136 mph)
- Min speed to become airborne: 44 knots (81·5 km/h; 51 mph)
- Service ceiling: 3,660 m (12,000 ft)
- Max range: 10·4 nm (19·3 km; 12 miles)
- Max endurance: 3 h

NASA

NATIONAL AERONAUTICS AND SPACE ADMINISTRATION

1520 H Street NW, Washington, DC 20546

HUGH L. DRYDEN FLIGHT RESEARCH CENTER

PO Box 273, Edwards, California 93523
Telephone: (805) 258 3311

NASA MINI-SNIFFER II

The Mini-Sniffer is a simple, low-cost vehicle platform, designed for high-altitude atmospheric research in remote areas, to measure air turbulence and atmospheric trace gas and to determine the constituents of particles in the atmosphere.

The first two prototype vehicles, designated Mini-Sniffer I, were described and illustrated in the 1975-76 *Jane's*. A third prototype, designated Mini-Sniffer II, made its first flight in the Summer of 1975; the description applies to the mission vehicle, which is fitted with a hydrazine-burning engine to permit flights to altitudes of up to 27,430 m (90,000 ft). The first flight with this engine was made in November 1976.

Payload instrumentation is being developed by the Wallops Flight Center and the National Oceanic and Atmospheric Administration to measure nitric oxide, chlorine, Freon 11 and 12, free oxygen, and the hydroxyl radical. Langley Research Center plans to use the Mini-Sniffer to make accurate measurements of fine turbulence which cannot be obtained with faster aircraft. Equipped with lightweight wire impact particle grab samplers developed by Ames Research Center, and a real-time telemetered particulate density sensor, the Mini-Sniffer can make low-speed manoeuvres through aerospace vehicle wakes or other suspected particle concentrations. Radiation sensor payloads being developed by the Atomic Energy Commission may allow the multiple and prompt monitoring of nuclear activity.

The Mini-Sniffer is also under consideration by the Jet Propulsion Laboratory as a potential RPV to collect rock samples and data on Mars.

TYPE: Remotely piloted research vehicle.

AIRFRAME: Mid-wing monoplane of twin-tailboom configuration, built entirely of foam plastics, glassfibre and wood. Wings have 20° sweepback at quarter-chord, 13% thickness/chord ratio, and variable dihedral on outer panels. Elevons on wing trailing-edges. Twin sweptback fins and rudders and enclosed tailplane. Non-retractable tricycle landing gear, without tyres.

POWER PLANT: One 3-22·4 kW (4-30 hp) Akkerman 235 piston engine, driving a two-blade constant-speed variable-pitch feathering pusher propeller. Typical rating 15 kW (20 hp). Single aluminium integral fuel tank in fuselage, for 26·5 litres (7 US gallons) of hydrazine monopropellant. Oil capacity 0·95 litres (1 US quart).

SYSTEMS AND EQUIPMENT: Alternator on Akkerman 235 engine provides electrical power during climb and cruise; 28V nickel-cadmium battery for use during unpowered flight. Resdel uplink control. SCI-680-PCM 16-channel data telemetry system. Vega radar transponder. NASA autopilot. Sun and magnetic sensors for wing levelling, airspeed hold and heading hold.

DIMENSIONS, EXTERNAL:
- Wing span: 6·71 m (22 ft 0 in)
- Wheel track: 1·14 m (3 ft 9 in)

DIMENSION, INTERNAL:
- Payload compartment volume: 0·033 m³ (1·16 cu ft)

WEIGHTS:
- Max payload: 22·7 kg (50 lb)
- Max T-O weight: 89 kg (196 lb)

PERFORMANCE (estimated):
- Max level speed at 21,340 m (70,000 ft): 160 knots (296 km/h; 184 mph)
- Stalling speed: 26 knots (49 km/h; 30 mph) IAS
- Max rate of climb at S/L: 792 m (2,600 ft)/min
- Service ceiling: 27,430 m (90,000 ft)
- Range with max payload: 434 nm (805 km; 500 miles)

LANGLEY RESEARCH CENTER

Hampton, Virginia 23665
Telephone: (804) 827 1110

NASA PROJECT DAST

Project DAST (Drones for Aerodynamic and Structural Testing) is conducted jointly by NASA's Langley and Dryden Flight Research Centers, utilising modified Firebee IIs as testbeds for high-risk evaluation of various research wing configurations.

The first of these, designated ARW-1 (for aeroelastic research wing), was due to begin flight testing in August 1979. Fabrication of a second type of wing (ARW-2), also of supercritical type, was to begin later the same year.

NORTHROP

NORTHROP CORPORATION—VENTURA DIVISION

1515 Rancho Conejo Boulevard, Newbury Park, California 91320
Telephone: (805) 498 3131
Telex: 659 220

GENERAL MANAGER: Kent Kresa
VICE-PRESIDENT, MARKETING: Vincent W. Howard
MANAGER, CORPORATE COMMUNICATIONS: Park H. Irvine

Northrop's Ventura Division designs and manufactures pilotless target aircraft and related equipment. It also produces glassfibre wing fairings for the Boeing 747 transport aircraft, an unmanned underwater vehicle (MK-30) as a target for US Navy anti-submarine warfare training, and torpedo modification kits.

Northrop Ventura (formerly Radioplane) undertook the design, development and construction of its first radio controlled target drone in the mid-thirties. Since then it has become a leader in the field of pilotless aircraft. A total of 77,077 drones had been delivered to the US military services and 25 allied nations by 1 January 1978.

Components of a Northrop MQM-74A are used in the XBQM-108 VATOL (vertical attitude take-off and landing) RPV described under the US Navy heading in this section.

NORTHROP KD2R5 BASIC TRAINING TARGET

This target drone is currently in use by the armed forces of 18 countries as a training device for ground-to-air gunnery and is used as a training target for surface-to-air missiles such as Seacat, Tigercat, Redeye, Blowpipe, Sparrow, Chaparral and Hawk.

Design began in 1946 and the prototype flew for the first time in 1947. Since then more than 55,000 of this type, including early KD2R versions, have been built and production continues.

TYPE: Remotely controlled aerial target.

AIRFRAME: High-wing monoplane, of aluminium alloy construction. No dihedral. Wing incidence 1° at root, −2° at tip. Ailerons and elevator servo-operated by D-9 actuators.

POWER PLANT: One 67 kW (90 hp) Northrop O-100-3 flat-four engine, driving a two-blade fixed-pitch wooden propeller. Steel integral fuel tank in mid-fuselage, capacity 44 litres (11·6 US gallons). Refuelling point in fuselage forward of wing.

LAUNCH AND RECOVERY: Surface launch from land or ship, by either rotary or zero-length launcher. Recovery by parachute released by radio command. Engine is stopped and parachute deploys automatically in event of serious damage by gunfire, or loss of radio control or electrical power.

GUIDANCE AND CONTROL: AN/ARW-79 radio command guidance system, with automatic altitude hold. Visual or radar tracking (radar or FM type tracking systems or equivalent).

EQUIPMENT: 28V battery for all electrical power. L-band tracking system, smoke generating kit, tow banner and many other accessories available to customer's requirements. For radar augmentation, two wingtip reflector pods are optional.

DIMENSIONS, EXTERNAL:
- Wing span: 3·50 m (11 ft 6 in)
- Wing area, gross: 1·74 m² (18·7 sq ft)
- Length overall: 3·85 m (12 ft 7½ in)
- Height overall: 0·76 m (2 ft 6 in)

WEIGHTS:
- Weight empty: 123 kg (271 lb)
- Max launching weight: 181 kg (400 lb)
- Max zero-fuel weight: 133 kg (292 lb)
- Max landing weight: 154 kg (340 lb)

PERFORMANCE:
- Max level speed at S/L and max cruising speed: 194 knots (359 km/h; 223 mph)
- Stalling speed: 58 knots (108 km/h; 67 mph)
- Max rate of climb at S/L: 1,341 m (4,400 ft)/min
- Service ceiling: 8,230 m (27,000 ft)
- Range at S/L with max fuel: 183 nm (338 km; 210 miles)

NORTHROP CHUKAR II

US military designation: MQM-74C

The MQM-74C is an improved version of the MQM-74A (1974-75 *Jane's*), evolved via an MQM-74B developmental model to meet requirements for a 500 knot (926 km/h; 576 mph) target. Since early 1974 more than 1,100 MQM-74Cs have been delivered to the US Navy, making more than 3,500 MQM-74 Chukars manufactured in all. Production of the MQM-74C is continuing.

Modified versions of the MQM-74C have been tested and operated as reconnaissance, electronic warfare and strike RPVs under the US Navy's Persistent Anti-Radiation Missile (PARM) and US Air Force's TED programmes. More recently, Northrop has tested a tactical reconnaissance and target acquisition version, known as the **Chukar-R**, fitted with a modular nose section mounting a Perkin-Elmer 35 mm camera and a Teledyne Brown TV camera, and incorporating preprogrammed navigation. Under US Navy contract, Northrop is also developing a new version of the MQM-74C known as the **BQM-74C** (described separately), which will be used by the US Navy as a cruise missile simulator and standard Navy aerial training target.

The basic Chukar II/MQM-74C target aircraft was designed to meet requirements for a small, lightweight target for anti-aircraft gunnery, surface-to-air missile training and weapon system evaluation. Chukar II is used at the NATO Missile Firing Installation (NAMFI) on the island of Crete in the Mediterranean. Meteor of Italy (which see) was selected by NATO's Hawk management office to provide Chukar II services at the Salto di Quirra range in Sardinia, and the Chukar II is used also in the Persian Gulf, to provide crew training and weapon system evaluation for the Imperial Iranian Navy.

TYPE: Radio-controlled recoverable target.

AIRFRAME: Shoulder-wing monoplane, of aluminium construction. No-dihedral detachable wings, each with electrically-actuated aileron. Tapered circular-section body, with underslung air intake duct. Inverted-Y tail unit, with 30° anhedral on tailplane, fixed vertical fin and electrically-actuated elevators.

POWER PLANT: One Williams Research Corporation Model WR24-7 (J400-WR-401) turbojet engine, rated at 0·8 kN (180 lb st). Fuel tank in centre of fuselage.

LAUNCH AND RECOVERY: Zero-length launching by means of two Mk 91 Mod 0 JATO rockets and a ZL-5 launcher. Normal recovery by automatic drone pull-up followed by main parachute deployment, initiated automatically in emergencies such as interruption of continuous radio signal or loss of parachute command channel. Alternative method consists of direct main parachute deployment and is initiated automatically on loss of electrical power. Main parachute housed in fuselage immediately aft of wing, with automatic disconnect on impact.

GUIDANCE AND CONTROL: Radio command guidance system. Out-of-sight control by automatic stabilisation and command, with radar tracking; in-sight control with visual acquisition aids. Proportional feedback stabilisation and control system for pitch and bank. Engine

NASA Mini-Sniffer II, with variable-dihedral wingtips

NASA ARW-1 supercritical wing on a quarter-scale wind tunnel model of a Project DAST Firebee II

Northrop KD2R5 basic training target, in service in 18 countries

DAST Firebee II with ARW-1 wing on B-52 launch aircraft *(Erik Simonsen)*

Northrop MQM-74C Chukar II target drones (Williams WR24-7 turbojet engine)

Northrop Chukar-R, with interchangeable nosecones for tactical reconnaissance or target use

throttle position, altitude hold initiation and recovery system initiation controlled by audio tone signals. Components include receiver, decoder, autopilot, aileron and elevator servos, altitude hold and airspeed pressure transducers. Command control antenna in upper forward fuselage.

EQUIPMENT (target): Electrical power from engine-driven alternator through a rectifier-regulator. 28V nickel-cadmium battery secondary power source used during glide. Onboard acquisition and tracking aids include fore and aft Luneberg lenses for passive radar augmentation, four wingtip-mounted MK-28 Mod 3 infra-red flares, pyrotechnic infra-red plume augmentors, active L-band augmentation, and a smoke system, designed to improve visual detection. Main payload compartment is in front fuselage between control equipment bay and fuel tank. Improved Manoeuvrability Package (IMP) successfully flight tested in 1976 has closed-loop control device installed in flight control system, enabling Chukar II to perform constant *g* manoeuvres at any of five selected levels up to and including 6*g*. A low-cost infra-red tow target, for use with the Chukar II system, was successfully flight-tested in early 1978. One can be attached to each wingtip and towed approx 30 m (100 ft) behind the Chukar.

DIMENSIONS, EXTERNAL:
- Wing span: 1·76 m (5 ft 9¼ in)
- Length overall: 3·87 m (12 ft 8½ in)
- Body diameter: 0·38 m (1 ft 3 in)
- Height overall: 0·71 m (2 ft 4 in)

WEIGHTS:
- Weight empty: 128·4 kg (283 lb)
- Max launching weight: 223 kg (492 lb)

PERFORMANCE:
- Max level speed at 6,100 m (20,000 ft): 515 knots (954 km/h; 593 mph)
- Max level speed at S/L: 475 knots (880 km/h; 547 mph)
- Econ cruising speed at S/L: 250 knots (463 km/h; 288 mph)
- Max rate of climb at S/L with full fuel: 1,780 m (5,840 ft)/min
- Service ceiling: 12,200 m (40,000 ft)
- Range at max speed at S/L: 205 nm (380 km; 236 miles)
- Range at max speed at 6,100 m (20,000 ft): 330 nm (611 km; 380 miles)
- Range at econ cruising speed at S/L: 245 nm (454 km; 282 miles)

NORTHROP CHUKAR III

US Navy designation: BQM-74C

The Chukar III is a target version of the MQM-74C Chukar II (which see) with added air-launch capability. It can be used as a cruise missile simulator, in training pilots for air-to-air combat, and as a target for anti-aircraft gunnery and surface-to-air missiles. Design began in November 1977, and construction of 10 pre-production examples started in September 1978; three of these had been completed by the end of January 1979, though none had flown at that time.

TYPE: Radio controlled recoverable target.

AIRFRAME: Shoulder-wing monoplane of aluminium construction. Northrop G-9224-080 wing section of 8% thickness/chord ratio. No-dihedral non-swept wings, each with electrically-actuated aileron. Semi-monocoque aluminium body, similar to that of MQM-74C, houses all equipment, power plant and fuel tank. Nose and tail skins removable for access to equipment and power plants. Underslung engine air intake. Inverted-Y aluminium tail unit, comprising fixed vertical fin, fixed tailplane halves (anhedral 30°) and two electrically actuated elevators.

POWER PLANT: One Williams Research Corporation Model WR24-7A (J400-WR-402) turbojet engine, rated at 0·8 kN (180 lb st). Pressurised fuel tank in centre of fuselage.

LAUNCH AND RECOVERY: Can be launched from ground or shipborne launcher in same manner as MQM-74C. Can also be air-launched from Grumman A-6E Intruder or McDonnell Douglas TA-4J Skyhawk (one under each wing); is also compatible with underwing launchers of Lockheed DP-2 Neptune or DC-130A Hercules. Parachute recovery, on land or from water, as for MQM-74C.

GUIDANCE AND CONTROL: Out-of-sight control by automatic stabilisation and command; radar tracking in-sight control, with visual acquisition aids. Proportional feedback stabilisation and control system for pitch and bank.

Engine throttle position, altitude hold initiation and recovery initiation are controlled by audio tone signals. Components include a Northrop digital avionics processor, vertical gyro, Motorola AN/DKW-3 integrated target control system, aileron and elevator servos, and altitude hold pressure transducer.

EQUIPMENT: Electrical power from engine-driven alternator through a rectifier-regulator. 28V nickel-cadmium battery secondary power source. Onboard acquisition and tracking aids include fore and aft Luneberg lenses, for passive radar augmentation, and a smoke system. Main payload compartment is in forward fuselage section. Equipment includes locator beacon, radar altimeter, seeker simulator (to duplicate cruise missile emissions), radar transponder for IFF, and scoring. Provisions include flight profile programmer with UHF command override; radar altimeter; active J-band, B-band, L-band and X-band radar augmentation; and Tacan receiver. System also includes payload kits for mobile sea range (MSR) operations.

DIMENSIONS, EXTERNAL:

Wing span	1·76 m (5 ft 9·4 in)
Wing area, gross	0·74 m² (8·0 sq ft)
Length overall	3·94 m (12 ft 11·4 in)
Height overall	0·72 m (2 ft 4·3 in)

WEIGHTS AND LOADING:

Basic operating weight empty	133 kg (294 lb)
Max payload	78·5 kg (173 lb)
Max launching weight	204 kg (451 lb)
Max wing loading	273 kg/m² (56 lb/sq ft)

PERFORMANCE (at max T-O weight):

Max level speed at 6,100 m (20,000 ft)	500 knots (927 km/h; 576 mph)
Econ cruising speed	300 knots (555 km/h; 345 mph)
Service ceiling	9,145 m (30,000 ft)
Max range	450 nm (833 km; 518 miles)

NORTHROP NV-130

Northrop and Beech were selected by the US Air Force in 1975 to develop and produce flight demonstration examples of a Tactical Expendable Drone System (TEDS). First flight of a Northrop NV-130 prototype was made on 22 January 1976. A total of 11 flights were made during the validation flight test programme. Systems definition and computer simulations were completed in early 1977.

The ECM effectiveness of the NV-130 was validated successfully, but funds for full-scale development were not approved in the US defence budget and the programme is at present inactive.

A description and illustration of the NV-130 can be found in the 1977-78 *Jane's*.

NORTHROP NV-135

US military designation: Harassment Weapons System (HWS)

The Northrop NV-135 candidate in the US Air Force's HWS (formerly LCEHV) programme is a mini-RPV designed to harass enemy radar defences. Three were built, and underwent successful flight testing in 1976.

Design and analysis were continued in preparation for the Request for Proposals expected to be issued by the US Air Force in mid-1979. As required by the USAF, Northrop will collaborate on the programme with a team from the Federal Republic of Germany.

Of sweptback flying wing configuration, with endplate fins, the NV-135 is of plastics construction, produced by a Northrop adaptation of the rotational moulding process. It is powered by an 8·2 kW (11 hp) two-cylinder two-stroke piston engine, driving a two-blade pusher propeller, and is controlled by a programmed and command guidance system.

DIMENSIONS, EXTERNAL:

Wing span	2·44 m (8 ft 0 in)
Length overall	1·28 m (4 ft 2½ in)
Body diameter	0·28 m (11 in)

WEIGHT:

Max launching weight	68 kg (150 lb)

PERFORMANCE:

Design speed	104 knots (193 km/h; 120 mph)
Max speed during flight tests	160 knots (296 km/h; 184 mph)
Design operating height	3,660 m (12,000 ft)
Height reached during flight tests	1,830 m (6,000 ft)
Design endurance	3-5 h

ROCKWELL INTERNATIONAL

ROCKWELL INTERNATIONAL CORPORATION, LOS ANGELES DIVISION

815 Lapham Street, El Segundo, California 90245

ROCKWELL INTERNATIONAL/NASA/US AIR FORCE HiMAT

HiMAT (Highly Manoeuvrable Aircraft Technology) is a programme evolved by NASA's Dryden Flight Research Center at Edwards AFB, California, and the US Air Force Flight Dynamics Laboratory (AFFDL) at Wright-Patterson AFB, Ohio. Its basic purposes are to speed up the progress of advanced design technology into the flight test phase; to assist designers in taking larger technological steps forward between generations of aircraft; and, more specifically, to provide a low-cost, low-risk means of testing the advanced manoeuvring capability of future aircraft. NASA began evolving control techniques for the HiMAT programme in 1975, first with ⅜-scale unpowered glassfibre models of the F-15 fighter and later with two modified BQM-34F Firebee IIs.

After receipt of programme proposals from Grumman Aerospace, McDonnell Aircraft Co and Rockwell International, NASA announced in October 1975 the award of an $11·8 million contract to Rockwell for the design and construction of two prototype HiMAT remotely piloted research vehicles (RPRVs). Major subcontractors are Teledyne Ryan Aeronautical (airborne flight control system) and Hydraulic Research Corpn (servo actuators).

To meet the requirements of the programme, HiMAT's design consists of a basic core vehicle which includes the engine and all essential subsystems. To the core vehicle are added, as modular units, the main wings, canard surfaces, tail surfaces, and engine intake and afterburner/exhaust structures. In this way the modular components can be replaced during the programme, at minimum cost, with others of alternative design. Among these is expected to be a so-called '2D' vectored-thrust exhaust nozzle; other features to be tested include advanced supercritical wings; variable-camber wings; deformable, self-trimming outer wings; CCV (control configured vehicle) techniques; a digital fly-by-wire system; and a variable-thrust engine control system.

The first HiMAT RPRV was delivered to NASA on 7 March 1978 and the second on 12 June 1978. The first free flight was made on 27 July 1979. The RPRVs are air-launched at about 13,720 m (45,000 ft) from a B-52 carrier aircraft.

The HiMAT is flown by a pilot in a ground-based control centre in which all of the aeroplane's flight parameters are displayed via telemetry from the RPRV. The ground-based cockpit is equipped with conventional aircraft controls. The pilot is aided in the landing manoeuvre by a televised view of the landing area taken with a TV camera mounted in the HiMAT.

The following description applies to the HiMAT prototypes:

TYPE: Remotely piloted research vehicle.

AIRFRAME: Mid-wing monoplane, of roughly tandem-delta configuration, with sharply-swept main wings and canard forebody surfaces having graphite composite skins. Glassfibre outer leading-edges; remainder of wings of aluminium, titanium and other materials. Main wings have neither dihedral nor anhedral, and have ailerons, elevons and elevators on the trailing-edges, and NASA 'winglets' at tips. Canard surfaces have marked dihedral and are fitted with elevators. Semi-monocoque area-ruled fuselage, with graphite composite skin. Twin, swept, outward-canted pivoted fins on short booms extending from trailing-edges of main wings at approx mid-span. Graphite composite fin skins. Retractable tricycle landing gear, of skid type for landing on dry lake bed at Edwards AFB. All units retract rearward, main units to form continuous fairing with wing/tail booms, nose unit into underside of engine air intake trunk.

POWER PLANT: One General Electric J85-GE-21 turbojet engine (15·6 kN; 3,500 lb st dry and 22·25 kN; 5,000 lb st with afterburning), mounted centrally in fuselage. Fuel capacity (JP-5) 295 kg (650 lb).

LAUNCH AND RECOVERY: Air-launched from B-52 carrier aircraft. Recovered by conventional runway landing.

GUIDANCE AND CONTROL: Primary control from ground console, by TV, telemetry, and radar link with onboard systems. If ground control is lost, backup inputs from the RPRV will be relayed to a TF-104G chase-plane. On occasions when the TF-104G is out of control range, the HiMAT has an onboard self-righting system that will bring the RPRV into constant-altitude, orbiting, subsonic flight until the former can resume control.

EQUIPMENT: Onboard equipment includes flight and control parameter sensors, 164 research instrumentation sensors (pressures, strain gauges, accelerometers), signal processors, data link to ground and chase-plane, backup flight control system computer, and TV camera.

DIMENSIONS, EXTERNAL:

Wing span	4·755 m (15 ft 7¼ in)
Length overall, incl probe	6·86 m (22 ft 6 in)
Height overall	1·31 m (4 ft 3·6 in)

WEIGHTS:

Weight empty	1,200 kg (2,645 lb)
Max air-launching weight	1,528 kg (3,370 lb)
Thrust/weight ratio	approx 1

PERFORMANCE (estimated):

Max level speed	Mach 1·6
Touchdown speed	180 knots (333 km/h; 207 mph)
Average research flight duration	30 min
Max endurance	1 h 14 min
g limit	+12

SPERRY

SPERRY FLIGHT SYSTEMS DIVISION, SPERRY RAND CORPORATION

PO Box 21111, Phoenix, Arizona 85036
Telephone: (602) 942 2311

SPERRY (CONVAIR/GENERAL DYNAMICS) F-102A DELTA DAGGER

USAF designations: QF-102 and PQM-102

Conversion of US Air Force F-102A fighters for remotely piloted operation, under the Pave Deuce programme, has resulted in three versions, as follows:

QF-102. Prototypes, with provision for manned operation. Five converted by Fairchild Aircraft Service Division.

PQM-102A. Initial unmanned version, of which 63 produced under subcontract to Sperry by Fairchild Aircraft Service Division. First flight 13 August 1974, first operational flight 25 June 1975. Remote control avionics mounted in cockpit, on ejection seat rails; onboard programmer for pre-programmed manoeuvres; external engine control for starting; two more batteries in addition to normal F-102A installation; extensively modified AC electrical system, including two parallel transformers; dual autopilots; Vega Laboratories dual command and telemetry systems. Other details in 1977-78 *Jane's*.

PQM-102B. Current unmanned version, of which 66 being converted by Sperry Flight Systems. Retains same operational characteristics as PQM-102A except for one low-altitude mode, which can be implemented for special missions by installing radar altimeter. Retains also dual autopilots (the manoeuvre programmer of the PQM-102A being used as a backup flight control and stability system) and dual Vega command guidance and telemetry systems. Scoring system; smoke, brake and explosive destruct systems; and lift compensation in altitude hold mode, are all improved. Modification of basic aircraft; avionics and operational complexity; and throttle quadrant, are all simplified. Additional batteries are reduced to one; second transformer installation is deleted, a slightly modified form of the basic F-102A AC system being used; aircraft wiring is simplified; and engine start is done in cockpit, eliminating need for external control unit. Flight control avionics are located in the nose bay. Manoeuvres can be initiated and programmed from fixed ground control site, using new PQM-102B auxiliary panel.

The PQM-102s are the first-ever fighter aircraft converted for drone duties with no provision whatever for manned operation, and cannot be flown except under remote control. The following description applies to the PQM-102B:

AIRFRAME: As F-102A (see 1961-62 *Jane's*).

POWER PLANT: One Pratt & Whitney J57-P-23A turbojet engine, rated at approx 45·4 kN (10,200 lb st) dry and 71·2 kN (16,000 lb st) with afterburning.

LAUNCH AND RECOVERY: Normal runway T-O and landing.

GUIDANCE AND CONTROL: Fully redundant digital tracking control system, in conjunction with AN/FPS-16 range radar. Simultaneous control of two targets has been demonstrated.

SPECIAL EQUIPMENT: Aft avionics bay, missile bay, cockpit and two pylon-mounted underwing pods available for payload. Digidops miss-distance scoring system standard (antennae aft of cockpit, under fuselage, and in fairing each side of tailpipe); installation and test of vector miss-distance indication (VMDI) is planned. Two types of scoring camera operational, covering forward and aft areas to provide missile approach angle, velocity and miss distance; these are mounted in front and at rear of cockpit. Flight control stabilisation system, comprising flight reference computer, interface coupler and air data computer, provides eight longitudinal/vertical and four lateral/directional modes, and interface between aircraft systems and command/telemetry system. Automatic control modes are provided for take-off, loss of command carrier, take-off abort, and other safety modes. Redundant AC and DC power systems, and redundant autopilot. Manoeuvre programmer can be pre-programmed for three or four manoeuvres, to run in any required sequence. Command/telemetry system provides for four proportional and 48 discrete commands, 22 proportional and 40 discrete telemetry channels; nine additional commands available via standard payload modification. Manoeuvre destruct and explosive destruct systems incorporated. Radar and infra-red augmentation not required, due to size of aircraft.

Pre-production Northrop BQM-74C Chukar III air-launchable target

Northrop NV-135 Harassment mini-RPV

One of the two Rockwell HiMAT research RPV prototypes

Convair F-102A arriving at Sperry's modification centre near Phoenix, Arizona, for conversion to a PQM-102 target drone

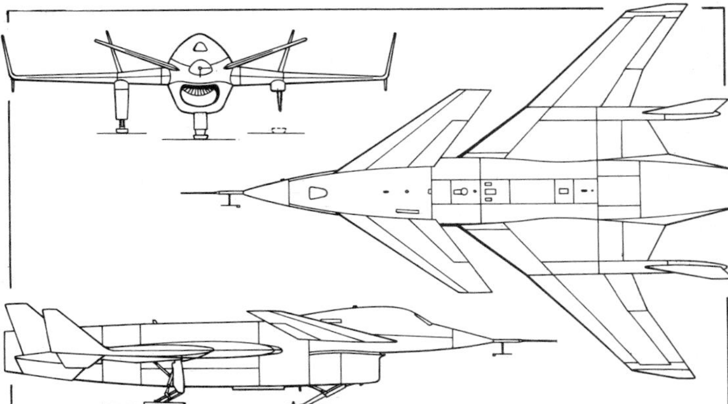

Rockwell International HiMAT research RPV *(Michael A. Badrocke)*

Teledyne Ryan BQM-34F Firebee II supersonic target

DIMENSIONS:
- Wing span: 11·62 m (38 ft 1½ in)
- Wing area, gross: 64·57 m² (695·0 sq ft)
- Length overall: 20·84 m (68 ft 4⅔ in)
- Height overall: 6·46 m (21 ft 2½ in)
- Payload volume (max, excl wing pods): 5·66 m³ (200 cu ft)

WEIGHTS:
- Basic mission weight: 9,076 kg (20,010 lb)
- Payload (max): 1,905 kg (4,200 lb)
- Mission operational T-O weight: 14,186 kg (31,276 lb)

PERFORMANCE:
- Max speed at altitude: Mach 1·2 (688 knots; 1,274 km/h; 792 mph)
- Operating height range: 61 m (200 ft) to 17,070 m (56,000 ft)
- Range (dictated by effective control range of guidance radar): more than 174 nm (322 km; 200 miles)
- Normal endurance of mission: 40-55 min
- *g* limit: +8

TELEDYNE RYAN
TELEDYNE RYAN AERONAUTICAL

2701 Harbor Drive, San Diego, California 92138
Telephone: (714) 291 7311

PRESIDENT: Teck A. Wilson
VICE-PRESIDENTS:
- F. X. Marshall (Target Programmes)
- H. B. Starkey (Special Programmes)
- J. M. Malloy (Administration, incl Public Relations)
- R. R. Schwanhausser (International RPV Requirements)

The former Ryan Aeronautical Company was an indirect successor to Ryan Airlines Inc, which produced the aeroplane in which Charles A. Lindbergh made the first nonstop flight from New York to Paris in 1927. In December 1969 the company was renamed Teledyne Ryan Aeronautical.

Current activities fall into two major categories, under the headings of Aerospace Systems and Electronic and Space Systems. The former group is concerned principally with the design, production and field operation of high-performance aerial jet targets and RPV systems.

Major production items at Teledyne Ryan's plant for many years have been the Firebee jet-powered targets and special-purpose vehicles (pre-programmed and remotely piloted) for various types of reconnaissance mission.

Teledyne Ryan BQM-34F Firebee II supersonic drones are being used in remotely piloted research vehicle (RPRV) test programmes at NASA's Dryden and Langley Research Centers. Teledyne Ryan itself conducted, under contract to NASA, a feasibility study involving the fitting of various different wing planforms and aerofoil sections to the Firebee II for test purposes. These included three types of supercritical wing, three types of supersonic wing, and a laminar-flow wing, and have led to NASA's DAST programme (which see).

Among other activities, Teledyne Ryan is studying a number of concepts for mini-RPVs.

TELEDYNE RYAN MODEL 124 FIREBEE I

USAF designation: BQM-34A
US Army designation: MQM-34D
US Navy designations: BQM-34A and BQM-34S

The Firebee I remotely piloted vehicle was developed as a joint US Air Force/Army/Navy project, in collaboration with the USAF Air Research and Development Command.

Glide flight tests of the original version began in March 1951, and the first powered flights were made that Summer at the USAF Holloman Air Development Center, Alamogordo, New Mexico. A total of 1,280 of these early Q-2A and KDA versions were built eventually for all three US services and for the RCAF, and full details of these can be found in previous editions of *Jane's*.

Development of the current **BQM-34A** (originally Q-2C) improved Firebee began on 25 February 1958. Construction of the prototype started on 1 May and it flew for the first time on 19 December 1958. The first production model flew on 25 January 1960.

By February 1978, a total of 5,893 Firebee Is (including more than 4,630 BQM-34A/S and MQM-34D targets) had been produced. These included Firebees supplied under contract to NATO for use in a missile test and evaluation programme, and a contract from the Japan Defence Agency for Firebees to support the training of missile and gunnery crews. The latter are being built by Fuji (which see). The latest US contracts, for 169 more Firebee Is, extend production into the 1980 calendar year.

Current Firebee targets for the US Navy incorporate a Motorola integrated track and control system (ITCS) or Vega Track and Control System (VTCS) and have the designation **BQM-34S**.

By 31 January 1978 Firebee I targets had provided more than 26,900 flights in support of weapon system and target research, development, test, evaluation, quality assurance, training and annual service practices conducted by the US Army, Navy and Air Force, and certain foreign governments. Since the current Firebee I and its predecessor models have been in operational use, target presentations have been made to virtually every surface-to-air and air-to-air weapon system in the US arsenal. To reduce the vulnerability of the target, and increase its cost-effectiveness, a 'non-kill' environment has been created and extensive use made of infra-red and/or radar augmented towed targets ('Towbees') or cloth banners, towed behind the Firebee on cables.

In November 1977 Teledyne Ryan successfully flew a BQM-34A using a company-developed all-digital Microprocessor Flight Control System (MFCS). This system permits the precise high-*g* manoeuvres required in test and evaluation of modern weapon systems.

RPVs (remotely piloted vehicles) using airframes developed from that of the Firebee I are described separately.

The following details refer to the standard BQM-34A target vehicle:

TYPE: Remotely piloted jet target vehicle.

AIRFRAME: Cantilever mid-wing monoplane, of aluminium alloy semi-monocoque construction. Three-spar wings, incorporating leading-edge droop. No dihedral or incidence. Sweepback at quarter-chord 45°. Single-spar ailerons, with Lear servo-actuators. Wingtips detachable. Provision for wingtip extensions. Tapered, circular-section body, with chemical-etched components. Glassfibre tailcone and nose section. Keel under central portion, to absorb landing impact. All tail surfaces swept 45° at quarter-chord. Multi-spar fin, with glassfibre tip housing guidance and control antenna. Trim rudder operated electrically by Bendix actuator. Single-spar tailplane, with glassfibre tips housing radar echo enhancing antennae. Ventral fin under tailcone, aft of main tail unit. Magnesium elevators powered by Lear servo.

POWER PLANT: One 7·56 kN (1,700 lb st) Teledyne CAE J69-T-29 turbojet engine. Integral fuel tank in forward fuselage, capacity 378 litres (100 US gallons). Provision for one 94·5 litre (25 US gallon) auxiliary fuselage tank and one 378 litre (100 US gallon) drop-tank under each wing. Oil capacity 5·75 litres (1·5 US gallons).

LAUNCH AND RECOVERY: Either air-launching, from suitably-modified aircraft, or ground-launching, using 50·3 kN (11,300 lb st) (nominal) solid-propellant JATO bottle. US Navy has launched BQM-34As from ships under way at up to 15 knots (27·5 km/h; 17 mph). Two-stage parachute recovery system operates automatically in event of target hit, loss of radio wave carrier from remote control station, engine failure, or upon command by remote control operator. To prevent damage by dragging, recovery system incorporates disconnect which releases parachute from Firebee on contact with ground or water.

GUIDANCE AND CONTROL: Remote control methods include choice of radar, radio, active seeker and automatic navigator, developed and designed by Teledyne Ryan. Normal method is through UHF radio link using AN/FRW-2 or SRW-4 ground transmitter and AN/DRW-29 airborne receiver. Target can be controlled either from manned aircraft or from surface station. Remote command includes activation of special scoring and augmentation equipment in target. Onboard beacon facilitates radar tracking; provision to install telemetry system to relay pertinent flight data to controller. Basic commands consist primarily of on/off functions, received by onboard radio receiver and relayed to appropriate subsystem. Motorola ITCS (integrated tracking and control system) in BQM-34S. BQM-34As currently being fitted with Vega DTCS (drone tracking and control system). Other types of remote command and tracking system can include microwave command and guidance system to control Firebee beyond line-of-sight from ground station through airborne relay station. Operational Firebees can be equipped with increased manoeuvrability flight control system for tactical air combat simulation which gives target capability to perform 4, 5 or 6*g* manoeuvres. Other systems include active and passive radar augmentation, and afterburning plume devices. Radar Altimeter Low Altitude Control System (RALACS), when added to Firebee I control system, permits precision low-altitude flights at 15 m (50 ft) over water and 30 m (100 ft) over land.

SYSTEMS: Electrical power only. Primary power furnished by 28V 200A DC engine-driven generator. Power for control systems furnished by 400Hz 115V 250W AC inverter; 28V 12·5Ah lead-acid battery provides power for electrical devices of recovery system and for control during pre-landing glide phase.

AVIONICS AND EQUIPMENT: AN/DRW-29 radio receiver with Dorsett TM-4-31A telemetry system, or DKW-2 guidance transponder, or DTCS Model 685-2 guidance system. A/A37G-3 or A/A37G-8 flight control system. Wide range of 'building block' operational equipment includes visual or radar-reflecting banner targets; radar or infra-red Towbee towed targets or tow target Doppler 'bird'; two underwing drop-tanks, 500 lb bombs or bomblet dispensers; AN/ALE-33 or other ECM containers; wingtip tow launchers, camera pods, scoring equipment, flares or other forms of infra-red augmentation, or reflector pods for radar augmentation. BQM-34A can be equipped with adjustable travelling wave tube amplifiers for use as radar echo enhancers in L, S, X and C frequency bands.

DIMENSIONS, EXTERNAL:

Wing span	3·93 m (12 ft 10·8 in)
Wing area, gross	3·34 m² (36·00 sq ft)
Length overall	6·98 m (22 ft 10·8 in)
Body diameter	0·94 m (3 ft 1·2 in)
Height overall	2·04 m (6 ft 8·4 in)

WEIGHTS:

Weight empty	680 kg (1,500 lb)
Basic gross weight	934 kg (2,060 lb)
Max launching weight	1,134 kg (2,500 lb)

PERFORMANCE:

Never-exceed speed Mach 0·96 (635 knots; 1,176 km/h; 731 mph at 15,240 m; 50,000 ft)

Max level speed at 1,980 m (6,500 ft) 600 knots (1,112 km/h; 690 mph)

Max cruising speed at 15,240 m (50,000 ft) at 816 kg (1,800 lb) AUW 547 knots (1,015 km/h; 630 mph)

Stalling speed, power on, at 816 kg (1,800 lb) AUW 101 knots (187 km/h; 116 mph)

Max rate of climb at S/L at 1,000 kg (2,200 lb) AUW 4,875 m (16,000 ft)/min

Operating height range 15 m-18,300 m (50 ft to more than 60,000 ft)

Endurance at 15,240 m (50,000 ft), incl 2 min 40 s glide after fuel expended 75 min 30 s

Max range 692 nm (1,282 km; 796 miles)

Flotation time with 25% fuel 24 h

TELEDYNE RYAN MODELS 147 and 255

USAF designation: AQM-34

The Model number 147, and the basic USAF designation AQM-34, encompass a large family of surveillance, reconnaissance and ECM RPVs evolved from the subsonic Firebee I target. The original Model 147A, which was little more than a modified Firebee I with a new guidance system and increased fuel capacity, was developed in 1962. Since then many hundreds of Model 147s have been delivered for operational use.

Details of all Model 147s, and their uses from 1964-74, can be found in the 1975-76 and later editions of *Jane's*. The surviving USAF RPVs are now in store, though available for reactivation if required. The major recent versions are as follows:

Model 147SD (AQM-34M). Low-altitude photographic reconnaissance version. Total of 78 built under USAF Compass Bin and Buffalo Hunter programmes. Pre-programmed digital computer, with Doppler guidance system. Fairchild KS-120A or F-415Y camera. Radar altimeter standard; some fitted in 1972 with Teledyne Systems Co Loran receivers and redesignated **Model 147SD Loran/AQM-34M(L).** Extended-range version, with underwing drop-tanks, also built. Served with 22nd Tactical Drone Squadron. One AQM-34M underwent flight testing at Edwards AFB, California, under USAF Compass Robin programme (see 1975-76 *Jane's* for details).

Model 147TF (AQM-34R). Built under USAF Compass Bin programme. Was also the second Combat Dawn version for Strategic Air Command: twenty ordered in 1971. Airframe externally similar to 147TE (see 1978-79 *Jane's*), but probe-type fairing on nose is omitted and there is a small blade antenna on top of the nosecone. Provision for underwing stores. Capable of cruising above 18,300 m (60,000 ft) at a speed of 420 knots (780 km/h; 485 mph).

Model 255 (AQM-34V). Tactical recoverable electronic warfare RPV. Update of 47 AQM-34H and J tactical electronic warfare RPVs, and 16 new-built AQM-34Vs, delivered in 1976 and later served with 432nd Tactical Drone Group, 11th Tactical Drone Squadron, Davis-Monthan AFB, Arizona. First flight conducted May 1976 by 6514th Test Squadron at Hill AFB, Utah. Incorporates active jamming provided by E-Systems (Melpar Division) and carries two Lundy ALE-2 or MB Associates ALE-38 chaff dispenser pods on underwing pylons. Primary mission was to precede strike aircraft to target, confusing enemy tracking equipment with chaff or other countermeasures. Air or ground launch capability, with prime recovery by MARS (mid-air retrieval system) by CH-3 or HH-53 helicopters. Compatible with Sperry Univac MDC (Multi Drone Control) installed in DC-130H, controlling up to eight vehicles at a time.

POWER PLANTS: Single Teledyne CAE turbojet engine, as follows:
147 SD: 8·54 kN (1,920 lb st) J69-T-41A.
147 TF: 12 kN (2,700 lb st) J100-CA-100.
255: J69-T-29.

LAUNCH AND RECOVERY: All models normally air-launched from DC-130A, E or H Hercules carrier/director aircraft. Recovery by CH-3 helicopter mid-air retrieval system (MARS). AQM-34V tested in ground launch in 1975 using Thiokol booster rocket and TRW thrust vector control.

GUIDANCE AND CONTROL: Teledyne Ryan radio command; or programme and command; or radio/microwave command guidance system. See also under individual model listings.

EQUIPMENT: See under individual model listings.

DIMENSIONS, EXTERNAL:

Wing span:	
147 SD	4·42 m (14 ft 6 in)
147 TF	9·75 m (32 ft 0 in)
Length overall:	
147 SD and TF	9·14 m (30 ft 0 in)
Body diameter:	
147 SD	0·94 m (3 ft 1·2 in)
147 TF	1·01 m (3 ft 3·6 in)

WEIGHTS:

Max launching weight:	
147 SD	1,412 kg (3,113 lb)
147 TF:	
without underwing stores	1,859 kg (4,100 lb)
with underwing stores	2,812 kg (6,200 lb)
AQM-34V	2,041 kg (4,500 lb)

TELEDYNE RYAN MODEL 166 FIREBEE II

US Navy designations: BQM-34E and BQM-34T
USAF designation: BQM-34F

Under contract to the US Navy and USAF, Teledyne Ryan Aeronautical produced the Model 166 Firebee II supersonic target vehicle, an advanced development of the BQM-34A Firebee I which can provide aerial target presentations above 18,300 m (60,000 ft) at a supersonic dash speed of Mach 1·5 for a period of 14 minutes.

Fourteen XBQM-34E development Firebee IIs were built under US Navy contract, and these underwent a successful operational test and evaluation programme in 1968-69. One static test airframe was also completed.

Three versions of the Firebee II have been built in quantity, as follows:

BQM-34E. For US Navy: 116 delivered. First operational flight 1 June 1972 at Pacific Missile Test Range. In service since 1973 with US Navy Squadron VC-8 in Puerto Rico.

BQM-34F. For US Air Force: 99 delivered. Slightly heavier than BQM-34E, with corresponding adjustment of performance, due to different augmentation and scoring systems and addition of recovery parachute for mid-air retrieval system (MARS).

BQM-34T. Follow-on production version for US Navy, incorporating Motorola integrated track and control system (ITCS). Total of 54 delivered.

Firebee II drones feature in a number of experimental programmes, including NASA's Project DAST (which see).

TYPE: Remotely piloted supersonic jet target vehicle.

AIRFRAME: Shoulder-wing monoplane. Sweepback 53° at leading-edge. Basic wing structure of aluminium honeycomb core, steel skins and leading-edge, machined aluminium trailing-edge and detachable aluminium wingtips. No ailerons. Conventional aluminium semi-monocoque fuselage, of frames, bulkheads and formers. Glassfibre nose radome. Protuberances avoided by designing external attachments and antennae to be flush. Nose radome, similar to that of Firebee I, houses radar augmentation system antenna and passive augmentation. Directly behind this is equipment compartment containing electrical, electronic and scoring systems, followed by central fuselage, consisting of fuel tank and structure for supporting wing. Inlet and oil tank assembly slung under equipment compartment. Inlet duct passes from inlet opening through fuel tank to engine, which is installed in fuselage half-shell integral with central fuselage structure. Entire aft portion of fuselage is removable subassembly which forms upper shell, covering engine. Sweptback (45°) all-moving horizontal tail surfaces; sweptback (53°) tapered fin and rudder. Horizontal tail surfaces used for roll and pitch control. Control surfaces actuated by electro-hydraulic actuator unit; this is self-contained package with two output shafts for horizontal tail surfaces and one for rudder, which is used for directional trim and yaw damping. Aluminium honeycomb cores, with steel skins. Aluminium leading- and trailing-edges. Fin tip is glassfibre housing for UHF antennae.

POWER PLANT: One 8·54 kN (1,920 lb st) Teledyne CAE J69-T-406 turbojet engine. Wing centre-section and main fuselage total fuel tank capacity 119 kg (263 lb) in BQM-34E and T, 151 kg (333 lb) in BQM-34F. External fuel pod capacity 181 kg (400 lb); weight of fuel plus tank, 210 kg (463 lb). With all tanks, target will perform subsonic flight missions with similar performance capability, endurance and range to those of subsonic BQM-34A. For supersonic flights, external pod is jettisoned. Oil capacity 5·75 litres (1·5 US gallons). Provision for 50·3 kN (11,300 lb st) (nominal) solid-propellant JATO bottle.

LAUNCH AND RECOVERY: Launched from ground or shipborne launcher, or from modified DP-2E Neptune or DC-130A or E Hercules aircraft. DP-2E can carry two Firebees underwing, DC-130 four; launched at altitudes up to 5,485 m (18,000 ft) at approx 200 knots (370 km/h; 230 mph). Recovery by two-stage parachute system similar to that of Firebee I. Can also be recovered from water or (BQM-34F only) by helicopter mid-air retrieval system. In a MARS recovery, helicop-

BQM-34A Firebee I target drone of the US Air Force

Helicopter retrieval of AQM-34R (Model 147TF)

Artist's impression of the Teledyne Ryan Firebrand naval supersonic target

Teledyne Ryan Model 255 (AQM-34V) electronic warfare RPV

ter snares 5·72 m (18 ft 9 in) diameter engagement parachute which extends above 24·08 m (79 ft 0 in) main parachute. Once engaged, the main parachute is released automatically. Provision for emergency recovery. In all versions, recovery parachutes are housed in fuselage tailcone. Recovery sequence preceded, at altitudes above 4,570 m (15,000 ft), by power-off glide, and can be initiated by remote command at any time during glide. When necessary to gain altitude and reduce speed for safe parachute deployment and recovery, a power-off climb is initiated automatically below 15,000 ft either by normal recovery command or if there is loss of engine power or generator failure.

GUIDANCE AND CONTROL: Frequency-modulated UHF radio guidance system, with 20 separate command channels, utilising AN/DRW-29 onboard radio receiver with compatible transmitter at remote control station. Motorola ITCS (integrated track and control system) in BQM-34T performs the functions of the tracking beacon, radio control receiver and telemetry system. Six-element automatic flight control system (AFCS) comprises three-axis rate gyro, vertical gyro, air data computer, flight control box, low-altitude control box, and three-axis electro-hydraulic actuator assembly. Positioning data provided by onboard radar tracking beacon, antennae for which are located on top of nose compartment and in lower aft portion of fuselage. Ten-channel telemetry system comprises data collection, conversion and FM/FM transmitting equipment in drone and receiving and data display units in remote control station. Flight control system continues to operate when engine or generator power is shut down at high altitude.

SYSTEMS: Electrical power only. Primary power furnished by 28V 200A DC engine-driven starter/generator. Power conversion by means of 250VA 400Hz 115V AC static inverter. Power for recovery system and for drone control during glide phase furnished by 28V 10Ah nickel-cadmium battery.

AVIONICS AND EQUIPMENT (BQM-34E and T): AN/DLQ-3 ECM equipment, AN/DRQ-4 missile scoring system, AN/APX-71 L-band beacon, special low-altitude radar altimeter kit for 15 m (50 ft) altitude, X- or C-band tracking beacons, AN/DRW-29 radio control receiver, Dorsett AN/AKT-21 telemetry system. Motorola ITCS in BQM-34T. Radar augmentation includes travelling wave tube (TWT) in S-, C- and X-band and nose-mounted Luneberg lens passive radar reflector. Infra-red augmentation by wingtip-mounted MK 37 Mod 0 flares. In general, Firebee II can be equipped with active and passive radar augmentors, electronic and photographic scoring systems, ECM, low-altitude radar sensing systems and IR flares or pods. Other augmentation equipment can include target identification, GCI tracking, variable radar-image size, augmented IR radiation and smoke system. Positive electronic identification provided by L-band IFF beacon.

DIMENSIONS, EXTERNAL:
Wing span:
BQM-34E and T — 2·71 m (8 ft 10·8 in)
BQM-34F — 2·95 m (9 ft 7·9 in)
Length overall — 8·89 m (29 ft 1·9 in)
Body diameter — 0·61 m (2 ft 0 in)
Height overall — 1·71 m (5 ft 7·2 in)

WEIGHTS (A: BQM-34E; B: BQM-34F; C: BQM-34T):
Weight empty:
A — 658 kg (1,452 lb)
B — 780·8 kg (1,721·4 lb)
Equipment payload:
A — 67 kg (147·6 lb)
C — 50·5 kg (111·4 lb)
Max launching weight:
A, air launch — 855·7 kg (1,886·5 lb)
B, air launch — 951 kg (2,097 lb)
A, ground launch — 1,036 kg (2,285 lb)
B, ground launch — 1,110 kg (2,447 lb)
C, ground launch — 1,030 kg (2,270 lb)

PERFORMANCE:
Max speed: at S/L — Mach 1·1
at 13,715 m (45,000 ft):
A — Mach 1·8
B — Mach 1·78
above 18,300 m (60,000 ft) — Mach 1·5
Operating height range — 15 m (50 ft) to 18,300 m (60,000 ft)
Service ceiling: A — 18,300 m (60,000 ft)
B — 16,765 m (55,000 ft)
Control range — 200 nm (370 km; 230 miles)
Typical range, external tank on:
low-altitude, subsonic cruise/transonic dash — 221 nm (409 km; 254 miles)
high-altitude, subsonic cruise/supersonic dash — 606 nm (1,123 km; 698 miles)
high-altitude, subsonic cruise throughout — 617 nm (1,142 km; 710 miles)
Max range — 774 nm (1,434 km; 891 miles)
Endurance (total time) — 1 h 14 min
Flotation time — 24 h

TELEDYNE RYAN MODELS 234 and 259

USAF designation: BGM-34

This RPV series was developed primarily for tactical strike and other defence suppression roles, reflecting plans to evolve combat drones for a variety of missions which at present require manned aircraft.

Details can be found in the 1975-76 and later editions of *Jane's*.

TELEDYNE RYAN FIREBRAND

US Navy designation: XBQM-111A

Initial US Navy funding of approx $3 million was announced in May 1977 for this new supersonic target, designed to simulate the threat posed by Soviet anti-shipping missiles. The total value of the development and construction programme will be $41·7 million.

The initial contract calls for the completion of nine targets: six for research and development and three for special tests. Known as the XBQM-111A Firebrand, the target will serve as a realistic 'enemy' in testing USN shipboard defence weapons under simulated combat conditions. Subject to the satisfactory completion of tests, production Firebrands are expected to be ordered in 1982.

TYPE: Recoverable supersonic target drone.

AIRFRAME: Shoulder-wing monoplane, with small delta wings (approx 63° sweep on leading-edges) set well back on tapered, circular-section body. Built mainly of aluminium alloy, with wings of aluminium honeycomb and bonded stainless steel skins. Differentially-operating elevons and rudder. Ram-air intake in base of fin.

POWER PLANT: Two Marquardt ramjets, each approx 22·24 kN (5,000 lb st), mounted externally one on each side of fuselage at rear. Fuel tank in centre of fuselage. Thiokol booster rockets.

LAUNCH AND RECOVERY: Air or surface launch. Fail-safe parachute recovery system, housed in fuselage between payload compartment (forward) and fuel tank.

GUIDANCE AND CONTROL: Pre-programmed radio command guidance system, using AN/AYK-14 flight control computer. Provision for manual override.

EQUIPMENT: Ram-air turbogenerator; batteries; Honeywell 7193 altimeter; Tacan; drag 'chute, recovery parachute and flotation bag; locator beacon; and destruct receiver. Mission equipment, in 0·17 m³ (6 cu ft) payload compartment in nose, includes ECM; active and passive radar augmentation; IR augmentation; expendable H-, I- and J-band emitter; and scoring system.

DIMENSIONS, EXTERNAL:
Wing span — 2·74 m (9 ft 0 in)
Wing area, gross — 3·72 m² (40·0 sq ft)
Length overall — 10·36 m (34 ft 0 in)
Body diameter — 0·71 m (2 ft 4 in)

WEIGHTS (surface launch):
Fuel — 998 kg (2,200 lb)
Payload — 113 kg (250 lb)
Max launching weight (incl booster) — 2,676 kg (5,900 lb)

US DEPARTMENT OF DEFENSE

Major areas in which the Department of Defense was concentrating RPV research during the late 1970s include the testing of a missile- or aircraft-launched mini-RPV; development and test of shipboard launch and recovery techniques; battery- and solar-powered RPVs; miniature infra-red and laser designator and rangefinder systems that will enable a mini-RPV to find targets and guide weapons at night; and data links resistant to hostile jamming. The use of mini-RPVs for hostile weapon and radar location is foreseen, using the air vehicle as a platform equipped with a lightweight high-performance radar, or a laser line-scanner, and a direct line-of-sight flash detector, or with an explosive charge to destroy a target. A small, low-cost system for locating a mortar projectile is being designed, and investigation of radar options for projectile tracking is in progress.

In addition to drone/RPV programmes for which hard-

USAF Flight Dynamics Laboratory XBQM-106, equipped with under-fuselage General Dynamics millimetre wave seeker

ware contracts have been awarded (described under the appropriate contractor's heading in this section), the following are among the more important programmes recently receiving attention by the three US services:

US AIR FORCE

Office of Information, Aeronautical Systems Division (AFSC), Wright-Patterson AFB, Ohio 45433
Telephone: (513) 253 7111

HWS (Harassment Weapons System). Mini-drone programme to develop a small, low-cost system to provide defence suppression of hostile air defences. Formerly known as LCEHV (Low Cost Expendable Harassment Vehicle). Will be ground-launched, to navigate autonomously to, and loiter in, the area of the hostile air defences. Its presence will draw the defences' fire, provoke radar silence, or (if ignored) will home in to allow an explosive charge to damage a hostile radar. System studies, by E-Systems' Melpar Division, Lockheed Missiles and Space Co and Northrop-Ventura have been submitted, and prototype airframes were built and flown by these companies in late 1976. Field tests at Nellis AFB (early 1976) and West Germany's Meppers Test Range (early 1977) were carried out with the USAF Axillary mini-RPV. These tests and additional subsystem testing (eg, warhead, launcher, navigation) were funded jointly by the USA and the Federal Republic of Germany.

The selected vehicle will weigh about 59 kg (130 lb) and measure about 3·05 m (10 ft) in wing span and length. In advance of the airframe, the USAF has initiated development of the sensor for the harassment system, and was evaluating competitive submissions for a passive radio frequency homing sensor in the Spring of 1979.

LAMPS (Low-Altitude Multi-Purpose System). Programme to develop low-altitude long-range RPV; not to be confused with US Navy's Light Airborne Multi-Purpose System manned helicopter.

XBQM-106. This experimental mini-RPV was designed and built by the USAF Flight Dynamics Laboratory, and was first flown in 1975. It is designed for easily-obtainable flexibility, and up to early 1979 six variants had flown, incorporating various alternative wing, nose, tail and engine configurations, and with payloads ranging from 11·3 to 45·4 kg (25-100 lb). Launch has been demonstrated from a Fairchild catapult.

The XBQM-106 is scheduled to flight test a fluidic autopilot developed by KBG Corporation.

The following description applies to the basic configuration:

AIRFRAME: Cantilever high-wing monoplane, with pod-and-boom fuselage, sweptback fin and rudder, dual-taper non-swept wings and non-swept horizontal tail. Twin, dependent endplate fins and rudders also tested. Construction mainly of foam plastics. Side force generators have been added.

POWER PLANT: One McCulloch MC-101A single-cylinder piston engine mounted above wing centre-section, usually driving a two-blade pusher propeller. Engines of 9-13·5 kW (12-18 hp) have been fitted, some with four-blade propeller.

LAUNCH AND RECOVERY: Launched by bungee-assisted trolley. Normal recovery by landing on ventral skid. Recovery using powered ram-air canopy has also been demonstrated.

GUIDANCE AND CONTROL: Radio and radar command guidance system standard. Real-time ground-based control system; USAF-developed autopilot or manual control optional. Aerodynamic control by ailerons, elevator and rudder. Special wings-level steering available via side-force control for accurate target strike experiments. Was to be used to flight-test acoustic guidance system developed by Northrop's Electro-Mechanical Division for mini-drones used in anti-tank attack role.

SPECIAL EQUIPMENT: Air-to-ground telemetry utilised on some missions. Wide variety of possible payloads, accommodated in nose sections of standard or modified shape.

DIMENSIONS, EXTERNAL:
Wing span 3·66 m (12 ft 0 in)
Wing area, gross 1·72 m² (18·5 sq ft)
Length overall 3·05 m (10 ft 0 in)

WEIGHTS:
Payload range 45-56 kg (100-125 lb)
Max T-O weight with 13·5 kW (18 hp) engine 100 kg (220 lb)
Max T-O weight 102 kg (225 lb)

PERFORMANCE:
Cruising speed 100 knots (185 km/h; 115 mph)
Max rate of climb at S/L 229 m (750 ft)/min
Service ceiling 3,050 m (10,000 ft)
Endurance up to 5 h

US ARMY

Public Affairs Office, US Army Troop Support and Aviation Materiel Readiness Command, 4300 Goodfellow Boulevard, St Louis, Missouri 63120

Aquila. Mini-RPV system technology demonstrator for reconnaissance, surveillance and target acquisition. Described under LMSC entry in this section. Programme has shown concept to be cost- and operationally effective. Full-scale engineering development due to begin in late 1979.

Electronic Warfare RPV. Programme to demonstrate 22·7-54·5 kg (50-120 lb) expendable/non-expendable mini-RPVs as an airborne platform for communication and non-communication jammers. Feasibility programme tentatively scheduled for completion in 1979. Future programme to be determined.

Little Scout. Scheduled to begin in late 1979 as follow-on programme to Aquila, providing operational tactical mini-RPV system capable of conducting reconnaissance, surveillance and target acquisition. Could be operational in early 1980s. Evaluation of potential power plants from Bennett and Teledyne CAE completed in December 1978.

US NAVY

Office of Information, Naval Air Systems Command, Department of the Navy, the Pentagon, Washington, DC 20361

David W. Taylor Naval Ship Research and Development Center VATOL (XBQM-108A). This US Navy programme is aimed at demonstrating vertical attitude take-off and landing (VATOL) aboard non-aviation ships. Tethered hover flight tests were successfully demonstrated on 29 September 1976. After refurbishment, free-flight hover tests on land were scheduled at the Pacific Missile Test Center during 1978. An operationally capable version will be built and tested aboard ship.

The VATOL test vehicle is a Navy in-house design that utilises parts of the Northrop MQM-74A target and the midcourse guidance system of a McDonnell Douglas AGM-84A Harpoon air-to-surface missile. The major changes were detailed in the 1977-78 *Jane's*.

TYPE: Vertical attitude take-off and landing test vehicle.

POWER PLANT: One Teledyne CAE YJ402-CA-400 turbojet engine (2·94 kN; 660 lb st) fitted for tethered hover tests, mounted in aft fuselage and fitted with vane-type thrust vector control system. Ventral air intake, in S-shaped ventral glassfibre duct. Fuel capacity 45·4 litres (12 US gallons). Teledyne CAE XJ402-CA-400 engine to be fitted for free-flight hover tests.

LAUNCH AND RECOVERY: Vertical attitude ('tail-sitting') take-off and landing. Can also take off and land in conventional (horizontal) attitude. Parachute recovery system of MQM-74A is retained for emergency use.

GUIDANCE AND CONTROL: For tethered hover tests, MQM-74A command and control receiver and decoder, housed in forward fuselage, were retained; Motorola integrated target control system (ITCS) will be fitted for free-flight hover tests. IBM/Lear Siegler midcourse guidance unit (MGU) from a McDonnell Douglas AGM-84A Harpoon air-to-surface missile provides guidance and control from take-off to terminal guidance takeover. It serves as both autopilot and inertial navigator by means of attitude reference assembly (ARA) in strapdown inertial sensor configuration; digital computer autopilot (DCA); and self-contained power supply. MGU sends control signals to elevon and rudder rotary electro-mechanical actuators via servo amplifiers for horizontal flight control. For control in vertical attitude (hover), signals are sent to linear electro-mechanical actuators that drive four vanes of high-temperature steel (Hastelloy X) located in engine exhaust. These vanes produce sufficient forces to provide control in pitch, roll and yaw.

SYSTEM AND EQUIPMENT: 28V DC electrical system. Power from ground support unit (two 65Ah batteries) used in tethered hover tests with YJ402 engine; in free-flight tests, will be taken from alternator mounted on XJ402

XBQM-108A VATOL (Vertical Attitude Take-Off and Landing) vehicle under development by US Navy

engine. Radar altimeter from Harpoon missile used to sense altitude in horizontal flight as well as in hover. Radar transmitting and receiving antennae located flush on wing undersurface, forward of elevons, during horizontal flight (one under each wing). As RPV transitions to a vertical attitude, antennae are spring-loaded and hinged, allowing them to rotate through 90° so that altitude can be measured during hover. Harpoon's signal conditioner and telemetry tray used to transmit more than 60 pieces of information on performance, engine parameters, flight control surface position and deflection rates.

DIMENSIONS, EXTERNAL:
Main wing span 2·21 m (7 ft 3 in)
Main wing area 2·02 m² (21·74 sq ft)
Foreplane span 1·10 m (3 ft 7½ in)
Foreplane area 0·46 m² (5·00 sq ft)
Body diameter 0·36 m (1 ft 2 in)
Length overall approx 3·58 m (11 ft 9 in)

WEIGHTS:
Fuel 42·6 kg (94 lb)
Max T-O weight 254 kg (560 lb)

PERFORMANCE:
Max cruising speed 400 knots (741 km/h; 460 mph)
Time to 1,525 m (5,000 ft) 8·8 s
Endurance approx 30 min

Naval Air Development Center QF-4B. QF-4B target version of McDonnell Douglas F-4B was developed by Naval Air Development Center for use at Pacific Missile Test Center. First aircraft was delivered in Spring 1972 to PMTC at Point Mugu for further flight development and subsequent use as supersonic target for new missile development. Flight testing was completed in January 1974.

QF-4B conversions are currently being produced by Naval Air Rework Facility, Cherry Point, North Carolina. Target is equipped for high-*g* manoeuvring and has provisions for photo and electronic scoring and ECM. Production expected to continue into 1980s. A follow-on version is under development to incorporate all-attitude manoeuvring.

Naval Surface Weapons Center HASPA. HASPA (High Altitude Superpressure Powered Aerostat) is programme for remotely piloted airship for high altitude (20,725 m; 68,000 ft) ocean surveillance and communications relay, sponsored by Air Systems Command of USN and managed by NSWC. Martin Marietta is a prime contractor. HASPA will be helium-filled, with an electric propulsion system, will be 101·50 m (333 ft) long, and have a diameter of 20·42 m (67 ft). Unpowered prototype, built by Sheldahl Inc, flown in 1976.

Naval Weapons Center QF-86. Twenty-nine North American F-86H Sabres were converted by Naval Weapons Center, China Lake, California, into QF-86H pilotless target aircraft, as described in 1977-78 *Jane's*. Two F-86F Sabres were undergoing prototype conversion at the NWC in 1978 into QF-86F pilotless target aircraft. Eventually, approx 50 F-86Fs are to be converted to QF-86F drones. The QF-86F and the existing QF-86H will be used as interim all-attitude manoeuvring targets.

AIR-LAUNCHED MISSILES

ARGENTINA

ARMED FORCES SCIENTIFIC AND TECHNICAL RESEARCH CENTRE

It was announced in the Spring of 1978 that two types of missile were under advanced development in Argentina. One is an anti-tank missile, in the class of the German Cobra, and was expected to become operational in 1979. The other is an air-to-surface missile in the class of the French AS.20, to arm naval fixed-wing aircraft and helicopters. Eight R & D rounds had been built by the Armed Forces Scientific and Technical Research Centre at the time of the announcement, with an evaluation batch of 50 missiles to follow. Guidance is by radio command. Only other details released by mid-1979 are as follows:

WEIGHTS:
Warhead 40 kg (88 lb)
Launching weight 115 kg (254 lb)

PERFORMANCE:
Max range 3·75 nm (7 km; 4·35 miles)

FRANCE

AÉROSPATIALE
SOCIÉTÉ NATIONALE INDUSTRIELLE AÉROSPATIALE
Division des Engins Tactiques

EXECUTIVE OFFICE: 2 rue Béranger, 92320 Châtillon sous Bagneux
Telephone: 657 11 80
Telex: 250881F

When Nord-Aviation became part of Aérospatiale, responsibility for its guided missiles, target vehicles and test vehicles was allocated to Aérospatiale's Tactical Missiles Division. Subsequently, this Division developed and put into production a new generation of short-range battlefield weapons, in association with MBB of Germany (see Euromissile entry in International section).

A total of 481,229 tactical missiles and 1,859 target and reconnaissance RPVs had been ordered from the Division and its overseas partners by January 1979. Employees totalled 5,800 at the beginning of 1979.

AÉROSPATIALE AS.11

The AS.11 is an air-to-surface version of the SS.11 line-of sight wire-guided battlefield missile. It is powered by a two-stage solid-propellant rocket motor. Directional control is achieved by varying the sustainer efflux through two side-nozzles.

In action, with a typical helicopter installation, the operator acquires the target by means of a stabilised and magnifying optical sight. As soon as the missile enters his field of vision after launch, he passes to it the signals needed to align it with the target, while keeping it above the terrain until impact. The signals are given by the operator by means of a control stick which makes it possible to send simultaneously up or down and port or starboard commands. The signals are transmitted to the missile over wires, wound on twin spools. Tracer flares are installed on the rear of the missile for visual reference.

The current AS.11 B.1 version is available with a variety of warheads, including an inert type for practice, the Type 140AC anti-tank warhead capable of perforating 60 cm (24 in) of armour plate, the Type 140AP02 explosive warhead (2·6 kg; 5·72 lb of explosive) which will penetrate an armoured steel plate 1 cm (0·4 in) thick at a range of 3,000 m (9,840 ft) and explode about 2·1 m (7 ft) behind the point of impact, and the Type 140AP59 high-fragmentation anti-personnel type with contact fuse.

The AS.11 B.1 and the basic surface-launched SS.11 B.1 have been supplied to all three French services and the armed forces of 27 other countries, including the USA and UK. Orders totalled 168,340 by January 1979, including surface-to-surface Harpons with automatic infra-red command guidance. Of these, 60% were for export. Licence manufacture was undertaken in Federal Germany and India. Production by Aérospatiale is expected to continue on a reduced scale until about 1985.

DATA: See table

AÉROSPATIALE AS.12

This spin-stabilised missile was derived from the AS.11 and has a warhead weighing 28·4 kg (62·6 lb), which makes it suitable for use against fortifications as well as tanks, ships and other vehicles. The current OP.3C warhead can pierce 40 mm (1·5 in) of armour and explode on the other side.

The AS.12 has a two-stage solid-propellant rocket motor and a command to line-of-sight guidance system. It can be air-launched at speeds up to about 200 knots (370 km/h; 230 mph), in conjunction with an APX 260 or APX 334 gyro-stabilised sight, and can be used at night with target illuminating equipment.

The AS.12 arms Breguet Atlantic and P-2 Neptune aircraft of the Royal Netherlands Navy, and is also carried by the Breguet Alizé. It is operational on helicopters of the French Navy, the Royal Navy and several other naval air arms.

A total of 8,309 AS.12s and surface-to-surface SS.12s had been ordered by January 1979, when manufacture was continuing. Of these, 79% were for export.

DATA: See table

AÉROSPATIALE LASSO

Work on this wire-guided spin-stabilised missile, proposed as a replacement for the AS.12 and SS.12, has been terminated. Details of Lasso can be found in the 1978-79 *Jane's*.

AÉROSPATIALE AS.15TT

The AS.15TT is projected by Aérospatiale as a lightweight all-weather missile for attacking surface targets of all tonnages at sea. It could be operated from comparatively slow-flying aircraft, such as ship-based or shore-based helicopters and maritime patrol aircraft, or from surface ships or coastal defence batteries. A helicopter such as the SA 365 Dauphin II could carry four, in pairs, on fuselage-side racks.

The general appearance of the AS.15TT is shown in the accompanying photograph of a model. It would use an extremely accurate automatic guidance system, and carry a warhead identical to that of the AS.12 missile.

Associated surface-surveillance radar is the Thomson-CSF Agrion 15, which has a 360° scan; is designed for automatic target tracking and determination of the differential target/missile range and bearing; and is able to operate in an ECM environment. As well as forming part of the AS.15TT system, the Agrion 15 can be used to designate over-the-horizon targets for long-range anti-ship missiles in the Exocet class.

In operation, the target would be detected and identified; the radar would be switched to automatic tracking and the missile launched. After a shallow descent, the AS.15TT would then follow a sea-skimming trajectory to the target, under entirely automatic guidance. The characteristics of the system are such that approach to the target and missile launch could be performed at very low altitude.

DATA: See table

AÉROSPATIALE AS.30 LASER

Developed as a successor to the original command-guided AS.30 (see 1976-77 *Jane's*), this tactical air-to-surface supersonic missile is intended to be compatible with all types of modern single-seat or multi-seat combat aircraft. It has a cylindrical body, cruciform sweptback wings which are canted to impart spin stabilisation, cruciform 'flip-out' tail-fins indexed in line with the wings, and a two-stage (boost and sustainer) solid-propellant rocket motor. A two-phase guidance system is utilised, comprising a pre-guidance phase on gyro reference, followed by laser terminal homing, by means of the missile's Thomson-CSF Ariel homing head.

Standard equipment required in the launch aircraft consists of an armament control panel, a firing button on the control column and an emergency jettison switch. Equipment associated specifically with the AS.30 Laser missile comprises launchers with the appropriate firing circuits, and a Thomson-CSF Atlis target illuminating pod.

Initial tests of an Atlis 1 pod under a French Air Force Jaguar A were made successfully at the CEV, Cazaux, in 1977. Test firings were scheduled to begin in early 1979.

DATA: See table

AÉROSPATIALE EXOCET AM39

Exocet is a missile that was devised originally to provide warships with all-weather attack capability against other surface vessels. The air-to-surface version is designated AM39. Propulsion is by a tandem two-stage solid-propellant motor, and the highly-destructive warhead is in the same order as that of a torpedo.

Compared with the surface-to-surface versions, the AM39 air-to-surface Exocet has a reduced launch weight and a new rocket motor that burns for 150 s, giving an increased range. Another modification to the propulsion system ensures a one-second delay in ignition after launch, allowing the missile to drop clear of the launch aircraft.

The AM39 has been selected for carriage by the French Navy's Atlantic and Super Etendard aircraft and by the Mirage F1. It is suitable for operation from medium-size helicopters, and has been ordered to equip Pakistani Sea Kings and Iraqi Super Frelons.

The missile's high subsonic flight profile consists of a pre-guidance phase, during which it travels towards the target, whose range and bearing have been determined by an airborne radar or ship's fire control computer and set up in the missile pre-guidance circuits before launch, and a final guidance phase during which the missile flies directly towards the target under the control of its active homing head. Throughout the flight the missile is maintained at a very low altitude (reported to be 2 to 3 metres; 6·5 to 10 ft) by an FM radio altimeter. Its homing head is reported to pick up the target over a range of up to 6·5 nm (12 km; 7·5 miles). Exocet is intended to operate efficiently in an ECM (electronic countermeasures) environment. It uses a modified version of the inertial low-level guidance system developed for the Kormoran missile and a sustainer motor similar to that of the Martel missile. Subcontractors to Aérospatiale include Electronique Marcel Dassault for the ADAC homing head, TRT for the AHV-7 radio altimeter, SNPE for the solid propellants, SERAT for the explosive charge, SFENA and SAGEM for accelerometers and gyroscopes, Jaeger for control surface actuators, and ECAN-Ruelle for servo control equipment.

Launch tests from a Super Frelon helicopter began in April 1973. The type of missile employed was an intermediate version of Exocet designated AM38, which consisted of a surface-to-surface MM38 fitted with the one-second ignition delay that is embodied in the AM39. In each of the powered launches, the missile dropped about 10 m (33 ft) in a stable, horizontal attitude from its pylon before ignition, despite rotor downwash.

Firings of AM39 missiles from a Super Frelon began in December 1976, and were followed by the first launches from a Super Etendard in the first half of 1977.

Carrying two Exocet AM39s and 5,000 litres (1,100 Imp gallons) of fuel, a Super Frelon can carry out a 6-hour patrol near its shore or ship base, or attack a specific target up to 350 nm (650 km; 400 miles) from base. Equipment added to the helicopter consists of two launch pylons, an operator's console, an Omera ORB-31D X-band search and tracking radar capable of acquiring targets the size of a fast patrol boat over a range of 28·5 nm (53 km; 33 miles) in sea state 4 or 5, an EMD Alto-2 Doppler radar altimeter, a SFIM CV-153 vertical gyro for a compass system, a compensated airspeed indicator and a Crouzet 70 computer.

Of the 103 production AM39s ordered by January 1979, more than 75% were for export.

RANGE (estimated):
launched from a helicopter at 60 knots (110 km/h; 69 mph) at a height of 100 m (330 ft)
28 nm (52 km; 32·25 miles)
launched from an Atlantic aircraft at heights between 300 and 5,000 m (1,000 ft and 16,400 ft)
29-32·25 nm (54-60 km; 33·5-37·25 miles)
launched from a Super Etendard aircraft at heights between 100 m (330 ft) and 10,000 m (33,000 ft)
32-37 nm (60-70 km; 37-43 miles)
For other data see table

ASMP

As mentioned in the 1977-78 *Jane's*, the original missile that was being developed under the ASMP (Air-Sol Moyenne Portée) designation reverted to definition study

Launch of an Aérospatiale AS.11 air-to-surface missile from an Alouette III helicopter

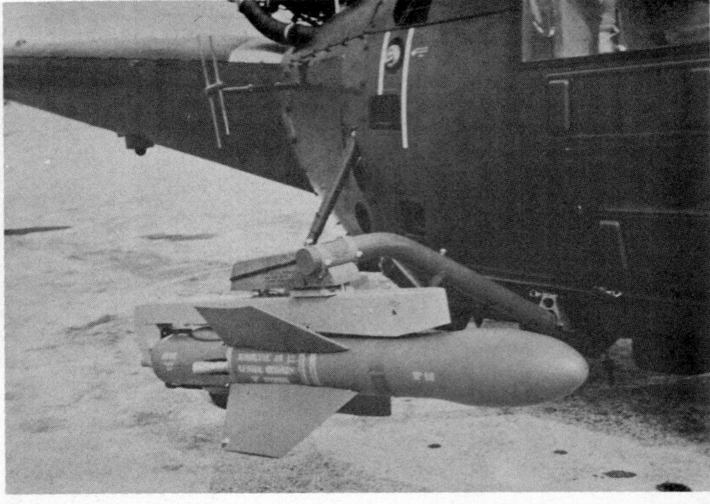

Aérospatiale AS.12 air-to-surface missile on an Alouette III helicopter

status when the ACF (Avion de Combat Futur) programme was cancelled. However, on 6 April 1978 it was announced that a new design and development contract for an air-to-surface medium-range missile (ASMP) had been awarded to Aérospatiale's Tactical Missiles Division, which will collaborate with ONERA and SNPE. Intended as the vehicle for the French Air Force's latest tactical nuclear warhead, ASMP was stated to benefit from ramjet engine research carried out by Aérospatiale and its predecessors, and from experience gained in developing the guidance systems for the Exocet and Pluton missiles. It will be carried initially by the Dassault Mirage 2000 tactical fighter, from about 1985.

The ASMP will be powered in supersonic cruising flight by a kerosene-burning ramjet, supplied with air by a pair of two-dimensional side intakes which will serve also as wings. Stability and control will be provided by two pairs of tail-fins and rudders, with guidance by an inertial system. Range is expected to be in the order of 40-54 nm (75-100 km; 46-62 miles) depending on launch and cruising height. Yield of the nuclear warhead is said to be between 100 and 150 kT, and ASMP is intended for stand-off use against heavily defended targets such as airfields, and command and communications centres.

It seems likely that the power plant will be a rocket-ramjet, with the solid-propellant launch booster integrated in the ramjet combustion chamber.

MATRA

SA MATRA

HEAD OFFICE: 4 rue de Presbourg, 75116-Paris
MANAGEMENT AND WORKS, POSTAL ADDRESS: BP No. 1, 78140-Vélizy
Telephone: 946 96 00
Telex: ENMATRA 698077F
PRESIDENT DIRECTOR-GENERAL: Jean-Luc Lagardère
DIRECTOR OF PUBLIC RELATIONS: Philippe Chassagny
CHIEF OF PRESS DEPARTMENT: Roland Sanguinetti

Since 1948, Matra has been engaged in extensive research and experimental work in the guided missile, propulsion and guidance fields. The wide range of weapon systems in current production includes a total of eight air-to-air, surface-to-air, air-to-surface and anti-ship missiles.

Other Matra weapon systems include the Durandal rocket-propelled penetration bomb for attacking runways; and the Beluga cluster weapon, developed in association with Thomson/Brandt, which dispenses 151 grenades or other munitions, lowered to the ground on individual brake-chutes.

MATRA R.530

Since 1963, more than 3,000 R.530 air-to-air missiles have been delivered to arm aircraft of 14 countries, including Mirage III and Mirage F1 interceptors of the French Air Force, F-8E(FN) Crusaders of the French Navy, and Mirages of the air forces of Argentina, Australia, Brazil, Colombia, Pakistan, South Africa and Venezuela. Production was scheduled to continue into 1979.

Suitable for use at heights from sea level to 21,000 m (69,000 ft), the R.530 is an all-weather missile, with interchangeable EMD AD-26 semi-active radar and SAT AD-3501 infra-red homing heads. It can be fired at the target from any relative direction.

The R.530 has a cylindrical body, with cruciform delta wings, two of which are fitted with ailerons, and cruciform tail control surfaces. It is powered by a dual-thrust (boost and sustainer) Hotchkiss-Brandt/SNPE Marie Antoinette solid-propellant rocket motor, rated at 83·36 kN (18,740 lb st).

Interchangeable Hotchkiss-Brandt fragmentation or continuous-rod warheads are available, each weighing 27 kg (60 lb) and fitted with a proximity fuse. Anti-jamming ECM devices are fitted to the AD-26 head.

DATA: See table

MATRA SUPER 530

This air-to-air weapon is being deployed initially as armament for the Dassault Mirage F1 interceptors of the French air force and will eventually arm also the Mirage 2000. Compared with the R.530, it has much improved aerodynamics, structure, radome, electronics and power plant, doubling both the acquisition distance and the effective range. It is an all-weather and all-sector weapon, with the ability to attack targets flying at an altitude 7,600 m (25,000 ft) higher or lower than that of the launch aircraft.

The Super 530 has an EMD Super AD-26 semi-active radar homing head. Its Angèle dual-thrust rocket motor, supplied by Thomson/Brandt, utilises Butalane propellant, with a much higher specific impulse than the motor of the R.530. The warhead is supplied by Thomson/Brandt, with a proximity fuse by Thomson-CSF; and advanced ECM anti-jamming circuits are fitted. Control is by means of the cruciform tail-fins.

Ramp-launch tests of the Super 530 began in January 1971, and the first controlled model was fired successfully on 27 February 1973. Five complete missiles had been fired successfully against airborne targets by early 1975; the first launch from a Mirage F1 was conducted successfully in January 1976, and operational evaluation by the French air force had reached an advanced stage by early 1979. Manufacture for the air force was started at the end of 1977, reaching mass production levels by January 1979.

DATA: See table

MATRA R.550 MAGIC

This air-to-air weapon system was intended initially to meet a French Air Force requirement for a highly-manoeuvrable short/medium-range 'dogfight' missile. Development was started in 1967 as a private venture and has continued under official contract since 1969.

The R.550 Magic has a 'double-canard' configuration, with a set of movable foreplane control surfaces immediately behind and indexed in line with cruciform fixed surfaces. The missile has an SNPE Romeo single-stage solid-propellant motor, an AD-3601 infra-red homing head with a cooled cell, manufactured by SAT, and a 12·5 kg (27·5 lb) warhead with 6 kg (13·2 lb) of explosive, impact and proximity fuses. It can utilise the same aircraft launcher as the Sidewinder which it replaces.

The Magic has wide range limits, is stressed for 30*g* manoeuvres and can be fired from an aircraft in a 6*g* turn, singly or at one second interval between rounds. There is no minimum launch speed; maximum is more than 700 knots (1,300 km/h; 805 mph), against targets in a forward sector of 140°.

The first air-launch of an R.550 complete with guidance equipment, against a target, took place at the Landes Test Centre on 11 January 1972, from a Gloster Meteor test aircraft. Delivery of the first production missiles for operational testing and evaluation by the French Air Force began in 1974. Full series manufacture began in 1975 and by the beginning of 1979 a total of 3,200 Magics had been delivered. Orders for training and operational rounds totalled 5,000, for 11 countries, at that time, and production was continuing at the rate of 100 a month at Salbris.

Adaptation to the Mirage III, Mirage 5, Mirage F1 and French Navy Crusader has been completed; adaptation to the Jaguar, Alpha Jet, Aermacchi M.B. 326K, and Super Étendard is under way, and Magic will also form the basic weapon of the Mirage 2000.

DATA: See table

GERMANY (FEDERAL REPUBLIC)

BODENSEEWERK

BODENSEEWERK GERÄTETECHNIK GmbH

HEAD OFFICE: Postfach 1120, 777-Überlingen
Telephone: (07 551) 811
Telex: 07 33924
LIAISON OFFICE: Bundeskanzlerplatz HI 1002, 5300-Bonn
Telephone: (02 221) 214432
UK OFFICE: 27-28 Crossway House, Bracknell, Berks RG12 1DA, England
Telephone: (0344) 26070 and 54782

Under the original NATO European production programme for the Sidewinder air-to-air missile, Bodenseewerk was prime contractor for the licence manufacture of 13,000 of the AIM-9B and FGW Mod 2 versions.

The company is now prime contractor for European production of the advanced AIM-9L Sidewinder, described under the NWC heading in the US section.

MBB

MESSERSCHMITT-BÖLKOW-BLOHM GmbH

HEAD OFFICE AND WORKS: Ottobrunn bei München, 8 München 80, Postfach 801220
Telephone: (089) 60 00 25 90

In addition to its manufacture of piloted aircraft, MBB has engaged in the development and manufacture of guided weapons for many years. It has achieved considerable success with its short-range surface-to-surface and surface-to-air battlefield missiles, some of which result from partnership with Aérospatiale of France.

Weapons in current production include an air-launched anti-shipping missile known as the Kormoran.

MBB KORMORAN

This roll-stabilised all-weather anti-shipping missile can be carried by any aircraft which is able to maintain a speed between Mach 0·6 and 0·95 during the attack, and which is equipped with target detection radar and an autonomous navigation system such as an inertial platform. The air-

Aérospatiale AS.30 Laser air-to-surface homing missile on a Jaguar

Super Frelon helicopter carrying two Exocet air-to-surface missiles

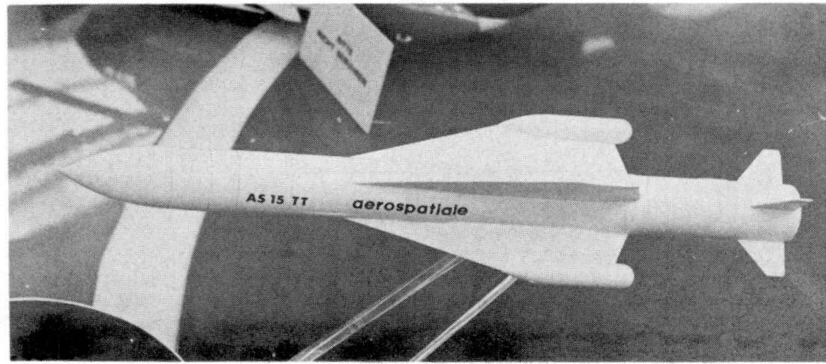

Model of Aérospatiale AS.15TT *(Brian M. Service)*

Matra R.550 Magic air-to-air missile on wingtip of Dassault Mirage F1

Matra Super 530 air-to-air missiles on underwing mountings of Mirage F1

Versions of the Matra R.530 air-to-air missile with semi-active radar guidance (left) and infra-red homing head (right)

craft's electronics must be supplemented by a position and homing indicator (PHI) and Kormoran firing equipment. Launch information is obtained from the aircraft's target detection radar, navigation system, and a navigation support device which adapts the signals representing velocity for the Kormoran airborne computer. In addition, if the missile is operated in an optical mode, instead of through target detection radar, the PHI has to be used in conjunction with computer co-ordinated data (CCD) and a vector addition unit (VAD).

Two built-in SNPE Prade boosters accelerate Kormoran to high subsonic cruising speed, which is then maintained by the SNPE Eole IV solid-propellant sustainer motor. The guidance system employs pre-guidance and homing phases, using a Thomson-CSF RE-576 radar terminal seeker. The new-type high-energy warhead, developed at MBB's Schrobenhausen works, weighs 160 kg (352 lb) and can penetrate 70-90 mm (2·75-3·5 in) of steel plate, making it effective against ships up to the size of a destroyer.

The launch aircraft can approach the target area at very low level, to escape detection by the ship's radar, by means of the PHI, with radar switched off. With the radar then turned on, the target is acquired and its position is fed into the PHI; the radar is again switched off while the aircraft takes up the optimum attack position. The radar is switched on, locked on to the target, and initial data are transmitted automatically to the missile. As soon as the missile has been launched under power, directly from the pylon, as little as 30 m (100 ft) above the water, the aircraft breaks away, outside the range of enemy anti-aircraft defences. The missile descends to its programmed flight level and locks on to the target, guided by inertial navigation aided by its radar altimeter. At a prescribed distance, the inertial system releases the active radar seeker. After this has locked on target, the inertial guidance is slaved and corrected in azimuth and range by the seeker head. At a short distance from the target the missile descends to its terminal flight level in order to hit the target just above the waterline.

The secondary optical firing mode, in which the pilot aims the missile by means of his optical weapon sight, is used against surprise targets, in the presence of extreme enemy ECM, or when the target is a small vessel, such as a fast patrol boat or minesweeper. Kormoran itself is immune to all known kinds of ECM.

In-plant testing of Kormoran was completed by early 1974, at which time official tests from F-104G Starfighter aircraft were under way. A preliminary production contract to equip F-104Gs of the German naval air arm was placed in 1974; it was followed by a full contract in November 1976, for 350 missiles and 56 aircraft installations, for which MBB is prime contractor. Seven qualification test firings in Autumn 1977 resulted in six direct hits on target and a seventh which met specification requirements. The first two series-production Kormorans were accepted by the naval air arm in December 1977. Kormoran will eventually arm Tornadoes of the German Navy.

DATA: See table

INTERNATIONAL PROGRAMMES

EUROMISSILE

EUROMISSILE GROUPEMENT D'INTÉRÊT ÉCONOMIQUE
7 rue Béranger, BP 84, 92320 Châtillon, France

Telephone: 657 12 44
Telex: EUROM 204691 F
PRESIDENT: Marcel Morer
SALES DIRECTORS: Pierre Froget and Georg Erlenwein

Euromissile is a Groupement d'Intérêt Economique formed by Aérospatiale of France and MBB of Germany. First products of the Euromissile team are three short-range battlefield weapons known as Milan, Hot and

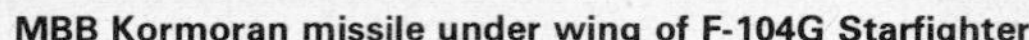

MBB Kormoran missile under wing of F-104G Starfighter

Launching a Hot missile from a Gazelle helicopter

Roland, developed initially for the armed services of France and Federal Germany. Hot is in production for both air-launched and surface-launched operation.

HOT

The Hot (High-subsonic, optically-guided, tube-launched) is a tube-launched wire-guided anti-tank missile suitable for both surface-to-surface and air-to-surface use. It has fins which fold down against the body when it is in its launching tube, and open out in flight. The power plant is a two-stage solid-propellant rocket motor. A jet-vane is used to steer the missile. Guidance is by automatic command to line of sight, with infra-red tracking.

The HLVS (Hot, stabilised localiser-sight) system offers magnifications of 3·2 × 17° field and 10·8 × 5° field. Sight limits are ±118° in bearing and +28°/−20° in elevation. To engage a target, the aimer maintains a sighting cross on the target, switches on the firing installation and selects a missile on the control box.

Flight testing of an operational Hot installation on an Aérospatiale/Westland SA 341 Gazelle helicopter, in conjunction with the HLVS stabilised sight system, was performed in 1973. With the target hidden from the sight of the pilot and missile operator before take-off, the helicopter proved able to acquire the target and launch a missile within 4 seconds of lift-off. Hit probability proved to be 90% over ranges varying from a minimum 400 m (1,310 ft) to a maximum of 4,000 m (13,125 ft) in hovering flight and 4,300 m (14,100 ft) in translational flight at speeds up to 100 knots (185 km/h; 115 mph). During missile flight, the helicopter was able to take evasive action at a turning speed of up to 6° per second.

Further helicopter trials, by the official services of France and Germany, took place during 1974, from a Gazelle and a BO 105 respectively. Since then France has adopted Hot as armament for the Gazelle helicopter; West Germany has selected it for the BO 105 M (PAH 1), and several other nations have ordered this weapon system for helicopter use. Series production began in 1976, and the first production units to equip helicopters were delivered in 1977. Hot was fired from Lynx and Dauphin helicopters during 1978.

DATA: See table

MATRA/BAe (HSD)

SA MATRA, 37 avenue Louis Breguet, 78140 Vélizy-Villacoublay, France
Telephone: 946 96 00

BRITISH AEROSPACE, Dynamics Group, Manor Road, Hatfield, Herts AL10 9LL, England
Telephone: Hatfield (30) 62300

AS.37/AJ.168 MARTEL

Martel (Missile Anti-Radar and TELevision) was manufactured in two versions, one using passive radar homing and the other TV guidance, with maximum commonality of structure and systems.

The anti-radar version (AS.37), produced by Matra in France, offers all-weather attack capability against radar antennae in several frequency bands. The television version (AJ.168) was produced in the UK by Hawker Siddeley Dynamics (now British Aerospace, Dynamics Group).

Production of Martel was completed in 1978, but it remains operational on a variety of aircraft, including the Buccaneer operated by the Royal Air Force, and the Mirage III-E, Jaguar and Atlantic operated by the French services. Details of both versions of the missile can be found in the 1978-79 *Jane's*.

ISRAEL

RAFAEL

RAFAEL ARMAMENT DEVELOPMENT AUTHORITY

Ministry of Defence, POB 2082, Haifa
Telephone: 04 714168

SHAFRIR

Shafrir is a short-range infra-red homing dogfight missile developed for use against aircraft at heights up to 18,000 m (60,000 ft). Many rounds have been fired against enemy aircraft since the current Mk 2 version entered service in 1969, with considerable success. This was particularly evident during the Yom Kippur War of October 1973, when Shafrir is claimed to have destroyed more than 100 Arab aircraft in air combat, representing a success rate of 60% in terms of the number of missiles fired.

Relatively small in size and simple in conception, Shafrir has a solid-propellant rocket motor and is a solid-state weapon, fully transistorised and with guidance by proportional navigation, for optimum results against manoeuvring targets.

The missile and its launcher are mounted under the wing of the aircraft on a specially-designed adapter which is capable of carrying other types of weapon as an alternative to Shafrir. Attachment is mechanical and the missile requires no support from the aircraft except for the firing circuit. When a target is detected within firing range, an audio signal is heard and a light is switched on automatically on the pilot's control panel as an indication that the firing button should be pressed. After launch, the missile tracks the target entirely automatically, and the warhead is detonated either on impact or by the proximity fuse within optimum distance of the target.

Shafrir Mk 3, under development, is expected to offer greater manoeuvrability and all-aspect launch capability.

Sales of the Mk 2 version are reported to have been made to several overseas customers, including Chile and Taiwan.

DATA: See table

LUZ

First reported in the 1974-75 *Jane's*, Luz-1 is now confirmed as a TV-guided air-to-surface missile developed and produced by Rafael Armament Development Authority. No details have been released officially, but in mid-1977 the Israeli Air Force was reported to be modifying its F-4E Phantom and IAI Kfir-C2 fighters to carry Luz. The missile's main purpose is said to be the destruction of enemy surface-to-air weapons, with a conventional warhead. Impervious to jamming, Luz is believed to have a maximum range of 43 nm (80 km; 50 miles) and a launch weight of 200 kg (440 lb).

ITALY

SELENIA

SELENIA INDUSTRIE ELETTRONICHE ASSOCIATE SpA

HEAD OFFICE AND WORKS: via Tiburtina km. 12.400, 00131 Rome
POSTAL ADDRESS: PO Box 7083, 00100 Rome
Telephone: 43601
Telex: 61106 Seleniat
PUBLIC RELATIONS: Gen Clemente Paolozzi

ASPIDE

This missile, already in production for use in the Albatros naval surface-to-air defence system, is under development as an all-weather all-aspect weapon for high-performance interceptors, and for use in the Spada ground-based low-altitude air defence system. It will improve the effectiveness of each of these weapon systems in terms of maximum missile range, operation at very low altitudes, multiple target engagement and resistance to advanced ECM. In particular, it is expected to enhance the dogfight and shootdown capabilities of the F-104S interceptors of the Italian Air Force.

Aspide has a single-stage solid-propellant rocket motor, supplied by SNIA Viscosa, which gives it a speed described as being "well in the hypersonic field". Its guidance system is of the semi-active radar type, developed by Selenia. The warhead is a fragmentation type produced by SNIA Viscosa.

The missile's final configuration is almost identical to that of the US Sparrow and the five missiles used in first-phase firing tests, concluded on 17 December 1975, were each powered by a licence-built Rocketdyne Mk 38 motor, as fitted in Sparrow. Second-phase testing involved five surface-to-air and five air-to-air firings, using missiles powered by the SNIA Viscosa motor developed especially for Aspide and fitted with an improved autopilot. Final testing was to involve fully-guided flights.

DATA: See table

SISTEL

SISTEL—SISTEMI ELETTRONICI SpA

HEAD OFFICE: via Tiburtina 1210, 00131 Rome
Telephone: 41 25 841
Telex: 68112 Sistelro
MANAGING DIRECTOR: Dott Manlio Lo Cascio

MARTE

In 1967, the Italian Navy initiated a development programme, known as Project Marte, to enhance the

Shafrir under wing of a Kfir fighter *(Israir)*

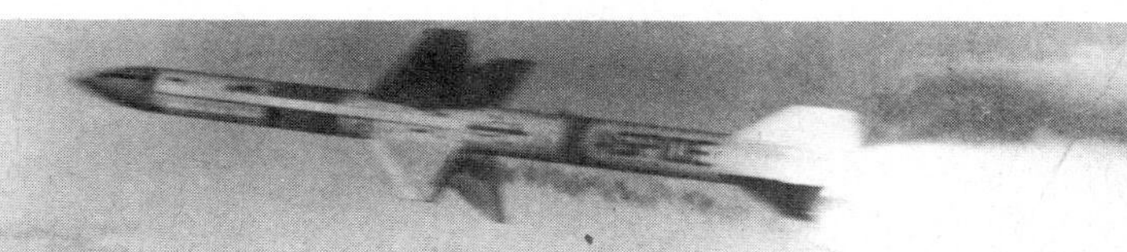

Ground-to-air firing of an Aspide missile in Sardinia

Mitsubishi ASM-1 anti-shipping missile

Sistel Sea Killer Mk 2 missile, as used in Marte air-to-surface weapon system

Artist's impression of Penguin Mk 3 on an F-16 of the Norwegian Air Force

capabilities of shore-based or shipborne helicopters by arming them with anti-shipping missiles. Eventually, Sistel's Sea Killer family of missiles was chosen as most suitable for this application, because of the weapons' all-weather operability, automatic guidance system, inherent insensibility to ECM and sea-skimming flight profile. The system has been studied for installation on a wide range of Agusta helicopters, with take-off weights varying from 3,000 kg to more than 10,000 kg (6,600-22,050 lb), dependent on the number of missiles to be carried and the possible requirement for simultaneous anti-submarine and surface strike capability.

Equipment added to the Marte helicopter is lightweight and easily operated. The radar performs navigation, search and target tracking as well as guidance of the missile in azimuth. Thus an SH-3D helicopter, fully equipped for surface strike and anti-submarine duties, and with an autopilot for instrument flying, can be assigned a 4¼ h maritime patrol at a search speed of 100 knots (185 km/h; 115 mph), carrying a crew of four. Total weight of the system is 1,320 kg (2,910 lb), including 158 kg (348 lb) for the radar, 600 kg (1,323 lb) for two Sea Killer Mk 2 missiles, 300 kg (661 lb) for electronic warfare equipment, and 22 kg (48 lb) for an optical sight.

In action, it can be assumed that the helicopter will locate a target in a few seconds of radar operation at the limit of radar range. To reduce the possibility of enemy recognition of the helicopter's radar interrogation, the airborne radar is then switched off and the aircraft descends in order to fly toward the target at the lowest practical height above the water. At an estimated distance just beyond missile range, the helicopter climbs again to missile launching height, re-acquires the target and launches a Sea Killer, which takes slightly more than one minute to reach the enemy ship.

The Sistel radar altimeter in the missile can be pre-set before launch to control the cruising height at values down to 3 m (9 ft 10 in) or less, depending on factors such as sea state. The altitude can be changed by command signal during flight, if required. Control in azimuth can be achieved either by automatic radar mode in all-weather conditions or by a standby fair-weather system, using an optical sight and joystick controller.

Initial firing trials of the Marte system, in flight, had been made successfully from an AB 204 helicopter by the Spring of 1973. The system was put into production subsequently for installation on Agusta SH-3D helicopters of the Italian Navy, utilising two Sea Killer Mk 2/Marte missiles and chin-mounted APQ-706 X-band track-while-scan radar supplied by SMA.

SISTEL SEA KILLER Mk 2

This two-stage missile is a development of the Sea Killer Mk 1 (see 1977-78 *Jane's*), with a heavier warhead and extended range. It is operational in surface-to-surface form on board four Vosper Mk 5 frigates of the Iranian Navy. With a small receiver modification, it is also the sea-skimming missile utilised in the Marte air-to-surface weapon system for helicopters.

POWER PLANT: SEP 299 solid-propellant booster, rated at 43·16 kN (9,702 lb st) for 1·6 s. SEP 300 solid-propellant sustainer, rated at 0·98 kN (220·5 lb st) for 73 s.

GUIDANCE: Alternative all-weather beam-rider/command/radio altimeter guidance, or optical radio command/radio altimeter guidance.

WARHEAD: High-explosive semi-armour-piercing with impact/proximity fuse.

DATA: See table

JAPAN

MITSUBISHI

MITSUBISHI DENKI KABUSHIKI KAISHA (Mitsubishi Electric Corporation)

HEAD OFFICE: 2-3, Marunouchi 2-chome, Chiyoda-ku, Tokyo 100

Telephone: 218 2111

PRESIDENT: Sadakazu Shindo

Mitsubishi Electric is prime contractor for licence production of Sparrow air-to-air missiles to arm F-4EJ fighters of the JASDF. This work began in FY 1972, and about 600 Sparrow IIIs were delivered, for air-to-air use, between 1974 and 1978. Production is continuing.

MITSUBISHI JUKOGYO KABUSHIKI KAISHA (Mitsubishi Heavy Industries Ltd)

HEAD OFFICE: 5-1 Marunouchi 2-chome, Chiyoda-ku, Tokyo 100

Mitsubishi Heavy Industries has Japanese government contracts to develop an air-to-surface anti-shipping missile.

MITSUBISHI AAM-2

Further development of this air-to-air missile was suspended in 1978, but the Japan Defence Agency is developing a new air-to-air 'dogfight' missile in co-operation with Mitsubishi, utilising technology evolved during the AAM-2 programme.

MITSUBISHI ASM-1

The Japanese government approved the expenditure of $44 million between FY 1973 and FY 1977 to cover the initial development phase of an anti-shipping missile to be carried by Mitsubishi F-1 attack aircraft of the JASDF. In November 1973 Mitsubishi Heavy Industries was selected as prime contractor for this missile, which is also suitable for ship or ground launching when fitted with a rocket booster. Subcontractors include Nissan Motor Co for the rocket motors.

Known as the ASM-1, the new missile is intended to travel to the target at a low altitude, using a Japan Aviation Electronics inertial system and TRT/Japan Radio ANV-7 radio altimeter for mid-course guidance, and a Mitsubishi Electronics active radar seeker for terminal guidance.

Twenty-five prototype missiles were bought in FY 1977-78 and the first two launches were made from a Mitsubishi T-2, flying at a height of 760 m (2,500 ft), on 12 and 13 December 1977, off Fukui in the Sea of Japan. Testing by the JDA's Technical Research and Development Institute was expected to be complete by May 1979, enabling the programme to be taken over by the JASDF. For this purpose, 10 more XASM-1s have been ordered for 1980 testing, and will be followed by 16 pre-production YASM-1s. Delivery of production ASM-1s is scheduled to begin in 1981.

DATA: See table

NORWAY

KONGSBERG

A/S KONGSBERG VAAPENFABRIKK

HEAD OFFICE AND WORKS: Postboks 25, N-3601 Kongsberg

Telephone: 034 38250

Telex: 11491 vaapn n

Defence Products Division

MARKETING MANAGER, DEFENCE EQUIPMENT: Jens Ch. Width

PUBLIC RELATIONS MANAGER: E. Frisvaag

This government-owned company was prime contractor for European production of the Bullpup air-to-surface missile and participated in other NATO-coordinated programmes such as those for the Sidewinder air-to-air missile and NATO Sea Sparrow. It is manufacturer of the Norwegian-developed Penguin anti-ship missile system.

PENGUIN

This anti-ship missile system was developed by the Norwegian Defence Research Establishment and A/S Kongsberg Vaapenfabrikk. It is in quantity production, and can be installed on ships, helicopters and other platforms.

In its ship-to-ship version, Penguin is delivered in a container with integral launch-rail and can utilise most existing types of shipboard fire-control systems. It embodies a two-stage solid-propellant rocket motor and an inertial guidance system with infra-red terminal homing. Its warhead weighs 120 kg (264 lb) and is similar to that of Bullpup, with a contact fuse.

The air-launched Penguin Mk 3 version is under development for carriage by F-16 fighters of the Norwegian Air Force. The Mk 3 will have an extended range and reduced wing span, and will dispense with the booster stage of the rocket motor fitted to the ship-launched versions. No dimensions, weights or performance data may yet be published; details of the ship-launched Penguin Mk 2 are included in the table at the end of this section.

SWEDEN

SBMC
SAAB-BOFORS MISSILE CORPORATION

Birger Jarlsgatan 6, 114 34 Stockholm

Telephone: 08 21 49 17
Telex: 12798 SBMC S

President: Arne Hult

This company was created jointly by Saab-Scania and Bofors, on 14 April 1978, to co-ordinate future missile activities within the two companies and to be responsible for marketing. The intention is that the work will continue to be located in the facilities of both parent companies, which remain responsible individually for weapons developed before the creation of SBMC. Details of three of these, the air-to-surface Saab RB04E and RB05A and Bofors RB53 Bantam wire-guided anti-tank missile, can be found in the 1977-78 *Jane's*.

UNION OF SOVIET SOCIALIST REPUBLICS

AIR-TO-AIR MISSILES

AA-1

NATO reporting name: Alkali

This first-generation Soviet air-to-air missile was produced as standard armament for the Sukhoi Su-9 and of the all-weather versions of the MiG-19, which continue in service with the air forces of the Soviet Union and some of its allies. Radars fitted to these interceptors are known to NATO as 'Spin Scan' and 'Scan Odd' respectively.

'Alkali' is a solid-propellant missile, with large delta cruciform wings at the rear and small cruciform foreplanes indexed in line with the wings. There appear to be control surfaces in the trailing-edges of the wings and 'Alkali' employs I/J-band semi-active radar homing. The warhead is carried immediately aft of the foreplanes.

Data: See table

K-13A (AA-2)

NATO reporting name: Atoll

This missile, which has the Soviet designation K-13A, has been seen under the wings of a variety of Soviet aircraft and is standard equipment on home and export versions of the MiG-21. It is almost identical to the first-generation American Sidewinder (AIM-9B) in size and configuration and appears to have a similar infra-red guidance system.

The body is cylindrical with cruciform control surfaces near the nose, indexed in line with the fixed cruciform tail-fins. There are no external cable or control conduits.

The triangular control surfaces have a compound sweep averaging about 60° on the leading-edge and 10° on the trailing-edge. They are linked in opposite pairs, with a maximum movement of 20-30°.

Leading-edge sweep on the tail-fins is about 40°, with straight trailing-edges. A small gyroscopically-controlled tab is inset in the trailing-edge of each fin, at the tip, presumably for anti-roll stabilisation but possibly with an added control function.

Nozzle diameter of the solid-propellant motor is 8 cm (3⅛ in). Weight and performance of 'Atoll' should be very similar to those of Sidewinder.

Data: See table

AA-2-2

NATO reporting name: Advanced Atoll

The latest multi-role versions of the MiG-21 ('Fishbed-J, K, L and N') carry a mix of standard infra-red 'Atolls' and a new version of this weapon with a radar homing head. For convenience, the radar version is known at present as 'Advanced Atoll'.

AA-3

NATO reporting name: Anab

First seen as underwing armament on the Yakovlev Yak-28P fighter ('Firebar') in the 1961 Soviet Aviation Day display, 'Anab' is a standard air-to-air missile in the Soviet Air Force. It was carried by Yak-28, Sukhoi Su-11 and Sukhoi Su-15 interceptors taking part in the 1967 air display at Domodedovo. All three types are fitted with the radar known to NATO as 'Skip Spin'.

'Anab' has a cylindrical body, with small cruciform canard control surfaces indexed in line with very large cruciform tail-fins. Both infra-red and I/J-band semi-active radar homing versions are operational, and have been built in thousands.

Data: See table

AA-5

NATO reporting name: Ash

'Ash' is the large air-to-air missile shown under the wings of Tupolev Tu-28P ('Fiddler') fighters in illustrations in the Aircraft section of this edition. It has cruciform wings and tail surfaces indexed in line, and is operational in two versions, which have infra-red and I/J-band semi-active radar homing heads respectively.

The radar fitted to the Tu-28P is known to NATO as 'Big Nose'. It has been suggested that the MiG-25 ('Foxbat-A') also carries 'Ash' as one of its alternative weapons. Several thousand of these missiles have been built.

Data: See table

AA-6

NATO reporting name: Acrid

This air-to-air missile was identified during 1975 as standard armament of the 'Foxbat-A' interceptor version of the MiG-25, which has fire control radar known to NATO as 'Fox Fire'. Its configuration is similar to that of 'Anab' but it is considerably larger. Photographs suggest that the version of 'Acrid' with an infra-red homing head is normally carried on each inboard underwing pylon, with a radar-homing version on each outer pylon. The latter is about 6·10 m (20 ft) long, with an estimated range of at least 20 nm (37 km; 23 miles). The wingtip fairings on the fighter, different in shape from those of 'Foxbat-B', are thought to house continuous-wave target illuminating equipment for the radar-homing missiles.

'Fox Fire' radar is believed to be evolved from the Tu-28P's 'Big Nose', with a detection range of 43-54 nm (80-100 km; 50-62 miles) and ability to track targets at 27 nm (50 km; 31 mile) range.

AA-7

NATO reporting name: Apex

This long-range air-to-air missile is one of two types of missile known to be carried as standard armament by interceptor versions of the MiG-23. No details are yet available, except that 'Apex' has a solid-propellant rocket motor and exists in two versions, with infra-red and semi-active radar homing heads, the latter operating in conjunction with the MiG-23's 'High Lark' fire control radar. 'Apex' is also reported to be an alternative weapon for the MiG-25.

Data: See table

AA-8

NATO reporting name: Aphid

Second type of air-to-air missile carried by the MiG-23, 'Aphid' is a close-range solid-propellant weapon with infra-red homing guidance.

The accompanying illustration suggests that it has a canard configuration, with small cruciform control surfaces immediately behind the hemispherical nose, indexed in line with the cruciform rear-mounted wings, which are similar in shape to those of 'Acrid'.

Data: See table

HELICOPTER MISSILES

AT-2

NATO reporting name: Swatter

No photographs of the Mil Mi-24 ('Hind-A and D') assault helicopter have yet shown missiles mounted on its wingtip launchers. However, there is no evidence to suggest that it carries wire-guided missiles. The only early Soviet anti-tank missile known to operate without wire guidance is 'Swatter', shown in surface-to-surface use in an accompanying illustration. Its employment on the Mi-24, and probably on the Ka-25 anti-submarine helicopter, was believed to be interim, pending availability of the new 'fire and forget' missile known in the West as the AS-8.

'Swatter' is controlled by elevons on the trailing-edges of its rear-mounted cruciform wings. The two small canard surfaces at the nose are also movable. The motor appears to exhaust through two vents diametrically opposed between the wings. Two more tubes, projecting rearward from opposite wings, probably house tracking flares. The blunt nose of 'Swatter' suggests the likelihood of a terminal homing system operating via the canard foreplanes.

Data: See table

AT-6

NATO reporting name: Spiral

New 'fire-and-forget' anti-tank missile carried by Mi-24 ('Hind-D') helicopter. Unconfirmed reports suggest that it is tube-launched, with a range of 3·75-5·3 nm (7-10 km; 4·3-6·2 miles), and homes on targets illuminated by a laser designator.

AIR-TO-SURFACE MISSILES

AS-2

NATO reporting name: Kipper

The missile carried by the Tu-16 ('Badger') in the 1961 Aviation Day display, and described as an anti-shipping weapon, has a conventional sweptwing aeroplane layout, with an underslung turbojet power plant. Radar is carried in the nose of the Tu-16 carrier aircraft, and guidance is believed to comprise initial beam-riding, subsequent pre-programmed flight under autopilot control, and infra-red terminal homing. A nuclear warhead can be fitted.

Data: See table

AS-3

NATO reporting name: Kangaroo

Largest of the air-to-surface missiles first seen in the Soviet Aviation Day display at Tushino in 1961, and known still to be operational in large numbers, was that carried by the Tu-95 ('Bear-B and C') and given the NATO reporting name 'Kangaroo'. It is a winged missile with an airframe similar in size and shape to a sweptwing turbojet-powered fighter aircraft. The tail unit is conventional, with sweepback on all surfaces. The vertical surfaces, concealed inside the launch aircraft until the missile is dropped, are of rhomboid form. A nuclear or high-explosive warhead can be fitted.

What was believed originally to be a radome on the missile's nose was identified subsequently as either a duct through which air can be fed to start the missile's turbojet engine prior to launching or a fairing over the air intake. Radar is carried in the nose of the Tu-95 launch aircraft and guidance is assumed to be by initial beam-riding and subsequent pre-programmed flight under autopilot control.

Data: See table

AS-4

NATO reporting name: Kitchen

The air-to-surface missile carried semi-submerged in the fuselage of the Tupolev Tu-22 ('Blinder') and variable-geometry Tu-26 ('Backfire-B'), and under the wings of the Tu-95 ('Bear'), looks considerably more advanced than the weapons already described. It has stubby delta wings and cruciform tail surfaces, and is believed to be powered by a liquid-propellant rocket engine. Guidance is reported to be inertial, with infra-red terminal homing. The speed of 'Kitchen' is probably high, and a choice of nuclear or high-explosive warhead can be assumed. About 1,000 are thought to have been delivered by 1976. More than one version is operational.

Data: See table

AS-5

NATO reporting name: Kelt

This air-to-surface missile, carried by the Tu-16 bomber, is externally similar to the earlier turbojet-powered 'Kennel' missile, which looked rather like a scaled-down unpiloted version of the MiG-15 fighter with a hemispherical radome above its air intake. On 'Kelt', both the ram-air intake and radome are replaced by a hemispherical nose fairing, probably housing a larger

'Anab' air-to-air missiles on a Yak-28P ('Firebar') fighter *(Flug Revue)*

Infra-red (left) and radar versions of 'Ash'

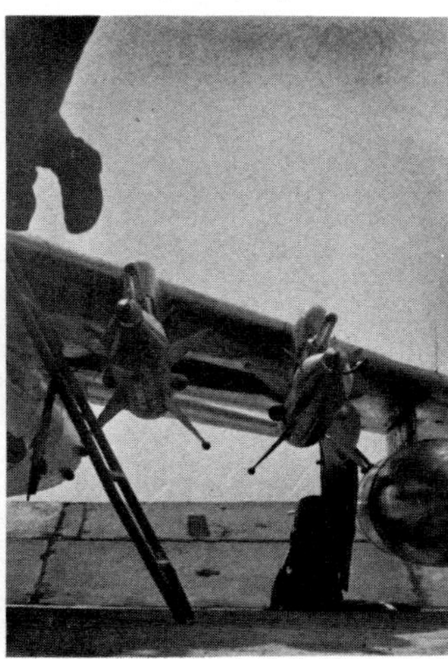

Two views of the missile known to NATO as 'Alkali' *(Tass)*

'Atoll' air-to-air missile under wing of Indian MiG-21

'Kingfish' missile carried by a Tu-16 *(JASDF)*

'Swatter' anti-tank missiles on BRDM vehicle. Missiles of this type are believed to arm Soviet helicopters *(Tass)*

radar. 'Kelt' is liquid-propellant rocket-powered and appears to be longer than 'Kennel'. Guidance is said to be by autopilot on a pre-programmed flight path, with radar terminal homing which can be switched from active to passive as required. Well over 1,000 'Kelts' are thought to have been delivered, with high-explosive warheads.

According to Israeli reports, about 25 'Kelts' were launched against Israeli targets by Tu-16s from Egypt during the Arab-Israeli War of October 1973. Twenty of the missiles were claimed as destroyed by the air and ground defences; the others hit two radar sites and a supply centre in Sinai.

DATA: See table

AS-6

NATO reporting name: Kingfish

First sighting of this formidable air-to-surface missile was by the pilot of a Japan Air Self-Defence Force F-86F in December 1977. When investigating a Tu-16 ('Badger') flying 43 nm (80 km; 50 miles) to the north of the Noto Peninsula, he was able to photograph the bomber, carrying a 'Kingfish' under its port wing. The missile has a cylindrical body with ogival nose, two short-span long-chord wings, and a cruciform tail unit with folding ventral fin. Propulsion is said to be by liquid-propellant rocket motor, with inertial midcourse guidance and active radar terminal homing, giving exceptional accuracy. Primary carrier is believed to be the Tu-26 ('Backfire').

DATA: See table

AS-7

NATO reporting name: Kerry

This tactical air-to-surface missile is reported to be carried by the Sukhoi Su-19 ('Fencer') fighter-bomber and other current Soviet close-support aircraft. It is said to have a radio command guidance system, to weigh about 1,200 kg (2,650 lb) and to have a range of 5·4 nm (10 km; 6·2 miles).

AS-8

AS-8 is believed to be the designation given in the West to the 'fire and forget' tactical missile that has been developed for the Mi-24 ('Hind-A and D') helicopter and will also arm a new Soviet lightweight attack helicopter now under development. Similar in concept to the US Hellfire, it is reported to have a max range of 4·3 nm (8 km; 5 miles) in its initial form, as delivered to Mi-24 units in 1977.

AS-X-9

A reported anti-radiation missile, with a range of 43-48 nm (80-90 km; 50-56 miles), to arm the Sukhoi Su-19 ('Fencer').

AS-X-10

Reported to be an electro-optical homing air-to-surface missile with a range of about 5·4 nm (10 km; 6·2 miles). A similar weapon, with a range of around 21·5 nm (40 km; 25 miles), is referred to in the USA as the Soviet

Launch of AS-2 ('Kipper') missile from a Tupolev Tu-16 ('Badger-C')

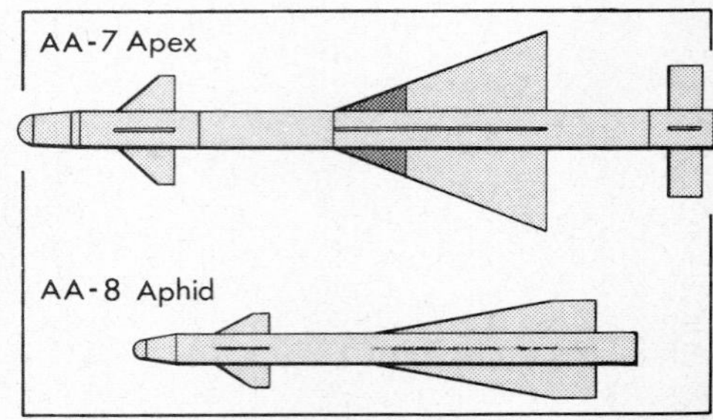

'Apex' and 'Aphid' missiles *(Michael A. Badrocke, with reference to data from Hasegawa Seisokusho Company)*

Advanced TASM (tactical air-to-surface missile) and is probably at a similar stage of development.

NEW MISSILE

US administration officials are reported to have said, on 1 February 1979, that the Soviet Union had begun to test a missile in the category of the USAF's ALCM. They claimed that at least eight missiles had been test-launched from Tu-26 ('Backfire') bombers during preceding months, over ranges of about 750 miles (650 nm; 1,200 km). This was said to be the first suggestion that the Soviet Union was testing long-range cruise missiles from its bombers.

The same US officials were quoted as saying that the maximum range of the new Soviet missile could be as much as 1,500 miles (1,300 nm; 2,400 km), but that it did not appear to have the high accuracy of the US ALCM designs or their ability to approach targets at tree-top heights.

UNITED KINGDOM

BAe

BRITISH AEROSPACE CORPORATION

CORPORATE HEADQUARTERS: Brooklands Road, Weybridge, Surrey KT13 0RN
Telephone: Weybridge (97) 45522
Telex: 27111

Dynamics Group

HEADQUARTERS: Six Hills Way, Stevenage, Herts SG1 2DA
Telephone: Stevenage (0438) 2422
Telex: 825125
CHAIRMAN AND CHIEF EXECUTIVE: G. R. Jefferson, CBE, BSc, CEng, MIMechE, FRAeS
GROUP DIRECTOR, AIR WEAPONS: L. G. Evans, MA, CEng, FRAeS
GROUP MARKETING DIRECTOR: L. A. Sanson, OBE
SECRETARY: M. W. Plimley, LLB
HEAD OF PUBLIC RELATIONS: M. K. Hird

Among weapons for which the Dynamics Group of British Aerospace is currently prime contractor are the Rapier and Seawolf surface-to-air missiles, the Sea Dart ship-to-air and ship-to-surface missile, and the Swingfire series of wire-guided anti-tank missiles; details of all of these can be found in *Jane's Weapon Systems.*

Production of the Martel long-range air-to-surface weapon jointly with SA Matra of France (see International section) has been completed, but the Dynamics Group of British Aerospace is developing a new air-launched sea-skimming missile, designated P3T, to replace Martel in the early 1980s. Development work on the SRAAM close-range air-to-air weapon (see 1977-78 edition) is restricted to a technology demonstration level. In full production is a medium-range all-weather air-to-air missile known as Sky Flash; the Sea Skua lightweight all-weather sea-skimming anti-ship missile is under development for service in the early 1980s.

Dynamics Group is the British 'daughter firm' for the Australian-developed Ikara long-range anti-submarine weapon for the Royal Navy. Other defence work includes development and manufacture of infra-red linescan systems which equip the Jaguar aircraft and the CL-89 surveillance RPV (see RPVs section).

SEA SKUA

This lightweight all-weather sea-skimming anti-ship missile is designed for operation from the Royal Navy's Lynx helicopter, to meet the threat from missile-firing fast patrol craft and to provide a good stand-off capability for the helicopter, with consequent protection from counter-attack. The complete helicopter-borne weapon system includes surveillance and tracking radar, fire control equipment, launching arrangements and up to four of the semi-active homing missiles. Main contractors are Dynamics Group of British Aerospace for the missile and fire control, Ferranti for the Seaspray radar, and Westland for the Lynx helicopter.

In addition to its ability to engage fast patrol boat targets, Sea Skua has a significant effectiveness against larger warships. It offers high lethality, with the capability of firing salvoes. The radar provides continuous surveillance, and includes facilities for weapon control and target identification.

Sea Skua is a quick-reaction system, at immediate readiness throughout the helicopter sortie, with a high degree of system reliability and full capability in a complex ECM environment. Wherever possible, it embodies existing, proven techniques and components. The solid-propellant boost and sustainer motor provides a high subsonic speed. Sea-skimming capability is conferred by a licence-built TRT radio altimeter, with Marconi Space and Defence Systems semi-active radar for terminal homing and a high-efficiency warhead actuated by a direct-action fuse. Simple go/no-go testing is all that is required on board ship before the missile is mounted on the helicopter.

The weapon system will enter service with the Royal Navy in the early 1980s and will be deployed widely on Lynx helicopters. It can be fitted to other medium-size helicopters and long-range maritime patrol aircraft.

DATA: See table

P3T

On 17 August 1977, Dr John Gilbert, UK Minister of State for Defence, announced that a sea-skimming anti-ship missile designated P3T was to be developed to replace Martel on RAF Buccaneer aircraft and to arm the interdictor/strike Tornado. It will be an active radar development of the present Martel (see 1978-79 *Jane's*), powered by a Microturbo TRI-60 turbojet engine instead of a rocket motor, for longer range. No other details are available; but the P3T is expected to enter service in the early 1980s and meets Royal Navy requirements for a missile to arm its Sea Harriers.

SABRE

Brief details of this lightweight air-to-surface missile, designed to meet the British AST 1227 requirement, became available at the 1978 Hanover Air Show. Based on the Rapier surface-to-air missile, Sabre would probably utilise a laser seeker developed by Martin Marietta, in conjunction with the Pave Spike target designation pod or the Atlis pod developed jointly by Thomson-CSF and Martin Marietta.

Unofficial sources have quoted a launching weight of 55 kg (120 lb) for Sabre, which is described as a supersonic all-weather weapon, able to manoeuvre at 25*g* and capable of penetrating the armour of a Soviet T-72 tank. A first-round kill probability of 80% is suggested, over a range of 2·7-3·2 nm (5-6 km; 3·1-3·7 miles) at low altitude. Aircraft for which it could provide primary armament include the Hawk and Alpha Jet.

SKY FLASH (XJ521)

Swedish Air Force designation: RB71

On 17 April 1973 Hawker Siddeley Dynamics (now British Aerospace Dynamics Group) announced that it had received a prime contract from the Ministry of Defence for project definition and pre-development studies of a new medium-range all-weather air-to-air missile based on the American AIM-7E Sparrow, which is itself in service with the RAF. Raytheon, the US Sparrow prime contractor, is participating in the programme through cross-licensing agreements with British Aerospace and Marconi Space and Defence Systems Ltd.

Project definition was completed in 1973, and it was announced on 26 February 1974 that Dynamics Group had received instructions from the Ministry of Defence to proceed with full development and initial production of the missile, now known as Sky Flash. A contract for full production was awarded in 1975, and aircraft to be armed with Sky Flash will include the RAF's Phantom and Tornado F.Mk 2. The first export contract, valued at £60 million, was announced in December 1978 and will provide Sky Flash missiles to arm the Swedish Air Force's Saab JA 37 Viggen all-weather fighter. Delivery of these will begin in mid-1980.

The 'boost and coast' Sky Flash has the same general configuration and dimensions as the Raytheon AIM-7E, but is fitted with a semi-active radar homing head of inverse monopulse design, developed by Marconi Space and Defence Systems under a Ministry of Defence contract. This has been designed as a completely self-contained unit with modular construction, which provides considerable flexibility in the overall design to cater for a wide range of different applications. Microstrip circuitry and the latest types of solid-state technology and micro-circuits have offered reliability, reduced size and high performance. The complete homing head is only 283 mm (11 in) long and can be fitted in any appropriate missile body of 180 mm (7 in) internal diameter.

The advanced radar proximity fuse is designed by EMI Electronics Ltd, and is claimed to offer a high single-shot kill capability against targets at high, medium and low altitudes. Dynamics Group has updated the autopilot and power systems, and is responsible for building the missile structure, as well as for assembly and test.

The successful completion of Sky Flash firing trials was announced in December 1977, by which time 22 missiles had been launched from US Navy F-4J Phantom aircraft over the Pacific Missile Test Center, California, in a variety of attack situations against targets representative of a range of hostile aircraft types. These included targets flying at subsonic and supersonic speeds, singly and in formation, and in severe ECM environments. Several missiles scored direct hits and others were classified as partial successes, simple remedial modifications being made to subsequent missiles. During the trials the snapdown capability of Sky Flash was demonstrated when a missile launched from medium altitude achieved a target 'kill' against an unaugmented QF-86 drone flying only 150 m (500 ft) above the ground. Aircraft from which Sky Flash has since been launched successfully include the General Dynamics F-16.

DATA: See table

UNITED STATES OF AMERICA

BOEING

BOEING AEROSPACE COMPANY

HEAD OFFICE AND WORKS: Seattle, Washington 98124

ALCM

USAF designation: AGM-86

The Air-Launched Cruise Missile (ALCM) is a small unmanned winged air vehicle capable of sustained subsonic flight following launch from an airborne carrier aircraft. It is propelled by a turbofan engine, incorporates a

The 'Badger-G' version of the Tupolev Tu-16, with two 'Kelt' missiles on underwing launchers

Two views of Tupolev Tu-95 ('Bear-B') with AS-3 ('Kangaroo') air-to-surface missile

Lynx HAS. Mk 2 of the Royal Navy, armed with Sea Skua missiles

Sky Flash medium-range all-weather air-to-air missiles

nuclear warhead, and is programmed to strike a predetermined surface target. Guidance is by a combination of inertial and terrain comparison (Tercom) techniques. In the terrain comparison mode the missile is kept on course by a computer which compares pre-programmed geographical features on its flight plan with the geography seen by its sensors during actual flight.

Boeing's AGM-86 ALCM design makes maximum use of the air vehicle developed under the former AGM-86A Subsonic Cruise Armed Decoy (SCAD) programme, for which Boeing was prime contractor.

When launched in large numbers, each of the missiles would have to be countered, making defence against them both difficult and costly. The missiles are intended to dilute defences and improve the ability of manned aircraft to penetrate to major targets. Small radar signature and low-level flight capability would enhance their effectiveness.

The ALCM is intended to have a nuclear warhead for 'hard target' kill capability, but is being considered also for decoy, reconnaissance and non-nuclear applications in Europe. In its initial form, designated **AGM-86A**, it was similar in overall dimensions to SRAM (short-range attack missile; see 1977-78 *Jane's*) and was suitable for carriage on the rotary launcher developed for this latter weapon, with wings and tail folded and engine air intake retracted. A B-52G was expected to carry 12 AGM-86As externally and 8 internally, complementing the aircraft's SRAMs and free-fall weapons. When carried externally, the missile was to have an underbelly auxiliary fuel tank fitted to increase its range.

Six test flights (three performance and three navigation/guidance) were conducted with AGM-86As between March and November 1976. Development is now centred on the **AGM-86B**. This has a fuselage more than 30% longer than that of the AGM-86A, to house sufficient fuel for double the range of the basic 'A'. On 1 February 1978, Boeing Aerospace received the first increment of a contract calling for a competitive fly-off between the AGM-86B and an air-launched version of the General Dynamics Tomahawk SLCM between June and November 1979. Department of Defense contracts funded a total of 24 Boeing/GD ALCMs in FY 1978, and a similar quantity in FY 1979, with a planned production purchase of 225 in FY 1980. A source selection decision is scheduled for January 1980, with an initial operational capability, comprising one squadron of B-52Gs externally loaded with ALCMs, by December 1982. Production of the winning ALCM is expected to total about 3,400.

Boeing Aerospace is responsible for the AGM-86B airframe, which differs in configuration from that of the Tomahawk. Williams Research Corporation supplied F107-WR-100 turbofan engines (2·67 kN; 600 lb st) for the advanced development phase ALCMs, with guidance by McDonnell Douglas. The first AGM-86B flight missile was scheduled for completion in Spring 1979.

Data: See table

FORD

FORD AEROSPACE & COMMUNICATIONS CORPORATION

Head Office: 20th Floor, 300 Renaissance Center, PO Box 43342, Detroit, Michigan 48243

Aeronutronic Division
Ford Road, Newport Beach, California 92663
Telephone: (714) 759 5996

Ford Aerospace & Communications Corporation, and its Philco predecessor, have produced Sidewinder air-to-air missiles and Chaparral surface-to-air missiles for the US armed services for many years. Details of the Sidewinder can be found under the NWC entry in this section.

GENERAL DYNAMICS

GENERAL DYNAMICS CORPORATION

HEAD OFFICE: Pierre Laclede Center, St Louis, Missouri 63105

Convair Division

5001 Kearny Villa Road, San Diego, California 92123

VICE-PRESIDENT AND GENERAL MANAGER: Dr Leonard F. Buchanan

Pomona Division

PO Box 2507, Pomona, California 91766

VICE-PRESIDENT AND GENERAL MANAGER: Ralph E. Hawes

The Pomona Division of General Dynamics is responsible for development and production of a wide variety of tactical weapon systems for the US Navy, US Army, US Air Force and friendly foreign powers. Current and recent products include the Standard Missile-1 naval ship-launched weapon, the Standard ARM anti-radiation missile, the Stinger advanced man-portable air defence weapon, and Phalanx, the Navy's all-weather automatic gun fire-control system. In pilot production is the longer-range Standard Missile-2.

In addition, the US Naval Air Systems Command has awarded a contract to Pomona for second-source production of the AIM-7F Sparrow air-to-air missile (see Raytheon entry).

Convair Division was selected in 1976 to develop the US Navy's Sea Launched Cruise Missile, under the designation BGM-109 Tomahawk. Variants are the USAF's Ground Launched Cruise Missile and the Tomahawk Air Launched Cruise Missile.

STANDARD ARM

US Navy designations: AGM-78 and RGM-66D

Production of this air-launched anti-radar missile has ended, although Standard ARM remains an important item in the USN and USAF inventories. Details can be found in the 1978-79 *Jane's*.

TOMAHAWK

USAF designation: AGM-109

On 17 March 1976, the US Secretary of the Navy announced that Convair Division of General Dynamics had been selected as prime contractor for the Navy's Sea Launched Cruise Missile (SLCM), which had been named Tomahawk. The contract, funded at $34·8 million, called for a flight of the first prototype missile in April 1976. The guidance systems, under development by McDonnell Douglas Astronautics Company—East, were to be integrated into the prototype, and flown as a complete weapon system in the early Autumn of 1976. Development has continued, and a mid-1980s IOC would be practicable if the Navy required the weapon.

General Dynamics is also developing the AGM-109 Air Launched Cruise Missile (ALCM), a variant of Tomahawk, for USAF Strategic Air Command, in competition with Boeing's AGM-86B. Like the latter (which see), the AGM-109 can be carried internally or externally on wing pylons, on B-52G bombers. Its planned mission is to provide additional targeting coverage and flexibility for penetrating bomber forces, by stressing enemy defences and reducing bomber exposure to the defences.

Another variant of Tomahawk, known as the Ground Launched Cruise Missile (GLCM), is being developed by General Dynamics for USAF's Tactical Air Command. This will provide an accurate all-weather theatre nuclear weapon system for deployment in highly-mobile form, and is intended to reach an IOC by the mid-1980s.

For its various applications, the Tomahawk missile is being developed in two basic forms, as follows:

Land Attack. Designed for use over ranges of more than 1,500 nm, this version has a McDonnell Douglas inertial navigation system with Terrain Contour Matching (Tercom). For launch from submarines, surface ships and land platforms, it is powered by an Atlantic Research Corporation solid-propellant booster motor, in the 31·1 kN (7,000 lb) thrust class, and a Williams Research Corporation F107-WR-400 cruise turbofan rated at 2·67 kN (600 lb st). The boost motor is not fitted for air-to-surface launch from strategic aircraft. This version has a nuclear warhead, and is intended to fly at low altitudes in all weathers.

The first fully guided land attack trial was conducted at White Sands Missile Range, New Mexico, on 5 June 1976. Tercom terrain avoidance capability was first used on 16 July 1976. The first demonstration of a land attack mission over a simulated target was made on 30 September 1976. A Tomahawk equipped with a dual-mode guidance system first demonstrated its precision accuracy against a simulated ground target on 31 January 1977.

Ship attack. Intended for use over ranges of more than 300 nm, this version differs from the land attack version basically in having a non-nuclear warhead, reduced fuel, and a modified form of the McDonnell Douglas guidance system fitted to the Harpoon missile.

The airframe is basically common to both the land attack and ship attack versions, with a cylindrical torpedo-shape body made of aluminium, tapering at the tail. Two narrow-chord wings are positioned approximately midway between the nose and tail. In the submarine-launched Tomahawk, the wings fold inside the body when the missile is in its submarine launch capsule and extend forward for cruising flight in the atmosphere. Cruciform folding tail surfaces are indexed in line with the wings. The ventral air intake for the cruise engine is retractable. Design emphasis is on low radar cross-section and minimum visual and infra-red signatures.

First air launch of an anti-ship Tomahawk was made from beneath the wing of a US Navy A-6 Intruder, at the Pacific Missile Test Center, on 29 March 1976. On 14 October 1976 a Tomahawk performed climb and descent manoeuvres during flight over the Pacific Ocean. Long-range over-the-horizon capability to search for and locate a target at sea was demonstrated on 7 December 1976.

A free-fall launch and mid-air engine start were made on 15 November 1976. On 24 February 1977, transition from boosted flight to cruising flight after the first launch from a land base was completed successfully. A series of survivability assessment flight tests was underway in early 1978. Competitive fly-off trials against the Boeing AGM-86B were to take place between June and November 1979. A source selection decision will be made in January 1980, permitting initial operational capability of the selected missile by December 1982.

Tomahawk development rounds are equipped with a parachute recovery system, enabling them to be refurbished and re-used.

DATA: See table

HUGHES

HUGHES AIRCRAFT COMPANY

CORPORATE OFFICE: Culver City, California 90230

CHAIRMAN OF THE BOARD AND CHIEF EXECUTIVE OFFICER: Dr Allen E. Puckett

PRESIDENT: John H. Richardson

Missile Systems Group

Canoga Park, California 91304

Telephone: (213) 883 2400

VICE-PRESIDENT AND GROUP EXECUTIVE: Dr Malcolm R. Currie

Electro-Optical & Data Systems Group

Culver City, California 90230

VICE-PRESIDENT AND GROUP EXECUTIVE: H. W. Boehmer

Hughes Aircraft began developing an air-to-air missile for the USAF in 1950, and this weapon has been in squadron use for many years as the Falcon. Currently, Hughes is producing an air-to-air missile named Phoenix for the US Navy, an air-to-surface missile named Maverick for the USAF, and a wire-guided anti-tank missile named TOW for the US Army and other customers. It is also engaged in prototype validation of an advanced medium-range air-to-air missile (AMRAAM).

PHOENIX

US Navy designation: AIM-54

Phoenix arms the Grumman F-14A Tomcat two-seat carrier-based fighter and is claimed to have capabilities exceeding those of any other air-to-air missile yet operational. It has a solid-propellant rocket motor, and is fitted with a large proximity-fused high-explosive warhead.

The launch aircraft's AWG-9 weapon control system is able to track an enemy aircraft, surface-launched cruise missile or air-to-surface missile, at high or low altitude, in any kind of weather, and launch the Phoenix missile. The data from the radar is processed by a solid-state, high-speed general-purpose digital computer, the output of which is displayed to the missile control officer in the launch aircraft on two displays: a 254 mm (10 in) cathode-ray tube and a 127 mm (5 in) multi-mode storage tube. The long-range high-power pulse Doppler radar has a planar array antenna, providing a 'look-down' capability that enables it to pick out moving targets from the ground clutter that normally obscures them on a conventional radar. The AWG-9 has a track-while-scan radar mode that makes it possible to launch up to six missiles and keep them on course while searching for other possible targets, all in the presence of sophisticated enemy countermeasures.

The first AWG-9 configured for the F-14A fighter was delivered to the US Navy in February 1970. Extensive use of hybrid circuits and new packaging techniques had enabled its weight to be reduced to less than 600 kg (1,320 lb), compared with 770 kg (1,700 lb) for earlier versions. The addition of air combat manoeuvre modes provided improved 'dogfight' capability, and the AWG-9 is able to launch other naval air-to-air weapons, including Sparrow 7E/7F and Sidewinder missiles, as well as Phoenix. It can also direct the firing of the M61 Vulcan 20 mm cannon.

Contractor testing was concluded on 13 June 1973 with a launch from an F-14A against a BQM-34E Firebee target II over a record range of 110 nm (204 km; 126 miles). The drone, augmented by radar signal to look as large as a bomber and equipped with an on/off blinking noise jammer, approached at an altitude of 15,850 m (52,000 ft) and speed of Mach 1·55. The F-14A, flying at 13,700 m (45,000 ft) and Mach 1·45, began tracking the Firebee at very long range and launched a single Phoenix at 110 nm. During flight, the Phoenix reached a high point in its trajectory of more than 30,500 m (100,000 ft) and then passed the drone within the lethal distance of its warhead.

Of the 56 Phoenix missiles launched from various aircraft during contractor tests, 43 were scored as hits. The success rate for the 17 missiles launched from the F-14A was 88%.

Effectiveness of Phoenix against low-flying anti-ship cruise missiles was demonstrated in August 1974, when the crew of a US Navy F-14 launched a Phoenix from a range of 19 nm (35 km; 22 miles) against a BQM-34 drone flying only 15 m (50 ft) above the sea to simulate such a missile. The unarmed Phoenix homed on the target and scored a hit by passing within the lethal distance of the warhead that is fitted to operational rounds. Subsequent testing by the contractor and fleet squadrons maintained an 85% firing success rate in more than 120 firings.

All F-14s built for the US Navy and Iranian Air Force are equipped to carry Phoenix. Production was initiated in late 1970, and continued missile purchases are envisaged up to 1986.

Phoenix entered first-line service in September 1974, when two squadrons of US Navy F-14s were deployed on board the nuclear-powered USS *Enterprise* for a six-month tour of duty in the Western Pacific. Six US carriers were operating F-14 fighter squadrons in 1978.

There are two versions of Phoenix, as follows:

AIM-54A. Initial production version, to which all details above apply. More than 2,000 had been built by the beginning of 1979, with manufacture of 210 approved for FY 1979 and budget requests for 180 for the US Navy in FY 1980.

AIM-54C. Improved version, with much enhanced ECCM capability and reliability. New target detecting device, digital electronics unit and autopilot, and solid-state transmitter/receiver. Fifteen engineering development models ordered. Scheduled to enter production in January 1982.

DATA: See table

AMRAAM

On 5 February 1979, the USAF announced that it had selected Hughes Aircraft Company's Missile Systems Group and Raytheon Company's Missile Systems Division to begin prototype validation on an advanced medium-range air-to-air missile (AMRAAM). This weapon is intended to replace the AIM-7 Sparrow in USAF and US Navy service, as primary armament of the F-14, F-15, F-16 and F/A-18 fighters.

The AMRAAM programme was initiated by a 13-month USAF/USN/USMC study of the likely air-to-air threat for the next 30 years, and the kind of beyond-visual-range weapon that would best meet such a threat.

Basic parameters laid down by the AMRAAM Joint System Program Office included an upper weight limit of about 160 kg (350 lb), with 90 kg (200 lb) as the desirable goal; all-weather capability; snapdown capability to permit interception of low-flying targets over land or sea; a resistance to ECM at least as good as that offered by current monopulse techniques; all-aspect launch and tracking ability; a minimum range at least equal to that of the AIM-7F Sparrow and a maximum range as great as the state of the art permits. These requirements seemed likely to demand inertial midcourse guidance and self-contained terminal homing such as active radar; however, it seemed likely that a missile with these features would appproach its target so closely that a conventional proximity-fused warhead weighing only 14-22 kg (30-50 lb) would be adequate.

No details of Hughes' AMRAAM missile have been released, but its general appearance is shown in the accompanying photograph of a full-scale model mounted on an F-15 fuselage station. Hughes claims that it will outperform the Sparrow, cost less to build and be one half as heavy as the earlier weapon. Its version of AMRAAM will offer maximum independence of the launching aircraft, and will enable the pilot to make launches against multiple targets with no changes in current cockpit procedures.

The AMRAAM validation phase is expected to last 33 months, after which the winning design will be taken through full-scale engineering development into production.

TOW

US Army designation: BGM-71A

Hughes Aircraft was prime contractor for development of this high-performance surface-to-surface and air-to-surface anti-tank missile, the basic characteristics of which are indicated by its name, as TOW is an acronym for Tube-launched, Optically-tracked, Wire-guided.

The basic ground-fired TOW system consists of a glassfibre launch tube, a tripod, a traversing and sighting unit, an electronic package, and missiles encased in shipping containers. Total weight of the entire weapon system, including missile, is approximately 91 kg (200 lb).

The missile has low aspect ratio wings and tail control surfaces that remain folded while in the launcher and flick

Full-scale model of the Boeing AGM-86B air-launched cruise missile

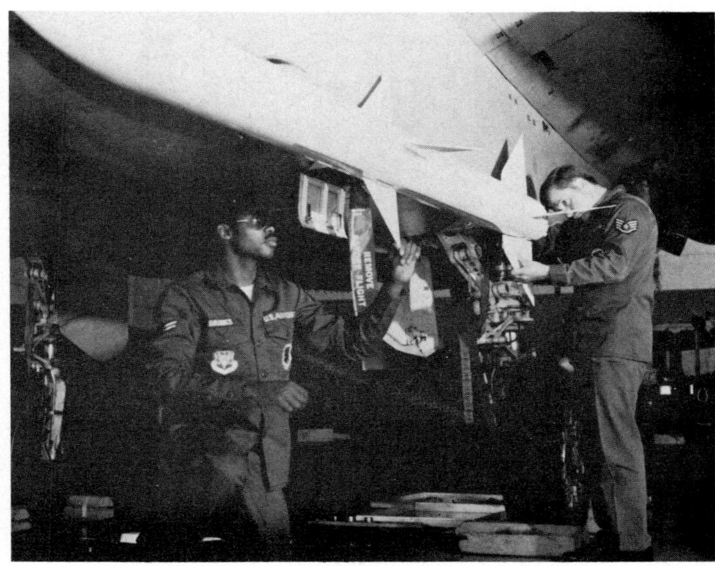

Model of Hughes' AMRAAM on F-15 fuselage station

Tomahawk under the wing of an A-6 Intruder test aircraft

The first fully guided Tomahawk flight after launch from an A-6 aircraft

Assembling the long-chord wings of an AIM-54A Phoenix air-to-air missile

BGM-71A TOW missile undergoing final inspection

Production line of AGM-65A Maverick TV-guided missiles

Planar wing version of GBU-15 glide bomb, with wings stowed, on B-52

open as the missile leaves the launch tube. The wings flick forward during extension, the tail surfaces rearward.

TOW is inserted into the rear end of the tube in its container, which forms an extension of the tube. Electrical and mechanical connections to the missile are made automatically during this operation. The Hercules K-41 solid-propellant motor gives two separate boost periods. It fires first to propel the missile from the launcher. The missile then coasts for a period after leaving the mouth of the tube, before the second stage of the booster fires.

The operator guides the missile by keeping the target centred in a telescopic sight. Movement of the sight generates electronic signals to correct the missile's course, the signals being passed through two wires. The warhead is a high-explosive shaped charge, developed under the Army Munitions Command, Picatinny Arsenal, New Jersey.

In its current form, TOW is a heavy assault weapon for use against tanks, armoured vehicles and gun emplacements over ranges of more than 3,750 m (12,300 ft). To permit its use from helicopters, Hughes developed under US Army contract a gyro-stabilised sight that would eliminate the effects of aircraft vibration and manoeuvres. As part of the XM-26 missile/launcher/sight subsystem, this was installed on a UH-1B helicopter, from which air-to-surface firing tests of TOW missiles were then made successfully at Redstone Arsenal, Alabama, with hits on moving tank targets over ranges of more than one mile.

Two UH-1Bs with early-model Hughes XM-26 sighting systems were shipped to Viet-Nam on 24 April 1972. After a short training period, during which each pilot-gunner fired one TOW missile for the first time, the aircraft were committed at Kontum to meet an expected armour threat. By 27 June, in 77 combat launches, they had scored 62 hits on point targets and had destroyed 39 armoured vehicles, trucks and howitzers, without themselves being hit by hostile fire.

As a result of these successes, the US Army embarked on a programme to convert AH-1G HueyCobras to AH-1Q/S Cobra/TOW standard, with improved M65 missile system. In addition, TOW arms helicopters of various types selected by foreign services, including the Hughes 500M-D Defenders of South Korea, Italy's Agusta A 109, AH-1Js supplied to Iran, and the British Army Lynx.

TOW has been in production for the US Army since 29 November 1968. By the beginning of 1979 a total of 220,000 missiles had been delivered from Hughes' factory at Tucson, Arizona, with production continuing at a rate of about 3,000 a month. Deployment to US troops in the USA and Europe began in November 1970, to replace the 106 mm recoilless rifle and the Entac and SS.11 missiles. Subsequently, TOW was ordered by 25 other countries. In more than 10,500 firings, including combat, TOW has demonstrated an operational reliability better than 96%, and 83% of the missiles have hit their target.

DATA: See table

MAVERICK

USAF designation: AGM-65

The Maverick is a precision-guided air-to-surface missile in the 500 lb class, which developed from a 1965 USAF concept. Following a competitive contract definition phase, Hughes received a $99 million fixed-price incentive contract to cover development, test and evaluation of the missile over a three-year period, starting in July 1968. The first unguided airborne launch took place at Edwards AFB, California, on 15 September 1969. In the first guided launch, at Holloman AFB, New Mexico, on 18 December 1969, the missile scored a direct hit on a stationary M-41 tank in a diving attack over medium range. Since then, more than 600 Mavericks have been fired during the development programme and in combat, with an overall record of 88% direct hits on their targets.

Production was initiated in mid-1971, and the USAF formally accepted the first production Maverick on 30 August 1972. More than 26,000 had been delivered by the beginning of 1979, and Maverick is operational on the A-7D, A-10A, F-4D/E and F-5E/F. In 1978 Maverick was being integrated on the F-111, F-16 and A-4M, and plans call for integration on the A-6E and AV-8B. It has been possible to adapt existing controls and displays in launch aircraft to operation of the Maverick weapon system. The minimum aircraft requirement is a raster-scan TV-type display in the cockpit and conventional control functions. A single-rail launcher has been developed for wing stations which cannot accommodate the standard three-round launcher.

In October 1973, Mavericks were used operationally by the Israeli Air Force during the Yom Kippur War, with spectacular success. Others have been delivered to Iran, Saudi Arabia, Sweden and Turkey, and were to be procured by Greece and South Korea during 1978. Sweden is integrating Maverick with the AJ37 version of the Viggen.

Two TV-guided versions were produced in quantity:

AGM-65A. Basic model with 5° field of view camera in the seeker, centroid tracker and single-stage solid-propellant boost/sustain rocket motor. Warhead in central portion of airframe. When triggered by contact fuse in the nose, a shaped-charge jet fires through the axis of the guidance unit into the target. First employed by USAF in Viet-Nam and the only version of Maverick yet made available to friendly foreign nations. Production terminated in favour of AGM-65B.

AGM-65B. 'Scene magnification' version of TV Maverick, with 2·5° field of view camera and associated minor changes to the guidance equations. Generally similar to AGM-65A, with same warhead. The USAF was training with this version in early 1978. Manufacture of 6,000 completed.

Missile reliability obviates the need for a missile check on aircraft, and operational use is in the 'fire and forget' mode. The pilot can slew the seeker for rapid lock-on to the target, using a TV visual display, launch the missile and immediately take evasive action while the missile guides itself to the target. Simplicity of operation was demonstrated by a successful firing from a Teledyne Ryan BGM-34 RPV.

Two further versions of Maverick are under development:

AGM-65C. Fitted with a Rockwell laser seeker which homes on a target illuminated by a ground or airborne laser designator. Can be used by day or night, as the pilot of the launch aircraft does not need to acquire the target visually. Provision is made for rendering the warhead inert, to protect friendly troops in the event of a designator failure or other loss of lock-on during close-support missions. Seventeen-month contractor testing, completed in Summer 1978, involved 15 launches against moving and stationary tanks, armoured personnel carriers and simulated bunkers, by day and night, from high and low altitudes, at various ranges and at speeds from slow to supersonic. Success rate exceeded 92% direct hits, with 12 targets illuminated by ground designators and 3 by designators on tactical aircraft. Near completion of engineering development in 1979, and undergoing flight tests for US Navy and Marine Corps utilisation.

AGM-65D. Has imaging infra-red (IIR) seeker, which tracks passively the natural thermal image of a tactical target, providing a pictorial display of the target to the pilot in darkness, haze and smoke. Lock-on, launch and 'fire and forget' homing flight as for AGM-65A/B. Full-scale engineering development started October 1978.

The basic shaped-charge warhead is designed to defeat heavy armour and reinforced concrete, making it most suitable for use against tanks and pillbox-type targets. An alternative blast/penetrator warhead is being developed to extend Maverick's capability against larger targets. This 300 lb class warhead will be employed first in the AGM-65C but is compatible with all versions of Maverick.

DATA: See table

GBU-15

Hughes Aircraft Company is responsible for developing the wing module and digital autopilot for the planar wing version of the US Air Force's GBU-15 air-to-surface glide bomb family, and for system integration.

The planar wing weapon (PWW), which is 4·04 m (13 ft 3 in) long, has 3·45 m (11 ft 4 in) span pivoted wings which extend after launch to increase its range. This enables the pilot of the launch aircraft to stand off at a safe distance while guiding the weapon accurately to the target. Its launching weight is 1,360 kg (3,000 lb).

The initial PWW is based on an MK 84 2,000 lb general-purpose bomb, with added TV guidance seeker and data link. It is planned eventually to deploy with Tactical Air Command a DME-guided PWW, which will be used in conjunction with the Lockheed U-2R Precision Location Strike System (PLSS) for all-weather area target attack. In this application, both the DME PWW and its target will be located in an electronic grid, and a ground-based computer will supply guidance commands to the weapon through the DME data link.

The GBU-15 series of weapons is described in more detail under the Rockwell International entry in this section. Flight testing of the planar wing version was continuing in 1979.

MDAC

MCDONNELL DOUGLAS ASTRONAUTICS COMPANY (A Division of McDonnell Douglas Corporation)

5301 Bolsa Avenue, Huntington Beach, California 92647
Telephone: (714) 896 3311
PRESIDENT: Robert L. Johnson
EXECUTIVE VICE-PRESIDENT: Ben G. Bromberg
VICE-PRESIDENT, ENGINEERING: Adrian P. O'Neal
VICE-PRESIDENT, MARKETING: Paul L. Smith

McDonnell Douglas Astronautics Company-St Louis

Box 516, St Louis, Missouri 63166
Telephone: (314) 232 0232
VICE-PRESIDENT AND GENERAL MANAGER: Erwin F. Branahl
VICE-PRESIDENT AND PROGRAMME MANAGER, HARPOON: Clifford D. Marks
VICE-PRESIDENT, ADVANCED MISSILE PROGRAMMES: R. Wayne Lowe

McDonnell Douglas Astronautics Company was formed on 26 June 1968, by merging the former Douglas Missile and Space Systems Division and the McDonnell Astronautics Company into a single management structure.

In the missile field, McDonnell Douglas Astronautics Company has developed and is producing the Harpoon anti-shipping missile for the US Navy and other customers, and is developing the Tomahawk cruise missile guidance system for the US Navy.

HARPOON

US Navy designations: AGM-84A and RGM-84A

The US Navy selected McDonnell Douglas as prime contractor for development of the Harpoon all-weather anti-ship missile in June 1971. The work was allocated to McDonnell Douglas Astronautics Company-East, with Texas Instruments Inc and Sperry Systems Management as major subcontractors.

The initial contract covered the development and demonstration of a number of engineering-model missiles over a two-year period. This phase of the programme was completed successfully on schedule, and was followed by a 30-month final development phase in which more than 30 missiles were launched from Harpoon-designated aircraft, ships and submarines. Production of 100 pilot missiles was authorised in 1974. A proportion of them was used for operational evaluation, which began in November 1975 and was completed in February 1977. The go-ahead for initial production had been given in July 1975, and authorisation for deployment on aircraft, surface ships and submarines was granted in July 1977.

The US Navy plans to equip all of its guided missile cruisers, guided missile destroyers, FF-1052 frigates, FFG-7 patrol frigates, DD-963 ASW destroyers and PHM-1 hydrofoil patrol craft; P-3C, A-6E and S-3A aircraft; and 594, 637, 688 and 700 class nuclear attack submarines with the Harpoon Weapon System (HWS). In addition the HWS has been procured by 12 allied nations for launch from surface ships, submarines and aircraft. More than 1,700 missiles are on order to supply these requirements, and production will continue until at least 1986.

The general configuration of the **AGM-84A** air-launched version of Harpoon is shown in the accompanying illustration. The Teledyne CAE J402-CA-400 turbojet power plant is housed in the rear of the body, with a ventral flush air intake.

Prior to launch, targeting data for Harpoon are provided by the command and launch subsystem, which interfaces with onboard systems. The Harpoon data processor, a general-purpose digital computer, receives targeting and attitude data from existing systems, and computes the necessary missile and launcher orders. After launch, guidance is provided by a midcourse guidance system consisting of a strapdown attitude reference assembly and digital computer. No inputs from the launch platform are required by the missile after launch. Cruise altitude is monitored by a radar altimeter, enabling the flight to the target to be made at low altitude, so offering both optimum target acquisition capability through reduction of clutter effects, and the ability to penetrate enemy defences. Offset launch capability is provided for all launch modes.

When the target comes within the search area of the active radar seeker, the high-resolution system detects and locks on to the target, even in rain and high sea states. Seeker lock-on is maintained until impact. Capability to perform high-*g* manoeuvres throughout flight permits successful operation against fast manoeuvring targets. A terminal 'pop-up' manoeuvre counters close-in defences and offers maximum warhead effectiveness. Counter-countermeasures devices are installed. The warhead is a penetration/high-explosive blast type.

DATA: See table

ASALM

Under USAF contracts dating back to June 1974, McDonnell Douglas and Martin Marietta are engaged on technology integration and flight dynamics development studies for an Advanced Strategic Air-Launched Missile (ASALM), in order to provide a technology base to meet future requirements for bomber penetration aids.

ASALM is conceived as a supersonic, highly-accurate, long-range missile, powered by an integral rocket/ramjet and capable of use in both air-to-surface and air-to-air bomber defence roles, including the destruction of enemy AWACS aircraft. Enemy defensive capabilities are those projected to be operational in the late 1980s, and ASALM was required to be compatible with the B-52 and FB-111 strategic bombers, carried internally on a rotary launcher or externally on wing pylons. It is intended to have a sophisticated guidance system, low radar and infra-red signatures, a nuclear warhead and sustained high-*g* manoeuvre capability.

Further contracts, covering design and ground testing of ASALM propulsion systems, have been awarded to the Marquardt Company and Chemical Systems Division of

Grumman A-6 Intruder carrying two Harpoons on underwing pylons

Artist's impression of McDonnell Douglas ASALM (Advanced Strategic Air-Launched Missile)

AIM-9H Sidewinder on McDonnell F-4 Phantom II

AGM-84A Harpoon air-to-surface anti-shipping missile

Sparrow (lower) and Sidewinder (upper, with protective nosecap) missiles on an F-14A Tomcat fighter of the US Navy *(Brian M. Service)*

AIM-9L advanced version of Sidewinder on US Navy F-4

UTC. The results of this aspect of the programme are expected to be generally applicable to other projects, including air-launched tactical missiles, surface-launched defensive missiles and a variety of air-to-air missiles.

The type of propulsion system proposed involves both solid rocket and liquid fuel ramjet technology. It will operate as a solid rocket booster until it reaches supersonic speeds. At that point, through a series of mechanical changes that take place in flight, it will become a ramjet. These changes entail the opening of air-inlets, nozzle changes and a switch to the burning of liquid fuel and air in the combustion chamber within a common system. Prior to the development of this concept, a ramjet required an external solid rocket booster to propel it to its supersonic velocity. The spent booster was then jettisoned.

NWC
NAVAL WEAPONS CENTER

China Lake, California 93555
Telephone: (714) 939 3555

The Naval Weapons Center is located 250 km (155 miles) northeast of Los Angeles, on the Mojave Desert. Its mission is to conduct a programme of warfare analysis, research, development, test, evaluation, systems integration and fleet engineering support in naval weapons systems, principally for air warfare, and to conduct investigations into related fields of science and technology. Weapons developed at the Center have included the Mighty Mouse 2·75 in folding-fin aircraft rocket, the 11·75 in Tiny Tim rocket, the Zuni 5 in folding-fin aircraft rocket, the Sidewinder air-to-air guided missile, the Snakeye 250/500 lb bomb with folding dive-brake retardation system to avoid fragmentation damage to the launch aircraft during low-level strikes, the Shrike and Standard ARM air-to-surface anti-radar missiles and the Walleye glide bomb. Production of many of these weapons was entrusted to commercial companies under whose entries they are, or were, described in *Jane's*.

SIDEWINDER

US military designation: AIM-9

The **AIM-9A** prototype version of the Sidewinder air-to-air missile was developed by the NWC and was first fired successfully on 11 September 1953. The **AIM-9B** first-generation production version was manufactured by Philco (now Ford Aerospace & Communications Corporation) and General Electric for the US Navy and the USAF, with a Naval Propellant Plant solid-propellant rocket motor and infra-red seeker, and was supplied to many foreign services. Production in the USA, from 1955, totalled more than 80,000 AIM-9Bs.

Although the US services no longer deploy the AIM-9B and its semi-active radar counterpart, the **AIM-9C**, other countries continue to utilise the 'B', of which licence manufacture was undertaken in Germany by Bodenseewerk, in association with subcontractors in the Netherlands, Denmark, Norway, Greece, Portugal and Turkey.

Also no longer deployed is the **AIM-9D**, which had higher speed and greater range than the 'B', from which it could be distinguished by its tapering nose, longer-chord nose fins and greater sweepback on the tail fins. This version had a Rocketdyne Mk 36 Mod 5 solid-propellant rocket motor, different guidance unit and continuous-rod warhead with proximity and impact fuses.

Of the developed versions of the infra-red homing Sidewinder produced for air-to-air use, to enhance and update the missile's capabilities, those in service with, or in production for, the US services in 1978 were as follows:

AIM-9E. Approximately 5,000 of this version were produced by Philco for the USAF, by modification of AIM-9Bs to have a new seeker section, Thiokol Mk 17 solid-propellant motor, refurbished electronics and wiring. Major increase in capability claimed. Production completed.

AIM-9G. Similar to AIM-9D but with off-boresight target acquisition and lock-on. Lead bias function moves missile impact point forward to a more vulnerable area on the target aircraft. Production by Raytheon for US Navy completed in FY 1970.

AIM-9H. Version for US Navy with improved close-range 'dogfight' capability. Basically similar to AIM-9G, but with solid-state guidance instead of vacuum tube electronics for improved reliability and maintainability, decreased minimum ranges and faster angle tracking rates. Production completed.

AIM-9J. Conversion of AIM-9Bs and 9Es, with new 'front end' to enhance 'dogfight' capability by improved manoeuvring ability. About 14,000 modified for USAF by Ford Aerospace to equip the F-15 Eagle and other types. Deliveries began in 1977 and have been completed.

AIM-9L. Third-generation version of Sidewinder. Rocketdyne/Bermite Mk 36 Mod 6 solid-propellant motor. Double-delta nose fins for improved inner boundary performance and better manoeuvrability. AM-FM conical scan for increased seeker sensitivity and improved tracking stability. Rate bias and active optical fuse for increased lethality and low susceptibility to countermeasures. Annular blast fragmentation warhead. Series of 20 joint service technical evaluation firings completed on 1 March 1975, including successful firings against PQM-102 targets, and with particular emphasis on difficult shots on the beam or forward quarter of the target. Planned procurement between FY 1976 and FY 1980 totals 3,550 for US Navy and more than 5,000 for the USAF (to arm the F-15 and F-16). Eventual total for the two services is expected to be 14,950. In FY 1976, Raytheon was contracted to deliver 1,300 AIM-9Ls and Ford Aerospace the remaining 210 missiles to qualify them for full production. Total of 2,900 provided under FY 1978 budget and 3,150 in FY 1979, with a further 2,370 requested in FY 1980 and 1,120 proposed for FY 1981. The AIM-9L was chosen in August 1977 to arm Phantom and Tornado F.Mk 2 aircraft of the Royal Air Force and Sea Harriers of the Royal Navy. It will also be deployed on Viggens of the Swedish Air Force.

AIM-9N. Version of AIM-9P for Foreign Military Sales.

AIM-9P. Improved version of AIM-9J produced by Ford Aerospace for USAF. Increased lethality due to fuse improvements. Reduced-smoke rocket motor.

Versions of Sidewinder under development in 1978 for proposed air-to-air use were as follows:

AIM-9J+ (J-3). Further improvement of AIM-9J, under development for USAF by Ford Aerospace. Increased target acquisition envelope, solid-state electronics and increased lethality due to fuse improvements. Proposed production by conversion of existing AIM-9Es and 9Js.

AIM-9M. Variant of AIM-9L with new closed-circuit IR cooling unit claimed to be less costly, easier to service and more effective than the open-cycle gas unit used in earlier versions. Under development for US Navy and USAF. Increased ECCM capability, improved background discrimination, reduced-smoke rocket motor. First batch of 42 units ordered from Hughes Aircraft by US Navy in 1978.

DATA: See table

RAYTHEON
RAYTHEON COMPANY

141 Spring Street, Lexington, Massachusetts 02173
Telephone: (617) 862 6600
Telex: 92-3455
CHAIRMAN OF THE BOARD AND CHIEF EXECUTIVE OFFICER: Thomas L. Phillips
PRESIDENT: D. Brainerd Holmes

Raytheon Company is prime contractor for the US Army's Patriot and Improved Hawk surface-to-air missile systems, and the US Navy/USAF Sparrow air-to-air missile. It produces the Dragon anti-tank missile for the US armed services, and versions of the US Navy/USAF Sidewinder air-to-air missile (described under NWC heading), and is the major subcontractor on the US Navy's Aegis advanced surface missile system.

Raytheon Company's Equipment Division is prime contractor for the NATO Sea Sparrow system, under development for the US Navy, the Royal Norwegian Navy, the Royal Danish Navy, the Royal Netherlands Navy, the Royal Belgian Navy and the Italian Navy.

SPARROW

US military designations: AIM-7 and RIM-7H

The AIM-7 Sparrow, developed by Raytheon Company for the US Naval Air Systems Command, is a radar-homing air-to-air missile with all-weather all-altitude operational capability. It can also be used against shipping targets from aircraft or ships.

The Sparrow equips McDonnell Douglas F-4 Phantom II aircraft of the US Navy, USAF, Royal Air Force, Greek Air Force, Iranian Air Force, Israeli Air Force, Republic of Korea Air Force and Spanish Air Force. The Lockheed F-104S fighters licence-built in Italy are Sparrow-armed, and both the USAF's McDonnell Douglas F-15 Eagle and the US Navy's Grumman F-14 Tomcat employ this missile. Mitsubishi is manufacturing more than 600 in Japan for the Japan Air Self-Defence Force, under licence from Raytheon.

Without change, the Sparrow is used on US Navy ships as a surface-to-air and anti-shipping weapon in the Basic Point Defense Surface Missile System. It is also used in Canadian ships in the Close Range Missile System.

The current, advanced, **AIM-7F** Sparrow is powered by a Hercules Mk 58 Mod 0 solid-propellant motor and has a Raytheon semi-active Doppler radar homing system, with a smaller solid-state seeker than that of earlier versions. The heavier continuous-rod warhead is actuated by a proximity fuse or contact fuse, and is mounted forward of the wings, instead of aft as on earlier versions. Manoeuvrability has been improved, and Sparrow is now considered a good dogfight missile as well as a good medium-range weapon with all-aspect capability, including shoot-down.

The AIM-7F is the fourth operational version of the Sparrow and is the only one that can be carried by the F-15. It has been fired successfully from a YF-16, but there is no current requirement for Sparrow armament on USAF F-16s. Production of the earlier AIM-7C, D and E models totalled 34,000 missiles, and the AIM-7F continues in production for the US Navy and USAF, with General Dynamics as second-source contractor. Total procurement under the AIM-7F programme is expected to provide 9,804 missiles for the US Navy and 9,150 for the USAF. The missile was approved for deployment at the beginning of 1977. Production of 1,725 was funded under the FY 1978 budget and 1,910 in FY 1979, with a further 1,560 requested in FY 1980 and 1,700 proposed for FY 1981 to meet USAF and USN requirements.

Development of an advanced monopulse seeker for the AIM-7F is underway, with the aims of reducing cost and overcoming present shortcomings in the ECM and look-down/clutter areas. Initial operational capability is planned for 1981.

A new missile known as Sky Flash, evolved from Sparrow, is in production for the Royal Air Force by Dynamics Group of British Aerospace (which see).

DATA: See table

ROCKWELL INTERNATIONAL
ROCKWELL INTERNATIONAL CORPORATION

Missile Systems Division
4300 East Fifth Avenue, Columbus, Ohio 43216

Rockwell International's Columbus (Ohio) Missile Systems Division is playing a major role in several important US weapon programmes. Brief details are given of the GBU-15 air-to-surface weapons and the Hellfire anti-armour weapon system which the Division is developing and/or producing for the US Army and Air Force.

HELLFIRE

The US Army announced in October 1976 that Rockwell International had won the competition for engineering development of the Hellfire (HELicopter-Launched, FIRE and forget) modular missile system. The company was awarded a $66·7 million contract for full-scale engineering development, including design, manufacture, testing and evaluation of the missile, launcher, ground and logistics support equipment. Rockwell is performing most of the work at Columbus, but propellant loading and final assembly are done at Redstone Arsenal, Alabama, under subcontract with Thiokol Chemical Company.

The initial version of Hellfire uses a laser seeker as its guidance module, and will equip the US Army's AH-64 advanced attack helicopter. Use of laser homing in the initial application of Hellfire is based on successful testing by the Army Missile Research and Development Command in Huntsville, Alabama, using Rockwell International Hornet missile airframes and Rockwell laser seekers. Hellfire is designed to accept other guidance modules, and current plans call for development of air-defence suppression and imaging IR seekers for this modular missile.

In November 1974 two test missiles, fitted with laser seekers supplied by Rockwell International, scored direct hits on two tank targets in the first successful ripple fire demonstration of such weapons at Redstone Arsenal. A US Army crew, flying an AH-1G HueyCobra helicopter, 'popped up' from cover and fired the first test missile at a tank illuminated by a ground-based laser designator. Less than one second later, the second missile was launched against a tank situated about 20 m (65 ft) from the first target and illuminated by an airborne laser on board a second AH-1G.

The Hellfire system's demonstrated rapid, ripple and indirect fire performance and effectiveness, coupled with the capability of being launched from a variety of helicopters, ground vehicles and fixed-wing aircraft, provides a significant improvement over current systems.

Hellfire is being developed in accordance with international standards of measurement (metric). Launch weight of the missile will be in the region of 41 kg (90 lb).

Engineering Development (ED) flight testing of Hellfire began in mid-1978. Testing up to the beginning of 1979 included unguided ballistic launches, a pre-programmed launch, and fully guided laser launches using the Tri-Service Laser Seeker also developed by Rockwell. One laser-guided Hellfire was launched from a JAH-1G testbed helicopter flying at low altitude. All flight tests under the ED phase of the programme have been successful.

GBU-8 (HOBOS) and GBU-15

The GBU-8 HOBOS (HOming BOmb System) is a modular weapon system developed under the USAF's electro-optical guided bomb (EOGB) programme. It consists of a guidance and control kit designed for easy installation on MK 84 (2,000 lb) and M118H1 (3,000 lb) general-purpose bombs. This installation does not alter the conventional bomb suspension, release or jettison functions, thus permitting the conversion of standard bombs into highly-accurate guided weapon systems.

Each kit consists of a forward guidance section, the warhead or interconnect section (including the bomb), and the aft control section.

The guidance or nose section consists of target seeker optics and sensor mounted on a gyro-stabilised platform, and the associated electronics which include a camera, platform and tracker electronics, and associated power supplies. The guidance section also furnishes reference signals to the autopilot located in the control section.

The warhead section consists of the MK 84 or M118H1 bomb with an interconnect assembly made up of four strakes, external electrical conduit, umbilical receptacle, and strake and umbilical receptacle attachment bands. The strakes are indexed in line with the wings to provide aerodynamic stability. The conduit transmits electrical signals between the guidance and control sections. The umbilical receptacle provides the necessary aircraft signal interface. Fusing of the HOBOS can be accomplished either electrically or mechanically.

The control or aft section consists of a cylindrical body with cruciform wings fitted with trailing-edge flap control surfaces for flight manoeuvring. The weapon system batteries and flight control system components are located within this section, including the autopilot which collects pitch and yaw steering data from the guidance section and converts this information into signals which drive the pneumatic control surface actuators.

The effectiveness of the HOBOS modular weapon system has been demonstrated fully in a large number of successful air drops, notably against targets such as aircraft in revetments, jungle roads and bridges in Viet-Nam.

Missile Systems Division has produced this weapon for the US Air Force, and it has been sold to several other countries through Foreign Military Sales.

USAF designation for this weapon system in its latest form is GBU-15(V)/B, covering a family of modular guided weapons. Adaptation to another warhead, such as the CBU-75 cluster munition, is possible; and several alternative types of guidance system may be utilised to provide day and night all-weather capability, including a laser seeker, imaging infra-red (IIR), and a midcourse system that includes distance measuring equipment (DME) for increased accuracy. Each system provides a glide bomb with self-contained guidance, high accuracy and moderate/long-range stand-off capability.

The modular elements consist of a group of interchangeable major assemblies which are combined to produce specific guided glide weapons. These configurations differ according to guidance, fusing, warhead and type of mission (direct attack or indirect attack).

In the indirect attack version, a data link module is used which allows control after launch. Further options available are cruciform and planar wings which provide the two basic weapons in the GBU-15(V)/B system.

The indirect attack version of the Cruciform Wing Weapon (CWW), shown in the accompanying illustration, has completed all development and testing and was expected to be the first of the GBU-15(V)/B weapons to be placed into service. (See also GBU-15 entry under the Hughes Aircraft heading in this section.)

DIMENSIONS:
- Length overall:
  - MK 84: 3·78 m (12 ft 5 in)
  - M118E1: 3·71 m (12 ft 2 in)
- Body diameter:
  - MK 84: 0·46 m (1 ft 6 in)
  - M118E1: 0·61 m (2 ft 0 in)
- Wing span:
  - MK 84: 1·12 m (3 ft 8 in)
  - M118E1: 1·32 m (4 ft 4 in)

WEIGHT:
- Launching weight:
  - MK 84: 1,016 kg (2,240 lb)
  - M118E1: 1,544 kg (3,404 lb)

MK 84 GBU-8 with new midcourse guidance, including DME, for increased accuracy

Hellfire missiles on Hughes YAH-64 advanced attack helicopter

Left to right: TV-guided HOBOS based on 2,000 lb MK 84 bomb; IR-guided HOBOS based on 2,000 lb MK 84 bomb; TV-guided HOBOS based on 3,000 lb M118 bomb

AGM-88A HARM air-to-surface missile

Cruciform Wing Weapon developed under GBU-15 programme

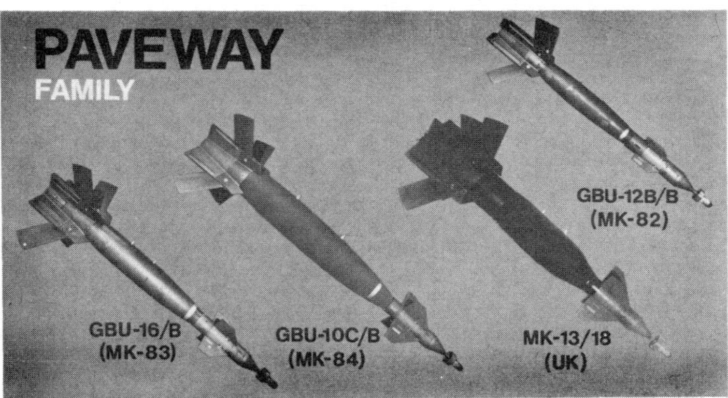

Paveway II laser-guided bombs

Paveway laser-guided weapons on a USMC AV-8A Harrier

TEXAS INSTRUMENTS

TEXAS INSTRUMENTS INCORPORATED

PO Box 6015, Dallas, Texas 75222
Telephone: (214) 238 2011
Telex: 7-3324

Texas Instruments has played a major part in many US missile programmes. The latest missile for which it is prime contractor is the AGM-88A HARM, of which brief details follow:

HARM

US Navy designation: AGM-88A

On 24 May 1974, Texas Instruments was named as prime contractor for HARM (High-speed Anti-Radiation Missile) by the US Naval Air Systems Command. The initial phase of the contract covered four months of basic design co-ordination and was followed by the Advanced Development Phase; during 1978 the programme progressed to engineering development. This is centred in the company's Dallas facilities, where production of the Shrike anti-radiation missile took place for more than a decade.

Few details of HARM may yet be published. Its basic configuration is conventional, with a slim cylindrical body, ogival head, cruciform double-delta wings at mid-length for simplified roll control, and cruciform tail fins indexed in line with the wings. The fixed antenna for proportional navigation is in the extreme nose, with the seeker. The smokeless solid-propellant dual-thrust rocket motor is provided by Thiokol.

The emphasis on high speed reflects experience gained in Viet-Nam, where Soviet surface-to-air missile radar systems sometimes detected the approach of US anti-radiation missiles such as the first-generation Shrike and ceased operation before the missile could lock on to them. In the case of the Navy's A-7E aircraft, HARM can cover a wide range of frequency spectra through the use of programmable digital processors in both the aircraft's AN/AWG-25 avionics equipment and the missile. The USAF will also utilise HARM on the F-4G 'Wild Weasel'. The missile has been launched successfully from F-4, A-6 and A-7 aircraft, and is readily adaptable to the F-18, AV-8B and F-16.

DATA: See table

PAVEWAY LASER GUIDED BOMBS

The Laser Guided Bomb (LGB) concept was introduced by Texas Instruments Incorporated in 1965. The US Air Force initiated an extensive development programme and the name Paveway was assigned to this. Texas Instruments builds the guidance units and rear wing assemblies, which are fitted to US MK 80 series bomb bodies. With minor modifications, the Paveway units have been installed on other aircraft ordnance, including the British MK 13/18 and 540 lb stores.

Paveway LGBs are semi-active laser-guided munitions which home on reflected laser energy from a target being illuminated by a laser designator. Day and night attacks can be accomplished against all types of tactical targets, since no intrinsic target signature is required. LGBs have been used effectively against anti-aircraft gun and missile installations, tanks, tracks, bridges, power stations, railroads, buildings, ships and caves.

Conventional bomb handling equipment is used for loading and fusing. No electrical interface to the delivery aircraft is required. Paveway munitions are delivered in a similar manner to conventional unguided munitions.

Continued development and engineering upgrading has added Paveway II to the family of weapons proven in Southeast Asia. Folding rear wings on the Paveway II have increased weapon performance and aircraft load density, increasing the number of aircraft, worldwide, that are compatible with the Paveway system.

The same laser detector and guidance unit is used with all weapons. The rear wing and control canards vary in size according to the size of the weapon.

Both Paveway I and II are currently in production for customers that include the US Air Force and Navy, Royal Air Force, Royal Netherlands Air Force, Iranian Air Force, Hellenic Air Force, Turkish Air Force, Canadian Armed Forces, Royal Saudi Air Force and Republic of Korea Air Force.

AIR-LAUNCHED MISSILES

Note: entries in italics are estimated

Country	Prime Contractor	Model	Length m (ft in)	Body diam cm (in)	Wing span m (ft in)	Launch weight kg (lb)	Cruising speed knots (km/h; mph)	Range	
France	Aérospatiale	AS.11	1·20 (3 11)	16·4 (6½)	0·50 (1 7½)	30 (66)	313 (580; 360)	300-3,000 m (985-9,850 ft)	Time of flight (propelled) 20-21 s. Min turning radius 1,000 m (3,300 ft)
	Aérospatiale	AS.12	1·87 (6 2)	21 (8¼)	0·65 (2 1½)	77 (170)	at impact 180 (335; 210)	6,000 m (19,685 ft)	Range in relation to surface. Time of flight 32 s
	Aérospatiale	AS.15TT	2·16 (7 1)	18·5 (7¼)	0·53 (1 8¾)	96 (212)	540 (1,000; 620)	more than 8 nm (15 km; 9·3 miles)	Warhead 30 kg (66 lb) Time of flight (propelled) 45·2 s
	Aérospatiale	AS.30 Laser	3·65 (11 11¾)	34·2 (13½)	1·00 (3 3¼)	520 (1,146)		5·4-6·5 nm (10-12 km; 6·2-7·5 miles)	Warhead 240 kg (529 lb)
	Aérospatiale	Exocet AM39	4·68 (15 4¼)	35 (13¾)	1·00 (3 3¼)	less than 650 (1,430)	Mach 0·93	see p.643	Warhead *160 kg (352 lb)*
	Matra	R.530	3·28 (10 9¼)	26 (10¼)	1·10 (3 7¼)	195 (430)	Mach 2·7	9·5 nm (18 km; 11 miles)	
	Matra	Super 530	3·54 (11 7¼)	26 (10¼)	0·64 (2 1¼)	227 (500)	*Mach 4·5*	*16-19 nm* *(30-35 km; 18·5-21·75 miles)*	Fin span 0·90 m (2 ft 11½ in). Operational ceiling above 21,350 m (70,000 ft)
	Matra	R.550 Magic	2·80 (9 2¼)	15·7 (6)	0·47 (1 6½)	88 (194)	Mach 2+	3·25 nm (6 km; 3·75 miles) at medium altitude; 5·4 nm (10 km; 6·2 miles) at high altitude	Fin span 0·65 m (2 ft 1½ in) Min range 500 m (1,640 ft)
Germany, Federal Rep	MBB	Kormoran	4·40 (14 5)	34 (13½)	1·00 (3 3¼)	600 (1,320)	*Mach 0·95*	*20 nm* *(37 km; 23 miles)*	
International	Euromissile	Hot	1·28 (4 2½)	14·4 (5¾)	*0·31 (1 0¼)	23·5 (51·8)	486 (900; 560)	400-4,000 m (1,310-13,125 ft)	Time of flight to 4,000 m 17 s. Warhead 6 kg (13·2 lb)
Israel	Rafael	Shafrir	2·47 (8 1¼)	16 (6¼)	0·52 (1 8½)	93 (205)		2·7 nm (5 km; 3·1 miles)	Warhead 11 kg (24·25 lb)
Italy	Selenia	Aspide	3·70 (12 1½)	20·3 (8)	1·00 (3 3¼)	220 (485)	*Mach 4*	*27-54 nm* *(50-100 km; 31-62 miles)*	Warhead *33 kg (73 lb)*
	Sistel	Sea Killer Mk 2	4·70 (15 5)	20·6 (8⅛)	1·00 (3 3¼)	300 (660)	Mach 0·74	over 10·8 nm (20 km; 12·4 miles)	Warhead 70 kg (154 lb)
Japan	Mitsubishi	ASM-1	3·95 (12 11½)	35 (13¾)	1·19 (3 10¾)	610 (1,345)	Mach 0·9	43-48 nm (80-90 km; 50-56 miles)	Warhead 200 kg (440 lb)
Norway	Kongsberg	Penguin Mk 2	3·05 (10 0)	28 (11)	1·40 (4 7)	330 (727)	Mach 0·8	15 nm (27 km; 17 miles)	Air-launched Mk 3 has shorter span, extended range
USSR		AA-1 'Alkali'	1·88 (6 2)	17·8 (7)	0·58 (1 10¾)	*90* *(200)*		3·2-4·3 nm (6-8 km; 3·7-5 miles)	
		AA-2 'Atoll' (K-13A)	2·80 (9 2)	12·0 (4¾)	0·45 (1 5¾)	70 (154)	Mach 2·5	2·5-3·5 nm (5-6·5 km; 3-4 miles)	Span of tail fins 0·53 m (1 ft 8¾ in)
		AA-3 'Anab'	*4·10* *(13 5)*	*28·0* *(11)*	*1·30* *(4 3)*			over 8·75 nm (16 km; 10 miles)	Length for IR version; radar version is 4·0 m (13 ft 1 in) long
		AA-5 'Ash'	*5·50* *(18 0)*					16 nm (30 km; 18·5 miles)	Length for IR version; radar version is 5·2 m (17 ft 0 in) long
		AA-7 'Apex'	*4·30* *(14 1¼)*	*24·0* *(9½)*	*1·05* *(3 5½)*	*320* *(705)*		*15 nm (27 km; 17 miles)*	
		AA-8 'Aphid'	*2·00* *(6 6¾)*	*13·0* *(5)*		*55* *(121)*		*3-4 nm* *(5·5-8 km; 3·5-5 miles)*	*Warhead 6 kg (13·2 lb)*
		'Swatter'	0·90 (2 11½)	15·0 (6)	0·65 (2 2)	25 (55)	290 (540; 335)	300-2,200 m (985-7,220 ft)	
		AS-2 'Kipper'	*9·50* *(31 0)*	*90* *(35·4)*	*4·88* *(16 0)*	*4,200* *(9,260)*	*Mach 1·2*	*115 nm* *(213 km; 132 miles)*	*Warhead 1,000 kg (2,200 lb)*
		AS-3 'Kangaroo'	14·90 *(48 11)*	*185* *(72·8)*	9·15 (30 0)	*11,000* *(24,250)*	Mach 1·8	350 nm (650 km; 400 miles)	*Nuclear or HE warhead 2,300 kg (5,070 lb)*
		AS-4 'Kitchen'	*11·30* *(37 0)*	*90* *(35·4)*	*3·00* *(9 10)*	*6,000+* *(13,225)*	*Mach 2+*	*160 nm* *(300 km; 185 miles)*	Range at low altitude *Warhead 1,000 kg (2,200 lb)*
		AS-5 'Kelt'	*9·45* *(31 0)*	*100* *(39·5)*	*4·57* *(15 0)*	*3,500* *(7,715)*	*Mach 0·9*	over 85 nm *(160 km; 100 miles)*	Range at low altitude *HE warhead; 1,000 kg (2,200 lb)*
		AS-6 'Kingfish'	*10·50* *(34 6)*		*2·50* *(8 2½)*		*Mach 3*	*120 nm* *(220 km; 135 miles)*	Range at low altitude

Note: entries in italics are estimated

Country	Prime Contractor	Model	Length m (ft in)	Body diam cm (in)	Wing span m (ft in)	Launch weight kg (lb)	Cruising speed knots (km/h; mph)	Range	
UK	British Aerospace	Sea Skua	*2·83 (9 3½)*	*27 (10½)*	*0·60 (1 11½)*	*147 (325)*			*Warhead 20 kg (44 lb)*
	British Aerospace	Sky Flash	3·66 (12 0)	20·3 (8)	1·02 (3 4¼)	193 (425)	Mach 4	27 nm (50 km; 31 miles)	
USA	Boeing Aerospace	AGM-86B ALCM	6·32 (20 9)	62 (24½)	3·66 (12 0)	1,282 (2,825)	approx 435 (805; 500)	approx 1,350 nm (2,500 km; 1,550 miles)	Height overall 1·19 m (3 ft 11 in)
	General Dynamics	AGM-109 Tomahawk	6·10 (20 0)	53 (21)	2·54 (8 4)	1,157 (2,550)	*478 (885; 550)*	over 1,300 nm (2,400 km; 1,500 miles)	Data for land attack version. Range of tactical version over 300 nm (555 km; 345 miles)
	Hughes	AIM-54A Phoenix	3·95 (13 0)	38 (15)	0·91 (3 0)	447 (985)	Mach 5+	108 nm + (200 km; 124 miles)	
	Hughes	BGM-71A TOW	1·17 (3 10)	15 (6)	0·34 (1 1½)	19 (42)	High subsonic	500-3,750 m (1,640-12,300 ft)	Warhead 3·9 kg (8·6 lb) Max range increased by 25% in 1978
	Hughes	AGM-65A Maverick	2·46 (8 1)	30 (12)	0·71 (2 4)	210 (462)		*12 nm (22 km; 14 miles)*	
	MDAC	AGM-84A Harpoon	3·84 (12 7)	34 (13½)	NA	526 (1,160)	High subsonic		
	NWC/ Raytheon	AIM-9G/H Sidewinder	2·87 (9 5)	13 (5)	*0·63 (2 0¾)	86 (190)	Mach 2·5	over 1·75 nm (3·35 km; 2 miles)	Warhead 11·4 kg (25 lb)
	Ford Aerospace	AIM-9J/P Sidewinder	2·83 (9 3½)	13 (5)	*0·56 (1 10)	72 (159)	Mach 2·5	over 1·75 nm (3·35 km; 2 miles)	Warhead 11·4 kg (25 lb)
	NWC/ Raytheon/ Ford Aerospace	AIM-9L Sidewinder	2·87 (9 5)	13 (5)	*0·63 (2 0¾)	86 (190)	Mach 2·5	over 3·75 nm (7 km; 4·35 miles)	Warhead 11·4 kg (25 lb)
	Raytheon	AIM-7F Sparrow	3·66 (12 0)	20 (8)	1·02 (3 4)	227 (500)	*Mach 3·5+*	*24 nm (44 km; 28 miles)*	
	Texas Instruments	AGM-88A HARM	4·17 (13 8)	25·4 (10)	1·13 (3 8½)	354 (780)		over 8·5 nm (16 km; 10 miles)	Altitude limits S/L to 12,200 m (40,000 ft)

*Fin span

SPACEFLIGHT

CANADA

SPAR

SPAR AEROSPACE LIMITED

Royal Bank Plaza South, Toronto M5J 2J2, Canada
Telephone: (416) 865 0480
Telex: 065-24240 Sparcal Tor
Chairman of the Board: L. D. Clarke
President: R. D. Richmond
Viee-President, Marketing: R. E. Marcille
Director, Public Relations: Hugh A. MacLean

Spar is an independent Canadian public company, active in varied fields of advanced technology and serving commercial, scientific and military markets.

Anik B, Canada's latest domestic communications satellite (described in the RCA entry in the US section), which was launched on 15 December 1978, contained two communications systems developed and built by Spar Aerospace Electronic Group.

Under Canadian/US co-operative arrangements, a Canadian team led by Spar is developing the remote manipulator system for the Space Shuttle programme. The team has, in addition, established a computer-controlled facility capable of simulating under laboratory conditions the performance of remote manipulator systems for space, Arctic, underwater and nuclear applications.

SHUTTLE REMOTE MANIPULATOR SYSTEM (SRMS)

The SRMS consists of a 15 m (50 ft) long mechanical arm with joints similar to a human shoulder, elbow and wrist. It will be operated by an astronaut, from the port-side aft crew station of the Orbiter flight deck, to deploy satellites into space from the vehicle's cargo bay, and to retrieve orbiting satellites for on-board servicing or return to Earth. It will be capable of handling satellites weighing up to 29,480 kg (65,000 lb), with a length of up to 18·28 m (60 ft) and maximum diameter of 4·57 m (15 ft). A second arm may be installed on the opposite side of the cargo bay when mission requirements dictate such a move.

Shuttle Remote Manipulator System (SRMS) under development by Spar

CHINA
(PEOPLE'S REPUBLIC)

China launched her first satellite (Norad designation *Chicom 1*) on 24 April 1970, and thus became the fifth country to orbit a payload using national resources, following the USSR, USA, France and Japan. The launch is believed to have taken place from the main Chinese rocket centre near Shuang Cheng Tsu, 800 km (500 miles) east of the nuclear test establishment of Lop Nor.

Brief details of the China 2, 3, 4 and 5 satellites were given in the 1976-77 *Jane's*. China 6 and 7 were briefly described in the 1978-79 *Jane's*. China 8, launched on 26 January 1978, and weighing an estimated 3,600 kg (8,000 lb), returned a re-entry module to Earth. The carrier vehicle re-entered and burned up on 7 February.

It is widely surmised that the development of the satellites and their launch vehicle has been managed by Dr Tsien Hsue-Shen, a scientist who was employed by the Jet Propulsion Laboratory in California as a member of a rocket design team during the second World War. After the war the Doctor worked at the Massachusetts Institute of Technology. He returned to China in 1955.

In November/December 1978 a Chinese delegation, led by Dr. Jen Hsin-min, Director of the Chinese Academy of Space Technology, held discussions with United States officials regarding possible US-Chinese cooperation in the peaceful utilisation of space technology. The discussions resulted in an informal agreement for purchase by the Chinese of a complete US civil satellite communications system, and of a ground station capable of receiving Earth resources information from US Landsat satellites.

FRANCE

AÉROSPATIALE

SOCIÉTÉ NATIONALE INDUSTRIELLE AÉROSPATIALE

Division Systèmes Balistiques et Spatiaux

Management: Route de Verneuil, BP 96, 78130-Les Mureaux
Telephone: 474-72-13
Telex: AISPA 696 759F
Director: P. M. Usunier

The Space and Ballistic Systems Division of Aérospatiale handles research, development, testing and engineering for entire missile and space vehicle systems, including a range of solid-propellant sounding rockets (see 1977-78 *Jane's*). Satellite programmes to which it is contributing include Intelsat V, H-Sat, Exosat, MAROTS, Phebus and Meteosat, for which it is prime contractor and which was launched on 23 November 1977.

Aérospatiale is a member of the CIFAS and COSMOS international consortia (see International section) and has founded a joint subsidiary, named Eurosatellite, with MBB and ETCA, for the development and marketing of applications satellites. The choice by ESA of the Phebus X spacecraft for the H-Sat programme is the first outcome of this co-operative venture.

ARIANE

This heavy three-stage launch vehicle is being developed in Europe as a co-operative project involving ten countries. The programme is financed by the European Space Agency, with the French space agency CNES as prime contractor. Ariane's payload potential will be 1,700 kg (3,748 lb) into a transfer orbit, or applications satellites of up to 925 kg (2,035 lb) weight in geostationary orbit, or with an ESA-developed apogee motor 967 kg (2,134 lb).

Aérospatiale is responsible for the design of Ariane and for integration of the entire vehicle. It is producing major structural elements of the first stage and is responsible for the final delivery of all three stages and the fairings.

SEP is developing the engines and associated subsystems. Matra is building the vehicle equipment bay, and ETCA is responsible for the checkout and launch command facilities.

The first test flight is scheduled for November 1979; the second for March 1980 with a payload consisting of Amsat, Cat and Firewheel; the third for June 1980 with a payload of APPLE, Cat and Meteosat 2, and the fourth for October 1980, with a payload of Cat, Exosat and MARECS A. The vehicle is expected to be fully operational in 1981.

Projected developments include lengthening the third stage fuel tank and the addition of strap-on boosters to increase the transfer orbit payload to 2,300 kg (5,070 lb) by 1982-83; and a dual launch system known as SYLDA, to permit the simultaneous launch of two 800-1,020 kg (1,763-2,248 lb) satellites.

Details of the individual stages are as follows:

L 140 FIRST STAGE

This first stage is made up of two identical steel tanks for the 145,000 kg (319,670 lb) of UDMH and nitrogen tetroxide propellants, linked together by means of a cylindrical skirt. It is powered by four Viking engines (each 611·25 kN; 137,412 lb st), carried on a cylindrical thrust frame and protected by fairings with fins. Burn time is 145 seconds.

An interstage skirt joins the first and second stages.

L 33 SECOND STAGE

The second stage comprises two light alloy tanks for 34,000 kg (74,955 lb) of UDMH and nitrogen tetroxide propellants, separated by a common bulkhead. The single Viking engine (713 kN; 160,280 lb thrust in vacuum) is linked to the stage by a conical thrust frame. Burn time is 132 seconds.

A cylindrical interstage skirt connects the second and third stages.

H 8 THIRD STAGE

The third stage is made of light alloy and houses 8,200 kg (18,075 lb) of liquid hydrogen and liquid oxygen propellants for its single HM7 cryogenic engine (60 kN; 13,485 lb thrust). Burn time is 570 seconds.

A cylindrical vehicle equipment bay is situated above the third stage. The equipment platform is an annular plate, the inside flange of which supports the payload attachment fittings.

DIMENSIONS:

Length: L 140 1st stage	18·40 m (60 ft 4½ in)
L 33 2nd stage	10·40 m (33 ft 1 in)
H 8 3rd stage	8·60 m (26 ft 2½ in)
Overall length	47·0 m (154 ft 2 in)
Body diameter: L 140	3·80 m (12 ft 5½ in)
L 33, H 8, equipment bay	2·60 m (8 ft 6½ in)

WEIGHTS:

L 140 1st stage	165,000 kg (363,760 lb)
L 33 2nd stage	37,600 kg (82,895 lb)
H 8 3rd stage	9,400 kg (20,725 lb)
Total weight at lift-off	207,000 kg (456,355 lb)

PHEBUS

Phebus (Polyvalent HEavy BUS) is a multi-purpose modular spacecraft, designed to perform a wide variety of applications missions. Launched by a vehicle in the Ariane class, Phebus will have a mass of approximately 900 kg (1,984 lb) in geostationary orbit, of which 150 to 350 kg (330 to 772 lb) will be available for payload.

The spacecraft and its subsystems are so designed that the same basic vehicle can, for the lowest possible cost, handle missions as varied as direct television, high-density telecommunications, Earth resources and observation.

Phebus is stabilised about three axes. The main body comprises two U-shaped structures, the service module and the payload module, which together form a cube with sides of about 2 m (6 ft 6¾ in). The solar arrays furnish from 1 to 6kW. According to energy requirements they can be either of the flexible fold-up type (high-energy mission) or of the lightweight/rigid type (medium-energy requirements). During launch the arrays are folded. When in orbit they are deployed and the overall wing span of the satellite, depending upon the configuration, varies from 15 to 40 m (49 to 131 ft).

The initial version, Phebus X, has been selected by ESA for the H-Sat programme. H-Sat's missions will be telecommunications, direct-TV, and in-flight qualification of new space technologies. Launch is planned for 1981.

SONATE

Sonate is a drum-shape telecommunications satellite, weighing 300 to 400 kg (660-880 lb). It is optimised for domestic or regional missions, involving point-to-point telecommunications, relay, data collection and transmission.

Utilising proven technologies and existing hardware, Sonate will be reliable and relatively inexpensive. Its configuration is based on the Meteosat spacecraft platform, and on Symphonie (4-6GHz) or OTS (12-14GHz) payloads, with a mechanically de-spun antenna. It will be spin-stabilized and will have more than 300W power at the end of its lifetime.

Sonate is configured for dual launch with Ariane/SYLDA, but users can choose between this method and the Space Shuttle with an upper stage (SSUS-D).

Mockup of Ariane three-stage launch vehicle

Artist's impression of the Phebus X configuration chosen for the H-Sat programme

Model of the Sonate communications satellite

MATRA
SA MATRA

MANAGEMENT AND WORKS: 37 avenue Louis Breguet, 78140-Vélizy
Telephone: 946.96.00
Telex: MATRA 698 077F
OFFICERS: See Missiles section

Matra is currently working on the Command and Data Management System for Spacelab, as contractor for ESA, and on the vehicle equipment bay for the Ariane European launcher.

Following successful operation in orbit of the Orbital Test Satellite (OTS), for which Matra developed the attitude and orbit control system, the company is developing within the MESH international consortium the attitude and orbit control system of the European Communication Satellite (ECS) and its maritime version (MARECS), and will integrate ECS.

Matra is also developing with CNES the French Earth Observation satellite SPOT, and is working, under ESA contract, on the Faint Object Camera (FOC) for NASA's Space Telescope.

GERMANY
(FEDERAL REPUBLIC)

DORNIER
DORNIER SYSTEM GmbH

Postfach 6136048, 7990 Friedrichshafen

Telephone: Immenstaad (07545) 81
Telex: 073 4359

GENERAL MANAGERS:
Dipl-Ing Silvius Dornier
Dipl-Ing Dr Jr Karl-Wilhelm Schäfer
Dr Ing Bernhard Schmidt
Dr Ing Helmut Ulke
Dipl-Kfm Klaus-Peter Thomé
PUBLIC RELATIONS: Gerhard Patt

Dornier System, a member company of the Dornier group, is engaged in activities involving spaceflight, new technologies, electronics and research. It is a major European contractor for the development of equipment for satellites, and for associated equipment such as the communications terminals mounted on German ships for use with the Marisat satellite system.

Within the STAR international consortium, Dornier System was responsible for design and manufacture of the attitude measuring equipment, booms and mechanisms of the GEOS research satellite launched on 20 April 1977, and led development of the international Sun/Earth explorer ISEE-B satellite launched on 22 October 1977.

Dornier System is now developing the environmental control and life support subsystem (ECLSS) and the instrument pointing system (IPS) for the Spacelab which is to be carried into orbit by the US Space Shuttle.

For Ariane, the European launch vehicle, Dornier is developing the second-stage tank structure.

ERNO

ERNO RAUMFAHRTTECHNIK GmbH

Hünefeldstrasse 1-5, Postfach 10 59 09, 2800 Bremen 1
Telephone: (0421) 5391
Telex: 024 5548
DIRECTORS:
Dipl-Ing Hans E. W. Hoffmann
RA Bernd Kosegarten

ERNO is an affiliated company of the Zentralgesellschaft VFW-Fokker GmbH, Düsseldorf. Its current space activities include work on the Spacelab to be carried into orbit by the Space Shuttle, the second stage of the Ariane European launch vehicle and the maritime communications satellite MARECS. Together with the US Marisat satellites, MARECS will form the INMARSAT global system for ship communications.

SPACELAB

Under development by a ten-nation consortium led by VFW-Fokker/ERNO, Spacelab is the largest European space project initiated in the present decade and will be the only manned payload for the American Space Shuttle. A typical payload will comprise a large module and two pallets with an overall length of 13·80 m (45 ft 3 in) and a diameter of 4·06 m (13 ft 4 in).

The first launch of the Space Shuttle with a Spacelab is scheduled for 1981. Four payload specialists will work in two shifts for periods of 7 to 30 days. Spacelab will remain in the cargo bay of the Orbiter during the mission and will be brought back to Earth when the Orbiter lands. The payload specialists will be able to work under normal atmospheric conditions in the pressurised module. For work on the pallet section pressure suits will be necessary.

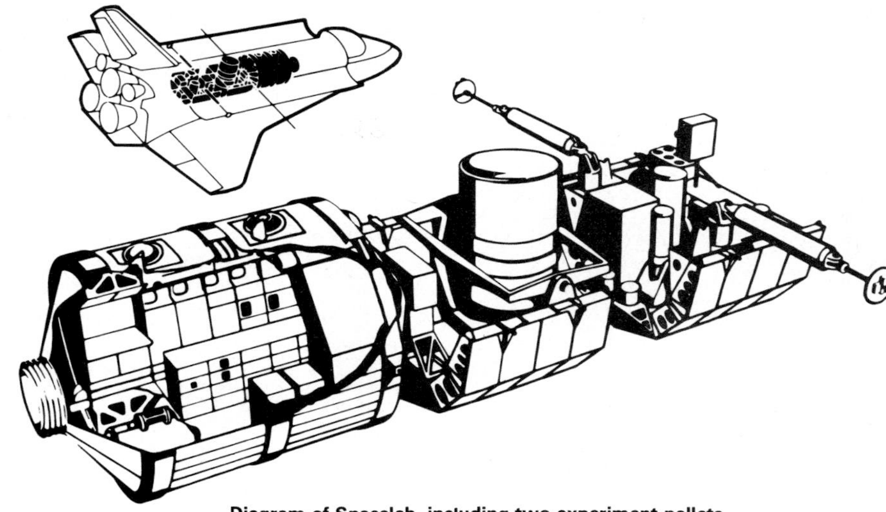

Diagram of Spacelab, including two experiment pallets

MBB

MESSERSCHMITT-BÖLKOW-BLOHM GmbH

Space Division
8012 Ottobrunn bei München
Telephone: (089) 60 00 25 90

In addition to its manufacture of piloted aircraft, Messerschmitt-Bölkow-Blohm is engaged in the development of guided weapons (see Air-Launched Missiles section), research rockets and satellites. Contributions to ten space programmes have been made since 1968, including the two Helios solar probes and the Symphonie communications satellites. Currently the company is building the Exosat X-ray satellite, under contract to ESA, and is a major subcontractor for the Intelsat V communications satellite (which see).

MBB is also developing the HM7 cryogenic engine for the Ariane launcher, and the trajectory and attitude control system for the Galileo Jupiter probe, sponsored by NASA and the Federal German Ministry of Research and Technology. In December 1978, the company submitted to that Ministry a proposal for a domestic TV-SAT satellite, designed to transmit three television programmes directly into every home from a geostationary orbit. The satellite is designed for a life of ten years in orbit, and includes triple-redundancy for critical electronic components and electric thrust units for orbit control.

OTRAG

ORBITAL TRANSPORT- UND RAKETEN AG

Herzogstrasse 39, 8000 München 40
Telephone: 089-320-1079
Telex: 528548 otragd
CHAIRMAN: Dr-Ing Kurt H. Debus
PRESIDENT: Dipl-Ing Lutz T. Kayser

OTRAG is developing as a private venture a low-cost satellite launch vehicle based on a building block concept, by which tank-plus-engine modules are clustered in increasing numbers to form larger vehicles.

The basic OTRAG building block is a two-tank/two-engine module, one tank containing white fuming nitric acid and the other kerosene. The two throttleable engines each develop 29·36 kN (6,600 lb st). Two such building blocks together form the smallest flight vehicle.

The tanks, which have a diameter of 27·0 cm (10·6 in), are made from cold-spun stainless steel. Length of the tanks on the basic vehicle is 6·0 m (19 ft 8 in), but this is increased for the larger vehicles. Each tank is filled with propellant to about two-thirds capacity. Compressed air occupies the remaining space and forces the propellant into the engine during flight. Radial injection and ablative thrust chambers are used, lined with a coating of asbestos and phenolic plastics resin.

Engine throttling capability is provided by ball valves, which allow propellants to pass from the tanks to the engines, and are opened or closed by actuators to provide full, 50% or zero thrust.

To achieve low cost, existing aerospace components or commercially available components are used wherever possible, examples of the latter being the fuel valves and their actuators.

Guidance is by an inertial platform and computer in the payload section. These send signals to each engine actuator unit, which in turn throttles the engines on one side or the other to control the attitude of the vehicle.

A basic flight vehicle, consisting of two modules, was successfully test-launched from North-Shaba in Zaïre on 17 May 1977, when an altitude of about 12,000 m (39,370 ft) was reached. A second launch, on 20 May 1978, utilised a cluster of four modules and reached a height of 30,000 m (98,400 ft). No 3 flight test took place on 5 June 1978, with a cluster of four modules and tank length of 12·0 m (39 ft 4 in).

From these basic flight vehicles OTRAG plans to evolve a series of efficient but relatively inexpensive launchers capable of undertaking a wide variety of duties. The first orbital insertion is planned for Summer 1980, with an 80-module vehicle; by 1981 it is hoped to launch a vehicle of more than 600 modules. On the larger vehicles the propellant tanks will be lengthened to a maximum of 40 m (131 ft), and the basic modules will be clustered in stages one inside the other. As one stage or 'layer' burns out, it will be jettisoned when the next outermost layer or stage ignites. The process will continue until only a slender core stage is left to insert the payload into orbit.

A 600-module vehicle could place a 10,000 kg (22,000 lb) payload in low Earth orbit, or 2,000 kg (4,409 lb) in geosynchronous orbit.

OTRAG 4-module launch vehicle

INDIA

ISRO

INDIAN SPACE RESEARCH ORGANISATION

F Block, Cauvery Bhavan, District Office Road, Bangalore 560 009
Telephone: 27371
Telex: 0845-499 IN
CHAIRMAN: Prof S. Dhawan

The Government of India set up a Space Commission in June 1972, backed by the Department of Space (DOS), and entrusted DOS with responsibility for conducting India's space programme. ISRO functions under DOS as its research and development organisation and for executing the space research activities.

ISRO operates and maintains the UN-sponsored Thumba Equatorial Rocket Launching Station (TERLS) near Trivandrum, and encourages international collaboration in space research experiments using rockets.

The activities of ISRO, which has its Headquarters at Bangalore, are carried out at the following centres:

Vikram Sarabhai Space Centre (VSSC)
ISRO PO, Trivandrum 695 022
Telephone: 4671 and 4791
Telex: 0884-201 IN and 0884-202 IN
DIRECTOR: Dr Brahm Prakash

VSSC serves as the main research and development centre for space technology. It is engaged in the development of sounding rockets and satellite launch vehicles.

Space Applications Centre (SAC)
Jodhpur Tekra, Ahmedabad 380 053
Telephone: 42700 and 43296
Telex: 012-239 IN
DIRECTOR: Prof Yash Pal

This Centre is concerned with space applications programmes of ISRO in the areas of satellite communications,

TV broacasting via satellite, survey of Earth resources and meteorological parameters from space/aerial platforms using remote sensing and satellite geodesy.

SHAR Centre
Sriharikota PO 524 124, Nellore District (AP)
Telephone: 2001 and 2345 (via Madras)
Telex: 041-394 and 041-7353 IN
DIRECTOR: N. Pant

This centre contains facilities for launching and flight testing large multi-stage sounding rockets. Facilities for launching satellites are under development. The centre also has facilities for the production of solid propellants and for the static testing of rocket motors. The main Indian ground station for tracking, commanding ISRO satellites and receiving telemetry data is located at this centre.

ISRO Satellite Centre (ISAC)
Peenya Industrial Estate, Bangalore 560 058
Telephone: 38262-69
Telex: 0845-325 IN
DIRECTOR: Prof U. R. Rao

This centre provides inputs for planning satellite programmes/missions of ISRO, and for the fabrication of satellites. It is the research centre for satellite technology.

The latest ISRO programmes are as follows:

SATELLITE LAUNCH VEHICLE (SLV-3)

This VSSC project has the objective of developing an indigenous satellite launch vehicle capable of putting a 40 kg (88 lb) satellite into elliptical Earth orbit. The four-stage solid-propellant vehicle, designated SLV-3, will have a maximum length of 23 m (75 ft 6 in) and will weigh 17,000 kg (37,480 lb) at lift-off. Thrust of the first stage will be 422 kN (95,000 lb). Inertial control and guidance will be employed.

The first launch, involving a Rohini RS-1 satellite, was scheduled for July 1979.

SEO SATELLITE

SEO (Satellite for Earth Observations) was scheduled to be launched from the Soviet Union in 1979, under an agreement between ISRO and the USSR Academy of Sciences. It will be placed in a near-circular orbit of 525 km (325 miles) nominal altitude with an inclination of 51°.

The primary payloads of the 425 kg (937 lb) satellite are two slow-scan TV cameras with a ground resolution of about 1 km (0·60 miles) and a microwave radiometer. The satellite is spin-stabilised with attitude control, and the spin rate is maintained by a cold gas system. SEO was fabricated at ISAC and its payloads at SAC.

The primary aim of launching this and similar satellites is to gain experience in techniques for obtaining scientific information in the areas of meteorology, forestry, hydrology and oceanography using satellite sensors.

ROHINI SATELLITE

The first Rohini Satellite (RS-1), which weighs 40 kg (88 lb), is designed to monitor the performance of the fourth stage of the SLV-3 vehicle which will inject the satellite into an Earth orbit. After the SLV-3 rocket becomes operational, it will be used to launch future Rohini scientific satellites.

APPLE SATELLITE

APPLE (Ariane Passenger Payload Experiment), a 630 kg (1,389 lb) experimental communications satellite, was under development in 1979. It is ISRO's first three-axis stabilised geostationary satellite, and will be used to develop the technology required for launching, positioning and controlling such satellites. APPLE is to be launched by an Ariane of the European Space Agency in 1980.

INTERNATIONAL PROGRAMMES

CIFAS

CONSORTIUM INDUSTRIEL FRANCO-ALLEMAND POUR LE SATELLITE SYMPHONIE (DEUTSCH-FRANZÖSICHES INDUSTRIE-KONSORTIUM FÜR DEN SATELLITEN SYMPHONIE)
BP 62, 78130-Les Mureaux, France
Telephone: 474.72.13
Telex: AIRSPA 60159F
ADMINISTRATOR: P. M. Usunier

This consortium was formed on 25 April 1968 in response to a request from the French and German governments for proposals to develop a telecommunications satellite named Symphonie. Members of the consortium, under the technical, industrial and commercial direction of Société Nationale Industrielle Aérospatiale (Division Systèmes Balistiques et Spatiaux), are Messerschmitt-Bölkow-Blohm, Thomson-CSF, SAT, Siemens-AG and AEG-Telefunken.

Symphonie communications satellite

SYMPHONIE

The first operational Symphonie telephone/television satellite was launched by a Delta vehicle on 19 December 1974, and reached its geostationary position over the South Atlantic, at longitude 11·5°W, on 8 January 1975, giving coverage of two zones through two elliptical beams, each of 13° × 8°. The first beam covers Europe, North and Central Africa; the second beam covers South America and the eastern parts of North and Central America. The second Symphonie was launched on 26 August 1975, and is also positioned at longitude 11·5°W.

The two satellites are used constantly for experiments, demonstrations, and a wide variety of operational services, including educational broadcasts to Africa, commercial television programmes and communications for the UN and UNESCO. Two transponders have a transmission capacity of 600 two-way telephone channels.

Symphonie was intended for 24-hour use over a five-year period. The basic programme called for three flight units, plus the necessary spares. The launch of the third satellite, a refurbished prototype, is planned as payload for one of the Ariane development flights.

COSMOS

ÉTUDES TECHNIQUES ET CONSTRUCTIONS AÉROSPATIALES SA (ETCA)
BP 97, 6000-Charleroi 1, Belgium

SOCIÉTÉ NATIONALE INDUSTRIELLE AÉROSPATIALE
BP 96, 78130-Les Mureaux, France

SOCIÉTÉ ANONYME DE TÉLÉCOMMUNICATIONS (SAT)
41 rue Cantagrel, 75624-Paris Cédex 13, France

MESSERSCHMITT-BÖLKOW-BLOHM GmbH (MBB)
8 München 80, Postfach 801 169, Germany

SIEMENS AG
8 München 70, Hofmannstrasse 51, Germany

MARCONI SPACE & DEFENCE SYSTEMS LTD
The Grove, Stanmore, Middlesex HA7 4LY, England

SELENIA SpA
CP 7083, 00100 Rome, Italy

The COSMOS consortium was formed in November 1970. It is involved in several major space programmes, notably Meteosat, of which details follow:

Meteosat geostationary meteorological satellite

METEOSAT

Aérospatiale of France, acting as prime contractor for the COSMOS consortium, was awarded a $56·76 million contract by ESA for development of this geosynchronous meteorological satellite in December 1973. The work culminated in launch of Meteosat 1 by a Delta 2914 vehicle on 23 November 1977. The satellite was continuing to send excellent pictures and other meteorological data in mid-1979. Launch of the second Meteosat is scheduled for May 1980, by a French Ariane vehicle.

Ford Aerospace assists Aérospatiale's Cannes establishment in co-ordinating and integrating the project. Of the other COSMOS members, MBB is responsible for the spacecraft structure; Marconi Space & Defence Systems supplies the attitude and orbit control system and checkout equipment, and is involved with Siemens on the satellite's main communications package.

Meteosat represents Europe's contribution to a worldwide Global Atmospheric Research Programme (GARP), intended to utilise also US and Japanese satellites to provide data for the World Weather Watch Organisation. Further details were given in the 1977-78 *Jane's*.

MESH

AERITALIA SpA
Piazzale V. Tecchio 51/A, 80125 Naples, Italy

BRITISH AEROSPACE DYNAMICS GROUP
Manor Road, Hatfield, Hertfordshire AL10 9LL

ERNO RAUMFAHRTTECHNIK GmbH
28 Bremen 1, Hünefeldstrasse 15, Postfach 1199, Germany

FOKKER-VFW
PO Box 7600, Schiphol Oost, The Netherlands

INTA
Departamento de Equipo y Armamento, Paseo del Pintor Rosales 34, Torrejon de Ardoz, Madrid 8, Spain

SA MATRA
BP No. 1, 78140-Vélizy, France

SAAB-SCANIA AKTIEBOLAG
S-581 88 Linköping, Sweden

This international consortium was formed in October 1966, the word MESH being an acronym of the initial letters of the four original founder members.

In addition to the OTS and ECS satellite programmes, MESH is involved in the maritime communications satellite MARECS, which employs basic ECS technology.

ECS

Development is proceeding of the European Communications Satellite (ECS), with British Aerospace Dynamics Group as prime contractor. ECS, based on the technology of OTS, will offer a fully operational regional satellite communications system, and will be capable of carrying a significant proportion of future European telephone, telex and TV traffic. The first ECS will be placed in geostationary orbit in 1981, by the European Ariane launcher, and it is planned that this should be followed by three more between then and 1990. The launches will be made from the equatorial site at Kourou in French Guiana.

OTS

This Orbital Test Satellite was produced under a three-year contract, with British Aerospace Dynamics Group as prime contractor, responsible for both development and launch support. It signifies completion of the technological and development phase of the European Communications Satellite programme.

OTS was to be placed in geostationary orbit in 1977, in order to demonstrate the operational capabilities of on-board high-technology communications payloads and spacecraft systems. It was intended also to test experimental advanced communications concepts and propagation assumptions in space. Shortly after launch, in September 1977, a failure in the Delta launch vehicle caused it to explode and the satellite was lost. The second OTS flight model was launched successfully on 11 May 1978 and arrived on station at 10°E on 21 May.

The primary aim of the OTS programme is to develop a space communications system which will make facilities available to European postal and telecommunications authorities grouped in CEPT (Conference Européenne des Postes et Télécommunications). These facilities will offer satellite links for a significant portion of inter-European telephony, telegraphy and telex traffic in the 1980s, and will satisfy the requirements of the EBU (European Broadcasting Union) or Eurovision relay.

MARECS

This maritime communications programme involves the initial procurement of two MARECS (the maritime version of ECS) satellites. They will serve the Eastern Atlantic and Indian Oceans, providing merchant shipping with instant communications to shore terminals by links vastly superior to the present highly congested HF circuits.

The basic structure, control and power systems are those of ECS, to which will be fitted complete communications packages being developed by MSDS. The first satellite will be launched in 1980, into geostationary orbit over the western Indian Ocean. The system will be augmented by further launches into different orbital locations, until INMARSAT has established a worldwide maritime satellite communications system.

To permit the use of simple shipborne and shore-based terminals, MARECS will be equipped with a high-efficiency 'shaped beam' antenna, coupled with a transistorised L-band power amplifier. Ships will use L-band frequencies to communicate to and from the satellite. As shore terminals will be able to use more sophisticated equipment, the shore-to-satellite frequency will be in the 6GHz band and satellite-to-shore communications will use the 4GHz band.

Artist's impression of OTS satellite in orbit

STAR

BRITISH AEROSPACE DYNAMICS GROUP
Stevenage-Bristol Division, Filton House, Bristol BS 99 7AR, England

CONTRAVES AG
Schaffhauserstrasse 580, CH-8052 Zurich 11, Switzerland

CGE-FIAR
Via G.B. Grassi 93, 20157 Milan, Italy

DORNIER SYSTEM GmbH
Postfach 648, 799 Friedrichshafen/Bodensee, Germany

TELEFONAKTIEBOLAGET L. M. ERICSSON
126 25 Stockholm, Sweden

MONTEDEL (MONTECATINI EDISON ELETTRONICA SpA)
Via E Bassini 15, 20133 Milan, Italy

SENER SA
Guzman el Bueno 133, Madrid 3, Spain

SOCIÉTÉ EUROPÉENNE DE PROPULSION
Tour Roussel-Nobel, Cédex 3, 92080-Paris Défense, France

THOMSON-CSF
173 boulevard Hausmann, 75360-Paris, Cédex 08, France

STAR (Satellites for Telecommunications, Applications and Research) companies are involved in several major space programmes, notably ISEE-2, of which details follow:

ISEE-2 EXPLORER SATELLITE

Dornier System is prime contractor for the International Sun-Earth Explorer (ISEE-2) satellite, on behalf of the STAR consortium. BAe supplied the spacecraft's attitude and orbit control subsystems, sensors, hinged booms for sensor deployment and mechanical ground support equipment. Sener was responsible for the 15 m (49 ft) antenna booms. The power developed by the solar array is 120W.

This is a joint NASA/ESA programme, involving three satellites. Two of these (ISEE-1 and ISEE-3) were developed under NASA auspices; ISEE-2 is the responsibility of the European Space Agency.

ISEE-1 and 2 were launched by a single Delta vehicle on 22 October 1977 and ISEE-3 was launched on 12 August 1978. The missions are intended to investigate solar-terrestrial relationships at the outermost boundaries of the Earth's magnetosphere. The satellites carry carefully matched scientific experiments from Europe and the US. Separating the satellites by a controlled distance makes it possible to compare their results.

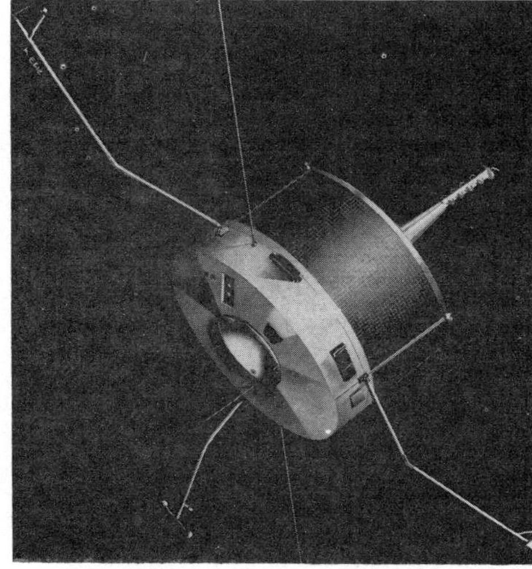

Artist's impression of ISEE-2 Explorer satellite

ITALY

AERITALIA

AERITALIA-SOCIETÀ AEROSPAZIALE ITALIANA p.a.
Diversified Activities Group
Headquarters: See Aircraft section
Executive Director: Ing Stefano Abba

Space Sector
Corso Marche, 41-10146-Turin
Telephone: (011) 33321
Telex: 23076 AERITOR

Aeritalia is engaged in research and development of missile and space vehicle systems. It is a member of the VFW-Fokker/ERNO Spacelab consortium and of the MESH European satellite consortium.

The Space Sector's current activities include work on the structure and heat shields for the Italian Alfa vehicle (described in 1977-78 *Jane's*) and its engine; design and manufacture of the Ariane test satellite CAT; work on the OTS, MARECS and ECS satellites and on the thermal control system for Spacelab. The Sector also worked on the Italian Sirio satellite for CNA (which see).

CNA

COMPAGNIA NAZIONALE AEROSPAZIALE
Via Salaria Km 9·3, 00199 Rome
Telephone: (06) 840 2941
Telex: 61295 CNASPA
Director General: Dott Antonio Teofilatto

This company succeeds the former Compagnia Industriale Aerospaziale, which was formed in 1965 for the design and development of aerospace systems. Its current parent companies are Aeritalia, Montedison Sistemi, Selenia and SNIA Viscosa.

The company was involved primarily in development of the Sirio satellite, produced under the sponsorship of the Consiglio Nazionale Ricerche (CNR) of Rome and launched on 25 August 1977. Sirio reached station at 15°W longitude on 8 September 1977 where it is involved in SHF propagation experiments. Brief details of this satellite were given in the 1977-78 *Jane's*.

CN Aerospaziale is currently developing Sirio 2, designed to support the METEOSAT and LASSO missions, under contract to the European Space Agency.

JAPAN

MITSUBISHI

MITSUBISHI JUKOGYO KABUSHIKI KAISHA (Mitsubishi Heavy Industries Ltd)
Mitsubishi Electric Corporation
5-1, Marunouchi, 2-chome, Chiyoda-ku, Tokyo 100
Officers: See Aircraft section
Manager, Space Systems Department: M. Hamada

Mitsubishi Heavy Industries has co-operated with the National Space Development Agency of Japan in the programme for the N-1 and N-2 launch vehicles; with the National Aerospace Laboratory, which supports rocket research; and with the Institute of Space and Aeronautical Science, University of Tokyo, which is a major contributor to scientific satellite programmes. It is also a designer and manufacturer of space subsystems, as well as ground support equipment.

Mitsubishi Electric Corporation designed and manufactured the CS satellite for NASDA (which see).

NASDA
NATIONAL SPACE DEVELOPMENT AGENCY OF JAPAN

2-4-1, Hamamatsu-cho, Minato-ku, Tokyo 105
Telephone: (03) 435-6111
Telex: J28424
President: Akiyoshi Matsuura
Director, Systems Planning Department: Koichi Yamaguchi

This Agency was established on 1 October 1969, with primary responsibility for Japanese development of satellites, launch vehicles, tracking systems, and associated facilities and equipment.

In addition to the programme of satellites to be launched by the N vehicle (which see), NASDA has another programme involving three geostationary satellites launched by US vehicles—Geostationary Meteorological Satellite (GMS) launched on 14 July 1977 and described in 1977-78 *Jane's*, the experimental Communications Satellite (CS) Sakura, launched on 15 December 1977, and the experimental Broadcasting Satellite (BSE) Yuri launched on 7 April 1978. CS and BSE are described in the 1978-79 *Jane's*.

The future NASDA programme calls for the launching of two more engineering satellites, a second met-sat, a geosurvey satellite, a second com-sat and a maritime observation satellite.

H-1 LAUNCH VEHICLE

This three-stage vehicle is being designed to launch heavy satellites in the mid-eighties. It will be able to launch satellites weighing 500 kg (1,102 lb) into geostationary orbit.

N LAUNCH VEHICLE

The three-stage N-1 launch vehicle is capable of putting a 920 kg (2,028 lb) satellite into a 200 km (124 mile) orbit or a 145 kg (320 lb) satellite into a geostationary orbit. The first stage consists of a Douglas DSV-3N-1 liquid-propellant (liquid oxygen/kerosene) rocket, with three Nissan (Thiokol TX-354-5) solid-propellant strap-on boosters (approx 1,471 kN; 330,600 lb st); the LE-3 second stage is powered by a storable liquid rocket (NTO/A-50), and the third stage by a Thiokol TE-364-3 solid rocket. The guidance system is of the strap-down radio command type. The N-2 vehicle has an extended long-tank DSV-3P-1, nine strap-on boosters and inertial guidance, and is designed to put a 350 kg (772 lb) satellite into geostationary orbit. It is scheduled to be tested in 1980, and will have an Aerojet AJ-10-118F second stage instead of the LE-3 of the N-1.

With the N vehicle NASDA launched the Ionosphere Sounding Satellite-B (ISS-B) on 16 February 1978, and the Experimental Communications Satellite (ECS) on 6 February 1979. The N vehicle is expected to be utilised for launching other satellites later, including ETS-3. Now in the project stage, ETS-3 is being designed to establish the production and operational technology of three-axis stabilised satellites with a high-accuracy attitude control system. Also being designed for launch by N vehicles are GS-1, a balloon-type satellite intended to establish a geodetic system, and MOS-1, an Earth and ocean survey satellite.

The main parameters of the N-1 and N-2 vehicles are:

Dimensions (approx):
- Length overall: (N-1) — 32·6 m (106 ft 11 in)
  - (N-2) — 35·0 m (114 ft 10 in)
- Diameter of first stage:
  - (N-1 and N-2) — 2·4 m (8 ft 2½ in)

Weight (approx): (N-1) — 90,000 kg (198,400 lb)
- (N-2) — 137,168 kg (302,400 lb)

First launching of N rocket

NISSAN
NISSAN JIDOSHA KABUSHIKI KAISHA (Nissan Motor Co Ltd)

Head Office: 17-1, 6-chome, Ginza, Chuo-ku, Tokyo
Aeronautical and Space Division: 5-1, 3-chome, Momoi, Suginami-ku, Tokyo
Telephone: Tokyo (390) 1111
Telex: 0-232-2271
Chairman: Katsuji Kawamata
President: Takashi Ishihara
Executive Managing Director: Kohichiro Tanaka
Manager, Aeronautical and Space Division: Kazuo Shibata

The Aeronautical and Space Division of Nissan is responsible for the major share of work on rockets and missiles in Japan. It has produced many sounding rockets (see 1977-78 *Jane's*) and many research rockets for the Japanese Aerospace Laboratory, Meteorological Agency and Antarctic Research Centre. Nissan has also developed a number of rocket motors of the kind used in the NASDA N satellite launch vehicle. The first-stage strap-on boosters are produced by Nissan under licence from Thiokol Corporation, USA, and the third-stage solid-propellant motors are procured and serviced by Nissan.

Mu ROCKET

Details of Mu-4S, Mu-3C, Mu-3C-1 and Mu-3C-2 satellite launching rockets were given in the 1977-78 *Jane's*. The Mu-3H launch vehicle is basically an Mu-3C with an improved M13 first stage. Brief details of the MS-T3 Tansei 3 and Exos-A satellites launched by Mu vehicles were given in the 1978-79 *Jane's*. Exos-B was launched on 16 September 1978 and placed in a 30,558 × 230 km (18,987 × 143 miles) orbit; when in orbit this scientific satellite was named Jikiken. Corsa-B (Hakucho), an X-ray observation satellite, was launched on 21 February 1979. The 120 kg (265 lb) scientific satellites Astro-A and Astro-B will be launched by improved Mu-3S boosters in the 1980s.

The following details apply to the Mu-3H:

Type: Solid-propellant three-stage satellite launch vehicle.

Power Plant: M13 first stage gives 866 kN (194,670 lb st) at sea level, and is supplemented by eight SB strap-on boosters, giving a total of 785 kN (176,440 lb st). The M22 second stage gives 360 kN (80,910 lb st) in vacuo and is fitted with liquid-injection thrust vector control. The M3A third stage gives 73·55 kN (16,535 lb st) in vacuo and has a similar control system.

Upper-stage spherical motor and Jikiken satellite

Dimensions:
- Length overall:
  - M13 1st stage — 14·98 m (49 ft 2 in)
  - M22 2nd stage — 4·87 m (16 ft 0 in)
  - M3A 3rd stage — 1·54 m (5 ft 1 in)
- Diameter:
  - M13 1st stage — 1·50 m (4 ft 11 in)
  - M22 2nd stage — 1·41 m (4 ft 7½ in)
  - M3A 3rd stage — 1·14 m (3 ft 9 in)

Weights:
- At launch:
  - M13 1st stage — 32,264 kg (71,130 lb)
  - SB boosters (8) — 3,825 kg (8,432 lb)
  - M22 2nd stage — 8,635 kg (19,037 lb)
  - M3A 3rd stage — 1,240 kg (2,734 lb)

Mu-3H-3 launch vehicle

UNION OF SOVIET SOCIALIST REPUBLICS

Available details of Soviet satellites, space probes and spacecraft have appeared in *Jane's* since the 1959-60 edition, together with descriptions of the A-2 and A-3 research rockets and meteorological rockets which are standard vehicles in constant use.

COSMOS SATELLITES

This series of satellites is continuing the Soviet programme of research into physical phenomena in space and the Earth's upper atmosphere; and into the technical problems involved in spaceflight and the development of spacecraft design and their systems; as well as conducting experiments of an applied nature of interest to science and the Soviet economy.

The wide terms of reference mean that a Cosmos satellite can vary from a small uninstrumented device to a large spacecraft capable of life support, and military applications. The majority of the scientific satellites are of a basic standard design in which various experiment payloads can be accommodated. They are cylindrical in shape, approximately 1·83 m (6 ft) long by 1·05 m (3 ft 6 in) in diameter and weigh about 360 kg (800 lb).

Cosmos 637, launched on 26 March 1974, was the first satellite in the series to be placed in a synchronous orbit. Positioned over the Indian Ocean, it is assumed to have been an early version of the Statsionar communications satellite announced by the Soviet authorities in 1970. Stat-

Cosmos scientific satellite *(Maurice Allward)*

Mockup of Cosmos 782 biological satellite, embodying components of Vostok manned spacecraft *(Tass)*

sionar 1, the first operational satellite of this class, was launched on 22 December 1975. (See the Raduga entry in this section.)

In October 1976, the Soviet authorities announced the creation of the Morsvyazsputnik Organisation, which is responsible for the management of Soviet maritime communications satellites.

MILITARY COSMOS

As the satellite table at the end of this section indicates, Cosmos designations are given to Soviet reconnaissance satellites and other types of military spacecraft.

Cosmos reconnaissance satellites are launched from the bases at Plesetsk and Tyuratam, usually into orbits with inclinations of 52°, 65° or 72°. Most eject capsules after 8 days and these are presumably recovered. Some have the capacity for in-flight frequency changing; others have a small manoeuvring capability for precise target coverage.

Cosmos 317 appeared to be the first of a new series of operational reconnaissance satellites with an 11-13 day life, instead of the 8 days of early versions. An unusual characteristic of some of the longer-life craft is the ejection of a capsule just before recovery. The ejected capsule goes into a slightly lower orbit, where it remains for several days until it decays naturally.

A number of test vehicles for the Soviet Union's Fractional Orbital Bombardment System were given Cosmos designations. Cosmos designations have also been given to spacecraft which have the capability of intercepting other satellites. Early 'interceptors' were Cosmos 249, 252, 374 and 375. In the first of a later series of typical tests, Cosmos 803, launched on 12 February 1976, was the target and was intercepted by Cosmos 804 and 814. Cosmos 804 executed three major manoeuvres and achieved a close intercept, after which it was manoeuvred out of orbit. Other Cosmos satellites used for intercept tests were described in the 1977-78 *Jane's*. Three distinct attack procedures appear to be used: Eccentric Orbit mode, where the attack satellite is launched into an eccentric orbit in which it makes a flyby of the target; Circular Orbit mode, where the attack satellite is injected into a circular orbit similar to that of the target, the interception being made at a slower flyby speed; Pop-Up mode, where the attack satellite intercepts within one revolution, in contrast to the other two modes, which require several revolutions. The Pop-Up mode of attack is difficult to counter, as there is little advance indication of an intended target.

Cosmos 629, launched from Plesetsk on 24 January 1974 into an orbit inclined at 62·8° to the equator, was the first recoverable reconnaissance satellite to employ this inclination. It has been used by the majority of reconnaissance satellites since then.

A number of Cosmos satellites have been launched into orbits suitable for ocean surveillance missions. The first of these was Cosmos 198, launched on 27 December 1967. Cosmos 651 and subsequent spacecraft in this series appear to be bigger, with a length of about 12 m (40 ft) compared with 6 m (20 ft) of the earlier satellites. All the satellites were launched into an initially low orbit of about 250 km (155 miles) but after a few weeks moved into an approximately circular orbit of 1,000 km (620 miles).

COSMOS LAUNCHERS

Two categories of launch vehicle appear to be used for Cosmos and Intercosmos satellites, and other Soviet spacecraft. One category is based on the structures and power plants of standard missiles, such as the SS-4 ('Sandal'), SS-5 ('Skean') and SS-9 ('Scarp'), with additional upper stages as required. The other combines the basic core vehicle developed originally for the Vostok manned spacecraft with a variety of upper stages. Examples are as follows:

SS-4 + Cosmos stage. First stage powered by 706·34 kN (158,800 lb st) RD-214 four-chamber liquid-propellant rocket engine, burning nitric acid and kerosene. Second stage powered by RD-119 single-chamber engine, burning liquid oxygen and dimethylhydrazine, and giving 107·87 kN (24,250 lb thrust) in vacuum. Typical launch, on 26 June 1974, orbited Cosmos 662, a 408 kg (900 lb) ellipsoid, 1·83 m (6 ft) long with a diameter of 1·22 m (4 ft), intended for scientific research. (Referred to as B-1 Cosmos in drawing on page 679).

SS-5 + Restart stage. A typical application for the SS-5 is to orbit satellites like Cosmos 655 and 661. Shaped as cylinders, 1·83 m (6 ft) long and 0·91 m (3 ft) in diameter, with paddle-type solar panels, these are thought to have navigation and/or electronic intelligence missions. (Referred to as C-1 Cosmos in drawing on page 679).

SS-9 + FOBS stage. Frequent launches of this vehicle are expected to contribute to continued development of Fractional Orbital Bombardment System techniques and/or to ocean surveillance missions. Satellites like Cosmos 651 and 654 normally remain in low parking orbit for two months, then split and move into a 104 min orbit.

Vostok core + Venus stage. This standard launch vehicle has many applications. It is used with an escape stage to orbit the 1,250 kg (2,750 lb) uprated Molniya 2 communications satellites. Typical military payloads were Cosmos 639, a manoeuvrable reconnaissance satellite intended probably to study the breakup of Arctic pack ice; and Cosmos 658, a reconnaissance satellite in the form of a four-ton sphere-cylinder, 5·0 m (16 ft 6 in) long, which remained in orbit for 12 days.

EKRAN

Ekran ('Screen') is the name given by Vasily Shamshin, Soviet First Deputy Minister of Communications, to a new generation of geostationary television relay satellites, although the first spacecraft in the series was given the international registration of Statsionar T.

Purpose of the satellite is to make it possible to set up a system of television communications throughout the whole of the Soviet Union.

Ekran is a direct-broadcast satellite, relaying television signals directly to community aerials throughout the country. Earlier Statsionar satellites are conventional relay spacecraft, transmitting programmes from Moscow to special Earth satellite stations in Russia and bordering countries.

The Ekran spacecraft is operating at 714MHz and, in addition to advanced relay equipment, embodies a three-axis Earth-directed orientation system, a power supply system using solar batteries which is independently orientated on the Sun, an orbital correction system, a radio telemetry system to transmit information on the functioning of the various systems, and a radio system for the accurate measurement of the orbital parameters and spacecraft control.

Ekran 1 (Statsionar T) was launched on 26 October 1976 into a geostationary orbit and then manoeuvred into its scheduled position at 90° E.

Ekran geostationary TV relay satellite, displayed at 1977 Paris Air Show *(Flight International)*

HORIZONT

Horizont ('Horizon') is the name given to a new series of communications satellites for telephone and television transmissions. The use of an inclined orbit gives better coverage for areas in the far north of the Soviet Union. The first Horizont satellite was launched on 19 December 1978 into an elliptical orbit with a significantly higher perigee than Molniya satellites.

INTERCOSMOS SATELLITES

Launched on 14 October 1969, Intercosmos 1 involved the co-operation of seven Socialist countries: Bulgaria, Czechoslovakia, Germany (Democratic Republic), Hungary, Poland, Romania and the USSR. The satellite carried scientific instruments developed and made in Czechoslovakia and Germany as well as in the USSR. Its programme was devoted mainly to research connected with the Sun, and involved simultaneous observations in the seven participating countries into radio-astronomical, ionospheric and optical phenomena.

Details of subsequent Intercosmos launches have been given in successive editions of *Jane's*. Spacecraft in this series launched during 1978 are listed in the satellite table at the end of this section.

METEOR

Meteor is the name given to the Soviet series of first-generation operational meteorological satellites, developed from Cosmos prototypes.

The satellites, which provide information about the state of the atmosphere both on the 'daylight' and 'night' sides of the Earth, are stabilised so that the camera lenses and infra-red instruments always point towards the Earth.

Information received from Meteors is supplied to the Soviet hydro-meteorological service and to the World Meteorological Service. Cloud cover picture charts are transmitted to Washington, Geneva, Tokyo, Sydney and other foreign weather services.

Meteor 1 was launched on 26 March 1969; and launchings have continued at a current rate of three or four per year.

The Meteor system consists of three satellites in orbital planes at 90° and 180° to each other, so that they pass over a given area of the Earth on the northbound pass at intervals of about 6 hours and 12 hours, and again during the southbound pass.

MOLNIYA

Molniya 1 (Lightning), launched on 23 April 1965, was a communications satellite placed in a highly elliptical orbit designed to provide the longest possible communications sessions between Moscow and Vladivostok. It was the first Soviet communications satellite. On 24 November 1971, **Molniya 2A**, the first of a new uprated version, was launched from Plesetsk.

Launches of both versions have continued, and the current operational system consists of four pairs of each type of Molniya circling the Earth in orbital planes spaced at 90° intervals. The planes rotate at the rate of about 1° a day, in order to maintain stationary ground tracks over the Earth throughout the year, thus providing predictable communications coverage over the whole of the USSR.

Molniya 3 is the latest version, embodying improved communications equipment able to accommodate colour television and new communications frequencies. The first of the new spacecraft was launched on 21 November 1974, and was placed in a normal Molniya-type 12 h 17 min orbit, with its 650 km (400 mile) perigee over the southern hemisphere and its apogee of 40,690 km (25,283 miles) over the northern hemisphere.

Prognoz 2 solar research satellite *(Tass)*

PROGNOZ

Launched on 14 April 1972, Prognoz 1 (Forecast) was the first of a series of satellites designed specifically to study processes of solar activity, and their influence on the interplanetary medium and the Earth's magnetosphere.

Prognoz is basically spherical, with four cruciform solar panels extended to provide power via an internal rechargeable chemical battery. The sphere, filled with an inert gas, contains telemetry equipment, temperature control components and the electrical system. Experiments on board are intended to measure: electromagnetic solar radiation generated simultaneously with solar flares; solar cosmic radiation; solar wind plasma; and radio waves.

Subsequent Prognoz launches have been recorded in the annual tables of satellites.

PROGRESS

Progress is a non-reusable unmanned spacecraft, designed to ferry supplies and equipment up to space stations of the Salyut type. A development of the basic two-man Soyuz spacecraft, it is lightened as much as possible, with all the normal Soyuz life support systems removed, to permit carriage of the maximum practicable payload. The propulsion module is almost unchanged; but the size of the instrument module is increased. The major change entails replacement of the standard Soyuz descent module with a tanker module carrying propellants.

Positioning, rendezvous, approach and docking can be effected automatically or controlled from Salyut. The freight compartment of Progress is hermetically sealed, so that, after the vehicle has docked, cosmonauts can work in comfort while transferring supplies to their space station.

After transfer of the supplies, the spacecraft is used as a receptacle for waste material such as spent oxygen regenerators and filters, empty food and water cartons, sewage and redundant flight documentation. It is then jettisoned, to burn up in the atmosphere on re-entry; recovery is not attempted.

Weight of the first Progress was announced as 7,020 kg (15,476 lb), of which 2,300 kg (5,071 lb) was cargo, 1,000 kg (2,204 lb) fuel and 1,300 kg (2,866 lb) food etc. Weight varies according to mission. Progress is 10·8 m (35 ft 5 in) long with a maximum diameter of 3·7 m (12 ft 2 in).

Progress 1. Launched on 20 January 1978, ferried supplies to Salyut 6, with which it docked on 22 January. While docked, the first-ever refuelling in space was conducted on 3 February, following checks by the crew of Soyuz 26. The spacecraft undocked on 6 February, and re-entered and burned up the next day.

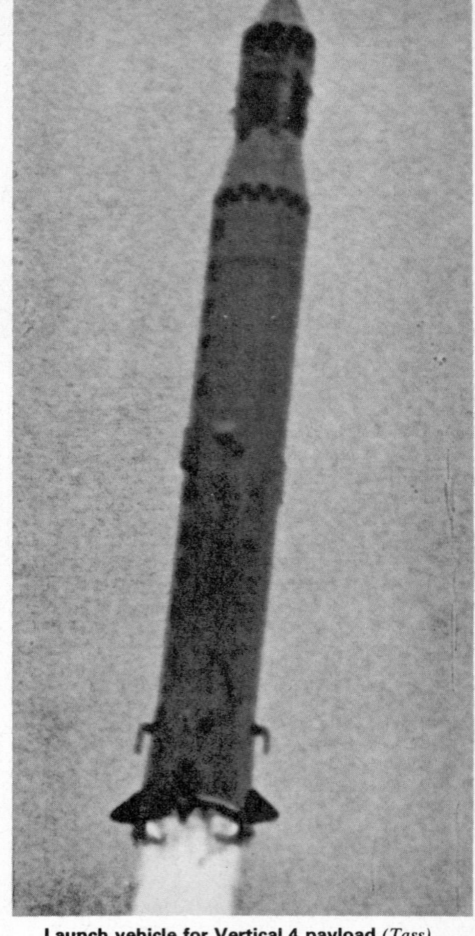

Launch vehicle for Vertical 4 payload *(Tass)*

Full-scale model of Molniya 2 communications satellite *(Brian M. Service)*

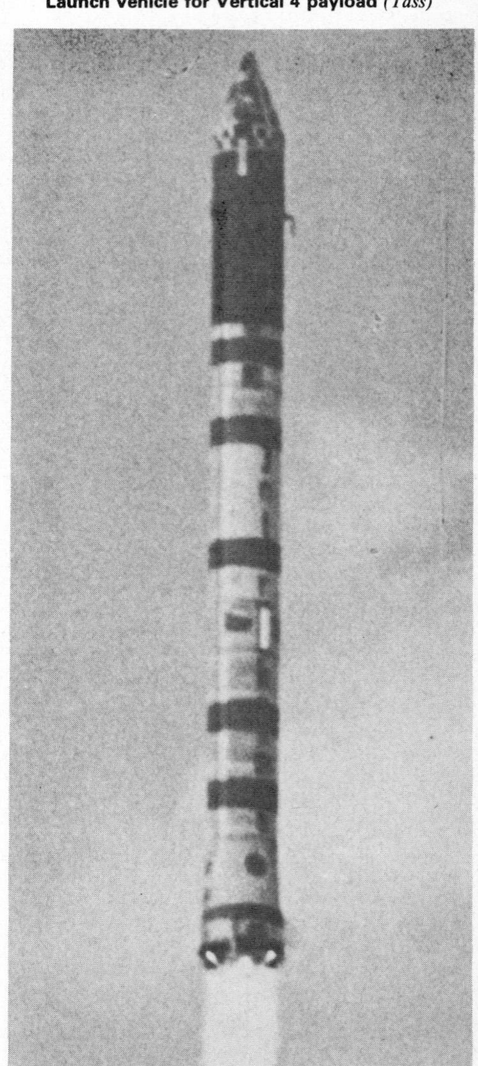

Launch vehicle for Intercosmos 16 satellite *(Tass)*

Progress 2. Launched on 7 July 1978, carried consumables to the Soyuz 29 (which see) crew aboard Salyut 6 (which see). Spacecraft docked on 9 July, using the recently vacated aft docking port.

Progress 3. Launched on 7 August 1978, carried mainly food to Salyut 6, still occupied by the Soyuz 29 crew. Docked on 10 August, using the port on the Salyut instrument unit, undocked 21 August.

Progress 4. Launched on 3 October 1978, carried more fuel and consumables to Salyut 6 for the crew of Soyuz 29. Docked on 6 October; refuelling completed by 13 October. On 20 October Progress 4's engines were used to raise the Salyut 6/Soyuz 31/Progress 4 complex from a 340 × 321 km (211 × 199 miles) orbit to a 362 × 359 km (225 × 223 miles) orbit. Undocked 24 October.

Progress 5. Launched on 12 March 1979, carried fuel, equipment, water, food, mail and other cargo to Salyut 6 for the crew of Soyuz 32 (which see), who had been busy reactivating the space station. Docked on 14 March. Progress 5 mission tested improvements in the design of unmanned transport spacecraft. Equipment carried included a television set on which programmes of USSR Central Television can be received, a Koltso radio system for communication between members of the crew and ground control, an improved Kristall furnace and a gamma-ray telescope. On 30 March the engine of the transport spacecraft was used to increase the orbit of the Salyut 6/Soyuz 32/Progress 5 complex.

RADUGA/STATSIONAR

Raduga (Rainbow) is the name of a Soviet system of geostationary-orbit communications satellites, the first operational version of which, **Statsionar 1**, was launched on 22 December 1975.

Statsionars are three-axis stabilised, and transmit at higher power levels than comparable US-launched Intelsat IV spacecraft. This enables them to communicate with smaller and therefore cheaper ground terminals. Currently, the spacecraft communicate with the Orbita network of ground stations set up for the Molniya programme.

Details of Statsionar launches can be found in the annual tables of satellites.

SALYUT

Salyut (Salute) spacecraft have served as orbital scientific stations for the crews of Soyuz manned spacecraft. Basically, the station is a stepped cylinder about 13 m (42 ft 8 in) long, from 2·13 m (7 ft) to 4·0 m (13 ft) in diameter, with a weight of 18½ tons.

Details of Salyut 1 and 2 can be found in the 1973-74 *Jane's*. Salyut 3 was described in the 1975-76 edition. Salyut 4 and 5 were described in the 1977-78 edition.

Salyut 6, launched on 29 September 1977, is a major development of Salyut 5, the main change being the embodiment of a second docking port so that two Soyuz-type spacecraft can be docked simultaneously. The additional port is located on the instrument section, opposite the original port on the transfer compartment. The two ports are identical, and the automatic rendezvous procedure is the same at both, but only the new port embodies refuelling facilities. Normal crew is two, increasing for short periods of time to four. Soviet sources indicate that the station can support six cosmonauts.

Internal modifications by comparison with early Salyuts include the installation of a folding shower cubicle, into which hot water is sprayed and recovered by an extractor pump. Sensors are fitted to register the impact of micrometeorites.

Major items of equipment installed in the Working Compartment include a BST-IM submillimetre telescope, an MKF-6M multi-spectral camera and a KT-140 high-resolution topographical camera system.

An initial programme of research involving Soyuz 26, 27 and 28, and Progress 1, was described in the 1978-79 *Jane's.* A second programme started on 16 June 1978 with the docking of Soyuz 29 (which see), crewed by Vladimir Kovalyonok and Alexander Ivanchenkov, who set a new endurance record for manned space flight of 140 days, ending on 2 November 1978.

During this period the two cosmonauts carried out an extensive programme of research and experiments, were visited by the crews of Soyuz 30 and 31 (which see), and were re-supplied with fuel, food and equipment ferried up by the Progress 2, 3 and 4 unmanned transport spacecraft (which see). Activities during the 140-day programme included a 2 h 5 min EVA on 29 July 1978 by Kovalyonok and Ivanchenkov, and a burn of the Progress 4 engines on 20 October to raise the Salyut's orbit. The second programme ended on 2 November 1978 with the return to Earth of the two cosmonauts in Soyuz 31.

A third programme started on 26 February 1979 with the docking of Soyuz 32 (which see) and the boarding of cosmonauts Lyakhov and Ryumin. An early problem was a fault which developed in one of the three propellant tanks aboard the space station.

SOYUZ SPACECRAFT

Developed for the Russian Earth-orbital space station programme, Soyuz spacecraft each comprise three basic sections or modules: a laboratory-cum-rest compartment (orbital module), a descent compartment (landing module) and a propulsion and instrument section (service module). The orbital module is mounted on the extreme nose of the craft, and communicates with the landing module via a hermetically-sealed hatch. The orbital and landing modules are pressurised to 1·01 bars (14·7 lb/sq in), have a combined internal volume of 9 m³ (318 cu ft) and can accommodate up to four cosmonauts.

Full-scale representation of the Salyut 3/4 type of space station *(Tass)*

The service module contains the main systems for orbital flight, together with a liquid-propellant propulsion system embodying two motors (one a standby) each with a thrust of 3·92 kN (880 lb). These allow midcourse manoeuvres, up to heights of 1,300 km (800 miles), and are used for the de-orbit manoeuvre. Another system provides attitude control. Attached to the service module is a solar-cell array having an area of about 14 m² (150 sq ft).

The landing module contains the parachutes and landing rockets. A backup parachute system is available in case of failure. The main parachute, preceded by a pilot 'chute, is deployed at 8,000 m (27,000 ft). Retro-rockets, operating at a height of about 1 m (3 ft) above the ground, ensure a landing velocity not exceeding 3 m/s (10 ft/s). The aerodynamic design of the landing module permits landing loads to be kept within 3-4*g*, although ballistic re-entries, involving loads of 8-10*g*, can be made if required. The overall length of the craft is about 9 m (30 ft), the diameter of the crew compartments about 2·1 m (7 ft) and the all-up weight about 6,000 kg (13,000 lb).

The Soyuz craft are equipped with an automatic control system for approach and docking manoeuvres, the technique and external aerials being similar to those employed on the Cosmos spacecraft 186 and 188, and 212 and 213.

The missions of Soyuz 1 to 28 were described in previous editions of *Jane's.*

Soyuz 29. Launched on 15 June 1978 with Col Vladimir Kovalyonok (commander) and Alexander Ivanchenkov (flt. engineer), Soyuz 29 docked with the forward docking port of Salyut 6 (which see) on 16 June, to continue the occupation of the space station begun by the crews of Soyuz 26-28 earlier in the year.

The two cosmonauts returned safely to Earth on 2 November 1978, after completing the then-longest manned space flight of 140 days, during which they were visited by the crews of Soyuz 30 and 31 (which see) and supplied with food, fuel and other supplies ferried to the space station by Progress 2, 3 and 4 (which see).

On 7 September 1978, Kovalyonok and Ivanchenkov entered the Soyuz 31 spacecraft (which see), undocked from Salyut 6 and, after the station had been rotated, re-docked, using the forward docking unit. This left the aft one, which has refuelling facilities, free for the Progress 4 supply spacecraft.

Kovalyonok and Ivanchenkov returned to Earth in Soyuz 31, the original crew of which used Soyuz 29 to return. During their long stay in space, Kovalyonok and Ivanchenkov carried out an extensive programme of research and experiments, including many with the Kristall space furnace. To assist re-adaptation to the Earth's gravitation after four and a half months of weightlessness, the two cosmonauts performed special exercises and wore vacuum suits during their last weeks in orbit. Towards the end of their mission they were also busy activating the Soyuz 31 spacecraft used for their return and 'mothballing' Salyut 6.

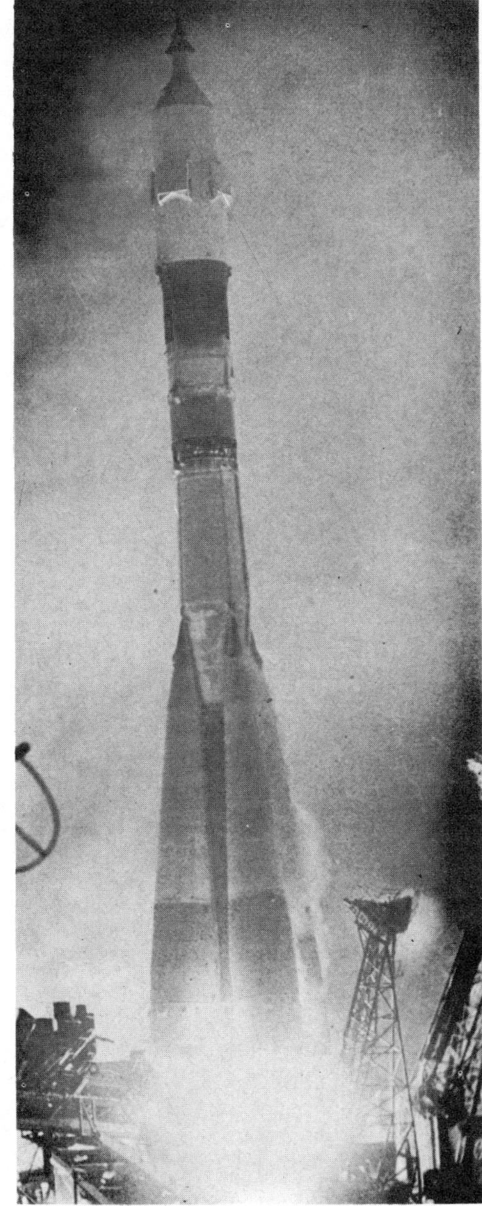
Launch of Soyuz 28 (Note: photograph could not be trimmed to show true vertical lift-off) *(Tass)*

Soyuz 30. Launched on 27 June 1978, Soyuz 30 was commanded by Lt Col Pyotr Klimuk with Major Miroslaw Giermaszewski of the Polish Air Force (acting as flight engineer). The spacecraft docked with the aft port of Salyut 6 (which see) on 28 June. There followed a seven-day programme of research, some of it prepared jointly by Soviet and Polish scientists. In particular, experiments were carried out involving the manufacture of semiconductor materials under conditions of weightlessness. On 2 July the Salyut 6/Soyuz 29/Soyuz 30 complex was orientated to enable a multizonal camera to photograph individual regions of the western Soviet Union. Soyuz 30 undocked on 5 July and returned safely to Earth.

Soyuz 31. Launched on 26 August 1978, Soyuz 31 was commanded by Col Valery Bykovsky, who had flown previously in Vostok 5 and Soyuz 22. In the seat normally occupied by the flight engineer was researcher Sigmund Jahn of the German Democratic Republic. The spacecraft docked with the port on the instrument unit of Salyut 6 (which see) on 27 August. After a programme of international research lasting seven days, Bykovsky and Jahn returned to Earth on 3 September using the Soyuz 29 spacecraft which had remained docked with Salyut 6 since 16 June 1977. Soyuz 31 was used by the crew of Soyuz 29 (which see) for their return to Earth.

Soyuz 32. Launched on 25 February 1979, Soyuz 32 was commanded by Lt Col Vladimir Lyakhov, with Valery Ryumin as flight engineer. On 26 February the spacecraft docked with Salyut 6 (which see), which had been orbiting in the unmanned mode since the departure of the Soyuz 29 crew on 2 November 1978, to begin a new programme of research and experiment. On boarding Salyut 6, Lyakhov and Ryumin started extensive maintenance checks and restoration work made necessary by the fact the station had been in space for nearly a year and a half, of which 250 days were in the manned mode. Of interest was the significant wear of cables and other mobile elements of radio communication units. On the check list were the rotating mechanism and seals of the 'Splav' experiment chamber which, in use, turns to expose its contents to space.

On 14 March the unmanned transport spacecraft Progress 5 (which see) docked with Salyut 6, bringing fuel and other supplies to the two cosmonauts.

SOYUZ LAUNCHER

The vehicle used for launching Soyuz spacecraft appears to be a development of the booster used for launching the original Vostok spacecraft, with some 11·8 m (36 ft) of additional upper staging and structures. To cater for the increased weight and bending moment the inter-stage truss is strengthened. During launch, the Soyuz vehicle is surmounted by an escape tower.

It is not possible to identify the current engines in the launch vehicle, or give their individual ratings. However, official Soviet reports have stated that the vehicle has a total thrust of around 60 million horsepower, which is three times the power quoted for the original Vostok launcher. The basic configuration has not changed. Thus, the first stage consists of a central core, powered by an engine with four primary nozzles and four verniers. This is surrounded by four wrap-round boosters, each with four primary nozzles and two verniers, so that 32 rocket chambers are fired simultaneously during lift-off.

Data given in a brochure issued by Aérospatiale of France suggest that the Soyuz launcher can insert payloads of up to 7,500 kg (16,535 lb) into low circular orbit; 2,400 kg (5,290 lb) into geostationary transfer orbit; and satellites of up to 1,100 kg (2,425 lb) into geostationary orbit.

VENUS

Venus is the name given to a series of spacecraft developed specifically to explore the planet Venus. Details of Venus 1 to 10 were given in earlier editions of *Jane's*, and the basic spacecraft was described in the 1977-78 edition.

Venus 11 was launched on 9 September 1978, and **Venus 12** on 14 September. The two spacecraft reached the planet in December 1978, and their descent modules landed on the surface on 25 and 21 December respectively (Venus 12, on a shorter flight path, arrived first). The descent modules sent back a great deal of information, that of Venus 11 transmitting for 95 minutes. The modules confirmed earlier discoveries of a predominantly carbon dioxide atmosphere, with a surface pressure about 88 times greater than that on the Earth, and a surface temperature of about 450°C.

VENUS LAUNCHER

Although basically similar in configuration to the launchers used for the Soviet manned spacecraft, the launcher for Venus probes appears to have elongated first and second stages, giving an increase in propellant tankage.

ZONDA LAUNCHER

A drawing purporting to show this largest known Soviet launch vehicle appeared in a brochure issued by Aérospatiale of France in 1977. The drawing, of which a copy appears on page 679, suggests that Zonda has the same configuration as the Soyuz vehicle. The first stage is shown as a large-diameter core, surrounded by six large boosters. The upper stages are attached by a truss structure.

Overall height of Zonda is shown as about 61·33 m (201 ft). It is stated to be able to insert a payload of 22,000 kg (48,500 lb) into low circular orbit; 5,000 kg (11,020 lb) into geostationary transfer orbit; and satellites weighing up to 1,600 kg (3,525 lb) into geostationary orbit.

UNITED KINGDOM

BAe
BRITISH AEROSPACE
Dynamics Group

HEAD OFFICE: Six Hills Way, Stevenage, Herts SG1 2DA

BRISTOL WORKS: PO Box 77, Filton House, Bristol BS99 7AR

HATFIELD WORKS: Manor Road, Hatfield, Herts AL10 9LL

CHAIRMAN AND CHIEF EXECUTIVE: G. R. Jefferson

GROUP MARKETING DIRECTOR: L. A. Sanson

GROUP PUBLIC RELATIONS MANAGER: M. K. Hird

Following nationalisation of major units of the UK aerospace industry, British Aircraft Corporation's Guided Weapons Division and Hawker Siddeley Dynamics Ltd became the Dynamics Group of British Aerospace on 1 January 1978. Both of the former concerns had played major roles in British and international space projects for many years, as described in previous editions of *Jane's*.

Among a wide variety of space technology programmes currently in hand, under contract to the European Space Agency and US companies, British Aerospace is leading the MESH international consortium as prime contractor for ESA's European Communications Satellite (ECS) and MARECS, a maritime version of ECS. The ECS project aims to provide a fully operational satellite communications system for Europe in the 1980s, providing bulk telephone transmissions in 'time division multiple-access' mode, and TV distribution to complement existing terrestrial systems. MARECS (described in the MESH entry) will provide direct telephone and telex links between ships in distant oceans and shore stations in the UK and elsewhere.

Also for ESA, British Aerospace in 1979 completed a study of the payload for an Earth Resources Survey Satellite System, and is currently developing and manufacturing the 33 m² (356 sq ft) 4kW solar array and the photon detector assembly for NASA's Space Telescope being built by Lockheed Missiles and Space Company. Other solar array work for spacecraft applications, under contract to ESA, includes development of a 6kW lightweight flexible fold-out array for communications satellites of the next decade, and proposals to augment Space Shuttle power, using solar power modules of up to 60kW.

As prime contractor of the STAR consortium, BAe was responsible for the ESA satellite GEOS-2 (launched 14 July 1978) which is studying the magnetosphere from geostationary orbit. Under contract to Marconi Space & Defence Systems, BAe was design authority for Britain's Ariel 6 scientific satellite, launched on 3 June 1979 for investigations into high energy physics. BAe built the engineering and flight satellite structures, and was responsible for the mechanical ground support equipment and most environmental testing.

BAe has also initiated long-term studies of the feasibility of solar power satellites. Stationed in geosynchronous orbit, these satellites would receive energy via large arrays of photo electric cells, convert it onboard into microwave radio energy, and beam it towards receiving antennae on the Earth's surface. There, the microwave energy would be converted to usable electrical power and fed into a supply grid.

As a member of the nine-nation European Spacelab consortium led by ERNO of West Germany, British Aerospace is working on the pallets (experiment-mounting platforms) for the Spacelab that is to be carried into orbit by the US Space Shuttle. The first Orbiter test flight pallet was delivered in November 1978.

Other British Aerospace activities concern high-speed data handling systems for aircraft, mathematical modelling of complex systems, HF notch antenna tuning units, microwave phased arrays, precision gyroscopes and inertial guidance equipment for the services and industry, and a wide range of reinforced and microwave plastics components for the marine, electronics and aerospace industries, including radomes, radar reflectors, antennae and structural components.

British Aerospace has developed under contract to Intelsat a microprocessor-based computer intended primarily for satellite attitude and orbit control applications. The system, designed to operate on less than 1W of power, is of modular construction so that its built-in memory can be expanded to meet a variety of needs.

Manufacture of the widely-used Skylark high-altitude sounding rocket continues. For details see 1977-78 *Jane's*.

Artist's impression of the European Communications Satellite

Artist's impression of the MARECS maritime communications satellite

MSDS
MARCONI SPACE AND DEFENCE SYSTEMS LTD

HEAD OFFICE: The Grove, Stanmore, Middlesex HA7 4LY

Telephone: (01) 954-2311

Telex: 22616

Marconi Space and Defence Systems, a member of GEC-Marconi Electronics, assembled and tested the hydrazine propulsion subsystem used to keep the NATO III communications satellite on station in its synchronous orbit. This series of satellites also embodies local oscillators built by MSDS; these act as highly stable frequency sources with which incoming signals to the satellites are mixed to produce the intermediate frequency suitable for the onboard electronics.

As a member of COSMOS consortium, MSDS provided the attitude control system and other equipment for Meteosat which, following a successful launch on 23 November 1977, is sending back excellent pictures and other meteorological data. MSDS will provide similar equipment for Exosat, a precision three-axis stabilised X-ray observatory. Under subcontract to Aérospatiale, it is responsible for attitude and orbit control systems on the Ariane launch vehicle. In association with the MESH international consortium, it is prime contractor for the maritime payload modules which will be mounted on the

UK 6 (Ariel 6) satellite

ECS platform to form the MARECS spacecraft. MSDS also completed, as prime contractor, integration of the flight model of the UK 6 scientific satellite.

UK 6 (ARIEL) SATELLITE

UK 6, Britain's sixth scientific satellite in the Ariel series, is intended to undertake investigations in the field of high-energy astrophysics, and carries three experiments. One is designed to study the ultra-heavy component of cosmic radiation; two other experiments are for observations of X-ray sources particular as to their time variations.

The satellite was funded by the Science Research Council and is managed from the Council's Appleton Laboratory at Slough, from where it is being controlled in orbit.

Ariel 6 is designed to have an operational life of two years, and was launched by a Scout rocket from Wallops Island into a 550 km (342 mile) circular orbit on 3 June 1979.

UNITED STATES OF AMERICA

BOEING

THE BOEING COMPANY

HEAD OFFICE AND WORKS: Seattle, Washington 98124

Boeing Aerospace Company
Space Systems Division

Box 3999, Seattle, Washington 98124

OFFICERS: See Aircraft section

Boeing Aerospace Company's Space Systems Division designed and built the base modules for the Applications Explorer Mission A and B satellites. The modules, containing all the spacecraft's support instrumentation, power system, communications, command and attitude control subsystems, are hexagons approximately 71 cm (28 in) across and 64 cm (25 in) long, weighing 91 kg (200 lb). Each module has solar panels with a total area of 2·2 m² (24 sq ft).

INERTIAL UPPER STAGE (IUS)

In August 1976 Boeing was selected by the US Air Force Space and Missile Systems Organization (SAMSO) to develop the Inertial Upper Stage (IUS) that will carry Space Shuttle payloads either to orbits not attainable by the Shuttle Orbiter or on to interplanetary trajectories. It has also been chosen as the upper stage for the Air Force's Titan 34-D rocket.

The IUS vehicles are designed in three sizes, using common components.

The basic two-stage vehicle is 5·0 m (16 ft 4½ in) long and 2·9 m (9 ft 6 in) in diameter. It consists of an aft skirt, a 9,707 kg (21,400 lb) aft-stage solid rocket motor generating an average of 189·5 kN (42,600 lb) of thrust, an interstage, a 2,722 kg (6,000 lb) forward stage solid rocket motor generating an average of 77·5 kN (17,430 lb) of thrust, and an equipment support structure which contains electronics for guidance and navigation, reaction control subsystem and electrical power. Its weight is 14,515 kg (32,000 lb).

The NASA twin-stage IUS uses two 9,707 kg (21,400 lb) motors and, except for the larger forward-stage motor and minor modifications to the interstage and equipment support structure, is quite similar to the basic two-stage vehicle. Tooling is identical for both vehicles. The NASA two-stage version is 6·64 m (21 ft 9½ in) long and weighs 20,956 kg (46,200 lb).

The three-stage vehicle combines the NASA twin-stage vehicle with a spinning version of the smaller 2,722 kg (6,000 lb) motor, acting as the third stage and providing increased performance for planetary missions. The three-stage vehicle is 8·3 m (27 ft 6 in) long and weighs 24,767 kg (54,600 lb).

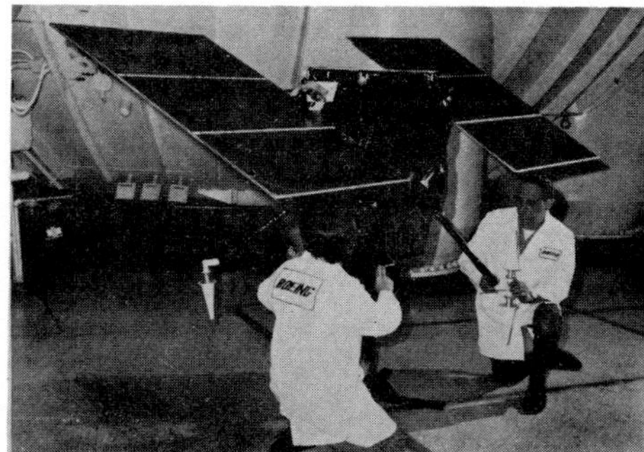

Applications Explorer Mission A satellite

Boeing's propulsion team member, Chemical Systems Division of United Technologies, will design and test all solid motors. Production deliveries are programmed to begin in 1980.

FAIRCHILD INDUSTRIES

FAIRCHILD INDUSTRIES INC

Germantown, Maryland 20767

OFFICERS AND DIVISIONS: See Aircraft section

In 1978 Fairchild was selected by NASA as the integration and test contractor for the Multimission Modular Spacecraft (MMS), a standard bus for many future NASA and DoD missions. The first launch using the MMS will be LANDSAT-D, scheduled for 1981. Shuttle compatible, retrievable and refurbishable, the MMS is also being considered for such missions as GRO, ERBS, UARS and COASTSAT.

Fairchild is responsible for producing the Stage Vehicle System for use on the Atlas E/F launch vehicle. Used as an interstage between Atlas and the NavStar Global Positioning Satellite System, it contains two tandem-mounted TE-M-364-4 solid rocket motors for providing transfer orbit insertion of the satellites. Of the planned total of seven satellites, five have been launched successfully into orbit, and the sixth was scheduled for April, 1979.

Fairchild was also responsible for the integration and test, and the manufacture of subsystems for the ISEE-3 satellite.

ISEE-3

Launched on 12 August 1978 by a Delta rocket from Cape Canaveral ISEE-3 (ISEE-B before launch) is designed to measure the isotropic concentration of solar and galactic cosmic rays, and investigate various solar, interplanetary and recently discovered astrophysical and magnetic phenomena. It carries twelve scientific experiments, and will provide a reference measurement for data collected by ISEE-1 and 2, launched into elliptical Earth orbits.

ISEE-3, on the other hand, was designed to operate at a hypothetical point in space where the gravities of the Sun and Earth/Moon systems balance out. This point, known as the Libration point, is about 1,500,000 km (930,000 miles) from the Earth. If placed exactly on this point, the spacecraft would move round the Sun at the same rate as the Earth. At this point, however, communications would be difficult, and to minimise the Sun's interference ISEE-3 is revolving about the Libration point at a distance of 145,000 km (89,900 miles). Frequent course corrections will be necessary to maintain this unusual heliocentric orbit.

Fairchild was responsible for integrating the final system and for fabricating selected subsystems, including the complete structural subsystem and the yo-yo de-spin system in which wire-like devices were designed to unwind from the spacecraft to slow its spin from 50 to 10 rpm, allowing deployment of the booms.

The ISEE-3 spacecraft is drum-shaped; it weighs about 453 kg (1,000 lb), and is 1·73 m (68 in) in diameter and 3·30 m (10 ft 10 in) high.

FORD

FORD AEROSPACE & COMMUNICATIONS CORPORATION

20th Floor, 300 Renaissance Center, PO Box 43342, Detroit, Michigan 48243

Telephone: (313) 568-7640

In addition to the satellites listed, Ford manufactured the Sakura experimental communications satellite, described under the NASDA entry in the Japanese section of the 1978-79 *Jane's*.

GEOSTATIONARY OPERATIONAL ENVIRONMENTAL SATELLITE (GOES)

Similar to the SMS satellites, described in the 1977-78 *Jane's,* but embodying improvements in communication systems performance and reliability, the 294 kg (647 lb) GOES-1 (Geostationary Operational Environmental Satellite) was built for the National Oceanic and Atmospheric Administration (NOAA) by Ford Aerospace & Communications Corporation's Western Development Laboratories Division, under a contract awarded through NASA's Goddard Space Flight Center.

GOES-1 was launched on 16 October 1975. GOES-2 was launched on 16 June 1977 and is now over the equator above South America, from which position it is observing the eastern half of the United States and the Atlantic Ocean. GOES-1 was replaced by GOES-3, launched on 16 June 1978; the former spacecraft being repositioned at 60° E.

GOES-2 is the first spacecraft of its type to be used as part of the Global Atmospheric Research Program (GARP) first Global Experiment.

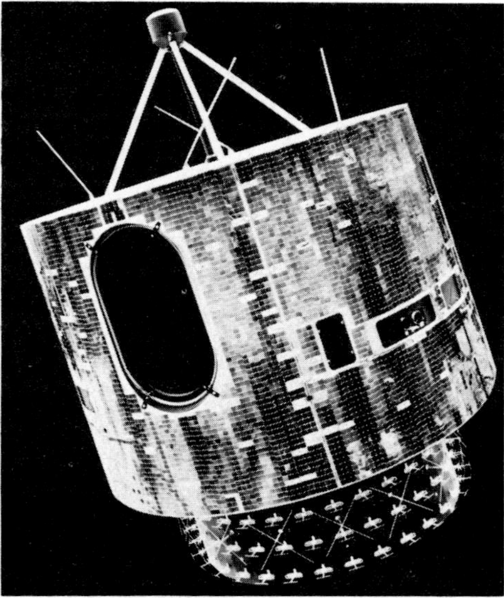

GOES Geostationary Operational Environmental Satellite

INTELSAT V

Ford Aerospace, under a contract administered by the Communications Satellite Corporation (COMSAT), is building seven Intelsat V communications satellites for the 102-nation International Telecommunications Satellite Organisation (INTELSAT). The first Intelsat V was scheduled to be launched in late 1979.

Intelsat V's capacity of 24,500 telephone half-circuits is twice that of Intelsat IVA. It is also the first satellite of the Intelsat series to be three-axis stabilised, using technology developed during the European Symphonie programme. Launch weight of the 6.4 m (21 ft) high satellite is 1,860 kg (4,100 lb). Planned life span is seven years.

NATO 3C

Built by Ford Aerospace & Communications Corporation, the third NATO 3 (described in the 1977-78 *Jane's*) communications satellite was launched on 19 November 1978 by a Delta rocket from Cape Canaveral Air Force Station. In synchronous orbit, it is positioned at longitude 50°W, midway between Africa and South America, and is being used as an 'orbital spare' in conjunction with its two sister satellites, NATO 3A and NATO 3B. NATO 3A is above the equator midway between Africa and South America, and in early 1979 was passing NATO communications traffic. NATO 3B, stationed at longitude 135°W, above the eastern Pacific off the west coast of the United States, was early in 1979 'on loan' to the US Defense Communications Agency to augment the Defense Satellite Communications System (DSCS).

Intelsat V structural thermal model

GENERAL DYNAMICS

GENERAL DYNAMICS CORPORATION

HEAD OFFICE: Pierre Laclede Center, St Louis, Missouri 63105

Convair Division

San Diego, California 92138

OFFICERS: See Aircraft section

Convair Division devotes a major part of its activity to production and launch of Atlas and Centaur space launch vehicles, as well as production of DC-10 fuselages. Convair is also developing the Tomahawk cruise missile for the US Navy, and producing the Space Shuttle Orbiter mid-fuselage for NASA.

ATLAS E and F

Atlas E and F series rockets were formerly ICBMs deployed at Strategic Air Command bases as part of the US strategic missile force. Phase-out of the Atlas ICBM force in 1965 made them available for conversion into launch vehicles, as described in previous editions.

ATLAS SLV

The Atlas Standardised Launch Vehicle (SLV) had its inception in Atlas, the United States' first intercontinental ballistic missile (ICBM). Two versions are currently in service:

SLV-3A, for use with Agena.

SLV-3D, for use with the Centaur D-1A.

These vehicles differ from their immediate predecessor, the SLV-3, mainly in increased tank length and rocket engine thrust.

Atlas is a 'stage-and-a-half' vehicle, consisting of side booster and central sustainer sections. The sustainer section includes the propellant tanks and a single rocket engine. The booster engines receive fuel from the sustainer tanks and are jettisoned midway into flight.

The engine system is the Rocketdyne MA-5, using liquid oxygen and RP-1 propellants. Total thrust developed is 1,917·4 kN (431,040 lb), including 1,646 kN (370,000 lb) total from the two boosters, 266·9 kN (60,000 lb) from the sustainer, and 4·6 kN (1,040 lb) total axial thrust from the two vernier rockets. All engines are ignited at lift-off.

Most of the electronic command and control functions for the SLV-3D are generated by its Centaur D-1A upper-stage electronics system. The SLV-3A has its own systems, independent of the upper stage, including radio guidance.

By the beginning of 1979, Atlas had been the booster for over 170 space launches, with many space 'firsts' to its credit. The world's first communications satellite was launched by Atlas in 1958, as were the first US manned orbital flights (Mercury). All US planetary spacecraft have been launched by Atlas or Centaur. In 1972 Pioneer 10 was started on its flight path to Jupiter with the highest velocity ever imparted to a spacecraft.

DIMENSIONS:

Diameter	3·05 m (10 ft 0 in)
Length:	
SLV-3A	24·0 m (78 ft 11 in)
SLV-3A/Agena	36·0 m (118 ft 0 in)
SLV-3D	21·2 m (69 ft 6 in)
SLV-3D/Centaur	39·9 m (131 ft 0 in)

PERFORMANCE:

Atlas/Centaur: See Centaur entry

Atlas SLV-3A/Agena:

3,856 kg (8,500 lb) into 185 km (115 mile) orbit

1,238 kg (2,730 lb) into synchronous transfer orbit

CENTAUR

Centaur was the first US high-energy upper stage and the first to utilise liquid hydrogen as a propellant. The current version is combined with the Atlas SLV-3D.

In April 1973, the first Atlas/Centaur D-1A launched Pioneer 11 on a Jupiter fly-by mission. Three more Intelsat IVs, Mariner 10, seven Intelsat IVAs, three Comstars (domestic communication satellites leased to AT and T by Comsat), the first two High Energy Astronomy Observatories (HEAO) and the US Navy's Fleetsatcom 1 have also been launched successfully by this vehicle. In early 1979, Atlas/Centaur D-1A had been assigned future missions extending into 1981. They include further launches of Comstars, Fleetsatcoms, High Energy Astronomy Observatories and Pioneer missions to orbit Venus and probe its atmosphere.

Centaur was also used as an upper stage for Titan IIIE, described in previous editions of *Jane's*.

Centaur D-1A retains the same propulsion and structural features as its predecessor, Centaur D, with stainless steel pressurised tanks and two 66·72 kN (15,000 lb st) Pratt & Whitney RL10A liquid oxygen/liquid hydrogen rocket engines. Specific impulse with this propellant combination is 445 s, the highest of any current space vehicle. Total propellants carried weigh 13,950 kg (30,750 lb). Attitude control is achieved by gimballing the two main engines or by clusters of small hydrogen peroxide rocket motors.

Several of the electronics components were redesigned for Centaur D-1A. The most significant addition is a 16,000 word capacity Teledyne digital computer. Navigation, guidance, vehicle stability, tank pressurisation, propellant management, telemetry formats and transmission, and event initiation are all controlled by the computer. Guidance, control and sequencing for the Atlas booster are provided by the Centaur D-1A electronics system.

Payloads are carried on adapters mounted on the forward end of the Centaur. A 3·05 m (10 ft) diameter fairing protects payloads for Centaur D-1A.

DIMENSIONS:

Centaur length	9·14 m (30 ft 0 in)
Centaur diameter	3·05 m (10 ft 0 in)
Atlas/Centaur length	39·9 m (131 ft 0 in)

PERFORMANCE:

Atlas/Centaur:

5,080 kg (11,200 lb) into 185 km (115 mile) circular orbit

1,860 kg (4,100 lb) into synchronous transfer orbit

590 kg (1,300 lb) to near planet

Atlas/Centaur AC-36 launch vehicle

GENERAL ELECTRIC

GENERAL ELECTRIC COMPANY SPACE DIVISION

HEAD OFFICE: Valley Forge Space Center, PO Box 8555, Philadelphia, Pennsylvania 19101

General Electric's Space Division is vehicle contractor for NASA's Landsat programme (formerly Earth Resources Technology Satellite, ERTS). It is also responsible for design and manufacture of Nimbus meteorological satellites, BSE (Broadcast Satellite Experimental) and DSCS III (Defense Satellite Communications Systems) satellites.

LANDSAT (ERTS)

Designed to study the resources of Earth from space, ERTS-1 (Earth Resources Technology Satellite) was launched by NASA on 23 July 1972. It was subsequently renamed Landsat-1 and is described in the 1977-78 *Jane's*. This spacecraft was retired by NASA on 16 January 1978, after operating for 5½ years and after revolutionising the technology of observing the Earth from space.

Landsat-2 (known formerly as ERTS-B) was launched on 22 January 1975, into an orbit similar to that of Landsat-1 but 180° out of phase from it to allow repetitive coverage of all portions of the Earth every nine days with two spacecraft, instead of once every 18 days with one spacecraft. Brief details of Landsat-2 were given in the 1977-78 *Jane's*. A third spacecraft in the series, Landsat-3, was launched on 5 March 1978. This embodies refined sensors which are supplying data significantly improved over those obtained from Landsats 1 and 2. The multispectral scanner subsystem (MSS) detects temperature differences in vegetation, bodies of water and urban areas by day and night. An improved return beam vidicon (RBV) sensor has increased the resolution of recorded images by 50 per cent, enabling areas as small as half an acre to be identified. The thermal data is providing information on plant stress, vigour and other changes characterised by temperature differences.

NIMBUS

Nimbus-7, the seventh satellite in an atmospheric research programme, was launched on 23 October 1978. Designed to gather data from the atmosphere and oceans, it is obtaining global information on air and water pollution for continuing research on climate and weather. In addition one of the sensors, called a Coastal Zone Colour Scanner (CZCS), is available to identify and track oil spills over eleven major ocean areas traversed by tankers.

Since Nimbus-1 was launched on 28 August 1964, the six spacecraft in the series have returned more than 400,000 TV pictures of the Earth's cloud cover, 51,000 hours of infra-red data, 42,000 hours of ultra-violet data, 185,000 hours of 'sounder' data on temperature and pressure and more than 16,000 hours of data on the Earth's heat balance.

Details of earlier Nimbus spacecraft are given in the 1974-75 *Jane's*.

Landsat-3 Earth resources technology satellite

HUGHES

HUGHES AIRCRAFT COMPANY

Culver City, California 90230

Telephone: (213) 391-0711

Current space programmes for which Hughes Aircraft is prime contractor include development and manufacture of the orbiter and multiprobe spacecraft for NASA's Pioneer Venus programme; Western Union's Westar, Comsat's Intelsat IV and IVA, Comsat General's Comstar, and Indonesia's Palapa telecommunications satellites; Comsat General's Marisat maritime satellites; Japan's first Geostationary Meteorological Satellite (GMS-1); the Geostationary Operational Environmental Satellites (GOES-D, E, F) for the US National Oceanic and Atmospheric Administration (NOAA), resulting from a contract awarded by NASA in December 1977; the Ku-band Integrated Radar and Communications Subsystem for NASA's Space Shuttle; and NASA's Orbiting Solar Observatory (OSO-I) satellite (see 1977-78 *Jane's*). The company is also engaged on development and manufacture of classified military satellite systems; Visible/Infrared Spin-Scan Radiometers (VISSR), used as the primary sensor on GMS and, with atmospheric sounder (VAS), on GOES-D, E, and F; Multispectral Scanners (MSS) used on Landsat spacecraft and a Thermatic Mapper for Landsat D; and on investigation and flight testing of experimental ion engines for advanced spacecraft.

INTELSAT IVA

Pending the availability of Intelsat V, Hughes built six improved Intelsat IVA spacecraft, with BAe as a principal subcontractor, to handle the world's mounting telecommunications traffic up to 1979. These new spacecraft have 20 transponders (individual receiver-transmitters) compared with 12 on Intelsat IV. A new advanced antenna system concentrates signal beams like spotlights into the communication and business centres on both sides of an ocean, via 16 of the 20 transponders. Using a technique called beam diversity or 'frequency re-use', the spacecraft casts spatially separate transmit-receive spot beams. These permit an Earth station in one beam to receive and transmit on the same frequencies as an Earth station in the other beam without interference. The result is an increase in capacity to 11,000 two-way telephone conversations or 20 colour TV channels, almost twice that of its predecessors.

The first Intelsat IVA, F-1, was launched successfully on 26 September 1975, followed by Intelsat IVA F-2 on 29 January 1976. The last of six Intelsat IVAs was launched on 31 March 1978. The $290 million programme has provided three operational satellites over the Atlantic Ocean and two over the Indian Ocean.

DIMENSIONS:

Diameter	2·36 m (7 ft 9 in)
Height overall	7·00 m (22 ft 11 in)

WEIGHT:

At launch	1,515 kg (3,340 lb)

MARISAT

Built by Hughes Aircraft Company for the Comsat General Corporation, three Marisat satellites were launched and placed into operational service in 1976. World's first commercial maritime telecommunications satellites, they were designed to provide rapid high-quality communications between ships at sea and shore offices. Telephone and telex messages may be exchanged without fear of interference or delay due to severe weather or ionospheric disturbances that might disrupt radio traffic. The satellites have thus improved significantly the communication of distress, safety, search and rescue, and weather reports.

Details of the Marisat satellites were given in the 1977-78 *Jane's*.

Intelsat IVA communications satellite

LOCKHEED

LOCKHEED MISSILES & SPACE COMPANY INC

(Subsidiary of Lockheed Corporation)

1111 Lockheed Way, Sunnyvale, California 94088
Telephone: (408) 742-6688
PRESIDENT: Robert A. Fuhrman
OTHER FACILITIES: Palo Alto and Santa Cruz, California
DIRECTOR, PUBLIC INFORMATION: George Mulhern

Lockheed Missiles & Space Company is heavily engaged in both missile work and the design, development and production of satellites and space vehicles.

AGENA D

The Agena satellite is used normally as the upper stage of a two-stage launcher, in combination with an Atlas, Thor, or Titan IIIB. The current Agena D version consists of a cylindrical body containing a Bell Aerosystems Model 8096 (YLR81-BA-11) restartable liquid-propellant rocket engine (71·2 kN; 16,000 lb st) and propellant tanks, telemetry, instrumentation, guidance and attitude control systems. It has carried most types of power supply, including a nuclear reactor electric power supply and an ion engine. The payload section (nosecone) can accommodate a wide variety of Earth-orbiting and space probes weighing up to several hundred pounds. The Agena system and its attached payload have functioned for more than six months in some missions for the USAF.

Agena D differs from earlier versions in being able to accept a variety of payloads, whereas its predecessors had integrated payloads. The restartable engine permits the satellite to change its orbit in space.

Since 1959, Agenas have served as satellite or booster on more missions than any other spacecraft in the world, having been used on well over 300 flights, representing approximately half of all US space missions.

Agena forms the basis of the new Seasat ocean survey satellite, described separately in this entry. A high proportion of the unidentified US satellites included in the table at the end of this section can be assumed to be Agena payloads of various kinds.

The following details refer to Agena D:

DIMENSIONS:

Length (typical)	7·09 m (23 ft 3 in)
Diameter	1·52 m (5 ft 0 in)

WEIGHTS (typical):

Propellant weight	6,148 kg (13,553 lb)
Vehicle weight empty	673 kg (1,484 lb)
Weight in orbit, less payload	579 kg (1,277 lb)

LOCKHEED/USAF 467 BIG BIRD

First launched on 15 June 1971, from Pt Arguello, this highly-advanced photographic reconnaissance satellite is reported to weigh about 11,340 kg (25,000 lb) and to be 15·25 m (50 ft) long. The first Big Bird was launched by a Titan IIID into an orbit of 299 × 183 km (186 × 144 miles), with an inclination of 96·41°. Its capabilities clearly included the same kind of close-look high-resolution photography as that of the recoverable type of Agena vehicle; and it is reported to have ejected a series of capsules for air-snatch recovery.

Big Bird is believed to process photographs taken by cameras and transmit information to Earth in the form of digital data by radio link. Some reports suggest that it also carries infra-red mapping and side-looking radar equipment. Its orbit takes its cameras within range of every point on the Earth twice in each period of 24 hours.

Big Birds continue to be launched at four-to-six-monthly intervals and have demonstrated an endurance of up to four months in orbit.

Although no official data have been released on US reconnaissance satellites, acknowledgement of their use for military purposes was made by President Carter during a speech at the Kennedy Space Center. In his statement, the President said: "Photo reconaissance satellites have become an important stabilizing factor in world affairs in the monitoring of arms agreements. They make an immense contribution to the security of all nations. We shall continue to develop them." An earlier indication of the value placed on information gained by satellite reconnaissance was given by the late President Lyndon Johnson, who said in March 1967: "We have spent $35-40,000 million on the space programme, and if nothing else had come out of it except the knowledge we have gained from space photography, it would be worth 10 times what the whole programme has cost, because tonight we know how many missiles the enemy has."

SEASAT

Seasat, an experimental oceanographic satellite built for NASA, was launched on 27 June 1978 from Vandenberg Air Force Base into a near-circular polar orbit of about 800 km (430 miles), so that it circled the Earth 14 times daily and covered 96% of the world's oceans every 36 hours. Radars and radiometers aboard the spacecraft were used to see through clouds and provide data on wave heights, currents, ocean temperatures, icebergs, storms, and coastal features. On 9 October, after three months of gathering extensive data, the satellite was silenced by an apparent power failure due, it is thought, to an electrical short in the slip ring assembly of the solar array. Nevertheless, the satellite proved its primary objective: that precise information on the state of the oceans could be obtained in this manner. It will require about 1½ years to process the data obtained. Full details of the 2,274 kg (5,000 lb) satellite and its special sensors were given in the 1978-79 *Jane's*. Future ocean survey satellites are planned for Space Shuttle launches in the mid-80s.

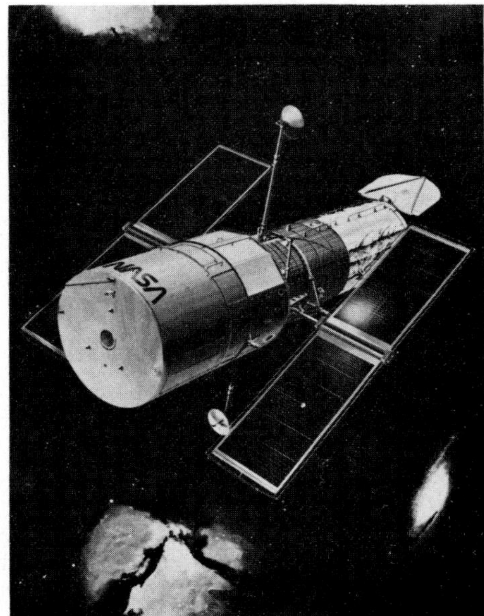

Artist's impression of NASA's Space Telescope

SPACE TELESCOPE

Lockheed Missiles & Space Company is building for NASA a Space Telescope which will be launched in 1983 as the most ambitious space astronomy project yet undertaken. Operating well above the optically obscuring effects of Earth's atmosphere, the telescope will be able to detect objects 50 times more faint and seven times further away than those which can be seen by telescopes on Earth. The solar array and photon detector assembly are being developed and manufactured by British Aerospace under contracts from the European Space Agency.

MARTIN MARIETTA

MARTIN MARIETTA CORPORATION

CORPORATE HEADQUARTERS: 6801 Rockledge Drive, Bethesda, Maryland 20034
Telephone: (301) 897-6000
CHAIRMAN AND CHIEF EXECUTIVE OFFICER: J. Donald Rauth
PRESIDENT AND CHIEF OPERATING OFFICER: Thomas G. Pownall
VICE-PRESIDENT, PUBLIC RELATIONS: Roy Calvin
AEROSPACE HEADQUARTERS: 6801 Rockledge Drive, Bethesda, Maryland 20034
PRESIDENT, MARTIN MARIETTA AEROSPACE: Laurence J. Adams

Baltimore Division
103 Chesapeake Park Plaza, Baltimore, Maryland 21220
Denver Division
PO Box 179, Denver, Colorado 80201
Telephone: (303) 973-3000
Orlando Division
PO Box 5837, Orlando, Florida 32805
Telephone: (305) 352-2000

Martin Marietta Aerospace produces missiles, spacecraft, launch vehicles, communications systems and electronic systems. It also fabricates precision components for the US Department of Defense and NASA, and conducts research related to defence and space systems.

The Denver Division produces the Titan III family of space boosters, defence systems, command and information systems, mobile transporter systems and external tanks for the Space Shuttle. Orlando Division produces advanced strategic air-launched missiles, communications systems, the Pershing surface-to-surface ballistic missile, the Patriot surface-to-air missile, strategic terminal interceptors, and tactical weapons systems. Baltimore Division fabricates structural components of aircraft, space vehicles and defence systems.

TITAN III

Titan III is America's standard heavy-duty space 'workhorse' booster and is used for both military and non-military space launch missions. It provides a high frequency launch capability for a wide variety of manned and unmanned payloads, ranging from 15,875 kg (35,000 lb) in Earth orbit to 3,175 kg (7,000 lb) for planetary missions to Mars, Jupiter and Saturn.

Martin Marietta, in addition to its role as systems integrating contractor, builds the airframe and liquid-propellant stages, supplies the flight control system, and is integrating contractor for facilities and launch operation at Cape Canaveral. Aerojet-General produces the liquid-propellant engines. UTC's Chemical Systems Division supplies the solid-propellant boosters used in the more powerful models. Guidance systems for the Titan IIIC and D are built by General Motors Corporation's Delco Division and Western Electric respectively.

The core section of Titan III consists of elements which provide a high degree of commonality throughout all configurations. It consists of two booster stages and an upper stage, known as Transtage, that can function both in the boost phase of flight and as a restartable space tug propulsion vehicle. All stages use storable liquid propellants and have gimbal-mounted thrust chambers for vehicle control.

Titan III exists in three current configurations:

Titan IIIB. Basically the first two stages of the core section. It can accommodate a variety of specialised upper stages. First launched on 29 July 1966. Series of launches continued through 1978, all with Agena upper stages and classified USAF payloads.

Titan IIIC. Consists of the core section, including the Transtage upper stage, with solid-propellant rocket motors attached to each side to function as a booster stage before ignition of main engines. Payloads include USAF and NASA unmanned military, scientific and communications satellites, including about 80% of all those placed into synchronous equatorial orbit from US launch sites.

Titan IIID. Basically similar to IIIC but has only a two-stage liquid-propellant core (without Transtage) and radio guidance instead of the standard inertial guidance. Able to accept a variety of upper stages. Reported to have been used to orbit the first Lockheed Big Bird advanced photo-reconnaissance spacecraft, weighing about 11,340 kg (25,000 lb), from Pt Arguello on 15 June 1971.

The first stage of the core section is 22·25 m (73 ft) long and 3·05 m (10 ft) in diameter. Its engines, which use a blend of hydrazine and unsymmetrical dimethylhydrazine (UDMH) for fuel, and nitrogen tetroxide as an oxidiser, have a 15 : 1 expansion ratio and are ignited at an altitude where efficiency is increased, giving a thrust of 2,339·6 kN (526,000 lb) in vacuum. The second stage is 7·10 m (23 ft 3½ in) tall and 3·05 m (10 ft) in diameter. Its engine uses the same propellants as the first stage and develops 453·7 kN (102,000 lb st).

The Transtage space propulsion vehicle is 4·57 m (15 ft) tall and 3·05 m (10 ft) in diameter and also uses UDMH/hydrazine and nitrogen tetroxide as propellants. The twin-chamber engine produces 71·17 kN (16,000 lb) of thrust and is capable of multiple restarts in space, which permits a wide variety of manoeuvres, including change of plane, change of orbit, and transfer to deep-space trajectory. Transtage also houses the control module for the entire vehicle, including the guidance system and segments of the flight control and vehicle safety systems.

Titan IIIC/D's solid-propellant booster motors are each 25·91 m (85 ft) long and 3·05 m (10 ft) in diameter. Each motor is built in five segments and develops more than 5,115·2 kN (1,150,000 lb st). The booster stage is steered by a thrust vector control system, which injects nitrogen tetroxide into the engine nozzle.

Titan 34-D. Instead of Transtage, future Titan IIIs will use the Boeing Inertial Upper Stage (which see) that is being developed for the Space Shuttle. Designated Titan 34-D, these vehicles will be used for some primary launches, as well as for backup of the Space Shuttle during that vehicle's transition period. The Titan 34-D is expected to replace current Titans, with an estimated requirement for 23 in the 1980s.

Titan IIIC heavy duty launch vehicle

MCDONNELL DOUGLAS

MCDONNELL DOUGLAS CORPORATION

McDonnell Douglas Astronautics Company (MDAC)

5301 Bolsa Avenue, Huntington Beach, California 92647

In March 1977 MDAC was awarded a Spacelab integration contract by NASA involving the design, development and fabrication of most of the Spacelab hardware for which NASA is responsible. This includes the crew transfer tunnel, verification flight instrumentation, mockups and ground support equipment. The contract also covers systems engineering and integration to develop Spacelab operational capability.

DSV-3 DELTA

Details of early versions of the Delta can be found in the 1971-72, 1972-73 and 1977-78 *Jane's*. Production is now centred on the DSV-3P, of which details follow:

DSV-3P Extended Long Tank Delta (also known as 'Straight-Eight' or '2000 Series Delta'). This launch vehicle has a constant 2·44 m (8 ft) diameter from the base of the boat-tail to the conical nose section of the shroud. This provides an enlarged volume, to accommodate larger payloads. The second stage, with a TRW LMDE engine, is suspended within the 2·44 m (8 ft) diameter barrel section. The first-stage length is increased by 3·05 m (10 ft) by comparison with earlier long-tank versions, providing an increase of 13,600 kg (30,000 lb) in propellant capacity. In addition, the MB-3-III main engine is replaced by a Rocketdyne RS-27 of 911·84 kN (205,000 lb st). As an alternative to the TE-364-3 motor, a higher-performing motor, the TE-364-4, is available as a third stage. The two-stage capability is increased to 1,880 kg (4,150 lb) into a 370 km (230 mile) circular orbit. The three-stage capability is increased to 700 kg (1,550 lb) into a synchronous transfer orbit.

DSV-3P (Delta 3914). First launched on 12 December 1975, this uprated version of the standard 'Straight-Eight' Delta utilises nine Castor IV solid-propellant strap-on motors in place of the nine Castor IIs used on the Delta 2914. Development costs were borne by MDAC, and will be recovered through a user charge imposed on non-government users of the vehicle. Dimensions are the same as for the standard DSV-3P Delta 2914, but firing weight is increased to 191,400 kg (422,000 lb). Delta 3914 is capable of putting a 930 kg (2,050 lb) payload into a geosynchronous transfer orbit.

The number of Deltas ordered, in many versions, totalled 157 by Spring 1979.

DIMENSIONS:

Length overall	35·15 m (115 ft 4 in)
Body diameter	2·44 m (8 ft 0 in)

WEIGHTS:

Firing weight of DSV-3P (2000 Series):	
3 solid motors	104,330 kg (230,000 lb)
6 solid motors	117,930 kg (260,000 lb)
9 solid motors	131,540 kg (290,000 lb)

PAYLOAD ASSIST MODULE

Two Payload Assist Module (PAM) rocket systems are being developed to improve the load-carrying capability of the McDonnell Douglas launch vehicle and for use on Space Shuttle missions. As many as four satellites, with PAM stages attached, could be launched during a single flight of the Shuttle Orbiter.

Both PAMs are solid-propellant spinning rockets. One, known as PAM-D, will be carried into low Earth orbit by the Space Shuttle and from that position will carry payloads of up to 1,110 kg (2,450 lb) into transfer orbit. Kick motors will then insert payloads into 35,880 km (22,300 mile) high geosynchronous orbits.

Six PAM-Ds have been ordered by Hughes Aircraft Company, and two by Ford Aerospace and Communications Corporation to help launch satellites which Ford is developing for the Government of India.

The second type of rocket, PAM-A, is intended to be used for handling payloads weighing up to 2,000 kg (4,400 lb) during Space Shuttle missions.

After insertion into low Earth orbit by the Shuttle, the upper stage will carry payloads into a transfer orbit where a kick motor will insert it into a circular geosynchronous orbit 35,880 km (22,300 miles) above the Earth. This upper stage will accommodate payloads of a size now being launched by Atlas-Centaur rockets. Six PAM-As were ordered by NASA in 1978.

Delta 117 launch vehicle for Explorer 55 satellite

NASA

NATIONAL AERONAUTICS AND SPACE ADMINISTRATION

HEADQUARTERS: Washington, DC 20546

ADMINISTRATOR: Dr Robert A. Frosch

NASA is responsible for co-ordinating and conducting virtually all US non-military space projects. Its Office of Space Transportation Systems is responsible for the Space Shuttle programme.

DYNAMICS EXPLORER

Dynamics Explorer is a NASA-sponsored programme which will investigate the interactive coupling between the Earth's magnetosphere, ionosphere and plasmasphere. It will utilise two coplanar polar orbiting spacecraft, constructed by RCA Astro-Electronics and described under the RCA entry in this section.

IUE SATELLITE

This International Ultraviolet Explorer satellite, launched on 26 January 1978 into a modified synchronous Earth orbit by NASA in co-operation with the European Space Agency and the British Research Council, is intended to study a wide range of celestial objects in one of the most important regions in the electromagnetic spectrum.

ISPM

In March 1979 NASA announced that it had signed an

agreement with the European Space Agency for a joint International Solar Polar Mission (ISPM) to be launched in 1983. Under the agreement, NASA and ESA will each provide a spacecraft. Both spacecraft will be launched simultaneously by the Space Shuttle, and will then be directed on a trajectory in the ecliptic plane (the plane containing all the planets) to Jupiter. The gravity of Jupiter will be used to redirect their paths out of the ecliptic plane, back to the Sun in trajectories—one northbound and one southbound—that are mirror images of each other, passing over the solar poles. Purpose of the mission is to extend scientific knowledge of the Sun.

PIONEER VENUS 1978

NASA sent both an orbiter and a multiprobe spacecraft to Venus in 1978 to conduct a detailed scientific examination of the planet's atmosphere and weather. Both spacecraft were built by Hughes Aircraft Co.

The orbiter was launched on 20 May and was inserted into Venusian orbit on 3 December; the multiprobe spacecraft was launched on 8 August and entered the Venusian atmosphere six days after arrival of the orbiter.

Weight of the orbiter was about 567 kg (1,250 lb) and that of the multiprobe spacecraft about 885 kg (1,950 lb). Both were about 2·44 m (8 ft) in diameter.

The orbiter, carrying 43 kg (95 lb) of instruments, was designed to study the Venusian atmosphere over one 243-day period. Most of the data-gathering was expected to occur when the craft was closest to the planet, for one hour a day.

The multiprobe spacecraft carried four separate probes which were released from the main body about 20 days before penetration of the atmosphere. Three of the probes were small, weighing about 86 kg (189 lb), including 2·7 kg (6 lb) of instruments. Most of the probe's weight was accounted for by the heatshields and pressure vessels. The probes measured atmospheric pressure and temperature, and investigated the exchange of heat energy between the Sun and atmosphere.

The fourth probe was larger, weighing about 291 kg (642 lb) and carrying about 28 kg (62 lb) of instrumentation. Its payload included a mass spectrometer and a gas chromatograph to provide details about the identity of components in the atmosphere.

All four probes were targeted to different locations on the surface, and were tracked during their 70 minute descent through the atmosphere, to gain information on winds and circulation patterns.

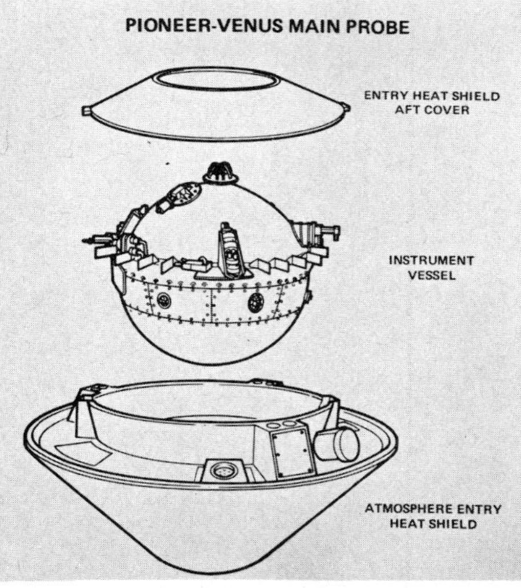

Pioneer Venus orbiter (foreground) and multiprobe spacecraft

After release of the probes the main body made a shallow entry into the atmosphere, obtaining measurements of the upper atmosphere until it burned up at an altitude of about 120 km (75 miles). The mission was highly successful, one of the small probes transmitting data for 67 minutes after impact.

SAGE (AEM-B)

SAGE (Stratospheric Aerosol and Gas Experiment) was launched on 18 February 1979 by a Scout vehicle, from Wallops Flight Center, into a nominal 600 km (370 miles) orbit.

Its purpose is to obtain measurements of global, spatial and temporal distributions of stratospheric aerosols and ozone, and to use these to study their effects on the Earth's radiation budget and environment.

Known also as the Applications Explorer Mission-B satellite, SAGE is a small, versatile, low-cost spacecraft which provides three-axis stabilisation for its viewing instruments. Structure consists of a base module containing attitude control, data handling, communications, command and power subsystems for the instrument module; and an instrument module containing the spectrometer and its supporting equipment. Two solar paddles for converting sunlight to electricity extend from the structure. A yo-yo despin system is located on the base module, below the solar array.

The SAGE sensor is a four-spectral channel radiometer, which measures the extinction of solar radiation during solar occultation. The spacecraft locks on to the Sun as it experiences a sunrise or sunset, and measures the Sun's brightness at four wavelengths. This information is interpreted in terms of vertical profiles of the atmospheric constituent that attenuated or dimmed the sunlight. Thirty profiles per day are being obtained in this manner, spread over latitude and longitude. Over a year, 10,000 profiles will be measured from latitude 78° S to 78° N.

Comparable aerosol data for the polar regions obtained by Nimbus 7 (which see) will complement SAGE.

SPACE SHUTTLE TRANSPORTATION SYSTEM

The Space Shuttle is the first re-usable space vehicle, consisting basically of two stages: a booster and an Orbiter. The Orbiter has a delta wing and looks very like a conventional aeroplane, but is powered by rocket engines. The liquid propellants for these engines are carried in a large external jettisonable tank, which will be attached to the Orbiter at lift-off. Two large solid-propellant jettisonable boosters will be mounted on opposite sides of the propellant tank for lift-off.

Prime contractors are Rockwell International (which see) for the Orbiter, Martin Marietta for the external tank, and Thiokol for the boosters. In operation, the Shuttle will be launched vertically, with all engines firing in both the boosters and Orbiter. At an altitude of about 43 km (27 miles), the booster stages will separate and descend into the sea by parachute, for recovery. The Orbiter will continue under its own power, and will jettison its large external propellant tank just before attaining orbit.

In space, the Orbiter will manoeuvre by means of two smaller rocket engines, also mounted in the rear-fuselage propulsion cluster. For minor course corrections and adjustments of attitude, the Orbiter has a series of small thrusters.

The Orbiter's main tasks are to place satellites into orbit, retrieve satellites from orbit, and repair and service satellites in orbit. It could be used to put a propulsive stage and satellite into precise low Earth orbit, for subsequent transfer to synchronous orbit or to an 'escape' mission into space. It could also be used for short-duration scientific and applications missions, as an orbiting research laboratory or reconnaissance vehicle, for space rescue, as a tanker for space refuelling, and for support of orbiting space stations.

On some flights a pressurised Spacelab, being developed by ten European countries under the leadership of the European Space Agency, will be carried in the payload bay.

Spacelab will be the means by which man-associated experiments can be performed in the Orbiter payload bay. It includes a pressurised enclosure housing support equipment (to make it habitable) as well as the experimental equipment. When sensors require direct exposure to the space environment, a pallet will be used in association with the pressurised enclosure. On other types of missions, a pallet may be used alone, with control of the instruments being exercised from the Orbiter cabin or even from the ground. The Spacelabs are being designed around a basic seven-day mission, which is extendable up to 30 days by trading payload weight and volume for the additional consumables necessary to accommodate the further time in orbit.

On conclusion of its mission, the Orbiter will fly back into the atmosphere towards its land base, protected by a new form of heat shielding which will survive 100 missions, unlike current ablative-type heatshields. Once through the re-entry phase, the Orbiter will be able to glide up to 950 nm (1,760 km; 1,100 miles) to its base, steered by aerodynamic controls.

Special equipment being developed for use on the Space Shuttle includes a new type of spacesuit and a rescue system known as a Personal Rescue Enclosure. This consists of a 0·86 m (34 in) diameter ball which contains its own short-term simplified life support and communication systems. The ball has three layers (urethane, Kevlar and an outside thermal protective layer) and a small viewing port of tough Lexan.

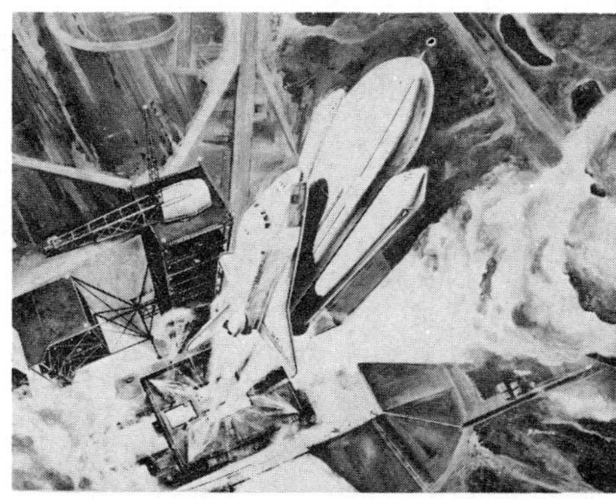

Artist's impression of Space Shuttle launch. The two boosters and the Orbiter main engine fire in parallel

Typical in-orbit experimental payload. An impression of a mission utilising the remote manipulator system

At low altitude the Orbiter goes into horizontal flight for an aircraft-type approach and landing

Orbiter OV-101 *Enterprise* completed approach and landing tests at NASA's Dryden Flight Research Center, California, in 1977, and ground vibration tests in 1978.

The first operational orbital mission is scheduled to be flown by the second Orbiter, OV-102, from the Kennedy Space Center, Florida, in the first half of 1981, following a series of test flights. Orbiter OV-102 is named *Columbia*; OV-099 will be named *Challenger*; OV-103, *Discovery*; and OV-104, *Atlantis*, after sea vessels used for exploration.

Basic dimensions and weights of the complete Space Transportation System are as follows:

DIMENSIONS, EXTERNAL:
- Wing span — 23·79 m (78 ft 0·68 in)
- Length overall — 56·14 m (184 ft 2·4 in)
- Length of external tank — 47 m (154 ft 2·4 in)
- Length of boosters — 45·46 m (149 ft 2·0 in)
- Height overall — 23·35 m (76 ft 7·2 in)

WEIGHTS:
- Shuttle complete — 1,984,305 kg (4,374,573 lb)
- Orbiter (empty) — 68,040 kg (150,000 lb)
- External tank (full) — 743,253 kg (1,638,565 lb)
- Boosters (2), each — 586,506 kg (1,293,004 lb)

THRUST:
- Total, at lift-off — 30,622 kN (6,925,000 lb)
- Orbiter, main engines (3), each — 1,608 kN (375,000 lb)
- Boosters (2), each — 12,899 kN (2,900,000 lb)

PERFORMANCE:
- Payload:
  - In 185 km (100 nm) orbit, due east: 29,485 kg (65,000 lb)
  - In 500 km (270 nm) orbit, 55° inclin: 11,340 kg (25,000 lb)
  - In 185 km (100 nm) polar orbit: 14,515 kg (32,000 lb)

VOYAGER

Two Mariner-type spacecraft, designated Voyager 1 and 2, were launched on a Jupiter-Saturn mission in 1977—Voyager 1 on 5 September and Voyager 2 on 20 August. They were intended to fly by both planets, and conduct exploratory investigations of the Jupiter and Saturn planetary systems. Voyager 1, flying faster than its companion, encountered Jupiter in March 1979, passing within 357,000 km (222,000 miles) of the planet. It took the first close-up pictures of Jupiter's four largest moons. The craft will arrive at Saturn in November 1980, flying past at a distance of 209,000 km (130,000 miles) and within 4,000 km (2,500 miles) of Titan, Saturn's largest moon. Voyager 2 reached Jupiter in July 1979, and will reach Saturn in August 1981. If all goes well, it will then be targeted for the first encounter with Uranus, some 2,700 million km (1,700 million miles) from Earth, in January 1986, before leaving the solar system.

The Voyagers were designed and built at NASA's Jet Propulsion Laboratory, California. Each of the 825 kg (1,820 lb) spacecraft carries wide-angle and narrow-angle television cameras and 10 scientific instruments. Major investigations include imaging, radio science, infrared and ultraviolet spectroscopy, magnetometry, charged particles, cosmic rays, photopolarimetry, planetary radio astronomy, plasma and particulate matter.

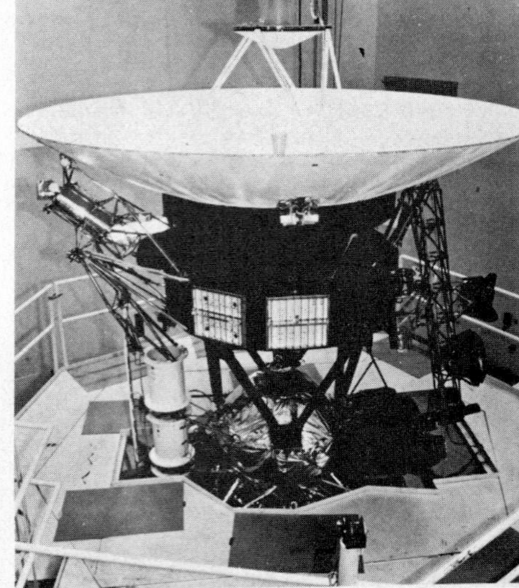

Jupiter-Saturn Voyager being vibration tested

RCA
RCA CORPORATION

President and Chief Executive Officer: Edgar H. Griffiths
Group Vice-President: Irving K. Kessler
Director, Public Affairs: Nicholas F. Pensiero

Government Systems Division
Cherry Hill Offices, Camden, New Jersey 08101
Telephone: (609) 234-1234

RCA is prime contractor for a number of major defence programmes, including the US Navy's Aegis advanced ship-to-air missile system, the USAF's Block 5D satellites, and Tiros meteorological satellites. It also produces many satellite subsystems and components, including the Closed Circuit Television (CCTV) camera system for the Space Shuttle.

Artist's impression of Anik B in orbit

ANIK B

Anik B was launched on 15 December 1978 into synchronous orbit by a Delta 3914 vehicle as part of Canada's domestic communications satellite system, operated by Telesat Canada. It is a derivative of the RCA Satcom spacecraft, with an all-up weight of 918 kg (2,023 lb), including about 90 kg (200 lb) of hydrazine propellant used for station keeping throughout its seven-year design life. The solar array initially provides 840W of power, which decreases naturally to 635W at end of life. Batteries supply power during periods of eclipse. The spacecraft is three-axis stabilised, with the antennae always pointing towards Canada with an accuracy of 0·25 degree.

Block 5D Air Force meteorological satellite

BLOCK 5D SATELLITE

Block 5D is the name given to new series of advanced meteorological satellites forming part of the Defense Meteorological Satellite Program (DMSP) managed by the Air Force Space and Missile Systems Organization.

Two DMSP satellites are normally in orbit at any one time providing weather data on a real-time basis to the Air Weather Service (AWS) and Navy ground and shipboard terminals located round the world. Data from the satellites are made available to civilian services through the Commerce Department's National Oceanic and Atmospheric Administration (NOAA).

The first Block 5D satellite was launched on 11 September 1976, the second on 5 June 1977. A third satellite was launched on 30 April 1978 and four additional Block 5Ds are being made by RCA Astro-Electronics. Details of the satellites are given in the 1977-78 edition.

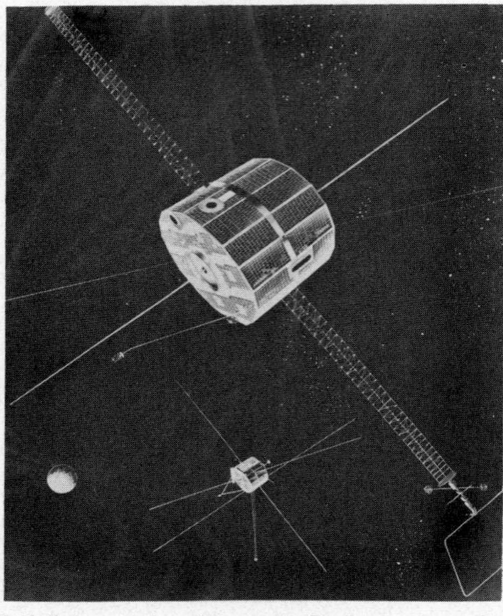

Artist's impression of Dynamics Explorer spacecraft

DYNAMICS EXPLORER

Dynamics Explorer (DE) is a NASA-sponsored programme which will investigate the interactive coupling between the Earth's magnetosphere, ionosphere and plasmasphere. It will utilise two coplanar polar orbiting spacecraft, designed by RCA Astro-Electronics; these will be launched by a single Delta 3914 into low and high elliptical orbits. The planned perigee altitude of both satellites is 250 km (155 miles); the apogee altitude of the low spacecraft is 1,000 km (620 miles) and that of the high spacecraft 4 to 6 Earth radii geocentric. The Dynamics Explorer launch is scheduled for 1981.

The Dynamics Explorer spacecraft is a derivative of the Atmosphere Explorer satellite. DE-A is estimated to weigh 258 kg (569 lb), of which 30 kg (66 lb) is science payload. DE-B will weigh approximately 305 kg (672 lb), of which 70 kg (154 lb) is for the experiments.

Of particular interest is the variety of experiment antennae and booms carried on both spacecraft. The high mission configuration (DE-A) accommodates two wire antennae 213 m (700 ft) long tip-to-tip, two 4 m (13 ft) flexible stem antennae, and two rigid booms 6 m (20 ft) long. The low mission spacecraft (DE-B) contains six 32 mm (1·25 in) diameter flexible stem antennae 11 m (36 ft) long, and a single rigid boom 6 m (20 ft) in length.

ITOS (NOAA) SATELLITE

Designed and built by RCA Astro-Electronics for NASA's Goddard Space Flight Center, the Improved Tiros Operational Satellite is capable of mapping the Earth's cloud cover at night as well as by day. Two complete scans of the Earth are thus possible each day rather than one.

When in orbit ITOS spacecraft are handed over to the National Oceanic and Atmospheric Administration and given the designation NOAA. Details of early ITOS spacecraft and NOAA launchings are given in the 1977-78 *Jane's*. Recent launchings are listed in the table of satellites at the end of this section. In early 1979 NOAA-4 and NOAA-5 were operational.

NOVA SATELLITE

The Nova satellite is an advanced version of the US Navy's Transit, and is part of the Navy's Navigation Satellite System.

Among various improvements, the satellite will be equipped with its own onboard station-seeking and station-keeping propulsion systems. The satellite also will require fewer position-updating transmissions from ground control stations than Transit. The new design was developed by the Applied Physics Laboratory of Johns Hopkins University, with support from RCA.

Nova will weigh approximately 136 kg (300 lb) in orbit and will utilise a 7·6 m (25 ft) long gravity boom for stabilisation.

The first of three satellites was scheduled for launch in late 1979 or early 1980, from Vandenberg Air Force Base, California, by a Scout rocket. In operation, the satellites will transmit signals that indicate their orbital positions. Using information derived from these signals, a ship or aircraft with the required onboard equipment will be able to determine its longitude and latitude to an accuracy 20 times greater than that offered by conventional radio or astro navigation.

Artist's impression of Nova navigational satellite

TIROS N

The first of a new generation of polar-orbiting weather satellites, designated TIROS-N, was launched on 13 October 1978 and is providing more information, more accurately and at a higher rate than the ITOS (NOAA) satellites. This is accomplished by carrying more advanced sensing devices, including: the Advanced Very High Resolution Radiometer (AVHRR), the Tiros Operational Vertical Sounder (TOVS), a French Data Collection System (DCS), and a Solar Environment Monitor (SEM). The data provided by these instruments will enable forecasters to predict climatic trends accurately up to a week in advance, and eventually to two weeks.

TIROS-N has an overall diameter of 1·88 m (6 ft 2 in) and is 3·71 m (12 ft 2 in) long. Weight at lift-off is 1,421 kg (3,127 lb); in-orbit weight is 689 kg (1,520 lb). Eight of the satellites have been procured to meet NOAA's operational requirements until 1985. Each will be launched by an Atlas E/F vehicle into a near-polar Sun-synchronous orbit at a nominal height of 833 km (517 miles) or 870 km (540 miles).

ROCKWELL INTERNATIONAL
ROCKWELL INTERNATIONAL CORPORATION
Space Systems Group

12214 Lakewood Boulevard, Downey, California 90241
Telephone: (213) 922-2111
PRESIDENT: George B. Merrick

Rockwell's Space Systems Group is comprised of three divisions: the Shuttle Orbiter Division which is responsible for design, development and test of Space Shuttle Orbiters; the STS Integration & Operations Division which is responsible for integrating NASA's Space Transportation System and payloads; and the Satellite Systems Division which has responsibility for design, development and test of the NavStar satellites of the Global Positioning System, as well as design, development and test of other satellites and space systems.

NAVSTAR

The NavStar global positioning system is intended to satisfy future precise positioning and navigation needs of all the US military services, and to have potential civil applications. NavStar is designed to provide suitably equipped users with highly accurate (to within 10 m; 30 ft) three-dimensional position and velocity information and a precise timing reference in real time. The NavStar spacecraft will be placed in subsynchronous, 12-hour circular orbits of about 20,170 km (12,530 miles) in three orbital planes at 63° inclination, with eight satellites per ring. The complete system of 24 satellites should be operational by 1985.

NavStar 1 was launched on 22 February 1978 by an Atlas F from Vandenberg AFB, and was followed by three more NavStars as detailed in the table of satellites at the end of this section. In concept validation phase testing, these four satellites have, in signals to ground, air and sea units, provided navigational data with three-dimensional accuracies better than design specifications.

The Global Positioning System (GPS) set (the user's or receiver's equipment) may be one of several models, installed or even hand-held in land, sea, air or space vehicles. The set comprises a combined radio receiver and computer, which locks on to NavStar signals from the four satellites that are most favourably located and computes the signal's time and range into navigational data. Key to the system is the use of highly accurate atomic clocks, of which three are installed on each of the 759 kg (1,673 lb) satellites; these will lose or gain only one second in 36,000 years.

SPACE SHUTTLE ORBITER

The National Aeronautics and Space Administration's Space Shuttle will be the world's first re-usable space transportation system, and will be the keystone of America's space programme through this century.

The Shuttle system includes the Orbiter stage, capable of carrying up to 29,484 kg (65,000 lb) of cargo into Earth orbit; an external propellant tank; and two solid-propellant rocket boosters. The Orbiter will lift off from Earth like a rocket, operate in orbit as a spacecraft, and return to land in a manner similar to that of a conventional aeroplane.

The first Shuttle Orbiter (OV-101 *Enterprise*) completed 13 flights during unpowered approach and landing tests (ALT) at NASA's Dryden Flight Research Center. Five unmanned captive flights with the Orbiter mated atop a Boeing 747 carrier were followed by three manned captive flights. The first of five free flights and landings was made on 12 August 1977, the last on 26 October.

Details of the overall operation of the Space Shuttle Transportation System are given in the NASA entry in this section.

The following description applies to Orbiter vehicle OV-102:

TYPE: Re-usable space transportation vehicle.

WINGS: Cantilever low-wing monoplane, of double-delta planform. Wing section NACA 0010 (modified). Sweepback 81° on inner leading-edges, 45° on outer leading-edges. Dihedral 3° 30′ on trailing-edges. The main wing assembly, for which Grumman is responsible, is primarily a conventional aluminium alloy structure made up of a corrugated spar web, truss-type ribs, and riveted skin/stringer and honeycomb skins. Wing has a very blunt leading-edge and is more than 1·52 m (5 ft) thick at the thickest point. Two-segment hydraulically-actuated elevons on each trailing-edge, for pitch and roll control, are of aluminium honeycomb construction with a titanium rubbing strip on each of their leading-edges. Hinged panels on the wing upper surface, of titanium sandwich, are used to seal the wing/elevon gap; these are the only areas of the wing not covered by the thermal protection system.

FUSELAGE: Conventional semi-monocoque aluminium alloy structure, built in three main portions. Forward fuselage contains the crew module, three forward electronics bays, forward reaction control system and nose-wheel unit. The mid-fuselage portion is an 18·28 m (60 ft) long section of primary load-carrying structure, built by General Dynamics (Convair) and includes the wing carry-through structure. Upper half of the mid-fuselage consists of structural payload bay doors, hinged along the side and meeting at the top centreline. These doors are of graphite epoxy bonded honeycomb sandwich construction, with a Nomex core, and are opened and closed by Curtiss-Wright actuators. The forward 9·14 m (30 ft) of each door incorporates Vought radiator panels that are hinged and latched to the inside of the door and can be deployed in orbit. Fixed aft radiator panels are attached to the remaining inner surface of each door. The aft fuselage interfaces with the removable orbital manoeuvring system (OMS) pods, the wing rear spar, the vertical tail assembly, the underbody flap, the external tank rear supports, the main propulsion system, the launch umbilical panel, the three aft electronics bays, and other discrete system equipment. A bulkhead heat-shield at the rear of the vehicle protects the main engine systems. A large body flap under the rear fuselage protects the main engine nozzles during re-entry, and is hydraulically-actuated to serve also as a trimming surface, particularly to compensate for the nose-up pitching moment induced when the rudder is in use as a speed brake.

TAIL UNIT: Vertical surfaces only, built by Fairchild Republic, of wedge-shaped section with 45° sweepback on fin leading-edge. Fin is a conventional aluminium alloy structure. The rudder/speed brake assembly has an aluminium honeycomb skin and is divided into upper and lower sections. Each of these is also split longitudinally and actuated individually to serve as both rudder and speed brake, operated by a Sundstrand hydraulic rotary actuator. The Inconel honeycomb seal over these is the only part of the vertical tail not covered by the thermal protection system. Mission requirements call for a locked rudder/speed brake during boost, orbit and re-entry. The speed brake control is provided from approx Mach 10 to Mach 5; from Mach 5 to landing the rudder and speed brake controls are combined as required. Primary system control is automatic, with manual override.

THERMAL PROTECTION SYSTEM: Almost the whole of the exterior of the Orbiter, a total area of some 1,103 m² (11,874 sq ft), is covered in one of four main types of thermal insulation. Two of these, known as HRSI (high-temperature re-usable surface insulation) and LRSI (low-temperature re-usable surface insulation) are the responsibility of Lockheed Missiles and Space Co, and are in the form of silica fibre-based quartz tiles. Some 34,000 tiles will cover 70 per cent of the surface (475·38 m²; 5,117 sq ft of HRSI and 281·68 m²; 3,032 sq ft of LRSI, covering most of the wings, fuselage and tail areas). The tiles are coated with reaction cured glass (RCG), the HRSI tiles giving protection from temperatures of 649-1,260°C (1,200-2,300°F) and the LRSI tiles from temperatures of 371-649°C (700-1,200°F). For temperatures below 371°C, some 304·36 m² (3,275 sq ft) of the surface, mostly on the cargo bay doors and mid-fuselage, is covered with coated Nomex felt. The nose-cap, and most of the wing leading-edges, a total of 38·00 m² (409 sq ft), are covered in a reinforced carbon-carbon (RCC) composite for which Vought is the subcontractor. Metal insulation is used along the elevon hinge lines. Total weight of the thermal insulation is 7,861 kg (17,332 lb).

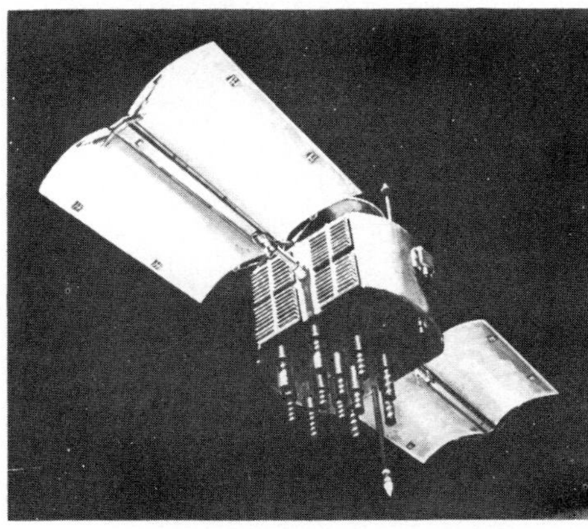

Artist's impression of NavStar satellite

LANDING GEAR: Retractable tricycle type, with twin wheels and Menasco oleo-pneumatic shock-absorbers on each unit. Hydraulic actuation, nose unit retracting forward into fuselage and main units forward into wings. Nose unit is steerable; main units are fitted with B. F. Goodrich brakes and Hydro-Aire anti-skid units. All units have Goodrich wheels and tyres. Landing gear is designed to facilitate safe landing at speeds of up to 221 knots (409 km/h; 254 mph). The main gear tyres are rated at 20,410 kg (45,000 lb) and the brakes at 240 × 10⁶ foot-lb.

BOOSTERS: Two Thiokol solid-propellant rocket boosters (each 12,899 kN; 2,900,000 lb st for lift-off) will be positioned under the wings of the Orbiter, attached one on each side of the Orbiter's external propellant tank.

MAIN PROPULSION: Three Rocketdyne SSME (Space Shuttle Main Engines) high-pressure liquid oxygen/liquid hydrogen engines, each rated at 1,668 kN (375,000 lb st) for lift-off and 2,090 kN (470,000 lb thrust) in space.

EXTERNAL PROPELLANT TANK: Contains the main propellants for the Orbiter. It is of aluminium alloy monocoque construction, with a 25 mm (1 in) thick foam external insulation. In the forward end of the tank is a 552·2 m³ (19,500 cu ft) tank holding 606,515 kg (1,337,358 lb) of liquid oxygen; in the aft end is a 1,523·5 m³ (53,800 cu ft) tank holding 101,812 kg (224,458 lb) of liquid hydrogen. Total propellant weight 708,427 kg (1,561,816 lb).

ORBIT MANOEUVRING ENGINES: Two Aerojet Liquid Rocket Company (ALRC) bi-propellant liquid rocket engines, running on monomethylhydrazine (MMH) and nitrogen tetroxide (N_2O_4), are used for the Orbiter's orbit manoeuvring subsystem (OMS). These engines are housed in pods, one on each side of the Orbiter's aft fuselage. The OMS engines, for which a usable total of 10,830 kg (23,876 lb) of propellant is carried, are used to position the Orbiter in orbit; each develops 26·7 kN (6,000 lb thrust) in space.

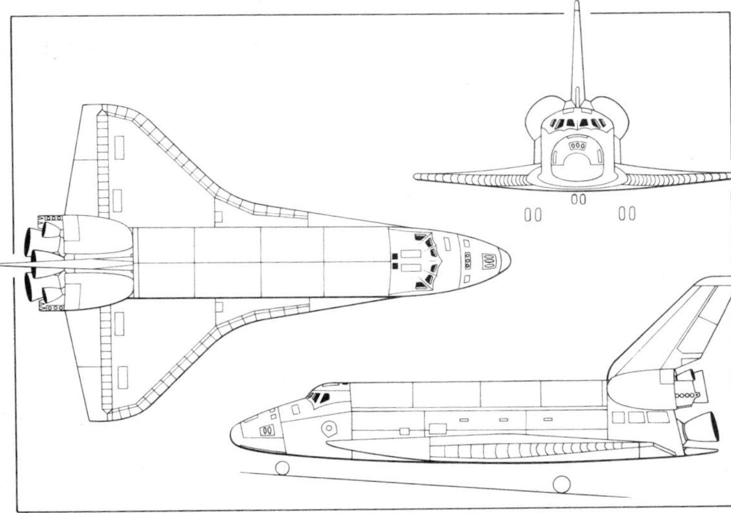

NASA/Rockwell International Space Shuttle Orbiter *(Michael A. Badrocke)*

Space Shuttle Orbiter vehicle OV-101, *Enterprise,* **approaching the runway at the end of an early unpowered flight test**

Reaction Control Engines: The Orbiter's reaction control subsystem (RCS) utilises thirty-eight Marquardt R-40A bipropellant liquid rocket engines (each 3·87 kN; 870 lb vacuum thrust) and six Marquardt R-1E bipropellant liquid rocket vernier thrusters (each 0·11 kN; 25 lb vacuum thrust). Fourteen of the R-40A engines are on the Orbiter's nose and 24 on the aft end, 12 in each OMS/RCS pod; there are two of the R-1E verniers on the nose and two in each aft pod. Propellants are the same as for the OMS engines; 1,096 kg (2,418 lb) is carried in the RCS tanks, and there is provision for crossfeed between the OMS and RCS tanks.

Crew Compartment: Self-contained crew module has a fuselage-side hatch for access, a hatch into the airlock from the mid-section, and a hatch from the airlock into the payload bay. It is divided into three levels, the upper (flight deck) level having side-by-side seating for two flight crewmen with dual controls. Behind them are seats for one or two mission specialists. On the middle deck are seats for three more mission specialists, three bunks, galley, hygiene section, airlock, four electronics bays, and payload bay access; for rescue missions, seats for three more persons can be fitted in place of the bunks. The lower deck contains environmental control equipment and crew equipment storage.

Payload Bay: In centre of fuselage, 18·29 m (60 ft) long and 4·57 m (15 ft) in diameter. Retractable manipulator arm on left hand side (with provision for a second one on the right), for deploying and retrieving payloads. Complete closed-circuit TV system by RCA Astro-Electronics includes a colour camera in the crew compartment and several black and white cameras in the cargo bay and on the manipulator arm. With special lighting, these will facilitate payload handling and provide TV coverage for engineers and the general public on Earth.

Systems: Environmental control and life support system, made up of four subsystems: atmosphere revitalisation subsystem (ARS), to control atmospheric environment for occupants and thermal environment for electronics; food, water and waste subsystem (FWW), to provide cooking, hygiene, and other life support functions; active thermal control subsystem (ATCS), to maintain subsystems and components within specified temperature limits and to provide, via payload door radiator panels, active heat rejection to protect payloads; and an airlock support subsystem. Three redundant hydraulic systems, each of 207 bars (3,000 lb/sq in), supply actuators for the elevons, body flap, rudder/speed brake, and power to actuate main engine thrust vector controls, landing gear, brakes and steering. Electrical power subsystem (EPS) consists, functionally, of a fuel cell power plants (FCP) subsystem, and a power reactant storage and distribution (PRSD) subsystem. There are three FCPs, each providing power at 27·5V to 32·5V DC over a power range of 2-12kW and each connected to one of the three main DC buses; these supply the primary in-flight electrical power used by the Shuttle, generated through the chemical combination and conversion of cryogenic oxygen and hydrogen. In the PRSD subsystem, enough of these materials is stored to provide a total of 1,530kWh of electrical energy to the Orbiter, including 50kWh to a payload over a seven-day period. Westinghouse remote power control system and master timing unit. Honeywell four-channel fly-by-wire electrical flight control subsystem for operation of all control surfaces and main engine controls. APU subsystem consists of three Sundstrand independent APUs (each 100·7 kW; 135 shp), deriving their energy from the decomposition of hydrazine (N_2H_4).

Electronics and Equipment: Fully fail-operational/fail-safe guidance, navigation and control system, including three Singer-Kearfott KT-70/SKN-2600 type inertial measuring units; triplex Ku-band microwave scan beam landing system, by the AIL Division of Cutler-Hammer; three Northrop rate gyro assemblies; three Hoffman L-band Tacan; three Bendix accelerometer assemblies; two Honeywell C-band radar altimeters; four AiResearch air data transducers; two Lear Siegler attitude director indicators; two Collins horizontal situation indicators; two Sperry alpha/Mach indicators; two Bendix altitude/vertical velocity indicators; two Bendix surface position indicators; two Sperry barometric altimeters; and two Sperry ATC transponders. Communications and tracking equipment includes one (optionally two) Ku-band rendezvous radar/satellite com; two Ball star trackers; two one-way Doppler extractors; two 100W Watkins-Johnson S-band TWT amplifiers; two P-band UHF for EVA/ATC com; Conrac S-band FM for Orbiter/ground and Orbiter/payload com; and Ku-band radio for Orbiter/ground com. Central data processing is by means of five IBM Advanced System/4 Pi Model AP-101 (modified) digital computers (each with a capacity for 65,000 32-bit words) and two mass memory units (each with capacity of 134 megabits). Four of the computers are interconnected to process guidance, navigation and control inputs and to relay commands to FBW flight control systems; the fifth is provided for independent backup and systems management.

Basic dimensions and weights of the Orbiter are:

Dimensions, external:	
Wing span	23·79 m (78 ft 0·68 in)
Wing aspect ratio	2·265
Wing mean aerodynamic chord	12·06 m (39 ft 6·81 in)
Length	37·26 m (122 ft 3·06 in)
Length of fuselage	32·775 m (107 ft 6·3 in)
Height	17·25 m (56 ft 7 in)
Dimensions, internal:	
Payload bay:	
Length	18·29 m (60 ft 0 in)
Diameter	4·57 m (15 ft 0 in)
Crew module: Volume	71·50 m³ (2,525 cu ft)
Areas:	
Wings, gross	249·91 m² (2,690 sq ft)
Elevons (total)	38·38 m² (413·14 sq ft)
Rudder/speed brake	9·09 m² (97·84 sq ft)
Vertical tail surfaces (total)	38·39 m² (413·25 sq ft)
Body flap	12·61 m² (135·75 sq ft)
Weights:	
Weight empty	68,040 kg (150,000 lb)
Design landing weight	85,275 kg (188,000 lb)
Performance:	
Orbital speed	approx 15,285 knots (28,325 km/h; 17,600 mph)
Nominal touchdown speed (unpowered)	180 knots (334 km/h; 208 mph) EAS

TRW

TRW DEFENSE AND SPACE SYSTEMS GROUP

1 Space Park, Redondo Beach, California 90278

Telephone: (213) 535-4321

Vice-President and General Manager: Dr George E. Solomon

Public Affairs and Communications Director: R. E. Trudel

TRW Defense and Space Systems Group has provided technical direction and systems engineering for the USAF Atlas/Titan/Minuteman missile programme since 1954. The company has also designed and built more than 150 spacecraft and scores of major subsystems. Its recent and current military and civilian contracts have included prime contracts for the NASA Pioneer, USAF DSCS II, international communications satellites and US Navy Fleet Communications Satellite.

DEFENSE SATELLITE COMMUNICATIONS SYSTEM, PHASE II (DSCS II)

The Phase II Defense Satellite Communications System (DSCS II) utilises synchronous-orbit, high-capacity, super high frequency communications satellites and surface terminals to provide reliable worldwide circuits for carrying essential military communications. The satellites are developed and produced by TRW Inc for the USAF.

Protected against interference, the satellites are each equipped with steerable narrow-beam antennae that focus a portion of the satellite's energy to areas 870 nm (1,600 km; 1,000 miles) in diameter. Within these specially illuminated areas, the narrow beam antennae allow small terminals to be used in place of more costly large terminals. The narrow beams are designed to be steered in a matter of minutes to different locations on the Earth's surface, and the satellites are so designed that they can be moved in a few days to new synchronous orbital positions. In this way coverage can be tailored to fit defence contingency communications all over the world.

The Phase II satellites each weigh 590 kg (1,300 lb), are 2·75 m (9 ft) in diameter and 3·95 m (13 ft) tall with antennae extended. Electrical power is supplied by solar arrays with an output of 535W at launch, decreasing to a minimum of 358W after five years. The X-band single-frequency conversion repeater has a bandwidth of 410MHz and capacity of 1,300 voice channels or up to 100 megabits per second of data.

The Earth-coverage antennae have a transmit beam-width of 18°, a gain of 16·8 dbi, and effective radiated power of 28 dbw. The narrow-coverage antennae have beamwidths of 2·6° and 6·5°, a gain of 33 dbi and 22 dbi, and an effective radiated power of 43 dbw and 32 dbw. They are steerable to ±10°.

First launch of two DSCS II satellites was on 3 November 1971, by Titan IIIC launch vehicle, from Cape Kennedy. Five more pairs had been launched by early 1979, at which time contracts were expected to fund a total of at least 16 satellites, to extend coverage into the 1980s.

FLEETSATCOM

The US Navy-sponsored Fleetsatcom satellite system will provide worldwide high-priority UHF communications between naval aircraft, ships, submarines, ground stations, Strategic Air Command and the Presidential command networks.

The first Fleetsatcom was launched by an Atlas-Centaur on 19 February 1978. In all, four of the three-axis stabilised satellites will be placed into geosynchronous equatorial orbit to provide complete Earth coverage, except for the polar regions. A fifth satellite will serve as a contingency spare. Fleetsatcoms have a design life of five years and provide more than 30 voice and 12 teletype channels.

The satellite consists of two major components, each with a basic 2·44 m (8 ft) hexagonal body. The payload module contains UHF and X-band communications equipment and antennae. Each of its six side panels carries related communications components. The 4·88 m (16 ft) parabolic UHF antenna is made up of ribs and mesh, and opens like an umbrella. The solar array, never shadowed, is exposed to sunlight in both folded and deployed configurations. Three nickel-cadmium batteries provide power during eclipse.

Weights:	
At lift-off	1,860 kg (4,100 lb)
In orbit	885 kg (1,950 lb)

HEAO

HEAO, a High Energy Astronomy Observatory, is designed to study some of the most intriguing mysteries in the universe; including pulsars, quasars, exploding galaxies and 'black holes' in space. The information gained may lead to a better understanding of the high energy universe and to new theories about energy production and high-density nuclear matter.

Three spacecraft, HEAO-A, B and C, are planned to undertake a three-mission programme.

HEAO-A is intended to survey and map X-ray sources throughout the celestial sphere and also measure low-energy gamma-ray flux. Rotating end-over-end, it is able to survey the entire sky in six months.

HEAO-B will manoeuvre and point for long periods at selected X-ray sources mapped by HEAO-A and smaller X-ray spacecraft. HEAO-C will conduct a survey of gamma ray emissions and study cosmic ray particles from our galaxy.

HEAO is 5·8 m (19 ft) long and weighs about 3,150 kg (7,000 lb), including 1,350 kg (3,000 lb) of experiments. Basically, the spacecraft consists of a common equipment module plus a mission-peculiar experiment module. The HEAO-A experiment module structure is six-sided. Three of the four experiments are designed to study certain attributes of the low-to-medium energy X-rays from galactic and extra-galactic discrete X-ray sources, as well as the diffuse X-ray background. The fourth experiment extends the observations into the low-energy gamma ray region of the spectrum.

Artist's impression of Fleetsatcom satellite

DSCS II defence communications satellite

In HEAO-B, which must point to specific stars or points in the sky, reaction wheels are added to provide a precise and highly accurate pointing capability of one arc minute or better.

HEAO-A, designated HEAO-1 in orbit, was launched by Atlas-Centaur 45 on 12 August 1977, from Cape Canaveral Air Force Station at the Kennedy Space Center, Florida. It returned excellent quality data, studying more than 300 stellar sources, until its supply of attitude control gas became exhausted in January 1979 and its mission ended. HEAO-B, designated HEAO-2 in orbit, was launched on 13 November 1978. Nicknamed *Einstein Observatory,* the spacecraft carries the first telescope capable of producing focused images showing the structure of X-ray objects. By the end of March 1979, among the 500 images transmitted were pictures of the brightest, most distant and most powerful objects yet observed to emit X-rays — quasars estimated to be more than 10,000 million light years from Earth.

HEAO-C was scheduled to be launched in late 1979.

IMEWS (USAF 647 SATELLITE)

The USAF's 647 series of satellites, for which TRW Systems is prime contractor, is intended to provide early warning of a hostile ballistic missile launch by detecting the infra-red emission from the missiles by means of an Aerojet-General infra-red 'telescope'. The programme is believed to be known now by the acronym IMEWS (Integrated Missile Early Warning Satellite) and to be the operational successor to the original Midas project.

A first launch, on 6 November 1970, was unsuccessful. The second launching, by a Titan IIIC from Cape Kennedy on 5 May 1971, is believed to have been successful. IMEWS-3 was launched on 1 March 1972, and IMEWS-4 on 12 June 1973. French reports suggest that the IMEWS satellite is cylindrical, weighs 820 kg (1,800 lb) at launch, has an inertial three-axis stabilisation system and measures approximately 3 m (9 ft 10 in) in diameter and 3 m (9 ft 10 in) in height; cruciform solar panels are said to span 7 m (23 ft). The same reports stated that the satellite carries high-resolution cameras, able to transmit photographs of any missiles that are located to a ground station 500 km (300 miles) north-west of Adelaide, Australia, for onward transmission via synchronous-orbit relay satellites to NORAD headquarters, Colorado Springs, USA.

VOUGHT

VOUGHT CORPORATION (Subsidiary of THE LTV CORPORATION)

Headquarters: PO Box 225907, Dallas, Texas 75265

Officers: See Aircraft section

Vought Corporation is prime contractor for the NASA/DoD Scout launch vehicle. It is also engaged in the fields of advanced defence systems, ramjet propulsion systems and laser technology.

SCOUT (XRM-91)

Scout was designed to make possible space, orbital and re-entry research at comparatively low cost. Its first stage is the 511·5 kN (115,000 lb st) Algol IIB (Aerojet Senior) by Aerojet-General, or Algol III (see below); the second stage is the 266·9 kN (60,000 lb st) Castor II by Thiokol; the third stage is the 93·41 kN (21,000 lb st) Antares II (X259) by Hercules Inc's Allegany Ballistics Laboratory; the current Altair III fourth stage, by Thiokol, develops 26·7 kN (6,000 lb st). Honeywell provides the simplified gyro guidance system. Spin stabilisation of the fourth stage is by Vought.

On 16 February 1961, a Scout became the first solid-propellant vehicle ever to put a satellite into orbit when it was used to launch the Explorer 9 inflatable sphere.

An enlarged heatshield, first used on 20 June 1971, provides a volume of 1·0 m³ (35·3 cu ft) and increases the diameter of the payload that Scout can carry to 1·0 m (3 ft 3¼ in). The Algol III first-stage motor provides a total impulse of 3,266,000 kg/s (7,200,000 lb/s) compared with about 2,476,000 kg/s (5,450,000 lb/s) for the Algol IIB. It increases the weight that Scout can put into a 500 km (310 mile) easterly orbit from 150 kg (330 lb) to approximately 193 kg (425 lb).

A fifth-stage velocity package is available which increases the Scout's hypersonic re-entry performance, makes possible highly-elliptical deep-space orbits, and extends the vehicle's probe capabilities to the Sun.

In addition to its use by NASA and the Department of Defense, Scout is used for international programmes, including those of the United Kingdom, Italy, France, Germany, the Netherlands and the European Space Agency (ESA). A total of 98 had been launched by January 1979.

Dimensions:

Overall height	22·92 m (75 ft 2½ in)
Max body diameter	1·14 m (3 ft 9 in)

Weight:

Launching weight	21,400 kg (47,185 lb)

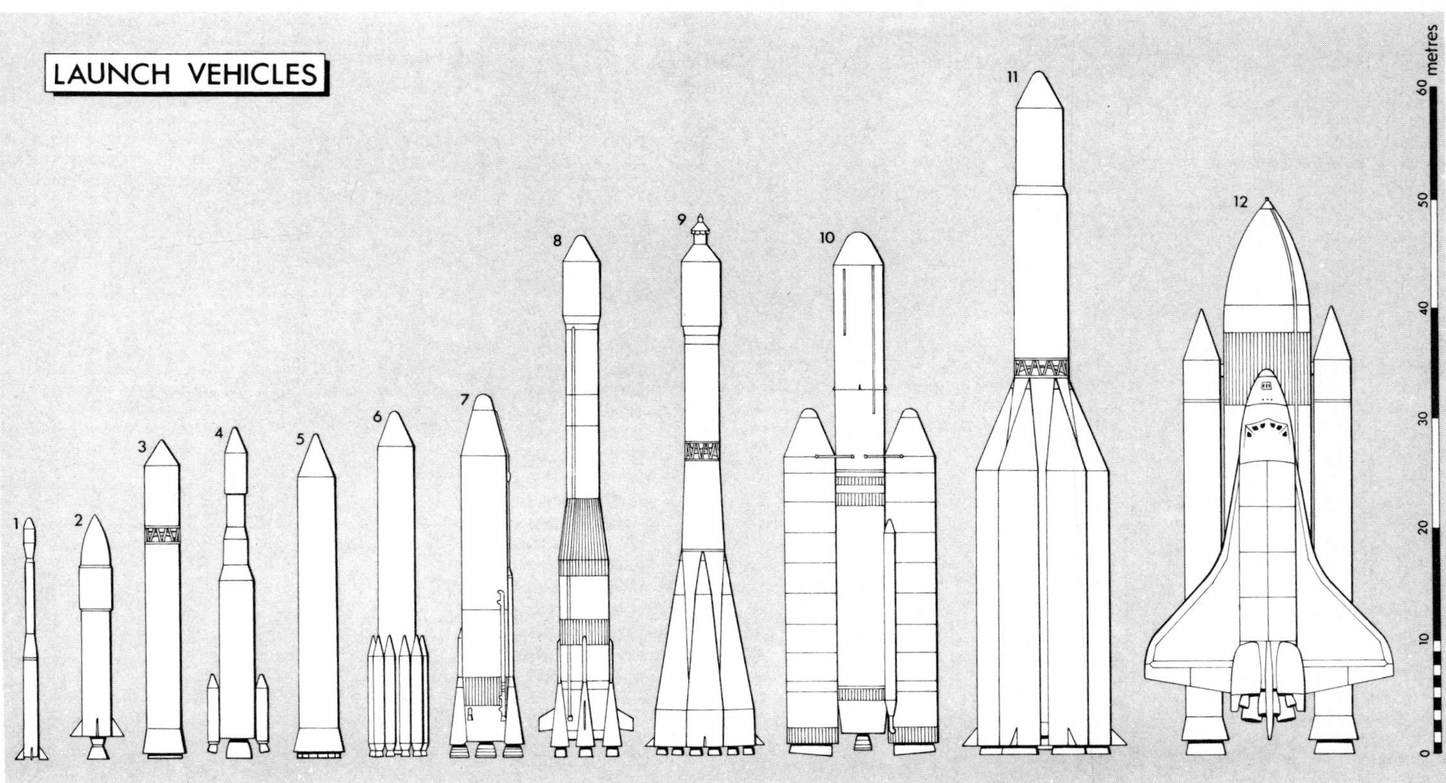

Launch vehicles: 1, Scout (USA); 2, Diamant BP-4 (France); 3, B-1 Cosmos (USSR); 4, N (Japan); 5, C-1 Cosmos (USSR); 6, Delta 3914 (USA); 7, Atlas-Centaur (USA); 8, Ariane (France); 9, A-2 Soyuz (USSR); 10, Titan IIIC (USA); 11, D-1e Zonda (USSR); 12, Space Shuttle (USA) *(Michael A. Badrocke)*

SATELLITES AND SPACECRAFT LAUNCHED DURING 1978

Note: Both the USA and USSR have withheld information on some launchings and this list may be incomplete. Data in italics are approximate or estimated.

Date	Origin	Name	Total weight kg	Total weight lb	Launch Vehicle	Apogee km	Apogee miles	Perigee km	Perigee miles	Inclin-ation	Lifetime	Remarks
6 Jan	USSR	Cosmos 974	*6,000*	*13,230*	—	334	207	178	111	62·81	13 days	*Reconnaissance satellite*
7 Jan	USA	Intelsat IVA (F-3)	1,511	3,331	Atlas-Centaur	35,806	22,249	35,768	22,225	0·3	Unlimited	Communications satellite.
10 Jan	USSR	Soyuz 27	*6,570*	*14,480*	—	237	147	190	118	88·71	65 days	Docked with Salyut 6. Crew Vladimir Dzhanibekov, Oleg Makarov.
10 Jan	USSR	Cosmos 975	*2,500*	*5,510*	—	653	406	634	394	81·22	*60 years*	Navigation satellite?
10 Jan	USSR	Cosmos 976-983	*40*	*88*	—	1,465	910	1,457	905	74·03	*9,000 years*	*Military communications satellites.*
13 Jan	USSR	Cosmos 984	*5,500*	*12,125*	—	291	181	206	128	62·81	13 days	*Reconnaissance satellite.*
17 Jan	USSR	Cosmos 985	*700*	*1,543*	—	1,022	635	945	587	82·94	*1,200 years*	Navigation satellite?
20 Jan	USSR	Progress 1	*7,020*	*15,476*	—	256	159	173	107	51·61	19 days	Unmanned ferry spacecraft. Carried supplies to Salyut 6.
24 Jan	USSR	Molniya-3 (9)	*1,500*	*3,306*	—	40,618	25,239	646	401	62·81	*12 years*	Communications satellite.
24 Jan	USSR	Cosmos 986	*6,000*	*13,230*	—	318	198	172	107	65·01	*14 days*	*Reconnaissance satellite.*
25 Jan	China	China 8	*3,600*	*7,937*	—	479	298	161	100	57·03	12 days	Purpose not known.
26 Jan	USA	IUE-1	—	—	Delta	45,888	28,513	25,669	15,950	28·63	Unlimited	International Ultra-Violet Explorer.
31 Jan	USSR	Cosmos 987	*6,000*	*13,230*	—	321	199	175	109	62·80	14 days	*Reconnaissance satellite.*
4 Feb	Japan	EXOS A (Kyoko)	103	227	Mu-3H	3,975	2,470	642	399	65·09	*300 years*	Scientific satellite investigating aurorae.
8 Feb	USSR	Cosmos 988	*6,000*	*13,230*	—	335	208	201	125	72·84	12 days	*Reconnaissance satellite.*
9 Feb	USA	Fleetsatcom 1	1,884	4,154	Atlas-Centaur	35,666	22,162	35,522	22,072	2·77	Unlimited	Military communications satellite.
14 Feb	USSR	Cosmos 989	*6,000*	*13,230*	—	318	198	169	105	65·05	14 days	*Reconnaissance satellite.*
16 Feb	Japan	ISS 2 (Ume 2)	140	309	N	1,224	761	975	606	69·37	*1,400 years*	Ionospheric sounding satellite.
17 Feb	USSR	Cosmos 990	*750*	*1,653*	—	809	503	783	487	74·05	*120 years*	Military communications satellite.
22 Feb	USA	NavStar 1 (NDS-1)	*450*	*992*	Atlas F	20,308	12,619	20,095	12,486	63·27	Unlimited	Navigation development satellite.
25 Feb	USA	USAF	—	—	—	—	—	—	—	—	—	Purpose not disclosed.
28 Feb	USSR	Cosmos 991	*700*	*1,543*	—	1,009	627	963	598	82·98	*1,200 years*	Navigation satellite?
2 Mar	USSR	Soyuz 28	*6,570*	*14,480*	—	246	153	192	119	51·63	8 days	Docked with Salyut 6. Crew Alexei Gubarev and Vladimir Remek.
2 Mar	USSR	Molniya-1 (39)	*1,000*	*2,200*	—	39,741	24,694	489	304	62·84	*12 years*	Communications satellite.
4 Mar	USSR	Cosmos 992	*5,500*	*12,125*	—	323	201	203	126	71·34	13 days	*Reconnaissance satellite.*
5 Mar	USA	Landsat 3	960	2,116	Delta	918	570	900	559	99·14	*100 years*	Earth resources survey satellite.
	USA	Oscar 8	27	60		917	570	903	561	98·99	*100 years*	Amateur radio satellite.
10 Mar	USSR	Cosmos 993	*6,000*	*13,230*	—	340	211	171	106	72·86	13 days	*Reconnaissance satellite.*
15 Mar	USSR	Cosmos 994	*700*	*1,543*	—	1,011	628	980	609	82·93	*1,200 years*	Navigation satellite?
16 Mar	USA	USAF	*13,300*	*29,320*	Titan IIID	240	149	160	99	96·43		'Big Bird' reconnaissance satellite.
	USA	USAF	*60*	*132*		645	401	639	397	95·83	*60 years*	Purpose not disclosed.
17 Mar	USSR	Cosmos 995	*5,500*	*12,125*	—	235	146	217	135	81·34	13 days	*Reconnaissance satellite.*
28 Mar	USSR	Cosmos 996	*700*	*1,543*	—	1,010	628	957	595	82·93	*1,200 years*	Navigation satellite?
30 Mar	USSR	Cosmos 997	*7,000*	*15,430*	—	210	130	195	121	51·60	1 orbit	—
	USSR	Cosmos 998	*7,000*	*15,430*		210	130	195	121	51·60	1 orbit	—
30 Mar	USSR	Cosmos 999	*6,000*	*13,230*	—	352	219	174	108	71·39	13 days	*Reconnaissance satellite.*
31 Mar	USSR	Cosmos 1000	*700*	*1,543*	—	1,012	629	965	600	82·93	*1,200 years*	Navigation satellite.
31 Mar	USA	Intelsat IVA	825	1,812	Atlas-Centaur	35,806	22,249	35,768	22,225	0·3	Unlimited	Communications satellite.
4 Apr	USSR	Cosmos 1001	*7,000*	*15,430*	—	228	142	200	124	51·62	11 days	—
6 Apr	USSR	Cosmos 1002	*5,500*	*12,125*	—	282	175	204	127	65·05	13 days	*Reconnaissance satellite.*
7 Apr	Japan	BSE 1 (Yuri)	678	1,495	Delta	35,786	22,236	35,784	22,235	0·08	Unlimited	Experimental Broadcasting Satellite.
8 Apr	USA	USAF	*700*	*1,543*	Atlas-Agena D	—	—	—	—	29·9	Unlimited	Monitors missile launchings.
20 Apr	USSR	Cosmos 1003	*6,000*	*13,230*	—	328	204	178	111	62·81	14 days	*Reconnaissance satellite.*
26 Apr	USA	HCMM	134	295	Scout	651	405	559	347	97·60	*60 years*	Heat Capacity Mapping Satellite.
1 May	USA	AMS 3	513	1,131	Thor-Burner 2	835	519	820	510	98·71	*80 years*	Advanced Meteorological Satellite.
5 May	USSR	Cosmos 1004	*5,500*	*12,125*	—	290	180	205	127	62·81	13 days	*Reconnaissance satellite.*
11 May	Europe	OTS 2	865	1,907	Delta	35,779	22,232	35,072	21,793	0·10	Unlimited	Orbital Test Satellite.
12 May	USSR	Cosmos 1005	*2,500*	*5,510*	—	652	405	625	388	81·24	*60 years*	—
12 May	USSR	Cosmos 1006	—	—	—	407	253	382	237	65·85	*15 months*	—
13 May	USA	NavStar 2 (NDS 2)	453	997	Atlas F	20,094	12,486	19,958	12,401	63·13	Unlimited	Navigation Development Satellite.
16 May	USSR	Cosmos 1007	*5,500*	*12,125*	—	350	217	168	104	72·83	13 days	*Reconnaissance satellite.*
17 May	USSR	Cosmos 1008	*900*	*1,984*	—	548	341	497	309	74·04	*10 years*	—
19 May	USSR	Cosmos 1009	—	—	—	1,384	860	965	600	65·84	3 orbits	Intercepted Cosmos 967.
20 May	USA	Pioneer Venus 1	582	1,283	Atlas-Centaur	In orbit round the Sun				—	Unlimited	Venus probe.
23 May	USSR	Cosmos 1010	*6,000*	*13,230*	—	229	142	215	134	81·38	13 days	Earth resources satellite.
23 May	USSR	Cosmos 1011	*700*	*1,543*	—	1014	630	960	597	82·91	*1,200 years*	Navigation satellite?
25 May	USSR	Cosmos 1012	*5,500*	*12,125*	—	265	165	202	126	62·80	13 days	*Reconnaissance satellite.*
2 June	USSR	Molniya-1 (40)	*1,000*	*2,205*	—	39,941	24,818	412	256	62·86	*12 years*	Communications satellite.
7 June	USSR	Cosmos 1013-20	*40*	*88*	—	1,500	932	1,475	917	74·02	*10,000 years*	*Military communications satellites.*
10 June	USSR	Cosmos 1021	*6,000*	*13,230*	—	316	196	172	107	65·03	13 days	*Reconnaissance satellite.*
10 June	USA	USAF	—	—	Titan IIIC	35,860	22,282	35,620	22,133	0·5	Unlimited	Missile early warning satellite?
12 June	USSR	Cosmos 1022	*6,000*	*13,230*	—	348	216	169	105	72·86	13 days	*Reconnaissance satellite.*
14 June	USA	USAF	*13,300*	*29,320*	Titan IIID	509	316	223	139	86·96	—	'Big Bird' reconnaissance satellite.
15 June	USSR	Soyuz 29	*6,570*	*14,480*	—	248	154	193	120	51·63		Docked with Salyut 6. Crew Vladimir Kovalyonok and Alexander Ivanchenkov.
16 June	USA	GOES 3	627	1,382	Delta	35,802	22,246	35,776	22,230	1·00	Unlimited	Meteorological satellite.
21 June	USSR	Cosmos 1023	*750*	*1,653*	—	805	500	783	487	74·08	*120 years*	—
27 June	USA	Seasat 1	2,300	5,071	Atlas-Agena D	800	497	776	482	108·02	*200 years*	Experimental ocean survey satellite.
27 June	USSR	Soyuz 30	*6,570*	*14,480*	—	239	149	198	123	51·65	8 days	Docked with Salyut 6. Crew Pyotr Klimuk and Miroslaw Giermaszewski.
28 June	USSR	Cosmos 1024	*1,250*	*2,755*	—	40,094	24,913	605	376	62·83	*12 years*	*Missile early warning satellite.*
28 June	USSR	Cosmos 1025	—	—	—	667	414	638	396	82·49	—	—
29 June	USA	Comstar IC	1,520	3,351	Atlas-Centaur	35,780	22,233	35,470	22,040	0·08	Unlimited	US domestic communications satellite
2 July	USSR	Cosmos 1026	*5,500*	*12,125*		247	153	207	129	51·78	4 days	—
7 July	USSR	Progress 2	*7,020*	*15,476*	—	235	146	182	113	51·61	28 days	Unmanned ferry spacecraft. Carried supplies to Salyut 6.
14 July	Europe	GEOS 2	573	1,263	Delta	35,592	22,116	25,640	15,932	0·77	Unlimited	Studying magnetosphere.
14 July	USSR	Molniya 1 (41)	1,000	2,205	—	39,769	24,711	606	377	62·83	*12 years*	—
18 July	USSR	Raduga 4	2,000	4,410	—	35,859	22,282	35,716	22,193	0·44	Unlimited	Communications satellite.
27 July	USSR	Cosmos 1027	*700*	*1,543*	—	1,004	624	966	600	82·94	*1,200 years*	*Navigation satellite*
5 Aug	USA	USAF	—	—	Titan IIIB/Agena D	—	—	—	—	—	—	—
5 Aug	USSR	Cosmos 1028	*6,000*	*13,230*	—	248	154	171	106	67·13	30 days	*Reconnaissance satellite.*
7 Aug	USSR	Progress 3	*7,020*	*15,476*	—	232	144	190	118	51·64		Unmanned ferry spacecraft. Carried food to Salyut 6.
8 Aug	USA	Pioneer Venus 2	904	1,993	Atlas-Centaur	In orbit round the Sun.				—	Unlimited	Venus probe.
12 Aug	USA	ISEE 3			Delta	In orbit round the Sun.				—	Unlimited	International Sun Earth Explorer.

Date	Origin	Name	Total weight kg	lb	Launch Vehicle	Apogee km	miles	Perigee km	miles	Inclin-ation	Lifetime	Remarks
22 Aug	USSR	Molniya 1 (42)	*1,000*	*2,205*	—	40,792	25,347	442	275	62·87	Unlimited	Communications satellite.
26 Aug	USSR	Soyuz 31	*6,600*	*14,550*	—	243	151	193	120	51·62	68 days	Docked with Salyut 6. Crew Valery Bykovsky and Sigmund Jahn.
29 Aug	USSR	Cosmos 1029	*6,000*	*13,230*	—	331	206	177	110	62·82	10 days	*Reconnaissance satellite.*
6 Sept	USSR	Cosmos 1030	*1,000*	*2,205*	—	40,128	24,934	610	379	62·78	*12 years*	*Missile early warning satellite.*
9 Sept	USSR	Venera 11	*5,000*	*11,020*	—	In orbit round the Sun.				—	Unlimited	Venus probe.
9 Sept	USSR	Cosmos 1031	*6,000*	*13,230*	—	347	216	182	113	62·84	13 days	*Reconnaissance satellite.*
14 Sept	USSR	Venera 12	*5,000*	*11,020*	—	In orbit round the Sun.						Venus probe.
16 Sept	Japan	Jikiken (Exos B)	90	199	Mu-3H	30,558	18,988	230	143	31·10	*5 years*	Scientific satellite.
19 Sept	USSR	Cosmos 1032	—	—	—	223	139	214	133	81·35	13 days	*Reconnaissance satellite.*
3 Oct	USSR	Cosmos 1033	*6,000*	*13,230*	—	234	145	204	127	81·40	13 days	*Reconnaissance satellite.*
3 Oct	USSR	Progress 4	*7,000*	*15,430*	—	248	154	185	115	51·65	23 days	Unmanned ferry spacecraft. Carried supplies to Salyut 6.
4 Oct	USSR	Cosmos 1034-41	*40*	*88*	—	1,482	921	1,402	871	74·01	*7,000 years*	*Military communications satellites.*
6 Oct	USSR	Cosmos 1042	*6,000*	*13,230*	—	306	190	180	112	89·37	13 days	*Reconnaissance satellite.*
7 Oct	USA	NavStar 3 (GPS 3)	*450*	*992*	Atlas F	20,310	12,620	20,283	12,603	62·81	Unlimited	Global Positioning System satellite.
10 Oct	USSR	Cosmos 1043	*2,500*	*5,510*	—	634	394	620	385	81·20	*60 years*	—
13 Oct	USSR	Molniya 3 (10)	*1,500*	*3,307*	—	40,828	25,369	432	268	62·79	*12 years*	Communications satellite.
13 Oct	USA	Tiros 11	734	1,618	Atlas F	864	537	849	528	98·92	*1,000 years*	Meteorological satellite.
17 Oct	USSR	Cosmos 1044	*5,500*	*12,125*		292	181	205	127	62·82	13 days	*Reconnaissance satellite.*
24 Oct	USA	Nimbus 7	907	2,000	Delta	955	593	943	586	99·28	*1,200 years*	Environmental satellite.
24 Oct	USSR	Intercosmos 18	*550*	*1,212*	—	761	473	414	257	82·97	*15 years*	International research satellite.
26 Oct	USSR	Cosmos 1045	—	—	—	1,724	1,071	1,688	1,049	82·60	*15,000 years*	—
		Radio 1	—	—		1,724	1,071	1,688	1,049	82·60	*15,000 years*	Amateur radio satellite.
		Radio 2	—	—		1,724	1,071	1,688	1,049	82·60	*15,000 years*	Amateur radio satellite.
30 Oct	USSR	Prognoz 7	*950*	*2,094*	—	202,965	126,117	483	300	65·00	*10 years*	Scientific satellite. Studying magnetosphere.
1 Nov	USSR	Cosmos 1046	*6,000*	*13,230*	—	353	219	212	132	72·9	13 days	*Reconnaissance satellite.*
13 Nov	USA	HEAO 2	3,150	6,945	Atlas-Centaur	542	337	523	325	95·08	*2 years*	High Energy Astronomy Observatory.
15 Nov	USSR	Cosmos 1047	*6,000*	*13,230*	—	378	235	182	113	72·9	13 days	*Reconnaissance satellite.*
16 Nov	USSR	Cosmos 1048	*750*	*1,653*	—	824	512	788	490	74·04	*100 years*	—
19 Nov	USA	NATO IIIC	*720*	*1,587*	Delta	35,783	22,235	35,495	22,056	4·41	Unlimited	NATO communications satellite.
21 Nov	USSR	Cosmos 1049	*6,000*	*13,230*	—	375	233	183	114	72·87	13 days	*Reconnaissance satellite.*
28 Nov	USSR	Cosmos 1050	*6,000*	*13,230*	—	298	185	258	160	62·8	13 days	*Reconnaissance satellite.*
5 Dec	USSR	Cosmos 1051-58	*40*	*88*	—	1,530	951	1,451	902	74·02	*10,000 years*	*Military communications satellites.*
7 Dec	USSR	Cosmos 1059	*6,000*	*13,230*	—	360	224	188	117	62·8	13 days	*Reconnaissance satellite.*
8 Dec	USSR	Cosmos 1060	*5,500*	*12,125*	—	311	193	209	130	65·03	13 days	*Reconnaissance satellite.*
11 Dec	USA	NavStar 4 (GPS 4)	*450*	*992*	Atlas F	20,288	12,606	20,183	12,541	63·29	Unlimited	Global Positioning System satellite.
14 Dec	USA	DSCS II (11)	*550*	*1,212*	Titan IIIC	36,412	22,625	35,797	22,243	2·50	Unlimited	Military communications satellite.
		DSCS II (12)	*550*	*1,212*		36,416	22,628	36,263	22,533	2·50	Unlimited	Military communications satellite.
14 Dec	USSR	Cosmos 1061	*5,500*	*12,125*	—	333	207	211	131	62·82	13 days	*Reconnaissance satellite.*
15 Dec	USSR	Cosmos 1062	*700*	*1,543*	—	548	341	508	316	74·04	*5 years*	—
16 Dec	Canada	Telesat 4	900	1,984	Delta	—	—	—	—	—	Unlimited	Communications satellite.
19 Dec	USSR	Cosmos 1063	*2,500*	*5,512*	—	661	411	632	393	81·23	*60 years*	—
19 Dec	USSR	Horizont	*2,000*	*4,409*	—	48,365	30,053	22,581	14,031	10·69	Unlimited	Communications satellite.
20 Dec	USSR	Cosmos 1064	*700*	*1,543*	—	991	616	435	270	82·95	*10 years*	—
22 Dec	USSR	Cosmos 1065	*550*	*1,212*	—	556	345	346	215	50·68	*2 years*	—
23 Dec	USSR	Cosmos 1066	*500*	*1,102*	-	*908*	*564*	*848*	*527*	*81·24*	*500 years*	May be weather satellite.
26 Dec	USSR	Cosmos 1067	*700*	*1,543*	—	1,226	762	1,184	736	82·98	*2,500 years*	—
26 Dec	USSR	Cosmos 1068	*6,000*	*13,230*	—	408	254	187	116	62·82	13 days	*Reconnaissance satellite.*
28 Dec	USSR	Cosmos 1069	*5,500*	*12,125*	—	290	180	244	152	62·82	13 days	*Reconnaissance satellite.*

AERO-ENGINES

ARGENTINA

CICARÉ
CICARÉ AERONAUTICA SC

Ave Ibañez Frocham s/n, CC24, Saladillo, Provincia de Buenos Aires (Comodoro Mantel, in Buenos Aires)
Telephone: 41-5260

Several types of Cicaré automotive engine have been produced in quantity for surface applications. Cicaré Aeronautica, formed in 1972, is developing light helicopters (see Aircraft section) and light-aircraft engines.

CICARÉ 4C2T

This light, low-cost engine is intended to replace the many Continental A65 and similar engines used in Argentina and other countries as a standard power unit for light aviation. It first ran in October 1973.

TYPE: Four-cylinder horizontally-opposed aircooled two-stroke piston engine.

CYLINDERS: Bore 74 mm (2·91 in). Stroke 76 mm (3·00 in). Swept volume 1,314 cc (80·18 cu in). Compression ratio 8·0 : 1. Cylinders on each side cast in light alloy as single unit complete with half crankcase. Steel liners.

PISTONS: Aluminium alloy castings, each with two compression rings and one scraper ring.

CONNECTING RODS: Forged steel, with needle-roller bearings in both big and small ends.

CRANKSHAFT: Four-throw steel forging carried in three ball bearings.

CRANKCASE: Divided on vertical centreline; each half cast complete with pair of cylinders.

INDUCTION: Twin carburettors, each equipped with hot-air anti-icing. Mixture passed through crankcase and thence through inlet and exhaust ports in cylinders.

FUEL: Mixture of 40 parts 80-octane gasoline to 1 part SAE.40 oil.

IGNITION: Dual magnetos, serving two Champion UK10, Autolite BT3 or PVI BT3 plugs per cylinder.

LUBRICATION: See under Fuel.

ACCESSORIES: Rear pads for 12V alternator and starter.

DIMENSIONS:
- Length: 810 mm (31·89 in)
- Width: 660 mm (25·98 in)
- Height: 550 mm (21·65 in)

WEIGHT, DRY:
- Estimated, with accessories: 68 kg (150 lb)

PERFORMANCE RATING:
- Max T-O: 52·2 kW (70 hp) at 3,500 rpm

Prototype Cicaré 4C2T, showing propeller shaft driven by gearbox at rear. Rated at 52·2 kW (70 hp)

SPECIFIC FUEL CONSUMPTION:
- Fuel/oil mix at optimum rating: 111 μg/J (0·66 lb/h/hp)

AUSTRALIA

CAC
COMMONWEALTH AIRCRAFT CORPORATION LIMITED

HEAD OFFICE AND WORKS: GPO Box 779H, Melbourne 3001, Victoria
Telephone: 640-771
OFFICERS: See Aircraft section

This company built the Rolls-Royce Avon and Viper and SNECMA Atar 9C turbojets, and supports these engines in service with the RAAF.

BELGIUM

FN
FABRIQUE NATIONALE HERSTAL SA

HEAD OFFICE AND WORKS: B-4400 Herstal
Telephone: (041) 64 08 00

FN has been making and overhauling jet engines since 1949. Its major current programme involves the production of components for the Pratt & Whitney F100-PW-100 fan module and core engine module for Belgium, Denmark, the Netherlands and Norway, and also for the USAF and for third-party countries; assembly and test of these modules; and final building and testing of the complete engines for the European consortium and for third-party countries. The first engine ran at FN in July 1978, and deliveries to F-16 production centres began two months later.

Participation in the Larzac jet engine programme involves final building and testing of the engines for Alpha Jet trainers supplied to the Belgian Air Force.

FN is also a member of the consortium which has put the Rolls-Royce Tyne turboprop back into production to power the Transall C-160 and Dassault-Breguet Atlantic ANG.

FN's share in the CFM56 project amounts to 5 per cent of the 50 per cent work-split due to SNECMA in this SNECMA-General Electric joint programme.

FN is still making parts for major engine manufacturers including Rolls-Royce (marine Tyne, Dart), SNECMA (Atar 9C, M53) and Pratt & Whitney (JT8D). FN also makes spare parts for the General Electric J79-11A and SNECMA Atar 9C, and for the FN-Boeing 553 gas turbine powering Swedish S tanks.

CANADA

ORENDA
HAWKER SIDDELEY CANADA LTD, Orenda Division

Box 6001, Toronto, AMF, Ontario L5P 1B3
Telephone: (416) 677-3250

VICE-PRESIDENT AND GENERAL MANAGER: R. F. Tanner
DIRECTOR OF ENGINEERING: B. A. Avery
DIRECTOR OF OPERATIONS: P. K. Peterson
DIRECTOR OF MARKETING: D. J. Caple
DIRECTOR OF FINANCE: K. R. Church

Main activities of Orenda Division are the manufacture of aircraft turbine engines and components, and the design and manufacture of industrial gas turbines.

An important activity is repair, overhaul and spares manufacture of J85-CAN-15 turbojets. These engines, similar to the J85-GE-15 described under General Electric on a later page, were in production at Orenda from 1967 until 1974.

Orenda also overhauls J85-CAN-40, J79-OEL-7 and Orenda turbojet engines. It supplies parts to Belgium, Canada, West Germany, Italy, the Netherlands, Norway, Pakistan, the United States and Venezuela.

P&WC
PRATT & WHITNEY AIRCRAFT OF CANADA LTD

HEAD OFFICE AND WORKS: PO Box 10, Longueuil, Quebec J4K 4X9
Telephone: (514) 677-9411
PRESIDENT AND CHIEF EXECUTIVE OFFICER: D. C. Lowe
EXECUTIVE VICE-PRESIDENT, OPERATIONS: E. L. Smith
VICE-PRESIDENTS:
- K. H. Sullivan (Marketing)
- L. D. Caplan (Finance and Administration)
- J. P. Beauregard (Materials and Procurement)
- A. L. Tontini (Personnel)
- R. H. Guthrie (Industrial and Marine Division)
- R. G. Raven (Helicopter and Systems Division)
- E. H. Schweitzer (Product Support)
- C. B. Wrong (Engineering)
- E. L. Hunter (Production)
- C. J. C. Pascoe (Counsel)

Pratt & Whitney Aircraft of Canada is a major subsidiary of United Technologies Corporation, Connecticut, USA, and is the UTC company responsible for engines for general aviation.

Original turbine work by the company was initiated by the concept and preliminary design of the JT12 (J60) turbojet, development and manufacture of which were taken over subsequently by Pratt & Whitney Aircraft. Design, development and manufacture of the PT6, ST6, PT6T and JT15D series of small turbine aero-engines represents over 70 per cent of the company's activities.

P&WC is owned 97 per cent by the United Technologies Corporation. Approximately 15 per cent of its sales are linked to defence requirements. It occupies more than 139,400 m² (1·5 million sq ft) of space in three plants and employs more than 6,000 persons.

In 1978 a total of 1,825 new engines were delivered. By 1 January 1979 P&WC had delivered more than 15,300 PT6A and 6B engines, and over 1,300 JT15D turbofans.

P&WC JT15D

Following a comprehensive performance study of small turbofan engines carried out by P&WC during 1965, detail design of a definitive engine, the 8·9-11·12 kN (2,000 lb to 2,500 lb st) JT15D was initiated in June 1966. First run of the new turbofan was on 23 September 1967.

Intended to power business aircraft, small transports and counter-insurgency combat aircraft in the 8,000 lb to 12,500 lb AUW category, the JT15D is an advanced technology two-spool front-fan engine having a minimum number of aerodynamic components. Major design objectives were a significant improvement in sfc, and simplicity of construction to ensure low first cost and maintenance costs. Other objectives were low noise levels, ease of handling, and the attainment of airline standards of reliability.

Initial application for the JT15D was the twin-engined Cessna Citation. Flightworthy prototype engines were delivered in August 1969 for the Citation's first flight in mid-September. By January 1979 a total of 1,049 JT15D-1 and -1A engines had been delivered for the Citation. Certificated to FAR Part 36 noise specifications, the JT15D-1-powered Citation is claimed to be the quietest executive jet flying. TBO of the D-1 engine is 3,000 h.

A second application for the engine was the Aérospatiale SN 601 Corvette twin-engined business jet. TBO of the JT15D-4 for this aircraft is 2,000 h; deliveries totalled 270 by January 1979.

In late 1976 Cessna announced the Citation II, for delivery in 1978. In January 1977 Cessna introduced the Citation I powered by the new JT15D-1A. By January 1979 total operating time on JT15D engines was 1,875,000 h.

The following description relates to the JT15D-1 except where indicated:

Type: Two-shaft turbofan.

Air Intake: Direct pitot intake without inlet guide vanes. Hot-air anti-icing for nose bullet.

Fan: Single-stage axial fan, aerodynamically related to that of the JT9D but on a much smaller scale. Forged disc fitted with 28 solid titanium blades secured by dovetail fixings riveted to disc. Blades have part-span shrouds. Casing, which forms the engine air intake, of forged stainless steel. Circular splitter ring behind fan, held between two rows of 33 inner wrapped-sheet stators and single row of 66 outer stator blades. Total air mass flow, 34 kg (75 lb)/s; bypass ratio about 3·3:1; bypass flow typically 26 kg (57·5 lb)/s; primary core air flow 8 kg (17·5 lb)/s; fan pressure ratio 1·5:1.

Compressor: Primary airflow enters eye of single-stage titanium centrifugal compressor. Single-sided impeller, with 16 full vanes and 16 splitter vanes, secured to shaft by special bolt and key-washer. Two-piece casing with diffuser in form of pipes containing straightening vanes. Overall pressure ratio almost 10:1. (JT15D-4 compressor airflow augmented by axial boost stage between fan and compressor.)

Combustion Chamber: Annular reverse-flow type. Outer casing of heat-resistant steel; flame tube of nickel alloy, supported on low-pressure turbine stator assembly. Spark igniters at 5 and 7 o'clock positions (viewed from rear).

Fuel System: Engine-driven sandwich-mounted pump delivering through FCU, flow divider and dual manifolds at 44·8 bars (650 lb/sq in); DP-LI pneumatic control unit mounted on pump on first 246 engines, subsequent engines having DP-L2 with dual metering valve.

Fuel Grades: JP-1, JP-4, JP-5 conforming to PWA Spec. 522.

Nozzle Guide Vanes: High-pressure ring of 15, air-cooled, integrally cast in cobalt alloy.

Turbine: Single-stage HP with 71 solid blades held in fir-tree roots. Two-stage LP with nickel alloy discs, first stage being cast integrally with 61 blades and second stage carrying 55 blades in fir-tree roots. LP fan shaft drives fan, with ball thrust bearing behind fan and roller gear and intershaft bearings; HP shaft drives centrifugal compressor, with front ball thrust bearing and rear roller bearing. Gas temperature 960°C before turbine, 562°C after turbine.

Jet Pipe: Nickel alloy cone and sheet-metal pipe. Provision made for adjusting the area to match engines and to trim performance.

Accessory Drives: Package under front of engine driven by power offtake from front of HP shaft.

Lubrication System: Integral oil system, with gear-type pump delivering at up to 5·52 bars (80 lb/sq in). Capacity, 9·0 litres (2·4 US gallons; 2·0 Imp gallons).

Oil Specification: PWA521 Type II.

Mounting: Hard or soft, according to customers' choice. Four main pads on front casing, arranged two on each side at 30° above and below horizontal. One rear mount at top or on either side of centreline.

Starting: Air-turbine starter or electric starter/generator.

Dimensions:	
Diameter:	
JT15D-1, -1A	691 mm (27·2 in)
JT15D-4	686 mm (27·0 in)
Length overall:	
JT15D-1, -1A	1,506 mm (59·3 in)
JT15D-4	1,600 mm (63·0 in)
Frontal area	0·37 m² (4 sq ft)
Weight, Equipped:	
JT15D-1, -1A	232·5 kg (514 lb)
JT15D-4	253 kg (557 lb)
Performance Ratings:	
T-O:	
JT15D-1, -1A	9·8 kN (2,200 lb st)
JT15D-4	11·12 kN (2,500 lb st)
Max continuous:	
JT15D-1, -1A	9·3 kN (2,090 lb st)
JT15D-4	10·56 kN (2,375 lb st)

Exterior (right) and cutaway drawing (below) of the P&WC JT15D-1 twin-spool turbofan (9·8 kN; 2,200 lb st)

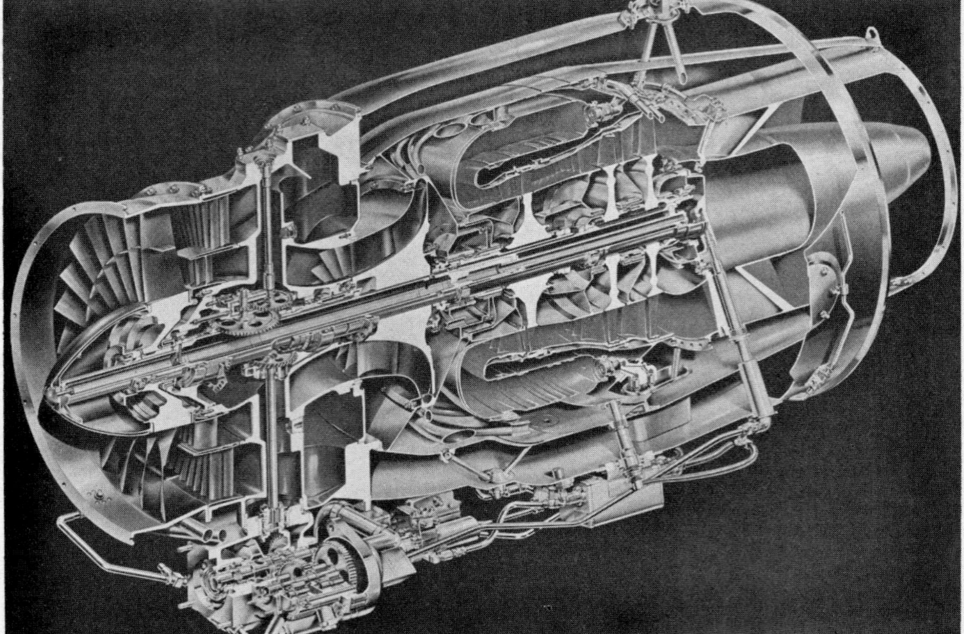

Specific Fuel Consumption (T-O):	
JT15D-1, -1A	15·30 mg/Ns (0·540 lb/h/lb st)
JT15D-4	15·92 mg/Ns (0·562 lb/h/lb st)

P&WC PT6A

The PT6A is a free-turbine turboprop, built in many versions. By January 1979 more than 10,000 had logged 31,600,000 h in some 4,000 aircraft registered in 112 countries.

An experimental PT6 ran for the first time in November 1959 and flight trials in the nose of a Beech 18 began in May 1961. Civil certification of the first production model, the 578 ehp PT6A-6, was granted in late 1963. Progressively higher rated versions have followed to power a wide variety of aircraft. In September 1977 P&WC introduced the PT6A-10 series, with ratings extending down to 354 kW (475 shp) for light and agricultural aviation. First engines in this group are expected to be the PT6A-11, -112, -14AG and -15AG.

Principal versions of the PT6A are as follows:

PT6A-6. Flat rated at 431 ekW; 410 kW (578 ehp; 550 shp) at 2,200 propeller rpm to 21°C, this version received civil certification in December 1963. A total of 350 PT6A-6s were built between then and November 1965. Among aircraft powered by the PT6A-6 are the de Havilland Canada Turbo-Beaver and early DHC-6 Twin Otter Series 100.

PT6A-11. Flat rated at 394 ekW; 373 kW (528 ehp; 500 shp) at 2,200 propeller rpm to 42°C. Certificated December 1977. Fitted to Piper Cheyenne I.

PT6A-112. Flat rated at 394 ekW; 373 kW (528 ehp; 500 shp) at 1,900 propeller rpm to 56°C.

PT6A-14AG. Flat rated at 433 ekW; 410 kW (580 ehp; 550 shp) at 2,200 propeller rpm to 54°C. Embodies design features for agricultural aviation.

PT6A-15AG. Flat rated at 533 ekW; 507 kW (715 ehp; 680 shp) at 2,200 propeller rpm to 22°C. Certificated October 1977, including operation on diesel fuel. Embodies design features for agricultural aviation.

PT6A-20. Flat rated at 432 ekW; 410 kW (579 ehp; 550 shp) at 2,200 propeller rpm to 21°C, the -20 offered improved reliability and increases in max continuous, max climb and max cruise power ratings over the PT6A-6. The PT6A-20 was certificated in October 1965. Between then and 1974 approximately 2,400 were built to power the Beech King Air B90, Beech Model 99, prototypes of the EMBRAER EMB-110 Bandeirante, de Havilland Canada DHC-6 Twin Otter Series 100 and 200, James Aviation (Fletcher FU-24) conversion, Marshall of Cambridge (Grumman) Goose conversion, McKinnon G-21C and G-21D Turbo-Goose (Grumman Goose) conversions, Pilatus PC-6/B1-H2 Turbo-Porter, prototype Pilatus PC-7 Turbo Trainer and the Swearingen Merlin IIA (which can be re-engined with the PT6A-27).

PT6A-20A. Similar to A-20; fitted to early Beech King Air C90.

PT6A-21. Flat rated at 432·5 ekW; 410 kW (580 ehp; 550 shp) at 2,200 propeller rpm to 21°C, the A-21 offers improved fuel consumption and reliability, mainly by mating the A-27 power unit with the A-20A gearbox. Certificated on 10 December 1974. Fitted to current Beech King Air C90. Total deliveries of -20, -20A and -21 exceed 2,700.

PT6A-25. Flat rated at 432·5 ekW; 410 kW (580 ehp;550 shp) at 2,200 propeller rpm to 33°C. Special oil system for sustained inverted flight. Certificated May 1976. Fitted to Beech T-34C.

PT6A-25A. Identical to -25 except for certain castings being made of magnesium alloy instead of aluminium alloy. Fitted to Pilatus PC-7.

PT6A-27. Flat rated at 553 ekW; 507 kW (715 ehp; 680 shp) at 2,200 propeller rpm to 22°C, attained by 12½ per cent increase in mass flow provided by larger-diameter compressor, at lower turbine temperatures than in PT6A-20. Production began in November 1967 and 1,715 had been delivered by January 1979. Production continues. Applications include the Hamilton Westwind II/III (Beech 18) conversions, Beech Model 99, Beech Model 99A, Beech U-21A and U-21D, de Havilland Canada DHC-6 Twin Otter Series 300, Pilatus/Fairchild Industries PC-6/B2-H2 Porter, Frakes Aviation (Grumman) Mallard conversion, IAI Arava, Let L-410A Turbolet, Saunders Aircraft ST-27A (de Havilland Heron) conversion and EMBRAER EMB-110 Bandeirante and EMB-312 single-engined military trainer.

The 553 ekW (715 ehp) P&WC PT6A-27 free-turbine turboprop

PT6A-28. Similar to the PT6A-27 and with the same T-O and max continuous ratings, this version has an additional normal cruise rating of 562 ehp available up to 21°C corresponding to the max cruise rating conditions of the -27. In addition the max cruise rating of the -28 gives 652 ehp up to the higher ambient of 33°C. This model continues in production, with 1,950 engines delivered by the beginning of 1979. Applications are Beech King Air E90 and A100, Piper Cheyenne II and EMBRAER Xingu.

PT6A 34. Flat rated at 584 ekW; 559 kW (783 ehp; 750 shp) at 2,200 propeller rpm to 31°C, this version has aircooled nozzle guide vanes to allow operation at higher turbine entry temperatures. For the IAI Arava, Saunders ST-28, Frakes Aviation (Grumman) Mallard conversion, Jetstream conversion and EMBRAER EMB-111.

PT6A-34B. Identical to -34 except for aluminium alloy replacing magnesium in major castings. Fitted to Beech T-44A.

PT6A-34AG. First model intended specifically for agricultural use, and certificated on diesel fuel. Retrofitted to Frakes conversion of Ag-Cat and Ayres Turbo-Thrush.

PT6A-135. Flat rated at 587 ekW; 559 kW (787 ehp; 750 shp) at 1,900 rpm. Changed drive ratio reduces propeller noise; hot-end modifications to permit higher cycle temperatures. Certificated July 1977. Fitted to Jetcrafters Taurus and Beech King Air C100.

PT6A-36. Flat rated at 586 ekW, 559 kW (786 ehp, 750 shp) at 2,200 rpm to 36°C. Similar to -34 but higher ratings. Certificated June 1977. Fitted to IAI Arava.

PT6A-38. Derated A-41, flat rated at 597 ekW; 559 kW (801 ehp; 750 shp) to 39°C. Certificated May 1975. Installed in Beech C-12A.

PT6A-41. Higher mass flow, aircooled stage-one turbine nozzle guide vanes and two-stage free turbine. T-O rating of 673 ekW; 634 kW (903 ehp; 850 shp) at 2,000 propeller rpm, available up to 41°C. Thermodynamic power is 812 ekW (1,089 ehp). By the beginning of 1979 more than 1,070 engines had been delivered for Beech Super King Air 200, Piper Cheyenne III and Gulfstream American Hustler.

PT6A-45A. Similar to PT6A-41 but with redesigned gearbox to transmit higher powers at reduced propeller speeds. Rated at 875·5 ekW; 875·0 kW (1,174 ehp; 1,173 shp) at 1,700 rpm to 8°C, or to 21°C with water injection. Certificated February 1976. Powers Shorts 330 and Mohawk 298.

PT6A-50. Similar to PT6A-41 with a longer, higher-ratio reduction gear to give lower propeller tip speed for quieter operation at T-O. Rating at T-O is 875·5 ekW; 835 kW (1,174 ehp; 1,120 shp) available with water injection up to 34°C at 1,210 propeller rpm. Certificated September 1976, and delivered same month for de Havilland Canada DHC-7.

Current TBO on all models up to -34 is 3,500 h. TBO on 38 and -50 is 2,000, and on -41 and -45A is 2,500 h.

The following data apply generally to the PT6A series:

Type: Free-turbine axial-plus-centrifugal turboprop engine.

Propeller Drive (all models up to and including PT6A-41): Two-stage planetary gear train. Ratio 15 : 1. Rotation clockwise when viewed from rear. Drive from free turbine. Flanged propeller shaft. Plain bearings. Higher-ratio reduction gears developed for PT6A-45A and -50.

Air Intake: Annular air intake at rear of engine, with intake screen. Aircraft-supplied alcohol anti-icing system or inertial separation anti-icing system.

Compressor: Three axial-flow stages, plus single centrifugal stage. Single-sided centrifugal compressor, with 26 vanes, made from titanium forging. Axial rotor of disc-drum type, with stainless steel stator and rotor blades. The stator vanes (44 first-stage, 44 second-stage, 40 third-stage) are brazed to casing. The rotor blades (16 first-stage, 32 second-stage and 32 third-stage) are dovetailed to discs. Discs through-bolted, with centrifugal compressor, to shaft. Fabricated one-piece stainless steel casing and radial diffuser. PT6A-27: compression ratio 6·7 : 1, air mass flow 3·1 kg/s (6·8 lb/s).

Combustion Chamber: Annular reverse-flow type of stainless steel construction, with 14 simplex burners around periphery of chamber. All versions up to A-34 have two glow plug igniters with option of two spark igniters; A-38 onwards, two spark igniters. PT6A-27 has one plug at 64° on starboard side of vertical centreline and one at 90° on port side.

Fuel System: Bendix DP-F2 pneumatic automatic fuel control system. Pneumatic computing section, fuel metering and regulating section, gas generator governor and free turbine governor. Primary and secondary flow manifolds with seven nozzles per manifold. PT6A-50 has DP-F3 with starting spill valve and motive flow systems.

Fuel Grade: Commercial jet fuels JP-1, JP-4, JP-5, MIL-J-5624. Use of aviation gasolines (MIL-G-5572) grades 80/87, 91/98, 100/130 and 115/145 permitted for a period of up to 150 h during any overhaul period.

Nozzle Guide Vanes: 29 nozzle guide vanes; A-34 onward, 14 aircooled HP vanes.

Turbines: Models up to A-34 have two single-stage axial; HP turbine (with 58 blades) drives compressor, and LP turbine (with 41 shrouded blades) drives output shaft. PT6A-38 onward have two-stage LP turbine. All blades have fir-tree root fixings.

Bearings: Each main rotor (gas generator and free turbine) supported by one ball and one roller anti-friction bearing.

Jet Pipe: Collector duct surrounding free-turbine shaft, exhaust through two ports on horizontal centreline.

Accessories: Mounting pads on accessory case (rear of engine) for starter/generator, hydraulic pump, aircraft accessory drive, vacuum pump and tachometer-generator. Mounting pad on the shaft-turbine reduction gear case for propeller overspeed governor, propeller constant-speed control unit and tachometer generator.

Lubrication System: One pressure and four scavenge elements in the pump stacks. All are gear type and are driven by the gas generator rotor. Engine has an integral oil tank with a capacity of 8·75 litres (2·3 US gallons). Oil supply pressure is 5·5 bars (80 lb/sq in) on PT6A-11 to -28, 5·85 bars (85 lb/sq in) on -34 to -36, and 7·25 bars (105 lb/sq in) on -38 to -50.

Oil Specification: CPW202, PWA522 Type II (7·5 cs vis) (MIL-L-23699, MIL-L-7808 for military engines).

Mounting: Up to A-34, three-point ring suspension. A-38 onward, four-point mounting, except -50 has base mounting.

Starting: Electric starter/generator on accessory case.

Dimensions:

Max diameter	483 mm (19 in)
Length, less accessories:	
PT6A-6 to -34	1,575 mm (62 in)
PT6A-38, -41	1,701 mm (67 in)
PT6A-45A	1,829 mm (72 in)
PT6A-50	2,133 mm (84 in)
Frontal area	0·18 m^2 (1·95 sq ft)

Weight, Dry:

PT6A-11, -21, -27, -28	136 kg (300 lb)
PT6A-112	144·7 kg (319 lb)
PT6A-14AG, -15AG	140·2 kg (309 lb)
PT6A-20	130 kg (286 lb)
PT6A-25	145·6 kg (321 lb)
PT6A-25A, -135	146·1 kg (322 lb)
PT6A-34, -36	141·1 kg (311 lb)
PT6A-38, -41	172 kg (380 lb)
PT6A-45A	192 kg (423 lb)
PT6A-50	263 kg (580 lb)

Performance Ratings:

T-O rating:

See under model listings

Max continuous rating:

PT6A-11	394 ekW; 373 kW (528 ehp; 500 shp) at 2,200 rpm (to 42°C)
PT6A-112	394 ekW; 373 kW (528 ehp; 500 shp) at 1,900 rpm (to 56°C)
PT6A-14AG	433 ekW; 410 kW (580 ehp; 550 shp) at 2,200 rpm (to 54°C)
PTA-20	432 ekW; 410 kW (579 ehp; 550 shp) at 2,200 rpm (to 56°C)
PT6A-21	432·5 ekW; 410 kW (580 ehp; 550 shp) at 2,200 rpm (to 33°C)
PT6A-25	432·5 ekW; 410 kW (580 ehp; 550 shp) at 2,200 rpm (to 33°C)
PT6A-15AG, -27, -28	533 ekW; 507 kW (715 ehp; 680 shp) at 2,200 rpm (to 22°C)
PT6A-34	584 ekW; 559 kW (783 ehp; 750 shp) at 2,200 rpm (to 30°C)
PT6A-36	586 ekW; 559 kW (786 ehp; 750 shp) at 2,200 rpm (to 36°C)
PT6A-135	587 ekW; 559 kW (787 ehp; 750 shp) at 1,900 rpm (to 29°C)
PT6A-38	597 ekW; 559 kW (801 ehp; 750 shp) at 2,200 rpm (to 39°C)
PT6A-41	673 ekW; 634 kW (903 ehp; 850 shp) at 2,000 rpm (to 41°C)
PT6A-45A	798 ekW; 761 kW (1,070 ehp; 1,020 shp) at 1,700 rpm (to 27°C)
PT6A-50	762 ekW; 725·5 kW (1,022 ehp; 973 shp) at 1,210 rpm (to 32°C)

Max cruise rating:

PT6A-11	394 ekW; 373 kW (528 ehp; 500 shp) at 2,200 rpm (to 37°C)
PT6A-112	394 ekW; 373 kW (528 ehp; 500 shp) at 1,900 rpm (to 48°C)
PT6A-14AG	394 ekW; 373 kW (528 ehp; 500 shp) at 2,200 rpm (to 42°C)
PT6A-15AG	as PT6A-27
PT6A-20	389 ekW; 369 kW (522 ehp; 495 shp) at 2,200 rpm
PT6A-21	390 ekW; 309 kW (523 ehp; 495 shp) at 2,200 rpm (to 15°C)
PT6A-25	432·5 ekW; 410 kW (580 ehp; 550 shp) at 2,200 rpm (to 33°C)
PT6A-27	486 ekW; 462 kW (652 ehp; 620 shp) at 2,200 rpm (to 21°C)
PT6A-28	486 ekW; 462 kW (652 ehp; 620 shp) at 2,200 rpm (to 33°C)
PT6A-34	545 ekW; 522 kW (731 ehp; 700 shp) at 2,200 rpm (to 19°C)
PT6A-135	548 ekW; 522 kW (735 ehp; 700 shp) at 2,200 rpm (to 28°C)
PT6A-36	548 ekW; 522 kW (735 ehp; 700 shp) at 2,200 rpm (to 28°C)
PT6A-38	597 ekW; 559 kW (801 ehp; 750 shp) at 2,000 rpm (to 27°C)
PT6A-41	673 ekW; 634 kW (903 ehp; 850 shp) at 2,000 rpm (to 28°C)
PT6A-45A	749 ekW; 713 kW (1,004 ehp; 956 shp) at 1,425 rpm (to 15°C)
PT6A-50	706 ekW; 671 kW (947 ehp; 900 shp) at 1,020-1,160 rpm (to 23°C)

Specific Fuel Consumption:

At T-O rating:

PT6A-11, -112	109·4 μg/J (0·647 lb/h/ehp)
PT6A-14AG, -21, -25	106·5 μg/J (0·630 lb/h/ehp)
PT6A-15AG, -27, -28	101·8 μg/J (0·602 lb/h/ehp)
PT6A-20	109·7 μg/J (0·649 lb/h/ehp)
PT6A-34	100·6 μg/J (0·595 lb/h/ehp)
PT6A-36, -41	99·7 μg/J (0·590 lb/h/ehp)
PT6A-135	98·9 μg/J (0·585 lb/h/ehp)
PT6A-38	106·3 μg/J (0·629 lb/h/ehp)
PT6A-45A, -50	94·6 μg/J (0·560 lb/h/ehp)

At max cruise rating:

PT6A-20	113·2 μg/J (0·670 lb/h/ehp)
PT6A-21	109·7 μg/J (0·649 lb/h/ehp)
PT6A-25	106·5 μg/J (0·630 lb/h/ehp)

The 875·5 ekW (1,174 ehp) P&WC PT6A-45A free-turbine turboprop

PT6A-27, -28 103·4 μg/J (0·612 lb/h/ehp)
PT6A-34 102·1 μg/J (0·604 lb/h/ehp)
PT6A-38 106·3 μg/J (0·629 lb/h/ehp)
PT6A-41 99·9 μg/J (0·591 lb/h/ehp)
PT6A-45A 97·7 μg/J (0·578 lb/h/ehp)
PT6A-50 98·5 μg/J (0·583 lb/h/ehp)
Oil Consumption:
Max 0·091 kg (0·20 lb)/h

P&WC T74

T74 is the US designation for military versions of the PT6A turboprop and PT6B turboshaft.

T74-CP-700. US Army counterpart of the PT6A-20. More than 300 T74-CP-700s have been delivered to Beech for 129 U-21A aircraft. Inertial separator system to protect against sand and dust ingestion.

T74-CP-702. Rated at 580 ekW (778 ehp) and retrofitted in Beech U-21 aircraft engaged in US Project Crazydog electronic countermeasures.

P&WC PT6B/PT6C

The PT6B is the commercial turboshaft version of the PT6A and has a lower-ratio reduction gear. Principal versions are:

PT6B-9. Rated at 410 kW (550 shp) at 6,230 rpm available to 25°C. Civil certification received in May 1965. Production complete.

PT6B-34. Similar to B-9 except based on PT6A-34. T-O rating 559 kW (750 shp) at 6,188 rpm to 35°C (2½ min contingency 671 kW; 900 shp to 15°C). Certificated July 1976. Installed in experimental Westland Lynx.

PT6C. This series of engines provides direct drive from the power turbine, with no reduction gearing.

Dimensions:
Max diameter 483 mm (19 in)
Length, less accessories, PT6B-34 1,499 mm (59·0 in)
Frontal area 0·18 m² (1·95 sq ft)
Weight, Dry:
PT6B-9 116 kg (255 lb)
PT6B-34 135 kg (298 lb)
Performance Ratings:
T-O:
See under model listings
Max cruise:
PT6B-9 362 kW (485 shp) at 6,230 rpm
PT6B-34 466 kW (625 shp) at 6,188 rpm (to 15°C)
Specific Fuel Consumption:
At T-O rating:
PT6B-9 112·4 μg/J (0·665 lb/h/shp)
PT6B-34 104·6 μg/J (0·619 lb/h/shp)
At max cruise rating:
PT6B-9 116·6 μg/J (0·69 lb/h/shp)
PT6B-34 110·4 μg/J (0·653 lb/h/shp)
Oil Consumption:
Max 0·091 kg (0·20 lb)/h

P&WC PT6T TWIN-PAC

First run in July 1968, the PT6T Twin-Pac comprises two PT6 turboshaft engines mounted side by side and driving into a combining gearbox to provide a single output drive. The engine was launched as a coupled power unit for a family of twin-engined helicopters based on the Bell Helicopter UH-1 series. First of these, jointly financed by Bell, P&WC and the Canadian government, was the 15-seat Bell Model 212, which first flew with the PT6T-3 in April 1969.

Installation of the 1,342 kW (1,800 shp) PT6T-3 in the Model 212, in addition to offering true engine-out capability, provides an additional 300 shp over the single-engine 205A and gives enhanced hot-day and high altitude performance. Qualified PT6T-3s became available in the third quarter of 1970 coincident with certification of the Model 212, which is also produced under licence by Agusta in Italy.

Another application of the PT6T-3 engine is for conversion from piston engine to turbine power of the Sikorsky S-58. The prototype S-58T flew in August 1970 and certification was received in April 1971.

In these two helicopter applications, total shaft-power output is limited by the helicopter transmission. In the Model 212 the 1,342 kW (1,800 shp) PT6T-3 is restricted to a T-O rating of 962 kW (1,290 shp) and 843 kW (1,130 shp) for continuous power. In the S-58T the limits are 1,122 kW (1,505 shp) at T-O and 935 kW (1,254 shp) for continuous operation. The PT6T-3 is easily adapted to such power requirements by a simple setting of its torque control. In the event of a power-section failure, torquemeters in the combining gearbox signal the other power section to maximum power. A single-engine 30-minute rating is included for use, at pilot discretion, in such contingencies.

An uprated Twin-Pac, the PT6T-6, was certificated in December 1974. The higher power is achieved by material and aerodynamic improvements to the compressor-turbine nozzle guide vanes and rotor blades. Installed in S-58T and Agusta-Bell 212. By the beginning of 1978 3 million equivalent PT6 hours had been flown by PT6T engines in 1,180 helicopters in 57 countries.

The 1,342 kW (1,800 shp) P&WC PT6T-3 Twin-Pac coupled free-turbine turboshaft

The following details describe the main features differing from those of the standard PT6:

Type: Coupled free-turbine turboshaft.

Shaft Drive: Combining gearbox comprises three separate gear trains, two input and one output, each contained within an individual sealed compartment and all interconnected by drive shafts. Overall reduction ratio 5 : 1. Input gear train comprising three spur gears provides speed reduction between power sections and output gearbox. The two drives into the output gearbox are via Formsprag fully-phased overrunning clutches with input third gear forming outer member of clutch, and interconnect shaft forming inner, overunning member. Output gear train comprises three helical spur gears, two input pinions meshing with single output gear.

Air Intakes: Additional inertial particle separator fitted upstream of engine to reduce sand and dust ingestion. High frequency compressor noise suppressed.

Fuel System: As PT6 with manual backup system, and dual manifold for cool starts. Automatic power sharing and torque limiting. Torquemeters provide signals to Bendix fuel system metering valves to maintain power at level set by pilot's selective-collective control. Fuel heaters.

Fuel Grades: JP-1, JP-4 and JP-5.

Jet Pipe: Single upward-facing exhaust port on each gas generator.

Accessories: Starter/generator and tacho-generator mounted on accessory drive case at front of each power section. Other accessory drives on combining gearbox, including individual power turbine speed governors and tacho-generators, and provision for blowers and aircraft accessories.

Lubrication System: Independent lubrication system on each power section for maximum safety during single-engine operation. Integral oil tanks. Separate oil system for output section of combining gearbox.

Oil Specification: PWA Spec 521. For military engines, MIL-L-7808 and -23699.

Starting: Electrical, with cold weather starting down to −54°C.

Dimensions:
Height 838 mm (33·0 in)
Width 1,118 mm (44·0 in)
Length 1,702 mm (67·0 in)
Weight, Dry (standard equipment):
PT6T-3 288 kg (635 lb)
PT6T-6 291 kg (642 lb)
Performance Ratings:
T-O (5 min):
Total output, at 6,600 rpm:
PT6T-3 1,342 kW (1,800 shp)
PT6T-6 1,398 kW (1,875 shp) (to 21°C)
Single power section only, at 6,600 rpm:
PT6T-3 671 kW (900 shp)
PT6T-6 (2½ min) 764 kW (1,025 shp)
30 minute power (single power section only), at 6,600 rpm 723 kW (970 shp)
Max continuous:
Total output, at 6,600 rpm:
PT6T-3 1,193 kW (1,600 shp)
PT6T-6 1,249 kW (1,675 shp) (to 19°C)
Single power section only, at 6,600 rpm:
PT6T-3 596·5 kW (800 shp)
PT6T-6 615 kW (825 shp) (to 19°C)
Cruise A:
Total output, at 6,600 rpm:
PT6T-3 932 kW (1,250 shp)
PT6T-6 1,014 kW (1,360 shp)
Single power section only, at 6,600 rpm:
PT6T-3 466 kW (625 shp)
PT6T-6 500 kW (670 shp)
Cruise B:
Total output, at 6,600 rpm:
PT6T-3 820 kW (1,100 shp)
PT6T-6 891 kW (1,195 shp)
Single power section only, at 6,600 rpm:
PT6T-3 410 kW (550 shp)
PT6T-6 440 kW (590 shp)
Ground idle, at 2,200 rpm 44·7 kW (60 shp) max
Specific Fuel Consumption:
At T-O and 30 minute ratings (total output):
PT6T-3 100·6 μg/J (0·595 lb/h/shp)
PT6T-6 100·0 μg/J (0·592 lb/h/shp)
At max continuous rating (total output):
PT6T-3 101·2 μg/J (0·599 lb/h/shp)
PT6T-6 101·9 μg/J (0·603 lb/h/shp)
At Cruise A rating (total output):
PT6T-3 106·1 μg/J (0·628 lb/h/shp)
PT6T-6 108·7 μg/J (0·643 lb/h/shp)
At Cruise B rating (total output):
PT6T-3 110·4 μg/J (0·653 lb/h/shp)
PT6T-6 114·4 μg/J (0·677 lb/h/shp)
Oil Consumption:
Max (for both gas generators) 0·18 kg (0·4 lb)/h

P&WC T400

Military version of the PT6T Twin-Pac, the T400-CP-400 has castings of aluminium instead of magnesium. For military roles, P&WC describes the T400 as producing a minimum infra-red signature. Military Qualification Tests (MQT) were completed in March 1970, and production deliveries started in the same month.

The T400 is used in the US Air Force and Navy Bell UH-1N (military version of the Model 212), the US Marine Corps Bell AH-1J, and the Canadian Armed Forces Bell CH-135. T400 field operations started in the middle of 1970.

TBO on the T400-CP-400 is 2,000 h on both the power section and reduction gearbox. By the beginning of 1979 deliveries totalled 511 CP-400 engines.

The T400-WV-402 is the military counterpart of the PT6T-6 and is used in the AH-1T. By the beginning of 1979 over 260 WV-402 had been delivered.

Dimensions (CP-400 and WV-402):
Height 828 mm (32·6 in)
Width 1,115 mm (43·5 in)
Length 1,659 mm (65·3 in)
Weight, Dry:
T400-CP-400 324 kg (714 lb)
T400-WV-402 338 kg (745 lb)
Performance Ratings:
Intermediate:
T400-CP-400 1,342 kW (1,800 shp) at 6,600 rpm
T400-WV-402 1,469 kW (1,970 shp) at 6,600 rpm
Max continuous:
T400-CP-400 1,141 kW (1,530 shp) at 6,600 rpm
T400-WV-402 1,248 kW (1,673 shp) at 6,600 rpm
Specific Fuel Consumption (Intermediate rating):
T400-WV-402 99·9 μg/J (0·591 lb/h/shp)
T400-CP-400 100·4 μg/J (0·594 lb/h/shp)

CHINA
(PEOPLE'S REPUBLIC)

NATIONAL AIRCRAFT ENGINE FACTORY

MAIN LOCATION: Shenyang

As related in the 1977-78 *Jane's,* the first aircraft engine made in numbers in the People's Republic of China was the Soviet M-11 radial.

In 1958 licences were obtained by the 2nd Ministry of Machine Building for two additional Soviet aircooled radial engines, the 194 kW (260 hp) Ivchenko AI-14R and 746 kW (1,000 hp) Shvetsov ASh-62IR (both described under Poland), fitted respectively to the locally-built Chinko No. 1 (Yak-12) and Fong Shou No. 2 (An-2). Both of these aircraft and their engines are believed to have been built in large numbers. By 1959 the Manchurian plants were licence-building the Soviet Mi-4 helicopter and the Czech Super Aero 45 light twin. It is thought that in each case the engine (respectively the 1,268 kW; 1,700 shp Shvetsov ASh-82V 14-cylinder radial and the 104·4 kW; 140 hp M 332 four-in-line, the latter last described in the 1971-72 *Jane's*) was also produced either at Shenyang or at one of the other national factories. One possibility is that the Czech engine was made in the works at Harbin, because it was there that the Chinese version of the Super Aero 45 was produced. Harbin may also have taken over the M-11FR programme, because from 1959-60 that factory manufactured the M-11-powered Hai Lun-kiang No. 1, a locally designed liaison aircraft resembling the Yak-12.

GAS TURBINE ENGINES

During the Korean War (1950-53) large numbers of MiG-15 fighters were ferried through Manchuria. Chinese technicians became familiar with the aircraft and its Klimov RD-45 (Rolls-Royce Nene derivative) engine. In 1955 a licence for the manufacture of the MiG-15 fighter and MiG-15UTI trainer was signed in Moscow, and from 1958 several hundred of the latter were produced, powered by the RD-45 of 24·24 kN (5,450 lb st). The MiG-15 fighter was apparently not built in China, but in 1959 the first Chinese F-4, a licence-built MiG-17, began a production run of well over 1,000 aircraft, all probably powered by Chinese-built Klimov VK-1 turbojets rated at 26·47 kN (5,950 lb st).

In February 1959 the Chinese signed a licence agreement for the manufacture of the MiG-19 supersonic fighter, powered by RD-9 turbojets. Soon afterwards the relationship with the Soviet Union was severed; but the Chinese, working alone, managed to fly a locally-built F-6 (MiG-19) in 1961, and have since constructed a number estimated to reach 1,500. Thus, probably more than 4,000 RD-9 engines have been made at Shenyang. A subsequent production programme concerned the F-7 (MiG-21). As described in the Aircraft section, this fighter and its R-11 axial turbojet were put into production in China without a licence or any Soviet help. Deliveries of the R-11 from Shenyang are thought to have begun in 1965.

Chinese versions or developments of the RD-9 are likely to have been used in locally produced military prototypes. One of these is the F-6bis (NATO *Fantan)* twin-engined strike fighter, which has been built in quantity. In 1979 the F-6 and F-6bis were still in production; but manufacture of the F-7 (MiG-21) was terminated soon after 1970.

In 1975, the Chinese government signed a preliminary contract with Rolls-Royce Ltd for the licensed manufacture of a supersonic afterburning Spey turbofan generally similar to the Spey 202/203 used in F-4 Phantom fighters of the RAF. The value of British contracts on this programme, which includes a new production plant, is tentatively put at £100 million. It is assumed that the engines will power military aircraft, probably of Chinese design, and that the Chinese objective is total self-sufficiency in their production and operation.

CZECHOSLOVAKIA

OMNIPOL
OMNIPOL FOREIGN TRADE CORPORATION

ADDRESS: Washingtonova 11, Prague 1

Telephone: 2126

Omnipol is responsible for exporting products of the Czech aviation industry and for supplying information on those products which are available for export.

AVIA
AVIA NARODNI PODNIK

199 03 Praha 9, Letňany

Telephone: Prague 89-51-21

Originally a member of the Czechoslovak Aviation Industry Group, Avia National Corporation was transferred to the Czechoslovak Automotive Industry (CAZ) Group in 1960. The company is at present engaged in series production of piston engines, as well as propeller and spare parts manufacture.

AVIA M 137

Designed to power light aerobatic, training, and single-engined and multi-engined sports aircraft, the 134 kW (180 hp) M 137A piston engine is a modification of the M 337 with fuel and oil systems for aerobatic operation and without a supercharger. It powers the Zlin 42 M and Z 526 F. The M 137AZ is a modified version, with the air intake port at the rear so that a dust filter can be incorporated. Details are as for M 337, with the following differences:

CRANKSHAFT: No oil holes for propeller control.

FUEL SYSTEM: Type LUN 5150 pump; system designed for sustained aerobatics.

STARTER: LUN 2131 electric.

DIMENSIONS:

Length	1,344 mm (52·9 in)
Width	443 mm (17·44 in)
Height	630 mm (24·80 in)

WEIGHT (including starter): 141·5 kg (312 lb)

PERFORMANCE RATINGS:

T-O	134 kW (180 hp) at 2,750 rpm
Max continuous	119 kW (160 hp) at 2,680 rpm
Max cruising	104·5 kW (140 hp) at 2,580 rpm

SPECIFIC FUEL CONSUMPTION:

At T-O rating	91·26 μg/J (0·540 lb/h/hp)
At max cruise rating	81·96 μg/J (0·485 lb/h/hp)

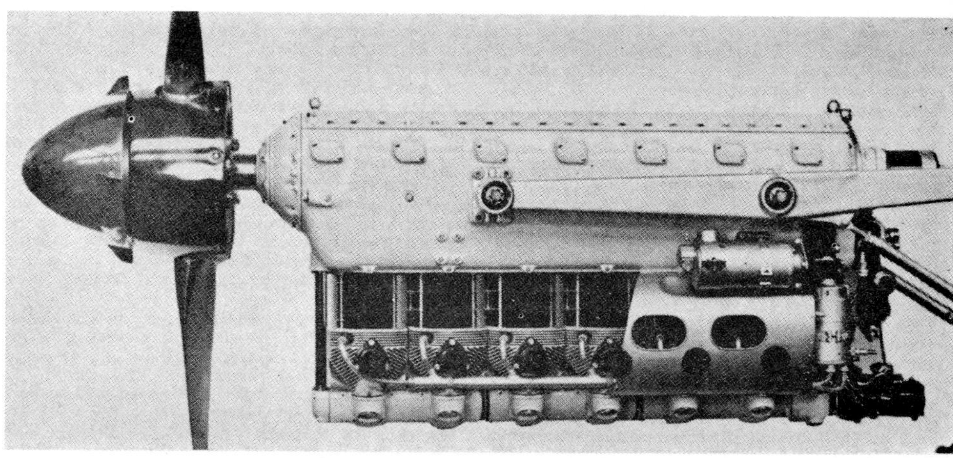

The 134 kW (180 hp) Avia M 137A six-cylinder aircooled piston engine

AVIA M 337

The M 337 six-cylinder aircooled supercharged engine powers several types of light aircraft that were built in Czechoslovakia, including the Morava L-200D, Zlin 43 and Zlin 726K. It can be supplied with hubs for fixed-pitch or controllable-pitch propellers.

TYPE: Six-cylinder inverted in-line aircooled, ungeared, supercharged and with direct fuel injection.

CYLINDERS: Bore 105 mm (4·13 in). Stroke 115 mm (4·53 in). Swept volume 5·97 litres (364·31 cu in). Compression ratio 6·3 : 1. Steel cylinders with cooling fins machined from solid. Cylinder bores nitrided. Detachable cylinder heads are aluminium alloy castings. Cylinder and head assembly attached to crankcase by four studs. Valve seats of special steel. Valve guides and sparking plug bushes of bronze.

PISTONS: Aluminium alloy stampings with graphited surfaces. Two compression rings and two knife-shaped scraper rings in common groove above gudgeon-pin. Gudgeon-pins secured by spring-circlips.

CONNECTING RODS: H-section aluminium alloy forgings. Two split big-ends bolted together by two bolts. Steel two-piece liner, lead-bronze plated.

CRANKSHAFT: Forged from special chrome-vanadium steel, machined all over. Nitrided crank-pins. Carried in seven steel-backed lead-bronze plated slide bearings which are lightly lead-lined, and in one ball thrust bearing at the front. Terminating in a wedge-shaped cone for the propeller hub mounting.

CRANKCASE: Heat-treated magnesium alloy (Elektron) casting, with top and front covers. Deep-sunk bearing covers forged from aluminium alloy, with double cross webs.

VALVE GEAR: Camshaft on the cylinder heads actuates the valves by means of rocker arms. Camshaft driven by vertical shaft and bevel gears. One inlet valve of heat-treated steel, one sodium-filled exhaust valve of austenitic steel with stellite seat. Nitrided valve stems.

IGNITION: Shielded type. Two vertical PAL-LUN 2221.13 magnetos with automatic sparking advance, driven by bevel gears. Two PAL L 22-62 sparking plugs per cylinder, 12 × 1·25 mm.

LUBRICATION: Dry sump pressure-feed type. The **M 337 AK** has a lubrication system cleared for sustained inverted operation.

SUPERCHARGER: Centrifugal type mounted on engine rear flange. Driven through a damping rubber coupling from crankshaft. Planetary gear, ratio 7·4 : 1, engaged via band friction clutch. Force feed lubrication of supercharger from main engine lubrication system.

FUEL SYSTEM: Low-pressure injection system. LUN 5152 pump driven from camshaft. Fuel injection nozzles located in front of intake valves. Automatic control in relation to engine manifold pressure. Fuel supplied to injection pump by fuel pressure pump located in common body with injection pump. (The M 337A has a unified fuel injection pump, type LUN 5150, and other minor changes. Specific fuel consumption is slightly higher.)

FUEL GRADE: Minimum 72-78 octane, with maximum TEL 0·06 per cent (volume).

COOLING: Airscoop on port side, designed to provide easy access to sparking plugs and easy removal of scoop and baffles.

STARTING: Electric starter combined with supercharger. Electric motor rotates the starter dog which is engaged by an electromagnet. Gears and clutch of supercharger serve the starter also.

ACCESSORIES: One 600W 28V dynamo. Electric rpm transmitter, drive 1 : 1. Propeller control unit. Mechanical tachometer on oil pump, drive 1 : 2. High-pressure hydraulic pump type P 6121A (to special order).

MOUNTING: Four engine-bearer feet with rubber dampers.

PROPELLER DRIVE: Direct left-hand tractor.

DIMENSIONS:

Overall length, without propeller boss	1,410 mm (55·51 in)
Width	472 mm (18·58 in)
Height	628 mm (24·72 in)
Frontal area	0·20 m² (2·15 sq ft)

WEIGHT, DRY: 148 kg (326·3 lb)

PERFORMANCE RATINGS:

T-O rating	157 kW (210 hp) at 2,750 rpm
Max continuous power	127 kW (170 hp) at 2,600 rpm
Max cruising power at 1,200 m (3,940 ft)	112 kW (150 hp) at 2,400 rpm

SPECIFIC FUEL CONSUMPTION:

At T-O rating	100·6 μg/J (0·595 lb/h/hp)
At max cruising power at 1,200 m (3,940 ft)	72·7 μg/J (0·430 lb/h/hp)

MOTORLET
MOTORLET NC, ZÁVOD JANA SVERMY

Prague-Jinonice
Telephone: Prague 522241
General Manager: Zdenek Horcík
Assistants to General Manager:
Technical Director: Ing Z. Pisařík
Economic Director: Ing Josef Svoboda
Production Director: Bohumil Hamerník
Head of Design Development: Ing Vladimír Pospísil

Motorlet National Corporation operates the main aero-engine establishment in Czechoslovakia, based on the former Walter factory at Jinonice, previously well known for its radial and in-line piston engines. Today, the Walter name continues in use only as a trade-mark for Motorlet piston and turbine engines.

Motorlet started turbine engine manufacture in 1952 with licensed production of the Soviet RD-45 centrifugal turbojet for MiG-15 fighters.

WALTER M 601

Second of Czechoslovakia's small turbine engines to enter production, the M 601 was designed to power the Czech L-410 twin-engined light transport aircraft. It drives a VJE-508 constant-speed three-blade propeller with hydraulically variable pitch.

The first version of the M 601, rated at 550 ehp, ran in October 1967. Development of a revised version, of increased diameter, started during 1968. The Let L-410M, powered by M 601 engines in place of the Canadian PT6A-34s fitted to the L-410A, was in Aeroflot service in Siberia in early 1979.

The Walter M 601 free-turbine turboprop, rated at 552 ekW (740 ehp)

Type: Free-turbine combined axial-and-centrifugal turboprop.
Propeller Drive: Reduction gear at front of engine with drive from free-turbine. Reduction ratio 14·9 : 1.
Air Intake: Annular intake at rear of engine, with debris screen, feeds air to compressor plenum chamber.
Compressor: Two axial stages plus single centrifugal stage. Pressure ratio 6·4 : 1 at 36,660 rpm gas generator speed. Air mass flow 3·25 kg (7·17 lb)/s.
Combustion Chamber: Annular combustor with rotary fuel injection and low-voltage ignition.
Compressor Turbine: Single-stage.
Power Turbine: Single-stage.
Fuel System: Low-pressure LUN 6590 system, with two-lever control providing gas-generator and power-turbine speed controls.
Fuel Grade: PL4, PL5 kerosene.
Jet Pipe: Collector duct surrounding power turbine shaft. Exhaust through two ports on horizontal centreline.
Accessories: Mounting pads on accessory case at rear of engine. Propeller controls mounted on reduction gear case at front of engine.
Lubrication System: Pressure gear-pump circulation. Integral oil tank and cooler.
Oil Specification: B3V synthetic oil.
Mounting: Three elastically-supported pins on compressor casing.
Starting: Electric.
Dimensions:
Diameter 420 mm (16·54 in)
Length 1,675 mm (65·95 in)
Weight, Dry: 178 kg (392·5 lb)
Performance Ratings:
T-O rating 552 ekW (740 ehp)
Cont. rating 485 ekW (650 ehp) to 18°C
Specific Fuel Consumption:
At T-O rating: 109·55 μg/J (0·648 lb/ehp/h)

FRANCE

G2P
GROUPEMENT POUR LES GROS PROPULSEURS À POUDRE

Head Office: 3 avenue du Général de Gaulle, 92800-Puteaux
Telephone: 778 15 15
Main Establishment: St Aubin de Médoc 33160
Administrator: Roger Guernon

SEP and SNPE (both listed in this section) formed G2P to ensure the close co-ordination of their activities and to act as prime contractor in the field of solid-propellant propulsion. Its activities are centred upon the motors of strategic missiles (MSBS, SSBS) and large tactical missiles (Pluton).

MICROTURBO
MICROTURBO SA

Head Office and Works: Chemin du Pont de Rupé, 31019-Toulouse Cédex
Telephone: (61) 70 07 77
Telex: 531442
Directorate:
G. Bayard
L. Pech (Commercial Director)
P. Calmels (Chief Engineer)

Microturbo was established in 1960 for the production of small gas turbines. The initial product was the Noelle 60290 free-turbine starter for the SNECMA Atar turbojet, and from this a wide range of units has been evolved.

Jointly with Soc. Soulé the company formed SA France-Engins (see RPVs and Targets section).

MICROTURBO COUGUAR 022

This single-shaft turbojet was developed as a power plant for small aircraft and RPVs. The 022 version powers the Australian GAF Turana target drone.

The installed engine, which incorporates only the equipment needed for flight, was designed to withstand the high mechanical and thermal stresses imposed by accelerated launch, telemetered shutdown and subsequent immersion in sea-water. Equipment for defuelling, refurbishing, refuelling, starting, ground running and pre-flight checkout is all accommodated in an associated servicing rig connected via an umbilical which is disconnected immediately prior to flight. Starting is accomplished by an air-impingement nozzle integral with the engine impeller shroud, the air supply being controlled from the servicing rig.

Dimensions:
Length (less jet pipe) 628 mm (24·725 in)
Length overall 853 mm (33·58 in)
Width 282 mm (11·1 in)
Height 386 mm (15·2 in)
Weight, Dry:
Basic, less jet pipe 26·5 kg (58·4 lb)
With control box 28·3 kg (62·4 lb)
Performance Ratings (ISA, S/L):
T-O and max continuous
0·79 kN (178 lb st) at 48,500 rpm
Idle 0·138 kN (31 lb st) at 28,000 rpm
Specific Fuel Consumption (ISA, S/L, static):
T-O and max continuous 35·4 mg/Ns (1·25 lb/h/lb st)

MICROTURBO TRS 18-046

This single-shaft turbojet was designed for installation in gliders, to impart a self-launch and climb capability, but has since been adapted for ultra-light aeroplanes such as the Bede BD-5J. It is in production, and an American Type Certificate was issued in May 1976. Applications in 1979 included the twin-jet NASA AD-1 slew-wing research aircraft and the Rutan Jet VariViggen of M Chagnes (see Homebuilt section).

The TRS 18-046 is of modular construction. The forward module incorporates the air intake, gearbox, electronic governing and protection unit and the start sequencing and indication unit. The 28V 600W starter/generator is located in the nose bullet. The oil tank, with submerged pump, is on the underside, and includes provision for inverted flight. The HP oil filter and pressure transducer are on the top of this module. Adjacent to the compressor are the probes for engine speed and air temperature.

The turbine module comprises: the one-piece centrifugal compressor, with diffuser and straightener vanes; the axial turbine rotor and nozzle diaphragm; and the main frame, carrying the rotor assembly on two ball bearings between the compressor and turbine. The aft module comprises: the turbine casing backplate, carrying the annular folded combustion chamber liner, exhaust cone and nozzle; 10 spill-type burners; two igniter plugs, used only during starting; and the jet pipe with thermocouple.

The fuel pump is driven electrically. The lubrication system is a closed circuit, with pressure supply to the rotor and gearbox bearings. The engine can be shut down and restarted in flight, and incorporates automatic fault and protection systems.

Dimensions:
Length 650 mm (25·59 in)
Width 325 mm (12·797 in)
Height 350 mm (13·78 in)
Weight, Dry:
Basic 32·0 kg (70·5 lb)
With igniter and voltage regulator 33·4 kg (73·63 lb)
Performance Rating (ISA, S/L):
T-O and max continuous
0·898 kN (202 lb st) at 44,000 rpm
Specific Fuel Consumption:
At above condition 36 mg/Ns (1·27 lb/h/lb st)

MICROTURBO TRS 18-056

This simplified version of the TRS 18-046 retains only the gas-generator section of earlier versions and was developed to power the France-Engins Mitsoubac and other RPVs. The lubrication system is of the total-loss type. During starting, the engine is cranked either by

Microturbo Couguar 022 single-shaft turbojet, rated at 0·79 kN (178 lb st)

Microturbo TRS 18-046 single-shaft turbojet, rated at 0·898 kN (202 lb st)

Microturbo TRS 18-056 single-shaft turbojet, rated at 0·98 kN (220·5 lb st)

impingement with air supplied from a bottle or by windmilling, according to the RPV in which it is installed. Ignition for starting is provided by an electrically fired cartridge. At shutdown, two independent systems shut off the fuel supply: one is an instantaneously actuated shut-off valve and the other releases the gas pressure from the fuel tank.

DIMENSIONS:
- Length: 600 mm (23·6 in)
- Width: 305 mm (12·0 in)
- Height: 345 mm (13·6 in)

WEIGHT, DRY:
- Basic, no jet pipe: 23·0 kg (50·7 lb)

PERFORMANCE RATING (ISA, S/L):
- T-O and max continuous: 0·98 kN (220·5 lb st) at 45,000 rpm

SPECIFIC FUEL CONSUMPTION:
- At above condition: 36 mg/Ns (1·27 lb/h/lb st)

MICROTURBO TRI 60

Representing a significant French development in the propulsion of cruise-type unmanned vehicles, the TRI 60 was designed under a contract from the Direction des Recherches et Moyens d'Essais. It is an extremely simple single-shaft turbojet for use in subsonic missiles and RPVs. The design has been biased towards minimal cost and absence of any maintenance or overhaul, though engine design life exceeds 20 hr. In 1976 the TRI 60 was selected to power the Aérospatiale C.22 RPV. In 1978 it was chosen for the British Aerospace P3T (Cruise Martel) missile.

The annular intake contains the accessory gearbox in the central bullet, together with an alternator or starter/generator; the struts house fuel and oil pipes. The simple axial compressor operates at a pressure ratio of about 4 : 1, with airflow of 5·6 kg (12·3 lb)/s, and is carried between front and rear bearings with labyrinth seals. The smokeless combustor is of the axial type, with multiple spray burners fed by a peripheral manifold. The axial turbine is overhung behind the rear bearing on the central diffuser housing.

An air bleed provides up to 1·5 per cent of total airflow. There is an engine-driven fuel pump, but lubrication is by either pre-lubricated bearings or a total-loss system from a pressurised reservoir. Speed control can be mechanical, electronic, fluidic or pneumatic, according to installation. Starting can be by impingement, electrical, cartridge or other means.

DIMENSIONS:
- Length overall: 882 mm (34·72 in)
- Envelope diameter: 310 mm (12·20 in)

WEIGHT, DRY: 45 kg (99·2 lb)

PERFORMANCE RATING (ISA, S/L):
- Max T-O: 3·43 kN (772 lb st) at 28,500 rpm

Microturbo TRI 60 turbojet in configuration used on C.22 RPV (mounted on dummy portion of fuselage, with nozzle to left)

SPECIFIC FUEL CONSUMPTION (as above): 35·4 mg/Ns (1·25 lb/h/lb)

RECTIMO
RECTIMO AVIATION SA

OFFICES AND WORKS:
Aérodrome de Chambéry, 73420-Savoie
Telephone: (79) 63 40 06
DIRECTOR: André Rosselot

Rectimo has manufactured over 500 Type 4 AR 1200 single-ignition derivatives of the Volkswagen four-cylinder aircooled car engine, which together with the larger 4 AR 1600 are used in the Sportavia RF4D powered glider and various ultra-light aircraft. The 30 kW (40 hp) 4 AR 1200 engine has a 1,192 cc cubic capacity, 7 : 1 compression ratio and weighs 61·5 kg (136 lb). Fuel consumption under cruise conditions is 11 litres (2·4 Imp gal)/h. The 4 AR 1600 produces 45·5 kW (61 hp) at T-O and has a cubic capacity of 1,600 cc and an 8 : 1 compression ratio. Weight is 64 kg (141 lb). Both engines have a maximum speed of 3,600 rpm.

Rectimo 4 AR 1200 piston engine of 30 kW (40 hp)

SACMA

Vinon sur Verdon

Preliminary details became available in mid-1977 of the family of light piston engines under development by this French company in a new factory inland from the Riviera. Covering a range of take-off power from 74 to 176 kW (100-240 hp), they utilise numerous automotive components, notably of Chrysler origin, to reduce cost and ensure proven performance. All models have watercooled opposed cylinders, turbocharger or rotary mixture distributor, and 3:1 reduction to the propeller shaft. The adjacent table lists the basic models to be offered. The 110 kW (150 hp) flat-four engine began running in a Socata Rallye in the Spring of 1977.

Socata Rallye testbed for the 112 kW (150 hp) SACMA engine *(Aviation Magazine International)*

T-O power kW (hp)	Crankshaft rpm	Dry weight kg (lb)	Fuel consumption 75% power cc/h (lb/h)	Oil capacity litres (pints)
74·5 (100)	3,600	113 (249)	19 (30)	3 (5·3)
89·5 (120)	3,600	113 (249)	23 (37)	3 (5·3)
112 (150)	5,400	115 (254)	28 (45)	4 (7)
134 (180)	3,600	135 (298)	33·5 (53)	6 (10·5)
179 (240)	5,400	140 (309)	45 (72)	6 (10·5)

SEP
SOCIÉTÉ EUROPÉENNE DE PROPULSION

3 avenue du Général de Gaulle, Tour Nobel, Cédex 3, 92080-Paris La Défense
Telephone: 772 12 12
Telex: 63906 Putau
CENTRES AND ESTABLISHMENTS: Bordeaux-Le Haillan, Bordeaux-Blanquefort, Vernon, Melun-Villaroche and Istres
PRESIDENT DIRECTOR GENERAL: P. Soufflet

SEP specialises in the design and development of all categories of propulsion systems and engines for aircraft, missiles, space launchers and satellites, and it possesses the most important rocket facilities in Europe. Two-thirds of its 2,200 personnel are engineers and technicians specialising in research, development and testing.

SEP HM4 liquid oxygen/liquid hydrogen rocket engine for upper-stage propulsion (40·4 kN; 9,080 lb)

SEP produces a wide range of solid- and liquid-propellant motors as sustainers and boosters for French and European guided and unguided missiles and space launchers. Some 60 different types of motor have been designed since 1950, including the three stages of the Diamant A and B and B P 4 French space launchers, the second stage and perigee motor of the ELDO Europa II launcher, and motors for the SSBS, MSBS and Pluton nuclear-warhead missiles. The company acquired experience in cryogenic-propellant rockets through developing the HM4 and HM7 engines.

Centre National d'Etudes Spatiales has entrusted SEP with the entire propulsion systems of the three stages of the L 3 S Ariane launch vehicle. A major engine for manned aircraft is the SEP 844 which provides thrust boost for Dassault Mirage III fighters in service with the French Air Force and other air forces.

Other SEP developments include engines using hybrid propellants, fluorine and fluorine compounds, monopropellants, compressed gases, as well as electric 'thrusters'. The company is now applying its missile and space technology to oceanology.

SEP HM4

The HM4 is the smaller of two upper-stage liquid-propellant rocket engines currently being developed by SEP.

TYPE: Liquid-propellant rocket engine.

PROPELLANTS: Liquid oxygen and liquid hydrogen.

THRUST CHAMBER ASSEMBLY: Four-chamber unit of 42 : 1 nozzle area ratio, regeneratively cooled, and with double-wall machined casing in stainless steel and Inconel X750. Operating sequence initiated by hydrogen pre-cooling and pre-opening of hydrogen injection valve. Concentric-tube propellant injection system with central oxygen flow. Pyrotechnic ignition. Combustion pressure 23·29 bars (337·8 lb/sq in) and temperature 2,627°C.

THRUST CHAMBER MOUNTING: Chambers hinged around axis concentric with engine axis.
PROPELLANT PUMPS: Axial-plus-centrifugal pumps, co-axial.
PROPELLANT FLOW: Liquid hydrogen flow rate 1·67 kg (3·67 lb)/s at 40 bars (580 lb/sq in). Liquid oxygen flow rate 8·33 kg (18·32 lb)/s at 36 bars (522 lb/sq in).
TURBINE: Two-stage axial-flow impulse unit in Inconel X750. Gas inlet temperature 617°C.
GAS GENERATOR: Liquid hydrogen flow rate 0·088 kg (0·19 lb)/s. Liquid oxygen flow rate 0·079 kg (0·17 lb)/s. Pyrotechnic ignition.
LUBRICATION SYSTEM: Uses tributyl phosphate spray into gaseous hydrogen.
STARTING: Solid-grain primer.
THRUST CONTROL: Thrust held constant by regulation of turbopump speed via control of gas generator propellant supply.
DIMENSIONS:
Height overall 1,170 mm (45·6 in)
Diameter overall 1,220 mm (46·5 in)
WEIGHT, DRY: 174 kg (382·8 lb)
PERFORMANCE:
Max thrust 40·4 kN (9,080 lb)
Overall propellant mixture ratio 5 : 1
Specific impulse 412

SEP P4

The P4 solid-propellant propulsion system was designed as the second stage of the French Navy's MSBS (underwater-to-surface ballistic missile), a weapon now equipped with the Rita II engine.

The P4 has a case of wound glass filament, weighing only 320 kg (705 lb). It is loaded with a grain of Isolane propellant, based on polyurethane binder, of high specific impulse. Ignition is by a solid-propellant microrocket on the front closure, which is also provided with controllable thrust-termination ports. The fixed nozzle is of carbon-fibre laminate with a graphite throat. Pitch and yaw control is effected by freon injection through four electrovalves. Roll is controlled by two separate steerable motors.

P4 is to replace Topaze as the second stage of the B P 4 version of the Diamant launch vehicle.
DIMENSIONS:
Length 2,500 mm (98·4 in)
Diameter 1,500 mm (59 in)
WEIGHT, LOADED: about 4,000 kg (8,820 lb)
PERFORMANCE:
Vacuum thrust 176·5 kN (39,680 lb)
Constant-thrust burn 55 s

SEP VIKING

The Viking series of turbopump-fed rocket engines was designed for simplicity and low cost. The thrust chamber, fed with unsymmetrical dimethyl hydrazine (UDMH) and nitrogen tetroxide (N_2O_4), has a single wall of HS 25 steel, coated with zirconium oxide, fuel-film cooled. The nozzle throat is of graphite. The light-alloy injector is of the radial type, with alternate doublets.

Mounted directly on the chamber, the turbopump has a two-stage Curtiss turbine, driven by propellant gases cooled by water. The turbine shaft carries impellers for UDMH, N_2O_4 and water. The gas-generator also provides on-board power and pressurises the tanks. Combustion pressure is regulated against a reference by varying turbine speed. Mixture ratio is maintained by controlling the flow of N_2O_4.

In 1972 SEP ran Viking I qualification tests of 150 s duration. The L 3 S Ariane vehicle will have a first stage, Lilo, with four Viking II engines now under development.

SEP P4 solid-propellant propulsion system for Diamant B P 4

Testing of the cluster began in 1976. The second-stage Ariane engine is Viking IV, a Viking II tuned for vacuum operation, with two-axis thrust vectoring. The nozzle has a bell shape, fabricated by welding rolled and Flo-turned steel sheet.
WEIGHT, DRY:
Viking II 776 kg (1,735 lb)
Viking IV 850 kg (1,876 lb)
PERFORMANCE:
Nominal S/L thrust:
Viking II 588·4 kN (132,275 lb)
Vacuum thrust: Viking II 686·5 kN (154,323 lb)
Viking IV 717·9 kN (161,378 lb)
Chamber pressure:
Viking II 55·5 bars (805 lb/sq in)
Vacuum specific impulse: Viking II 278·6
Viking IV 292·3

SEP HYDRAZINE THRUSTER

SEP has for a long period been engaged in the development of small monopropellant thrusters for satellite attitude and orbit control. Most of this work has been based on hydrazine, decomposed through a catalyst to serve as a monopropellant. The present SEP hydrazine propulsion system uses CNESRO 1 catalyst, developed jointly by SEP and the Faculté des Sciences of Paris.

SEP delivered to CNES (Space Centre of Toulouse) a flight model of its hydrazine micropropulsion system, comprising: surface-tension tank, engine, European CNESRO catalyst, hydrazine electrovalve, sensor and on-board electronics. This micropropulsion system was assembled on the D-5A satellite, launched by Diamant B P 4. During endurance testing a D-5A thruster operated continuously for 145,000 s, without attention to the catalyst bed.

SEP has since developed a larger thruster for mounting on the GEOS satellite. During qualification testing this thruster operated for 8,600 s (specified time 7,800 s) in 34,000 impulses, and for 3,400 s in continuous operation (specification 3,000 s). In the following data this thruster is referred to as GM, the earlier unit being referred to as D-5A.
WEIGHT, DRY:
D-5A 0·18 kg (0·397 lb)
GM 0·35 kg (0·771 lb)

SEP hydrazine thruster system for D-5A satellite, shown with conical fairing removed

Propulsion bay of Lilo, first stage of the L 3 S Ariane launch vehicle, showing the four SEP Viking II engines. Total S/L thrust is 2,353·6 kN (529,100 lb)

CHAMBER PRESSURE:
D-5A 15·3-30·5 bars (222-442 lb/sq in)
GM 10-30 bars (145-435 lb/sq in)
ELECTRICAL LOAD:
D-5A 5W
GM 6W
THRUST:
D-5A 0·0028-0·0016 kN (0·629-0·359 lb)
GM 0·014-0·006 kN (3·15-1·35 lb)
SPECIFIC IMPULSE (Vacuum):
D-5A, GM 215-230

TYPICAL SEP SOLID-PROPELLANT ROCKET ENGINES

Type	Thrust at S/L	Duration of Thrust (s)	Total Weight	Length	Diameter
SEP 163 Sioule	1·4 kN (315 lb)	37	40 kg (88 lb)	1,745 mm (68·7 in)	141 mm (5·5 in)
SEP 6854 Odet	37 kN (8,320 lb)	4	124 kg (273 lb)	2,560 mm (101 in)	226 mm (8·9 in)
SEP 7382 Yonne	94 kN (21,130 lb)	20	1,250 kg (2,756 lb)	4,062 mm (160 in)	584 mm (23 in)
SEP 7392 Rance	162·8 kN (36,520 lb)	17·5	1,565 kg (3,450 lb)	4,605 mm (181·3 in)	578 mm (22·7 in)
SEP 7342 Vienne	293 kN (65,860 lb)	4·6	846 kg (1,870 lb)	3,195 mm (125·8 in)	590 mm (23·2 in)
SEP 299 Arz	43·15 kN (9,702 lb)	1·6	57·5 kg (126·78 lb)	1,076 mm (42·2 in)	250 mm (9·8 in)
SEP 300 Drac	0·96 kN (215·8 lb)	73	52·5 kg (115·76 lb)	1,100 mm (43·3 in)	207 mm (8·1 in)
SEP Dropt	40 kN (9,000 lb)	45	751 kg (1,655·9 lb)	1,500 mm (59 in)	800 mm (31·5 in)
SEP Ball	4·2 kN (944 lb)	4·3	23·1 kg (50·9 lb)	430 mm (16·9 in)	221 mm (8·7 in)
SEP Trap	Start 8·05 kN (1,809 lb) Cruise 1·78 kN (402 lb)	Start 3·8 Cruise 10·2	45·2 kg (99·75 lb)	835 mm (32·87 in)	221 mm (8·7 in)
SEP Arc	Start 1·90 kN (20,233 lb) Start 2·53 kN (11,915 lb) Cruise 14·1 kN (3,170 lb)	Start 10·1 Start 20·2 Cruise 3·5	57 kg (125·7 lb)	2,306 mm (90·8 in)	157 mm (6·2 in)
SEP Ciron (GEOS)	16·4 kN (3,687 lb)	45	300 kg (661 lb)	1,070 mm (42·1 in)	684 mm (26·9 in)
SEP Mage	30·4 kN (6,835 lb)	40	345 kg (761 lb)	1,170 mm (46·1 in)	764 mm (30·1 in)

SEP ION THRUSTER

Like other electric thrusters that generate a jet of charged ions, this device uses caesium as the working fluid. Caesium from the supply tank is vaporised and ionised between the hollow cathode and inner anode in the presence of a powerful magnetic field. The ions are accelerated through an electrostatic grid and then neutralised by a secondary hollow cathode immediately downstream. Its useful life is to amount to 10,000 h of cumulative operation, enabling the engine to perform missions ranging from 7 to 10 years in orbit.

WEIGHT, DRY: 1·5 kg (3·3 lb)

PERFORMANCE:

Thrust	6·7 mN or about 0·00067 kg
Flow-rate of caesium	0·5 gr (0·0011 lb)/h
Beam orientation	±20°
Power input	250W
Specific impulse	5,000

SEP ion thruster, using caesium ions to give very small thrust at high specific impulse

SEP HM7

Under development for upper-stage propulsion, the HM7 is a 70·06 kN (15,750 lb) liquid oxygen/liquid hydrogen engine. It is also referred to in the entry for MBB of West Germany.

TYPE: Liquid-propellant rocket engine.

PROPELLANTS: Liquid oxygen and liquid hydrogen.

THRUST CHAMBER ASSEMBLY: Single-chamber unit of 48 : 1 nozzle area ratio, regeneratively cooled, and of stainless steel tube construction. Operating sequence initiated by hydrogen pre-cooling and pre-opening of hydrogen injection valve. Concentric-tube propellant injection system with central oxygen flow. Pyrotechnic ignition. Combustion pressure 35 bars (507·5 lb/sq in) and temperature 2,727°C.

THRUST CHAMBER MOUNTING: Gimballed assembly, turbopump integral with chamber.

PROPELLANT PUMPS: Axial-plus-centrifugal pumps, coaxial.

PROPELLANT FLOWS: Liquid hydrogen flow rate 2·76 kg (6·07 lb)/s at 65 bars (942·5 lb/sq in). Liquid oxygen flow rate 14·21 kg (31·26 lb)/s at 52 bars (754 lb/sq in).

TURBINE: Two-stage axial-flow impulse unit in Inconel X 750. Gas inlet temperature 617°C.

GAS GENERATOR: Liquid hydrogen flow rate 0·133 kg (0·29 lb)/s. Liquid oxygen flow rate 0·12 kg (0·26 lb)/s. Pyrotechnic ignition.

LUBRICATION SYSTEM: Uses tributyl phosphate spray into gaseous hydrogen.

STARTING: Solid grain primer.

THRUST CONTROL: Thrust held constant by regulation of turbopump speed via control of gas generator propellant supply.

DIMENSIONS:

Height overall	1,617 mm (63·06 in)
Diameter overall	847 mm (33·03 in)

WEIGHT, DRY: 145 kg (319 lb)

PERFORMANCE:

Max thrust in vacuo	70·06 kN (15,750 lb)
Overall propellant mixture ratio	5·15 : 1
Specific impulse	425

SEP HM7 high-energy upper-stage rocket engine (vacuum thrust 70·06 kN; 15,750 lb)

SNECMA

SOCIÉTÉ NATIONALE D'ÉTUDE ET DE CONSTRUCTION DE MOTEURS D'AVIATION

HEAD OFFICE: 2 boulevard Victor, 75724 Paris Cedex 15
Telephone: 554 92 00
Telex: 202 834 Motav

CHAIRMAN AND MANAGING DIRECTOR: René Ravaud

DIRECTOR, PERSONAL ASSISTANT TO THE CHAIRMAN: Jean Calmon

DEPUTY MANAGING DIRECTOR FOR AERO-ENGINE PROGRAMMES AND MARKETING: Jean Péquignot

DIRECTOR FOR AERO-ENGINE DEVELOPMENT AND PRODUCTION: Jean Ségui

DIRECTOR FOR SUBSIDIARY COMPANIES AND DIVISIONS: Gérard Jousseaume

PERSONNEL DIRECTOR: Jean Pascaud

DIRECTOR, FINANCE AND PLANNING: Jean Sollier

DIRECTOR FOR INTERNATIONAL RELATIONS: Jean Crépin

GENERAL SECRETARY: Henri Forsans

TECHNICAL DIRECTOR: Pierre Lachaume

PUBLIC RELATIONS (PRESS): Philippe Dreux

Villaroche Centre: 77550-Moissy-Cramayel

Design, development and ground test centre. A subsidiary establishment for flight and noise tests is located at Istres.

Evry-Corbeil:

RN 7; BP 81, 91003-Evry Cedex

Engine production, quality control, service, procurement and laboratories for research and development.

Gennevilliers:

291 Avenue d'Argenteuil, BP 30, 92234-Gennevilliers

Forging and casting production, complete machining of mechanical parts.

Suresnes—ELECMA Division:

22 Quai Galliéni, 92150-Suresnes

Design, development and production of electronic equipment, especially electronic control systems for the aircraft industry.

SNECMA (Société Nationale d'Etude et de Construction de Moteurs d'Aviation) was born on 29 August 1945 from the merger of several aero-engine companies: Gnome et Rhône, Société Anonyme des Moteurs Renault pour l'Aviation, Société Générale de Mécanique et d'Aviation (former Moteurs Lorraine), and Groupe d'Etudes des Moteurs à Huile Lourde.

These companies already had a long aeronautical tradition and SNECMA has always devoted its main activity to aero-engines. More than 4,850 Atar turbojets have been ordered; they have played a significant part in the worldwide success of Mirage fighters. SNECMA is developing the M53 turbojet for fighters of the next decade.

SNECMA is also participating in the following international collaborative programmes:

The Olympus 593 for Concorde, developed and produced with Rolls-Royce; the CF6-50 for the Airbus A300, for which engine SNECMA and MTU in Germany are partners with General Electric; the CF6-32, in cooperation with General Electric; the CFM56, which SNECMA shares equally with General Electric, but with FN associated within SNECMA's share; the Larzac, produced in co-operation with Turboméca and with production also involving the German companies MTU and KHD, and FN in Belgium; and the Tyne, produced by a consortium (SNECMA, MTU, Rolls-Royce, FN).

SNECMA ATAR

The Atar is a single-shaft military turbojet first run in 1946 and since developed and cleared for flight at Mach numbers greater than 2. Major versions are:

Atar 9C. Compared with the earlier 9B this introduced a new compressor, a self-contained starter and an improved overspeed which comes into operation automatically when the aircraft reaches Mach 1·4, giving power equivalent to a sea level thrust of 62·76 kN (14,110 lb st). Equips most Mirage III and 5.

Atar 9K-50. Derived from the Atar 9C. Designed to offer improved subsonic specific fuel consumption, increased thrust for supersonic acceleration and improved overhaul life. The main improvements are in an entirely redesigned turbine with blades not forged but cast and coated with refractory metal from the vapour phase. Stages 1 and 8 of the compressor have been redesigned, resulting in pressure ratio raised from 6 : 1 to 6·15 : 1, coupled with slightly augmented mass flow. The control and electronic equipment have been revised and extended to improve the security of single-engined aircraft. The 9K-50 is the power plant of all production Mirage F1 versions and the Mirage 50.

Atar 8K-50. This is essentially the 9K-50, the latest variant in production, re-engineered to have a simple unaugmented jet-pipe and fixed nozzle, for the Super Etendard. All parts are protected against sea corrosion. The 8K-50 completed its 150 h official type test in May 1975. Production deliveries began in May 1977.

DIMENSIONS:

Diameter	1,020 mm (40·2 in)
Length overall:	
Atar 8K-50	3,936 mm (155 in)
Atar 9C, 9K-50	5,944 mm (234 in)

WEIGHTS:

Dry, complete with all accessories:	
Atar 8K-50	1,155 kg (2,546 lb)
Atar 9C	1,456 kg (3,209 lb)
Atar 9K-50	1,582 kg (3,487 lb)

PERFORMANCE RATINGS:

Max with afterburner:	
Atar 9C	58·9 kN (13,230 lb st) at 8,400 rpm
Atar 9K-50	70·6 kN (15,870 lb st) at 8,400 rpm
Max without afterburner:	
Atar 8K-50	49 kN (11,025 lb st) at 8,550 rpm
Atar 9C	42 kN (9,430 lb st) at 8,400 rpm
Atar 9K-50	49·2 kN (11,055 lb) st

SPECIFIC FUEL CONSUMPTION:

At max rating with afterburner:	
Atar 9C	57·5 mg/Ns (2·03 lb/h/lb st)
Atar 9K-50	55·5 mg/Ns (1·96 lb/h/lb st)
At max rating without afterburner:	
Atar 8K-50	27·5 mg/Ns (0·97 lb/h/lb st)
Atar 9C	28·6 mg/Ns (1·01 lb/h/lb st)
Atar 9K-50	27·5 mg/Ns (0·97 lb/h/lb st)

OIL CONSUMPTION: 1·5 litres (2·64 Imp pints)/h

SNECMA M53

The M53 is a single-shaft turbofan—more strictly a continuous-bleed turbojet—capable of propelling fighter aircraft at high altitude at Mach 2·5. The first application is in the Mirage 2000, being developed for the Armée de l'Air. The engine is of modular construction.

The single shaft comprises a three-stage fan and five-stage compressor driven by a two-stage turbine designed for operation at high gas temperature. There are no inlet guide vanes. Max airflow is 86 kg (190 lb)/s. Between the

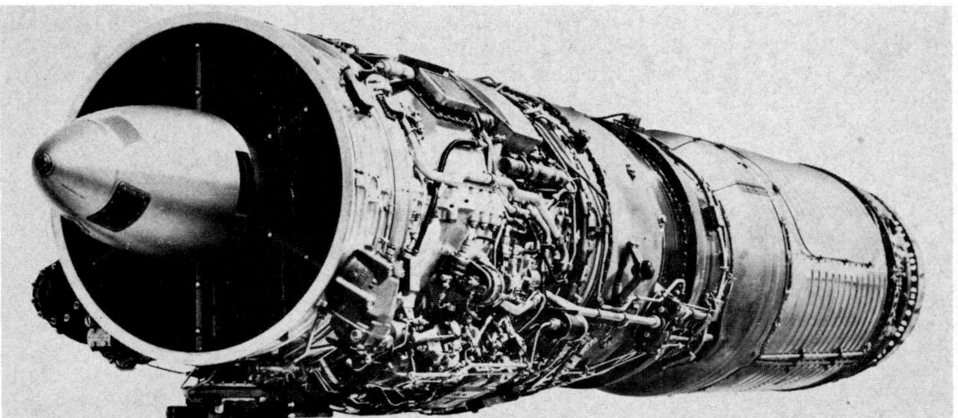

SNECMA Atar 9K-50 turbojet of 70·6 kN (15,870 lb st) with afterburner

fan and compressor is a mid-frame incorporating accessory drives and front roller bearing and ball thrust bearing. The annular combustion chamber is designed for smoke-free operation. The turbine delivery casing incorporates the third bearing. Fuel to the combustion chamber and reheat system, and the multi-flap nozzle, are controlled by a fuel system monitored by an ELECMA electronic computer.

The first prototype engine was tested in February 1970, 18 months after programme go-ahead. The second ran in August, and achieved maximum rpm after 30 minutes of operation. Military rating (51 kN; 11,466 lb) was reached in October, three months ahead of contractual commitment. Testing with afterburner began in November 1970. The first official test took place at 54·92 kN (12,346 lb) in May 1971. In the same month a 50 h test was run at afterburning thrusts up to 81·39 kN (18,298 lb), 98 per cent of the nominal rating. In September thrust exceeded the nominal figure, at 83·4 kN (18,740 lb), and in December simulated altitude trials began at Saclay. By March 1972 three prototype M53 engines were running. Flight trials began on 18 July 1973 in the starboard pod of a Caravelle testbed. The supersonic flight envelope is being explored with the Mirage F1-M53 flying testbed, which first flew in December 1974. In July 1977 an official 50-h test was completed at 88·5 kN. In early 1979 running time exceeded 9,000 h.

The initial M53-2 version is rated at 83.4 kN (18,740 lb st). Development is now centred on the M53-5, data for which are given below. This will be the engine of the production Mirage 2000.

DIMENSIONS:
- Overall length: 4,853 mm (191 in)
- Max diameter: 1,055 mm (42·0 in)

WEIGHT, DRY: 1,450 kg (3,195 lb)

PERFORMANCE RATINGS:
- Max thrust, with afterburner: 88·3 kN (19,840 lb)
- Max thrust, cold: 55 kN (12,350 lb)

SPECIFIC FUEL CONSUMPTION:
- At max cold rating: 24·64 mg/Ns (0·87 lb/h/lb st)

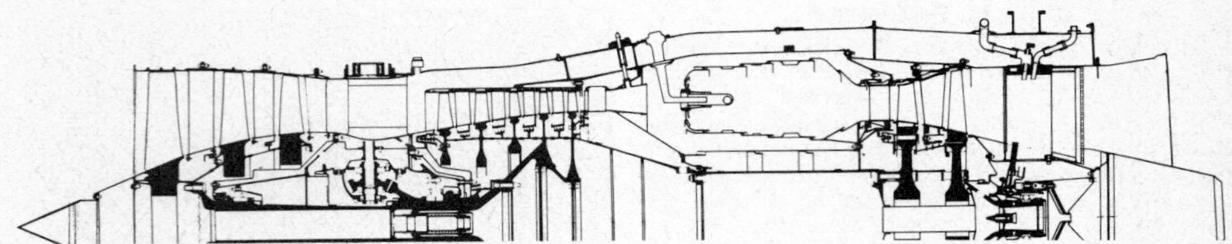

Longitudinal section through the SNECMA M53 showing LP and HP sections on single shaft (pressure ratio, 9·3 at 10,500 rpm) and bypass duct

SNECMA M53 augmented bypass turbojet of 88·3 kN (19,840 lb st)

CFM INTERNATIONAL CFM56

SNECMA decided in the Autumn of 1971 to develop the CFM56, a subsonic turbofan in the ten-tonne-thrust (22,000 lb) class, in co-operation with General Electric. The French and US companies are splitting all the work on a 50/50 basis. The project is covered more fully under CFM in the International section.

GE/SNECMA/MTU CF6-50

To provide engines for the Airbus Industrie A300 SNECMA and MTU of Federal Germany participate in a co-production programme with General Electric to make the CF6-50 turbofan. SNECMA performs assembly and test, and manufactures parts, with a total share on a cost basis of 26·8 per cent. MTU's share is 10·0 per cent, and GE supplies the balance. The SNECMA/GE production agreement has been extended to include the CF6-45, to power initial A310 versions, and the CF6-80.

GE/SNECMA CF6-32

This engine, described like other CF6 versions in the US section, is expected to have thrust in the 130-170 kN (30,000-38,000 lb st) range. SNECMA is responsible for the LP turbine, turbine rear frame, and accessory gearbox, and for some of the testing of complete engines.

SNECMA/ROLLS-ROYCE OLYMPUS 593

SNECMA collaborated with Rolls-Royce in development and manufacture of the Olympus 593 turbojet for the Concorde. (See under 'Rolls-Royce/SNECMA' in the International section.)

SNECMA/TURBOMÉCA LARZAC

This 13·8 kN (2,966 lb st) turbofan was designed jointly by SNECMA and Turboméca, to power business jets, military liaison aircraft and trainers. A description of the Larzac is given under the entry for Turboméca-SNECMA GRTS, in this section.

SNECMA/MTU/RR/FN TYNE

Under Rolls-Royce licence, the Tyne 22 turboprop for the Transall C-160, was, in October 1977, put back into production by the original four-nation consortium, with the original work-split. SNECMA's share will be made by Hispano-Suiza, and assembly and test will be at Sochata-SNECMA, Châtellerault. First delivery 1980. The similar Tyne 21 is also to be re-ordered, to power the ANG (Atlantic Nouvelle Génération).

SNPE

SOCIÉTÉ NATIONALE DES POUDRES ET EXPLOSIFS

HEADQUARTERS: 12 Quai Henri IV, 75181 Paris Cédex 04
Telephone: 277 15 70
Telex: 22356 Poudres Paris

USINE DE SAINT MÉDARD

St Médard-en-Jalles (Gironde)
Telephone: (56) 44 21 25

Established by Royal Decree in 1679, the former Poudrerie Nationale de St Médard was one of the largest establishments in the Service des Poudres. In October 1971 the SDP was taken over by the SNPE, a national company responsible for all solid propellant charges from pistol ammunition to an ICBM.

Brief details of some current production motors are given in the table. Composite propellants include polybutadiene, polychlorates of vinyl or polyurethane, ammonium perchlorate (with additions such as dispersed aluminium) and numerous other composite propellants, often with 12-15 separate ingredients, as well as the more traditional double-base extruded propellants (type SD) derived from cordite and similar gun propellants which are made cheaply in sizes up to 200 mm (7·9 in) diameter.

SD motors are used mainly for such applications as anti-tank missiles and take-off boosters. The plastic/plastolane composites are cast in free blocks, whereas the isolite/isolane/butalite/butalane series are case-bonded permanently into the metal vehicle stage which is also sometimes fabricated at St Médard.

The establishment has test-fired a 255 kN (57,320 lb) motor of 2 m (78·8 in) diameter, and at the 1969 Paris Salon exhibited an inert segment weighing approximately 10,000 kg (22,000 lb) and of 3 m (118 in) diameter to demonstrate its capacity to make segments suitable for Titan IIIC.

Since 1959 the establishment has been manufacturing the rocket motor of the US Hawk missile under licence, and in turn has licensed the governments of India and Pakistan to make the plastolane motors used in Aérospatiale sounding rockets.

PRINCIPAL SNPE MOTORS

Motor	Application	Total Impulse kN-s (lb-s)	Duration (s)	Diameter mm (in)	Charge weight kg (lb)
Isolane propellant					
P.16 (Type 902)	SSBS first stage	40,993 (9,215,350)	76	1,500 (59)	16,000 (35,275)
P.10 (Type 903)	SSBS second stage	—	—	1,500 (59)	10,000 (22,050)
P.10 (Type 904)	MSBS first stage	—	—	1,500 (59)	10,000 (22,050)
P.4 (Rita)	MSBS second stage	9,709 (2,182,580)	55	1,500 (59)	4,000 (8,820)
P.6					
Polka	Masurca boost	1,569 (352,740)	4·6	560 (22)	690 (1,521)
Jacée	Masurca cruise	618 (138,900)	26	400 (15·75)	320 (705)
Plastolite/plastolane					
Marie-Antoinette	Matra R. 530	78·46 (17,635)	9	203 (8)	42·5 (93·7)
Vénus	Malafon boost	167 (37,480)	2·9	275 (10·8)	92 (203)
Épervier	AS.30 boost	105 (23,600)	2	330 (13)	57 (126)
Mammouth	VE.110 test vehicle	3,609 (811,300)	18·2	800 (31·5)	1,910 (4,210)
Stromboli	Aérospatiale Dragon	1,422 (319,675)	16·5	550 (21·6)	685 (1,510)
SD					
Mk 43	2·75 in rocket	—	1·5	62 (2·45)	2·65 (5·84)
CT.20	CT.20 boost trolley	—	2	92 (3·62)	90 (198)

TURBOMÉCA
SOCIÉTÉ TURBOMÉCA

Bordes, 64320 Bizanos
Telephone: (15-59) 32 84 37
Telex: 560928
OTHER WORKS: Mézières S/Seine (Yvelines) and Tarnos (near Bayonne)
PARIS OFFICE: 1, Rue Beaujon, Paris 8e
PRESIDENT AND DIRECTOR-GENERAL: J. R. Szydlowski

The Société Turboméca was formed in 1938 by M Szydlowski and M Planiol to develop blowers, compressors and turbines for aeronautical use. Today, it is the leading European manufacturer of small turbine aero-engines. Since it first started development of gas turbines in 1947, the company has developed about 50 different types of power plant of which some 15 have entered production and ten types have been manufactured under licence in five countries.

By 1 January 1979, a total of 16,684 Turboméca engines for fixed and rotary-wing applications and aircraft auxiliary duties had been delivered to customers in 97 countries, including France. Approximately 14,000 more engines have been built under licence by what are today Rolls-Royce Ltd in the UK, Teledyne CAE in the US, ENMASA in Spain, Hindustan Aeronautics Ltd in India, Bet-Shemesh in Israel and state factories in Romania and Yugoslavia.

Total covered floor area for Turboméca's three plants at Bordes, Mézières and Tarnos is 135,396 m² (1,457,390 sq ft). At 1 January 1979 the company employed a total of 4,375 people.

Turboméca has 45·6 per cent participation in CGTM, 50 per cent in RRTI, 26 per cent in CGR, 50 per cent in Turboméca SNECMA, 50 per cent in Astadyne (APU development with ABG-Semca), 50 per cent in MTU-Turboméca, 50 per cent in Rolls-Royce Turboméca, 51 per cent in Bet-Shemesh Engines, 22·08 per cent in Ormat Turbines and 100 per cent in Turboméca do Brasil.

ROLLS-ROYCE TURBOMÉCA ADOUR

This turbofan was developed jointly by Rolls-Royce and Turboméca for the SEPECAT Jaguar tactical strike fighter and advanced trainer. Other versions were developed subsequently for the BAe Hawk and Mitsubishi T-2 and F-1. A brief description of the Adour is given in the International section.

TURBOMÉCA ASTAFAN

The Astafan is a low-consumption lightweight turbofan of high by-pass ratio, low noise level design which made its first run during the Summer of 1969. Comprising an Astazou turboprop power section, operating at constant speed, driving a single-stage variable-pitch fan via reduction gearing, it is being developed in several versions corresponding to different development stages of the Astazou. All have the high bypass ratio of 7 : 1 and are characterised by very low specific fuel consumption. Variable-pitch blading facilitates constant-speed operation and permits off-loading of the engine during starting.

The following are the first versions under development:

Astafan IIG. Variant developed for military trainer applications; selected for Aérospatiale Fouga 90.

Astafan III. Derived from the Astazou XVIII, with air-cooled turbine.

Astafan IV. Derived from the Astazou XX, with three-stage axial high-pressure compressor.

Flight development of prototype Astafan engines began in a Hawk Commander on 8 April 1971. Two podded underwing Astafans replaced the original piston engines, conferring a substantial improvement in flight performance and a reduction in noise and vibration.

On 24 January 1976 an Aero Commander 690 flew at Pau for the first time powered by two Astafan IVF6 engines, similar to the basic Astafan IV but rated at 10·49 kN (2,359 lb) take-off thrust and with even lower noise and fuel consumption.

TYPE: Single-shaft turbofan with geared fan.

ENTRY CASING: Annular light alloy entry cowl and fan duct supported on double row of air straightener vanes downstream of fan rotor.

FAN: Single-stage fan with variable-incidence rotor blading overhung at front without entry guide vanes. Drive from gas generator section is via two-stage epicyclic gear train housed in cylindrical casing forming inner wall of fan duct. Astafan IV has fan of increased diameter (700 mm; 27·5 in).

COMPRESSOR, COMBUSTION SYSTEM AND TURBINE: Same as Astazou XVIII. Normal gas-generator operating speed, 43,000 rpm. (Astafan IV has Astazou XX compressor, running at 42,000 rpm.)

JET PIPE: Fixed type with straight frustum inner cone.

ACCESSORIES: Mounted on casing forming rear of secondary air intake.

FUEL SYSTEM: Independent control systems for starting and normal operation. Fuel regulator maintains speed constant with pilot operating single lever controlling fan blade pitch hydraulically to vary thrust output. Turboméca 'thermic' load limiter controls turbine entry temperature.

FUEL GRADES: AIR 3404A, 3405 or 3407A.

LUBRICATION SYSTEM: Pressure lubrication to bearings and reduction gear, with annular engine-mounted oil tank.

Turboméca Astafan III geared variable-pitch turbofan on testbed, giving 8·34 kN (1,870 lb st)

STARTING: Automatic electrical starting with compressor blow-off valve and fan in minimum pitch.

DIMENSIONS:

Length overall:	
Astafan IIG	1,980 mm (77·95 in)
Astafan III	2,030 mm (80·0 in)
Astafan IV	2,218 mm (87·5 in)
Max diameter over fan cowl:	
Astafan IIG	693 mm (27·3 in)
Astafan III	665 mm (26·2 in)
Astafan IV	780 mm (30·7 in)

WEIGHTS:

Equipped Astafan IIG	285 kg (628 lb)
Astafan III bare engine	210 kg (462 lb)
Equipped Astafan III	approx 230 kg (507 lb)
Astafan IV bare engine	220 kg (485 lb)

PERFORMANCE RATINGS:

T-O dry:	
Astafan IIG	6·88 kN (1,543 lb st)
T-O, wet:	
Astafan III	8·34 kN (1,870 lb st)
Astafan IV	12·06 kN (2,710 lb st)

SPECIFIC FUEL CONSUMPTION:

At T-O rating:	
Astafan IIG	10·76 mg/Ns (0·38 lb/h/lb st)
Astafan III	10·34 mg/Ns (0·365 lb/h/lb st)
Astafan IV	8·78 mg/Ns (0·310 lb/h/lb st)

TURBOMÉCA-SNECMA LARZAC

This small turbofan has been developed jointly by Turboméca and SNECMA to power military trainers and other small aircraft. A description of the Larzac is given under Turboméca-SNECMA GRTS.

TURBOMÉCA MARBORÉ

The Marboré turbojet is the most widely used of Turboméca's range of gas turbines. By 1 January 1979, a total of 4,332 Marboré II engines of 3·92 kN (880 lb) st had been delivered by Turboméca and a further 10,000 by Continental Aviation and Teledyne CAE (see US section) as the J69.

This initial version of the engine was joined in production by the 4·71 kN (1,058 lb st) Marboré VI with receipt of type approval in June 1962. By 1 January 1979, a total of 1,106 Marboré VI turbojets had been built.

The Marboré VI was also built under licence in Spain by ENMASA as the Marboré M21.

The following particulars relate to the Marboré VI:

TYPE: Single-shaft centrifugal-flow turbojet.

AIR INTAKE: Annular sheet metal nose intake bolted to front of light alloy compressor casing.

COMPRESSOR: Single-sided impeller machined from two alloy forgings, shrunk on steel shaft and locked and dowelled to maintain alignment. Pressure ratio 3·84 : 1. Air mass flow 9·8 kg (21·6 lb)/s.

COMBUSTION CHAMBER: Composed of inner and outer sheet metal casings, forming annular flame tube. Two primary flows enter from opposite ends of chamber, rear stream through hollow turbine nozzle guide vanes.

FUEL SYSTEM: Fuel, pumped through hollow impeller shaft, is fed to combustion zone by rotating injector disc around periphery of which are vents. Fuel is vented by centrifugal force, being atomised in the process.

FUEL GRADE: AIR 3405 (JP-1).

NOZZLE GUIDE VANES: Twenty-five sheet steel cooled by primary air.

TURBINE: Single-stage with thirty-seven blades. Gas temperature 613°C at 21,500 rpm.

JET PIPE: Inner and outer sheet metal casings.

ACCESSORY DRIVES: Gear casing in central compressor housing with drives for fuel and oil pumps. Connecting shaft to underside of accessories gear case above compressor casing. Accessories include tachometer generator and electric starter. Take-off (4 hp continuous) for remotely-driven accessory box.

LUBRICATION SYSTEM: Pressure type. Single gear-type pump serves front gear casing, two main bearings and rpm governor. Three scavenge pumps return bearing oil to tank via cooler. Normal oil pressure 2·76 bars (40 lb/sq in).

OIL SPECIFICATION: AIR 3512 (mineral) or AIR 3513A (synthetic).

MOUNTING: Four points, with Silentbloc rubber mountings, two at front and two at rear.

STARTING: Air Equipement 24V electric starter or compressed air starter. Two Turboméca igniter plugs.

DIMENSIONS:

Length with exhaust cone but without tailpipe	1,416 mm (55·74 in)
Width	593 mm (23·35 in)
Height	631 mm (24·82 in)

WEIGHT, DRY:

Equipped	140 kg (309 lb)

PERFORMANCE RATINGS:

T-O	4·71 kN (1,058 lb st) at 21,500 rpm
Cruising	4·21 kN (925 lb st) at 20,500 rpm

SPECIFIC FUEL CONSUMPTION:

At T-O rating	30·87 mg/Ns (1·09 lb/h/lb st)
At cruising rating	30·31 mg/Ns (1·07 lb/h/lb st)

TURBOMÉCA ARBIZON

Announced in 1970, the Arbizon is a simple single-shaft turbojet, known originally as the TR281 and derived from the Turmo IIIC₃ turboshaft. Intended for the propulsion of missiles and RPVs, it has single-stage axial and centrifugal compressors and a single-stage turbine.

Arbizon IIIB. Original version, for Otomat cruise missile. Four-lobed bellmouth inlet ducts surround front face carrying electric starter and other accessories. Mass flow 6 kg (13·2 lb)/s; pressure ratio 5·5. Total of 96 built by 1 January 1979.

Turboméca Arbizon IV short-life turbojet (underside shown, with inlet to left)

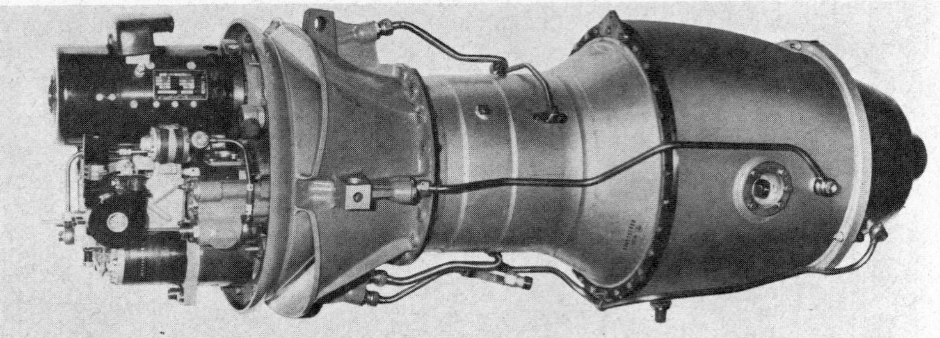

Turboméca Arbizon III expendable turbojet, rated at 3·73 kN (836 lb st)

Arbizon IV. Smaller version, under development. Design life 30 hours. Air-impingement starter.

DIMENSIONS:

Diameter of combustion chamber:	
Arbizon IIIB	405 mm (15·95 in)
Max diameter:	
Arbizon IV	330 mm (13·00 in)
Length overall, with accessories:	
Arbizon IIIB	1,361 mm (53·58 in)
Arbizon IV	1,025 mm (40·35 in)

WEIGHT, DRY:

Arbizon IIIB	115 kg (253 lb)
Arbizon IV	60 kg (132 lb)

PERFORMANCE RATINGS:

T-O: Arbizon IIIB	3·73 kN (836 lb st) at 33,000 rpm
Arbizon IV	3·61 kN (809 lb st)
Max continuous:	
Arbizon IIIB	3·24 kN (727 lb st) at 32,000 rpm
Arbizon IV	3·30 kN (741 lb st)

SPECIFIC FUEL CONSUMPTION:

At max continuous rating:	
Arbizon IIIB	31·44 mg/Ns (1·11 lb/h/lb st)
Arbizon IV	29·29 mg/Ns (1·034 lb/h/lb st)

TURBOMÉCA ARRIEL

This turboshaft engine is being used initially in two Aérospatiale helicopters, the single-engined AS 350 Ecureuil and twin-engined SA 365 Dauphin. It could also power a future version of the SA 341 Gazelle.

The Arriel is intended to have low first cost, low maintenance cost and low specific weight. It is characterised by modular construction, and is expected eventually to form the basis for a single-shaft turboprop and a turbofan in the 4·90 kN (1,100 lb st) class. The gas generator ran in 1973. The first complete engine ran on the bench on 7 August 1974. Flight development began on 17 December 1974 in the SA 341-02 Gazelle, which had been converted for Arriel development by Aérospatiale and the CGTM. The twin-engined SA 365 first flew on 24 January 1975, and the AS 350 Ecureuil on 14 February 1975. By 1979 Aérospatiale had ordered 222 Arriel I engines. Of these, 78 had been delivered, with FAA certification.

TYPE: Single-shaft axial-plus-centrifugal free-turbine turboshaft.

AIR INTAKE: Direct pitot entry to axial compressor.

COMPRESSOR: Single-stage axial compressor, machined from titanium forging. Supersonic centrifugal stage also machined from titanium. High rotational speed for maximum attainable pressure ratio (9:1).

COMBUSTION CHAMBER: Annular chamber, with flow radially outwards and then inwards. Centrifugal fuel injection without central tube.

GAS-GENERATOR TURBINE: Two integral cast axial stages with solid blades. Turbine shield capable of disc containment.

POWER TURBINE: Single axial stage with inserted blades.

JET PIPE: Exhaust diffuser fabricated by welding.

REDUCTION GEAR: Light alloy gearbox, containing two stages of helical gears, giving drive at 6,000 rpm to output shaft extending whole length of engine, with drive connections to both front and rear. Hydraulic torquemeter.

Turboméca Arriel I free-turbine turboshaft, with initial ratings up to 508 kW (681 shp)

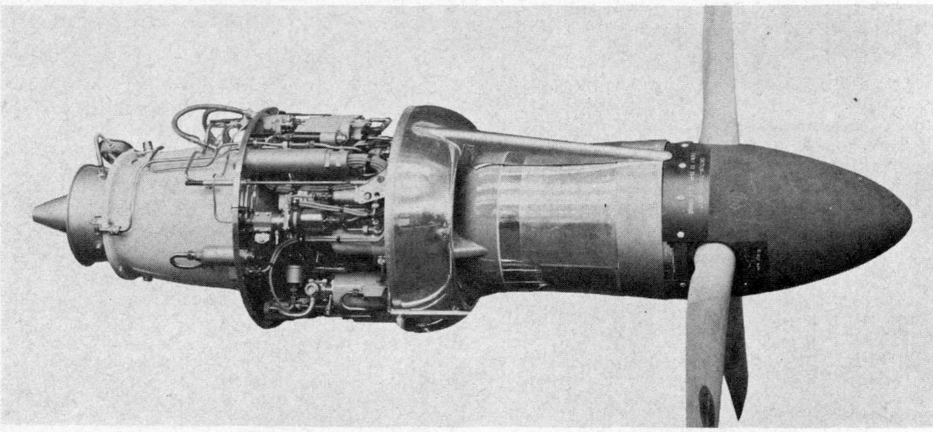

Turboméca Astazou XIVC turboprop engine, rated at 636 ekW (853 ehp)

ACCESSORY DRIVES: Two bevel gears and radial quill shaft drive accessory gearbox at front end, carried between compressor case and output shaft. Main pad provides for optional 12,000 rpm alternator; other drives for oil pumps, tachometer generator, governor and starter.

LUBRICATION SYSTEM: Independent circuit. Oil from tank passes through gear pump and metallic-cartridge filter. Return from engine via three gear scavenge pumps. Temperature probe and pressure switch to verify operation.

OIL SPECIFICATION: AIR 3512 (mineral) or AIR 3513A (synthetic).

MOUNTING: Multi-point flanges allow easy mounting in single or twin installation.

STARTING: Electric starter or starter/generator.

DIMENSIONS:

Length, excl accessories	1,090 mm (42·91 in)
Height overall	569 mm (22·40 in)
Width	430 mm (16·93 in)

WEIGHT, DRY:

With all engine accessories	109 kg (240 lb)

PERFORMANCE RATINGS:

Max contingency, initial	508 kW (681 shp)
Max contingency, later	544 kW (730 shp)
Take-off and intermediate contingency	478 kW (641 shp)
Max continuous	441·5 kW (592 shp)

SPECIFIC FUEL CONSUMPTION:

Max contingency	93·1 μg/J (0·551 lb/h/shp)
Intermediate continegency	96·8 μg/J (0·573 lb/h/shp)

TURBOMÉCA ASTAZOU TURBOPROP

The Astazou is the major turboprop in the Turboméca range and is in production in its 636 kW (853 ehp) Astazou XIVC and 760·6 kW (1,020 ehp) Astazou XVI versions. The Astazou XIV was certificated by the French airworthiness authorities in October 1968, followed by ARB/FAA certification of the Astazou XIVC and C1 in March 1969.

Current versions of the Astazou are:

Astazou XII. Powered Shorts Skyvan Srs 2 at 690 shp and Pilatus Turbo-Porter PC-6/A1-H2 at 700 ehp.

Astazou XIV (alias AZ14). Developed from Astazou XII. Powers early Jetstream business aircraft at 853 ehp.

Astazou XVI (alias AZ16). Higher rated version of Astazou XIV and first engine to enter production with new Turboméca aircooled turbine. The XVID, without starter/generator, powers the standard Jetstream; the XVIZ powers the Nord 260A. The Astazou XVIG, equipped for sustained inverted flight, was certificated by the Services Officiels Français on 30 April 1971; it powers the Argentinian Pucará combat aircraft. By the beginning of 1979, 164 Astazou XVI engines had been built.

Astazou XVIII. Higher rated version of Astazou XVI which first ran in early 1969 with T-O rating of 860·5 kW (1,154 ehp).

Astazou XX. Under development. This engine has two transonic axial compressor stages in titanium, in addition to the centrifugal stage machined in steel. Maximum T-O rating is 1,075 ekW (1,442 ehp).

Details of the Astazou series of turboshafts are given separately.

TYPE: Single-shaft axial-plus-centrifugal turboprop.

REDUCTION GEAR: Mounted in tapered cylindrical casing at front of engine, with two-stage epicyclic reduction gear having helical primary gears and straight secondary gears. Reduction ratio 24·115 : 1 (XVIG, 21·8 : 1). (Astazou XX gearbox incorporates torquemeter.)

AIR INTAKE: Annular air intake at rear of reduction gear casing. Hot-air de-icing.

COMPRESSOR: Two-stage axial followed by single-stage centrifugal with single-sided impeller. Two rows of stator blades aft of each axial rotor. Centrifugal stage has radial and axial diffusers. (Astazou XX has a four-stage compressor, comprising three axial followed by one centrifugal.)

COMBUSTION SYSTEM: Reverse-flow annular type with centrifugal fuel injector using rotary atomiser disc. Ignition by two ventilated torch igniters.

TURBINE: Three-stage axial with blades integral with discs. (Air cooling provided for Astazou XVI, XVIII and XX.) Discs attached by curvic couplings and bolts.

JET PIPE: Fixed type with curved inner cone.

ACCESSORIES: Mounted on casing forming rear of air intake. Drive pads provided for starter/generator, oil pump, fuel pump and speed governor, tacho-generator, AC generator and hydraulic pump.

MOUNTING: Trunnion located on each side of turbine casing front flange, plus third trunnion on underside of turbine casing.

FUEL SYSTEM: Automatic constant-speed system with propeller Beta-control and Turboméca 'thermic' load limiter and speed governor.

FUEL GRADES: AIR 3404, 3405, or 3407.

LUBRICATION SYSTEM: Pressure lubrication to bearings and reduction gear, with 8 litre (14 pint) oil tank mounted at front of engine.

OIL SPECIFICATION: AIR 3515 or synthetic AIR 3573.

STARTING: Electric.

DIMENSIONS:
Diameter over intake cowl 546 mm (21·5 in)
Overall length, incl propeller 2,047 mm (80·6 in)

WEIGHTS:
With accessories:
Astazou XIV approx 206 kg (454 lb)
Astazou XVID 205 kg (452 lb)
Astazou XVIG 228 kg (502 lb)
Astazou XVIZ 213 kg (468 lb)
Astazou XVIII approx 205 kg (452 lb)
Astazou XX 220 kg (484 lb)

PERFORMANCE RATINGS:
T-O:
Astazou XIV 636 ekW; 596·5 kW (853 ehp; 800 shp) at 43,000 rpm
Astazou XVID 722·5 ekW; 681 kW (969 ehp; 913 shp) at 43,089 rpm
Astazou XVIG, XVIZ 760·5 ekW; 720 kW (1,020 ehp; 965 shp) at 43,000 rpm
Astazou XVIII 860·5 ekW; 813 kW (1,154 ehp; 1,090 shp) at 43,000 rpm
Astazou XX 1,075 ekW; 1,030 kW (1,442 ehp; 1,381 shp) at 42,000 rpm

Max continuous:
Astazou XIV 574 ekW; 537 kW (770 ehp; 720 shp) at 43,000 rpm
Astazou XVID 626·5 ekW; 586 kW (840 ehp; 786 shp) at 43,089 rpm
Astazou XVIG, XVIZ 696·5 ekW; 654 kW (934 ehp; 877 shp) at 43,000 rpm
Astazou XVIII 809 ekW; 768 kW (1,085 ehp; 1,030 shp) at 43,000 rpm
Astazou XX 951·5 ekW; 907·5 kW (1,276 ehp; 1,217 shp) at 42,000 rpm

SPECIFIC FUEL CONSUMPTION:
At T-O rating:
Astazou XIV 92·4 μg/J (0·547 lb/h/shp)
Astazou XVI (all versions) 88·7 μg/J (0·525 lb/h/shp)
Astazou XVIII 85·3 μg/J (0·505 lb/h/ehp)
Astazou XX 75·9 μg/J (0·449 lb/h/ehp)

TURBOMÉCA ASTAZOU TURBOSHAFT

This turboshaft series of the Astazou family is derived from the early second-generation Astazou II turboprop fitted to the Mitsubishi MU-2 and Pilatus Turbo-Porter. Variants are as follows:

Astazou IIA. Rated at 390 kW (523 shp) and powers the Aérospatiale SA 318C Alouette II Astazou helicopter. Total of 732 built by 1977.

Astazou III. Definitive turboshaft for Anglo-French helicopter programme for production SA 341 Gazelle. Derived from Astazou IIA but with revised profile of turbine, using higher temperature alloy to match power needs of SA 341. Astazou IIIA, B, C and N for Gazelle versions all certificated in June 1972; uprated IIIA2, B2, C2 and N2 certificated May 1978. Produced jointly by Turboméca and Rolls-Royce Ltd, with 844 delivered by 1979.

Astazou XIVB and XIVF. In production for the SA 319B Alouette III; XIVB is civil and XIVF military. Flat rated to 441 kW (591 shp) (one hour) up to 4,000 m (13,125 ft) or +55°C.

Astazou XIVH. In production for SA 341 Gazelle, with much increased power. Flat-rated to transmission limit, to remove all altitude and temperature limitations. Certificated October 1974. Total of all XIV versions, 459 by 1979.

Astazou XVIIIA. Further increase in power gained by improved turbine, allowing higher gas temperature. Powers SA 360 Dauphin; 27 delivered by 1978.

Astazou XX. Fourth axial compressor stage added. Designed for operation in hot and high countries. Intended to power SA 361 helicopter.

The following description relates to the Astazou IIIN except where indicated:

TYPE: Single-shaft axial-plus-centrifugal turboshaft.

REDUCTION GEAR: Similar to Astazou XIV turboprop. Reduction ratio 7·039 : 1 (Astazou XIVB/F, 7·345; XVIA, XVIIIA, 7·375).

AIR INTAKE: Annular air intake at rear of reduction gear casing.

COMPRESSOR: Single-stage axial (IIA, IIN, IIIN), two-stage axial (XIV, XVIII) or three-stage axial (XX) followed by single-stage centrifugal with single-sided impeller. Air mass flow 2·5 kg/s (5·5 lb/s).

COMBUSTION SYSTEM: Similar to Astazou XIV.

TURBINE: Similar to Astazou XIV.

JET PIPE: Similar to Astazou XIV.

ACCESSORIES: Five drive pads on casing forming rear of air intake.

MOUNTING: At front by flange located at power take-off section, and at rear by two lugs on accessory mounting pad section.

FUEL SYSTEM: Automatic constant speed control with speed governor.

LUBRICATION SYSTEM: Pressure type with gear type pumps. Oil tank of 8 litre (14 pint) capacity mounted at front of engine.

STARTING: Electrical, automatic.

DIMENSIONS:
Height: Astazou IIA 458 mm (18 in)
Astazou III, XIVH 460 mm (18·1 in)
Astazou XVIA, XVIIIA 698 mm (27·48 in)
Astazou XX 721 mm (28·4 in)
Width: Astazou IIA 480 mm (18·8 in)
Astazou III, XIVH 460 mm (18·1 in)
Length overall: Astazou IIA 1,272 mm (50·0 in)
Astazou III, XIVB/F 1,433 mm (56·3 in)
Astazou XVIA, XVIIIA 1,327 mm (52·2 in)
Astazou XIVH 1,470 mm (57·9 in)
Astazou XX 1,529 mm (60·22 in)

WEIGHTS:
Equipped:
Astazou III 147 kg (324 lb)
Astazou III (suffix 2) 150 kg (330 lb)
Astazou XIVB/F 166 kg (366 lb)
Astazou XVIA, XVIIIA 155 kg (341 lb)
Astazou XIVH 160 kg (353 lb)
Astazou XX 195 kg (430 lb)

PERFORMANCE RATINGS:
Max power: Astazou IIA 390 kW (523 shp)
Astazou III 441·5 kW (592 shp)
Astazou III (suffix 2) 481 kW (645 shp)
Astazou XX 750 kW (1,005 shp)
One hour: Astazou XIVB/F 440·7 kW (591 shp)
Astazou XVIA 651 kW (873 shp) maintained at sea level to 30°C
Astazou XVIIIA 651 kW (873 shp) maintained at sea level to 40°C
Max continuous: Astazou IIA 352·7 kW (473 shp)
Astazou III 390 kW (523 shp)
Astazou III (suffix 2) 441·5 kW (592 shp)
Astazou XIVB/F 405 kW (543 shp)
Astazou XVIA, XVIIIA 600 kW (805 shp)
Astazou XIVH flat-rated in SA 341 to 440·7 kW (591 shp) to 55°C or 4,000 m (13,125 ft)
Astazou XX 675 kW (905 shp)

SPECIFIC FUEL CONSUMPTION:
At max power rating:
Astazou IIA 105·3 μg/J (0·623 lb/h/shp)
Astazou III 108·7 μg/J (0·643 lb/h/shp)
Astazou III (suffix 2) 109·9 μg/J (0·65 lb/h/shp)
Astazou XIVB/F 105·5 μg/J (0·624 lb/h/shp)
Astazou XVIA 93·8 μg/J (0·555 lb/h/shp)
Astazou XVIIIA 91·3 μg/J (0·540 lb/h/shp)
Astazou XX 85·9 μg/J (0·508 lb/h/shp)

TURBOMÉCA BASTAN

The Bastan turboprop is one of the second generation of Turboméca engines, characterised by their two-stage axial-centrifugal compressor. The Bastan VIC rated at 786·7 kW (1,055 ehp) powers the Aérospatiale N 262 and was certificated by the Services Officiels Français and the FAA in 1964. The 1,000 ehp Bastan VID powers the Argentinian GII.

A second version, the Bastan VII, flat rated at 780 kW (1,046 shp), is derived from the Bastan VI and powers the Aérospatiale Frégate. The Bastan VII was certificated by the Services Officiels Français on 3 August 1970. Total production of Bastan VI and VII is 560 engines.

TYPE: Single-shaft axial-plus-centrifugal turboprop.

REDUCTION GEAR: Two-stage epicyclic type. Ratio 1 : 21·0957. Propeller shaft carried in ball bearing at front.

AIR INTAKE: Annular intake at rear of reduction gear.

COMPRESSOR CASING: Central portion carries rear ball bearing for compressor shaft.

COMPRESSOR: Single axial stage for Bastan VIC, and two axial stages for Bastan VII, followed by single centrifugal stage. On Bastan VII first axial rotor blades are titanium and pin-mounted in disc, and second axial rotor blades are light alloy integral with disc. Bastan VIC pressure ratio 5·83 : 1 and air mass flow 4·5 kg (10 lb)/s. Bastan VII pressure ratio 6·68 : 1 and mass flow 5·9 kg (13·1 lb)/s. Water-methanol injection in Bastan VIC.

COMBUSTION CHAMBER: Direct-flow annular type. Usual Turboméca rotary atomiser fuel injection system. Two torch igniters. Gas temperature before turbine 870°C.

TURBINE: Three-stage axial-flow.

JET PIPE: Annular welded sheet assembly.

ACCESSORY DRIVE: Upper pinion train drives dynamo starter, propeller governor and fuel pump with fuel metering device. Lower gear drives electric tachometer transmitter, fuel pump, 20kVA alternator and landing gear pump. All accessories mounted on intake casing.

MOUNTING: Three attachment points, two lateral, one at bottom of engine.

ENGINE CONTROL: By two governors. One adjusts fuel flow entering engine so that it is maintained at the value set by the power control lever, as a function of the variations of pressure and temperature at the engine air intake. The second governor maintains the propeller rpm at the value set by the rpm control lever, by varying propeller pitch.

STARTING: Automatic starter/generator on Bastan VII.

DIMENSIONS:
Height: Bastan VIC 775·5 mm (30·53 in)
Width: Bastan VIC 685 mm (26·97 in)
Diameter: Bastan VII 550 mm (21·7 in)
Length: Bastan VIC 1,548·6 mm (60·95 in)
Bastan VII 1,911 mm (75·2 in)

Turboméca Astazou XX turboshaft, rated at 750 kW (1,005 shp)

The 780 kW (1,046 shp) Turboméca Bastan VII single-shaft turboprop powering the Frégate

WEIGHT, DRY:
Fully equipped:
Bastan VIC 322 kg (710 lb)
Bastan VII approx 370 kg (816 lb)
PERFORMANCE RATINGS (S/L, ISA):
Bastan VIC:
T-O and max continuous 700·4 ekW; 595 kW (1,060 ehp; 798 shp) at 33,500 rpm
Bastan VII:
T-O 1,089 ekW; 780 kW (1,460 ehp; 1,046 shp) at 32,000 rpm maintained up to 40°C or to 3,650 m (11,975 ft)
SPECIFIC FUEL CONSUMPTION:
Bastan VIC, T-O 98·4 μg/J (0·582 lb/h/ehp)
Bastan VII, T-O 88·7 μg/J (0·525 lb/h/ehp)

TURBOMÉCA ARTOUSTE III

The Artouste IIIB is a single-shaft turboshaft derived from the Artouste II. It is a member of the second generation of Turboméca engines with two-stage axial-centrifugal compressor and three-stage turbine. The Artouste IIIB has a pressure ratio of 5·2 : 1. Air mass flow is 4·3 kg/s (9·5 lb/s) at 33,300 rpm.

Type approval at the rating given below was received on 25 May 1961, following completion of a 150-hour official type test. Production at Turboméca continues. In addition, Artouste IIIBs are being built under licence in India by Hindustan Aeronautics Ltd.

The Artouste IIIB, which powers the Aérospatiale SA 316B Alouette III, obtained FAA certification in March 1962 and in August 1968 similar certification of the Artouste IIC1, C2, C5 and C6, powering the SE 3130 and 313B Alouette II Artouste, was also obtained.

An uprated version, the Artouste IIID, was certificated on 30 April 1971. It differs in having a reduction gear giving 5,864 rpm at the driveshaft (instead of 5,773 rpm) and in slightly revised equipment. The IIID powers a late version of the Alouette III. A total of 2,215 Artouste III engines had been built by January 1979.

DIMENSIONS:
Length 1,815 mm (71·46 in)
Height 627 mm (24·68 in)
Width 507 mm (19·96 in)
WEIGHT, DRY:
Fully equipped:
Artouste IIIB 182 kg (400 lb)
Artouste IIID 178 kg (392 lb)
PERFORMANCE RATINGS (maintained up to 55°C at S/L or up to approximately 4,000 m; 13,150 ft):
T-O:
Artouste IIIB 420 kW (563 shp)
Artouste IIID 440 kW (590 shp)
Max continuous (both) 405 kW (543 shp)
SPECIFIC FUEL CONSUMPTION:
T-O:
Artouste IIIB 128·8 μg/J (0·762 lb/h/shp)
Artouste IIID 126·2 μg/J (0·747 lb/h/shp)
Max continuous (both) 130·1 μg/J (0·77 lb/h/shp)

MTU-TURBOMÉCA MTM 80

This proposed new helicopter engine is discussed in the Addenda.

TURBOMÉCA TURMO

The Turmo free-turbine engine is in service in both turboshaft and turboprop versions.

The main variants are as follows:

Turmo IIIC$_3$. This was the original power plant of the triple-engined SA 321 Super Frelon helicopter. Maximum contingency rating is 1,104 kW (1,480 shp).

Turmo IIIC$_4$. Developed from Turmo IIIC$_3$ and with a maximum contingency rating of 1,032 kW (1,384 shp), this all-weather version is manufactured jointly by Turboméca and Rolls-Royce to power SA 330 Puma twin-engined helicopters under the Franco-British helicopter agreement of October 1967. Certificated by the Services Officiels Français on 9 October 1970. Total production of IIIC$_4$ and IV by 1979 was 1,439 engines.

Turmo IIIC$_5$, IIIC$_6$, IIIC$_7$. Similar to Turmo IIIC$_3$ but with different ratings. The SA 321F and 321J Super Frelons powered by these engines obtained French certification in June 1968. Total production of Super Frelon engines (including E series), 549.

Turmo IIID. Turboprop version, similar in basic construction to Turmo IIIC series but with output speed limited to 6,000 rpm.

Turmo IIIE$_3$. Similar to Turmo IIIC$_3$ but with different ratings. In production for SA 321 Super Frelon.

Turmo IIIE$_6$. Higher turbine temperature.

Turmo IV. The Turmo IVA is a civil engine derived from the IIIC$_4$, with a maximum contingency rating of 1,057 kW (1,417 shp). The IVB is a military version having the same ratings as the IIIC$_4$.

The following description applies generally to the Turmo IIIC$_3$, C$_4$, C$_5$ and E, except where indicated:

TYPE: Free-turbine axial-plus-centrifugal turboshaft.

REDUCTION GEAR: Turmo IIIC$_3$, C$_5$ and E$_3$ fitted with rear-mounted reduction gear mounted in bifurcated exhaust duct with rear-facing power take-off shaft. Turmo IIIC$_4$ is a direct-drive engine.

AIR INTAKE: Annular forward-facing intake, with de-icing in Turmo IIIC$_4$ and C$_5$.

The 420 kW (563 shp) Turboméca Artouste IIIB single-shaft helicopter turboshaft

COMPRESSOR: Single-stage axial followed by single-stage centrifugal with single-sided impeller. Two rows of light alloy stator blades aft of axial stage. Centrifugal stage has steel radial and axial diffusers; impeller located by lugs on turbine shaft. Axial rotor blades, titanium in Turmo IIIC$_3$, C$_5$ and E$_3$ and steel in Turmo IIIC$_4$, pin-mounted in steel disc with integral shaft. Pressure ratio 5·9 : 1 on Turmo IIIC$_3$. Air mass flow 5·9 kg (13 lb)/s.

COMBUSTION SYSTEM: Reverse-flow annular type with centrifugal fuel injector using rotary atomiser disc. Ignition by two ventilated torch igniters.

GAS GENERATOR TURBINE: Two-stage axial unit with integral rotor blades.

POWER TURBINE: Two-stage axial unit in Turmo IIIC$_3$, C$_5$ and E$_3$, and single-stage in Turmo IIIC$_4$. In all advanced production engines of IIIC$_4$ derivation the power turbine speed is 22,840 rpm under all high-power conditions.

JET PIPE: Fixed type with lateral bifurcated exhaust duct in Turmo IIIC$_3$, C$_5$ and E$_3$, and single lateral duct on Turmo IIIC$_4$.

ACCESSORIES: Mounted above and below intake casing with drive pads for oil pump, fuel control unit, electric starter, tacho-generator and, on Turmo IIIC$_4$, oil cooler fan. Control unit remote drive also provided on Turmo IIIC$_4$ from bevel gear drive on power turbine output shaft.

MOUNTING: Two lateral supports fitted to lower part of turbine casing at rear flange output shaft protection tube. On Turmo IIIC$_4$, also on reduction gear case.

FUEL SYSTEM: Fuel control unit for gas generator on Turmo IIIC$_3$, C$_5$ and E$_3$, with speed limiter for power turbine also fitted on E$_3$. Constant-speed system fitted on Turmo IIIC$_4$ power turbine, with speed limiter also fitted on gas generator.

FUEL GRADE: AIR 3405 for Turmo IIIC$_4$.

LUBRICATION SYSTEM: Pressure type with oil cooler and 13 litre (23 Imp pint) tank at front of engine on Turmo IIIC$_4$, with oil tank only around intake casing on Turmo IIIC$_3$, C$_5$ and E$_3$, and by intake accessory drive gear on Turmo IIIC$_4$.

OIL SPECIFICATION: AIR 3155A, or synthetic AIR 3513, for Turmo IIIC$_4$.

STARTING: Automatic system with electric starter motor.

DIMENSIONS:
Height:
Turmo IIIC$_3$, C$_5$ and E$_3$ 716·5 mm (28·2 in)
Turmo IIIC$_4$ 719 mm (28·3 in)
Turmo IIID$_3$ 926 mm (36·5 in)
Width:
Turmo IIIC$_3$, C$_5$ and E$_3$ 693 mm (27·3 in)
Turmo IIIC$_4$ 637 mm (25·1 in)
Turmo IIID$_3$ 934 mm (36·8 in)
Length:
Turmo IIIC$_3$, C$_5$ and E$_3$ 1,975·7 mm (78·0 in)
Turmo IIIC$_4$ 2,184 mm (85·5 in)
Turmo IIID$_3$ 1,868 mm (73·6 in)

WEIGHT, DRY:
Turmo IIIC$_3$ and E$_3$, fully equipped 297 kg (655 lb)
Turmo IIIC$_5$, IIIC$_6$ and IIIC$_7$ 325 kg (716 lb)
Turmo IIIC$_4$, equipped engine 225 kg (496 lb)
Turmo IIID$_3$, basic engine 365 kg (805 lb)
PERFORMANCE RATINGS:
T-O: Turmo IIIC$_3$, D$_3$ and E$_3$ 1,104 kW (1,480 shp)
Turmo IIIE$_6$ 1,181 kW (1,584 shp)
Max contingency:
Turmo IIIC$_4$ at 33,800 gas-generator rpm 1,032 kW (1,384 shp)
Turmo IIIC$_6$ at 33,550 gas-generator rpm 1,156 kW (1,550 shp)
Turmo IIIC$_7$ at 33,800 gas-generator rpm 1,201 kW (1,610 shp)
Turmo IVA at 33,950 gas-generator rpm 1,057 kW (1,417 shp)
Turmo IVC at 33,800 gas-generator rpm 1,163 kW (1,560 shp)
T-O and intermediate contingency:
Turmo IIIC$_5$ 1,050 kW (1,408 shp)
SPECIFIC FUEL CONSUMPTION:
At T-O rating:
Turmo IIIC$_3$ and E$_3$ 101·9 μg/J (0·603 lb/h/shp)
Turmo IIID$_3$ 104·1 μg/J (0·616 lb/h/shp)
At max contingency rating:
Turmo IIIC$_4$, C$_5$, C$_6$, C$_7$ and IV 106·8 μg/J (0·632 lb/h/shp)
Turmo IVA 106·3 μg/J (0·629 lb/h/shp)

TURBOMÉCA/ROLLS-ROYCE RTM 321

Proposal for collaborative turboshaft engine in the 1,120/1,490 kW (1,500/2,000 shp) class, referred to under Rolls-Royce Turboméca in the Addenda.

TURBOMÉCA MAKILA

This new turboshaft engine, rated at an initial 1,323·5 kW (1,775 shp) for take-off and intermediate contingency, is under development to power the Aérospatiale Super Puma helicopter. Derived partly from the Turmo family, it incorporates all the latest features of the company's advanced engines, including: rapid-strip modular construction; three axial stages of compression plus one centrifugal; later fuel inlet to centrifugal atomiser; two-stage gas-generator turbine (probably with cooled blades); two-stage free power turbine; and lateral exhaust.

During 1974 this engine was confirmed as partner to the Arriel in laying the foundation for the company's marketing in the next 15 years. The world market for this size of engine is put at 10,000 units. The first engine was delivered for bench test in 1976, and the gas generator went on test in November of that year. The first complete Makila engine ran in January 1977 and flew in June of that year.

The following data are provisional:

DIMENSIONS:
Length, intake face to rear face 1,395 mm (54·94 in)

The 1,032 kW (1,384 shp) Turboméca Turmo IIIC$_4$ turboshaft which powers the SA 330 Puma helicopter

Width 530 mm (20·9 in)
Height 514 mm (20·25 in)
WEIGHT, DRY: 210 kg (463 lb)
PERFORMANCE RATINGS (ISA, S/L):
Max contingency
1,424 kW (1,910 shp) at 36,300 gas-generator rpm
T-O and intermediate
1,323·5 kW (1,775 shp) at 35,500 gas-generator rpm
Max continuous
1,215·5 kW (1,630 shp) at 34,750 gas-generator rpm
SPECIFIC FUEL CONSUMPTION:
Max contingency 80·4 μg/J (0·476 lb/h/shp)
T-O and intermediate 80·8 μg/J (0·478 lb/h/shp)
Max continuous 82·3 μg/J (0·487 lb/h/shp)

Turboméca Makila free-turbine turboshaft, with initial ratings up to 1,424 kW (1,910 shp)

The Turboméca Turmastazou XIV free-turbine turboshaft, rated at 663 kW (889 shp)

TURBOMÉCA TURMASTAZOU

The Turmastazou turboshaft engine comprises the Astazou single-seat turboprop with the addition of a free-turbine. Development is proceeding on the five engines built by March 1969.

TYPE: Free-turbine axial-plus-centrifugal turboshaft.

POWER DRIVE: Direct at rear of engine. No reduction gear fitted.

AIR INTAKE: Annular forward-facing intake at front of engine, feeding direct to compressor inlet.

COMPRESSOR AND COMBUSTION SYSTEM: Similar to Astazou.

COMPRESSOR TURBINE: Two-stage axial unit with rotor blades integral with turbine discs. Discs through-bolted with curvic couplings.

POWER TURBINE: Two-stage axial unit with rotor blades integral with turbine discs. Discs through-bolted with curvic couplings. Constant output speed 29,000 rpm.

JET PIPE: None fitted as standard.

ACCESSORIES: Mounted on compressor casing behind oil tank. Drive pads fitted for oil pump, tacho-generator, fuel control unit, starter/generator, AC generator and hydraulic pump (optional).

FUEL SYSTEM: Automatic control system with constant speed control of free-turbine.

LUBRICATION SYSTEM: Pressure type system with gear pump. Oil tank mounted around front of engine.

STARTING: Automatic electrical starting.

DIMENSIONS:
Height 552 mm (21·7 in)
Width 440 mm (17·3 in)
Length overall 1,332 mm (52·4 in)
WEIGHT:
Complete with accessories 160 kg (352 lb)
PERFORMANCE RATINGS (T-O):
Turmastazou XIV 663 kW (889 shp)
Turmastazou XVI 735 kW (986 shp)
SPECIFIC FUEL CONSUMPTION:
Turmastazou XIV and XVI:
T-O 86·9 μg/J (0·507 lb/h/shp)

TURBOMÉCA DOUBLE TURMASTAZOU

The Double Turmastazou free-turbine coupled turboshaft comprises two Turmastazou turboshafts coupled by a combining gearbox to drive a common output shaft. The engine is intended for twin-engined helicopter installations. It is specified for a new helicopter by Agusta, to which company an engine has been delivered.

The Double Turmastazou XIV comprises two Turmastazou XIV engines and is under development at 1,775 shp. A higher-powered model, the 2,071 shp Double Turmastazou XVI, is derived from the Astazou XVI. In both cases the usual output shaft speed is 6,600 rpm.

TURBOMÉCA-SNECMA

GROUPEMENT TURBOMÉCA-SNECMA (GRTS)

1 rue Beaujon, BP 37-08, 75362 Paris Cédex 08
Telephone: 924-18-61

ADMINISTRATORS:
R. Florentini
E. Delfour

MANAGEMENT CONTROL COMMITTEE:
R. Martin
F. Rigaud

FINANCIAL COMMISSARY: C. Hirt

Announced in March 1969, Groupement Turboméca-SNECMA is a company formed jointly by Société Turboméca and SNECMA to be responsible for the design, development, manufacture, sales and service support of the Larzac all-axial small turbofan launched in 1968 as a joint venture by the two companies. Groupement Turboméca-SNECMA has no capital at present and comprises primarily a joint management organisation to produce the engine.

Turboméca-SNECMA Larzac 04 two-shaft turbofan, rated at 13·18 kN (2,966 lb st)

TURBOMÉCA-SNECMA LARZAC

Originally this small turbofan was planned for a wide range of applications, and the first prototype was a 9·8 kN (2,200 lb st) engine aimed at the commercial market. This type of engine ran in May 1969 and began flight development in a pod carried by a Constellation in March 1971. By this time the main immediate market had shifted to military trainers, and GRTS designed the Larzac 04 for this purpose.

In February 1972 the Larzac 04 was selected for a joint Franco-German programme to provide propulsion for the Alpha Jet (see International entry in Aircraft section). In addition to the two French partners in GRTS, two German companies, MTU and KHD, were added to the programme. Both have played a part in the manufacture of prototype engines and the achievement of endurance tests. All four companies are sharing in production and post-certification development. Complete engines are assembled in both countries for the Alpha Jet programme. The first production engine was delivered in September 1977. The work split is France 56·5 per cent, Germany 43·5. Engines for Belgium are assembled and tested by FN.

Bench testing of the Larzac 04 began in May 1972. Flight development with the Constellation testbed began in March 1973, and with a Falcon 10 in July 1973. The first Alpha Jet flew on 26 October 1973, and qualification of the Larzac 04 was accomplished on schedule in May 1975. The rating given is at a turbine entry temperature of 1,130°C; growth thrust potential greater than 15 per cent is forecast without dimensional change.

In September 1972 the French Services Officiels approved an agreement between GRTS and Teledyne CAE covering the production, marketing and after-sales support of the Larzac in the United States and Canada.

The Larzac 04 has a two-stage fan, four-stage HP compressor, annular combustion chamber with vaporising burners, single-stage HP turbine with cooled blades and single-stage LP turbine. Maximum airflow is 27·6 kg (60·8 lb)/sec, pressure ratio 10·6 and by-pass ratio 1·13. A single fixed-area jet pipe is used. All accessories are driven by the HP spool and grouped under the fan case. The engine is mounted by an isostatic suspension on either side of the centre of gravity. The engine is of modular design and is intended to produce minimum noise and smoke.

DIMENSIONS:
Overall length of basic engine 1,179 mm (46·4 in)
Overall diameter 602 mm (23·7 in)
WEIGHT, DRY:
Larzac 04 290 kg (640 lb)
T-O THRUST (S/L, static):
Larzac 04 13·18 kN (2,966 lb)
SPECIFIC FUEL CONSUMPTION:
Larzac 04 20·1 mg/Ns (0·71 lb/h/lb st)

GERMANY
(FEDERAL REPUBLIC)

ERNO
ERNO RAUMFAHRTTECHNIK GmbH

Address: Hünefeldstrasse 1-5, 2800 Bremen
Telephone: 0421 538 2305

This VFW-Fokker subsidiary claims to be Europe's leading producer of hydrazine-based motor systems. Most of its products in this field are small thrusters for space applications. Thrusts range from 0·05 N to 2·5 kN (0·011-557 lb) for motors operating at about 1,000°C and from 0·001 N to 4·0 N (0·0002-0·899 lb) for cold-gas thrusters. Spacecraft using ERNO thrusters include Intelsat III, Aeros A/B, MAROTS and OTS.

KHD
KLÖCKNER-HUMBOLDT-DEUTZ AG

Address: 5 Köln (Cologne) 80, Postfach 80 05 09
Telephone: Cologne (0221) 8221

KHD is a leading manufacturer of diesel engines and trucks. In its subsidiary at Oberursel it concentrates its activities in the gas-turbine field. It designs, manufactures and services gas turbines, power transmissions and complete power systems for aircraft, road vehicles, marine craft and industrial applications. Its most important gas turbine is the T312, the compact lightweight APU (auxiliary power unit) of the Panavia Tornado, providing full shaft power of 114 kW (153 hp) or full air bleed of 0·22 kg (0·49 lb)/s or a combination. KHD also supplies the complete Tornado secondary power system linking the T312 to a cross-shaft coupled to each main engine.

KHD is also participating in production of the T64 turboshaft (see MTU in this section) and Larzac turbofan (see Turboméca-SNECMA in this section).

LIMBACH
LIMBACH MOTORENBAU

Head Office and Works: Kotthausener Str 5, D-533 Königswinter 21, Sassenberg
Telephone: (02244) 2322
President: P. Limbach

This company manufactures four-stroke piston engines for ultra-light aeroplanes and powered gliders. All are of similar basic design, though one sub-type has a greater cylinder stroke, and a new range about to go into production has substantially larger capacity.

LIMBACH SL 1700

Several variants of this engine have been certificated by the Luftfahrt-Bundesamt (Federal Office of Civil Aviation). Apart from the first sub-type listed below all are four-stroke (Otto) engines:

Limbach SL 1700D. Dual-ignition. Not certificated. Fitted to Sportavia-Pützer RF7.

Sportavia-Limbach SL 1700E. Basic engine of the current range. Fitted to Sportavia/Pützer RF5 and RF5B.

Limbach SL 1700EA. Differs in having front-end starter and different induction system. Fitted to Scheibe SF-25C Falke.

Limbach SL 1700EAI. Similar to EA except equipped to drive Hoffmann variable-pitch propeller. Fitted to Scheibe SF-28.

Limbach SL 1700EB. Similar to E except for having increased cylinder stroke and twin carburettors.

Limbach SL 1700EBI. Similar to EB except equipped to drive Hoffmann variable-pitch propeller. Fitted to Schleicher ASK 16.

Limbach SL 1700EC. Similar to E except for having a carburettor intake heating box.

Limbach SL 1700 ECI. Similar to EC except equipped to drive Hoffmann variable-pitch propeller.

Sportavia-Limbach SL 1700EI. Similar to E except equipped to drive Hoffmann variable-pitch propeller. Optional for RF5B.

Unless otherwise stated, the following description refers to the SL 1700E:

Type: Four-cylinder horizontally-opposed aircooled piston engine.

Cylinders: Bore 88 mm (3·46 in). Stroke 69 mm (2·71 in) (EB, EBI, 74 mm; 2·87 in). Swept volume 1,680 cc (102·51 cu in) (EB, EBI, 1,800 cc; 108·56 cu in). Compression ratio 8 : 1.

Induction: Stromberg-Zenith 150CD carburettor (two in EB, EBI). (EA, EAI, one Zenith 28 RX2).

Fuel Grade: 90 octane.

Ignition: Single Slick 4030 magneto feeding one Bosch WB 240 ERT 1 plug in each cylinder.

Starting: One Fiat 0·5 hp starter (EA, EAI, one Bosch 0·3 kW; 0·4 hp).

Accessories: Ducellier 250W alternator (EA, EAI, 150W Ducati); APG 17.09.001 fuel pump (EA,EAI, 17.09.001A).

Dimensions:
Length overall:
SL 1700D 649 mm (25·6 in)
SL 1700EA, EAI 558 mm (22·0 in)
SL 1700E, EI, EC, ECI 618 mm (24·33 in)
other variants 580 mm (22·8 in)
Width overall:
SL 1700D 800 mm (31·5 in)
SL 1700EA, EAI 770 mm (30·3 in)
other variants 764 mm (30·1 in)
Height overall:
SL 1700D 451 mm (17·8 in)
SL 1700EA, EAI 392 mm (15·4 in)
other variants 368 mm (14·5 in)

Weight, Dry:
SL 1700E, EI 73 kg (161 lb)
SL 1700EA, EAI 70 kg (154 lb)
SL 1700EB, EBI, EC, ECI 74 kg (164 lb)

Performance Ratings:
T-O:
SL 1700D 48·5 kW (65 hp) at 3,600 rpm
SL 1700E, EI, EC, ECI 51 kW (68 hp) at 3,600 rpm
SL 1700EA, EAI 44·7 kW (60 hp) at 3,550 rpm
SL 1700EB, EBI 53·7 kW (72 hp) at 3,600 rpm
Continuous:
SL 1700E, EI, EC, ECI 45·5 kW (61 hp) at 3,200 rpm
SL 1700EA, EAI 41·7 kW (56 hp) at 3,300 rpm
SL 1700EB, EBI 49·2 kW (66 hp) at 3,200 rpm

Limbach L 2000/L 2400/L 2600 series (all similar in appearance) flat-four four-stroke. These engines are initially rated at 52·2, 59·6 and 67 kW (70, 80 and 90 hp)

LIMBACH L 2000-2600

Instead of planning a single new engine—the SL 2400 introduced in the 1975-76 *Jane's*—Limbach is developing similar engines in three sizes. The smallest is the L 2000 of just under 2,000 cc capacity; the intermediate L 2400 has larger bore, and the largest, the L 2600, combines the larger bore with longer stroke. In 1979 the demand did not appear to justify the costs of certification.

Type: Four-cylinder horizontally-opposed aircooled four-stroke piston engine.

Cylinders: Bore (L 2000) 94 mm (3·70 in), (L 2400, 2600) 103 mm (4·06 in). Stroke (L 2000, 2400) 71 mm (2·79 in), (L 2600) 78·5 mm (3·09 in). Swept volume (L 2000) 1,970 cc (120·2 cu in), (L 2400) 2,368 cc (144·49 cu in), (L 2600) 2,616 cc (159·62 cu in). Compression ratio 8 : 1.

Induction: One Marvel-Schebler 3 PA carburettor fed by APG 20.09.001 fuel pump.

Fuel Grade: 90 octane.

Ignition: Two Slick 4001 magnetos, with Slick high-temperature harness feeding two Bosch WB 240 ERT 1 plugs in each cylinder.

Starter: Bosch 0·3 kW (0·4 hp) electric.

Accessories: Limbach 250W alternator; oil capacity 4 litres (8·4 Imp pints).

Dimensions (L 2400):
Length 640 mm (25·20 in)
Width 790 mm (31·10 in)
Height 378 mm (14·88 in)

Weight, Dry:
L 2000 D-I 91 kg (201 lb)
L 2400 D-I 92 kg (203·5 lb)
L 2600 D-I 93 kg (205 lb)

Performance Rating (T-O and max continuous):
L 2000 D-I 52·2 kW (70 hp) at 3,000 rpm
L 2400 D-I 59·6 kW (80 hp) at 3,000 rpm
L 2600 D-I 67 kW (90 hp) at 3,000 rpm

LIMBACH L 275E

This engine is intended for low-cost propulsion of RPVs and ultra-light aircraft.

Type: Two-cylinder horizontally-opposed two-stroke air-cooled piston engine.

Cylinders: Cast aluminium alloy with Nicasil liner. Bore 66 mm (2·6 in). Stroke 40 mm (1·57 in). Swept volume 274 cc (16·72 cu in).

Induction: Two all-attitude diaphragm carburettors.

Fuel Grade: 90 octane, mixed 25:1 with two-stroke oil.

Ignition: 12V Bosch transistorised, one Bosch WK 175T6 plug per cylinder.

Accessories: Leistritz-type turbo silencer (muffler).

Dimensions:
Length overall 226 mm (8·89 in)
Width overall 390 mm (15·35 in)
Height overall 187 mm (7·36 in)

Weight (with silencer): 7·5 kg (16·53 lb)

Performance Rating: 18 kW (24 hp) at 7,300 rpm

Below left, Sportavia-Limbach SL 1700E flat-four four-stroke engine, rated at 51 kW (68 hp)

Below centre, Limbach SL 1700EA flat-four four-stroke engine, rated at 44·7 kW (60 hp)

Below right, Limbach L 275E two-stroke for ultra-light and RPV applications, to be rated at 18 kW (24 hp)

MBB
MESSERSCHMITT-BÖLKOW-BLOHM GmbH

8 München 80, Postfach 801 220
Telephone: (0811) 6 00 01
Development and Production Centres: Ottobrunn bei München; Lampoldhausen; Hamburg; and Bölkow-Apparatebau GmbH at Nabern and Schrobenhausen

As noted in the Aircraft section, Messerschmitt-Bölkow and Hamburger Flugzeugbau merged in 1969 to form the MBB group. The former Bölkow element of this group is engaged in the design and development of a wide variety of medium- and high-energy rocket engines and motors. Other activities include thrust augmentation by afterburning, engine casing design, propellant insulation and mounting, and preparatory work towards series production and reliability.

Other recent development of liquid-propellant engines by MBB has embraced advanced thermodynamic combustion engines, injection and cooling of engines of low thrust level and engines with high- and medium-energy storable propellants.

MBB MONOPROPELLANT GAS-GENERATORS

MBB has produced 13 different types of gas-generator, with flow rates from 0·00018 kg (0·0004 lb) to 8·2 kg (18·2 lb)/s and using the propellants N_2H_4, N_2H_4 + H_2O, and H_2O_2 + H_2O. The bigger gas-generators are operating with catalytic and thermic decomposition. The smallest generator supplies a cold-gas satellite attitude-control system, while the bigger types are for propellant-tank pressurisation.

MBB STORABLE ROCKET ENGINES

This engine family includes motors of 0·01/0·03/0·05/0·08/0·3/0·4/0·5/97·9 kN (2·2/6·6/11/18/66/88/110/22,000 lb) thrust. Except for the 0·01 kN (2·2 lb) engine, which uses MMH/N_2O_4, all other engines run on AZ50/N_2O_4. The 0·01 kN (2·2 lb) engine is in use as the attitude-control thruster for the Franco-German Symphonie communications satellite; it is designed for steady-state and pulse-mode operation. The 0·4 kN (88 lb) engine was the vernier for the German third stage of the ELDO-A launcher, and in modified form it was to be used as the apogee motor for ELDO-II. This engine is highly qualified and in several ELDO-A launches has operated in space without failure. A total of 135 was produced. In 1973 a new tactical missile engine was developed, operating at thrust levels of 23·5 kN (5,290 lb); 11·77 kN (2,646 lb); 7·85 kN (1,764 lb). The 98 kN (22,000 lb) engine was developed as the prototype power plant for an artillery rocket.

MBB HIGH-ENERGY ROCKET ENGINES

MBB has worked with the cryogenic propellant combination H_2/F_2 since 1962. After the installation of a fluorine liquefaction facility and a technology programme for a 0·3 kN (66 lb) engine, the development of a 4·9 kN (1,100 lb) engine started in 1967-68. It was the aim to use a cluster of two engines of this size as a 'kick stage' for space probes. The programme was discontinued after the first series of tests with regeneratively-cooled chambers had showed high combustion efficiency. The propellant combination H_2/O_2 was used from 1962 in three engine projects at the thrust levels of 0·3/6·67/9·34 kN (66/1,500/2,100 lb). The 66 lb H_2/O_2 engine was presented in 1966 as a flight prototype, the first cryogenic rocket engine in Germany. The engine incorporated integral propellant valves and an ignition system. In altitude-simulation tests a specific impulse of 415 s was achieved and multiple restart capability and throttleability were demonstrated. For possible post-Apollo programme participation, the 1,500 lb and 2,100 lb engines were developed in 1970-72. Both are regeneratively cooled, electrically ignited, restartable and pulsable (10Hz). They have high performance and a combustion efficiency of more than 98%. In 1972-73 an LH_2/LO_2 engine rated at 5·0 kN (1,125 lb) in vacuum conditions was developed for multiple-restart use in upper stages. This engine can be throttled over a range of 8 : 1 (possibly 10 : 1).

Since 1973, in partnership with SEP of France, MBB has developed the HM7 engine to power the third stage of the European Ariane space launch vehicle. This LH_2/LO_2 engine has a vacuum thrust of 60 kN (13,500 lb). Its regeneratively cooled thrust chamber of milled copper operates at a pressure of 30 bars (435 lb/sq in), and the specific impulse is 444. Total thrust-chamber weight is 63 kg (138·9 lb). The nozzle extension, with an area-ratio of 61, is dump-cooled with LH_2. By the start of 1977, a total of 220 firings had been completed on MBB's high-pressure test facility under sea-level and simulated altitude conditions. Thrust-chamber qualification was due in May 1977. SEP is Ariane propulsion prime contractor. MBB's role is to supply the thrust chamber and main propellant valves.

MBB HIGH-PRESSURE ENGINES

In the course of development of high-pressure liquid-rocket engines MBB developed a turbopump engine utilising staged combustion in 1963. This 49 kN (11,000 lb) lox/kerosene engine was the first to run in the western world, with turbine exhaust completely burned in the main combustor. It was designed for 96·5 bars (1,400 lb/sq in) abs and was throttleable at 14 : 1, and remains the first and most powerful turbopump rocket engine developed in Federal Germany since 1945.

For the storable propellants UDMH/N_2O_4 a 9·8 kN (2,200 lb) pressure-fed engine was developed and tested at chamber pressures of more than 193 bars (2,800 lb/sq in) abs to demonstrate high-performance injection systems and electroformed thrust-chamber technology for corrosive propellants.

MBB developed and fabricated some 133·44 kN (30,000 lb) H_2/O_2 engines designed for 270 bars (3,000 lb/sq in) abs. These were tested at Rocketdyne's facilities in California up to chamber pressures of 276 bars (4,000 lb/sq in) abs without failure. The electroforming thrust-chamber technology demonstrated in this programme is now the baseline for the Space Shuttle Main Engine of Rocketdyne (which see).

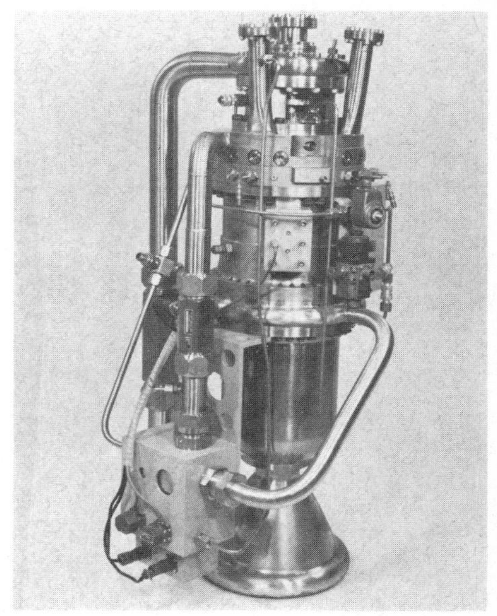

MBB 49 kN (11,000 lb) sea-level thrust lox/kerosene rocket engine

MBB RAM ROCKETS

Since 1965 MBB has been developing ram rocket engines with liquid and solid propellants, and liquid-fuelled ramjet engines, for the propulsion of missiles with supersonic cruise speed and long range capability.

MBB has studied high-energy boron propellants as well as medium-energy composite grains, UDMH, MMH and kerosene. For missile applications, studies were carried out with semi-integrated and fully integrated engines with many configurations of air inlet. These studies were supported by half-scale burning tests (net thrust 4·0 kN; 899 lb) and aerodynamic tests in wind-tunnels.

Solid-propellant ram rockets are inherently simple in structure and have high reliability because of hypergolic ram combustion.

MBB solid-propellant ram rocket on combustion test in a wind tunnel

MTU
MOTOREN-UND-TURBINEN-UNION MÜNCHEN GmbH

München-Allach, Dachauer Str 655 (postal address, 8 München 50, Postfach 50 06 40)
Telephone: (089) 1489-1
Board of Management MTU Group:
Dr Ernst Zimmermann (President)
Dr Hans Dinger (Executive Vice-President)
Dr Peter Beer
Hubert Dunkler
Dr Wolfgang Hansen
Günter Welsch

MTU München is owned half by Maschinenfabrik Augsburg-Nürnberg AG (MAN) and half by Daimler-Benz AG, and now manages all the aircraft engine programmes formerly managed by MAN Turbo and Daimler-Benz.

MTU handles service support for the J79-MTU-J1K/17A and T64-MTU-7 engines made by MTU under General Electric licence. It also handles service support and parts manufacture of such civil engines as the JT3D, JT8D and CF6, as well as Lycoming piston engines.

The MTU J79-MTU-J1K turbojet with afterburner

MTU/GE CF6

Under the terms of a licence agreement signed with the International General Electric Company, MTU has approximately a 10 per cent share in the manufacture of the CF6-50 engine for the Airbus A300, together with SNECMA. The main task of MTU is production of the complete HP turbine.

PRATT & WHITNEY JT10D

MTU is a partner, with Fiat of Italy, in this new turbofan described in the US part of this section.

ROLLS-ROYCE TYNE

MTU has a 28 per cent share in the production of a further batch of about 170 Tyne engines for the re-opened Transall production line. In addition MTU has assumed responsibility for service support of all Tyne 21 engines (Atlantic) and Tyne 22 (Transall), including engines used by civil operators.

TURBO-UNION RB.199

MTU München's largest programme is a 40 per cent share in this engine, more than 2,000 of which are now in production as described under Turbo-Union in the International part of this section.

SNECMA/TURBOMÉCA LARZAC

MTU has approximately a 25 per cent share in production of this French engine used in the Alpha Jet. MTU will also support the hot-end components for the Luftwaffe.

ALLISON 250-C20B

MTU is licence-producing 687 of these turboshaft engines, designated 250-MTU-C20B, for the PAH-1 and VBH helicopter programmes (see MBB in Aircraft section). MTU also suports C20 and C20B engines used by civil operators.

MTU/TURBOMÉCA MTM 380

This is a proposed new turboshaft for helicopters, especially the proposed PAH-2 anti-tank helicopter. Final drive from the power turbine would be via a co-axial shaft. Rated at 800 kW (1,100 shp) it is intended to offer direct competition to the Rolls-Royce Gem, in the production of which Turboméca shares. For further details see Addenda.

PARODI

ROLAND PARODI

Address: Klettgau-Erzingen

This engineer has developed a four-cylinder four-stroke aircooled piston engine for ultra-light aircraft and powered gliders. With various designations in the HP 45 series, these are derived from a Honda design, with a new crankcase and lubrication system. Crankshaft speed of 8,000 rpm is reduced by belt to about 2,800 at the propeller. Maximum ratings are 33·12 or 36·4 kW (45 or 50 hp).

PIEPER

PIEPER MOTORENBAU GmbH

Address: 495 Minden/Westf, Postfach 1229
Telephone: (0571) 34088

Pieper is manufacturing the 45 hp Stamo MS 1500-1 modified Volkswagen four-cylinder aircooled piston engine for the Scheibe SF-25B Falke two-seat powered glider. The capacity of this is 1,500 cc, compression ratio 7·2 : 1, length 640 mm (25 in), width 745 mm (29·3 in), height 395 mm (15·5 in), and dry weight 52 kg (115 lb). The MS 1500-1 operates on either 80/86 or 90 octane fuel, and is started by a pull-cord. Production has now also begun of the MS 1500-2, with electric starter and generator. This increases overall height to 450 mm (17·7 in) and dry weight to 60 kg (132 lb). By 1979 well over 600 engines had been delivered, and the period between complete overhauls had been extended to 1,000 h.

Pieper MS 1500-1 four-cylinder four-stroke engine, rated at 33·6 kW (45 hp)

PULCH

OTTO PULCH

Hölderlinstrasse 21, 7513 Spöck-Stutensee
Telephone: 07249-8509

PULCH 003

As a private venture Otto Pulch (OUV, EAA-Chapter 308) has developed a four-stroke radial piston engine for light aircraft. Using BMW motorcycle cylinders and pistons, he designed a new crankcase and connecting-rod assembly, reduction gear and dual ignition system. The first prototype Pulch 003A ran in Autumn 1976. In summer 1977 it was awarded the Wolf-Hirth-Preis by *Flug Revue* magazine as the most outstanding achievement in light aircraft technology in Germany in 1977. The second prototype Pulch 003B, incorporating substantial improvements, ran in 1978, and has a demonstrated noise level of only 96 dBA at full power at a distance of 10 m (33 ft). The 003B is described as "an ideal engine for homebuilt aircraft," and will be available in kit form.

Type: Six-cylinder radial aircooled piston engine.

Cylinders: Pulch 003A (BMW R 90/6), Bore, 90 mm (3·55 in). Stroke, 70 mm (2·76 in). Swept volume, 2,700 cc (165 cu in). Pulch 003B (BMW R 100S) Bore, 94 mm (3·71 in). Stroke, 70 mm (2·76 in). Swept volume, 2,900 cc (177 cu in).

Induction: Pulch 003A, two SUM carburettors. Pulch 003B, fuel-injection system, Bosch K-Jetronic.

Ignition: Both versions, electronic system.

Propeller Drive: Geared, ratio (003A) 2·29:1, (003B) 2·56:1.

Dimensions:
- Length overall:
  - Pulch 003A, 003B — 800 mm (31·5 in)
- Width overall:
  - Pulch 003A, 003B — 750 mm (29·55 in)

Weight, Dry:
- Pulch 003A — 110 kg (242·5 lb)
- Pulch 003B — 120 kg (264·5 lb)

Performance Rating (T-O):
- Pulch 003A — 110 kW (150 hp) at 5,000 rpm
- Pulch 003B — 132 kW (180 hp) at 5,500 rpm

PULCH THREE-CYLINDER

A new engine for motorised gliders was to run in Autumn 1979. It has three four-stroke BMW cylinders driving a vertical crankshaft and with 1:3 angle box to the propeller shaft. Swept volume is 1,500 cc (91·7 cu in) and rating 55 kW (75 hp).

Pulch 003A six-cylinder radial, to be rated at 110 kW (150 hp)

RFB

RHEIN-FLUGZEUGBAU GmbH
(Subsidiary of VFW-Fokker GmbH)

Head Office and Main Works: D-4050 Mönchengladbach 1, Flugplatz, Postfach 408
Telephone: (0 21 61) 662031
Officers: See Aircraft section

Though not a constructor of aircraft engines, Rhein-Flugzeugbau is marketing a Fan Pod as a complete unit for fitment to power-assisted sailplanes and ultra-light aircraft, as well as to surface vehicles.

RFB FAN POD SG 85

This is a fixed-geometry pod marketed as a complete unit for installation by the purchaser. It was run on the bench in 1974, with Fichtel & Sachs Wankel engines, and was subsequently flight tested in a Blanik sailplane. In certain types of motor-glider with side-by-side seating it should be possible to make the installation retractable.

Engine: Dual rotating-combustion (Wankel-type) engines mounted in tandem. Fichtel & Sachs KM 914/2 V-85 engines are regarded as standard, with a combined rating of 50 hp. Engines are equipped with 12V starter and generator, and with silenced exhaust system.

Fan Rotor: Three-blade fan moulded in Friedel-Krafts reinforced plastics material, with hard erosion-resistant strip along each leading-edge. Direct drive from engines without separate bearings. Rotating spinner.

Fan Duct: Single shell in FK sandwich reinforced plastics with PUR foam filling.

Pylon: Light alloy construction, with downward projecting spigot attachment 200 mm (8 in) long mating with airframe.

Fuel Grade: Automotive gasoline and oil mixture in ratio 30 : 1.

Dimensions:
- Length — 1,200 mm (47·24 in)
- Fan duct external diameter — 750 mm (29·53 in)
- Height, incl aircraft spigot — 1,000 mm (39·37 in)

L-13 Blanik motor-glider in sustained flight with RFB SG 85 fan pod

Weight, Dry: 56 kg (123·5 lb)

Performance Rating:
- Full throttle, S/L — 0·932 kN (209·5 lb st)

Fuel Consumption:
- At full throttle (5,500 rpm), S/L — 15 l (3·3 Imp gal)/h
- At cruise at 5,000 rpm, S/L — 11·5 l (2·5 Imp gal)/h

Noise (full throttle, from 305 m; 1,000 ft) — 57 dBA

Prototype installation of RFB fan pod SG 85, as mounted for flight testing on Blanik motor-glider (0·932 kN, 209·5 lb st at S/L)

INDIA

HAL
HINDUSTAN AERONAUTICS LTD

Indian Express Building, Vidhana Veedhi, PO Box 5150, Bangalore 560 001
Telephone: 76091
OFFICERS: See Aircraft section

The Bangalore and Koraput Engine Divisions of HAL comprise the main aero-engine design, development and manufacturing elements of the Indian aircraft industry.

BANGALORE COMPLEX (Engine Division)

This Division is engaged in the manufacture of gas-turbine engines. The Adour 804 engines for all except the initial batch of Jaguars for the Indian Air Force will be manufactured by HAL under Rolls-Royce/Turboméca licence. The Orpheus 701 to power the Ajeet and Kiran II, the Orpheus 703 to power the Marut and the Dart 531 to power the BAe 748 are made under licence from Rolls-Royce. The Artouste IIIB to power the Alouette III and SA 315 is made under licence from Turboméca. The division also overhauls Dart, Avon, Orpheus, Artouste, Gnome and J34 engines for the Indian Air Force and other customers.

KORAPUT DIVISION

This Division of HAL is located at Koraput in Orissa. It was established to manufacture under Soviet government licence the Tumansky R-11 afterburning turbojet for HAL-built MiG-21 fighters. With help from the Soviet Union, the first engine was run on the bench (which it was used to calibrate) in early 1969. The company declines to comment on widespread reports of subsequent licence-production of the R-11-F2S-300 and R-13 (SPS).

INDONESIA

LAPAN
LEMBAGA PENERBANGAN DAN ANTARIKSA NASIONAL
(The National Institute of Aeronautics and Space)

HEAD OFFICE: Jalan Pemuda Persil No 1, Jakarta Timur
MAILING ADDRESS: PO Box 3048, Jakarta
Telephone: (021) 48 28 02
CHAIRMAN: Air Vice-Marshal J. Salatun
VICE-CHAIRMAN: Prof Wiranto Arismunandar

PUSAT TEKNOLOGI DIRGANTARA
(Aerospace Technology Centre)

Rumpin Airfield, Bogor, West Java
HEAD, AEROSPACE TECHNOLOGY CENTRE: Dr Haryono Djojodihardjo
MANAGER, ROCKET DEVELOPMENT PROJECT: Ir Kisman Subandhi

LAPAN was established in 1963, to exploit indigeneous capabilities in aeronautics and space in support of the National Five Year Plan. At the beginning of 1978 LAPAN had 527 personnel, of whom 195 were university graduates, divided among the Space Applications Centre (Jakarta), the Aerospace Technology Centre (Rumpin Airfield, near Bogor), the Atmospheric and Space Research Centre (Bandung) and the Aerospace Study Centre (Jakarta).

In 1974 LAPAN began the design of the RC-741 liquid propellant rocket engine, the first prototype of which was completed in February 1978. The RC-741 is the first liquid-propellant rocket engine made in Indonesia. In early 1979 it was about to undergo static tests at LAPAN's Aerospace Technology Centre.

LAPAN RC-741

The RC-741 is designed for use in a boosted single-stage sounding rocket.

TYPE: Single-chamber liquid-propellant rocket engine.
PROPELLANTS: RFNA and xylidine, mixture ratio 3:1.
THRUST CHAMBER: Single chamber of 7:1 nozzle area ratio, using regenerative and radiative cooling, and with double-wall machined casing. Wall material nickel-chrome steel. Co-axial propellant injection, with hypergolic ignition. Combustion pressure 55·7 bars (808·28 lb/sq in) and temperature 2,700°C.
MOUNTING: Chamber bolted on four mountings concentric with engine axis.
PROPELLANT PUMPS: Centrifugal.
PROPELLANT FLOW: Fuel flow 2·45 kg (5·4 lb)/s; oxidiser flow rate 8·12 kg (17·9 lb)/s.
TURBINE: Single-stage axial impulse type.
THRUST CONTROL: Thrust held constant by regulation of turbopump speed via control of gas-generator propellant supply.

DIMENSIONS: Length overall	605 mm (23·819 in)
Diameter overall	210 mm (8·268 in)
WEIGHT, DRY:	41 kg (90·38 lb)
PERFORMANCE (S/L): Max thrust	2,100 kg (4,630 lb)
Specific impulse	240 s

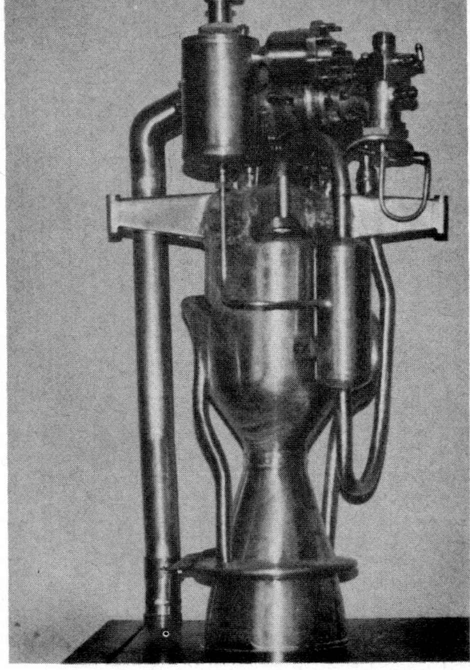

The LAPAN RC-741 liquid rocket engine (2,100 kg; 4,630 lb thrust)

INTERNATIONAL PROGRAMMES

CFM INTERNATIONAL
CFM INTERNATIONAL SA

160 Avenue de Versailles, 75016 Paris, France
Telephone: 524 43 62
CHAIRMAN AND CHIEF EXECUTIVE: J. C. Malroux
EXECUTIVE OFFICERS:
N. Epstein (Marketing and Product Support)
J. C. Malroux (acting) (Projects)
A. O. Kohn (Technical)
J. F. Sullivan (Finance)
T. G. Homburg (Logistic and Product Support Services)

CFM International, a joint company, was formed by General Electric and SNECMA in early 1974 to provide overall programme management for the CFM56 engine and a single customer interface for sales and service. Owned and managed on a 50/50 share basis, the company has been staffed with experienced people from the two parent companies.

In addition to the CFM International management team which directs the overall programme, the parent companies have their own CFM56 programme managers. For SNECMA, this position is held by J. Rossignol. His GE counterpart is R. B. Smith. The two men contribute to overall direction in conjunction with the Chief Executive.

The SNECMA/GE agreement is not a profit-sharing arrangement. Responsibilities for hardware design, development and production are assigned through CFM International on an equal basis to the parent companies. Each company then assumes responsibility and funding for its assigned task throughout the life of the programme. This is a unique concept among international co-operative ventures in the aerospace field. SNECMA has from the outset been agreeable to participation of other European engine companies within its 50 per cent share. FN of Belgium has joined SNECMA for certain low-pressure system components.

GE is responsible for design integration, the core engine and the main engine control. The core engine is that of the F101 turbofan developed for the B-1 bomber. SNECMA is responsible for the low-pressure system, reverser, gearbox and accessory integration and engine installation.

Each company is responsible for its assigned hardware from design through development, production and product improvement. CFM International will provide the planning and integration of the product support programme.

CFM INTERNATIONAL CFM56

In the late 1960s General Electric and SNECMA made independent studies of the market requirement for the next generation of high bypass ratio engines. The GE studies were centered around an engine designated GE13, the core of which is now being used in the F101. SNECMA's studies were based on an engine designated M56. Each company concluded that a large market existed for a high bypass ratio engine in the ten tonne class (97·86-106·76 kN; 22,000-24,000 lb st), with low noise, low emissions and low fuel consumption, coupled with ease of maintenance and low operating costs.

In April 1971 SNECMA began a search for possible partners to undertake development of a commercial engine in this class. By December 1971 SNECMA had chosen GE as its partner and, after obtaining French government approval, detailed design activity began. Work was stopped, however, in September 1972 when the export licence restriction applied by the US State Department Office of Munitions Control made the programme untenable for the two companies. It was not resumed on a joint basis until September 1973, when negotiations led to a workable licensing agreement which also protected US technology. Since that time, a working agreement and management structure have been defined and engine certification is scheduled for 1979, at the completion of 7,500 hours of development testing. Design targets include low noise characteristics below ICAO Annex 16, 1977 revision (CAN V), low emissions (to meet the lower EPA regulations expected to be in force at engine certification) and low fuel consumption, coupled with design simplicity.

The first CFM56 demonstrator engine ran at the GE Evendale plant on 20 June 1974. The engine reached its full rated thrust within 10 hours of running, with fuel consumption lower than specification. Since then, 11 more engines have entered the test programme. The engine first flew in a USAF YC-15 as part of the AMST development programme. Engine-development flight testing began in March 1977 when an engine installed with a full-length fan duct flew in a Caravelle at the SNECMA flight-test centre.

All certification ingestion tests have been completed. An aggressive programme of endurance testing is being followed, to complete more than 20,000 extra-severe cycles, simulating short-haul service, before entry into service. Noise testing has demonstrated predicted levels.

By the end of 1979 total running time will exceed 8,000 h. A total of 12 engines will be built for the development programme. CFM International has planned several versions of the CFM56. Ratings between 80 and 122 kN (18,000 and 27,500 lb st) have been projected within the existing fan diameter. In early 1979 four ratings were announced: The full level given below; a re-rating at 83·6 kN (18,800 lb); a thrust of 80·0 kN (18,000 lb) with smaller fan of 1·52 m (60 in) diameter; and the CFM56 DR-18 rated at 80·0 kN but with new lightweight fan of 1·4 m (55 in) diameter.

A development programme to flight-test the Model 707 aircraft with CFM56 propulsion is being carried out by Boeing. Other potential commercial applications are numerous. The engine size is ideal for derivative or re-engined versions of existing aircraft such as the DC-8-60 series, a four-engined A300 derivative, and the twin-engined BAe One-Eleven, DC-9, Boeing 737 and Mercure. Several airframe companies in the United States and Europe are developing preliminary designs in the two-, three- and four-engine categories for service in the 1980s

CFM56 engine 006 (97·86 kN; 22,000 lb st) prior to flight testing in Caravelle

and 1990s. In addition to this large commercial market, an extensive military market has been identified. The CFM56 has been offered for the proposed McDonnell Douglas C-15 transport, for retrofit in the US Air Force KC-135 tanker fleet, and is being considered for other military derivatives of the 707. It will be suitable for other military transport, patrol and tanker aircraft.

TYPE: Two-shaft turbofan for subsonic applications.

AIR INTAKE: Direct pilot entry, without inlet guide vanes.

FAN: Single-stage axial. Forged titanium disc holding 44 inserted titanium blades, each with a tip shroud to form a continuous peripheral ring. Fan and the attached LP compressor (booster) run in front roller bearing and rear ball bearing. Pointed conical spinner rotates with fan. Alloy steel fan frame of continuous ring construction, carried by 12 radial struts of low thickness/chord ratio well downstream of fan. Max airflow 376 kg (830 lb)/s. Bypass ratio 6 : 1.

LP COMPRESSOR: Three axial stages on titanium drum bolted to fan disc serve as booster to supercharge core. Downstream flow curves inwards to match diameter of HP compressor. In this section is main fan frame and sumps and bearings for front end of both shafts. Ring of bleed doors allows core airflow to escape into fan duct at low power settings. Bleed doors are closed at all normal flight power settings.

HP COMPRESSOR: Nine-stage axial with tapering tip diameter. Rotor of high-strength corrosion-resistant alloy, with blades of titanium (to stage 3) or steel. Stators steel, with first four stators variable. Split titanium front casing with steel liners. Based upon HP compressor of F101, with minor modifications. Overall pressure ratio in 25 : 1 class.

COMBUSTION CHAMBER: Fully annular with advanced film cooling. Based upon F101 combustor but modified for reduced emissions. Level of pollution from the core is claimed to be below that of any engine at present in airline service.

HP TURBINE: Single-stage axial with aircooled stator and rotor blades. Entry gas temperature in 1,260°C class. High stage loading. HP system carried in only two bearings.

LP TURBINE: Four-stage axial.

EXHAUST UNIT (FAN): Constant-diameter duct of sound-absorbent construction. Outer cowl and engine cowl form convergent plug nozzle, with airframe-mounted reverser.

EXHAUST UNIT (CORE): Fixed-area type with convergent plug nozzle. Sound-absorbent construction.

ACCESSORY DRIVE: Gearbox in front sump transmits drive from front of HP spool, via radial shaft in fan frame, to transfer gearbox mounted on underside of fan case. Drive faces on both front and rear sides. Air starter at transfer gearbox.

FUEL SYSTEM: Hydromechanical with electronic trim.

LUBRICATION: Non-pressure-regulated system.

DIMENSIONS:

Front flange diameter	1,828 mm (72·0 in)
Length, excl spinner	2,430 mm (95·7 in)

WEIGHT, DRY: 2,005 kg (4,420 lb)

PERFORMANCE RATINGS:

Max T-O 106·8 kN (24,000 lb st) flat rated to 30°C

Cruise at 9,144 m (30,000 ft) at Mach 0·80 28·26 kN (6,350 lb st)

SPECIFIC FUEL CONSUMPTION:

Cruise rating, as above 18·4 mg/Ns (0·65 lb/h/lb st)

GARRETT/VOLVO FLYGMOTOR

THE GARRETT CORPORATION

HEAD OFFICE: 9851 Sepulveda Boulevard, Los Angeles, California 90009, USA

Telephone: (213) 670-0131

VOLVO FLYGMOTOR AB

HEAD OFFICE: 461 81 Trollhättan, Sweden.

Telephone: 0520-30100

Agreement on co-operative development of a low bypass ratio derivative of the TFE731 turbofan engine (described under Garrett in the US section) was signed on 2 March 1978 in Trollhättan. The agreement was approved later by the US and Swedish authorities.

GARRETT/VOLVO FLYGMOTOR TFE1042

With this new engine the two parent companies are aiming at the market for the next generation of training, ground support, lightweight strike and fighter aircraft.

The TFE1042 will be offered at two ratings, one **(1042-5)** with a thrust of 16·15 kN (3,630 lb) at S/L ISA, and another **(1042-6)** with 18·95 kN (4,260 lb). This latter version will also be offered with an afterburner, giving 30·23 kN (6,800 lb) as the **1042-7**.

The engine will be developed around the core of the commercial TFE731 turbofan and will utilise the same accessory drive system. Garrett will provide the manufacturing facilities for all parts common to the two engine models, and will be responsible for the overall design. Volvo Flygmotor will be responsible for the detail design and manufacture of the uncommon parts, such as the new two-stage fan, fan gearbox and afterburner.

The first phase of the development programme was to lead to a prototype engine test in August 1979. Flight prototype engines can be made available in two years from the start, Saab-Scania having agreed to provide a flight-test aircraft.

TYPE: Two-shaft military turbofan, with geared front fan. Optional fully modulated afterburner.

AIR INTAKE: Direct entry, fixed, without inlet guide vanes.

FAN: Two-stage axial, with titanium inserted blades. Total airflows and by-pass ratios at max rating, S/L ISA, are: (1042-5) 33·6 kg (74·1 lb)/s, 0·84:1; (1042-6, -7) 35·6 kg (78·4 lb)/s, 0·70:1.

COMPRESSORS, COMBUSTION CHAMBER, FUEL SYSTEM; and ACCESSORY DRIVES: As TFE731

TURBINES: Single axial-HP stage with aircooled inserted blades and cooled nozzle guide vanes (basically as TFE731-33). Turbine inlet temperature for TFE1042-5 is similar to that of TFE731-3. For 1042-6 and-7, turbine temperature is increased, requiring cooling also of guide vanes and blades of first stage of three-stage LP turbine.

EXHAUST SYSTEM: Mixed fan and turbine exhaust discharged to atmosphere through common convergent nozzle. For augmented version, mixed streams pass through afterburner with outer casing of titanium and inner wall of special alloys. One high-energy spark igniter. Fuel-actuated fully-variable iris-type con-di nozzle. Aircraft-mounted digital system containing torque-motor valves for afterburner fuel metering and nozzle actuation.

MOUNTINGS: Main mount transmitting thrust, weight and moment is at front frame. Engine can be mounted from either side. Single mount on turbine casing for vertical loads only.

SHAFTING: HP spool consists of HP turbine and HP compressor, on shaft supported by one roller bearing and one ball bearing. This drives accessory gearbox through tower-shaft transfer box. LP spool consists of LP turbine and LP compressor, interconnected by curvic couplings and supported on one ball bearing at compressor and one roller bearing at turbine. Drives fan through reduction gear with ratio of 1·416:1. Fan shaft supported by roller bearing under first-stage fan disc and ball thrust bearing under second-stage disc.

DIMENSIONS:

Length:	
1042-5, -6	1,620 mm (63·75 in)
1042-7	3,545 mm (140 in)
Max diameter	676 mm (26·6 in)

WEIGHT, DRY:

1042-5	363 kg (800 lb)
1042-6	370 kg (815 lb)
1042-7	544 kg (1,200 lb)

PERFORMANCE RATINGS (SL, ISA):

Max T-O:	
1042-5	16·15 kN (3,630 lb st)
1042-6	18·95 kN (4,260 lb st)
1042-7 (dry)	18·37 kN (4,130 lb st)
1042-7 (augmented)	30·23 kN (6,800 lb st)

SPECIFIC FUEL CONSUMPTION (ratings as above):

1042-5	19·6 mg/Ns (0·692 lb/h/lb st)
1042-6	20·6 mg/Ns (0·728 lb/h/lb st)
1042-7 (dry)	21·2 mg/Ns (0·749 lb/h/lb st)
1042-7 (augmented)	63·5 mg/Ns (2·24 lb/h/lb st)

ROLLS-ROYCE/ALLISON

ROLLS-ROYCE LIMITED

HEAD OFFICE: 65 Buckingham Gate, London SW1E 6AT, England

THE DETROIT DIESEL ALLISON DIVISION, GENERAL MOTORS CORPORATION

HEAD OFFICE: Detroit, Michigan, USA

Co-operation between Rolls-Royce and Allison started in November 1958, when the two companies began work on the design and development of high-performance jet engines for commercial and military applications.

ALLISON/ROLLS-ROYCE TF41

Manufacturers' designations: Rolls-Royce Spey RB. 168-62 and -66, Allison Model 912-B3 and -B14

In August 1966 Allison and Rolls-Royce were awarded a joint contract by USAF Systems Command for the development and production of an advanced version of the RB.168-25 Spey turbofan, to power Vought A-7D Corsair II fighter-bomber aircraft for the USAF.

Development and production were undertaken jointly by Rolls-Royce and Allison, with Rolls-Royce supplying parts common to existing Spey variants and Allison, which is manufacturing under licence, being responsible for items peculiar to the TF41. This provided an approximately 50/50 division of manufacturing effort, but with Allison also undertaking assembly, test and delivery.

Design of the RB.168-62 started in June 1966 and, following the award of the USAF contract, the engine was given the USAF designation TF41-A-1. Major change compared with the RB.168-25 is the move forward of the bypass flow split into the LP compressor, to give a larger three-stage fan followed by a two-stage IP compressor, all five stages being driven by the two-stage LP turbine. The number of HP compressor stages is reduced from 12 to 11, the HP turbine remaining at two stages. These modifications raise the mass flow and the bypass ratio (from 0·7 : 1 to 0·76 : 1). No afterburner is fitted.

Other design changes compared with the RB.168-25 include omission of the fan inlet guide vanes, the first rotor stage being overhung on a bearing supported by the first-stage stator vanes. The fan and IP compressor are of more modern aerodynamic design, and the HP and LP turbine nozzle throat areas have been increased to pass the additional flow. The HP turbine is of modified aerodynamic design, and an annular exhaust mixer replaces the RB.168-25's chuted design.

First run of the TF41-A-1/RB.168-62 was at Rolls-Royce, Derby, in October 1967, the first Allison engine following at Indianapolis in March 1968.

A second version of the TF41 is the A-2, developed for the US Navy and ordered in 1968 to power the Vought A-7E Corsair. Differences are slight, although the thrust rating is appreciably increased by raising the engine speed. This required re-stressing the disc of the LP turbine and HP compressor. Mass flow is slightly increased, the bypass ratio being 0·74 : 1. The engine has additional protection against corrosion.

By 1977 more than 1,300 engines had been delivered, and production of the TF41 for the A-7 is expected to

Cutaway drawing of the Allison/Rolls-Royce TF41-A-1 (Spey RB.168-62) turbofan (64·5 kN; 14,500 lb st)

continue into the 1980s. In combat service both versions of the TF41 have shown outstanding reliability. The exceptional overhaul life (for a combat engine) of 1,500 h has been reached.

TYPE: Military turbofan.

AIR INTAKE: Direct entry, fixed, without intake guide vanes.

COMPRESSOR: Two-shaft axial. 3 fan stages, 2 intermediate stages on same shaft and 11 high-pressure stages. All rotor blades carried on separate discs. Fan and LP rotor blades of titanium, held by dovetail roots in slots broached in discs which are bolted together through curvic couplings and similarly attached to the stubshafts. HP rotor blades also of titanium, except stages 9, 10 and 11 of stainless steel, the first HP stage being pinned and the remainder being dovetailed into broached slots; discs similarly bolted together but driven through splined shaft coupling. Overall pressure ratio 20 : 1 (A-2, 21·4 : 1); mass flow 117 kg/s (258 lb/s) (A-2, 119 kg/s; 263 lb/s). HP compressor pressure ratio, 6·2 : 1; mass flow, 67 kg/s (148 lb/s).

COMBUSTION CHAMBER: Tubo-annular, with 10 interconnected Ni-Co alloy flame tubes in steel outer casing. Duple spray atomising burner at head of each chamber. High-energy 12-joule igniter plug in chambers 4 and 8.

FUEL SYSTEM: Hydromechanical HP system with automatic acceleration and speed control and emergency manual override. Variable-stroke dual fuel pump.

FUEL GRADE: JP-4 (A-2, JP-5).

NOZZLE GUIDE VANES: Two HP stages with air cooling; two LP stages uncooled.

TURBINE: Impulse-reaction axial type, two HP stages and two LP. All blades forged in Ni-Co alloy; first HP stage blades cooled internally by HP compressor air.

JET PIPE: Fixed, heat-resistant steel.

ACCESSORY DRIVES: External gearbox driven by radial shaft from HP system; provision for starter, fuel boost pump, two hydraulic pumps, HP fuel pump, fuel control, HP tachometer, CSD and alternator, permanent-magnet generator, LP fuel pump and oil pumps. Additional low-speed (LS) gearbox, driven from LP shaft, serving LP rotor governor and tachometer.

LUBRICATION SYSTEM: Self-contained, with engine-mounted tank, fuel/oil heat exchanger and gear type pump; pressure 3·45 bars (50 lb/sq in). Tank capacity: A-1, 4·5 litres (1·0 Imp gal); A-2, 10·3 litres (2·27 Imp gal).

MOUNTING: Main ball-type trunnions on compressor intermediate casing; rear tangential steady-type at rear of bypass duct.

STARTING: Integral gas turbine (air turbine).

DIMENSIONS:

Length overall	2,610 mm (102·6 in)
Intake diameter	953 mm (37·5 in)
Height overall	1,026 mm (40 in)

WEIGHT, DRY:

A-1	1,353 kg (2,980 lb)
A-2	1,370 kg (3,018 lb)

PERFORMANCE RATING (Max T-O):

A-1	64·5 kN (14,500 lb st) to ISA +8°C
A-2	66·7 kN (15,000 lb st) to ISA

SPECIFIC FUEL CONSUMPTION (Max T-O):

A-1	17·93 mg/Ns (0·633 lb/h/lb st)
A-2	18·33 mg/Ns (0·647 lb/h/lb st)

ROLLS-ROYCE/SNECMA

ROLLS-ROYCE LTD

HEAD OFFICE: 65 Buckingham Gate, London SW1E 6AT, England

Telephone: 01-222-9020

SOCIÉTÉ NATIONALE D'ÉTUDE ET DE CONSTRUCTION DE MOTEURS D'AVIATION

HEAD OFFICE: 2 Boulevard Victor, 75724 Paris cédex 15, France

Telephone: 554-92-00

Rolls-Royce Ltd and SNECMA were jointly responsible for the Olympus 593 turbojet of the Anglo-French Concorde supersonic transport. They also tested M45S series turbofan engines incorporating high bypass ratio geared fans with variable-pitch blades.

ROLLS-ROYCE/SNECMA M45SD-02 (RB.410D-2)

Ultra-quiet demonstrator engine based on M45H but driving Dowty Rotol variable-pitch fan. Joint programme by Rolls-Royce, Dowty Rotol and SNECMA, with funding shared by industry and the British government.

The demonstrator engine, designated M45SD-02 and with the Rolls-Royce project number of RB.410D-2, ran at the government engine test station at Aston Down, Glos, in April 1975. Since then the objectives of the test programme have been met, with noise measurement having been undertaken by SNECMA at their Istres facility. The engine is now stored awaiting a possible future test programme. This demonstrator engine fully verified the characteristics of the quiet geared variable-pitch turbofan (described in the 1978-79 *Jane's*). The 66·8 kN (15,000 lb st) RB. 410-11 could be a definitive version for civil and military R/STOL transports.

ROLLS-ROYCE/SNECMA OLYMPUS 593

The Olympus 593 was developed by Rolls-Royce Ltd in Britain and SNECMA in France as the power plant for the Concorde supersonic airliner. The work was shared on a 60%/40% basis, respectively. Rolls-Royce produced the gas generator and SNECMA the convergent/divergent exhaust nozzle, thrust reverser and afterburner system.

Full certification of the Olympus 593 Mk 610 was achieved in September 1975, when total running time exceeded 50,000 h. In January 1976, at the start of scheduled services by British Airways and Air France, more than 54,000 h had been run. This far exceeded the time logged by any other engine at the start of service (and does not include the much greater time logged by earlier Olympus engines). By the end of 1978 a further 82,800 h had been flown in scheduled service.

Details of the Olympus 593 were given in the 1978-9 *Jane's*.

ROLLS-ROYCE TURBOMÉCA

ROLLS-ROYCE TURBOMÉCA LIMITED

4/5 Grosvenor Place, London SW1, England

Telephone: 01-235-3641

This company was formed jointly by Rolls-Royce and Turboméca in June 1966 to control the design, development and production programmes for the Adour two-shaft turbofan. The main function of the company is to receive contracts from the British Ministry of Defence on the Adour for both the British and French governments. The company can also enter into commercial contracts for the sale of the Adour to customers other than the British and French governments and grant licences for its manufacture.

ROLLS-ROYCE TURBOMÉCA ADOUR

The Adour was designed originally for the SEPECAT Jaguar strike/trainer aircraft to meet requirements laid down by the British and French joint air and naval staffs. It is a two-shaft turbofan engine fitted with an integral, modulated afterburner of advanced design. The whole engine is simple and robust and contains features permitting modular exchange, major engine sections being replaceable in the field, avoiding the need for return to an overhaul base.

The complete propulsion unit has been designed for an overhaul life of 1,000 h. The engine temperatures and rotational speeds are moderate and a thrust growth of the order of 40 per cent within the confines of existing installations is envisaged.

Bench testing began at Derby on 9 May 1967. Engines are assembled at Derby (R-R) and Tarnos (Turboméca) from parts made at single sources in Britain and France. Turboméca makes the compressors, casings and external pipework (to preserve Anglo-French parity the afterburner is subcontracted to SNECMA); Rolls-Royce makes the remainder. By January 1979 total flight time exceeded 450,000 h on over 1,400 engines.

The Adour has been selected for the Japanese Mitsubishi T-2 trainer and F-1 fighter/support aircraft, and since 1970 Ishikawajima-Harima Heavy Industries has

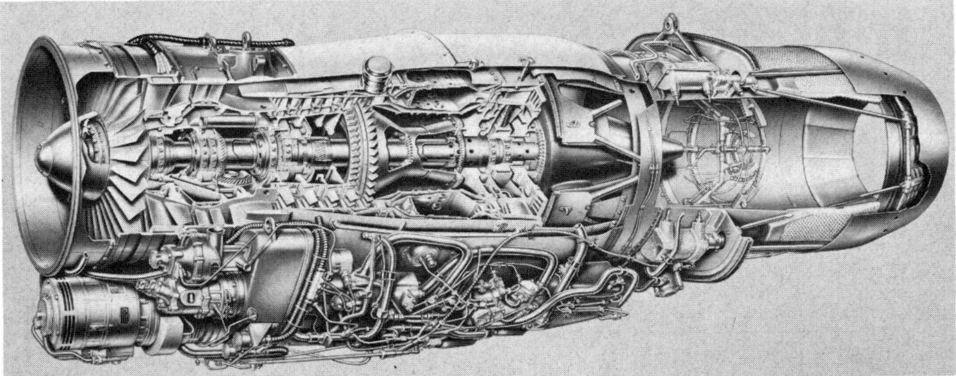

Cutaway drawing of the Rolls-Royce Turboméca Adour Mk 102 augmented turbofan (32·5 kN; 7,305 lb st)

been producing the Adour under a licence agreement. In 1972 a non-afterburning Adour was selected to power the British Aerospace (HS) Hawk advanced trainer. Further applications of the Adour are under consideration.

Current versions of the engine are as follows:

Adour Mk 102. Standard production engine for Jaguars in service with RAF and Armée de l'Air. Qualified in 1972.

Mk 104. Uprated RT.172-26 version similar to Mk 804; RAF Mk 102 engines are being converted to this standard.

Mk 151. Non-afterburning version for Hawk. Internal components and certification temperatures identical to Mk 102 and Mk 801A. Qualified in 1975.

Mk 801A. Japanese designation TF40-IHI-801A. Standard production engine for Mitsubishi T-2 and F-1. Qualified in 1972. (See Ishikawajima-Harima in Japanese section.)

Mk 804. Uprated engine for Jaguar International. Installationally interchangeable with Mk 102. General increase in thrust of some 10 per cent, with greater increase at high forward speeds (rating with full afterburner at Mach 0·9 at S/L, ISA increased by 27 per cent) giving improved aircraft performance throughout flight envelope. Qualified in 1976.

Mk 851. Non-afterburning version of Mk 804 for export Hawk; ordered by Finland and Indonesia.

RT.172-56. Further uprated for increased thrust and greatly reduced specific fuel consumption, with changed LP compressor blading and HP and LP turbines. Rated at 25·4 kN (5,700 lb st) at S/L. Has achieved guaranteed performance. Installationally interchangeable with earlier versions. For delivery in 1980.

RT.172-58. Augmented version of -56, with increased fuel flow to afterburner. Rated at 37·4 kN (8,400 lb st) at S/L. For delivery in 1980. Powers Indian Jaguar; engines supplied initially from Europe but later to be assembled by Hindustan Aeronautics with increasing Indian-manufactured content.

Further versions of the Adour, giving substantial increases in thrust, are projected.

The following description refers to the Adour Mk 102:

TYPE: Two-shaft turbofan for subsonic and, with augmentation, supersonic aircraft.

INTAKE: Formed by forward extension of fan casing. No radial struts or inlet guide vanes.

FAN: Two-stage. Rotating spinner, anti-iced by turbine-bearing cooling air, on front of first-stage disc. Individually replaceable blades with no part-span or tip shrouds. Fixed stators and exit vanes. Whole unit overhung ahead of front LP roller bearing of squeeze-film type. Full-length by-pass duct leading to afterburner. By-pass ratio, 0·80 : 1.

COMPRESSOR: Five-stage compressor on HP shaft. Large-diameter double-conical shaft for rigidity with bolted curvic couplings. Wide-chord blades of titanium. Steel stator blades. Overall pressure ratio 11 : 1.

COMBUSTION CHAMBER: Annular, with straight-through flow. Fitted with 18 air-spray fuel nozzles and two igniter plugs. Engine fuel system by Lucas GTE.

HP TURBINE: Single-stage, aircooled.

LP TURBINE: Single-stage. Both turbine bearings of squeeze-film type.

JET PIPE: Fully modulated afterburner of compact, short-length design incorporating four concentric but staggered spray rings and vapour gutters. Catalytic igniters between inner gutters. Variable nozzle has eight master and eight slave petals positioned by eight-sided frame moved axially by four fuel-operated nozzle rams. Afterburner fuel flow and nozzle system by Dowty Fuel Systems, with vapour-core pump.

DIMENSIONS:

Inlet diameter (all)	559 mm (22 in)
Max width (all)	762 mm (30 in)
Max height (all)	1,041 mm (41 in)
Length:	
Mks 102, 801A, 804	2,970 mm (117 in)
Mks 151, 851	1,956 mm (77 in)

WEIGHT, DRY: See table

PERFORMANCE RATINGS: See table

SPECIFIC FUEL CONSUMPTION (Mk 102):

S/L static, dry 21 mg/Ns (0·74 lb/h/lb st)

Mach 0·8, 11,890 m (39,000 ft) 27 mg/Ns (0·955 lb/h/lb st)

Rolls-Royce Turboméca Adour 151 for British Aerospace (HS) Hawk T.1, rated at 23·12 kN; 5,200 lb st

Version	Application	Weight dry kg (lb)	Max S/L thrust kN (lb st)
* Mk 102	Jaguar	755 (1,665)	32·5 (7,305)
Mk 151 (Mk 851 export)	Hawk	595 (1,312)	23·1 (5,200)
* Mk 801A (TF40-IHI-801A)	T-2, F-1	755 (1,665)	32·5 (7,305)
* Mk 104 (RT.172-26, Mk 804)	Jaguar	767 (1,690)	35·6 (8,000)
RT.172-56		655 (1,444)	25·4 (5,700)
* RT.172-58		780 (1,720)	37·4 (8,400)

* afterburning versions

ROLLS-ROYCE TURBOMÉCA RTM 321

Several sources have reported joint engineering development of this turboshaft engine in the 1,120/1,490 kW (1,500/2,000 shp) class. An obvious application would be the WG.34 Sea King Replacement helicopter. Neither engine manufacturer had made an announcement by April 1979, but see Addenda.

TURBO-UNION

TURBO-UNION LTD

PO Box 3, Filton, Bristol BS12 7QE, England

Munich Office: 8 Munich 81, Arabellastrasse 4/7, Federal Republic of Germany

Telephone: 0272-693871

Formed in October 1969, this international company was established to manage the entire programme for the RB.199 engine for the Panavia Tornado multi-role combat aircraft. Shares are held in the ratio Fiat Aviazione SpA, 20 per cent; MTU München GmbH, 40 per cent; Rolls-Royce Ltd, 40 per cent. The stated intention is that the overall work-share shall be in proportion to the numbers of aircraft bought by the three partner countries.

TURBO-UNION RB.199

A three-shaft augmented turbofan of extremely advanced design, the RB.199 has a lightweight fan based on that of the Pegasus on a reduced scale, an advanced afterburner designed for an extremely wide operating envelope, and an integral thrust-reverser. The RB.199 offers low fuel consumption for long-range dry cruise, even at sea level, and approximately 100 per cent thrust augmentation with full afterburner for combat manoeuvre and supersonic acceleration. Further design goals included minimal weight and frontal area, moderate first cost and economic maintenance and overhaul. Strip, inspection and rebuild are facilitated by modular construction, and by the use of advanced manufacturing techniques to reduce the number of separate components.

The first RB.199 ran in September 1971. Flight testing began in April 1973 with an engine installed in a dummy portion of the Tornado, complete with inlet and duct system and 27 mm Mauser gun, carried beneath a Vulcan flying test bed.

The first Tornado flew on 14 August 1974. Aircraft P.02 flew at Warton on 30 October 1974. By that time more than 2,000 hours had been logged in static testing and 320 hours of subsonic flight with the Vulcan. Afterburner light-up has consistently been exemplary, and as early as January 1974 main-engine relight had been demonstrated 1,525 m (5,000 ft) higher than demanded by specification for entry into service, and 3,050 m (10,000 ft) higher than specification for initial flying. The 150 hr FQT (Formal Qualification Test) was completed in November 1978.

The following are principal existing or projected versions of the RB.199 which have been announced officially or unofficially:

RB.199-34R. Designation of the basic engine adopted to power the Tornado. The released figures for performance given later apply to this engine in Mk 101 form.

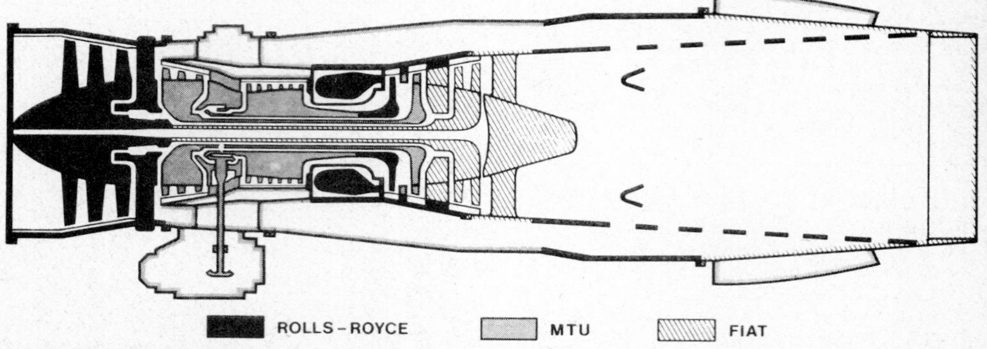

Simplified section through Turbo-Union RB.199 showing portions for which each company is responsible

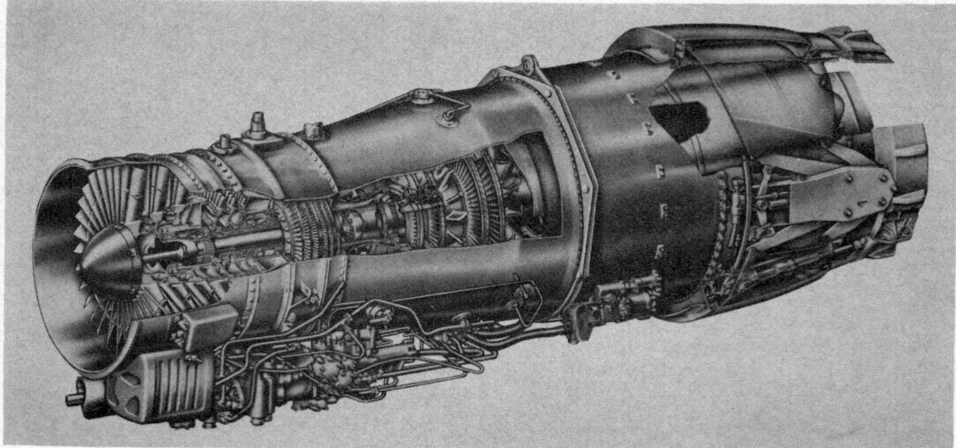

Cutaway drawing of Turbo-Union RB.199-34R three-shaft augmented turbofan

RB.199-01. Initial engine used in flight development. For prototype flight clearance a reduced performance was accepted, dry thrust being 11 per cent below that required for FQT and maximum augmented thrust 19 per cent below; both figures were well within the allowed limits.

RB.199-02. Has an increased annulus area in IP and LP turbines, achieved by minor redesign of the blades within the existing turbine casing. In addition to improving the development potential of the engine, the immediate effect was to enable the engine to deliver increased thrust at existing temperatures. A bench engine built to the -02 standard had demonstrated final FQT specification thrust, both dry and with afterburner at lower turbine gas temperatures than had previously been achieved. It had demonstrated an sfc 5·0 per cent better than that achieved with any -01 engine, and an afterburning sfc better than that required for FQT.

RB.199-03. Embodies significant improvements to fan and afterburner, giving increased performance. Tornado flying with -03 engines began in March 1977, and engines to this standard powered most Tornado flying throughout 1978.

RB.199-04. Flight-development version corresponding to initial production standard; entered Tornado flying programme in March 1978.

RB.199 Mk 101. This designation applies to the initial production-standard engine, as ordered in July 1976. During 1978 the first production engines were delivered, and Tornado flying with production engines began in October 1978.

RB.199 derivatives. Versions are being considered for air-superiority fighters and, without afterburner, for various applications including trainer and attack aircraft.

RB.199 uprated. Turbo-Union is reported to have studied an advanced RB.199 rated at 79·6 kN (17,900 lb st) with maximum augmentation. Such an engine could power later Tornado versions or the projected Hindustan HF-73. A third potential application is in developments of the McDonnell Douglas/Northrop F-18.

The following description refers to the RB.199-34R Mk 101:

Type: Three-shaft augmented turbofan with integral afterburner and reverser.

Intake: Annular with no inlet guide vanes.

Fan: Three-stage axial, aerodynamically derived from that of Pegasus. Discs and blades of titanium alloy. Maximum air mass flow approx 70 kg (154 lb)/s. Bypass ratio more than 1 : 1.

IP Compressor: Three-stage axial. Rotor and casing of titanium alloy.

HP Compressor: Six-stage axial. Overall pressure ratio greater than 23 : 1.

Combustion Chamber: Annular, with vaporising burners. Combustion without visible smoke.

HP Turbine: Highly loaded single stage with advanced cooling techniques. Entry gas temperature over 1,327°C.

IP Turbine: Single-stage axial, with cooled rotor blades.

LP Turbine: Two-stage axial.

Jet Pipe: Close-coupled afterburner, giving fully modulated augmentation. Maximum gas temperature over 1,627°C. Convergent fully variable final nozzle with minimised base area, matched to wide range of flight conditions. Nozzle flaps actuated by four screwjacks driven by an air motor via a translating shroud.

Reverser: Target type, with upper and lower clamshells driven by an air motor.

Accessories: Radial shaft drives packaged external gearbox carrying hydromechanical portion of main and afterburner fuel system. Fuel control of advanced electronic type. Engine gearbox mechanically connected to aircraft gearbox and KHD starter gas-turbine.

Dimensions:
Max diameter 870 mm (34·25 in)
Overall length approx 3,200 mm (126 in)

Weight, Dry: approx 816 kg (1,800 lb)

Performance Ratings:
T-O dry over 35 kN (8,000 lb) st
T-O with max afterburning over 66 kN (15,000 lb) st

ISRAEL

BET-SHEMESH
BET-SHEMESH ENGINES LTD

Mobile Post Haela, Bet-Shemesh
Telephone: 02-911661-2

The first section of a 12,077 m² (130,000 sq ft) Israeli aero-engine factory, Bet-Shemesh Engines Ltd, was inaugurated officially on 15 January 1969. The company was owned 49 per cent by the Israeli government and 51 per cent by Turboméca SA and the manufacturing plant was based on the Turboméca factory at Tarnos. On 1 January 1977 Israel Aircraft Industries (IAI) took over the Israeli shareholding and assumed responsibility for management. Over the subsequent year the number of employees increased from 550 to more than 800.

At first Bet-Shemesh manufactured turboprop components on behalf of Turboméca. By 1973 complete Marboré VI turbojets for CM 170 Super Magister trainers were being produced. The company also manufactures parts of the Marboré II, Artouse II and III, Turmo II and Astazou II. Today the plant is the centralised source for all aircraft gas-turbine manufacture in Israel; but it has not been disclosed whether Bet-Shemesh plays any role in providing or supporting J79 engines. The company is unofficially reported to have been developing the M-6F, a turbofan based on the Marboré and rated at 15·1 kN (3,400 lb st).

ITALY

ALFA-ROMEO
SOCIETÀ PER AZIONI ALFA-ROMEO

Via Gattamelata 45, 20149 Milan
Telephone: Milan 3977
Aviation Works: 80038 Pomigliano D'Arco, Naples
Telephone: 8841 344

Alfa-Romeo participated in the European production programme for General Electric J79-GE-11A turbojets to power Lockheed F-104G Starfighters. It is collaborating with Rolls-Royce in the manufacture and overhaul of Gnome H.1000, H.1200 and H.1400 turboshafts. A licence agreement has also been signed for the manufacture of General Electric T58 and T700 turboshafts.

Alfa-Romeo was prime contractor for the manufacture, under General Electric licence, of the J85-GE-13A turbojet to power the G91Y aircraft. It is manufacturing the hot section of the J79-GE-19 turbojet for the F-104S, as well as many parts for the J79-11B, -17 and -1K. Alfa-Romeo manufactures CF6 combustors under subcontract to General Electric; assembles the kits and overhauls P&WC PT6T engines for the AB 212 helicopter; under GE licence it is responsible for the hot section of the T64-P4D turboprop co-produced with Fiat; and participates in development and hot-section component manufacture for the Turbo-Union RB.199 for the Panavia Tornado. The company would probably be a major partner in Italian development and licence production of the Rolls-Royce Spey 807 for the AMX aircraft. It is continuing to study a gas turbine engine in the 373 kW (500 hp) class for general aviation use (see Rolls-Royce Alfa-Romeo RB.318 in UK part of this section).

The company overhauls many engines of Rolls-Royce, General Electric and Pratt & Whitney manufacture.

Alfa-Romeo is a member of the Finmeccanica-IRI group of companies.

CSTM
CENTRO STUDI TRASPORTI MISSILISTICI (Missile Transport Research Centre)

Head Office: Via Squarcialupo 19-A, 00162 Rome
Telephone: 423.833
President: Glauco A. Partel

CSTM has begun work on the P-77 self-pressurised monopropellant rocket engine. Starting and reaction is by a special heating system.

FIAT
FIAT AVIAZIONE SpA

Via Nizza 312, 10127 Torino, Italy
Telephone: (011) 6399
Telex: 23320 Fiatavio
Chairman: C. E. Rossi
Managing Director: G. C. Boffetta
Production Director: S. Innocenti Torrini
Design and Engineering Director: L. La Rocca

Fiat Aviazione SpA was incorporated in 1976 as a wholly Fiat-owned company. It took over all the aero-engine activities carried out formerly by the Fiat Aviation Division, and the participation in Turbo-Union Ltd and Turbomotori Internazionale, as well as control of Motoravio Sud at Brindisi where overhaul of jet and piston engines and construction of jet engine parts are carried out.

Fiat's main aircraft engine programmes now concern the Turbo-Union RB.199, Rolls-Royce Viper 600, Pratt & Whitney JT10D and General Electric J79, J85, CF6 and T64, all of which are referred to below. In addition the company overhauls many types of engine, including the J79 and Orpheus, and the R-2800 piston engine. It is engaged in the design, development and production of the LM 2500 marine gas turbine, in collaboration with General Electric, and the design and production of main gearboxes for Aérospatiale helicopters.

TURBO-UNION RB.199

Fiat holds 20 per cent of the shares of Turbo-Union Ltd, the joint company set up to produce the RB.199-34R engine for the Panavia Tornado. Fiat's responsibility is the LP turbine and shaft, exhaust diffuser, jetpipe and nozzle. The programme is described under Turbo-Union in the International part of this section.

PRATT & WHITNEY JT10D

Since 1974 Fiat has been responsible for design and development of the accessory drive gearbox for the Pratt & Whitney JT10D civil turbofan engine. The programme is described under Pratt & Whitney in the US part of this section.

GENERAL ELECTRIC CF6

Fiat is engaged in the manufacture of components for the CF6 civil turbofan for both General Electric and SNECMA. For GE the company supplies complete accessory gearboxes, transfer gearboxes, inlet gearboxes and shafts. SNECMA is supplied with various gearbox components and shafts for CF6-50 engines for the Airbus A300.

GENERAL ELECTRIC T64-P4D

This free-turbine turboprop powers most versions of the Aeritalia G 222 military transport aircraft. Under a licence agreement between the General Electric Company and the Italian government, the engine is being manufactured in Italy under the leadership of Fiat as prime contractor.

GENERAL ELECTRIC J79-19

This afterburning turbojet powers most versions of the Lockheed F-104S fighters of the Italian Air Force. Fiat, as prime contractor for Italy, produced the engine under a licence agreement between the General Electric Company and the Italian government.

GENERAL ELECTRIC J85-13

With Alfa-Romeo as prime contractor, Fiat participated in production under licence of the J85-13A, power plant of the Aeritalia G91Y aircraft.

ROLLS-ROYCE VIPER 600

Development of this turbojet for business aircraft and military trainers is in collaboration with Rolls-Royce. Fiat's responsibility extends to all components rearward of the compressor housing (except turbine discs and blades), together with the exhaust assembly and silencer designed to meet noise legislation. The Viper 600 is described in the Rolls-Royce entry in this section.

PIAGGIO
INDUSTRIE AERONAUTICHE E MECCANICHE RINALDO PIAGGIO SpA

Head Office: Viale Brigata Bisagno 14, 16129 Genoa (426)
Telephone: 540 521
Works and Officers: See Aircraft section

The Aero Engine Division of Piaggio is currently manufacturing the following engines under various licence agreements: Rolls-Royce Viper 11, 526, 540 and 632-43 turbojets to power the Aermacchi M.B. 326 and 339 and Piaggio PD-808 (a sublicence for the manufacture of the Viper 11 and 540 was issued to Atlas Aircraft to power South African-built M.B. 326 aircraft); Avco Lycoming T53-L-13A and L-13B and T55-L-11A turboshaft engines ordered by the Italian government for installation in Bell 204B/205 and CH-47C Chinook helicopters, respectively; and Lycoming VO-435 and GSO-480 piston engines.

SNIA VISCOSA
DEFENCE AND SPACE DIVISION

Via Sicilia 162, 00187 Rome
Telephone: (06) 4680
Telex: 610114 SNIA
FACTORIES: Colleferro (Rome) and Ceccano (Frosinone)
DIVISION MANAGER: Ing E. Svizzeretto
CHIEF OF ROCKET, MISSILES AND SPACE R & D DEPARTMENT: Ing P. Laurienzo

The SNIA Viscosa Defence and Space Division is engaged in the production of conventional ammunition and the research, design and production of solid propellants, solid-propellant rocket motors, complete rockets and missiles, as well as air-to-surface and surface-to-surface unguided weapons. It possesses all necessary installations for the production of double-base solid propellants. Composite solid-propellant grains and motors incorporating polyurethane or polybutadiene polymers as binder are also produced in all sizes.

Complete propulsion units of up to 1,500 mm (59 in) diameter, with combustion times ranging from a fraction of a second to about 1 minute, are manufactured by SNIA Viscosa's Defence and Space Division for use in military rockets and missiles.

SNIA's Defence and Space Division produced the motors for the Italian Sparrow air-to-air missile programme, and developed an advanced motor for the Aspide air-to-air missile, now coming into the production phase. The Division is also involved in the development of many weapon systems in co-operation with such companies as MBB, OTO Melara, Breda Meccanica Bresciana and Sistel.

In the space field, a new amagnetic high-performance apogee motor, with a titanium-alloy case and improved polybutadiene propellant, was developed and qualified for the Italian Sirio experimental satellite successfully launched in August 1977. The solid-propellant apogee motor for the GEOS satellite, developed and qualified in co-operation with SEP of France, has operated twice successfully, in April 1977 and July 1978. For OTS and Meteosat, a high-performance apogee motor with carbon-fibre case was qualified by a consortium formed by SNIA, SEP and MAN. The same consortium has since begun development of a larger apogee motor for Ariane payloads. SNIA has also completed, on behalf of CNES, the development and qualification of retro and ullage motors for the separation of all three stages of the Ariane vehicle.

JAPAN

IHI
ISHIKAWAJIMA-HARIMA JUKOGYO KABUSHIKI KAISHA (Ishikawajima-Harima Heavy Industries Co Ltd)

HEAD OFFICE: No 2-1, 2 chome, Ohte-Machi, Chiyoda-ku, Tokyo
AERO ENGINE AND SPACE DEVELOPMENT GROUP: 3-5-1, Mukodai-cho, Tanashi-shi, Tokyo 188
Telephone: (0424) 66-1252
PRESIDENT: Dr Hisashi Shinto
EXECUTIVE VICE-PRESIDENT: Dr Osamu Nagano
MANAGING DIRECTOR AND GENERAL MANAGER, AESD GROUP: Dr Kaneichiro Imai

In February 1960 IHI began the licence production of General Electric J79-IHI-11A turbojet engines for Japanese-built Lockheed F-104J Starfighters.

Under further licensing agreements with General Electric, IHI is producing the J79-IHI-17 turbojet for the McDonnell Douglas F-4EJ, the T58 turboshaft for helicopters and other applications, including the propulsion of air cushion vehicles and hydrofoil boats, and the T64-IHI-10 turboprop engine to power the JMSDF's PS-1 anti-submarine flying-boat and US-1 search and rescue amphibian, and the Kawasaki P-2J maritime patrol aircraft. By January 1979 deliveries totalled 664 T58s, 376 T64s and 571 J79s.

The manufacture of the Rolls-Royce Turboméca Adour augmented turbofan in Japan under licence agreement received government approval in September 1970. Its production began in early 1973, under the Japanese designation TF40-IHI-801A, to power the supersonic T-2 trainer and F-1 fighter.

IHI was nominated in 1978 as prime contractor of Pratt & Whitney F100 engines for the F-15 fighter and Allison T56 engines for the Lockheed P-3C. Kawasaki and Mitsubishi will be subcontractors.

IHI undertakes overhaul and repair of Pratt & Whitney JT8D and Rolls-Royce RB.211 commercial turbofans, and General Electric J79, T58 and T64, and R-R Turboméca TF40 military engines, and Turboméca Artouste and Astazou turboshafts.

Prior to the start of licence production, in April 1959, IHI had been responsible for the J3 turbojet engine which had been under development by the Nippon Jet-Engine Company since 1956. The J3-IHI-7 version is installed in Fuji T-1B intermediate jet trainer and Kawasaki P-2J aircraft.

IHI participated in developing the XJ11 liftjet, as well as the JR100 and JR200 built under supervision of the NAL. In addition, in collaboration with Mitsubishi and Kawasaki, IHI made the prototypes of the FJR710 turbofan. The JR100, JR200 and FJR710 are described in the NAL entry.

IHI is co-operating with JDA in the development of small turbofans in the 11·8 kN (2,645 lb) thrust class.

IHI F3 (CFJ 810)

This new military turbofan was unveiled at the International Gas Turbine Conference in England in April 1978. Development had begun just two years earlier, with funding by the JDA's Technical Research & Development Institute. The initial Phase I (XF3) form has a single-stage fan with bypass ratio of 1·9, five-stage transonic compressor, 12-burner combustion chamber and single-stage HP and LP turbines. Rating in this form is to be 11·79 kN (2,650 lb st). Later, a more powerful Phase II engine (XF3-20) is to have a two-stage fan, two-stage LP turbine and higher turbine temperature. This engine, rated at 13·7 kN (3,080 lb st), was expected to begin air-testing in a C-1 transport in 1979. The eventual version is intended for the MT-X twin-engined trainer, at a rating of 15·66 kN (3,520 lb st).

For possible civil applications, a derivative engine with single-stage fan of 3:1 bypass ratio is planned under the designation CFJ810. It would be rated at 14·68 kN (3,307 lb st).

Ishikawajima-Harima J3-IHI-7C turbojet engine (13·7 kN; 3,090 lb st)

IHI J3

The J3-IHI-7C is a derivative of the J3-1, of which a description appeared in the 1959-60 *Jane's,* under the entry for 'Nippon Jet-Engine Company'. It is installed in the Kawasaki P-2J aircraft currently in service with the JMSDF, and is in production. By September 1978 deliveries totalled 239.

An experimental version with augmentation reached a thrust of 20·2 kN (4,542 lb) during bench tests in December 1972. The J3-IHI-7D is an uprated version (15·2 kN, 3,415 lb st), which is replacing the -7C in P-2J aircraft.

The following data apply to the J3-IHI-7C:

TYPE: Axial-flow turbojet.
AIR INTAKE: Annular nose air intake. Anti-icing system for front support struts.
COMPRESSOR: Eight-stage axial-flow type, built of Ni-Cr-Mo steel. Rotor consists of a series of discs and spacers bolted on to shaft. Rotor and stator blades of AISI 403 steel. Stator blades brazed on to fabricated base which is fixed in casing with circumferential T-groove. Rotor blades dovetailed to discs. Light alloy casing in upper and lower sections, flange-jointed together. Pressure ratio 4·5 : 1. Air mass flow 25·4 kg (56 lb)/s.
COMBUSTION CHAMBER: Annular type. AISI 321 steel outer casing. L 605 steel flame tube. Thirty fuel supply pipes located in combustion chamber outer casing and 30 vaporiser tubes located at front of flame tube. Ignition by low-voltage high-energy spark plug in each side of combustion chamber.
FUEL SYSTEM: Hydromechanical, with IHI FC-2 fuel control.
FUEL GRADE: JP-4.
NOZZLE GUIDE VANES: Single row of aircooled fabricated vanes.
TURBINE: Single-stage axial-flow type. Disc bolted to shaft. Precision-forged blades.
BEARINGS: Rotating assembly carried in front (double ball) and rear (roller) compressor rotor bearings and rear (roller) turbine shaft bearing.
JET PIPE: Fixed-area type.
ACCESSORY DRIVES: On gearbox under compressor front casing.
LUBRICATION SYSTEM: Forced-feed system for main bearings and gear case. Dry sump. Vane-type positive displacement supply and scavenge pump.
OIL SPECIFICATION: MIL-L-7808.
MOUNTING: Three-point suspension, with one pickup by a pin on starboard side of compressor front casing and a trunnion on each side of the compressor rear casing.
STARTING: Electrical starter in intake bullet fairing.
DIMENSIONS:
- Length, less tailpipe — 1,661 mm (65·4 in)
- Length overall with rear cone — 1,994 mm (78·5 in)
- Diameter overall — 627 mm (24·7 in)
- Frontal area — 0·28 m² (3·01 sq ft)

WEIGHT, DRY:
- Bare — 380 kg (838 lb)
- With accessories — 430 kg (948 lb)

PERFORMANCE RATING:
- T-O — 13·7 kN (3,090 lb st)

SPECIFIC FUEL CONSUMPTION:
- At T-O rating — 29·74 mg/Ns (1·05 lb/h/lb st)

OIL CONSUMPTION:
- At normal rating (max) — 0·60 litres (1·06 Imp pints)/h

IHI TF40-IHI-801A

This is the Rolls-Royce Turboméca Adour augmented turbofan engine, as built under licence by IHI. For details see Rolls-Royce Turboméca entry in International section.

KAWASAKI
KAWASAKI JUKOGYO KABUSHIKI KAISHA (Kawasaki Heavy Industries Ltd)

2-16-1 Nakamachi-Dori, Ikuta-ku, Kobe
Telephone: Kobe (078) 341-7731
WORKS: Akashi, Hyogoken
OFFICERS: See Aircraft section

Kawasaki's factory at Akashi started repair, overhaul and component manufacturing for aircraft engines, on behalf of the US armed forces and the Japan Defence Agency, in 1953. Since then, it has overhauled more than 11,500 engines, mainly of the Allison J33, General Electric J47, Rolls-Royce Orpheus, Westinghouse J34, and Kawasaki KT5311A and KT5313B series. Since 1968 the company has also been making spare parts for the J33, and since 1973 for the Orpheus.

In 1967, under a licence agreement with Avco Lycoming, Kawasaki started manufacturing T53 turboshaft engines. Deliveries of the resulting KT5311A, KT5313B and T53-K-13B engines totalled 230 units by early 1979.

Kawasaki shares in parts manufacturing for the Pratt & Whitney F100 engine for the F-15 fighter and the JT8D engines produced by MHI for the Kawasaki C-1 medium-range military transport aircraft, and also for the Rolls-Royce Turboméca Adour produced by IHI for the Mitsubishi T-2 supersonic trainer and F-1.

MITSUBISHI

MITSUBISHI JUKOGYO KABUSHIKI KAISHA (Mitsubishi Heavy Industries Ltd)

Head Office: 5-1, Marunouchi 2 chome, Chiyoda-ku, Tokyo 100

Engine Works: Daiko Plant, Nagoya Aircraft Works, 1-1, Daiko-cho, Higashi-ku, Nagoya 455

Telephone: Nagoya (052) 721-3111

Komaki North Plant, Nagoya Aircraft Works, 1200, Higashi-Tanaka, Komaki-Shi, Aichi 485

Telephone: Komaki (0568) 79-2111

Officers: See Aircraft section

Since 1952 Mitsubishi has been responsible for the repair and overhaul of engines of the Japan Defence Agency and domestic and foreign airlines.

In 1967 Mitsubishi resumed its activity in the aviation gas-turbine field by undertaking manufacture of the CT63 turboshaft engine to power Hughes 369HM helicopters of the JGSDF under a licence agreement with Allison. A total of 217 engines were delivered to the Japan Defence Agency by March 1978. In 1972, under licence agreement with Pratt & Whitney Aircraft, Mitsubishi began the manufacture of the JT8D-M-9 turbofan. The first was delivered in January 1973. By 1980 a total of 71 engines are to be delivered to the Japan Defence Agency for use in the Kawasaki C-1 military transport. Deliveries by September 1978 had reached 63.

In collaboration with IHI and Kawasaki, Mitsubishi participates in the FJR710 turbofan programme (see NAL entry).

NAL

NATIONAL AEROSPACE LABORATORY

Address: 1880 Jindaiji-machi, Chofu City, Tokyo

Telephone: 0422-47-5911

Director: Toshio Kawasaki

Head of Aero-Engine Division: Masakatsu Matsuki

The National Aerospace Laboratory (NAL) is a government establishment responsible for research and development in the field of aeronautical and space science. Since 1962 it has extended its activity to include V/STOL techniques. The decision was made in that year to initiate development of an engine to fulfil the requirement for a lightweight lift-jet power plant for VTOL aircraft.

The more advanced NAL/IHI JR200 was developed in 1966, the NAL/IHI JR220 was completed in 1971.

In 1971 the Agency of Industrial Science and Technology, Ministry of International Trade and Industry (MITI), funded a high by-pass ratio turbofan engine (FJR710) development programme. NAL has completed the basic design of this engine, and many component tests are being made at NAL. The FJR710 is being developed by an industry consortium comprising IHI, Kawasaki and Mitsubishi, in co-operation with NAL and MITI.

MITI/NAL FJR710 two-shaft turbofan (49 kN; 11,025 lb st)

MITI/NAL FJR710

In the late 1960s the Japanese government and industry, seeking an engine programme that might remain competitive for many years, decided to embark on the design of a subsonic turbofan of high by-pass ratio. After a preliminary study by the NAL, funding was provided by the Ministry of International Trade and Industry in 1971 for a prototype demonstrator and test programme.

NAL has managed the design of the resulting FJR710. Manufacture of the prototype and development engines was subcontracted to IHI, Kawasaki and Mitsubishi. The first engine made its first run in May 1973. By the end of 1978 six engines (three FJR710/10 and three FJR710/20 with small changes) had run a total of 1,300 hours. Tests completed included 150-hour endurance and low-cycle fatigue. In November 1977 high-altitude performance testing was successfully completed at the NGTE in Britain.

In the 1978-79 *Jane's* brief details were given in the Addenda of the more powerful FJR710-600; but NAL has deleted all mention of this, saying only "the first engine of the second phase ran in December 1978". NAL makes no mention of the proposed C-1 testbed, rebuilt with upper-surface blowing from four FJR710-20s. The current test programme is hoped to lead to a production engine in the 44·5-66·8 kN (10,000-15,000 lb st) class.

The following description applies to the prototype engine, and is provisional:

Type: Two-shaft high by-pass ratio turbofan for subsonic commercial or military aircraft.

Air Intake: Direct annular entry around fan spinner.

Fan: Single-stage fan, with rotating spinner and inserted titanium blades with part-span shrouds. Metal fan duct held by eight aerofoil struts, preceded by ring of flow-straightening vanes. By-pass ratio 6·5 : 1.

Compressor: Mechanically independent HP compressor. Multi-stage axial assembly with inserted blades of titanium and, at delivery end, high-nickel alloy. Several rows of variable stator blades held in upper and lower half-casings and operated by peripheral rings scheduled by hydraulic ram.

Combustion Chamber: Smokeless annular type.

Turbine: Two-stage HP gas-generator turbine with cooled blades. Multi-stage LP fan turbine.

Jet Pipe: Fixed area.

Dimensions (approx):

Length	3,300 mm (130 in)
Diameter	1,520 mm (60 in)

Weight, Dry: 980 kg (2,160 lb)

Performance Ratings (ISA):

T-O 49 kN (11,025 lb st)

Cruise at 6,100 m (20,000 ft) at Mach 0·7 16·7 kN (3,748 lb st)

Specific Fuel Consumption:

T-O	9·83 mg/Ns (0·347 lb/h/lb st)
Cruise, as above	17·7 mg/Ns (0·623 lb/h/lb st)

NAL/IHI JR200 and JR220

Following work on the NAL/IHI JR100, NAL designed and developed the higher-thrust NAL/IHI JR200 of improved thrust/weight ratio, and this was manufactured by IHI. Development has now been suspended.

An improved version, the NAL/IHI JR220 with higher pressure ratio and higher turbine entry temperature, is under initial development.

The following details relate to the JR200:

Type: Single-shaft axial lift-jet.

Air Intake: Forward-facing annular type.

Compressor: Five-stage axial unit of 4 : 1 pressure ratio and 37·2 kg (82 lb)/s air mass flow at 12,450 rpm. Air bleed 3 kg (6·6 lb)/s.

Combustion Chamber: Annular type.

Turbine: Single-stage axial unit with 850°C entry temperature.

Jet Pipe: Fixed area.

Weight, Dry: 127 kg (280 lb)

Performance Ratings:

Max without air bleed	20·4 kN (4,585 lb st)
Max with air bleed	17·8 kN (4,012 lb st)

Specific Fuel Consumption:

At max rating, without air bleed 32·0 mg/Ns (1·13 lb/h/lb st)

At max rating, with air bleed 33·2 mg/Ns (1·17 lb/h/lb st)

XENOAH

XENOAH COMPANY

Head Office: 2-142-1 Sakuragaoka, Higashiyamato, Tokyo 189

This company produces a range of small high-speed two-stroke piston engines which have gained wide acceptance for the propulsion of many kinds of vehicles, and for other applications. They are being used in a number of ultra-light aircraft of both homebuilt and factory-built types.

XENOAH G72C-C

This engine has been type-tested by the JCAB and FAA (Pacific-Asia) and was certificated by the JCAB on 24 July 1978; FAA certification followed on 5 June 1979.

Type: Three-cylinder aircooled two-stroke piston engine.

Cylinders: Bore 72·0 mm (2·835 in). Stroke 59·5 mm (2·342 in). Swept volume 726·7 cc (44·34 cu in). Compression ratio 7·0.

Induction: Three Mikuni VM34SS float-type carburettors with mixture control. Two Mikuni DF52-501 fuel pumps. One Mikuni 4M-501 oil injection pump.

Fuel Grade: 100/130 octane gasoline and Shell Super two-stroke oil injected separately into induction system.

Ignition: Dual capacitor-discharge.

Exhaust System: 3:1 manifold and tuned silencer.

Starting: Hitachi SI 08-62 electric starter, 12V, 1kW.

Accessories: Optional Mitsubishi 14V 35A alternator and mounting bracket for instrument vacuum pump.

The Xenoah G72C-C three-cylinder engine

DIMENSIONS:
Length with exhaust manifold 564 mm (22·2 in)
Width including carburettors 443 mm (17·44 in)
Height overall (incl plugs) 390 mm (15·35 in)
WEIGHT, DRY:
Bare 59·4 kg (131 lb)
With exhaust system, silencer, starter, alternator and vacuum pump 71·2 kg (157 lb)

PERFORMANCE RATING:
Max T-O 44·8 kW (60 hp) at 6,080 rpm
Max continuous 40·3 kW (54 hp) at 6,080 rpm

SPECIFIC FUEL CONSUMPTION:
Max at 75% power (33·6 kW; 45 hp) 135 μg/J (0·8 lb/h/hp)

FUEL CONSUMPTION:
Max at 75% power 22·5 litres (4·95 Imp gallons; 5·95 US gallons)/h

POLAND

PZL
POLSKIE ZAKLADY LOTNICZE

HEADQUARTERS: ul. Miodowa 5, 00251 Warsaw

SALES REPRESENTATIVE: Pezetel, ul. Przemyslowa 26, 00450 Warsaw

Telephone: Warsaw 285071

The entire Polish aircraft industry is subordinate to the Zjednoczenie Przemyslu Lotniczego i Silnikowego PZL (Aircraft and Engine Industry Union). Pezetel handles all export sales of Polish aeronautical material.

BORZECKI
JOZEF BORZECKI

Wroclaw, ul. Sernicka 20/4

BORZECKI 2RB

The 2RB is a small piston engine designed and built by J. Borzecki for use in motor gliders. The prototype was built in 1970 and in the same year underwent bench tests. A flat-four, it may be used with tractor or pusher propeller. The engine began flight testing in early 1972 in the Borzecki Alto-Stratus motor glider. Development is continuing. The engine is based on the Riedel engine used to start German turbojets in World War 2.

TYPE: Four-cylinder two-stroke horizontally-opposed air-cooled piston engine.

CYLINDERS: Bore 70 mm (2·76 in). Stroke 35 mm (1·38 in). Swept volume 540 cc (33 cu in). Compression ratio 7·2 : 1. Aluminium alloy cylinders and heads attached to crankcase by four studs. Steel liners.

PISTONS: Aluminium alloy, with two compression rings.

CONNECTING RODS: Milled from steel.

CRANKSHAFT: Steel shaft, supported in four ball bearings and one ball-thrust bearing at the front.

CRANKCASE: Aluminium alloy case, divided at the vertical longitudinal and transverse centrelines with aft cover.

INDUCTION: Jawa 250 motor-cycle carburettor.

FUEL: Mixture of 76 octane petrol and oil.

IGNITION: Battery ignition. One M14-250 14 mm (0·55 in) sparking plug per cylinder.

MOUNTING: Four rubber dampers at rear of crankcase or four studs at cylinder heads.

PROPELLER DRIVE: Direct tractor or pusher.

DIMENSIONS:
Length overall, with propeller boss 450 mm (17·7 in)
Width 250 mm (9·8 in)
Height, with carburettor 260 mm (10·2 in)
WEIGHT, DRY: 15 kg (33 lb)
PERFORMANCE RATINGS:
T-O 17·9 kW (24 hp) at 6,000 rpm
Continuous 12 kW (16 hp) at 4,500 rpm

The Borzecki 2RB light piston engine

SPECIFIC FUEL CONSUMPTION:
At max T-O rating 145·3 μg/J (0·86 lb/h/shp)
At continuous rating 126·75 μg/J (0·75 lb/h/shp)

IL
INSTYTUT LOTNICTWA (Aeronautical Institute)

HEADQUARTERS: Al. Krakowska 110/114, 02-256 Warsaw-Okecie

Telephone: Warsaw 460993

MANAGING DIRECTOR: Dr Ing Andrzej Wierzba

DEPUTY DIRECTOR: Dipl Ing Jerzy Grzegorzewski

CHIEF OF TECHNICAL INFORMATION DIVISION: Dipl Ing Andrzej Glass

The Aeronautical Institute is an establishment concerned with aeronautical research, aerodynamic tests, strength tests, test flights of aeroplanes, helicopters and gliders, aviation equipment, materials, technical information and standardisation. The Institute has a special manufacturing plant responsible for constructing prototypes to its own design.

IL SO-1

The Aeronautical Institute designed the SO-1 turbojet to power the Polish TS-11 Iskra (Spark) jet basic trainer. It was designed to permit the full range of aerobatics, including inverted flight. Guaranteed overhaul life is 200 hours. Production was handled by the WSK-Rzeszów, as noted in that organisation's entry.

TYPE: Single-shaft axial-flow turbojet.

AIR INTAKE: Annular intake casing manufactured as a cast shell. Fixed inlet guide vanes.

COMPRESSOR CASING: Manufactured as a cast shell in two parts, split along horizontal centreline, in aluminium alloy.

COMPRESSOR: Seven-stage axial-flow compressor. Drum-type rotor built up of disc assemblies, with constant diameter over tips of rotor blades. Carried in ball bearing at front and roller bearing at rear. Steel stator blades bonded with resinous compound into slots in carrier rings. Rotor of steel and duralumin, with first three blade rows of steel and remainder of aluminium alloy. Pressure ratio 4·8.

COMBUSTION CHAMBER: Annular type with 24 integral vaporisers. Outer casing made of welded steel.

FUEL SYSTEM: Two independent systems supplied by one pump. Starting system consists of six injectors, with direct injection. Main system consists of twelve twin injectors with outlets towards the vaporisers.

IL SO-1 turbojet (9·8 kN; 2,205 lb st), initial power plant of the TS-11 Iskra (Spark) trainer *(BIIL)*

FUEL SPECIFICATION: Kerosene P-2 or TS-1.

TURBINE: Single-stage axial-flow type. Blades attached to disc by fir-tree roots. Supported in roller bearing at rear.

JET PIPE: Outer tapered casing and central cone connected by streamlined struts. Nozzle area adjusted by exchangeable inserts.

LUBRICATION SYSTEM: Open type for rear compressor and turbine bearings, supplied by separate pumps. Closed type for all other lubrication points, fed by separate pumps.

OIL SPECIFICATION: Type AP-26 (synthetic).

ACCESSORY DRIVES: Gearbox mounted at bottom of air intake casing and driven by bevel gear shaft from front of compressor.

STARTING: 27V starter/generator and bevel gear shaft, driven by aircraft battery or ground power unit, mounted on air intake casing.

DIMENSIONS:
Length overall 2,151 mm (84·7 in)
Width 707 mm (27·8 in)
Height 764 mm (30·1 in)
WEIGHT, DRY: 303 kg (668 lb)
PERFORMANCE RATINGS:
T-O 9·8 kN (2,205 lb st) at 15,600 rpm
Max cont 8·7 kN (1,958 lb st) at 15,100 rpm
SPECIFIC FUEL CONSUMPTION:
At T-O rating 29·6 mg/Ns (1·045 lb/h/lb st)
OIL CONSUMPTION: 0·8 litres (1·4 Imp pints)/h

IL SO-3

This improved version of the SO-1 replaced the earlier type in production at the WSK-Rzeszów. The SO-3 is intended for tropical use and incorporates minor changes in compressor, combustion chamber and turbine, data remaining the same as for the SO-1. It is fitted to all current versions of the TS-11. TBO has been doubled, to 400 hours. In 1978 the improved SO-3B was on test.

JANOWSKI
JAROSLAW JANOWSKI

Lodz 11, ul. Nowomiejska 2/29

JANOWSKI SATURN 500

The Saturn 500 was designed by Mr Jaroslaw Janowski and built by Mr S. Polawski for the Janowski J-1 ultra-light amateur-built aircraft (see Homebuilt section). The prototype Saturn 500 was built in 1969. This two-cylinder two-stroke engine may be used with tractor or pusher propeller, and is intended for ultra-light aircraft built by amateurs.

In 1972 work began on a new version of the Saturn 500, with new cylinder heads, improved crankshaft and dual ignition. Its rating (max T-O) is increased to 30 hp; dry weight is believed to be about 25 kg (55 lb).

The following description applies to the initial 25 hp version:

TYPE: Two-cylinder two-stroke horizontally-opposed air-cooled piston engine.

CYLINDERS: Bore 70 mm (2·76 in). Stroke 65 mm (2·56 in). Swept volume 500 cc (30·5 cu in). Compression ratio 8·5 : 1. Steel barrels with aluminium alloy cylinder heads. Cylinder and head assembly attached to crankcase by four studs.

PISTONS: Of aluminium alloy. Two compression rings and one oil scraper ring.

CONNECTING RODS: Steel forgings.

CRANKSHAFT: Steel counterbalanced shaft, supported in two lead-bronze plain bearings and one ball-thrust bearing at the front.

CRANKCASE: Aluminium alloy case, split in the vertical plane, with front and aft covers.

INDUCTION: Two BVF 28N1 carburettors.

FUEL: Petrol/oil mixture using aviation 90 octane.

IGNITION: Two magnetos. One M14-250 14 mm (0·55 in) sparking plug per cylinder.

MOUNTING: Four rubber dampers at rear of crankcase.

PROPELLER DRIVE: Direct tractor or pusher.
DIMENSIONS:
 Length overall, with propeller boss 430 mm (16·93 in)
 Width, without sparking plugs 515 mm (20·27 in)
WEIGHT, DRY: 27 kg (59·5 lb)
PERFORMANCE RATING:
 T-O 18·65 kW (25 hp) at 4,000 rpm
SPECIFIC FUEL CONSUMPTION:
 Max T-O rating 118·23 μg/J (0·70 lb/h/hp)
 Normal cruising power 111·48 μg/J (0·66 lb/h/hp)

Saturn 500 two-cylinder two-stroke engine designed by Jaroslaw Janowski

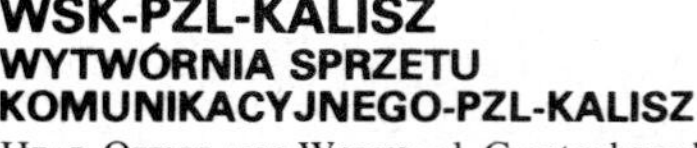

WSK-PZL-KALISZ
WYTWÓRNIA SPRZETU KOMUNIKACYJNEGO-PZL-KALISZ

HEAD OFFICE AND WORKS: ul. Czestochowska 140, 62800 Kalisz
Telephone: 74081, 74091
GENERAL MANAGER: Dipl Ing Henryk Jaruzel

In 1952 the Soviet Union transferred responsibility for manufacture and service support of Soviet aircooled radial piston engines to the WSK (transport equipment manufacturing centre) at Kalisz.

Current production is centred on: the 1,000 hp ASh-62IR (Polish designation ASz-62IR) for all versions of the An-2; and the 260 hp AI-14RA for the PZL-104 Wilga (see Aircraft section). Production of the ASz-62IR exceeds 14,000 engines. WSK-Kalisz has developed a version of the AI-14 with electric starter, the AI-14RC.

PZL (IVCHENKO) AI-14R

The original 260 hp AI-14R version of this nine-cylinder aircooled radial engine has been produced in very large quantities, in both the Soviet Union and Poland. Since 1960 several later versions have gone into production in the Soviet Union for fixed-wing aircraft and helicopters. Both of the following were developed at Kalisz.

AI-14RA. Basic production engine, rated at 194 kW (260 hp); fitted to Yak-12, Yak-18, PZL-101A Gawron and PZL-104 Wilga 3.

AI-14RC. Version fitted with electric starter.

The following description refers to the AI-14RA:

TYPE: Nine-cylinder single-row aircooled radial, geared and supercharged.
CYLINDERS: Bore 105 mm (4·125 in). Stroke 130 mm (5·125 in). Displacement 10·16 litres (620 cu in). Nitrided steel barrel; cast light alloy head incorporating air starting valve. Two spark plugs and single inlet and exhaust valves. Compression ratio 5·9.
PISTONS: Aluminium forgings, each with two chromium-plated compression rings, upper oil control ring with slot and, on skirt, tapered scraper ring.
CONNECTING RODS: One master rod, with lead-bronze big-end bearing; eight link rods articulated by steel cemented knuckle pins fixed in the master-rod cheeks against rotation and secured laterally by retaining strips.
CRANKSHAFT: Heat-treated steel in two parts, the front portion being gripped in the split cheek of the rear portion and held by a pinch bolt. Both portions carry a counterweight, the rear counterweight being pendulous type which balances inertia forces and also serves as vibration damper. Shaft held in two main roller bearings and ball thrust bearing in crankcase front cover.
CRANKCASE: Front and rear forgings in heat-treated light alloy, joined by nine bolts. At the rear a mixture collector receives the mixture from the supercharger.
VALVE GEAR: Each valve is opened by push/pull rod, from a cam plate geared to rotate in opposition to the crankshaft.
INDUCTION SYSTEM: Carburettor type, with choke tube upstream of supercharger.
FUEL GRADE: 70 to 100 octane.)

PZL AI-14RA piston engine

SUPERCHARGER: Aluminium forged impeller.Magnesium cast diffuser
LUBRICATION: Gear-type pressure and scavenge pumps.
IGNITION: Left magneto serves front plugs, right serves rear; automatic timing and fully screened.
PROPELLER DRIVE: Three planetary gears, ratio 0·787.
STARTING: By compressed air from airborne or ground compressor or bottle-fed through distributor to cylinder-head valves (and to purge lower cylinders of drained liquid).
DIMENSIONS:
 Diameter 985 mm (38·78 in)
 Length 956 mm (37·63 in)
WEIGHT, DRY 197 kg (434 lb)
PERFORMANCE RATINGS:
 Max T-O 194 kW (260 hp) at 2,350 rpm
 Cruise (60% max continuous) 98·4 kW (132 hp) at 1,730 rpm
SPECIFIC FUEL CONSUMPTION:
 Max T-O 95-104·3 μg/J (0·562-0·617 lb/h/shp)
 Cruise 76·4-83·8 μg/J (0·452-0·496 lb/h/shp)

PZL (SHVETSOV) ASz-62R

Power plant of the An-2 transport biplane, the ASz-62R is a 1,000 hp nine-cylinder aircooled radial engine. It was developed from the Wright Cyclone R-1820 by Arkadiya Shvetsov's bureau in the Soviet Union, as the ASh-62. Several variants have been built in the Soviet Union, including the ASh-62IR/TK driving a turbo-compressor to maintain 850 hp up to a height of 9,500 m (31,000 ft).

ASz-62IR. Standard power plant of the Li-2 (Soviet DC-3) and all versions of the An-2 except for the An-2M. Transferred to WSK-PZL-Kalisz in 1959.

All versions have a cylinder bore of 155·5 mm (6⅛ in), swept volume of 29·87 litres (1,823 cu in) and compression ratio of 6·4 : 1.

PZL ASz-62IR piston engine

The planetary reduction gear has a ratio of 0·637 : 1.
DIMENSIONS:
 Length overall, without power take-off 1,130 mm (44·50 in)
 Diameter 1,375 mm (54·13 in)
WEIGHT, DRY:
 Without power take-off 567 kg (1,250 lb)
PERFORMANCE RATINGS:
 T-O 1,000 hp at 2,200 rpm
 Rated power 820 hp at 2,100 rpm
 (75% power) 615 hp at 1,910 rpm
 Max continuous (90% power) 738 hp at 2,030 rpm
 Cruise (50% power) 410 hp at 1,670 rpm
SPECIFIC FUEL CONSUMPTION:
 T-O 112 μg/J (0·661 lb/h/shp)
 Cruise 80 μg/J (0·474 lb/h/shp)

WSK-PZL-RZESZÓW
WYTWÓRNIA SPRZETU KOMUNIKACYJNEGO-PZL-RZESZÓW

HEAD OFFICE AND WORKS: ul. Obrońców Stalingradu 120, 35078 Rzeszów, Postbox 340
Telex: 83411
GENERAL MANAGER: Dipl Ing Jozef Rokoszak

WSK-Rzeszów, founded in 1938 as PZL-Rzeszów, at first produced Bristol Pegasus and Walter Junior and Minor engines under licence. After World War 2 the works expanded considerably. The first product was the Soviet M-11D, followed by series production of the ASz-62IR and LiT-3 piston engines and HO-10 and SO-1 turbojets.

Current production is centred on: the Soviet-designed GTD-350 turboshaft, together with WR-2 reduction gear for Mi-2 helicopters; the tropicalised SO-3 turbojet for the TS-11 Iskra trainer; and the PZL-3S piston engine for agricultural aircraft. The SO-3 is described (with the SO-1) on an earlier page, under the heading IL.

PZL GTD-350

The GTD-350 is a free-turbine helicopter power plant. In the version used in the twin-engined Mi-2, the drive is taken from the rear, with the twin jet pipes of each engine exhausting to port (port engine) and starboard (starboard engine). The GTD-350 can be supplied with downward-facing jet pipe and with drive from the front, if required.

PZL (Isotov) GTD-350 turboshaft engine (322 kW; 431 shp)

Though developed and initially produced by the Isotov bureau in the Soviet Union, it is now in production only in Poland. WSK-Rzeszów has developed a new version rated at 358 kW (480 shp) designated GTD-350P. TBO of the GTD-350 is 3,000 hours, and work is in hand to extend it.

TYPE: Axial/centrifugal-flow free-turbine turboshaft engine.
AIR INTAKE: Annular intake casing and inlet guide vanes of

stainless steel. Automatic de-icing of inlet guide vanes and central bullet by air bleed from compressor.

Compressor: Seven axial stages and one centrifugal stage, all of steel, connected together with a tie-bolt. Discs shrunk-fitted to shaft. Blades of axial stages have dovetail roots. Shaft carried in front roller bearing and rear ball bearing. Pressure ratio 6·05 : 1. Air mass flow 2·19 kg (4·83 lb)/s at 45,000 rpm.

Compressor Casing: Horizontally-split aluminium alloy casing, with stator blades brazed to semi-rings. No diffuser blades.

Combustion Chamber: Reverse-flow type with air supply through two tubes. Centrifugal duplex single-nozzle burner. Ignition system comprises burner and semiconductor spark-plug. Eight thermocouples at gas outlet.

Fuel System: Includes NR-40TA pump governor with shut-off cock, which feeds fuel to burner, controls gas-generator rpm and limits max output; RO-40TA power turbine rpm governor, DS-40 signal transmitter controlling bleed valves; and electromagnetic valve to provide fuel for starting. Provision against power-turbine overspeed and (GTD-350P only) helicopter transmission overload.

Fuel Grade: TS-1 or TS-2.

Compressor Turbine: Single-stage turbine with aircooled disc. Shrouded blades with fir-tree roots. Precision-cast fixed guide vanes. Turbine casing has metal-graphite insert in plane of blades. Shaft supported in ball bearing at rear. Temperature before turbine 970°C (GTD-350P, 985°C).

Power Turbine: Two-stage constant-speed type (24,000 rpm). Shrouded blades with fir-tree roots. Discs bolted together. Stator blades welded to rings. Airflow is again reversed aft of power turbine.

Jet Pipes: Two fixed-area jet pipes.

Reduction Gearing: Two sets of gears, with ratio of 0·246 : 1, in cast magnesium alloy casing. Output shaft speed, 5,900 rpm.

Lubrication System: Closed type. Gear-type pump with one pressure and four scavenge units. Nominal oil pressure 2·94±0·5 bars (43 lb/sq in). Oil cooler and oil tank, capacity 12·5 litres (2·75 Imp gallons), fitted to airframe.

Oil Grade: B3-W (synthetic).

Accessories: STG3 3kW starter/generator, NR-40T governor pump, D1 tachometer generator and oil pumps mounted on reduction gear casing and driven by gas-generator. RO-40T rotating speed governor, D1 tachometer generator and centrifugal breather, also mounted on reduction gear casing, driven by power turbine.

Starting: STG3 starter/generator suitable for operation at up to 4,000 m (13,125 ft) altitude.

Dimensions:
- Length overall: 1,385 mm (54·53 in)
- Max width: 520 mm (20·47 in)
- Width (with jet pipes): 626 mm (24·65 in)
- Max height: 630 mm (24·80 in)
- Height (with jet pipes): 760 mm (29·9 in)

Weight, Dry:
- Less jet pipes and accessories: 135 kg (298 lb)

Performance Ratings:
- Max contingency at 97% max gas-generator rpm:
  - GTD-350: 322 kW (431 shp)
  - GTD-350P: 358 kW (480 shp)
- T-O rating (6 min) at 94% max gas-generator rpm:
  - GTD-350: 295 kW (395 shp)
  - GTD-350P: 331 kW (444 shp)
- Nominal rating (1 h) at 89% gas-generator rpm:
  - GTD-350: 235 kW (315 shp)
  - GTD-350P: 257 kW (345 shp)
- Cruising rating (II)
  - 210 kW (281 shp) at 86·5% gas-generator rpm
- Cruising rating (I)
  - 173 kW (232 shp) at 83·5% gas-generator rpm

PZL-Franklin 6AS-350A with turbocharger

Specific Fuel Consumption:
- T-O: 136 μg/J (0·805 lb/h/shp)
- Nominal: 146 μg/J (0·861 lb/h/shp)
- Cruising (II): 154 μg/J (0·913 lb/h/shp)
- Cruising (I): 165 μg/J (0·978 lb/h/shp)

Oil Consumption:
- Max: 0·3 litres (0·53 Imp pints)/h

PZL-3S

With ancestry going back via the LiT-3 to the AI-26W, this radial was the only type in its class to be developed in the 1970s. It has an FAA Type Certificate and Polish CACA certificate to BCAR. Applications include the PZL-106A Kruk, and conversions of the Grumman Ag-Cat and Rockwell Thrush Commander.

Type: Seven-cylinder aircooled radial.

Cylinders: Bore 155·5 mm (6·12 in). Stroke 155 mm (6·1 in). Swept volume 20·6 litres (1,265 cu in). Compression ratio 6·4 : 1.

Pistons: Forged aluminium.

Induction System: Float-type carburettor. Mechanically driven supercharger.

Fuel Grade: Aviation gasoline, minimum 91 octane.

Lubrication: Gear-type oil pump. Oil grade Aero Shell 100 or other to MIL-L-6082.

Propeller Drive: Direct. Provision for constant-speed propeller Type US-132000 or Dowty Rotol R303/3-110-F.

Accessories: ANG 6423 Prestolite alternator and two output shafts, one 27 hp (35 max) for spraying pump and the other 5 hp.

Starting: Electrical.

Dimensions:
- Diameter: 1,267 mm (49·88 in)
- Length: 1,110 mm (43·72 in)

Weight, Dry: 411 kg (906 lb)

Performance Ratings:
- Max T-O: 448 kW (600 hp) at 2,200 rpm
- Max continuous: 410 kW (550 hp) at 2,050 rpm
- Cruise (75 per cent): 310 kW (415 hp) at 2,000 rpm

Specific Fuel Consumption:
- T-O, max cont: 105 μg/J (0·61 lb/h/hp)
- Cruise: 86 μg/J (0·51 lb/h/hp)

PZL-3R

This is the geared version of the PZL-3S. The following are the main differences:

Propeller Drive: Planetary gear of 0·7 ratio. Provision for constant-speed propeller, Type US-133000.

PZL-3S seven-cylinder radial

Dimension: Length 1,271 mm (50·06 in)

Weight, Dry: 446 kg (983 lb)

PZL-FRANKLIN ENGINES

In 1975 Pezetel acquired rights to manufacture and market the entire range of aircooled piston engines formerly produced by the Franklin Engine Company (Aircooled Motors) of the United States. These engines are being produced in Poland for light aircraft of all kinds, including helicopters and motor-gliders.

A version of the Ogar motor-glider was to fly in 1978 with the 2A-120C (later -120CP). Type testing the 4A-235B3 (for the PZL-110 Rallye) has been completed, and twin-engined flying with 6A-350C1R (right) and C1L (left) were to be completed in early 1978. The 6AS-350 is on test.

All these engines are of the horizontally-opposed type, with cylinders of 117·48 mm (4·625 in) bore and 88·9 mm (3·5 in) stroke. All have direct drive and operate on 100/130 grade fuel. Accessories normally include electric starter, alternator and fuel pump. Other details are tabulated:

PZL-FRANKLIN ENGINES

Engine model	Cylinder arrangement	Capacity cc (cu in)	Compression ratio	Max T-O rating at S/L (kW, hp at rpm)	Overall dimensions mm (in) length	width	height	Weight dry kg (lb)	Remarks
2A-120C	2 horiz	1,916 (117)	8·5	45 (60) at 3,200	581 (22·9)	795 (31·3)	515 (20·3)	75·8 (167)	
4A-235B	4 horiz	3,850 (235)	8·5	93(125) at 2,800	774 (30·5)	795 (31·3)	637 (25·1)	117·6 (259)	
6A-350C	6 horiz	5,735 (350)	10·5	164 (220) at 2,800	952 (37·5)	795 (31·3)	641 (25·25)	167 (367)	
6AS-350A	6 horiz	5,735 (350)	7·4	186·4 (250) at 2,800*	1,097 (43·2)	868 (34·2)	983 (38·7)	189 (417)	turbocharged
6A-350D	6 horiz	5,735 (350)	10·5	175 (235) at 3,200	825 (32·5)	795 (31·3)	642 (25·3)	145 (320)	helicopter engine
6V-350B	6 vert	5,735 (350)	10·5	175 (235) at 3,200	968 (38·0)	795 (31·3)	779 (30·6)	144 (320)	helicopter engine

*Rated at 175 kW (235 hp) at 2,800 rpm at 5,000 m (16,400 ft).

SOUTH AFRICA

ATLAS
ATLAS AIRCRAFT CORPORATION OF SOUTH AFRICA (PTY) LTD

Address and Officers: See Aircraft section

Atlas is manufacturing the Rolls-Royce Viper 540 turbojet under sublicence from Piaggio of Italy, for use in Atlas Impala attack trainers.

SWEDEN

FLYGMOTOR

VOLVO FLYGMOTOR AB

Head Office and Works: S-461 01 Trollhättan
Telephone: 0520-301-00

This company was founded in 1930 and began by building under licence the Bristol Pegasus I aero-engine, under the designation My VI. Since 1970 Volvo Flygmotor has been a wholly owned subsidiary of AB Volvo.

Volvo Flygmotor AB holds a licence to build Rolls-Royce Avon engines and is also engaged in research and development work on turbojet engines, ramjet engines and rocket engines. Its major current programme involves the production of two versions of the RM8 supersonic turbofan developed from the Pratt & Whitney JT8D to power different sub-types of the Saab 37 Viggen combat aircraft.

It is also engaged in the development of experimental hybrid and liquid-fuel rocket engines. The company has a technical collaboration agreement on ramjet development with Rolls-Royce Ltd.

Volvo Flygmotor is the manufacturer of the combustion (thrust) chambers for the first and second stages of the Ariane European space launcher. The engines concerned, Viking II and Viking IV, are described in the SEP entry of the French section.

FLYGMOTOR RM8

The RM8 is a Swedish military version of the Pratt & Whitney JT8D civil subsonic turbofan which Flygmotor has developed to power the Saab 37 Viggen supersonic multi-purpose combat aircraft.

Until 1970 the main effort was devoted to development and manufacture of the RM8A version for the AJ 37, SF 37, SH 37 and SK 37 versions of the Viggen. Production was almost complete by the beginning of 1979. In late 1970 a substantially modified version, the **RM8B,** was planned to meet the propulsion requirements of the fighter Viggen, the JA 37. Research at Pratt & Whitney and Flygmotor showed that a changed design could improve the reliability of operations at high altitudes and in severe manoeuvres, as well as increase thrust in all regimes. In collaboration with Pratt & Whitney the design of the RM8B was completed in late 1971. The major change to improve functional reliability at high altitude involved taking the first stage off the LP compressor and adding it to the fan, giving a three-stage fan and three-stage LP spool, both having a revised aerodynamic configuration according to the latest P & W research. To increase thrust the RM8B has a four-nozzle burner combustion system and a new HP turbine. Delivery of production RM8B engines began in 1978.

The following description refers to the RM8A:

Type: Axial-flow two-spool turbofan with modulated afterburner.

Air Intake: Annular, with 19 fixed inlet guide vanes.

Fan: Two-stage front fan. Titanium blades.

LP Compressor: Four-stage axial-flow, integral with fan stages, on inner of two concentric shafts. Blades of titanium. Steel casing.

HP Compressor: Seven-stage axial-flow on outer hollow shaft. Blades made of special high-temperature alloys. Overall pressure ratio 16·5 : 1. By-pass ratio approximately 1 : 1. Total air mass flow 145 kg (320 lb)/s.

Combustion Chamber: Cannular type with nine cylindrical flame tubes, each downstream of a single Duplex fuel nozzle. Two high-energy spark plugs, each with its own igniter box.

HP Turbine: Single-stage axial-flow, with cast aircooled blades.

LP Turbine: Three-stage axial-flow, with cast blades. Exit guide vanes after turbine.

Afterburner: Double-skinned to provide duct for cooling air. Outer skin of titanium. Inner skin of special alloys. One hot-streak igniter. Hydraulically-actuated fully-variable nozzle, using fuel as the operating fluid.

Bearings: Main shafts run in total of six bearings.

Control Systems: There are two systems. The main system for the gas-generator comprises a Bendix hydromechanical control of advanced design. A further Bendix unit controls the fuel flow to the afterburner and the nozzle area. A single power lever controls thrust from maximum afterburner down to idle; further movement below idle actuates the fuel cut-off valve.

Mounting: Three-point. Main mountings on each side of compressor casing; one under turbine casing.

Accessory Drive: Via gearbox, under engine, driven from HP turbine shaft.

Dimensions:

Length overall:	
RM8A	6,160 mm (242·5 in)
RM8B	6,230 mm (245·25 in)
Max diameter (both versions)	1,397 mm (55 in)
Inlet diameter (both)	1,030 mm (40·55 in)

Weight, Dry:

RM8A	2,100 kg (4,630 lb)
RM8B	2,350 kg (5,181 lb)

Volvo Flygmotor RM8B augmented turbofan for JA 37 fighter version of Viggen, rated at 125 kN (28,110 lb st) with maximum augmentation

Performance Ratings (ISA, S/L):

Max T-O, augmented:	
RM8A	115·6 kN (25,990 lb st)
RM8B	125 kN (28,110 lb st)
Max T-O, dry:	
RM8A	65·6 kN (14,750 lb st)
RM8B	72 kN (16,200 lb st)

Specific Fuel Consumption:

Max augmented:	
RM8A	70·0 mg/Ns (2·47 lb/h/lb st)
RM8B	71·4 mg/Ns (2·52 lb/h/lb st)
Max dry:	
RM8A	17·8 mg/Ns (0·63 lb/h/lb st)
RM8B	18·1 mg/Ns (0·64 lb/h/lb st)
Max continuous (both)	17·3 mg/Ns (0·61 lb/h/lb st)

GARRETT/FLYGMOTOR TFE 1042

This collaborative family of turbofans is covered in the International part of this section.

FLYGMOTOR VR35

The VR35 is a prepackaged liquid-propellant rocket engine with positive expulsion of the storable inhibited red fuming nitric acid (IRFNA) and Hydyne propellants. A solid-propellant gas generator delivers the expelling gas and programmes the thrust into a boost phase followed by a sustain blow-down period.

The positive expulsion is accomplished by a gas-pressurised piston for the fuel, contained in a central tank, and an inward-collapsible aluminium bladder for the oxidiser in its concentric tank. This expulsion system enables the engine to be fired under any acceleration direction, a capability which is essential for a missile engine with a thrust programme that includes the sustain phase.

Another advantage with this type of engine is the completely smoke-free exhaust, leaving no signature at launch or during flight.

The VR35 is used in the Saab-Scania RB05 air-to-surface missile, which is one of the main weapons for the AJ 37 Viggen (see Air-Launched Missiles section).

Dimensions:

Length overall	1,770 mm (69·7 in)
Max diameter	300 mm (11·8 in)

Weight:	127 kg (280 lb)
Propellant Mass Fraction:	0·59
Operating Temperature Range:	−50°C to +65°C

Performance:

Boost	20-25 kN (4,496-5,620 lb) depending on temperature
Sustain	5 kN (1,124 lb)
Total impulse	160 kN s (35,970 lb-s)

Volvo Flygmotor VR35 prepackaged liquid rocket on static test at dive angle

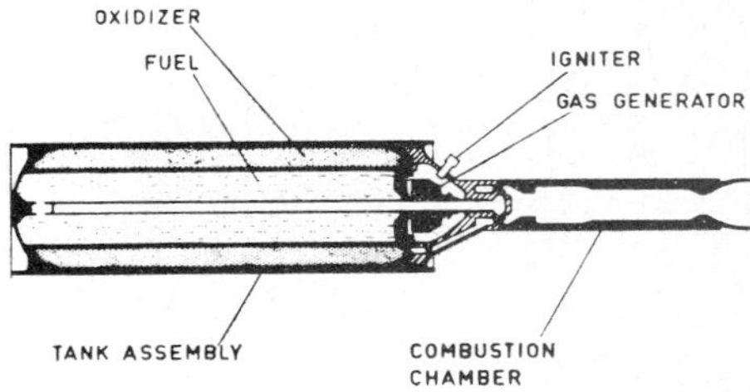

VR35 longitudinal cross-section

FLYGMOTOR RAMJETS

Ramjet engine research and development have been under way at Volvo Flygmotor since 1952, when the company's underground high-pressure air magazine was completed. The stored air drives the combustion test rigs and wind tunnels necessary for this kind of work.

The engine research culminated in several flight tests with the RR2, designed for a Mach number of 2·85 and intended for pod-mounting on a ground-to-air missile. The RR2 engine has a diameter of 260 mm (10·25 in) and an empty weight 42·0 kg (92·5 lb). The kerosene-type fuel is stored in the missile main body and is delivered to the ramjet combustion chamber by means of an air-driven turbopump integrated into the engine forebody.

The main research effort is now directed towards an integral rocket-ramjet engine. This new concept is a ramjet engine containing a solid- propellant grain in its combustion chamber. The rocket is fired to launch and accelerate the vehicle. After completion of the boost phase the chamber is used for ramjet combustion. The transition between the boost and the ramjet-sustain phase is accomplished by suddenly increasing the nozzle area, opening the air inlet and injecting the liquid fuel.

Two basic types of rocket-ramjet have been investigated and tested. The **RRX1** has a circumferential nose air intake and is designed for a Mach number of 5·0. The body diameter is 190 mm (7·5 in). The **RRX5** has four side-mounted air intakes to free the nose for a missile warhead and guidance. It is intended for a Mach-number range of 1·8-3·5, with a diameter varying between 300-450 mm (11·8 and 17·7 in).

Research is in hand on solid ducted rockets of simpler form using fuel-rich gases from underoxidised solid propellant.

UNION OF SOVIET SOCIALIST REPUBLICS

GDL

The Gas Dynamics Laboratory was founded in Leningrad in 1929. Since that time it has completed a very large number of rocket-engine programmes, mainly using liquid propellants. The laboratory has occupied many facilities, but is still headquartered in Leningrad. Four of its best-known engines are described below.

GDL RD-107

This four-chamber liquid-propellant rocket engine was developed during 1954 to 1957. The RD-107 and its derivatives have been in use for many years as first-stage engines for the launch vehicles for Vostock, Voskhod and derived programmes. Each complete RD-107 comprises four main chambers and two small vernier chambers.

Exhibition model of the RD-107 rocket engine, with two-chamber vernier engine in front *(TAM Air et Cosmos)*

TYPE: Four-chamber liquid-propellant rocket engine.

PROPELLANTS: Liquid oxygen and kerosene.

THRUST CHAMBERS: Four primary thrust chambers of double-wall construction, with fabricated corrugations between walls and inner walls of copper or copper-rich alloy. Conical nozzles. All-welded heads. Flat-plate injectors, with concentric rings of tubes in which propellants are pre-mixed before injection. Estimated diameters: throat 150-165 mm (6-6·5 in), nozzle 685 mm (27 in). Combustion pressure 60·8 bars (882 lb/sq in).

VERNIER CHAMBERS: Two chambers of double-wall construction, with finning between walls. Estimated diameters: throat 75 mm (3 in), nozzle 305 mm (12 in).

TURBOPUMP: One single-shaft turbopump mounted in tubular thrust frame and feeding all chambers. Assembly comprises turbine exhaust hood containing coiled heat exchanger, single-sided shrouded centrifugal kerosene pump, double-sided shrouded centrifugal liquid oxygen pump, gearbox, and two auxiliary centrifugal pumps, one of which supplies the monopropellant gas generator. Fuel lines to main chambers pass through common valve.

The 706·4 kN (158,800 lb) thrust GDL RD-214 rocket engine used to power the first stage of the Cosmos launcher. Vacuum rating 725·7 kN (163,142 lb)

PERFORMANCE (in vacuum):

Rated thrust	1,000 kN (224,870 lb)
Specific impulse	314 s

GDL RD-119

This more modern single-chamber liquid-propellant engine, which has been in use since 1962, forms the second-stage engine of a launch vehicle for Cosmos research satellites. More than 1,000 of these satellites have been launched, using two-, three- and four-stage launch vehicles of various types and having lifting capacities ranging from hundreds of pounds to 7·6 tonnes (7·5 tons).

TYPE: Single-chamber liquid-propellant rocket engine.

PROPELLANTS: Liquid oxygen and dimethyl-hydrazine.

THRUST CHAMBER: Single fixed chamber, possibly of tubular-wall construction, with fuel entry above base of nozzle. Estimated diameters: throat 100 mm (4 in), nozzle 940 mm (37 in). Combustion pressure 81·1 bars (1,176 lb/sq in).

TURBOPUMP: One single-shaft turbopump, driven by monopropellant (hydrazine) gas generator. Exhaust from gas generator taken to multiple auxiliary nozzles for control in roll, pitch and yaw.

PERFORMANCE (in vacuum):

Rated thrust	108 kN (24,250 lb)
Specific impulse	352 s

The RD-219 powers the second stage of launchers; a nitric acid/UDMH engine, its twin chambers have vacuum thrust of 883 kN (198,441 lb)

GDL RD-214

This neat liquid-propellant rocket engine, developed at GDL in 1952-57, has been adopted as the standard first-stage propulsion for launching the Cosmos series of Soviet satellites. It has four thrust chambers, burning nitric acid and kerosene, each chamber being rated at 176·6 kN (39,700 lb) thrust at sea level. Vacuum rating of the engine is 725·7 kN (163,142 lb). The propellants are fed by a single large turbopump group mounted above the chamber group, the fuel being supplied straight to a bolted connection on the welded chamber heads and the nitric acid passing through part-flexible pipes to the regeneratively cooled chamber nozzle and throat. Chamber pressure is given by GDL as 3·1 bars (45 kg/cm²) and specific impulse as 246. The four chambers are rigidly fixed to the Cosmos launcher first stage, vehicle control being accomplished by four refractory deflector vanes, one per chamber, mounted on the vehicle skirt control packages and projecting into the rocket exhaust. More than 1,000 RD-214 engines have been flown from Kapustin Yar on non-recoverable Cosmos missions.

GDL RD-219

Since the mid-1950s the emphasis in Soviet development of large liquid-propellant rockets has swung from lox/kerosene to storable mixtures, particularly RFNA/UDMH. This combination offers good specific impulse, can be left in the vehicle tanks indefinitely and is hypergolic. The first large GDL engine of this type to be disclosed was the RD-219, a twin-chamber unit developed in 1958-61 and used for second-stage propulsion of large vehicles (possibly the SS-9 ICBM, or the Type G or Proton/Zond launcher). The chambers have a vacuum expansion ratio, and are fed by a single turbopump. They are fixed rigidly to a welded tubular thrust frame extending down to the vehicle skirt.

PERFORMANCE (in vacuum):

Rated thrust	883 kN (198,441 lb)
Specific impulse	293.

GLUSHENKOV

This design bureau became known in 1969 when it was revealed as that responsible for the TVD-10 engines fitted in the Beriev Be-30 STOL transport. The TVD-10 is a small turboprop in the 950 shp class, supplied to Beriev as a complete cowled unit with a reversing propeller produced specially for this application. The engine air intake is positioned below the propeller axis, but no details of the TVD-10 have yet been made available. It has been reported that it was mainly due to difficulties with the TVD-10 that the Be-30 programme was terminated in 1973.

In 1978 the improved TVD-10B, rated at 723 kW (970 shp) went into production for the An-28 twin-engined STOL aircraft. It is also reported that the TVD-10B powers the An-3 agricultural aircraft. In 1979 photographs were released of one of these engines mounted in a Yak-18PM fully aerobatic trainer.

Glushenkov is also responsible for the 671 kW (900 shp) GTD-3 turboshaft engine, two of which power the Kamov Ka-25 helicopter. This engine and the TVD-10 appear to have a generally similar layout, with a free power turbine, and it is possible that they use a common gas generator.

ISOTOV

GENERAL DESIGNER IN CHARGE OF BUREAU: Sergei Pietrovich Isotov

This bureau was responsible for the GTD-350 and TV2-117A turboshaft engines which power the Mil Mi-2 and Mi-8 helicopters respectively. The former is in production in Poland, and is described under the WSK-PZL-Rzeszów entry in this edition. Isotov was also responsible for the TVD-850 turboprop engines which powered early Antonov An-28 transport aircraft (see Aircraft section).

ISOTOV TV2-117A

The power plant of the Mi-8 comprises two TV2-117A engines coupled through a VR-8A gearbox. As is common with modern Soviet helicopters, the engines and gearbox are delivered and thereafter treated as a single unit. The complete package incorporates a control system (separate from the control system of each gas generator) which maintains desired rotor speed, synchronises the power of both engines, and increases the power of the remaining engine if the other should fail.

The TV2 engine is of conservative design, being biased in favour of long and trouble-free life rather than attempting to rival the small size and weight of some Western engines in the same power class.

TYPE: Free-turbine helicopter turboshaft engine.

AIR INTAKE: Direct pitot, with main front casing providing vertical upper and lower drive-shafts to accessory packages. Main accessory group above the engine projects ahead of intake face. Casing incorporates variable-incidence inlet vanes.

COMPRESSOR: Ten-stage axial. Construction principally in titanium to reduce weight in comparison with the steel

Isotov TV2-117A turboshaft engine (1,118 kW; 1,500 shp)

that would otherwise be used. Inlet guide vanes and stators of stages 1, 2 and 3 are of variable incidence to facilitate starting and increase compressor efficiency over a wide speed range; for the same reasons the casing incorporates automatic blow-off valves. Pressure ratio 6·6 : 1 at 21,200 rpm.

COMBUSTION CHAMBER: Annular, with eight burner cones. Fabricated from inner and outer diffuser casings, flame tube, casing, burners, and anti-icing bleed air pipe.

FUEL GRADE: T-1 or TS-1 to GOST 10227-62 specification (Western equivalents, DERD.2494, MIL-F-5616).

TURBINE: Two-stage axial compressor turbine bolted to rear of splined shaft with front extension to drive accessories. Solid rotor blades, held by fir-tree roots in discs cooled by bleed air (first disc 10th-stage air, all other discs 8th-stage). First- and second-stage stators have 51 and 47 inserted blades respectively. Free power turbine of similar two-stage design; its rotors have 43 and 37 blades respectively.

EXHAUST UNIT: Large fixed-area duct which deflects the gas out at 60°. It comprises a pipe, pipe shroud and tie-band, shroud connector links and exhaust pipe attachments. The exhaust pipe and shroud together form a double-wall assembly which minimises heat transfer into the power plant nacelle, the pipe being cooled by air circulating in the double wall.

OUTPUT SHAFT: The main drive-shaft is an extension of the power turbine rotor shaft. It conveys torque from the free turbine to the overrunning clutch of the helicopter main gearbox (VR-8A) and is also coupled to the speed governor of the free-turbine rotor. Max output speed 12,000 rpm; main rotor speed 192 rpm.

ACCESSORIES: Mounted on the main drive box above the intake casing, in which a train of bevel and spur gears provides drives for airframe and engine accessories. The engine automatic control system includes a fuel system, hydraulic system, anti-icing system, gas temperature restriction system, engine electric supply and starting system, and monitoring instruments. The hydraulic system positions the variable stators according to a preset programme, depending on compressor speed and air temperature at the inlet; it also sends electrical signals to control the starter/generator system, close the starting bleed air valves and restrict peak gas temperature to 600°C. Air up to 1·8 per cent of the total mass flow can be used to heat the intake and other parts liable to icing. Fire extinguishant can be released manually by the pilot, upon receipt of a fire warning, through a series of spray rings and pipes.

LUBRICATION: Pressure circulation type. Oil is supplied by the upper pump and scavenged from the five main bearings by the lower pump, returned through the helicopter-mounted air/oil heat exchanger and thence to the helicopter tank. The oil seals and air/oil labyrinth seals are connected to a centrifugal breathing system.

OIL GRADE: Synthetic, permitting operation at oil temperatures above 200°C, combined with easy starting at minus 40°C without heating the oil. Grade B-3V to MRTU 38-1-157-65 (nearest foreign substitute Castrol 98 to DERD.2487). Consumption, not over 0·5 litre per hour per engine.

STARTING: Electrical, fuel, and ignition systems are integrated. The SP3-15 system comprises DC starter/generator, six storage batteries, control panel, ground supply receptacle, and control switches and relays; of these all are airframe mounted except for the GS-18TP starter/generator which cranks the compressor during the starting cycle. The ignition unit comprises a control box, two semiconductor plugs, solenoid valve, and switch. The starting fuel system comprises an automatic starting unit on the NR-40V fuel regulating pump, constant-pressure valve, and two igniters.

DIMENSIONS:
Length, with accessories and exhaust pipe — 2,835 mm (111·5 in)
Length, intake face to rotor gearbox connection — 2,391 mm (94·25 in)
Width — 547 mm (21·5 in)
Height — 745 mm (29·25 in)

WEIGHT, DRY:
Engine, without generator, transducers, etc — 330 kg (727 lb)
VR-8A gearbox, less entrapped oil — 745 kg (1,642 lb)

PERFORMANCE RATINGS:
T-O (S/L, static) — 1,118 kW (1,500 shp)
Cruise (122 knots; 225 km/h; 140 mph at 500 m; 1,640 ft) — 746 kW (1,000 shp)

SPECIFIC FUEL CONSUMPTION:
T-O, as above — 102·4 μg/J (0·606 lb/h/shp)
Cruise, as above — 115·4 μg/J (0·683 lb/h/shp)

ISOTOV TVD-850

Power plant of early Antonov An-28 STOL transports, the TVD-850 turboprop has a rating of 810 shp. The cowled engine looks almost identical to the Turboméca Astazou, and the reduction gearbox must be housed in the centre of an annular air intake section. This engine appears to have lost in competition with the Glushenkov TVD-10B.

IVCHENKO

The collective headed by general designer Alexander G. Ivchenko until his death in June 1968 was based in a factory at Zaparozhye in the Ukraine. The bureau is now headed by General Designer Lotarev, who has his own entry on a later page.

The first engine with which Ivchenko was associated officially was the 41 kW (55 hp) AI-4G piston engine used in the Kamov Ka-10 ultra-light helicopter. He progressed ultimately, via the widely used AI-14 and AI-26 piston engines, to become one of the Soviet Union's leading producers of gas turbine engines. Since 1952 all Soviet piston engines have been assigned to Poland (see under WSK-PZL-Kalisz in Polish section).

IVCHENKO AI-20

This engine was developed as the NK-4 at the Kuznetsov bureau in 1947-52, with the assistance of German engineers. Eventually preferred to the VK-2, it was ordered into production, and the Zaporozhye collective was charged with the final refinement and production.

Redesignated AI-20, it was produced from 1955 in several versions for aircraft that included the An-10, An-12, An-32, Be-12, Il-18 and Il-38.

AI-20K. Rated at 2,942 kW (3,945 ehp). Used in Il-18V, An-10A and An-12.

AI-20M. Initial T-O rating of 3,124 kW (4,190 ehp). Used in Il-18D/E, An-10A and An-12. Probably fitted to Il-38 and Beriev M-12. Capable of operation on a wide range of fuels and lubricating oils. Power increased to 3,169 kW (4,250 ehp) for later engines as in detailed description below. Uprated again for An-32.

The AI-20 was designed to operate reliably in all temperatures from −60°C to +55°C at heights up to 10,000 m (33,000 ft). It is a constant-speed engine, the rotor speed being maintained at 12,300 rpm by automatic variation of propeller pitch. Gas temperature after turbine is 560°C in both current versions. TBO of the AI-20K was 4,000 h in the Spring of 1966; the same life was reached by the -20M in 1968.

In the Il-18 installation, the AI-20 turboprop is supplied as a complete power plant with cowling, mounting and automatically-feathering reversible-pitch four-blade propeller.

TYPE: Single-shaft turboprop.

AIR INTAKE: Inner and outer cones connected by six radial struts. Outer casing carries accessories and front mountings. Centre casing carries reduction gear.

COMPRESSOR: Ten-stage assembly of discs running in roller bearing in front casing, joined to first disc by tubular extension shaft, and ball-thrust bearing in combustion chamber casing on through-bolted rear shaft. Magnesium alloy stator casing in upper and lower halves, bolted together. Pressure ratio 9·2 under altitude cruise conditions. Air mass flow 20·7 kg (45·6 lb)/s.

Ivchenko AI-20M turboprop of 3,169 ekW (4,250 ehp) *(courtesy of Aviation Magazine International, Paris)*

COMBUSTION CHAMBER: Annular chamber with ten burner cones welded to front ring, and separate inner and outer shrouds. Burners anchored by flanges on chamber casing. Pilot burners and ignition plugs at top of casing.

FUEL GRADE: T-1 or TS-1 to GOST-10227-62 (DERD.2492, JP-1 to MIL-F-5616).

TURBINE: Three stages overhung on cantilevered shaft running in roller bearing in tapered cone of combustion chamber casing and splined to compressor drive-shaft. Rotor blades shrouded at inner and outer ends and installed in pairs in slots in aircooled discs. Stator blades secured in grooves in casing, first stage being aircooled and second stage being hollow to ensure uniform heating.

JET PIPE: Fixed-area type with five radial struts. Nozzle area 0·225 m² (2·42 sq ft).

REDUCTION GEAR: Planetary type, incorporating six-cylinder torquemeter and negative-thrust transmitter (type IKM), with self-checking device, for autofeathering AV-681 propeller. Ratio 0·08732 (input speed 12,300 rpm except ground-idle 10,400 rpm).

LUBRICATION: Pressure-feed type with full re-circulation; hourly consumption not over 0·8 litres (0·175 Imp pints).

OIL GRADE: Mixture 75% transformer oil GOST 982-56 or MK-8 to GOST 6457-66 (equivalent to DERD.2490 or MIL-O-6081B) and 25% MS-20 or MK-22 to GOST 1013-49 (DERD.2472 or MIL-O-6082B).

ACCESSORIES: Engine and airframe accessories driven off compressor front extension shaft, via radial shafts at 6 and 12 o'clock. Full ice-protection and fire-extinguishing systems.

STARTING: Two electric starter/generators, Type STG-12 TMO-1000, supplied from ground source or from APU Type TG-16.

DIMENSIONS:
Length — 3,096 mm (121·89 in)
Width — 842 mm (33·15 in)
Height — 1,180 mm (46·46 in)

WEIGHT, DRY: 1,040 kg (2,292 lb)

PERFORMANCE RATINGS:
T-O — 3,169 kW (4,250 ehp)
Cruise (350 knots; 650 km/h; 404 mph at 8,000 m; 26,000 ft) — 2,013 kW (2,700 ehp)

SPECIFIC FUEL CONSUMPTION:
T-O — 104·3 μg/J (0·617 lb/h/shp)
Cruise, as above — 73·3 μg/J (0·434 lb/h/shp)

IVCHENKO AI-24

This turboprop powers the An-24 and its derivatives. Production began in 1960 and the following data refer to engines of the second series, which were in production by the Spring of 1966.

The AI-24 of 1,875 kW (2,515 ehp) powered the An-24V Series I, and was followed by the AI-24A with provision for water injection, in the main production version of that aircraft.

The more powerful AI-24T of 2,103 kW (2,820 ehp) with water injection is used in the An-26. This engine has in-flight vibration monitoring, automatic relief of power overloads and gas temperature behind the turbine, and auto-shutdown and feathering.

The AI-24 is a constant-speed engine, maintained at 15,100 rpm by automatic variation of propeller pitch. The engine is flat-rated to maintain its nominal output to 3,500 m (11,500 ft). TBO was 3,000 hours in the Spring of 1966; by 1968 the later AI-24T had reached 4,000 h.

TYPE: Single-shaft turboprop.

AIR INTAKE: Large magnesium alloy casting, comprising inner and outer cones joined by four radial struts. Carries accessories, reduction gear, front mountings and compressor inlet guide vanes.

COMPRESSOR: Ten-stage axial. Stainless steel rotor, comprising rigidly-connected discs carrying dovetailed blades. Front shaft runs in roller bearing and is bolted to propeller drive-shaft of reduction gear; rear shaft runs in ball-thrust bearing and is splined to turbine shaft. Welded steel casing in bolted left and right halves, with welded front and rear connecting flanges. Pressure ratio (max continuous, 6,000 m; 18,300 ft, 272 knots; 505 km/h; 314 mph) 7·85 : 1. Air mass flow 14·4 kg (31·7 lb)/s.

COMBUSTION CHAMBER: Annular, of spot-welded heat-resistant steel, with eight simplex burners inserted into swirl-vane heads. Contains two starting units, each comprising a body, pilot burner and igniter plug.

FUEL GRADE: T-1, TS-1 to GOST 10227-62 (DERD.2494 or MIL-F-5616).

TURBINE: Three-stage axial. Three discs carry solid blades in fir-tree roots, and are automatically centred on each other when connected by stay-bolts to the extended flange at the rear of the turbine shaft. Shaft splined to compressor rear shaft and held by tie-rod; runs in roller bearing ahead of first turbine disc. Three stator diaphragms through-bolted together and to combustion-chamber casing. First nozzle diaphragm cooled by secondary air from combustion chamber. Rotor/stator sealing effected by soft inserts mounted in grooves in nozzle assemblies. Peak exhaust temperature during starting 750°C.

JET PIPE: Fixed-area type. Inner and outer rings connected by three hollow struts carrying 12 thermocouples.

REDUCTION GEAR: Planetary type, incorporating hydraulic torquemeter and electromagnetic negative-thrust transmitter for propeller auto-feathering. Magnesium alloy casing. Front flange of propeller shaft has end splines and 12 stud holes for type AV-72 propeller (AI-24T drives AV-72T propeller). Ratio 0·08255.

LUBRICATION: Pressure circulation system; hourly consumption not over 850 gr (1·87 lb).

OIL GRADE: Mixture of 75% transformer oil GOST 982-56 or MK-8 (DERD.2490 or MIL-O-6081B) and 25% MS-20 or MK-22 (DERD.2472 or MIL-O-6082B).

ACCESSORIES: Mounted on front casing are starter/generator, alternator, propeller speed governor and centrifugal breather. Below casing are oil unit, air separator and removable box containing LP and HP fuel pumps and drives to hydraulic pump and tachometer generators. Also on front casing are an aerodynamic probe, ice detector, and negative-thrust feathering valve, torque transmitter and oil filter.

STARTING: Electric STG-18TMO starter/generator supplied from ground power or from TG-16 APU.

DIMENSIONS:
- Length overall: 2,346 mm (92·36 in)
- Width: 677 mm (26·65 in)
- Height: 1,075 mm (42·32 in)

WEIGHT, DRY: 600 kg (1,323 lb)

PERFORMANCE RATINGS:
- T-O:
  - AI-24A: 1,875 kW (2,515 ehp)
  - AI-24T: 2,103 kW (2,820 ehp)
- Cruise rating at 243 knots (450 km/h; 280 mph) at 6,000 m (18,300 ft):
  - AI-24A: 1,156 kW (1,550 ehp)
  - AI-24T: 1,178 kW (1,580 ehp)

SPECIFIC FUEL CONSUMPTION:
- At cruise rating:
  - AI-24A: 91·3 μg/J (0·540 lb/h/shp)
  - AI-24T: 90·1 μg/J (0·533 lb/h/shp)

OIL CONSUMPTION: 0·85 kg (1·87 lb)/h

The 1,875 ekW (2,515 ehp) Ivchenko AI-24 turboprop *(courtesy of Aviation Magazine International, Paris)*

Ivchenko AI-25 turbofan (14·68 kN; 3,300 lb st)

IVCHENKO AI-25

This turbofan powers the three-engined Yakovlev Yak-40 STOL transport. The Aeroflot Yak-40 has the basic AI-25 engine, but the Yak-40B of the Soviet Air Force has an AI-25 with an aircooled HP turbine and rating of 17·13 kN (3,850 lb st). The AI-25 also powers the Czech L-39 trainer, and it was to be manufactured by Motorlet, Czechoslovakia, as the Walter Titan. The emergence of the Polish WSK-PZL-Mielec M-15 agricultural aircraft led to transfer of AI-25 activity to Poland, and mass production is now likely to take place in that country to provide engines for an M-15 programme estimated at 3,000 aircraft for the Soviet Union alone.

The Ivchenko bureau planned the engine for small transports, trainers and business jet aircraft. It is claimed to have an exceptional margin of flow stability and to be unusually robust and simple.

TYPE: Two-shaft turbofan.

AIR INTAKE: Fabricated from titanium sheet. Central bullet and intake leading-edges anti-iced by hot bleed air.

FAN: Three-stage axial. Drum/disc construction with pin-jointed blades. Casing and fan duct of magnesium alloy. Peak pressure ratio, 1·695 at 10,750 rpm. By-pass ratio 2.

COMPRESSOR: Eight-stage axial. Drum/disc construction of titanium, with aluminium and magnesium casing. Dovetailed blades. Peak pressure ratio, 4·68 at 16,640 rpm. Overall pressure ratio, 8.

COMBUSTION CHAMBER: Annular. Inner and outer casings joined upstream to 12 burner heads with stabilisers.

FUEL GRADE: T-1, TS-1 to GOST 10227-62 (DERD.2494, MIL-F-5616).

TURBINE: Single-stage HP turbine; two-stage LP turbine. Shrouded solid rotor blades held by fir-tree roots in cooled discs.

JET PIPE: Plain fixed convergent nozzles for core and by-pass airflow. No mixer.

LUBRICATION: Self-contained, pressure circulating.

OIL GRADE: MK-8 to GOST 6457-66 or MK-6 to GOST 10328-63 (Western equivalents, DERD.2490 or MIL-O-6081B). Consumption 0·3 litres (0·53 Imp pints)/h.

ACCESSORIES: All shaft-driven accessories mounted on gearbox on underside of engine and driven off HP spool. Equipment includes automatic fire extinguishing (agent can be supplied into oil-contacted labyrinth cavities), ice protection, automatic starting and control system, oil-system chip detector and casing vibration monitor.

STARTING: Pneumatic. Air starter type SV-25 is supplied from ground hose coupling or from APU type AI-9 or an operating engine bleed. System claimed to develop high torque for rapid start in any climatic condition, and to be cleared for exceptional number of starts in given overhaul life.

DIMENSIONS:
- Length overall: 1,993 mm (78·46 in)
- Width overall: 820 mm (32·28 in)
- Height overall: 895 mm (35·24 in)

WEIGHT, DRY:
- Without accessories: 290 kg (639 lb)

PERFORMANCE RATINGS:
- T-O: 14·68 kN (3,300 lb st)
- Long-range cruise rating, 6,000 m (20,000 ft) and 296 knots (550 km/h; 342 mph): 3·49 kN (785 lb st)

SPECIFIC FUEL CONSUMPTION:
- T-O: 15·86 mg/Ns (0·56 lb/h/lb st)
- Cruise, as above: 23·71 mg/Ns (0·837 lb/h/lb st)

KOLIESOV

During an official tour of the Soviet aircraft industry in mid-1973, a representative of *Air Force Magazine* was told of the existence of the hitherto-unreported Koliesov Engine Design Bureau. It was then developing an alternative engine to the Kuznetsov NK-144, the power plant used in the Tu-144 and, probably, in the Tupolev Tu-22M bomber, known to NATO as 'Backfire'.

The Koliesov engine was described as a variable-geometry, variable by-pass ratio engine which functions as a turbojet in supersonic flight and as a turbofan in the subsonic regime. No such advanced design exists in the West. This engine could power the reported new Soviet strategic bomber (unofficially said to be the Tu-160).

Soviet engine designers are reported to be experimenting also with hypersonic vehicles powered by scramjet propulsion systems and capable of operating in the Mach 5 to Mach 7 range.

KUZNETSOV

GENERAL DESIGNER IN CHARGE OF BUREAU: Nikolai Dmitrievich Kuznetsov

Kuznetsov was deputy to General V. Ya. Klimov during the Second World War. In the late 1940s his own bureau at Kuibyshev developed a series of large turboprop and turbofan engines. One of the first, the NK-4, was transferred to Ivchenko, and is described under that collective's heading, as the AI-20. The much larger NK-12 turboprop was used in the Tu-95 and Tu-126 military aircraft and in the Tu-114 civil transport, and was produced subsequently in small numbers for the An-22. The NK-8 and NK-144 may no longer be produced in their original forms.

KUZNETSOV NK-8

One of the first Soviet civil turbofans, the NK-8 has been developed through a number of variants, the most powerful of which is the NK-144 supersonic augmented engine for the Tupolev Tu-144 supersonic transport. Basic versions are the 99·1 kN (22,273 lb st) **NK-8-4** which originally powered the Ilyushin Il-62 four-engined transport, and the further-developed 93·2 kN (20,950 lb) **NK-8-2** which was the original engine of the Tupolev Tu-154. At one time it was planned to replace the NK-8-2 by the Soloviev D-30K, which replaced the NK-8-4 in the Il-62M. It is believed that all current Tu-154A/B aircraft are powered by the **NK-8-2U** of greater thrust (details unknown in the West). The NK-8-4 remains in service with several Il-62 (not Il-62M) operators, including LOT.

TYPE: Two-shaft turbofan.

AIR INTAKE: Fabricated from outer ring, inner splitter and welded stator blades (15 in core airflow, 30 ahead of fan). Hot-air ice-protection.

FAN: Two-stage axial, with anti-flutter sweptback blades on first rotor stage. Pressure ratio 2·15 at 5,350 rpm. By-pass ratio 1·02 (NK-8-2, 1·00).

COMPRESSOR: Two IP stages on fan shaft. Six-stage HP compressor. Construction of both rotors and stators, including blading, almost wholly of titanium alloy. Core pressure ratio, 10·8 at 6,950 HP rpm (NK-8-2, 10 at 6,835 rpm).

COMBUSTION CHAMBER: Annular, with 139 burners. Claimed to produce no visible smoke.

FUEL GRADE: T-1 and TS-1 to GOST 10227-62 or T-7 to GOST 12308-66 (equivalent to Avtur 50 to DERD.2494 or MIL-F-5616).

TURBINE: Single-stage HP turbine, two-stage LP turbine, all with shrouded rotor blades, aircooled discs and hollow nozzle blades (stators). All shafting carried between shock-absorbing bearings at each end, with labyrinth and contact (rubbing) graphite seals to prevent gas leakage. Gas temperature, not over 870°C (1,143°K) ahead of turbine, not over 670°C (NK-8-2, 650°C) downstream, both values sea level, static.

JET PIPE: Mixer leads by-pass flow into common jet pipe which may be fitted with blocker/cascade-type reverser giving up to 48% (NK-8-2, 45%) reverse thrust, and noise suppressor.

LUBRICATION: Continuous pressure feed and recirculation. Oil consumption not over 1·3 kg (2·87 lb)/h. Pressure not less than 2·28 bars (33 lb/sq in).

OIL GRADE: Mineral oil MK-8 or MK-8P to GOST 6457-66 (DERD.2490 or MIL-O-6081B). External tank on left side of front casing.

ACCESSORIES: These include automatic flight-deck warning of vibration exceeding permissible limit, ice and fire. All accessories grouped beneath fan duct casing. Engine claimed to need no attention for long periods, other than inspection of fuel and oil filters. RTA-26-9-1 turbine gas temperature controller by Smiths Industries.

STARTING: HP spool driven by constant-speed drive type PPO-62M, or started pneumatically by air from APU type TA-6, from ground hose or by air from another engine (NK-8-2, pneumatic starter only). Time to idling speed not over 80 s. Engine can be windmill-started in the air under all conditions, up to altitudes of 11,000 m (36,000 ft).

DIMENSIONS:
NK-8-4:
Length, no reverser 5,100 mm (201 in)
NK-8-2:
Length, with reverser 5,288 mm (208·19 in)
Length, without reverser 4,762 mm (187·48 in)
Diameter 1,442 mm (56·8 in)

WEIGHT, DRY:
NK-8-4:
No reverser 2,100 kg (4,629 lb)
With reverser 2,400 kg (5,291 lb)
NK-8-2:
No reverser 2,100 kg (4,629 lb) max
With reverser 2,350 kg (5,180 lb) max

PERFORMANCE RATINGS:
NK-8-4:
T-O rating 99·1 kN (22,273 lb st)
Cruise rating at 11,000 m (36,000 ft) and 458 knots (850 km/h; 530 mph) 27 kN (6,063 lb st)
NK-8-2:
T-O rating 93·2 kN (20,950 lb st)
Cruise (as above) 17·65 kN (3,968 lb st)

SPECIFIC FUEL CONSUMPTION:
At cruise rating at 11,000 m (36,000 ft) and 458 knots (850 km/h; 530 mph):
NK-8-4 22·1 mg/Ns (0·78 lb/h/lb st)
NK-8-2 21·53 mg/Ns (0·76 lb/h/lb st)

KUZNETSOV NK-86

Though described by the Ilyushin aircraft bureau as a new engine, this turbofan of 127·5 kN (28,660 lb st) appears to be closely related to the lower-thrust NK-8 series used in the Il-62 and Tu-154. The thrust is the same as the unaugmented rating of the NK-144 (see below) and the NK-86 may bear an even closer resemblance to the supersonic engine, which was itself derived from the NK-8. Four NK-86s power the Il-86 wide-body transport.

KUZNETSOV NK-144

This is the two-spool augmented turbofan developed for the Soviet Union's first supersonic transport aircraft, the Tu-144. It is a development of the NK-8 and the first five pre-production NK-144s completed some 1,500 hours of bench-testing by October 1965. The engine flew in at least one testbed aircraft before the start of the Tu-144 flight programme in 1968.

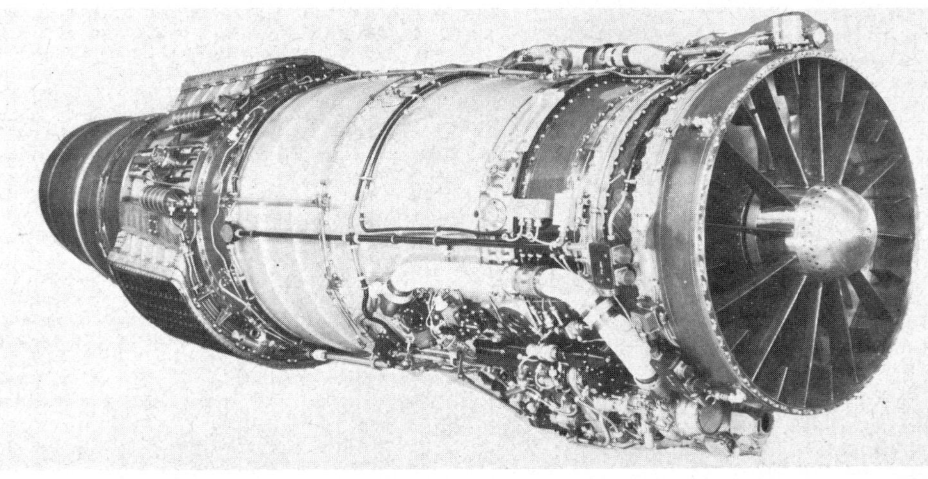

Kuznetsov NK-8-2 turbofan with thrust reverser (93·2 kN; 20,950 lb st)

Since 1972 the afterburner augmentation has been increased, raising maximum rating from 171·6 kN (38,580 lb) to the figure given below. A version of the NK-144 is believed to be the engine of at least the first sub-type of the Tupolev Tu-22M supersonic bomber known to NATO as 'Backfire'.

The NK-144 is reported to have a two-stage titanium fan, three-stage IP compressor, eleven-stage HP compressor, annular combustion chamber, single-stage HP turbine and two-stage LP turbine. Aircooled blades are used in the HP turbine, and titanium is used extensively in construction of the engine. By-pass ratio is reported to be 1 : 1, maximum mass flow 250 kg (551 lb)/s, and pressure ratio 15 : 1. The jet pipe incorporates an afterburner, with hydraulically-actuated variable-area nozzle. Gas temperature at turbine entry is 1,050°C.

DIMENSIONS:
Length overall 5,200 mm (204·7 in)
Diameter 1,500 mm (59 in)

WEIGHT:
Without jet pipe, but with afterburner 2,850 kg (6,283 lb)

PERFORMANCE RATINGS:
Max, without afterburning 127·5 kN (28,660 lb st)
Max, with afterburning 196·1 kN (44,090 lb st)

KUZNETSOV NK-12M

Designed at Kuibishev under the leadership of N. D. Kuznetsov and former German engineers, the NK-12M is the most powerful turboprop engine in the world. In its original form as the NK-12M it developed 8,948 kW (12,000 ehp). The later NK-12MV is rated at 11,033 kW (14,795 ehp) and powers the Tupolev Tu-114 transport, driving four-blade contra-rotating propellers of 5·6 m (18 ft 4 in) diameter. As the NK-12MA, rated at 11,185 kW (15,000 shp), it powers the Antonov An-22 military transport, with propellers of 6·2 m (20 ft 4 in) diameter. A third application is in the Tupolev Tu-95 bomber and its derivatives, and Tu-126 'AWACS'.

The NK-12M has a single 14-stage axial-flow compressor. Compression ratio varies from 9 : 1 to 13 : 1 according to altitude, and variable inlet guide vanes and blow-off valves are necessary. A cannular-type combustion system is used: each flame tube is mounted centrally on a downstream injector, but all tubes merge at their maximum diameter to form an annular secondary region. The single turbine is a five-stage axial. Mass flow is 65 kg (143 lb)/s.

The casing is made in four portions, from sheet steel, precision welded. An electric control for variation of propeller pitch is incorporated, to maintain constant engine speed.

DIMENSIONS:
Length 6,000 mm (236·2 in)
Diameter 1,150 mm (45·3 in)

WEIGHT, DRY: 2,350 kg (5,181 lb)

PERFORMANCE RATINGS:
T-O 11,033 kW (14,795 ehp)
Nominal power 8,826 kW (11,836 ehp) at 8,300 rpm
Idling speed 6,600 rpm

Kuznetsov NK-12MV single-shaft turboprop of 11,033 ekW (14,795 ehp)
(courtesy of Aviation Magazine International, Paris)

LOTAREV

GENERAL DESIGNER IN CHARGE OF BUREAU: Vladimir Lotarev

LOTAREV D-36

As successor to Alexander Ivchenko at Zaparozhye, Vladimir Lotarev has developed the turbofan engine that powers the An-72 and Yak-42. With a by-pass ratio of 5·34 : 1 the D-36 is the first avowed turbofan—as distinct from a by-pass turbojet—to emerge in the Soviet Union. Bench testing was in progress in September 1973, and flights in a pod carried beneath a Tu-16 testbed aircraft preceded the Yak-42 first flight by several years.

No details had been disclosed as this edition went to press, though Western engineers visiting the Soviet Union report that the D-36 is a more advanced and modern engine than other Soviet commercial gas turbines.

WEIGHT, DRY: 1,080 kg (2,480 lb)

PERFORMANCE RATINGS:
T-O rating 62·76 kN (14,110 lb st)
Cruise rating at 8,000 m (26,200 ft) at Mach 0·84 15·6 kN (3,505 lb st)

SPECIFIC FUEL CONSUMPTION:
At T-O rating 10·76 mg/Ns (0·38 lb/h/lb st)
At cruise rating as above 18·7 mg/Ns (0·66 lb/h/lb st)

LYULKA

General Designer in Charge of Bureau: Arkhip Mikhailovich Lyulka

During the late 1930s Arkhip Lyulka worked on the design of an axial turbojet that became an early war casualty. In 1942 he planned a more advanced engine that finally materialised as the TR-1, of 12·75 kN (2,866 lb st), run on the bench in 1944 and used in the Ilyushin Il-22 four-jet bomber and Sukhoi Su-11 twin-jet fighter prototypes, both of 1947. Ultimately, in 1948, this pioneer Soviet-designed turbojet was developed to give 14·71 kN (3,307 lb st).

In 1946 Lyulka began the design of a very ambitious axial engine to give a thrust of 44·13 kN (9,920 lb), and in 1950 this began bench trials under the designation AL-5. Although of basically simple, single-shaft configuration, with a seven-stage compressor and single-stage turbine, the AL-5 was more powerful than any Western engine apart from the prototype Olympus and J57. By 1951 it was rated at 45·1 kN (10,140 lb st) and flew in the prototype Ilyushin Il-30 twin-jet bomber; later in 1951-52 uprated AL-5 engines, giving a static thrust of 49·1 kN (11,032 lb), powered the Il-46 twin-jet bomber and the transonic Lavochkin La-190 and Yakovlev Yak-1000 fighters. An advanced civil version of the same engine, the AL-5 rated at 53·93 kN (12,125 lb st) powered the Tu-110 four-engined derivative of the Tu-104 airliner that did not go into production (at the time, in 1959, this engine was reported in the West as the 'Lu-4').

By the time the AL-5 was running, Lyulka had conducted extensive research with axial compressors having supersonic airflow through some or all of the stages. It was clear that, if problems of flow breakdown and inefficiency could be resolved, such a compressor would enable turbojets to be made much smaller and lighter for a given thrust and with greater thrust per unit frontal area, and thus much better suited to the propulsion of supersonic fighters. By 1952 a supersonic-compressor engine had been designed and built. This, the AL-7, became Lyulka's first major success.

LYULKA AL-7

The first AL-7 ran on the bench in late 1952 and the first production version was cleared for use in 1954 at a design rating of 63·74 kN (14,330 lb st). Its initial application was on the Il-54, yet another Ilyushin twin-jet bomber that failed to see production, despite the fact that its speed at low altitude of 620 knots (1,150 km/h; 714 mph) was probably unrivalled by any other bomber in 1955. In the same year the Sukhoi Su-7 single-seat ground-attack fighter was designed around the AL-7F afterburning version of this engine, with thrust increased by about 40 per cent (see data below). By 1956 the Su-7 was flying, and the AL-7F had also been chosen for the basically similar Su-9 all-weather fighter. Subsequently the -7F was also produced for the Su-11 and -11U.

By 1958 a further developed version of the basic unaugmented engine, the AL-7PB, had been chosen by Beriev for the Be-10 reconnaissance flying-boat, which—apart from being the only pure-jet flying-boat ever to go into service anywhere—set up a number of world records for speed, load-carrying and altitude. Other versions of the AL-7, in both cases of the -7F afterburning family, powered the unsuccessful Tu-98 bomber and La-250 strike fighter of 1956.

The AL-7F, or a development of it, has been persistently reported to be the power plant of the Tu-28P twin-engined interceptor. This is not confirmed. The Tu-28P is considered to need greater thrust, greater even than provided by the AL-21 which was not available when the Tu-28 entered service in the early 1960s.

Type: Single-shaft axial-flow turbojet, available with or without afterburner.

Air Intake: Central bullet fairing and 14 fixed aerofoil struts anti-iced by compressor bleed air.

Compressor: Nine-stage axial (probably eight stages in original AL-7 design). First two stages widely separated axially, with variable stators ahead of second stage. Each stage has blades inserted in centreless disc held by peripheral spacers at correct distance from adjacent discs, the whole being coupled together finally by the central drive-shaft in tension. Pressure ratio probably about 8 : 1.

Combustion Chamber: Annular type with perforated inner flame tube. Multiple downstream fuel injectors inserted through cups in forward face of liner. Liner outer casing provided with multiple inward secondary-air injection ducts.

Turbine: Two-stage axial-flow type. Both wheels overhung behind rear bearing; front disc bolted to flange on hollow tubular driveshaft which, in turn, is splined to rear of compressor shaft running in main centre bearing which locates compressor axially against end loads.

Afterburner (AL-7F): Comprises upstream diffuser and downstream combustion section. Pilot combustor on turbine exit cone includes single nozzle ring and flame-holder; main spray ring and gutter flame-holder assembly located further downstream at greater radius. Refractory liner in combustion section. Variable-area nozzle, with multiple hinged flaps which govern nozzle size and profile according to signals from reheat control system based on turbine exit temperature and throttle lever position.

Accessories: Fuel pump and control unit, oil pumps, hydraulic pump, electric generator, tachometer and other items grouped into quickly replaceable packages beneath compressor casing.

Performance Ratings:

Max rating:

AL-7F, unaugmented	68·64 kN (15,432 lb st)
AL-7F, afterburning	98·1 kN (22,046 lb st)
AL-7PB	63·74 kN (14,330 lb st)

LYULKA AL-21

When continued development of the Su-7 family by the Sukhoi bureau was matched with increased thrust it was logical to suppose that the engine would be a derivative of the AL-7. This is now reported to have happened, and the designation AL-21 has been given. The AL-21 resembles the AL-7 closely, and may be installationally interchangeable, but has significant improvements to the compressor and other components. The first production version was the AL-21F-3, for the Su-17 variable-geometry tactical aircraft. The very important twin-engined Su-19 has engines in the same thrust class and possibly from the Lyulka bureau.

Performance Ratings:

Max S/L, unaugmented	80·1 kN (18,000 lb st)
Max S/L, afterburning	109 kN (24,500 lb st)

MIKULIN

General Designer in Charge of Bureau: Alexander Alexandrovich Mikulin

Eighty years old on 16 February 1975, Mikulin has been engaged in aircraft engine design since 1916. Notable Vee-12 water-cooled engines from his designs were the AM-13, AM-34, AM-38 (used in the Il-2 and Il-10 Stormovik) and AM-42.

Very large numbers of M-11 five-cylinder radial engines have been built in the Soviet Union and (from 1949) Poland to power a variety of light aircraft and helicopters. Best-known variants are the 93 kW (125 hp) M-11D and the 119 kW (160 hp) M-11FR which powers the Yak-18 primary trainer. Brief descriptions appeared in the 1975-76 *Jane's*.

The large turbojet described below was designed immediately after the second World War. Though a version was fitted to M-4 four-engined prototypes, it is not known if Mikulin's bureau developed the much more powerful 'D-15' engine fitted to later M-4 aircraft.

MIKULIN RD-3M-500

The basic RD-3M (or AM-3M) single-spool axial-flow turbojet was developed under the design leadership of P. F. Zubets from the original Mikulin M-209 (civil RD-3 or AM-3) engine which powers the Tu-16 and early M-4 bombers and was adapted for the USSR's first jet transport, the Tu-104.

The RD-3M-500 was evolved, in turn, from the RD-3M and powers the Tu-104A and Tu-104B commercial transports. It has a simple basic configuration, with an eight-stage axial-flow compressor, annular-type combustion system with 14 flame tubes, and a two-stage turbine. The compressor casing is made in front, centre and rear portions, the front casing housing a row of inlet guide vanes. A bullet fairing mounted centrally in the annular ram-air intake houses a type S-300M gas-turbine starter, developing 90-100 hp at 31,000-35,000 rpm. The jet pipe consists of a central cone and fixed nozzle with an orifice diameter of approximately 840 mm (33 in). Pressure ratio is 6·4 : 1; temperature after turbine 720°C.

Dimensions:

Length overall	5,340 mm (210·23 in)
Diameter	1,400 mm (55·12 in)

Performance Rating:

T-O	93·15 kN (20,940 lb st)

SHVETSOV

Founder of Bureau: Arkadiya Dmitrievich Shvetsov

Arkadiya Shvetsov had meteoric rise to fame with his aircooled radial engines based on original US designs, which transformed Soviet fighters, bombers and transport aircraft during and after the second World War. The most important, and most powerful, of these engines was the ASh-82 series, derived from the Pratt & Whitney Twin Wasp, which at ratings up to 1,491 kW (2,000 hp) powered Lavochkin fighters, the Tu-2 and Tu-4 bombers, Il-12 and -14 transports and Mi-4 and Yak-24 helicopters (see 1975-76 *Jane's*). The ASh-62, originally based on the Wright Cyclone, was made in large numbers at ratings in the 750 kW (1,000 hp) class for the Li-2 and An-2. The ASh-62M agricultural version, developed by Vedeneev, and all An-2 engines after 1952, were transferred with all other Soviet aircooled radials to Poland (see WSK-PZL-Kalisz and WSK-PZL-Rzeszów in Polish part of this section). Another important Shvetsov piston engine was the 545 kW (730 hp) ASh-21, fitted to the Yak-11. All these engines have been described in earlier editions.

SOLOVIEV

General Designer in Charge of Bureau: P. A. Soloviev

Engines for which Soloviev's design team is responsible include the turbofans fitted in the Ilyushin Il-62M and Il-76 and Tupolev Tu-124 and Tu-134 transport aircraft, and the turboshafts which power the Mi-6, Mi-10 and V-12 helicopters.

SOLOVIEV D-15

This engine was first reported, in 1959, as that fitted to the four-engined Type 201-M aircraft which gained a number of world records for speed and altitude. Over the years it has become apparent that the aircraft was a special Myasishchev M-4, and that the engine was standard in the later service versions of this aircraft. Details of the D-15 are still unknown in the West, but it is probably safe to deduce that it is a two-shaft by-pass turbojet (low by-pass ratio turbofan). It is likely that it laid the foundation upon which Soloviev's bureau produced the civil D-20 and D-30, both of which are considerably smaller engines.

Performance Rating:

T-O	128·6 kN (28,660 lb st)

SOLOVIEV D-20P

The D-20P is a two-spool turbofan fitted to the Tupolev Tu-124 twin-engined passenger transport. Of conservative design, it underwent prolonged testing before entering service. It was designed for maximum economy and reliability over the range of ambient temperatures between −40°C and 40°C.

Type: Two-shaft turbofan (by-pass turbojet).

Air Intake: Eight radial struts and central bullet fairing, de-iced by hot bleed air from fourth HP stage (from final stage at low rpm).

Fan: Three-stage axial, with supersonic blading in first stage. Mass flow 113 kg (249 lb)/s at 8,550 rpm. Pressure ratio (S/L, static at max cont 7,900 rpm) 2·4 : 1. By-pass ratio 1 : 1.

Compressor: Eight-stage axial. Automatically-controlled flap valves downstream of the third and fourth stages bleed air into the fan duct to stabilise behaviour. Pressure ratio (at max continuous, 11,170 rpm) 5 : 1; overall pressure ratio 13 : 1.

Combustion Chamber: Can-annular, with 12 flame tubes each fitted with duplex burner.

Fuel grade: T-1, TS-1 to GOST 10227-62 (Avtur-50 to DERD.2494, MIL-F-5616).

Turbine: Single-stage HP turbine with cast blades; stator blades and both sides of disc cooled by bleed air. Two-stage LP turbine with forged blades. Max gas temperature downstream of turbine 650°C.

Jet Pipe: Concentric pipes for fan airflow and core gas, terminating in supersonic nozzles of fixed-area type.

Lubrication: Open type, with oil returned to tank. Consumption in flight, not over 1 kg (2·2 lb)/h. Typical pressure 3·4-4·5 kg/cm² (50-64 lb/sq in).

Oil Grade: Mineral oil MK-8 or MK-8P to GOST 6457-66 (DERD.2490 or MIL-O-6081B).

Accessories: Two gearboxes provide drives for starter/generator, tachometer, air compressors, hydraulic pump, oil pump and other controls and instruments. For re-starting in flight, an altitude sensing device meters fuel flow appropriate to height. An automatic fire extinguishing system is fitted. De-icing of the air intake and inlet guide vanes is controlled automatically. The engine also has oil chip detectors, vibration monitors and turbine gas temperature limiters.

Starting: Electric (DC) system, incorporating STG-18TM starter/generator.

Dimensions:

Length overall	3,304 mm (130 in)
Diameter, bare	976 mm (38·3 in)

Weight, Dry:	1,468 kg (3,236 lb)

Soloviev D-20P turbofan (52·96 kN; 11,905 lb st)

Performance Ratings:
Max T-O rating 52·96 kN (11,905 lb st)
Long-range cruise, Mach 0·75, 11,000 m (36,000 ft) 10·79 kN (2,425 lb st)
Specific Fuel Consumption:
Max T-O 20·4 mg/Ns (0·72 lb/h/lb st)
Long-range cruise, as above 25·5 mg/Ns (0·90 lb/h/lb st)

SOLOVIEV D-25V

D-25V is the Soloviev bureau designation for the free-turbine turboshaft which powers the Mil Mi-6, Mi-10 and V-12 helicopters and was also fitted to the Kamov Ka-22 experimental convertiplane. It is usually referred to by its official designation of **TV-2BM**.

The complete helicopter power plant comprises two D-25V engines, identical except for handed jet pipes, and an R-7 gearbox. The latter has four stages of large gear-wheels providing an overall ratio of 69·2 : 1. The R-7 is 2,795 mm (110·04 in) high, 1,551 mm (61·06 in) wide and 1,852 mm (72·91 in) long. Its dry weight is 3,200 kg (7,054 lb), more than that of the pair of engines.

The D-25V is flat rated to maintain rated power to 3,000 m (10,000 ft) or to temperatures up to 40°C at sea level.

The D-25VF turboshafts fitted to the Mil V-12 helicopter are uprated to 6,500 shp. These engines are believed to incorporate a zero stage on the compressor and to operate at higher turbine gas temperatures. The following details apply to the basic D-25V:

Type: Single-shaft turboshaft with free power turbine.
Air Intake: Six hollow radial struts, the two vertical struts housing splined shafts driving upper and lower accessory drive boxes. Vertical struts de-iced by oil drained from upper drive box; four inclined struts and bullet fairing de-iced by hot oil returned from engine to tank.
Compressor: Nine-stage axial. Comprises fixed inlet guide vane assembly, first-stage stator ring, upper and lower casings with dovetailed stator blades, ninth-stage stator ring and exit vanes, rotor, and air blow-off valves. Pressure ratio 5·6 at T-O power, 10,530 rpm.
Combustion Chamber: Can-annular. Assembled from diffuser (the structural basis of the engine), inner shroud, 12 flame tubes with transition liners, diaphragm and compressor-shaft shroud.
Fuel Grade: T-1, TS-1 to GOST 10227-62 (DERD.2494, MIL-F-5616).
Turbine: Single-stage compressor turbine, overhung behind rear roller bearing. Two-stage power turbine, overhung on end of rear output shaft. Both turbines rotate counter-clockwise, seen from the rear. Normal power turbine rpm, 7,800-8,300; maximum 9,000. Transmission shaft in three universally-jointed sections, allowing for 10 mm (4 in) misalignment between engine and gearbox.
Jet Pipe: Large fabricated assembly in heat-resistant steel, curved out to side to allow rotor transmission to pass through duct wall in aircooled protecting pipe.
Lubrication: Pressure circulation at 3·45-4·41 bars (50-64 lb/sq in). Separate systems for gas-generator and for power turbine, transmission and gearbox.
Oil Grade: Gas-generator, MK-8 to GOST 6457-66 or transformer oil to GOST 982-56. Power turbine and gearbox, mixture (75-25 Summer, 50-50 Winter) of MK-22 or MS-20 to GOST 1013-49 and MK-8 or transformer oil. Hourly oil consumption, gas-generator not over 1 kg (2·2 lb), power turbine and transmission not over 2 kg (4·4 lb).
Accessories: SP3-12TV electric supply and starting system; fuel supply to separate LP and HP systems; airframe accessories driven off upper and lower gearboxes on inlet casing.
Starting: The SP3-12TV system starts both engines and also generates electric current. It comprises an STG-12TM starter/generator on each engine, igniter unit, two spark plugs with cooling shrouds, two switch-over contactors, solenoid air valve, pressure warning, PSG-12V control panel and electro-hydraulic cutout switch of the TsP-23A centrifugal governor. In the starter mode the system draws current from a ground supply receptacle or from batteries.
Dimensions:
Length overall, bare 2,737 mm (107·75 in)
Length overall with transmission shaft 5,537 mm (218·0 in)
Width 1,086 mm (42·76 in)
Height 1,158 mm (45·59 in)
Weight, Dry:
With engine-mounted accessories 1,325 kg (2,921 lb)
Performance Ratings:
T-O 4,101 kW (5,500 shp)
Rated power 3,504 kW (4,700 shp)
Cruise (1,000 m; 3,280 ft, 135 knots; 250 km/h; 155 mph) 2,983 kW (4,000 shp)
Specific Fuel Consumption:
T-O, as above 108 μg/J (0·639 lb/h/shp)
Cruise, as above 118·1 μg/J (0·699 lb/h/shp)

SOLOVIEV D-30

This two-spool turbofan powers the Tu-134 twin-engined airliner and is derived from the D-20. Major portions of the core and carcase are similar, but the complete power plant is larger than the D-20, and more powerful and efficient.

In turn the D-30 has been developed into the considerably larger D-30K, described separately. They showed a continuing allegiance to the form of power plant pioneered by Rolls-Royce as the 'by-pass turbojet', a term still used in the Soviet Union to describe these engines, in which the LP system comprises several stages and the by-pass ratio is not greater than unity (in the West most turbofans have single-stage fans with a by-pass ratio of from 3 to 8).

Type: Two-shaft turbofan (by-pass turbojet).
Air Intake: Titanium alloy assembly, incorporating air bleed anti-icing of centre bullet and radial struts.
Fan: Four-stage axial (LP compressor). First stage has shrouded titanium blades held in disc by pinned joints. Pressure ratio (T-O rating, 7,700 rpm, S/L, static), 2·65 : 1. Mass flow 125 kg (265 lb)/s. By-pass ratio 1 : 1.
Compressor: Ten-stage axial (HP compressor). Drum and disc construction, largely of titanium. Pressure ratio (T-O rating, 11,600 rpm, S/L, static), 7·1 : 1. Overall pressure ratio, 17·4 : 1.
Combustion Chamber: Can-annular, with 12 flame tubes fitted with duplex burners.
Fuel Grade: T-1 and TS-1 to GOST 10227-62 (equivalent to DERD.2494 or MIL-F-5616).
Turbine: Two-stage HP turbine. First stage has cooled blades in both stator and rotor. LP turbine also has two stages. All discs aircooled on both sides, and all blades shrouded to improve efficiency and reduce vibration. All shaft bearings shock-mounted.
Jet Pipe: Subsonic fixed-area type, incorporating main and by-pass flow mixer with curvilinear ducts of optimum shape. D-30-2 engine of Tu-134A fitted with twin-clamshell (Rolls-type) reverser.
Lubrication: Open type, with oil returned to tank.
Oil Grade: Mineral oil MK-8 or MK-8P to GOST 6457-66 (equivalent to DERD.2490 or MIL-O-6081B). Consumption in flight not over 1·0 kg (2·2 lb)/h.
Accessories: Automatic ice-protection system, fire extinguishing for core and by-pass flows, vibration detectors on casings, oil chip detectors and automatic limitation of exhaust gas temperature to 620°C at take-off or when starting and to 630°C in flight (5 min limit). Shaft-driven accessories driven via radial bevel-gear shafts in centre casing, mainly off HP spool, accessory gearboxes being provided above and below centre casing and fan duct. D-30-2 carries constant-speed drives for alternators.
Starting: Electric DC starting system incorporating STG-12TVMO starter/generators.
Dimensions:
Overall length 3,983 mm (156·8 in)
Base diameter of inlet casing 1,050 mm (41·3 in)
Weight, Dry: 1,550 kg (3,417 lb)
Performance Ratings:
T-O 66·68 kN (14,990 lb st)
Long-range cruise rating, 11,000 m (36,000 ft) and Mach 0·75 12·75 kN (2,866 lb st)
Specific Fuel Consumption:
T-O 17·56 mg/Ns (0·62 lb/h/lb st)
Cruise, as above 21·81 mg/Ns (0·77 lb/h/lb st)

SOLOVIEV D-30K

Despite its designation, this turbofan is very different from the D-30 described previously. It is larger, and has a much higher rating, a by-pass ratio considerably higher, and very few parts (in the core) common to the D-30.

The basic **D-30KU** version, to which the specification details below apply, replaced the Kuznetsov NK-8 as power plant of the Ilyushin Il-62M long-range transport. The more powerful **D-30KP**, rated at 117·7 kN (26,455 lb st), powers the Ilyushin Il-76 freight transport. Clamshell-type thrust reversers are fitted to all four engines of this aircraft, and to the outer engines of the Il-62M. These reversers are not an integral part of the engine but are airframe assemblies incorporated in the nacelle.

Type: Two-shaft turbofan, with integral flow mixer and reverser.
Air Intake: Fabricated from titanium alloy. Fixed spinner and 26 cambered inlet guide vanes anti-iced by air bled from sixth or eleventh stage of HP compressor (depending on rpm). Integral front roller bearing for LP shaft.

The 4,101 kW (5,500 shp) Soloviev D-25V turboshaft

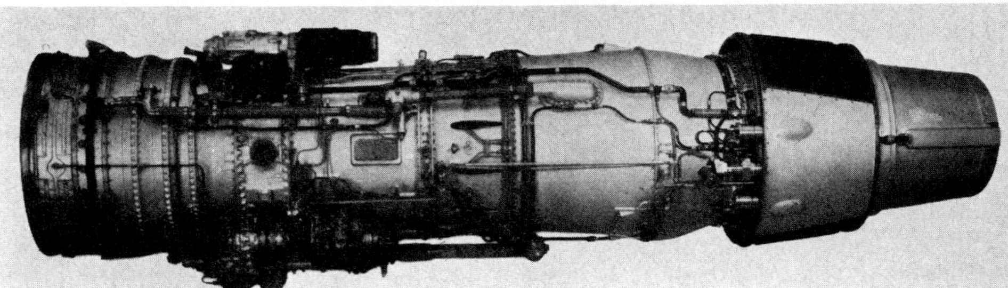
Soloviev D-30 turbofan (66·68 kN; 14,990 lb st) with thrust reverser

FAN (LP Compressor): Three stages, mainly of titanium alloy. First-stage rotor blades held in dovetail slots, with part-span anti-vibration snubbers. Other two stages have pinned rotor blades. Spool rotates between front roller bearing and rear ball bearing, with additional roller bearing behind LP turbine. Drum/disc construction, coupled with tie-bolt and driven by splined shaft connection. Mass flow at take-off, 269 kg (593 lb)/s at 4,730 rpm (87·9 per cent), with by-pass ratio of 2·42.

DIVISION CASING: Linking the LP and HP compressors, this is the main structural attachment band to the aircraft. Magnesium-alloy casting, held by front and rear rows of peripheral bolts. Carries LP mid bearing and HP front bearing and incorporates vertical radial drive to front drive box for accessories on underside.

HP COMPRESSOR: Eleven stages. Drum/disc rotor, with discs centred on shaft by rectangular splines. Rotor blades held in dovetail slots, first two stages having part-span snubbers. Construction of titanium alloys, except for shafts, rear casing, and rotor blades and discs of stages 9-11, and stator vanes of stages 10-11, which are steel. To reduce blade vibration inlet guide vanes are turned through up to 30° according to preset programme over speed range of 7,900-9,600 rpm, while air is bled from fifth and sixth stages under transient conditions; in addition a closed peripheral chamber with perforated walls surrounds the first-stage rotor blades. HP shaft supported in front roller bearing in division casing, ball thrust bearing at rear of compressor spool and roller bearing ahead of turbine. Casing split horizontally. Overall pressure ratio (S/L, static) 20 at HP speed of 10,460 rpm (96 per cent).

COMBUSTION CHAMBER: Cannular type with 12 flame tubes in annular chamber. Each tube comprises hemispherical head and eight short sections welded with gaps for dilution air. Single swirl-type main/pilot burner centred in each tube. Igniter plugs in two tubes. Outer casing and duct shroud provided with longitudinal joints for access to flame tubes and HP turbine nozzle ring.

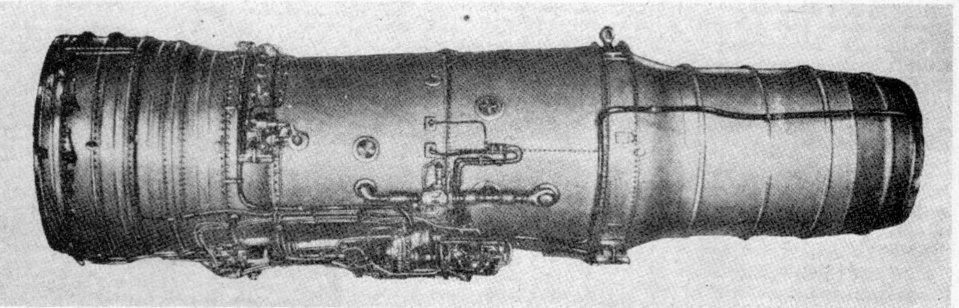

Soloviev D-30KU turbofan (108 kN; 24,250 lb st)

FUEL GRADE: T-1, TS-1, GOST-10227-62, A-1 (D1655/63t), DERD.2494 or 2498, Air 3405/B or 3-GP-23e.

TURBINES: Two-stage HP turbine with first-stage nozzles, part of second-stage nozzles and both sets of discs and rotor blades cooled by HP bleed air. Second-stage rotor blades tip-shrouded. Both discs interchangeable. Take-off inlet gas temperature 1,122°C. Four-stage LP turbine with uncooled shrouded rotor blades carried in four identical discs cooled by by-pass air.

JET PIPE: Downstream of LP turbine a rear support frame serves as the rear structural band attaching the engine to the aircraft. This frame incorporates the rear LP shaft roller bearing and 12 thermocouples, and also includes the 16-chute mixer for the core and by-pass flows.

LUBRICATION: Closed type, with oil returned to tank. Incorporates fuel/oil heat exchanger and centrifugal air separator with metal-particle warning unit.

OIL GRADE: MK-8 or MK-8P to GOST 6467-66 (mineral) or BNII NP-50-1-4F to GOST 13076-67 (synthetic) or Western equivalents.

ACCESSORIES: Front and rear drive boxes underneath engine carry all shaft-driven accessories. Differential constant-speed drive to alternator and air-turbine starter.

STARTING: Pneumatic air-turbine starter fed by ground supply, APU or cross-bleed from running engine. Start cycle time to idling rpm, 40-80 s depending on ambient temperature (limits, −60° to +50°C). In-flight starting up to 9,000 m (27,430 ft) by windmilling.

DIMENSIONS:

Length with reverser	5,700 mm (224 in)
Inlet diameter	1,464 mm (57·6 in)
Maximum diameter of casing	1,560 mm (61·4 in)

WEIGHT, DRY:

With reverser	2,650 kg (5,842 lb)
Without reverser	2,300 kg (5,071 lb)

PERFORMANCE RATINGS (ISA):

T-O 108 kN (24,250 lb st) to 21°C
Cruise at 11,000 m (36,000 ft) and Mach 0·8 27 kN (6,063 lb st)

SPECIFIC FUEL CONSUMPTION:

At T-O rating	13·88 mg/Ns (0·49 lb/h/lb st)
Cruise, as above	19·83 mg/Ns (0·70 lb/h/lb st)

TUMANSKY

Academician Sergei K. Tumansky, who died in 1973, left a legacy of turbojet and by-pass jet engines which were the propulsion basis on which the MiG bureau created the MiG-21, in worldwide service, and the extremely high-performance MiG-25. Tumansky is believed also to have designed the engine of the MiG-23/-27 and Su-15.

TUMANSKY R-11 and R-13

Designated TRD Mk R37F (turbojet R37F) by the Soviet armed forces, the R-11/R-13 family have been built in very large numbers, and two versions have been licence-built by HAL in India. At least one version is produced, without a licence, in China.

A single-shaft turbojet with afterburner, the R-11 entered production in 1956 with dry and afterburning ratings of 38·25 kN (8,600 lb) and 50 kN (11,240 lb) respectively. In 1959 a world speed record was set by the E-66, powered by an R-11-F2-300, with the same dry rating but a new afterburner giving a maximum thrust of 58·36 kN (13,120 lb). This engine also powered the production variant of the E-66, the MiG-21F, as well as the MiG-21PF, FM, FL and possibly other versions.

A very similar engine is the R-11-F2S-300, which powers the Indian-built MiG-21M. It is believed that versions of the R-11 power all known versions of the twin-engined Yak-28.

The R-13-300 incorporates major changes to handle an increased airflow, and has dry and afterburning ratings of 50 kN (11,240 lb) and 64·72 kN (14,550 lb) respectively. It powers the latest known MiG-21 versions, including the MF. It is believed not to be installationally interchangeable with the R-11 series.

Tumansky R-11 built under licence by HAL in India

TUMANSKY R-266

In about 1961 the Tumansky bureau began the design of a jet engine with afterburner considerably more powerful than the R-11 and intended for flight at speeds higher than Mach 3. This engine was adopted by the MiG bureau for the MiG-25 twin-engined fighter. Existence of this Mach 3·2 aircraft was disclosed in April 1965 when its first world record was announced. At that time the aircraft was referred to as the E-266, and its engine as the TRD Mk 31. Thrust rating was given as 98·1 kN (22,046 lb).

Most production versions of the MiG-25 have a pair of R-266 engines. These are extremely simple afterburning turbojets similar in concept to the earlier de Havilland Gyron. The single-shaft compressor has five stages and works at a peak pressure-ratio of about 7 : 1. The single-stage turbine is reported to be uncooled, an extraordinary feature for a Mach 3 engine. Construction is mainly of steel, with a little titanium. Turbine entry temperature is estimated at only 847°C (again a scarcely credible low figure). At supersonic speeds almost all the thrust is provided by the variable inlets, three-ring afterburner and variable nozzle. Special T-6 fuel is used with freezing point of −62·2°C and flash point of 54·4°C. Dry and augmented ratings are (S/L, static) 9,300 kg (20,500 lb) and 12,250 kg (27,010 lb).

A more powerful (R-266F ?) engine powers the latest 'Foxbat' interceptor (said to be the MiG-25MP), and possibly other variants. This engine is rated at 14,000 kg (30,865 lb st), and is almost certainly the same as the RD-F engines of the same rating which power the E-266M aircraft which set time-to-height records in 1975.

TUMANSKY MiG-23 ENGINE

Despite its importance, the engine of the MiG-23 is unknown in the West, though generally attributed to the Tumansky bureau. Basic design of the single-engined variable-geometry MiG-23 dates from 1962-63. Prototypes were flying by 1967, and the MiG-27 tactical attack version was in service by 1970. This has an engine, unofficially said to be designated R-29B, designed for STOL and low-level operation, with large LP compressor (fan) and simple afterburner. Dry and augmented ratings are estimated at 66·72 kN (15,000 lb) and 88·96 kN (20,000 lb) respectively. The engine is installed with simple fixed inlets and has a short two-position nozzle. The MiG-23S all-weather fighter has an engine sharing a common core but having a smaller LP compressor and large afterburner. This engine is designed for supersonic operation at Mach 1·8-2·1, and is fed by fully-variable supersonic inlets and discharges through a large fully modulated primary and secondary nozzle of variable profile. Dry and augmented ratings are estimated at 78·5 kN (17,635 lb) and 112·8 kN (25,350 lb) respectively. As far as can be judged, the same engine is fitted to the MiG-23U two-seat trainer, though it has been suggested that the lower-thrust R-27 is fitted to most aircraft (of all versions) for export.

By early 1979 Western observers seemed to be agreed that a smaller, but possibly related, engine is used in the Su-15 interceptor; the designation is said to be R-25, and the dry and augmented thrusts are given as 40 kN (9,000 lb st) and 23·85 kN (16, 500 lb st) respectively.

VEDENEEV

General Designer in Charge of Bureau: Ivan M. Vedeneev

This designer was responsible for the improvement and development of certain models of the AI-14 piston engine designed by the Ivchenko bureau. He also developed the ASh-62M, produced in Poland as the ASz-62M, from Shvetsov's ASh-62IR nine-cylinder radial. He now heads his own bureau.

M-14V-26

Derived from the Ivchenko AI-14 family of engines for fixed-wing aircraft, the M-14V-26 powers the Kamov Ka-26 helicopter. In this installation the stub-wing carries an engine on each tip. Beneath the rotor an R-26 gearbox combines the power of the engines and distributes it equally between the two co-axial main rotors turning in opposite directions.

It is said to incorporate all the experience gained in many years of developing engines in this class, and shows numerous areas of refinement compared with the AI-14 series. The engine has forced cooling by an axial fan driven via a friction clutch and extension shaft ahead of the main output bevel box at 1·452 times crankshaft speed. The engine planetary gearbox has a ratio of 0·309 and incorporates friction and ratchet clutches. The central R-26 gearbox has a ratio of 0·34; it also drives the generator, hydraulic pump, oil pump and tachometer generator.

Dimensions:
- Diameter 985 mm (38·78 in)
- Length 1,145 mm (45·08 in)

Weight, Dry: 245 kg (540 lb)

Performance Ratings:
- T-O 242 kW; 325 hp at 2,800 rpm
- Max continuous I 205 kW; 275 hp at 2,450 rpm
- Max continuous II 142 kW; 190 hp at 2,350 rpm
- Cruise I 142 kW; 190 hp at 2,350 rpm
- Cruise II 108 kW; 145 hp at 2,350 rpm

Specific Fuel Consumption:
- At cruise ratings 77·7 μg/J (0·46 lb/h/hp)

VEDENEEV M-14P

With this engine Vedeneev reverted to the original fixed-wing application, apparently independently of the Ivchenko bureau. The M-14P is used with direct drive to a fixed-pitch two-blade propeller in the Moscow Aviation Institute OSKB-1-3PM and the Yak-18T.

In the former aircraft the T-O rating is given as 242 kW (325 hp), and in the Yak-18T as 269 kW (360 hp).

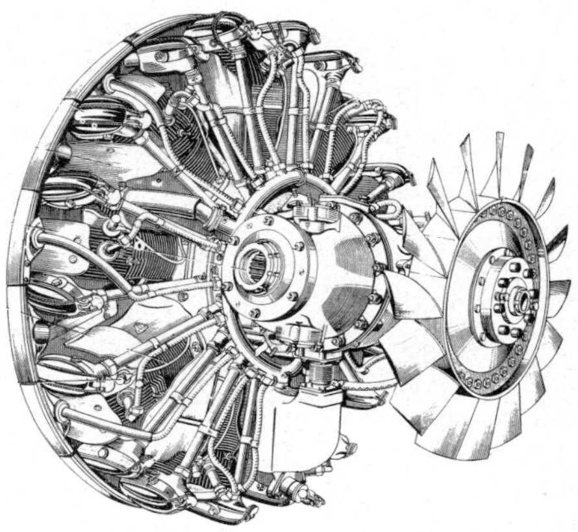

Vedeneev M-14V-26 radial piston engine, with cooling fan, for Kamov Ka-26 helicopter

ENGINES OF UNKNOWN DESIGN

1. **RU 19-300.** Auxiliary turbojet of 8·83 kN (1,985 lb st) for which the initial application was in the Antonov An-24/26/30 transports. Mounted in the rear of the starboard nacelle in place of the TG-16 APU, the RU 19-300 provides additional take-off thrust and also drives an integrally-mounted generator to relieve the aircraft's AI-24T turboprops of supplying electrical power during take-off. This arrangement increases the An-24RV's take-off performance under hot and high conditions, and improves single-engine handling and stability. After take-off, the auxiliary turbojet is shut down and the AI-24Ts are coupled mechanically to the engine-mounted generators. In this dual role the RU 19-300 provides 2·16 kN (485 lb st) for take-off. During flight the auxiliary turbojet is available for use as an APU. The version installed in the An-30 is designated RU 19A-300.

In 1976 it became known in the West that the RU 19 is used to power the La-17 target (see RPVs and Targets section in 1977-78 *Jane's*).

2. **Lift-Jet.** Soviet design bureaux conducted extensive research into jet lift from the late 1950s, and purpose-designed lift-jets were probably flying by 1962 (possibly much earlier). At the 1967 air show at Domodedovo three lift-jet V/STOL research aircraft were displayed. A MiG aircraft based on the MiG-21 had two lift-jets in the mid-fuselage, with a single large inlet door above. A larger MiG, with fuselage and tail closely similar to the eventual MiG-23 but with a small delta wing, had a similar arrangement, differing in detail design of the dorsal door. A Sukhoi aircraft, similar to the twin-engined Su-15, had three lift engines fed by two upper doors. All these installations had large open slots in the dorsal doors (which were hinged at the rear) and transverse louvres filling the ventral jet aperture (probably hinged and under pilot control to give variable forward thrust). Photographs of these aircraft last appeared in the 1971-72 *Jane's*. The two lift-jets used in the Yak-36 VTOL aircraft carried on board the carrier *Kiev* are probably developments of the same engines, though details are not yet known. They could be turbojets or turbofans. The inlet door has open louvres, and it is safe to assume pilot-controlled exit cascades. Thrust estimates for these engines are agreed at around 26·7 kN (6,000 lb) each.

3. **Lift/Cruise Engine.** The Yakovlev V/STOL research aircraft (NATO 'Freehand') demonstrated at the 1967 Domodedovo air show was powered by a twin-nozzle vectored-thrust propulsion system. The use of a large bifurcated nose intake and only two exhaust nozzles suggests that the installation may have used two standard turbojets or turbofans, each fitted with a single swivelling nozzle. On balance, however, it is likely that the 'Freehand' research aircraft used the same large single engine as the Yak-36 combat aircraft carried on board the *Kiev*. This is probably a turbofan, similar in essentials to the British Pegasus and Anglo-German RB.193 (used in the VAK 191B), but with the entire efflux discharged through left and right rear nozzles. The HP spool must be bled to provide air for the reaction control jets at the tail and wingtips. There is no afterburning in this engine, and estimates put its T-O thrust in the 89 kN (20,000 lb st) class.

UNITED KINGDOM

BRISTOL AEROJET
BRISTOL AEROJET LIMITED

Head Office and Works: Banwell, Weston super Mare, Somerset BS24 8PD
Telephone: Banwell (0934-82) 2251
Telex: 44259

Directors:
- Dr F. Llewellyn Smith, CBE (Chairman)
- R. M. Howarth (Managing Director)
- G. A. Harrison
- N. D. Ware
- M. G. Hatley (USA)
- W. J. Blood (USA)
- B. H. McFeely (USA)
- D. P. Nelson (USA)

In 1952 a team was formed to meet the rocket-motor requirements of early British guided missile projects. This team constituted the nucleus of Bristol Aerojet, formed in 1958 by the Bristol Aeroplane Company and the Aerojet-General Corporation of California. The company specialises in the design, development and production of solid-propellant and packaged liquid-propellant rocket motors for missile and research rocket applications.

Bristol Aerojet has supplied production motors for the Bloodhound, Seaslug, Seacat, Tigercat, Rapier, Seawolf, Sea Skua, USD-501, Skylark, Skua, Petrel, Fulmar and INTA Flamenco, and for other flight and ground applications.

The company's rocket-motor manufacturing processes have been licenced to Breda Meccanica Bresciana in Italy and to Instituto Nacional de Tecnica Aerospatial (INTA) in Spain, and are used under different arrangements in Canada and Australia. Under an agreement with the British government the company is supplying British 'plastic' propellant manufacturing and filling technology and equipment for a rocket-motor filling facility set up by INTA, and is able to supply a similar service to other approved organisations.

Bristol Aerojet produces rocket motors to customer requirements, undertakes launcher design, and provides a technical service for assembly and firing of experimental rockets at British and overseas ranges. The company also produces research rockets and ballistic targets.

BRISTOL AEROJET LIQUID MOTORS

Pre-filled, fully sealed motors have been developed in collaboration with the MoD Propellants, Explosives and Rocket Motor Establishment. Flight-proven motors give complex thrust/time programmes on command, and have a shut-down and re-start capability. The simple propellants are smoke-free and offer instant readiness after long storage.

BRISTOL AEROJET SOLID MOTORS

The following details may be published of the principal types of solid rocket motor manufactured by Bristol Aerojet Ltd:

Motor Name	Diam mm (in)	Length mm (in)	Burn Time (s)	Total impulse (kN-s)	Application
Bantam	125 (4·92)	1,473 (58)	33·6	52·0	Skua
Chick	68 (2·68)	554 (21·8)	0·18	4·45	Skua and Petrel boost
Cuckoo	431·8 (17)	1,312 (51·65)	4·1	360·0	Skylark boost
Goldfinch	431·8 (17)	2,224 (87·56)	3·6	701·0	Skylark boost
Lapwing	176·8 (6·96)	1,826 (71·9)	25·0	153·0	Petrel
Raven	431·8 (17)	5,232 (206)	30·0	1,510·0	Skylark
Siskin	141·2 (5·56)	600·0 (23·62)	3·58	16·5	
Waxwing	712 (28)	(spherical)	55·0	845·5	
Heron	257·3 (10·13)	3,364 (132·45)	3·1	418	Flamenco/Fulmar
Snipe	259·8 (10·23)	2,212 (87·1)	15·5	237	Flamenco/Fulmar

DOWTY ROTOL
DOWTY ROTOL LTD

Cheltenham Road East, Gloucester GL2 9QH
Telephone: 0452 712424

Known primarily as a producer of propellers and related rotary devices, Dowty Rotol has developed the propulsion system described below. Though *Jane's* does not include propellers as such, this new development—in the form of an integrated propulsion unit—is exceptional.

DOWTY DUCTED PROPULSOR

Starting with the premise that propeller-driven aircraft are too noisy to meet future noise legislation, and in many cases even existing limits (80 dBA flyover), Dowty began in 1972 to seek an answer. One is the propeller of increased diameter, turning at lower rpm and driven through a large gearbox. This was soon discarded as too costly, heavy and limited in noise reduction, and as generally inapplicable to existing general-aviation aircraft because of propeller-blade clearance and landing gear height. A much better answer was found to be the multi-blade ducted fan, looking superficially like a high bypass ratio turbofan, which can produce not only dramatic reduction in noise but also markedly increased aircraft performance.

In the Spring of 1976 a static test rig was run, driven by a 224 kW (300 hp) Continental IO-520. The fan had seven blades and a diameter of 1,219 mm (48·0 in). The target

Close-up of Dowty Ducted Propulsor on the Islander

static thrust was 5·38 kN (1,200 lb st) and the achieved figure at first build was 5·56 kN (1,250 lb st). The target noise at 305 m (1,000 ft) was 65 dB; the achieved figure was 62 dB. Further development showed how to obtain substantial net thrust from the engine cooling air and exhaust, ducted to a propulsive nozzle at the rear of the nacelle. Very good engine cooling was achieved, despite the extra-tight cowling, and vibration was reduced well below that with a propeller.

In the Autumn of 1976 the Islander was selected as a suitable research and demonstrator aircraft, and Miles-Dufon at Shoreham handled the conversion of both engines (224 kW/300 hp Lycoming IO-540), each being lowered on a pylon below the wing and coupled direct to a fan with large spinner and seven aluminium variable-pitch blades running inside a specially profiled duct carried on six downstream flow-straightener vanes. At full power the 1,219 mm (48 in) fan has a tip speed of only 172 m (565 ft)/s, compared with 287 m (942 ft)/s for the original 2,032 mm (80·0 in) propeller. The reduction in noise is exceptional, and there is a gain in thrust. The Ducted Propulsor Islander flew on 10 June 1977, and has given remarkable demonstrations of quietness and improved performance in the hands of the test pilot, Neville Duke. Noise in the cabin and on the ground has been reduced from about 85 to 65 dB, far below any future environmentalist goal. There are many side benefits, such as reduced pollution from leaner mixture.

Britten-Norman Islander testbed for Dowty Ducted Propulsor

LEONIDES

HARKER & ASSOCIATES

40 Pont Street, London SW1X 0AD
Telephone: 01-584-6720, 01-584-4725

Formerly of Rolls-Royce, Mr Harker is trying to get the Alvis Leonides nine-cylinder geared aircooled radial into agricultural aviation. Over 2,000 h have been flown with the Leonides 125/7 of 418 kW (560 hp) in an Ag-Cat and a Rockwell Thrush Commander R in California, and two Ag-Cat B aircraft are certificated and in use. Approximately 300 used engines are available for use. The intention is to start new production, and negotiations to this end are in progress with companies in the USA and the UK.

Harker & Associates can offer overhauls, and hopes to offer new engines of the Leonides 531 (long-stroke 485 kW, 650 hp) type in 1980. Alvis is supplying technical assistance and spares.

Installation of Leonides 125/7 in Ag-Cat (popularly called Leo-Cat)

LUCAS

LUCAS AEROSPACE LTD

Head Office: Shirley, Solihull, West Midlands B90 2JJ
Telephone: 021-744-8522
Chairman: B. F. W. Scott

Lucas Aerospace was formed in 1971 to bring together Lucas Gas Turbine Equipment Ltd and Rotax Ltd. The Electrical Division at Hemel Hempstead is producing the CT 3201, originally designed by Rover as the TJ.125.

LUCAS CT 3201

This small turbojet was developed as a power plant for surveillance RPVs. Delivery of production engines to MBLE is continuing, for the Belgian company's Epervier surveillance RPV. Discussions are in progress with other drone manufacturers.

Type: Single-shaft turbojet.
Air Intake: Aluminium alloy bifurcated.
Compressor: Single-stage centrifugal. Cast aluminium with steel rotating guide vanes. Rotor hydraulically pressed to shaft. Mass flow 0·93 kg (2·05 lb)/s.
Combustion Chamber: Annular reverse-flow. Six spray burners. High-energy 2 Joule igniter.
Fuel System: Double-datum piston type.
Fuel Grade: JP-4, JP-5 and equivalents.
Turbine: Single, radial-flow, 12 blades integral with steel disc. Retained by sleeve/bolt on shaft, hung behind needle and roller bearings. Inlet gas temperature 917°C.
Accessory Drives: Fuel pump and alternator between intakes driven by toothed belts.
Lubrication System: Self-contained, 100 cc. SAE.5 below 25°C, SAE.10 above.
Dimensions:
Length overall 584 mm (23·0 in)
Max width 269 mm (10·6 in)
Max depth 311 mm (12·25 in)
Weight, Dry: 18·6 kg (41·0 lb)
Performance Ratings:
Max thrust at ISA 0·51 kN (114 lb)
Reduced thrust 0·32 kN (73 lb)

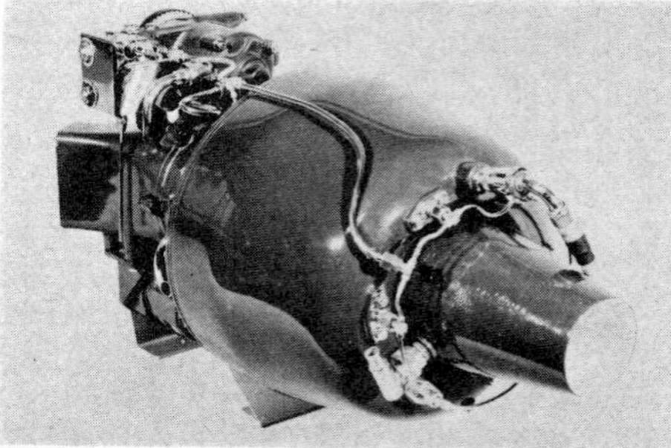
Lucas CT 3201 turbojet of 0·51 kN (114 lb st) as fitted to the MBLE Épervier RPV

Specific Fuel Consumption:
At max rating 37·1 mg/Ns (1·31 lb/h/lb st)

NPT

NOEL PENNY TURBINES LTD

Siskin Drive, Toll Bar End, Coventry CV3 4FE
Telephone: 0203-301528
Directors:
E. R. Ponsford (Chairman)
R. N. Penny (Managing Director)
The Earl of Minto
S. Penny (Secretary)

Noel Penny Turbines was incorporated in 1972. It continues to derive much of its turnover from packaged research and engineering programmes for world-wide clients across the entire spectrum of small gas turbines. It also manufactures its own products.

With modular design philosophy, basic gasifier units can be built up to cover a wide variety of duties. The NPT 101 and 401 turbojets are also available as NPT 109 and 409 blower modules, providing large volumes of low-pressure uncontaminated air for hovercraft and airfield servicing use.

NPT is developing engines of high power/weight and power/bulk ratios which will combine low first cost with economy of operation. Again, the modular design concept will enable these to be offered as single- or two-shaft units, in turbojet, turboprop or ground-power form.

The current aerospace programme is concentrated on small turbojets for unmanned vehicles. Several projects are subject to security classification, but the NPT 401A and simple low-cost NPT 151 and 251 can be described.

NPT 401A, 251

The following description refers to the NPT 401A; NPT 251 differences are given in brackets.

Type: Single-shaft turbojet.
Air Intake: Forward-facing annular.

COMPRESSOR: Axial stage followed by centrifugal in cast aluminium alloy (centrifugal, cast steel). Maximum airflow 2·27 kg (4·99 lb)/s (1·85 kg; 4·07 lb/s, pressure ratio 5·02).

COMBUSTION CHAMBER: Reverse-flow annular with vaporising burners. Single 3 kV spark igniter.

FUEL SYSTEM: LP, pressurised-inlet electric pump, electronic control.

FUEL GRADES: Kerosene, Jet A-1, JP-5.

TURBINE: Single-stage axial, integral blades, cast nickel alloy. Max inlet gas temperature 955°C (1,087°C).

ACCESSORY DRIVES: Alternator on compressor shaft.

LUBRICATION: Total-loss oil mist.

MOUNTING: Pads at compressor-housing flange.

STARTING: External air source on compressor.

DIMENSIONS:
- Diameter: 343 mm (13·5 in)
- Length: NPT 401A: 597 mm (23·5 in)
- NPT 251: 577 mm (22·72 in)

WEIGHT, DRY:
- NPT 401A: 43 kg (95 lb)
- NPT 251: 34 kg (75 lb)

PERFORMANCE RATING (Max S/L):
- NPT 401A: 1·468 kN (330 lb st)
- NPT 251: 1·335 kN (299 lb st)

SPECIFIC FUEL CONSUMPTION (Max rating):
- NPT 401A: 28·8 mg/Ns (1·016 lb/h/lb st)
- NPT 251: 33·4 mg/Ns (1·18 lb/h/lb st)

NPT 151

This recently developed small turbojet is a low-cost engine for single-mission vehicles. It may be adapted later to longer-life applications.

TYPE: Single-shaft turbojet.

AIR INTAKE: Forward-facing annular.

COMPRESSOR: Centrifugal, aluminium alloy. Maximum airflow 1·25 kg (2·75 lb)/s.

COMBUSTION CHAMBER: Straight-through annular with vaporising burners. Ignition by electrically fired pyrotechnic cartridge.

FUEL SYSTEM: LP single-speed, pump mounted on compressor shaft. Control by pump mechanical governor and acceleration unit.

FUEL GRADES: Jet A-1, JP-5.

TURBINE: Inward-radial flow, cast nickel alloy. Max inlet temperature 897°C.

ACCESSORY DRIVES: None.

LUBRICATION: Total-loss oil mist.

MOUNTING: Three brackets on front casing.

STARTING: Windmilling, or by external air source on compressor.

Noel Penny NPT 401A turbojet

DIMENSIONS:
- Diameter: 275 mm (10·83 in)
- Length: 310 mm (12·2 in)

WEIGHT, DRY: 15·0 kg (33·0 lb)

PERFORMANCE RATING (Max S/L): 0·672 kN (151 lb st)

SPECIFIC FUEL CONSUMPTION (Max rating): 34 mg/Ns (1·20 lb/h/lb st)

ROLLASON

ROLLASON AIRCRAFT AND ENGINES LTD

Brighton, Hove and Worthing Joint Municipal Airport, Shoreham-by-Sea, Sussex BN4 5FJ
Telephone: Shoreham-by-Sea 62680

In support of its manufacture (now ended) of the Druine Turbulent light aeroplane, Rollason Aircraft and Engines Ltd undertook the conversion of Ardem 4CO2 power plants for this aircraft, from motor car engines.

Rollason has developed versions of the Ardem engine with capacities of 1,500 or 1,600 cc. Any of these engines can be installed in Nipper aircraft. The Mk X is also used in the Australian Corby Starlet and other homebuilts. A version with single ignition and electric starter powers the Slingsby-built Motor-Falke.

ARDEM Mk X (1,500 cc)

The standard model has a compression ratio of 7·8 : 1 and gives 33·6 kW (45 hp) at 3,300 rpm for take-off, with a fuel consumption of 17 litres (3·75 Imp gallons)/h at max rating. In addition, a high-compression version is available, as follows:

CYLINDERS: Bore 83 mm (3·27 in). Stroke 69 mm (2·72 in). Cast steel barrels, light alloy heads. Compression ratio 8·5 : 1.

PISTONS: Aluminium alloy high-compression pistons, each with two compression rings and one scraper ring. Floating gudgeon pins.

CONNECTING RODS: White metal bearings in big-end. Bronze bearings in little-end.

CRANKSHAFT: Runs in four white metal bearings.

CRANKCASE: Magnesium case.

VALVE GEAR: Two valves per cylinder. Camshaft geared to crankshaft.

INDUCTION: Zenith 32 KL P10 carburettor.

FUEL GRADE: 80 octane.

IGNITION: Lucas SR4 magneto mounted below engine, with chain drive. Two Lodge LH spark plugs per cylinder.

LUBRICATION: Wet sump type, with single gear-type pump.

OIL SPECIFICATION: Shell W80.

PROPELLER DRIVE: Direct drive.

ACCESSORIES: SEV 46C fuel pump.

DIMENSIONS:
- Length: 426 mm (16·75 in)
- Width: 750 mm (29·50 in)
- Height: 559 mm (22·00 in)

PERFORMANCE RATING:
- Max: 39·5 kW (53 hp) at 3,600 rpm

FUEL CONSUMPTION:
- At max rating: 18·2 litres (4·0 Imp gallons)/h

ARDEM Mk XI (1,600 cc)

After extensive testing this engine was approved and is produced as the Ardem Mk XI. It differs from the Mk X in having cylinders of 85·5 mm (3·365 in) bore and dual ignition.

WEIGHT:
- With accessories: 71·6 kg (158 lb)

PERFORMANCE RATINGS:
- Max: 41 kW (55 hp) at 3,300 rpm
- Cruise: 26·5 kW (35·5 hp) at 2,500 rpm

FUEL CONSUMPTION:
- At cruise rating: 12·5 litres (2·75 Imp gallons)/h

ROLLS-ROYCE

ROLLS-ROYCE LIMITED

HEAD OFFICE: 65 Buckingham Gate, London SW1E 6AT
Telephone: 01-222-9020

MAIN LOCATIONS:
PO Box 3, Filton, Bristol BS12 7QE
Telephone: 0272-693871
PO Box 31, Moor Lane, Derby DE2 8BJ
Telephone: 0332-42424
PO Box 72, Ansty, Coventry CV7 9JR
Telephone: 0203-613211
Leavesden, Watford WD2 7BZ
Telephone: 09273-74000
Scottish group of factories to the south of Glasgow

CHAIRMAN AND CHIEF EXECUTIVE: Sir Kenneth Keith

VICE CHAIRMEN:
D. J. Pepper
Marshal of the Royal Air Force Sir Denis Spotswood

MANAGING DIRECTOR, AERO DIVISION: D. A. Head

LONG TERM PLANNING DIRECTOR: R. T. Whitfield

BOARD MEMBERS:
Sir George Burton
Sir St John Elstub
Sir Arthur Knight
A. R. G. Raeburn
Sir Peter Thornton
S. L. Higginbottom

FOREIGN AFFAIRS ADVISER: Sir John Russell

COMPANY SECRETARY: J. R. L. Southam

Rolls-Royce Ltd, which produces a range of gas turbines and ramjets, retains the experience in aircraft engines built up over more than 60 years by the predecessor companies that it incorporated. The company also represents British experience in lightweight high-power gas turbines for industrial and marine purposes, since such engines were first derived from aircraft gas turbines.

More than 220 million hours of operating experience have been accumulated with Rolls-Royce civil and military gas turbines, which are used by 241 airlines and 98 armed forces.

In addition to the products designed, developed and manufactured solely in Britain, the company works with partners abroad on a number of joint civil and military aircraft engine programmes. Licences for the manufacture of Rolls-Royce engines or components are also held by many countries throughout the world.

The main activities are at Derby, Glasgow, Bristol, Coventry and Leavesden, where aircraft gas turbines are produced, and at Ansty, where aircraft gas turbine techniques are applied to industrial and marine uses. A total of 58,570 people are employed.

Rolls-Royce engines in commercial service include the RB.211, Spey, M45H and Conway turbofans, Avon, Viper and RB.162 turbojets, and Dart and Tyne turboprops. New civil engines include the RB.211-535, RB.401 and proposed RB.432. Military engines include the Pegasus vectored-thrust turbofan and Odin ramjet, as well as versions of the Spey, Conway, Avon, Viper, Dart and Tyne. Helicopter engines include the Gem, Gnome and (with Turboméca) Turmo and Astazou. Under the International heading in this section are described the RB.199 (Turbo-Union), Adour (with Turboméca), Olympus 593 and M45SD-02 (with SNECMA) and TF41 (with Detroit Diesel Allison).

Versions of several Rolls-Royce aircraft gas turbines are used as power units for large and small ships, hydrofoils, air cushion vehicles, electricity-generating sets, gas and oil pumping equipment and for other industrial uses.

ROLLS-ROYCE TURBOMÉCA ADOUR

This turbofan was designed by Rolls-Royce and Turboméca. It is described in the International part of this section.

ROLLS-ROYCE RB.199

This advanced augmented turbofan is the power unit for the Panavia Tornado. The RB.199 programme is managed by Turbo-Union (see International part of this section).

ROLLS-ROYCE RB.211

The RB.211 is a family of advanced technology three-shaft turbofans of high by-pass ratio and high pressure ratio, with thrusts so far announced from 163 kN (36,720 lb) to 244·65 kN (55,000 lb). The engine was selected by Lockheed in March 1968 to power the L-1011 TriStar, and later by Boeing as an alternative option on the 747. In August 1978 the lowest-thrust version was selected as launch engine for the Boeing 757.

Rolls-Royce initiated design studies of three-shaft turbofans in 1961 and a twin-spool engine, the RB.178, was tested in 1967 to provide relevant component and gas generator experience. Among the advantages afforded by a three-shaft layout are its ready use of a high pressure ratio with fewer compressor and turbine stages whilst maintaining excellent handling. The need for compressor variable stator mechanisms can also be minimised and the rotating assemblies can be made relatively short and rigid while preserving light construction. As a result the RB.211 has demonstrated outstandingly low seal and aerofoil wear, thus maintaining a high level of performance throughout engine life.

For the Lockheed TriStar, Rolls-Royce developed and now manufactures the complete propulsion system, comprising the engine, fan airflow reverser, pod cowlings and related systems, and noise attenuation for the intake, fan cowl and turbine exhaust duct.

The engine is divided into seven modules. This permits rapid change of engine parts, and enables service life to be set up individually for each module. It also facilitates rapid repair, as a damaged or time-expired module can be replaced with the engine installed in the aircraft. Maximum provision is made for in-service monitoring of engine condition and visual inspection on the ground of all engine sections.

The RB.211 combustion chamber is of annular design, giving significant advantages over tubo-annular systems in terms of reduced cost, weight and length, and improved efficiency. The reduced length makes a two-bearing HP system possible, with both bearings located away from the high temperatures of the combustion area. Detailed design has been aimed at reducing exhaust contaminants to a minimum. To reduce fan noise the RB.211 has no inlet guide vanes. Throughout the compressors and turbines the blade spacing, and the numerical ratios of rotor and stator blades in each stage, have been carefully chosen for minimum noise generation consistent with optimum performance. Additional noise attenuation is achieved by the use of acoustic lining material in the intake, fan and turbine exhaust ducts.

The **RB.211-22B**, the standard engine of the L-1011-1 TriStar, is flat rated at 187 kN (42,000 lb st) to 28·9°C. This engine was certificated in February 1973 by the CAA and in April 1973 by the FAA. By the end of 1977 more than 570 engines had been delivered, and engine flight hours in service were in excess of 4·5 million.

The **RB.211-524** represents the initial step in the RB.211's programme of growth. It preserves maximum commonality with the -22B but has increased core airflow, slightly higher turbine gas temperature and improved component efficiency. The -524 entered airline service in 1977 with the L-1011 and 747.

Engines for the extended-range TriStar are rated at

213·5 kN (48,000 lb) to 28·9°C and are designated RB.211-524. Engines for B.747 aircraft have identical configuration but have been certificated at 222·4 kN (50,000 lb) to 28·9°C and are designated **RB.211-524B.**

The **RB.211-524D** is an improved engine for heavier versions of the Boeing 747 and other aircraft. It is rated at 235·75 kN (53,000 lb st) and is scheduled for certification in 1980.

The **RB.211-524G** is an improved-performance engine due to be certificated in 1981 at 244·65 kN (55,000 lb st).

The **RB.211-535C** is rated at 166 kN (73,390 lb st) for the Boeing 757. In this application a policy of flexible thrust rating means that the -535C will be unlikely to operate at thrusts greater than 149 kN (33,500 lb st). It has the HP module of the RB.211-22B, a six-stage IP compressor and a scaled-down version of the RB.211-524B fan. Fan airflow is 25 per cent lower than that of the -22B, and core airflow 16 per cent lower. The engine runs at lower temperatures, pressures and velocities than the 22B, resulting in exceptionally low noise and high propulsive efficiency.

The **RB.211-535D** is offered for future applications at a rating of 172 kN (38,700 lb st).

The following description relates to the RB.211-22B:

TYPE: Three-shaft axial turbofan.

AIR INTAKE: Forward-facing pitot.

LP FAN: Single-stage overhung fan driven by LP turbine, the whole rotor assembly being supported on three bearings. Front bearing is large roller, squeeze-film supported behind fan. Axial location of rotor is by inter-shaft ball bearing in rear end of IP compressor drum. LP turbine supported on roller bearing, squeeze-film mounted in exhaust cone panel. Rotating spinner supported from fan rotor disc and hot-air anti-iced via central feed-tube within shaft. Titanium alloy used for 33 fan rotor blades, and steel for 70 fan outlet guide vanes. Titanium fan disc bolted with curvic coupling to LP shaft. Aluminium fan casing. Total fan airflow (T-O rating), 626 kg (1,380 lb)/s (-524, 657·7 kg; 1,450 lb). By-pass ratio 5 : 1 (-524, 4·4 : 1.)

IP COMPRESSOR: Seven-stage compressor rotor driven by IP turbine and supported on three bearings located directly in support panels. Front squeeze-film bearing is roller. Mid bearing at rear of IP compressor is ball bearing providing axial location for IP rotor. Rear bearing is roller, squeeze-film supported in panel between HP and IP turbines. Two drums, one of titanium discs welded together and the other of welded steel discs, are bolted to form one rotor, carrying titanium rotor blades. Aluminium and steel casings carry aluminium and stator steel blades. Single-stage titanium variable inlet guide vanes.

HP COMPRESSOR: Six-stage compressor rotor driven by HP turbine connected by large-diameter shaft and carried on ball location bearing at front and roller bearing mounted at the rear in panel behind HP turbine disc. Welded titanium discs, a single steel disc and welded nickel alloy discs are bolted together to form the rotor, carrying titanium, steel and nickel alloy blades. Steel casing carries steel and Nimonic stator blades. Overall pressure ratio 25 : 1.

COMBUSTION CHAMBER: Fully annular, with steel outer casings and Nimonic combustor. Downstream fuel injection by 18 airspray burners with annular atomisers. Ignition by high-energy igniter plugs in Nos 8 and 12 burners.

HP TURBINE: Single-stage axial unit with nozzle guide vanes and Nimonic rotor blades, both rows aircooled. Convection and film-cooled blades mounted in Nimonic disc by fir-tree roots.

IP TURBINE: Single-stage axial unit with Nimonic nozzle guide vanes and Nimonic rotor blades. NGVs aircooled. Rotor blades fir-tree mounted in Nimonic disc.

LP TURBINE: Three-stage axial unit with Nimonic rotor blades fir-tree mounted in steel discs.

JET PIPE: Steel jet pipe without spoiler.

ACCESSORY DRIVES: Radial drive from HP shaft to gearbox on fan casing. Accessories driven include integrated-drive generator and aircraft hydraulic pumps.

LUBRICATION SYSTEM: Continuous circulation 'dry sump' system with single gear-type pressure pump and multiple gear-type scavenge pumps. Oil tank 21 litres (37 Imp pints) capacity integral with gearbox.

MOUNTING: Two-point mounting system. Front mount on fan casing takes thrust, vertical and side-loads. Rear link mount on exhaust casing takes torsional, side and vertical loads. Both mounts are fail-safe and allow for carcase expansion.

DIMENSIONS:	
Length overall	3,033 mm (119·4 in)
Intake diameter	2,172 mm (85·5 in)
WEIGHT, DRY:	
RB.211-22B	4,171 kg (9,195 lb)
RB.211-524B	4,452 kg (9,814 lb)
PERFORMANCE RATINGS:	
T-O, flat rated to 28·9°C:	
RB.211-535C	166 kN (37,390 lb st)
RB.211-22B	187 kN (42,000 lb st)
RB.211-524	213·5 kN (48,000 lb st)
RB.211-524B	222·4 kN (50,000 lb st)
RB.211-524D	235·75 kN (53,000 lb st)
RB.211-524G	244·65 kN (55,000 lb st)
T-O flat-rated to 34·2°C:	
RB.211-535D	175 kN (39,410 lb st)
Cruise at 10,670 m (35,000 ft) and Mach 0·85:	
RB.211-22B	41·8 kN (9,400 lb st)
RB.211-524B	51 kN (11,550 lb st)
SPECIFIC FUEL CONSUMPTION:	
At cruise rating, as above:	
RB.211-22B	18·1 mg/Ns (0·640 lb/h/lb st)
RB.211-524B	18·6 mg/Ns (0·657 lb/h/lb st)

Rolls-Royce RB.211-524B three-shaft turbofan (222·4 kN; 50,000 lb st)

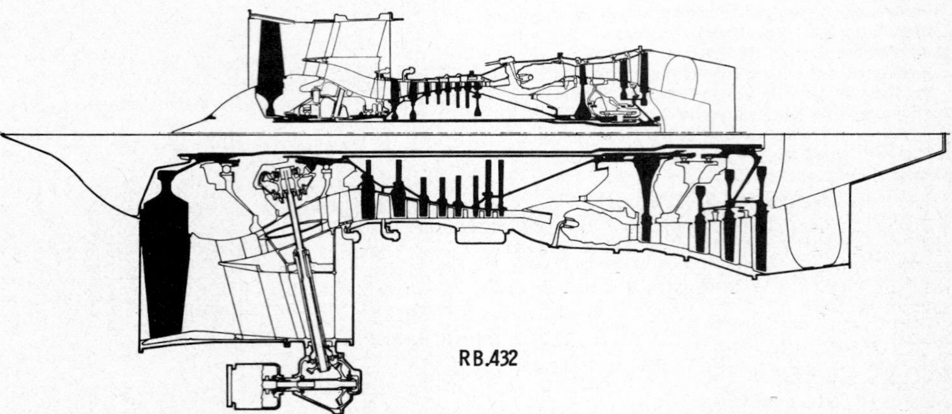

The proposed RB.432 would be largely a scale-up of the RB.401 with an added LP turbine stage. The bottom half of this drawing shows the RB.432-03 of September 1978. A later drawing appears in the Addenda

ROLLS-ROYCE RB.432

This engine is regarded as a possible replacement for the Spey turbofan, in its subsonic transport applications, though in February 1979 it still had no launch application. The RB.432 is a totally new engine, though strongly based on a scale-up of the RB.401 demonstrator with added third LP turbine stage. It has thermodynamic cycle and mechanical design parameters for minimum noise, exhaust pollution, and cost of manufacture and maintenance. Maximum airflow is 250 kg (551 lb)/s; cruise pressure ratio and bypass ratio respectively are 18·0 and 4·9.

DIMENSIONS:	
Diameter (fan case)	1,460 mm (57·5 in)
Length (flange to flange)	2,261 mm (89·0 in)
WEIGHT, DRY	1,580 kg (3,480 lb)
RATINGS:	
Max T-O (S/L, static)	71-80 kN (16,000-18,000 lb st)
Cruise Mach 0·8 at 9,145 m (30,000 ft)	19·8 kN (4,460 lb st)

ROLLS-ROYCE RB.163 CIVIL SPEY

Design of the Spey RB.163 began in September 1959, and the first engine ran at the end of December 1960. Civil Speys are in service in the Trident, BAe One-Eleven, Grumman Gulfstream II and F28 Fellowship, and in the C-8A augmentor-wing research aircraft of NASA. In 1978 the Spey was selected for the Gulfstream III, which like current One-Elevens has noise-suppressing features; it was also subject of a major collaborative production programme between Rolls-Royce and the government of Romania.

The following versions of the civil Spey are in service:

Mk 505-5F. T-O rating of 44·6 kN (10,050 lb st) at 12,150 rpm, for Trident 1C.

Mk 506-14. T-O rating of 46·3 kN (10,410 lb st) at 12,530 rpm, for One-Eleven.

Mk 506-14A. As 506-14 with smaller capacity turbine.

Mk 511-8 and 511-14. T-O rating of 50·7 kN (11,400 lb st) at 12,390 rpm. Mk 511-5 for Trident, Mk 511-8 for Gulfstream II and Mk 511-14 for One-Eleven.

Mk 511-5W and 511-14W. As 511-5 and 511-14 but with water injection to maintain rating to 35°C.

Assembly of the IP compressor of the RB.211-535C, rated at 166 kN (37,390 lb st)

Mk 512-5 and 512-14. T-O rating 53·0 kN (11,930 lb st) in Mk 512-5/50 for Trident 3B, Mk 512-5W and 5W/50 at same rating for Trident 2E, Mk 512-14E at 55·26 kN (12,420 lb st) for One-Eleven, and Mk 512-14W at and Mk 512DW at 55·8 kN (12,550 lb st), all at 12,640 rpm.

Mk 555-15H. Lightened and simplified version, with T-O rating of 43·8 kN (9,850 lb). For F28 Fellowship. Has changed company project number of **RB.183.** Current production version is the 555-15H, flat rated at 44·0 kN (9,900 lb) to 29·7°C; on a 40°C day it gives 6 per cent higher T-O thrust than the 555-15.

The military versions are described separately.

The following details refer specifically to the Spey Mk 512-14DW, as fitted to the BAe One-Eleven Series 500, except where indicated:

TYPE: Two-spool axial-flow turbofan engine.

AIR INTAKE: Annular, with bleed air thermal anti-icing.

COMPRESSOR: Two spools. Five-stage (four-stage on Mks 505, 506 and 555) low-pressure (LP) and 12-stage high-pressure (HP). First-stage HP stator vanes variable-incidence. LP compressor steel drum type, pinned to shaft. HP compressor is of the steel disc type, first stage bolted to shaft, remaining stages splined. HP stator blades steel; LP stators aluminium. LP rotor blades aluminium (Mk 512 titanium 1st stage); HP blades steel and titanium. Stators slotted into casing; rotor blades pinned or dovetailed. LP casing two-piece magnesium. HP casing two-piece steel. Pressure ratio 21·2 : 1 (15·0 on Mk 505 and 555, 17·2 on Mk 506, 18·9 on Mk 510 and 511). Air mass flow 94·4 kg (208 lb)/s (90·27 kg; 200 lb on Mk 505 and 555, 92 kg; 203 lb on Mk 506, 92·5 kg; 204 lb on Mk 510 and 511). By-pass ratio 0·64 : 1 (1·0 on Mk 505, 555 and 506).

COMBUSTION CHAMBER: Tubo-annular with 10 Nimonic sheet liners. Duplex downstream burners, one per chamber. High energy igniters in chambers 4 and 8.

FUEL SYSTEM: Plessey LP pump feeding through fuel-cooled oil cooler and Marston Excelsior fuel heater to LP filter at inlet to Lucas GD pump. HP metered by Lucas regulator, embodying combined speed and acceleration control and fed through Lucas LP governor and shut-off valve to Duple spray nozzles. Maximum pressure 124 bars (1,800 lb/sq in).

FUEL GRADE: DERD.2482 or 2486.

WATER INJECTION SYSTEM: (engines bearing 'W' suffix): Water supplied by Lucas air turbopump through engine-mounted automatic shut-off valve to injector passages in fuel spray nozzles (water sprays into primary airflow through flame tube swirlers).

NOZZLE GUIDE VANES: Hollow cast in nickel-based alloy. HP aircooled.

TURBINES: Two two-stage. First HP aircooled. HP discs nickel-based alloy, bolted to shaft (HP discs steel on Mks 505, 506 and 555). LP discs creep-resisting ferritic steel. Nickel-based alloy blades attached by fir-tree roots.

BEARINGS: LP compressor supported in roller bearings, plus ball thrust bearing. HP compressor has front roller bearing and ball thrust bearing. Turbine bearings all roller type flexibly mounted.

JET PIPE: Fixed-area stainless steel sheet.

REVERSER AND SUPPRESSOR: Normally internal clamshell (Gulfstream II target type, not Rolls-Royce supplied, and F28 has no reverser). Five- or six-chute silencing nozzles available.

ACCESSORY DRIVES: Port gearbox, driven from LP rotor, carries LP governor and LP tacho. Starboard gearbox, driven from HP rotor, carries LP and HP fuel pumps, fuel regulator, main oil pumps, airflow control rpm signal transmitter, starter and HP tacho. Provision in starboard gearbox for aircraft ancillaries.

LUBRICATION SYSTEM: Self-contained continuous circulation. Single pressure pump feeds oil from tank through fuel-cooled oil cooler and HP filter to gearboxes and shaft bearings. Five main scavenge pumps. Tank capacity 6·8 litres (12 Imp pints). Usable oil 5·1 litres (9 Imp pints). Normal pressure 2·41-3·45 bars (35-50 lb/sq in).

OIL SPECIFICATION: DERD.2487.

MOUNTING: Two trunnions, two saddle mountings and one rear mounting.

STARTING: Plessey 220 air-turbine starter. Rotax alternative on Mks 505, 511 and 512; AiResearch on Mk 555.

DIMENSIONS:

Length, less tailpipe:	
Mk 505, 506, 555	2,795 mm (110·0 in)
Mk 510, 511	2,911 mm (114·6 in)
Diameter:	
Mk 505, 506, 555	940 mm (37·0 in)
Mk 510, 511	942 mm (37·1 in)

WEIGHT, DRY:

Mk 505-5	998 kg (2,200 lb)
Mk 506-14	1,024 kg (2,257 lb)
Mk 506-14AW	1,038 kg (2,288 lb)
Mk 510-5, 511-5	1,049 kg (2,312 lb)
Mk 510-14, 511-14	1,058 kg (2,332 lb)
Mk 510-14W, 511-14W	1,188 kg (2,621 lb)
Mk 511-5W	1,050 kg (2,317 lb)
Mk 512	1,168 kg (2,574 lb)
Mk 555-15	1,008 kg (2,222 lb)

Rolls-Royce Spey 555 simplified turbofan rated at 44·0 kN (9,900 lb st)

PERFORMANCE RATINGS:

Max T-O: See under series descriptions

Max continuous:	
Mk 505	42 kN (9,450 lb st) at 12,260 rpm
Mk 506	44·4 kN (9,990 lb st) at 12,385 rpm
Mk 511	48·7 kN (10,940 lb st) at 12,240 rpm
Mk 512, Mk 512DW	51·5 kN (11,580 lb st) at 12,450 rpm
Mk 555-15	42·1 kN (9,470 lb st) at 11,900 rpm
Typical cruise rating at 450 knots (834 km/h; 518 mph) at 9,750 m (32,000 ft):	
All versions	13·7 kN (3,070 lb st)

SPECIFIC FUEL CONSUMPTION:

At T-O rating:	
Mk 505	15·9 mg/Ns (0·560 lb/h/lb st)
Mk 506	15·95 mg/Ns (0·563 lb/h/lb st)
Mk 511	17·3 mg/Ns (0·612 lb/h/lb st)
Mk 555-15	15·9 mg/Ns (0·560 lb/h/lb st)
At typical cruise rating:	
Mks 505, 506	21·5 mg/Ns (0·760 lb/h/lb st)
Mk 510, 511	22·3 mg/Ns (0·790 lb/h/lb st)
Mks 512, 555	22·7 mg/Ns (0·800 lb/h/lb st)

OIL CONSUMPTION:

Max (all Marks)	0·42 litres (0·75 Imp pints)/h

ROLLS-ROYCE RB.168 MILITARY SPEY

The military Spey RB.168 incorporates modifications to meet higher-duty conditions.

Design of the RB.168-1, Mk 101, started in November 1960; this mark powers the Hawker Siddeley Buccaneer strike aircraft.

The RB.168-25R (Mks 202/3) supersonic engine with afterburner has a dry rating of 54·5 kN (12,250 lb) plus a 70 per cent static augmentation and powers the McDonnell Douglas Phantom FG.1 and FGR.2. Major change is the introduction of a robust shaft-and-disc LP compressor. As with Mk 101, use is made of HP compressor bleed air for aircraft BLC purposes. A Plessey gas-turbine starter is fitted. Augmentation is thrust-modulating from an initial boost, at sea level static, of six per cent.

In December 1975 the chairman of Rolls-Royce signed contracts with the Chinese government for an initial supply of supersonic augmented Spey engines and for licence-production of such engines in China. The initial agreement is valued at over £80 million, and the eventual total, including plant and equipment, is expected to exceed £100 million.

In 1978 the Spey was selected by Aeritalia for the proposed AMX (G91 replacement) aircraft; if this materialises, engines will be produced at least partly under licence by Italian companies. The engine selected is the unaugmented Mk 807, rated at 49·0 kN (11,030 lb st), derived from the Mk 101 and the civil Spey 555. The development and production of the Mk 807 is expected to be a two-nation programme lasting into the next century.

The Spey RB.168-20 Mk 250, closely based on the commercial Spey, powers the British Aerospace (HS) Nimrod. Embodying extensive anti-corrosion treatment, this variant provides a higher thrust than its civil counterpart, through operation at higher rpm and higher turbine entry temperature. Provision is made for driving a large alternator.

DIMENSIONS:

Diameter	825 mm (32·5 in)
Length:	
Mks 101, 250	2,985 mm (117·5 in)
Mks 202, 203	5,204 mm (204·9 in)

WEIGHT, DRY:

Mk 101	1,181 kg (2,603 lb)
Mk 250	1,227 kg (2,704 lb)
Mks 202, 203	1,857 kg (4,093 lb)

PERFORMANCE RATING:

Max T-O:	
Mk 101	49·1 kN (11,030 lb st)
Mks 202, 203	91·25 kN (20,515 lb st)
Mk 250	53·4 kN (11,995 lb st)

ROLLS-ROYCE/ALLISON SPEY TF41

Versions of the Spey produced jointly by Rolls-Royce and the Detroit Diesel Allison Division of General Motors are described in the International section.

ROLLS-ROYCE M45

Collaboration between Rolls-Royce Bristol and SNECMA on the M45 series of advanced turbofan engines began in late 1964, and a formal agreement was signed in February 1965. First of the series to be built was the M45F demonstrator engine, which ran for the first time in June 1966.

Under the collaborative agreement a subsonic civil version, the M45H, was developed for the VFW 614 transport. This engine was certificated in 1974 and since 1975 has been in scheduled airline service. In 1976 the companies mutually agreed that Rolls-Royce Ltd should take over full responsibility for the M45H, which is now entirely a Rolls-Royce Ltd product.

M45H-01 ran in January 1969 and was developed to power the twin-engined VFW 614 short-haul airliner, on which it is mounted in unique overwing pods. The M45H-01, with a take-off thrust of 35·0 kN (7,865 lb), passed its type approval test in August 1974.

Modular construction, using ten modules, has been incorporated to reduce strip time for repair and overhaul.

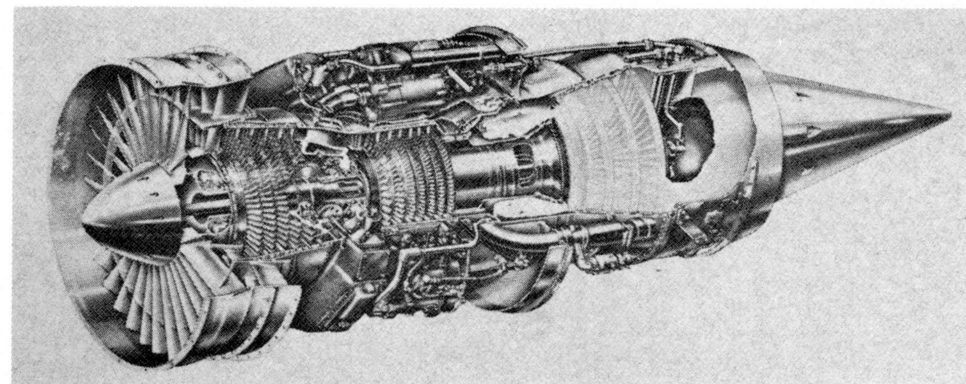

Cutaway drawing of Rolls-Royce M45H-01 civil turbofan, rated at 35·0 kN (7,865 lb st)

Internal inspection for 'on-condition' maintenance is possible by means of borescopes. In addition magnetic chip-detectors, fine filtration in the oil scavenge line and vibration measuring devices assist in giving early warning of incipient failure.

Low gas velocities result in noise levels substantially lower than those of most current engines. The omission of fan inlet guide vanes, and the relatively large fan rotor/stator spacing, result in low compressor noise levels.

Derivatives of the M45H-01 under consideration at present include:

The ultra-quiet demonstrator engine, designated **M45SD-02,** remains a collaborative programme with SNECMA, and is described under the two companies in the International part of this section.

The following particulars apply to the M45H-01:

Type: Twin-spool turbofan.

Air Intake: Pitot, designed to integrate with VFW 614 short-cowl pod.

Fan: Single-stage axial unit integral with the LP system. Blades, in titanium, have snubbers at approximately two-thirds of blade height. Inlet guide vanes omitted to reduce icing problems, weight, cost and noise. Fan centrifuging effect and use of snubbers reduce risk of damage from foreign object ingestion. Mass flow 108 kg/s (238 lb/s). By-pass ratio 3·0 : 1.

LP Compressor: Five-stage axial unit of constant root diameter, driven by LP turbine. Rotor is of monobloc construction to give smooth running and long life. Fan and LP compressor rotor overhung on LP front shaft carried on bearings supported from compressor intermediate casing. Front bearing is main ball thrust unit. Rear bearing is roller providing radial location for interconnection of LP front and rear shafts. Fan and LP compressor casing are single ring assemblies giving stiff construction with high degree of circularity. This, together with use of abradable spacer coatings, gives enhanced compressor efficiency through small blade tip clearances. All compressor stators are punched and brazed into stator rings, eliminating stator wear and fretting. Low-pressure air bleed provided to ventilate accessory zone. No variable-geometry blading.

Intermediate Casing: One-piece casing carrying engine and aircraft accessories, and gearbox. Internally provides support for fan/LP compressor bearings and for HP compressor front bearing. Contains accessory drive gears from LP and HP shafts.

HP Compressor: Seven-stage axial unit of constant tip diameter, driven by HP turbine. Rotor uses multi-disc construction with through bolts and curvic couplings. Front stub shaft carried on main ball thrust bearing supported by compressor intermediate casing. Rear HP disc bolted to HP turbine shaft. HP compressor casing and stator mounting as for LP compressor. High-pressure air bleed provided for aircraft cabin air-conditioning and, when required, engine nose cowl anti-icing system. No variable-geometry blading. Overall pressure ratio 16 : 1.

Combustion System: Short-length annular chamber with vaporising burners.

HP Turbine: Single-stage with air-cooled rotor blading.

LP Turbine: Three-stage axial.

Jet Pipe: Plug nozzle type.

Fuel System: Dowty hydro-mechanical system. Fuel from first-stage centrifugal pump passes through fuel heater and filter, and thence to second-stage gear pump to main control system and acceleration control. Centrifugal governors on LP and HP shafts cause fuel spill-back in event of more than 2 per cent shaft overspeed.

Accessories: Include fuel heater, engine oil cooler, fuel control units, LP and HP governors, alternators, constant speed unit, oil tank, air starter, hydraulic and lubricating pumps.

Lubrication System: Gear-type pressure pump feeds oil to all main bearings, LP and HP drives and accessory gearbox. Oil scavenged from front and rear compartments and from accessory gearbox passes through fuel-cooled oil cooler before returning to tank.

Starting: Air starter on HP accessory gearbox.

Dimensions:

Fan intake diameter 909 mm (35·8 in)
Overall length 2,795 mm (110·0 in)

Weight:

Max, basic 662 kg (1,460 lb)

Performance Ratings:

T-O rating (S/L, ISA) 35·0 kN (7,865 lb st)
Cruise (Mach 0·6, 6,096 m/20,000 ft ISA) 12·9 kN (2,900 lb)

Specific Fuel Consumption:

At T-O rating 12·89 mg/Ns (0·455 lb/h/lb st)
At cruise rating:
Mach 0·60 and 6,096 m (20,000 ft) ISA 20·08 mg/Ns (0·709 lb/h/lb)

ROLLS-ROYCE TYNE

The 4,570 ekW (6,100 ehp) Tyne 22 two-shaft turboprop has been put back into production for the additional Transall C-160 aircraft to be built by Aérospatiale. Like engines for previous Transall aircraft they are made by a consortium comprising Rolls-Royce, SNECMA, MTU and FN. Brief details are given under SNECMA.

Limited production is also being undertaken of the Tyne 20 Mk 801, derated to 4,090 ekW (5,480 ehp) for an export version of the Aeritalia G222.

ROLLS-ROYCE DART

Beginning life in 1945 at 738 kW (990 hp), this classic turboprop was developed to give 2,420 ekW (3,245 ehp) in military and 2,256 ekW (3,025 ehp) in civil versions. Current production of new engines is centred on the less powerful models listed in the accompanying table. About 7,000 Dart engines have been delivered, and demand remains strong.

Type: Single-shaft centrifugal-flow turboprop engine.

Reduction Gear: Double helical high-speed train and final helical drive. Ratio in current engines: 0·093.

Air Intake: Circular intake with annular duct leading to impeller eye of first-stage compressor. Oil tank cast integral with casing. Secondary air intake supplies air to oil cooler.

Compressor: Two-stage centrifugal. Each impeller has nineteen vanes and steel rotating guide vanes. Mass air flow at maximum rpm typically 10·66 kg (23·5 lb)/s at 5·62 : 1 pressure ratio.

Combustion Chambers: Seven inclined flame tubes with atomisers for downstream injection. High-energy igniter plugs in Nos. 3 and 7 chambers.

Fuel System: Variable-stroke pump delivers fuel to burners through flow control unit, which incorporates a filter, throttle valve, shut-off cock and barometric pressure control. Automatically-progressive injection of water/methanol to maintain take-off power under high ambient temperature. System linked with throttle lever to prohibit use except at take-off rpm. Fuel filter de-icing by hot air from compressor.

Turbine: Three-stage axial.

Exhaust Unit: Inclined to suit installation.

Accessory Drives: Gearbox drive from main-shaft centre-coupling immediately behind compressor.

Lubrication: Integral oil tank (14 litres; 25 Imp pints) feeds via standpipe and feathering pump through tank base, to ensure feathering possible even after prolonged system oil leak. Gear pump supplies oil to all bearings and reduction-gear jets.

Controls: Throttle interconnected with propeller controller and high-pressure cock linked with feathering controls. Propeller feathered by moving shut-off cock past closed position.

Mounting: Four feet at 90° on compressor casing, although only three need be used.

Dimensions, Weights and Performance:

See table.

ROLLS-ROYCE ALFA-ROMEO RB.318

This engine in the 448 kW (600 shp) class for general aviation is running in Italy but has not been announced by Rolls-Royce.

ROLLS-ROYCE VIPER

This turbojet remains in production for civil and military customers. More than 5,000 Vipers have been ordered by 41 countries, 29 of which have chosen the engine for trainer and light attack aircraft.

Current versions are as follows:

Viper 11 (Mk 200 Series). Single-shaft seven-stage axial-flow compressor driven by single-stage turbine. Air mass flow 20 kg/s (44 lb/s). Type-tested at 11·12 kN (2,500 lb st) and powers Jindivik Mk 3 drone, BAC Jet Provost T.4 and 5, Yugoslav Soko Galeb and Hindustan HJT-16 Kiran trainers.

A Viper 11 version, the 22-1, was built under licence in Italy by Piaggio for the Aermacchi M.B.326 trainer and by Atlas of South Africa and Commonwealth Aircraft of Australia for similar aircraft.

Viper 500 Series. Development with increased airflow, achieved by zero stage on compressor. Major applications early HS.125 (Mks 521, 522) and PD-808 executive aircraft (Mk 526) and BAC 167 Strikemaster (Mk 535), Aermacchi M.B.326GB (Mk 540) and Soko Jastreb (Mk 531) training and light combat aircraft. Mk 540 built under licence by Piaggio and Atlas.

Viper 600 Series. Eight-stage axial-flow compressor driven by two-stage turbine; annular vaporising combustion chamber. Take-off rating 16·7 kN (3,750 lb st) civil and 17·8 kN (4,000 lb st) military. Agreement signed with Fiat (Italy) in July 1969 for technical collaboration in design, development and production (see Fiat entry).

The civil Viper 601 powers the HS.125-600, and the military Viper 632 is fitted to the Aermacchi M.B.326K and M.B.339. An engine similar to the 632 powers the VTI/CIAR Orao/IAR-93. The Viper 632 is now built under licence in Italy, Romania and Yugoslavia.

The following details apply to the Viper 600 series:

Type: Single-shaft axial turbojet.

The 1,700 ekW (2,280 ehp) Rolls-Royce Dart 535 single-shaft turboprop, typical of the versions in production

ROLLS-ROYCE DART TURBOPROP ENGINES (current production)

Mark Number	Take-off Guaranteed Maximum Power	Maximum Cruise Rating and Specific Fuel Consumption (250 knots; 463 km/h; 288 mph at 6,100 m; 20,000 ft)	Maximum Basic Dry Weight	Length (without jet pipe)	Diameter	Application
535-2	1,700 ekW; 1,551 kW (2,280 ehp; 2,080 shp) at 15,000 rpm	957 kW (1,284 shp); 104 μg/J; at 14,200 rpm	639 kg (1,409 lb)	2,496 mm (98·27 in)	963 mm (37·9 in)	BAe.748
536-7R	1,730 ekW; 1,580 kW (2,320 ehp; 2,120 shp) at 15,000 rpm	957 kW (1,284 shp); 104 μg/J; at 14,200 rpm	639 kg (1,409 lb)	2,496 mm (98·27 in)	963 mm (37·9 in)	F 27

Air Intake: Direct pitot. Anti-icing by hot compressor air. No inlet guide vanes.
Compressor: Eight-stage. Steel drum-type rotor with disc assemblies. Magnesium alloy casing with blow-off valve. Stator blades mounted in carrier rings slotted into casing. All stator blades and 1st, 2nd and 8th stage rotor blades of steel; remainder aluminium alloy. Zero-stage and first-stage rotor blades attached by fir-tree roots; stages 3-8 riveted. Pressure ratio 5·8 : 1. Air mass flow 26·5 kg (58·4 lb)/s.
Combustion Chamber: Short annular type with 24 vaporising burners and six starting atomisers. Electric ignition.
Fuel System: Hydromechanical, consisting primarily of fuel pump, barometric fuel control and air/fuel ratio control.
Fuel Grade: JP-1 or JP-4.
Turbine: Two-stage axial. Shrouded blades attached to discs by fir-tree roots and locking strips. Discs attached by Hirth couplings.
Bearings: Ball-thrust type at forward end of compressor, roller bearings at centre section and at rear end of combustion chamber inner casing.
Jet Pipe: Cone of heat-resisting steel rings butt-welded together. (Viper 601: eight-lobe convoluted nozzle to meet FAR Pt 36 noise requirements).
Accessory Drives: Gearbox driven from front of compressor by bevel gear.
Lubrication System: Self-contained. Recirculatory system supplying front bearing and gearbox, metered feed supplied to centre and rear bearings by micro-pumps. Military version fully aerobatic.
Oil Specification: Mobil Jet 2, Shell ASTO 500 and Castrol 580.
Mounting: Civil: cantilevered, side mounted, single spherical bearing in centre-section casing, with top and bottom links and attachment at intake casing. Military: trunnion mounted at centre-section with additional support at intake casing.
Starting: 24V starter/generator.
Dimensions:
Max casing diameter:
All versions 624 mm (24·55 in)
Length (flange to flange):
Viper 11 1,626 mm (64·0 in)
Viper 521, 522 (plus jet pipe and nozzle) 2,159 mm (85·0 in)
Viper 531, 535, 540, 632 1,806 mm (71·1 in)
Viper 601 (plus jet pipe) 2,270 mm (89·4 in)
Weights, Dry:
Viper 11 284 kg (625 lb)
Viper 521 336 kg (740 lb)
Viper 522, 531 345 kg (760 lb)
Viper 526 340 kg (750 lb)
Viper 535 331 kg (730 lb)
Viper 540 342 kg (755 lb)
Viper 601, 632 358 kg (790 lb)
Performance Ratings:
T-O:
Viper 11 11·12 kN (2,500 lb st)
Viper 521, 531 13·9 kN (3,120 lb st)
Viper 522, 526, 535, 540 14·9 kN (3,360 lb st)
Viper 601 16·7 kN (3,750 lb st)
Viper 632 17·8 kN (4,000 lb st)
Specific Fuel Consumption:
Viper 11 30·3 mg/Ns (1·07 lb/h/lb st)
Viper 500 series 28·3 mg/Ns (1·00 lb/h/lb st)
Viper 601 26·6 mg/Ns (0·94 lb/h/lb st)
Viper 632 27·5 mg/Ns (0·97 lb/h/lb st)
Oil Consumption:
All versions 0·57 litres (1 Imp pint)/h

ROLLS-ROYCE RB.401

The RB.401 is a two-shaft, medium by-pass ratio, turbofan in the 24·5 kN (5,500 lb) thrust class. It is aimed principally at the business jet market, but could also have application to trainer/light attack aircraft.

A demonstrator engine, the RB.401-06, ran on the testbed on 21 December 1975. The engine now under development for the business-aviation market is the RB.401-07. This engine first ran in November 1977, exceeding its T-O rating after six hours of testing, with fuel flow within 2·0 per cent of brochure specification.

The RB.401 incorporates components already proven in company research programmes, with technology which reads across from the RB.211 and other advanced commercial engines. It has been designed to meet all foreseeable requirements regarding noise and exhaust pollution, in addition to having an extremely low specific fuel consumption.

The following data apply to the RB.401-07:
Type: Two-shaft turbofan.
Fan: Single-stage axial, based on latest RB.211 technology. Low aspect ratio titanium blades without snubbers. Maximum airflow 82·5 kg (182 lb)/s. Bypass ratio 4·2 : 1.
By-Pass Duct: Full-length, giving installational simplicity with optimum overall nacelle performance.
Intermediate Casing: One-piece magnesium casting incorporating accessory-gearbox drive.

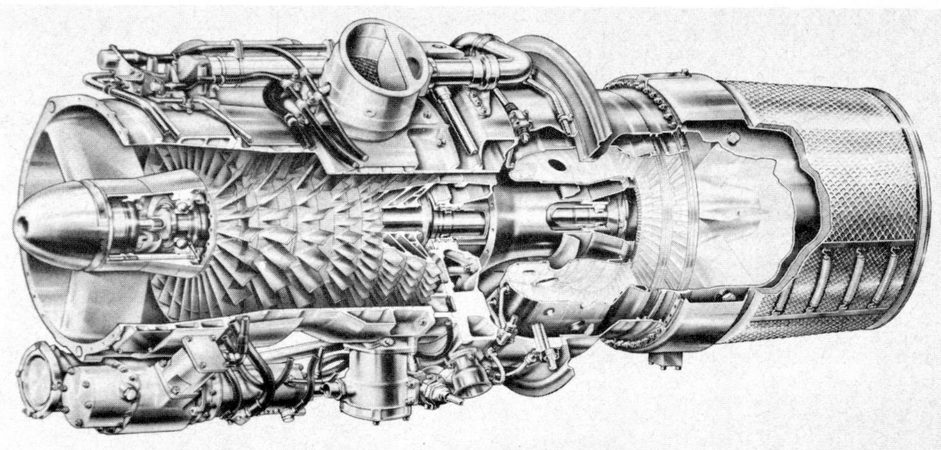

Cutaway drawing of the Rolls-Royce Viper 632 single-shaft turbojet (take-off rating 17·8 kN; 4,000 lb st)

HP Compressor: Eight-stage axial. Titanium rotor blades and nickel-alloy stator blades. Inlet guide vanes and first-stage stators have variable stagger. Pressure ratio of HP spool alone, 11·5 : 1.
Combustion System: Annular, with vaporising burners.
Fuel System: Hydromechanical, with provision for electronic supervision of engine parameters.
Turbines: Single-stage HP turbine, with aircooled rotor and stator blades. Two-stage LP turbine, with uncooled fully-shrouded blades.
Lubrication System: Self-contained, including tank, pumps, filter, scavenge strainer, tubes, fittings, and cooler.
Dimensions:
Length, flange to flange 1,544 mm (60·8 in)
Diameter, fan casing 823 mm (32·4 in)
Weight, Dry: 447 kg (985 lb)
Performance Ratings:
T-O (flat-rated to 15°C):
S/L, ISA 24·7 kN (5,540 lb st)
Cruise:
Mach 0·7 and 12,000 m (40,000 ft) ISA 5·0 kN (1,130 lb)
Specific Fuel Consumption:
T-O 12·72 mg/Ns (0·449 lb/h/lb st)
Cruise (as above) 20·0 mg/Ns (0·707 lb/h/lb)

ROLLS-ROYCE ORPHEUS

This single-spool turbojet was initiated in December 1953 as a private venture. The Orpheus 701 was type-tested in November 1956 at 20·1 kN (4,520 lb st) and is used in the Gnat fighter; a modified version powers the Indian HAL Ajeet.

The Mk 703, rated at 21·6 kN (4,850 lb st), is in service with the Indian Air Force in the Hindustan HF-24 Marut fighter. For all Indian applications the engine is built under licence at Bangalore by Hindustan Aeronautics Limited (HAL). A description appeared in the 1967-68 *Jane's*.

ROLLS-ROYCE OLYMPUS

The Olympus was the first British two-spool turbojet. The engines currently in service with the Vulcan B.2 are the Mk 301 (89 kN; 20,000 lb). From these has been derived a range of Industrial Olympus in worldwide use for power generation and gas pumping, and Marine Olympus in use as propulsion units for medium and large warships of twelve navies.

Details of the more powerful Olympus 593 for the Concorde are given in the International section.

ROLLS-ROYCE PEGASUS

The Pegasus is a turbofan for V/STOL applications. It has two main rotating systems which are mechanically independent and rotate in opposite directions, thus minimising gyroscopic effects. It has a three-stage axial-flow fan of transonic design and an eight-stage high-pressure compressor, each driven by a two-stage turbine. Thrust vectoring is achieved by four rotatable nozzles simultaneously operated and symmetrically positioned on each side of the engine. The front nozzles discharge by-pass air, whilst the rear nozzles discharge the turbine efflux. The total thrust is divided between the four nozzles, and the resultant thrust passes through a fixed point irrespective of nozzle angle, thus minimising aircraft control problems. HP bleed air is used for aircraft stabilisation. The Pegasus was the first engine designed with an overhung fan, without inlet guide vanes, requiring no anti-icing.

By varying the angle of the nozzles, an aircraft powered by the Pegasus can take off vertically or with a short run or with a conventional long run. The reserve of power in the normal runway take-off allows for an appreciable increase in payload. The engine is stressed for operation up to Mach 2, ISA tropopause, at maximum thrust.

The Pegasus ran in August 1959, and flight trials in the Hawker Siddeley P.1127 prototypes began in October 1960. The **Pegasus 3,** which powered prototype P.1127 aircraft, was rated at 60 kN (13,500 lb st). The engine entered service in the Harrier with the RAF in 1969 and later with the AV-8A of the USMC and Matador of the Spanish Navy. These aircraft have the Pegasus 11 Mk 103, rated at 95·6 kN (21,500 lb st).

This engine is cleared to use VIFF (vectoring in forward flight) to enhance combat manoeuvrability. A variant of the Pegasus 11 is the **Mk 104** for maritime operation. The LP and intermediate casings are of corrosion-resistant materials, and the gearbox drive is strengthened for higher electrical power generation. The Mk 104 powers the first 34 Sea Harriers ordered for the Royal Navy. In US service the Pegasus 11 has the British designation **Mk 803** and the US designation **F402-RR-402.**

The proposed engine for the McDonnell Douglas/BAe AV-8B (Advanced Harrier) is the **F402-RR-404** with improved maintainability and TBO of not less than 1,000 hours. The US Navy AV-8B+ will be powered by an F402 with new fan giving 6·72 kN (1,500 lb) additional T-O thrust. The first of two YAV-8B prototypes powered by F402 engines with new front nozzles began flight development in November 1978.

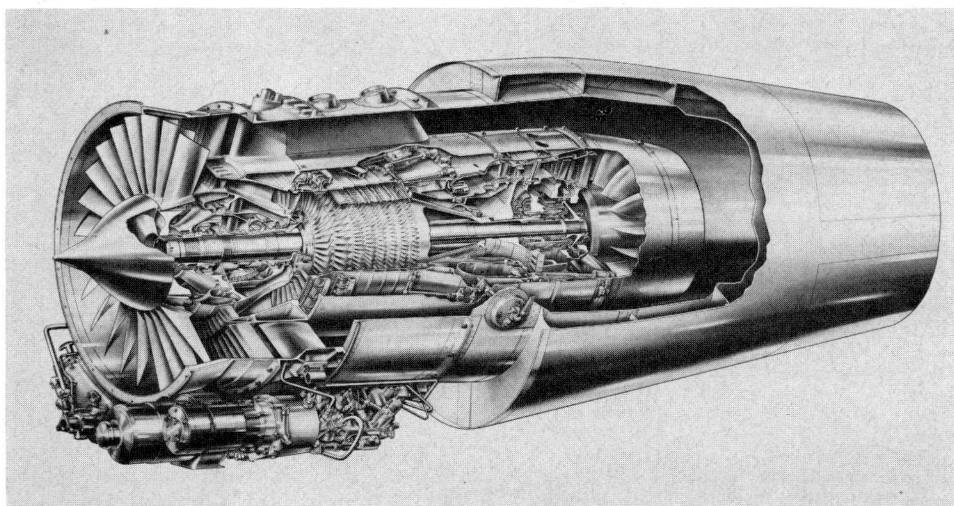

Cutaway drawing of the Rolls-Royce RB.401-07 turbofan (24·7 kN; 5,540 lb st)

The following data apply specifically to the Pegasus 11:

Type: Two-shaft vectored-thrust turbofan.

Air Intake Casing: One-piece casting in ZRE magnesium-zirconium alloy (Mk 104, aluminium).

Fan: Three-stage axial, overhung ahead of front bearing. Titanium blades with part-span snubbers. Maximum airflow 196 kg (432 lb)/s. Pressure ratio 2·3 : 1. By-pass ratio 1·4 : 1.

Intermediate Casing: Houses front fan bearing, accessory drives and HP compressor front bearing. All engine-driven accessories mounted above this casing.

HP Compressor: Eight-stage with titanium rotor blades. Overall pressure ratio 14 : 1.

Combustion System: Annular, with low-pressure vaporising burner system.

Fuel System: Hydromechanical, comprising centrifugal backing pump, gear-type pressure pump, HP shut-off cock and overspeed governors and emergency manual control.

Turbines: Two-stage HP turbine and two-stage LP turbine. First-stage HP blades precision cast. Remaining three rotor stages have forged blades. Both HP stages aircooled.

Thrust Nozzles: Two steel cold front-thrust nozzles and two Nimonic hot thrust nozzles, actuated by duplicated air motors through shafts and chains. Vectored-thrust control by pilot command lever.

Lubrication System: Self-contained, comprising pressure pump and three scavenge pumps, with fuel-cooled oil cooler.

Mounting: Four-point suspension, with main trunnions on each side of delivery casing and tie link at rear of turbines.

Starting: Gas-turbine starter/APU on intermediate casing.

Dimensions:

Length, without nozzles	2,510 mm (98·84 in)
Diameter, fan casing	1,220 mm (48·05 in)
Length, with nozzles	3,480 mm (137 in)

Weight, Dry (without nozzles):

Mk 103	1,404 kg (3,096 lb)
Mk 104	1,429 kg (3,148 lb)

Performance Ratings:
See under sub-type descriptions.

ROLLS-ROYCE ODIN

The Odin ramjet powers the British Aerospace Sea Dart, which has been developed to meet a Royal Navy and NATO requirement for a medium-range guided weapon system for small warships. The Sea Dart is in service with HMS *Bristol* and Type 42 destroyers of the Royal and Argentine Navies and will equip the anti-submarine cruiser HMS *Invincible*. The ramjet forms an integral part of the missile body, and gives a longer range and better performance characteristics against fast-manoeuvring targets than a solid-rocket-powered missile. Details of the Odin are classified.

ROLLS-ROYCE TURBOMÉCA RTM.321

This projected turboshaft engine is briefly referred to under the International heading and in the Addenda.

ROLLS-ROYCE GEM

The Gem was designed and developed at Leavesden, for the Lynx helicopter. Although this is an element of the Anglo-French helicopter programme, the Gem development programme has been funded entirely by the British government. Production engine deliveries, with a proportion of parts supplied by Turboméca of France, began in 1975. In 1978 the Arab British Engine Company was formed to build an expected 750 Gems and spares under licence in Egypt.

Choice of a two-spool gas generator gives fast response to power demand without the need for a complex control system. Conservative stressing and thermo-dynamic loading, and use of proven design and manufacturing techniques, are features which experience has shown to contribute to engine reliability.

The design concept of the engine is based upon seven major modules, each capable of being assembled, tested and released as interchangeable units for service use in the interest of reducing the operator's product support commitments.

The nine main bearings each have labyrinth seals pressurised by LP compressor air which also cools the bearings and minimises heat transfer to the oil, and oil cooler and fan requirements.

Provision is made for in-flight and on-ground condition monitoring systems. Features include access ports for intrascope inspection of each LP compressor stage, HP compressor, combustor, LP turbine and power turbine, and mountings for vibration pickups.

Three versions have been announced:

Gem Mk 10001. Engine-change unit for Lynx, rated at 671 kW (900 shp). In quantity production, shared with Turboméca. Entered service in 1976.

Gem 2. Export military engine, rated at 900 shp. In service with foreign governments.

Gem 4. First stage of uprating programme; rated at 1,050 shp. Based on Gem 2 with modified LP compressor to increase mass flow by approximately 10 per cent, together with small increase in turbine entry temperature. In production for 4,762 kg (10,500 lb) Lynx.

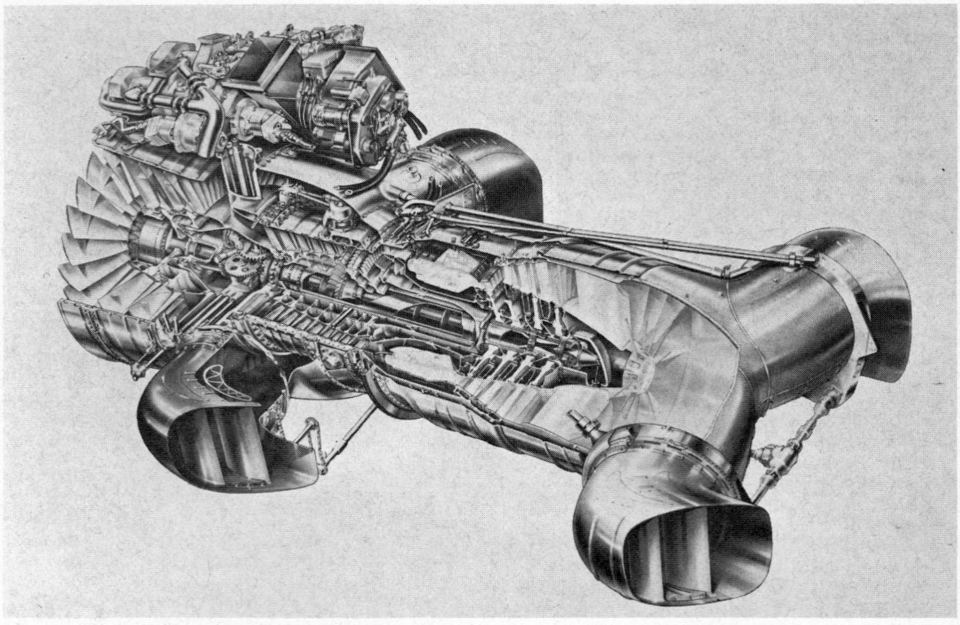

Cutaway drawing of the Rolls-Royce Pegasus 103 turbofan (95·6 kN; 21,500 lb st)

Gem 41. Further power growth with minimal change to Gem 4 to provide new range of ratings to meet future helicopter requirements. Fitted to Westland WG.30 Lynx derivative.

The following description relates to the Gem Mk 10001; other versions are generally similar:

Type: Free-turbine turboshaft, with two-spool gas generator.

Air Intake: Annular forward facing.

Shaft Drive: Compact single-stage double-helical reduction gear with rotating planet cage carried by ball bearing at front and roller bearing at rear. Reduction gear mounted within intake casing and driven by power turbine shaft. Gearbox comprises No. 1 module, and power turbine shaft No. 2 module. Gearbox provides governed output speed of 6,000 rpm. No. 2 module provides for signal to phase-displacement torquemeter (customer option).

LP Compressor: Four-stage axial. LP compressor and intake case comprise No. 3 module.

HP Compressor: Single-stage centrifugal impeller having alternate inducer and radial vanes. Combined radial-and-axial diffuser feeds compressor delivery air to annular combustor. Overall pressure ratio 12·0 : 1.

Combustion Chamber: Fully annular reverse-flow with air-atomiser fuel sprays supplied by external fuel manifold. High-energy ignition box mounted on power turbine/jet pipe case.

HP Turbine: Single-stage axial close-coupled to HP impeller. Rotor blades and aircooled nozzle guide vanes based on R-R Dart technology. HP spool with compressor intermediate casing and combustor comprise No. 4 module.

LP Turbine: Single-stage axial with shrouded rotor blades, drives LP compressor. LP turbine and main shaft comprise No. 6 module.

Power Turbine: Two-stage axial with shrouded rotor blades. Rear of power drive shaft drives output speed governor and overspeed fuel cut-off trip mechanism via spur and bevel gear train in exhaust cone. Power turbine and jet pipe form No. 7 module.

Jet Pipe: Short-length duct with casing extending forward to combustor rear casing. Four cruciform struts integral with exhaust cone.

Accessory Drives: Bevel gear on front of HP compressor shaft drives accessory shaft extending through compressor intermediate casing to spiral bevel gear drive to accessory wheelcase mounted atop intermediate casing. Drives provided for starter/generator, fuel pump, oil cooler fan and other accessories. Wheelcase forms No. 5 module.

Fuel System: Plessey fuel system with fluidics circuit providing fully automatic control, and power matching for multi-engine installation. Also automatic restoration of power from 'good' engine in event of single engine failure. Incorporates fuel filter.

Lubrication System: Engine-mounted oil tank and cooler to provide self-contained system. Magnetic chip detectors fitted in each scavenge line. Oil filter incorporated in accessory wheelcase.

Dimensions:

Height overall	596 mm (23·5 in)
Width overall	575 mm (22·6 in)
Length overall	1,095 mm (43·1 in)

Weight, Dry:

Gem 10001, 2	150 kg (330 lb)
Gem 4	156 kg (343 lb)

Cutaway drawing of the Rolls-Royce Gem free-turbine turboshaft, with initial service rating of 671 kW (900 shp)

PERFORMANCE RATINGS:
Max contingency (2½ min):
Gem 10001, 2 671 kW (900 shp)
Gem 4 783 kW (1,050 shp)
Gem 41-1 835 kW (1,120 shp)
Intermediate contingency (1 hr)/max T-O (5 min):
Gem 10001, 2 619 kW (830 shp)
Gem 4 734·5 kW (985 shp)
Gem 41-1 746 kW (1,000 shp)
Max continuous:
Gem 10001, 2 559 kW (750 shp)
Gem 4 645 kW (865 shp)
Gem 41-1 664 kW (890 shp)
SPECIFIC FUEL CONSUMPTION:
Max T-O:
Gem 10001, 2 89·57 μg/J (0·53 lb/h/shp)
Gem 4 86·19 μg/J (0·51 lb/h/shp)
Gem 41-1 82·47 μg/J (0·488 lb/h/shp)
50 per cent max T-O:
All versions 111·5 μg/J (0·66 lb/h/shp)

ROLLS-ROYCE GNOME

Gnome is the name given to the versions of the General Electric T58 turboshaft which Rolls-Royce manufactures in the UK. The first ran on 5 June 1959.

The major difference between the Gnome and T58 lies in the replacement of the Hamilton Standard fuel control system by a Lucas system controlled by an electrical computer.

By January 1979 more than 1,800 Gnome engines had been delivered. To date, four versions have been announced:

H.1000. Initial version, rated at 783 kW (1,050 shp). Power plant for military Whirlwind HAR.Mk 9, HAR.Mk 10 and HCC.Mk 12, civil S-55 Series 3 and Agusta-Bell 204B.

H.1200. Rated at 932 kW (1,250 shp). Used in Agusta-Bell 204B, Boeing Vertol 107 and some Kawasaki KV-107/II-5s. Coupled version for Wessex Mks 2, 5, 50 and 60 series comprises two H.1200s driving through a coupling gearbox designed and manufactured by Rolls-Royce.

H.1400. Rated at 1,044 kW (1,400 shp). Based on the H.1200, with modified compressor to increase airflow. Turbine diaphragm cooling redesigned to increase temperature capacity and life. Dimensions unchanged.

H.1400-1. Rated at 1,145 kW (1,535 shp). Uprated from H.1400, without change in size or weight, by increasing gas-generator speed and using improved gas-generator turbine-blade material allowing increased temperature. In production for Westland Sea King and Commando.

In addition a new two-stage power turbine permits further increases in power. Developments are under consideration for using this power turbine at ratings of 1,298 kW (1,740 shp), 1,376 kW (1,845 shp) and 1,547 kW (2,075 shp).

The following description refers specifically to the H.1400-1 turboshaft version:

TYPE: Axial-flow free-turbine turboshaft engine.

AIR INTAKE: Annular forward-facing. Centre housing carrying front main bearing supported by four radial struts. Struts and inlet guide vanes anti-iced with hot compressor bleed air and oil drainage.

COMPRESSOR: Ten-stage axial. Controlled variable incidence for inlet guide vanes and first three rows of stator blades. Air mass flow 6·26 kg (13·8 lb)/s.

COMBUSTION SYSTEM: Straight-through annular chamber with outer casing split along horizontal centreline. Sixteen Simplex-type fuel injectors, eight on each of two sets of manifolds. One Lodge capacitor-discharge high-energy igniter plug.

FUEL SYSTEM: Lucas hydromechanical units, comprising variable-stroke multi-plunger pump, flow control unit and throttle controlled by HSDE electrical control computer and throttle actuator.

FUEL GRADE: DERD.2452, 2453, 2454, 2486, 2494 and 2498 (NATO F44, F34, F40, F35 and F43).

GAS-PRODUCER TURBINE: Two-stage, coupled to compressor shaft by conical shaft. Extended-root blading with fir-tree attachments.

POWER TURBINE: Single-stage free turbine. Extended-root blading with fir-tree attachments.

EXHAUST SYSTEM: Curved exhaust ducting arranged to suit individual applications.

REDUCTION GEAR: Optional double-helical gear providing reduction from nominal 19,500 rpm power turbine speed to 6,600 rpm at output shaft. Provision for power take-off to left or right.

ACCESSORY DRIVES: Quill shaft drive through lower intake strut. Fuel and lubrication systems mounted beneath compressor casing. Power take-off shaft up to 100 shp on primary reduction gear casing for separate accessories gearbox.

LUBRICATION: Fully scavenged gear pumps. Serck oil cooler.

MOUNTING: Three forward mounting faces on intake casing. Two rear mounting faces on upper portion of primary gear casing. When no reduction gear fitted, rear mounting face on engine centreline at power-turbine output shaft housing.

STARTING: Rotax electric starter in nose bullet.

DIMENSIONS:
Length:
H.1000, H.1200, H.1400-1 (all ungeared) 1,392 mm (54·8 in)
Coupled H.1200 (Wessex) 1,747 mm (68·8 in)
Max height:
H.1000, H.1200, H.1400-1 (all ungeared) 549 mm (21·6 in)
Coupled H.1200 (Wessex) 1,031 mm (40·6 in)
Max width:
H.1000, H.1200 (ungeared) 462 mm (18·2 in)
H.1400-1 (ungeared) 577 mm (22·7 in)
Coupled H.1200 (Wessex) 1,059 mm (41·7 in)
WEIGHT, DRY:
H.1000 (ungeared) 134 kg (296 lb)
H.1200 (ungeared) 142 kg (314 lb)
H.1400-1 (ungeared) 148 kg (326 lb)
Reduction gearbox 52·6 kg (116 lb)
Coupled H.1200 with coupling gearbox:
for Wessex 422 kg (930 lb)
PERFORMANCE RATINGS (at power-turbine shaft):
Max contingency (2½ min; multi-engine aircraft only):
H.1200 1,007 kW (1,350 shp)
H.1400-1 1,238 kW (1,660 shp)
Max one-hour (single engine):
H.1000 783 kW (1,050 shp)
H.1200 932 kW (1,250 shp)
H.1400-1 1,145 kW (1,535 shp)
Max continuous:
H.1000 671 kW (900 shp)
H.1200 783 kW (1,050 shp)
H.1400-1 932 kW (1,250 shp)
SPECIFIC FUEL CONSUMPTION:
At max contingency rating:
H.1200 104·4 μg/J (0·618 lb/h/shp)
H.1400-1 102·75 μg/J (0·608 lb/h/shp)

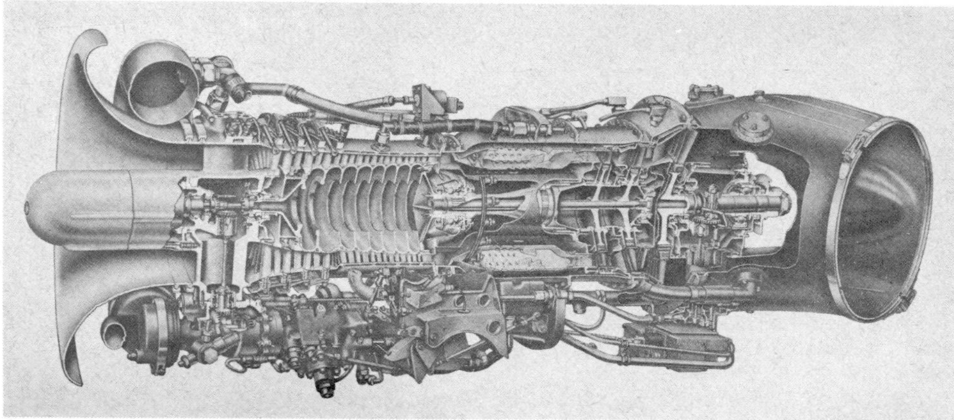

Cutaway drawing of the Rolls-Royce Gnome H.1400-1 free-turbine turboshaft, rated at 1,238 kW (1,660 shp)

ROLLS-ROYCE MOTORS

ROLLS-ROYCE MOTORS LTD

HEAD OFFICE: Crewe, Cheshire CW1 3PL
Telephone: 0270-55155
MAIN LOCATIONS:
Crewe (Car Division, Specialist and Light Aircraft Engine Division, Precision Components Division)
Shrewsbury, Salop SY1 4DP (Diesel Division, Military Engine Division)
London NW (Mulliner Park Ward Division)
DIRECTORS:
I. J. Fraser (Chairman)
D. A. S. Plastow (Managing Director)
C. S. Aston
A. R. Fenn
H. P. N. Benson
L. W. Harris (Commercial Director)
T. Neville (Financial Director)
H. Wuttke
P. J. Vinson
DIRECTOR OF GROUP PUBLIC RELATIONS: W. D. J. Roscoe

Rolls-Royce Continental piston engines; left, O-200, rated at 74·5 kW (100 hp); right, O-240, rated at 97 kW (130 hp)

Rolls-Royce Motors, which began operations on 24 April 1971, comprises the businesses formerly carried on by the Motor Car and Oil Engine Divisions of the former Rolls-Royce Ltd. The company has four factories employing 10,000 people; annual turnover is more than £120 million. It is unconnected with today's Rolls-Royce Ltd.

Under the terms of a licence agreement signed in 1960 with Teledyne Continental Motors of the United States, Rolls-Royce Motors markets Continental light-aircraft engines and spare parts throughout the world, with the exception of North and South America and certain Far Eastern countries. Five models from the Continental range are manufactured by the company's Specialist and Light Aircraft Engine Division at Crewe, and these are described hereafter.

ROLLS-ROYCE CONTINENTAL C90

This is the 70·8 kW (95 hp) Continental C90 four-cylinder engine built under licence.

ROLLS-ROYCE CONTINENTAL O-200-A

This is the 74·5 kW (100 hp) Continental O-200-A four-cylinder engine, built under licence.

ROLLS-ROYCE CONTINENTAL O-240-A

The O-240-A is the first light-aircraft engine to be developed by Rolls-Royce Motors in conjunction with Teledyne Continental. Rolls-Royce took over the programme in 1968 with a view to developing the engine specifically for the European market. Certification was completed in January 1970 and FAA Type Validation was awarded in February 1971. Production deliveries began in mid-1970, initially for the Reims Aviation Aerobat and Rollason Condor. The O-240 is being marketed in the United States by Teledyne Continental Motors.

Type: Four-cylinder, horizontally-opposed, aircooled, carburetted, unsupercharged.

Cylinders: Bore 112·5 mm (4·438 in). Stroke 98·4 mm (3·875 in). Capacity 3,933 cc (240 cu in). Compression ratio 8·5 : 1. Cast aluminium alloy finned heads are screwed and shrunk on to forged steel barrels.

Pistons: Heat-treated aluminium alloy. Two compression rings and one oil control ring above the gudgeon pin, one scraper below. Fully floating, ground steel tube gudgeon pins with pressed-in aluminium end plugs.

Connecting Rods: Forged steel I-section. Big-end bearings are thin steel backed overlay plated copper lead. Little-end bearings are roller bronze bushings.

Crankshaft: Alloy steel forgings, nitrided all over for greater fatigue strength, having three journals running in thin steel backed overlay plated copper lead bearings.

Note: The new IO-368 is described in the Addenda.

Rolls-Royce Continental IO-360 piston engine, rated at 156·6 kW (210 hp)

Crankcase: Cast aluminium alloy, split along the vertical centreline.

Valve Gear: Two valves per cylinder. Steel inlet valves with hardened tips. Steel exhaust valves with hardened tips faced with Stellite F. Valve seats shrunk into position. Camshaft, in centre of crankcase beneath the crankshaft, driven by gear from the crankshaft.

Induction: Float-type carburettor with a manual mixture control.

Fuel Grade: 100/130 octane minimum.

Ignition: Two Slick type 4001 or two Bendix Scintilla S4LN-21 magnetos on rear of crankcase driven by gears from camshaft. Two Champion REM 38EC, REM 38W or Lodge RSE 23/3R 18 mm spark plugs per cylinder.

Lubrication System: Wet sump. Magnesium crankcase cover houses the engine-driven gear type oil pump. An oil pressure relief valve is mounted in the cover. Provision is made for an airframe-mounted oil cooler and optional full-flow filter.

Propeller Drive: Direct drive, clockwise when viewed from rear. ARP 502 Type 1 flange.

Accessories: Ford 15V 60A alternator. Mechanical tachometer drive from oil pump at rear of engine. Fuel pump is operated from an eccentric on the camshaft at front of engine. An AND 20,000 accessory drive pad is provided at the front of the crankcase.

Starting: Prestolite EO 19508 12V starter.

Mounting: Four rear-mounted ring type mounting brackets to which vibration isolators can be attached.

Dimensions:
- Length: 826 mm (32·5 in)
- Width: 798 mm (31·4 in)
- Height: 633 mm (24·9 in)

Weight, Dry: incl accessories 112 kg (246 lb)

Performance Ratings:
- Take-off: 97 kW (130 hp) at 2,800 rpm
- Maximum recommended cruise: 72·7 kW (97·5 hp) at 2,540 rpm

Specific Fuel Consumption:
- Max rich: 81·1 μg/J (0·48 lb/h/hp)
- Max lean: 71·0 μg/J (0·42 lb/h/hp)

Oil Consumption:
- Maximum: 2·53 μg/J (0·015 lb/h/hp)

ROLLS-ROYCE CONTINENTAL O-300

This is the 108 kW (145 hp) Continental O-300 six-cylinder engine, built under licence.

ROLLS-ROYCE CONTINENTAL IO-360

This is the 156·6 kW (210 hp) Continental IO-360 six-cylinder horizontally-opposed aircooled engine built under licence. The turbocharged TSIO-360 of 156·6 or 168 kW (210 or 225 hp) is also produced by Rolls-Royce Motors.

WESLAKE

WESLAKE AEROMARINE ENGINES LTD

Brunswick Industrial Centre, Ashford, Kent TN23 2EH

Telephone: Ashford (0233) 25153

Telex: 966185

Officers:

B. D. Blackwell, MA, BSc(Eng)

W. T. C. Miller, OBE, MA, CEng, MIMechE, MInstM

Secretary: K. Stansfield

Divisional Manager: D. P. Short, MA, CEng, MIMechE

On 1 May 1979 Weslake Aeromarine Engines Ltd was acquired by Westland Aircraft Ltd, whose subsidiary company, Normalair-Garrett Ltd, from that date undertook the management control and operational responsibility for the Ashford facility, where a range of RPV engines is being produced.

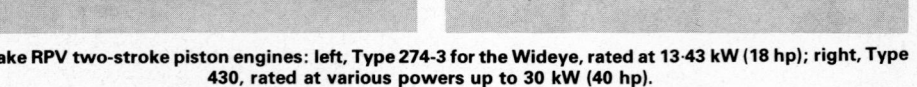

Weslake RPV two-stroke piston engines: left, Type 274-3 for the Wideye, rated at 13·43 kW (18 hp); right, Type 430, rated at various powers up to 30 kW (40 hp).

WESLAKE TYPE 116

Two-cylinder two-stroke rated at 5·5 kW (7·5 hp). Details restricted.

WESLAKE TYPE 274

The Type 274 is the first production engine available. It is being produced in two basic versions for RPVs, ACVs (Hovercraft) and powered hang gliders.

Type: Two-cylinder aircooled two-stroke, simultaneous-firing (274-6 loop scavenged).

Cylinders: Die-cast aluminium with plated bore (274-6, treated bore). Bore 66 mm (2·60 in). Stroke 40 mm (1·575 in). Capacity 274 cc (42·50 cu in).

Connecting Rods: Forged steel, caged needle bearing at both ends (274-3, single-piece; 274-4, -6, split type).

Crankshaft: Forged steel. 274-3, three-piece, vertical, running in caged needle and thrust bearings at both ends, with drive at both ends. 274-4 and -6, single-piece with large-diameter propeller mounting at one end.

Crankcase: 274-3, two-piece cast in LM25 aluminium with mounts for vertical operation. 274-4, similar but rear radial mounts. 274-6, single-piece with radial anti-vibration mounts.

Induction: 274-3 and -4, twin Tillotson carburettors incorporating fuel pump. 274-6, single carburettor at rear feeding through rotary disc valve.

Fuel Grade: 274-3, regular road-vehicle gasoline plus branded two-cycle oil in ratio 50:1. 274-4, same in ratio 25:1. 274-6, three-star gasoline plus oil in ratio 25:1 reducing to 50:1.

Ignition: 274-3 and -4, specially developed SEM electronic flywheel magneto, type AM3/90; fully shielded, no external power. 274-6, modified AM3/90.

Dimensions:
- Length: 274-3, -4: 228·5 mm (9·0 in)
- 274-6: 355·5 mm (14·0 in)
- Width: 355·5 mm (14·0 in)
- Height: 228·5 mm (9·0 in)

Weight, Dry (complete to run):
- 274-3, -4: 7·7 kg (17·0 lb)
- 274-6: 7·26 kg (16·0 lb)

Performance Rating:
- 274-3, -4, -6: 13·43 kW (18 hp) at 6,500 rpm

Specific Fuel Consumption:
- 274-3, -4, -6: below 186 μg/J (1·1 lb/h/hp)

WESLAKE TYPE 430

This is a larger two-cylinder two-stroke engine, generally following the principles of the 274. Single-piece connecting rods drive a three-piece crankshaft driving at both ends. A twin-plug version is available.

Dimensions:
- Length: 305 mm (12·0 in)
- Width: 432 mm (17·0 in)
- Height: 254 mm (10·0 in)

Weight, Dry (complete): 11·3 kg (25·0 lb)

Performance Rating: up to 30 kW (40 hp)

Specific Fuel Consumption: 149 μ/J (0·8 lb/h/lb)

WESLAKE TYPE 548

This is basically a four-cylinder version of the 274-6, with an aluminium or magnesium alloy crankcase incorporating ports for reed-valve induction.

Weight, Dry: 16·3 kg (36·0 lb)

Performance Rating: 26·9 kW (36 hp)

WESLAKE TYPE 860

A four-cylinder two-stroke; details restricted.

WESLAKE TYPE 1527

Based on well-proven production components, this is a flat-four four-stroke aircooled RPV engine.

Cylinders: Die-cast aluminium barrels and heads. Aluminium liner with internal coating. Bore 90·0 mm (3·54 in). Stroke 60 mm (2·36 in). Capacity 1,527 cc (93·2 cu in).

Crankshaft: Single-piece, four-throw, three-bearing.

Induction: Twin Stromberg or Weber carburettors.

Fuel Grade: Pump four-star or Avgas 100R.

Ignition: Lucas Rita breakerless system.

Dimensions:
- Length: 355·5 mm (14·0 in)
- Width: 647·4 mm (25·5 in)
- Height (dry-pump version): 228·5 mm (9·0 in)

Weight, Dry (inc starter): under 45·4 kg (100·0 lb)

Performance Rating (ISA): 74·6 kW (100 hp) at 5,500 rpm

Specific Fuel Consumption (at rating): under 84·5 μg/J (0·5 lb/h/hp)

UNITED STATES OF AMERICA

AEROJET

AEROJET-GENERAL CORPORATION (Subsidiary of The General Tire & Rubber Company)

9100 East Flair Drive, El Monte, California 91734
Telephone: (213) 572-6000
CHAIRMAN OF THE BOARD: M. G. O'Neil
PRESIDENT: J. H. Vollbrecht

Aerojet Solid Propulsion Company

PRESIDENT: Jack L. Heckel (acting)

Aerojet-General Corporation has activities in four major areas of business: chemicals, electronics, engineering and construction, and mechanical systems and metal products. In the chemicals area, Aerojet Solid Propulsion Company develops, produces and tests solid-propellant rocket motors for aerospace and defence programmes. In the mechanical systems area, Aerojet Liquid Rocket Company is active in research, development, testing and production of liquid-propellant rocket engines and sounding rockets for defence and aerospace programmes, and waterjet propulsion systems for US Navy craft and Army amphibious vehicles. Aerojet also has 50 per cent ownership and is the manager of Bristol Aerojet which develops and produces rocket motor systems for the British Ministry of Defence (see UK section).

Aerojet is a wholly owned subsidiary of The General Tire & Rubber Company, Akron, Ohio, and had 8,716 employees in December 1977.

Applications of the Corporation's rocket technology include:

Aerojet Solid Propulsion Company (ASPC), Sacramento, California. Development and manufacture of the second-stage motors for the US Air Force Minuteman ICBM, the motors for Hawk, Sparrow and Standard ARM, and the first stage of the Scout launch vehicle.

Aerojet Liquid Rocket Company (ALRC), Sacramento, California. Development and manufacture of all liquid-fuel stages for the US Air Force Titan family of vehicles, and Aerobee and Astrobee sounding rockets.

AEROJET TITAN III ENGINES

The production of Titan III first, second and Transtage engines for use as booster propulsion on the Titan family of vehicles has been under way continuously since 1962 by Aerojet Liquid Rocket Company and its predecessor Aerojet organisations. These engines, utilising storable propellants, develop 2,353 kN (529,000 lb), 445 kN (100,000 lb) and 71·2 kN (16,000 lb) thrust respectively. Their flight reliability is in the 90-99 per cent class. The nominal weights of these engines are 1,977, 564 and 196 kg (4,360, 1,245 and 432 lb) respectively. These weights are below those of other comparable liquid rocket engines.

In January 1978 ALRC was awarded a $38·5 million contract by the USAF Space and Missile Organisation for nine additional Titan propulsion systems. This will extend production through June 1981.

AEROJET SPACE SHUTTLE OMS ENGINE

The Space Shuttle Orbiter has two Orbiter Manoeuvring System (OMS) engines, in pods on each side of the vertical stabiliser (fin). The OMS engine, produced by ALRC, provides thrust for orbit insertion, circularisation and plane change, rendezvous and de-orbit manoeuvres. The propellants are monomethylhydrazine (MMH) and nitrogen tetroxide. At launch the basic system carries

ALRC Space Shuttle OMS engine

AEROJET SOLID PROPULSION COMPANY MOTORS

Name	Designation	Fuel	Oxidiser	Average thrust kN (lb)	Max length m (in)	Max dia m (in)	Total weight kg (lb)	Remarks/Primary Application
Strategic Motors								
Minuteman 2nd stage	SR19-AJ-1	Polybutadiene	NH_4ClO_4	269·5 (60,000)	4·01 (162)	1·32 (52)	7,076 (15,600)	Minuteman LGM-30G second stage, titanium case, single submerged nozzle, liquid injection TVC.
Polaris 1st stage	A3P	Polyurethane	NH_4ClO_4	—	4·62 (182)	1·37 (54)	10,886 (24,000)	Polaris A3, glass case, four rotatable nozzles; nitroplasticiser additive.
Tactical Motors								
Phoenix	Mk 60 Mod 0	Polybutadiene	NH_4ClO_4	—	1·78 (70)	0·38 (15)	199 (439)	Propulsion for Navy's fleet-defence air-to-air missile.
Sparrow III, AIM-7E	Mk 52 Mod 2	Polybutadiene	NH_4ClO_4	—	1·32 (52)	0·2 (8)	68·5 (151)	Propulsion for Navy's Sparrow air-to-air missile and UK BAe Sky Flash.
Shrike	Mk 53 Mod 2	Polybutadiene	NH_4ClO_4	—	1·32 (52)	0·2 (8)	71 (157)	Propulsion for Navy's AGM-45 anti-radiation air-to-surface missile.
Shrike, Improved	Mk 78 Mod 0	Polyurethane	NH_4ClO_4	—	1·30 (51)	0·2 (8)	78 (172)	Dual-thrust propulsion for anti-radiation air-to-surface missile.
Tartar	Mk 1 Mod 0	Polyurethane	NH_4ClO_4	—	2·62 (103)	0·34 (13·5)	345 (760)	Dual-thrust propulsion for Navy ship-to-air missile.
Tartar, Improved	Mk 27 Mod 2, 3	Polyurethane	NH_4ClO_4	—	2·62 (103)	0·34 (13·5)	354 (780)	Dual-thrust propulsion for Navy ship-to-air missile.
Standard Missile	Mk 56 Mod 2	Polybutadiene Polyurethane	NH_4ClO_4	—	2·62 (103)	0·34 (13·5)	411·5 (907)	Dual-thrust propulsion for Navy ship-to-air Missile Type 1, MR.
Harpoon	MX-(TBD)B446-2	Polyurethane	NH_4ClO_4	—	0·61 (24)	0·34 (13·5)	119 (262)	Booster for Navy Harpoon anti-ship missile.
2·75 in FFAR, Improved	SR105-AJ-1	Polybutadiene	NH_4ClO_4	—	0·34 (33)	0·07 (2·75)	5·9 (13)	Air-launched forward firing.
Hawk	XM22E8	Polyurethane	NH_4ClO_4	—	2·77 (109)	0·36 (14)	388 (856)	Dual-thrust motor for Army's surface-to-air Hawk missile.
Hawk, Improved	XM112	Polyurethane	NH_4ClO_4	—	2·77 (109)	0·36 (14)	395 (870)	Dual-thrust motor for Army's surface-to-air Hawk missile.
Launch Vehicle Boosters and Space Motors								
Alcor 1B		Polybutadiene	NH_4ClO_4	44·5 (10,000)	1·43 (76)	0·51 (20)	455·5 (1,004)	Third stage of Athena test vehicle and 2nd stage for Astrobee 1500 launch vehicle.
Astrobee F		HTPB	NH_4ClO_4	169/37 (38,000/ 8,300)	7·11 (280)	0·43 (15)	1,255 (2,768)	Dual-thrust sounding rocket (200 lb to 235 miles altitude).
SVM-4A	SVM-4A	Polybutadiene	NH_4ClO_4	—	1·52 (60)	0·94 (37)	706 (1,557)	Apogee-boost motor for Intelsat IV synchronous communications satellite.
SVM-5	SVM-5	Polybutadiene	NH_4ClO_4	21·8 (4,900)	0·91 (36)	0·76 (30)	318·5 (702)	Apogee-boost motor for NASA Synchronous Meteorological Satellite.
SVM-7	SVM-7	Polybutadiene	NH_4ClO_4	43·2 (9,520)	1·45 (57)	0·76 (30)	440 (970)	Apogee-boost motor for RCA Comsat.
Gas Generators and JATOs								
Turbine Start Cartridge		Butyl Rubber	NH_4NO_3	n.a.	0·41 (16)	0·18 (7)	11 (24)	For Titan II first stage.
Turbine Start Cartridge		Butyl Rubber	NH_4NO_3	n.a.	0·48 (19)	0·10 (4)	5·5 (12)	For Titan II second stage.
Gas Gen Mk 46		Butyl Rubber	NH_4NO_3	n.a.	1·09 (43)	0·305 (12)	—	Prime power source for the Navy's Mk 46 Mod 0 torpedo.
Controllable Motors								
SCCSRM		Polyurethane	NH_4ClO_4	—	0·38 (15)	0·51 (20)	415 (915)	Single-chamber controllable solid-rocket motor.
Air Launched (VTM)		Polybutadiene	NH_4ClO_4	—	1·37 (54)	0·43 (17)	185 (407)	Variable-thrust motor; has both thrust-magnitude and vector control.
Air-to-Air Controllable (ATAC)		Polybutadiene	NH_4ClO_4	—	1·70 (67)	0·20 (8)	95 (210)	Throttling over wide temperature range.
Stop-Start Motor (SSM)		Polyurethane	NH_4ClO_4	—	2·21 (87)	0·51 (20)	396·5 (874)	Stop/start operation on command.

4,087 kg (9,010 lb) of usable MMH and 6,743 kg (14,866 lb) of usable oxidiser. The following are chief characteristics:

Thrust (in vacuo)	26·7 kN (6,000 lb)
Chamber Pressure (in vacuo)	8·62 bars (125 lb/sq in)
Specific Impulse	313·2 s
Mixture Ratio	1·65 : 1
Nozzle Area Ratio (flight)	55 : 1
Dry Weight	118 kg (260 lb)
Thrust Vector Limits	±7°
Storage Life	10 years
Firing Life (100 missions)	15 h
Number of Starts	1,000
Longest Single Firing	1,250 s

AEROJET HAWK MOTOR

The single-chamber solid-propellant rocket motor of the Hawk surface-to-air missile was the first dual-thrust dual-grain motor to be mass-produced.

Within its single propellant mass, the motor has an inner core of propellant constituting a short-duration booster grain which launches and accelerates the missile to supersonic speed. When this inner core is consumed, a slower-burning outer core, forming the sustainer portion of the propellant, takes over and keeps the missile at the required velocity.

An Improved Hawk propulsion system, using an upgraded and higher-impulse polyurethane propellant, passed its qualification testing at the US Army Test and Evaluation Command, White Sands Missile Range. Several hundred Improved Hawk motors have been test fired and flight tested without failure, demonstrating the same high degree of reliability and long life as the Basic Hawk motor. The Improved Hawk motor is now in production at Sacramento. Aerojet Solid Propulsion Company has signed agreements with several foreign firms for its production.

AEROJET MINUTEMAN MOTORS

Aerojet Solid Propulsion Company produces the second stage of LGM-30G Minuteman III. This motor has polybutadiene/ammonium perchlorate propellant packaged in a titanium case, and the single submerged nozzle has liquid injection thrust-vector control. Loaded weight is 7,076 kg (15,600 lb) and average thrust 269·5 kN (60,000 lb).

AEROJET STANDARD MISSILE MOTOR

This motor is a dual-thrust design for the boost and sustain phases of the Standard I medium-range missile trajectory. This motor fits the same envelope as the test motors that were used in an earlier version of Standard Missile. The chamber has been lengthened, and the extension or blast tube eliminated, to accommodate more propellant and increase performance. These motors have been in production for the US Navy since 1970. Improvement is expected in the future to enhance missile performance.

AEROJET SPARROW / SHRIKE MOTORS

The Mark 52 and Mark 53 motors are the sustainer or 'all boost' thrust units for the Sparrow AIM-7E and Shrike AGM-45A missiles. They are similar in construction and dimensions. The principal difference lies in the performance characteristics, which are tailored to match the air-to-air and air-to-ground missions. These motors have been in production since the mid-1960s and several thousand have been produced to meet US Navy and Air Force requirements. In 1969 an improvement programme was initiated to develop the Mark 78 motor. This is a dual-thrust (boost and sustain) motor which greatly enhances the performance of the AGM-45B Improved Shrike. Production of this motor started in 1972, with several thousand produced to date.

AEROJET HARPOON BOOSTER MOTOR

The Harpoon booster motor is used to launch the RGM-84 surface-launched version of the US Navy's Harpoon missile. It is mounted in tandem and provides thrust during the boost phase before the cruise engine starts. The motor has completed all research and development and is now in production. The design incorporates many advanced features such as a submerged nozzle, developed over many years by Aerojet Solid Propulsion Company. Use of this missile/motor combination is planned for many fleet units of the US Navy and other navies.

AEROJET SPACE VEHICLE MOTORS (SVM)

The Aerojet family of space vehicle motors provides a wide range of impulse for synchronous orbit insertion, retrograde or upper-stage propulsion applications in communications, meteorological and research satellites. Communications and meteorological satellites have been placed in synchronous orbit by SVM-1, -2, -4A, -5, -6, -6A, -7 and -7A motors. The motors differ mainly in size (diameter) and use glass-filament-wound cases, advanced propellant and modern nozzle materials. Mechanical-electrical safe-and-arming devices are included in the basic configuration. Impulse flexibility for new applications can be obtained by minor variations in case length and/or propellant loading. Details were given in the 1976-77 *Jane's*.

ASPC Minuteman III second-stage motor

AEROJET ALCOR 1B

The Alcor 1B is a high-performance Aerojet Solid Propulsion Company motor featuring a high specific-impulse polybutadiene propellant and extremely light-weight inert components. The nozzle is a unique combination of laminated reinforced-plastics materials, and the chamber is a very thin, welded, high-strength titanium 6Al-4V alloy structure. This highly efficient chamber has demonstrated excellent resistance to external flight loads in structural tests.

The Alcor 1B is used as third stage on the Athena test vehicle and is the second-stage propulsion system on the Astrobee 1500 launch vehicle. It can be applied as an upper-stage sounding rocket motor, a small component test vehicle, a synchronous orbit injection motor, or an upper-stage booster for low and medium orbits. The motor can be spin-stabilised and is fabricated to a very small thrust-misalignment tolerance (0·0004 radians angular and 0·51 mm; 0·020 in linear). This motor has been used on more than 100 flights without a failure.

AEROJET ASTROBEE F

The Astrobee F is a dual-thrust sounding-rocket motor incorporating many of the design features, including HTPB propellant, of the successful Astrobee D. The boost thrust averages 169 kN (38,000 lb) for 3 s followed by a sustain thrust of 3,765 kg (8,300 lb) for 53 s. The 381 mm (15 in) diameter motor is designed to be compatible with the Aerobee payload systems and vehicle facilities. The initial Astrobee F test design is capable of delivering 90·7 kg (200 lb) payloads up to altitudes of 378 km (235 miles). By 1979 over 20 successful flights had been made.

ASPC motor for Standard I MR surface-to-air missile

ASPC Mk 78 motor for Improved Shrike

ASPC SVM-7 space-vehicle motor

ASPC boost motor for RGM-84 Harpoon missile

ALLISON

DETROIT DIESEL ALLISON DIVISION, GENERAL MOTORS CORPORATION

Detroit, Michigan
Telephone: (313) 531-7100
Indianapolis Operations: PO Box 894, Indianapolis, Indiana 46206
Telephone: (317) 244-1511
General Manager: Donald J. Atwood
General Sales Manager: Chester B. Clum
Manager, Indianapolis Operations: Edward B. Colby

Detroit Diesel Allison's Gas Turbine Operations continue to produce T56 turboprop engines for the Lockheed C-130 Hercules, Lockheed P-3 Orion and Grumman E-2 Hawkeye. The commercial counterpart of the T56, the Model 501, powers the Lockheed Electra, commercial Hercules and Convair 580 airliners.

The Allison T63 small gas turbine, and its commercial counterpart, the Model 250, have been developed through many versions with numerous applications, as listed under each model heading. A turboprop version of the Model 250 was certificated in March 1969 for light fixed-wing aircraft applications.

It was announced in January 1976 that Allison and Rolls-Royce of England would develop and produce jointly a version of the Rolls-Royce Spey turbofan engine, under the designation TF41, to power advanced versions of the LTV A-7 Corsair II aircraft. The TF41 remains in production for the US Navy's A-7E carrier-based attack aircraft. Further details can be found in the International section.

ALLISON MODEL 250

US military designation: T63

The Model 250 is a small turboshaft engine in which power is derived from a free power turbine and is delivered through an offset gearbox which includes all accessory drive pads.

A development contract for the T63 military version was received by Allison in June 1958 and the engine was first run in the Spring of 1959. Details of early versions last appeared in the 1978-79 *Jane's*; the following are current models:

T63-A-720. Hot-end improvements, increasing T-O rating to 313 kW (420 shp). Corresponds to commercial C20B. In production for the Bell OH-58C.

250-B17. Announced in 1972, the B17 is an uprated version of the earlier B15 turboprop, corresponding to the C20 turboshaft. Current model is the **B17B,** operating at 17°C higher turbine gas temperature and with hot-end improvements similar to those of the C20B, which maintain full power at high ambient temperatures. The B17B entered production in September 1974. In production for Turbostar 402 conversions, Turbostar 414, GAF Nomad N22 and 24, Ahrens AR-404, SIAI-Marchetti SM.1019E and a growing variety of agricultural aircraft modifications.

250-C20B. Introduced in 1974, and rated at 313 kW (420 shp). In production for Bell 206B JetRanger III and 206L LongRanger, MBB BO 105D, Agusta A 109A, Hughes 500D, and Soloy UH-12E and Bell 47G conversions.

250-C28. Representing Series III of the Model 250 evolutionary process, the 373 kW (500 shp) C28 is a near-total redesign. The axial multi-stage compressor, one of the primary features of the original design, has been eliminated. Instead a single-stage front-entry centrifugal impeller is used, handling a considerably increased airflow. The philosophy behind Series III was to reduce noise and emissions, and despite the increase in power the sound pressure level of the bare engine has been reduced. The compressor-acceleration bleed is eliminated, and the exhaust leaves through a single low-velocity stack which also has a minimal infra-red signature. The main gearbox has new gears with increased helix and decreased pressure angles. Flight-cleared prototype engines were first available in September 1975 in two forms: C28B, with particle separator; C28C with plain inlet. Certificated December 1977.

250-C28B. Improved model with 2½-min rating of 410 kW (550 shp).

250-C28C. Improved model with 2½-min rating of 410 kW (550 shp).

250-C30. Representing Series IV of the Model 250 growth programme, the C30 has a more advanced single-stage compressor, handling a higher mass flow at an increased pressure ratio. The engine has numerous new features, one of which is dual ignition to comply with FAR Pt 29. The C30 will have an initial rating of 485 kW (650 shp). Prototype engines were delivered in 1976. Certification was completed in March 1978.

The following description applies to Model 250 engines currently in production or development:

TYPE: Light turboshaft or turboprop.

COMPRESSOR: The C20, C20B, and B17B incorporate an axial/centrifugal compressor with six axial stages and one centrifugal. The C28B and C and the C30 have a single-stage centrifugal compressor only. Pressure ratio: C20, 7·0:1; C20B, B17B, 7·2:1: C28B/C, C30, 8·5:1. Air mass flow: C20, 1·5 kg (3·4 lb)/s; C20B, B17B, 1·56 kg (3·45 lb)/s; C28B/C, 2·02 kg (4·45 lb)/s; C30, 2·54 kg (5·6 lb)/s.

COMBUSTION CHAMBER: Single can-type chamber at rear of engine. Single duplex fuel nozzle in rear face of chamber. One igniter on C20, C20B, B17B, C28B/C. Dual igniters on C30, optional on C28B/C.

TURBINES: Two-stage gas-producer turbine and two-stage free power turbine. Integrally-cast rotor blades and wheels. Gas-producer turbine outlet temperature: C20B, B17B, 810°C; C28B/C, 730°C; C30, 740°C.

GEARCASE: Magnesium casting which forms primary structure of engine and contains all power and accessory gear trains, torque sensor and oil pumps. Compressor and turbine assemblies bolted to front and rear faces respectively. Rated shp available at either front or rear output-shaft spline or any combination totalling both. Turboshaft output speed, 6,016 rpm. Turboprop output speed, 2,030 rpm.

CONTROL SYSTEM: Pneumatic-mechanical system consisting essentially of fuel pump and filter assembly, gas producer fuel control and power turbine governor (B17B, hydromechanical; C20B, C28, C30, pneumatic-mechanical).

FUEL: Primary fuels are ASTM-A or A-1 (Model 250-C20, ASTM D-1655) and MIL-T-5624, JP-4, JP-5 and diesel fuel.

LUBRICATION: Dry sump.

OIL SPECIFICATION: MIL-L-7808 and MIL-L-23699.

DIMENSIONS:

Length:

B17B	1,143 mm (45·0 in)
C20B	1,046 mm (40·8 in)
C28B	1,239 mm (48·78 in)
C28C	1,032 mm (40·63 in)
C30	1,097 mm (43·2 in)

Width:

B17B, C20B	483 mm (19·0 in)
C28, C30	557 mm (21·94 in)

Height:

B17B	572 mm (22·5 in)
C20B	589 mm (23·2 in)
C28, C30	638 mm (25·13 in)

WEIGHT, DRY:

B17B	88·4 kg (195 lb)
C20B	71·5 kg (158 lb)
C28	99·3 kg (219 lb)
C28B	104 kg (230 lb)
C28C	102·5 kg (226 lb)
C30	106·6 kg (235 lb)

PERFORMANCE RATINGS (S/L, ISA):

T-O:

C20B (5 min)	313 kW (420 shp)
C28, 28B, 28C (30 min)	373 kW (500 shp)
C30 (2½ min)	522 kW (700 shp) to 32·2°C

Max continuous:

B17B	287 kW (385 shp)
C20B	298 kW (400 shp)
C28	373 kW (500 shp)
C30	485 kW (650 shp)

Cruise B (75 per cent):

B17B	205 kW (275 shp)
C20B	207 kW (278 shp)
C28	274 kW (367 shp)
C30	312 kW (418 shp)

SPECIFIC FUEL CONSUMPTION:

At T-O rating:

B17B	110·7 μg/J (0·655 lb/h/shp)
C20B	110 μg/J (0·650 lb/h/shp)
C28	102·5 μg/J (0·606 lb/h/shp)
C30	100 μg/J (0·592 lb/h/shp)

At cruise B rating:

B17B	121 μg/J (0·716 lb/h/shp)
C20B	120 μg/J (0·709 lb/h/shp)
C28	112 μg/J (0·664 lb/h/shp)
C30	111 μg/J (0·657 lb/h/shp)

ALLISON GMA 300

This is the latest core engine developed under the USAF/USN Ategg (Advanced Turbine Engine Gas Generator) programme. Projected applications include a wide range of turbofans, some with variable-pitch blades, and turboshaft engines for air and surface applications.

ALLISON GMA 500

Advanced 600 kW (800 shp) class demonstrator engine under development for US Army.

ALLISON T56

Current versions of the T56 are as follows:

T56-A-14. Rated at 3,661 ekW (4,910 ehp). Generally similar to T56-A-15, but seven-point suspension like T56-A-10W and detail changes. Powers the P-3B and C Orion.

T56-A-15. Rated at 3,661 ekW (4,910 ehp). Introduced aircooled turbine blades. Powers C-130H (all versions), C-130K, HC-130N, HC-130P and some AC-130s.

T56-A-422. Rated at 3,661 ekW (4,910 ehp). Powers Grumman E-2C Hawkeye and C-2A Greyhound.

T56-A-423. Rated at 3,661 ekW (4,910 ehp). Powers US Navy versions of the C-130.

Including the Model 501 commercial engines, production of these engines reached 11,000 by February 1976. Production is likely to continue into the early 1980s.

Model 501-D22D. This civil engine was proposed in 1977 to power the Lockheed L-400 Twin Hercules. It incorporates water/alcohol augmentation and auto-feathering.

Model 501-M71. The latest version of T56/501 offered for C-130 and P-3 aircraft would have 24 per cent greater power and 10 per cent lower s.f.c.

The following details apply to the T56-A-15:

TYPE: Axial-flow turboprop engine.

PROPELLER DRIVE: Combination spur/planetary gear type, primary step-down by spur, secondary by planetary. Overall gear ratio 13·54 : 1. Power section rpm 13,820. Cast magnesium reduction-gear housing. Gearbox assembly supported from power section by main drive shaft casing 711 mm (28 in) long and two inclined struts. Weight of gearbox assembly approximately 249 kg (550 lb) with pads on rear face for accessory mounting.

AIR INTAKE: Circular duct on engine face. Thermal de-icing.

COMPRESSOR: Fourteen-stage axial-flow. Series of fourteen discs with rotor blades dovetailed in peripheries and locked by adjacent discs. Rotor assembly tie-bolted to shaft which runs on one ball and one roller type bearing. Fifteen rows of stator blades, welded in rings. Disc, rotor and stator blades and four-piece cast casing of stainless steel. Compressor inlet area 1,004 cm²

The 313 kW (420 shp) Allison Model 250-C20B turboshaft engine

The 485 kW (650 shp) Allison Model 250-C30 turboshaft engine

The 3,661 ekW (4,910 ehp) Allison T56-A-15 turboprop engine which powers late versions of the Lockheed C-130 Hercules transport

(155·65 sq in). Pressure ratio 9·5 : 1. Air mass flow 14·70 kg (32·4 lb)/s.

COMBUSTION CHAMBER: Six stainless steel cannular-type perforated combustion liners within one-piece stainless steel outer casing. Fuel nozzles in forward end of each combustor liner. Primary ignition by two igniters in diametrically-opposite combustors.

FUEL SYSTEM: High-pressure type. Bendix control system. Water/alcohol augmentation system available.

FUEL GRADE: MIL-J-5624, JP-4 or JP-5.

NOZZLE GUIDE VANES: Hollow aircooled blades of special high-temperature alloy.

TURBINE: Four-stage. Rotor assembly consists of four stainless steel discs, with first stage having hollow air-cooled blades of special high-temperature alloy, secured in peripheries of discs by fir-tree roots. Discs splined to rotor shaft which runs on front and rear roller bearings. Steel outer turbine casing. Gas temperature before turbine 1,076°C.

JET PIPE: Fixed. Stainless steel.

ACCESSORY DRIVES: Accessory pads on rear face of reduction-gear housing at front end of engine.

LUBRICATION SYSTEM: Low-pressure. Dry sump. Pesco dual-element oil pump. Normal oil supply pressure 3·8 bars (55 lb/sq in).

OIL SPECIFICATION: MIL-L-7808.

MOUNTING: Three-point suspension.

STARTING: Air turbine, gearbox-mounted.

DIMENSIONS:

Length (all current versions)	3,708 mm (146 in)
Width (all current versions)	686 mm (27 in)
Height:	
A-15, A-422, A-423	991 mm (39 in)
A-14	1,118 mm (44 in)

WEIGHT, DRY:

A-14	855 kg (1,885 lb)
A-15	828 kg (1,825 lb)
A-422	859 kg (1,984 lb)
A-423	836 kg (1,844 lb)
D22D	840 kg (1,851 lb)

PERFORMANCE RATINGS (S/L, ISA, static):

T-O:

D22D augmented
3,730 kW (5,000 shp) at 13,820 rpm

A-14, A-15, A-422, A-423, D22D
3,661 ekW; 3,424 kW (4,910 ehp; 4,591 shp) at 13,820 rpm

Normal:

A-14, A-15, A-422, A-423, D22D
3,255 ekW; 3,028 kW (4,365 ehp; 4,061 shp) at 13,820 rpm

SPECIFIC FUEL CONSUMPTION:

At max rating:

A-14, A-15 — 84·67 μg/J (0·501 lb/h/ehp)

At normal rating:

A-14, A-15, A-422, A-423 — 87·4 μg/J (0·517 lb/h/ehp)

OIL CONSUMPTION:

A-14, A-15 — 1·3 litres (0·35 US gallons)/h

ALTURDYNE

ALTURDYNE

8050 Armour Street, San Diego, California 92111

Telephone: (213) 565-2131

PRESIDENT: Frank Verbeke

This company, "dedicated to bringing the advantages of the small gas turbine to new areas of industry and commerce", has developed small engines for RPVs and ultralight aircraft. It was formed in 1970 and employs 90. At present it purchases the basic gas generator and incorporates this into a complete engine for various purposes. The two main products are of 112 kW (150 hp) and 187 kW (250 hp).

The larger units are based upon the Solar T62 Titan single-shaft gas turbine (last described in *Jane's* for 1975-76). Alturdyne is marketing turboshaft, air compressor, turboprop and turbojet versions of this engine in the 187-260 kW (250-350 shp) class. The turbojet weighs 32 kg (70 lb) and has a take-off rating of 1·1 kN (250 lb st). The data below are for the turboprop, with normal propeller speed of 2,600 rpm.

DIMENSIONS:

Length (without propeller shaft)	667 mm (26·25 in)
Width	286 mm (11·25 in)
Height (without optional sump)	460 mm (18·12 in)

WEIGHT, DRY: 56·7 kg (125 lb)

PERFORMANCE RATING:

T-O, S/L — 187 kW (250 shp)

Rated at 187 kW (250 shp) the shaft-drive Alturdyne engine based on the T62 can be used as a turboshaft or, as shown here, a turboprop *(Howard Levy)*

ATLANTIC RESEARCH

ATLANTIC RESEARCH CORPORATION

5390 Cherokee Avenue, Alexandria, Virginia 22314

Telephone: (703) 354-3400

This is a privately held company of some 920 employees, organised into four operating divisions: Propulsion, Research and Technology, Teleproducts, and Advanced Programs. The Propulsion Division is a leading designer and manufacturer of small solid-propellant rockets and gas generators; it also produces industrial mixers and air-purification systems (for example, for all US Navy nuclear submarines). R & T includes in its work many areas relevant to aerospace propulsion. Teleproducts is concerned mainly with communications. APD's work is very diverse.

ARC SOLID ROCKET MOTORS

Atlantic Research claims to make solid propellants that "propel missiles, spin satellites, provide thrust-vector control, inflate air cushions, produce non-toxic exhaust, burn fast, burn slow, separate nose shrouds, gobble up electrons, produce smoke, produce no smoke, radiate IR or lase". The company supplies sustainer motors for Terrier and Standard ship/air missiles, the launch and sustainer motors for Redeye and Stinger infantry/air missiles, the complete Arcas, Super Arcas and Boosted Arcas meteorological and atmosphere-research rockets, motors for later Minuteman ICBMs that eject shrouds and perform other functions, the gas generator for UpSTAGE (unaffected by extreme launch acceleration), the gas generators and auxiliary rockets for the Polaris and Poseidon programmes, and the very-long-burning dual-pressure gas generator for C-4 Trident. ARC Propulsion Division is under contract to General Dynamics Convair Division to design and manufacture the boost motor for the BGM-109 sea-launched Tomahawk cruise missile, and to Vought to supply the solid propulsion system for GSRS (General Support Rocket System). R & T Division is involved in external-burning rockets.

AVCO LYCOMING

AVCO LYCOMING STRATFORD DIVISION OF AVCO CORPORATION

HEAD OFFICE: 550, South Main Street, Stratford, Connecticut 06497

Telephone: (203) 378-8211

PRESIDENT OF AVCO CORPORATION: George L. Hogeman

VICE-PRESIDENTS (STRATFORD):

J. S. Bartos (General Manager)
M. T. Anderson (Quality)
A. J. Burrows (Washington Operation)
P. J. Foley (Engine Program Management)
M. J. Leff (Marketing and Product Support)
S. L. Rosenberg (Finance)
M. S. Saboe (Engineering)
J. F. Shanley (Administration)
W. I. Tierney (Personnel)
E. L. Wilkinson (Operations)

Avco Lycoming Stratford is the gas-turbine manufacturing division of Avco Corporation. Together with the Williamsport division, it forms the Avco Lycoming Engine Group.

Stratford division is producing several families of engines, including the T53, T55, LTS 101 and LTP 101, with turboshaft, turboprop, turbofan, industrial and marine variants. Over 20,000 T53 and T55 engines have been produced, with production ensured to the end of the 1970s. Several versions of the LTS 101 have been certificated. The LTS 101 turboshaft powers the Bell 222, the Aérospatiale AS 350, the MBB/Kawasaki BK 117, and the Agusta A 129. The LTP 101 turboprop was selected to power the Piaggio PD 166, the prototype Britten-Norman Turbo-Islander, the Snow Air Tractor, Riley Aircraft turbo conversions, the Page Aircraft Turbo Thrush and Ag-Cat conversions, the Aerospace Fletcher Cresco, and the Dornier Turbo-Skyservant. The PLT 27 is being evaluated for several applications. The ALF 502 turbofan has completed FAA certification and has been selected for the Canadair Challenger and the British Aerospace 146.

Avco Lycoming is working upon two significant development contracts. For NASA, Stratford will build and demonstrate a high by-pass ratio turbofan of 7·1 kN (1,600 lb st), with low fuel consumption aimed at general aviation but also suitable for use in training aircraft. The US Army selected Avco Lycoming to develop an advanced technology engine in the 600 kW (800 shp) range.

AVCO LYCOMING ALF 502

The ALF 502 turbofan is being developed primarily for applications in the commercial and executive market. It is

FAA type certificated at 29·8 kN (6,700 lb st). The core gas-generator is the T55.

The ALF 502 was launched as a commercially directed, company-sponsored effort in 1969. Its first application was in the Northrop A-9A, with the military engine designation F102. Nonetheless, the engine design remained aimed at the commercial requirement for low cost of operation and high reliability. Construction was made totally modular, and the basic design was refined to satisfy commercial needs of long life and low cost of operation, with on-condition maintenance instead of a fixed TBO. Thus, a TBO of 4,000 h has been granted, with on-condition authorization.

The ALF 502 has flown in several aircraft, demonstrating low noise signature, and at simulated altitudes up to 22,900 m (75,000 ft).

It has been selected for the Canadair Challenger in 502L form at 33·4 kN (7,500 lb st), and for the British Aerospace 146 in 502H standard at 29·8 kN (6,700 lb st). Initial Challenger flying was done on the 502H, but the more powerful model was installed in early 1979. Should a military BAe 146 be ordered it would probably be powered by the F102 at 502L rating. It also powers the four-engined NASA Quiet Short-haul Research Aircraft (QSRA).

Engine deliveries off production tooling were made in December 1977, with quantity production starting in 1979.

Type: High by-pass ratio, two-shaft geared turbofan.

Fan Module: Cast fan frame includes four engine mounts 90° apart, and may be used for mounting thrust reverser. Fan rotor blades are base and part-span shrouded and individually replaceable. Containment ring surrounds rotor. Mounted directly behind rotor, (6,700 lb st engines) is single or (7,500 lb st engines) two stages of compression. Individually replaceable fan exit stators are located to minimise noise. Inlet spinner bolted to fan rotor is anti-iced by oil flow. Anti-icing of compressor stators by bleed air. Accessory gearbox on fan frame takes HP shaft power. Additional services such as fuel, oil, pneumatic and electrical lines, are routed through other hollow struts. Reduction gear within centre of fan frame couples LP turbine to fan. By-pass ratio: 502H, 5·89; 502L, 5·0.

Compressor: Core supercharged by one or two LP stages, as described above. HP compressor has seven axial stages and single radial stage, driven by two-stage HP turbine. Supported by roller bearing and aft ball bearing. Acceleration bleed control between stages 6 and 7 operated by main fuel control. Upper and lower casings contain stator half-rings, removable for maintenance, and borescope ports. Overall pressure ratio 13·7.

Turbine: HP has two air-cooled stages. LP has two stages, splined to fan reduction gear. All rotor blades base shrouded: LP additionally tip shrouded.

Combustion Chamber: One-piece annular combustor wraps around turbine. Atomising nozzles inserted through outer chamber at rear. Four customer bleed ports around exterior. Combustion liner and housing bolted to compressor diffuser. Disconnecting permits removal of cumbustor/turbine module, providing access to HP turbine. Borescope ports permit inspection of combustor and turbine without removal.

Avco Lycoming ALF 502L geared turbofan rated at 33·4 kN (7,500 lb st)

Accessory Drives: Accessory gearbox carries main fuel control, oil pump and filter, tachometer (if required) and provisions for customer accessories.

Exhaust Unit: Fan and core exhaust include flanges for bolted ducts and nozzles.

Dimensions:

Diameter	1,067 mm (42·0 in)
Length overall	1,443 mm (56·8 in)

Weight, Dry:

ALF 502H, 502R	565 kg (1,245 lb)
ALF 502L	578 kg (1,275 lb)

Performance Ratings (T-O, S/L, static):

ALF 502H, 502R	29·8 kN (6,700 lb)
ALF 502L	33·4 kN (7,500 lb)

Specific Fuel Consumption (T-O):

All versions	11·9 mg/Ns (0·42 lb/h/lb st)

AVCO LYCOMING ALF 101

Supported by NASA through the QCGAT (Quiet Clean General-Aviation Turbofan) programme, the ALF 101 is a simple turbofan based on the same gas-generator as the LTP 101 turboprop and LTS 101 turboshaft. It naturally becomes a two-shaft engine, the independent power turbine driving the large single-stage fan of 9:1 by-pass ratio via a reduction gearbox. In early 1979, details had not been disclosed beyond the design T-O thrust of 7·2 kN (1,620 lb st) and dry weight of 156 kg (343 lb).

AVCO LYCOMING LTS 101

US military designation: YT702-LD-700

This series of small turboshaft engines includes seven models with maximum power ratings between 459 and 548 kW (615 and 735 shp) and output speeds of 6,000 or 9,265 rpm. All commercial models are certificated by the FAA, and the military YT702 has completed a 60 hour PFRT. This simple modular engine was designed to provide low life cycle costs. It has a single axial compressor stage followed by a single centrifugal stage, a reverse-flow annular combustor, and single-stage axial gas-generator and power turbines. The front-mounted gearbox provides forward or aft drives, or a combination. The radial-flow inlet provides for an optional particle separator. Mass flow is 2·03 kg (4·8 lb)/s, and pressure ratio 8·5 : 1.

The LTS 101 first flew in a Bell JetRanger testbed in 1973. Since then it has been selected to power the Bell 222 light twin-engined helicopter and the Aérospatiale AS 350 single-engined helicopter, it has also flown in the Aérospatiale SA 366 light twin-engined helicopter. It also powers the MBB/Kawasaki BK 117 light twin-engined helicopter and the Agusta A 129. Lycoming has also

AVCO LYCOMING GAS TURBINE ENGINES

Manufacturer's and civil designation	Military designation	Type*	T-O Rating kN (lb st) or max kW (hp)	SFC μg/J; ‡ mg/Ns (lb/h/hp; ‡lb/h/lb st)	Weight dry less tailpipe kg (lb)	Max dia mm (in)	Length overall mm (in)	Remarks
T5313B	—	ACFS	1,044 kW (1,400 shp)	98 (0·58)	245 (540)	584 (23)	1,209 (47·6)	Powers Bell 205A
T5317A	—	ACFS	1,119 kW (1,500 shp)	99·7 (0·59)	256 (564)	584 (23)	1,209 (47·6)	Based on T5319A
T5319A	—	ACFS	1,342 kW (1,800 shp)	96·3 (0·57)	256 (564)	584 (23)	1,209 (47·6)	Awaiting FAA certification
—	T53-L-11	ACFS	820 kW (1,100 shp)	115 (0·68)	225 (496)	584 (23)	1,209 (47·6)	Bell UH-1B, D, F; Kaman H-43
T5311A	—	ACFS	820 kW (1,100 shp)	115 (0·68)	225 (496)	584 (23)	1,209 (47·6)	Bell 204B
—	T53-L-13B	ACFS	1,044 kW (1,400 shp)	98 (0·58)	245 (540)	584 (23)	1,209 (47·6)	Advanced UH-1s and AH-1G
—	T53-L-702	ACFS	1,417 kW (1,900 shp)	94·6 (0·56)	254 (561)	584 (23)	1,209 (47·6)	Military T5319A
—	T53-L-703	ACFS	1,155 kW (1,549 shp)	101·4 (0·60)	247 (545)	584 (23)	1,209 (47·6)	Bell AH-1Q, AH-1S TOW/Cobra
LTC1K-4C	—	ACFS	1,417 kW (1,500 shp)	98 (0·58)	247 (545)	584 (23)	1,209 (47·6)	Canadair CL-84
T5321A	—	ACFP	1,393 ekW (1,868 ehp)	96·3 (0·57)	306 (675)	584 (23)	1,656 (65·2)	Turboprop T5319A
—	T53-L-15	ACFP	897 ekW (1,203 ehp)	101·4 (0·60)	274 (605)	584 (23)	1,483 (58·4	Grumman OV-1D
LTC4R-1	—	ACFP	2,837 ekW (3,804 ehp†)	87·9 (0·52)	422 (930)	615 (24·2)	1,580 (62·2)	Turboprop T55-L-11A
—	T55-L-7B	ACFS	1,976 kW (2,650 shp)	104·8 (0·62)	263 (580)	615 (24·2)	1,118 (44)	Boeing CH-47A, Bell HueyTug
—	T55-L-7C	ACFS	2,125 kW (2,850 shp)	101·4 (0·60)	267 (590)	615 (24·2)	1,118 (44)	Boeing CH-47B and Bell 214A
T5508D (LTC4B-8D)	—	ACFS	1,750 kW (2,347 shp) (flat-rated)	106·5 (0·63)	274 (605)	610 (24)	1,118 (44)	Bell 214A, 214B
—	T55-L-11A	ACFS	2,796 kW (3,750 shp)	89·6 (0·53)	322 (710)	615 (24·2)	1,181 (46·5)	Boeing CH-47C
LTC4B-12	—	ACFS	3,430 kW (4,600 shp)	86·2 (0·51)	329 (725)	615 (24·2)	1,118 (44)	Improved T55-L-11A
LTS 101-600	YT702-LD-700	ACFS	459 kW (615 shp)	98 (0·58)	110 (241)	584 (23)	785 (30·9)	{ Bell 222, Aérospatiale
LTS 101-700	—	ACFS	507 kW (680 shp)	94 (0·56)	110 (241)	584 (23)	785 (30·9)	{ AS 350
LTP 101-600	—	ACFP	462 ekW (620 ehp)	93 (0·55)	148 (325)	533 (21)	914 (36)	{ B-N Turbo-Islander, Piaggio
LTP 101-700	—	ACFP	522 ekW (700 ehp)	93 (0·55)	148 (325)	533 (21)	914 (36)	{ P.166-DL3, Air Tractor AT 302
PLT-27	—	ACFS	1,529 kW (2,050 shp)	76·1 (0·45)	145 (320)	437 (17·2)	965 (38)	In development
ALF 502H, R	—	ACFF	29·8 kN (6,700 lb)	‡11·89 (‡0·42)	565 (1,245)	1,067 (42)	1,443 (56·8)	FAA certificated; BAe 146
—	F102-LD-100	ACFF	35 kN (7,860 lb)	‡11·89 (‡0·42)	500 (1,100)	1,041 (41)	1,422 (56)	NASA QSRA
ALF 502L	—	ACFF	33·4 kN (7,500 lb)	‡11·89 (‡0·42)	579 (1,275)	1,067 (42)	1,443 (56·8)	Canadair Challenger

*ACFS = axial plus centrifugal, free-turbine shaft; ACFP = axial plus centrifugal, free-turbine propeller; AFS = axial, free-turbine shaft; ACFF = axial plus centrifugal, free-turbine fan

†2,752 kW (3,690 shp); also has military rating of 2,574 ekW/2,494 kW (3,452 ehp/3,344 shp).

Avco Lycoming turbine engines in the 600 shp class (from left to right): LTS 101-600B/650A (459 kW; 615 shp), LTS 101-650C (504 kW; 675 shp) and LTP 101 (462 ekW; 620 ehp)

received US Government contracts which will provide a turbofan and an airborne APU both based on the LTS 101 core.

DIMENSIONS:
- Length: 785 mm (30·9 in)
- Width: 406 mm (16·0 in)
- Height:
  - LTS 101-600A/600B/650A: 568 mm (22·38 in)
  - LTS 101-650C: 483 mm (19·0 in)

WEIGHT, DRY:
- LTS 101-600A/600B/650A: 110 kg (241 lb)
- LTS 101-650: 105 kg (232 lb)

PERFORMANCE RATINGS:
- 2·5 min contingency:
  - LTS 101-650A, 650C: 504 kW (675 shp)
- T-O:
  - LTS 101-600A, -600B, -650A,-650C: 459 kW (615 shp)
  - LTS 101-700: 507 kW (680 shp)
- Maximum continuous:
  - LTS 101-600A, -600B, -650A, -650C: 440 kW (590 shp)

SPECIFIC FUEL CONSUMPTION (T-O rating):
- LTS 101-600A, -600B, -650A: 95·8 μg/J (0·567 lb/h/shp)
- LTS 101-650C: 95·6 μg/J (0·566 lb/h/shp)

AVCO LYCOMING LTP 101

The LTP 101 is a turboprop derived from the LTS 101. It incorporates a free power turbine, provisions for tractor or pusher installation, hydraulic propeller governor, axi-symmetric inlet and all-weather protection. The output shaft speed lies in the range 1,700-1,950 rpm, consistent with available three-blade reversible propellers. It is of modular construction.

FAA certification was received in 1976. The LTP 101 was then selected for the Piaggio P.166-DL3, Britten-Norman Turbo-Islander prototype, Air Tractor and Aerospace Fletcher agricultural aircraft, Riley conversions of Cessna 360 and 421, Page Aircraft Turbo Thrush and Ag-Cat conversions, Dornier Turbo-Skyservant and Schapel Super Swat. Production deliveries have commenced.

DIMENSIONS:
- Length overall: 938 mm (36·94 in)
- Height overall: 521 mm (20·53 in)

WEIGHT, DRY: 147 kg (325 lb)

PERFORMANCE RATINGS (S/L, ISA):
- T-O:
  - LTP 101-600: 462 ekW (620 ehp)
  - LTP 101-700: 522 ekW (700 ehp)
- Max continuous:
  - LTP 101-600: 410 ekW (585 ehp)

SPECIFIC FUEL CONSUMPTION:
- All above ratings: 92·9 μg/J (0·55 lb/h/ehp)

AVCO LYCOMING LTC1
US military designation: T53

The T53 is a turboshaft with a free power turbine, which was developed under a joint USAF/US Army contract. A total of 18,000 units had logged over 26·2 million hours of operation, with every US armed service and in 29 other countries, by January 1979.

Licences for manufacture of the T53 are held by Klöckner-Humboldt-Deutz in Germany, Piaggio in Italy and Kawasaki in Japan.

Versions currently in production or under development are as follows:

T53-L-13. Uprated version of L-11, which it superseded in production in August 1966.Redesigned 'hot end' and initial stages of compressor section to provide substantially increased power for hot-day and high-altitude performance. Four turbine stages, compared with two in earlier models, and variable-incidence inlet guide vanes combined with redesigned first two compressor stages, permit greater airflow and lower turbine temperatures. This version has atomising combustor to facilitate operation on a wider range of fuels. Powers Bell UH-1C and UH-1D and AH-1G HueyCobra. The **T5313A** commercial version of the T53-L-13 received FAA type cetification in Spring 1968 and powers Bell 205A.

T53-L-701. Turboprop version of the L-13 incorporating the Lycoming 'split-power' propeller reduction gear. Produced for Grumman OV-1D previously powered by T53-L-15, and specified for stretched version of Air-Metal AM-C111. In production for T-CH-1 (Taiwan).

T53-L-703. Turboshaft engine similar to L-13. Flat rated for AH-1Q and AH-1S HueyCobra.

LTC1K-4C. Generally similar to the T53-L-13, but incorporating special seals to allow operation in the attitude range from 105° nose up to 90° nose down. Has 10-minute rating of 1,500 shp and Powered Canadair CL-84-1 VTOL aircraft; powers Bell XV-15 tilt-rotor VTOL aircraft.

T5319A. Latest growth version of T53 turboshaft family. Improvements over L-13 include new gearing, improved cooling of first gas producer turbine nozzle plus aircooled blades in first turbine rotor. Also incorporates new materials in other turbine stages. Rated at 1,800 shp at take-off.

T5317A. Lower-powered version of -19A with take-off rating limited to 1,500 shp by use of standard L-13 reduction gear.

T5321A. Turboprop version of -19A with 'split-power' gear. Uses standard SBAC No. 4 propeller shaft with through-the-shaft oil provisions.

The following details apply to the T53-L-13 and L-701:

TYPE: Free-turbine turboshaft engine.

AIR INTAKE: Annular casing of magnesium alloy, with 6 struts supporting reduction gearbox and front main bearings. Anti-icing by hot air tapped from engine.

COMPRESSOR: Five axial stages followed by a single centrifugal stage. Four-piece magnesium alloy casing with one row of variable-incidence inlet guide vanes and five rows of steel stator blades, bolted to one-piece steel alloy diffuser casing with tangential outlet to combustion chamber. Rotor comprises one stainless steel and four aluminium alloy discs with stainless steel blades and one titanium impeller mounted on shaft supported in forward ball thrust and rear roller bearings. Compression ratio 7·4 : 1. Air mass flow 4·85 kg/s (10·7 lb/s) at 25,240 gas producer rpm.

COMBUSTION CHAMBER: Annular reverse-flow type, with one-piece sheet steel outer shell and annular liner. Twenty-two atomising fuel injectors.

FUEL CONTROL SYSTEM: Hydromechanical controls for gas generator and for power sections. Chandler Evans TA-2S system with one dual fuel pump. Pump pressure 41·4 bars (600 lb/sq in). Main and emergency flow controls. Separate interstage air bleed control.

FUEL GRADE: ASTM A-1, MIL-J-5624, MIL-F-26005A, JP-1, JP-4, JP-5, CITE.

TURBINE: Four axial-flow turbine stages. Casing fabricated from sheet steel. First two stages, driving compressor, use hollow aircooled stator vanes and cored-out cast steel rotor blades and are mounted on outer co-axial shaft to gas producer. Second two stages, driving reduction gearing, have solid steel blades, and are spline-mounted to shaft.

EXHAUST UNIT: Fixed-area nozzle. Steel outer casing and inner cone, supported by four radial struts.

ACCESSORIES: Electric starter or starter/generator (not furnished). Bendix-Scintilla TGLN high-energy ignition unit. Two igniter plugs.

LUBRICATION: Recirculating system, with gear pump with one pressure and one scavenge unit. Filter. Pump pressure 4·83 bars (70 lb/sq in).

OIL GRADE: MIL-L-7808, MIL-L-23699.

DIMENSIONS:
- Length overall:
  - L-13: 1,209 mm (47·6 in)
  - L-701: 1,483 mm (58·4 in)
  - T5321A: 1,656 mm (65·2 in)
- Diameter:
  - All versions: 584 mm (23·0 in)

WEIGHT, DRY:
- Less tailpipe:
  - L-13: 249 kg (549 lb)
  - T5317A, T5319A: 256 kg (564 lb)
  - T5321A: 306 kg (657 lb)
  - LTC1K-4C, L-703: 247 kg (545 lb)
  - L-701: 312 kg (688 lb)

PERFORMANCE RATINGS:
- Max at S/L:
  - L-13: 1,044 kW (1,400 shp)
  - L-701: 1,082 ekW; 1,044 kW (1,451 ehp; 1,400 shp plus 0·57 kN (128 lb) at 20,430 rpm
  - LTC1K-4C, T5317A: 1,119 kW (1,500 shp)
  - T5319A: 1,342 kW (1,800 shp)
  - T5321A: 1,393 ekW; 1,342 kW (1,868 ehp; 1,800 shp)
  - L-703: 1,107 kW (1,485 shp) to 28°C

SPECIFIC FUEL CONSUMPTION:
- At max rating:
  - L-13, LTC1K-4C: 98 μg/J (0·58 lb/h/shp)

Cutaway drawing of the 1,044 kW (1,400 shp) Avco Lycoming T53-L-13 turboshaft engine

L-701, T5319A, T5321A
96·3 μg/J (0·57 lb/h/shp)
T5317A 99·7 μg/J (0·59 lb/h/shp)
L-703 101·4 μg/J (0·60 lb/h/shp)
OIL CONSUMPTION:
All versions 450 gr (1·0 lb)/h

AVCO LYCOMING LTC4

US military designation: T55

This engine is based on the T53 design concept but with higher mass flow. It was developed under a joint USAF/US Army contract. Total operating time by early 1978 was 3·4 million hours. Most of this time was logged by L-7 versions fitted to the CH-47A and CH-47B Chinook.

Current production and development versions are as follows:

T55-LTC4B-8D. Modified version of the T55-L-7C. Powers Bell 214A and 214C utility helicopters for Iran, flat rated to transmission limit of 1,678 kW (2,250 shp).

T5508D. Commercial version of LTC4B-8D. Powers Bell 214B.

T55-L-11 (LTC4B-11B). Uprated and redesigned version of L-7, with a second stage added to the compressor turbine, and variable-incidence inlet guide vanes ahead of the compressor. First two compressor stages transonic. New atomising fuel nozzles. Powers CH-47C Chinook, first deliveries having been made in August 1968.

T55-L-712. Supersedes the T55-L-11 and specified for the US Army's modernised Boeing Vertol CH-47D. The basic engine is the T55-L-11D, with wide-chord compressor blades and welded rotor. Improvements in design and materials are aimed at achieving a time between overhauls of 2,500 hr. Military qualification was due in mid-1978.

LTC4B-12. Growth version with 3,430 kW (4,600 shp) maximum power rating, 3,258 kW (4,370 shp) on hot day. Higher turbine entry temperature and increased turbine cooling.

LTC4R-1. Turboprop version of L-11 with Lycoming split-power reduction gear.

The following description applies to the T55-L-11 and LTC4R-1:

TYPE: Free-turbine turboshaft engine.

AIR INTAKE: Annular type casing of magnesium alloy with four struts supporting reduction gearbox and front main bearings. Anti-icing by hot air tapped from engine. Provision for intake screens.

COMPRESSOR: Seven axial stages followed by a single centrifugal stage. Two-piece magnesium alloy stator casing with one row of variable inlet guide vanes and seven rows of steel stator blades, bolted to steel alloy diffuser casing to which combustion chamber casing is attached. Rotor comprises seven stainless steel discs and one titanium impeller mounted on shaft supported in forward ball-thrust bearing and rear roller bearing. Pressure ratio 8·2 : 1. Air mass flow 12·25 kg (27 lb)/s.

COMBUSTION CHAMBER: Annular reverse-flow type. Steel outer shell and inner liner. Twenty-eight fuel burners with downstream injection.

FUEL SYSTEM: Hamilton Standard JFC 31 fuel control system. Gear-type fuel pump, with gas producer and power shaft governors, flow control with altitude compensation and shut-off valve.

FUEL GRADE: MIL-J-5624 grade JP-4, JP-5, MIL-F-46005A or CITE.

TURBINE: Two mechanically independent axial turbines.

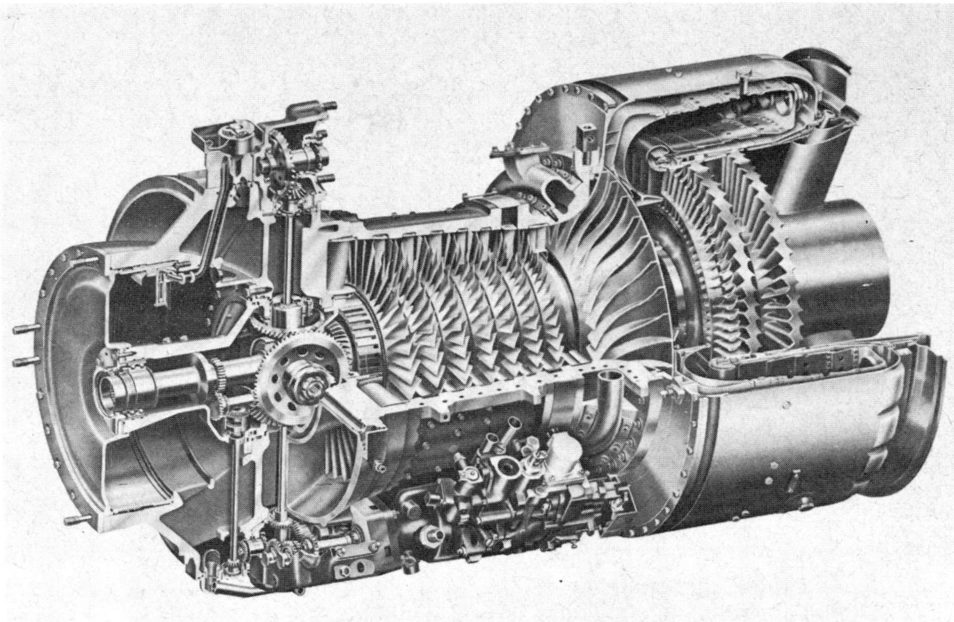

Avco Lycoming T5508D (LTC4B-8D) turboshaft, flat-rated at 1,678 kW (2,250 shp)

Gas-generator turbine has single stage (two stages on T55-L-11 series) with cored-out cast steel blades having inner cooling airflow. Disc flange-bolted to drive shaft. Hollow stator vanes. Two-stage power turbine has solid steel blades.

EXHAUST UNIT: Fixed-area nozzle, with inner cone, supported by six radial struts.

ACCESSORIES: Electric starter or starter/generator, or air or hydraulic starter. Bendix-Scintilla TGLN high-energy ignition unit. Four igniter plugs.

LUBRICATION: Recirculating type. Integral oil tank and cooler on L-11, external tank for 4R-1.

OIL GRADE: MIL-L-7808, MIL-L-23699.

DIMENSIONS:
Diameter (all versions) 616 mm (24·25 in)
Length overall:
L-7, LTC4B-8D, T5508D, LTC4B-12
1,119 mm (44·03 in)
L-9, LTC4R-1 1,580 mm (62·2 in)
L-11A 1,181 mm (46·5 in)

WEIGHT, DRY:
L-7B 263 kg (580 lb)
L-9, LTC4R-1 422 kg (930 lb)
L-11A 322 kg (710 lb)
LTC4B-8D, T5508D 274 kg (605 lb)
LTC4B-12 329 kg (725 lb)

PERFORMANCE RATINGS (T-O, S/L):
L-7B 1,976 kW (2,650 shp)
L-9, LTC4R-1 2,837 kW (3,804 ehp); (2,752 kW; 3,690 shp plus 1·27 kN; 285 lb st)
L-11A 2,792 kW (3,750 shp)
LTC4B-8D, T5508D 2,200 kW (2,950 shp)
flat rated to 1,678 kW (2,250 shp)
LTC4B-12 3,430 kW (4,600 shp)

SPECIFIC FUEL CONSUMPTION (T-O, S/L):
L-7B 104·8 μg/J (0·62 lb/h/shp)
L-9, LTC4R-1, L-11A 89·6 μg/J (0·53 lb/h/shp)
LTC4B-8D, T5508D (flat rated)
106·5 μg/J (0·63 lb/h/shp)
LTC4B-12 86·2 μg/J (0·51 lb/h/shp)

AVCO LYCOMING PLT 27 SERIES

US military designation: T405

The PLT 27 series forms a new generation of two-spool free-turbine turboshaft engines. Advanced technology increases power per pound of fuel and power to weight, while reducing size, increasing reliability and furthering modular maintenance principles.

The baseline PLT 27 of 1,529 kW (2,050 shp) has been tested in both front-drive (PLT 27A) and rear-drive (27B) configurations. Its development is paralleling the AGT XM1 vehicular turbine which has been selected to power the next American main battle tank. Conservative turbine temperatures in the PLT 27 provide readily attainable early growth. In all configurations, inlet particle separator and infra-red kits can be provided. A later growth version is the PLT 27C (rear drive) or 27D (front drive).

DIMENSIONS:
Max diameter 444 mm (17·5 in)
Length overall 985 mm (38·8 in)

WEIGHT, DRY:
PLT 27A/B 166/184 kg (366/406 lb)
PLT 27C/D 165/186 kg (365/410 lb)

PERFORMANCE RATINGS (S/L Std Day):
PLT 27A/B 1,529 kW (2,050 shp)
PLT 27C/D 1,864 kW (2,500 shp)

SPECIFIC FUEL CONSUMPTION (S/L Std Day):
PLT 27 A/B 76·1 μg/J (0·45 lb/h/shp)
PLT 27 C/D 72·7 μg/J (0·43 lb/h/shp)

Two versions of the Avco Lycoming PLT 27 advanced turboshaft: left, PLT 27A/B 1,529 kW (2,050 shp); right, PLT 27C/D 1,864 kW (2,500 shp)

AVCO LYCOMING WILLIAMSPORT DIVISION

Williamsport, Pennsylvania 17701
Telephone: (717) 323-6181

VICE-PRESIDENTS:
Peter J. Goodwin (General Manager)
A. E. Light (Engineering)
S. T. Jedrziewski (Sales and Service)
W. R. Bower (Operations)
H. A. Schuck (Controller)
F. W. Riddell (Advanced Planning)

Williamsport Division is engaged primarily in production of the well-known Lycoming series of horizontally-opposed aircooled reciprocating engines ranging from 110 to 450 hp. Turbocharging is being offered on additional models and the horsepower, in some cases, has been increased. Development efforts are being directed to improvements resulting in lower cost of manufacturing and longer time between overhauls, to help offset increasing labour and material costs. During recent years FAA approval has been received for several new engine models. Turbocharged versions of four- and six-cylinder engines have been certificated, along with several versions of new high-compression, simplified-design engines.

AVCO LYCOMING O-235 SERIES

Smallest and basic engine of the Lycoming range. Four cylinders of 111 mm (4⅜ in) bore and 98·4 mm (3⅞ in) stroke. The high-compression O-235-L2C is the most recent production version of the O-235, used in several

AVCO LYCOMING HORIZONTALLY-OPPOSED PISTON ENGINES

Engine Model*	No. of Cylinders	Rated output at Sea Level kW (hp) at rpm	Capacity litres (cu in)	Compression Ratio	Fuel grade Minimum	Weight Dry kg (lb)	Length Overall mm (in)	Width Overall mm (in)	Height Overall mm (in)	Gear Ratio†
O-235-C	4	86 (115) at 2,800	3·85 (233)	6·75	80/87	97·5 (215)	751 (29·56)	812 (32·00)	569 (22·53)	D
O-235-H	4	86 (115) at 2,600	3·85 (233)	6·75	80/87	96 (213)	738 (29·05)	812 (32·00)	569 (22·40)	D
O-235-L	4	86 (115) at 2,600 78 (105) at 2,400	3·85 (233)	8·5	100	98 (218)	738 (29·05)	812 (32·00)	569 (22·40)	D
O-320-A	4	112 (150) at 2,700	5·2 (319·8)	7·0	80/87	110 (243)	751 (29·56)	819 (32·24)	584 (22·99)	D
O-320-D	4	119 (160) at 2,700	5·2 (319·8)	8·5	91/96	114 (253)	808 (31·82)	819 (32·24)	488 (19·22)	D
O-320-E	4	112 (150) at 2,700	5·2 (319·8)	7·0	80/87	113 (249)	738 (29·05)	819 (32·24)	584 (22·99)	D
O-320-H	4	119 (160) at 2,700	5·2 (319·8)	9·0	100	115 (253)	819 (32·26)	830 (32·68)	621 (24·46)	D
AEIO-320-E	4	112 (150) at 2,700	5·2 (319·8)	7·0	80/87	117 (258)	738 (29·05)	819 (32·24)	589 (23·18)	D
O-360-A	4	134 (180) at 2,700	5·92 (361)	8·5	91/96	118 (260)	808 (31·82)	848 (33·37)	488 (19·22)	D
LO-360-A	4	134 (180) at 2,700	5·92 (361)	8·5	91/96	120 (266)	808 (31·82)	848 (33·37)	488 (19·22)	D
O-360-C	4	134 (180) at 2,700	5·92 (361)	8·5	91/96	116 (258)	757 (29·81)	848 (33·37)	625 (24·59)	D
IVO-360-A	4	134 (180) at 2,900	5·92 (361)	8·5	100	124 (274)	762 (30·00)	848 (33·37)	583 (22·95)	DV
TO-360-C	4	157 (210) at 2,575 to 3,048 m (10,000 ft)	5·92 (361)	7·3	100	154 (343)	876 (34·50)	921 (36·25)	534 (21·02)	D
IO-360-A	4	149 (200) at 2,700	5·92 (361)	8·7	100	133 (293)	757 (29·81)	870 (34·25)	491 (19·35)	D
IO-360-B	4	134 (180) at 2,700	5·92 (361)	8·5	100	122 (268)	757 (29·81)	848 (33·37)	631 (24·84)	D
IO-360-C	4	149 (200) at 2,700	5·92 (361)	8·7	100	134 (298)	855 (33·65)	870 (34·25)	495 (19·48)	D
LIO-360-C	4	149 (200) at 2,700	5·92 (361)	8·7	100	138 (306)	855 (33·65)	870 (34·25)	495 (19·48)	D
HIO-360-C	4	153 (205) at 2,900	5·92 (361)	8·7	100	132 (291)	791 (31·14)	870 (34·25)	495 (19·48)	D
HIO-360-D	4	142 (190) at 3,200 to 1,280 m (4,200 ft)	5·92 (361)	10·0	100	132 (290)	894 (35·23)	904 (35·62)	495 (19·48)	D
HIO-360-E	4	142 (190) at 2,900	5·92 (361)	8·0	100	132 (290)	797 (31·36)	870 (34·25)	507 (19·97)	D
AEIO-360-A	4	149 (200) at 2,700	5·92 (361)	8·7	100	139 (307)	780 (30·70)	870 (34·25)	492 (19·35)	D
AEIO-360-B	4	134 (180) at 2,700	5·92 (361)	8·5	91/96	125 (277)	738 (29·05)	848 (33·37)	631 (24·84)	D
AEIO-360-H	4	134 (180) at 2,700	5·92 (361)	8·5	91/96	122 (270)	738 (29·05)	848 (33·37)	631 (24·84)	D
VO-435-A	6	186 (250) at 3,200 T-O 194 (260) at 3,400	7·1 (434)	7·3	80/87	181 (399)	882 (34·73)	853 (33·58)	612 (24·13)	DV
VO-435-B	6	197 (265) at 3,200	7·1 (434)	8·7	100	189 (420)	1,002 (39·46)	866 (34·11)	610 (24·02)	DV
TVO-435-D	6	201 (270) at 3,200	7·1 (434)	7·3	100	209 (465)	882 (34·73)	853 (33·58)	906 (35·67)	DV
GO-480-G	6	209 (280) at 3,000 T-O 220 (295) at 3,400	7·8 (479·7)	8·7	100	201 (444)	981 (38·64)	842 (33·12)	712 (28·02)	0·642
GSO-480-B	6	253 (340) at 3,400	7·8 (479·7)	7·3	100	231 (513)	1,252 (49·31)	842 (33·12)	840 (33·08)	0·642
IGSO-480-A	6	239 (320) at 3,200 to 3,350 m (11,000 ft) T-O 254 (340) at 3,400	7·8 (479·7)	7·3	100	233 (513)	1,208 (47·56)	842 (33·12)	579 (22·81)	0·642
O-540-B	6	175 (235) at 2,575	8·86 (541·5)	7·2	80/87	166 (366)	945 (37·22)	848 (33·37)	624 (24·56)	D
O-540-E	6	194 (260) at 2,700	8·86 (541·5)	8·5	91/96	167 (368)	976 (38·42)	848 (33·37)	624 (24·56)	D
O-540-G	6	194 (260) at 2,700	8·86 (541·5)	8·5	91/96	174 (386)	999 (39·34)	848 (33·37)	624 (24·56)	D
O-540-J	6	175 (235) at 2,400	8·86 (541·5)	8·5	100	162 (357)	989 (38·93)	848 (33·37)	519 (20·43)	D
VO-540-B	6	227 (305) at 3,200	8·86 (541·5)	7·3	80/87	202 (446)	882 (34·73)	880 (34·70)	617 (24·29)	D V
VO-540-C	6	227 (305) at 3,200 to 915 m (3,000 ft)	8·86 (541·5)	8·7	100	200 (441)	882 (34·73)	880 (34·70)	649 (25·57)	D V
IO-540-C	6	186 (250) at 2,575	8·86 (541·5)	8·5	91/96	170 (375)	976 (38·42)	848 (33·37)	622 (24·46)	D
IO-540-E	6	216 (290) at 2,575	8·86 (541·5)	8·7	100	187 (416)	999 (39·34)	870 (34·25)	498 (19·60)	D
IO-540-K	6	224 (300) at 2,700	8·86 (541·5)	8·7	100	201 (443)	999 (39·34)	870 (34·25)	498 (19·60)	D
IO-540-S	6	224 (300) at 2,700	8·86 (541·5)	8·7	100	201 (444)	997 (39·24)	870 (34·25)	498 (19·60)	D
IO-540-T	6	194 (260) at 2,700	8·86 (541·5)	8·5	91/96	171 (381)	989 (38·93)	848 (33·37)	546 (21·50)	D
AEIO-540-D	6	194 (260) at 2,700	8·86 (541·5)	8·5	91/96	174 (386)	999 (39·34)	848 (33·37)	621 (24·46)	D
IGSO-540-A	6	268 (360) at 3,200 to 3,200 m (10,500 ft) T-O 283 (380) at 3,400	8·86 (541·5)	7·3	100	250 (551)	1,441 (56·74)	870 (34·25)	515 (20·30)	0·642
TIO-540-A	6	231 (310) at 2,575 to 4,575 m (15,000 ft)	8·86 (541·5)	7·3	100	232 (511)	1,304 (51·34)	870 (34·25)	577 (22·71)	D
TIO-540-C	6	186 (250) at 2,575 to 4,575 m (15,000 ft)	8·86 (541·5)	7·2	100	205 (456)	1,026 (40·38)	848 (33·37)	770 (30·33)	D
TIO-540-F	6	242 (325) at 2,575 to 4,575 m (15,000 ft)	8·86 (541·5)	7·3	100	233 (514)	1,304 (51·34)	870 (34·25)	570 (22·42)	D
LTIO-540-F	6	242 (325) at 2,575 to 4,575 m (15,000 ft)	8·86 (541·5)	7·3	100	233 (514)	1,304 (51·34)	870 (34·25)	570 (22·42)	D
TIO-540-J	6	261 (350) at 2,575 to 4,575 m (15,000 ft)	8·86 (541·5)	7·3	100	235 (518)	1,308 (51·50)	870 (34·25)	573 (22·56)	D
LTIO-540-J	6	261 (350) at 2,575 to 4,575 m (15,000 ft)	8·86 (541·5)	7·3	100	235 (518)	1,308 (51·50)	870 (34·25)	573 (22·56)	D
TIO-540-R	6	261 (350) at 2,500 254 (340) to 4,575 m (15,000 ft)	8·86 (541·5)	7·3	100	238 (524)	1,309 (51·52)	870 (34·25)	574 (22·60)	D
TIO-540-S	6	224 (300) at 2,700 to 3,660 m (12,000 ft)	8·86 (541·5)	7·3	100	228 (502)	1,004 (39·56)	915 (36·02)	667 (26·28)	D
TIO-541-E	6	283 (380) at 2,900 to 4,575 m (15,000 ft)	8·86 (541·5)	7·3	100	270 (596)	1,282 (50·70)	905 (35·66)	640 (25·17)	D
TIGO-541-D	6	336 (450) at 3,200 314 (420) at 4,575 m (15,000 ft)	8·86 (541·5)	7·3	100	311 (685)	1,470 (57·90)	885 (34·86)	611 (24·05)	0·667
TIGO-541-E	6	317 (425) at 3,200 to 4,575 m (15,000 ft)	8·86 (541·5)	7·3	100	319 (704)	1,462 (57·57)	885 (34·86)	575 (22·65)	0·667
IO-720-A	8	298 (400) at 2,650	11·84 (722)	8·7	100	257 (567)	1,179 (46·41)	870 (34·25)	573 (22·53)	D
IO-720-B	8	298 (400) at 2,650	11·84 (722)	8·7	100	252 (556)	1,218 (47·97)	870 (34·25)	530 (20·88)	D

*Model designation code: A, Aerobatic; AE, Aerobatic engine; G, Geared; H, Helicopter; I, Fuel injected; L, Left-hand rotation crankshaft; O, Opposed-cylinders; S, Supercharged; T, Turbocharged; V, Vertical crankshaft; †D, Direct drive; V, Vertical mounting

Avco Lycoming O-235-L rated at 86 kW (115 hp)

The 175 kW (235 hp) Avco Lycoming O-540-J six-cylinder engine

The 317 kW (425 hp) Avco Lycoming TIGO-541-E six-cylinder engine

The 298 kW (400 hp) eight-cylinder Avco Lycoming IO-720-A1A engine

primary trainers. It requires 100-octane (minimum) aviation fuel.

AVCO LYCOMING O-320 and IO-320 SERIES

Cylinder bore increased to 130 mm (5⅛ in). The O-320 is an engine in the 112-119 kW (150-160 hp) class. Both carburetted and fuel-injected versions are produced in low- and high-compression models for use with 80/87 or 100-octane minimum grade fuels, respectively. Fully aerobatic models are available.

AVCO LYCOMING O-360 and IO-360 SERIES

The O-360 series is basically the same as the O-320 except for an increase in stroke to 111 mm (4⅜ in). Like the O-320, this engine is manufactured with low or high compression, with carburettor or fuel injection. The various models include aerobatic capability, a specific design for helicopters and a turbocharged version. The IO-360 is built in several versions; the IO-360-A series has fuel injection, tuned induction and high-output cylinders, while the IO-360-B series has continuous-flow port injection and standard cylinders.

Latest addition to this family is the TO-360-C series rated at 157 kW (210 hp). These engines have a simple turbocharger, controlled mechanically by the pilot's throttle.

AVCO LYCOMING O-540 and IO-540 SERIES

The O-540 is basically a direct-drive, six-cylinder version of the four-cylinder O-360. It is available in low- and high-compression versions, and the VO-540 is in production as a helicopter powerplant with crankshaft vertical. Fuel-injected IO-540 models are manufactured in a variety of configurations, with rating of 186-224 kW (250-300 hp). An aerobatic version is available. Many of these engines, particularly in the higher horsepower range, have a tuned induction system. Continuous monitoring and computer analysis of engine service records has made it possible to increase the recommended time between overhaul (TBO) for these engines; most models have a TBO of 2,000 h. The most recent members of this family are the -J series of direct-drive engines.

The 231 kW (310 hp) Avco Lycoming TIO-540 six-cylinder engine fitted to the Piper Navajo C

AVCO LYCOMING TIO-540 SERIES

This is a turbocharged version of the fuel-injected IO-540, with tuned induction. It is manufactured in a wide range of horsepowers and is used in the Piper Turbocharged Aztec, the Rockwell Commander 700 and all unpressurised models of the Piper Navajo. The latest addition to the TIO-540 series is the -S model with simple turbocharger interconnected with the pilot's throttle.

AVCO LYCOMING TIO-541 SERIES

Although the displacement of this turbocharged, six-cylinder series is the same as the TIO-540, the TIO-541 and geared TIGO-541 are totally redesigned. The accessory housing is an integral part of the crankcase, and the new design features allow these engines to operate at the high end of the Lycoming power spectrum. The TIO-541-E is rated at 283 kW (380 hp) and the geared TIGO-541-E at 317 kW (425 hp). Times between overhauls are recommended at 1,600 and 1,200 h, respectively. A double-scroll blower is available to provide cabin pressurisation.

AVCO LYCOMING IO-720 SERIES

This eight-cylinder version of the IO-540 is used in a variety of aircraft at ratings from 280 to 298 kW (375 to 400 hp). Time between overhauls is 1,800 h (1,200 in agricultural applications).

AVCO LYCOMING NEW RANGE

Avco Lycoming, Williamsport, is continuing the development of a new series of high-performance, normally-aspirated and turbocharged flat opposed piston engines. In addition, extensive study and testing are being devoted to finding ways of reducing noise and improving overall efficiency.

BELL

BELL AEROSPACE TEXTRON

HEAD OFFICE AND WORKS: PO Box 1, Buffalo, New York 14240

Telephone: (716) 297-1000

OFFICERS: See Aircraft section

Bell has been engaged in the design, development and production of liquid-propellant rocket engines since 1946.

A single-chamber engine which Bell developed originally to power a nuclear weapon pod to be carried by the B-58 Hustler bomber is now being used in modified form in the Agena space vehicle and provides upper-stage propulsion for numerous spacecraft. The latest version is able to offer multiple re-start capability and was used for the Gemini rendezvous programme. The Agena vehicles used in this programme were also fitted with a Bell-produced secondary propulsion system of 0·071 kN (16 lb) and 0·88 kN (200 lb) S/L thrust radiation-cooled rocket motors for fine adjustment of their velocity prior to the docking manoeuvre.

On 20 February 1979, Bell completed 20 years of space

Bell Agena single-chamber liquid-propellant rocket engine

use of the Agena series of engines. In that time the Models 8096, described hereunder, and 8247 had been used in almost 340 missions by the US Air Force and NASA.

BELL MODEL 8096 AGENA ENGINE

This engine was first developed as the power plant for one of the weapon pods that was to be carried by the B-58 Hustler supersonic bomber. It is used in modified form, with gimballed chamber, as the power unit of the Lockheed-built Agena vehicle, forming the second stage of the Thor-Agena, Atlas-Agena and other space vehicles.

During its development the engine has undergone five major modifications, each resulting in an improvement in specific impulse. The present version, designated Model 8096, has a specific impulse of nearly 300 s, which is more than 10% better than the original version of 1959, an increase equivalent to 225 kg (500 lb) in payload for Earth orbital missions.

The Model 8096 engine is a single-chamber pump-fed engine, running on red fuming nitric acid and unsymmetrical dimethyl-hydrazine (UDMH) hypergolic propellants. It gives 71 kN (16,000 lb) S/L thrust, and has re-start capability in space. This feature can be used, for example, to change from a circular to an elliptical orbit.

The Model 8096 engine has the ability to be re-started twice in space. It powers the Agena vehicles used in many US Air Force and NASA programmes.

Bell has qualified the Agena engine to run on high-density acid (HDA), which burns at increased temperature to give increased thrust and efficiency; it requires a silicone additive to protect the thrust chamber. A higher-performance baffled injector has been developed and qualified for the current production engine. The company is investigating future propellant combinations and potential Agena applications in the Space Shuttle programme.

DIMENSIONS:
- Length overall: approx 2,134 mm (84 in)
- Nozzle diameter: 825·5 mm (32·5 in)

WEIGHT: approx 132 kg (290 lb)

PERFORMANCE:
- Thrust: 71 kN (16,000 lb)
- Chamber pressure approx: 34·5 bars (500 lb/sq in)
- Specific impulse: approx 300 s

CSD

CHEMICAL SYSTEMS DIVISION (A division of United Technologies Corporation)

HEADQUARTERS: Sunnyvale, California 94086
Telephone: (408) 739-4880
DIVISION PRESIDENT: Barnet R. Adelman
DIVISION SENIOR VICE-PRESIDENTS:
Dr David Altman
Eugene Roberts

CSD is currently engaged in research, development and production of rockets, rocket propellants and advanced propulsion systems, as well as a range of 'spin-off' by-products. Since its founding in the late 1950s it has conducted a continuous programme of rocket technology and is now producing a variety of advanced space propulsion systems for both the Department of Defense and the National Aeronautics and Space Administration.

CSD's largest programme is the production of 3,048 mm (120 in) diameter, segmented solid-propellant booster rockets. Other programmes described hereafter include the Algol III and FW-5 rocket motors, all of which are fully operational.

In 1976 a specially formed subsidiary, United Space Boosters Inc (USBI), was selected by NASA as boost assembly contractor for the Space Shuttle. USBI will be responsible, under a $122 million contract, for assembly, checkout, launch, post-launch disassembly and refurbishment of the motors for re-use. The present contract covers six development flights by March 1980, with an option for 21 operational flights extending into 1982.

CSD 3,048 mm (120 in) SEGMENTED MOTOR

Mass-produced at CSD's Coyote, California, rocket production facility, this 3,048 mm (120 in) diameter solid-propellant rocket motor centre segment is interchangeable with any other centre segment. Its cylindrical metal case is manufactured from high-strength steel (D6AC) and heat treated to an ultimate strength of 13,790 bars (200,000 lb/sq in). Less than 12·7 mm (0·5 in) thick, each case is equipped with clevis-type end joints with holes for cylindrical fastening pins. Loaded with propellant, a synthetic rubber (polybutadiene acrylonitrile) with aluminium additives as fuel and ammonium perchlorate as oxidiser, a segment has an overall length of 3,276 mm (10 ft 9 in) and weighs 36,400 kg (80,300 lb). Designed as the basic building block for large solid-propellant booster rockets, the segmented motor can be assembled in from one- to seven-segment configurations with thrusts ranging from 1,112-6,673 kN (250,000 to 1·5 million lb). A fully configured motor contains a destruct system, a forward-end ignition system a liquid-injection thrust-vector control system for steering and has its own staging sequence capability.

CSD has made progress in the development of more efficient and economical means of fabricating the steel motor cases used in the 120 in programme, through production processes known as internal roll extrusion and shear forming. Both techniques reduce production time and result in a more reliable and economical product.

A five-segment configuration of this motor is used in pairs as the zero (launch) stage of the US Air Force Titan IIIC and D space launch vehicles. Operating together, the 26·12 m (86 ft) tall motors produce a thrust of 10,675 kN (2,400,000 lb). Launched for the first time on 18 June 1965, the boosters have flown 48 successful missions in as many launches, using 96 motors.

Production continued in 1975, following a $59 million US Air Force contract for 16 five-segment motors for delivery in 1976 and 1977. This raised total purchase by the USAF Space and Missile Systems Organisation to 116. An additional $50 million contract calls for 20 more motors for delivery in the 13 months from June 1979.

In early 1979 CSD was completing production of five-segment motors and starting development and production of 5½-segment motors for the Titan 34D, the advanced version of the US Air Force's standard space launch vehicle. Two 5½-segment rocket boosters will launch the Titan 34D on its maiden flight from Cape Canaveral in mid-1980. The ten-ton additional half-motor segment is located just below the rocket's forward closure. In 1978 CSD received contract awards for $89 million for eight pairs of the 5½-segment systems.

Essentially a lengthened version of the five-segment motor, a seven-segment motor has been statically test-fired four times. Producing a record 6,227 kN (1·4 million lb) of thrust, the motors operated perfectly while testing an advanced steering system, called an ullage blow-down, which is now used on all flights of Titan IIIC and IIID vehicles.

CSD IUS

In October 1976 the US Air Force awarded the Boeing/CSD team a contract to develop the Inertial Upper Stage (IUS) for the Space Shuttle and the Titan 34D space launch vehicle. CSD's all-solid IUS proposal won the award over five competitors' liquid-propellant submissions. The Air Force cited highest reliability and safety at lowest cost in its choice. The Boeing/CSD IUS completed its validation phase on 19 December 1977, after a successful test firing of the 2,310 mm (91 in) diameter rocket motor at the Arnold Engineering Development Center (AEDC). During the firing, the 9,979 kg (22,000 lb) motor encountered no difficulties during an unusually long (154 s) burn. Key components, including the advanced flight-weight nozzle, proved their survivability. Average thrust was 173·6 kN (39,000 lb) and maximum 249·2 kN (56,000 lb) at a simulated altitude of 33,800 m (111,000 ft).

Full-scale development of the IUS propulsion system began on 1 March 1978 under a $32 million contract award from Boeing Aerospace. The propulsion system for the two-stage IUS consists of two solid rocket motors designed by CSD: a 2·31 m (91 in) aft motor containing 9,707 kg (21,400 lb) of propellant and a 1·6 m (63 in) forward stage motor with 2,722 kg (6,000 lb) of propellant. In May 1978 CSD received a $3 million award from Boeing to develop the thrust vector control (TVC) servo-actuator system to control the moveable nozzle. The basic TVC system consists of two controllers and four actuators powered by 28V batteries. In December 1978 CSD received a $2 million award to produce a servo-actuator system to raise the IUS to deployment position inside the Shuttle Orbiter's cargo bay.

CSD ALGOL III

CSD is in full production of Algol III, a more powerful solid-propellant first stage for NASA's Scout space launch vehicle. 9·14 m (30 ft) tall and 1·14 m (45 in) in diameter, the improved solid booster permits an increase of 40-54 per cent in the Scout's payload/weight capability. When loaded with its propellant (PBAN with aluminium additives and ammonium perchlorate oxidiser) Algol III weighs 13,605 kg (30,000 lb). Its nozzle is fabricated from steel with a graphite cloth-phenolic and silica cloth-phenolic cone liner. Ignition is by a small nose-mounted solid rocket. Producing 623 kN (140,000 lb) of lift-off thrust, Scout burns for 75 s to boost the Scout to an altitude of 48 km (30 miles) before burnout. The motor flew for the first time in August 1972 and by the end of 1977 had completed 15 missions.

About three launches per year are planned for the 1980s. Algol III is believed to be the only launch vehicle that will remain in production after the Shuttle becomes operational.

CSD FW-5

The FW-5 is designed interchangeable with existing upper-stage motors. While its primary application is that of an apogee motor, it can be used for orbital, probe or re-entry missions, as well as retro-rocket propulsion for space vehicles.

The FW-5 is 691 mm (27·2 in) diameter and has an overall length of 1,123 mm (44·2 in). Its case is fabricated from glassfibre and epoxy resin, with a cylindrical wall thickness of 3·3 mm (0·13 in) and end domes with solar isotensoid contours with a nominal wall thickness of 15·2 mm (0·60 in). The igniter and nozzle attachment fittings

Full-scale mockup of Boeing IUS, showing the forward and aft CSD motors

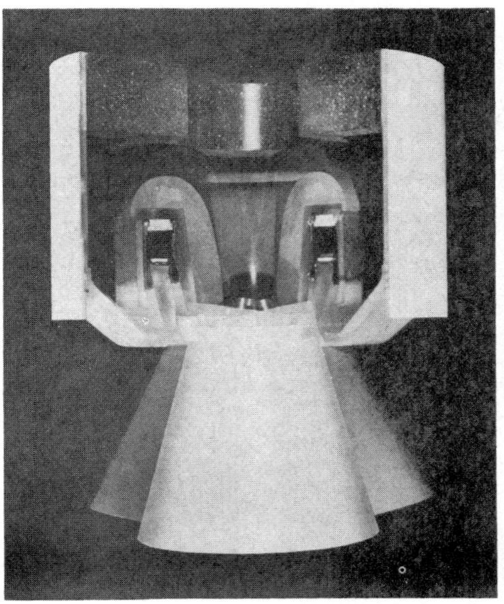

Three of CSD's advanced rocket nozzle systems: left, cutaway model showing operation of Techroll; centre, a test EEC during firing; right, a hot ball and socket

are fabricated from aluminium, and the aluminium interstage flange is bonded and riveted to the integrally-wound glassfibre skirt of the motor case.

The standard FW-5 has an inert weight of 29·7 kg (65·6 lb) and a propellant weight of 260 kg (575 lb), resulting in a motor mass fraction of 0·89. The average motor thrust is 25·04 kN (5,630 lb) with a burn time of 42·1 s.

FW-5 operated perfectly on its first mission in November 1972 when it placed Telesat Canada's Anik communications satellite into final orbit. The second Anik was put on station by an FW-5 in April 1973, followed by a third in May 1975.

By 1978 the FW-5 had completed seven additional consecutive successful flights on the Delta 2914 launch vehicle. The FW-5 was used to put on station communications satellites such as the Anik, Westar, Marisat, and Palpa. CSD has also developed a version of the FW-5 with a 178 mm (7·0 in) extension to the nozzle exit cone. The flight unit was to be used to launch the Martin-Marietta/Denver Scatha satellite in early 1979.

CSD ADVANCED-TECHNOLOGY MOTOR

This motor is being developed for the US Air Force by CSD for use in future space missions. It is 914 mm (36 in) diameter and 1,828 mm (72 in) long, contains 1,134 kg (2,500 lb) of propellant, and has thrust in the 67-89 kN (15,000-20,000 lb) class. The Kevlar filament-wound motor was test fired on 28 September 1978 at the Arnold Engineering Development Center for 60 s at a simulated altitude of 30,500 m (100,000 ft). The motor was spun at 100 rpm to simulate inflight conditions. It utilized a fixed carbon nozzle containing a pyrolytic graphite washer throat and two-dimensional involute carbon/carbon throat support and exit cone. The nozzle entrance employed three-dimensionally reinforced carbon/carbon. The programme was to culminate in 1979 with a second test firing. This motor utilised a redesigned case for improved performance, a carbon/carbon ITE and different propellant.

CSD BOOSTER SEPARATION MOTOR

In late 1975 NASA selected CSD to develop and produce solid-propellant booster separation motors (BSM) to be used on the first six development flights of the Space Shuttle programme beginning in 1980.

The BSMs will be used to separate the two reusable solid rocket boosters (SRB) approximately 110 seconds after launch of the Space Shuttle. Each SRB will require eight BSMs, four forward and four aft, which will fire for less than a second to achieve safe separation. In September 1978 the motor passed acceptance by NASA. Sixteen were then shipped to Kennedy Space Center, the first of 104 ordered for Shuttle development flights.

Each BSM has a length of 838 mm (33·0 in) and a diameter of 327 mm (12·88 in), with a weight of 73·0 kg (161 lb). It uses CSD UTP-19048 (HTPB) propellant, and will have 62·5 kN-s (14,000-lb-s) minimum total impulse WEB action time, and 67·0 kN-s (15,000-lb-s) minimum action time. Burn-time (WEB) performance time limit is 0·8 s. Maximum thrust called for is 129·5 kN (29,000 lb), with a WEB action time average thrust of 82·6 kN (18,500 lb) minimum.

CSD HAHST HYBRID PROPULSION

CSD's hybrid rocket for the Department of Defense High Altitude High-Speed Target (HAHST) drone (see under Beech heading in the RPVs and Targets section) is 330 mm (13 in) in diameter, has an overall length of 3,556 mm (140 in), and weighs 390 kg (860 lb). It uses a polybutadiene and methyl methacrylate fuel grain, and nitric acid as its liquid oxidiser. Ablative-cooled, its thrust ranges from 0·88-5·34 kN (200 to 1,200 lb) at altitudes

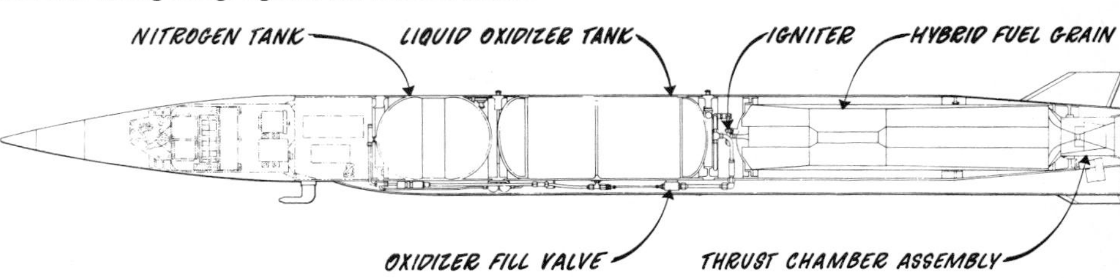

Longitudinal section of supersonic target vehicle with CSD hybrid propulsion, showing disposition of solid fuel grain and liquid propellants

between 10,670 and 30,480 m (35,000 and 100,000 ft). The HAHST successfully completed all its initial flight-readiness test-firings in 1973. In 1978 the HAHST was successfully flown three times by the US Navy at the Pacific Missile Test Center; engineering development of the HAHST was to begin in 1979.

CSD LIQUID ROCKET ENGINES

The company's liquid rockets range in size from 1,321 mm (52 in) long and 660 mm (26 in) in diameter and weighing 32·6 kg (72 lb) to 1,918 mm (75·5 in) long, 1,219 mm (48 in) in diameter and weighing 83·9 kg (185 lb). Their propellant is 50/50 hydrazine and unsymmetrical dimethyl hydrazine and nitrogen tetroxide. The engine nozzles are a composite structure with a glassfibre shell and silica-phenolic liner. Ignition is hypergolic.

CSD AIR-BREATHING PROPULSION

In early 1973, CSD was selected to spearhead the efforts of its parent, United Technologies Corporation, in the research and development of ramjet propulsion systems, with the support of UTC's Hamilton Standard Division and United Technologies Research Center. In mid-1973 CSD was awarded a contract by the US Navy to research, design and develop a Modern Ramjet Engine (MRE). Called an integral rocket/ramjet, the propulsion device involves both solid rocket and liquid fuel ramjet technology. It operates as a solid rocket booster until it reaches supersonic speeds. At that point, through a series of mechanical changes that take place in flight, it becomes a ramjet. These changes involve the opening of air inlets, an increase in the nozzle diameter and a switch to the burning of liquid fuel and air in the combustion chamber within a common system. The propulsion technology acquired in carrying out this project will be applied to the development of an advanced air-to-air missile system.

In mid-1974 CSD was awarded another ramjet programme by the US Air Force, to design and ground test an advanced integral rocket/ramjet propulsion system which would satisfy the requirements of an advanced strategic air-launched missile (ASALM).

In the ASALM programme, CSD had by 1978 embarked on a project to demonstrate the feasibility of two design approaches, one by McDonnell Douglas, the other by Martin Marietta. CSD was carrying out extensive ground testing, including numerous hot firings at its ramjet test facility near San Jose. This testing also involved simulated flight-test missions, in preparation for the next phase of development.

In mid-1977, the division received a subcontract from Vought, funded by the Navy, to refine the earlier Advanced Low Volume Ramjet (ALVRJ) (see Vought entry). In late 1977 CSD received a contract to develop the technology base for a high-speed ramjet propulsion system up to Mach 6.

Also in late 1977, CSD was awarded an Air Force contract to develop a solid-fuelled, ducted-rocket propulsion system. Called DRED (Ducted Rocket Engine Development), the system will be applied to high-performance, advanced air-to-air missiles, which will be operational in the 1980s. Working with CSD in Phase I of the programme will be Vought and Atlantic Research.

In the ducted rocket a solid rocket fuel produces a fuel-rich gas. This is injected into a combustion (ram-burner) chamber, mixed with ram air and further burned to provide sustained thrust at supersonic speeds. The ram air is introduced through inlet ducts alongside the proposed 152 mm (6 in) diameter, 3,048 mm (10 ft) long vehicle. Compared to a conventional rocket, the ducted rocket is claimed to offer many times the thrust duration, permitting powered flight all the way to a target and a greater range with less weight.

CSD's work in the Solid Fuelled Ramjet (SFRJ) area has progressed to a ground test demonstration of an air-to-surface missile configuration of heavy-weight hardware. The division is now proceeding with a Validation Of Concept programme for a proposed air-to-air weapon system, and under a 1978 contract is also investigating ramjet propulsion for US Army flight vehicles.

ADVANCED PROPULSION TECHNOLOGY

Testing of CSD's patented Techroll joint continues. This is a fluid-filled, constant-volume bearing which allows easy pivoting of the nozzle by the steering system. It is considered to be the first major improvement in rocket steering in almost a decade. Both IUS motors use the Techroll seal. Other uses being researched include a main rotor bearing for helicopters and a joint in high-pressure and transmission lines.

The extendible exit cone (EEC) is a device which mechanically enlarges as a rocket motor fires in space, improving performance by over five per cent. The first test at operational pressures and temperatures of an EEC system for ICBM nozzle applications was successfully carried out in June 1977. This CSD system uses nested cones of an advanced composite material, which lock into place by a latching mechanism.

CSD is continuing developmental work on its Bolt Extrusion Thrust Termination (BETT) system, considered the only new thrust-termination system for solid rocket motors developed in the last 20 years. BETT replaces nozzle flange bolts with a combination of explosive-released and extrudable bolts. Upon command, explosive bolts are actuated and the nozzle moves aft, dropping the motor's internal pressure drastically. This halts propellant burning and neutralizes motor thrust. A 1978 test of the system used a 2·34 m (92 in) Kevlar case. Upon command all explosive bolts operated within 0·001 s and the nozzle moved 146 mm (5·76 in) rearward in 0·016 s. Two tests of BETT on third-stage Minuteman motors were scheduled for early 1979.

CSD's "hot ball and socket" rocket steering system employs an integral carbon/carbon nozzle and thrust vector control system without the use of any seals, insulators or metallic structures. The materials are self-lubricating, and loads are transmitted between the surfaces even while white hot. This allows ball diameter to be reduced to a minimum, sharply reducing vectoring torque. The hot ball and socket completed its first test firing in 1978 under contract to the US Naval Sea Systems Command.

CURTISS-WRIGHT

CURTISS-WRIGHT CORPORATION, WOOD-RIDGE FACILITY

HEAD OFFICE AND WORKS: One Passaic St, Wood-Ridge, New Jersey 07075
Telephone: (201) 777-2900
CHAIRMAN OF THE BOARD AND PRESIDENT: T. Roland Berner
EXECUTIVE VICE-PRESIDENTS:
Charles E. Ehringer
Richard P. Sprigle
VICE-PRESIDENT, ENGINEERING: A. F. Kossar
VICE-PRESIDENTS:
D. Lasky
W. Figart

The Wood-Ridge facility of Curtiss-Wright Corporation is engaged in the research, development and licensing of Wankel-type rotary engines, manufacture of engine parts, aircraft and industrial engine overhaul, electric power generation systems and advanced marine and turbine technology.

CURTISS-WRIGHT SETE

In competition with Garrett-AiResearch and Pratt & Whitney, Curtiss-Wright is participating in the SETE (Supersonic Expendable Turbine Engine) programme of the US Navy. The objective is the cheapest possible jet engine capable of unfailingly-reliable instant starting and flight propulsion, under severe conditions of manoeuvre, over a wide band of speeds and heights, on a single flight of a missile. Details are restricted, but several sources give thrust class as 10·23 kN (2,300 lb st).

CURTISS-WRIGHT RC ENGINES

In 1958 Curtiss-Wright Corporation obtained a licence for the NSU-Wankel type of rotating-combustion (RC) engine and embarked on a major programme of independent development of a range of such engines aimed at a wide spectrum of applications. At first the company concentrated on large engines in the power range around 500 hp for aircraft use, but during the past decade much smaller engines have dominated the hardware test and development programme, some of which has been funded by US military agencies, including the Naval Air Systems Command.

Most research has been carried out on versions of the **RC2-60** (twin rotors each of about 0·983 litre; 60 cu in capacity), rated at up to 149 kW (200 hp) at 5,500 rpm and with possible future potential to reach twice this rotational speed in view of the near-perfect balance. One of these engines powered the Lockheed Q-Star acoustic research aircraft, specially designed for miniumum noise level (see 1971-72 *Jane's*). Further testing has been completed successfully in a Cessna Cardinal light aircraft and Hughes TH-55 training helicopter.

In 1965 the 310 hp **RC2-90** was run, with helicopter applications in mind, and the 1·47 litre (90 cu in) rotor has since been used in extensive development of stratified charge engines capable of operating on a range of fuels including JP-4 and JP-5 gas turbine kerosenes.

Curtiss-Wright RC2-75, rated at 254 kW (340 hp), on bench with three-blade propeller

The **RC2-75-Y3** is one of a very important family of engines, regarded as optimally sized for a wide range of general aviation aircraft. As the designation indicates, it is based on two rotors each of nominal 1·23 litres (75 cu in) capacity, and has liquid cooling and a geared drive. Engine development had in early 1975 progressed to running engines with propellers on static testbeds.

In May 1976 NASA awarded Curtiss-Wright a contract to perform a six-month effort involving a "Programme for Characteristic Data of an Experimental Rotary Combustion Aircraft Engine". The RC2-75 was tested as initially designed to obtain performance and exhaust emission data. Results indicate that 1980 EPA standards could be met for carbon monoxide and oxides of nitrogen. Hydrocarbon results were slightly above the standard; however, Company engineers feel it is likely that the total EPA 1980 emissions requirement can be realised by employing known modifications which do not include add-on devices or sacrifices in performance or durability. A second NASA contract was awarded in November 1977 to explore the effect of such modifications, and in 1979 this work was continuing to give limited gains in reduced fuel consumption and exhaust pollution.

DIMENSIONS:
Length 798 mm (31·4 in)
Width 602 mm (23·7 in)
Height 546 mm (21·5 in)
WEIGHTS:
Basic, dry 127 kg (280 lb)
Installed, with starter, oil cooler, oil tank, coolant and radiator and mounting brackets 167 kg (368 lb)
PERFORMANCE RATING:
Max T-O 254 kW (340 hp) at 7,000 rpm

DREHER

DREHER ENGINEERING COMPANY

708 Lincoln Boulevard, Santa Monica, California 90402
Telephone: (213) 395-6510

Mr Max Dreher, an aeronautical engineer, has built a series of small turbojet engines over a period of 24 years. One of them, known as the TJD-76 Baby Mamba, was mounted on his Prue 215A all-metal 12·0 m sailplane as an auxiliary turbojet.

Development of the TJD-76C has been virtually completed, apart from the recent addition of an automatic fuel control device which is operating well and will later be applied to the larger engines. During the past year it has become evident that the main market favours the TJD-76E, and a suitable production manufacturer is being sought.

Two views of the Dreher Baby Mamba single-shaft turbojet: *(left)* TJD-76C on mount; *(right)* TJD-76C Jet Pack installed on sailplane. Thrust rating is 0·245 kN (55 lb st)

DREHER TJD-76C BABY MAMBA

This new version of the Baby Mamba is lighter and introduces several mechanical and aerodynamic improvements, including a tachometer generator for direct rpm reading.

TYPE: Single-shaft turbojet.
AIR INTAKE: At front. Air flow 0·50 kg (1·1 lb)/s.
COMPRESSOR: Single-stage mixed-flow. Single 17-4 PH stainless steel impeller with sixteen vanes. Splined to shaft and supported in two ball bearings. Mixed-flow two-stage diffuser of 347 stainless steel. Pressure ratio 2·8 : 1.
COMPRESSOR CASING: Of 2024 aluminium alloy and 347 stainless steel.
COMBUSTION CHAMBER: Annular type with Hastelloy X outer casing and flame tube. Vaporising system with fuel/air pre-mix. One spark plug in flame tube.
FUEL SYSTEM: Manual with pressurised fuel supply, or electrically-driven fuel pump. Fuel pressure 5·52 bars (80 lb/sq in). Automatic system for drone applications.
FUEL GRADE: Kerosene or petrol.
NOZZLE GUIDE VANES: Single axial stage, with sixteen investment-cast vanes in Stellite 31.
TURBINE: Single-stage axial-flow, with nineteen integrally-cast blades, of Inconel 713 LC. Gas temperature 770°C before turbine, 675°C after turbine, at continuous cruising power.
JET PIPE: Fixed type, with jet pipe and cone of Hastelloy X.
LUBRICATION: Air/oil mist system with total loss, using bleed air equivalent to 2·5 per cent of total mass flow. Capacity 1 litre (2 US pints).
OIL GRADE: MIL-L-7808E (Turbo 15).
MOUNTING: Two rigid connections on diffuser section and one flexible connection on turbine section.
STARTING: Compressed air 10·34 bars (150 lb/sq in), via three nozzles driving turbine wheel.
DIMENSIONS:
Length overall 416 mm (16·38 in)
Diameter 151 mm (5·94 in)
WEIGHTS:
Dry 6·4 kg (14·1 lb)
Complete with fuel tank 10·0 kg (22 lb)
PERFORMANCE RATINGS:
Max 0·245 kN (55 lb st)
Continuous 0·20 kN (45 lb st)
SPECIFIC FUEL CONSUMPTION:
at max rating 42·5 mg/Ns (1·5 lb/h/lb st)
OIL CONSUMPTION:
at max rating 25 cc/min

DREHER TJD-76D and E

These versions were derived from the TJD-76C in 1972 to meet a need for a very low-cost short-life unit for the propulsion of mini-RPVs and other expendable vehicles. Both have similar performance to the TJD-76C but weigh approximately 6·5 kg (14·33 lb), complete with 2 kW alternator. Envelope diameter is 165 mm (6·5 in) and length 400 mm (15·75 in).

DSI
DEVELOPMENTAL SCIENCES INC

15747 East Valley Boulevard, City of Industry, California 91749
Telephone: (213) 330-6865
PRESIDENT: Dr Gerald R. Seemann

DSI RESONATING RAMJET

This simple engine consists of an inlet diffuser, inlet with turning vanes, fuel injectors, flameholder, combustion chamber, transition section, tailpipe and nozzle. It is fabricated by welding from 321 stainless steel. Certain area ratios are critical to successful operation at approximately 300Hz. Flight Mach number ranges from 0·5 to 0·95.

DSI has both flown and tunnel-tested this engine. In its basic form it is a very low-cost power plant. Recently, development has been proceeding under contract for the propulsion of a ground-launched RPV, and tests have been made at the US Navy Air Propulsion Test Center (engine) and Army Proving Ground at Yuma (booster ejection).

Among suitable fuels are propane (gas or liquid), gasoline (petrol), JP-4 and JP-5. Fuel is fed by a pump to multiple injector nozzles, with fuel scheduling regulated by a Mach number feedback. For cold starting the combustion chamber is fitted with a 5 s Holex igniter. The engine is available in sizes smaller and larger than that described below.

DIMENSIONS:
Length overall 1,270 mm (50 in)
Width (or height) 197 mm (7·75 in)
Height (or width) 279 mm (11·0 in)
WEIGHT, DRY: 13·6 kg (30 lb)

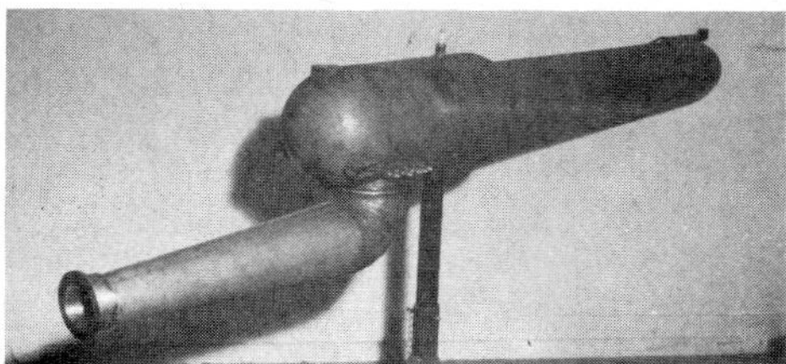

Developmental Sciences resonating ramjet in 0·89 kN (200 lb) thrust size

PERFORMANCE RATING (S/L):
Max thrust at Mach 0·7 0·89 kN (200 lb)
SPECIFIC FUEL CONSUMPTION: 3·5-4·8

GARRETT-AIRESEARCH
AIRESEARCH MANUFACTURING COMPANY of Arizona (a division of The Garrett Corporation)

Sky Harbor Airport, 111 S 34th St, PO Box 5217, Phoenix, Arizona 85010
Telephone: (602) 267-3011
VICE-PRESIDENT AND MANAGER: Jack Marinick
SALES MANAGER: Malcolm E. Craig

The Garrett Corporation's AiResearch Manufacturing Company of Arizona, at Phoenix, has been called the world's largest producer of small gas turbines. Development of the first Garrett small turbines began in 1946 and the division claims to have produced over 70% of the total of gas-turbine units with power ratings from 60 to 2,500 hp built in the United States and Europe.

GARRETT-AIRESEARCH ATF3
US military designation: F104-GA-100

Considered to be the first three-spool engine to run in the United States, the Garrett-AiResearch ATF3 is the first engine in the world to combine the three-spool features with a reverse-flow combustion system and turbines, and mixed-flow exhaust.

The arrangement of components allows the fan design to be determined largely independently of the gas-generator compressor requirements, and permits operation at optimum fan speed. Omission of fan inlet guide vanes, mixing of the gas-generator exhaust with the fan airflow, and double reversal of the internal airflow enable the ATF3 to offer significant reductions in overall noise generation.

Other design considerations include reliability, maintainability and elimination of visible smoke. The accessories are revealed by removing the tailcone fairing, and their positioning at the rear of the engine is claimed to reduce installed drag.

All design and early development of the ATF3 took place at the AiResearch Torrance (Los Angeles) facility. The conceptual design was completed in early 1966, and testing of demonstrator engines was initiated in May 1968. Under US Air Force contract, the ATF3 successfully completed preliminary flight rating tests in 1972 at 18 kN (4,050 lb) thrust. Both the aerodynamic and mechanical design criteria were established around sea-level, ISA +15°C take-off rating of 22·46 kN (5,050 lb).

In May 1976 it was announced that the ATF3-6 had been selected by Dassault-Breguet to power the Falcon 20G business jet, with US coast-to-coast range. Commercial certification was achieved in early 1979 after 15,000 hours of testing, and production shipments began in that year. The ATF3-6 is offered under a retrofit programme for existing Falcon 20 aircraft. It powers the HU-25A Falcon Guardian that is in production for the US Coast Guard.

TYPE: Three-shaft axial-flow turbofan.

INTAKE: Direct pitot, fixed type. No inlet vanes or struts. Total airflow 73·5 kg/s (162 lb/s).

LOW-PRESSURE (FAN) SYSTEM: Single-stage titanium fan, driven by three-stage IP turbine. By-pass ratio 2·8 at take-off.

INTERMEDIATE-PRESSURE SYSTEM: Five-stage titanium axial IP compressor, each stage having a separate disc, driven by two-stage LP turbine. Airflow is then delivered to rearward-facing HP compressor via eight tubes feeding into an annular duct concentric with the by-pass duct. Core airflow 18·15 kg (40 lb)/s.

HIGH-PRESSURE SYSTEM: Single-stage titanium centrifugal compressor, driven by single-stage HP turbine. IP airflow enters the single-sided impeller from the rear. Overall pressure ratio (T-O) 21, (high-altitude cruise) 25.

COMBUSTION SYSTEM: Reverse-flow annular type.

TURBINES: Single-stage HP, three-stage IP and two-stage LP turbines drive, respectively, the HP, fan (LP) and IP compressors. IP and LP turbines have fully shrouded blades. Aircooled first-stage nozzle vanes and HP rotor blades. Exhaust gases turned 180° through eight sets of cascades to mix with fan by-pass flow.

FUEL SYSTEM: Electromechanical, incorporating solid-state computer. Manual emergency backup system.

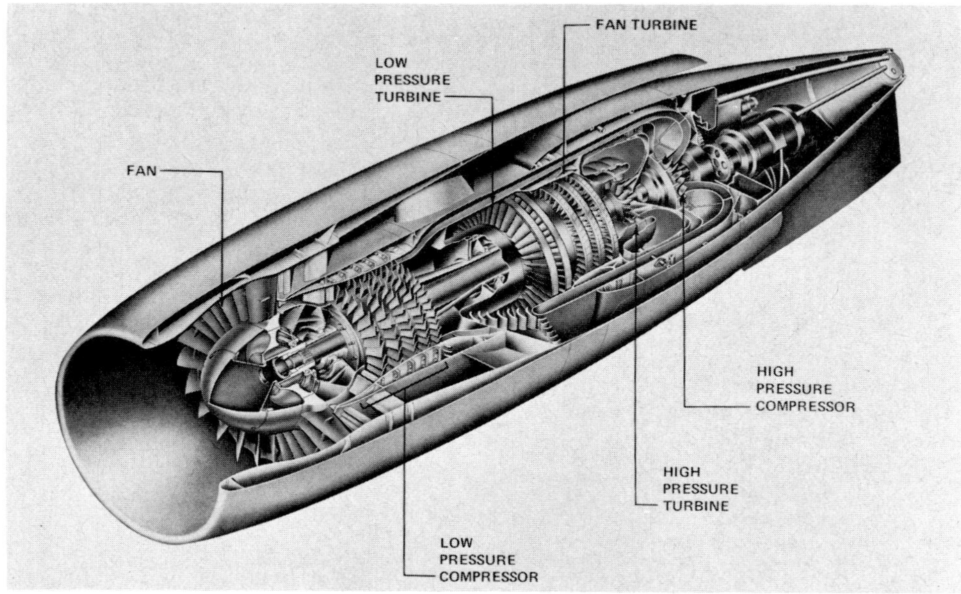

Cutaway of the Garrett-AiResearch ATF3-6 three-shaft turbofan with double flow-reversal (22·46 kN; 5,050 lb st)

ACCESSORY DRIVES: Three drive pads on rear-mounted gearbox driven by HP shaft, providing for hydraulic pump, starter/generator and one spare. Accessory cooling by fan discharge air which is exhausted through a nozzle at the tip of the fairing.

EXHAUST SYSTEM: Mixed fan and turbine exhaust discharged to atmosphere through annular nozzle surrounding combustion section.

LUBRICATION SYSTEM: Self-contained hot-tank type; tank integral with gearbox.

MOUNTING: Two-plane pickup system.

STARTING: Electrical or pneumatic.

DIMENSIONS:
ATF3-6:
Length 2,316 mm (91·2 in)
Max diameter 853 mm (33·6 in)
WEIGHT, DRY:
ATF3-6 431 kg (950 lb)
PERFORMANCE RATINGS (uninstalled):
T-O (S/L, static):
ATF3-6 22·46 kN (5,050 lb), ISA+15°C
Cruise (12,200 m; 40,000 ft at Mach 0·8):
ATF3-6 4·5 kN (1,012 lb)
SPECIFIC FUEL CONSUMPTION:
At T-O rating (S/L, ISA static) 13·6 mg/Ns (0·48 lb/h/lb st)
At cruise (as above) 22·38 mg/Ns (0·79 lb/h/lb st)

GARRETT-AIRESEARCH TFE731

Announced in April 1969, the TFE731 is a two-spool geared turbofan designed to confer US coast-to-coast range upon business jet aircraft. Use of a geared fan confers flexibility in operation and yields optimum performance both at low altitudes and at up to 15,250 m (50,000 ft).

Component testing began in March 1969. The first engine ran in September 1970, and was tested at Phoenix in a Learjet 25. FAA certification and first production deliveries to Dassault for the Falcon 10 took place in August 1972.

In October 1972 it was stated that the Lockheed JetStar would be re-engined with the TFE731-3, flat rated at 16·46 kN (3,700 lb st) by a modest increase in turbine inlet temperature. The TFE731-3 was certificated in 1974. The modified aircraft is designated JetStar II, and first flew in July 1974. AiResearch Aviation is converting a number of JetStar I aircraft to have TFE 731-3 power.

Since 1973 the TFE731, in various sub-types, has been selected for the Gates Learjet 35/36, Cessna Citation III, Dassault-Breguet Falcon 50, HS 125-700, IAI 1124 Westwind, Rockwell International's Sabreliner 65A, CASA C-101 trainer and light attack aircraft, Learjet 54/55/56 Longhorn, and ICX X-Avia, and proposals have been made for RPV and other short-life programmes.

By early 1979 deliveries of TFE731-2 and -3 engines had reached 1,600. Output had risen to 40 per month, with expansion planned to rise to 50 per month.

TYPE: Turbofan with two shafts and geared front fan.

AIR INTAKE: Direct pitot, fixed, without guide vanes.

FAN: Single-stage axial titanium fan, with inserted blades. The fan shaft is connected directly to the planetary gearbox ring gear. Max fan airflow, sea level static, 51·25 kg (113 lb)/s (-3, 53·7 kg; 118·3 lb/s; -4, 54·6 kg; 120·4 lb/s). By-pass ratio 2·66 (-3, 2·80; -4, 2·28).

COMPRESSOR: Low-pressure compressor has four stages (TFE731-4, five stages), each with a separate disc. Rotors and stators have inserted blades and vanes. High-pressure compressor, carried on a separate shaft running at higher speeds, is centrifugal. Overall pressure ratio (S/L, static): -2, 14·0; -3, 14·6; -4, 17·5.

COMBUSTION CHAMBER: Annular combustion chamber of reverse-flow type, with 12 fuel nozzles inserted radially and injecting fuel tangentially.

FUEL SYSTEM: Hydro-electronic, with single-lever control to mechanical and electronic elements.

TURBINES: High-pressure turbine has a single axial stage with inserted blades. Low-pressure turbine has three axial stages, all with inserted blades. Average inlet gas temperature to HP turbine, S/L, max T-O thrust, 1,010°C (-3 and -4, higher).

JET PIPE: Short fan duct facilitating installation of fan reverser. Fixed core nozzle.

ACCESSORY DRIVES: Accessories driven from HP spool are grouped around underside of the forward section of the fan duct. Pads are provided on the front side of the accessory gearbox for the airframe-type accessories: hydraulic pump, starter/generator or starter motor and alternators. Pads on the back side of the gearbox drive the engine accessories: fuel control unit and oil pump.

DIMENSIONS:
Intake diameter 716 mm (28·2 in)
Length overall (-2, -3) 1,263 mm (49·73 in)
Width 869 mm (34·20 in)
Height overall 992 mm (39·07 in)
WEIGHT, DRY:
TFE731-2, -3 329 kg (725 lb)
PERFORMANCE RATINGS:
Max T-O (S/L, 24·4°C):
TFE731-2 15·57 kN (3,500 lb st)

TFE731-3	16·46 kN (3,700 lb st)
Cruise (12,200 m; 40,000 ft at Mach 0·8):	
TFE731-2	3·36 kN (755 lb)
TFE731-3	3·64 kN (817 lb)
SPECIFIC FUEL CONSUMPTION:	
Max T-O (as above):	
TFE731-2	13·88 mg/Ns (0·49 lb/h/lb st)
TFE731-3	14·33 mg/Ns (0·506 lb/h/lb st)
Cruise (as above):	
TFE731-2	23·08 mg/Ns (0·815 lb/h/lb)
TFE731-3	23·65 mg/Ns (0·835 lb/h/lb)

GARRETT-AIRESEARCH/FLYGMOTOR TFE1042

This low-by-pass derivative of the TFE731 is a joint project with Volvo Flygmotor of Sweden and is described in the International part of this section.

GARRETT-AIRESEARCH ETJ131

Evolving from Garrett's long turbocharger experience, the ETJ131 turbojet is designed for military applications such as low-cost decoys and target vehicles. Although details are not available, it is generally known that the design uses turbocharger components mated to a single-can combustor. In the 0·445 kN (100 lb) thrust class, the engine is described as "low-cost, with very simplified controls". Unofficial sources report the engine has been tested at 0·89 kN (200 lb) with an afterburner. The company designation is Model 1030, and it is based on the T18A turbocharger.

GARRETT-AIRESEARCH TJE341

In the 4·45 kN (1,000 lb) thrust class, the TJE341 turbojet is derived from earlier Garrett low-cost expendable engine technology and demonstration programmes. Intended initial application is in medium-range RPVs now under study. The TJE341 has a re-usable rating for recoverable RPVs, yet is expected to retain the overall simplicity and potentially low production cost that were design goals for earlier Garrett turbojets.

GARRETT-AIRESEARCH TPE331

US military designation: T76

Originally based upon extensive experience with APUs, this was the first AiResearch engine for aircraft propulsion; it has since been the main product which has helped to provide funding for later engines. The military T76 has achieved only modest sales, but the civil TPE331 has been most successful and developed in a series of versions. Deliveries in mid-1979 were at the rate of more than 50 engines per month, and total deliveries then exceeded 6,000. Flight time exceeded 15,000,000 hours.

The following are major versions:

TPE331 series I, II. Initial production version, FAA certificated in February 1965. Rated at 451 ekW; 429 kW plus 0·33 kN (605 ehp; 575 shp plus 75 lb st). Redesignated **TPE331-25/61** and **-25/71** and produced until 1970. Powers Mitsubishi MU-2 (A to E models), Fairchild Industries/Pilatus Porter, Carstedt Jet Liner, Volpar Super Turbo 18, Aerospace FU-24, Rockwell International Hawk Commander and 680 and DHC-2 Turbo Beaver.

TPE331-1 series. Certificated December 1967 at 526 ekW; 496 kW plus 0·44 kN (705 ehp; 665 shp plus 100 lb st). Powers Mitsubishi MU-2 (F and G), Pilatus Turbo-Porter and Fairchild Industries AU-23A Peacemaker, Mid West CJ600, Volpar Turboliner, Interceptor 400, Rockwell International Turbo Commander and (customer option) Thrush Commander, Swearingen Merlin IIB and Aerospace Fletcher 1284, Marsh Turbo Thrush and Marsh Turbo Ag-Cat.

TPE331-2 series. The -201 was certificated in December 1967 at 563 ekW; 533 kW plus 0·45 kN (755 ehp; 715 shp plus 102 lb st). Powers Shorts Skyvan, CASA 212 pre-series and Volpar Turbo Goose and Turbo Beaver.

TPE331-3 series. Certificated in March 1970 at 674 ekW; 626 kW plus 0·71 kN (904 ehp; 840 shp plus 159 lb st). Uprated gas generator with increased airflow and pressure ratio, but same turbine temperature as in original TPE 331. Powers Swearingen Merlin III, IV and Metro, and Century Jetstream III.

TPE331-5/6 series. The -251 was certificated in March 1970; this matches the gas generator of the -3 series with the 715 shp gearbox, and is flat-rated to 2,134 m (7,000 ft). Powers Shorts Skyvan 3 (-201), Beech King Air B100

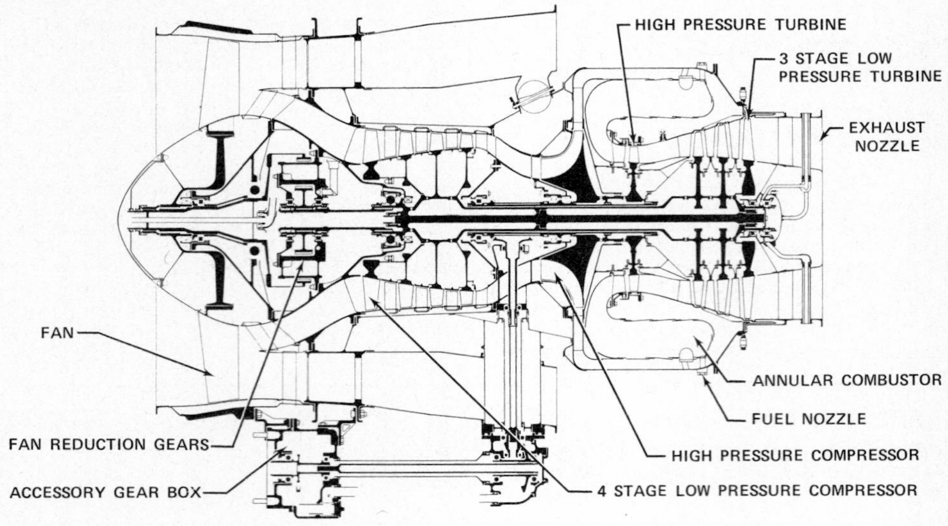

Cross-section (top) and external view (above) of the 15·57 kN (3,500 lb st) Garrett-AiResearch TFE731-2 geared front-fan engine

Garrett-AiResearch ETJ131 low-cost turbojet for short-life applications (0·445 kN; 100 lb st class). The air inlet is on the left, the combustor at upper right and the jet pipe behind at lower right

Garrett-AiResearch TPE331 series commercial turboprop engine. This has the air intake below the spinner, unlike the T76 military engines

(-252), CASA 212 Aviocar (-251) and Rockwell International Turbo Commander 690A (-251). The -5 designation indicates output speed of 1,591 rpm; the -6 has an output speed of 2,000 rpm.

TPE331-8. Matches compressor and gearbox of -251 with new turbine section. Thermodynamic power of 676 ekW; 645 kW (865 shp plus 47·7 kg, 105 lb st), but flat rated at 533 kW (715 shp) to 36°C. Certification was received in September 1976. Powers Cessna Conquest.

TPE331-9. Rated at 645 kW (865 shp).

TPE331-10. Rated at 746 kW 1,000 shp. Certificated February 1978 and for use in new MU-2 models, Merlin IIIB, Jetstream and CASA 212.

TPE331-9, -10, -11. New models under development with ratings 533 kW (715 shp) to 746 kW (1,000 shp). Certification scheduled for mid-1979.

T76. Military engine, with gas generator similar to TPE331-1 series but with front end inverted, to give inlet above instead of below spinner. Two versions, originally designated T76-G-10 and G-12 and restyled G-410 and G-411, respectively giving clockwise and anticlockwise propeller rotation (seen from rear). Development near completion of revised T76-G-420/421 rated at 776 kW (1,040 shp), with certification in September 1976. All models power Rockwell International OV-10 Bronco.

The TPE331 and T76 are of similar frame size, and the following data apply generally to both models:

Type: Single-shaft turboprop.

Propeller Drive: Two-stage reduction gear, one helical spur and one planetary, with overall ratio of 20·865 : 1 or 26·3 : 1. Rotation clockwise or anticlockwise.

Air Intake: Single scoop intake duct at top (T76) or bottom of engine, at front. Provision for bleed air de-icing.

Compressor: Tandem two-stage centrifugal type. Each impeller is single-sided, and is made from titanium. First-stage casing of magnesium, with aluminium diffuser. Second-stage casing and diffuser of stainless steel. Mass flow, 2·61 kg (5·78 lb)/s for 25/61, 25/71, 2·81 kg (6·2 lb)/s for -1, 2·80 kg (6·17 lb)/s for -2 and T76, 3·52 kg (7·75 lb)/s for -251 and 3·54 kg (7·8 lb)/s for -3. Pressure ratio 8·0 for 25/61, 25/71, 8·34 for -1, 8·54 for 2 and T76, 10·37 for -251 and -3.

Combustion Chamber: Annular type of high-temperature alloy. High-energy capacitor discharge ignition. Igniter plug on turbine plenum.

Fuel System: Woodward or Bendix control system for use with Beta propeller governing control system. Five radial primary nozzles in continuous operation. Ten axial simplex nozzles. Max fuel pressure 41·4 bars (600 lb/sq in).

Fuel Grade: (TPE331): Aviation turbine fuels ASTM designation D1655-64T types Jet A, Jet B and Jet A-1; MIL-F-5616-1, Grade JP-1.

Fuel Grade: (T76): MIL-L-5624F(2), Grades JP-4 and JP-5; MIL-G-5572, Grade 115/145.

Nozzle Guide Vanes: Axial vanes made from Inco 713C castings.

Turbine: Three-stage axial-flow type. Discs of first two stages of Inco 100, third stage of Inco 713C, attached to shaft by curvic couplings. Blades cast integrally with disc. Turbine inlet gas temperature, 987°C for 25/61, 25/71, 993°C for T76, 1,005°C for all other models.

Jet Pipe: Fixed type, stainless steel.

Accessories: AND 20005 Type XV-B tachometer generator, AND 20002 Type XII-D starter/generator, AND 20010 Type XX-A propeller governor and AND 20001 Type XI-B hydraulic pump, all mounted on aft face of accessories case.

Lubrication System: Medium-pressure dry sump system. Gerotor internal gear-type pressure and scavenge pumps. Normal oil supply pressure 6·90 bars (100 lb/sq in). Provision for automatic fuel filter anti-icing.

Oil Specification: MIL-L-23699-(1) or MIL-L-7808.

Mounting: Five-point suspension. Three pads on aft face of accessory case, two pads at aft end of turbine plenum.

Starting: Pad for 399A starter/generator on aft face of accessory case.

Dimensions (approx):
- Length overall:
  - TPE331: 1,092 to 1,168 mm (43-46 in)
  - T76: 1,118 mm (44 in)
- Width:
  - TPE331: 533 mm (21 in)
  - T76: 483 mm (19 in)
- Height:
  - TPE331: 660 mm (26 in)
  - T76: 686 mm (27 in)

Weights, Dry:
- TPE331-25/61, 71: 152 kg (335 lb)
- TPE331-1, -2: 152·5 kg (336 lb)
- T76: 155 kg (341 lb)
- TPE331-251: 163 kg (360 lb)
- TPE331-3: 161 kg (355 lb)

Performance Ratings:
- T-O: see under model listings
- Military (30 min):
  - T76-G-410/411: 533 kW; 563 ekW (715 shp; 755 ehp)
- Normal:
  - T76-G-410/411: 485 kW; 514·5 ekW (650 shp; 690 ehp)
- Max cruise (ISA, 3,050 m; 10,000 ft and 250 kt; 463 km/h; 288 mph):
  - TPE331-25/61, 71: 332 kW (445 shp)
  - TPE331-1: 404 kW (542 shp)
  - TPE331-2, T76: 430 kW (577 shp)
  - TPE331-251, -3: 529·5 kW (710 shp)

Specific Fuel Consumption:
- At T-O rating:
  - TPE331-25/61, 71: 111·5 μg/J (0·66 lb/h/shp)
  - TPE331-1: 107·0 μg/J (0·633 lb/h/shp)
  - TPE331-2: 99·4 μg/J (0·588 lb/h/shp)
  - TPE331-251: 105·8 μg/J (0·626 lb/h/shp)
  - TPE331-3: 99·7 μg/J (0·59 lb/h/shp)
  - T76-G-410/411: 101·4 μg/J (0·60 lb/h/shp)

Oil Consumption:
- Max: 0·009 kg (0·02 lb)/h

GARRETT-AIRESEARCH TSE331-3U

This turboshaft, derived from the TPE331-3 turboprop, was certificated in April 1970. It powers the Sikorsky S-55T helicopter conversion certificated by Aviation Specialties Inc of Mesa, Arizona, flat rated at 522 kW (700 shp).

Type: Single-shaft turboshaft with front end drive.

Power Drive: Two-stage reduction gear, one helical spur and one planetary, with overall ratio of 16·410 : 1.

Air Intake: Single scoop intake duct at top front of engine. Provision for bleed air anti-icing.

Compressor: Two-stage centrifugal. Tandem, single-sided titanium impellers are attached to the shaft by curvic couplings. First-stage casing of magnesium with aluminium diffusers. Second-stage casing and diffusers of stainless steel. Pressure ratio 10·32 : 1.

Combustion Chamber: Annular type of high-temperature alloy. High-energy capacitor discharge ignition. Igniter plug on turbine plenum.

Fuel System: Woodward fuel control for automatic speed control and fuel metering to match engine power to rotor load. Fuel filter, fuel shut-off valve, fuel-flow divider and manifold drain valve, fuel manifold and nozzle assemblies (five primary, ten secondary), start-fuel system and fuel anti-ice system.

Fuel Grade: Aviation turbine fuels ASTM designation D1655-68T, Types Jet A, A-1, and B, MIL-T-5624G-1, Grades JP-4 and JP-5, MIL-F-5161-1, Grade JP-1.

Nozzle Guide Vanes: Axial vanes made from Inco 713C castings.

Turbine: Three-stage axial-flow type. Discs of first two stages of Inco 100, third stage of Inco 713C, attached to shaft by curvic couplings. Blades cast integrally with disc.

Exhaust Duct: Fixed type. Cone and jet pipe both of stainless steel.

Accessories: AND 20005 Type XV-B tachometer generator, AND 20002 Type XII-D starter/generator, AND 20001 Type XI-B hydraulic pump, all mounted on aft face of accessories case.

Lubrication System: Medium-pressure dry sump system. Gerotor internal gear type pressure and scavenge pumps. Normal oil supply pressure 6·90 bars (100 lb/sq in). Provision for automatic fuel filter anti-icing.

Oil Specification: MIL-L-23699A or MIL-L-7808D.

Mounting: Five-point suspension. Three pads on aft face of accessory case, two pads at aft end of turbine plenum.

Starting: Pad for 300A starter/generator on aft face of accessory case.

Dimensions (approx):
- Length overall: 1,118 mm (44 in)
- Width: 533 mm (21 in)
- Height: 686 mm (27 in)

Weight, Dry: 161 kg (355 lb)

Performance Ratings:
- T-O: 596·5 kW (800 shp)
- Max continuous: 522 kW (700 shp)

Specific Fuel Consumption:
- T-O: 99·7 μg/J (0·59 lb/h/shp)

Oil Consumption:
- Max: 0·009 kg (0·02 lb)/h

GENERAL ELECTRIC

GENERAL ELECTRIC COMPANY AIRCRAFT ENGINE GROUP

1000 Western Avenue, Lynn, Massachusetts 01910
Telephone: (617) 594-0100

Group Locations: Lynn and Everett, Massachusetts; Cincinnati, Ohio; Rutland and Ludlow, Vermont; Hooksett, New Hampshire; and Albuquerque, New Mexico. Also test facilities at Edwards Air Force Base, California, and Peebles, Ohio. Further facilities at Seattle, Washington; Arkansas City, Kansas; Ontario, California.

Vice-President and Group Executive: F. O. MacFee Jr

Military Engine Division:
Vice-President and General Manager: J. N. Krebs

Airline Programs Division:
Vice-President and General Manager: L. V. Tomasetti

Commercial Engine Division:
Vice-President and General Manager: J. E. Worsham

Engineering Division:
Vice-President and General Manager: B. H. Rowe

Manufacturing Division:
Vice-President and General Manager: R. F. Letts

Marine and Industrial Department:
General Manager: O. R. Bonner

Strategic Planning:
Vice-President: R. H. Goldsmith

Project and Technology Assessment:
Vice-President: E. Woll

International Engine Programs:
General Manager: Jack I. Hope

Current products of the GE Aircraft Engine Group include the F101, F103, F404, J79, J85, T58, T64, T700 and TF34 for military use, and the CF6, CF34, CF700, CJ610, CT58, CT7 and CT64 for the commercial and general aviation market. In partnership with SNECMA of France a company was formed to develop and market the CFM56 turbofan, as described in the International part of this section under CFM International.

General Electric J79-GE-17 turbojet (79·24 kN; 17,820 lb st with afterburning)

GENERAL ELECTRIC J79

Development of the J79, America's first high-compression variable-stator turbojet, began in 1952. In addition to US manufacture, it was produced by Orenda of Canada to power the Canadair CF-104/F-104G (MAP), by Ishikawajima-Harima in Japan for the licence-built F-104DJ, and by MTU of Germany, Fiat of Italy and FN of Belgium for the European-built F-104G. The Italian production team, including Alfa-Romeo, also produced the J79-GE-19, an improved engine similar to the J79-GE-17 but configured for the F-104S Starfighter. More than 17,000 J79s had been built by GE and licensees by January 1979.

Derivatives of the J79 have been the CJ805-3 turbojet and CJ805-23 turbofan, powering the Convair 880 and

990 Coronado airliners, respectively, as well as the LM1500 industrial and marine gas turbine.

Versions of the J79 in service are as follows:

J79-GE-7A. Built under licence by Orenda (as J79-OEL-7) for Canadair CF-104.

J79-GE-8. McDonnell Douglas F-4B and RF-4B. Air mass flow 76·5 kg (169 lb)/s. Pressure ratio 12·9 : 1.

J79-GE-10. RA-5C and F-4J. Pressure ratio 13·5 : 1. Improved -10A has smoke-free combustor for F-4S.

J79-GE-11A. Lockheed F-104G. Built under licence in Japan (as J79-IHI-11A), Germany, Italy, Belgium and Canada.

J79-GE-15. Powers F-4C, F-4D and RF-4C for USAF. Similar to J79-GE-8 except for self-contained starting.

J79-GE-17. Similar to J79-GE-10, but for F-4E, F-4G, RF-4E, F-4EJ and F-4F; similar engine used in IAI Kfir.

J79-GE-19. F-104S and F-104A. Differs from J79-GE-10/17 only in external characteristics. Guided expansion jet nozzle. Afterburner provides continuous fuel-flow modulation from 1,225 kg (2,700 lb)/h to 15,420 kg (34,000 lb)/h.

The following details apply to all J79 variants except where otherwise indicated:

TYPE: Variable-stator single-shaft axial-flow turbojet.

AIR INTAKE: Annular type.

COMPRESSOR: Seventeen-stage axial-flow. Details in 1977-78 *Jane's*.

COMBUSTION CHAMBER: Cannular type consisting of 10 combustion cans. Details in 1978-79 *Jane's*.

FUEL SYSTEM: Hydromechanical, details in 1977-78 *Jane's*.

FUEL GRADE: JP-4 or JP-5.

TURBINE: Three-stage, details in 1977-78 *Jane's*.

AFTERBURNER: Details in 1978-79 *Jane's*.

ACCESSORY DRIVES: Details in 1978-79 *Jane's*.

LUBRICATION: Details in 1978-79 *Jane's*.

OIL SPECIFICATION: Details in 1978-79 *Jane's*.

MOUNTING: Details in 1978-79 *Jane's*.

STARTING: Details in 1978-79 *Jane's*.

DIMENSIONS:
Length overall:
J79-GE-7A, 11A — 5,283 mm (207·96 in)
J79-GE-8 — 5,295 mm (208·45 in)
J79-GE-10, 17, 19 — 5,301 mm (208·69 in)
Diameter at compressor:
J79-GE 7A, 8, 11A, 15 — 973 mm (38·3 in)
J79-GE-10, 17, 19 — 992 mm (39·06 in)

WEIGHT, DRY:
J79-GE-7A — 1,644 kg (3,625 lb)
J79-GE-8 — 1,676 kg (3,695 lb)
J79-GE-10 — 1,749 kg (3,855 lb)
J79-GE-11A — 1,658 kg (3,655 lb)
J79-GE-15 — 1,678 kg (3,699 lb)
J79-GE-17, 19 — 1,745 kg (3,846 lb)

PERFORMANCE RATINGS:
T-O, with afterburning:
J79-GE-7A, 11A — 70·3 kN (15,800 lb st)
J79-GE-8, 15 — 75·6 kN (17,000 lb st)
J79-GE-10, 17, 19 — 79·24 kN (17,820 lb st)
Military:
J79-GE-7A, 11A — 44·5 kN (10,000 lb st)
J79-GE-8, 15 — 48·5 kN (10,900 lb st)
J79-GE-10, 17, 19 — 52·5 kN (11,810 lb st)
Cruise:
J79-GE-7A, 11A — 11·8 kN (2,650 lb st)
J79-GE-8, 10, 15, 17, 19 — 11·6 kN (2,600 lb st)

SPECIFIC FUEL CONSUMPTION:
At T-O rating:
J79-GE-7A, 11A — 55·8 mg/Ns (1·97 lb/h/lb st)
J79-GE-8 — 54·67 mg/Ns (1·93 lb/h/lb st)
J79-GE-15 — 55·1 mg/Ns (1·945 lb/h/lb st)
J79-GE-10, 17, 19 — 55·66 mg/Ns (1·965 lb/h/lb st)
At military rating:
J79-GE-8, 15 — 24·36 mg/Ns (0·86 lb/h/lb st)
J79-GE-7A, 10, 11A, 17, 19 — 23·79 mg/Ns (0·84 lb/h/lb st)
At cruise rating:
J79-GE-7A, 8, 11A, 15 — 29·74 mg/Ns (1·05 lb/h/lb st)
J79-GE-10, 17, 19 — 26·91 mg/Ns (0·95 lb/h/lb st)

General Electric J85-21 turbojet (22·2 kN; 5,000 lb st with afterburning)

GENERAL ELECTRIC J85

The following are major versions of the J85 small military turbojet, the -21 being the main production version. By 1979 more than 12,000 J85 engines had been delivered to air forces in 26 nations.

J85-4A. Powers the Rockwell International T-2C Buckeye trainer.

J85-5. Afterburning version with 6·6 : 1 thrust-to-weight ratio; powers Northrop T-38 Talon supersonic trainer.

J85-13. Developed from J85-5, with increased turbine inlet temperature for Northrop F-5A/B supersonic fighter. As the J85-13A, licence-built by Alfa-Romeo, also powers the Aeritalia G91Y.

J85-15. Version of J85-13 with improved turbine and hydraulically actuated exhaust nozzle to power CF-5 and NF-5. Manufactured under licence in Canada by Orenda.

J85-17A/B. Powers Saab 105G attack/reconnaissance aircraft and Cessna A-37B attack aircraft. Also used as take-off and climb booster for Fairchild C-123K and AC-119K.

J85-21. Higher airflow version with zero stage to give total of nine compressor stages. Equipped with afterburner for supersonic aircraft. Powers Northrop F-5E/F Tiger II.

J85/J1. Non-afterburning derivative with nine-stage compressor.

Civil version of the J85 is the CJ610 turbojet, to which the aft-fan CF700 turbofan is closely related. Both are described separately.

The following data refer specifically to the J85-21:

TYPE: Single-shaft turbojet.

AIR INTAKE: Annular type, surrounding central bullet fairing. Variable-incidence inlet guide vanes, with hot-air anti-icing.

COMPRESSOR: Nine-stage axial-flow type, with variable inlet guide vanes and first three stator stages. Titanium rotor blades, first two stages having part-span shrouds. Discs joined at periphery. Casing in upper and lower halves. Pressure ratio approximately 8·3 : 1. Air mass flow 24·0 kg (53·0 lb)/s.

COMBUSTION CHAMBER: Annular type with perforated liner. Twelve duplex fuel injectors. Ports in outer casing facilitate inspection of liner.

TURBINE: Two-stage axial-flow type. Casing is in halves, split horizontally. Turbine inlet temperature 977°C.

AFTERBURNER: Consists of a diffuser and a combustor. A pilot burner with four spraybars and a main burner of 12 spraybars are located in the diffuser section. Combustion is initiated by a single igniter plug and is then self-sustained. Nozzle position governs exit area and is regulated automatically by the afterburner control system as a function of turbine exit temperature and throttle lever position.

LUBRICATION: Positive displacement, pressurised recirculating type.

STARTING: Air impingement starter on afterburning engines. Provision for starter/generator on non-afterburning engines.

DIMENSIONS:
Length overall — 2,858 mm (112·5 in)
Max diameter — 533 mm (21·0 in)

WEIGHT, DRY:
J85-21 — 310 kg (684 lb)

PERFORMANCE RATINGS:
Max rating, with afterburner — 22·2 kN (5,000 lb st)
Military rating, without afterburner: — 15·6 kN (3,500 lb st)

SPECIFIC FUEL CONSUMPTION:
At max rating, with afterburner: — 60·3 mg/Ns (2·13 lb/h/lb st)
At military rating, without afterburner: — 28·3 mg/Ns (1·00 lb/h/lb st)

GENERAL ELECTRIC CJ610

Announced in May 1960, the CJ610 is a power plant tailored for commercial and executive aircraft of 5,700-7,500 kg (12,500-16,500 lb) gross weight. It is essentially similar to the basic J85 turbojet, without afterburner.

By January 1979, a total of 1,850 CJ610s had accumulated more than 5,000,000 h. TBO reached 4,000 h in 1977.

There are six versions:

CJ610-1, CJ610-4. Initial production versions, differing only in accessory gearbox location.

CJ610-5, CJ610-6. Developed versions of -1 and -4 respectively, providing increased T-O thrust. Power Gates Learjet 24D, 25B and 25C, Hansa and IAI Westwind 1121.

CJ610-8, CJ610-9. Developed for production deliveries beginning in 1969. Power Hansa, IAI Westwind 1123 and NAL (Japan) experimental VTOL.

CJ610-8A. FAA certificated in April 1977 for operation at up to 15,500 m (51,000 ft), to give better economy and over-weather capability to Learjet Century III 24E, 24F, 25D and 25F. Main differences are longer-life turbine and turbine-nozzle area change.

DIMENSIONS:
Length overall:
CJ610-1, -5, -9 — 1,298 mm (51·1 in)
CJ610-4, -6, -8, -8A — 1,153 mm (45·4 in)
Max flange diameter — 449 mm (17·7 in)

WEIGHT, DRY:
CJ610-1 — 181 kg (399 lb)
CJ610-4 — 176 kg (389 lb)
CJ610-5 — 183 kg (402 lb)
CJ610-6 — 180 kg (396 lb)
CJ610-8, -8A — 185 kg (407 lb)
CJ610-9 — 191 kg (421 lb)

General Electric CJ610-4 (12·7 kN; 2,850 lb st) and (right) CJ610-5 (13·1 kN; 2,950 lb st) turbojet engines

PERFORMANCE RATINGS (guaranteed):
T-O:

CJ610-1, -4	12·7 kN (2,850 lb st)
CJ610-5, -6, -8A	13·1 kN (2,950 lb st)
CJ610-8, -9	13·8 kN (3,100 lb st)

Max continuous:

CJ610-1, -4	12 kN (2,700 lb st)
CJ610-5, -6	12·4 kN (2,780 lb st)
CJ610-8, -9	13 kN (2,925 lb st)
CJ610-8A	12·7 kN (2,850 lb st)

SPECIFIC FUEL CONSUMPTION:
At T-O rating:

CJ610-1, -4	28·05 mg/Ns (0·99 lb/h/lb st)
CJ610-5, -6, -8, -9	27·75 mg/Ns (0·98 lb/h/lb st)
CJ610-8A	27·5 mg/Ns (0·97 lb/h/lb st)

At max continuous rating:

CJ610-1, -4, -8A	27·5 mg/Ns (0·97 lb/h/lb st)
CJ610-5, -6	27·2 mg/Ns (0·96 lb/h/lb st)
CJ610-8, -9	27·2 mg/Ns (0·96 lb/h/lb st)

GENERAL ELECTRIC CF700

Like the CJ610 turbojet, the CF700 is also derived from the J85 engine. Utilising the same gas generator, it is an aft-fan turbofan suitable for military and commercial aircraft. Since it can be tilted while in steady-state operation and operate vertically, it affords lift/cruise capability in VTOL aircraft.

FAA certification of the original version was received on 1 July 1964. The uprated CF700-2D was certificated in early 1968. The CF700-2D has an improved compressor turbine with higher thermodynamic efficiency. The CF700-2D2 incorporates a new design of tailpipe.

CF700 engines power the Dassault-Breguet Falcon 20 and Rockwell Sabre 75A executive transports. By 1974 the TBO had reached 3,000 h. By January 1979 more than 1,100 CF700s had flown 3,000,000 h.

The general description of the J85 turbojet applies also to the CF700, with the following additional assembly:

AFT FAN: Single-stage free-floating fan. By-pass ratio 1·6 : 1. Mass air flow through fan 39·9 kg (88·0 lb)/s.

DIMENSIONS:

Overall length, compressor nose to tailcone tip	1,912 mm (75·57 in)
Length, flange to flange	1,361 mm (53·6 in)
Max diameter	840·4 mm (33·1 in)
Max diameter less fan	447 mm (17·6 in)

WEIGHT, DRY:

CF700-2C	330 kg (725 lb)
CF700-2D, -2D2	334 kg (737 lb)

PERFORMANCE RATINGS:
Max T-O (flat-rated to 30°C):

CF700-2C	18·35 kN (4,125 lb st)
CF700-2D	18·90 kN (4,250 lb st)
CF700-2D2	20·02 kN (4,500 lb st)

Max continuous:

CF700-2C	17·8 kN (4,000 lb st)
CF700-2D, 2D2	18·3 kN (4,120 lb st)

SPECIFIC FUEL CONSUMPTION:
Max T-O:

CF700-2C, -2D, -2D2	18·4 mg/Ns (0·65 lb/h/lb st)

Max continuous:

CF700-2C, -2D	18·4 mg/Ns (0·65 lb/h/lb st)
CF700-2D2	18·1 mg/Ns (0·64 lb/h/lb st)

GENERAL ELECTRIC F404

The F404 is an advanced technology augmented turbofan described as being "in the 16,000 lb thrust class". It is the US Navy derivative of the YJ101 engine flown in the USAF YF-17 aircraft (see *Jane's* 1975-76). The changed designation from J to F (turbofan) reflects a higher by-pass ratio, and the number in the 400-series indicates funding by the US Navy.

In contrast, the YJ101 was funded by the US Air Force, in April 1972, to power the twin-engined Northrop YF-17 Air Combat Fighter. Seven engines in two YF-17 prototypes logged 719 h in 302 flights. These test flights explored a large part of the flight envelope, and a maximum of Mach 2·05 was reached at 12,500 m (41,000 ft). All engine commitments were achieved during the seven-month YF-17 flight programme.

In May 1975 the US Navy selected the McDonnell Douglas/Northrop team to develop its Navy Air Combat Fighter (NACF), designated F-18 Hornet. The F-18 is a derivative of the YF-17, powered by two F404 engines. The F404 was also selected for the single-engined F-5G, but this proposal (originally for Taiwan) had not gone ahead by Spring 1979.

Compared with that of the J101, the F404 fan diameter is increased less than 25·4 mm (1·0 in) while increasing the by-pass ratio from 0·20 to 0·34. The fan is driven by a slightly larger LP turbine. The technology, and the core, comprising the HP compressor, combustion chamber and HP turbine, remain the same.

First F404 engine test took place one month ahead of schedule in January 1977 and soon demonstrated sea-level production performance. Preliminary flight rating test took place in May 1978 and first F-18 flight took place in November 1978. By early 1979 more than 2,000 h of factory development testing had been completed, including 250 with afterburner and 150 at simulated altitude. A total of nine engines were to be delivered in 1978 and 24 in 1979, and MQT (Model Qualification Test) was due in

General Electric CF700-2D turbofan (18·9 kN; 4,250 lb st)

July 1979. The first production delivery is scheduled for December 1979.

TYPE: Two-shaft augmented low-ratio turbofan (turbojet with continuous by-pass bleed).

AIR INTAKE: Plain annular. Fixed central bullet, fixed and variable inlet vanes.

FAN: Three-stage axial. Outer flow diverted to by-pass duct. By-pass ratio 0·34. Airflow 63·5 kg (140 lb)/s.

HP COMPRESSOR: Seven-stage axial. Overall pressure ratio, 25 : 1 class.

COMBUSTION CHAMBER: Single-piece annular.

HP TURBINE: Single-stage axial. Highly loaded aircooled blades.

LP TURBINE: Single-stage axial.

EXHAUST SYSTEM: Close-coupled high-augmentation afterburner with combustion in both core and by-pass flows. Convergent-divergent exhaust nozzle with hydraulic actuation.

CONTROL SYSTEM: Electrical-hydromechanical.

DIMENSIONS:

Length overall	4,030 mm (158·8 in)
Max diameter	880 mm (34·8 in)

WEIGHT, DRY: approx 908 kg (2,000 lb)

PERFORMANCE RATING:

Max T-O	71·2 kN (16,000 lb st) class

GENERAL ELECTRIC TF34

It was announced in April 1968 that the US Naval Air Systems Command had awarded General Electric a contract for development of the TF34. This high by-pass ratio turbofan had won a 1965 US Navy competition aimed at providing a tailor-made engine in the 40 kN (9,000 lb st) category for the VS(X) aircraft by 1972 within a budget of $96 million. In August 1972 the **TF34-GE-2,** the initial variant for the VS(X) application (the Lockheed S-3A Viking), completed its Model Qualification Test (MQT) and subsequently entered production. The S-3A entered fleet service in February 1974, and GE and the US Navy have defined a 4,000 h TBO extension programme.

In January 1975 GE began shipment of the **TF34-GE-400A,** which replaced the GE-2 as S-3A engine. The later model incorporates various improvements, with changed external piping, an adaptive control system for optimising accessory power extraction, and a simplified rocket gas ingestion system.

In 1970 the TF34 was selected to power the twin-engined Fairchild Republic A-10A Thunderbolt II attack aircraft to compete in the AX competition. The A-10A application led in July 1972 to an Air Force contract for development of the **TF34-GE-100.** This was re-engineered to minimise unit price. It has a long fan duct and side mountings. The GE-100 flew in the first A-10A in May 1972. The A-10A won the AX competition, and the TF34-GE-100 was formally qualified for production in October 1974.

In 1974 a third version of the TF34, most nearly resembling the GE-2, was selected to provide auxiliary (thrust) power for the Sikorsky S-72 RSRA (Rotor Systems Research Aircraft) for NASA and the US Army.

TYPE: Two-shaft high by-pass ratio turbofan.

AIR INTAKE: Plain annular intake. No fixed inlet struts or guide vanes. Small spinner rotates with fan.

FAN: Single-stage fan has blades forged in titanium, without part-span shrouds. Blades replaceable with engine installed. Performance at max S/L rating, mass flow 153 kg (338 lb)/s at 7,365 rpm with pressure ratio 1·5. By-pass ratio 6·2.

COMPRESSOR: 14-stage axial on HP shaft. Inlet guide vanes and first five stators variable. First nine rotor stages titanium, remainder high-nickel alloy. Performance at max S/L rating, core airflow 21·3 kg (47 lb)/s at 17,900 rpm with pressure ratio 14 : 1, overall engine pressure ratio 21.

COMBUSTION CHAMBER: Annular Hastelloy chamberliner and front dome, providing ports for primer nozzles, igniters and 18 carburetting burners.

TURBINE: Two-stage HP gas generator turbine with convection-cooled rotor blades and stator vanes, the first-stage nozzle vanes having film and impingement cooling. Four-stage LP fan turbine with tip-shrouded blades. Turbine entry gas temperature 1,225°C maximum.

FUEL SYSTEM: Contamination-resistant, carburetting type. Integrated hydromechanical control unit with electronic amplifier. Fuel grade JP-4 or JP-5.

ACCESSORY DRIVES: Engine and customer accessories mounted around horseshoe-shaped gearbox, fitting closely around lower half of compressor casing. Radial shaft drive from front of HP shaft.

LUBRICATION: Enclosed, pressurised, dual system with vent along centre shaft.

DIMENSIONS:
Max diameter:

TF34-GE-400A	1,326 mm (52·2 in)
TF34-GE-100	1,259 mm (48·6 in)
Basic length (both)	2,540 mm (100·0 in)

WEIGHT, DRY:

TF34-GE-400A	661 kg (1,458 lb)
TF34-GE-100	647 kg (1,427 lb)

PERFORMANC RATINGS:
Max T-O (S/L, static):

TF34-GE-400A	41·3 kN (9,275 lb st)
TF34-GE-100	40·3 kN (9,065 lb st)

General Electric F404 augmented turbofan (71·2 kN; 16,000 lb st class)

General Electric TF34-GE-400A turbofan of 41·3 kN; 9,275 lb st

Specific Fuel Consumption:
Max T-O, S/L static:
TF34-GE-400A 10·3 mg/Ns (0·363 lb/h/lb st)
TF34-GE-100 10·5 mg/Ns (0·370 lb/h/lb st)

GENERAL ELECTRIC CF34

In April 1976 General Electric's General Aviation Engine Department, at Lynn, announced the CF34 as a new turbofan in the 31-36 kN (7,000-8,000 lb st) class for business and commercial aircraft. A natural derivative of the military TF34 at Cincinnati, the CF34 will be closely similar to the TF34-100, but with external configuration tailored to FAA and customer requirements.

Total fan airflow will be 139 kg (307 lb)/s, with pressure ratio 1·4. Core pressure ratio will be 12·5, giving overall pressure ratio of 17·5. By-pass ratio is to be 6·3.

Dimensions: As TF34-100

Weight, Dry: 692 kg (1,525 lb)

Performance Ratings:
T-O (S/L static)
35·5 kN (7,990 lb st) flat-rated to 22·8°C
Cruise (11,000 m; 36,000 ft at Mach 0·8)
7·83 kN (1,760 lb)

Specific Fuel Consumption:
T-O, as above 10·18 mg/Ns (0·359 lb/h/lb st)
Cruise, as above 19·48 mg/Ns (0·687 lb/h/lb)

GENERAL ELECTRIC CF6

US military designation (CF6-50E): F103-GE-100

On 11 September 1967 General Electric announced the commitment of corporate funding for development of the CF6 turbofan for the then-forthcoming generation of wide-body transports. From the initial family of 142 to 160 kN (32,000 lb to 36,000 lb st) CF6 two-shaft engines announced in September 1967 to cover the anticipated thrust requirements of the Lockheed and McDonnell Douglas airbus projects, the CF6 evolved through a series of variants to the CF6-6D, flat rated at 178 kN (40,000 lb) to 31°C and tailored to the McDonnell Douglas DC-10 Series 10 intermediate-range transport. Announcement that this engine had been selected by United Air Lines and American Airlines was made on 25 April 1968. Further orders have since been placed by many airlines for the CF6-6, 45, 50 and 80 series.

Basic configuration of the CF6-6 comprises a '1¼-stage' fan driven by a five-stage LP turbine energised by a slightly modified TF39 core engine, consisting of a 16-stage HP compressor, annular combustor and two-stage turbine. Modifications have been introduced to enable the accessory systems to suit airline installation requirements, while other changes are aimed at enhancing reliability, durability and maintainability.

CF6-6D. Initial 178 kN (40,000 lb st) version of engine in production for intermediate-range DC-10 Series 10. First ran on 21 October 1968 and 18 days later attained 203·5 kN (45,750 lb st). Following a series of successful factory and outdoor tests, engine was released for production in February 1969. The second CF6-6D, built to the production configuration, first ran in May 1969. By December 1970 a total of 30 engines had been shipped and flight testing with a single engine hung on the starboard inner pylon of a B-52 had extended to 15,250 m (50,000 ft), Mach 0·896 and 420 knots (779 km/h; 484 mph) indicated airspeed. Delivery of flight test engines to McDonnell Douglas started in late 1969, with aircraft first flight following in September 1970. Certification of the CF6-6D for commercial service was granted by the FAA in September 1970, and the engine entered airline service in the DC-10 Series 10 in August 1971.

CF6-6D1. In August 1971 this growth version was FAA certificated and offered to take advantage of the demonstrated margin of the -6D. The D1 rating is increased by 1,000 lb to 182·4 kN (41,000 lb st) at 28·9°C. By 1979 more than 400 6-6D and 6-6D1 engines had been delivered.

CF6-32. Proposal for a reduced-thrust engine, to suit anticipated market needs. Briefly described in the Addenda to the 1977-78 *Jane's,* it was in Spring 1979 still too fluid a proposal to be included in the main text of this edition; but see Addenda.

CF6-45A and -45B. Economical de-rated CF6-50E (described later) giving flat rating of 206·8 kN (46,500 lb st) to 36·1°C (-45A for 747SR) or 43·3°C (-45B for 747SP and 45B2 for Airbus A310 and on offer for Boeing 767).

CF6-50A. Announced by GE in January 1969, the 218 kN (49,000 lb st) CF6-50A is a growth version of the CF6-6. The increased thrust is achieved by increased flow through the core engine (reducing the by-pass ratio from 5·9 to 4·4) at slightly decreased turbine entry temperature. A major change is the introduction of two additional stages behind the single-stage LP compressor of the CF6-6, with no change in the turbofan's external dimensions. To provide for flow matching between the two rotors, variable by-pass doors are incorporated between the LP and HP compressors. A 41 per cent scale model fan with three-stage compressor and variable by-pass doors started testing in January 1969. In October 1970 a CF6-50A attained a thrust of 258 kN (58,000 lb) in a test cell at 5·6°C. FAA certification testing was completed in March 1972. The CF6-50A entered airline service in December 1972 in the DC-10 Series 30. The CF6-50 series also powers the Airbus Industrie A300 and some versions of the Boeing 747.

CF6-50C. The CF6-50C is rated at 226·8 kN (51,000 lb st) up to 30°C. Higher thrust is provided by an increase in turbine temperature, with improved cooling of hot-section components. Certificated November 1973.

CF6-50C1/E1. Rated 233·5 kN (52,500 lb st) to 30°C.

CF6-50E. (Military designation **F103-GE-100).** This engine is rated to give 233·5 kN (52,500 lb st) up to 26°C. Certificated November 1973. Powers some versions of Boeing 747-200 and E-4A.

CF6-50C2/E2. Similar to C1 and E1 but improved s.f.c. and e.g.t. margins and new fan case and blades with improved bird-strike resistance. Certification 1978.

CF6-50L2. Rated at 240·2 kN (54,000 lb st) to 30°C. Certification in 1978.

CF6-50M. Growth version for rating at 246·9 kN (55,500 lb st). To be made available as required.

CF6-80. Simplified engine with four-stage LP turbine similar to CF6-32, reducing weight and length yet with reduced fuel consumption. Launched November 1977 as choice of American and Delta for 767-200, with ratings from 196 kN (44,000 lb) (-80A) to 213-240 kN (48,000-54,000 lb) (-80B) and adopted for Airbus A310 in place of CF6-45B2. First run scheduled for November 1979, with Certification due in 1981.

By January 1978 CF6-6 engines had accumulated over 4,345,000 engine hours. Engine-attributable three-month in-flight shut-down rate was 0·07 per 1,000 h. During the same time period 740 CF6-50 engines had accumulated over 4,320,000 h with engine-attributable in-flight shut-down rate of 0·05 per 1,000 h. See Addenda.

The following data relate to the CF6-6D, with the differing features of the CF6-50 series also detailed.

Type: Two-shaft high by-pass ratio commercial turbofan.

Air Intake: Single forward-facing annular configuration.

Fan: Single-stage fan with integrally-mounted single-stage LP compressor (described together as a 1¼-stage fan), both driven by LP turbine. Fan has rotating spinner and omits inlet guide vanes. Blade-containment shroud provided against possible blade failure. The 38 fan rotor blades are individually removable from the thick-section disc bolted to forward conical extension of LP shaft system. Blade aerofoil has anti-vibration shrouds at two-thirds span. Fan exit airflow split between LP compressor and fan slipstream. Fan frame has 12 radial struts across fan slipstream exit. Fan frame provides support for LP and HP rotor front bearings, fan being overhung ahead of large-diameter ball-thrust bearing with rear roller bearing ahead of core engine. Blades, discs, spool of titanium; exit guide vanes of aluminium; fan frame and shaft of steel; spinner and fan case of aluminium alloy. Total airflow 593 kg/s (1,307 lb/s), by-pass ratio 5·9 : 1. Configuration of CF6-50 is similar but with two added LP stages and by-pass doors (described below). Total airflow 654 kg (1,439 lb)/s; by-pass ratio 4·4 : 1.

A typical General Electric CF6-50 series turbofan, rated at up to 246·9 kN (55,500 lb st)

LP Compressor: Single-stage compressor acting as booster to airflow into core engine. Rotor blades carried on rear rim of tapered drum bolted to rear of fan disc. Stators cantilevered off short-chord shroud ring, supported by radial outer struts and radial/tangential inner struts located on fan front frame. Compressor exit flow free to balance between core engine and fan slipstream exit. Configuration of CF6-50 modified to three compressor booster stages carried on flanged rotor drum. Continuous shroud extends to fan front frame with 12 integral by-pass doors located between canted radial struts in fan exit inner casing. These doors maintain proper flow matching between the fan/LP system and core by opening at low power settings to permit LP supercharged flow to bleed into the fan airstream. The doors are closed during take-off and cruise.

HP Compressor: Sixteen-stage compressor of near-constant tip diameter, with inlet guide vanes and first six stator rows having variable incidence. Provision for interstage air bleed for airframe use and engine cooling. Rotor is of combined drum-and-disc construction with front stage and rear three stages overhung on conical shaft providing location on HP front bearing and HP main shaft. All rotor blades held in rabbeted discs and individually replaceable without rotor disassembly. Stages 1-14 blades forged titanium, 15-16 steel. Stages 1-10 disc titanium, 11-16 and aft casing Inconel 718. Casing split on horizontal centreline: stator vanes held in dovetail slots and replaceable individually. Stages 1-2 stators titanium, 3-15 steel; inlet guide vanes titanium, outlet guide vanes steel. Double-skin inner casing shrouds the LP main shaft. Outlet frame contains compressor diffuser and incorporates support structure for HP rotor mid-bearings. Overall pressure ratio (T-O), 24·2 (6D), 24·7 (6D1). Core airflow (F6-6D) 86 kg (190 lb)/s. CF6-50A has 15th and 16th stages removed to pass greater core airflow of 121 kg (267 lb/s) and reduce pressure and temperature of air entering combustion chamber. Improved materials and strengthened structure in later stages. Overall pressure ratio (T-O), 27·1 (45B), 28·6 (50A), 29·5 (50C), 30·3 (50E), 32·4 (50M).

Combustor: Fully annular with comprehensive film-cooling. Separate snout, dome and inner/outer skirts, with nozzles, igniter, leads and manifold externally removable. Dome contains ports for two igniters and axial swirler cups for 30 fuel nozzles. Igniters of high-voltage surface-gap type with energy level of 2·0 joules, each igniter operated independently. Forged steel nozzles with liner of Hastelloy X. Nozzle and dome designed to minimise smoke, and entrance diffuser has gradual profile to assure low temperature gradient to turbine under all flight conditions. CF6-50 combustor is shorter, of improved material (HS 18-8), and can be removed with fuel nozzles in place.

HP Turbine: Two-stage aircooled turbine with 1,290°C entry temperature. Rotor blades are film and convection cooled. Rotor blades cast from René 80; discs and forward and rear shafts of Inconel 718. First-stage nozzle guide vanes supported at inner and outer ends, second-stage cantilevered from outer ends, with inner ends carrying interstage labyrinth seals. First-stage vanes cast from X40 and film cooled by compressor discharge pressure. Second-stage vanes are cast from René 80 material and are convection cooled. Vanes are welded into pairs to decrease number of gas leakage paths. Thin-section discs with heavy-section centreless hubs are bolted to front and rear conical shafts, including conical and arched inter-disc diaphragms. Configuration for CF6-50 is similar but introduces improved materials and cooling, and blades are not Siamesed but individual.

LP Turbine: Five-stage constant tip-diameter turbine with nominal 871°C inlet temperature. Rotor blades tip-shrouded and cast in René 77, not aircooled. Forward and rear shafts, case and discs of Inconel 718. First-stage nozzle guide vanes supported at inner and outer ends, remaining stages are cantilevered from outer ends, with inner ends carrying inter-stage labyrinth seals. Stages 1-3 guide vanes cast in six-vane segments in René 77, stages 4 and 5 cast in pairs in René 41. Vanes held in slots machined in the two half-stator casing. Drum and centreless disc construction, located on LP rotor by front and rear conical diaphragms attached to third- and fourth-stage discs. Front diaphragm attached to LP main shaft, rear diaphragm to rear stub shaft. Drive to rotor by means of long fan midshaft. On CF6-50 a four-stage LP turbine is used, all stages being modified in geometry and cooled by 7th HP-stage compressor air instead of 9th.

Exhaust Unit (Fan): Fixed-area annular duct with outer cowl and engine cowl forming convergent plug nozzle for fan slipstream.

Exhaust Unit (Turbine): Short-length fixed-area exhaust duct with convergent plug nozzle. Provision for exhaust thrust reverser.

Thrust Reverser (Fan): Annular cascade reverser with blocker doors across fan duct. For reverse thrust, rear portion of fan outer cowl translates aft on rotating ballscrews to uncover cascade vanes. Blocker doors (16) flush-mounted in cowl on link arms hinged in inner cowl, rotate inwards to expose cascade vanes and block fan duct. Reverser hinged at top to open in L/R halves for access to HP casing and combustor.

Thrust Reverser (Turbine): Post nozzle exit, cascade type. Two cascade screens are mounted in vertical plane on fixed pivot aft of turbine exhaust and are enclosed in fairing forming aerofoil-shaped plug. Aft translation of fairing uncovers cascades which open across nozzle exit and divert turbine exhaust radially outward and slightly forward in horizontal plane. Configuration for CF6-50 similar to fan thrust reverser with nine blocker doors, but not split. CF6-50 available with long fixed core nozzle; short nozzle also designed, for performance improvement. Acoustic treatment is provided in the nozzle flow path.

Rotor Support System: Eight bearings (four for each rotor) at seven locations. Fan and LP compressor carried on ball thrust bearing (1) behind fan disc and roller bearing (2) at front of LP main shaft; both bearings mounted in fan front frame structure, which also supports HP compressor front roller bearing (3). LP turbine carried on roller bearings at front and rear of turbine rotor assembly—rear bearing (7) being mounted in spider structure across turbine exit, and front bearing (6) on major spider structure between HP and LP turbines. HP compressor carried at rear on adjacent roller bearing (4R) and ball-thrust bearing (4B) at interconnection with HP turbine front conical shaft, both bearings being mounted on support structure integral with compressor outlet diffuser. A roller bearing (5), mounted in the inter-turbine structure, carries the aft HP conical shaft.

Accessory Drive: This consists of the inlet gearbox, radial gearbox, radial driveshaft, transfer gearbox, horizontal driveshaft and accessory gearbox. The inlet gearbox is located in the forward sump of the engine. The gearbox transfers energy from the core-engine (HP) rotor to the radial driveshaft located in a housing aft of the bottom vertical strut of the fan frame. The transfer gearbox is mounted on the bottom of the fan frame. Accessory mounting pads are provided on both the forward and aft faces of the gearbox. The engine accessories mounted on the gearbox are starter, fuel pump, main engine control, lubrication pump and tachometer. Pads are also provided for mounting the aircraft hydraulic pumps, constant-speed drive and alternator.

Fuel System: Hydromechanical fuel control system regulates steady-state fuel flow and schedules acceleration and deceleration fuel flow. It also schedules and powers variable-stator vane position. A governor in the Woodward control provides core-engine speed stability during steady-state operation. During transient operation, core-engine fuel flow is scheduled on the basis of throttle position, compressor inlet temperature, compressor discharge pressure and core-engine speed. The fuel control and fuel pump are mounted in the accessory package as an integrated unit which avoids interconnecting high-pressure fuel lines and potential leakage points (they are separable for change or maintenance). This configuration provides a single drive mounting flange. The filter, fuel/oil heat exchanger and control pressurising valve may be removed individually without removing the entire assembly. The fuel manifold is double-wall constructed for safety and mounted on the exterior of the engine. For CF6-50, fuel control is modified to provide scheduling function for LP compressor variable by-pass doors.

Fuel Grades: Fuels conforming to ASTM-1655-65T, Jet A, Jet A1 and Jet B, and MIL-T-5624G2 grades JP-4 or JP-5 are authorised, but Jet A is primary specification.

Lubrication System: Dry-sump centre-vented system in which oil is pressure-fed to each engine component requiring lubrication. Oil is removed from the sump areas by scavenge pumps, passed through a fuel/oil heat exchanger and filter to the engine tank. Nominal lubrication system pressure is 2·07-6·21 bars (30-90 lb/sq in) above sump reference pressure. All pressure and scavenge pumps and filters are located in the lubrication centre on the forward side of the gearbox.

Oil Specification: Conforming to General Electric specification D50TFI classes A & B, equivalent to MIL-L-7808 or MIL-L-23699A.

Mounting: Main thrust mount located on the inner fan frame; aft mount located on the turbine mid-frame.

Starting: Air-turbine starter mounted on the front of the accessory gearbox at the through shaft.

Noise Suppression Equipment: Acoustic panels integrated with fan casing, fan front frame and thrust reverser.

Dimensions:

Fan tip diameter	2,195 mm (86·4 in)
Max width (cold)	2,390 mm (94·1 in)
Max height (over gearbox)	2,675 mm (105·3 in)
Length overall (cold):	
CF6-6D	4,775 mm (188 in)
CF6-50 series	4,648 mm (183 in)

Weight, Dry (basic engine):

CF6-6D, -6D1	3,679 kg (8,111 lb)
CF6-45A/B, -50E, -50E1	3,851 kg (8,490 lb)
CF6-50A, -50C, -50C1	3,892 kg (8,580 lb)
CF6-50M	4,083 kg (9,002 lb)
Fan and turbine reverser:	
CF6-6D, -6D1	932 kg (2,054 lb)
CF6-50A, -50C	968 kg (2,135 lb)
CF6-50E	962 kg (2,121 lb)
CF6-50M	972 kg (2,143 lb)

Performance Ratings:

Max T-O, uninstalled ideal nozzle:
See under model listings

Max altitude and Mach No:
CF6-6 and -50: 13,700 m (45,000 ft) at Mach 1·0

Max cruise at 10,670 m (35,000 ft) and Mach 0·85, flat rated to ISA + 10°C, uninstalled, real nozzle:

CF6-6D	40·3 kN (9,060 lb)
CF6-6D1	40·9 kN (9,200 lb)
CF6-45A	47·3 kN (10,630 lb)
CF6-50A, -50C	48·0 kN (10,800 lb)
CF6-50E, -45B	50·3 kN (11,300 lb)
CF6-50L2	52·9 kN (11,900 lb)
CF6-50M	53·2 kN (11,956 lb)

Specific Fuel Consumption:

At T-O thrust, as above:

CF6-6D	9·86 mg/Ns (0·348 lb/h/lb st)
CF6-6D1	9·91 mg/Ns (0·350 lb/h/lb st)
CF6-45A, -45B	10·36 mg/Ns (0·366 lb/h/lb st)
CF6-50A	10·90 mg/Ns (0·385 lb/h/lb st)
CF6-50C	11·05 mg/Ns (0·390 lb/h/lb st)
CF6-50E	10·65 mg/Ns (0·376 lb/h/lb st)
CF6-50L2	10·59 mg/Ns (0·374 lb/h/lb st)
CF6-50M	10·79 mg/Ns (0·381 lb/h/lb st)

Oil Consumption: 0·9 kg (2·0 lb)/h

GENERAL ELECTRIC F101

The F101-GE-100 is the engine designed by General Electric for the Rockwell International B-1 strategic bomber.

In November 1976 the F101 completed its Product Verification testing. This qualified the engine for initial production. PV is a new concept replacing the previous MQT (Model Qualification Test). At that time 23 YF101 and 23 F101 engines had run over 12,000 h and logged 1,600 h in 74 flights. In 1978 the engine was still flying intensively, and in 1979 the US Air Force and Navy were jointly funding the F101X, with $41 million in 1979 and $16 million requested as a follow-on. The F101X is a possible replacement engine for the F-14 and F-16 should improvements to their existing engines fail to yield expected benefits. Further details, see Addenda.

General Electric F101 augmented turbofan, rated in the 133 kN (30,000 lb st) class

Air Intake: Direct pitot with 20 fixed radial vanes with variable trailing flaps.
Fan: Two axial stages. Solid titanium blades with tip shrouds for improved clearance control. Inlet guide vanes and for vanes installed in horizontally split titanium casing which permits blades and vanes to be individually replaceable. Pressure ratio, over 2. Airflow, approximately 159 kg (350 lb)/s.
Compressor: The high stage-loading technology developed in the GE1 series of engines (see 1973-74 *Jane's*) has been applied to the F101 axial compressor to obtain, in nine stages, a pressure ratio exceeding 11. Rotor constructed by inertia-welding separate discs into drum. First six rotor stages titanium alloy, stages 7-9 Inconel 718. Inlet guide vanes and stator vanes 1-3 steel, with variable incidence; remainder Inconel 718, fixed. Repairability and maintenance enhanced by split compressor casing, with front section of titanium and rear of steel, allowing blades and vanes to be individually replaceable. Borescope inspection ports permit visual inspection of vanes, blades and clearances.
Combustion Chamber: Very short, annular machined Hastelloy X. LP injection with air-blast swirler to atomise fuel into dome area. Smokeless combustion downstream gives a uniform temperature profile at HP turbine nozzle.
HP Turbine: Air-cooled, single-stage, high-energy-extraction design. Light weight achieved by use of advanced materials and manufacturing processes. Blades and vanes are hollow airfoils in René 125, convective- and film-cooled. Stationary shroud is segmented and cooled, giving growth characteristics compatible with rotor to provide tip-clearance control.
LP Turbine: Two-stage assembly. First stators of thoria-dispersed nickel-chrome with René 95 rotor disc and René 125 blades. Second stage of René 80. Shaft of Inconel 718. All blades uncooled. Blades individually replaceable; vanes replaceable in segmented groups.
Afterburner: Fully modulated augmentation. Fan and core flows each supplied through 28 augmentor chutes and mixed downstream of turbine. Reheat fuel supplied initially to core flow only, giving automatic light-up with minimal jump in thrust. Further increase in augmentor fuel-flow causes additional outer spraybars and circular flameholder gutters to come into operation, until at maximum augmentation combustion is complete across the whole engine flow. Fan air at about 121°C used to provide film-cooling of augmentor duct wall of Inconel 625.
Propelling Nozzle: Exhaust duct of welded titanium. Variable-area, variable-profile primary and secondary nozzles, each of multiple-flap type. Eight primary rams drive translating ring, cams and links to secure optimum independent profile of both nozzles over wide range, with con-di operation in supersonic cruise at all levels.
Accessory Drives: Main accessory gearbox self-contained module at 6 o'clock on fan casing. Drives main and augmentor fuel pumps, fuel boost pump, fuel control, lube pressure and scavenge pumps, hydraulic pump, alternator and power take-off shaft. Integral lube and hydraulic tanks.
Dimensions:
Length overall 4,596 mm (181 in)
Intake diameter 1,397 mm (55 in)
Weight, Dry: about 1,814 kg (4,000 lb)
Performance Ratings:
Cold about 75·6 kN (17,000 lb st)
Full augmentation over 133·4 kN (30,000 lb st)

GENERAL ELECTRIC T58

The T58 is a small free-turbine turboshaft engine which was developed for helicopter propulsion for the US Navy Bureau of Weapons. A civil version, the CT58, was awarded a Type Certificate by the FAA on 1 July 1959 and is described separately.

Hydromechanical constant-speed control system features in the T58 maintains essentially constant rotor speed by regulating the engine power automatically, so eliminating the need for speed adjustment by the pilot during normal operation.

Rolls-Royce Ltd produces modified versions of the T58 under licence in the United Kingdom as the Gnome. The T58 is also licensed for manufacture in Italy and Japan. Industrial and marine version of the T58 is the LM100. By January 1978 more than 7,000 T58 engines had been manufactured.

Versions currently in service or in production are as follows:

T58-GE-3. Five-minute rating of 988 kW (1,325 shp). Powers Bell UH-1F.

T58-GE-5. Five-minute rating of 1,119 kW (1,500 shp). Powers Sikorsky CH-3E, HH-3E/F and NASA RSRA (Sikorsky S-72).

T58-GE-8E, F. Rated at 1,007 kW (1,350 shp). Powers Boeing Vertol CH-46A, Kaman SH-2, Sikorsky SH-3A/G and HH-52A.

T58-GE-10. Rated at 1,044 kW (1,400 shp). Powers Sikorsky SH-3D/H, and Boeing Vertol CH-46D/F.

T58-GE-16. Rated at 1,394 kW (1,870 shp). US military qualified. Aircooled gas-generator turbine and two-stage power turbine. Powers Boeing CH-46E.

T58-GE-100. Uprated T58-GE-5. Ten-minute rating 1,119 kW (1,500 shp) to 15°C or 1,100 kW (1,475 shp) to 26°C. Powers selected CH/HH-3E. Qualified 1976.

Type: Free-turbine turboshaft.
Air Intake: Annular intake casing with four hollow radial struts supporting central housing for starter drive clutch and front main roller bearing. Casing and struts anti-iced by air bled from compressor.
Compressor: Ten-stage axial-flow. Variable-incidence inlet guide vanes. First three of the eleven rows of stator blades also have variable incidence. One-piece steel construction for last eight stages of rotor hub. Casing divided into upper and lower halves. Pressure ratio 8·4 : 1. Air mass flow 5·62 kg (12·4 lb)/s in T58-GE-3 and 8E, 6·21 kg (13·7 lb)/s in T58-GE-5, -10 and -100, 6·30 kg (13·9 lb)/s in T58-GE-16.
Combustion Chamber: Annular type. Sixteen fuel nozzles (eight on each of two manifolds) mounted on front of inner liner. Dual capacitor discharge ignition unit. Outer casing in two halves to facilitate inspection.
Gas Generator Turbine: Two-stage short-chord axial-flow type, coupled directly to compressor by hollow conical shaft. Centre ball thrust bearing, rear roller bearing. Cooling by air bled from compressor. T58-GE-16 has aircooled first-stage turbine nozzle and blades and second-stage nozzle.
Power Turbine: Single-stage (two-stage in T58-GE-16) axial-flow type, mechanically independent of gas generator turbine. Operated nominally at 19,500 rpm. Engines with single-stage power turbine can have reduction gear giving output at 6,000 rpm. Power turbine accessory drive unit and flexible feed-back cable provide a speed signal to the control.
Torque Sensor Speed Decreaser Gearbox (optional): Gearbox with integral lubrication system. Reduces power speed to 6,000 rpm. Assembly includes an integral torque sensing system.
Jet Exhaust: Two positions (90° left or right) on all versions. T58-GE-16 can also be supplied with downward-ejecting or multiple-position exhaust.
Controls (except T58-GE-10 and -16): Free turbine constant-speed control. Hydromechanical controls.
Controls (T58-GE-10, -16): Integrated hydro-mechanical/electrical power control system for isochronous speed governing and twin-engine load sharing.
Accessory Drives: Engine accessories driven from compressor shaft. Airframe accessories mounted on free-turbine reduction gearbox or rotor hub.
Dimensions:
Max width:
except T58-GE-16 526 mm (20·7 in)
T58-GE-16 607 mm (23·9 in)
Length overall:
except T58-GE-16 1,499 mm (59·0 in)
T58-GE-16 1,626 mm (64·0 in)
Weight, Dry:
T58-GE-3 140 kg (309 lb)
T58-GE-5, -100 152 kg (335 lb)
T58-GE-8E, F 138 kg (305 lb)
T58-GE-10 159 kg (350 lb)
T58-GE-16 201 kg (443 lb)
Performance Ratings:
Five-minute:
See under model listings
Military:
T58-GE-3 988 kW (1,325 shp) at 20,960 rpm
T58-GE-5, 10 1,044 kW (1,400 shp) at 19,500 rpm
T58-GE-8E, F 1,007 kW (1,350 shp) at 19,500 rpm
T58-GE-16 1,394 kW (1,870 shp) at 19,500 rpm
T58-GE-100 1,119 kW (1,500 shp) at 19,500 rpm
Cruise:
T58-GE-3 798 kW (1,070 shp)
T58-GE-5, 10 932 kW (1,250 shp)
T58-GE-8E, F 857·5 kW (1,150 shp)
T58-GE-16 1,320 kW (1,770 shp)
T58-GE-100 1,015 kW (1,360 shp) at 19,500 rpm
Specific Fuel Consumption:
At military rating:
T58-GE-3 103 μg/J (0·61 lb/h/shp)
T58-GE-5, 8E/F, 10, 100 101 μg/J (0·60 lb/h/shp)
T58-GE-16 89·5 μg/J (0·53 lb/h/shp)
At cruise rating:
T58-GE-3 106·5 μg/J (0·63 lb/h/shp)
T58-GE-5, 100 103 μg/J (0·61 lb/h/shp)
T58-GE-8E, F 105 μg/J (0·62 lb/h/shp)
T58-GE-10 105 μg/J (0·62 lb/h/shp)
T58-GE-16 91 μg/J (0·54 lb/h/shp)

GENERAL ELECTRIC CT58

The commercial version of the T58 is designated CT58 and was the first US helicopter turbine to receive FAA certification.

Current versions are as follows:

CT58-110. Rated at 932 kW; 1,250 shp (1,007 kW; 1,350 shp for 2½ min) at 19,500 rpm. Air mass flow 5·67 kg (12·7 lb)/s. Pressure ratio 8·2 : 1.

CT58-140. Rated at 1,044 kW; 1,400 shp (1,119 kW; 1,500 shp for 2½ min) at 19,500 rpm. Air mass flow 6·21 kg (13·7 lb)/s. Pressure ratio 8·4 : 1.

The CT58 powers the Sikorsky S-61 and S-62 and Boeing Vertol 107 Model II.

Dimensions:
Max width 406 mm (16·0 in)
Length overall 1,500 mm (59·0 in)
Weight, Dry:
CT58-110 143 kg (315 lb)
CT58-140 154 kg (340 lb)
Performance Ratings:
2½ min and normal T-O:
See under model listings
Cruise:
CT58-110 783 kW (1,050 shp)
CT58-140 932 kW (1,250 shp)
Specific Fuel Consumption:
At normal T-O rating 103 μg/J (0·61 lb/h/shp)
At cruise rating:
CT58-110 108 μg/J (0·64 lb/h/shp)
CT58-140 105 μg/J (0·62 lb/h/shp)

GENERAL ELECTRIC T64

The T64 is a versatile aircraft gas turbine engine which was developed initially for the US Navy. The basic T64 turboshaft engine becomes a turboprop with the addition of a two-part speed-reduction gearbox.

Current versions include:

T64-GE-7. Direct-drive turboshaft rated at 2,928 kW (3,925 shp). Powers US Air Force CH-53B, CH-53C and HH-53C. Also powers VFW-built CH-53D/G. Produced under licence by MTU (see entry under Germany, Federal Republic).

T64-GE-7A. Direct-drive turboshaft flat-rated at 2,935 kW (3,936 shp) to 28°C. Powers Sikorsky S-65.

T64-GE-10. Turboprop engine with propeller gearbox above centreline. Rated at 2,215 kW (2,970 shp). Produced under licence by Ishikawajima Harima Heavy Industries in Japan for Shin Meiwa PS-1 flying-boat (four engines) and Kawasaki P-2J patrol aircraft (two engines).

The 1,394 kW (1,870 shp) General Electric T58-GE-16 turboshaft

T64-GE-413A. Direct-drive turboshaft rated at 2,935 kW (3,936 shp). Two engines power the US Navy CH-53D and RH-53D.

T64-GE-415. Growth version with improved combustion liner and turbine cooling. Max rating 3,266 kW (4,380 shp). Powers Sikorsky RH-53D and three-engined CH-53E helicopters.

CT64-GE-820. CT64-820-1, -2 and -3 turboprops based on early turboshaft versions power DHC-5C Buffalo and prototype Aeritalia G222. FAA certificated CT64-820-4 has improved components of T64-415 and is flat-rated at 2,336 kW (3,133 shp) to 38°C, in production for DHC-5D Buffalo.

T64-P4D. Turboprop version flat rated at 2,535 kW (3,400 shp) to 45°C. Two P4D engines power most Aeritalia G222 transports. Production by Fiat, supported by Alfa-Romeo, with deliveries beginning in 1975.

All T64s are qualified to operate from 100° nose-up to 45° nose-down. The T64 was designed for extensive growth: current production engines rated at 3,266 kW (4,380 shp) are a result of growth made possibly largely by aircooling of the first-stage gas generator turbine rotor and stator. The addition of aircooling to the second turbine stage provides further horsepower growth beyond 3,729 kW (5,000 shp) without significant change in external dimensions.

By January 1979 a total of over 2,000 T64 engines of all kinds had been delivered by GE to customers in 13 countries. In addition licences to produce the T64 are held by MTU in Germany, Fiat in Italy, Rolls-Royce in Britain and IHI in Japan.

TYPE: Free-turbine turboshaft/turboprop engine.

COMPRESSOR: Fourteen-stage axial-flow. Single-spool steel rotor for -10 and -820-1/2/3. Titanium and steel compressor for -7A, -413A, -415, -P4D and CT64-820-4. Inlet guide vanes and first four stages of stator blades variable. Compressor blades can be removed individually without rotor disassembly. Casing flanged along centreline. Stator blades removable. Air mass flow per second: -10, 11·6 kg (25·5 lb); -7A, -413A, 12·8 kg (28·3 lb); -415, 13·3 kg (29·4 lb); -820-4, 11·9 kg (26·2 lb); P4D, 12·2 kg (27·0 lb). Pressure ratio: 10, -820-4, 12·5; -7A, -413A, 14·1; -415, 14·8; P4D, 13·0.

COMBUSTION CHAMBER: Annular type. Double fuel manifold feeds twelve duplex-type fuel nozzles with external flow divider. Nozzles mounted on outer diffuser wall of compressor rear frame.

GAS GENERATOR TURBINE: Two-stage axial-flow type, coupled directly to compressor rotor by spline connection.

POWER TURBINE: Two-stage axial-flow type, mechanically independent of gas generator turbine.

REDUCTION GEAR: Remotely-mounted basic reduction gear for turboprop versions is offset and accessible for inspection and replacement. Gear-driven by power turbine, using co-axial shafting through the compressor. Propeller gear ratio 13·44 : 1.

STARTING: Mechanical, airframe supplied.

DIMENSIONS:

Length:

T64-GE-7A, 413A, -415	2,006 mm (79 in)
T64-GE-10, P4D	2,793 mm (110 in)
CT64-820	2,870 mm (113 in)

Width:

T64-GE-7A, -413A, -415	60 mm (26·0 in)
T64-GE-10, -P4D, -820	683 mm (26·9 in)

Height:

T64-GE-7A, 413A, -415	825 mm (32·5 in)
T64-GE-10, -P4D	1,168 mm (46 in)
CT64-820	1,026 mm (40·4 in)

WEIGHT, DRY:

T64-GE-413A	325 kg (716 lb)
T64-GE-7A, -415	327 kg (720 lb)
T64-GE-10	529 kg (1,167 lb)
CT64-820-1	513 kg (1,130 lb)
CT64-820-2, -4	520 kg (1,145 lb)
CT64-820-3	518 kg (1,140 lb)
T64-P4D	538 kg (1,188 lb)

PERFORMANCE RATINGS:

Max rating (sea level):

T64-GE-10

2,215 kW (2,970 shp) at 1,160 output rpm

T64-GE-7A, -413A	2,935 kW (3,936 shp)
CT64-820-4	2,336 kW (3,133 shp)
T64-P4D	2,535 kW (3,400 shp)
T64-415	3,266 kW (4,380 shp)

SPECIFIC FUEL CONSUMPTION (S/L):

At max rating:

T64-GE-7A, -415	79·4 μg/J (0·47 lb/h/shp)
T64-GE-10	84·5 μg/J (0·50 lb/h/shp)
T64-GE-413A, P4D	81 μg/J (0·48 lb/h/shp)
CT64-820-4	83 μg/J (0·49 lb/h/shp)

GENERAL ELECTRIC T700

Under a contract awarded by the US Army Aviation Materiel Laboratories Propulsion Division, General Electric initiated a two-year demonstration programme in August 1967 to design, build and test a new 1,118·5 kW (1,500 shp) advanced technology turboshaft. Designated GE12, the engine was developed by the Aircraft Engine Group's Military Engine Division. During the latter part of 1968 the basic contracts for the GE12 and competing Pratt & Whitney ST9 demonstrator turboshaft were extended to the end of 1969 and additional work was also funded to carry the GE12 programme through to 30 September 1971. The GE12 demonstrator was illustrated in the 1971-72 *Jane's*.

The 2,935 kW (3,936 shp) General Electric T64-GE-413A turboshaft

A new competition was conducted in 1971 to provide the power plant for the Army's projected utility tactical transport system (UTTAS) proposed as a replacement for the present Bell UH-1 family of Army helicopters. In late 1971 it was announced that the winner was the GE engine, and that a contract for a production version, the T700-GE-700, was being negotiated with the US Army Aviation Systems Command.

The first T700 engine was tested in February 1973. Shipment of ground test engines was accomplished on schedule in February 1974, and flight qualification testing was completed ahead of schedule in August 1974. Shipments for UTTAS flight aircraft began immediately, with first flights of the Boeing YUH-61A and Sikorsky YUH-60A following during the autumn of 1974. Identical T700 engines powered the two advanced attack helicopter (AAH) contenders, the Bell YAH-63A and Hughes YAH-64A.

In December 1976 the first contract for production engines was received to power the winning Sikorsky UH-60A Black Hawk. Engines have been delivered from early 1978. The Hughes AH-64 was also selected over its rival, with a production decision due in 1980. By 1979 more than 40,000 h had been logged, including 20,000 flying in the four competing helicopters. A Navy T700, with 95-97 per cent commonality, has been selected for the Sikorsky SH-60B (LAMPS Mk III) helicopter (Light Airborne Multi-Purpose System).

The T700 has been designed to be compatible with the Army's special operating and environmental conditions, and embodies high reliability, simplicity of maintenance, low vulnerability to combat damage, and high performance combined with compact dimensions. Use is made of higher pressure ratios and turbine entry temperatures than with existing small turboshafts to assist in reducing size and weight.

To reduce vulnerability, all external lines and leads are short in length and are grouped compactly for minimum exposure. Self-contained electrical and lubrication systems are fitted. Multiple mounting points allow for ease of installation and the necessary airframe connections have been minimised and are located close to the engine centreline. The whole engine is of modular construction for swift field maintenance or section replacement without special tools.

GE has announced studies for derivatives, including a family of turbojets for RPVs and other fixed-wing aircraft. Other possibilities include turboprops and high by-pass ratio turbofans, while front and rear drive modifications make surface applications possible.

A programme of growth has been started to meet the widening spectrum of applications. As envisioned, 10 per cent greater power will be available from the existing basic engine. Addition of an LP booster (zero stage) will then provide 20-30 per cent growth, depending on the increase in turbine temperature chosen. These growth versions are planned to be interchangeable with the present T700-GE-700 aircraft installation.

TYPE: Ungeared free-turbine turboshaft engine.

INTAKE: Annular type, with anti-iced integral inlet particle separator containing no moving parts yet designed to remove 95 per cent of sand, dust and foreign-object

General Electric T700-GE-700 turboshaft engine, showing (light coloured duct rising at mid-section) the extractor for solid particles removed by the inlet separator. Intermediate (T-O) rating, 1,151 kW (1,543 shp)

ingestion. Extracted matter discharged by separator blower driven from accessory gearbox.

COMPRESSOR: Combined axial/centrifugal. Five axial stages and single centrifugal stage mounted on same shaft. Each axial stage is one-piece 'blisk' (blades plus disc) in AM355 steel highly resistant to erosion. Inlet guide vanes and first two stator stages are variable. Pressure ratio, about 15 : 1. Airflow about 4·5 kg (10 lb)/s at 44,720 rpm.

COMBUSTION CHAMBER: Fully annular. Compact short-length configuration, designed for maximum reliability and long life. Central fuel injection to maximise acceptance of contaminated fuel and give minimal smoke generation and uniform temperature profile into the turbine. Flame tube is machined ring in Hastelloy X. Ignition system obtains power from separate winding on engine-mounted alternator and serves dual plugs.

TURBINE: Two-stage gas-generator (HP) turbine operates at gas temperatures exceeding 1,100°C. First-stage nozzle investment-cast in X40. Second-stage nozzle investment-cast in two-vane segments in R80. Discs, cooling plates, and blades of both stages clamped by five short tiebolts; five larger bolts then tighten turbine to shaft, driving via curvic joint. Rated shaft speed (S/L, ISA, max T-O power), 44,720 rpm. Two-stage free power turbine, designed for high efficiency at part-power levels (especially 30 and 60% of military power), with tip-shrouded blades and segmented nozzles. Power turbine inlet temperature at intermediate power, 827°C. Nozzle guide vanes René 77, rotor discs Inco 718, rotor blades René 80 uncooled. Output speed, 17,000-21,000 rpm. Power output shaft for front drive.

CONTROLS: Hydromechanical control can be replaced in less than 12 minutes and requires no adjustment or lockwire. Electrical control, coupled with hydromechanical control, provides twin-engine speed and torque matching.

ACCESSORIES: Grouped at top of engine, together with engine control system, for maximum simplicity, accessibility and combat survivability. Integral lubrication supply tank, plus an emergency supply of mist lubrication following total loss of main supply. Torque sensor provides signal to electrical control system.

DIMENSIONS:

Length overall	1,181 mm (46·5 in)
Width	635 mm (25 in)
Height overall	584 mm (23 in)

WEIGHT, DRY (with particle separator): 188 kg (415 lb)

PERFORMANCE RATINGS:

Intermediate (30 min)	1,151 kW (1,543 shp)
Max continuous	933 kW (1,251 shp)
75% max continuous	699 kW (937 shp)

SPECIFIC FUEL CONSUMPTION:

Intermediate	79·25 μg/J (0·469 lb/h/shp)
Max continuous	80·6 μg/J (0·477 lb/h/shp)
75%	87 μg/J (0·514 lb/h/shp)

GENERAL ELECTRIC CT7

In September 1976 General Electric announced the introduction of a new commercial helicopter engine based on the T700 military engine developed for the US Army. Certification testing to Federal Aviation Administration standards was completed in April 1977.

DIMENSIONS:

Length	1,194 mm (47·0 in)
Width	635 mm (25·0 in)
Height	584 mm (23·0 in)

WEIGHT, DRY: 195 kg (430 lb)

PERFORMANCE RATINGS (S/L, static, 15°C):

Contingency (2½ min)	1,209 kW (1,620 shp)
T-O (5 min) and en route contingency (30 min)	1,164 kW (1,560 shp)
Max cruise	940 kW (1,260 shp)

GESCHWENDER

GESCHWENDER AEROMOTIVE INC

4131 NW 36 Street, Bldg. 978, Lincoln, Nebraska 68524
Telephone: (402) 470 3333

Geschwender Aeromotive Inc has developed a series of liquid-cooled V-8 engines for aviation use. These engines use the 351 and 460 CID (cubic-inch displacement) engine blocks with horsepower ranging from 330 to 430 normally aspirated, and over 600 with the addition of a turbocharger on the 460.

The conversion incorporates a reducton unit which uses a high-velocity chain to transmit the power from the crankshaft to the propeller. Standard ratios are 1·923:1, 2·307:1 and 2·423:1. These ratios meet a wide variety of engines and propeller applications.

The primary objective of Geschwender Aeromotive is to provide engines for agricultural aviation. A prototype engine installed on a Funk airframe had accumulated in excess of 700 h at time of publication. Full Federal Aviation Administration certification is anticipated during calendar year 1979.

The corporation has also done some preliminary development on smaller liquid-cooled engines of the Ford V-4 and Pinto types for the homebuilt market. Production of engines for this market is planned for mid-1979. This secondary objective is to provide engines that will add realism to scale replica World War 2 liquid-cooled aircraft.

DIMENSIONS:

Length overall	1,422 mm (56·5 in)
Width	584 mm (23·0 in)
Height	635 mm (25·0 in)

WEIGHT, DRY:

351 CID	272 kg (600 lb)
460 CID	318 kg (700 lb)

MAX POWER (S/L):

351 CID	280 kW (375 hp) at 5,400 rpm
460 CID normally aspirated	336 kW (450 hp) at 5,500 rpm
460 CID turbocharged	448 kW (600 hp)

Prototype development flying has been done mainly with a 400 CID engine (300 kW, 400 hp) installed in a Funk 23B

GLUHAREFF

EMG ENGINEERING COMPANY

18518J South Broadway Avenue, Gardena, California 90248
Telephone: (213) 321-8699

Eugene M. Gluhareff, a pioneer of ultra-light rotorcraft, has been developing a unique type of air-breathing jet engine which he considers to offer notable advantages over all other systems for rotor tip-drive. The first model is the G8-2, which was designed in 1955 and fully developed over the next ten years for tip-drive or sailplane auxiliary propulsion. It has also been used for surface application in a go-kart, and in numerous static rigs sold to universities and other organisations. Production has been hard pressed to keep up with demand, a fast-growing market being radio-controlled flight vehicles. Manned platforms and small helicopters are also proving to be a large market for various sizes of the family of engines described below.

GLUHAREFF G8-2

Although extremely simple, the G8 series corresponds to no prior jet system. The design is based on propane, a readily-available volatile fuel. The pressure of the liquid propane in the tank delivers the fuel, via a needle valve serving as the throttle, to the burner unit. The fuel enters the burner duct and is immediately vaporised in a hot heat-exchanger. Vapour then passes back down an insulated pipe to the injector where its residual pressure is converted to kinetic energy. The high-velocity gas jet induces air through three 'supercharger' intakes, each synchronised to the internal flow, which gives the correct final fuel/air ratio to the mixture entering the combustion chamber. Here the mixture is initially ignited by a spark plug and thereafter burns continuously. The intake ducts are tuned to each other to create one-way flow. Resonance in the tailpipe is undesirable and is prevented by making the propelling nozzle of fishtail shape.

At first production was concentrated on two sizes of jet unit. The G8-2-15 is 914 mm (36 in) long; has a tailpipe diameter of 89 mm (3·5 in) and weighs 2·5 kg (5·5 lb). The equivalent horsepower at 644 km/h (400 mph) is 19·2. The G8-2-40 is 978 mm (38·5 in) long, has a tailpipe diameter of 127 mm (5·0 in) and weighs 5·2 kg (11·5 lb). The equivalent horsepower at 644 km/h (400 mph) is 46·0.

Static thrust (S/L, ISA) for the smaller unit, the G8-2-15, ranges from 0·004 kN (1 lb) at nozzle pressure of 1·38 bars (20 lb/sq in) to 0·067 kN (15 lb) at about 8·96 bars (130 lb/sq in). At the lower end the specific fuel consumption is over 10, but at higher powers levels off close to 6 in early units. Addition of a ram-air scoop reduces static performance (max about 0·047 kN; 10·5 lb), but raises dynamic thrust at 91·5 m (300 ft)/s from 0·071 kN (15·9 lb) to 0·078 kN (17·5 lb). Altitude performance has been explored statically, on a mountain; more than 0·053 kN (12 lb) thrust was available at 2,455 m (8,050 ft), the greatest height reached.

By 1979 three more models were available, the G8-2-20, -80 and -130, respectively rated at 0·089, 0·36 and 0·59 kN (20, 80 and 130 lb st), and a G8-2-250 (1·1 kN, 250 lb st) was on bench test. The best specific fuel consumption had been dramatically reduced from 170 mg/Ns (6 lb/h/lb st) to only 21·8 mg/Ns (0·77 lb/h/lb st).

The units are manufactured by Gluhareff's subsidiary EMG Engineering Co. Customers have the option of buying plans only, a construction package, partly prefabricated or an assembly kit or finished engine.

Gluhareff G8-2-15 jet unit, rated at 0·067 kN (15 lb st), without ram-air scoop

JACOBS

PAGE INDUSTRIES INC

HEAD OFFICE: C.E. Page Airport, PO Box 191, Yukon, Oklahoma 73099
Telephone: (405) 354-5385
PRESIDENT: O. J. Butts
VICE-PRESIDENT AND TREASURER: Currie Smith
VICE PRESIDENT, ENGINEERING: Merrill H. Bumbaugh

Page Industries is the successor to the Jacobs Aircraft Engine Co, which had manufactured aircooled radial piston engines since 1929. Current production is centred upon the various versions of the R-755 described below.

JACOBS R-755

This long-established seven-cylinder radial is being manufactured in several versions. The basic engine is the **R-755A** which is the subject of the detailed description. The current engines in this series are the R-755A2, and the A2M with dual ignition. The **R-755B** has a lower power rating, and is available as the R-755B1, driving a fixed-pitch propeller, and the B2 which can have a control valve for a two-position propeller or provision for a hydraulically-operated constant-speed propeller. The **R-755S** is a turbocharged version, available with dual ignition as the R-755SM.

The Piper Pawnee Brave PA-36-285 conversion uses the R-755S engine driving a Hamilton Standard 2B20-AG-CF 6135A-11S propeller as modified by Pacific Propeller Inc of Kent, Washington. Approval for the conversion is held by STC Engineering, of Oklahoma City.

TYPE: Seven-cylinder aircooled radial piston engine.

CYLINDERS: Bore 133 mm (5·25 in). Stroke 127 mm (5 in). Swept volume 12·3 litres (757 cu in). Barrels machined from steel forgings with close-spaced fins. Aluminium alloy heads screwed and shrunk on. Aluminium-bronze valve-seats shrunk into heads.

PISTONS: Forged aluminium alloy. Three compression rings and one scraper ring above gudgeon-pin (piston-pin) and two scraper rings below. Fully-floating nitrided gudgeon-pins.

CONNECTING RODS: One-piece steel master rod. Forged aluminium alloy link rods bearing directly upon nitrided-steel pins.

CRANKSHAFT: Two-piece clamp type, machined from forgings in chrome-nickel-molybdenum steel.

CRANKCASE: Assembled from five parts. Aluminium alloy.

VALVE GEAR: Cam ring, drive gears, tappets and pushrods all in nose section, with all moving parts enclosed.

Tulip-type inlet valves and sodium-cooled exhaust valves, each with two springs.
INDUCTION: Single updraught Stromberg NA-R7A carburettor. R-755S and SM have this carburettor fed at up to 35 in Hg by AiResearch exhaust-gas turbocharger between Nos. 2 and 3 cylinders. System set to maintain power to 5,945 m (19,500 ft), with aneroid relief valve to prevent overboosting beyond 36 in Hg. Manifold pressure controlled by throttle.
FUEL: 80 octane (755S, SM, 80/87 octane).
IGNITION: One Scintilla magneto and battery distributor, incorporating automatic advance (engines with "M" suffix, two magnetos).
LUBRICATION: Single unit comprising gear pressure pump and two scavenge pumps feeds all plain bearings. Dry sump. Automatic valve lubrication. Optional provision to operate adjustable-pitch or constant-speed propeller.
PROPELLER DRIVE: Direct, RH tractor, SAE 20 spline.
MOUNTING: Choice of eight locations incorporated around rear main crankcase.
DIMENSIONS:
Diameter 1,118 mm (44 in)
Length overall 1,020 m (40 7/32 in)
WEIGHT, DRY:
R-755A, B1 229 kg (505 lb)
R-755B2 232 kg (511 lb)
R-755S 261 kg (576 lb)
R-755SM 264 kg (583 lb)
PERFORMANCE RATINGS:
Rated power:
R-755A 224 kW (300 hp) at 2,200 rpm
R-755B 205 kW (275 hp) at 2,200 rpm
R-755S, SM:
rated power 205 kW (275 hp) at 2,030 rpm maintained to 5,945 m (19,500 ft); take-off (1 min limit) 261 kW (350 hp) at 2,200 rpm

Jacobs R-755A seven-cylinder radial piston engine, rated at 224 kW (300 hp)

MARQUARDT

THE MARQUARDT COMPANY (a division of CCI Corporation)

HEAD OFFICE: 16555 Saticoy Street, Van Nuys, California 91409
Telephone: (213) 781 2121
PRESIDENT: G. H. Hanauer
VICE-PRESIDENTS:
K. E. Woodgrift (Engineering)
A. L. Sorensen (Operations)
B. E. Huston (Finance)
C. Long (Advanced Programs)

The Marquardt Corporation was formed in November 1944 to undertake research and development of ramjet engines, and it produced the first American subsonic ramjet in 1945. Its main engineering business continues to be advanced aerospace propulsion and the supply of ram-air turbine power systems. A major portion of sales is currently associated with manufacture of sophisticated structures and components for the aerospace industry, and the production of clustered munition ordnance.

Marquardt is currently developing security-classified types of composite rocket/air-breathing propulsion systems for the US Air Force and Navy. These are regarded by the company as likely to lead to a new generation of power plants for supersonic strategic missiles and expendable tactical vehicles.

In the field of precision control rockets, Marquardt is engaged in developing reaction control engines for the Space Shuttle (the R-40A described separately). Recently, the control rocket work has been expanded to include development of a monopropellant rocket system for a classified programme, and advanced development activities for a hydrogen/oxygen water electrolysis rocketry system. A complete range of monopropellant and bipropellant rockets, precision valves and rocketry components is now being marketed.

Marquardt maintains extensive test facilities at Van Nuys for research and testing of air-breathing rocket engines, and controls and accessories. Total land area occupied exceeds 56 acres, and covered buildings exceed 46,400 m² (500,000 sq ft); employment exceeds 900.

MARQUARDT DUCTED ROCKET

In October 1977 Marquardt announced a new $2 million contract from the US Air Force Aero Propulsion Laboratory for further work on the ducted-rocket propulsion system. According to the company president: "It is designed to combine the best features of the ramjet engine and the solid rocket into a simple low-cost high-efficiency propulsion system. It employs a fuel-rich solid-rocket gas-generator and, like the basic ramjet, utilises the atmosphere as its primary source for oxidiser. The specific impulse is significantly higher than that of conventional solid rockets, yet it maintains the inherent simplicity desired for tactical applications".

The programme's objective is to demonstrate system performance in flight-weight hardware, culminating in an integrated engine demonstration in September 1979. Supporting Marquardt are Hughes (integration of aircraft, missile and engine), and Rocketdyne McGregor Division (solid-rocket gas-generator). Applications centre on both tactical and strategic missiles.

MARQUARDT FIREBRAND RAMJET

In May 1977 Marquardt began work on a Teledyne Ryan contract, expected to be valued at about $6 million, for design and development of ramjet engines for the Teledyne Ryan Firebrand (see RPVs and Targets section). Each Firebrand will be powered by two of the new engines. At completion of the present programme in February 1982 six R & D targets and two special test vehicles will have flown; a production quantity is expected to follow. Firebrand will be highly supersonic, simulating advanced anti-ship missiles, and is designed to be reusable.

MARQUARDT R-40A

This precision control rocket is being developed and qualified for the Space Shuttle orbiter vehicle.
TYPE: Liquid-propellant reaction control rocket.
PROPELLANTS: Nitrogen tetroxide and monomethyl hydrazine.

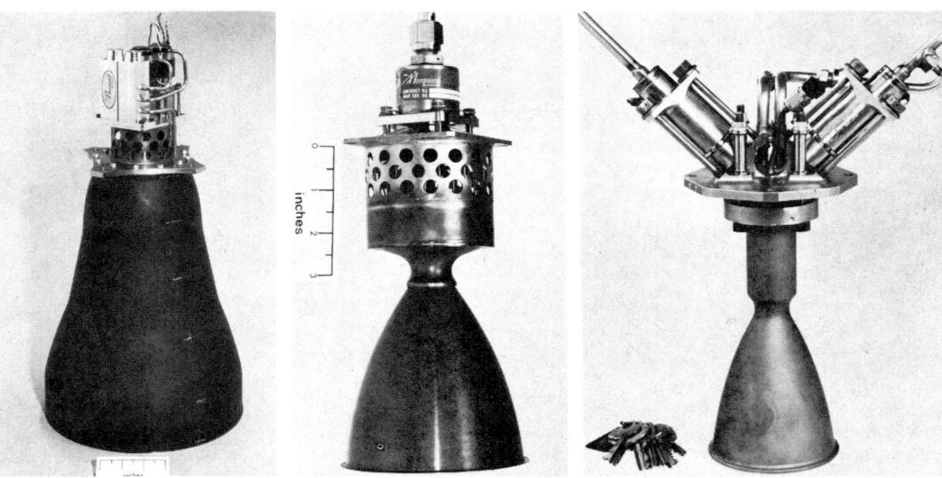

Precision control rocket engines by Marquardt *(from left to right):* **R-40A 3·87 kN (870 lb), R-30 0·69 kN (155 lb), R-1E 0·11 kN (25·0 lb), all ratings being in vacuum**

THRUST CHAMBER ASSEMBLY: Single chamber. Area ratio 20. Made of welded coated columbium, with welded-on orthogonal and scarfed nozzle extension in same material. Internal film cooling. Exterior insulated for buried installation. Started by electrical signal to on/off solenoid valve. Multiple doublet injector with hypergolic ignition.
THRUST CHAMBER MOUNTING: Flange bolt circle on injector head.
PROPELLANT FEED SYSTEM: Pressurised tanks, with feed of 0·526 kg (1·16 lb)/s fuel and 0·838 kg (1·85 lb)/s oxidant at 16·4 bars (238 lb/sq in abs).
DIMENSIONS:
Length overall 457 mm (18·0 in)
Nozzle exit diameter 267 mm (10·5 in)
WEIGHT, DRY: 6·3 kg (14·0 lb)
PERFORMANCE RATINGS:
Max thrust (vacuum) 3·87 kN (870 lb)
Chamber pressure 10·5 bars (152 lb/sq in)
Specific impulse 286

MARQUARDT R-30

This precision control rocket has been qualified for use on the kick stage of the USAF Defense Meteorological Satellite and NASA Tiros-No.
TYPE: Liquid monopropellant precision control rocket.
PROPELLANT: Hydrazine.
THRUST CHAMBER: Single chamber. Area ratio 22. Fabricated in L605 stainless steel. Shell 405 catalyst bed in combustion chamber. Multiple element injection.
THRUST CHAMBER MOUNTING: Fixed, by flange bolt circle on injector head.
PROPELLANT FEED SYSTEM: Pressurised tank. Flow rate 0·297 kg (0·657 lb)/s at 31 bars (450 lb/sq in abs).
DIMENSIONS:
Length overall 273 mm (10·75 in)
Diameter 103 mm (4·0 in)
WEIGHT, DRY: 1·36 kg (3·0 lb)
PERFORMANCE RATINGS:
Max thrust (vacuum) 0·69 kN (155 lb)
Chamber pressure 15·5 bars (225 lb/sq in)
Specific impulse 236

MARQUARDT R-1E

This small high-performance rocket was qualified for use on the reaction control subsystem of the subsequently-abandoned USAF Manned Orbital Laboratory, and is now being qualified as the vernier engine for the Space Shuttle Orbiter.
TYPE: Liquid bipropellant rocket for use in space.
PROPELLANTS: Nitrogen tetroxide and monomethyl hydrazine.
THRUST CHAMBER: Single chamber. Minimum area ratio 26 with orthogonal and scarfed nozzles. Made of metal-coated columbium. Insulated for buried installation. Started by electrical signal to on/off solenoid valve. Single doublet injector with hypergolic ignition.
THRUST CHAMBER MOUNTING: Fixed, by flange bolt circle on injector head.
PROPELLANT FEED SYSTEM: Pressurised tank. Flow rate 0·016 kg (0·0354 lb)/s fuel and 0·0256 kg (0·565 lb)/s oxidant.
DIMENSIONS:
Length overall 241 mm (9·5 in)
Width 145 mm (5·7 in)
Height (depth) 103 mm (4·0 in)
WEIGHT, DRY: 1·0 kg (2·20 lb)
PERFORMANCE RATINGS:
Max thrust (vacuum) 0·11 kN (25·0 lb)
Chamber pressure 7·45 bars (108 lb/sq in)
Specific impulse (area ratio 40) 275

MARQUARDT MA210/212

Two versions of this low-cost ramjet engine have been developed. The pitot-inlet MA210-XAA is designed primarily for the high-subsonic speed regime of Mach 0·7 to 0·9, although it has been tested at Mach 2·0. The conical-inlet version, MA212-XAA, provides higher thrust and better cruise fuel consumption in supersonic flight conditions. The engines use the same combustor system with an interchangeable inlet-diffuser assembly selected for either subsonic or supersonic flight operation. Both versions are of single-wall all-steel construction with two-point mounting to the vehicle pylon. Ignition is by pyrotechnic flare.
DIMENSIONS:
Length overall:
MA210-XAA 2,070 mm (79 in)
MA212-XAA 2,134 mm (84 in)
Diameter 381 mm (15 in)
WEIGHT, DRY:
MA210-XAA 31·75 kg (70 lb)
MA212-XAA 35·2 kg (77·5 lb)

Performance:
Operating envelope:
MA210-XAA S/L to 9,145 m (30,000 ft), Mach 0·7-1·5
MA212-XAA S/L to 18,300 m (60,000 ft), Mach 1·0-2·5
Design thrust (net):
MA210-XAA 2·94 kN (660 lb), S/L, Mach 0·9
MA212-XAA 6·05 kN (1,360 lb), 12,200 m (40,000 ft), Mach 2·5

Marquardt MA212-XAA conical-inlet supersonic ramjet (net thrust 6·05 kN; 1,360 lb at Mach 2·5 at 12,200 m; 40,000 ft)

NELSON

NELSON AIRCRAFT CORPORATION

Head Office: PO Box 454, Irwin, Pennsylvania 15642
Telephone: (412) 863-5900
President: Charles R. Rhoades
Vice-President: Lawrence J. Rhoades

Nelson Aircraft Corporation, among its many industrial activities, produces to order the Nelson H-63 four-cylinder two-cycle aircooled engine, which has been certificated by the FAA as a power unit for single-seat helicopters, and is now available also as a power plant for propeller-driven aircraft. All these engines are capable of sustained inverted flight. Recommended overhaul period is 800 hours.

NELSON FOUR-STROKE RANGE

Nelson Aircraft is developing a new range of lightweight four-stroke engines. They will be compact, and will have liquid cooling. The three sizes have outputs of 44·7 kW (60 hp), 89·5 kW (120 hp) and 112 kW (150 hp). Dry weights are, respectively, 39·95 kg (88 lb), 57·2 kg (126 lb) and 70·37 kg (155 lb).

By 1978 the 112 kW (150 hp) engine and a range of 89·5 kW (120 hp) engines had been run. Emphasis is on the latter. Future engines will include a Roots-type blower running at the 6,000 rpm of the engine, propeller speed being 2,000 rpm.

NELSON H-63

US military designation: YO-65

Developed originally as a power unit for single-seat helicopters, the H-63 is now available in five versions, as follows:

H-63C. Basic helicopter power unit for vertical installation. Battery ignition and direct drive. Certificated by FAA. Supplied as complete power package, including clutch, cooling fan and shroud.

H-63CP. Basically as H-63C, but without clutch, fan and shroud. Intended primarily for installation in horizontal position, with direct drive to propeller. FAA certificated.

H-63CPM. Magneto ignition (see 'Ignition' in detail description).

H-63CPMR, CPR. Versions with speed-reducing propeller drive (see 'Power Take-off' in detail description).

Nelson has developed a 1·07 m (42 in) wooden propeller with glassfibre covering for use with the H-63. It is suitable for either tractor or pusher installation.

Type: Four-cylinder horizontally-opposed aircooled, two-stroke.

Cylinders: Bore 68·3 mm (2[11]/16 in). Stroke 70 mm (2¾ in). Total capacity 1·03 litres (63 cu in). Compression ratio 8 : 1. Each complete cylinder is machined from an aluminium alloy casting, the bore being porous-chrome plated for wear resistance. Cylinders bolted to and detachable from crankcase.

Pistons: Aluminium alloy casting. Two piston rings. Two needle roller bearings pressed in boss. Piston (gudgeon) pin pressed into small end of connecting rod.

Connecting Rods: Alloy steel forging. Caged roller bearing at big-end.

Crankshaft: Four-throw. Nitralloy shaft on ball and roller bearings.

Crankcase: Two-piece case divided on horizontal centreline. Each half is a magnesium alloy casting.

Induction: Nelson diaphragm-type all-angle fuel control carburettor. Hot-air anti-icing. Fuel/oil mixture valves nrom crankcase through specially-designed rotary valve driven by crankshaft. Intake to and exhaust from cylinders through ports. Exhaust stacks are of aluminium alloy.

Nelson four-stroke prototype engine in 89·5 kW (120 hp) size

First photograph of the Nelson H-63CPR with speed-reducing chain drive. Maximum rating will be 35·4 kW (47·5 hp)

Fuel: 80/87 octane gasoline and SAE 30 ash-free-base oil in 16 : 1 mixture for fuel and lubrication.

Ignition (except M models): Battery-type dual-ignition with automatic retard for starting. (M models): Two Slick magnetoes. Two Champion D-9 or 5 COM spark plugs per cylinder.

Lubrication: See under 'Fuel'.

Power Take-off: (H-63C): Hollow shaft extension from Salisbury centrifugal clutch output drive. (R models): Hy-Vo high-speed chain drive with ratio of 8 : 5 (0·0625).

Starting: 12V DC Autolite electric motor and Bendix drive.

Cooling: (H-63C): Centrifugal aluminium fan and two-piece glassfibre shrouding designed to maintain all temperatures within acceptable limits on an FAA hot day of 37·8°C, S/L. (Other versions): by propeller slipstream.

Mounting: Four Lord-type mounts, two on each half of crankcase.

Dimensions (H-63C):
Length 508 mm (20·0 in)
Height 376 mm (14·8 in)
Width 605 mm (23·8 in)

Weight, Dry:
H-63C, with accessories 34·5 kg (76 lb)
H-63CP, with accessories 30·8 kg (68 lb)
H-63CPM 30·9 kg (68·0 lb)

The 35·8 kW (48 hp) Nelson H-63CP for fixed-wing aircraft

The 32 kW (43 hp) Nelson H-63C four-cylinder two-stroke engine

H-63CPR, H-63CPMR 38·6 kg (85·0 lb)

Power Ratings:
T-O:
H-63C 32 kW (43 hp) at 4,000 rpm
H-63CP, H-63CPM 35·8 kW (48 hp) at 4,400 rpm
H-63CPR, H-63CPMR 35·4 kW (47·5 hp) at 2,750 output rpm
Max continuous:
H-63C 32 kW (43 hp) at 4,000 rpm
H-63CP, H-63CPM 33·6 kW (45 hp) at 4,000 rpm
H-63CPR, H-63CPMR 33·25 kW (44·6 hp) at 2,500 output rpm

Fuel Consumption:
R models
16 litres (4·2 US gal; 3·47 Imp gal)/h at 2,500 output rpm

NORTHROP

NORTHROP CORPORATION, VENTURA DIVISION

1515 Rancho Conejo Boulevard, Newbury Park, California 91320
Telephone: (805) 498-3131

In 1972 Northrop Corporation acquired the rights to this engine from McCulloch Corporation. The 4318 series continues in production at Ventura Division, to power the KD2R-5 basic training target (see RPVs and Targets section).

NORTHROP MODEL 4318F

US military designation: O-100-3

Type: Four-cylinder horizontally-opposed aircooled two-stroke.

Cylinders: Bore 80·8 mm (3[3]/16 in). Stroke 79·4 mm (3⅛ in). Displacement 1·6 litres (100 cu in). Compression ratio 7·8 : 1. Die-cast aluminium with integral head and hard chrome plated walls. Self-locking nuts secure cylinders to crankcase studs.

Pistons: Cast aluminium. Two rings above pins. Piston (gudgeon) pins of case-hardened steel.

Connecting Rods: Forged steel. 'Free-roll' silver-plated bearings at big-end. Small-end carries needle bearing. Lateral position of rod controlled by thrust washers between piston pin bosses and small-end.

Crankshaft: Four-throw one-piece steel forging on four anti-friction bearings, two ball and two needle, one with split race for centre main bearing.

Crankcase: One-piece heat-treated permanent-mould aluminium casting, closed at rear end with cast aluminium cover which provides mounting for magneto.

Valve Gear: Fuel mixture for scavenging and power

stroke introduced to cylinders through crankshaft-driven rotary valves and ported cylinders.

Induction: Crankcase pumping type. Diaphragm-type carburettor with adjustable jet.

Fuel Specification: Grade 100/130 aviation fuel mixed in the ratio 20 parts fuel with one part 40SAE two-cycle outboard motor oil.

Ignition: Single magneto and distributor. Directly connected to crankshaft through impulse coupling for easy starting. Radio noise suppressor included. BG type RB 916S, AC type 83P or Champion REM-38R spark plugs. Complete radio shielding.

Lubrication: Oil mixed with fuel as in conventional two-stroke engines.

Propeller Drive: RH tractor. Keyed taper shaft.

Starting: By separate portable hydraulic starter.

Mounting: Three mounting lugs provided with socket for rubber mounting bushings.

Dimensions:

Length	686 mm (27·0 in)
Width	711 mm (28·0 in)
Height	381 mm (15·0 in)

Weight, Dry:

Less propeller hub	34·9 kg (77 lb)

Power Rating:

Rated output 62·6-71·6 kW (84-96 hp) at 4,100 rpm

Specific Consumption (fuel/oil mixture at S/L at rated power): 127 µg/J (0·75 lb/h/shp)

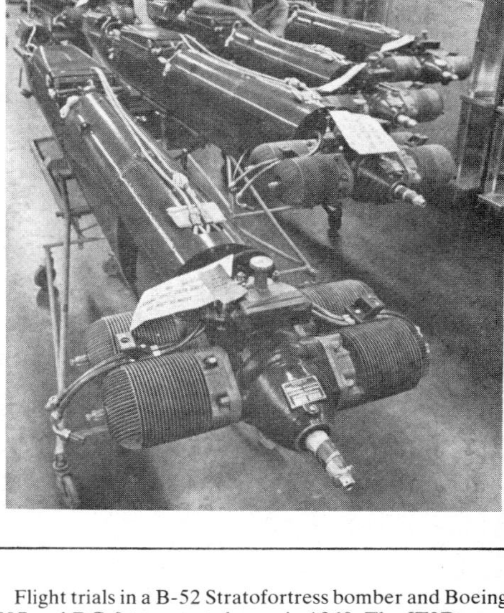

Production of Northrop Ventura targets powered by O-100-3 piston engines rated at 62·6-71·6 kW (84-96 hp)

PRATT & WHITNEY

THE PRATT & WHITNEY AIRCRAFT GROUP OF UNITED TECHNOLOGIES CORPORATION

Group Headquarters: East Hartford, Connecticut 06108

Telephone: (203) 565-4321

Group President: Bruce N. Torell

Group Executive Vice-President, Technology and Strategic Planning: Richard J. Coar

Group Public Relations Director: Edward R. Cowles

Commercial Products Division

East Hartford, Connecticut

Division President: David J. Hines

Government Products Division

West Palm Beach, Florida

Division President: Edmund V. Marshall

Manufacturing Division

East Hartford, Connecticut

Division President: Donald Nigro

Pratt & Whitney Aircraft of Canada

See separate entry under Canada.

Pratt & Whitney Aircraft was formed in 1925 and rapidly became a world leader in aircraft piston engines. It is now the world's largest producer of gas-turbine engines.

On 23 April 1976 Pratt & Whitney was restructured as the Pratt & Whitney Aircraft Group, composed of four divisions listed above.

Commercial Products Division is responsible for commercial aircraft engines. Government Products Division is responsible for military engines. Manufacturing Division provides plant and facilities for making the products of the CPD and GPD. Pratt & Whitney Aircraft of Canada (P&WC), which has its own entry under that country on an earlier page, is responsible for engines for general aviation.

The Pratt & Whitney Aircraft Group has approximately 33,000 employees at locations in Connecticut, and about another 12,000 in Florida and Canada.

Excluding P&WC, the divisions of the Group had by 1978 manufactured more than 60,000 gas-turbine engines, most of them for aircraft. These engines had accumulated over 408 million flight hours in military and commercial service. Most of this time has been logged by the JT3D, JT8D and JT9D turbofans on which the major part of the world's air transport is based.

In August 1975 Pratt & Whitney and Rolls-Royce signed an agreement for joint further development of the Pegasus vectored-thrust turbofan, which includes an option to take up a manufacturing licence for the British engine.

PRATT & WHITNEY JT8

US military designation: J52

The J52 is a medium-sized turbojet which was designed under the auspices of the US Navy Bureau of Weapons. It powers all versions of the Grumman A-6 Intruder/Prowler attack and ECM aircraft and current versions of the McDonnell Douglas A-4 Skyhawk.

J52-P-6A, 6B, 8A, 8B. Rated at 37·8 kN (8,500 lb) (6A, 6B) or 41·4 kN (9,300 lb) (8A, 8B). Powers A-4E, A-4F, TA-4F, TA-4J, A-6A, A-6B, A-6C, A-6E.

J52-P-408. Rated at 50 kN (11,200 lb). Powers A-4F, A-4M, some export A-4 versions, EA-6B.

The J52 is a two-spool turbojet, with total of 12 compressor stages, a 'cannular' type combustion system fed by 36 dual-orifice injectors and independent high-pressure and low-pressure single-stage turbines. Pressure ratio ranges from 12·4 to 14·5 : 1. Several advanced design features are incorporated to achieve the rating increases with a minimum change in engine envelope and weight compared to previous JT8 (J52) models. These include two-position inlet guide vanes and aircooled first-stage turbine vanes and blades. In addition, the burner cans include features for reduced smoke.

Dimensions:

Diameter	796 mm (31·36 in)
Length (P-408)	3,020 mm (118·9 in)

Weight, Dry:

J52-P-408	1,052 kg (2,318 lb)

Performance Ratings:

See under model listings

PRATT & WHITNEY JT4

US military designation: J75

Last described in the 1970-71 *Jane's*, about 50 of these large two-shaft turbojets, of J75-P-13 type, are being rebuilt by Pratt & Whitney Aircraft to power Lockheed TR-1 reconnaissance aircraft. Afterburners will be removed and other changes made.

PRATT & WHITNEY JT3D

US military designation: TF33

The JT3D is a turbofan version of the J57 turbojet, handling almost 2·5 times more air than the J57 and with pressure ratio ranging from 13 : 1 on the JT3D-1 to 14·3 : 1 on the JT3D-8A (TF33-P-7).

Evolution from the J57 involved removal of the first three stages of the J57 compressor and replacement by two fan stages. Of considerably larger diameter than the compressor, the fan extends well outside the compressor casing. The third-stage turbine on the J57 was enlarged and a fourth stage added to provide the power necessary to drive the low-pressure compressor rotor and integral fan.

The JT3D produces 50% more take-off and 27% more cruise thrust than the J57, while giving a 13% better cruising specific fuel consumption.

Flight trials in a B-52 Stratofortress bomber and Boeing 707 and DC-8 transports began in 1960. The JT3D powers all late versions of these aircraft. The Lockheed C-141A StarLifter military transport uses the TF33-P-7 version, with an additional stage of compression. In January 1973 the -7 engine, modified to incorporate additional accessory drives, was selected to power the Boeing E-3A (AWACS) aircraft. Designation of the E-3A engine is TF33-PW-100A (JT3D-8B).

More than 8,480 JT3D turbofans, including converted JT3C engines, had been delivered by the end of 1978. Additional engines remain to be delivered.

Dimensions:

Diameter:

JT3D-3B	1,350 mm (53·14 in)
TF33-PW-100A	1,373 mm (54·06 in)

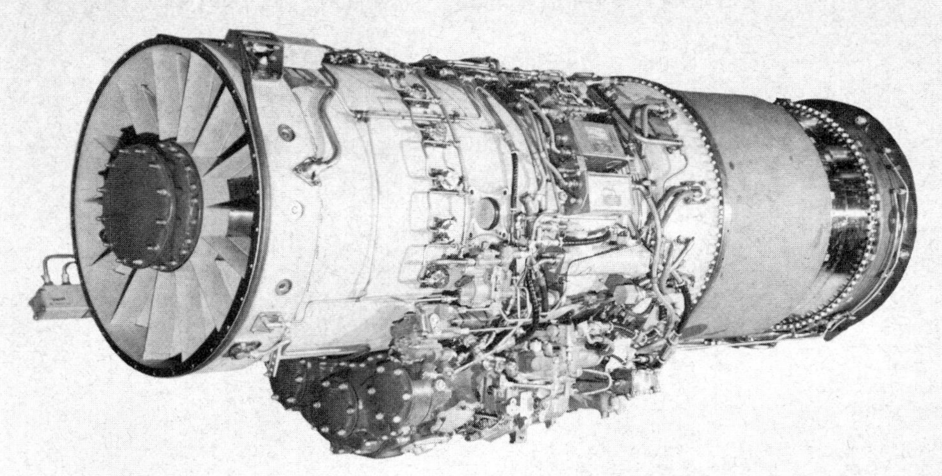

Pratt & Whitney J52-P-408 two-shaft turbojet rated at 50 kN (11,200 lb st)

Pratt & Whitney TF33-P-7 turbofan rated at 93·4 kN (21,000 lb st)

Length:
JT3D-3B 3,479 mm (137 in)
TF33-PW-100A 3,607 mm (142 in)
Weight, Dry:
JT3D-3B 1,969 kg (4,340 lb)
TF33-PW-100A 2,173 kg (4,790 lb)
Performance Ratings (T-O, S/L, static):
JT3D-3B 80 kN (18,000 lb st)
TF33-PW-100A 93·4 kN (21,000 lb st)
Specific Fuel Consumption (T-O rating):
JT3D-3B 15·5 mg/Ns (0·535 lb/h/lb st)
TF33-PW-100A 15·86 mg/Ns (0·560 lb/h/lb st)

PRATT & WHITNEY JT8D

This turbofan engine was developed as a company-sponsored project to power the Boeing 727. It was later selected for other types of aircraft, and supersonic military versions of the JT8D have been developed in Sweden by Volvo Flygmotor (see RM8 in that company's entry).

Construction of the JT8D is largely of steel and titanium. An annular by-pass duct runs the full length of the engine, with balanced mixing of the hot and cold air streams in the tailpipe.

The JT8D entered commercial service on 1 February 1964. It has since become the most widely used commercial jet engine, over 9,000 having logged more than 140 million flight hours.

The following are the basic versions:

JT8D-1, -1A, -1B. Initial version rated at 62·3 kN (14,000 lb st). Powers Boeing 727-100 and -100C, McDonnell Douglas DC-9-10 and -10F, and Aérospatiale Caravelle 10B and 10R.

JT8D-7, -7A, -7B. Develops 62·3 kN (14,000 lb st) to 28·9 °C at S/L. Specified for Boeing 727-100, -100C and 200, Boeing 737-100 and -200, McDonnell Douglas DC-9-10, -30 and -30F, Aérospatiale Caravelle 10R and 11R.

JT8D-9, -9A. Develops 64·5 kN (14,500 lb st) to 28·9°C at S/L. Specified for Boeing 727-100, -100C and 200, 737-200, -200C and T-43A, McDonnell Douglas DC-9-20, -30, -40, C-9A, C-9B and VC-9C, Aérospatiale Caravelle 12 and Kawasaki C-1. Deliveries began in July 1967. Produced under licence in Japan (see entry under Mitsubishi).

JT8D-11. Develops 66·7 kN (15,000 lb st) to 28·9°C at S/L. Specified for McDonnell Douglas DC-9-20, -30 and 40 series aircraft and Boeing 727-200. Deliveries began in November 1968.

JT8D-15. Develops 69 kN (15,500 lb st) to 28·9°C. FAA certification was received and deliveries began in April 1971. Selected for Dassault Mercure, Boeing Advanced 727 and 737, and DC-9. Entered service 1972.

JT8D-17. Develops 71·2 kN (16,000 lb st) to 28·9°C. Certificated on 1 February 1974 (tenth anniversary of JT8D-1 entry to airline service). Entered service July 1974. More than 800 ordered by December 1977 for advanced versions of Boeing 727 and 737, DC-9 and McDonnell Douglas YC-15 prototypes.

JT8D-17R. Alternative T-O rating 72·95 kN (16,400 lb) but has capability of providing 4·448 kN (1,000 lb) additional thrust in the event of significant thrust loss on any other engine. Certificated at 77·40 kN (17,400 lb st) T-O rating in April 1976. Delivery for Advanced 727-200 August 1976 and certification with reserve-thrust feature November 1976.

JT8D-200 Series. The first member of this series is the JT8D-209, rated at 82·2 kN (18,500 lb st) to 25°C, for normal use and 85·6 kN (19,250 lb st) to 28·9°C following loss of thrust on any other engine. This reduced-noise derivative of the JT8D family is substantially redesigned. The JT8D-209 combines the HP compressor, HP turbine spool and combustion section of the JT8D-9 with advanced LP technology derived from the NASA JT8D Refan Programme and other recently developed P&WA engines. The 200 Series offers substantially increased thrust with reduced noise and specific fuel consumption, together with the established reliability and low maintenance cost of the JT8D HP spool. The new single-stage fan has increased diameter. The new six-stage LP compressor, integral with the fan, offers increased pressure ratio. The LP turbine has 20 per cent greater annular area and achieves a higher efficiency. Surrounding the engine is a new by-pass duct. The exhaust system includes a 12-lobe internal mixer to provide forced mixing of the fan and primary streams. A JT8D-209 prototype engine began flight development in a McDonnell Douglas YC-15 on 4 March 1977. Later that month Pratt & Whitney launched the -209 as a commercial product, the first application being the DC-9-55, a stretched version of the DC-9. On 20 October 1977 McDonnell Douglas announced full-scale production of this aircraft, re-designated the DC-9 Super 80. FAA certification of the JT8D-209 was scheduled for mid-1979. The JT8D-209A, identical to the 209 but without a mixer, was the engine selected for the McDonnell Douglas C-15 candidate for the USAF AMST programme.

The first -200 growth engine, the JT8D-217, has been offered for growth versions of the DC-9-80 in late 1980. This engine is rated at 88·96 kN (20,000 lb st), with 92·75 kN (20,850 lb st) available following loss of thrust on any other engine.

Since February 1970 all new JT8D engines have incorporated smoke-reduction hardware, and conversion kits are available for in-service engines. Low-emission burners using aerating nozzles are being developed for the JT8D and will be used in all JT8D-200 series production. Two noise-reduction options are also available for all JT8D models. Maximum TBO for the JT8D is 16,800 h.

Type: Axial-flow two-spool turbofan.

Air Intake: Annular with 19 fixed inlet guide vanes (23 in 200 series).

Fan: Two-stage front fan (200 Series, single stage). First stage has 27 titanium blades (30 in -1 and -7; 34 in 209) dovetailed into discs. First-stage blades have integral shroud at about 61% span. Airflow: -1, -1A, -7, -7A, 143 kg (315 lb)/s; -9, -9A, 145 kg (319 lb)/s; -11, -15, 146 kg (322 lb)/s; -17, 147 kg (324 lb)/s; 17R, 148 kg (326 lb)/s; -209, 213 kg (469 lb)/s; -217, 217 kg (483 lb)/s. By-pass ratio: -1, -1A, -7, -7A, 1·10; -9, -9A, 1·04; -11, 1·05; -15, 1·03; -17, 1·02; -17R, 1·00; 209, 1·78; -217, 1·70.

LP Compressor: Six-stage (-200 series, seven-stage) axial, integral with fan stages, on inner of two concentric shafts. Blades made of titanium. Shaft carried in double ball bearings, either half of each bearing being able to handle the complete loading.

HP Compressor: Seven-stage axial-flow on outer hollow shaft which, like the inner shaft, is carried in double ball bearings. One-piece casing. Blades made of steel or titanium. Pressure ratio: -1, -1A, -7, -7A, 15·8; -9, -9A, 15·9; -11, 16·2; -15, 16·5; -17, 16·9; -17R, 17·3; -209, 17·1; -217, 18·6.

Combustion Chamber: Cannular type with nine cylindrical flame-tubes, each downstream of a single Duplex burner and discharging into a single annular nozzle.

HP Turbine: Single-stage axial-flow. Solid blades in -1 to 9 and -209, aircooled in -11 and later, and -217; guide

Pratt & Whitney JT8D-209 two-shaft turbofan rated at 85·6 kN (19,250 lb st) to 28·9°C

Pratt & Whitney JT8D-17R two-shaft turbofan rated at 77·40 kN (17,400 lb st) to 25°C

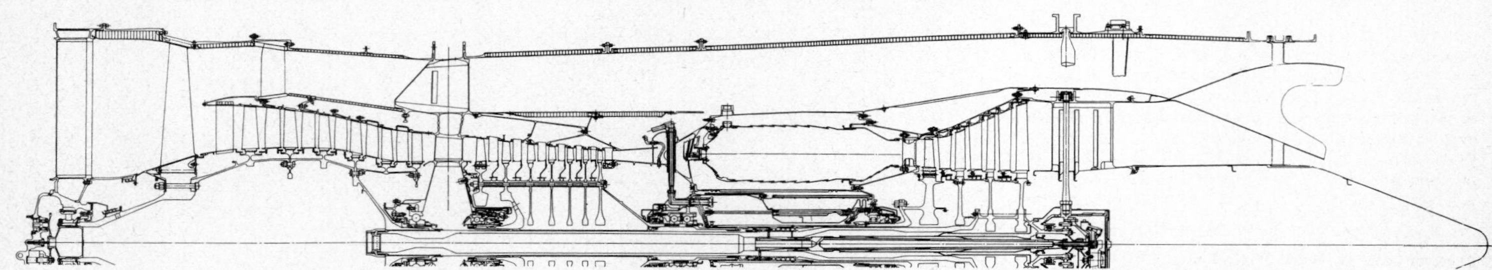

Longitudinal section drawing of upper half of Pratt & Whitney JT8D-209 rated at 85·6 kN (19,250 lb st) to 28·9°C

vanes hollow and aircooled in all models.

LP TURBINE: Three-stage axial-flow. Solid blades and guide vanes.

DIMENSIONS:

Diameter:

-1 to -17	1,080 mm (42·5 in)
-209, -217	1,431 mm (56·34 in)

Length:

-1 to -17	3,048 mm (120·0 in)
-209, -217	3,835 mm (151·0 in)

WEIGHT, DRY:

JT8D-1, -1A, -1B	1,431 kg (3,155 lb)
JT8D-7, -7A, -7B	1,454 kg (3,205 lb)
JT8D-9, -9A	1,475 kg (3,252 lb)
JT8D-11, -15	1,501 kg (3,309 lb)
JT8D-17	1,510 kg (3,330 lb)
JT8D-17R	1,549 kg (3,415 lb)
JT8D-209	2,001 kg (4,410 lb)
JT8D-217	2,048 kg (4,515 lb)

PERFORMANCE RATINGS:

T-O thrust (S/L, static): see model descriptions

Max cruise thrust (10,665 m; 35,000 ft at Mach 0·8):

JT8D-1, -1A	15·7 kN (3,520 lb)
JT8D-7, -7A	16·1 kN (3,630 lb)
JT8D-9, -9A	18·2 kN (4,100 lb)
JT8D-11	17·6 kN (3,950 lb)
JT8D-15	18·3 kN (4,100 lb)
JT8D-17, -17R	18·9 kN (4,240 lb)
(at 9,145 m; 30,000 ft at Mach 0·8)	
JT8D-209	21·9 kN (4,945 lb)
JT8D-217	23·9 kN (5,380 lb)

SPECIFIC FUEL CONSUMPTION:

T-O rating:

JT8D-1, -1A, -7, -7A	16·57 mg/Ns (0·585 lb/h/lb st)
JT8D-9, 9A	16·85 mg/Ns (0·595 lb/h/lb st)
JT8D-11	17·56 mg/Ns (0·620 lb/h/lb st)
JT8D-15	17·84 mg/Ns (0·630 lb/h/lb st)
JT8D-17	18·27 mg/Ns (0·645 lb/h/lb st)

Max cruise rating, as above:

JT8D-1, -1A	22·24 mg/Ns (0·785 lb/h/lb st)
JT8D-7, -7A	22·38 mg/Ns (0·790 lb/h/lb st)
JT8D-9, -9A	22·86 mg/Ns (0·807 lb/h/lb st)
JT8D-11	23·14 mg/Ns (0·817 lb/h/lb st)
JT8D-15	22·97 mg/Ns (0·811 lb/h/lb st)
JT8D-17, -17R	23·37 mg/Ns (0·825 lb/h/lb st)
JT8D-209	20·70 mg/Ns (0·731 lb/h/lb st)
JT8D-217	21·35 mg/Ns (0·754 lb/h/lb st)

PRATT & WHITNEY JT9D

US military designation (JT9D-7): F105-PW-100

Based on technology stemming from the USAF heavy freighter propulsion of 1961-63, the JT9D was the first of the new era of very large, high by-pass ratio turbofans on which the design of the present generation of wide-body commercial transports rests.

In its basic design the JT9D is compact, being shorter than the JT3D, and has two shafts, each supported in two bearings. In cruising flight the installed sfc is 22-23% lower than for the JT3D or JT8D. Careful attention has been paid to maintenance.

First run of the JT9D was in December 1966, and first engine flight test, with the engine mounted on the starboard inboard pylon of a Boeing B-52E, was in June 1968. The first flight of the Boeing 747 occurred on 9 February 1969. The DC-10-40 flew on 28 February 1972.

Versions of the JT9D include:

JT9D-3. The initial production model, rated at 193·5 kN (43,500 lb) to 26·7°C. Fitted to first production Boeing 747. Engines delivered from April 1969 and certificated the following month.

JT9D-3A. Incorporates water injection for wet rating of 200 kN (45,000 lb) to 26·7°C. Powers Boeing 747-100 and -200B. Engines delivered from December 1969 and certificated on 9 January 1970.

JT9D-7. This engine incorporates improvements resulting from -3A service experience. The LP compressor has blades and vanes sloped back perpendicular to the inclined core airflow for increased stability and life; pylon-matched fan exit vanes reduce sfc; HP compressor discs have a longer life, and the stators are driven through a low-friction mechanism; a short-cone hooded burner increases durability and reduces smoke emission far below the visible level; changes to HP and LP turbines increase life, and improved HP disc sealing improves performance. The -7 was certificated in June 1971. It powers the 747-200B, C, F and SR, raising the certificated take-off weight from 322,050 to 351,530 kg (710,000 to 775,000 lb). On 30 November 1971 the 747-200 was certificated at full weight and thrust, and with a fixed-inlet cowl, quieter than the original type with blow-in doors (104 EPNdB 'traded' compared with 112).

JT9D-7A. This incorporates a number of aerodynamic improvements which provide higher component efficiencies. The result is an increased thrust capability at the same turbine temperature. This has been reflected in rating increases over the JT9D-7. A version of the -7A, with improved component efficiencies to reduce specific fuel consumption, powers the 747SP.

JT9D-7F. Aerodynamically identical to the JT9D-7A, the -7F has first- and second-stage turbine rotor blades and second-stage stator vanes of directionally solidified material, allowing a rise in turbine gas temperature. This is reflected in further increase in thrust. The -7F permits operation at the Boeing 747 basic structural limit of 362,870 kg (800,000 lb). The -7F was certificated in September 1974; first deliveries were made in March 1975.

JT9D-7J. Aerodynamically identical to -7F this has improved cooling and HP turbine to achieve -7F wet T-O rating without water injection.

JT9D-7R. Selected for Boeing 767-200 (JT9D-7R4D) and by Swissair for Airbus A310-220 (-7R4C). Maximum commonality with other -7 engines with reduced weight and improved maintainability and surge-margin levels, plus low SFC deterioration rate. Accessory drive box on core as in other -7 series but thrust frame eliminated. Certification due July 1980. See Addenda.

JT9D-20. In this engine the T-O rating with water injection has been increased to 220 kN; 49,400 lb to 30°C. With this engine, the DC-10-20 was redesignated DC-10-40 and certificated at a gross weight of 530,000 lb for dry operation. At the wet rating **(JT9D-20W)** it is certificated at 251,745 kg (555,000 lb). The D-20 is similar to the D-7, except for external configuration changes such as accessory-gearbox location, thrust-transmitting points and plumbing hardware locations. The gearbox is under the fan exit casing, and the new mounting has enabled the thrust-frame yoke (added to earlier engines to prevent ovalising of the casing) to be eliminated. The D-20 was certificated in October 1972.

JT9D-59A. This engine is the first member of the family of growth versions selected to power the DC-10 and A300B. It evolved from an intensive component development programme begun in 1970, which led to the running of a complete experimental engine at 276 kN (62,000 lb st). The Dash 59A differs from earlier JT9D engines mainly in the following respects: the fan has a diameter approximately 25·4 mm (one inch) larger and reprofiled blades of higher efficiency; the low-pressure compressor has a zero (fourth) stage and is completely redesigned and the whole hot end is entirely redesigned. The burners are recontoured, an HP turbine carbon seal is added, the HP turbine rotor blades are of directionally solidified PWA 1422 superalloy, the HP turbine annulus is of greater area, and the LP turbine is mechanically and aerodynamically redesigned. The carcase of the engine is stressed for 249 kN (56,000 lb st). With a dry rating of 236 kN (53,000 lb) the JT9D-59A was certificated on 12 December 1974; production deliveries began in January 1975. These engines are configured for installation in a common nacelle, developed jointly by P&WA and Rohr Industries, for the 747, DC-10 and A300B. The growth potential of this size of engine is predicted at 267 kN (60,000 lb).

JT9D-70A. This is the corresponding growth version of the JT9D for the Boeing 747. The engine was certificated on 12 December 1974, and first deliveries were made in January 1975 at a rating of 236 kN (53,000 lb). First

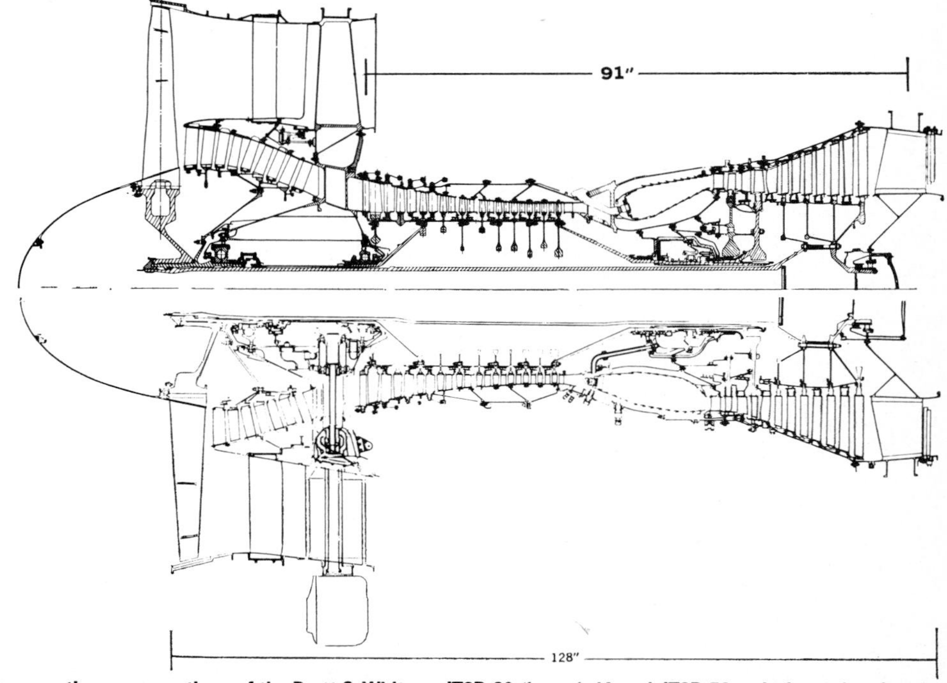

Comparative cross-sections of the Pratt & Whitney JT9D-20 *(lower half)* and JT9D-59 turbofans, showing the latter's redesigned fan, LP compressor, combustion chamber and turbine

Pratt & Whitney JT9D-59A turbofan, rated at 236 kN (53,000 lb st)

application is the 747F certificated at 371,946 kg (820,000 lb).

JT9D-7Q, -7Q1. These have the same gas path as the 59A and -70A but an exterior configured like the -7 (a totally different engine, despite the designation) for installation in the Boeing 747-200 nacelle. The combination of improved performance, reduced drag and reduced propulsion-system weight significantly improve 747-200 performance. The -7Q was certificated in October 1978.

Since entry to service on 21 January 1970 the JT9D has gained experience in the 747 more rapidly than any previous engine. Within one year 653 engines had been delivered, and early in 1973 the total exceeded 1,132. Rate of delivery has since slowed but the total now exceeds 1,790 and flight time in early 1979 was in excess of 27 million hours.

The following description applies to early versions of the JT9D, with data for later models given in parentheses:

Type: Two-shaft turbofan of high by-pass ratio.

Intake: Direct pitot, annular fixed geometry (except that airframe inlet on early 747 aircraft has blow-in side doors around periphery). No inlet guide vanes ahead of fan. Airflow improved by rotating spinner.

Fan: Single stage, with 46 titanium blades of 4·6 aspect ratio and two part-span shrouds held by dovetails in steel LP rotor. Downstream are 108 aluminium alloy exit guide vanes (96 on the -59A, -70A and -7Q), followed by nine discharge-case radial struts. Fan case of stainless steel and aluminium alloy, designed to contain fan blades. Discharge case lined with perforated acoustic material. Nominal airflow 684 kg (1,509 lb)/s at 3,650 rpm (-7, 698 kg; 1,540 lb/s at 3,750 rpm; -59A, 70A, 734 kg; 1,619 lb/s). Pressure ratio; typically 1·6 : 1. By-pass ratio: -3A, 5·17 : 1; -7, 5·15 : 1; -59A, -70A, 4·9 : 1.

LP Compressor: Three stages (JT9D-59A, -70A, 7Q/Q1, four different stages), rotating with fan. Rotor made up of rings, spacers and conical disc splined to steel LP shaft and held by lock-nut ahead of fan and overhung ahead of main LP ball thrust bearing. Hydraulically opened bleed ring at LP exit to increase flight-idle stall margin and excess air during deceleration. Rotor stages have 124, 132 and 130 dovetailed blades of titanium alloy. First stator stage anti-iced by 9th stage bleed air. Stator stages have 88, 128 and 126 titanium vanes and 120 (4th stage) nickel alloy vanes, all riveted to outer rings. Casing of aluminium alloy. Core airflow typically 118 kg (260 lb)/s (all versions).

HP Compressor: Eleven stages. All stages have rings or centreless discs with integral spacers carried on conical discs at 3rd and 11th stages on HP shaft of titanium alloy (front) and high-nickel alloy (rear), bolted at rear hub. Rotor stages have 60, 84, 102, 100, 110, 108, 104, 94 and 100 dovetailed titanium blades and 102 and 90 nickel alloy blades. Stator has 76, 70, 80, 106, 100 and 112 titanium alloy vanes and 126, 146, 154, 158 and 92 vanes of nickel alloy, all brazed to inner and outer rings. First four stator stages are variable, positioned by hydraulic actuator to provide adequate stall margin for starting, acceleration and part-power operation. Casing of titanium alloys (last two stages, nickel alloy) has bleed ports supplying 8th-stage air for airframe requirements. Max HP speed: -3A, 7,580 rpm; -7, 8,000 rpm. Overall engine pressure ratio: -3A, 21·5 : 1; 7, 22·3 : 1; -59A, -70A, 24 : 1.

Combustion Chamber: The diffuser case, which extends from the HP compressor to the midpoint of the combustion section, incorporates two sets of bleed ports for 15th-stage air for airframe requirements. The forward set takes air from the outside case via an integral manifold and the rear set bleeds air from the inner diameter via four of the ten radial struts. The combustor itself is fabricated in nickel alloy and is annular, with the forward end of the liner extended in 20 conical primary zones held in 20 burners fed from external fuel manifolds. In early models (-3A, -7 and -20), the outer casing can be slid forward over the diffuser for access to the HP turbine. Ignition by dual AC 4-joule capacitor system serving two plugs just above chamber centreline on each side.

Fuel System: Pressure type with hydraulic control system operating at up to 76 bars (1,100 lb/sq in). Main components are fuel control, pump, fuel/air heater and fuel/oil heat exchanger. Provision for water injection, as customer option, with regulator, piping and spray nozzles, adds 18·1 kg (40 lb) to engine weight.

Fuel Grade: P&W specification PWA 522.

HP Turbine: Two stages. Both have high-nickel discs splined to HP shaft, secured by lock-nut, carrying high-nickel blades in fir-tree roots; first stage has 116 aircooled blades and second has 138 solid blades. Stators have 66 and 90 high-nickel alloy vanes, both rows aircooled. Turbine inlet temperature (-3A, max T-O), typically 1,243°C (-59A, -70A, 1,350-1,370°C).

LP Turbine: Four stages. Stages have 108, 126, 122 and 116 solid nickel alloy blades held in fir-tree roots in discs of nickel alloy (last disc, iron alloy). Stators have 122, 120, 110 and 102 solid nickel alloy vanes. Exhaust gas temperature after turbine, typically 452°C (-3A) or 482°C (-7, -20).

Jet Pipe: Fixed Inconel assembly, with large central plug cone.

Reverser: Fan duct reverser comprises a translating sleeve (the rearmost portion of fan duct) which moves aft, causing long links to close the blocker doors and simultaneously pulling aft the cascade vanes. Primary (core) reverser, largely of Inconel 625, uses fixed cascades which are uncovered by aft movement of translating sleeves to which are hinged blocker doors pulled by links against the central nozzle plug. No primary reverser is used on -59A, -70A or -7Q.

Accessory Drives: Main accessory gearbox driven by tower bevel shaft from front of HP spool and mounted under central diffuser case (-20, -59A, -70A, under fan discharge case). Main driven accessories include CSD, fuel pump and control, starter, hydraulic pump, alternator and N_2 tachometer; Boeing 747 includes primary reverser motor and the DC-10-40 a second hydraulic pump and a fuel boost pump. The box also includes numerous lubrication system items, and provides for hand-turning the HP spool during borescope inspection.

Lubrication System: Pressure feed through fuel/oil cooler to four main bearings and return through scavenge pumps (-20 also centrifugal scavenge) to 18·8-37·6 litre (5-10 US gal; 4·16-8·32 Imp gal) tank.

Oil Grade: PWA 521 (blend of synthetic and/or mineral oils).

Mounting: From above, in two planes. Front mount (-3A, -7) is double flange at top of fan discharge case, absorbing vertical and side loads. On -20, -59A, -70A the mount is rectangular block above intermediate case, taking vertical and side loads, and thrust brackets at 40° each side of vertical on intermediate-case outer flange. Rear mount (-3A, -7) in double flange above casing in plane of turbine LP bearing, to which engine thrust is transmitted via Y-shaped thrust frame from intermediate case in arrangement that prevents thrust loads reaching (and distorting) the turbine exhaust case. On 20, -59A, -70A, the frame is eliminated and rear mount takes only vertical, side and torsional loads.

Starting: Pneumatic, by HamStan PS 700 or AiResearch ATS100-384 (DC-10, PS 700 only). Supplied at 2·76-3·10 bars (40-45 lb/sq in) from APU, ground cart or cross-bleed.

Dimensions:

JT9D-3A, -7, -7A, -7F, -7J, -7R, -20:	
Diameter	2,428 mm (95·6 in)
Length (flange to flange)	3,256 mm (128·2 in)
JT9D-59A, -70A, -7Q, -7Q1:	
Diameter	2,466 mm (97·7 in)
Length	3,358 mm (132·2 in)

Weight, Dry:

Guaranteed, including standard equipment:	
JT9D-3A	3,905 kg (8,608 lb)
JT9D-7, -7A	3,982 kg (8,780 lb)
JT9D-7F, -7J	4,014 kg (8,850 lb)
JT9D-7R	3,853 kg (8,495 lb)
JT9D-20	3,833 kg (8,450 lb)
JT9D-59A	4,146 kg (9,140 lb)
JT9D-70A	4,153 kg (9,155 lb)
JT9D-7Q, -7Q1	4,262 kg (9,395 lb)

Performance Ratings:*

T-O, dry:	
JT9D-3A	196·9 kN (44,250 lb) to 26·7°C
JT9D-7	206 kN (46,300 lb) to 26·7°C
JT9D-7A	208·29 kN (46,950 lb) to 26·7°C
JT9D-7F	213·5 kN (48,000 lb) to 26·7°C
JT9D-7J	222·5 kN (50,000 lb st) to 30°C
JT9D-7R	197·1 kN (44,300 lb st) to 30°C
JT9D-20	206 kN (46,300 lb) to 28·9°C
JT9D-59A, -70A, -7Q	236 kN (53,000 lb) to 30°C
JT9D-7Q1	242 kN (54,500 lb st) to 30°C
T-O, wet:	
JT9D-3A	203·8 kN (45,800 lb) to 26·7°C
JT9D-7	213·1 kN (47,900 lb) to 30°C
JT9D-7A	215·8 kN (48,500 lb) to 30°C
JT9D-7F*	222·5 kN (50,000 lb) to 30°C
JT9D-20*	220 kN (49,400 lb) to 30°C
Max cruise performance, 10,665 m (35,000 ft) at Mach 0·85:	
JT9D-3A, -7	45·4 kN (10,200 lb)
JT9D-7A	47·5 kN (10,680 lb)
JT9D-7F, -7J	49·2 kN (11,050 lb)
JT9D-7R	47·9 kN (10,760 lb)
JT9D-20	47·5 kN (10,680 lb)
JT9D-59A*, -70A*, -7Q*	53·2 kN (11,950 lb)
JT9D-7Q1	54·3 kN (12,200 lb)

Specific Fuel Consumption:

At dry T-O rating, S/L static, ISA:	
JT9D-3A	9·80 mg/Ns (0·346 lb/h/lb st)
JT9D-7	10·08 mg/Ns (0·356 lb/h/lb st)
JT9D-7A	10·11 mg/Ns (0·357 lb/h/lb st)
JT9D-7F*	10·34 mg/Ns (0·365 lb/h/lb st)
JT9D-20*	9·89 mg/Ns (0·349 lb/h/lb st)
JT9D-59A, -70A*	10·57 mg/Ns (0·373 lb/h/lb st)
JT9D-7Q*	10·66 mg/Ns (0·376 lb/h/lb st)
Cruise, Mach 0·85, 10,665 m (35,000 ft):	
JT9D-3A	17·84 mg/Ns (0·630 lb/h/lb st)
JT9D-7	18·01 mg/Ns (0·636 lb/h/lb st)
JT9D-7A	18·16 mg/Ns (0·641 lb/h/lb st)
JT9D-7F*	18·55 mg/Ns (0·655 lb/h/lb st)
JT9D-20*	17·67 mg/Ns (0·624 lb/h/lb st)
JT9D-59A*, -70A*	17·67 mg/Ns (0·624 lb/h/lb st)
JT9D-7Q*	18·66 mg/Ns (0·659 lb/h/lb st)

Ideal nozzles

PRATT & WHITNEY JT10D

Pratt & Whitney Aircraft is continuing to study the design and marketing of a second-generation turbofan for future commercial transports. Work on the JT10D began in 1972 and the first JT10D flight-weight demonstrator engine ran on 9 August 1974. On 19 August, it achieved a thrust of 102·3 kN (23,000 lb).

P&WA has been working with airframe manufacturers and airlines to develop an engine configuration that will result in minimum trip fuel consumption with low emission levels, and will reduce the man-hours required for engine installation and flight-line maintenance. The JT10D uses the JT9D modular maintenance concept, but with fewer parts per module. It consists of seven modules, each individually replaceable. In addition, the individual parts in the modules are designed to be readily accessible, and easily removed and replaced. The engine incorporates low-noise features of the JT9D, including the use of a high by-pass ratio, a single-stage fan without inlet guide vanes, wide axial separation between the blade and vane rows, and a moderate fan tip speed. The engine is designed to be compatible with acoustically treated nacelles to achieve aircraft noise levels below FAR.36 requirements.

By February 1975 design work had been initiated on a derivative of the demonstrator, designated JT10D-2. This engine, with a take-off thrust of 109 kN (24,500 lb), was designed to meet requirements for various commercial and military applications.

In response to a call for increased thrust requirements from commercial operators, P&WA began studies in July 1976 for an alternative engine, designated JT10D-4. This had a take-off thrust rating of 129 kN (29,000 lb st).

Participating with P&WA in the development of the

Pratt & Whitney JT10D demonstrator, run at 102·3 kN (23,000 lb st)

JT10D are Motoren- und Turbinen-Union GmbH (MTU) of Federal Germany and Fiat SpA of Italy. P&WA is expected to bear 83·2 per cent of the programme; MTU 12·8 per cent and Fiat 4 per cent. A collaboration agreement between these companies was signed in July 1977.

In the fourth quarter of 1977 P&WA, recognising the need for a wide range of thrusts for the various new aircraft requirements which were emerging, redirected the JT10D programme to the development of a family of engines which would use common HP compressor, burner, HP turbine and bearings and shafts, and which, with various fans, LP compressors and LP turbines, would cover the thrust range from 111·2 to 155·7 kN (25,000 to 35,000 lb st). Concurrently it was decided to incorporate the latest technology into the engine, so that it would not only have the advantage of all the first-generation high-bypass engines' service experience but would be better able to take advantage of future improvements in technology as they occur. At the end of 1978 further changes were still being considered. The company announced that the JT10D had been "resized to 36 000 lb st" for certification in March 1982, without an LP compressor; with the latter added the engine would be more powerful still—almost twice the power originally considered, indicative of substantial changes.

TYPE: Two-shaft turbofan of high by-pass ratio.

AIR INTAKE: Direct front entry. No inlet guide vanes or anti-icing.

FAN: Single stage. Titanium forged hub with 40 inserted titanium alloy blades with part-span shrouds. Downstream are single row of exit guide vanes and radial struts supporting fan case. Rotating fan spinner. Bypass ratio 5 : 1 to 7 : 1.

LP COMPRESSOR: Zero, one or two stages.

HP COMPRESSOR: Twelve stages. Overall engine pressure ratio 27 : 1 to 35 : 1.

COMBUSTION CHAMBER: Annular, with flame tube fabricated in nickel alloy.

HP TURBINE: Two-stage axial with aircooled blades.

LP TURBINE: Four- or five-stage axial.

WEIGHT, DRY: 2,359-3,583 kg (5,200-7,900 lb)

PERFORMANCE RATING (T-O, S/L, static): See text.

PRATT & WHITNEY JTF10A

US military designation: TF30

Development of this high-compression two-spool turbofan was begun in 1958 as a private venture, and resulted in testing of the first turbofan with afterburning. It was chosen subsequently as the power plant for the General Dynamics F-111.

The version used initially in the F-111 was designated TF30-P-1 (JTF10A-20) which provides 82·3 kN (18,500 lb st) with afterburning. It was superseded in the F-111A by the TF30-P-3 (JTF10A-21) which provides the same thrust with reduced sea level supersonic specific fuel consumption. The F-111D is powered by the TF30-P-9 (JTF10A-36) engine with afterburning, rated at 92·7 kN (20,840 lb st). The FB-111 bomber is equipped with the TF30-P-7 (JTF10A-27D) engine, which is in the 89 kN (20,000 lb) thrust class with afterburning. The F-111F is equipped with the TF30-P-100 (JTF10A-32C) engine, an advanced version with higher thrust. The Vought A-7A and A-7B Corsair II tactical attack aircraft are powered by the TF30-P-6 (JTF10A-8) and TF30-P-408 (JTF10A-16A), these being simplified versions without afterburning and rated at 50·5 kN (11,350 lb) and 59·6 kN (13,400 lb st) respectively.

Most recent application of the TF30 is the US Navy's Grumman F-14A Tomcat fighter, powered by the **TF30-P-412A,** a modified TF30-P-12, with a revised form of afterburning nozzle. The P-412A has an afterburning rating of 93 kN (20,900 lb st). In 1977 the P-412A was modified to **TF30-P-414** standard with new first-stage compressor rotor blades and strengthened fan case to ensure containment. The US Navy is converting F-14A engines to P-414 standard.

The most advanced TF30 production version was the

Pratt & Whitney TF30-P-412A afterburning turbofan, rated at 93 kN (20,900 lb st)

USAF **TF30-P-100,** qualified in January 1971, in which weight is held below 1,815 kg (4,000 lb) while increasing thrust to the 111 kN (25,000 lb) class, with reduced fuel consumption.

Time between overhauls of the various TF30 models varies from 850 h (P-100) to 1,500 h.

TYPE: Two-shaft axial-flow turbofan.

INTAKE: Direct pitot annular type with 23 fixed inlet guide vanes (19 on P-8 and P-408). Hollow vanes pass anti-icing air.

FAN: Three stages (two on P-8 and P-408). Rotor and stator and casings all of titanium, except for steel containment case on P-412A. Three rotor stages have 28 (with part-span shrouds), 36 and 36 blades, all dovetailed; stator stages have 44, 44 and 48 vanes, all rivet-retained. Pressure ratio 2·14 to 2·4. Mass flow typically 112 kg (247 lb)/s (P-100 118 kg; 260 lb/s).

LP COMPRESSOR: Six stages (seven on P-8 and P-408), constructed integrally with fan to form nine-stage spool. Wholly of titanium construction, except stator blades of steel.

HP COMPRESSOR: Seven stages, constructed mainly of nickel-based alloy.

COMBUSTION CHAMBER: Can-annular, with steel casing and eight Hastelloy X flame cans each held at the front by four dual-orifice burners. Spark igniters in chambers 4 and 5.

FUEL SYSTEM: HP system (above 69 bars; 1,000 lb/sq in), with conventional hydromechanical control. Main elements comprise fuel pump, filter, fuel control, P & D valve and nozzles. Separate afterburner system for A/B engines. No water injection.

FUEL GRADE: JP-4, JP-5.

HP TURBINE: Single stage, with aircooled nozzle guide vanes (stators) of cobalt alloy and aircooled rotor blades of nickel-based alloy (P-100 vanes and blades of directionally solidified alloy). Max gas temperature, early models 1,137°C, P-100 1,240°C.

LP TURBINE: Three stages of nickel-based alloys. Rotor stages have 94, 96 and 80 (P-100, 72) fir-tree root blades. Gas temperature after turbine, typically 587°C.

JET PIPE (non-A/B engine): Simple steel pipe where fan airflow and core gas mix before passing through fixed nozzle.

AFTERBURNER: Diffuser leads to combustion section comprising double-wall outer duct and inner liner carrying five-zone combustion system. Ignition by auxiliary squirt in A/B diffuser, coupled with main squirt in No. 4 burner can which produces hot-streak of fuel through the turbine (P-100 engine, fully modulated light-up by 4-joule electrical ignition system). Max gas temperature 1,677°C.

NOZZLE (A/B engines): Primary nozzle has variable area, with six hinged segments actuated by engine-fuel rams (P-100, 18 iris segments translated along curved profile by six long-stroke rams). Ejector nozzle has six blow-in doors with free tail-feathers.

ACCESSORY DRIVES: Main gearbox under compressor, driven by bevel shaft from HP spool. Contains major elements of lubrication and breather systems. Drive pads at front and rear for main and A/B fuel pumps, main oil pump, N_2 tachometer, starter, fluid power pumps and power take-off.

LUBRICATION SYSTEM: Self-contained dry-sump hot-tank system. Accessory gearbox housing forms 15 litre (4 US gal; 3·3 Imp gal) tank. Oil circulated at 3·10 bars (45 lb/sq in) through pump, filter, coolers (air/oil on airframe, fuel/oil on engine and A/B fuel/oil cooler) and three main bearing components; returned by scavenge pumps and deaerator.

OIL GRADE: MIL-L-7808.

MOUNTING: Two-planar. Front peripheral pair of flanges absorb vertical, side and thrust loads; rear pair of peripheral flanges (in line with No. 6 bearing behind LP turbine) absorb vertical and side loads.

STARTING: Air-turbine starter on left forward drive pad of accessory gearbox.

DIMENSIONS:

Max diameter:	
TF30-P-414	1,293 mm (50·9 in)
TF30-P-100	1,242 mm (48·88 in)
Length overall:	
TF30-P-414	5,987 mm (235·7 in)
TF30-P-100	6,139 mm (241·7 in)

WEIGHT, DRY:

TF30-P-414	1,860 kg (4,100 lb)
TF30-P-100	1,807 kg (3,985 lb)

PERFORMANCE RATINGS (T-O, S/L):

TF30-P-414	93 kN (20,900 lb st)
TF30-P-100	111·7 kN (25,100 lb st)

SPECIFIC FUEL CONSUMPTION (T-O):

TF30-P-414	78·75 mg/Ns (2·78 lb/h/lb st)
TF30-P-100	69·40 mg/Ns (2·450 lb/h/lb st)

PRATT & WHITNEY JTF22

US military designations: F100 and F401

Stemming partly from the JTF16 demonstrator engine designed in 1965-66, the JTF22 is an advanced-technology military turbofan with afterburner for supersonic applications. Basic development was funded as a demonstrator programme for the US Air Force. In February 1970 the decision was taken to use the JTF22 core engine as the basis of two highly refined power units: the **F100-PW-100** (JTF22A-25A) for the twin-engined McDonnell Douglas F-15 Eagle fighter for the US Air Force, and the **F401-PW-400** (JTF22A-24A) for the twin-engined Grumman F-14B Tomcat fighter prototype for the US Navy. Subsequently, the F100 was adopted for the single-engined General Dynamics F-16, production versions of which are powered by a slightly modified engine designated **F100-PW-200.**

Some 3,000 hours of development testing were accomplished between 1968 and the 60 hr PFRT (preliminary flight rating test) in February 1972. The 150 hr QT (qualification test) was completed in October 1973. In

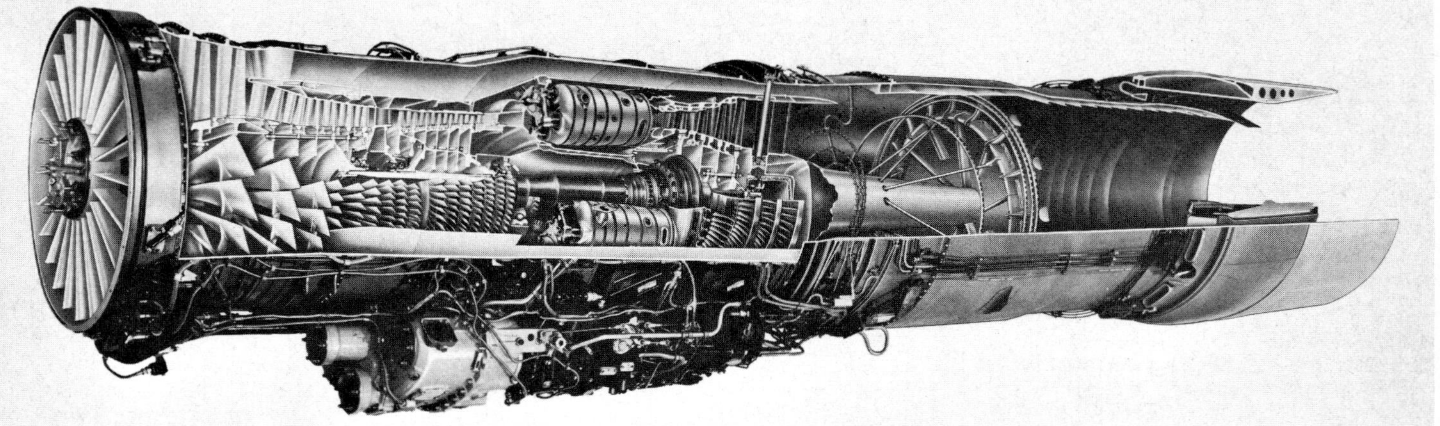

Cutaway drawing of Pratt & Whitney TF30-P-100 afterburning turbofan, rated at 111·7 kN (25,100 lb st)

Pratt & Whitney F100-PW-100 augmented turbofan rated at 106·2 kN (23,810 lb st) with full afterburning and shown also below in longitudinal cross-section

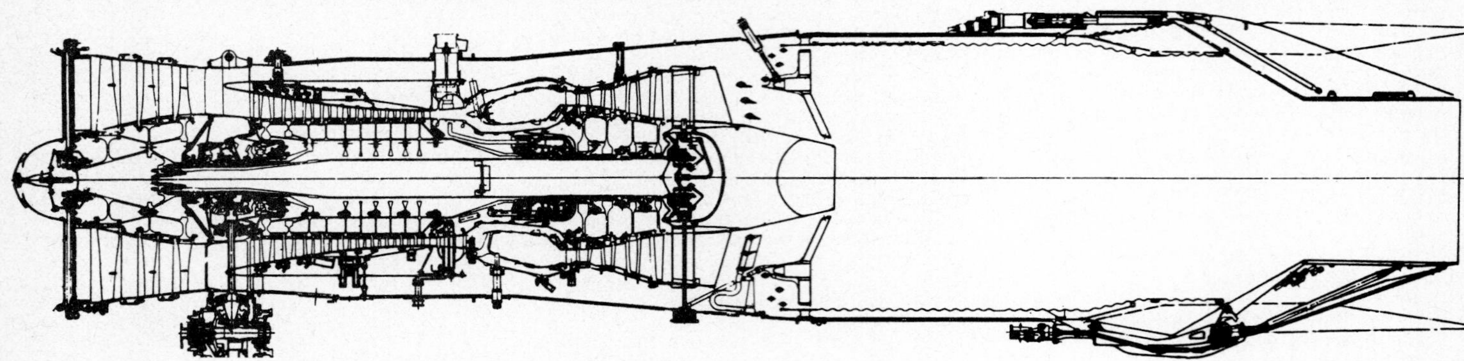

October 1978 running time exceeded 455,000 h, of which more than 236,000 h had been in the F-15 and 3,200 in the F-16. More than 1,000 engines had been delivered, and shipments were at the rate of 20 per month. The F100 has a current maximum operating time interval of 1,250 h.

The prototype F401 ran in September 1972 and two flight-cleared engines flew in an F-14B development aircraft in June 1973. The US Navy-funded F401 has the same core as the F100 but a larger fan and afterburner. It powers the Rockwell XFV-12A V/STOL prototype, in which the entire engine efflux can be diverted to ducts along the wing and canard foreplane.

Type: Two-shaft turbofan with high-augmentation afterburner.

Intake: Direct pitot type. Fabricated titanium, with fixed nose bullet. Single row of 21 inlet guide vanes, with hot-air anti-iced leading-edges and variable-camber trailing-edge flaps.

Fan: Three stages (3½ in F401 which has added single-stage LP compressor downstream of fan to supercharge core). Fan blades have part-span shrouds. Discs of titanium 6-2-4-6, blades titanium 8-1-1. Entry diameter 928 mm (36·5 in) (F401 960 mm; 37·8 in). By-pass ratio 0·7 (F401 0·65).

Compressor: Ten-stage axial, on HP shaft. First three stages have variable stators. Discs 1-2, forged Ti 6-2-4-6; 3, forged Ti 8-1-1; 4, forged PWA 1016; 5, 7 and 9, PWA 1027; 6, 8 and 10, Gatorized (isothermal squeeze forging) IN-100. Blades 1-3, Ti 8-1-1; 4, Ti 6-2-4-6; 5-9 Incoloy 901; 10, PWA 1005. Pressure ratio 8 : 1. Overall engine pressure ratio 25 : 1 (F401 26·9 : 1).

Combustion Chamber: Annular. Fabricated in nickel alloy with film cooling throughout. Large-diameter duplex fuel nozzles. Primary atomising stage used at all times, with secondary air-blast stage operative at high fuel flow rates. Capacitor-discharge ignition.

HP Turbine: Two stages. Discs forged IN-100. Blades PWA 1422 directionally solidified alloy with PWA 73 coating; first rotor impingement cooled, second with convective (HP bleed air) only. Maximum gas temperature 1,399°C (both engines). Maximum speed 13,450 rpm (both engines).

LP Turbine: Two stages. Discs forged IN-100. Blades, uncooled, cast in IN-100 with PWA 73 coating. Modified LP turbine in F401. Maximum speed 10,400 rpm (F401, 9,400 rpm).

Afterburner: Five concentric spray rings in flow from core engine; two slightly farther downstream in by-pass airflow. Flameholder assembly downstream of spray nozzles, with high-energy electrical ignition to give modulated light-up. Outer by-pass duct and other major portions, fabricated in sheet and stringer titanium. Interior liner of coated refractory material.

Nozzle: Multi-flap balanced-beam articulated nozzle giving very wide range in area and profile.

Control System: Unified hydromechanical fuel and nozzle-area control, with electronic engine control.

Dimensions:

Overall diameter:	
F100	1,180 mm (46·5 in)
F401	1,283 mm (50·5 in)
Length, excl bullet:	
F100	4,851 mm (191·0 in)
F401	5,070 mm (199·6 in)

Weight, Dry:

F100	1,371 kg (3,020 lb)
F401	1,596 kg (3,520 lb)

Performance Ratings (S/L, ISA):

Max T-O, dry:	
F100	66·7 kN (15,000 lb st) class
F401	66·7 kN (15,000 lb st) class
Max T-O, augmented:	
F100	111·2 kN (25,000 lb st) class
F401	133·4 kN (30,000 lb st) class

PRATT & WHITNEY RL10

The RL10 rocket engine, for the propulsion of space vehicle upper stages, is a regeneratively cooled, turbopump-fed engine with a single chamber. The current RL10A-3-3 production version is rated at 66·7 kN (15,000 lb) thrust at an altitude of 61,000 m (200,000 ft), and has a nominal specific impulse of 444 s. Propellants are liquid oxygen and liquid hydrogen, injected at a nominal oxidizer-to-fuel mixture ratio of 5·0 : 1. Rated engine thrust is achieved at a nominal design chamber pressure of 27·6 bars (400 lb/sq in) absolute, with a nominal nozzle area ratio of 57 : 1. The engine can be used for multi-engine installation on an interchangeable basis and is capable of multiple starts after extended coast periods.

First deliveries were made in August 1960 for use in NASA's Centaur stage of the Atlas-Centaur rocket, which is powered by two RL10 engines. A six-engine cluster of RL10A-3 engines powered the S-IV stage of the Saturn I, achieving a perfect performance record for the entire launch programme. Over 9,500 RL10 firings have been accomplished, and 140 engines have flown on operational Saturn and Centaur vehicles, accomplishing 216 successful in-flight starts. In the Titan-Centaur 5 mission two RL10 engines accomplished a record seven in-flight starts, five of them after spacecraft separation. Between two starts there was a 5·25 h coast at zero-*g*.

Pratt & Whitney RL10A-3-3 rocket engine

Experimental versions of the RL10 have been tested at the Pratt & Whitney Aircraft Group's Government Products Division. These tests include variable-thrust operation, low idle operation, pumped idle operation, operation with a 205 : 1 ratio nozzle extension, operation on fluorine/hydrogen, lox/propane and flox/methane propellants. NASA ordered additional RL10 engines to power Centaur missions during the late 1970s.

ROCKETDYNE

ROCKETDYNE DIVISION OF ROCKWELL INTERNATIONAL

Headquarters: 6633 Canoga Ave, Canoga Park, California 91304

Telephone: (213) 884-4000

Other Facilities: Santa Susana, California

President: N. J. Ryker

Executive Vice-President: N. C. Reuel (Advanced Programmes)

Vice-Presidents:
D. J. Sanchini (SSME Programme Manager)
S. J. Domokos (Laser Programmes)
E. B. Monteath (MX Programme)
M. C. Ek (Engineering and Test)
J. C. McMillen (Finance and Administration)

Rocketdyne is a division of Rockwell International, devoted primarily to the design and manufacture of rocket engines for the US Air Force and Army and the National Aeronautics and Space Administration. It was established as a separate division on 8 November 1955.

Rocketdyne liquid-propellant engines power more than three-quarters of all large US space vehicle stages.

ROCKETDYNE SSME

On 13 July 1971, the Rocketdyne Division of Rockwell International was selected by the US National Aeronautics and Space Administration to design and develop the main engine for the orbiter stage of the US Space Shuttle. Three of these engines provide a total of 6,272 kN (1,410,000 lb) vacuum thrust.

Two large solid-propellant boosters are strapped on the sides of the orbiter's expendable propellant tank which will carry the liquid oxygen and liquid hydrogen for the three main engines in the orbiter. The orbiter rides piggyback on the propellant tank in a parallel configuration. The solid motors and the three Space Shuttle Main Engines (SSME) produce 28,469 kN (6,400,000 lb st) to lift the vehicle from the pad in a conventional vertical flight path. The solid motors will burn out at about 40 km (25 miles) altitude, separate from the orbiter stage, and be lowered by parachutes into the ocean for recovery. The three main engines will continue to power the vehicle to near orbit; the external tank will then separate and be de-orbited and disposed in a safe area of the ocean. After mission completion the orbiter will re-enter the Earth's atmosphere and manoeuvre to a landing site for an unpowered horizontal landing similar to that of a conventional jet aircraft.

In overall configuration, the SSME is slightly smaller in size than the F-1 engine used in the Saturn V vehicle first stage. It burns liquid oxygen and liquid hydrogen propellants and has been designed for high reliability, reusability, multiple re-start capability and low cost. It is capable of 7½ h of burn time, accrued during 55 flights. Modified airline maintenance procedures are used to service the engine between flights without removing it from the vehicle.

The design combines the merits of high-chamber-pressure operation, an optimum-performance contoured bell-shaped nozzle, and a regeneratively-cooled thrust chamber, capable of 11° gimballing, for maximum performance and long life. The chamber wall is cooled so efficiently that it is at 567°C, although the combustion temperature is about 3,300°C. No propellants are wasted in the cooling process. The combustion chamber wall is made of slotted metal, rather than tubes, using Rocketdyne-developed NARloy-Z, a copper alloy that is easily machined, has higher strength than pure copper, and has very high thermal conductivity. Tubes are incorporated in the lower nozzle section.

The SSME is controlled by a unique system incorporating dual-redundant digital computers. This system monitors engine parameters such as pressure and temperature and the engine is automatically adjusted to operate at the required thrust and mixture ratio. The system also develops a record of engine operating history for maintenance purposes to improve serviceability and extend total engine life.

In 1978 testing continued at the Santa Susana Field Laboratory and National Space Technology Laboratories. A third single-engine test position has been activated at the Santa Susana site and testing of engine 0201 has been initiated. Engine 0002 was tested on both A-1 and A-2 test stands at NSTL. The engine, which was in test continuously for over two years, accumulated over 1,200 s in 82 tests. Engine 2002 has accumulated over 4,600 s in 34 tests, both in the three-engine Main Propulsion Test Article cluster and in single-engine testing.

SSME 0005 successfully completed simulation of the Preliminary Flight Certification while accumulating 12,000 s on the A-1 test stand. This consisted of more than 5,000 s of operating time, most of which was at rated power level (RPL); 300 s of this time was at 102 per cent RPL. During this test series, five consecutive tests were conducted for the flight duration of 520 s.

Major SSME programme milestones were reached during the year, demonstrating the increasing maturity of the engine design. More than 34,000 s of engine hot-fire time were accumulated during the development programme in 1978.

COMBUSTION CHAMBER: Channel-wall construction with regenerative cooling by the hydrogen fuel. Concentric-element injector.

TURBOPUMPS: Two low-pressure pumps boost the inlet pressures for two high-pressure pumps. Dual preburners provide turbine-drive gases to power the high-pressure pumps. Hydrogen-pump discharge pressure is 478·3 bars (6,937 lb/sq in) at 37,250 rpm; it develops 56,554 kW (75,840 hp).

CONTROLLER: Honeywell digital computer controller provides closed-loop engine control, in addition to data processing and signal conditioning for control, check-out, monitoring engine status, and maintenance data acquisition.

CONTROLS: A hydraulic-actuation control system is used. The dual-redundant self-monitoring servo-actuators respond to signals from the controller to position the ball valves. A pneumatic system provides backup for the hydraulic system for engine cut-off. Main subcontractors: Honeywell Inc (controller); Hydraulic Research and Manufaturing Co (actuators).

MAINTENANCE: Engine to be maintained using airline-type maintenance procedure for on-the-vehicle servicing. Time between overhauls is 55 flights or 7·5 h of cumulative operation.

DIMENSIONS:

Length	4,242 mm (13 ft 11 in)
Diameter at nozzle exit	2,388 mm (7 ft 10 in)

PERFORMANCE:

S/L thrust (one engine)	1,668 kN (375,000 lb)
Vacuum thrust	2,091 kN (470,000 lb)
Specific impulse	455 s
Chamber pressure	207 bars (3,000 lb/sq in)
Throttling ratio	2 : 1
Expansion ratio:	
Test	35 : 1
Flight	77·5 : 1

Rocketdyne assemblers installing the third SSME on to its handler prior to delivery in December 1977

ROCKETDYNE RS-27

The RS-27 power plant consists of an RS2701A main engine and two LR101-NA-11 vernier engines. The verniers provide vehicle control during flight and vehicle stabilisation prior to stage separation. The RS-27 is used as the booster propulsion system for the Delta launch vehicle, replacing the Rocketdyne MB-3 (USAF designation LR79) propulsion system.

The RS2701A is a single-chamber bipropellant fixed-thrust gimballed engine. It utilises liquid oxygen and RP-1 propellants at a nominal mixture ratio of 2·245 : 1. Its rated thrust is 911·8 kN (205,000 lb) at sea level, with a maximum duration of 242 s. The thrust and mixture ratio are controlled by fixed orifices. The engine is a hybrid design which utilises the turbopump, turbine, gas generator, valves and thrust chamber of the H-1 engine, and the control system, start system and component-packaging arrangement of the MB-3 engine.

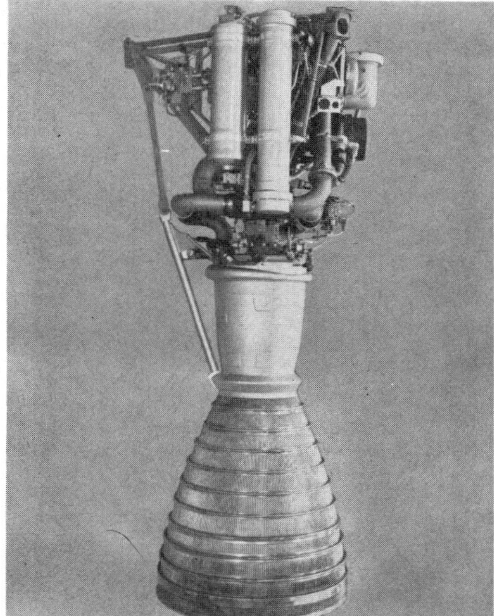

Rated at 911·8 kN (205,000 lb) at sea level, the RS2701A is the main engine of the Rocketdyne RS-27 propulsion system

DIMENSIONS:

Overall length	3,607 mm (11 ft 10 in)
Envelope max diameter	1,900 mm (6 ft 4 in)
WEIGHT, DRY (approx):	1,025 kg (2,261 lb)

The Rocketdyne MA-5 propulsion system comprises a central sustainer and two booster engines, and (not shown) two small vernier engines for fine control of vehicle velocity and trajectory

ROCKETDYNE MA-5

USAF designations: YLR89-NA-7 booster, YLR105-NA-7 sustainer and YLR101-NA-15 vernier

The MA-5 propulsion system consists of a dual-chamber liquid-propellant booster engine, a single-chamber liquid-propellant sustainer engine, and two vernier engines to control vehicle roll and to trim final velocity and directional control after burnout of the sustainer. This propulsion system powers the Atlas-Agena and Atlas-Centaur launch vehicles.

The design consists of two gimballed tubular-wall booster chambers, with twin-turbopump feed for the liquid oxygen and RP-1 propellants, and a single gimballed tubular-wall sustainer chamber, with similar feed. Ignition of both boosters and the sustainer engine takes place shortly before the vehicle is launched. Each YLR89-NA-7 booster is rated at 1,646 kN (370,000 lb) but can be derated to 1,495 kN (336,000 lb). The YLR105-NA-7 is rated at 267 kN (60,000 lb) but can be derated to 254 kN (57,000 lb). The YLR101 verniers are rated at 3 kN (669 lb) each.

Production is continuing, and the MA-5 is being used to boost launches scheduled through 1981.

DIMENSIONS:
- Length: 2,490 mm (98·0 in)
- Diameter, nozzle exit: 1,242 mm (48·88 in)

WEIGHT, DRY:
- Booster: 1,424 kg (3,140 lb)
- Sustainer: 471 kg (1,037 lb)

ROCKETDYNE MA-3

USAF designations: LR89-NA-5 booster, LR105-NA-5 sustainer, and LR101-NA-7 vernier

The MA-3 propulsion system consists of two independent liquid-propellant booster engines, a single-chamber liquid-propellant sustainer engine, and two vernier engines to control vehicle roll and to trim final velocity and directional control after burnout of the sustainer. This propulsion system is used to power Atlas E/F launch vehicles.

The booster and sustainer engines consist of gimballed tubular-wall thrust chambers, and independent bipropellant turbopumps for liquid oxygen and RP-1. The vernier has a gimballed solid-wall regeneratively cooled thrust chamber which receives propellants from the sustainer and propellant tanks after sustainer shutdown. Both the booster engines and sustainer engines are ignited prior to vehicle lift-off, whereas the vernier engines are ignited approximately 3.5 seconds after the sustainer is started. Each LR89-NA-5 booster engine is rated at 734 kN (165,000 lb) and the LR105-NA-5 sustainer is rated at 254 kN (57,000 lb). The LR101-NA-7 vernier engines are rated at 4·45 kN (1,000 lb) each.

Although not currently in production, the MA-3 is being used to boost launch vehicles through 1983.

DIMENSIONS:
- Length: 3,371 mm (132·7 in)
- Diameter, nozzle exit: 1,242 mm (48·88 in)

WEIGHT, DRY:
- Booster (each): 626 kg (1,380 lb)
- Sustainer: 412 kg (909 lb)

ROCKETDYNE P8E-9

Rocketdyne has been under contract to the US Army since August 1971 to deliver production quantities of the P8E-9 rocket engine to power the Lance surface-to-surface missile; previous Lance propulsion had been procured through Vought, the prime contractor. The P8E-9 operates on storable bipropellants (IRFNA, inhibited red fuming nitric acid, and UDMH, unsymmetrical dimethyl hydrazine). The engine uses dual concentric thrust chambers for booster and sustainer operation, with propellants fed from pressurised tanks. Ignition is hypergolic, and chamber and nozzle cooling of both chambers is ablative.

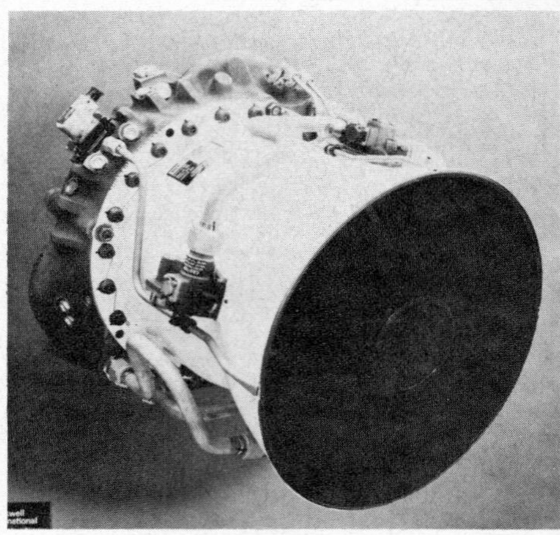

Rocketdyne P8E-9 packaged liquid rocket engine for Lance, rated at 222·4-22·24 kN (50,000/5,000 lb)

Start of the system is initiated by ignition of the solid-propellant gas generator, which pressurises the propellant tanks, provides engine start, and provides a gas flow through side-mounted spin nozzles for missile rotation. Booster duration is 6 s, with both booster and sustainer engines operating; sustainer operation continues for 120 s with variable thrust. Booster thrust is in the 222·4 kN (50,000 lb) class and sustainer thrust range is from 22·24 kN (5,000 lb) to zero. Area ratio values are 5·7 (booster) and 4·0 (sustainer). Mixture ratio is 3·4, chamber pressure is 65·5 bars (950 lb/sq in), and the motor measures 492·8 mm (19·4 in) long by 538·5 mm (21·2 in) diameter.

ROTORWAY

ROTORWAY INC

14805 S. Interstate 10, Tempe, Arizona 85284
Telephone: (602) 963-6652
GENERAL MANAGER: Al Newell

RotorWay Inc is a builder of small helicopters (see entry in Aircraft section). For a considerable period it has been developing its own power plant, for these and for other light aircraft. The following is preliminary information:

ROTORWAY RW-100

This is the fixed-wing version of the RotorWay horizontally opposed four-cylinder engine. Like the growing number of builders or converters of water-cooled general-aviation engines, the company expects the RW-100 to be competitive with established aircooled units. It is demonstrating the ability to cruise at 90-95 per cent of maximum power, and thus offers slightly greater cruise power than larger aircooled engines, for fractionally less installed weight, smaller bulk, similar consumption, but using 92-octane automotive fuel, with extended aircraft range and much-reduced noise. The RW-100 is offered normally aspirated as a tractor or pusher engine.

DIMENSIONS:
- Length, excl exhaust: 610 mm (24·0 in)
- Width overall: 781 mm (30·75 in)
- Height overall: 457 mm (18·0 in)

WEIGHT, DRY: 74·8 kg (165 lb)
PERFORMANCE RATING: 74·6 kW (100 hp) at 3,000 rpm
SPECIFIC FUEL CONSUMPTION: 64·2 μg/J (0·38 lb/h/shp)

ROTORWAY RW-133

This engine was designed to power the Scorpion Too light helicopter, but is expected to find a wide market. It was designed with the following objectives in mind: high power/weight ratio; improved fuel economy; reduced noise and emissions; smooth operation; and long, reliable life. It has been developed with and without turbocharger.

RotorWay RW-100 horizontally-opposed fixed-wing engine (74·6 kW; 100 hp)

RotorWay RW-133 vertical-crankshaft turbocharged helicopter engine (flat-rated at 119·4 kW; 160 hp)

TYPE: Horizontally-opposed, vertical-crankshaft, water-cooled four-stroke piston-engine.

CYLINDERS: Offset left and right for plain connecting rods side-by-side. Swept volume 2·19 litres (133 cu in). Compression ratio 9·6 : 1.

INDUCTION: Through circular air cleaner to single downdraught carburettor with fixed main jet and adjustable idle jet.

IGNITION: Aircraft-type magnetos, dual ignition.

LUBRICATION: Oil temperature 82°-99°C. Oil pressure 2·72-4·1 bars (40-60 lb/sq in).

COOLING: Closed water system, operating temperature 82°C.

WEIGHT, DRY (with starter):
- Without turbocharger: 77·1 kg (170 lb)
- With turbocharger: 83·9 kg (185 lb)

PERFORMANCE:
- Without turbocharger 99·2 kW (133 hp) at 4,500 rpm
- With turbocharger (flat-rated) 119·4 kW (160 hp) at 4,500 rpm

TELEDYNE CAE

TELEDYNE CAE DIVISION OF TELEDYNE INC

HEAD OFFICE: 1330 Laskey Road, Toledo, Ohio 43697
Telephone: (419) 470-3000
PRESIDENT: James L. Murray
EXECUTIVE VICE-PRESIDENT: Raymond Ortiz
VICE-PRESIDENTS:
- Dennis E. Barbeau (Engineering)
- Eugene R. Sullivan (Finance)
- Robert P. Schiller (Marketing, Plans, Contracts)
- Frank X. Marsh (Programmes)

The headquarters for management, marketing, finance, engineering and production is the Toledo, Ohio, facility of over 32,500 m² (350,000 sq ft).

From 1951 until 1960 almost all development was based on Turboméca designs. By far the most important of these was the Marboré, from which stemmed the J69 series of turbojets on which the manufacturing programme has depended. Since 1960 Teledyne CAE has embarked on an in-house development programme on a large scale. To a considerable degree the newer Teledyne CAE engines are aimed at target drones, unmanned reconnaissance aircraft and cruise missiles.

In September 1978 Teledyne CAE was selected by Williams Research as the latter's licensee to be second-source manufacturer of the F107-WR-101 and -400 cruise-missile engines. Full production is planned for early 1980.

TELEDYNE CAE 352 and 356

US military designation: J69

The J69 was originally the Turboméca Marboré, which has been developed to meet American requirements. Four versions are currently available as follows:

J69-T-25 (Teledyne CAE Model 352-5A). Long-life version, which powers the Cessna T-37B trainer and is FAA certificated as the Model CJ69-1025. Its air mass flow is 9 kg (19·8 lb)/s. Operational ceiling is 13,720 m (45,000 ft).

J69-T-29 (Teledyne CAE Model 356-7A). Powers the Teledyne Ryan BQM-34A subsonic target drone. Operational ceiling is 18,300 m (60,000 ft). This is a Marboré II with a single-stage transonic axial compressor supercharging the centrifugal stage.

J69-T-41A (Teledyne CAE Model 356-29A). Transonic axial compressor and revised centrifugal stage handling airflow of 13·5 kg (29·8 lb)/s with pressure ratio of 5·45 : 1. Operational ceiling in excess of 21,030 m (69,000 ft). In production as improved version of J69-T-29 powering special-purpose subsonic RPVs.

YJ69-T-406 (Teledyne CAE Model 356-34A). Produced for the US Navy's BQM-34E and the USAF's BQM-34F supersonic target drones. Initial qualification testing was completed during 1967 and deliveries of production engines began in 1970. The T-406 engine can propel the BQM-34E to Mach 1·5 at 18,300 m (60,000 ft) altitude. Future development of the T-406 engine involves addition of an advanced axial compressor stage and an afterburner for Mach 2·5 drone performance; another project would have an aircooled turbine.

The J69-T-29, YJ69-T-406 and J69-T-41A have a single-stage axial compressor ahead of the standard centrifugal compressor. Combustion system and turbine arrangements are basically the same as on the J69-T-25.

DIMENSIONS (nominal):
- Length overall:
  - J69-T-25: 899 mm (35·39 in)
  - YJ69-T-406, J69-T-41A and J69-T-29: 1,138 mm (44·8 in)
- Width:
  - J69-T-25: 566 mm (22·30 in)
  - J69-T-41A, J69-T-29: 568 mm (22·36 in)
  - YJ69-T-406: 572 mm (22·52 in)

WEIGHT, DRY:
- J69-T-25: 165 kg (364 lb)

J69-T-29	154 kg (341 lb)
J69-T-41A	159 kg (350 lb)
YJ69-T-406	163 kg (360 lb)

Performance Ratings:
Max rating:

J69-T-25	4·56 kN (1,025 lb) at 21,730 rpm
J69-T-29	7·56 kN (1,700 lb) at 22,000 rpm
J69-T-41A	8·54 kN (1,920 lb) at 22,000 rpm
YJ69-T-406	8·54 kN (1,920 lb) at 22,150 rpm

Normal rating:

J69-T-25	3·91 kN (880 lb) at 20,700 rpm
J69-T-29	6·12 kN (1,375 lb) at 20,790 rpm
J69-T-41A	7·34 kN (1,650 lb) at 20,900 rpm
YJ69-T-406	7·65 kN (1,719 lb) at 21,450 rpm

Specific Fuel Consumption:
At max rating:

J69-T-25	32·30 mg/Ns (1·14 lb/h/lb st)
J69-T-41A, J69-T-29	31·16 mg/Ns (1·10 lb/h/lb st)
YJ69-T-406	31·44 mg/Ns (1·11 lb/h/lb st)

TELEDYNE CAE 356-28A

US military designation: J100-CA-100

The Model 356-28A was developed by Teledyne CAE as a power plant for RPVs and other unmanned aircraft. The engine is derived from the J69 family but has no parts in common with the J69 family. It has a two-stage transonic axial compressor ahead of the centrifugal stage, handling a mass flow of 20·4 kg (44·9 lb)/s with a pressure ratio of 6·3 : 1. The combustion chamber is annular with centrifugal fuel injection. The turbine has two axial stages, each fitted with replaceable blades. Fixed geometry is used throughout, although the engine is at present operating at altitudes in excess of 22,860 m (75,000 ft).

The J100-CA-100 completed a 108 h qualification test in June 1969. Applications include the Teledyne Ryan 147TE and 147TF medium-altitude intelligence-collection RPVs.

Dimensions:
Length, intake flange to jet pipe flange 1,225 mm (48·21 in)

Max width	629 mm (24·75 in)
Max height	663 mm (26·10 in)

Weight, Dry: 195 kg (430 lb)

Performance Ratings:

Max	12·01 kN (2,700 lb st) at 20,700 rpm
Normal	10·81 kN (2,430 lb st) at 20,120 rpm

Specific Fuel Consumption:
At max rating 31·16 mg/Ns (1·10 lb/h/lb st)

TELEDYNE CAE 356-28E

Brief details of this high-altitude turbojet were given in the 1978-9 edition.

TELEDYNE CAE 356-28F

US military designation: J100-CA-101

This version of the J100 has been optimised for low-altitude performance with minimal cost. Changes include a slight increase in shaft speed, revised radial-diffuser vane angle and reduced turbine inlet nozzle area. Application has not been disclosed.

Dimensions:

Length overall	1,234 mm (48·6 in)
Max width	627 mm (24·7 in)
Max height	643 mm (25·3 in)

Weight, Dry: 195 kg (430 lb)

Performance Ratings:
Military S/L static 13·6 kN (3,050 lb)

Specific Fuel Consumption:
Military S/L static 31·16 mg/Ns (1·10 lb/h/lb st)

TELEDYNE CAE 365

US military designation: LJ95

This family of engines had its inception in a lift-jet, the Model 365-7, developed for the US Air Force as the XLJ95-T-1. Details remain classified, except that the engine is in the 22·24 kN (5,000 lb st) class, has an above-average turbine gas temperature and offers a ratio of thrust to weight exceeding 20 : 1, yet is intended for propulsion of manned aircraft.

TELEDYNE CAE 370

US military designation: J402-CA-400

This low-cost expendable engine was designed for the propulsion of cruise-type missiles and is in production for the US Navy AGM-84A and RGM-84A Harpoon missiles. The J402 is noteworthy for its compact component and accessory disposition, giving minimum frontal area. Though the entire design minimises production time and cost, high reliability was a prime requirement. Flight limits are 12,200 m (40,000 ft) and Mach 0·9 continuous or Mach 1·1 for limited periods. Engine life is reported unofficially to be 1 h.

In 1974 the J402-CA-400 was selected as cruise power plant for the tactical versions of the US Navy Tomahawk Sea Launched Cruise Missile. In partnership with the competing SLCM contractors, Vought Systems Division and GD Convair, Teledyne CAE supported extensive testing, leading to selection of the GD tactical SLCM in mid-1976. Subsequently there were changes in the Tomahawk programme, and though the J402 has been flown in Tomahawk test flights the missile now has a turbofan engine of different manufacture.

Teledyne CAE J69-T-29 turbojet of 7·56 kN (1,700 lb st)

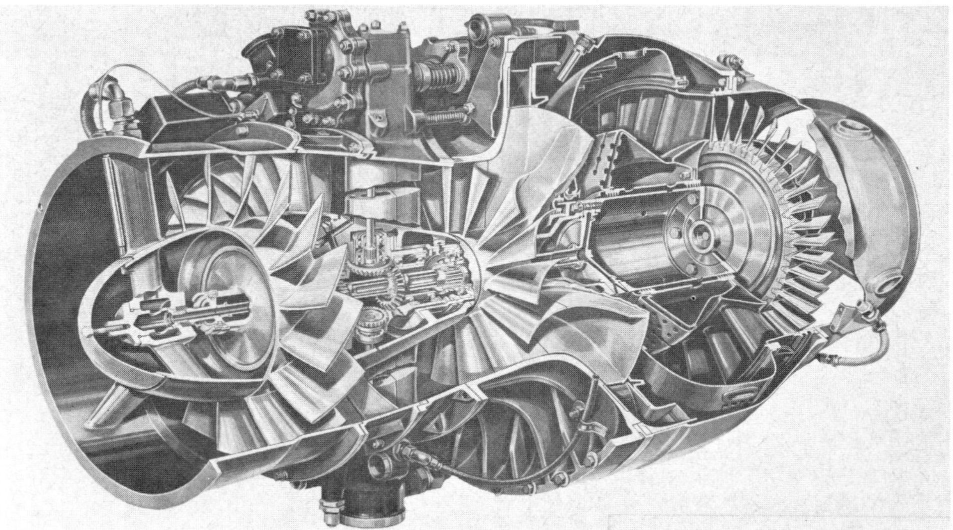

Teledyne CAE YJ69-T-406 turbojet of 8·54 kN (1,920 lb st)

Teledyne CAE J100-CA-100 turbojet of 12·01 kN (2,700 lb st)

Type: Single-shaft turbojet.

Intake: Direct pitot inlet with four struts.

Compressor: Single transonic axial compressor with precision cast construction. Single centrifugal compressor with precision cast construction. Max airflow 4·35 kg (9·6 lb)/s. Pressure ratio 5·8.

Combustion Chamber: Annular type.

Fuel System: Low-pressure supply to centrifugal injection nozzles in compressor shaft. Electronic control system with automatic sequencing and regulation to meet demands of missile flight profile.

Turbine: Single-stage axial.

Jet Pipe: Fixed-area.

Accessories: Pyrotechnic starting and ignition systems. Optional integral alternator and alternator regulator to give 6 kW of DC power.

Mounting: Four main mountings disposed radially around main (compressor diffuser) frame.

Dimensions:

Length (excl bullet)	748 mm (29·44 in)
Overall diameter	318 mm (12·52 in)

Weight, Dry: 45·36 kg (100 lb)

Performance Rating:
Max S/L static 2·94 kN (660 lb) at 41,200 rpm

Specific Fuel Consumption (S/L, static): 34·0 mg/Ns (1·20 lb/h/lb st)

TELEDYNE CAE 372-2

US military designation: J402-CA-700

This turbojet is in production for the Beech MQM-107 variable-speed training target. It is based on the Model 370 (J402) but differs in detail engineering and equipment, reflecting the need for repeated missions of extended duration. The electronic fuel control governs engine operation throughout the starting cycle and over the whole operating range. A shaft-mounted high-speed

Teledyne CAE J402-CA-400 expendable low-cost turbojet of 2·94 kN (660 lb st)

This slightly retouched photograph was in 1979 the only illustration of the Teledyne CAE 455H-2 turbofan demonstrator cleared for publication

alternator provides 1·2 kW of DC power. Engine life is unofficially reported to be 15 h.

DIMENSIONS:
- Length (excl bullet) 753 mm (29·65 in)
- Overall diameter 317 mm (12·50 in)

WEIGHT, DRY: 52 kg (115 lb)

PERFORMANCE RATING:
- Max S/L static 2·85 kN (640 lb) at 40,400 rpm

SPECIFIC FUEL CONSUMPTION (S/L, static): 33·71 mg/Ns (1·19 lb/h/lb st)

TELEDYNE CAE 373

A growth version of the basic J402 described above, the CAE 373 is a new turbojet in the 4·00-4·45 kN (900-1,000 lb st) class. Addition of a second axial compressor stage increases pressure ratio to 8·7 : 1 and airflow to 6·2 kg (13·7) lb/s. The engine retains low-cost features but is designed for both expendable and long-life applications. It will be available with various starting options and either high-speed alternator or a centreline reduction gear and starter/generator. The CAE 373 is a company-funded development, and a demonstrator engine ran in 1976. It is intended for missile and RPV applications.

Teledyne CAE J402-CA-700 turbojet of 2·85 kN (640 lb st) for MQM-107 variable-speed training target

TELEDYNE CAE 440/555

A possible basis for a wide family of advanced small engines for the period after 1975, the 440 and 555 core engines developed as a result of the company's participation in the US Air Force Advanced Turbine Engine Gas Generator programme. Like ATEGG studies by other companies, the Models 440 and 555 have design parameters (pressure ratio, turbine entry temperature and specific fuel consumption) similar to those of the most advanced large engines. Most likely applications of these engine cores would be in turbofans in the 13·3-22·24 kN (3,000-5,000 lb) thrust class for piloted aircraft or high-performance RPVs. A photograph appeared in the 1978-79 *Jane's*.

TELEDYNE CAE 455

In 1979 preliminary details were disclosed of the Model 455H-2, first of the three rival JTDE (Joint Technology Demonstrator Engine) types to complete initial objectives for the US Air Force and Navy APSI (Aircraft Propulsion Subsystem Integration) programme. The 455H-2 uses a USAF-sponsored LP (fan) turbine, Navy-sponsored single-stage fan and HP spool based on the Model 555 described previously. It is intended to lead to a new family of durable, low-cost engines in the 31 kN (7,000 lb st) class for cruise missiles, trainers and liaison aircraft until the end of the century.

TELEDYNE CAE 490

This is the French-designed Turboméca-SNECMA Larzac (see Turboméca-SNECMA GRTS in French section), an 'exclusive agreement' for which was announced by Teledyne CAE in January 1973. The American company will "market, manufacture and service" the European turbofan for the United States and Canada.

The president of Teledyne CAE said that the Larzac, the initial US version of which is designated Model 490-4, "provides a valuable new source of flight-ready jet engines for strike and trainer aircraft, missiles and remotely piloted vehicles". A Model 490-4 demonstrator engine began running at Toledo in March 1973, and it is planned eventually to market a commercial Model 490-6. The CAE 490 is also being evaluated as a candidate engine for a future US Navy and/or US Air Force undergraduate pilot trainer.

TELEDYNE CONTINENTAL
TELEDYNE CONTINENTAL MOTORS
Aircraft Products Division

PO Box 90, Mobile, Alabama 36601
Telephone: (205) 438-3411
PRESIDENT: D. G. Bigler
EXECUTIVE VICE-PRESIDENT: J. H. Engler
VICE-PRESIDENTS:
- S. A. Riggs (Marketing)
- R. Hillard (Operations)
- J. V. Miller (Controller)
- L. Waters (Engineering)
- K. C. Oehler (Personnel and Industrial Relations)

DIRECTOR, OF SERVICE: Larry Anderson
DIRECTOR OF FIELD INVESTIGATION: Robert Moore
MANAGER OF COMMUNICATIONS: Don Fairchilds

In 1927, the former Continental Motors Corporation, one of the largest automobile engine manufacturers in the world, produced its first aero-engine, a sleeve-valve air-cooled radial incorporating the Argyll (Burt-McCollum) patents, which had been purchased by the Corporation from the British Argyll Company in 1925.

In 1931 the 38 hp A40 flat-four was put on the market. This was followed by the A50, A65, A75, A80 and C90 engines.

In October 1960 it was announced that Rolls-Royce Ltd of England had acquired the licence to manufacture and sell certain engines from the complete range of Continental piston engines throughout the world, apart from the Americas and certain countries in the Far East. (See Rolls-Royce Motors Ltd in UK section.)

CONTINENTAL O-200 SERIES

The O-200-A engine is a four-cylinder horizontally-opposed aircooled engine. It is fitted with a single updraught carburettor, dual magnetos and starter and generator.

The O-200-B is similar to the O-200-A, but is designed for pusher installation.

For other details see table.

CONTINENTAL IO-360 SERIES

The IO-360 is a six-cylinder horizontally-opposed air-cooled engine with fuel injection. Design and materials are generally similar to those of IO-346-A (1970-71 *Jane's*), except for number and size of cylinders. Accessories include oil cooler, two magnetos, propeller governor drive, vacuum pump and 24V alternator. The IO-360 has a sandcast crankcase, with the accessory case mounted at the rear. The cylinders are shell-moulded.

The IO-360-C has dual accessory drive. The TSIO-360-A, B and C have a turbocharger pressurised induction system, revised fuel system, starter and accessory drive, scavenge pump and full-flow oil cooler. These engines power the Cessna T337 Skymaster. The TSIO-360-E, F and G are equipped with a complete exhaust system, and the turbocharger is engine mounted. The LTSIO-360-E is identical except that the crankshaft rotates in the opposite direction; they power the Piper Seneca II, Arrow III and Mooney 231.

For further details see table.

CONTINENTAL O-470 SERIES

Engines in the O-470 series (including the E-185 and E-225) are all basically similar. Engines prefixed 'IO' have direct fuel-injection.

The 168 kW and 172 kW (225 hp and 230 hp) models have a compression ratio of 7 : 1, the 186 kW (250 hp) models a ratio of 8 : 1, and the 194 kW (260 hp) models a ratio of 8·6 : 1. The exception is the O-470-U, which has a ratio of 8·6 : 1 and runs on 100LL grade fuel.

The following description refers specifically to the O-470-R, but is generally applicable to all versions:

TYPE: Six-cylinder horizontally-opposed aircooled.

CYLINDERS: Bore 127 mm (5 in). Stroke 101·6 mm (4 in). Swept volume 7·5 litres (471 cu in). Compression ratio 7 : 1. Forged steel barrels with integral cooling fins. Heat-treated cast aluminium alloy heads screwed and shrunk on to barrels.

PISTONS: Aluminium. Four rings, two compression and one oil control above pin and scraper ring below. Steel gudgeon pins with permanently forged-in aluminium end plugs.

CONNECTING RODS: Forged steel. Trimetal bronze replaceable type big-end bearings, bronze bushing little-ends.

CRANKSHAFT: One-piece six-throw chrome-nickel-molybdenum steel forging. Outer surfaces nitrided. One 5th and one 6th order counterweights attached to shaft. Five bearings of replaceable shell type.

CRANKCASE: Two-piece heat-treated aluminium casting divided at vertical lengthwise plane through crankshaft, with integral cast accessory section. The O-470-S and IO-470-VO have squirt nozzles installed in the crank-case to provide oil cooling to the piston inner dome.

The 149 kW (200 hp) Teledyne Continental TSIO-360-E

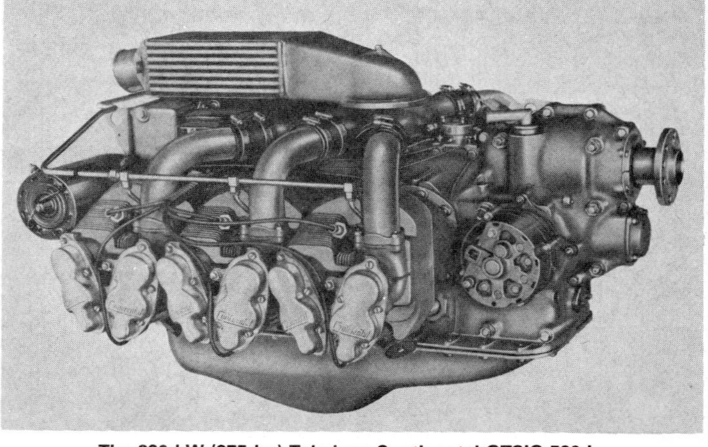

The 280 kW (375 hp) Teledyne Continental GTSIO-520-L

VALVE GEAR: Two poppet-type valves per cylinder: one steel inlet and one steel exhaust with Stellite seat. Camshaft gear-driven from crankshaft in lower part of crankcase.
INDUCTION: Updraught gravity-feed carburettor.
FUEL: 80/87 octane (most models use 100LL/100).
IGNITION: Two magnetos on top of accessory section. Two spark plugs per cylinder. Shielded ignition harness.
LUBRICATION: Pressure type. Oil cooler on front of crankcase. Oil filter in crankcase. One impeller type pump. Oil pressure 2·07-4·14 bars (30-60 lb/sq in).
PROPELLER DRIVE: RH drive. Direct. Flanged propeller shaft. Provision for constant-speed propeller.
ACCESSORIES: Generator on accessory section. Drives for vacuum pump and tachometer.
STARTING: Electric starter.
MOUNTING: Four mounting points, one at each lower corner of crankcase.
DIMENSIONS, WEIGHTS AND PERFORMANCE:
See table.

CONTINENTAL IO-520 SERIES

These engines are basically similar to the IO-470, but with cylinders of larger bore. They are fitted with an alternator driven either by a belt or by a face gear on the crankshaft. All IO-520 series engines are rated at 213 kW (285 hp) except for the IO-520-D, -E and -F which have a take-off rating of 224 kW (300 hp). IO-520 engines power the Beechcraft Baron and Bonanza, Navion and Cessna 210. New in 1970 were the generally similar IO-520-J, -K and -L, also rated at 213 kW (285 hp) (-K and -L are cleared to 224 kW (300 hp) at 2,850 rpm at take-off). The IO-520-M was developed in 1975 for use in the Cessna 310, replacing the IO-470-V.

The TSIO-520 series are turbocharged. Take-off rating is 213 kW (285 hp) except for the -E and -G, rated at 224 kW (300 hp), and the TSIO-520-J rated at 231 kW (310 hp) and equipped with an intercooler and provision for an overboost valve. These engines power the Cessna 414, 320D, T210 and 210F, and turbocharged Bonanza. The TSIO-520-L was developed for use in the Beech Pressurised Baron. It develops 231 kW (310 hp) at 2,700 rpm, has a complete exhaust system and an engine mounted turbocharger. The TSIO-520-N is used in the Cessna 340A and 414.

For other details see table.

CONTINENTAL GTSIO-520

This is similar to the TSIO-520 range but is geared and uprated. The -C model, rated at 254 kW (340 hp) at 3,200 rpm, powers the Cessna 411. The GTSIO-520-D, rated at 280 kW (375 hp) at 3,400 rpm, powers the Cessna 421. The -K has an integral turbocharger and complete exhaust system; the most powerful Continental engine in production, used in the Rockwell Commander 685. The -G is used in a military application, the -H powers the Cessna 421A Golden Eagle. The -L is used in the Cessna 421C and the -M in the Cessna Titan.

REPRESENTATIVE TELEDYNE CONTINENTAL HORIZONTALLY-OPPOSED ENGINES

Engine Model	No. of Cylinders	Bore and Stroke mm (in)	Capacity litres (cu in)	Power Ratings kW (hp) at rpm: Take-off	M.E.T.O.	Comp. Ratio	Dry Weight* kg (lb)	Dimensions: Length mm (in)	Width mm (in)	Height mm (in)	Octane Rating
O-200-A	4	103·2×98·4 (4 1/16×3 7/8)	3·28 (201)	74·5 (100) at 2,750	74·5 (100) at 2,750	7·0	99·8 (220)	725 (28·53)	802 (31·56)	589 (23·18)	80/87
IO-360-D	6	112·5×98·4 (4 7/16×3 7/8)	5·9 (360)	157 (210) at 2,800	157 (210) at 2,800	8·5	148·3 (327)	877 (34·53)	798 (31·40)	618 (24·33)	100/130
TSIO-360-C, D	6	112·5×98·4 (4 7/16×3 7/8)	5·9 (360)	168 (225) at 2,800	168 (225) at 2,800	7·5	136 (300)	910† (35·84)	838 (33·03)	603 (23·75)	100/130
TSIO-360-E, F	6	112·5×98·4 (4 7/16×3 7/8)	5·9 (360)	149 (200) at 2,575	149 (200) at 2,575	7·5	175 (385)	1,437§ (56·58)	795 (31·30)	671 (26·44)	100/130
IO-470-H	6	127×101·6 (5×4)	7·7 (471)	194 (260) at 2,625	194 (260) at 2,625	8·6	202·5 (446·5)	1,100 (43·31)	852 (33·56)	502 (19·75)	100/130
O-470-R, S	6	127×101·6 (5×4)	7·7 (471)	172 (230) at 2,600	172 (230) at 2,600	7·0	193·2 (426)	915 (36·03)	852 (33·56)	723 (28·42)	80/87
TSIO-470-D	6	127×101·6 (5×4)	7·7 (471)	194 (260) at 2,600	194 (260) at 2,600	7·5	231·8 (511)	1,465 (58·07)	852 (33·56)	514 (20·25)	100/130
IO-520-A	6	133×101·6 (5¼×4)	8·5 (520)	213 (285) at 2,700	213 (285) at 2,700	8·5	215·9 (476)	1,053 (41·41)	852 (33·56)	502 (19·75)	100/130
IO-520-BA	6	133×101·6 (5¼×4)	8·5 (520)	213 (285) at 2,700	213 (285) at 2,700	8·5	207·3 (457)	1,009 (39·71)	853 (33·58)	678 (26·71)	100/130
IO-520-D	6	133×101·6 (5¼×4)	8·5 (520)	224 (300) at 2,850	213 (285) at 2,700	8·5	208·2 (459)	949 (37·36)	901 (35·46)	604 (23·79)	100/130
IO-520-M	6	133×101·6 (5¼×4)	8·5 (520)	213 (285) at 2,700	213 (285) at 2,700	8·5	188 (415)	1,189 (46·80)	852 (33·56)	518 (20·41)	100/130
TSIO-520-B	6	133×101·6 (5¼×4)	8·5 (520)	213 (285) at 2,700	213 (285) at 2,700	8·5	219 (483)	1,490 (58·67)	852 (33·56)	516 (20·32)	100/130
TSIO-520-C	6	133×101·6 (5¼×4)	8·5 (520)	213 (285) at 2,700	213 (285) at 2,700	7·5	208 (458)	1,040† (40·91)	852 (33·56)	509 (20·04)	100/130
TSIO-520-E	6	133×101·6 (5¼×4)	8·5 (520)	224 (300) at 2,700	224 (300) at 2,700	7·5	219 (483)	1,010† (39·75)	852 (33·56)	527 (20·74)	100/130
TSIO-520-J, N	6	133×101·6 (5¼×4)	8·5 (520)	231 (310) at 2,700	231 (310) at 2,700	7·5	221·3 (487·8)	997 (39·25)	852 (33·56)	516 (20·32)	100/130
TSIO-520-L	6	133×101·6 (5¼×4)	8·5 (520)	231 (310) at 2,700	231 (310) at 2,700	7·5	244·5 (539)	1,286 (50·62)	852 (33·56)	508 (20·02)	100/130
TSIO-520-M, R	6	133×101·6 (5¼×4)	8·25 (520)	231 (310) at 2,700	213 (285) at 2,600	7·5	198 (436)	1,040† (40·91)	852 (33·56)	598 (23·54)	100/130
GTSIO-520-C	6	133×101·6 (5¼×4)	8·5 (520)	254 (340) at 3,200	254 (340) at 3,200	7·5	252·7 (557)	1,081 (42·56)	880 (34·04)	587 (23·1)	100/130
GTSIO-520-F, K	6	133×101·6 (5¼×4)	8·5 (520)	324 (435) at 3,400	324 (435) at 3,400	7·5	290·3 (640)	1,426 (56·12)	880 (34·04)	664 (26·15)	100/130
GTSIO-520-H, L‡, M‡	6	133×101·6 (5¼×4)	8·5 (520)	280 (375) at 3,400	280 (375) at 3,400	7·5	250 (550·37)	1,081 (42·56)	880 (34·04)	680 (26·78)	100/130

*With accessories; †Not including turbocharger;
‡Similar to -H except length 1,114 mm (43·87 in) and weight 248 kg (547 lb) (-M, height 662 mm; 26·08 in)

THERMO-JET

THERMO-JET STANDARD INC

PO Box 55976, Houston, Texas 77055
Telephone: (713) 465-5735
MANAGER: John A. Melenric

This company specialises in the design and manufacture of valveless pulse-jet units for remotely piloted vehicles and the homebuilt aircraft markets. These engines are devoid of moving parts and are characterised by multiple reverse-flow air inlets to a combustion chamber in which is burned propane, butane or compressed natural gas, obviating the need for a fuel pump. Intermittent combustion and expulsion takes place at a cycle frequency determined by the chamber size and geometry and combustion pressure.

At present Thermo-Jet is offering four sizes of unit, described separately below. Each has a structure fabricated in Type 321 stainless steel, with Type 304 stainless fuel piping and 2024 T4 aluminium fuel nozzles. The throttle regulates fuel flow only. To start, ignition is provided by a hand-cranked magneto connected through a plug and socket to a Champion CJ-6 sparking plug. The throttle is then advanced to the vapour mode and the engine lights up. Once running, the throttle is switched to the liquid mode for normal operation. Combustion chamber mean temperature is 1,150°C in each unit.

THERMO-JET J7-300

Smallest of the company's units, this has three air inlets to a duct terminating in a straight-pipe exhaust tube.

DIMENSIONS:
- Diameter: 178 mm (7 in)
- Length: 1,245 mm (49·0 in)

WEIGHT, DRY: 3·63 kg (8·0 lb)

PERFORMANCE:
- (for max power):
  - Thrust at S/L: 0·09 kN (21 lb)
  - Specific impulse: 735 s
  - Mean effective pressure: 0·21 bars (3 lb/sq in)
  - Cycle frequency: 119 cps
- (for max endurance):
  - Thrust at S/L: 0·031 kN (7 lb)
  - Specific impulse: 950 s
  - Mean effective pressure: 0·07 bars (1 lb/sq in)
  - Cycle frequency: 119 cps

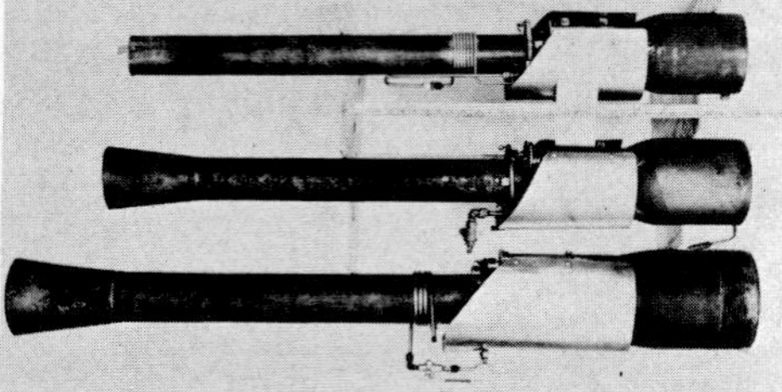
From the top: Thermo-Jet J7-300, J8-200 and J10-200

SPECIFIC FUEL CONSUMPTION:
- Max power: 139 mg/Ns (4·9 lb/h/lb st)
- Max endurance: 108 mg/Ns (3·8 lb/h/lb st)

THERMO-JET J8-200

This larger unit has two air intakes and an exhaust tube with flared end.

DIMENSIONS:
- Diameter: 203 mm (8 in)
- Length: 1,422 mm (56 in)

WEIGHT, DRY: 4·99 kg (11·0 lb)

PERFORMANCE:
- (for max power):
  - Thrust at S/L: 0·133 kN (30 lb)
  - Specific impulse: 720 s
  - Mean effective pressure: 0·19 bars (2·8 lb/sq in)
  - Cycle frequency: 98 cps
- (for max endurance):
  - Thrust at S/L: 0·044 kN (10 lb)
  - Specific impulse: 1,000 s
  - Mean effective pressure: 0·07 bars (1 lb/sq in)
  - Cycle frequency: 91 cps

SPECIFIC FUEL CONSUMPTION:
- Max power: 141·8 mg/Ns (5·0 lb/h/lb st)
- Max endurance: 102 mg/Ns (3·6 lb/h/lb st)

THERMO-JET J10-200

This further enlarged unit has two air inlets to a duct having a flared exhaust tube nozzle.

DIMENSIONS:
- Diameter: 254 mm (10 in)
- Length: 1,778 mm (70 in)

Thermo-Jet J13-202 valveless pulse-jet (0·40 kN; 90 lb st)

WEIGHT, DRY: 8·8 kg (19·5 lb)

PERFORMANCE:
- (for max power):
  - Thrust at S/L: 0·244 kN (55 lb)
  - Specific impulse: 692 s
  - Mean effective pressure: 0·186 bars (2·7 lb/sq in)
  - Cycle frequency: 69 cps
- (for max endurance):
  - Thrust at S/L: 0·08 kN (18 lb)
  - Specific impulse: 945 s
  - Mean effective pressure: 0·07 bars (1 lb/sq in)
  - Cycle frequency: 65 cps

SPECIFIC FUEL CONSUMPTION:
- Max power: 147 mg/Ns (5·2 lb/h/lb st)
- Max endurance: 108 mg/Ns (3·8 lb/h/lb st)

THERMO-JET J13-202

Largest and newest of the present range, this unit has two air inlets to a duct having a flared exhaust tube nozzle.

DIMENSIONS:
- Diameter: 330 mm (13 in)
- Length: 2,311 mm (91 in)

WEIGHT, DRY: 15 kg (33 lb)

PERFORMANCE:
- (for max power):
  - Thrust at S/L: 0·40 kN (90 lb)
  - Specific impulse: 655 s
  - Mean effective pressure: 0·19 bars (2·8 lb/sq in)
  - Cycle frequency: 58 cps
- (for max endurance):
  - Thrust at S/L: 0·142 kN (32 lb)
  - Specific impulse: 900 s
  - Mean effective pressure: 0·07 bars (1 lb/sq in)
  - Cycle frequency: 56 cps

SPECIFIC FUEL CONSUMPTION:
- Max power: 156 mg/Ns (5·5 lb/h/lb st)
- Max endurance: 113 mg/Ns (4·0 lb/h/lb st)

THIOKOL

THIOKOL CORPORATION

CORPORATE OFFICE: PO Box 1000 Newtown, Pennsylvania 18940
Telephone: (215) 968-5911
GOVERNMENT SYSTEMS GROUP: PO Box 9258 Ogden, Utah 84409
Telephone: (801) 399-1191
SOLID PROPELLANT ROCKET MOTOR PLANTS: Elkton, Maryland; Huntsville, Alabama; Marshall, Texas; Brigham City, Utah
PYROTECHNIC AND ORDNANCE PLANTS: Shreveport, Louisiana; Marshall, Texas
CHAIRMAN OF THE BOARD, PRESIDENT AND CHIEF EXECUTIVE: R. E. Davis
VICE-PRESIDENT AND TREASURER: A. P. Roeper
GROUP VICE-PRESIDENTS:
R. N. Thompson (Chemical)
James M. Stone (Government Systems)
E. R. Kearney (General Products)

Organized in 1929, Thiokol Chemical Corporation produced and marketed the first synthetic rubber manufactured in the United States. In 1943, the discovery by Thiokol of liquid polymer, a new type of synthetic rubber, paved the way for the practical development of the 'case-bonded' principle of rocket power plant design. The company's polysulphide liquid polymer proved to be the catalyst for the first mass production of efficient solid-propellant rocket motors, as well as for the development of large solid-propellant motors. The firm's operations have now been organised into separate groups to serve widening areas of related products. Reflecting this diversity, the name has been changed to Thiokol Corporation.

Details of some of the more important solid-propellant rocket motors used in missiles, sounding rockets, spacecraft and space launch vehicles are given below. Important current rocket motor activity, of which details cannot be reported, includes: production of gas generators for the Poseidon missile; recent completion of production of the TX-481 Maverick motor, and engineering development of the TX-486 motor for the Patriot air-defence missile.

In 1974 Thiokol Corporation was awarded a contract to develop the solid rocket motors for the NASA Space Shuttle.

THIOKOL SPACE SHUTTLE SRM

The Space Shuttle Solid Rocket Motor is a segmented design which is 3·708 m (146 in) in diameter, 38·1 m (125 ft) long, weighs 569,268 kg (1,255,000 lb), and contains 503,000 kg (1,109,000 lb) of propellant. The SRM is cast in four segments, which are rail-shipped to launch sites at Kennedy Space Center and Vandenberg Air Force Base. At the sites the motors are stacked vertically in pairs as part of the Solid Rocket Booster for the Space Shuttle.

At lift-off, the SRMs are burning in parallel with the three Space Shuttle liquid main engines mounted in the orbiter. The two SRMs develop 10,533,000 kN (1,368,000 lb) average thrust each (vacuum conditions) and burn for about two minutes. Thrust-vector control for each SRM is provided by a flexible-bearing movable nozzle, driven by two hydraulic actuators.

After burnout, the two boosters are separated from the vehicle, which continues under the power of the three main engines. The boosters fall into the Earth's atmosphere, where parachutes are deployed to control impact velocity into the ocean. The boosters are then towed back to the launch site, disassembled, preserved, and returned to the factory for propellant reloading (see under CSD in this section).

The motor case consists of 11 weld-free ring-rolled forgings fabricated from Ladish D6AC steel. The ends of the forged case sections are machined to form tang-and-clevis joints by means of which the sections are assembled into 'casting segments'. Four casting segments (consisting of a forward segment, two centre segments and one aft segment) make up the basic manufacturing and shipping configuration of a single SRM.

The propellant is a PBAN terpolymer composite, bonded to the asbestos-silica filled nitrile-butadiene rubber internal insulation by means of a compatible liner. The propellant grain in the forward end is configured to an 11-point star which transitions into a tapered centre-perforated (CP) cross-section for the centre and aft sections of the motor. The nozzle is a 20·4 per cent submerged, omni-directionally movable, flexible-bearing nozzle with a throat diameter of 1·38 m (54·5 in) and an exit-plane diameter of 3·76 m (148 in). The nozzle consists of insulated aluminium and steel components. The flexible bearing which provides thrust vector control (TVC) consists of a series of 10 semi-spherical steel shims laminated between flexible elastomer pads.

The ignition system is mounted internally at the forward end of the forward segment. The system consists of an electro-mechanical safe/arm device, an initiator which is a small, multi-nozzled rocket motor containing about 0·7 kg (1·5 lb) of fast-burning propellant, and the main igniter which is an insulated steel-case rocket motor containing about 59 kg (130 lb) of fast-burning propellant. A moulded-silica throat insert in the main igniter directs the flame pattern to the SRM's main propellant grain. Ignition time for the SRM is approximately 0·25 s.

THIOKOL SSUS-A MOTOR

The Thiokol TU-844 motor provides propulsion for the McDonnell Douglas Spinning Solid Upper Stage (SSUS-A) which launches Atlas-Centaur-class payloads from the Space Shuttle. The motor is a slightly modified third-stage Minuteman III with TVC and roll-control systems removed. Lengths of the nozzle and case are optimised to minimise Space Shuttle user changes. The motor uses an S-901 glassfibre case and is loaded with CTPB propellant. It is 2·12 m (83·4 in) long and 1·32 m (52 in) in diameter, and weighs 3,662 kg (8,074 lb).

TRIDENT MOTORS

The three propulsion stages for the Trident C-4 fleet ballistic missile are being developed and manufactured

Thiokol Space Shuttle SRM being prepared for static firing

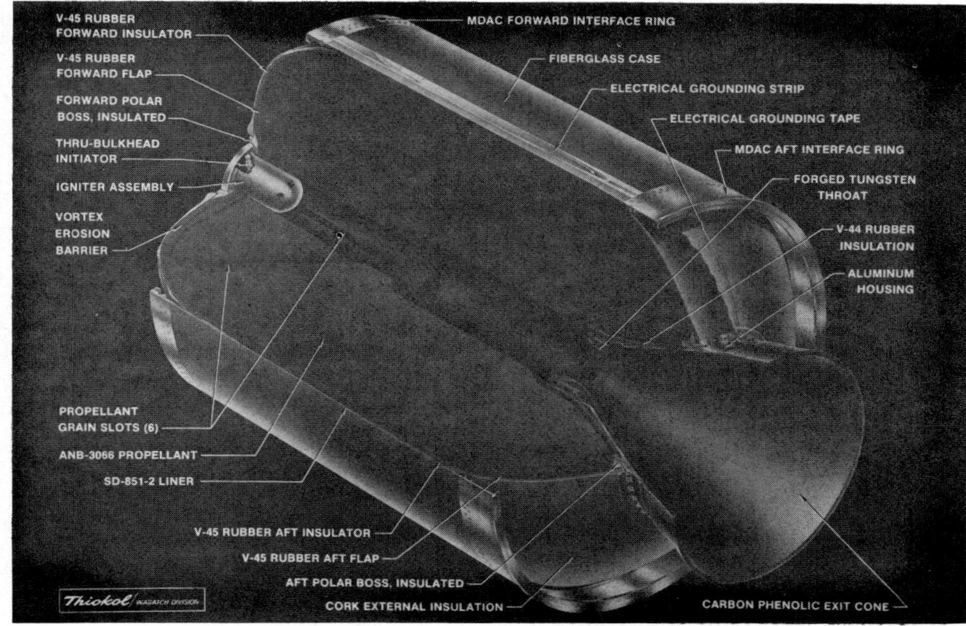

Thiokol SSUS-A motor shown as cutaway drawing

jointly by Thiokol and Hercules Inc. The motors are loaded with high-energy cross-linked double-base propellant. High-performance subsystems, including Kevlar cases, flex-seal TVC and low-erosion nozzles, have been developed and are being manufactured by the joint venture. Technical data are classified.

POSEIDON FIRST-STAGE MOTORS

The motors for the Poseidon C-3 fleet ballistic missile were manufactured jointly by Thiokol and Hercules Inc. Dimensions and performance of the propulsion stages are not available, due to the classified nature of the programme. Production has been completed, and the motors are currently deployed in the Navy's Poseidon fleet ballistic missile.

THIOKOL MINUTEMAN THIRD-STAGE MOTOR

US military designation: SR73-AJ-1

The SR73-AJ-1 is the third-stage rocket motor for the Minuteman III missile. It is 2·36 m (93 in) long, 1·32 m (52 in) in diameter, and weighs 3,649 kg (8,046 lb). The motor supplies 155·1 kN (34,876 lb) of thrust over a 59·6 s burn time. The motor utilises an S-901 glassfibre case loaded with CTPB propellant, a fixed nozzle, LITVIC system and hot-gas roll control system.

THIOKOL MINUTEMAN FIRST-STAGE MOTOR

US military designation: M-55-A1

The TU-122 is the first-stage rocket motor for the Minuteman II and III ICBMs. The motor is approximately 7·62 m (25 ft) in length, 1·68 m (5 ft 6 in) in diameter, and weighs 22,680 kg (50,000 lb). It provides approximately 889·5 kN (200,000 lb) thrust during a 60 s firing time. The motor utilises a D6AC steel case loaded with PBAN propellant. It has four movable nozzles capable of an 8° vector angle.

THIOKOL LONG-LIFE SRAM MOTOR

Thiokol is under contract to Boeing to improve the ageing and life of the motor for the USAF's AGM-69 SRAM missile. A motor with a projected service life of over 10 years has been developed and is currently being qualified. The SRAM motor is 2·54 m (100 in) long, 0·44 m (17·5 in) in diameter, and is loaded with 449 kg (990 lb) of HTPB propellant. The grain configuration consists of an aft-end boost grain and a forward sustain grain. They are separated by a barrier and have separate igniters. The motor has a fixed nozzle and a steel case.

THIOKOL TX-174

The TX-174 is the first stage of the Pershing tactical weapon system. The motor case is a thin-wall flight design fabricated from modified AISI H-11 or type D6AC steel. The contoured nozzle has an expansion ratio for sea-level operation.

The TX-174 has an overall length of 2·61 m (102·61 in) and an outside diameter of 1·02 m (40 in). The nominal propellant weight is 2,019 kg (4,451 lb). The nominal total weight of the TX-174 is 2,270 kg (5,004 lb). It provides an average thrust of 117 kN (26,290 lb) and a total impulse of 1,017,200 lb-s. The web burning time is 38·30 s. The TX-174 utilises a cylindrical-core propellant configuration.

THIOKOL TX-175

The TX-175 is the sustainer stage for the Pershing. The motor case is a thin-wall flight design fabricated from modified AISI H-11 or type D6AC steel. The forward dome of the case has three ports for impulse control. The contoured nozzle is sized for altitude operation.

The TX-175 has an overall length of 2·46 m (96·72 in) and an outside diameter of 1·02 m (40·0 in). The nominal propellant weight is 1,263 kg (2,785 lb). The nominal total weight of the TX-175 is 1,471 kg (3,244 lb). At vacuum conditions, it provides an average thrust of 85·5 kN (19,220 lb) and a total impulse of 757,200 lb-s. The web burning time is 39·0 s. The TX-175 utilises a cylindrical-core propellant configuration.

THIOKOL TX-30

The TX-30 is the sustainer of the Nike-Hercules missile. Overall length including blast tube is 4·43 m (174·4 in), and diameter 0·72 m (28·4 in). Total weight is 1,288 kg (2,840 lb) with a propellant weight of 985 kg (2,172 lb). Average thrust is 63·2 kN (14,200 lb) for a burning time of 26·6 s. Total impulse is 399,000 lb-s.

THIOKOL TX-261

The TX-261 is a PBAA-propellant version of the Nike-Hercules sustainer, with an altitude expansion nozzle instead of a blast tube/nozzle as on the TX-30. It is used in a variety of applications, including Pershing Drop Boost Test Vehicle and Defense Nuclear Agency Project Flame for re-entry vehicle nosecone evaluations. It is also used as the second stage of the ARPAT (Advanced Research Projects Agency Terminal) test vehicle. The motor is 2·92 m (114·89 in) long and 0·72 m (28·44 in) in diameter. Its total loaded weight is 1,301 kg (2,870 lb). Propellant weight is 1,054 kg (2,324 lb). Sea-level thrust is 254·5 kN (57,200 lb) over a total burning time of 8·92 s for a total impulse of 546,800 lb-s.

THIOKOL TX-306

The TX-306 is one of a group of motors that can be used separately, or in combination, for a wide variety of applications. It has a spherical configuration. Its contoured nozzle provides 20 : 1 expansion ratio for altitude applications. It was used in conjunction with TX-33, TX-261 and TE-M-29 motors to provide propulsion for the ARPAT target vehicle. As the third stage of that vehicle it accelerated simulated warheads during high-velocity intercept tests. The TX-306 is 739 mm (29·11 in) in diameter and with nozzle it is 1·20 m (47·31 in) long. Its case-bonded, composite propellant weighs 312 kg (688 lb), and its total weight is 383 kg (845 lb). It provides an average thrust of 59·6 kN (13,400 lb). Its total burning time is approximately 11 s and its total impulse is 158,000 lb-s at sea level.

THIOKOL TE-260G

The TE-260G rocket motor for the Subroc missile incorporates both directional control and thrust reversal. It consists of a cylindrical case containing the Thiokol propellant charge, a dual forward bulkhead design incorporating a thrust-reversal system, and an aft bulkhead containing four nozzles, each of which is equipped with a jetevator thrust vector control system. Six cable-carrying conduits run the full length of the case on the inside wall to allow guidance signals to be transmitted to the aft vector control system.

The TE-260G employs a composite solid propellant which is bonded to the case wall. Its principal constituents are polyurethane fuel binder and ammonium perchlorate oxidiser in a propellant system designed to provide a high specific impulse and a low burning rate. Thiokol developed the polyurethane system specifically to meet the Subroc requirements.

THIOKOL TU-289

US military designation: SR49-TC-1

The TU-289 solid-propellant rocket motor powers the AIR-2A Genie unguided air-to-air missile. It replaced an earlier motor, and has an improved propellant which increases the storage life and permits the missile to be deployed in a wide range of environmental temperatures. This motor remained in production through 1978.

THIOKOL TX-354

TX-354 motors are used in a variety of applications such as first and second stages, and as strap-on boosters for launch vehicles. The TX-354-3 has a high-altitude nozzle and is used as the second stage of the Scout vehicle. TX-

Thiokol Long-life SRAM motor

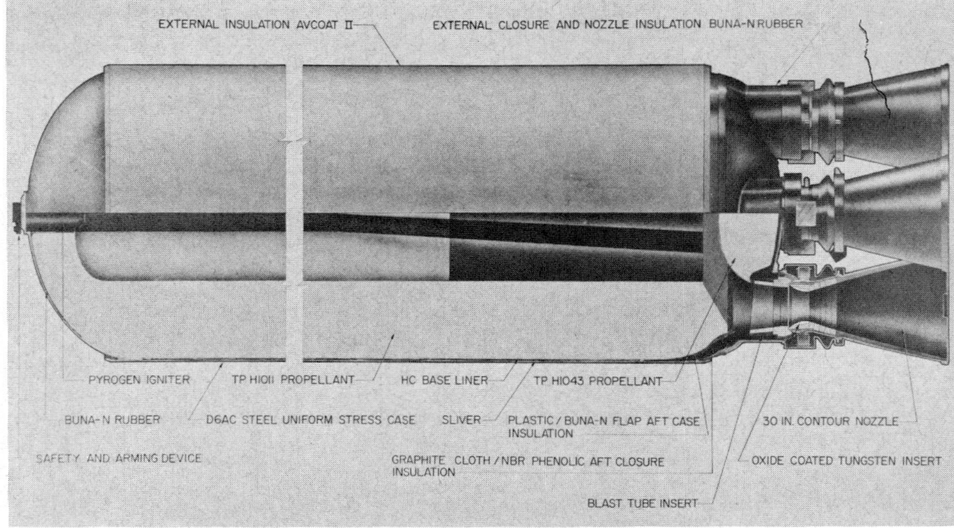

Part longitudinal section of Thiokol Minuteman first-stage motor

354-4 has a sea-level straight nozzle and is used as a first stage for the Stripi vehicle with Recruit strap-on motors. TX-354-5 is the strap-on booster for the Delta vehicle. It has an 11° canted sea-level nozzle and is used in groups of three, six, or nine. TX-354 weighs 4,320 to 4,410 kg (9,525 to 9,743 lb). The case without nozzle is 5,130 mm (202 in) long and has a diameter of 787 mm (31 in). Sea-level thrust is 232 kN (52,150 lb) over a total burning time of 39 s for a total impulse of 886,043 kg-s (1,953,400 lb-s).

THIOKOL TX-481 (MAVERICK)

TX-481 motors are used in the AGM-65A and AGM-65B Maverick missiles. The motor has an overall length of 1,020 mm (40·16 in), is 272 mm (10·7 in) in diameter, and has a total weight of 47·2 kg (104 lb). The case and blast-tube are aluminium. The composite propellant employs a Thiokol polysulphide polymer binder with ammonium perchlorate oxidiser. The motor operates in a boost/sustain mode with thrust levels of 44·5 kN (10,017 lb) in boost for 0·575 s and 9·68 kN (2,175 lb) in sustain phase for 3·495 s. The overall impulse is 6,169 kg-s (13,600 lb-s). The operational temperature range for the motor is −54°C to 71·1°C. Excellent shelf life has been demonstrated.

Production of motors for the A and B models of Maverick began in 1972 and was continuous through 1978 at delivery rates varying from approximately 250 to 1,000 motors per month. The total quantity of motors delivered is 26,213; batch acceptance static firings totalled 1,299.

THIOKOL TX-486 (PATRIOT)

The TX-486 motor is the propulsion system for the Patriot missile which provides defence against high-performance aircraft. The overall length of the motor is 3,302 mm (130 in) and its outside diameter is 406 mm (16·0 in). It weighs approximately 590 kg (1,300 lb). Ballistic parameters for the motor are classified. The motor case is D6AC steel, and the nozzle adapter is 4130 steel. Silica phenolic materials are employed in the nozzle throat and exit cone. The propellant and liner use a hydroxyl-terminated polybutadiene polymer binder; ammonium perchlorate is the propellant oxidiser. The Engineering Development programme for the motor was successfully completed in 1978. Initial production is scheduled for early 1981.

THIOKOL TX-581

The TX-581 (Castor II-X) is an extended-length version of the TX-354 (Castor II) motor and was developed as a strap-on booster with an 11° canted nozzle. It can also be used in first- or second-stage applications with a straight nozzle. The motor is 787·4 mm (31 in) in diameter, 8,000 mm (315 inches) long and weighs about 5,806 kg (12,800 lb). Sea-level performance provides an average thrust of approximately 339·4 kN (76,300 lb) over a total burning time of 35·8 s, giving a total impulse of 1,195,164 kg-s (2,634,900 lb-s), a 35 per cent increase over Castor II.

THIOKOL TX-526

TX-526 motors are used in a variety of booster/strap-on applications. The TX-526-0 motor, combined with four Recruit strap-on motors, is the booster for the Athena H vehicle. The TX-526-1 with 7° canted nozzle is qualified for strap-on booster applications. The TX-526-2 with 11° canted nozzle is used as a strap-on booster for the Delta 3914 vehicle, with each vehicle having nine motors. The 9,093 mm (358 in) long, 1,016 mm (40 in) diameter solid-propellant motor weighs 10,550 kg (23,250 lb). It provides an average thrust of 379·3 kN (85,270 lb), with a total burning time of approximately 58 s for a total impulse of 2,159,544 kg-s (4,760,900 lb-s) at sea-level.

THIOKOL TX-633 (MAVERICK)

US military designation: SR-114-TC-1

The TX-633 was developed as a reduced-smoke version of the Maverick rocket motor (see TX-481). Qualification testing was completed in 1977.

Compared with the original Maverick motor, the reduced-smoke model produces equal performance within the same envelope, varying only in the propellant and liner system, ignition system and protective closure. Motor case, blast-tube, nozzle, grain configuration and insulation are identical to the original model. The propellant and liner for this motor employ a hydroxyl-terminated polybutadiene polymer binder; the oxidiser is ammonium perchlorate. The reduced-smoke version of the motor could phase in with the next element of production.

THIOKOL HARM MOTOR

US military designation: XAGM-88A

The HARM motor is a reduced-smoke, dual-thrust rocket that powers the Navy's High-speed Anti-Radiation Missile. The motor is approximately 254 mm (10 in) in diameter and 2,120 mm (83·5 in) long. It utilises a D6AC steel case loaded with 127 kg (280 lb) of reduced-smoke, non-aluminized HTPB propellant, and has a single fixed nozzle. The propellant grain provides a boost/sustain thrust profile.

THIOKOL TE-M-416 TOMAHAWK

The Tomahawk is a high-performance motor designed specifically for use in sounding rocket systems. It is used in the Tomahawk vehicle as a single stage and in several other vehicles, such as Nike-Tomahawk and Terrier-Tomahawk, as the second stage. The motor is 3,607 mm (142 in) long and has a diameter of 229 mm (9 in). It weighs 220 kg (486 lb) and produces 48·9 kN (11,000 lb) thrust at sea level. This motor has been used by NASA in scale studies of the Shuttle SRM acoustic effects on an operational launch.

THIOKOL TE-M-29-8

Super Recruit, TE-M-29-8, is an improved version of previous Recruit motor configurations. The burn-time motor total impulse is increased from 55,000 to 62,000 lb-s, while keeping burn time unchanged. Weight is increased by about 6 per cent.

THIOKOL TE-M-307 (APACHE)

The TE-M-307-3 rocket motor was designed for second-stage applications, and therefore includes a 20 second delay igniter. It is 2,741 mm (107·91 in) long, 174·2 mm (6·86 in) in diameter and is used both as a sounding rocket and as a target missile. The TE-M-307-4 version was designed for single-stage applications. It uses the same loaded case and headcap assembly as the TE-M-307-3, with a 3·32 : 1 expansion ratio nozzle and an instantaneous TE-P-415 pyrogen. It is also used as a sounding rocket and as a target missile.

THIOKOL TE-M-364 (STAR-37)

The TE-M-364-2 (STAR-37B) is a 939·8 mm (37 in) diameter spherical main retro-rocket designed for the Surveyor and modified for use on the Burner II stage. Modifications consisted of increasing propellant loading to 653 kg (1,440 lb) and strengthening the attachment structure to accommodate higher inertial loads.

The TE-M-364-3 (STAR-37D) is a Surveyor main retro-rocket modified for use as third stage propulsion on the Improved Delta vehicle. Modifications consisted of again increasing propellant load, to 1,440 lb, redesigning the attachment structure to mate with the Delta launch vehicle and changing the diameter to 952·3 mm (37·49 in).

The TE-M-364-4 (STAR-37E) is an elongated version of the Delta motor, the AP/hydrocarbon/Al propellant grain being increased in mass from 653 kg (1,440 lb) to 1,040 kg (2,290 lb) by adding a 355 mm (14 in) cylinder to the case. Average thrust is 68·8 kN (15,472 lb) for a burn time of 41·96 s. This motor provides third-stage propulsion on Improved Delta.

The TE-M-364-19 (STAR-37F) is a shorter (1,518 mm) version of the Delta motor, accommodating 865·5 kg (1,908 lb) of propellant. The nozzle is of composite asbestos, glass and graphite phenolic structure. The titanium case has a 178 mm (7 in) cylindrical section. Average thrust is 59·8 kN (13,440 lb) for a burn time of 40 s. It provides the impulse to circularise the orbit of the Fleetsatcom satellite at the apogee of the launch orbit. This motor has been selected as the AKM (apogee-kick motor) for Intelsat V.

The TE-M-364-11 (STAR-37G) is a very similar extended Delta motor, likewise used for Improved Delta third-stage propulsion. Average thrust is 62·9 kN (14,145 lb) for a burn time of 45·48 s.

The TE-M-364-14 (STAR-37N) is a version having a propellant loading of 557·9 kg (1,230 lb). Average thrust is 38·4 kN (8,634 lb) for a burn time of 37·7 s. This motor provides third-stage propulsion on the Japanese N vehicle.

The TE-M-364-15 (STAR-37S) is a titanium (6Al-4V) spherical-cased version with modified attachment and propellant loading of 657·7 kg (1,450 lb). Average thrust is 43·5 kN (9,790 lb) for a burn time of 42·2 s. It provides the third-stage propulsion for weather satellites flown on the USAF Thor vehicle.

THIOKOL TE-M-442-1 (STAR-26B)

This motor is spherical, 663 mm (26·1 in) in diameter and 839 mm (33·05 in) long; propellant weight is 238 kg (525 lb) and total motor weight is 261 kg (576 lb). The TE-M-442-1 was developed from the TE-M-442 of 1965 and features a case of titanium instead of steel. It flies as an additional stage to the standard Burner II launch vehicle, atop the TE-M-364-2 second stage.

THIOKOL TE-M-479 (STAR-17)

The TE-M-479 is a 442 mm (17·4 in) spherical rocket motor developed for NASA's Radio Astronomy Explorer satellite programme. The motor is 687 mm (27·06 in) long and serves as the apogee kick stage which makes the orbit of the spacecraft truly circular. Total motor weight is 78·8 kg (173·8 lb); propellant weight is 69·4 kg (153 lb). High mass-fraction and excellent performance reproducibility characterise this motor for space systems application. The TE-M-479 was first flown in July 1968.

THIOKOL TE-M-521 (STAR-17A)

This 444 mm (17·5 in) diameter and 980 mm (38·6 in) long motor was developed by adding a 175 mm (6·9 in) straight section to the spherical TE-M-479 (RAE) motor. The TE-M-521 has a propellant weight of 112 kg (247 lb) and a total weight of 123·9 kg (273·2 lb). It served to 'circularise' the orbit of the Skynet I, NATO I and IMP-H and -J satellites. The motor has a titanium case and flight-proven propellant.

THIOKOL TE-M-541/542 (STAR-6)

This small glassfibre motor measures 157 mm (6·2 in) in diameter and 356 mm (14 in) long and serves in a classified space application. Using the same hardware, with minor insulation changes, the motor is loaded to either of two configurations: 4·85 kg (10·7 lb), 1,395 kg-s (3,075 lb-s) total impulse, 5·99 kg (13·2 lb) total weight (TE-M-541); and 3·27 kg (7·2 lb), 930 kg-s (2,050 lb-s) total impulse, 4·8 kg (10·6 lb) total weight (TE-M-542). These motors have an extensive flight history.

THIOKOL TE-M-473 (SANDHAWK)

The Sandhawk TE-M-473 is a high-performance 330 mm (13 in) diameter, 5,105 mm (201 in) long rocket motor designed for sounding rocket use. It features a regressive thrust-time trace, which results in near-constant vehicle acceleration during its 15 s burn time and provides an extremely smooth flight environment. This motor is suited for use in single-stage, two-stage and three-stage vehicle configurations.

THIOKOL TE-M-236 (SARV RETRO)

This is a retrograde motor for an unmanned satellite. It uses an internal-burning case-bonded grain weighing 18·3 kg (40·34 lb) in a case of 4130 steel, with a re-entrant conical rear closure to keep overall length to only 324 mm (12·76 in). Burn-time (7·5 s) average thrust is 5·6 kN (1,250 lb).

THIOKOL TE-M-640 ALTAIR III (STAR-20)

This 0·5 m (19·67 in)-diameter, 1·49 m (58·45 in)-long motor is the fourth stage of the Scout launch vehicle. The 273·3 kg (602·5 lb) AP/CTPB/Al propellant grain is cast in a filament-wound glassfibre case. The external nozzle is a composite of graphite, plastics and steel. Motor weight is 26·9 kN (6,050 lb) for a burn time of 27·8 s.

THIOKOL TE-M-458 (STAR-13)

This is a deceleration motor used in the Anchored Interplanetary Monitoring Platform (AIMP) programme. The 31 kg (68·3 lb) charge of AP/Al urethane is contained in a spherical case of 6Al-4V titanium, with graphite/vitreous silica phenolic nozzle. Loaded weight is 35·65 kg (78·6 lb) and average thrust 3·8 kN (850 lb) for a burn time of 21·8 s.

THIOKOL TE-M-516 (STAR-13A)

This apogee-boost motor is made by mating the propellant and nozzle of the TE-M-444 with the case and igniter of the TE-M-458. Average thrust is 5·8 kN (1,309 lb) for a burn time of 15·3 s. The motor was used as an injection

Thiokol TE-M-364-19 (STAR-37F) motor

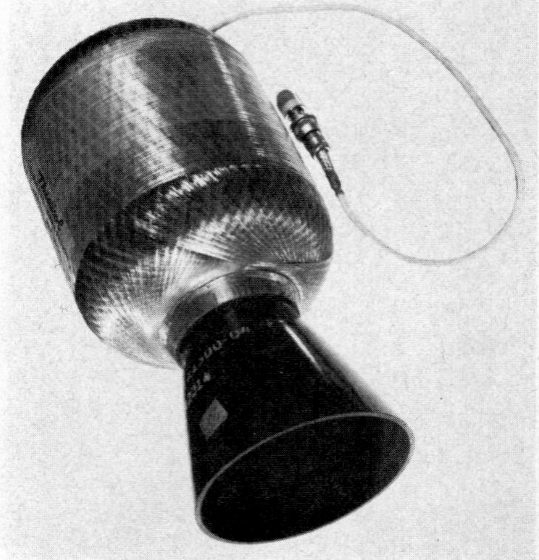

Thiokol TE-M-541 (STAR-6) motor

stage of the Thor Burner II carrying two satellites: Secor and Aurora.

THIOKOL TE-M-604 (STAR-24)

This apogee-boost motor has a 199·5 kg (439·8 lb) charge of AP/hydrocarbon/Al propellant contained in a spherical case of 6Al-4V titanium with graphite/carbon phenolic nozzle. Average thrust is about 20 kN (4,500 lb) for a burn time of 30·21 s. The motor was used as the apogee kick stage on the UK Skynet II and USAF Space Test Platform, and successfully placed the Lageos spacecraft in orbit. It was modified for use on the NASA IUE, and was the orbit-insertion motor for the Pioneer-Venus spacecraft which reached Venus in 1978.

THIOKOL TE-M-616 (STAR-27)

This 694 mm (27·3 in) diameter, 1,303 mm (51·3 in) long apogee boost motor has a 334 kg (736 lb) charge of AP/CTPB/Al propellant in a case of 6 Al-4V titanium and a graphite/carbon-phenolic nozzle. It has a Model 2130 remotely located electromechanical safe/arm device. Motor weight is 363 kg (800 lb); mass fraction is 0·920. Propellant weight can be reduced up to 25 per cent. Average thrust in vacuum is 27 kN (6,080 lb) for a burn time of 34·2 s. This motor was used to place in orbit the Canadian Communications Technology, Japanese Geometeorological, Japanese Broadcast and several USAF Navstar satellites. It is also used for the USAF P78-1 and NASA GOES satellites.

THIOKOL TE-M-696/TE-M-697 SPIN/DESPIN MOTORS

These qualified 35 mm (1·38 in) diameter motors were developed to provide total impulse reproducibility of 0·77 per cent. The propellant provides exhaust with low radar signature through a canted nozzle. The titanium alloy case minimises weight, and the TAM molybdenum nozzle controls thrust vector. The spin motor is 142 mm (5·6 in) long, weighs 0·28 kg (0·62 lb), and delivers 377·5 N (84·9 lb) thrust in vacuum for 0·30 s. The de-spin motor is 92 mm (3·6 in) long, weighs 0·23 kg (0·51 lb), and delivers 219·2 N (49·3 lb) thrust in vacuum for 0·29 s.

THIOKOL TE-M-700 (STAR-30)

This 762 mm (30 in) diameter, 1,508 mm (59·37 in) long apogee-boost motor has a 472·7 kg (1,042 lb) charge of AP/HTPB/Al propellant in a case of 6Al-4V titanium and with a graphite/carbon-carbon nozzle. The aft-end igniter is initiated by a Model 2130 remotely located safe/arm device. Motor weight is 505·3 kg (1,114 lb); propellant mass fraction is 0·935. The propellant weight can be increased 6 per cent and decreased 10 per cent. Average thrust in vacuum is 26·6 kN (5,980 lb) over a 51·5 s burn time.

THIOKOL TE-M-711 (STAR 48)

This 1,247 mm (49·1 in) diameter, 1,829 mm (72 in) long perigee kick motor has 1,996 kg (4,400 lb) of AP/HTPB/Al propellant in a case of 6Al-4V titanium and has a deeply submerged nozzle with a graphite throat insert and carbon/carbon exit cone. The aft-end igniter is initiated from a remotely located Model 2130 safe/arm device. Motor weight is 2,109 kg (4,650 lb); propellant mass fraction is 0·946. Average thrust in vacuum is 66 kN (14,900 lb) over an 85 s burn time. The motor is being developed for the Payload Assist Module for spacecraft launches from the Delta launch vehicle and Space Shuttle.

THIOKOL TE-M-762 ANTARES III (STAR 31)

This 762 mm (30 in) diameter, 2,873 mm (113 in) long motor has 1,228 kg (2,840 lb) of AP/HTPB/Al propellant in a filament-wound Kevlar case and a carbon/phenolic nozzle with a carbon/carbon throat insert. Motor weight is 1,393 kg (3,070 lb), including external insulation. Average thrust is 80 kN (18,000 lb) over a 46 s burn time. The motor is being qualified as an improved third stage for the Scout launch vehicle and was scheduled for initial flight in late 1979.

TRW

TRW DEFENSE AND SPACE SYSTEMS GROUP

HEAD OFFICE: One Space Park, Redondo Beach, California 90278

Telephone: (213) 535-4321

TRW developed, built and launched the first monopropellant hydrazine propulsion system to enter and be started in space.

TRW is testing a wide variety of chemical propulsion engines. One of these, the man-rated Lunar Module Descent Engine, landed Astronauts on the Moon. Another engine was built to provide midcourse trajectory corrections for the Mariner '69 missions to Mars and the Mariner 10 (Venus-Mercury) missions. TRW provided the monopropellant hydrazine orbit-adjust propulsion system for three NASA Atmospheric Explorer Satellites launched in 1973, 1974 and 1975.

TRW's propulsion research programmes include low-thrust monopropellant, bipropellant, colloid, ion, radioisotope and electro-thermal engines. In addition, an active research programme in low-cost propulsion technology is being continued. Tests of TRW rocket engines are conducted at the company's test site at San Juan Capistrano, California.

TRW TR-201 (DELTA)

A bipropellant engine designed for vacuum operation, the TR-201 serves as propulsion of the second stage of the NASA/McDonnell Douglas Delta launch vehicle. This is one of NASA's standard production launch vehicles.

TYPE: Liquid bipropellant rocket engine.

PROPELLANTS: Nitrogen tetroxide and 50/50 mix of hydrazine and UDMH.

THRUST CHAMBER: Single chamber. Area ratio 43. Chamber of quartz phenolic construction with ablative cooling. Nozzle of columbium, with radiation cooling. Co-axial injector with hypergolic ignition. Starting by 28V electrical signal to on/off solenoid valves.

THRUST CHAMBER MOUNTING: Gimbal attachment above injector.

PROPELLANT FEED SYSTEM: Pressure feed system by McDonnell Douglas Astronautics. Gas pressure 15·51 bars (225 lb/sq in). Flow rate 5·62 kg (12·4 lb)/s fuel and 8·92 kg (19·7 lb)/s oxidant.

DIMENSIONS:

Length overall	2,156 mm (84·9 in)
Nozzle diameter	922 mm (36·3 in)

WEIGHT, DRY: 113 kg (250 lb)

PERFORMANCE RATING:

Max thrust (vacuum)	43·6 kN (9,800 lb)
Combustion pressure	7·03 bars (102 lb/sq in)
Combustion temperature	2,700°C
Specific impulse	302

TRW TR-201 Delta engine, with vacuum thrust of 43·6 kN (9,800 lb)

VOUGHT

VOUGHT CORPORATION

HEAD OFFICE: PO Box 225907, Dallas, Texas 75265

Telephone: (214) 266-2695

OFFICERS: See Aircraft section

VOUGHT LVRJ

This Low-Volume Ram Jet was developed by Vought for the US Navy. Five successful flights were made, with range exceeding 161 km (100 miles) and speed exceeding 2,736 km/h (1,700 mph). In a follow-on STM (Supersonic Tactical Missile) programme for the US Navy, Vought is continuing development of the integral rocket/ramjet vehicle, incorporating "lower-cost propulsion components" and a guidance system.

Vought LVRJ carried by A-7E Corsair

WILLIAMS

WILLIAMS RESEARCH CORPORATION

2280 W Maple Road, Walled Lake, Michigan 48088

Telephone: (313) 624-5200

PRESIDENT: Sam Williams

VICE-PRESIDENTS:
- E. L. Klein (General Manager)
- John Jones (Engineering)
- David C, Jolivette (Public Relations)

Sam Williams believed in 1956 that gas-turbine technology could be extended down to very small sizes, and that if a small turbojet were made available it would find a market. The WR2 first ran at a thrust of 0·31 kN (70 lb) in 1962 and has since been developed into the WR2-6 and WR24-6. The more advanced WR19 uses an aerodynamically similar core and Williams Research is also building a range of shaft-drive engines.

All versions of the US Air Force and Navy cruise missiles, ALCM and Tomahawk, are propelled by the F107 turbofan. New engine production facilities for the F107 are being established in Ogden, Utah, and in September 1978 Teledyne CAE was named as second-source producer, with mass production due in early 1982.

WILLIAMS WR2 and WR24

US military designation (WR24): J400

Air enters at the eye of a single-sided light alloy centrifugal compressor which handles an air mass flow of 1 kg (2·2 lb)/s at a pressure ratio of 4·1 : 1. After passing through the diffuser which provides the structural basis for the engine the air divides, part of it flowing radially inwards as primary combustion airflow and the main bulk entering the short outward-radial annular combustor, through dilution apertures around the outer and rear face of the flame tube.

Fuel is sprayed centrifugally through a group of fine holes in the main compressor drive shaft. Surrounding the fuel pipe along the centreline of the main drive shaft is a cool airflow bled from the diffuser, which escapes through holes in the drive shaft to cool the combustion flames and reduce metal shaft and bearing temperatures, the main bearing being behind the compressor. A single igniter is mounted in the chamber at 12 o'clock. The hot gas, at about 955°C, then turns inwards and exits rearwards through the single-stage axial turbine and simple jet pipe.

The first production versions of the WR2 are the WR2-6, fitted to the Canadair AN/USD-501 high-performance battlefield reconnaissance vehicle; and the WR24-6 and -7 (YJ400-WR-400 and J400-WR-401) which power, respectively, the Northrop Chukar I and II target drones. The WR2-6 has a variable-area exhaust nozzle with translating central bullet, and drives a DC generator. The WR24 family have a minimal fixed-area jet pipe and drive a 4,000Hz alternator. The WR24-7 runs at higher temperature than the WR24-6 and incorporates detail modifications which increase mass flow to 1·36 kg (3 lb)/s and pressure ratio to 5·3. The WR24-17, not yet in production, is further uprated though similar externally. More than 4,000 WR2 and WR24 turbojets had been delivered by 1979.

Left: **Williams Research WR2-6 turbojet, for the Canadair CL-89 (AN/USD-501) reconnaissance drone (0·56 kN; 125 lb st).** *Right:* **Williams Research WR24-7 turbojet (0·76 kN; 170 lb st); the 0·89 kN (200 lb st) WR24-17 is visually identical**

Dimensions:

Overall length:

WR2-6	566 mm (22·3 in)
WR24-6	490 mm (19·3 in)
WR24-7, WR24-17	about 635 mm (25 in)

Max diameter:

WR2-6, WR24-6	274 mm (10·8 in)
WR24-7, WR24-17	about 305 mm (12 in)

Weight, Dry:

WR2-6, WR24-6	about 13·6 kg (30 lb)
WR24-7	20 kg (44·0 lb)

Maximum Ratings (S/L, static):

WR2-6	0·56 kN (125 lb) at 60,000 rpm
WR24-6	0·54 kN (121 lb) at 60,000 rpm
WR24-7	0·76 kN (170 lb)
WR24-17	0·89 kN (200 lb)

Specific Fuel Consumption:

WR2-6, WR24-6	35·41 mg/Ns (1·25 lb/h/lb st)

WILLIAMS WR19

To produce this two-shaft turbofan Williams Research used the WR2 as core and added an additional fan, axial compressor and drive turbine on a separate shaft, together with a by-pass duct. The LP turbine is related to those developed for the company's shaft-drive engines.

The WR19 was the power plant used in the Bell Aerosystems Flying Belt. It has also been used in the Williams Aerial Systems Platform (WASP) and Kaman Stowable Aircrew VEhicle Rotoseat (SAVER). From it has been derived the US Air Force/Navy F107, and the WR44 for general aviation, described separately.

In early 1970 the company received a $1,400,000 contract from the USAF for further development of a turbofan for future decoys. The company is making great efforts to increase the maximum gas temperature, particularly in the WR19 and derived engines. At present the temperature actually used is about 955°C, with potential of the present materials (Haynes 31 cobalt-base alloy for inlet guide vanes, Inco 100 for first-stage turbine blades and Inco 713 for other hot parts) limited to about 1,010°C.

Despite the mechanical difficulty of working on such small components, with turbine rotor discs and blades cast as single units, Williams is experimenting with aircooled turbine rotor blades and expects soon to be able to operate at gas temperatures higher than 1,100°C. The WR19 would be the first engine offered with cooled blades, and it also continues the company philosophy of using specially developed alternators, governors and other accessories capable of running at the full 60,000 rpm of the main shaft.

An advanced version of the WR19 is the F107 described separately.

Air Intake: Direct pitot type with four struts but no fixed inlet guide vanes. Unlike most WR2 engines the WR19 has a plain annular entry instead of a side intake downstream of an alternator or generator on the nose of the main shaft.

Compressor: Two-stage metal fan and two-stage axial IP compressor on common shaft leading to HP centrifugal compressor, handed to rotate in opposite direction to minimise gyroscopic couple. Total air mass flow, about 2 kg (4·4 lb)/s; overall pressure ratio, 8·1; by-pass ratio, approximately 1 : 1.

Combustion Chamber: Folded annular type, with fuel sprayed from revolving slinger on HP shaft. Dilution airflow admitted through perforated liner; cooling air injected through two sets of holes in HP shaft. Single igniter mounted diagonally on engine upper centreline.

Fuel System: Fuel fed at low pressure through transfer seal into pipe in HP shaft and ejected at high centrifugally-induced pressure, through calibrated fine orifices drilled radially through HP shaft in line with combustion chamber.

Turbine: Single-stage axial-flow HP turbine, with Haynes 31 nozzle guide vanes and rotor wheel cast as single unit in Inco IN 100. Two-stage LP turbine, again with both wheels cast as single units, in Inco 713. Provision to be made for aircooling to raise entry gas temperature from 955°C to above 1,100°C.

Williams Research WR19-3-1 two-shaft turbofan. Rating is 3·19 kN (718 lb st)

Jet Pipe: Mixer unit immediately downstream of LP turbine allows by-pass flow to merge with core gas flow to pass through plain propelling nozzle.

Accessories: Fuel and control system, filters, oil pump, tacho-generator and optional other accessories grouped into flat packages around upper part of fan/IP compressor casing. Starting system, depending on application, drives HP spool.

Mounting: Depending on application, main mounting above centrifugal diffuser casing with two double-lug pickups on horizontal centreline at LP turbine casing.

Dimensions:

Length overall	787 mm (31·0 in)
Width	338 mm (13·31 in)
Height	407 mm (16·20 in)

Weight, Dry:

With starter/generator	64·0 kg (141·0 lb)

Performance Rating (S/L, static):

Standby/T-O (wet)	3·19 kN (718 lb)
Maximum continuous	2·22 kN (500 lb st)

WILLIAMS WR19-A7

US military designation: F107

The F107 two-shaft turbofan is an advanced and uprated WR19 designed to propel the US Air Force ALCM (Air Launched Cruise Missile). Rated in the 2·67 kN (600 lb st) class, the F107 also powers the General Dynamics Convair Tomahawk Sea Launched Cruise Missile, and in 1978 emerged in a third form for ALCM-B. Williams has emerged clear winner in the competition to propel US cruise missiles, simplifying the attempt to maximise commonality exerted since 1977 by the JCMPO (Joint Cruise Missiles Project Office). All F107 versions are basically similar, but differ in mission and equipment, as follows:

F107-WR-100. Also designated WR19-A7, this was the engine selected for the Boeing AGM-86A ALCM, making the first ALCM flight at White Sands on 5 March 1976. Prototype engines only.

F107-WR-101. Selected to power the Boeing AGM-86B (ALCM-B). Improved configuration and performance. Qualification testing began in October 1978.

F107-WR-102. Selected to power the General Dynamics AGM-109 Tomahawk ALCM (Air-Launched Cruise Missile).

F107-WR-400. Selected to power the General Dynamics BGM-109 SLCM (Sub/Ship-Launched Cruise Missile) and the GLCM (Ground-Launched Cruise Missile) for the USAF, all versions of Tomahawk. An early 400 engine powered the first Tomahawk to fly (air-launched by A-6A) on 5 June 1976.

Type: Two-shaft turbofan.

Air Intake: Direct pitot type.

LP Compressor: Two-stage fan coupled to two-stage IP compressor.

HP Compressor: Single-stage centrifugal.

Williams Research F107-WR-100 two-shaft turbofan, developed for the Air-Launched Cruise Missile. Rating is "in the 2·67 kN/600 lb st class"

Williams Research F107-WR-101 two-shaft turbofan for AGM-86B

Williams Research F107-WR-102 two-shaft turbofan for AGM-109 Tomahawk

Williams Research F107-WR-400 two-shaft turbofan for BGM-109 Tomahawk SLCM and GLCM

COMBUSTION CHAMBER: Folded annular with rotary fuel injection.
TURBINE: Single-stage HP, two-stage LP.
ACCESSORIES: Grouping varies with sub-type. Self-contained lubrication system. Solid-propellant gas-impingement starter.
DIMENSIONS:

Length overall:	
F107-WR-100	800 mm (31·5 in)
F107-WR-101	1,232 mm (48·5 in)
F107-WR-102, -400	937 mm (36·9 in)
Envelope diameter	305 mm (12 in)

WEIGHT, DRY:

F107-WR-100	58·7 kg (130 lb)
F107-WR-101	64·0 kg (141 lb)
F107-WR-102	65·8 kg (145 lb)
F107-WR-400	64·4 kg (142 lb)

PERFORMANCE RATING: 2·67 kN (600 lb st) class

WILLIAMS WR 44

In February 1978 Foxjet International signed a contract for exclusive supply for three years of the WR44-800 turbofan to power the twin-engined Foxjet. A single WR44 has also been considered as a rear engine/APU in one version of the Gulfstream American Hustler.

Development of the WR44 began in 1971, using the WR19 as a basis. By-pass ratio was increased to 3, and overall pressure ratio increased. Claimed to be outstandingly quiet and suitable for general-aviation applications, the WR44 was expected to power the Foxjet on its first flight and to be certificated in 1980.

DIMENSIONS:

Length (with tailpipe)	1,143 mm (45·0 in)
Max diameter	419 mm (16·5 in)

WEIGHT, DRY 87·5 kg (193 lb)

PERFORMANCE RATING (S/L):
T-O 3·78 kN (850 lb st)

WILLIAMS WR34

This family of simple turboshaft engines is aimed at a wide spectrum of applications, including aviation. Based on a centrifugal compressor and radial inflow turbine, it is robust and reliable, and has unchanged configuration over power outputs from 11-26 kW (15-35 hp) at output speeds of 3,600, 6,000, or 12,000 rpm. Equipped weight is 29·5 kg (65 lb).

Williams Research WR34 turboshaft

ADDENDA

AIRCRAFT

ARGENTINA

TENSA

On 14th September 1979, Cessna announced that it had signed a long-term manufacturing and distribution agreement with TENSA, a manufacturing and aircraft marketing organisation in Argentina. Initially, TENSA will assemble three single-engined and two multi-engined Cessna types for the Argentine market. Later plans call for production of additional single-engined models and three further piston- and turboprop-powered multi-engined aircraft. Cessna estimates that 420 aircraft will be produced in Argentina during the next five years. It will also introduce its Cessna Pilot Center flight training programme into that country.

Under an earlier agreement, Cessna single-engined aircraft, including the Model 150, 150 Aerobat, Skylane and AGwagon, were assembled by the FMA at Córdoba from 1966 to 1976.

FMA IA 58B Bravo, with heavier armament and improved avionics compared with the IA 58A Pucará. Details on page 4. *(J. M. G. Gradidge)*

BRAZIL

EMBRAER (page 10)

EMBRAER EMB-120

This new 30-passenger commuter airliner is to be powered by two Pratt & Whitney Aircraft of Canada PT7A-1 turboprop engines, each rated at 1,119 kW (1,500 shp) from S/L to about 3,050 m (10,000 ft).

CANADA

DE HAVILLAND CANADA (page 21)

DHC-6 TWIN OTTER

Sales of the Twin Otter reached 700 on 2 October 1979, with the announcement that Widerøe's Flyveselskap A/S of Norway had ordered its 18th aircraft of this type. Delivery is planned for September 1980.

DHC-7 DASH 7

Orders and options for the Dash 7 reached 59 in September 1979, when Henson Aviation of Maryland ordered one, with options on two more. The first will be delivered in May 1980.

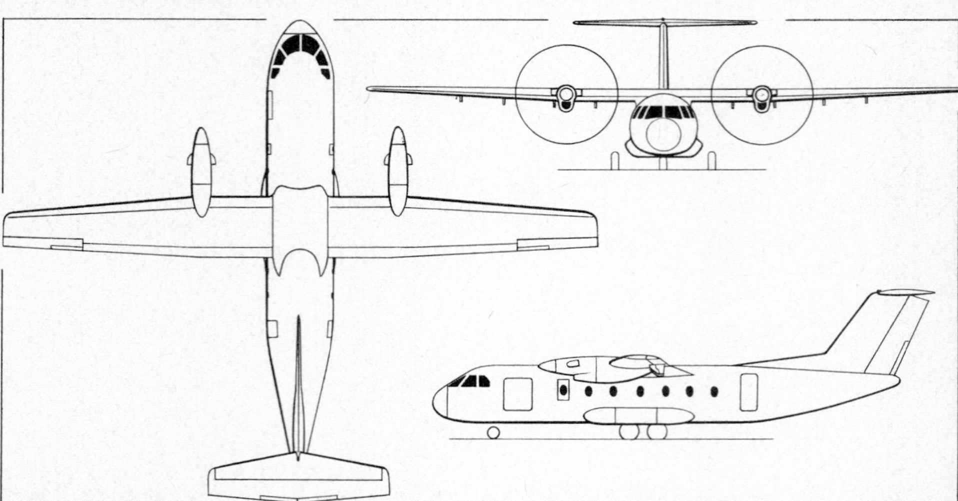

Aérospatiale AS35, as currently envisaged with two Turboméca Makila turboprop engines *(Pilot Press)*

FRANCE

AÉROSPATIALE (page 40)

AÉROSPATIALE AS35

Market studies have indicated the need for a relatively small short-haul transport with 30 to 40 seats, to replace the 15/20-seat turboprop aircraft now used by third-level operators. The AS35 has been projected to meet this requirement, with the capability of design 'stretch' to 50 seats as traffic increases.

Aérospatiale believes that, by taking advantage of modern technology, the AS35 would be able to offer a 20-50% improvement in fuel consumption per seat by comparison with current aircraft, making possible a reduction of 10-20% in cost per seat-mile. Noise and pollution levels would be low, and a feature of the configuration is the ease with which the rear fuselage can be modified to produce an all-cargo version with capability to airdrop bulky freight or parachute troops.

The AS35 is intended to meet FAR Pt 25 requirements. Aérospatiale would like to develop it as a collaborative project with other manufacturers, and believes that production aircraft could be in service within four years of programme launch.

The following information should be regarded as provisional. No dimensions or precise specification data are yet defined.

Type: Twin-turboprop short-haul transport.

Wings: Cantilever high-wing monoplane, comprising a constant-chord centre-section and tapered outer panels. Dihedral on outer panels only. Ailerons and flaps along entire trailing-edge. Trim tab in each aileron.

Fuselage: Structure of constant section throughout main cabin. Conical rear fuselage of passenger versions would be replaced on ambulance and cargo versions by a wider, more upswept rear fuselage and beaver-tail, with lower surface made up of loading ramp and doors.

Tail Unit: Cantilever T tail with sweptback vertical surfaces, horn-balanced elevator and large dorsal fin. Tabs in rudder and elevator.

Prototype Aérospatiale AS 355E Ecureuil 2/Twinstar six-seat twin-turbine helicopter

Dassault Mystère-Falcon 20FH development aircraft for the new Mystère-Falcon 20 Series H, described on page 59 *(J. M. G. Gradidge)*

Landing Gear: Retractable tricycle type. Single nosewheel. Each main gear comprises two wheels in tandem, which retract into a fairing built on to the bottom of the fuselage.

Power Plant: Two turboprop engines in 1,120-1,490 kW (1,500-2,000 shp) class. Engines under consideration in 1979 included the Turboméca Makila of 1,423 kW (1,908 shp).

ACCOMMODATION: Crew of two, and 36, 40 or 44 passengers in four-abreast seating, with centre aisle. Wardrobe, galley, toilet and baggage compartment, in pairs, at front and back of cabin. Doors at front and rear of passenger cabin on port side. Service door on starboard side, opposite rear door. Emergency exit at front of cabin on each side. Ambulance version accommodates 18 stretcher patients, in three tiers of three on each side of cabin, with seat at rear for attendant.

WEIGHTS (approx):
Payload 3,500-4,500 kg (7,715-9,920 lb)
Max T-O weight 15,000 kg (33,070 lb)

PERFORMANCE (typical, estimated):
Normal cruising speed 250 knots (460 km/h; 287 mph)
T-O run 1,000 m (3,280 ft)
Range with max payload over 800 nm (1,480 km; 920 miles)

AÉROSPATIALE FOUGA 90

First flight of the prototype Fouga 90 following replacement of its original Astafan IIG engines with Astafan IVGs (each 7·75 kN; 1,740 lb st) was made on 26 September 1979.

AÉROSPATIALE AS 355E ECUREUIL 2/TWINSTAR

The prototype AS 355E (F-WZLA) flew for the first time on 27 September 1979. At that date, orders totalled 186, for 49 customers in 9 countries. Orders for the single-engined AS 350 Ecureuil/Astar totalled 460 for 17 countries on the same date, by which 105 had been delivered.

GERMANY (FEDERAL)

MBB (page 76)

MBB HFB 320 HANSA JET

As a result of the success of the three Hansa Jet ECM trainers already in service, the German Federal Defence Technology and Procurement Office ordered four more of these aircraft for the Luftwaffe in late 1977. The first of these (D-CANO) flew for the first time on 22 August 1979 and, after production flight testing, was ferried to Rome in October to have its special avionics installed by Elettronica SpA. It is scheduled for delivery to the Luftwaffe in early 1980.

Full details of the basic Hansa Jet can be found in the 1973-74 *Jane's*.

MBB BO 105 L

This new version of the BO 105 (see page 76) has more powerful engines and an uprated transmission, permitting operation at a higher gross weight. The description of the BO 105 CB applies also to the BO 105 L, except as follows:

ROTOR DRIVE: Main transmission, type ZF-FS 112, is rated for a twin-engine input of 294 kW (395 shp) per engine, or a single engine input of 368 kW (493 shp) continuous, or 404 kW (542 shp) for 2·5 min.

POWER PLANT: Two Allison 250-C28C turboshaft engines, each rated at 410 kW (550 shp) for 2·5 min, and with a 5 min take-off or max continuous power rating of 373 kW (500 shp). Fuel system generally as for BO 105 CB, but max standard capacity 380 kg (838 lb).

First of the new batch of HFB 320 Hansa Jet ECM trainers completed by MBB's Commercial Aircraft Division

SYSTEMS: As for BO 105 CB, except 24V battery is of 25Ah capacity.

WEIGHTS:
Weight empty 1,250 kg (2,756 lb)
Max T-O weight, internal load 2,400 kg (5,291 lb)
Max T-O weight, external load 2,500 kg (5,512 lb)

PERFORMANCE (at max T-O weight):
Never-exceed speed at S/L 146 knots (270 km/h; 168 mph)
Max cruising speed at S/L 136 knots (252 km/h; 157 mph)
Max rate of climb at S/L 600 m (1,970 ft)/min
Max operating height 6,100 m (20,000 ft)
Service ceiling, one engine out 2,880 m (9,450 ft)
Hovering ceiling IGE 4,000 m (13,120 ft)
Hovering ceiling OGE 3,440 m (11,290 ft)
Range at S/L, standard fuel, max internal payload, no reserves 248 nm (460 km; 286 miles)

INTERNATIONAL

AIRBUS INDUSTRIE (page 86)

AIRBUS A300

Orders received in September/October 1979 include 3 additional A300B2-200s for Toa Domestic Airlines, bringing their total to 9 firm orders; and additional A300B4-100s for Iberia, which has now placed firm orders for 9, plus options on 5 more. Orders for the A300 total 183 as a result, plus 78 options.

ISRAEL

IAI (page 101)

IAI WESTWIND 2

At the US National Business Aircraft Association Convention, in September 1979, Israel Aircraft Industries displayed the prototype of the new Westwind 2 (4X-CMK), which will supplement the Westwind I in production. It flew for the first time in the Spring of 1979 and is expected to receive certification by early 1980, enabling deliveries to begin during the second half of that year.

The Westwind 2 has IAI's new 'Sigma' wing of advanced aerodynamic profile and fitted with winglets above the tip-tanks. The elliptical cabin section increases seated headroom and allows a flat rather than 'trenched' cabin floor, an airline-type flushing toilet, and improved placing of the overhead passenger service units. Standard features and equipment include thrust reversers, a lift-dump system, fully-modulated anti-skid brakes, wide-profile tyres, single-point refuelling, strobe lights, dual batteries, digital weather radar, radio altimeter, Collins APS-80 autopilot and a full range of Collins Pro-Line solid-state avionics.

New 'Sigma' wings and winglets identify IAI's Westwind 2

Standard seating is for a crew of two and 10 passengers.

The Garrett-AiResearch TFE 731 turbofans of the Westwind I are retained on the Westwind 2.

WEIGHTS:
Basic empty weight 5,820 kg (12,830 lb)
Operating weight empty, excl fuel 7,258 kg (16,000 lb)
Max T-O weight 10,660 kg (23,500 lb)
Max landing weight 8,618 kg (19,000 lb)

PERFORMANCE (at max T-O weight):
Max operating Mach No. Mach 0·80
Max cruising speed Mach 0·76
Normal cruising speed Mach 0·74
Initial cruising height 11,275 m (37,000 ft)
Balanced T-O field length 1,600 m (5,250 ft)
Landing field length 747 m (2,450 ft)
Range with 4 passengers and NBAA/VFR reserves 2,900 nm (5,370 km; 3,337 miles)

ITALY

R. PIAGGIO (page 121)

PIAGGIO P.166-DL3-MAR

Piaggio has proposed the P.166-DL3-MAR as a medium-range maritime surveillance version of the standard P.166-DL3. Applications would include coastguard, anti-smuggling, maritime traffic, fishery and pollution control, and search and rescue. The P.166-DL3-MAR would be equipped with an integrated search/detection/identification/plotting and reporting system, plus four underwing pylons for external weapons or other stores. It would be able to operate from unprepared strips, day or night, in all weathers.

AIRFRAME AND POWER PLANT: As for standard P.166-DL3, except for changes necessary to install specialised equipment.

AVIONICS AND EQUIPMENT: According to customer and mission requirements. Typical packages can include 180° scan search radar, two Vinten aerial cameras, Doppler or other suitable navigation system, and operator's console; or 360° search radar, low light level TV camera with monitor and recorder, Doppler/Omega navigation system and tactical co-ordinator's console.

WEIGHTS:
Weight empty, without operational equipment 2,460 kg (5,424 lb)
Operational equipment (conventional package) 400 kg (882 lb)
Weight empty, equipped 2,860 kg (6,306 lb)
Operational weight 3,206 kg (7,069 lb)
Fuel 1,094 kg ((2,411 lb)
Max T-O weight 4,300 kg (9,480 lb)

PERFORMANCE (typical mission with crew of three, cruising to search area at 170 knots; 315 km/h; 196 mph at 3,050 m; 10,000 ft, maintaining search at 140 knots; 259 km/h; 161 mph at 1,220 m; 4,000 ft, 30 min reserves):
At 40 nm (74 km; 46 miles) from base:
time on station 6 h 0 min
total mission time 6 h 30 min
At 200 nm (370 km; 230 miles) from base:
time on station 4 h 0 min
total mission time 6 h 20 min
At 360 nm (667 km; 415 miles) from base:
time on station 2 h 0 min
total mission time 6 h 15 min
At 440 nm (815 km; 506 miles) from base:
time on station 1 h 0 min
total mission time 6 h 0 min

USSR

MIL (page 197)

MIL Mi-8

The following military versions of this helicopter may now be identified by NATO reporting names:

Hip-C. Basic assault transport, as illustrated on page 200. Twin rack for stores on each side of cabin.

Hip-E. World's most heavily armed helicopter. In service with Soviet armed forces, as illustrated on page 199. One flexibly-mounted 12·7 mm machine-gun in nose. Triple stores rack on each side of cabin, able to carry up to 192 rockets in six suspended packs plus 4 'Swatter' anti-tank missiles above racks.

Hip-F. Variant of 'Hip-E' for export. Missile armament changed to 6 'Saggers'.

MIL Mi-24

The two latest versions that may be identified by NATO reporting names are:

Hind-E. For Soviet armed forces. Armed with tube-launched and probably laser-guided missiles (NATO 'Spiral').

Hind-F. As 'Hind-E' for export. Reported to carry 'Sagger' missiles. Operators include East Germany, Libya, Afghanistan and Ethiopia.

Yakovlev Yak-36 (NATO 'Forger-A') hovering over the flight deck of the *Kiev (Tass)*

UNITED KINGDOM

BRITISH GLIDING ASSOCIATION

Address: Kimberly House, Vaughan Way, Leicester
Chief Technical Officer: R. B. Stratton

BGA SUPERMUNK

BGA Supermunk, a converted Chipmunk 22 with Lycoming O-360 engine

First flown on 20 August 1979, the Supermunk (G-BBNA) is a conversion of a British-built de Havilland Chipmunk Mk 22 to accept a Lycoming flat-four engine in place of the original Gipsy Major in-line power plant. The conversion was started in April 1979 by officers of the BGA, and was undertaken in order to improve the performance and serviceability of the aircraft in the role of glider tug. In the Autumn of 1979, pre-certification development flying was continuing, and some performance figures remained to be established; nevertheless, the aircraft had already satisfied expectations in regard to improvements in take-off performance and in turnround time during towing trials.

A description of the Chipmunk has appeared in previous editions of *Jane's*. The following details summarise the airframe, power plant and other changes embodied in the Supermunk version:

Airframe: Basically as standard Chipmunk Mk 22 aft of firewall. Forward of firewall, engine is installed on a US-built welded steel tube dynafocal mounting, and is encased in a new two-piece cowling of fire-resistant polyester GRP. Not cleared for spinning or aerobatics; other limitations as for Chipmunk Mk 22.

Power Plant: One 134 kW (180 hp) Lycoming O-360-A4A flat-four engine, driving a Sensenich two-blade metal propeller from a Piper Cherokee 180. Fuel system incorporates both mechanical and electrical pumps.

Accommodation: Seats for two persons in tandem, as in Chipmunk, under one-piece rearward-sliding framed canopy. Front cockpit instrumentation altered to accommodate different engine instruments. Original flight instruments retained in rear cockpit, but some engine instruments have been removed.

Systems: 12V (instead of 24V) electrical system includes generator, starter and single 35Ah battery. Vacuum pump to drive gyro instruments.

Dimensions, external:
- Wing span: 10·46 m (34 ft 4 in)
- Wing area, gross: 15·98 m² (172 sq ft)
- Length overall: 7·84 m (25 ft 8½ in)
- Height overall: 2·13 m (7 ft 0 in)
- Propeller diameter: 1·93 m (6 ft 4 in)

Weights:
- Weight empty: 652 kg (1,438 lb)
- Max T-O weight: 952 kg (2,100 lb)

Performance (established up to Autumn 1979):
- Cruising speed at 2,450 rpm: 106 knots (196 km/h; 122 mph) IAS
- Cruising speed at 2,300 rpm: 97 knots (180 km/h; 112 mph) IAS
- Max rate of climb at S/L (pilot only, plus max fuel): 360 m (1,180 ft)/min
- Rate of climb as glider tug, depending on type and weight of glider: 152-244 m (500-800 ft)/min

CRANFIELD (page 240)

Under the leadership of Mr John J. Spillman of the College of Aeronautics, Cranfield has developed sets of wingtip 'sails' which can be made integrally with new plastics wingtips for the Piper Pawnee agricultural aircraft. Flight testing of the three-sail tips illustrated has confirmed that they offer reductions in drag, fuel consumption and wake vortex effects, as well as reducing wasteful spray drift at the extremities of the spraybars.

NASA was testing in a wind tunnel a set of five-sail tips on a Pawnee model in the Summer of 1979. The British National Research Development Corporation retains the patents for the sails, which it is hoped to market to Pawnee operators.

Wingtip 'sails' on a Piper Pawnee

TO SOLAR-POWERED AIRCRAFT DEVELOPMENTS

Address: 5A Lyndhurst Gardens, London NW3

This company was formed by Mr Freddie To, in order to build a solar-powered aircraft that he had devised. Design of the aircraft, known as the Solar One, was undertaken by Mr David Williams, and the first short hop was claimed in December 1978. A flight of nearly three-quarters of a mile (1,200 m) was made by Mr Ken Stewart at Lasham Airfield, Hampshire, on 13 June 1979. The flight was made at a maximum height of about 25 m (80 ft) and at a maximum speed of about 35 knots (65 km/h; 40 mph). A second flight was made on the same day by Mr Bill Maidment.

SOLAR ONE

This first successful British solar-powered aircraft has a glider configuration. The built-up framework structure is of wood, covered with a thin heat-shrunk plastics material known as Solarfilm. To simplify stowage and transport, the long-span cantilever wing is made in three sections, with a laminated spruce girder main box-spar. A Wortmann FX180 wing section is used. The all-moving fin and tailplane are detachable.

The solar cells above the wing roots are visible in this view of Solar One *(Flight International)*

A two-blade propeller, at the top of a pylon in front of the cockpit, is driven through 3:1 reduction gearing by four Bosch permanent magnet electric motors, linked by a chain drive. The batteries to power the motors consist of 24 nickel-cadmium cells, with a capacity of 25Ah, which store the energy supplied by 750 solar cells, each 76 mm (3 in) diameter, attached to the upper surface of the root section of the wings, aft of the spar.

Dimensions, external:
Wing span	20·73 m (68 ft 0 in)
Wing area, gross	24·15 m² (260 sq ft)
Length overall	6·71 m (22 ft 0 in)
Propeller diameter	1·60 m (5 ft 3 in)

Weight:
Weight empty	105 kg (230 lb)

WESTLAND (page 250)

WESTLAND COMMANDO

The first of 15 Sea King HC.Mk 4 troop transport and logistic support helicopters for the Royal Navy (ZA290), similar to the Westland Commando, made its first flight on 26 September 1979.

UNITED STATES OF AMERICA

BEECHCRAFT (page 262)

It was announced on 2 October 1979 that Raytheon Company and Beech Aircraft Corporation had agreed in principle to merge. Beech will continue to be operated as a separate entity under its present management, at its present locations. The separate board of directors for Beech will include appropriate Raytheon representation.

BEECHCRAFT SUPER KING AIR MODEL F90

Deliveries of the Super King Air F90 began in mid-1979, shortly after FAA certification of this sixth member of the King Air range of corporate transport aircraft. Basically, it combines the pressurised fuselage of the King Air 90 with reduced-span wings similar to those of the King Air 100, and a T tail assembly similar to that of the Super King Air 200.

New Beechcraft assemblies and technology are utilised throughout its construction, and the PT6A-135 turboprop engines drive slow-turning four-blade propellers to reduce airport and in-flight noise. Cabin pressurisation is increased to 0·34 bars (5·0 lb/sq in) to give a sea level environment at 3,350 m (11,000 ft), a 1,525 m (5,000 ft) environment at 5,595 m (18,360 ft), and a 3,050 m (10,000 ft) environment at an altitude of 8,075 m (26,500 ft).

Type: Seven/ten-seat twin-turboprop business aircraft.

Wings: Similar to King Air 100. De-icing system standard.

Fuselage: Similar to King Air 90.

Tail Unit: Similar to Super King Air 200. Tailplane de-icing standard.

Landing Gear: Retractable tricycle type, with twin-wheel main units and single steerable nosewheel.

Power Plant: Two 559 kW (750 shp) Pratt & Whitney Aircraft of Canada PT6A-135 turboprop engines, each driving a Hartzell FT 101 73 four-blade propeller with optional reverse pitch. Automatic fuel transfer system, engine anti-icing, propeller de-icing, and ice-free fuel venting system, are standard.

Accommodation: Two seats side by side on flight deck. Seats for five to eight persons in main cabin, in deep-cushioned chairs. Passengers screened from flight deck and toilet by partitions at front and rear of cabin. Space for 183 kg (403 lb) of baggage. Windscreen anti-icing standard.

System: Pressurisation system differential 0·34 bars (5·0 lb/sq in).

Avionics: Standard avionics package includes dual nav/com, marker beacon, glideslope, DME and transponder.

Dimensions, external:
Wing span	13·99 m (45 ft 10¾ in)
Wing area, gross	25·98 m² (279·7 sq ft)
Length overall	12·13 m (39 ft 9½ in)
Height overall	4·60 m (15 ft 1¼ in)
Tailplane span	5·61 m (18 ft 4¾ in)
Propeller diameter	2·34 m (7 ft 8 in)
Passenger door: Height	1·31 m (4 ft 3¾ in)
Width	0·69 m (2 ft 3 in)

Dimensions, internal:
Cabin, excl flight deck: Length	3·89 m (12 ft 9 in)
Width	1·37 m (4 ft 6 in)
Height	1·45 m (4 ft 9 in)
Avionics compartment volume	0·45 m³ (16 cu ft)

Weights and Loadings:
Weight empty	3,003 kg (6,622 lb)
Max T-O and landing weight	4,966 kg (10,950 lb)
Max ramp weight	5,003 kg (11,030 lb)
Max wing loading	190·8 kg/m² (39·1 lb/sq ft)
Max power loading	4·4 kg/kW (7·3 lb/shp)

Performance (A: at max T-O weight; B: at 4,309 kg/9,500 lb AUW; C: at 4,082 kg/9,000 lb AUW):

Max cruising speed (B):
at 3,660 m (12,000 ft)	267 knots (495 km/h; 307 mph)
at 5,490 m (18,000 ft)	260 knots (482 km/h; 299 mph)
at 7,925 m (26,000 ft)	251 knots (465 km/h; 289 mph)
Take-off speed (A)	107 knots (198 km/h; 123 mph)
Accelerate/stop decision speed (A)	107 knots (198 km/h; 123 mph)
Approach speed (A)	105 knots (195 km/h; 121 mph)
Stalling speed (A), power off: flaps up	94 knots (175 km/h; 109 mph)
32·5% flap	84 knots (156 km/h; 97 mph)
100% flap	77 knots (143 km/h; 89 mph)
Max rate of climb at S/L: A	725 m (2,380 ft)/min
C	947 m (3,108 ft)/min
Rate of climb at S/L, one engine out: A	183 m (599 ft)/min
C	289 m (947 ft)/min
Service ceiling: A	9,084 m (29,802 ft)
C	above 9,450 m (31,000 ft)
Service ceiling, one engine out: A	4,395 m (14,419 ft)
C	5,919 m (19,420 ft)
T-O run (A), flaps up	637 m (2,090 ft)
T-O run to 15 m (50 ft) (A), flaps up	871 m (2,856 ft)
Landing from 15 m (50 ft) (A), without propeller reversal	907 m (2,977 ft)
Landing run (A), without propeller reversal	578 m (1,895 ft)

Cruising range at max cruise power, with reserves:
at 3,660 m (12,000 ft)	960 nm (1,779 km; 1,105 miles)
at 5,490 m (18,000 ft)	1,160 nm (2,149 km; 1,335 miles)
at 7,925 m (26,000 ft)	1,440 nm (2,669 km; 1,658 miles)

Cruising range at max range power, with reserves:
at 3,660 m (12,000 ft)	1,179 nm (2,185 km; 1,357 miles)
at 5,490 m (18,000 ft)	1,369 nm (2,537 km; 1,576 miles)
at 7,925 m (26,000 ft)	1,576 nm (2,920 km; 1,814 miles)

CESSNA (page 308)

CESSNA CUTLASS RG

Cessna announced on 15 August 1979 the introduction of a new four-seat lightplane with retractable landing gear which it claims to be the lowest priced aircraft in this category. Known as the Cutlass RG, it combines the airframe of the Model 172 Skyhawk with the retractable landing gear developed for the Skylane RG. Power is provided by a 134 kW (180 hp) Lycoming O-360-F1A6 flat-four engine, driving a two-blade constant-speed metal propeller. Two fuel tanks, one in each wing, have a combined usable capacity of 235 litres (62 US gallons).

The Cutlass RG became available in late 1979, together with a Cutlass RGII with avionics and equipment as detailed for the Skyhawk II, plus the optional Nav Pac. Equivalent versions designated F Cutlass RG and F Cutlass RGII are to be assembled under licence by Reims Aviation in France.

Cessna Cutlass RG four-seat lightplane with retractable landing gear

Dimensions, external: As for Skyhawk except:
Length overall	8·36 m (27 ft 5 in)
Tailplane span	3·43 m (11 ft 3 in)
Wheel track	2·59 m (8 ft 6 in)
Propeller diameter	1·94 m (6 ft 4½ in)

Weights and Loadings (A: Cutlass RG; B: Cutlass RGII):
Weight empty: A	707 kg (1,558 lb)
B	725 kg (1,598 lb)
Max T-O and landing weight: A, B	1,202 kg (2,650 lb)
Max ramp weight: A, B	1,206 kg (2,658 lb)
Max wing loading: A, B	74·4 kg/m² (15·2 lb/sq ft)
Max power loading: A, B	8·97 kg/kW (14·7 lb/hp)

Performance (at max T-O weight):
Max level speed at S/L	145 knots (269 km/h; 167 mph)
Cruising speed, 75% power at 2,740 m (9,000 ft)	140 knots (259 km/h; 161 mph)
Stalling speed, flaps up, power off	54 knots (100 km/h; 62 mph) CAS
Stalling speed, flaps down, power off	50 knots (93 km/h; 58 mph) CAS
Max rate of climb at S/L	244 m (800 ft)/min
Service ceiling	5,120 m (16,800 ft)
T-O run	287 m (940 ft)
T-O to 15 m (50 ft)	511 m (1,675 ft)
Landing from 15 m (50 ft)	408 m (1,340 ft)
Landing run	191 m (625 ft)
Range with max fuel, recommended lean mixture, with allowances for engine start, taxi, T-O, climb and 45 min reserves	720 nm (1,334 km; 829 miles)
Range with max fuel at econ cruising speed, allowances as above	840 nm (1,557 km; 967 miles)

GATES LEARJET (page 338)

GATES LEARJET SEA PATROL

A prototype of this special missions version of the Learjet was exhibited at the 1979 Paris Air Show, before making a worldwide demonstration tour. This aircraft (N80SM) is a modified Learjet 35A, with a slightly larger cabin than the equally suitable 36A, enabling more observers to be carried during demonstrations.

Equipment available for the Sea Patrol Learjet includes Litton AN/APS-504(V)2 sea surveillance radar, with 360° sweep from the underbelly radome and digital CFAR clutter suppression; low light level TV with video tape and scan conversion; forward-looking infra-red sensors; Daedalus DS-1210 multi-spectral scanner with tape data storage and hard copy printer; minicomputers for data processing; ASW sonobuoy drop and detection equipment; a hardpoint under each wing with an Alkan 165B ejector for survival equipment, flares or up to 220 kg (485 lb) of other stores; drop hatch for rescue gear; high-intensity searchlight; reconnaissance, mapping or LOROP cameras; HF, VHF and UHF homers; GNS-500A VLF Omega navigation system; side-looking airborne radar; Bendix RDR 1300B weather radar; and hand held cameras with nav information interface.

Items fitted to the demonstrator make it suitable for location and detection of surface vessels, identification of targets, determination of target activities, and storage of permanent video tape and photographic records of target image, with position, time and date.

Performance (Learjet 36A):
Operating speed at 11,275-12,500 m (37,000-41,000 ft)	407 knots (753 km/h; 468 mph)
Operating speed at 4,575-7,620 m (15,000-25,000 ft)	323 knots (598 km/h; 371 mph)
Operating speed, S/L to 610 m (2,000 ft)	257 knots (475 km/h; 295 mph)
Rate of climb at S/L	1,380 m (4,525 ft)/min
Range at high altitude	2,502 nm (4,633 km; 2,879 miles)
Range at medium altitude	1,810 nm (3,352 km; 2,083 miles)
Range at low altitude	1,168 nm (2,163 km; 1,344 miles)

Gates Learjet 35A Sea Patrol demonstration aircraft

LOCKHEED (page 368)

LOCKHEED L-1011 TRISTAR

An order from British Airways for 6 more L-1011-200s, announced on 13 September 1979, brings the total of TriStar orders (230) and options (71) past the 300 mark.

MCDONNELL DOUGLAS (page 381)

MCDONNELL DOUGLAS DC-9 SUPER 80

The first DC-9 Super 80 flew for the first time on 18 October 1979. Orders for the Super 80 at that time totalled 68, with options on 24 more.

TEXAS HELICOPTER CORPORATION (page 451)

TEXAS HELICOPTER WASP

This company is producing currently three conversions of Bell Model 47 helicopters, as follows:

Wasp. Two single-seat versions, based on the military OH-13E (company designation **M74**) and OH-13H (**M74A**), which received FAA certification on 3 May 1976 and 31 August 1977 respectively. A combined total of 31 of these aircraft had been ordered and 33 converted by 1 September 1979. Many are employed on agricultural work. Other uses include transport, fish spotting and law enforcement.

Wasp II. Under the company designation **M79S**, Texas Helicopters completed the design of a tandem two-seat conversion of the military TH-13T. Conversion of a prototype began in March 1978, followed by the first production example in January 1979; this latter aircraft flew for the first time on 13 February 1979.

The description which follows applies to all three versions, as detailed:

Type: Lightweight general utility helicopter.

Rotor System: Two-blade semi-rigid main rotor, with interchangeable blades of all-metal construction. Wooden blades optional for Wasp M74. Blades attached to hub by grips. Conventional swashplate assembly for cyclic-pitch and collective-pitch control. Blades do not fold. Brake on main rotor optional. Two-blade all-metal tail rotor assembly, with blades of light alloy honeycomb. Tracking tabs on main rotor blades.

Rotor Drive: Through centrifugal clutch and two-stage planetary transmission. Steel shaft drive to tail rotor with 90° gearbox at aft end of tailboom. Main rotor/engine rpm ratio M74: 0·111; M74A/M79S: 0·06.

Fuselage: In three sections: centre, rear fuselage and cabin. Centre section is a welded stainless steel tube structure to carry the engine and cabin. Rear section is also a steel tube structure of A130 steel, triangular in cross-section, and serves as a support for the tail rotor drive shaft.

Tail Unit: All versions have a small ventral fin constructed of light alloy honeycomb sandwich. Both versions of Wasp have very small fixed horizontal surfaces at forward end of ventral fin. Wasp II has a small all-moving tailplane of light alloy honeycomb sandwich construction. Trim tab on elevator.

Landing Gear: Tubular fixed skid type. Shock-absorption by flexing of cross tubes. Two small ground handling wheels standard. Float kit optional.

Power Plant (Wasp M74): One 149 kW (200 hp) Lycoming TVO-435-AIE vertically-mounted flat-six engine. One fuel tank aft of engine with capacity of 110 litres (29 US gallons). Refuelling points at each side of tank. Oil capacity 7·6 litres (2 US gallons).

Power Plant (Wasp M74A, Wasp II): One Lycoming TVO-435 vertically-mounted flat-six engine, with max T-O rating of 179 kW (240 hp) for 2 min on Wasp M74A, and of 201 kW (270 hp), for 5 min on Wasp II. Fuel capacity Wasp M74A as M74; Wasp II has two fuselage-mounted fuel tanks with a combined capacity of 216 litres (57 US gallons). Refuelling point at top of each tank. Oil capacity as above.

Accommodation: Both versions of Wasp seat a pilot only, with door on each side. Wasp II seats pilot and passenger in tandem, with two doors on starboard side. Cabin of all three versions ventilated; heating and air-conditioning optional.

Texas Helicopter Corporation M74 Wasp single-seat conversion of a Bell OH-13E

Systems: Hydraulic system, with manual backup, for operation of flight controls. Electrical system supplied by 24V battery.

Avionics and Equipment: Radio optional on Wasp II only. Blind-flying instrumentation standard only on Wasp II. Special equipment available includes agricultural spraygear, cargo hook, racks, and cable cutter.

Dimensions, external (A: Wasp M74; B: Wasp M74A; C: Wasp II):

Diameter of main rotor:
- A, B — 10·70 m (35 ft 1¼ in)
- C — 11·31 m (37 ft 1¼ in)

Diameter of tail rotor:
- A, B, C — 1·73 m (5 ft 8¼ in)

Main rotor blade chord:
- A, B, C — 0·28 m (11 in)

Length overall, excl main rotor:
- A, B — 9·59 m (31 ft 5½ in)
- C — 9·93 m (32 ft 7 in)

Height to top of rotor hub:
- A, B, C — 2·88 m (9 ft 5½ in)

Dimensions, internal:

Cabin: Length:
- A, B — 1·40 m (4 ft 7 in)
- C — 2·74 m (9 ft 0 in)

Max width:
- A, B — 0·66 m (2 ft 2 in)
- C — 0·74 m (2 ft 5 in)

Max height:
- A, B — 1·35 m (4 ft 5 in)
- C — 1·19 m (3 ft 11 in)

Areas:

Main rotor blades (each):
- A, B — 1·65 m² (17·71 sq ft)
- C — 1·73 m² (18·63 sq ft)

Tail rotor blades (each):
- A, B, C — 0·11 m² (1·2 sq ft)

Main rotor disc:
- A, B — 90·02 m² (969 sq ft)
- C — 100·69 m² (1083·87 sq ft)

Tail rotor disc:
- A, B, C — 2·35 m² (25·31 sq ft)

Ventral fin:
- A, B, C — 0·36 m² (3·86 sq ft)

Horizontal tail surfaces (total):
- A, B — 0·19 m² (2 sq ft)

Tailplane:
- C — 0·42 m² (4·5 sq ft)

Weights and Loadings:

Weight empty:
- A, B — 649 kg (1,430 lb)
- C — 721 kg (1,590 lb)

Max T-O weight:
- A — 1,111 kg (2,450 lb)
- B — 1,247 kg (2,750 lb)
- C — 1,451 kg (3,200 lb)

Max disc loading:
- A — 12·34 kg/m² (2·53 lb/sq ft)
- B — 13·85 kg/m² (2·84 lb/sq ft)
- C — 14·41 kg/m² (2·95 lb/sq ft)

Max power loading:
- A — 7·46 kg/kW (12·25 lb/hp)
- B — 6·97 kg/kW (11·46 lb/hp)
- C — 7·22 kg/kW (11·85 lb/hp)

Performance (at max T-O weight):

Never-exceed speed:
- A, B — 87 knots (161 km/h; 100 mph)
- C — 92 knots (170 km/h; 106 mph)

Max level speed:
- A, B — 87 knots (161 km/h; 100 mph)
- C — 92 knots (170 km/h; 106 mph)

Max cruising speed:
- A, B, C — 74 knots (137 km/h; 85 mph)

Econ cruising speed:
- A, B, C — 69·5 knots (129 km/h; 80 mph)

Range with max fuel, no reserves:
- A, B — 130 nm (241 km; 150 miles)
- C — 200 nm (370 km; 230 miles)

Range with 163 litres (43 US gallons) fuel, no reserves:
- C — 169 nm (314 km; 195 miles)

HOMEBUILT AIRCRAFT

AUSTRIA

WESTERMAYER
OSKAR WESTERMAYER

Hauptstrasse 11, A-2161 Poysbrunn

Herr Westermayer, Austrian Director of the International Gyroplane Association, has built four small rotorcraft, of which brief details follow:

WESTERMAYER WE 01

Completed in 1969, the WE 01 (OE-AXW) is similar in general configuration to the Bensen B-8M. It is powered by a 48·5 kW (65 hp) 1,800 cc Volkswagen engine and has a two-blade teetering rotor, made originally of wood but now fitted with Gfk blades.

Dimensions, external:
- Rotor diameter — 6·90 m (22 ft 7½ in)

Length of fuselage	3·10 m (10 ft 2 in)
Height overall	2·00 m (6 ft 6¾ in)
WEIGHTS:	
Weight empty	155 kg (342 lb)
Max T-O weight	270 kg (595 lb)
PERFORMANCE:	
Max level speed	65 knots (120 km/h; 75 mph)
Cruising speed	48 knots (90 km/h; 56 mph)
Max rate of climb at S/L	120-180 m (393-590 ft)/min
T-O run	100 m (328 ft)
Range with max fuel	86 nm (160 km; 99 miles)

WESTERMAYER WE 02

Testbed for a new Gfk rotor, with teetering hub and automatic pitch change from pre-rotation to flight pitch.

WESTERMAYER WE 03

More refined rotorcraft (OE-AXB, illustrated) used to flight test various early forms of the rotor head used on the WE 04. Powered by 2,600 cc Volkswagen engine.

WESTERMAYER WE 04

Similar to the WE 03 in general configuration, the WE 04 (OE-AXR) represents the fully-developed Westermayer single-seat rotorcraft. It was built in 1978 and embodies a number of design features new to aircraft in this category, including all-glassfibre rotor blades and a patented helicopter-type rotor head that provides cyclic and collective pitch to the blades, offering improved stability and safety. The blades are pre-spun to 500 rpm prior to take-off and pitched to +7° for flight.

The blades are made from Gevetex Glasrovings and cloth, with a Rohacell 31 foam core, bonded with CIBA epoxy resin in heated steel moulds. Blade section is NACA 8H-12.

The fuselage is made of metal and Gfk, with wood covering on the cabin and a side-hinged (to starboard) one-piece canopy/windscreen. A non-retractable tricycle landing gear is fitted, with steerable nosewheel and a small bumper wheel at the rear of the tailboom. The horizontal tail surfaces are fixed, but there is a large rudder with a ground-adjustable tab on its trailing-edge. All tail surfaces are wooden-covered.

Westermayer WE 03 light rotorcraft *(M. Hooks)*

Power plant is a 52·2 kW (70 hp) 2,600 cc Volkswagen engine, driving a two-blade wooden fixed-pitch pusher propeller. Normal autorotative rotor rpm in cruising flight is 380-400.

DIMENSIONS, EXTERNAL:	
Rotor diameter	7·40 m (24 ft 3½ in)
Rotor blade chord, constant	18 cm (7·09 in)
Length of fuselage	3·92 m (12 ft 10½ in)
Height overall	2·20 m (7 ft 2½ in)
Propeller diameter	1·38 m (4 ft 6½ in)
WEIGHTS:	
Weight empty	230 kg (507 lb)
Max T-O weight	340 kg (750 lb)
PERFORMANCE:	
Max level speed	81 knots (150 km/h; 93 mph)
Cruising speed	65 knots (120 km/h; 75 mph)
Max rate of climb at S/L	300 m (985 ft)/min
T-O run	10 m (33 ft)
Range with max fuel	135 nm (250 km; 155 miles)

CANADA

K & S
K & S AIRCRAFT

4623 Fortune Road SE, Calgary, Alberta T2A 2A7
Telephone: (403) 272 3658

K & S Aircraft is continuing to sell to amateur constructors plans of its popular SA 102·5 Cavalier two-seat light aircraft. Also available are plans of the new SA 103 and SA 104 Cavalier, and the SA 105 Super Cavalier with retractable landing gear.

K & S SA 102·5 CAVALIER

TYPE: Two-seat or '2+2' light aircraft.

WINGS: Cantilever low-wing monoplane. Wing section NACA 23015 at root, NACA 23012 at tip. Dihedral 6°. Incidence 3° 30′ at root, washed out to 1° at tip. No sweepback at quarter-chord. Single wooden box-spar, plywood leading-edge, and auxiliary rear spar to carry aileron and flap loads. Diagonal I-section drag spar between front and rear spar in each wing. Entire centre-section is plywood-covered and contoured to serve as cabin seat. Outer panels covered with Dacron synthetic fabric, finished with a polyurethane compound. Single-slotted Frise-type ailerons of spruce and plywood. Cable-operated split flaps of spruce and birch ply. Optional plans available for building wing in three pieces and for electrical actuation of flaps.

FUSELAGE: Truss-type structure, with four main longerons, of spruce and birch plywood construction. Cockpit canopy and doors of moulded glassfibre, rear part of top-decking fabric-covered.

TAIL UNIT: Cantilever structure, with sweptback vertical surfaces. All-wood construction, with Dacron covering. Fixed-incidence tailplane. Elevators operated by push-rods. Trim tab in starboard elevator.

LANDING GEAR: Non-retractable tricycle type. All units have spring steel legs of K & S design. Wheel size 5·00-5, tyre pressure 40 lb/sq in (2·8 kg/cm²), on all units. For rough-field operation, 6·00-6 main wheels with low-profile tyres are used optionally. Expanding-shoe brakes, operated hydraulically by dual toe-controls. Glassfibre wheel fairings. Alternative 1,500 lb (680 kg) capacity floats or ski landing gear optional.

POWER PLANT: Wide choice of four-cylinder engines available, including 85, 90 or 100 hp Continental, 125-130hp Franklin Sport 4A, 108 or 115 hp Lycoming O-235, or 125 or 135 hp Lycoming O-290. Choice of wood or metal, fixed-pitch or variable-pitch propellers, with diameters from 5 ft 6 in (1·68 m) to 6 ft 0 in (1·83 m). Whichever engine is used, an extension shaft (3 to 5 in; 7·6 to 12·7 cm) is fitted between the propeller and the engine crankshaft, permitting the use of more streamlined cowling panels and a reduction in the compression of airflow between the propeller and engine. All fuel in permanent wingtip tanks, with choice of two sizes: 17 or 20 US gallons (64 or 75 litres) each. Oil capacity 1·5-1·8 US gallons (5·7-6·8 litres), according to engine fitted.

ACCOMMODATION: Side-by-side seating for pilot and one adult passenger, with optional rear jump-seat for two small children in what would normally be the baggage area. Without this rear seat, up to 125 lb (56·7 kg) of baggage can be carried, depending upon engine and equipment installations. Forward-opening door on each side of heated and ventilated cabin.

K & S SA 105 Super Cavalier built by Mr Hank Q. Johnson

AVIONICS AND EQUIPMENT: Standard nav/com equipment, including 1 or 2 VHF sets. ADF and transponder optional.

DIMENSIONS, EXTERNAL:	
Wing span, over tip-tanks	27 ft 4 in (8·33 m)
Width, outer wing panels folded	11 ft 11 in (3·63 m)
Wing area, gross	118·0 sq ft (10·96 m²)
Wing aspect ratio	6·25
Length overall	22 ft 0 in (6·71 m)
Height overall	7 ft 4 in (2·23 m)
Wheelbase	4 ft 6 in (1·37 m)
Propeller diameter	see under 'Power Plant'
WEIGHTS AND LOADINGS:	
Basic operating weight empty	900 lb (408 kg)
Max T-O weight	1,500 lb (680 kg)
Max wing loading	12·7 lb/sq ft (2·60 kg/m²)
Max power loading (85 hp engine)	17·6 lb/hp (7·98 kg/hp)
PERFORMANCE (at max T-O weight, 125 hp Lycoming engine):	
Never-exceed speed	199 knots (230 mph; 370 km/h)
Max level speed at 7,000 ft (2,135 m)	160 knots (185 mph; 297 km/h)
Max cruising speed	143 knots (165 mph; 265 km/h)
Econ cruising speed	134 knots (155 mph; 249 km/h)
Stalling speed, flaps up	43·5 knots (50 mph; 81 km/h) IAS
Stalling speed, flaps down	35 knots (40 mph; 65 km/h) IAS
Max rate of climb at S/L	over 1,700 ft (518 m)/min
Service ceiling	16,000 ft (4,875 m)
T-O run	350 ft (107 m)
T-O to 50 ft (15 m)	1,000 ft (305 m)
Landing from 50 ft (15 m)	1,300 ft (396 m)
Landing run	600 ft (183 m)
Max range, no reserves	720 nm (830 miles; 1,335 km)

K & S SA 103 CAVALIER

This aircraft combines a simplified version of the SA 105 airframe with a non-retractable tailwheel type landing gear. It provides a roomier cabin than the SA 102·5, for improved passenger comfort and increased baggage space, and allows use of the plentiful engines in the 93-134 kW (125-180 hp) category that are currently available.

K & S SA 104 CAVALIER

The SA 104 differs from the SA 103 in having a non-retractable tricycle landing gear similar to that of the SA 102·5.

K & S SA 105 SUPER CAVALIER

Although similar in general configuration to the SA 102·5, the SA 105 is an entirely new design, with only the ailerons and wingtip tanks interchangeable between the two types. Overall dimensions are slightly greater, offering improved comfort and more baggage space; and a retractable tricycle landing gear is standard.

K & S does not recommend the SA 105 for inexperienced builders or for pilots with fewer than 50 hours logged. First example to fly was the aircraft shown in the accompanying illustration (N17HJ), built by Mr Hank Q. Johnson of Memphis, Tennessee. This is powered by a 149 kW (200 hp) Lycoming IO-360 flat-four engine in a Gulfstream American Traveler cowling, without a propeller extension, which compromises its appearance and performance by comparison with the basic K & S design. Max cruising speed is 191 knots (354 km/h; 220 mph) at 2,135 m (7,000 ft) with a constant-speed propeller; econ cruising speed is 156-165 knots (289-305 km/h; 180-190 mph); and max rate of climb at S/L 760 m (2,500 ft)/min.

The following description applies to the standard SA 105 built to K & S plans:

TYPE: Two-seat all-wood light aircraft.

WINGS: Cantilever low-wing monoplane. Wing section NACA 23015 at root, NACA 23010 at tip. Dihedral at chord line 6° from roots. Washout 2° 30′ between ribs 0 and 5. All-wood structure of Sitka spruce spars, fir/mahogany marine ply ribs, and leading-edge skin of

Finnish birch plywood. Fabric covering aft of main spar, except for plywood walkways at roots, and tips. Ailerons of similar construction to wings. Mechanical (optionally electrically operated) three-position (15°, 30°, 45°) simple flaps, able to be set at negative angles of −4°, −8° or −12° for cruising flight. Glassfibre canted wingtip tanks.

FUSELAGE: Truss structure, with four longerons, of Sitka spruce and Finnish birch plywood. Cockpit roof, side window/door frames and engine cowling of glassfibre. Rear fuselage and rear part of top-decking fabric covered.

TAIL UNIT: Cantilever wood structure, with sweptback vertical surfaces. Fin and tailplane plywood covered; control surfaces fabric covered. Trim tab in starboard elevator.

LANDING GEAR: Retractable tricycle type, with mechanical (optionally electric or hydraulic) actuation. Main units retract inward into wing roots, nosewheel rearward. Spring steel legs. All three wheels size 5·00-5. Brakes on main wheels, toe-operated from port seat.

POWER PLANT: One Lycoming or Franklin flat-four engine, with propeller extension shaft. Recommended are 112-119 kW (150-160 hp) Lycoming O-320/IO-320, driving a variable-pitch or constant-speed propeller. Min recommended power plant is 93 kW (125 hp) Franklin 4A-235 or Lycoming O-290/O-290-D/O-290-G driving a fixed-pitch propeller. Max recommended is 149 kW (200 hp) Lycoming O-360/IO-360. Other suitable engines include the new Javelin Aircraft Ford conversion with ground-adjustable wooden propeller. Normal capacity of wing-tip tanks 127 litres (28 Imp gallons). Optional sump tanks (with engines over 112 kW; 150 hp) raise total capacity to 152·75 litres (33·6 Imp gallons). Capacity of tip-tanks manufactured by K & S is greater than capacity quoted.

ACCOMMODATION: Two seats side by side in enclosed cabin. Dual controls. Forward-hinged window/door on each side. Baggage space aft of seats, capacity 104 kg (229 lb). (Note: restricted T-O weight of Canadian-registered aircraft does not permit this baggage allowance.)

DIMENSIONS, EXTERNAL:
- Wing span over tip-tanks: 8·31 m (27 ft 3⅝ in)
- Wing area, gross, flaps up: 10·87 m² (117 sq ft)
- Length overall: 7·25 m (23 ft 9½ in)
- Wheel track: 2·58 m (8 ft 5½ in)
- Wheelbase: 1·33 m (4 ft 4¼ in)
- Propeller diameter: 1·83 m (6 ft 0 in)

WEIGHTS:
- Weight empty: 431-454 kg (950-1,000 lb)
- Max T-O weight: Canada 680 kg (1,500 lb)
- elsewhere 816 kg (1,800 lb)

PERFORMANCE (estimated, at AUW of 816 kg; 1,800 lb. A, 93 kW; 125 hp; B, 112 kW; 150 hp; C, 134 kW; 180 hp):
- Never-exceed speed: 200 knots (370 km/h; 230 mph)
- Max cruising speed:
  - A 143-148 knots (265-273 km/h; 165-170 mph)
  - B 152-156 knots (281-289 km/h; 175-180 mph)
  - C 165-174 knots (305-322 km/h; 190-200 mph)
- Stalling speed, flaps up: 56·5-61 knots (105-113 km/h; 65-70 mph) IAS
- Stalling speed, flaps down 15°: 43·5-48 knots (81-89 km/h; 50-55 mph) IAS
- Max rate of climb at S/L:
  - A 183-213 m (600-700 ft)/min
  - B 274-305 m (900-1,000 ft)/min
  - C 365-396 m (1,200-1,300 ft)/min
- T-O run:
  - A 305 m (1,000 ft)
  - B 244 m (800 ft)
  - C 183 m (600 ft)

FRANCE

DELEMONTEZ-CAUCHY

Aérodrome de Persan-Beaumont, Val d'Oise

Among new amateur-built aircraft which took part in the RSA meeting at Brienne-le-Château in July 1979 was a small two-seater designated DC-1, with a configuration reminiscent of that of the well-known Jodel series of designs. It had been built over a period of 18 months by M Alain Cauchy, with design assistance from M Jean Delemontez, President-Director General of Avions Jodel SA, and had flown for the first time on 6 July 1979.

DELEMONTEZ-CAUCHY DC-1

TYPE: Low-cost two-seat light aircraft.

WINGS: Cantilever low-wing monoplane. Single-spar wing, with wide-span centre-section of constant chord and thickness, and two tapered outer panels set at a coarse dihedral (12°). All-wood structure. Plywood-covered leading-edge forward of spar; fabric covering aft of spar. Fabric-covered wooden ailerons.

FUSELAGE: Plywood-covered wood structure of basically rectangular section, with rounded top-decking.

TAIL UNIT: Cantilever wood structure. No fin. Tailplane plywood-covered; elevators and rudder fabric-covered.

LANDING GEAR: Non-retractable tailwheel type. Cantilever main legs with rubber-in-compression shock-absorption. Steerable tailwheel.

POWER PLANT: One 1,600 cc converted Volkswagen motorcar engine, driving a two-blade wooden fixed-pitch propeller made by Evra to Delemontez design.

ACCOMMODATION: Two seats side by side in enclosed cabin. Centrally-mounted control column and dual rudder pedals.

DIMENSIONS, EXTERNAL:
- Wing span: 7·40 m (24 ft 3½ in)
- Wing area, gross: 9·45 m² (101·7 sq ft)
- Length overall: 7·40 m (24 ft 3½ in)

DIMENSION, INTERNAL:
- Cabin: Max width: 1·00 m (3 ft 3¼ in)

WEIGHT:
- Weight empty: 216 kg (476 lb)

PERFORMANCE (measured on first flight, pilot only):
- Max level speed: 113 knots (210 km/h; 130 mph)
- Max cruising speed (75% power): 86 knots (160 km/h; 99 mph)
- Approach speed: 43 knots (80 km/h; 50 mph)
- Max rate of climb at S/L: 240 m (785 ft)/min
- T-O run: 120 m (394 ft)
- Landing run: 100 m (328 ft)

GRINVALS

Aircraft exhibited at the 1979 Paris Air Show under the auspices of the RSA (Réseau du Sport de l'Air) included the four-seat all-plastics Orion, designed and built by M Grinvals with the assistance of M Calvel, whose Frelon motor glider is described in this Addenda. The Orion project had first attracted attention at the 1977 RSA meeting at Brienne-le-Château, where a radio-controlled scale model was demonstrated. The full-scale prototype was not quite complete, lacking its tail-mounted propeller, when shown at Le Bourget and Brienne in the Summer of 1979.

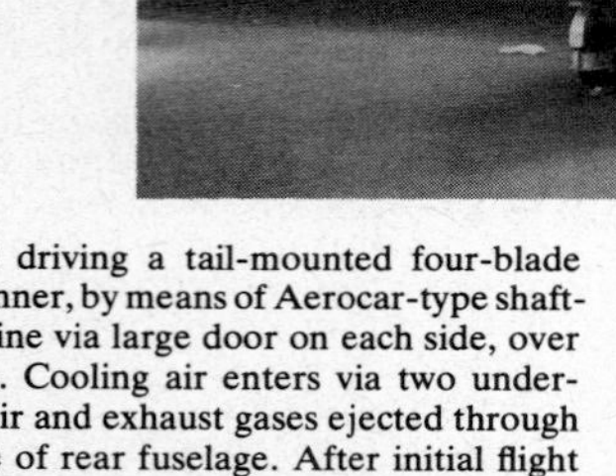

The four-seat Grinvals Orion, awaiting its tail-mounted propeller *(J. M. G. Gradidge)*

GRINVALS ORION

The entire airframe of the Orion is made of glassfibre, reinforced locally with carbon fibre and Kevlar.

TYPE: Four-seat all-plastics light aircraft.

WINGS: Cantilever low-wing monoplane, built in one piece tip-to-tip, and installed in housing moulded into under-surface of fuselage. Wing section NACA 43015 at root, NACA 43012 at tip. Dihedral 4° 18′ from root. Incidence 2° 18′ at root, 0° 18′ at tip. Aileron and slotted flap along entire trailing-edge of each wing. No tabs.

FUSELAGE: All-plastics structure of ovoid section, with integral tail fin and wing-root stubs and fillets.

TAIL UNIT: Cantilever T-tail, with fixed tailplane, horn-balanced elevator and inset rudder. Fixed ventral fin. Tab in elevator.

LANDING GEAR: Retractable tricycle type, with single wheel on each unit. Electrical retraction, nosewheel forward, main units inward under fuselage. Manual emergency actuation. Main gear fully enclosed when retracted, by doors attached to legs. All three legs of Wittman cantilever leaf-spring type. Hydraulic disc brakes on main wheels. Tailskid under ventral fin to protect propeller in taildown attitude.

POWER PLANT: Prototype has one Lycoming flat-four engine, of 112-134 kW (150-180 hp), mounted inside rear fuselage and driving a tail-mounted four-blade propeller, with spinner, by means of Aerocar-type shafting. Access to engine via large door on each side, over wing trailing-edge. Cooling air enters via two underbelly scoops; hot air and exhaust gases ejected through ducts on each side of rear fuselage. After initial flight trials, and certification, the prototype is planned to flight test alternative power plants, including Wankel and 112 kW (150 hp) SACMA engines.

ACCOMMODATION: Four persons, in pairs, in enclosed cabin, or three persons, depending on engine power. Upward-opening window/door on each side, forward of wing. Large baggage space at rear of cabin. Dual controls.

DIMENSIONS, EXTERNAL:
- Wing span: 9·00 m (29 ft 6½ in)
- Wing chord at root: 1·50 m (4 ft 11 in)
- Wing chord at tip: 1·00 m (3 ft 3½ in)
- Wing aspect ratio: 7·2
- Wing area, gross: 11·25 m² (121·1 sq ft)
- Length overall: 6·70 m (21 ft 11¾ in)
- Tailplane span: 3·30 m (10 ft 10 in)
- Wheel track: 2·90 m (9 ft 6 in)
- Propeller diameter: 1·50 m (4 ft 11 in)

DIMENSIONS, INTERNAL:
- Cabin: Length: 2·30 m (7 ft 6½ in)
- Max height: 1·10 m (3 ft 7¼ in)
- Max width: 1·10 m (3 ft 7¼ in)

WEIGHTS (A, 112 kW; 150 hp: B, 134 kW; 180 hp):
- Weight empty, equipped: A 535 kg (1,180 lb)
  - B 550 kg (1,213 lb)
- Max T-O weight: A 975 kg (2,150 lb)
  - B 990 kg (2,183 lb)

PERFORMANCE (estimated, at max T-O weight):
- Max level speed, three occupants:
  - A 162 knots (300 km/h; 186 mph)
- Max level speed, three/four occupants:
  - B 173 knots (320 km/h; 199 mph)
- Max cruising speed: A 146 knots (270 km/h; 168 mph)
  - B 156 knots (290 km/h; 180 mph)

POTTIER (page 482)

POTTIER P.50TR BOUVREUIL

The Bouvreuil single-seat sporting monoplane built in Switzerland by M Sugnaux, of Billens, flew for the first time on 27 July 1979 and was displayed at the 1979 RSA meeting at Brienne in France. This aircraft (HB-YBF) has a 74·5 kW (100 hp) Continental O-200 engine, slotted flaps and electrically-retractable tailwheel-type landing gear. It differs from plans in having extended and cambered wingtips, and two underwing attachments for camera pods or external fuel tanks. Its load factors for aerobatics are calculated as +12/−7*g*. Equipment includes VHF radio and VOR.

DIMENSIONS, EXTERNAL:
- Wing span: 6·48 m (21 ft 3 in)
- Wing area, gross: 7·5 m² (80·7 sq ft)
- Length overall: 5·25 m (17 ft 2¾ in)
- Height overall: 1·70 m (5 ft 7 in)

WEIGHT:
- Weight empty: 360 kg (794 lb)

PERFORMANCE (estimated):
- Max level speed: 167 knots (310 km/h; 192 mph)
- Max cruising speed: 151 knots (280 km/h; 174 mph)
- Landing speed: 43 knots (80 km/h; 50 mph)

RÉSEAU DU SPORT DE L'AIR

Under the aegis of the RSA, a number of French amateur designer/constructors exhibited their latest products at the 1979 Paris Air Show. Two of the completed aircraft, the Calvel Frelon motor glider and the Grinvals Orion homebuilt aircraft, are described separately in this Addenda. The following homebuilt was also among those exhibited:

Koenig Tom-Pouss. This small side-by-side two-seat

light aircraft is of epoxy/carbon fibre construction and is powered by a fan-cooled 1,700 cc Volkswagen engine, mounted at the rear of the fuselage pod and driving a pusher propeller. Twin tailbooms carry the inverted-V tail unit, and there is a fixed NASA-type winglet at each wingtip. Large 'flaperons' on the wing trailing-edges provide high lift augmentation and roll control. Pitch and yaw control are assured by the combined elevator/rudders which can be operated both differentially and collectively. Maximum speed is quoted as 143 knots (265 km/h; 165 mph).

The Koenig Tom-Pouss, of epoxy/carbon fibre construction *(J. M. G. Gradidge)*

GERMANY (FEDERAL)

Becker Mistral CP 301 (see page 484)

Eich JE-2 Gyroplane (Continental A65 engine)

UNITED STATES OF AMERICA

EICH
JAMES EICH

1820 W Grand Avenue, Alhambra, California 91801
Telephone: (213) 289 1983

After gaining considerable experience from flying a Barnett J-3M rotorcraft, Mr Eich designed and built a two-seat gyroplane of which details follow. Design started in 1975 and construction of the prototype began the following year. First flight was achieved in 1977.

EICH JE-2 GYROPLANE

TYPE: Two-seat light autogyro.

ROTOR SYSTEM: Two-blade aluminium teetering rotor. Six struts forming the rotor pylon pick up the top of the fuselage structure at the corners of the front (passenger's) cockpit.

FUSELAGE: Square-section welded girder structure of chrome-molybdenum steel tubing, covered with Dacron and finished with Stits Poly-dope.

TAIL UNIT: Fixed horizontal stabiliser, triangular ventral fin and rudder. Fin is of Dacron, integral with fuselage covering. Stabiliser and rudder are of sheet aluminium, with simple ribs and spars of aluminium tubing.

LANDING GEAR: Non-retractable tricycle type. Spring-in-compression shock-absorption. Main-wheel tyres size 5·00-5. Steerable nosewheel with tyre size 4·00-5. Go-kart brakes.

POWER PLANT: One 48·5 kW (65 hp) Continental A65 engine, driving a two-blade Eich fixed-pitch tractor propeller. One fuel tank aft of firewall, capacity 60·5 litres (16 US gallons).

ACCOMMODATION: Two seats in tandem in open cockpits. Dual controls.

DIMENSIONS, EXTERNAL:

Diameter of main rotor	7·92 m (26 ft 0 in)
Rotor blade chord	0·187 m (7⅜ in)
Length overall	4·27 m (14 ft 0 in)
Height overall	2·44 m (8 ft 0 in)
Wheel track	1·83 m (6 ft 0 in)
Wheelbase	1·65 m (5 ft 5 in)
Propeller diameter	1·78 m (5 ft 10 in)

WEIGHTS:

Weight empty	200 kg (440 lb)
Max T-O weight	385·5 kg (850 lb)

PERFORMANCE:

Max cruising speed at 915 m (3,000 ft)	69·5 knots (129 km/h; 80 mph)
Econ cruising speed at 915 m (3,000 ft)	52 knots (96·5 km/h; 60 mph)
Max rate of climb at 915 m (3,000 ft)	91·5 m (300 ft)/min
T-O run	305 m (1,000 ft)
Landing run	15 m (50 ft)
Range	156 nm (290 km; 180 miles)

FISHER-VAN NORMAN
DICK FISHER and CHARLES VAN NORMAN

FISHER-VAN NORMAN REPLICA P-51D MUSTANG

Mr Dick Fisher, an operations project engineer with NASA, and Mr Charles Van Norman, an engineer with the USAF Flight Test Center at Edwards Air Force Base, have designed and built a ⅔-scale replica of a North American P-51D Mustang fighter of the Second World War. The complete project occupied their spare time for 14 years and each man devoted about 5,000 hours to construction of the aircraft over the final 11-year period. The first flight was made in July 1978.

2/3-scale replica of a P-51D Mustang, built by Mr Dick Fisher and Mr Charles Van Norman *(Howard Levy)*

TYPE: Single-seat scale replica fighter.

WINGS: Cantilever all-wood structure, covered with plywood and an outer skin of Dacron fabric, finished with automotive acrylic enamel. Electrically-actuated flaps.

FUSELAGE: All-wood semi-monocoque structure, covered with plywood and an outer skin of Dacron fabric, finished with automotive acrylic enamel.

TAIL UNIT: Conventional cantilever structure of similar construction to wings. Electric pitch trim.

LANDING GEAR: Retractable tailwheel type. Main legs from a Globe Swift. Hydraulically-actuated main units; electrically-actuated tailwheel.

POWER PLANT: One 149 kW (200 hp) Ranger 6-440-C5 engine, driving a two-blade propeller with spinner. Fuel capacity 113·5 litres (30 US gallons).

ACCOMMODATION: Single seat under blown canopy.

WEIGHTS:

Weight empty	658 kg (1,450 lb)
Max T-O weight	839 kg (1,850 lb)

PERFORMANCE:

Max level speed over	174 knots (322 km/h; 200 mph)
Max rate of climb at S/L	305-457 m (1,000-1,500 ft)/min
Range with max fuel at 148 knots (274 km/h; 170 mph)	434 nm (805 km; 500 miles)
Endurance with max fuel	3 h

INTERNATIONAL HELICOPTERS
INTERNATIONAL HELICOPTERS INC

PO Box 107, Mayville, New York 14757
PRESIDENT: Gary M. Weatherlow
VICE-PRESIDENT: Robert G. Dart

On 2 January 1979, this company announced that it had completed the purchase of Helicom Inc, which had produced and marketed kits for single-seat and two-seat homebuilt helicopters since the early 1960s. It transferred the entire operation from Long Beach, California, to the facilities of Aero Industries at Dart Airport (Detroit Sectional) in Mayville, NY, and began production of Commuter IIA kits immediately.

INTERNATIONAL HELICOPTERS COMMUTER IIA

A detailed description of the original Helicom Commuter Jr Model H-1A single-seat helicopter last appeared in the 1972-73 *Jane's*. The Commuter IIA is a more powerful two-seater, of generally similar configuration but embodying a number of refinements. Details of these, and a photograph of the aircraft, were not available when this edition closed for press. The following details should be regarded as provisional:

TYPE: Two-seat light helicopter.

ROTOR SYSTEM: Two-blade main rotor and two-blade tail rotor of aluminium alloy construction. All-steel drive system, with no V-belts. Specially-designed centrifugal clutch.

FUSELAGE: Basic steel tube truss structure. Glassfibre and Plexiglas cabin enclosure. Rear structure not covered.

TAIL UNIT: Small horizontal stabiliser and triangular ventral fin.

LANDING GEAR: Steel tube skids, with optional ground handling wheels.

POWER PLANT: One 112 kW (150 hp) Lycoming O-320 flat-four engine, with dual ignition, mounted vertically aft of cabin. Two cylindrical fuel tanks, one each side of main rotor driveshaft, above engine.

ACCOMMODATION: Two seats side by side. Conventional helicopter controls.

LACO

Banning Municipal Airport, PO Box 415, Desert Hot Springs, California 92240
Telephone: (714) 329 0955

LACO 125

Mr Joe Laven designed, built and has flown a two-seat light biplane known as the LACO. Design started in May 1971 and, following construction of two scale models to check the basic configuration, construction of a prototype began in April 1972. First flight was achieved on 29 May 1977 at the hands of Stolp Starduster test pilot Mr Eric Shilling.

TYPE: Two-seat light biplane.

WINGS: Braced single-bay biplane. Wing section NACA 2412. Dihedral 2° on lower wings only. Incidence 2° on lower wings only. Conventional structure, with two spruce spars, spruce capstrips, mahogany ribs, aluminium leading-edge and chrome-molybdenum steel fittings, all fabric covered. N-type interplane struts each side; two N-type struts support centre of upper wing above fuselage. Modified Frise-type ailerons on lower wings only, of similar construction to wings but with aluminium trailing-edge. No flaps or trim tabs.

FUSELAGE: Welded Warren truss structure of chrome-molybdenum steel tubing, with mahogany formers and spruce stringers, fabric covered.

TAIL UNIT: Conventional braced structure of welded chrome-molybdenum steel tube, fabric covered. Trim tab optional, but not fitted to prototype.

LANDING GEAR: Non-retractable tailwheel type, with steerable tailwheel. Polyurethane spring shock-absorption of LACO design. Cleveland main wheels, size 6·00-6. McKay Aero Research MF-7 main-wheel fairings. Cleveland hydraulic brakes.

LACO 125, designed and built by Mr Joe Laven

POWER PLANT: One 93 kW (125 hp) Continental C-215-2 flat-four engine, driving a McCauley two-blade fixed-pitch propeller. Fuel tank in fuselage, capacity 91 litres (24 US gallons). Oil capacity 7·5 litres (2 US gallons).

ACCOMMODATION: Two seats in tandem in open cockpits.

SYSTEMS: Engine-driven generator, lights and 30A starting system.

AVIONICS: Genave-100 channel transceiver.

DIMENSIONS, EXTERNAL:

Wing span, upper	6·93 m (22 ft 8¾ in)
Wing span, lower	6·29 m (20 ft 7½ in)
Wing chord, upper (constant)	1·14 m (3 ft 9 in)
Wing chord, lower (constant)	1·07 m (3 ft 6 in)
Wing area, gross	13·94 m² (150 sq ft)
Length overall	5·94 m (19 ft 6 in)
Height overall	2·18 m (7 ft 2 in)
Tailplane span	2·64 m (8 ft 8 in)
Wheel track	1·88 m (6 ft 2 in)
Wheelbase	4·47 m (14 ft 8 in)
Propeller diameter	1·83 m (6 ft 0 in)

WEIGHTS:

Weight empty	390 kg (860 lb)
Max T-O weight	635 kg (1,400 lb)

PERFORMANCE:

Never-exceed speed	139 knots (257 km/h; 160 mph)
Max level speed	108 knots (200 km/h; 124 mph)
Max cruising speed	98 knots (182 km/h; 113 mph)
Stalling speed, power off	49 knots (90 km/h; 56 mph)
Stalling speed, power on	43·5 knots (80·5 km/h; 50 mph)
Max rate of climb at S/L	259 m (850 ft)/min
Range with max fuel	245 nm (455 km; 283 miles)

MacCREADY (page 528)

Dr PAUL MacCREADY

GOSSAMER ALBATROSS

The Gossamer Albatross man-powered aircraft was developed from the Gossamer Condor, with which a team headed by Dr Paul MacCready won a £50,000 Kramer Prize for the first figure-of-eight flight around two pylons half a mile apart by an aircraft propelled entirely by a man, on 23 August 1977. The Albatross is similar in configuration to the Condor, but has fewer external bracing wires and has structural members made of carbon fibre reinforced plastics (CFRP) tubing for optimum strength/weight ratio. The piloting position is upright rather than semi-reclined. Weight of the Albatross slightly exceeds that of the Condor, due mainly to the 2 litres (3·5 Imp pints) of drinking water provided for the pilot and the installation of a small Motorola Handi Talki communications radio with Bell Telephone earphone.

On 12 June 1979 the Gossamer Albatross completed successfully the first crossing of the English Channel by an aircraft propelled entirely by a man. Piloted by Mr Bryan Allen, who had gained the £50,000 prize in the Condor in 1977, it took off from Folkestone, England, at 05.51 h BST and landed on the beach at Cap Gris Nez, France, at 08.40 h BST. Straight-line distance covered was about 20 nm (37 km; 23 miles). Indicated airspeed varied from an initial 12-13 knots (22-24 km/h; 14-15 mph) to a later 9·5-10·5 knots (17·5-19·5 km/h; 11-12 mph). Average height above the sea was 0·5-2 m (2-6 ft), with a minimum of about 0·15 m (6 in) and maximum of 7·5 m (25 ft). This achievement gained a Kremer Prize of £100,000.

A second Gossamer Albatross, built as a backup for the cross-Channel flight, differs only in detail from the aircraft used on the successful attempt and described hereafter:

TYPE: Single-seat man-powered aircraft.

WINGS: Wire-braced high-wing monoplane, made in four panels, joined by light alloy tubes inside spar. Wing section Lissaman 7776. Thickness/chord ratio 11·5%. Moderate dihedral, constant from roots. Average sweepback at spar (28% chord) 7° 30′. Single spar of 50 mm (2 in) diameter CFRP tube; Styrofoam (expanded polystyrene) ribs with CFRP capstrips and stiffeners; Styrofoam leading-edge skin and Du Pont Mylar transparent heat-shrunk plastic film covering. Wingtips warped by starboard 'handlebar' control. No other control surfaces on wings. Kingpost of 25 mm (1 in) CFRP tubing provides overwing attachment for bracing wires.

Bryan Allen leaving the cliffs of Dover on 12 June 1979

FUSELAGE: Basic structure of CFRP tubing; formers of CFRP strip with Styrofoam core; leading-edge and bottom covering of Styrofoam sheet, with inset window in line with pilot's head; Mylar film covering. Holes in leading-edge and vents in trailing-edge maintain flow of air through interior. Rhomboidal shape and aerofoil section of fuselage gondola enable it to act as vertical stabilising surface, requiring no additional fin area.

FOREPLANE: Wire-braced universally-pivoted structure of similar construction to wings, carried on a bowsprit of 38 mm (1·5 in) CFRP tubing. Fore and aft movement of pilot's port 'handlebar' grip controls foreplane pitch. Sideways movement operates servo-tabs on trailing-edge near tips, to provide roll and directional control.

LANDING GEAR: Two small fixed wheels at base of fore and aft gondola structural members, diameter 125 mm (5 in) and 100 mm (4 in) respectively.

MOTIVE POWER: Man-power on bicycle pedals, transmitted by chain drive to two-blade pusher propeller mounted on light alloy/CFRP shaft. Computer-designed propeller has Eppler 193 basic section; each blade is made in six pieces from expanded polystyrene, bonded on to a CFRP tube and covered with Kevlar cloth.

DIMENSIONS, EXTERNAL:

Wing span	28·60 m (93 ft 10 in)
Wing area	44·03 m² (474 sq ft)
Wing aspect ratio	18·6
Canard span	5·59 m (18 ft 4 in)
Canard area	5·95 m² (64 sq ft)
Propeller diameter	4·11 m (13 ft 6 in)

WEIGHTS AND LOADING:

Weight empty	31·75 kg (70 lb)
T-O weight with 63·5 kg (140 lb) pilot	97·5 kg (215 lb)
Wing loading	2·21 kg/m² (0·45 lb/sq ft)

McCARLEY (page 529)

After the photograph of the prototype Mini-Mac had been printed, we learned that the gentleman standing by the aircraft was not the late Mr Charles E. McCarley. The Editor offers his sincere regrets for this wrong assumption.

Rutan VariEze high-performance tail-first monoplane built in Switzerland **(see page 539)** *(Roland Eichenberger)*

SEQUOIA AIRCRAFT CORPORATION (page 540)

SEQUOIA FALCO F.8L

Sequoia Aircraft Corporation is offering plans to build the Falco F.8L high-performance low-wing monoplane, designed in Italy by Ing Stelio Frati and first flown on 15 June 1955. The aircraft was last marketed in Italy by Aeromere. In its current form, for amateur construction, it incorporates minor changes, and the performance data given below apply to the Sequoia Falco F.8L fitted with a 119 kW (160 hp) Lycoming O-320-B3B flat-four engine, although Lycoming engines of 100·5 kW (135 hp) and 112 kW (150 hp) can be installed. Component parts and kits for the Sequoia Falco F.8L will be available from outside suppliers, details of which can be obtained through Sequoia Aircraft.

Type: Two-seat light monoplane.

Wings: Cantilever low-wing monoplane. Laminar-flow NACA $64_2$212½ wing section at root, NACA $64_2$210½ at tip. Thickness/chord ratio 12½% at root and 10% at tip. Dihedral 5°. Incidence at root 3°. Washout 4°. All-wood one-piece single-spar structure built integrally with forward portion of fuselage. Plywood-covered, with overall fabric covering. Frise-type ailerons and electrically-operated split flaps can be of wood and fabric or all-metal construction. Optional leading-edge modification gives milder stall and slightly reduced cruising speed.

Fuselage: Plywood-covered semi-monocoque structure, with wooden frames and longerons, fabric covered overall. Normally built in two sections, comprising a centre-section integral with the wings, and a tailcone; but can be built in one piece.

Tail Unit: Cantilever type. All-wood tailplane and fin integral with rear portion of fuselage. Rudder and elevators can be of wood and fabric or all-metal construction. Controllable trim tab in starboard elevator.

Italian-built Falco F.8L two-seat light monoplane
(James Gilbert)

Landing Gear: Retractable tricycle type. Manual or optional electrical retraction, with mechanical emergency actuation. Oleo-pneumatic shock-absorbers. Single-disc hydraulic brakes. Steerable nosewheel.

Power Plant: One Lycoming O-290-D2B, O-320-A2A or O-320-B3B flat-four engine of 100·5 kW (135 hp), 112 kW (150 hp) or 119 kW (160 hp) respectively, driving a fixed-pitch or constant-speed (except for O-290 engine) two-blade propeller with spinner. Fuel in two metal tanks, capacity 118 litres (31·2 US gallons).

Accommodation: Enclosed cabin for two persons side by side. Rearward-sliding transparent canopy. Dual controls standard. Cabin heated and ventilated. Baggage locker behind seats. Provision for fitting seat for a child of not more than 40 kg (88 lb) weight in baggage space.

Systems: Electrical system of 12V or 24V for cabin lighting, landing lights, navigation lights, strobes, etc.

Dimensions, external:
- Wing span 8·00 m (26 ft 3 in)
- Wing area, gross 10 m² (107·5 sq ft)
- Wing aspect ratio 6·4
- Length overall 6·50 m (21 ft 4 in)
- Height overall 2·29 m (7 ft 6 in)

Weights (O-320-B3B engine):
- Weight empty 550 kg (1,212 lb)
- Max T-O weight 820 kg (1,808 lb)
- Max aerobatic weight 748 kg (1,650 lb)

Performance (O-320-B3B engine):
- Never-exceed speed 208 knots (386 km/h; 240 mph)
- Max level speed at S/L 184 knots (341 km/h; 212 mph)
- Cruising speed at 1,830 m (6,000 ft), 75% power 165 knots (306 km/h; 190 mph)
- Stalling speed, flaps and wheels down 54 knots (100 km/h; 62 mph)
- Max rate of climb at S/L 347 m (1,140 ft)/min
- Service ceiling 5,790 m (19,000 ft)
- Range at econ cruising speed 755 nm (1,400 km; 870 miles)

STRIPLIN
STRIPLIN AIRCRAFT CORPORATION

PO Box 2001, Lancaster, California 93534
Telephone: (805) 945 2522

President: Kenneth Striplin

This company is developing a foot-launched powered hang glider known as the FLAC (Foot Launched Air Cycle), which was flown for the first time on 24 October 1978 by 19 year old Paul Striplin, who had logged only 9 h as a student pilot at that time. Testing has been completed, and Striplin Aircraft Corporation is marketing the FLAC in the form of a Quick Flight Kit, which requires only assembly, and an Economy Kit containing all materials to build the complete glider. It does not sell engines, but is able to recommend suitable power plants. The following data apply to the prototype:

STRIPLIN FLAC

Type: Foot-launched rigid-wing powered hang glider.

Wings: Cantilever high-wing monoplane of constant chord. Special German laminar-flow wing section. Wings moderately sweptback. No dihedral. Structure fabric-covered aft of spar. Elevon control surfaces attached to trailing-edge near tips operate collectively as elevators, differentially as ailerons. Large endplates on wingtips each carry a control surface at the rear, operated independently as rudders, collectively as airbrakes. Wings fold for transportation.

Fuselage: Glassfibre pod suspended from wings, with large windscreen and open sides. Bomb-bay type doors in bottom open for foot launching.

Striplin Foot Launched Air Cycle

Landing Gear (auxiliary): Tricycle type, with non-retractable main units and retractable steerable nosewheel. Laminated glassfibre legs. Optional main-wheel fairings.

Power Plant (optional): Prototype has a go-kart engine, with reduction gear, driving a small pusher propeller.

Accommodation: Pilot only, on hammock-type seat. Side-stick control actuates elevons; foot pedals operate rudders.

Dimensions, external:
- Wing span 9·75 m (32 ft 0 in)
- Wing span, folded 5·64 m (18 ft 6 in)
- Wing chord (constant) 1·37 m (4 ft 6 in)
- Wing area 14·4 m² (155 sq ft)
- Wing aspect ratio 6·3
- Length of fuselage pod 2·31 m (7 ft 7 in)
- Height overall 1·22 m (4 ft 0 in)
- Wheel track 1·07 m (3 ft 6 in)

Weight:
- Weight empty 71 kg (156 lb)

Performance (provisional):
- Max level speed over 48 knots (89 km/h; 55 mph)
- T-O speed on wheels at 1,220 m (4,000 ft) 18·5 knots (34 km/h; 21 mph)
- Rate of climb at 1,220 m (4,000 ft)91 m (300 ft)/min

UFM
ULTRALIGHT FLYING MACHINES

Santa Clara, California

UFM SOLAR RISER

Mr Larry Mauro, designer of the Easy Rider biplane hang glider, has built a solar-powered aircraft, called the Solar Riser. Based on the hang glider, the Solar Riser has a power system incorporating solar panels with 300 cells, giving a total of 40V 10A power output. Associated equipment includes a battery and a 2·24 kW (3 hp) General Design electric motor of the type developed originally for the Apollo spacecraft programme. To convert the hang glider into a simple research aeroplane, a pilot nacelle and a tricycle landing gear are also fitted.

The Solar Riser is claimed to have been the first solar-powered aircraft to fly, and by mid-1979 had completed six flights, totalling 10 minutes flying time. The first flight, in late April 1979, covered a distance of about 805 m (2,640 ft), at an altitude of 12·2 m (40 ft). Normal flying time is from 1 to 3 minutes. The current research and development programme is aiming at a flight of one hour, but improvements to the aircraft and its power system could eventually lead to flights of about two hours.

Type: Single-seat solar-powered biplane.

Wings: Based on Easy Rider hang glider, with aluminium alloy spars, ribs, leading- and trailing-edges, stainless steel interplane struts, and Dacron skin. Upper wing top surface is covered with solar panels made up of 300 cells.

UFM Solar Riser solar-powered aeroplane
(Henry Artof)

Fuselage: Small and basic nacelle for pilot, with electric motor mounted at rear.

Landing Gear: Non-retractable tricycle type.

Power Plant: One 2·24 kW (3 hp) General Design electric motor, driving a 1·04 m (3 ft 5 in) diameter Soarmaster pusher propeller.

Dimensions, external:
- Wing span 9·14 m (30 ft 0 in)
- Wing chord (constant) 1·04 m (3 ft 5 in)
- Length overall 2·44 m (8 ft 0 in)

Weights:
- Weight empty 57 kg (125 lb)
- Max T-O weight 131·5 kg (290 lb)

Performance:
- Max level speed, approx 17·3 knots (32 km/h; 20 mph)
- T-O run 23-61 m (75-200 ft)
- Endurance (to date) 1 to 3 min

SAILPLANES

AUSTRALIA

DAVID BETTERIDGE

c/o Box 390, Morphett Vale, South Australia 5162

Mr Betteridge has designed an unusual motor glider, the general appearance of which is shown in an accompanying photograph. It was test-flown by Mr Colin Scott at Aldinga, South Australia, in early 1979, and was due to be put into production by Free Flight Gliders towards the end of that year.

Of sweptwing tail-less configuration, with a swept fin and rudder at each wingtip, the aircraft has a single-seat open cockpit and is powered by a 175 cc Yamaha motorcycle engine, driving a pusher propeller. A tailwheel-type non-retractable landing gear is fitted.

The prototype is built of aluminium and plywood, but glassfibre will be used for production aircraft, which will be capable of being dismantled and carried on a car trailer.

SPECIFICATION:

Wing span	10·00 m (32 ft 9¾ in)
Length overall	3·00 m (9 ft 10 in)
Weight empty	180 kg (397 lb)
T-O and landing run	50 m (165 ft)

Prototype motor glider designed by Mr David Betteridge of South Australia *(Advertiser Newspapers Ltd)*

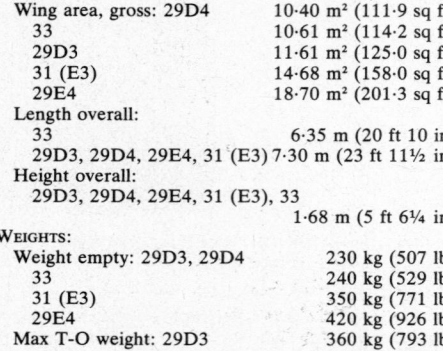

JOHN BUCHANAN

Mr Buchanan is building the prototype of a new sailplane which he describes as "just a pod big enough to fit the pilot, with a wing attached". The wing, constructed of carbon-fibre and glassfibre, is of swept configuration, with a 15 metre span (49 ft 2½ in), narrow chord and very high aspect ratio. It is mid-mounted on the small, streamlined fuselage pod, at the rear of which is a small sweptback fin; there are no horizontal tail surfaces. A flush-fitting one-piece cockpit transparency encloses the pilot. Fuselage length is 3·70 m (12 ft 1¾ in).

Mr Buchanan, who is a graduate aeronautical engineer from the Cranfield Institute of Technology in England and a former RAAF pilot, is building the sailplane under a $A10,000 grant from the Australian government.

FRANCE

JACQUES CALVEL

CALVEL FRELON (HORNET)

Calvel Frelon ultra-light powered glider *(J. M. G. Gradidge)*

Illustrated in an accompanying photograph, the Frelon was built by M Jacques Calvel, a specialist in the use of laminated plastics materials.

TYPE: Single-seat ultralight powered glider.

AIRFRAME: Braced high-wing monoplane. Wing section Wortmann FX-61-184. Slight dihedral from roots; single wing bracing strut each side. Airbrake in upper surface of each wing, well inboard of aileron and close to trailing-edge. Main load-bearing structure of cabin is of metal tubing, around which is built a streamlined pod-shaped nacelle tapering off to a 12 cm (4¾ in) diameter tubular tailboom. Cantilever tail unit comprises a sweptback fin with horn-balanced rudder, a small ventral fin, and a low-set, non-swept, one-piece all-moving tailplane. Non-retractable tricycle landing gear, with streamlined wheel fairings. Steerable nosewheel has metal leg, main units have legs of glassfibre laminates. Except for cabin framework and nosewheel leg, entire airframe is of glassfibre/epoxy laminates, with metal fittings. One-piece flush-fitting cockpit transparency.

POWER PLANT: One 20 kW (27 hp) piston engine, installed in nacelle on top of fuselage, aft of cabin, and driving a two-blade fixed-pitch wooden propeller with spinner.

DIMENSIONS, EXTERNAL:

Wing span	10·40 m (34 ft 1½ in)
Wing chord, constant	0·65 m (2 ft 1½ in)
Wing area, gross	7·80 m² (83·96 sq ft)
Wing aspect ratio	13·5
Length overall	5·40 m (17 ft 8½ in)
Height overall	1·50 m (4 ft 11 in)
Propeller diameter	0·65 m (2 ft 1½ in)

WEIGHTS AND LOADING:

Weight empty	135 kg (297 lb)
Max T-O weight	220 kg (485 lb)
Max wing loading	28 kg/m² (5·7 lb/sq ft)

PERFORMANCE (estimated):

Max level speed	59 knots (110 km/h; 68 mph)
Cruising speed	43 knots (80 km/h; 50 mph)
Stalling speed	24·5 knots (45 km/h; 28 mph)

ROMANIA

ICA-BRASOV (page 574)

IS-29

The current basic version of this versatile sailplane is the **IS-29D2**, described in the main Sailplanes section. The following are all variants of the IS-29D2 design:

IS-29D3. Club Class version, with 16·5 m span wings, non-retractable landing gear and unpainted (allochrome) finish.

IS-29D4. With 15 m span wings, 80° max flap setting, airbrakes, and (to come) provision for 120 litres (26·4 Imp gallons) water ballast.

IS-29DM. Powered version of D2; see separate description which follows.

IS-29E2. With 19 m span wings and interconnected flaps and ailerons. To be offered with 100 litres (22 Imp gallons) water ballast. Details as in main section.

IS-29E4. High-performance version, with 24 m span wings, built in four sections, and interconnected flaps and ailerons.

IS-29EM. Powered version of E3; see separate description which follows.

IS-31 (E3). With 20 m span wings and interconnected flaps and ailerons. To be offered with 100 litres (22 Imp gallons) water ballast. Prototype flying; not yet certificated in mid-1979.

IS-33. Racing version, with 15 m span wings fitted with 'flaperons'. To be offered with 150 litres (33 Imp gallons) water ballast.

IS-29EM motor glider (Rectimo 4AR-1200 engine)

DIMENSIONS, EXTERNAL:

Wing span: 29D4, 33	15·00 m (49 ft 2½ in)
29D3	16·50 m (54 ft 1½ in)
31 (E3)	20·00 m (65 ft 7½ in)
29E4	24·00 m (78 ft 9 in)
Wing area, gross: 29D4	10·40 m² (111·9 sq ft)
33	10·61 m² (114·2 sq ft)
29D3	11·61 m² (125·0 sq ft)
31 (E3)	14·68 m² (158·0 sq ft)
29E4	18·70 m² (201·3 sq ft)
Length overall:	
33	6·35 m (20 ft 10 in)
29D3, 29D4, 29E4, 31 (E3)	7·30 m (23 ft 11½ in)
Height overall:	
29D3, 29D4, 29E4, 31 (E3), 33	1·68 m (5 ft 6¼ in)

WEIGHTS:

Weight empty: 29D3, 29D4	230 kg (507 lb)
33	240 kg (529 lb)
31 (E3)	350 kg (771 lb)
29E4	420 kg (926 lb)
Max T-O weight: 29D3	360 kg (793 lb)
29D4	480 kg (1,058 lb)
33	500 kg (1,102 lb)
29E4, 31 (E3)	530 kg (1,168 lb)

PERFORMANCE:

Best glide ratio:	
29D3 at 50 knots (93 km/h; 58 mph)	37·5
29D4 at 59 knots (110 km/h; 68·5 mph)	37
29E4 at 57 knots (105 km/h; 65·5 mph)	51
31 (E3) at 59 knots (110 km/h; 68·5 mph)	48
33 at 61·5 knots (114 km/h; 71 mph)	41
Min sinking speed:	
29D3 at 42 knots (78 km/h; 48·5 mph)	0·58 m (1·90 ft)/s
29D4 at 46·5 knots (86 km/h; 53·5 mph)	0·65 m (2·13 ft)/s
29E4 at 45·5 knots (84 km/h; 52·5 mph)	0·40 m (1·31 ft)/s
31 (E3) at 49 knots (90 km/h; 56 mph)	0·50 m (1·64 ft)/s
33 at 46·5 knots (86 km/h; 53·5 mph)	0·64 m (2·10 ft)/s
Stalling speed:	
29D3, 29E4	37 knots (68 km/h; 42·5 mph)
33	40·5 knots (75 km/h; 47 mph)
29D4, 31 (E3)	41·5 knots (76 km/h; 47·5 mph)

Max speed (smooth air):
29E4, 31 (E3) 119 knots (220 km/h; 137 mph)
29D3, 29D4 121 knots (225 km/h; 140 mph)
33 130 knots (240 km/h; 149 mph)
g limits: 29D4 +4·0/−1·5
29D3, 29E4, 31 (E3), 33 +5·3/−2·65

IS-29DM and IS-29EM

These two motor gliders, of which prototypes have been flown, are respectively powered versions of the IS-29D2 and IS-29E3, fitted with a 29 kW (39 hp) Rectimo 4AR-1200 engine driving a Hoffmann HO-V42 propeller; fuel capacity is 27 litres (6 Imp gallons). A retractable rubber-sprung Tost monowheel, diameter 345 mm, is fitted; the Tost tailwheel has a diameter of 210 mm. Production aircraft are expected to be available by mid-1980.

DIMENSIONS, EXTERNAL:
Wing span: DM 15·00 m (49 ft 2½ in)
EM 20·00 m (65 ft 7½ in)
Wing area, gross: DM 10·20 m² (109·8 sq ft)
EM 14·68 m² (158·0 sq ft)
Length overall: DM, EM 7·00 m (22 ft 11½ in)
Height overall: DM, EM 1·75 m (5 ft 9 in)
Propeller diameter: DM, EM 1·36 m (4 ft 5½ in)
WEIGHTS:
Weight empty: DM 310 kg (683 lb)
EM 400 kg (882 lb)
Max T-O weight: DM 440 kg (970 lb)
EM 530 kg (1,168 lb)
PERFORMANCE (power on):
Max level speed:
DM, EM 119 knots (220 km/h; 137 mph)
Cruising speed: DM 92 knots (170 km/h; 106 mph)
EM 86 knots (160 km/h; 99 mph)
Stalling speed: DM 43·4 knots (80·3 km/h; 50 mph)
EM 42 knots (77 km/h; 48 mph)
Max rate of climb at S/L: DM 180 m (590 ft)/s
EM 150 m (492 ft)/s
Service ceiling: DM, EM 4,500 m (14,765 ft)
T-O to 15 m (50 ft): DM 370 m (1,215 ft)
EM 400 m (1,315 ft)
Range with max fuel:
DM, EM 270 nm (500 km; 310 miles)
PERFORMANCE (power off):
Best glide ratio: DM 32
EM 42
Min sinking speed: DM 0·70 m (2·30 ft)/s
EM 0·55 m (1·80 ft)/s

SWITZERLAND

EFF (ENTWICKLUNGSGEMEINSCHAFT FÜR FLUGZEUGBAU

Buchstrasse 23, CH-8302 Augwil
Telephone: (01) 813 3244
PRESIDENT: T. Bircher

EFF PROMETHEUS

After four years of design work, construction of the Prometheus began in 1975, and it flew for the first time on 22 June 1978.

TYPE: Two-seat twin-jet motor glider; g limits +4·0/−4·0.

AIRFRAME: Cantilever monoplane. Wing section Wortmann FX-67-170-17. Wings have aluminium main spar, with plywood skin and glassfibre/foam sandwich infill. Trailing-edge 'flaperons'. DFS upper-surface airbrakes. Forward fuselage built of wood, with glassfibre skin; rear fuselage is of glassfibre sandwich, as are the fixed-incidence T tailplane and elevator. Retractable tricycle landing gear, comprising twin main wheels with Goodyear tyres (diameter 127 mm; 5 in, pressure 4·3 bars; 62·4 lb/sq in) and Tost brake; and single nosewheel with General Tire and Rubber Co tyre (pressure 5 bars; 72·5 lb/sq in). Nosewheel is oleo-sprung, main wheels by rubber blocks. Seats for two persons side by side; VFR instrumentation standard, IFR optional.

POWER PLANT: Two 0·88 kN (198 lb st) Microturbo TRS 18 turbojet engines. Fuel in two 73 litre (16 Imp gallon) wing tanks and two 14 litre (3 Imp gallon) fuselage tanks: total fuel capacity 174 litres (38 Imp gallons). Oil capacity 2 litres (0·4 Imp gallons).

DIMENSIONS, EXTERNAL:
Wing span 19·40 m (63 ft 7¾ in)
Wing chord, mean aerodynamic 0·989 m (3 ft 3 in)
Wing area, gross 17·64 m² (189·9 sq ft)
Wing aspect ratio 21·3
Length overall 8·30 m (27 ft 2¾ in)
Height overall 1·70 m (5 ft 7 in)
WEIGHTS AND LOADINGS:
Weight empty, equipped 735 kg (1,620 lb)
Max T-O weight 999 kg (2,202 lb)
Max wing loading 56·6 kg/m² (11·6 lb/sq ft)
Max power loading 567·6 kg/kN (5·56 lb/lb st)
PERFORMANCE:
Not released at time of closing for press

HANG GLIDERS

GERMANY (FEDERAL)

PROF DIPL-ING BERNHARD E. R. J. DE TEMPLE

Am Pfingstborn 23, 6501 Heidesheim/Rhein
Telephone: 06132 58566

TEMPLE-FLÜGEL TF-1

The Temple-Flügel (Temple-Wing) TF-1 rigid-wing hang glider is unusual in that pre-stressed sheets of foam plastics are used in the wings and tail unit to provide firm lifting surfaces which are virtually insensitive to dynamic loads. Because these surfaces are pre-stressed, they do not become deformed in flight. Other advantages accruing from the use of foam plastics include low constructional and repair costs.

Prof de Temple first tested this concept in the form of a model, which was flown in 1963. A full-size prototype was built in 1978, and the first manned flight in this aircraft was made in Austria on 13 August of that year.

AIRFRAME: Constant-chord non-swept wings, with bowed profile and 4° dihedral from roots. Basic airframe structure is of aluminium alloy tubes and U-sections, with ferritic and stainless steel bolts and screws. Tail unit is an inverted V, supported by twin tailbooms and having an included angle of 104°. Wing and tail lifting surfaces are of pre-stressed Styropor foam plastics, a biologically inert material; their profiles are especially suitable for flight at low Reynolds numbers, though this type of wing could possibly be flown at higher speeds. Steel cables above and below wings permit control of the aircraft by wing-warping and raising tail unit.

DIMENSIONS:
Wing span 10·30 m (33 ft 9½ in)
Wing chord, constant 1·46 m (4 ft 9½ in)
Length overall 5·00 m (16 ft 4¾ in)
Height overall 3·00 m (9 ft 10 in)
Tail unit span 2·80 m (9 ft 2¼ in)
AREAS:
Wings, gross 15·00 m² (161·5 sq ft)
Tail unit (projected):
horizontal 2·52 m² (27·13 sq ft)
vertical 1·00 m² (10·76 sq ft)
WEIGHTS:
Weight empty 48 kg (106 lb)

Temple-Flügel TF-1 rigid-wing hang glider

Max T-O weight 138 kg (304 lb)
PERFORMANCE:
Best glide ratio 8·8
Min sinking speed 1·38 m (4·53 ft)/s
Max level speed approx 24 knots (44 km/h; 27 mph)

UNITED STATES OF AMERICA

ELECTRA FLYER INTERNATIONAL

700 Comanche NE, Albuquerque, New Mexico 87107
Telephone: (505) 344 3444
PRESIDENT: Larry Newman

Latest known products of this company are as follows:

Cirrus 5. Airframe of anodised aluminium, with vinyl-coated stainless steel cables. Standard features include quick tensioner kingpost, triple deflexers, keel pocket. Available in four sizes (C5A, C5B, C5C and C5D).

SPECIFICATION:
Span: C5A 10·12 m (33 ft 2½ in)
C5B 9·45 m (31 ft 0 in)
C5C 8·75 m (28 ft 8½ in)
C5D 7·99 m (26 ft 2½ in)
Leading-edge: C5A 6·10 m (20 ft 0 in)
C5B 5·67 m (18 ft 7¼ in)
C5C 5·27 m (17 ft 3½ in)
C5D 4·81 m (15 ft 9½ in)
Keel: C5A 2·93 m (9 ft 7¼ in)
C5B 2·74 m (9 ft 0 in)
C5C 2·53 m (8 ft 3½ in)
C5D 2·32 m (7 ft 7¼ in)
Nose/billow angle (all) 112/1·0°
Wing area: C5A 18·58 m² (200·0 sq ft)
C5B 16·26 m² (175·0 sq ft)
C5C 13·94 m² (150·0 sq ft)
C5D 11·61 m² (125·0 sq ft)
Wing aspect ratio (all) 5·5
Weight: C5A 23·1 kg (51 lb)
C5B 20·9 kg (46 lb)
C5C 18·6 kg (41 lb)
C5D 17·7 kg (39 lb)
Pilot weight range: C5A 73-100 kg (160-220 lb)
C5B 59-77 kg (130-170 lb)
C5C 50-64 kg (110-140 lb)
C5D 36-50 kg (80-110 lb)
Best glide ratio (all) 8
Min sinking speed (all) 76 m (250 ft)/min
Stalling speed (all) 16 knots (29 km/h; 18 mph)

Dove. Airframe of similar materials to Cirrus. Standard features include quick tensioner kingpost, keel pocket. No deflexers. Available in four sizes (A, B, C and D).

SPECIFICATION:
Span: A 10·12 m (33 ft 2½ in)
B 9·45 m (31 ft 0 in)
C 8·75 m (28 ft 8½ in)
D 7·99 m (26 ft 2½ in)
Leading-edge: A 6·10 m (20 ft 0 in)
B 5·67 m (18 ft 7¼ in)
C 5·27 m (17 ft 3½ in)
D 4·81 m (15 ft 9½ in)
Keel: A 3·23 m (10 ft 7¼ in)
B 3·05 m (10 ft 0 in)
C 2·83 m (9 ft 3½ in)
D 2·62 m (8 ft 7¼ in)
Nose/billow angle (all) 112/1·75°
Wing area: A 20·44 m² (220·0 sq ft)
B 18·02 m² (194·0 sq ft)
C 15·61 m² (168·0 sq ft)
D 13·47 m² (145·0 sq ft)
Wing aspect ratio: A, B, C 1·8
D 1·7
Weight: As for Cirrus 5A/B/C/D respectively
Pilot weight range: As for Cirrus 5A/B/C/D respectively
Best glide ratio (all) 7
Min sinking speed (all) 55 m (180 ft)/min
Stalling speed (all) 14 knots (26 km/h; 16 mph)

Electra Floater. High-performance glider for intermediate and advanced pilots. Airframe of similar materials to Cirrus. Standard features include applied leading-edge, coated cables, quick-folding crossbar. Available in four sizes (Floater 165, 185, 205 and 230).

SPECIFICATION:
Span: 165 9·21 m (30 ft 2½ in)
185 9·75 m (32 ft 0 in)
205 10·27 m (33 ft 8¼ in)
230 10·88 m (35 ft 8¼ in)
Leading-edge: 165 5·18 m (17 ft 0 in)
185 5·49 m (18 ft 0 in)
205 5·79 m (19 ft 0 in)
230 6·10 m (20 ft 0 in)
Keel: 165 2·81 m (9 ft 2½ in)
185 2·97 m (9 ft 9 in)
205 3·12 m (10 ft 3 in)
230 3·32 m (10 ft 10¾ in)
Nose/billow angle (all) 120/0·5°
Wing area: 165 15·33 m² (165·0 sq ft)
185 17·19 m² (185·0 sq ft)
205 19·05 m² (205·0 sq ft)
230 21·37 m² (230·0 sq ft)
Wing aspect ratio (all) 5·53
Weight: 165 24 kg (53 lb)
185 25 kg (55 lb)
205 26 kg (57 lb)
230 29·5 kg (65 lb)
Pilot weight range: 165 45-68 kg (100-150 lb)
185 59-77 kg (130-170 lb)
205 68-86 kg (150-190 lb)
230 77-100 kg (170-220 lb)
Stalling speed (all)
15-16 knots (27·5-29 km/h; 17-18 mph)

Olympus. High-performance glider, with which many national and international distance and altitude gain records have been set. Airframe of similar materials to Cirrus. Standard features include triple deflexers, glassfibre battens, locking tips for 18° washout. Can be fitted with 7·5 kW (10 hp) Chrysler two-stroke engine in Soarmaster PP-106 power pack with 2 litres (0·5 US gallons) fuel and Kevlar propeller.

Standard unpowered Olympus available in three sizes (140, 160 and 180), as follows:

SPECIFICATION:

Span: 140	10·06 m (33 ft 0 in)
160	10·67 m (35 ft 0 in)
180	10·92 m (35 ft 10 in)
Leading-edge: 140	5·79 m (19 ft 0 in)
160	5·94 m (19 ft 6 in)
180	6·20 m (20 ft 4 in)
Keel: 140	1·86 m (6 ft 1¼ in)
160	2·29 m (7 ft 6 in)
180	2·62 m (8 ft 7¼ in)
Nose/billow angle: 140	122/0·15°
160, 180	123/0·15°
Wing area: 140	12·91 m² (139·0 sq ft)
160	14·68 m² (158·0 sq ft)
180	16·63 m² (179·0 sq ft)
Wing aspect ratio: 140	7·83
160	7·70
180	7·20
Weight: 140	21·8 kg (48 lb)
160	22·7 kg (50 lb)
180	23·6 kg (52 lb)
Pilot weight range: 140	52-63·5 kg (115-140 lb)
160	66-77 kg (145-170 lb)
180	79-100 kg (175-220 lb)
Best glide ratio (all)	9
Min sinking speed (all)	61 m (200 ft)/min
Stalling speed (all)	11·5 knots (21 km/h; 13 mph)

RPVs & TARGETS

CANADA

CANADAIR (page 616)

CANADAIR CL-227

The CL-227 is scheduled to enter service with the Canadian Armed Forces in 1985. It is reported that the operational version will be fitted with a US turboprop engine, and will have propellers of 2·59 m (8 ft 6 in) diameter; payload capacity (TV camera or infra-red sensor) will be increased to 30 kg (66 lb).

GERMANY (FEDERAL)

VFW-FOKKER (page 620)

VFW-FOKKER RT 910 TUCAN

This new mini-RPV was displayed in model form at the 1979 Paris Air Show. Intended for real-time reconnaissance and target acquisition, the Tucan appears to have a broadly similar configuration to the prototype mini-RPV described in the main section, but without the latter's canard control surfaces. Main sensors are said to be a laser designator for daylight operations, and a stabilised mini-FLIR for night use. The RPV has a radio command guidance system, and telemetry for relaying visual and signal data. Launch is by catapult, recovery by parachute. The scale model displayed at Paris, which weighs 20 kg (44 lb), is powered by a 5·6 kW (7·5 hp) PEWO Bully two-cylinder engine mounted at the tail, can fly at up to 108 knots (200 km/h; 124 mph), and was to be used for flight tests and for the training of pilots who will later control the full-scale RPV. The full-size Tucan is expected to weigh 95 kg (209 lb), of which 30 kg (66 lb) will be payload, and to have a maximum speed of 135 knots (250 km/h; 155 mph) at heights up to 3,000 m (9,850 ft).

INTERNATIONAL

AN/USD-502 (page 621)

AN/USD-502/CL-289

At the 1979 Paris Air Show, Canadair announced that the first test flights of the CL-289 would take place in December 1979, and operational trials in 1981. Production is scheduled to begin in 1983.

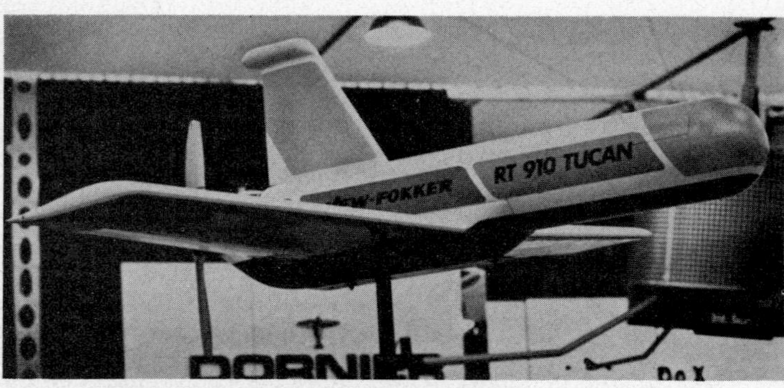

Model of the VFW-Fokker RT 910 Tucan mini-RPV *(Brian M. Service)*

Israel Aircraft Industries Scout mini-RPV

ISRAEL

IAI

ISRAEL AIRCRAFT INDUSTRIES

Ben Gurion International Airport, Lydda (Lod)
Telephone: (03) 973 111
Telex: Isravia 031102 and 031114

IAI SCOUT

Israel Aircraft Industries has designed and built a mini-RPV, known as the Scout, primarily for real-time battlefield reconnaissance and surveillance of target areas. The complete system comprises the Scout aircraft, ground control station, launcher and retrieval net.

Other military and civil applications include missile site reconnaissance, battlefield control, target identification, strike force control, artillery targeting, border patrol, coastal and waterway control, and damage assessment.

Scouts are operational with the Israeli armed services and with undisclosed export customers.

AIRFRAME: Cantilever high-wing monoplane. Fuselage is a rectangular-section nacelle; twin inward-canted fins and rudders, supported by twin tailbooms extending from wings outboard of fuselage. No landing gear on catapult-launched version, but a non-retractable tricycle gear can be fitted, if required, for operation from paved strips. Modular construction, with large access panels. Low detection signatures.

POWER PLANT: One 9 kW (12 hp) aircooled piston engine, installed in rear of fuselage nacelle and driving a specially designed two-blade pusher propeller. Fuel is a 20:1 petrol/oil mixture.

LAUNCH AND RECOVERY: Truck-mounted pneumatic rail launcher, and trailer- or truck-mounted recovery net, are standard. Conventional runway T-O and landing available optionally, if landing gear is fitted.

GUIDANCE AND CONTROL: Radio command guidance system. Aerodynamic control by ailerons, elevator and rudder. For recovery, aircraft is guided semi-automatically by an optical device into centre of retrieval net.

SPECIAL EQUIPMENT: TV camera, with telephoto lens, mounted in fuselage on stabilised platform servo-controlled for vibration damping. Large transparent hemispherical blister under centre of fuselage nacelle. Camera can rotate and scan through 360° in azimuth and 0-90° in pitch. Field of view adjustable, representing at an altitude of 915 m (3,000 ft) an area 600 × 800 m (1,970 × 2,625 ft) with wide-angle focus or 39 × 52 m (128 × 170 ft) with close-up focus for high resolution. Alternatively, aircraft can be fitted with panoramic camera to scan an area within 60° on each side of flight path. Configuration permits development of other payload packages, to customer's requirements.

DIMENSIONS, EXTERNAL:

Wing span	3·59 m (11 ft 9½ in)
Length overall	3·50 m (11 ft 6 in)

WEIGHTS:

Payload	13·6 kg (30 lb)
Fuel	12·2 kg (27 lb)
Launching weight	91 kg (200 lb)

PERFORMANCE (typical):

Max level speed	80 knots (148 km/h; 92 mph)
Speed for max range	55 knots (102 km/h; 63 mph)
Stalling speed	38 knots (71 km/h; 44 mph)
Rate of climb at S/L	152 m (500 ft)/min
Max operating altitude	3,050 m (10,000 ft)
Flight endurance	4 h 30 min

SWEDEN

FoA

FÖRSVARETS FORSKNINGSANSTALT (National Defence Research Institute)

Linnegatan 89, Fack, 104 50 Stockholm 80
Telephone: (08) 63 18 00
CHAIRMAN AND DIRECTOR-GENERAL: N. H. Lundquist

FoA SKATAN

The Skatan system was designed under a Swedish government contract of 1969 to provide short-range daylight-only reconnaissance and surveillance over zones immediately behind the forward edge of the battle area (FEBA). The complete system comprises miniature aircraft, a radio transmitter and telescopic antenna, two pairs of binoculars, and a case for cameras and film processing equipment.

TYPE: Short-range battlefield reconnaissance mini-RPV.

AIRFRAME: Shoulder-wing monoplane, with constant-chord wings and square-section fuselage. Non-retractable tailwheel-type landing gear. Construction of balsa wood proposed, which would give typical lifetime of 5-10 missions. Extremely small radar signature; not affected by ECM in programmed flight.

POWER PLANT: One 1·2 kW (1·6 hp) O.S. Max H80/RC 13·23 cc single-cylinder glow-plug engine, driving a two-blade propeller. Fuel, contained in a tank of 0·5 litres (0·11 Imp gallons) capacity, is a mixture of methanol (70%), castor oil (25%) and nitromethane (5%).

LAUNCH AND RECOVERY: Conventional T-O and landing, under radio control, is standard; alternative parachute recovery system available optionally.

GUIDANCE AND CONTROL: Radio command guidance. Aircraft can be guided by manual control throughout flight, controlled in line-of-sight by use of two pairs of binoculars (one of low magnification for very close range control, and a higher-magnification pair for use at longer range), mounted co-axially; manual guidance can also be effected by use of radar data and triangulation instead of binoculars. Of these, the distance-calculation method has proved to be the most effective. Alternatively, drone can be fitted with an automatic flight control system for pre-programmed flight. An aneroid device and altimeter are linked to an onboard control to maintain operating altitude within an accuracy of 20 m (66 ft). Using this system, the onboard radio receiver can be switched off over the surveillance area, avoiding ECM while the aircraft photographs the area below. Aerodynamic control of the drone is by movement of conventional ailerons and tail control surfaces.

SPECIAL EQUIPMENT: Two onboard camera systems have been tested: an f/2·8 Canon with 40 mm lens, and an f/1·4 Nikon F with 50 mm lens. Of these the former is cheaper, but has not yielded fully satisfactory picture clarity; the latter, while providing much better results, is considered too expensive for Swedish Army requirements. Other potential payloads include radio relay equipment, jammers, smoke generators, laser target designator, TV camera, radar reflector, or (in 'kamikaze' role) small attack weapons.

DIMENSIONS, EXTERNAL:
- Wing span: 2·14 m (7 ft 0¼ in)
- Length overall: 1·61 m (5 ft 3½ in)

WEIGHTS:
- Weight without camera: 4·4 kg (9·7 lb)
- T-O weight with 0·4 litres (0·09 Imp gallons) fuel:
  - with Canomatic M70 camera: 6·0 kg (13·2 lb)
  - with Nikon F camera: 7·4 kg (16·8 lb)

PERFORMANCE:
- Max level speed: 54 knots (100 km/h; 62 mph)
- Optimum operating height: 300-500 m (985-1,640 ft)
- T-O run (on tarmac, zero wind): 7 m (23 ft)
- Landing run: 20 m (66 ft)
- Line-of-sight control range: 2·7 nm (5 km; 3·1 miles)
- Typical mission times:
  - briefing and preparation: 5-10 min
  - out and back flight: 7-10 min
  - film removal and processing: 5-10 min
  - total time: 17-30 min

UNITED KINGDOM

BRITISH AEROSPACE, DYNAMICS GROUP

Manor Road, Hatfield, Hertfordshire
Telephone: Hatfield (30) 62300

BAe FLYBAC

This small RPV has been used many times by the Royal Aircraft Establishment in a continuing programme of research and testing, concerned with the military applications of RPVs. Few details are available, except that a primary need in the programme has been to instrument all vehicles to permit autonomous or remote pilot control, telemetry of the onboard systems, and parachute recovery for reasons of range safety.

Flybac is powered by a 1·34 kW (1·8 hp) Webra piston engine.

DIMENSIONS, EXTERNAL:
- Wing span: 2·00 m (6 ft 6¾ in)
- Length overall: 1·47 m (4 ft 9¾ in)
- Height overall: 0·41 m (1 ft 4¼ in)

WEIGHTS:
- Max payload: 3 kg (6·6 lb)
- Max launching weight: 11 kg (24·25 lb)

PERFORMANCE:
- Cruising speed: 39 knots (72 km/h; 45 mph)
- Max range: 13 nm (24 km; 15 miles)
- Max endurance: 20 min

BAe STABILEYE

BAe Stabileye Mk 1 climbing away after launch

Exhibited at the 1979 Paris Air Show, Stabileye is a mini-RPV for day and night surveillance, equipped with a Linescan 204 infra-red camera system. The image obtained by the camera can be projected on a screen in the ground control station, signals being transmitted by radio data link, or recorded on film for analysis on completion of mission.

General configuration is that of a bulbous, pod-shaped nacelle, with shoulder-mounted constant-chord wings, twin tailbooms and twin fins and rudders. The power plant drives a 'pusher' propeller at the rear of the central nacelle.

Stabileye Mk 1 has been flown hundreds of times with different payloads during the RAE's RPV research programme. At least 18 had been built by the Autumn of 1979, one of which had flown 40 times. This version has a 60 cc Rowena piston engine, rated at 3 kW (4 hp).

Stabileye Mk 2, which had not flown by September 1979, has a 5·5 kW (7·5 hp) Weslake 116 engine.

DIMENSIONS, EXTERNAL:
- Wing span: 3·10 m (10 ft 2 in)
- Wing area: 1·65 m² (17·75 sq ft)
- Length overall: 2·60 m (8 ft 6½ in)
- Height overall: 0·89 m (2 ft 11 in)

WEIGHTS (A, Stabileye Mk 1; B, Mk 2):
- Max payload: A 8 kg (17·6 lb); B 15 kg (33 lb)
- Max launching weight: A 42 kg (92·5 lb); B 55 kg (121 lb)

PERFORMANCE:
- Max level speed: A 78 knots (144 km/h; 90 mph); B 93 knots (173 km/h; 107 mph)
- Cruising speed: A 68 knots (126 km/h; 78 mph); B 83 knots (155 km/h; 96 mph)
- Stalling speed: A 39 knots (72 km/h; 45 mph); B 43 knots (79 km/h; 49 mph)
- Max range: B 86 nm (160 km; 99 miles)
- Max endurance: A 30 min; B 1 h 0 min

CRANFIELD (page 240)

MARCONI AVIONICS/CRANFIELD INSTITUTE OF TECHNOLOGY MACHAN

Machan is the latest of a series of mini-RPVs which have been developed under UK government contract for systems research at the Royal Aircraft Establishment. Prime contractor, responsible for project management, payloads and ground support, is Marconi Avionics. Design and manufacture of the Machan airframe, including the control system, has been undertaken by the Cranfield Institute of Technology.

The general appearance of the **Cranfield A2** vehicle for the Machan system is shown in the accompanying photograph of a model. It has unswept wing of constant chord on a fuselage with a diamond-shape cross section. Horizontal and vertical tail control surfaces are carried on the duct for the rear-mounted ducted propeller, which is driven by a 13·43 kW (18 hp) Weslake 274-6 two-cylinder aircooled two-stroke engine. Recovery gear consists of a parachute, housed in a pod above the fuselage, and two wing-mounted skids.

(Machan is the name of the platform, built in a tree, from which tigers were hunted and killed in India.)

Model of Cranfield A2 vehicle for the Machan RPV system

DIMENSIONS, EXTERNAL:
- Wing span: 3·7 m (12 ft 1·7 in)
- Wing area: 1·8 m² (19·38 sq ft)
- Length overall: 2·13 m (6 ft 11·85 in)
- Height overall: 0·55 m (1 ft 9·65 in)

WEIGHTS:
- Max payload: 15 kg (33·1 lb)
- Max launching weight: 70 kg (154·3 lb)

PERFORMANCE (estimated):
- Max level speed: 116 knots (216 km/h; 134 mph)
- Typical operating speed: 68 knots (126 km/h; 78 mph)
- Stalling speed: 50 knots (94 km/h; 58 mph)
- Max range: 130 nm (240 km; 150 miles)
- Max endurance: 2 h

FLIGHT REFUELLING LTD (page 624)

ASAT

Flight Refuelling Ltd has designed a jet-propelled target drone to meet a Ministry of Defence (RAF) requirement known as ASAT (Advanced Subsonic Aerial Target). This requirement calls for a level speed in excess of 400 knots (741 km/h; 461 mph) and a steady state manoeuvring capability of up to 6*g*. A contract has been received to build eight flight vehicles, of which the first is expected to fly before the end of 1980. If approved, the drone is expected to be produced at the rate of about 50 per year.

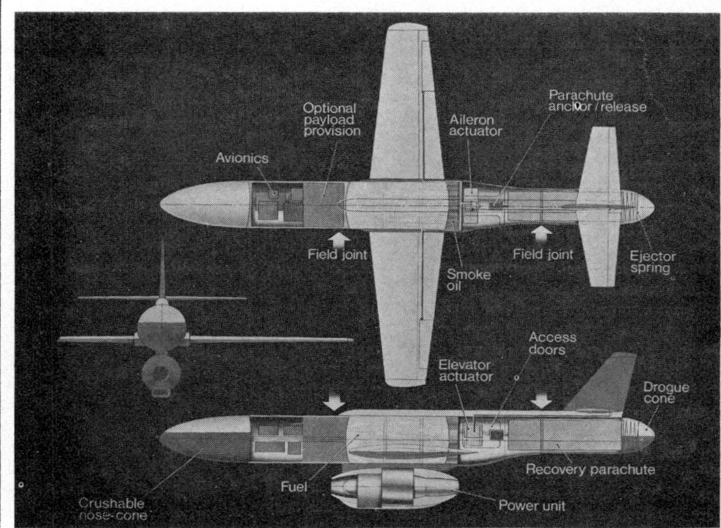

Flight Refuelling ASAT (Advanced Subsonic Aerial Target)

The max fuel load of 60 kg (132 lb) permits sortie times in excess of 1 h. Approach and intercept legs of a typical mission total nearly 5·5 nm (10 km; 6·2 miles), over the whole of which the target vehicle is flown at more than 400 knots (741 km/h; 461 mph) at S/L. Ten such circuits can be repeated at 4·5 min intervals. During less demanding operations, or where more time is required between presentations, the rate of fuel usage will be lower and the vehicle can be loitered at 3,000 m (9,845 ft) altitude for more than 90 min, with full allowances for T-O, climb, descent and recovery.

TYPE: Subsonic target drone.

AIRFRAME: Cantilever low/mid-wing monoplane. Wings and tail surfaces (sweptback fin, non-swept tailplane and elevators) folded from flat aluminium alloy sheet, without compound forming. Wings are each attached to fuselage by four bolts, are fitted with plain ailerons, and are interchangeable port/starboard. Tailplane held in place by fin, via two studs. Aluminium alloy fuselage, of circular cross-section, with crushable nosecone to absorb ground impact. Nosecone attachment and body joints made by hand-clamps. Nosecone is expendable, and is replaced after each flight. Cylindrical GRP canister in rear fuselage, housing recovery parachutes. Engine pod attached under fuselage by two bolts.

POWER PLANT: One 1·08 kN (242·5 lb st) Microturbo TRS 18-075 turbojet engine, built under licence by Ames Industrial Ltd and mounted in pod under centre of fuselage. Fuel tank in centre of fuselage, between wings; aft of this is a smaller tank for oil, which can be injected into jetpipe, on command from ground, to produce smoke.

LAUNCH AND RECOVERY: Proposed launch from three-wheeled trolley, running on a circular track 100 m (330 ft) in diameter and attached by cable to an anchor point at its centre. Aircraft will reach T-O speed in three laps of this track, equivalent to a straight-line T-O run of more than 1,000 m (3,280 ft), and with this system can always be launched into wind. Irvin day and night parachute recovery system, consisting of a cluster of three cruciform 'chutes, stowed in GRP canister which is rear-loaded into aft fuselage and covered by an ejector spring and drogue tailcone.

GUIDANCE AND CONTROL: Marconi Avionics control system, using a low-cost autopilot complemented by a microprocessor-based ground control station which utilises radar data as the basis for more sophisticated control and guidance functions. Aerodynamic control by ailerons and elevators, actuators for which are in rear fuselage, between fuel/oil tanks and parachute compartment.

EQUIPMENT: Large bay in forward fuselage, aft of nosecone, for avionics and optional payload.

DIMENSIONS, EXTERNAL:	
Wing span	3·00 m (9 ft 10 in)
Length overall	4·00 m (13 ft 1½ in)
WEIGHTS:	
Max payload	20 kg (44 lb)
Max fuel load	60 kg (132 lb)
Max launching weight	200 kg (441 lb)

AIR-LAUNCHED MISSILES

SWEDEN

SBMC (page 648)

The Swedish government decided, on 26 April 1979, to commission the Swedish Defence Material Administration to negotiate with Saab Bofors Missile Corporation the procurement of a new anti-ship missile system for which Saab-Scania will be prime contractor. The missile, designated RBS 15, will be deployed initially as armament for Swedish torpedo boats of the 'Spica' class, with which it will become operational in 1985. Second stage of the programme will involve adapting the same weapon to meet Swedish Air Force requirements for its next type of attack aircraft.

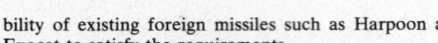

Artist's impression of the Swedish RBS 15 anti-ship missile

RBS 15

The RBS 15 anti-ship missile, shown in an accompanying illustration, is the first project undertaken by the Saab Bofors Missile Corporation. Other Swedish companies such as Philips Electronics Industries will participate in the programme, which was launched after studies of the capability of existing foreign missiles such as Harpoon and Exocet to satisfy the requirements.

As currently envisaged, the RBS 15 will require very little pre-launch preparation. All calculations will be performed automatically by a fire control computer, which will also control the status of the complete weapon system. The missile itself will be of the 'fire and forget' type, with a turbojet engine for long range at sea-skimming height, an ECM-resistant homing system, and a heavy and effective warhead.

DIMENSIONS:	
Length overall	4·35 m (14 ft 3¼ in)
Body diameter	0·50 m (1 ft 7¾ in)
Wing span, folded	0·85 m (2 ft 9½ in)
WEIGHT:	
Launching weight, without booster	560 kg (1,235 lb)

UNITED KINGDOM

BRITISH AEROSPACE (page 650)

P3T

An artist's impression of the P3T 'fire and forget' anti-ship missile was made available at the 1979 Paris Air Show. As anticipated, the configuration follows closely that of the Anglo-French Martel, except for the addition of an underbelly air intake for the Microturbo engine, which will give a much longer range than the solid-propellant rocket motor of the earlier weapon.

The P3T's sea-skimming height control system is already well proven in flight trials. It will be an all-weather missile, with an onboard computer employing the latest microprocessing technology, and an active radar homing head developed by Marconi Space & Defence Systems. Prior to launch, the computer will be supplied with target positional information from the carrier aircraft. The computer will control the flight path of the P3T until the target is acquired by the seeker during the final sea-skimming phase of the attack.

British Aerospace announced on 31 July 1979 that it had completed the definition phase of the programme, as a result of which it had been awarded a contract to develop and evaluate the P3T and to supply an initial production quantity. Wholly funded by the UK Ministry of Defence, the weapon will arm RAF Buccaneer and Tornado aircraft and the Royal Navy's Sea Harriers.

Artist's impression of BAe P3T anti-ship missile

Mockup of BAe Sabre air-launched missile (see page 650) exhibited at 1979 Paris Air Show *(Brian M. Service)*

UNITED STATES OF AMERICA

HUGHES (page 652)

MAVERICK

Integration of Maverick with the F-16, F-111 and Saab AJ 37 Viggen has been completed as planned. The A-4M Skyhawk II will be equipped with the new AGM-65E version of the missile, when development has been completed. Another carrier-based aircraft with which Maverick will be integrated is the F/A-18 Hornet.

Greece has deployed Maverick with its air force, as expected. Delivery to South Korea was awaiting US Congressional approval in Summer 1979.

Latest news concerning advanced versions of Maverick is as follows:

AGM-65C. This laser homing development version seems likely to be superseded by the AGM-65E.

AGM-65D. Now requested for US Navy as well as USAF. Naval version, known as Infra-red Attack Weapon, will utilise the same basic airframe, rocket motor and enlarged warhead as the Marine Corps AGM-65E.

AGM-65E. Development of AGM-65C, with laser guidance, for US Marine Corps deployment on A-4M and F/A-18. Will have new 135 kg (298 lb) blast/penetrator warhead, with delayed action fuse, for close air support and attacks on ships and hardened shelters.

SPACEFLIGHT

INDIA

ISRO (page 663)

BHASKARA

Bhaskara, India's second scientific satellite, was launched from the Soviet Union on 7 June 1979. Its purpose is to monitor Earth resources.

USSR

COSMOS (page 666)

The Soviet authorities have announced that the mission of Cosmos 1076, launched on 12 February 1979, was oceanographic in nature. The satellite carries sensors capable of monitoring water temperature.

PROGRESS

Progress 5. The engines of this supply ship were used to raise the orbit of the Salyut 6 space station on 30 March and 2 April 1979. On 3 April, Progress 5 separated from Salyut.

Progress 6. This cargo ship docked with Salyut 6 on 15 May 1979, carrying fuel, equipment, experiment materials and provisions. It separated on 8 June, to free its docking port for Soyuz 34.

Progress 7. Launched on 28 June 1979, Progress 7 docked with Salyut 6 two days later, bringing fuel for the space station's manoeuvring engines, equipment and supplies for the crew. It was used to push Salyut 6 into an orbit of about 411 × 399 km (255 × 248 miles), the highest yet achieved by such a spacecraft. After separating on 20 July, Progress 7 made a controlled re-entry over the Pacific on the same day.

SOYUZ

Soyuz 32. On 15 July 1979, Soyuz 32 cosmonauts Lyakhov and Ryumin surpassed the previous longest stay in orbit—139 days 14 h 47 min 32 s by the crew of Soyuz 29. Measurements made on board Salyut 6 at that time showed that Ryumin's weight had increased by more than half a kg—the first time that an astronaut had been known to increase his mass in orbit. A suggested reason is the improved diet made possible by the use of Progress supply craft to replenish food stocks on board the space station. The crews' diet can now include canned goods as well as fresh fruit and vegetables. Soyuz 32 was recovered on Earth, unmanned, on 13 June 1979, carrying the results of some of the experiments performed on board Salyut 6.

Soyuz 33. Launched on 10 April 1979, Soyuz 33 carried Nikolai Rukavishnikov (commander), with Bulgarian Major Georgi Ivanov as co-pilot. The spacecraft rendezvoused with Salyut 6 but was unable to dock with the space station owing to malfunction of an approach correction power unit. The mission was aborted and an emergency return to Earth made safely.

Soyuz 34. This spacecraft was launched on 6 June 1979 and sent unmanned to dock with Salyut 6 on 8 June 1979. It ferried scientific equipment and consumables to the space station, but its primary purpose was to provide a means of return for Lyakhov and Ryumin, whose Soyuz 32 had reached the end of its nominal orbital lifetime of about 80 days. It landed safely back on Earth, about 170 km (105 miles) southeast of Dzhezkazgan, on 19 August 1979, carrying the two cosmonauts, who had spent 175 days and 36 min in space.

UNITED STATES OF AMERICA

DEPARTMENT OF DEFENSE

ASAT

It was reported in 1979 that funds have been allocated within the Pentagon Space Defense programme for the development of anti-satellite technology. A miniature anti-satellite (ASAT) vehicle is proposed, which would destroy its targets by direct collision. Faced with the threat of similar Soviet weapons, funds have also been allocated to improve the survivability of US spacecraft under explosive or laser attack, to develop onboard sensors capable of detecting whether the carrier spacecraft has been detected by radar, illuminated by laser energy or physically touched by another vehicle. Electro-optical and electronic countermeasures technology is also being developed for Defense Meteorological Satellite, Defense Support Programme and NavStar Global Positioning System spacecraft.

NASA (page 674)

NASA's long-abandoned Skylab orbital laboratory re-entered Earth's atmosphere on 11 July 1979. Debris was scattered over a wide area of the Indian Ocean and parts of southwestern Australia, but no casualties or damage to property were reported.

SPACE SHUTTLE

On 28 June 1979, NASA's Administrator, Dr Robert A. Frosch, told a subcommittee of the House of Representatives that it would no longer be possible to meet the target date of 9 November for the first launch of the Space Shuttle. Stated causes were delays in engine testing and in the production and installation of the quartz tiles that will provide thermal protection for the Orbiter *Columbia* during re-entry.

At least 10,000 of the tiles remained to be bonded to the vehicle's metal structure at that time, and NASA officials speculated that a realistic first flight target was June or July 1980. This is likely to defer the first operational launch from February 1981 to September 1981, and Satellite Business Systems, RCA, Comsat and NOAA have been warned that they will probably have to switch to more costly expendable Delta or Atlas Centaur launch vehicles if planned satellite launch dates are to be met.

AERO-ENGINES

INTERNATIONAL

MTU/TURBOMÉCA

MTU/TURBOMÉCA MTM 380

This turboshaft engine will be developed by MTU/Turboméca SARL, a joint company owned equally by both partners. The reason for developing the engine, with a specification almost identical to that of the Rolls-Royce Gem, is said to be to power the proposed PAH-2 Franco-German anti-tank helicopter. MTU is responsible for the combustion chamber, gas generator and power turbine, the French partner being assigned the rest, representing a 50/50 work-split by cost. The first gas generator was scheduled to run before the end of 1979.

The MTM 380 is of modular design and is intended for minimum emissions.

COMPRESSOR: Single-shaft, with four axial stages (with variable stators on at least the first two) and one centrifugal stage. Mass flow over 3 kg (6·6 lb)/s. Pressure ratio about 13.

COMBUSTION CHAMBER: Reverse-flow annular with vaporising burners.

TURBINES: Two-stage aircooled gas-generator turbine. Two-stage power turbine.

CONTROL SYSTEM: Digital.

DIMENSIONS:
- Length: 990 mm (38·98 in)
- Max diameter: 475 mm (18·7 in)

WEIGHT, DRY: about 145 kg (320 lb)

RATINGS:
- Max T-O: 1,050 shp (772 kW)
- Contingency: 1,340 shp (1,000 kW)

ROLLS-ROYCE TURBOMÉCA (page 703)

ROLLS-ROYCE TURBOMÉCA RTM 321

At the 1979 Paris Salon Rolls-Royce and Turboméca both exhibited full-scale display examples of this new turboshaft engine which they are to develop jointly, subject to government approval. A demonstrator programme was expected to be agreed in July 1979. No mention was made of Alfa-Romeo of Italy, which had been the first company to mention the project (page 705). Though Westland has ordered 11 General Electric T700 engines for the WG 34 helicopter programme, the two engine companies hope that the RTM 321 will be adopted as the standard production engine on this helicopter. It offers an alternative to the T700 in other new helicopters in the 7/11-tonne class. The RTM 321 incorporates all the experience gained with such modern engines as the Gem and Makila to achieve extreme simplicity, good sfc and low costs. It comprises four modules and can be configured for any desired installation, with front or rear drive.

COMPRESSOR: Three-stage axial, single-stage centrifugal.

COMBUSTION CHAMBER: Annular reverse-flow.

TURBINES: Two-stage (presumably aircooled, but not yet announced) gas-generator turbine. Two-stage power turbine.

WEIGHT: approx 180 kg (396 lb)

RATINGS:
- Max contingency: initially in 1,300 kW (1,750 shp) range, rising later to 1,865 kW (2,500 shp)
- Intermediate: initially in 783 kW (1,050 shp) range
- Long-range cruise: initially in 582 kW (780 shp) range

SPECIFIC FUEL CONSUMPTION:
- Intermediate: 86·0 μg/J (0·509 lb/h/shp)
- Cruise, as above: 86·2 μg/J (0·51 lb/h/shp)

MTU/Turboméca MTM 380 turboshaft engine *(Brian M. Service)*

Rolls-Royce Turboméca RTM 321 turboshaft engine *(Brian M. Service)*

RR/MDD/BAe/RAE

In March 1979 the first results were announced of an advanced noise-suppressing nozzle that could enable future supersonic transports to meet "noise regulations currently governing subsonic aircraft operating in the United States". The installation, comprising seven different configurations of mixer nozzle and surrounding ejector, was designed by McDonnell Douglas after five years of preliminary research into SST noise suppression. It was fitted by British Aerospace and Rolls-Royce to a modified Viper turbojet with a pressure ratio "typical of Advanced Supersonic Transport engines", and flown in a BAe HS 125 of the Royal Aircraft Establishment on prolonged testing past a measurement site on one of the towers of the Severn Bridge. Rolls-Royce eight-lobe and conical nozzles were used as reference. The extremely encouraging results led to further testing in a wind tunnel at the NASA Ames Research Center, using the entire nacelle from the 125.

McDonnell Douglas advanced noise-suppressing nozzle on Viper turbojet of HS 125

USSR

LOTAREV (page 715)

LOTAREV D-36

It is confirmed that two of these engines are fitted in the An-72, with special air-bleed provisions for BLC purposes. Rating is given as 63·74 kN (14,330 lb st).

UNITED KINGDOM

BONNER
AERO BONNER LTD

ADDRESS:
Shoreham Airport, East Sussex BN4 5FJ
Telephone: 079-17-5764

This company has been developing an aircraft conversion of a British V-6 motorcar engine. In 1976 the first flight prototype engine was installed in a Chipmunk (actually a former winner of the King's Cup race) and was exhibited statically at the SBAC show at Farnborough. The flight test programme began on 2 July 1979.

BONNER SUPER SAPPHIRE

This engine for general aviation is a watercooled development of a standard production car engine. Early bench development has been most successful and the Super Sapphire is expected to set a new level of cheap, lightweight, compact, quiet and smooth power for aircraft requiring engines in the 149 kW (200 hp) class. Mr Bonner considers the conversion too extensive for homebuilders to undertake themselves, but will entertain enquiries for complete engines.

TYPE: Six-cylinder four-stroke piston engine, turbocharged and with geared drive.
CYLINDERS: V-6 configuration. Watercooled. Swept volume 3,000 cc (183 cu in).
INDUCTION: Turbocharged. Direct fuel injection.
IGNITION: Dual, with one magneto and one coil.
LUBRICATION: Dry sump.
PROPELLER DRIVE: Reduction gear with quill shaft, 0·5 ratio.
DIMENSIONS:
Length overall 914 mm (36·0 in)
Width overall 457 mm (18·0 in)
Height overall 609 mm (24·0 in)
WEIGHT, DRY: 149 kg (328 lb)
PERFORMANCE RATING:
Max T-O 149 kW (200 hp) at 5,500 rpm
FUEL CONSUMPTION:
At cruise (74·5 kW; 100 hp) 34 litres (7·5 Imp gal)/hr

The new Continental Rolls-Royce IO-368 light aircraft engine announced jointly by Teledyne Continental Motors and Rolls-Royce Motors Ltd at the 1979 Paris Air Show

ROLLS-ROYCE GEM

The Westland WG 30 helicopter is powered by two Gem 41-1 turboshaft engines, each with 2½ min contingency rating of 836 kW (1,120 shp), 30 min power of 791 kW (1,060 shp) and continuous power rating of 671 kW (900 shp).

ROLLS-ROYCE MOTORS (page 727)

At the 1979 Paris Salon this company and Teledyne Continental of the United States announced jointly a completely new flat-four aircooled piston engine, the Continental Rolls-Royce IO-368. Unlike all previous light-aircraft engines built by Rolls-Royce Motors, the IO-368 has been a Crewe product from its earliest design stages. Full details will appear in the next edition of *Jane's*.

ROLLS-ROYCE (page 721)

On 11 June 1979 Rolls-Royce and Airbus Industrie signed an agreement to "initiate a programme to develop versions of the A300 and A310 powered by RB.211 engines". Work is going ahead on studying the most efficient installation and pod design.

ROLLS-ROYCE RB.432

Inevitably this advanced, simple, low-emissions turbofan has developed beyond being a scaled RB.401, as shown by the accompanying drawing released in April 1979. The following are new data:

DIMENSIONS:
Diameter (fan case) 1,581 mm (62·5 in)
Length (flange to flange) 2,420 mm (95·3 in)
WEIGHT, DRY: 1,806 kg (3,981 lb)
RATINGS:
Max T-O 75·6-84·5 kN (17,000-19,000 lb st)
Cruise, Mach 0·75, 10,670 m (35,000 ft) 17·79 kN (4,000 lb)

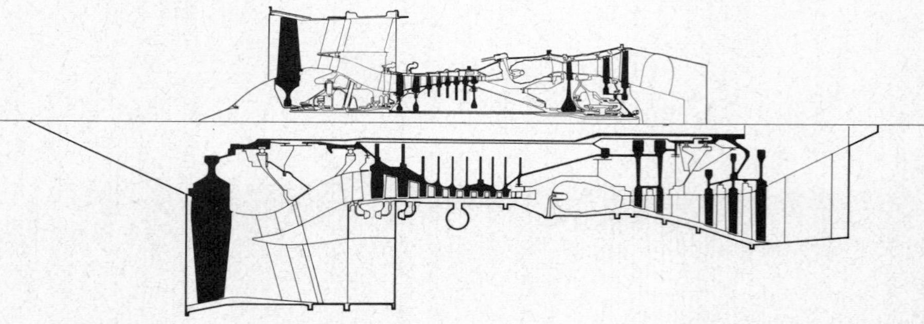

A new longitudinal section of the Rolls-Royce RB.432 (lower half) compared with the RB.401 (upper half) to the same scale

UNITED STATES OF AMERICA

GENERAL ELECTRIC (page 743)

GENERAL ELECTRIC CF6

Like Pratt & Whitney (page 788), GE has consolidated all its wide-body engine experience into a highly competitive new family of engines in the CF6-80 family. These are shorter, due to elimination of the turbine mid-frame and introduction of a new combustor and compressor rear frame. Fan blades are improved, and the compressor is all-steel and has long-life variable-stator bushings. The standard production engine for the Boeing 767-200 as ordered by American and Delta is the CF6-80A, with accessories on the core. The standard engine for the Airbus A310 as ordered by Lufthansa and KLM is the CF6-80A1, with accessories on the fan case. There is also a CF6-80B with increased mass flow and reduced bypass ratio, and a CF6-80C with 4,115 mm (162 in) fan, fifth LP turbine stage and the highest thrust of the series.

FAN: Diameter 2,195 mm (86·4 in) (80C, 2,286 mm, 90·0 in); mass flow, 650 kg (1,433 lb)/s (80B, 680 kg, 1,500 lb; 80C, 746 kg, 1,645 lb); bypass ratio 4·66 (80B, 4·28; 80C, 4·58).

LENGTH: 3,988 mm (157 in) (80C, 4,115 mm, 162 in)

WEIGHT, DRY:

80A	3,826 kg (8,435 lb)
80A1, 80B	3,769 kg (8,310 lb)
80C	about 3,900 kg (8,600 lb)

PERFORMANCE RATINGS:

Max T-O: 80A, A1	213 kN (48,000 lb st) to 33°C
80B	240 kN (54,000 lb st) to 30°C
80C	249 kN (56,000 lb st) to 30°C
Cruise, Mach 0·8 at 10,670 m (35,000 ft):	
80A, A1	36·3 kN (8,170 lb st)
80B	42·2 kN (9,480 lb st)
80C	42·5 kN (9,550 lb st)

GENERAL ELECTRIC CF6-32

By the time this edition appears this simplified, reduced-thrust CF6 will probably have been ordered for the Boeing 757. From the start it has been a joint venture with SNECMA of France, and in June 1979 Volvo Flygmotor of Sweden announced 6 per cent participation, with responsibility for manufacturing the rotor front extension shaft, compressor rotor drum, all variable stators, and HP and combustor casings. Alfa-Romeo SpA of Italy is also a manufacturing participant.

The first of seven engines was to run in August 1979, and certification is due in early 1982.

The Dash-32 uses the CF6-6 core with the latest improvements (Dash-6D2C), mated with a smaller fan with only 36 blades. The LP booster is removed, together with the turbine mid-frame. The HP turbine blades and vanes are of Dash-50 type but operated at -6D2C speed and temperature. The LP turbine has only four stages and its casing is 360° with no joint. The new gearbox, tailored to 757-size aircraft, is under the fan case.

FAN: Diameter 1,930 mm (76·0 in); mass flow 501 kg (1,104 lb)/s; bypass ratio 4·7. Overall engine pressure ratio 24·3.

LENGTH: 3,734 mm (147·0 in)

WEIGHT, DRY: 3,223 kg (7,105 lb)

PERFORMANCE RATINGS:

T-O 162 kN (36,500 lb st)

Cruise, Mach 0·8 at 11,580 m (38,000 ft) 36·9 kN (8,290 lb st)

GENERAL ELECTRIC F101-X

This advanced military augmented turbofan is being developed for American and other supersonic fighters, and in particular is a candidate engine for re-engining the F-14 Tomcat and F-16. Based largely on components from the F101, YJ101 and F404, the F101-X was announced in June 1979. At that time development was being accelerated under a $79·7 million US Air Force contract, leading to flight test in both the F-14 and F-16 in 1981. An alternative designation is DFE (Derivative Fighter Engine). The first of three prototypes is to run at Evendale in January 1980.

FAN: Inlet guide vanes with variable trailing flaps. Three axial stages scaled up from F404, with solid titanium blades. Split case. Blades and vanes individually replaceable. Pressure ratio greater than 3. Mass flow approx 122 kg (270 lb)/s. Bypass ratio 0·87.

COMPRESSOR: Similar to F101, with nine stages on one-piece inertia-welded rotor. Inlet guide vanes and first three stators variable. Split casing is titanium at front and steel at rear. Blades and vanes individually replaceable. Pressure ratio over 10.

COMBUSTION CHAMBER: Similar to F101, with very short annular design fed by dual cone nozzles injecting into 20 small scroll cups.

HP TURBINE: Identical to F101. Advanced single stage with hollow blades and vanes both impingement and film-cooled. Blades individually replaceable without rotor disassembly. Segmented shroud providing tip clearance control.

LP TURBINE: Based on F101, with two stages, tip-shrouded but uncooled. Blades individually replaceable; second-stage vanes replaceable in groups.

AFTERBURNER: Scaled from F101. Mixed-flow with convoluted mixer of fan and core streams in plane of flameholder, where ignition begins on inner ring. Core oxygen is 90 per cent consumed upstream of fuel injection into bypass air.

NOZZLE: Scaled from F404 with primary, divergent and outer flaps and seals. Translating hydraulically powered ring drives triple flaps with hinged connections running on cams and rollers.

DIMENSIONS:

Diameter	1,270 mm (50·0 in)
Length (F-16)	5,156 mm (203·0 in)

WEIGHT, DRY: not disclosed

RATING:

T-O 116-129 kN (26,000-29,000 lb st) class

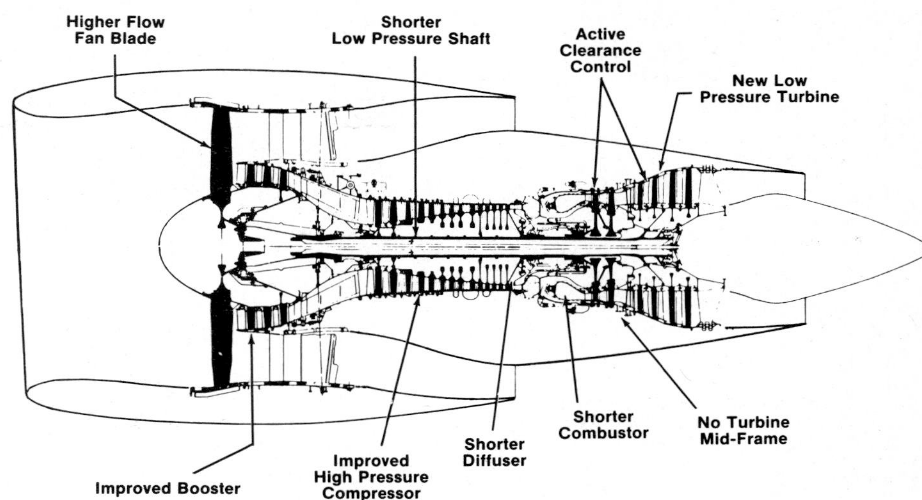

Features of the General Electric CF6-80A

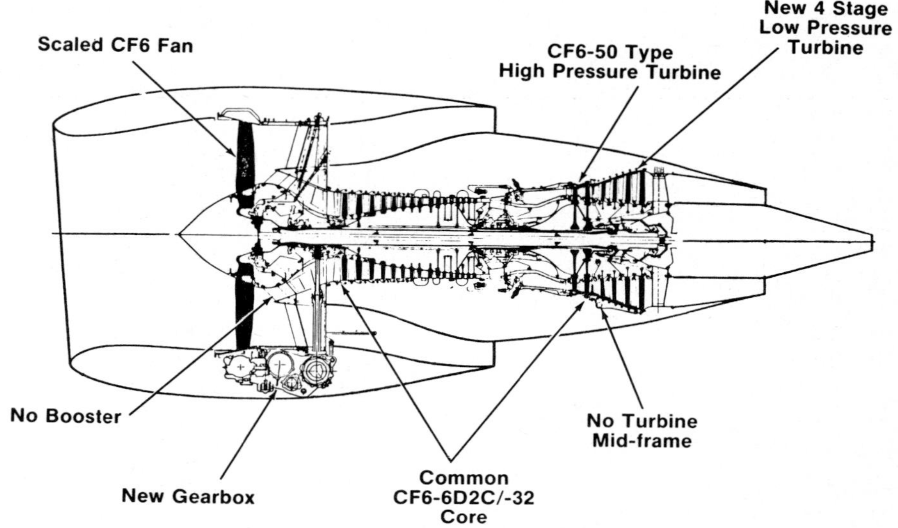

Features of the General Electric CF6-32

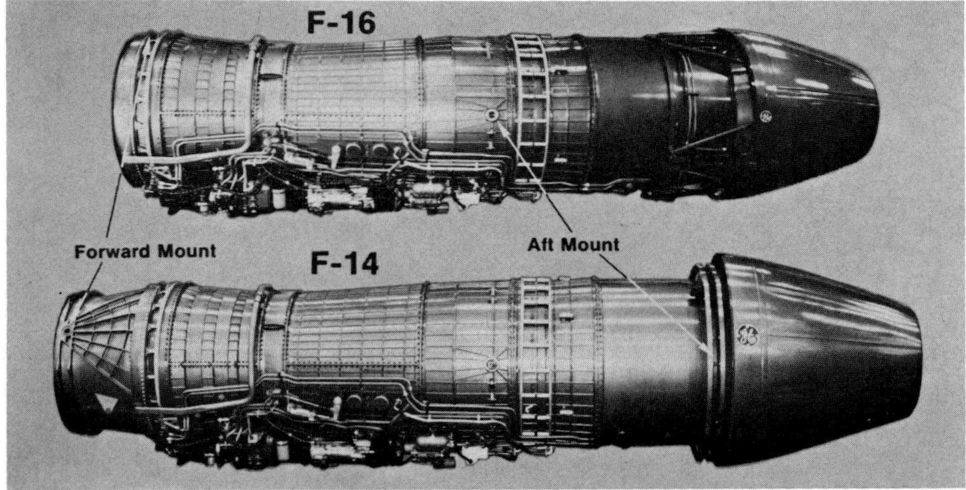

Comparative side elevations of the General Electric F101-X Derivative Fighter Engine, showing the inlet extension, different mountings and different nozzle of the F-14 installation

PRATT & WHITNEY (page 753)

PRATT & WHITNEY JT9D

All previous experience with the JT9D turbofan engine for wide-bodied aircraft has been incorporated into the JT9D-7R4 family, designed initially to power the Airbus A310 and Boeing 767 but applicable to other wide-body aircraft. Derived from the JT9D-7A, the new family have a fan with 25·4 mm (1·0 in) greater diameter and improved aerodynamics, a zero stage on the LP compressor, improved aerofoil-section blades in the HP compressor and single-crystal HP turbine blades. The specific fuel consumption is approximately 6 per cent lower than that of the Dash-7A, and turbine temperatures are significantly reduced. The following are major versions, the first four being scheduled for certification and delivery in 1980:

JT9D-7R4A. Rated at 198·46 kN (44,300 lb st). To be fitted to Boeing 767-200 of United.

JT9D-7R4B. Rated at 206·53 kN (46,100 lb st).

JT9D-7R4C. Rated at 210·11 kN (46,900 lb st). First engine selected for A310, by Swissair.

JT9D-7R4D. Rated at 215·04 kN (48,000 lb st). Selected for Boeing 767 by Pacific Western.

JT9D-7R4E. Rated at 224·0 kN (50,000 lb st).

JT9D-7R4F. Rated at 232·96 kN (52,000 lb st).

JT9D-7R4G. Rated at 241·92 kN (54,000 lb st).

JT9D-7R4H. Rated at 250·88 kN (56,000 lb st).

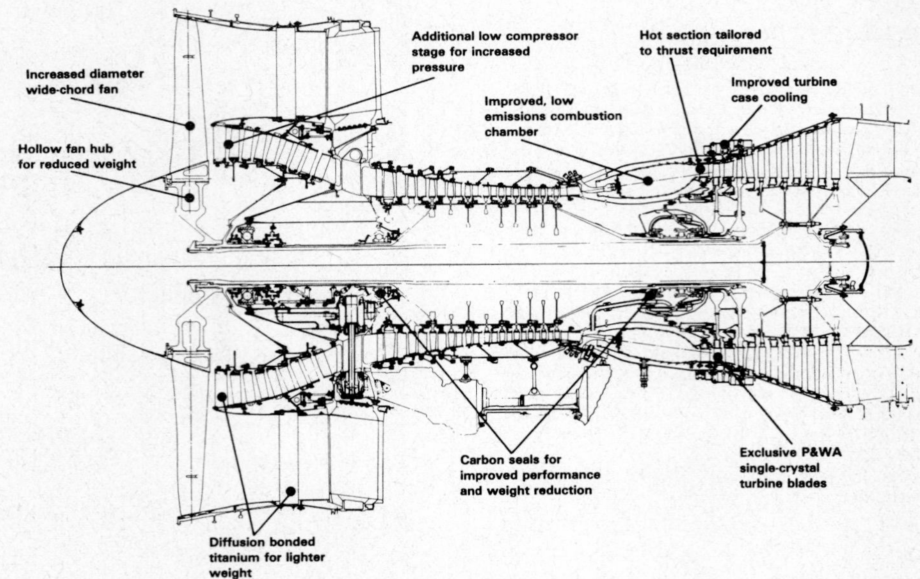

Features of the Pratt & Whitney JT9D-7R4 series

INDEXES

(Items in italics refer to the ten previous editions)

AIRCRAFT

B

C

D

M

N

O

T

U

V

Z

SAILPLANES AND HANG GLIDERS

LIGHTER-THAN-AIR

RPVs AND TARGETS

AIR-LAUNCHED MISSILES, SPACEFLIGHT

C

D

E

F

G

H

I

T

U

V

W

X

Y

Z

AERO-ENGINES

A

K

L

M

N

O

P

U

V

W

X

Y

Z

Printed in England by Netherwood Dalton & Co. Ltd., Huddersfield